91ST EDITION

EDITOR & PUBLISHER®

International DATA BOOK

The Encyclopedia of the Newspaper Industry

BOOK 1: DAILIES

2012

Editorial: 17782 Cowan, Suite C, Irvine, CA 92614 – (949) 660-6150; Fax (949) 660-6172
Customer Service: (888) 732-7323

International
DATA BOOK®

Published annually by Editor & Publisher, the oldest publishers' and advertisers' periodical in the United States

With which has been merged: ***The Journalist***, establisher March 22, 1884; ***Newspaperdom***, March 22, 1892; ***The Fourth Estate***, March 1, 1894; ***Editor & Publisher***, June 29, 1901; ***Advertising***, January 22, 1925.

CORPORATE OFFICES (949) 660-6150
FAX (949) 660-6172
EDITOR-IN-CHIEF *Jeff Fleming*
jeff@editorandpublisher.com
MANAGING EDITOR *Kristina Ackermann*
kristina@editorandpublisher.com
ART DIRECTOR *Robert Martin Jr.*
robert@editorandpublisher.com
EDITORIAL ASSISTANT *Nu Yang*
nu.yang@editorandpublisher.com
PROOFREADER *Judy Wilkin*
SALES MANAGER *Ralph Bayless*, ext. 204
ralph@editorandpublisher.com
CLASSIFIED ADVERTISING SALES *Jon Sorenson*
(800) 887-1615 FAX (866) 605-2323
classifieds@editorandpublisher.com
SUBSCRIPTION SERVICES (888) 732-7323
CIRCULATION MANAGER *Amelia Salazar*, ext. 217
amelia@editorandpublisher.com
CIRCULATION ASSISTANTS *Rick Avila*, ext. 254
Kristina Salazar, ext. 255
PRODUCTION *Mike Miller*, ext. 219
mike@editorandpublisher.com
TECHNOLOGY DIRECTOR *Adam Tessin*
adam@editorandpublisher.com
WEB DEVELOPER *Ryan Baker*
DIGITAL ASSISTANT *Bryan Sheehy*, ext. 257
DIRECTOR OF ADV./OPERATIONS *Janette Hood*, ext. 201
janette@editorandpublisher.com
ACCOUNTING *Stacey Iannotti*, ext. 213
stacey@editorandpublisher.com

EDITORIAL & ADVERTISING MAILING ADDRESS
17782 COWAN, STE. C, IRVINE, CA 92614

WWW.EDITORANDPUBLISHER.COM

Editor & Publisher is printed in the U.S.A.

duncan mcintosh company inc.

DUNCAN McINTOSH CO.
FOUNDED BY:
Editor and Publisher • Duncan McIntosh Jr.
Co-Publisher • Teresa Ybarra McIntosh (1942-2011)

17782 Cowan, Suite C, Irvine, CA 92614, (949) 660-6150; fax (949) 660-6172; www.editorandpublisher.com;

ISBN 1-930732-54-6 (Book 1) ISBN 1-930732-55-4 (Book 2)

Letter from the Publisher...

Welcome to the 91st edition of the Editor & Publisher International Data Book. The Data Book offers hundreds of thousands of facts about the newspaper industry.

The listings in this directory are designed to give you the information you need about newspapers – fast. The directory is available both in print and on the Web at www.editorandpublisher.com/databook, enabling you to search, retrieve and export data in seconds for your own personal use.

The Data Book in print is divided into two volumes with the following content. Book I features detailed listings for U.S. and Canadian daily newspapers, including contact information, personnel, circulation, advertising rates, mechanical specifications, commodity consumption and equipment. Users will also find listings of U.S. and Canadian daily newspaper groups; syndicates and news services; both conventional and interactive companies offering products and services to the industry; associations; newspaper brokers and appraisers; advertising representatives; and much more.

Book 2 offers extensive data on the non-daily newspaper industry with listings of community weekly newspapers, shopper/TMC publications, specialty and niche publications (including alternative, college and university papers, journalism schools, African American, Hispanic, Jewish, ethnic, real estate and other publications), non-daily newspaper groups and industry organizations.

The Who's Where directory of industry professionals with phone numbers, titles, and company names has been divided into two sections, one for Dailies and one for Weeklies. The Daily Newspaper Who's Where contacts are conveniently bound into the back of this book. The Who's Where directory for Weekly Newspapers is bound into the back of Book 2 for Weekly Newspapers.

As of February 1, 2012, daily newspapers in the United States numbered 1,382. Total U.S. daily newspaper circulation was 44.4 million. The number of U.S. Sunday newspapers totaled 900 with circulation of 48.5 million. Additional information can be found in the Ready Reckoner charts, which appear on pages v through vi of this front section.

Editor and Publisher thanks the people of the newspaper industry and in businesses supporting the industry for their help in providing us with accurate information for the 91st edition of the International Year Book. Please continue to direct questions, comments and suggestions to us at (949) 660-6150.

Sincerely,

Duncan McIntosh
President

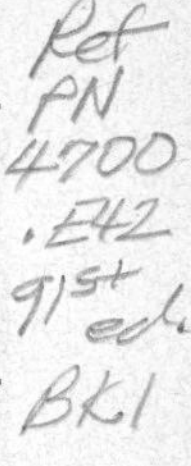

TABLE OF CONTENTS
2012 EDITOR & PUBLISHER INTERNATIONAL DATA BOOK

BOOK 1: DAILIES
FRONT PAGES

BOOK 2: WEEKLIES
FRONT PAGES

NEWSPAPER ADVERTISING

A SUMMARY OF NEWSPAPER ADVERTISING TRENDS COMPILED BY EDITOR & PUBLISHER FROM MEDIA RECORDS AND NAA REPORTS

LINAGE TOTALS - 1963 to 1970

Note: Figures from 1963 to 1970 are in thousands of lines; department store advertising is included in retail figures

YEAR	RETAIL	DEPARTMENT STORE	GENERAL	AUTOMOTIVE	FINANCIAL	CLASSIFIED	TOTAL ADVERTISING
1963	1,442,817	508,402	261,747	141,877	53,588	695,888	2,595,917
1964	1,673,186	593,476	292,549	159,729	60,867	787,135	2,973,466
1965	1,776,702	627,924	288,528	170,366	63,350	858,631	3,157,577
1966	1,863,633	652,845	310,287	182,894	73,184	924,255	3,354,253
1967	1,897,081	657,266	297,106	158,506	69,946	878,114	3,300,753
1968	1,917,404	625,691	296,134	170,958	72,838	923,724	3,381,058
1969	2,003,022	629,340	300,080	173,623	81,677	1,017,084	3,575,486
1970	2,014,880	613,212	275,156	161,570	74,907	917,262	3,443,775

DOLLAR OUTLAY - 1971 to 2010

Note: On Jan. 1, 1971, the Media Records base was increased to 64 from 52 cities, and the terms from it's report "Total Agate Lines" to "Dollar Outlay." Numbers are in thousands of dollars; department store advertising is included in retail figures.

YEAR	RETAIL	DEPARTMENT STORE	GENERAL	AUTOMOTIVE	FINANCIAL	CLASSIFIED	TOTAL ADVERTISING
1971	1,807,304	536,930	455,356	100,765	103,099	751,652	3,218,176
1972	2,004,666	567,833	504,377	102,514	122,137	914,868	3,648,562
1973	2,044,095	561,770	479,183	99,783	138,898	1,024,153	3,786,112
1974	2,078,760	562,583	491,508	104,191	126,023	966,673	3,767,155
1975	2,363,965	634,965	547,099	93,264	130,810	982,229	4,117,367
1976	3,129,474	793,497	752,267	144,538	147,394	1,522,474	5,696,147
1977	3,129,474	793,497	752,267	144,538	147,394	1,522,474	5,696,147
1978	3,579,933	871,250	826,614	151,004	201,670	1,884,505	6,643,726
1979	3,959,802	891,902	937,792	192,961	236,771	2,201,717	7,529,043
1980	4,396,320	954,411	1,122,701	183,568	297,962	2,191,773	8,192,324
1981	5,067,750	1,092,674	1,379,698	225,627	387,152	2,514,923	9,575,150
1982	5,282,855	1,151,824	1,419,610	265,013	398,732	2,497,840	9,864,050
1983	5,028,265	1,140,450	1,482,434	248,470	327,427	2,698,155	9,784,751

Note: Since 1984, the dollar volume has been supplied by the newspaper advertising bureau, now part of Newspaper Association of America. The large increase in all subsequent years occurs because these figures include all newspapers nationwide.

YEAR	RETAIL	DEPARTMENT STORE	GENERAL	AUTOMOTIVE	FINANCIAL	CLASSIFIED	TOTAL ADVERTISING
1984	12,784,000		3,081,000			7,657,000	23,522,000
1985	13,443,000		3,352,000			8,375,000	25,170,000
1986	14,311,000		3,376,000			9,303,000	26,990,000
1987	15,227,000		3,494,000			10,691,000	29,412,000
1988	15,790,000		3,821,000			11,586,000	31,197,000
1989	16,504,000		3,948,000			11,916,000	32,368,000
1990	16,652,000		4,122,000			11,506,000	32,280,000
1991	15,839,000		3,924,000			10,587,000	30,350,000
1992	16,041,000		3,834,000			10,764,000	30,639,000
1993	16,859,000		3,853,000			11,157,000	31,869,000
1994	17,496,000		4,149,000			12,464,000	34,109,000
1995	18,099,000		4,251,000			13,742,000	36,092,000
1996	18,344,000		4,667,000			15,065,000	38,076,000
1997	19,242,000		5,315,000			16,773,000	41,330,000
1998	20,331,000		5,721,000			17,873,000	43,925,000
1999	20,907,000		6,732,000			18,650,000	46,289,000
2000	21,409,000		7,653,000			19,608,000	48,670,000
2001	20,679,000		7,004,000			16,622,000	44,305,000
2002	20,994,000		7,210,000			15,898,000	44,102,000
2003	21,341,000		7,797,000			15,801,000	44,939,000
2004	22,012,000		8,083,000			16,608,000	46,703,000
2005	22,187,000		7,910,000			17,312,000	47,409,000
2006	22,120,910		7,504,895			16,985,536	46,611,341
2007	21,018,000		7,005,000			14,186,000	42,209,000
2008	18,768,570		5,995,934			9,975,014	34,739,518
2009	14,218,000		4,424,000			6,179,000	24,821,000
2010	12,926,051		4,221,075			5,648,110	22,795,236

* To present a truer picture of advertising trends, all linage carried in the three metropolitan New York City dailies that struck for 90 days August to November 1978 hs been excluded from 1978 totals and 1977 figures have been correspondingly adjusted.

* Source: Research Department of the Newspaper Association of America, 3/11.

BASIC DATA FOR ADVERTISING SPACE BUYERS

Morning

Period Ended	Total number of papers	Total net circulation	Total column inch rate	milinch rate	Relation of milinch rate to milinch rate for the preceeding 2 years
12/31/11	980	41,562,085	$70,767.01	$1,702.68	increase $261.60 + 15.36%
12/31/09	869	43,421,084	$62,001.81	$1,427.90	increase $17.39 + 1.22%
			10,795,519 AM plus 2,625,565 PM through combination		
12/31/08	872	42,939,680	$62,445.50	$1,454.26	increase $129.54 + 8.91%
			42,757,749 AM plus 181,931 PM through combinations		
12/31/07	867	44,745,057	$61,155.81	$1,366.76	increase $114.08 + 8.35%
			44,547,744 AM plus 197,313 PM through combinations		
12/31/06	833	45,708,175	$58,628.68	$1,282.67	increase $129.00 + 10.06%
			45,441,416 AM plus 266,729 PM through combinations		
12/31/05	817	46,402,988	$56,736.35	$1,222.69	increase $167.70 + 13.72%
			46,122,614 AM plus 280,734 PM through combinations		
12/31/04	814	47,483,349	$51,502.53	$1,084.64	increase $75.54 + 6.97%
			46,887,490 AM plus 595,859 PM through combinations		
12/31/03	787	47,614,150	$48,820.93	$1,025.34	increase $48.34 + 4.71%
			46,930,215 AM plus 683,935 PM through combinations		
12/31/02	777	47,314,102	$46,975.77	$992.85	increase $51.50 + 5.20%
			46,617,163 AM plus 696,939 PM through combinations		
12/31/01	776	47,102,993	$45,272.34	$961.14	increase $77.89 + 8.10%
			46,821,480 AM plus 281,513 PM through combinations		
12/31/00	766	47,120,047	$43,423.91	$921.56	increase $88.04 + 9.55%

Afternoon

Period Ended	Total number of papers	Total net circulation	Total column inch rate	milinch rate	Relation of milinch rate to milinch rate for the preceeding 2 years
12/31/11	470	4,543,326	$8,177.16	$1,799.82	decrease $19.70 - 1.08%
12/31/09	528	6,413,488	$12,032.42	$1,876.10	decrease $108.79 - 5.80%
			(5,482,151 PM plus 931,337 AM through combinations)		
12/31/08	546	6,858,369	$12,090.92	$1,762.94	decrease $60.23 - 3.42%
			5,839,770 PM plus 1,018,559 AM through combinations		
12/31/07	565	7,238,621	$12,824.47	$1,771.67	increase $186.46 + 10.52%
			6,193,856 PM plus 1,044,765 AM through combinations		
12/31/06	614	8,436,773	$13,783.60	$1,633.75	increase $162.56 + 9.95%
			6,887,784 PM plus 1,548,989 AM through combinations		
12/31/05	645	8,159,398	$12,538.29	$1,536.67	increase $169.71 + 11.05%
			(7,222,429 PM plus 936,969 AM through combinations)		
12/31/04	653	9,327,047	$13,111.15	$1,405.71	increase $116.50 + 8.29%
			7,738,648 PM plus 1,588,399 AM through combinations		
12/31/03	680	9,987,734	$13,265.68	$1,328.20	increase $24.81 + 1.87%
			8,255,136 PM plus 1,732,598 AM through combinations		
12/31/02	692	10,334,154	$12,919.94	$1,250.22	decrease $79.02 - 6.32%
			8,568,994 PM plus 1,765,160 AM through combinations		
12/31/01	704	9,555,908	$12,963.07	$1,356.55	increase $137.94 + 10.17%
			(8,756,566 PM plus 799,342 AM through combinations)		
12/31/00	727	10,078,235	$13,121.14	$1,301.93	increase $186.73 + 14.34%

Sunday

Period Ended	Total number of papers	Total net circulation	Total column inch rate	milinch rate	Relation of milinch rate to milinch rate for the preceeding 2 years
12/31/11	1015	50,880,930	-	-	-
12/31/09	919	46,895,201	$75,207.37	$1,603.70	increase $106.90 + 6.67%
			(46,849,960 Sunday plus 45,241 AM and PM through combinations)		
12/31/08	902	49,162,344	$75,630.08	$1,538.37	increase $142.32 + 9.25%
			(49,114,892 Sunday plus 47,452 AM and PM through combinations)		
12/31/07	907	51,347,859	$74,722.80	$1,455.23	increase $154.84 + 10.64%
			(51,246,332 Sunday plus 101,527 AM and PM through combinations)		
12/31/06	907	53,279,897	$71,227.96	$1,336.86	increase $157.63 + 13.37%
			(53,175,299 Sunday plus 104,598 AM and PM through combinations)		
12/31/05	914	55,376,702	$69,991.16	$1,263.91	increase $200.08 + 15.83%
			(55,270,381 Sunday plus 106,321 AM and PM through combinations)		
12/31/04	915	57,862,287	$63,332.56	$1,094.54	increase $86.92 + 7.94%
			(57,753,013 Sunday plus 109,274 AM and PM through combinations)		
12/31/03	917	58,883,978	$60,834.09	$1,033.12	increase $75.97 + 7.35%
			(58,494,695 Sunday plus 459,188 AM and PM through combinations)		
12/31/02	913	59,680,781	$58,613.95	$982.12	increase $90.80 + 9.30%
			(58,780,299 Sunday plus 900,482 AM and PM through combinations)		
12/31/01	913	62,020,333	$57,813.89	$932.18	increase $109.95 + 11.79%
			(59,090,364 Sunday plus 2,929,969 AM and PM through combinations)		
12/31/00	917	62,598,913	$53,237.36	$850.46	increase $80.32 + 9.44%

Note: Circulation reflects "Total Average Circulation," which consists of a publication's paid and verified print and digital editions. Total average circulation also includes any paid and verified branded editions. (ABC recommends not making any direct comparisons of data to prior years.)

READY RECKONER OF ADVERTISING RATES AND CIRCULATIONS

1,382 daily newspapers (931 morning, 451 evening and including 26 all-day) and 900 Sunday

Number of newspapers as of Feb. 1, 2012 with circulation as reported for six months primarily ending on Sept. 30, 2011

STATE	NUMBER OF DAILY NEWSPAPERS				MORNING PAPERS NET CIRCULATION SEPT. 30, 2011		AFTERNOON PAPERS NET CIRCULATION SEPT. 30, 2011		TOTALS		SUNDAY PAPERS NET CIRCULATION SEPT. 30, 2011	
	Population 2010 Census	AMs	PMs	Total	AM Circulation	Inch rates including all combinations	PM Circulation	Inch rates including all combinations	Total AM & PM Circulation	Minimum rates for AM & PM coverage	Number of papers	Sunday circulation
Alabama	4,779,736	25	1	26	498,424	$922.82	6,000	$9.50	504,424	$932.32	20	624,283
Alaska	710,231	5	2	7	71,135	$200.63	5,724	$23.45	76,859	$224.08	3	72,379
* Arizona	6,392,017	13	1	14	480,568	$904.54	12,095	$7.95	492,663	$912.49	11	700,966
Arkansas	2,915,918	15	12	27	364,154	$628.60	55,552	$145.23	419,706	$773.83	15	485,884
California	37,253,956	73	10	83	5,714,146	$5,103.36	81,658	$317.82	5,795,804	$5,421.18	58	4,751,294
* Colorado	5,029,196	24	6	30	749,417	$1,517.44	27,423	$68.38	776,840	$1,585.82	17	890,315
Connecticut	3,574,097	14	2	16	403,182	$1,155.65	37,207	$80.65	440,389	$1,236.30	13	596,791
Delaware	897,934	2	0	2	94,469	$205.00	0	$0.00	94,469	$205.00	2	142,200
District of Columbia	601,723	2	0	2	574,613	$1,276.64	0	$0.00	574,613	$1,276.64	2	891,446
Florida	18,801,310	37	0	37	1,910,920	$4,572.20	0	$0.00	1,910,920	$4,572.20	36	2,718,505
Georgia	9,687,653	31	2	33	602,585	$1,832.15	18,702	$29.00	621,287	$1,861.15	27	906,244
Hawaii	1,374,810	5	0	5	234,770	$331.49	0	$0.00	234,770	$331.49	5	196,484
Idaho	1,567,582	8	1	9	158,635	$267.32	5,000	$13.50	163,635	$280.82	9	273,507
* Illinois	12,830,632	31	30	61	1,554,899	$2,675.13	200,184	$387.94	1,755,083	$3,063.07	27	2,023,367
* Indiana	6,483,802	36	31	67	792,869	$1,320.47	203,228	$548.84	996,097	$1,869.31	27	1,088,182
* Iowa	3,046,355	17	20	37	358,153	$818.15	136,323	$284.82	494,476	$1,102.97	12	531,242
Kansas	2,853,118	12	24	36	201,583	$429.50	113,545	$242.85	315,128	$672.35	10	226,810
* Kentucky	4,339,367	12	7	19	356,937	$829.55	65,953	$124.57	422,890	$954.12	13	534,026
Louisiana	2,967,297	18	8	26	426,519	$765.25	53,173	$79.80	479,692	$845.05	20	514,396
Maine	1,328,361	5	2	7	152,604	$183.38	15,166	$30.00	167,770	$213.38	4	177,388
Maryland	5,773,552	8	2	10	326,310	$512.12	38,133	$59.27	364,443	$571.39	8	508,763
* Massachusetts	6,547,629	16	14	30	656,647	$1,645.22	259,759	$344.51	916,406	$1,989.73	19	1,055,904
Michigan	9,883,640	22	23	45	706,082	$1,896.40	372,720	$657.94	1,078,802	$2,554.34	25	1,458,981
Minnesota	5,303,925	17	8	25	655,978	$878.59	80,533	$157.28	736,511	$1,035.87	16	991,776
Mississippi	2,967,297	12	11	23	201,826	$235.16	81,025	$114.66	282,851	$349.82	19	292,356
Missouri	5,988,927	19	22	41	568,117	$1,852.56	130,557	$217.71	698,674	$2,070.27	20	883,272
Montana	989,415	9	3	12	277,885	$349.06	9,554	$24.50	287,439	$373.56	8	262,325
* Nebraska	1,826,341	7	9	16	179,888	$180.21	134,775	$130.41	314,663	$310.62	6	292,806
Nevada	2,700,551	6	1	7	273,977	$468.94	5,632	$15.30	279,609	$484.24	5	264,491
New Hampshire	1,316,470	9	0	9	140,307	$227.38	0	$0.00	140,307	$227.38	6	146,124
* New Jersey	8,791,894	17	0	17	800,698	$1,393.31	5,610	$0.00	806,308	$1,393.31	14	1,039,844
* New Mexico	2,059,179	9	6	15	181,552	$321.51	41,443	$79.69	222,995	$401.20	12	226,899
* New York	19,378,102	38	15	53	5,919,922	$6,106.10	352,540	$324.41	6,272,462	$6,430.51	40	6,643,077
* North Carolina	9,535,483	41	6	47	894,701	$1,592.95	67,437	$111.18	962,138	$1,704.13	39	1,200,687
North Dakota	672,591	6	5	11	130,949	$241.83	16,162	$60.43	147,111	$302.26	8	148,457
* Ohio	11,536,504	49	35	84	1,659,264	$2,906.75	283,067	$652.74	1,942,331	$3,559.49	42	2,323,771
Oklahoma	3,751,351	12	25	37	295,889	$649.63	141,553	$280.21	437,442	$929.84	30	558,940
* Oregon	3,831,074	8	9	17	311,438	$437.71	202,146	$148.18	513,584	$585.89	12	547,159
* Pennsylvania	12,702,379	58	22	80	2,368,149	$5,442.89	225,497	$426.74	2,593,646	$5,869.63	44	3,020,271
Puerto Rico	3,725,789	1	0	1	178,005	$0.00	0	$0.00	178,005	$0.00	1	209,901
* Rhode Island	1,052,567	4	1	5	143,466	$368.17	12,465	$22.00	155,931	$390.17	3	146,649
South Carolina	4,625,364	15	1	16	440,005	$884.42	6,409	$11.95	446,414	$896.37	13	592,710
South Dakota	814,180	7	4	11	104,597	$184.06	21,974	$57.95	126,571	$242.01	4	105,050
* Tennessee	6,346,105	13	12	25	535,523	$1,190.27	130,229	$181.26	665,752	$1,371.53	20	862,913
* Texas	25,145,561	58	23	81	2,080,846	$4,324.98	114,262	$279.59	2,195,108	$4,604.57	77	3,122,226
Utah	2,763,855	6	0	6	298,240	$596.17	0	$0.00	298,240	$596.17	6	371,623
Vermont	625,711	8	1	9	99,321	$192.15	5,695	$16.00	105,016	$208.15	4	87,608
Virginia	8,001,024	21	3	24	2,699,110	$1,192.98	21,971	$47.00	2,721,081	$1,239.98	17	758,753
Washington	6,724,540	15	6	21	686,960	$1,229.30	67,735	$115.31	754,695	$1,344.61	16	875,912
West Virginia	1,852,994	10	8	18	153,418	$387.98	66,548	$160.47	219,966	$548.45	11	194,880
* Wisconsin	5,686,986	19	14	33	592,864	$1,310.02	147,358	$434.55	740,222	$1,744.57	18	904,891
Wyoming	563,626	6	3	9	58,165	$105.02	20,244	$42.80	78,409	$147.82	6	65,718
TOTALS	310,919,701	931	451	1,382	40,320,681	$65,243.11	4,099,966	$7,568.34	44,420,647	$72,811.45	900	48,510,446

* Indicates population groups including one or more of the 26 all-day newspapers counted both in AM & PM columns, but only once in the total

Circulation for these papers is equally divided between AMs & PMs

Note: Circulation reflects "Total Average Circulation," which consists of a publication's paid and verified print and digital editions. Total average circulation also includes any paid and verified branded editions. (ABC recommends not making any direct comparisons of data to prior years.)

CIRCULATION OF U.S. DAILY NEWSPAPERS BY CIRCULATION GROUPS

NUMBER OF DAILY NEWSPAPERS				MORNING PAPERS NET CIRCULATION SEPT. 30, 2011		AFTERNOON PAPERS NET CIRCULATION SEPT. 30, 2011		TOTALS		SUNDAY PAPERS NET CIRCULATION SEPT. 30, 2011	
Circulation	AMs	PMs	Total	AM Circulation	Inch rates including all combinations	PM Circulation	Inch rates including all combinations	Total AM & PM Circulation	Minimum rates for AM & PM coverage	Number of papers	Sunday circulation
More than 1,000,000	4	0	4	6,731,000	$1,340.00	0	$0.00	6,731,000	$1,340.00	2	3,671,892
500,001 - 1,000,000	5	0	5	2,725,775	$3,417.95	0	$0.00	2,725,775	$3,417.95	9	6,435,951
* 100,001 - 500,000	69	0	69	13,453,972	$25,788.60	398,496	$0.00	13,852,468	$25,788.60	88	19,533,461
50,001 - 100,000	79	2	81	5,445,899	$10,794.41	168,977	$152.40	5,614,876	$10,946.81	96	6,713,746
* 25,001 - 50,000	148	12	160	5,128,486	$9,071.23	453,399	$618.18	5,581,885	$9,689.41	166	5,751,063
* 10,001 - 25,000	303	79	382	4,914,321	$9,426.41	1,128,909	$2,305.22	6,043,230	$11,731.63	281	4,735,559
* 5,001 - 10,000	200	182	382	1,492,693	$3,764.50	1,326,298	$2,669.68	2,818,991	$6,434.18	194	1,427,020
* 5,000 or less	123	176	299	428,535	$1,640.01	623,887	$1,822.86	1,052,422	$3,462.87	64	241,754
TOTALS	931	451	1,382	40,320,681	$65,243.11	4,099,966	$7,568.34	44,420,647	$72,811.45	900	48,510,446

*Indicates population groups including one or more of the 26 all-day newspapers counted both in AM & PM columns, but only once in the total
Circulation for these papers is equally divided between AMs & PMs

READY RECKONER OF ADVERTISING RATES AND CIRCULATIONS - CANADA

100 daily newspapers (64 morning, 36 evening) and 25 Sunday

Number of newspapers as of February 1, 2012 with circulations mainly as reported for six months ended September 30, 2011

NUMBER OF DAILY NEWSPAPERS					MORNING PAPERS NET CIRCULATION SEPT 30, 2011		AFTERNOON PAPERS NET CIRCULATIOON SEPT 30, 2011		TOTALS		SUNDAY PAPERS NET CIRCULATION SEPT 30, 2011	
PROVINCE	Population Statistics Canada July 2011	AMs	PMs	Total	AM Circulation	Inch rates including all combinations	PM Circulation	Inch rates including all combinations	Total AM & PM Circulation	Minimum rates for AM & PM coverage	Number of Papers	Sunday Circulation
Alberta	3,645,257	6	3	9	334,096	$27.36	23,781	$4.66	357,877	$32.02	5	336,929
British Columbia	4,400,057	8	7	15	410,117	$41.25	22,726	$7.36	432,843	$48.61	5	248,009
Manitoba	1,208,268	2	3	5	132,954	$12.71	19,279	$3.63	152,233	$16.34	3	174,338
New Brunswick	751,171	4	0	4	102,622	$10.57	0	$0.00	102,622	$10.57	0	0
Newfoundland and Labrador	514,536	2	0	2	26,317	$2.25	0	$0.00	26,317	$2.25	0	0
Nova Scotia	921,727	5	1	6	159,478	$10.66	6,540	$1.40	166,018	$12.06	1	97,283
Ontario	12,851,821	23	19	42	1,456,316	$158.81	170,601	$27.96	1,626,917	$186.77	6	680,598
Prince Edward Island	140,204	2	0	2	25,046	$2.18	0	$0.00	25,046	$2.18	0	0
Quebec	7,903,001	10	0	10	818,485	$50.23	0	$0.00	818,485	$50.23	5	500,669
Saskatchewan	1,033,381	2	2	4	94,074	$9.83	13,658	$2.43	107,732	$12.26	0	0
Yukon Territory	33,897	0	1	1	0	$0.00	1,820	$1.61	1,820	$1.61	0	0
TOTALS	33,403,320	64	36	100	3,559,505	$325.85	258,405	$49.05	3,817,910	$374.90	25	2,037,826

Note: Circulation reflects "Total Average Circulation," which consists of a publication's paid and verified print and digital editions. Total average circulation also includes any paid and verified branded editions. (ABC recommends not making any direct comparisons of data to prior years.)

CIRCULATION OF DAILY NEWSPAPERS OF CANADA BY CIRCULATION GROUPS

NUMBER OF DAILY NEWSPAPERS				MORNING PAPERS NET CIRCULATION SEPT 30, 2011		AFTERNOON PAPERS NET CIRCULATIOON SEPT 30, 2011		TOTALS		SUNDAY PAPERS NET CIRCULATION SEPT 30, 2011	
Circulation	AMs	PMs	Total	AM Circulation	Inch rates including all combinations	PM Circulation	Inch rates including all combinations	Total AM & PM Circulation	Minimum rates for AM & PM coverage	Number of Papers	Sunday Circulation
More than 500,000	0	0	0	0	$0.00	0	$0.00	0	$0.00	0	0
250,001 - 500,000	2	0	2	575,297	$69.27	0	$0.00	575,297	$69.27	1	295,589
100,001 - 250,000	12	0	12	1,672,822	$126.43	0	$0.00	1,672,822	$126.43	9	1,178,809
50,001 - 100,000	8	0	8	552,198	$51.19	0	$0.00	552,198	$51.19	3	228,114
25,001 - 50,000	11	0	11	393,977	$39.58	0	$0.00	393,977	$39.58	6	245,456
10,001 - 25,000	18	10	28	292,577	$28.75	135,485	$21.20	428,062	$49.95	5	83,459
10,000 or less	13	26	39	72,634	$14.87	122,920	$27.85	195,554	$42.72	1	6,399
TOTALS	64	36	100	3,559,505	$330.09	258,405	$49.05	3,817,910	$379.14	25	2,037,826

Note: Circulation reflects "Total Average Circulation," which consists of a publication's paid and verified print and digital editions. Total average circulation also includes any paid and verified branded editions. (ABC recommends not making any direct comparisons of data to prior years.)

Note: Circulation reflects "Total Average Circulation," which consists of a publication's paid and verified print and digital editions. Total average circulation also includes any paid and verified branded editions. (ABC recommends not making any direct comparisons of data to prior years.)

TOP 100 DAILY NEWSPAPERS IN THE U.S.

New York (NY) The Wall Street Journal (m-mon to sa) 2,096,169
McLean (VA) USA TODAY (m-mon to fri) 1,784,242
New York (NY) The New York Times (m-mon to fri) 1,150,589
New York (NY) NY Daily News (m-mon to fri) 605,677
Los Angeles (CA) Los Angeles Times (m-mon to fri) 572,998
San Jose (CA) San Jose Mercury News (m-mon to fri) 527,568
New York (NY) New York Post (m-mon to fri) 512,067
Washington (DC) The Washington Post (m-mon to fri) 507,465
Chicago (IL) Chicago Tribune (m-mon to fri) 425,370
Dallas (TX) The Dallas Morning News (m-mon to fri) 409,642
Melville (NY) Newsday (m-mon to fri) 404,542
Chicago (IL) Chicago Sun-Times (m-mon to fri) 389,353
Houston (TX) Houston Chronicle (m-mon to fri) 369,710
Denver (CO) The Denver Post (m-mon to fri) 353,115
Philadelphia (PA) The Philadelphia Inquirer (m-mon to fri) 331,134
Minneapolis (MN) Star Tribune (m-mon to fri) 298,147
Phoenix (AZ) The Arizona Republic (m-mon to fri) 292,838
Santa Ana (CA) The Orange County Register (m-mon to fri) 270,809
New York (NY) amNew York (m-mon to fri) 266,852
Springfield (VA) The Washington Examiner (m-mon to fri) 259,906
Cleveland (OH) The Plain Dealer (m-mon to fri) 243,299
Seattle (WA) The Seattle Times (m-mon to fri 242,814
Portland (OR) The Oregonian (All day-mon to fri) 242,784
Saint Petersburg (FL) Tampa Bay Times (m-mon to fri) 240,024
Detroit (MI) Detroit Free Press (m-mon to fri) 234,579
San Francisco (CA) San Francisco Chronicle (m-mon to fri) 220,515
San Diego (CA) The San Diego Union-Tribune (m-mon to fri) 219,347
Las Vegas (NV) Las Vegas Review-Journal (m-mon to fri) 213,078
Newark (NJ) The Star-Ledger (m-mon to fri) 210,586
Boston (MA) The Boston Globe (m-mon to fri) 205,939
Sacramento (CA) The Sacramento Bee (m-mon to fri) 199,921
Kansas City (MO) The Kansas City Star (m-mon to fri) 199,222
Saint Louis (MO) St. Louis Post-Dispatch (m-mon to fri) 191,631
Fort Worth (TX) Fort Worth Star-Telegram (m-mon to fri) 189,795
Milwaukee (WI) Milwaukee Journal Sentinel (m-mon to fri) 188,819
Saint Paul (MN) St. Paul Pioneer Press (m-mon to fri) 188,081
Pittsburgh (PA) Tribune-Review (m-mon to fri) 187,875
Little Rock (AR) Arkansas Democrat-Gazette (m-mon to fri) 179,134
Honolulu (HI) Honolulu Star-Advertiser (m-mon to fri) 178,082
San Juan (PR) El Nuevo Dia (m-mon to fri) 178,005
Atlanta (GA) Atlanta Journal-Constitution (m-mon to fri) 173,884
Pittsburgh (PA) Pittsburgh Post-Gazette (m-mon to fri) 173,160
Indianapolis (IN) The Indianapolis Star (m-mon to fri) 171,662
Orlando (FL) Orlando Sentinel (m-mon to fri) 171,418
Baltimore (MD) The Baltimore Sun (m-mon to fri) 170,510
Miami (FL) The Miami Herald (m-mon to fri) 160,505
Buffalo (NY) The Buffalo News (All day-mon to fri) 152,074
Fort Lauderdale (FL) Sun-Sentinel Co. (m-mon to fri) 147,860
Woodland Park (NJ) The Record, Herald News (m-mon to fri) 146,523
Norfolk (VA) The Virginian-Pilot (m-mon to fri) 145,785
Charlotte (NC) The Charlotte Observer (m-mon to fri) 145,595
Louisville (KY) The Courier-Journal (m-mon to fri) 142,801
Cincinnati (OH) The Cincinnati Enquirer (m-mon to fri) 140,877
Detroit (MI) The Detroit News (m-mon to fri) 139,128
Tampa (FL) The Tampa Tribune (m-mon to fri) 138,172
San Antonio (TX) San Antonio Express-News (m-mon to fri) 137,514
New Orleans (LA) The Times Picayune (m-mon to fri) 135,716
Hartford (CT) The Hartford Courant (m-mon to fri) 135,363
Columbus (OH) The Columbus Dispatch (m-mon to fri) 135,330
Omaha (NE) Omaha World-Herald (All day-mon to fri) 135,282
Oklahoma City (OK) The Oklahoman (m-mon to fri) 132,294
Los Angeles (CA) Investor's Business Daily (m-mon to fri) 127,896
Raleigh (NC) The News & Observer (m-mon to fri) 127,138
Rochester (NY) Democrat and Chronicle.com (m-mon to fri) 124,987
Providence (RI) The Providence Journal (m-mon to fri) 122,558
Nashville (TN) The Tennessean (m-mon to fri) 120,805
Austin (TX) Austin American-Statesman (m-mon to fri) 119,885
Boston (MA) Boston Herald (m-mon to fri) 113,798
Toledo (OH) The Blade (m-mon to fri) 113,786
Springfield (OH) Springfield News-Sun (m-mon to fri) 112,451
Riverside (CA) The Press-Enterprise (m-mon to fri) 112,084
Memphis (TN) The Commercial Appeal (m-mon to fri) 111,618
Richmond (VA) Richmond Times-Dispatch (m-mon to fri) 110,732
Salt Lake City (UT) The Salt Lake Tribune (m-mon to fri) 105,746
Des Moines (IA) The Des Moines Register (m-mon to fri) 105,151
Fresno (CA) The Fresno Bee (m-mon to fri) 104,991
Neptune (NJ) Asbury Park Press (m-mon to fri) 104,582
Birmingham (AL) The Birmingham News (m-mon to fri) 102,991
Los Angeles (CA) La Opinion (m-mon to fri) 100,608
Arlington Heights (IL) Daily Herald (m-mon to fri) 99,629
Jacksonville (FL) The Florida Times-Union (m-mon to fri) 99,280
Philadelphia (PA) The Philadelphia Daily News (m-mon to fri) 97,694
Tulsa (OK) Tulsa World (m-mon to fri) 97,580
West Palm Beach (FL) The Palm Beach Post (m-mon to fri) 95,620
Dayton (OH) Dayton Daily News (m-mon to fri) 93,259
Allentown (PA) The Morning Call (m-mon to fri) 93,175
Grand Rapids (MI) The Grand Rapids Press (e-mon to fri) 92,842
Knoxville (TN) Knoxville News Sentinel (m-mon to fri) 91,867
Woodland Hills (CA) Daily News (m-mon to fri) 89,990
Tucson (AZ) Arizona Daily Star (m-mon to fri) 89,874
Lexington (KY) Lexington Herald-Leader (m-mon to fri) 89,050
Akron (OH) Akron Beacon Journal (m-mon to fri) 87,780
Albuquerque (NM) Albuquerque Journal (m-mon to fri) 87,109
Munster (IN) The Times (m-mon to fri) 86,894
Madison (WI) Wisconsin State Journal (m-mon to fri) 84,191
Charleston (SC) The Post and Courier (m-mon to fri) 82,261
New Castle (DE) The News Journal (m-mon to fri) 81,749
Mobile (AL) Press-Register (m-mon to fri) 81,003
Syracuse (NY) The Post-Standard (m-mon to fri) 80,720
Long Beach (CA) Press-Telegram (m-mon to fri) 79,925

TOP 10 DAILY NEWSPAPERS IN CANADA

Toronto (ON) The Globe and Mail (m-mon to fri) 309,154
Toronto (ON) Toronto Star (m-mon to fri) 266,143
Montreal (QC) Le Journal de Montreal (m-mon to fri) 206,490
Montreal (QC) La Presse (m-mon to fri) 205,411
Vancouver (BC) The Vancouver Sun (m-mon to fri) 156,769
Toronto (ON) National Post (m-mon to fri) 146,245
Vancouver (BC) The Province (m-mon to fri) 144,996
Toronto (ON) The Toronto Sun (m-mon to fri) 141,144
Calgary (AB) Calgary Herald (m-mon to fri) 124,559
Montreal (QC) The Gazette (m-mon to fri) 116,446

Note: Circulation reflects "Total Average Circulation," which consists of a publication's paid and verified print and digital editions. Total average circulation also includes any paid and verified branded editions. (ABC recommends not making any direct comparisons of data to prior years.)

TOP 100 SUNDAY NEWSPAPERS IN THE U.S.

Newspaper	Circulation
New York (NY) The Wall Street Journal	2,026,740
New York (NY) The New York Times	1,645,152
Houston (TX) Houston Chronicle	911,564
Los Angeles (CA) Los Angeles Times	905,920
Washington (DC) The Washington Post	846,019
Chicago (IL) Chicago Tribune	781,128
New York (NY) NY Daily News	667,638
Detroit (MI) Detroit Free Press	639,350
San Jose (CA) San Jose Mercury News	602,566
Minneapolis (MN) Star Tribune	543,633
Denver (CO) The Denver Post	538,133
Philadelphia (PA) The Philadelphia Inquirer	482,457
Melville (NY) Newsday	476,723
Phoenix (AZ) The Arizona Republic	472,200
Atlanta (GA) Atlanta Journal-Constitution	410,022
Cleveland (OH) The Plain Dealer	403,945
Saint Petersburg (FL) Tampa Bay Times	403,229
Chicago (IL) Chicago Sun-Times	400,506
Santa Ana (CA) The Orange County Register	397,764
New York (NY) New York Post	379,673
Dallas (TX) The Dallas Morning News	374,653
Boston (MA) The Boston Globe	360,186
San Antonio (TX) San Antonio Express-News	344,120
Seattle (WA) Seattle Post-Intelligencer/Seattle Times	333,937
Newark (NJ) The Star-Ledger	333,601
Saint Louis (MO) St. Louis Post-Dispatch	332,825
Milwaukee (WI) Milwaukee Journal Sentinel	326,262
Pittsburgh (PA) Pittsburgh Post-Gazette	317,439
Baltimore (MD) The Baltimore Sun	314,253
Indianapolis (IN) The Indianapolis Star	313,057
Portland (OR) The Oregonian	300,922
Kansas City (MO) The Kansas City Star	300,450
San Diego (CA) The San Diego Union-Tribune	293,423
San Francisco (CA) San Francisco Chronicle	287,226
Orlando (FL) Orlando Sentinel	286,982
Cincinnati (OH) The Cincinnati Enquirer	285,345
Sacramento (CA) The Sacramento Bee	269,660
Little Rock (AR) Arkansas Democrat-Gazette	266,798
Columbus (OH) The Columbus Dispatch	265,892
Tampa (FL) The Tampa Tribune	259,590
Louisville (KY) The Courier-Journal	257,611
Saint Paul (MN) St. Paul Pioneer Press	252,796
Buffalo (NY) The Buffalo News	235,671
Fort Worth (TX) Fort Worth Star-Telegram	230,809
Fort Lauderdale (FL) Sun-Sentinel Co.	224,763
Nashville (TN) The Tennessean	224,440
Des Moines (IA) The Des Moines Register	216,648
Charlotte (NC) The Charlotte Observer	213,803
San Juan (PR) El Nuevo Dia	209,901
Miami (FL) The Miami Herald	209,116
Pittsburgh (PA) Tribune-Review	202,181
Hartford (CT) The Hartford Courant	199,661
Oklahoma City (OK) The Oklahoman	197,270
Raleigh (NC) The News & Observer	191,923
Austin (TX) Austin American-Statesman	186,803
Las Vegas (NV) Las Vegas Review-Journal	186,785
Norfolk (VA) The Virginian-Pilot	176054
Springfield (OH) Springfield News-Sun	175,995
Birmingham (AL) The Birmingham News	175,497
Rochester (NY) Democrat and Chronicle.com	173,429
Woodland Park (NJ) The Record, Herald News	172,660
Omaha (NE) Omaha World-Herald	170,381
Richmond (VA) Richmond Times-Dispatch	164,137
Jacksonville (FL) The Florida Times-Union	159,312
Neptune (NJ) Asbury Park Press	157,723
New Orleans (LA) The Times Picayune	155,435
Grand Rapids (MI) The Grand Rapids Press	152,231
Toledo (OH) The Blade	150,119
Dayton (OH) Dayton Daily News	149,268
Memphis (TN) The Commercial Appeal	146,594
Tucson (AZ) Arizona Daily Star	143,358
Fresno (CA) The Fresno Bee	140,929
Tulsa (OK) Tulsa World	140,126
Syracuse (NY) The Post-Standard	139,130
Honolulu (HI) Honolulu Star-Advertiser	135,555
Columbia (SC) The State	129,715
Riverside (CA) The Press-Enterprise	129,409
Providence (RI) The Providence Journal	129,024
Albany (NY) Times Union	128,001
Akron (OH) Akron Beacon Journal	125,227
New Castle (DE) The News Journal	124,693
West Palm Beach (FL) The Palm Beach Post	123,488
Allentown (PA) The Morning Call	123,409
Salt Lake City (UT) The Salt Lake Tribune	122,782
Knoxville (TN) Knoxville News Sentinel	120,881
Madison (WI) Wisconsin State Journal	119,192
Greenville (SC) The Greenville News	118,686
Lexington (KY) Lexington Herald-Leader	117,980
Mechanicsburg (PA) The Patriot-News	116,609
Albuquerque (NM) Albuquerque Journal	113,361
Arlington Heights (IL) Daily Herald	107,499
Colorado Springs (CO) Gazette	107,001
Chattanooga (TN) Chattanooga Times Free Press	103,419
Fort Wayne (IN) The Journal Gazette	102,861
Tacoma (WA) The News Tribune	102,645
Baton Rouge (LA) The Advocate	102,240
Mobile (AL) Press-Register	101,808
Springfield (MA) The Republican	101,471
Wichita (KS) The Wichita Eagle	100,199
Woodland Hills (CA) Daily News	98,939

TOP 10 SUNDAY NEWSPAPERS IN CANADA

Newspaper	Circulation
Toronto (ON) Toronto Star	295,589
Montreal (QC) Le Journal de Montreal	209,175
Toronto (ON) The Toronto Sun	187,433
Vancouver (BC) The Province	158,146
Winnipeg (MB) Winnipeg Free Press	122,654
Calgary (AB) Calgary Herald	114,642
Ottawa (ON) The Ottawa Citizen	105,143
Edmonton (AB) Edmonton Journal	100,026
Halifax (NS) The Chronicle Herald	97,283
Vanier (QC) Le Journal de Quebec	87,741

U.S. AND CANADIAN MULTINEWSPAPER CITIES

NOTE: This list includes 35 cities in the United States and 9 cities in Canada as of Feb 1, 2010. Newspapers publishing under the 8 joint operating agreements are indicated with a (*). The 11 U.S. cities and 1 Canadian city with newspapers of common ownership are indicated by an (+). The national newspapers are not included.

TUCSON, AZ
Arizona Daily Star (m-mon to fri; m-sat; S)*
Tucson Citizen (e-mon to fri; m-sat)*
The Dialy Territorial (m-mon to fri)

LOS ANGELES, CA
Daily Commerce (e-mon to fri)
Investor's Business Daily (m-mon to fri)
La Opinion (Spanish) (m-mon to fri; m-sat; S)
Los Angeles Times (m-mon to fri; m-sat; S)
Daily News (m-mon to fri; m-sat; S)

SAN DIEGO, CA
The Daily Transcript (m-mon to fri)
The San Diego Union-Tribune (m-mon to fri; m-sat;S)

SAN FRANCISCO, CA
San Francisco Chronical (all day-mon to fri; m-sat;S)
The Examiner (m-mon to fri; S)

SAN MATEO, CA
San Mateo County Times (e-mon to fri; m-sat)
San Mateo Daily Journal (m-mon to sat)

ASPEN, CO
Aspen Daily News (m-mon to sat; S)
The Aspen Times (m-mon to sat)

BOULDER, CO
Daily Camera (m-mon to fri; m-sat)*
Colorado Daily (m-mon to fri)

WASHINGTON, DC
The Washington Post (m-mon to fri, m-sat. S)
The Washington Times (m-mon to fri;S)

MIAMI, FL
Diario Las Americas (Spanish) m-tues to sat;S)
The Miami Herald (m-mon to fri; m-sat;S)
El Nuevo Herald (m-mon to fril m-sat;S)

CHICAGO, IL
Daily Herald (m-mon to fri, m-sat; S)
SouthtownStar (m-mon to fri; m-sat;S)
Chicago Sun-Times (m-mon to fri, m-sat;S)
Chicago Tribune (m-mon to fri, m-sat;S)

FORT WAYNE, IN
The Journal Gazaette (m-mon to fri, m-sat;S)*
The News-Sentinel (e-mon to fri, e-sat)+

BOSTON, MA
The Christian Science Monitor (m-mon to fri)
The Boston Glove (m-mon to fri, m-sat)
Boston Herald (m-mon to fri, m-sat;S)

DETROIT, MI
Detroit Free Press (m-mon to fri, m-sat; S)*
The Detroit News (m-mon to fri, m-sat)*

COLUMBIA, NO
Columbia Missourian (m-mon to fri;S)
Columbia Daily Tribune (e-mon to fri, m-sat;S)

LAS VEGAS, NV
Las Vegas Sun (m-mon to fri, m-sat;S)*
Las Vegas Review-Journal (m-mon to fri, m-sat;S)*

TRENTON, NJ
The Times (m-mon to fri, m-sat;S)
The Trentonian (m-mon to fri, m-sat;S)

NEW YORK, NY
am New York (m-mon to fri)
El Diario La Prensa (Spanish) (m-mon to fri, m-sat;S)
Daily News (m-mon to fri, m-sat;S)
New York Post (m-mon to fri, m-sat;S)
The New York times (m-mon to fri, m-sat;S)
The Wall Street Journal (m-mon to fri, m-sat)
Holy (Spanish) m-mon to fri;S)

OGDENSBURG, NY
Courier-Observer (m-tues to sat)*
The Journal (m-mon to fri)*

PORTLAND, OR
Daily Journal of Commerce (m-mon to fri)
The Oregonian (all day-mon to fri, m-sat;S)

FRANKLIN-OIL CITY, PA
The Derrick (m-mon to sat)*
The News-Herald (m-mon to sat)*

LANCASTER, PA
Intelligencer Journal (m-mon to fri; m-sat)*
Lancaster News Era (e-mon to fri; e-sat)*

PHILADELPHIA, PA
The Philadelphia Inquirer (m-mon to fri; m-sat;S)
The Philadelphia Daily News (m-mon to fri, m-sat)*

WILKES-BARRE, PA
The Citizens' Voice (m-mon to fri;m-sat)
Times Leader (m-mon to sat;S)

YORK, PA
York Daily Records (m-mon to fri;m-sat)*
The York Dispatch (e-mon to fri)*

KINGSPORT, TN
Daily News (m-tues to thur; wknd)
Kingsport Times-News (m-mon to fri;m-sat;S)

DALLAS, TX
Al Dia (m-mon to sat)
The Dallas Morning News (m-mon to fri,m-sat;S)

SALT LAKE CITY, UT
The Deseret News (m-mon to fri;m-sat;S)*
The Salt Lake Ttribune (m-mon to fri;m-sat;S)*

SEATTLE, WA
Seattle Daily Journal of Commerce (m-mon to sat)
The Seattle Times (m-mon to fri;m-sat;S)

CHARLESTON, WV
Charleston Gazette (m-mon to fri)*
Charleston Daily Mall (e-mon to fri)*

PARKERSBURG, WV
The Parkersburg News (m-mon to fri, m-sat,S+
The Parkersburg Sentinel (e-mon to fri)+

WHEELING, WV
The Intelligencer (m-mon to fri, m-sat)*
Wheeling News-Register (e-mon to fri;S)

MADISON, WI
The Capital Times (e-mon to fri;e-sat)+
Wisconsin State Journal (m-mon to fri;m-sat;S)

CANADA

CALGARY, AB
Calgary Herald (m-mon to fri,m-sat;S)
The Calgary Sun (m-mon to fri;m-sat)

EDMONTON, AB
Edmonton Journal (m-mon to fri, m-sat;S)
The Edmonton sun (m-mon to fri;m-sat)

VANCOUVER, BC
The Province (m-mon to fri;S)+
The Vancouver Sun (m-mon to fri;m-sat)*

WINNEPEG, MB
Winnepeg Free Press (m-mon to fri,m-sat;S)
The Winnepeg Sun (m-mon to fri;m-sat;S)

OTTOWA, ON
The Ottawa Citizen (m-mon to fri,m-sat;S)
Le Droit (m-mon to fri,m-sat)
The Ottawa Sun (m-mon to fri;m-sat;S)

TORONTO, ON
National Post (m-mon to fri;m-sat)
The Globe and Mall (m-mon to ri;m-sat)
The Toronto Start (m-mon to fri,m-sat;S)
The Toronto Sun (m-mon to fri,m-sat;S)

MONTREAL, D.C.
Le Devoir (m-mon to fri,m-sat)
The Gazette (m-mon to fri;,-sat;S)
Le Journaal de Montreal (m-mon to fri,m-sat;S)
La Presse (m-mon to fri;m-sat;S)

QUEBEC, DC
Le Journal de Quebec (m-mon to fri;m-sat;S)
Le Soleil (m-mon to fri;m-sat;S)

SHERBOOKE, QC
The Records (m-mon to fri)
La Tribune (m-mon to fri;m-sat)

MECHANICAL EQUIPMENT — ABBREVIATIONS

COMPOSITION

TYPESETTERS

AG — Agfa-Gevaert
AU — Autologic
AX — Automix
Bg — Bobst Graphic
COM — Compugraphic
Dy — Dymo
F — Fairchild
Fi — Filmotype
Fo — Fotosetter
Fr — Friden
HCM — Hell/HCM
Hd — Headliner
HI — Harris
Ik — Itek
Jus — Justowriter
L — Lanston
LC — Linofilm Composer
M — Mergenthaler
Ma — Morisawa
MGD — MGD-Rockwell
MON — Monotype
Ph — Photon
Pr — Protype
Pt — Photo Typositor
So — Simmons-Owega
SP — Star Parts
Sr — Singer
ST — Stripprinter
TC — Titus Communications
V — Varityper
Va — Varisystems
VG — Visual Graphics

FRONT-END HARDWARE & SOFTWARE

ACT — Automated Complete Typesetting
AG — Agfa-Gevaert
AP — Associated Press
APP — Apple
AT — Atex
AU — Autologic
AX — Automix
BD — Berthold NA
Bee — Beehive
BF — Basic 4
Bg — Bobst Graphic
BR — Bunker Ramo
Bs — Burroughs
C — Chemco
CD — Crosfield Data Systems
CDS — Computer Double Screen
CJ — Collier-Jackson
CM — Cincinnati Milacron
COM — Compugraphic
CPU — Computext
Cp — CompuScan
CS — Computer Services
CSI — Computer Systems Inc.
Cx — Camex
Da — Datapoint
DD — Delta Data
DEC — Digital Equipment Corp.
DL — Data Logic
DS — Data Disc
DTI — Digital Technology International
Dy — Dymo
ECR — ECRM
EKI — Electric Knowledge Inc.
En — Entrex
ES — Evans & Southerland
ESE — Editorial System Engineering Co.
FSI — Freedom Systems Integrators
Gn — Genisis
HAS — Hastech
Hel — Hell
HI — Harris
HP — Hewlett Packard
Hw — Honeywell
Hx — Hendrix
Hz — Hazeltine
IBM — International Business Machines
III — Information International Inc.
Ik — Itek
In — Infotron
INS — Independent Network Services
ISSI — Integrated Software Systems Inc.
KC — Key Corp.
Kk — Kodak
Lf — Leaf Systems
LIP — Logicon-Intercomp
Lk — Lektromedia
LNS — Lee Newspapers Services
LS — Lear-Siegler
M — Mergenthaler
Mac — Macintosh
MD — Micro Data
MeD — Mega Data
MGD — MGD-Rockwell
Mh — Mohr
Mk — Mycro-Tek
MON — Monotype
MPS — Morris Publishing Systems
Mx — Memorex
NEC — Newspaper Electronics Corp.
NW — Neasi-Weber
Omn — Omnitext
Omo — Omron
On — Ontel
Op — Omptimix
OS — One Systems
PBS — Publishing Business Systems
PEP — Perception Electronic

PUBLISHING

PS — Peripheral Systems
QPS — Quark Publishing Systems
Ra — Raytheon
RSK — Radio Shack
RZ — Royal Zenith
SCS — Software Consulting Services
SII — System Integrators Inc.
SMS — Stauffer Media Systems
Syc — Sycor
SyD — Systems Development
TC — Titus Communications
Te — Telcom
TI — Texas Instruments
TM — Teleram
Tr — Teleray
TRW — TRW-Fujitsu
TS — Tal-Star
Tt — Teleterm
Tx — Telex
Uni — Univac
V — Varityper
Va — Varisystems
X — Xerox
XIT — Xitron
ZC — Zentec Corp.

AUDIOTEX

DJ — Dow Jones
TEDS — Toronto Star Edition Design System
TMS — Tribune Media Services
VNN — Voice News Network

OCR READERS

APP — Apple
COM — Compugraphic
Cp — CompuScan
Da — Datatype
Di — Digitek
ECR — ECRM
Hx — Hendrix
M — Mergenthaler
MGD — MGD-Rockwell

PLATE-MAKING

PLATE SYSTEMS

AU — Autologic
B — Brown
CD — Crosfield Data Systems
DiL — DiLitho
DP — DuPont
Dyn — Dynaflex
ECM — EOCOM
F — Fairchild
He — Hercules (Merigraph)
LE — LogEtronics
LP — Laser-Plate
LX — Grace (Letterflex)
Mag — Magnesium
Na — Napp
Nat — National
Rf — Richflex
WL — Western Litho
Z — Zinc

PLATE PROCESSORS

B — Brown
Be — Beach
BM — Ball Metal
CEM — Chemcut
Dow — Dow Chemical
DP — DuPont
Dyn — Dynaflex
He — Hercules (Merigraph)
Ic — Iconics
LG — Laser Graphics
LX — Grace (Letterflex)
MAS — Master
Na — Napp
Nat — National
Nu — nuArc
Ny — Nyloprint
Tas — TasopeSearch
Wd — Wood
WL — Western Litho

CAMERAS

AG — Agfa-Gevaert
B — Brown
Bo — Borrowdale
Br — Bruning
C — Chemco
CL — Clydedale
Co — Consolidated
COM — Compugraphic
DAI — Dainippon
DSA — D.S. America (SCREEN)
ECR — ECRM
Go — Goodkin
Ik — Itek
K — Kenro
Kk — Kodak
Kl — Klimsch
L — Lanston
LE — LogEtronics
MG — ModiGraphic
Nu — nuArc
R — Robertson
Sm — Statmaster
VG — Visual Graphics
W — Western

AUTOMATIC FILM PROCESSORS

AG — Agfa-Gevaert
AU — Autologic
C — Chemo
DP — DuPont
Kk — Kodak
Kr — Kreonite
LE — LogEtronics
P — Pako
WL — Western Litho

COLOR SEPARATION SYSTEMS

AG — Agfa-Gevaert
BKY — Berkey
C — Chemco
Ca — Carlson
Eh — Ehrenreich
Hel — Hell
KFM — K&F Printing Systems International
Kk — Kodak
Lf — Leaf Systems
RZ — Royal Zenith
WDS — Warner MDS

PRESSROOM

DILITHO SYSTEMS

DI — Dahlgren
G — Goss
HI — Harris
In — Inland
RPM — Smith RPM Co.
Ry — Ryco Graphic
T — Taft
Wd — Wood

PRESSES

Bk — Babcock
Cb — Crabtree
FAU — Faustel
Fin — Fincor
FOL — Flex-O-Line
G — Goss
GE — General Electric
H — Hoe
Ha — Hantscho
HAR — Hoe-Aller
HI — Heidleberg-Harris
KB — Koenig & Bauer
KP — King Press
MAN — MAN/Roland USA
MHI — Mitsubishi Heavy Ind.
MOT — Motter
SC — Scott
SLN — Solna
TKS — Tokyo Kikai Seisakusho
Tp — Thatcher-Pacer
Wd — Wood
WPC — Web Press Corp.

PRESS CONVERSION SYSTEMS

KDS — Kidder Stacy
KFM — K&F Printing Systems International
PEC — Publishers Equip. Corp.
PMC — Press Machinery Corp.
RKW — Rockwell
RPM — Smith RPM Co.

REPROPORTIONING SYSTEMS

CS — Combined Services
FLS — Flurographic Services

MAILROOM

STACKERS

BG — Baldwin-Gegenheimer
CH — Cutler-Hammer
DG — Didde Glaser
Fg — Ferag
HI — Heidelberg-Harris
HL — Hall
Id — IDAB
KAN — Kansa
MM — Muller-Martini
MRS — Mailroom Systems
NJP — Nolan Jampol
PPK — Pace Pack
QWI — Quipp
RKW — Rockwell
SH — Sta-Hi
St — Stepper

INSERTERS/STUFFERS

D — Dexter
DG — Didde Glaser
Fg — Ferag
G — Goss
Gr — Graphicart
HI — Harris
I — Insertomatic
KAN — Kansa
KR — Kirk-Rudy
LEG — Leger Inc.
M — Mergenthaler
Mc — McCain
Mg — Magnacratt
MM — Muller-Martini
S — Sheridan
SH — Sta-Hi
St — Stepper

BUNDLE TYERS

AMP — Ampag
Bu — Bunn
Ca — Carlson
Cn — Cranston
Cr — Crawford
CYP — Cypack
Eb — Ebby
Gd — Gerrard
Gs — General Strapping
HL — Hall
Id — IDAB
In — Inland
It — Interlake
J — Jampol
Mc — McCain
Md — MidStates
MLN — Signode
MM — Muller-Martini
MVP — Metaveppa
NJP — Nolan Jampol
OVL — Ovalstrapping
PM — Paper Man
QWI — Quipp
S — Sheridan
Sa — Saxmayer
SHt — SatoHit
Si — Parker-Signode
St — Stepper
Ty — Tyler
Us — USSteel
Ws — Walla Star
WT — Wire-Tyer

ADDRESSERS

Am — Addressograph-Multigraph
AVY — Avery
BH — Bell & Howell
Ch — Cheshire
Dm — Dick Mailer
El — Elliott
Gd — Gerrard
GL — Galley List
Gp — Graphotype
Hw — Honeywell
IBM — International Business Machines
KAN — Kansa
KR — Kirk-Rudy
Mg — Magnacraft
Pa — Pollard-Alling
PB — Pitney-Bowes
Rp — Roto-Strip Printer
RSK — Radio Shack
SC — Scriptomatic
Sp — Speedomat
SRC — Standard Register Co.
St — Stepper
Wm — Wing Mailer

DELIVERY SYSTEMS

CBM — Custom Built Machinery
EDS — EDS-IDAB
Fg — Ferag
FMC — FMC Corp.
KAN — Kansa
RKW — Rockwell
SIH — SI Handling

LIBRARY SYSTEMS

AT — Atex
ATT — AT&T
BH — Bell & Howell
CCC — Capital Cities Communications
DDC — Documaster
DEC — Digital Equipment
GE — General Electric
IBM — International Business Machines
IFK — Info-Ky
IXA — Infotex Assoc.
LIP — Logicon-Intercomp
MED — Mead
QLS — QL Systems
SII — System Integrators Inc.
SMS — Stauffer Media Systems

COMMUNICATIONS

FACSIMILE EQUIPMENT

ABD — AB Dick
Ao — Apeco
AP — Associated Press
ATT — AT&T
CD — Crosfield Digital Systems
CP — Canadian Press
DF — Data Fax
Dm — Daycom
ECM — EOCOM
Hel — Hell
Ho — Hogan
IBM — International Business Machines
III — Information International Inc.
LI — Litcom
Mag — Magnavox
Mh — Muirhead
Px — Pressfax
Q — Quickfax
QWI — Quipp
Rem — Remington
SN — Scanatron
SW — Stewart Warner
Uf — Unifax
UPI — United Press International
VI — Vistatype
Wr — Warwick
Wx — Westrex
X — Xerox

DATA COMMUNICATIONS

AMS — American Satellite
DTG — Datalog
EPT — Epic Technology
GAN — Gandalf Data
Mot — Motorola
XIT — Xitron

BUSINESS COMPUTERS

ALR — Advanced Logic Research
APP — Apple
AT — Atex
ATT — AT&T
Bs — Burroughs
CJ — Collier-Jackson
DEC — Digital Equipment Corp.
DG — Data General
EKI — Electric Knowledge Inc.
HP — Hewlett Packard
Hw — Honeywell
IBM — International Business Machines
Mac — Macintosh
Mk — Mycro-Tek
NEC — Newspaper Electronics Corp.
PBS — Publishing Business Systems
RSK — Radio Shack
TI — Texas Instruments
Uni — Univac
Wa — Wang

The table of abbreviations is for major equipment manufacturers listed in section I & III. Companies not found in the above list are entered in full.

Section I

Daily Newspapers Published in the United States and Canada

DAILY NEWSPAPERS PUBLISHED IN THE UNITED STATES

EXPLANATION OF SYMBOLS AND ABBREVIATIONS FOR U.S. DAILIES

ABC definitions follow lines of urban development, trading habit or political boundary. Publishers may report their circulation by city zone and retail trading zone or by newspaper designated market. These are established with approval of the Audit Bureau of Circulations.

ABC-city zone (ABC-CZ) – Area described as the corporate city center or target area of circulation.

ABC-retail trading zone (ABC-RTZ) - Area beyond the City Zone whose residents regularly trade to an important degree with the retail merchants in the City Zone.
Newspaper Designated Market (ABC-NDM). The geographical area which a newspaper considers to be the market it serves. Publisher members have the option of reporting circulation according to just the new NDM or in combination with a City Zone and/or Retail Trading zone figure.

HH-Households

NEWSPAPER PUBLICATIONS
AND CIRCULATION
(d) – daily
(m) – morning
(e) – evening
(S) – Sunday
(all day) – several editions published through the day

CIRCULATION
Figures preceded by "ABC" indicate circulation from the ABC publisher's statement for period ending Sept. 30, 2011, unless otherwise noted.

All other figures are from newspapers' sworn postal statements.

ADVERTISING RARTES
Maximum rate per inch (open inch rate) for general (national) display advertising is shown where available for each edition of the paper and for combinations between editions and other daily papers.

NEWS SERVICES
AP – Associated Press
AFP – Agency France-Presse
CO – Canadian Press
CN 0 - Capital News Service
CNS – Copley News Service
CQ – Congressional Quarterly Service
SCM - Christian Science Monitor
DF – Data Features
DJ – Dow Jones
GNS – Gannett News Service
HN – Hearst Newspapers
INS – Independent Network Systems
LAT-WP - Los Angeles Times-Washington Post News Service
MCT – McClatchy-Tribune Information Services
NEA – Newspaper Enterprise Association
NYT – New York Times News Service
ONS – Ottawa News
PNS – Pacific News Service
RN – Reuters News Agency
SHNS - Scripps-Howard Newspaper Service
SNS – Sterling News Service
TMS – Tribune Media Service
UPI – United Press International

For table of abbreviations of equipment and manufacturer, see front pages.

ALABAMA

ALEXANDER CITY

ALEXANDER CITY OUTLOOK

548 Cherokee Rd., Alexander City, Ala., 35011; gen tel (256) 234-4281; adv tel (256) 234-4281; ed tel (256) 234-4281; gen fax (256) 234-6550; adv fax (256) 234-6550; ed fax (256) 234-6550; gen e-mail editor@alexcityoutlook.com; web site www.alexcityoutlook.com

Published: Tues, Wed, Thur, Fri, Sat
Weekday Frequency: m
Circulation: 5,300; 5,300(sat); 5,300(sun)
Last Audit: September 30, 2001
Price: 7.00/mo; 138.00/yr.
Advertising: Open inch rate $13.90
News services: Landon Media Group.
Politics: Independent.
Not Published: Christmas.
Special Editions: Bridal (Apr); Back-to-School (Aug); Christmas Greetings (Dec); Parade (Feb); Home Town Business (Jan); FYI (Jul); Spring Fashion (Mar); Graduation (May); Gift Guide (Nov); Fall Fashion (Sept).
Special Weekly Sections: Lake Martin Fish Wrapper (Fri); Education (Thur); Automotive (Wed).
Magazines: Parade (S); American Profile (Weekly).
Pub. Kenneth Boone
Bus. Mgr. Darlene Yates
Gen. Mgr. Roger Steele
Acct. Exec. Mary Ann Foy
Acct. Exec. Doug Patterson
Circ. Mgr. Fran Cassiano
Prodn. Mgr. Lee Champion
Market Information: TMC.
Mechanical available: Offset; Black and 3 ROP colors; insert accepted; page cutoffs - 22 3/4.
Mechanical Specifications: Type page 13 x 21 1/2; E - 6 cols, 2 1/16, 1/8 between; A - 6 cols, 2 1/16, 1/8 between; C - 9 cols, 2 1/16, 1/8 between.
Commodity Consumption: Avg. Page Number Per Issue - Daily 12; Avg. Page Number Per Issue - Plates Used 2000; widths 27 1/2; Newsprint Used - Short Tons 240; Printing Ink Used - Pages Printed 3696.
Equipment; Editorial Hardware – 7-APP/Mac; Editorial Equipment – 3-APP/Mac, 2-APP/Mac LaserWriter.; Classified Hardware – 2-APP/Mac.; Production Equipment – Nu; Cameras – CL. PRESSROOM: Line 1 – 5-KP/News King. MAILROOM: Counter stackers – BG/Count-O-Veyor 104A; Bundle tying machines – 1/Ca.

ANDALUSIA

ANDALUSIA STAR-NEWS

207 Dunson St., Andalusia, Ala., 36420-0403; gen tel (334) 222-2402; ed tel (334) 222-2402; gen fax (334) 222-6597; ed fax (334) 222-6597; ed e-mail editor@andalusiastarnews.com; web site www.andalusiastarnews.com

Published: Tues, Wed, Thur, Fri, Sat
Weekday Frequency: m
Saturday Frequency: m
Circulation: 3,395; 3,600(sat)
Last Audit: March 31, 2007
Price: 8.00/mo; 88.00/yr.
Advertising: Open inch rate $9.80
News services: NEA.
Politics: Independent. **Established:** 1939
Not Published: New Year; Christmas.
Special Editions: Baseball (Apr); Football (Aug); Progress (Feb); Chamber Guide (Jan); Pride In America (Jun); Home Improvement (Mar); Graduation (May); Fall Fashion (Sept).
Special Weekly Sections: Health Page (Fri); TV (Sat); Business/Financial Page (Thur); Education (Tues); Agriculture (Wed).
Magazines: American Profile (Weekly).
Pub. ..... Michele Gerlach
Adv. Mgr. ..... Ruck Ashworth
Circ. Dir. ..... Jeff Moore
News Ed. ..... Stephanie Nelson
Prodn. Mgr. ..... Chris Love
Market Information: ADS; TMC.
Mechanical available: Offset; Black and 3 ROP colors; insert accepted - by request; page cutoffs - 22 7/8.
Mechanical Specifications: Type page 13 x 21 1/2; E - 6 cols, 2 1/16, 1/8 between; A - 6 cols, 2 1/16, 1/8 between; C - 9 cols, 1 3/8, 1/8 between.
Commodity Consumption: Avg. Page Number Per Issue - Daily 12; Avg. Page Number Per Issue - Plates Used 7500; widths 27 1/2; Newsprint Used - Short Tons 600; Printing Ink Used - Black 20000; Printing Ink Used - Color 500.
Equipment; Editorial Hardware – 6-APP/Mac Quadra 610, 2-APP/Power Mac 8100, 1-APP/Power Mac 8500, 10-APP/Mac G3, 2-APP/Mac 8500; Editorial Equipment – 2-V/Panther 3990 Imagesetter, XYQUEST/270 Mb drive, XYQUEST/28.8 modem, Polaroid/SprintScan 35; Editorial Printers – 2-APP/Mac LaserWriter 810 Pr CLASSIFIED: Front-end Software – Baseview/Class Manager Plus.; Classified Hardware – APP/Mac G3; Classified Printers – APP/Mac LaserWriter 810 Pro, Xante/Accel-a-Writer 8200 DISPLAY: Ad make-up applications – QPS/QuarkXPress 4.0, Adobe/Acrobat 2.1; Display Hardware – 2-APP/Mac G3; Display Printers – APP/Mac LaserWriter 810 Pro, Xante/Accel-a-Writer 8200 PRODUCTION: Pagination Software – QPS/QuarkXPress 4.0.; Production Equipment – Nat/Universal 33 Subtractive; Cameras – Horizontal/Clyesdale; Scanners – 2-HP/ScanJet IIcx, 1-Lf/Leafscan 35, 1-Polaroid/Sprintscan 35ES PRESSROOM: Line 1 – 10-KP/News King single width 1994; Folders – KP/KJ 6; Reels and Stands – 6 MAILROOM: Counter stackers – BG/Count-O-Veyor; Inserters and stuffers – KAN/480; Bundle tying machines – Wilton; Addressing machine – 2/Dispensa-Matic/16. BUSINESS COMPUTERS: Business Software – Microsoft/Excel; Business Hardware – Dell/PC

ANNISTON

THE ANNISTON STAR

4305 McClellan Blvd., Anniston, Ala., 36206; gen tel (256) 236-1551; ed tel (256) 235-9556; gen fax (256) 241-1991; adv fax (256) 241-1984; ed fax (256) 241-1991; gen e-mail news@annistonstar.com; web site www.annistonstar.com

Published: Mon, Tues, Wed, Thur, Fri, Sat, Sun
Weekday Frequency: m
Saturday Frequency: m
Circulation: 19,563; 22,045(sat); 21,039(sun)
Last Audit: ABC September 30, 2011
Price: 13.50/mo; 153.00/yr.
Advertising: Open inch rate $40.00
News services: AP, NYT.
Politics: 1883
Own facility?: Y
Special Editions: Healthy Living
Special Weekly Sections: TV Star (Fri)
Magazines: Parade (S).
LongLeaf
Chrmn./Pub. ..... H. Brandt Ayers
Pres ..... Phillip A. Sanguinetti
Vice Pres., Opns. ..... Ed Fowler
HR Mgr. ..... Elaine Estes
Circ. Dir. ..... Dennis Dunn
Circ. Mgr. ..... Donnie Bowman
Ed. ..... Bob Davis
Mng. Ed. ..... Anthony Cook
Ed. at Large ..... John Fleming
Columnist ..... George Smith
Features Ed. ..... Lisa Davis
Metro Ed. ..... Ben Cunningham
News Ed. ..... Phillip Tutor
Photo Ed. ..... Trent Penny
Assistant VP for Operations ..... Robert Jackson
Controller ..... Scott Calhoun
Advertising Manager ..... Dollie Robinson
Market Information: Split run; TMC.
Mechanical available: Offset; Black and 3 ROP colors; insert accepted; page cutoffs - 22.
Mechanical Specifications: Type page 9.88 x 21
Commodity Consumption: Avg. Page Number Per Issue - Daily 30; Avg. Page Number Per Issue - Plates Used 25288; Avg. Page Number Per Issue - Sunday 62; widths 25; Newsprint Used - Short Tons 2255; Printing Ink Used - Black 50242; Printing Ink Used - Color 5645; Printing Ink Used
Equipment EDITORIAL: Front-end Software – Microsoft/Windows, Microsoft/Word.; Editorial Hardware – PC LAN, Microsoft/Windows NT Server 4.0; Editorial Printers – HP/LaserJet 4MV CLASSIFIED: Front-end Software – Baseview/Classified.; Classified Hardware – Microsoft/Windows NT Server 4.0; Classified Printers – HP/LaserWriter DISPLAY: Ad make-up applications – Microsoft/Word, APP/Mac Appleshare; Layout Software – MEI.; Display Hardware – Microsoft/NT Server; Display Printers – HP/LaserWriter PRODUCTION: Pagination Software – InDesign; Production Equipment – SCREEN PlateRite News 2000 Thermal Platesetter PRESSROOM: Line 1 – 12 DGM 850; Folders – 2; Pasters – 6 Jardis Pasters MAILROOM: Counter stackers – Quipp 400; Inserters and stuffers – 1-Mueller/227 GMA SLS 1000; Bundle tying machines – Dynaric ; Business Hardware – IBM/AS-400
Delivery method: Mail, Newsstand, Private Carrier, Racks

ATHENS

THE NEWS-COURIER

410 W. Green St., Athens, Ala., 35611; gen tel (256) 232-2720; gen fax (256) 233-7753; adv e-mail advertising@athensnews-courier.com; web site www.enewscourier.com

Published: Tues, Wed, Thur, Fri, Sat, Sun
Weekday Frequency: m
Circulation: 6,126; 6,126(sat); 7,299(sun)
Last Audit: September 30, 2009
Price: 52.00/yr (local), $78.00/yr (elsewhere).
Advertising: Open inch rate $10.42
News services: AP.
Politics: Independent.
Advertising not accepted: Beer and liquor.
Special Editions: Senior Citizens (Quarterly).
Special Weekly Sections: TV Times (Fri); Kid's Corner (Thur); Home Solutions (Tues); Food Day (Wed).
Magazines: TV Tab (Fri); Relish (Monthly); USA WEEKEND Magazine (S); American Profile (Weekly).
Pub. ..... Ann Laurence
Adv. Mgr., Classified ..... Faye McElyea
Circ. Mgr. ..... Connie Witt
Mng. Ed. ..... Kelly Kazek
Market Information: TMC; Zoned editions.
Mechanical available: Offset; Black and 3 ROP colors; insert accepted; page cutoffs - 22 3/4.
Mechanical Specifications: Type page 13 x 21 1/2; E - 6 cols, 2 1/16, 1/8 between; A - 6 cols, 2 1/16, 1/8 between; C - 8 cols, 1 3/4, 1/8 between.

Commodity Consumption: Avg. Page Number Per Issue - Daily 24; Avg. Page Number Per Issue - Plates Used 9000; Avg. Page Number Per Issue - Sunday 48; widths 28; Newsprint Used - Short Tons 44; Printing Ink Used - Black 13000; Printing Ink Used - Color 1750; Printing Ink Used -

Equipment EDITORIAL: Front-end Software – QPS/QuarkXPress 4.0, Adobe/Photoshop 5.0.; Editorial Hardware – APP/Mac; Editorial Equipment – 6-ECR/Autokon; Editorial Printers – 1-HP/4MV, 1-APP/Mac 810 CLASSIFIED: Front-end Software – Baseview.; Classified Hardware – APP/Mac; Classified Equipment – COM/4961, COM/2414; Classified Printers – APP/Mac 810 DISPLAY: Ad make-up applications – Multi-Ad/Creator 4.0, Adobe/Photoshop 5.0.; Display Hardware – APP/Mac G3; Display Printers – 1-APP/Mac LaserPrinter; Production Equipment – Caere/OmniPage 6.0.

BIRMINGHAM

THE BIRMINGHAM NEWS

2201 4th Ave. N., Birmingham, Ala., 35203; gen tel (205) 325-2222; adv tel (205) 325-2261; ed tel (205) 325-2444; gen fax (205) 325-2283; adv fax (205) 325-3217; ed fax (205) 325-2283; web site www.bhamnews.com

Published: Mon, Tues, Wed, Thur, Fri, Sat, Sun

Weekday Frequency: m

Saturday Frequency: m

Circulation: 102,991; 101,700(sat); 175,497(sun)

Last Audit: ABC September 30, 2011

Price: 135.20/yr (m&S).

Advertising: Open inch rate $183.60(m-fri)

News services: AP, MCT, NNS, Independent News Service.

Politics: Independent.

Special Editions: Aarons 499/Talladega (Apr); FLW Fishing Championship (Aug); Prime Time Living (Dec); Bridal Guide (Jan); Prime Time Living (Jun); Prime Time Living (Mar); Summer Go Guide (May); Holiday Gift Catalog (Nov); Prime Time Living (Sept).

Special Weekly Sections: City Scene-entertainment (Fri); Punch-TV listing (S).

Magazines: Parade (S).

Pub. ....V.H. Hanson
Vice Pres., Sales/Mktg. ....Maggie Krost
Dir., HR ....Ellen Williams
Credit Mgr...................................Milicent Yeager
Mgr., Purchasing ....Wade Walker
Recruitment Team Leader..........Victoria Howell
Research Mgr. ....Stephanie Y. Handy
Adv. Dir. ....Roland Weeks
Adv. Dir., Bus. Devel.........................Carl Bates
Mktg. Dir. ....Robert West
Circ.Vice Pres. ....Troy Niday
Circ. Asst. Dir. ....Jim Keeble
Circ. Mgr., South Zone ....Patti Bearden
Circ. Mgr., State........................Jerry Reynolds
Ed......................................Thomas V. Scarritt
Exec. Ed. ....Hunter George
Asst. Mng. Ed. ....Pamela Dugan
Asst. Mng. Ed. ....Scott Walker
Art Dir. ....Wayne Marshall
Bus./Finance Ed.....................Jerry Underwood

Market Information: Split run; TMC; Zoned editions.

Mechanical available: Offset; Black and 3 ROP colors; insert accepted; page cutoffs - 22 3/4.

Mechanical Specifications: Type page 12 1/2 x 21 3/4; E - 6 cols, 2 1/16, 1/8 between; A - 6 cols, 2 1/16, 1/8 between; C - 10 cols, 1 3/8, 1/16 between.

Commodity Consumption: Avg. Page Number Per Issue - Daily 58; Avg. Page Number Per Issue - Plates Used 183219; Avg. Page Number Per Issue - Sunday 140; widths 31 1/4; Newsprint Used - Short Tons 33500; Printing Ink Used - Black 742000; Printing Ink Used - Color 189000; Printin

Equipment EDITORIAL: Front-end Software – HI/Informix Database.; Editorial Hardware – 2-CSI/1170, 2-APP/Mac Plus, 30-HI/Newsmaker, 4-HI/Sun Sparc 20; Editorial Equipment – 7-

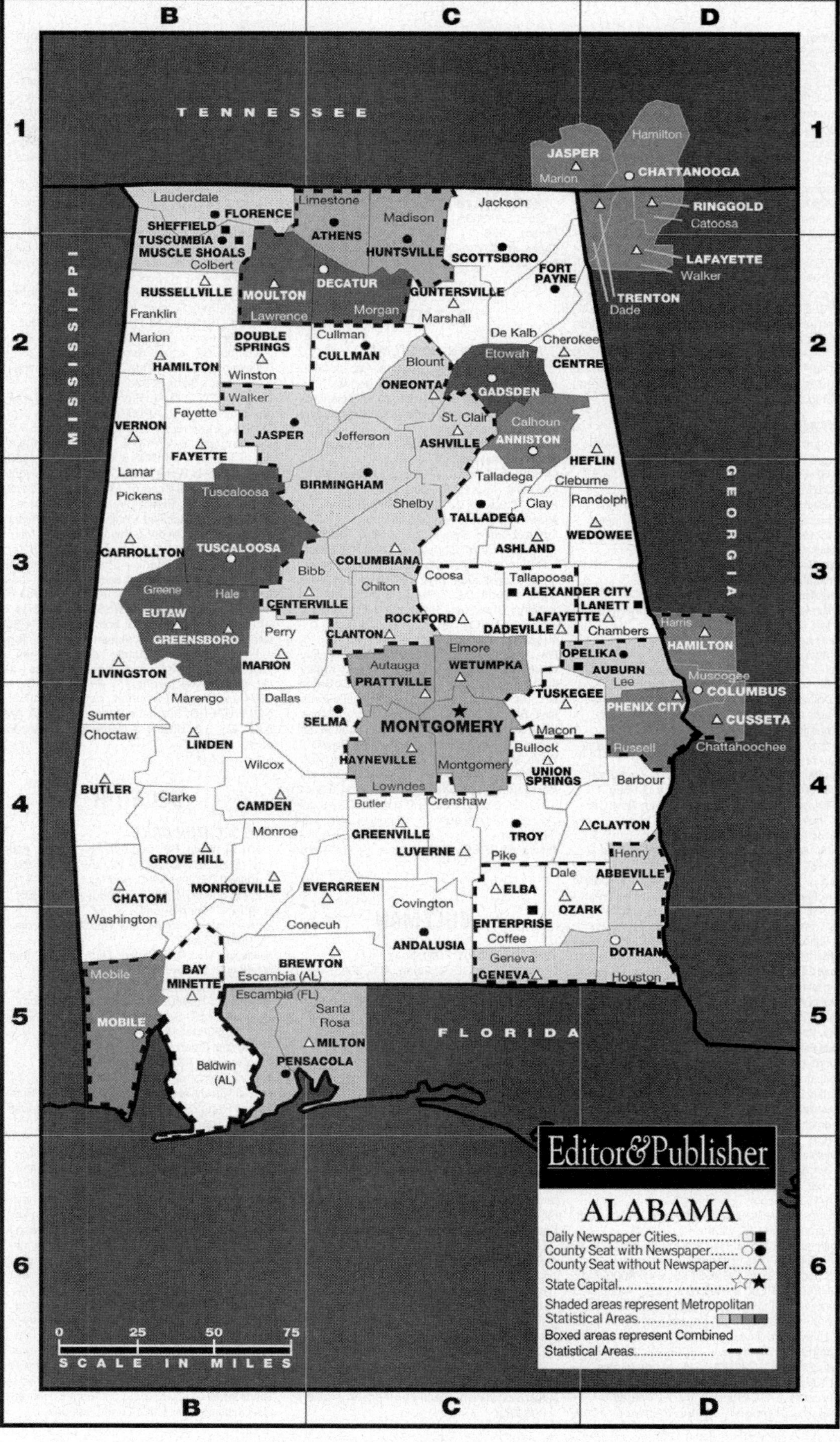

HI/Page Layout Sys, 62-CSI/EDIT 112, 41-CSI/EDIT 90, 110-PC; Editorial Printers – HP/2100 PLC CLASSIFIED: Front-end Software – PPI/Classified 3.0.; Classified Hardware – CSI/Sys 2400, 2-Compaq/4100; Classified Equipment – 54-CSI/112 B, 75-MS/NT workstations; Classified Printers – HP/4100 DISPLAY: Ad make-up applications – GEAC/Advertising 8.01; Layout Software – 4-HI/8900 Display Ad Sys, 6-HI/Workstation, 2-HI/2100.; Display Hardware – 3-FTA claspag, 3-Compaq/2100 PRODUCTION: Pagination Software – HI.; Production Equipment – 2-WL/III, 1-AU/APS 6, 1-LE/LD24AC, 2-LE/24L, Micro/3; Scanners – 2-ECR/Autokon 1000, 1-LE/480, Kk/RSF 2035+ PRESSROOM: Line 1 – 21-G/Metroliner w/12 half decks; Folders – 4-G/3:2; Pasters – 21; Press control system – EAE/Print 4 System. MAILROOM: Counter stackers – 3-HL/DUK-Carriers, 4-HL/Monitor, 6-QWI/401; Inserters and stuffers – 3-S/72P; Bundle tying machines – 14-Dynaric/1500, 4/Power Strap. BUSINESS COMPUTERS: Business Software – CJAIMS; Business Hardware – 1-V/8545-II, Dec/Alpha, Compaq/2100

BIRMINGHAM POST-HERALD

2200 4th Ave. N., Birmingham, Ala., 35203; gen tel (205) 325-2222; adv tel (800) 283-4015; ed tel (205) 325-2214; gen fax (205) 325-2410; gen e-mail mailbox@postherald.com; ed e-mail mailbox@postherald.com; web site www.postherald.com

Published: Sat
Saturday Frequency: m
Circulation: 8,019; 150,353(sat)
Last Audit: September 30, 2004
Price: 33.80/26 wks; 5.65/mo; 67.60/yr (mon to fri); 16.90/13wk.
News services: AP, SHNS, NYT.
Politics: Independent.
Note: The Birmingham Post-Herald (e) and Birmingham News (mS) are corporately and editorially separate. The Birmingham News acts as agent for Birmingham Post Co. in printing, circulating and selling advertising space in Birmingham Post-Herald. The Saturday circ
Special Editions: Football '05 (Aug); Apartment & Condo Living (Jun); Home & Garden Show (Mar); Summer Fun (May); New Car Show (Nov).
Special Weekly Sections: Kudzu (Fri); Sports Monday (Mon); Your Money (Thur); Business Tuesday (Tues); Food Day (Wed).
Sec. ....Denise Kuprionis
Adv. Mgr., Administrative Opns. ....Mike West
Ed./Pub./Pres. ....Jim Willis
Asst. Mng. Ed. ....John Staed
Columnist ....Elaine Witt
Editorial Page Ed. ....Karl Seitz
Food Ed. ....Wade Kwon
Librarian ....Sonja Franks
News Ed. ....Susan Robinson
Online Ed. ....Dave Sharp
Pub. Serv. Dir. ....Becky Gallagher
Real Estate Ed. ....Shawn Ryan
Sports Ed. ....Scott Adamson
Audiotex Mgr. ....Jeff Carlton
Market Information: ADS; Split run; TMC.
Mechanical available: Offset; Black and 3 ROP colors; insert accepted; page cutoffs - 22 3/4.
Mechanical Specifications: Type page 13 x 21 3/4; E - 6 cols, 2 1/16, 1/8 between; A - 6 cols, 2 1/16, 1/8 between; C - 10 cols, 1 3/8, 1/16 between.
Commodity Consumption: Avg. Page Number Per Issue - Daily 36; widths 54.
Equipment: Editorial Hardware – 2-CSI/1170, 2-APP/Mac Plus; Editorial Equipment – 15-CSI/Edit 112, 35-CSI/Edit 90, 3-HI/8000 PLS, 2-HI/8900 PLS, 2-HI/2100 PLS.; Classified Hardware – CSI/Sys 2400; Classified Equipment – 54-CSI/112 B.; Layout Software – CJ.; Display Hardware – HI/XP-21 PRODUCTION: Pagination Software – HI/XP-21.; Production Equipment – 2-AU/APS-6 Imaging Sys, 1-AU/3850, 1-LE/LD24C, 2-LE/24L, Micro/3; Cameras – 2-C/Spartan III, 1-C/Marathon, 1-C/Mod; Scanners – 2-ECR/Autokon 1000, Kk/RSF 20354, 2-Umax/D-16L PRESSROOM: Line 1 – 21-G/Metroliner; Folders – 4-G/3:2; Pasters – 21 MAILROOM: Counter stackers – 7-HL/Monitor, 1-HL/AT, 3-RKW/GPS 3000; Inserters and stuffers – 3-S/72P; Bundle tying machines – 8/MLN, 2-/Power Strap.; Audio Hardware – Brite Voice Systems; Business Hardware – 1-V/8545-II, 2-DEC/Alpha

CLEVELAND NEWSPAPERS, INC.

525 Office Park Dr., Birmingham, Ala., 35223-2413; gen tel (205) 870-1684; gen fax (205) 870-9531

Politics: 1956
Chrmn. of Bd./Vice Pres ....C. Lee Walls
Pres./CEO ....C. Lee Walls

CLANTON

THE CLANTON ADVERTISER

1109 Seventh St. N., Clanton, Ala., 35045-2113; gen tel (205) 755-5747; gen fax (205) 755-5857; gen e-mail newsroom@clantonadvertiser.com; web site www.clantonadvertiser.com

Published: Tues, Wed, Thur, Fri, Sat, Sun
Weekday Frequency: m
Circulation: 5,000; 5,000(sat); 5,000(sun)
Last Audit: March 29, 2006
Price: 70.20/mo; 26.73/3mo, $39.96/6mo.
Advertising: Open inch rate $11.95
Special Editions: Senior Scene (Apr); Football Preview (Aug); Christmas Greetings (Dec); Progress (Feb); Bridal Guide (Jan); Faces and Places (Jul); Peach Festival (Jun); Life in the South (Mar); Graduating Seniors (May); Christmas Songbook (Nov); Holiday Cookbook (Oct); H
Magazines: American Profile (Weekly).
Pres./Pub. ....Michael R. Kelley
Office Mgr. ....Peggy Kelley
Adv. Dir. ....Zack Bates
Circ. Dir. ....Michelle Price
Mng. Ed. ....Brent Maze
News Ed. ....Scott Mims
Sports Ed. ....Stephen Dawkins
Prodn. Mgr. ....Jimmy Ruff
Prodn Supvr., Mailroom ....Teresa Patterson
Mechanical Specifications: Type page 11 5/8 x 21 1/2; E - 6 cols, 1 5/6, 1/8 between; A - 6 cols, 1 5/6, 1/8 between; C - 10 cols, 1 1/16, 7/64 between.
Equipment PRESSROOM: Line 1 – G/Community.

CULLMAN

THE CULLMAN TIMES

300 4th Ave. SE, Cullman, Ala., 35055-3611; gen tel (256) 734-2131; gen fax (256) 737-1020; adv fax (256) 737-1006; ed fax (256) 737-1020; gen e-mail cullman@cullmantimes.com; ed e-mail news@cullmantimes.com; web site www.cullmantimes.com

Published: Tues, Wed, Thur, Fri, Sat, Sun
Weekday Frequency: m
Saturday Frequency: m
Circulation: 10,000; 10,000(sat); 10,500(sun)
Last Audit: Sworn March 31, 2007
Price: 9.00/mo; 118.00/yr.
Advertising: Open inch rate $16.70
Insert rate: 40
News services: AP.
Politics: Independent. **Established:** 1901
Special Editions: Consumer How To Guide (Apr); Sound Off (Aug); Christmas Greetings (Dec); Bridal Guide (Feb); Prime Times (Jan); Prime Times (Jul); Reader's Choice Awards (Jun); Spring Fashion (Mar); Graduation (May); Alabama Auto Guide (Monthly); Thanksgiving Day (Nov);
Special Weekly Sections: Church Page (Fri); Opinion Page (S); Used Auto Buyers Guide (Sat); Nascar Page (Thur); Outdoors (Tues); Best Food Day-Farm Page (Wed).
Magazines: Relish (Monthly)American Profile (Weekly).
Pub. ....Bill Morgan
Bus. Mgr. ....Pete Lewter
Adv. Dir. ....Kathy McLeroy
Retail Adv. Mgr. ....Burl Wilson
Circ. Mgr. ....Sam Mazzara
Mng. Ed. ....Derek Price
Lifestyles Ed. ....Tiffany Green
News Ed. ....Amanda Shavers-Davies
Sports Ed. ....Justin Graves
Market Information: ADS; TMC.
Mechanical available: Offset; Black and 3 ROP colors; insert accepted - hi-fi; page cutoffs - 22 3/4.
Mechanical Specifications: Type page 12 x 21 1/2; E - 6 cols, 1 7/8, 1/8 between; A - 6 cols, 1 7/8, 1/8 between; C - 8 cols, 1 1/3, 1/8 between.
Commodity Consumption: Avg. Page Number Per Issue - Daily 20; Avg. Page Number Per Issue - Plates Used 11000; Avg. Page Number Per Issue - Saturday 10; Avg. Page Number Per Issue - Sunday 60; widths 25; Newsprint Used - Short Tons 1189; Printing Ink Used - Black 16000; Printin
Equipment EDITORIAL: Front-end Software – Microsoft/Word 6.1, APP/Mac Write Now 4.0, QPS/QuarkXPress.; Editorial Hardware – 7-COM/Intrepid, 6-APP/Mac, 8-APP/Mac; Editorial Printers – APP/Mac Laser Writer 560, Xante/Accel-a-Writer 8200 CLASSIFIED: Front-end Software – 5-Baseview/Ad Manager Pro, 2-Baseview/Class Flow.; Classified Hardware – 4-APP/Mac; Classified Printers – Xante/Accel-a-Writer 8200; Layout Software – 6-APP/Mac.; Display Printers – Xante/Accel-a-Writer 8200; Production Equipment – Pre Press/Panther Plus Imagesetter, Gluntz & Jensen/Multi-Line 21; Cameras – 1-R, 1-Cl, Kk/Image Maker; Scanners – APP/Mac II. PRESSROOM: Line 1 – 10-HI/Cotrell V-30 1993; Folders – HI/JF-25C (Main), HI/JF-25B (Aux).; Inserters and stuffers – 1-MM/308 Biliner; Bundle tying machines – 1/Bu, 1-/Power Strapper; Wrapping singles – 1-/St; Addressing machine – 1-/Am, 1-/KR, 1-KR/4-up head, Prism/Ink Jet. BUSINESS COMPUTERS: Business Software – PBS, AM 3.0, CMS 3.0; Business Hardware – SUN, E-450

DECATUR

THE DECATUR DAILY

201 First Ave. SE, Decatur, Ala., 35601; gen tel (256) 353-4612; adv tel (256) 340-2382; ed tel (256) 340-2433; gen fax (256) 340-2411; adv fax (256) 340-2366; ed fax (256) 340-2411; gen e-mail news@decaturdaily.com; web site www.decaturdaily.com

Published: Mon, Tues, Wed, Thur, Fri, Sat, Sun
Weekday Frequency: m
Saturday Frequency: m
Circulation: 18,890; 20,312(sat); 23,848(sun)
Last Audit: ABC September 30, 2011
Price: 10.50/mo; 126.00/yr.
Advertising: Open inch rate $34.45
News services: AP, NYT, SHNS, TMS.
Politics: Democrat. **Established:** 1912
Special Weekly Sections: Agriculture (Mon); Business Page (S); Church Page (Sat); Building Page (Tues); Shopping Bag (Wed).
Magazines: Parade (S).
Pres./Pub. ....Barrett C. Shelton
Gen. Mgr. ....Clint Shelton
Controller/Personnel Mgr. ....Wendy Bobo
Adv. Mgr., Classified ....David Benoy
Adv. Mgr., Retail ....Crystal Brown
Circ. Dir. ....Wayne Burdon
Bus. Writer ....Eric Flerschauer
Editorial Page Ed. ....Tom Wright
Educ. Writer ....Bayne Hughes
Entertainment/Amusements Ed. ....Andrea Brunty
Environmental Writer ....Paul Huggins
Living Today Ed. ....Andria Brunty
Metro Ed. ....Regina Wright
Asst. Metro Ed. ....Franklin Harris
Photo Dept. Ed. ....John Godbey
Religion Ed. ....Melanie Smith
Sports Writer ....Mark Edwards
Market Information: TMC; Zoned editions.
Mechanical available: Offset; Black and 3 ROP colors; insert accepted; page cutoffs - 22 3/4.
Mechanical Specifications: Type page 11 1/2 x 21 1/2; E - 6 cols, 1 15/16, 1/8 between; A - 6 cols, 1 15/16, 1/8 between; C - 10 cols, 1 1/16, 1/16 between.
Commodity Consumption: Avg. Page Number Per Issue - Daily 32; Avg. Page Number Per Issue - Plates Used 20000; Avg. Page Number Per Issue - Sunday 68; widths 25; Newsprint Used - Short Tons 2200; Printing Ink Used - Black 58000; Printing Ink Used - Color 6000; Printing Ink Used
Equipment EDITORIAL: Front-end Software – APT.; Editorial Hardware – 10-Compaq/386, 24-AST/286; Editorial Equipment – 2-V/XP 1000, 1-Ultre/4000 Imagesetter CLASSIFIED: Front-end Software – APT.; Classified Hardware – APT; Classified Equipment – Okidata DISPLAY: Ad make-up applications – APT; Layout Software – APT.; Display Hardware – 7-APP/Mac PRODUCTION: Pagination Software – APT/ACT, QPS/QuarkXPress 3.32.; Production Equipment – Adobe/Photoshop 6.0, APP/Mac G3, APP/Mac G4; Cameras – SCREEN; Scanners – Umax/Majicsan PRESSROOM: Line 1 – 7-G/Urbanite, 1-G/3-color unit single width; Reels and Stands – 2 MAILROOM: Counter stackers – QWI/350; Inserters and stuffers – HI; Bundle tying machines – Dynaric/NP 1500; Addressing machine – KR; Other equipment – MM/TI528. AUDIO: Audio Software – Brite; Audio Hardware – Brite, Brite BUSINESS COMPUTERS: Business Software – INSI; Business Hardware – IBM/AS-400

DEMOPOLIS

DEMOPOLIS TIMES

315 E. Jefferson St., Demopolis, Ala., 36732; gen tel (334) 289-4017; gen fax (334) 289-4019; ed e-mail news@demopolistimes.com; web site www.demopolistimes.com

Published: Tues, Wed, Thur, Fri, Sat, Sun
Weekday Frequency: m
Circulation: 2,850; 2,850(sat); 2,850(sun)
Last Audit: March 28, 2007
Advertising: Open inch rate $9.00
Politics: 1905
Magazines: American Profile (Weekly).
Pub. ....Jason Cannon
Gen. Mgr. ....Bernice Smith
Sports Ed. ....Jeremy Smith
Mechanical Specifications: Type page 13 1/3 x 21 1/2; E - 6 cols, 1/6 between; A - 6 cols, 1/6 between; C - 10 cols, between.

DOTHAN

THE DOTHAN EAGLE

227 N. Oates St., Dothan, Ala., 36301; gen tel (334) 792-3141; adv tel (334) 792-3141; ed tel (334) 792-3141; gen fax (334) 712-7979; adv fax (334) 712-7975; ed fax (334) 712-7979; ed e-mail news@dothaneagle.com; web site www.dothaneagle.com

Group: Metro Newspaper Advertising Services, Inc.
Published: Mon, Tues, Wed, Thur, Fri, Sat, Sun
Weekday Frequency: m
Saturday Frequency: m
Circulation: 27,996; 26,410(sat); 28,746(sun)
Last Audit: ABC September 30, 2011
Price: 11.30/mo; 166.80/yr.
Advertising: Open inch rate $45.00
News services: AP, NEA.
Politics: Independent.
Special Editions: Wire Grass Outdoors (Monthly); Football Weekend (Nov); Football Weekend (Oct); New Car (Quarterly); Football Weekend (Sept); Golf (Spring); Golf (Summer).
Special Weekly Sections: Home & Garden (Fri); Expanded Business Pages (S); Church Page (Sat); Food (Wed).

Magazines: Relish (Monthly); USA WEEKEND Magazine (S).
Pub....Jim Whittum
Controller...Bobby Jesswein
Adv. Mgr....Jerry Morgan
Mgr., Mktg....Stephanie Madden
Mng. Ed....Ken Tuck
Asst. Mng. Ed....Andrew Small
City Ed....Kendall Clinton
Editorial Page Ed....William Perkins
Lifestyle Ed....Linnea McClellan
News Ed....Kristin Branch
Sports Ed....Jon Johnson
Mgmt. Info Servs. Mgr....David Shuemake
Prodn. Mgr....Charlie Gibson
Prodn. Mgr., Pressroom...Tim Slater
Market Information: Split run; TMC; Zoned editions.
Mechanical available: Offset; Black and 3 ROP colors; insert accepted; page cutoffs - 22 3/4.
Mechanical Specifications: Type page 13 x 21 1/2; E - 6 cols, 2 1/16, 3/16 between; A - 6 cols, 2 1/16, 3/16 between; C - 9 cols, 1 3/8, 1/16 between.
Commodity Consumption: Avg. Page Number Per Issue - Daily 32; Avg. Page Number Per Issue - Sunday 68; widths 27 1/2; Newsprint Used - Short Tons 2100; Printing Ink Used - Pages Printed 37000.
Equipment; Editorial Hardware – CText; Editorial Printers – V/5300.; Classified Hardware – CText; Classified Printers – V/5300.; Layout Software – SCS/Layout 8000.; Display Hardware – CText; Display Printers – V/5300 PRODUCTION: Pagination Software – QPS/QuarkXPress 3.3.; Production Equipment – Caere/OmniPage, 2-Tegra/5300 Film device; Cameras – 1-LE/121-V242, 1-R/432; Scanners – 2-Umax, 1-Umax/PowerLook PRESSROOM: Line 1 – 12-G/Urbanite single width (64 page capacity). MAILROOM: Counter stackers – 2-Id/2000-4000; Inserters and stuffers – 8-GMA/Station, GMA/SLS 1000 (DTP); Bundle tying machines – 1-Dynaric/Auto Strapper; Wrapping singles – Mailroom control system ☐ GMA; Addressing machine – KR/320; Other equipment –MM/CH4100. BUSINESS COMPUTERS: Business Software – Oracle, PBS, ATT, CText, Microsoft/Windows; Business Hardware – HP

ENTERPRISE

THE ENTERPRISE LEDGER

106 N. Edwards St., Enterprise, Ala., 36330; gen tel (334) 347-9533; gen fax (334) 347-0825; gen e-mail ledgernews@eprisenow.com; web site www.eprisenow.com
Published: Tues, Wed, Thur, Fri, Sun
Weekday Frequency: m
Circulation: 10,209; 10,724(sun)
Last Audit: March 31, 1998
Price: 10.30/mo; 166.80/yr.
Advertising: Open inch rate $19.25
News services: Papert (Landon).
Politics: Independent.
Special Editions: Fort Rucker Appreciation (Apr); Football (Aug); Brides (Jan); Women in Business (Jul); Progress (Jun); NASCAR Racing (Mar); Graduation (May); Cookbook (Oct).
Special Weekly Sections: Automotive (Fri); Food (Wed).
Magazines: Real Estate (Monthly); Apartment Living (Quarterly).
Pub....Jim Whittum
Adv. Dir....Ameria Wilder
Online Adv. Mgr...Kelli McQueen
Circ. Mgr....Elmer Deel
Mng. Ed....Danny Lewis
Sports Ed....Jeremy Wise
Market Information: Split run; TMC; Zoned editions.
Mechanical available: Offset; Black and 3 ROP colors; insert accepted; page cutoffs - 22 3/4.
Mechanical Specifications: Type page 13 x 21 1/2; E - 6 cols, 2 1/16, 1/8 between; A - 6 cols, 2 1/16, 1/8 between; C - 9 cols, 1 1/2, 1/8 between.
Commodity Consumption: Avg. Page Number Per Issue - Daily 10; Avg. Page Number Per Issue - Sunday 16; Newsprint Used - Metric Tons 70; Newsprint Used - Short Tons 510.
Equipment EDITORIAL: Front-end Software – QPS/QuarkXPress.; Editorial Hardware – Mk/3000, 1-APP/Mac Centris 610, 1-XYQUEST/Power User 88mg; Editorial Equipment – Ethernet, 1-AG/Arcus Scanner, 1-Nikon/Coolscan; Classified Hardware – Mk. PRODUCTION: Pagination Software – Adobe/Photoshop.; Production Equipment – 1-APP/Mac Quadra 630, 1-APP/Mac IIci, APP/Mac LaserWriters, V/5100; Cameras – 1-SCREEN/DT-C240-DST BUSINESS COMPUTERS: Business Software – Lotus 3.1 plus, Lotus 2.2, WordPerfect 6.0; Business Hardware – ATT/3B2-500, Oracle

FLORENCE

TIMESDAILY

219 W. Tennessee St., Florence, Ala., 35630; gen tel (256) 766-3434; adv tel (256) 740-4736; ed tel (256) 740-5721; gen fax (256) 740-4700; adv fax (256) 740-4700; ed fax (256) 740-4717; web site www.timesdaily.com
Published: Mon, Tues, Wed, Thur, Fri, Sat, Sun
Weekday Frequency: m
Saturday Frequency: m
Circulation: 25,535; 24,693(sat); 28,309(sun)
Last Audit: ABC September 30, 2011
Price: 13.00/4 wks; 169.00/yr.
Advertising: Open inch rate $49.10
News services: AP.
Politics: Independent.
Own facility?: Y
Special Editions: Explore the Shoals (Apr); High School Football (Aug); Progress (Feb); Money Matters (Jan); Living Here (Jul); Senior Living (Jun); Lawn and Garden (Mar); Graduation (May); High School Basketball (Nov); Readers Choice (Oct).
Shoals Woman (every other month);Tennessee Valley Brides (annual);TNValley-Homefinder (monthly); TNValleyWheels (biweekly)
Special Weekly Sections: Currents (Fri); Best Food Day (Wed).
Magazines: Shoals Woman (Every other month); Shoals Magazine (Quarterly); USA Weekend (S)Explore the Shoals (AprProgress (Feb); Money Matters (Jan); Living Here (Jul); Senior Living (Jun); Tennessee Valley Brides (annual);TNValley-Homefinder (monthly); TNValleyWheels (biweekly)
Pub....Darrell R. Sandlin
Controller...Donna Lawhead
Adv. Dir....Melody Bishop
Adv. Mgr., Classified Call Ctr....Erica Mayfield
Adv. Mgr., Display...Renita Jimmar
Circ. Dir....Michael McKillip
Exec. Ed....Scott Morris
Mng. Ed....Mike Goens
City Ed....Sherhonda Allen
Lifestyle Ed....Teri T. Thornton
Night Ed....Christine Fink
News Asst....Valerie Sherer
Photo Ed....Matthew T. McKean
Sports Ed....Gregg Dewalt
Asst. Sports Ed....Jeff McIntyre
Dir., ITS/Pre Press Serv....Chris Giroir
Online Dir....Paul Crawford
Prodn. Mgr., Distr....Anthony Arnold
Prodn. Mgr., Pre Press...Lin Reynolds
Prod. Dir....Kevin Blurton
Market Information: TMC.
Mechanical available: Offset; Black and 3 ROP colors; insert accepted; page cutoffs - 22.
Mechanical Specifications: Type page 11 x 21; E - 6 cols, 1 15/16, 3/16 between; A - 6 cols, 1 5/8, 3/16 between; C - 9 cols, 11/16, 1/16 between.
Commodity Consumption: Avg. Page Number Per Issue - Daily 31; Avg. Page Number Per Issue - Plates Used 24500; Avg. Page Number Per Issue - Sunday 35.3; widths 13 1/2; Newsprint Used - Short Tons 3115; Printing Ink Used - Black 64000; Printing Ink Used - Color 9000; Printing In
Equipment EDITORIAL: Front-end Software – CPU.; Editorial Hardware – PC; Classified Hardware – PC DISPLAY: Ad make-up applications – ATS; Layout Software – QPS/QuarkXPress.; Display Hardware – APP/Mac; Scanners – 1-PixelCraft/8000. PRESSROOM: Line 1 – Oct-97; Press Drives – 1997; Folders – 1, 1-G/Urbanite 1997; Pasters – 6 MAILROOM: Counter stackers – 5-QWI/350-400W; Inserters and stuffers – NP1472; 632 Inserter; Bundle tying machines – Power Strap; Dynaric; Other equipment –1-MM/Stitcher-Trimmer 1528/29, 4-Fox/321 w/Stacker.; Audio Hardware – Brite Voice Systems BUSINESS COMPUTERS: Business Software – INSI

FORT PAYNE

FORT PAYNE NEWSPAPERS, INC.

PO Box 680349, Fort Payne, Ala., 35968-0349; gen tel (256) 845-2550; gen fax (256) 845-7459; gen e-mail news@times-journal.com; web site www.times-journal.com
Published: Mon, Tues, Wed, Thur, Fri, Sat, Sun
Price: 72.00/yr; 79.00.
Advertising: Open inch rate $8.85

THE TIMES-JOURNAL

811 Greenhill Blvd. NW, Fort Payne, Ala., 35967; gen tel (256) 845-2550; adv tel (256) 845-2550; ed tel (256) 845-2550; gen fax (256) 845-7459; adv fax (256) 845-7459; ed fax (256) 845-7459; gen e-mail tjnews@times-journal.com; web site www.times-journal.com
Published: Tues, Wed, Thur, Fri, Sat
Weekday Frequency: m
Saturday Frequency: m
Circulation: 4,850; 5,519(sat)
Last Audit: September 30, 2009
Price: 72.00/yr.
Advertising: Open inch rate $10.95
Politics: Independent.
Not Published: Thanksgiving; Christmas.
Magazines: American Profile (Weekly).
Owner...Lissa Walls Vahldiek
Adv. Mgr....Gloria Jackson
Circ. Mgr....Tammy Stevens
Ed....J.D. Davidson
Mng. Ed....Jared Felkins
Market Information: TMC; Zoned editions.
Mechanical available: Offset; Black and 3 ROP colors; insert accepted; page cutoffs - 21 1/2.
Mechanical Specifications: Type page 13 x 21 1/2; E - 6 cols, 2 1/16, 1/8 between; A - 6 cols, 2 1/16, 1/8 between; C - 6 cols, 2 1/16, 1/8 between.
Commodity Consumption: Avg. Page Number Per Issue - Daily 16; Avg. Page Number Per Issue - Plates Used 2500; widths 27 1/2; Newsprint Used - Short Tons 250; Printing Ink Used - Black 3600; Printing Ink Used - Color 300; Printing Ink Used - Pages Printed 3600.
Equipment; Editorial Hardware – Mk, APP/Mac.; Classified Hardware – APP/Mac.; Display Hardware – APP/Mac.; Production Equipment – 1-WL/30A; Cameras – AG/Repromaster/3800. PRESSROOM: Line 1 – 5-G/Community; Folders – 1; Inserters and stuffers – KAN/320; Addressing machine – 2-Am/1900, 2-El/3101.; Business Hardware – IBM

GADSDEN

THE GADSDEN TIMES

401 Locust St., Gadsden, Ala., 35901; gen tel (256) 549-2000; adv tel (256) 549-2075; ed tel (256) 549-2050; gen fax (256) 549-2013; adv fax (256) 549-2013; ed fax (256) 549-2105; adv e-mail timesadv@gadsdentimes.com; ed e-mail news@gadsdentimes.com; web site www.gadsdentimes.com
Published: Mon, Tues, Wed, Thur, Fri, Sat, Sun
Weekday Frequency: m
Saturday Frequency: m
Circulation: 15,396; 17,024(sat); 17,459(sun)
Last Audit: ABC September 30, 2011
Price: 11.00/mo; 135.82/yr.
Advertising: Open inch rate $36.50
Insert rate: varies by paging and frequency commitment
News services: AP, NYT.
Politics: Independent. **Established:** 1867
Own facility?: Y
Special Editions: Football (Aug); County Focus Editions (4) (Feb); Home & Garden (Mar); Graduation (May); Basketball (Nov).
Special Weekly Sections: Religious News (Fri); People (Mon); Real Estate (S); Health News (Thur); Home (Tues); Food (Wed).
Magazines: Parade (S).
Pub....Glen Porter
Bus. Office Mgr....Richard Davis
Exec. Ed....Ron Reaves
Photo Dept. Mgr....Marc Golden
Reporter...Lisa Rogers
Travel/Women's Ed....Cyndi Nelson
System Coord....Pat Baines
Market Information: TMC.
Mechanical available: Offset; Black and 3 ROP colors; insert accepted; page cutoffs - 22 3/4.
Mechanical Specifications: Type page 13 x 21 1/2; E - 6 cols, 2 1/16, 1/8 between; A - 6 cols, 2 1/16, 1/8 between; C - 9 cols, 1 11/32, 3/32 between.
Commodity Consumption: Avg. Page Number Per Issue - Daily 24; Avg. Page Number Per Issue - Plates Used 14000; Avg. Page Number Per Issue - Sunday 52; widths 27; Newsprint Used - Metric Tons 1718; Newsprint Used - Short Tons 1894; Printing Ink Used - Black 42100; Printing Ink U
Equipment EDITORIAL: Front-end Software – Baseview.; Editorial Hardware – APP/Mac-SH; Editorial Printers – AU, AG/Accuset CLASSIFIED: Front-end Software – Baseview.; Classified Hardware – APP/Mac G4; Classified Printers – AU, AG/Accuset DISPLAY: Ad make-up applications – Multi-Ad/Creator 3.8; Layout Software – APP/Mac.; Display Hardware – APP/Mac G3; Display Printers – AU, AG/Accuset PRODUCTION: Pagination Software – QPS 4.0.; Production Equipment – Mac Base/AG Accuset, 1-Konica/K-280, QPS 3.31; Scanners – Mk/SilverScan, Mk/ScanMaker III, Kk, Nikon/Coolscan; Folders – 1; Reels and Stands – 6; Business Hardware – ADV/36
Delivery method: Mail, Newsstand, Private Carrier, Racks

HUNTSVILLE

THE HUNTSVILLE TIMES

2317 S. Memorial Pkwy., Huntsville, Ala., 35801; gen tel (256) 532-4000; adv tel (256) 532-4250; ed tel (256) 532-4400; gen fax (256) 532-4420; adv fax (256) 532-4183; ed fax (256) 532-4420; gen e-mail htimes@htimes.com; adv e-mail bill.joyner@htimes.com; ed e-mail htimes@htimes.com; web site www.htimes.com
Group: Metro Suburbia, Inc./Newhouse Newspapers
Published: Mon, Tues, Wed, Thur, Fri, Sat, Sun
Weekday Frequency: m
Saturday Frequency: m
Circulation: 44,462; 44,441(sat); 68,811(sun)
Last Audit: ABC September 30, 2011
Price: 12.70/mo (eS); 140.40/yr.
Advertising: Open inch rate $71.17
News services: AP, LAT-WP, NNS, MCT.
Politics: Independent.
Special Editions: Madison Showcase (Apr); College/Pro Football (Aug); Year End Drive Away (Dec); Home & Remodeling Show (Feb); The Boomers (Jan); The Arts Council (Jul); Top Of Class (Jun); Women's Expo (Mar); Memorial Day Drive Away (May); The Perfect Gift Guide (Nov); Ca

Special Weekly Sections: TV Times (Fri); Money Matters (Mon); Family Times (Sat); High School Sports (Thur); Health & Science (Tues); Food Pages (Wed).
Magazines: Parade (S).
Pres./Pub. ....Robert D. Ludwig
Controller ....Robert Carothers
Asst. Controller..........................Anita McCain
Adv. Mgr., Classified ....Sheila Runnels
Adv. Mgr., Major Accts. ....Joe Bagwell
Adv. Mgr., Retail ....Steve Wilson
Mktg. Mgr. ....Carol Casey
Circ. Dir. ....Frank Maier
Ed. ....Kevin Wendt
City Desk Ed. ....Shelly Haskins
Design Ed. ....Doug Mendenhall
Editorial Page Ed. ....John Ehinger
Entertainment/Leisure Ed. ....Deborah Storey
Health Ed. ....Kenneth Kesner
News Ed. ....Joe Duncan
Asst. News Ed. ....Stephen Lomax
Outdoors Ed. ....Alan Clemons
Chief Photographer ....Mike Mercier
Regl. Ed. ....Mike Hollis
Religion Ed. ....Yvonne Betowt
Market Information: TMC; Zoned editions.
Mechanical available: Offset; Black and 3 ROP colors; insert accepted; page cutoffs - 21 1/4.
Mechanical Specifications: Type page 12 x 21; E - 6 cols, 2, 3/16 between; A - 6 cols, 2, 3/16 between; C - 10 cols, 1 1/4, 1/6 between.
Commodity Consumption: Avg. Page Number Per Issue - Daily 42; Avg. Page Number Per Issue - Plates Used 46800; Avg. Page Number Per Issue - Sunday 119; widths 50; Newsprint Used - Short Tons 8400; Printing Ink Used - Black 175600; Printing Ink Used - Color 66300; Printing Ink U
Equipment EDITORIAL: Front-end Software – SII/INL Sys, Decade, Coyote III.; Editorial Hardware – Tandem/CLX, 54-IBM/286-30, 6-Compaq/386-25; Editorial Equipment – APP/Mac Graphics System, Merlin/T1; Editorial Printers – HP/III, HP/IV, Compaq/PageMarq 15 CLASSIFIED: Front-end Software – SII/ICP Sys, Northwood/Class Page.; Classified Hardware – Tandem/CLX, 12-IBM/286-30; Classified Equipment – PC; Classified Printers – Genicom/LW455 Linewriter, HP/4 DISPLAY: Ad make-up applications – Multi-Ad/Creator, CNI/Ad Tracker, QPS/QuarkXPress, Adobe/Illustrator, IAL/System; Layout Software – 3-SII/IAL.; Display Hardware – APP/Mac, APP/Power Mac; Display Printers – HP/LaserJet III, HP/5 SI PRODUCTION: Pagination Software – QPS/QuarkXPress.; Production Equipment – WL/Litho Plater, AP Server, 2-AII/APS 3850; Scanners – 1-ECR/Autokon 1030, ECR/Autokon 1000, CD/6306 Scanner, 4-AG/Argus II, 4-Polaroid/SprintScan PRESSROOM: Line 1 – 8-TKS/M-72 black units; Line 2 – 4-TKS/M-72 Half Decks Spot Color Unit; Line 3 – 1-TKS/M-72 4 Color Satellite Unit; Line 4 – 1-TKS/M-72 Standalone Black Unit; Reels and Stands – 9-TKS/M-72 Reels & Stands; Press control system – TKS/Press Control MAILROOM: Counter stackers – 4-QWI/200, 1-Id/440; Inserters and stuffers – 2-HI/1372 Inserters; Bundle tying machines – 4-Dynaric/Strapper NP-1; Wrapping singles – 4-QWI/Bottom Wrap; Addressing machine – 2/KR. AUDIO: Audio Software – One Link 5.08; Audio Hardware – Voice News Network/Tribune Media Service, One Link BUSINESS COMPUTERS: Business Software – INSI/OS400 2.1.0; Business Hardware – 1-IBM/400-RISC 500

JASPER

DAILY MOUNTAIN EAGLE

1301 Viking Dr., Jasper, Ala., 35501; gen tel (205) 221-2840; gen fax (205) 221-6203; gen e-mail jasper@mountaineagle.com; adv e-mail advertising@mountaineagle.com; web site www.mountaineagle.com
Published: Mon, Tues, Wed, Thur, Fri, Sat, Sun
Weekday Frequency: m
Saturday Frequency: m
Circulation: 9,406; 10,018(sat); 9,671(sun)
Last Audit: ABC September 30, 2011
Price: 9.00/mo; 123.00/yr (county carrier).
Advertising: Open inch rate $17.08
News services: AP.
Politics: Independent.
Not Published: Christmas.
Special Editions: Atlanta Braves (Apr); Football (Aug); Letters to Santa (Dec); Progress (Feb); Senior Citizen (Jul); Home Folks (Jun); Graduation (May); Gift Guide (Nov); Women's World (Oct); Newcomer's Guide (Sept).
Magazines: TV Guide (Fri); USA WEEKEND Magazine (S); Business & Industrial Review (Tues); Best Food (Wed); American Profile (Weekly).
Office/Credit Mgr. ....Charlotte Keeton
Adv. Dir. ....Jerry Geddings
Adv. Mgr., Classified ....Sandra Lawson
Circ. Mgr. ....................................J.H. Boshell
Ed. ....Jerome Wassmann
Mng. Ed. ....Ron Harris
Editorial Page Ed. ....Brian Kennedy
Sports Ed. ....Jonathan Bentley
Prodn. Mgr. ....Michael Keeton
Market Information: ADS; TMC.
Mechanical available: Offset; Black and 3 ROP colors; insert accepted; page cutoffs - 22 3/4.
Mechanical Specifications: Type page 13 x 21 1/2; E - 6 cols, 5/16, 1/8 between; A - 6 cols, 5/16, 1/8 between; C - 6 cols, 5/16, 1/8 between.
Commodity Consumption: Avg. Page Number Per Issue - Daily 20; Avg. Page Number Per Issue - Sunday 34; widths 25; Newsprint Used - Short Tons 600.
Equipment; Editorial Hardware – Mk; Editorial Equipment – 12-Mk.; Production Equipment – 2-Mk/Ad Touch, 2-APP/Mac LaserWriter Plus; Cameras – 1-R/Corsair, 1-DAI/5161. PRESSROOM: Line 1 – 8-WPC/Web Leader; Line 2 – 3-WPC/Quadcolor; Folders – 2-WPC/2:1. MAILROOM: Counter stackers – 1-BG/Count-O-Veyor; Inserters and stuffers – 4-DG/320; Bundle tying machines – 1/Sa; Addressing machine – 1-Ch/730.

LANETT

THE VALLEY TIMES-NEWS

220 N. 12th St., Lanett, Ala., 36863; gen tel (334) 644-8100; adv tel (334) 644-8110; ed tel (334) 644-8123; gen fax (334) 644-5587; adv e-mail advertising@valleytimes-news.com; ed e-mail news@valleytimes-news.com; web site www.valleytimes-news.com
Published: Mon, Tues, Wed, Thur, Fri
Weekday Frequency: e
Circulation: 6,000
Last Audit: October 1, 2002
Price: 6.00/mo; 100.00/yr.
Advertising: Open inch rate $9.50
Insert rate: $50/m
News services: AP.
Politics: Independent. **Established:** 1950
Not Published: Christmas.
Own facility?: Y
Special Editions: Christmas Greetings (Dec); Progress (Jun); Cookbook (Nov); Car Care (Oct); Fall Fashion (Sept).
Adv. Dir. ....Phillip Jones
Classified Mgr. ....Martha Milner
Ed. ....Cy Wood
Graphics Ed. ....Kathy Reeves
News Ed. ....Wayne Clark
Sports Ed. ....Scott Sickler
Prodn. Foreman, Pressroom ....David Cardino
Prodn. Foreman, Engraving ....Jerry Hudman
Market Information: TMC.
Mechanical available: Offset; Black and 3 ROP colors; insert accepted; page cutoffs - 22 3/4.
Mechanical Specifications: Type page 13 x 21 1/2; E - 6 cols, 2 1/8, 1/4 between; A - 6 cols, 2 1/8, 1/4 between; C - 9 cols, 1 1/2, 1/8 between.
Commodity Consumption: Avg. Page Number Per Issue - Daily 16; Avg. Page Number Per Issue - Plates Used 5200; widths 14; Newsprint Used - Short Tons 460; Printing Ink Used - Black 1800; Printing Ink Used - Color 300; Printing Ink Used - Pages Printed 5300.
Equipment EDITORIAL: Front-end Software – Mk, APP/Mac.; Editorial Hardware – Mk, PC; Editorial Printers – 2-COM/308 Laser CLASSIFIED: Front-end Software – Mk.; Classified Hardware – Mk, PC, APP/Mac; Classified Printers – 2-COM/308 Laser DISPLAY: Ad make-up applications – Mk, APP/Mac.; Display Hardware – APP/Mac, COM, PC; Display Printers – 2-COM/308; Production Equipment – 1-LE/LD-1800A; Cameras – Roconex/1-B. PRESSROOM: Line 1 – 6-G/Community; Folders – G/2:1; Pasters – 1 MAILROOM: Counter stackers – 1/BG; Bundle tying machines – 1-/BG. BUSINESS COMPUTERS: Business Software – APP/Mac; Business Hardware – 1-RSK/Model III, 1-Bs/B96-40

MOBILE

PRESS-REGISTER

401 N. Water St., Mobile, Ala., 36602; gen tel (251) 219-5400; adv tel (251) 219-5545; ed tel (251) 219-5632; adv fax (251) 219-5068; ed fax (251) 219-5799; adv e-mail shall@press-register.com; ed e-mail news@press-register.com; newsroom@mobileregister.com; web site www.press-register.com
Published: Mon, Tues, Wed, Thur, Fri, Sat, Sun
Weekday Frequency: m
Saturday Frequency: m
Circulation: 81,003; 77,206(sat); 101,808(sun)
Last Audit: ABC September 30, 2011
Price: 6.50/mo (d), $11.00/mo (dS); 130.20/yr.
Advertising: Open inch rate $81.21
News services: AP, LAT-WP, MCT, NEW, SHNS, Religious News, NYT.
Politics: Independent.
Special Editions: Home Builders Association (Apr); Parade of Homes (Aug); Holiday Gift Guide (Dec); Home Builders Showcase (Feb); Better Business Bureau (Jan); Automotive Hot Sellers (Jul); Soil & Sea (Jun); Easter (Mar); Congratulations Graduates (May); Jr. League Christm
Special Weekly Sections: TV Supplement (Fri); Farm Page (Mon); Travel Page (S); Church Pages (Sat).
Magazines: Parade (S).
Controller/Treasurer ....Vicki Catlett
Dir., HR ....Lee Stringfellow
Adv. Mgr., Classified ....Britt Pickett
Adv. Mgr., Nat'l ....Wanda Jacobs
Adv. Mgr., Retail ....Steve Hall
Dir., Mktg./Promo. ....Randy Granger
Circ. Dir. ....George Markevicz
Circ. Mgr., Home Delivery ....Wayne Carrier
Circ. Mgr., Opns. ....Bill Van Hook
Circ. Mgr., Single Copy ....Jim McKeel
Vice Pres., News/Ed. ....Michael Marshall
Mng. Ed. ....Dewey English
Bus./Finance Ed. ..............................K.A. Turner
Editorial Page Ed. ....Frances Coleman
Environmental Reporter ....Ben Raines
Farm/Agriculture Ed. ....Charles Croft
Features Ed. ....Debbie Lord
Graphics Ed. ....Thom Dudgeon
Growth/Environmental Ed ....Bill Finch
Health/Medical Reporter ....Monique Curet
Market Information: ADS; Split run; TMC; Zoned editions.
Mechanical available: Letterpress (direct); Black and 3 ROP colors; insert accepted; page cutoffs - 21 1/2.
Mechanical Specifications: Type page 11 3/5 x 20 1/2; E - 6 cols, 1 4/5, 1/8 between; A - 6 cols, 1 4/5, 1/8 between; C - 10 cols, 1 9/32, 1/32 between.
Commodity Consumption: Avg. Page Number Per Issue - Daily 76; Avg. Page Number Per Issue - Plates Used 97830; Avg. Page Number Per Issue - Saturday 65; Avg. Page Number Per Issue - Sunday 159; widths 27 3/8; Newsprint Used - Short Tons 16318; Printing Ink Used - Black 463710;
Equipment EDITORIAL: Front-end Software – HI/NME 3.31.006, HI/NMP 1.8.19, XP21 3.6.; Editorial Hardware – 2-Sun/Ultra 2, 2-Sun/Sparc 20; Editorial Printers – HP/LaserJet 6, HP/DesignJet 1055cm CLASSIFIED: Front-end Software – Tandem/D20 Operating Sys, ICP.; Classified Hardware – SII/Sys 77; Classified Printers – Centronics/351, HP/LaserJet 6 DISPLAY: Ad make-up applications – Multi-Ad/Creator, Adobe/Photoshop; Layout Software – AII/Ad Manager Production System.; Display Hardware – Sun/Micro Sys, APP/Power Mac; Display Printers – AII/APS 2000 (proof), 3-HP/1155 Plotters, 3-HP/500 b/w Printers PRODUCTION: Pagination Software – HI/XP21.; Production Equipment – 2-AU/APS-6-10-8C, 2-MAS, 2-Alpha RIP, 1-AII/3850, 1-AII/350 wide, 1-Graphix RIP; Cameras – 1-C/Newspager; Scanners – Sharp PRESSROOM: Line 1 – 12-G/Mark I (4 half decks); Folders – 2-G/2:1; Pasters – 12-G/RTP; Reels and Stands – 12 MAILROOM: Counter stackers – 6-HL/Monitor, 4/Quipp 401; Inserters and stuffers – 2-HI/1372P, 1-HI/1472P; Bundle tying machines – 8-/Dynaric; Addressing machine – 2-/Ch; Other equipment –1-MM/335. BUSINESS COMPUTERS: Business Software – Microsoft/Windows NT, Microsoft/Windows 95, Microsoft/Office 97, Platinum 4.6A, Abra Suite 5.21, MicroSystems Specialists Inc.; Business Hardware – 1-HP/979

MONTGOMERY

ADVERTISER CO.

200 Washington Ave., Montgomery, Ala., 36101; gen tel (334) 262-1611; gen fax (334) 261-1579; adv fax (334)262-1502; web site www.momtgomeryadvertiser.com
Published: Mon, Tues, Wed, Thur, Fri, Sat, Sun
Price: 182.00/yr.
Advertising: Open inch rate $7.40

MONTGOMERY ADVERTISER

425 Molton St., Montgomery, Ala., 36104; gen tel (334) 262-1611; adv tel (334) 261-1563; ed tel (334) 261-1524; gen fax (334) 261-1579; adv fax (334) 261-1591; ed fax (334) 261-1505; web site www.montgomeryadvertiser.com
Group: Gannett Co., Inc.
Published: Mon, Tues, Wed, Thur, Fri, Sat, Sun
Weekday Frequency: m
Saturday Frequency: m
Circulation: 31,495; 34,054(sat); 43,807(sun)
Last Audit: ABC September 30, 2011
Price: 182.00/yr.
Advertising: Open inch rate $113.04
News services: AP, SHNS, MCT, GNS, PR Newswire.
Politics: Independent.
Special Editions: Coupon Book (Apr); Game Day College (Aug); SEC Game Day (Dec); Health & Fitness (Feb); Coupon Book (Jan); Hyundai (Jul); Restaurant Guide (Jun); Gulf Coast Tab (Mar); Health & Fitness (May); Holiday Gift Guide (Nov); Coupon Book (Oct); First Methodist Ven
Special Weekly Sections: Religion (Fri); TV Week (S); Home & Garden (Sat); Go (weekly entertainment) (Thur); Health (Tues); Food (Wed).
Magazines: USA WEEKEND Magazine (S).
President & Publisher ....Samuel Martin
Exec. Ed. ....Wanda Lloyd
Editorial Page Ed. ....Kenneth Hare
Features Ed. ....Rick Harmon
News Ed. ....Terry Manning
Director of Sales & Marketing ....Karen Walker
Director of Operations ....Jim Zajas
Circulation Manager ....Barry Whitman
Market Information: Split run; TMC; Zoned editions.
Mechanical available: Offset; Black and 3 ROP colors; insert accepted - samples; page cutoffs - 20 1/2.
Mechanical Specifications: Type page 11 5/8 x 20 1/2; E - 6 cols, 1 5/6, 1/8 between; A - 6 cols, 1 5/6, 1/8 between; C - 10 cols, between.
Commodity Consumption: Avg. Page Number Per Issue - Daily 46; Avg. Page Number Per

Issue - Plates Used 114000; Avg. Page Number Per Issue - Sunday 55; widths 37 1/2; Newsprint Used - Metric Tons 7010; Newsprint Used - Short Tons 7728; Printing Ink Used - Black 118960; Printing
Equipment EDITORIAL: Front-end Software – Harris/Newsmaker 2.5, HI/Newsmaker Editorial 3.5.; Editorial Hardware – 70-Dell/Optiplex, Sun/Enterprise 450; Editorial Printers – HP, Unity/1600 XL, HP/8150 CLASSIFIED: Front-end Software – Harris/AdPower, HI/CASH 2.1.9.; Classified Hardware – 20-Dell/Optiplex, Dell/Power Edge 90; Classified Printers – HP/4si DISPLAY: Ad make-up applications – QPS/QuarkXPress, Adobe/Photoshop 5.5; Layout Software – SCS/Layout 8000.; Display Hardware – 17-APP/Power Mac G4; Display Printers – HP LaserJet 5, HP LaserJet/8550 PRODUCTION: Pagination Software – Solaris 2.5, HI/Newsmaker Pagination 4.0.; Production Equipment – 2-V/Pro Panther 36, 1-V/5300-B; Cameras – 1-C; Scanners – 2-ECR, ScanView/ScanMate 5000 Drum Scanner, Kk/2035S, HP/ScanJet 4C, Nikon/LS 2000 PRESSROOM: Line 1 – Aug-96; Folders – G/3:2 (144 page); Pasters – G/RTP; Reels and Stands – 8-G/3-Arm. MAILROOM: Counter stackers – 6-QWI/350; Inserters and stuffers – NP/1472; Bundle tying machines – 5-Dynaric/NP-2; Wrapping singles – 1-Bu/Tying Machine, 5-QWI/Viper Bottom Wraps; Addressing machine – Barstrom/In-Line; Other equipment –MM/321 TV Stitcher-Trimmer. BUSINESS COMPUTERS: Business Software – Microsoft/Office Pro 1997; Business Hardware – IBM/AS-400 9406-300

OPELIKA

OPELIKA-AUBURN NEWS

2901 Society Hill Rd., Opelika, Ala., 36804; gen tel (334) 749-6271; gen fax (334) 749-1228; web site www.oanow.com
Published: Mon, Tues, Wed, Thur, Fri, Sat, Sun
Weekday Frequency: m
Saturday Frequency: m
Circulation: 13,583; 13,705(sat); 14,303(sun)
Last Audit: ABC September 30, 2011
Price: 11.75/mo.; 141.00/yr.
Advertising: Open inch rate $31.60
News services: AP.
Politics: Independent.
Special Weekly Sections: Best Automotive Days (Fri); Best Real Estate Days (S); Church Page (Sat); Business Pages (Thur); Business Pages (Tues); Living Pages (Wed).
Magazines: USA WEEKEND Magazine (S).
Pub. ....James W. Rainey
Vice Pres. ....Alan Davis
Classified Mgr. ....Crystal Russel
Circ. Dir. ....Jerry May
Editorial Page Ed.........................Joe McAdory
Sports Ed. ....Mike Szvetitz
Prodn. Mgr. ....Tim Maxwell
Market Information: ADS; TMC.
Mechanical available: Offset; Black and 3 ROP colors; insert accepted; page cutoffs - 22.
Mechanical Specifications: Type page 11 1/2 x 21 1/2; E - 6 cols, 1 3/4, 1/6 between; A - 6 cols, 1 3/4, 1/6 between; C - 6 cols, 1 3/4, 1/6 between.
Commodity Consumption: Avg. Page Number Per Issue - Daily 60; Avg. Page Number Per Issue - Sunday 122; widths 25; Newsprint Used - Short Tons 675.
Equipment EDITORIAL: Front-end Software – QPS/QuarkXPress, Baseview.; Editorial Hardware – APP/Mac; Editorial Printers – V CLASSIFIED: Front-end Software – Baseview.; Classified Hardware – APP/Mac DISPLAY: Ad make-up applications – Baseview.; Display Hardware – APP/Mac IIcx; Display Printers – V; Production Equipment – 1-Nu, Pre Press/Panther Plus; Cameras – Amergraph. PRESSROOM: Line 1 – 8-G/Community 1976; Folders – SC/499.; Inserters and stuffers – 4/KAN; Bundle tying machines – MLN/Sprint. BUSINESS COMPUTERS: Business Software – Unix; Business Hardware – PBS

SCOTTSBORO

THE DAILY SENTINEL

701 Veterans Dr., Scottsboro, Ala., 35768; gen tel (256) 259-1020; adv tel (256) 259-1020; ed tel (256) 259-1020; gen fax (256) 259-2709; adv fax (256) 259-2709; ed fax (256) 259-2709; adv e-mail advertising@dailysentinel.com; web site www.thedailysentinel.com
Published: Tues, Wed, Thur, Fri, Sat
Weekday Frequency: m
Saturday Frequency: m
Circulation: 3,895; 4,228(sat)
Last Audit: September 30, 2009
Price: 72.00/yr; 19.75/3mo, $38.50/6mo.
Advertising: Open inch rate $9.20
News services: AP, TMS.
Politics: Independent.
Not Published: Christmas.
Special Editions: Car Care (Apr); Back-to-School (Aug); Lawn & Garden (Mar); Graduation (May); Industry (Nov); Car Care (Oct).
Special Weekly Sections: TV Guide (Fri).
Magazines: American Profile (Weekly).
Pub. ....Brad Shurett
Adv. Dir. ....Kelvin Parker
Circ. Mgr. ....Randy Lewis
Mng. Ed. ....Kim Bonner
Sports Ed....................................Jason Bowen
Prodn. Mgr. ....Junior Lewis
Market Information: Split run; TMC; Zoned editions.
Mechanical available: Black and 3 ROP colors; insert accepted - cards; page cutoffs - 21 1/2.
Mechanical Specifications: Type page 13 x 21 1/2; E - 6 cols, 2 1/16, 1/8 between; A - 6 cols, 2 1/16, 1/8 between; C - 9 cols, 1 1/2, 1/16 between.
Commodity Consumption: Avg. Page Number Per Issue - Daily 16; Avg. Page Number Per Issue - Sunday 28; widths 27 1/2; Newsprint Used - Short Tons 280; Printing Ink Used - Black 12000; Printing Ink Used - Color 1075; Printing Ink Used - Pages Printed 4472.
Equipment EDITORIAL: Front-end Software – Microsoft/Word, QPS/QuarkXPress.; Editorial Hardware – APP/Mac Quadra 610; Editorial Printers – APP/Mac LaserWriter Pro 810 CLASSIFIED: Front-end Software – Baseview/Class Manager Plus, Baseview/Fraw.; Classified Hardware – APP/Mac Quadra 610 DISPLAY: Ad make-up applications – Multi-Ad/Creator, QPS/QuarkXPress.; Display Hardware – APP/Mac Quadra 610; Display Printers – APP/Mac LaserWriter Pro 810 PRODUCTION: Pagination Software – QPS/QuarkXPress 4.0.; Production Equipment – Konica/Imagesetter; Cameras – C/Marathon; Scanners – Ap PRESSROOM: Line 1 – 5; Line 2 – 4-KP/Color King 1992; Line 3 – 2-KP/Color 1999.; Press Drives – W/House Motors, GE/Motors MAILROOM: Counter stackers – Mid-Atlantic; Bundle tying machines – 1/Strapex, 1-/Strapex; Addressing machine – 1-/KR.; Business Hardware – IBM, Packard Bell/Force I

SELMA

THE SELMA TIMES-JOURNAL

1018 Water Ave., Selma, Ala., 36701; gen tel (334) 875-2110; adv tel (334) 875-2110; ed tel (334) 875-2110; gen fax (334) 872-4588; adv fax (334) 875-5896; ed fax (334) 875-5896; adv e-mail ads@selmatimesjournal.com; ed e-mail editor@selmatimesjournal.com; web site www.selmatimesjournal.com
Group: Boone Newspapers, Inc.
Published: Tues, Wed, Thur, Fri, Sat, Sun
Weekday Frequency: m
Saturday Frequency: m
Circulation: 8,500; 8,500(sat); 10,000(sun)
Last Audit: Sworn September 30, 2002
Price: 12.95/mo; 155.40/yr; 38.85/3mo.
Advertising: Open inch rate $15
Insert rate: $77/M
News services: AP
Politics: Independent. **Established:** 1827
Not Published: Monday
Own facility?: Y
Special Editions: Battle of Selma (Apr); Kickoff-Football (Aug); Horizons-Progress (Feb); FYI-For Your Information (Jul); Graduation (May); Chamber of Commerce (Nov); Phone Book (Sep)
Magazines: Parade (S).
Pres./Pub. ....Dennis Palmer
Vice Pres./Bus. Mgr. ....Jay Davis
Cir. Dir........................................Shane Gaut
Editor ....TIm Reeves
Prodn. Mgr....................................Fred Scott
Market Information: Split run; TMC; Zoned editions.
Mechanical available: Offset; Black and 3 ROP colors; insert accepted; page cutoffs - 22 3/4.
Mechanical Specifications: Type page 13 x 21 1/2; E - 6 cols, 2 1/16, 1/8 between; A - 6 cols, 2 1/16, 1/8 between; C - 10 cols, 1 3/8, 1/16 between.
Commodity Consumption: Avg. Page Number Per Issue - Daily 16; Avg. Page Number Per Issue - Plates Used 6400; Avg. Page Number Per Issue - Sunday 28; widths 27 1/2; Newsprint Used - Short Tons 960; Printing Ink Used - Black 44000; Printing Ink Used - Color 2000; Printing Ink Us
Equipment; Editorial Hardware – APP/Mac. CLASSIFIED: Front-end Software – Baseview 1.; Classified Hardware – APP/Mac; Classified Equipment – APP/Mac; Layout Software – 4-APP/Mac.; Production Equipment – Kodak, Trendsetter direct to plate PRESSROOM: Line 1 – 10-KP/News King. MAILROOM: Counter stackers – 1/BG; Inserters and stuffers – By hand; Bundle tying machines – 1-/Bu; Addressing machine – 1-/KR.; Business Hardware – PC
Delivery method: Mail, Newsstand, Private Carrier, Racks

TALLADEGA

THE DAILY HOME

6 Sylacauga Hwy., Talladega, Ala., 35160; gen tel (256) 362-1000; adv tel (256) 362-1000; ed tel (256) 362-1000; gen fax (256) 299-2197; adv fax (256) 299-2197; ed fax (256) 362-2192; gen e-mail news@dailyhome.com; web site www.dailyhome.com
Published: Tues, Wed, Thur, Fri, Sat, Sun
Weekday Frequency: m
Circulation: 9,872; 9,872(sat); 9,872(sun)
Price: 10.00/mo (carrier/mail); 111.00/yr.
Advertising: Open inch rate $15.80
News services: AP.
Politics: Independent.
Not Published: Christmas.
Special Editions: Winston 500 (Apr); Football (Aug); Spirit of Christmas (Dec); Vacation Drawing (Feb); Update (Jan); Lakeside Living (Jul); Lakeside Living (Jun); Home & Garden (Mar); Graduation Tab (May); Christmas Gift Guide (Nov); Adopt A Pet Classified Promotion (Oct)
Special Weekly Sections: TV Guide (Fri); Religion Page (Sat); Food Page (Wed).
Magazines: Parade (S).
Adv. Dir. ....Pam Adamson
Adv. Mgr., Retail Sales ....Sandy Carden
Classified Mgr. ....Carrie Hutto
Circ. Mgr...................................Kandi George
Ed. ....Carol Pappas
Assoc. Ed. ....Janice Keith
City Ed....................................Graham Hadley
Community Calendar Ed...................Lisa Taylor
Lifestyles Ed. ....Laura Nation
Photo Ed....Bob Crisp
Sports Ed. ....Heather Baggett
Asst. Sports Ed..........................Lavante Young
Webpage Coord. ....Jim Smothers
Market Information: ADS; Split run; TMC; Zoned editions.
Mechanical available: Offset; Black and 3 ROP colors; insert accepted; page cutoffs - 22 3/4.
Mechanical Specifications: Type page 13 x 21 1/2; E - 6 cols, 2 1/16, 1/8 between; A - 6 cols, 2 1/16, 1/8 between; C - 9 cols, 1 3/8, 1/16 between.
Commodity Consumption: Avg. Page Number Per Issue - Daily 16; Avg. Page Number Per Issue - Plates Used 10644; widths 27 1/2; Newsprint Used - Short Tons 577; Printing Ink Used - Black 18460; Printing Ink Used - Color 3000; Printing Ink Used - Pages Printed 5346.
Equipment EDITORIAL: Front-end Software – Aldus/PageMaker, Microsoft/Word, QPS/QuarkXPress.; Editorial Hardware – APP/Mac; Editorial Equipment – HP/Flatbed Scanner, Polaroid/Film Scanner; Editorial Printers – APP/Mac LaserWriter I CLASSIFIED: Front-end Software – Baseview.; Classified Hardware – APP/Mac; Classified Printers – APP/Mac LaserWriter I DISPLAY: Ad make-up applications – Aldus/PageMaker, Microsoft/Word.; Display Hardware – APP/Mac; Display Printers – APP/Mac LaserWriter I; Production Equipment – AG/Imagesetter; Cameras – 1-C/19 x 23. PRESSROOM: Line 1 – 6-G/Community, 2-G/Universal Color Unit; Folders – 1; Reels and Stands – 2-Roll/Stand. MAILROOM: Counter stackers – 1-BG/106; Inserters and stuffers – 6/DG; Bundle tying machines – 1-Ty-Tech/Tyer, 3-/Bu; Addressing machine – 1-/KR.; Business Hardware – IBM

TROY

THE MESSENGER

918 S. Brundidge St., Troy, Ala., 36081; gen tel (334) 566-4270; adv tel (334) 670-6305; ed tel (334) 670-6323; gen fax (334) 566-4281; adv fax (334) 566-4281; ed fax (334) 566-4281; adv e-mail deedie.carter@troymessenger.com; web site www.troymessenger.com
Published: Tues, Wed, Thur, Fri, Sun
Weekday Frequency: m
Circulation: 2,814; 2,814(sun)
Last Audit: September 30, 2005
Price: 8.40/mo; 108.00/yr.
Advertising: Open inch rate $14.90
News services: NEA.
Note: For printing information see Andalusia Star News.
Magazines: American Profile (Weekly).
Adv. Dir. ....Deedie Carter
Ed...Stacy Graning
Features Ed. ....Jaine Treadwell
Sports Ed. ....Matt Nascone
Market Information: TMC; Zoned editions.
Mechanical available: Offset; Black and 3 ROP colors; insert accepted.
Mechanical Specifications: Type page 13 1/2 x 21 1/2; E - 6 cols, 2, 1/4 between; A - 6 cols, 2, 1/4 between; C - 9 cols, 1 5/16, 1/4 between.
Commodity Consumption: Avg. Page Number Per Issue - Sunday 54.
Equipment; Editorial Hardware – Mk/Newswriter.; Classified Hardware – Mk.; Layout Software – APP/Mac LC II, Mk/Newswriter.; Production Equipment – Mk/LaserWriter.

TUSCALOOSA

THE TUSCALOOSA NEWS

315 28th Ave., Tuscaloosa, Ala., 35401; gen tel (205) 345-0505; adv tel (205) 345-0505; ed tel (205) 345-0505; gen fax (205) 722-0187; adv fax (205) 722-0175; ed fax (205) 722-0187; adv e-mail ad@tuscaloosanews.com; web site www.tuscaloosanews.com
Group: The New York Times
Published: Mon, Tues, Wed, Thur, Fri, Sat, Sun
Weekday Frequency: m
Saturday Frequency: m
Circulation: 27,274; 26,881(sat); 31,926(sun)
Last Audit: ABC September 30, 2011
Price: 3.50/wk (mS); 182.00/yr ; 14.00/4wk.
Advertising: Open inch rate $63.20
News services: AP, NYT.
Politics: Independent.
Own facility?: Y
Special Editions: University of Alabama Today

(Aug); Fall Homes Decorating (Dec); Focus (Feb); Back-to-School (Jul); Family-owned Businesses (Jun); Focus (Mar); Outdoors (May); Parade of Homes (Oct); Outdoors (Sept).
Special Weekly Sections: Church Page (Fri); TV Click (S); Best Food Day (Wed).
Magazines: Parade (S).
Pub.....Tim Thompson
HR/Administrative Asst......Carla Gillespie
Adv. Mgr., Retail.....Angela Young-Hobbs
Circ. Mgr......Tony Heaps
Exec. Ed......Douglas Ray
City Ed.....Katherine Lee
Editorial Page Ed......Ben Windham
Librarian.....Betty Slowe
Photo Dept. Mgr......Robert Sutton
Exec. Sports Ed......Tommy Deas
Mng. Sports Ed......Harold Stout
Theater/Music Ed......Mark Cobb
New Media Coord......Chris Rattey
Opns. Dir......Paul Hass
Prodn. Dir., Pre Press.....Sam Kirkwood
Prodn. Mgr., Mailroom.....Henry Burt
Prodn. Mgr., Pre Press.....Chuck Jones
Prodn. Mgr., Pressroom.....Wade Morrison
Market Information: TMC.
Mechanical available: Offset; Black and 3 ROP colors; insert accepted - any size; page cutoffs - 22 3/4.
Mechanical Specifications: Type page 13 x 21 1/2; E - 6 cols, 2 1/16, 1/8 between; A - 6 cols, 2 1/16, 1/8 between; C - 9 cols, 1 3/8, 1/16 between.
Commodity Consumption: Avg. Page Number Per Issue - Daily 44; Avg. Page Number Per Issue - Plates Used 37000; Avg. Page Number Per Issue - Sunday 90; widths 27; Newsprint Used - Short Tons 4300; Printing Ink Used - Black 104000; Printing Ink Used - Color 16000; Printing Ink Us
Equipment EDITORIAL: Front-end Software – CompuText.; Editorial Hardware – PC, Microsoft/Windows NT; Editorial Printers – HP/5000 CLASSIFIED: Front-end Software – AT/IAS, Computext.; Classified Hardware – PC, Microsoft/Windows NT; Classified Printers – HP/5000 DISPLAY: Ad make-up applications – QPS/QuarkXPress, Adobe/Photoshop; Layout Software – CompuText.; Display Hardware – APP/Mac; Display Printers – QMS, HP/Color PRODUCTION: Pagination Software – CompUtext.; Production Equipment – 2-COM/9600, 1-Nu/Flip Top FT52UPNS; Cameras – 1-C/Spartan III, 1-R; Scanners – 2-Kk/RFS 2035+, 2-X/11x17 Flatbed PRESSROOM: Line 1 – 10-G/Urbanite, 1-G/Urbanite (3 color); Press Drives – 2; Pasters – 8-Ebway/H535000; Press control system – 2; Press registration system – KFM/Pin System. MAILROOM: Counter stackers – 3-HL/Monitor; Inserters and stuffers – 1-S/10-48P; Bundle tying machines – 1-MLN/ML, 1/Power Strap, 1-MLN/MLEE, 1-Dynaric/NP-2; Addressing machine – 1-/KR.; Audio Hardware – Brite Voice Systems; Business Hardware – IBM/AS-400

ALASKA

ANCHORAGE

ANCHORAGE DAILY NEWS

1001 Northway Dr., Anchorage, Alaska, 99508; gen tel (907) 257-4200; adv tel (907) 257-4444; ed tel (907) 257-4305; gen fax (907) 257-4246; adv fax (907) 257-4246; ed fax (907) 258-2157; ed e-mail newsroom@adn.com; web site www.adn.com
Group: Metro Newspaper Advertising Services, Inc.
Published: Mon, Tues, Wed, Thur, Fri, Sat, Sun
Weekday Frequency: m
Saturday Frequency: m
Circulation: 43,794; 43,683(sat); 50,287(sun)
Last Audit: ABC September 30, 2011
Price: 12.50/mo; 135.00/yr; 72.50/6mo.
Advertising: Open inch rate $116.80
News services: AP, NYT, LAT-WP, MCT, RN, CNS, DJ, TMS, UPI.
Politics: Independent. **Established:** 1946
Own facility?: Y
Special Editions: Woman's Show (Apr); Fall Homebuilders Show (Aug); Last Minute Gifts (Dec); Iditarod (Feb); Health & Fitness (Jan); Hunting (Jul); Spring Home Improvement (Jun); Spring Homebuilders Show (Mar); Trucks, 4x4s & RVs (May); Snowmachining (Nov); College Plannin
Special Weekly Sections: LIFE (Fri); TV News (S); Food (Wed).
Magazines: Parade (S).
Pub./Pres......Patrick Doyle
Ed......Patrick Dougherty
City Ed......David Hulen
Columnist.....Beth Bragg
Community News Ed......Rose Cox
Copy Desk Chief.....Jim Macknicki
Editorial Page Ed......Larry Persily
Educ. Reporter.....Katie Pesznecker
Features Ed......Kathleen McCoy
Film/Theater Ed......Mark Baechtel
Food Ed......T.C. Mitchell
Finance.....Jerry Hug
Retail Ad Manager.....Joni Vakalis
Classified Manager.....Kit Hagen
Dir., Finance.....David Ryan
Dir., Organizational Devel......Nancy Manes
Credit Mgr......Jim Donahue
Vice Pres. Adv......Lee Leschper
Adv. Mgr., Retail.....Michael Wiley
Mktg. Mgr......Jane Lee
Bus. Ed......Bill White
Market Information: ADS; TMC; Zoned editions.
Mechanical available: Offset; Black and 3 ROP colors; insert accepted; page cutoffs - 21 1/8.
Mechanical Specifications: Type page 11 5/8 x 20 7/8; E - 6 cols, 1 7/8, 3/16 between; A - 6 cols, 1 7/8, 3/16 between; C - 10 cols, 1 7/25, 1/8 between.
Commodity Consumption: Avg. Page Number Per Issue - Daily 64; Avg. Page Number Per Issue - Plates Used 95749; Avg. Page Number Per Issue - Sunday 126; widths 25; Newsprint Used - Metric Tons 12617; Printing Ink Used - Black 157142; Printing Ink Used - Color 126199; Printing In
Equipment; Editorial Hardware – 510-Compaq PC, Win 2000, Sun 420 Servers, DTI News 5.4; Editorial Equipment – 2-Linotronic/530, 1-HP/755cm Color Proofer, HP/1050 Color Proofer; Editorial Printers – 2-ECR, Imagesetter/, Harlequin/Rip. CLASSIFIED: Front-end Software – DTI 5.01.; Classified Hardware – 40-APP/Mac G3, Sun/450 Server; Classified Equipment – Sun/450 Unix servers; Classified Printers – 2-ECR, 2-Linotype/530, Imagesetter, Harlequin/Rip DISPLAY: Ad make-up applications – QPS/QuarkXPress, Macromedia/Freehand, Adobe/Illustrator, Adobe/Photoshop, Engage/Content Server; Layout Software – MEI/ALS, Engage/Technology Content Server.; Display Hardware – APP/Mac G3, APP/Mac G4; Display Printers – 2-Linotronic/RIP, 2-ECR, Harlequin/Rip PRODUCTION: Pagination Software – QPS/QuarkXPress, DTI/I; Production Equipment – Caere/OmniPage, 1-ECR 6200, 2-Linotype-Hell/5301, 2-HP/51050 Color Proofer, 1-Glunz & Jensen/550, 1-Glunz & Jensen/720; Cameras – 2-C/Spartan III; Scanners – 1-Hel/Topaz, 1-Hel/Opal, 1-Fuji/C550, 1-Fuji/2750 PRESSROOM: Line 1 – 9-G/Headliner offset double width 1986; Line 3 – 4-HL/V-30 Heatset single width 1995; Press Drives – 9-GE/Motors, Fin/Controllers, 2-GE Motor/Fin/Control, 1-GE w/GE/Controllers; Folders – 2-G/3:2 (144 page MAILROOM: Counter stackers – 4-Hall/HT II, 3-QWI/401; Inserters and stuffers – 1-HI/14-72, 1-GMA/S-1000, MM/227 5:1; Bundle tying machines – 1/Power Strap, 2-Signode/Spirit, 4-Dynamic/NP 1500, 2-Signode/LB2000, 2-QWI/Viper, PBS/Insert Management; Addressing machine – Addressing machin BUSINESS COMPUTERS: Business Software – 4-PC Pentium III; Business Hardware – 2-HP/3000 918-RXs, 2-HP/3000 918-RXs
Delivery method: Private Carrier

FAIRBANKS

FAIRBANKS DAILY NEWS-MINER

200 N. Cushman St., Fairbanks, Alaska, 99707; gen tel (907) 456-6661; adv tel (907) 459-7548; ed tel (907) 459-7572; gen fax (907) 452-5054; adv fax (907) 451-8962 (display); ed fax (907) 452-7917; gen e-mail editor@newsminer.com; adv e-mail ads@newsminer.com; ed e-mail newsroom@newsminer.com; web site www.newsminer.com
Published: Mon, Tues, Wed, Thur, Fri, Sat, Sun
Weekday Frequency: m
Saturday Frequency: m
Circulation: 13,143; 13,206(sat); 16,382(sun)
Last Audit: ABC September 30, 2011
Price: 14.00/mo; 175.80/yr.
Advertising: Open inch rate $25.88
News services: AP, NYT.
Politics: Independent.
Not Published: Memorial Day; Labor Day; Christmas (unless it falls on a Sunday).
Special Editions: Building (Apr); Back-to-School (Aug); Christmas Greeter (Dec); Valentine's Day (Feb); Hunting (Jul); Visitor's Guide (Jun); Winter Carnival (Mar); Christmas Shopper (Nov); Winter Survival (Sept).
Special Weekly Sections: Outdoors (Fri); Kaleidoscope (arts & entertainment) (Thur); Food (Wed).
Magazines: Parade (S).
Pub......Marilyn Romano
Gen. Mgr., Digital Express.....Richard Harris
Dir., Finance.....Katherine Strle
Credit Mgr......Cassey Kelley
HR Mgr......Jim Shanklin
Purchasing Agent.....Mary O'Shea
Mgr., Educ. Serv. (NIE).....Joe Wagner
Adv. Dir......Paula Kothe
Adv. Mgr., Classified.....Alice Hansen
Adv. Mgr., Promo......Danita Swensson
Circ. Dir......Tom Gilligan
Mng. Ed......Rod Boyce
Asst. Mng. Ed......Sam Bishop
Educ. Reporter.....Marmian Grimes
Food Ed......Patricia Watts
Graphics Ed......Dee Dee Hammond
News Ed......Chris Talbott
Mechanical available: Offset; Black and 3 ROP colors; insert accepted; page cutoffs - 22 3/4.
Mechanical Specifications: Type page 12 7/8 x 21; E - 6 cols, 2 1/16, 1/8 between; A - 6 cols, 2 1/16, 1/8 between; C - 10 cols, 1 1/4, 1/12 between.
Commodity Consumption: Avg. Page Number Per Issue - Daily 30; Avg. Page Number Per Issue - Plates Used 14000; Avg. Page Number Per Issue - Sunday 76; widths 25; Newsprint Used - Short Tons 1632; Printing Ink Used - Black 31500; Printing Ink Used - Color 3500; Printing Ink Used
Equipment EDITORIAL: Front-end Software – HI/PEN System.; Editorial Hardware – 31-PC 486; Editorial Equipment – 1-Lf/AP Leaf Picture Desk, 1-APP/Power Mac G3; Editorial Printers – Panasonic, 1-APP/Mac LaserWriter II, Okidata CLASSIFIED: Front-end Software – HI/CASH, Microsoft/Windows 95.; Classified Hardware – 15-Pentium/PC; Classified Printers – 3-Okidata DISPLAY: Ad make-up applications – Multi-Ad/Creator 3.7; Layout Software – 2-SCS/Layout 8000, 5-APP/Power Mac G3.; Display Hardware – 2-SCS/Layout 8000; Display Printers – 1-HP/1600C, 1-Case/Printer, 1-HP/Laserjet 6MP PRODUCTION: Pagination Software – HI/XP-21 Images.; Production Equipment – TextBridge/Pro 98, 2-Gluntz & Jensen; Cameras – 1-R/16 x 20, 1-W/20 x 24; Scanners – 1-ECR/Autokon 8400 PRESSROOM: Line 1 – 11-G/Urbanite; Line 2 – 4-G 1965; Line 3 – Jan-70; Line 4 – 1-G/Urbanite 1996; Line 5 – 1-G/Urbanite 1997; Line 6 – 4-G/Urbanite 1998; Press Drives – 1-HP/75, 1-HP/100; Folders – 1-G/2:1; Reels and Stands – 6-G/Urbanite; Press control system – 2 MAILROOM: Counter stackers – QWI/108; Inserters and stuffers – 1-MM/227, 1-MM/227; Bundle tying machines – 2-MLN/EE; Wrapping singles – 1-PRM/720; Addressing machine – 1-IBM/AS-400; Other equipment –1-MM/286 QFL, 1-MM/1620 QFL. BUSINESS COMPUTERS: Business Software – Microsoft/Word, Microsoft/Excel, Libra, Abra Cadabra, Human Resources, Geac/Vision Shift; Business Hardware – 1-IBM/AS-400, 15-Gateway, Novell/LAN, Microsoft/Windows NT SQL

JUNEAU

JUNEAU EMPIRE

3100 Channel Dr., Juneau, Alaska, 99801-7814; gen tel (907) 586-3740; adv tel (907) 586-3740; ed tel (907) 586-3740; gen fax (907) 586-9097; adv fax (907) 586-9097; ed fax (907) 586-3028; ed e-mail editor@juneauempire.com; web site www.juneauempire.com
Group: Morris Communications Inc.
Published: Mon, Tues, Wed, Thur, Fri, Sun
Weekday Frequency: m
Circulation: 4,371
Price: 13.50/mo; 141.45/yr.
Advertising: Open inch rate $22.00
News services: AP, MCT.
Politics: Independent. **Established:** 1912
Not Published: Saturday
Own facility?: Y
Special Editions: Salmon Derby (Aug); Christmas (Dec); George Washington's Birthday (Feb); Legislature (Jan); Juneau Guide (May); High School Basketball Preview (Nov); Lifestyles (Oct).
Special Weekly Sections: Neighbors (Fri); TV Week (S); Preview (Thur); Spotlight (Tues); Neighbors (Wed).
Magazines: Juneau Guide - tourism/travel
Profile: Daily Newspaper Publisher
Publisher.....Mark Bryan
Advertising Manager.....Leah Nelson
Managing Editor.....John Moses
Circulation/Mailroom Director Vitto Kleinschmidt
Production Director.....Bob Honea
Market Information: ADS.
Mechanical available: Offset; Black and 3 ROP colors; insert accepted; page cutoffs - 22 1/2.
Mechanical Specifications: Type page 13 x 21; E - 6 cols, 2 1/16, 1/8 between; A - 6 cols, 2 1/16, 1/8 between; C - 8 cols, 1 1/2, 1/8 between.
Commodity Consumption: Avg. Page Number Per Issue - Daily 23; Avg. Page Number Per Issue - Plates Used 6000; Avg. Page Number Per Issue - Sunday 24; widths 27; Newsprint Used - Metric Tons 380; Printing Ink Used - Black 6000; Printing Ink Used - Color 300.
Equipment EDITORIAL: Front-end Software – MPS/Tecs 2.; Editorial Hardware – Gateway; Editorial Equipment – AG/1500; Editorial Printers – APP/Mac II NTX CLASSIFIED: Front-end Software – MPS.; Classified Hardware – Gateway; Classified Printers – Toshiba, Epson DISPLAY: Ad make-up applications – Multi-Ad/Creator, QPS/QuarkXPress.; Display Hardware – APP/Macs, APP/Power Mac; Display Printers – AG/1500, HP/LaserJet 4 Plus; Production Equipment – 2-M/202N; Cameras – C/Spartan III. PRESSROOM: Line 1 – 7-G/Community single width; Folders – 1-G/Community, G/SC (with Balloon former). MAILROOM: Counter stackers – BG/Count-O-Veyor; Inserters and stuffers – KAN/8 units & counter; Bundle tying machines – .; Audio Hardware – Morris Publishing System, Samsung; Business Hardware – Gateway, IBM/PS2
Delivery method: Newsstand, Private Carrier, Racks

KENAI

PENINSULA CLARION

150 Trading Bay 1, Kenai, Alaska, 99611;

gen tel (907) 283-7551; adv tel (907) 283-7551; ed tel (907) 283-7551; gen fax (907) 283-3299; adv fax (907) 283-8144; ed fax (907) 283-3299; gen e-mail news@peninsulaclarion.com; web site www.peninsulaclarion.com
Published: Mon, Tues, Wed, Thur, Fri, Sun
Weekday Frequency: m
Circulation: 5,710; 5,710(sun)
Last Audit: September 28, 2001
Price: 8.50/mo; 100.00/yr.
Advertising: Open inch rate $20.15
News services: AP.
Politics: Independent.
Not Published: New Year; Memorial Day; Independence Day; Labor Day; Thanksgiving; Christmas.
Special Editions: Mother's Day (Apr); Hunting (Aug); Greetings (Dec); Industry (Feb); Fathers' Day (Jun); Recreation Guide (May); Real Estate (Monthly); Coupon Book (Quarterly).
Special Weekly Sections: Outdoor (Fri); Peninsula LIfe (S); What's Happening (Thur); School News (Wed).
Pub. ....Stan Pitlo
Purchasing Agent/Controller ....Jane Russell
Circ. Dir. ....Evy Gebhardt
Exec. Ed. ....Larry Campbell
Mng. Ed. ....Will Morrow
Asst. Ed. ....Dori Lynn Anderson
Sports Ed. ....Jeff Helminiak
New Media Dir. ....Vincent Nusunginya
Prodn. Mgr., Post Press/Mailroom ....Doug Munn
Market Information: TMC.
Mechanical available: Offset; Black and 3 ROP colors; insert accepted - all; page cutoffs - 21 1/2.
Mechanical Specifications: Type page 13 x 21 1/2; E - 6 cols, 2, 1/6 between; A - 6 cols, 2, 1/6 between; C - 8 cols, 1 1/2, 1/6 between.
Commodity Consumption: Avg. Page Number Per Issue - Daily 20; Avg. Page Number Per Issue - Plates Used 8000; widths 34; Newsprint Used - Metric Tons 304; Printing Ink Used - Black 3400; Printing Ink Used - Color 2300.
Equipment; Editorial Hardware – APP/Mac.; Classified Hardware – APP/Mac.; Production Equipment – 2-Nu, XIT/Cadet, ECR/Imagesetter; Cameras – 1-R. PRESSROOM: Line 1 – 8-G/Offset single width 1992; Press Drives – 2-Fin/60 h.p.; Folders – 2; Reels and Stands – 3 MAILROOM: Counter stackers – 1/BG; Inserters and stuffers – 1-/St; Bundle tying machines – 3-/Bu; Wrapping singles – 1-/St; Addressing machine – 1-/St; Other equipment –2-It/Stitcher, 1-Ch/Trimmer.; Audio Hardware – Morris Communications Corp; Business Hardware – Gateway/EV500

SOUTHEASTERN NEWSPAPERS, INC.

150 Trading Bay #1, Kenai, Alaska, 99611; gen tel (907) 283-7551; gen fax (907) 283-3299; adv e-mail evy.gebhardt@peninsulaclarion.com; web site www.peninsulaclarion.com
Published: Mon, Tues, Wed, Thur, Fri, Sat, Sun
Weekday Frequency: m
Circulation: 5,044; 4,881(sun)
Price: 132.00/yr.
Advertising: Open inch rate $15.45
Pub. ....Stan Pitlo

KETCHIKAN

KETCHIKAN DAILY NEWS

501 Dock St., Ketchikan, Alaska, 99901; gen tel (907) 225-3157; adv tel (907) 225-3157; ed tel (907) 225-3157; gen fax (907) 225-1096; adv fax (907) 225-1096; ed fax (907) 225-1096; gen e-mail news@ketchikandailynews.com; adv e-mail kdn@kpunet.net; web site www.ketchikandailynews.com
Published: Mon, Tues, Wed, Thur, Fri, Sat
Weekday Frequency: m
Circulation: 4,117; 4,117(sat)
Last Audit: September 28, 2001
Price: 142.00/yr.
Advertising: Open inch rate $15.80
News services: AP.
Politics: Independent.
Not Published: New Year; Memorial Day; Independence Day; Labor Day; Veteran's Day; Thanksgiving; Christmas.
Special Editions: Christmas Card Edition (Annually).
Magazines: First City Scene (Sat).
Co-Pub. ....Lew Williams
Co-Pub. ....Tena Williams
Circ. Mgr. ....Lecile Kiffer
Mng. Ed. ....Terry Miller
Market Information: TMC.
Mechanical available: Offset; Black and 3 ROP colors; insert accepted - anything; page cutoffs - 22 1/2.
Mechanical Specifications: Type page 13 1/2 x 21; E - 6 cols, 2 1/16, 1/8 between; A - 6 cols, 2 1/16, 1/8 between; C - 9 cols, 1 1/2, 1/16 between.
Commodity Consumption: Avg. Page Number Per Issue - Daily 14; Avg. Page Number Per Issue - Plates Used 11000; Avg. Page Number Per Issue - Sunday 72; widths 30; Newsprint Used - Short Tons 212; Printing Ink Used - Black 7200; Printing Ink Used - Color 1000; Printing Ink Used -
Equipment; Editorial Hardware – APP/Mac.; Classified Hardware – Point 4.; Production Equipment – 1-COM/8400, APP/Mac LaserWriter II, COM/3400 Laserprinter; Cameras – 1-R/Vertical. PRESSROOM: Line 1 – 3-G/Community; Line 2 – 1-G/Universal; Folders – 1-G/2:1.; Addressing machine – 3/Wm.

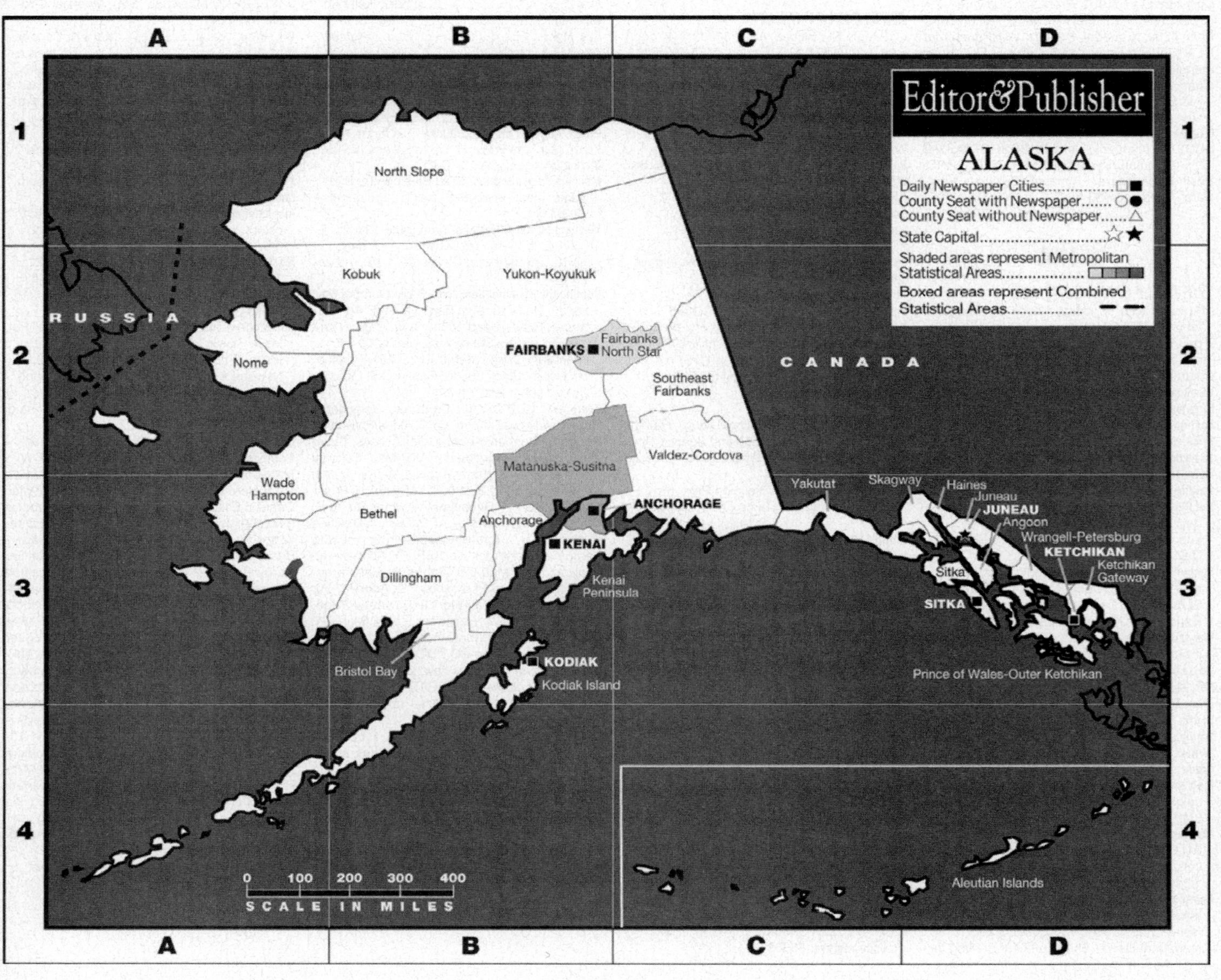

KODIAK

KODIAK DAILY MIRROR

1419 Selig St., Kodiak, Alaska, 99615; gen tel (907) 486-3227; gen fax (907) 486-3088; web site www.kodiakdailymirror.com
Published: Mon, Tues, Wed, Thur, Fri
Weekday Frequency: e
Circulation: 2,849
Last Audit: September 30, 2004
Price: 10.00/mo; 150.00/yr.
Advertising: Open inch rate $12.75
News services: AP, CNS, TMS.
Politics: 1940
Special Editions: Coast Guard Supplement (Aug); Holiday Gift Guide (Dec); Adventure Guide (Jul); Graduation (Jun); ComFish (Mar); Crab Festival (May).
Special Weekly Sections: TV (Fri); Gardengate (Mon); Outdoors (Tues); Best Food Days (Wed).
Pub. ....Richard Harris
Ed..Derek Clarkston
Market Information: TMC.
Mechanical available: Offset; Black and 3 ROP colors; insert accepted - any; page cutoffs - 22 3/4 Folded.
Mechanical Specifications: Type page 11 1/2 x 21; E - 6 cols, 3 3/4, 3/16 between; A - 6 cols, 3 3/4, 3/16 between; C - 6 cols, 3 3/4, 3/16 between.
Commodity Consumption: Avg. Page Number Per Issue - Daily 10.
Equipment EDITORIAL: Front-end Software – Microsoft/Word.; Editorial Hardware – APP/Power Mac 7200; Editorial Printers – HP/LaserJet CLASSIFIED: Front-end Software – Fourth Dimension.; Classified Hardware – 1-APP/Mac Quadra 630 DISPLAY: Ad make-up applications – Aldus, Adobe/PageMaker 6.0; Display Hardware – APP/Mac G3; Production Equipment – Nu/Flip Top FT40UP; Cameras – SCREEN/Companica 516. PRESSROOM: Line 1 – 5-G/Community. BUSINESS COMPUTERS: Business Software – Synaptic; Business Hardware – Compaq/586-166

SITKA

THE DAILY SITKA SENTINEL

112 Barracks St., Sitka, Alaska, 99835; gen tel (907) 747-3219; gen fax (907) 747-8898; gen e-mail sitkanews@hotmail.com; web site www.sitkasentinel.com
Published: Mon, Tues, Wed, Thur, Fri
Weekday Frequency: e
Circulation: 2,875
Last Audit: October 9, 2006
Price: 85.00/yr.
Advertising: Open inch rate $10.70
News services: AP.
Politics: Independent. **Established:** 1940
Not Published: New Year; Washington's Birthday; Memorial Day; Independence Day; Labor Day; Alaska Day (Oct 18); Veteran's Day; Thanksgiving; Christmas.
Special Editions: Back-to-School (Aug); Christmas Greetings (Dec); Boat Show (Mar); Summer Visitors (May); Christmas Shopping Issue (Nov); Moonlight Madness (Oct).
Magazines: Sitka Weekend (TV & Entertainment) (Fri).
Office Mgr.....................................Libby Mears
Adv. Mgr. ....Catherine Bagley
Exec. Ed.....................................Thad Poulson
Sports Ed. ....Craig Giammona
Women's Ed. ....Sandy Poulson
Writer ....Shannon Haughland
Prodn., Head Pressman............Michael Bagley
Mechanical available: Offset; Black and 3 ROP colors; insert accepted; page cutoffs - 22 3/4.
Mechanical Specifications: Type page 13 1/2 x 21; E - 6 cols, 2 1/16, 1/8 between; A - 6 cols, 2 1/16, 1/8 between; C - 6 cols, 2 1/16, 1/8 between.
Commodity Consumption: Avg. Page Number Per Issue - Daily 10; Avg. Page Number Per Issue - Plates Used 1560; widths 29; Newsprint Used - Short Tons 48; Printing Ink Used - Black 900; Printing Ink Used - Color 30; Printing Ink Used - Pages Printed 2600.
Equipment EDITORIAL: Front-end Software – TC.; Editorial Hardware – 10-IBM; Editorial Equipment – Multitech/900, 6-Northgate/286-12, 3-PC 386; Editorial Printers – HP/Laser Jet, Xante/Accel-a-Writer 3G CLASSIFIED: Front-end Software – TC 1.348.; Classified Hardware – IBM; Classified Printers – HP/Laser Jet, Xante/Accel-a-Writer 3G DISPLAY: Ad make-up applications – Aldus/PageMaker, Adobe/Illustrator, Adobe/Photo Shop; Layout Software – APP/Mac.; Display Printers – Xante/Accel-a-Writer 3G PRODUCTION: Pagination Software – Adobe/Page Maker.; Production Equipment – 1-Nu/Flip Top, HP/Laser Jet; Cameras – 1-K, 1-SCREEN/640-C; Scanners – HP PRESSROOM: Line 1 – 4-G/Community; Folders – 1; Bundle tying machines – Felins/Paktyer; Addressing machine – Wm. BUSINESS COMPUTERS: Business Software – Peachtree; Business Hardware – 3-Microsoft/Windows

ARIZONA

BISBEE

BISBEE DAILY REVIEW

12 Main St., Bisbee, Ariz., 85603-0127; gen tel (520) 432-2231; gen fax (520) 432-2356; gen e-mail svhads@transedge.com; ed e-mail svhnews@transedge.com; web site www.svherald.com
Group: ANA Ad Services, Inc. (Arizona Newspaper Association)
Wick Communications Co Inc
Published: Mon, Tues, Wed, Thur, Fri, Sat, Sun
Weekday Frequency: m
Saturday Frequency: m
Circulation: 604; 590(sat); 605(sun)
Last Audit: Sworn September 30, 2011
Price: 12.50/mo; 150.00/yr.
Advertising: Open inch rate $15.25 weekdays
Insert rate: 55.65
News services: AP, NYT.
Politics: Independent. **Established:** 1898
Note: For information on printing and production see the Sierra Vista Daily Herald. Advertisements in the Daily Review (mS) are included in the Sierra Vista Herald (mS).
Advertising not accepted: N
Own facility?: Y
Special Editions: Back-to-School (Aug); Health & Fitness (Jan); Business and Service Directory (Mar); Christmas Opening (Nov); Year in Review (Jan).
Special Weekly Sections: Religion Page (Fri); Outdoors Page (T); Taste (Wed). Tempo-Ent (Th)
Profile: Community newspaper
Pub. ....Philip Vega
Bus. Mgr. ....Joan Hancock
Dir., Mktg. ....Patricia Wick
Mng. Ed. ....Eric Petermann
Sports Ed. ....Matt Hickman
Prodn. Mgr. ....Scott Green
Prodn. Mgr., Mailroom ....Ron Temple
Circulation Manager ....Ray Taylor
Market Information: TMC; Zoned editions.
Mechanical available: Offset; Black and 3 ROP colors; insert accepted - all; page cutoffs - 21.
Mechanical Specifications: Type page 9 29/32 x 21; E - 6 cols, 1 17/32, 5/6 between; A - 6 cols, 1 17/32, 5/6 between; C - 9 cols, 1, 11/12 between.
Commodity Consumption: Avg. Page Number Per Issue - Daily 24; Avg. Page Number Per Issue - Sunday 36; widths 22; Newsprint Used - Metric Tons 800; Printing Ink Used - Black 5200; Printing Ink Used - Color 1000; Printing Ink Used - Pages Printed 9096.
Equipment CLASSIFIED: Front-end Software – Baseview.; Layout Software – 5-APP/Mac.
Zip Codes served: 85603
Delivery method: Mail, Newsstand, Private Carrier, Racks

BULLHEAD CITY

MOHAVE VALLEY DAILY NEWS

2435 Miracle Mile, Bullhead City, Ariz., 86442; gen tel (928) 763-2505; adv tel (928) 763-2505; ed tel (928) 763-2505; gen fax (928) 763-7820; adv fax (928) 763-7820; ed fax (928) 763-7820; gen e-mail mvdnews@mohavedaily.news; adv e-mail director@npgcable.com; ed e-mail mvdnedit@mohavedailynews.com; web site www.mohavedailynews.com
Published: Mon, Tues, Wed, Thur, Fri, Sun
Weekday Frequency: m
Circulation: 7,609; 8,509(sun)
Last Audit: ABC September 30, 2011
Price: 83.60/yr; 25.06/3mo.
Advertising: Open inch rate $23.90
News services: AP.
Special Editions: Home Improvement & Gardening (Apr); Seniors (Feb); Business Profiles (Jul); The Best of (Jun); NCAA Finals (Mar); Life in Colorado (May); The Best of (Nov); Women in Business (Oct); Home Improvement & Gardening (Sept).
Special Weekly Sections: Colorado River Weekender (Fri).
Magazines: USA WEEKEND Magazine (S).
Pub...Chuck Rathbun
Gen. Mgr. ....Paul Stubler
Bus. Mgr...................................Sue Anderson
Adv. Supvr., Classified ....Kathy Jones
Ed. ....Bill McMillen
Entertainment Ed. ....Alan Marciochi
Sports Ed................................Daniel McKillop
Dir., Opns.............................Nancy Darmofal
Prodn. Supvr., Camera/Stripping ......Carlos Ruiz
Prodn. Mgr., Pre Press..................Patricia Fisk
Market Information: ADS; TMC.
Mechanical available: Offset; Black and 3 ROP colors; insert accepted - most; page cutoffs - 22 3/4.
Mechanical Specifications: Type page 13 x 21; E - 6 cols, 1 13/16, 1/6 between; A - 6 cols, 1 13/16, 1/6 between; C - 8 cols, 1 1/2, 1/6 between.
Commodity Consumption: Avg. Page Number Per Issue - Daily 18; Avg. Page Number Per Issue - Plates Used 18000; Avg. Page Number Per Issue - Sunday 32; widths 12 1/2; Newsprint Used - Metric Tons 1251; Printing Ink Used - Black 30500; Printing Ink Used - Color 17034; Printing In
Equipment EDITORIAL: Front-end Software – Baseview/NewsEdit Pro, QPS, Aldus/Freehand, Adobe/Photoshop, Adobe/Color Access, Baseview.; Editorial Hardware – APP/Mac; Editorial Printers – Xante/Accel-a-Writer 3G, Xante/Accel-a-Writer 8300 CLASSIFIED: Front-end Software – Baseview/Ad Manager Pro.; Classified Hardware – APP/iMac; Classified Printers – Xante/Accel-a-Writer 8300, Xante/Accel-a-Writer 3G DISPLAY: Ad make-up applications – Multi-Ad/Creator 6, Aldus/Freehand 10.0, Adobe/Photoshop 7.0, Adobe/Color Access, Adobe/Illustrator 9.0, Adobe/PageMaker 6.5; Display Hardware – APP/Mac G4; Display Printers – Xante/Accel-a-Writer 8300, Xante/Accel-a-Writer 3G PRODUCTION: Pagination Software – Baseview, Quark 4.0.; Production Equipment – GTS/OLIC, 2-Post Script/Level 3, 2-Pre Press/Panther Pro V; Cameras – B; Scanners – Lf, Microtek, Umax/Flatbed, Nikon/Coolscan LS-2000 PRESSROOM: Line 1 – 3-WPC/Atlas single width, 1-WPC/Marc 25; Line 2 – 1-WPC/Quad stack single width, 3-WPC/Marc 25; Folders – WPC (1/4-1/2), WPC/Mark 25 1999; Reels and Stands – 4; Inserters and stuffers – 2/KAN; Bundle tying machines – MLN/2EE, OVL, It; Other equipment –Challenger/3Knife Trimmer. BUSINESS COMPUTERS: Business Software – Quattro/Pro; Business Hardware – Qantel

CASA GRANDE

CASA GRANDE DISPATCH

200 W. Second St., Casa Grande, Ariz., 85122; gen tel (520) 836-7461; adv tel (520) 426-3814; ed tel (520) 836-7461; gen fax (520) 836-0343; adv fax (520) 836-8522; ed fax (520) 836-0343; gen e-mail ads@trivalleycentral.com; web site www.trivalleycentral.com
Published: Tues, Wed, Thur, Fri, Sat, Sun
Weekday Frequency: m
Saturday Frequency: m
Circulation: 7,208; 7,145(sat); 7,522(sun)
Last Audit: ABC September 30, 2011
Price: $10.50/mo (motor route); 126.00/yr.
Advertising: Open inch rate $14.17
News services: AP.
Politics: Independent.
Not Published: New Year; Memorial Day; Independence Day; Labor Day; Thanksgiving; Christmas.
Own facility?: Y
Special Editions: Home Improvement (Apr); Back-to-School (Aug); Christmas (Dec); O'Odham Tash (Indian Days) (Feb); Customer Appreciation (Jul); Car Care (Jun); Spring Fashion (Mar); Graduation (May); Real Estate (Monthly); Gift Guide (Nov); Cotton Issue (Oct).
Special Weekly Sections: Casa Grande Valley TV Roundup (Sat); Tri-Valley Dispatch (Wed).
Magazines: Pinal Ways (Quarterly); USA WEEKEND Magazine (Sat); American Profile (Weekly).
Dir., Mktg. ....Kara K. Cooper
Circ. Dir...Jim Martin
Editorial Page Ed. ....Donovan M. Kramer
News Ed....................................Larry Lockhart
Sports Ed. ....Ed Petruska
Data Processing Mgr., Prodn. Systems Rob Williams
Mgmt. Info Servs. Mgr., Bus. Applications Andre Phillips
Prodn. Dir. ....Mark Urseth
Market Information: ADS; TMC.
Mechanical available: Offset; Black and 3 ROP colors; insert accepted; page cutoffs - 22 3/4.
Mechanical Specifications: Type page 13 x 21 1/2; E - 6 cols, 2 1/16, 1/8 between; A - 6 cols, 2 1/16, 1/8 between; C - 8 cols, 1 9/16, 1/8 between.
Commodity Consumption: Avg. Page Number Per Issue - Daily 26; Avg. Page Number Per Issue - Plates Used 2643; widths 27 1/2; Newsprint Used - Metric Tons 430; Printing Ink Used - Black 6556; Printing Ink Used - Color 670; Printing Ink Used - Pages Printed 8087.
Equipment EDITORIAL: Front-end Software – Baseview/NewsEdit Pro IQUE, Baseview/Wire Manager IQ Pro, QPS/QuarkXPress 3.32.; Editorial Hardware – APP/Power Mac, APP/Mac Quadra; Editorial Equipment – Phrasea/Archive (photo/text); Editorial Printers – APP/Mac LaserWriter IIq CLASSIFIED: Front-end Software – Baseview/Class Manager 3.0.6.; Classified Hardware – APP/Mac Quadra 630; Classified Printers – Okidata DISPLAY: Ad make-up applications – Multi-Ad/Creator 4.0, QPS/QuarkXPress 3.32.; Display Hardware – APP/Power Mac; Display Printers – APP/Mac LaserWriter Pro 16/600, Xante/Accel-a-Writer 8200, Tektronix/Phaser 300 PRODUCTION: Pagination Software – QPS/QuarkXPress 3.32.; Production Equipment – Caere/OmniPage Direct, AG/Accuset 1500, AG/Viper RIP, Vista/88; Cameras – 1-DAI/C-260-D PRESSROOM: Line 1 – 13-G/Community; Line 2 – 4; Line 3 – 2, 3; Folders – 2-G/Suburban (with balloon), G/SSC. MAILROOM: Counter stackers – 2-BG/105; Inserters and stuffers – 1-KAN/480 Inserter; Bundle tying machines – 2-MLN/ML2EE; Addressing machine – 1/Wm.; Business Hardware – GEAC/Vision Shift, Covalent
Delivery method: Newsstand, Private Carrier

DOUGLAS

THE DAILY DISPATCH

530 11th St., Douglas, Ariz., 85307; gen tel (520) 364-3424; adv tel (520) 364-3424; ed tel (520) 364-3424; gen fax (520) 364-6750; adv fax (520) 364-6750; ed fax (520) 364-6750; gen e-mail publisher@douglasdispatch.com; web site www.douglasdispatch.com
Published: Tues, Wed, Thur, Fri, Sat, Sun
Weekday Frequency: e
Circulation: 2,169
Last Audit: September 30, 2003
Price: 7.50/mo; 75.00/yr.
Advertising: Open inch rate $7.95(wknd)
News services: AP, Capitol Media Services.
Politics: Independent. **Established:** 1902
Advertising not accepted: Tobacco.
Special Editions: Visitor's Guide (Apr); High School Sports (Aug); Christmas (Dec); Sweetheart Specials (Feb); Customer Appreciation (Jan); Visitor's Guide (Jul); Viva! Douglas (Jun); Business and Professional (Mar); Graduation (May); Holiday Shopping Guide (Nov); Car Care
Special Weekly Sections: Church Page (Fri); TV Guide (S); Education (Thur); Health and Fitness (Tues); Business (Wed).
Magazines: SE Magazine (Quarterly); USA WEEKEND Magazine (S).
Bookkeeper..............................Kimberly Hicks
Adv. Mgr.............................Davin Dominguez
Circ. Mgr...................................Wendy Parra
Editorial Page Ed. ....Lawrence L. Blaskey
Sports Ed................................Bruce Whetten
Market Information: ADS; TMC.
Mechanical available: Offset; Black and 2 ROP colors; insert accepted - cards; page cutoffs - 21.
Mechanical Specifications: Type page 13 x 21; E - 6 cols, 2 1/16, 1/8 between; A - 6 cols, 2 1/16, 1/8 between; C - 6 cols, 2 1/16, 1/8 between.
Commodity Consumption: Avg. Page Number Per Issue - Daily 10; Avg. Page Number Per Issue - Saturday 16; widths 13 3/4; Printing Ink Used - Pages Printed 2496.
Equipment EDITORIAL: Front-end Software – Adobe/Photoshop 7.0, Microsoft/Word 5.1, QPS/QuarkXPress 6.5.; Editorial Hardware – APP/iMac, APP/Mac G3; Editorial Equipment – APP/Mac CLASSIFIED: Front-end Software – Baseview.; Classified Hardware – APP/Mac Centris 610; Classified Printers – QMS/860 DISPLAY: Ad make-up applications – QPS/QuarkXPress 6.5, Adobe/Photoshop 7.0; Layout Software – APP/Mac G4.; Display Printers – HP/5000N; Production Equipment – APP/Mac Performa 6400; Cameras – 1-LE/4 Vertical; Scanners – Umax/S-6E. PRESSROOM: Line 1 – 3-G/Community.; Business Hardware – APP/Mac

FLAGSTAFF

ARIZONA DAILY SUN

1751 S. Thompson St., Flagstaff, Ariz., 86001; gen tel (928) 774-4545; adv tel (928) 774-4545; ed tel (928) 556-2241; gen fax (928) 773-1934; ed fax (928) 774-4790; gen e-mail azdsnews@azdailysun.com; adv e-mail hhansen@azdailysun.com; ed e-mail rwilson@azdailysun.com; web site www.azdailysun.com
Published: Mon, Tues, Wed, Thur, Fri, Sat, Sun
Weekday Frequency: m
Saturday Frequency: m
Circulation: 10,002; 10,541(sun)
Last Audit: ABC September 30, 2011
Price: 12.75/mo; 153.00/yr.
Advertising: Open inch rate $40.48
News services: AP, MCT, TMS, CSM.
Politics: Independent. **Established:** 1883
Not Published: Christmas.
Own facility?: Y
Special Editions: Pigskin Preview (Aug); Best of Flagstaff (Dec); Design An Ad (Feb); Winterfest (Jan); Cardinals (Jul); Rodeo (Jun); 99 Things (May); Best of Flagstaff (Nov); Calendar (Oct).
Special Weekly Sections: Sundial (TV Listings) (S); Flagstaff Has It (Tues).
Magazines: Relish (Monthly); Parade (S).
Pres./Pub....................................Don Rowley
Classified Adv. Dir. ....Heidi Hansen
Circ. Mgr. ....Jeremy Alexander
City/Metro Ed. ....Laura Clymer
Editorial Page Ed. ....Randy Wilson
Educ. Ed...................................Betsey Bruner
Photo Ed........................................Jake Bacon
Sports Ed. ....Keith Jiron
Gen. Mgr., Electronic Media ....Michelle Lopez
Prodn. Dir. ....Edward D'Hooge
Prodn. Mgr., Pressroom ....William Smith
Market Information: TMC.
Mechanical available: Offset; Black and 3 ROP colors; insert accepted; page cutoffs - 22 3/4.
Mechanical Specifications: Type page 11 5/8 x 21 1/2; E - 6 cols, 2 1/16, 1/8 between; A - 6 cols, 2 1/16, 1/8 between; C - 8 cols, 1 1/2, 1/8 between.
Commodity Consumption: Avg. Page Number Per Issue - Daily 24; Avg. Page Number Per Issue - Plates Used 9090; Avg. Page Number Per Issue - Sunday 34; widths 12 1/2; Newsprint Used - Metric Tons 1040000; Printing Ink Used - Black 34000; Printing Ink Used - Color 8100; Printing I
Equipment EDITORIAL: Front-end Software – QPS/QuarkXPress, Baseview.; Editorial Hardware – APP/Mac; Editorial Equipment – APP/Mac II Graphics; Editorial Printers – APP/Mac LaserPrinter CLASSIFIED: Front-end Software – Mactive.; Classified Hardware – PC; Layout Software – Adobe/InDesign.; Display Hardware – APP/Mac PRODUCTION: Pagination Software – QPS/QuarkXPress, Adobe/Photoshop.; Production Equipment – Amerigraph/437, LaserMaster/1200XLO, LaserMaster/1800x60, 2-AU/3850; Cameras – 2-SCREEN/Vertical; Scanners – HP/ScanJet IIc PRESSROOM: Line 1 – 15-G/Community (3 stacked units, plus 2-high); Press Drives – 2-HP/75; Folders – 1-G/SSC, 1; Reels and Stands – 2, 1. MAILROOM: Counter stackers – 1-BG/Count-O-Veyor 109; Inserters and stuffers – 1-Harris 848, 1-KAN/480; Bundle tying machines – Si/Spirit, 2/Oval Strapper; Addressing machine – ScrippSat; Other equipment – 1-Rima/Counter Stacker, 3-/Knife Trimmer. BUSINESS COMPUTERS: Business Software – PBS, Phoenix, Falcon
Zip Codes served: 86001,86004, 86015, 86017, 86018, 86040, 86045, 86046, 86047, 86351, 86033, 86023, 86339
Delivery method: Mail, Newsstand, Private Carrier, Racks

KINGMAN

KINGMAN DAILY MINER

3015 Stockton Hill Rd., Kingman, Ariz., 86401; gen tel (928) 753-6397; adv tel (928) 753-6397; ed tel (928) 753-6397; gen fax (928) 753-5661; adv fax (928) 753-5661; ed

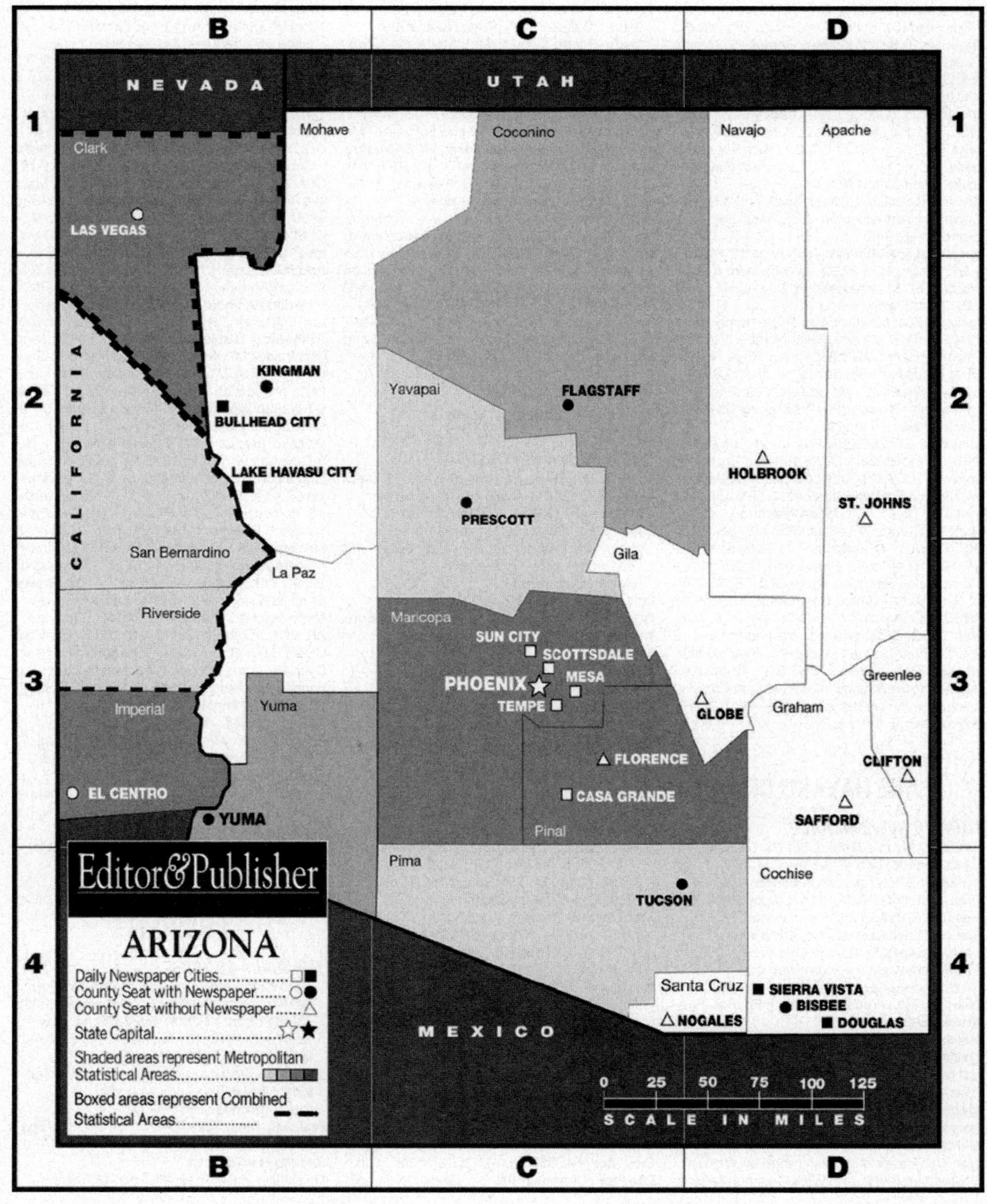

fax (928) 753-3796; gen e-mail kingmannewspapers@mcimail.com; adv e-mail advert@ctaz.com; ed e-mail opinion@kingmandailyminer.com; web site www.kingmandailyminer.com
Group: ANA Ad Services, Inc. (Arizona Newspaper Association)
Published: Mon, Tues, Wed, Thur, Fri, Sun
Weekday Frequency: m
Circulation: 7,969; 8,172(sun)
Last Audit: September 30, 2008
Price: 15.00/mo (mail); 93.60/yr; 6.50/4wk (carrier), $15.00/4wk (mail).
Advertising: Open inch rate $17.80
News services: AP, Papert (Landon).
Politics: Independent.
Advertising not accepted: Tobacco products.
Special Editions: Business Showcase (Apr); Back-to-School (Aug); Last Minute Christmas (Dec); Top 10 Stories of the Year (Jan); Soap Box Derby (Jul); Welcome to Kingman (Jun); Home & Garden (Mar); Park & Recreation Book (May); Christmas Kick-Off (Nov); Destination Kingman
Special Weekly Sections: Church/Religion (Fri); Business (S); Food (Tues); Outdoors (Wed).
Magazines: Relish (Monthly); Parade (S); American Profile (Weekly).
Pub. .... Robin Mauser
Adv. Dir. .... Colleen Machado
Circ. Dir. .... Kandy Cummins
Ed .... Mark Borgard
News Ed. .... Rich Thurlow
Prodn. Dir. .... Paul Mauser
Market Information: TMC.
Mechanical available: Offset; Black and 3 ROP colors; insert accepted - poly bags; page cutoffs - 22 3/4.
Mechanical Specifications: Type page 12 1/2 x 21 1/2; E - 6 cols, 1 27/32, 1/8 between; A - 6 cols, 1 27/32, 1/8 between; C - 6 cols, 1 27/32, 1/8 between.
Commodity Consumption: Avg. Page Number Per Issue - Daily 16; Avg. Page Number Per Issue - Plates Used 5304; Avg. Page Number Per Issue - Sunday 22; widths 13 3/4; Newsprint Used - Metric Tons 289; Printing Ink Used - Black 9739; Printing Ink Used - Color 1948; Printing Ink Us
Equipment EDITORIAL: Front-end Software – QPS/QuarkXPress. CLASSIFIED: Front-end Software – CAMS. DISPLAY: Ad make-up applications – Adobe/Illustrator 2.0, QPS/QuarkXPress 3.1, Adobe/Photoshop 2.5, Multi-Ad/Creator 4.1, Caere/OmniPage. PRODUCTION: Pagination Software – QPS/QuarkXPress.; Production Equipment – Caere/OmniPage; Cameras – SCREEN/C-240-D; Scanners – Umax, Polaroid/SprintScan 35 PRESSROOM: Line 1 – 8-G/Suburban, 8; Folders – G/SC, G/Suburban; Reels and Stands – 2 MAILROOM: Counter stackers – 2-HL/Monitor; Inserters and stuffers – SH/1372 (12 pocket); Bundle tying machines – 2-MLN/2A; Addressing machine – KR; Other equipment –MM/221, 6-Pocket/Saddle Stitcher.

LAKE HAVASU CITY

TODAY'S NEWS-HERALD

2225 W. Acoma Blvd., Lake Havasu City, Ariz., 86403; gen tel (928) 453-4237; adv tel (928) 453-4237; ed tel (928) 453-4237; gen fax (928) 855-9892; adv fax (928) 855-9892; ed fax (928) 855-2637; gen e-mail sales@havasunews.com; adv e-mail ads@havasunews.com; ed e-mail news@havasunews.com; web site www.havasunews.com
Published: Mon, Tues, Wed, Thur, Fri, Sat, Sun
Weekday Frequency: m
Saturday Frequency: m
Circulation: 9,815; 9,815(sat); 10,503(sun)
Last Audit: September 30, 2008
Price: 9.71/mo; 80.89/yr.
Advertising: Open inch rate $23.42
News services: AP.
Politics: Independent.
Note: This paper is equally owned by Western Newspapers Inc. and Wick Communications.
Special Editions: Holiday Shopping Guide (Dec); Winter Visitor's Guide (Feb); Meet Your Merchant (Mar); Summer Guide (May); Winter Visitor's Guide (Nov); London Bridge Days (Oct).
Special Weekly Sections: Entertainment (Fri); Sunday Comics (S).
Magazines: American Profile (Weekly).
Pub. .... Mike Quinn
Controller .... Sandy Stangifer
Adv. Dir. .... David Alley
Circ. Mgr. .... Jim Abdon
Mng. Ed .... Becci Maxedon
News Ed. .... Steve Stovall
Sports Ed. .... Blair Schilling
Prodn. Mgr. .... Kelly Parks
Market Information: TMC.
Mechanical available: Black and 3 ROP colors; insert accepted - envelopes, cards; page cutoffs - 21.
Mechanical Specifications: Type page 13 x 21; E - 6 cols, 2 1/16, 1/4 between; A - 6 cols, 2 1/16, 1/4 between; C - 6 cols, 2 1/16, 1/4 between.
Commodity Consumption: Avg. Page Number Per Issue - Daily 28; Avg. Page Number Per Issue - Plates Used 12880; Avg. Page Number Per Issue - Sunday 32; widths 25; Newsprint Used - Short Tons 6825; Printing Ink Used - Black 10400; Printing Ink Used - Color 2600; Printing Ink Used
Equipment EDITORIAL: Front-end Software – Microsoft/Word, Aldus/PageMaker, QPS/QuarkX-Press.; Editorial Hardware – 12-APP/Mac CLASSIFIED: Front-end Software – Multi-Ad/CAMS.; Classified Hardware – 2-APP/Power Mac DISPLAY: Ad make-up applications – Multi-Ad/Creator.; Display Hardware – APP/Mac PRODUCTION: Pagination Software – QPS/QuarkXPress 3.3.; Production Equipment – Microtek; Cameras – Scanners ☐ Microtek/II SI, Microtek PRESSROOM: Line 1 – Press control system ☐ 1993. BUSINESS COMPUTERS: Business Software – Vision Data; Business Hardware – ATT/Unix PC

PHOENIX

THE ARIZONA REPUBLIC

200 E. Van Buren St., Phoenix, Ariz., 85004; gen tel (602) 444-4000; adv tel 602-444-3902; ed tel (602) 444-8499; gen fax (602) 444-8044; adv fax (602) 444-8788; ed fax (602) 444-8044; ed e-mail opinions@arizonarepublic.com; web site www.azcentral.com
Group: Gannett Co., Inc.
Published: Mon, Tues, Wed, Thur, Fri, Sat, Sun
Weekday Frequency: m
Saturday Frequency: m
Circulation: 292,838; 322,514(sat); 472,200(sun)
Last Audit: ABC September 30, 2011
Price: 4.45/wk; 231.40/yr.
Advertising: Open inch rate $668.00
News services: AP, LAT-WP, NYT, SHNS, RN, MCT, HN, CSM, GNS, TMS.
Politics: Independent. **Established:** 1887
Special Editions: Working (Apr); Football Extra Preview (Aug); Fiesta/College Bowl Preview (Dec); Spring Training/Baseball Preview (Feb); Phoenix Open (Jan); Mercury/WNBA Preview (Jun); Arizona Inc. (May); Working (Oct); Rep AZ Best (Sept).
Special Weekly Sections: Preview (Fri); Computing (Mon); Arts & Ideas (S); Wheels (Sat); ALT (Teens) (Thur); RV Outdoors (Tues); Food (Wed).
Magazines: Vista (Fri); USA WEEKEND Magazine (S).
Profile: The Arizona Republic is Arizona's leading provider of news and information, and has published a daily newspaper in Phoenix for more than 110 years. As the state's premier media company, The Republic is much more than a newspaper. It is part of a multimedi
Pres./Pub .... John Zidich
Exec. Vice Pres./CFO .... Jon Held
Vice Pres., Community Rel. .... Gene D'Adamo
Dir., HR .... Mike Spector
Admin. Asst. .... Patsy Rivera
Circ. Asst. Dir. .... Jack Saunders
Circ. Opns. Mgr. .... Steve Reed
Exec. Ed. .... Nicole Carroll
Gen. Mgr., Scottsdale Republic .... Mike Ryan
Deputy Ed., Presentation/Sports .... Tracy Collins
Deputy Mng. Ed., Page One .... Keira Nothaft
A & E Rep. Ed .... Stacy Sullivan
SVP/News and Audience Development Randy Lovely
Director/Retail & National Advertising Chris Stegman
VP/Digital Media .... Mike Coleman
VP/Production .... Bob Kotwasinski
Market Information: Split run; TMC; Zoned editions.
Mechanical available: Offset; Black and 3 ROP colors; insert accepted - samples, post-it notes; page cutoffs - 22 3/4.
Mechanical Specifications: Type page 13 x 21 1/2; E - 6 cols, 1 3/4, 1/8 between; A - 6 cols, 1 3/4, 1/8 between; C - 10 cols, 1 1/8, 1/16 between.
Commodity Consumption: Avg. Page Number Per Issue - Daily 88; Avg. Page Number Per Issue - Plates Used 792123; Avg. Page Number Per Issue - Saturday 220; Avg. Page Number Per Issue - Sunday 193; widths 27; Newsprint Used - Metric Tons 107802; Printing Ink Used - Black 1821000;
Equipment EDITORIAL: Front-end Software – CCI, Microsoft/Word Office.; Editorial Hardware – Sun/Sparc 4500, CCI; Editorial Printers – HP CLASSIFIED: Front-end Software – PGL, Mactive Adbase 2.24.; Classified Hardware – 2-Sun 4800, PCs; Classified Equipment – dat*, MECLS, Multibox; Classified Printers – HP/Desktops DISPLAY: Ad make-up applications – Adobe/InDesign CS2, QPS/QuarkXPress 6.5, Adobe/Photoshop CS2, Adobe/Illustrator CS2 11, Adobe/Acrobat-Distiller 7.0, Mosaic/Inspector; Display Hardware – 2-Sun/E4500, APP/Mac; Display Printers – 2-HP/Laser, Techtronic 780, Xerox, Mosaic Multiples, 6-See-Color PRODUCTION: Pagination Software – CCI.; Production Equipment – III/Laser Setter, 5-AII/3850 Typesetter, APP/Mac; Scanners – 2-Scitex/Smart Scan PRESSROOM: Line 1 – 9-G/Metroliner; Line 2 – 9-G/Metroliner; Line 3 – 9-G/Headliner offset; Line 4 – 9-G/Colorliner; Line 5 – 9-G/Colorliner; Line 6 – 9-G/Colorliner; Line 7 – 9-G/Colorliner; Line 8 – 10-G/Universal 4S; Folders – 7-G/3:2; Pasters – 63; Reels and Stands – Reels and Sta MAILROOM: Counter stackers – 36-HL/Monitor, 1-HL/HT, 4-QWI/351; Inserters and stuffers – 6/AM Graphics/NP 2299; Bundle tying machines – 32-/Power Strap, 4-/Dynamics. AUDIO: Audio Software – Micro Voice/Audiotext 2000; Audio Hardware – AP, VNN, AT/2000, Sun/Sparc 100 BUSINESS COMPUTERS: Business Software – Microsoft, Cyborg, Lotus Notes, Oracle:financials, In-house; Business Hardware – Bull/DPS-8000, Sun/2000, 4-Sun/4000
Zip Codes served: The Arizona Republic provides delivery to all zip codes in Maricopa, Pinal, Yavapai, Gila and Graham counties. Select zip codes in Coconino, Navajo, Apache, Greenlee, Cochise and Pima counties. Only small SCS delivery in Mohave, La Paz and Yuma counties.
Delivery method: Mail, Newsstand, Private Carrier, Racks

PRESCOTT

THE DAILY COURIER

1958 Commerce Center Cir., Prescott, Ariz., 86301; gen tel (928) 445-3333; adv tel (928) 776-8122; ed tel (928) 445-3333; gen fax (928) 445-4916; adv fax (928) 445-4756; ed fax (928) 445-2062; adv e-mail pnigraph@prescottaz.com; ed e-mail pnieditorial@prescottaz.com; web site www.prescottaz.com
Published: Mon, Tues, Wed, Thur, Fri, Sat, Sun
Weekday Frequency: m
Saturday Frequency: m
Circulation: 14,405; 15,433(sat); 15,544(sun)
Last Audit: ABC September 30, 2011
Price: 2.55/wk; 11.05/mo; 132.60/yr.
Advertising: Open inch rate $25.30
News services: Western Newspapers Inc..
Politics: Independent.
Special Editions: Home Improvement Tab (Apr); Business Profiles (Feb); Yavapai County Mature Living (Jul); Frontier Days (Jun); Tourist Treasures (May); Women In Business (Oct); Fall Home Improvement (broad) (Sept).
Special Weekly Sections: Real Estate (Fri); Business (S).
Magazines: Today's Real Estate (Monthly); Parade (S); American Profile (Thur).
Pub./CEO .... Kit Atwell
Personnel Dir. .... Barbara Hansen
Ed. .... Ben Hansen
Mng. Ed. .... Tim Wiederaenders
City Ed .... Steve Stockmar
City Ed .... Scott Daravanis
Asst. Prodn. Dir. .... Gary Brinkman
Market Information: ADS; TMC.
Mechanical available: Offset; Black and 3 ROP colors; insert accepted; page cutoffs - 22.
Mechanical Specifications: Type page 11 3/4 x 21 1/2; E - 6 cols, between; A - 6 cols, between; C - 6 cols, between.
Commodity Consumption: Avg. Page Number Per Issue - Daily 30; Avg. Page Number Per Issue - Plates Used 4500; Avg. Page Number Per Issue - Sunday 60; widths 12 1/2; Newsprint Used - Metric Tons 1870; Printing Ink Used - Black 28000; Printing Ink Used - Color 12000; Printing Ink
Equipment EDITORIAL: Front-end Software – Adobe/Photoshop, QPS/QuarkXPress 4.0, Microsoft/Word, Aldus/Freehand.; Editorial Hardware – APP/Mac 19 color monitor; Editorial Equipment – AG/Focus Scanner; Editorial Printers – APP/Mac LaserWriter 16-1600 PS; Classified Hardware – 6-APP/Mac Beige G3, 1-APP/Mac 7200/120, 1-APP/Mac Powerbook G3, 1-APP/Apple Design Keyboard, 1-Kensington/Keyboard, 1-APP/Mac Pro Plus Keyboard, 1-APP/Apple 14 Monitor, 1-APP/Apple 17 Monitor, 5-Sony/Monitors; Classified Equipment – 1-Umax/Astra 2200S S; Display Hardware – 4-APP/Mac Blue/White G3, 4-APP/Mac Beige G3, 2-APP/Mac G4, 3-APP/Apple Design Keyboards, 2-APP/Mac USB Keyboards, 5-APP/Mac Pro Plus Keyboards, 3-APP/Apple 1705 Monitor, 1-Optiquest/Monitor, 6-Sony/Monitor; Display Printers – 1-Lexmart C910, 1-Xante/Ac PRODUCTION: Pagination Software – Adobe/Acrobat 4.0, MultiAd/Creator2, Flightcheck 4.5r22, Adobe/Illustrator 9.0, Adobe/Indesign 2.0, Insposition 2.5.4, Adob; Production Equipment – 2-Pre Press/Panther Fast Track CTP, 3-Sony/Monitors, 3-APP/USB Extended Keyboards, 3-APP/USB Optical Mouse PRESSROOM: Line 1 – 1-G/Community; Line 2 – 1-DIDDE/UV; Press Drives – 2, 1, 150, 100, 75; Folders – 1-G/Universal 45, 1-G/SSC; Reels and Stands – 6-Enkel/Splicer. MAILROOM: Counter stackers – 1-HL/Monitor, 1-QWI; Inserters and stuffers – HI/Sheridan 1372, MM/227; Bundle tying machines – Strap-Pack/Strapper 35-80 AKN, MLN/ML2-EE, Si/LB 2000, Si/LB 2330; Addressing machine – 3/Dispensa-matic; Other equipment –Mc/2000 6-Pocke; Business Hardware – DEC/200, APP/Mac PowerBook 160, APP/Mac PowerBook 550, Mk/ScanMaker IIG Scanner, APP/Mac LaserWriter II NTX, 2-DEC/server, 6-DEC/VT-420 monitor, 2-DEC/VT-220 monitor, DEC/LA-424 Desktop printer, C.Itoh/Dot Matrix Printer, AST/PC, APP/Mac Plus,

PRESCOTT NEWSPAPERS, INC.

PO Box 312, Prescott, Ariz., 86302; gen tel (928) 445-3333

SIERRA VISTA

SIERRA VISTA HERALD

102 Fab Ave., Sierra Vista, Ariz., 85635; gen tel (520) 458-9440; gen fax (520) 459-0120; adv e-mail svhads@transedge.com; ed e-mail svhnews@transedge.com; web site www.svherald.com

Group: ANA Ad Services, Inc. (Arizona Newspaper Association)
Published: Mon, Tues, Wed, Thur, Fri, Sat, Sun
Weekday Frequency: m
Saturday Frequency: m
Circulation: 7,642; 7,315(sat); 7,895(sun)
Last Audit: Sworn September 30, 2011
Price: 12.50/mo; 150.00/yr.
Advertising: Open inch rate $15.25,weekdays
Insert rate: 55.65
News services: AP, NYT.
Politics: Independent. **Established:** 1955
Note: Advertisements in the Sierra Vista Herald (mS) are automatically included in the Bisbee Daily Review (mS).
Advertising not accepted: N
Own facility?: Y
Special Editions: Business and Service Directory (Apr); Christmas Opening (Dec); Health Directory (Jan); Back-to-School (Jul); Picture Your Home (Real Estate Magazine) (Monthly); Southeast Arizona Traveler (Oct). Year in Review (Jan.1)
Special Weekly Sections: Religion Page (Fri); Business (Mon); Comics (S); Real Estate (Sat); Taste (Wed).Tempo-Ent (Thu)
Magazines: USA WEEKEND Magazine (S); American Profile (Tues).
Profile: Community newspaper
Co-Chrmn. ....Robert Wick
Co-Chrmn. ....Walter M. Wick
Pub. ....Philip Vega
Adv. Dir. ....Becky Bjork
Dir., Mktg. ....Patricia Wick
Circ. Mgr. ....Ray Taylor
Sports Ed. ....Matt Hickman
Data Processing Mgr. ....Joan Hancock
IT Mgr. ....Don Judd
Prodn. Mgr., Composing ....Tracy Edwards
Prodn. Foreman, Press/Camera .Rhett Hartgrove
Managing Editor ....Eric Petermann
Market Information: Split run; TMC; Zoned editions.
Mechanical available: Offset; Black and 3 ROP colors; insert accepted - all; page cutoffs - 21.
Mechanical Specifications: Type page 9 89/100 x 21; E - 6 cols, 1 56/100, 5/6 between; A - 6 cols, 1 56/100, 5/6 between; C - 9 cols, 1, 58/100 between.
Commodity Consumption: Avg. Page Number Per Issue - Daily 24; Avg. Page Number Per Issue - Sunday 40; widths 22; Newsprint Used - Metric Tons 800; Printing Ink Used - Black 12000; Printing Ink Used - Color 5100; Printing Ink Used - Pages Printed 9096.
Equipment EDITORIAL: Front-end Software – Baseview.; Editorial Hardware – APP/Mac; Editorial Printers – APP/Mac CLASSIFIED: Front-end Software – Baseview.; Classified Hardware – APP/Mac; Classified Printers – APP/Mac; Layout Software – Adobe/Creative Suite.; Display Hardware – APP/Mac; Display Printers – APP/Mac PRODUCTION: Pagination Software – Adobe/Creative Suite.; Production Equipment – Southern Lithoplate MX33 PRESSROOM: Line 1 – 15-G/Community; Press control system – Perretta MAILROOM: Counter stackers – BG/Count-O-Veyor 106; Inserters and stuffers – 1-HI/Sheridan; Bundle tying machines – 2-Wilton/Strap Pack 55-80; Mailroom control system – Prism. BUSINESS COMPUTERS: Business Software – Vision Data; Business Hardware – DEC
Zip Codes served: 85635, 85650, 85615, 85616, 85636, 85603
Delivery method: Mail, Newsstand, Private Carrier, Racks

SUN CITY

DAILY NEWS-SUN

10102 Santa Fe Dr., Sun City, Ariz., 85351; gen tel (623) 977-8351; adv tel (623) 876-3690; ed tel (623) 876-2520; gen fax (623) 876-3698; adv fax (623) 876-3689; ed fax (623) 876-3698; adv e-mail advertising@yourwestvalley.com; web site www.yourwestvalley.com
Published: Mon, Tues, Wed, Thur, Fri, Sat
Weekday Frequency: m
Saturday Frequency: m
Circulation: 6,463; 6,463(sat)
Last Audit: ABC September 30, 2011
Price: 1.85/wk; 8.00/mo; 65.00/yr.
Advertising: Open inch rate $21.29
News services: AP, DJ, ONS.
Politics: Independent. **Established:** 1957
Special Editions: Choices (Apr); Funeral Planner (Jun); Spring Home Improvement (Mar); Senior Caregivers (May); Holiday Gift Guides (Nov); Fall Home Improvement (Oct).
Special Weekly Sections: Week's End/Business Review (Sat); Weekender/Entertainment (Thur); Food & Nutrition (Tues); Travel (Wed).
Magazines: TV/Entertainment (Fri); USA WEEKEND Magazine (Sat).
Pub. ....Jason Joseph
Adv. Dir. ....Penny Bruns
Circ. Dir. ....Dianne Woods
Ed. ....Maryanne Leyshon
Exec. Ed. ....Dan McCarthy
Features Ed. ....Claudia Sherrill
Sports Ed. ....Rich Bolas
Prodn. Mgr., Press ....James Dickey
Market Information: ADS; TMC.
Mechanical available: Offset; Black and 3 ROP colors; insert accepted - all; page cutoffs - 22 3/4.
Mechanical Specifications: Type page 11 5/8 x 21 1/2; E - 6 cols, 1 7/8, 1/8 between; A - 6 cols, 1 7/8, 1/8 between; C - 9 cols, 1 7/8, 1/8 between.
Commodity Consumption: Avg. Page Number Per Issue - Daily 34; Avg. Page Number Per Issue - Plates Used 12000; widths 30; Newsprint Used - Metric Tons 2818; Printing Ink Used - Black 60000; Printing Ink Used - Color 13000; Printing Ink Used - Pages Printed 10430.
Equipment EDITORIAL: Front-end Software – DTI.; Editorial Hardware – SUN; Editorial Equipment – 2-Canon/Digital Cameras; Editorial Printers – 2-HP CLASSIFIED: Front-end Software – DTI.; Classified Hardware – Sun; Classified Equipment – 1-Umax/Scanner; Classified Printers – 2-HP DISPLAY: Ad make-up applications – DTI; Layout Software – DTI.; Display Hardware – SUN; Display Printers – 3-HP PRODUCTION: Pagination Software – DTI.; Production Equipment – NuArc; Cameras – C/Spartan III PRESSROOM: Line 1 – 8-G/Urbanite; Folders – 1-G/Urbanite 1000; Reels and Stands – 2-G/High; Press registration system – Burgess/Carlson. MAILROOM: Counter stackers – 2-HL/Quiad; Inserters and stuffers – GMA; Bundle tying machines – 2/Dynaric ND1500; Wrapping singles – Mailroom control system □ Lincs/GMA. BUSINESS COMPUTERS: Business Software – MS/Office; Business Hardware – IBM/AS-400, HP/Vectra

TEMPE

EAST VALLEY TRIBUNE

1620 W Fountainhead Parkway #219, Tempe, Ariz., 85282; gen tel (480) 898-6500; adv tel (480) 898-6475; ed tel (480) 898-6514; adv fax (480) 898-6463; ed fax (480) 898-6362; adv e-mail golocal@evtrib.com; ed e-mail forum@evtrib.com; newstips@evtrib.com; web site www.eastvalleytribune.com
Published: Wed, Fri, Sun
Weekday Frequency: m
Last Audit: Sworn September 30, 2008
Advertising: Open inch rate $75.95
News services: AP, Scripps, Capitol
Not Published: Mon, Tues, Thur, Sat.
Special Editions: Best of East Valley (Apr); Varsity Xtra High School Football Season Kickoff (Aug); GetOut Performing Arts Expo (Sept); East Valley Business Expo (Oct); East Valley Guide (Oct); Active Adults - Senior Lifestyles(Oct - Apr)
Magazines: Parade (S). Spry, Relish
Publisher ....Rick Flowers
Local Sales Manager ....Jim Nephew
Adv. Mgr., Nat'l ....Bridget Luna
Mng. Ed. ....Bob Romantic
Market Information: Zoned editions available
Mechanical Specifications: Type page 10 x 12.75 ; @RecordBody:**Commodity Consumption:** Avg. Page Number Per Issue - Daily 50; Avg. Page Number Per Issue - Plates Used 156000; Avg. Page Number Per Issue - Saturday 90; Avg. Page Number Per Issue - Sunday 100; widths 50; Newsprint Used - Short Tons 2458; Printing Ink Used - Black 39636; Print
Equipment; Layout Software – DTI. PRODUCTION: Pagination Software – DTI/PageSpeed 4.1, DTI/AdSpeed 4.1.; Other equipment – Mc/Quarter Folder Stitcher-Trimmer.
Delivery method: Private Carrier, Racks

TUCSON

ARIZONA DAILY STAR

4850 S. Park Ave., Tucson, Ariz., 85726-6807; gen tel (520) 573-4400; adv tel (520) 573-4366; ed tel (520) 573-4235; gen fax (520) 573-4107; adv fax (520) 573-4343; ed fax (520) 573-4141; ed e-mail letters@azstarnet.com; web site www.azstarnet.com
Published: Mon, Tues, Wed, Thur, Fri, Sat, Sun
Weekday Frequency: m
Saturday Frequency: m
Circulation: 89,874; 106,375(sat); 143,358(sun)
Last Audit: ABC September 30, 2011
Price: 2.90/wk; 13.00/mo; 156.00/yr.
News services: AP, NYT, MCT, SHNS, DJ, DF, TMS.
Politics: Independent. **Established:** 1877
Note: Advertising is sold in combination with Tucson Citizen (e) for $210.20(d) & $292.10(S). Individual newspaper rates not made available. For detailed production information, see Tucson Newspapers listing.
Special Weekly Sections: Caliente (entertainment) (Fri); TV Week (S); Food & More (Wed).
Magazines: USA WEEKEND Magazine (S).
Mng. Ed. ....Bobbie Jo Buel
Asst. Mng. Ed. ....Teri Hayt
Asst. Mng. Ed. ....Dennis Joyce
Books Ed. ....Valerie Vinyard
Bus. Ed. ....Jill Spitz
Copy Chief ....George Campbell
Editorial Page Ed. ....Ann Brown
Entertainment/Features/Travel Ed. Maria Parham
Film Critic ....Phil Villarreal
Food/Home Ed. ....Kristen Cook
Graphics Ed. ....Jose Merino
Health/Medical Ed. ....Stephnie Innes
Starnet Online Ed. ....John Bolton
High School Sports Ed. ....Ryan Finley
Sports Ed. ....Jennin Corner
Science/Technology Ed. ....Norma Coile
Reader Advocate ....Debbie Kornmiller
Radio/Television Ed. ....Dave Skog
Metro Ed. ....Hipolito R. Corella
News/Research Servs. Dir. ....Elaine Raines
Market Information: Split run; TMC; Zoned editions.
Mechanical available: Offset; Black and 3 ROP colors; insert accepted - single sheet flyers; page cutoffs - 22 3/4.
Mechanical Specifications: Type page 12 x 21 1/2; E - 6 cols, 1 4/5, between; A - 6 cols, 1 4/5, between; C - 10 cols, 1 1/10, between.
Equipment EDITORIAL: Front-end Software – QPS.; Editorial Hardware – MS/NT, APP/Mac Desktop; Editorial Printers – HP/LaserJet IV CLASSIFIED: Front-end Software – TECS-2 4.2.; Classified Hardware – Proteon/PC Network; Classified Printers – HP/4000 Laser Jet, Tektronix/Phaser 300 DISPLAY: Ad make-up applications – Baseview/Ad Manager 2.8, QPS/QuarkXPress 4.04; Layout Software – MEI, ALS.; Display Hardware – APP/Mac, Sun, Microsoft; Display Printers – DEC/LA 120, Tekronix/Phaser 300, HP/2500C, HP/LaserJet 4050 PRODUCTION: Pagination Software – HI/8900 Classified 7.6, QPS 2.08.; Production Equipment – 4-APP/Mac Power PC, 2-III/3810 Imagesetter, 3-3850 Sierras; Scanners – Umax/100 PRESSROOM: Line 1 – 8-G/Metro 3127A doublewidth (4 half decks); Line 2 – 8-G/Metro 3128A doublewidth (4 half decks); Press Drives – 16; Folders – 4-G/3:2; Reels and Stands – G/Harmonic Drive; Press registration system – WPC/Metro Color 4/4 Tower. MAILROOM: Counter stackers – 4-GMA, 3-QWI/400, 4-QWI/500, 2-QWI/500C; Inserters and stuffers – 1/SLS 1000 10:1, 2-/SLS 3000 22:1, GMA/PTH; Bundle tying machines – 6-/MLN, 3-/Power Strap, 2-HI/RS-25; Wrapping singles – 4-QWI/Bottom Wrap, 4-QWI/Vipers w/Ink Jet Labe; Business Hardware – IBM/AS-400

THE DAILY TERRITORIAL

3280 E. Hemisphere Loop, Ste. 180, Tucson, Ariz., 85706; gen tel (520) 294-1200; adv tel (520) 294-1200; ed tel (520) 294-1200; gen fax (520) 294-4040; adv fax (520) 294-4040; ed fax (520) 295-4071; adv e-mail advertising@azbiz.com; ed e-mail editor@azbiz.com; web site www.azbiz.com
Group: Wick Communications
Published: Mon, Tues, Wed, Thur, Fri
Weekday Frequency: m
Circulation: 753
Price: 100.00/yr; 45.00/3mo, $70.00/6mo.
Advertising: Open inch rate $5.45
News services: American Newspaper Representatives Inc..
Politics: Independent. **Established:** 1920
Not Published: New Year; Memorial Day; Independence Day; Labor Day; Thanksgiving; Christmas; all postal holidays.
Pub. ....Thomas Lee
Adv. Dir. ....Jill A'Hearn
Adv. Mgr., Legal ....Monica Akyol
Circ. Dir. ....Laura Horvath
Ed. ....David Hatfield
Art Dir. ....Andrew Arthur
Prodn. Mgr. ....Greg Day
Mechanical available: Offset; Black and 3 ROP colors; insert accepted; page cutoffs - 22 3/4.
Mechanical Specifications: Type page 10 1/4 x 13; E - 4 cols, 2 3/8, 1/8 between; A - 4 cols, 2 3/8, 1/8 between; C - 6 cols, 1 1/2, 3/16 between.
Commodity Consumption: Avg. Page Number Per Issue - Daily 24; Avg. Page Number Per Issue - Plates Used 1500; widths 27 1/2; Newsprint Used - Short Tons 39; Printing Ink Used - Black 650; Printing Ink Used - Pages Printed 7000.
Equipment; Editorial Hardware – 1-Mk/3000, 10-PC; Editorial Equipment – Mk.; Classified Hardware – Mk/3000, 1-PC. DISPLAY: Ad make-up applications – Aldus/PageMaker, Aldus/Freehand; Layout Software – Mk.; Display Hardware – APP/Mac; Display Printers – APP/Mac LaserWriter II, HP/Laserwriter 4MV (11x17) PRODUCTION: Pagination Software – Adobe/PageMaker 6.5.; Production Equipment – Microtek/Scanmaker Plus, HP/Laserwriter 4MV (11x17), Pre Press/Panther Plus 46; Cameras – 1-SCREEN/Companica-6500D, 1-AG/20 x 24; Scanners – Umax/Powerlook II PRESSROOM: Line 1 – 6-HI/V-15A; Line 2 – Atlas/Web Leader 2000; Folders – 1 MAILROOM: Counter stackers – BG/Count-O-Veyor; Bundle tying machines – 2-Ace/Tyer; Addressing machine – 1-Ch/612.; Business Hardware – NCR/LAN Sys

INSIDE TUCSON BUSINESS

3280 E. Hemisphere Loop, Ste. 174, Tucson, Ariz., 85702; gen tel (520) 294-1200; adv tel (520) 294-1200; ed tel (520) 294-1200; gen fax (520) 294-4040; adv fax (520) 294-4040; ed fax (520) 295-4071; adv e-mail adv@azbiz.com; ed e-mail editor@azbiz.com; web site www.InsideTucsonBusiness.com
Group: Wick Communications
Published: Fri
Circulation: 1,774
Last Audit: Sworn June 1, 2010
Politics: 1991

TUCSONCITIZEN.COM

4850 S. Park Ave., Tucson, Ariz., 85714; gen tel (520) 573-4561; adv tel (520) 573-4366; ed tel (520) 573-4614; adv fax (520) 573-4407; gen e-mail

mevans@tucsoncitizen.com; web site www.tucsoncitizen.com
Group: Gannett Co., Inc.
Published: Mon, Tues, Wed, Thur, Fri, Sat, Sun
Weekday Frequency: All day
Saturday Frequency: All day
Circulation: 19,851; 19,557(sat)
Last Audit: September 30, 2008
News services: GNS
Politics: 1870
Note: Advertising is sold in combination with Arizona Daily Star.
Own facility?: Y
Administrator/Editor........................Mark Evans

YUMA

YUMA SUN

2055 S. Arizona Ave., Yuma, Ariz., 85364; gen tel (928) 783-3333; adv tel (928) 539-6800; gen fax (928) 343-1009; adv fax (928) 343-1009; ed fax (928) 782-7369; adv e-mail advertising@yumasun.com; ed e-mail news@yumasun.com; web site www.yumasun.com
Group: Freedom Communications
Published: Mon, Tues, Wed, Thur, Fri, Sat, Sun
Weekday Frequency: m
Saturday Frequency: m
Circulation: 15,461; 15,461(sat); 16,117(sun)
Last Audit: September 30, 2008
Advertising: Open inch rate $34.23
News services: AP.
Politics: Independent.
Own facility?: Y
Special Editions: Health Connections (Every other month, odd months); Healthy Yuma (every other month, even months); Yuma's Best (Feb); Ag in Yuma (Mar.); Living in Yuma (May; Southwest Living (quarterly); Raising Yuma (quarterly); Dove Hunting (Aug. or Sept); Visiting in Yuma (Oct.); Gift Guides (Nov. and Dec.); PAWS pet adoption tab (monthly).
Special Weekly Sections: Business/Financial (S); Religion (Sat); Food (Tues); Business/Financial (Wed).
Pub..Joni Brooks
Manager, Human Resources...........Justin Cook
National Advertising Sales Representative Brian Owens
Marketing Manager...............Adrianne Wagner
Circ. Dir.......................................Bob Roeser
Assignments Editor..............Roxanne Molenar
Editor, Bajo El Sol....................John Vaughn
Special Content Editor...................Randy Hoeft
Editor..Terry L. Ross
Features Editor............................Darin Fenger
Sports Editor.........................Edward Carifio
Adv. Mgr., Classified..................Tisha Sullivan
Market Information: TMC/ Marketplace
Mechanical available: Offset; Black and 3 ROP colors; insert accepted; page cutoffs - 21.
Mechanical Specifications: Type page 11 13/16 x 21; E - 6 cols, 1/6 between; A - 6 cols, 1/6 between; C - 6 cols, 1/6 between.
Commodity Consumption: Avg. Page Number Per Issue - Daily 24; Avg. Page Number Per Issue - Plates Used 19748; Avg. Page Number Per Issue - Saturday 25; Avg. Page Number Per Issue - Sunday 47; widths 12 1/2; Newsprint Used - Metric Tons 1466; Printing Ink Used - Black 36408; Pr
Equipment: Editorial Hardware – 30-APP/Mac G3; Editorial Equipment – 1-APP/Mac Quadra 605, 1-APP/Mac Quadra 610, SMS/Stauffer Gold, Lf/AP Leaf Picture Desk, 1-Umax/Scanner, 1-Lf/Leafscan, 1-APP/Power Mac 60066, 1-Gateway/7500, 1-APP/Mac Quadra 800, Sun/Microsystems Server, Sybase/Datab CLASSIFIED: Front-end Software – Atex; Classified Hardware – PCs; Classified Equipment – Atex cloud; Classified Printers – HP/4000 DISPLAY: Ad make-up applications – Atex ; Display Hardware – PCs; Display Printers – 1-QMS/1660 PRODUCTION: Pagination Software – Atex PRESSROOM: Line 1 – 9-G/Urbanite 1970. MAILROOM: Counter stackers – 1-Id/2100, 1-MM/CN25; Inserters and stuffers – 1-MM/Alphaliner 10:1; Bundle tying machines – 1-MLN/2EE, 1/MLN, 1-Sterling/MR40CH; Other equipment –1-MC/1800 Stitcher-Trimmer.; Audio Hardware – PCs BUSINESS COMPUTERS: Business Software – Atex; Great Plains; Business Hardware – PCs
Delivery method: Mail, Private Carrier, Racks

ARKANSAS

ARKADELPHIA

ARKADELPHIA SIFTINGS HERALD

205 S. 26th St., Arkadelphia, Ark., 71923-0010; gen tel (870) 246-5525; gen fax (870) 246-6556; gen e-mail publisher@siftingsherald.com; adv e-mail advertising@siftingsherald.com; ed e-mail news@siftingsherald.com; web site www.siftingsherald.com
Published: Mon, Tues, Wed, Thur, Fri
Weekday Frequency: e
Circulation: 2,656
Last Audit: October 9, 2002
Price: 5.00/mo (home delivery); 99.00(mail)/yr.
Advertising: Open inch rate $12.80
News services: AP.
Politics: Democrat.
Advertising not accepted: Adoption ads; Alcohol.
Not Published: New Year; Memorial Day; Independence Day; Labor Day; Thanksgiving; Christmas.
Magazines: American Profile (Weekly).
Interim Pub..................................Clark Smith
Adv. Mgr..................................Sherry Kizziar
Circ. Mgr...................................Donnie Hollis
News Ed,.............................Wendy Ledbetter
Market Information: TMC.
Mechanical available: Offset; Black and 3 ROP colors; insert accepted; page cutoffs - 22 3/4.
Mechanical Specifications: Type page 13 1/2 x 21 1/2; E - 6 cols, 2, 1/6 between; A - 6 cols, 2, 1/6 between; C - 9 cols, 1 1/3, 1/6 between.
Commodity Consumption: Avg. Page Number Per Issue - Daily 10; widths 27; Newsprint Used - Short Tons 100.
Equipment EDITORIAL: Front-end Software – Aldus/PageMaker.; Editorial Hardware – APP/Mac; Editorial Printers – APP/Mac LaserWriter CLASSIFIED: Front-end Software – Baseview.; Classified Hardware – APP/Mac; Classified Printers – APP/Mac DISPLAY: Ad make-up applications – Multi-Ad/Creator.; Display Hardware – APP/Mac; Display Printers – APP/Mac LaserWriter; Production Equipment – Nu; Cameras – SCREEN/Companica 640c. PRESSROOM: Line 1 – 5-KP/News King.; Bundle tying machines – Ca/Band-Tyer; Addressing machine – Wm.; Business Hardware – IBM

BATESVILLE

BATESVILLE GUARD

258 W. Main St., Batesville, Ark., 72501-6711; gen tel (870) 793-2383; gen fax (870) 793-9268; gen e-mail news@guardonline.com; adv e-mail advertising@guardonline.com; web site www.guardonline.com
Group: Arkansas Press Services
Published: Mon, Tues, Wed, Thur, Fri
Weekday Frequency: e
Circulation: 9,067
Last Audit: October 1, 2002
Price: 5.00/mo (in county), $5.50/mo (out of county), $7.00/mo (out of state); 65.50/yr.
Advertising: Open inch rate $10.78
News services: AP.
Politics: Independent. **Established:** 1876
Not Published: Memorial Day; Independence Day; Thanksgiving; Christmas.
Special Editions: Batesville USA (Apr); Fair Time (Aug); Spirit of Christmas (Dec); Valentine Gift Guide (Feb); Brides (Jan); White River Water Carnival (Jul); Father's Day (Jun); Baseball (Mar); Graduation (May); Basketball (Nov); Hunting (Oct).
Special Weekly Sections: Education (Fri); Outdoors (Thur); Business (Tues); Agriculture (Wed).
Magazines: River Country Tab (Fri); American Profile (Weekly).
Pub.......................................Dr. O.E. Jones
Gen. Mgr.......................................Pat Jones
Adv. Dir./Promo. Mgr......................Mike Smith
Circ. Dir...............................Christine Brown
Mng. Ed...................................Angelia Roberts
Asst. Mng. Ed...........................Andrea Bruner
Assoc. Ed.......................................Larry Stroud
Photo Ed................................Stephanie Ewell
Online Mgr...............................J. Ross Jones
Prodn. Mgr., Pressroom................Don Stitcher
Mechanical available: Offset; Black and 2 ROP colors; insert accepted; page cutoffs - 22 3/4.
Mechanical Specifications: Type page 13 x 21; E - 6 cols, 2 1/16, 1/8 between; A - 6 cols, 2 1/16, 1/8 between; C - 6 cols, 2 1/16, 1/8 between.
Commodity Consumption: Avg. Page Number Per Issue - Daily 23.
Equipment: Editorial Hardware – 8-TC, 1-XIT/Portable XPT II.; Classified Hardware – 1-TC.; Production Equipment – 3-LC; Cameras – 1-B. PRESSROOM: Line 1 – 1-F/20-page.; Bundle tying machines – 2/Sa.; Business Hardware – 3-IBM/Sys 36

BENTON

THE SALINE COURIER

321 N. Market St., Benton, Ark., 72015-3734; gen tel (501) 315-8228; adv tel (501) 315-8228; ed tel (501) 315-8228; gen fax (501) 315-1230; adv fax (501) 315-1920; ed fax (501) 315-1920; adv e-mail dwills@bentoncourier.com; ed e-mail news@bentoncourier.com; subscription@bentoncourier.com; web site www.bentoncourier.com
Group: Horizon Publications
Published: Mon, Tues, Wed, Thur, Fri, Sat, Sun
Weekday Frequency: e
Saturday Frequency: m
Circulation: 6,005; 6,005(sat); 6,005(sun)
Last Audit: Sworn September 30, 2001
Price: 8.00/mo; 93.00/yr.
Advertising: 15.10 natl
Insert rate: 61.00
News services: AP.
Politics: 1876
Not Published: none.
Own facility?: Y
Special Editions: American Home Week/Home Improvement (Apr); Back-to-School (Aug); Christmas (Dec); Business Profile (Feb); Summer Recreation Guide (Jun); Fashion/Bridal (Mar); Spring Car Care (May); Cooking (Nov); Fall Car Care (Oct); Hunting (Sept).
Special Weekly Sections: Religion (Sat); Living (S); Neighbors (Lifestyle) (Thur); Business (Tues); Food & Good Health (Wed).
Magazines: TV Magazine (S); American Profile (Weekly).
Bus. Mgr....................................Vicki Dorsch
Assoc. Ed.............................Lynda Hollenback
Prodn. Mgr..........................Patricia Stuckeys
Publisher...................................Terri Leifeste
Addvertising Director....................David Wills
Editor...Brent Davis
Market Information: TMC
Mechanical available: Offset; Black and 3 ROP colors; insert accepted; page cutoffs - 22 3/4.
Mechanical Specifications: Type page 13 x 21 1/2; E - 6 cols, 1 4/5, 1/8 between; A - 6 cols, 1 4/5, 1/8 between; C - 9 cols, 1 11/50, 1/8 between.
Commodity Consumption: Avg. Page Number Per Issue - Daily 16; Avg. Page Number Per Issue - Plates Used 2080; Avg. Page Number Per Issue - Sunday 26; widths 25; Newsprint Used - Short Tons 27.24; Printing Ink Used - Black 2000; Printing Ink Used - Pages Printed 4160.
Equipment EDITORIAL: Front-end Software – QPS/QuarkXPress, Baseview/NewsEdit.; Editorial Hardware – 9-APP/Mac; Editorial Equipment – V/Imagesetter CLASSIFIED: Front-end Software – Baseview/Class.; Classified Hardware – 2-APP/Mac DISPLAY: Ad make-up applications – QPS, Adobe/Photoshop; Layout Software – APP/Mac II, APP/Mac IIcx, APP/Mac IIfx, APP/Mac Quadra 700.; Display Hardware – APP/Mac II NT; Display Printers – 2-APP/Mac LaserWriter Plus, V/Imagesetter PRODUCTION: Pagination Software – Scanners Â 2-Microtek/Neg. Scanner, APP/Mac Flatbed Scanner.; Production Equipment – V/Imagesetter, 2-APP/Mac Laser, APP/Mac LaserWriter Plus; Cameras – 1-B PRESSROOM: Line 1 – 8-G/Community. MAILROOM: Counter stackers – 1/BG; Bundle tying machines – 2-/Bu.; Business Hardware – Baseview
Zip Codes served: 72015, 72019, 72022, 72002, 72011, 72103, 72167
Delivery method: Newsstand, Private Carrier, Racks

BENTONVILLE

BENTON COUNTY DAILY RECORD

104 SW A St., Bentonville, Ark., 72712; gen tel (479) 271-3700; adv tel (479) 271-3730; ed tel (479) 271-3713; gen fax (479) 271-3744; adv fax (479) 273-7777; ed fax (479) 271-3744; gen e-mail aronline@arkansasonline.com; adv e-mail circulation@arkansasonline.com; web site www.nwaonline.com
Group: Arkansas Press Services
Published: Mon, Tues, Wed, Thur, Fri, Sat, Sun
Weekday Frequency: m
Saturday Frequency: m
Circulation: 17,975; 17,975(sat); 19,635(sun)
Last Audit: September 30, 2006
Price: 7.00/mo; 109.00/yr.
Advertising: Open inch rate $14.91
News services: AP, NYT.
Politics: Independent.
Special Editions: Wal-Mart Shareholders Meeting (Jun).
Special Weekly Sections: Outdoors (Fri); Legal Transactions (Mon); School News (S); Church (Sat); Westside Benton Co. (Wed).
Magazines: Parade (S).
Adv. Mgr........................................Jim Quillen
Circ. Mgr..................................George Loftus
Ed....Mike Jones
Features Ed............................Tonya McKeiver
News Ed...Kent Marts
Political Ed.............................Gary Lookodoo
Online Mgr....................................Roger Frye
Market Information: ADS; Split run; TMC; Zoned editions.
Mechanical available: Offset; Black and 3 ROP colors; insert accepted; page cutoffs - 22 3/4.
Mechanical Specifications: Type page 13 x 21; E - 6 cols, 2 1/16, 1/8 between; A - 6 cols, 2 1/16, 1/8 between; C - 9 cols, 1 1/4, between.
Commodity Consumption: Avg. Page Number Per Issue - Daily 22; Avg. Page Number Per Issue - Plates Used 12000; Avg. Page Number Per Issue - Saturday 22; Avg. Page Number Per Issue - Sunday 60; widths 29 1/2; Newsprint Used - Short Tons 1400; Printing Ink Used - Black 28000; Pri
Equipment EDITORIAL: Front-end Software – Baseview, Novell/Netware, XYQUEST/XyWrite, QPS.; Editorial Hardware – APP/Mac; Editorial Printers – 2-APP/Mac LaserWriter IIg CLASSIFIED: Front-end Software – Baseview.; Classified Printers – APP/Mac LaserWriter II NT DISPLAY: Ad make-up applications – Aldus/PageMaker, Canuis, QPS/QuarkXPress; Layout Software – APP/Mac.; Display Hardware – APP/Mac; Display Printers – APP/Mac LaserWriter II NT; Production Equipment – APP/Mac LaserWriter II NT, Pre Press/Panther Pro; Cameras – SCREEN/30 x 40; Scanners – 5-Mi-

crotek/Flatbed, Umax, 4-Nikon/Negative Scanner. PRESSROOM: Line 1 – 12-G/Community; Folders – 1-G/SSC; Reels and Stands – 2-G/Community (stacked). MAILROOM: Counter stackers – Fg/M-71; Bundle tying machines – 2-MLN/Strapper; Addressing machine – KR. BUSINESS COMPUTERS: Business Software – PBS/MediaPlus; Business Hardware – PBS

BLYTHEVILLE

BLYTHEVILLE COURIER NEWS

900 N. Broadway, Blytheville, Ark., 72316; gen tel (870) 763-4461; adv tel (870) 763-4461; ed tel (870) 763-4461; gen fax (870) 763-6874; adv fax (870) 763-6874; ed fax (870) 763-6874; adv e-mail cnadv@couriernews.net; ed e-mail aweld@couriernews.net; web site www.couriernews.net

Group: Arkansas Press Services
Published: Tues, Wed, Thur, Fri, Sun
Weekday Frequency: e
Circulation: 3,128; 3,090(sun)
Last Audit: September 30, 2008
Price: 8.50/mo; 110.00/yr.
Advertising: Open inch rate $10.00
News services: AP.
Politics: Independent.
Advertising not accepted: Certain types requiring investments.
Not Published: New Year; Christmas.
Special Editions: Income Tax (Jan).
Special Weekly Sections: Church Page (Fri); Senior Outlook (Mon); Kids Page (S); Business (Thur); Health & Environment (Tues); Best Food Day (Wed).
Magazines: TV Magazine (Fri); Relish (Monthly); Color Comics (S).

Pub. .... David Tennyson
Adv. Mgr. .... Bess Ann Pease
Circ. Mgr. .... Melissa Andrew
Mng. Ed. .... Mark Brassfield
Ed. .... Andy Weld
Prodn. Foreman, Pressroom .... Susie Robison

Market Information: TMC.
Mechanical available: Offset; Black and 3 ROP colors; insert accepted - all; page cutoffs - 21 1/2.
Mechanical Specifications: Type page 13 1/2 x 21 1/2; E - 6 cols, 2 1/16, 1/8 between; A - 6 cols, 2 1/16, 1/8 between; C - 9 cols, 1 3/8, 1/8 between.
Commodity Consumption: Avg. Page Number Per Issue - Daily 14; Avg. Page Number Per Issue - Plates Used 2500; Avg. Page Number Per Issue - Sunday 20; widths 27 1/2; Newsprint Used - Short Tons 800; Printing Ink Used - Pages Printed 4368.
Equipment EDITORIAL: Front-end Software – QPS, Baseview/NewsEdit, Multi-Ad/Creator.; Editorial Hardware – 2-APP/Mac Power Book, 3-APP/Mac Quadra, 2-APP/Mac Classic; Editorial Equipment – Microtek/ScanMaker; Editorial Printers – APP/Mac ImageWriter CLASSIFIED: Front-end Software – Baseview, Microsoft, QPS.; Classified Hardware – APP/Mac Quadra 605 DISPLAY: Ad make-up applications – Multi-Ad/Creator 3.6; Display Hardware – 2-APP/Mac Quadra 610; Display Printers – APP/Mac LaserWriter Pro 810 PRODUCTION: Pagination Software – QPS.; Production Equipment – TI/OmniPage; Cameras – 1-R/1975, LE/500 PRESSROOM: Line 1 – 8-G/Community; Folders – 1-G/SC, 1-G/Community.; Inserters and stuffers – KAN/320 2:1; Bundle tying machines – 1-Felin/11313, 1-Us/GMH; Addressing machine – 1-El/300.; Business Hardware – Software □ Vision Data, Microsoft/Excel

CAMDEN

CAMDEN NEWS

113 Madison Ave., Camden, Ark., 71701-0798; gen tel (870) 836-8192; gen fax (870) 837-1414; gen e-mail camnews@cablelynx.com; adv e-mail advertising@camdenarknews.com; ed e-mail

sports@camdenarknews.com; web site www.camdenarknews.com
Group: Arkansas Press Services
Published: Mon, Tues, Wed, Thur, Fri
Weekday Frequency: e
Circulation: 4,342
Last Audit: September 24, 2003
Price: 8.25/mo; 99.00/yr; 24.75/3mo, $49.50/6mo .
Advertising: Open inch rate $13.10
News services: AP.
Politics: Independent. **Established:** 1920
Note: Subscribers to the Camden News (e) & the Magnolia Banner-News (e) receive the Sunday edition of the El Dorado News-Times (mS). See the El Dorado listing for Sunday circulation & advertising rates.
Not Published: New Year; Independence Day; Christmas.
Special Editions: Industrial Progress (Apr); Football (Aug); Bridal (Jan); Home, Lawn, & Garden (Mar); Cookbook (Oct); Fall Fashion (Sept).
Magazines: Relish (Monthly); Food (Tues); American Profile (Weekly).
Broadcast Affiliations: Radio KAMD-FM.
Pub....Walter E. Hussman
Gen. Mgr.....Sue Silliman
Bus. Mgr.....Pam Hulse
Adv. Mgr.....Susan Silliman
Circ. Mgr.....LaDonna Foster
Mng. Ed....Jim Edwards
Sports Ed.....Kelly Blair
Market Information: TMC.
Mechanical available: Offset; Black and 3 ROP colors; insert accepted.
Mechanical Specifications: Type page 13 x 21 1/2; E - 6 cols, 2 1/16, 1/8 between; A - 6 cols, 2 1/16, 1/8 between; C - 8 cols, 1 3/8, 1/16 between.
Commodity Consumption: Avg. Page Number Per Issue - Daily 12; widths 25; Newsprint Used - Short Tons 90; Printing Ink Used - Black 818; Printing Ink Used - Color 146; Printing Ink Used - Pages Printed 2782.
Equipment EDITORIAL: Front-end Software – QPS/QuarkXPress 4.1, Baseview.; Editorial Equipment – 7-APP/Mac G4, 7-APP/iMac; Editorial Printers – Epson/DXF 5000 3.2 CLASSIFIED: Front-end Software – Baseview 3.3.; Classified Equipment – 2-APP/iMac; Layout Software – 1-APP/Super Mac 8500, 20 Color Monitors, Scanners. PRODUCTION: Pagination Software – QPS/QuarkXPress 4.1.; Production Equipment – Adobe/Photoshop 6.0, Caere/OmniPage 8.0 BUSINESS COMPUTERS: Business Software – Sun/System; Business Hardware – 1-Compaq/386-25, 2-Wyse

CONWAY

LOG CABIN DEMOCRAT

1058 Front St., Conway, Ark., 72033; gen tel (501) 327-6621; adv tel (501) 505-1226; ed tel (501) 505-1233; gen fax (501) 327-6787; adv fax (501) 505-1284; ed fax (501) 327-6787; gen e-mail mail@thecabin.net; adv e-mail ads@thecabin.net; ed e-mail editorial@thecabin.net; web site www.thecabin.net
Published: Mon, Tues, Wed, Thur, Fri, Sat, Sun
Weekday Frequency: e
Circulation: 10,234; 10,234(sat); 10,234(sun)
Last Audit: October 1, 2003
Price: 8.75/mo; 93.00/yr.
Advertising: Open inch rate $15.95
News services: AP, SHNS.
Politics: Democrat. **Established:** 1879
Special Editions: Toad Suck Daze (Apr); Football (Aug); Last Minute Gift Guide (Dec); Bridal Tab (Feb); Red Tag Sale (Jan); Newcomer's Guide (Jul); June Shopping Spree (Jun); Spring Fashion (Mar); Mother's Day Gift Guide (May); Christmas Gift Guide (Nov); Auto Car Care (Oc
Special Weekly Sections: Church Directory (Fri); Business Page (S); Best Food Day (Tues); Education Page (Wed).
Magazines: USA WEEKEND Magazine (S); American Profile (Weekly).
Adv. Dir.....Rhonda Overbey
Circ. Mgr.....Amber Mcnaulty
Ed.....Rick Fahr
Mng. Ed....Waylon Harris
City Ed....Mark Burke
Pressroom Supvr.....Gary Mitchell
Pre Press Mgr.....Terri Freeman
Market Information: TMC.
Mechanical available: Offset; Black and 3 ROP colors; insert accepted; page cutoffs - 21 1/2.
Mechanical Specifications: Type page 15 1/4 x 21 1/2; E - 6 cols, 2 1/16, 1/8 between; A - 6 cols, 2 1/16, 1/8 between; C - 7 cols, 2 1/16, 1/8 between.
Commodity Consumption: Avg. Page Number Per Issue - Daily 16; Avg. Page Number Per Issue - Plates Used 12000; Avg. Page Number Per Issue - Sunday 30; widths 29; Newsprint Used - Short Tons 500; Printing Ink Used - Black 9000; Printing Ink Used - Color 500.
Equipment EDITORIAL: Front-end Software – Baseview/NewsEdit.; Editorial Hardware – Mk, APP/Mac; Editorial Equipment – APP/Mac; Editorial Printers – Laser CLASSIFIED: Front-end Software – Baseview/Ad Manager Pro.; Classified Hardware – 2-Mk, APP/Mac; Classified Printers – Laser; Layout Software – Dell/3255X.; Display Printers – HP/LaserJet III PRODUCTION: Pagination Software – Baseview/NewsEdit.; Production Equipment – ECR/PelBox 1245CS, MON/Rip Express 1.02; Cameras – 1-R/480; Scanners – COM PRESSROOM: Line 1 – 6-HI/Cotrell; Folders – 1 MAILROOM: Counter stackers – Stobb/PI; Inserters and stuffers – MM/227E; Bundle tying machines – 1-Bu/63685; Wrapping singles – 1-Sa/EM, 1-St/730; Addressing machine – 1-Wm/28297.; Business Hardware – 1-IBM/Sys 34, APP/Mac

DE QUEEN

DE QUEEN DAILY CITIZEN

404 De Queen Ave., De Queen, Ark., 71832; gen tel (870) 642-2111; ed tel (870) 642-2111; gen fax (870) 642-3138; gen e-mail dqbee@ipa.net; web site www.dequeen.com
Group: Arkansas Press Services
Published: Mon, Tues, Wed, Thur, Fri
Weekday Frequency: e
Circulation: 2,592
Price: 7.00/mo (city delivery), $6.00/mo (outside county); 75.00/yr.
Advertising: Open inch rate $6.75
News services: AP.
Politics: Democrat. **Established:** 1939
Not Published: New Year; Independence Day; Labor Day; Thanksgiving; Christmas.
Special Editions: Back-to-School (Aug); Spring Car Care (Mar); Christmas Shopper (Nov); Fall Car Care (Oct).
Special Weekly Sections: Education (Fri); Business (Mon); Outdoors (Thur); Consumer News (Wed).
Pub....Anita Marshall
Adv. Mgr.....Melissa Blakenship
Circ. Mgr.....Beth Hughes
Ed.....Scott Smith
Society Ed.....Linda Russell
Sports Ed.....Mark Bishop
Prodn. Supt.....Shane Pate
Market Information: TMC.
Mechanical available: Offset; Black and 1 ROP colors; insert accepted; page cutoffs - 22 3/4.
Mechanical Specifications: Type page 15 1/4 x 21; E - 7 cols, 2 1/16, 1/8 between; A - 7 cols, 2 1/16, 1/8 between; C - 7 cols, 2 1/16, 1/8 between.
Commodity Consumption: Avg. Page Number Per Issue - Daily 12; Avg. Page Number Per Issue - Plates Used 2100; widths 32; Newsprint Used - Short Tons 90; Printing Ink Used - Black 1700; Printing Ink Used - Color 75; Printing Ink Used - Pages Printed 3120.
Equipment; Editorial Hardware – HI, APP/Mac; Editorial Printers – HP. CLASSIFIED: Front-end Software – BMF.; Classified Hardware – HI, PC; Classified Printers – Epson; Layout Software – 2-APP/Mac II.; Display Printers – 2-HP/11 x 17; Production Equipment – 1-APP/Mac Laser, 2-HP; Cameras – 1-R/500; Scanners – Microtek. PRESSROOM: Line 1 – 3-HI/Cotrell V-15A 1969; Folders – 1; Inserters and stuffers – KAN; Bundle tying machines – Bu; Addressing machine – St; Other equipment –Rosback Stitcher. BUSINESS COMPUTERS: Business Software – BMF; Business Hardware – 3-PC

EL DORADO

EL DORADO NEWS-TIMES

111 N. Madison Ave., El Dorado, Ark., 71731; gen tel (870) 862-6611; adv tel (870) 862-6611; ed tel (870) 862-6611; gen fax (870) 862-5226; adv fax (870) 862-9482; ed fax (870) 862-9482; ed e-mail editorial@eldoradonews.com; web site www.eldoradonews.com
Group: WEHCO Media
Published: Mon, Tues, Wed, Thur, Fri, Sat, Sun
Weekday Frequency: m
Saturday Frequency: m
Circulation: 9,413; 9,413(sat); 13,713(sun)
Last Audit: ABC September 30, 2011
Price: 10.25/mo;123.00/yr.
Advertising: Open inch rate $21.00
Insert rate: $61.00 per m
News services: AP.
Politics: Independent. **Established:** 1876
Note: The Sunday edition of the El Dorado News-Times (mS) is called The Sunday News. It is a combined edition of the El Dorado News-Times, Camden News (e) & Magnolia Banner-News (e). The Sunday News is distributed to subscribers in Union County, Columbia County and Ouachita County in southern Arkansas.
Own facility?: Y
Special Editions: Spring Fashion (Apr); Back-to-School (Aug); Progress (Mar); Graduation (May); Christmas Catalogue (Nov); Fall Fashion (Sept).
Special Weekly Sections: Living (S).
Magazines: Relish (Monthly); USA WEEKEND Magazine (S);
Pub....Walter E. Hussman
Gen. Mgr.....Betty Chatham
Adv. Dir.....Nichole Patterson
Circ. Mgr.....Scott Bramlett
Entertainment Ed.....Rod Harrington
Features Ed.....Janice McIntire
News Ed.....Chris Qualls
Online Ed.....Shea Wilson
Sports Ed.....Tony Burns
Prodn. Mgr., Pressroom....Iva Gail Riser
Market Information: TMC.
Mechanical available: Offset; Black and 3 ROP colors; insert accepted; page cutoffs - 22 3/4.
Mechanical Specifications: Type page 13 x 21 1/2; E - 6 cols, 1 5/8, 3/16 between; A - 6 cols, 1 5/8, 13/16 between; C - 8 cols, 1 3/16, 1/8 between.
Commodity Consumption: Avg. Page Number Per Issue - Daily 16; Avg. Page Number Per Issue - Plates Used 6074; Avg. Page Number Per Issue - Sunday 28; widths 25; Newsprint Used - Short Tons 457; Printing Ink Used - Black 7772; Printing Ink Used - Color 1206; Printing Ink Used -
Equipment EDITORIAL: Front-end Software – Baseview 3.2.2.; Editorial Hardware – 5-APP/Mac G4, 12-APP/iMac; Editorial Equipment – Nikon/Cool Scan 4; Editorial Printers – 1-Microtek/Flatbed Scanner CLASSIFIED: Front-end Software – Baseview/Ad Manager Pro 2.05.; Classified Hardware – 3-APP/Mac; Classified Equipment – HP/Laserjet 4050 DISPLAY: Ad make-up applications – QPS/QuarkXPress 4.1; Display Hardware – 5-APP/Power Mac G4 PRODUCTION: Pagination Software – Multi-Ad/Creator 6.0.; Production Equipment – Caere/OmniPage 8.0; Cameras – C/Spartan III; Scanners – Epson/1280 PRESSROOM: Line 1 – 4-G/Urbanite (8 pgs on each unit). MAILROOM: Counter stackers – Systems Technology/Count-O-Veyor; Bundle tying machines – 1-Ca/Band tyer, Sterling; Addressing machine – Wm.
Delivery method: Mail, Private Carrier, Racks

NEWS-TIMES PUBLISHING CO.

111 N. Madison, El Dorado, Ark., 71731; gen tel (870) 862-6611; adv tel 870-862-6611; ed tel 870-862-6611; gen fax (870) 862-5226; adv fax 870-862-9482; ed fax 870-862-9482; gen e-mail editorial@eldoradonews.com; adv e-mail advertising@eldoradonews.com; ed e-mail cqualls@eldoradonews.com; web site www.eldoradonews.com
Group: Wehco Media, Inc.
Published: Mon, Tues, Wed, Thur, Fri, Sat, Sun
Weekday Frequency: m
Saturday Frequency: m
Circulation: 9,413; 9,413(sat); 13,713(sun)
Price: 123.00/yr.
Advertising: Open inch rate $25.65
Insert rate: $65 per M
News services: Associated Press
Politics: 1889
Advertising not accepted: Y
Own facility?: Y
Zip Codes served: 71730, 71765, 71749, 71759, 71762, 71758
Delivery method: Mail, Newsstand, Private Carrier, Racks

FAYETTEVILLE

NORTHWEST ARKANSAS TIMES

212 N. East Ave., Fayetteville, Ark., 72702-1607; gen tel (479) 442-1700; adv tel (479) 442-1700; ed tel (479) 442-1700; gen fax (479) 442-5477; adv fax (479) 442-5477; ed fax (479) 442-1714; web site www.nwaonline.com
Circulation: 17,807; 17,807(sat); 20,381(sun)
Last Audit: September 30, 2007
Price: 10.75/mo; 109.00/yr.
Advertising: Open inch rate $16.26
News services: Landon Media Group.
Advertising not accepted: No obscene ads.
Magazines: Parade (S).
Pub.....Jeff Jeffus
Dir., Finance....Sandra Thompson
Dir., HR....Broderick Daniels
Admin. Asst.....Patricia Smith
Adv. Dir., Sales/Mktg.....Jim Blankenship
Adv. Mgr., Classified....Kaye Hunton
Adv. Mgr., Retail....Brian Parson
Circ. Dir.....Hector Cueva
Exec. Ed.....Greg Harton
Mng. Ed.....Christie Swanson
Features Ed.....Cassie Hussman
Photo Dept.....Andy Shupe
Sports Ed.....Terry Wood
Dir., IT....Mat Costa
Online Mgr.....Steven Jarvis
Prodn. Mgr., Plant....Eric Haley
Market Information: ADS; TMC.
Mechanical available: Offset; Black and 3 ROP colors; insert accepted - cards, coupon books, small items; page cutoffs - 22.
Mechanical Specifications: Type page 11 5/8 x 21 1/2; E - 6 cols, 1 5/6, 1/8 between; A - 6 cols, 1 5/6, 1/8 between; C - 9 cols, 1 1/4, 1/8 between.
Commodity Consumption: Avg. Page Number Per Issue - Daily 12; Avg. Page Number Per Issue - Plates Used 16243; Avg. Page Number Per Issue - Sunday 20; widths 50; Newsprint Used - Short Tons 518; Printing Ink Used - Black 11616; Printing Ink Used - Color 4699; Printing Ink Used
Equipment EDITORIAL: Front-end Software – Adobe/InDesign, Baseview/NewsEdit Pro 4.0, QWE.; Editorial Hardware – APP/Mac; Editorial Equipment – 2-V/6990 negative printer, Lf/AP Leaf Picture Desk; Editorial Printers – Pre Press/Panther Imagesetter CLASSIFIED: Front-end Software – DTI/Classified 5.3.; Classified Hardware – APP/Mac DISPLAY: Ad make-up applications – Managing Editor/ALS; Layout Software – Baseview/Production Manager Pro 2.0, APP/Mac.; Display Hardware – 2-Mk, Baseview; Display Printers – APP/Mac LaserWriter II PRODUCTION: Pagination Software – Adobe/; Production Equipment – 2-V/VT6000W,

1-Pre Press, 1-Pre Press/Panther Plus 36, 4-APP/Mac G4, 2-AG/Imagesetter 1500, 2-Dell/Image Controller, 2-XIT/Image Controller; Cameras – B, R; Scanners – Companica/680C, 2-Tecsu/18x22-1200 OPI Flatbed, TS-2070 PRESSROOM: Line 1 – 8-G/Headliner offset; Folders – Hoe/Colormatic 3:2/2:1; Pasters – 9-Hoe/Colormatic Auto Paster. MAILROOM: Counter stackers – Quipp; Inserters and stuffers – Titan/13/72s; Bundle tying machines – Sterling; Addressing machine – Ch/596 (heat activated). BUSINESS COMPUTERS: Business Software – Unix/OS, Informix, Vision Data 5.0; Business Hardware – Vision Data (mainframe)

FORREST CITY

TIMES-HERALD

222 N. Izard St., Forrest City, Ark., 72335-1699; gen tel (870) 633-3130; adv tel (870) 633-3130; ed tel (870) 633-3130; gen fax (870) 633-0599; adv fax (870) 633-0599; ed fax (870) 633-0599; gen e-mail fctimes@thnews.com; ed e-mail tamjohns@thnews.com; web site www.thnews.com

Published: Mon, Tues, Wed, Thur, Fri
Weekday Frequency: e
Circulation: 4,500
Last Audit: September 30, 2006
Price: 121.00/yr.
Advertising: Open inch rate $11.64
News services: AP.
Politics: Independent. **Established:** 1871
Not Published: New Year; Independence Day; Thanksgiving; Christmas.
Pub. Emer. ....Trent Bonner McCollum
Pub. ....Weston McCollum Lewey
Adv. Mgr. ....Jim Wirski
Classified Adv. Mgr. ....Betty Bridges
Mng. Ed. ....Tamara Johnson
Sports Ed. ....Fred Conley
Market Information: TMC.
Mechanical available: Offset; Black and 3 ROP colors; insert accepted - cards; page cutoffs - 22 1/2.
Mechanical Specifications: Type page 13 x 21; E - 6 cols, 2 1/16, 1/8 between; A - 6 cols, 2 1/16, 1/8 between; C - 9 cols, 1 3/8, 1/16 between.
Commodity Consumption: Avg. Page Number Per Issue - Daily 20; widths 28; Printing Ink Used - Pages Printed 3400.
Equipment EDITORIAL: Front-end Software – Baseview.; Editorial Hardware – APP/Mac; Editorial Equipment – AG/Accuset 800; Editorial Printers – Xante CLASSIFIED: Front-end Software – Baseview.; Classified Hardware – APP/Mac 7200 PRODUCTION: Pagination Software – Baseview, QPS/QuarkXPress.; Production Equipment – AG/Accuset 800; Cameras – 1-R; Scanners – AG/DuoScan PRESSROOM: Line 1 – 6-G/Community (balloon former w/ color hump); Press Drives – Press registration system □ Stoesser/PIN Register System.; Inserters and stuffers – KAN/320 6 Station; Bundle tying machines – Malow.; Business Hardware – RSK/16

TIMES-HERALD PUBLISHING CO., INC.

222 N. Izard St., Forrest City, Ark., 72335; gen tel (870) 633-3130; gen fax (870) 633-0599; gen e-mail mwirski@thnews.com; web site www.thnews.com
Published: Mon, Tues, Wed, Thur, Fri, Sat, Sun
Price: 95.75/yr.
Advertising: Open inch rate $10.80

FORT SMITH

TIMES RECORD

3600 Wheeler Ave., Fort Smith, Ark., 72901; gen tel (479) 785-7700; adv tel (479) 785-7727; ed tel (479) 785-7742; gen fax (479) 785-7741; adv fax (479) 785-7741 (classified); ed fax (479) 784-0413; adv e-mail kconey@swtimes.com; ads@swtimes.com; ed e-mail jhansen@swtimes.com; web site www.swtimes.com
Published: Mon, Tues, Wed, Thur, Fri, Sat, Sun
Weekday Frequency: m
Saturday Frequency: m
Circulation: 34,904; 34,904(sat); 39,887(sun)
Last Audit: September 30, 2009
Price: 9.95/mo (dS); 101.28/yr.
Advertising: Open inch rate $40.98
News services: AP.
Politics: Independent.
Magazines: TV Today (S).
Pub. ....Gene Kincy
Adv. Dir. ....John Speck
Adv. Mgr., Classified ....Julie Newman
Mgr., Cor. Accts. ....Kevin Coney
Dir., Promo. ....Mike Davis
Circ. Dir. ....Dennis Arnoldaussen
Circ. Mgr. ....Glen Hogue
Exec. Ed ....Byron Tate
City Ed. ....Judi Hansen
Theater/Music Ed. ....Scott Smith
Travel Ed. ....Tina Dale
Prodn. Mgr. ....Eddy Metz
IT Dir. ....Carl Nobel
Prodn. Mgr., Pressroom ....Mike Fryette
Market Information: Zoned editions.
Mechanical available: Offset; Black and 3 ROP colors; insert accepted; page cutoffs - 21 1/2.
Mechanical Specifications: Type page 13 x 21 1/2; E - 6 cols, 2 1/16, 1/8 between; A - 6 cols, 2 1/16, 1/8 between; C - 9 cols, 1 5/16, 1/16 between.
Commodity Consumption: Avg. Page Number Per Issue - Daily 48; Avg. Page Number Per Issue - Plates Used 45000; Avg. Page Number Per Issue - Sunday 72; widths 54; Newsprint Used - Metric Tons 4400; Printing Ink Used - Black 15000; Printing Ink Used - Color 7000; Printing Ink Use
Equipment EDITORIAL: Front-end Software – Baseview.; Editorial Hardware – 21-APP/Mac G4, 12-APP/Mac G3, 30-APP/iMac; Editorial Equipment – 6-Digital Cameras, 4-Digital Card Readers; Editorial Printers – 1-APP/8500, 1-HP/Color 8550 CLASSIFIED: Front-end Software – Baseview.; Classified Hardware – 11-APP/G4, 3-APP/iMac; Classified Equipment – 3-Digital Camera, 1-Digital Card Reader; Classified Printers – 1-HP/4050 DISPLAY: Ad make-up applications – Baseview, QPS/QuarkXPress, Aldus/Freehand, Adode/Photoshop; Layout Software – ALS/Managing Editor.; Display Hardware – 2-APP/G4, 1-APP/iMac, APP/7200/120; Display Printers – 2-HP/4050 PRODUCTION: Pagination Software – Baseview, QPS/QuarkXPress, Adobe/Indesign.; Production Equipment – 2-Nu, KFM, Anitic/Plate Processor PRESSROOM: Line 1 – G/Cosmo double width; Pasters – 6-G/Cosmo.; Business Hardware – HP/9000

HARRISON

HARRISON DAILY TIMES

111 W. Rush Ave., Harrison, Ark., 72601-4218; gen tel (870) 741-2325; gen fax (870) 741-5632; gen e-mail harrisondaily@harrisondaily.com; ed e-mail news@harrisondaily.com; web site www.harrisondaily.com
Group: Arkansas Press Services
Published: Tues, Wed, Thur, Fri, Sat
Weekday Frequency: m
Circulation: 8,184; 9,185(sat)
Last Audit: Sworn March 17, 2010
Price: 5.00/mo (carrier); 99.00/yr.
Advertising: Open inch rate $12.92
News services: AP.
Politics: Independent. **Established:** 1876
Special Editions: Farm (Monthly).
Special Weekly Sections: TV Magazine-Focus (Fri).
Magazines: USA WEEKEND Magazine (S).
Pub ....Ronnie E. Bell
Bus. Mgr. ....Carol Lawson
Adv. Mgr. ....Jason Overman
Circ. Mgr. ....Richard Hudleson
Bus./Finance Ed. ....Donna Braymer
City/Metro Ed. ....James White
Fashion/Style Ed. ....Yvonne Cone
Food Ed. ....Jane Dunlap Christenson
Photo Ed. ....Dwain Lair
Political/Gov't Ed. ....Lee Dunlap
Sports Ed. ....Jeff Brasel
Television/Film Ed. ....Lynn Blevins
Prodn. Mgr., Composing ....Julie Lockett
Prodn. Mgr., Pressroom ....Leon Lane
Market Information: TMC.
Mechanical available: Offset; Black and 3 ROP colors; insert accepted; page cutoffs - 22 3/4.
Mechanical Specifications: Type page 13 x 21 1/2; E - 6 cols, 2 1/16, 1/8 between; A - 6 cols, 2 1/16, 1/8 between; C - 8 cols, 1 1/2, 1/8 between.
Commodity Consumption: Avg. Page Number Per Issue - Daily 20; Newsprint Used - Short Tons 559; Printing Ink Used - Black 2000; Printing Ink Used - Color 250; Printing Ink Used - Pages Printed 5000.
Equipment; Editorial Hardware – Mk, APP/Mac; Editorial Equipment – APP/Mac II, 10-Mk/400, 3-APP/Mac; Editorial Printers – 2-APP/Mac LaserWriter 630 Pro, 1-APP/Mac LaserWriter NTX.; Classified Equipment – 1-Mk.; Production Equipment – 1-Linotype-Hell/Linotronic 190 RIP 20; Cameras – VG/670 C Vertical. PRESSROOM: Line 1 – 7-G/Community (DEV color deck); Folders – 1; Inserters and stuffers – 1/St, 4-/KAN; Bundle tying machines – 2-/Bu; Wrapping singles – 1-St/Collator-tyer (ST-3 unit); Addressing machine – 1-/Ch.; Business Hardware – 5-RSK, APA

HELENA

THE DAILY WORLD

417 York St., Helena, Ark., 72342; gen tel (870) 338-9181; gen fax (870) 338-9184; ed e-mail editorial@helena-arkansas.com; composing@helena-arkansas.com; web site www.helena-arkansas.com
Published: Tues, Wed, Thur, Fri
Weekday Frequency: m
Circulation: 2,157
Last Audit: September 20, 2004
Price: 9.00/mo; 128.00/yr.
Advertising: Open inch rate $13.00
News services: AP.
Politics: Independent.
Not Published: Christmas.
Special Editions: Cooking School Tab (Apr); Football (Aug); Christmas Tab (Dec); Drug Info Tab (Feb); Progress (Jul); Baseball (Jun); Farm & Garden (Mar); Graduation (May); Christmas Wishbook (Nov); Blues Festival (Oct).
Special Weekly Sections: Grocery Day (Tues).
Magazines: American Profile (Fri).
Pub. ....Clark Smith
Bus. Mgr. ....Carolyn Brown
Display Adv. Mgr. ....Ann Puckett
Mng. Ed. ....Randy Hogan
Sports Ed. ....Larry Binz
Staff Writer ....Betty Adams
Web Mgr. ....Michele Page
Prodn. Mgr., Composing/Classified Jennifer Barnhill
Market Information: TMC.
Mechanical available: Offset; Black and 3 ROP colors; insert accepted - standing cards; page cutoffs - 21.
Mechanical Specifications: Type page 12 17/20 x 21 1/2; E - 6 cols, 2 1/16, 1/8 between; A - 6 cols, 2 1/16, 1/8 between; C - 8 cols, 1 9/16, 1/8 between.
Commodity Consumption: Avg. Page Number Per Issue - Daily 10; Avg. Page Number Per Issue - Plates Used 2879; widths 27; Newsprint Used - Short Tons 155; Printing Ink Used - Black 2235; Printing Ink Used - Color 416; Printing Ink Used - Pages Printed 2688.
Equipment EDITORIAL: Front-end Software – Microsoft/Word 5.1, QPS/QuarkXPress 4.1.; Editorial Hardware – APP/Mac; Editorial Printers – APP/Mac LaserWriter Select CLASSIFIED: Front-end Software – Baseview.; Classified Hardware – APP/Mac, APP/iMac 2000; Classified Printers – APP/Mac LaserWriter Pro DISPLAY: Ad make-up applications – Multi-Ad/Creator; Layout Software – APP/Mac G-3.; Display Hardware – APP/Mac; Display Printers – APP/Mac LaserWriter Pro PRODUCTION: Pagination Software – QPS/QuarkXPress 4.1.; Production Equipment – Nu/Flip Top FT40UP; Cameras – 1-SCREEN/640-c Companica; Scanners – 2-Microtek PRESSROOM: Line 1 – 5-G/Community; Folders – 1-G/Community. MAILROOM: Counter stackers – BG/Count-O-Veyor; Bundle tying machines – Bu/BT-16.; Business Hardware – 1-RSK

HOPE

HOPE STAR

522 W. Third St., Hope, Ark., 71802; gen tel (870) 777-8841; gen fax (870) 777-3311; gen e-mail hopestar71802@yahoo.com; web site www.hopestar.com
Group: Arkansas Press Services
Published: Mon, Tues, Wed, Thur, Fri
Weekday Frequency: e
Circulation: 3,031
Last Audit: October 1, 2003
Price: 8.00/mo; 79.00/yr.
Advertising: Open inch rate $15.60
News services: AP.
Politics: Independent. **Established:** 1899
Advertising not accepted: Classifieds offering home work.
Not Published: New Year; Memorial Day; Independence Day; Labor Day; Thanksgiving; Christmas.
Special Editions: Watermelon Festival (Jul); Progress (Mar); Graduation (May).
Magazines: Star Time Entertainment (weekly TV section) (Fri); American Profile (Weekly).
Pub. ....Clark Smith
Adv. Dir. ....Richard Haycox
Circ. Dir. ....Donnie Hollis
Ed. ....Ken McLemore
Pressroom Mgr. ....Darrell Terry
Market Information: ADS; TMC.
Mechanical available: Offset; Black and 3 ROP colors; insert accepted - all; page cutoffs - 22 3/4.
Mechanical Specifications: Type page 13 x 21 1/2; E - 6 cols, 2 1/16, 1/8 between; A - 6 cols, 2 1/16, 1/8 between; C - 6 cols, 2 1/16, 1/8 between.
Commodity Consumption: Avg. Page Number Per Issue - Daily 16; Avg. Page Number Per Issue - Plates Used 7400; widths 27 1/2; Newsprint Used - Short Tons 270; Printing Ink Used - Black 2500; Printing Ink Used - Color 1500; Printing Ink Used - Pages Printed 3970.
Equipment; Editorial Hardware – 4-APP/Mac IIci; Editorial Equipment – 6-HI/1250, 5-COM/Computype, 6-APP/Mac Performa; Editorial Printers – LaserMaster/XL 1200.; Classified Hardware – APP/Mac Network.; Layout Software – APP/Mac.; Production Equipment – APP/Mac LaserWriter NTX; Cameras – 1-B/Caravelle 18 x 24. PRESSROOM: Line 1 – 5-WPC/Marc 25; Reels and Stands – 5 MAILROOM: Counter stackers – BG/Count-O-Veyor; Bundle tying machines – 4-Sa/EM10755; Wrapping singles – 4/Sa; Addressing machine – 1-Ch/500, 1-Ch/730.; Business Hardware – IBM/Sys 34

HOT SPRINGS

THE SENTINEL-RECORD

300 Spring St., Hot Springs, Ark., 71901; gen tel (501) 623-7711; adv tel (501) 623-7711; ed tel (501) 623-7711; gen fax (501) 623-2984; adv fax (501) 623-2984; ed fax (501) 623-8465; adv e-mail production@hotsr.com; ed e-mail editor@hotsr.com; web site www.hotsr.com
Published: Mon, Tues, Wed, Thur, Fri, Sat, Sun
Weekday Frequency: m
Saturday Frequency: m
Circulation: 16,128; 17,138(sat); 17,005(sun)
Last Audit: ABC September 30, 2011

Price: 10.50/mo; 119.70/yr.
Advertising: Open inch rate $29.85
News services: AP.
Politics: Independent. **Established:** 1877
Special Editions: Senior Resource (Aug); Christmas (Dec); Mail-it-Away (Feb); Senior Scene (Monthly).
Special Weekly Sections: TV Magazine (S).
Magazines: Relish (Monthly); USA WEEKEND Magazine (Sat); American Profile (Weekly).
Pub.....Walter E. Hussman
Gen. Mgr......Nat Lea
Adv. Dir......Penny Thornton
Editorial Page Ed......Melinda Gassaway
Lifestyles Ed......Marilyn Holsapple
Online Ed......Mark Gregory
Photo Ed......Richard Rasmussen
Photographer.....Alison Harbour
Real Estate Ed......Lynda Lampinen
Religion Ed.....Linda Arneson
Sports Ed......Robert Wisener
Teen-Age/Youth Ed......Matthew Hoffman
Prodn. Mgr., Distr......Danny Leftridge
Prodn. Mgr., Pre Press.....Jimmy Robertson
Market Information: TMC.
Mechanical available: Offset; Black and 3 ROP colors; insert accepted; page cutoffs - 22 3/4.
Mechanical Specifications: Type page 11 5/8 x 21 1/4; E - 6 cols, 1 3/4, 1/8 between; A - 6 cols, 1 3/4, 1/8 between; C - 9 cols, 1 1/4, 1/8 between.
Commodity Consumption: Avg. Page Number Per Issue - Daily 24; Avg. Page Number Per Issue - Plates Used 12000; Avg. Page Number Per Issue - Sunday 42; widths 25; Newsprint Used - Short Tons 1250; Printing Ink Used - Black 30000; Printing Ink Used - Color 2550; Printing Ink Used
Equipment EDITORIAL: Front-end Software – Baseview.; Editorial Hardware – APP/Mac CLASSIFIED: Front-end Software – Baseview.; Classified Hardware – APP/Mac; Classified Printers – Okidata DISPLAY: Ad make-up applications – Multi-Ad 4.3; Layout Software – Mk/Ad Manager.; Display Hardware – APP/Mac; Display Printers – AG/Accuset 1500 PRODUCTION: Pagination Software – QPS 4.1.; Production Equipment – TI/OmniPage; Scanners – HP PRESSROOM: Line 1 – 7-G/Urbanite 1967; Reels and Stands – G/7. MAILROOM: Counter stackers – 2-HL/Monitor, 1-QWI/Sport II; Inserters and stuffers – 1-KAN/480; Bundle tying machines – MLN/MLN2A, Si/Portable BUSINESS COMPUTERS: Business Software – PBS, Circulation, Ad Management; Business Hardware – IBM

JONESBORO

THE JONESBORO SUN

518 Carson St., Jonesboro, Ark., 72401; gen tel (870) 935-5525; gen fax (870) 935-6659; adv fax (870) 935-1674; ed fax (870) 935-5823; adv e-mail llynn@jonesborosun.com; web site www.jonesborosun.com
Group: Arkansas Press Services
Published: Mon, Tues, Wed, Thur, Fri, Sat, Sun
Weekday Frequency: m
Saturday Frequency: m
Circulation: 19,830; 19,830(sat); 22,564(sun)
Last Audit: March 31, 2008
Price: 165.60/yr.
Advertising: Open inch rate $30.43
News services: AP.
Politics: Democrat.
Advertising not accepted: Y
Own facility?: Y
Special Editions: Farm Family, Academic All-stars, ASU Campus Guide, High School Football/Basketball, NEA Pride, NEA District Fair, Chamber Leadership, Local Favorites, Sun Outdoors, NEA Harvest, Let's Eat Out, Susan G. Komen Cancer Awareness, Christmas Open House
Special Weekly Sections: Lifestyle (S); Church Page (Sat); Food (Wed).Entertainment (Thurs(
Magazines: TV Guide (S).
Pub.....David Mosesso
Adv. Dir.....Lisa Lynn
Adv. Mgr., Nat'l.....Dennell Whittingham
Editorial Page Ed.....Roy Ockert
News Ed.....Maria Flora
Sports Ed......Kevin Turbeville
Prodn. Foreman, Composing.....Roger Brumley
Prodn. Foreman, Pressroom.....Joe Tidwell
Controller.....Michael Shain
Circulation Director.....Lorri Householder
Controller/Bus. Mgr......Jeremy Arling
Adv. Mgr., Classified.....Kim Smith
Adv. Mgr., Retail Sales.....Patricia Lander
Circ. Mgr......Richard Bales
Market Information: TMC.
Mechanical available: Offset; Black and 3 ROP colors; insert accepted; page cutoffs - 21 1/2.
Mechanical Specifications: Type page 11 x 21 1/2; E - 6 cols, 2, 1/8 between; A - 6 cols, 2, 1/8 between; C - 8 cols, 1 1/2, 1/8 between.
Commodity Consumption: Avg. Page Number Per Issue - Daily 32; Avg. Page Number Per Issue - Plates Used 15000; Avg. Page Number Per Issue - Sunday 64; widths 22; Newsprint Used - Short Tons 2000; Printing Ink Used - Pages Printed 13000.
Equipment EDITORIAL: Front-end Software – MediaSpan CLASSIFIED: Front-end Software – MediaSpan PRODUCTION: Pagination Software – Prestelligence PRESSROOM: Line 1 – 8-G/Urbanite 1986; Line 6 – Feb-86; Folders – 1-G/2:1; Reels and Stands – 2-G/4 Tier; Press control system – 2-1986. MAILROOM: Counter stackers – Newstack, 1-Id/660, 1-Id/2200; Inserters and stuffers – HI/1372, W/ARS; Bundle tying machines – 2/MLN; Addressing machine – 1-/KR, 2-/CYP.
Delivery method: Mail, Newsstand, Private Carrier, Racks

LITTLE ROCK

ARKANSAS DEMOCRAT-GAZETTE

121 E. Capitol Ave., Little Rock, Ark., 72201; gen tel (501) 378-3400; adv tel (501) 378-3437; ed tel (501) 378-3485; gen fax (501) 378-3591; adv fax (501) 378-3591; gen e-mail news@ardemgaz.com; web site www.arkansasonline.com
Published: Mon, Tues, Wed, Thur, Fri, Sat, Sun
Weekday Frequency: m
Saturday Frequency: m
Circulation: 179,134; 180,530(sat); 266,798(sun)
Last Audit: ABC September 30, 2011
Price: 12.50/mo; 135.00/yr; 35.00/3mo, $70.00/6mo.
Advertising: Open inch rate $347.00
News services: AP, LAT-WP, SHNS, NYT, MCT, Bloomberg.
Politics: Independent.
Note: Arkansas Democrat-Gazette owns two daily newspapers as well at eight weekly newspapers all located in Arkansas.
Special Editions: Football (Aug); Christmas Gift (Dec); Racing (Jan); Spring Fashion (Mar); Basketball (Nov).
Special Weekly Sections: Weekend Arkansas (Fri); Health (Mon); TV Magazine (local, offset) (S).
Magazines: Relish (Monthly); Parade (S); American Profile (Weekly).
Pub.....Walter E. Hussman
Vice Pres., Opns......Lynn Hamilton
Vice Pres./Gen. Mgr......Paul R. Smith
Controller.....Terrell Strickland
Mgr., Accounting.....Adam Jordan
Bus. Mgr......Judy Nethercutt
Mgr., Data Processing/Typeset.....Clay Carson
Mgr., Personnel.....Kay Brewer
Adv. Dir......John Mobbs
Adv. Dir., Classified.....Scott Stine
Adv. Mgr., Classified Inside Sales.....Katie Nikpour
Adv. Mgr., Recruitment.....Gary Troutman
Adv. Mgr., Retail Sales.....David Brown
Adv. Mgr., Retail Sales.....Carol Dawson
Adv. Supvr., Customer Sales.....Phyllis White
Adv. Supvr., Opns......Gail Newton
Dir., Promo.....Estel Jeffery
Circ. Dir......Larry Graham
Exec. Ed......Griffin Smith
Deputy Ed......Frank Fellone
Market Information: Split run; Zoned editions.
Mechanical available: Offset; Black and 3 ROP colors; insert accepted; page cutoffs - 22.
Mechanical Specifications: Type page 11 5/8 x 20 1/2; E - 6 cols, 1 5/6, 1/8 between; A - 6 cols, 1 5/6, 1/8 between; C - 9 cols, 1 1/5, 1/12 between.
Commodity Consumption: Avg. Page Number Per Issue - Daily 93; Avg. Page Number Per Issue - Plates Used 242700; Avg. Page Number Per Issue - Sunday 142; widths 55; Newsprint Used - Short Tons 29356; Printing Ink Used - Black 433647; Printing Ink Used - Color 269472; Printing In
Equipment EDITORIAL: Front-end Software – Baseview.; Editorial Hardware – APP/Mac; Editorial Equipment – APP/Mac, PCs; Editorial Printers – 4-AG/Accuset-1500 CLASSIFIED: Front-end Software – DTI.; Classified Hardware – Novell/LAN, 45-APP/Mac; Classified Printers – 4-AG/Accuset-1500 DISPLAY: Ad make-up applications – Multi-Ad/Creator; Layout Software – MEI.; Display Hardware – Novell/LAN, APP/Mac; Display Printers – 4-AG/Accuset-1500 PRODUCTION: Pagination Software – QPS/QuarkXPress.; Production Equipment – 4-AG/Accuset-1500, 3-Newark; Cameras – Scanners ÃÂ Nikon, Lf/Leafscan 35-45, HP/Sharp 8 x 10; Scanners – Nikon, Lf/Leafscan 35-45, HP/Sharp 8 x 10 PRESSROOM: Line 1 – 9-G/Headliner 1987; Line 2 – 9-G/Headliner 1988; Line 3 – Line 4 ÃÂ 8-G/Headliner 1996; Folders – 4-G/3:2, 1-H/3:2, 1-H/2:1; Pasters – 18-G/C-45, 8; Reels and Stands – G/RTP. MAILROOM: Counter stackers – 5-HL/HT, 3-HL/Monitor, 6/QWI; Inserters and stuffers – 2-HI/1372, 1-MM/7:1, 4-HI/1372, 1-MM/6:1; Bundle tying machines – 2-/Power Strap/Model 5, 1-MLN/News 90, 4-MLN/MLN2A, 6-/QWI; Addressing machine – 3-/Ch; Other equipment – MM/Stitc; Audio Hardware – Telepublishing Inc, Newspaper Voice Services BUSINESS COMPUTERS: Business Software – Unix/SCO, PBS; Business Hardware – IBM/AS-400, IBM/RS 6000, Client Server Network

MAGNOLIA

BANNER-NEWS

134 S. Washington St., Magnolia, Ark., 71753-3523; gen tel (870) 234-5130; adv tel (870) 234-5130; ed tel (870) 234-5130; gen fax (870) 234-2551; adv fax (870) 234-2551; ed fax (870) 234-2551; adv e-mail advertising@bannernews.net; ed e-mail news@bannernews.net; web site www.bannernews.net
Published: Mon, Tues, Wed, Thur, Fri, Sun
Weekday Frequency: e
Circulation: 4,100; 17,200(sun)
Last Audit: Sworn September 29, 2006
Price: 8.25/mo; 105.00/yr.
Advertising: Open inch rate $10.06
Insert rate: $60 per m
News services: AP.
Politics: 1878
Note: The Banner-News is printed at the El Dorado News-Times. For detailed production information, see the El Dorado News-Times listing. Subscribers to the Banner-News (e), the Camden News (e), and the El Dorado News-Times (mS) receive the Sunday edition of the
Not Published: New Year; Christmas.
Own facility?: Y
Special Editions: Blossom Festival (Apr); Bride (Jan); Progress (May); Fall Fashion (Sept).
Magazines: Relish (Monthly); American Profile (Weekly).
Pub.....Walter E. Hussman
Gen. Mgr......Susan Gill
Circ. Mgr......Maebelle Green
Mng. Ed......Jamie Davis
Sports Ed......Chris Gilliam
Market Information: TMC.
Mechanical available: Offset; Black and 3 ROP colors; insert accepted; page cutoffs - 21 1/2.
Mechanical Specifications: Type page 13 x 21 1/2; E - 6 cols, 2 1/16, 1/16 between; A - 6 cols, 2 1/16, 1/16 between; C - 8 cols, 1 3/8, 1/16 between.
Commodity Consumption: Avg. Page Number Per Issue - Daily 10; Avg. Page Number Per Issue - Sunday 24.
Equipment EDITORIAL: Front-end Software – Baseview.; Editorial Hardware – IBM; Editorial Printers – Epson CLASSIFIED: Front-end Software – Baseview.; Classified Hardware – IBM; Classified Printers – HP DISPLAY: Ad make-up applications – APP/Mac Display Ad Makeup System.; Display Hardware – Printers APP/Mac LaserWriter II; Bundle tying machines – Cyclone; Addressing machine – Novell/LAN.
Delivery method: Mail, Newsstand, Private Carrier, Racks

MALVERN

MALVERN DAILY RECORD

219 Locust St., Malvern, Ark., 72104; gen tel (501) 337-7523; adv tel same ext 216; ed tel ext 215; gen fax (501) 337-1226; adv fax same; ed fax same; gen e-mail mdrecord@sbcglobal.net; adv e-mail mdradvertising@ sbcglobal.met; ed e-mail mdrecord@sbcglobal.net
Group: Arkansas Press Services
Published: Tues, Wed, Thur, Fri, Sat
Weekday Frequency: e
Saturday Frequency: m
Circulation: 3,500
Last Audit: Sworn September 30, 2006
Price: 7.00/mo (city), $7.50/mo (outside city); 84.00/yr.
Advertising: Open inch rate $11.45
News services: AP.
Politics: 1914
Own facility?: Y
Special Editions: Christmas (Dec); Progress (Jan); Thanksgiving/Christmas Kick-off (Nov).
Magazines: Food Days (Mon); Consumer Review (Thur); Food Days (Wed); American Profile (Weekly).
Bus. Mgr......Kim Taber
Adv. Dir......Richard Folds
Circ. Mgr......Kathi Ledbetter
News Ed......Mark Bivens
Online Ed......James Liegh
Sports Ed......LaJuan Monney
Composing Mgr......Jessica Mathis
Market Information: TMC.
Mechanical available: Offset; Black and 4 ROP colors; insert accepted; page cutoffs - 22 3/4.
Mechanical Specifications: Type page 13 x 21 1/2; E - 6 cols, 2 1/16, 1/8 between; A - 6 cols, 2 1/16, 1/8 between; C - 9 cols, 1 1/3, 1/8 between.
Commodity Consumption: Avg. Page Number Per Issue - Daily 14; Avg. Page Number Per Issue - Plates Used 2393; widths 27 1/2; Newsprint Used - Short Tons 165; Printing Ink Used - Black 1150; Printing Ink Used - Color 482; Printing Ink Used - Pages Printed 3640.
Equipment EDITORIAL: Front-end Software – Baseview, QPS/QuarkXPress.; Editorial Hardware – APP/Mac; Editorial Printers – APP/Mac LaserWriter IIg CLASSIFIED: Front-end Software – Baseview.; Classified Hardware – APP/Mac DISPLAY: Ad make-up applications – QPS/QuarkXPress; Layout Software – APP/Mac.; Display Hardware – Printers APP/Mac LaserWriter IIg; Production Equipment – Nat/A-250; Cameras – B. PRESSROOM: Line 1 – G. MAILROOM: Counter stackers – BG; Addressing machine – Wm.; Business Hardware – 3-Wyse
Delivery method: Mail, Newsstand, Private Carrier, Racks

MOUNTAIN HOME

THE BAXTER BULLETIN

16 W. 6th St., Mountain Home, Ark., 72653-

3508; gen tel (870) 508-8000; adv tel (870) 508-8080; ed tel (870) 508-8050; gen fax (870) 508-8020; adv fax (870) 508-8020; ed fax (870) 508-8020; adv e-mail addir@baxterbulletin.com; ed e-mail newsroom@baxterbulletin.com; web site www.baxterbulletin.com
Published: Mon, Tues, Wed, Thur, Fri, Sat
Weekday Frequency: m
Saturday Frequency: m
Circulation: 9,156; 9,156(sat)
Last Audit: ABC September 30, 2011
Price: 19.75/3mo, $35.88/6mo.
Advertising: Open inch rate $12.60
News services: AP, GNS.
Politics: Independent.
Special Editions: Health (Apr); Back-to-School (Aug); Letters to Santa (Dec); Baxter County Fact Book (Feb); Chronology (Jan); Home Show (Mar); Twin Lakes Real Estate Guide (Monthly); Christmas Gift Guide (Nov); Baxter County Fair (Sept).
Special Weekly Sections: TV Book (Fri); Technology (Mon); Faith/Religion (Sat); Entertainment (Thur); Health/Fitness (Tues); Food (Wed).
Magazines: Living Well Magazine (Every other month); USA WEEKEND Magazine (Sat).
Gen. Mgr. ....Tom Tate
Online Adv. Mgr./Adv. Dir. .Kelly Freudensprung
Online Mgr. ....Daniel Greer
Dir., Opns.................................Doug Webster
Market Information: TMC.
Mechanical available: Offset; Black and 3 ROP colors; insert accepted; page cutoffs - 22 3/4.
Mechanical Specifications: Type page 11 5/8 x 21; E - 6 cols, 1 5/6, 1/8 between; A - 6 cols, 1 5/6, 1/8 between; C - 6 cols, 1 5/6, 1/8 between.
Commodity Consumption: Avg. Page Number Per Issue - Daily 22; Avg. Page Number Per Issue - Plates Used 8900; widths 12 1/2; Newsprint Used - Metric Tons 520; Newsprint Used - Short Tons 574; Printing Ink Used - Black 15500; Printing Ink Used - Color 4000; Printing Ink Used - P
Equipment EDITORIAL: Front-end Software – Baseview/NewsEdit Pro 3.5.; Editorial Hardware – Mk/3000; Editorial Equipment – 9-Mk/PC CLASSIFIED: Front-end Software – Baseview/Ad Manager Pro 2.6.; Classified Equipment – 3-Epson/PC; Layout Software – MEI/Ad Force 4.0.; Display Hardware – Software QPS/QuarkXPress 4.11 PRODUCTION: Pagination Software – QPS/QuarkXPress 4.11.; Production Equipment – 2-COM/8400; Cameras – 1-C/Spartan III; Scanners – Umax PRESSROOM: Line 1 – 6-G/Community, 2-Dauphin/Graphic Units. MAILROOM: Counter stackers – 1/BG; Inserters and stuffers – 1-/MM; Bundle tying machines – 2-/Bu, 1-Samuel/Strapper; Addressing machine – 1-KR, 1-Profit Packaging/P3.; Business Hardware – 1-IBM/AS-400

PARAGOULD

PARAGOULD DAILY PRESS

1401 W. Hunt St., Paragould, Ark., 72450; gen tel (870) 239-8562; gen fax (870) 239-8565; adv fax (870) 239-3636; ed fax (870) 239-8565; adv e-mail advertising@paragoulddailypress.com; web site www.paragoulddailypress.com
Group: Arkansas Press Services
Published: Tues, Wed, Thur, Fri, Sat, Sun
Weekday Frequency: m
Circulation: 5,539; 5,539(sat); 6,291(sun)
Last Audit: September 30, 2006
Price: 10.25/mo; 117.00/yr.
Advertising: Open inch rate $8.95
News services: AP.
Politics: Independent.
Advertising not accepted: Dating services; Abortion; Adoption.
Not Published: New Year; Labor Day; Christmas.
Special Editions: Travel (Apr); Fall Fashions (Aug); Christmas (Dec); Loose Caboose Festival (Jul); Family-Owned Business (Jun); Spring Fashions (Mar); Thanksgiving (Nov); Outdoors (Oct); Football (Sept).
Special Weekly Sections: Entertainment (Fri); Weddings (S); Outdoors (Sat); Farm (Thur); Business (Tues); Food (Wed).
Magazines: Television (S).
Pub. ....Scott Perkins
Mng. Ed................................Janie Ginocchio
Sports Ed..............................Mike McKinney
Prodn. Mgr., Composing..........Debbie Robeson
Market Information: TMC.
Mechanical available: Offset; Black and 3 ROP colors; insert accepted; page cutoffs - 23 5/16.
Mechanical Specifications: Type page 11 5/8 x 21 1/2; E - 6 cols, 1 5/6, 1/8 between; A - 6 cols, 1 5/6, 1/16 between; C - 9 cols, 1 7/20, 1/8 between.
Commodity Consumption: Avg. Page Number Per Issue - Daily 16; Avg. Page Number Per Issue - Plates Used 6000; Avg. Page Number Per Issue - Sunday 22; widths 25; Newsprint Used - Short Tons 500; Printing Ink Used - Black 85000; Printing Ink Used - Color 20000; Printing Ink Used
Equipment EDITORIAL: Front-end Software – QPS, APP/Appleworks 6.0, QPS/QuarkXPress 4.1, Text Edit Plus.; Editorial Hardware – APP/Mac; Editorial Printers – HP/LaserJet 5000N CLASSIFIED: Front-end Software – Baseview, QPS.; Classified Hardware – APP/Mac; Classified Printers – Okidata/Pacemark 3410 DISPLAY: Ad make-up applications – Multi-Ad/Creator, Adobe/Photoshop, Caere/OmniPage; Layout Software – APP/Mac.; Display Hardware – 1-APP/Mac G3, 3-APP/Mac G4; Display Printers – HP/LaserJet 5000N, HP/2500 CM PRODUCTION: Pagination Software – QPS/QuarkXPress 4.1.; Production Equipment – 2-APP/Mac Laser Plus, Pelbox/UR-30, APP/Mac G-3; Cameras – 1-C/Spartan III; Scanners – Nikon/Film Scanner PRESSROOM: Line 1 – 6-G/Community (balloon former); Folders – 1; Inserters and stuffers – KAN/320 4 pocket; Bundle tying machines – 1-Sa/4592; Addressing machine – 1-El/3300.

PINE BLUFF

PINE BLUFF COMMERCIAL

300 Beech St., Pine Bluff, Ark., 71601; gen tel (870) 534-3400; adv tel (870) 543-1452; ed tel (870) 543-1456; gen fax (870) 534-0113; adv fax (870) 534-0113; ed fax (870) 534-0113; adv e-mail pbcads@pbcommercial.com; ed e-mail news@pbcommercial.com; web site www.pbcommercial.com
Group: Arkansas Press Services
Published: Mon, Tues, Wed, Thur, Fri, Sat, Sun
Weekday Frequency: m
Saturday Frequency: m
Circulation: 11,600; 11,600(sat); 12,091(sun)
Last Audit: September 30, 2009
Price: 8.75/mo; 105.00/yr (carrier).
Advertising: Open inch rate $20.70
News services: AP, MCT, NEA.
Politics: Independent.
Special Editions: Good News Tab (Apr); Football Tab (Aug); Wedding Tab (Feb); FYI Community Information Tab (Jul); Garden & Home Improvement (Mar); Wrap It Up Early (Nov); Fall Hunting/Fishing Guide Tab (Sept).
Special Weekly Sections: Weekend Entertainment (Fri); Business News (S); TV (Sat); Business News (Wed).
Magazines: USA WEEKEND Magazine (S).
Broadcast Affiliations: ABC; CBS; NBC; UPN; Fox.
Pub..Michael Hengel
Bus. Mgr...............................Marci Davenport
Automotive Ed...........................Jennifer Smith
City/Metro Ed............................Sandra Hope
Educ./School Ed.............................Rick Joslin
Photo Ed...Joe Torres
Regl. Ed. ....Kersh Hall
Travel Ed..............................Eva Marie Pearson
Mgmt. Info Servs./Online Mgr. ....Pat Poe
Prodn. Foreman, Composing Richard Northington
Prodn. Foreman, Mailroom..........Gloria Wilburn
Prodn. Foreman, Pressroom ................T.C. Day
Market Information: TMC; Zoned editions.
Mechanical available: Offset; Black and 3 ROP colors; insert accepted; page cutoffs - 21.
Mechanical Specifications: Type page 11 5/8 x 21; E - 6 cols, 1 4/5, 1/6 between; A - 6 cols, 1 4/5, 1/6 between; C - 9 cols, 1 1/5, 1/6 between.
Commodity Consumption: Avg. Page Number Per Issue - Daily 24; Avg. Page Number Per Issue - Plates Used 19000; Avg. Page Number Per Issue - Sunday 48; widths 13 3/4; Newsprint Used - Metric Tons 1100; Newsprint Used - Short Tons 1212; Printing Ink Used - Black 50000; Printing I
Equipment EDITORIAL: Front-end Software – Baseview/NewsEdit PRO 1998.; Editorial Hardware – APP/Mac G3; Editorial Printers – Pre Press/Panther Plus, Pre Press/Panther Plus 136, HP/Laser Jet 4MV CLASSIFIED: Front-end Software – Baseview/Admanager Pro.; Classified Hardware – APP/Mac G3; Classified Printers – Pre Press/Panther Plus, Pre Press/Panther Plus 136, HP/Laser Jet 4MV DISPLAY: Ad make-up applications – Aldus/Freehand 6.0, QPS/QuarkXPress 4.0; Layout Software – APP/Mac G-3s.; Display Hardware – Printers ÃŒï¿½ Pre Press/Panther Plus, Pre Press/Panther Plus 136, HP/Laser Jet 4MV PRODUCTION: Pagination Software – Baseview.; Production Equipment – Graham/S-1-27; Cameras – Kk/5060B, C/Marathon; Scanners – 5-Microtek/Scanmaker E6, 5-Vmax, 1-Mirage II PRESSROOM: Line 1 – 9-G/Urbanite; Folders – 1 MAILROOM: Counter stackers – QWI/350; Inserters and stuffers – 2-MM/227; Bundle tying machines – EAM-Mosca, 1-MLN/2A; Addressing machine – 1-KR/211.; Business Hardware – 9-HP/917LX3000, Link/MC5

RUSSELLVILLE

THE COURIER

201 E. Second St., Russellville, Ark., 72801; gen tel (479) 968-5252; gen fax (479) 968-2832; adv fax (479) 967-9361; ed fax (479) 968-4037; adv e-mail michelle@couriernews.com; ed e-mail editor@couriernews.com; web site www.couriernews.com
Published: Tues, Wed, Thur, Fri, Sat, Sun
Weekday Frequency: m
Saturday Frequency: m
Circulation: 8,000; 8,000(sat); 10,000(sun)
Last Audit: Sworn September 20, 2002
Price: 9.75/mo; 117.00/yr.
Advertising: Open inch rate $19.75
News services: AP,
Politics: Independent. **Established:** 1875
Not Published: Monday
Own facility?: Y
Special Editions: Welcome to the Valley (Apr); Football (Aug); Active Lifestyles (Dec); Women's (Feb); Home Life (Jan); Home Life (Jul); Boats, Spokes, Auto (Jun); Agriculture (Mar); Home Life (May); Home Life (Nov); Progress (Oct); Home Life (Sept).
Special Weekly Sections: Church Directory (Fri); Real Estate (S); Business Review (Tues); Best Food Day (Wed).
Magazines: USA WEEKEND Magazine (S).
Pub.......................................David Meadows
Bus. Mgr. ....Kelly Davis
Adv. Dir. ....Michelle Harris
Circ. Mgr...Mike Geiss
Mng. Ed.....................................Sean Ingram
Production coordinator ....Adam Franks
Market Information: TMC.
Mechanical available: Offset; Black and 3 ROP colors; insert accepted; page cutoffs - 22 3/4.
Mechanical Specifications: Type page 12 1/2 x 21 1/2; E - 6 cols, 1 4/5, 1/8 between; A - 6 cols, 1 4/5, 1/8 between; C - 9 cols, 1 1/6, 1/8 between.
Commodity Consumption: Avg. Page Number Per Issue - Daily 20; Avg. Page Number Per Issue - Plates Used 5000; Avg. Page Number Per Issue - Saturday 24; Avg. Page Number Per Issue - Sunday 40; widths 25; Newsprint Used - Short Tons 2247; Printing Ink Used - Black 30000; Printing
Equipment EDITORIAL: Front-end Software – MediaSpan, InDesign; Editorial Hardware – Mac G-5's x 9; Editorial Equipment – 1-Microtek/300G Flatbed Scanner; Editorial Printers – HP Laserwriter CLASSIFIED: Front-end Software – MediaSpan; Classified Hardware – 1-APP/Mac G-5 1-APP/Mac G-5 1-APP/Mac G-5610, ; Classified Printers – HP LaswerWriter Plus DISPLAY: Ad make-up applications – MediaSpan; Display Hardware – G-5's x5 ; Display Printers – HP Laser Writer PRODUCTION: Pagination Software – InDesign.; Production Equipment – Mac G-5's PRESSROOM: Line 1 – 8-G/Urbanite 1993; Folders – G/Quarter, G/Half, G/Upper, G/Lower. MAILROOM: Counter stackers – 1/BG; Inserters and stuffers – 4-MM/227-7; Bundle tying machines – 1-/Strapex; Wrapping singles – 3-/SA; Addressing machine – 2-/KR. BUSINESS COMPUTERS: Business Software – MSSI, Great Plains; Business Hardware – 1-Zeos/486 PC, 3-EKI/televideo Mac G-5's
Delivery method: Mail, Private Carrier, Racks

SEARCY

DAILY CITIZEN

3000 E. Race Ave., Searcy, Ark., 72143-4808; gen tel (501) 268-8621; gen fax (501) 268-6277; adv e-mail classifieds@thedailycitizen.com; ed e-mail editor@thedailycitizen.com; web site www.thedailycitizen.com
Published: Tues, Wed, Thur, Fri, Sat, Sun
Weekday Frequency: m
Circulation: 5,686; 5,686(sat); 5,686(sun)
Last Audit: October 1, 2004
Price: 8.25/mo; 117.00/yr.
Advertising: Open inch rate $13.00
News services: AP, NEA.
Politics: Independent.
Special Weekly Sections: Weekend Review (Fri); Business Review (Mon); Business News (S); Business News (Thur); Merchant's Market (Tues); Best Food Day (Wed).
Magazines: Color Comics (S).
Pub...Mike Murphy
Adv. Dir. ....Pat Tullos
Circ. Mgr................................Jessica Jackson
Ed. ....Jay Strasner
Mng. Ed.................................Warren Watkins
Community Ed. ....Wendy Waring
News Ed....................................Gabe Calzada
Sports Ed................................Quinton Bagley
Market Information: TMC.
Mechanical available: Offset; Black and 3 ROP colors; insert accepted; page cutoffs - 22 7/8.
Mechanical Specifications: Type page 13 x 21 1/2; E - 6 cols, 2 1/16, 1/8 between; A - 6 cols, 2 1/16, 1/8 between; C - 9 cols, 1 3/8, 1/16 between.
Commodity Consumption: Avg. Page Number Per Issue - Daily 20; Avg. Page Number Per Issue - Plates Used 4500; Avg. Page Number Per Issue - Sunday 30; widths 27; Newsprint Used - Short Tons 440; Printing Ink Used - Black 13200; Printing Ink Used - Color 1000; Printing Ink Used -
Equipment EDITORIAL: Front-end Software – Baseview.; Editorial Hardware – APP/Mac Classics (networked); Editorial Printers – APP/Mac LaserPrinters CLASSIFIED: Front-end Software – Baseview.; Classified Hardware – APP/Mac IIs; Classified Printers – APP/Mac LaserPrinters DISPLAY: Ad make-up applications – Multi-Ad/Creator.; Display Hardware – APP/Mac IIs; Display Printers – APP/Mac LaserPrinters; Production Equipment – 1-Nat; Cameras – 1-R. PRESSROOM: Line 1 – 6-HI/V-15A.; Bundle tying machines – 2/Bu.; Business Hardware – APP/Mac II, IBM/PCs

SPRINGDALE

THE MORNING NEWS OF NORTHWEST ARKANSAS

2560 N. Lowell Rd., Springdale, Ark., 72765; gen tel (479) 751-6200; adv tel (479) 872-5000; ed tel (479) 872-5030; gen fax (479) 872-5077; adv fax (479) 872-5079; ed fax (479) 872-5055; adv e-mail advertise@nwaonline.com; ed e-mail news@nwaonline.com; web site www.nwaonline.com

Published: Mon, Tues, Wed, Thur, Fri, Sat, Sun
Weekday Frequency: m
Saturday Frequency: m
Circulation: 28,448; 35,270(sat); 35,685(sun)
Last Audit: September 30, 2009
Price: 8.30/mo; 77.65/yr.
Advertising: Open inch rate $29.59
News services: AP.
Politics: Independent. **Established:** 1881
Advertising not accepted: NC-17 movies.
Special Weekly Sections: Weekend (Fri); Et Cetera (Mon); Business (Other); TV Today (S); Religion (Sat); Outdoor (Thur); Your Family (Tues); Food (Wed).
Magazines: Northwest Arkansas Health (Quarterly); USA WEEKEND Magazine (S).
Pub. ....Tom Stallbaumer
Bus. Mgr. ....Sandy Renfroe
Adv. Dir. ....Kent Eikenberry
Circ. Dir. ....Steve Austin
Ed...Rusty Turner
Mng. Ed.............................Lisa Thompson
Bus. Ed. ....Bruce Castleberry
Entertainment Ed........................Becca Martin
Living Ed.................................Debbie Miller
Metro Ed................................Jennifer Cook
Metro Ed...............................Donna Lonchar
Metro Ed. ....Leeanna Walker
Photo Ed. ....Spencer Tirey
Political Ed.............................Brenda Blagg
Sports Ed...................................Chip Souza
Data Processing Mgr. ....Steve Spahr
Mgmt. Info Servs. Mgr...............Chris Dunivan
Prodn. Mgr., Pressroom ....Eddy Metz
Mechanical available: Offset; Black and 3 ROP colors; insert accepted - single sheets; page cutoffs - 22.
Mechanical Specifications: Type page 10 1/2 x 21; E - 6 cols, 1 61/100, 1/6 between; A - 6 cols, 1 61/100, 1/6 between; C - 9 cols, 1 9/100, 2/25 between.
Commodity Consumption: Avg. Page Number Per Issue - Daily 56; Avg. Page Number Per Issue - Plates Used 108000; Avg. Page Number Per Issue - Sunday 106; widths 12 1/2; Newsprint Used - Metric Tons 5000; Printing Ink Used - Black 50000; Printing Ink Used - Color 45500; Printing
Equipment EDITORIAL: Front-end Software – Baseview/NewsEdit Pro IQUE.; Editorial Hardware – 33-APP/iMac, 11-APP/Mac G3 233, 11-APP/iBook, 2-APP/Powerbook G#; Editorial Equipment – Canon/Fax 630, Nikon/LS-100 Scanner, AG/Scanner; Editorial Printers – Xante/Accel-a-Writer 3N CLASSIFIED: Front-end Software – Baseview/Ad Manager Pro.; Classified Hardware – 14-APP/iMac; Classified Equipment – Canon/Facsimile, Minolta/copier, PB/postage meter, 1-Swintec/4040; Classified Printers – TI, APP/Mac LaserWriter 630 DISPLAY: Ad make-up applications – Managing Editor/ALS, AdForce, Quark 4.11, Adobe/Photoshop 7, Adobe/Illustrator 10, Baseview/Production Manager Pro; Display Hardware – 9-APP/Mac G3 400, 3-APP/Mac G3 233; Display Printers – 1-HP/4MV, 1-Tektronix/Phaser 780, 1-Xante/3N, Xante/3G PRODUCTION: Pagination Software – Baseview, QPS/QuarkXPress.; Production Equipment – 3-APP/Mac LaserWriter II, Xante 8200, APP/Mac Laser Pro 630, 2-Pre Press/Panther Plus Imagesetter; Cameras – SCREEN/C-680-C; Scanners – 4-Ap PRESSROOM: Line 1 – 18-DGM/850; Line 2 – 18-DGM/850; Folders – 4-DGM/1255; Pasters – 20 MAILROOM: Counter stackers – 4/HL, 2-QWI/401, 1-QWI/Sport; Inserters and stuffers – 2-HI/1472A; Bundle tying machines – 3-Dynaric; Wrapping singles – 2-Monarch/Bottom Wrap, 2-HI; Addressing machine – 4-/Wm. BUSINESS COMPUTERS: Business Software – HP/MPEIX 5.5, UDMS 5.6, ABII, CJ/Class 8.02H, DB/General 7.1, CJ/AIM 8.02H, Progress/4GL, RDBMS 6.2BO4; Business Hardware – 1-HP/927LX(3000), Compaq/Proliant 1600

STUTTGART

STUTTGART DAILY LEADER

111 W. Sixth St., Stuttgart, Ark., 72160; gen tel (870) 673-8533; gen fax (870) 673-3671; ed e-mail editor@stuttgartdailyleader.com; web site www.stuttgartdailyleader.com

Group: Arkansas Press Services
Published: Mon, Tues, Wed, Thur, Fri
Weekday Frequency: e
Circulation: 2,397
Last Audit: September 27, 2002
Price: 6.75/mo; 79.00/yr.
Advertising: Open inch rate $12.00
News services: AP, TMS.
Politics: Independent.
Advertising not accepted: Abortion; 900 numbers.
Not Published: New Year; Memorial Day; Labor Day; Thanksgiving; Christmas.
Special Weekly Sections: Church Directory (Fri); Business and Review Page (Wed).
Magazines: TV (Every other week); Fifty-plus (Monthly); American Profile (Weekly).
Pub....Clark Smith
Office Mgr..........................Stephanie Sowell
Display Adv. Mgr. ....Jim Kennedy
Classified Adv. Mgr. ....Peggy Synco
Circ. Mgr...............................Willene Boehn
Mng. Ed. ....Lesley Valadez
Website Mgr.............................Daniel Kelso
Market Information: TMC.
Mechanical available: Offset; Black and 3 ROP colors; insert accepted - any; page cutoffs - 22 3/4.
Mechanical Specifications: Type page 13 x 21 1/2; E - 6 cols, 2 1/16, 1/8 between; A - 6 cols, 2 1/16, 1/8 between; C - 9 cols, 1 3/8, 1/16 between.
Commodity Consumption: Avg. Page Number Per Issue - Daily 14; Avg. Page Number Per Issue - Plates Used 4200; widths 28; Newsprint Used - Short Tons 220; Printing Ink Used - Black 6000; Printing Ink Used - Color 1000; Printing Ink Used - Pages Printed 3640.
Equipment EDITORIAL: Front-end Software – QPS/QuarkXPress 3.11, Baseview/NewsEdit.; Editorial Hardware – APP/Mac Performa 6200CD, APP/Power Mac 7200; Editorial Equipment – Umax/Color Scanner; Editorial Printers – APP/Mac LaserWriter NTX, GCC/Elite 600, APP/Mac-4/600 CLASSIFIED: Front-end Software – Baseview/Class Manager Plus.; Classified Hardware – APP/Mac, APP/Power Mac 7200; Classified Equipment – Umax/Color Scanner, ZIP drive; Classified Printers – APP/Mac NTX, GCC/Elite 600 DISPLAY: Ad make-up applications – QPS/QuarkXPress, Multi-Ad/Creator 6.0; Layout Software – APP/Mac, APP/Power Mac 7200.; Display Hardware – 6-APP/Mac NTX; Display Printers – GCC/Elite 600, APP/Mac-4/600 PRODUCTION: Pagination Software – QPS/QuarkXPress 3.11.; Production Equipment – Umax, Adobe/Photoshop; Cameras – 1-SCREEN/Auto film processors PRESSROOM: Line 1 – 6-G/Community; Folders – G/Suburban.; Bundle tying machines – Felins/Tying.

WEST MEMPHIS

CRITTENDEN PUBLISHING CO.

111 E. Bond St., West Memphis, Ark., 72301; gen tel (870) 735-1010; gen fax (870) 735-1020; gen e-mail etnews@midsouth.gr.com; etnews@midsouth.gr.com; web site www.theeveningtimes.com

Published: Mon, Tues, Wed, Thur, Fri, Sat, Sun
Price: 75.00/yr.

TIMES

1010 Hwy. 77 N., Marion, Ark., 72364; gen tel (870) 735-1010; adv tel (870) 735-1010; ed tel (870) 735-1010; gen fax (870) 735-1020; adv fax (870) 735-1020; ed fax (870) 735-1020; gen e-mail news@theeveningtimes.com; adv e-mail retailadv@theeveningtimes.com; web site www.theeveningtimes.com

Published: Mon, Tues, Wed, Thur, Fri
Weekday Frequency: m
Circulation: 8,000
Last Audit: Sworn September 30, 2005
Price: 6.50/mo; 75.00/yr.
Advertising: Open inch rate $13.92
News services: AP.
Politics: 1943
Not Published: Christmas.
Own facility?: Y
Special Editions: Agriculture (Apr); Pigskin Preview (Aug); Christmas Greetings (Dec); Valentine Pages (Feb); Financial Preview (Jan); Back-to-School Tab (Jul); Pre-July 4th Specials (Jun); Bridal Tab (Mar); Spring Car Care (May); Golden Times (Monthly); Holiday Gift Guide
Special Weekly Sections: Church News (Fri); Farm News (Thur); Business (Tues).
Magazines: American Profile (Weekly).
Adv. Dir. ....Nick Coulter
Circ. Mgr. ....Joey Scalzo
Alex Coulter
Mike Coulter
Business manager..........................Alice Rains
Managing Editor.........................Mike Douglas
Pub..................................Alexander Coulter
Office/Credit Mgr. ....Alice Raines
Market Information: TMC.
Mechanical available: Offset; Black and 3 ROP colors; insert accepted; page cutoffs - 23 3/4.
Mechanical Specifications: Type page 11 3/4 x 21 1/2; E - 6 cols, 1 7/10, 1/8 between; A - 6 cols, 3 3/5, 1/16 between; C - 9 cols, 1 1/10, 1/8 between.
Commodity Consumption: Avg. Page Number Per Issue - Daily 24; Avg. Page Number Per Issue - Plates Used 4194; widths 25; Newsprint Used - Metric Tons 1427; Newsprint Used - Short Tons 29483; Printing Ink Used - Black 90000; Printing Ink Used - Color 1622; Printing Ink Used - Pa
Equipment EDITORIAL: Front-end Software – Baseview/NewsEdit Pro, QPS/QuarkXPress.; Editorial Hardware – Printers ◻ ECR CLASSIFIED: Front-end Software – CText.; Classified Hardware – Baseview/Ad Manager Pro, QPS/QuarkXPress; Classified Printers – ECR DISPLAY: Ad make-up applications – Adobe/PageMaker, Adobe/Photoshop, QPS/QuarkXPress, Adobe/Illustrator; Layout Software – APP/Mac G4, APP/Mac G3, APP/Power Mac 8600.; Display Printers – Accel-A-Writer, ECR PRODUCTION: Pagination Software – QPS/QuarkXPress.; Production Equipment – APP/Mac, PCs; Cameras – C/Spartan III; Scanners – Canon/Flatbed, Canon/Coldscan PRESSROOM: Line 1 – 6-KP/News King 1974; Folders – KP/Newsking; Reels and Stands – 6-Roll/Stands; Press control system – GE/SP 200.; Inserters and stuffers – KAN; Bundle tying machines – 2/Akebono; Addressing machine – St; Other equipment – MM/4-Pocket Stitcher-Trimmer. BUSINESS COMPUTERS: Business Software – QuarkXPress; Business Hardware – IBM/386-486, APP/Mac
Delivery method: Mail, Private Carrier, Racks

CALIFORNIA

AUBURN

AUBURN JOURNAL, INC.

1030 High St., Auburn, Calif., 95603-4707; gen tel (530) 885-5656; adv tel (530) 852-0225; ed tel (530) 852-0245; gen fax (530) 885-7235; adv fax (530) 885-4511; ed fax (530) 887-1231; gen e-mail ajournal@goldcountrymedia.com; adv e-mail circulation@goldcountrymedia.com; ed e-mail ajournal@goldcountrymedia.com; dericr@goldcountrymedia.com; web site www.auburnjournal.com

Group: U.S. Suburban Press, Inc.
Published: Mon, Tues, Wed, Thur, Fri, Sun
Weekday Frequency: m
Circulation: 9,520; 9,639(sun)
Last Audit: ABC September 30, 2011
Price: 125.00/yr; 35.75/3mo, $65.00/6mo.
Advertising: Open inch rate $24.30
News services: AP, U.S. Suburban Press Inc., TMS, UPI.
Politics: Independent. **Established:** 1872
Note: Auburn Journal, Inc. is owned by Brehm Communications Inc. Through it's subsidiaries, Democrat Co., Gull Communications, Hi-Desert Publishing Co., Inc., News West Publishing Company Inc., Penny Power Publications Inc., Placer Community Newspapers, Inc. a
Special Editions: Stampede (Apr); Back to School (Aug); Gift Catalog 4 (Dec); I Do! (Feb); Healthy Living (Jan); Auburn Journal's Best of the Best (Jul); Active - Living Life After 55 (Mar); Auburn Spring Home Show (May); Gift Catalog 1 (Nov); Women In Business (Oct); Aubu
Special Weekly Sections: Placer Home & Garden (Fri); Business (S); Food (Wed).
Magazines: USA WEEKEND Magazine (S).
Pub. ....Tony Hazarian
Bus. Dir......................................Staci Orlando
Bus. Opns. Mgr. ....Sandy Stockton
Adv. Dir., Classified..........Suzanne Stevenson
Adv. Mgr. ....Beth O'Brien
Circulation Dir. ....Kelly Leibold
Ed...Deric Rothe
Bus./Finance Ed. ....Gloria Young
News Ed. ....Michelle Miller-Carl
Sports Ed. ....Todd Mordhorst
Gen. Mgr., Print Div. ....Jim Easterly
Prodn. Mgr., Post Press...........Randy Jaworski
Prodn. Mgr., Pressroom................Keith Bowen
Prodn. Supvr., Imaging ....Mary Hazelwood
Pub. ....Tommy Hazarian
Market Information: TMC.
Mechanical available: Offset; Black and 3 ROP colors; insert accepted - Polybags; page cutoffs - 22.
Mechanical Specifications: Type page 10 x 21; E - 6 cols, 1 9/16, 1/8 between; A - 6 cols, 1 9/16, 1/8 between; C - 6 cols, 1 9/16, 1/8 between.
Commodity Consumption: Avg. Page Number Per Issue - Daily 22; Avg. Page Number Per Issue - Plates Used 30000; Avg. Page Number Per Issue - Sunday 48; widths 34; Newsprint Used - Metric Tons 1877; Printing Ink Used - Black 25000; Printing Ink Used - Color 15000; Printing Ink Us
Equipment EDITORIAL: Front-end Software – APT.; Editorial Hardware – PC; Editorial Equipment – 25-IBM/PC; Editorial Printers – 2-LaserMaster/, 2-Pre Press/Panther Plus Imagesetter CLASSIFIED: Front-end Software – APT.; Classified Hardware – PC; Classified Printers – 2-LaserMaster, 2-Pre Press/Panther Plus Imagesetter; Layout Software – Multi-Ad/Creator.; Display Hardware – APP/Mac; Display Printers – Cannon/Image Class C2100, Xante/Accel-a-Writer 3G; Production Equipment – Caere/OmniPage Pro; Scanners – Umax, Polaroid/SprintScan. PRESSROOM: Line 1 – 18-G/Community SSC, 2-DGM/430; Press Drives – 4-Fin/75hp; Folders – 2-G/SSC; Reels and Stands – 7; Inserters and stuffers – KAN/480 5:1, MM/7:1; Bundle tying machines – 2/Bu, 3-Si; Addressing machine – KR; Other equipment –MM/492R Folder.; Business Hardware – Qantel/Q29BS

BAKERSFIELD

THE BAKERSFIELD CALIFORNIAN

1707 Eye St., Bakersfield, Calif., 93301-0440; gen tel (661) 395-7500; adv tel (661)

395-7437; ed tel (805) 395-7364; gen fax (661) 395-7280; adv fax (661) 395-7406; ed fax (805) 395-7519; adv e-mail circulation@bakersfield.com; ed e-mail local@bakersfield.com; sports@bakersfield.com; web site www.bakersfield.com
Published: Mon, Tues, Wed, Thur, Fri, Sat, Sun
Weekday Frequency: m
Saturday Frequency: m
Circulation: 43,228; 45,481(sat); 52,508(sun)
Last Audit: ABC September 30, 2011
Price: 13.50/mo (mS); 161.86/yr (carrier).
Advertising: Open inch rate $104.21
News services: AP, NYT, McClatchy, CSM.
Politics: 1897
Special Editions: Relay for Life ROP Pages (Apr); Holiday Worship (Dec); Wedding Planner (Feb); Kern Life (Jul); Best of Kern County (May); Focus on Living (Monthly); Harvest Home Show (Oct); Kern County Fair Guide (Sept).
Special Weekly Sections: Business (S); Homes (Sat); Eye on Entertainment (Thur).
Magazines: Parade (S); Latino Weekly Magazine (Weekly).
Broadcast Affiliations: NBC; FOX; ABC; CBS.
Pres./CEO ....Richard Beene
Chrmn. of the Board/Pub...Ginger F. Moorhouse
Sr. Vice Pres./CFO ....Motoko Komatsubara
Vice Pres., Sales/Circ./Mktg./Opns. ...John Wells
Vice Pres., HR ....Nancy Chaffin
Adv. Mgr., Display ....Anita Davis
Adv. Mgr., Classified ....Sally Ellis
Vice Pres., Audience Devel. .....Mary Lou Fulton
Circ. Mgr., Single Copy ....Ellen Rink
Vice Pres./Exec. Ed. ....Mike Jenner
Mng. Ed. ....Steve Mullen
Asst. Mng. Ed., Design/Prodn. ....James Bennett
Asst. Mng. Ed., Projects ....Lois Henry
Design Ed. ....Glenn Hammett
Editorial Page Ed. ....Dianne Hardisty
Lifestyles Ed. ....Jennifer Self
News Ed. ....Christine Peterson
Photo Dir. ....Alex Horvath
Sports Ed. ....Tony Lacava
Market Information: Split run; TMC.
Mechanical available: Offset; Black and 3 ROP colors; insert accepted - product samples, donation bags; page cutoffs - 22 1/20.
Mechanical Specifications: Type page 13 x 21; E - 6 cols, 2 1/16, 1/8 between; A - 6 cols, 2 1/16, 1/8 between; C - 10 cols, 1 3/8, 1/8 between.
Commodity Consumption: Avg. Page Number Per Issue - Daily 56; Avg. Page Number Per Issue - Plates Used 97260; Avg. Page Number Per Issue - Sunday 80; widths 27 1/4; Newsprint Used - Metric Tons 8503; Printing Ink Used - Black 183000; Printing Ink Used - Color 93000.
Equipment EDITORIAL: Front-end Software – QPS.; Editorial Hardware – APP/Mac, 40-APP/Mac G3, 51-APP/Mac G4; Editorial Printers – HP CLASSIFIED: Front-end Software – DTI/Class Speed.; Classified Hardware – 13-PC DISPLAY: Ad make-up applications – Multi-Ad/Creator, Adobe/Photoshop 4.0; Layout Software – MEI/ALS.; Display Hardware – APP/Mac G4; Display Printers – HP/DesignJet 75S, HP/5 MU PRODUCTION: Pagination Software – QPS/QuarkXPress.; Production Equipment – WL/Lith V, 2-AU/3850, 2-AII, AII/3850; Cameras – C/Spartan III, Walzberg, AG/8200; Scanners – Nikon, Kk PRESSROOM: Line 1 – 8-TKS/(4 half decks) 1983; Folders – 2-TKS/3:2; Pasters – 8 MAILROOM: Counter stackers – 3-HL/Monitor; Inserters and stuffers – Fg/8:1; Bundle tying machines – Power Strap/PL6; Addressing machine – Domino/Jet Array Ink Jet Printer.; Audio Hardware – Brite Voice Systems BUSINESS COMPUTERS: Business Software – PBS; Business Hardware – Sun/1000E

BANNING

THE RECORD GAZETTE

218 N. Murray, Banning, Calif., 92220; gen tel (951) 849-4586; adv tel (951) 849-4586 ext 30; ed tel (951) 849-4586 ext 29; gen fax (951) 849-2437; adv fax (951) 849-2437; ed fax (951) 849-2437; gen e-mail editor@recordgazette.net; adv e-mail sales@recordgazette.net; ed e-mail news@recordgazette.net; web site www.recordgazette.net
Published: Fri
Last Audit: March 21, 2007
Price: 5.25/mo; 22.00/yr.
Advertising: Open inch rate $11.00
Politics: Independent. **Established:** 1908
Not Published: New Year; Memorial Day; Independence Day; Labor Day; Thanksgiving; Christmas.
Special Editions: Home Improvement (Apr); Back to School (Aug); Our Town Newcomers (Jun); Pass Progress (Mar); Stagecoach Days (Oct); Oktoberfest (Sept).
Special Weekly Sections: Entertainment (Fri); Senior Citizens (Mon); Health (Thur); Home & Garden (Tues); Entertainment (Wed).
Magazines: Sun Lakes Life (Monthly).
Pub. ....Toebe Bush
Circ. Mgr. ....Richard Klein
Ed. ....Charles G. Ferrell
Prodn. Mgr. ....Cheri Mitchell
Prodn. Mgr., Pressroom ....Jose Bayron
Market Information: TMC.
Mechanical Specifications: Type page 11 1/2 x 21 1/2; E - 6 cols, 1 13/16, 1/8 between; A - 6 cols, 1 13/16, 1/16 between; C - 9 cols, 1 3/16, 1/8 between.
Commodity Consumption: Avg. Page Number Per Issue - Daily 14; Avg. Page Number Per Issue - Plates Used 3200; Newsprint Used - Metric Tons 130; Printing Ink Used - Black 3000; Printing Ink Used - Color 600; Printing Ink Used - Pages Printed 3650.
Equipment; Editorial Hardware – ScrippSat.; Classified Hardware – ScrippSat. DISPLAY: Ad make-up applications – Adobe/PageMaker, Adobe/Illustrator, Macromedia/Freehand, Microsoft/Word, Microsoft/Excel; Display Hardware – Negative/Scanner with built-in CD-Rom, Desktop/Scanners, CD-Roms (external); Display Printers – 2-HP/5MP, 1-Unity/1800 PRODUCTION: Pagination Software – Adobe/PageMaker 6.5.; Production Equipment – Caere/OmniPage Pro 5.0; Cameras – 1-K/Vertical PRESSROOM: Line 1 – 4-G/Community 1964; Folders – 1; Inserters and stuffers – MM/227; Bundle tying machines – 1/CyKlop; Addressing machine – 3-/Wm.; Business Hardware – DEC

BARSTOW

DESERT DISPATCH

130 Coolwater Ln., Barstow, Calif., 92311-3222; gen tel (760) 256-2257; adv tel (760) 256-2257; ed tel (760) 256-2257; gen fax (760) 256-0685; adv fax (760) 256-0685; ed fax (760) 256-0685; web site www.desertdispatch.com
Published: Mon, Tues, Wed, Thur, Fri, Sat, Sun
Weekday Frequency: m
Saturday Frequency: m
Circulation: 3,259; 3,259(sat); 28,565(sun)
Last Audit: September 30, 2009
Price: 2.11/wk; 91.35/yr; 8.45/4wk.
News services: AP.
Politics: Independent.
Note: The Barstow Desert Dispatch (mS) has a combination rate of $46.00 with the Victorville Daily Press (mS). The two papers publish a combined Sunday edition, the Press-Dispatch; the combination rate for the Press-Dispatch is $52.00. Individual newspaper rate
Not Published: New Year; Memorial Day; Independence Day; Labor Day; Thanksgiving; Christmas.
Special Editions: Exploring Barstow (Apr); Main St. USA (Aug); Letters to Santa (Dec); Presidents' Day (Feb); Gettysburg Address (Jan); Declaration of Independence (Jul); Parade of Homes (Jun); Battle Colors (Mar); Memorial Day (May); Veterans Day (Nov); Parade of Homes (O
Special Weekly Sections: Real Estate (Fri); Business Page (Mon); Religion Page (Sat); Food (Wed).
Magazines: Weekender Magazine (Fri); On TV (S).
Pub. ....Stephan Wingert
Finance Dir. ....Robert Fitzsimmons
Adv. Dir. ....Bea Lint
Promo. Sales Mgr. ....Barbara Miller
Ed. in Chief ....Scott Shackford
Women's Ed. ....Kay Lavato
Mgmt. Info Servs. Mgr. ....Josh Brunton
Online Mgr. ....David Schrimpf
Prodn. Mgr., Composing ....Harry Pontius
Circ. Dir. ....Jackie Parsons
Sports Ed. ....Matt Peter
Market Information: ADS.
Mechanical available: Web Offset; Black and 3 ROP colors; insert accepted; page cutoffs - 21 1/2.
Mechanical Specifications: Type page 14 x 22 3/4; E - 6 cols, 2 1/16, 1/8 between; A - 6 cols, 2 1/16, 1/8 between; C - 9 cols, 1 1/3, 1/8 between.
Commodity Consumption: Avg. Page Number Per Issue - Daily 12; Avg. Page Number Per Issue - Saturday 14; widths 12 1/2; Newsprint Used - Short Tons 270.
Equipment; Editorial Hardware – Software ☐ Baseview, QPS/QuarkXPress. CLASSIFIED: Front-end Software – Baseview.; Classified Hardware – Printers ☐ TI/Omni800 DISPLAY: Ad make-up applications – QPS/QuarkXPress, Aldus/PageMaker, Aldus/FreeHand, Claris/MacDraw; Layout Software – APP/Mac, Baseview.; Production Equipment – Baseview, QPS/QuarkXPress.; Business Hardware – Software ☐ PBS

BENICIA

BENICIA HERALD

820 First St., Benicia, Calif., 94510; gen tel (707) 745-0733; gen fax (707) 745-8583; gen e-mail beniciaherald@gmail.com
Group: U.S. Suburban Press, Inc.
Published: Tues, Wed, Thur, Fri, Sun
Weekday Frequency: m
Circulation: 2,707; 2,707(sun)
Last Audit: December 31, 2007
Price: 4.50/mo; 62.00/yr.
Advertising: Open inch rate $12.60
News services: Papert (Landon), U.S. Suburban Press Inc..
Politics: 1898
Not Published: New Year; Independence Day; Labor Day.
Special Weekly Sections: Entertainment (Thur).
Magazines: USA WEEKEND Magazine (S).
Adv. Mgr. ....Pam Poppe
Circ. Mgr. ....Joe Smith
Market Information: TMC.
Mechanical available: Offset; Black and 3 ROP colors; insert accepted; page cutoffs - 22 1/2.
Mechanical Specifications: Type page 12 1/2 x 21 1/2; E - 6 cols, 2, 1/8 between; A - 6 cols, 2, 1/8 between; C - 8 cols, 1 1/2, 1/8 between.
Commodity Consumption: Avg. Page Number Per Issue - Daily 14; Avg. Page Number Per Issue - Plates Used 3500; Avg. Page Number Per Issue - Sunday 22; widths 27; Newsprint Used - Metric Tons 175; Printing Ink Used - Black 5200.
Equipment EDITORIAL: Front-end Software – QPS/QuarkXPress.; Editorial Hardware – APP/Mac; Classified Hardware – IBM.; Layout Software – APP/Mac AdMaker. PRESSROOM: Line 1 – 8; Business Hardware – IBM/AS-400

CAMARILLO

VENTURA COUNTY STAR

550 Camarillo Center Dr., Camarillo, Calif., 93010-7700; gen tel (805) 437-0000; adv tel (805) 437-0000; ed tel (805) 437-0000; oth tel (800) 221-7827; gen fax (805) 437-0465; ed e-mail calendar@vcstar.com; web site www.vcstar.com
Group: E.W. Scripps Metro Suburbia, Inc./Newhouse Newspapers
Published: Mon, Tues, Wed, Thur, Fri, Sat, Sun
Weekday Frequency: m
Saturday Frequency: m
Circulation: 61,621; 65,776(sat); 91,827(sun)
Last Audit: ABC September 30, 2011
Price: 3.555/wk; 15.38/mo; 184.60/yr.
Advertising: Open inch rate $141.00
News services: AP, NYT, McClatchy, SHNS, MCT, NEA, TMS.
Politics: Independent. **Established:** 1925
Own facility?: Y
Special Editions: Extra! (TMC weekly)
The Lighthouse (Naval Base Ventura County County bi-weekly);
Siglo 21 (Spanish weekly);
I do! (January and July);
Spelling Bee (March);
Star Scholar Awards (April);
Readers' Choice (May);
Medical & Healthcare Directory (May);
Graduation (June)
Eldercare (July);
Ventura County Fair (August);
Living Here (October)
Breast Cancer Awareness (October);
Women Today (November);
Special Weekly Sections: Time Out (Fri); CARS (Sat.); Homes (Sun)
Magazines: Parade (S); Dash; Athlon Sports
Pres./Pub. ....George H. Cogswell
Dir., Finance ....Denice Atcheson
Adv. Mgr., Classified, Multimedia Nate Rodriguez
Adv. Mgr., Sales ....Art Williams
Dir., Mktg. ....Monica White
Circ. Dir., Home Delivery ....John Rotter
Circ. Dir., Sales/Retention ....Russ Briley
Circ. Mgr., Single Copy ....Maggie Browne
Mng. Ed. ....John Moore
Asst. Mng. Ed. ....Mike Blackwell
Asst. Mng. Ed. ....DeAnn Justesen
Bus. Ed. ....Jim Medina
Entertainment Ed. ....Mark Wyckoff
News Ed. ....Darrin Peschka
Photography Dir. ....Ray Meese
Adv. Sr. Vice Pres. ....Francesca Lewis
Circ. Vice Pres., Opns. ....Steven A. Smith
Vice Pres./Ed. ....Joe R. Howry
News Ed. ....Amanda Reiter
Opinion Page Ed. ....Marianne Ratcliff
Market Information: TMC; Zoned editions.
Mechanical available: Offset; Black and 3 ROP colors; insert accepted; page cutoffs - 22 3/4.
Mechanical Specifications: Type page 10 3/4 x 21 1/2; E - 6 cols, 1 35/50, 1/10 between; A - 6 cols, 1 35/50, 1/10 between; C - 10 cols, 98/100, 1/10 between.
Commodity Consumption: Avg. Page Number Per Issue - Daily 61.41; Avg. Page Number Per Issue - Plates Used 96000; Avg. Page Number Per Issue - Sunday 95.46; widths 50; Newsprint Used - Metric Tons 13573; Printing Ink Used - Black 300600; Printing Ink Used - Color 50136; Printin
Equipment EDITORIAL: Front-end Software – QPS, QPS/QuarkXPress 4.04.; Editorial Hardware – APP/PowerMac, APP/iMac; Editorial Equipment – Printers ☐ HP/4si mx, Data Products/Typhoon 6 CLASSIFIED: Front-end Software – AT.; Classified Hardware – Pentium/PCs, Compaq; Classified Printers – HP/4si mx DISPLAY: Ad make-up applications – QPS/QuarkXPress, Adobe/Photoshop, Adobe/Acrobat, Macromedia/Freehand, Adobe/PDF, Adobe/Illustrator; Layout Software – QPS/QuarkXPress, MEI/ALS, AT.; Display Hardware – APP/Power Mac; Display Printers – Typhoon, HP/755C Plotter, HP/Plotter 2500, QMS 2060 PRODUCTION: Pagination Software – QPS, MEI/ALS.; Production Equipment – Offset, 4-MS/NT Dec Alpha RIP; Cameras – 1-C/Spartan III; Scanners – 1-AII/3750, 1-Scitex/Smart 340L PRESSROOM: Line 1 – 10-TKS/3 Color Decks double width 1997; Folders – 1-TKS/Folder 3:2; Pasters – 10; Press registration system – ABB/WPC. MAILROOM: Counter stackers – 8-HL/Monitor, Fg, 2-QWI/Dual Halls; Inserters and stuffers – 2-NP/630, AM Graphics, HI/Finishing System; Bundle tying machines – 10/Sterling; Mailroom control system – Prima; Addressing machine – 1-/Domino Jet System.

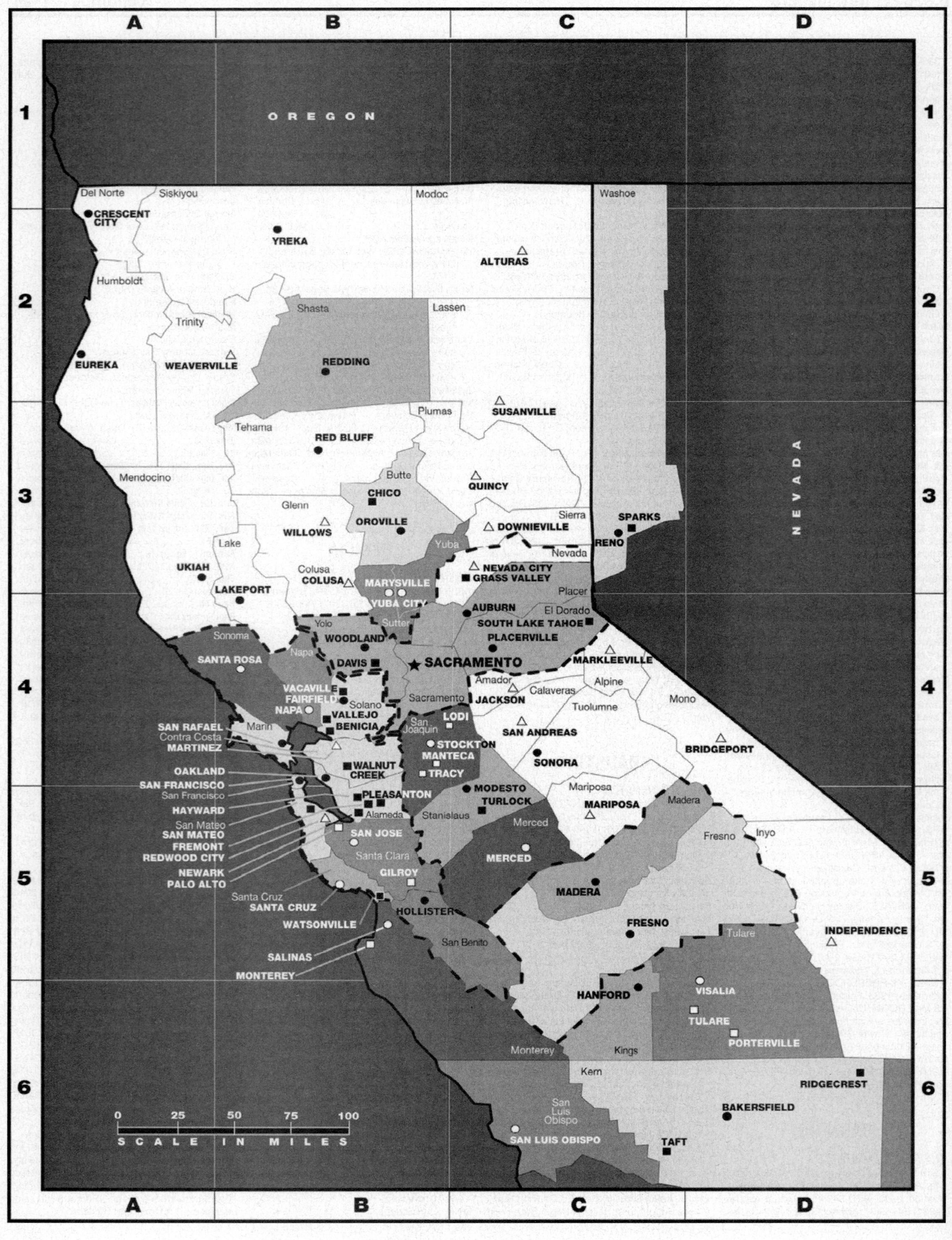
A
B
C
D
1
2
3
4
5
6
OREGON
NEVADA
Del Norte
CRESCENT CITY
Siskiyou
YREKA
Modoc
ALTURAS
Washoe
Humboldt
Trinity
EUREKA
WEAVERVILLE
Shasta
REDDING
Lassen
SUSANVILLE
Plumas
Tehama
RED BLUFF
Mendocino
Butte
CHICO
QUINCY
Glenn
OROVILLE
WILLOWS
DOWNIEVILLE
Sierra
SPARKS
RENO
Lake
Yuba
Nevada
UKIAH
Colusa
COLUSA
MARYSVILLE
NEVADA CITY
GRASS VALLEY
LAKEPORT
YUBA CITY
Placer
AUBURN
El Dorado
Yolo
Sutter
SOUTH LAKE TAHOE
Sonoma
WOODLAND
PLACERVILLE
Napa
SANTA ROSA
DAVIS
SACRAMENTO
MARKLEEVILLE
Amador
Alpine
VACAVILLE
FAIRFIELD
Calaveras
Sacramento
JACKSON
Mono
NAPA
Solano
Tuolumne
VALLEJO
BENICIA
SAN RAFAEL
Marin
San Joaquin
LODI
SAN ANDREAS
Contra Costa
MARTINEZ
STOCKTON
BRIDGEPORT
MANTECA
SONORA
WALNUT CREEK
OAKLAND
TRACY
SAN FRANCISCO
San Francisco
MODESTO
Mariposa
PLEASANTON
TURLOCK
HAYWARD
MARIPOSA
Madera
Alameda
Stanislaus
San Mateo
SAN MATEO
Merced
SAN JOSE
Inyo
FREMONT
Fresno
REDWOOD CITY
Santa Clara
MERCED
NEWARK
GILROY
PALO ALTO
MADERA
Santa Cruz
SANTA CRUZ
HOLLISTER
WATSONVILLE
FRESNO
INDEPENDENCE
Tulare
San Benito
SALINAS
MONTEREY
VISALIA
HANFORD
TULARE
PORTERVILLE
Monterey
Kings
Kern
RIDGECREST
BAKERSFIELD
San Luis Obispo
SAN LUIS OBISPO
TAFT
0
25
50
75
100
SCALE IN MILES

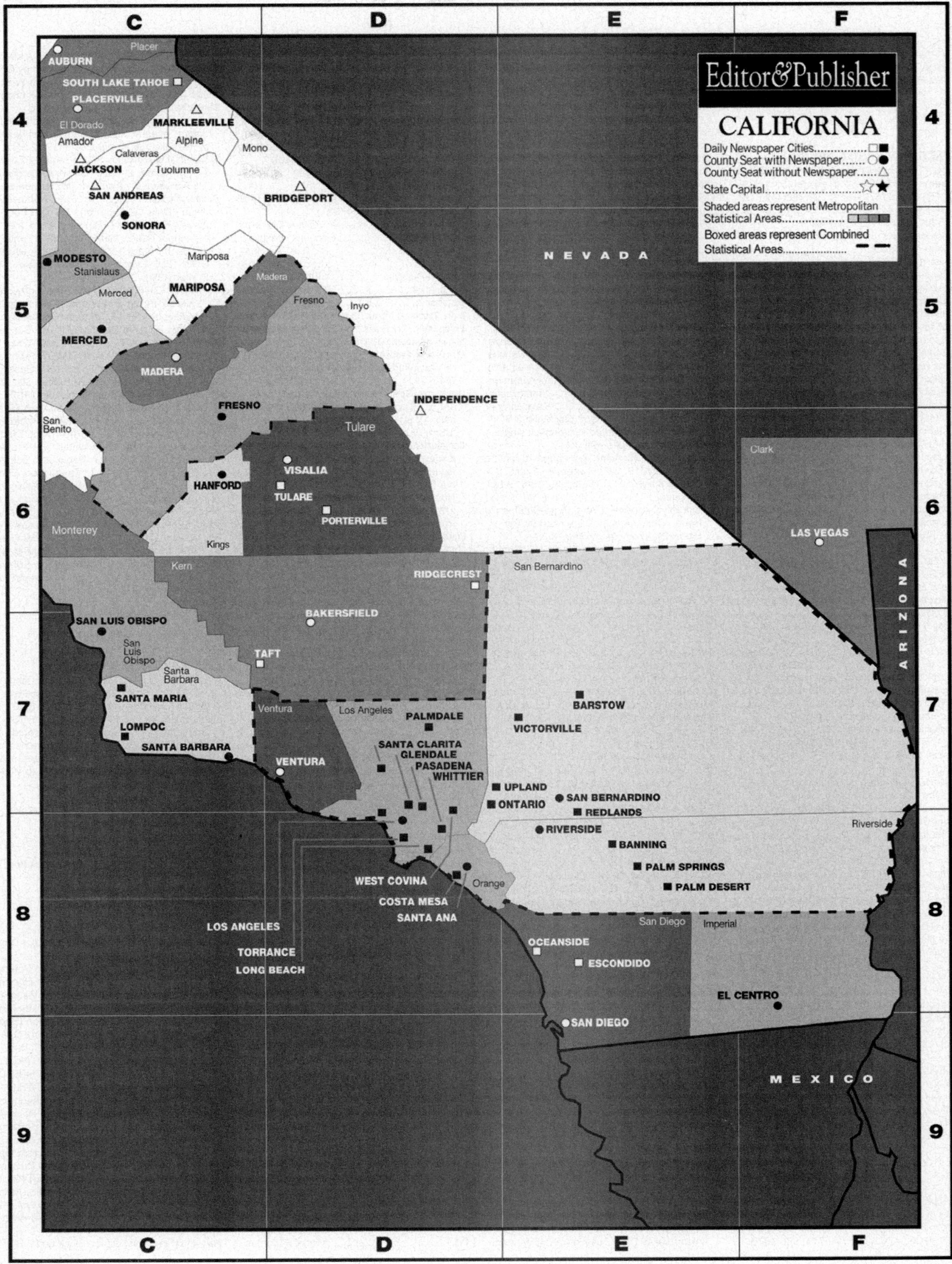

C
D
E
F
4
5
6
7
8
9
Editor&Publisher
CALIFORNIA
Daily Newspaper Cities
County Seat with Newspaper
County Seat without Newspaper
State Capital
Shaded areas represent Metropolitan Statistical Areas
Boxed areas represent Combined Statistical Areas
NEVADA
ARIZONA
MEXICO
AUBURN
Placer
SOUTH LAKE TAHOE
PLACERVILLE
El Dorado
MARKLEEVILLE
Amador
Alpine
Mono
Calaveras
JACKSON
Tuolumne
SAN ANDREAS
BRIDGEPORT
SONORA
MODESTO
Mariposa
Stanislaus
Madera
Merced
MARIPOSA
Fresno
Inyo
MERCED
MADERA
FRESNO
INDEPENDENCE
San Benito
Tulare
VISALIA
HANFORD
TULARE
PORTERVILLE
Monterey
Kings
Clark
LAS VEGAS
Kern
RIDGECREST
San Bernardino
SAN LUIS OBISPO
BAKERSFIELD
San Luis Obispo
TAFT
Santa Barbara
SANTA MARIA
BARSTOW
Ventura
Los Angeles
PALMDALE
VICTORVILLE
LOMPOC
SANTA CLARITA
GLENDALE
SANTA BARBARA
PASADENA
VENTURA
WHITTIER
UPLAND
SAN BERNARDINO
ONTARIO
REDLANDS
RIVERSIDE
Riverside
BANNING
PALM SPRINGS
WEST COVINA
Orange
PALM DESERT
COSTA MESA
SANTA ANA
LOS ANGELES
San Diego
Imperial
OCEANSIDE
TORRANCE
ESCONDIDO
LONG BEACH
EL CENTRO
SAN DIEGO

Zip Codes served: Ventura County
Delivery method: Mail, Newsstand, Private Carrier, Racks

CHICO

CHICO ENTERPRISE-RECORD

400 E. Park Ave., Chico, Calif., 95928-7127; gen tel (530) 891-1234; adv tel (530) 896-7751; ed tel (530) 896-7754; gen fax (530) 342-3617; adv fax (530) 891-9204; ed fax (530) 342-3617; gen e-mail chicoer@chicoer.com; web site www.chicoer.com
Group: MediaNews Group
Published: Mon, Tues, Wed, Thur, Fri, Sat, Sun
Weekday Frequency: m
Saturday Frequency: m
Circulation: 28,815; 30,522(sat); 32,072(sun)
Last Audit: ABC September 30, 2011
Price: 10.70/mo (carrier); 179.62/yr.
Advertising: Open inch rate $30.29
News services: AP, NEA, SHNS.
Politics: Independent.
Special Editions: Home & Garden Issue (Apr); University (Aug); Last Minute Gift Guide (Dec); Chico Outlook (Feb); Salute to Agriculture Tab (Mar); Silver Dollar Fair Tab (May); Senior's Tab (Monthly); Christmas Opening (Nov); Health & Wellness Tab (Quarterly); Chico Expo (
Magazines: Relish (Monthly); USA WEEKEND Magazine (S); TV Times (Sat).
Pub. ....Gregg McConnell
Controller ....Robert Gardner
Dir., HR ....Maureen Garrity
Ed ....David Little
City Ed. ....Steve Schoonover
News Ed. ....Michelle King
Sports Ed. ....Dave Davies
Online Dir. ....Fred Crosthwaite
Systems Mgr. ....Ray Kirk
Prodn. Foreman, Pressroom ....Sean Johnson
Circulation Director ....Jay Gillispie
Asst. to Pub. ....Natalie Noziska
Circ. Dir. ....Clay Eubank
Market Information: TMC; Zoned editions.
Mechanical available: Offset Press; Black and 3 ROP colors; insert accepted - flyers printed in-house; page cutoffs - 22.
Mechanical Specifications: Type page 10 1/4 x 21; E - 6 cols, 1 9/16, 1/8 between; A - 6 cols, 1 9/16, 1/8 between; C - 10 cols, 31/32, 1/16 between.
Commodity Consumption: Avg. Page Number Per Issue - Daily 25; Avg. Page Number Per Issue - Plates Used 45900; Avg. Page Number Per Issue - Saturday 37.5; Avg. Page Number Per Issue - Sunday 50; widths 25; Newsprint Used - Metric Tons 2760; Printing Ink Used - Black 48000; Prin
Equipment EDITORIAL: Front-end Software – Baseview, QPS/QuarkXPress.; Editorial Hardware – APP/Mac CLASSIFIED: Front-end Software – Baseview.; Classified Hardware – APP/Mac; Layout Software – Baseview.; Display Hardware – APP/Mac; Display Printers – Software ◻ Multi-Ad/Creator, Adobe/Photoshop, QPS/QuarkXPress PRODUCTION: Pagination Software – Baseview, QPS/QuarkXPress.; Production Equipment – 2-Pre Press/Panther Imagesetter, 1-OLEC/OV 33 HD; Cameras – 1-R/LE PRESSROOM: Line 1 – 4-MAN/Uniman 4 x 2 (2 color decks, double width); Folders – 2; Pasters – 4-MEG. MAILROOM: Counter stackers – 2-HL/Monitor, 1/QWI; Inserters and stuffers – 2-/MM; Bundle tying machines – 1-/MLN, I-/It; Addressing machine – 3-/Wm.; Business Hardware – CJ
Delivery method: Mail, Newsstand, Private Carrier, Racks

COSTA MESA

DAILY PILOT

1375 Sunflower Ave., Costa Mesa, Calif., 92626-1665; gen tel (714) 966-4600; adv tel (714) 966-4663; gen fax (714) 966-4679; adv fax (714) 966-4675; gen e-mail dailypilot@latimes.com; web site www.dailypilot.com
Published: Tues, Wed, Thur, Fri, Sat, Sun
Weekday Frequency: m
Saturday Frequency: m
Circulation: 24,600; 29,500(sat); 29,500(sun)
Last Audit: March 5, 2008
Price: 2.65/wk; 30.00/mo; 104.00/yr.
Advertising: Open inch rate $29.90
News services: Papert (Landon), U.S. Suburban Press Inc..
Politics: Independent.
Special Editions: Healthy, Wealthy & Wise (Apr); New Year (Dec); Annual Almanac (Feb); Healthy, Wealthy & Wise (Jan); Healthy, Wealthy & Wise (Jul); Menu Guide (Jun); Toshiba Senior Golf Classic (Mar); Student Design-an-Ad (May); Gift Guide (Nov); Top 103 (Sept).
Special Weekly Sections: Auto Pilot (Sat).
Magazines: Real Estate (Sat).
Adv. Dir. ....Lisa Cosenza
Ed. ....John Canalis
City Ed. ....Imran Vittachi
News Ed. ....Paul Anderson
Photo Ed. ....Mark Dustin
Sports Ed. ....Steve Virgen
Mechanical available: Offset; Black and 3 ROP colors; insert accepted - card stock single sheet; page cutoffs - 22 3/4.
Mechanical Specifications: Type page 13 x 21; E - 6 cols, 2 1/16, 1/8 between; A - 6 cols, 2 1/16, 1/8 between; C - 10 cols, 1 3/8, 1/16 between.
Commodity Consumption: Avg. Page Number Per Issue - Daily 14; Avg. Page Number Per Issue - Saturday 24; widths 13 3/4; Newsprint Used - Metric Tons 1319; Printing Ink Used - Black 36800; Printing Ink Used - Color 16000.
Equipment EDITORIAL: Front-end Software – QPS, Dewar/System with QuarkXPress.; Editorial Hardware – Ik, Dewar/Sys IV, APP/Mac, PC; Editorial Equipment – Output, AG/Accuset 1500; Editorial Printers – HP/LaserJet 4MV, HP/LaserJet 5P CLASSIFIED: Front-end Software – Intertext.; Classified Hardware – PC; Classified Printers – HP/Laser, V/with Tegra Controller DISPLAY: Ad make-up applications – Multi-Ad/Creator, QPS/QuarkXPress, Adobe/Photoshop; Layout Software – MEI/ALS.; Display Hardware – APP/Mac 8100; Display Printers – HP/LaserJet 4MV, APP/Mac LaserWriter 630, HP/8000, Cyclone; Production Equipment – 2-V, 1-Nu/UPNS, 1-BKY/Adlux 5KW; Cameras – 1-Ik/530 Stat camera; Scanners – AG/6100 Stat Camera, Howtek/Color Scanner. PRESSROOM: Line 1 – 8-HI/N1600; Folders – 1-HI/2:1; Pasters – 7-MEG/500; Reels and Stands – 7-MEG/500. MAILROOM: Counter stackers – 2-Id/NS440; Inserters and stuffers – 1-S/24P; Bundle tying machines – 2-MLN/MLN2A; Addressing machine – 1-El/8000-1. BUSINESS COMPUTERS: Business Software – CJ/OP; Business Hardware – HP/3000

COVINA

SAN GABRIEL VALLEY TRIBUNE

1210 Azusa Canyon Rd., West Covina, Calif., 91790; gen tel (626) 962-8811; gen fax (626) 962-8849; adv fax (626) 795-5515; ed fax (626) 338-9157; gen e-mail news.tribune@sgvn.com; web site www.sgvtribune.com
Published: Mon, Tues, Wed, Thur, Fri, Sat, Sun
Weekday Frequency: m
Saturday Frequency: m
Circulation: 58,632; 33,937(sat); 80,022(sun)
Last Audit: ABC September 30, 2011
Price: 36.00/2mo.
News services: AP, CNS, MCT, Scripps-McClatchy, BPI, DJ, TMS, NYT.
Politics: Independent.
Note: The Los Angeles Newspaper Group includes the Long Beach Press-Telegram (mS), Los Angeles Daily News (mS), Ontario Inland Valley Daily Bulletin (mS), Pasadena Star-News (mS), Redlands Daily Facts (eS), San Bernardino County Sun (mS), San Gabriel Valley Tri
Special Editions: The Body (Apr); Local Business (Aug); The Rose Magazine (Dec); The Body (Jan); Seen Magazine (Jul); Health Beat (Jun); Health Beat (Mar); Water Awareness (May); Holiday Guide (Nov); The Body (Oct); College & Prep Football (Sept).
Special Weekly Sections: Career Site (S); Home Buyer (Sat).
Magazines: Relish (Monthly); U Magazine (mS) (Other); TV Magazine (S).
Pub. ....Steve Lambert
HR/Admin. Mgr. ....Rachel A. Vasquez
Mng. Ed. ....Steve Hunt
Bus. Ed. ....Kevin Smith
Editorial Page Ed. ....Steve Scauzillo
Features Ed. ....Catherine Gaugh
Librarian ....Sharon Brawley
Mgr., Technical Servs. ....Terry Frazier
Prodn. Mgr., Pre Press ....Pedro Garcia
Market Information: ADS; TMC.
Mechanical available: Offset; Black and 3 ROP colors; insert accepted; page cutoffs - 22 3/4.
Mechanical Specifications: Type page 11 1/2 x 21 1/4; E - 6 cols, 1 13/16, 1/8 between; A - 6 cols, 1 13/16, 1/8 between; C - 10 cols, 1 1/6, 1/16 between.
Commodity Consumption: Avg. Page Number Per Issue - Daily 46; Avg. Page Number Per Issue - Plates Used 65038; Avg. Page Number Per Issue - Saturday 86; Avg. Page Number Per Issue - Sunday 84; widths 12 1/2; Newsprint Used - Metric Tons 4993; Printing Ink Used - Black 102469; P
Equipment EDITORIAL: Front-end Software – SII/Editorial.; Editorial Hardware – SII/Server Net; Editorial Equipment – 75-SII/Coyote 3, 2-SII/PC; Editorial Printers – 5-HP CLASSIFIED: Front-end Software – SII/Czar II.; Classified Hardware – 1-SII/Server Net; Classified Equipment – 27-SII/Coyote 3; Classified Printers – 3-HP DISPLAY: Ad make-up applications – SII/IAL; Layout Software – SII/IAL, 4-Compaq/Ring Stations.; Display Hardware – 6-APP/Mac, 3-Compaq; Display Printers – Proofers, HP PRODUCTION: Pagination Software – SII/INL 9.2.; Production Equipment – 2-AIL/3850, 2-Polaroid, QPS; Cameras – 1-Spartan/III, 1-C/Newspager, 1-C/Spartan III; Scanners – 2-Lf/Leafscan 35, 10-Compaq, 2-Polaroid PRESSROOM: Line 1 – 7-G/HO 1989; Line 2 – Jul-90; Folders – 3; Pasters – 14; Reels and Stands – 14; Press control system – G/MPCS. MAILROOM: Counter stackers – 5-Id/2000, 2-Id/440, 1/QWI; Inserters and stuffers – 4-GMA/SLS 1000; Bundle tying machines – 8-/Power Strap/PSN5, 2-/Dynaric; Wrapping singles – Addressing machine ◻ 2-Videojet/VMS. BUSINESS COMPUTERS: Business Software – CJ, Ultipro (Payroll); Business Hardware – HP/969

CRESCENT CITY

THE DAILY TRIPLICATE

312 H St., Crescent City, Calif., 95531; gen tel (707) 464-2141; adv tel (707) 464-2141; ed tel (707) 464-2141; gen fax (707) 464-5102; adv fax (707) 464-5102; ed fax (707) 464-5102; gen e-mail tripnews@triplicate.com; web site www.triplicate.com
Published: Tues, Wed, Thur, Fri, Sat
Weekday Frequency: m
Saturday Frequency: m
Circulation: 4,738; 5,850(sat)
Last Audit: September 30, 2008
Price: 1.75/wk; 7.00/mo; 66.00/yr.
Advertising: Open inch rate $16.80
News services: AP.
Politics: Independent.
Not Published: New Year; Thanksgiving; Christmas.
Special Editions: Fair (Aug); Bridal (Jan); July 4 (Jul); Vacation (May); Car Care (Oct).
Special Weekly Sections: TV Magazine (Sat).
Pub. ....Michele Thomas
Adv. Mgr. ....Cindy Vosburg
Circ. Mgr. ....Tammy Britt
Ed. ....Richard Wiens
Prodn. Mgr., Opns ....John Johnson
Market Information: ADS; Split run; TMC.
Mechanical available: Offset; Black and 3 ROP colors; insert accepted - samples, at newspaper's discretion; page cutoffs - 22 3/4.
Mechanical Specifications: Type page 13 x 21 1/2; E - 6 cols, 2, 1/6 between; A - 6 cols, 2, 1/6 between; C - 9 cols, 1 3/8, 1/12 between.
Commodity Consumption: Avg. Page Number Per Issue - Daily 17; Avg. Page Number Per Issue - Plates Used 7800; widths 13 1/2; Newsprint Used - Metric Tons 358; Printing Ink Used - Black 10600; Printing Ink Used - Color 1300; Printing Ink Used - Pages Printed 4398.
Equipment EDITORIAL: Front-end Software – QPS/QuarkXPress 3.32, Adobe/Photoshop 6.0, Adobe/Illustrator 8.0.; Editorial Hardware – 7-APP/Mac; Editorial Equipment – HP/Scanner; Editorial Printers – APP/Mac LaserWriter IIq, HP/LaserWriter IV M CLASSIFIED: Front-end Software – QPS/QuarkXPress 3.31, Baseview 2.2.; Classified Hardware – APP/Mac; Classified Printers – APP/Mac LaserWriter IIg DISPLAY: Ad make-up applications – QPS/QuarkXPress 3.32, Adobe/Illustrator 8.0, Adobe/Photoshop 6.0; Display Hardware – APP/Mac; Display Printers – APP/Mac LaserWriter IIg, HP LaserWriter 4M PRODUCTION: Pagination Software – QPS/QuarkXPress 4.0.; Production Equipment – HP/LaserJet 400 MV, Konica/Imagesetter; Cameras – SCREEN; Scanners – HP PRESSROOM: Line 1 – 6-G/Community single width 1989. MAILROOM: Counter stackers – 1-HL/Monitor; Inserters and stuffers – 1-Mc/5-into-1; Bundle tying machines – EAM-Mosca. BUSINESS COMPUTERS: Business Software – Microsoft/Excel, WordPerfect, Microsoft/Word; Business Hardware – PC Clone

DAVIS

THE DAVIS ENTERPRISE

315 G St., Davis, Calif., 95616; gen tel (530) 756-0800; adv tel (530) 756-0800; ed tel (530) 756-0800; gen fax (530) 756-6707; adv fax (530) 756-6707; ed fax (530) 756-1668; gen e-mail newsroom@davisenterprise.net; graphics@davisenterprise.net; adv e-mail ads@davisenterprise.net; ed e-mail newsroom@davisenterprise.net; web site www.davisenterprise.com
Group: U.S. Suburban Press, Inc.
Published: Mon, Tues, Wed, Thur, Fri, Sun
Weekday Frequency: e
Circulation: 8,031; 8,142(sun)
Last Audit: September 30, 2009
Price: 1.97/wk (plus tax); 7.88/mo (plus tax); 95.00/yr (plus tax).
Advertising: Open inch rate $21.20
News services: AP, NYT, SHNS.
Politics: 1897
Not Published: New Year; Presidents' Day; Memorial Day; Independence Day; Labor Day; Thanksgiving; Christmas.
Special Editions: Picnic Day (Apr); Yolo County Fair (Aug); Holiday Gift Guide (Dec); Design an Ad (Jan); All in the Family (Jul); Visitors Guide (Jun); Best of Yolo (Mar); Holiday Gift Guide (Nov); California Man Triathlon (Sept).
Special Weekly Sections: Automotive (Fri); Special Features (S); Restaurant (Thur); Business Focus (Tues); Best Food Day (Wed).
Magazines: Relish (Monthly); USA WEEKEND Magazine (S); Weekend Magazine (Thur).
Pub./Vice Pres./Sec. ....Burt McNaughton
Adv. Dir. ....Nancy Hannell
Arts Ed. ....Derrick Bang
Automotive Ed. ....Staci Dennis
Educ./Schools Ed. ....Jeff Hudson
Living/Lifestyle Ed. ....Linda DuBois
Photo Ed. ....Wayne Tilcock
Political/Gov't Ed. ....Debbie Davis
Religion Ed. ....Cory Golden
Prodn. Foreman, Pressroom ....Richard White
Market Information: TMC.
Mechanical available: Offset; Black and 3 ROP

colors; insert accepted; page cutoffs - 21 1/2.
Mechanical Specifications: Type page 11 9/10 x 21; E - 6 cols, 1 7/8, 1/8 between; A - 6 cols, 1 7/8, 1/8 between; C - 10 cols, 1 3/16, 1/16 between.
Commodity Consumption: Avg. Page Number Per Issue - Daily 28; Avg. Page Number Per Issue - Sunday 48; widths 25; Newsprint Used - Short Tons 1300; Printing Ink Used - Pages Printed 8596.
Equipment EDITORIAL: Front-end Software – Baseview, QPS/QuarkXPress.; Editorial Hardware – APP/Mac G4; Editorial Printers – AG/Imagesetters, IPTech/RIP CLASSIFIED: Front-end Software – Baseview, QPS/QuarkXPress.; Classified Hardware – APP/Mac G4; Classified Printers – Hyphen/RIP, AG/Accuset 1000, HP/5000 DISPLAY: Ad make-up applications – Corel Draw, Adobe/Photoshop, QPS/QuarkXPress; Layout Software – QPS/QuarkXPress.; Display Hardware – Pentium/PC; Display Printers – HP/4M, AG/Imagesetters, Hyphen/RIP, Tektronix/850 (Color) PRODUCTION: Pagination Software – QPS/QuarkXPress 4.04.; Production Equipment – Lf/AP Leaf Picture Desk, AG/Accuset, I P Tech/RIP; Cameras – 1-Acti/204D, Kk/RFS 2035+; Scanners – HP/ScanJet 4C, Polaroid/Sprint Scan PRESSROOM: Line 1 – 10-G/SC; Line 2 – 1-G/U; Folders – 1 MAILROOM: Counter stackers – BG/108; Inserters and stuffers – 1-KAN/480, 1-KAN/Multi-feed; Bundle tying machines – 3-MLN/ML2EE. BUSINESS COMPUTERS: Business Software – Microsoft/Word, Lotus, Vision Data; Business Hardware – Sun/Sparc II server

DANVILLE

SAN RAMON VALLEY TIMES

524 Hartz Ave, Danville, Calif., 94506; gen tel (925) 743-2202
Group: MediaNews Group Inc

EL CENTRO

IMPERIAL VALLEY PRESS

205 N. Eighth St., El Centro, Calif., 92243; gen tel (760) 337-3400; adv tel (760) 337-3430; ed tel (760) 337-3425; gen fax (760) 353-3003; adv e-mail advertising@ivpressonline.com; ed e-mail editor@ivpressonline.com; web site www.ivpressonline.com
Published: Mon, Tues, Wed, Thur, Fri, Sat, Sun
Saturday Frequency: m
Circulation: 8,911; 8,911(sat); 9,854(sun)
Last Audit: September 30, 2009
Price: 9.00/mo (carrier); 100.00/yr (carrier).
Advertising: Open inch rate $27.50
News services: AP.
Politics: Independent. **Established:** 1901
Special Editions: Women of Imperial Valley (Aug); California Midwinter Fair (Feb); Inland Empire (Jan); County Progress (Jul); Graduation (Jun); Sweet Onion Festival (May); Business Journal (Monthly); Cattle Call Tab (Oct); Football Preview (Sept).
Special Weekly Sections: Church Page (Fri); Lifestyles (S); Youth Page (Sat); Farm Page (Thur); Food Page (Tues).
Magazines: Relish (Monthly); TV Plus (TV Guide) (S); American Profile (Tues).
Pres./Pub. ....Teresa Zimmer
Adv. Dir. ....Tracy Kelley
Ed. ....Brad Jennings
Graphics Ed. ....Joan Duncan-Bush
News Ed. ....Peggy Dale
Sports Ed. ....Mario Renteria
Market Information: ADS; TMC.
Mechanical available: Offset; Black and 3 ROP colors; insert accepted; page cutoffs - 22 3/4.
Mechanical Specifications: Type page 11 3/5 x 21 1/2; E - 6 cols, 1 4/5, 1/8 between; A - 6 cols, 1 4/5, 1/8 between; C - 9 cols, 1 1/5, 4/5 between.

Commodity Consumption: Avg. Page Number Per Issue - Daily 26; Avg. Page Number Per Issue - Plates Used 52000; Avg. Page Number Per Issue - Sunday 40; widths 12 1/2; Newsprint Used - Short Tons 725; Printing Ink Used - Black 21000; Printing Ink Used - Color 10500; Printing Ink
Equipment EDITORIAL: Front-end Software – ACT, Microsoft/Word 6.0, QPS/QuarkXPress 3.3.; Editorial Hardware – PC; Editorial Equipment – AG/Accuset 1000; Editorial Printers – 2-Xante/Accel-a-Writer CLASSIFIED: Front-end Software – ACT.; Classified Hardware – PC; Classified Equipment – Xante; Classified Printers – AG/Imagesetter, Graphic Enterprises/Pro Setter 1000 DISPLAY: Ad make-up applications – Mk/Managing Editor 2.0; Layout Software – MEI/ALS.; Display Hardware – PC; Display Printers – Graphic Enterprises/Pro Setter 1000, LaserMaster/Unity 1800XL-0 PRODUCTION: Pagination Software – QPS/QuarkXPress 4.1.; Production Equipment – 2-Xante/Accel-a-Writer 8200, AG/Accuset 1000; Cameras – Companica; Scanners – AG/Flatbed PRESSROOM: Line 1 – G/Urbanite 1061; Line 2 – G/Urbanite 1061; Line 3 – G/Urbanite 1061; Line 4 – G/Urbanite 1061; Line 5 – G/Urbanite 1061; Line 6 – G/Urbanite 1061; Line 7 – G/Urbanite 1061; Folders – 1; Pasters – Folders ÂD 1. MAILROOM: Counter stackers – 2/HL; Inserters and stuffers – 2-/KAN; Bundle tying machines – Sterling. BUSINESS COMPUTERS: Business Software – PBS; Business Hardware – Sun/PC Server

ESCONDIDO

NORTH COUNTY TIMES

207 E. Pennsylvania Ave., Escondido, Calif., 92025; gen tel (760) 839-3333; adv tel (760) 740-3541; ed tel (760) 839-3333; gen fax (760) 740-5454; adv fax (760) 740-5464; ed fax (760) 745-3769; ed e-mail kdavy@nctimes.com; web site www.nctimes.com
Group: U.S. Suburban Press, Inc.
Published: Mon, Tues, Wed, Thur, Fri, Sat, Sun
Weekday Frequency: m
Saturday Frequency: m
Circulation: 75,727; 53,422(sat); 80,920(sun)
Last Audit: ABC September 30, 2011
Price: 2.94/wk (carrier); 11.90/mo; 142.80/yr (carrier).
Advertising: Open inch rate $91.00
News services: AP, MCT, NYT, Cox News Service.
Politics: Independent. **Established:** 1995
Special Editions: Last Minute Gift Guide (Dec); San Diego Auto Show (Jun).
Special Weekly Sections: Trips/Places (S).
Magazines: Parade (S); Preview (entertainment guide) (Thur).
Profile: Suburban daily newspaper whose emphasis is on local news in North County and Southwest Riverside county.
Pub. ....Peter York
Pub., Temecula ....Haward Wahl
Finance Dir. ....Jim Eruinfma
HR Dir. ....Peggy Chapman
Adv. Dir. ....Pam Rumer
Circ. Dir. ....Mark Henschen
Ed. ....Kent Davy
Mng. Ed. ....W. Russell Harris
Mng. Ed. ....Dan McSwain
Asst. Mng. Ed., Online ....Michael Donnelly
City Ed., Coastal ....Melanie Marshall
City Ed., Inland ....Bob Masingale
Features Ed. ....Laura Groch
Sports Ed. ....Loren Nelson
Online Dir. ....Brett Sondrup
IT Mgr. ....Bill Pavich
Prodn. Dir. ....Doug Ranes
Prodn. Mgr. ....Stephanie Woodard
Market Information: ADS; TMC; Zoned editions.
Mechanical available: Offset; Black and 3 ROP colors; insert accepted; page cutoffs - 22.
Mechanical Specifications: Type page 13 x 21; E - 6 cols, 2, 1/6 between; A - 6 cols, 2, 1/6 between; C - 10 cols, 1 1/4, 1/24 between.
Commodity Consumption: Avg. Page Number Per Issue - Daily 45; Avg. Page Number Per Issue - Plates Used 180000; Avg. Page Number Per Issue - Saturday 45; Avg. Page Number Per Issue - Sunday 66; widths 25; Newsprint Used - Metric Tons 10800; Printing Ink Used - Black 122206; Pri
Equipment EDITORIAL: Front-end Software – Microsoft/Windows 95, QPS/QuarkXPress, Lotus Notes 4.64.; Editorial Hardware – IBM/Thinkpad, APP/Mac, PC; Editorial Equipment – Nikon/D1; Editorial Printers – Lexmark/2080, IBM/Optra, HP/500 CLASSIFIED: Front-end Software – Lotus/Notes 4.64, Microsoft/Windows NT.; Classified Hardware – IBM/PC, APP/Mac G3; Classified Printers – Lexmark/2080 DISPLAY: Ad make-up applications – Microsoft/Windows 95; Layout Software – SCS/Layout.; Display Hardware – IBM/PC, APP/Mac; Display Printers – HP/4 PRODUCTION: Pagination Software – QPS/QuarkXPress 4.0.; Production Equipment – 3-Lf/AP Leaf Picture Desk, 1-1 Step Anitec/Plate Processor; Scanners – 2-Epson/836X2, 3-Kk/PFS 2035, 2-Epson/2450 PRESSROOM: Line 1 – 5-G/HO (3 half decks) 1990; Line 2 – 7-G/HO (3 half decks); Press Drives – 5-Allen/Bradley/Digital, 6-Fin/Analog; Folders – 2-G/2:1, 2-G/3:2; Pasters – 5-G/CT-45. MAILROOM: Counter stackers – 3-Id/2000, 2-HL/Monitor, 1-MM/310, 1/HL; H4; Inserters and stuffers – 2-GMA/SLS 1000 6:1, 2-MM/Byliners 6:1; Bundle tying machines – 4-/Dynaric; Other equipment –Bottom Wrap, 3-Id, 2-/QWI, 1-MM/Stitcher-Trimmer. BUSINESS COMPUTERS: Business Software – DB: S, Unix-Vision Data; Business Hardware – PC

EUREKA

MEDIA NEWS GROUP

PO Box 3580, Eureka, Calif., 95502-3580; gen tel (707) 441-0500; gen fax (707) 441-0565

TIMES-STANDARD

930 6th St., Eureka, Calif., 95501-1112; gen tel (707) 441-0500; adv fax (707) 441-0565; ed fax (707) 441-0501; ed e-mail editor@times-standard.com; web site www.times-standard.com
Published: Mon, Tues, Wed, Thur, Fri, Sat, Sun
Weekday Frequency: m
Saturday Frequency: m
Circulation: 18,436; 17,499(sat); 19,757(sun)
Last Audit: ABC September 30, 2011
Price: 12.30/mo; 134.07/yr.
Advertising: Open inch rate $34.75
News services: AP.
Politics: Independent. **Established:** 1854
Special Editions: Vacation the North Coast (Apr); Humboldt County Fair Tab (Aug); Gift Guide (Dec); Spring Bridal (Feb); Fact Book (Jun); Best Of (Mar); Design-an-Ad (May); Women in Business Tab (Oct); Football Preview (Sept).
Special Weekly Sections: TV Times (S); Northern Lights (Thur); Senior Citizens (Tues).
Magazines: Relish (Monthly); USA WEEKEND Magazine (S).
Pub. ....Dave Kuta
Controller ....Claudette Lemon
Adv. Dir. ....Shonnie Bradbury
Display Adv. Dir. ....Zach Harrington
Circ./Mktg. Dir. ....Peter Fennell
Mng. Ed. ....Kimberly Wear
City Ed. ....James Faulk
Copy Desk Chief ....Cheryl Karnes
Copy Ed. ....Jessica Richelderfer
Entertainment Ed. ....Chris Durant
Lifestyle Ed. ....Heather Shelton
Photo Ed. ....Rich Bickel
Restore/Preserve Ed. ....Kathy Dillon
Sports Ed. ....Ray Aspuria
Interactive Mgr. ....Jeffrey Soderberg
Prodn. Dir. ....Jason Kennedy
Mailroom Mgr. ....Mike Styczinski
Market Information: ADS; TMC.
Mechanical available: Offset; Black and 3 ROP colors; insert accepted - bags, samples; page cutoffs - 21 1/2.
Mechanical Specifications: Type page 11 13/16 x 21 1/2; E - 6 cols, 1 5/8, 1/8 between; A - 6 cols, 1 7/8, 1/8 between; C - 10 cols, 1 1/4, 1/16 between.
Commodity Consumption: Avg. Page Number Per Issue - Daily 28; Avg. Page Number Per Issue - Plates Used 16000; Avg. Page Number Per Issue - Saturday 28; Avg. Page Number Per Issue - Sunday 48; widths 12 1/2; Newsprint Used - Short Tons 1680; Printing Ink Used - Black 38000; Pri
Equipment EDITORIAL: Front-end Software – QPS/QuarkXPress 6.0.; Editorial Hardware – 18-Mk, 20-APP/Mac; Editorial Equipment – 4-APP/Mac G3 Server; Editorial Printers – Canon/Imagerunner 330 CLASSIFIED: Front-end Software – Baseview/Ad Manager Pro 2.0.; Classified Hardware – 6-APP/iMac; Classified Equipment – 4-APP/iMac; Classified Printers – APP/Mac LaserWriter DISPLAY: Ad make-up applications – Multi-Ad/Creator 2; Layout Software – 6-APP/Mac G3.; Display Printers – Konica/Marlin PRODUCTION: Pagination Software – QPS/QuarkXPress 6.0, MEI/ALS 2.5, Baseview/NewsEdit Pro 3.2.1.; Production Equipment – HP/LaserJet 8100N, Epson/Color Printer 7500; Cameras – 1-R/432 Mark II, 1-LE/121 PRESSROOM: Line 1 – 8-G/Urbanite 1990; Folders – G/2:1. MAILROOM: Counter stackers – 2/MM; Inserters and stuffers – 2-/MM; Bundle tying machines – 1-MLN/ML1EE; Wrapping singles – 1-Am/1997B; Addressing machine – GEAC; Other equipment – MM/Stitcher-Trimmer. BUSINESS COMPUTERS: Business Software – Microsoft/Office; Business Hardware – NewzWare, GEAC

FAIRFIELD

DAILY REPUBLIC

1250 Texas St., Fairfield, Calif., 94533; gen tel (707) 425-4646; gen fax (707) 425-5924; adv e-mail drads@dailyrepublic.net (Retail); drclass@dailyrepublic.net (Classified); web site www.dailyrepublic.com
Published: Mon, Tues, Wed, Thur, Fri, Sat, Sun
Weekday Frequency: m
Saturday Frequency: m
Circulation: 17,089; 17,089(sat); 18,123(sun)
Last Audit: September 30, 2009
Price: 10.20/mo; 122.40/yr (carrier), $135.29 (mail, in-county).
Advertising: Open inch rate $27.47
News services: AP, NYT, SHNS.
Politics: Independent.
Advertising not accepted: Tobacco.
Special Editions: American Home Week (Apr); Annual Welcome (Aug); Thanksgiving Morning (Nov); Cookbook (Oct); Solano Seniors (Other); Solano Summer (Summer).
Special Weekly Sections: Automobiles (Fri); Religion (S); Religion (Sat); Best Food Day (Wed).
Magazines: Relish (Monthly); USA WEEKEND Magazine (S); Real Estate Magazine (Sat); American Profile (Weekly).
Pres./CEO ....Foy McNaughton
Pub. ....Bill James
Adv. Dir. ....Sharon Guy
Adv. Mgr., Nat'l ....Brian Kermoade
Tailwind Ed. ....Nick DeCicco
Asst. Sports Ed. ....Brian Arnold
Copy Ed. ....Susan Winslow
Design Ed. ....Maureen Fissolo
News Ed. ....Shawn Miller
Online/Projects Ed. ....Kathleen L'Ecluse
Photo Ed. ....Brad Zweerink
Sports Ed. ....Paul Farmer
IT Dir. ....Joe Boydston
Opns. Dir. ....T. Burt McNaughton
Prodn. Foreman, Pressroom ....Larry Mammen
Market Information: TMC.
Mechanical available: Offset; Black and 3 ROP colors; insert accepted - all types; page cutoffs - 22 3/4.
Mechanical Specifications: Type page 11 7/8 x 21 3/8; E - 6 cols, 1 7/8, 1/8 between; A - 6 cols, 1 7/8, 1/8 between; C - 10 cols, 1 3/16, 1/8 between.
Commodity Consumption: Avg. Page Number Per Issue - Daily 42; Avg. Page Number Per

Issue - Plates Used 8320; Avg. Page Number Per Issue - Sunday 68; widths 25; Newsprint Used - Metric Tons 1700; Printing Ink Used - Pages Printed 1640.
Equipment EDITORIAL: Front-end Software – Baseview/NewsEdit Pro IQUE.; Editorial Hardware – APP/Mac G4, APP/Mac G3; Editorial Equipment – IPTech/Turbo RIP CLASSIFIED: Front-end Software – Baseview.; Classified Hardware – 10-APP/Mac; Classified Printers – HP/4MV; Layout Software – 3-COM/Dawn (online), 5-APP/Mac Network.; Display Hardware – APP/Mac G3 PRODUCTION: Pagination Software – QPS/QuarkXPress 4.12.; Production Equipment – 2-Birmy/Setter, 2-Accuset/1000; Cameras – 1-Danagraph; Scanners – 2-Kk/2750, 2-HP/6100 PRESSROOM: Line 1 – 9-G/Urbanite; Folders – 1 MAILROOM: Counter stackers – 2-BG/Count-O-Veyor; Inserters and stuffers – 2-KAN/480; Bundle tying machines – 1/MLN; Addressing machine – 2-/Am, 1-Ch/725. BUSINESS COMPUTERS: Business Software – Vision Data; Business Hardware – 1-IBM, Sun/Ultra 1

FREMONT

THE ARGUS

37468 Fremont Blvd., Fremont, Calif., 94536-3705; gen tel (510) 353-7027; ed tel (510) 353-7001; gen fax (510) 353-7029; adv fax (510) 353-7047; ed fax (510) 353-7029; gen e-mail bangcirc@bayareanewsgroup.com; ed e-mail ccnnewsrelease@bayareanewsgroup.com; web site www.insidebayarea.com
Published: Mon, Tues, Wed, Thur, Fri, Sat, Sun
Weekday Frequency: m
Saturday Frequency: m
Circulation: 26,619; 24,978(sat); 25,798(sun)
Last Audit: September 30, 2007
Price: 155.00/yr.
Advertising: Open inch rate $125.00
News services: NYT, AP, LAT-WP, SHNS, McClatchy, Bloomberg.
Politics: Independent. **Established:** 1960
Note: For detailed mechanical equipment information, see the Oakland Tribune listing.
Special Editions: My Town-Fremont (Apr); I Do-Bridal (Feb); PARCA (Jan); My Town-Newark (Jul); Almanac (Mar); Daytrips (May); California Home (Monthly); Bay Area Best (Oct); NFL Preview (Sept).
Special Weekly Sections: Automotive (Fri); NFL Mondays in Sports (Mon); Careers (S); Real Estate (Sat); Food (Wed).
Magazines: Relish (Monthly); TV Week (S).
Pub. ....John Armstrong
Sr. Vice Pres., Adv./Mktg. ....Steven Brisaud
Sr. Vice Pres., Prodn. ....Dennis Miller
Adv. Vice Pres., Classified/Local Retail Lilian Mitchinson
Mgr., Mktg./Promo ....Melanie Keiholtz
Mktg. ....Deborah Nordstrom
Circ. Vice Pres. ....Jim Dove
Circ. Dir. ....Daniel Cruey
Ed. ....Steve Waterhouse
Mng. Ed. ....Pete Wevurski
Arts Ed. ....Monique Beeler
Automotive Ed. ....Kelly Lopez
Bus. Ed ....Drew Voros
City Ed. ....Rick La Plante
Editorial Page Ed. ....Tom Tuttle
Features Ed. ....Keith Jones
Food Ed. ....Danielle Centoni
Religion Writer ....Jennifer Carnig
Sports Ed. ....Mike Lefkow
Data Processing Mgr. ....Manny Sardinia
Market Information: TMC.
Mechanical available: Black and 3 ROP colors; insert accepted; page cutoffs - 20 1/2.
Mechanical Specifications: Type page 12 x 21 1/2; E - 6 cols, 2 1/16, 1/8 between; A - 6 cols, 2 1/16, 1/8 between; C - 10 cols, 1 1/4, 1/32 between.
Commodity Consumption: Avg. Page Number Per Issue - Daily 72; Avg. Page Number Per Issue - Plates Used 28000; Avg. Page Number Per Issue - Sunday 96; widths 50; Newsprint Used - Metric Tons 3675; Printing Ink Used - Black 72000; Printing Ink Used - Color 7500; Printing Ink Use
Equipment EDITORIAL: Front-end Software – Novell 9.11, XYQUEST/XyWrite, HI/XP21, HI/NME, HI/NMP.; Editorial Hardware – PC; Editorial Printers – HP/5000N CLASSIFIED: Front-end Software – Mactive.; Classified Hardware – PC DISPLAY: Ad make-up applications – Xenix, Multi-Ad/Creator; Layout Software – SCS/Layout 8000.; Display Hardware – APP/Mac 9600, APP/Mac G3, APP/Mac G4 PRODUCTION: Pagination Software – HI/2100 2.1.; Production Equipment – 6-Nu, 1-W, 1-Nat, 1-AN, 1-SL; Cameras – 4-C; Scanners – 4-HP, 1-Epson, 1-Scitex PRESSROOM: Line 1 – 13-G/Urbanite single width 1978; Line 2 – 13-G/Urbanite single width 1984; Line 3 – 13-G/Urbanite single width 1993; Line 4 – 7-MAN/Lithomatic II double width 1990; Line 5 – 7-G/Urbanite single width 1990; Line 6 – 15-G/Urbanite single width 1998 MAILROOM: Counter stackers – 10-HL/Monitor, 3-QWI/SP, 2/Compass; Inserters and stuffers – 2-HI/1372P, 1-GMA/16:1, 1-GMA/8:1; Bundle tying machines – 10-MLN/2A, 4-/Dynamic, 1-/Power Strap, 4-/Bu; Addressing machine – 1-/Ch, 2-/KR. BUSINESS COMPUTERS: Business Software – CJ; Business Hardware – 1-HP/300 957

TRI-CITY VOICE

39737 Paseo Padre Parkway, Fremont, Calif., 94538; gen e-mail tricityvoice@aol.com; web site tricityvoice.com
Published: Tues, Fri

FRESNO

THE FRESNO BEE

1626 E. St., Fresno, Calif., 93786-2006; gen tel (559) 441-6233; adv tel (559) 441-6092; ed tel (559) 441-6330; adv fax (559) 441-6458; ed fax (559) 441-6499; adv e-mail classads@fresnobee.com; ed e-mail metro@fresnobee.com; web site www.fresnobee.com
Group: Newspapers First, Inc.
Published: Mon, Tues, Wed, Thur, Fri, Sat, Sun
Weekday Frequency: m
Saturday Frequency: m
Circulation: 104,991; 116,674(sat); 140,929(sun)
Last Audit: ABC September 30, 2011
Price: 3.08/wk; 13.34/mo; 160.16/yr.
Advertising: Open inch rate $279.25
News services: AFP, AP, NYT, LAT-WP, MCT, SHNS.
Politics: Non-Partisan. **Established:** 1922
Special Weekly Sections: Career Builder (Other); Real Estate (S); Today's Home (Sat); House & Garden (Thur); Food (Wed).
Magazines: 7 Magazine (Fri); Color Comics (S).
Pres./Pub. ....William Fleet
Regl. Vice. Pres., Finance ....Walt Kletke
Vice Pres., Custom Publications ..Valerie Bender
Controller ....Glynna Billings
Vice Pres., HR ....Laura Janigian
Adv. Sr. Vice Pres., Sales/Strategic Mktg. John Coakley
Adv. Dir., Classified ....Valerie Vaz
Adv. Dir., Display ....David Dakin
Vice Pres., Community Rel./Sr. Circ. Mgr. Ken Hatfield
Mgr., Research ....Ghassane Habib
Circ. Vice Pres. ....Thomas Cullinan
Circ. Sr. Mgr. ....Dan Baptista
Circ. Mgr., Home Delivery ....Marshall McDowell
Circ. Mgr., Mktg. ....Lisa Birrell
Circ. Mgr., Sales ....Cheryl Maciel
Circ. Mgr., Single Copy ....Matt Steele
Circ. Mgr., Systems ....Jim Fotes
Exec. Ed./Sr. Vice Pres. ....Betsy Lumbye
Editorial Page Ed./Vice Pres. ....James Boren
Mng. Ed ....Jack Robinson
Market Information: ADS; Split run; TMC; Zoned editions.
Mechanical available: Flexographic; Black and 3 ROP colors; insert accepted - poly bags; page cutoffs - 22.
Mechanical Specifications: Type page 9 7/8 x 21; E - 6 cols, 1.55, .115 between; A - 6 cols, 1.55, 1/8 between; C - 6 cols, 1.55, .115 between.
Commodity Consumption: Avg. Page Number Per Issue - Daily 60; Avg. Page Number Per Issue - Plates Used 275862; Avg. Page Number Per Issue - Saturday 80; Avg. Page Number Per Issue - Sunday 108; widths 49; Newsprint Used - Metric Tons 21471; Printing Ink Used - Black 453900; Pr
Equipment EDITORIAL: Front-end Software – Unisys/Hermes, Unisys/Wire Center.; Editorial Hardware – 150-HP/Vectra VE8, 30-HP/Kzyzx xu, 12-Sun/E 450; Editorial Equipment – AII/Output Manager NT, 2-DEC; Editorial Printers – 2-HP/Design Jet 1055CM, 12-HP/LaserJet 5000 CLASSIFIED: Front-end Software – Scoop, SII/SCP, Coyote/XA, SII/Czar II.; Classified Hardware – Tandem/K1004, 3-HP/Apollo 715, 50-HP/EPC, 2-Sun/Ultra 10; Classified Printers – 6-HP/5000 DISPLAY: Ad make-up applications – QPS/QuarkXPress, AII/Ad Manager; Layout Software – MEI/ALS.; Display Hardware – Sun/Sparc Stations, APP/Mac; Display Printers – AII/3850, HP/Design Jet 1055 CM PRODUCTION: Pagination Software – Unisys/Hermes 5.5.; Production Equipment – Na/FP IV, 2-Na/Flex-V, 5-Loge, 5-III/3850; Cameras – 1-C/Newspager II, 1-C/Marathon; Scanners – 2-Scitex/Eversmart Pro, 2-Eskofot/Full Page PRESSROOM: Line 1 – 6-MAN/Print Couples, 22-MAN/Flexoman double width 1991; Line 2 – 6-MAN/Print Couples, 22-MAN/Flexoman M double width 1991; Line 3 – 6-MAN/Print Couples, 22-MAN/Flexoman M, 18-1992; Folders – MAN/4:3:2; Pasters – 18-HUR/50 Hi Speed Utilized Reel T MAILROOM: Counter stackers – 2/Compass 180, 1-Id/2000, 2-HL/HT; Inserters and stuffers – 3-HI/1472P; Bundle tying machines – 4-/Power Strap/PSN-6, 6-/Samuel Strap; Wrapping singles – 6-HL/Bottom Wrap; Addressing machine – 1-/Kirk Rudy, 1-Prism/InkJet Online System

GILROY

THE DISPATCH

6400 Monterey St., Gilroy, Calif., 95021-2365; gen tel (408) 842-6400; adv tel (408) 842-6400; ed tel (408) 842-9687; gen fax (408) 842-7105; ed fax (408) 842-2206; adv e-mail cindyc@gilroydispatch.com; classified@dispatch.com; ed e-mail editor@garlic.com; web site www.gilroydispatch.com
Published: Tues, Fri
Weekday Frequency: m
Circulation: 4,800
Last Audit: Sworn
Advertising: Open inch rate $12.50
News services: McClatchy
Politics: Independent. **Established:** 1868
Advertising not accepted: N
Own facility?: Y
Special Editions: Many
Pub. ....Stephen Staloch
Adv. Mgr., Retail ....Cindy Courter
Dir., Circ./Sales/Opns. ....Walt Glines
Exec. Ed. ....Mark Derry
Sports Ed. ....Josh Weaver
Prodn. Mgr., Pre Press ....Chuck Gibbs
Prodn. Mgr., Pressroom ....Sam Montoya
Mechanical Specifications: Type page 13 x 21 1/2; E - 6 cols, 2 1/16, 1/6 between; A - 6 cols, 2 1/16, 1/6 between; C - 10 cols, 1 7/32, 1/6 between.
Delivery method: Newsstand, Private Carrier

GLENDALE

GLENDALE NEWS-PRESS

221 N Brand Blvd 2nd Floor, Glendale, Calif., 91203-2609; gen tel (818) 637-3200; web site www.glendalenewspress.com

GRASS VALLEY

THE UNION

464 Sutton Way, Grass Valley, Calif., 95945; gen tel (530) 273-9561; adv tel (530) 273-9567; ed tel (530) 477-4203; gen fax (530) 273-1854; adv fax (530) 273-1854; ed fax (530) 477-4292; gen e-mail letters@theunion.com; adv e-mail ads@theunion.com; web site www.theunion.com
Published: Mon, Tues, Wed, Thur, Fri, Sat
Weekday Frequency: m
Circulation: 15,339; 15,339(sat)
Last Audit: September 30, 2009
Price: 9.75/mo; 109.00/yr.
Advertising: Open inch rate $29.98
News services: AP.
Politics: Independent.
Advertising not accepted: That which requires payment in advance.
Special Editions: Best of Nevada County (Apr); Fair (Aug); Bride (Jan); Home & Garden (Mar); Football (Sept).
Special Weekly Sections: Business (Mon); Home and Garden (Sat); Religious (Thur); Community/Society (Tues); Food (Wed).
Magazines: American Profile (Weekly).
Pub. ....Jeff Ackerman
Circ. Dir. ....Craig Underwood
Ed. ....Jeff Pelline
City Ed. ....Trina Kleist
Entertainment Ed. ....Pam Jung
Sports Ed. ....Brian Hamilton
Mgmt. Info Servs./Online Mgr. ....Tom Harbert
Prodn. Dir. ....Lee Brant
Prodn. Mgr., Press ....Gary Clelan
Market Information: TMC.
Mechanical available: Offset; Black and 3 ROP colors; insert accepted; page cutoffs - 22 3/4.
Mechanical Specifications: Type page 13 x 21 1/2; E - 6 cols, 2 1/16, 1/8 between; A - 6 cols, 2 1/16, 1/8 between; C - 9 cols, 1 3/8, 1/16 between.
Commodity Consumption: Avg. Page Number Per Issue - Daily 32; widths 27; Newsprint Used - Metric Tons 1014; Printing Ink Used - Black 9900; Printing Ink Used - Color 6482; Printing Ink Used - Pages Printed 9659.
Equipment; Editorial Hardware – APP/Mac. CLASSIFIED: Front-end Software – Baseview/Ad Manager Pro.; Classified Hardware – APP/Mac, APP/iMac; Layout Software – APP/Mac.; Display Hardware – Ethernet/Ap Talk, 7-APP/Mac Centris; Production Equipment – APP/Mac; Cameras – 1-SCREEN/Ver. PRESSROOM: Line 1 – 7-G/Community (2 stack color). MAILROOM: Counter stackers – 1-BG/MFG; Inserters and stuffers – 2/MM, MM/227; Bundle tying machines – 1-/MLN, 1-/Bu. BUSINESS COMPUTERS: Business Software – PBS/Media Plus; Business Hardware – Sun/Sparc server

HANFORD

THE SENTINEL

300 W. 6th St., Hanford, Calif., 93230; gen tel (559) 582-0471; adv tel (559) 582-0471; ed tel (559) 582-0471; gen fax (559) 582-0512; ed fax (559) 587-1876; web site www.hanfordsentinel.com
Published: Mon, Tues, Wed, Thur, Fri, Sat
Weekday Frequency: e
Saturday Frequency: e
Circulation: 8,556; 8,612(sat); 9,680(sun)
Last Audit: ABC September 30, 2011
Price: 11.00/mo (carrier).
Advertising: Open inch rate $31.50
News services: AP.
Politics: Independent. **Established:** 1886
Special Editions: Bridal Tab (Feb); Dairy (Jun); Home Improvement (Mar); Home Show (May); Christmas Opening (Nov); Progress (Oct); Football (Sept).
Special Weekly Sections: Community Page (Fri); Student News (Mon); Health (S); Church Page (Sat); Farm Page (Thur); Best Food Day (Tues); Home & Garden (Wed).
Magazines: Relish (Monthly); USA WEEKEND

Magazine (S); Parade (Weekly).
Pub. Manuel Collazo
Adv. Mgr. Eacrica Hruby
Circ. Dir. Greg Barkley
Mng. Ed. Jackie Kaczmarek
City Ed. Jon Earnest
Sports Ed. Rich Degive
Photo Ed. Apolinar Fanseca
Prodn. Mgr., Mailroom Todd Nelson
Market Information: Split run; TMC.
Mechanical available: Offset; Black and 3 ROP colors; insert accepted; page cutoffs - 22 3/4.
Mechanical Specifications: Type page 13 x 21 1/2; E - 6 cols, 2 1/16, 1/8 between; A - 6 cols, 2 1/16, 1/8 between; C - 9 cols, 1 3/8, 1/16 between.
Commodity Consumption: Avg. Page Number Per Issue - Daily 26; Avg. Page Number Per Issue - Plates Used 14000; Avg. Page Number Per Issue - Sunday 26; widths 13 1/4; Newsprint Used - Metric Tons 1344; Printing Ink Used - Black 45000; Printing Ink Used - Color 4500; Printing Ink
Equipment EDITORIAL: Front-end Software – Baseview/NewsEdit Pro IQUE 3.2.2.; Editorial Hardware – APP/Mac; Editorial Printers – QMS/2060 CLASSIFIED: Front-end Software – Synaptic.; Classified Hardware – 4-ScrippSat; Classified Printers – QMS/820 Turbo DISPLAY: Ad make-up applications – Ad Force; Layout Software – Ad Force, MEI.; Display Hardware – APP/Mac; Display Printers – QMS/2060; Production Equipment – 2-AU/APS, 3850 Color Imager, Noritsu, QMS/2060 1800 x 60, ECR/Scriptsetter VRL-36/HS; Cameras – 1-SCREEN/Companica 660c; Scanners – Tecsa/TS2470. PRESSROOM: Line 1 – 7-G/Community floor, 1-G/Stacked, 4-G/Stacked 4-high; Folders – 1 MAILROOM: Counter stackers – 1/Rima; Inserters and stuffers – 1-MM/227E; Bundle tying machines – 1-MLN/ML2EE, 1-/Sterling. BUSINESS COMPUTERS: Business Software – Lotus, SmartSuite, Microsoft/Office, WordPerfect, CDA; Business Hardware – 8-Mk/Acer, 2-Dell/Dimensions XPS P200s, HP/Laser Jet

HAYWARD

THE DAILY REVIEW

22533 Foothill Blvd., Hayward, Calif., 94541-4109; gen tel (510) 661-2626; adv tel (510) 293-2491; ed tel (510) 293-2482; gen fax (510) 293-2499; ed fax (510) 293-2490; gen e-mail bangcirc@bayareanewsgroup.com; ed e-mail ccnnewsrelease@bayareanewsgroup.com; web site www.insidebayarea.com/review
Published: Mon, Tues, Wed, Thur, Fri, Sat, Sun
Weekday Frequency: m
Saturday Frequency: m
Circulation: 31,183; 28,185(sat); 30,491(sun)
Last Audit: September 30, 2007
Price: 154.00/yr.
Advertising: Open inch rate $149.00
News services: NYT, AP, LAT-WP, SHNS, McClatchy, Bloomberg.
Politics: Independent.
Note: For detailed mechanical equipment information, see the Oakland Tribune listing.
Special Editions: My Town-San Leandro/San Lorenzo (Apr); I Do-Bridal (Feb); Alameda Spring Home & Gardens (Jan); Fremont Art & Wine Festival (Jul); My Town-Hayward/Castro Valley (Jun); Almanac (Mar); Powell Ranch Rodeo (May); California Home (Monthly); Sausage & Suds-San L
Special Weekly Sections: Preview (Fri); NFL Mondays in Sports (Mon); Real Estate (S); Real Estate (Sat); Food (Wed).
Magazines: Relish (Monthly); TV Week (S).
Pres./CEO/Pub. John Armstrong
Vice Pres., Finance Tina McCollum
Vice Pres., Adv./Mktg. Bob Gray
Vice Pres., Adv. Wayne Wedgeworth
Vice Pres., HR Bob Jandusa
Adv. Dir. Alex Budyszewick
Adv. Mgr., Nat'l Rick Hunz
Research Mgr. Margaret Lin
Coord., Mktg./Promo. Melanie Keilholtz
Circ. Vice Pres. Jim Dove
Circ. Dir. Harold Strong
Circ. Dir., Opns. Scott Kinter
Ed. John Bowman
Editorial Page Ed. Tom Tuttle
Features Ed. Kari Hulac
Local Politics/City Hall Writer Michelle Miyers
Photo Ed. Ron Riesterer
Regl. Ed. Mike Oliver
Sports Ed. Jon Becker
Market Information: ADS; TMC.
Mechanical available: Black and 3 ROP colors; insert accepted; page cutoffs - 20 1/2.
Mechanical Specifications: Type page 12 x 21 1/2; E - 6 cols, 2 1/16, between; A - 6 cols, 2 1/16, between; C - 10 cols, 1 1/4, between.
Commodity Consumption: Avg. Page Number Per Issue - Daily 59; Avg. Page Number Per Issue - Plates Used 27000; Avg. Page Number Per Issue - Sunday 89; widths 37 1/2; Newsprint Used - Metric Tons 6456; Printing Ink Used - Black 136000; Printing Ink Used - Color 9550; Printing In
Equipment EDITORIAL: Front-end Software – Novell 4.11, XYQUEST/XyWrite 3.54, HI/NME, HI/NMP, HI/XP21.; Editorial Hardware – PC CLASSIFIED: Front-end Software – HI/Cash.; Classified Hardware – PC DISPLAY: Ad make-up applications – Xenix, SCS/Layout 8000, Multi-Ad/Creator; Layout Software – SCS/Layout 8000.; Display Hardware – APP/Mac 9600, APP/Mac G3, APP/Mac G4 PRODUCTION: Pagination Software – HI/2100 2.1.; Production Equipment – 6-III/Graphix Color Imagers, 1-W, 1-Nat, 1-AN, 1-SL; Cameras – 4-C; Scanners – 4-HP, 1-Epson, Scitex PRESSROOM: Line 1 – 13-G/Urbanite single width 1978; Line 2 – 13-G/Urbanite single width 1984; Line 3 – 13-G/Urbanite single width 1993; Line 4 – 7-MAN/Lithomatic II double width 1989; Line 5 – 7-G/Community single width 1990; Line 6 – 15-G/Urbanite single width 199 MAILROOM: Counter stackers – 10-HL/Monitor, 3-QWI/SP, 2/Compass; Inserters and stuffers – 2-HI/1372P, 1-GMA/16:1, 1-GMA/8:1; Bundle tying machines – 4-/Dynamic, 1-/Power Strap, 4-/Bu; Addressing machine – 1-/Ch, 2-/KR.

HOLLISTER

FREE LANCE

350 Sixth St., Ste. 101, Hollister, Calif., 95023-1417; gen tel (831) 637-8555; adv tel (831) 599-9228; gen fax (831) 842-0427; adv fax (831) 637-4104; gen e-mail info@freelancenews.com; web site www.hollisterfreelance.com
Published: Tues
Circulation: 3,221
Last Audit: ABC September 30, 2011
Advertising: Open inch rate $13.00
Politics: Independent.
Pub. Stephen P. Staloch
Vice. Pres., Adv. David Marin
Adv. Servs. Mgr. Cindy Courter
Circ. Mgr. Robert Rodriguez
Circ. Mgr. Walt Glines
Ed. Kollin Kosmicki
Sports Ed. Andrew Matheson
Mechanical Specifications: Type page 13 x 21 1/2; E - 6 cols, 2 1/16, 1/8 between; A - 6 cols, 2 1/16, 1/8 between; C - 10 cols, 1 7/32, 1/8 between.

LAKEPORT

LAKE COUNTY RECORD-BEE

2150 S. Main St., Lakeport, Calif., 95453-0849; gen tel (707) 263-5636; gen fax (707) 263-0600; ed e-mail letters@record-bee.com; obits@record-bee.com; web site www.record-bee.com
Published: Tues, Wed, Thur, Fri, Sat
Weekday Frequency: m
Saturday Frequency: m
Circulation: 5,874; 6,690(sat)
Last Audit: ABC September 30, 2011
Price: 90.80/yr.
Advertising: Open inch rate $13.94
News services: AP.
Politics: Independent.
Special Weekly Sections: Real Estate (Sat); Lifestyles (Wed).
Magazines: Relish (Monthly); TV Spotlight (Sat); American Profile (Weekly).
Pub. Gary D. Dickson
Bus. Mgr. Karen McNish
Adv. Dir. Christine Hammers
Circ. Dir. Jim Davis
Ed. Rick Kennedy
Sports Ed. Brian Sumpter
Graphics Prodn. Dir. Carol Wilbur
Asst. Prodn. Mgr. Dan Mello
Prodn. Mgr., Mailroom Jose Contreras
Market Information: TMC.
Mechanical available: Offset; Black and 3 ROP colors; insert accepted - 8 1/2 x 11; page cutoffs - 22 3/4.
Mechanical Specifications: Type page 13 x 21; E - 6 cols, 2 1/16, 1/8 between; A - 6 cols, 2 1/16, 1/8 between; C - 8 cols, 1 1/2, 1/8 between.
Commodity Consumption: Avg. Page Number Per Issue - Daily 16; Avg. Page Number Per Issue - Plates Used 8000; widths 28; Newsprint Used - Metric Tons 900; Printing Ink Used - Black 11000; Printing Ink Used - Pages Printed 6500.
Equipment EDITORIAL: Front-end Software – QPS/QuarkXPress, Baseview, Adobe/Photoshop.; Editorial Hardware – 4-APP/Mac 7100, APP/Mac 4400, 2-APP/Mac 475, 1-APP/Mac 7200; Editorial Equipment – Polaroid/SprintScan 35, AG/Studio Star Scanner; Editorial Printers – APP/Mac LaserWriter 16-160 PS CLASSIFIED: Front-end Software – Baseview/Ad Manager Pro 1.0.4.; Classified Hardware – 3-APP/Mac 4400; Classified Printers – APP/Mac LaserWriter 16-600, Okidata/line Printer DISPLAY: Ad make-up applications – Multi-Ad/Creator 4.1, QPS/QuarkXPress 3.32, Adobe/Photoshop 4.01; Display Hardware – 3-APP/Mac 7300, 2-APP/Mac 8100; Display Printers – APP/Mac LaserWriter 8500 PRODUCTION: Pagination Software – QPS/QuarkXPress 3.32, Baseview/Extensions.; Production Equipment – Caere/OmniPage Pro; Cameras – SCREEN/250 PRESSROOM: Line 1 – 6-WPC/Web Leader.; Inserters and stuffers – 6-MM/227; Bundle tying machines – 1/Bu, 2-/Strapex; Addressing machine – 1-/Ch; Other equipment –MM/DSS Trimmer, MM/JAV Stitcher.; Business Hardware – DEC/Micro VAX 3100-40

LODI

LODI NEWS-SENTINEL

125 N. Church St., Lodi, Calif., 95240-2102; gen tel (209) 369-2761; adv tel (209) 369-2761; ed tel (209) 369-7035; gen fax (209) 369-1084; adv fax (209) 369-1084; ed fax (209) 369-6706; adv e-mail ads@lodinews.com; ed e-mail news@lodinews.com; web site www.lodinews.com
Published: Mon, Tues, Wed, Thur, Fri, Sat
Weekday Frequency: m
Saturday Frequency: m
Circulation: 14,852; 14,852(sat)
Last Audit: September 30, 2009
Price: 8.75/mo; 105.00/yr.
Advertising: Open inch rate $23.03
News services: AP, LA Times/McClatchy.
Politics: Independent. **Established:** 1881
Advertising not accepted: Y
Not Published: New Year; Memorial Day; Independence Day; Labor Day; Christmas.
Own facility?: Y
Special Editions: Senior services (Jan); Brides (Feb); Visitors Guide (May); Home Improvement Guide (Jun); How-To Guide (July); Grape & Wine Festival (Sept); Christmas (Dec).
Special Weekly Sections: Business/Stock Market (Fri); Church (Sat); Business/Stock Market (Thur); Business/Stock Market (Tues); Best Food Day (Wed).
Magazines: USA WEEKEND Magazine (Sat).
Pub. Marty Weybret
Circ. Mgr. Steve Knape
Ed. Richard Hanner
Bus. Page Ed. Jordan Guinn
City Ed. Rich Hanner
Lodi Living Ed. Lauren Nelson
News Ed. Brian Craig
Photo Ed. Brian Feulner
Religion Page Ed. Ross Farrow
Society Page Ed. Pamela Bauserman
Sports Ed. Scott Howell
Mgr., Internet Servs. Simon Birch
Mgr., Opns. Matt Silva
Composing Mgr. Julie Govette
Ad Director Tracy Kelley
Adv. Dir. Kimberly Anger
Market Information: TMC
Mechanical available: Offset; Black and 3 ROP colors; insert accepted - coupons; page cutoffs - 22 3/4.
Mechanical Specifications: Type page 10 15/16 x 21 1/2; E - 6 cols, 1 3/4, 3/16 between; A - 6 cols, 1 13/16, 1/8 between; C - 8 cols, 1 1/4, 1/8 between.
Commodity Consumption: Avg. Page Number Per Issue - Daily 24; Avg. Page Number Per Issue - Plates Used 7965; Avg. Page Number Per Issue - Saturday 32; widths 24; Newsprint Used - Metric Tons 738; Printing Ink Used - Black 20937; Printing Ink Used - Color 4498; Printing Ink Use
Equipment EDITORIAL: Front-end Software – Baseview/NewsEdit Pro IQUE 3.22.; Editorial Hardware – APP/Mac G3; Editorial Equipment – ECR/Jetsetter 6200; Editorial Printers – Xante/Accel-a-Writer 3G CLASSIFIED: Front-end Software – Baseview/Ad Manager Pro.; Classified Hardware – APP/Mac G3; Classified Equipment – ECR/Jetsetter 6200; Classified Printers – QMS/2060 Print System DISPLAY: Ad make-up applications – QPS/QuarkXPress 4.0, Multi-Ad/Creator 4.03; Layout Software – MEI/ALS Page Director 2.5.; Display Hardware – APP/Mac G3; Display Printers – Xante/Accel-a-Writer 3G PRODUCTION: Pagination Software – QPS/QuarkXPress 4.0.; Production Equipment – Caere/OmniPage Pro 8.0, Adobe/Photoshop 4.0, Adobe/Photoshop 6.0; Cameras – 1-Acti; Scanners – Microtek/1850 si, 2-Umax/Powerlook II, Polaroid/SprintScan 35, 1-Epson/Expression 636 PRESSROOM: Line 1 – 13-1979, G/Community single width; Folders – 2-G/2:1. MAILROOM: Counter stackers – 1/KAN; Inserters and stuffers – 1-KAN/9 station; Bundle tying machines – 1-/MLN; Addressing machine – 1-/St.
Zip Codes served: 95220, 95227, 95237, 95240, 95242, 95253, 95258, 95632, 95686
Delivery method: Mail, Newsstand, Private Carrier, Racks

LOMPOC

THE LOMPOC RECORD

115 N. H St., Lompoc, Calif., 93436; gen tel (805) 736-2313; adv tel 805-737-1039; ed tel 805-266-0942; adv fax (805) 736-5654; ed fax (805) 735-5118; web site www.lompocrecord.com
Published: Mon, Tues, Thur, Fri, Sun
Weekday Frequency: m
Circulation: 4,793; 4,412(sat); 4,672(sun)
Last Audit: September 30, 2009
Price: 7.90/mo (local), $10.97/mo (elsewhere); 88.00/yr.
Advertising: Open inch rate $28.94
News services: AP.
Politics: Independent.
Own facility?: Y
Special Editions: Welcome to the Central Coast (Aug); Flower Festival (Jun).
Special Weekly Sections: Church Page (Fri); Best Automobile Days (S); Business Page (Tues); Real Estate (Wed).
Magazines: TV Record (Fri); Relish (Monthly); Access (S).
Publisher Cynthia Schur
Exec. Ed. Tom Bolton

City Ed. ....Bo Poertner
Sports Ed. ....Elliott Stern
IT/Web Admin. ....Braxton Carroll
Prodn. Mgr. ....George Fischer
Bus. Mgr. ....Donna Dimock
Circ. Dir. ....Rich Macke
Market Information: TMC.
Mechanical available: Web Offset; Black and 3 ROP colors; insert accepted; page cutoffs - 21 1/2.
Mechanical Specifications: Type page 13 x 21 1/2; E - 6 cols, 2 1/16, 1/8 between; A - 6 cols, 2 1/16, 1/8 between; C - 8 cols, 1 1/2, 1/8 between.
Commodity Consumption: Avg. Page Number Per Issue - Daily 20; Avg. Page Number Per Issue - Plates Used 3272; Avg. Page Number Per Issue - Sunday 28; widths 27; Newsprint Used - Metric Tons 500; Printing Ink Used - Black 10000; Printing Ink Used - Color 396; Printing Ink Used -
Equipment EDITORIAL: Front-end Software – Baseview.; Editorial Hardware – APP/Mac CLASSIFIED: Front-end Software – Baseview.; Classified Hardware – APP/Mac; Classified Printers – TI/Omni 800 DISPLAY: Ad make-up applications – Mk, Multi-Ad/Creator, QPS/QuarkXPress.; Display Hardware – APP/Mac; Display Printers – HP/4MV; Production Equipment – 2-Pre Press/Panther Plus; Cameras – Nu/Vertical Camera. PRESSROOM: Line 1 – 5-G/Community 1977, G/Community; Folders – G/Community, G/SC.; Bundle tying machines – 1/Bu, Si/ML2EE. BUSINESS COMPUTERS: Business Software – CJ/AIM 7.0; Business Hardware – HP/System 3000
Zip Codes served: 93436
Delivery method: Mail, Newsstand, Private Carrier, Racks

LONG BEACH

PRESS-TELEGRAM

300 Ocean Gate, Ste. 150, Long Beach, Calif., 90844; gen tel (562) 435-1161; adv tel (562) 499-1243; ed tel (562) 499-1337; adv fax (562) 435-5415; ed fax (562) 499-1277; ed e-mail ptnews@presstelegram.com; web site www.presstelegram.com
Published: Mon, Tues, Wed, Thur, Fri, Sat, Sun
Weekday Frequency: m
Saturday Frequency: m
Circulation: 79,925; 64,116(sat); 68,119(sun)
Last Audit: ABC September 30, 2011
Price: 149.00/yr.
News services: AP, MCT, NYT, McClatchy, City News Service, Entertainment News Wire, TMS.
Politics: Independent.
Note: The Los Angeles Newspaper Group includes the Long Beach Press-Telegram (mS), Los Angeles Daily News (mS), Ontario Inland Valley Daily Bulletin (mS), Pasadena Star-News (mS), Redlands Daily Facts (eS), San Bernardino County Sun (mS), San Gabriel Valley Tri
Special Editions: Grand Prix (Apr); Back To School (Aug); Chronology (Dec); Love Lines-Class (Feb); Careers and Education (Jan); Millenium Bride (Jul); Father's Day (Jun); Pre-Owned Vehicles (Mar); Grad Tab (May); LB Marathon (Nov); Halloween (Oct); Olympics (Sept).
Special Weekly Sections: Weekend/Taste (Fri); Business Monday (Mon); So. California Live! (Mon-fri); TV (quarterfold) (S); Real Estate (Sat); Food (Wed).
Magazines: Relish (Monthly); Access (S).
Pub. ....Mark Ficcara
Adv. Dir. ....Greg Pedersen
Adv. Mgr., Classified ....Diane Stumpp
Dir., Mktg. ....Lynn Komadina
Circ. Dir. ....Dennis Schafer
Vice Pres., Circ. ....Joe Robidoux
Exec. Ed. ....Rich Archbold
Exec. Ed., News ....Jim McCormack
Exec. Ed., Sports ....Jeff Parenti
Bus. Ed. ....Charlotte Aiken
City Ed., Day ....Rose Fitzpatrick
City Ed., Night ....Ed Kamlan
Design Ed. ....Christine Strobel
Editorial Page Ed. ....Larry Allison
Features Ed. ....Marlene Greer
Food Ed. ....Alessandra Djurklou
Librarian ....Bob Andrew
News Ed. ....John Futch
Radio/Television Ed. ....Robin Deemer
Restaurant Reviews Ed. ....Al Rudis
Market Information: ADS; Split run; TMC; Zoned editions.
Mechanical available: Offset; Black and 3 ROP colors; insert accepted; page cutoffs - 22.
Mechanical Specifications: Type page 13 x 21; E - 6 cols, 2 1/16, 1/8 between; A - 6 cols, 2 1/16, 1/8 between; C - 10 cols, 1 1/4, 1/16 between.
Commodity Consumption: Avg. Page Number Per Issue - Daily 52; Avg. Page Number Per Issue - Plates Used 85000; Avg. Page Number Per Issue - Sunday 100; widths 50; Newsprint Used - Metric Tons 14000; Printing Ink Used - Black 587000; Printing Ink Used - Color 90000; Printing Ink
Equipment EDITORIAL: Front-end Software – SII/Editorial.; Editorial Hardware – SII/Tandem CLASSIFIED: Front-end Software – SII/Czar.; Classified Hardware – SII/Tandem DISPLAY: Ad make-up applications – APP/Mac, QPS/QuarkXPress; Layout Software – SCS/Layout 8000, SII/IAL.; Display Hardware – 16-APP/Mac G4 PRODUCTION: Pagination Software – CSI/1170, SII/INL & IAL.; Production Equipment – 2-AU/APS6-108C, AU/Soft PIP RIPs, 2-AU/3750; Cameras – 1-C/Newspager, C/Spartan III BUSINESS COMPUTERS: Business Software – CJ/AIM, Microsoft/Access Window, Adobe/Photoshop 3.01, Adobe/Illustrator, QuarkXPress, CJ/AIM 7.01.G, CJ/Layout 2.01.E, CJ/AD Tracking 5.01.C, CJ/CIS 4.01.H, CJ 2.09.M, CJ 8.02.D, CJ 7.02.D, Microsoft/Office Windo; Business Hardware – HP/3000 Series 967

PRESS-TELEGRAM PUBLICATIONS, INC.

300 Ocreangate, Ste 1400, Long Beach, Calif., 90844; gen tel (562) 435-1161; adv tel (562) 499-1312; ed tel (562) 499-1267; gen fax (562)499-1325; adv fax (562)499-1474; ed fax (562) 499-1277; web site www.presstelegram.com
Group: Media News Group
Published: Mon, Tues, Wed, Thur, Fri, Sat, Sun
Weekday Frequency: m
Saturday Frequency: m
Price: 148.80/yr.
Advertising: Open inch rate $43.58
Publisher ....Linda Lindus

LOS ANGELES

DAILY COMMERCE

915 E. First St., Los Angeles, Calif., 90012-4042; gen tel (213) 229-5300; ed tel (213) 229-5358; gen fax (213) 229 5481; adv fax (213) 229 5481; gen e-mail audreymiller@dailyjournal.com; web site www.dailyjournal.com
Published: Mon, Tues, Wed, Thur, Fri
Weekday Frequency: e
Circulation: 1,254
Last Audit: September 24, 1998
Price: 640.00/yr.
Advertising: Open inch rate $12.00
News services: AP, LAT-WP, NYT.
Politics: Independent. **Established:** 1888
Special Editions: Special Focus (Monthly).
Magazines: Real Estate in Review (Monthly).
Pub. ....Gerald L. Salzman
Adv. Rep. ....Audrey Miller
Circ. Mgr. ....Ray Chagolla
Ed. ....Lisa Churchill
Mgmt. Info Servs. Mgr. ....Ky Tu
Prodn. Mgr. ....Manuel Azuiler
Mechanical available: Offset; Black and 4 ROP colors; insert accepted; page cutoffs - 11.
Mechanical Specifications: Type page 10 x 13 1/2; E - 4 cols, 2, 1/4 between; A - 4 cols, 2 3/8, 1/2 between; C - 3 cols, 3, 1/2 between.
Commodity Consumption: Avg. Page Number Per Issue - Daily 64.
Equipment EDITORIAL: Front-end Software – APT/ACT, Microsoft 2.1, QPS 3.1.; Editorial Hardware – AT, IBM/486, Viewsonic/20 inch monitor; Editorial Printers – HP/LaserJet; Classified Hardware – AT.; Production Equipment – 3-COM/8600.

DAILY JOURNAL CORP.

915 E. First St., Los Angeles, Calif., 90012-4042; gen tel (213) 229-5300; gen fax (213) 680-3682; gen e-mail sheila_sadaghiane@dailyjournal.com; web site www.dailyjournal,com
Published: Mon, Tues, Wed, Thur, Fri, Sat, Sun
Price: 640.00/yr.
Advertising: Open inch rate $63.00
Politics: 1880

INVESTOR'S BUSINESS DAILY

12655 Beatrice St., Los Angeles, Calif., 90066-7300; gen tel (310) 448-6000; adv tel (310) 448-6700; ed tel (310) 448-6373; gen fax (310) 577-7301; adv fax (310) 577-7301; ed fax (310) 577-7350; ed e-mail IBD-news@investors.com; web site www.investors.com
Published: Mon, Tues, Wed, Thur, Fri
Weekday Frequency: m
Circulation: 127,896
Last Audit: Sworn September 30, 2009
Price: 329.00/yr; 205.00/6mo, $549.00/2yr, $789.00/3yr.
News services: AP
Politics: 1984
Not Published: New Year; Martin Luther King Jr. Day; Presidents' Day; Good Friday; Memorial Day; Independence Day; Labor Day; Thanksgiving; Christmas.
Profile: Editorial focuses on the daily news' potential to impact both businesses and investments. IBD is read predominantly by mid to top management-those dedicated to senior business careers who have higher than average disposable income with which to invest. Th
Vice Pres., Customer Rel. ....Margo Schuster
Adv. Mgr., Opns. (W. Coast) ....Kathy Murray
Adv. Mgr., Opns. (E. Coast) ....Janice Janendo
Vice Pres., Mktg ....Ralph Perrini
Vice Pres., Internet Mktg. ....Harlan Ratzky
Circ. Vice Pres. ....Doug Fuller
Ed ....Wesley F. Mann
Exec. Ed. ....Chris Gessel
Mng. Ed ....Susan Warfel
Technology Bureau Chief, Silicon Valley Mike Krey
Assoc. Ed. ....Terry Jones
Graphic Arts Ed. ....Mary Ann Edwards
Leaders Ed. ....Bucky Fox
New America Ed ....Ken Hoover
Mutual Funds/Personal Finance Ed. Doug Rogers
To The Point Ed. ....Ed Carson
To The Point Ed. ....Ken Popovich
Prodn. Ed. ....Mark Sharar
Vice Pres./Nat'l Adv. Dir. ....Terri Chiodo
Asst. Ed ....Ken Brown
Market Information: Split run.
Mechanical available: Web Offset; Black and 3 ROP colors; insert accepted; page cutoffs - 22.
Mechanical Specifications: Type page 11 5/8 x 20 3/4; E - 6 cols, 1 7/8, 1/8 between; A - 6 cols, 1 7/8, 1/8 between; C - 8 cols, 1 2/3, 1/16 between.
Commodity Consumption: Avg. Page Number Per Issue - Daily 34; Avg. Page Number Per Issue - Plates Used 12000; widths 25; Newsprint Used - Metric Tons 4490; Newsprint Used - Short Tons 4950; Printing Ink Used - Black 74000.
Equipment EDITORIAL: Front-end Software – HAS/Tops 5 2.4.; Editorial Equipment – APP/Mac, HP/5SI; Editorial Printers – Printronix/P 600, HP/LaserJet 4, HP/LaserJet 5 CLASSIFIED: Front-end Software – Admax, Classpag 8.0.; Classified Hardware – PC DISPLAY: Ad make-up applications – Adobe/PageMaker, Admax 6.5, QPS/QuarkXPress 3.32, HAS/Tops 5 2.4, Adobe/Illustrator 6.0, SCS; Layout Software – HAS, APP/Mac, Layout/8000.; Display Hardware – HAS, APP/Mac, PC; Display Printers – HP/5SI, Linotype-Hell/Linotronic 500, XIT PRODUCTION: Pagination Software – HAS/Tops 5 2.4.; Production Equipment – W, III/3750, SCREEN/Photace DS C 260D; Cameras – SCREEN/Photace DS C 260D; Scanners – CD, ECR/Autokon, 2-III/3750 PRESSROOM: Line 1 – 13-G/Urbanite single width 1992, 13-RKW/U5055 single width 1992, 3-RKW/U5055 single width 1994; Press Drives – 2-Fin/SPC 3000 1992, 1-Fin/SPC 3000 1994; Folders – 1-RKW/U5055; Pasters – 3-Jardis/FP4540 1994, 10-Jardis/FP4540. MAILROOM: Counter stackers – Id/NS660, Id/2100; Bundle tying machines – OVL/JP80, OVL/Constellation K-101, OVL/Constellation 415, 2-OVL/JB40; Addressing machine – KAN/500 BL2, Barstrom, Scitex/Ink Jet 5000.; Business Hardware – Bs/A9
Delivery method: Mail, Newsstand, Private Carrier, Racks

LOS ANGELES TIMES MEDIA GROUP

202 W. First St., Los Angeles, Calif., 90012; gen tel (213) 237-5000; ed tel (213) 237-7000; web site www.latimes.com
Group: Tribune Company
Published: Mon, Tues, Wed, Thur, Fri, Sat, Sun
Weekday Frequency: All day
Saturday Frequency: All day
Circulation: 657,467; 783,664(sat); 983,702(sun)
Last Audit: September 30, 2009
Advertising: www.latimes.com/mediakit
News services: Business Wire, PR Newswire, AP, RN, LAT-WP, City News Service, Bloomberg Business News, AFP, PNS, TMS, CQ.
Advertising not accepted: Y
Own facility?: Y
Special Weekly Sections: Health (Mon); Career-Builder (S); Home (Sat); Calendar Weekend (Thur); Food (Wed).
Magazines: LA, Los Angeles Times Magazine (color, offset) (S-montly).
Broadcast Affiliations: Tribune Broadcasting
Profile: The Los Angeles Times, a Tribune Publishing company, is the largest metropolitan daily newspaper in the country and the winner of 30 Pulitzer Prizes. The Times
Publisher/CEO, Los Angeles Times
President/CEO, Tribune Company
Eddy Hartenstein
Exec. Vice Pres., Bus. Servs. ....Bill Nagel
Sr. Vice Pres./CFO ....Chris Avetisian
Sr. Vice Pres./Gen. Counsel ....Julie K. Xanders
Sr. Vice Pres., Opns. ....Russ Newton
SVP, Admin ....Gwen Murakami
VP, Communications ....Nancy Sullivan
Chief Revenue Office, EVP Advertising John T. O'Loughlin
Adv. Dir., Classified, Real Estate Leslie Lindemann
Adv. Dir., Retail ....Shannon Hanes
Adv. Dir., Retail ....Jeffrey Young
SVP, Digital ....Emily Smith
SVP, Advertising and Targeted Media Pompe Scott
VP, Film Advertising ....Berns Francie
VP, Media and Live Entertainment ..Farish Stacie
Director, Events and Strategic Partnerships Mastoris Anne
VP, Advertiser Marketing and Events Anna Magzanyan
VP, Revenue Development ....Collins Jennifer
President, COO ....Kathy Thomson
Editor ....Russ Stanton
Managing Editor, Online ....Orr Jimmy
Managing Editor, News ....Davan Maharaj
Deputy Managing Editor ....Marc Duvoisin
Assistant Managing Editor ....Sallie Hofmeister
Associate Editor ....Randy Harvey
Deputy Managing Editor
Colin Crawford
Assistant Managing Editor ....Joe Eckdahl
Assistant Managing Editor ....Michael Whitley
Editor of the Editorial Pages ..Nicholas Goldberg
Editor, Op-Ed and Sunday Opinion ....Sue Horton
Assistant Managing Editor ....Henry Fuhrmann
Assistant Managing Editor ....Alice Short
Editor at Large ....Jim Newton
Assistant Managing Editor ....Ashley Dunn
Vice President,
Legal and Deputy General Counsel
Karlene Goller
Commodity Consumption: Avg. Page Number Per

Issue - Daily 114; Avg. Page Number Per Issue - Plates Used 2770380; Avg. Page Number Per Issue - Saturday 114; Avg. Page Number Per Issue - Sunday 220; widths 25; Newsprint Used - Metric Tons 291284; Printing Ink Used - Black 534782
Equipment DISPLAY: Ad make-up applications – Managing Editor/ALS, NW/Admarc 7.0, Engage/Dataflow, Microsoft/Windows 98; Layout Software – MEI/ALS.; Press Drives – 16; Folders – 32; Pasters – Pasters
Delivery method: Newsstand, Private Carrier, Racks

LOS ANGELES TIMES

202 W. 1st Street, Los Angeles, Calif., 90012; gen tel 213.237.5000; web site http://www.latimes.com/
Published: Mon, Tues, Wed, Thur, Fri, Sat, Sun
Weekday Frequency: m
Saturday Frequency: m
Circulation: 572,998; 637,983(sat); 905,920(sun)
Last Audit: ABC September 30, 2011
Politics: Independent.
EVP/Advertising......................John O'Loughlin
Adv. Mgr. ....Hector Cabral
Ed...Dan Evans
City Ed...Jason Wells
Sports Ed. ....Grant Gordon

LA OPINION

700 South Flower Street, Suite 3000, Los Angeles, Calif., 90017; gen tel (213) 896-2150; adv tel (213) 896-2300; ed tel (213) 896-2333; gen fax (213) 896-2151; adv fax (213) 896-2080; ed fax (213) 896-2171; ed e-mail editorial@laopinion.com; editor@laopinion.com; web site www.impre.com/laopinion
Published: Mon, Tues, Wed, Thur, Fri, Sat, Sun
Weekday Frequency: m
Saturday Frequency: m
Circulation: 100,608; 59,342(sat); 41,572(sun)
Last Audit: ABC September 30, 2011
Price: 167.71/yr (d), $83.85/6mths (d); 41.93/3mo,
Advertising: Open inch rate $94.31
News services: AP, EFE, CNS, AFP, NOTIMEX, UPI, PR Newswire, PRWEB
Politics: Independent. **Established:** 1926
Own facility?: N
Special Editions: Calendario Torneo (Jan); Calendario Torneo (March); Mujeres Destacadas (March); Dodgers Calendar (April); Angels Calendar (April); Mothers Day (May); Cinco de Mayo (May); MLB All Star (July); 4th of July Special (July); Mexican Soccer League (July); Back to School La Opinion (July/August); Back to School Contigo (August); Fiestas Patrias (Sept); Gift Ideas (Nov); Gift Ideas (Dec).
Special Weekly Sections: Futbol (Fri); Vida y Estilo (S); Negocios (Business Section) (Tues); Vida y Estilo (Lifestyle Section) (Wed).
Magazines: Main News (daily), Ciudad (daily), Negocios (daily), hola LA (Everyday except thurs.), La Vibra (Thursdays) Deportes (daily), Clasificados (daily)
Executive Assistant / Admin ...Patricia Shepherd
CEO and Publisher ....Monica Lozano
Circ. Dir.....................................Jim Pellegrino
Executive Editor............................Pedro Rojas
VP Integrated Marketing ....Mary Zerafa
Vice Chrmn. ....Jose Lozano
Dir. IT..Bob Mason
Mechanical available: Open Web Offset; Black and 3 ROP colors; insert accepted - upon approval; page cutoffs - 22 3/4.
Mechanical Specifications: Type page 12 1/2 x 21 1/2; E - 6 cols, 1 7/8, 3/16 between; A - 6 cols, 1 7/8, between; C - 10 cols, 1 1/16, between.
Commodity Consumption: Avg. Page Number Per Issue - Daily 47.4; Avg. Page Number Per Issue - Plates Used 48000; Avg. Page Number Per Issue - Saturday 60.7; Avg. Page Number Per Issue - Sunday 61.6; widths 27 1/2; Newsprint Used - Metric Tons 11547; Printing Ink Used - Black 30
Equipment EDITORIAL: Front-end Software – SII.; Editorial Hardware – 52-SII/K-100 Himalaya Risc; Editorial Equipment – RSK/Tandy 2000; Editorial Printers – HP 1050 C Plus, HP Design Jet 1050C CLASSIFIED: Front-end Software – SII.; Classified Hardware – 52-SII/K-100 Himalaya Risc; Classified Printers – Ricoh Aticio 5500/MC4500 DISPLAY: Ad make-up applications – DTI/AdSpeed; Layout Software – DTI.; Display Hardware – 3-Sun/Sparc 20; Display Printers – 3-HP/LaserPrinter; Production Equipment – 2-COM/8600, 1-ECR/VR 36, 1-ECR/VR 30, 1-AG/Arcus, 1-Pre Press/Panther 62, 1-ECR/Knockout; Cameras – R/500, 1-B/Horizontal; Scanners – 1-Nikon/Slide Scanner, 1-Optronics/Prosetter Drum Scanner, 1-APP/Mac Quadra 950, 1-APP/Mac Quadra 650. PRESSROOM: Line 1 – 10-G/Urbanite U1247 single width; Line 2 – 10-G/Urbanite U1379 single width; Folders – G/Series 1000; Pasters – 18-Enkel/Autoweb 2500; Press control system – Fin/Consoles. MAILROOM: Counter stackers – 3/NJP, 1-/EZ; Bundle tying machines – 2-Bu/Tristar 210, 5-OVL/415; Addressing machine – 1-/BH, Ap/IIe.; Audio Hardware – Micro Voice System BUSINESS COMPUTERS: Business Software – DSI/Papertrack; Business Hardware – PBS/Business System, IBM/380 Risc System, Ricoh Aticio 5500
Delivery method: Newsstand, Racks

MADERA

MADERA TRIBUNE

100 E. 7th St., Madera, Calif., 93638; gen tel (559) 674-2424; adv tel (559) 674-2424; ed tel (559) 674-8134; gen fax (559) 673-0944; adv fax (559) 673-6526; ed fax (559) 673-0944; gen e-mail maderatribune@maderatribunet.net; ed e-mail news@maderatribune.net; web site www.maderatribune.com
Published: Mon, Tues, Wed, Thur, Fri, Sat
Weekday Frequency: m
Saturday Frequency: m
Circulation: 4,379; 4,496(sat)
Last Audit: September 30, 2005
Price: 9.00/mo; 66.00/yr.
Advertising: Open inch rate $14.00
News services: AP.
Politics: Independent. **Established:** 1892
Not Published: New Year's Day; Memorial Day; July 4; Labor Day; Thanksgiving; Christmas.
Special Editions: Madera Business Extravaganza (Apr); Back-to-School (Aug); Last Minute Gift Guide (Dec); FFA Tab (Feb); Brides Guide (Jan); Rural Routes/Salute to Ag Broad Sheet (Jul); Father's Day (Jun); Pride in Madera County (Mar); Mother's Day (May); Holiday Gift Guid
Special Weekly Sections: Financial (Fri); Financial (Mon); Religion (Sat); Financial (Thur); People (Tues); People (Wed).
Magazines: USA WEEKEND Magazine (Sat).
Adv. Dir........................................Ellen Beach
Ed. ....Charles P. Doud
Sports Ed...................................Paul Stanford
Dir., Opns...................................Leonard Soliz
Market Information: TMC.
Mechanical available: Offset; Black and 3 ROP colors; insert accepted - 3 x 5; page cutoffs - 22 3/4.
Mechanical Specifications: Type page 13 x 21; E - 6 cols, 2 1/16, 1/8 between; A - 6 cols, 2 1/16, 1/8 between; C - 9 cols, 1 3/8, 1/16 between.
Commodity Consumption: Avg. Page Number Per Issue - Daily 20; Avg. Page Number Per Issue - Plates Used 10510; widths 25; Newsprint Used - Metric Tons 300; Printing Ink Used - Black 10623; Printing Ink Used - Color 1843; Printing Ink Used - Pages Printed 10510.
Equipment EDITORIAL: Front-end Software – Baseview/NewsEdit Pro.; Editorial Hardware – APP/Mac; Editorial Printers – APP/Mac CLASSIFIED: Front-end Software – Baseview.; Classified Hardware – COM, APP/Mac; Classified Printers – APP/Mac DISPLAY: Ad make-up applications – Multi-Ad/Creator; Layout Software – APP/Mac.; Display Hardware – APP/Mac; Display Printers – APP/Mac PRODUCTION: Pagination Software – QPS/QuarkXPress 4.0.; Production Equipment – Nuarc; Folders – 2; Bundle tying machines – 1-Bu/16 2X, 1/MLN. BUSINESS COMPUTERS: Business Software – CJ; Business Hardware – IBM/Sys 34, HP/Sys, IBM

MANTECA

MANTECA BULLETIN

531 E. Yosemite Ave., Manteca, Calif., 95336; gen tel (209) 249-3500; adv tel (209) 249-3500; ed tel (209) 249-3500; gen fax (209) 249-3559; adv fax (209) 249-3551; ed fax (209) 249-3559; adv e-mail ads@mantecabulletin.com; ed e-mail news@mantecabulletin.com; web site www.mantecabulletin.com
Group: Morris Multimedia, Inc.
Published: Mon, Tues, Wed, Thur, Fri, Sat, Sun
Weekday Frequency: m
Saturday Frequency: m
Circulation: 5,451; 5,451(sat); 5,451(sun)
Last Audit: Sworn September 30, 2010
Price: 86.20/yr.
Advertising: $14.33/inch Open rate
Insert rate: 63/m Open rate
News services: AP; MNCC
Politics: 1908
Not Published: Christmas.
Own facility?: Y
Special Editions: HS Football Preview (Aug); Pumpkin Fair (Oct); Sidewalk Fair (Apr)
Special Weekly Sections: BulletinExtra On-the-Road (Fridays); Home Guide (Saturday);
Magazines: American Profile (Weekly); Relish (monthly); Spry (monthly)
Profile: Manteca Daily Newspaper serving South San Joaquin Co. California
Editorial Page Ed. ....Dennis Wyatt
Composing & Commercial Print Mgr. .Kay Garcia
Group Publisher ....Dave Winegarden
Advertising Director ....Chuck Higgs
Circulation Director.....................Drew Savage
Business Manager...............Tamara Foreman
Pressroom Manager.............Howard Santiago
City Editor........................Rose Albano-Risso
Sports Editor ....Jonamar Jacinto
I.T. Manager ....Adam Wright
Pub. ....Paul Mahony
Adv. Mgr. ....Teri Garcia
Circ. Mgr. ....Amy Hitchcock
Prodn. Mgr..................................Steve Curtis
Market Information: TMC.
Mechanical available: Offset; Black and 3 ROP colors; insert accepted - all; page cutoffs - 22.
Mechanical Specifications: Type page 12 x 21; E - 6 cols, 1 5/8, 1/8 between; A - 6 cols, 1 7/8, 1/8 between; C - 10 cols, 7/8, 1/8 between.
Commodity Consumption: Avg. Page Number Per Issue - Daily 20; Avg. Page Number Per Issue - Plates Used 9000; Avg. Page Number Per Issue - Sunday 26; widths 25; Newsprint Used - Metric Tons 575; Printing Ink Used - Black 15500; Printing Ink Used - Color 3300.
Equipment EDITORIAL: Front-end Software – Baseview/NewsEdit Pro.; Editorial Hardware – 10-APP/Mac G3; Editorial Printers – HP/LaserJet 4MV CLASSIFIED: Front-end Software – Baseview.; Classified Hardware – 6-APP/Mac G3; Classified Printers – APP/Mac Pro 630 DISPLAY: Ad make-up applications – QPS/QuarkXPress, Baseview, Adobe/Photoshop; Layout Software – 6-APP/Mac G4.; Display Printers – HP/8000N PRODUCTION: Pagination Software – QPS/QuarkXPress.; Production Equipment – HP/8000N, Pre Press/Panther, Konica/EV Jetsetter 9100; Cameras – 1-B; Scanners – 4-HP, 2-Umax PRESSROOM: Line 1 – 13-G/Community; Line 2 – 3; Line 3 – 1; Press Drives – Fin/75 h.p., Twin/150 hp; Folders – 1-G/SC. MAILROOM: Counter stackers – 1-BG/Count-O-Veyor; Bundle tying machines – 3/Bu; Addressing machine – 1-/Am. BUSINESS COMPUTERS: Business Software – MAS 90; Business Hardware – 4-Pentium/network with Microsoft Windows 2000
Zip Codes served: 95336, 95337, 95330, 95366, 95231, 95206
Delivery method: Mail, Newsstand, Private Carrier, Racks

MARYSVILLE

APPEAL-DEMOCRAT

1530 Ellis Lake Dr., Marysville, Calif., 95901; gen tel (530) 741-2345; adv tel (530) 741-2345; ed tel (530) 741-2400; gen fax (530) 741-1061; adv fax (530) 741-2086; ed fax (530) 741-0140; gen e-mail appeal@syix.com; web site www.appeal-democrat.com
Published: Mon, Tues, Wed, Thur, Fri, Sat, Sun
Weekday Frequency: m
Saturday Frequency: m
Circulation: 17,679; 17,679(sat); 18,306(sun)
Last Audit: September 30, 2009
Price: 33.00/mo; 88.75/yr.
Advertising: Open inch rate $27.80
News services: AP, MCT, TMS.
Politics: Libertarian. **Established:** 1853
Special Editions: Pets (Apr); Medical Directory (Dec); New Neighbors (Feb); Brides (Jan); Y-S Fair (Jul); Graduation (Jun); Home Improvement (Mar); Spirit of Freedom (Nov); Home Improvement (Sept).
Special Weekly Sections: Life (S); Real Estate (Sat); Food (Wed).
Magazines: USA WEEKEND Magazine (S); Weekender (Thur).
Broadcast Affiliations: WLNE New Bedford, MA; WRGB Schenectady, NY; KTVL Medford, OR; WLNE Providence, RI; WTVC Chattanooga, TN; KFDM Beaumont, TX; KFDM Port Arthur, TX.
Profile: Daily newspaper serving the northern California counties of Yuba, Sutter, and Colusa.
Pub. ....Dave Schmall
Asst. to Pub. ....Melony Sanchez
Bus. Mgr. ....Mike Burman
Adv. Dir. ....Debbie Baggett
Adv. Mgr., Classified....................Nancy Brown
Adv. Mgr., Nat'l................Stephanie Azevedo
Circ. Dir. ....Joe Kraus
Entertainment Ed..........................Josh Kendrix
Features Ed................................Susan Benitez
News Ed......................................Todd Hansen
Photo Ed...................................Chris Kauffman
Sports Ed...................................Bryan Demain
Prodn. Foreman, Mailroom ......Cindy Alexander
Prodn. Foreman, Pressroom ....Engel Avalos
Market Information: TMC.
Mechanical available: Offset; Black and 3 ROP colors; insert accepted - sample pouch, poly bag; page cutoffs - 22 3/4.
Mechanical Specifications: Type page 11 5/8 x 21 1/2; E - 6 cols, 1 13/16, 1/8 between; A - 6 cols, 1 13/16, 1/8 between; C - 9 cols, 1 3/16, 1/8 between.
Commodity Consumption: Avg. Page Number Per Issue - Daily 34; Avg. Page Number Per Issue - Plates Used 16000; Avg. Page Number Per Issue - Saturday 34; Avg. Page Number Per Issue - Sunday 48; widths 25; Newsprint Used - Metric Tons 1507; Printing Ink Used - Black 27270; Printi
Equipment EDITORIAL: Front-end Software – Dewar/Sys IV, Baseview.; Editorial Hardware – APP/Mac, Baseview; Editorial Equipment – APP/Power Mac, HP/8000; Editorial Printers – Pre Press/Panther Pro, Varityper CLASSIFIED: Front-end Software – Baseview.; Classified Hardware – APP/Mac, Baseview; Layout Software – MEI.; Display Hardware – APP/Mac PRODUCTION: Pagination Software – Baseview.; Production Equipment – Caere/Omni-Page Pro 7.0.1, Pre Press/Panther Pro 36 Imagesetter; Cameras – C/Spartan III; Scanners – Nikon/Coolscan 35mm PRESSROOM: Line 1 – 8-G/Urbanite (1 color hump) 1986; Pasters – 7 MAILROOM: Counter stackers – 1-BG/Count-O-Veyor 108; Inserters and stuffers – 2-MM/227; Bundle tying machines – 1-MLN/ML2EE, 1-MLN/Spirit; Wrapping singles – 1-Id; Mailroom control system – 1/HL. BUSINESS COMPUTERS: Business Software – Great Plains; Business Hardware – PC

MENLO PARK

PALO ALTO DAILY NEWS

255 Constitution Dr., Menlo Park, Calif., 94025-1108; gen tel (650) 391-1000; adv tel (650) 391-1028; ed tel (650) 391-1337; ed e-mail news@paloaltodailynews.com; web site www.paloaltodailynews.com

Published: Mon, Tues, Wed, Thur, Fri, Sat, Sun
Weekday Frequency: m
Saturday Frequency: m
Circulation: 47,585; 49,282(sat); 49,464(sun)
Last Audit: March 31, 2007
Price: 1.85/wk; 8.00/mo; 96.00/yr.
Advertising: Open inch rate $20.00
News services: AP, NYT, Bay City News.
Politics: Independent.
Special Editions: Back-to-School (Aug); Holiday Gift Guide (Dec); Bride (Jan); Reader's Choice Awards (Jun); Home Improvement (Monthly); Holiday Gift Guide (Nov); Bride (Sept).
Special Weekly Sections: Autos (Fri); Computing (Mon); Autos (S); Autos (Sat); Autos (Thur); Fashion (Tues); Travel (Wed).
Adv. Mgr., Classified................Michael Relayo
Exec. Ed...................................Mario Dianda
Mng. Ed...................................Jamie Casini
City Ed.....................................Jason Green
Asst. City Ed..........................Victor Gonzales
Copydesk Chief...............................Kevin Kelly
Sports Ed...................................Greg Frazier
Opns. Mgr.................................Paulo Pereira
Prodn./Creative Servs. Mgr..........Christine Eng
Market Information: TMC.
Mechanical available: Offset; Black and 3 ROP colors; insert accepted.
Mechanical Specifications: Type page 13 x 21.
Commodity Consumption: Avg. Page Number Per Issue - Daily 52; Avg. Page Number Per Issue - Saturday 52.
Equipment EDITORIAL: Front-end Software – Baseview/NewsEdit Pro, QPS/QuarkXPress 3.31.; Editorial Hardware – 10-APP/Mac G4; Editorial Printers – HP/5, NewGen/Imager Plus 12xf CLASSIFIED: Front-end Software – Baseview/Class Manager Plus.; Classified Hardware – 2-APP/Power Mac 7200-90; Classified Printers – HP/LaserJet 5mp DISPLAY: Ad make-up applications – QPS/QuarkXPress 3.31.; Display Hardware – 6-APP/Power Mac 7500/100; Display Printers – NewGen/Imager Plus 12xf PRODUCTION: Pagination Software – QPS/QuarkXPress 3.31.; Production Equipment – Lf/AP Leaf Picture Desk; Scanners – HP/ScanJet 3C PRESSROOM: Line 1 – 5-KP/Web Leader single width; Folders – 5; Business Hardware – APP/Mac G4

MERCED

MERCED SUN-STAR

3033 N. G St., Merced, Calif., 95341-0739; gen tel (209) 722-1511; adv tel (209) 385-2499; ed tel (209) 384-3811; gen fax (209) 385-2468; adv fax (209) 385-2468; ed fax (209) 385-2460; ed e-mail editor@mercedsun-star.com; web site www.mercedsun-star.com

Published: Mon, Tues, Wed, Thur, Fri, Sat
Weekday Frequency: m
Saturday Frequency: m
Circulation: 11,976; 15,373(sat)
Last Audit: ABC September 30, 2011
Price: 12.50/mo; 105.00/yr.
Advertising: Open inch rate $46.75
News services: AP.
Politics: Independent.
Special Editions: Senior Scene (Monthly).
Special Weekly Sections: Health Pages (Tues).
Magazines: Preview/Entertainment (Fri); UC Merced (Quarterly); Parade (S); TV Update (Sat).
Pub.................................Debra Kuykendall
Dir., Finance............................Laurie De Bie
Adv. Dir.....................................Larry Dovichi
Vice Pres., Circ..........................Michael Miller
Features Ed...............................Barbara Hale
Local News Ed.......................Michelle Robison
Prodn. Mgr.........................Mike Schlotthauer
Market Information: ADS; TMC.
Mechanical available: Offset; Black and 3 ROP colors; insert accepted - card inserts; page cutoffs - 22 3/4.
Mechanical Specifications: Type page 13 x 21; E - 6 cols, 2 1/16, 1/8 between; A - 6 cols, 2 1/16, 1/8 between; C - 9 cols, 1 3/8, 1/16 between.
Commodity Consumption: Avg. Page Number Per Issue - Daily 34.4; Avg. Page Number Per Issue - Plates Used 42416; Avg. Page Number Per Issue - Saturday 66; widths 12 1/2; Newsprint Used - Metric Tons 1019.4; Printing Ink Used - Black 4800; Printing Ink Used - Color 2250; Printin
Equipment EDITORIAL: Front-end Software – Baseview.; Editorial Hardware – APP/Mac; Editorial Printers – HP/LaserJet CLASSIFIED: Front-end Software – Baseview.; Classified Hardware – APP/Mac; Classified Printers – HP/LaserJet DISPLAY: Ad make-up applications – Synaptic.; Display Hardware – IBM; Display Printers – Okidata/Microline 591 PRODUCTION: Pagination Software – Baseview, QPS/QuarkXPress 4.0.; Production Equipment – 1-Accuset/800, 1-Konica/CRT Autokon, 1-Konica/K-550; Cameras – 1-C/Spartan I, 1-SCREEN/Companica 650 CR (color); Scanners – Umax/1200, Polaroid/SprintScan, ECR/Autokon PRESSROOM: Line 1 – 8-G/Urbanite; Folders – 1-G/2:1. MAILROOM: Counter stackers – 1-G/Stackmaster; Inserters and stuffers – 4/MM; Bundle tying machines – 3-MLN/ML2EE, 1-EAM-Mosca; Addressing machine – 2-/KR.; Business Hardware – 2-IBM/486

MODESTO

THE MODESTO BEE

1325 H St., Modesto, Calif., 95354; gen tel (209) 578-2000; adv tel (209) 521-7777; ed tel (209) 578-2330; gen fax (209) 578-2095; adv fax (209) 578-2271; gen e-mail cservice@modbee.com; web site www.modbee.com

Group: Newspapers First, Inc.
Published: Mon, Tues, Wed, Thur, Fri, Sat, Sun
Weekday Frequency: m
Saturday Frequency: m
Circulation: 59,361; 61,205(sat); 72,406(sun)
Last Audit: ABC September 30, 2011
Price: 11.25/mo (carrier), $7.25/mo (mon, sat & S only); 119.60/yr.
Advertising: Open inch rate $136.10
News services: AP, NYT, LAT-WP, MCT, MNS.
Politics: Non-Partisan.
Special Editions: Living in the Valley (Aug); SUV & Ski (Dec); Health & Fitness (Feb); Bridal (Jan); NSA Girl's Softball (Jul); Father's Day (Jun); Progress (Mar); Graduation (May); Oakdale Business (Nov); Readers' Choice (Oct); Homescape (Spring); NASCAR (Summer).
Special Weekly Sections: Scene (Fri); Monday Life (Mon); Your Home (S); Faith & Values (Sat); Buzz (Thur); Currents (Tues); Healthy Living (Wed).
Magazines: Parade (S).
Dir., Finance..........................Walter E. Kletke
Adv. Vice Pres............................Tim Ritchey
Adv. Mgr., Inside Sales.........Deanna Whitmore
Circ. Mgr., Acquisition....................Patty Tharp
Circ. Mgr., Distr..................Craig Mackenzie
Exec. Ed.....................................Mark Vasche
Editorial Page Ed...............................Judy Sly
Farm/Agriculture Writer..............Rich Estrada
Graphics Dir................................Jim Lawrence
Health/Medical Reporter...............Ken Carlson
Chief Photographer......................Debbie Noda
Sports Ed......................................Brian Clark
Technology Writer.......................Patrick Giblin
Television/Film Writer......................Pat Clark
Theater/Music Writer...................Lisa Millegan
Wine Writer..................................Tim Moran
Online Dir.................................Eric Johnston
Work/Money Team Leader..................Dave Hill
Market Information: ADS; Split run; TMC; Zoned editions.
Mechanical available: Flexography; Black and 3 ROP colors; insert accepted - tabloids, minis, standards, free standing; page cutoffs - 22.
Mechanical Specifications: Type page 13 x 21; E - 6 cols, 2 1/16, 1/8 between; A - 6 cols, 2 1/16, 1/8 between; C - 10 cols, 1 1/2, 1/16 between.
Commodity Consumption: Avg. Page Number Per Issue - Daily 55; Avg. Page Number Per Issue - Plates Used 89232; Avg. Page Number Per Issue - Sunday 73; widths 40 1/2; Newsprint Used - Short Tons 10777; Printing Ink Used - Black 324000; Printing Ink Used - Color 95000; Printing I
Equipment EDITORIAL: Front-end Software – Unisys/Hermes.; Editorial Hardware – 6-Compaq, DEC/Alpha; Editorial Equipment – 9-IBM/PC CLASSIFIED: Front-end Software – NetLinx Czar, NetLinx Coyote XA.; Classified Hardware – SII/Tandem, 6-Compaq, Tandem DISPLAY: Ad make-up applications – Multi-Ad/Creator 2; Layout Software – MEI/ALS.; Display Hardware – 13-APP/Mac G3; Display Printers – AG PRODUCTION: Pagination Software – Unisys/Hermes 4.0, SCP II.; Production Equipment – Na/Flex, III, 1-Autologic 3850; Scanners – AG/T2000, Umax PRESSROOM: Line 1 – 8-G/Flexoliner; Press Drives – Rockwell/Allen Bradley; Folders – 2-G/Sovereign; Pasters – 8; Reels and Stands – 8-G/CT-50 RTP. MAILROOM: Counter stackers – 2-HL/HTII, 1-HL/HTII dual carrier, 2-HI/Olympian; Inserters and stuffers – HI/NP 2299; Bundle tying machines – 4/Power Strap/PSN5, 1-/Power Strap/PSN6, 1-/MLN; Wrapping singles – 3-HL/Monarch, 1-/EDS; Mailroom control system – HI/Prima BUSINESS COMPUTERS: Business Software – CJ; Business Hardware – DEC/VAX 4600, PBS/Circulation Mgmt. 3.2

MONTEREY

THE MONTEREY COUNTY HERALD

8 Upper Ragsdale Dr., Monterey, Calif., 93940; gen tel (831) 372-3311; adv tel (831) 646-4300; ed tel (831) 646-4352; adv fax (831) 646-4394 (retail); ed fax (831) 372-8401; web site www.montereyherald.com

Published: Mon, Tues, Wed, Thur, Fri, Sat, Sun
Weekday Frequency: m
Saturday Frequency: m
Circulation: 23,101; 23,101(sat); 60,843(sun)
Last Audit: ABC September 30, 2011
Price: 13.60/mo ; 180.00/yr .
Advertising: Open inch rate $74.45
News services: AP, LAT-WP, NYT, MCT.
Politics: Independent.
Special Editions: Classic Car Weekend (Aug); Holiday Gift Guide (Dec); Wedding Planner (Feb); AT&T Pro-Am Golf (Jan); California Rodeo Salinas (Jul); Discover Carmel Valley 1 (Jun); Senior 1 (Mar); Focus on Salinas (May); Discover Carmel Valley 2 (Nov); Cherry's Jubilee Ca
Special Weekly Sections: Health/Science (Fri); Life (Mon); Arts & Leisure (S); Real Estate Tab (Sat); Go! (Thur); Family (Tues); Taste (Wed).
Magazines: TV Week (S).
CFO....................................Juan Jose Sierra
Pub......................................Gary Omernick
Online Ed..................................Lisa Mitchell
Features Ed...................................Mike Hale
Political Ed...............................Royal Calkins
Prodn. Mgr., Publishing Systems Jeremy Patterson
Exec. Ed...................................Joe Livernois
Market Information: TMC.
Mechanical available: Flexography; Black and 3 ROP colors; insert accepted; page cutoffs - 22 1/4.
Mechanical Specifications: Type page 13 x 21; E - 6 cols, 2 1/16, 1/8 between; A - 6 cols, 2 1/16, 1/8 between; C - 9 cols, 1 3/8, 1/16 between.
Commodity Consumption: Avg. Page Number Per Issue - Daily 44; Avg. Page Number Per Issue - Plates Used 35000; Avg. Page Number Per Issue - Sunday 80; widths 12 1/2; Newsprint Used - Short Tons 3500; Printing Ink Used - Black 144480; Printing Ink Used - Color 3780; Printing Ink
Equipment EDITORIAL: Front-end Software – Dewar/Disc Sys III.; Editorial Hardware – 10-PC, 25-Visual Display Terminals; Editorial Equipment – 2-PrePress/Tegra with 5000 processors & 50001 Imagers; Editorial Printers – 1-Dataproducts/LZR CLASSIFIED: Front-end Software – DTI/Class, Dewar/Disc Sys III.; Classified Hardware – 22-PC DISPLAY: Ad make-up applications – QPS/QuarkXPress.; Display Hardware – 14-APP/Mac; Production Equipment – 2-Tegra/Varityper/XP-1000, 2-Tegra/Varityper 5000 RIP, 1-AG/Avantra 25, 1-Bidco, 2-Cascade/RIP; Cameras – 2-C/Spartan III; Scanners – HP/ScanJet Plus, ECR/Autokon 1000DC. PRESSROOM: Line 1 – 7-G/Flexoliner 1988; Folders – 2 MAILROOM: Counter stackers – 2-MM/310, 1-MM/375, 1-TMSI/Compass 180; Inserters and stuffers – 2-MM/308 Biliner; Bundle tying machines – 2/MLN, 2-Sterling/MR45CH. BUSINESS COMPUTERS: Business Software – CJ/AIM; Business Hardware – 1-DEC/VAX-4200, 1-DEC/VAX-4300, 5-APP/Mac, 24-IBM

NAPA

NAPA VALLEY REGISTER

1615 2nd St., Napa, Calif., 94559-0050; gen tel (707) 226-3711; adv tel (707) 257-3003; gen fax (707) 252-0247; adv fax (707) 257-3003; gen e-mail napanews@napanews.com; ed e-mail napaopinion@napanews.com; web site www.napavalleyregister.com

Group: Metro Newspaper Advertising Services, Inc.
Published: Mon, Tues, Wed, Thur, Fri, Sat, Sun
Weekday Frequency: m
Saturday Frequency: m
Circulation: 14,130; 13,504(sat); 13,914(sun)
Last Audit: ABC September 30, 2011
Price: 12.50/mo; 139.00/yr.
Advertising: Open inch rate $26.90
News services: AP.
Politics: Independent.
Own facility?: Y
Special Editions: Once Upon A Time (Apr); Football (Aug); Wishbooks (Dec); Bridal (Feb); Healthwise (Jan); The Best Years (Jul); County Fair (Jun); Spring Home & Garden (Mar); Napa Solano Home & Garden (May); Auto Showcase (Nov); Transamerica Golf (Oct); Heirlooms (Sept).
Special Weekly Sections: Real Estate (S); Senior Citizens (Sat); Art & Entertainment (Thur); Food & Wine (Wed).
Magazines: Relish (Monthly); USA WEEKEND Magazine (S).
Pub....Brenda Speth
Bus. Mgr......................................Tracy Hardy
HR Mgr.................................Peggy Chapman
Adv. Dir................................Norma Kostecka
Circ. Dir.......................................Joe Brasil
Mng. Ed.......................................Bill Kisliuk
City Ed......................................David Ryan
Living/Lifestyle Ed...................Sasha Paulsen
Opinion Ed...................................Doug Ernst
Religion Ed....................................Tina Barni
Sports Ed...............................Randy Johnson
Mgmt. Info Servs. Mgr..................John Herrick
Webmaster.................................Peter Wierich
Prodn. Foreman, Composing.....Mary Lou Gilley
Prodn. Foreman, Pressroom/Platemaking John Hawkley
Market Information: Split run; TMC.
Mechanical available: Offset; Black and 3 ROP colors; insert accepted; page cutoffs - 22 3/4.
Mechanical Specifications: Type page 13 x 21 1/2; E - 6 cols, 1 5/8, 1/8 between; A - 6 cols, 1 7/8, 1/8 between; C - 10 cols, 1 1/8, 1/16 between.
Commodity Consumption: Avg. Page Number Per Issue - Daily 24; Avg. Page Number Per Issue - Plates Used 12000; Avg. Page Number Per Issue - Sunday 56; widths 25; Newsprint Used - Metric Tons 1600; Printing

Ink Used - Black 15000; Printing Ink Used - Color 2500; Printing Ink Use
Equipment EDITORIAL: Front-end Software – Baseview.; Editorial Hardware – 25-APP/Mac; Editorial Printers – 2-LaserMaster/Unity 1800 x 60, 2-AU/3850 CLASSIFIED: Front-end Software – Synaptic.; Classified Hardware – 5-ScrippSat; Classified Printers – LaserMaster/Unity DISPLAY: Ad make-up applications – QPS/QuarkXPress, QPS, Adobe/Photoshop, Archetype/Corel Draw; Display Hardware – 5-ScrippSat; Display Printers – 3-LaserMaster/Unity PRODUCTION: Pagination Software – QPS/QuarkXPress 3.31.; Production Equipment – 5-LaserMaster/Unity; Cameras – 1-MG; Scanners – HP/ScanJet IIc PRESSROOM: Line 1 – 7-G/Urbanite; Folders – 1 MAILROOM: Counter stackers – 1/BG; Inserters and stuffers – 2-MM/6:1; Bundle tying machines – 1-/MLN; Addressing machine – American Business Computers.; Audio Hardware – US Audiotex; Business Hardware – 6-ScrippSat

NOVATO

MARIN INDEPENDENT JOURNAL

150 Alameda del Prado, Novato, Calif., 94949-6665; gen tel (415) 883-8600; adv tel (415) 883-8600; ed tel (415) 883-8600; gen fax (415) 382-0549; adv fax (415) 382-1535; ed fax (415) 883-5458; ed e-mail tosubscribe@marinij.com; localnews@marinij.com; web site www.marinij.com
Published: Mon, Tues, Wed, Thur, Fri, Sat, Sun
Saturday Frequency: m
Circulation: 26,548; 26,548(sat); 28,815(sun)
Last Audit: September 30, 2009
Price: 3.20/wk; 166.40/yr.
Advertising: Open inch rate $156.00
News services: AP, Bay City News Service, McClatchy, NYT, TMS.
Politics: Independent.
Special Editions: Health & Fitness (Apr); Real Estate (Aug); Holiday Gift Guide Series (Dec); Summer Camps (Feb); Bridal Showcase (Jan); Real Estate (Jul); Real Estate (Jun); Fashion (Mar); Mountain Play (May); Marin Homes (Monthly); Auto Showcase (Nov); Real Estate (Oct);
Special Weekly Sections: Lifestyles-Health & Fitness (Mon); Lifestyles-Home & Garden (Sat); IJ Weekend (Thur); Lifestyles-Food & Drink (Wed); Motorway (Weekly).
Magazines: Relish (Monthly); USA WEEKEND Magazine (S).
Pres./Pub. ....Mario van Dongen
Adv. Mgr. ....Ron Thayer
Circ. Dir. ....Wally Tiedemann
Exec. Ed. ....Matthew Wilson
City Ed. ....Robert Sterling
Editorial Page Ed. ....Doug Bunnell
Graphics Design Ed. ....Beth Renneisen
Lifestyles Ed. ....Brent Ainsworth
Page One Ed. ....Joe Konte
Sports Ed. ....Dave Allen
Prodn. Mgr., Opns. ....Tom Jensen
Prodn. Mgr., Pressroom ....Bob Phillips
Market Information: ADS; Split run.
Mechanical available: Offset; Black and 3 ROP colors; insert accepted - CD's, packages like Handiwipes, etc.; page cutoffs - 22 3/4.
Mechanical Specifications: Type page 11 5/8 x 21 1/2; E - 6 cols, 1 13/16, 1/8 between; A - 6 cols, 1 13/16, 1/8 between; C - 10 cols, 1 1/8, 1/5 between.
Commodity Consumption: Avg. Page Number Per Issue - Daily 44; Avg. Page Number Per Issue - Plates Used 36980; Avg. Page Number Per Issue - Sunday 88; widths 27; Newsprint Used - Short Tons 4800; Printing Ink Used - Black 107000; Printing Ink Used - Color 32500; Printing Ink Us
Equipment EDITORIAL: Front-end Software – APP/Mac G3 4.6.8, Baseview.; Editorial Hardware – Baseview; Editorial Equipment – 50-AT/ADT; Editorial Printers – 1-QMS CLASSIFIED: Front-end Software – APT/ACT Classified.; Classified Hardware – 1-Dell/PC; Classified Printers – HP/4MP LaserJet DISPLAY: Ad make-up applications – Multi-Ad/Creator, QPS/QuarkXPress, Adobe/Pagemaker, Adobe/Photoshop; Display Hardware – 4-APP/Mac, Intel/Pentium fileserver, 3-AT; Display Printers – Tektronix/III PXi, APP/Mac LaserWriter 630 PRODUCTION: Pagination Software – Baseview, Adobe/InDesign CS.; Production Equipment – 1-Lf/AP Leaf Picture Desk, 2-Purup/Eckoprint, Barco; Scanners – Truvell/Color, 1-EC, Kk/RFS 2035, Nikon/AF 3510, Nikon/LS1000, Umax/5-12 Vista, AG/Arcus II, 2-Tecsa/Full Page 5240 PRESSROOM: Line 1 – 7-H/Lithomatic II double width; Press Drives – Bardal; Folders – 1-H/3:2, 1-H/2:1; Reels and Stands – 7; Press registration system – WPC/Microtrak. MAILROOM: Counter stackers – 2-HL/Monitor, 1-HL/Dual Carrier, 1-HL/HT-2, 1-Gammerler/570; Inserters and stuffers – 1-GMA/SLS 2000 10:2; Bundle tying machines – 2-MLN/2A, 3/Dynaric, 3-QWI/Viper; Wrapping singles – 1-St/600; Addressing machine – 1-Ch/542, 2-Barstrom; Business Hardware – IBM/AS-400

OAKLAND

THE ALAMEDA NEWSPAPER GROUP

401 13th St., Tribune Tower, Oakland, Calif., 94612; gen tel (510) 293-2426; gen fax (510) 293-2712

ONTARIO

INLAND VALLEY DAILY BULLETIN

2041 E. 4th St., Ontario, Calif., 91764-2605; gen tel (909) 987-6397; adv tel (909) 987-6397; ed tel (909) 987-6397; gen fax (909) 466-0235; adv fax (909) 989-8287; ed fax (909) 948-9038; adv e-mail adv@inlandnewspapers.com; ed e-mail citydesk@inlandnewspapers.com; news@dailybulletin.com; news.tips@inlandnewspapers.com; web site www.dailybulletin.com
Published: Mon, Tues, Wed, Thur, Fri, Sat, Sun
Weekday Frequency: m
Saturday Frequency: m
Circulation: 60,936; 47,348(sat); 60,516(sun)
Last Audit: ABC September 30, 2011
Price: 184.80/yr (carrier); 10.64/4wk.
News services: AP, CNS, MCT, NYT.
Politics: Independent.
Note: The Los Angeles Newspaper Group includes the Long Beach Press-Telegram (mS), Los Angeles Daily News (mS), Ontario Inland Valley Daily Bulletin (mS), Pasadena Star-News (mS), Redlands Daily Facts (eS), San Bernardino County Sun (mS), San Gabriel Valley Tri
Special Weekly Sections: City News (Fri); Real Estate (S); Real Estate (Sat); Food (Wed).
Magazines: Relish (Monthly); USA WEEKEND Magazine (S).
CEO/Pub. ....Fred Hamilton
Gen. Mgr. ....Peggy delToro
Finance Dir. ....Kathy Johnson
Adv. Vice Pres. ....Gene Pearlman
Circ. Vice Pres. ....Kathy Michalak
Exec. Ed. ....Frank Pine
Mng. Ed. ....Jeff Keating
Sr. Ed./Editorial Page Ed. ....Mike Brossart
Automotive Ed. ....Al Noseworthy
Asst. City Ed., Los Angeles Co. ....Joe Blackstock
Features Ed. ....Carla Sanders
Online Ed. ....Kent Salas
Photo Ed. ....Jeff Malet
Sports Ed. ....Louis Brewster
Prodn. Vice Pres. ....John Wartinger
Market Information: ADS; TMC; Zoned editions.
Mechanical available: Offset; Black and 3 ROP colors; insert accepted - single sheet flyers; page cutoffs - 22 3/4.
Mechanical Specifications: Type page 13 x 21 1/2; E - 6 cols, 1 4/5, 1/8 between; A - 6 cols, 1 4/5, 1/8 between; C - 10 cols, 1 7/100, 1/16 between.
Commodity Consumption: widths 25; Newsprint Used - Metric Tons 8100; Printing Ink Used - Black 125500; Printing Ink Used - Color 35400.
Equipment EDITORIAL: Front-end Software – Baseview, QPS/QuarkXPress.; Editorial Hardware – APP/Mac; Editorial Equipment – APP/Power Mac, APP/Mac G3; Editorial Printers – XIT/486 Clipper, APP/Mac LaserWriter Plus IIg, Pre Press/Panther Pro 46, Pre Pres/Panther Laserwriter CLASSIFIED: Front-end Software – SII.; Classified Hardware – 22-PC; Classified Equipment – APP/Mac; Classified Printers – HP/LaserJet 4M Plus, Pre Press/Panther Pro 46 Imagesetter DISPLAY: Ad make-up applications – Aldus/FreeHand 7.0, Microsoft/Works 4.0, Multi-Ad/Creator, Adobe/Illustrator 6.0, Adobe/Photoshop; Display Hardware – APP/Mac Quadra 610, APP/Mac G3, APP/Power Mac 8100, APP/Mac G4; Display Printers – Pre Press/Panther Pro 46 Imagesetters, HP/750 Color Plotter PRODUCTION: Pagination Software – Baseview, QPS/QuarkXPress 4.0.; Production Equipment – Pre Press/Panther Pro 46, 3-P/7225, 1-P/26RA; Cameras – C/Spartan III; Scanners – ECR/Autokon 1000 PRESSROOM: Line 1 – 7-MAN/Uniman 4 x 2 double width (4 color decks) 1986; Line 2 – 7-MAN/Uniman 4 X 2 double width (4 color decks) 1988; Folders – 4-MAN/2:1; Pasters – 14-MEG, 3. MAILROOM: Counter stackers – 4-HL/Monitor; Inserters and stuffers – 2-MM/227S; Bundle tying machines – 5/MLN. BUSINESS COMPUTERS: Business Software – Unix 3.0.12-1, Xi/Textspooler 15.1, Progress 5.2E, HP/MPE XL-IX, Cobol/II-XL, Data General 6.1, CJ, UDMS/Report Writer 4.0; Business Hardware – Unisys/6000-70, HP/3000 927-LX

PALM SPRINGS

THE DESERT SUN

750 N. Gene Autry Trail, Palm Springs, Calif., 92262; gen tel (760) 322-8889; gen fax (760) 778-4512; adv fax (760) 778-4528; ed fax (760) 778-4654; adv e-mail mkrans@palmspri.gannett.com; michelle.krans@thedesertsun.com; web site www.thedesertsun.com
Published: Mon, Tues, Wed, Thur, Fri, Sat, Sun
Weekday Frequency: m
Saturday Frequency: m
Circulation: 32,858; 36,462(sat); 40,406(sun)
Last Audit: ABC September 30, 2011
Price: 3.28/wk (includes tax); 13.10/mo; 144.13/yr.
Advertising: Open inch rate $106.75
News services: AP, GNS.
Politics: Independent. **Established:** 1927
Special Editions: Home Sweet Home (Apr); Football (Aug); Restaurant Guide (Dec); Riverside County Date Festival (Feb); Bob Hope Golf Classic (Jan); Newsweek & Evert Cup Tennis Championships (Mar); Keeping Cool & Summer Fun (May); Pure Gold Coupons (Monthly); Discover the C
Special Weekly Sections: Restaurant Review (Fri); Youth Page/Teen Voice (Mon); Desert Home (S); Real Estate (Sat); Desert Driver (Thur); Golf Notes (Tues); Prep Sports (Wed).
Magazines: Weekend Entertainment Guide (Fri); Desert Magazine (Monthly); TV Magazine (Sat).
Pres./Pub. ....Richard A. Ramhoff
Controller ....Sherri Maurer
Adv. Dir. ....Dominique Shwe
Circ. Dir. ....Greg Castro
Circ. Mgr., Home Delivery ....Kevin Kreisler
Community Conversations Ed. ....James Folmer
Features Ed. ....Barbara Lowell
Photo Ed. ....James Ku
Sports Ed. ....Matt Solinsky
Market Information: TMC.
Mechanical available: Offset; Black and 3 ROP colors; insert accepted; page cutoffs - 22 1/16.
Mechanical Specifications: Type page 13 x 21; E - 6 cols, 2, 1/8 between; A - 6 cols, 2, 1/8 between; C - 10 cols, 1 1/5, 1/8 between.
Commodity Consumption: Avg. Page Number Per Issue - Daily 55; Avg. Page Number Per Issue - Plates Used 65504; Avg. Page Number Per Issue - Sunday 72; widths 50; Newsprint Used - Metric Tons 6486; Printing Ink Used - Black 122790; Printing Ink Used - Color 18347; Printing Ink U
Equipment EDITORIAL: Front-end Software – SCS, Good News.; Editorial Hardware – Dell/Poweredge Server; Editorial Printers – HP/5-51 CLASSIFIED: Front-end Software – SII.; Classified Hardware – Tandem DISPLAY: Ad make-up applications – SCS/Layout 8000; Layout Software – SCS/Layout 8000.; Display Hardware – Dell/286, Dell/386; Display Printers – Dataproducts/LZR1200, APP/Mac LaserWriter 5SI, APP/Mac LaserWriter 12-660 (color) PRODUCTION: Pagination Software – SCS/Goodnews.; Production Equipment – 2-Harlequin/RIP, 2-AII/3850, 1-ECR 4550; Cameras – 1-C/Spartan III, 1-C/Newspager; Scanners – 2-ECR/Autokon 1000 PRESSROOM: Line 1 – 6-G/HO (3 half decks); Line 2 – 1989; Folders – 1-G/Double, G/3:2; Pasters – Reels and Stands ◻ 6-G/CT-50; Press control system – G/MPCS. MAILROOM: Counter stackers – Id/NS660, 3-Id/NS2000; Inserters and stuffers – H/14-72; Bundle tying machines – Power Strap; Addressing machine – 1/Ch.; Business Hardware – 1-IBM/Sys AS400, 1-IBM/Sys AS400

PALMDALE

ANTELOPE VALLEY PRESS

37404 N. Sierra Hwy., Palmdale, Calif., 93550-9343; gen tel (661) 273-2700; adv tel (661) 273-2700; ed tel (661) 273-2700; gen fax (661) 947-4870; adv fax (661) 947-4870; ed fax (661) 947-4870; gen e-mail email@avpress.com; ed e-mail editor@avpress.com; letters@avpress.com; web site www.avpress.com
Group: Antelope Valley Newspapers Inc Antelope Valley Newspapers Inc
Published: Mon, Tues, Wed, Thur, Fri, Sat, Sun
Weekday Frequency: m
Saturday Frequency: m
Circulation: 19,344; 19,344(sat); 23,354(sun)
Last Audit: Sworn September 30, 2010
Price: .50 daily, $1.50 Sunday, 199.00 year
Advertising: Open inch rate $70.90 daily, $76.75 Sunday commisssionable
News services: Metro, AP, TMS, N YT, Bloomberg, CNS, CSM, MCT.
Politics: 1915
Advertising not accepted: N
Own facility?: Y
Special Editions: Annual Fair (Aug); Annual Future Leaders (Feb); Annual Welcome (Oct).Sring and Fall Home; @RecordBody:**Special Weekly Sections:** Automotive (Fri); Real Estate (S); Food (Wed).
Magazines: Antelope Valley Lifestyle (Monthly); Parade (Weekly).Relish monthly, American Profile monthly
Pub. ....William C. Markham
Vice Pres./Gen. Mgr. ....Cherie Bryant
Adv. Dir., Retail ....Jay Curran
Mng. Ed. ....Charles Bostwick
Ed. ....Dennis Anderson
Bus./Finance Ed. ....James Skeen
Editorial Page Ed. ....William Warford
Entertainment/Amusements Ed. Lavender Vroman
Fashion/Style Ed. ....Liane Roth
Photo Ed. ....Ron Siddle
Real Estate Ed. ....Dean MacDonald
Special Sections Ed. ....Karen Maeshiro
Prodn. Mgr., Opns. ....Dennis Birks
Classified Advertising Director .Gina Mazzapica
Sports Editor ....Jay Heater
Marketing Director ....Cheryl Fletcher
Classified Advertising Director .Gina Mazzapica
Sports Editor ....Jay Heater
Marketing Director ....Cheryl Fletcher
Market Information: ADS; TMC.
Mechanical available: Offset; Black and 4 ROP colors; insert accepted; page cutoffs - 22 3/4.
Mechanical Specifications: Type page 22 1/8 x 21

1/2; E - 6 cols, 2 1/16, 1/8 between; A - 6 cols, 2 1/16, 1/8 between; C - 9 cols, 1 3/8, 1/16 between.

Commodity Consumption: Avg. Page Number Per Issue - Daily 34; Avg. Page Number Per Issue - Plates Used 47020; Avg. Page Number Per Issue - Saturday 46; Avg. Page Number Per Issue - Sunday 68; widths 12 1/2; Newsprint Used - Metric Tons 2824; Printing Ink Used - Black 106656; P

Equipment EDITORIAL: Front-end Software – DTI 55/In Copy; Editorial Hardware – Sun V440, StorEdge 330; Editorial Equipment – Mac G4, Mac G5; Editorial Printers – HP 8150 CLASSIFIED: Front-end Software – DTI 5.5; Classified Hardware – SunFire V120, StorEdge 330, Sun V440; Classified Equipment – Mac GA; Classified Printers – HP 2300, HP 1300 DISPLAY: Ad make-up applications – DTI 5.5/In Design; Display Hardware – Quad G5; Display Printers – HP 8150, HP 755, HP 1055 PRODUCTION: Pagination Software – DTI 5.5, Fusion RIP, Highwater Q2 Load balancer, Frist proof pro, DynaStrip 5 page pairer; Production Equipment – HP 1055 Color Proofer, 755 Color Proofer, 2 AII 3850's; Cameras – 2-C, R/440, 1-C/Spartan 3; Scanners – Epson 3200 Photo PRESSROOM: Line 1 – 10-G/Urbanite ; Press Drives – 3-HP/100; Folders – 1-G/Urbanite 1000 Series; Pasters – 7-Enkel/Automatic; Press control system – G/Console; Press registration system – Duarte/Pin System. MAILROOM: Counter stackers – 3-Id/2100; Inserters and stuffers – AM Graphics/NP 630; Bundle tying machines – 2/Dynaric; Mailroom control system – Amerigraph/Icon; Addressing machine – KR/Communications. BUSINESS COMPUTERS: Business Software – PBS, SBS, Edgil, Bellatrix, Global; Business Hardware – Dell power edge 2800, Dell power edge 2900

Zip Codes served: 93536, 93551, 93534, 93535, 93550, 93560, 93552, 93543, 93505, 93510, 93501, 93591, 93532, 93553, 93561, 93523, 93516, 93544, 91355, 91390, 91351

Delivery method: Mail, Private Carrier, Racks

PALO ALTO

THE WALL STREET JOURNAL-WESTERN EDITION

1701 Page Mill Rd., Palo Alto, Calif., 94304; gen tel (630) 493-2800; adv tel (415) 765-6131; adv fax (415) 398-0929; adv e-mail nora.millare@dowjones.com; web site www.wfj.com

Published: Mon, Tues, Wed, Thur, Fri, Sat
Weekday Frequency: m
Saturday Frequency: m
Circulation: 1,700,000; 1,400,000(sat)
Not Published: Presidents' Day; Memorial Day; Independence Day; Labor Day; Thanksgiving; Christmas.

Pub. ....Leslie Hinton
Adv. Mgr. ....Chris Collins
Circ. Mgr. ....Lynne K Brennen
Ed. in Chief ....Robert Thompson
Mgmt., Sec. ....Nora Millare

Mechanical available: Offset; Black and 3 ROP colors; insert accepted; page cutoffs - 22 3/4.

Commodity Consumption: Avg. Page Number Per Issue - Daily 52; widths 60.

Equipment; Production Equipment – 3-W, 1-Doutlilt, 5-Nu; Cameras – 2-C; Scanners – 2-ECR. PRESSROOM: Line 1 – 12-G/Metro Double Width; Line 2 – 12; Line 3 – 12-G/Metro Double Width; Line 4 – 12; Press Drives – 4; Folders – 2, 2; Pasters – 20, 20; Reels and Stands – 20, 20; Press control system – 4 MAILROOM: Counter stackers – 8/QWI; Bundle tying machines – 13-/Sterling, 9-/Powerstrap, 4-/OVL; Addressing machine – 8-/AVY. BUSINESS COMPUTERS: Business Software – Word processing; Business Hardware – IBM/3090

PASADENA

PASADENA STAR-NEWS

911 E. Colorado Blvd., Pasadena, Calif., 91109-1772; gen tel (626) 578-6300; adv tel (626) 578-6300; ed tel (626) 578-6300; gen fax (626) 432-5248; adv fax (626) 432-5247; ed fax (626) 432-5248; gen e-mail business@sgvn.com; ed e-mail news.starnews@sgvn.com; sports@sgvn.com; features@sgvn.com; web site www.pasadenastarnews.com

Published: Mon, Tues, Wed, Thur, Fri, Sat, Sun
Weekday Frequency: m
Saturday Frequency: m
Circulation: 25,154; 24,555(sat); 38,212(sun)
Last Audit: ABC September 30, 2011
Price: 4.00/wk.
News services: AP, CNS, Scripps-McClatchey, DJ, NYT, TMS.
Politics: Independent.
Note: The Los Angeles Newspaper Group includes the Long Beach Press-Telegram (mS), Los Angeles Daily News (mS), Ontario Inland Valley Daily Bulletin (mS), Pasadena Star-News (mS), Redlands Daily Facts (eS), San Bernardino County Sun (mS), San Gabriel Valley Tri
Special Editions: Earth Day (Apr); Pro Football Tab (Aug); The Rose Magazine (Dec); The Body (Jan); Hot Blues and Cool Jazz (Jul); Health Beat (Jun); Health Beat (Mar); Water Awareness (May); Holiday Guide (Nov); Rodeo Tab (Oct); Think Environmental (Sept).
Special Weekly Sections: Home Buyer (S); Home Buyer (Sat).
Magazines: Relish (Monthly); USA WEEKEND Magazine (S).

Pub. ....Lary Kline
Dir., Finance ....Rosa Lopez
HR/Admin. Mgr. ....Rachel A. Vasquez
Adv./Classified Dir. ....Randy Heltsley
Circ. Dir. ....Mike Belles
Circ. Mgr., Home Delivery ....Dennis Wagner
Circ. Mgr., Single Copy ....Dennis Schaffer
Ed. ....Larry Wilson
Exec. Ed. ....Talmage Campbell
Mng. Ed. ....Steve Hunt
Bus. Ed. ....Kevin Smith
City Ed. ....Bob Rector
Asst. City Ed. ....Janette Williams
Editorial Page Ed. ....Steve Scauzillo
Editorial Page Writer ....Linda Beckman
Features Ed. ....Catherine Gaugh
Librarian ....Linda Hammes
Sports Ed. ....Doug Spoon
Visuals Ed. ....Tim Berger
Mgr., Technical Servs. ....Terry Frazier

Market Information: ADS; TMC; Zoned editions.
Mechanical available: Offset; Black and 3 ROP colors; insert accepted; page cutoffs - 22 3/4.
Mechanical Specifications: Type page 11 1/2 x 21 1/4; E - 6 cols, 1 13/16, 1/8 between; A - 6 cols, 1 13/16, 1/8 between; C - 10 cols, 1 1/16, 1/16 between.
Commodity Consumption: Avg. Page Number Per Issue - Daily 46; Avg. Page Number Per Issue - Plates Used 50600; Avg. Page Number Per Issue - Saturday 86; Avg. Page Number Per Issue - Sunday 84; widths 50; Newsprint Used - Metric Tons 4147; Printing Ink Used - Black 63962; Printi
Equipment EDITORIAL: Front-end Software – SII/Editorial.; Editorial Hardware – SII/Server-Net; Editorial Equipment – 75-SII/Coyote, 2-SII/PC 22; Editorial Printers – 5-HP CLASSIFIED: Front-end Software – SII/Czarll.; Classified Hardware – 1-SII/ServerNet; Classified Equipment – 27-SII/Coyote 3; Classified Printers – 3-HP DISPLAY: Ad make-up applications – SII/IAL; Layout Software – SII/IAL, 4-Compaq/Ring Stations.; Display Hardware – 6-APP/Mac, 3-Compaq; Display Printers – Proofers, HP PRODUCTION: Pagination Software – SII/INL 9.2.; Production Equipment – AP Web Server, APP/Mac, QPS; Cameras – 2-C/Spartan III, 1-C/Newspager; Scanners – 10-Compaq, 2-Lf/Leafscan 35, 2-Polaroid PRESSROOM: Line 1 – 7-G/HO 1989; Line 2 – Jul-90; Folders – 3; Pasters – 14; Reels and Stands – 14; Press control system – G/MPCS. MAILROOM: Counter stackers – 5-Id/2000, 2-Id/440, 1/QWI; Inserters and stuffers – 4-GMA/SLS 1000; Bundle tying machines – 5-/Power Strap/PSN5, 2-/Dynaric; Wrapping singles – Addressing machine Â□ 2-Videojet/VMS. BUSINESS COMPUTERS: Business Software – CJ, Ultipro (payroll); Business Hardware – HP/969

PLACERVILLE

MOUNTAIN DEMOCRAT

1360 Broadway, Placerville, Calif., 95667-1088; gen tel (530) 622-1255; gen fax (530) 622-7894; gen e-mail mtdemo@mtdemocrat.net; adv e-mail adorders@mtdemocrat.com; web site www.mtdemocrat.com

Group: McNaughton Newspapers Inc.
Published: Mon, Tues, Wed, Fri
Weekday Frequency: m
Circulation: 11,001
Last Audit: Sworn September 30, 2006
Price: 80.00/yr; 22.00/3mo, $38.00/6mo.
Advertising: Open inch rate $22.10
News services: NYT, U.S. Suburban Press Inc..
Politics: Republican. **Established:** 1851
Advertising not accepted: N
Not Published: Tues.; Thurs.; Sat.; and Sun.
Own facility?: Y
Special Editions: Home and Garden (Apr); Medical Section (May); Home Improvement (Oct); Best of El Dorado County (Oct)
Special Weekly Sections: Real Estate (Fri); American Profile (Fri); Best Food Day (Wed).
Magazines: Relish (Monthly); American Profile (Weekly).
Profile: Dating back to California's Gold Rush days, the Mountain Democrat is the oldest newspaper in continuous publication in the state. The Mountain Democrat is an award-winning suburban newspaper covering the high growth West Slope of El Dorado County, Califor

Publisher ....Richard B. Esposito
Adv. Dir. ....Ian Balentine
Circ. Mgr. ....Gerry Ulm
Mng. Ed. ....Pat Lakey
Features Ed. ....Mimi Escabar
Sports Ed. ....Liz Kane
Online Contact ....Michael Raffety
Production Manager ....Letty Baumgardner
Online Editor ....David Martinelli

Market Information: TMC.
Mechanical available: Offset; Black and 3 ROP colors; insert accepted - Poly Bags; page cutoffs - 21 5/8.
Mechanical Specifications: Type page 12 x 21; E - 6 cols, 1 15/16, 1/8 between; A - 6 cols, 1 15/16, 1/8 between; C - 10 cols, 1 1/4, 1/8 between.
Commodity Consumption: widths 26 1/2.
Equipment EDITORIAL: Front-end Software – Wordpress; Editorial Hardware – AP/Mac; Editorial Printers – HP, HP CLASSIFIED: Front-end Software – Baseview.; Classified Hardware – AP/Mac; Classified Printers – HP, AG DISPLAY: Ad make-up applications – QPS/QuarkXPress, Adobe/Photoshop; Layout Software – APP/Mac.; Display Hardware – APP/Mac; Display Printers – APP/Mac, HP PRODUCTION: Pagination Software – Adobe/Photoshop, QPS/QuarkXPress.; Production Equipment – AG; Scanners – Epson, Umax BUSINESS COMPUTERS: Business Software – VisionData; Business Hardware – VisionData
Delivery method: Mail, Newsstand, Private Carrier, Racks

PLEASANTON

TRI-VALLEY HERALD/SAN RAMON VALLEY HERALD

127 Spring St., Pleasanton, Calif., 94588; gen tel (925) 734-8600; adv tel (925) 416-4710; ed tel (925) 416-4757; gen fax (925) 416-4850; adv fax (510) 293-2381; ed fax (925) 416-4850; gen e-mail bangcirc@bayareanewsgroup.com; ed e-mail bgoll@angnewspapers.com; web site www.trivalleyherald.com

Published: Sat, Sun
Saturday Frequency: m
Circulation: 31,317; 28,255(sat); 30,549(sun)
Last Audit: September 30, 2007
Price: 120.51/yr.
Advertising: Open inch rate $172.00
News services: NYT, AP, LAT-WP, SHNS, McClatchy, Bloomberg.
Politics: Independent.
Note: For detailed mechanical equipment information, see the Oakland Tribune listing.
Special Editions: My Town-Dublin (Apr); I Do-Bridal (Feb); Grapevine-Livermore (Jan); Fremont Art & Wine Festival (Jul); My Town-Pleasanton (Jun); Almanac (Mar); Daytrips (May); California Home (Monthly); Bay Area Best (Oct); NFL Preview (Sept).
Special Weekly Sections: Preview (Fri); NFL Mondays in Sports (Mon); Careers (S); Real Estate (Sat); Food (Wed).
Magazines: Relish (Monthly); TV Week (S).

Pres./Pub. ....John Armstrong
Exec. Vice Pres., Adv./Mktg. ....Bob Gray
Sr. Vice Pres., Prodn. ....Dennis Miller
Vice Pres., Circ. ....Jim Dove
Vice Pres., HR ....Robert Jendusa
Mgr., HR ....Karen Austin
Adv. Mgr., Nat'l ....Rick Hunz
Adv. Mgr., Retail ....Karen Frank
Mktg. Dir. ....Melanie Keilholtz
Circ. Dir. ....Brad Nichols
Circ. Dir., Opns. ....Mary O'Brien
Ed. ....Bob Goll
City Ed. ....Dave Boitano
Entertainment Ed. ....Jeanie Wakeland
Fashion Ed. ....Jolene Thym
Features Ed. ....Kari Hulac
Features Ed. ....Keith Jones
Financial Ed. ....Drew Voros
Food Ed. ....Jodi Chade

Market Information: TMC; Zoned editions.
Mechanical available: Black and 3 ROP colors; insert accepted; page cutoffs - 20 1/2.
Mechanical Specifications: Type page 12 x 21 1/2; E - 6 cols, 2 1/16, 1/8 between; A - 6 cols, 2 1/16, 1/8 between; C - 10 cols, 1 1/4, 1/32 between.
Commodity Consumption: Avg. Page Number Per Issue - Daily 72; Avg. Page Number Per Issue - Plates Used 30841; Avg. Page Number Per Issue - Sunday 98; widths 37 1/2; Newsprint Used - Metric Tons 3950; Printing Ink Used - Black 80000; Printing Ink Used - Color 7500; Printing Ink
Equipment EDITORIAL: Front-end Software – XYQUEST/XyWrite, HI/NME, HI/NMP.; Editorial Hardware – PC, Novell; Editorial Printers – HP/5000N CLASSIFIED: Front-end Software – Mactive.; Classified Hardware – PC DISPLAY: Ad make-up applications – Xenix, SCS/Layout 8000, Multi-Ad/Creator; Layout Software – SCS/Layout 8000.; Display Hardware – APP/Mac 9600, APP/Mac G3, APP/Mac G4 PRODUCTION: Pagination Software – HI/NMP 3.5.; Production Equipment – 6-AII/Graphics Color Imagers (3850), 1-W, 1-MAS, 2-WI, 1-Nat, 1-AN, 1-SL; Cameras – 4-C; Scanners – 4-HP, 1-Epson, 1-Scitex PRESSROOM: Line 1 – 13-G/Urbanite single width 1978; Line 2 – 13-G/Urbanite single width 1984; Line 3 – 13-G/Urbanite single width 1993; Line 4 – 7-MAN/Lithomanic II double width 1989; Line 6 – 15-G/Urbanite single width 1998; Line 7 – 6-MAN/Roland double width 1989 MAILROOM: Counter stackers – 10-HL/Monitor, 3-QWI/SP, 2/Compass; Inserters and stuffers – 1-GMA/16:1, 1-GMA/8:1; Bundle tying machines – 4-/Dynamic, 1-/Power Strap; Addressing machine – 1-/Ch, 2-/KR. BUSINESS COMPUTERS: Business Software – CJ; Business Hardware – 1-HP/3000 987-200SX

VALLEY TIMES

127 Spring St., Pleasanton, Calif., 94566; gen tel (925) 462-4160; adv tel (925) 847-2118; ed tel (925) 847-2112; gen fax (925) 847-2177; adv fax (925) 847-2177; ed fax (925) 847-2189; gen e-mail rclemens@cc-

times.com; ed e-mail vtletters@cctimes.com; web site www.contracostatimes.com
Published: Mon, Tues, Wed, Thur, Fri, Sat, Sun
Weekday Frequency: m
Saturday Frequency: m
Circulation: 44,354; 44,354(sat); 46,559(sun)
Last Audit: September 30, 1998
Price: 7.50/mo (carrier); 159.64/yr.
News services: AP, U.S. Suburban Press Inc., Newspapers First.
Politics: Independent.
Note: Contra Costa Newspapers daily group includes the Pleasanton Valley Times (mS), Richmond West County Times (mS) and Walnut Creek Contra Costa Times (mS). The group advertising rates are $228.00(d) and $254.00(S). Individual newspaper rates not made availab
Special Editions: Christmas (5 times) (Dec); Spring Home & Garden (Feb); Fall Home & Garden (Oct); Football Preview (Sept).
Special Weekly Sections: Auto (Fri).
Pub. ....John Armstrong
Vice Pres., Adv. ....Peter Herschberger
Adv. Mgr. ....Lynn Marleau
Circ. Mgr. ....Frank Eiras
Ed. ....Kelly Gust
News Ed. ....Sam Richards
Sports Ed. ....Marcus Thompson
Prodn. Dir. ....Donald Jochens
Prodn. Mgr., Pressroom ....Werner Reuper
Market Information: ADS; TMC; Zoned editions.
Mechanical available: Offset; Black and 3 ROP colors; insert accepted - min size 6 x 8 on 40lbs stock, max size 13 3/4; page cutoffs - 22 3/4.
Mechanical Specifications: Type page 13 x 21; E - 6 cols, 2 1/16, 1/8 between; A - 6 cols, 2 1/16, 1/8 between; C - 10 cols, 1 1/4, 1/16 between.
Commodity Consumption: Avg. Page Number Per Issue - Daily 70; Avg. Page Number Per Issue - Plates Used 66769; Avg. Page Number Per Issue - Sunday 140; widths 27 1/2; Newsprint Used - Metric Tons 5322; Printing Ink Used - Black 87278; Printing Ink Used - Color 33316; Printing I
Equipment EDITORIAL: Front-end Software – Dewar, AT, Microsoft/Word.; Editorial Hardware – AT/9000, PC 486-66; Editorial Equipment – 22-AT/Reporter; Classified Hardware – AT/9000; Classified Equipment – SII, 6-AT/Reporter, DEC/220. DISPLAY: Ad make-up applications – Multi-Ad/Creator 3.8; Layout Software – SCS/Layout 8000.; Display Hardware – APP/Power Mac; Display Printers – APP/Mac LaserWriter PRODUCTION: Pagination Software – Dewar, QPS/QuarkXPress. MAILROOM: Counter stackers – 7-QWI/100, 6-QWI/300, 4-MM/288; Inserters and stuffers – 1-HI/1372, 1-HI/1472, 1-HI/2299, 2-MM/275; Bundle tying machines – 8/Dynaric, 4-/MLN, 3-/Bu; Wrapping singles – 1-St/Shanklin; Addressing machine – 1-/Ch, 1-/St. BUSINESS COMPUTERS: Business Software – Lotus, Microsoft/Word, Microsoft/Excel; Business Hardware – PCs, APP/Mac SE

PORTERVILLE

THE PORTERVILLE RECORDER

115 E. Oak Ave., Porterville, Calif., 93257; gen tel (559) 784-5000; adv tel (559) 784-5000; ed tel (559) 784-5000; gen fax (559) 784-1172; adv fax (559) 784-5245; ed fax (559) 784-1689; gen e-mail recorder@portervillerecorder.com; web site www.portervillerecorder.com
Published: Mon, Tues, Wed, Thur, Fri, Sat
Weekday Frequency: m
Circulation: 9,402; 8,700(sat)
Last Audit: Sworn September 30, 2006
Price: 12,45/mo (plus tax); 91.14/yr (plus tax).
Advertising: Open inch rate $17.20
News services: AP, MCT, NEA, TMS.
Politics: Independent. **Established:** 1909
Advertising not accepted: Y
Not Published: Sunday
Own facility?: Y
Special Editions: Medical Directory (Feb); Bridal (Jan); Readers Choice (Jul); Graduation & Scholarships (Jun); South County Pride (Mar); Porterville Fair (May); Holiday Gifts (Nov); Women in Business (Oct); Living Here (Sept).
Special Weekly Sections: Financial, Health and Fitness (Sat); Arts & Entertainment (Thur); Schools (Tues).
Magazines: USA WEEKEND Magazine (Sat); The Buzz (Thur).
Editor and Publisher ....Mark Fazzone
Bus. Mgr. ....Craig Dimmitt
Adv. Dir. ....Gunter Copeland
Adv. Supvr. ....Josie Chapman
Circ. District Mgr. ....Vidi Acuna
Circ. District Mgr. ....Rhonda Haskins
Ed. ....Claudia Elliott
Asst. Mng. Ed., Features Anita Stackhouse-Hite
Asst. Sports Ed. ....Jason Peterson
Visuals Dir. ....Reneh Agha
IT Mgr. ....Steve Lublin
New Media Mgr. ....Jon Taylor
Prodn. Mgr. ....Speed Gamble
Market Information: Split run; TMC.
Mechanical available: Offset; Black and 3 ROP colors; insert accepted; page cutoffs - 22 3/4.
Mechanical Specifications: Type page 13 x 21; E - 6 cols, 2 1/16, 1/8 between; A - 6 cols, 2 1/16, 1/8 between; C - 9 cols, 1 5/16, 1/8 between.
Commodity Consumption: Avg. Page Number Per Issue - Daily 21; Avg. Page Number Per Issue - Plates Used 10900; Avg. Page Number Per Issue - Saturday 32; widths 25; Newsprint Used - Metric Tons 606; Printing Ink Used - Black 11129; Printing Ink Used - Color 4820; Printing Ink Us
Equipment EDITORIAL: Front-end Software – Baseview/NewsEdit Pro IQ 3.2.3, QPS/QuarkXPress 4.03.; Editorial Hardware – 8-APP/Mac G3, 6-Umax; Editorial Equipment – 2-APP/Mac 8600 Server; Editorial Printers – 1-HP/8000, 2-ECR/Imagesetter CLASSIFIED: Front-end Software – Baseview/Ad Manager Pro 2.06.; Classified Hardware – 4-APP/Mac G3; Classified Equipment – 1998-APP/Mac G3 Server; Classified Printers – 1-HP/8000, 2-ECR/Imagesetter DISPLAY: Ad make-up applications – QPS/QuarkXPress 4.03; Display Hardware – 4-APP/Mac 7300; Display Printers – 1-HP/8000, ECR/Imagesetter PRODUCTION: Pagination Software – QPS/QuarkXPress 4.03.; Production Equipment – 1-Nu/Plate Burner, APP/Mac Quadra 950; Cameras – Acti/225; Scanners – Flatbed, Nikon PRESSROOM: Line 1 – 8-G/Community; Folders – 1-G/2:1.; Bundle tying machines – 2/Us, 1-/MLN.; Business Hardware – 1-Packard Bell/Novell, 3-IBM/PC 80, 2-IBM/30, Novell, 1-Genecom/4440XT, 4-Compaq, 1-Packard Bell/Visionary
Delivery method: Mail, Newsstand, Private Carrier, Racks

RED BLUFF

DAILY NEWS

545 Diamond Ave., Red Bluff, Calif., 96080; gen tel (530) 527-2151; ed tel (530) 527-2153; gen fax (530) 527-3719; adv fax (530) 527-5774; ed fax (530) 527-9251; adv e-mail advertise@redbluffdailynews.com; ed e-mail editor@redbluffdailynews.com; newsdesk@redbluffdailynews.com; web site www.redbluffdailynews.com
Published: Mon, Tues, Wed, Thur, Fri, Sat
Weekday Frequency: m
Saturday Frequency: m
Circulation: 6,358; 6,117(sat)
Last Audit: ABC September 30, 2011
Price: 7.09/mo (plus tax); 85.08/yr (plus tax).
Advertising: Open inch rate $20.60
News services: AP, NYT, SHNS.
Politics: Independent.
Not Published: Christmas.
Special Editions: Rodeo (Apr); Back-To-School (Aug); Future Ad Designers (Dec); Red Bluff Today (Feb); Corning Today (Jan); Fourth of July (Jul); Health (Mar); Women (May); Farm/City (Nov); Antiques & Collectables (Oct); Tehama Dist. Fair (Sept).
Special Weekly Sections: Top Picks (Fri); Church and Farm Page (Sat); Entertainment (Thur); Best Food Day (Tues); Business Page (Wed).
Magazines: Relish (Monthly); USA WEEKEND Magazine (Sat); American Profile (Weekly).
Pub./Adv. Dir. ....Greg Stevens
Bus. Mgr. ....Daleen Baker
Ed. ....Chip Thompson
Online Ed. ....Sonia Owensby
Prodn. Mgr. ....Sandra Valdivia
Market Information: TMC.
Mechanical available: Offset; Black and 3 ROP colors; insert accepted; page cutoffs - 22 1/2.
Commodity Consumption: Avg. Page Number Per Issue - Daily 20; Avg. Page Number Per Issue - Plates Used 5090; Avg. Page Number Per Issue - Saturday 24; widths 27 1/2; Newsprint Used - Metric Tons 300; Printing Ink Used - Black 14975; Printing Ink Used - Color 775; Printing Ink
Equipment EDITORIAL: Front-end Software – Baseview.; Editorial Hardware – 6-APP/Power Mac 7600-12, 4-APP/Power Mac 7200-90; Editorial Printers – HP/LaserJet 4MV CLASSIFIED: Front-end Software – Baseview.; Classified Hardware – 5-APP/Power Mac 7200-90; Classified Printers – 1-Okidata/Pacemark 3410, 1-HP/LaserJet 4MV DISPLAY: Ad make-up applications – Baseview, Ad Force; Layout Software – Ad Force.; Display Hardware – APP/Power Mac 7200-90; Display Printers – HP/Laserjet 4MV PRODUCTION: Pagination Software – Baseview.; Production Equipment – 2-HP/Laser Jet 4MV, 2-APP/Power Mac 7600-120; Cameras – Acti/Process, 3M/Imager PRESSROOM: Line 1 – 4-G/Urbanite (balloon former) 1980; Folders – 1-G/2:1; Reels and Stands – Press control system ÃÂ 1980. MAILROOM: Counter stackers – BG/Count-O-Veyor; Bundle tying machines – 2/Cyclone. BUSINESS COMPUTERS: Business Software – SSPS; Business Hardware – Brainworks/PCs

REDDING

RECORD SEARCHLIGHT

1101 Twin View Blvd., Redding, Calif., 96003-1531; gen tel (530) 243-2424; adv tel (530) 225-8241; ed tel (530) 225-8211; gen fax (530) 242-8672; adv fax (530) 225-8212; ed fax (530) 225-8236; gen e-mail info@redding.com; adv e-mail rrsretail@scripps.com; ed e-mail letters@redding.com; web site www.redding.com
Published: Mon, Tues, Wed, Thur, Fri, Sat, Sun
Weekday Frequency: m
Saturday Frequency: m
Circulation: 20,576; 22,145(sat); 24,134(sun)
Last Audit: ABC September 30, 2011
Price: 14/mo; 168.00/yr.
Advertising: Open inch rate $52.77
News services: AP, LAT-WP, McClatchy, SHNS, MCT, TMS.
Politics: Independent. **Established:** 1938
Own facility?: Y
Special Editions: Best of North State - Annual Health Care - Annual
Special Weekly Sections: Automotive (Fri); Travelin' (Mon); Real Estate (S); Garden (Sat); Outdoor Sports (Thur); Best Food Day (Wed).
Magazines: Parade (S).
Broadcast Affiliations: KHSL (CBS); KNVN (ABC); KRCR (ABC).
Pres./Pub. ....Shanna Cannon
Dir., Mktg./Convergence Michelle Martin-Streeby
Mng. Ed. ....Carole Ferguson
City Ed. ....Maline Hazle
Editorial Page Ed. ....Bruce Ross
Living/Lifestyle Ed. ....Damon Arthur
Photo Ed. ....Andreas Fuhrmann
HR Manager ....Kelly Tucker
Finance Manager ....Rob Lowes
Account Development Manager - Advertising Kathy Soper
Sr. Director Operations ....Robbie Parham
Editor ....Silas Lyons
Market Information: ADS; TMC.
Mechanical available: Offset; Black and 3 ROP colors; insert accepted - all; page cutoffs - 22 3/4.
Mechanical Specifications: Type page 11 1/2 x 21 1/4; E - 6 cols, 1 3/4, 1/8 between; A - 6 cols, 1 3/4, 1/8 between; C - 10 cols, 1 3/32, 1/16 between.
Commodity Consumption: Avg. Page Number Per Issue - Daily 40; Avg. Page Number Per Issue - Plates Used 50400; Avg. Page Number Per Issue - Sunday 44; widths 50; Newsprint Used - Metric Tons 3000; Printing Ink Used - Black 54116; Printing Ink Used - Color 21000; Printing Ink Us
Equipment EDITORIAL: Front-end Software – Dewar, HI.; Editorial Hardware – PC; Editorial Printers – V, TB/GUA 5100, TB/GUA 5380E, HP/LaserJet 4MV CLASSIFIED: Front-end Software – HI/CASH, Microsoft/Windows.; Classified Hardware – PC; Classified Printers – HP DISPLAY: Ad make-up applications – Archetype/Corel Draw 9.0; Layout Software – Archetype/Corel Draw, Microsoft/Windows.; Display Hardware – PC; Display Printers – HP/LaserJet 4MV PRODUCTION: Pagination Software – HI/NMP.; Production Equipment – 2-Amerigraph/Magnum 323, APP/Mac, Kk/RFS 2035 Plus; Cameras – 1-Acti/504-D; Scanners – Scitex/Smart 540, Kk/RFS 2035 Plus PRESSROOM: Line 1 – 7-HI/N1650 double width 1982; Folders – 2; Pasters – 7-MEG; Reels and Stands – 7-MEG. MAILROOM: Counter stackers – 3/HL; Inserters and stuffers – GMA/1000; Bundle tying machines – 2-MLN/2A; Addressing machine – KR. BUSINESS COMPUTERS: Business Software – PBS/Adv Mgt 2.8, PBS/Circ Mgt 2.7; Business Hardware – PBS, Sun/Sparc 10
Delivery method: Mail, Newsstand, Private Carrier, Racks

REDLANDS

REDLANDS DAILY FACTS

700 Brookside Ave., Redlands, Calif., 92373; gen tel (909) 793-3221; adv tel (909) 793-3221; ed tel (909) 793-3221; gen fax (909) 793-9588; adv fax (909) 793-9588; ed fax (909) 793-9588; gen e-mail editor@redlandsdailyfacts.com; adv e-mail ads@redlandsdailyfacts.com; ed e-mail editor@redlandsdailyfacts.com; web site www.redlandsdailyfacts.com
Published: Mon, Tues, Wed, Thur, Fri, Sat, Sun
Weekday Frequency: m
Saturday Frequency: m
Circulation: 6,956; 6,938(sat); 7,125(sun)
Last Audit: ABC September 30, 2011
Price: 1.71/wk; 182.00/yr; 6.84/4wk.
News services: AP.
Note: The Los Angeles Newspaper Group includes the Long Beach Press-Telegram (mS), Los Angeles Daily News (mS), Ontario Inland Valley Daily Bulletin (mS), Pasadena Star-News (mS), Redlands Daily Facts (eS), San Bernardino County Sun (mS), San Gabriel Valley Tri
Special Weekly Sections: Dining Guide (Fri); Local Business Features (Mon); Great Escapes (Other); Cultural Arts (S); Lifestyle (Thur); Church News (Tues); Food Advertising (Wed).
Magazines: Relish (Monthly); USA WEEKEND Magazine (S).
Pub. ....Fred Hamilton
Circ. Dir. ....Dan Heasley
Adv. Rep, Classified ....Melinda Torres
Adv. Rep, Classified ....Cathy Wilson
Community Ed. ....Jennifer Dobbs
News Ed. ....Betty Tyler
Web Site Administrator ....John Wartenger
Mechanical available: Offset; Black and 3 ROP colors; insert accepted; page cutoffs - 22.
Mechanical Specifications: Type page 11 1/2 x 21; E - 6 cols, 2 1/16, 1/8 between; A - 6 cols, 2 1/16, 1/8 between; C - 10 cols, 1 7/100, 1/8 between.
Commodity Consumption: Avg. Page Number Per Issue - Daily 16; Avg. Page Number Per

Issue - Plates Used 6500; Avg. Page Number Per Issue - Sunday 20; widths 12 1/2; Newsprint Used - Metric Tons 240; Printing Ink Used - Black 15500; Printing Ink Used - Color 600; Printing Ink Us

Equipment CLASSIFIED: Front-end Software – SII.; Classified Hardware – PC; Layout Software – Ad Force. PRODUCTION: Pagination Software – Baseview.; Production Equipment – Caere/OmniPage Pro 2.12, 2-NewGen/Turbo PS-480; Scanners – 1-Microtek/600-GS; Folders – 1; Business Hardware – Collier Jackson

RICHMOND

WEST COUNTY TIMES

PO Box 318, Richmond, Calif., 94806; gen tel (510) 758-8400; adv tel (510) 262-2714; ed tel (510) 262-2731; gen fax (510) 262-2719; adv fax (510) 262-2719; ed fax (510) 262-2776; ed e-mail letters@cctimes.com; web site www.contracostatimes.com

Published: Mon, Tues, Wed, Thur, Fri, Sat, Sun
Weekday Frequency: m
Saturday Frequency: m
Circulation: 32,263; 32,263(sat); 33,231(sun)
Last Audit: September 30, 1998
Price: 9.18/mo (carrier); 173.00/yr.
News services: AP, LAT-WP, NYT, States News Service, McClatchy.
Politics: Independent.
Note: Contra Costa Newspapers daily group includes the Richmond West County Times (mS), Pleasanton Valley Times (mS) and Walnut Creek Contra Costa Times (mS). The group combination rates are $228.00(d) and $254.00(S). Individual newspaper rates not made availab
Magazines: Bloomberg Financial (S).
Adv. Mgr. ....Patrice Zettner
Circ. Mgr., Home Delivery ....Zonna Thomas
Ed ....Scott Corey
Mng. Ed. ....Chris Lopez
Educ. Writer ....Kara Shire
Photo Chief ....Mark DuFrene
Religion Writer ....Mary Reiley
Sports Ed. ....Phil Jensen
Mgmt. Info Servs. Mgr. ....Dave Anderson
Prodn. Mgr., Pressroom ....Werner Reuper
Publisher ....Tully Mac
Market Information: ADS; TMC; Zoned editions.
Mechanical available: Offset; Black and 3 ROP colors; insert accepted - all; page cutoffs - 22 3/4.
Mechanical Specifications: Type page 13 x 21 1/2; E - 6 cols, 2 1/16, 1/8 between; A - 6 cols, 2 1/16, 1/8 between; C - 10 cols, 1 1/4, 1/16 between.
Commodity Consumption: Avg. Page Number Per Issue - Daily 54; Avg. Page Number Per Issue - Sunday 70; widths 55; Newsprint Used - Metric Tons 3038; Printing Ink Used - Black 70000; Printing Ink Used - Color 15000.
Equipment; Editorial Hardware – AT/9000, 3-IBM; Editorial Equipment – 21-IBM/PC, 5-RSK/TRS 100.; Classified Hardware – SII.; Layout Software – SCS/Layout 8000.

RIDGECREST

THE DAILY INDEPENDENT

224 E. Ridgecrest Blvd., Ridgecrest, Calif., 93555; gen tel (760) 375-4481; adv tel (760) 375-4481; ed tel (760) 375-4481; gen fax (760) 375-4880; adv fax (760) 375-4880; ed fax (760) 375-4880; gen e-mail editor@ridgecrestca.com; web site www.ridgecrestca.com

Published: Tues, Wed, Thur, Fri, Sat
Weekday Frequency: m
Circulation: 7,900; 7,900(sat)
Last Audit: March 31, 2002
Price: 7.75/mo; 90.00/yr (carrier).
Advertising: Open inch rate $11.58
News services: AP.
Politics: Independent.
Special Editions: Christmas Carols & Greetings (Dec); Independent Babies (Jan); Graduation Congratulations (Jun); Home Show (Mar); Spring Car Care (May); Fall Home Improvement (Nov); New Car Buyers Guide (Oct); Fall Sports (Sept).
Special Weekly Sections: Real Estate (Fri); Business (S); Automotive (Thur); Automotive (Tues); Best Food Day (Wed).
Magazines: American Profile (Weekly).
Pub. ....John Watkins
Display Adv. Mgr. ....Paula McKay
Classified Adv. Mgr. ....Rodney Connors
Circ. Mgr. ....Brian Voigt
Ed ....Nathan Ahle
City Ed. ....Nathaniel Lidle
Sports Ed. ....Cheeto Barrera
Market Information: Split run; TMC.
Mechanical available: Offset; Black and 3 ROP colors; insert accepted; page cutoffs - 22 3/4.
Mechanical Specifications: Type page 13 x 21 1/2; E - 6 cols, 2 1/16, 1/8 between; A - 6 cols, 2 1/16, 1/8 between; C - 9 cols, 1 1/3, 1/12 between.
Commodity Consumption: Avg. Page Number Per Issue - Daily 20; Avg. Page Number Per Issue - Sunday 24; widths 32; Newsprint Used - Metric Tons 550.
Equipment; Editorial Hardware – APP/Mac; Editorial Equipment – 2-APP/Mac ci. CLASSIFIED: Front-end Software – Baseview.; Classified Hardware – APP/iMac, APP/Mac G4; Layout Software – APP/Mac G4.; Display Hardware – APP/iMac PRODUCTION: Pagination Software – ECR/Panther Pro.; Production Equipment – 1-Nu; Cameras – AG PRESSROOM: Line 1 – 9-G; Folders – 1; Press registration system – Duarte/PIN System.; Inserters and stuffers – MM; Bundle tying machines – MLN.; Business Hardware – PBS

RIVERSIDE

THE PRESS-ENTERPRISE

3450 14th St., Riverside, Calif., 92501-3812; gen tel (951) 684-1200; adv tel (951) 368-9250; ed tel (951) 368-9460; gen fax (951) 368-9023; adv fax (951) 368-9009; ed fax (951) 368-9023; gen e-mail customer-care@pe.com; ed e-mail penews@pe.com; letters@pe.com; web site www.pe.com

Published: Mon, Tues, Wed, Thur, Fri, Sat, Sun
Weekday Frequency: m
Saturday Frequency: m
Circulation: 112,084; 112,963(sat); 129,409(sun)
Last Audit: ABC September 30, 2011
Price: 2.75/wk; 143.00/yr.
Advertising: Open inch rate $211.28
News services: AP, CNS, DJ, MCT, NYT, SHNS, Cox, TMS.
Politics: Independent. **Established:** 1878
Special Editions: Southwest Career Expo (Apr); People to Know (Aug); Holiday Entertaining (Dec); Easy Street (Feb); Super Sunday Classified (Jan); San Bernardino Career Expo (Jun); Golf Magazine (Mar); Valley-Wide Recreation (May); Holiday Planner (Nov); Farmers Fair (Oct)
Special Weekly Sections: Travel (S); Auto-Driving (Sat); Living (Thur); Health & Fitness (Tues); Food (Wed).
Magazines: The Guide (weekly entertainment tab) (Fri).
CEO/Publisher ....Ronald Redfern
SVP Finance and Publishing Ops ....Ed Lasak
Adv. Mgr., Display ....Bobbi Meyer
Adv. Mgr., Major Accts. ....Tom Paradis
Adv. Mgr., Regl ....Pam Ayala
Adv. Mgr., Regl. ....Russ Stewart
Vice Pres., News/Exec. Ed. ....Maria DeVarenne
Deputy Mng. Ed. ....Nels Jensen
Columnist ....Dan Bernstein
Editorial Ed. ....Gale Hammons
SVP Advertising and Interactive Dev. ....Ken Nelson
VP Circulation and Distribution ....Aaron Kotarek
General Manager/Hispanic Media Frank Escobedo
Dir Multimedia Sales Dev ....John Kerr
Director Gen and Major Accounts ....Anita Davis
Mgr Innovation/Business Dev Andrew McFadden
Interactive Development Director ....Paul McAfee
Recruitment/SMB Sales Mgr. ..Jeannie Goodman
Adv. Mgr., Gen. ....Brad Gardner
Adv. Mgr., Real Estate ....Darlene Clayton
Adv. Mgr., Regl. ....Joe Hudon
Adv. Mgr., Regl. ....Marlene Placak
Adv. Mgr., Regl. ....Gerry Tomczak
Mgr., Promo. ....Donna Dawson
PR Mgr. ....Tom Phillips
Circ. Mgr., Home Delivery ....Mike Kreiser
Mng. Ed. ....John Gryka
Online Ed. ....Bob Wardrop
Market Information: Split run; TMC; Zoned editions.
Mechanical available: Offset; Black and 3 ROP colors; insert accepted; page cutoffs - 22.
Mechanical Specifications: Type page 11 5/8 x 21; E - 6 cols, 2 1/16, 1/8 between; A - 6 cols, 2 1/16, 1/8 between; C - 10 cols, 1 3/16, 1/16 between.
Commodity Consumption: Avg. Page Number Per Issue - Daily 68; Avg. Page Number Per Issue - Plates Used 258274; Avg. Page Number Per Issue - Saturday 124; Avg. Page Number Per Issue - Sunday 118; widths 12 1/2; Newsprint Used - Metric Tons 29000; Newsprint Used - Short Tons 320
Equipment EDITORIAL: Front-end Software – AT 4.67.; Editorial Hardware – 9-AT/Series 60; Editorial Printers – Okidata, HP CLASSIFIED: Front-end Software – AT, CText.; Classified Hardware – CText, IMB/RS 6000 Sybase DISPLAY: Ad make-up applications – Multi-Ad; Layout Software – Aii.; Display Hardware – AII/Ad Manager, APP/Mac, 36-AII/Ad Manager 2.6; Display Printers – Tektronix, HP, Plotter; Production Equipment – 3-Glunz & Jensen/35 HD, 2-III/3810 Laser, 1-III/3850 Sierra, 1-III/3850 Sierra, 4-III/3850 SST, 2-III/3850W SST, LE/Max 26; Cameras – 1-C/Marathon, 1-C/Spartan III; Scanners – 2-ECR/Autokon 1000, 1-III/3750. PRESSROOM: Line 1 – 9-G/HO-Double Width 1987; Line 2 – 9-G/HO-Double Width 1987; Line 3 – 9-G/HO-Double Width 1987; Press Drives – 27; Folders – 6; Reels and Stands – 24, 45; Press control system – 3-G/MPCS. MAILROOM: Counter stackers – 7-HL/Monitor, 1-Id/NS660, 5-QWI/400; Inserters and stuffers – 3-HI/NP 1372, 1-HI/NP 1472; Bundle tying machines – 8-Si/MLN, 2/Bu, 3-/Sterling, 3-Dynaric/NP 1500; Mailroom control system – QWI/Conveyors & Controls, QWI/On-Line; Addressing machine – Addressi AUDIO: Audio Software – Micro Voice/Audiotext 2000; Audio Hardware – IT Network, Micro Voice/Audiotext 2000 BUSINESS COMPUTERS: Business Software – CJ, HP/9000 k570; Business Hardware – 2-DEC/VAX 6410, 2-DEC/Alpha Server 4000

SACRAMENTO

THE SACRAMENTO BEE

2100 Q St., Sacramento, Calif., 95816; gen tel (916) 321-1000; adv tel (916) 321-1234; ed tel (916) 321-1851; gen fax (916) 321-1109; ed fax (916) 321-1109; ed e-mail opinion@sacbee.com; web site www.sacbee.com

Group: Newspapers First, Inc.
Published: Mon, Tues, Wed, Thur, Fri, Sat, Sun
Weekday Frequency: m
Saturday Frequency: m
Circulation: 199,921; 215,761(sat); 269,660(sun)
Last Audit: ABC September 30, 2011
Price: 226.20/yr; 53.50/13wk.
Advertising: Open inch rate $405.00
News services: AP, Bloomberg, CT, MCT, LAT-WP, NYT, SHNS, DJ, GNS, HN.
Politics: Non-Partisan. **Established:** 1857
Own facility?: Y
Special Weekly Sections: Friday's Ticket (Fri); Travel (S); Home & Garden (Sat); Taste (Wed).
Magazines: Parade (S).
Pres./Pub. ....Cheryl Dell
Sr. Vice Pres., Finance ....Gary Strong
Vice Pres., HR ....Linda Brooks
Adv. Sr. Vice Pres. ....Francesca Lewis
Adv. Dir., Major Accts. ....Jill Threde
Adv. Mgr. ....Steve Briggs
Adv. Mgr., Classified/Real Estate ..John Castillon
Adv. Mgr., Market Analysis ....Darrell Kunken
Adv. Mgr., Nat'l ....Suzanne Deegan
Adv. Mgr., Reg'l ....Eric Luchini
Adv. Mgr., Retail Sales ....K. Ann Rollin
Adv. Mgr., Retail Territories ....Jim Paquett
Audience Devel./Membership Servs. Sr. Vice Pres. Dan Schaub
Audience Devel. Dir. ....Maria Ravera
Audience Devel./Membership Servs. Mgr., Admin./Opns. ....Mark Montgomery
Audience Devel./Membership Servs. Mgr., Opns. Gary Pitts
Market Information: TMC.
Mechanical available: Offset; Black and 4 ROP colors; insert accepted; page cutoffs - 22.
Mechanical Specifications: Type page 11 1/2 x 21; E - 6 cols, 1 81/100, 1/8 between; A - 6 cols, 1 81/100, 1/8 between; C - 6 cols, 1 1/10, 1/8 between.
Commodity Consumption: Avg. Page Number Per Issue - Daily 90; Avg. Page Number Per Issue - Plates Used 540000; Avg. Page Number Per Issue - Saturday 140; Avg. Page Number Per Issue - Sunday 176; widths 50; Newsprint Used - Metric Tons 59011; Printing Ink Used - Black 1066814;
Equipment EDITORIAL: Front-end Software – Unisys/Hermes 5.5.; Editorial Hardware – PC; Editorial Printers – HP/LaserJet CLASSIFIED: Front-end Software – SII.; Classified Hardware – SII/Sys 55; Classified Printers – HP/LaserJet DISPLAY: Ad make-up applications – Cx 8.0; Layout Software – Ad Mgr..; Display Printers – 2-HP 25DDCP PRODUCTION: Pagination Software – Unisys/Hermes 5.5.; Production Equipment – 3-Aii/3850, 2-Aii/3850 Wide, 1-KFM/Verifier, 1-Nu/Flip Top; Scanners – 2-Eskofot/20245, Scitex/Eversmart PRESSROOM: Line 1 – 11-G/Metroliner (double width) 1981; Line 2 – 11-G/Metroliner (double width) 1981; Line 3 – 11-G/Metroliner (double width) 1981; Line 4 – 36-G/Colorliner couples (double width) 1989; Folders – PPK/Imperial 3:2; Pasters – 9-G/RTP; Reels and Stands – Reels and Stands MAILROOM: Counter stackers – 22-QWI/300, 4-Id/200; Inserters and stuffers – 6/AM Graphics/2299; Bundle tying machines – 18-Dynaric/NP-1, 24-Dynaric/NP-2, 21-Dynaric/PNP-1; Mailroom control system – Prima, Denex.

SALINAS

THE SALINAS CALIFORNIAN

123 W. Alisal St., Salinas, Calif., 93901; gen tel (831) 754-4131; adv tel (831) 754-4133; ed tel (831) 754-4260; gen fax (831) 754-4104; ed fax (831) 754-4293; gen e-mail newsroom@salinas.gannett.com; ed e-mail newsroom@salinas.gannett.com; web site www.thecalifornian.com

Published: Mon, Tues, Wed, Thur, Fri, Sat
Weekday Frequency: m
Saturday Frequency: m
Circulation: 9,037; 13,545(sat)
Last Audit: ABC September 30, 2011
Price: 10.25/mo; 142.91/yr.
Advertising: Open inch rate $59.84
News services: AP, GNS, LAT-WP.
Politics: Independent. **Established:** 1871
Special Editions: Welcome to Monterey County (Apr); Healthfocus (Aug); Holiday Planning Guides (Dec); Wineries (Feb); Wedding & Event Planner (Jan); Rodeo (Jul); Wedding & Event Planner (Jun); Our Towns (Mar); Home Sweet Home (May); Healthfocus (Nov); Agriculture Wrap Up (
Special Weekly Sections: Television (Sat); Entertainment & Dining (Thur); Food Day (Tues); Health & Wellness (Wed).
Magazines: USA WEEKEND Magazine (Sat).
Gen. Mgr. ....Terry Feinberg
Dir., HR/Community Aff. ....Teri James
Adv. Dir. ....Danna Arvig
Circ. Opns. Mgr. ....Nick Losada
Mng. Ed ....Anjanette Delgado
Digital Ed. ....Ria Megnin
Editorial Page Ed. ....Roberto Robledo

Features Ed. ....Katherine Ball
Sr. News Ed. ....Mike Nemeth
Photo Chief ....Richard Green
Web Developer ....Gonzalo N. Maravilla
Prodn. Dir. ....Cortland Hunt
Prodn. Opns. Mgr. ....Paul Kurowski
Pre Press Mgr. ....Gabe Vasquez
Market Information: Split run; TMC.
Mechanical available: Web Offset; Black and 3 ROP colors; insert accepted - all, 3 to 13 3/4; page cutoffs - 22 1/16.
Mechanical Specifications: Type page 11 5/8 x 21; E - 6 cols, 2 1/16, 1/6 between; A - 6 cols, 2 1/16, 1/12 between; C - 9 cols, 1 3/8, 1/12 between.
Commodity Consumption: Avg. Page Number Per Issue - Daily 32; Avg. Page Number Per Issue - Plates Used 66000; Avg. Page Number Per Issue - Saturday 50; widths 25; Newsprint Used - Short Tons 1667; Printing Ink Used - Black 58186; Printing Ink Used - Color 9236; Printing Ink Us
Equipment EDITORIAL: Front-end Software – APT 3.; Editorial Equipment – Printers □ HP/8000 CLASSIFIED: Front-end Software – APT.; Classified Hardware – PC Compatible; Classified Printers – HP/Laserwriter DISPLAY: Ad make-up applications – Multi-Ad/Creator 2, QPS/QuarkXPress 4.04, ALS 3.0; Layout Software – ALS.; Display Hardware – APT; Display Printers – HP/LaserJet 4MV, Ricoh/Color Printer PRODUCTION: Pagination Software – APT.; Production Equipment – 2-Anocoil, Konica/EV Jetsetters; Scanners – Epson/Perfection 1680, Howtek/Scanmaster 4500, Tecsa/1850 Copy DOT PRESSROOM: Line 1 – 10-G/Urbanite 1986; Folders – 1 MAILROOM: Counter stackers – QWI/400; Inserters and stuffers – HI/1372, Mueller/Martini 321; Bundle tying machines – Signode/MLN 2E; Addressing machine – Kirk Rudy; Other equipment –Mc/2000 Stitcher-Trimmer.; Business Hardware – IBM/AS-400

SAN BERNARDINO

SAN BERNARDINO COUNTY SUN

4030 N. Georgia Blvd., San Bernardino, Calif., 92407-1847; gen tel (909) 889-9666; ed tel (909) 386-3877; adv fax (909) 884-2536; ed fax (909) 885-8741; ed e-mail citydesk@sbsun.com; web site www.sbsun.com
Published: Mon, Tues, Wed, Thur, Fri, Sat, Sun
Weekday Frequency: m
Saturday Frequency: m
Circulation: 57,415; 49,864(sat); 57,500(sun)
Last Audit: ABC September 30, 2011
Price: Home Delivery: $4.35. Single Copy: 0.75 (Mon-Fri) and $1 (Sat & Sun)
News services: AP, MCT, GNS, SHNS, McClatchy, City News Service.
Politics: Independent.
Note: The Los Angeles Newspaper Group includes the Long Beach Press-Telegram (mS), Los Angeles Daily News (mS), Ontario Inland Valley Daily Bulletin (mS), Pasadena Star-News (mS), Redlands Daily Facts (eS), San Bernardino County Sun (mS), San Gabriel Valley Tri
Own facility?: Y
Special Editions: Nursing in the Inland Empire (Nov); Health & Fitness (5 times/yr) (Other); News of the City (Quarterly); Home & Garden (Semi-yearly); Route 66 (Sept).
Special Weekly Sections: Weekend (Fri); Business File (Mon); Business Sunday (S); Home Guide (Sat); Gardening (Tues); Food (Wed).
Magazines: Relish (Monthly); TV Week (S).
Broadcast Affiliations: KCBS-TV.
Pub./CEO ....Fred Hamilton
Finance Dir. ....Kathy Johnson
Vice Pres., HR ....Louise Kopitch
Adv. Acct. Exec., New Media ....Gail Donahue
Adv. Exec., Employment Classifieds Norma Sapp
Mktg. Dir. ....Rick Sweeney
Circ. Mgr., Home Delivery ....Lynn Brokow
Circ. Mgr., Home Delivery ....Debby Wilson
Ed. ....Steve Lambert
Exec. Ed. ....Frank Pine
Mng. Ed., New Media ....Sandy Kobrin
Asst. Mng. Ed., Metro ....Joseph Calderon
Rialto/Fontana reporter ....Jim Steinberg
Columnist ....John Weeks
VP Circulation Inland Division ....Joe Robidoux
VP Circulation, Los Angeles Newspaper Group David Williams
Senior Editor ....Kimberly Guimarin
Adv. Dir. ....Gene Pearlman
Adv. Mgr. ....Sandra Gray
Editorial Page Ed. ....Carolyn Schatz
Editorial Page Asst. ....Christina Brock
Features Ed. ....Carla Sanders
Market Information: Split run; TMC; Zoned editions.
Mechanical available: Offset; Black and 3 ROP colors; insert accepted; page cutoffs - 22.
Mechanical Specifications: Type page 12 1/2 x 21; E - 6 cols, 2, 1/8 between; A - 6 cols, 2, 1/8 between; C - 10 cols, 1 1/4, 1/16 between.
Commodity Consumption: Avg. Page Number Per Issue - Daily 54; Avg. Page Number Per Issue - Plates Used 120000; Avg. Page Number Per Issue - Saturday 68; Avg. Page Number Per Issue - Sunday 88; widths 54; Newsprint Used - Metric Tons 8400; Printing Ink Used - Black 401610; Prin
Equipment; Editorial Hardware – 1-AT/Series 60, 1-HI/Newsmaker 1.6.53; Editorial Equipment – AT, MON/Postscript, APP/Mac Graphics Systems; Editorial Printers – MON/Laser Express. CLASSIFIED: Front-end Software – AT 4.67.; Classified Hardware – AT/Series 60; Classified Equipment – MON/Postscript; Classified Printers – MON/Laser Express DISPLAY: Ad make-up applications – Multi-Ad/Creator 4.0.1; Layout Software – MEI/ALS 8000.; Display Hardware – 14-APP/Mac; Display Printers – MON/Postscript PRODUCTION: Pagination Software – HI/Newsmaker.; Production Equipment – WL, 2-Futuro/Monotype; Cameras – 1-C/Pager II; Scanners – ECR/Autokon 8400, ECR/Autokon 1000 PRESSROOM: Line 1 – 6-G/Headliner Offset (4 wide) 1992; Line 2 – 6-G/Headliner Offset (4 wide) 1992; Line 3 – 6-G/Headliner Offset (4 wide) 1992; Folders – 6-G/3:2 (160 page); Pasters – 18-G/CT50; Press control system – G/MPCS. MAILROOM: Counter stackers – QWI; Inserters and stuffers – 3/AM Graphics/NP 1472; Bundle tying machines – 4-MLN/EM1016A; Mailroom control system – QWI; Addressing machine – 2-/Ch, 2-Barstrom/on-line; Other equipment – Mc/Stitcher-Trimmer. BUSINESS COMPUTERS: Business Software – WordPerfect, Lotus; Business Hardware – IBM/AS-400
Zip Codes served: 91701 91730 91739 91786 92220 92223 92252 92277 92284 92301 92307 92308 92311 92313 92314 92315 92316 92320 92324 92325 92327 92335 92336 92337 92339 92342 92345 92346 92347 92352 92354 92358 92359 92371 92373 92374 92376 92377 92382 92392 92394 92397 92399 92401 92404 92405 92407 92408 92410 92411
Delivery method: Mail, Newsstand, Private Carrier, Racks

SAN DIEGO

THE DAILY TRANSCRIPT

2131 Third Ave., San Diego, Calif., 92101; gen tel (619) 232-4381; adv tel (619) 232-4381; ed tel (619) 232-4381; gen fax (619) 239-5716; adv fax (619) 239-4312; ed fax (619) 236-8126; gen e-mail editor@sddt.com; adv e-mail sales@sddt.com; ed e-mail editor@sddt.com; web site www.sddt.com
Published: Mon, Tues, Wed, Thur, Fri
Weekday Frequency: m
Circulation: 6,404
Last Audit: March 31, 1998
Price: 120.68/yr.
Advertising: Open inch rate $100.00
News services: AP, Bloomberg.
Politics: Independent. **Established:** 1886
Special Editions: Soaring Dimensions (Aug); San Diego Sourcebook (Dec); Commercial Real Estate Report (Jan); Health Care (Jun); San Diego Business Resource Guide (May); Inside Biotech (Oct); Architecture & Design (Sept).
Special Weekly Sections: Weekend Watch (Fri); Business Matters (Mon); High Performance (Thur); Tech Talk (Tues); Law Briefs (Wed).
Magazines: Monday Memo (Mon); The Lenders (Thur).
Pub./CEO ....Robert Loomis
Mgr., HR ....Patricia Techaira
Adv. Dir., Classified ....Andrea Lane
Dir., Mktg./Promo. ....Christine Tran
Circ. Mgr. ....Shelly Barry
Ed. ....Joseph Guerin
Exec. Ed. ....George Chamberlin
Real Estate Ed. ....Richard Spaulding
Dir., Info Systems ....Joey Schmitt
Prodn. Mgr. ....Steve Lovelace
Market Information: ADS.
Mechanical available: Offset; Black and 3 ROP colors; insert accepted; page cutoffs - 21 1/2.
Mechanical Specifications: Type page 13 x 21 1/2; E - 6 cols, 2 1/16, 1/8 between; A - 6 cols, 2 1/16, 1/8 between; C - 8 cols, 1 1/2, 1/8 between.
Commodity Consumption: Avg. Page Number Per Issue - Daily 36; Avg. Page Number Per Issue - Plates Used 7500; widths 13 3/4; Newsprint Used - Short Tons 600; Printing Ink Used - Black 10000; Printing Ink Used - Color 200; Printing Ink Used - Pages Printed 9360.
Equipment EDITORIAL: Front-end Software – Mircosoft/Word.; Editorial Hardware – APP/Mac CLASSIFIED: Front-end Software – Baseview.; Classified Hardware – APP/Mac; Layout Software – HP/3000.; Display Hardware – 3-APP/Mac IIcx, APP/Mac Radius Monitor; Display Printers – APP/Mac LaserWriter II NTX PRODUCTION: Pagination Software – QPS/QuarkXPress.; Production Equipment – Nu/Carbon; Cameras – R, LE/48D 24 x 48 PRESSROOM: Line 1 – 5-KP/News King; Line 2 – Ryobi/2800 CD 11X17; Folders – 1-KP/2:1. MAILROOM: Counter stackers – 1-BG/Count-O-Veyor 105; Inserters and stuffers – MM/327 4 Station; Bundle tying machines – MLN/Spirit Model 257; Addressing machine – KR. BUSINESS COMPUTERS: Business Software – CJ; Business Hardware – HP/3000 Micro XE

THE SAN DIEGO UNION-TRIBUNE

350 Camino De La Reina, San Diego, Calif., 92108-3003; gen tel (619) 299-3131; ed tel (619) 293-1211; gen fax (619) 293-1896; ed fax (619) 260-5081; gen e-mail customer-support@signonsandiego.com; ed e-mail news@uniontrib.com; letters@uniontrib.com; web site www.signonsandiego.com
Published: Mon, Tues, Wed, Thur, Fri, Sat, Sun
Weekday Frequency: m
Saturday Frequency: m
Circulation: 219,347; 225,918(sat); 293,423(sun)
Last Audit: ABC September 30, 2011
Price: 18.50/mo (includes tax); 196.00/yr (includes tax).
Advertising: Open inch rate $459.00
News services: Landon Media & Metro Suburbia, CNS, NYT, MCT, RN, DF, DJ, LAT-WP, NNS, SHNS, TMS.
Politics: Republican. **Established:** 1868
Special Editions: Going Green (Apr); San Diego's Best (Aug); Auto Show (Dec); Super Bowl (Feb); NFL Playoffs (Jan); Summer Adventures (Jul); Summer Adventures (Jun); SD Best Ballot (Mar); Passport (May); Holiday Gift Guide (Nov); Dining Guide (Oct); NFL Football Preview (S
Special Weekly Sections: Work Week (Mon); Arts (S); Wheels (Sat); Night & Day (Entertainment Guide) (Thur); Health and Fitness (Tues); Quest (Wed).
Magazines: Dining Around (Central) (Annually); SD Home (Every other month); SD Health (Other); Fashion Forward (Semi-yearly).
Pres./Pub. ....Ed Moss
Pub., Enlace ....Francisco Mata
Sr. Vice Pres., Bus. Channels ....Bill Nagel
Vice Pres./CFO ....Jessica Walker
Vice Pres./Chief Revenue Officer Scott T. Whitley
Vice Pres., HR ....Bobbie Espinosa
Controller/Mgr., Bus. Servs. ....Gary Pekala
Budget/Analysis Mgr. ....Ron Parra
Credit Mgr. ....Vickie Bolinger
Purchasing Mgr. ....Dorothy Young
Adv. Dir., Bus. Channels/Opns. Kimi Moore-Macias
Adv. Dir., Major Media Sales ....Rita Jurczyk
Adv. Sales Dir., Ret. Communities ....Lynn Banda
Adv. Gen. Mgr., SD Marketplace (Class.) Corinne Lynch
Adv. Mgr., Bus. Channels/Gen. Mgr., Lifestyles/Entertainment ....Chris Lavin
Adv. Budget Mgr. ....Betty Symons
Dir., Mktg. ....George Bonaros
Dir., Direct Mktg. ....Laura Tarabini
Mgr., Community Pub. Rel. ......Drew Schlosberg
Circ. Dir., Sales ....Frank Horvath
Market Information: Split run; TMC; Zoned editions.
Mechanical available: Offset; Black and 3 ROP colors; insert accepted; page cutoffs - 22 3/4.
Mechanical Specifications: Type page 11 1/2 x 21 1/2; E - 6 cols, 1 7/8, 1/6 between; A - 6 cols, 1 7/8, 1/6 between; C - 10 cols, 1 1/10, 1/20 between.
Commodity Consumption: Avg. Page Number Per Issue - Daily 95; Avg. Page Number Per Issue - Plates Used 697727; Avg. Page Number Per Issue - Sunday 207; widths 25; Newsprint Used - Metric Tons 67178; Printing Ink Used - Black 1353948; Printing Ink Used - Color 1213087; Printing
Equipment EDITORIAL: Front-end Software – SII/Sys 55.; Editorial Hardware – Tandem/Clx, 350-Micron/P2; Editorial Equipment – III/Postscript, AII/Oman NT 3850; Editorial Printers – HP/LaserJets CLASSIFIED: Front-end Software – SII/Czar II.; Classified Hardware – Tandem/ServerNet, 185-Pentium; Classified Equipment – III/Postscript, SII/Scoop II, SII/SCP Pagination; Classified Printers – HP/LaserJets, APP/Mac LaserWriter DISPLAY: Ad make-up applications – Dataflow, Imageflow, Viewflow; Layout Software – Cascade, 20-APP/Mac.; Display Hardware – 4-Sparc/20s, 2-DEC/Alpha NFS Servers PRODUCTION: Pagination Software – SII/Classified.; Production Equipment – 7-AII/3850, 1-KFM/Twin Drawer, 1-P/26 RA, 1-P/DL 260, 1-P/1800IS, 1-P/26 RT, 2-AG/660, 4-Glunz & Jensen, Konica/28D Processor, 2-LE/LL2218, 1-LE/LL21D; Scanners – 4-AG/Arcus, 3-AII/3750 PRESSROOM: Line 1 – 2-G/Metro towers 4/4 1999, 9-G/Metro double width (5 half decks) 1973; Line 2 – 2-G/Metro towers 4/4 1999, 9-G/Metro double width (5 half decks) 1973; Line 3 – 2-G/Metro towers 4/4 1999, 9-G/Metro double width (5 half decks) 1973; Line 4 – 2-G/Me MAILROOM: Counter stackers – 23-QWI/350, 2-QWI/SJ400; Inserters and stuffers – 4-AM Graphic/2299 20:1; Bundle tying machines – 24-Dynaric/NP2, 1-Dynaric/RLM1; Wrapping singles – 16-QWI/Cobra, 1-QWI/Viper; Mailroom control system – HI/AMCS, HI/Omni 200E; Addressing machine – Addressing; Audio Hardware – Pacific Bell BUSINESS COMPUTERS: Business Software – Microsoft/Office 2000; Business Hardware – 2-DEC/VAX 7610

SAN FRANCISCO

SAN FRANCISCO CHRONICLE

901 Mission Street, San Francisco, Calif., 94103-2988; gen tel (415) 777-1111; adv tel (415) 777-7250; ed tel (415) 777-7100; adv fax (415) 896-6410; ed fax (415) 896-1107; adv e-mail advertise@sfchronicle.com; ed e-mail chronfeedback@sfchronicle.com; web site www.sfgate.com/chronicle
Group: Hearst Corporation
Published: Mon, Tues, Wed, Thur, Fri, Sat, Sun
Weekday Frequency: m
Saturday Frequency: m
Circulation: 220,515; 221,746(sat); 287,226(sun)
Last Audit: ABC September 30, 2011
Price: Weekly Rates: $9.95 (Daily+Sunday), $8.05 (Daily only), $7.25 (W-Su), $7 (Th-

Su), $5.45 (F-Su), $4.50 (Sunday only)
News services: AP, Bloomberg, Getty, MCT, NYT, WP
Politics: Independent. **Established:** 1865
Special Weekly Sections: Thursday: 96 Hours, Ovation; Sunday: Food&Wine, Home&Garden, Style, Travel, Insight, Book Review, Real Estate
Magazines: Parade (S).
Publisher & Chairman ....Frank Vega
Vice Pres., Finance/CFO ....Suzy Cain
Sr. Vice Pres., Adv ....Jeff Bergin
Adv. Vice Pres., Nat'l ....Hernan Ponce
Vice Pres., Circ. ....Chris Blaser
Deputy Mng. Ed., Features ....Meredith White
Managing Editor ....Stephen Proctor
Sr. Art Dir. ....Matthew Petty
Arts Critic ....Kenneth Baker
Sports Ed. ....Alan Saracevic
President ....Mark Adkins
MIS Director ....Melorie Acevedo
Vice Pres., Marketing ....Kelly Harville
Editor/Exec. Vice Pres. ....Ward Bushee
Asst. Mng. Editor, Presentation ....Frank Mina
Editorial Operations ....Allen Matthews
Director, Retail Adv. ....Karleen Arnink-Pate
Vice Pres.- Digital ....Mark Ugar
Metro Editor ....Audrey Cooper
Business Editor ....Kevin Keane
Production Operations Manager....Robin Erskine
Market Information: Split run; TMC; Zoned editions.
Mechanical available: Offset, Heatset Offset; Black and 3 ROP colors; insert accepted - all; page cutoffs - 21 inches
Mechanical Specifications: Image area 10.08 x 20.25; E - 5 cols, 1.88, 1/6 between cols; A - 6 cols, 1.49, 1/6 between cols; C - 6 cols, 1.49, 1/6 between cols.
Commodity Consumption: Avg. Page Number Per Issue - Daily 78; Avg. Page Number Per Issue - Plates Used 785264; Avg. Page Number Per Issue - Saturday 66; Avg. Page Number Per Issue - Sunday 212; widths 50; Newsprint Used - Metric Tons 111614; Newsprint Used - Short Tons 123032;
Equipment EDITORIAL: Front-end Software – CCI NewsDesk, AlfaQuest PrintExpress, SCC MediaServer, MEI ALS, NewsColor, Agfa Intellitune; Editorial Hardware – Sun i86, Mac; Editorial Printers – HP/DesignJet, HP/LaserJet CLASSIFIED: Front-end Software – Atex AdManager, SCS Classified Pagination; Classified Hardware – PC IBM, PC DELL; Classified Equipment – Linux VM; Classified Printers – HP/LaserJet 1200, HP/LaserJet 3850, HP LaserJet 5M DISPLAY: Ad make-up applications – DPS Ad Tracker, OneVision Asura, Agfa Intellitune; Layout Software – Multi-Ad/Creator 8.5.1, QPS/QuarkXPress 4.11.; Display Hardware – Apple G5; Display Printers – Compaq/Pagemarq, AII/3850, HP/4M, HP/5M; Production Equipment – 3-Kodak CTP Platemakers, 3-Kodak? Plate Processors, Burgess Plate Handling System PRESSROOM: Line 1 – 3-MAN/Roland XXL Triple Wide (3 units 4/4, 1 tower can be split into two 2/2 webs) (1 unit has optional Heatset) (Fremont) 2009; Line 2 – 3-MAN/Roland XXL Triple Wide (3 units 4/4, 1 tower can be split into two 2/2 webs) (1 unit has optional Heatset) (Fremont) 2009; Line 3 – 3-MAN/Roland XXL Triple Wide (3 units 4/4, 1 tower can be split into two 2/2 webs) (1 unit has optional Heatset) (Fremont) 2009width (9 half decks) (Richmond) 1990; Line 4 – Presses 1 & 2 AND Presses 2 & 3 can be duplexed together.; Line 5 – Press 3 has quaterfolding capabilities.; Press Drives – Baumueller; Folders – 3-MAN/Roland 2:5:5 Jaw Folders ; Pasters – 12-MAN/Roland; Reels and Stands – 12-MAN/Roland (4 per press); Press control system – MAN/Roland; Press registration system – QIPC MAILROOM: Counter stackers – 10-Fg, 4-QWI/Packman; Inserters and stuffers – 5-Fg (each with 1 press feeder, 2 disc feeders and 10 pocket feeders), 2 MagnaPak 33:1; Bundle tying machines – 6-Ferag, 10-Ferag Cross Tie, 4-Mosca; Mailroom control system – Goss Omnizone; Other equipment –10 QWI Bottomwrappers BUSINESS COMPUTERS: Business Software – Neasi-Weber Admarc, DTI Circulation, Atex AdManager, DPS AdTracker; Business Hardware – Sun i86, Mac
Delivery method: Newsstand, Private Carrier, Racks

SAN JOSE

SAN JOSE MERCURY NEWS

750 Ridder Park Dr., San Jose, Calif., 95190-2432; gen tel (408) 920-5000; adv tel (408) 920-5589; ed tel (408) 920-5912; gen fax (408) 288-8060; adv fax (408) 920-2750; ed fax (408) 920-5244; ed e-mail letters@mercurynews.com; web site www.mercurynews.com
Group: Newspapers First, Inc.
Published: Mon, Tues, Wed, Thur, Fri, Sat, Sun
Weekday Frequency: m
Saturday Frequency: m
Circulation: 527,568; 507,221(sat); 602,566(sun)
Last Audit: ABC September 30, 2011
Price: 3.30/wk; 14.65/mo; 175.80/yr.
Advertising: Open inch rate $566.00
News services: AP, NYT, LAT-WP, CNS, DJ, MCT.
Politics: 1851
Special Editions: SV 150 (Apr); Venture Capital (Aug); Venture Capital (Feb); AT&T Pebble Beach (Jan); Asia (Jun); Cruises (Mar); Mexico (May); Venture Capital (Nov); Model Preview-Trucks (Oct); E-Business (Sept).
Special Weekly Sections: Eye (Entertainment Tab) (Fri); Business Monday (Mon); TV (S); Real Estate (Sat); Venture (Thur); Science & Health (Tues); Food & Wine (Wed).
Magazines: USA WEEKEND Magazine (S).
Chrmn./Pub. ....Jeff Kiel
Vice Pres./CFO ....Lisa Buckingham
Vice Pres., HR/Labor.......Kathleen Slattery Hall
Vice Pres., Opns. ....Dave Bauer
Dir., Acctg. ....Tina Tragarz
Adv. Dir., Classified............Pete Herschberger
Adv. Dir., Nat'l ....Phyllis Weber
Adv. Dir., Opns. ....Mary Evans
Adv. Dir., Retail ....Michael Turpin
Adv. Dir., Targeted Delivery ....Don Poepping
Mgr., Mktg. Commun./Special Sections Dan Breeden
Mgr., Research ....Angela York
Circ. Vice Pres. ....David Rounds
Circ. Dir., Sales/Admin. ....Darren Beevor
Circ. Mgr., Home Delivery..........Melvina Ponzio
Circ. Mgr., Single Copy ....Bruce Emsley
Circ. Mgr., Transportation..............Tom Weldon
Exec. Ed. ....David J. Butler
Deputy Mng. Ed., Convergence...Katherine Fong
Asst. Mng. Ed., Editing............Herschel Kenner
Market Information: ADS; TMC; Zoned editions.
Mechanical available: Offset; Black and 3 ROP colors; insert accepted; page cutoffs - 22 3/4.
Mechanical Specifications: Type page 11 1/2 x 21 1/4; E - 6 cols, 1 4/5, 1/6 between; A - 6 cols, 1 4/5, 1/6 between; C - 10 cols, 1 1/10, 3/25 between.
Commodity Consumption: Avg. Page Number Per Issue - Daily 94; Avg. Page Number Per Issue - Plates Used 681600; Avg. Page Number Per Issue - Saturday 101; Avg. Page Number Per Issue - Sunday 226; widths 40 1/2; Newsprint Used - Metric Tons 62555; Printing Ink Used - Black 16098
Equipment EDITORIAL: Front-end Software – SII.; Editorial Hardware – SII, SII/Servernet; Editorial Equipment – SII/Coyote 430; Editorial Printers – HP CLASSIFIED: Front-end Software – SII.; Classified Hardware – SII/Servernet; Classified Printers – HP DISPLAY: Ad make-up applications – QPS/QuarkXPress, AII/Ad Manager; Layout Software – AII.; Display Hardware – Sun/Sparc Ultra; Display Printers – 3-HP/2500, 3-HP/LaserJet PRODUCTION: Pagination Software – 2-CCI/Newsdesk on Sun Enterprise 6500 with 40 Solaris PC.; Production Equipment – 4-III/3850 Pagesetter, 2-Scitex/Dolev 400, 1-WL/Lith 7; Cameras – 1-C/Newspagers; Scanners – 3-AG/Horizon, 1-HCM/3800, 1-Eskoscan/263615, 1-AII/3750 PRESSROOM: Line 1 – 10-G/Metro double width (6 decks); Line 2 – 10-G/Headliner double width (6 decks); Line 3 – 10-G/Headliner double width (6 decks); Line 4 – 10-G/Headliner double width (6 decks); Press Drives – Allen Bradley/2Press, Fin/2Press; Folders – 4-G/144 p MAILROOM: Counter stackers – 6-HT, 2-QWI/351, 2-QWI/401, 2-QWI/501; Inserters and stuffers – 1-GMA/2000 32:2, 1-GMA/SLS 1000 20:2, 1-GMA/SLS 1000 28:2; Bundle tying machines – 11-Dynaric/NP-2, 7-Samuel/NT40. BUSINESS COMPUTERS: Business Software – CJ/AIM-CIS, Oracle Financial; Business Hardware – 1-HP/959-300

SAN LUIS OBISPO

THE TRIBUNE

3825 S. Higuera St., San Luis Obispo, Calif., 93401; gen tel (805) 781-7800; adv tel (805) 781-7844; ed tel (805) 781-7902; gen fax (805) 781-7870; ed fax (805) 781-7905; gen e-mail newsroom@thetribunenews.com; adv e-mail classifiedsells@thetribunenews.com; ed e-mail letters@thetribunenews.com; web site www.sanluisobispo.com
Published: Mon, Tues, Wed, Thur, Fri, Sat, Sun
Weekday Frequency: m
Saturday Frequency: m
Circulation: 33,104; 34,548(sat); 37,733(sun)
Last Audit: ABC September 30, 2011
Price: 15.50/mo
Advertising: Open inch rate $60.18
News services: AP, Scripps-McClatchy Western Services, MCT, CNS, LAT-WP, NYT, TMS.
Politics: Independent. **Established:** 1869
Own facility?: Y
Special Editions: Vintages (Other).
Special Weekly Sections: Home and Garden (friday), Central Coast Living (Sunday), Ticket Entertainment (Thursday)
Magazines: Ticket (Fri); Real Estate Monthly (Monthly); TV Book (S).
President and Publisher ....Bruce Ray
VP/Human Resources...............Devon P. Goetz
Director of Advertising ....Terrie Banish
Advertising Manager ....Lori Haynes
VP/Online and Marketing ....Sergio Holguin
Home Delivery Manager.................Cathy Veley
VP/Executive Editor.....................Sandra Duerr
Managing Editor ....Tad Weber
Presentation Editor..........................Joe Tarica
VP/Production ....Don Dodds
Pre-Press Manager...................James Morgan
Circ. Dir./Vice Pres. ....Jeff Brinley
Circ. Mgr., Customer Serv. ....Cliff Thompson
Circ. Mgr., Single Copy ....Dan Larabee
Circ. Mgr., Zone ....Jeanne Horishny
Circ. Coord., NIE ....Jon Madden
Editorial Page Ed.............................Bill Morem
Features Ed..............................Rochelle Reed
News Ed. ....Andy Castagnola
Sports Ed. ....Neil Pascale
Market Information: TMC.
Mechanical available: Offset; Black and 3 ROP colors; insert accepted; page cutoffs - 21 3/4.
Mechanical Specifications: Type page 9.875 x 21 1/2; E - 6 cols, 1 7/8, 1/8 between; A - 6 cols, 1 7/8, 1/8 between; C - 10 cols, 1 1/8, 1/32 between.
Equipment EDITORIAL: Front-end Software – APP/Mac OS, Claris/Works, QPS/QuarkXPress, Adobe/Photoshop.; Editorial Hardware – 45-APP/Mac, 3-TI/810; Editorial Equipment – 1-HP/33491A; Editorial Printers – 3-HP/LaserJet CLASSIFIED: Front-end Software – DTI. Class Speed Suite v 4.2.3; Classified Hardware – DTI, APP/Mac Solaris sys; Classified Equipment – APP/Mac (for Ad Makeup); Display Hardware – APP/Mac; Display Printers – 1-APP/Mac LaserWriter Plus PRODUCTION: Pagination Software – MEI/ALS 5.2.0.; Production Equipment – 2-APP/Mac LaserWriter Plus, ECR/45-50, ECR/Jetsetter; Scanners – Epson 4180 PRESSROOM: Line 1 – 14-G/Urbanite single width; Press Drives – 3, 1; Folders – 1, 1; Pasters – 6; Reels and Stands – 4-G/Urbanite. MAILROOM: Counter stackers – Quip 500; Inserters and stuffers – SLS 2000 12:2; Bundle tying machines – Samual NT 40; Addressing machine – Ch; Other equipment –MM. BUSINESS COMPUTERS: Business Software – PBS/MediaPlus; Business Hardware – PBS

SAN MATEO

SAN MATEO COUNTY TIMES

477 9th Ave., Ste. 110, San Mateo, Calif., 94402-1858; gen tel (650) 348-4411; adv tel (650) 348-4454; ed tel (650) 348-4332; gen fax (650) 348-4479; adv fax (650) 348-4450; ed fax (650) 348-4446; gen e-mail angclass@angnewspapers.com; bangcirc@bayareanewsgroup.com; ed e-mail ccnnewsrelease@bayareanewsgroup.com; web site www.mercurynews.com
Published: Mon, Tues, Wed, Thur, Fri, Sat, Sun
Weekday Frequency: e
Saturday Frequency: m
Circulation: 24,417; 21,935(sat)
Last Audit: September 30, 2008
Price: 137.85/yr.
Advertising: Open inch rate $141.00
News services: AP, NYT, McClatchy, SHNS, CNS, LAT-WP, Bloomberg.
Politics: Independent-Republican.
Special Editions: Baseball Preview (Apr); Humane Society (Feb); Alameda Springs Home & Gardens (Jan); Fremont Art & Wine Festival (Jul); Wine Walk (Jun); Almanac (Mar); My Town-The Peninsula (May); California Home (Monthly); Bay Area Best (Oct); NFL Preview (Sept).
Special Weekly Sections: Automotive (Fri); NFL Mondays in Sports (Mon); Careers (S); Real Estate (Sat); Food (Wed).
Magazines: USA WEEKEND Magazine (Sat).
Pres./Pub. ....Ron Schueler
Assoc. Pub. ....Jerry Fuchs
Adv. Dir. ....Anne Artoux
Adv. Mgr., Display.........................Tim Biringer
Mgr., Mktg./Promo................Melanie Keilholtz
Promo. Coord............................Melissa Brown
Circ. Dir.......................................Edward Jow
Ed...Terry Winckler
Exec. Ed...................................Jennifer Aquino
Mng. Ed......................................Pete Wevurski
Bus. Ed....Drew Voros
Editorial Page Ed...........................Tom Tuttle
Food Ed. ....Danielle Centoni
Lifestyle Ed.....................................Kari Hulac
Photo Ed. ....Ron Riesterer
Regl. Ed......................................Mike Oliver
Sports Ed...................................Glenn Reeves
Telecom Mgr................................Sam Lovato
Plant Mgr., Mailroom ....Randy McLeod
Prodn. Mgr., Opns. ....Roger Stanley
Market Information: TMC.
Mechanical available: Offset; Black and 3 ROP colors; insert accepted - product samples; page cutoffs - 20 1/2.
Mechanical Specifications: Type page 12 x 21 1/2; E - 6 cols, 2 1/16, 1/8 between; A - 6 cols, 2 1/16, 1/8 between; C - 10 cols, 1 3/16, 1/16 between.
Commodity Consumption: Avg. Page Number Per Issue - Daily 42; Avg. Page Number Per Issue - Plates Used 20000; widths 54 3/4; Newsprint Used - Metric Tons 4200; Printing Ink Used - Black 156500; Printing Ink Used - Color 18000; Printing Ink Used - Pages Printed 13146.
Equipment EDITORIAL: Front-end Software – HI/NME, HE/NMP.; Editorial Hardware – Novell DISPLAY: Ad make-up applications – Xenix, Multi-Ad/Creator; Layout Software – SCS/Layout 8000.; Display Hardware – APP/Mac 9600, APP/Mac G3, APP/Mac G4; Production Equipment – 6-Nu, 1-W, 1-Nat, 1-AN, 1-SL; Cameras – 4-C; Scanners – 4-HP, 1-AG, 1-Scitex.; Line 2 – 13-G/Urbanite single width 1978; Line 3 – 13-G/Urbanite single width 1984; Line 4 – 13-G/Urbanite single width 1993; Line 5 – 7-MAN/Lithomatic II 1989; Line 6 – 7-G/Urbanite 1990; Line 7 – 15-G/Urbanite single width 1998; Line 8 – 6-MAN/Roland do MAILROOM: Counter stackers – 10-HL/Monitor, 3-QWI/SP, 2/Compass; Inserters and stuffers – 2-HI/1372P, 1-GMA/6:1, 1-GMA/8:1; Bundle tying machines – 10-MLN/2A, 1-/Power Strap, 4-/Dynamic, 4-/Bu; Addressing machine – 1-/Ch, 2-/KR.; Busi-

ness Hardware – IBM/Sys AS-400, 15-IBM

SAN MATEO DAILY JOURNAL

800 S. Claremont St., Ste. 210, San Mateo, Calif., 94402; gen tel (650) 344-5200; gen fax (650) 344-5290; gen e-mail info@smdailyjournal.com; adv e-mail ads@smdailyjournal.com; ed e-mail news@smdailyjournal.com; web site www.smdailyjournal.com

Published: Mon, Tues, Wed, Thur, Fri, Sat
Weekday Frequency: m
Circulation: 14,800; 14,800(sat)
Last Audit: March 12, 2001
Advertising: Open inch rate $20.00
News services: AP.
Special Editions: Easter (Apr); Summer Shopping (Aug); Post-Holiday Clearance (Dec); Valentine's Day (Feb); Post-Holiday Clearance (Jan); Summer Shopping (Jul); Summer Employment (Jun); St. Patrick's Day (Mar); Summer Employment (May); Holiday Gift Guide (Nov); Holiday Emp
Special Weekly Sections: Automotive (Fri); Automotive (Sat); Kids Korner (Thur); Health (Tues); Education Directory (Wed).
Magazines: Relish (Monthly).
Pub. ....Jerry Lee
Ed. ....Jon Mays
Copy Ed./Page Designer ....Erik Oeverndiek
Prodn. Mgr. ....Nicola Zeuzem
Mechanical available: Black; insert accepted; page cutoffs - 16.
Mechanical Specifications: Type page 10 x 15 1/2; E - 5 cols, 1 4/5, between; A - 6 cols, 1 1/2, between; C - 6 cols, 1 1/2, between.
Commodity Consumption: Avg. Page Number Per Issue - Daily 28; Avg. Page Number Per Issue - Saturday 36.
Equipment EDITORIAL: Front-end Software – QPS/QuarkXPress, Baseview/NewsEdit Pro.; Editorial Hardware – APP/Mac CLASSIFIED: Front-end Software – Baseview/AdManager Pro, QPS/QuarkXPress, Adobe/Illustrator, Adobe/Photoshop, Multi-Ad/Creator.; Classified Hardware – APP/Mac DISPLAY: Ad make-up applications – Baseview/Ad Manager Pro.; Display Hardware – APP/Mac PRODUCTION: Pagination Software – QPS/QuarkXPress.

SANTA ANA

THE ORANGE COUNTY REGISTER

625 N. Grand Ave., Santa Ana, Calif., 92701-4347; gen tel (714) 796-7000; adv tel (714) 796-7914; ed tel (714) 796-7951; gen fax (714) 796-5052; adv fax (714) 558-7544; ed fax (714) 796-3657; ed e-mail letters@ocregister.com; web site www.ocregister.com

Published: Mon, Tues, Wed, Thur, Fri, Sat, Sun
Weekday Frequency: m
Saturday Frequency: m
Circulation: 270,809; 247,202(sat); 397,764(sun)
Last Audit: ABC September 30, 2011
Price: 3.01/wk; 13.04/mo; 156.52/yr.
Advertising: Open inch rate $467.51
News services: AP, MCT, NYT, McClatchy.
Note: The Orange County Register operates a separate printing facility in Anaheim.
Special Editions: The Collection (Apr); Holiday Gift Guide II (Dec); LA Auto Show (Jan); Orange County Fair (Jul); Used Car/Auto Service (Jun); Home Beautiful (Mar); Health & Hospital (May); The Collection III (Nov); Las Vegas Live (Oct); Best of Orange County (Sept).
Special Weekly Sections: Home & Garden (Fri); Commentary (S); Saturday (Sat); Venture (Thur); Health & Fitness (Wed).
Magazines: Parade (S).
CEO/ Pub. ....Terry Horne
Vice Pres., Commentary/Opinion ....Cathy Taylor
Vice Pres., Circ. ....Larry Riley
Sr. Vice Pres./Ed. ....Ken Brusic
Deputy Ed., Design ....Brenda Shoun
CFO/Vice Pres., Finance ....Diane Siegfried
Dir., Admin./News ....Catherine Reiland
Sr. Vice Pres., Sales/Mktg. ....Debbie Holzkamp
Adv. Dir., Local Retail ....Lori Dean
Adv. Dir., Retail/Merchandise/Food Jack Nemeth
Adv. Dir., Classified ....Gary Tackett
Dir., Customer Acquisition/Serv. ....Sophia Bien
Dir., Market Research ....Bob Olinto
Dir., New Bus. ....Kevin Olson
Dir., Single Copy ....Paula Olsen
Mgr., Mktg. Communication ....Bob Gary
Deputy Ed., Cities/Zoned Products ....Jeff Light
Deputy Ed., Features/Bus. ....Robin Doussard
Writing Coach ....Lucille DeView
Sr. Team Leader/Bus. Ed. ....Glenn Hall
Market Information: ADS; Split run; TMC.
Mechanical available: Offset; Black and 3 ROP colors; insert accepted; page cutoffs - 22 3/4.
Mechanical Specifications: Type page 11 1/2 x 21 1/2; E - 6 cols, 1 3/4, 1/8 between; A - 6 cols, 1 3/4, 1/8 between; C - 10 cols, 1 3/22, 1/8 between.
Commodity Consumption: Avg. Page Number Per Issue - Daily 100; Avg. Page Number Per Issue - Plates Used 720000; widths 50; Newsprint Used - Metric Tons 120000; Printing Ink Used - Black 1800000; Printing Ink Used - Color 475000.
Equipment EDITORIAL: Front-end Software – AT.; Editorial Hardware – 14-AT/J-11, CCI; Editorial Printers – Printronix, Okidata CLASSIFIED: Front-end Software – AT, Mactive.; Classified Hardware – 12-AT/J-11; Classified Equipment – Infoswitch/ACD; Classified Printers – Printronix, Okidata DISPLAY: Ad make-up applications – Unix, III; Layout Software – III.; Display Hardware – Sun/Microsystems PRODUCTION: Pagination Software – Mactive, CCI.; Production Equipment – 4-M/L-500, 2-M/L-530, 1-ECR/ScriptSetter IV; Cameras – 1-C/Newspager, R/481, C/Spartan III; Scanners – 2-ECR/Autokon 1000DE, ECR/Autokon AII PRESSROOM: Line 1 – 11-G/Metro 1979; Line 2 – 11-G/Metro 1979; Line 3 – 11-G/Metro 1982; Line 4 – 11-G/Headliner 1984; Line 5 – 11-G/Headliner 1985; Line 6 – 11-G/Metro 1989; Folders – 2-G/Single, 4-G/Double Out; Pasters – G/Static Belt RIP; Reels and Stands – G/Y C MAILROOM: Counter stackers – 5-SH/251, 9-GPS/3000, 2-Id/2000, 2-HL/440; Inserters and stuffers – 1/MM, GMA/SLS 1000 16:1; Bundle tying machines – 17-MLN/2E; Wrapping singles – 3-/Si; Addressing machine – 3-/Ch; Other equipment –2-/MM. AUDIO: Audio Software – QNX; Audio Hardware – Centigram/IVR BUSINESS COMPUTERS: Business Software – Admarc, Microsoft/Office 97 Pro Discus, Lawson GL/AD; Business Hardware – HP/9000-K570, IBM/9672, 32-AT/PDPJ

SANTA BARBARA

SANTA BARBARA NEWS-PRESS

715 Anacapa St., Santa Barbara, Calif., 93101-2203; gen tel (805) 564-5200; adv tel (805) 963-4391; ed tel (805) 564-5200; gen fax (805) 564-5270; adv fax (805) 966-1421; ed fax (805) 966-6258; adv e-mail classad@newspress.com; ed e-mail news@newspress.com; web site www.newspress.com

Published: Mon, Tues, Wed, Thur, Fri, Sat, Sun
Weekday Frequency: m
Saturday Frequency: m
Circulation: 25,273; 24,484(sat); 25,151(sun)
Last Audit: ABC September 30, 2011
Price: 2.59/wk ; 144.56/yr.
Advertising: Open inch rate $63.86
News services: AP, NYT, MCT, SHNS, DJ, TMS.
Politics: Independent.
Special Editions: Home and Decorator (Apr); Back to School (Aug); Gift Guide (Dec); Weddings (Feb); Business Outlook (Jan); Fiesta (Jul); Fashion (Mar); Chefs (May); The Season Begins (Nov); Surf (Oct); Prep Football (Sept).
Special Weekly Sections: Sports (S); Religion (Sat).
Magazines: USA WEEKEND Magazine (S).
Co-Pub. ....Wendy Mccaw
Co-Pub ....Arthur von Wiesenberger
CFO/Dir., Opns. ....Norman Colavincenzo
Adv. Dir. ....Fred Mariea
Dir., Community Rel. ....Graham Brown
Customer Serv. Mgr. ....Jacky Barnard
Mng. Ed. ....Linda Strean
Editorial Page Ed. ....Travis K. Armstrong
Features Ed. ....Gary Robb
Librarian ....Cass Cara
Photo/Graphics Ed. ....Len Wood
Spec. Sections Ed. ....Anne Peyrat
Sports Columnist ....John Zant
Dir., Systems ....Raul Gil
MIS Mgr. ....Rick Merrick
Web Designer/Developer ....Mary Beckman
Prodn. Dir. ....Bob Yznaga
Prodn. Mgr., Distr. ....Steve Kuster
Prodn. Mgr., Press ....Matt Armstrong
Prodn. Mgr., Publishing Servs. ....Sharon Moore
Market Information: Split run; TMC.
Mechanical available: Offset; Black and 3 ROP colors; insert accepted; page cutoffs - 22.
Mechanical Specifications: Type page 13 x 21; E - 6 cols, 2 1/16, 1/8 between; A - 6 cols, 2 1/16, 1/8 between; C - 9 cols, 1 3/8, 1/16 between.
Commodity Consumption: Avg. Page Number Per Issue - Daily 48; Avg. Page Number Per Issue - Plates Used 137000; Avg. Page Number Per Issue - Sunday 124; widths 55; Newsprint Used - Metric Tons 5181; Printing Ink Used - Black 118361; Printing Ink Used - Color 72144; Printing Ink
Equipment EDITORIAL: Front-end Software – DTI.; Editorial Hardware – APP/PowerMac, Sun/Sparc; Editorial Printers – DEC, HP CLASSIFIED: Front-end Software – DTI/ClassSpeed 4.2.; Classified Hardware – APP/Power Mac, Sun/Sparc; Classified Equipment – Grand Junction/Fast Ethernet Switches; Classified Printers – HP, Dataproducts, III/3850 DISPLAY: Ad make-up applications – CJ; Layout Software – CJ.; Display Hardware – DEC/VAX, DTI/AdSpeed, 30-APP/Mac Quadra; Display Printers – DEC, HP, Dataproducts, Canon/Laser Printer PRODUCTION: Pagination Software – DTI, QPS/QuarkXPress 3.3, Adobe/PageMaker 5.0, Adobe/FreeHand 5.0.; Production Equipment – 2-G, J, III/Graphic Cobe Imager, DTI; Scanners – ECR III/3750, Nikon 35mm, CD, 5-Umax/Flatbed PRESSROOM: Line 1 – 4-G/Metrocolor (2 towers; 1 mono; 1 HO w/half deck) 1993; Folders – G/3:2 double single delivery 1993; Pasters – 5-G/CT-45; Reels and Stands – 5-G/CT-45; Press control system – G/MCPS2. MAILROOM: Counter stackers – 4/QWI; Inserters and stuffers – 1-HI/NP 630; Bundle tying machines – 4-/Dynaric; Wrapping singles – 3-/QWI; Mailroom control system – Am/AMCS, MM/Print roll, Davario/Conveyor; Addressing machine – 1-/Ch; Other equipment –MM/Stitcher-T BUSINESS COMPUTERS: Business Software – CJ, MCBA, Microsoft, DTI; Business Hardware – DEC/VAX

SANTA CLARITA

THE SIGNAL

PO Box 801870, Santa Clarita, Calif., 91380-1870; gen tel (661) 259-1234; gen fax (661) 254-8068; adv fax (661) 259-2081; ed fax (661) 255-9689; gen e-mail info@the-signal.com; web site www.the-signal.com

Published: Mon, Tues, Wed, Thur, Fri, Sat, Sun
Weekday Frequency: m
Saturday Frequency: m
Circulation: 9,265; 10,318(sat); 9,017(sun)
Last Audit: Sworn September 30, 2010
Price: 6.50/mo; 50.00/yr.
Advertising: Open inch rate $39.90
Insert rate: $32.60
News services: AP.
Politics: Conservative. **Established:** 1919
Own facility?: Y
Special Weekly Sections: Entertainment (Fri); Valley Homes (S); Religion (Sat); Lifestyles/Features (Tues); Lifestyles/Features (Wed).
Market Information: TMC.
Mechanical available: Offset; Black and 3 ROP colors; insert accepted; page cutoffs - 22 3/4.
Mechanical Specifications: Type page 12 x 21 1/4; E - 6 cols, 1 7/8, 1/8 between; A - 6 cols, 1 7/8, 1/8 between; C - 10 cols, 1, 1/8 between.
Commodity Consumption: Avg. Page Number Per Issue - Daily 30; Avg. Page Number Per Issue - Plates Used 37000; Avg. Page Number Per Issue - Sunday 64; widths 25; Newsprint Used - Metric Tons 2400; Printing Ink Used - Black 64000; Printing Ink Used - Color 5200; Printing Ink Use
Equipment EDITORIAL: Front-end Software – Baseview.; Editorial Hardware – APP/Mac; Editorial Printers – Xante/3 G CLASSIFIED: Front-end Software – Baseview.; Classified Hardware – APP/Mac; Classified Printers – TI/Omni 800 DISPLAY: Ad make-up applications – Baseview; Layout Software – Baseview.; Display Hardware – APP/Mac PRODUCTION: Pagination Software – QPS 4.1.1.; Production Equipment – 2-Nu/Flip Top FT52, 1-MAS/Newspeed; Cameras – 1-Acti PRESSROOM: Line 1 – 10-G/Urbanite 1985; Folders – 2; Pasters – 8 MAILROOM: Counter stackers – 1-MM/K231, 1-MM/310; Inserters and stuffers – 2-MM/227; Bundle tying machines – 2/MLN, 1-MLN/MLEE. BUSINESS COMPUTERS: Business Software – IBM/Acct Mate; Business Hardware – PC

SANTA MARIA

SANTA MARIA TIMES

3200 Skyway Dr., Santa Maria, Calif., 93455; gen tel (805) 925-2691; adv tel (805) 925-2691; ed tel (805) 925-2691; gen fax (805) 928-5657; adv fax (805) 928-5657; ed fax (805) 928-5657; web site www.santamariatimes.com

Published: Mon, Tues, Wed, Thur, Fri, Sat, Sun
Weekday Frequency: m
Saturday Frequency: m
Circulation: 13,961; 12,672(sat); 18,382(sun)
Last Audit: ABC September 30, 2011
Price: 11.00/mo; 110.40/yr.
Advertising: Open inch rate $52.11
News services: AP, GNS, MCT, NYT, SHNS, TMS.
Politics: Independent.
Special Editions: Santa Maria Strawberry Festival (Apr); Readers' Choice (Aug); Last Minute Gift Guide (Dec); Farm & Agriculture (Feb); Wedding Guide (Jan); Mid-State Fair (Jul); Flower Festival (Jun); Personal Improvement (Mar); Fire Safety (May); Coupon Direct (Monthly);
Special Weekly Sections: Health (Fri); Travel (S); Home & Garden (Sat); Senior (Thur); Scrapbook (Tues); Food (Wed).
Magazines: Relish (Monthly); USA WEEKEND Magazine (S).
Adv. Vice Pres. ....Cynthia Schur
Circ. Dir. ....Rich Macke
Exec. Ed. ....Tom Bolton
Mng. Ed. ....Dave Bemis
Asst. Mng. Ed. ....Len Wood
Features Ed. ....Dana Gran
Online Ed. ....Gary Robb
Sports Ed. ....Elliott Stern
Asst. Sports Ed. ....Dan Watson
Web Developer ....Jose Aquino
Prodn. Mgr. ....George Fischer
Market Information: TMC.
Mechanical available: Offset; Black and 3 ROP colors; insert accepted - upon prior quote only; page cutoffs - 22 3/4.
Mechanical Specifications: Type page 11 5/8 x 21 1/2; E - 6 cols, 1 13/16, 1/8 between; A - 6 cols, 2 1/16, 1/8 between; C - 10 cols, 1 1/32, 1/16 between.
Commodity Consumption: Avg. Page Number Per Issue - Daily 26; Avg. Page Number Per Issue - Plates Used 30000; Avg. Page Number Per Issue - Sunday 52; widths 12 1/2; Newsprint Used - Metric Tons 1900; Printing Ink Used - Black 40000; Printing Ink Used - Color 3000; Printing Ink
Equipment EDITORIAL: Front-end Software – QPS/QuarkXPress 4.11, Adobe/Photoshop 6.0, Macromedia/Freehand 9, Baseview/NewsEdit Pro 3.6.1, SII.; Editorial Hardware – 15-

APP/Power Mac G3, 3-APP/Power Mac 7300, 2-APP/Power Mac G4; Editorial Equipment – 1-Umax/Astra 4000n Scanner; Editorial Printers – 1-QMS/2060 CLASSIFIED: Front-end Software – Baseview/Ad Manager Pro.; Classified Hardware – 9-APP/iMac G3; Classified Equipment – APP/Mac G4 Server; Classified Printers – HP/8150n DISPLAY: Ad make-up applications – QPS/QuarkXPress 4.11; Display Hardware – 7-APP/Power Mac G3; Display Printers – 1-QMS/2060 PRODUCTION: Pagination Software – QPS/QuarkXPress 4.11, Multi-Ad/Creator 2 6.5.; Production Equipment – 1-Nu PRESSROOM: Line 1 – 10-G/Urbanite single width; Folders – 1 MAILROOM: Counter stackers – QWI; Inserters and stuffers – HI/1372; Bundle tying machines – 2/MLNEE; Addressing machine – Wm/from computer lists. BUSINESS COMPUTERS: Business Software – PBS: Circ, PBS: Adv; Business Hardware – PBS

SANTA ROSA

THE PRESS DEMOCRAT

427 Mendocino Ave., Santa Rosa, Calif., 95401-6313; gen tel (707) 546-2020; adv tel (707) 546-2020; ed tel (800) 660-5056; gen fax (707) 521-5330; adv fax (707) 521-5334; ed fax (707) 521-5330; ed e-mail letters@pressdemo.com; web site www.pressdemocrat.com

Published: Mon, Tues, Wed, Thur, Fri, Sat, Sun
Weekday Frequency: m
Saturday Frequency: m
Circulation: 56,017; 59,187(sat); 61,314(sun)
Last Audit: ABC September 30, 2011
Price: 17.99/mo; 216.00/yr.
Advertising: Open inch rate $120.00
News services: NYT, AP, LAT-WP, McClatchy, Bay City News Service, TMS, MCT.
Politics: 1857
Special Editions: Sonoma Co. Skiers Info. Guide (Nov); Fall Home & Garden (Sept).
Special Weekly Sections: Ticket (Fri); Sonoma Sunday (S); Church (Sat); Teen Life (Tues); Food Life (Wed).
Magazines: Santa Rosa Magazine (Quarterly); TV Week (S); Savor Wine Country Magazine (Semi-yearly).

Pub. .... Bruce Kyse
Controller .... Sandy McAdler
Innovation Dir. .... Kristin Houston
Adv. Dir. .... Carolyn McCulligh
Adv. Mgr. .... Bridget Gieseke
Adv. Mgr., Nat'l .... Barbara Mitchel
Online Adv. .... Nicol Harris
Dir., Mktg. .... Cindy Butner
Circ. Mgr. .... Dava Amador
Ed. .... Heather Irwin
Exec. Ed .... Catherine Barnett
Mng. Ed. .... Robert Swofford
Sr. Ed. .... Chuck Buxton
Sr. Ed., Presentation .... George Millener
Books Ed .... Patty Hayes
Editorial Page Ed .... Paul Gullixson
Entertainment Ed .... Dan Taylor
News Ed .... James Fremgen
Online Ed. .... Greg Retsinas

Market Information: ADS; Split run; TMC.
Mechanical available: Offset; Black and 3 ROP colors; insert accepted; page cutoffs - 22.
Mechanical Specifications: Type page 11 5/8 x 20 3/4; E - 6 cols, 1 13/16, 1/8 between; A - 6 cols, 1 13/16, 1/8 between; C - 6 cols, 1 13/16, 1/8 between.
Commodity Consumption: Avg. Page Number Per Issue - Daily 66; Avg. Page Number Per Issue - Plates Used 122000; Avg. Page Number Per Issue - Sunday 132; widths 25; Newsprint Used - Metric Tons 13870; Printing Ink Used - Black 285000; Printing Ink Used - Color 110000; Printing I
Equipment EDITORIAL: Front-end Software – Unisys 4.0.; Editorial Hardware – Unisys/Publishing System, Sun/Server, Compaq/Prosignia; Editorial Equipment – PC; Editorial Printers – 5-HP/Laser Jet CLASSIFIED: Front-end Software – AT/Advantage 1.4.8305, MEI/CLS, Atex.; Classified Hardware – Atex, Compaq/Proliant 6000, Compaq, HP; Classified Equipment – RE/Magazine Production Unit, 11-Dell; Classified Printers – HP/4000TN DISPLAY: Ad make-up applications – Multi-Ad/Creator, III/Ad Manager, QPS/QuarkXPress, Baseview/Managing Editor CLS; Layout Software – APP/Mac.; Display Hardware – APP/Mac, III/Ad Manager PRODUCTION: Pagination Software – MEI/CLS 2.6.; Production Equipment – 2-P/SC 250, 1-CD/635E; Cameras – 1-C/260D; Scanners – Nikon, CD, Autokon/1000 PRESSROOM: Line 1 – 8-G/Headliner (4 decks) 1986; Folders – 2-G/3:2 (144); Pasters – G/RPT. MAILROOM: Counter stackers – 6/QWI; Inserters and stuffers – 2-/AM Graphics/6305 22/24, 1-/AM Graphics/NP 630 22 hopper, 1-/AM Graphics/NP 630 26 hopper; Bundle tying machines – 6-/Power Strap/PSN6, 4-/Dynaric; Wrapping singles – 1-HI/650 Saddle Binder, PowerStrap AUDIO: Audio Software – Brite Voice Systems; Audio Hardware – ITN, AP StockQuote, Brite Voice Systems BUSINESS COMPUTERS: Business Software – Admarc, Lawson, INSI; Business Hardware – IBM/AS-400 Model E50

PRESS DEMOCRAT PUBLISHING CO.

427 Mendocino Ave., Santa Rosa, Calif., 95401; gen tel (707) 526-8659

SCOTTS VALLEY

SANTA CRUZ SENTINEL

1800 Green Hills Rd., Ste. 210, Scotts Valley, Calif., 95066; gen tel (831) 423-4242; gen fax (831) 423-1154; ed fax (831) 429-9620; gen e-mail sentcity@santa-cruz.com; ed e-mail news@santacruzsentinel.com; web site www.santacruzsentinel.com

Published: Mon, Tues, Wed, Thur, Fri, Sat, Sun
Weekday Frequency: m
Saturday Frequency: m
Circulation: 20,992; 20,992(sat); 21,351(sun)
Last Audit: September 30, 2009
Price: 3.30/wk; 117.00/yr.
Advertising: Open inch rate $42.18
News services: AP, McClatchy, NYT.
Politics: Non-Partisan. **Established:** 1856
Not Published: New Year; Memorial Day; Labor Day; Thanksgiving; Christmas.
Special Editions: Back to School (Aug); Last Minute Gift Guide (Dec); Forecast (Feb); Bride & Groom (Jan); Wharf to Wharf Race (Jul); Antiques (Jun); Home & Garden (Mar); Holiday Gift Guide (Nov); Employment Digest (Oct); Santa Cruz County Fair (Sept).
Special Weekly Sections: Spotlight-Entertainment & Dining (Fri); Seniors (Mon); Education (S); Sports-Breaking Away (Thur); Best Food Day (Wed).
Magazines: Relish (Monthly); TV Magazine (S).

Pub. .... Mike Jung
Ed. .... Tom Honig
Books Ed .... Chris Watson
Bus. Ed. .... Julie Copeland
City Desk .... Len La Barth
Copy Desk Chief .... Marc DesJardins
Features Ed .... Stacy Vreeken
Film/Theater Ed .... Wallace Baine
Photo Ed. .... Bill Lovejoy
Sports Ed. .... Tom Moore
Travel Ed .... Stacey Vreeken
Internet Mgr. .... Arlene Hudson
Opns. Dir. .... Mike Blaesser

Market Information: ADS; Split run; TMC.
Mechanical available: Offset; Black and 3 ROP colors; insert accepted - product samples; page cutoffs - 22 3/4.
Mechanical Specifications: Type page 13 x 21 1/2; E - 6 cols, 2 1/16, 1/8 between; A - 6 cols, 2 1/16, 1/8 between; C - 9 cols, 1 3/8, 1/16 between.
Commodity Consumption: Avg. Page Number Per Issue - Daily 38; Avg. Page Number Per Issue - Plates Used 35000; Avg. Page Number Per Issue - Saturday 36; Avg. Page Number Per Issue - Sunday 60; widths 25; Newsprint Used - Metric Tons 2150; Newsprint Used - Short Tons 2368; Print
Equipment EDITORIAL: Front-end Software – QPS/QuarkXPress 3.32, Microsoft/Word 6.0, Dewar/View 2.11.; Editorial Hardware – IBM/300 PL CLASSIFIED: Front-end Software – Dewarview/Enterprise.; Classified Hardware – IBM/300PL DISPLAY: Ad make-up applications – QPS/QuarkXPress 3.32, Microsoft/Word 6.0; Display Hardware – IBM/300 PL; Display Printers – HP/LaserJet 4 PRODUCTION: Pagination Software – QPS/QuarkXPress 3.31.; Production Equipment – 1-WL; Cameras – Ik/550, Ik/555; Scanners – Kk/RFS 2035 PRESSROOM: Line 1 – 6-G/Headliner 1985; Pasters – 5; Reels and Stands – 5 MAILROOM: Counter stackers – 3/QWI; Inserters and stuffers – 2-GMA/6:1-8:1; Bundle tying machines – 2-/Power Strap, 1-/OVL. AUDIO: Audio Software – MNA, BBS, VDC; Audio Hardware – J H Zerbey Newspaper Inc, PC 486, 4-MB; Business Hardware – 1-IBM/AS-400

SONORA

THE UNION DEMOCRAT

84 S. Washington St., Sonora, Calif., 95370-4711; gen tel (209) 532-7151; adv tel (209) 588-4555; ed tel (209) 588-4525; gen fax (209) 532-5139; adv fax (209) 532-5139; ed fax (209) 532-6451; adv e-mail ads@uniondemocrat.com; ed e-mail newsroom@uniondemocrat.com; letters@uniondemocrat.com; web site www.uniondemocrat.com

Group: Western Communications
Published: Mon, Tues, Wed, Thur, Fri
Weekday Frequency: e
Circulation: 10,024
Last Audit: ABC September 30, 2011
Price: 7.00/mo; 78.00/yr.
Advertising: Open inch rate $19.50
News services: AP.
Politics: 1854
Not Published: New Year; Memorial Day; Independence Day; Labor Day; Thanksgiving; Christmas.
Own facility?: Y
Special Editions: Back-to-School (Aug); Letters to Santa (Dec); Dollars and Sense (Jan); MotherLode Fair (Jul); Senior Lifestyle (Jun); Home & Garden (Mar); MotherLode Roundup (May); Holiday Treasures (Nov); Career Woman (Oct).
Special Weekly Sections: Health & Medicine (Mondays); Food&Drink (Tues); Business (Wed); Travel & Leisure (Thurs); Entertainment tab (Thurs); Community (Friday)
Magazines: American Profile (Wed).

Pub. .... Ron Horton
Bus. Mgr. .... Lynne Fernandez
Adv. Dir. .... Gary Piech
Adv. Mgr., Classified .... Peggy Pietrowicz
Ed. .... Craig Cassidy
Mng. Ed., Features .... Margie Hiser
Sports Ed. .... Bill Rozak
Theater/Music Ed. .... Gary Linehan
Coord., Systems/Web .... Derek Rosen
Prodn. Mgr., Opns./Press .... Rick Quillen
Circulation Manager .... Sharon Sharp
Circ. Dir. .... Michele Rockwell

Market Information: Split run; TMC.
Mechanical available: Web Offset; Black and 3 ROP colors; insert accepted; page cutoffs - 23.
Mechanical Specifications: Type page 11 1/2 x 21 1/2; E - 6 cols, 2, 1/6 between; A - 6 cols, 2, 1/6 between; C - 8 cols, 1 1/3, 1/6 between.
Commodity Consumption: Avg. Page Number Per Issue - Daily 30; Avg. Page Number Per Issue - Plates Used 8400; widths 12 1/2; Newsprint Used - Short Tons 554; Printing Ink Used - Black 8500; Printing Ink Used - Color 1400; Printing Ink Used - Pages Printed 7620.
Equipment EDITORIAL: Front-end Software – Baseview, QPS/QuarkXPress, Adobe/Photoshop, Adobe/Illustrator.; Editorial Hardware – APP/Mac; Editorial Equipment – Nikon/35mm Scanner, Umax/Powerlook II; Editorial Printers – V, APP/Mac, HP; Classified Hardware – APP/Mac; Classified Printers – V, APP/Mac DISPLAY: Ad make-up applications – QPS/QuarkXPress, Adobe/Photoshop, Adobe/Illustrator; Layout Software – Other; Display Hardware – APP/Mac; Display Printers – V/Imagesetters, ECR/3650, Pre Press/Panther Plus, Epson/Stylus 3000 PRODUCTION: Pagination Software – QPS/QuarkXPress 4.0.; Production Equipment – Caere/OmniPage Pro, Pre Press/Panther Plus; Cameras – SCREEN/Companica 5161; Scanners – Nikon/LS-1000 PRESSROOM: Line 1 – 8-G/Community single width.; Inserters and stuffers – 6-KAN/480; Bundle tying machines – Dynaric; Addressing machine – Wm. BUSINESS COMPUTERS: Business Software – PBS; Business Hardware – 7-PC Clone
Delivery method: Mail, Newsstand, Private Carrier, Racks

SOUTH LAKE TAHOE

TAHOE DAILY TRIBUNE

3079 Harrison Ave., South Lake Tahoe, Calif., 96150-7931; gen tel (530) 541-3880; adv tel (530) 541-3880; ed tel (530) 541-3880; gen fax (530) 541-0373; adv fax (530) 541-8238; ed fax (530) 541-0373; ed e-mail editor@tahoedailytribune.com; web site www.tahoedailytribune.com

Published: Wed, Thur, Fri, Sat
Weekday Frequency: m
Saturday Frequency: m
Circulation: 1,000; 1,000(sat)
Last Audit: Sworn October 1, 2001
Price: 15/mo (carrier); 143/yr (carrier)
News services: AP.
Politics: Independent. **Established:** 1952
Not Published: Sun-Tues
Own facility?: Y
Special Editions: Almanac Series (Feb).
Special Weekly Sections: Entertainment (Fri).
Magazines: Tahoe Magazine (May and November) (Twice-Annually); Lake Tahoe Action (Thurs); Tahoe Tastes (February and August) (Twice-Annually); Best of Tahoe (July) (Annually)

Ed. .... Annie Flanzraich
Action Ed. .... Tim Parsons
Pub. .... Mary Jurkonis
Adv. Sales Coord .... Loretta Shirley
Circ. Mgr. .... Tim Woods
Mng. Ed. .... Elaine Goodman
Exec. Ed. .... Ryan Slabaugh
Mulitmedia Ed. .... Jeff Munson
Sports Ed .... Steve Yingling

Market Information: ADS; TMC.
Mechanical available: Web Offset; Black and 3 ROP colors; insert accepted - on request; page cutoffs - 22 3/4.
Mechanical Specifications: Type page 12 7/8 x 21 1/2; E - 6 cols, 2, 1/8 between; A - 6 cols, 2, 1/8 between; C - 9 cols, 1 1/3, 1/9 between.
Commodity Consumption: Avg. Page Number Per Issue - Daily 20; Avg. Page Number Per Issue - Saturday 32(fri); widths 27 1/2.
Equipment EDITORIAL: Front-end Software – QPS/QuarkXPress 3.1.; Editorial Hardware – 1-APP/Mac; Editorial Equipment – Lf/AP Leaf Picture Desk; Editorial Printers – APP/Mac LaserWriter II NTX CLASSIFIED: Front-end Software – Fourth Dimension.; Classified Hardware – APP/Mac; Classified Printers – APP/Mac LaserWriter II NTX DISPLAY: Ad make-up applications – QPS/QuarkXPress 3.1, Aldus/FreeHand; Layout Software – 6-APP/Mac SE, 2-APP/Mac II.; Display Hardware – APP/Mac; Display Printers – APP/Mac LaserWriter II NTX; Production Equipment – 2-Microcraft/Translator II, APP/Mac IINTX. PRESSROOM: Line 1 – 16-G/Community; Folders – 1 MAILROOM: Counter stackers – 1/BG; Inserters and stuffers – 4-/MM; Bundle tying machines – 2-/MLN. BUSINESS COMPUTERS: Business Software – PBS
DTI; Business Hardware – Unisys
Zip Codes served: 96150+
Delivery method: Newsstand, Private Carrier, Racks

STOCKTON

THE RECORD

530 E. Market St., Stockton, Calif., 95202-3009; gen tel (209) 943-6397; adv tel (209) 546-8200; ed tel (209) 546-8250; gen fax (209) 546-8186; adv fax (209) 546-8232; ed fax (209) 546-8288; gen e-mail editor@recordnet.com; adv e-mail advertising@recordnet.com; ed e-mail newsroom@recordnet.com; web site www.recordnet.com

Group: Dow Jones
Published: Sun
Weekday Frequency: m
Saturday Frequency: m
Circulation: 42,488; 49,611(sat); 51,994(sun)
Last Audit: ABC September 30, 2011
Price: 199.00/yr.
Advertising: Call
Insert rate: Call
News services: AP, MCT.
Politics: 1895
Own facility?: Y
Special Editions: Pinnacle (Annually); Asparagus Festival (Apr); Back-to-School (Aug); Outlook 1 (Feb); Holiday Guide (Nov); Home Life (Quarterly); Best of San Joaquin (Sept).
Special Weekly Sections: Entertainment - Thursdays; Automotive - Friday; Real Estate - Sat/Sun; Travel - Sunday; @RecordBody:**Magazines:** San Joaquin Lifestyles (bi-monthly); San Joaquin Woman (bi-monthly)
Pub. ....Roger Coover
Credit Mgr. ....Claudine Dunham
Adv. Dir. ....Deitra Kenoly
Circ. Director ....Peter Gutierrez
Editor ....Mike Klocke
Mng. Editor ....Donald W. Blount
Editorial Page Ed. ....Eric Grunder
Metro Editor ....Kevin Parrish
Online Editor ....Tara Cuslidge
Sports Editor ....Bob Highfill
Dir., Info Tech ....Stewart Willis
Tech Servs. Mgr. ....Ken Damilano
Prodn. Dir., Opns. ....Damian Glick
Safety, Environmental, Maintenance Mgr. Jim Frankel
CFO ....Charles Scott
Adv. Servs. Mgr. ....Ral Weekly
Metro Ed. ....Barbara Zumwalt
Prodn. Mgr., Pressroom ....Joey Givens
Market Information: ADS; TMS
Mechanical available: Offset; Black and full color ROP colors; insert accepted - commercial flyers; page cutoffs - 22 3/4.
Mechanical Specifications: Type page 11 5/8 x 21 1/2; E - 6 cols, 1 5/6, 1/6 between; A - 6 cols, 1 5/6, 1/6 between; C - 10 cols, 1 1/16, 1/12 between.
Commodity Consumption: Avg. Page Number Per Issue - Daily 52; Avg. Page Number Per Issue - Plates Used 80000; Avg. Page Number Per Issue - Sunday 74; widths 50; Newsprint Used - Metric Tons 6373; Printing Ink Used - Black 219200; Printing Ink Used - Color 70775; Printing Ink U
Equipment; Editorial Hardware – APP/Mac, PC; Editorial Printers – HP, CLASSIFIED: Front-end Software – Mactive/Classified 2.24, SQL/Server 2000.; Classified Hardware – Dell/6450 Cluster Server; Classified Equipment – Hyphen/Mac RIP, OPI/Hyphen DISPLAY: Ad make-up applications – Adobe/Illustrator, Adobe/Photoshop; Layout Software – HI/Jazbox, Managing Editor/ALS 4.2.; Display Printers – HP PRESSROOM: Line 1 – 10-TKS; Press Drives – 7-ABB; Folders – 1-TKS; Pasters – 7-Brock; Reels and Stands – 7-TKS; Press control system – ABB, Brock; Press registration system – Quad Tech. MAILROOM: Counter stackers – 2-HI/Olympic NP 500, 2-QWI/Packman; Inserters and stuffers – 1-HI/1472P; Bundle tying machines – 2-Dynaric/NP 1500 HS; Mailroom control system – G; Other equipment –2-Accraply/Labeler.
Zip Codes served: San Joaquin County
Delivery method: Newsstand, Private Carrier, Racks

STOCKTON NEWSPAPERS, INC.

530 E. Market St., Stockton, Calif., 95202; gen tel (209) 546-8241; gen fax (209) 547-8182

TAFT

DAILY MIDWAY DRILLER

800 Center St., Taft, Calif., 93268; gen tel (661) 763-3171; gen fax (661) 763-5638; ed e-mail editor@bay.rr.com; web site www.taft-midwaydriller.com

Published: Mon, Tues, Wed, Thur, Fri
Weekday Frequency: e
Circulation: 4,900
Price: 5.80/mo; 55.77/yr.
Advertising: Open inch rate $8.35
News services: AP.
Politics: Independent. **Established:** 1916
Not Published: New Year; Memorial Day; Independence Day; Labor Day; Thanksgiving; Christmas.
Special Weekly Sections: Religion (Fri); Opinion (Thur); Business (Tues); Lifestyle (Wed).
Office Mgr. ....Deanna Long
Circ. Mgr. ....Melissa Robertson
Ed. ....John Watkins
City Ed. ....Doug Keeler
Sports Ed. ....Sara Mitchell
Prodn. Mgr. ....Carrie Cole
Market Information: TMC.
Mechanical available: Offset; Black and 1 ROP colors; insert accepted; page cutoffs - 21 1/2.
Mechanical Specifications: Type page 13 x 21 1/2; E - 6 cols, 2 1/16, 1/8 between; A - 6 cols, 2 1/16, 1/8 between; C - 6 cols, 2 1/16, 1/8 between.
Commodity Consumption: Avg. Page Number Per Issue - Daily 8; Avg. Page Number Per Issue - Plates Used 3500; widths 14; Newsprint Used - Metric Tons 132; Printing Ink Used - Pages Printed 2214.
Equipment; Editorial Hardware – 3-IBM, 2-IBM/AT; Editorial Printers – 1-HP/LaserJet II.; Classified Hardware – 1-IBM/AT; Classified Equipment – 1-Okidata/99.; Display Hardware – Printers ☐ QMS; Display Printers – QMS; Production Equipment – 1-COM/IV, 1-HP/Laserprinter; Cameras – 1-B. PRESSROOM: Line 1 – 4-G/Community; Folders – 1; Inserters and stuffers – 1-MM/EM 10; Bundle tying machines – 2/Bu; Addressing machine – 1-/Am.; Business Hardware – 1-IBM/AT, 1-Mk/Acer 486

TORRANCE

DAILY BREEZE

21250 Hawthorne Blvd., Ste. 170, Torrance, Calif., 90503-4066; gen tel (310) 540-5511; adv tel (310) 540-5511; ed tel (310) 540-5511; gen fax (310) 772-6281; adv fax (310) 543-4796; ed fax (310) 540-6272; gen e-mail askus@dailybreeze.com; ed e-mail newsroom@dailybreeze.com; calendar@dailybreeze.com; web site www.dailybreeze.com

Group: MediaNews Group
Published: Mon, Tues, Wed, Thur, Fri, Sat, Sun
Weekday Frequency: m
Saturday Frequency: m
Circulation: 74,653; 63,362(sat); 64,245(sun)
Last Audit: ABC September 30, 2011
News services: AP, City News Service, SHNS, Religion News Service
Note: The Los Angeles Newspaper Group includes the Long Beach Press-Telegram (mS), Los Angeles Daily News (mS), Ontario Inland Valley Daily Bulletin (mS), Pasadena Star-News (mS), Redlands Daily Facts (eS), San Bernardino County Sun (mS), San Gabriel Valley Tribune
Own facility?: N
Special Editions: South Bay's Best (Aug); Source (July);
Chronology (Nov); Holiday Worship (Dec); Holiday Entertainment (Nov) Oh Baby (Jan); People of Distinction (Novl); High School Graduation (Jun); Auto Preview (Nov); Wedding Guide (March & October)
Special Weekly Sections: Food (Wed); Health (Thurs); Home+Garden (Sat); Home Guide: Real Estate (Sat)
Magazines: USA WEEKEND Magazine (S).
Circ. Mgr., Customer Serv. ....Jim Vita
Vice Pres., Consumer Mktg ....Ron Hasse
Editor ....Toni Sciacqua
Business ....Muhammed El-Hasan
City Editor ....Frank Suraci
Columnist ....John Bogert
Features Editor ....Leo Smith
Visuals ....Chuck Bennett
VP Advertising ....Jim Shaw
Publisher ....Jack Klunder
Mechanical available: Offset; Black and 3 ROP colors; insert accepted - flexi, products samples, single sheets; page cutoffs - 22 3/4.
Mechanical Specifications: Type page 12 1/2 x 21 1/4; E - 6 cols, 2 1/16, 1/8 between; A - 6 cols, 2 1/16, 1/8 between; C - 10 cols, 1 1/4, 1/16 between.
Equipment PRESSROOM: Line 1 – Outsourced to Southwest Offset Printing, Gardena, CA
Zip Codes served: 90245, 90247, 90248, 90249, 90250, 90254, 90260, 90266, 90274, 90275, 90277, 90278, 90501, 90502, 90503, 90504, 90505, 90506, 90710, 90717, 90731, 90732, 90744, 90745, 90746, 90747
Delivery method: Mail, Newsstand, Private Carrier, Racks

TRACY

TRACY PRESS

145 W. 10th St., Tracy, Calif., 95376; gen tel (209) 835-3030; gen fax (209) 835-0655; adv fax (209) 832-5383; gen e-mail tp-news@tracypress.com; adv e-mail tpads@tracypress.com; web site www.tracypress.com

Published: Wed, Sat
Last Audit: November 10, 2009
Advertising: Open inch rate $24.20
Politics: Independent. **Established:** 1898
Pres./Pub. ....Robert S. Matthews
Adv. Dir. ....Lisa Cracraft
Mktg. Mgr. ....Lisa Carcraft
Circ. Mgr. ....Nancy Mathews
Ed. ....Cheri Matthews
Graphics Ed ....Ryan Carpenter
News Ed. ....Eric Firpo
Prodn. Mgr., Pressroom ....John Wilson

TURLOCK

TURLOCK JOURNAL

138 S. Center St., Turlock, Calif., 95380; gen tel (209) 634-9141; gen fax (209) 632-8813; adv e-mail adinfo@turlockjournal.com; ed e-mail news@turlockjournal.com; web site www.turlockjournal.com

Published: Wed, Sat
Last Audit: March 31, 2003
Price: 8.50/mo (plus tax); 102.00/yr (plus tax).
Advertising: Open inch rate $13.91
Insert rate: $39.00/M.
Politics: 1904
Gen. Mgr. ....Kristi Massey
Circ. Mgr. ....Kelli Threet
Ed. ....Kristina Hacker
Mechanical Specifications: Type page 13 x 21 1/2; E - 6 cols, 2 1/16, 1/8 between; A - 6 cols, 2 1/16, 1/8 between; C - 9 cols, 1 5/16, 1/8 between.

UKIAH

UKIAH DAILY JOURNAL

590 S. School St., Ukiah, Calif., 95482; gen tel (707) 468-3500; adv tel (707) 468-3500; ed tel (707) 468-3526; gen fax (707) 468-5780; ed fax (707) 468-3544; gen e-mail udj@pacific.net; web site www.ukiahdailyjournal.com

Published: Mon, Tues, Wed, Thur, Fri, Sat, Sun
Weekday Frequency: e
Saturday Frequency: m
Circulation: 5,606; 5,606(sat); 5,888(sun)
Last Audit: ABC September 30, 2011
Price: 12.00/mo; 132.86/yr.
Advertising: Open inch rate $17.28
News services: AP.
Politics: Independent. **Established:** 1860
Special Editions: Home & Garden (Apr); Redwood Empire Fair Official Program (Aug); Christmas Songbook (Dec); Auto Show (Feb); Ukiah Lifestyles/Almanac (Jul); Summer Fun Coupon Book (Jun); Holy Week Directory (Mar); Mother's Day Dining/Gift Guide (May); Homemakers School (O
Special Weekly Sections: On The Market (Fri); Lifestyles (Thur); People (Tues); Business News (Wed).
Magazines: Relish (Monthly); On TV (S); American Profile (Weekly).
Pub. ....Kevin McConnell
Vice Pres., Finance/Controller ....Ronald Mayo
Adv. Retail Mgr. ....Sue Whitman
Circ. Dir. ....Melanie Doty
Asst. Ed. ....Jody Martinez
Online Ed. ....K.C. Meadows
Chief Photographer ....MacLeod Pappidas
Webpage Ed. ....Brittany Deshell
Prodn. Mgr., Composing ....Suzanne Whitman
Market Information: ADS; TMC.
Mechanical available: Offset; Black and 3 ROP colors; insert accepted - spadea, gatefolds; page cutoffs - 22 3/4.
Mechanical Specifications: Type page 12 x 21; E - 6 cols, 1 9/10, 1/8 between; A - 6 cols, 1 9/10, 1/8 between; C - 9 cols, 1 1/4, 1/16 between.
Commodity Consumption: Avg. Page Number Per Issue - Daily 20; Avg. Page Number Per Issue - Plates Used 6000; Avg. Page Number Per Issue - Sunday 28; widths 25; Newsprint Used - Metric Tons 420; Printing Ink Used - Black 6000; Printing Ink Used - Color 500.
Equipment EDITORIAL: Front-end Software – Baseview/NewsEdit.; Editorial Hardware – APP/Mac; Editorial Equipment – Epson/1200C Flatbed Scanner, Nikon/Scanner; Editorial Printers – HP/5000N CLASSIFIED: Front-end Software – Baseview/Class Manager Pro, Baseview/Class Flow.; Classified Hardware – APP/Mac; Classified Printers – APP/Mac LaserWriter Select 360, HP/5000N DISPLAY: Ad make-up applications – Multi-Ad/Creator 4.0, QPS/QuarkXPress 3.32, Microsoft/Word 5.1, Adobe/Photoshop 3.0, Adobe/Illustrator 7.0, Adobe/Acrobat 4.0; Layout Software – 3-APP/Mac.; Display Hardware – Printers ☐ HP/5000N PRODUCTION: Pagination Software – QPS/QuarkXPress 3.31, Baseview/Class Flow.; Production Equipment – Caere/OmniPage 3.0; Scanners – Epson/1200C Flatbed Scanner, Epson/Flatbed-636, HP/4MV, Nikon/LS1000 BUSINESS COMPUTERS: Business Software – Lotus 1-2-3 5.0; Business Hardware – Compaq, Samsung, AR, HP, CJ

VACAVILLE

THE REPORTER

916 Cotting Ln., Vacaville, Calif., 95688; gen tel (707) 448-6401; adv tel (707) 448-6401; ed tel (707) 448-2200; gen fax (707) 447-7405; adv fax (707) 447-7405; ed fax (707) 447-8411; gen e-mail newsroom@thereporter.com; adv e-mail advertising@thereporter.com; web site www.thereporter.com

Published: Mon, Tues, Wed, Thur, Fri, Sat, Sun
Weekday Frequency: m
Saturday Frequency: m
Circulation: 17,221; 16,195(sat); 17,569(sun)
Last Audit: September 30, 2009
Price: 10.75/mo; 160.00/yr.
Advertising: Open inch rate $75.00
News services: AP.
Politics: Independent. **Established:** 1883
Special Weekly Sections: Auto (Fri); Home (S); Religion (Sat); Prime Time (Tues); Food (Wed).
Magazines: Relish (Monthly); USA WEEKEND Magazine (S); American Profile (Weekly).
Pub. ....Steve Smith

HR Dir. ....Shannon Hogan
Adv. Dir. ....Debra Tavey
Circ. Dir. ....Maria Dennison
Circ. Mgr. ....Eric Robanske
Ed. ....Diane Barney
City Ed. ....Robin Miller
Editorial Page Ed. ....Karen Nolan
Entertainment/Amusements Ed. Richard Bammer
Features Ed. ....Greg Trott
Photo Ed. ....Rick Roach
Sports Ed. ....Tim Roe
Prodn. Mgr. ....Brent Dobbier
Webmaster ....James Price
Market Information: TMC.
Mechanical available: Offset; Black and 3 ROP colors; insert accepted; page cutoffs - 22 3/4.
Mechanical Specifications: Type page 13 1/4 x 21; E - 6 cols, 2 1/16, 1/8 between; A - 6 cols, 2 1/16, 1/8 between; C - 10 cols, 1 3/16, 1/8 between.
Commodity Consumption: Avg. Page Number Per Issue - Daily 36; Avg. Page Number Per Issue - Plates Used 6038; Avg. Page Number Per Issue - Saturday 60; Avg. Page Number Per Issue - Sunday 92; widths 25; Newsprint Used - Metric Tons 1720; Printing Ink Used - Black 5000; Printing
Equipment; Editorial Hardware – HI; Editorial Printers – APP/Mac 810, V/6000. CLASSIFIED: Front-end Software – CText 2.1.; Classified Hardware – CText, 12-PC; Classified Printers – APP/Mac LaserWriter Plus; Layout Software – 8-APP/Mac network.; Display Hardware – IBM/486 fileserver, APP/Mac; Display Printers – V/6000 PRODUCTION: Pagination Software – HI/8900.; Production Equipment – 1-APP/Mac LaserWriter NTX, 1-V/VT-600; Cameras – SCREEN; Scanners – 1-APP/Mac PRESSROOM: Line 1 – 7-DEV/Horizon (upper/lower former); Folders – DEV/V50. MAILROOM: Counter stackers – HL/Monitor, Id/Marathoner; Inserters and stuffers – GMA/SLS 1000 8:1; Bundle tying machines – Ace/50, Power Strap/PSN-6; Wrapping singles – Mailroom control system ÃÂ Id/Conveyors, Id/Bottom wrap, Id/Truckloaders. BUSINESS COMPUTERS: Business Software – CJ/AIM 5.01, CIS 4.01, GL, AP; Business Hardware – HP/927LX

VALLEJO

VALLEJO TIMES-HERALD

440 Curtola Pkwy., Vallejo, Calif., 94590; gen tel (707) 644-1088; adv tel (707) 644-1141; ed tel (707) 644-1141; gen fax (707) 553-6877; adv fax (707) 553-6877; ed fax (707) 643-0128; adv e-mail smccullough@timesheraldonline.com; web site www.timesheraldonline.com
Published: Mon, Tues, Wed, Thur, Fri, Sat, Sun
Weekday Frequency: m
Saturday Frequency: m
Circulation: 13,580; 13,199(sat); 13,777(sun)
Last Audit: September 30, 2009
Price: 9.00/mo; 116.00/yr.
Advertising: Open inch rate $88.00
News services: AP, SHNS, McClatchy, Bay City News.
Politics: Independent. **Established:** 1875
Special Editions: Baseball Preview (Apr); I Do-Bridal (Feb); Super Bowl (Jan); Fremont Art & Wine Festival (Jul); Daytrips (May); California Home (Monthly); Grand National Rodeo-Cow Palace (Oct); NFL Preview (Sept).
Special Weekly Sections: Automotive (Fri); NFL Mondays in Sports (Mon); Real Estate (S); Real Estate (Sat); Food (Wed).
Magazines: Relish (Monthly); USA WEEKEND Magazine (S); American Profile (Weekly).
Pub. ....Steve Smith
Adv. Dir. ....Shelly McCullough
Classified Mgr. ....Sally Schulz
Ed. ....Ted Vollmer
Mng. Ed. ....Jack Bungart
City Ed. ....Mary Enbom
Community Ed. ....Richard Freeman
Copy Ed. ....Malcolm Donahoo
Librarian ....Lerecia Davis
Interactive Mgr. ....James Price
Pre Press Mgr. ....Lisa Lerseth
Market Information: TMC.
Mechanical available: Offset; Black and 3 ROP colors; insert accepted; page cutoffs - 21 1/2.
Mechanical Specifications: Type page 12 x 21 1/2; E - 6 cols, 2, 1/8 between; A - 6 cols, 2, 1/8 between; C - 10 cols, 1 1/8, 3/16 between.
Commodity Consumption: Avg. Page Number Per Issue - Daily 31; Avg. Page Number Per Issue - Plates Used 8000; Avg. Page Number Per Issue - Sunday 40; widths 12 1/2; Newsprint Used - Metric Tons 1240; Printing Ink Used - Black 45000; Printing Ink Used - Color 16900; Printing Ink
Equipment EDITORIAL: Front-end Software – Baseview.; Editorial Hardware – APP/Mac; Editorial Equipment – Printers APP/Mac 8500, APP/Mac 16-600 CLASSIFIED: Front-end Software – Baseview.; Classified Hardware – APP/Mac; Classified Printers – Lexmark/Optra T DISPLAY: Ad make-up applications – Multi-Ad/Creator 3.8; Layout Software – Page Director/ALS.; Display Hardware – APP/Mac; Display Printers – APP/Mac LaserWriter 8500, 3-APP/Mac LaserWriter 16-600 PRODUCTION: Pagination Software – Baseview.; Production Equipment – 2-Nu, Devotec 20; Cameras – 1-C/A2024; Scanners – Polaroid/SprintScan 35, LaCie/Silverscanner III PRESSROOM: Line 1 – 13-G/Urbanite, 1-1986; Press Drives – 2-GE/200 LP; Folders – 1-G/900 Series; Reels and Stands – 2 MAILROOM: Counter stackers – 3-QWI/350; Inserters and stuffers – 2-MM/227, 1/MM; Bundle tying machines – 1-/OVL, 2-/Power Strap; Addressing machine – 1-/Ch. BUSINESS COMPUTERS: Business Software – CJ, Unix/SCO, Progress; Business Hardware – 1-HP/3000-LX, ALR/Unix

VICTORVILLE

DAILY PRESS

13891 Park Ave., Victorville, Calif., 92392; gen tel (760) 241-7744; adv tel (760) 241-7744; ed tel (760) 951-6236; gen fax (760) 241-7145; adv fax (760) 241-7145; ed fax (760) 241-1860; gen e-mail stephan_wingert@link.freedom.com; adv e-mail acallahan@vvdailypress.com; ed e-mail don_holland@link.freedom.com; web site www.highdesert.com
Published: Mon, Tues, Wed, Thur, Fri, Sat, Sun
Weekday Frequency: m
Saturday Frequency: m
Circulation: 25,059; 23,230(sat); 28,565(sun)
Last Audit: September 30, 2009
Price: 2.53/wk; 113.46/yr; 10.13/4wk.
News services: AP, MCT.
Politics: Independent. **Established:** 1937
Note: The Victorville Daily Press (m) has a combination rate of $46.00 with the Barstow Desert Dispatch (m). The two papers publish a combined Sunday edition, the Press-Dispatch; the combination rate for the Press-Dispatch is $52.00. Individual newspaper rates
Special Editions: Letters to Santa/Christmas Greetings (Dec); Progress (Feb); Parenting Guide (Jan); High Desert Guidebook (Jul); Job Fair/Recruitment (Mar); San Bernardino County Fair Program (May); High Desert Opportunity (Oct); Health & Better Living (Quarterly); Footba
Special Weekly Sections: Wheels (Fri); Business (Mon); On TV (S); Real Estate (Sat); Health & Fitness (Thur); Family (Tues); Cookery (Wed).
Magazines: USA WEEKEND Magazine (S); American Profile (Sat).
Pub. ....Stephan T. Wingert
Bus. Mgr. ....Robert Fitzsimmons
Adv. Dir. ....Angie Callahan
Promo. Sales Mgr. ....Barbara Miller
Ed. ....Don Holland
Editorial Page Ed. ....Stephen M. Williams
News Ed. ....Mike Lamb
Mgmt. Info Servs. Mgr. ....Joshua Brunton
New Media Mgr. ....Jane Rowan
Prodn. Dir. ....Harry Pontius
Circ. Mgr. ....Jackie Parsons
Features Ed. ....Veronica Hill
Market Information: ADS; TMC.
Mechanical available: Offset; Black and 3 ROP colors; insert accepted - comic spadea, samples, catalogs; page cutoffs - 22 3/4.
Mechanical Specifications: Type page 11 5/8 x 21 1/2; E - 6 cols, 1 5/6, 1/8 between; A - 6 cols, 1 5/6, 1/8 between; C - 9 cols, 1 3/16, 1/16 between.
Commodity Consumption: Avg. Page Number Per Issue - Daily 36; Avg. Page Number Per Issue - Plates Used 23854; Avg. Page Number Per Issue - Saturday 38; Avg. Page Number Per Issue - Sunday 56; widths 25; Newsprint Used - Metric Tons 2541; Printing Ink Used - Black 51042; Printi
Equipment EDITORIAL: Front-end Software – Baseview, QPS/QuarkXPress.; Editorial Equipment – Lf/Leafscan 45, APP/Mac Quadra 950, XYQUEST, Lf/AP Graphics Server; Editorial Printers – HP/DeskJet 1200c, V/5300B, Panasonic, APP/Mac LaserWriter II NTX, Xante/8200, Tektronix/Phaser 560 CLASSIFIED: Front-end Software – Baseview.; Classified Printers – Okidata DISPLAY: Ad make-up applications – Multi-Ad, QPS/QuarkXPress, Macromedia/Freehand, Baseview/Prod. Mgr. Pro; Layout Software – MEI/ALS.; Display Hardware – STA/386, 3-APP/Mac; Display Printers – APP/Mac LaserWriter II, Genicom/3410 PRODUCTION: Pagination Software – Baseview, QPS/QuarkXPress.; Production Equipment – 2-Kk; Scanners – X PRESSROOM: Line 1 – 10-G/Urbanite 1980; Folders – 2; Pasters – 6-Enkle. MAILROOM: Counter stackers – QWI/350, QWI/500; Inserters and stuffers – GMA/SLS 1000 (8 heads); Bundle tying machines – 1/Power Strap, 1-/Dynaric; Other equipment – 1-/MM 15g. BUSINESS COMPUTERS: Business Software – PBS; Business Hardware – IBM/Network, AT/11-Station, 3-COM/Network

VISALIA

TULARE ADVANCE-REGISTER

330 N. West St., Visalia, Calif., 93291; gen tel 559-735-3200; adv tel 559-735-3231; ed tel 559-735-3277; gen fax 559-733-0826; adv fax 559-735-3396; ed fax 559-735-3399; web site www.tulareadvanceregister.com
Group: Gannett Co., Inc.
Published: Mon, Tues, Wed, Thur, Fri, Sat
Weekday Frequency: m
Saturday Frequency: m
Price: $9.75/mo
Not Published: Sunday
Special Editions: Health & Fitness (Jan);World AG Expo (Feb); Job Fair (Apr); Health & Fitness (Apr); Living Here (May); Medical Directory (June); Health & FItness (July); Tulare County Fair (Sept); Kids Fest (Nov); Get Fit (Dec); Real Estate Plus (Semi-monthly)
President & Publisher ....Amy Pack
Controller ....Mari Benko-Wylie
Executive Editor ....Linda Green
Advertising Director ....Davis Taylor
Operations Manager ....David Sutton
Delivery method: Mail, Newsstand, Private Carrier, Racks

VISALIA NEWSPAPERS, INC.

330 N. West St., Visalia, Calif., 93279; gen tel (559) 735-3200; gen fax (559) 733-0826; adv e-mail ads@visaliatimesdelta.com; web site www.visaliatimesdelta.com
Published: Mon, Tues, Wed, Thur, Fri, Sat
Politics: 1859

VISALIA TIMES-DELTA

330 N. West St., Visalia, Calif., 93291-6010; gen tel (559) 735-3200; adv tel (559) 735-3231; ed tel (559) 735-3277; gen fax (559) 733-0826; adv fax (559) 735-3396; ed fax (559) 735-3399; gen e-mail publisher@visaliatimesdelta.com; adv e-mail classified@visaliatimesdelta.com; retail@visaliatimesdelta.com; ed e-mail news@visaliatimesdelta.com; web site www.visaliatimesdelta.com
Published: Mon, Tues, Wed, Thur, Fri, Sat
Weekday Frequency: m
Saturday Frequency: m
Circulation: 18,161; 22,609(sat)
Last Audit: ABC September 30, 2011
Price: 13.43/mo
News services: AP, GNS, NYT, TMS.
Politics: 1859
Not Published: Sunday
Special Editions: Health & Fitness (Jan);World AG Expo (Feb); Job Fair (Apr); Health & Fitness (Apr); Living Here (May); Medical Directory (June); Health & FItness (July); Tulare County Fair (Sept); Kids Fest (Nov); Get Fit (Dec); Real Estate Plus (Semi-monthly)
Special Weekly Sections: Real Estate Plus (Thurs); The Shopper (Thur); Food (Wed).
Magazines: Vista (Mon); USA Weekend(Sat).
Pres./Pub. ....Amy L. Pack
Controller ....Mari Benko-Wylie
Adv. Mgr., Classified Inside Sales Debbie Lowe-Guzman
Exec. Ed. ....Linda Green
City Ed. ....Jim Houck
Opinion Page Ed. ....Paul Hurley
Spanish Language Ed. ....Eduardo Stanley
Prodn. Mgr., Opns. ....David Sutton
Advertising director ....Davis Taylor
Media Sales Manager ....Martin MJ Gocke
Daily Editor ....Melinda Morales
Adv. Dir. ....Vaughn Kessler
Circ. Sales/Opns. Mgr. ....Jessica Dungca
Sr. Ed. ....Jamie Butow-Gonzales
Features Ed. ....Marty Burleson
Dir., Info Technology ....Deanne Gober
Prodn. Dir. ....Cortland Hunt
Market Information: Split run; TMC.
Mechanical available: Offset; Black and 3 ROP colors; insert accepted - Poly Bags; page cutoffs - 22.
Mechanical Specifications: .
Commodity Consumption: Newsprint Used - Metric Tons 2499; Newsprint Used - Short Tons 2755; Printing Ink Used - Black 45800; Printing
Equipment PRESSROOM: Line 1 – 10-G/Urbanite 1986 MAILROOM: Counter stackers – 1-QWI/1000, 1-HI/RS25, 1-G/Overstacker, 1-HI/RS25; Inserters and stuffers – 1-HI/848; Bundle tying machines – 2/MLN, 1-/MLN; Wrapping singles – 1-/QWI; Addressing machine – 1-/Ch
Delivery method: Mail, Newsstand, Private Carrier, Racks

VISALIA TIMES-DELTA & TULARE ADVANCE-REGISTER

330 N. West St., Visalia, Calif., 93291-6010; gen tel (559) 735-3200; adv tel (559) 735-3231; ed tel (559) 688-0521; gen fax (559) 688-7503; adv fax (559) 688-7503; ed fax (559) 735-3278; gen e-mail tularenews@visaliatimesdelta.com; adv e-mail rdillon@visaliatimesdelta.com; ed e-mail news@visaliatimesdelta.com; web site www.visaliatimesdelta.com
Published: Mon, Tues, Wed, Thur, Fri, Sat
Weekday Frequency: m
Saturday Frequency: m
Circulation: 5,874; 6,003(sat)
Last Audit: September 30, 2008
Price: 7.75/mo; 105.00/yr.
News services: AP, GNS.
Politics: Independent. **Established:** 1882
Note: Advertising is sold in combination with Visalia Times-Delta (m) for $54.09(d) and $60.31(m-sat). Individual newspaper rates not made available.
Special Editions: Farm Equipment Show (Feb); Dairy Month (Jun); Clubs & Organizations (May); Football Rivalry (Nov); Football Kick-off (Sept).
Special Weekly Sections: Church Features (Sat); Best Food Day (Wed).
Magazines: Choices Magazine-Visalia (Fri); Vista (Mon); USA WEEKEND Magazine (Sat).

Pres./Pub. ....Amy L. Pack
Adv. Dir. ....Vaughn Kessler
Circ. Distr. Mgr. ....Theresa Simpson
Exec. Ed. ....Linda Green
City Ed. ....Jim Houck
Sports Ed. ....Kevin McCusker
Dir., Information Systems..........Dee Dee Gober
Data Processing Mgr. ....Gary Woodside
Mgr., Opns.............................Mike Hazelwood
Prodn. Mgr., Pre Press ....Theresa Mullins
Market Information: TMC.
Mechanical available: Offset; Black and 4 ROP colors; insert accepted - single sheet; page cutoffs - 21 3/8.
Mechanical Specifications: Type page 13 x 21 1/2; E - 6 cols, 2 1/16, 1/8 between; A - 6 cols, 2 1/16, 1/8 between; C - 10 cols, 1 1/4, 1/16 between.
Commodity Consumption: Avg. Page Number Per Issue - Daily 14; Avg. Page Number Per Issue - Plates Used 2600; widths 14; Newsprint Used - Metric Tons 303; Printing Ink Used - Black 4200; Printing Ink Used - Color 1500; Printing Ink Used - Pages Printed 4963.
Equipment EDITORIAL: Front-end Software – Baseview, SII/Sys 55.; Editorial Hardware – SII/Sys 55, APP/Mac Quadra, Tandem/TNSII, 28-SII/Coyote QB; Editorial Equipment – 3-APP/Mac; Editorial Printers – Centronics/351, APP/Mac LaserWriter IIf CLASSIFIED: Front-end Software – SII/Sys 55.; Classified Hardware – SII/Sys 55, Tandem/TNSII, 7-SII/Coyote QB; Classified Printers – Centronics/351 DISPLAY: Ad make-up applications – Smart Dummy; Layout Software – Smart Dummy/Ad Layout System.; Display Hardware – PC; Display Printers – HP/LaserJet III; Production Equipment – 2-Nu, 2-APP/Mac LaserWriter II NTX, ECR/RIP, ECR/Autokon, 1-RZ; Cameras – 1-C, 1-Nu. PRESSROOM: Line 1 – 10-G/Urbanite 1986. MAILROOM: Counter stackers – 1-QWI/1000, 1-HI/RS25, 1-G/Overstacker; Inserters and stuffers – 1-HI/848; Bundle tying machines – 2/MLN; Wrapping singles – 1-/QWI; Addressing machine – 1-/Ch.

WATSONVILLE

REGISTER-PAJARONIAN

100 Westridge Dr., Watsonville, Calif., 95076-6602; gen tel (831) 761-7300; adv tel (831) 761-7351; ed tel (831) 761-7322; gen fax (831) 722-8386; adv fax (831) 722-8386; ed fax (831) 761-7338; gen e-mail businessoffice@register-pajaronian.com; adv e-mail advertising@register-pajaronian.com; ed e-mail newsroom@register-pajaronian.com; web site www.register-pajaronian.com
Published: Mon, Tues, Wed, Thur, Fri, Sat, Sun
Weekday Frequency: e
Saturday Frequency: m
Circulation: 5,268; 5,268(sat)
Last Audit: March 31, 2007
Price: 7.95/mo (home), $9.95/mo (mail); 95.40/yr (home), $128.25/yr (mail).
Advertising: Open inch rate $27.75
News services: AP, SHNS.
Politics: Independent. **Established:** 1868
Not Published: New Year; Christmas.
Special Editions: Home Improvement (Monthly); Progress (Oct).
Special Weekly Sections: Real Estate (Fri); Education (Sat); Business (Thur); Best Food Day (Tues).
Magazines: TV Weekly (Sat).
Pub. ....Tom Cross
Controller...................................Michael Rand
Office Mgr................................Kelly Nicholson
Mgr., Nat'l Adv..........................Jeanie Johnson
Circ. Dir...............................Carmen Johnson
News Ed. ....David Carkhuff
Sports Ed. ....Michael Oppenheimer
Prodn. Foreman, Press ....Alfie Morris
Market Information: TMC.
Mechanical available: Offset; Black and 3 ROP colors; insert accepted; page cutoffs - 22 3/4.
Mechanical Specifications: Type page 13 x 21; E - 6 cols, 2 1/16, 1/8 between; A - 6 cols, 2 1/16, 1/8 between; C - 9 cols, 1 3/8, 1/16 between.
Commodity Consumption: Avg. Page Number Per Issue - Daily 20; Avg. Page Number Per Issue - Plates Used 13000; widths 27 1/2; Newsprint Used - Metric Tons 1000; Printing Ink Used - Black 24000; Printing Ink Used - Color 3000; Printing Ink Used - Pages Printed 7963.
Equipment; Editorial Hardware – 26-SII; Editorial Equipment – 5-RSK/TRS 80 model 100 remote terminal.; Classified Hardware – 4-SII.; Layout Software – 2-COM.; Production Equipment – 2-COM/Videosetter, 2-COM/Advantage; Cameras – 1-C/Spartan II. PRESSROOM: Line 1 – 6-G/Urbanite; Folders – 1; Bundle tying machines – 1/MLN.; Business Hardware – INSI

WEST COVINA

PASADENA STAR-NEWS

911 Colorado Blvd., 1210 Azusa Canyon, West Covina, Calif., 91790; gen tel (626) 578-6300; gen fax (626) 792-9413; web site www.pasadenastarnews.com
Published: Mon, Tues, Wed, Thur, Fri, Sat, Sun
Note: For additional information, see listing in Daily Section under Seattle, WA.

WHITTIER DAILY NEWS

1210 Azusa Canyon, West Covina, Calif., 91790; gen tel (562) 698-0955; gen fax (562) 698-0450; gen e-mail robert.gonzales@sgvn.com; web site www.whittierdailynews.com
Price: 34.00/8 weeks.
Advertising: Open inch rate $25.05

WHITTIER

THE WHITTIER DAILY NEWS

7612 Greenleaf Ave., Whittier, Calif., 90602; gen tel (562) 698-0955; gen fax (562) 698-0450; adv fax (562) 907-6743; ed fax (562) 698-0450; gen e-mail news.wdn@sgvn.com; web site www.whittierdailynews.com
Published: Mon, Tues, Wed, Thur, Fri, Sat, Sun
Weekday Frequency: m
Saturday Frequency: m
Circulation: 14,827; 13,881(sat); 19,655(sun)
Last Audit: ABC September 30, 2011
Price: 4.00/wk.
News services: AP, CNS, MCT, Scripps-McClatchy, BPI, DJ, NYT, United Media.
Politics: Independent.
Note: The Los Angeles Newspaper Group includes the Long Beach Press-Telegram (mS), Los Angeles Daily News (mS), Ontario Inland Valley Daily Bulletin (mS), Pasadena Star-News (mS), Redlands Daily Facts (eS), San Bernardino County Sun (mS), San Gabriel Valley Tri
Special Editions: The Body (Apr); Pro Football Tab (Aug); The Rose Magazine (Dec); The Body (Jan); The Body (Jul); Health Beat (Jun); Health Beat (Mar); Water Awareness (May); Holiday Guide (Nov); The Body (Oct); Dining Guide (Sept).
Special Weekly Sections: Career Site (S); New Home Buyer (Sat).
Magazines: Relish (Monthly); U Magazine (mS) (Other); Seen Magazine (Quarterly); TV Magazine (S).
Pub. ....Ron L. Wood
Dir., Finance ....Rosa Lopez
HR/Admin. Mgr. ....Rachel A. Vasquez
Adv./Classified Dir. ....Sergio Verdejo
Circ. Dir.......................................Mike Belles
Circ. Mgr., Single Copy ....Dennis Wagner
Circ. Mgr., Home Delivery ....Dennis Schaffer
Ed. ....Tim Traegeer
Exec. Ed. ....Talmage Campbell
Mng. Ed. ....Steve Hunt
Bus. Ed. ....Kevin Smith
City Ed. ....Hector Gonzalez
Editorial Page Writer................Linda Beckman
Features Ed...........................Catherine Gaugh
Opinions Ed. ....Steve Scauzillo
Sports Ed. ....Doug Spoon
Visuals Ed. ....Tim Berger
Mgr., Technical Servs...................Terry Frazier
Prodn. Dir. ....Ron Berry
Prodn. Mgr., Mailroom ....Jose Avila
Market Information: ADS; TMC.
Mechanical available: Offset; Black and 3 ROP colors; insert accepted; page cutoffs - 22 3/4.
Mechanical Specifications: Type page 11 1/2 x 21 1/2; E - 6 cols, 1 13/16, 1/8 between; A - 6 cols, 1 13/16, 1/8 between; C - 10 cols, 1 1/16, 1/16 between.
Commodity Consumption: Avg. Page Number Per Issue - Daily 48; Avg. Page Number Per Issue - Plates Used 27000; Avg. Page Number Per Issue - Saturday 82; Avg. Page Number Per Issue - Sunday 80; widths 12 1/2; Newsprint Used - Metric Tons 2020; Printing Ink Used - Black 40300; Pr
Equipment EDITORIAL: Front-end Software – SII/Editorial.; Editorial Hardware – SII/Server-Net; Editorial Equipment – 75-SII/Coyote 35, 2-SII/PC; Editorial Printers – 5-HP CLASSIFIED: Front-end Software – SII/Czar II.; Classified Hardware – 1-SII/ServerNet; Classified Equipment – 27-SII/Coyote 3; Classified Printers – 3-HP DISPLAY: Ad make-up applications – SII/IAL; Display Hardware – 6-APP/Mac, 3-Compaq; Display Printers – Proofers, HP PRODUCTION: Pagination Software – SII/INL 9.2.; Production Equipment – 2-WL, APP/Mac, QPS; Cameras – 1-Spartan/III, 1-C/Newspager, 1-C/Spartan II; Scanners – 2-Lf/Leafscan 35, 10-Compaq, 2-Polaroid PRESSROOM: Line 1 – 7-G/HO 1989; Line 2 – Jul-90; Folders – 3; Pasters – 14; Reels and Stands – 14; Press control system – G/MPCS. MAILROOM: Counter stackers – 5-Id/2000, 2-Id/440, 1/QWI, Id/2000; Inserters and stuffers – 4-GMA/SLS 1000; Bundle tying machines – 5-/Power Strap/PSN-5, 2-/Dynaric; Addressing machine – 2-Videojet/VMS. BUSINESS COMPUTERS: Business Software – CJ, Ultipro; Business Hardware – HP/969

WOODLAND

THE DAILY DEMOCRAT

711 Main St., Woodland, Calif., 95695; gen tel (530) 662-5421; gen fax (530) 662-1288; gen e-mail news@dailydemocrat.com; adv e-mail adreps@dailydemocrat.com; web site www.dailydemocrat.com
Published: Tues, Wed, Thur, Fri, Sat, Sun
Weekday Frequency: e
Saturday Frequency: e
Circulation: 8,048; 8,048(sat); 7,961(sun)
Last Audit: ABC September 30, 2011
Price: 8.50/mo (city), $9.00/mo (county).
Advertising: Open inch rate $24.24
News services: AP, NYT, TMS.
Politics: Independent. **Established:** 1857
Special Editions: Home & Garden (Apr); Childcare Directory (Aug); Christmas Express (Dec); Bridal Tab (Feb); Ad Packages (Jan); Made in Woodland (Jul); Class (Graduation) (Jun); National Ag Tab Sun (Mar); National Police (May); Holiday Gift (Nov); National Cosmetology Mont
Special Weekly Sections: Business (Fri); Farm Page (Sat); Ag Pages (Thur); Food (Wed).
Magazines: Relish (Monthly); USA WEEKEND Magazine (S); American Profile (Weekly).
Pub. ....Jim Gleim
Bus. Mgr. ....Wendy Patrick
Adv. Dir. ....Allison Perkes
Circ. Mgr. ....Idelle Nicado
Ed....Jim Smith
Sports Ed. ....Bruce Burton
Internet Mgr................................James Price
Pre Press Mgr................................Nancy Nusz
Market Information: TMC.
Mechanical available: Offset; Black and 3 ROP colors; insert accepted; page cutoffs - 22 3/4.
Mechanical Specifications: Type page 13 x 21 1/2; E - 6 cols, 2 1/16, 1/8 between; A - 6 cols, 2 1/16, 1/8 between; C - 10 cols, 1 3/8, 1/16 between.
Commodity Consumption: Avg. Page Number Per Issue - Daily 16; Avg. Page Number Per Issue - Plates Used 8000; Avg. Page Number Per Issue - Saturday 24; Avg. Page Number Per Issue - Sunday 24; widths 27; Newsprint Used - Metric Tons 460; Printing Ink Used - Pages Printed 6350.
Equipment; Editorial Hardware – SII; Editorial Equipment – APP/Mac IIcx; Editorial Printers – 1-TI/Omni 800, 1-APP/Mac LaserWriter NT. CLASSIFIED: Front-end Software – Baseview.; Classified Printers – 1-TI/Omni 800 DISPLAY: Ad make-up applications – Multi-Ad; Layout Software – Baseview/ALS.; Display Hardware – 1-APP/Mac IIci, 1-APP/Mac IIcx, 1-APP/Power Mac 6100-66; Display Printers – 1-APP/Mac LaserWriter II, 1-HP/LaserJet; Production Equipment – 2-NewGen/Laser printers; Cameras – Acti/225. PRESSROOM: Line 1 – 8-G/Community 1970; Folders – 1 MAILROOM: Counter stackers – 1/BG; Bundle tying machines – 1-/MLN.; Business Hardware – ALR/REVQ, 1-HP/3000-917LX

WOODLAND HILLS

DAILY NEWS

21860 Burbank Blvd., Ste. 200, Woodland Hills, Calif., 91367; gen tel (818) 713-3000; adv tel (818) 713-3232; ed tel (818) 713-3636; gen fax (818) 713-0058; adv fax (818) 713-0062; adv e-mail ads@dailynews.com; web site www.dailynews.com
Published: Mon, Tues, Wed, Thur, Fri, Sat, Sun
Weekday Frequency: m
Saturday Frequency: m
Circulation: 89,990; 86,471(sat); 98,939(sun)
Last Audit: ABC September 30, 2011
Price: 2.99/wk; 12.96/mo; 155.48/yr.
News services: AP, MCT, NYT, City News Service, McClatchy.
Politics: Independent.
Note: The Los Angeles Newspaper Group includes the Long Beach Press-Telegram (mS), Los Angeles Daily News (mS), Ontario Inland Valley Daily Bulletin (mS), Pasadena Star-News (mS), Redlands Daily Facts (eS), San Bernardino County Sun (mS), San Gabriel Valley Tri
Special Weekly Sections: High School Football Special (in season) (Fri); So. Cal. Wheels (Mon); Real Estate (S); Real Estate (Sat); Best Food Day (Wed).
Magazines: Relish (Monthly); Access (S).
Pub...Jack Klunder
VP Finance.................................Dan Scofield
Adv. Vice Pres. ....Michael Reagan
Adv. Dir.,...................................Mike McMullin
Dir., Mktg./Pub. Rel. ....Bill Vanlaningham
Dir., Mktg. Research ....Liz Hamm
Ed. ....Carolina Garcia
Restaurant Critic ....Larry Lipson
Columnist ....Dennis McCarthy
Photo Dir. ....Dean Musgrove
Entertainment/Book Ed. ....Robert Lowman
Features Ed...................................Sharyn Betz
Metro Ed....................................Barbara Jones
Market Information: ADS; Split run; TMC; Zoned editions.
Mechanical available: Offset; Black and 4 ROP colors; insert accepted - product samples; page cutoffs - 22.
Mechanical Specifications: Type page 11 1/2 x 21; E - 6 cols, 1 13/16, 1/8 between; A - 6 cols, 1 13/16, 1/8 between; C - 10 cols, 1 1/16, 1/16 between.
Commodity Consumption: Avg. Page Number Per Issue - Daily 71; Avg. Page Number Per Issue - Plates Used 300.572; Avg. Page Number Per Issue - Saturday 102; Avg. Page Number Per Issue - Sunday 148; widths 12 1/2; Newsprint Used - Metric Tons 32661; Newsprint Used - Short Tons 39
Equipment EDITORIAL: Front-end Software – SII.; Editorial Hardware – Tandem/Server; Editorial Equipment – 1-DEC/VAX 6620, 2-DEC/VAX 6610, 1-DEC/Alpha 1000 CLASSIFIED: Front-end Software – SII.; Classified Hardware – Tandem/Server DISPLAY: Ad make-up applications – Geac/Advertising 8.02;

Layout Software – SCS/Layout 8000.; Display Hardware – HP/997; Display Printers – HP/5SI PRODUCTION: Pagination Software – DTI.; Production Equipment – 2-AU/APS-6-108, 1-KFM/Flat Express II, 4-AU/3850, 1-SCREEN/LD-281-Q, 2-Konica/K400, 2-Konica/K550, 20-LE/2120; Cameras – C/Spartan III; Scanners – 2-AU/3750, 2-AU/APS COM PRESSROOM: Line 1 – 11-G/Headliner Offset double width 1989; Line 2 – 11-G/Headliner Offset double width 1989; Line 3 – 11-G/Headliner Offset double width 1990; Folders – 6-G/3:2; Pasters – 10-GH/Digital; Reels and Stands – 30 MAILROOM: Counter stackers – 14-HL/Monitor HT, 2-QWI/SJ400; Inserters and stuffers – 2-HI/1472, 1-HI/1372, 1-GMA/SLS 1000; Bundle tying machines – 2-MLN/2A, 14/Power Strap/PSN, 2-OVL/Strapmaster, Si; Wrapping singles – 13-HL/440 Bottom Wrap, 2-/Power Strap/Bottom BUSINESS COMPUTERS: Business Software – Geac; Business Hardware – HP/997

YREKA

SISKIYOU DAILY NEWS

309 S. Broadway, Yreka, Calif., 96097; gen tel (530) 842-5777; gen fax (530) 842-6787; gen e-mail publisher@siskiyoudaily.com; adv e-mail advertising@siskiyoudaily.com; ed e-mail editor@siskiyoudaily.com; web site www.siskiyoudaily.com

Published: Mon, Tues, Wed, Thur, Fri
Weekday Frequency: e
Circulation: 5,554
Last Audit: October 1, 2003
Price: 7.25/mo (in county), $8.60/mo (out of county); 78.30/yr (carrier), $82.08/yr (mail).
Advertising: Open inch rate $15.00
News services: AP.
Politics: Independent.
Not Published: New Year; Independence Day; Thanksgiving; Christmas.
Special Editions: Spring Car Care (Apr); Siskiyou Golden Fair (Aug); Year-End Review (Dec); Chamber Information Book (Jun); Progress (Mar); Holiday Gift Guide (Nov); Football Kick-off (Sept).
Special Weekly Sections: TV Spotlight (Fri).
Magazines: Siskiyou Spotlight Tab (Fri); Siskiyou County Properties (Real Estate) (Monthly); American Profile (Weekly).
Pub. .... Rod Dowse
Bookkeeper/Purchasing Agent .... Pat Mills
Adv. Dir. .... David Nelmes
Circ. Mgr. .... Jean Smith
Mng. Ed. .... Mike Slizewski
Sports Ed. .... Dan Murphy
Market Information: TMC.
Mechanical available: Offset; Black and 3 ROP colors; insert accepted; page cutoffs - 22 3/4.
Mechanical Specifications: Type page 13 x 21 1/2; E - 6 cols, 2 1/16, 1/8 between; A - 6 cols, 2 1/16, 1/8 between; C - 8 cols, 1 1/2, 1/8 between.
Commodity Consumption: Avg. Page Number Per Issue - Daily 18; Avg. Page Number Per Issue - Plates Used 3241; widths 34; Newsprint Used - Metric Tons 360; Newsprint Used - Short Tons 394; Printing Ink Used - Black 6000; Printing Ink Used - Color 1500; Printing Ink Used - Pages
Equipment EDITORIAL: Front-end Software – Baseview, QPS/QuarkXPress.; Editorial Hardware – APP/Mac; Editorial Equipment – HP/Scanner; Editorial Printers – APP/Mac LaserWriter Pro 600, APP/Mac LaserWriter Pro 630 CLASSIFIED: Front-end Software – Baseview, QPS/QuarkXPress.; Classified Hardware – APP/Mac; Classified Printers – APP/Mac LaserWriter, Dot Matrix DISPLAY: Ad make-up applications – APP/Mac, QPS/QuarkXPress; Layout Software – APP/Mac, QPS/QuarkXPress.; Display Hardware – APP/Mac; Display Printers – APP/Mac LaserWriter II, APP/Mac LaserWriter Pro 600 PRODUCTION: Pagination Software – QPS/QuarkXPress 4.0.; Production Equipment – 2-APP/Mac LaserWriter II NTX, 1-COM/88, 1-COM/IV, APP/Mac LaserWriter Pro 600, APP/Mac LaserWriter Pro 630, PrePress/Panther Pro 46; Cameras – 1-SCREEN/Vertical PRESSROOM: Line 1 – 6-G/Community single width 1980; Folders – 1-G/Community.; Bundle tying machines – 1/Us; Addressing machine – 1-/Wm. BUSINESS COMPUTERS: Business Software – Microsoft; Business Hardware – Pentium/PC

COLORADO

ALAMOSA

ALAMOSA NEWSPAPERS, INC.

401-407 State Ave., Alamosa, Colo., 81101; gen tel (719) 589-2553; gen fax (719) 589-6573

THE VALLEY COURIER

2205 State Ave., Alamosa, Colo., 81101-1099; gen tel (719) 589-2553; gen fax (719) 589-6573; adv e-mail ads@alamosanews.com; ed e-mail news@alamosanews.com; web site www.alamosanews.com

Group: News Media Corporation
Published: Tues, Wed, Thur, Fri, Sat
Weekday Frequency: m
Saturday Frequency: m
Circulation: 5,300; 5,500(sat)
Last Audit: Sworn September 30, 2006
Price: 10.95/mo (carrier); 103.00/yr (within the San Luis Valley, CO); 142.00/yr (outside the Valley).
Advertising: Open inch rate $18.65
Insert rate: Based on size/weight
News services: AP.
Not Published: New Year; Memorial Day; Independence Day; Labor Day; Thanksgiving; Christmas.
Own facility?: Y
Special Editions: Home Improvement (Apr); Back-to-School (Aug); Christmas (Dec); Rodeo (Jul); Summer Lifestyle (May); Ski (Nov); Hunting (Sept).
Special Weekly Sections: Outdoors (Fri); Agriculture (Thur).
Publisher/Adv. Dir. .... Keith R. Cerny
Circ. Mgr. .... Shasta Quintana
Editor .... Ruth Heide
Prodn. Foreman, Pressroom .... Vernon Trujillo
Sports Editor .... Eric Flores
Adv. Mgr., Classified .... Yolanda Martinez
Sports Ed. .... Lloyd Engen
Mechanical available: Offset; Black and 3 ROP colors; insert accepted; page cutoffs - 21 1/2.
Mechanical Specifications: Type page 11 1/2 x 21 1/2; E - 6 cols, 1 13/16, 1/8 between; A - 6 cols, 1 13/16, 1/8 between; C - 8 cols, 1 1/3, 1/8 between.
Commodity Consumption: Avg. Page Number Per Issue - Daily 14; Avg. Page Number Per Issue - Plates Used 2520; Avg. Page Number Per Issue - Saturday 14; widths 13 3/4; Newsprint Used - Short Tons 100; Printing Ink Used - Pages Printed 3598.
Equipment EDITORIAL: Front-end Software – APP/Mac.; Editorial Hardware – APP/Mac; Editorial Printers – 2-APP/Mac LaserPrinter CLASSIFIED: Front-end Software – Mk.; Classified Hardware – Mk, APP/Mac; Classified Printers – APP/Mac DISPLAY: Ad make-up applications – APP/Mac; Display Hardware – APP/Mac; Display Printers – APP/Mac LaserPrinter PRODUCTION: Pagination Software – Aldus/PageMaker 4.0.; Production Equipment – 1-Nu, 1-COM/2961, 1-COM/7200; Cameras – 1-R; Scanners – APP/Scanner PRESSROOM: Line 1 – 6-G/Community.; Folders – 8-1988.; Inserters and stuffers – 6; Bundle tying machines – 1; Addressing machine – 1; Business Hardware – IBM/PC
Delivery method: Mail, Newsstand, Private Carrier, Racks

ASPEN

ASPEN DAILY NEWS

517 E. Hopkins Ave., Aspen, Colo., 81611; gen tel (970) 925-2220; ed fax (970) 920-2118; gen e-mail aspnews@aspendailynews.com; web site www.aspendailynews.com

Published: Mon, Tues, Wed, Thur, Fri, Sat, Sun
Weekday Frequency: m
Saturday Frequency: m
Circulation: 12,500; 12,500(sat); 12,500(sun)
Last Audit: January 10, 1997
Price: 36.00/mo; 400.00/yr.
Advertising: Open inch rate $8.50
News services: AP.
Politics: Independent.
Special Editions: Winter Guide (Dec); Winterskol (Jan); Summer Guide (Jun); Winternational (Mar); Spruce Up for Spring (May); 24 Hours of Aspen (Nov).
Special Weekly Sections: Time Out (Thur); Mountain Marketplace (Wed).
Owner .... David N. Danforth
Bus. Mgr. .... Tedra Bates
Adv. Dir. .... Lynn Chaffier
Circ. Mgr. .... Rafael Perez
Mng. Ed. .... Catherine Lutz
Ed. .... Troy Hooper
Web/Assoc. Special Sections Ed. Damien Williamson
Mechanical available: Offset Web; Black and 3 ROP colors; insert accepted - will contract to print inserts; page cutoffs - 14 1/2.
Mechanical Specifications: Type page 10 1/4 x 14; E - 4 cols, 2 7/16, 1/3 between; A - 6 cols, 1 1/2, 1/6 between; C - 6 cols, 1 1/2, 1/6 between.
Commodity Consumption: Avg. Page Number Per Issue - Daily 36; Avg. Page Number Per Issue - Plates Used 3000; Avg. Page Number Per Issue - Saturday 24; widths 29 1/2; Newsprint Used - Metric Tons 350; Printing Ink Used - Pages Printed 12064.
Equipment EDITORIAL: Front-end Software – QPS/QuarkXPress 3.3.; Editorial Hardware – 4-APP/Mac Quadra 610; Editorial Equipment – 8-APP/Mac LC III; Editorial Printers – 2-APP/Mac LaserWriter, GCC/SelectPress 600 CLASSIFIED: Front-end Software – Baseview/Ad Manager Pro.; Classified Hardware – 2-APP/Mac LC III; Classified Printers – GCC/SelectPress 600 DISPLAY: Ad make-up applications – QPS/QuarkXPress 3.3; Layout Software – QPS.; Display Hardware – 1-APP/Power Mac; Display Printers – APP/Mac LaserWriter 360 PRODUCTION: Pagination Software – QPS/QuarkXPress 3.3.; Production Equipment – Adobe/Photoshop 3.0, 3-COM/Editwriter 7500, APP/Mac IIcx, APP/Mac LaserWriter II NTX; Cameras – AG/Repromaster 1100, SCREEN/Auto Companica; Scanners – 2-APP/Mac IIcx, Umax/Vista T630 PRESSROOM: Line 1 – 5-G/Community; Folders – G/Community. BUSINESS COMPUTERS: Business Software – Proprietary; Business Hardware – APP/Mac SE30, APP/Mac Classic

THE ASPEN TIMES

310 E Main St, Aspen, Colo., 81611; gen tel (970)Â 925-3414; adv tel (970) 925-3414; ed tel (970) 925-3414; gen fax (970) 925-6240; adv fax (970) 925-6240; ed fax (970) 925-9156; gen e-mail mail@aspentimes.com; adv e-mail ads@aspentimes.com; web site www.aspentimes.com

Group: Swift Communications
Published: Mon, Tues, Wed, Thur, Fri, Sat
Weekday Frequency: m
Circulation: 11,000; 11,000(sat)
Last Audit: March 31, 2006
Advertising: Open inch rate $11.00
News services: AP, LAT-WP, NYT.
Politics: Independent.
Special Editions: Restaurant Guide (Dec); Style (Jun).
Magazines: Weekend (Fri).
Pub. .... Jenna Weatherred
Bus. Mgr. .... Nancy Boprow
Adv. Dir. .... Gunilla Israel
Circ. Mgr. .... Bob Lombardi
Mng. Ed .... Rick Carroll
Arts Ed. .... Stewart Oksenhorn
Sports Ed. .... Jon Maletz
Market Information: ADS; TMC.
Mechanical available: Offset; Black and ROP colors; insert accepted; page cutoffs - 16.
Mechanical Specifications: Type page 11 1/2 x 17 1/4; E - 5 cols, 1 9/10, 1/6 between; A - 5 cols, 1 9/10, 1/6 between; C - 5 cols, 1 9/10, 1/6 between.
Commodity Consumption: Avg. Page Number Per Issue - Daily 36.
Equipment EDITORIAL: Front-end Software – Baseview.; Editorial Hardware – 12-APP/Mac LC II, APP/Mac ci; Editorial Printers – LaserMaster/, AG CLASSIFIED: Front-end Software – Baseview.; Classified Hardware – 2-APP/Mac vx, APP/Mac LC II DISPLAY: Ad make-up applications – Baseview; Layout Software – 2-APP/Mac ci.; Display Hardware – APP/Mac; Production Equipment – 3-APP/Mac LaserPrinter, Pre Press/Panther Imagesetter; Cameras – LE. PRESSROOM: Line 1 – 5-WPC/Web Leader; Reels and Stands – 5 MAILROOM: Counter stackers – BG; Bundle tying machines – Bu.; Business Hardware – Osicom

UTE CITY TEA PARTY LTD.

517 E. Hopkins Ave, Aspen, Colo., 81611; gen tel (970) 925-2220; gen fax (970) 920-2118

AURORA

AURORA SENTINEL

14305 E. Alameda Ave., Ste. 200, Aurora, Colo., 80012; gen tel (303) 750-7555; adv tel (303) 750-7555; ed tel (303) 750-7555; gen fax (303) 750-7699; adv fax (303) 750-7699; ed fax (720) 449-9033; gen e-mail news@aurorasentinel.com; adv e-mail advertise@aurorasentinel.com; web site www.aurorasentinel.com

Published: Mon, Tues, Wed, Thur, Fri
Weekday Frequency: m
Circulation: 46,000
Last Audit: January 4, 2008
Price: 19.95/yr.
Advertising: Open inch rate $8.00
News services: AP, CNS, TMS.
Politics: 1908
Not Published: New Years; Memorial Day; Independence Day; Labor Day; Christmas.
Special Weekly Sections: Entertainment (Fri); Health (Mon); Home (Thur); Food (Wed).
Pub./Pres. .... Harrison Cochran
Bus. Mgr. .... Liisa Morrissey
Adv. Dir. .... Ellyn Gebhardt
Classified Mgr. .... Staci Giomi
Circ. Dir. .... Bob Guerrero
Ed. .... Dave Perry
Mng. Ed. .... Aaron Cole
Sports Ed. .... Courtney Oakes
Prodn. Supvr. .... Jennifer Elbel
Market Information: TMC.
Mechanical available: Black and 4 ROP colors; insert accepted - we print; page cutoffs - 14.
Mechanical Specifications: Type page 10 x 14; E - 5 cols, 1 9/10, 1/8 between; A - 5 cols, 1 9/10, 1/8 between; C - 7 cols, 1 1/3, 1/9 between.
Equipment EDITORIAL: Front-end Software – CS3. CLASSIFIED: Front-end Software – Adforce 5.2.; Layout Software – Adforce 5.2. PRODUCTION: Pagination Software – CS3.; Production Equipment – Texbridge/Pro

BOULDER

BOULDER PUBLISHING, INC.

1048 Pearl, Boulder, Colo., 80302; gen tel (303) 442-1202

COLORADO DAILY

1048 Pearl St., Boulder, Colo., 80302; gen tel (303) 443-6272; gen fax (303) 443-9357; gen e-mail editor@coloradodaily.com; adv e-mail advertising@coloradodaily.com; ed e-mail editor@coloradodaily.com; web site

www.coloradodaily.com
Published: Mon, Tues, Wed, Thur, Fri
Weekday Frequency: m
Circulation: 15,329
Last Audit: March 31, 2007
Price: 250.00/yr.
Advertising: Open inch rate $21.00
News services: CSM, MCT, UPI.
Politics: Independent. **Established:** 1892
Special Editions: Menu Guide (Apr); Welcome Back Fall (Aug); Graduation (Dec); CU & Boulder's Best (Feb); Welcome Back Spring (Jan); Boulder Summer (Jun); Graduation (May); Boulder Winter (Oct); Stadium Stampede (6 editions in Oct & Nov) (Other).
Special Weekly Sections: Real Estate (Fri); Our Town (Mon); Visitors' Edition (daily during summer) (Other); Food & Drink (Thur); The Arts (Tues); Body & Soul (Wed).
Adv. Dir. .... Andrew Mirrington
Circ. Mgr. .... Neal Donahue
Mng. Ed. .... Bronson Hilliard
Entertainment Ed. .... Oakland Childers
Opinion Page Ed. .... Brad Weisman
Pre Press/Systems Mgr. .... Chad DiPrince
Prodn. Supvr., Pressroom .... John Christopher
Mechanical available: Black and 3 ROP colors; insert accepted.
Mechanical Specifications: Type page 11 1/2 x 15; E - 6 cols, 1 1/2, 3/8 between; A - 6 cols, 1 1/2, 3/8 between; C - 8 cols, 1 1/4, 1/8 between.
Equipment EDITORIAL: Front-end Software – QPS/QuarkXPress.; Editorial Hardware – PC, APP/Mac CLASSIFIED: Front-end Software – Account Scout.; Classified Hardware – 4-PC DISPLAY: Ad make-up applications – Account Scout; Layout Software – Baseview/Managing Editor, Ad Force.; Display Hardware – 8-PC PRODUCTION: Pagination Software – QPS/QuarkXPress.; Production Equipment – Nu/FT40 V6 UPNS; Scanners – Scitex PRESSROOM: Line 1 – 8-G/Community 1972, 2-Dauphin/DGM 430 1998; Line 8 – Press Drive ÂÐ Baldor/P36801410155; Press Drives – Folders ÂÐ Rockwell/SSC. MAILROOM: Counter stackers – BG/Count-O-Veyor; Bundle tying machines – Dynaric/RLM-1. BUSINESS COMPUTERS: Business Software – Fake Brains-Advertising, Quick Books-Accounting; Business Hardware – PC

DAILY CAMERA

1048 Pearl St., Boulder, Colo., 80302-5111; gen tel (303) 442-1202; adv tel (303) 473-1401; adv fax (303) 473-1144; ed fax (303) 449-9358; web site www.dailycamera.com
Published: Mon, Tues, Wed, Thur, Fri, Sat, Sun
Weekday Frequency: m
Saturday Frequency: m
Circulation: 24,850; 25,169(sat); 26,980(sun)
Last Audit: ABC September 30, 2011
Price: 2.50/wk; 10.00/mo; 130.00/yr.
Advertising: Open inch rate $64.02
News services: AP, LAT-WP, NYT, SHNS.
Politics: Independent. **Established:** 1891
Special Editions: Summer Camping (Apr); Back-to-School (Aug); Holiday Guide (Dec); Wedding Guides (Feb); Home & Garden/HGTV Mag. (Jul); Wedding Guides (Jun); Home & Gardens/HGTV Mag. (Mar); Bolder Boulder Race Guide (May); School Choice Guide (Nov); Voter's Guide (Oct).
Special Weekly Sections: At Home (Fri); Business Plus (Mon); Memories (S); Tech Plus (Thur); Youth Page (Tues); Food (Wed).
Magazines: Parade (S).
Pub. .... Al Manzi
Personnel Dir. .... Mary Hentschel
Mgr., Mktg./Promo./New Media . Jill Stravolemos
City Ed. .... Kevin Kaufman
Features Ed. .... Erika Stutzman Deakin
Data Processing Dir. .... Jim Dubey
Prodn. Dir. .... Tina Kruzel
Prodn. Mgr., Pre Press .... Bettina Kruzel
Prodn. Mgr., Pressroom .... Dale Leppert
Market Information: ADS; TMC; Zoned editions.
Mechanical available: Offset; Black and 3 ROP colors; insert accepted - product samples; page cutoffs - 22 3/4.
Mechanical Specifications: Type page 11 5/8 x 21 1/2; E - 6 cols, 1 5/6, 1/8 between; A - 6 cols, 1 5/6, 1/8 between; C - 9 cols, 1 1/16, 1/36 between.
Commodity Consumption: Avg. Page Number Per Issue - Daily 54; Avg. Page Number Per Issue - Plates Used 99550; Avg. Page Number Per Issue - Sunday 114; widths 37 31/100; Newsprint Used - Metric Tons 5757; Newsprint Used - Short Tons 6346; Printing Ink Used - Black 126921; Print
Equipment EDITORIAL: Front-end Software – HI 3.5, HI.; Editorial Hardware – Intel/PC, Sun/Enterprize Servers, APP/Mac; Editorial Equipment – APP/Server; Editorial Printers – HP/5si CLASSIFIED: Front-end Software – HI/Ad Power.; Classified Hardware – 2-Pentium/PC Servers, 18-Pentium/PC Clients; Classified Equipment – HI/Ad Pag DISPLAY: Ad make-up applications – SCS/Layout 8000 10; Display Hardware – 2-Pentium/PC; Display Printers – HP/Laser 5si PRODUCTION: Pagination Software – QPS/QuarkXPress 6.5, HI/Newsmaker Pagination.; Production Equipment – 2-Autologic/3850, 1-Nu/UPNS PRESSROOM: Line 1 – 5-G/Metro double width 1972; Line 2 – 5-G/Community single width (Custom-Built 3-knife trimmer) 1979; Folders – 2-G/Metro, 1-G/Community SSC; Pasters – 5; Reels and Stands – 5 MAILROOM: Counter stackers – 1-Id/2100, 1-QWI/350, 1-QWI/300, 1/HL Monitor; Inserters and stuffers – Valley Remanufacturing/S-1372; Bundle tying machines – 2-/Power Strap/PSN5, Power Strap/PSN6, 2-ST/MR45CH; Wrapping singles

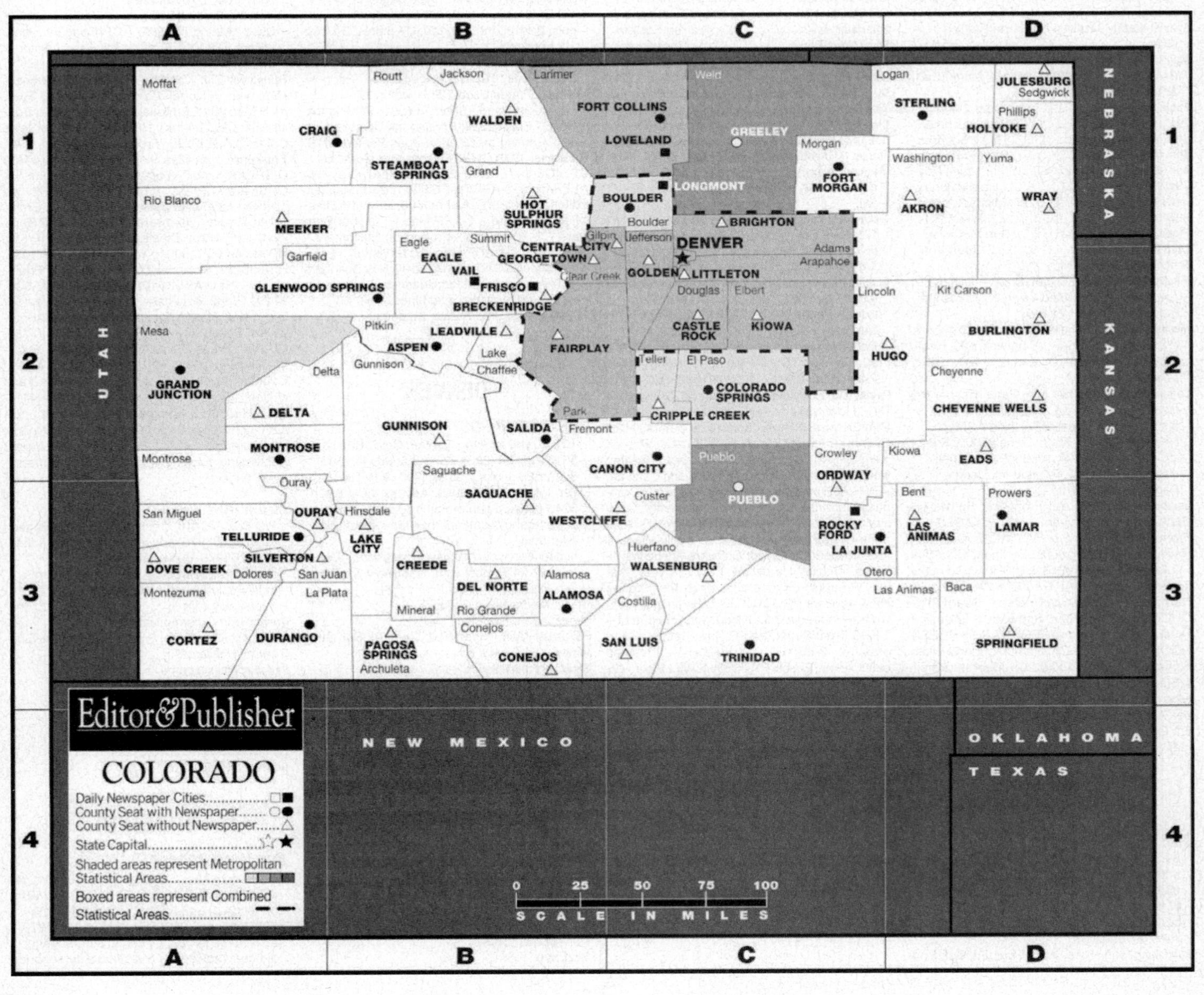

– 2-/Power Strap/Mark V Underwrapper BUSINESS COMPUTERS: Business Software – PBS/CM, PBS/AM, PeopleSoft AAP, AGL, PAY; Business Hardware – Sun/Solaris

CANON CITY

THE CANON CITY DAILY RECORD

701 S. 9th St., Canon City, Colo., 81212-4911; gen tel (719) 275-7565; adv tel (719) 275-7565; ed tel (719) 275-7565; gen fax (719) 275-1353; adv fax (719) 275-1353; ed fax (719) 275-1353; web site www.canoncitydailyrecord.com

Group: Prairie Mountain Publishing
Published: Mon, Tues, Wed, Thur, Fri, Sat
Weekday Frequency: m
Saturday Frequency: m
Circulation: 7,055; 7,055(sat)
Last Audit: September 30, 2009
Price: 8.00/mo (carrier), $9.00/mo (mail); 93.00/yr (carrier), $108.00/yr (mail).
Advertising: Open inch rate $15.00
News services: AP.
Politics: Independent. **Established:** 1875
Not Published: Christmas.
Own facility?: Y
Special Editions: Community Report (Progress Edition) (Apr); Bridal Guide (Feb); Real Estate Preview (Semi-monthly); Hunting Guide (Sept).
Special Weekly Sections: American Profile (Weekly).
Magazines: The Scene (Mon-fri); Relish (Monthly); USA WEEKEND Magazine (Sat); American Profile (Weekly).

Publisher ....Dean Lehman
Pub. ....Edward Lehman
Gen. Mgr./Ed. ....Terry Cochran
Bus. Mgr. ....Glenna Phillips
Adv. Dir. ....Jami Roy
Circ. Mgr. ....Harold Jones
News Ed. ....Michael Alcala
Prodn. Mgr. ....Alan Polk
Prodn. Mgr., Pre Press ....Sue McCulloch
Lead Press Operator ....Todd Kohl

Market Information: TMC.
Mechanical available: Offset; Black and 3 ROP colors; insert accepted - single, broadsheet, tab; page cutoffs - 22 3/4.
Mechanical Specifications: Type page 10 1/2 x 21 1/2; E - 6 cols, 1 5/8, 1/8 between; A - 6 cols, 1 5/8, 1/8 between; C - 9 cols, 1 1/16, 1/8 between.
Commodity Consumption: Avg. Page Number Per Issue - Daily 20; Avg. Page Number Per Issue - Plates Used 7400; widths 27 1/2; Newsprint Used - Metric Tons 87000; Printing Ink Used - Black 19000; Printing Ink Used - Color 3000; Printing Ink Used - Pages Printed 6240.
Equipment EDITORIAL: Front-end Software – GN3; Editorial Hardware – PC, CLASSIFIED: Front-end Software – APT/ACT.; Classified Hardware – PC, Compaq/Prolinea; Classified Printers – Okidata/193 Plus DISPLAY: Ad make-up applications – APT/ACT, AdMax; Display Hardware – PC; Display Printers – Sharp PRODUCTION: Pagination Software – InDesign; Production Equipment – ECR/VLR 36 PRESSROOM: Line 1 – 13-G/Community single width; Folders – 1 MAILROOM: Counter stackers – 1/BG; Inserters and stuffers – KAN/480; Bundle tying machines – 1-/Malow, 1-/Ca, 1-MLN/Strapper; Addressing machine – Automecha/Accufast ST; Other equipment –Champion/Stitcher-Trimmer.

COLORADO SPRINGS

THE GAZETTE

30 S. Prospect St., Colorado Springs, Colo., 80903; gen tel (719) 632-5511; adv tel (719) 636-0306; ed tel (719) 636-0266; gen fax (719) 636-0118; adv fax (719) 476-4858; ed fax (719) 636-0202; web site www.gazette.com

Published: Mon, Tues, Wed, Thur, Fri, Sat, Sun
Weekday Frequency: m
Saturday Frequency: m
Circulation: 77,840; 77,840(sat); 89,896(sun)
Last Audit: Sworn September 30, 2009
Price: varies/deals
Advertising: Open inch rate $142.21
News services: AP, MCT/LAT-WP
Politics: 1872
Own facility?: Y
Special Editions: Auto Show (Apr); Parade of Homes (Aug); Holiday Lights (Dec); BRIDE (Feb); From House to Home (Jan); U.S. Senior Open (Jul); Peak Performers (Jun); From House to Home (Mar); Best of the Springs (May); Dining Guide (Nov); The Road Ahead Auto Preview (Oct);
Special Weekly Sections: Food (Wed.); Out There (Thu.); go!, Wheels (Fri.), Springs Houses (Sat.); Life, SpringsJobs, Springs Home & Style (Sun.)
Magazines: Pikes Peak Parent (Monthly); Parade (S).

Interim Publisher ....Mike Burns
Business Editor ....Bill Radford
Regional Director HR ....Katherine Florman
Adv. Dir., Sales Opns. ....Vicki Cederholm
Vice Pres., Mktg. ....Liz Cobb
Vice Pres./Ed. ....Jeff Thomas
Dir., Interactive Content/Audience Devel. Carmen Boles
Local News Editor ....Joanna Bean
Local News Editor ....Sue McMillin
Editorial Page Ed. ....Wayne Laugesen
Entertainment Ed. ....Warren Epstein
Local News Editor ....Dena Rosenberry
Photo Dir. ....Stuart Wong
Sports Ed. ....Jim O'Connell
Dir., IT ....Brad Shaw
Vice Pres., Opns. ....Jerry Buck
Circ. Vice Pres. ....Cory Arcarese
Circ. Dir., Consumer Sales ....Adel Ibrahim

Market Information: ADS; TMC.
Mechanical available: Offset; Black and 3 ROP colors; insert accepted; page cutoffs - 22 3/4.
Mechanical Specifications: Type page 10 5/8 x 21 1/2; E - 6 cols, 1 5/8, 3/16 between; A - 6 cols, 1 5/8, 3/16 between; C - 10 cols, 15/16, 1/8 between.
Commodity Consumption: Avg. Page Number Per Issue - Daily 61; Avg. Page Number Per Issue - Plates Used 179754; Avg. Page Number Per Issue - Saturday 109; Avg. Page Number Per Issue - Sunday 94; widths 50; Newsprint Used - Metric Tons 14400; Printing Ink Used - Black 291632; Pr
Equipment EDITORIAL: Front-end Software – DTI NewsSpeed 7; Editorial Hardware – Sun/Servers, PCs; Editorial Equipment – Dell Clients; Editorial Printers – HP/Laser Printer, Xerox/HP/Kyocersa Color Laser Printer, Nikon/Digital CLASSIFIED: Front-end Software – PBS AdPlus; Classified Hardware – HP-Compaq; Classified Equipment – Dell clients; Classified Printers – Kyocera/Laser PrinterHP Laser printer DISPLAY: Ad make-up applications – DTI AdSpeed 7; Layout Software – PBS/MediaPlus.; Display Hardware – Sun/Servers; Display Printers – Kyocera/Laser Printer, Xerox, HP & Kyocera PRODUCTION: Pagination Software – Harlequin 5.5.; Production Equipment – 1 KPG TrendSetter, 2 KPG NewsSetters; Cameras – 2-LE/121; Scanners – Desktop only:Canon, Epson PRESSROOM: Line 1 – 7-MAN/5 Color Deck double width offset 1982; Line 2 – 7-MAN/5 Color Deck double width offset 1985; Line 3 – 9-G/Community single width offset 1996; Folders – 4-MAN/3:2, 1-G/SC; Pasters – 14; Reels and Stands – 14 MAILROOM: Counter stackers – 5-HL/Monitor3, 2-Compass/180, 2-Quipp/501, 1-HL/Dual Carrier, 1-HL/Dual Carrier; Inserters and stuffers – 1-GMA/SLS 2000 12:2, 1-GMA/SLS 2000 12:2; Bundle tying machines – 1-LB/News Signode, 2-MLN/Portable, 2-LB/X2000 Signode, 1-Dynaric BUSINESS COMPUTERS: Business Software – PBS-Circ. Hosted/Local PBS AdPlus; Business Hardware – HP-Compaq
Delivery method: Private Carrier, Racks

CRAIG

CRAIG DAILY PRESS

466 Yampa Ave., Craig, Colo., 81625; gen tel (970) 824-7031; adv tel (970) 824-7031; ed tel (970) 824-7031; gen fax (970) 824-6810; adv fax (970) 824-6810; ed fax (970) 824-6810; gen e-mail bjacobson@craigdailypress.com; adv e-mail bjacobson@craigdailypress.com; ed e-mail jgrubbs@craigdailypress.com; web site www.craigdailypress.com

Published: Sat
Saturday Frequency: m
Circulation: 3,400; 9,600(sat)
Last Audit: March 8, 2007
Price: 7.50/mo; 66.00/yr.
Advertising: Open inch rate $10.19
News services: AP.
Politics: 1891
Special Weekly Sections: Saturday Northwest (Sat).
Magazines: American Profile (Weekly).

Pub. ....Bryce Jacobson
Adv. Dir. ....Renee Campbell
Circ. Mgr. ....Amy Fontenot
Ed. ....Jennifer Grubbs
Prodn. Mgr. ....Meg Wortman

Market Information: TMC.
Mechanical available: Offset; Black and 3 ROP colors; insert accepted; page cutoffs - 17.
Mechanical Specifications: Type page 10 13/16 x 16; E - 5 cols, 2 1/16, 1/8 between; A - 5 cols, 2 1/16, 1/8 between; C - 5 cols, 2 1/16, 1/8 between.
Commodity Consumption: Avg. Page Number Per Issue - Daily 16; Avg. Page Number Per Issue - Plates Used 2280; widths 17; Newsprint Used - Short Tons 91; Printing Ink Used - Black 2800; Printing Ink Used - Color 100; Printing Ink Used - Pages Printed 5016.
Equipment EDITORIAL: Front-end Software – QPS/QuarkXPress.; Editorial Hardware – 6-APP/Mac II, 2-APP/Mac SE30, 1-APP/Mac IIci; Editorial Printers – Hyphen/600, HP/4MV; Classified Hardware – 1-APP/Mac II.; Layout Software – 2-APP/Mac II.; Production Equipment – 1-V/VT600, 1-APP/Mac LaserWriter, 1-Hyphen/Copal 600; Cameras – 1-K, Nat; Scanners – 1-Truvell, 1-APP/Mac Scanner, 1-HP/Scanner.; Bundle tying machines – 1/Bu, 1-MLN/ML2EE; Addressing machine – 2-/Wm.; Business Hardware – 1-ATT

DENVER

THE DENVER POST

101 W. Colfax Ave., Denver, Colo., 80202-5315; gen tel (303) 820-1010; adv tel (303) 892-2525 (class.); ed tel (303) 954-1201; gen fax (303) 820-1406; adv fax (303) 892-5243 (class.); gen e-mail hr@denvernewspaperagency.com; reach@denverpost.com; ed e-mail subscribervipdesk@denverpost.com; newsroom@denverpost.com; web site www.denverpost.com

Group: Media News Group
Newspapers First, Inc.
Published: Mon, Tues, Wed, Thur, Fri, Sat, Sun
Weekday Frequency: m
Saturday Frequency: m
Circulation: 353,115; 389,576(sat); 538,133(sun)
Last Audit: ABC September 30, 2011
Price: $225.65/48 weeks
Advertising: Open inch rate $847.32(m-fri); $879.82 (sat); $1,029.48 (sun)
News services: AP, NYT, LAT-WP, Bloomberg, McClatchy.
Note: For detailed business information see Denver Newspaper Agency listing.
Special Editions: The Deal
Going Green
National Western Stock Show
Home Show
Parade of Homes
Komen Race for the Cure
Denver Auto Show
Ski Expo
Magazines: Parade (S)
Color Comics (S)
TV (S)
USA Weekend (S)
Broadcast Affiliations: KUSA; WB2.

Pub. ....William Dean Singleton
Exec VP of Strategy OPS & IT ....Bernie Szachara
Ed. ....Gregory Moore
Mng. Ed., Opns. ....Jeanette Chavez
Assoc. Ed., Staff Devel. Carla Kimbrough Robinson
Book Ed. ....Tom Walker
City Ed. ....Leeann Colacioppo
Entertainment Ed. ....Edward Smith
Asst. Entertainment Ed. ....Bill Porter
Fashion/Style Ed. ....Suzanne Brown
Features Ed. ....Judith Howard
Graphics Dir. ....Blair Hamill
Editorial Librarian ....Vicki Makings
Nat'l Ed. ....Michelle Fulcher
Nat'l Foreign Ed. ....Dan Meyers
Online Ed. ....Howard Saltz
Photography Dir. ....John Sunderland
Photo Assignment Ed. ....JeAlison Hale
Political Ed. ....Rebecca Cantwell
Sports Ed. ....Kevin Dale

Market Information: TMC and Electronic Edition
Mechanical available: Offset; Black and 3 ROP colors; insert accepted.
Mechanical Specifications: Type page 12 x 21; ROP 6 cols, 1.75, 1/8 between; Class: 10 cols, 1.06, 1/16 between.
Commodity Consumption: widths 50; Newsprint Used - Metric Tons 87770; Printing Ink Used - Black 1580000; Printing Ink Used - Color 87770.
Equipment EDITORIAL: Front-end Software – Hemmes; Editorial Hardware – SII/61 Risc, APP/Mac G4; Editorial Printers – Centronics/351, DEC/LA 180, HP/2500, Cyclone/Savin Color CLASSIFIED: Front-end Software – AT, Enterprise 1.4.; Classified Hardware – Sun/450 DISPLAY: Ad make-up applications – QPS/QuarkXPress 4.1, INDesign, DPS, Ad Tracker; Layout Software – Unisys, AT, Enterprise; Display Hardware – Compaq/NT Services, APP/Mac; Display Printers – HP/5SI, HP/4MV, HP/2500, Xante/8200, HP/1055, HP/855ON, Rainbow/2730; Production Equipment – 2-AU/APS-6 1085, DIT/Line 303-820-1710, Glunz & Jensen/Online, AG/SelectSet 5000; Cameras – Konica/Newspager, C/Spartan III; Scanners – 3-AG/Horizon, 2-AII/3750, CD, Kk.; Press Drives – 3, 2; Pasters – G/CT-45; Reels and Stands – G/CT-45. MAILROOM: Counter stackers – 41/QWI; Inserters and stuffers – Fg/Drum 5 Lines, 3-HI/13-72, 1-HI/14-72, 4-HI/630-23; Bundle tying machines – 23-/OVL, 23-/Power Strap, 15-/Sterling, 2-/Dynaric; Mailroom control system – Burt Technologies; Addressing machine – Domi; Audio Hardware – InterConnect

MOUNTAIN WEEKLY

P.O.Box 460446, Denver, Colo., 80246; gen tel 9703765975; adv tel 9703765975; ed tel 9703765975; gen e-mail info@mtnweekly.com; adv e-mail advertising@mtnweekly.com; web site mtnweekly.com

Group: Swift Communications
Published: Mon, Tues, Wed, Thur, Fri, Sat, Sun
Weekday Frequency: m
Saturday Frequency: m
Circulation: 2,000; 300(sat)
Price: Free
Politics: 2004
Advertising not accepted: N
Zip Codes served: 80246,81224
Delivery method: Mail

DURANGO

DURANGO HERALD

1275 Main Ave., Durango, Colo., 81301; gen tel (970) 247-3504; adv tel (970) 247-3504; ed tel (970) 247-3504; gen fax (970) 259-5011; adv fax (970) 259-8817; ed fax (970) 259-5011; gen e-mail herald@durangoherald.com; adv e-mail classified@durangoher-

ald.com; advertising@durangoherald.com; ed e-mail letters@durangoherald.com; briefs@durangoherald.com; web site www.durangoherald.com
Published: Mon, Tues, Wed, Thur, Fri, Sat, Sun
Weekday Frequency: m
Saturday Frequency: m
Circulation: 8,045; 8,045(sat); 8,504(sun)
Last Audit: ABC September 30, 2011
Advertising: Open inch rate $14.65
News services: AP, NYT, CNS.
Politics: Independent-Republican. **Established:** 1881
Special Editions: Southwest Summer (Apr); Focus on Business (Feb); County Fair (Jul); Newcomers (Jun); Christmas Gift Guide (Nov); Southwest Winter (Oct).
Special Weekly Sections: Religion (Fri); Arts & Entertainment (Mon); Business (S); Arts & Entertainment (Thur); TV (Tues); Education (Wed).
Magazines: USA WEEKEND Magazine (Sat); Cross Currents (Semi-monthly).
Pub. ....Richard G. Ballantine
Gen. Mgr. ....Sharon Hermes
Dir., Adv./Mktg. ....Dennis Hanson
Circ. Mgr. ....Julio Goicoechea
Arts/Entertainment Ed. ....Pat Miller
City Ed. ....Tom Sluis
Editorial Page Ed. ....Bill Roberts
IT Mgr. ....David Tabar
Market Information: TMC.
Mechanical available: Offset; Black and 3 ROP colors; insert accepted; page cutoffs - 22 7/8.
Mechanical Specifications: Type page 13 x 21; E - 6 cols, 2, 1/8 between; A - 6 cols, 2, 1/8 between; C - 7 cols, 1 3/4, 1/8 between.
Commodity Consumption: Avg. Page Number Per Issue - Daily 27; Avg. Page Number Per Issue - Plates Used 4184; Avg. Page Number Per Issue - Saturday 20; Avg. Page Number Per Issue - Sunday 46; widths 27 1/2; Newsprint Used - Metric Tons 600; Printing Ink Used - Black 7500; Print
Equipment EDITORIAL: Front-end Software – QPS/QuarkXPress, APT.; Editorial Hardware – 28-Pentium/90 486 PC; Editorial Equipment – Pre Press/Panther 34P Imagesetter, Lf/AP Leaf Picture Desk, Microtek/Scanmaker III; Editorial Printers – NewGen, HP/4MV, HP/5000, HP/MVP5 CLASSIFIED: Front-end Software – QPS/QuarkXPress, APT.; Classified Hardware – 4-Pentium/PC-90 486; Classified Equipment – Pre Press/Panther 34P Imagesetter; Classified Printers – TI/500, NewGen DISPLAY: Ad make-up applications – Aldus/FreeHand, Aldus/PageMaker, QPS/QuarkXPress; Layout Software – ACT.; Display Hardware – PC 486; Display Printers – HP/4MV, HP/5000 PRODUCTION: Pagination Software – QPS/QuarkXPress, APT.; Production Equipment – TI/OmniPage, Prepress/Panther/34P; Scanners – Tecsa/Scanner, GEI PRESSROOM: Line 1 – 5-KP/News King single width 1979, 1-KP/News King 1994, 4-KP/News King single width 1998; Folders – KP/KJ8 1998.; Inserters and stuffers – KAN/480; Bundle tying machines – MLN.; Business Hardware – PBS, SBS

FORT COLLINS

THE COLORADOAN

1300 Riverside Ave., Fort Collins, Colo., 80524; gen tel (970) 493-6397; adv tel (970) 224-7701; ed tel (970) 224-7730; adv fax (970) 224-7726; ed fax (970) 224-7899; gen e-mail news@coloradoan.com; adv e-mail advertising@coloradoan.com; ed e-mail opinion@coloradoan.com; web site www.coloradoan.com
Published: Mon, Tues, Wed, Thur, Fri, Sat, Sun
Weekday Frequency: m
Saturday Frequency: m
Circulation: 20,601; 21,552(sat); 26,079(sun)
Last Audit: ABC September 30, 2011
Price: 2.80/wk; 145.60/yr.
Advertising: Open inch rate $68.35
News services: AP, GNS, LAT-WP.
Politics: Independent.
Special Editions: Coloradoan Golf (Apr); Football Preview (Aug); Parks & Recreation (Dec); Best in the Business (Feb); Bridal Magazine (Jan); Parks and Recreation (Jul); Greeley Stampede (Jun); Remodel Magazine (Mar); Volunteer Guide (May); Volunteer Guide (Nov); Best of F
Special Weekly Sections: Make & Model (Fri); Business Edge (Mon); Xplore (S); At Home (Sat); Northern Colorado Homes (Thur); CareerBuilder (Tues).
Magazines: USA WEEKEND Magazine (S).
Profile: The Fort Collins Coloradoan is the market leader for local news, advertising, and other information in the Fort Collins area. The Coloradoan is a news and information company that publishes the leading daily newspaper in Northern Colorado. The company is
Pres./Pub. ....Kim Roegner
Controller ....Jennifer Salazar
Dir., HR ....Corina McCalahan
Adv. Dir. ....Gabe Aguirre
Adv. Mgr., Retail Sales ....Michael Lin
Circ. Dir. ....Kathy Jack-Romero
Circ. Mgr., Opns. ....Susan Giglio
Exec. Ed. ....Robert Moore
Editorial Page Ed. ....Kathleen Duff
Online Content Ed. ....Betty Grace Mickey
Chief Photographer ....V. Richard Haro
Sports Ed. ....Sean Duff
Online Sales Mgr. ....Kate Gannon
Market Information: TMC.
Mechanical available: Offset; Black and 3 ROP colors; insert accepted; page cutoffs - 22 3/4.
Mechanical Specifications: Type page 13 x 21 1/2; E - 6 cols, 2 1/16, 1/8 between; A - 6 cols, 2 1/16, 1/8 between; C - 10 cols, 1 3/8, 1/16 between.
Commodity Consumption: Avg. Page Number Per Issue - Daily 46; Avg. Page Number Per Issue - Plates Used 61082; Avg. Page Number Per Issue - Sunday 81; widths 27 1/4; Newsprint Used - Short Tons 3296; Printing Ink Used - Black 48748; Printing Ink Used - Color 33217; Printing Ink
Equipment EDITORIAL: Front-end Software – ACT/APT 3.0.; Editorial Hardware – 26-Pentium/PC 266, Dell; Editorial Equipment – APP/Leaf Digital Server, DiGiCol/Archive; Editorial Printers – HP/4000, 2-HP/8000 CLASSIFIED: Front-end Software – ACT/APT Classified 3.5.0, QPS/QuarkXPress 4.0.; Classified Printers – HP/4000 DISPLAY: Ad make-up applications – Multi-Ad/Creator 6.5.8, QPS/QuarkXPress 6.0, Adobe/Illustrator 10, Adobe/Photoshop 7, Multi-Ad/Creator Pro; Display Hardware – Monotype/News Express, HP/1050C, 16-IBM/Thinkpad 1.2g, 4-Dell/700; Display Printers – HP/8000, 3-HP/4000 PRODUCTION: Pagination Software – ACT/APT 3.6.0.; Production Equipment – 2-Nu/FT4OUPNS, 2-Mon/Ripexpress; Cameras – Scanners ☐ Microtek PRESSROOM: Line 1 – 18-G/Urbanite; Folders – 2-G/2:1; Pasters – 9 MAILROOM: Counter stackers – 3/PPK, 2-QWI/351, 2-Gammerler/STC-70; Inserters and stuffers – GMA/SLS 1000A, 5-AF-100/Hopper loaders; Bundle tying machines – Sp/300, 2-Sterling/MH40, 2-Ovalstrapping 2000/NS; Addressing machine – 1-Barstrom/on-line; Other equipment –Other equipment ☐

FORT COLLINS NEWSPAPERS, INC.

PO Box 1577, Fort Collins, Colo., 80522; gen tel (970) 493-6397; gen fax (970) 224-7798

FORT MORGAN

FORT MORGAN TIMES

329 Main St., Fort Morgan, Colo., 80701; gen tel (970) 867-5651; gen fax (970) 867-7448; gen e-mail fmtimes@fmtimes.com; adv e-mail ads@fmtimes.com; web site www.fortmorgantimes.com
Published: Mon, Tues, Wed, Thur, Fri, Sat
Weekday Frequency: e
Circulation: 3,186; 3,186(sat)
Last Audit: September 30, 2009
Price: 10.00/mo; 108.00/yr.
Advertising: Open inch rate $12.00
News services: AP.
Politics: Independent. **Established:** 1884
Not Published: Legal holidays.
Special Editions: Senior Living (Apr); Back to School (Aug); Christmas Greetings/Letters to Santa (Dec); Income Tax Preparation Guide (Feb); Soil Conservation District Annual Meeting (Jan); Morgan County Fair (Jul); July 4th/Rodeo (Jun); Progress (Mar); Graduation (May); C
Special Weekly Sections: TV Schedule (Sat).
Magazines: American Profile (Weekly).
Gen Mgr. ....Julie Tonsing
Adv. Mgr. ....Teresa Leake
Circ. Mgr. ....Josephina Monsivais
Ed. ....John Brennan
Bus. Ed. ....Dan Barker
Farm/Agriculture Ed. ....Jesse Chaney
Sports Ed. ....Rich Headley
Market Information: TMC.
Mechanical available: Offset; Black and 3 ROP colors; insert accepted - half-fold; page cutoffs - 22 3/4.
Mechanical Specifications: Type page 11 13/16 x 21 1/2; E - 4 cols, 2 13/16, 1/8 between; A - 6 cols, 1 13/16, 1/8 between; C - 6 cols, 1 13/16, 1/8 between.
Commodity Consumption: Avg. Page Number Per Issue - Daily 21; Avg. Page Number Per Issue - Plates Used 4771; Avg. Page Number Per Issue - Saturday 12; widths 25; Newsprint Used - Metric Tons 173; Printing Ink Used - Black 3900; Printing Ink Used - Color 320; Printing Ink Used
Equipment EDITORIAL: Front-end Software – Baseview, QPS/QuarkXPress, Adobe/Photoshop.; Editorial Hardware – 12-APP/Mac, Ethernet, APP/Mac Server; Editorial Printers – 2-APP/Mac LaserWriter II, Xante/Accel-a-Writer CLASSIFIED: Front-end Software – Baseview.; Classified Hardware – 1-APP/Mac Plus; Classified Printers – APP/Mac LaserWriter II, Xante/Accel-a-Writer DISPLAY: Ad make-up applications – QPS/QuarkXPress; Layout Software – 2-APP/Mac Plus, 1-Murata/F-32 Fax, QPS/QuarkXPress.; Display Printers – APP/Mac LaserWriter II, Xante/Accel-a-Writer PRODUCTION: Pagination Software – QPS/QuarkXPress.; Production Equipment – 1-Nu/Sink, Jobo/Processor; Cameras – 1-R, B/Horizontal PRESSROOM: Line 1 – 6-G/Community; Folders – 1-G/2:1, 1-G/Community.; Inserters and stuffers – Manual; Bundle tying machines – 1-Marlow/Mc; Addressing machine – AKI/Addressograph, AKI/Labeler, AKI/Electronic Labeler.

FRISCO

SUMMIT DAILY NEWS

40 W. Main St., Frisco, Colo., 80443; gen tel (970) 668-3998; adv tel (970) 668-3998; ed tel (970) 668-3998; gen fax (970) 668-3859; adv fax (970) 668-3859; ed fax (970) 668-0755; gen e-mail news@summitdaily.com; web site www.summitdaily.com
Published: Mon, Tues, Wed, Thur, Fri, Sat, Sun
Weekday Frequency: All day
Saturday Frequency: All day
Advertising: Open inch rate $14.35
News services: AP.
Politics: 1989
Note: The Summit Daily News is printed at the Colrado Mountain News Media plant. For detailed commodity consumption, advertising and production, see Vail Daily News listing.
Special Weekly Sections: Summit Scene (Fri); Summit Homes & Properties (Sat).
Mgmt. Info Servs. Mgr. ....Greg Treece
Publisher ....Matt Sandberg
Mechanical available: Offset; Black and ROP colors; insert accepted; page cutoffs - 15 1/4.
Mechanical Specifications: Type page 10 5/8 x 16; E - 6 cols, 1 1/2, 1/6 between; A - 6 cols, 1 1/2, 1/6 between; C - 7 cols, 1 1/2, 1 3/8 between.
Commodity Consumption: Avg. Page Number Per Issue - Daily 48; Avg. Page Number Per Issue - Saturday 52; Avg. Page Number Per Issue - Sunday 48; widths 33 1/2; Newsprint Used - Metric Tons 600; Printing Ink Used - Black 8800; Printing Ink Used - Pages Printed 15000.
Equipment EDITORIAL: Front-end Software – QPS/QuarkXPress, Adobe/Photoshop.; Editorial Hardware – APP/Mac CLASSIFIED: Front-end Software – Baseview.; Classified Hardware – APP/Mac; Classified Equipment – APP/Mac; Classified Printers – APP/Mac LaserWriter IIg DISPLAY: Ad make-up applications – QPS, Adobe/Illustrator, Adobe/Photoshop; Layout Software – APP/Mac.; Display Hardware – APP/Power Mac PC PRODUCTION: Pagination Software – MEI/ALS.; Production Equipment – Nu; Cameras – AG; Scanners – Kk, HP PRESSROOM: Line 1 – 10; Folders – DGM/Quarter. MAILROOM: Counter stackers – HL; Inserters and stuffers – MM/227; Bundle tying machines – Signode.; Business Hardware – Unix, PBS

GLENWOOD SPRINGS

GLENWOOD SPRINGS POST INDEPENDENT

2014 Grand Ave., Glenwood Springs, Colo., 81601-4116; gen tel (970) 945-8515; adv tel (970) 945-8515; ed tel (970) 947-5537; gen fax (970) 945-4487; adv fax (970) 945-8518; ed fax (970) 945-4487; web site www.postindependent.com
Published: Mon, Tues, Wed, Thur, Fri, Sat, Sun
Weekday Frequency: m
Saturday Frequency: m
Circulation: 5,064; 5,064(sat); 5,064(sun)
Last Audit: September 30, 1998
Price: 8.50/mo; 102.00/yr.
Advertising: Open inch rate $13.65
News services: AP.
Politics: Independent.
Not Published: New Year; Christmas.
Special Editions: Christmas (Dec); Recreation (Feb); Summer Recreation Guides (May); Holiday Kick-off (Thanksgiving) (Nov); Hunting (Oct).
Special Weekly Sections: Mountain Leisure (Fri); Church (Sat); Business (Thur); Education (Tues); Best Food Day (Wed).
Magazines: Tourism Magazine (Feb) (Annually); Parade (S).
Pub. ....Jenna Weatherred
Adv. Dir. ....Gunilla Asher
Circ. Coord. ....Melissa Boutwell
Classified Adv. Sup ....Lisa Parmelee
Mng. Ed. ....Dale Shrull
Market Information: TMC.
Mechanical available: Offset; Black and 3 ROP colors; insert accepted; page cutoffs - 22 3/4.
Mechanical Specifications: Type page 13 x 21 1/2; E - 6 cols, 2 1/4, 1/6 between; A - 6 cols, 2 1/4, 1/6 between; C - 6 cols, 2 1/4, 1/6 between.
Commodity Consumption: Avg. Page Number Per Issue - Daily 16; Avg. Page Number Per Issue - Plates Used 2500; widths 34; Newsprint Used - Short Tons 800; Printing Ink Used - Black 10000; Printing Ink Used - Color 1800; Printing Ink Used - Pages Printed 5000.
Equipment EDITORIAL: Front-end Software – QPS/QuarkXPress, Baseview/Extension.; Editorial Hardware – APP/Mac; Editorial Equipment – APP/Mac Scanner; Editorial Printers – APP/Mac LaserWriter II NTXs CLASSIFIED: Front-end Software – Baseview, QPS/QuarkXPress.; Classified Hardware – APP/Mac IIsi; Classified Printers – APP/Mac LaserWriter II NTX DISPLAY: Ad make-up applications – Multi-Ad/Creator, QPS/QuarkXPress; Layout Software – Ad Force by Ad Manager, Inc.; Display Hardware – APP/Mac IIsi; Display Printers – APP/Mac LaserWriter II GS; Production Equipment – MON/1270; Cameras – Acti. PRESSROOM: Line 1 – 6-G/Community (upper former); Folders – G/2:1.; Bundle tying ma-

chines – 1/OVL, 1-/MLN; Addressing machine – Automecha/Accufast, Intermountain. AUDIO: Audio Software – SMS; Audio Hardware – APP/Mac; Business Hardware – Epson

GRANBY

SKY-HI NEWS

424 E. Agate Ave., Granby, Colo., 80446; gen tel (970) 887-3334; gen fax (970) 887-3204; web site www.skyhidailynews.com
Published: Mon, Tues, Wed, Thur, Fri
Last Audit: N/A
Advertising: Open inch rate $9.00
Pub. ....Kim Burner
Adv. Rep. ....Tess Conger
Circ. Mgr. ....Darin Foran
Mng. Ed. ....Autumn Philips
Prodn. Mgr. ....John Marte

GRAND JUNCTION

THE DAILY SENTINEL

734 S. Seventh St., Grand Junction, Colo., 81501; gen tel (970) 242-5050; gen fax (970) 241-6860; adv fax (970) 241-6860; ed fax (970) 244-8578; gen e-mail letters@gjds.com; adv e-mail classified@gjds.com; web site www.gjsentinel.com
Published: Mon, Tues, Wed, Thur, Fri, Sat, Sun
Weekday Frequency: m
Saturday Frequency: m
Circulation: 24,348; 23,707(sat); 27,124(sun)
Last Audit: ABC September 30, 2011
Price: 2.75/wk; 117.00/yr (carrier), 260.00/yr (mail).
Advertising: Open inch rate $50.89
News services: AP, Cox News Service, NYT (Pony).
Politics: Independent.
Special Editions: Food and Fitness (Apr); Grand Valley Values (Aug); Late Shopper's Guide (Dec); Grand Valley Values (Feb); Coupon Book (Jan); Home Improvement Directory (Jul); Grand Valley Values (Jun); Baseball (Mar); Coupon Book (May); Coupon Book (Nov); Grand Valley Va
Special Weekly Sections: Out & About (Fri); Business (S); Religion (Sat); Best Food Day (Wed).
Magazines: Parade (S).
Exec. Sec. ....Robin Dearing
Adv. Dir. ....Dennis Mitchell
Mktg. Dir. ....Lynn Lickers
Circ. Dir., Opns. ....Bud Winslow
Circ. Mgr. ....Tracy Gettman
Ed ....Dennis Herzog
Mng. Ed. ....Laurena Mayne Davis
City Ed ....Tim Harty
Editorial Page Ed. ....Bob Silbernagel
Features Ed. ....Todd Powell
Graphics Ed./Art Dir. ....Robert Garcia
News Ed. ....Brian Harvey
Photo Ed. ....Christopher Tomlinson
Political Writer ....Charles Ashby
Sports Ed. ....Patti Arnold
Mgr., Mgmt. Info Servs. ....Bob Eicher
Prodn. Foreman, Pressroom ....Joe Craig
Prodn. Foreman, Pressroom ....Scott Crabtree
Market Information: Split run; TMC.
Mechanical available: Offset; Black and 3 ROP colors; insert accepted; page cutoffs - 22 3/4.
Mechanical Specifications: Type page 12 x 21; E - 6 cols, 1 7/8, 1/6 between; A - 6 cols, 1 7/8, 1/6 between; C - 9 cols, 1 3/16, 1/6 between.
Commodity Consumption: Avg. Page Number Per Issue - Daily 28; Avg. Page Number Per Issue - Saturday 28; Avg. Page Number Per Issue - Sunday 44; widths 37 1/2; Newsprint Used - Short Tons 3000; Printing Ink Used - Pages Printed 13600.
Equipment EDITORIAL: Front-end Software – DTI.; Editorial Hardware – APP/Mac CLASSIFIED: Front-end Software – DTI.; Classified Hardware – APP/Mac; Layout Software – APP/Mac.; Display Hardware – APP/Mac; Display Printers – Software ÃÂ DTI PRODUCTION: Pagination Software – DTI.; Production Equipment – 1-Nat/A250, DTI PRESSROOM: Line 1 – 5-G/Headliner; Folders – 2-G/2:1. MAILROOM: Counter stackers – 2-QWI/350B; Inserters and stuffers – 1-GMA/SLS 1000; Bundle tying machines – 1-CYP/RTV-7-600.; Audio Hardware – Newspaper Voice Systems BUSINESS COMPUTERS: Business Software – CJ; Business Hardware – HP/E3000

GRAND JUNCTION FREE PRESS

145 N. Fourth St., Grand Junction, Colo., 81501; gen tel (970) 243-2200; web site www.gjfreepress.com
Group: Swift Communications

GRAND JUNCTION NEWSPAPERS, INC.

734 S. 7th St., Grand Junction, Colo., 81501; gen tel (970) 242-5050; gen fax (970) 241-6860

GREELEY

GREELEY DAILY TRIBUNE

501 8th Ave., Greeley, Colo., 80631; gen tel (970) 352-0211; adv tel (970) 352-0211; ed tel (970) 352-0211; gen fax (970) 352-7817; adv fax (970) 352-4059; ed fax (970) 356-5780; gen e-mail gtribune@greeleytrib.com; ed e-mail nnemec@greeleytrib.com; web site www.greeleytrib.com
Published: Mon, Tues, Wed, Thur, Fri, Sat, Sun
Weekday Frequency: m
Saturday Frequency: m
Circulation: 18,985; 18,985(sat); 20,802(sun)
Last Audit: September 30, 2009
Price: 9.50/mo; 102.00/yr (carrier/mail).
Advertising: Open inch rate $37.18
News services: LAT-WP, AP.
Politics: Independent. **Established:** 1870
Advertising not accepted: Vending machines; Fortune telling; Ads soliciting money; Libido enhancement.
Special Editions: Stampede (Jul); Panorama (Mar); Homes On Parade (May); Holiday Magazine (Nov); Click (Oct); Homes On Parade (Sept).
Special Weekly Sections: Preview TV/Entertainment (Fri); People/Senior (S); Education (Sat); Outdoors (Thur); Family/Health (Wed).
Magazines: USA WEEKEND Magazine (S).
Pub. ....Bart Smith
Grp. Pub. ....Steve Weaver
Adv. Dir. ....Stephanie Schafer
Circ. Dir. ....Joe Luethmers
Ed. ....Randy Bangert
Mng. Ed. ....Kelly Tracer
Action Line Ed ....Mike Peters
City Ed. ....Sharon Dunn
Editorial Page Ed. ....Nancy Nemec
Entertainment Ed. ....Donovan Henderson
Farm/Agriculture Ed. ....Bill Jackson
Sports Ed. ....Nate Miller
Mgmt. Info Servs. Mgr. ....Jeff Kelly
Prodn. Mgr., Mailroom ....Ron Heil
Prodn. Foreman, Pressroom ....Robert Rodd
Prodn. Mgr., Pre Press ....Dustin Bell
Market Information: TMC; Zoned editions.
Mechanical available: Offset; Black and 3 ROP colors; insert accepted; page cutoffs - 22 3/4.
Mechanical Specifications: Type page 13 x 21 1/2; E - 6 cols, 2 1/16, 1/8 between; A - 6 cols, 2 1/16, 1/8 between; C - 9 cols, 1 1/2, 1/8 between.
Commodity Consumption: Avg. Page Number Per Issue - Daily 32; Avg. Page Number Per Issue - Saturday 52; Avg. Page Number Per Issue - Sunday 68; widths 25; Newsprint Used - Metric Tons 2300; Printing Ink Used - Black 49500; Printing Ink Used - Color 23000; Printing Ink Used - P
Equipment EDITORIAL: Front-end Software – QuarkXPress 4.1, Baseview.; Editorial Hardware – APP/G4; Editorial Printers – HP/LaserJet CLASSIFIED: Front-end Software – Baseview/AD Manager Pro.; Classified Hardware – APP/iMac; Classified Printers – HP/LaserJet DISPLAY: Ad make-up applications – QuarkXPress; Layout Software – APP/G4.; Display Printers – HP/LaserJet PRODUCTION: Pagination Software – QuarkXPress.; Production Equipment – 2-Pre Press/Panther Pro G2, 1-DP PRESSROOM: Line 1 – 13-G/Urbanite; Line 2 – G/Community; Folders – 2; Reels and Stands – G. MAILROOM: Counter stackers – 2/BG; Inserters and stuffers – S/1372 12:1; Bundle tying machines – MLN; Addressing machine – 1-/Ch. BUSINESS COMPUTERS: Business Software – PBS; Business Hardware – Sun/Sparc Server 670 mp

LA JUNTA

LA JUNTA TRIBUNE-DEMOCRAT

422 Colorado Ave., La Junta, Colo., 81050; gen tel (719) 384-4475; gen fax (719) 384-5999; gen e-mail mail@ljtd.com; web site www.lajuntatribunedemocrat.com
Published: Mon, Tues, Wed, Thur, Fri
Weekday Frequency: e
Circulation: 3,721
Last Audit: March 31, 2005
Price: 4.00/mo (local); 62.00/yr (mail).
Advertising: Open inch rate $10.05(e-fri)
News services: AP.
Politics: Independent.
Not Published: New Year; Memorial Day; Independence Day; Labor Day; Thanksgiving; Christmas.
Special Editions: Spring Fashion (Apr); Kids Rodeo (Aug); Progress (Jan); Christmas Shopping (Nov).
Special Weekly Sections: Agriculture (Fri); Best Food Day (Tues); Best Food Day (Wed).
Magazines: This Week in La Junta (Sat).
Circ. Mgr. ....Reeda Ojeda
Ed. ....Candi Hill
Market Information: TMC.
Mechanical available: Offset; Black and 3 ROP colors; insert accepted; page cutoffs - 22 3/4.
Mechanical Specifications: Type page 10 13/16 x 14 1/4; E - 5 cols, 2 1/16, 1/8 between; A - 5 cols, 2 1/16, 1/8 between; C - 5 cols, 2 1/16, 1/8 between.
Commodity Consumption: Avg. Page Number Per Issue - Daily 14; widths 29; Newsprint Used - Metric Tons 200; Printing Ink Used - Black 6900; Printing Ink Used - Color 420; Printing Ink Used - Pages Printed 4364.
Equipment; Editorial Hardware – 5-Mk/4001.; Classified Hardware – 1-Mk/4001.; Layout Software – 2-COM/Powerview.; Production Equipment – 1-COM/2961, 1-COM/8400; Cameras – 1-Acti. PRESSROOM: Line 1 – 1-G/Community; Folders – 1-G/2:1.; Bundle tying machines – 1/Bu; Addressing machine – 1-/KR.; Business Hardware – 1-IMS/International

LONGMONT

DAILY TIMES-CALL

PO Box 299, Longmont, Colo., 80502-0299; gen tel (303) 776-2244; web site www.longmontfyi.com

TIMES-CALL

350 Terry St., Longmont, Colo., 80501-5440; gen tel (303) 776-2244; adv tel (303) 776-7440; ed tel (303) 776-2244; gen fax (303) 678-8615; adv fax (303) 774-8088; ed fax (303) 678-8615; ed e-mail opinion@times-call.com; news@times-call.com; web site www.timescall.com
Published: Mon, Tues, Wed, Thur, Fri, Sat, Sun
Weekday Frequency: m
Saturday Frequency: m
Circulation: 18,193; 18,193(sat); 19,911(sun)
Last Audit: ABC September 30, 2011
Price: 18.00/mo (mail); 216.00/yr (mail).
Advertising: Open inch rate $29.15
News services: AP, U.S. Suburban Press Inc., The Newspaper Network (TNN).
Politics: Independent. **Established:** 1871
Special Editions: Inside & Out (Apr); Longmont Magazine (Aug); Holiday Gifts (Dec); Bridal (Feb); Health Magazine (Jan); Fair & Rodeo (Jul); Health Directory (Jun); Progress (Mar); Graduation (May); Coupon Book (Monthly); Longmont Magazine (Nov); A Taste of Home (Oct); Boo
Special Weekly Sections: Faith (Fri); Schools (Mon); Business (S); Home & Real Estate Weekly (Sat); Outdoors (Thur); Pulse (Tues); Cuisine (Wed).
Magazines: Relish (Monthly); USA WEEKEND Magazine (S); American Profile (Sat).
Profile: Daily newspaper covering Boulder, Weld and Larimer Counties in Colorado.
Pres./Ed. ....Dean G. Lehman
Pub. ....Edward Lehman
Dir., Cor. Finance ....Tom Krough
Mgr., HR ....Deanna Riley
Adv. Dir. ....John DiMambro
Adv. Mgr., Display ....Penny Dille
Promos./Community Servs. Coord. Karen Friesner
NIE Coord. ....Cindy Piller
Circ. Dir., Cor. ....Maurice Elhart
Mng. Ed ....John Vahlenkamp
Bus. Ed. ....Tony Kindelspire
City Ed. ....Rob Spencer
Day Ed. ....Travis Pryor
Editorial Page Ed. ....Jenn Ooton
News Ed. ....K.J. Ritter
Chief Photographer ....Richard Hackett
Special Sections Ed. ....Kristi Ritter
Sports Ed. ....Brian Howell
Web Ed. ....Paula Aven Gladych
Mgmt. Info Servs. Mgr. ....Suzanne Barrett
Market Information: Split run; TMC.
Mechanical available: Offset; Black and 3 ROP colors; insert accepted; page cutoffs - 22 3/4.
Mechanical Specifications: Type page 11 1/4 x 21 1/4; E - 6 cols, 1 3/4, 1/8 between; A - 6 cols, 1 3/4, 1/8 between; C - 9 cols, 1 1/4, 1/8 between.
Commodity Consumption: Avg. Page Number Per Issue - Daily 41; Avg. Page Number Per Issue - Plates Used 168000; Avg. Page Number Per Issue - Saturday 41; Avg. Page Number Per Issue - Sunday 81; widths 34; Newsprint Used - Metric Tons 1772; Printing Ink Used - Black 28352; Print
Equipment EDITORIAL: Front-end Software – SCS/GN3, SCS/Tark Archive System.; Editorial Hardware – Dell/Windows 2000, Dell/Workstations; Editorial Equipment – AP/AdSend; Editorial Printers – ECR/4550 Knockouts, HP/LaserJet CLASSIFIED: Front-end Software – SCS/Classified/Admax.; Classified Hardware – Dell/Linux Servers, Dell/Windows 2000/XP; Classified Printers – HP/Laserjets DISPLAY: Ad make-up applications – Dell/Windows 2000/XP; Layout Software – SCS/Layout 8000.; Display Hardware – Dell/Linux; Display Printers – HP/LaserJets PRODUCTION: Pagination Software – SCS/GoodNews 3.; Production Equipment – 2-Burgess/Vacolux, Windows/2000; Cameras – C/Spartan III PRESSROOM: Line 1 – 9-G 1974 (4 units), 1975 (1 unit), 1976 (2 units), 1994 (1 unit); Press Drives – 1994; Folders – 1-G/Urbanite, 1. MAILROOM: Counter stackers – 2-QWI/400, QWI/350; Inserters and stuffers – GMA/SLS 2000 12:1; Bundle tying machines – 2-Samuel/NT 30, Power Strap/200; Addressing machine – VideoJet; Other equipment –Mc/Stitcher-Trimmer 4:1. BUSINESS COMPUTERS: Business Software – Microsoft Office XP, Open Office 1.03; Business Hardware – HP/3000 & 922LX

TIMES-CALL PUBLISHING CORP.

350 Terry St., Longmont, Colo., 80501; gen tel (303) 776-2244; gen fax (303) 776-0837

LOVELAND

DAILY REPORTER-HERALD

201 E. 5th St., Loveland, Colo., 80537; gen tel (970) 669-5050; gen fax (970) 667-1111; adv fax (970) 663-6892; ed fax (970) 667-1111; gen e-mail news@reporter-herald.com; adv e-mail temler@reporter-herald.com; ed e-mail news@reporter-herald.com; web site www.reporterherald.com

Published: Mon, Tues, Wed, Thur, Fri, Sat, Sun
Weekday Frequency: m
Saturday Frequency: m
Circulation: 15,494; 15,494(sat); 20,997(sun)
Last Audit: ABC September 30, 2011
Price: 9.85/mo, $18.00/mo (mail); 118.20/yr.
Advertising: Open inch rate $27.31
News services: AP, LAT-WP, TMS.
Politics: Independent.
Special Editions: Vacation Guide (Apr); Corn Roast (Aug); Community photo calendar (Dec); Making a Difference (Feb); Wedding (Jan); Loveland Snapshot (Jul); Tour of New Homes (Jun); Home and Garden How-To (Mar); Women in Business (May); Coupon Book (Monthly); Holiday Open
Special Weekly Sections: Auto Weekly (Fri); Neighbors (Mon); Comics (S); Realty Guide (Sat); Outpost (Thur); School Page (Tues); Berthoud Bulletin (Wed).
Magazines: Health Line (Monthly); USA WEEKEND Magazine (S); American Profile (Sat).
Pub. ....Edward Lehman
HR Coord. ....Marge Reiber
Adv. Dir. ....Linda Story
Mgr., Mktg./Promo. ....Linda Larsen
Circ. Mgr. ....John Ellis
Ed. ....Kenneth J. Amundson
Mng. Ed. ....Christine Kapperman
Editorial Page Ed. ....Kenneth J Amundson
Editorial Writer ....Dean G. Lehman
Librarian ....Linda Mitchell
Sports Ed. ....Mike Brohard
Online Mgr. ....Bill Schmich
Prodn. Creative Servs. Mgr. ....Dennis Book
Market Information: Split run; TMC.
Mechanical available: Offset; Black and 3 ROP colors; insert accepted - rotos; page cutoffs - 22 3/4.
Mechanical Specifications: Type page 11 5/8 x 21 1/2; E - 6 cols, 1 5/6, 1/8 between; A - 6 cols, 1 5/6, 1/8 between; C - 9 cols, 1 3/16, 1/8 between.
Commodity Consumption: Avg. Page Number Per Issue - Daily 28; Avg. Page Number Per Issue - Saturday 36; Avg. Page Number Per Issue - Sunday 40.
Equipment EDITORIAL: Front-end Software – Good News.; Editorial Hardware – Dell; Editorial Equipment – 1-APP/Mac II, Lf/AP Leaf Picture Desk, APP/Mac Quadra CLASSIFIED: Front-end Software – WebTerm X.; Classified Hardware – Dell DISPLAY: Ad make-up applications – WebTerm X; Layout Software – SCS/Class Pag.; Display Hardware – SCS, Dell; Cameras – AG.; Bundle tying machines – 1/Bu; Addressing machine – 1-/El.; Business Hardware – 1-HP/3000

LOVELAND PUBLISHING CO.

201 E. 5th St., Loveland, Colo., 80537; gen tel (970) 669-5050; gen fax (970) 667-1111

MONTROSE

THE MONTROSE DAILY PRESS

3684 N. Townsend Ave., Montrose, Colo., 81401; gen tel (970) 249-3444; adv tel (970) 249-3444; ed tel (970) 249-3444; gen fax (970) 249-3331; adv fax (970) 249-3331; ed fax (970) 249-2370; gen e-mail dailypress@montrosepress.com; adv e-mail ads@montrosepress.com; ed e-mail editor@montrosepress.com; web site www.montrosepress.com
Group: Wick Communications
Published: Tues, Wed, Thur, Fri, Sat, Sun
Weekday Frequency: m
Saturday Frequency: m
Circulation: 5,400; 5,400(sat); 5,400(sun)
Last Audit: Sworn March 31, 2008
Price: 9.00/mo; 115.00/yr (in state)
Advertising: Open inch rate $12.50
News services: AP.
Politics: Independent.
Not Published: Mondays
Own facility?: Y
Special Editions: January ....
Sun ....Year in review
Sun....Lifestyles

February....
Thur ....Home, Garden, Business Expo
Sat ....Answer Book

March....
Sat....Spring Sports Preview
Sat....Home & Garden w/Earth Day

April....
Sun ....Destination Montrose
Sun....Lifestyles

May....
Sat....Graduation Tab
Thur....Montrose County Fair Book

June....
Outlook editions....
Tues....Agriculture
Wed ....Community
Thurs ....Non-profits
Fri ....Health
Sat....Industry
Sun....Photo Expo

July....
Thur ....M. County Fair and Rodeo
Sun....Lifestyles

August....
Thur ....Olathe Sweet Corn
Sat ....Back to School
Thur....Fall Sports Preview

September ....
Sat....Best of the Valley

October ....
Sat ....Energy Guide
Sun ....Destination Montrose
Sun ....Lifestyle

November ....
Thur....Veterans Tab
Sat....Winter Sports Tab
Sun....Holiday Gift guide

Special Weekly Sections: Scene Magazine (Fridays), Focus (Sundays), Automotive & Real Estate (Friday)
Magazines: TV Showtime (Fri); Parade (Sun).
Adv. Dir. ....Tim Frates
Circ. Dir. ....Phil Ashley
Features Ed. ....Elaine Hale Jones
News Ed. ....Katharhynn Hydlberg
Sports Ed. ....Matt Lindberg
Prodn. Mgr., Mailroom ....Denny Haulman
Publisher ....Francis Wick
Managing Editor ....Mike Easterling
Market Information: ADS; TMC; Zoned editions.
Mechanical available: Offset; Black and 3 ROP colors; insert accepted - full or part run, quarter folded; page cutoffs - 21 1/2.
Mechanical Specifications: Type page 10 x 21; E - 6 cols, 2 1/16, 1/8 between; A - 6 cols, 2 1/16, 1/8 between; C - 8 cols, 1 1/2, 1/8 between.
Commodity Consumption: Avg. Page Number Per Issue - Daily 20; Avg. Page Number Per Issue - Plates Used 7000; Avg. Page Number Per Issue - Sunday 36
Equipment EDITORIAL: Front-end Software – QPS/QuarkXPress.; Editorial Hardware – APP/Imacs; Editorial Printers – Xante CLASSIFIED: Front-end Software – Baseview.; Classified Hardware – 2-Mk, APP/Imacs; Classified Printers – Xante DISPLAY: Ad make-up applications – QPS/QuarkXPress; Layout Software – APP/Imacs.; Production Equipment – Linotype-Hell/LaserWriter; Cameras – 1-Nu/2024, 1-AG; Scanners – Equipment ÂŒ QPS/QuarkXPress. PRESSROOM: Line 1 – 6-G/Community; Folders – 1; Reels and Stands – 6; Bundle tying machines – 2/Bu; Addressing machine – 1-St/1200.; Business Hardware – 2-RSK/TRS 80, 2-RSK/1000 HD, 2-IBM
Zip Codes served: 81401, 81402, 81403, 81425, 81432
Delivery method: Newsstand, Private Carrier, Racks

PRESS PUBLISHING CO.

535 S. 1st St., Montrose, Colo., 81401; gen tel (970) 249-3444; gen fax (970) 249-3331

PUEBLO

THE PUEBLO CHIEFTAIN

825 W. Sixth St., Pueblo, Colo., 81003; gen tel (719) 544-3520; adv tel (719) 544-3520; ed tel (719) 544-3520; gen fax (719) 542-3329; adv fax (719) 546-3235; gen e-mail pueblo@chieftain.com; adv e-mail chiefad@pueblo.com; classads@chieftain.com; ed e-mail newsroom@chieftain.com; web site www.chieftain.com
Published: Mon, Tues, Wed, Thur, Fri, Sat, Sun
Weekday Frequency: m
Saturday Frequency: m
Circulation: 43,071; 43,071(sat); 45,388(sun)
Last Audit: ABC September 30, 2011
Price: 11.95/mo
Advertising: Open inch rate $73.30
News services: AP, MCT, TMS.
Politics: 1868
Own facility?: Y
Special Editions: Colorado State Fair (Aug); Holiday Greetings (Dec); Graduation (Jun); Spring Home & Garden (Mar); Classroom Chieftain (May); Active Years, 50 & Above (Monthly); Winterfest (Nov); Generation X-tra (Quarterly); Fall Home Improvement (Sept).
Special Weekly Sections: Real Estate (Fri); Real Estate (S); Best Food Day (Wed).
Magazines: Relish (Monthly); Parade (S); TV Magazine (Sat).
Broadcast Affiliations: KOAA-TV-NBC; KRDO-TV-ABC; KKTV-TV-CBS; KRFX-FOX.
Gen. Mgr. ....Marvin Laut
Mgr., Bus. Office/Purchasing Agent Diane Tafoya
Adv. Dir., Mktg./Online Publishing Bernie Schutz
Adv. Mgr., Display ....Bob Hudson
Circ. Dir. ....Matt Butorac
Ed. ....Robert H. Rawlings
Mng. Ed., News ....Steve Henson
Mng. Ed., Prodn. ....Chris Woodka
Bus. Ed. ....Dennis Darrow
City Ed. ....Larry Lopez
Editorial Page Ed. ....Charles Campbell
Lifestyle Ed. ....Peter Strescino
Photo Dir. ....Chris McLean
Radio/Television Ed. ....Cheri Zanotelli
Sports Ed. ....Judy Hildner
Market Information: Split run; TMC.
Mechanical available: Offset; Black and 3 ROP colors; insert accepted; page cutoffs - 22.
Mechanical Specifications: Type page 13 x 21 1/2; E - 6 cols, 2 1/16, 1/8 between; A - 6 cols, 2 1/16, 1/8 between; C - 9 cols, 1 3/8, 1/16 between.
Commodity Consumption: Avg. Page Number Per Issue - Daily 34; Avg. Page Number Per Issue - Plates Used 38000; Avg. Page Number Per Issue - Sunday 56; widths 27; Newsprint Used - Metric Tons 5200; Printing Ink Used - Black 120000; Printing Ink Used - Color 20000; Printing Ink U
Equipment EDITORIAL: Front-end Software – Crosstalk.; Editorial Hardware – HI/PEN System, 23-HI, HI/PLS 8300, 5-HI/8860; Editorial Equipment – IBM/PC; Editorial Printers – HP/LaserJet II CLASSIFIED: Front-end Software – HI/CPS software.; Classified Hardware – HI 8300, 10-HI 8864; Classified Printers – Dataproducts B600 DISPLAY: Ad make-up applications – HI/PLS-SCS, PBS/AM; Layout Software – SCS/Layout 8000, PBS/AM.; Display Hardware – 3-HI/8860, 1-HI/8900, IBM/PS2, IBM/RS 6000; Display Printers – ALPS/P2100 PRODUCTION: Pagination Software – DTI.; Production Equipment – KFM, AG/Litex 26, Norscreen MS 250 PRESSROOM: Line 1 – 6-MAN/Roland uniset (single width) 32 couples 1996; Folders – 2-MAN/Roland Jaw; Pasters – 6; Press control system – MAN/Roland Pecom. MAILROOM: Counter stackers – 2-HL/Monitor, 3-HL/Dual Carrier; Inserters and stuffers – 2-HI/1372R; Bundle tying machines – 5-Sterling/Tying Machine; Addressing machine – VideoJet 4000; Other equipment –Stitcher-Trimmer, MM/Bravo T.; Business Hardware – 1-IBM/Sys 36, 1-IBM/5225, 1-Decision Data/6708, 4-IBM/PC, 1-IBM/RS6000, 19-Dell/PC
Delivery method: Mail, Newsstand, Private Carrier, Racks

STAR-JOURNAL PUBLISHING CORP.

PO Box 36, Pueblo, Colo., 81002; gen tel (719) 544-3520; gen fax (719) 542-3329; web site chieftain.com
Published: Mon, Tues, Wed, Thur, Fri, Sat, Sun
Weekday Frequency: m
Saturday Frequency: m
Circulation: 46,448; 46,448(sat); 48,228(sun)
Politics: 1868
Delivery method: Mail, Newsstand, Private Carrier, Racks

ROCKY FORD

ROCKY FORD DAILY GAZETTE

912 Elm Ave., Rocky Ford, Colo., 81067; gen tel (719) 254-3351; adv tel (719) 254-3351; ed tel (719) 254-3351; gen fax (719) 254-3354; adv fax (719) 254-3354; ed fax (719) 254-3354; gen e-mail news@rockyforddailygazette.com
Published: Mon, Tues, Wed, Thur, Fri
Weekday Frequency: e
Circulation: 3,013
Last Audit: October 1, 2001
Price: 5.00/mo; 60.00/yr (outside trade area).
Advertising: Open inch rate $5.85
Politics: Republican.
Not Published: New Year; Memorial Day; Independence Day; Labor Day; Thanksgiving; Christmas.
Special Weekly Sections: Best Religious Day (Fri); Best Sports Days (Mon); Best Area Communities Reach (Thur); Best Business Day (Tues); Best Food Days (Wed).
Magazines: Television (Fri).
Adv. Mgr. ....Laura Thompson
Circ. Dir. ....Pamela Griego
Prodn. Mgr., Pressroom ....J.R. Thompson
Mechanical available: Offset; Black and 3 ROP colors; insert accepted; page cutoffs - 22 3/4.
Mechanical Specifications: Type page 13 x 21; E - 6 cols, 2 1/16, 1/8 between; A - 6 cols, 2 1/16, 1/8 between; C - 6 cols, 2 1/16, 1/8 between.
Commodity Consumption: Avg. Page Number Per Issue - Daily 34.
Equipment EDITORIAL: Front-end Software – Microsoft/Word, Aldus/SuperPaint, Aldus/PageMaker.; Editorial Hardware – APP/Mac, APP/Power Mac; Editorial Printers – APP/Mac LaserWriter II NT, APP/Mac LaserWriter Plus, HP/LaserJet IV M; Classified Hardware – APP/Mac; Classified Equipment – Software ☐ Microsoft/Word. DISPLAY: Ad make-up applications – Aldus/PageMaker 6.0; Layout Software – APP/Mac.; Display Hardware – APP/Power Mac; Display Printers – Software ☐ Aldus/PageMaker 6.0 BUSINESS COMPUTERS: Business Software – Checkmark; Business Hardware – APP/Mac

SALIDA

THE MOUNTAIN MAIL

125 E. Second St., Salida, Colo., 81201; gen tel (719) 539-6691; gen fax (719) 539-6630; web site www.themountainmail.com
Published: Mon, Tues, Wed, Thur, Fri
Weekday Frequency: m
Circulation: 3,494
Price: 57.00/yr.
Advertising: Open inch rate $8.50
News services: Papert (Landon).
Not Published: Christmas.
Pub. ....Merle Baranczyk
Admin. Dir. ....Karen Hasselbrink
Adv. Mgr. ....Vicki Vigil
Circ. Mgr. ....Sandra Christensen
Mng. Ed. ....Paul Goetz

Sports Ed. ....Kevin Hoffman
Online Contact ....Holly Russell
Online Mgr. ....Joerge Hasselbrink
Prodn. Mgr. ....Morris Christensen
Market Information: TMC.
Mechanical available: Offset; Black and 2 ROP colors; insert accepted; page cutoffs - 15 3/4.
Mechanical Specifications: Type page 10 1/2 x 15 3/4; E - 5 cols, 2, 1/8 between; A - 5 cols, 2, 1/8 between; C - 5 cols, 2, 1/8 between.
Commodity Consumption: Avg. Page Number Per Issue - Daily 16; Avg. Page Number Per Issue - Plates Used 1500; widths 33 1/2; Newsprint Used - Metric Tons 215; Newsprint Used - Short Tons 94; Printing Ink Used - Black 2000; Printing Ink Used - Color 100; Printing Ink Used - Page
Equipment EDITORIAL: Front-end Software – QPS/QuarkXPress 3.33, Adobe/Photoshop 5.0, Adobe/Illustrator 5.0.; Editorial Hardware – APP/Mac; Editorial Printers – Xante/8100, Xante/8200; Classified Hardware – 2-APP/Mac. DISPLAY: Ad make-up applications – QPS/QuarkXPress; Layout Software – 2-APP/Mac.; Display Hardware – APP/Macs PRODUCTION: Pagination Software – QPS/QuarkXPress 3.31.; Production Equipment – 2-APP/Mac; Cameras – 1-Acti/183; Scanners – LaCie/Silver Scanner II, Polaroid/SprintScan PRESSROOM: Line 1 – 7-G/Community; Folders – 1; Addressing machine – 2/Wm. BUSINESS COMPUTERS: Business Software – Synaptic; Business Hardware – EPS

STEAMBOAT SPRINGS

STEAMBOAT PILOT & TODAY

1901 Curve Plz., Steamboat Springs, Colo., 80487; gen tel (970) 879-1502; adv tel (970) 871-4218; ed tel (970) 871-4221; oth tel (970) 871-4202; gen fax (970) 879-2888; gen e-mail sstanford@SteamboatToday.com; adv e-mail advertising@SteamboatToday.com; ed e-mail editor@SteamboatToday.com; web site www.steamboattoday.com
Group: WorldWest LLC
Published: Mon, Tues, Wed, Thur, Fri, Sat, Sun
Weekday Frequency: m
Saturday Frequency: m
Circulation: ; 5,600(sun)
Last Audit: Sworn November 25, 2008
Advertising: Open inch rate $13.45
Insert rate: $75.00/M.
Politics: 1884
Advertising not accepted: N
Own facility?: Y
Magazines: At Home in Steamboat Springs
Colorado Hunter
Explore Steamboat
Profile: WorldWest, LLC
COO, The World Company ....Suzanne Schlicht
General Manager ....Scott Stanford
Circ. Mgr. ....Steve Balgenorth
Mechanical Specifications: Type page 14 x 21 1/2; E - 6 cols, 2 1/8, 1/4 between; A - 6 cols, 2 1/8, 1/4 between; C - 6 cols, 2 1/8, 1/4 between.
Delivery method: Racks

STEAMBOAT TODAY

1901 Curve Plz., Steamboat Springs, Colo., 80487; gen tel (970) 879-1502; adv tel (970) 879-1502; ed tel (970) 879-1502; gen fax (970) 879-2888; adv fax (970) 879-2888; ed fax (970) 879-2888; gen e-mail info@steamboatpilot.com; web site www.steamboatpilot.com
Published: Mon, Tues, Wed, Thur, Fri, Sat
Weekday Frequency: m
Saturday Frequency: m
Circulation: 9,523; 7,768(sat)
Last Audit: March 31, 2008
Advertising: Open inch rate $11.25
News services: AP.
Special Weekly Sections: 4 Points (Fri).
Magazines: American Profile (Sat).
Pub ....Suzanne Schlicht
Circ. Dir. ....Steve Balgenorth
Ed. ....Brent Boyer
City Ed. ....Mike Lawrence
News Ed. ....Allison Miriani
Sports Ed./Photographer ....John Russell
Online Devel. Mgr. ....Tyler Jacobs
Internet Servs. Mgr. ....Scott Stanford
Mechanical available: Offset; Black and 1 ROP colors; insert accepted.
Mechanical Specifications: Type page 10 1/2 x 14; E - 4 cols, between; A - 4 cols, between; C - 4 cols, between.
Commodity Consumption: Avg. Page Number Per Issue - Daily 20.
Equipment EDITORIAL: Front-end Software – Claris/Works, QPS/QuarkXPress, APP/Mac Laserwriter II.; Editorial Hardware – APP/Power Mac; Editorial Printers – HP/LaserJet CLASSIFIED: Front-end Software – DOS.; Classified Hardware – IBM DISPLAY: Ad make-up applications – QPS/QuarkXPress, Adobe/Illustrator, Adobe/Photoshop; Layout Software – APP/Power Mac.; Display Hardware – APP/Power Mac; Display Printers – HP/LaserJet, Xante PRODUCTION: Pagination Software – QPS/QuarkXPress 4.0.; Production Equipment – Ultra/Plus Flip Top, Polaroid/SprintScan; Cameras – Kk/50603 Image Maker PRESSROOM: Line 1 – 5-G/Community double width 1992; Press Drives – Fin/902.; Bundle tying machines – Akebono.

STERLING

JOURNAL-ADVOCATE

504 N. Third St., Sterling, Colo., 80751; gen tel (970) 522-1990; adv tel (970) 522-1990; ed tel (970) 522-1990; gen fax (970) 522-2320; adv fax (970) 522-2320; ed fax (970) 522-2320; web site www.journal-advocate.com
Published: Mon, Tues, Wed, Thur, Fri, Sat, Sun
Weekday Frequency: e
Saturday Frequency: m
Circulation: 3,723; 3,723(sat)
Last Audit: September 30, 2009
Price: 8.50/mo; 78.00/yr.
Advertising: Open inch rate $13.90
News services: AP.
Politics: Independent. **Established:** 1884
Advertising not accepted: Adoptions.
Not Published: New Year; Memorial Day; Independence Day; Labor Day; Thanksgiving; Christmas.
Special Editions: Rodeo & Fair (Aug); Christmas Greetings (Dec); Profiles (Feb); Progress (Mar); Travel/Tourism (May); Newcomers (Nov).
Special Weekly Sections: Agriculture (Fri); Television (Sat); Entertainment (Thur); Lifestyles (Tues); Food (Wed).
Magazines: American Profile (Sat).
Pub. ....David McClain
Bus. Mgr. ....Julie Tonsing
Adv. Dir. ....Sharon Friedlander
Ed. ....Forrest Hershberger
News Ed. ....Sara Waite
Regl. Ed. ....Judy Debus
Prodn. Dir. ....Michael Foster
Pre Press Mgr. ....Duane Miles
Market Information: ADS; Split run; TMC; Zoned editions.
Mechanical available: Offset; Black and 3 ROP colors; insert accepted - product samples, paper bags; page cutoffs - 22 3/4.
Mechanical Specifications: Type page 12 x 21 1/2; E - 6 cols, 1 5/6, 1/8 between; A - 6 cols, 1 5/6, 1/8 between; C - 8 cols, 1 1/3, 1/8 between.
Commodity Consumption: Avg. Page Number Per Issue - Daily 16; Avg. Page Number Per Issue - Saturday 16; widths 25; Newsprint Used - Short Tons 240.
Equipment EDITORIAL: Front-end Software – Baseview/NewsEdit, QPS/QuarkXPress.; Editorial Hardware – APP/Mac, APP/Power Mac; Editorial Equipment – Nikon/LS 2000, Minolta/QuickScan; Editorial Printers – HP/LaserJet 2100, Xante/1200dpi, Xante/36 CLASSIFIED: Front-end Software – Baseview.; Classified Hardware – APP/Mac; Classified Printers – APP/Mac ImageWriter, HP/LaserJet 2100 DISPLAY: Ad make-up applications – QPS/QuarkXPress, Multi-Ad/Creator; Layout Software – APP/Mac II.; Display Hardware – APP/Mac; Display Printers – APP/Mac, Xante/1200dpi, HP/LaserJet 2100; Production Equipment – Nu, HP/LaserJet 2100, Xante/8200, Xante/1200dp, Konica/6000 EV-jetsetter; Cameras – 1-Acti/125. PRESSROOM: Line 1 – 6-G/Community Offset (24 Page/Broadsheet Capacity).; Bundle tying machines – 2/Bu; Addressing machine – Dispensa-Matic. BUSINESS COMPUTERS: Business Software – Nomads/Listmaster; Business Hardware – IBM

TELLURIDE

TELLURIDE DAILY PLANET

307 E. Colorado Ave., Telluride, Colo., 81435; gen tel (970) 728-9788; gen fax (970) 728-8061; adv e-mail advertising@tellurideplanet.com; ed e-mail editor@tellurideplanet.com; web site www.telluridenews.com
Published: Mon, Tues, Wed, Thur, Fri
Weekday Frequency: m
Circulation: 3,841
Last Audit: September 30, 1997
Price: 29.00/yr.
Advertising: Open inch rate $12.72
Note: Printed at Montrose, CO. For detailed production and mechanical specifications, refer to Montrose Daily Press listing.
Magazines: American Profile (Weekly).
Pub. ....Andrew Mirrington
Adv. Mgr. ....Maureen Pelisson
Retail Adv. ....Nick LeClaire
Ed. ....Matthew Beaudin
Asst. Ed. ....Katie Klingsporn
Photo Ed. ....Erin Raley
Prodn. Mgr. ....Kevin Deleu

TRINIDAD

THE CHRONICLE-NEWS

200 W. Church St., Trinidad, Colo., 81082; gen tel (719) 846-3311; gen fax (719) 846-3612; gen e-mail news@trinidadchronicle-news.com; web site www.thechronicle-news.com
Published: Mon, Tues, Wed, Thur, Fri
Weekday Frequency: e
Circulation: 3,275
Last Audit: September 30, 2001
Price: 44.00/yr (outside county), $42.00/yr (in county).
Advertising: Open inch rate $11.58
News services: AP.
Politics: Independent.
Not Published: Thanksgiving; Christmas.
Special Editions: Rodeo (Other).
Special Weekly Sections: TV Entertainment (Thur).
Magazines: Parade (Weekly).
Pub ....Aileen Hood
Prodn. Mgr. ....Sheila Hamlan
Market Information: Split run; TMC.
Mechanical available: Offset; Black and 1 ROP colors; insert accepted; page cutoffs - 22 3/4.
Mechanical Specifications: Type page 13 x 22; E - 6 cols, 2 1/16, 1/8 between; A - 6 cols, 2 1/16, 1/8 between; C - 8 cols, 1 1/2, 1/8 between.
Commodity Consumption: Avg. Page Number Per Issue - Daily 8; widths 13 3/4; Newsprint Used - Short Tons 44; Printing Ink Used - Black 1800; Printing Ink Used - Color 50.
Equipment EDITORIAL: Front-end Software – QPS/QuarkXPress 3.32.; Editorial Hardware – APP/Power Mac 8500; Editorial Printers – Xante/Accel-a-Writer 8200 CLASSIFIED: Front-end Software – Baseview/Class Manager, FoxBase.; Classified Hardware – APP/Mac Quadra 630; Classified Printers – Xante/Accel-a-Writer 8200 DISPLAY: Ad make-up applications – QPS/QuarkXPress 3.32, Adobe/Photoshop 3.2, Adobe/Illustrator.; Display Hardware – APP/Power Mac 8100; Display Printers – Xante/Accel-a-Writer 8200 PRODUCTION: Pagination Software – QPS/QuarkXPress 3.32.; Production Equipment – 1-Nu; Cameras – 1-R/500 PRESSROOM: Line 1 – 2-KP/Color King.; Addressing machine – 1/Am.

VAIL

VAIL DAILY

40780 US Hwy. 6 & 24, Vail, Colo., 81658-0081; gen tel (970) 949-0555; adv tel (970) 949-0555; ed tel (970) 949-0555; gen fax (970) 949-7096; adv fax (970) 949-7094; ed fax (970) 949-7096; gen e-mail publisher@vaildaily.com; ed e-mail editor@vaildaily.com; web site www.vaildaily.com
Published: Mon, Tues, Wed, Thur, Fri, Sat, Sun
Weekday Frequency: m
Saturday Frequency: m
Circulation: 10,525; 10,525(sat); 9,332(sun)
Last Audit: September 30, 2000
Price: 30.00/yr (S only).
Advertising: Open inch rate $13.65
News services: AP.
Special Editions: Taste of Vail (Apr); Rocky Mtn. Wedding Guide (Feb); Best of the Vail Valley (Jan); Eagle County Rodeo Program (Jul); High Country Homestyle (Jun); Vail Valley Summertime (May); Vail Valley Holiday Guide (Nov).
Special Weekly Sections: Mountain Homes & Properties Real Estate (S); Religion (Sat); Education (Thur); The Marketplace (Tues); Food & Wine (Wed).
Bus. Mgr. ....Rob Tramazo
Adv. Dir. ....Lance Fahrney
Sales Mgr. ....Graham Danzoll
Mktg. Dir. ....Mark Bricklin
Circ. Mgr. ....Kip Tingle
Ed./Pub. ....Don Rogers
Mng. Ed. ....Matt Zalaznick
Asst. Mng. Ed. ....Edward Stoner
Arts/Entertainment Ed. ....Caramie Schnell
Bus. Ed. ....Scott Miller
Community Ed. ....Lauren Glendenning
Sports Ed. ....Chris Freud
Prodn. Mgr., Press ....Jim Hemig
Prodn. Mgr., Pre Press ....Tommy Kubitsky
Mechanical available: Offset; Black and 3 ROP colors; insert accepted; page cutoffs - 22 3/4.
Mechanical Specifications: Type page 10 2/3 x 16; E - 5 cols, 2, 1/6 between; A - 5 cols, 2, 1/6 between; C - 7 cols, 1 2/5, 1/6 between.
Commodity Consumption: Avg. Page Number Per Issue - Daily 54; Avg. Page Number Per Issue - Saturday 54; Avg. Page Number Per Issue - Sunday 90; widths 33 1/2; Printing Ink Used - Black 5000; Printing Ink Used - Color 250.
Equipment EDITORIAL: Front-end Software – Baseview.; Editorial Hardware – APP/Mac; Editorial Printers – APP/Mac LaserWriter CLASSIFIED: Front-end Software – Baseview.; Classified Hardware – PC, APP/Mac; Classified Printers – HP DISPLAY: Ad make-up applications – QPS/QuarkXPress, Adobe.; Display Hardware – APP/Mac; Display Printers – APP/Mac LaserPrinter, HP PRODUCTION: Pagination Software – MEI/ALS 2.0.; Production Equipment – Pre Press/Panther Plus; Cameras – AG; Scanners – HP PRESSROOM: Line 1 – 10-KP/News King 1985; Folders – 1-KP/KJ-8. MAILROOM: Counter stackers – HL Monitors; Inserters and stuffers – MM; Bundle tying machines – MLN.; Business Hardware – PBS

CONNECTICUT

BRIDGEPORT

CONNECTICUT POST

410 State St., Bridgeport, Conn., 06604; gen tel (203) 333-0161; adv tel (203) 330-6236; ed tel (203) 330-6384; gen fax (203) 336-3373; adv fax (203) 336-3373; ed fax (203) 367-8158; ed e-mail jsmith@ctpost.com; web site www.connpost.com
Published: Mon, Tues, Wed, Thur, Fri, Sat, Sun
Weekday Frequency: m
Saturday Frequency: m
Circulation: 48,661; 33,573(sat); 73,000(sun)
Last Audit: ABC September 30, 2011
Price: 4.50/wk.
Advertising: Open inch rate $132.90
News services: AP, MCT, LAT-WP, CNS, NYT, SHNS, TMS.
Politics: Independent.
Special Editions: Summer Education (Apr); Higher Education (Aug); Holiday Gift Guide 2 (Dec); Bact to School/College (Fall); President's Day Auto (Feb); Education (Jan); Retirement Options (Jul); Trumbull Day (Jun); New York Auto Show (Mar); Stratford Day (May); Christmas
Special Weekly Sections: Auto/Truck (Fri); Seniors (Mon); Arts/Theater (S); Religion (Sat); Preview (Thur).
Magazines: Preview/Entertainment Guide (Fri); Relish (Monthly); USA WEEKEND Magazine (S); Parade (Weekly).
Pub. .... John Geauguscine
CFO .... Lance Deda
Mgr., HR .... Sharon C. Ferguson
Adv. Dir. .... Elliott Huron
Adv. Mgr., Art Servs. .... George Zariff
Adv. Mgr., Classified .... Nancy Toth
Adv. Mgr., Retail .... Kim Boath
Adv. Mgr., Nat'l .... Dorothy Cicerro
Circ. Dir. .... John Truitt
Ed. .... Thomas Baden
Asst. Mng. Ed., Prodn. .... Todd Hollis
Editorial Page Ed. .... Michael Daly
Features Ed. .... Sev Rinaldi
Metro Ed. .... John Schwing
Photo/Graphics Ed. .... Cathy Zuraw
Sports Ed. .... Gary Rogo
State News Ed. .... Anna Amato
Facility Mgr. .... James Shay
IT Dir. .... Robert Walsh
Online Mgr. .... Carol Dauber
Market Information: Split run; TMC; Zoned editions.
Mechanical available: Offset; Black and 3 ROP colors; insert accepted; page cutoffs - 21 1/2.
Mechanical Specifications: Type page 11 5/8 x 20 1/4; E - 6 cols, 1 5/6, 1/8 between; A - 6 cols, 1 5/6, 1/8 between; C - 10 cols, 1 2/25, 1/16 between.
Commodity Consumption: Avg. Page Number Per Issue - Daily 46; Avg. Page Number Per Issue - Plates Used 95000; Avg. Page Number Per Issue - Sunday 96; widths 12 1/2; Newsprint Used - Metric Tons 9682; Newsprint Used - Short Tons 10675; Printing Ink Used - Black 187880; Printing
Equipment EDITORIAL: Front-end Software – Digital/3000 Alpha Chip, QPS/QuarkXPress 3.3, AT/Dewarview 2.1.; Editorial Hardware – Digital/3000 Alpha Chip; Editorial Printers – HP/LaserJet IV M, AU/APS Broadsheet CLASSIFIED: Front-end Software – AT.; Classified Hardware – Digital/3000 Alpha Chip; Classified Printers – Epson DISPLAY: Ad make-up applications – Multi-Ad; Layout Software – Managing Editor/ALS.; Display Hardware – DEC/VAX 6310, III/4700A; Display Printers – DEC/LP25, DEC/LP27, Genicom PRODUCTION: Pagination Software – Dewar/View 2.1, Computext/CompoClass.; Production Equipment – 4-LE, 2-Digital/RIP, III/3850; Cameras – 2-C/Spartan III; Scanners – Epson PRESSROOM: Line 1 – 9-G/Metro offset (5 half decks); Folders – 2-G/3:2; Pasters – 11 MAILROOM: Counter stackers – 3-HL/Monitor HTs, 1-HL/Dual Carrier; Inserters and stuffers – 2-GMA/SLS 1000 18:1; Bundle tying machines – 4-OVL/JP40, 1-OVL/415, 1-MLN/EE.; Audio Hardware – City Line, Brite Voice Systems BUSINESS COMPUTERS: Business Software – CJ; Business Hardware – 2-DEC/VAX, III/6310, III/4700A

BRISTOL

THE BRISTOL PRESS

99 Main St., Bristol, Conn., 06010-6541; gen tel (860) 584-0501; ed tel (860) 585-9283; gen fax (860) 584-2192; ed e-mail editor@bristolpress.com; web site www.bristolpress.com
Group: U.S. Suburban Press, Inc.
Published: Mon, Tues, Wed, Thur, Fri, Sat
Weekday Frequency: m
Saturday Frequency: m
Circulation: 5,955; 5,955(sat)
Last Audit: ABC September 30, 2011
Price: 174.20/yr.
Advertising: Open inch rate $42.26
News services: AP.
Politics: Independent. **Established:** 1871
Note: The Bristol Press shares a combined Sunday edition, The Herald Press, with The Middletown Press (m) and (New Britain) Herald (e). See the Herald listing for circulation.
Special Editions: Home Improvement (Apr); Back-to-School (Aug); Holiday Celebration (Dec); Home Show (Feb); Bridal (Jan); Bridal (Jun); Business & Industry Review (Mar); Summertime (May); Gift Guide (Nov); Home Improvement (Oct).
Special Weekly Sections: Family Life (Mon); Religion (Sat); Tempo (Thur); Health (Tues); Food (Wed).
Pub. .... Mike Schroeder
Dir., HR .... Robyn Roy
Adv. Dir. .... Nancy Frede
Adv. Mgr., Classified .... Jody Skomars
Exec. Ed. .... James Smith
City Ed. .... Erin King
Editorial Page Ed. .... William Sarno
Librarian .... Virginia Rogers
Photo Ed. .... Michael Orazzi
Political Ed. .... Steve Collins
Religion Ed. .... Tim Dumont
Sports Ed. .... Mike Blais
Women's Ed. .... Maureen Hamel
Prodn. Mgr., Pre Press .... James Bousquet
Market Information: TMC.
Mechanical available: Offset; Black and 3 ROP colors; insert accepted; page cutoffs - 22 3/4.
Mechanical Specifications: Type page 12 x 21 1/2; E - 6 cols, 2 1/16, 1/8 between; A - 6 cols, 2 1/16, 1/8 between; C - 10 cols, 1 3/8, 1/8 between.
Commodity Consumption: Avg. Page Number Per Issue - Daily 24; Avg. Page Number Per Issue - Plates Used 11800; Avg. Page Number Per Issue - Saturday 32; widths 25; Newsprint Used - Short Tons 980; Printing Ink Used - Black 3700; Printing Ink Used - Color 820; Printing Ink Used
Equipment EDITORIAL: Front-end Software – DDS/622, Microsoft/Windows, Novell, CNI/Database.; Editorial Hardware – 17-Pentium/486; Editorial Printers – Xante/Accel-a-Writer 8200 CLASSIFIED: Front-end Software – AT.; Classified Hardware – ALR/PC 486; Classified Equipment – QMS/2210 Printer DISPLAY: Ad make-up applications – Multi-Ad; Display Hardware – 6-APP/Mac cx, APP/Mac ci, APP/Mac Classic, 1-APP/Mac SE; Display Printers – NewGen/660B PRODUCTION: Pagination Software – QPS/QuarkXPress 3.32.; Production Equipment – 24-SQ, C/Spartan III; Cameras – C/Spartan II, ECR/8400 Autokon II, AG/Repromaster 2000 BUSINESS COMPUTERS: Business Software – CJ, INSI; Business Hardware – HP/3000

DANBURY

THE NEWS-TIMES

333 Main St., Danbury, Conn., 06810; gen tel (203) 744-5100; adv tel (203) 744-5100; ed tel (203) 731-3347; adv fax (203) 792-4211; ed fax (203) 792-8730; ed e-mail editor@newstimes.com; web site www.newstimes.com
Group: Hearst
Published: Mon, Tues, Wed, Thur, Fri, Sat, Sun
Weekday Frequency: m
Saturday Frequency: m
Circulation: 18,804; 13,795(sat); 30,545(sun)
Last Audit: ABC September 30, 2011
Price: $364.00/yr
Advertising: Open inch rate $52.40
News services: AP, DJ, MCT, ONS.
Politics: Independent. **Established:** 1883
Own facility?: Y
Special Editions: Real Estate Showcase (Monthly); Inside Business (Quarterly).
Special Weekly Sections: Weekend Entertainment Guide (Fri); Sports Plus (Mon); Cookbook (S); Religion Page (Sat); Business Plus (Thur); Food (Wed).
Magazines: Relish (Monthly); Parade (S).
Circulation Opertaions Manager .... David Parks
Human Resources Manager .... Cheri Panzica
Editor .... Art Cummings
Entertainment Ed. .... Linda Tuccio-Koonz
IT Help Desk .... Rich Joudy
Prodn. Mgr., Pre Press .... Nicole London
Publisher .... Shawn Palmer
Multimedia Sales Director .... Kelly Tremaine
Multimedia Sales Manager .... Loraine Marshall
Director of Operations .... Ron Darr
Managing Editor .... Jacqueline Smith
Bus. Mgr. .... Brian Jenkinsen
Design Ed. .... Kevin Hudson
Sports Ed. .... Jason Sonski
Webmaster .... Sean Clarke
Market Information: TMC.
Mechanical available: Offset; Black and 4 ROP colors; insert accepted - mini tabs, cards, merchandise; page cutoffs - 22 3/4.
Mechanical Specifications: Type page 13 x 21; E - 6 cols, 2 1/16, 1/8 between; A - 6 cols, 2 1/16, 1/8 between; C - 9 cols, 1 3/8, 1/16 between.
Commodity Consumption: Avg. Page Number Per Issue - Daily 40; Avg. Page Number Per Issue - Plates Used 80000; Avg. Page Number Per Issue - Sunday 72; widths 40 1/2; Newsprint Used - Metric Tons 5000; Printing Ink Used - Black 144000; Printing Ink Used - Color 9000; Printing In
Equipment; Editorial Hardware – AT, Dewar/View. DISPLAY: Ad make-up applications – Adobe/Photoshop; Layout Software – MEI/ALS.; Display Hardware – PC; Display Printers – HP PRODUCTION: Pagination Software – AT.; Production Equipment – 2-ECR/Knockout 4050, AG/Accuset 1000; Cameras – 1-C/Spartan II MAILROOM: Counter stackers – QWI; Inserters and stuffers – 14-SCS/2000; Bundle tying machines – 2/OVL; Addressing machine – Prism.; Business Hardware – IBM/AS-400

GREENWICH

GREENWICH TIME

1455 E. Putnam Ave., Ste. 101, Greenwich, Conn., 06830; gen tel (203) 625-4400; adv tel (203) 964-2425; ed tel (203) 625-4444; gen fax (203) 625-4419; adv fax (203) 964-2278; gen e-mail letters.greenwichtime@scni.com; web site www.greenwichtime.com
Group: Heast Media Services
Published: Mon, Tues, Wed, Thur, Fri, Sat, Sun
Weekday Frequency: m
Saturday Frequency: m
Circulation: 7,061; 5,578(sat); 10,370(sun)
Last Audit: ABC September 30, 2011
Price: 4.20/wk; 16.80/mo; 184.60/yr.
News services: AP, LAT-WP, MCT.
Politics: Independent. **Established:** 1877
Note: Printed at the Connecticut Post Plant. For detailed mechanical equipment information, see the Stamford Advocate listing. Advertising is sold in combination with the Stamford Advocate (mS) for $80.80(d) and $89.70(S). Individual newspaper rates not made a
Advertising not accepted: Y
Not Published: New Year; Christmas.
Own facility?: N
Special Editions: New York Auto Show (Apr); Survey of Education (Aug); Great Gift Ideas (Dec); Cruise/Guide (Feb); Weddings (Jan); Travel (Jul); Water, Water, Water (Jun); Home (Mar); New England Vacations (May); Holiday Countdown (Nov); Kitchen & Bath (Oct); Bahamas Trave
Special Weekly Sections: Weekend (Fri); Family Room (Mon); Travel (S); Life & Style (Thur); Health (Tues); Food (Wed).
Magazines: Parade (S).
Profile: Local community newspaper
Publisher .... Michelle McAbee
Editor .... David McCumber
Sports Editor .... Chris McNamee
Vice Pres. Operations .... Craig Allen
Prodn. Mgr., Pre Press .... Dennis Tidrick
Group Publisher .... John DeAugustine
Business Editor .... Stephanie Borise
Managing Editor .... Albert Yuravich
Market Information: Split run; TMC; Zoned editions.
Mechanical available: Offset; Black and 3 ROP colors; insert accepted; page cutoffs - 22 3/4.
Mechanical Specifications: Type page 12 x 21 1/2; E - 6 cols, 1 7/8, 1/6 between; A - 6 cols, 1 7/8, 1/6 between; C - 10 cols, 1 7/8, 1/6 between.
Commodity Consumption: Avg. Page Number Per Issue - Daily 37; Avg. Page Number Per Issue - Plates Used 18000; Avg. Page Number Per Issue - Saturday 20; Avg. Page Number Per Issue - Sunday 104; widths 37 1/2; Newsprint Used - Metric Tons 1500; Printing Ink Used - Black 35505; P
Equipment EDITORIAL: Front-end Software – QPS/QuarkXPress, Adobe/Photoshop, Baseview/Newsedit Pro IQUE, Adobe/Illustrator.; Editorial Hardware – 30-APP/Mac; Editorial Equipment – Lf/AP Leaf Picture Desk, APP/Mac, Kk/Scanners; Editorial Printers – Graphic Enterprises/PS 3, III/3850 CLASSIFIED: Front-end Software – DTI/Class Speed, Baseview/Ad Manager, Plan Builder.; Classified Hardware – 3-APP/Mac G3, DTI/Enterprise 450; Classified Printers – AII/3850, HP/4050 DISPLAY: Ad make-up applications – Multi-Ad/Creator, QPS/QuarkXPress; Layout Software – 13-APP/Mac, AII/SQL, Baseview.; Display Hardware – APP/Mac; Display Printers – APP/Mac LaserWriters, Graphic Enterprises/PS 3; Production Equipment – 2-Nu/Flip Top, 2-WL/38D; Scanners – Kk/Scanner, 2-Linotype-Hell.; Folders – 2; Pasters – 9-MEG/Automatic; Reels and Stands – MEG. MAILROOM: Counter stackers – 1-QWI/3500, 1-QWI/3500, 1/QWI; Inserters and stuffers – 1-HI/1472; Bundle tying machines – 4-OVL/JP40; Addressing machine – 2-KR/215, 1-Barstrom/In-Line; Other equipment –HI/Stitcher-Trimmer.; Business Hardware – 1-DEC/VAX 4100, CJ
Zip Codes served: 06830, 06831, 06807, 06870, 06878
Delivery method: Mail, Newsstand, Private Carrier, Racks

HARTFORD

THE HARTFORD COURANT

285 Broad St., Hartford, Conn., 06115-3785; gen tel (860) 241-6200; adv tel (860) 241-6221; ed tel (860) 241-6484; gen fax (860) 241-3863; adv fax (860) 241-3864; ed fax (860) 241-3865; gen e-mail letters@courant.com; adv e-mail info@courant.com; ed e-mail news@courant.com; web site www.hartford-courant.com; www.courant.com
Group: Metro Newspaper Advertising Services,

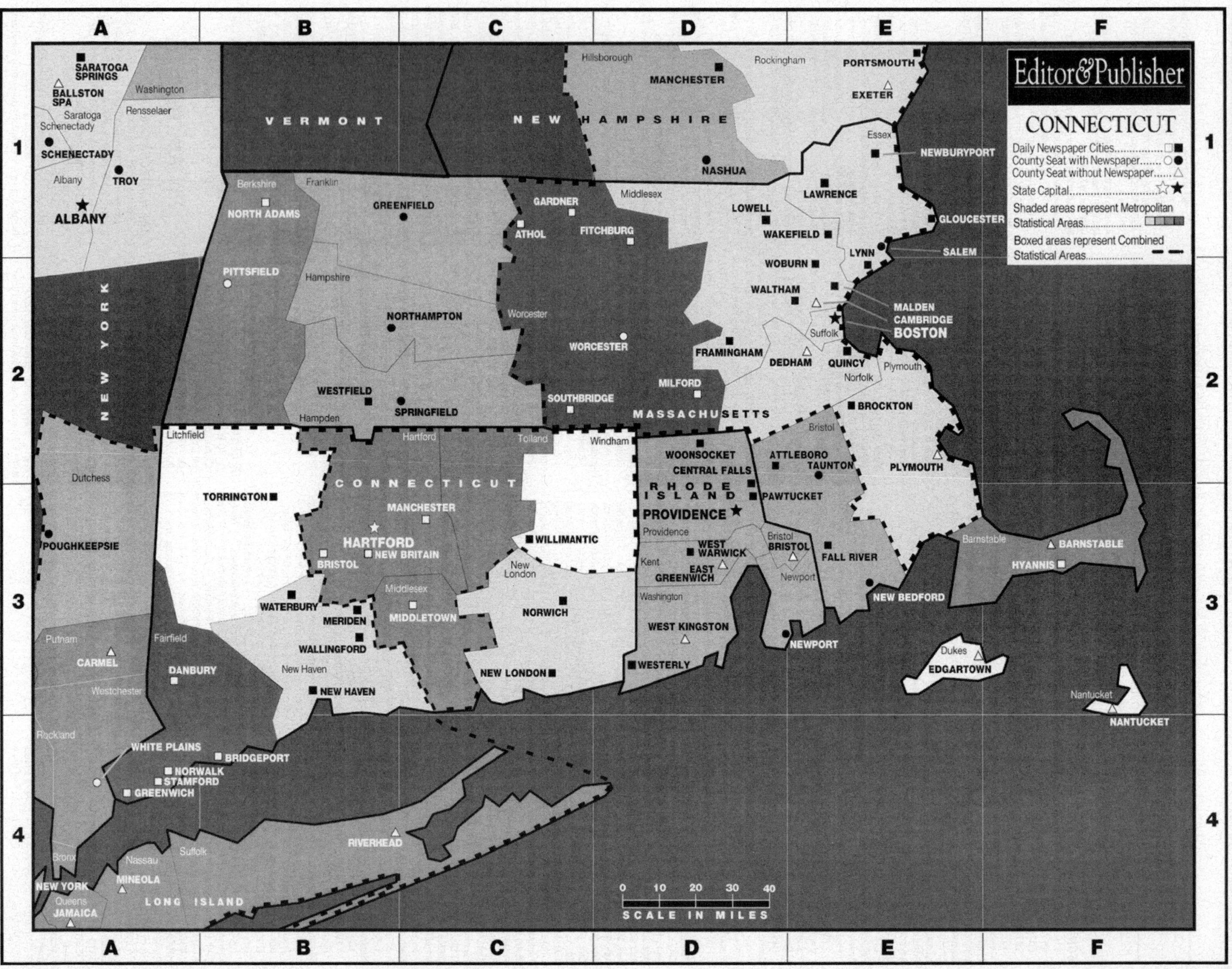
Editor&Publisher
CONNECTICUT
Daily Newspaper Cities
County Seat with Newspaper
County Seat without Newspaper
State Capital
Shaded areas represent Metropolitan Statistical Areas
Boxed areas represent Combined Statistical Areas
VERMONT
NEW HAMPSHIRE
NEW YORK
MASSACHUSETTS
CONNECTICUT
RHODE ISLAND
LONG ISLAND
SARATOGA SPRINGS
BALLSTON SPA
Washington
Saratoga
Rensselaer
Schenectady
SCHENECTADY
Albany
TROY
ALBANY
Hillsborough
MANCHESTER
Rockingham
PORTSMOUTH
EXETER
NASHUA
Essex
NEWBURYPORT
Berkshire
Franklin
NORTH ADAMS
GREENFIELD
GARDNER
ATHOL
FITCHBURG
Middlesex
LOWELL
LAWRENCE
WAKEFIELD
GLOUCESTER
LYNN
SALEM
WOBURN
PITTSFIELD
Hampshire
WALTHAM
MALDEN
CAMBRIDGE
BOSTON
Suffolk
NORTHAMPTON
Worcester
WORCESTER
FRAMINGHAM
DEDHAM
QUINCY
Plymouth
Norfolk
MILFORD
WESTFIELD
SPRINGFIELD
SOUTHBRIDGE
Hampden
BROCKTON
Litchfield
Hartford
Tolland
Windham
Bristol
WOONSOCKET
CENTRAL FALLS
ATTLEBORO
TAUNTON
PLYMOUTH
Dutchess
TORRINGTON
PAWTUCKET
PROVIDENCE
Providence
MANCHESTER
HARTFORD
BRISTOL
NEW BRITAIN
WILLIMANTIC
POUGHKEEPSIE
WEST WARWICK
Kent
EAST GREENWICH
New London
Bristol
BRISTOL
Newport
FALL RIVER
Barnstable
BARNSTABLE
HYANNIS
Middlesex
MIDDLETOWN
WATERBURY
MERIDEN
Washington
NORWICH
NEW BEDFORD
WALLINGFORD
Putnam
Fairfield
CARMEL
DANBURY
WEST KINGSTON
NEWPORT
Westchester
New Haven
NEW HAVEN
NEW LONDON
WESTERLY
Dukes
EDGARTOWN
Nantucket
NANTUCKET
Rockland
WHITE PLAINS
BRIDGEPORT
NORWALK
STAMFORD
GREENWICH
RIVERHEAD
Bronx
Nassau
Suffolk
NEW YORK
MINEOLA
Queens
JAMAICA
0 10 20 30 40
SCALE IN MILES

Inc.
Published: Mon, Tues, Wed, Thur, Fri, Sat, Sun
Weekday Frequency: m
Saturday Frequency: m
Circulation: 135,363; 139,628(sat); 199,661(sun)
Last Audit: ABC September 30, 2011
Price: 4.50/wk; 218.40/yr.
Advertising: Open inch rate $430.00
News services: AP, Bloomberg, DJ, Entertainet, MCT, LAT-WP, RN Photo.
Politics: Independent.
Special Editions: Guide To Education (Apr); Mark Twain Days (Aug); At Work-Weekly Education (Dec); President's Day Auto I (Feb); Family Ski (Jan); Guide To Education (Jul); Cape Cod & The Islands (Jun); Gardening (Mar); Summer Activity Guide (May); Early Ski (Nov); Home De
Magazines: USA WEEKEND Magazine (S).
Pres./Pub./CEO ....Richard Graziano
Vice Pres./CFO ....Richard S. Feeney
Controller ....Robert R. Rounce
Cor. Affairs/Commun. Consultant Andrea Savastra
Vice Pres., Adv. ....Nancy A. Meyer
Adv. Dir., Classified ....Mary Lou Stoneburner
Adv. Dir., Regl./Major ....Mark Lukas
Adv. Mgr., Courant Direct Sales.....Kathy Enders
Adv. Mgr., Regl. Sales ....Susan Faust
Vice Pres., Mktg./Cor. Affairs......Nancy Benben
Mktg. Mgr. ....Doreen Madden
Circ. Vice Pres. ....David Bennett
Circ. Mgr., Retail Sales...................Susan Kerr
Circ. Mgr., Opns. ....Brian McEnery
Circ. Mgr., Strategic Planning/Finance Micheal Vortherms
Circ. Mgr., Single Copy ....Camille Stinton
Dir., Content....................................Jeff Levine
Interim Ed. ....Naedine Hazell
Vice Pres./Editorial Page Ed. ..Carolyn Lumsden
Mng. Ed. ....G. Claude Albert
Market Information: ADS; Split run; TMC; Zoned editions.
Mechanical available: Offset; Black and 3 ROP colors; insert accepted - product samples; page cutoffs - 22 3/4.
Mechanical Specifications: Type page 11 5/8 x 21 1/2; E - 6 cols, 1 13/16, 1/8 between; A - 6 cols, 1 13/16, 1/8 between; C - 10 cols, 1 3/32, 1/16 between.
Commodity Consumption: Avg. Page Number Per Issue - Daily 66; Avg. Page Number Per Issue - Plates Used 400000; Avg. Page Number Per Issue - Saturday 72; Avg. Page Number Per Issue - Sunday 118; widths 24 7/8; Newsprint Used - Metric Tons 29000; Printing Ink Used - Black 114000
Equipment: Editorial Hardware – 4-IBM/RS6000, Pentium/300NT; Editorial Equipment – HP, 8-HP/InkJet Plotter; Editorial Printers – Software □ CCI/Layout 5.5.4.22. CLASSIFIED: Front-end Software – AT/Enterprise 1.4.8.; Classified Hardware – 4-AT/9000, 67-AT/9000 SDT, 2-IBM/RS6000, Pentium/100NT; Classified Printers – 5-AII/3850, III/Postscript Proofers DISPLAY: Ad make-up applications – Adobe/InDesign CS2, Adobe/Photoshop CS2, QPS/QuarkXPress 6.0; Layout Software – Layout/8000.; Display Hardware – 32-APP/Power Mac, APP/Mac G3, APP/Mac G4; Display Printers – 5-AII/3850 PRODUCTION: Pagination Software – AT/R5 Classified Pagination, QPS/QuarkXPress, CCI/Editorial Pagination.; Production Equipment – Caere/OmniPage, 2-Scitex/Dolev 400, 3-KFM/VIPB; Scanners – 2-Scitex/Smartscanner, 1-Eskofot/2450 PRESSROOM: Line 1 – 8-G/Metro offset (4 half decks) 1976; Line 2 – 8-G/Metro offset (4 half decks) 1976; Line 4 – 8-G/Metro offset (4 half decks) 1986; Line 5 – 1986, 8-G/Metro offset (4 half decks) 1986; Folders – 6-G/3:2. MAILROOM: Counter stackers – 2-HL/Monitor, 6-QWI/351, 3-NP/160; Inserters and stuffers – 2-GMA/3000, 1/KR; Bundle tying machines – 6-/Dynaric, 3-Dynaric/Offline; Wrapping singles – 3-/Great Lakes; Addressing machine – 4-/Ch, 2-Domino/On Line Ink Jetting, 2-/KAN. BUSINESS COMPUTERS: Business Software – PBS/MediaPlus, Microsoft/Office, Peoplesoft; Business Hardware – HP/3000, IBM/RS6000

MANCHESTER

JOURNAL INQUIRER

306 Progress Dr., Manchester, Conn., 06042-9011; gen tel (860) 646-0500; adv tel (860) 646-0500; ed tel (860) 646-0500; gen fax (860) 646-9867; adv fax (860) 643-1180; ed fax (860) 646-9867; gen e-mail news@journalinquirer.com; adv e-mail jiads@journalinquirer.com; ed e-mail letters@journalinquirer.com; web site www.journalinquirer.com
Published: Mon, Tues, Wed, Thur, Fri, Sat, Sun
Weekday Frequency: e
Saturday Frequency: e
Circulation: 30,701; 34,026(sat); 34,026(sun)
Last Audit: ABC September 30, 2011
Price: 2.70/wk; 140.40/yr.
Advertising: Open inch rate $56.00
News services: AP, NYT, SHNS.
Politics: Independent. **Established:** 1968
Special Editions: Spring Home & Garden (Apr); Back-to-School (Aug); Washington's Birthday Auto (Feb); Super Sunday (Jan); Discovery (Jul); Fall Brides (Jun); Business & Industry (Mar); Dining Out Guide (May); Sleighbell (Nov); Inside Football (Oct); Fall Sports (Sept).
Special Weekly Sections: Parade (S); USA Weekend (Sat); Time Out (Thur); Food Day (Wed).
Magazines: Relish (Monthly); American Profile (Weekly).
Pub.......................................Elizabeth S. Ellis
Vice Pres., Finance ....Walter Rudewicz
Adv. Vice Pres. ....William K. Sybert
Circ. Dir. ....Gary Hatania
Circ. Mgr., Home Delivery...........Patrick McCue
Mng. Ed./Vice Pres., News ....Chris Powell
Asst. Mng. Ed. ....Lee Giguere
Asst. Mng. Ed./News Ed. ....Ralph W. Williams
Consumer Columnist ....Harlan Levy
Editorial Page Ed. ....Keith C. Burris
Living Section Ed..................Richard Tambling
Photo Ed. ....Adrian Keating
Sports Ed....................................Brian Coyne
State Ed. ....Julie Sprengelmeyer
Television/Radio Ed......................Matt Buckler
Town News Ed., E. Windsor/Manchester/S. Windsor/Windsor/Windsor Locks .Nancy Thompson
Town News Ed., Ellington/Stafford ..Chris Dehnel
Prodn. Vice Pres. ....Timothy Noon
Online Mgr. ....Dan Hatch
Market Information: TMC; Zoned editions.
Mechanical available: Offset; Black and 3 ROP colors; insert accepted - single sheet; page cutoffs - 21 5/8.
Mechanical Specifications: Type page 10 1/2 x 14; E - 5 cols, 2, 1/6 between; A - 5 cols, 2, 1/6 between; C - 8 cols, 1 1/3, 1/6 between.
Commodity Consumption: Avg. Page Number Per Issue - Daily 64; widths 14 3/4; Newsprint Used - Short Tons 3100; Printing Ink Used - Black 86000; Printing Ink Used - Color 3000.
Equipment EDITORIAL: Front-end Software – Microsoft/Windows NT 4.0, CNI.; Editorial Hardware – Compaq/ML530; Editorial Equipment – 65-IBM/PC, 4-APP/Power Mac; Editorial Printers – 2-HP/8100N CLASSIFIED: Front-end Software – PPI.; Classified Hardware – 3-Ik/Model 40; Classified Printers – HP/8100N; Layout Software – MEI.; Display Hardware – 4-APP/Power Mac G3, 4-APP/Power Mac G4; Display Printers – HP/8100 PRODUCTION: Pagination Software – QPS/QuarkXPress 4.1.; Production Equipment – 2-Nu/Flip Top UP, 1-Glunz & Jensen/K550, 2-Glunz & Jensen K720; Cameras – 1-C; Scanners – 1-Minolta/Dimage, 1-Polaroid/Sprint Scan 35 Plus PRESSROOM: Line 1 – 10-HI/845 2000; Folders – 1; Pasters – 6-MEG; Press registration system – 1 MAILROOM: Counter stackers – 2-HL/Dual Carrier; Inserters and stuffers – HI/1472; Bundle tying machines – 1/Power Strap, 3-/Sterling; Addressing machine – 1-Domino/Ink Jet. BUSINESS COMPUTERS: Business Software – INS-I; Business Hardware – IBM/AS-400

MERIDEN

RECORD-JOURNAL

11 Crown St., Meriden, Conn., 06450-0915; gen tel (203) 235-1661; adv tel (203) 317-2303; gen fax (203) 639-0210; adv fax (203) 235-4048; adv e-mail advertising@record-journal.com; ed e-mail newsroom@record-journal.com; web site www.record-journal.com
Published: Mon, Tues, Wed, Thur, Fri, Sat, Sun
Weekday Frequency: m
Saturday Frequency: m
Circulation: 15,990; 17,270(sun)
Last Audit: Sworn December 31, 2008
Price: 5.25/wk; 22.75/month; 208.00/yr.
Advertising: Open inch rate $36.54
News services: AP, NYT, RNS.
Politics: 1867
Not Published: Christmas.
Own facility?: Y
Special Editions: Spring Home & Garden (Apr); Bus & Homeroom (Aug); Holiday Gift Pages (Dec); President's Day Auto (Feb); Weddings (Jan); Services Guide (Jul); Summertime (Jun); Design-An-Ad (Mar); Business & Industry (May); Holiday Shopping (Nov); Celebrate Wallingford (O
Special Weekly Sections: Health & Fitness (Fri); Front Porch (Mon); Neighbors (S); Enjoy! (Thur); Home (Tues); Great Taste (Wed).
Magazines: Parade (S)
Sr. Vice Pres., Sales/Mktg............Michael Killian
Sr. Vice Pres. ....Tim Ryan
Circ. Dir. ....David Pare
Ed..Eliot C. White
Mng. Ed................................Ralph Tomaselli
City Ed. ....Eric Cotton
News Ed. ....Michael Misarski
Chief Photographer..........................Chris Zajac
Sr. Writer......................................Jeffery Kurz
Asst. Sports Ed. ....Bryant Carpenter
vp/new media ....elizabeth white
Market Information: TMC.
Commodity Consumption: Avg. Page Number Per Issue - Daily 33; Avg. Page Number Per Issue - Plates Used 24000; Avg. Page Number Per Issue - Sunday 70; widths 50; Newsprint Used - Metric Tons 2400; Printing Ink Used - Black 25000; Printing Ink Used - Color 2000; Printing Ink Use
Equipment PRESSROOM: Line 1 – outsource; Folders – 2-WH/2:1; Pasters – 5, 2. BUSINESS COMPUTERS: Business Software – CJ
Delivery method: Mail, Newsstand, Private Carrier, Racks

MIDDLETOWN

THE MIDDLETOWN PRESS

386 Main St., 4th Fl., Middletown, Conn., 06457; gen tel (860) 347-3331; gen fax (860) 347-3380; ed e-mail editor@middletownpress.com; web site www.middletownpress.com
Group: U.S. Suburban Press, Inc.
Published: Mon, Tues, Wed, Thur, Fri, Sat
Weekday Frequency: m
Saturday Frequency: m
Circulation: 6,114; 6,114(sat)
Last Audit: September 30, 2009
Price: 3.75/wk; 161.20/yr.
Advertising: Open inch rate $23.21
News services: AP, NYT, LAT-WP.
Politics: Independent.
Note: The Middletown Press shares a combined Sunday edition with The New Haven Register.
Special Editions: Summer Entertaining (Apr); College Student's Guide (Aug); Last Minute Gift Guide (Dec); Valentine (Feb); Super Bowl (Jan); Hartford Open (Jul); Middlesex Summer (Jun); March Madness (Mar); Summer Preview (May); Coupon Book (Monthly); Thanksgiving (Nov); M
Special Weekly Sections: Auto (Fri); Seniors (Mon); Real Estate (Sat); Entertainer (Thur); Health (Tues); Food (Wed)
Magazines: Parade (Weekly).
Editor.................................Viktoria Sundqvist
Michael Giannone
John Gallacher
Tracy Hale
Sam Spencer
Leslie Friedlander
Lisa Basile
Jeff Mill
Jonathan Burton
Kelly Oleksiw
Claire Michalewicz
Cathy Avalone
Pub....................................Daniel A. Moriarty
Circ. Dir....................................Beth Turnhee
Asst. Ed. ....Paul Nicholas
Features Ed. ....Cassandra Day
Sports Ed. ....Jeremie Smith
Prodn. Mgr.........................Barbara Ouellette
Market Information: TMC.
Mechanical available: Offset; Black and 3 ROP colors; insert accepted - pocket books, free-standing stuffers, etc.; page cutoffs - 21 3/8.
Mechanical Specifications: Type page 13 x 22 1/2; E - 6 cols, 1 7/8, 1/8 between; A - 6 cols, 1 7/8, 1/8 between; C - 9 cols, 1 3/8, 3/16 between.
Commodity Consumption: Avg. Page Number Per Issue - Daily 26; Avg. Page Number Per Issue - Saturday 28; widths 27 1/2.
Equipment EDITORIAL: Front-end Software – Prestige (remote); Editorial Hardware – HP laptops, Netbooks; Classified Printers – Xante DISPLAY: Ad make-up applications – Mk/Ad Builder, Multi-Ad, QPS/QuarkXPress.; Production Equipment – 1-C.; Bundle tying machines – 1-Sa/Ty.

NEW BRITAIN

THE HERALD

One Ct. St., 4th Fl., New Britain, Conn., 06051; gen tel (860) 225-4601; gen fax (860) 229-5718; ed fax (860) 223-8171; ed e-mail letters@newbritainherald.com; web site www.newbritainherald.com
Published: Mon, Tues, Wed, Thur, Fri, Sat, Sun
Weekday Frequency: m
Saturday Frequency: m
Circulation: 5,624; 5,624(sat); 9,898(sun)
Last Audit: ABC September 30, 2011
Price: 3.25/wk (carrier); 174.20/yr.
Advertising: Open inch rate $72.73
News services: AP.
Politics: Independent. **Established:** 1880
Note: The Herald Press is a combined Sunday edition of The Bristol Press (e), Middletown Press (m) and (New Britain) Herald (e).
Special Editions: Senior Citizens (Apr); Coupon Book (Aug); Christmas Song Book (Dec); Presidents' Sale (Feb); Health & Fitness (Jan); Crazy Days (Jul); Father's Day Co-op (Jun); Basketball (Mar); Mother's Day Dining (May); Homefinder (Monthly); Thanksgiving Dining (Nov);
Special Weekly Sections: Your Weekend (Fri); Property Transfers (Mon); Health and Tech (S); Rental Guide (Sat); Auto (Thur); Classroom (Tues); Best Food Day (Wed).
Magazines: USA WEEKEND Magazine (S).
Pub...............................Michael E. Schroeder
Circ. Dir....................................Brenda Kelley
Exec. Ed. ....James Smith
Sports Ed....Matt Straub
Prodn. Mgr., Pre-Press ....Barbara Ouellette
Market Information: Split run; TMC; Zoned editions.
Mechanical available: Offset; Black and 3 ROP colors; insert accepted; page cutoffs - 21 3/4.
Mechanical Specifications: Type page 12 x 21 1/2; E - 6 cols, 1 5/6, 1/6 between; A - 6 cols, 1 5/6, 1/6 between; C - 10 cols, 1 1/4, 1/16 between.
Commodity Consumption: Avg. Page Number Per Issue - Daily 28; Avg. Page Number Per Issue - Plates Used 20000; Avg. Page Number Per Issue - Saturday 28; Avg. Page Number Per Issue - Sunday 34; widths 24 7/8; Newsprint Used - Metric Tons 1824; Printing Ink Used - Black 59000; Pr
Equipment EDITORIAL: Front-end Software –

CNI, Microsoft/Word for Windows, QPS/QuarkXPress.; Editorial Hardware – CNI, 25-Pentium/100-166; Editorial Equipment – 2-Ultre/4000 Imagesetters; Editorial Printers – 2-Xante/8200; Classified Hardware – AT; Classified Equipment – 5-Pentium/ALR; Classified Printers – Software ÂD AT. DISPLAY: Ad make-up applications – Multi-Ad, QPS/QuarkXPress.; Display Hardware – 7-APP/Mac; Display Printers – 2-QMS/860; Production Equipment – 2-Ultra/4000, 1-Nu/Flip Top; Cameras – 1-C/Marathon; Scanners – Lf/Leafax 35. PRESSROOM: Line 1 – 6-G/Metro (2 half decks); Folders – 1; Pasters – 6; Reels and Stands – 6 MAILROOM: Counter stackers – 1-SH/Backup, 1-QWI/351; Inserters and stuffers – 2-MM/227; Bundle tying machines – 1/CYP, 2-/Sa, 2-/Bu, 1-/MLN, 2-MLN/2A; Addressing machine – 1-/Ch. BUSINESS COMPUTERS: Business Software – Vision Data; Business Hardware – Sun/Micro Systems

NEW HAVEN

NEW HAVEN REGISTER

40 Sargent Dr., New Haven, Conn., 06511-5918; gen tel (203) 789-5200; adv tel (203) 789-5437; ed tel (203) 789-5650; gen fax (203) 789-5209; adv fax (203) 865-8360 (class); ed fax (203) 865-7894; gen e-mail letters@nhregister.com; adv e-mail ktremaine@nhregister.com; ed e-mail jkramer@nhregister.com; web site www.nhregister.com

Group: Metro Newspaper Advertising Services, Inc.
Published: Mon, Tues, Wed, Thur, Fri, Sat, Sun
Weekday Frequency: m
Saturday Frequency: m
Circulation: 64,562; 38,012(sat); 96,205(sun)
Last Audit: ABC September 30, 2011
Price: 4.75/wk; 20.58/mo; 222.00/yr.
Advertising: Open inch rate $188.30
News services: AP, SHNS, LAT-WP, MCT, NYT, TMS.
Politics: Independent. **Established:** 1812
Special Editions: NCAA Section (Apr); Courses & Careers (Aug); Holiday Gift Guides (Dec); Internet Guide (Feb); Walter Camp Football Foundation (Jan); Menu Guide (Jul); International Festival Arts/Ideas (Jun); Home Show (Mar); Zoomers (May); Business Expo (Nov); Luxury Liv
Special Weekly Sections: Weekend (Fri); Money Monday (Mon); Home/Real Estates (S); Financial/Business (Sat); Business (Thur); Food (Wed).
Magazines: USA WEEKEND Magazine (S); Parade (Weekly).
Pub. ....Edward Condra
Credit Mgr. ....Helen Rogers
Display Adv. Dir........................Kelly Tremaine
Promo. Mgr. ....Kristen Alves
Circ. Mgr.......................................Tim Solt
Ed. ....Jack Kramer
Mng. Ed. ....Mark Brackenbury
Arts/Travel Ed. ....Donna Doherty
Bus. Ed. ....Cara Baruzzi
Editorial Page Ed. ....Charles P. Kochakian
Capitol Bureau Chief.....................Greg Hladky
Entertainment Ed....................Patrick Ferrucci
Graphics Ed...................................Ann Dallas
Librarian.......................................Angel Diggs
Living Ed. ....Richard Sandella
Photo Ed......................................Vern Williams
Radio/Television Ed..............Joseph Amarante
Sports Ed. ....Sean Barker
State/City Ed.................Helen Bennett Harvey
Market Information: Split run; TMC; Zoned editions.
Mechanical available: Offset; Black and 3 ROP colors; insert accepted - die cut, straight edge one side; page cutoffs - 22 2/25.
Mechanical Specifications: Type page 12 x 21; E - 6 cols, 1 7/8, 1/8 between; A - 6 cols, 1 7/8, 1/8 between; C - 10 cols, 1 1/4, 1/16 between.
Commodity Consumption: Avg. Page Number Per Issue - Daily 44; Avg. Page Number Per Issue - Plates Used 192800; Avg. Page Number Per Issue - Saturday 57; Avg. Page Number Per Issue - Sunday 100; widths 37 1/2; Newsprint Used - Metric Tons 10664; Newsprint Used - Short Tons 9674
Equipment EDITORIAL: Front-end Software – Prestige.; Editorial Hardware – AT; Editorial Equipment – 9-APP/Mac, 40-RSK/100, 24-IBM/PS 2, Lf/AP Leaf Picture Desk; Editorial Printers – Panasonic/1124, NEC/P5300 CLASSIFIED: Front-end Software – AT/Release 4.7.7.; Classified Hardware – AT/with 30 workstation; Classified Equipment – 8-APP/Mac; Classified Printers – Epson/FX1050, Lintronic, HP/LaserPrinter DISPLAY: Ad make-up applications – Multi-Ad/Creator 4.0.1, QPS/QuarkXPress 4.04; Layout Software – MEI/ALS 25.; Display Hardware – APP/Mac G3; Display Printers – APP/Mac, MON/600 PRODUCTION: Pagination Software – Prestige.; Production Equipment – 2-MON/Express 1200, 2-PPRM-STR/600, 1-Lf/Leafscan 45, 2-Glunz & Jensen; Cameras – 2-C/Spartan III PRESSROOM: Line 1 – 7-G/Metroliner-3272 double width (3 half decks); Line 2 – 7-G/Metroliner 3273 double width (3 half decks); Folders – 2-G/Imperial 3:2; Reels and Stands – 14-G/45 RTP 3-arm; Press control system – G/EPCS-PAR. MAILROOM: Counter stackers – 4-GMA/CombiStack, 1-MM/310, 1-HL/Monitor, 1-HL/Dual Carrier, 2-QWI/501, 1-QWI/451; Inserters and stuffers – 1-GMA/SLS 2000 22:1, 2-GMA/SLS 3000 16:2; Bundle tying machines – 4-Dynaric; Other equipment –Addressing machine D 2-Ch/525E, 1-Ch/582-N BUSINESS COMPUTERS: Business Software – INSI, CJ; Business Hardware – IBM/AS-400 E50, DEC/4000

NEW LONDON

THE DAY PUBLISHING COMPANY

47 Eugene O'Neill Dr., New London, Conn., 06320-1231; gen tel (860) 442-2200; ed tel 8604401000; gen fax (860) 442-5599; adv fax (860) 442-5443; ed fax (860) 442-0420; adv e-mail advertising1@theday.com; ed e-mail editor@theday.com; web site www.theday.com

Published: Mon, Tues, Wed, Thur, Fri, Sat, Sun
Weekday Frequency: m
Saturday Frequency: m
Circulation: 25,494; 24,985(sat); 29,004(sun)
Last Audit: ABC September 30, 2011
Price: 4.83/wk; 251.16/yr.
Advertising: Open inch rate $41.90 D; $47.72 Sunday
Insert rate: SS $45.90 Full Run CPM
News services: AP, CQ, NYT, MCT, New England News Service, TMS.
Politics: Independent. **Established:** 1881
Own facility?: Y
Special Editions: Education Guide (Bi-annually); DaySaver - Coupons (Monthly); Special Auto (Bi-annually); Dining (Annually); Song Book (Annually); Gift Guide (Annually)
Special Weekly Sections: Real Estate (Fri); Auto (Sat); Church Page (Sat); Weekend Entertainment (Thur); Food (Wed).
Magazines: Mystic Places Magazine (Annually); Go Westerly Magazine (Annually), Grace Magazine (Bi-Monthly); Sound & Country Magazine (Quarterly)
Dir., Finance......................Robert Tousignant
Chief, Staff/Dir., HR.........Mary-Jane McGinnis
Accounting Manager ....Timothy Hinchey
Accounting Manager...........Maryellen Solinsky
Director of Advertising..............Christine Neves
Post-Press/Distribution Operations Manager Robert D. Ford
Publisher ....Gary Farrugia
Managing Editor ....Tim Cotter
Director of Operations ....William Langman
Director of Audience Development Daniel Williams
Executive Editor.......................Timothy Dwyer
Director of Information Technology..Shane Dixon
Commercial Print Sales Manager..Michael Flaig
Product Manager....................Colleen Proctor
Press Manager ....Timothy Tighe
Advertising Services Manager...Christine Brown
Classified Advertising Manager Bence Strickland
Sales Development Manager ....David Gellar
Membership Marketing Manager..........Katie Fox
Managing Editor/Multimedia.......Sally Stapleton
Deputy Managing Editor/News Operations Carol McCarthy
AME/Reporters ....Lisa McGinley
Purchasing Agent...........................Mel Seeger
Adv. Mgr., Classified ....Richard Zesk
Adv. Mgr., Classified/Telephone Sales Roberta McLaughlin
Adv. Dir. ....Shawn E. Palmer
Adv. Mgr., Retail..........................Diane Martin
Mktg. Res. Mgr.........................William Hoelzel
Tourism Mktg. Specialist ....Gail Baker
Circ. Dir.....................................Mark L. Barry
Circ. Mgr. ....Janet M. Ballestrini
Circ. Mgr., Special Prog...........Elizabeth Suson
Circ. Mgr., Sales ....Matthew R. Dery
Market Information: TMC; Zoned editions.
Mechanical available: Offset; Black and 3 ROP colors; insert accepted - product samples accepted with conditions; page cutoffs - 21.
Mechanical Specifications: Type page 12 1/4 x 21; E - 6 cols, 2 1/16, 1/8 between; A - 6 cols, 2 1/16, 1/8 between; C - 10 cols, 1 7/32, 1/16 between.
Commodity Consumption: Avg. Page Number Per Issue - Daily 43; Avg. Page Number Per Issue - Plates Used 39018; Avg. Page Number Per Issue - Saturday 48; Avg. Page Number Per Issue - Sunday 62; widths 27; Newsprint Used - Metric Tons 4000; Printing Ink Used - Black 60700; Printi
Equipment EDITORIAL: Front-end Software – MediaSpectrum/ContentWatch; Editorial Hardware – IBM/Lenovo; Editorial Printers – HP/Konica CLASSIFIED: Front-end Software – Miles 33/Futureproof; Classified Hardware – IBM; Classified Printers – HP/Konica DISPLAY: Ad make-up applications – Adobe CS3; Display Hardware – IBM/Apple; Display Printers – HP/Konica PRESSROOM: Line 1 – 7-G/Headliner Offset double width 1988; Line 2 – 1-HI/248 Sheet; Line 3 – Komori/GS228P Sheet 2003; Line 4 – 1-Ryobi/envelope; Press Drives – Allen Bradley; Folders – G/Imperial 3:2, 2; Pasters – G/RTP4S; Reels and Stands – 7; Press control system – Press control system MAILROOM: Counter stackers – 2-QWI/200, 3-QWI/350, 1-QWI/400; Inserters and stuffers – S/NP630 22-stations; Bundle tying machines – 6/Power Strap, 3-/Power Strap/3/4 Wraps, 3-Matthews/Ink Jet System; Mailroom control system – QWI/Programmer, ICON/300; Addressing machine – Addressing m BUSINESS COMPUTERS: Business Software – Microsoft (various); Business Hardware – IBM/Lenovo
Delivery method: Newsstand, Private Carrier, Racks

THE DAY PUBLISHING CO.

47 Eugene O'Neill Dr., New London, Conn., 06320-1231; gen tel (860) 442-2200; gen fax (860) 442-5599; web site www.theway.com

Price: 200.20/yr.
Advertising: Open inch rate $39.83

NORWALK

THE HOUR PUBLISHING CO.

1 Selleck St., 4th Floor, Norwalk, Conn., 06855-1117; gen tel (203) 846-3281; adv tel (203) 354-1090; ed tel 203-354-1062; oth tel (203) 3541020; gen fax (203) 846-9897; adv fax (203)846-9897; ed fax (203) 840-1802; oth fax (203) 354-1128; gen e-mail lsura@thehour.com; adv e-mail jbrosz@thehour.com; ed e-mail news@thehour.com; business@thehour.com; sports@thehour.com; faith@thehour.com; web site www.thehour.com

Published: Mon, Tues, Wed, Thur, Fri, Sat, Sun
Weekday Frequency: m
Saturday Frequency: m
Circulation: 16,055; 16,055(sat); 28,054(sun)
Last Audit: ABC September 30, 2011
Price: .75 Daily, 2.00 Sunday
Advertising: $34.15/col inch daily, $22.00 / col inch weeklies
Insert rate: $40 per thousand
News services: AP, MCT.
Politics: Neutral. **Established:** 1871
Not Published: None
Own facility?: N
Special Editions: The Stamford Times Wilton Villager
Special Weekly Sections: Health (Tues); Entertainment (Thur); Fitness (Tues); Best Food (Wed).
Magazines: USA WEEKEND Magazine (S); American Profile (Weekly). Relish (Monthly), Spry (Monthly)
Pub./COO ....Chet Valiante
Advertising Director...................Debra Hanson
Classified Supervisor...............Jocelyn Battista
Bus. Systems Mgr.............................Peter Kish
Co-Managing Editor, Bus. Ed. ....Chris Bosak
Editor Emeritus...........................John P. Reilly
Copy Editor, Religion Ed............Carol Hofmann
Asst. Sports Ed. ....George Albano
Vice Pres., Opns. ....Mark C. Koch
VP Sales & Marketing ....John Brosz
President......................................Brett Whitton
Asst. Circulation Director ....Darlene Temple
Co-Managing Editor ....Jerrod Ferrari
Regional Editor - The Stamford Times & Wilton Villager..................................Jeremy Soulliere
City Editor...................................James Walker
Managing Sports Editor...................John Nash
Production Director..................Robert Marsala
Web Development Director ....Matt Terenzio
Market Information: TMC.
Commodity Consumption: Avg. Page Number Per Issue - Daily 38; Avg. Page Number Per Issue - Saturday 44; Avg. Page Number Per Issue - Sunday 64; widths 54; Newsprint Used - Metric Tons 1700; Newsprint Used - Short Tons 1112; Printing Ink Used - Black 37760; Printing Ink Used -
Equipment EDITORIAL: Front-end Software – Baseview/NewsEdit Pro IQUE 3.2.3.; Editorial Hardware – 4-APP/Mac 7200, 1-APP/Mac 9600, 1-APP/Mac 8600, 36-APP/Mac G3; Editorial Equipment – 1-Dell/Pentium PC; Editorial Printers – 2-HP/LaserJet 8000 CLASSIFIED: Front-end Software – Baseview/Ad Manager Pro 2.06.; Classified Hardware – 8-APP/Mac G3; Classified Printers – 1-GCC/Elite XL DISPLAY: Ad make-up applications – CJ; Layout Software – CJ.; Display Hardware – 2-HP/3000 PRODUCTION: Pagination Software – QPS/QuarkXPress 4.1.; Production Equipment – Caere/OmniPage Pro 7.0, AP/Picture Desk Server; Scanners – JK&A/1Z70 BUSINESS COMPUTERS: Business Software – CJ; Business Hardware – 2-HP/3000
Zip Codes served: Too many to list.
Delivery method: Mail, Newsstand, Private Carrier, Racks

NORWICH

THE BULLETIN

66 Franklin St., Norwich, Conn., 06360; gen tel (860) 887-9211; adv tel (860) 887-9211; ed tel (860) 887-9211; gen fax (860) 887-1949; adv fax (860) 887-1949; ed fax (860) 887-9666; ed e-mail news@norwichbulletin.com; web site www.norwichbulletin.com

Published: Mon, Tues, Wed, Thur, Fri, Sat, Sun
Weekday Frequency: m
Saturday Frequency: m
Circulation: 17,023; 17,023(sat); 20,531(sun)
Last Audit: ABC September 30, 2011
Price: $3.95/week 7 day
Advertising: Open inch rate $56.95
News services: AP, GNS.
Politics: 1791
Own facility?: Y
Special Editions: Spring Home & Garden (Apr); Back-to-School (Aug); Holiday Gift Guides (Dec); Home Improvement (Feb); Job Fair (Jan); Back-to-School (Jul); Job Fair (Jun); Job Fair (Mar); Spring Home & Garden (May); Job Fair (Nov); Job Fair (Sept).
Special Weekly Sections: Real Estate (Fri); Sunday Open House (S); APB Cars (Sat); Town & Country (Thur); APB Jobs (Wed).
Magazines: USA WEEKEND Magazine (S).
Controller/Director of Operations Nadine McBride
Exec. Editor.....................................Jim Konrad

Editorial Page Ed. ....Ray Hackett
Advertising Director....................Dan Graziano
Market Information: Split run; TMC.
Mechanical available: Offset; Black and 3 ROP colors; insert accepted - sample bags; page cutoffs - 22 3/4.
Mechanical Specifications: Type page 11 5/8 x 21 1/2; E - 6 cols, 1 5/6, 1/8 between; A - 6 cols, 1 5/6, 1/8 between; C - 10 cols, 1 1/25, 1/12 between.
Commodity Consumption: Avg. Page Number Per Issue - Daily 24; Avg. Page Number Per Issue - Plates Used 26000; Avg. Page Number Per Issue - Sunday 32; widths 50; Newsprint Used - Metric Tons 2331; Printing Ink Used - Black 85000; Printing Ink Used - Color 10000; Printing Ink Us
Equipment EDITORIAL: Front-end Software – Microsoft/Word 97, QPS/QuarkXPress 3.32.; Editorial Hardware – 5-MS/NT Server, 39-PC; Editorial Printers – Pre Press/Panther Pro; Display Hardware – PC PRODUCTION: Pagination Software – QPS/QuarkXPress 4.11.; Production Equipment – Pre Press/Panther Plus, Adobe/Photoshop; Scanners – Kk/RFS 2035 Plus, Microtek; Other equipment –MM.
Delivery method: Mail, Newsstand, Private Carrier, Racks

STAMFORD

THE ADVOCATE

9 River Bend Dr. S., Stamford, Conn., 06901; gen tel (203) 964-2200; adv tel (203) 964-2425; ed tel (203) 964-2293; adv fax (203) 964-2278; ed fax (203) 964-2345; adv e-mail ads@scni.com; ed e-mail letters.advocate@scni.com; web site www.stamfordadvocate.com
Published: Mon, Tues, Wed, Thur, Fri, Sat, Sun
Weekday Frequency: m
Saturday Frequency: m
Circulation: 12,938; 8,951(sat); 21,516(sun)
Last Audit: ABC September 30, 2011
Price: 4.20/wk; 16.80/mo; 184.60/yr.
News services: AP, LAT-WP, MCT.
Politics: Independent. **Established:** 1829
Note: Advertising is sold in combination with the Greenwich Time (mS) for $80.80(d) and $89.70(S). Individual newspaper rates not made available.
Special Editions: Garden (Apr); Educational Outlook (Aug); Steppin Out New Years (Dec); Business & Economic Review (Feb); Educational Outlook (Jan); Healthy Connections (Jul); Summer Party Guide (Jun); NY Auto Show (Mar); Health & Wellness (May); Stamford Business Outlook
Special Weekly Sections: Family (Mon); Travel (S); Life & Style (Thur); Health (Tues); Food (Wed).
Magazines: Color Comics (S).
Vice Pres., Opns./Circ. Dir. ....Craig Allen
Pub...................................Michelle McAbee
Mgr., Mktg. Serv. ....Vincent Yade
Ed.......................................David McCumber
Bus. Ed. ....James Zebora
Editorial Page Ed. ....Tom Mellano
Sports Ed....................................Tom Renner
Prodn. Mgr., Pre Press................Dennis Tidrick
Prodn. Mgr., Transportation.....Trevor Viechweg
Prodn. Supvr., Pagination-Night......Robert Reed
Market Information: Split run; TMC; Zoned editions.
Mechanical available: Offset; Black and 3 ROP colors; insert accepted; page cutoffs - 22 3/4.
Mechanical Specifications: Type page 11 5/8 x 21 1/2; E - 6 cols, 1 7/8, 1/6 between; A - 6 cols, 1 7/8, 1/6 between; C - 10 cols, 1 1/8, 1/6 between.
Commodity Consumption: Avg. Page Number Per Issue - Daily 44; Avg. Page Number Per Issue - Plates Used 110000; Avg. Page Number Per Issue - Saturday 30; Avg. Page Number Per Issue - Sunday 112; widths 50; Newsprint Used - Metric Tons 5000; Printing Ink Used - Black 85000; Prin
Equipment EDITORIAL: Front-end Software – QPS/QuarkXPress 4.1, Adobe/Photoshop, Baseview/NewsEdit Pro IQUE, Adobe/Illustrator.; Editorial Hardware – 75-APP/Mac; Editorial Equipment – Lf/AP Leaf Picture Desk, Nikon/Scanners; Editorial Printers – Graphic Enterprises/PS 3, III/3850 CLASSIFIED: Front-end Software – DTI/ClassSpeed.; Classified Hardware – 1-DTI/Enterprise 450, 35-APP/Mac G3; Classified Printers – AII/3850, HP/4050 DISPLAY: Ad make-up applications – Multi-Ad/Creator, QPS/QuarkXPress 4.1; Layout Software – 13-APP/Mac, AII/SQL Admanager.; Display Hardware – APP/Mac; Display Printers – APP/Mac LaserWriters, Graphic Enterprises/PS 3, III/3850 PRODUCTION: Pagination Software – QPS/QuarkXPress 4.1.; Production Equipment – 3-III/3850, 1-KFM; Scanners – Kk/scanner, 1-Linotype-Hell, 1-Linotype-Hell PRESSROOM: Line 1 – 8-HI/1660 offset double width 1982, 2-HI/1660 double width 1991; Folders – 2; Pasters – 9-MEG/Automatic; Reels and Stands – MEG. MAILROOM: Counter stackers – 1-QWI/3500, 1-QWI/3500, 1-QWI/3500; Inserters and stuffers – 1-HI/1472 online; Bundle tying machines – 4-OVL/JP40; Addressing machine – 2-KR/215; Other equipment –HI/Stitcher-Trimmer.; Business Hardware – 1-DEC/VAX 4100, CJ

SOUTHERN CONNECTICUT NEWSPAPERS, INC.

75 Tresser Blvd., Stamford, Conn., 06901; gen tel (203) 964-2200; gen fax (203) 964-2278 (Display A
Published: Mon, Tues, Wed, Thur, Fri, Sat, Sun
Saturday Frequency: m
Circulation: 31,886; 14,529(sat); 31,886(sun)
Last Audit: ABC September 30, 2011
Price: 210.00/yr.
Advertising: Open inch rate $71.40

TORRINGTON

THE REGISTER CITIZEN

59 Field Street, Torrington, Conn., 06790-0058; gen tel (860) 489-3121; adv tel 860-489-3121, ext. 312; ed tel 860-489-3121, ext. 5; gen fax (860) 489-6790; gen e-mail editor@registercitizen.com; adv e-mail adassist@registercitizen.com; ed e-mail editor@registercitizen.com; web site www.registercitizen.com
Published: Mon, Tues, Wed, Thur, Fri, Sat, Sun
Weekday Frequency: m
Saturday Frequency: m
Circulation: 5,338; 5,338(sat); 5,841(sun)
Last Audit: ABC September 30, 2011
Price: 3.20/wk; 12.80/mo; 166.40/yr.
Advertising: Open inch rate $25.19
News services: AP.
Politics: Independent. **Established:** 1874
Special Editions: Home Improvement (Apr); Fall Festivals (Aug); First Night (Dec); Progress (Feb); Bridal (Jan); Torrington (Jul); Graduation (Jun); Car Care (Mar); Memorial Day Activities (May); Christmas Gift Guide (Nov); Fall Car Care (Oct); Fall Bridal (Sept).
Special Weekly Sections: Entertainment (Thursday); Real Estate (S); Food (Thur); Health & Science (Tues); @RecordBody:**Magazines:** Comics (S).
Pub...Matt DeRienzo
Adv. Dir....................................Tilda Crossman
Adv. Mgr., Classified...................Bob Reneson
Adv. Mgr., Online Sales.....................Bernie Re
Circ. Dir.......................................Timothy Lee
Ed. ....Jordan Fenster
Mng. Ed. ....Liz Strillacci
Sports Ed.....................................Garrett Dale
Market Information: ADS; Split run; TMC; Zoned editions.
Mechanical available: Offset; Black and 3 ROP colors; insert accepted - single card; page cutoffs - 22 3/4.
Mechanical Specifications: Type page 13 x 21 1/4; E - 6 cols, 1 7/8, 1/8 between; A - 6 cols, 1 7/8, 1/8 between; C - 9 cols, 1 3/8, 1/16 between.
Commodity Consumption: Avg. Page Number Per Issue - Daily 24; Avg. Page Number Per Issue - Plates Used 18600; Avg. Page Number Per Issue - Saturday 24; Avg. Page Number Per Issue - Sunday 32; widths 30; Newsprint Used - Short Tons 1990; Printing Ink Used - Black 45000; Printin
Delivery method: Mail, Newsstand, Private Carrier, Racks

WATERBURY

REPUBLICAN-AMERICAN

389 Meadow St., Waterbury, Conn., 06722-2090; gen tel (203) 574-3636; adv tel (203) 574-3636; ed tel (203) 574-3636; adv fax (203) 754-0644; ed fax (203) 596-9277; gen e-mail releases@rep-am.com; adv e-mail adres@rep-am.com; web site www.rep-am.com
Published: Mon, Tues, Wed, Thur, Fri, Sat, Sun
Weekday Frequency: m
Saturday Frequency: m
Circulation: 43,694; 41,878(sat); 49,874(sun)
Last Audit: ABC September 30, 2011
Price: 17.34/mo (dS); 208.00/yr (dS).
Advertising: Open inch rate $61.02(m-thur)
News services: AP, MCT, Bloomberg.
Politics: 1922
Not Published: Christmas.
Own facility?: Y
Special Editions: Gardening (Apr); Careers/Education (Dec); Bridal (Jan); Summer Lifestyles (May); Travel-Winter (Nov); Bridal/Fashions (Oct); Autumn Lifestyles (Sept).
Special Weekly Sections: Religion Page (Fri); Accent (S); Wheels Section (Sat); Weekend (Thur); Today's Woman (Tues); Food Features (Wed).
Magazines: Parade (S).
Dash (monthly) on Sun.
Controller...................................Kevin Larche
Asst. Pub./Bus. Mgr. ....William B. Pape
Adv. Dir., Mktg. ....Fred Hull
Adv. Mgr., Retail ....Susan Sprano
Adv. Mgr., Retail........................Richard Welch
Exec. Ed. ....Jonathan F. Kellogg
Publisher and Editor.................William J. Pape
Litchfield Co. Ed. ....Anne Karolyi
Night Ed....................................Martin Begnal
News System Editor................Howard Fielding
Exec. Sports Ed.............................Lee Lewis
Associate Features Editor Tracey O'Shaughnessy
Wire Ed.......................................Ed Goodman
Dir., Opns. ....Andrew J. Pape
Prodn. Mgr. ....Ray Creighton
Prodn. Foreman, Mailroom ....Mark Lehner
Metro Editor ....Tom Ferriter
AME/Features Editor ....Debra Aleksinas
Market Information: ADS; Split run; TMC; Zoned editions.
Mechanical available: Offset; Black and 3 ROP colors; insert accepted - single sheets; page cutoffs - 22 3/4.
Mechanical Specifications: Type page 11 5/8 x 21 1/4; E - 6 cols, 1 3/4, 1/8 between; A - 6 cols, 1 3/4, 1/8 between; C - 9 cols, 1 1/4, 1/16 between.
Commodity Consumption: Avg. Page Number Per Issue - Daily 42; Avg. Page Number Per Issue - Plates Used 92400; Avg. Page Number Per Issue - Sunday 110; widths 12 1/2; Newsprint Used - Metric Tons 6722; Newsprint Used - Short Tons 7410; Printing Ink Used - Black 137300; Printing
Equipment EDITORIAL: Front-end Software – Saxotech, Microsoft/Word, QPS/QuarkXPress.; Editorial Hardware – 4-MT/NT Servers, 56-PC,20-APP/Mac; Editorial Printers – 1-HP/LaserPrinter, HP/Design Jet 1055 CH CLASSIFIED: Front-end Software – Miles 33/Feature Proof, Miles 33/Beacon.; Classified Hardware – Dell 6300 HPDL 380 WM 2003; Classified Printers – 2-HP/LaserPrinter 4MS; Layout Software – Miles 33/Beacon.; Display Hardware – 2-MS/NT Servers, 12-APP/Mac, 1-PC; Display Printers – Dataproducts, HP PRODUCTION: Pagination Software – Polka Dots; Production Equipment – 2 HPDL380; Scanners – 2-HP/4C PRESSROOM: Line 1 – 6-G/Metro double width (2 decks) 1969; Folders – G/2:1; Pasters – 6; Reels and Stands – 6 MAILROOM: Counter stackers – 6/QWI; Inserters and stuffers – 1-HI/1472 online, 1-HI/1372; Bundle tying machines – 4-MLN/2A, 1-Ca/Tyers, 3-Dynaric/NP-3; Wrapping singles – 2-HL/Bottom Wrap, 1-QWI; Mailroom control system – MM; Addressing machine – 1-/Ch; Other equipment –Other equ BUSINESS COMPUTERS: Business Software – Great Plains 5.0, AR/Datasciences; Business Hardware – Compaq/NT Server, Dell/6300 NT Server
Delivery method: Mail, Newsstand, Private Carrier, Racks

WILLIMANTIC

THE CHRONICLE

1 Chronicle Rd., P.O. Box 148, Willimantic, Conn., 06226; gen tel (860) 423-8466; adv tel (860) 423-8466; ed tel (860) 423-8466; gen fax (860) 423-7641; adv fax (860) 423-7641; ed fax (860) 423-6585; gen e-mail chron@thechronicle.com; ed e-mail news@thechronicle.com; web site www.thechronicle.com
Published: Mon, Tues, Wed, Thur, Fri, Sat
Weekday Frequency: e
Saturday Frequency: m
Circulation: 6,506; 6,506(sat)
Last Audit: September 30, 2009
Price: 2.40/wk.
Advertising: Open inch rate $24.65
News services: Reuters, McClatchy Tribune News Services
Politics: 1877
Not Published: New Year; Memorial Day; Independence Day; Labor Day; Thanksgiving; Christmas.
Own facility?: Y
Special Editions: Back-to-School (Aug); Gift Gallery (Dec); Bridal (Jan); Summer Guide (Jun); Spring Special (May); Christmas (Nov); Harvest Values (Oct); Sports (Sept).
Special Weekly Sections: Real Estate (Mon); Society/Wedding (Sat); Arts (Thur); Food (Wed).
Magazines: Album (Sat); American Profile (Weekly).
Purchasing Agent ....Kevin B. Crosbie
Adv. Dir. ....Jean Beckley
Circ. Dir. ....Mark Banfield
Ed..Charles Ryan
Bus./Finance Ed. ....Ron Robillard
Sports Ed. ....Mike Sypher
Prodn. Foreman, Pressroom ....Peter Linkkila
Market Information: ADS; TMC.
Mechanical available: Offset; Black and 3 ROP colors; insert accepted; page cutoffs - 21 1/2.
Mechanical Specifications: Type page 13 x 21 1/2; E - 6 cols, 2 1/16, 1/8 between; A - 6 cols, 2 1/16, 1/8 between; C - 9 cols, 1 9/16, 1/16 between.
Commodity Consumption: Avg. Page Number Per Issue - Daily 16; Avg. Page Number Per Issue - Saturday 24; widths 27 1/2; Newsprint Used - Short Tons 375; Printing Ink Used - Pages Printed 9000.
Equipment EDITORIAL: Front-end Software – CText.; Editorial Hardware – 20-CText, IBM; Editorial Printers – HP CLASSIFIED: Front-end Software – Vision Data.; Classified Hardware – 4-Vision Data; Classified Printers – APP/Mac LaserWriter NT DISPLAY: Ad make-up applications – QPS/QuarkXPress.; Display Hardware – 6-IBM; Display Printers – HP; Production Equipment – Nat; Scanners – HP. PRESSROOM: Line 1 – 5-WPC/Web Leader; Line 2 – 2-WPC/Web Leader.; Inserters and stuffers – KAN/480; Bundle tying machines – MLN. BUSINESS COMPUTERS: Business Software – Vision Data; Business Hardware – DEC/Micro VAX II
Delivery method: Mail, Newsstand, Private Carrier, Racks

DELAWARE

DOVER

DELAWARE STATE NEWS

110 Galaxy Dr., Dover, Del., 19901; gen tel (302) 674-3600; adv tel (302) 741-8207; gen fax (302) 741-8261; gen e-mail dsnnews@newszap.com; adv e-mail dsnads@newszap.com; ed e-mail dsnnews@newszap.com; web site www.newszap.com

Published: Mon, Tues, Wed, Thur, Fri, Sat, Sun
Weekday Frequency: m
Saturday Frequency: m
Circulation: 12,720; 12,720(sat); 17,507(sun)
Last Audit: September 30, 2009
Price: 145.60/yr.
Advertising: Open inch rate $29.80
News services: AP, MCT, LAT-WP, TMS.
Politics: 1953
Special Editions: January Bridal (Jan); Annual Medical Directory (May); Holiday Gift Guide (Nov); Quarterly Employment (Quarterly); NASCAR Race Tabs (Sept).
Special Weekly Sections: Entertainment (Fri); Entertainment (S).
Magazines: TV & Leisure (S).
Pub. ....Tamra Brittingham
Adv. Vice Pres. ....Darel LaPrade
Adv. Mgr., Classified ....Heather Cregar
Mng. Ed. ....Andrew West
Asst. Mng. Ed. ....Drew Ostroski
Entertainment Ed. ....Gwen Guerke
Sports Ed. ....Andy Walter
Webmaster ....Linda Snyder
Prodn. Mgr., Distr. ....Don Clendaniel
Market Information: TMC.
Mechanical available: Offset; Black and 3 ROP colors; insert accepted; page cutoffs - 21 1/4.
Mechanical Specifications: Type page 11 5/6 x 21 1/2; E - 6 cols, 1 5/6, 1/8 between; A - 6 cols, 1 5/6, 1/8 between; C - 9 cols, 1 3/8, 1/8 between.
Commodity Consumption: Avg. Page Number Per Issue - Daily 24; Avg. Page Number Per Issue - Sunday 48; widths 25.
Equipment EDITORIAL: Front-end Software – AT/Dewar View 3.0, MS/Word 97.; Editorial Hardware – IBM/Unix, Dell/Optiplex Y Enspiron, APP/Mac; Editorial Printers – HP/LaserJet 5000 CLASSIFIED: Front-end Software – AT/Enterprise.; Classified Hardware – IBM/Unix, Dell/Optiplex; Classified Printers – HP/LaserJet 8000 DISPLAY: Ad make-up applications – QPS/QuarkXPress 4.0, Adobe/Photoshop 6.0, Adobe/Illustrator 9.0, Macro Media/Freehand 9.0; Layout Software – SCS/Layout 8000.; Display Hardware – APP/Mac; Display Printers – HP/Design Jet PRODUCTION: Pagination Software – AT/Dewar View 3.0.; Production Equipment – 2-Mon/Panther Pro 62, MS/Windows NT; Cameras – C/Spartan III PRESSROOM: Line 1 – 7-G/Urbanite; Line 2 – 6-G/Community; Folders – 3 MAILROOM: Counter stackers – 1-BG/Count-O-Veyor, 1-HL/Monitor 708-724-6100; Bundle tying machines – 1-MLN/MI1EE, 1-MLN/ML2EE; Addressing machine – Ch/596. BUSINESS COMPUTERS: Business Software – PBS; Business Hardware – IBM/Unix

WILMINGTON

THE NEWS JOURNAL

950 W. Basin Rd., New Castle, Del., 19720; gen tel (302) 324-2500; adv tel (302) 324-2650; ed tel (302) 324-2990; gen fax (302) 324-5518; adv fax (302) 324-2620; ed fax (302) 324-2595; web site www.delawareonline.com

Published: Mon, Tues, Wed, Thur, Fri, Sat, Sun
Weekday Frequency: m
Saturday Frequency: m
Circulation: 81,749; 80,057(sat); 124,693(sun)
Last Audit: ABC September 30, 2011
Price: 3.75/wk (dS); 15.00/mo (dS); 195.00/yr (dS).
Advertising: Open inch rate $175.20
News services: AP, GNS, LAT-WP, Baltimore Sun.
Politics: Independent.
Special Editions: Travel (Apr); Football (Aug); Shopping Guide (Dec); Careers (Feb); Spring Brides (Jan); Academic All Stars (Jun); Camp Guide (Mar); Beach Guide (May); Education (Oct); Travel (Sept).
Special Weekly Sections: Garden/Home (Fri); Family (Mon); Best Food Day (S); Auto (Sat); Crossroads (Thur); Best Food Day (Wed).
Magazines: 55 Hours (Entertainment) (Fri); USA WEEKEND Magazine (S).
Pres./Pub. ....W. Curtis Riddle
Vice Pres., Finance ....Don Lemire
Vice Pres., HR ....Dolores Pinto
Controller ....Kevin Huff
Vice Pres., Adv. ....Dennis Sheely
Adv. Dir., Retail ....Amy Newton
Mktg. Mgr. ....J.B. Braun
Vice Pres., Circ. ....Michael S. Kane
Circ. Mgr., Single Copy ....M. Lynn Davis
Circ. Mgr., Sales/Mktg. ....Steve Urbish
Circ. Mgr., Home Delivery Sales ....Alexis Ziobro
Circ. Mgr., Opns. ....Hector Garcia
Circ. Mgr., Newspapers in Educ. Shirley Price-Roane
Vice Pres., News/Exec. Ed. ....David Ledford
Asst, Mng. Ed. ....Greg Burton
Asst. Mng. Ed. ....Jill Fredel
Bus. Ed. ....Merritt Wallick
Editorial Page Ed. ....John Sweeney
Night Ed. ....Phil Freedman
Sports Ed. ....Jason Levine
Market Information: ADS; TMC; Zoned editions.
Mechanical available: Offset; Black and 3 ROP colors; insert accepted - card inserts, custom-designed; page cutoffs - 21 1/8.
Mechanical Specifications: Type page 13 1/8 x 21 1/4; E - 6 cols, 2 1/16, 1/8 between; A - 6 cols, 2 1/16, 1/8 between; C - 10 cols, 1 1/4, 1/16 between.
Commodity Consumption: Avg. Page Number Per Issue - Daily 52; Avg. Page Number Per Issue - Plates Used 95000; Avg. Page Number Per Issue - Sunday 120; widths 54 1/2; Newsprint Used - Metric Tons 17500; Newsprint Used - Short Tons 19290; Printing Ink Used - Black 405000; Printi
Equipment EDITORIAL: Front-end Software – QPS 2.0.10.; Editorial Hardware – IBM/Server, APP/Mac, PC; Editorial Equipment – 1-Color-master/Plus, IBM, MS/NT Advanced Server, GMTI/Digital Archive; Editorial Printers – ECR/3850, ECR/Wildcat XL180 DTP CLASSIFIED: Front-end Software – Unisys 3.0.; Classified Hardware – IBM/Server, 35-PC DISPLAY: Ad make-up applications – Genesys; Layout Software – SCS/Layout 8000, APP/Mac with QuarkXPress.; Display Hardware – IBM/AS-400; Display Printers – HP/LaserJet III, Spectraset PRODUCTION: Pagination Software – QPS 2.0.10.; Production Equipment – W/Optical Plate Bender, KFM, ECR/Wildcat XL 180, Barco; Scanners – 2-Kk/2035 Pro, Umax/1200 PRESSROOM: Line 1 – 8-G/Headliner Offset 1989, 1-G/Metrocolor Tower 1994; Line 2 – 8-G/Headliner Offset 1989, 1-G/Metro color tower 1994; Folders – 4; Pasters – 16-G/RTP CT50; Reels and Stands – Press registration system Â□ 2-G/Quadtech. MAILROOM: Counter stackers – 3-HL/Monitor, 13/QWI; Inserters and stuffers – 1-GE/1372, 2-HI/1472; Bundle tying machines – 8-/Power Strap; Wrapping singles – 5-/Power Strap 3/4 wrap; Addressing machine – 2-/Barstrom, 3-/Barstrom; Other equipment – 1-/MM.; Audio Hardware – Lucent/Overture 250 BUSINESS COMPUTERS: Business Software – Genesys :Circ, Adv, Lawson :Fin, Cyborg :Payroll; Business Hardware – IBM/AS-400

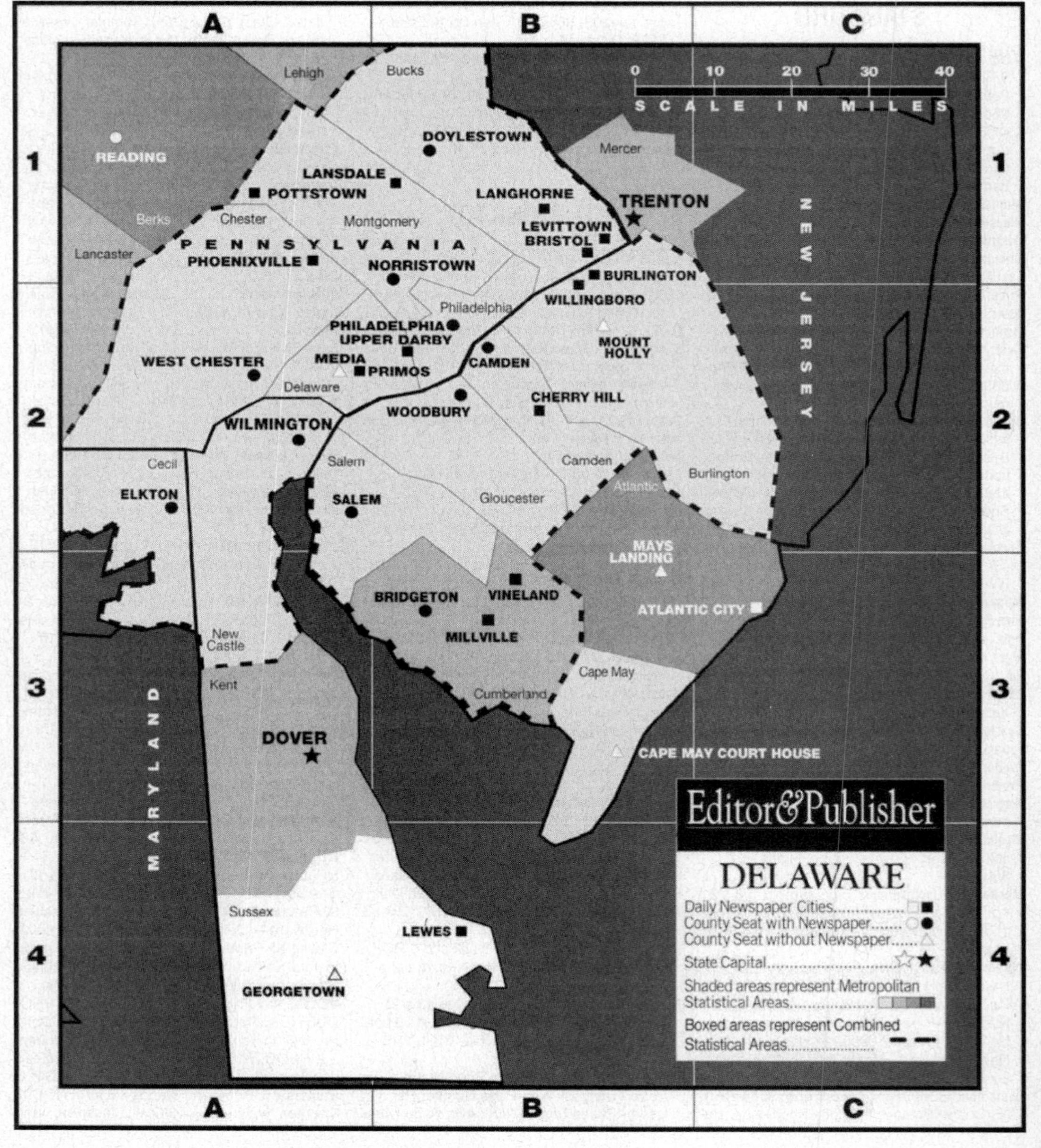

DISTRICT OF COLUMBIA

WASHINGTON

THE WASHINGTON POST

1150 15th St. NW, Washington, D.C., 20071; gen tel (202) 334-6000; adv tel (202) 334-7642 (Nat'l Adv); adv fax (202) 334-5561 (Nat'l Adv); ed fax (202) 334-5547 (Nat'l News); web site www.washingtonpost.com

Published: Mon, Tues, Wed, Thur, Fri, Sat, Sun
Weekday Frequency: m
Saturday Frequency: m
Circulation: 507,465; 485,528(sat); 846,019(sun)
Last Audit: ABC September 30, 2011
Price: 62.40/yr (d), $78.00/yr (S), $127.40/yr (d&S).
Advertising: Open inch rate $1,169.00
News services: AFP, AP, CT, DJ, MCT, NEA, NNS, RN.
Politics: Independent.
Special Editions: Home & Design (Apr); Football Preview (Aug); Holiday Guide Feature (Dec); Cruise (Feb); Bridal Feature (Jan); Homes Showcase (Jul); Homes Showcase (Jun); Home Showcase (Mar); Outdoor Living Feature (May); Ski (Nov); Bermuda & the Bahamas (Oct); Fall Fashi
Special Weekly Sections: Weekend Tab (Fri); Health Tab (Tues); Food Section (broadsheet) (Wed).
Magazines: Washington Post Magazine (S).
Profile: Major newspaper for Washington, DC and surrounding metropolitan areas
Chrmn.................................Boisfeuillet Jones
Pres., Washington Post Media/Pub. Katharine Weymouth
Pres./Gen. Mgr. ....Stephen P. Hills
Vice Pres. at Large...........Benjamin C. Bradlee
Vice Pres./Bus. Mgr. ....Theodore C. Lutz
Vice Pres., Personnel/Admin./Controller Margaret Schiff
Vice Pres., Affiliates.................Lionel Neptune
Vice Pres., Circ. ....David Dadisman
Vice Pres., Devel................Gerald M. Rosberg
Vice Pres., Gov't Affairs........Carol D. Melamed
Vice Pres., Labor...................Patricia A. Dunn
Vice Pres., Opns. ....Michael Clurman
Vice Pres., Prodn. ....Jim Coley
Adv. Dir., Bus. Devel.............Joyce Richardson
Adv. Dir., Classified ....Larry Keating
Adv. Dir., Nat'l ....Rick Tippett
Dir., Recruitment Adv. ....Wendy Evans
Dir., Mktg. Commun......................Rich Handloff
Mgr., Creative Servs./Consumer Media Susan Heyman
Circ. Dir., Home Delivery ....Gregg Fernandes
Market Information: Split run; TMC; Zoned editions.
Mechanical available: Letterpress and offset; Black and 3 ROP colors; insert accepted; page cutoffs - 22.
Mechanical Specifications: Type page 12 x 21; E - 6 cols, 1 15/16, 1/8 between; A - 6 cols, 1 15/16, 1/8 between; C - 10 cols, 1 1/8, 1/16 between.
Commodity Consumption: Avg. Page Number Per Issue - Daily 110; Avg. Page Number Per Issue - Plates Used 1098265; Avg. Page Number Per Issue - Sunday 200; widths 54 7/8; Newsprint Used - Short Tons 250000; Printing Ink Used - Black 6050000; Printing Ink Used - Color 570000; Pri
Equipment; Editorial Hardware – SII/Synthesis 66.; Classified Hardware – SII/Synthesis 66. DISPLAY: Ad make-up applications – Multi-Ad/Creator; Layout Software – MEI, Mk/Ad Director.; Display Printers – GE/Proofer PRODUCTION: Pagination Software – ECI.; Production Equipment – Na, 6-Titan, 4-C/220, 1-WL/Lith 10, 1-WL/Lith 3, KFM/Auto Benders; Cameras – 1-C/Marathon, 1-C/Newspager PRESSROOM: Line 1 – 42-G/Mark I (5:G); Line 2 – 18-G/Mark II (3:G); Line 3 – 31-G/Metro (2:G); Line 4 – 10-TKS/Offset (1-TKS); Line 5 – 46-G/MKI (6:G); Folders – 2-G/2:1, 14-G/3:2; Pasters – 133, 10. MAILROOM: Counter stackers – 28-HL/Monitor, 6-Id/330, 5-Id/440, 2-Id/220; Inserters and stuffers – 2-S/72P, 3-HI/Collator, 6-GMA/SLS 1000, 1-GMA/SLS 1000 16:1; Bundle tying machines – 6-GMA/SLS 1000, 16-MLN/MLN2, 2-MLN/2AHS, 24-MLN/2A.; Audio Hardware – Micro Voice BUSINESS COMPUTERS: Business Software – Microsoft/Windows 98, Microsoft/Windows NT, Microsoft/Windows 95; Business Hardware – IBM, Oracle, DSI

THE WASHINGTON TIMES

3600 New York Ave. NE, Washington, D.C., 20002-1947; gen tel (202) 636-3000; adv tel (202) 636-3030; ed tel (202) 636-3000; gen fax (202) 636-8906; adv fax (202) 526-9348; ed fax (202) 715-0037; gen e-mail general@washingtontimes.com; adv e-mail advertising@washingtontimes.com; web site www.washingtontimes.com

Group: Metro Newspaper Advertising Services, Inc.
Published: Mon, Tues, Wed, Thur, Fri, Sun
Weekday Frequency: m
Circulation: 67,148; 45,427(sun)
Last Audit: September 30, 2009
Price: 2.50/wk; 117.00/yr; 29.25/13wk.
Advertising: Open inch rate $107.64
News services: MCT, AP, RN, CNS, Bloomberg, AFP, SHNS, Cox News Service, UPI, CSM, London Daily Telegraph, Xinhua News Service, CN, NEA.
Politics: Independent. **Established:** 1982
Note: Effective June 1, 2008, this newspaper changed its publishing plan from (m-mon to fri; m-sat; S) to (m-mon to fri; S).
Special Editions: Tee Time (Annually); Baseball Preview (Apr); Football Preview (Aug); Bride (Jan); Beach Living (Jun); Tourist Guide (May); International (Monthly); Gift Guide (Nov); Active Adults (Quarterly); Small Business Adminstration (Semi-yearly).
Special Weekly Sections: Show (Fri); Employment Extra (Mon); Family Times (S); Travel (Sat); Washington Weekend & Calendar (Thur); Food (Wed).
Magazines: American Profile (Fri); Relish (Monthly); USA WEEKEND Magazine (S); Washington's Finest (Semi-monthly).
Acting Pres./Pub.....................Jonathan Slevin
Assoc. Pub. ....Robert Morton
Vice. Pres., HR.........................Sonya Jenkins
Dir., Facilities.......................Mark Frankowski
Adv. Mgr., Interactive ....Eric Rasnic
Adv. Mgr., Major Accts. ....Art Crofoot
CMO ....Thomas Culligan
Dir., Mktg. ....Brian Bauman
Mgr., Art Graphics ....Patrick Crofoot
Mgr., Research ....Goldie Butler
Circ. Mgr., Customer Serv..........Jackie Jackson
Circ. Mgr., Systems..........................Lisa Gray
Online Mng. Ed.........................David Eldridge
Deputy Mng. Ed., Admin. ....Ted Agres
Asst. Mng. Ed., Graphics.......Joseph W. Scopin
Asst. Mng. Ed., News ....Geoffrey Etnyre
Asst. Mng. Ed, Spec. Section Features Maria Stainer
Capitol Hill Bureau Chief ....Stephen Dinan
Denver Bureau Chief...........Valerie Richardson
Market Information: ADS; Split run.
Mechanical available: Offset; Black and 3 ROP colors; insert accepted - polybag samples; magazines; page cutoffs - 22 3/4.
Mechanical Specifications: Type page 11 5/8 x 21 1/2; E - 6 cols, 1 5/6, 1/8 between; A - 6 cols, 1 5/6, 1/8 between; C - 10 cols, 1 3/50, 1/8 between.
Commodity Consumption: Avg. Page Number Per Issue - Daily 62; Avg. Page Number Per Issue - Plates Used 80000; Avg. Page Number Per Issue - Saturday 58; Avg. Page Number Per Issue - Sunday 62; widths 25; Newsprint Used - Metric Tons 14700; Newsprint Used - Short Tons 16170; Pri
Equipment EDITORIAL: Front-end Software – Managing Editor/ALS, Saxotech/Saxopress 5.5.; Editorial Hardware – 2-Sun/Enterprise 450, 8-Dell/Pentium, 200-APP/iMac; Editorial Equipment – 40-APP/Mac Page Makeup Workstation; Editorial Printers – 3-HP/18150 CLASSIFIED: Front-end Software – Atex/Enterprise 1.7.; Classified Printers – HP/LaserJet DISPLAY: Ad make-up applications – MEI/Roundhouse, QPS/QuarkXPress 6.5, Adobe/Illustrator; Display Hardware – 2-DEC/Alpha 4100, 22-APP/Power Mac; Display Printers – 3-Xante/Accel-a-Writer 8200, 1-Epson/3000 Color Printer, 1-HP/1000 Color PRODUCTION: Pagination Software – QPS/QuarkXPress 6.5.; Production Equipment – TI/OmniPage Pro 5.0, 2-WL/Lith-X-Pozer III PRESSROOM: Line 1 – 10-G/Urbanite; Line 2 – 10-G/Urbanite; Line 3 – 14-G/Urbanite; Line 4 – 14-G/Urbanite; Pasters – 32-Cary/FP4540; Reels and Stands – 32-Cary/CLFP; Press control system – 10-Fin/Drive. MAILROOM: Counter stackers – 4-Gammerler, 4-QWI/502; Inserters and stuffers – 1-HI/1372P, 1-K&M/1372; Bundle tying machines – 2-MLN/2A, 6/Power Strap, 2-Mosca/Cross Strap; Wrapping singles – 4-G/Bottom Wrap; Mailroom control system – HL; Addressing machine – 1-Pr; Audio Hardware – BlueStreak Media BUSINESS COMPUTERS: Business Software – Microsoft/Word, Microsoft/Excel, Powerpoint; Business Hardware – 2-DEC/Alpha 4100, 300-APP/Mac, 90-IBM/PC, 20-Dell/PowerEdge 2450, 5-Dell/PowerEdge 2650

FLORIDA

BOCA RATON

BOCA RATON NEWS

1141 S. Rogers Cir., Ste. 7, Boca Raton, Fla., 33487; gen tel (561) 893-6400; adv tel (561) 893-6500; ed tel (561) 893-6600; gen fax (561) 893-6674; adv fax (561) 893-6674; ed fax (561) 893-6677; gen e-mail copydesk@bocanews.com; adv e-mail sales@bocanews.com; web site www.bocanews.com

Published: Mon, Tues, Thur, Fri, Sun
Weekday Frequency: m
Circulation: 13,673; 14,339(sun)
Price: 65.00/yr; 21.45/3mo, $37.70/6mo.
Advertising: Open inch rate $37.73
News services: AP, MCT.
Politics: Independent.
Special Weekly Sections: Weekend (Fri); Society (Mon); Boca Life (S); Real Estate News & Review (Sat).
Magazines: TV Book (S).
Pub. ....Craig Swill
Adv. Mgr., Classified ....Nancy Smith
Adv. Mgr., Natl./Major Accts...........Lew Roberts
Exec. Vice Pres., Sales...........Richard Ciarliello
City Ed. ....Dale King
Society Ed. ....Kip Sheffield
Sports Ed. ....John Johnston
Admin./Tech. Mgr. ....Eric Nudleman
Mechanical available: Offset; Black and 3 ROP colors; insert accepted - any; page cutoffs - 22 3/4.
Mechanical Specifications: Type page 13 x 21 1/2; E - 6 cols, 2, 3/16 between; A - 6 cols, 2, 3/16 between; C - 10 cols, 1 1/4, 1/16 between.
Commodity Consumption: Avg. Page Number Per Issue - Daily 40; Avg. Page Number Per Issue - Plates Used 140000; Avg. Page Number Per Issue - Sunday 180; widths 27; Newsprint Used - Metric Tons 2869.
Equipment EDITORIAL: Front-end Software – QPS/QuarkXPress, Microsoft/Word.; Editorial Hardware – 10-APP/Mac, 20-PC; Classified Hardware – HI/8300,, 7-HI/8860, 2-HI/8863. DISPLAY: Ad make-up applications – QPS/QuarkXPress, Aldus/FreeHand, Adobe/Illustrator, Adobe/Photoshop; Layout Software – 8-APP/Mac. PRODUCTION: Pagination Software – QPS/QuarkXPress.; Production Equipment – 2-COM/8600, 2-AU/APS-6, 1-Tegra/Varityper; Cameras – 1-C/Spartan III, 1-AG/2024; Scanners – 1-ECR/Autokon 1000, Lf/Leafscan 45, 2-HP/ScanJet 4C PRESSROOM: Line 1 – 10-G/Urbanite; Press Drives – 2; Folders – 2-G/2:1; Pasters – 6-WEB/Qwi; Press control system – 2-Fin/Control Console. MAILROOM: Counter stackers – 1-BG/108, 1-Id/2000; Inserters and stuffers – 2-MM/227; Bundle tying machines – 1/MLN, 1-/Dynaric; Wrapping singles – Id/Under Crafter BUSINESS COMPUTERS: Business Software – CJ; Business Hardware – 1-HP/3000

BRADERTON

BRADENTON HERALD

PO Box 921, Bradenton, Fla., 34206-0921; gen tel (941) 748-0411; web site www.bradentonherald.com

Published: Mon, Tues, Wed, Thur, Fri, Sat, Sun
Weekday Frequency: m
Saturday Frequency: m
Circulation: 28,612; 30,031(sat); 40,019(sun)
Last Audit: ABC September 30, 2011

BROOKSVILLE

HERNANDO TODAY

15299 Cortez Blvd., Brooksville, Fla., 34613; gen tel (352) 544-5200; adv tel (352) 544-5232; ed tel (352) 544-5280; gen fax (352) 799-5246; adv fax (352) 544-5255; ed e-mail dchichester@hernandotoday.com; cwessels@hernandotoday.com; web site www.hernandotoday.com

Published: Mon, Tues, Wed, Thur, Fri, Sat, Sun
Weekday Frequency: m
Saturday Frequency: m
Circulation: 15,053; 15,053(sat); 15,053(sun)
Last Audit: October 4, 2002
Price: .75/wk; 32.50/yr.
Advertising: Open inch rate $33.40(m-fri)
Note: For detailed press information, see the Tampa Tribune.
Special Weekly Sections: Out & About (Fri); Trib TV (S); Classified Automotive (Sat); Health Today (Thur); Sports (Wed).
Magazines: Relish (Monthly); USA WEEKEND Magazine (S).
Broadcast Affiliations: WFLA-TV (Channel 8) Tampa.
Pub.................................Duane L. Chichester
Office Mgr. ....Denise Nohejl
Adv. Mgr., Classified.....................Anne Collier
Adv. Mgr., Retail.........................Brenda Miton
Circ. Mgr. ....Terry Thompson
Ed. ....Chris Wessel
Community News Ed. ....Timothy Howsare
Special Sections Ed......................Paula Nelson
Sports Ed. ....Tony Castro
Online Mgr. ....Michael Terry
Market Information: TMC.
Mechanical available: Offset; Black and 3 ROP colors; insert accepted; page cutoffs - 22.
Mechanical Specifications: Type page 13 x 21; E - 6 cols, 2 1/2, 1/6 between; A - 6 cols, 2 1/2, 1/6 between; C - 10 cols, 1 1/5, 1/6 between.
Equipment EDITORIAL: Front-end Software – CText, Novell 3.12.; Editorial Hardware – PC 486 100MHz; Editorial Equipment – HP/Netserver; Editorial Printers – QMS/1660E CLASSIFIED: Front-end Software – SII.; Classified Hardware – SII/Coyote 15; Classified Printers – Epson/Action Laser II DISPLAY: Ad make-up applications – AIM; Layout Software – CJ/World Class Series.; Display Hardware – HP/700-94; Display Printers – Epson/DFX-8000 PRODUCTION: Pagination Software – QPS/QuarkXPress 3.32.; Production Equipment – Omni/PagePro; Cameras – Companica/680 C Vertical; Scanners – Danagraf/Scanmate 21.4, Umax/Vista S6, AG/Arcus II BUSINESS COMPUTERS: Business Software – Microsoft/Office; Business Hardware – HP/Vectra 4-100

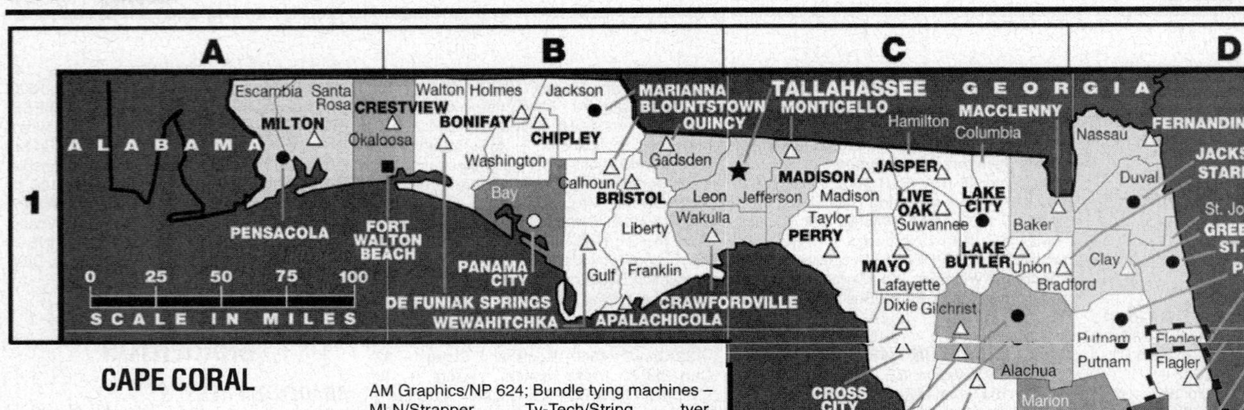

CAPE CORAL

CAPE CORAL BREEZE

2510 Del Prado Blvd., Cape Coral, Fla., 33904; gen tel (239) 574-1110; adv tel (239) 574-1110; ed tel (239) 574-1110; gen fax (239) 573-2318; adv fax (239) 574-3403; ed fax (239) 574-5693; adv e-mail breezecorpads@flguide.com; ed e-mail news@breezenewspapers.com; web site www.cape-coral-daily-breeze.com

Published: Tues, Thur, Sat
Weekday Frequency: m
Saturday Frequency: m
Circulation: 1,072; 1,072(sat)
Last Audit: Sworn October 1, 2002
News services: AP.
Politics: Independent. **Established:** 1961
Advertising not accepted: N
Not Published: New Year (unless on a Sat); Memorial Day; Independence Day; Labor Day; Thanksgiving; Christmas.
Own facility?: N
Special Editions: Progress Edition (Apr); Newcomers Guide (Aug); Caroling Book (Dec); Valentine's Day (Feb); Best of The Cape Ballot Ads Start (Jan); July 4th Page (Jul); Father's Day (Jun); Visitors Guide (Mar); Memorial Day Flag (May); Veterans Salute (Nov); Visitor's Gu
Special Weekly Sections: RPM (Sat).
Publisher ....Scott Blonde
Adv. Dir. ....Renee Brown
Mng. Ed. ....Chris Strine
Editorial Dir. ....Valarie Harring
Photo Dept. Mgr. ....Michael Pistello
Sports Ed. ....Jim Linette
Prodn. Mgr., Press..........................Henry Keim
Circulation Director ....Smith Barbara
Advertisng Director ....Jim Konig
Market Information: TMC.
Mechanical available: Offset; Black and 3 ROP colors; insert accepted - single sheets; page cutoffs - 22.
Mechanical Specifications: Type page 11 3/4 x 21 1/2; E - 6 cols, 2 1/16, 1/4 between; A - 8 cols, 1 3/8, 3/16 between; C - 8 cols, 1 3/8, 3/16 between.
Commodity Consumption: Avg. Page Number Per Issue - Daily 24; Avg. Page Number Per Issue - Plates Used 30000; Avg. Page Number Per Issue - Saturday 56; widths 34; Newsprint Used - Short Tons 2100; Printing Ink Used - Black 44000; Printing Ink Used - Color 14000; Printing Ink U
Equipment EDITORIAL: Front-end Software – QPS/QuarkXPress 3.32.; Editorial Hardware – APP/Power Mac G3; Editorial Printers – HP/LaserJet 4MV CLASSIFIED: Front-end Software – ONI/Class 0.5.4.; Classified Hardware – Daktech/52X Max; Classified Printers – HP/LaserJet 2100TN DISPLAY: Ad make-up applications – Multi-Ad/Creator 4.01; Layout Software – Metro/CDs.; Display Hardware – Umax/C500; Display Printers – HP/LaserJet 4MV PRODUCTION: Pagination Software – QPS/QuarkXPress 3.32.; Production Equipment – 1-Nu/Flip Top, Graham/S 3-27; Cameras – 1-C/Pager, SCREEN/690D, C/Page Camera 1292; Scanners – HP, RZ/4050 Scanner PRESSROOM: Line 1 – 8-HI/V-15 single width 1990; Folders – 1, HI/JF-25; Pasters – 1-BG/Acumeter SY 1243; Reels and Stands – 4-Martin/Splicers. MAILROOM: Counter stackers – 109-BG/Count-0-Veyor, Rima/RS25, Rima/RS10; Inserters and stuffers – HI, S/624, AM Graphics/NP 624; Bundle tying machines – MLN/Strapper, Ty-Tech/String tyer, Akebono/Strapper; Addressing machine – KR; Other equipment –MM/Stitcher-T; Business Hardware – NCR
Delivery method: Mail, Newsstand, Private Carrier, Racks

CHARLOTTE HARBOR

CHARLOTTE SUN

23170 Harborview Road, Charlotte Harbor, Fla., 33980; gen tel (941) 206-1000; adv tel (941) 206-1214; ed tel (941) 206-1100; gen fax (941) 629-2085; adv fax (941) 629-4499; ed fax (941) 629-2085; gen e-mail info@sun-herald.com; adv e-mail gnickerson@sun-herald.com; web site www.yoursun.com

Group: Sun Coast Media Group, Inc.
Published: Mon, Tues, Wed, Thur, Fri, Sat, Sun
Weekday Frequency: m
Saturday Frequency: m
Circulation: 34,569; 29,612(sat); 42,483(sun)
Last Audit: ABC September 30, 2011
Price: 144.45/yr (carrier).
Advertising: Open inch rate $65.80
Insert rate: Open rate single sheet $40
News services: MCT, AP Limited, AP Photo Feed, Bloomberg-Washington Post, News Service of Florida, St. Petersburg Times
Politics: Independent. **Established:** 1977
Not Published: None
Own facility?: Y
Special Editions: Charlotte Sun
Englewood Sun
North Port Sun
Venice Gondolier Sun
Special Weekly Sections: Feeling Fit (Sun.); Weekly Heralds (Wed.); Let's Go (Wed.); Waterline (Thu.); Automotive (Sat.); Real Estate (Sat.); Shopping & Entertainment (Sunday)
Magazines: USA Weekend
Harbor Style
Profile: Newspaper publishing
President, Sun Coast Media Group, Inc./Sun Newspapers/Pub....................David Dunn-Rankin
Advertising Director ....Glen Nickerson
Executive Editor The Sun................Chris Porter
Managing Editor.........................John Hackworth
Circulation Director ....Mark Yero
VP of Marketing ....Debbie Dunn-Rankin
Viewpoint Editor........................Brian Gleason
Features Editor......................Donna Davidson
Sports Editor...................................Pat Obley
Charlotte Sun Editor.........................Rusty Pray
Deputy Sports Editor.................Mark Lawrence
Asst Sports Editor ....Matthew Stevens
Charlotte Sun Systems Editor ....Jim Merchant
Class/Telmktg Manager.......................Geri Kotz
Systems Manager.........................Ed McIntosh
Press Room Manager ....Chris Germann
Mgr., HR ....Mary Skaggs
Adv. Mgr., Classified ....Frank Ledo
Vice Pres., Mktg.....................Robert Whitfield
Circ. Dir........................................Joe Gallimore
Exec. Ed. ....Jim Gouvellis
Mng. Ed......................................Buddy Martin
Bus. Ed....Dan Means
Buzz Ed......................................Leigh Sprimont
Deputy City Ed.......................Lorraine Roberts
Asst. City Ed. ....Bob Reddy
Features Ed..............................Donna Davidson
Internet Ed. ....Scott Corwin
Photo Ed. ....Paul Schmidt
Exec. Sports Ed. ....Pat Obley
Asst. Sports Ed. ....Dave Mondt
Data Processing Mgr...............Joanne Hackney
Market Information: Split run; TMC; Zoned editions.
Mechanical available: Offset; Black and ROP colors; insert accepted; page cutoffs - 22.
Mechanical Specifications: Type page 10 x 20.75; E - 6 cols, 21, 1/8 between; A - 6 cols, 21, 1/8 between; C □ 6 cols, 16, 1/8 between.
Commodity Consumption: Avg. Page Number Per Issue - Daily 44; Avg. Page Number Per Issue - Plates Used 46800; Avg. Page Number Per Issue - Sunday 40; widths 27 1/4; Newsprint Used - Short Tons 4000; Printing Ink Used - Black 12500; Printing Ink Used - Color 7200; Printing Ink
Equipment EDITORIAL: Front-end Software – DTI Content Publisher/Adobe InDesign & In-Copy; Editorial Hardware – Dell (Lattitude E6500 series and Inspiron 1500 series); Editorial Equipment – FA/Compact, FP/230B; Editorial Printers – Konica BizHub CLASSIFIED: Front-end Software – Brainworks.; Classified Hardware – Dell Workgroup Server; Classified Printers – Konica BizHub DISPLAY: Ad make-up applications – Multiad Creator Pro 8.5; Layout Software – MEI.; Display Hardware – Dell Workgroup Server; Display Printers – Konica BizHub PRODUCTION: Pagination Software – MEI/ALS 2.0.2rl.; Production Equipment – Kodak Trendsetter 150 CTP, Kodak PDF workflow, Newsmanager/Preps. Nela Vision Bender.; Scanners – Epson Scanner PRESSROOM: Line 1 – 12-G/Urbanite U-5019 5 units DGM 850; Folders – 2 goss 5000 series folders 2 goss quarter folders; Pasters – 7 JARDIS flying pasters 1-MARTIN zero speed paster; Reels and Stands – Press control system □ 2-Fin/2193E-150-38D, 1-Fin/2193E-100-38D. MAILROOM: Counter stackers – 1-HI/251017, 1-HL/Monitor, 1-BG/105; Inserters and stuffers – 1-HI/848; Bundle tying machines – 1-MLN/ML2EE, 1-MLN/A1672A, 1/Bu. BUSINESS COMPUTERS: Business Software – Saxotech-Data Sciences Inc; Business Hardware – Dell Workgroup Server
Zip Codes served: 33834, 33873, 33890, 33921, 33946, 33947, 33948, 33950, 33952, 33953, 33954, 33955, 33980, 33981, 33982, 33983, 34223, 34224, 34229, 34266, 34269, 34275, 34285, 34286, 34287, 34288, 34289, 34291, 34292, 34293
Delivery method: Mail, Newsstand, Private Car-

rier, Racks

CRYSTAL RIVER

CITRUS COUNTY CHRONICLE

1624 N. Meadowcrest Blvd., Crystal River, Fla., 34429; gen tel (352) 563-6363; adv tel (352) 563-5592; ed tel (352) 563-5660; gen fax (352) 563-5665; adv fax (352) 563-5665; ed fax (352) 563-3280; adv e-mail advertising@chronicleonline.com; ed e-mail newsdesk@chronicleonline.com; web site www.chronicleonline.com

Published: Mon, Tues, Wed, Thur, Fri, Sat, Sun
Weekday Frequency: m
Saturday Frequency: m
Circulation: 22,343; 22,343(sat); 27,603(sun)
Last Audit: ABC September 30, 2011
Price: 81.03/yr.
Advertising: Open inch rate $48.35
News services: AP.
Special Editions: Home Improvement (Apr); Football (Aug); Gift Guide (Dec); Business Almanac (Feb); Income Tax Guide (Jan); Snowbird (Jul); Nature Coast (Jun); Fair Guide (Mar); Hurricane Tab (May); Seniors Illustrated (Monthly); Crystal River Merchants (Nov); Festival of
Special Weekly Sections: Entertainment (Fri); Homefront (S); Religion (Sat); Food (Thur); Health (Tues); Education (Wed).
Magazines: USA WEEKEND Magazine (S).
Pub. ....Gerry Mulligan
Community Affairs Dir. ....Neale Brennan
Adv. Dir. ....John Provost
Circ. Dir. ....Kathie Stewart
Ed. ....Charles Brennan
Mng. Ed. ....Mike Arnold
Chief Copy Desk Ed. ....Cheryl Jacob
Photo Ed. ....Matthew Beck
Sports Ed. ....John Coscia
Prodn. Mgr. ....Tom Feeney
Prodn. Mgr., Pressroom ....Mike Weaver
Market Information: TMC; Zoned editions.
Mechanical available: Web Offset; Black and 3 ROP colors; insert accepted; page cutoffs - 22 3/4.
Mechanical Specifications: Type page 13 x 21 1/2; E - 6 cols, 2 1/16, 1/8 between; A - 6 cols, 2 1/16, 1/8 between; C - 10 cols, 1 1/8, 1/8 between.
Commodity Consumption: Avg. Page Number Per Issue - Daily 24; Avg. Page Number Per Issue - Plates Used 16000; Avg. Page Number Per Issue - Sunday 50; widths 25; Newsprint Used - Short Tons 1970; Printing Ink Used - Black 54000; Printing Ink Used - Color 7000; Printing Ink Used
Equipment EDITORIAL: Front-end Software – XYQUEST/XyWrite, QPS/QuarkXPress 3.3.; Editorial Hardware – CText; Editorial Printers – ECR/11 X 17 proof printer CLASSIFIED: Front-end Software – APT. DISPLAY: Ad make-up applications – Multi-Ad/Creator, QPS/QuarkXPress; Layout Software – APP/Mac.; Display Hardware – APP/Mac PRODUCTION: Pagination Software – Layout 8000.; Production Equipment – Caere/OmniPage, APP/Mac, AG/Online; Cameras – AG; Scanners – 3-Nikon, 2-AG PRESSROOM: Line 1 – 7-G/Community SC (1 univ offset color), 1-DGM/4-high Color; Folders – G/Community SC, DGM/1030; Pasters – 7-Jardis/Splicers. MAILROOM: Counter stackers – 1-HL/Monitor, QWI/401; Inserters and stuffers – 1-AM/Graphics NP 1372 w/icon, 1-MM/8:1; Bundle tying machines – 2-MLN/Strapper; Addressing machine – KR; Other equipment –HI/Stitcher-Trimmer. BUSINESS COMPUTERS: Business Software – Lotus; Business Hardware – IBM/Sys 36

DAYTONA BEACH

DAYTONA BEACH NEWS-JOURNAL

901 Sixth St., Daytona Beach, Fla., 32117-8099; gen tel (386) 252-1511; adv tel (386) 252-1511; ed tel (386) 252-1511; gen fax (386) 258-8469; ed fax (386) 258-8465; adv e-mail adv@news-jrnl.com; ed e-mail letters@news-journalonline.com; web site www.news-journalonline.com

Group: Halifax Media
Published: Mon, Tues, Wed, Thur, Fri, Sat, Sun
Weekday Frequency: m
Saturday Frequency: m
Circulation: 61,023; 67,064(sat); 82,989(sun)
Last Audit: ABC September 30, 2011
Price: 14.13/mo; 169.47/yr; 84.74/26wk.
Advertising: Open inch rate $196.10
News services: AP
Politics: Democrat.
Own facility?: Y
Special Editions: Palm Coast How to Guide (Apr); Football Preview (NFL) (Aug); Letters to Santa (Dec); Volusia County Schools Newsletter (Every other month); Bridal Guide (Feb); Prospectus (Jan); Speed (Jul); Disaster Guide (Jun); Garden & Leisure Lifestyle Show (Mar); Par
Special Weekly Sections: Fishing News (Fri); Health & Fitness (Mon); Real Estate (S); School News (Sat); Senior Citizen News (Thur); Fishing News (Tues); Food Features (Wed).
Magazines: Homes & Property (Monthly); TV Journal (S).
Profile: This service features Associated Press news, local coverage, community service and tourist information, discussion forums, software file libraries, an online almanac with information about the local area and various links to advertisers' Web sites
Mgr., Mktg. Devel. ....Brad Gordner
Mgr., Strategic Mktg. ....Lori Kopp
Circ. Mgr. ....John K. Shaw
Mng. Ed. ....Cory Lancaster
Deputy Mng. Ed., News ....Cal Massey
Deputy Mng. Ed., Prodn. ....Chris Seymour
Asst. Mng. Ed. ....Derek Catron
CEO & Publisher, Halifax Media Michael Redding
Editor ....Pat Rice
Advertising Director ....Mike Baskin
Chrmn. of the Board ....Marc L. Davidson
Pres./CEO/Pub. ....Georgia M. Kaney
CFO ....David Kendall
Mgr., Accounting ....Ellen Andrews
Community Rel. Mgr. ....Kathy Tiller
Circ. Dir. ....Douglas R. Davis
Circ. Sales/Mktg. Mgr. ....Larry Saffer
Co-Ed ....Marc Davidson
Ed. ....Donald Lindley
Sr. Mng. Ed. ....Troy Moore
Mng. Ed., Online ....Tony Briggs
Deputy Mng. Ed., Visuals ....Kelly Markowitz
Asst. Mng. Ed., Metro ....Kathy Kelly
Market Information: ADS; Split run; TMC; Zoned editions.
Mechanical available: Offset; Black and full color ROP colors; insert accepted - samples; page cutoffs - 22.
Mechanical Specifications: Type page 11 5/8 x 20 3/4; E - 6 cols, 1 13/16, 1/8 between; A - 6 cols, 1 13/16, 1/8 between; C - 9 cols, 1 1/4, 1/16 between.
Commodity Consumption: Avg. Page Number Per Issue - Daily 44; Avg. Page Number Per Issue - Plates Used 183600; Avg. Page Number Per Issue - Saturday 50; Avg. Page Number Per Issue - Sunday 114; widths 54; Newsprint Used - Short Tons 15598; Printing Ink Used - Black 320850; Pri
Equipment EDITORIAL: Front-end Software – HI/Newsmaker 3.31, Microsoft/Windows NT, Microsoft/Wor; Editorial Hardware – 2-Sun/Ultra2, 3-Sun/Sparc 10 Server, 2-Sun/Sparc Storage Arrays, 50-Dell/Dimension XPS T450, 20-Dell/Dimension V350, 10-Dell/Optiplex; Editorial Printers – QMS/1660, MON/Proofer, HP/8100N CLASSIFIED: Front-end Software – Cx/Intertext, HI.; Classified Hardware – AST/Bravo MS 5166M, 37-IBM PS/1; Classified Printers – 2-Digital/L030W Companion, Okipage/6e; Display Hardware – DEC/Alpha-4610, SCS/Layout 8000, HP/200, APP/Mac G3 Server, Micronet/Array, APP/Mac 950, APP/Mac 840, APP/Mac 7100, APP/Mac 9600, APP/Mac 7300, APP/Mac G3; Display Printers – Dec/LA30, QMS/PS-860, QMS/2060, QMS/1660, Tektronix/Phaser 300, Tektronix/380 PRODUCTION: Pagination Software – HI/Newsmaker 2.0; Production Equipment – 2-MON/ExpressMaster 25, 3-MON/RIP Express, 3-Sun/Ultra Sparc 2Xs, SCREEN/Doubletruck Imagesetter, Harlequin/RIP; Cameras – 2-C, 1-Payea, 1-C/Spartan; Scanners – 3-ECR/Autokon, 1-SCREEN/608 Scanner, HP/ScanJet Plus PRESSROOM: Line 1 – 14-G/Metroliner; Folders – 2-G/3:2, 2-G/2:1; Pasters – 12 MAILROOM: Counter stackers – 1-QWI/100, 5-QWI/200, 2-QWI/310, 3-QWI/350, 2-MM/CS70-338; Inserters and stuffers – HI/1472, HI/1372, HI/2299, NP/120 Gripper Conveyor; Bundle tying machines – 8-Dynaric/NP-2, 2-Dynaric/NP-1, 4-Malow/50-S String Typer; Wrapping singles – Wrapping singles AUDIO: Audio Software – Unix 3.01; Audio Hardware – Brite Voice Systems, AP StockQuote II, 2-Pentium/100; Business Hardware – 2-DEC/Alpha 4610
Delivery method: Mail, Newsstand, Private Carrier, Racks

FORT LAUDERDALE

SUN-SENTINEL CO.

200 E. Las Olas Blvd., Fort Lauderdale, Fla., 33301; gen tel (954) 356-4000; gen fax (954) 356-4555; web site www.sun-sentinel.com

Published: Mon, Tues, Wed, Thur, Fri, Sat, Sun
Weekday Frequency: m
Saturday Frequency: m
Circulation: 147,860; 176,618(sat); 224,763(sun)
Last Audit: ABC September 30, 2011
Politics: 1910
Note: Sun-Sentinel Co. is owned by the Tribune Co.
Pres. ....Robert Gremillion
Sr. Vice Pres. ....Earl Maucker
Sr. Vice Pres./Pub ....Howard Greenberg
Commun. Mgr. ....Kevin Courtney

FORT MYERS

THE NEWS-PRESS

2442 Dr. Martin Luther King Jr. Blvd., Fort Myers, Fla., 33901-3987; gen tel (239) 335-0200; adv tel (239) 335-0335; ed tel (239) 335-0350; gen fax (239) 334-0239; adv fax (239) 334-0239; ed fax (239) 334-0708; gen e-mail community@news-press.com; web site www.news-press.com

Published: Mon, Tues, Wed, Thur, Fri, Sat, Sun
Weekday Frequency: m
Saturday Frequency: m
Circulation: 54,761; 61,137(sat); 76,470(sun)
Last Audit: ABC September 30, 2011
Price: 3.50/wk; 14.00/mo; 182.00/yr; 45.50/13wk.
Advertising: Open inch rate $151.30
News services: AP, GNS, MCT, TMS.
Politics: Independent.
Special Editions: Commerce & Growth (Apr); Minivans (Aug); Holiday Gift Guide (Dec); Golf Guide (Feb); Visitor's Guide (Jan); The Best (Jul); Best Ballots (Jun); Careers (Mar); Bonita's Best (May); Newcomer's Magazine (Nov); New Car Preview (Oct); Country Club Living (Sept
Special Weekly Sections: Gulfcoasting Entertainment (Fri); Business Monday (Mon); Tropicalia (S); Home & Garden (Sat); Healthy Living (Tues); Food (Wed).
Magazines: USA WEEKEND Magazine (S).
Exec. Asst. Pres./Pub. ....Deb Waller
Vice Pres., Opns. ....Mike Monscour
Vice Pres., Finance ....Matt Petro
Vice Pres., HR ....Ann Weinberg
Adv. Sr. Vice Pres., Sales/Mktg. ...Nancy Solliday
Retail Sales Mgr. ....Jim Wyatt
Circ. Vice Pres. ....Bob Sutherland
Circ. Dir. ....Ken McCloud
Exec. Ed./Vice Pres., News ....Terry Eberle
Sr. Mng. Ed. ....Cindy McCurry-Ross
Asst. Mng. Ed. ....Sheldon Zoldan
Bus. Ed. ....Steve McQuilkin
Cape Coral Ed. ....Tom Hayden
Digest Ed. ....Bob Rathgeber
Digital Ed. ....Mark Bickel
Editorial/Community Conversation Ed. David Plazas
Grandeur Ed. ....Tracy Jones
Lehigh Ed. ....Casey Logan
Lifestyles Ed. ....Tammy Ayer
Asst. Metro Ed. ....Andrew Jarosh
Market Information: ADS; Split run; TMC; Zoned editions.
Mechanical available: Offset; Black and 3 ROP colors; insert accepted; page cutoffs - 22 3/4.
Mechanical Specifications: Type page 11 3/4 x 21 1/2; E - 6 cols, 1 5/6, 1/8 between; A - 6 cols, 1 5/6, 1/8 between; C - 10 cols, 1 1/8, 1/16 between.
Commodity Consumption: Avg. Page Number Per Issue - Daily 89; Avg. Page Number Per Issue - Plates Used 240000; Avg. Page Number Per Issue - Sunday 168; widths 37 1/2; Newsprint Used - Short Tons 25503; Printing Ink Used - Black 400000; Printing Ink Used - Color 300000; Printin
Equipment EDITORIAL: Front-end Software – QPS, Quickwire.; Editorial Hardware – IBM/Netfinity Server, APP/Mac Dispatch Server; Editorial Equipment – AU/OMAN Servers, Lf/AP Leaf Picture Desk, GMTI/Digicol Archive; Editorial Printers – HP, All CLASSIFIED: Front-end Software – Mactive/Pongrass.; Classified Hardware – SII/Tandem; Classified Equipment – Fax Action; Classified Printers – HP, All DISPLAY: Ad make-up applications – Microsoft/Windows 2000, Multi-Ad/Creator; Layout Software – SCS/Layout 8000.; Display Hardware – APP/Mac, IBM/Netfinity; Display Printers – HP, All PRODUCTION: Pagination Software – QPS 4.11.; Production Equipment – 2-Anacoil, CA/MX33; Scanners – 2-Linotype-Hell/Topaz, 2-Tecsa/GEI PRESSROOM: Line 1 – 8-G/Metro (4 half decks) 1974, 2-Goss/Uniliner 4/4 Towers 2004; Line 2 – 1980-G/Metro (4 half decks) 8, 2-Goss/Uniliner 4/4 Towers 2004; Press Drives – Metros/DC motors/60hp, Uniliners/Shaftless indramat 35hp; Folders – 4-G/3:2; Pasters – 16-G/Met MAILROOM: Counter stackers – 4-HL/HI, 5-QWI/350, 3-Gammerler/STC 70, 1-QWI/500; Inserters and stuffers – 1-HI/2299, 1-HI/NP 1372; Bundle tying machines – 5-Dynaric/1500, 1-Dynaric/5000; Wrapping singles – 5-QWI/Viper 3/4 Wraps; Mailroom control system – QWI/BDS BUSINESS COMPUTERS: Business Software – Genesys; Business Hardware – IBM/AS-400

THE NEWS-PRESS MEDIA GROUP

2442 Dr. Martin Luther King Jr. Blvd., Fort Myers, Fla., 33901-3987; gen tel 239.335.0200; adv tel 239.335.0520; ed tel 239.335.0224; oth tel 239.335.0362; adv fax 239.344.4742; ed fax 239.334.0708; gen e-mail response@news-press.com; adv e-mail advertise@news-press.com; ed e-mail mailbag@news-press.com; web site www.news-press.com

Published: Mon, Tues, Wed, Thur, Fri, Sat, Sun
Weekday Frequency: m
Saturday Frequency: m
Circulation: 59,316; 70,879(sat); 87,241(sun)
Advertising: Open inch rate $70.85 b/w Daily
Own facility?: Y
Equipment PRESSROOM: Line 1 – 20 Goss Metro Couples
16 Goss Uniliner Tower Couple; Line 2 – 20 Goss Metor Couple
16 Goss Uniliner Tower Couples; Press Drives – Fincor 5126; Folders – (2) Goss Imperial 3:2 Rotary; Pasters – (8) Brock Solutions
(8) Goss MGD; Reels and Stands – Goss; Press control system – Goss Work Station MAILROOM: Counter stackers – Quipp 350 (5)
Quipp 500 (1)
Gammerler (3); Inserters and stuffers – 2299 (1) 1372 (1); Bundle tying machines – Dynaric 1500 (5)
Dynaric 5000 (1)
Dynaric 2400 (1); Wrapping singles – Quipp Viper (5); Mailroom control system – Icon (2) Omnizone; Addressing machine – Kansa 550 Domino Jet Array

FORT WALTON BEACH

FLORIDA FREEDOM NEWSPAPERS

200 Racetrack Rd., Fort Walton Beach, Fla., 32547; gen tel (850) 863-1111; gen fax (850) 862-5230; gen e-mail patr@nwfdailynews.com; web site www.nwf-dailynews.com
Price: 171.20/yr.
Advertising: Open inch rate $25.00
Insert rate: $54.00/M.

NORTHWEST FLORIDA DAILY NEWS

200 Racetrack Rd. NW, Fort Walton Beach, Fla., 32547; gen tel (850) 863-1111; adv tel (850) 863-1111; ed tel (850) 863-1111; gen fax (850) 862-5230; adv fax (850) 863-9348; ed fax (850) 863-7834; ed e-mail news@nwfdailynews.com; web site www.nwfdailynews.com
Published: Mon, Tues, Wed, Thur, Fri, Sat, Sun
Weekday Frequency: m
Saturday Frequency: m
Circulation: 28,407; 28,407(sat); 33,386(sun)
Last Audit: September 30, 2009
Price: 13.00/mo; 150.00/yr (d, mail), $180.00/yr (dS, mail).
Advertising: Open inch rate $50.00
News services: AP, NEA, MCT.
Politics: Independent. **Established:** 1946
Special Editions: Football (Aug); Gift Guide (Dec); Home Improvement (Mar); Vacation Guide (May).
Special Weekly Sections: Showcase/Entertainment (Fri); Moneysense (S); Food (Wed).
Magazines: Parade (S).
Pub.............Tom Conner
Adv. Dir.............Craig Hatcher
Mktg. Dir.............Michelle Macleod
Circ. Dir.............Darrell Snyder
Mng. Ed.............Colin Lipnicky
Art Ed.............Ken Maines
City Ed.............Lee Frost
Editorial Page Ed.............Jim Shoffner
Photo Ed.............Mark Kulaw
Showcase Ed.............Brenda Shoffner
Sports Ed.............Adam Pruiett
Webmaster............Del Stone
Mechanical available: Offset; Black and 3 ROP colors; insert accepted - all; page cutoffs - 22 3/4.
Mechanical Specifications: Type page 13 x 21 1/2; E - 6 cols, 2 1/16, 1/8 between; A - 6 cols, 1 13/16, 1/16 between; C - 9 cols, 1 1/11, 1/8 between.
Commodity Consumption: Avg. Page Number Per Issue - Daily 42; Avg. Page Number Per Issue - Sunday 82; widths 13 3/4; Newsprint Used - Metric Tons 3500; Newsprint Used - Short Tons 3000; Printing Ink Used - Pages Printed 17438.
Equipment EDITORIAL: Front-end Software – APT.; Editorial Hardware – PC; Editorial Printers – HP/8000 CLASSIFIED: Front-end Software – APT.; Classified Hardware – PC; Classified Printers – HP/4000 DISPLAY: Ad make-up applications – Multi-Ad/Creator 2; Layout Software – Multi-Ad/Creator 2, QPS/QuarkXPress.; Display Hardware – PC; Display Printers – APP/Mac Applewriter 8500; Production Equipment – V/Plain Paper, 1-LE/26; Cameras – C/Spartan III; Scanners – Equipment ☐ QPS/QuarkXPress 4.02. PRESSROOM: Line 1 – 9-G/Urbanite (3 color unit); Folders – 1; Pasters – 8 MAILROOM: Counter stackers – 1-HL/Monitor; Inserters and stuffers – GMA; Bundle tying machines – 2-MLN/EE, 1/Dynaric.; Business Hardware – PC

GAINESVILLE

THE GAINESVILLE SUN

2700 SW 13th St., Gainesville, Fla., 32608; gen tel (352) 378-1411; adv tel (352) 374-5012; ed tel (352) 374-5075; gen fax (352) 374-5099; adv fax (352) 338-3125; ed fax (352) 338-3128; web site www.gainesville.com
Published: Mon, Tues, Wed, Thur, Fri, Sat, Sun
Weekday Frequency: m
Saturday Frequency: m
Circulation: 29,024; 30,003(sat); 41,480(sun)
Last Audit: ABC September 30, 2011
Price: 3.00/wk; 169.00/yr.
Advertising: Open inch rate $101.00
News services: AP, NYT, LAT-WP, MCT, SHNS, TMS.
Politics: Independent.
Special Editions: Gainesville Magazine (Apr); Gainesville Magazine (Aug); Gainesville Magazine (Dec); Gainesville Magazine (Feb); Wedding Book (Jan); Travel-Caribbean Value Season (Jul); Gainesville Magazine (Jun); Travel-Summer in Europe (Mar); Travel-USA & Canada (May);
Special Weekly Sections: Weekend (Fri); Worklife (Mon); Campus (Other); TV Weekend (Sat); Scene (Thur).
Magazines: Parade (S).
Pub.............James E. Doughton
Controller............Jeffrey Pole
Mgr., Bus. Office............Raymond Ferrara
Bus. Devel. Mgr.............James Holmes
Adv. Dir.............Susan Pinder
Adv. Asst. Mgr., Classified............Naomi Williams
Adv. Coord., Nat'l............Dorie Clark
Online Sales Mgr.............Craig Grant
Circ. Dir.............Jim Miller
Circ. Mgr., Opns............Bob Carpentieri
Exec. Ed.............Jim Osteen
Mng. Ed.............Jacki Levine
Bus. Ed.............Anthony Clark
Amusements/Entertainment Ed...Dave Schlenker
Editorial Page Ed.............Ron Cunningham
Educ. Writer, Higher............Nathan Crabbe
Educ. Writer, Lower............Cindy Swirko
Health Ed.............Diane Chun
Metro Ed.............Jon Rabiroff
Metro Ed.............Sean McCrory
Market Information: ADS; Split run; TMC.
Mechanical available: Offset; Black and 3 ROP colors; insert accepted - all; page cutoffs - 22.
Mechanical Specifications: Type page 11 5/8 x 21; E - 6 cols, 2 1/16, 1/8 between; A - 6 cols, 2 1/16, 1/8 between; C - 10 cols, 1 3/16, 1/8 between.
Commodity Consumption: Avg. Page Number Per Issue - Daily 44; Avg. Page Number Per Issue - Plates Used 71100; Avg. Page Number Per Issue - Sunday 80; widths 13 1/4; Newsprint Used - Short Tons 9414; Printing Ink Used - Black 151200; Printing Ink Used - Color 52700; Printing In
Equipment EDITORIAL: Front-end Software – DTI/SpeedWriter, DTI/SpeedPlanner, DTI/Page-Speed 4.2.; Editorial Hardware – AT/9000, APP/Mac; Editorial Printers – 2-HP/8000, 2-AU/APS Ace 1 3N CLASSIFIED: Front-end Software – DTI/ClassSpeed 4.23.; Classified Hardware – APP/Mac DISPLAY: Ad make-up applications – DTI/AdSpeed, DTI/SpeedPlanner 4.23; Layout Software – DTI/AdSpeed, DTI/Ad-Manager, DTI/SpeedPlanner.; Display Hardware – 6-APP/Mac Pagination, 2-APP/Mac Text Input; Display Printers – 2-HP/8000, 2-AU/APS-HS-3850, 1-ECR/4550 PRODUCTION: Pagination Software – DTI/PageSpeed 4.23.; Production Equipment – Caere/OmniPage, 2-AU/APS 3850 HS, 1-ECR/4550; Cameras – 1-C/Newspager; Scanners – CD/646IE Color Scanner, Kk/Pro Rfs 2035, Umax/PowerLook, Umax/Ultra Vision PRESSROOM: Line 1 – 7-G/Headliner offset (5 half decks); Folders – 2-G/2:1 (with 1 motter stitch online stitching head); Pasters – 7; Reels and Stands – 7 MAILROOM: Counter stackers – 2-Id/2200, 2-QWI/350, 1-QWI/610; Inserters and stuffers – HI/1472P; Bundle tying machines – 1-MLN/2A, 2-Dynaric/NP2; Wrapping singles – 2-QWI/Viper w/Fox Ink Jet Printers; Addressing machine – 1/Ch, 1-/KR, Domino/Online, InkJet; Other equipment –Other; Audio Hardware – Brite Voice Systems BUSINESS COMPUTERS: Business Software – Microsoft/Office 97; Business Hardware – 1-IBM/AS 400

JACKSONVILLE

THE FLORIDA TIMES-UNION

One Riverside Ave., Jacksonville, Fla., 32202; gen tel (904) 359-4111; adv tel (904) 359-4111; ed tel (904) 359-4280; gen fax (904) 359-4478; adv fax (904) 359-4452; ed fax (904) 359-4478; web site www.jacksonville.com
Group: ????
????
Morris Communications Corpration
Published: Mon, Tues, Wed, Thur, Fri, Sat, Sun
Weekday Frequency: m
Saturday Frequency: m
Circulation: 99,280; 108,565(sat); 159,312(sun)
Last Audit: ABC September 30, 2011
Price: 4.67wk; 20.26/mo; 222.39/yr; 60.79/13wk.
Advertising: Open inch rate $283.00
News services: AP
Politics: Independent. **Established:** 1864
Note: Advertising is sold in combination with St. Augustine Record (mS) for $243.00(d), $259.00(m-sat) and $279.00(S).
Advertising not accepted: Y
Own facility?: Y
Special Editions: TPC (May), Fl/Ga (October) Football (August)
Special Weekly Sections: Home (Sat); Drive (Saturday) Religion (Saturday) Skirt! (Monday) Health (Wednesday)
Magazines: USA WEEKEND Magazine (S).
Pub.............Lucy Talley
Gen. Mgr.............Robert E. Martin
Controller, Div.............W. Mitchel Denning
Personnel Dir.............Carol Holmes
Adv. Mgr., Nat'l Accts.............Jim Leewe
Mgr., Promo.............Karen Brashear
Ed.............Frank Denton
Mng. Ed.............Carole Fader
Art Dir.............Steve Nelson
Bus. Ed.............Wayne Ezell
Bus. Writer............Timothy Gibbons
Features Ed.............Jeff Reece
Film/Theater Ed.............Matt Soergel
VP- Finance and Strategic Planning Delinda Fogel
VP- Circulation/Marketing............Amy McSwain
VP-Operations............Robert Todd
VP Advertising............Mark Lane
Adv. Dir., Classified............Geraldine Kotz
Circ. Dir.............Malcolm Drownell
Circ. Dir., Distr. Ctr.............Greg Webb
Circ. Mgr., Distr./Home Delivery.....Bill Brashear
Asst. Mng. Ed.............Joe Adams
Copy Ed.............Robin Hadley
Fashion Ed.............Linda Hanks
Market Information: ADS; Split run; Zoned editions.
Mechanical available: Offset; Black and 3 ROP colors; insert accepted; page cutoffs - 22 3/4.
Mechanical Specifications: Type page 11 5/8 x 21 1/2; E - 6 cols, 1 13/16, 1/8 between; A - 6 cols, 1 13/16, 1/16 between; C - 10 cols, 1 1/8, 1/16 between.
Commodity Consumption: Avg. Page Number Per Issue - Daily 54; Avg. Page Number Per Issue - Plates Used 289000; Avg. Page Number Per Issue - Saturday 84; Avg. Page Number Per Issue - Sunday 130; widths 37 1/2; Newsprint Used - Metric Tons 30000; Printing Ink Used - Black 661340
Equipment EDITORIAL: Front-end Software – DTI/Editorial v4.3, AII/Output MGR v2.5, Adobe/PS/3.; Editorial Hardware – DTI, Sun/Server, 250-APP/Mac; Editorial Equipment – 4-AII/3850 Imagesetter; Editorial Printers – HP, Xante, XIT CLASSIFIED: Front-end Software – DTI 5.01.; Classified Hardware – DTI, Sun/Server, 65-APP/Mac; Classified Printers – Epson, HP DISPLAY: Ad make-up applications – Archtype, Op, Adobe/PS/3, Alpha; Layout Software – 12-APP/Mac G3, AII/AdManager 3.1.; Display Hardware – Sun/Sparc Server 450, Intel/NT; Display Printers – X, 2-HP 2500, Typhoon, 1-HP/1055 CM PRODUCTION: Pagination Software – Media Spectrum Ad Watch and Content Wacth; DTI Pagination; Production Equipment – Lf/AP Leaf Picture Desk, 2 Kodak Trendsetter 200 CTP devices; Accutech Optical registration and Benders 10, 5-APP/Mac, 2-III/3850H, 2-III/3850H PRESSROOM: Line 1 – G/Metro 3213 8Units, 4 color decks 20 print couples; Line 2 – G/Metro: 3076; 9 units, 5 color decks, 23 print couples; Line 3 – G/Metro 3019 9 units, 5 decks, 23 print couples; Folders – 6-G/3:2 4; Pasters – 23; Reels and Stands – 23 MAILROOM: Counter stackers – 3-HI/HT, 4-QWI/501, 8-QWI/401; Inserters and stuffers – 2-HI/MP 632; Bundle tying machines – 6-Dynaric/3000; Wrapping singles – Manual.; Audio Hardware – PEP; Business Hardware – SAP
Accounting/Ad Order Entry
PBS Circulation Management
Delivery method: Mail, Newsstand, Private Carrier, Racks

KEY WEST

THE KEY WEST CITIZEN

3420 Northside Dr., Key West, Fla., 33040; gen tel (305) 292-7777; adv tel (305) 292-7777; ed tel (305) 292-7777; gen fax (305) 294-0768; adv fax (305) 294-0768; ed fax (305) 294-0768; web site www.keysnews.com
Published: Mon, Tues, Wed, Thur, Fri, Sat, Sun
Weekday Frequency: m
Saturday Frequency: m
Circulation: 7,998; 7,998(sat); 8,301(sun)
Last Audit: ABC September 30, 2011
Price: 12.00/mo; 102.00/yr.
Advertising: Open inch rate $27.48
News services: AP.
Politics: Independent. **Established:** 1876
Own facility?: Y
Special Editions: Back-to-School (Aug); Destination Weddings (Feb); Hemingway Days (Jul); Hurricane Tab (Jun); Locals Guide (Monthly); Gift Guide (Nov); Fantasy Fest (Oct); Healthfile (Quarterly); Home Improvement (Sept).
Special Weekly Sections: Church Page (Fri); Florida Keys Life (S); Paradise Entertainment (Thur).
Magazines: Comics (S).
Pub.............Paul Clarin
Production Director............Randy Erickson
Ed.............Tom Tuell
News Ed.............Cheryl Smith
Paradise Ed.............Nadja Hansen
Photo Ed.............Mike Hentz
Exec. Sports Ed.............Ralph Marrow
Mgmt. Info Servs. Mgr.............John McCormick
Circ. Manager............Tonya Parks
Business Editor............Mandy Miles
Advertising Director............David Singleton
Market Information: ADS; TMC.
Mechanical available: Offset; Black and 3 ROP colors; insert accepted; page cutoffs - 21 1/2.
Mechanical Specifications: Type page 13 x 21 1/2; E - 6 cols, 2 1/16, 1/8 between; A - 6 cols, 2 1/16, 1/8 between; C - 9 cols, 1 5/16, 1/16 between.
Commodity Consumption: Avg. Page Number Per Issue - Daily 18; Avg. Page Number Per Issue - Plates Used 7800; Avg. Page Number Per Issue - Sunday 32; widths 12 1/2; Newsprint Used - Short Tons 399; Printing Ink Used - Black 18047; Printing Ink Used - Color 800; Printing Ink Use
Equipment EDITORIAL: Front-end Software – Baseview.; Editorial Hardware – APP/Mac, Mk, PC; Editorial Printers – HP/5000 CLASSIFIED: Front-end Software – AdManager/Pro.; Classified Hardware – APP/Mac iMac; Classified Printers – HP/4050 DISPLAY: Ad make-up applications – Adobe/Photoshop, Adobe/Illustrator, QPS, QPS/QuarkXPress; Layout Software – Baseview, APP/Mac.; Display Hardware – APP/Mac Quadra 8100, APP/Mac G3; Display Printers – Epson/3000c, HP/8000, Pre Press/Panther PRODUCTION: Pagination Software – Adobe/Illustrator, Adobe/Photoshop, QPS/QuarkXPress, QPS.; Production Equipment – Panther/Pro 62, V/5300; Cameras – SCREEN/Companica 680C; Scanners – AG/Arcus Plus PRESSROOM: Line 1 – 9-G/1109SS; Folders – 1; Inserters and stuffers –

7/MM; Bundle tying machines – 1-/OVL; Addressing machine – 1-/El.; Audio Hardware – Software ☐ Infotext; Business Hardware – ATT
Delivery method: Mail, Newsstand, Private Carrier, Racks

THE KEY WEST CITIZEN
3420 Northside Drive, Key West, Fla., 33040; gen tel (305) 292-7777; adv tel (305) 292-7777; ed tel (305) 292-7777; adv fax 305-295-8013; ed fax 305-295-3008; ed e-mail editor@keysnews.com; web site www.keysnews.com
Group: Cooke Communications Florida LLC
Published: Mon, Tues, Wed, Thur, Fri, Sat, Sun
Weekday Frequency: m
Saturday Frequency: m
Own facility?: Y
Delivery method: Mail, Newsstand, Private Carrier, Racks

LAKE CITY

LAKE CITY REPORTER
180 E. Duval St., Lake City, Fla., 32055; gen tel (386) 752-1293; adv tel (386) 752-1293; ed tel (386) 752-1293; gen fax (386) 752-9400; adv fax (386) 752-9400; ed fax (386) 752-9400; adv e-mail abutcher@lakecityreporter.com; ed e-mail rbridges@lakecityreporter.com; web site www.lakecityreporter.com
Published: Tues, Wed, Thur, Fri, Sat, Sun
Weekday Frequency: m
Saturday Frequency: m
Circulation: 8,887; 8,887(sat); 8,887(sun)
Last Audit: Sworn September 30, 2007
Price: 83.46/yr (carrier), $96.00/yr (mail).
Advertising: Open inch rate $19.50
News services: AP, SHNS.
Politics: 1874
Not Published: Monday
Own facility?: Y
Special Editions: Suwannee Valley Vacation Guide (Jan.); Rodeo magazine (March); North Florida Living (Apr); Football (Aug); Song Book (Dec); Physicians Directory (Jan); Columbia Style Biz (Jul); Best of the Best (May); Home for the Holidays (Nov); Guide to Columbia County (Oct); County Fair magazine (Oct.); Health & Nutrition (Sept).
Special Weekly Sections: Real Estate (Fri); @RecordBody:**Magazines:** Parade (S); American Profile (Weekly).
Publisher....................................Todd Wilson
Controller...................................Sue Brannon
Sports Ed. ....Tim Kirby
IT Mgr. ....Dave Kimler
Advertising Director..................Ashley Butcher
Editor...................................Robert Bridges
Circulation Director ....Mandy Brown
Adv. Dir. ....Lynda Strickland
Circ. Dir. ....Russell Waters
Ed...Tom Mayer
Mng. Ed...................................Jerry Spaeder
Market Information: TMC.
Mechanical available: Offset; Black and 3 ROP colors; insert accepted - hand bill size; page cutoffs - 22 1/4.
Mechanical Specifications: Type page 13 x 21 1/2; E - 6 cols, 1 5/6, 1/8 between; A - 6 cols, 1 5/6, 1/8 between; C - 6 cols, 1 5/6, 1/8 between.
Commodity Consumption: widths 13 3/4.
Equipment EDITORIAL: Front-end Software – Baseview, QPS, Adobe/Photoshop.; Editorial Hardware – APP/Macs; Editorial Printers – Panther/Imagesetter, Xante/Accel-a-Writer, APP/Laserwriter CLASSIFIED: Front-end Software – Baseview.; Classified Hardware – APP/Macs; Classified Printers – Xante/Accel-a-Writer, APP/Laserwriter DISPLAY: Ad make-up applications – QPS/QuarkXPress.; Display Hardware – APP/Macs; Display Printers – Xante/Accel-a-Writer, APP/Laserwriter PRODUCTION: Pagination Software – Baseview.; Production Equipment – Panther; Business Hardware – IBM/AS-400
Delivery method: Mail, Newsstand, Private Carrier, Racks

LAKELAND

LAKELAND LEDGER PUBLISHING CORP.
300 West Lime St., Lakeland, Fla., 33815; gen tel (863) 802-7000; gen fax (863) 802-7813

THE LEDGER
300 W. Lime St., 300 West Lime Street, Lakeland, Fla., 33815; gen tel (863) 802-7000; adv tel (863) 802-7406; ed tel (863) 802-7519; gen fax (863) 802-7804; adv fax (863) 802-7813; ed fax (863) 802-7849; gen e-mail customerservice.classified@theledger.com; web site www.theledger.com
Published: Mon, Tues, Wed, Thur, Fri, Sat, Sun
Weekday Frequency: m
Saturday Frequency: m
Circulation: 41,309; 40,358(sat); 62,756(sun)
Last Audit: ABC September 30, 2011
Price: 3.67/wk (carrier); 190.85/yr.
Advertising: Open inch rate $121.67
News services: AP, NYT, MCT, LAT-WP.
Politics: Independent. **Established:** 1924
Own facility?: Y
Special Editions: Back-to-School (Aug); Year In Review (Dec); Automotive (Jan); Football (Jul); Spring Health Care (Mar); Mayfaire-By-The-Lake (May); Today's Senior (Monthly); Reader's Choice (Nov); Parade of Homes (Oct); Fall Health Care (Sept).
Special Weekly Sections: Entertainment (Fri); Pro Football (Mon); Travel (S); Real Estate (Sat); Food (Thur); Medical (Tues).
Magazines: Parade (S).
Broadcast Affiliations: New York Times Company Broadcast Group.
Pub./Pres.................................Jerome Ferson
Dir., HR............................Anthony Rodriguez
Adv. Dir........................................Dawn Willis
Adv. Mgr., Classified/Display.........Kim Edwards
Mng. Ed....................................Lenore Devore
Art Dir......................................Mark Williams
East Polk Ed.......................................Jeff Kline
Editorial Page Ed. ....Kevin Bouffard
Asst. Editorial Page Ed. ....Glenn Marston
Farm/Agriculture Ed. ....Lynn Maddox
Health/Medical Ed.......................Robin Adams
Home/Garden Ed. ....Lyle McBride
Online Ed. ....Barry Friedman
Outdoors Ed............................Delwin Milligan
Political/Gov't Ed. ....Bill Rufty
Circ. Mgr...............................Robert Copeland
Exec. Ed. ....Skip M. Perez
Market Information: ADS; TMC; Zoned editions.
Mechanical available: Offset; Black and 3 ROP colors; insert accepted - spadea comic wraps; page cutoffs - 22.
Mechanical Specifications: Type page 13 x 21 1/2; E - 6 cols, 2 1/16, 1/8 between; A - 6 cols, 2 1/16, 1/8 between; C - 9 cols, 1 3/8, between.
Commodity Consumption: Avg. Page Number Per Issue - Daily 72; Avg. Page Number Per Issue - Plates Used 380327; Avg. Page Number Per Issue - Sunday 136; widths 54; Newsprint Used - Metric Tons 14814; Printing Ink Used - Black 280000; Printing Ink Used - Color 170000; Printing I
Equipment EDITORIAL: Front-end Software – AT/SYSDECO.; Editorial Hardware – AT/SYSDECO, APP/Mac Press-to-Go; Editorial Equipment – Lf/AP Leaf Picture Desk, AP/Leafax, APP/Laserphoto; Editorial Printers – AU/Laserprinter, Okidata CLASSIFIED: Front-end Software – AT/SYSDECO Classified Pagination.; Classified Hardware – AT/SYSDECO-Classified Pagination DISPLAY: Ad make-up applications – AT/Classpage FPO; Layout Software – SCS/Layout 8000, SCS/LYNX.; Display Hardware – AT/LAS; Display Printers – HP/8000 Laser Jet PRODUCTION: Pagination Software – AT/Classpage FPO, AT, Press 2go, QPS/QuarkXPress.; Production Equipment – Kk/RFS 2035, 2-Microtek/600, CD/5400; Cameras – 1-C/Spartan; Scanners – 1-Kk/RFS 2035, 2-PixelCraft/7650X, 1-Howtek/D4000 PRESSROOM: Line 1 – 2; Folders – 2; Pasters – 8-G/RIP (ea. press); Reels and Stands – 8; Press control system – G/Control; Press registration system – G/Pin Register. MAILROOM: Counter stackers – 8-QWI/350; Inserters and stuffers – 1-HI/RS25, 4-GMA/2000 14:1; Bundle tying machines – 8/Power Strap/News Tyers; Mailroom control system – Machine Design; Addressing machine – 1-/Ch, 1-/St.; Audio Hardware – Brite; Business Hardware – IBM/AS-400
Zip Codes served: 33565, 33566, 33567, 33801, 33803, 33805, 33809, 33810, 33811, 33812, 33813, 33815, 33823, 33827, 33830, 33834, 33835, 33837, 33896, 33897, 33838, 33839, 33841, 33843, 33844, 33850, 33851, 33853, 33859, 33855, 33856, 33860
Delivery method: Mail, Newsstand, Private Carrier, Racks

LEESBURG

THE DAILY COMMERCIAL
212 E. Main St., Leesburg, Fla., 34748; gen tel (352) 365-8200; adv tel (352) 365-8240; ed tel (357) 365-8266; gen fax (352) 365-1951; gen e-mail news@dailycommercial.com; web site www.dailycommercial.com
Published: Mon, Tues, Wed, Thur, Fri, Sat, Sun
Weekday Frequency: m
Saturday Frequency: m
Circulation: 21,203; 21,203(sat); 20,922(sun)
Last Audit: September 30, 2007
Price: 5.95/mo; 63.97/yr.
Advertising: Open inch rate $26.56
News services: AP, NYT.
Politics: Independent.
Special Editions: Home Improvement (Apr); Women's Quarterly (Aug); Holiday Gift Guide (Dec); Women's Quarterly (Feb); Super Bowl Preview (Jan); For Your Health (Mar); Women's Quarterly (May); Women's Quarterly (Nov); Welcome Back (Oct).
Special Weekly Sections: Weekend (Fri); Real Estate (Sat); Best Food Day (Thur).
Magazines: TV Week (offset) (S); USA WEEKEND Magazine (Thur).
Broadcast Affiliations: LSCC-TV; Comcast; Time-Warner.
Pub. ....Ron Wallace
Adv. Dir....................................Steve Skaggs
Circ. Dir......................................Tina Reader
News Ed...Bill Koch
Prodn. Mgr., Pressroom.........James Bilderback
Mechanical available: Offset; Black and 3 ROP colors; insert accepted; page cutoffs - 22 3/4.
Commodity Consumption: Avg. Page Number Per Issue - Daily 32; Avg. Page Number Per Issue - Plates Used 72000; Avg. Page Number Per Issue - Sunday 60; widths 27 1/2; Newsprint Used - Short Tons 3780; Printing Ink Used - Black 124000; Printing Ink Used - Color 18000; Printing In
Equipment EDITORIAL: Front-end Software – Baseview/NewsEdit Pro 3.0, Baseview/IQUE, QPS/QuarkXPress.; Editorial Hardware – 8-StarMax/4000, 12-StarMax/3000, 10-APP/Mac G4; Editorial Printers – Teletype/MOD 40, Xante/Accel-a-Writer 8200, GCC/Elite XL 616, APP/Mac LaserWriter Pro 16 CLASSIFIED: Front-end Software – Baseview/Ad Manager Pro 1.0.4.; Classified Hardware – 9-StarMax/4000; Classified Printers – APP/Mac 4/600 DISPLAY: Ad make-up applications – QPS/QuarkXPress, Adobe/Photoshop, Adobe/Illustrator.; Display Hardware – 5-StarMax/4000; Display Printers – Xante/Accel-a-Writer 8200, GCC/Elite XL616, APP/Mac LaserWriter Pro; Production Equipment – 2-Pre Press/Panther Pro 36, 1-C/80, 1-C/80RA, 1-Konica/K-550; Cameras – 1-C, 1-LE; Scanners – Kk/RFS 2035, 2-AG/StudioScan. PRESSROOM: Line 1 – 10-G/Urbanite; Folders – 1; Pasters – 6 MAILROOM: Counter stackers – 4/QWI, 2-Id; Inserters and stuffers – 1-HI/848; Bundle tying machines – 2-/MLN, 1-MLN/Spirit; Addressing machine – 1-/Ch.; Audio Hardware – Brite Voice Systems, AP; Business Hardware – IBM/Sys 36

MARIANNA

JACKSON COUNTY FLORIDAN
4403 Constitution Ln., Marianna, Fla., 32448; gen tel (850) 526-3614; adv tel (850) 526-3614; ed tel (850) 526-3614; gen fax (850) 482-4478; adv fax (850) 482-4478; ed fax (850) 482-4478; gen e-mail editorial@jcfloridan.com; adv e-mail sales@jcfloridan.com; ed e-mail editorial@jcfloridan.com; web site www.jcfloridan.com
Group: Media General
Published: Tues, Wed, Thur, Fri, Sun
Weekday Frequency: m
Circulation: 5,073; 5,278(sun)
Last Audit: ABC September 30, 2011
Price: 9.95/mo; 119.40/yr.
Advertising: Open inch rate $22.65
News services: AP, SHNS.
Politics: Independent.
Not Published: Saturday, Monday
Special Editions: Senior Citizen (Apr); Football (Aug); Marianna Christmas Bucks (Dec); Visitor's Guide Supplement (Feb); Income Tax (Jan); Senior Citizen (Jul); Visitor's Guide Supplement (Jun); Home & Garden (Mar); Mother's Day (May); Farm City (Nov); Back To School (Sep
Special Weekly Sections: Religion (Fri); Business (S); Health (Thur); Education (Tues); Agriculture (Wed).
Magazines: Relish (Monthly); USA WEEKEND Magazine (S); American Profile (Weekly).
Profile: http://www2.jcfloridan.com/contact_us/circulation/
Adv. Dir./Publisher...................Valeria Roberts
Circ. Mgr..................................Dena Oberske
Mng. Ed. ....Mike Becker
Photo Ed. ....Mark Skinner
Sports Ed.....................................Dustin Kent
Market Information: TMC.
Mechanical available: Offset; Black and 3 ROP colors; insert accepted; page cutoffs - 22 3/4.
Mechanical Specifications: Type page 12 x 21 1/2; E - 6 cols, 1 3/4, 1/6 between; A - 6 cols, 1 3/4, 1/6 between; C - 6 cols, 1 3/4, 1/6 between.
Commodity Consumption: Avg. Page Number Per Issue - Daily 12; Avg. Page Number Per Issue - Sunday 16; widths 25 1/2; Printing Ink Used - Black 4200; Printing Ink Used - Pages Printed 3288.
Delivery method: Mail, Newsstand, Private Carrier, Racks

MELBOURNE

FLORIDA TODAY
One Gannett Plaza, Melbourne, Fla., 32940; gen tel (321) 242-3500; adv tel 321-242-3765; ed tel 321-242-3621; gen fax (321) 253-0071; adv fax 321-242-6618; ed fax 321-242-6620; oth fax 321-242-6601; gen e-mail sshook@floridatoday.com; adv e-mail jprice@floridatoday.com; ed e-mail bstover@floridatoday.com; web site www.floridatoday.com
Group: Gannett Co., Inc, 7950 Jones Branch Drive, McLean, VA
Gannett Co., Inc.
Publishers Representatives of Florida, Inc.
Published: Mon, Tues, Wed, Thur, Fri, Sat, Sun
Weekday Frequency: m
Saturday Frequency: m
Circulation: 59,038; 62,809(sat); 85,496(sun)
Last Audit: ABC September 30, 2011
Price: $1.00 (mon-sat); $1.50 (sun); $20.05/month (7-day); $10.14/month (Sun); $12.68/month (weekend)
Advertising: Open inch rate: $79.67 (mon-sat) / $128.37 (sun)
News services: AP, Gannett Content One
Politics: Independent. **Established:** 1966

Advertising not accepted: Y
Own facility?: Y
Special Editions: HealthSource; Health & Medicine; Brevard County Moms; Fact Book; @RecordBody:**Special Weekly Sections:** TGIF Weekend (Fri); Money Monday (Mon); Arts & Leisure (S); Saturday Real Estate (Sat); Big Auto Book (Thur); Health and Fitness (Tues).
Magazines: USA Weekend (sun)
Broadcast Affiliations: WESH: NBC; WKMG: CBS; WFTV: ABC; WOFL (Fox).
Profile: Brevard County, Population 543,376 - HH 229,692
President and Publisher..........Mark Mikolajczyk
Executive Editor..............................Bob Stover
Controller................................Robert Van Epp
Sales and Marketing Director.........Greg Watson
Multi Media Advertising Manager Kim Robedeau
Strategic Marketing Solutions Director Gina Kaiser
Credit Mgr. ....Sharon Secord
Operations Director ....John Vizzini
Adv. Dir..Chris Wood
VP/South Region, HR Business Partner Team Julie Lusk
Assistant Controller.................Landra Burgess
Adv. Mgr., Retail.....................Janet Gallagher
Systems Manager ....Dan Patellis
Adv. Mgr., Classified ....Kay Wartell
Operations Production Manager....Bob Campbell
Distribution Operations Manager Cedric Johnson
Circ. Mgr., Info..............................David Popp
National / Majors Manager..............Julian Price
Retail Sales Manager ....Leween Jones
Retail Sales Manager ....Mike Coppage
Aerospace/Aviation Ed......................John Kelly
Automotive Manager..............Spencer Henney
Editorial Page Ed...........................John Glisch
Packaging Center Manager ....Marcus Greco
Editorial Writer.......................Annette Clifford
Local Editor....................................John Kelly
Multimedia Editor ....Jeff Meesey
Features Ed..............................Deidre Gordon
Public Interest Editor........................Matt Reed
Food Ed........................Suzy Fleming Leonard
Delivery News Editor..................Eric Garwood
Sports Editor..............................Mike Parsons
Visuals Editor..............................Tim Walters
Custom Content Editor ....Suzy Leonard
Business Editor....................Adam Lowenstein
Enterprise Editor / space, family, education Mara Bellaby
Enterprise Editor/county, state, environment John McCarthy
Enterprise Editor/breaking news, military, religion Lee Nessel
Market Information: Electronic Edition; Sunday Select; TMC
Mechanical available: Offset; Black and 3 ROP colors; preprinted inserts accepted
Mechanical Specifications: Type page 10x21. 6 cols, 1 5/6, 1/8 between
Commodity Consumption: Avg. Page Number Per Issue - Daily 68; Avg. Page Number Per Issue - Plates Used 160000; Avg. Page Number Per Issue - Sunday 148; widths 50; Newsprint Used - Metric Tons 14292; Newsprint Used - Short Tons 15754; Printing Ink Used - Black 230817; Printing
Equipment EDITORIAL: Front-end Software – HI/NewsMaker Editorial 4.5.; Editorial Hardware – 2-Sun/Enterprise 450; Editorial Equipment – HI/NewsMaker Pagination; Editorial Printers – Epson CLASSIFIED: Front-end Software – HI/AdPower, HI/AdPower.; Classified Hardware – Gateway; Classified Equipment – HI/Classified AdPag; Classified Printers – Florida Data DISPLAY: Ad make-up applications – Adobe/Creative Suite, QPS/QuarkXPress 4.11, Multi-Ad/Creator Pro 6.5, File Maker Pro, DPS/AdTracker, DPS/AdTracker 5.0.1, Aldus/FreeHand 9.0; Display Hardware – APP/Mac; Display Printers – HP/Color Laser Jet, HP/Jaser Jet, Tektronix/Phaser 780 PRODUCTION: Pagination Software – HI/NewsMaker.; Production Equipment – 2-CD/646IE, Anites/SN48 Processor, WL/Lithobender; Scanners – 2-Linotype-Hell/Topaz, 1-Kk/RFS 2035 Plus PRESSROOM: Line 1 – 16-G/Headliner Offset double width; Line 2 – 8-G/C150 Community offset single width; Press Drives – Fin; Folders – r-G/3:2, 1-G/1:1, Twafolder; Pasters – 16-G/45 RTP, 2-Enkel/Zero Speed Pasters; Reels and Stands – Static belt tension 3 arm reels; Press control system – Fin/Drive; Press registration system – KFM MAILROOM: Counter stackers – 1-MM, 2-HL/Dual Carrier, 2-QWI/Dual Carrier, 2-HL/Monitor, 2-QWI/401, 1-Gammerler/KL503, 1-Gammerler/STC-700; Inserters and stuffers – 1-Mailstar, 2-HI/630, 1-HI/632; Bundle tying machines – 3-Dynaric/NP 1500, 3-Power Strap, Newstyer/2000; Wrapping singles – 3-HL/Bottom Wrap, 3-HI/Bottomwrap, 2-QWI/Viper Bottomwrap; Mailroom control system – 2-Prima/Icon 300; Addressing machine – 1-Ch, 1-Barstrom; Other equipment –MM/Prima Trimmer, 2-Accraply, 1-Cannon/Series II Cart Loader. BUSINESS COMPUTERS: Business Software – Cyborg, Lawson, Gen ledger, Corporate 1997 : Adv, Circ; Business Hardware – 1-IBM/AS-400 Model F45, IBM/AS-400 500-2141
Zip Codes served: Brevard County, FL
Delivery method: Mail, Newsstand, Private Carrier, Racks

MIAMI

DIARIO LAS AMERICAS

2900 NW 39th St., Miami, Fla., 33142; gen tel (305) 633-3341; adv tel (305) 633-3341; ed tel (305) 633-3341; gen fax (305) 635-7668; adv fax (305) 635-4002; ed fax (305) 635-7668; adv e-mail advertising@diariolasamericas.com; ed e-mail editorial@diariolasamericas.com; web site www.diariolasamericas.com
Published: Tues, Wed, Thur, Fri, Sat, Sun
Weekday Frequency: m
Circulation: 69,132; 69,132(sat); 69,132(sun)
Last Audit: February 12, 2001
Price: 73.83/yr.
Advertising: Open inch rate $32.25
News services: AFP, EFE, NYT, NYT Spanish.
Politics: Independent.
Not Published: New Year; Good Friday; Memorial Day; Independence Day; Labor Day; Thanksgiving; Christmas.
Special Editions: Latin Chamber of Commerce (Apr); Carnival Miami (Feb); Colombia Independence Day (tab) (Jul); Weddings (Mar); Cuban Independence Day (May); South Florida Auto Show (Nov); Hispanic Heritage Festival (Oct); Nicaragua Independence Day (tab) (Sept).
Special Weekly Sections: Auto Review (S); Best Food Day (Thur); Vida Sana (Health) (Wed).
Magazines: La Revista (Every other week).
Asst. Pub. ....Maribel Suarez
Bus. Mgr./Controller..................Victor M. Vega
Credit Mgr. ....Daniel Medina
Adv. Dir. ....Alejandro Aguirre
Adv. Mgr., Nat'l..................Bertha V. Enriquez
Adv. Mgr., Classified...................Jose A. Yuste
Ed. ....Horacio Aguirre
Deputy Ed. ....Alejandro J. Aguirre
Food Ed. ....Virginia Godoy
News Ed...................................Gustavo Pena
Society Ed......................Luis David Rodriguez
Data Processing Mgr.............Jesus Hernandez
Prod. Mgr. ....Gustavo De La Osa
Mechanical available: Offset; Black and 3 ROP colors; insert accepted - free fall, cards, etc.; page cutoffs - 21.
Mechanical Specifications: Type page 13 x 21; E - 6 cols, 2 1/16, 1/8 between; A - 6 cols, 2 1/16, 1/8 between; C - 10 cols, 1/8 between.
Commodity Consumption: Avg. Page Number Per Issue - Daily 32; Avg. Page Number Per Issue - Plates Used 11500; Avg. Page Number Per Issue - Sunday 56; widths 13 3/4; Newsprint Used - Short Tons 2500; Printing Ink Used - Black 40600; Printing Ink Used - Color 1000.
Equipment EDITORIAL: Front-end Software – AT/APM4 Pagination, Microsoft/Windows, Microsoft/Word, Novell/Network 4.0, Archetype/Designer, Adobe/Photoshop.; Editorial Hardware – Compaq/Pro Liner Servers; Editorial Equipment – Sharp/Scanner; Editorial Printers – 2-QMS/8600, HP, Epson, Okidata, QMS/Hammerhead 2060 CLASSIFIED: Front-end Software – Novell/Network 3.12. DISPLAY: Ad make-up applications – Novell/Network 4.0, Archetype/Designer; Layout Software – 30-Compaq, Compaq/Server.; Display Hardware – Compaq/ProLiner; Display Printers – Seiko, QMS/860 Printers PRODUCTION: Pagination Software – AT/APM4.; Production Equipment – 2-COM/Universal, NA/A250, 1-COM/19IN-Dawn; Cameras – 1-Ik/530, 1-Ik/560, 1-Spartan/1244; Scanners – Sharp/JX-600 PRESSROOM: Line 1 – 8-G/U 686; Folders – 2-G/U-686; Pasters – 8-Cary/Compact Splicer. MAILROOM: Counter stackers – 1-Id; Addressing machine – 1/KR.; Business Hardware – 6-DEC/CPU 1123

EL NUEVO HERALD

One Herald Plaza, Miami, Fla., 33132; gen tel 1-800-843-4372; web site www.miamiherald.com
Published: Mon, Tues, Wed, Thur, Fri, Sat, Sun
Weekday Frequency: m
Saturday Frequency: m
Circulation: 57,381; 53,429(sat); 72,687(sun)
Last Audit: ABC September 30, 2011

THE MIAMI HERALD

1 Herald Plz., Miami, Fla., 33132-1693; gen tel (305) 350-2111; adv tel (305) 376-3161; ed tel (305) 376-2287; adv fax (305) 376-2094; ed fax (305) 376-5287; adv e-mail adsbyemail@herald.com; web site www.miamiherald.com
Group: Metro Newspaper Advertising Services, Inc.
Published: Mon, Tues, Wed, Thur, Fri, Sat, Sun
Weekday Frequency: m
Saturday Frequency: m
Circulation: 160,505; 127,037(sat); 209,116(sun)
Last Audit: ABC September 30, 2011
Price: 3.10/wk; 161.20/yr; 12.40/4wk.
Advertising: Open inch rate $406.00
News services: AP, DJ, MCT, LAT-WP, SOU, TV Data.
Special Weekly Sections: Weekend (2 Zones) (Fri); Business Monday (Mon); Focus (S); Wheels & Waves (Thur); Neighbors (12 Zones) (Wed).
Magazines: Parade (S).
Pres./Pub..........................David A. Landsberg
Vice Pres., Finance/CFO ....Susan Rosenthal
Vice Pres./Broward Bus. Mgr........Donna Dickey
Vice Pres./CFO ....Susan A. Rosenthal
Vice Pres., Targeted Publications .....Dory Trinka
Vice Pres., HR/Asst. to Pub. ....Elissa Vanaver
Gen. Mgr., MiamiHerald.com ....Raul Lopez
Adv. Dir., Classified....................Patricia Royal
Adv. Dir., Local ....David Jost
Adv. Dir., Nat'l...........................Matthew Fine
Interactive Sales Mgr...................Jackie Kaplan
Vice Pres., Mktg./Bus. Devel. ....Willard Soper
Circ. Vice Pres..........................Terry Whitney
Vice Pres./Exec. Ed.............Anders Gyllenhaal
Dir., Int'l Edition ....Tony Espetia
Mng. Ed., Multimedia.....................Rick Hirsch
Mng. Ed., News ....Dave Wilson
Mng. Ed., Presentations/Opns. ....Liza Gross
Asst. Mng. Ed., Broward ....Pat Andrews
Dir., Photography ....Luis Rios
Market Information: ADS; Split run; TMC; Zoned editions.
Mechanical available: Offset; Black and 3 ROP colors; insert accepted - single sheets; page cutoffs - 22.
Mechanical Specifications: Type page 11 5/8 x 21; E - 6 cols, 1 13/16, 1/6 between; A - 6 cols, 1 5/6, 1/8 between; C - 10 cols, 1 1/6, 1/8 between.
Commodity Consumption: Avg. Page Number Per Issue - Daily 85; Avg. Page Number Per Issue - Plates Used 900000; Avg. Page Number Per Issue - Saturday 106; Avg. Page Number Per Issue - Sunday 218; widths 49 7/8; Newsprint Used - Metric Tons 80974; Newsprint Used - Short Tons 892
Equipment EDITORIAL: Front-end Software – SII/Coyote 3, SII/Layout.; Editorial Hardware – SII/Tandem Servernet, 350-HP/PC; Editorial Printers – HP/5000, OMS/2060; Classified Hardware – 180-HP/PC; Classified Printers – HP/5000. DISPLAY: Ad make-up applications – SCS/Layout 8000, Managing Editor/ALS; Layout Software – SCS/Layout 8000, Cascade, MEI.; Display Hardware – PC, Novell, Unix, APP/Mac; Display Printers – HP/5000 PRODUCTION: Pagination Software – QPS/QuarkXPress 4.11, SII/Layout 1.94.; Production Equipment – 4-WL/38-G, 2-WL/OPB, 5-AII/3850; Scanners – 2-Eskofot/2636, 2-Tecsa, 1-Howtek/Scanmaster 2500, 1-Howtek/Scanmaster 6500 PRESSROOM: Line 1 – 3-G/Newsliner double width 1997, 2-G/Newsliner double width 1999; Folders – 5, 3, 5; Pasters – 45-G/CT50; Reels and Stands – 45-CT/50. MAILROOM: Counter stackers – 2-QWI/300, 2-QWI/300, 2-QWI/300, 1-QWI/350, 10-QWI/350, 4-QWI/350, 3-QWI/350; 6-QWI/350, 4-QWI/400, 2-QWI/400; Inserters and stuffers – 1-HI/1372P, 1-HI/1372P, 2-HI/1472P, 1-HI/1572, 2-GMA/SLS1000A; Bundle tying machines – 1-Dynaric/NP- AUDIO: Audio Software – Omnivox Apex; Audio Hardware – 2-PC BUSINESS COMPUTERS: Business Software – CJ 6.03K, Admarc 7.0.D; Business Hardware – 1-HP/3000, 1-HP/3000, 1-HP/9000

THE MIAMI HERALD PUBLISHING CO.

One Herald Plaza, Miami, Fla., 33132-1693; gen tel (305) 350-2111; gen fax (305) 376-2329; web site http://www.miami.com/mld/miamiherald/

NAPLES

NAPLES DAILY NEWS

1100 Immokalee Rd., Naples, Fla., 34110; gen tel (239) 262-3161; adv tel (239) 262-3161 (display); ed tel (239) 263-4863; gen fax (239) 263-4816; adv fax (239) 263-4703 (class); ed fax (239) 263-4816; gen e-mail info@naplesnews.com; adv e-mail classad@naplesnews.com (classified); sales@naplesnews.com (internet sales); web site www.naplesnews.com
Published: Mon, Tues, Wed, Thur, Fri, Sat, Sun
Weekday Frequency: m
Saturday Frequency: m
Circulation: 45,136; 47,732(sat); 55,453(sun)
Last Audit: ABC September 30, 2011
Price: 4.97/wk; 59.65/mo; 226.69/yr.
Advertising: Open inch rate $104.74
News services: AP, SHNS, NYT.
Politics: Independent.
Special Editions: Newcomers (Apr); Back-to-School (Aug); Newcomers (Dec); Ambience (Feb); Newcomers (Jan); In Business (Jul); Parents & Kids (Jun); Newcomers (Mar); Parents & Kids (May); Real Estate Marketplace (Monthly); Homes for the Holidays (Nov); Portfolio of Homes (O
Special Weekly Sections: Fashion (Fri); Business Monday (Mon); Business (S); Religion (Sat); Health (Tues); Food (Wed).
Magazines: Visitor's Guide (Other); Comics (S).
Pres./Pub....................................Chris Doyle
Dir., Finance ....Debbie Landreth
Asst. to Pub...................................Trish Priller
Adv. Mgr.......................................Kurt Aderson
Adv. Mgr., Major Accts..................Rick Kendall
Adv. Mgr., Nat'l/Co-op...................Paula Monty
Circ. Dir.......................................Tom Janning
Ed. ....Philip P. Lewis
City Ed....Allen Bartlett
Editorial Page Ed. ....Jeffrey Lytle
Homes/Ambience Ed. .Harriet Howard Heithaus
News Ed....Tim Aten
Real Estate Ed. ....Jim Lockhart
Sports Ed. ....Greg Hardwig
Mgr., IS/Pre Press ....Cathy Rodrick
Online/New Media Dir....................Andrea Lynn
Mgr., Packaging.........................Glenn Williams
Prodn. Mgr., Pressroom ....Cassay Cote
Market Information: Zoned editions.
Mechanical available: Offset; Black and 3 ROP colors; insert accepted; page cutoffs - 23 9/16.
Mechanical Specifications: Type page 13 x 22 1/4; E - 6 cols, 2 1/16, 1/8 between; A - 6 cols, 2 1/16, 1/8 between; C - 10 cols, 1 1/5, 1/8 between.
Commodity Consumption: Avg. Page Number Per

Issue - Daily 63; Avg. Page Number Per Issue - Plates Used 78520; Avg. Page Number Per Issue - Sunday 172; widths 27 1/2; Newsprint Used - Metric Tons 8539; Printing Ink Used - Black 180000; Printing Ink Used - Color 75000; Printing

Equipment EDITORIAL: Front-end Software – HI/NME.; Editorial Hardware – HI/Newsmaker; Editorial Printers – Epson, IBM, Konica, HP CLASSIFIED: Front-end Software – HI/Ad-Power.; Classified Hardware – Dell/200; Classified Printers – Epson/DFX 5000, Konica/Laser, HP DISPLAY: Ad make-up applications – SCS; Layout Software – SCS/Layout 8000.; Display Hardware – Sun/Sparc 20; Display Printers – HP/LaserJet III, C.Itoh/C1400, Data products/1550, Techtronic Phaser PRODUCTION: Pagination Software – QPS/QuarkXPress 3.31, HI/XP-21-DASH, HI/XP-21 NMP, HI/XP-21 NME.; Production Equipment – 2-AU/3850 Doublewidth, WL/Lith-X-Pozer III, WL/Lithobender SD 30, Automated/Optical Film Punch; Scanners – Scitex/System, Kk/2035, Graphic Enterprises/3050 Copy Dot PRESSROOM: Line 1 – 9-G/Metro double width (5 half decks) 1994; Press Drives – 10-HP/75; Folders – 3-G/3:2 double; Pasters – 9; Reels and Stands – G/reels. MAILROOM: Counter stackers – 6-HL/Monitor; Inserters and stuffers – 1-S/1472, 1-S/1272P; Bundle tying machines – 1/Power Strap/PSN-2, 2-/Power Strap/PSN-6, 3-Dynaric/NP 1500; Wrapping singles – 4-/CH, 1-HL/Underwrap; Mailroom control system – 2-/PC, Image Packagi BUSINESS COMPUTERS: Business Software – PBS: Microsoft/Office; Business Hardware – Sun/Sparc

NEW SMYRNA BEACH

THE OBSERVER

508 Canal St., New Smyrna Beach, Fla., 32168; gen tel (386) 427-1000; adv fax (386) 424-9858; gen e-mail news@nsb-observer.com; web site http://www.sevob-server.com/

Published: Thur
Last Audit: Sworn March 31, 2006
Price: 30.00/yr.
Advertising: Open inch rate $13.75
Politics: Independent.
Owner/Pub. ....Michele Lott
Gen. Mgr., Sales/Mktg. ....Doug Hodson
Circ. Mgr. ....Myriah Chandler
Ed. ....Robert Burns
Prodn. Dir. ....Roy Padrick
Mechanical Specifications: Type page 13 x 21 1/2; E - 6 cols, 2 1/16, 1/8 between; A - 6 cols, 2 1/16, 1/8 between; C - 8 cols, 1 1/2, 1/8 between.

OCALA

OCALA STAR-BANNER

2121 SW 19th Avenue Rd., Ocala, Fla., 34471; gen tel (352) 867-4010; adv tel (352) 867-4098; ed tel (352) 867-4013; gen fax (352) 867-4028; adv fax (352) 867-4028; ed fax (352) 867-4018; ed e-mail tom.mcniff@starbanner.com; web site www.ocala.com

Published: Mon, Tues, Wed, Thur, Fri, Sat, Sun
Weekday Frequency: m
Saturday Frequency: m
Circulation: 29,625; 31,336(sat); 40,272(sun)
Last Audit: ABC September 30, 2011
Price: 3.98/wk.
Advertising: Open inch rate $101.00(m-thur to fri)
News services: AP, NYT
Politics: NonPartisan. **Established:** 1866
Own facility?: Y
Special Editions: Hurricane Guide, Living Here (area guide)
Special Weekly Sections: Religion (Sat); Go (local entertainment) (Thur); Health & Fitness (Sun); Big Sun Homes (real estate) (Sat)
Magazines: Real Estate Review (Sat); Parade (S);
Publisher ....Allen Parsons
Adv. Mgr., Classified ....Melody Day
Adv. Mgr., Retail ....Steve Martin
Community Relations ....Mary Baggs
Home Delivery Manager ....Bill Hayter
Managing Editor ....Tom McNiff
Editorial Page Ed. ....Brad Rogers
Assistant Managing Editor ....Jim Ross
Photo Editor ....Alan Youngblood
Sports Ed. ....Andy Marks
Advertising Director ....Susan Pinder
Executive Editor ....Jim Osteen
Online Community Editor ....Richard Anguiano
Market Information: TMC, Sunday Select
Mechanical available: Offset; Black and 3 ROP colors; insert accepted.
Mechanical Specifications: Type page 13 x 21 1/3; E - 6 cols, 2 1/16, 1/8 between; A - 6 cols, 2 1/16, 1/8 between; C - 9 cols, 1 3/8, 1/16 between.
Commodity Consumption: Avg. Page Number Per Issue - Daily 56; Avg. Page Number Per Issue - Plates Used 56300; Avg. Page Number Per Issue - Sunday 76; widths 54; Newsprint Used - Short Tons 6474; Printing Ink Used - Black 107900; Printing Ink Used - Color 32000; Printing Ink Us

Equipment EDITORIAL: Front-end Software – DTI/Pagespeed, DTI/SpeedPlanner, DTI/SpeedDriver.; Editorial Hardware – 2-AT/Series 60, 15-PC Power pagination editing station; Editorial Equipment – 46-AT; Editorial Printers – 1-QMS/860 CLASSIFIED: Front-end Software – AT/Advantage.; Classified Hardware – 15-PC, MS/NT Server DISPLAY: Ad make-up applications – DTI/SpeedPlanner, DTI/Ad-Speed; Layout Software – DTI/SpeedPlanner.; Display Hardware – 1-IBM, 12-APP/Mac workstation; Display Printers – 2-QMS/860, 1-Phaser/300i PRODUCTION: Pagination Software – DTI/SpeedPlanner, DTI/Speed-Driver, MEI/Page Director.; Production Equipment – 1-AU/APS-6 5-8, 3-Pre Press/Panther Pro 46, 1-C/80RA, 2-P/Online; Cameras – 1-C/Spartan III 1270, 1-C/Newspager PRESSROOM: Line 1 – 5-G/Headliner 1988; Folders – 1 MAILROOM: Counter stackers – 3/QWI; Inserters and stuffers – 1-/HI; Bundle tying machines – 3-/MLN; Other equipment –1-MM/Stitcher-Trimmer. AUDIO: Audio Software – Brite Voice Systems; Audio Hardware – Brite Voice Systems; Business Hardware – 1-IBM/AS-400 36

Delivery method: Newsstand, Private Carrier, Racks

OKEECHOBEE

OKEECHOBEE NEWS

107 SW 17th St., Ste. D, Okeechobee, Fla., 34974; gen tel (863) 763-3134; gen fax (863) 763-5901; adv fax (863) 763-7949; gen e-mail okeenews@newszap.com; adv e-mail okecompo@strato.net; ed e-mail okeditor@newszap.com; web site www.newszap.com

Published: Mon, Tues, Wed, Thur, Fri, Sat, Sun
Weekday Frequency: m
Saturday Frequency: m
Circulation: 2,583; 2,583(sat); 2,583(sun)
Last Audit: September 30, 2001
Price: 2.41/wk; 10.17/mo, $17.35/mo (mail); 117.70/yr, $201.43/yr (mail).
Advertising: Open inch rate $19.08
News services: AP.
Special Editions: Back to School (Aug); Christmas Greeting Ads (Dec); Medical Information Guide (Jan); Okeechobee County Fact Book (Mar); Graduation (May); Real Estate Magazine (Monthly); Christmas Gift Guide (Nov).
Adv. Dir. ....Judy Kasten
Circ. Mgr. ....Janet Madray
Ed. ....Katrina Elsken
Sports Ed. ....Charles Murphy
Prodn. Mgr., Pressroom ....Ginny Guy
Market Information: TMC.
Mechanical available: Web Offset; Black and 3 ROP colors; insert accepted.
Mechanical Specifications: Type page 11 5/8 x 21 1/2; E - 6 cols, 1 5/8, between; A - 6 cols, 1 5/8, between; C - 9 cols, 1 1/5, between.

Equipment EDITORIAL: Front-end Software – Microsoft/Word, QPS/QuarkXPress.; Editorial Hardware – APP/Mac DISPLAY: Ad make-up applications – QPS/QuarkXPress, Adobe/Photoshop; Layout Software – APP/Mac.

ORLANDO

ORLANDO SENTINEL

633 N. Orange Ave., Orlando, Fla., 32801-2833; gen tel (407) 420-5000; adv tel (407) 420-5100; ed tel (407) 420-5411; adv fax (407) 420-5768; ed fax (407) 420-5350; adv e-mail classified_ad@orlandosentinel.com; ed e-mail insight@orlandosentinel.com; web site www.orlandosentinel.com; www.elsentinel.com

Group: Metro Newspaper Advertising Services, Inc.
Published: Mon, Tues, Wed, Thur, Fri, Sat, Sun
Weekday Frequency: m
Saturday Frequency: m
Circulation: 171,418; 184,000(sat); 286,982(sun)
Last Audit: ABC September 30, 2011
Price: 3.95/wk; 17.12/mo; 189.60/yr (mS).
Advertising: Open inch rate $369.00(m-thur to fri)
News services: NYT, MCT, LAT-WP, AP, Cox News Service, CQ, TMS.
Politics: Independent. **Established:** 1876
Own facility?: Y
Special Editions: Dealer's Choice (Apr); Football Preview (Aug); Holiday Dining (Dec); Lake County Spring Parade of Homes (Feb); Florida Forecast (Jan); Hot Cars (Jul); Career Builder Xtra (Jun); Bay Hill Invitational (Mar); Hurricane Survival Guide (May); Auto Show I (Nov
Special Weekly Sections: Rush! (Fri); Central Florida Business (Mon); Travel (S); El Sentinel (Sat); Ride (Thur); Good Eating (Wed).
Magazines: Parade (S).
Profile: Orlando Sentinel Communications, publisher of the Orlando Sentinel and Orlando Sentinel.com, is a wholly owned subsidiary of Tribune Company, chicago. In addition to newspaper publishing (since 1876) and Web publishing, the company is involved in deirect
Pub. ....Howard Greenberg
Sr. Vice Pres./Gen. Mgr., Orlando Sentinel Communications ....Avido Khahaifa
Compensation/Commun. Mgr. ....Dyana Burke
Adv. Vice Pres./Dir. ....John D'Orlando
Adv. Sr. Mgr., Delivery ....Jack Curtin
Adv. Mgr., Bus. ....Rich Miller
Vice Pres., Interactive ....Linda Schaible
Circ. Vice Pres. ....Bert Ortiz
Circ. Mgr., Subscriber Servs. ....Dave Elder
Ed. ....Charlotte H. Hall
Mng. Ed. ....Mark Russell
Assoc. Mng. Ed., Bus. ....Gail Rayos
Assoc. Mng. Ed., Features ....Kim Marcum
Assoc. Mng. Ed., Photo/Design/Visuals Bonita Burton
Ed., Recruitment/Staff Devel. ....Dana Eagles
Arts/Entertainment Ed. ..Mary Frånces Emmons
Bus. News Ed. ....Ned Popkins
City Ed. ....Lisa Cianci
Lifestyles Ed ....Barry Glenn
Market Information: ADS; Split run; TMC; Zoned editions.
Mechanical available: Offset; Black and 3 ROP colors; insert accepted - product samples; page cutoffs - 22 1/25.
Mechanical Specifications: Type page 12 x 20 7/8; E - 6 cols, 2 1/16, 1/8 between; A - 6 cols, 2 1/16, 1/8 between; C - 10 cols, 1 1/8, 1/8 between.
Commodity Consumption: Avg. Page Number Per Issue - Daily 115; Avg. Page Number Per Issue - Plates Used 629000; Avg. Page Number Per Issue - Saturday 140; Avg. Page Number Per Issue - Sunday 300; widths 50; Newsprint Used - Metric Tons 54432; Printing Ink Used - Black 891460;

Equipment EDITORIAL: Front-end Software – CCI/Newsdesk 5.5.5, Microsoft/Windows NT XP 4.0.; Editorial Hardware – IBM/RS 6000; Editorial Equipment – 350-PC; Editorial Printers – HP, GEI, OSE CLASSIFIED: Front-end Software – Czar I, Coyote/3 1.4, SCS/Claspag 4.44.; Classified Hardware – 4-SII/Sys 77 S7002; Classified Equipment – Ad-Star, Fax Action, GDT/Gateway DISPLAY: Ad make-up applications – CCI/Addesk Production 5.5.3, Solaris 2.6; Layout Software – SCS/Layout 8000.; Display Hardware – 2-Sun/Sparc 5, 6-Sun/Sparc 1000E, 6-Sun/Ultra 2, 2-Sun/Ultra 250; Production Equipment – 4-3850 SST-Wide, 9-APP/Mac, 3-Sharp/2X-610; Cameras – 1-C/Newspager; Scanners – 2-Eskofot. PRESSROOM: Line 1 – 27-G/Metro double width, 4-G/Imperial double width 1981; Line 2 – 18-G/Head double width, 3-G/Imperial double width 1985; Line 3 – 5-G/Newsliner 4 over 4 color towers, digital inking; Press Drives – Fin; Folders – 7-G/3:2; Pasters – 45-G/RTP; Reels and Stands – Reel MAILROOM: Counter stackers – 13-QWI/351, 2-QWI/401, 6-QWI/501, 4-BG/Exactistack Count-o-veyor; Inserters and stuffers – 2-HI/2299, 2-SLS/3000 30:22, 1-HI/1630; Bundle tying machines – 5-GMA/Combistack, 5-Dynaric/NP 2-3, 5-Dynaric/RLM-1, 1-Dynaric/DF-2400, 7-Signode AUDIO: Audio Software – QNX 3.21; Audio Hardware – IT Networks, 2-Brite Voice Systems/4820 R-1939 BUSINESS COMPUTERS: Business Software – WordPerfect, Microsoft/Word, Microsoft/Excel, Microsoft/Access, Microsoft/Office 97; Business Hardware – IBM/PS-2 Pentium, Dell/6x100, Dell/CPI, Dell/LS

PALATKA

PALATKA DAILY NEWS

1825 St. Johns Ave., Palatka, Fla., 32178-0777; gen tel (386) 312-5200; gen fax (386) 312-5209; web site www.palatkadailynews.com

Published: Tues, Wed, Thur, Fri, Sat
Weekday Frequency: m
Saturday Frequency: m
Circulation: 11,804; 13,309(sat)
Last Audit: September 30, 2008
Price: 6.89/mo; 86.72/yr.
Advertising: Open inch rate $22.11
News services: AP.
Politics: Independent.
Not Published: Christmas.
Special Editions: Back-to-School (Aug); Fact Book (Feb); Meet the Manager (Jan); Blue Crab Festival (May); Gift Guide (Nov); Create a Beautiful Home (Oct); Industry Appreciation (Sept).
Special Weekly Sections: Currents (Fri); Health and Fitness Page (Wed).
Pub. ....Rusty Starr
Adv. Dir. ....Mary Kaye Wells
Circ. Dir. ....John Allender
Ed. ....Larry Sullivan
Sports Ed. ....Andy Hall
Market Information: TMC; Zoned editions.
Mechanical available: Offset; Black and 3 ROP colors; insert accepted - small catalogs, cards; page cutoffs - 22 3/4.
Mechanical Specifications: Type page 13 x 21 1/2; E - 6 cols, 2 1/16, 1/8 between; A - 6 cols, 2 1/16, 1/8 between; C - 9 cols, 1 3/8, 1/16 between.
Commodity Consumption: Avg. Page Number Per Issue - Daily 24; Avg. Page Number Per Issue - Plates Used 8500; widths 27 1/2; Newsprint Used - Short Tons 780; Printing Ink Used - Black 18400; Printing Ink Used - Color 1500; Printing Ink Used - Pages Printed 6100.

Equipment EDITORIAL: Front-end Software – Computext.; Editorial Hardware – 8-IBM/486, 5-PC Pagination Station; Editorial Equipment – APP/Mac IIcx, APP/Mac 300, Shava/Telebridge, Microcom/9600 Modem, Lf/AP Leaf Picture Desk, APP/Mac vx; Editorial Printers – 1-APP/Mac LaserWriter II NTX CLASSIFIED: Front-end Software – Computext/CompuClass.; Classified Hardware – Computext/CompuClass;

Classified Printers – APP/Mac LaserWriter II DISPLAY: Ad make-up applications – Multi-Ad/Creator, QPS/QuarkXPress, Adobe/Photoshop.; Display Hardware – 1-APP/Mac II, 1-APP/Mac IIci, 1-APP/Mac Quadra 950; Display Printers – 1-DEC/VT 820 Plain Paper, 1-Pre Press/Panther Plus PRODUCTION: Pagination Software – Computext/Comet.; Production Equipment – TI/OmniPage, 1-Konica/K550; Scanners – 2-Microtek/II XE, 1-Kk/RFS 2035; Addressing machine – Ch/586.; Audio Hardware – Brite Voice Systems BUSINESS COMPUTERS: Business Software – Microsoft/Excel, Microsoft/Word, INSI; Business Hardware – IBM/S-36, PC Network

PALM BEACH

PALM BEACH DAILY NEWS

265 Royal Palm Way, Suite 100, Palm Beach, Fla., 33480; gen tel (561) 820-3800; adv tel (561) 820-3815; ed tel (561) 820-3865; gen fax (561) 820-3802; adv fax (561) 655-4594; ed fax (561) 655-4594; web site www.palmbeachdailynews.com

Published: Mon, Tues, Wed, Thur, Fri, Sat, Sun
Price: 185.84
Advertising: Open inch rate $34.27
Politics: 1897

PANAMA CITY

THE NEWS HERALD

501 W. 11th St., Panama City, Fla., 32401; gen tel (850) 747-5000; adv tel (850) 747-5030; ed tel (850) 747-5070; gen fax (850) 747-5018; adv fax (850) 763-4636; ed fax (850) 747-5097; gen e-mail news@pcnh.com; web site www.newsherald.com

Group: Freedom Communications, Inc.
Published: Mon, Tues, Wed, Thur, Fri, Sat, Sun
Weekday Frequency: m
Saturday Frequency: m
Circulation: 23,773; 23,773(sat); 28,993(sun)
Last Audit: September 30, 2009
Price: 167.88/yr; 13.16/4wk.
Advertising: Open inch rate $50.00
News services: AP, MCT.
Politics: 1937
Own facility?: Y
Special Weekly Sections: TV Times (Fri); Lifestyle & Viewpoint (S); Religion (Sat); Outdoors (Thur); Food (Wed).
Magazines: Parade Magazine (S).
Division Vice Pres./Pub. ....Karen E. Hanes
Regl. Controller/FP&A ....Robert Delaney
Regl. HR Dir. ....Lorraine Grimes
Adv. Dir. ....Pamela Gregory
Regl. Classified Dir. ....Irene Field
Adv. Mgr., Classified ....Glenda Sullivan
Adv. Mgr., Creative Servs. ....Joye McCormick
Ed. ....Mike Cazalas
Editorial Page Ed. ....Scott Kent
Online Ed. ....Tony Simmons
Exec. Sports Ed. ....Pat McCann
IT Servs. ....David Sinnett
Prodn. Dir., Opns. ....Ron Smith
Regional Circulation Director .....Sharon Heckler
Circ. Dir., Regl. ....Mike Miller
Regl. Dir., Content ....Patrick Rice
Market Information: ADS.
Mechanical available: Offset; Black and 3 ROP colors; insert accepted; page cutoffs - 21.
Mechanical Specifications: Type page 11 2/3 x 20; E - 6 cols, 1 13/16, 1/8 between; A - 6 cols, 1 13/16, 1/8 between; C - 9 cols, 1 1/4, 1/16 between.
Commodity Consumption: Avg. Page Number Per Issue - Daily 36; Avg. Page Number Per Issue - Plates Used 27500; Avg. Page Number Per Issue - Sunday 72; widths 12 1/2; Newsprint Used - Metric Tons 4300; Printing Ink Used - Pages Printed 17176.
Equipment EDITORIAL: Front-end Software – APT.; Editorial Hardware – PC; Editorial Printers – HP/5MX CLASSIFIED: Front-end Software – APT.; Classified Hardware – PC; Classified Printers – HP/4000, HP/5SI DISPLAY: Ad make-up applications – APT; Layout Software – APT.; Display Hardware – PC; Display Printers – HP/750, HP/5MX PRODUCTION: Pagination Software – APT.; Production Equipment – Kk/Newsway PRESSROOM: Line 1 – 28 unit Goss Universal; Press Drives – Shaftless; Folders – 2; Reels and Stands – 10; Press control system – EAE; Press registration system – Manual MAILROOM: Counter stackers – 2-Gaemmeler; Inserters and stuffers – SLS 3000 - 12 heads; Bundle tying machines – 3 Dynaric and 1 Sterling; Wrapping singles – 2-/Bu; Addressing machine – KAN
Delivery method: Mail, Newsstand, Private Carrier, Racks

PENSACOLA

PENSACOLA NEWS JOURNAL

101 E. Romana St., Pensacola, Fla., 32502; gen tel (850) 435-8500; adv tel (850) 435-8554; ed tel (850) 435-8542; gen fax (850) 435-8633; adv fax (850) 469-8213; ed fax (850) 435-8633; gen e-mail news@pnj.com; ed e-mail news@pnj.com; web site www.pnj.com

Group: Metro Suburbia, Inc./Newhouse Newspapers
Published: Mon, Tues, Wed, Thur, Fri, Sat, Sun
Weekday Frequency: m
Saturday Frequency: m
Circulation: 40,219; 38,033(sat); 60,246(sun)
Last Audit: ABC September 30, 2011
Price: 3.25/wk; 17.29/mth; 169.00/yr.
Advertising: Open inch rate $190.11
News services: AP, GNS.
Special Editions: Football (Aug); Hurricane (May).
Special Weekly Sections: Weekender (Fri); TV Week (S).
Magazines: USA WEEKEND Magazine (S).
Pub./Pres. ....Kevin Doyle
Dir., Finance ....Tom Hartley
Dir., Adv. Sales ....Bobby Rice
Adv. Mgr., Retail ....Nadja Silvey
Adv. Mgr., Inside Sales ....Debora Lefort
Dir., Market Devel. ....Becca Boles
Strategic Mktg. Mgr. ....Gregory L. Clay
Circ. Dir. ....Pat Daugherty
Exec. Ed. ....Richard Schneider
Mng. Ed. ....Gray Biel
Archives Mgr. ....Earl Melvin
Content Ed. ....Tom Ninestine
Editorial Page Ed. ....Carl Wernicke
Market Information: ADS; TMC; Zoned editions.
Mechanical available: Offset; Black and 3 ROP colors; insert accepted - min 4 x 7-80 lbs stock; page cutoffs - 22.
Mechanical Specifications: Type page 11 5/8 x 20 3/4; E - 6 cols, 1 5/6, 1/8 between; A - 6 cols, 1 5/6, 1/8 between; C - 10 cols, 1, 1/8 between.
Commodity Consumption: Avg. Page Number Per Issue - Daily 45; Avg. Page Number Per Issue - Plates Used 59279; Avg. Page Number Per Issue - Sunday 94; widths 25; Newsprint Used - Metric Tons 6825; Newsprint Used - Short Tons 7523; Printing Ink Used - Black 228915; Printing Ink
Equipment EDITORIAL: Front-end Software – Harris Newsjaz 2.0.; Editorial Hardware – IBM/XSeries Servers; Editorial Printers – Accel A Writer 45 CLASSIFIED: Front-end Software – Mactive Adbase.; Classified Hardware – Dell/Poweredge Server; Classified Equipment – Mobile Advertising Sales System DISPLAY: Ad make-up applications – Multi-Ad/Creator; Layout Software – MEI ALS.; Display Hardware – 7-APP/Mac PRODUCTION: Pagination Software – Harris/NewsJaz 2.0, M Active PGL.; Production Equipment – KFM/Twin-Line Semi-auto, 2-AU/APS PIP II, 1-AU/3850; Scanners – Tecsa PRESSROOM: Line 1 – 7-G/Headliner Offset double width 1997; Press Drives – 5-Fin/125 h.p. Digital; Folders – 2-G/3:2 160 PG; Pasters – 1997; Press control system – G/MPCS. MAILROOM: Counter stackers – 2-Id/2200, 1-HL/Monitor, 2/Quipp 400, 1-/Compass 180; Inserters and stuffers – AM Graphics/630 21 hopper; Bundle tying machines – 2-Dynaric/NP-1, 2-Dynaric/NP-1, 2-Dynaric/NP 1500; Mailroom control system – Id/TCP Bundle Control Syste; Audio Hardware – Octel BUSINESS COMPUTERS: Business Software – Microsoft/Office 97 Desktop Suite; Business Hardware – IBM/AS-400E 9406-620

SAINT AUGUSTINE

THE ST. AUGUSTINE RECORD

1 News Pl., Saint Augustine, Fla., 32086; gen tel (904) 829-6562; adv tel (904) 819-3475; gen fax (904) 819-3538; adv fax (904) 819-3557; ed fax (904) 819-3558; adv e-mail ads@staugustinerecord.com; ed e-mail editor@staugustinerecord.com; web site www.staugustine.com

Published: Mon, Tues, Wed, Thur, Fri, Sat, Sun
Weekday Frequency: m
Saturday Frequency: m
Circulation: 16,701; 17,728(sat); 20,046(sun)
Last Audit: ABC September 30, 2011
Price: 12.91/mo.-154.92/yr
Advertising: Open inch rate $26.00
News services: AP, MCT, LAT-WP, Morris News Service.
Politics: Independent.
Note: Advertising is sold in combination with Jacksonville Florida Times Union (mS) for $243.00(d), $259.00(m-sat) and $279.00(S).
Special Editions: Active Lifestyles (Apr); Back-to-School (Aug); Christmas Greetings (Dec); Bridal (Feb); Active Lifestyles (Jan); Active Lifestyles (Jul); Just Say No (Mar); Real Estate Today (May); Holiday Style & Fashion (Nov); Explore St. John's (Oct); Football (Sept).
Special Weekly Sections: Arts & Entertainment (Fri); Lifestyle (S); The Welcome Mat (Sat); Food (Thur).
Magazines: Relish (Monthly); USA WEEKEND Magazine (S).
Publisher ....Ron Davidson
Circ. Dir. ....Bill Mitchell
Circ. Mgr. ....Paul Kennedy
Ed. ....Peter Ellis
Assoc. Ed. ....Richard Prior
Assignment Ed. ....Peter Guinta
Compass Ed. ....Renee Unsworth
Editorial Page Ed. ....Margo Pope
Features Ed. ....Anne Heymen
Health Ed. ....Shaun Ryan
Sports Ed. ....Justin Barney
Prodn. Dir. ....Steve Carswell
Special Projects Dir. ....Gail Cumiskey
Prodn. Superintendent, Mailroom ...Michael Ford
Prodn. Superintendent, Pre Press ....Jeff Taylor
Prodn. Superintendent, Pressroom Jeffry Johnson
Advertising Director ....Tonya Clay
Market Information: TMC.
Mechanical available: Offset; Black and 3 ROP colors; insert accepted - odd size; page cutoffs - 22 3/4.
Mechanical Specifications: Type page 11 5/8 x 21 1/12; E - 6 cols, 1 5/6, 1/6 between; A - 6 cols, 1 5/6, 1/6 between; C - 9 cols, 11/72 between.
Commodity Consumption: Avg. Page Number Per Issue - Daily 28; Avg. Page Number Per Issue - Plates Used 25000; Avg. Page Number Per Issue - Saturday 62; Avg. Page Number Per Issue - Sunday 54; widths 12 7/16; Newsprint Used - Metric Tons 1200; Printing Ink Used - Black 19000; P
Equipment EDITORIAL: Front-end Software – DTI 5.2.; Editorial Hardware – IBM, 40-APP/Mac; Editorial Equipment – AG/1500 Imagesetter; Editorial Printers – XIT/Navigator, HP CLASSIFIED: Front-end Software – DTI 5.2.; Classified Hardware – IBM, DTI; Classified Printers – Epson DISPLAY: Ad make-up applications – Adobe/InDesign, DTI 5.2; Layout Software – MEI/ALS.; Display Hardware – APP/Mac; Display Printers – XIT/Navigator, HP PRODUCTION: Pagination Software – DTI 5.2.; Production Equipment – XIT/Navigator, Ag/1500; Cameras – AG/Accuset 1500 PRESSROOM: Line 1 – 10 1/2-G/Urbanite; Folders – G/Urbanite Half; Reels and Stands – HI/Roll Stands; Press registration system – Carlson. MAILROOM: Counter stackers – 1/MM; Inserters and stuffers – 1-MM/227S; Bundle tying machines – 2-MLN/ML2EE; Addressing machine – 1-Am/1900, KAN. AUDIO: Audio Software – MPS/Audiotex, Brite; Audio Hardware – AP SelectStox, Gateway/2000 BUSINESS COMPUTERS: Business Software – PBS; Business Hardware – IBM

SAINT PETERSBURG

TAMPA BAY TIMES

490 1st Ave. S., Saint Petersburg, Fla., 33701-4204; gen tel (727) 893-8111; adv tel (727) 894-1141; gen fax (727) 893-8675; adv fax (727) 892-2209; gen e-mail local@tampabay.com; ed e-mail local@tampabay.com; web site www.tampabay.com

Group: Newspapers First, Inc.
Published: Mon, Tues, Wed, Thur, Fri, Sat, Sun
Weekday Frequency: m
Saturday Frequency: m
Circulation: 240,024; 235,650(sat); 403,229(sun)
Last Audit: ABC September 30, 2011
Price: 4.00/wk; 187.98/yr; 51.98/13wk.
Advertising: Open inch rate $770.00
News services: AP, NYT, LAT-WP, SHNS, MCT.
Special Editions: Clearwater Fun 'n Sun (Apr); Football (Aug); Personal Best (Every other month); Hernando Profiles (Feb); School Search (Jan); Wedding Guides (Jul); West Virginia (Jun); Chasco Fiesta (Mar); Hurricane (May); Home Search (Monthly); Holiday Gift Guide (Nov);
Special Weekly Sections: Arts & Entertainment (S); HomeLink (Sat); Weekend (Entertainment) (Thur); Taste (Wed).
Magazines: Bay (Every other month); Sunday Comics (S).
Chrmn./CEO/Ed. ....Paul Tash
Vice Pres./CFO ....Jana Jones
Vice Pres./Sec. ....Andrew P. Corty
Vice Pres./Pub., Tampa ....Joe DeLuca
Dir., HR/Diversity Officer ....Sebastian Dortch
Dir., Cor. Giving ....Nancy Waclawek
Adv. Mgr. ....Mark Shurman
Adv. Mgr., Classified ....Michelle Mitchell
Mgr., Creative Strategy ....Kerry O'Reilly
Community/Events Mgr. ....Dave LaBell
Staff-Commun. Mgr. ....Jounice Nealy-Brown
Editor/Vice President ....Neil Brown
Dir., Editorial/Creative, Times Targeted Media Gretchen Letterman
Sr. Ed. ....Jim Booth
Ed., North Suncoast ....Bill Stevens
Mng. Ed., Enterprise ....Mike Wilson
Mng. Ed., Tampa Bay ....Joe Childs
Deputy Managing Editor, Features Jeanne Grinstead
Market Information: Split run; TMC; Zoned editions.
Mechanical available: Offset; Black and 4 ROP colors; insert accepted - pre-approved samples; page cutoffs - 22 3/4.
Mechanical Specifications: Type page 11 27/100 x 21 1/2; E - 6 cols, 2 1/16, 1/8 between; A - 6 cols, 2 1/16, 1/8 between; C - 10 cols, 1 5/16, 1/16 between.
Commodity Consumption: Avg. Page Number Per Issue - Daily 76; Avg. Page Number Per Issue - Plates Used 936424; Avg. Page Number Per Issue - Saturday 106; Avg. Page Number Per Issue - Sunday 158; widths 48; Newsprint Used - Short Tons 54383; Printing Ink Used - Black 1014601; P
Equipment; Editorial Printers – 5-HP/LaserJet. CLASSIFIED: Front-end Software – Mactive/AdBase. DISPLAY: Ad make-up applications – In-house; Layout Software – III, Inhouse/Layout Sys.; Display Hardware – Printers ☐ 2-APP/Mac LaserWriter; Production Equipment – 4-KPG/85, 2-Anitec/SN48, 4-Trendsetter 200. PRESSROOM: Line 1 – 21-G/Metroliner double width; Line 2 – 21-G/Metroliner double width; Line 3 – 21-G/Metroliner double width; Folders – 5-G/single, 4-G/double; Pasters – 63; Reels and Stands – 63 MAILROOM: Counter stackers – 5-QWI/350, 24-QWI/400; Inserters

and stuffers – 5-S/1472, 1-HI/In-Line 30 632; Bundle tying machines – 9-Dynaric/NP, 12-Dynaric/NP-2, 17-Dynaric/NP3, 2-Mosca/Z-5; Wrapping singles – 10-QWI/Viper 30, 16-QWI/Viper 50; Mailroom control system – Mailroom control s

SANFORD

SANFORD HERALD

217 E. First St., Sanford, Fla., 32771; gen tel (407) 322-2611; gen fax (407) 323-9408; gen e-mail rlavender@mysanfordherald.com; web site www.mysanfordherald.com
Group: North Carolina Press Service, Inc.
Published: Wed, Sun
Last Audit: February 25, 2005
Price: 36.00/yr.
Advertising: Open inch rate $8.00
Insert rate: $60.00/M.
Politics: 1908
Pub. ....Gene Kruckemyer
Adv. Dir./Classified Mgr. ....Roxzie Lavender
Circ. Mgr. ....Wanda Kourpanidis
Ed. ....Glenn Judah
Mechanical Specifications: Type page 13 x 21 1/2; E - 6 cols, 2 1/16, 1/8 between; A - 6 cols, 2 1/16, 1/8 between; C - 8 cols, 1 1/2, 1/8 between.
Zip Codes served: 32771, 32772, 32773, 32750, 32779, 32746, 32765

SARASOTA

SARASOTA HERALD-TRIBUNE

1741 Main St., Sarasota, Fla., 34236; gen tel (941) 953-7755; adv tel (941) 361-4000; ed tel (941) 361-4990; gen fax 941-361-4580; adv fax (941) 361-4095; ed fax (941) 361-4880; adv e-mail heather.potts@heraldtribune.com; ed e-mail tom.tryon@heraldtribune.com; web site www.heraldtribune.com
Group: Publishers Representatives of Florida, Inc.
Published: Mon, Tues, Wed, Thur, Fri, Sat, Sun
Weekday Frequency: m
Saturday Frequency: m
Circulation: 63,864; 65,481(sat); 83,140(sun)
Last Audit: ABC September 30, 2011
Price: 164.84/yr; 15.85/5wk, $41.21/13wk, $82.42/26wk.
Advertising: Open inch rate $185.38
News services: AP, LAT-WP, NYT.
Politics: Independent. **Established:** 1925
Own facility?: Y
Special Editions: Golf Guide (Apr); Year-End Auto Clearance (Aug); Auto Showcase (Dec); Dining Guide (Feb); Jubilee (Jan); Dining Guide (Jul); Suncoast Off-shore Program (Jun); Wine Fest (Mar); Hurricane (May); Holiday Gift Guide (Nov); Season (Oct); Clubs (Sept).
Special Weekly Sections: Ticket (Entertainment) (Fri); Business Weekly (Mon); Perspective (S); HomeLife (Sat); Cuisine (Wed).
Magazines: Comics (S).
Broadcast Affiliations: Sarasota News Now (SNN6).
Publisher ....Diane McFarlin
Asst. Adv. Dir. ....Shari Brickley
Adv. Mgr., Nat'l ....Jennifer Tamman
Circ. Mgr., Retention ....Jennifer Eichorn
Exec. Ed. ....Mike Connelly
Asst. Mng. Ed. ....Deborah Winsor
Venice Bureau Ed. ....David Hackett
Books Ed. ....Susan Rife
Bus. Ed. ....Matt Sauer
Columnist ....David Grimes
Columnist ....Tom Lyons
Columnist, Charlotte ....Eric Ernst
Critic, Theater/Television ....Jay Handelman
Editorial Page Ed. ....Thomas Lee Tryon
News Ed. ....Kyle Booth
News Bus. Mgr. ....Janice Gehle
Photo Dir. ....Mike Lang
Market Information: Zoned editions.
Mechanical available: Offset; Black and 4 ROP colors; insert accepted; page cutoffs - 22.
Mechanical Specifications: Type page 11 5/8 x 21; E - 6 cols, 1 4/5, 1/8 between; A - 6 cols, 1 4/5, 1/8 between; C - 10 cols, 1 4/5, 1/6 between.
Commodity Consumption: Avg. Page Number Per Issue - Daily 86; Avg. Page Number Per Issue - Plates Used 282500; Avg. Page Number Per Issue - Sunday 215; widths 41; Newsprint Used - Metric Tons 18560; Printing Ink Used - Black 385000; Printing Ink Used - Color 114400; Printing I
Equipment EDITORIAL: Front-end Software – AT.; Editorial Hardware – AT CLASSIFIED: Front-end Software – AT.; Classified Hardware – AT DISPLAY: Ad make-up applications – Cx, QPS/QuarkXPress, Multi-Ad/Creator; Layout Software – AT.; Display Hardware – Sun; Production Equipment – KFM/Plate Express, 4-III/3850, WL/III; Scanners – ECR/1000, ECR/2045, ECR/8400, Nikon/Scanners. PRESSROOM: Line 1 – G/(18 unit lines with 1 4-color tower & 3 decks) 1994; Folders – Imperial/144-page; Pasters – G/RTP 45 DIA; Press control system – G/MPCS III; Press registration system – WPC/Web Control. MAILROOM: Counter stackers – 6/QWI; Inserters and stuffers – 3-HI/NP 1372; Bundle tying machines – 2-/Power Strap/PSN, 5-/Dynaric; Wrapping singles – 8-HL/Monarch; Addressing machine – 1-Ch/S42.; Audio Hardware – Brite Voice Systems BUSINESS COMPUTERS: Business Software – Admarc; Business Hardware – 2-IBM/4381, III/TECS 2

SEBRING

HIGHLANDS TODAY

315 US Hwy. 27 N., Sebring, Fla., 33870; gen tel (863) 386-5800; adv tel (863) 386-5800; ed tel (863) 386-5800; gen fax (863) 382-1076; adv fax (863) 382-1076; ed fax (863) 382-2509; gen e-mail highlandstoday@highlandstoday.com; adv e-mail retailads@highlandstoday.com; web site www.highlandstoday.com
Published: Mon, Tues, Wed, Thur, Fri, Sat, Sun
Weekday Frequency: m
Saturday Frequency: m
Circulation: 16,609; 16,609(sat); 16,609(sun)
Last Audit: September 30, 1996
Price: 1.00/wk; 13.91/mo; 55.64/yr.
Advertising: Open inch rate $28.65
News services: AP, TMS.
Note: For detailed press information, see the Tampa Tribune.
Special Editions: 101 Things to do in the Heartland (Jan); 12 Hours of Sebring Race Tab (Mar).
Special Weekly Sections: Business (S); Religion (Sat).
Magazines: USA WEEKEND Magazine (Fri); American Profile (Mon).
Pub. ....Tina Gottus
Adv. Dir. ....Morgan Miller
Circ. Dir. ....Vince Liles
Ed. ....Richard Hensley
Sports Ed. ....Mark Pinson
Market Information: Zoned editions.
Mechanical available: Black and 3 ROP colors; insert accepted; page cutoffs - 21.
Mechanical Specifications: Type page 13 x 21; E - 6 cols, 1 3/4, 1/8 between; A - 6 cols, 1 3/4, 1/8 between; C - 10 cols, 1 5/8, 1/8 between.

STUART

TREASURE COAST NEWS/PRESS-TRIBUNE

1939 S. Federal Hwy., Stuart, Fla., 34995-9009; gen tel (772) 287-1550; adv tel (772) 287-1550; ed tel (772) 287-1550; gen fax (772) 221-4175; adv fax (772) 221-4250; ed fax (772) 221-4246; gen e-mail feedback@tcpalm.com; adv e-mail sales@tcpalm.com; web site www.tcpalm.com
Published: Mon, Tues, Wed, Thur, Fri, Sat, Sun
Weekday Frequency: m
Saturday Frequency: m
Circulation: 66,989; 66,515(sat); 86,286(sun)
Last Audit: ABC September 30, 2011
Price: 2.54/wk; 11.00/mo; 122.00/yr.
Advertising: Open inch rate $208.20
News services: AP, NEA, NYT, SHNS.
Politics: Independent.
Special Editions: Character Counts (); Leisure Time (Aug); Hurricane (Jun); Treasure Guide (Nov); Coupon Book (Quarterly).
Special Weekly Sections: Real Estate Preview (Fri); Real Estate Preview (S); Real Estate Preview (Sat).
Magazines: Parade (S).
Broadcast Affiliations: WPTV-News Channel 5-West Palm Beach.
Pres. ....Thomas E. Weber
Vice Pres./Gen. Mgr. ....Rebecca K. Freeman
Controller ....Rebecca Whittemore
Dir., HR ....Janice Green
Finance Dir. ....David E. Buckey
Adv. Dir. ....Robert Brunjes
Mktg. Dir. ....Rick Baxter
Circ. Dir. ....Don Hornbeck
Ed. ....Mark Tomasik
Metro Ed. ....Mike Cannan
News Ed. ....Dennis Durkee
Sports Ed. ....Mike Graham
Television/Film Ed. ....Bill Deyoung
Entertainment Ed. ....Marilyn Vauer
IT Dir. ....Ed Lindoo
Prodn. Dir., Opns. ....Mike O'Leary
Prodn. Mgr., Creative Servs. ....Michael Johnson
Prodn. Mgr., Post Press ....Tim Warren
Market Information: ADS; Split run; TMC; Zoned editions.
Mechanical available: Offset; Black and 3 ROP colors; insert accepted; page cutoffs - 21.
Mechanical Specifications: Type page 11 5/8 x 20 3/8; E - 6 cols, 2 1/16, 1/8 between; A - 6 cols, 2 1/16, 1/8 between; C - 9 cols, 1 3/8, 1/8 between.
Commodity Consumption: Avg. Page Number Per Issue - Daily 62; Avg. Page Number Per Issue - Plates Used 300000; Avg. Page Number Per Issue - Saturday 80; Avg. Page Number Per Issue - Sunday 106; widths 55; Newsprint Used - Metric Tons 6759; Printing Ink Used - Black 124000; Pri
Equipment EDITORIAL: Front-end Software – HI/Newsmaker Editorial.; Editorial Hardware – HI/Newsmaker Editorial, 2-Sun/Ultra II Servers; Editorial Equipment – 7-HI/2100, HI/XP-21 Pagination, 4-Sun; Editorial Printers – 3-HP/4000 CLASSIFIED: Front-end Software – R4 4.2.; Classified Hardware – DTI, 1-Sun/Ultra I, 12-APP/Mac 7600, 3-APP/Mac 8500, 1-APP/Mac 9500; Classified Printers – APP/Mac 12-640 DISPLAY: Ad make-up applications – SCS/Layout 8000, Multi-Ad/Creator, QPS/QuarkXPress, Adobe/Photoshop; Layout Software – 4-APP/Mac, 5-APP/Power; Display Hardware – PC 386, 5-APP/Mac Power PC; Display Printers – HP/LaserJet, QMS/230 Color Printer PRODUCTION: Pagination Software – HI/HMP (3.5).; Production Equipment – APP/Mac 7.0, AG/Imagemaster 5000, Futuro; Scanners – Scitex/Smart 342L, Scitex/Eversmart PRESSROOM: Line 1 – 10-MAN/Regioman 8-couple-towers; Line 2 – 2-MAN/Regioman 4-couple-units; Line 3 – ABD/11 x 17; Line 4 – ABD/13 x 17 1/2; Folders – 1-MAN/double jaw KFZ 2:3:3, MAN/single jaw KFZ 2:3:3; Pasters – 5-MEG. MAILROOM: Counter stackers – 2-HL/Monitor, 1-HT/Monitor, Dug/Carrick; Inserters and stuffers – 1-GMA/SLS 1000; Bundle tying machines – Power Strap/PSN5, Power Strap/PSN6, 2-Newstyer/2000; Wrapping singles – 3-HL/Monarch; Mailroom control system – Newscom; Other equipment –Other AUDIO: Audio Software – Zimmers Interactive; Audio Hardware – VNN, PC 486; Business Hardware – Software □ PBS: Ad/Circ Management

TALLAHASSEE

TALLAHASSEE DEMOCRAT

277 N. Magnolia Dr., Tallahassee, Fla., 32301; gen tel (850) 599-2100; adv tel (850) 671-6544; ed tel (850) 599-2170; adv fax (850) 942-0185; ed fax (850) 599-2224; adv e-mail jvale@tallahassee.com; ed e-mail letters@tallahassee.com; web site www.tallahassee.com
Group: Federated Publications/Gannett
Published: Mon, Tues, Wed, Thur, Fri, Sat, Sun
Weekday Frequency: m
Saturday Frequency: m
Circulation: 32,673; 34,273(sat); 46,138(sun)
Last Audit: ABC September 30, 2011
Price: 22.00/mo; 264.05/yr.
News services: MCT, AP, TMS, GNS.
Politics: 1905
Own facility?: Y
Special Editions: Living Here (Aug); Home & Design (Every other month); College Football Preview (Fall); Business Outlook (Feb); North Florida Home Show (Jan); Chamber of Commerce (Jul); Legislature 2008 (Mar); Money Clip (Monthly); Holiday Planner (Nov); Physicians & Health; Your Health (monthly); Moms like Me (Monthly);
Special Weekly Sections: Limelight (Fri); Life & Arts (S); Religion (Sat); Food (Thur); Families (Tues); Home & Garden (Wed); Career-Builder (Weekly).
Magazines: USA WEEKEND Magazine (S).
Retail Adv. Mgr. ....Cari Evans
Controller ....Scott LaFuria
Community Rel. Mgr. ....Jeanie Booth
Mktg & Nondaily Mgr. ....Marjorie Schoelles
Circ. Mgr. ....Richard Kay
FSView Gen. Mgr. ....Eliza LePorin
Exec. Ed. ....Bob Gabordi
Bus. Ed. ....Dave Hodges
State Editor ....Paul Flemming
Community Conversation/Editorial Page Ed. Mary Ann Lindley
Digital/Systems Ed. ....Bjorn Morton
Features/Custom Content Ed. ....Kati Schardl
Managing Ed. ....Rebeccah Cantley
Digital Media Dir. ....Chris Counts
Prepress, Postpress, IT Mgr ....Randy Fingeroot
Opns./Circ. Dir. ....Bill Taylor
Sales and Marketing Director ....Richard Reeves
Sports Ed. ....Ira Schoffel
Digitial Communities Ed./Photo Ed. ..Holly Moore
Pres. & Publisher ....Patrick E. Dorsey
Research & New Business Manager Kenneth Allewelt
Circulation Sales Specialist ....Daria Cornelius
Adv. Dir. ....Donna Moore
Metro Ed. ....Byron Dobson
News Ass't ....Debra Galloway
Sports Ed. ....Jim Lamar
Mechanical available: Offset; Black and 3 ROP colors; insert accepted - product samples; page cutoffs - 22 3/4.
Mechanical Specifications: Type page 10 1/8 x 21 1/2; E - 6 cols, 1 9/16, 1/6 between; A - 6 cols, 1 9/16, 1/6 between; C - 9 cols, 1 3/8, 1/16 between.
Commodity Consumption: Page Number Per Issue □ Daily 28; Avg. Page Number Per Issue - Plates Used 106000; Avg. Page Number Per Issue □ Sunday 56; widths 22; Newsprint Used - Metric Tons 2,077; Newsprint Used - Short Tons 2,289; Printing Ink Used - Black 38,072 lbs; Printing
Equipment EDITORIAL: Front-end Software – DTI 7.3 ; Editorial Hardware – 2x sunfire v440; Editorial Printers – HP5000 CLASSIFIED: Front-end Software – DTI/Classified 5.3.; Classified Hardware – 2-Sun/Enterprise 450, 21-IBM/PC Workstation; Classified Printers – Variety DISPLAY: Ad make-up applications – DTI; Layout Software – DTI Speedplanner 7.3; Display Hardware – 2x Sunfire V440; Display Printers – HP 5000 PRODUCTION: Pagination Software – DTI 7.3; Production Equipment – 2-Anacoil/LX45, Anacoil/Thermal PRESSROOM: Line 1 – 7-G/Metro double width (4 decks) 1979; Line 2 – 6-G/Urbanite single width; Folders – 1-G/Metro, 1, 1-G/Urbanite, 2-G/Uniflow 2:1; Pasters – 7-G/Automatic RTP; Reels and Stands – 4-G/Urbanite high roll stand. MAILROOM: Counter stackers – 1-MM/310-20, 2-Baldwin/108, 3-QWI/400; Inserters and stuffers – 1-Titan G60 22 heads; Bundle tying machines – 2-Samuel/NT 440, 3-Samuel/Newstyer 2000;

Wrapping singles – 3-QWI/50 bottom wrap, 1-Samuel BUSINESS COMPUTERS: Business Software – Word Processing
Zip Codes served: 31792, 32301. 32302, 32303, 32304, 32305, 32306, 32308, 32309, 32310, 32311, 32312, 32317, 32320, 32321, 32322, 32323, 32324, 32327, 32328, 32330, 32331, 32332, 32333, 32334, 32337, 32340, 32343, 32344, 32346, 32347, 32348, 32351, 32352, 32355, 32358, 32361, 32399, 32421, 32424, 32425, 32428, 32446, 32447, 32448, 32456, 32460, 39817, 39819, 39827, 39828, 39897
Delivery method: Mail, Newsstand, Private Carrier, Racks

TAMPA

THE TAMPA TRIBUNE

202 S. Parker St., Tampa, Fla., 33606-2395; gen tel (813) 259-7711; adv tel (813) 259-7455 (retail); ed tel (813) 259-7600; gen fax (813) 258-8107 (adv); adv fax (813) 259-7903 (class); ed fax (813) 259-8080; adv e-mail tboclassified@tbo.com; web site www.tampatrib.com; www.weathercenter.com; www.tbo.com
Group: Towmar Representaciones S.A.
Published: Mon, Tues, Wed, Thur, Fri, Sat, Sun
Weekday Frequency: m
Saturday Frequency: m
Circulation: 138,172; 135,614(sat); 259,590(sun)
Last Audit: ABC September 30, 2011
Price: 3.00/wk (mS); 156.00/yr (mS).
Advertising: Open inch rate $500.00
News services: AP, NYT, MCT, TMS, LAT-WP.
Politics: Independent. **Established:** 1895
Own facility?: Y
Special Editions: Gasparilla (Jan); Strawberry Fest, Outdoor Expo (Mar); Summer Camps, Green Living (Apr); Quince (Jun); Florida Bride, Welcome Back USF, Best of (Aug); Bucs Preview, Festival Del Sabor (Sep); Think Pink (Oct); Winter Resident Guide, Presents Aplenty (Nov)
Special Weekly Sections: Friday Extra (Fri); Real Estate (S); CarSeeker (Sat); 4You (Sat); Baylife & Travel (Sun); Home Inside & Out (Sun)
Magazines: Parade (S).
Broadcast Affiliations: WFLA-TV News Channel 8
Pres./Pub. ....Denise E. Palmer
Vice Pres., Opns. ....William Barker
Controller ....Bob Amos
Asst. Controller ....Robert N. Wayne
Mgr., Human Resources ....Ric Sierra
Adv. Vice Pres., Sales ....Bob Geiger
Adv. Mgr., Majors/National ....Joe Gess
Dir., Ad Ops ....Bernie Petrich
Dir., Market Devel. ....Ted Stasney
Circ. Mgr., Systems ....Brian Keena
Circulation Director ....Tommie McLeod
Managing Editor ....Duke Maas
Dir., Content (TBO) ....Loren Omoto
Mgr., Packaging & Transportation ...Stan Volland
Mgr., Pressroom ....George Buddy Kerr
Editor, Opinions ....Joe Guidry
Vice Pres., Admin. ....Kermit Kauffman
Gen. Mgr. ....Rusty Coates
Credit Mgr. ....Charles Wilson
Adv. Mgr., NW Regl. Sales ....Brenda Minton
Adv. Mgr., Telesales ....Nancy Summers
Mktg. Mgr. ....Fran Solomon
Telemarketing Mgr. ....Alan Williams
Circ. Opns. Mgr., Metro ....Gary May
Circ. Opns. Mgr., State ....Dan Warnock
Circ. Mgr., Mktg. ....Terry Thompson
Market Information: ADS; Split run; TMC; Zoned editions.
Mechanical available: Offset; Black and 3 ROP colors; insert accepted; page cutoffs - 22.
Mechanical Specifications: Type page 11 5/8 x 21; E - 6 cols, 1 3/4, 1/8 between; A - 6 cols, 1 3/4, 1/8 between; C - 10 cols, 1 1/16, 1/8 between.
Commodity Consumption: Avg. Page Number Per Issue - Daily 76; Avg. Page Number Per Issue - Plates Used 547755; Avg. Page Number Per Issue - Sunday 158; widths 24 7/8; Newsprint Used - Short Tons 55282; Printing Ink Used - Black 730716; Printing Ink Used - Color 328545.
Equipment EDITORIAL: Front-end Software – CCI/News Gate, HI/NewsMaker Pagination.; Editorial Hardware – 10-SII/K1000, Tandem, 4-Sun/Ultra Sparc; Editorial Equipment – 200-PC with Coyote-3; Editorial Printers – ECR/4550 Imagesetters CLASSIFIED: Front-end Software – Mactive/Ad Base.; Classified Hardware – 10-SII/K1000, SII/Tandem; Classified Equipment – 120-PCs with Coyote-3; Classified Printers – ECR/4550 Imagesetters, 7-Ad Proof/Printers DISPLAY: Ad make-up applications – CJ/Layout, QuarkXPress, Adobe/InDesign, xPance; Layout Software – CJ/Layout-8000.; Display Hardware – HP/900 PRODUCTION: Pagination Software – CCI/New Desk.; Production Equipment – 3-WL/Lith-X-Pozer III, 3-ECR/4550, 2-III/3850, 1-ECR/9100; Scanners – 2-HP/ScanJet Flatbed, 1-Kk/3750, 1-Umax PRESSROOM: Line 1 – 16-TKS/M-72 double width, 4, 8; Line 2 – 16-TKS/M-72 double width, 4, 8; Folders – 4-TKS/Double; Pasters – 20, 16; Reels and Stands – 20, 16; Press control system – TKS/NPC.; Press registration system – CTP MAILROOM: Counter stackers – 23/QWI; Inserters and stuffers – 2-HI/1472, 6-GMA/SLS 1000, 1-/HI Heidelberg; Bundle tying machines – 1-/Power Strap, 16-/Dynaric.; Mailroom control system – SAM BUSINESS COMPUTERS: Business Software – Peoplesoft HRMS, Microsoft/Office2003, Microsoft/Windows XP XP, GEAC World Class Advertising System, WinStar; Business Hardware – 1-HP/900

THE VILLAGES

THE VILLAGES DAILY SUN

1100 Main St., The Villages, Fla., 32159; gen tel (352) 753-1119; adv tel (352) 753-1119; ed tel (352) 753-1119; gen fax (352) 751-7995; adv fax (352) 751-7996; ed fax (352) 753-7787; adv e-mail advertising@thevillagesmedia.com; ed e-mail larry.croom@thevillagesmedia.com; web site www.thevillagesdailysun.com
Group: U.S. Suburban Press, Inc.
Published: Mon, Tues, Wed, Thur, Fri, Sat, Sun
Weekday Frequency: m
Saturday Frequency: m
Circulation: 35,369; 35,369(sat); 37,102(sun)
Last Audit: ABC September 30, 2011
Price: 10.00/mo; 51.40/yr.
Advertising: Open inch rate $24.00
Insert rate: $56/M
News services: AP.
Politics: 1997
Special Editions: Salute to Business (Apr); Football Preview (Aug); Paradise in Pictures (Feb); Golfest (Jan); Social Security (Mar); Hurricane Preparedness Guide (May); Wheels Car Show (Nov); Newcomers (Sept).
Magazines: Sound Clips (Every other month); Relish (Monthly); Parade Magazine (S); American Profile (Weekly): Athlon Sports (Monthly); Dash (Monthly)
Broadcast Affiliations: WVLG AM 640; VNN Channel 2.
Pub. ....Philip Markward
Gen. Mgr. ....Jim Sprung
Adv. Mgr., Sales/Mktg. ....Dan Sprung
Circ. Dir. ....John Gagnon
CSR Mgr. ....Wendy Crowther-Barnes
Exec. Ed. ....Larry Croom
Mng. Ed. ....Matt Fry
Mng. Ed. ....Meta Minton
Asst. Mng. Ed. ....Curt Hills
Lifestyles Ed. ....Holly Lawler
Opinion Page Ed. ....Mark Francis
Photo Ed. ....Bill Mitchell
Sports Ed. ....Keith Chartrand
Dir., Opns. ....Steven Infinger
Prodn. Mgr., Opns. ....Ingo Fockler
Market Information: Split run; Zoned editions.
Mechanical available: Offset; Black and 3 ROP colors; insert accepted; page cutoffs - 22 3/4.
Mechanical Specifications: Type page 11 5/8 x 21 7/16; E - 6 cols, 1 11/16, 3/16 between; A - 6 cols, 1 11/16, 3/16 between; C - 6 cols, 1 13/16, 1/8 between.
Commodity Consumption: Avg. Page Number Per Issue - Daily 64; Avg. Page Number Per Issue - Plates Used 60000; Avg. Page Number Per Issue - Sunday 92; widths 27 1/2; Newsprint Used - Metric Tons 4000; Printing Ink Used - Black 84000; Printing Ink Used - Color 55000; Printing In
Equipment EDITORIAL: Front-end Software – WoodWing/QPS/QuarkXPress/InDesign/CS5; Editorial Hardware – Apple Servers
Apple PCs; Editorial Printers – HP CLASSIFIED: Front-end Software – QPS/QuarkXPress, Baseview. CircManagerPro; Classified Hardware – Apple Servers
Apple PC's; Classified Printers – HP DISPLAY: Ad make-up applications – AdManagerPro/QPS/QuarkXPress. InDesign; Display Hardware – Apple Servers
Apple PCs; Display Printers – HP PRODUCTION: Pagination Software – PuzzleFlow Automator; Production Equipment – Pre Press/2-Kodak Trendsetter News CTP; Scanners – Nikon, Microtek. PRESSROOM: Line 1 – 3 - DGM color towers/1 Goss Community color tower; Line 2 – 4 DGM color towers / 2 mono units; Press Drives – 2 Fincor 125HP drives, 4 Fincor 150 HP drives ; Folders – DGM 1035, DGM 1240; Reels and Stands – 13 Jardis Splicers; Press registration system – QTI Multicam MAILROOM: Counter stackers – Quipp Packman, Gammer; Inserters and stuffers – KANSA, Muller Martini 3000; Bundle tying machines – Dynaric; Business Hardware – Dell PC's
IBM AS400

WEST PALM BEACH

PALM BEACH NEWSPAPERS, INC.

2751 S. Dixie Hwy., West Palm Beach, Fla., 33416-4700; gen tel (561) 820-4100; gen fax (561) 820-4136
Pub. Tim Burke

THE PALM BEACH POST

2751 S. Dixie Hwy., West Palm Beach, Fla., 33405-1233; gen tel (561) 820-4100; adv tel (561) 820-4300; ed tel (561) 820-4401; gen fax (561) 820-4136; adv fax (561) 837-8434; ed fax (561) 820-4445; ed e-mail pb_metro@pbpost.com; pb_sports@pbpost.com; pb_business@pbpost.com; web site www.pbpost.com
Group: Metro Newspaper Advertising Services, Inc.
Published: Mon, Tues, Wed, Thur, Fri, Sat, Sun
Weekday Frequency: m
Saturday Frequency: m
Circulation: 95,620; 98,278(sat); 123,488(sun)
Last Audit: ABC September 30, 2011
Price: 3.25/wk; 161.20/yr.
Advertising: Open inch rate $180.77
News services: AP, Bloomberg, LAT-WP, NYT, PR Newswire, Cox.
Politics: Independent. **Established:** 1908
Special Editions: SunFest (Apr); Football (Aug); Holiday Gift Guide (Dec); Treasure Coast Fairs & Festivals (Feb); Super Bowl (Jan); Back To School (Jul); Palm Beach Medical Society Directory (Jun); Home & Garden (Mar); Discover Florida (May); Palm Beach Post Financial Sho
Special Weekly Sections: TGIF (Entertainment tab) (Fri); Inside Business (Mon); Travel (S); Weekend Stocks (Sat); Food & Dining (Thur); Local News Tabs (Wed).
Magazines: Color Comics (S).
Vice Pres./Gen. Mgr. ....Charles Gerardi
Vice Pres., HR ....Linda Murphy
Controller ....Caroll Barrett
Credit Mgr. ....Susan Meldonian
Adv. Vice Pres. ....Douglas Grossman
Adv. Dir., Opns. ....Gregg Harr
Adv. Mgr., Retail, Bureau Offices Steve Waxelbaum
Dir., Mktg. Servs. ....Laura Cunningham
Dir., Sales/Mktg./Single Copy ....Mark Sasser
Internet Mktg. Mgr. ....Michelle Ruzgar
Mgr., Research/Sales Presentations Suzanne Willcox
Circ. Vice Pres. ....Barry Berg
Circ. Mgr., Admin. Servs. ....Linda Campbell
Circ. Mgr., Opns. ....Rich Schnars
Exec. Ed./Pub. ....Tim Burke
Mng. Ed. ....Bill Rose
Asst. Mng. Ed., Bus. ....Rick Christie
Asst. Mng. Ed., Photo ....Pete Cross
Asst. Mng. Ed., Projects ....Bill Greer
Market Information: Split run; TMC; Zoned editions.
Mechanical available: Offset; Black and 3 ROP colors; insert accepted; page cutoffs - 23 9/16.
Mechanical Specifications: Type page 11 5/8 x 22 1/2; E - 6 cols, 1 5/6, 1/8 between; A - 6 cols, 1 5/6, 1/8 between; C - 10 cols, 1 11/100, 1/16 between.
Commodity Consumption: Avg. Page Number Per Issue - Daily 81; Avg. Page Number Per Issue - Plates Used 450000; Avg. Page Number Per Issue - Saturday 119; Avg. Page Number Per Issue - Sunday 153; widths 12 1/2 ; 43 1/8; Newsprint Used - Short Tons 44136; Printing Ink Used - Bl
Equipment EDITORIAL: Front-end Software – DTI/Editorial 4.3.; Editorial Hardware – 8-Sun, 105-APP/Power Mac G4; Editorial Equipment – 6-Networks in Bureaus CLASSIFIED: Front-end Software – AT/Do Fax, DTI/Class Speed 5.5.; Classified Hardware – Sun/OTI, 55-APP/Mac G4; Classified Equipment – Ricoh/77 Fax; Classified Printers – HP/5000 N DISPLAY: Ad make-up applications – DTI/Adspeed 5.5; Layout Software – DTI/AdInput, DTI/Planbuilder.; Display Hardware – Sun/DTI, 6-APP/Mac G 4; Display Printers – APP/Mac Laser Writer 8500 PRODUCTION: Pagination Software – DTI 4.3, Pagespeed 4.3, Speedplanner 4.3, Adspeed 5.5, Classpeed 5.5, DTI/Planbuilder 3.8.; Production Equipment – Harlequin/Rips 5.12, Vision Bender, Scitex/Eversmart Pro II, 2-AU/APS, 2-3850 SST, 2-AU/APS 3850 SST Wide PRESSROOM: Line 1 – 24-G/Metro (12 color decks) double width; Line 2 – 8-G/Suburban single width; Line 3 – 6-G/Colorliner double width; Folders – 4; Pasters – 32; Reels and Stands – 32 MAILROOM: Counter stackers – 1/HL, HI/Rima, 7-/QWI; Inserters and stuffers – 3-GMA/SLS 1000, 1-/Stepper Solo; Bundle tying machines – 11-/Dynaric, 3-Dynaric/RLM-1; Wrapping singles – 4-/Constellation, 2-/MLN; Mailroom control system – GMA; Addressing machine – K; Other equipment –Id/Bottom Wrap, Samuel Strapping. BUSINESS COMPUTERS: Business Software – Labrador; Business Hardware – Unisys/2200

WINTER HAVEN

NEWS CHIEF

455 Sixth St. NW, Winter Haven, Fla., 33881; gen tel (863) 401-6900; ed e-mail news@newschief.com; features@newschief.com; web site www.polkonline.com
Published: Mon, Tues, Wed, Thur, Fri, Sat, Sun
Weekday Frequency: m
Saturday Frequency: m
Circulation: 3,754; 3,754(sat); 5,398(sun)
Last Audit: ABC September 30, 2011
Price: 1.78/wk; 99.65/yr.
Advertising: Open inch rate $19.85
News services: AP, SHNS, DF, LAT-WP.
Politics: Independent.
Special Editions: Citrus Exposition (Feb); Newcomer's Guide (Jan); Outlook (Mar).
Special Weekly Sections: Home Finder (Sat).
Magazines: Real Estate (Fri); Relish (Monthly); Retirement Living (Other); USA WEEKEND Magazine (S).
Pub. ....Nelson Kirkland
Bus. Mgr. ....Bruce Baker
Classified Adv. Mgr. ....Jacki Unger-Poole
Circ. Dir. ....Jeff Amero
Exec. Ed. ....Roger Ballas
Mng. Ed. ....Joe Braddy
Lifestyle Ed. ....Meredith Jean Morton
Sports Ed. ....Jason Martin

Prodn. Dir. ....Dennis Wilkinson
Market Information: TMC.
Mechanical available: Offset; Black and 3 ROP colors; insert accepted; page cutoffs - 22 3/4.
Mechanical Specifications: Type page 13 x 21 1/2; E - 6 cols, 2 1/16, 1/8 between; A - 6 cols, 2 1/16, 1/8 between; C - 6 cols, 2 1/16, 1/8 between.
Commodity Consumption: Avg. Page Number Per Issue - Daily 40; Avg. Page Number Per Issue - Sunday 71; widths 25; Newsprint Used - Short Tons 2150.
Equipment EDITORIAL: Front-end Software – Caere/OmniPage.; Editorial Hardware – 6-APP/G3 PowerMac fileserver, 1-APP/Mac fx fileserver, 5-APP/iMac; Editorial Equipment – APP/Mac Scanner CLASSIFIED: Front-end Software – BaseView/AJ Manager 3.X.; Classified Hardware – APP/Mac G3 fileserver, 13-APP/Mac G3; Classified Printers – HP/4100 DISPLAY: Ad make-up applications – QuarkPress 4.11, Photoshop SS; Layout Software – 1-APP/Mac G4 Server, 8-APP/Mac G35 and G45.; Display Printers – 1-HP/5000, 1-HP/8550 PRODUCTION: Pagination Software – QuarkPress 4.11-.; Production Equipment – 2-V/4000 RIP/5500 Typesetter, Nikon; Cameras – 1-C/Spartan II; Scanners – Howtek PRESSROOM: Line 1 – 6-G/Urbanite (1 3-color); Line 2 – 8-HI/V-15A (Color deck); Folders – 1, 1. MAILROOM: Counter stackers – 1-MM/1231, 1-QWI/928; Inserters and stuffers – 1-S/NP524, 1-MM/227; Bundle tying machines – 2-MLN/MLN; Addressing machine – 1/El, 1-KAN/Labeler.; Business Hardware – ATT/6386 E-33 WGS

GEORGIA

ALBANY

THE ALBANY HERALD

126 N. Washington St., Albany, Ga., 31701; gen tel (229) 888-9300; adv tel (229) 888-9398; ed tel (229) 888-9344; gen fax (229) 888-9357; adv fax (229) 888-9394; ed fax (229) 888-9356; gen e-mail news@albanyherald.com; adv e-mail class@albanyherald.surfsouth.com; ed e-mail letters@albanyherald.com; web site www.albanyherald.com
Group: Southern Community Newspapers, Inc.
Published: Mon, Tues, Wed, Thur, Fri, Sat, Sun
Weekday Frequency: m
Saturday Frequency: m
Circulation: 17,868; 16,366(sat); 21,027(sun)
Last Audit: Sworn September 30, 2009
Price: 16.95/mo; 182.95/yr.
Advertising: Open inch rate $58.15
News services: AP.
Politics: 1891
Own facility?: Y
Special Editions: (February)Albany Tech, Bridal Show, Dougherty Schools, Outlook 2011 (March) marathon/marti Gras, Health Wise, Albany Panthers, South Georgia Woman (April) Sports Hall of Fame, Health Wise, 40 under 40, Readers Choice (May) South Georgia Woman, Graduation, Health Wise, Fun Guide 50 (June) Homebuyer's Guide, Lifestyle Expo (July) Homebuyer's Guide, South Georgia Woman, Health Wise (August) Football Preview, Health Wise, Homebuyer's Guide (September) Homebuyers Guide, Georgia Peanut Tour, South Georgia Woman (October) ASU Homecoming, Metro Guide, Health Wise, homebuyer's Guide (November) Holiday Open House, Veterans, Holiday Gift Guide II, South Georgia Woman
Special Weekly Sections: AAA Express TMC, The Emblem (US Marince Corp Newspaper), Real Estate Showcase, Southview
Magazines: Comic Section (S); Homebuyer's Guide (monthly), USA Weekend (S)
Broadcast Affiliations: None
President/Publisher................Michael Gebhart
Advetising Director ....Kevin Austin
Adv. Accts. Rep., Nat'l/Major ....Phil Cody
Editor ....Jim Hendricks
Mng. Ed.......................................Danny Carter
Metro Editor...........................Carlton Fletcher
Sports Editor ....Danny Aller
Director of Operations....................Lynn Ridder
Prodn. Supvr., Composing..............Don Kimsey
Prodn. Supvr., Mailroom...........Charles Holsey
General Manager ....John Hetzler
Circulation Director........................Michael Hill
Market Information: Prime Plus- Zoned Editions Wednesday, AAA/Herald Express-TMC Tuesdays - Sunday Select -Opt in Free Product-Sundays
Mechanical available: Offset; Black and 3 ROP colors; insert accepted; page cutoffs - 22 3/4.
Mechanical Specifications: Type page 11x 21 1/2; E - 6 cols, 1 7/8, 1/6 between; A - 6 cols, 1 7/8, 1/6 between; @RecordBody:**Commodity Consumption:** Avg. Page Number Per Issue - Daily 25; Avg. Page Number Per Issue - Plates Used 16492; Avg. Page Number Per Issue - Sunday 62; widths 25; Newsprint Used - Short Tons 3250; Printing Ink Used - Black 52500; Printing Ink Used - Color 17900; Printing Ink Used
Equipment EDITORIAL: Front-end Software – SCS Scoop; In Design; Adobe Photo Shop and Illustrator; Microsoft Word; Editorial Hardware – Dell PC; Editorial Printers – 3-APP/Mac Laser-Printers CLASSIFIED: Front-end Software – SCS/Classified 8000.; Classified Hardware – SCS/Class, 10-Falco/VDT, 2-IBM/PS2, 1-APP/Mac Quadra, 2-Dell/466XE Networked; Classified Printers – 2-PostScript/Laser Printers DISPLAY: Ad make-up applications – Multi-Ad/Creator; Layout Software – SCS.; Display Hardware – 5-APP/Mac IIci; Display Printers – 2-PostScript/Laser Printer PRODUCTION: Pagination Software – SCS, QPS/QuarkXPress.; Production Equipment – 1-Nat/A340, 2-LE; Cameras – C/Spartan III, C/Newspager PRESSROOM: Line 1 – 9-G/Urbanite 1977; Folders – G/2:1; Press control system – 3-Fin/Control Console. MAILROOM: Counter stackers – 3-MM/310, 1-MM/288; Inserters and stuffers – 3-MM/227; Bundle tying machines – 3-Dynaric/NP2 AUDIO: Audio Software – New Horizons/Info-Connect; Audio Hardware – Info-Connect, Texas Micro/486; Business Hardware – SCS, 2-Dell, 20-Falco
Zip Codes served: 31701,31707,31709,31710,31719,31721,31010,31015,31714,31714,31716,31719,31730,31744,31763,31765,31768,31779,31780,31781,31784,31787,31789,31791,31793,31794,31795,31796,31832,39813,39817,39819,39823,39826,39834,39837,39840,39841,39842,39845,39846,39851,39859,39862,39870,39877,39886
Delivery method: Mail, Newsstand, Private Carrier, Racks

THE ALBANY HERALD PUB. CO., INC.

126 N. Washington St., Albany, Ga., 31701; gen tel (229) 888-9300; gen fax (229) 888-9357

AMERICUS

AMERICUS TIMES-RECORDER

101 Hwy. 27 E., Americus, Ga., 31709; gen tel (229) 924-2751; adv tel (229) 924-2751; gen fax (229) 928-6344; gen e-mail her.editorial@gaflnews.com; ed e-mail beth.alston@gaflnews.com; web site www.americustimesrecorder.com
Published: Tues, Wed, Thur, Fri, Sun
Weekday Frequency: m
Circulation: 6,962; 6,917(sun)
Last Audit: December 3, 2009
Price: 8.66/mo.
Advertising: Open inch rate $33.85
News services: AP, TNN.
Politics: Independent. **Established:** 1879
Not Published: New Year; Memorial Day; Independence Day; Labor Day; Christmas.
Special Editions: Car Care (Apr); Football (Aug); Holiday Cookbook (Dec); Business & Service Directory (Feb); Insurance Week (Jan); Christmas in July (Jul); Summer Recreation (Jun); Lawn & Garden (Mar); Mother's Day (May); ValueTown-Thanksgiving (Nov); Home-Owned Business
Special Weekly Sections: Church News (Fri); Best Food Day (Tues).
Magazines: South Georgia Rural Living (Monthly); Parade (S).
Pub. ....Dan Sutton
Circ. Dir. ....Zelmi Melscon
Mng. Ed. ....Beth Alston
Sports Ed.................................Chris Whitaker
Mgmt. Info Servs. Mgr.................Hubby Brooks
Market Information: TMC.
Mechanical available: Offset; Black and 3 ROP colors; insert accepted - single sheet; page cutoffs - 22 3/4.
Mechanical Specifications: Type page 13 x 21 1/2; E - 6 cols, 2 1/16, 1/8 between; A - 6 cols, 2 1/16, 1/8 between; C - 9 cols, 1 7/8, 1/16 between.
Commodity Consumption: Avg. Page Number Per Issue - Daily 14; Avg. Page Number Per Issue - Plates Used 2650; Avg. Page Number Per Issue - Saturday 14; Avg. Page Number Per Issue - Sunday 24; widths 27 1/2; Newsprint Used - Short Tons 206; Printing Ink Used - Black 2500; Printi
Equipment EDITORIAL: Front-end Software – QPS/QuarkXPress.; Editorial Hardware – 7-APP/Mac LC III, 2-APP/Mac Centris 610; Editorial Equipment – Pre Press/Panther Pro 46; Editorial Printers – HP/LaserJet 4MV; Classified Hardware – 1-APP/Mac Centris 610; Classified Equipment – 4-ATT. DISPLAY: Ad make-up applications – Multi-Ad/Creator, Aldus/FreeHand, Adobe/Illustrator, QPS/QuarkXPress; Layout Software – APP/Mac IIci, APP/Mac Centris 610.; Display Hardware – APP/Mac IIci, APP/Mac 610 Centris; Display Printers – 2-APP/Mac Laser-Printer, Tegra/Varityper/5060W, Tegra/Varityper/600W PRODUCTION: Pagination Software – QPS/QuarkXPress 3.32.; Production Equipment – Caere/OmniPage Pro 2.12, APP/Mac 610 Centris; Cameras – B/Horizontal, SCREEN/Vertical PRESSROOM: Line 1 – G/Community (upper former); Folders – G/Half, G/Quarter.; Inserters and stuffers – KR/4-pocket; Bundle tying machines – MLN/Auto Bundler.; Business Hardware – PBS

ATHENS

ATHENS BANNER-HERALD

1 Press Pl., Athens, Ga., 30601; gen tel (706) 549-0123; adv tel (706) 208-2281; ed tel (706) 208-2212; gen fax (706) 543-5234; adv fax (706) 543-5234; ed fax (706) 208-2246; gen e-mail news@onlineathens.com; adv e-mail adreps@onlineathens.com; web site www.onlineathens.com
Published: Mon, Tues, Wed, Thur, Fri, Sat, Sun
Weekday Frequency: m
Saturday Frequency: m
Circulation: 19,580; 19,580(sat); 25,914(sun)
Last Audit: ABC September 30, 2011
Price: 9.95/mo; 99.00/yr.
Advertising: Open inch rate $35.27
News services: AP, BPI, LAT-WP.
Politics: Independent.
Special Editions: Golf Guide (Apr); College Football (Aug); Gift Guide (Dec); Spotlight 1 (Feb); Top Citizen (Jan); Locally Owned Business (Jun); Spotlight 2 (Mar); Twilight Criterium (May); New Car Intro (Nov); Gameday (Oct); Senior Living/Primetime (Quarterly); Gameday (
Special Weekly Sections: Home & Garden (Fri); School Pages (Mon); Pet Pages (Sat); Neighbor Page (Thur); Health Page (Tues); Food (Wed).
Magazines: Relish (Monthly); Homefront (S); Marquee (Entertainment) (Thur).
Controller, Division ....Greg Williamson
Adv. Dir. ....Angela Smith
Adv. Mgr., Online Sales..................Alan Brown
Mktg. Dir. ....George James
Circ. Dir. ....Ron Forrest
Exec. Ed. ....Jason Winders
Arts/Entertainment Ed. ....Julie Phillips
Bus./Finance Ed. ....Don Nelson
Editorial Page Ed......................Jim Thompson
Features Ed. ....Courtney Pomeroy
Metro Ed. ....Roger Nielsen
Oconee Ed. ....Wayne Ford
Online Ed. ....David Bill
Photo Dir. ....John Curry
Prodn. Dir................................Gary Cleveland
Prodn. Mgr., Mailroom.........Dennis McCraven
Market Information: ADS; Split run; TMC; Zoned editions.
Mechanical available: Offset; Black and 3 ROP colors; insert accepted; page cutoffs - 22 3/4.
Mechanical Specifications: Type page 11 5/8 x 21 1/4; E - 6 cols, 2 1/16, 1/8 between; A - 6 cols, 1 13/16, 1/8 between; C - 10 cols, 1 1/16, 5/64 between.
Commodity Consumption: Avg. Page Number Per Issue - Daily 28; Avg. Page Number Per Issue - Plates Used 80000; Avg. Page Number Per Issue - Saturday 40; Avg. Page Number Per Issue - Sunday 94; widths 24 7/8; Newsprint Used - Metric Tons 2900; Newsprint Used - Short Tons 3100; P
Equipment EDITORIAL: Front-end Software – Baseview 3.5.6, Adobe/Illustrator 9.0, QPS/QuarkXPress 6.5, Adobe/Acrobat 3.0, Adobe/Creative Suite 2.; Editorial Hardware – 21-Gateway/2000, 2-APP/Power Mac, 2-Gateway/2000, Umax/5900, APP/Mac G4; Editorial Printers – 1-HP/5M, 1-HP/5000 GN Printer CLASSIFIED: Front-end Software – DTI 5.42.; Classified Hardware – 8-Gateway; Classified Printers – HP/5000 Gn DISPLAY: Ad make-up applications – Adobe/Creative Suite 2, QPS/QuarkXPress 6.5, 6-Outlook/Express 4.5; Layout Software – MEI/ALS 4.2.; Display Hardware – 2-APP/Mac G4, 6-APP/Mac G3; Display Printers – Tektronix/Color Printer, 2-HP/5M, 2-HP/5000 GN PRODUCTION: Pagination Software – QPS/QuarkXPress 4.11, Adobe/Photoshop 7.0, Adobe/Creative Suite 2.; Production Equipment – Ap Windows 2000 Photo Server, 2-AG/1500, 2-APP/Mac G3; Scanners – 1-Kk/2035 PRESSROOM: Line 1 – 12-G/Urbanite; Folders – G/2:1. MAILROOM: Counter stackers – 3-HL/HT II, 1/Stackpack, 2-QWI/Soin, 2-TMSI; Inserters and stuffers – 1-/AM Graphics/048P, NP/848; Bundle tying machines – G-3/Titan, 3-Dynamic; Wrapping singles – 2-/Samuels, 1-/QWI; Addressing machine – 2-/Ch; Other equipment –2-/Ga AUDIO: Audio Software – VG/9000, TRT (customer aplication); Audio Hardware – MPS, 2-Gateway/2000, APP/Stockserver BUSINESS COMPUTERS: Business Software – WordPerfect 5.0, PC file, Lotus/1-2-3, Microsoft/Windows, MPS, Microsoft/Word, Microsoft/Excel; Business Hardware – PBS, Bay Network Hub, IBM/RISC 6000, Raid Tower, Gateway, IBM, HP/5M

ATLANTA

ATLANTA JOURNAL-CONSTITUTION

223 Perimeter Center Parkway, N.E., Atlanta, Ga., 30346; gen tel (404) 526-5889; adv tel (404) 577-5772; ed tel (404) 526-5395; gen fax (404) 526-5199; ed fax (404) 526-5199; gen e-mail listen@ajc.com; ed e-mail hpost@ajc.com; web site www.ajc.com
Group: COX Enterprises, Inc.
Published: Mon, Tues, Wed, Thur, Fri, Sat, Sun
Weekday Frequency: m
Saturday Frequency: m
Circulation: 173,884; 186,034(sat); 410,022(sun)
Last Audit: ABC September 30, 2011
Price: 3.95/wk (7 days); 17.12/mo; 191.02/yr.
Advertising: Open inch rate $762.90
News services: Cox News Service, AP, DJ, LAT-WP, NYT, MCT, CNS, CQ, NNS, PNS, SHNS, TMS.
Politics: 1990
Special Editions: Breast Cancer Education (An-

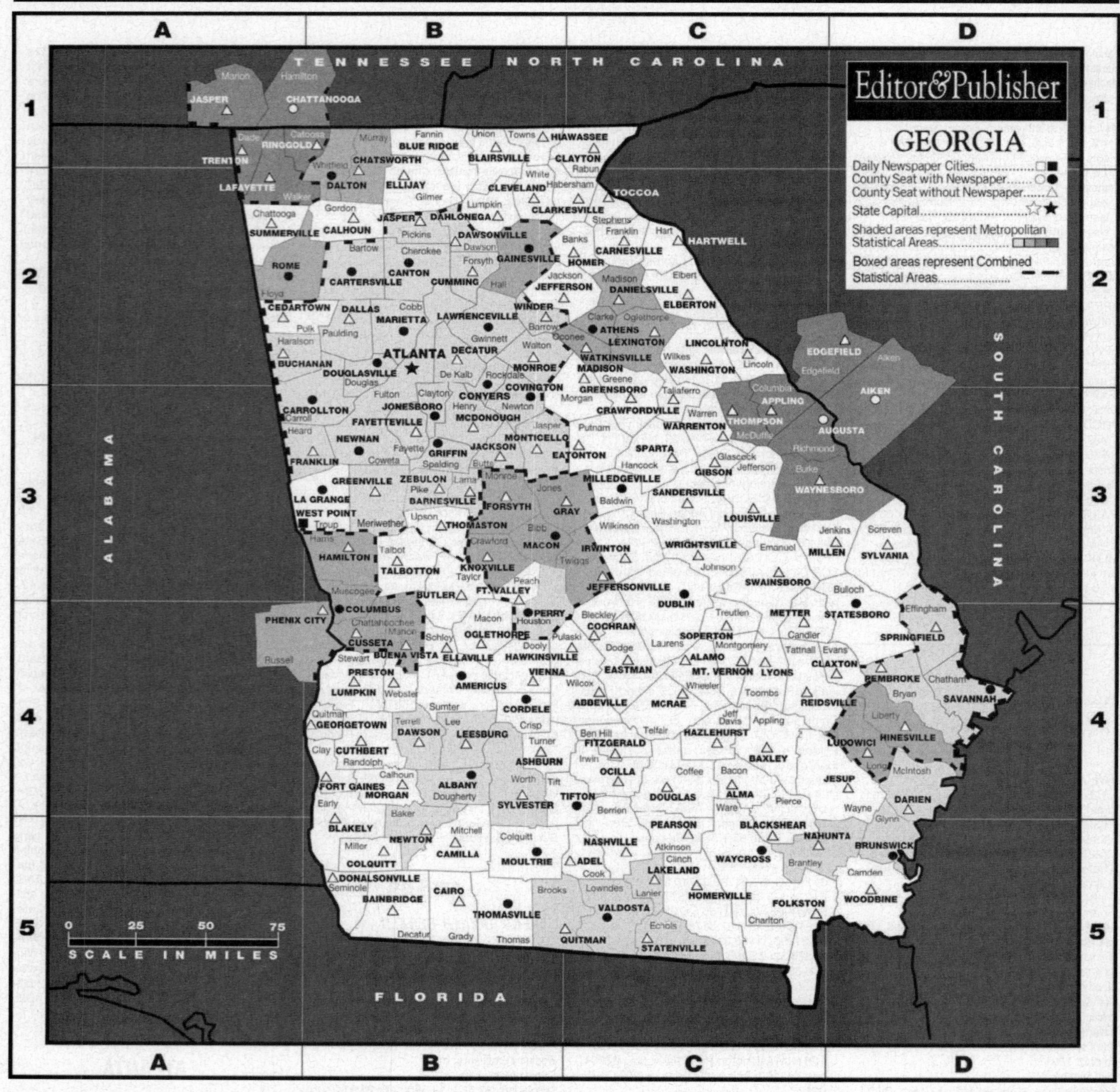

nually); Golf/Masters (Apr); Back to School (Aug); Holiday Gift Guides (Dec); Brides (Feb); Safety Vehicles (Jan); Peachtree Road Race (Jul); Executive Homes (Jun); Braves Baseball Preview (Mar); Fun in the Sun (May); Pulse (Mon

Special Weekly Sections: Sports Weekend (Fri); Horizon (Mon); Travel (S); Faith & Values (Sat); Community Editions (Thur); Healthy Living (Tues); Atlanta Tech (Wed).

Magazines: Color Comics (S).

Pres./Publisher .... Mike Joseph
Pub. .... Doug Franklin
Vice Pres., Legal Affairs .... Charles Parker
Controller .... Chad Richardson
Dir., HR .... Bill Jones
Dir., Purchasing .... Al Abrash
Adv. Vice Pres., Classified/Internet .... Larry Kline
Adv. Vice Pres., Retail .... Mike Perricone
Adv. Dir., Major Accts. .... Sammy McDaniel
Adv. Dir., Nat'l/Sales .... Debbie Reetz
Adv. Dir., Retail/Territory Sales ..... Karen Walker
Adv. Mgr., Clipper/Direct Mktg. .... Ron Ade
Adv. Mgr., Opns. .... Diane Ludington
Vice Pres., Mktg. .... Amy Chown
Vice Pres., Strategic Mktg. .... Paula Rattray
Dir., Mktg. Devel. .... Laura Inman
Mktg. Mgr., Classified/Territory .... Chris Hood
Mktg. Opns. Mgr. .... Bill Means
Circ. Vice Pres. .... Robert W. Eickhoff
Circ. Sr. Dir., Consumer Sales/Retention Mike Burlingame
Dir., HR .... Jason Smith

Market Information: ADS; Split run; TMC; Zoned editions.

Mechanical available: Offset; Black and 3 ROP colors; insert accepted - zoned areas; page cutoffs - 21 1/4.

Mechanical Specifications: Type page 12 5/8 x 21 1/4; E - 6 cols, 1 13/16, 1/8 between; A - 6 cols, 1 13/16, 1/8 between; C - 10 cols, 1 1/16, 1/8 between.

Commodity Consumption: Avg. Page Number Per Issue - Daily 93; Avg. Page Number Per Issue - Plates Used 1113000; Avg. Page Number Per Issue - Saturday 136; Avg. Page Number Per Issue - Sunday 235; widths 12 1/2; Newsprint Used - Short Tons 128250; Printing Ink Used - Black 2860

Equipment EDITORIAL: Front-end Software – DTI.; Editorial Hardware – 620-APP/Mac, 175-APP/Mac Powerbook; Editorial Equipment – 18-Sun/Server, 2-Dell/Gu55 Server; Editorial Printers – HP, Xante, Canon CLASSIFIED: Front-end Software – In-house.; Classified Hardware – 145-IBM/3192, 2-Ad Star DISPLAY: Ad make-up applications – NW/Admarc, NW/Discuss; Layout Software – DTI/Speed Planner.; Display Hardware – IBM 9672 PRODUCTION: Pagination Software – DTI.; Production Equipment – 4-KFM/Bender single width, 2-Cx/Bidco, Glunz & Jensen/K2; Cameras – 4-C/Spartan; Scanners – 1-Howtek, 2-ECR/1800, 2-ECR/Autokon 1000, 2-Pixel Craft (tab size), 1-Scitex/Smartscan, 1-Tecsa/TS2470, 1-Tecsa/TS2570 PRESSROOM: Line 1 – 4-TKS/(20 half decks; 4 satellites) (Gwinnett); Line 2 – 2-TKS/7000CD tower units (Gwinnett); Line 3 – 4-TKS/(20 half decks; 4 satellites) (Fulton); Folders – 8-TKS/(Fulton), 8-TKS/(Gwinnett); Reels and Stands – 40, 40. MAILROOM: Counter stackers – 13-SH/257 (Fulton), 16-QWI/300-350 (Gwinnett); Inserters and stuffers – 1-NP/1472, 3-QWI/201, 4-QWI/200 (Reach), 2-GMA/SLS 2000 30:2 (Gwinnett), 1-GMA/SLS 2000 36:2 (Gwinnett), 1-QWI/400 (Reach); Bundle tying machines – 11-Si/Fulton, 14 BUSINESS COMPUTERS: Business Software – CA, Global; Business Hardware – IBM/9672 RC4

AUGUSTA

THE AUGUSTA CHRONICLE

725 Broad St., Augusta, Ga., 30901; gen tel (706) 724-0851; gen fax (706) 828-4273; gen e-mail newsroom@augustachronicle.com; adv e-mail adsales@augustachronicle.com; ed e-mail letters@augustachronicle.com; web site www.augustachronicle.com

Group: Metro Newspaper Advertising Services, Inc.
Published: Mon, Tues, Wed, Thur, Fri, Sat, Sun
Weekday Frequency: m
Saturday Frequency: m
Circulation: 58,519; 62,860(sat); 75,402(sun)
Last Audit: ABC September 30, 2011
Price: 13.00/mo; 156.00/yr.
Advertising: Open inch rate $102.05(m-fri)
News services: AP, MCT, Morris, SHNS, LAT - WP.
Politics: Independent. **Established:** 1785
Special Editions: Masters Golf (Apr); Back-to-School (Aug); Gift Guides (Dec); Primetime (Feb); Brides (Jan); Primetime Diversity (Jul); Triple Crown (Mar); Graduation (May); PrimeTime (Quarterly); Hunting & Fishing (Sept).
Special Weekly Sections: Applause (Fri); Today's Home (S); Religion (Sat); Xtreme (Tues); Food (Wed).
Magazines: Relish (Monthly); USA WEEKEND Magazine (S).
Broadcast Affiliations: WJBF (ABC); WRDW (CBS); WAGT (NBC); WFXG (FOX).
Pres. ....Donald W. Bailey
Pub. ....William S. Morris
CFO ....Martin Pippin
Credit Mgr. ....Kathy Hammons
Adv. Dir. ....Tonney Bennar
Adv. Mgr., Delivery ....Janet Culver
Adv. Mgr., Display ....Kate Cooper-Metts
Adv. Acct. Mgr. ....Lorie Tate
Mgr., Newspapers in Educ. ....Melisa Siman
Circ. Mgr. ....Jeff Hartley
Circ. Mgr., Sales/Mktg. ....Paul Mcmanaman
Mng. Ed. ....Elizabeth Adams
Editorial Cartoonist ....Rick McKee
Editorial Page Ed. ....Michael Ryan
Features Ed. ....Tharon Giddens
Metro Ed. ....Bill Kirby
News Ed. ....John Gogick
Outdoors Ed. ....Rob Pavey
Sports Ed. ....John Boyette
Audiotex Mgr. ....Lowell Dorn
Market Information: ADS; Split run; TMC; Zoned editions.
Mechanical available: Offset; Black and 3 ROP colors; insert accepted; page cutoffs - 22 3/4.
Mechanical Specifications: Type page 11 5/8 x 21 1/2; E - 6 cols, 2 1/16, 1/8 between; A - 6 cols, 2 1/16, 3/32 between; C - 10 cols, 1 3/16, 1/8 between.
Commodity Consumption: Avg. Page Number Per Issue - Daily 42; Avg. Page Number Per Issue - Plates Used 106500; Avg. Page Number Per Issue - Saturday 52; Avg. Page Number Per Issue - Sunday 92; widths 37 1/2; Newsprint Used - Short Tons 10278; Printing Ink Used - Black 170040;
Equipment EDITORIAL: Front-end Software – MPS.; Editorial Equipment – APP/Power Mac; Editorial Printers – Pre Press/Panther CLASSIFIED: Front-end Software – DTI, APP/Mac.; Classified Hardware – DTI, APP/Mac; Classified Printers – Pre Press/Panther DISPLAY: Ad make-up applications – Multi-Ad/Creator, QPS/QuarkXPress, Adobe/Photoshop; Display Hardware – APP/Mac, APP/Mac NTX, APP/Power Mac; Display Printers – XIT/Clipper, Tektronix/Phaser PRODUCTION: Pagination Software – QPS/Qu; Production Equipment – Caere/OmniPage, 1-KFM/Twin Drawer, 1-AG/1500, Xante/Accel-a-Writer 8200 ps, 2-Pre-Press/Panther Pro 62, 2-Glunz & Jensen/280; Cameras – 1-C/Spartan, 1-C/Marathon; Scanners – Nikon/ScanTouch AX-1200, Kk/Film Scanner RFS-2035 PRESSROOM: Line 1 – 5-G/Metro (2 color decks) 1968, 2-G/Metro 1969, 3-G/Metro (3 color decks) 1988; Press Drives – 10; Folders – 2-G/3:2, 2-G/2:1; Pasters – 10; Reels and Stands – 10 MAILROOM: Counter stackers – 5/Quipp 351; Inserters and stuffers – 2-MM/227, 2-GMA/SLS 2000; Bundle tying machines – 5-/Dynaric; Addressing machine – 8-/Wm, 1-/KR. AUDIO: Audio Software – PEP/Voice Print 9000, TRT; Audio Hardware – Morris Information Services, Gateway/2000 BUSINESS COMPUTERS: Business Software – PBS/Circ. 3.2, PBS/Adv. 2.8; Business Hardware – 2-IBM/RISC6000

BRUNSWICK

THE BRUNSWICK NEWS

3011 Altama Ave., Brunswick, Ga., 31520-4626; gen tel (912) 265-8320; gen fax (912) 264-4973; adv e-mail advertising@thebrunswicknews.com; ed e-mail editor@thebrunswicknews.com; newsroom@thebrunswicknews.com; web site www.thebrunswicknews.com

Published: Mon, Tues, Wed, Thur, Fri, Sat
Weekday Frequency: m
Saturday Frequency: m
Circulation: 17,800; 17,800(sat)
Price: 5.00/mo; 60.00/yr.
Advertising: Open inch rate $19.95
Insert rate: $37-$69 CPM
News services: AP, NEA.
Politics: Independent. **Established:** 1902
Not Published: Independence Day; Thanksgiving; Christmas.
Own facility?: Y
Special Editions: Newcomers Guide (Apr); Football (Aug); Christmas Greetings (Dec); Wedding Bells (Feb); Outlook Glynn (Jan); Back to School (Jul); Hurricane Survival (Jun); Tour of Homes (Mar); Graduation (May); Holiday Gift Guide (Nov); Celebration (Oct); Health and Fitn
Special Weekly Sections: Business (Fri); Wedding & Engagement (Mon); Sunday Drive (Sat); Business (Wed).
Magazines: Relish (Monthly; Spry (monthly); American Profile (Weekly).
Vice Pres./Gen. Mgr. ....Ron Maulden
Adv. Dir. ....Heath Slapikas
Circ. Dir. ....Frank Lane
Ed. ....Buff Leavy
Mng. Ed. ....Kerry Klumpe
Editorial Page Ed. ....C.H. Leavy
Lifestyle Ed. ....Mary Starr
News Ed. ....Hank Rowland
Sports Ed. ....Dave Jordan
Data Processing Mgr. ....Mark Young
Mechanical available: Offset; Black and 3 ROP colors; insert accepted; page cutoffs - 22 3/4.
Mechanical Specifications: Type page 13 x 21; E - 6 cols, 2 1/16, 1/8 between; A - 6 cols, 2 1/16, 1/8 between; C - 8 cols, 1 1/2, 1/8 between.
Commodity Consumption: Avg. Page Number Per Issue - Daily 42; Avg. Page Number Per Issue - Plates Used 14000; Avg. Page Number Per Issue - Saturday 42; widths 27 1/2; Newsprint Used - Short Tons 1250; Printing Ink Used - Black 24950; Printing Ink Used - Color 4550; Printing In
Equipment EDITORIAL: Front-end Software – Baseview. CLASSIFIED: Front-end Software – Baseview, QPS/QuarkXPress.; Display Hardware – Baseview. PRODUCTION: Pagination Software – Baseview.; Production Equipment – Nu/Flip Top, DP; Cameras – C/Spartan III PRESSROOM: Line 1 – 8-G/Community 1974.; Inserters and stuffers – 1/DG; Addressing machine – Papertrack System.; Business Hardware – Papertrak/System
Delivery method: Newsstand, Private Carrier, Racks

CANTON

CHEROKEE TRIBUNE

521 E. Main St., Canton, Ga., 30114; gen tel (770) 479-1441; adv tel (770) 479-1441; ed tel (770) 479-1441; gen fax (770) 479-3505; adv fax (770) 479-3505; ed fax (770) 479-3505; gen e-mail bjacoby@cherokeetribune.com; web site www.cherokeetribune.com

Group: U.S. Suburban Press, Inc.
Published: Mon, Tues, Wed, Thur, Fri, Sat, Sun
Weekday Frequency: m
Saturday Frequency: m
Circulation: 4,492; 4,492(sat); 4,820(sun)
Last Audit: ABC September 30, 2011
Price: 30.45/13wk, $57.75/26wk, $107.63/53wk.
Advertising: Open inch rate $15.75
News services: AP.
Special Weekly Sections: Real Estate (S).
Magazines: USA WEEKEND Magazine (S).
Pub. ....Otis Brumby
Adv. Mgr. ....Kim Fowler
Circ. Mgr. ....Matt Heck
Ed. ....Barbara Jacoby
Market Information: ADS; TMC.
Mechanical available: Offset; Black and ROP colors; insert accepted.
Mechanical Specifications: Type page 11 5/8 x 21.

CARROLLTON

TIMES-GEORGIAN

901 Hayes Mill Rd., Carrollton, Ga., 30117; gen tel (770) 834-6631; gen fax (770) 834-9991; gen e-mail publisher@times-georgian.com; web site www.times-georgian.com

Published: Tues, Wed, Thur, Fri, Sat, Sun
Weekday Frequency: m
Circulation: 8,019; 8,019(sat); 7,849(sun)
Last Audit: March 31, 2008
Price: 9.50/mo; 104.00/yr; 54.65/6mo (mail), $106.45/yr (mail).
Advertising: Open inch rate $34.00
News services: AP.
Politics: Independent.
Special Editions: Auto (Fall).
Magazines: USA WEEKEND Magazine (S).
Pub. ....Leonard Woolsey
Bus. Mgr. ....Michael Shaine
Adv. Dir., Classified ....David Bigg
Circ. Dir. ....John Knoll
Mng. Ed. ....Bruce Browning
Lifestyles Ed. ....Kathryn Campbell
Sports Ed. ....Corey Cusick
Market Information: TMC.
Mechanical available: Offset; Black and 3 ROP colors; insert accepted; page cutoffs - 22 3/4.
Mechanical Specifications: Type page 13 x 21 1/2; E - 6 cols, 2 1/16, 1/8 between; A - 6 cols, 2 1/16, 1/8 between; C - 9 cols, 1 1/2, 1/8 between.
Commodity Consumption: Avg. Page Number Per Issue - Daily 17; Avg. Page Number Per Issue - Plates Used 12000; Avg. Page Number Per Issue - Sunday 24; widths 28; Newsprint Used - Short Tons 1500; Printing Ink Used - Black 30000; Printing Ink Used - Color 6000; Printing Ink Used
Equipment EDITORIAL: Front-end Software – Baseview, Baseview/NewsEdit Pro, QPS/QuarkXPress.; Editorial Hardware – 11-APP/Mac; Editorial Printers – 1-APP/Mac LaserWriter II NTX, APP/Mac Printer CLASSIFIED: Front-end Software – Baseview/Ad Manager Pro.; Classified Hardware – 5-APP/Mac DISPLAY: Ad make-up applications – Multi-Ad/Creator.; Display Hardware – 9-APP/Mac PRODUCTION: Pagination Software – QPS/QuarkXPress 3.32.; Production Equipment – Caere/Omnipage Pro 6.0; Cameras – 1-C/Spartan III PRESSROOM: Line 1 – 9-G/Community. MAILROOM: Counter stackers – 1-BG/Count-O-Veyor; Inserters and stuffers – 2/MM; Bundle tying machines – 2-/MLN; Addressing machine – 1-/KR. BUSINESS COMPUTERS: Business Software – Baseview/Ap Manager Pro; Business Hardware – 6-APP/Mac

CARTERSVILLE

CARTERSVILLE NEWSPAPERS

251 S. Tennessee St., Cartersville, Ga., 30120; gen tel (770) 382-4545; gen fax (770) 382-2711

THE DAILY TRIBUNE NEWS

251 S. Tennessee St., Cartersville, Ga., 30120-0070; gen tel (770) 382-4545; gen fax (770) 382-2711; gen e-mail news@daily-tribune.com; adv e-mail jennifer.moates@daily-tribune.com; ed e-mail news@daily-tribune.com; web site www.daily-tribune.com

Published: Mon, Tues, Wed, Thur, Fri, Sun
Weekday Frequency: m
Circulation: 5,833; 5,833(sat); 6,508(sun)
Last Audit: ABC September 30, 2011
Price: $98.95 yr
Advertising: Open inch rate $10.70
News services: AP.
Politics: 1946
Not Published: Thanksgiving; Christmas.
Own facility?: Y
Special Editions: Earth Day Tab (Apr); Christmas Greetings (Dec); Medical Tab (Feb); Chamber Tab (Jan); Progress (Jul); Graduation (Jun); Holiday Cookbook (Nov).
Special Weekly Sections: Real Estate (Fri); Business News Day (S).
Magazines: Relish (Monthly); TV Outlook (S); American Profile (Weekly).
Ed. ....Johnette Dawson
Women's News Ed. ....Elizabeth Cochran
Prodn. Dir., Pre Press ....William Bramlett
Prodn. Dir., Pressroom ....Byron Pezzarossi
Market Information: TMC; Zoned editions.
Mechanical available: Offset; Black and 3 ROP colors; insert accepted - any; page cutoffs - 22 3/4.
Mechanical Specifications: Type page 13 x 21 1/2; E - 6 cols, 2 1/16, 1/8 between; A - 6 cols, 2 1/16, 1/8 between; C - 6 cols, 2 1/16, 1/8 between.
Commodity Consumption: Avg. Page Number Per Issue - Daily 21.03; Avg. Page Number Per Issue - Plates Used 9457; widths 28; Newsprint Used - Short Tons 604; Printing Ink Used - Black 17771; Printing Ink Used - Color 2785; Printing Ink Used - Pages Printed 6520.
Equipment EDITORIAL: Front-end Software – Baseview 3.3.; Editorial Hardware – APP/Mac; Editorial Equipment – 7-APP/Mac; Editorial Printers – APP/Mac LaserWriter Pro 630 CLASSIFIED: Front-end Software – Baseview.; Classified Hardware – 2-APP/Mac; Classified Printers – APP/Mac LaserWriter Pro 630 DISPLAY: Ad make-up applications – Multi-Ad/Creator, QPS/QuarkXPress 3.3, Aldus/FreeHand; Layout Software – APP/Mac.; Display Hardware – 4-APP/Mac, 4-Radius/81-110; Display Printers – APP/Mac LaserWriter Pro 630 PRODUCTION: Pagination Software – Baseview, QPS/QuarkXPress.; Production Equipment – C/Powermatic-66F, Adobe/Photoshop, V/3990; Cameras – 1-C/Spartan III; Scanners – 1-AG/Arcus II, 1-AG/Arcus Plus, 1-Polaroid/SprintScan 35 PRESSROOM: Line 1 – 7-WPC/Web Leader (2-Color quad); Line 3 – 4-WPC/Web Leader (1-Color quad); Line 4 – 3-WPC/Web leader (1-Color quad); Folders – 5 MAILROOM: Counter stackers – 1/Mid America Graphics; Inserters and stuffers – MM/7:1; Bundle tying machines – 2-/Bu, 1-Strapex/Solomat; Addressing machine – 3-/Dispensa-Matic/16.; Business Hardware – DEC/PC XL 466D2, 1-Mk/Digital
Delivery method: Mail, Private Carrier, Racks

COLUMBUS

COLUMBUS LEDGER-ENQUIRER

17 W. 12th St., Columbus, Ga., 31901; gen tel (706) 324-5526; adv tel (706) 571-8553; ed tel (706) 571-8565; gen fax (706) 576-6236; adv fax (706) 576-6236; ed fax (706) 576-6290; web site www.ledger-enquirer.com

Published: Mon, Tues, Wed, Thur, Fri, Sat, Sun
Weekday Frequency: m
Saturday Frequency: m
Circulation: 31,975; 30,858(sat); 41,526(sun)
Last Audit: ABC September 30, 2011
Price: 3.92/wk; 17.00/mo; 204.00/yr.
Advertising: Open inch rate $69.25
News services: AP, MCT.
Politics: Non-Partisan.
Special Editions: GA Coastal (Apr); Careers (Feb); Business & Industry (Jan); Golf Guide (Jul); N. GA Mountains (Jun); Gulf Coast (Mar); Golf Guide (May); Christmas Open House Directory (Nov); Business & Industry (Oct); Panama City Beach Festival (Sept).
Special Weekly Sections: Business (Fri); Money Today (Mon); Living/Society (S); Business (Sat); Excellent Views (Thur); Business (Tues); Food (Wed).
Magazines: Parade (S).
Broadcast Affiliations: ABC, CBS, NBC, FOX.
Pres./Pub. ....Valerie Canepa
Dir., HR ....Jim Daugherty
Adv. Dir. ....Rodney Mahone
Circ. Dir. ....John Kelly
Circ. Mgr., Single Copy ....Pat Chitwood
Exec. Ed. ....Ben Holden
Assoc. Ed. ....Dusty Nix
Columnist ....Tim Chitwood
Entertainment Writer ....Brad Barnes
Features Ed. ....Dawn Minty
Metro Ed./Planning ....Dimon Kendrick-Holmes
News Ed. ....Larry Foley
Sports Ed. ....Kevin Price
Chief Technician ....Jimmy Mann
Prodn. Foreman, Platemaking ....David Crute
Market Information: ADS; TMC; Zoned editions.
Mechanical available: Offset; Black and 3 ROP colors; insert accepted - product samples; page cutoffs - 22.
Mechanical Specifications: Type page 13 x 21; E - 6 cols, 2, 1/6 between; A - 6 cols, 2, 1/6 between; C - 10 cols, 1 3/16, 1/9 between.
Commodity Consumption: Avg. Page Number Per Issue - Daily 44; Avg. Page Number Per Issue - Plates Used 60000; Avg. Page Number Per Issue - Sunday 78; widths 54; Newsprint Used - Metric Tons 5543; Newsprint Used - Short Tons 6110; Printing Ink Used - Black 69898; Printing Ink U
Equipment EDITORIAL: Front-end Software – DTI.; Editorial Hardware – APP/Mac, SII/3, DTI; Editorial Printers – 1-HP/2564B, 1-HP/LJ III, 1-HP/LJ II CLASSIFIED: Front-end Software – DTI.; Classified Hardware – DTI; Classified Printers – 1-Centronics, 1-HP/LaserJet DISPLAY: Ad make-up applications – HI, Aldus/FreeHand, QPS/QuarkXPress, Multi-Ad/Creator, Adobe/Illustrator, Adobe/Photoshop, Adobe/Acrobat, AP AdSend, DTI; Layout Software – APP/Mac, DTI.; Display Hardware – APP/Mac PRODUCTION: Pagination Software – DTI.; Production Equipment – 2-3., Imagemaster/1200, MON/1270, MON/NT RIP; Cameras – Autokon, C/Spartan; Scanners – Microtek/Scanmaster Plus III, Howtek PRESSROOM: Line 1 – 6-G/Headliner Offset 1989; Reels and Stands – G/RTP-50. MAILROOM: Counter stackers – QWI, Id/440, Id/660; Inserters and stuffers – 1-HI/1572; Bundle tying machines – 5/MLN; Addressing machine – 4-/Ch. AUDIO: Audio Software – Definity/G3; Audio Hardware – ATT/Audix BUSINESS COMPUTERS: Business Software – CJ/AIM-CIS; Business Hardware – HP/955

THE R. W. PAGE CORP.

17 W. 12th St., Columbus, Ga., 31901; gen tel (706) 324-5526; gen fax (706) 576-6290

CONYERS

THE ROCKDALE CITIZEN

969 S. Main St., Conyers, Ga., 30012; gen tel (770) 483-7108; adv tel (770) 483-7108; ed tel (770) 483-7108; adv fax (770) 761-4048; ed fax (770) 483-5797; gen e-mail alice.queen@rockdalecitizen.com; adv e-mail brenda.bennett@rockdalecitizen.com; ed e-mail news@rockdalecitizen.com; web site www.rockdalecitizen.com
Published: Tues, Wed, Thur, Fri
Weekday Frequency: m
Circulation: 4,335; 4,335(sat); 6,709(sun)
Last Audit: September 30, 2009
Price: 120.32/yr.
Advertising: Open inch rate $22.78
News services: AP, TMS.
Politics: Independent. **Established:** 1953
Special Editions: Meet Your Merchants (Apr); High School Football (Aug); Old Fashion Christmas (Dec); Community Living (Feb); Bridal Guide (Jan); Fun in the Sun (Jun); Home & Garden (Mar); Readers Choice (Nov); Readers Choice (Oct); How to Guide (Sept).
Special Weekly Sections: Real Estate (Thur).
Magazines: USA WEEKEND Magazine (S).
Pub. ....Alice Queen
Adv. Dir. ....Brenda Bennett
Retail Adv. Rep. ....Rachel Hayes
Circ. Dir. ....Thom Bell
Mng. Ed. ....Jay Jones
Features Ed. ....Karen Rohr
Sports Ed. ....Jeff Gillespie
Mechanical available: Offset; Black and 4 ROP colors; insert accepted; page cutoffs - 22.
Mechanical Specifications: Type page 12 x 21 1/2; E - 6 cols, 1 7/8, 1/8 between; A - 6 cols, 1 7/8, 1/8 between; C - 10 cols, 1/8 between.
Commodity Consumption: Avg. Page Number Per Issue - Daily 28; Avg. Page Number Per Issue - Saturday 32; Avg. Page Number Per Issue - Sunday 32; widths 25.
Equipment EDITORIAL: Front-end Software – Baseview/NewsEdit Pro.; Editorial Hardware – APP/Power Mac; Editorial Printers – APP/Mac CLASSIFIED: Front-end Software – Baseview/ClassFlow 1.1.2.; Classified Hardware – APP/Power Mac; Classified Printers – APP/Mac, HP DISPLAY: Ad make-up applications – Adobe/Illustrator, Adobe/Photoshop, QPS/QuarkXPress.; Display Hardware – APP/Power Mac; Display Printers – HP PRODUCTION: Pagination Software – QPS/QuarkXPress 4.0.; Production Equipment – 2-ECR/VRL-80, SCREEN/220; Cameras – SCREEN/C-670-D; Scanners – 1-Nu/2024V-C, 4-Microtek/II HR PRESSROOM: Line 1 – 12-G/Urbanite 1997; Line 2 – Enkel/Splicers; Line 3 – 16-DEM/430; Press Drives – 2-A/B; Pasters – Enkel/G Web; Press registration system – Stoesser/Pin System through Platebender. MAILROOM: Counter stackers – 2/KAN, 1-/Gammler; Inserters and stuffers – 2-KAN/480; Bundle tying machines – 3-/StraPak. BUSINESS COMPUTERS: Business Software – Baseview; Business Hardware – APP/Mac Power Mac

CORDELE

CORDELE DISPATCH

306 W. 13th Ave., Cordele, Ga., 31015-2348; gen tel (229) 273-2277; gen fax (229) 273-7239; web site www.cordeledispatch.com
Published: Tues, Wed, Thur, Fri, Sun
Weekday Frequency: m
Circulation: 4,590; 4,590(sun)
Last Audit: September 30, 2000
Advertising: Open inch rate $21.50
News services: Community Newspaper Holdings, Inc..
Politics: Independent. **Established:** 1908
Not Published: Saturday; Monday.
Special Weekly Sections: Religious Page (Fri); Business (S); Restaurants (Thur); Best Food Days (Tues).
Magazines: Relish (Monthly); Parade (S).
Adv. Dir. ....Chris Mann
Mng. Ed. ....Peggy King
Sports Ed. ....Harvey Simpson
Prodn. Compositor ....Betty Ruis
Prodn. Compositor ....Cathy Strickland
Market Information: TMC.
Mechanical available: Offset; Black and 3 ROP colors; insert accepted - standing card, specialties; page cutoffs - 22 3/4.
Mechanical Specifications: Type page 13 x 21 1/2; E - 6 cols, 2 1/16, 1/8 between; A - 6 cols, 2 1/16, 1/8 between; C - 9 cols, 1 3/8, 1/16 between.
Commodity Consumption: Avg. Page Number Per Issue - Daily 14; Avg. Page Number Per Issue - Plates Used 2990; widths 32; Newsprint Used - Short Tons 220; Printing Ink Used - Black 10000; Printing Ink Used - Color 1500; Printing Ink Used - Pages Printed 3500.
Equipment EDITORIAL: Front-end Software – FSI.; Editorial Hardware – 1-APP/Mac Quadra 950, 4-APP/Mac LC III, 2-APP/Mac Centris 610, 1-APP/Mac IIcx; Editorial Equipment – TI/Omni 800 CLASSIFIED: Front-end Software – FSI.; Classified Hardware – APP/Mac Centris 610 DISPLAY: Ad make-up applications – Multi-Ad/Creator, Aldus/FreeHand, QPS/QuarkXPress; Layout Software – 1-APP/Mac IIcx.; Display Hardware – APP/Mac Centris 610 PRODUCTION: Pagination Software – QPS/QuarkXPress 3.3.; Production Equipment – Caere/OmniPage, V/5060, V/5300, DEC/VT-820; Cameras – 1-R; Scanners – Lf/Leafscan 35, AG/Arcus Plus; Press registration system – Duarte/Pin Registration System.; Bundle tying machines – 1/Midstates, 1-MLN/SP300; Addressing machine – 1-/El, 1-/Am. AUDIO: Audio Software – Computer Group/Ads-on-Call; Audio Hardware – Mk/Touch 386 PC BUSINESS COMPUTERS: Business Software – Lotus 1-2-3, WordPerfect; Business Hardware – ATT

COVINGTON

THE NEWTON CITIZEN

7121 Turner Lake Rd., Covington, Ga., 30014; gen tel (770) 787-7303; ed fax (770) 787-8603; gen e-mail alice.queen@newtoncitizen.com; adv e-mail advertising@newtoncitizen.com; ed e-mail news@newtoncitizen.com; web site www.newtoncitizen.com
Published: Sun
Circulation: 5,892; 16,210(sat); 16,210(sun)
Last Audit: April 21, 2004
Price: 62.26/yr.
Advertising: Open inch rate $22.78
Adv. Dir. ....Brenda Bennett
Circ. Dir. ....Thom Bell
Ed. ....Alice Queen
City Ed. ....Barbara Knowles

CUMMING

FORSYTH COUNTY NEWS

302 Veterans Memorial Blvd., Cumming, Ga., 30040; gen tel (770) 887-3126; gen fax (770) 889-6017; web site www.forsythnews.com
Published: Wed, Thur, Fri, Sun
Weekday Frequency: m
Circulation: 12,500; 13,500(sun)
Last Audit: Sworn March 31, 2006
Price: 56.00/yr; 35.00/6mo.
Advertising: Open inch rate $16.45
Politics: 1908
Special Editions: Newcomers (Jul); Progress (Mar).
Magazines: USA Weekend (S); American Profile (Weekly).
Pub. ....John Hall
Adv. Mgr. ....Ryan Garmon
Office Mgr. ....Sabrena Moctezuma
Circ. Dir. ....Mark Golding
Ed. ....Kevin Atwill
Market Information: TMC; Zoned editions.

FORSYTH COUNTY NEWS

302 Veterans Memorial Blvd., Cumming, Ga., 30040; gen tel (770) 887-3126; gen fax (770) 889-6017; web site www.forsythnews.com
Price: 56.00/yr; 35.00/6mo.
Advertising: Open inch rate $16.45
Politics: 1908
Advertising not accepted: Y
Special Editions: USA Weekend (S); American Profile (Weekly).
Special Weekly Sections: Newcomers (Jul); Progress (Mar).
Pub. ....John Hall
Office Mgr. ....Sabrena Moctezuma
Ed. ....Kevin Atwill
Circulation Director ....Samuil Nikolov
Advertising Manager ....Ryan Garmon
Accounting Manager ....DeAnne Major
Adv. Dir. ....Rusty Williamson
Circ. Dir. ....Mark Golding
Market Information: TMC; Zoned editions.
Zip Codes served: 30040,30041,30028,30534,30506,30024,30097,30004,30005,30107
Delivery method: Mail, Newsstand, Private Carrier, Racks

DALTON

THE DAILY CITIZEN

308 S. Thornton Ave., Dalton, Ga., 30720; gen tel (706) 217-6397; adv tel (706) 272-7709; ed tel (706) 272-7735; gen fax (706) 275-6641; adv fax (706) 272-7743; ed fax (706) 275-6641; gen e-mail internet@daltoncitizen.com; adv e-mail jeffmutter@daltoncitizen.com; ed e-mail internet@daltoncitizen.com; web site www.daltoncitizen.com
Published: Mon, Tues, Wed, Thur, Fri, Sat, Sun
Weekday Frequency: m
Saturday Frequency: m
Circulation: 11,040; 11,040(sat); 10,426(sun)
Last Audit: September 30, 2009
Price: 10.95/mo; 131.40/yr.
Advertising: Open inch rate $19.50
News services: AP, SHNS.
Politics: Independent.
Special Editions: Progress (Mar).
Special Weekly Sections: Entertainment (Sat).
Magazines: Relish (Monthly); USA WEEKEND Magazine (S).
Pub. ....William Bronson
Bus. Mgr. ....Laddie Tony
Adv. Dir. ....Gary Jones
Bus. Ed. ....Jamie Jones
News Ed. ....Wes Chance
Sports Ed. ....Larry Fleming
Online Mgr. ....Victor Miller
Prodn. Mgr., Post Press ....Norma Jackson
Market Information: TMC.
Mechanical available: Offset; Black and 3 ROP colors; insert accepted; page cutoffs - 21 1/2.
Mechanical Specifications: Type page 11 1/2 x 21 1/2; E - 6 cols, 1 13/16, 5/32 between; A - 6 cols, 1 13/16, 5/32 between; C - 6 cols, 1 13/16, 5/32 between.
Commodity Consumption: Avg. Page Number Per Issue - Plates Used 7200; Avg. Page Number Per Issue - Sunday 36; widths 25; Newsprint Used - Short Tons 620; Printing Ink Used - Black 12000; Printing Ink Used - Color 2000; Printing Ink Used - Pages Printed 7700.
Equipment:; Editorial Hardware – APP/Mac; Editorial Equipment – APP/Mac Graphics Network, APP/Mac. CLASSIFIED: Front-end Software – FSI.; Classified Hardware – APP/Mac PRODUCTION: Pagination Software – QPS/QuarkXPress, Multi-Ad/Creator, Macromedia/Freehand.; Production Equipment – Pre Press/Panther 2042; Scanners – Umax/Mirage PRESSROOM: Line 1 – 10-G/Community.; Inserters and stuffers – 1-MM/6-1; Bundle tying machines – 1-Bu/String Tying Machine; Addressing machine – 1/KR, 1-/KAN. BUSINESS COMPUTERS: Business Software – Microsoft/Office 97; Business Hardware – ICanon (ATT)

DOUGLASVILLE

DOUGLAS COUNTY SENTINEL

8501 Bowden St., Douglasville, Ga., 30134; gen tel (770) 942-6571; adv tel (770) 942-6571; ed tel (770) 942-6571; gen fax (770)

949-7556; adv fax (770) 949-7556; ed fax (770) 949-7556; gen e-mail news@douglascountysentinel.com; adv e-mail kari@douglascountysentinel.com; ed e-mail news@douglascountysentinel.com; web site www.douglascountysentinel.com
Published: Tues, Wed, Thur, Fri, Sat, Sun
Weekday Frequency: m
Saturday Frequency: m
Circulation: 3,666; 3,666(sat); 3,113(sun)
Last Audit: March 31, 2008
Advertising: Open inch rate $21.00
News services: AP.
Politics: Independent. **Established:** 1902
Special Weekly Sections: TV Weekly (Sat); Business (Tues); Food Day (Wed).
Magazines: USA WEEKEND Magazine (S).
Pub. ....Leonard Woolsey
Adv. Mgr. ....Kari White
Circ. Dir. ....John Knoll
Sports Ed. ....Darryl Maxie
Systems Mgr. ....Ricky Stilley
Editor ....Mitch Sneed
News Ed. ....Sheila Erwin
Online Ed. ....Bill Fordham
Paulding County News Ed. ....Chris Barker
Market Information: TMC.
Mechanical available: Offset; Black and 3 ROP colors; insert accepted - hi-fi; page cutoffs - 11 1/16 x 21 1/2.
Mechanical Specifications: Type page 13 5/8 x 21 1/2; E - 6 cols, 2 1/16, 1/8 between; A - 6 cols, 2 1/16, 1/8 between; C - 10 cols, 1 1/16, 1/8 between.
Equipment; Editorial Hardware – 1-EKI, 7-EKI/Televideo.; Classified Hardware – 3-PC. DISPLAY: Ad make-up applications – Adobe/Photoshop 6,4,3, Adobe/Illustrator 8,9, QuarkXpress 4.1; Layout Software – 4-APP/Mac.; Display Hardware – OS 10.5; Display Printers – HP/Laserjet 5000, Lanier 5635

DUBLIN

THE COURIER HERALD

115 S. Jefferson St., Dublin, Ga., 31040-2449; gen tel (478) 272-5522; adv tel (478) 272-5522; gen fax (478) 272-2189; adv fax (478) 272-2189; adv e-mail advertising@courier-herald.com; ed e-mail news@courier-herald.com; web site www.courier-herald.com
Published: Mon, Tues, Wed, Thur, Fri, Sat
Weekday Frequency: e
Saturday Frequency: e
Circulation: 9,398; 9,398(sat)
Last Audit: ABC September 30, 2011
Price: 10.00/mo; 159.00/yr.
Advertising: Open inch rate $14.00
News services: AP.
Politics: Independent. **Established:** 1876
Not Published: New Year; Independence Day; Labor Day; Thanksgiving; Christmas.
Special Editions: Gardening (Apr); Football (Aug); Wedding Planner (Jan); St. Patrick's (Mar); Graduation (May); Holiday Gift Guide (Nov); New Car & Auto Guide (Oct).
Special Weekly Sections: Religion (Sat); Business (Thur); Education (Tues); Best Food Day (Wed).
Magazines: USA WEEKEND Magazine (Sat).
Gen. Mgr. ....Carol Porter
Adv. Dir. ....Pam Burney
Adv. Mgr., Classified ....Melissa Sanders
Circ. Mgr. ....Cheryl Gay
Ed ....DuBose Porter
Photo Ed. ....Joey Wilson
Mgmt. Info Servs. Mgr. ....Griffin Lovett
Online Mgr. ....Jonthan Dye
Prodn. Mgr. ....Elizabeth Mimbs
Market Information: TMC.
Mechanical available: Offset; Black and 3 ROP colors; insert accepted - max size 11 x 14; page cutoffs - 22 3/4.
Mechanical Specifications: Type page 13 x 21 1/2; E - 6 cols, 2 1/16, 1/8 between; A - 6 cols, 2 1/16, 1/8 between; C - 6 cols, 2 1/16, 1/8 between.
Commodity Consumption: Avg. Page Number Per Issue - Daily 19; Avg. Page Number Per Issue - Plates Used 6000; widths 27 1/2; Newsprint Used - Short Tons 496; Printing Ink Used - Black 10450; Printing Ink Used - Color 1565; Printing Ink Used - Pages Printed 5966.
Equipment; Editorial Hardware – Mk.; Classified Hardware – Mk.; Layout Software – 2-APP/Mac IIcx.; Display Hardware – APP/Mac Radius 19 color monitor; Production Equipment – 1-APP/Mac LaserWriter NT, 1-Dataproducts/11 x 17; Cameras – 1-CL/Horizontal, 1-R/Vertical; Scanners – 1-APP/Mac, 1-Mirror/Color scanner.; Line 6 – 8-G/SC (with Gev-Flexicolor half deck); Folders – 1-G/SC.; Bundle tying machines – 2/AMP, 1-/MLN, 1-/Bu; Addressing machine – 1-/Ch.; Business Hardware – MTI/Micro-Computer

GAINESVILLE

THE TIMES

345 Green St. NW, Gainesville, Ga., 30503-0838; gen tel (770) 532-1234; adv tel (770) 532-1234; ed tel (770) 532-1234; gen fax (770) 532-7085; adv fax (770) 532-8187; ed fax (770) 532-0457; gen e-mail nbaggs@gainesvilletimes.com; adv e-mail sjones@gainesvilletimes.com; ed e-mail news@gainesvilletimes.com; web site www.gainesvilletimes.com
Published: Mon, Tues, Wed, Thur, Fri, Sat, Sun
Weekday Frequency: m
Saturday Frequency: m
Circulation: 22,000; 22,000(sat); 26,000(sun)
Last Audit: Sworn September 30, 2008
Price: 169.00/yr, $104/yr (fri, sat, S); 42.25/13 wks, $84.50/26wks.
Advertising: Open inch rate $47.95
News services: AP, AP Sportswire, AP Photo, AP Graphics.
Politics: 1947
Own facility?: Y
Special Editions: Back to School (Aug); Newcomers Guide (Feb); Health Watch (quarterly); Progress (Mar); Summer Guide (May); Business Link (Monthly); Fall Guide (Sept.)
Special Weekly Sections: Health & Fitness (Mon); Church Page (Sat); Get Out (Thur); Food (Wed).
Magazines: USA WEEKEND Magazine (S); Get Out (Thur).
Pub. ....Dennis Stockton
Gen. Mgr. ....Norman Baggs
Adv. Dir. ....Sherrie Jones
Adv. Supvr., New Bus.Devel. ....Melisa Sizemore
Circ. Dir. ....Garry Tinsley
Exec. Ed. ....Mitch Clarke
Mng. Ed. ....Keith Albertson
Asst. Life Ed ....Shannon Casas
New Media Ed ....Michael Beard
Sports Ed. ....Brent Holloway
Mgmt. Info Servs. Mgr. ....DeJuan Woodward
Prodn. Dir. ....Mark Hall
Sr. Design Ed. ....Kristen Morales
Market Information: TMC.
Mechanical available: Offset; Black and 3 ROP colors; insert accepted - mini-tabs; page cutoffs - 22 3/4.
Mechanical Specifications: Type page 13 x 21 1/2; E - 6 cols, 2 1/16, 1/8 between; A - 6 cols, 2 1/16, 1/8 between; C - 10 cols, 1 3/16, 1/16 between.
Commodity Consumption: Avg. Page Number Per Issue - Daily 24; Avg. Page Number Per Issue - Plates Used 44350; Avg. Page Number Per Issue - Sunday 70; widths 27; Newsprint Used - Metric Tons 5832; Printing Ink Used - Black 134870; Printing Ink Used - Color 86147; Printing Ink U
Equipment EDITORIAL: Front-end Software – Scoop; Editorial Hardware – 21-PC P166, 9-PC P200, 1-Pentium/PC Pro 2000; Editorial Printers – 1-Lexmark/Optra, 1-HP/LaserJet 4MV CLASSIFIED: Front-end Software – APT/V2.; Classified Hardware – 5-PC P166, 1-Pentium/Pro 200 PC; Classified Equipment – SyQuest/Disc Reader; Classified Printers – 1-Lexmark/Optra DISPLAY: Ad make-up applications – APT; Layout Software – APT.; Display Hardware – 1-PC/P200, 3-APP/Mac 8500, 3-APP/Mac 8100, 1-APP/Mac 7200, 1-APP/Mac 7100; Display Printers – 2-APP/Mac LaserWriter 630, 1-Xante/Accel-a-Writer; Production Equipment – 2-ECR/4550 Imagesetter with PC RIP, 1-ECR/Autokon 1000 DE, Pre Press/Panther Plus, Epson/Stylus Proxl Proofer, Xante/Accel-a-Writer 8900 Plain Paper, 2-ECR/4500; Scanners – ECR/Autokon 1000 DE, AG/Arcus Plus, Umax/Flat PRESSROOM: Line 1 – 4-G/Urbanite 1970, 8-G/Urbanite 1982, 2-G/Urbanite 1984, 1-G/Urbanite 1985; Press Drives – 4-Fin/100 h.p. Drive Motors; Folders – G/Urbanite U775, G/Urbanite U1362; Pasters – 8 MAILROOM: Counter stackers – 1-QWI/300, 1/PPK, 1-QWI/351; Inserters and stuffers – 3-/MM; Bundle tying machines – 2-/Bu, 2-/MLN; Addressing machine – 1-Barstrom/Labeler, 1-/Ch; Other equipment –1-MM/Minuteman Stitcher-Trimmer.; Audio Hardware – Software ÃÂÃÂÃÂÃÂÃÂ Octel
Delivery method: Newsstand, Private Carrier

GRIFFIN

GRIFFIN DAILY NEWS

323 E. Solomon St., Griffin, Ga., 30224; gen tel (770) 227-3570; adv tel (770) 227-3276; gen fax (770) 412-1678; adv e-mail advertising@griffindailynews.com; ed e-mail editor@griffindailynews.com; web site www.griffindailynews.com
Published: Tues, Wed, Thur, Fri, Sat, Sun
Weekday Frequency: m
Circulation: 6,936; 6,936(sat); 6,246(sun)
Last Audit: March 31, 2008
Price: 13.50/mo.
Advertising: Open inch rate $24.80
News services: AP.
Politics: Independent.
Not Published: Christmas.
Special Editions: Progress (Apr); Football (Aug); Valentines (Feb); Super Bowl (Jan); Vacation (Jun); Spring Fashion (Mar); Youth Sports (May); Newcomer's Guide (Sept).
Special Weekly Sections: TV Notes (S).
Magazines: USA WEEKEND Magazine (S).
Pub. ....David Clevenger
Adv. Dir. ....Joy Gaddy
Adv. Acct. Exec. ....Amy Davis
Circ. Dir. ....Mark Golding
Mng. Ed. ....Tim Daly
Asst. Mng. Ed ....Anthony Rhoades
City Ed. ....Sheila Marshall
Sports Ed. ....John Sullivan
Market Information: ADS; TMC; Zoned editions.
Mechanical available: Offset; Black and 3 ROP colors; insert accepted - single sheets; page cutoffs - 21 1/2.
Mechanical Specifications: Type page 13 x 21 1/2; E - 6 cols, 2, 1/6 between; A - 6 cols, 2, 1/6 between; C - 9 cols, 1 1/3, 1/6 between.
Commodity Consumption: Avg. Page Number Per Issue - Daily 18; Avg. Page Number Per Issue - Sunday 70; widths 27 1/2; Newsprint Used - Short Tons 300; Printing Ink Used - Black 34000; Printing Ink Used - Color 5400.
Equipment EDITORIAL: Front-end Software – Baseview/NewsEdit Pro IQue, QPS/QuarkXPress 4.04.; Editorial Hardware – APP/Mac; Classified Hardware – APP/Mac; Classified Equipment – TI/Omni 800; Classified Printers – QMS/2060. DISPLAY: Ad make-up applications – Aldus/FreeHand, Adobe Illustrator 8.01, Photoshop 5.5, Acrobat Exchange 3.0, Multi-Ad/Creator 4.0.3, QPS/QuarkXPress 4.04; Layout Software – 2-APP/Power Mac 4400, APP/Mac; Display Hardware – APP/Mac; Display Printers – QMS/2060 PRODUCTION: Pagination Software – QPS/QuarkXPress 4.04.; Production Equipment – Caere/OmniPage, QMS/2060; Cameras – 1-C/Spartan II; Scanners – 2-APP/Mac One Scanner PRESSROOM: Line 1 – 8-G 1968; Folders – SC/Community. MAILROOM: Counter stackers – 1-BG/Count-O-Veyor; Inserters and stuffers – 1-MM/5 pocket; Bundle tying machines – 1/Bu; Addressing machine – KAN/Zip Code Separator, KAN/Label Applicator.; Business Hardware – 1-Cumulus/GLC 1220 W

JONESBORO

NEWS/DAILY

138 Church St., Jonesboro, Ga., 30236; gen tel (770) 478-5753; gen fax (770) 473-9032; adv fax (770) 472-2121; ed fax (770) 472-2060; gen e-mail info@news-daily.com; web site www.news-daily.com
Published: Mon, Tues, Wed, Thur, Fri, Sat, Sun
Weekday Frequency: m
Circulation: 2,090
Last Audit: September 30, 2008
Advertising: Open inch rate $15.70
News services: AP.
Politics: Independent. **Established:** 1970
Special Editions: Spring Tour of Homes (Apr); Football Kick-off (Aug); Christmas Gift Guide (Dec); Bride's Tour (Feb); Progress (Jan); Newcomer's Guide (Jul); Spring Car Care (Mar); Welcome Summer (May); Meet the Merchants (Oct); Introduction to New Cars (Sept).
Special Weekly Sections: Business (Fri); Religion (Sat); Living (Thur).
Magazines: Relish (Monthly); USA WEEKEND Magazine (Sat).
Pub. ....Bonnie Pratt
Bus. Mgr. ....Donna Sanders
Adv. Dir. ....Christy Collier
Ed. ....Chet Fuller
Columnist/Entertainment Critic ....Joel Hall
Sports Ed. ....Doug Gorman
Prodn. Foreman, Pressroom ....Gary Toohey
Prodn. Mgr., Mailroom/Distr. ....Leonard Crane
Market Information: Split run; TMC.
Mechanical available: Offset; Black and 3 ROP colors; insert accepted; page cutoffs - 21 1/2.
Mechanical Specifications: Type page 13 x 21 1/2; E - 6 cols, 2 1/16, 1/8 between; A - 6 cols, 2 1/16, 1/8 between; C - 6 cols, 2 1/16, 1/8 between.
Commodity Consumption: Avg. Page Number Per Issue - Daily 22; widths 28; Newsprint Used - Short Tons 540.
Equipment; Editorial Hardware – COM/One Sys.; Display Hardware – COM/Power View.; Production Equipment – 11-COM/8400; Cameras – 1-C/17 x 24, 1-K/Vertical 16 x 22. PRESSROOM: Line 1 – 6-KP/News King; Line 2 – 8-KP/News King; Folders – 14; Reels and Stands – 6 MAILROOM: Counter stackers – 1/BG; Bundle tying machines – 2-/Bu; Addressing machine – 1-/Ch.

LAGRANGE

LA GRANGE DAILY NEWS

105 Ashton St., LaGrange, Ga., 30240; gen tel (706) 884-7311; adv tel (706) 884-7315; ed tel (706) 884-7316; gen fax (706) 884-8712; ed e-mail editor@lagrangenews.com; web site www.lagrangenews.com
Published: Mon, Tues, Wed, Thur, Fri, Sat, Sun
Saturday Frequency: m
Circulation: 13,400; 13,400(sat); 13,400(sun)
Last Audit: May 2, 2003
Price: 9.50/mo; 114.00/yr (carrier), $152.75/yr (mail).
Advertising: Open inch rate $12.84
News services: AP, NEA.
Politics: Independent. **Established:** 1843
Not Published: Christmas.
Magazines: USA WEEKEND Magazine (S); American Profile (Weekly).
Pub. ....Lynn McLamb
Bus. Mgr. ....Judy Phillips
Adv. Mgr., Classified ....Carla Jones
Circ. Dir. ....Brian Moncrief
Ed. ....Andrea Lovejoy
News Ed. ....Dan Baker
Sports Ed. ....Kevin Eckleberry
Prodn. Mgr. ....Roland Foiles
Graphics Mgr. ....Toni Simmons
Market Information: TMC; Zoned editions.
Mechanical available: Offset; Black and 3 ROP colors; insert accepted; page cutoffs - 22.
Mechanical Specifications: Type page 13 3/4 x 21 1/2; E - 6 cols, 1 5/6, 1/8 between; A - 6 cols, 1 5/6, 1/8 between; C - 9 cols, 1 3/16, 1/16 between.

Commodity Consumption: Avg. Page Number Per Issue - Daily 14; Avg. Page Number Per Issue - Plates Used 8300; widths 25; Newsprint Used - Short Tons 575; Printing Ink Used - Pages Printed 7200.
Equipment; Editorial Hardware – COM/One Sys.; Layout Software – 3-COM/On-line.; Production Equipment – COM/OS; Cameras – 1-B, 1-C. PRESSROOM: Line 1 – 7-G; Folders – 2; Business Hardware – 1-Bs/90

LAWRENCEVILLE

GWINNETTE DAILY POST

725 Old Norcross Rd., Lawrenceville, Ga., 30045; gen tel (770) 963-9205; adv tel (770) 963-9205; ed tel (770) 339-5850; gen fax (770) 277-5271; adv fax (770) 338-7350; ed fax (770) 339-8081; gen e-mail news@gwinnettdailypost.com; adv e-mail advertising@gwinnettdailypost.com; ed e-mail letters@gwinnettdailypost.com; web site www.gwinnettdailypost.com
Published: Tues, Wed, Thur, Fri, Sat, Sun
Weekday Frequency: m
Price: 72.00/yr.
Advertising: Open inch rate $92.36
News services: AP, U.S. Suburban Press Inc..
Politics: Independent.
Note: Gray Television, Inc. owns 28 television stations as well as the shopper, Albany (GA) Albany Area Advertiser.
Special Editions: Back To School (Aug); Bridal (Feb); Progress (Jan); College Bound (Jun); Bell South Classic (Mar); Business Review (Oct).
Special Weekly Sections: Automotive (Fri); Travel (S); Restaurants (Sat); Medical (Tues).
Magazines: USA WEEKEND Magazine (S).
Broadcast Affiliations: GNET-TV Gwinnett, GA.
Pub. ....J.K. Murphy
Financial Dir. ....Susan Andrews
Adv. Dir., Retail ....Brenda Bohn
Adv. Mgr., Classified ....Kellie Moore
Adv. Mgr., Legal Notices ....Cindy Carter
Adv. Mgr., Major Accts ....Janet McCray
Circ. Dir. ....Thom Bell
Circ. Mgr., Sales/Customer Serv. ...Sherry Brown
Ed. ....Todd Cline
Copy Desk Chief ....Nate McCullough
Graphics Ed. ....Nicole Finley
Photo Ed. ....Anthony Stalcup
Sports Ed. ....Will Hammock
Tech. Dir./Online Mgr. ....Howard F. Reed
Prodn. Mgr., Distribution ....Ken Walker
Chrmn./CEO/Dir. ....J. Mack Robinson
Vice Chrmn. ....Hilton H. Howell
Sr. Vice Pres., Finance/CFO ....James C. Ryan
Vice Pres., Law/Devel. ....Robert A. Beizer
Market Information: ADS.
Mechanical available: Offset; Black and 3 ROP colors; insert accepted; page cutoffs - 22.
Mechanical Specifications: Type page 13 x 21; E - 6 cols, 2 1/36, 1/6 between; A - 6 cols, 2 1/36, 1/6 between; C - 9 cols, 1 1/2, 1/6 between.
Commodity Consumption: Avg. Page Number Per Issue - Daily 40; Avg. Page Number Per Issue - Saturday 40; Avg. Page Number Per Issue - Sunday 52; widths 25.
Equipment EDITORIAL: Front-end Software – Baseview.; Editorial Hardware – APP/Macs; Editorial Printers – APP/Mac CLASSIFIED: Front-end Software – Baseview, QPS/QuarkXPress 4.0.; Classified Hardware – APP/iMacs; Classified Printers – APP/Macs DISPLAY: Ad make-up applications – QPS/QuarkXPress 4.0; Layout Software – Baseview.; Display Hardware – APP/Mac; Display Printers – APP/Mac PRODUCTION: Pagination Software – QPS/QuarkXPress 4.0.; Production Equipment – ECR PRESSROOM: Line 1 – 10-G/Urbanite 1997; Folders – G/Urbanite. MAILROOM: Counter stackers – KAN; Inserters and stuffers – KAN; Bundle tying machines – . BUSINESS COMPUTERS: Business Software – Baseview; Business Hardware – PC

MACON

THE TELEGRAPH

120 Broadway, Macon, Ga., 31201-3444; gen tel (478) 744-4200; adv tel (478) 744-4256; ed tel (478) 744-4411; gen fax (478) 744-4385; adv fax (478) 744-4297; ed fax (478) 744-4385; web site www.macon.com
Group: McClatchy Newspapers, Inc.
Metro Newspaper Advertising Services, Inc.
Published: Mon, Tues, Wed, Thur, Fri, Sat, Sun
Weekday Frequency: m
Saturday Frequency: m
Circulation: 44,895; 46,011(sat); 66,344(sun)
Last Audit: ABC September 30, 2011
Price: 3.45/wk; 14.95/mo; 179.40/yr.
Advertising: Open inch rate $86.50
News services: AP, MCT, LAT-WP, HN, NYT, TMS.
Politics: Independent. **Established:** 1826
Special Editions: Spring Home (Apr); Football (Aug); Tax Guide (Feb); Brides (Jan); Cherry Blossom Festival (Mar); Fall Garden (Oct).
Special Weekly Sections: Out & About (Fri); Personal Finance (S); College Game Day (Sat); Personal Technology (Thur); Best Food Day (Wed).
Magazines: Med Trends (May, Aug, Nov) (Other); Home Hunter (S).
Broadcast Affiliations: WMAZ (CBS); WMGT (NBC); WPGA (ABC); WGXA (FOX).
Pres./Pub. ....George McCanless
CFO ....Conna Hardy
Adv. Mgr., Classified ....Clero Wright
Circ. Vice Pres. ....Dave Gossett
Circ. Mgr. ....Phil Schroder
Circ. Single Copy Mgr. ....Robert Bailey
Exec. Ed ....Sherrie Marshall
Editorial Columnist ....Charles Richardson
News Ed. ....Oby Brown
News Ed. ....Ben Yoder
Chief, Photography ....Woody Marshall
Sports Ed. ....Daniel Shirley
Sports Columnist ....Michael Lough
IT Mgr. ....Joe Mendoza
Adv. Mgr., Retail ....Lisa Berrian
Interactive Mgr. ....Ryan Gilchrest
Market Information: ADS; Split run; TMC; Zoned editions.
Mechanical available: Flexographic; Black and 3 ROP colors; insert accepted; page cutoffs - 22.
Mechanical Specifications: Type page 11 3/4 x 21 1/8; E - 6 cols, 1 7/8, 1/8 between; A - 6 cols, 1 7/8, 1/8 between; C - 10 cols, 1 7/100, 1/5 between.
Commodity Consumption: Avg. Page Number Per Issue - Daily 46; Avg. Page Number Per Issue - Plates Used 133886; Avg. Page Number Per Issue - Sunday 98; widths 54; Newsprint Used - Metric Tons 8001; Newsprint Used - Short Tons 8817; Printing Ink Used - Black 285476; Printing Ink
Equipment EDITORIAL: Front-end Software – Saxotech; Editorial Hardware – DTI, Sun/Ultra Enterprise Servers, APP/Macs; Editorial Equipment – MON/4550, MON/1270, 2-MON/News Express; Editorial Printers – HP/Lasers CLASSIFIED: Front-end Software – DTI.; Classified Hardware – Sun/Ultra Enterprise Servers, APP/Macs; Classified Equipment – MON/4550, MON/1270, 2-MON/News Express; Classified Printers – HP/Lasers DISPLAY: Ad make-up applications – QPS/QuarkXPress, AdSpeed; Layout Software – MEI.; Display Hardware – Sun/Ultra Enterprise Servers, APP/Macs; Display Printers – APP/Mac LaserWriter, HP/Lasers PRODUCTION: Pagination Software – DTI.; Production Equipment – 2-MON/1200 News Express, 1-Na/FPII, 3-Glunz & Jensen BUSINESS COMPUTERS: Business Software – Microsoft/Excel, Microsoft/Word, Reflections, Monarc, CJ/AIM-CIS; Business Hardware – 1-HP/3000 Series 957

MARIETTA

MARIETTA DAILY JOURNAL

580 Fairground St., Marietta, Ga., 30061; gen tel (770) 428-9411; adv tel (770) 428-9411; ed tel (770) 428-9411; gen fax (770) 422-9533; adv fax (770) 428-7945; ed fax (770) 422-9533; gen e-mail mdjnews@mdjonline.com; adv e-mail advertising@mdjonline.com; ed e-mail letters@mdjonline.com; web site www.mdjonline.com; www.cherokeetribune.com
Group: U.S. Suburban Press, Inc.
Published: Mon, Tues, Wed, Thur, Fri, Sat, Sun
Weekday Frequency: m
Saturday Frequency: m
Circulation: 15,621; 15,621(sat); 15,970(sun)
Last Audit: ABC September 30, 2011
Price: 10.00/mo; 107.63/yr.
Advertising: Open inch rate $24.95
News services: AP, SHNS, CNS, LAT-WP, TMS.
Politics: Independent. **Established:** 1866
Special Editions: Lawn & Garden (Apr); Football Preview (Aug); Gift Guide (Dec); Progress (Feb); Year-in-Review (Jan); Fact Book (Jul); Father's Day (Jun); Brides (Mar); Spring Car Care (May); Thanksgiving (Nov); Fall Home & Garden (Sept).
Special Weekly Sections: Automotive (Fri); Lifestyle (S).
Magazines: Going Out (local entertainment) (Fri); USA WEEKEND Magazine (S).
Pres. ....Otis A. Brumby
Pub. ....Otis A. Brumby
Assoc. Pub. ....Jay Whorton
Accounting Mgr. ....JoAnne Shivley
HR Mgr. ....Lee Garrett
Adv. Dir. ....Wade Stephens
Mng. Ed. ....Billy Mitchell
Columnist ....Bill Kinney
Columnist ....Dick Yarbourgh
Editorial Page Ed. ....Joe Kirby
Photo Dept. Mgr. ....Damion Guarnieri
Online Mgr. ....Zuriel Reyes
Prodn. Mgr. ....David Tallmadge
Prodn. Mgr., Distr. ....Matt Heck
Prodn. Mgr., Mailroom ....Pat McClesky
Prodn. Mgr., Pre Press ....Leigh Braddy
Market Information: ADS; TMC.
Mechanical available: Offset; Black and 3 ROP colors; insert accepted; page cutoffs - 21.
Mechanical Specifications: Type page 11 5/8 x 21; E - 6 cols, 1 5/6, 2/5 between; A - 6 cols, 2, 2/5 between; C - 10 cols, 2/5 between.
Commodity Consumption: Avg. Page Number Per Issue - Daily 36; Avg. Page Number Per Issue - Plates Used 122100; Avg. Page Number Per Issue - Sunday 48; widths 50; Newsprint Used - Short Tons 5803; Printing Ink Used - Black 124000; Printing Ink Used - Color 48000; Printing Ink U
Equipment EDITORIAL: Front-end Software – Ik.; Editorial Hardware – Ik; Editorial Equipment – ECR/Scriptsetter; Editorial Printers – Okidata, Xante, QMS/6100, QMS/4032, HP/5000 CLASSIFIED: Front-end Software – Ik.; Classified Hardware – Ik; Classified Printers – Panasonic DISPLAY: Ad make-up applications – QPS/QuarkXPress 4.11, Adobe/Photoshop 7.0, Adobe/Illustrator 10; Layout Software – QPS/QuarkXPress 4.11.; Display Hardware – 6-PC; Display Printers – Okidata, Xante PRODUCTION: Pagination Software – ACT.; Production Equipment – 1-Konica, EV/Jetsetter, ECR/Scriptsetter; Cameras – 1-C/Spartan, 1-C/Spartan III PRESSROOM: Line 1 – 5-MAN/4 x 2 double width 1995; Press Drives – 3 MAILROOM: Counter stackers – 3-HL/Monitor; Inserters and stuffers – 3/KR; Bundle tying machines – 4-/Bu, 2-Si. BUSINESS COMPUTERS: Business Software – APT, PBS, Quark XPress, Microsoft Word, SBS; Business Hardware – 1-IBM/RSC 6000, Compaq/5500

MILLEDGEVILLE

THE UNION-RECORDER

165 Garrett Way, Milledgeville, Ga., 31059-0520; gen tel (478) 452-0567; adv tel (478) 453-1430; ed tel (478) 453-1450; gen fax (478) 453-1449; adv fax (478) 453-1439; ed fax (478) 453-1459; ed e-mail newsroom@unionrecorder.com; web site www.unionrecorder.com
Published: Tues, Wed, Thur, Fri, Sat
Weekday Frequency: m
Circulation: 7,416; 7,416(sat)
Last Audit: September 30, 2003
Price: 80.30/yr.
Advertising: Open inch rate $15.80
News services: AP.
Politics: Independent.
Special Editions: Football (Aug); Gift Ideas (Dec); Black History (Feb); Focus on Milledgeville (Jul); Home Improvement & Gardening (Mar); Graduation (May); Gift Guide (Nov); Historic Guide to Milledgeville (Oct).
Special Weekly Sections: Schools (Fri); Family (Sat); Health (Tues); Wedding Planner (Weekly).
Magazines: TV Magazine (Fri); Relish (Monthly); USA WEEKEND Magazine (Sat).
Pub. ....Keith E. Barlow
Bus. Mgr. ....Lynda Jackson
Adv. Dir. ....Erin Simmons
Circ. Dir. ....Michael Evans
Mng. Ed. ....Natalie Davis
City Ed. ....Jonathan Jackson
Prodn. Dir. ....Keith Justice
Market Information: ADS; TMC.
Mechanical available: Offset; Black and 3 ROP colors; insert accepted; page cutoffs - 22 3/4.
Mechanical Specifications: Type page 11 3/4 x 21 1/2; E - 6 cols, 1 3/4, 1/8 between; A - 6 cols, 2 1/16, 1/8 between; C - 9 cols, 1, 1/16 between.
Commodity Consumption: Avg. Page Number Per Issue - Daily 16; Avg. Page Number Per Issue - Plates Used 10000; widths 29; Newsprint Used - Metric Tons 1200; Printing Ink Used - Black 40000; Printing Ink Used - Color 10000; Printing Ink Used - Pages Printed 5500.
Equipment EDITORIAL: Front-end Software – Baseview/NewsEd.; Editorial Hardware – APP/Mac; Editorial Printers – Xante/8200, Unity/1800 PMR CLASSIFIED: Front-end Software – Baseview/Ad Manage Pro.; Classified Hardware – APP/Macs; Classified Printers – Xante/8200 DISPLAY: Ad make-up applications – QPS/QuarkXPress, Aldus/Illustrator, Aldus/FreeHand, Adobe/Photoshop; Display Hardware – APP/Power Mac 9500; Display Printers – Xante/8200 PRODUCTION: Pagination Software – QPS/QuarkXPress 4.01.; Production Equipment – Caere/OmniPage Pro 8.0, Pre Press/Panther Plus 46; Cameras – C/Spartan III; Scanners – Lf/Leafscan 35, Polaroid/Sprint ScanPlus, HP/2CX PRESSROOM: Line 1 – 7-G/Community.; Folders – 1; Inserters and stuffers – MM/5 Head; Bundle tying machines – Bu/Plastic and string. BUSINESS COMPUTERS: Business Software – Microsoft/Office 4.0; Business Hardware – Canyon Lake Software, Navision, Baseview/Ad Manager-Pro

MOULTRIE

THE MOULTRIE OBSERVER

25 N. Main St., Moultrie, Ga., 31768; gen tel (229) 985-4545; adv tel (229) 985-4545; ed tel (229) 985-4545; gen fax (229) 985-3569; adv fax (229) 985-3569; ed fax (229) 985-3569; gen e-mail dwain.walden@gaflnews.com; ed e-mail dwain.walden@gaflnews.com; web site www.moultrieobserver.com
Published: Tues, Wed, Thur, Fri, Sat, Sun
Weekday Frequency: m
Circulation: 7,198; 7,198(sat); 7,198(sun)
Price: 8.58/mo; 93.46/yr, $109.20/yr (mail).
Advertising: Open inch rate $21.05
News services: AP.
Politics: Independent. **Established:** 1894
Special Editions: Brides (Apr); Back-to-School (Aug); Progress (Jul); Colquitt Pride (Jun); Home, Lawn & Garden (Mar); Super Mom (May); Agricultural Exposition (Oct); New Car (Sept).
Special Weekly Sections: Health Scene (Mon); TV Week (Sat); Dining Guide (Thur).
Magazines: Chamber of Commerce Guide (An-

nually); Relish (Monthly); Parade (S).
Adv. Dir. ....Charlie Bankston
Adv. Mgr., Nat'l/Major Accts. ....Laura Rogers
Circ. Dir. ....Shawn Highsmith
Mng. Ed. ....Dwain Walden
Prodn. Foreman, Composing...Glenda Apperson
Market Information: TMC.
Mechanical available: Offset; Black and 3 ROP colors; insert accepted; page cutoffs - 22 3/4.
Mechanical Specifications: Type page 13 x 21 1/2; E - 6 cols, 2 1/16, 1/8 between; A - 6 cols, 2 1/16, 1/8 between; C - 9 cols, 1 1/4, 1/8 between.
Commodity Consumption: Avg. Page Number Per Issue - Daily 20; Avg. Page Number Per Issue - Plates Used 4000; widths 27 1/2; Newsprint Used - Short Tons 330; Printing Ink Used - Black 8500; Printing Ink Used - Color 500; Printing Ink Used - Pages Printed 6260.
Equipment EDITORIAL: Front-end Software – FSI/Edit.; Editorial Hardware – APP/Mac CLASSIFIED: Front-end Software – FSI.; Classified Hardware – APP/Mac; Layout Software – PBS.; Production Equipment – 2-Dy/Mark 4, 4-COM/4961, 1-COM/2961, 1-COM/7200; Cameras – 1-C/Spartan II, ECR/Autokon. PRESSROOM: Line 1 – 8-G/Community; Folders – 1-G/2:1.; Bundle tying machines – 2/Bu; Addressing machine – 2-/Wm. AUDIO: Audio Software – FSI; Audio Hardware – APP/Mac; Business Hardware – IBM/AS-400

OBSERVER PUBLISHING CO.
25 N. Main St., Moultrie, Ga., 31768; gen tel (229) 985-4545; gen fax (229) 985-3569

NEWNAN

THE TIMES-HERALD
16 Jefferson St., Newnan, Ga., 30263; gen tel (770) 253-1576; gen fax (770) 253-2538; gen e-mail colleen@newnan.com; adv e-mail lamar@newnan.com; ed e-mail ellen@newnan.com; web site www.times-herald.com
Published: Mon, Tues, Wed, Thur, Fri, Sat, Sun
Weekday Frequency: m
Saturday Frequency: m
Circulation: 10,990; 10,990(sat); 10,990(sun)
Last Audit: September 29, 2003
Price: 89.00/yr.
Advertising: Open inch rate $17.00
News services: AP.
Magazines: USA WEEKEND Magazine (S).
Pres. ....William W. Thomasson
Vice Pres. ....Marianne Thomasson
Pub. ....Sam Jones
Controller ....Diana Shellabarger
Adv. Mgr. ....Lamar Truitt
Sales/Mktg. Dir. ....Colleen Mitchell
Circ. Dir. ....Naomi Jackson
Assignment Ed. ....Winston Skinner
Copy Ed ....Will Blair
Coweta Close-Up Ed. ....Angela Webster
Features Ed. ....Jeff Bishop
News Ed. ....Ellen L. Corker
Sports Ed. ....Tommy Camp
Tech. Mgr. ....Steve Hill
Market Information: TMC.
Mechanical available: Offset; Black and 3 ROP colors; insert accepted.
Equipment EDITORIAL: Front-end Software – QPS/QuarkXPress.; Editorial Hardware – APP/Mac CLASSIFIED: Front-end Software – Baseview.; Classified Hardware – APP/Mac

PERRY

THE HOUSTON HOME JOURNAL
1210 Washington St., Perry, Ga., 31069; gen tel (478) 987-5499; adv tel 478-987-1823; gen fax 478-988-9194; adv fax 478-988-9193; adv e-mail jevans@sunmulti.com; ed e-mail kriner@sunmulti.com; web site www.hhjnews.com
Published: Wed, Sat
Weekday Frequency: m
Saturday Frequency: m
Circulation: 14,000; 14,000(sat)
Last Audit: Sworn October 1, 2004
Advertising: Open inch rate $12.00
Insert rate: 40/M
Politics: 1870
Not Published: Monday, Tuesday, Thursday, Friday, Sunday
Own facility?: Y
Ed. ....Daniel F. Evans
Lifestyle Ed. ....Charlotte Perkins
Prodn. Mgr., Mailroom ....Jimmy Townsend
Prodn. Mgr., Opns. ....Billy Townsend
Mechanical Specifications: Type page 11 5/8 x 21; E - 6 cols, 5/6, between; A - 6 cols, 1 5/6, between; C - 8 cols, 1 5/16, between.
Zip Codes served: 31069, 31047, 31088, 31093
Delivery method: Mail

ROME

NEWS PUBLISHING CO.
305 E. 6th Ave., Rome, Ga., 30162-1633; gen tel (706) 290-5200 (Circ); gen fax (706) 232-9632

ROME NEWS-TRIBUNE
305 E. 6th Ave., Rome, Ga., 30162; gen tel (706) 291-6397; adv tel (706) 290-5220; ed tel (706) 290-5252; gen fax (706) 232-9632; adv fax (706) 232-9632; ed fax (706) 234-6478; gen e-mail romenewstribune@rn-t.com; web site www.romenews-tribune.com
Published: Mon, Tues, Wed, Thur, Fri, Sat, Sun
Weekday Frequency: m
Saturday Frequency: m
Circulation: 14,921; 14,921(sat); 15,466(sun)
Last Audit: September 30, 2009
Price: 9.62/mo; 94.06/yr.
Advertising: Open inch rate $28.66
News services: NYT, AP, NEA, MCT.
Politics: Independent.
Own facility?: Y
Special Editions: Administrative Professionals (Apr); Harmon Football Forecast (Aug); Santas Letters (Dec); Prime Time (Every other month); Review and Forecast (Feb); Bride's World I (Jan); Rome Symphony (Jul); Medical (Jun); Review and Forecast (Mar); Memorial Classified
Special Weekly Sections: Roman Record (Mon); Roman Life (S); Tribune Viewers Guide (Sat); Young Romans (Tues); Best Food Guide (Wed).
Magazines: Business Tab (Mon); Parade (S); TV/Cable Program Magazine (Sat); Youth Tab (Tues).
Pub ....Otis M. Raybon
Adv. Dir. ....Mike Schuttinga
Circ. Dir. ....Robert Ronco
Ed. ....Charlotte Atkins
Mng. Ed. ....Mike Colombo
Editorial Page Ed. ....John Willis
Sports Ed. ....David Dawson
Dir., Information Technology ....Matt Debord
Data Processing Mgr. ....Mike Deaton
Prodn. Dir., Dispatch ....Tona Deaton
Prodn. Mgr., Press ....Rob Broadway
Market Information: Split run; TMC.
Mechanical available: Offset; Black and 3 ROP colors; insert accepted; page cutoffs - 22 3/4.
Mechanical Specifications: Type page 11 1/2 x 21 1/4; E - 6 cols, 1 5/6, 1/8 between; A - 6 cols, 1 5/6, 1/8 between; C - 9 cols, 1 9/50, 1/16 between.
Commodity Consumption: Avg. Page Number Per Issue - Daily 22; Avg. Page Number Per Issue - Plates Used 21000; Avg. Page Number Per Issue - Saturday 22; Avg. Page Number Per Issue - Sunday 42; widths 25; Newsprint Used - Short Tons 1200; Printing Ink Used - Black 17500; Printin
Equipment EDITORIAL: Front-end Software – Novell/Network 4.1, Microsoft/NT 4.0.; Editorial Hardware – 1-Compaq/Proliant Server, 27-Compaq/2000 DeskPro; Editorial Equipment – ACT; Editorial Printers – HP/5000 CLASSIFIED: Front-end Software – ACT.; Classified Hardware – Intergraph/IS 8000 Server, 7-Compaq/2000 DeskPro, Microsoft/NT Server; Classified Printers – HP/5000 DISPLAY: Ad make-up applications – QPS/QuarkXPress.; Display Hardware – 3-Compaq/2000 DeskPro; Display Printers – HP/5000 PRODUCTION: Pagination Software – ACT.; Production Equipment – LaserMaster/1200dpi, ECR/4550, ECR/VRL 36; Scanners – HP/ScanJet 5P, Nikon/LS-2000, Microtech/ScanMaker V6000, GEI/Tecsa 5000 Full Page PRESSROOM: Line 1 – 15 unit Dgm 430; Folders – 1 MAILROOM: Counter stackers – Stima/Poly Wrap Insert 12.1; Inserters and stuffers – Newstec/SLS 1000 10:2; Bundle tying machines – 1-MLN/MLEE; Mailroom control system – Prism; Addressing machine – KR/Inkjet, 1-Prism/InkJet Labeling System. BUSINESS COMPUTERS: Business Software – PBS CM 2.7, PBS/AM 2.8, SBS-GL; Business Hardware – 1-IBM RS6000
Delivery method: Mail, Newsstand, Private Carrier, Racks

SAVANNAH

SAVANNAH MORNING NEWS
1375 Chatham Pkwy., Savannah, Ga., 31405-0301; gen tel (912) 236-9511; adv tel (912) 652-0250; ed tel (912) 652-0300; gen fax (912) 236-8909; adv fax (912) 652-0260; ed fax (912) 234-6522; web site www.savannahnow.com
Published: Mon, Tues, Wed, Thur, Fri, Sat, Sun
Weekday Frequency: m
Saturday Frequency: m
Circulation: 37,197; 37,197(sat); 55,377(sun)
Last Audit: ABC September 30, 2011
Price: 13.00/mo; 156.00/yr.
Advertising: Open inch rate $110.00
News services: AP, NEA, MCT, LAT.
Politics: Independent.
Special Weekly Sections: Diversions (Fri); Government (Mon); Business & Employment Exchange (S); Behind the Wheel (Sat); Food (Wed).
Magazines: Relish (Monthly); USA WEEKEND Magazine (S).
Pub ....Michael Traynor
HR Dir. ....Frankie Fort
Adv. Dir. ....Randy Mooney
Adv. Mgr., Classified ....Ken Boler
Adv. Mgr., Real Estate ....Linda Horan
Adv. Mgr., Display ....Cynthia Barnes
Acct. Mgr. ....Elena Mitchell
Dir., Mktg./Promo. ....Stacy Jennings
Circ. Dir. ....Todd Timmons
Circ. Mgr ....David Ellis
Exec. Ed. ....Susan Catron
Community Ed. ....Steve Corrigan
Editorial Page Ed. ....Tom Barton
Editorial Writer ....Edward Fulford
Editorial Writer ....Scott Kent
Educ. Reporter ....Jenel Few
Environmental Reporter ....Mary Landers
Gov't/Bus. Ed. ....Pamela E. Walck
Justice Ed. ....Suzanne Donovan
News Planning Ed. ....Stephen Komives
Market Information: ADS; TMC; Zoned editions.
Mechanical available: Offset; Black and 3 ROP colors; insert accepted - odd sizes subject to approval; page cutoffs - 22 3/4.
Mechanical Specifications: Type page 11 1/2 x 21 1/2; E - 6 cols, 1 3/4, 3/16 between; A - 6 cols, 1 3/4, 3/16 between; C - 9 cols, 1 1/16, 1/16 between.
Commodity Consumption: Avg. Page Number Per Issue - Daily 44; Avg. Page Number Per Issue - Plates Used 110528; Avg. Page Number Per Issue - Saturday 56; Avg. Page Number Per Issue - Sunday 96; widths 12 1/2; Newsprint Used - Short Tons 6800; Printing Ink Used - Black 13612; Pr
Equipment EDITORIAL: Front-end Software – DTI/Edit 5.2, QPS/QuarkXPress, Adobe/Illustrator, Aldus/FreeHand.; Editorial Hardware – IBM/AT, APP/Mac 8100-80, APP/Mac IIfx, APP/Mac SE, APP/Mac 8500-100; Editorial Equipment – IBM/Selectric; Editorial Printers – HP/4, III/XIT, HP/5000 CLASSIFIED: Front-end Software – DTI/Classified 5.0.; Classified Hardware – IBM/AT; Classified Printers – IBM/2391 DISPLAY: Ad make-up applications – Multi-Ad/Creator, Aldus/FreeHand, Adobe/Illustrator, QPS/QuarkXPress, PBS, Adobe/Photoshop; Display Hardware – APP/Mac; Display Printers – APP/Mac LaserWriter IIg, Tektronix/Phaser III, III/XIT, Clipper/Navigator, HP/1200C PRODUCTION: Pagination Software – QPS/QuarkXPress, Archetype/OPI, Adobe/Illustrator, Adobe/In Des; Production Equipment – 2-Nu/Flip Top FT40UPNS, AG/Accuset 1500, Nu/Vacuum plate burner; Cameras – 1-C/Spartan III; Scanners – Polaroid/SprintScan, Nikon/ScanTouch, Epson/G36, Ag/Studio Star PRESSROOM: Line 1 – 7-G/3176; Folders – 2-G/2:1; Pasters – 7; Reels and Stands – 7 MAILROOM: Counter stackers – 1-HL/HT-2, 3-TMSI/Compass 180; Inserters and stuffers – MM/227, 3-MM/6:1, Heidelberg/632 14:1; Bundle tying machines – 2-Dynaric/NP-2, 2-Dynaric/NP 1500; Addressing machine – 2/Ch, 1-/KR, Videojet/7000; Other equipment – QWI/Bottom Wra BUSINESS COMPUTERS: Business Software – Microsoft/Excel, WordPerfect, Microsoft/Word; Business Hardware – Gateway 2000 P5-90

STATESBORO

STATESBORO HERALD
1 Proctor St., Statesboro, Ga., 30458; gen tel (912) 764-9031; adv tel (912) 764-9031; ed tel (912) 489-9400; gen fax (912) 489-8181; adv fax (912) 489-8181; ed fax (912) 489-9445; adv e-mail jmelton@statesboroherald.com; ed e-mail jhealy@statesboroherald.com; web site www.statesboroherald.com
Group: Morris Multimedia, Inc.
Published: Tues, Wed, Thur, Fri, Sat, Sun
Weekday Frequency: m
Saturday Frequency: m
Circulation: 7,442; 7,442(sat); 7,926(sun)
Last Audit: Sworn September 27, 2002
Price: 3.23/wk.
Advertising: Open inch rate $13.04
Insert rate: Ask for quote
News services: AP, The Newspaper Network, SHNS.
Politics: Independent. **Established:** 1937
Not Published: Mondays
Own facility?: Y
Special Editions: Bridal (Apr); Community Pride (Feb); Newcomer's Guide (Jun); Home Improvement (Mar); Georgia Southern University New Student Guide (May); Healthy Living (Nov); Best
Special Weekly Sections: TV Tab (S); Community Voice (Thur); Business Tuesday (Tues).
Magazines: Parade (S).
Pres. ....Joe McGlamery
Pub. ....Randy Morton
Regl. Controller ....Jennifer Lewis
Adv. Dir. ....Jan Melton
Adv. Mgr., Classified ....Pamela Pollard
Print Adv. Mgr. ....Kelly Dailey
Circ. Mgr. ....Darrell Elliott
Asst. Ed. ....Eddie Ledbetter
Market Information: TMC.
Mechanical available: Offset; Black and 3 ROP colors; insert accepted; page cutoffs - 22.
Mechanical Specifications: Type page 10 1/2 x 21; E - 6 cols, 1 16/25, 1/8 between; A - 6 cols, 1 16/25, 1/8 between; C - 6 cols, 1 16/25, 1/6 between.
Commodity Consumption: Avg. Page Number Per Issue - Daily 20; Avg. Page Number Per Issue - Plates Used 42298; Avg. Page Number Per Issue - Saturday 24; Avg. Page Number Per Issue - Sunday 32; widths 25; Newsprint Used - Short Tons 2665; Printing Ink Used - Black 45237; Printing
Equipment; Editorial Hardware – Dell; Editorial Equipment – DTI; Editorial Printers – HP Laserjet5000 CLASSIFIED: Front-end Software – DTI; Classified Hardware – Dell; Classified Printers – HP laserjet 5000 DISPLAY: Ad make-up applications – InDesign; Layout Software – 3 Dell Servers PRODUCTION: Pagination Software – InDesign; Production Equipment –

Kodak direct to plate PRESSROOM: Line 1 – 12-G/Community 1993; Folders – Dec-93; Pasters – 9 MAILROOM: Counter stackers – Heidelberg-Harris; Inserters and stuffers – Alphaliner, 1997; Bundle tying machines – Signode; Business Hardware – Dell
Zip Codes served: 30458;30461
Delivery method: Mail, Newsstand, Private Carrier, Racks

THE STATESBORO HERALD

#1 Proctor Street, Herald Square, Statesboro, Ga., 30458; gen tel (912) 764-9031; adv tel 9124899401; ed tel 9124899402; gen fax 9124898181; adv fax 9124898181; ed fax 9124899445; adv e-mail jmelton@statesboroherald.com; ed e-mail jhealy@statesboroherald.com; web site www.statesboroherald.com
Group: Morris Multimedia
Published: Tues, Wed, Thur, Fri, Sat, Sun
Weekday Frequency: m
Saturday Frequency: m
Circulation: 7,145; 7,145(sat); 7,583(sun)
Insert rate: avg $49/m
News services: AP, FOX News, Morris Multimedia
Politics: 1937
Advertising not accepted: Y
Not Published: Mondays
Own facility?: Y
Special Editions: Community Pride (Feb)
City Guide (May)
Newcomer Guide (June)
Special Weekly Sections: LIfestyles (Sun) Business (Tue) Education (Wed) Community (Thur) Real Estate (Fri) Entertainment (Sat)
Magazines: TV tab
Moments
Connect
Broadcast Affiliations: Morris Network
Market Information: University, Agriculture, Industry
Mechanical available: std 6 col x 21 in
tab 6 col x 10.5 in
Mechanical Specifications: 1 col 1.64 in
2 col 3.41 in
3 col 5.18 in
4 col 6.96 in
5 col 8.73 in
6 col 10.5 in
Equipment EDITORIAL: Front-end Software – Adobe CS4 Production Standard, InCopy, CS4 Web Premium; Editorial Hardware – CanoScan LiDE60, Dell GX760, GX 620 (4), GX520 (2), Latitude E6500, E5500, Nikon D300S, Nikon Coolpix (2); Editorial Equipment – RadioShack Scanner; Editorial Printers – HP5200N CLASSIFIED: Front-end Software – DIT MediaPlus8.9.2; Classified Hardware – Dell GX520 (2), CanoScan4400F flatbed scanner, Sharp EL-1197P; Classified Equipment – n/a; Classified Printers – HP5000N DISPLAY: Ad make-up applications – Citrix Media Plus Display, MS Office, SnagIt9, Dropbox; Display Hardware – Dell D610 Laptops (4), D620, D830; Display Printers – HP5200N PRODUCTION: Pagination Software – FlipQ, Adobe CS4 Production Premium; Production Equipment – TriCaster Studio, SmartFade 1248, Altman 1000L lighting system, KinoFlo DivaLite 400, SmithVictor SBQ-1 Softbox (2), Prompter People teleprompter (2) iKam teleprompter, Panasonic TH-50PH9 display (4), Libec T58 tripod, Optiplex GX620 (2); Cameras – Panasonic AG HVX200P studio, Canon XHA1S, Canon GL-2 (2); Scanners – CanoScan 1220U PRESSROOM: Line 1 – 16 units Goss Community; Press Drives – 3 Fincor Drives 75/125/125; Folders – Goss Community SSC w/upper former. Two 4-HI color stacks; Pasters – 9 Enkel Splicers; Press control system – 3 Fincor Controllers; Press registration system – Quad Tech motorized registration MAILROOM: Counter stackers – Muller Martini, Rima RS-2520S; Inserters and stuffers – Muller Martini Alphaliner 14 pocket; Bundle tying machines – Signode LB-2000 (3); Wrapping singles – n/z; Mailroom control system – n/a; Addressing machine – n/a; Other equipment – Challenge Champion, McCain MT-571A AUDIO: Audio Software – Adobe Soundbooth, Adobe Premier; Audio Hardware – Yamaha MG16/6FX mixing console, Samson CT7 wireless mic system, Airwave AT3000 receiver, AT3002 transceiver, AudioTechnicaPro41 mic(4), Rode NTG-1 mic (2) Electrovoice RE20 mic(2), Arrakis ARC-10 radio console, innkeeper 2 digital hybrid, Comrex Blue Box, NuMark MP102 CD player, Sennheiser HD202 headphones (6) JBL Pro speakers, Midland GTX XtraTalk (4), Radio Shack Pro-106 scanner, Dell OptiPlex 760, GX 620 (2). BUSINESS COMPUTERS: Business Software – DTI MediaPlus 8.9.2, iCVerify, MS Office SBE; Business Hardware – Unifi35 Smartboard, PltneyBowes G900 mailer, imagistics in4720 copier, Okifax 5780, HP5000N, Dell GX520 (3).
Zip Codes served:
30458;30461;30452;30450;30415;31321;31308;30467;30439;30417
Delivery method: Mail, Newsstand, Private Carrier, Racks

THOMASVILLE

THOMASVILLE TIMES-ENTERPRISE

106 South St., Thomasville, Ga., 31792; gen tel (229) 226-2400; gen fax (229) 228-5863; ed e-mail mark.lastinger@gaflnews.com; web site www.timesenterprise.com
Published: Tues, Wed, Thur, Fri, Sat, Sun
Weekday Frequency: m
Circulation: 8,293; 8,293(sat); 8,291(sun)
Last Audit: September 30, 2009
Price: 10.95/mo; 126.00/yr.
Advertising: Open inch rate $22.05
News services: AP.
Politics: Independent.
Advertising not accepted: Vending machine; Stuffing envelopes.
Not Published: New Year; Independence Day; Labor Day; Christmas.
Special Editions: Rural Living (Monthly).
Special Weekly Sections: Church Pages (Fri); Business (S); Weekend Page (Thur); Best Food Days (Tues); Best Food Days (Wed).
Magazines: Relish (Monthly); Color Comics (S).
Pub ....Norman Bankston
Adv. Dir. ....Chris White
Adv. Mgr., Major/Nat'l Accts. ....Laura Rogers
Circ. Dir. ....Thomas H. Clements
Mng. Ed. ....Mark Lastinger
Prodn. Mgr. ....Monte Kilcrease
Prodn. Mgr., Composing ....Travis Ouzts
Market Information: ADS; Split run; TMC; Zoned editions.
Mechanical available: Offset; Black and 3 ROP colors; insert accepted - free standing; page cutoffs - 22 1/2.
Mechanical Specifications: Type page 13 x 21 1/2; E - 6 cols, 2 1/16, 1/8 between; A - 6 cols, 2 1/16, 1/8 between; C - 9 cols, 1 5/16, 1/8 between.
Commodity Consumption: Avg. Page Number Per Issue - Daily 18; Avg. Page Number Per Issue - Plates Used 3717; Avg. Page Number Per Issue - Sunday 40; widths 27 1/2; Newsprint Used - Short Tons 375; Printing Ink Used - Black 8200; Printing Ink Used - Color 500; Printing Ink Used
Equipment EDITORIAL: Front-end Software – QPS/QuarkXPress, FSI.; Editorial Hardware – FSI; Classified Hardware – APP/Mac.; Production Equipment – 1-APP/Mac LaserWriter, Tegra/Varityper, 2-APP/Mac, 1-Mk/AdComp; Cameras – SCREEN/Vertical; Scanners – Lf/Leafscan. PRESSROOM: Line 1 – 8-G, 7-G/Community (1 color unit).; Inserters and stuffers – 5/MM; Bundle tying machines – 1-/OVL; Addressing machine – 3-Wm/5. BUSINESS COMPUTERS: Business Software – WordPerfect 6.0, Lotus 4.1; Business Hardware – 6-ATT/Business Sys

TIFTON

THE TIFTON GAZETTE

211 N. Tift Ave., Tifton, Ga., 31794; gen tel (229) 382-4321; adv tel (229) 382-4321; ed tel (229) 382-4321; gen fax (229) 387-7322; adv fax (229) 387-7322; ed fax (229) 387-7322; gen e-mail ttg.editorial@gaflnews.com; ed e-mail ttg.editorial@gaflnews.com; web site www.tiftongazette.com
Published: Tues, Wed, Thur, Fri, Sat, Sun
Weekday Frequency: m
Circulation: 9,046; 9,046(sat); 9,046(sun)
Price: 2.90/wk; 112.36/yr.
Advertising: Open inch rate $29.05
News services: AP.
Politics: Independent. **Established:** 1888
Not Published: Christmas.
Special Editions: Love Affair Tab (Apr); Back-to-School (Aug); Christmas Greetings (Dec); Love Lines (Feb); Health & Fitness (Jan); Home-owned Business (Jul); Home and Garden (Mar); Mother's Day (May); Holiday Gift Guide (Nov); Shop Early (Oct); Oktoberfest (Sept).
Special Weekly Sections: Entertainment (Fri); Education (Thur); Best Food Day (Wed).
Magazines: Parade (S).
Pub. ....Frank Sayles
Office Mgr. ....Jetty Tanner
Adv. Mgr. ....Lisa Beckham
Adv. Mgr., Retail Sales ....Kitty Stone
Promo. Mgr. ....Melody Cowart
Circ. Mgr. ....Rachel Wainwright
Mng. Ed. ....Florence Rankin
Sports Ed. ....Steve Carter
Market Information: TMC.
Mechanical available: Offset; Black and 3 ROP colors; insert accepted - any; page cutoffs - 22 3/4.
Mechanical Specifications: Type page 13 x 21 1/2; E - 6 cols, 2 1/16, 1/8 between; A - 6 cols, 2 1/16, 1/8 between; C - 9 cols, 1 3/8, 1/16 between.
Commodity Consumption: Avg. Page Number Per Issue - Daily 17; Avg. Page Number Per Issue - Plates Used 4400; widths 27; Newsprint Used - Short Tons 280; Printing Ink Used - Black 11800; Printing Ink Used - Pages Printed 5200.
Equipment; Editorial Hardware – Mk/1100.; Classified Hardware – Mk/1100.; Production Equipment – 2-Mk/Laserwriter; Cameras – 1-III/Newsprint. PRESSROOM: Line 1 – 6-G/Community; Folders – 1 MAILROOM: Counter stackers – BG; Bundle tying machines – 1/Bu, 1-/Staplex; Addressing machine – 2-/Wm.; Business Hardware – ATT

VALDOSTA

VALDOSTA DAILY TIMES

201 N. Troup St., Valdosta, Ga., 31601; gen tel (229) 244-1880; adv tel (229) 244-1880; ed tel (229) 244-1880; gen fax (229) 244-2560; adv fax (229) 244-2560; ed fax (229) 244-2560; gen e-mail vdt.editorial@gaflnews.com; ed e-mail vdt.editorial@gaflnews.com; web site www.valdostadailytimes.com
Group: Publishers Representatives of Florida, Inc.
Published: Mon, Tues, Wed, Thur, Fri, Sat, Sun
Weekday Frequency: m
Saturday Frequency: m
Circulation: 14,077; 14,077(sat); 16,166(sun)
Last Audit: September 30, 2009
Price: 2.99/wk; 13.45/mo; 142.00/yr (home delivery).
Advertising: Open inch rate $27.30
News services: AP, SHNS.
Politics: Independent. **Established:** 1867
Special Editions: Football (Aug); Cookbook (Jun); Yearbook (Mar); Living Here (Nov).
Special Weekly Sections: Business Page (S); Church Page (Sat); Food Page (Tues).
Magazines: Relish (Monthly); Parade (S).
Broadcast Affiliations: WTLH Fox 49.
Pub. ....Sandy Sanders
Adv. Mgr., Nat'l/Major ....Laura Rogers
Vice Pres., Circ. ....Andrew Wardle
Mng. Ed. ....Kay Harris
News Ed. ....Kelli Hernandez
Lifestyle Ed. ....Elizabeth Butler
Online Ed. ....Iskren Georgiev
Sports Ed. ....Christian Malone
Vice Pres., Technology ....Hubby Brooks
Vice Pres., Prodn. ....Vince Cribb
Prodn. Mgr., Mailroom ....Lyold Kitchens
Market Information: ADS; TMC.
Mechanical available: Offset; Black and 3 ROP colors; insert accepted; page cutoffs - 22 3/4.
Mechanical Specifications: Type page 11 1/2 x 21 1/2; E - 6 cols, 1 4/5, 1/6 between; A - 6 cols, 1 4/5, 1/6 between; C - 6 cols, 1 13/16, 1/6 between.
Commodity Consumption: Avg. Page Number Per Issue - Daily 24; Avg. Page Number Per Issue - Plates Used 80000; Avg. Page Number Per Issue - Sunday 50; widths 25; Newsprint Used - Short Tons 3093; Printing Ink Used - Black 35252; Printing Ink Used - Color 64830; Printing Ink Use
Equipment EDITORIAL: Front-end Software – FSI, QPS/QuarkXPress 3.32, Multi-Ad/Creator 4.03, Adobe/Illustrator 7, Adobe/Photoshop 4.0.; Editorial Hardware – FSI, APP/Mac; Editorial Printers – Xante/Accel-A-Writer 8300, Pre Press/Panther Pro 46, Pre Press/Panther Pro 62, Canon/360 PS CLASSIFIED: Front-end Software – Baseview 2.1.1, QPS/QuarkXPress 3.32.; Classified Hardware – Baseview, APP/Mac; Classified Equipment – Pre Press/Panther Pro 62; Classified Printers – HP/5000; Layout Software – QPS/QuarkXPress, Multi-Ad/Creator. PRODUCTION: Pagination Software – FSI, Multi-Ad/Creator, QPS/QuarkXPress.; Production Equipment – Nu/FT40V6, Pre Press/Panther Pro 46, Pre Press/Panther Pro 62; Cameras – 1-LE/121, C, SCREEN/C 680; Scanners – Umax/Mirage, Umax/Mirage II PRESSROOM: Line 1 – 16-2000; Folders – 1, 1. MAILROOM: Counter stackers – 2-MM/(3 station automatic inserter), 2/Sheridan, 2-/Monitors HT, 2-/Compass 100; Inserters and stuffers – 2-GMA/SLS-1000; Bundle tying machines – 2-Signode, 2-/PowerStrap, 2-/Samuel; Addressing machine – 1-/Kick Rudy; Other equipment –Other equipment ☐; Business Hardware – PBS, Oracle

WAYCROSS

WAYCROSS JOURNAL-HERALD

400 Isabella St., Waycross, Ga., 31502; gen tel (912) 283-2244; adv tel (912) 287-2244; ed tel (912) 283-2244; gen fax (912) 283-2815; adv fax (912) 285-5255; ed fax (912) 283-2815; ed e-mail newsroom@wjhnews.com; web site www.wjhnews.com
Published: Mon, Tues, Wed, Thur, Fri, Sat
Weekday Frequency: e
Saturday Frequency: e
Circulation: 9,304; 9,304(sat)
Last Audit: Sworn September 25, 2003
Price: 11.50 mo./138.00 yr.
Advertising: Open inch rate $15.00
Insert rate: $50 CPM
News services: AP.
Politics: Democrat. **Established:** 1875
Advertising not accepted: Y
Not Published: Labor Day,Christmas, Thanksgiving, July 4
Own facility?: Y
Special Editions: Football (Aug); Christmas (Dec); Bridal (Feb); Spring (Mar); Cookbook (Oct); Fair (Sept).
Special Weekly Sections: TV (Sat).
Pub. ....Roger L. Williams
Adv. Mgr., Nat'l ....Van Carter
Adv. Mgr., Classified ....Debbie Rowell
Local Display Mgr. ....Ava Hendricks
Mgr., Promo ....Donnie Carter
Circ. Mgr. ....Donna Cox
Amusements Ed. ....Scott Cooper
Film/Theater Ed. ....Gary Griffin
Food/Garden Ed. ....Myra Thrift
Photo Dept. Mgr. ....James Hooks
Picture Ed. ....Jack Williams
Mechanical available:
Editorial:QuarkXPress,Photoshop, Adobe Illustrator;Advertising:MultiAd Creator and QuarkXPress;Circulation:IBM

Mechanical Specifications: type page: 12 x 20.25, display adv.: 6 cols.; classified adv. 9 cols.
Commodity Consumption: Avg. Page Number Per Issue - Daily 24; Avg. Page Number Per Issue - Plates Used 13000; widths 27 1/2; Newsprint Used - Short Tons 460; Printing Ink Used - Black 40000; Printing Ink Used - Color 3000.
Equipment EDITORIAL: Front-end Software – QPS 3.31.; Editorial Hardware – APP/Mac, Mk/1100 Plus; Editorial Equipment – 1-COM/7200H; Editorial Printers – APP/Mac LaserPrinter; Classified Hardware – 2-Mk/Touchwriter Plus; Classified Printers – APP/Mac LaserPrinter. DISPLAY: Ad make-up applications – Multi-Ad/Creator 3.6.1; Layout Software – APP/Mac.; Display Hardware – APP/Mac; Display Printers – APP/Mac LaserPrinter PRODUCTION: Pagination Software – QPS 3.31.; Production Equipment – TI/Omni-Page 3.1, 1-BKY; Cameras – 1-C/Spartan III PRESSROOM: Line 1 – 10-unit Goss Community offset press; Inserters and stuffers – KAN/402; Addressing machine – IBM/Sys 36.; Business Hardware – 1-IBM/Sys 54
Zip Codes served: 31501,31510,31516,31550,31551,31552,31564,31650
Delivery method: Private Carrier, Racks

HAWAII

HILO

HAWAII TRIBUNE-HERALD

355 Kinoole St., Hilo, Hawaii, 96720; gen tel (808) 935-6621; adv tel (808) 935-6621; ed tel (808) 935-6621; gen fax (808) 969-9100; adv fax (808) 969-9100; ed fax (808) 961-3680; adv e-mail asledge@hawaiitribune-herald.com; ed e-mail htrib@hawaiitribune-herald.com; web site www.hawaiitribune-herald.com
Group: Stephens Media Company, LLC
Published: Mon, Tues, Wed, Thur, Fri, Sat, Sun
Weekday Frequency: m
Saturday Frequency: m
Circulation: 18,007; 18,007(sat); 20,270(sun)
Last Audit: Sworn September 30, 2009
Price: 11.25/mo; 135.00/yr.
Advertising: Open inch rate $31.74
Insert rate: 87.00 p/m
News services: AP.
Politics: Independent.
Own facility?: Y
Special Editions: American Home Week (Apr); Christmas Gift Guide (Dec); Bride (Feb); Home Improvement (Jun).
Special Weekly Sections: Church (Fri); Best Food Day (S); Best Food Day (Tues).
Magazines: USA WEEKEND Magazine (S).
Pub. .... Ted E. Dixon
Adv. Dir. .... Alice Sledge
Ed. .... David Bock
Prodn. Mgr., Pre Press .... Arlan Vierra
Cir Dir .... Thad Henderson
Circ. Dir. .... William Crawford
Market Information: TMC.
Mechanical available: Offset; Black and 3 ROP colors; insert accepted; page cutoffs - 21 1/2.
Mechanical Specifications: Type page 12 x 21 1/2; E - 6 cols, 1 7/8, 1/6 between; A - 6 cols, 1 7/8, 1/6 between; C - 9 cols, 1 1/4, 2/15 between.
Commodity Consumption: Avg. Page Number Per Issue - Daily 24; Avg. Page Number Per Issue - Sunday 44; widths 12 1/2; Newsprint Used - Metric Tons 1200; Printing Ink Used - Pages Printed 10500.
Equipment EDITORIAL: Front-end Software – Adobe/InDesign.; Editorial Hardware – APP/Mac, QPS/QuarkXPress 4.11, Baseview/News Edit Pro 3.2.3; Editorial Equipment – Nikon/LS 1000, Epson/1200 Scanners; Editorial Printers – LaserMaster/, APP/Mac, Epson/3000 CLASSIFIED: Front-end Software – Baseview/Ad Manager Pro.; Classified Hardware – APP/Mac; Classified Printers – NewGen, HP/1300 CP, Epson/1520, DISPLAY: Ad make-up applications – Adobe/InDesign, Baseview/Ad Manager Pro, Adobe/Photoshop, Adobe/Illustrator; Layout Software – Baseview.; Display Hardware – APP/Mac G3; Display Printers – Xante/Accel-aWriter; Production Equipment – Mk, 2-PrePress Solutions/Panther 36Plus; Cameras – Nu; Scanners – Epson, HP, Nikon, Microtek. PRESSROOM: Line 1 – 8-G/Urbanite; Folders – 1 MAILROOM: Counter stackers – Quipp 500; Inserters and stuffers – MM/227; Bundle tying machines – Sig LB2330; Addressing machine – Videojet 7300 BUSINESS COMPUTERS: Business Software – CJ; Business Hardware – CJ

HONOLULU

HONOLULU STAR-ADVERTISER

500 Ala Moana Boulevard #7-500, Honolulu, Hawaii, 96813; gen tel (808) 529-4700; adv tel (808) 529-4700; ed tel (808) 529-4747; gen fax (808) 529-4898; adv fax (808) 529-4898; ed fax (808) 529-4750; adv e-mail displayads@staradvertiser.com; ed e-mail citydesk@staradvertiser.com; web site www.staradvertiser.com
Group: Oahu Publications, Inc.
Newspapers First, Inc.
Published: Mon, Tues, Wed, Thur, Fri, Sat, Sun
Weekday Frequency: m
Saturday Frequency: m
Circulation: 178,082; 123,848(sat); 135,555(sun)
Last Audit: ABC September 30, 2011
Price: $19.95/month
Advertising: Open rate $205 pci (M/T/Sa), $220 pci (W/Th/F), $260 pci (Su)
Insert rate: Single Sheet CPM $78.82 Daily, $83.53 Sunday
Politics: 2010
Advertising not accepted: N
Own facility?: Y
Special Editions: Ala Moana (Mar, Jul, Nov), Young at Heart (Mar & Sep), Easter (Apr), Summer School (Apr), Earth Day (Apr), Military Appreciation (Apr), Nurses Week (May), Hawaii's Best (Jun), Back to School (Jul), Progress (Jul), Staycation (Aug), University of Hawaii Sports (Aug-May), Football Fever (Aug-Dec), Parade of Homes (Oct), Top Restaurants (Oct), Credit Union (Oct), Holiday Gift Guides (Nov-Dec)
Special Weekly Sections: tgif (Fri), Dining Out (Sun), Hawaii Renovation (Sun)
Magazines: 101 Things to Do, AKA (U. of Hawaii Athletics), Aulani (Disney Aulani Resort in-room magazine), Go Kailua, Halekulani Living (Halekulani Hotel in-room magazine), HILuxury, Luana (Fairmont Hotels in-room magazine), Ola (Hilton Grand Waikikian in-room magazine)
Profile: Newspaper
President and Publisher .... Dennis Francis
Senior Vice President, Marketing .... Dave Kennedy
Senior Vice President, Advertising .... Glenn Zuehls
Vice President / Editor .... Frank Bridgewater
Vice President / Technology .... Roger Forness
Production Director .... Marty Black
Director of Digital Media .... Troy Fujimoto
Human Resources Director .... Rebecca Stolar
Circulation Director .... Steve Tomino
Controller .... TC Gray
Director of Consumer Sales/Retention .... Joe Leong
Pres./Pub. .... Lee P. Webber
Vice Pres., Finance .... Richard Fuke
Controller .... Amy Kunz
Adv. Vice Pres. .... Clint Schroeder
Circ. Vice Pres. .... Michael Cusato
Circ. Mgr., Customer Serv. .... Merilee Lucas
Circ. Mgr., Home Delivery .... Steve Tomino
Circ. Mgr., Single Copy .... Lester Kodama
Circ. NIE Coord. .... Jennifer Dang
Ed. .... Mark Platte
Mng. Ed., Content .... Marsha McFadden
Mng. Ed., Digital/Multimedia .... Sandra S. Oshiro
Asst. Bus. Ed. .... Alan Yonan
Deputy City Ed. .... Dave Dondoneau
Asst. City Ed. .... Maureen O'Connell
Asst. City Ed. .... John Windrow
Asst. City Ed. .... Dan Woods
Asst. City Ed. .... Andy Yamaguchi
Database/Special Projects Ed. .... Stephen Downes
Editorial/Opinion Ed. .... Jeanne Mariani-Belding
Mechanical available: Offset Presses; Black + 3 ROP Colors; Inserts Accepted - Preprints, Post-it Notes; 70,000 CPM; 6 Sections; Page Cutoff 21.
Mechanical Specifications: Type page 11 x 21; E - 6 cols, 1 - 1/2, 1/8 between; A - 6 cols, 1 - 1/2, 1/8 between; C - 10 cols, 7/8, 3/32between.
Equipment EDITORIAL: Front-end Software – Newsedit Pro; Editorial Hardware – Mac OS X CLASSIFIED: Front-end Software – ATEX; Classified Hardware – Dell/Windows; Classified Printers – HP DISPLAY: Ad make-up applications – ATEX; Layout Software – QuarkXPress; Display Hardware – Dell/Windows; Cameras – Canon PRESSROOM: Line 1 – 6 Towers Man Roland Regioman 2004; Line 2 – 6 Towers Man Roland Regioman 2004; Press Drives – VFD - Shaftless; Folders – KFZ 80 (2-3-3) Jaw Folder System; Pasters – CD-13; Reels and Stands – CD-13; Press control system – PECOM; Press registration system – PECOM MAILROOM: Counter stackers – 4 - Quipp 501
1 - Quipp 401
4 - Muller Martini Combi Stacks; Inserters and stuffers – 2 - GMA/SLS 2000; Bundle tying machines – 4-Dynaric NP 3000
4-Dynaric NP 1500; Mailroom control system – SAM; News Grip Links; Addressing machine – 2 - Scitex 5120 Ink Jet Lablers; Other equipment –Muller Martini Buffering System; 2 - Kansa 1/4 Folders; 2 - Accraply Labelers; 4 - Quipp Auto Cartloader; Business Hardware – Dell/Windows
Delivery method: Mail, Newsstand, Private Carrier, Racks

KAILUA-KONA

WEST HAWAII TODAY

75-5580 Kuakini Hwy., Kailua-Kona, Hawaii, 96740-1647; gen tel (808) 329-9311; gen fax (808) 329-3659; ed fax (808) 329-4860; gen e-mail wht@aloha.net; adv e-mail tfosso@westhawaiitoday.com; web site www.westhawaiitoday.com
Published: Mon, Tues, Wed, Thur, Fri, Sat, Sun
Weekday Frequency: m
Saturday Frequency: m
Circulation: 10,341; 10,341(sat); 12,478(sun)
Last Audit: September 30, 2009
Price: 9.00/mo; 108.00/yr.
Advertising: Open inch rate $24.00
News services: AP.
Politics: Independent.
Special Editions: Kona Coffee Festival (Nov); Football (Sept).
Special Weekly Sections: Entertainment (Fri); Travel (S); Automotive (Thur); Food (Tues).
Magazines: USA WEEKEND Magazine (S).
Pub. .... Richard M. Asbach
Bus. Office Mgr. .... Lana Taira
Adv. Dir. .... Tracey Fosso
Adv. Mgr., Sales .... June Howard
Circ. Dir. .... John Shackelford
Editorial Page Ed. .... Reed Flickinger
Marine Activities .... James Quirk
Real Estate Ed. .... Brenda Jensen
Prodn. Supvr., Press .... Mike Freyette
Prodn. Supvr., Composing .... Ron Hoffer
Market Information: TMC.
Mechanical available: Offset; Black and 3 ROP colors; insert accepted - card-70 lbs bound stock; page cutoffs - 22 3/4.

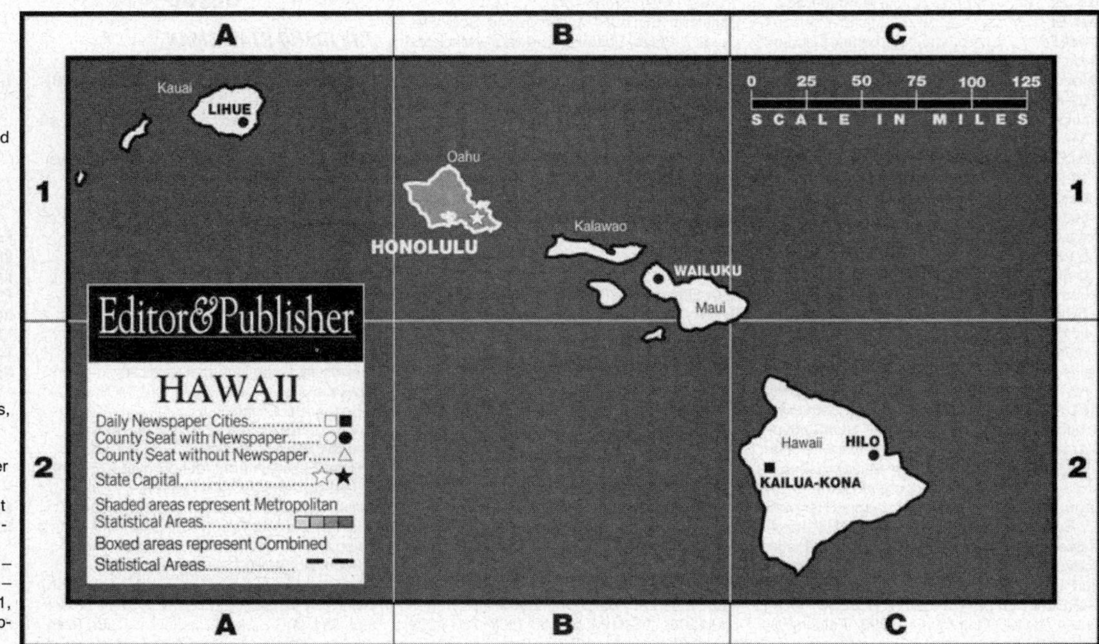

Mechanical Specifications: Type page 11 5/8 x 21 1/2; E - 6 cols, 1 3/4, 3/16 between; A - 6 cols, 1 3/4, 3/16 between; C - 9 cols, 1 3/16, 1/8 between.
Commodity Consumption: Avg. Page Number Per Issue - Daily 48; Avg. Page Number Per Issue - Plates Used 10000; Avg. Page Number Per Issue - Sunday 100; widths 32; Newsprint Used - Metric Tons 780; Printing Ink Used - Black 20000; Printing Ink Used - Color 2500; Printing Ink Use
Equipment EDITORIAL: Front-end Software – Adobe/Illustrator CS2, Adobe/InDesign CS2, Adobe/Photoshop CS2, Baseview.; Editorial Hardware – APP/Mac; Editorial Printers – 1-Xante/Accel-a-Writer 3N CLASSIFIED: Front-end Software – Baseview/AdManager Pro, QPS/QuarkXPress.; Classified Hardware – APP/Mac; Classified Printers – HP DISPLAY: Ad make-up applications – Adobe/CS2; Layout Software – 5-APP/Mac G4.; Display Printers – 2-Xante/Accel-a-Writer 3N PRODUCTION: Pagination Software – Adobe/CS2.; Production Equipment – 1-Pre Press/Panther Pro 36-HS, 1-Mon/Ultra 36; Cameras – 1-LE/490 vertical PRESSROOM: Line 1 – 8-G/Community; Press Drives – 2-Fin/60 h.p.; Folders – 1-G/SC. MAILROOM: Counter stackers – MM/310; Inserters and stuffers – MM/227; Bundle tying machines – 2-MLN/Strapper; Addressing machine – 3/Wm.

LIHUE

THE GARDEN ISLAND

3-3137 Kuhio Hwy., Lihue, Hawaii, 96766-0231; gen tel (808) 245-3681; adv tel (808) 245-3681; ed tel (808) 245-3681; gen fax (808) 245-5286; adv fax (808) 245-5286; web site www.thegardenisland.com
Published: Mon, Tues, Wed, Thur, Fri, Sat, Sun
Weekday Frequency: m
Saturday Frequency: m
Circulation: 11,259; 11,259(sat); 8,763(sun)
Last Audit: ABC September 30, 2011
Price: 9.75/mo (carrier), $45.00/mo (1st class mail); 99.00/yr (carrier), $180.00/yr (2nd class mail).
Advertising: Open inch rate $23.00
News services: AP, TMS, LAT-WP.
Politics: Independent. **Established:** 1902
Special Editions: TGI Homes (Monthly); Essential Kauai (Quarterly).
Special Weekly Sections: Kauai Times (S).
Magazines: USA WEEKEND Magazine (S).
Pres./Pub. ....Randy Kozerski
Adv. Dir ....Casey Quel
Asst. Ed. ....Nathan Eagle
Asst. Ed. ....Michael Levine
Sports Ed. ....Lanaly Cabalo
Prodn. Mgr. ....Richard Stein
Market Information: ADS; TMC; Zoned editions.
Mechanical available: Offset; Black and 3 ROP colors; insert accepted; page cutoffs - 22 3/4.
Mechanical Specifications: Type page 12 1/2 x 21 1/2; E - 6 cols, 1 13/16, 1/8 between; A - 6 cols, 2, 1/8 between; C - 6 cols, 1 13/16, 1/8 between.
Commodity Consumption: Avg. Page Number Per Issue - Daily 32; Avg. Page Number Per Issue - Sunday 40; widths 25; Newsprint Used - Metric Tons 747; Printing Ink Used - Black 29850; Printing Ink Used - Color 26188; Printing Ink Used - Pages Printed 6370.
Equipment; Editorial Hardware – Baseview; Editorial Printers – 2-QMS/820 T, LaserMaster/1800. CLASSIFIED: Front-end Software – ScrippSat.; Classified Hardware – Sun/Suntype; Classified Printers – Okidata/Microline, QMS/393 DISPLAY: Ad make-up applications – Archetype/Designer, Archetype/Corel Draw; Layout Software – Baseview.; Display Hardware – 2-ScrippSat; Display Printers – QMS, LaserMaster/1800x60 PRODUCTION: Pagination Software – APP/Mac.; Production Equipment – Nu/Flip Top FT4OUP; Cameras – SCREEN/Companica 690 E PRESSROOM: Line 1 – 12-G/Community 1993; Folders – 1 MAILROOM: Counter stackers – 1-B/108; Inserters and stuffers – MM/227E; Bundle tying machines – Bu/String Tyer and Plastic Strap; Other equipment –1-MM/235.

KAUAI PUBLISHING CO.

PO Box 231, Lihue, Hawaii, 96766; gen tel (808) 245-3681; gen fax (808) 245-5286

WAILUKU

THE MAUI NEWS

100 Mahalani St., Wailuku, Hawaii, 96793; gen tel (808) 244-3981; adv tel (808) 242-6363; ed tel (808) 242-6343; gen fax (808) 242-6315; adv fax (808) 242-6390; ed fax (808) 242-9087; adv e-mail adsales@mauinews.com; ed e-mail citydesk@mauinews.com; web site www.mauinews.com
Published: Mon, Tues, Wed, Thur, Fri, Sat, Sun
Weekday Frequency: m
Saturday Frequency: m
Circulation: 17,081; 17,081(sat); 19,418(sun)
Last Audit: ABC September 30, 2011
Price: 15.00/mo; 155.00/yr.
Advertising: Open inch rate $40.25
Insert rate: 65/m
News services: AP,
Advertising not accepted: Y
Special Editions: Back-to-School (Aug); Kahului Industrial Area Christmas (Dec); Bridal Fair (Feb); Outlook (Economic Outlook Tab) (Jan); Maui Contractors Assoc.-Building & Materials Expo (Jun); Graduation (May); First Hawaiian Auto Show (Nov); Aloha Festivals (Oct); Parad
Special Weekly Sections: Real Estate (Fri); Weekly TV Tab (S); Maui Scene (Thur); Super Market Ads (Tues)., Scene Magazine (Entertainment) Thurs.
Magazines: Parade (S).
Pub. ....Joe Bradley
Adv. Mgr., Retail ....Dawne Miguel
Circ. Mgr. ....Chris Minford
Ed. ....David Hoff
City Ed. ....Brian Perry
Features Ed. ....Rick Chatenever
News Ed. ....Lee Imada
Sports Ed. ....Brad Sherman
Market Information: TMC.
Mechanical available: Offset; Black and 3 ROP colors; insert accepted; page cutoffs - 21
Mechanical Specifications: Type page 11x19.75
Commodity Consumption: Avg. Page Number Per Issue - Daily 40; Avg. Page Number Per Issue - Sunday 80; widths 27; Newsprint Used - Metric Tons 1800.
Equipment EDITORIAL: Front-end Software – Quark X-Press; Editorial Hardware – Macintosh; Editorial Equipment – IMACS for page layout CLASSIFIED: Front-end Software – FSI.; Classified Hardware – PC DISPLAY: Ad make-up applications – Ad Force 4. Creator 8; Layout Software – Macintosh; Display Hardware – Macintosh; Display Printers – HP 5200; Production Equipment – 2 Kodak Trendsetter CTP units PRESSROOM: Line 1 – 12 DGM Advantage II units MAILROOM: Counter stackers – MM/TYP 267; Inserters and stuffers – 1 K&M 14 into 1 inserter; Bundle tying machines – MLN/Wilton; Addressing machine – St.; Business Hardware – IBM
Delivery method: Mail, Newsstand, Private Carrier, Racks

IDAHO

BLACKFOOT

MORNING NEWS

34 N. Ash St., Blackfoot, Idaho, 83221; gen tel (208) 785-1100; gen fax (208) 785-4239; gen e-mail mnews@cableone.net; adv e-mail wingram@cableone.net; web site www.am-news.com
Published: Mon, Tues, Wed, Thur, Fri, Sat
Weekday Frequency: m
Saturday Frequency: m
Circulation: 4,800; 4,800(sat)
Price: 89.00/yr; 23.00/3mo (carrier), $26.55/3mo (mail).
Advertising: Open inch rate $14.86
News services: AP.
Politics: Independent.
Not Published: Christmas.
Own facility?: Y
Special Editions: Progress (Mar); Outdoors (May-Aug); State Fair (Aug); Seniors (Sept).
Special Weekly Sections: Religion News (Fri); Agriculture (Sat); Food Day (Wed).
Magazines: Outdoors (Fri); American Profile (Weekly).
Adv. Mgr. ....Wayne Ingram
Circ. Mgr. ....Tom Daily
Ed. ....Robert Hudson
Sports Ed. ....Mark High
Prodn. Mgr. ....Kelly Koontz
Prodn. Mgr., Mailroom ....Leonard Martin
Market Information: TMC.
Mechanical available: Offset; Black and 3 ROP colors; insert accepted; page cutoffs - 22 3/4.
Mechanical Specifications: Image area - 10.12 x 21.5; 6 columns.
Commodity Consumption: Avg. Page Number Per Issue - Daily 15.5; Avg. Page Number Per Issue - Saturday 16; widths 27 1/2.
Equipment EDITORIAL: Front-end Software – InDesign; Editorial Hardware – Mac Mini's; Editorial Printers – Pre Press - Two Panther 46 Imagesetters, HP/5000 Laser. CLASSIFIED: Front-end Software – Baseview/Ad Pro, Baseview/Classflow.; Classified Hardware – Mac Mini's DISPLAY: Ad make-up applications – InDesign, Adobe/Acrobat, Adobe/Photoshop, Adobe/Illustrator; Display Hardware – Mac Mini's; Display Printers – PrePress - Two Panter 46 Imagesetters; Production Equipment – Mac Mini's - PrePress - Two Panther 46 Imagesetters PRESSROOM: Line 1 – 9; Folders – KP/KJ-6. MAILROOM: Counter stackers – 1-BG/Count-O-Veyor; Inserters and stuffers – MM/227E 2:1; Bundle tying machines – 2/Bu; Addressing machine – 1-/Sp. BUSINESS COMPUTERS: Business Software – List Master Systems; Business Hardware – PC's
Delivery method: Mail, Newsstand, Private Carrier, Racks

BOISE

THE IDAHO STATESMAN

1200 N. Curtis Rd., Boise, Idaho, 83706-1239; gen tel (208) 377-6200; adv tel (208) 377-6350; ed tel (208) 377-6400; gen fax (207) 377-6230; adv fax (208) 377-6309; ed fax (208) 377-6449; adv e-mail advertising@idahostatesman.com; ed e-mail newsroom@idahostatesman.com; web site www.idahostatesman.com
Published: Mon, Tues, Wed, Thur, Fri, Sat, Sun
Weekday Frequency: m
Saturday Frequency: m
Circulation: 47,724; 51,861(sat); 77,111(sun)
Last Audit: ABC September 30, 2011
Price: 3.25/wk; 187.00/yr; 13.00/4wk, $26.00/8wk (mS), $18.40/8wk (m), $16.00/8wk (S).
Advertising: Open inch rate $125.20
News services: AP, GNS, LAT-WP, MCT, Scripps-McClatchy.
Politics: Independent. **Established:** 1864
Special Editions: Legislative Tab (Jan); Boise River Festival (Jun); Idaho Private 75 (Oct); Best of Treasure Valley (Sept).
Special Weekly Sections: Parade (Fri); Scene (Entertainment Tab) (Fri); Automotive-Classified Std (Sat); Rec (Outdoor Tab) (Thur); Food Std (Wed).
Pres. ....Mi-Ai Parrish
Vice Pres., Sales/Mktg. ....Travis Quast
Asst. Circ. Dir ....Ed Allen
Adv. Mgr., Retail ....Steve Howard
Books Ed ....Vickie Gowler
Outreach Customer Serv. Coord. ....Binna Jensen
Bus. Ed. ....Mike Mahamy
Editorial Page Ed. ....Kevin Richert
Editorial Writer ....Chuck Malloy
Educ. Reporter ....Seth Preston
Entertainment/Amusements Ed. ....Michael Deeds
Environmental Reporter ....Rocky Barker
Farm/Agriculture Reporter ....John Tucker
Food/Home Ed. ....Vickie Ashwill
Graphics Ed./Art Dir. ....Tim Jones
Librarian ....Kris Watson
Metro Ed. ....Bill Manny
Photo Ed. ....Kim Hughes
Market Information: ADS; TMC; Zoned editions.
Mechanical available: Offset; Black and 3 ROP colors; insert accepted; page cutoffs - 23 9/16.
Mechanical Specifications: Type page 13 x 22; E - 6 cols, 2 1/25, 1/6 between; A - 6 cols, 2, 1/4 between; C - 10 cols, 1 1/4, 1/12 between.
Commodity Consumption: Avg. Page Number Per Issue - Daily 53; Avg. Page Number Per Issue - Plates Used 121610; Avg. Page Number Per Issue - Sunday 82; widths 54; Newsprint Used - Metric Tons 8185; Newsprint Used - Short Tons 9023; Printing Ink Used - Black 145390; Printing Ink
Equipment EDITORIAL: Front-end Software – QPS.; Editorial Hardware – 2-AT/1170S, Microsoft/NT Server, APP/Macs; Editorial Equipment – Newsview, APP/Mactext; Editorial Printers – HP CLASSIFIED: Front-end Software – DTI.; Classified Hardware – 2-AT/1170, AT, Unix/Server, APP/Macs; Classified Equipment – Celera/OCR and scanner for legals, Preference-PC; Classified Printers – HP DISPLAY: Ad make-up applications – QPS/QuarkXPress 3.32; Layout Software – APP/Mac, QPS/QuarkXPress.; Display Hardware – APP/Mac; Display Printers – HP PRODUCTION: Pagination Software – DTI (classified), QPS/(news).; Production Equipment – All/Sierra, 1-WL/Lith 5, 1-AG; Cameras – 2-C; Scanners – 1-Microtek/ScanMaker II, Horizon/Scanner, PixelCraft/8200 PRESSROOM: Line 1 – 9-G/Metro; Folders – 1; Pasters – 9-G/Automatic. MAILROOM: Counter stackers – 1-Id/440, 1-Id/550, 3/HI, 2-Heidelberg/Olympian; Inserters and stuffers – 1-HI/1472P; Bundle tying machines – 3-MLN/2A; Addressing machine – 1-/Ch; Other equipment –MM/TV Quarterfolder/s/t.; Audio Hardware – Micro Voice BUSINESS COMPUTERS: Business Software – Microsoft/Office 97; Business Hardware – 1-IBM/AS-400 Model 640

COEUR D'ALENE

COEUR D'ALENE PRESS

201 Second St., Coeur d'Alene, Idaho, 83814; gen tel (208) 664-8176; adv tel (208) 664-0226; ed tel (208) 664-8176; gen fax (208) 664-0212; adv fax (208) 664-0212; ed fax (208) 664-0212; gen e-mail jthompson@cdapress.com; ed e-mail editor@cdapress.com; web site www.cdapress.com
Published: Sun
Circulation: 21,340; 21,340(sat); 28,500(sun)
Last Audit: October 1, 2001
Price: 9.00/mo, $9.50/mo (motor route).
Advertising: Open inch rate $37.07
News services: AP, NEA.
Politics: Independent. **Established:** 1903
Note: The North Idaho Sunday serves the five northern counties in Idaho and is a combined effort of three dailies and three weeklies: Coeur d'Alene Press (m), Sandpoint Bonner County Daily Bee (m), Kellogg Shoshone News-Press (m), Priest River Times (w), Bonner
Special Editions: Coupon Book (Monthly).
Special Weekly Sections: Real Estate (S); Auto Plus (Sat).
Magazines: Relish (Monthly); USA WEEKEND Magazine (S); CDA Magazine (Semi-yearly); American Profile (Weekly).
Pub. ....James Thompson

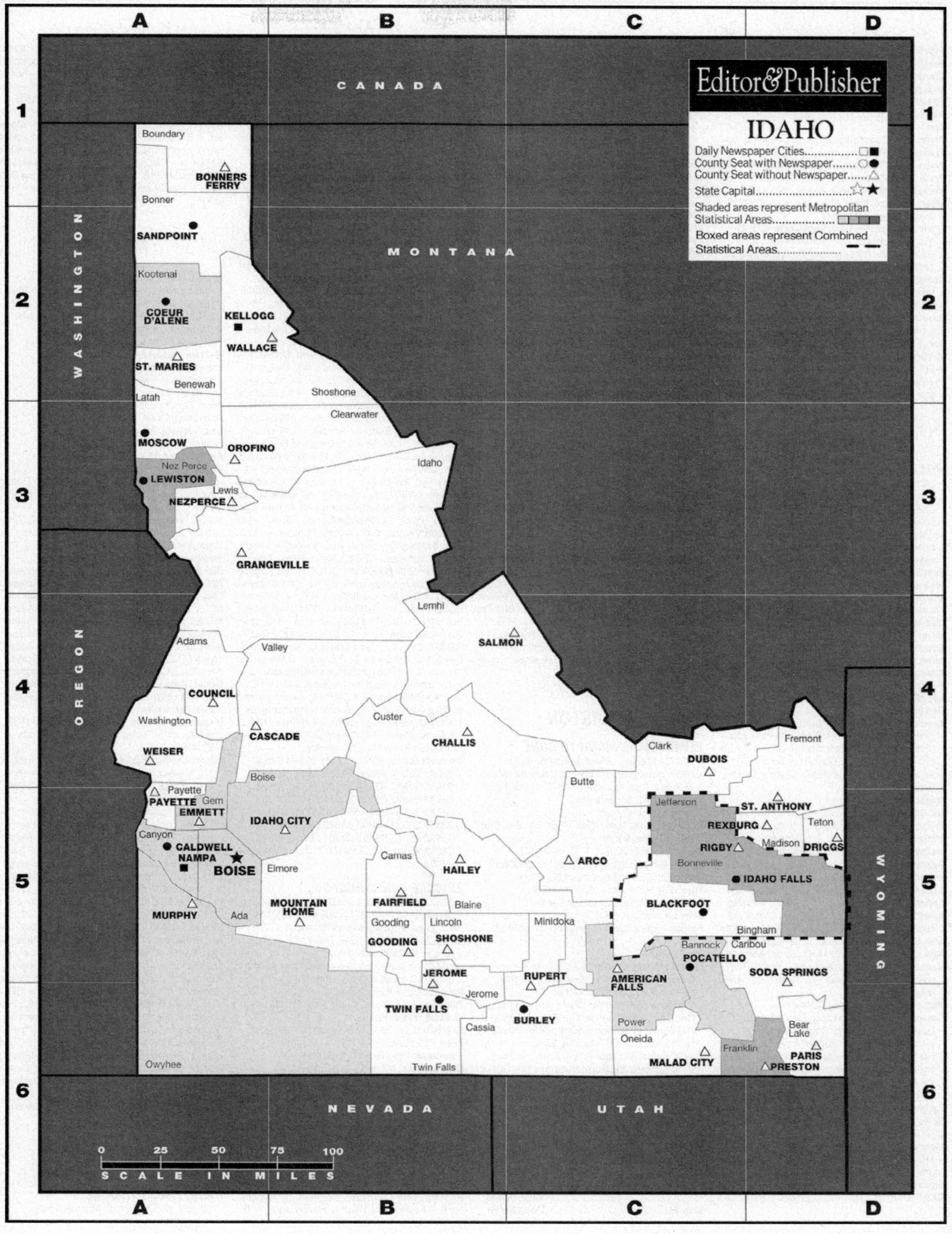
Editor&Publisher
IDAHO
Daily Newspaper Cities
County Seat with Newspaper
County Seat without Newspaper
State Capital
Shaded areas represent Metropolitan Statistical Areas
Boxed areas represent Combined Statistical Areas
CANADA
MONTANA
WASHINGTON
OREGON
WYOMING
NEVADA
UTAH
Boundary
BONNERS FERRY
Bonner
SANDPOINT
Kootenai
COEUR D'ALENE
KELLOGG
WALLACE
ST. MARIES
Benewah
Shoshone
Latah
Clearwater
MOSCOW
OROFINO
Nez Perce
LEWISTON
Idaho
Lewis
NEZPERCE
GRANGEVILLE
Lemhi
SALMON
Adams
Valley
COUNCIL
Washington
CASCADE
Custer
CHALLIS
WEISER
Boise
Payette
PAYETTE
Gem
EMMETT
IDAHO CITY
Butte
Clark
DUBOIS
Fremont
Jefferson
ST. ANTHONY
REXBURG
Teton
Madison
RIGBY
DRIGGS
Bonneville
IDAHO FALLS
Canyon
CALDWELL
NAMPA
BOISE
Elmore
Camas
HAILEY
ARCO
MURPHY
Ada
MOUNTAIN HOME
FAIRFIELD
Blaine
BLACKFOOT
Bingham
Gooding
Lincoln
Minidoka
GOODING
SHOSHONE
Bannock
Caribou
POCATELLO
JEROME
RUPERT
AMERICAN FALLS
SODA SPRINGS
Jerome
TWIN FALLS
BURLEY
Power
Cassia
Oneida
Bear Lake
Franklin
MALAD CITY
PARIS
PRESTON
Owyhee
Twin Falls
0 25 50 75 100
SCALE IN MILES
A B C D
1 2 3 4 5 6

Bus. Mgr./Purchasing Agent ....Frank Granier
Adv. Dir. ....Paul Burke
Classified Adv. Dir. ....Jen Porter
Circ. Dir. ....Dan Phillips
Editorial Page Ed. ....Mike Patrick
News Ed. ....Bill Buley
Sports Ed. ....Mark Nelke
Prodn. Mgr., Composing ....Judd Jones
Prodn. Mgr., Mailroom....................Brad Oliver
Prodn. Mgr., Mailroom....................Sally Botaw
Prodn. Mgr., Pressroom..............Ken Montreuil
Market Information: TMC; Zoned editions.
Mechanical available: Offset; Black and 3 ROP colors; insert accepted.
Mechanical Specifications: Type page 13 x 21 1/2; E - 6 cols, 2 1/16, 1/8 between; A - 6 cols, 2 1/16, 1/8 between; C - 8 cols, 1 3/8, 1/8 between.
Commodity Consumption: Avg. Page Number Per Issue - Daily 40; Avg. Page Number Per Issue - Sunday 72.
Equipment; Editorial Hardware – 1-Dy/Cps 300.; Classified Hardware – 1-Dy/Cps 300.; Production Equipment – 2-Dy/Cps 300; Cameras – 1-K/Vertical 24. PRESSROOM: Line 1 – 4-G/Community.; Inserters and stuffers – 3/M; Bundle tying machines – 1-Bu/PP8-6; Addressing machine – 1-Ch/500PM.

IDAHO FALLS

POST REGISTER

333 Northgate Mile, Idaho Falls, Idaho, 83401; gen tel (208) 522-1800; adv tel (208) 522-1800; gen fax (208) 529-3142; adv fax (208) 529-3142; ed fax (208) 529-9683; adv e-mail bacor@postregister.com; ed e-mail news@postregister.com; web site www.postregister.com
Published: Tues, Wed, Thur, Fri, Sat, Sun
Weekday Frequency: m
Saturday Frequency: m
Circulation: 27,200; 27,200(sat); 29,500(sun)
Last Audit: Sworn September 30, 2009
Price: 13.50/mo; 162.00/yr.
Advertising: Open inch rate $20.25
Insert rate: Variable
News services: AP, SHNS, MCT.
Politics: 1880
Not Published: Christmas.
Own facility?: Y
Special Editions: New Car Guide (Oct); Back to School (Aug); Estate & Financial Planning (Feb); Homemakers School (Mar); Home Improvement/Home & Garden (Monthly); Winter Recreation Guide (Nov); Medical Guide (Apr, Oct).
Magazines: Parade (S).
Dir. Bus. Admin. ....Ivy Berry
Promo./Community Affairs Mgr.....Kate Salomon
Editor and Publisher..................Roger Plothow
Managing Editor......................Rob Thornberry
Opinions Ed...............................Corey Taule
Production and Systems Dir. ....Karen Fioretti
Sales Director.................................Brett Acor
Commercial Printing Mgr.............Mark Merkley
Advertising Manager.........................Mark Hill
Classified Ad. Mgr...........................Hilary Witt
Asst. to the Publisher...............Bonnie Hansen
Market Information: ADS; TMC; Zoned editions.
Mechanical available: Offset; Black and 3 ROP colors; insert accepted - free-standing cards; page cutoffs - 21.
Mechanical Specifications: Contact us.
Commodity Consumption: Avg. Page Number Per Issue - Daily 36; Avg. Page Number Per Issue - Plates Used 20000; Avg. Page Number Per Issue - Sunday 68; widths 12 1/2; Newsprint Used - Metric Tons 2800; Printing Ink Used - Black 49000; Printing Ink Used - Color 16000; Printing In
Equipment; Classified Hardware – DTI; Layout Software – DTI; Production Equipment – All CTP PRESSROOM: Line 1 – 16-unit Goss Magnum; Pasters – Yes; Inserters and stuffers – 1-Goss Magnapak; 1-GMA/SLS 1000; Mailroom control system – Goss Omnizone; Addressing machine – Yes BUSINESS COMPUTERS: Business Software – PBS

KELLOGG

SHOSHONE NEWS-PRESS

401 Main St., Kellogg, Idaho, 83837; gen tel (208) 783-1107; gen fax (208) 784-6791; gen e-mail ccamppell@shoshonenews-press.com; web site www.shoshonenews-press.com
Published: Sun
Circulation: 3,315; 3,315(sat); 28,500(sun)
Last Audit: October 1, 2001
Price: 9.75/mo (carrier), $10.25/mo (motor route); 156.00/yr.
Advertising: Open inch rate $14.52
News services: AP, NEA.
Politics: Independent. **Established:** 1897
Note: The North Idaho Sunday serves the five northern counties in Idaho and is a combined effort of three dailies and three weeklies: Coeur d'Alene Press (m), Sandpoint Bonner County Daily Bee (m), Shoshone News-Press (m), Priest River Times (w), Bonners Ferry
Not Published: Legal holidays.
Special Editions: Progress (Other).
Magazines: Relish (Monthly); The North Idaho Advertiser (Other); Visitor's Guide Tab (Thur); American Profile (Weekly).
Pub. ....Dan Drewry
Adv. Specialist..............................Linn Reese
Office Mgr.........................Christy Champpell
Mng. Ed.....................................Nick Rotunno
Market Information: TMC.
Mechanical available: Offset; Black and 3 ROP colors; insert accepted - any; page cutoffs - 22 3/4.
Mechanical Specifications: Type page 13 x 21 1/2; E - 6 cols, 2 1/16, 1/8 between; A - 6 cols, 2 1/16, 1/8 between; C - 8 cols, 1 1/2, 1/16 between.
Commodity Consumption: Avg. Page Number Per Issue - Daily 18; Avg. Page Number Per Issue - Sunday 72.
Equipment; Editorial Hardware – APP/Mac SE30.; Classified Hardware – 1-APP/Mac SE30.; Production Equipment – 1-Nu. PRESSROOM: Line 1 – 4-G/Community; Folders – 1-G/Community.; Bundle tying machines – 1/It; Addressing machine – 2-/Am.; Business Hardware – 2-DEC/UT220 B2

LEWISTON

LEWISTON MORNING TRIBUNE

505 Capital St., Lewiston, Idaho, 83501-0957; gen tel (208) 743-9411; adv tel (800) 745-9411; adv fax (208) 746-7341; ed fax (208) 746-1185; web site www.lmtribune.com
Published: Mon, Tues, Wed, Thur, Fri, Sat, Sun
Weekday Frequency: m
Saturday Frequency: m
Circulation: 20,626; 20,626(sat); 21,599(sun)
Last Audit: Sworn September 30, 2004
Price: $14.50/mo (dS), $8.70/mo (S).
Advertising: Open inch rate $18.44
News services: AP, MCT.
Politics: Independent-Democrat. **Established:** 1892
Own facility?: Y
Special Editions: Students (Apr); Nez Perce Fair (Aug); Christmas Greeters (Dec); Explorations (Feb); Getting Married (Jan); Coupons (Jul); Health Beat (Jun); Spring Car Care (Mar); Agriculture (May); Getting Ready (Nov); At Home (Oct); From House to Home (Quarterly); Roundup Edition
Special Weekly Sections: Arts & Entertainment (Fri); Agriculture (Mon); Business (S); Outdoors (Thur); Food (Wed).
Magazines: Parade (S).
Broadcast Affiliations: KLEW TV (CBS).
Profile: Daily newspaper and web commercial printing.
Gen. Mgr. ....Wayne Hollingshead
Controller..................................Philip Charlo
Adv. Dir. ....Bob Reitz
Circ. Dir................................Michael McBride
Ed. ....Nathan Alford
Mng. Ed. ....Doug Bauer
City Ed...................................Craig Clohessy
Editorial Page Ed. ....Marty Trillhause
Environmental Ed. ....Eric Barker
Garden Ed...............................Jeanne DePaul
Graphics Ed./Art Dir. ....Brian Beesley
Health/Medical Ed.........................Susan Engle
News Ed.....................................Bill Furstenau
Pressroom Manager.........................Jay Brown
Librarian..................................Phyllis Collins
Market Information: TMC.
Mechanical available: Offset; Black and 3 ROP colors; insert accepted - sample packets; page cutoffs - 22 3/4.
Mechanical Specifications: Type page 12 1/2 x 21 1/2; E - 6 cols, 1 13/16, 1/8 between; A - 6 cols, 1 13/16, 1/8 between; C - 9 cols, 1 1/4, 1/8 between.
Commodity Consumption: Avg. Page Number Per Issue - Daily 32; Avg. Page Number Per Issue - Plates Used 36500; Avg. Page Number Per Issue - Sunday 57; widths 34; Newsprint Used - Metric Tons 2150; Printing Ink Used - Black 105000; Printing Ink Used - Color 12200; Printing Ink U
Equipment EDITORIAL: Front-end Software – QPS 3.3, Microsoft/Windows 98, Dewar/DewarView, Microsoft/Word 6.0, Sybase 11.5, Novell/Netware 4.11, Windows NT 4.0.; Editorial Hardware – AT, Compaq/Windows NT 4.0, Genic/P4 Pentium; Editorial Equipment – Pentium II, Linix; Editorial Printers – HP/5SIMX, HP/8000N CLASSIFIED: Front-end Software – Sybase 11.5, AT/Enterprise, Microsoft/Word 6.0, Microsoft/Word 6.0, AT/Press, Windows NT 4.0.; Classified Hardware – Pentium I; Classified Printers – HP/1200 DISPLAY: Ad make-up applications – Microsoft/Windows 98, Aldus/PageMaker 6.5, Archetype/Corel Draw 3.0, Microsoft/Word 6.0, Adobe/Photoshop 5.0, Macromedia/Freehand 7.0, Adobe/Illustrator; Layout Software – SCS/Layout 8000.; Display Printers – HP 8000N PRODUCTION: Pagination Software – Dewar/View 1.40, QPS/QuarkXPress 3.31, Microsoft/Word 6.0.; Production Equipment – 1-B/5KW, 2-Harlequin/RIP, ECRM/VLR, ECRM/5100; Cameras – 1-C/Spartan III; Scanners – 2-HP/Scanner PRESSROOM: Line 1 – Man Roland Uniset 75; Press Drives – 2; Folders – 2; Pasters – 4; Reels and Stands – 4-Roll/Stand; Press registration system – Stoesser/Register Systems. MAILROOM: Counter stackers – 2-BG/104; Inserters and stuffers – 2-MM/227E; Bundle tying machines – 1-MLN/ML2EE; Addressing machine – 1/MG.; Audio Hardware – Software ☐ PBX audiotext; Business Hardware – Newzware
Zip Codes served: 83501 83541 83524 83540 83545 83544 83520 83553 83546 83827 83539 53533 83554 83530 83522 82526 83549 83552 83525 83531 83832 83535 83843/844 83537 83871 83823 83855 83857 83834 83806 83872 83523 83543 83536 83555 99403 99401 99402 99347 99102 99111 99113 99130 66161 99163/164 99179

TRIBUNE PUBLISHING CO.

505 Capital Street, Lewiston, Idaho, 83501; gen tel (208) 743-9411; adv tel (208) 746-4237; ed tel (208) 848-2272; gen fax (208) 746-7341; adv fax (208) 746-7343; ed fax (208) 746-1185; adv e-mail ads@lmtribune.com; ed e-mail letters@lmtribune.com; web site www.lmtribune.com
Group: Tribune Publishing Co.
Published: Mon, Tues, Wed, Thur, Fri, Sat, Sun
Weekday Frequency: m
Circulation: 22,783; 22,285(sat); 23,985(sun)
Price: 159.00/yr.
Advertising: Open inch rate $19.85
News services: AP and McClatchy
Politics: 1892
Own facility?: Y
Special Weekly Sections: Outdoors, art and entertainment, close to home, opinion, business and Sunday A.M.
Equipment EDITORIAL: Front-end Software – Doris; Editorial Hardware – WXP; Editorial Printers – HP CLASSIFIED: Front-end Software – Aprofit; Classified Hardware – WXP; Classified Printers – HP DISPLAY: Ad make-up applications – Newzware; Display Hardware – WXP; Display Printers – HP PRODUCTION: Pagination Software – Harlequin preps; Production Equipment – Harlequin; Cameras – Nikon; Scanners – HP PRESSROOM: Line 1 – Man Roland; Press Drives – Man Roland; Folders – Man Roland; Pasters – Megtec; Reels and Stands – Megtec MAILROOM: Counter stackers – Rima; Inserters and stuffers – Muellers; Bundle tying machines – Rima AUDIO: Audio Software – Call nanabe Cisco; Audio Hardware – HP BUSINESS COMPUTERS: Business Software – Newzware; Business Hardware – WLK WXP

MOSCOW

MOSCOW-PULLMAN DAILY NEWS

409 S. Jackson St., Moscow, Idaho, 83843; gen tel (208) 882-5561; gen fax (208) 883-8205; ed e-mail editor@dnews.com; web site www.dnews.com
Published: Mon, Tues, Wed, Thur, Fri, Sat
Weekday Frequency: m
Saturday Frequency: m
Circulation: 6,140; 6,500(sat)
Last Audit: Sworn September 30, 2004
Price: 9.83/mo; 110.55/yr.
Advertising: Open inch rate $13.24
News services: AP, SHNS.
Politics: Independent.
Not Published: Memorial Day; Labor Day.
Special Editions: Tax Help (Apr); Fall Ag (Aug); Bridal (Feb); Brides (Jan); Agriculture (Mar); Mother's Day (May); Christmas Opening (Nov); Brides (Oct); Football (Sept).
Special Weekly Sections: Slice of Life (Sat); Arts & Entertainment (Thur); Business (Sat).
Magazines: USA Weekend (Weekly).
Broadcast Affiliations: None
Gen. Mgr. ....Wayne Hollingshead
Adv. Mgr. ....Craig Staszkow
Circ. Mgr. ....Mike McBride
Ed. ....Nathan Alford
Arts Ed. ....Alan Solan
City Ed. ....Murf Raquet
News Ed. ....Alan Solan
Sports Ed. ....Devin Rokyta
Photo Ed............................Geoff Crimmins
Opinion Page Ed............................Murf Raquet
Managing Editor ....Lee Rozen
Market Information: ADS; TMC.
Mechanical available: Offset; Black and 3 ROP colors; insert accepted - all; page cutoffs - 22 3/4.
Mechanical Specifications: Type page 13 x 21 1/2; E - 6 cols, 2 1/16, 1/8 between; A - 6 cols, 2 1/16, 1/8 between; C - 9 cols, 1 3/8, 1/16 between.
Commodity Consumption: Avg. Page Number Per Issue - Daily 22; Avg. Page Number Per Issue - Plates Used 8500; Avg. Page Number Per Issue - Saturday 32; widths 27 1/2; Newsprint Used - Metric Tons 511; Printing Ink Used - Black 20000; Printing Ink Used - Color 2000; Printing Ink
Equipment EDITORIAL: Front-end Software – QPS.; Editorial Hardware – APP/Macs; Editorial Printers – QMS, HP, Xante CLASSIFIED: Front-end Software – Printers ☐ Sony, HP; Classified Hardware – APP/Macs DISPLAY: Ad make-up applications – QPS; Layout Software – APP/Macs.; Display Hardware – APP/Macs; Display Printers – QMS/Laser Printers PRODUCTION: Pagination Software – QPS.; Production Equipment – QMS, Adobe/Photoshop; Cameras – SCREEN; Scanners – Lf, Microtek PRESSROOM: Line 1 – 5-HI/Cotrell V-25; Folders – 1; Reels and Stands – 4-HI/Cotrell. MAILROOM: Counter stackers – 7-KAN/480; Bundle tying machines – 1-MLN/ML2EE.; Business Hardware – CDS
Delivery method: Mail, Newsstand, Private Carrier, Racks

NAMPA

IDAHO PRESS-TRIBUNE

1618 N. Midland Blvd., Nampa, Idaho,

83651; gen tel (208) 467-9251; adv tel (208) 468-9251; ed tel (208) 467-9251; gen fax (208) 467-9562; adv fax (208) 467-1863; ed fax (208) 467-9562; gen e-mail newsroom@idahopress.com; web site www.idahopress.com
Published: Mon, Tues, Wed, Thur, Fri, Sat, Sun
Weekday Frequency: m
Saturday Frequency: m
Circulation: 18,276; 18,276(sat); 20,832(sun)
Last Audit: September 30, 2009
Price: 10.75/mo (city carrier), $11.25/mo (motor route).
Advertising: Open inch rate $21.83
News services: AP, SHNS.
Politics: Independent.
Special Editions: Homemakers School (Apr); Caldwell Night Rodeo (Aug); Holiday Gift Guide (Dec); Cavalcade (Feb); Newcomer's Guide (Jul); Graduation (Jun); Mom of the Year (May); Holiday Delights (Nov); Get Ready for Winter (Oct); Healthy Living (Sept).
Special Weekly Sections: M.O.R.E. (Fri); Health Page (Mon); Family (S); Religion (Sat); Movie Review (Thur); People (Wed).
Magazines: Relish (Monthly); Parade (S).
Broadcast Affiliations: KTVB; KNIN; KTRV; KBCI.
Profile: Daily newspaper, shopper, web site and niche products serving Canyon County, Idaho.
Pub....Rick Weaver
Bus. Mgr....Rhonda McMurtrie
Adv. Supvr., Classified...Becky Thompson
Asst. Mng. Ed....David Woosley
Community Ed....Kaye Steffler
Editorial Page Ed...Vickie Schaffeld Holbrook
Sports Ed....Tom Fox
Prodn. Dir., Mailroom...Joe Hansen
Prodn. Dir., Press...Daniel Paris
Prodn., Post Press...Charlene Holmberg
Market Information: ADS; TMC.
Mechanical available: Offset; Black and 3 ROP colors; insert accepted - almost all; page cutoffs - 21 1/2.
Mechanical Specifications: Type page 12 1/2 x 20 1/2; E - 6 cols, 2 1/16, 1/8 between; A - 6 cols, 2 1/16, 1/8 between; C - 9 cols, 1 3/8, 1/16 between.
Commodity Consumption: Avg. Page Number Per Issue - Daily 32; Avg. Page Number Per Issue - Plates Used 15000; Avg. Page Number Per Issue - Sunday 42; widths 25; Newsprint Used - Metric Tons 1800; Printing Ink Used - Black 4500; Printing Ink Used - Color 1300; Printing Ink Used
Equipment EDITORIAL: Front-end Software – Baseview/NewsEdit Pro 2.0.; Editorial Hardware – APP/Power Mac 8100-80, APP/Mac G3, APP/Mac G4, APP/iMac; Editorial Equipment – Printers ☐ 2-AG/Accuset 1100 CLASSIFIED: Front-end Software – Baseview/Class Manager 3.2.; Classified Hardware – APP/Mac Quadra 630; Classified Printers – APP/Mac ImageWriter, Okidata/320; Display Hardware – 4-APP/Mac IIci, 1-APP/Mac IIfx, 3-APP/Mac Classic, 1-Sun/Sparc ELC. PRODUCTION: Pagination Software – QPS/QuarkXPress 4.0.; Production Equipment – 1-Nu/Flip Top FT 40LNS, AG/P-3400, PS/Laserprinter, 2-Accuset/Imagesetters; Cameras – 2-SCREEN/680C, Sony/MVC-2000 Digital, Canon/RV301-Digital, QuickTake 150; Scanners – APP/Mac, Polaroid/Neg Scanner PRESSROOM: Line 1 – 16-DGM/440. MAILROOM: Counter stackers – Schur; Bundle tying machines – 1-MLN/ML2-EE, Si/LB-News 3000; Other equipment –Consolidated/225, 3/Knife, Stitch-Trimmer. AUDIO: Audio Software – The Vital System 5.04.05; Audio Hardware – New Horizons, ZEOS/486DX/Pantera BUSINESS COMPUTERS: Business Software – Media Plus, PBS, SBS; Business Hardware – Sun/Ultrabox

POCATELLO

IDAHO STATE JOURNAL

305 S. Arthur Ave., Pocatello, Idaho, 83204; gen tel (208) 232-4161; gen fax (208) 233-8007; adv fax (208) 233-1642; adv e-mail adsales@journalnet.com; ed e-mail newsclerk@journalnet.com; web site www.journalnet.com
Published: Mon, Tues, Wed, Thur, Fri, Sat, Sun
Weekday Frequency: m
Saturday Frequency: m
Circulation: 16,361; 16,361(sat); 17,456(sun)
Last Audit: September 30, 2009
Price: 18.75/mo; 225.00/yr.
Advertising: Open inch rate $25.15
News services: AP, MCT, SHNS.
Politics: Independent.
Special Weekly Sections: Church (Fri); Youth Page (Mon); HomeLife (Sat); Escapes (Thur); Teen Page (Tues); Best Food Day (Wed).
Magazines: Parade (S); TV Journal (Sat).
Pub....Bill Kunerth
Office Mgr....Henry Johnson
Circ. Dir....Nathan Slater
Circ. Mgr., Newspapers in Educ./Sales Matthew Plooster
Mng. Ed....Ian Fennell
City Ed....John O'Connell
Community Ed....Jodeane Albright
Photo Ed....Doug Lindley
Sports Ed....Tim Flagstad
Dir., Info Tech Servs....Justin Smith
Market Information: ADS; TMC.
Mechanical available: Offset; Black and 3 ROP colors; insert accepted; page cutoffs - 22 3/4.
Mechanical Specifications: Type page 13 x 21 1/2; E - 6 cols, 2 1/16, 1/8 between; A - 6 cols, 2 1/16, 1/8 between; C - 9 cols, 1 3/8, 1/16 between.
Commodity Consumption: Avg. Page Number Per Issue - Daily 32; Avg. Page Number Per Issue - Plates Used 9000; Avg. Page Number Per Issue - Saturday 32; Avg. Page Number Per Issue - Sunday 62; widths 13 3/4; Newsprint Used - Metric Tons 1300; Printing Ink Used - Black 56032; Pri
Equipment EDITORIAL: Front-end Software – Baseview/NewsEdit, QPS/QuarkXPress 3.32.; Editorial Hardware – APP/Mac; Editorial Printers – HP/4M-2, HP/LaserJet 5000 CLASSIFIED: Front-end Software – Baseview.; Classified Hardware – APP/Mac; Classified Printers – APP/Mac ImageWriter II, HP/LaserJet 4M DISPLAY: Ad make-up applications – QPS/QuarkXPress 4.0, Adobe/Illustrator 6.0, Adobe/Photoshop 5.0; Layout Software – 1-APP/Power Mac 7200, 2-APP/Power Mac 750; Display Printers – APP/Mac Laser Writer IIg, HP/Color LaserJet 4500 PRODUCTION: Pagination Software – QPS/QuarkXPress 4.0.; Production Equipment – AG/Accuset 1000, Graham M28; Cameras – 1-K, 1-Argile/16 x 23; Scanners – Nikon PRESSROOM: Line 1 – 7-G/Urbanite single width 1968; Folders – 1-G/5000; Press registration system – Duarte/Punch System. MAILROOM: Counter stackers – 1/BG; Inserters and stuffers – 2-MM/217E; Bundle tying machines – 2-Si; Other equipment –Mc/Stitcher-Trimmer. AUDIO: Audio Software – Vital System 5.04.05; Audio Hardware – Market Link, Pony/486-66 BUSINESS COMPUTERS: Business Software – PBS; Business Hardware – Sun/Sparc fileserver

POST FALLS

POST FALLS PRESS

PO Box 39, Post Falls, Idaho, 83877-0039; gen tel (208) 773-7502; web site http://www.cdapress.com/

REXBURG

THE STANDARD-JOURNAL

23South 1st East, Rexburg, Idaho, 83440-0010; gen tel (208) 356-5441; gen fax (208) 356-8312; gen e-mail kgeisler@uvsj.com; ed e-mail editor@uvsj.com; web site www.rexburgstandardjournal.com
Group: Pioneer Newspapers
Published: Tues, Wed, Thur, Sat
Weekday Frequency: e
Saturday Frequency: m
Circulation: 5,000; 5,000(sat)
Price: $8 month/ 75.00/yr.
Advertising: Open inch rate $13.50
Insert rate: $55 /M Single Sheet
Politics: 1881
Not Published: Sun, Monday, Wednesday
Own facility?: Y
Audience Development Director..Jeremy Cooley
Publisher...Kristy J. Geisler
Editor...Robert Patten
Mng. Ed....Matt Flitton
Zip Codes served: 83440, 83445

SANDPOINT

BONNER COUNTY DAILY BEE

310 Church St., Sandpoint, Idaho, 83864; gen tel (208) 263-9534; gen fax (208) 263-9091; ed fax (208) 263-9091; ed e-mail bcdailybee@cdapress.com; web site www.bonnercountydailybee.com
Published: Sun
Circulation: 4,537; 4,537(sat); 28,500(sun)
Last Audit: September 25, 2002
Price: 13.00/mo (carrier), 24.00/mo (mail); 156.00/yr (carrier), 288.00/yr (mail).
Advertising: Open inch rate $12.95
News services: AP.
Politics: Independent. **Established:** 1966
Note: The North Idaho Sunday serves the five northern counties in Idaho and is a combined effort of three dailies and three weeklies: Coeur d'Alene Press (m), Bonner County Daily Bee (m), Kellogg Shoshone News-Press (m), Priest River Times (w), Bonners Ferry He
Not Published: Legal holidays.
Special Editions: Spring (Mar); North Idaho Tourist Guide (May); Winter Sports (Nov).
Special Weekly Sections: Best Food Day (Tues).
Magazines: Relish (Monthly); American Profile (Weekly).
Pub....David Keyes
Bus. Mgr....Carolyn Inge
Adv. Dir....Kathy Hubbard
News Ed....Keith Kinnaird
News Room Ed....Caroline Lobsinger
Sports Ed....Eric Plummer
Market Information: TMC.
Mechanical available: Offset; Black and 3 ROP colors; insert accepted; page cutoffs - 22 3/4.
Mechanical Specifications: Type page 13 x 21 1/2; E - 6 cols, 2 1/16, 1/8 between; A - 6 cols, 2 1/16, 1/8 between; C - 8 cols, 1 5/8, 1/8 between.
Commodity Consumption: Avg. Page Number Per Issue - Daily 14; Avg. Page Number Per Issue - Sunday 72.
Equipment; Editorial Hardware – APP/Mac SE.; Classified Hardware – APP/Mac SE.; Production Equipment – DP.; Addressing machine – 1/St.; Business Hardware – CIT

TWIN FALLS

THE TIMES-NEWS

132 Fairfield St. W., Twin Falls, Idaho, 83301-5492; gen tel (208) 733-0931; adv tel (208) 733-0931; ed tel (208) 733-0931; gen fax (208) 734-5538; web site www.magicvalley.com
Published: Mon, Tues, Wed, Thur, Fri, Sat, Sun
Weekday Frequency: m
Saturday Frequency: m
Circulation: 17,508; 17,508(sat); 21,509(sun)
Last Audit: ABC September 30, 2011
Price: 4.35/wk; 205.40/yr.
Advertising: Open inch rate $28.35
News services: AP, LAT-WP, MCT.
Politics: Independent. **Established:** 1904
Special Editions: Fair & Farm (Aug); Summer Fun Guide (May); Home (Sept).
Special Weekly Sections: TV/Entertainment (Fri); Health/Fitness/Fashion (Mon); Business (S); Church Page (Sat); TNT (Thur); Food & Home (Wed).
Magazines: TV Magazine (Fri); Parade (S); Magic Valley Ag Weekly (Sat).
Pub....Brad Hurd
Controller...John Knerler
Adv. Dir....John Pfeifer
Adv. Mgr., Classified...Deby Johnson
Dir., Mktg....Greg Taylor
Circ. Dir....Trisha Mitchell
Ed....James Wright
Ad Weekly Ed....Carol Dumas
Editorial Page Ed....David Cooper
Features Ed....Virginia Huthins
Online Ed....Tracey Emery
Photo Dept. Mgr....R. Ashley Smith
Sports Ed....Matt Christensen
Market Information: ADS; Split run; TMC; Zoned editions.
Mechanical available: Offset; Black and 3 ROP colors; insert accepted; page cutoffs - 21 1/2.
Mechanical Specifications: Type page 12 1/2 x 21 1/2; E - 6 cols, 2 1/16, 1/8 between; A - 6 cols, 2 1/16, 1/8 between; C - 9 cols, 1 3/8, 1/16 between.
Commodity Consumption: Avg. Page Number Per Issue - Daily 36; Avg. Page Number Per Issue - Sunday 52; widths 25; Newsprint Used - Metric Tons 2100; Printing Ink Used - Pages Printed 14800.
Equipment EDITORIAL: Front-end Software – Lotus/Notes 4.6.; Editorial Hardware – Sun, Mk; Editorial Printers – 1-Linotype-Hell/Linotronic 500, ECR/Pelbox, APP/Mac LaserPrinter CLASSIFIED: Front-end Software – Lotus/Notes 4.6.; Classified Hardware – Sun; Classified Equipment – PC 4-286DG; Classified Printers – APP/Mac LaserPrinters DISPLAY: Ad make-up applications – QPS/QuarkXPress; Layout Software – APP/Mac G4.; Display Hardware – APP/Mac G4; Display Printers – 1-Linotype-Hell/Linotronic 500, ECR/Pelbox, APP/Mac LaserWriters; Production Equipment – ECR/Pelbox, Linotype-Hell/Linotronic 500, APP/Mac LaserWriter; Cameras – Canon; Scanners – Truvell, Nikon. PRESSROOM: Line 1 – 7-G/Urbanite (Cole/3 Knife trimmer); Line 2 – 1-G/Urbanite color deck; Folders – 1, 1-G/quarter folder; Press control system – 2-Fin/control, 2-DC Motors/100 h.p.. MAILROOM: Counter stackers – 1-HL/Monitors; Inserters and stuffers – MM/227; Bundle tying machines – MLN; Wrapping singles – Id; Other equipment –MM/Stitcher. AUDIO: Audio Software – Tribune Publishing Company/Vicki; Audio Hardware – In-house, IBM/486; Business Hardware – Sun/Sparc, Compaq

ILLINOIS

ALTON

ALTON TELEGRAPH PRINTING CO.

111 E. Broadway, Alton, Ill., 62002; gen tel (618) 463-2500; gen fax (618) 463-9829

THE TELEGRAPH

111 E. Broadway, Alton, Ill., 62002; gen tel (618) 463-2500; adv tel (618) 463-2550; ed tel (618) 463-2563; gen fax (618) 463-9829; adv fax (618) 463-0951; ed fax (618) 463-9829; gen e-mail telegraph@thetelegraph.com; web site www.thetelegraph.com
Published: Mon, Tues, Wed, Thur, Fri, Sat, Sun
Weekday Frequency: m
Saturday Frequency: m
Circulation: 24,032; 22,873(sat); 25,002(sun)
Last Audit: September 30, 2007
Price: 3.50/wk; 182.00/yr.
Advertising: Open inch rate $39.60
News services: AP, NEA, SHNS.

Politics: Independent. **Established:** 1836
Advertising not accepted: Ads requesting readers to send money for any reason; 900 numbers; unless they publish fee per call.
Special Editions: Senior Living (Apr); Back-to-School (Aug); Wrap it Up (Dec); Focus (Feb); Brides & Grooms (Jan); Bridal Guide (Jul); The Guide (Jun); Home Improvement (Mar); Heroes (May); Holiday Dining (Nov); Car Care (Oct); Fall Home Improvement (Sept).
Special Weekly Sections: Business (Fri); TV Week (S); River Bend Express (Thur); Food (Wed).
Magazines: USA WEEKEND Magazine (S); American Profile (Weekly).
Pub....James E. Shrader
Controller....Rick Thompson
Adv. Dir.....Johnny Aguirre
Circ. Mgr.....Barbara Horstman
Asst. City Ed.....Steve Whitworth
Editorial Page Ed.....Dan Brannan
Medical/Hospital Ed.....Corey Stulce
News Ed....Dennis Grubaugh
Online Ed.....Laura Griffith
Photo Dept. Mgr.....John Badman
Sports Ed.....Pete Hayes
Asst. Sports Ed....Greg Shashack
Mgmt. Info Servs. Mgr.....Everett Hicks
Prodn. Mgr.....Karla Suttles
Prodn. Supvr., Mailroom....Gerald Harrison
Prodn. Foreman, Pressroom....Dave Sweetman
Market Information: TMC; Zoned editions.
Mechanical available: Offset; Black and 3 ROP colors; insert accepted - spadeas, free-standing insert; page cutoffs - 21 3/8.
Mechanical Specifications: Type page 12 x 22 3/4; E - 6 cols, 1 7/8, 1/8 between; A - 6 cols, 1 7/8, 1/8 between; C - 10 cols, 1 1/8, 1/16 between.
Commodity Consumption: Avg. Page Number Per Issue - Daily 33; Avg. Page Number Per Issue - Plates Used 48428; Avg. Page Number Per Issue - Saturday 30; Avg. Page Number Per Issue - Sunday 71; widths 50; Newsprint Used - Short Tons 2210; Printing Ink Used - Black 36230; Printin
Equipment EDITORIAL: Front-end Software – QPS/QuarkXPress, Microsoft/Word.; Editorial Hardware – Compaq; Editorial Equipment – Lf/AP Leaf Picture Desk, APP/Mac, Nikon/Scanner; Editorial Printers – 1-Panasonic/KX P1624, 2-HP/8100; Classified Hardware – Compaq; Classified Printers – 2-HP/8100. DISPLAY: Ad make-up applications – QPS/QuarkXPress, Adobe/Freehand, Multi Ad Creator; Layout Software – APP/Mac.; Display Printers – 3-APP/Mac Scanners PRODUCTION: Pagination Software – QPS/QuarkXPress 6.0.; Production Equipment – 2-Tegra/XP-1000, 2-Tegra/Varityper/XP-1000, 1-Hyphen/Dash 72E; Cameras – 1-Commodore/2638 PRESSROOM: Line 1 – 7-MAN/Uniman 4 x 2 1986; Press Drives – 3-GE/DC 300 1986; Folders – Feb-86; Pasters – 6-MEG 1986; Reels and Stands – 7-MEG 1986. MAILROOM: Counter stackers – 2-HL/Monitor; Inserters and stuffers – 1-MM/4 bay, AM Graphics/NP 848; Bundle tying machines – 1-MLN/ML2EE, 1-MLN/ML2CC; Wrapping singles – Manual; Addressing machine – 1-Cheshire/525-E. BUSINESS COMPUTERS: Business Software – INSI, Transient Management Systems, Vision Data, AR 2000, Great Plains; Business Hardware – IBM/AS-400

ARLINGTON HEIGHTS

DAILY HERALD

155 E. Algonquin Rd., Arlington Heights, Ill., 60005-4617; gen tel (847) 427-4300; adv tel (847) 427-4624; ed tel (847) 427-4300; gen fax (847) 427-1550; adv fax (847) 427-1203; gen e-mail sales@dailyherald.com; adv e-mail sales@dailyherald.com; ed e-mail news@dailyherald.com; web site www.dailyherald.com
Published: Mon, Tues, Wed, Thur, Fri, Sat, Sun
Weekday Frequency: m
Saturday Frequency: m
Circulation: 99,629; 95,939(sat); 107,499(sun)
Last Audit: ABC September 30, 2011
Price: 5.95/wk; 309.40/yr; 42.00/8wk.
Advertising: Open inch rate $133.95 Daily; $136.30 Sunday
Insert rate: Open Full 8 page tab Daily $57, Sunday $59
News services: AP, CSM, RN, Bloomberg.
Politics: Independent. **Established:** 1872
Note: Listing covers 28 editions of the Daily Herald serving markets in Cook, Du Page, Kane, Lake, McHenry and Will counties.
Not Published: NONE
Own facility?: Y
Magazines: USA WEEKEND Magazine (S).
Chrmn. Emeritus....Daniel Baumann
Chairman/Pub./President/CEO....Douglas K. Ray
Vice Chrmn./Exec. Vice Pres. Robert Y. Paddock
Sr. Vice Pres., Director of Content and Strategic Planning....Colin O'Donnell
Sr. Vice Pres./Treasurer....Kent Johnson
Vice Pres./Dir., HR....Betsy Kmiecik
Sr. Vice Pres., Gen. Mgr. and Dir. of Sales Scott Stone
Asst. Vice Pres./Dir., Innovation and Audience Development....M. Eileen Brown
Asst. V.P., Adv. Dir.....Jason Hegna
Adv. Mgr., Div. Sales....Karyn Kraske
Adv. Mgr., Nat'l Sales....Elizabeth Reifert
Asst. Vice Pres./Mgr., Mktg./Promo. James A. Cook
Mgr., Mktg. and Research Servs....John Graham
Circ. Vice Pres.....James J. Galetano
Circ. Mgr.....John G. Janos
Circ. Mgr., New Bus.....Wayne S. Gebis
Circ. Mgr., Single Copy Sales..Joseph M. Marek
Market Information: Split run; TMC; Zoned editions.
Mechanical available: Offset; Black and 3 ROP colors; insert accepted; page cutoffs - 21 1/2.
Mechanical Specifications: Type page 11 1/8 x 21; E - 6 cols, 1 5/7, 2/13 between; A - 6 cols, 1 5/7, 2/13 between; C - 10 cols, 1 1/12, 1/11 between.
Commodity Consumption: Avg. Page Number Per Issue - Daily 84; Avg. Page Number Per Issue - Plates Used 286000; Avg. Page Number Per Issue - Saturday 126; Avg. Page Number Per Issue - Sunday 150; widths 12 1/2; Newsprint Used - Metric Tons 24976; Newsprint Used - Short Tons 275
Equipment EDITORIAL: Front-end Software – Saxotech.; Editorial Hardware – IBM/Netfinity NT Cluster; Editorial Printers – III/Postscript CLASSIFIED: Front-end Software – At/Enterprise.; Classified Hardware – Compaq/Proliant NT Cluster; Classified Printers – III/Postscript DISPLAY: Ad make-up applications – QPS/QuarkXPress, Adobe/Illustrator, Macromedia/Freehand, Adobe/InDesign, Adobe/Acrobat, Adobe/Photoshop, Asura, Soluero; Layout Software – PPI/Plan Page.; Display Hardware – DEC/VAX 1000; Display Printers – Hp/4000 PRODUCTION: Pagination Software – InDesign; Production Equipment – Autologic/Agfa PRESSROOM: Line 1 – MAN/Roland Regioman 48 pages double wide; Line 2 – MAN/Roland Regioman 48 pages double wide; Folders – 2; Pasters – 12; Inserters and stuffers – 3/AM Graphics/630 20:1; Other equipment – Challenge/Cutter. BUSINESS COMPUTERS: Business Software – GEAC, Ledger, Payables; Business Hardware – 2-DEC/VAX 4000-700
Delivery method: Mail, Newsstand, Private Carrier, Racks

AURORA

THE BEACON NEWS

495 N. Commons Dr., Ste. 200, Aurora, Ill., 60504-8295; gen tel (630) 978-8880; gen fax (630) 978-8509; adv e-mail rwall@scn1.com; web site www.suburbanchicagonews.com/beaconnews
Published: Mon, Tues, Wed, Thur, Fri, Sat, Sun
Weekday Frequency: m
Saturday Frequency: m
Circulation: 24,342; 23,604(sat); 25,835(sun)
Last Audit: September 30, 2009
Price: 3.00/wk; 156.00/yr, $208.00/yr (mail); 39.00/13wk, $78.00/6mo.
News services: CNS, AP, NEA, NYT.
Politics: Independent.
Note: Suburban Chicago Newspapers includes the Aurora Beacon News (mS), Elgin Courier News (mS), Joliet Herald News (mS), Naperville Sun (mS) and Waukegan Lake County News-Sun (e). The group combination rate is $170.50 (dS). Individual newspaper rates not made
Special Editions: Destination Spring Travel (Apr); Windfall of Homes (Aug); Readers Choice Awards (Dec); Auto Show (Feb); Health Extra (Jan); Education Outlook (Jul); Wedding Planner (Jun); Education Outlook (Mar); Education Outlook (Nov); Home Improvement (Oct); Windfall
Special Weekly Sections: Religion (Fri); Real Estate Showcase (S); New Homes (Sat); Go (Thur); Food (Wed).
Magazines: TV Program Guide (S); USA WEEKEND Magazine (Sat).
Pres./Pub.....Fred Lebolte
HR Dir.....Kathy Earley
Adv. Vice Pres.....Robert Wall
Mgr., Promo.....Christine Weber
Ed.....Rick Nagel
Assoc. Ed.....John Russell
News Ed.....Tom Johnson
Photo Ed.....Marianne Mather
Special Sections Ed.....Dan Waitt
Sports Ed.....Chris Sosa
Market Information: ADS; Split run; TMC; Zoned editions.
Mechanical available: Offset; Black and 3 ROP colors; insert accepted - single sheet, product samples; page cutoffs - 22 3/4.
Mechanical Specifications: Type page 13 x 21; E - 6 cols, 2 1/25, 1/6 between; A - 6 cols, 2 1/8, 1/6 between; C - 10 cols, 1 3/16, 1/16 between.
Commodity Consumption: Avg. Page Number Per Issue - Daily 30; Avg. Page Number Per Issue - Sunday 44; widths 27; Newsprint Used - Metric Tons 1953; Printing Ink Used - Black 44000; Printing Ink Used - Color 13000; Printing Ink Used - Pages Printed 11800.
Equipment EDITORIAL: Front-end Software – SII.; Editorial Hardware – Cybergraphics/; Editorial Printers – HP CLASSIFIED: Front-end Software – Centronics/Print Station 351.; Classified Hardware – Cybergraphics; Classified Printers – HP DISPLAY: Ad make-up applications – DTI; Layout Software – DTI.; Display Hardware – APP/Mac; Display Printers – APP/Mac LaserWriter; Business Hardware – DEC/VAX

THE COURIER NEWS

Same, Aurora, Ill., 60504; gen tel 630-978-8168; adv tel 630-978-8310; ed tel 630-978-8168; gen fax 630-978-8184; ed fax 630-978-8184; gen e-mail news@stmedianetwork.com; adv e-mail ilkclassified@stmedianetwork.com; ed e-mail news@stmedianetwork.com; web site courienewsonline.com
Published: Mon, Tues, Wed, Thur, Fri, Sun
Weekday Frequency: m
Saturday Frequency: m
Circulation: 8,717; 8,717(sat); 8,786(sun)
Last Audit: September 30, 2009
Price: 3.00/wk; 156.00/yr, $208.00/yr (mail).
News services: AP, Sun-Times Media
Politics: Independent. **Established:** 1875
Not Published: Saturday
Own facility?: N
Special Editions: Destination Spring Travel (Apr); Windfall of Homes (Aug); Readers Choice (Dec); Auto Show (Feb); Health Extra (Jan); Education Outlook (Jul); Health Extra (Jun); Education Outlook (Mar); Health Extra (Nov); Home Improvement (Oct); Health Extra (Sept).
Special Weekly Sections: Auto (Daily); Entertainment (Friday); New Homes (Friday)
Magazines: TV Week (Fri); USA WEEKEND Magazine (S).
Bus. Ed.....Nick Petersen
News Ed.....Marty O'Mara
Sports Ed.....R.J. Gerber
Commodity Consumption: Avg. Page Number Per Issue - Daily 22; Avg. Page Number Per Issue - Sunday 66; widths 41 1/4; Newsprint Used - Metric Tons 3103; Printing Ink Used - Black 106500; Printing Ink Used - Color 12400; Printing Ink Used - Pages Printed 10911.
Equipment CLASSIFIED: Front-end Software – Dewar.; Classified Hardware – AST/386; Classified Printers – Dataproducts DISPLAY: Ad make-up applications – CJ; Layout Software – CJ.; Display Hardware – Dewar; Business Hardware – CJ
Delivery method: Mail, Newsstand, Private Carrier, Racks

THE NAPERVILLE SUN

495 N. Commons Drive, Aurora, Ill., 60504; gen tel (630) 978-8825; gen fax (630) 978-8832; gen e-mail thesun@scn1.com; web site www.suburbanchicagonews.com
Group: Sun Times Media
Published: Wed, Fri, Sun
Weekday Frequency: All day
Circulation: 13,543; 13,399(sun)
Last Audit: Sworn September 30, 2009
Price: 13.00/wk; 26.00/mo; 79.30/yr.
Note: Suburban Chicago Newspapers includes the Aurora Beacon News (mS), Elgin Courier News (mS), Joliet Herald News (mS), Naperville Sun (mS) and Waukegan Lake County News-Sun (e). The group combination rate is $170.50 (dS). Individual newspaper rates not made
Advertising not accepted: Y
Magazines: USA WEEKEND Magazine (S).
Advertising Sales Manager....Mary Kulak
Mechanical Specifications: Type page 11 x 13; E - 5 cols, 2 1/16, between; A - 5 cols, 2 1/16, between; C - 8 cols, 1 3/16, between.
Delivery method: Newsstand, Private Carrier, Racks

BELLEVILLE

BELLEVILLE NEWS-DEMOCRAT

120 S. Illinois St., Belleville, Ill., 62220-0427; gen tel (618) 234-1000; adv fax (618) 235-0556; ed fax (618) 234-9597; gen e-mail letters@bnd.com; adv e-mail adinfo@bnd.com; ed e-mail newsroom@bnd.com; web site www.bnd.com
Published: Mon, Tues, Wed, Thur, Fri, Sat, Sun
Weekday Frequency: m
Saturday Frequency: m
Circulation: 47,129; 44,675(sat); 57,576(sun)
Last Audit: ABC September 30, 2011
Price: 3.25/wk (home delivery); 169.00/yr; 42.25/13wk.
Advertising: Open inch rate $69.00
News services: NYT, AP.
Politics: Independent.
Special Editions: Baseball (Apr); Fall Bridal (Aug); Wrap it Up (Dec); Home Builders' Show Tab (Feb); Auto Show Tab (Jan); Active Times (Jul); Senior Citizens Tab (Jun); Home Improvement Tab (Mar); Metro East Information Tab (May); Christmas Wishbook (Nov); Auto Care Tab (
Special Weekly Sections: Home/Fashion (Fri); Parenting/School (Mon); TV Magazine (S); Religion (Sat); Entertainment (Thur); Medicine/Science (Tues); Food (Wed).
Magazines: Parade (S).
Pres./Pub.....Jay Tebbe
Mktg. Ed.....Brandy Steely
Adv. Mgr., Classified....Brenda Fedak
Dir., HR/Mktg.....Jeanne Newton
Circ. Dir.....John Grove
Circ. Mgr.....Eric Freeman
Exec. Ed.....Jeff Couch
City Ed.....Gary Dotson
Editorial Page Ed.....Lori Browning
Librarian....Carla Anderson
Lifestyle Ed.....Patrick Kuhl
News Ed.....Candace Mount
Chief Photographer....Tim Vizer
Sports Ed.....Joseph Ostermeier
Prodn. Mgr., Pressroom....Larry Hofmeister
Prodn. Foreman, Composing....Mary Feltman

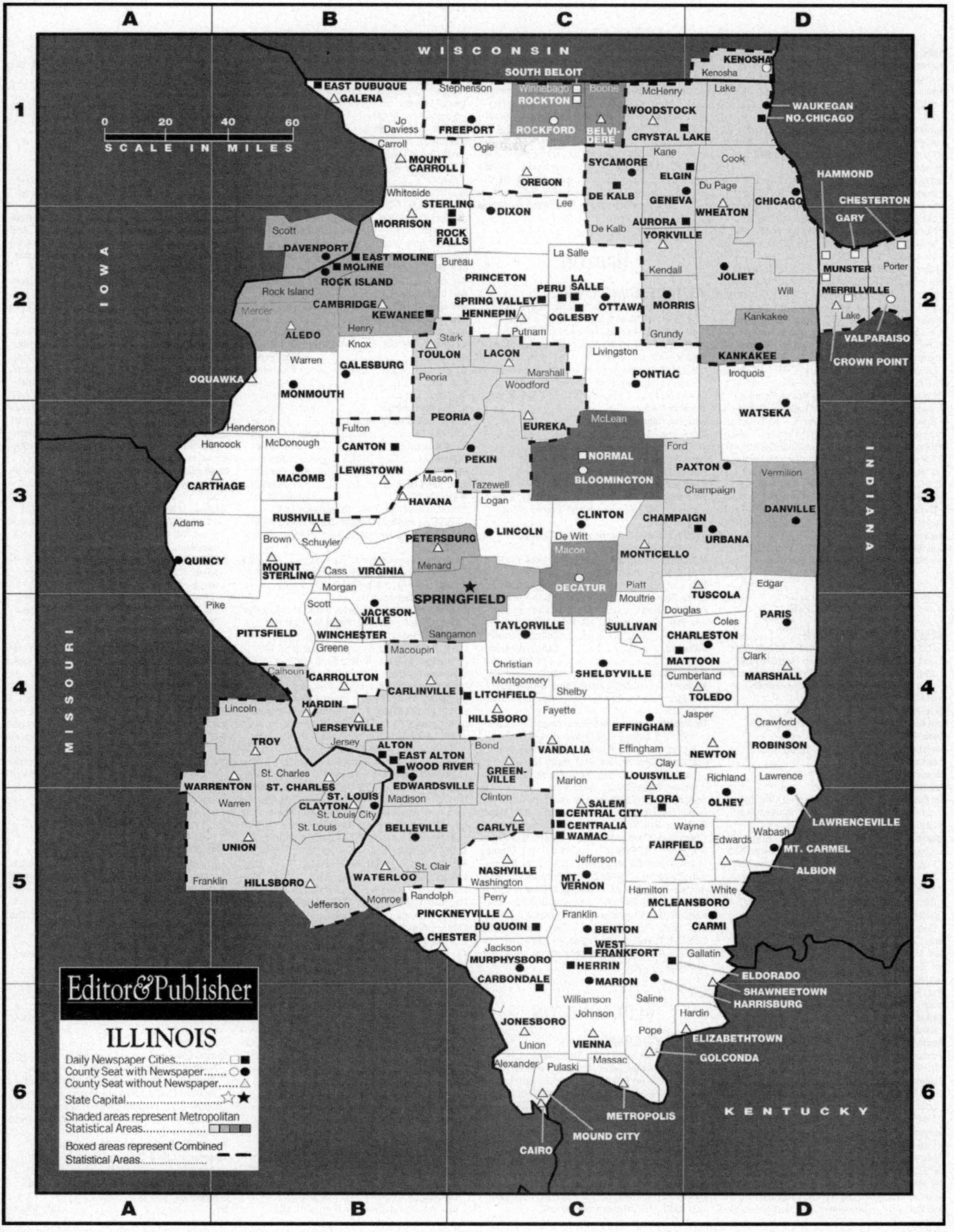

Editor&Publisher
ILLINOIS
Daily Newspaper Cities
County Seat with Newspaper
County Seat without Newspaper
State Capital
Shaded areas represent Metropolitan Statistical Areas
Boxed areas represent Combined Statistical Areas
SCALE IN MILES
WISCONSIN
IOWA
MISSOURI
INDIANA
KENTUCKY
SPRINGFIELD
CHICAGO
PEORIA
ROCKFORD
BLOOMINGTON
NORMAL
DECATUR
CHAMPAIGN
URBANA
JOLIET
DANVILLE
QUINCY
GALESBURG
KANKAKEE
EDWARDSVILLE
BELLEVILLE
ALTON
CARBONDALE
CAIRO
ST. LOUIS
DAVENPORT
ROCK ISLAND
MOLINE
GARY
HAMMOND
VALPARAISO

Prodn. Foreman, Mailroom.............Don Bradley
Market Information: Split run; TMC; Zoned editions.
Mechanical available: Offset; Black and 3 ROP colors; insert accepted; page cutoffs - 22 3/4.
Mechanical Specifications: Type page 11 3/5 x 21 1/2; E - 6 cols, 1 7/9, 1/6 between; A - 6 cols, 1 7/9, 1/6 between; C - 10 cols, 1 1/12, 1/6 between.
Commodity Consumption: Avg. Page Number Per Issue - Daily 36; Avg. Page Number Per Issue - Plates Used 32700; Avg. Page Number Per Issue - Saturday 42; Avg. Page Number Per Issue - Sunday 64; widths 25; Newsprint Used - Metric Tons 6000; Printing Ink Used - Black 139500; Print
Equipment EDITORIAL: Front-end Software – Baseview.; Editorial Hardware – APP/Mac Client Server; Editorial Printers – APP/Mac, Dataproducts/ CLASSIFIED: Front-end Software – PPI.; Classified Hardware – PC; Classified Printers – Pre Press/Panther Pro 46 Imagesetter DISPLAY: Ad make-up applications – In-house; Layout Software – MEI/ALS.; Display Hardware – DEC/VAX; Display Printers – HP PRODUCTION: Pagination Software – Baseview 4.1.; Production Equipment – Pre Press/Panther Pro Imagesetter; Cameras – C/Spartan; Scanners – Epson PRESSROOM: Line 1 – 14-G/Urbanite; Line 2 – 7-G/Community; Folders – G/Urbanite, 1-G/Folder w/balloon, 2-G/Community Folders, 1. MAILROOM: Counter stackers – 1-HL/Monitor, 2-HL/Monitor, 1-QWI/Sport, 1-HL/HT; Inserters and stuffers – GMA/SLS 1000 8:2, GMA/SLS 2000; Bundle tying machines – 1-Dynaric/NP2, Dynaric/NP2, 1-Dynaric/NP1, 1-Dynaric/NP2, 1-Dynaric/NP2; Addressing machine – GMA/Inkjet BUSINESS COMPUTERS: Business Software – Microsoft/Office; Business Hardware – APP/Mac, PC, DEC/VAX

BELVIDERE

BELVIDERE REPUBLICAN

130 S. State St., Belvidere, Ill., 61008-3630; gen tel (815) 547-0084; gen fax (815) 547-3045; ed e-mail bdrnews@rvpublishing.com; web site www.belvideredailyrepublican.net
Published: Tues, Wed, Fri
Circulation: 4,136
Last Audit: Estimate September 30, 2000
Price: 7.00/mo; 85.00/yr.
Advertising: Open inch rate $13.50
Insert rate: $35.00/M.
News services: AP, NEA.
Politics: Republican.
Not Published: New Year; Memorial Day; Independence Day; Labor Day; Thanksgiving; Christmas.
Special Editions: Farming (Apr); Fair (Aug); Christmas Greetings (Dec); Tax Guide (Feb); Progress (Jan); Information Guide (Jul); Spring (Mar); Senior (May); Super Saver Coupons (Monthly); Early Christmas Gift (Nov); Health & Fitness (Oct); Fall (Sept).
Special Weekly Sections: Youth Page (Mon); Business (Tues); Best Food Day (Wed).
Pub...............................Pete Cruger
Gen. Mgr...............................Randy Johnson
Adv. Sales..............................Debra Warner
Circ. Mgr...............................Lindy Sweet
Mng. Ed...................Melanie Bradley Marshall
Prodn. Mgr...............................Linda Lano
Market Information: Split run; TMC; Zoned editions.
Mechanical available: Offset; Black and 3 ROP colors; insert accepted - any; page cutoffs - 22 3/4.
Mechanical Specifications: Type page 10 1/4 x 13; E - 5 cols, 2 1/14, 1/12 between; A - 5 cols, 2 1/14, 1/12 between; C - 8 cols, 1 2/5, 1/12 between.
Commodity Consumption: Avg. Page Number Per Issue - Daily 18.
Equipment EDITORIAL: Front-end Software – QPS/QuarkXPress, Baseview/NewsEdit.; Editorial Hardware – APP/Mac; Editorial Printers – NewGen/Imager Plus 12 CLASSIFIED: Front-end Software – Baseview/Classified.; Classified Hardware – APP/Mac; Classified Printers – APP/Mac LaserWriter Plus; Display Hardware – APP/Mac. PRODUCTION: Pagination Software – Baseview/NewsEdit.; Production Equipment – 3-APP/Mac 9500, APP/Mac 7100; Cameras – 3-APP/Mac 9500, APP/Mac 7100; 1-R; Scanners – APP/Mac PRESSROOM: Line 1 – 8-G/Suburban 1993. MAILROOM: Counter stackers – 1-BG/Count-O-Veyor; Inserters and stuffers – 1/Mc; Bundle tying machines – 4-/Bu; Addressing machine – 1-/Am, 1-/MG BUSINESS COMPUTERS: Business Software – QPS, Baseview/NewsEdit; Business Hardware – 3-TC

BENTON

BENTON EVENING NEWS

111 E. Church St., Benton, Ill., 62812; gen tel (618) 438-5611; adv tel (618) 438-5611; ed tel (618) 438-5611; gen fax (618) 435-2413; adv fax (618) 435-2413; ed fax (618) 435-2413; gen e-mail terrak@clearwave.com; web site www.bentoneveningnews.com
Published: Mon, Tues, Wed, Thur, Fri, Sat, Sun
Weekday Frequency: e
Saturday Frequency: m
Circulation: 3,472; 3,472(sat)
Last Audit: September 28, 2002
Price: 10.50/mo; 116.00/yr.
Advertising: Open inch rate $10.75
News services: AP.
Not Published: New Year; Memorial Day; Independence Day; Labor Day; Thanksgiving; Christmas.
Special Editions: Progress (Mar); Todays Women (Quarterly).
Magazines: American Profile (Fri); USA WEEKEND Magazine (Sat).
Pub...............................Daniel Malkovich
Office. Mgr...............................Diana Packard
Adv. Mgr., Retail..................Terra Kerkemeyer
Adv. Mgr., Classified.........Sandy Vukadinovich
Circ. Mgr...............................Stmisty Darnell
Online Ed...............................Diana Winson
Sports Ed...............................Phil Knapper
Prodn. Mgr...............................Michelle Boner
Mechanical available: Laser; Black and 3 ROP colors; insert accepted - all; page cutoffs - 21 1/2.
Mechanical Specifications: Type page 12 x 21 1/2; E - 6 cols, 2, 1/6 between; A - 6 cols, 2, 1/6 between; C - 8 cols, 1 1/2, 1/6 between.
Commodity Consumption: Avg. Page Number Per Issue - Daily 14; Avg. Page Number Per Issue - Saturday 20; widths 25.
Equipment EDITORIAL: Front-end Software – Microsoft/Word.; Editorial Hardware – APP/iMac; Editorial Printers – APP/Mac LaserWriter II; Classified Hardware – APP/iMac; Classified Printers – APP/Mac LaserWriter II.; Display Hardware – APP/iMac. PRODUCTION: Pagination Software – QPS/QuarkXPress 3.31.; Production Equipment – Adobe/Photoshop 2.5; Cameras – SCREEN/Companica 680C; Scanners – Nikon/Coolscan, Scanmaker II XE; Bundle tying machines – 1/Bu. BUSINESS COMPUTERS: Business Software – Nomads/Listmaster; Business Hardware – Club America

BLOOMINGTON

THE PANTAGRAPH

301 W. Washington St., Bloomington, Ill., 61701; gen tel (309) 829-9000; adv tel (309) 829-9000; ed tel (309) 829-9000; adv fax (309) 829-9104; ed fax (309) 829-7000; gen e-mail mailbox@pantagraph.com; adv e-mail advertising@pantagraph.com; ed e-mail newsroom@pantagraph.com; web site www.pantagraph.com
Published: Mon, Tues, Wed, Thur, Fri, Sat, Sun
Weekday Frequency: m
Saturday Frequency: m
Circulation: 39,349; 35,755(sat); 42,786(sun)
Last Audit: ABC September 30, 2011
Price: 4.30/wk; 18.20/mo; 218.40/yr.
Advertising: Open inch rate $80.70
News services: AP, McClatchey.
Politics: Independent. **Established:** 1837
Special Editions: Spring Home & Garden I (Apr); Football Fever (Aug); Agri-Business (Feb); Health (Jan); Readers Choice (Jul); How To Guide (Jun); Annual Report (Mar); Community Guide (May); Hometown Holidays (Nov); Auto Preview (Oct); Fall Home & Garden II (Sept).
Special Weekly Sections: Home Market (Real Estate Guide) (Fri); Sunday Comics (spot, full color) (S); Select TV (Sat).
Magazines: Relish (Monthly); Parade (S); American Profile (Wed).
Pub...............................Richard Johnston
Gen. Mgr...............................Barry L. Winterland
Adv. Dir...............................Loretta Vance
Adv. Dir., Sales..............................Shannon Brinker
Adv. Mgr., Classified Sales......Bernard Beoletto
Adv. Mgr., Majors/Nat'l..............................Steve Lahr
Mktg. Servs. Mgr...............................Jonell Kehias
Community Rel. Dir...........Wendy Montgomery
Circ. Dir...............................Bob Scott
Ed..............................Mark Pickering
Mng. Ed...............................Julie Gerke
Bus. Ed...............................Karen Hansen
Capitol Bureau Chief..............................Kurt Erickson
Columnist/Online Producer..................Bill Flick
Day Desk Ed...............................Jane Pickering
Entertainment Ed...............................Dan Craft
Features Ed...............................Chuck Blystone
Health Ed...............................Paul Swiech
Asst. News Ed...............................Dan McNeile
Night City Ed...............................Roger Miller
Market Information: TMC; Zoned editions.
Mechanical available: Offset; Black and 3 ROP colors; insert accepted; page cutoffs - 21 1/2.
Mechanical Specifications: Type page 11 5/8 x 21 1/4; E - 6 cols, 1 13/16, 1/8 between; A - 6 cols, 1 13/16, 1/8 between; C - 9 cols, 1 3/16, 1/8 between.
Commodity Consumption: Avg. Page Number Per Issue - Daily 40; Avg. Page Number Per Issue - Plates Used 80000; Avg. Page Number Per Issue - Sunday 60; widths 37 1/2; Newsprint Used - Metric Tons 5080; Newsprint Used - Short Tons 5600; Printing Ink Used - Black 110000; Printing
Equipment EDITORIAL: Front-end Software – QPS/QuarkXPress 4.11.; Editorial Hardware – 50-Compaq/2000 Desk Pro, Compaq/Proliant 1600, Novell 4.11; Editorial Equipment – APP/Server; Editorial Printers – HP/8100 CLASSIFIED: Front-end Software – Mactive 2.21.; Classified Hardware – Mactive/SOL 2000, Compaq/ML530 Server, 25-Dell/Pentium III; Classified Printers – HP/4M Plus DISPLAY: Ad make-up applications – Multi-Ad/Creator 6.5; Layout Software – DPS/AD-Tracker.; Display Hardware – 12-APP/Mac, Compaq/Proiant ML370; Display Printers – HP/1050 Plotter, 1-HP/8150, 1-HP/5500 DN PRODUCTION: Pagination Software – APP/Mac; Production Equipment – Nu/Flip Top, HP/1050, MON/RIP Express ImageMaster 1000, 2-MON/RIP Express Imagemaster 1500; Cameras – C/Marathon; Scanners – 1-AG/1236X 325, 1-AG/Duoscan T1200, Kk/RFS 2035, Epson/836 XL, Microtech/9800 XL, AG/Duoscan F40 PRESSROOM: Line 1 – 9-G/Cosmo 3516 1975; Folders – 1-G/3:2; Reels and Stands – 7-G/3516. MAILROOM: Counter stackers – 1-Id/NS660, 1-HL/Monitor, HT/II; Inserters and stuffers – 2-GMA/SLS 1000; Bundle tying machines – 2/MLN, 2-/Dynaric; Wrapping singles – 1-QWI/Underwrap, 1-SH/Underwrap; Addressing machine – 1-Ch/596. BUSINESS COMPUTERS: Business Software – In-house; Business Hardware – 1-IBM/AS-400E

CANTON

DAILY LEDGER

53 W. Elm St., Canton, Ill., 61520; gen tel (309) 647-5100; gen fax (309) 647-4665; adv fax (309) 649-1047; adv e-mail ads@cantondailyledger.com; web site www.cantondailyledger.com
Published: Mon, Tues, Wed, Thur, Fri, Sat, Sun
Weekday Frequency: e
Saturday Frequency: m
Circulation: 5,428; 5,428(sat)
Last Audit: October 9, 2001
Price: 122.00/yr.
Advertising: Open inch rate $12.30
News services: AP.
Politics: Independent. **Established:** 1849
Not Published: New Year; Memorial Day; Independence Day; Labor Day; Thanksgiving; Christmas.
Special Editions: Lawn & Garden (Apr); Agriculture (Aug); Christmas Wishbook (Dec); Agriculture (Feb); Income Tax (Jan); Bridal (Jul); Father's Day (Jun); Car Care (Mar); Home Improvement (May); Turkey Give-away (Nov); Home Improvement (Oct); Pre-Labor Day (Sept).
Magazines: Channel Guide (Fri); American Profile (Weekly).
Pub...............................Scott Koon
Bus. Mgr...............................Carla Spotser
Adv. Mgr...............................Jackie Caulkins
Features Ed...............................Larry Eskridge
News Ed...............................John Froehling
Online Ed...............................Linda Woods
Sports Ed...............................Steve Shank
Prodn. Mgr...............................Darin Smith
Prodn. Mgr., Composing...........Debbie Roberts
Prodn. Mgr., Post Press..................Rick Bybee
Market Information: TMC.
Mechanical available: Offset; Black and 3 ROP colors; insert accepted; page cutoffs - 22 3/4.
Mechanical Specifications: Type page 12 x 21 1/2; E - 6 cols, 1 3/4, 1/8 between; A - 6 cols, 1 3/4, 1/8 between; C - 8 cols, 1 3/16, 1/16 between.
Commodity Consumption: Avg. Page Number Per Issue - Daily 14; Avg. Page Number Per Issue - Plates Used 3500; widths 12 1/2; Newsprint Used - Short Tons 458; Printing Ink Used - Black 19500; Printing Ink Used - Color 3900; Printing Ink Used - Pages Printed 4770.
Equipment; Editorial Hardware – APP/Mac G4.; Classified Hardware – APP/Mac G4.; Production Equipment – 3-APP/Mac G4, Pre Press/Panther ImageSetter; Cameras – 1-SCREEN; Scanners – SCREEN C/680, C. PRESSROOM: Line 1 – 6-G/Community; Folders – 1; Press control system – G/Community 50DC (Suburban Control).; Bundle tying machines – Bu/67590; Addressing machine – Dispensa-Matic/16; Other equipment –3-K/Trimmer.; Business Hardware – 2-IBM/PC

CARBONDALE

THE SOUTHERN ILLINOISAN

710 N. Illinois Ave., Carbondale, Ill., 62901-1283; gen tel (618) 529-5454; gen fax (618) 457-2935; web site www.southernillinoisan.com
Published: Mon, Tues, Wed, Thur, Fri, Sat, Sun
Weekday Frequency: m
Saturday Frequency: m
Circulation: 25,845; 25,816(sat); 33,471(sun)
Last Audit: ABC September 30, 2011
Price: 3.50/wk; 14.00/4wk; 169.00/yr.
Advertising: Open inch rate $59.10
News services: AP, MCT, SHNS, TMS.
Not Published: National Holidays (less Christmas)
Own facility?: Y
Special Editions: Spring Lawn & Garden (Apr); Football Preview (Aug); Holiday Wishes (Dec); Auto Racing (Feb); Southern Illinois Tourism Guide (Jan); Jackson City Visitor's Guide (Jul); Locally Owned Business (Jun); Spring Home Improvement (Mar); Southern Illinois Guide (M
Special Weekly Sections: Flipside (Thur).
Magazines: Life & Style in Southern Illinois (quarterly); Southern Business Journal (monthly); Parade (S); American Profile (Weekly).
Ed...............................Gary Metro

Mng. Ed. ....Mark Fitton
Editorial Page Ed. ....Marilyn Helstead
Features Ed. ....Cara Recine
Sports Ed. ....Les Winkeler
Prodn. Mgr. ....Bill Brasher
Prodn. Mgr., Pre Press ....David Fiedler
Publisher ....Bob Williams
Advertising Director ....Jason Woodside
Marketing & Circulation Director Trisha Woodside
Pub. ....Dennis DeRossett
Adv. Coord., Nat'l ....Brien Hays
Circ. Mgr. ....John Russell
Photo Ed. ....Chuck Novara
Opns. Mgr. ....Abby Hatfield
Market Information: ADS; Split run; TMC; Zoned editions.
Mechanical available: Offset; Black and 3 ROP colors; insert accepted - We-Prints; page cutoffs - 22 3/4.
Mechanical Specifications: Type page 12 x 21 1/2; E - 6 cols, 1 7/8, 5/32 between; A - 6 cols, 1 7/8, 5/32 between; C - 6 cols, 1 7/8, 5/32 between.
Commodity Consumption: Avg. Page Number Per Issue - Daily 32; Avg. Page Number Per Issue - Plates Used 41000; Avg. Page Number Per Issue - Sunday 76; widths 25; Newsprint Used - Metric Tons 1930; Newsprint Used - Short Tons 2865; Printing Ink Used - Black 90000; Printing Ink U
Equipment EDITORIAL: Front-end Software – HI.; Editorial Hardware – HI; Editorial Printers – HP CLASSIFIED: Front-end Software – HI.; Classified Hardware – HI; Classified Printers – HP/8000 DISPLAY: Ad make-up applications – HI; Layout Software – HI/PLS.; Display Hardware – HI/XP-21; Display Printers – HP/AU PRODUCTION: Pagination Software – HI/AU.; Production Equipment – AU/Laser, Lf/AP Leaf Picture Desk, HI; Cameras – 1-C/Spartan III; Scanners – AU, Nikon/Scanner, Umax/Powerlook 2, Astra, HP/ScanJet 5P PRESSROOM: Line 1 – 8-G/Urbanite (balloon former); Folders – 2-G/2:1, 1-G/1:4; Reels and Stands – 8-G/Stands. MAILROOM: Counter stackers – 1/HI; Inserters and stuffers – 2-MM/270, 8-/HI; Bundle tying machines – 1-/Sa, 2-Si; Addressing machine – Ch; Other equipment –Normandy.; Business Hardware – IBM/AS-400
Zip Codes served: Southern Illinois
Delivery method: Mail, Newsstand, Private Carrier, Racks

CARMI

CARMI TIMES

323 E. Main St., Carmi, Ill., 62821; gen tel (618) 382-4176; gen fax (618) 384-2163; adv e-mail advertising@carmitimes.com; ed e-mail editorial@carmitimes.com; web site www.carmitimes.com
Published: Mon, Tues, Wed, Thur, Fri
Weekday Frequency: e
Circulation: 2,718
Last Audit: September 29, 2003
Price: 9.75/mo; 113.00/yr.
Advertising: Open inch rate $10.92
News services: AP.
Politics: Independent.
Not Published: New Year; Memorial Day; Independence Day; Labor Day; Thanksgiving; Christmas.
Adv. Mgr. ....Linda Prince
Circ. Mgr. ....Brenda Pennington
City News Ed. ....Braden Willis
Online Ed. ....Barry Cleveland
Society/Women's Ed. ....Twaila Bridges
Sports Ed. ....Toby Brown
Market Information: TMC.
Mechanical available: Offset; Black and 3 ROP colors; insert accepted; page cutoffs - 21 1/2.
Mechanical Specifications: Type page 13 x 21 1/2; E - 6 cols, 2, 1/8 between; A - 6 cols, 2, 1/8 between; C - 8 cols, 1 1/2, 1/16 between.
Commodity Consumption: Avg. Page Number Per Issue - Daily 10; widths 27 1/2; Newsprint Used - Metric Tons 200; Printing Ink Used - Pages Printed 3000.
Equipment EDITORIAL: Front-end Software – Microsoft/Word, Aldus/PageMaker.; Editorial Hardware – 5-APP/Mac Plus, 1-APP/Mac Classic, 1-APP/Mac Classic II; Editorial Printers – APP/Mac LaserWriter II, APP/Mac ImageWriter DISPLAY: Ad make-up applications – Aldus/PageMaker, Aldus/FreeHand; Layout Software – 2-APP/Mac SE, 1-APP/Mac IIsi.; Display Printers – 1-APP/Mac LaserWriter II NTX; Production Equipment – X, 1-LU. PRESSROOM: Line 1 – 1-G; Line 2 – G.; Addressing machine – 1/Am, 1-Ap/Mac ImageWriter.

CENTRALIA

MORNING SENTINEL

232 E. Broadway, Centralia, Ill., 62801-9110; gen tel (618) 532-5604; adv tel (618) 532-5604; ed tel (618) 532-5601; gen fax (618) 532-1212; adv fax (618) 532-1212; gen e-mail news@morningsentinel.com; web site www.morningsentinel.com
Published: Mon, Tues, Wed, Thur, Fri, Sat, Sun
Weekday Frequency: m
Saturday Frequency: m
Circulation: 13,926; 13,926(sat); 13,926(sun)
Last Audit: September 30, 2009
Price: 1.50/wk; 78.00/yr (carrier).
Advertising: Open inch rate $10.50
News services: AP.
Politics: Independent. **Established:** 1863
Not Published: New Year; Memorial Day; Independence Day; Labor Day; Thanksgiving; Christmas.
Special Weekly Sections: Church (Fri); Lifestyles (Mon-fri); Farm (S); Lifestyles (Sat); Education (Thur).
Magazines: Telly Times (Fri); Comics (S).
Office Mgr. ....Julie Copple
Pub. ....John Perrine
Pub. ....William Perrine
Adv. Mgr. ....Daniel Nichols
Circ. Dir. ....Chuck Koepke
Farm Ed./Features Ed. ....Judith Joy
Sr. Ed. ....LuAnn Droege
Prodn. Supvr., Composing ....Terri Kelly
Prodn. Mgr. ....Dave Hurley
Market Information: Split run; TMC; Zoned editions.
Mechanical available: Offset; Black and 3 ROP colors; insert accepted - 3 x 5 in size to 15 x 11 1/2; page cutoffs - 22 3/4.
Mechanical Specifications: Type page 13 x 21 1/4; E - 6 cols, 2 3/16, 1/16 between; A - 6 cols, 2 3/16, 1/16 between; C - 8 cols, 2 1/16, 1/16 between.
Commodity Consumption: Avg. Page Number Per Issue - Daily 23; Avg. Page Number Per Issue - Plates Used 5614; Avg. Page Number Per Issue - Sunday 64; widths 16 1/2; Newsprint Used - Metric Tons 750; Printing Ink Used - Black 6000; Printing Ink Used - Color 100; Printing Ink Use
Equipment: Editorial Hardware – 13-Mk, 1-APP/Mac.; Classified Hardware – Mk/1100 Plus, 2-Mk. DISPLAY: Ad make-up applications – QPS/QuarkXPress, Adobe/Illustrator; Layout Software – 2-Mk/Ad Comp, APP/Mac Quadra 650, APP/Mac.; Display Printers – QMS/860, APP/Mac LaserWriter II; Production Equipment – 2-M/202, APP/Mac LaserWriter, APP/Mac LaserWriter II, QMS/860, Hyphen/Spectraset 2400; Cameras – 1-R/481; Scanners – AG/Arcus, Kk/RFS Film Scanner. PRESSROOM: Line 1 – 6-G/Urbanite Offset 1972; Folders – 1; Reels and Stands – 6-G/Roll Stand.; Inserters and stuffers – 1/MM; Bundle tying machines – 2-/Bu; Addressing machine – Ultra Comp/PC (with Panasonic Printer for Labels).

CHARLESTON

MID-ILLINOIS NEWSPAPERS

307 6th St., Charleston, Ill., 61920; gen tel (217) 345-7085; gen fax (217) 345-7090

CHICAGO

CHICAGO DEFENDER

4445 S. King Dr., Chicago, Ill., 60653; gen tel (312) 225-2400; adv tel (312) 225-2400; ed tel (312) 225-2400; gen fax (312) 225-6954; adv fax (312) 225-9231; ed fax (312) 225-9231; ed e-mail editorial@chicagodefender.com; web site www.chicagodefender.com
Group: Real Times Media, Inc.
Published: Wed
Weekday Frequency: m
Circulation: 14,479
Last Audit: March 31, 2011
Price: 36.00/yr (mail).
News services: NNPA, AP.
Politics: 1905
Not Published: Mon, Tue, Thu, Fri, Sat, Sun
Special Editions: Easter Special (Apr); Back-to-School (Aug); Shopping Guide (Christmas-Kwanzaa) (Dec); African-American History Month (Feb); Dr. Martin Luther King, Jr. (Jan); Health & Fitness (Jun); Career Week (Mar); Healthcare & Wellness (Nov); Financial (Sept).
Broadcast Affiliations: NBC; WGN (TV); WVON radio.
President ....Michael House
Managing Editor ....Kathy Chaney
CFO, Dir. of Fin & Bus Op ....Carol Bell
Mechanical available: Offset; Black and 3 ROP colors.
Mechanical Specifications: Type page 10 1/4 x 12 1/4; E - 5 cols, 2 1/16, 1/8 between; A - 5 cols, 2 1/16, 1/8 between; C - 5 cols, 2 1/16, 1/8 between.
Commodity Consumption: Avg. Page Number Per Issue - Weekly 36
Delivery method: Mail, Newsstand, Racks

CHICAGO SUN-TIMES

350 N. Orleans St., 10th Fl., Chicago, Ill., 60654-1700; gen tel (312) 321-3000; gen fax (312) 321-2299; adv fax (312) 321-9655; web site www.suntimes.com
Group: Metro Newspaper Advertising Services, Inc.
Published: Mon, Tues, Wed, Thur, Fri, Sat, Sun
Weekday Frequency: m
Saturday Frequency: m
Circulation: 389,353; 239,368(sat); 400,506(sun)
Last Audit: ABC September 30, 2011
Advertising: Open inch rate $608.00
News services: AP, UPI, DJ, LAT-WP, RN, Chicago City News Bureau.
Politics: Independent.
Special Editions: Baseball Preview (Apr); Education Guide (Aug); 10 Days & Counting (Dec); Black History Month (Feb); Bride & Groom (Jan); Bride & Groom (Jul); Education Guide (Mar); Mother's Day Greeting Ads (May); Holiday Gift Guide (Nov); Bulls/NBA Preview (Oct); Energy
Special Weekly Sections: Autotimes (Fri); Autotimes (Mon); TV Preview (S); Autotimes (Wed).
Magazines: USA WEEKEND Magazine (S).
Chrmn./CEO, Sun-Times Media Grp. Jeremy Halbreich
Pub. ....John Barron
Vice Pres., Labor Rel. (Chicago Sun-Times/Chicago Grp.) ....Ted Rilea
Adv. Vice Pres. ....Gladys Arroyo
Adv. Vice Pres., Classified ....Jim Dyer
Adv. Dir., Art/Entertainment/Local Markets David D. Ruiz
Adv. Vice Pres., Cor. Accts ......Dean R. Spencer
Adv. Dir., Local ....Dave Sherman
Vice Pres., Mktg. ....Willie Wilkov
Strategic Mktg. Mgr. ....Josephine Lisuzzo
Circ. Dir., Distr. ....Michael Perrone
Circ. Dir., Opns. ....Peter Belluomini
Circ. Dir., Sales ....Robert Edwards
Circ. Dir., Single Copy Sales ....Sandra Mather
Ed. in Chief ....Don Hayner
Mng. Ed. ....Andrew Herrmann
Asst. to Ed. ....Toby Roberts
Bus. Ed. ....Polly Smith
Editorial Cartoonist ....Jack Higgins
Editorial Page Ed. ....Tom McNamee
Market Information: ADS; Split run; TMC; Zoned editions.
Mechanical available: Offset; Black and 3 ROP colors; insert accepted - Polybags; page cutoffs - 23 9/16.
Mechanical Specifications: Type page 10 1/4 x 12; E - 6 cols, 1 9/16, 1/6 between; A - 6 cols, 1 9/16, 1/6 between; C - 8 cols, 1 3/16, 1/8 between.
Commodity Consumption: Avg. Page Number Per Issue - Daily 128; Avg. Page Number Per Issue - Plates Used 544674; Avg. Page Number Per Issue - Sunday 144; widths 57 1/2; Newsprint Used - Metric Tons 80000; Printing Ink Used - Black 1424457; Printing Ink Used - Color 667071; Prin
Equipment EDITORIAL: Front-end Software – AT 7.0.; Editorial Hardware – 8-AT/J-11, 200-IBM/486 DX-2; Editorial Equipment – 25-AT, IBM/RS 6000, 15-IBM/Power PC CLASSIFIED: Front-end Software – AT 7.0.; Classified Hardware – 4-AT/J-11, 60-IBM/486 DX-2; Classified Equipment – 2-AT, 2-IBM/RS 6000 pagination DISPLAY: Ad make-up applications – Multi-Ad/Creator.; Display Hardware – 12-APP/Mac; Display Printers – 3-AU/6600; Production Equipment – 3-AU/APS-5, Na, 1-Kk/Kodamatic 24, 1-P/Lith; Cameras – 2-C/Newspager, 1-C/Marathon, 1-C/Spartan III; Scanners – 1-SCREEN/608G Color Scanner. PRESSROOM: Line 1 – 21-G/Mark I Headliner; Line 2 – 21-G/Mark I Headliner; Line 3 – 24-G/Mark I Headliner; Folders – 10; Reels and Stands – 8-W/C-SE-5B, 1-W/CFP, 12-G/Digital Pilot, 21-G/Amplidine, 12-G/Selsyn. MAILROOM: Counter stackers – 12-HL/Sta-Hi ZS7S, 2-HL/Dual Carrier; Inserters and stuffers – 2-S/272P, 1/AM Graphics/2299; Bundle tying machines – 12-MLN/MLN2A, 9-/Power Strap/PSN6; Addressing machine – PC Systems.; Business Hardware – 1-IBM/370

CHICAGO TRIBUNE

435 N. Michigan Ave., Chicago, Ill., 60611; gen tel (312) 222-3232; adv tel (800) 974-7520; ed tel (312) 222-3001; gen fax (312) 222-2595; gen e-mail tribletter@tribune.com; adv e-mail classadinfo@tribune.com; ed e-mail metro@tribune.com; sports@tribune.com; sunday@tribune.com; business@tribune.com; web site www.chicagotribune.com
Group: Towmar Representaciones S.A.
Published: Mon, Tues, Wed, Thur, Fri, Sat, Sun
Weekday Frequency: m
Saturday Frequency: m
Circulation: 425,370; 335,417(sat); 781,128(sun)
Last Audit: ABC September 30, 2011
Price: 4.40/wk; 228.80/yr.
Advertising: Open inch rate $1,135.00
News services: AP, RN, NYT, TMS, DJ, MCT.
Politics: Independent.
Special Editions: Education Today-Summer (Apr); Fall Fashion (Aug); Year in Pictures (Dec); Cruise Planner (Feb); Winter Breaker (Jan); Golf (Jun); Education Today-Spring (Mar); Midwest Vacations (May); Ski Time (Nov); Follow the Sun (Oct); Fall/Winter Cruises (Sept).
Special Weekly Sections: Friday (Fri); Business Technology (Mon); Transportation (S); New Homes (Sat); Cars (Thur); Good Eating (Wed).
Magazines: Parade (S).
Broadcast Affiliations: WLS-TV Chicago ABC; WBBM-TV Chicago CBS; FOX-TV Chicago FOX; WMAQ-TV Chicago NBC; WTTW-TV Chicago PBS.
Pub. ....Tony Hunter
Sr. Vice Pres./Gen. Mgr. ....Richard Malone
Vice Pres., Finance/CFO ....Phil Doherty
Vice Pres., HR ....Janice Jacobs
Vice Pres., Devel. ....Owen Youngman
Dir., Technical Devel. ....Scott Tafelski
Dir., Technical Opns./Help Desk ....Sarp Uzkan
Dir., Client Servs. ....Deepak Agarwal
Adv. Sr. Vice Pres. ....Robert Fleck
Adv. Vice Pres., Sales ....Douglas Thomas
Adv. Vice Pres., Interactive ....Joe Farrell
Adv. Dir., Classified ....Barbara Swanson
Adv. Dir., Devel. ....Kathy Manilla

Adv. Dir., Network......................Ron Goldberg
Adv. Dir., Devel......................Susan Zukrow
Adv. Dir., Planning/Analysis......Margaret Durkin
Adv. Dir., Preprint......................John Wollney
Adv. Dir., Regl. Accounts.............Steve Brooks
Sr. Mgr., Multimedia Mktg..........Tom Garritano
Dir., Brand Mktg.......................Kelly Shannon
Market Information: Split run; TMC; Zoned editions.
Mechanical available: Offset; Black and 3 ROP colors; insert accepted - product samples,cd's,shopping bags; page cutoffs - 22.
Mechanical Specifications: Type page 13 x 21; E - 6 cols, 2 1/16, 1/8 between; A - 6 cols, 2 1/16, 1/8 between; C - 9 cols, 1 3/8, 1/16 between.
Commodity Consumption: Avg. Page Number Per Issue - Daily 56; Avg. Page Number Per Issue - Plates Used 1300000; Avg. Page Number Per Issue - Sunday 80; widths 41 1/4; Newsprint Used - Metric Tons 200000; Printing Ink Used - Black 4000000; Printing Ink Used - Color 1000000; Pri
Equipment EDITORIAL: Front-end Software – CCI Newsdesk 5.5.5.22t.; Editorial Hardware – PC Workstations/CCI Newsdesk; Editorial Printers – Xerox/Phaser 4400N CLASSIFIED: Front-end Software – Coyote/3 Client 51136.vvvv.001.; Classified Hardware – Dell/Optiplex GX100 Workstation; Classified Printers – HP/Laserjet 5, HP/LJ 4000, HP LJ4050, HP/LJ 4100, HP/LJ 4500, HP/LJ 4600, Lexmark/4226 DISPLAY: Ad make-up applications – CCI Addesk 5.5.5adp38h; Display Hardware – Mac/PC Workstations; Display Printers – Xerox/Phaser 4400N, HP/1050, HP/2000 PRODUCTION: Pagination Software – cci Newsdesk 5.5.5.22t.; Production Equipment – 3-Mk/Lasercompll, 3-Xenotron/UX 90, 2-L/300, 1-L/500, 1-Pixel, 1-Lynart; Cameras – 1-SCREEN/Rollmatic 475 PRESSROOM: Line 1 – 90-G/Metroliner offset presses (2 color decks per press), 8-G/Metroliner Offset Units, 3, 1, 1; Line 2 – 10-RKW/Metrocolor Press Units(Added to end of existing presses), 9-G/Metroliner Offset Units, 2, 1; Line 3 – 9-G/Metroliner Offset Units, 2, MAILROOM: Counter stackers – 25-SH/257S, HL/HT, 17-Quipp/350, 9-Quipp/400, 12-Quipp/350 Stackers; Inserters and stuffers – 5-S/72P, 1-HI/1372P, AM Graphics/NP 2299, AM Graphics/NP100, 4-Heidelberg/2299 with 22 hoppers, 2-Heidelberg/2299 with 21 hoppers, 3-Harris; Business Hardware – 4-DEC/KL 10, IBM/3083 JX3, IBM/3090-18 E, IBM/4381-R14

TIMES-COURIER

2110 Woodfall Dr #10, Charleston, Ill., 61920-3058; gen tel (217) 345-7085; web site www.jg-tc.com
Published: Mon, Tues, Wed, Thur, Fri, Sat
Weekday Frequency: m
Saturday Frequency: m
Circulation: 4,817; 4,724(sat)
Last Audit: ABC September 30, 2011

THE WALL STREET JOURNAL-CENTRAL EDITION

1 S. Wacker Dr., Ste. 2100, Chicago, Ill., 60606-4677; gen tel (312) 750-4000; adv tel (312) 750-4020; ed tel (312) 750-4104; adv fax (312) 750-4009; ed fax (312) 750-4153; ed e-mail newseditors@wsj.com; web site www.wsj.com
Not Published: Presidents' Day; Memorial Day; Independence Day; Labor Day; Thanksgiving; Christmas.
Gen. Mgr.................................Daniel Bernard
Mechanical available: Offset; Black and 3 ROP colors; insert accepted; page cutoffs - 22 3/4.
Commodity Consumption: Avg. Page Number Per Issue - Daily 54.
Equipment; Production Equipment – 7-Douthitt, 5-W, 2-Nu; Cameras – 2-C/Spartan III, 1-C/Newspager; Scanners – 2-ECR. PRESSROOM: Line 1 – 12-G/Metro-Double Width; Line 2 – 12-G/Metro-Double Width; Line 3 – 12; Line 4 – 12; Line 5 – 12; Line 6 – 12; Line 7 – 12; Press Drives – 2, 3, 7; Folders – 3-G/Metro, 4; Pasters – 30, 40; Reels and Stands – 30, 40; Press control system – 7 MAILROOM: Counter stackers – 14/QWI; Bundle tying machines – 19-/OVL, 16-/Sterling, 8-/Power Strap; Addressing machine – 14-/CCL.; Business Hardware – 3-IBM/3090

CLINTON

CLINTON JOURNAL

111 S. Monroe St., Clinton, Ill., 61727; gen tel (217) 935-3171; adv tel (217) 935-3171; ed tel (217) 935-3171; gen fax (217) 935-6086; adv fax (217) 935-6086; ed fax (217) 935-6086; ed e-mail news@clintondailyjournal.com; web site www.theclintonjournal.com
Group: News Media Corporation
Published: Tues, Fri, Sat
Circulation: 1,800; 6,500(sat)
Last Audit: Sworn November 25, 2008
Advertising: Open inch rate $15.90
Advertising not accepted: Y
Not Published: M, W Th, Sat, Sun
Own facility?: N
Circ. Mgr...............................Diane Robertson
Ed....Gordon Woods
Katy Pyne
Susan Munoz
Mechanical Specifications: Type page 11 1/2 x 21 1/2; E - 8 cols, 1 3/4, 1/8 between; A - 8 cols, 1 3/4, 1/8 between; C - 8 cols, 1 3/4, 1/8 between.
Delivery method: Mail, Private Carrier, Racks

CRYSTAL LAKE

NORTHWEST HERALD

7717 S. Rte. 31, Crystal Lake, Ill., 60014; gen tel (815) 459-4040; adv tel (815) 459-4040; ed tel (800) 589-8910; gen fax (815) 477-4960; adv fax (815) 477-4960; ed fax (815) 459-5640; gen e-mail information@shawmedia.com; adv e-mail advertising@shawmedia.com; ed e-mail tips@nwherald.com; web site www.nwherald.com
Group: Shaw Media
Published: Mon, Tues, Wed, Thur, Fri, Sat, Sun
Weekday Frequency: m
Saturday Frequency: m
Circulation: 31,192; 31,192(sat); 34,666(sun)
Last Audit: ABC September 30, 2011
Price: 4.50/wk; 234.00/yr
News services: AP, Gatehouse, Washington Post/Bloomberg News Service, Illinois Statehouse News
Politics: 1851
Note: Production outsourced to commercial printer.
Own facility?: Y
Special Editions: Medley of Homes (Apr); Prep Football Guide (Aug); Last Minute Gift (Dec); Progress (Feb); Books of Lists (Jan); Summer Home & Garden (Jun); Spring Home Improvement (Mar); Hometown Holidays (Nov); Every Thing for Your Home (Sept), Chicago Bears Football Preview
Special Weekly Sections: Wheels (Fri), Sidetracks (Thurs), Savor (Wed), Screen (Fri), Neighbors (Sat), Slice (Sun & Tues)
Magazines: Relish (Monthly); USA Weekend (Weekly); American Profile (Weekly), Spry (Monthly), Athlon Sports (Monthly)
Publisher......................................John Rung
VP/News & Content..........................Chris Krug
Editor...Dan McCaleb
VP/Finance...................................Stacia Hahn
VP/Production................................Kevin Elder
Advertising Director.......................Mike Harvel
I.T. Director................................Steve Sulouff
Classified Manager........................Shelly Bissell
VP/Marketing & Circulation...........Kara Hansen
Major/National Ad Director.............Jim Ringness
Adv. Vice Pres...............................J. Tom Shaw
VP/Marketing & Circulation...........Kara Hansen
Mng. Ed., Interactive Media...........Mike Weiler
Community News Ed., Bus..........Chris Freeman
Features Ed............................Scott Helmchen
Sports Ed.......................................Eric Olson
Prodn. Mgr., Pressroom................Kevin Lyons
Equipment EDITORIAL: Front-end Software – Roxen; Editorial Hardware – Mac CLASSIFIED: Front-end Software – VisionData; Classified Hardware – Sun/Mac DISPLAY: Ad make-up applications – InDesign; Display Hardware – Mac BUSINESS COMPUTERS: Business Software – VisionData; Business Hardware – Sun/Mac
Zip Codes served: McHenry County
Delivery method: Newsstand, Private Carrier, Racks

DANVILLE

COMMERCIAL NEWS

17 W. North St., Danville, Ill., 61832-5765; gen tel (217) 446-1000; adv tel (217) 447-5115; ed tel (217) 447-5155; gen fax (217) 446-9825; ed fax (217) 446-6648; gen e-mail info@dancomnews.com; ed e-mail newsroom@dancomnews.com; web site www.commercial-news.com
Published: Mon, Tues, Wed, Thur, Fri, Sat, Sun
Saturday Frequency: m
Circulation: 11,194; 11,194(sat); 12,801(sun)
Last Audit: September 30, 2009
Price: 2.85/wk.
Advertising: Open inch rate $21.00
News services: AP, SHNS.
Politics: Independent. **Established:** 1866
Special Editions: Turn the Key (Monthly).
Special Weekly Sections: Farm Page (Fri); Home Place (Thur); Best Food Day (Wed).
Magazines: Televiev (Fri); USA WEEKEND Magazine (S).
Pub...Chris Voccio
Circ. Dir...................................Kevin Cothron
Ed....Larry Smith
City Ed...Mary Wicoff
Sports Ed.......................................Chad Dare
Prodn. Dir.................................Garry Swaney
Prodn. Mgr., Mailroom.............Michelle Besse
Market Information: TMC; Zoned editions.
Mechanical available: Offset; Black and 3 ROP colors; insert accepted - 3 x 5 cards, single sheets 8 1/2 x 11; page cutoffs - 22 3/4.
Mechanical Specifications: Type page 11 5/8 x 21 1/2; E - 6 cols, 1 5/6, 1/8 between; A - 6 cols, 1 5/6, 1/8 between; C - 9 cols, 1 3/8, 1/8 between.
Commodity Consumption: Avg. Page Number Per Issue - Daily 24; Avg. Page Number Per Issue - Plates Used 52196; Avg. Page Number Per Issue - Sunday 48; widths 25; Newsprint Used - Metric Tons 1256; Newsprint Used - Short Tons 1384; Printing Ink Used - Black 30449; Printing Ink U
Equipment EDITORIAL: Front-end Software – APT/editorial.; Editorial Hardware – PC's; Editorial Printers – Unity, Ultra, H550, HP CLASSIFIED: Front-end Software – APT/Classified.; Classified Hardware – PC's; Classified Printers – Unity/Ultra 4550, HP DISPLAY: Ad make-up applications – QPS/QuarkXPress, Adobe/Pagemaker; Layout Software – APT/Display.; Display Printers – Deskjet 1600, HP4, 4550 PRODUCTION: Pagination Software – APT 2.06.04, QPS/QuarkXPress 4.0.; Production Equipment – 1-Nu, Ultra, 1-LS/2600R; Cameras – 1-C/Spartan III; Scanners – XRS 6C 24bit Color Scanner, Unimak Mirage D-16L, Polaroid Sprintscan 35 PRESSROOM: Line 1 – 6-HI/845; Folders – 1-HI/2:1; Reels and Stands – 6, 6-CW/Reel. MAILROOM: Counter stackers – 1-Quipp/350, 1-Compass/Compass; Inserters and stuffers – 1-GMA/SLS 1000 (10:1); Bundle tying machines – 1-Sterling/MN45, 2-Sterling/Portables; Addressing machine – 1/KAN.; Business Hardware – 1-IBM/AS-400 CE-10, 1-DEC/PDP 11-70

DE KALB

NORTHERN ILLINOIS PUBLISHING CO.

1586 Barber Greene Rd., De Kalb, Ill., 60115; gen tel (815) 756-4841; gen fax (815) 756-2079

DECATUR

HERALD & REVIEW

601 E. William St., Decatur, Ill., 62523; gen tel (217) 429-5151; adv tel (217) 421-6920; ed tel (217) 421-6979; gen fax (217) 421-6913; adv fax (217) 421-6913; ed fax (217) 421-7965; gen e-mail hrnews@herald-review.com; ed e-mail hrnews2@herald-review.com; web site www.herald-review.com
Published: Mon, Tues, Wed, Thur, Fri, Sat, Sun
Weekday Frequency: m
Saturday Frequency: m
Circulation: 28,018; 28,018(sat); 43,089(sun)
Last Audit: ABC September 30, 2011
Price: 3.80/wk (dS), $1.87/wk (satS); 197.60/yr (dS), $97.50/yr (satS).
Advertising: Open inch rate $55.85
News services: AP, Metro Surburbia Inc..
Politics: Independent.
Special Editions: Christmas Storybook (Other).
Special Weekly Sections: Entertainment (Fri); Business (S); Religion/Family (Sat); Teens (Thur); Food/Health (Wed).
Magazines: Parade (S).
Pub....Todd Nelson
Controller......................Stephen C. Brodbeck
Ed...Gary Sawyer
Mng. Ed....................................David Dawson
Reporter.............................Robert Fallstrom
Bus. Ed........................................Scott Perry
Entertainment Ed.............................Tim Cain
Opinion Page Ed..........................Dave Dawson
Exec. Sports Ed...........................Mark Tupper
Sports Ed...................................Mike Albright
Data Processing Supvr..................Karen Woare
Tech. Servs. Mgr........................Brad Marshall
Online Mgr............................Beth McCormick
Prodn. Mgr., Press...............Chuck Rutherford
Market Information: ADS; Split run; TMC; Zoned editions.
Mechanical available: Flexography; Black and 3 ROP colors; insert accepted; page cutoffs - 21 5/8.
Mechanical Specifications: Type page 13 x 21 1/2; E - 6 cols, 2 1/16, 1/8 between; A - 6 cols, 2 1/16, 1/8 between; C - 9 cols, 1 3/8, 1/16 between.
Commodity Consumption: Avg. Page Number Per Issue - Daily 28; Avg. Page Number Per Issue - Plates Used 37005; Avg. Page Number Per Issue - Sunday 68; widths 50; Newsprint Used - Metric Tons 3486; Printing Ink Used - Black 98100; Printing Ink Used - Color 35974; Printing Ink Us
Equipment; Editorial Hardware – CText/Dateline-Expressline; Editorial Printers – AG/Avantra 25.; Classified Hardware – CText/Advision ALPS; Classified Printers – AG/Avantra 25. DISPLAY: Ad make-up applications – QPS/QuarkXPress; Layout Software – MEI/ALS.; Display Hardware – Cascade Dataflow/Image Flow; Display Printers – AG/Avantra 25; Production Equipment – 2-AG/Avantra 25 Laser Drum Imager, 1-Na/Consolux; Cameras – C/Spartan III; Scanners – Kk/2035, Pixelcraft/8200. PRESSROOM: Line 1 – KBA/Colormax 1994; Folders – H/Double 3:2. MAILROOM: Counter stackers – 1-HL/Monitor, 2-QWI/300, 1-QWI/351; Inserters and stuffers – 1-MM/227 5:1, HI/1372, Phillipsburg/6:1; Bundle tying machines – 2/Power Strap/PSN6, 3-MLN/2A, 2-Bu/String Tyer; Wrapping singles – 2-/Bu; Addressing machine – 1-BH/Mg 1530,; Business Hardware – IBM/AS-400

DIXON

B.F. SHAW PRINTING CO.

113-115 Peoria Ave., Dixon, Ill., 61021; gen tel (815) 284-2222; gen fax (815) 284-2870

SAUK VALLEY NEWSPAPERS

113 S. Peoria Ave., Dixon, Ill., 61021; gen tel (815) 284-2224; adv tel (815) 284-2222; ed tel (815) 284-2222; gen fax (815) 625-9390; adv fax (815) 626-5365; ed fax (815) 625-9390; ed e-mail news@svnmail.com; web site www.saukvalley.com
Published: Mon, Tues, Wed, Thur, Fri, Sat, Sun

Weekday Frequency: e
Saturday Frequency: e
Circulation: 17,684; 18,146(sun)
Last Audit: ABC September 30, 2011
Price: 3.00/wk; 12.55/mo; 147.00/yr; 39.00/13wk, $75.00/26wk.
News services: AP, CNS, SHNS.
Politics: Republican. **Established:** 1851
Note: The Dixon Telegraph (e, wknd) has a combination rate of $30.27 with The Sterling Daily Gazette (e, wknd). Individual newspaper rates not made available.
Not Published: New Year; Memorial Day; Independence Day; Labor Day; Thanksgiving; Christmas.
Special Editions: Career Guide (Apr); Whiteside County Fair (Aug); Last Minute Gift Guide (Dec); Internet Directory (Feb); Health & Fitness (Jan); Dixon Sidewalk Sale (Jul); Dixon Petunia Festival (Jun); Home & Garden (Mar); Today's Farm (May); Senior Echo (Monthly); Baske
Special Weekly Sections: Church News (Fri); Grocery Days (Mon); Brides (Other); Entertainment (Thur); Grocery Days (Tues); Grocery Days (Wed).
Pub. ....Trevis Mayfield
Adv. Mgr. ....Jennifer Baratta
Mgr., Mktg./Promo. ....Ed Bushman
Circ. Mgr. ....Sheryl Gulbranson
Mng. Ed ....Larry Lough
Editorial Page Ed..................Kathleen Schultz
New Media Mgmt. ....Bob Wendt
Sports Ed. ....Will Larkin
Travel Ed. ....Andrea Mills
Prodn. Mgr. ....Ernie Appleyard
Market Information: TMC.
Mechanical available: Offset; Black and 3 ROP colors; insert accepted - all; page cutoffs - 22 3/4.
Mechanical Specifications: Type page 11 5/8 x 21 1/2; E - 6 cols, 1 5/6, 1/8 between; A - 6 cols, 1 5/6, 1/8 between; C - 9 cols, 1 1/4, 1/8 between.
Commodity Consumption: Avg. Page Number Per Issue - Daily 22; Avg. Page Number Per Issue - Plates Used 8745; Avg. Page Number Per Issue - Saturday 24; Avg. Page Number Per Issue - Sunday 44; widths 25; Newsprint Used - Short Tons 729; Printing Ink Used - Black 7000; Printing I
Equipment EDITORIAL: Front-end Software – Baseview 3.21.; Editorial Hardware – 28-APP/Mac; Editorial Printers – 2-HP/8150 N CLASSIFIED: Front-end Software – Baseview.; Classified Hardware – 8-APP/Mac; Classified Printers – 1-Okidata/Microline 320 dot matrix, 1-HP/8100 N DISPLAY: Ad make-up applications – QPS/QuarkXPress 4.1, Adobe/Photoshop 6.0, Adobe/Illustrator 9.0.; Display Hardware – 7-APP/Mac; Display Printers – 2-HP/LaserJet 8150N PRODUCTION: Pagination Software – Baseview 3.21.; Production Equipment – 1-Nu/Flip Top FT40L, 1-ECR/5100, Konica K-28; Cameras – 1-B/4000-C, Nu/SSTE 2024SB; Scanners – 2-AG/Arcus II PRESSROOM: Line 1 – 8-G/Urbanite; Line 2 – 7-HI/V-15A w/Glue Line; Folders – 1 MAILROOM: Counter stackers – Exact/Stack, QWI/Sport II Stacker; Inserters and stuffers – HI/1372; Bundle tying machines – 3-B/18, Dynaric/RLM-1, Sterling/GR45; Addressing machine – 1/Dispensa-Matic, Ch/595.; Business Hardware – ATT, APP/Mac, Convergent/S480

TELEGRAPH

113 S. Peoria Ave, Dixon, Ill., 61021; gen tel (815) 284-2222
Published: Mon, Tues, Wed, Thur, Fri
Weekday Frequency: e
Circulation: 7,291
Last Audit: ABC September 30, 2011

DU QUOIN

DU QUOIN EVENING CALL

9 N. Division St., Du Quoin, Ill., 1405; gen tel (618) 542-2133; adv tel (618) 542-2133; ed tel (618) 542-2133; gen fax (618) 542-2726; adv fax (618) 542-2726; ed fax (618) 542-2726; gen e-mail duquoin@varizon.net; web site www.duquoin.com
Published: Tues, Wed, Thur, Fri, Sat
Weekday Frequency: e
Saturday Frequency: m
Circulation: 3,800; 3,800(sat)
Last Audit: September 30, 2005
Price: 9.00/mo; 96.00/yr; 26.00/3mo.
Advertising: Open inch rate $9.75
News services: AP.
Politics: Independent. **Established:** 1895
Not Published: New Year; Memorial Day; Independence Day; Labor Day; Thanksgiving; Christmas.
Special Editions: Spring Home Improvements (Apr); Du Quoin State Fair (Aug); Tax Guide Tab (Feb); Bridal Show (Jan); Progress (Mar); Christmas Preview (Nov); Fall Home Improvements (Oct).
Special Weekly Sections: American Weekend (Fri); Business (Sat).
Magazines: USA WEEKEND Magazine (Sat); American Profile (Weekly).
Office Mgr. ....Debra Burns
Adv. Dir. ....Terri Fisher
Adv. Mgr., Classified...............Amanda Hargis
Circ. Mgr. ....Patti Malinee
News Ed....................................Craig Shrum
Science Ed.....................John H. Croessman
Sports Ed. ....Jeff Profitt
Prodn. Mgr................................Doug Daniels
Market Information: TMC.
Mechanical available: Offset; Black and 4 ROP colors; insert accepted; page cutoffs - 21 1/2.
Mechanical Specifications: Type page 13 4/5 x 23; E - 6 cols, 2 1/16, 1/8 between; A - 6 cols, 2 1/16, 1/8 between; C - 8 cols, 1 1/4, 1/8 between.
Commodity Consumption: Avg. Page Number Per Issue - Daily 14; Avg. Page Number Per Issue - Plates Used 3600; Avg. Page Number Per Issue - Saturday 28; Printing Ink Used - Pages Printed 5000.
Equipment EDITORIAL: Front-end Software – Microsoft/Word 4.0, Mk/NewsWriter.; Editorial Hardware – APP/Mac Plus; Editorial Printers – APP/Mac LaserWriter II NT CLASSIFIED: Front-end Software – Multi-Ad/CAMS.; Classified Hardware – APP/Mac; Classified Printers – APP/Mac LaserWriter II NT DISPLAY: Ad make-up applications – Multi-Ad/Creator; Display Hardware – APP/Mac LC III, APP/Mac IIsi; Display Printers – APP/Mac LaserWriter II NT PRODUCTION: Pagination Software – QPS/QuarkXPress.; Production Equipment – APP/Mac LC III, Quantra/610; Cameras – SCREEN/C-680-C Vertical; Scanners – Microtek/Image Scanner, TI/OMNI Page Professional PRESSROOM: Line 1 – G/Community.; Bundle tying machines – 1/Bu; Addressing machine – IBM/Listmaster.; Business Hardware – APP/Mac IIe, IBM/XT, Hyundai/386, Club America/286

EDWARDSVILLE

EDWARDSVILLE INTELLIGENCER

117 N. Second St., Edwardsville, Ill., 62025; gen tel (618) 656-4700; adv tel (618) 656-4700; ed tel (618) 656-4700; gen fax 618-656-*7618; adv fax (618) 656-7618; ed fax (618) 659-1677; adv e-mail amyschaake@edwpub.net; ed e-mail news@edwpub.net; web site www.edwpub.com
Group: Hearst
Published: Mon, Tues, Wed, Thur, Fri, Sat
Weekday Frequency: e
Saturday Frequency: m
Circulation: 4,288; 4,288(sat)
Last Audit: September 30, 2007
Price: 5.30/2wk; 121.00/48wk.
Advertising: Open inch rate $17.20
News services: AP, HN.
Politics: Independent. **Established:** 1862
Not Published: New Year; Independence Day; Labour Day; Memorial Day; Thanksgiving; Christmas.
Special Editions: Good News (Apr); Fall Sports (Aug); Christmas Greetings (Dec); Draw-an-Ad (Feb); Auto Show (Jan); Customer Appreciation (Jun); Spring Sports (Mar); Travel & Leisure (May); Veterans Day (Nov); Harvest Homefest (Oct); Answer Book/Madison Co. (Sept).
Special Weekly Sections: Real Estate (Fri); Family (Mon); Best Food Day (Sat).
Magazines: Weekender (Entertainment) (Sat).
Pub. ....Denise Vonder Haar
Adv. Mgr. ....Schaake Amy
Assistant Editor ....Bill Tucker
Mgmt. Info Servs. Mgr. ....Ron Harris
Prodn. Supvr., Mailroom..............Nick Tennyson
Prodn. Dir., Adv. Design Serv. ....Jennifer Dyer
Prodn. Foreman, Press/Camera ....David White
Opns. Mgr.............................Rosemary Kebel
Managing editor ....Carl Green
Sports editor ....Bill Roseberry
Market Information: TMC.
Mechanical available: Offset; Black and 3 ROP colors; insert accepted; page cutoffs - 22 3/4.
Mechanical Specifications: Type page 12 7/8 x 21 1/2; E - 6 cols, 2 1/16, 1/8 between; A - 6 cols, 2 1/16, 1/8 between; C - 9 cols, 1 3/8, 1/16 between.
Commodity Consumption: Avg. Page Number Per Issue - Daily 18; Avg. Page Number Per Issue - Plates Used 9500; widths 27; Newsprint Used - Short Tons 535; Printing Ink Used - Black 8100; Printing Ink Used - Color 1000; Printing Ink Used - Pages Printed 5588.
Equipment; Editorial Hardware – APP/Mac Quadras, APP/Mac LC IIIs; Editorial Equipment – 4-RSK/Tandy TRS 100; Editorial Printers – Software Â QPS/QuarkXPress. CLASSIFIED: Front-end Software – FSI/Classified.; Classified Hardware – 2-APP/Mac Quadra 605; Classified Printers – 1-TI DISPLAY: Ad make-up applications – Multi-Ad/Creator, APP/Mac System 7.1, QPS/QuarkXPress 3.3; Layout Software – 2-Mk.; Display Hardware – 2-APP/Power Mac 7200, 2-APP/Mac Quadra 650; Display Printers – APP/Mac LaserWriter IIg, Lynx/Imagesetter, Imager/Plus 12 PRODUCTION: Pagination Software – FSI.; Production Equipment – 4-APP/Mac LaserWriter, Dataproducts/LZR-1560, APP/Mac LaserWriter IIg, Lynx/Imagesetter; Cameras – 1-R; Scanners – 1-APP/Mac Scanner, Nikon PRESSROOM: Line 1 – 7; Folders – 1-KP/KJ-6. MAILROOM: Counter stackers – 1/BG; Inserters and stuffers – 1-KAN/320, 4-KAN/Station inserter; Bundle tying machines – 2-Bu/String Tying Machine; Addressing machine – 1-Automecha/Accufast PL-M; Other equipment –Challenge/3 Knife Trimmer 12x12, Challenge/Single; Audio Hardware – Zimmers Interactive BUSINESS COMPUTERS: Business Software – Infinum, MSExcel, MS/Word; Business Hardware – 3-IBM/486 DX2, 2-ALR/Powerflex, 3-Packard Bell/486 DX2, Compaq/286, 1-IBM/AST 486 DX2
Zip Codes served: 62025

EFFINGHAM

EFFINGHAM DAILY NEWS

201 N. Banker St., Effingham, Ill., 62401; gen tel (217) 347-7151; adv tel (217) 347-7151; ed tel (217) 347-7151; gen fax (217) 342-9315; adv fax (217) 342-9315; ed fax (217) 342-9315; gen e-mail edn@effinghamdailynews.com; web site www.effinghamdailynews.com
Published: Mon, Tues, Wed, Thur, Fri, Sat
Weekday Frequency: e
Saturday Frequency: e
Circulation: 10,120; 10,120(sat)
Last Audit: ABC September 30, 2011
Price: 1.75/wk; 7.40/mo; 87.00/yr.
Advertising: Open inch rate $16.00
News services: AP.
Politics: Independent.
Not Published: New Year; Memorial Day; Independence Day; Labor Day; Thanksgiving; Christmas.
Special Editions: Spring Car Care (Apr); Farm Fair (Aug); Bridal Tab (Feb); Health & Fitness (Jan); Christmas in July (Jul); Youth League Baseball (Jun); Girl Scout (Mar); Graduation (May); Christmas Opening (Nov); Restaurant Month (Oct); Fall Car Care (Sept).
Special Weekly Sections: Church Page (Fri); Food Page (Mon); School Page (Sat); Farm/Business (Thur); Horizons (Tues); Outlook (Wed).
Magazines: USA WEEKEND Magazine (Sat); American Profile (Weekly).
Pub......................................Steve Raymond
Bus. Mgr. ....Karen Mettendorf
Adv. Dir....................................Ken Goeckner
Circ. Mgr...................................Todd Buenker
Mng. Ed. ....Donna Riley-Gordon
Lifestyles Ed...................................Mary Holle
Sports Ed. ....Millie Lange
Composing Suprv....................Linda Niebrugge
Market Information: ADS; TMC.
Mechanical available: Offset; Black and 3 ROP colors; insert accepted; page cutoffs - 22 3/4.
Mechanical Specifications: Type page 13 x 21 1/2; E - 6 cols, 1 7/8, 1/8 between; A - 6 cols, 2 1/14, 1/8 between; C - 9 cols, 1 9/16, 1/8 between.
Commodity Consumption: Avg. Page Number Per Issue - Daily 24; Avg. Page Number Per Issue - Plates Used 8500; Avg. Page Number Per Issue - Saturday 28; widths 25; Newsprint Used - Short Tons 1200; Printing Ink Used - Black 27132; Printing Ink Used - Color 2035; Printing Ink Use
Equipment EDITORIAL: Front-end Software – Baseview/Managing Editor, Baseview/NewsEdit.; Editorial Hardware – APP/Mac, APP/iMac G3, APP/iMac G4; Editorial Printers – ECR, Prepress/Panther Plus 36 CLASSIFIED: Front-end Software – Baseview/Ad Manager Pro.; Classified Hardware – 3-APP/Mac; Classified Printers – Prepress/Panther Plus 36 DISPLAY: Ad make-up applications – Multi-Ad/Creator 2.5; Layout Software – QPS/QuarkXPress 3.1.; Display Hardware – APP/Mac; Display Printers – Prepress/Panther Plus 36 PRODUCTION: Pagination Software – QPS/QuarkXPress 4.0.; Production Equipment – 1-Nu/FT46V6UPNS, Prepress/Panther Plus 36; Cameras – 1-B/4000C, 1-SCREEN/670D PRESSROOM: Line 1 – 13-G/SC; Folders – 1-G/SC. MAILROOM: Counter stackers – 1/MM, 1-/Newsstack; Inserters and stuffers – 5-MM/267; Bundle tying machines – 1-MM/TABA 310-20, 2-MLN/ML2EE, 1-MLN/Spirit; Addressing machine – 1-/CH, 1-KR/215. BUSINESS COMPUTERS: Business Software – Vision Data; Business Hardware – Vision Data, PC, Accts receivable-Circ, Accts payable/gen ledger

ELGIN

THE COURIER-NEWS

PO Box 531, Elgin, Ill., 60121-0531; gen tel (847) 888-7800; web site www.suburbanchicagonews.com/couriernews/

FLORA

THE CLAY COUNTY ADVOCATE-PRESS

105 W. North Ave., Flora, Ill., 62839; gen tel (618) 662-2108; adv tel (618) 662-2108; ed tel (618) 662-2108; gen fax (618) 662-2939; adv fax (618) 662-2939; ed fax (618) 662-2939; adv e-mail advertiz@bspeedy.com; web site www.advocatepress.com
Published: Mon, Tues, Wed, Thur, Fri
Weekday Frequency: e
Circulation: 3,166
Last Audit: October 1, 2001
Price: 1.50/wk; 70.50/yr (in county), $84.50/yr (out of county).
Advertising: Open inch rate $7.60
News services: NEA, AP.
Politics: Independent. **Established:** 1886
Not Published: New Year; Memorial Day; Independence Day; Labor Day; Thanksgiving; Christmas.

Special Editions: Progress (Jun).
Special Weekly Sections: TV Listings - TAB (Weekly).
Adv. Mgr. ....Bob Hiemenz
Circ. Mgr. ....Bonnie Mason
News Ed. ....Mary Ann Maxwell
News Ed. ....Brian Turner
Sports Ed. ....Keith Gibson
TV Guide Ed. ....John Klanke
Market Information: TMC; Zoned editions.
Mechanical available: Offset; Black and 2 ROP colors; insert accepted - require quarter fold size; page cutoffs - 21.
Mechanical Specifications: Type page 13 3/4 x 21; E - 6 cols, 2 1/16, 1/8 between; A - 6 cols, 2 1/16, 1/8 between; C - 6 cols, 2 1/16, 1/8 between.
Commodity Consumption: Avg. Page Number Per Issue - Daily 12.

FREEPORT

THE JOURNAL-STANDARD

27 S. State Ave., Freeport, Ill., 61032; gen tel (815) 232-1171; adv tel (815) 232-0171; ed tel (815) 232-0157; gen fax (815) 232-3601; adv fax (815) 232-0104; ed fax (815) 232-0105; gen e-mail strosley@journalstandard.com; web site www.journalstandard.com
Published: Tues, Wed, Thur, Fri, Sat, Sun
Weekday Frequency: m
Circulation: 12,187; 12,187(sat); 12,330(sun)
Last Audit: March 31, 2008
Price: 2.90/wk; 171.60/yr.
Advertising: Open inch rate $17.19
News services: AP, CNS, MCT.
Politics: Independent.
Advertising not accepted: Mail order; Work at home.
Special Editions: Dream Homes (Apr); Football Tab (Aug); Homefront (Every other month); Home & Garden (Mar); Summer Calendar (May); Christmas Gift Guide (Nov).
Special Weekly Sections: Entertainment (Fri); Education (Mon); Lifestyle (S); Religion (Thur); Country View (Tues); Best Food Day (Wed).
Magazines: Parade (S); American Profile (Weekly).
Pub ....Steve Trosley
Adv. Mgr., Display ....Ann Young
Circ. Mgr. ....Jan Blair
Mng. Ed. ....Eric Petermann
Market Information: TMC; Zoned editions.
Mechanical available: Offset; Black and 3 ROP colors; insert accepted - machine insertable; page cutoffs - 21 1/2.
Mechanical Specifications: Type page 11 5/8 x 21 1/4; E - 6 cols, 1 5/6, 1/8 between; A - 6 cols, 1 5/6, 1/8 between; C - 9 cols, 1 1/5, 1/8 between.
Commodity Consumption: Avg. Page Number Per Issue - Daily 32; Avg. Page Number Per Issue - Plates Used 13500; widths 12 1/2; Newsprint Used - Metric Tons 1100; Printing Ink Used - Black 24000; Printing Ink Used - Color 6000; Printing Ink Used - Pages Printed 11500.
Equipment EDITORIAL: Front-end Software – QPS/QuarkXPress.; Editorial Hardware – 3-Compaq/386, 15-Amdek/VDT, APP/Power Mac 7100, 2-APP/Mac II, 6-APP/Mac IIci, 2-APP/Mac IIcx, Sun/Storage System 2gig/Editorial; Editorial Equipment – NEC/CD-Rom; Editorial Printers – 1-APP/Mac LaserWriter, APP/Mac LaserWriter CLASSIFIED: Front-end Software – Vision Data/Island Write.; Classified Hardware – Sun/Sparc II Server, Sun/Sparc Terminals; Classified Printers – Dataproducts DISPLAY: Ad make-up applications – QPS/QuarkXPress, Adobe/Illustrator; Display Hardware – 5-APP/Mac II, 1-APP/Mac IIci, APP/Mac with Radius monitors; Display Printers – APP/Mac LaserWriter, Imager/1200L, Hyphen RIP; Production Equipment – ECR/Pelbox, Sun/Storage System 4gig, OPI; Scanners – AG/7A Flatbed-Slide Scanner, APP/Mac Scanner, Kk/Slide-Negative Scanner. PRESSROOM: Line 1 – 1959; Line 2 – 7-G/Urbanite 1994. MAILROOM: Counter stackers – 2-HL/Monitor; Inserters and stuffers – 1-MM/227; Bundle tying machines – OVL; Mailroom control system – HL. BUSINESS COMPUTERS: Business Software – Vision Data; Business Hardware – Sun/Micro, DEC/VT420s

GALESBURG

THE REGISTER-MAIL

140 S. Prairie St., Galesburg, Ill., 61401; gen tel (309) 343-7181; adv tel (309) 343-7181; ed tel (309) 343-7181; gen fax (309) 342-5171; adv fax (309) 342-5171; ed fax (309) 343-2382; web site www.galesburg.com
Published: Mon, Tues, Wed, Thur, Fri, Sat, Sun
Weekday Frequency: m
Saturday Frequency: m
Circulation: 9,742; 9,742(sat); 10,214(sun)
Last Audit: ABC September 30, 2011
Price: 10.80/mo; 117.50/yr.
News services: AP.
Politics: Independent.
Note: The Galesburg Register-Mail (eS) has a combination rate of $86.16(d) and $97.30(S) with the Peoria Journal Star (mS). Individual newspaper rates not made available.
Not Published: New Year; Memorial Day; Independence Day; Labor Day; Thanksgiving; Christmas.
Special Editions: Lawn & Garden (Apr); Football (Aug); Gift Ads (Dec); Bridal Tab (Feb); Senior Citizens (Jan); Knox Co. Fair (Jul); Farmers' Forecast (Jun); Ag Day (Mar); Real Estate (May); Basketball (Nov); Farmers' Forecast (Oct); Senior Citizens (Sept).
Special Weekly Sections: TV (Fri).
Magazines: Parade (S).
Pub ....Tony Scott
Adv. Mgr., Classified ....Carol A. Uhlmann
Adv. Mgr., Retail ....Mark Ebner
Circ. Mgr. ....Krista Maciel
Circ. Mgr. ....David Spence
Circ. Mgr., Distr. ....Trent Avery
Ed ....Tom Martin
Bus. Ed ....John Pulliam
Features Ed. ....Jane Carlson
Local News Ed. ....Robert Buck
Sports Ed ....Mike Trueblood
Prodn. Mgr. ....John Bown
Prodn. Mgr., Mailroom ....Mike Spah
Prodn. Foreman, Pre Press ....Ron McGarry
Market Information: TMC.
Mechanical available: Offset; Black and 3 ROP colors; insert accepted; page cutoffs - 22 5/8.
Mechanical Specifications: Type page 13 3/4 x 22 5/8; E - 6 cols, 2, 1/6 between; A - 6 cols, 2, 1/6 between; C - 9 cols, 1 2/5, between.
Commodity Consumption: Avg. Page Number Per Issue - Daily 27; Avg. Page Number Per Issue - Plates Used 8600; widths 27 1/2; Newsprint Used - Short Tons 1040; Printing Ink Used - Black 28000; Printing Ink Used - Color 1500; Printing Ink Used - Pages Printed 8350.
Equipment EDITORIAL: Front-end Software – Dewar.; Editorial Hardware – Dewar; Editorial Equipment – APP/Mac Photo System, Lf/AP Leaf Picture Desk; Editorial Printers – T/300, Okidata/182 CLASSIFIED: Front-end Software – Dewar.; Classified Hardware – Dewar DISPLAY: Ad make-up applications – Multi-Ad/Creator; Layout Software – Multi-Ad/Creator.; Display Hardware – APP/Mac; Display Printers – APP/Mac; Production Equipment – 2-Nu, 1-Nat; Cameras – 1-SCREEN. PRESSROOM: Line 1 – 4-Wd/double width, Wd/Lithoflex; Line 2 – 3-G/Community; Line 3 – 10-WPC/Atlas (w/2-Quadra-color unit); Folders – 2; Inserters and stuffers – MM/228E 5:1; Bundle tying machines – Strapper; Addressing machine – KAN/500. BUSINESS COMPUTERS: Business Software – Vision Data; Business Hardware – ATT, Vision Data

HARRISBURG

THE DAILY REGISTER

35 S. Vine St., Harrisburg, Ill., 62946; gen tel (618) 253-7146; adv tel (618) 253-7734; ed tel (618) 253-7146; gen fax (618) 252-0863; ed fax (618) 252-0863; gen e-mail gwilson@yourclearwave.com; adv e-mail dwilson@yourclearwave.com; ed e-mail editor@yourclearwave.com; web site www.dailyregister.com
Published: Mon, Tues, Wed, Thur, Fri
Weekday Frequency: e
Saturday Frequency: m
Circulation: 4,556; 4,556(sat)
Last Audit: September 30, 2000
Price: 2.10/wk; 12.00/mo.
Advertising: Open inch rate $13.70
News services: AP.
Politics: Independent.
Not Published: New Year; Independence Day; Labor Day; Thanksgiving; Christmas.
Magazines: American Profile (Fri); USA WEEKEND Magazine (Sat).
Bus. Mgr. ....Kay Brandsasse
Adv. Mgr. ....Doris A. Wilson
Mng. Ed. ....Terry Geese
Online Mgr. ....George Q. Wilson
Prodn. Mgr. ....Gatha Moore
Mechanical available: Offset; Black and 3 ROP colors; insert accepted; page cutoffs - 21 3/4.
Mechanical Specifications: Type page 12 1/2 x 21 1/2; E - 6 cols, 2 1/16, 1/8 between; A - 6 cols, 2 1/16, 1/8 between; C - 9 cols, 1 3/8, 1/16 between.
Commodity Consumption: Avg. Page Number Per Issue - Daily 16; Avg. Page Number Per Issue - Plates Used 5600; widths 25; Newsprint Used - Short Tons 310; Printing Ink Used - Black 9300; Printing Ink Used - Color 1300; Printing Ink Used - Pages Printed 19710.
Equipment; Editorial Hardware – APP/Mac; Editorial Equipment – 2-APP/Mac PowerBook 140B. CLASSIFIED: Front-end Software – Multi-Ad.; Classified Hardware – APP/Mac; Layout Software – APP/Mac.; Display Hardware – Software □ Multi-Ad; Production Equipment – 1-LE; Cameras – 1-R.; Bundle tying machines – 1/Bu; Addressing machine – 2-/Wm.; Business Hardware – IBM
Delivery method: Mail, Newsstand, Private Carrier, Racks

ELDORADO DAILY JOURNAL

35 S. Vine St., Harrisburg, Ill., 62946-0248; gen tel (618) 253-7146; gen fax (618) 252-0863; gen e-mail dwilson@yourclearwave.com; ed e-mail editor@yourclearwave.com; web site www.dailyregister.com
Published: Mon, Tues, Wed, Thur, Fri
Weekday Frequency: e
Circulation: 1,103; 1,103(sat)
Last Audit: December 31, 1997
Advertising: Open inch rate $13.70
News services: AP.
Not Published: New Year; Independence Day; Labor Day; Christmas.
Magazines: TV Guide (Fri); USA WEEKEND Magazine (Sat).
Pub ....George Q. Wilson
Mktg. Dir. ....Doris Wilson
Mng. Ed ....Terry Geese
Prodn. Mgr. ....Gatha Moore
Mechanical available: Offset; Black and 1 ROP colors; insert accepted.
Mechanical Specifications: Type page 13 3/4 x 21 1/2; E - 6 cols, 2 1/16, 1/8 between; A - 6 cols, 2 1/16, 1/8 between; C - 8 cols, 1 2/3, 1/8 between.
Commodity Consumption: Avg. Page Number Per Issue - Daily 26.
Equipment; Editorial Hardware – 2-APP/Mac.; Bundle tying machines – 1/Bu.
Delivery method: Mail, Newsstand, Private Carrier, Racks

JACKSONVILLE

JACKSONVILLE JOURNAL-COURIER

235 W. State St., Jacksonville, Ill., 62650-1048; gen tel (217) 245-6121; adv tel (217) 245-6121; ed tel (217) 245-6121; gen fax (217) 245-1226; adv fax (217) 245-4570; ed fax (217) 245-1226; ed e-mail editors@myjournalcourier.com; web site www.myjournalcourier.com
Published: Mon, Tues, Wed, Thur, Fri, Sat, Sun
Weekday Frequency: m
Saturday Frequency: m
Circulation: 11,044; 11,044(sat); 11,550(sun)
Last Audit: ABC September 30, 2011
Price: 3.65/wk; 16.50/mo; 175.00/yr (carrier), $172.00/yr (mail).
Advertising: Open inch rate $20.50
News services: AP, MCT, SHNS.
Politics: Independent. **Established:** 1830
Special Editions: Back-to-School (Aug); New Year's Eve (Dec); Fall Auto Care Tab (Fall); Valentine Idea (Feb); July $ Days (Jul); Father's Day (Jun); Tax Preparation (Mar); Graduation Tab (May); Modern Farmer (Other); Spring Auto Tab (Spring); Summer Bridal Tab (Summer).
Special Weekly Sections: Church Page (Fri); Society (S); Fling (Thur); Food (Wed).
Magazines: USA WEEKEND Magazine (S); American Profile (Weekly).
Pub. ....Kent A. Kilpatrick
Circ. Dir. ....Ronald Hance
Ed. ....David C.L. Bauer
Photo Dept. Mgr. ....Steve Wermowski
Sports Ed. ....Dennis Mathes
Prodn. Mgr. ....Jeff Lonergan
Prodn. Mgr., Pressroom ....Steve Pahlmann
Prodn. Foreman, Mailroom ....Jim Van Hyning
Market Information: TMC.
Mechanical available: Offset; Black and 3 ROP colors; insert accepted; page cutoffs - 22 3/4.
Mechanical Specifications: Type page 12 1/2 x 21 1/2; E - 6 cols, 1 7/8, 1/8 between; A - 6 cols, 1 7/8, 1/8 between; C - 9 cols, 1 3/16, 1/8 between.
Equipment PRESSROOM: Line 1 – 8-G/Urbanite 1992.

JOLIET

THE HERALD NEWS

3109 W. Jefferson St., Joliet, Ill., 60435-4733; gen tel (815) 439-7530; adv tel (815) 729-6137; gen fax (815) 729-6059; adv fax (815) 729-6392; ed fax (815) 729-6059; gen e-mail heraldnews@scn1.com; adv e-mail scnmedia@scn1.com; ed e-mail HeraldNews@scn1.com; web site www.suburbanchicagonews.com
Published: Mon, Tues, Wed, Thur, Fri, Sat, Sun
Weekday Frequency: m
Saturday Frequency: m
Circulation: 35,757; 35,229(sat); 39,197(sun)
Last Audit: September 30, 2009
Price: 3.25/wk; 169.00/yr (carrier), $208.00/yr (mail).
News services: AP, CNS, NYT.
Politics: Independent.
Note: Suburban Chicago Newspapers includes the Aurora Beacon News (mS), Elgin Courier News (mS), Joliet Herald News (mS), Naperville Sun (mS) and Waukegan Lake County News-Sun (e). The group combination rate is $170.50 (dS). Individual newspaper rates not made
Special Editions: Destination Spring Travel (Apr); Windfall of Homes (Aug); Readers Choice Awards (Dec); New Homes Spring Buyers (Feb); Super Suburban Jobs (Jan); Education Outlook (Jul); Wedding Planner (Jun); Education Outlook (Mar); Education Outlook (Nov); Home Improve
Special Weekly Sections: Automotive (Fri); Community Calendar (Mon); Health (S); Church (Sat); Weekend (Thur); Consumer Page (Tues); Food Page (Wed).
Magazines: USA WEEKEND Magazine (S); TV Update (Sat).

Adv. Mgr., Retail Sales................Steve Vanisko
Circ. Mgr., Regl................................Ray Kartis
Mng. Ed................................David Monaghan
Features Ed. ....Sue Baker
News Ed..................................Matt Cappelini
Sports Ed........................................Dick Goss
Online Mgr................................Steve Sumner
Market Information: Split run; TMC; Zoned editions.
Mechanical available: Offset; Black and 3 ROP colors; insert accepted - any; page cutoffs - 21.
Mechanical Specifications: Type page 13 x 21; E - 6 cols, 2 1/16, 3/16 between; A - 6 cols, 2 5/32, 1/16 between; C - 10 cols, 1 3/8, 1/16 between.
Commodity Consumption: Avg. Page Number Per Issue - Daily 30; Avg. Page Number Per Issue - Sunday 56; widths 13 3/4; Newsprint Used - Metric Tons 3600; Printing Ink Used - Black 155000; Printing Ink Used - Color 30000; Printing Ink Used - Pages Printed 12500.
Equipment EDITORIAL: Front-end Software – SII.; Editorial Hardware – SII/Sys 55, 25-SII/Coyote, SII/Coyote 3, SII/MTX; Editorial Equipment – 1-APP/Mac II, 1-APP/Mac IIci, 1-APP/Mac SE; Editorial Printers – 1-TI/810, APP/Mac LaserWriter NTX DISPLAY: Ad make-up applications – CJ.; Display Hardware – DEC; Display Printers – OMS/Laser Printer PRODUCTION: Pagination Software – QPS/QuarkXPress 6.0, AU/Grafix Rips 4, Apscom (send) 4, Apscom (receive) 4.; Production Equipment – 2-AU/APS-108, 2-AU/APS-6000 Proofers, 4-Sierra/3850 Imagers, 2-HP/8000 b/w Proofers; Cameras – 2-B; Scanners – 1-ECR/Autokon 2030, 1-Howtek/4500 PRESSROOM: Line 1 – 4-G/Colorliner 2065 double width 1992; Line 2 – 4-G/Colorliner 2066 double width 1992; Reels and Stands – 10-G/CT50. MAILROOM: Counter stackers – 6/QWI, 2-/HL; Inserters and stuffers – 2-GMA/SLS 1000 14:1; Bundle tying machines – 8-/Power Strap; Addressing machine – 2-/AVY, 1-/Ch. BUSINESS COMPUTERS: Business Software – Archetype/Corel Draw, MicroGraphics/Designer; Business Hardware – DEC

KANKAKEE

THE DAILY JOURNAL

8 Dearborn Sq., Kankakee, Ill., 60901-0632; gen tel (815) 937-3300; adv tel (815) 937-3355; ed tel (815) 937-3367; gen fax (815) 937-3301; adv fax (815) 395-4630; ed fax (815) 937-3876; gen e-mail webmaster@daily-journal.com; adv e-mail advertising@daily-journal.com; ed e-mail editorial@daily-journal.com; web site www.daily-journal.com
Published: Mon, Tues, Wed, Thur, Fri, Sat
Weekday Frequency: e
Saturday Frequency: m
Circulation: 21,959; 27,487(sat)
Last Audit: Sworn September 30, 2008
Price: 1.75/wk; 91.00/yr (carrier/motor route).
Advertising: Open inch rate $36.86
Insert rate: $32.20
News services: AP; GateHouse
Politics: 1853
Not Published: Memorial Day; Independence Day; Labor Day; Thanksgiving.
Own facility?: Y
Special Editions: House & Garden (Apr); Medical Guide (Aug); All Wrapped Up In One (Dec); Weddings (Spring); Parenting (Feb); Life in Balance (Jan); Chicago Bears Training Camp Program (Jul); Progress (Mar); Graduation (May); HomeFinder (Monthly); Holiday Guide I (Nov); @RecordBody:**Special Weekly Sections:** TV Weekly
Magazines: Relish (Monthly); USA WEEKEND Magazine (Sat); American Profile (Tues).
Pub....................................Len Robert Small
Vice Pres., Finance...........Joseph E. Lacaeyse
Gen. Mgr...............................Kenneth Munjoy
Bus. Mgr. ....Cindy Liptak
Adv. Dir. ....Mr. Neil Shannon
Mktg. Mgr....................................Amy Fields
Circ. Mgr. ....Chad Campbell
Mng. Ed. ....Susy Schultz
Dir., Network Opns. Ctr................Wade LeBeau
Prodn. Dir.................................Kevin Norden
Prodn. Foreman, Press (Day).........David Grams
Prodn. Foreman, Press (Night) ....Larry King
Prodn. Mgr., Distr. ....Terry W. LaVoie
Metro Ed. ....Mike Frey
Asst. Metro Ed.........Rachael Reynolds-Soucie
Asst. Metro Ed., Sports/Innovations Caleb Benoit
Chief Photographer ....Mike Voss
Market Information: Split run; TMC.
Mechanical available: Offset; Black and 3 ROP colors; insert accepted; page cutoffs - 22 3/4.
Mechanical Specifications: Type page 10 19/50 x 21 1/2 ; E - 6 cols, 1 16/25, 11/100 between; A - 6 cols, 1 16/25, 11/100 between; C - 6 cols, 1 16/25, 11/100 between.
Commodity Consumption: Avg. Page Number Per Issue - Daily 32; Avg. Page Number Per Issue - Plates Used 34000; Avg. Page Number Per Issue - Sunday 76; widths 25; Newsprint Used - Metric Tons 2300; Printing Ink Used - Black 42640; Printing Ink Used - Color 37400; Printing Ink Us
Equipment EDITORIAL: Front-end Software – MediaSpan/NewsEdit IQ.; Editorial Hardware – Mac Servers and Workstations; Editorial Printers – 2-HP/Laserjet 8150 CLASSIFIED: Front-end Software – DTI; Classified Hardware – PC Workstations and servers.; Classified Printers – HP Laser Printer DISPLAY: Ad make-up applications – QuarkXPress 6, Adobe CS3 (InDesign, Ilustrator, Acrobat, and Photoshop); Display Hardware – APP/Mac; Display Printers – HP/LaserJet 8000, Ricoh color PRODUCTION: Pagination Software – Polkadots Prepageit; Production Equipment – Dell Servers and RIPS; Scanners – Epson/10000 XL Epson/1688 PRESSROOM: Line 1 – 7-G/Metro (3 Color Deck, 2 Tol); Folders – 2; Pasters – 6; Reels and Stands – 6 MAILROOM: Counter stackers – 4-Id/2000, 3/MM, 1-GMA/1000; Inserters and stuffers – 1-MM/227, 1-MM/308; Bundle tying machines – 6-/Dynaric; Addressing machine – Ch/525E. BUSINESS COMPUTERS: Business Software – Microsoft/Office DTI; Business Hardware – PC Workstations and Servers.
Delivery method: Mail, Newsstand, Private Carrier, Racks

KEWANEE

STAR-COURIER

105 E. Central Blvd., Kewanee, Ill., 61443-0836; gen tel (309) 852-2181; adv tel (309) 852-2181; ed tel (309) 852-2181; gen fax (309) 852-0010; adv fax (309) 852-0010; ed fax (309) 852-0010; ed e-mail editor@starcourier.com; web site www.starcourier.com
Published: Tues, Wed, Thur, Fri, Sat
Weekday Frequency: m
Circulation: 4,739; 4,739(sat)
Last Audit: October 1, 2004
Price: 2.45/wk; 9.70/mo; 110.70/yr; 56.80/6mo.
Advertising: Open inch rate $14.25
News services: AP.
Politics: Independent.
Not Published: New Year; Memorial Day; Independence Day; Labor Day; Thanksgiving; Christmas.
Special Editions: Home Improvement (Apr); Hogsmopolitan (Aug); Bridal (Jan); People Making a Difference (Jul); Fair Tab (Jun); 101 Things to do in Henry County (May); Farm Tab (Monthly).
Special Weekly Sections: Athlete of the Week (Fri); Forever Young (Mon); Day Trip (Thur); Outdoors (Tues); Home & Garden (Wed).
Magazines: American Profile (Weekly).
Pub..Dee Evans
Classified Adv. Mgr.......................Jolene Clark
Lifestyle Ed. ....Margi Washburn
News Ed. ....Dave Clarke
Sports. Ed. ....Mike Landis
Market Information: ADS; TMC.
Mechanical available: Offset; Black and 3 ROP colors; insert accepted; page cutoffs - 22 3/4.
Mechanical Specifications: Type page 13 x 21 1/2; E - 6 cols, 2 1/16, 1/8 between; A - 6 cols, 2 1/16, 1/8 between; C - 9 cols, 1 3/8, 1/16 between.
Commodity Consumption: Avg. Page Number Per Issue - Daily 16; Avg. Page Number Per Issue - Plates Used 9500; Avg. Page Number Per Issue - Saturday 16; widths 13 3/4; Newsprint Used - Metric Tons 308.3; Printing Ink Used - Black 4500; Printing Ink Used - Color 500; Printing Ink
Equipment; Editorial Hardware – APP/Mac; Editorial Equipment – 8-COM/Computype, 1-TC; Editorial Printers – HP, APP/Mac. CLASSIFIED: Front-end Software – Baseview.; Classified Hardware – APP/Mac; Classified Printers – APP/Mac DISPLAY: Ad make-up applications – QPS/QuarkXPress.; Display Hardware – APP/Mac; Display Printers – HP, APP/Mac PRODUCTION: Pagination Software – QPS/QuarkXPress.; Production Equipment – APP/Mac; Scanners – 1-GMS/E-Z-Scan II PRESSROOM: Line 1 – 4-G/Colorliner.; Bundle tying machines – 2/Bu. BUSINESS COMPUTERS: Business Software – Microsoft/Access, Microsoft/Excel, Microsoft/Word; Business Hardware – 4-IBM/PC-KT, 2-Compaq/386-S

LA SALLE

NEWS-TRIBUNE

426 Second St., La Salle, Ill., 61301-2334; gen tel (815) 223-3200; gen fax (815) 223-2543; ed fax (815) 224-6443; adv e-mail sales@newstrib.com; web site www.newstrib.com
Published: Mon, Tues, Wed, Thur, Fri, Sat
Weekday Frequency: e
Saturday Frequency: e
Circulation: 16,650; 17,010(sat)
Last Audit: September 30, 2009
Price: 1.95/wk; 7.80/mo; 89.70/yr.
Advertising: Open inch rate $29.00
News services: AP.
Not Published: New Year's Day; Christmas; Memorial Day; July 4th; Labor Day; Thanksgiving.
Special Editions: Meet The Bankers (Apr); Summer Festivals (Aug); A Year in Memoriam (Dec); Logo Contest (Feb); Meet The Bankers (Jan); A-Z Guide (Jul); Financial Focus (Jun); Teen Prom Guide (Mar); Money Smart (May); IVAR (Jan-Sept) (Monthly); Design An Ad (Nov); A-Z Guid
Magazines: USA WEEKEND Magazine (Sat).
Pres. ....Peter Miller
Pub. ....Joyce McCullough
Cor. Accounting Mgr........................Craig Baker
Adv. Dir...................................Scott Stavrakas
Circ. Dir. ....William Delorme
Lifestyle Ed..............................Cindy Rolando
News Ed. ....Craig Sterrett
Online Ed..............................Linda Kleczewski
Picture Ed..................................Kemp Smith
Online Mgr...............................Diane Seghers
Prodn. Mgr., Mailroom.......................Fort Miller
Prodn. Mgr., Pre Press ....Joseph Zokal
Prodn. Mgr., Pressroom ....Jeff Hoos
Market Information: ADS; Split run; TMC.
Mechanical available: Offset; Black and 3 ROP colors; insert accepted; page cutoffs - 21 3/4.
Mechanical Specifications: Type page 11 5/8 x 21 1/2; E - 6 cols, 1 5/6, 1/8 between; A - 6 cols, 1 5/6, 1/8 between; C - 9 cols, 1 1/16, 1/8 between.
Commodity Consumption: Avg. Page Number Per Issue - Daily 22; Avg. Page Number Per Issue - Plates Used 19011; widths 11 5/8; Newsprint Used - Short Tons 768; Printing Ink Used - Black 17293; Printing Ink Used - Color 5307; Printing Ink Used - Pages Printed 7964.
Equipment; Editorial Hardware – APT; Editorial Printers – AG/Accuset 1000, HP. CLASSIFIED: Front-end Software – Informatel.; Classified Hardware – PC; Classified Printers – AG/Accuset 1000, HP/4 DISPLAY: Ad make-up applications – APT 2001; Layout Software – QPS/QuarkXPress 4.1, Multi-Ad/Illustrator 8.0, Adobe/Photoshop 5.0, Adobe/Acrobat.; Display Hardware – APP/Mac; Display Printers – 2-AG/Accuset 1000, HP/5000, Tektronix/780 PRODUCTION: Pagination Software – Informatel.; Production Equipment – 2-COM, 1-AG/Accuset 1000, 1-Nikon/Coolscan; Scanners – Microtek PRESSROOM: Line 1 – 8-G/Urbanite 1972.; Inserters and stuffers – KAN/760; Bundle tying machines – ML2EE, MS Sterling/SSM 40, Si/LB-2000; Addressing machine – KR/511-515; Other equipment –MM.

LAWRENCEVILLE

DAILY RECORD

1209 State St., Lawrenceville, Ill., 62439; gen tel (618) 943-2331; adv tel (618) 943-2331; ed tel (618) 943-2331; gen fax (618) 943-3976; adv fax (618) 943-3976; ed fax (618) 943-3976; adv e-mail ads@lawdailyrecord.com; ed e-mail lawnews@lawdailyrecord.com; web site www.lawdailyrecord.com
Published: Mon, Tues, Wed, Thur, Fri
Weekday Frequency: e
Circulation: 3,964
Last Audit: September 30, 2000
Price: 69.00/yr.
Advertising: Open inch rate $7.50
News services: AP, CNS.
Politics: Independent.
Advertising not accepted: 900 numbers; Massage parlors.
Not Published: New Year; Memorial Day; Independence Day; Labor Day; Thanksgiving; Christmas.
Special Editions: Kreative Kids (Apr); Back-to-School (Aug); Christmas Greetings (Dec); Tax Guide (Feb); Summer Savings (Jul); Senior Citizen Salute (Jun); Spring Ag Salute (Mar); American Home Week (May); Christmas Opening (Nov); Working Women (Oct); Fall Festival (Sept).
Special Weekly Sections: Outdoors (Thur); Business & Money (Wed).
Magazines: TV Section (Fri).
Pub.......................................Kathleen Lewis
Adv. Dir....................................Sandie Young
Circ. Mgr.................................Joyce Tredway
News Writer................................Ashley Smith
Sports Ed. ....Bill Richardson
Mgr., Mgmt. Info Servs...........Michael Van Dorn
Layout Mgr............................Beverly Johnson
Market Information: ADS; TMC; Zoned editions.
Mechanical available: Offset; Black and 4 ROP colors; insert accepted - all, quarter folded (max. size 7 x 11); page cutoffs - 22 3/4.
Mechanical Specifications: Type page 13 x 21; E - 6 cols, 1 5/8, 1/8 between; A - 6 cols, 1 5/8, 1/8 between; C - 9 cols, 1 3/8, 1/16 between.
Commodity Consumption: Avg. Page Number Per Issue - Daily 10.
Equipment EDITORIAL: Front-end Software – Baseview/NewsEdit Pro 1.1.; Editorial Hardware – APP/Mac; Editorial Printers – 2-Xante/Accel-a-Writer 8200 CLASSIFIED: Front-end Software – Hypercard.; Classified Hardware – APP/Mac; Classified Printers – Xante/Accel-a-Writer 8200 DISPLAY: Ad make-up applications – Adobe/Illustrator, Multi-Ad/Creator; Layout Software – APP/Mac ci, Xante/Accel-a-Writer 8200.; Display Hardware – APP/Mac; Display Printers – Xante/Accel-a-Writer 8100A PRODUCTION: Pagination Software – QPS/QuarkXPress 3.3.; Production Equipment – 1-APP/Mac LaserWriter; Bundle tying machines – 1/US; Addressing machine – 1-/Am. BUSINESS COMPUTERS: Business Software – Microsoft/Word 5.0, Microsoft/Excel 5.0; Business Hardware – APP/Mac

LINCOLN

THE COURIER

2201 Woodlawn Rd., Lincoln, Ill., 62656-0740; gen tel (217) 732-2101; gen fax (217) 732-7039; gen e-mail courier@lincol-

ncourier.com; web site www.lincolncourier.com
Published: Mon, Tues, Wed, Thur, Fri, Sat, Sun
Weekday Frequency: e
Saturday Frequency: m
Circulation: 5,623; 5,813(sat)
Last Audit: September 30, 2007
Price: 2.45/wk; 10.60/mo; 117.84/yr.
News services: AP, CNS, SHNS.
Politics: Independent.
Note: The Lincoln Courier (e) has a combination rate of $74.13 with the Springfield State Journal-Register (mS). Individual newspaper rates not available.
Not Published: New Year; Memorial Day; Independence Day; Labor Day; Thanksgiving; Christmas.
Special Editions: County Fair (Aug); Progress (Mar).
Special Weekly Sections: Entertainment (Sat); Lifestyles (Wed).
Magazines: American Profile (Weekly).
News Ed. ....Dan Tackett
Market Information: TMC.
Mechanical available: Offset; Black and 3 ROP colors; insert accepted; page cutoffs - 21 1/4.
Mechanical Specifications: Type page 13 x 21; E - 6 cols, 2 1/16, 1/8 between; A - 6 cols, 2 1/16, 1/8 between; C - 9 cols, 1 3/8, 1/16 between.
Commodity Consumption: Avg. Page Number Per Issue - Daily 28; Avg. Page Number Per Issue - Plates Used 10400; widths 13 3/4; Newsprint Used - Short Tons 277; Printing Ink Used - Black 5280; Printing Ink Used - Color 650.
Equipment EDITORIAL: Front-end Software – Dewar/Disc Net, Dewar/Sys II, Dewar/Sys IV, Dewar/Discovery.; Editorial Equipment – Lf/AP Leaf Picture Desk; Editorial Printers – XIT/Clipper CLASSIFIED: Front-end Software – Dewar/Disc Net.; Classified Printers – XIT/Clipper DISPLAY: Ad make-up applications – Dewar/Disc Net, Dewar/Sys II, Dewar/Sys IV, Dewar/Discovery.; Display Hardware – 1-Dewar/Discovery; Production Equipment – XIT/Clipper; Cameras – R/500, C/Marathon. PRESSROOM: Line 1 – 7-G/Community 1978.; Bundle tying machines – MLN, 2-Si.

LITCHFIELD

NEWS-HERALD

112 E. Ryder St., Litchfield, Ill., 62056; gen tel (217) 324-2121; gen fax (217) 324-2122; adv fax (217) 324-2122; gen e-mail lfd-news@litchfieldil.com
Published: Mon, Tues, Wed, Thur, Fri
Weekday Frequency: e
Circulation: 5,218
Last Audit: October 29, 2004
Price: 16.00/yr (mail, local), $20.00/yr (mail).
Advertising: Open inch rate $3.80
News services: AP.
Politics: Independent-Democrat.
Not Published: New Year; Memorial Day; Independence Day; Labor Day; Veteran's Day; Thanksgiving; Christmas.
Special Editions: Dollar Day (Aug); Back-to-School (Fall); Dollar Day (Feb); Christmas (Nov); Great Outdoors (Spring).
Bus. Mgr. ....John C. Hanafin
Adv. Dir ....Debbie Kuethe
Circ. Mgr. ....Lisa Land
Wire Ed. ....Michelle Romanus
Prodn. Supt. ....James Keith
Mechanical available: Offset; Black and 3 ROP colors; insert accepted; page cutoffs - 22 3/4.
Mechanical Specifications: Type page 14 x 21 1/2; E - 8 cols, 1 2/3, 1/8 between; A - 8 cols, 1 2/3, 1/8 between; C - 8 cols, 1 2/3, 1/8 between.
Commodity Consumption: Avg. Page Number Per Issue - Daily 28.
Equipment; Editorial Hardware – 4-COM/MDT 350.; Production Equipment – 2-COM/2961HS, 1-COM/ACM9000; Cameras – 1-DSA/Companica-64OC. PRESSROOM: Line 1 – 4-G/Community.; Bundle tying machines – 1/B; Addressing machine – 1-Am/1900.

MACOMB

MACOMB JOURNAL

203 N. Randolph St., Macomb, Ill., 61455; gen tel (309) 833-2114; gen fax (309) 833-2346; adv fax (309) 833-2345; gen e-mail lynne@mcdonoughvoice.com; adv e-mail lynne @mcdonoughvoice.com; ed e-mail editor@mcdonoughvoice.com; web site www.mcdonoughvoice.com
Group: GateHouse Media
Published: Tues, Wed, Thur, Fri, Sat
Weekday Frequency: m
Saturday Frequency: m
Circulation: 3,800; 5,000(sat)
Last Audit: Sworn September 30, 2000
Price: 35/mo; 125.00/yr.
Advertising: Open inch rate $14.00
Insert rate: $60/M Single sheet
News services: AP, LAT-WP.
Not Published: Memorial Day; Independence Day; Labor Day; Thanksgiving; Christmas (unless on a Sunday).
Own facility?: Y
Special Editions: Restaurant Directory
Business directory
Central Illinois Family Magazine (Monthly)
Western Illinois University Coupon book
Special Weekly Sections: Church (Fri); Seniors (Mon); Lifestyles (S); Entertainment (Happenings) (Thur); Agriculture (Tues);Health (Wed).Business (Sat)
Magazines: Parade (S); American Profile (Weekly).Relish (Tuesday) Spry (Tuesday) Central Illinois Family Magazine (First Wed. month)
Publisher. Ad Director ....Lynne Campbell
Editor....................................Pospeschil Jodi
Sports ....Bower Ryan
Graphics........................Amanda Donaldson
Pub. ....Pam McDowell
Adv. Mgr., Classified...........Joanne VanWinkle
Adv. Mgr., Display ....Jane Hasley
Circ. Mgr. ....Autumn Bentzinger
Ed. ....Oliver Wiest
Sports Ed. ....Shelby Burget
Prodn. Mgr. ....Amanda Link
Market Information: TMC.
Mechanical available: Offset; Black and 3 ROP colors; insert accepted; page cutoffs - 22 3/4.
Mechanical Specifications: Type page 13 x 21 1/2; E - 6 cols, 2 1/16, 1/8 between; A - 6 cols, 2 1/16, 1/8 between; C - 10 cols, 1 1/4, 1/16 between.
Commodity Consumption: Avg. Page Number Per Issue - Daily 14; Avg. Page Number Per Issue - Sunday 28; widths 25; Newsprint Used - Metric Tons 427; Printing Ink Used - Pages Printed 4884.
Equipment EDITORIAL: Front-end Software – QPS/QuarkXPress, Microsoft/Word.; Editorial Hardware – APP/iMac, APP/Mac G4; Editorial Equipment – Nikon/Super Coolscan LS1000; Editorial Printers – APP/Mac LaserWriter NTX, HP/LaserJet CLASSIFIED: Front-end Software – CAMS.; Classified Hardware – APP/Mac 7200-75; Classified Printers – HP/LaserJet 5MP DISPLAY: Ad make-up applications – QPS/QuarkXPress, Multi-Ad/Creator; Display Hardware – APP/Mac G4; Display Printers – APP/Mac LaserWriter NTX, APP/Mac Pro 810l ; Biz Hub PRODUCTION: Pagination Software – QPS/QuarkXPress 5.0.; Production Equipment – TI/OmniPage Professional, TI/Omni-Page Professional, APP/Mac Pro 810, Mk, APP/Mac LaserWriter NTX, APP/Mac Pro 810; Cameras – R, R; Scanners – HP/ScanJet IIcx, HP/ScanJet IIcx PRESSROOM: Line 1 – 7-G/Community 1970.; Bundle tying machines – 2/Bu.; Business Hardware – Software Â MSSI
Zip Codes served: 61455, 61422, 62326,61420, 61438,61450,62367
Delivery method: Mail, Newsstand, Private Carrier, Racks

MARION

THE MARION DAILY REPUBLICAN

502 W. Jackson St., Marion, Ill., 62959-0490; gen tel (618) 993-2626; adv tel (618) 993-2626; ed tel (618) 993-2626; gen fax (618) 993-8326; adv fax (618) 993-8326; ed fax (618) 993-8326; ed e-mail editor@dailyrepublicannews.com; web site www.dailyrepublicannews.com
Published: Tues, Wed, Thur, Fri, Sat
Weekday Frequency: e
Saturday Frequency: m
Circulation: 3,600; 3,600(sat)
Last Audit: March 31, 2008
Price: 116.40/yr.
Advertising: Open inch rate $11.65
News services: AP.
Not Published: Independence Day; Christmas.
Magazines: USA WEEKEND Magazine (Sat); American Profile (Weekly).
Adv. Dir. ....Jonathan Bricks
Adv. Mgr., Classified ....Betty Caraker
Circ. Supvr. ....Jim Noble
Mng. Ed. ....Tim Petrowich
News Ed. ....Bill Swinford
Photo Ed. ....Tom Kane
Sports Ed. ....Justin Walker
Prodn. Mgr., Composition...............Steve Triest
Market Information: TMC.
Mechanical available: Offset; Black and 4 ROP colors; insert accepted - min. 8 1/2 x 11; page cutoffs - 21 1/2.
Mechanical Specifications: Type page 13 x 21 1/2; E - 6 cols, 2 1/16, 1/8 between; A - 6 cols, 2 1/16, 1/8 between; C - 8 cols, 1 5/8, 1/16 between.
Commodity Consumption: Avg. Page Number Per Issue - Daily 16.
Equipment EDITORIAL: Front-end Software – Microsoft/Word.; Editorial Hardware – 1-APP/Mac II; Editorial Printers – APP/Mac LaserWriter II CLASSIFIED: Front-end Software – Baseview.; Classified Hardware – APP/Mac; Classified Printers – APP/Mac LaserWriter II DISPLAY: Ad make-up applications – Aldus/PageMaker; Layout Software – APP/Mac.; Display Hardware – 4-APP/Mac; Display Printers – APP/Mac LaserWriter IIg; Production Equipment – Nu/FT40U3VP; Cameras – B.; Bundle tying machines – 2/Bu. BUSINESS COMPUTERS: Business Software – Nomads/Listmaster; Business Hardware – 2-Club America/486

MARSHALL

MARSHALL ADVOCATE

610 Archer Ave., Marshall, Ill., 62441; gen tel (217) 826-3600; gen fax (217) 826-3700; gen e-mail stromnews@joink.com
Published: Mon, Tues, Wed, Fri, Sat
Weekday Frequency: All day
Circulation: 4,711
Last Audit: Sworn N/A
Advertising: Open inch rate $6.00
Insert rate: $75.00/M.
Politics: 1996
Own facility?: N
Pub. ....Gary Strohm
Pub. ....Melody Strohm
Assistant Publisher ....Joni Graeff
Delivery method: Mail, Newsstand, Racks

MATTOON

JOURNAL-GAZETTE

100 Broadway Ave., Mattoon, Ill., 61938; gen tel (217) 235-5656; gen fax (217) 238-6886; gen e-mail editorial@jg-tc.com; web site www.jg-tc.com
Published: Mon, Tues, Wed, Thur, Fri, Sat
Weekday Frequency: m
Saturday Frequency: m
Circulation: 8,846; 8,646(sat)
Last Audit: September 30, 2009
Price: 2.50/wk; 123.00/yr; 31.50/13wk.
News services: AP.
Politics: Independent. **Established:** 1905
Note: Advertising is sold in combination with the Charleston (IL) Times-Courier for $19.75 (m). Individual newspaper rates not made available.
Not Published: New Year; Memorial Day; Independence Day; Labor Day; Christmas.
Special Editions: Farm (Jan); Bagelfest (Jul); Graduation (May); Thanksgiving Day (Nov); Automotive (Oct).
Special Weekly Sections: Newspapers in Education (Mon); School News-Sports-Lifestyle (Sat); Farm Feature (Thur); About People (Tues); Lifestyle-Food (Wed).
Magazines: USA WEEKEND Magazine (Sat).
Pub...Carl Walworth
Adv. Dir. ....Tammy Jordan
Circ. Dir...............................Robin Thompson
Mng. Ed........................................William Lair
Features Ed. ....Beth Heldebrandt
Sports Ed. ....Brian Nielsen
Mechanical available: Offset; Black and 3 ROP colors; insert accepted; page cutoffs - 22 3/4.
Mechanical Specifications: Type page 11 1/2 x 21 1/2; E - 6 cols, 1 3/4, 1/6 between; A - 6 cols, 1 3/4, 1/6 between; C - 6 cols, 1 3/4, 1/6 between.
Commodity Consumption: Avg. Page Number Per Issue - Daily 26; widths 27 1/2.
Equipment EDITORIAL: Front-end Software – Sun/Micro Sys, Unix/Arbotext, Lotus/Notes 4 6.4, Domino Server, Windows/NT.; Editorial Hardware – 16-Sun/SLC, 6-Sun/Sparc II, Dell/Optiplex 6-1; Editorial Printers – Xante/Accel-a-Writer 8200, HP/LaserJet 4MV, ECR/1085 CLASSIFIED: Front-end Software – Sun/OS (with Vision Data 4GL).; Classified Hardware – Sun/XWindows, Dell/GX 110; Classified Printers – 1-HP/IIIP, HP/4050N DISPLAY: Ad make-up applications – QPS/QuarkXPress 3.32, Adobe/Photoshop 3.05, Adobe/Illustrator 6.0; Layout Software – SCS/Layout 8000.; Display Hardware – 7-APP/Mac II, 2-APP/Mac SE30, 1-APP/Mac ci, 1-APP/Power Mac 9500; Display Printers – ECR/1085 PRODUCTION: Pagination Software – QPS/QuarkXPress 3.32, SCS/Lynx 3.1.; Production Equipment – Caere/OmniPro 5.0, Lf/Leafscan 35; Cameras – SCREEN/Companica 680C; Scanners – 2-HP/ScanJet Plus, AG/Horizon PRESSROOM: Line 1 – 12-G/Community; Folders – 1 MAILROOM: Counter stackers – 1-BG/Count-O-Veyor 106; Inserters and stuffers – 2-MM/227E; Bundle tying machines – 1-Bu/BT16, 3-MLN/ML2EE; Addressing machine – 2-Wm/5.; Business Hardware – 1-Compaq/386, Sun/4110

TIMES-COURIER

100 Broadway Ave., Mattoon, Ill., 61938; gen tel (217) 235-5656; gen fax (217) 238-6885; gen e-mail editorial@jg-tc.com; adv e-mail advertising@jg-tc.com; ed e-mail editorial@jg-tc.com; web site www.jg-tc.com
Published: Mon, Tues, Wed, Thur, Fri, Sat
Weekday Frequency: m
Saturday Frequency: m
Circulation: 5,495; 5,211(sat)
Last Audit: September 30, 2009
Price: 2.50/wk; 123.00/yr; 31.50/26wk.
News services: AP.
Politics: Independent.
Note: The Times-Courier is printed at the Mattoon Journal-Gazette plant. For detailed mechanical equipment information, see the Mattoon Journal-Gazette listing. The Times-Courier has an advertising combination rate of $19.75 (m) with the Journal-Gazette. Indivi
Not Published: New Year; Memorial Day; Independence Day; Labor Day; Christmas.
Special Editions: Farm (Jan); Bagelfest (Jul); Graduation (May); Christmas (Nov); Automotive Guide (Oct).
Special Weekly Sections: Church (Fri); Newspapers in Education (Mon); Sports/Lifestyle (Sat); Farm Features (Thur); About People (Tues); Lifestyle/Food (Wed).
Magazines: USA WEEKEND Magazine (Sat).
Pub...Carl Walworth
Adv. Dir. ....Tammy Jordan
Circ. Mgr..........................Marjorie Rutherford
Mng. Ed........................................William Lair

Features Ed. ....Beth Hildebrandt
Sports Ed. ....Brian Neilsen
Mechanical available: Offset; Black and 3 ROP colors; insert accepted; page cutoffs - 22 3/4.
Mechanical Specifications: Type page 11 1/2 x 21 1/2; E - 6 cols, 1 3/4, 1/6 between; A - 6 cols, 1 3/4, 1/6 between; C - 9 cols, 1 1/8, 1/8 between.
Commodity Consumption: Avg. Page Number Per Issue - Daily 26; widths 25.
Equipment EDITORIAL: Front-end Software – Sun/OS Solaris 2 4.2, Lotus/Notes 4.6.4.; Editorial Hardware – 2-Sun/SPARC 20, 6-Sun/SPARC 2, 15-Dell/Optiplex G1; Editorial Printers – HP/4MV CLASSIFIED: Front-end Software – Sun/OS (with Vision Data 4GL).; Classified Hardware – 1-Sun/Xwindows, 4-Dell/Optiplex GX110; Classified Printers – HP/II, HP/4050N DISPLAY: Ad make-up applications – APP/Mac System 9.2.1; Layout Software – SCS/8000 Layout.; Display Hardware – APP/Mac G3; Display Printers – HP/HMV, ECR/1085 PRODUCTION: Pagination Software – QPS/QuarkXPress 4.11, Lynx 3.3, SCS.; Production Equipment – Nu/Flip Top 40 V6 4PNS; Scanners – Epson/3600, AGFA/Horizon PRESSROOM: Line 1 – 12-G/Community; Press Drives – 2 MAILROOM: Counter stackers – Count-O-Veyer/105; Inserters and stuffers – M; Bundle tying machines – MM/227; Wrapping singles – Si/ML2EE; Addressing machine – Wm.; Business Hardware – Vision Data

MOLINE

THE DISPATCH

1720 5th Ave., Moline, Ill., 61265-7907; gen tel (309) 764-4344; adv tel (309) 757-5019; ed tel (309) 757-4999; gen fax (309) 797-0311; adv fax (309) 797-0321; ed fax (309) 757-4992; gen e-mail info@qconline.com; adv e-mail advertising@qconline.com; ed e-mail press@qconline.com; web site www.qconline.com
Published: Mon, Tues, Wed, Thur, Fri, Sat, Sun
Weekday Frequency: m
Saturday Frequency: m
Circulation: 37,400; 41,800(sat); 43,500(sun)
Last Audit: Sworn March 31, 2006
Price: 4.45/wk; 12.00/mo; 161.20/yr.
News services: MCT, NYT, AP, NEA, Bloomberg.
Politics: Independent.
Note: Advertising is offered in combination with The Rock Island Argus (mS) for $61.06 (d) and $63.82 (S). Individual newspaper rates not made available.
Not Published: Christmas.
Own facility?: Y
Special Editions: QC Q & A (Aug); Holiday Gift Guide (Dec); Home Builders Show (Feb); Home Improvement (Jan); Back to School (Jul); Lawn & Garden (Mar); Summer Events (May); Holiday Cookbook (Nov); Fall Home Improvement (Oct); Bridal Guide (Sept).
Special Weekly Sections: TV Week (combined with Rock Island Argus) (S); Religion (Sat); Entertainment (Thur); Best Food Day (Wed).
Magazines: USA WEEKEND Magazine (S).
Pub. ....Gerald J. Taylor
Bus. Mgr. ....Scott Aswege
Dir., HR ....Donna Herbig
Adv. Mgr., Retail ....Rhoni Perrine
Dir., Promos./Special Projects ....Steve Flatt
Assoc. Mng. Ed. ....Mike Romkey
Editorial Page Ed. ....Kenda Burrows
Food Ed. ....Brandy Welvaert
Librarian....................................Laura Yeater
Life Ed.....................................Laura Fraembs
Metro Ed. ....Joe Beach
Online Ed. ....George Cottay
Photo Dir. ....Terry Herbig
Radio/TV Ed. ....Sean Leary
Religion Ed............................Leon Lagerstam
Science Ed. ....Carolyn Hardin
Sports Ed. ....Marc Nesseler
Data Processing Mgr...................Sue Gramling
Market Information: Split run; TMC; Zoned editions.
Mechanical available: Offset; Black and 3 ROP colors; insert accepted - self-adhesive notes.
Mechanical Specifications: Type page 11 5/8 x 21 1/2; E - 6 cols, 1 5/8, 1/8 between; A - 6 cols, 1 5/8, 1/8 between; C - 9 cols, 1 5/8, 1/8 between.
Commodity Consumption: Avg. Page Number Per Issue - Daily 39.15; Avg. Page Number Per Issue - Plates Used 26869; Avg. Page Number Per Issue - Sunday 99.15; widths 50; Newsprint Used - Short Tons 3660; Printing Ink Used - Black 46211; Printing Ink Used - Color 18480; Printing I
Equipment EDITORIAL: Front-end Software – XYQUEST/XyWrite, QPS 5.0.; Editorial Hardware – 1-CText, 1-IBM; Editorial Equipment – HP/ScanJet, PC 486; Editorial Printers – Epson/Laser II; Classified Hardware – 66-PC 486, 2-Gb HD 16 Mega-Ram; Classified Printers – Copal/600, HP, Compex/420. DISPLAY: Ad make-up applications – SCS/Layout 8000 10; Layout Software – SCSI.; Display Hardware – PC 486-66; Display Printers – HP/Laser II PRODUCTION: Pagination Software – QPS 5.0.; Production Equipment – 1-B/5000, 1-Anacoil/Subtractive, CK Optical/6%; Scanners – 2-AG/Duoscan T2000XL PRESSROOM: Line 1 – 7-HI/1650; Folders – 1-HI/3:2; Pasters – 6-HI/Registron; Reels and Stands – 6-HI/Registron. MAILROOM: Counter stackers – 3-QWI/401; Inserters and stuffers – GMA/SLS 2000; Bundle tying machines – 2-Dynaric/NP-1; Addressing machine – 1-Ch/715; Other equipment –MM/235 Stitcher-trimmer.; Business Hardware – 1-IBM/400, 10-IBM/PC
Delivery method: Mail, Newsstand, Private Carrier, Racks

MOLINE DISPATCH PUBLISHING COMPANY, L.L.C

1720 5th Ave., Moline, Ill., 61265; gen tel (309) 764-4344; gen fax (309) 797-0311
Published: Mon, Tues, Wed, Thur, Fri, Sat, Sun
Weekday Frequency: m
Saturday Frequency: m
Circulation: 36,135; 36,135(sat); 40,345(sun)

MONMOUTH

DAILY REVIEW ATLAS

400 S. Main St., Monmouth, Ill., 61462; gen tel (309) 734-3176; adv tel (309) 734-3176; ed tel (309) 734-3176; gen fax (309) 734-7649; adv fax (309) 734-7649; ed fax (309) 734-7649; web site www.reviewatlas.com
Published: Mon, Tues, Wed, Thur, Fri, Sat, Sun
Weekday Frequency: e
Saturday Frequency: m
Circulation: 3,159; 3,159(sat)
Last Audit: September 30, 1996
Price: 70.00/yr.
Advertising: Open inch rate $10.90
News services: AP.
Politics: Independent.
Not Published: New Year; Memorial Day; Independence Day; Labor Day; Christmas.
Magazines: Senior Citizens Magazine (Monthly); Weekend Update (Sat); Channel Guide-Television Guide Section (Weekly).
Gen. Mgr. ....Tony Scott
Adv. Mgr.....................................Wendy Todd
Circ. Mgr....................................Brian Elliott
Sports Ed. ....Marty Pouchette
Prodn. Mgr................................Barb Simmons
Market Information: TMC.
Mechanical available: Offset; Black and 3 ROP colors; insert accepted; page cutoffs - 22 3/4.
Mechanical Specifications: Type page 13 x 21 1/2; E - 6 cols, 2 1/16, 1/8 between; A - 6 cols, 1 3/8, 1/8 between; C - 9 cols, 1 3/8, 1/16 between.
Commodity Consumption: Avg. Page Number Per Issue - Daily 10; Avg. Page Number Per Issue - Plates Used 3696; widths 27 1/2; Newsprint Used - Short Tons 103; Printing Ink Used - Black 14000; Printing Ink Used - Color 2600; Printing Ink Used - Pages Printed 3696.
Equipment; Editorial Hardware – 6-Mk.; Classified Hardware – 4-APP/Mac.; Layout Software – APP/Mac Desktop, APP/Mac Plus. PRODUCTION: Pagination Software – Baseview.; Production Equipment – LE; Cameras – 1-B; Bundle tying machines – 2/Bu; Addressing machine – 2-/Am.; Business Hardware – 2-IBM/PC, AT

MORRIS

MORRIS DAILY HERALD

1804 Division St., Morris, Ill., 60450; gen tel (815) 942-3221; gen fax (815) 942-0988; gen e-mail news@morrisdailyherald.com; web site www.morrisdailyherald.com
Published: Tues, Wed, Thur, Fri, Sat
Weekday Frequency: e
Saturday Frequency: m
Circulation: 5,294; 5,294(sat)
Last Audit: September 30, 2009
Price: 2.00/wk; 93.60/yr.
Advertising: Open inch rate $15.88
News services: AP, NEA.
Politics: Republican.
Not Published: New Year; Memorial Day; Independence Day; Labor Day; Thanksgiving; Christmas.
Special Editions: Football (Aug); Vision (Feb); Basketball (Nov); Corn Fest (Sept).
Special Weekly Sections: Religion (Fri).
Magazines: USA WEEKEND Magazine (Fri); Relish (Monthly); American Profile (Weekly).
Pub. ....Gerry Burke
Adv. Mgr. ....Sandy Pistole
Mng. Ed.................................Patrick Graziano
City Ed. ....Mark Molone
Sports Ed. ....Tim Smith
Prodn. Foreman, Pressroom.....Doug Harrington
Mechanical available: Offset; Black and 3 ROP colors; insert accepted - any; page cutoffs - 22 3/4.
Mechanical Specifications: Type page 11 5/8 x 21 1/2; E - 6 cols, 1 5/6, 1/8 between; A - 6 cols, 1 5/6, 1/8 between; C - 8 cols, 1 17/50, 1/8 between.
Commodity Consumption: Avg. Page Number Per Issue - Daily 28; Avg. Page Number Per Issue - Plates Used 7000; widths 25; Newsprint Used - Metric Tons 350; Printing Ink Used - Black 8000; Printing Ink Used - Color 6000; Printing Ink Used - Pages Printed 6900.
Equipment EDITORIAL: Front-end Software – Baseview, QPS.; Editorial Hardware – 4-APP/iMac 2000, 4-APP/Mac G3 2000, APP/IBook 2000; Editorial Equipment – APP/Mac Scanner; Editorial Printers – 2-HP/Laser Printer, 2-HP/LaserPrinter CLASSIFIED: Front-end Software – Baseview, QPS.; Classified Hardware – 2-APP/iMac, 2-APP/G3; Classified Printers – 1-HP/LaserPrinter DISPLAY: Ad make-up applications – QPS/QuarkXPress; Layout Software – 2-APP/iMac 2000, 2-APP/G3.; Display Hardware – APP/Mac; Display Printers – 2-APP/Mac LaserPrinter PRODUCTION: Pagination Software – Baseview, QPS/QuarkXPress 4.0.; Production Equipment – 1-APP/Mac, Konic/5100T, Konica/EV Jetsetter, 1-APP/G4 2000, Konica/3100S, Konica/EV Jetsetter 2000; Cameras – B PRESSROOM: Line 1 – 8-G; Folders – 2 MAILROOM: Counter stackers – 2/BG; Bundle tying machines – 3-/BU; Addressing machine – 3-/Wm. BUSINESS COMPUTERS: Business Software – Vision Data; Business Hardware – 3-Bs, Dell, 3-APP/Mac

MORRIS PUBLISHING CO.

1804 Division St., Morris, Ill., 60450; gen tel (815) 942-3221; gen fax (815) 942-0988

MOUNT CARMEL

DAILY REPUBLICAN REGISTER

115 E. 4th St., Mount Carmel, Ill., 62863; gen tel (618) 262-5144; gen fax (618) 263-4437; adv fax (618) 263-4437; gen e-mail news@mtcarmelregister.com; adv e-mail creativeads@mtcarmelregister.com; web site www.tristate-media.com/drr
Published: Mon, Tues, Wed, Thur, Fri
Weekday Frequency: All day
Circulation: 3,581
Last Audit: Sworn October 10, 2003
Price: 7.00 to 13.16 mo; 84.00 to 158.00/yr.
Advertising: Open inch rate $12.15 Weekly & Annual contracts available.
Insert rate: $40m starting
News services: AP.
Politics: Independent. **Established:** 1839
Not Published: New Year; Memorial Day; Independence Day; Labor Day; Thanksgiving; Christmas.
Own facility?: Y
Special Editions: Bridal Fair, Healthy Lifestyles, Progress, Prom Expo (Jan); Soil & Water, Financial/Tax, FFA, Valentines, Savvy Lifestyles (Feb); Home & Garden, Kids & Family, Spring (Mar); Spring Car Care, Prom, Bridal, Easter (Apr); Mother's Day, Graduation, Memorial Day, Home Show, Savvy Lifestyles (May); Little League, Summer Coupon Book, Meet Your Merchants, Father's Day, Outstanding Student (Jun); 4th of July, Bridal, Ag Days, Various County Fairs, Christmas In July (Jul); 4-H, Guide to Edwards County, Fall Sports, Savvy Lifestyles, Back To School (Aug); Ribberfest, Labor Day, Parent & Child, Fall Home Improvement, Guide to Wabash County (Sep); Fall Coupon Book, Homecoming, Bridal, Firefighters Salute, Chamber of Commerce Annual (Oct); Holiday Gift Guide #1, Holiday Gift Guide #2, Savvy Lifestyles (Nov); Holiday Gift Guide #3, Holiday Gift Guide #4, Holiday Gift Guide #5, Songbook, Winter Sports, and Wellness Guide
Magazines: American Profile (Weekly-Tuesday); USA Weekend Edition (Weekly-Friday); Savvy Lifestyles (quarterly); Real Estate Homes (monthly) and Outdoor News (monthly).
Pub. ....Phil Summers
Features Ed...................................Phil Gower
News Ed. ....Laura Easter
Sports Ed. ....Bob Livingston
Mechanical available: Offset; Black and 3 ROP colors; insert accepted; page cutoffs - 22 3/4.
Mechanical Specifications: Type page 10.875 x 21; E - 6 cols, 1.708, 1/8 between; A - 6 cols, 1.708, 1/8 between; C - 8 cols, 1.25, 1/8 between.
Commodity Consumption: Avg. Page Number Per Issue - Daily 12; Avg. Page Number Per Issue - Plates Used 5500; widths 25; Newsprint Used - Short Tons 250; Printing Ink Used - Black 1800; Printing Ink Used - Color 200; Printing Ink Used - Pages Printed 9000.
Equipment EDITORIAL: Front-end Software – QPS/QuarkXPress.; Editorial Hardware – 5-APP/Mac; Editorial Printers – 2-APP/Mac LaserWriter CLASSIFIED: Front-end Software – Baseview.; Classified Hardware – 2-APP/Mac; Classified Printers – APP/Mac LaserWriter DISPLAY: Ad make-up applications – Multi-Ad/Creator 6.; Display Hardware – 3-APP/Mac; Display Printers – APP/Mac LaserWriter PRODUCTION: Pagination Software – QPS/QuarkXPress 4.0.; Inserters and stuffers – Inserting done by hand.; Bundle tying machines – 1-Sa/50; Addressing machine – Wing-mailed labels. BUSINESS COMPUTERS: Business Software – Comet; Business Hardware – 2-PC
Zip Codes served: 62863, 62811, 62852, 62855, 62818, 62815, 62806, 62844, 62410, 62476 and mixed zips.
Delivery method: Mail, Newsstand, Private Carrier, Racks

MOUNT VERNON

REGISTER-NEWS

911 Broadway St., Mount Vernon, Ill., 62864; gen tel (618) 242-0113; gen fax (618) 242-8286; web site www.register-news.com
Published: Mon, Tues, Wed, Thur, Sat
Weekday Frequency: e

Saturday Frequency: m
Circulation: 10,260; 10,260(sat)
Last Audit: September 30, 1997
Price: 7.50/mo; 84.00/yr (mail); 22.00/3mo.
Advertising: Open inch rate $13.44
News services: AP.
Politics: Independent.
Special Editions: Lawn & Garden (Apr); Sweetcorn/Watermelon Festival (Aug); Christmas (Dec); Focus (Feb); Bridal (Jan); Illinois Engine Show (Jul); Father's Day (Jun); Home Improvement (Mar); Mother's Day (May); Christmas Openings (Nov); Fall Home Improvement (Oct); Cedar
Special Weekly Sections: Business (Fri); Church Page (Sat); Best Food Day (Wed).
Magazines: Relish (Monthly); USA WEEKEND Magazine (Sat).
Pub...Bob Dennis
Bus. Mgr..................................Brenda Moore
Adv. Mgr...Erin Smith
Mng. Ed.......................................Jeremy Hall
City Ed...Paul Lorenz
Market Information: TMC; Zoned editions.
Mechanical available: Offset; Black and 3 ROP colors; insert accepted; page cutoffs - 22 3/4.
Mechanical Specifications: Type page 13 x 21 1/2; E - 6 cols, 2 1/16, 1/8 between; A - 6 cols, 2 1/16, 1/8 between; C - 9 cols, 1 3/8, 1/16 between.
Commodity Consumption: Avg. Page Number Per Issue - Daily 28.
Equipment EDITORIAL: Front-end Software – Baseview.; Editorial Hardware – APP/Mac; Editorial Equipment – APP/Mac; Editorial Printers – APP/Mac CLASSIFIED: Front-end Software – Baseview.; Classified Hardware – APP/Mac; Classified Printers – APP/Mac, HP/4V DISPLAY: Ad make-up applications – Baseview; Layout Software – Adforce.; Display Hardware – APP/Mac; Display Printers – APP/Mac, HP/5V PRODUCTION: Pagination Software – Baseview.; Production Equipment – 1-Nu; Cameras – 1-Acti/V24; Scanners – Lf/Leafscan 35, APP/Mac, AVR, Microtek PRESSROOM: Line 1 – 9-G/Community; Folders – 1; Bundle tying machines – 1/Bu, 1-/Malow. BUSINESS COMPUTERS: Business Software – Vision Data; Business Hardware – HP

OLNEY

OLNEY DAILY MAIL

206 Whittle Ave., Olney, Ill., 62450; gen tel (618) 393-2931; gen fax (618) 392-2953; adv e-mail Advertising2@olneydailymail.com; ed e-mail editor@olneydailymail.com; web site www.olneydailymail.com
Group: GateHouse Media
Published: Mon, Tues, Wed, Thur, Fri
Weekday Frequency: e
Circulation: 3,675
Last Audit: Sworn September 26, 1998
Price: 115.50/yr.
Advertising: Open inch rate $17.15
News services: AP.
Politics: Independent. **Established:** 1898
Not Published: New Year; Memorial Day; Independence Day; Labor Day; Thanksgiving; Christmas.
Own facility?: Y
Special Editions: Its About Family
Richland County Shopper
Special Weekly Sections: School Life (Tues).
Magazines: American Profile (Weekly).
Spry (Monthly).
USA Weekend (Weekly).
Office Mgr...................................Leslie Geier
Editor..Mark Allen
Publisher.....................................Ray McGrew
Prodn. Supvr., Press................Mark Roberson
Market Information: TMC.
Mechanical available: Offset; Black and 3 ROP colors; insert accepted; page cutoffs - 21 1/2.
Mechanical Specifications: Type page 10.5 x 21 1/2; E - 6 cols, 1/6 between; A - 6 cols, 1/6 between; C - 8 cols, 1/6 between.
Commodity Consumption: Avg. Page Number Per Issue - Daily 14; Avg. Page Number Per Issue - Plates Used 3600; Avg. Page Number Per Issue - Saturday 12; widths 23; Newsprint Used - Short Tons 200; Printing Ink Used - Black 4840; Printing Ink Used - Color 700; Printing Ink Us
Equipment EDITORIAL: Front-end Software – Adobe CLASSIFIED: Front-end Software – TC.; Classified Hardware – Apple; Classified Printers – HP DISPLAY: Ad make-up applications – Adobe PRESSROOM: Line 1 – 7-G/Community 1965.; Business Hardware – IBM

OTTAWA

THE TIMES

110 W. Jefferson St., Ottawa, Ill., 61350-0618; gen tel (815) 433-2000; adv tel (815) 433-2002; ed tel (815) 433-2000; adv fax (815) 433-1626; ed fax (815) 433-1639; gen e-mail dtimes@udnet.net; adv e-mail sherryp@ottawadailytimes.com; ed e-mail press@inottawa.com; web site www.mywebtimes.com
Published: Mon, Tues, Wed, Thur, Fri, Sat, Sun
Weekday Frequency: e
Saturday Frequency: m
Circulation: 14,064; 14,064(sat)
Last Audit: September 30, 2009
Price: 2.10/wk; 105.00/yr.
Advertising: Open inch rate $18.90
News services: NEA, AP, TMS.
Politics: Republican.
Not Published: New Year; Memorial Day; Independence Day; Labor Day; Thanksgiving; Christmas.
Special Editions: Spring Lawn & Garden (Apr); Football Preview (Aug); Holiday Gift Guide (Dec); Spring Farm (Feb); Bridal Guide (Jan); Summer Farm (Jul); Dining & Entertainment (Jun); Home Improvement (Mar); Graduation (May); Real Estate/Realtor Guide (Monthly); Basketball
Magazines: Parade (Weekly).
Pub...John Newby
Bus. Mgr.......................................Cindy Liptak
Adv. Mgr................................Sherry Patterson
Adv. Supvr., Classified................Mindy Crouch
Circ. Dir................................Cynthia J. Liptak
Editorial Page Ed...........................Dan Hrabel
Online Ed........................................Lonny Cain
Photo Ed....Tom Sistak
Wire Ed.....................................Paul Carpenter
Mgr., Electronics..........................Jerry Battles
Prodn. Foreman, Press.................Richard Todd
Prodn. Mgr., Mailroom................Art Dougherty
Mechanical available: Offset; Black and 3 ROP colors; insert accepted - all; page cutoffs - 22 3/4.
Mechanical Specifications: Type page 13 x 21 1/2; E - 6 cols, 2 1/16, 1/8 between; A - 6 cols, 2 1/16, 1/8 between; C - 10 cols, 1 3/16, 1/16 between.
Commodity Consumption: Avg. Page Number Per Issue - Daily 22; widths 27 1/2; Newsprint Used - Metric Tons 622; Printing Ink Used - Black 27000; Printing Ink Used - Color 2000; Printing Ink Used - Pages Printed 6906.
Equipment EDITORIAL: Front-end Software – Cascade/Imageflow, FSI/Edit, FSI/Pagination.; Editorial Hardware – 13-APP/Mac, 8-APP/Mac G3, 1-APP/Power Mac G3 Server, 1-Sun/Sparc Station 5, 1-Microsoft/Windows NT Server; Editorial Printers – APP/Mac LaserWriter Pro 630 CLASSIFIED: Front-end Software – FSI/Class, QPS/QuarkXPress 4.04.; Classified Hardware – 3-DTK/PC; Classified Printers – HP/MP3 DISPLAY: Ad make-up applications – Multi-Ad/Creator 2 3.7.1, Intermedia; Display Hardware – 1-APP/Mac IIsi, 1-APP/Mac Centris 610; Display Printers – 1-APP/Mac Pro 630, HP/Color Laserjet 4500 N PRODUCTION: Pagination Software – QPS/QuarkXPress 4.04, FSI.; Production Equipment – TI/OmniPage 3.0, APP/Mac Laser Pro 8800, 2-Pre Press/Panther Pro 36; Cameras – R/480; Scanners – 2-Umax/1200 Flatbed Scanner, 1-Nikon/3510 Slide Film Scanner, 1-Polaroid/CoolScan 2000 PRESSROOM: Line 1 – 7-G/Urbanite (balloon former) 1968; Folders – 1-G/2:1.; Bundle tying machines – Bu/16, MLN/ML2, 2-Bu/Tying Machine, 1-MLN/MLE 22 Strapper; Addressing machine – 2-Sp/2605.; Business Hardware – 1-Magitronic, PC 486, 7-Wyse/Model 50, Microsoft/Windows NT Server, 6-PC

PARIS

PARIS BEACON-NEWS

218 N. Main St., Paris, Ill., 61944-0100; gen tel (217) 465-6424; adv tel (217) 465-6424; ed tel (217) 465-6424; gen fax (217) 466-5078; adv fax (217) 466-5078; ed fax (217) 466-5078; adv e-mail advertising@parisbeacon.com; circulation@parisbeacon.com; ed e-mail news@parisbeacon.com; web site www.parisbeacon.com
Published: Mon, Tues, Wed, Thur, Fri, Sat
Weekday Frequency: e
Circulation: 5,002; 5,002(sat)
Last Audit: September 29, 2004
Price: 2.00/wk (carrier); 96.00/yr (mail).
Advertising: Open inch rate $10.00
News services: AP, CNS.
Politics: Independent-Republican. **Established:** 1848
Not Published: New Year; Memorial Day; Independence Day; Labor Day; Thanksgiving; Christmas.
Special Weekly Sections: Weekender (Fri).
Magazines: American Profile (Fri).
Pub....Kevin Cothron
Circ. Dir.....................................Melody Newby
Online Ed...................................Kathy Rhoads
School Ed.......................................Gary Henry
Sports Ed.....................................Scott Dosch
Mechanical available: Offset; Black and 3 ROP colors; insert accepted; page cutoffs - 22 3/4.
Mechanical Specifications: Type page 13 3/4 x 21; E - 6 cols, 2, 1/8 between; A - 6 cols, 2, 1/16 between; C - 8 cols, 1 3/8, 1/8 between.
Commodity Consumption: Avg. Page Number Per Issue - Daily 12; Avg. Page Number Per Issue - Saturday 8; widths 28; Newsprint Used - Short Tons 170; Printing Ink Used - Black 5700; Printing Ink Used - Color 250.
Equipment EDITORIAL: Front-end Software – QPS/QuarkXPress 3.31, Adobe/Photoshop 4.0.6, Aldus/FreeHand 4.0; Editorial Hardware – APP/Mac 6100, APP/Power Mac 7100, Ap/iMac-APP/Power Mac G3; Editorial Equipment – Polaroid/SprintScan 35, Microtek/Scan Maker II; Editorial Printers – HP/LaserJet IV Plus, NewGen/Imager 12 CLASSIFIED: Front-end Software – QPS/QuarkXPress 3.31.; Classified Hardware – APP/Power Mac 6100; Classified Printers – NewGen/Imager 12 DISPLAY: Ad make-up applications – Multi-Ad/Creator 4.0.; Display Hardware – APP/Power Mac 6100; Display Printers – NewGen/Imager Plus 12; Production Equipment – COM/7900 Universal, APP/Mac LaserWriter; Cameras – 1-B, R, LE/500; Scanners – Polaroid/SprintScan 35, Microtek/Scan Maker II. PRESSROOM: Line 1 – 6-G/Community (double former). MAILROOM: Counter stackers – 1-BG/Count-O-Veyor; Bundle tying machines – 1/Bu; Addressing machine – 1-/Dispensa-Matic. BUSINESS COMPUTERS: Business Software – Baseview/Circulation Pro; Business Hardware – APP/Power Mac 6300

PEKIN

PEKIN DAILY TIMES

20 S. Fourth St., Pekin, Ill., 61555; gen tel (309) 346-1111; adv tel (309) 346-1111; ed tel (309) 346-1111; gen fax (309) 346-9815; adv fax (309) 346-9815; ed fax (309) 346-1446; adv e-mail advertise@pekintimes.com; ed e-mail news@pekintimes.com; web site www.pekintimes.com
Published: Mon, Tues, Wed, Thur, Fri, Sat, Sun
Weekday Frequency: e
Saturday Frequency: m
Circulation: 10,767; 10,767(sat)
Last Audit: September 30, 2001
Price: 2.45/wk; 122.00/yr.
Advertising: Open inch rate $21.00
News services: AP, TMS.
Politics: Independent.
Not Published: New Year; Memorial Day; Independence Day; Labor Day; Christmas.
Special Weekly Sections: Religion (Fri); Local Features (Sat); Kid's Page (Tues); Home and Garden (Wed).
Magazines: American Profile (Sat); Parade (Weekly).
Pub....Gregg Ratliff
Bus. Mgr.................................Mike Vetroczky
Adv. Dir.....................................Michelle Long
Circ. Mgr......................................Tony Marino
Ed...Michelle Teheux
Graphics Ed./Art Dir...................Dennis Mitchell
Sports Ed...Jim Haas
Market Information: Split run; TMC; Zoned editions.
Mechanical available: Offset; Black and 3 ROP colors; insert accepted; page cutoffs - 22 3/4.
Mechanical Specifications: Type page 11 1/2 x 21 1/2; E - 6 cols, 1 39/50, 1/8 between; A - 6 cols, 1 39/50, 1/16 between; C - 9 cols, 1 13/100, 1/8 between.
Commodity Consumption: Avg. Page Number Per Issue - Daily 25; Avg. Page Number Per Issue - Plates Used 4200; widths 25; Newsprint Used - Metric Tons 800; Printing Ink Used - Black 18000; Printing Ink Used - Color 1500; Printing Ink Used - Pages Printed 7800.
Equipment EDITORIAL: Front-end Software – Sun/OS 413 UBI, Solaris 2.6, Linux 6.1.; Editorial Hardware – Sun/Sparc Station, APP/Mac G3; Editorial Printers – HP/Laserjet 4 MV, HP/4050; Classified Hardware – 1-OS/40, Sun/Ultra; Classified Printers – Hp/4MV.; Layout Software – APP/Mac G3. PRODUCTION: Pagination Software – QPS/QuarkXPress 4.1.; Production Equipment – 1-Nu, 2-APP/Mac LaserWriter, ECR/Autokon, ECR/Pelbox 1085; Cameras – 1-R/580; Scanners – Nikon/LS 1000, Epson/836X1 PRESSROOM: Line 1 – 7-G/Urbanite; Folders – 1; Reels and Stands – 1-G/8. MAILROOM: Counter stackers – 2-Id/Marathon; Inserters and stuffers – 1/MM; Bundle tying machines – 2-Bu/201; Wrapping singles – 1-/Cr; Addressing machine – 1-/Am, 1-Ch/527.; Business Hardware – 2-ATT/3B1, 1-Sun/Sparc 402

PEORIA

JOURNAL STAR

1 News Plz., Peoria, Ill., 61614-8033; gen tel (309) 686-3000; adv tel (309) 686-3035 (national); ed tel (309) 686-3296; adv fax (309) 686-3079 (class); gen e-mail news@pjstar.com; web site www.pjstar.com
Published: Mon, Tues, Wed, Thur, Fri, Sat, Sun
Weekday Frequency: m
Saturday Frequency: m
Circulation: 59,090; 63,192(sat); 71,946(sun)
Last Audit: ABC September 30, 2011
Price: 4.25/wk; 210.60/yr.
News services: AP, LAT-WP, SNS, CNS, TMS.
Politics: Independent.
Note: The Peoria Journal Star(mS) has a combination rate of $86.16(d) and $97.30(S) with the Galesburg Register-Mail(eS). Individual newspaper rates not made available.
Special Weekly Sections: Kids (Mon); Home Builder (S); TV Week (Sat); Business (Tues); Best Food Day (Wed).
Magazines: Active Times (Monthly); Parade (S); Cue (Entertainment/Leisure Guide) (Thur).
Controller......................................Brian Kier
Vice Pres./Gen. Mgr......................Ken Mauser
Asst. Gen. Mgr..............................Gene Clime
Asst. Gen. Mgr.......................Justin McConnell
Credit Mgr.....................................Joe Dunlap
Adv. Mgr., Retail.........................Sue Patterson
Mgr., Mktg./Pub. Affairs..................Phil Jordan
Circ. Mgr....................................Bruce Nielsen
Mng. Ed.......................................John Plevka

Asst. Mng. Ed., Sunday Features/Servs. Sally McKee
Bus. Ed. ....Paul Gordon
City Ed., Night ....Anthony Smith
Entertainment Ed. ....Danielle Hatch
Head Librarian................................Judy Hicks
Lifestyles Ed. ....Jennifer Davis
Metro Ed...Mike Cecil
Neighbors Ed. ....Jennifer Towery
News Ed. ....Kelly VanLaningham
Market Information: Split run; TMC; Zoned editions.
Mechanical available: Offset; Black and 3 ROP colors; insert accepted; page cutoffs - 21 1/2.
Mechanical Specifications: Type page 11 5/8 x 20 53/100; E - 6 cols, 1 5/6, 3/16 between; A - 6 cols, 1 5/6, 3/16 between; C - 9 cols, 1 6/25, 3/32 between.
Commodity Consumption: Avg. Page Number Per Issue - Daily 42; Avg. Page Number Per Issue - Plates Used 96000; Avg. Page Number Per Issue - Sunday 82; widths 50; Newsprint Used - Metric Tons 8000; Printing Ink Used - Black 115000; Printing Ink Used - Color 71000; Printing Ink U
Equipment EDITORIAL: Front-end Software – ATS/Media Desk 3.4.; Editorial Hardware – HI/NewsMaker CLASSIFIED: Front-end Software – HI/AD Power 2.3, ADPAG.; Classified Hardware – HI/AD Power; Classified Printers – HP/8500 DISPLAY: Ad make-up applications – AII/Ad Manager 5, Multi-Ad/Creator 6.5; Layout Software – SCS/Layout 8000 10.; Display Hardware – APP/Power Mac PRODUCTION: Pagination Software – HI/AdPag.; Production Equipment – Glunz & Jensen/85V, Adobe/Photoshop; Cameras – 1-B/24, 1-C/Newspager II; Scanners – 5-Nikon, 1-Eskofot/2034 PRESSROOM: Line 1 – 6-MAN/Geoman; Reels and Stands – MAN/CD13 Reel Splicer; Press registration system – Grafikontrol. MAILROOM: Counter stackers – 4-QWI/500, 3-QWI/300, 1-GMA/6 Station Buffer, 2-GMA/Unwinders; Inserters and stuffers – 2-GMA/16:2; Bundle tying machines – 8-Dynaric; Wrapping singles – 4-QWI/Bottom Wrap.; Audio Hardware – Brite, Accu-Weather, AP Stockquote II, Brite; Business Hardware – IBM/AS-400 620

PONTIAC

THE DAILY LEADER

318 N. Main St., Pontiac, Ill., 61764-1930; gen tel (815) 842-1153; adv fax (815) 842-4388; gen e-mail ldrnews@mchsi.com; web site www.pontiacdailyleader.com
Published: Mon, Tues, Wed, Thur, Sat
Weekday Frequency: e
Saturday Frequency: m
Circulation: 4,784; 4,784(sat)
Price: 9.90/mo; 106.60/yr.
Advertising: Open inch rate $11.87
News services: AP.
Politics: Independent.
Not Published: New Year; Memorial Day; Independence Day; Labor Day; Christmas.
Special Editions: Progress (Mar).
Special Weekly Sections: Business Page (Thur); Agriculture Page (Tues).
Magazines: USA WEEKEND Magazine (Sat); American Profile (Weekly).
Pub. ....Pam Mc Dowell
Adv. Mgr. ....Gary DeVault
Circ. Mgr. ....Roger Swearingen
News Ed./Sports Ed. ....Erich Murphy
Prodn. Mgr. ....Linda Melvin
Market Information: TMC.
Mechanical available: Offset; Black and 3 ROP colors; insert accepted; page cutoffs - 22 3/4.
Mechanical Specifications: Type page 13 x 21 1/2; E - 6 cols, 2 1/16, 1/8 between; A - 6 cols, 2 1/16, 1/8 between; C - 8 cols, 1 1/2, 1/4 between.
Commodity Consumption: Avg. Page Number Per Issue - Daily 14; Avg. Page Number Per Issue - Plates Used 6000; Avg. Page Number Per Issue - Saturday 10; widths 27 1/2; Newsprint Used - Short Tons 700; Printing Ink Used - Black 20000; Printing Ink Used - Color 3000; Printing Ink
Equipment EDITORIAL: Front-end Software – Baseview. CLASSIFIED: Front-end Software – CAMS, Multi-Ad. DISPLAY: Ad make-up applications – Multi-Ad/Creator, QPS/QuarkXPress.; Production Equipment – 2-B/2332; Cameras – 1-R/580, 1-VG/POS-1-CPS. PRESSROOM: Line 1 – 6-G/Community; Line 2 – Cole/Rotary Trimmer; Folders – 1, 1. MAILROOM: Counter stackers – 1-BG/Count-O-Veyor; Bundle tying machines – 2/Bu, 2-/Malow; Addressing machine – 1-MG/1530.

QUINCY

THE QUINCY HERALD-WHIG

130 S. Fifth St., Quincy, Ill., 62301; gen tel (217) 223-5100; adv tel (217) 221-3303; adv fax (217) 221-3397; ed fax (217) 221-3395; gen e-mail whig@whig.com; ed e-mail mhilfrink@whig.com; web site www.whig.com
Group: Metro Newspaper Advertising Services, Inc.
Published: Mon, Tues, Wed, Thur, Fri, Sat, Sun
Weekday Frequency: e
Saturday Frequency: m
Circulation: 17,070; 17,070(sat); 20,872(sun)
Last Audit: ABC September 30, 2011
Price: 11.35/mo; 128.05/yr; 34.05/3mo, $19.50/3mo (wknd only).
Advertising: Open inch rate $34.72
News services: AP, Scripps-Howard.
Politics: Independent.
Not Published: New Year; Memorial Day; Independence Day; Labor Day; Thanksgiving; Christmas.
Special Editions: Home Improvement (Apr); Progress (Mar); Basketball (Nov); Car Care (Oct); Fast Forward (Quarterly); Football (Sept).
Special Weekly Sections: Home and Garden (Mon); Workplace (S); Food (Wed).
Magazines: Parade (S); TV Week Mini Book (Sat).
Broadcast Affiliations: KTIV-TV Sioux City, IA; WGEM-AM/WGEM-FM Quincy, IL; WGEM-TV Quincy, IL; WREX Rockford, IL; WSJV-TV Elkhart, IN; KTTC-TV Rochester, MN; WVVA-TV Bluefield, WV.
Gen. Mgr. ....Michael B. Hilfrink
Pub. ....Thomas A. Oakley
Adv. Dir. ....Tom Kelling
Adv. Mgr., Sales.................Karen Shanholtzer
Editorial Page Ed. ....Doug Wilson
Farm Ed. ....Debbie Gurtz Husar
Features Ed. ....Don Crim
Page 1 Ed....................................Kevin Murphy
Photo Ed.....................................Phil Carlson
Sports Ed. ....Don O'Brien
Online Contact...........................Holly Wagner
Prodn. Dir., Opns..................Joe Genenbacher
Market Information: Split run; TMC.
Mechanical available: Offset; Black and 3 ROP colors; insert accepted; page cutoffs - 22.
Mechanical Specifications: Type page 12 x 21; E - 6 cols, 2 1/16, 1/8 between; A - 6 cols, 2 1/16, 1/8 between; C - 9 cols, 1 3/8, 1/16 between.
Commodity Consumption: Avg. Page Number Per Issue - Daily 24; Avg. Page Number Per Issue - Plates Used 21500; Avg. Page Number Per Issue - Sunday 52; widths 12 1/2; Newsprint Used - Metric Tons 1550; Printing Ink Used - Black 42000; Printing Ink Used - Color 28000; Printing In
Equipment EDITORIAL: Front-end Software – Baseview 8.0.; Editorial Hardware – APP/Mac; Editorial Equipment – APP/Mac; Editorial Printers – Page/Marq 20, Lexmark CLASSIFIED: Front-end Software – Baseview.; Classified Hardware – APP/Mac; Classified Printers – Okidata/192 DISPLAY: Ad make-up applications – Multi-Ad/Creator, QPS/QuarkXPress; Layout Software – APP/Mac.; Display Hardware – 5-APP/Mac 7300-120; Display Printers – 2-LaserMaster/1000, Compaq/20 PRODUCTION: Pagination Software – Baseview 8.0, QPS/QuarkXPress.; Production Equipment – Pre Press/Panther Pro 13.3, Pre Press/Panther Plus 46; Cameras – R; Scanners – Microtek, Microtek/600ZS Scanner, PixelCraft/8200, Nikon/Coolscan 1000 PRESSROOM: Line 1 – 8-G/Urbanite 1989; Folders – 1 MAILROOM: Counter stackers – HL/Monitors; Inserters and stuffers – HI/13/72; Bundle tying machines – MLN/330, MLN/LS 300, Dynaric; Mailroom control system – 1-MM/Stitcher-Trimmer 948125. AUDIO: Audio Software – SMS; Audio Hardware – Voice News Network, SMS, IBM/Pentium BUSINESS COMPUTERS: Business Software – INSI: Bus, Circ; Business Hardware – IBM/AS-400

ROBINSON

DAILY NEWS

302 S. Cross St., Robinson, Ill., 62454; gen tel (618) 544-2101; adv tel (618) 544-2101; ed tel (618) 544-2101; gen fax (618) 544-9533; adv fax (618) 544-9533; ed fax (618) 544-9533; adv e-mail ads@robdailynews.com; ed e-mail news@robdailynews.com; web site www.robdailynews.com
Published: Mon, Tues, Wed, Thur, Fri, Sat, Sun
Weekday Frequency: e
Saturday Frequency: m
Circulation: 5,933; 5,933(sat)
Last Audit: September 30, 2003
Price: 1.25/wk; 5.00/mo; 59.00/yr.
Advertising: Open inch rate $9.50
News services: AP.
Not Published: New Year; Memorial Day; Independence Day; Labor Day; Thanksgiving; Christmas.
Special Editions: American Homes (Apr); LTC (Aug); Tax Guide (Feb); 4-H Fair (Jul); Agriculture (Mar); Heath Toffee Festival (May); Veteran's Salute (Nov); Working Women (Oct); Robinson Fall Festival (Sept).
Pub./Bus. Mgr./Sec./Treasurer.........Kathy Lewis
Adv. Mgr., Classified ....Dinah Corder
Circ. Mgr., Promo. ....Bob Fox
Ed...Greg Bilbney
Social Ed. ....Michelle Wagner
Sports Ed.....................................Josh Brown
Data Processing Mgr. ....Winnie Piper
Prodn. Foreman, Press...........Gregg Cummins
Mechanical available: Offset; Black and 4 ROP colors; insert accepted; page cutoffs - 21.
Mechanical Specifications: Type page 13 x 21; E - 6 cols, 1 5/6, 1/8 between; A - 6 cols, 1 5/6, 1/8 between; C - 9 cols, 1 1/6, 1/8 between.
Commodity Consumption: Avg. Page Number Per Issue - Daily 16.
Equipment EDITORIAL: Front-end Software – Baseview, QPS/QuarkXPress, Adobe/Photoshop.; Editorial Hardware – 7-Mk, 7-APP/Mac; Editorial Printers – Xante, LaserMaster/Unity; Classified Hardware – APP/Mac, Sun; Classified Printers – Xante, LaserMaster/Unity, QMS. DISPLAY: Ad make-up applications – Multi-Ad/Creator, QPS, Adobe/Photoshop, Adobe/Illustrator; Layout Software – APP/Mac.; Display Hardware – APP/Mac; Display Printers – Xante, LaserMaster/Unity; Production Equipment – 2-COM/Unisetter, 1-COM/4961, 1-COM/7200; Cameras – 1-B/Caravel. PRESSROOM: Line 1 – 6-G/Community; Folders – 1-G/2:1. MAILROOM: Counter stackers – 1-BG/Count-O-Veyor; Bundle tying machines – 2/Bu; Mailroom control system – Addressing machine Â□ 1-Am/Speed-umat 2600. BUSINESS COMPUTERS: Business Software – Baseview; Business Hardware – Mk, APP/Mac

ROCK ISLAND

THE ROCK ISLAND ARGUS

1724 4th Ave., Rock Island, Ill., 61201-7907; gen tel (309) 764-4344; adv tel (309) 764-4344; ed tel (309) 797-0321; gen fax (309) 797-0321; adv fax (309) 797-0321; ed fax (309) 797-0321; gen e-mail press@qconline.com; adv e-mail advertising@qconline.com; ed e-mail press@qconline.com; web site www.qconline.com
Published: Mon, Tues, Wed, Thur, Fri, Sat, Sun
Weekday Frequency: m
Saturday Frequency: m
Circulation: 36,146; 36,146(sat); 40,365(sun)
Last Audit: Sworn March 31, 2006
Price: 4.2/wk; 16.99/mo; 218.40/yr.
News services: AP, NEA, NYT, MCT, CNS.
Politics: Independent.
Note: Advertising offered in combination with The Moline Dispatch (mS) for $61.06 (d) and $63.82 (S). Individual newspaper rates not made available.
Not Published: Christmas.
Own facility?: Y
Special Editions: Home Improvement (Apr); Football (Aug); Last Minute Gift Guide (Dec); Progress (Feb); PGA Golf Event (Jul); Lawn & Garden (Mar); Summer Events (May); Holiday Cookbook (Nov); Bridal Guide (Oct); Home Improvement (Sept).
Special Weekly Sections: Business (Other); Farm Page (S); Church Page (Sat); Entertainment (Thur); Best Food Day (Wed).
Magazines: USA WEEKEND Magazine (S).
Adv. Dir. ....Val Yazbec
Adv. Mgr., Nat'l ....Jessico Licko
Adv. Mgr., Nat'l ....Jon Melin
Adv. Mgr., Retail ....Will Parks
Mgr., Promo./Special Projects...........Steve Flatt
Circ. Dir. ....John Newby
Ed. ....Gerald J. Taylor
Mng. Ed...............................Roger Ruthhart
Assoc. Mng. Ed. ....Mike Romkey
Action Line Ed...................................Jeff Dick
Bus./Finance Ed. ....Joe Beach
Columnist......................................John Marx
Editorial Page Ed. ....Murray Hancks
Features Ed. ....Joe Payne
Film/Theater Ed. ....Sean Leary
Market Information: Split run.
Mechanical available: Offset; Black and 3 ROP colors; insert accepted - self-adhesive notes.
Mechanical Specifications: Type page 13 x 21 1/2; E - 6 cols, 1 5/6, 1/8 between; A - 6 cols, 1 5/6, 1/8 between; C - 9 cols, 1 1/4, 1/16 between.
Commodity Consumption: Avg. Page Number Per Issue - Daily 39.15; Avg. Page Number Per Issue - Plates Used 26814; Avg. Page Number Per Issue - Sunday 99.15; widths 50; Newsprint Used - Short Tons 1972; Printing Ink Used - Black 22464; Printing Ink Used - Color 8685; Printing In
Equipment EDITORIAL: Front-end Software – XYQUEST/XyWrite, QPS/QuarkXPress 5.; Editorial Hardware – 1-CText; Editorial Equipment – HP/ScanJet, PC 486-66; Editorial Printers – Software □ XYQUEST/XyWrite, QPS/QuarkXPress 5. CLASSIFIED: Front-end Software – Ward-Vision.; Classified Hardware – PC 486 66Mhz; Classified Equipment – Copal/600, Comrex/420; Classified Printers – HP DISPLAY: Ad make-up applications – SCS/Layout 8000 10; Layout Software – SCS.; Display Hardware – PC 486-66; Display Printers – HP/Laser II PRODUCTION: Pagination Software – QPS 3.3.; Production Equipment – Anacoil, AG/3850; Scanners – AG/Horizon PRESSROOM: Line 1 – 7-HI/1650; Folders – 2-HI/3:2; Pasters – 6-HI/Registron; Reels and Stands – 6-HI/Registron.; Inserters and stuffers – GMA/SLS 2000; Addressing machine – 1-Ch/715.; Business Hardware – 1-IBM/400, 10-IBM

ROCKFORD

ROCKFORD REGISTER STAR

99 E. State St., Rockford, Ill., 61104; gen tel (815) 987-1200; adv tel (815) 987-1300; ed tel (815) 987-1359; gen fax (815) 964-2472; adv fax (815) 962-6578; ed fax (815) 987-1365; web site www.rrstar.com
Group: Metro Newspaper Advertising Services, Inc.
Published: Mon, Tues, Wed, Thur, Fri, Sat, Sun
Weekday Frequency: m
Saturday Frequency: m
Circulation: 53,661; 41,598(sat); 60,548(sun)

Last Audit: ABC September 30, 2011
Price: 3.75/wk; 195.00/yr.
Advertising: Open inch rate $164.92
News services: AP, GNS, MCT, LAT-WP.
Politics: Independent. **Established:** 1855
Advertising not accepted: Y
Own facility?: Y
Special Editions: Real Estate Marketplace (Monthly).
Special Weekly Sections: Wheels (Fri); Business Monday (Mon); Go (Other); Real Estate (S); Espejo (Weekly).
Magazines: USA WEEKEND Magazine (S); American Profile (Weekly).
Adv. Mgr., Classified ....Michele Massoth
Circ. Mgr., Opns. ....Joe Schlickman
Asst. Mng. Ed. ....Doug Gass
Asst. Mng. Ed. ....Jennifer Pollock
Editorial Page Ed............................Wally Haas
Sports Ed. ....Randy Ruef
Prodn. Dir. ....Kris Smith
Prodn. Mgr., Bldg. Serv./Distr. Ctr......Tom Hickey
Pub. ....Scott Bowers
Gen. Mgr........................................Tom Lasley
Exec. Ed.......................Linda G. Cunningham
News Ed....................................Marv Clemons
Prodn. Mgr..................................Carey Sydow
Prodn. Mgr., Press Opns..................Steve Rock
Market Information: TMC.
Mechanical available: Offset; Black and 3 ROP colors; insert accepted.
Mechanical Specifications: Type page 11 1/8 x 19 1/4; E - 6 cols, 1 3/4, 1/8 between; A - 6 cols, 1 3/4, 1/8 between; C - 10 cols, 1 2/25, 1/25 between.
Commodity Consumption: Avg. Page Number Per Issue - Daily 40; Avg. Page Number Per Issue - Plates Used 66075; Avg. Page Number Per Issue - Saturday 48; Avg. Page Number Per Issue - Sunday 72; widths 12; Newsprint Used - Metric Tons 8177; Newsprint Used - Short Tons 9014; Print
Equipment EDITORIAL: Front-end Software – Saxotech.; Editorial Hardware – SII/Synthesis 66XR, Tandem/K1000; Editorial Printers – HP/LaserJet IV, HP/DesignJet 755CM CLASSIFIED: Front-end Software – SII/Release 6.0.1, ATS.; Classified Hardware – Tandem/K1000, SII DISPLAY: Ad make-up applications – QPS/QuarkXPress 4.11, Multi-Ad/Creator 2; Layout Software – Managing Editor/ALS, Adobe/InDesign.; Display Hardware – 13-APP/Mac; Display Printers – HP/LaserJet 4MV, HP/8100, HP/755CM, HP/1055CM PRODUCTION: Pagination Software – MEI/ALS.; Production Equipment – 1-Pre Press/Panther, 1-AG/Avantra; Scanners – Microtek/Scanmaker III, Epson/836XL PRESSROOM: Line 1 – KBA 2006; Folders – 2, 2-KBA; Reels and Stands – 8, 6-KBA/EAE; Press control system – 1991; Press registration system – Microtrack/9500. MAILROOM: Counter stackers – 2-HL/Monitor HT, 4-QWI/401; Inserters and stuffers – Hopper/632E 29; Bundle tying machines – 2/Dynaric, 4-/Sterling; Wrapping singles – Bu; Mailroom control system – Omnizone; Addressing machine – KAN/600. BUSINESS COMPUTERS: Business Software – Micosoft/Office 2000; Business Hardware – 11-IBM/AS-400
Delivery method: Mail, Newsstand, Private Carrier, Racks

SAINT CHARLES

KANE COUNTY CHRONICLE

333 N. Randall Rd., Ste. 2, Saint Charles, Ill., 60174; gen tel (630) 232-9222; gen fax (630) 444-1645; ed fax (630) 232-4962; gen e-mail editorial@kcchronicle.com; adv e-mail advertising@kcchronicle.com; web site www.kcchronicle.com
Group: U.S. Suburban Press, Inc.
Published: Tues, Wed, Thur, Fri, Sat, Sun
Weekday Frequency: m
Saturday Frequency: m
Circulation: 11,320; 11,050(sat); 11,050(sun)
Last Audit: ABC September 30, 2011
Price: 2.70/wk; 8.67/mo; 104.00/yr.
Advertising: Open inch rate $31.57
News services: AP, SHNS, TMS.
Special Editions: Profiles/People (Mar); Clip & Save Coupon Book (Monthly).
Special Weekly Sections: Wheels (Fri); Neighbors (Sat); Bon Appetit (Thur); Lifestyle (Wed).
Magazines: Relish (Monthly); American Profile (Weekly).
Pub...Don Bricker
Adv. Dir. ....Karen Pletsch
Adv. Dir., Classified ....Lynn Laurie
Mktg. Coord.............................Leslie Shambo
Circ. Mgr., Distr./Sales ....Kara Hansen
Ed...Joe Grace
Sports Ed. ....Jay Schwab
Prodn. Dir. ....Kevin Elder
Prodn. Mgr., Mailroom..................Clem Garcia
Prodn. Mgr., Pressroom ....Ted Robinson
Market Information: ADS; TMC.
Mechanical available: Offset; Black and 3 ROP colors; insert accepted - min. overall size 8 1/2 x 11; page cutoffs - 22 3/4.
Mechanical Specifications: Type page 13 x 21; E - 6 cols, 2 1/16, 1/6 between; A - 6 cols, 2 1/16, 1/6 between; C - 9 cols, 1 5/16, 1/6 between.
Commodity Consumption: Avg. Page Number Per Issue - Daily 24; Avg. Page Number Per Issue - Plates Used 26000; Avg. Page Number Per Issue - Saturday 24; widths 12 1/2; Newsprint Used - Metric Tons 1400; Printing Ink Used - Black 29000; Printing Ink Used - Color 9800; Printing I
Equipment EDITORIAL: Front-end Software – Baseview/NewsEdit, QPS/QuarkXPress.; Editorial Hardware – Baseview; Editorial Printers – Compaq/PageMarq 15 CLASSIFIED: Front-end Software – Baseview 1.0.SC, QPS/QuarkXPress 4.0.; Classified Hardware – Printers ◻ Dataproducts/1560, AG/Accuset 1000 Imagesetters DISPLAY: Ad make-up applications – Multi-Ad/Creator 3.7, QPS/QuarkXPress 4.0, Adobe/Illustrator 7.0, Adobe/Photoshop 4.0; Display Hardware – 1-APP/Power Mac; Display Printers – AG/Accuset 1000, AG/Studio Scanner, Dataproducts/1560 Laser Printer, Nikon/2000 PRODUCTION: Pagination Software – QPS/QuarkXPress 4.0.; Production Equipment – Southern Litho, 2-AG; Cameras – B; Scanners – AG/Horizon Plus, APP/Mac One PRESSROOM: Line 1 – 8-G/Urbanite single width 1995; Folders – G/1000 Series. MAILROOM: Counter stackers – BG/167, MM; Inserters and stuffers – MM/227; Bundle tying machines – MLN, Bu. BUSINESS COMPUTERS: Business Software – Baseview, QuarkXPress, Multi-Ad; Business Hardware – APP/Mac

SHELBYVILLE

DAILY UNION

100 W. Main St., Shelbyville, Ill., 62565-1652; gen tel (217) 774-2161; adv tel (217) 774-2161; ed tel (217) 774-2161; gen fax (217) 774-5732; adv fax (217) 774-5732; ed fax (217) 774-5732; gen e-mail publisher@shelbyvilledailyunion.com; web site www.shelbyvilledailyunion.com
Published: Mon, Tues, Wed, Thur, Fri
Weekday Frequency: e
Circulation: 4,156
Price: 50.00/yr.
Advertising: Open inch rate $5.10
News services: AP.
Politics: Independent.
Not Published: New Year; Independence Day; Labor Day; Thanksgiving; Christmas.
Special Editions: Recreation Sections (Apr); Recreation (Aug); Lake Shelbyville (Jul); Recreation Sections (Jun); Lake Shelbyville (May).
Magazines: Relish (Monthly); American Profile (Weekly).
Pub..Paul Semple
Circ. Mgr. ....Jodi Large
Adv. Mgr......................................Rory Sands
Mng. Ed..............................Frank Mulholland
Sports Ed. ....John Curtis
Market Information: TMC.
Mechanical available: Offset; Black and 3 ROP colors; insert accepted; page cutoffs - 22 3/4.
Mechanical Specifications: Type page 15 1/2 x 21 1/2; E - 6 cols, 2 1/14, 1/8 between; A - 6 cols, 2 1/14, 1/8 between; C - 6 cols, 2 1/14, 1/8 between.
Commodity Consumption: Avg. Page Number Per Issue - Daily 10.
Equipment EDITORIAL: Front-end Software – Pageview/NewsEdit.; Editorial Hardware – APP/Mac; Editorial Printers – APP/Mac DISPLAY: Ad make-up applications – QPS/QuarkXPress 4.0; Layout Software – 2-APP/Mac.; Display Hardware – APP/Power Mac; Display Printers – APP/Mac; Bundle tying machines – 2/Bu. BUSINESS COMPUTERS: Business Software – Vision Data; Business Hardware – Vision Data

SPRINGFIELD

THE STATE JOURNAL-REGISTER

One Copley Plz., Springfield, Ill., 62701-1927; gen tel (217) 788-1300; adv tel (217) 788-1360; ed tel (217) 788-1517; adv fax (217) 788-1352; ed fax (217) 788-1551; gen e-mail sjr@sj-r.com; adv e-mail advertise@sj-r.com; ed e-mail sjr@sj-r.com; web site www.sj-r.com
Published: Mon, Tues, Wed, Thur, Fri, Sat, Sun
Weekday Frequency: m
Saturday Frequency: m
Circulation: 44,709; 45,174(sat); 50,319(sun)
Last Audit: ABC September 30, 2011
Price: 20.99/mo.; 241.80/yr.
Advertising: Open inch rate $89.05
News services: AP, MCT, GateHouse News Service
Politics: Independent. **Established:** 1831
Note: The State Journal-Register (mS) has a combination rate of $80.95 with the Lincoln Courier (e). Individual newspaper rates not made available.
Special Editions: Fall Festival Guide (Aug); Mother's Day Gifts (May); Welcome to Your Health (Monthly); Holiday Events Calender (Nov); SO Magazine (Other); Fall Home Improvement (Sept)., Seniors (monthly), & Home & Garden (monthly)
Special Weekly Sections: Be Healthy Springfield (Mon); City Guide (Other); Beliefs (S); At Home (Sat); A&E (Thur); The Voice (Tues); Food (Wed).
Magazines: Parade (S)., Relish, Dash, & Athlon
Director of operations..................Mike Kreppert
HR Mgr. ....Inez Harris
Adv. Dir., Sales ....Gary Tyler
Adv. Mgr., Outside Sales...........Shawna Ludlow
Adv. Supvr., Classified Sales ......Melissa Wilson
Adv. Supvr., Retail ....Nick Bressan
Audience Devel. Mgr. ....Edie Weaver
Exec. Ed...............................Jon Broadbooks
Mng. Ed., Content...............................Erin Orr
Mng. Ed., Digital Delivery...............Mike Turley
Bus. Ed..Tim Landis
Editorial Page Ed...................Matthew Dietrich
Food Ed......................................Kathryn Rem
Metro Ed. ....Gary Schieffer
Night Metro Ed. ....Mike Kienzler
Day News Ed.....................................Ted Wolf
Online Ed. ....Jason Piscia
Photo Ed...Rich Saal
Asst. Photo Ed. ....Ted Schurter
Publisher................................Walt T. Lafferty
Market Information: Split run; TMC.
Mechanical available: Offset; Black and 3 ROP colors; insert accepted; page cutoffs - 22 3/4.
Commodity Consumption: Avg. Page Number Per Issue - Daily 40; Avg. Page Number Per Issue - Plates Used 60000; Avg. Page Number Per Issue - Saturday 42; Avg. Page Number Per Issue - Sunday 68; widths 50; Newsprint Used - Metric Tons 5700; Printing Ink Used - Black 130000; Print
Equipment EDITORIAL: Front-end Software – ATS/Media Desk.; Editorial Hardware – Dell; Editorial Printers – HP/LaserJet CLASSIFIED: Front-end Software – ATS/Advisor.; Classified Hardware – Dell/Power Edge 2550; Classified Printers – HP/LaserJet DISPLAY: Ad make-up applications – QPS/QuarkXPress 5.0; Layout Software – MEI/ALS.; Display Hardware – Dell; Display Printers – HP/Laser Jet, HP/2000, HP/1050, HP/2500 PRODUCTION: Pagination Software – Northwood Publishing/Class Page.

STERLING

SAUK VALLEY MEDIA

3200 E. Lincolnway, Sterling, Ill., 61081; gen tel (815) 625-3600; gen fax (815) 625-9390; adv e-mail jbaratta@saukvalley.com; web site www.saukvalley.com
Group: Sauk Valley (Shaw) Media
Published: Mon, Tues, Wed, Thur, Fri, Sat
Weekday Frequency: m
Saturday Frequency: m
Circulation: 10,067
Last Audit: September 30, 2009
Price: 3.00/wk; 12.55/mo; 147.00/yr; 39.00/13wk, $75.00/26wk.
News services: AP, CNS, United Media Service, SHNS.
Politics: Independent. **Established:** 1854
Note: The Sterling Daily Gazette (e, wknd) has a combination rate of $30.27 with the Dixon Telegraph (e, wknd). Individual newspaper rates not made available.
Not Published: New Year; Memorial Day; Independence Day; Labor Day; Thanksgiving; Christmas.
Own facility?: Y
Special Editions: Career Guide (Apr); Today's Farm (Aug); Sterling Sights & Sounds (Dec); Internet Directory (Feb); Health & Fitness (Jan); Dixon Sidewalk Sale (Jul); Dixon Petunia Festival (Jun); Extra Circulation Sunday (Mar); Mother's Day (May); Senior Echo (Monthly); F
Magazines: TV Week (Fri); USA WEEKEND Magazine (S); Big E (Entertainment Guide) (Thur).
Pub. ....Trevis Mayfield
Advertising Director ....Jennifer Baratta
Circulation Director.............Sheryl Gulbranson
Exec. Ed....Larry Lough
Community Editor ....Andrea Mills
Chief Photographer......................Alex Paschal
Online Mgr. ....Robert Wendt
Production Director ....Ernie Appleyard
Prodn. Foreman, Press..................Larry Bowlin
IT Manager ....Phil Gaulrapp
Finance Director ....Joanne Doherty
Market Information: TMC.
Mechanical available: Offset; Black and 3 ROP colors; insert accepted - any; page cutoffs - 22 3/4.
Mechanical Specifications: Type page 11 3/5 x 21 1/2; E - 6 cols, 1 5/6, 1/8 between; A - 6 cols, 1 5/6, 1/8 between; C - 6 cols, 1 1/4, 1/8 between.
Commodity Consumption: Avg. Page Number Per Issue - Daily 22; Avg. Page Number Per Issue - Plates Used 5031; Avg. Page Number Per Issue - Saturday 24; Avg. Page Number Per Issue - Sunday 44; widths 12 1/2; Newsprint Used - Short Tons 1080; Printing Ink Used - Black 7000; Print
Equipment EDITORIAL: Front-end Software – Baseview/NewsEdit Pro IQue 2.2.2.; Editorial Hardware – 28-APP/Power Mac 7100; Editorial Printers – 2-HP/8150N CLASSIFIED: Front-end Software – Baseview/Ad Manager Pro V 1.0.4.B.; Classified Hardware – APP/Mac; Classified Printers – Okidata, 1-HP/8100N DISPLAY: Ad make-up applications – QPS/QuarkXPress 4.1, Adobe/Photoshop 6.0, Adobe/Illustrator 9.0.; Display Hardware – 7-APP/Power Mac 7100; Display Printers – 2-HP/LaserJet 8150N PRODUCTION: Pagination Software – Baseview 3.31.; Production Equipment – 1-ECR/9100, Konica K-28; Scanners – Nikon/LS 1000, AG/Studio Star PRESSROOM: Line 1 – 8-G/Urbanite double width 1995; Folders – 2 MAILROOM: Counter stackers – Exact/Stack, QWI/Sport II; Inserters and stuffers – HI/1372; Bundle tying machines – Dynaric/RLM-1; Addressing machine – Dispensamatic Ct/595. BUSINESS COMPUTERS: Business Software – Unix; Business Hardware – ATT/3B2500

STREATOR

THE TIMES-PRESS

115 Oak St., Streator, Ill., 61364; gen tel (815) 673-3771; gen fax (815) 672-9332; web site www.times-press.com
Published: Mon, Wed, Fri
Last Audit: September 30, 2000
Price: 1.75/wk.
Advertising: Open inch rate $12.00
News services: AP.
Politics: Republican.
Advertising not accepted: Tobacco.
Not Published: New Year; Memorial Day; Independence Day; Labor Day; Thanksgiving; Christmas.
Special Editions: Progress (Apr); Football (Aug); Christmas (Dec); Bridal (Jan); Baseball (Jul); Farm (Mar); Basketball (Nov); Home Fixup (Sept).
Special Weekly Sections: TV Guide (Fri).
Magazines: American Profile (Fri).
Gen. Mgr. ....Cynthia J. Liptak
Adv. Mgr. ....Anne Hinterlong
Circ. Mgr. ....John Babczak
Mng. Ed. ....Don Hrabal
Prodn. Mgr. ....Richard Todd
Mechanical available: Offset (Printed in Ottawa, IL); Black and 3 ROP colors; insert accepted; page cutoffs - 22 3/4.
Mechanical Specifications: Type page 11 1/2 x 21 1/2; E - 6 cols, 1 4/5, 1/8 between; A - 6 cols, 1 4/5, 1/8 between; C - 9 cols, 1 7/50, 1/8 between.
Equipment EDITORIAL: Front-end Software – Microsoft/NT Server 3.5, Oracle 7.0, FSI.; Editorial Hardware – 12-APP/Mac; Editorial Printers – NewGen/1200, QMS/1660; Classified Hardware – Mk/1100 Plus; Classified Printers – TI/810. DISPLAY: Ad make-up applications – Multi-Ad/Creator, QPS/QuarkXPress, Broderbund/Typestyler; Layout Software – APP/Mac.; Display Hardware – 1-APP/Mac G3, 2-APP/Power Mac 7200; Display Printers – APP/Mac LaserWriter 8500; Production Equipment – LE/LD 2600A-Loopline; Cameras – 1-B/500L, R/500L; Scanners – Epson, Abaton. PRESSROOM: Line 1 – G/Urbanite.; Bundle tying machines – 2/Bu; Wrapping singles – 1-Cr/1255-263L; Addressing machine – 1-Am/2605, 1-Am/2600.; Business Hardware – 1-IMS/Televideo

TAYLORVILLE

BREEZE-COURIER

212 S. Main St., Taylorville, Ill., 62568; gen tel (217) 824-2233; adv tel (217) 824-2233; ed tel (217) 824-2233; gen fax (217) 824-2026; adv fax (217) 824-2026; ed fax (217) 824-2026; ed e-mail breezenews@ctitech.com; web site www.breezecourier.com
Published: Mon, Tues, Wed, Thur, Fri, Sun
Weekday Frequency: e
Circulation: 5,408; 5,557(sun)
Last Audit: September 30, 2009
Price: 7.50/mo; 85.00/yr.
Advertising: Open inch rate $8.50
News services: AP.
Politics: Independent.
Not Published: New Year; Thanksgiving; Christmas.
Special Editions: Home Improvement (Apr); Back-to-School (Aug); First Baby (Dec); Senior Citizens (Feb); Tax Tab (Jan); County Fair (Jul); Bridal (Jun); Agriculture (Mar); Winter Sports (Nov); Car Care (Oct); Fall Home Improvement (Sept).
Special Weekly Sections: TV Tab (S).
Magazines: American Profile (S).
Exec. Vice Pres. ....Wilda Quinn Cooper
Credit Mgr. ....Cheryl McClelland
Circ. Dir. ....Brian Lindsey
Ed. ....Marylee C. Lasswell
Sports Ed. ....Brad Mcay
Online Mgr. ....Joe Dorr
Prodn. Mgr. ....Jeff Nation
Market Information: Split run; TMC; Zoned editions.
Mechanical available: Offset; Black and 3 ROP colors; insert accepted - any size; page cutoffs - 21.
Mechanical Specifications: Type page 11 5/8 x 21; E - 6 cols, 1 5/6, 1/8 between; A - 6 cols, 1 5/6, 1/8 between; C - 9 cols, 1 3/16, 1/8 between.
Commodity Consumption: Avg. Page Number Per Issue - Daily 18; Avg. Page Number Per Issue - Sunday 24.
Equipment EDITORIAL: Front-end Software – Baseview, QPS, Adobe/Photoshop.; Editorial Hardware – APP/Mac; Editorial Equipment – Microtek/Scanner, Nikon/Coolscan, Kk/DCS200 Digital camera; Editorial Printers – MON, APP/Mac LaserWriters, HP/LaserJet CLASSIFIED: Front-end Software – Baseview.; Classified Hardware – APP/Mac; Classified Printers – HP DISPLAY: Ad make-up applications – QPS/Quark 4.0; Layout Software – APP/Mac.; Display Hardware – APP/Mac; Display Printers – APP/Mac LaserWriter II NTX, HP/8100 N PRODUCTION: Pagination Software – QPS/QuarkXPress 4.0.; Production Equipment – 1-B/1500, HP PRESSROOM: Line 1 – 4-G/Community; Folders – 1; Inserters and stuffers – 2-MM/227E, 2-MM/277; Bundle tying machines – 1-Bu/7; Addressing machine – 1/Am. BUSINESS COMPUTERS: Business Software – QPS, Adobe/Photoshop, TI/OmniPage, Baseview; Business Hardware – APP/Mac

BREEZE PRINTING CO.

212 S. Main St., Taylorville, Ill., 62568; gen tel (217) 824-2233; gen fax (217) 824-2026

TINLEY PARK

SOUTHTOWNSTAR

6901 W. 159th St., Tinley Park, Ill., 60477-2327; gen tel (708) 633-6700; adv tel (708) 633-4800; ed tel (708) 633-6777; gen fax (708) 633-5999; adv fax (708) 633-6850; ed fax (708) 633-6770; gen e-mail news@southtownstar.com; web site www.southtownstar.com
Published: Mon, Tues, Wed, Thur, Fri, Sat, Sun
Weekday Frequency: m
Saturday Frequency: m
Circulation: 34,746; 30,026(sat); 50,389(sun)
Last Audit: September 30, 2009
Price: 125.00/yr.
Advertising: Open inch rate $100.00
News services: AP, CNS, NYT, NEA, DJ, Entertainment News Wire, Wall Street Journal.
Politics: Independent.
Special Weekly Sections: TGIF! (Fri); Family Life (Mon); Home Guide (S); Auto Guide (Sat); Working (Thur); Cyber Scene (Tues); Food (Wed).
Magazines: USA WEEKEND Magazine (S).
Pres./Pub. ....Murdoch Davis
Sr. Vice Pres. ....John P. Kern
Adv. Dir., Retail ....Steve Vanisko
Adv. Dir., Classified ....John Doolin
Circ. Dir. ....Robert Edwards
Ed. ....Michelle Holmes
Deputy Mng. Ed. ....John O'Brien
Deputy Mng. Ed. ....Dennis Robaugh
Bus. Ed. ....Bob Bong
Commentary Ed ....Karen Sorensen
Entertainment Ed ....Jessi Virtusio
Food Ed. ....Donna Vickroy
Metro Ed ....Paula Carlson
Metro Ed ....Wynne Everett
Photo Ed. ....Larry Ruehl
Sports Ed. ....Phil Arvia
Prodn. Dir. ....Kevin Bartlett
Prodn. Mgr., Post Press ....Chester Parson
Market Information: Split run; TMC; Zoned editions.
Mechanical available: Offset; Black and 3 ROP colors; insert accepted; page cutoffs - 22 3/4.
Mechanical Specifications: Type page 11 1/3 x 21 1/2; E - 6 cols, 1 4/5, between; A - 6 cols, 1 4/5, between; C - 10 cols, 1 2/25, between.
Commodity Consumption: Avg. Page Number Per Issue - Daily 64; Avg. Page Number Per Issue - Sunday 76; widths 50.
Equipment EDITORIAL: Front-end Software – III/Tecs 2.; Editorial Hardware – PC 286 8MHz CLASSIFIED: Front-end Software – III/Tecs 2.; Classified Hardware – PC 286 8MHz DISPLAY: Ad make-up applications – HI; Layout Software – APP/Mac, CJ.; Display Hardware – HI/8300, HI/8900; Display Printers – 3-Tegra/Varityper 5510, 2-Tegra/Varityper 1000P, 1-Hyphen/Dash, 1-GCC/SelectPress; Production Equipment – 2-LE, 1-P, 1-C; Cameras – 1-C/Spartan II, 1-C/Newspager, 1-B; Scanners – X, Howtek/Colorscan, 2-X, 2-ImageTex, Kk/2035. PRESSROOM: Line 1 – 17-G/Metro; Line 2 – 9-G/Urbanite; Folders – 3, G/2:1, 1-G/3:2. MAILROOM: Counter stackers – 2-QWI/300, 3-Monitor/HT, 2-HL/Sta-Hi; Inserters and stuffers – 2-GMA/SLS 1000 6:1, 1-GMA/SLS 1000 4:1; Bundle tying machines – 3/MLN, 10-MLN/2A, 1-/Spirit, 2-MLN/News 90; Addressing machine – 3-/Ch. BUSINESS COMPUTERS: Business Software – CJ; Business Hardware – 4-DEC/VAX

WATSEKA

TIMES-REPUBLIC

1492 E. Walnut St., Watseka, Ill., 60970; gen tel (815) 432-5227; gen fax (815) 432-5159; adv fax (815) 432-6779; gen e-mail watseka@intranix.com; web site www.watseka-timesrepublic.com
Published: Mon, Tues, Wed, Thur, Fri
Weekday Frequency: m
Circulation: 2,373
Last Audit: September 30, 2006
Price: 94.00/yr (carrier), $104.00/yr (mail, IL).
Advertising: Open inch rate $10.95
News services: AP.
Politics: Independent-Republican.
Advertising not accepted: Adoptions; unless by a lawyer.
Not Published: Thanksgiving; Christmas.
Special Editions: Twin State Farmer (Every other month); Bridal (Other); Twin State News & Views (Quarterly).
Pub. ....Don Hurd
Online Ed. ....Carla Waters
Market Information: TMC.
Mechanical available: Offset; Black and 1 ROP colors; insert accepted - single sheets; page cutoffs - 15.
Mechanical Specifications: Type page 10 1/4 x 14; E - 6 cols, 1 3/5, 1/6 between; A - 6 cols, 1 3/5, 1/6 between; C - 6 cols, 1 3/5, 1/6 between.
Commodity Consumption: Avg. Page Number Per Issue - Daily 20; Avg. Page Number Per Issue - Plates Used 6000; widths 30; Newsprint Used - Metric Tons 340; Printing Ink Used - Black 12000; Printing Ink Used - Color 500; Printing Ink Used - Pages Printed 4780.
Equipment EDITORIAL: Front-end Software – Baseview/NewsEdit.; Editorial Hardware – 5-APP/Mac; Editorial Printers – 1-Xante/Accel-a-Writer 8200, HP/LaserJet 8100 Series CLASSIFIED: Front-end Software – Baseview/Ad Manager Pro, QPS/QuarkXPress.; Classified Hardware – 1-APP/Mac, 4-APP/iMac; Classified Equipment – HP/laser Jet 2100TN; Classified Printers – HP/Laser Jet 8100 Series, 1-Xante/Accel-a-Writer 8200 DISPLAY: Ad make-up applications – 3-Multi-Ad/Creator 3.5, Microsoft/Word, QPS/QuarkXPress, Multi-Ad/Creator 4.0; Layout Software – Other ☐; Display Printers – 1-Xante/Accel-a-Writer 8200, HP/Laser Jet 8100 Series PRODUCTION: Pagination Software – QPS/QuarkXPress 4.0.; Production Equipment – TI/OmniPage 2.12, HP/Laser Jet 8100 Series; Cameras – 1-Nu, 1-R PRESSROOM: Line 1 – 4-KP/News King 1976; Folders – 1 MAILROOM: Counter stackers – 1/CH; Bundle tying machines – 4-/Bu; Addressing machine – 1-/Ch. BUSINESS COMPUTERS: Business Software – Microsoft/Windows 95, Microsoft/Word, Microsoft/Excel; Business Hardware – 2-IBM/Sys 36

WAUKEGAN

THE LAKE COUNTY NEWS-SUN

2383 N. Delany Rd., Waukegan, Ill., 60087; gen tel (847) 336-7000; adv tel (847) 249-7296; ed tel (847) 249-7200; gen fax (847) 249-7202; adv fax (847) 249-7248; ed fax (847) 249-7202; adv e-mail asonnenberg@pioneerlocal.com; ed e-mail nsforum@scnl.com; web site www.news-sunonline.com
Published: Wed
Last Audit: Estimate November 7, 2002
Price: 3.50/wk (carrier); 169.00/yr (carrier), $221.00/yr (mail).
Advertising: Open inch rate $25.00
Insert rate: $35.00/M.
News services: AP.
Politics: Independent.
Note: Suburban Chicago Newspapers includes the Aurora Beacon News (mS), Elgin Courier News (mS), Joliet Herald News (mS), Naperville Sun (mS) and Waukegan Lake County News-Sun (m). The group combination rate is $170.50 (dS). Individual newspaper rates not made
Special Weekly Sections: SEARCHchicagoautos (Fri).
Magazines: USA WEEKEND Magazine (Sat).
Broadcast Affiliations: CBS2.
Adv. Dir. ....Andrea Sonnenberg
Circ. Dir. ....Jay Beaton
Circ. Mgr., Reader Sales/Serv. Christine Wertman
Mng. Ed. ....Chris Cashman
News Ed. ....Charles Selle
Sports Ed. ....Jeff Bonato
Online Mgr. ....Ivonne Cueva
Pub. ....David Rutter
Mechanical available: Offset; Black and 4 ROP colors; insert accepted - single sheet flyers; page cutoffs - 11.
Mechanical Specifications: Type page 13 x 21; E - 6 cols, 2, between; A - 6 cols, 2 1/16, between; C - 10 cols, between.
Equipment EDITORIAL: Front-end Software – Tandem, SII/Editorial.; Editorial Hardware – SII/CLX Non-Stop; Editorial Equipment – 3-RSK/TRS 1000, 3-SII/Coyote PC, 46-SII/Coyote terminal, APP/Mac 8100, Howtek/Scanner, APP/Mac Quadra, 3-APP/Mac 7100; Editorial Printers – 4-APP/Mac LaserWriter II NTX CLASSIFIED: Front-end Software – SII/Classified, Tandem.; Classified Hardware – SII/CLX Non-Stop; Classified Equipment – 4-SII/Coyote terminal; Classified Printers – 1-CText/515 DISPLAY: Ad make-up applications – CJ 7.01G; Layout Software – CJ.; Display Hardware – CJ; Display Printers – DEC/Server 17
Zip Codes served: 60085

WEST FRANKFORT

THE DAILY AMERICAN

111 S. Emma St., West Frankfort, Ill., 62896; gen tel (618) 932-2146; adv tel (618) 932-2146; ed tel (618) 932-2146; gen fax (618) 937-6006; adv fax (618) 937-6006; ed fax (618) 937-6006; ed e-mail editor@dailyamericannews.com; web site www.dailyamericannews.com
Published: Mon, Tues, Wed, Thur, Fri, Sat, Sun
Weekday Frequency: e
Saturday Frequency: m
Circulation: 3,510; 3,510(sat)
Last Audit: October 1, 2001
Price: 2.40/wk; 9.50/mo.
Advertising: Open inch rate $10.25
News services: AP, TMS.
Politics: Independent.
Not Published: New Year; Memorial Day; Independence Day; Labor Day; Thanksgiving; Christmas.
Special Editions: Progress (Feb); Bridal (Jan); Fourth of July Celebration (Jun); Homes (Monthly); Home Improvement (Oct).
Magazines: USA WEEKEND Magazine (Fri); Sports Saturday (Sat); American Profile (Weekly).
Adv. Mgr. ....Diann Walthes
Adv. Mgr., Classified ....Megan Clifton

Market Information: ADS; TMC.
Mechanical available: Offset; Black and 4 ROP colors; insert accepted; page cutoffs - 21 1/2.
Mechanical Specifications: Type page 13 3/4 x 21 1/2; E - 6 cols, 2 1/16, 1/8 between; A - 6 cols, 2 1/16, 1/8 between; C - 8 cols, 1 1/2, 1/8 between.
Commodity Consumption: Avg. Page Number Per Issue - Daily 14; Avg. Page Number Per Issue - Saturday 28.
Equipment EDITORIAL: Front-end Software – QPS, Multi-Ad/Creator, Microsoft, Adobe/Photoshop.; Editorial Hardware – APP/Mac 610, APP/Mac 605; Editorial Printers – APP/Mac 630; Classified Hardware – IBM. DISPLAY: Ad make-up applications – QPS, Multi-Ad/Creator, Adobe/Photoshop; Layout Software – APP/Mac 650, APP/Mac 800.; Display Printers – APP/Mac 630 PRODUCTION: Pagination Software – QPS 3.3.; Production Equipment – V PRESSROOM: Line 1 – 11-G/Community; Folders – G/Suburban. MAILROOM: Counter stackers – St; Inserters and stuffers – St; Bundle tying machines – .

LIBERTY GROUP PUBLISHING

111-15 S. Emma St., West Frankfort, Ill., 62896; gen tel (618) 932-2146; gen fax (618) 937-6006

DAILY CHRONICLE

1586 Barber Greene Rd, DeKalb, Ill., 60115; gen tel (815) 756-4841; adv tel (815) 756-4841; ed tel (815) 756-4841; gen fax (815) 756-2079; adv fax (815) 756-2079; ed fax (815) 756-2079; gen e-mail information@shawmedia.com; web site www.daily-chronicle.com
Group: Shaw Media
Published: Mon, Tues, Wed, Thur, Fri, Sat, Sun
Weekday Frequency: m
Saturday Frequency: m
Circulation: 8,863; 9,663(sat); 9,663(sun)
Last Audit: ABC September 30, 2011
Price: 3.00/week; 156.00/yr.
News services: AP, TMS, Gatehouse News Service, Washington Post/Bloomberg
Politics: 1880
Note: Production outsourced to commercial printer.
Own facility?: Y
Special Editions: Progress (Apr); Back-to-School (Aug); Gift Guide (Dec); Farm Forecast (Jan); Spring Fashion (Mar); Home Improvement-Lawn & Garden (May); Christmas (Nov); Fall Farm (Oct); Fall Home Improvement (Sept).
Magazines: USA WEEKEND Magazine (Weekly), Relish (Monthly), American Profile (Weekly), Spry (Monthly), Athlon Sports (Monthly)
Publisher ....Don Bricker
Advertising Director ....Karen Pletsch
VP/Marketing & Circulation ....Kara Hansen
Editor ....Jason Schaumburg
VP/Finance ....Stacia Hahn
I.T. Director ....Steve Sulouff
VP/Production ....Kevin Elder
Classified Manager ....Shelly Bissell
Major/National Ad Director ....Jim Ringness
Fin. Dir. ....Lindsay Shull
Mng. Ed. ....Kristen Schmidt
Copy Ed. ....David Fixner
Lifestyles Ed ....Cindy DiDonna
News Ed. ....Inger Koch
Photo Ed. ....Holly Lundh
Sports Ed ....Steve Nemeth
Equipment EDITORIAL: Front-end Software – Roxen; Editorial Hardware – Mac CLASSIFIED: Front-end Software – VisionData; Classified Hardware – Sun/Mac DISPLAY: Ad make-up applications – InDesign; Display Hardware – Mac BUSINESS COMPUTERS: Business Software – VisionData; Business Hardware – Sun/Mac
Zip Codes served: DeKalb County
Delivery method: Newsstand, Private Carrier, Racks

INDIANA

ANDERSON

THE HERALD BULLETIN

1133 Jackson St., Anderson, Ind., 46016; gen tel (765) 640-4820; ed tel (765) 622-1212; gen fax (765) 640-4820; ed fax (765) 640-4815; ed e-mail newsroom@heraldbulletin.com; web site www.theheraldbulletin.com
Published: Mon, Tues, Wed, Thur, Fri, Sat, Sun
Weekday Frequency: m
Saturday Frequency: m
Circulation: 18,691; 18,691(sat); 20,422(sun)
Last Audit: September 30, 2009
Price: 3.00/wk (mS); 156.00/yr.
Advertising: Open inch rate $45.00
News services: AP.
Politics: Independent.
Special Editions: Spring Auto Guide (Apr); Fall Football (Aug); Visitor's Guide (Dec); Winter Clearance (Feb); Active Times (Jan); USA Proud (Jul); Father's Day Pages (Jun); Visitor's Guide (Mar); Mother's Day Gift Guide (May); Gift Guide (Nov); Active Times (Oct); Manufac
Special Weekly Sections: Food (Mon); Homes (S).
Magazines: Parade (S).
Pub. ....Henry Bird
Adv. Dir., Regl. ....Joe DeBik
Circ. Dir ....Amy Winter
Editorial Asst. ....Tammy Everitt
Photo Chief ....John Cleary
Asst. Content Ed. ....Stephen Dick
Prodn. Mgr., Distr. ....Susan Brooks
Market Information: ADS; Split run; TMC.
Mechanical available: Offset; Black and 3 ROP colors; insert accepted; page cutoffs - 22 3/4.
Mechanical Specifications: Type page 13 x 21 1/2; E - 6 cols, 2 1/16, 1/8 between; A - 6 cols, 2 1/16, 1/8 between; C - 9 cols, 1 3/8, 1/16 between.
Commodity Consumption: Avg. Page Number Per Issue - Daily 30; Avg. Page Number Per Issue - Plates Used 37350; Avg. Page Number Per Issue - Saturday 28; Avg. Page Number Per Issue - Sunday 52; widths 13 1/2; Newsprint Used - Metric Tons 2614; Newsprint Used - Short Tons 2881; P
Equipment EDITORIAL: Front-end Software – CText.; Editorial Hardware – CText, 2-DEC/433 ST; Editorial Equipment – 23-DEC/333C, 2-DEC/420SX, 1-DEC/466LP2, 5-Compaq/DeskPro 133; Editorial Printers – V/4000-5300E, 1-Pre Press/Panther Pro 46 CLASSIFIED: Front-end Software – CText.; Classified Hardware – 2-DEC/433 ST; Classified Equipment – 10-DEC/333C; Classified Printers – 1-C.Itoh DISPLAY: Ad make-up applications – SCS/Layout 8000; Layout Software – Archetype/Designer.; Display Hardware – 2-IBM/PS2; Display Printers – 1-C.Itoh PRODUCTION: Pagination Software – QPS 3.312.; Production Equipment – Nu/Ultra Violet burner, 1-V/Pan; Cameras – 2-SCREEN/6500C; Scanners – 1-Sharp/1200R, 1-Lf/AP Leaf 35mm, ECR/Autokon, 3-AG/Arcus PRESSROOM: Line 1 – 8-G/Urbanite single width; Folders – 1; Reels and Stands – 6-G/Stands. MAILROOM: Counter stackers – 1/HL, 1-/HI; Inserters and stuffers – 1-MM/SLS 2000; Bundle tying machines – 1-/MLN, 1-/Bu; Addressing machine – KR, FMC; Other equipment –1-MM/Fox Saddle Stitcher-Trimmer. AUDIO: Audio Software – Zimmers Interactive, IBS; Audio Hardware – UNN, Tribune Media, PC 486 BUSINESS COMPUTERS: Business Software – Oracle: Financials, PBS: Circ, Adv; Business Hardware – 2-HP/9000

ANGOLA

HERALD-REPUBLICAN

45 S. Public Sq., Angola, Ind., 46703; gen tel (260) 665-3117; gen fax (260) 665-2322; gen e-mail info@kpcnews.net; ed e-mail news@kpcnews.net; web site www.kpcnews.com
Published: Mon, Tues, Wed, Thur, Fri, Sat, Sun
Weekday Frequency: m
Saturday Frequency: m
Circulation: 4,410; 4,410(sat); 4,665(sun)
Last Audit: ABC September 30, 2011
Price: 162.00/yr.
Advertising: Open inch rate $14.35
Insert rate: 47M
News services: AP, SHNS.
Note: All production of the Herald-Republican is done at the central plant in Kendallville.
Not Published: New Year; Memorial Day; Independence Day; Labor Day; Christmas.
Own facility?: Y
Special Editions: Wedding Planner (Feb); Steuben County Answer Book (Jan); Big Bang 4th of July Sale (Jul); All In The Family Business (Jun); Angola Chamber Guide (Mar); Summer in Northeast Indiana (May).
Special Weekly Sections: Outdoor Life (Fri); Homes To Own (S).
Magazines: USA WEEKEND Magazine (S).
Pres./CEO/Pub. ....Terry Housholder
CFO ....Donna Scanlon
Mgr., HR ....Nancy Sible
Adv. Dir. ....Karen Bloom
Circ. Dir. ....Bruce Hakala
Ed. ....Michael Marturello
News Ed. ....Amy Oberlin
Sports Ed. ....Ken Fillmore
Online Ed. ....James Tew
Prodn. Mgr., Composing ....Jane Minick
GM/VP Sales Mktg ....Don Cooper
Market Information: ADS; TMC; Zoned editions.
Mechanical Specifications: Type page 13 x 21 1/2; E - 6 cols, 2, 1/6 between; A - 6 cols, 2 1/16, 1/6 between; C - 9 cols, 1 3/8, 1/6 between.
Equipment EDITORIAL: Front-end Software – ACT.; Layout Software – Multi-Ad 4.0, QPS/QuarkXPress, Adobe/PageMaker 6.5.; Display Hardware – PC, APP/Mac, ECR/ImageSetter Sun PRESSROOM: Line 1 – 6-G/Community.
Delivery method: Mail, Newsstand, Private Carrier, Racks

AUBURN

THE STAR

118 W. 9th St., Auburn, Ind., 46706; gen tel (260) 925-2611; adv tel (260) 925-2611; ed tel (260) 925-2611; gen fax (260) 925-2625; adv fax (260) 925-2625; ed fax (260) 925-2625; gen e-mail kpc@kpcnews.net; ed e-mail dkurtz@kpcnews.net; web site www.kpcnews.com
Published: Mon, Tues, Wed, Thur, Fri, Sat, Sun
Weekday Frequency: m
Saturday Frequency: m
Circulation: 6,776; 6,776(sat); 6,023(sun)
Last Audit: ABC September 30, 2011
Price: 14.75/mo, $7.00/mo (S); 160.00/yr, $84.00/yr (S).
Advertising: Open inch rate $28.71
News services: AP.
Politics: Independent. **Established:** 1871
Note: All production of the The Star is done at the central plant in Kendallville.
Not Published: New Year; Memorial Day; Independence Day; Labor Day; Thanksgiving; Christmas.
Own facility?: Y
Special Editions: Salute To Industry (Aug); Wedding Planner (Feb); Auburn Chamber Guide (Jan); Big Bang 4th of July (Jul); All In The Family Business (Jun); Sectional Basketball Preview (Mar); Graduation (May); Holiday Gift Guide (Nov); Apple Festival (Oct); ACD Festival (
Special Weekly Sections: Outdoor Life (Fri); Business Page (Other); Homes To Own (S); Agri-Business (Sat); Entertainment Page (Thur); Best Food Day (Wed).
Magazines: USA WEEKEND Magazine (S).
Pres./CEO/Pub. ....Terry Housholder
CFO ....Donna Scanlon
Mgr., HR ....Nancy Sible
Circ. Dir. ....Bruce Hakala
Adv. Vice Pres., Sales/Mktg. ....Bret Jacomet
Adv. Dir. ....Karen Bloom
Ed. ....Dave Kurtz
Sports Ed. ....Mark Murdock
Composing Mgr. ....Jane Minick
VP of Sales/Marketing ....Don Cooper
Market Information: ADS; TMC; Zoned editions.
Mechanical available: Offset; Black and 3 ROP colors; insert accepted - product samples; page cutoffs - 22 3/4.
Mechanical Specifications: Type page 11 1/2 x 21 1/2; E - 6 cols, 1 13/16, 1/8 between; A - 6 cols, 1 13/16, 1/8 between; C - 9 cols, 1 1/6, 1/8 between.
Commodity Consumption: Avg. Page Number Per Issue - Daily 14; Avg. Page Number Per Issue - Plates Used 14400; Avg. Page Number Per Issue - Saturday 24; widths 32; Newsprint Used - Metric Tons 1083; Newsprint Used - Short Tons 3300; Printing Ink Used - Black 6000; Printing Ink
Equipment EDITORIAL: Front-end Software – Baseview, QPS/QuarkXPress.; Editorial Hardware – 12-APP/Mac; Editorial Equipment – 6-RSK/TRS 80 Model 100; Editorial Printers – 2-APP/Mac LaserWriter CLASSIFIED: Front-end Software – Baseview, QPS/QuarkXPress.; Classified Hardware – 3-APP/Mac; Classified Printers – 2-APP/Mac LaserWriter DISPLAY: Ad make-up applications – QPS/QuarkXPress, Multi-Ad.; Display Hardware – 9-APP/Mac; Display Printers – 2-APP/Mac LaserWriter PRODUCTION: Pagination Software – QPS/QuarkXPress 4.0.; Production Equipment – 2-AG/Imagesetter 1200, Luntz & Jensen, 1-Tek Color/4C Printer; Cameras – 1-B, 1-Kk/Image Maker IM600; Scanners – APP/Mac, 1-AG/Arcus, 2-AG/Arcus Plus, 1-Kk/RFS 2035 PRESSROOM: Line 1 – 1-G/Floor SSC Units 1988, 1-Stalk/Pathfinder 1988; Line 2 – 2-G/4-High 1999; Folders – 2-G/SSC; Pasters – 2-KTI/Splicer; Press control system – 1-Ebway/Industries Pneumatic Master Control. MAILROOM: Counter stackers – 1/The Stacker Machine Co/S-N 316-19, 1-BG/Count-O-Veyor; Inserters and stuffers – 1-KAN/5 pocket, KAN/Twin Stacker, MM/Saddlebinder 4 pocket, 1-Challenge/Single Knife; Bundle tying machines – 1-Akebono/Strapper, IT; Other equipment –Other equipment ☐ BUSINESS COMPUTERS: Business Software – Baseview/Ad Manager Pro 2.02, Dynamic Great Plains, Baseview/Circulation Pro 1.8.0; Business Hardware – 1-Compaq/Proliant 5000
Delivery method: Mail, Newsstand, Private Carrier, Racks

BEDFORD

HERALD-TIMES, INC.

813 16th St., Bedford, Ind., 47421; gen tel (812) 275-3355; gen fax (812) 275-4191
Politics: 1942

THE TIMES-MAIL

813 E. 16th St., Bedford, Ind., 47421-0849; gen tel (812) 275-3355; adv tel (812) 277-7210; gen fax (812) 275-4191; adv fax (812) 275-4191; ed fax (812) 277-3472; gen e-mail tmnews@tmnews.com; adv e-mail brian@tmnews.com; ed e-mail mikel@tmnews.com; web site www.tmnews.com
Published: Sun
Circulation: 11,218; 11,218(sat); 40,171(sun)
Last Audit: September 30, 2008
Price: 11.95/mo; 156.00/yr.
Advertising: Open inch rate $37.16
News services: AP.
Politics: Independent.
Note: This publication shares a joint Sunday edition with the Bloomington (IN) Herald-Times (mS) and the Martinsville (IN) Reporter-Times (eS).

Not Published: New Year; Memorial Day; Independence Day; Labor Day; Christmas.
Special Editions: Business Expo (Apr); Back-to-School (Aug); Holiday Gift Guide (Dec); Area Dining Guide (Feb); Financial Focus (Jan); City-Wide Sidewalk Sale (Jul); Women in Business (Jun); Kitchen, Bath and Furniture (Mar); Summer Fun (May); Prime Advantage (Monthly); Th
Special Weekly Sections: TV Week (Fri).
Magazines: Parade (S).

Controller .... Mark P. Wozniak
Adv. Dir. .... Martha Shedd
Adv. Mgr., Classified .... Angie Blanton
Circ. Mgr. .... Joe Green
Ed. in Chief .... Scott C. Schurz
Ed. .... Debbie Turner
Mng. Ed. .... Michael S. Lewis
Bus./Finance Ed. .... Krystal Slaten
Health/Medical Ed. .... Diana Wires
Living/Lifestyle Ed. .... Susan Hayes
Online Ed. .... Marla Jones
Photo Ed. .... Rich Janzaruk
Political/Gov't Ed. .... Mike Lewis
Religion Ed. .... Glendora Goodwin
Sports Ed. .... Justin Sokeland

Market Information: Split run; TMC.
Mechanical available: Offset; Black and 3 ROP colors; insert accepted - standing card; page cutoffs - 22 3/4.
Mechanical Specifications: Type page 13 x 21; E - 6 cols, 2 1/16, 1/8 between; A - 6 cols, 2 1/16, 1/8 between; C - 9 cols, 1 3/8, 1/16 between.
Commodity Consumption: Avg. Page Number Per Issue - Daily 26; Avg. Page Number Per Issue - Sunday 64; widths 32; Newsprint Used - Short Tons 1040; Printing Ink Used - Black 56414; Printing Ink Used - Color 43639; Printing Ink Used - Pages Printed 8003.
Equipment EDITORIAL: Front-end Software – Baseview/IQUE Server.; Editorial Hardware – APP/Mac 9150-120 Workgroup Server; Editorial Printers – 2-Dataproducts/LZR 1580 CLASSIFIED: Front-end Software – Baseview/Ad Manager Pro.; Classified Hardware – Novell/Server; Classified Printers – 1-Dataproducts/LZR 1580 DISPLAY: Ad make-up applications – Adobe/Photoshop, Aldus/PageMaker, Multi-Ad/Creator, QPS/QuarkXPress, Aldus/Free-Hand; Layout Software – 2-AU/APS5, APP/Mac.; Display Hardware – 6-APP/Power Mac; Display Printers – Dataproducts/Laser-Printer 1580, APP/Mac LaserWriter II NTX PRODUCTION: Pagination Software – QPS/QuarkXPress, Ba; Production Equipment – 2-Hardot/15.75 Imagesetter, Pre Press/Panther Pro 46, Pre Press/Panther Pro 46 HS, Adobe/PageMaker, Macromedia/Freehand, Multi-Ad; Cameras – 1-Screen/C-260-D; Scanners – 1-Lf/Leafscan 45, 3-Kk/RFE 2035, APP/Mac PRESSROOM: Line 1 – 15-G/Community single width (Color); Folders – 1-G/SC1045 Balloon Double Former, 1-G/SC1045. MAILROOM: Counter stackers – 1-BG/Stabb Brick, Rima/RS25; Inserters and stuffers – 2-KAN/480; Bundle tying machines – 1-FMC/APM2A, 1-Sa/SR2A, 2/Dynaric, 2-/Bu, 1-/Interlake, Sterling; Addressing machine – Ch, KR; Other equipment –Mc/S2000 Stitcher-Trimmer 4 Po; Business Hardware – 1-DEC/VAX, 1-DEC/Rainbow, IBM

BLOOMINGTON

THE HERALD-TIMES

1900 S. Walnut St., Bloomington, Ind., 47401; gen tel (812) 332-4401; adv tel (812) 331-4279; gen fax (812) 331-4285; adv fax (812) 331-4285; ed fax (812) 331-4383; gen e-mail htnews@heraldt.com; adv e-mail adsales@heraldt.com; ed e-mail htnews@heraldt.com; web site www.heraldtimesonline.com
Published: Sun
Circulation: 25,732; 28,408(sat); 40,171(sun)
Last Audit: September 30, 2008
Price: 14.95/mo; 167.40/yr.
Advertising: Open inch rate $37.16
News services: AP.
Politics: Independent-Republican. **Established:** 1877
Note: This publication shares a joint Sunday edition with the Bedford (IN) Times-Mail (mS) and the Martinsville (IN) Reporter-Times (eS).
Not Published: New Year; Memorial Day; Independence Day; Labor Day; Christmas (unless on Sunday).

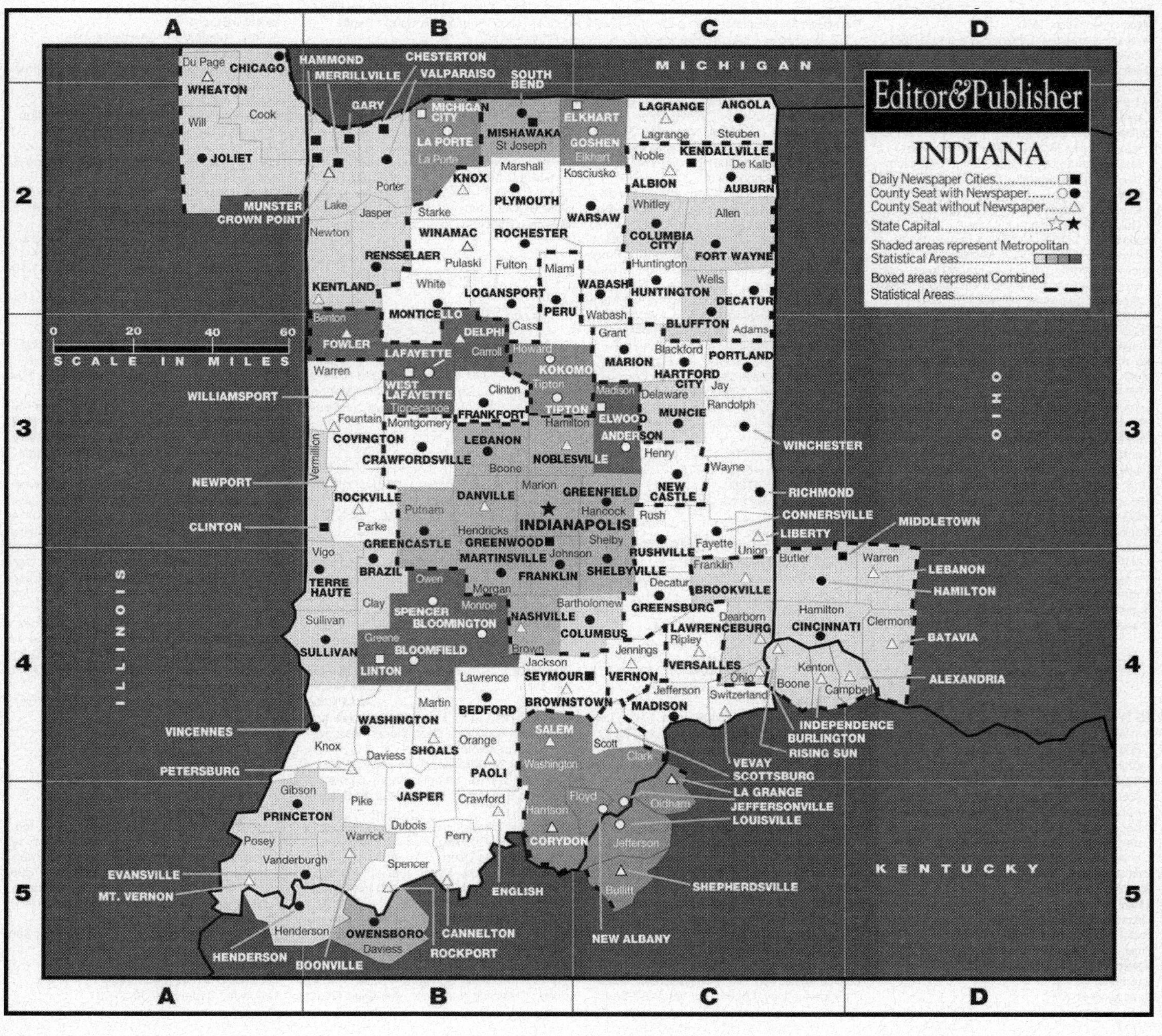

Special Editions: Reader's Choice (Apr); Westside Shopper (Dec); Home Lifestyles (Every other month); MCBA Home Show (Jan); Picnic with the Pops (Jun); Family (Mar); Parade of Homes (May); Buy It Now (Monthly); Eastside Shopper (Nov); Rental Guide (Quarterly); Bridal (Semi
Special Weekly Sections: Your Weekend (Fri); Neighbors (Mon-fri); Outdoor (S); More Weekend (Sat); Experience (Thur); Youth Ink (Tues); Food Section (Wed).
Magazines: Relish (Monthly); Parade (S); American Profile (Wed).
Pub./Purchasing Agent..........E. Mayer Maloney
Dir., HR..........Kim Sutton
Mktg. Mgr...........Brooke McCluskey
Circ. Dir...........Tim D. Smith
Ed. in Chief..........Scott C. Schurz
Mng. Ed...........Andrea Murray
Editorial Page Ed...........Robert Zaltsberg
Features/Lifestyle Ed...........William Strother
Photo Dept. Mgr...........David Snodgress
Online Mgr...........Todd Davidson
Prodn. Mgr., Pre Press..........Greg Davinport
Prodn. Dir...........Brad Clarke
Advertising Director..........Laurie Ragle
Adv. Dir...........Cory Bollinger
Sports Ed...........Chris Korman
Market Information: TMC.
Mechanical available: Offset; Black and 3 ROP colors; insert accepted; page cutoffs - 22.
Mechanical Specifications: Type page 11 5/8 x 21; E - 6 cols, 1 5/6, 1/6 between; A - 6 cols, 1 5/6, 1/6 between; C - 9 cols, 1 1/4, 1/10 between.
Commodity Consumption: Avg. Page Number Per Issue - Daily 36; Avg. Page Number Per Issue - Plates Used 22000; Avg. Page Number Per Issue - Sunday 64; widths 55; Newsprint Used - Short Tons 2750; Printing Ink Used - Black 80000; Printing Ink Used - Color 20900; Printing Ink Use
Equipment EDITORIAL: Front-end Software – Dewar/View, Microsoft/Windows, Microsoft/Word 2.0, QPS/QuarkXPress 3.2.; Editorial Hardware – 2-DEC/Micro VAX 3000; Editorial Equipment – AU/OPI Server, 2-AU/3850; Editorial Printers – HP/4MV CLASSIFIED: Front-end Software – APT.; Classified Hardware – DEC/Alphasaver 2000 DISPLAY: Ad make-up applications – Adobe/InDesign, Multi-Ad, SCS/Layout 8000; Layout Software – APP/Mac.; Display Hardware – APP/Mac fileserver PRODUCTION: Pagination Software – Dewar.; Production Equipment – 2-AU/3850, 1-Nu/Flip Top FT40V6UPNS; Cameras – Nu/Horizontal; Scanners – 2-Linotype-Hell/Saphire, 1-Linotype-Hell/S3300 Drum PRESSROOM: Line 1 – 5-KB/(3 color humps) double width 1985; Folders – 2-KB/3:2 KF 80 Jaw; Pasters – MEG; Reels and Stands – 5-MEG. MAILROOM: Counter stackers – 1-QWI/300, 1-Rima/RS30, 2-HL/Dual Carrier; Inserters and stuffers – 1-KAN/480 6:1, 1/AM Graphics/NP 630 13:1; Bundle tying machines – 2-/Power Strap/PSN20; Addressing machine – 1-/KR, 1-/Ch, 1-/Ink Jet.; Business Hardware – 2-DEC/VAX 3900, Microsoft/Windows NT

BLUFFTON

NEWS-BANNER

125 N. Johnson St., Bluffton, Ind., 46714; gen tel (260) 824-0224; adv tel (260) 824-0224; ed tel (260) 824-0224; gen fax (260) 824-0700; adv fax (260) 824-0700; ed fax (260) 824-0700; gen e-mail email@news-banner.com; adv e-mail email@news-banner.com; ed e-mail newsroom@news-banner.com; web site www.news-banner.com
Published: Mon, Tues, Wed, Thur, Fri, Sat
Weekday Frequency: e
Saturday Frequency: m
Circulation: 4,691; 4,691(sat)
Last Audit: Sworn October 1, 2003
Price: 11.40/mo; 119.00/yr; $54.95/yr (online).
Advertising: Open inch rate $13.70
Insert rate: varies
News services: AP.
Politics: Independent. **Established:** 1892
Not Published: New Year; Memorial Day; Independence Day; Labor Day; Thanksgiving; Christmas.
Own facility?: Y
Special Editions: Christmas Greetings (Dec); Progress (Jun); Senior Lifestyle (Quarterly).
Special Weekly Sections: Entertainment Guide (Sat); Internet/ModernLiving (Thur); Agricultural (Tues); House & Home (Wed).
Magazines: USA WEEKEND Magazine (Sat).
Chrmn...........George B. Witwer
Pres./Pub...........Mark F. Miller
Controller..........Martha Poling
Adv. Mgr., Classified..........Jean Bordner
Dir., Mktg...........Dianne Witwer
Circ. Dir...........Mary Battiste
Asst. Ed...........David Schultz
Mng. Ed...........Glen Werling
Arts/Entertainment Ed...........Barbara Barbieri
Editorial Page Ed...........Mark Miller
Sports Ed...........Paul Beitler
Prodn. Supt...........Howard Jones
Online Ed...........Jerry Battiste
Market Information: TMC.
Mechanical available: Offset; Black and 2 ROP colors; insert accepted; page cutoffs - 22 3/4.
Mechanical Specifications: Type page 10 1/2 x 21 1/2; E - 6 cols, 1 5/8, 3/20 between; A - 6 cols, 1 5/8, 3/20 between; C - 6 cols, 1 5/8, 3/20 between.
Commodity Consumption: Avg. Page Number Per Issue - Daily 13; Avg. Page Number Per Issue - Plates Used 6000; Avg. Page Number Per Issue - Saturday 14; widths 23; Newsprint Used - Short Tons 270; Printing Ink Used - Black 11300; Printing Ink Used - Color 375; Printing Ink U
Equipment EDITORIAL: Front-end Software – QPS/QuarkXPress 3.32, Baseview, Adobe/Photoshop 5.0.; Editorial Hardware – APP/Mac G3, APP/Power Mac, 2-APP/Mac G4; Editorial Printers – APP/Mac 8500 CLASSIFIED: Front-end Software – Baseview/ClassAct/FP 3.; Classified Hardware – APP/Mac, APP/iMac DISPLAY: Ad make-up applications – 6-Multi-Ad/Creator, QPS/QuarkXPress 4.1, Adobe/Photoshop.; Display Hardware – APP/Mac G3, APP/Mac G4; Display Printers – Xante PRODUCTION: Pagination Software – QPS/QuarkXPress 3.32.; Production Equipment – 1-Nu; Cameras – 1-Nu PRESSROOM: Line 1 – 4-G/Community 1975.; Bundle tying machines – 2/Bs.; Business Hardware – Software ☐ Vision Data
Zip Codes served: 46714, 46777, 46759, 46778, 46766, 46781, 46731, 46770, 46791, 46799, 46798, 46792, 47359
Delivery method: Mail, Newsstand, Private Carrier, Racks

NEWS-BANNER PUBLICATIONS, INC.

125 N. Johnson St., Bluffton, Ind., 46714; gen tel (260) 824-0224; gen fax (260) 824-0700
Politics: 1892

BRAZIL

THE BRAZIL TIMES

100 N. Meridian St., Brazil, Ind., 47834; gen tel (812) 446-2216; adv tel (812) 446-2216; ed tel (812) 446-2216; gen fax (812) 446-0938; adv fax (812) 446-0938; ed fax (812) 446-0938; gen e-mail news@thebraziltimes.com; adv e-mail ads@thebraziltimes.com; ed e-mail news@thebraziltimes.com; web site www.thebraziltimes.com
Published: Mon, Wed, Thur, Fri, Sat
Weekday Frequency: e
Saturday Frequency: m
Circulation: 4,633; 4,633(sat)
Last Audit: September 29, 2003
Price: 7.30/mo; 99.00/yr.
Advertising: Open inch rate $14.70(e-mon)
News services: AP.
Not Published: New Year; Memorial Day; Independence Day; Labor Day; Veteran's Day; Thanksgiving; Christmas.
Special Editions: Christmas Greetings (Dec); Football (Fall); New Year's Baby (Jan); Graduation (May); Business & Industry (Other).
Special Weekly Sections: Best Food Day (Mon); School News Page (Sat); Agri-Business (Tues).
Magazines: Relish (Monthly); Weekender (Sat).
Pub...........Randy List
Gen. Mgr...........Lynne Llewellyn
Bus. Mgr...........Denise Frazier
Adv. Rep...........John Adamson
Circ. Mgr...........Karen Barnhart
Ed...........Jason Moon
Sports Ed...........Carey Fox
Market Information: ADS; TMC.
Mechanical available: Offset; Black and 3 ROP colors; insert accepted; page cutoffs - 22 3/4.
Mechanical Specifications: Type page 11 5/8 x 21 1/2; E - 6 cols, 1 13/16, 1/8 between; A - 6, cols, 1 13/16, 1/8 between; C - 9 cols, 1 3/16, 1/16 between.
Commodity Consumption: Avg. Page Number Per Issue - Daily 10; Avg. Page Number Per Issue - Plates Used 1200; widths 27 1/2; Newsprint Used - Metric Tons 190; Printing Ink Used - Black 10000; Printing Ink Used - Color 1500; Printing Ink Used - Pages Printed 3120.
Equipment EDITORIAL: Front-end Software – Baseview/NewsEdit 2.0, Adobe/Photoshop 4.0, QPS/QuarkXPress 3.31. CLASSIFIED: Front-end Software – Baseview. DISPLAY: Ad make-up applications – Multi-Ad/Creator 3.7; Layout Software – Multi-Ad/Creator, QPS/QuarkXPress. PRODUCTION: Pagination Software – QPS/QuarkXPress 4.0.; Production Equipment – 1-LE/LD-18; Cameras – 1-R/480 PRESSROOM: Line 1 – 6-G/Community single width. MAILROOM: Counter stackers – 1-BG/Count-O-Veyor; Bundle tying machines – 1/Malow.

CHESTERTON

CHESTERTON TRIBUNE

193 S. Calumet Rd., Chesterton, Ind., 46304; gen tel (219) 926-1131; adv tel (219) 926-1131; ed tel (219) 926-1131; gen fax (219) 926-6389; adv fax (219) 926-6389; ed fax (219) 926-6389; gen e-mail chestertontrib@earthlink.net; web site www.chestertontribune.com
Published: Mon, Tues, Wed, Thur, Fri
Weekday Frequency: e
Circulation: 4,500
Last Audit: Sworn October 1, 2001
Price: 6.00/mo; 72.00/yr.
Advertising: Open inch rate $7.40
News services: AP.
Politics: 1884
Not Published: New Year; Memorial Day; Independence Day; Labor Day; Thanksgiving; Christmas.
Special Editions: Sidewalk Sale (Jul); Christmas Shopping Guide (Nov).
Bus. Mgr...........Betty Canright
Ed...........Warren H. Canright
Webmaster..........David Canright
Adv. Dir...........Dick Harlan
Circ. Mgr...........Alma Rabe
Community Ed...........Alexandra Newman
Mechanical available: Offset; Black; insert accepted; page cutoffs - 22.
Mechanical Specifications: Type page 13 x 21; E - 6 cols, 2 1/16, 1/8 between; A - 6 cols, 2 1/16, 1/8 between; C - 6 cols, 2 1/16, 1/8 between.
Commodity Consumption: Avg. Page Number Per Issue - Daily 12; Avg. Page Number Per Issue - Plates Used 1524; widths 27 1/2; Newsprint Used - Metric Tons 80; Printing Ink Used - Black 2375; Printing Ink Used - Pages Printed 3048.
Equipment EDITORIAL: Front-end Software – Baseview.; Editorial Hardware – Baseview/NewsEdit Pro; Editorial Printers – HP/LaserJet 5000N, HP/LaserJet 4050N CLASSIFIED: Front-end Software – Baseview/Classified.; Classified Hardware – APP/Mac Quadra; Classified Printers – HP/LaserJet 4050N DISPLAY: Ad make-up applications – Quark; Layout Software – Quark.; Display Hardware – APP/Mac G4; Display Printers – HP/LaserJet 5000N; Production Equipment – HP/LaserJet 5000N; Cameras – R. PRESSROOM: Line 1 – 3-G/Community; Folders – 1; Addressing machine – Baseview.
Zip Codes served: 46304; 46384; 46383
Delivery method: Mail, Private Carrier, Racks

CLINTON

THE DAILY CLINTONIAN

422 S. Main St., Clinton, Ind., 47842-0309; gen tel (765) 832-2443; adv tel (765) 832-2443; ed tel (765) 832-2443; adv fax (765) 832-2560; adv e-mail cccc@mikes.net; web site www.ccc-clintonian.com
Published: Mon, Tues, Wed, Thur, Fri
Weekday Frequency: e
Circulation: 5,045
Last Audit: Sworn October 1, 2003
Price: 1.95/wk.
Advertising: Open inch rate $8.00
Insert rate: Varies - contact Adv
News services: AP.
Politics: Republican. **Established:** 1912
Advertising not accepted: N
Not Published: New Year; Thanksgiving; Christmas.
Own facility?: Y
Special Editions: Christmas (Dec); Graduation (May); Il Bollettino (Sept).
Sec./Treasurer..........Diane E. Waugh
Prodn. Foreman, Composing/Pressroom George B. Carey
Mechanical available: Offset; Black and 2 ROP colors; insert accepted - hand stuffing in-plant; page cutoffs - 22 3/4.
Mechanical Specifications: Type page 15 1/2 x 21; E - 7 cols, 2 1/16, 1/8 between; A - 7 cols, 2 1/16, 1/8 between; C - 7 cols, 2 1/16, 1/8 between.
Commodity Consumption: Avg. Page Number Per Issue - Daily 10; Avg. Page Number Per Issue - Plates Used 7650; widths 17 1/2; Newsprint Used - Short Tons 240; Printing Ink Used - Black 7350; Printing Ink Used - Color 575; Printing Ink Used - Pages Printed 3720.
Equipment EDITORIAL: Front-end Software – Microsoft/Windows Server 2003; Editorial Hardware – 7 PC; Editorial Equipment – AP/Server, Epson/Scanner; Editorial Printers – Xante/4G, Xante/3G, 2-HP/4050 TN
2 HP 4200 CLASSIFIED: Front-end Software – Synaptic.; Classified Hardware – 3-PC; Classified Printers – 4 HP, 2 Xante DISPLAY: Ad make-up applications – Corel Draw X3; Display Hardware – 3 PCs; Display Printers – Xante; Production Equipment – 1-Nu/30x40 UP; Cameras – 1-B/Caravelle; Scanners – 3-Epson PRESSROOM: Line 1 – 4-KP/Color King; Folders – 1 MAILROOM: Counter stackers – 1-BG/Count-O-Veyor; Bundle tying machines – 2/Bu, 1-/Plastic Strap; Addressing machine – 1-Net Jet Labeler. BUSINESS COMPUTERS: Business Software – Microsoft/WindowsXP Pro; Business Hardware – 2-PC
Delivery method: Mail, Newsstand, Private Carrier

COLUMBIA CITY

THE POST & MAIL

927 W. Connexion Way, Columbia City, Ind., 46725-0837; gen tel (260) 244-5153; adv tel (260) 244-5153; ed tel (260) 244-5153; gen fax (260) 244-7598; adv fax (260) 244-7598; ed fax (260) 244-7598; gen e-mail postandmail@earthlink.net; web site www.thepostandmail.com
Published: Mon, Tues, Wed, Thur, Fri, Sat, Sun
Weekday Frequency: e
Saturday Frequency: m
Circulation: 4,058; 4,058(sat)
Last Audit: September 30, 2003

Price: 10.20/mo (carrier), $12.00/mo (motor route); 156.00/yr.
Advertising: Open inch rate $8.95
News services: AP.
Politics: Independent.
Not Published: New Year; Memorial Day; Independence Day; Labor Day; Christmas.
Special Editions: Home & Garden Tab (Apr); 4-H Tab (Aug); Progress (Feb); Taxes & Finances Tab (Jan); Old Settlers Day (Community Festival) Program (Jul); Car Care Tab (May); TV Monthly (Monthly); High School Sports Tab (Nov).
Magazines: USA WEEKEND Magazine (Sat); American Profile (Weekly).
Pub...Doug Brown
Bus. Mgr. ....Cindy Johnson
Adv. Mgr. ....Mick Long
Circ. Mgr.....................................Sally Ballard
Editorial Page Ed. ....Ruth Stanley
Obituary Ed. ....Laura Beucler
Market Information: TMC.
Mechanical available: Offset; Black and 3 ROP colors; insert accepted - max 29; page cutoffs - 21 1/2.
Mechanical Specifications: Type page 13 x 21 1/2; E - 6 cols, 1 3/4, 1/8 between; A - 6 cols, 1 3/4, 1/8 between; C - 9 cols, 1 1/8, 1/8 between.
Commodity Consumption: Avg. Page Number Per Issue - Daily 16; widths 25.
Equipment; Editorial Hardware – Mk, APP/Mac; Editorial Equipment – 5-Mk; Editorial Printers – APP/Mac.; Classified Hardware – 1-Mk.; Display Hardware – APP/Mac; Display Printers – APP/Mac LaserPrinter.; Production Equipment – 1-Ic; Cameras – 1-SCREEN; Scanners – Microtek.; Bundle tying machines – 2/Bu.

COLUMBUS

THE REPUBLIC

333 Second St., Columbus, Ind., 47201; gen tel (812) 372-7811; adv tel (812) 379-5652; ed tel (812) 379-5665; gen fax (812) 372-1634; adv fax (812) 379-5776; ed fax (812) 379-5711; adv e-mail advertise@therepublic.com; ed e-mail editorial@therepublic.com; web site www.therepublic.com
Published: Mon, Tues, Wed, Thur, Fri, Sat, Sun
Weekday Frequency: m
Saturday Frequency: m
Circulation: 18,693; 18,693(sat); 20,154(sun)
Last Audit: September 30, 2009
Price: 12.50/mo (home delivery); 145.50/yr.
Advertising: Open inch rate $26.05
News services: AP, NEA, SHNS, MCT.
Politics: Independent-Republican. **Established:** 1872
Special Editions: Business Profiles (Apr); Education (Aug); Year-in-Review (Dec); Tourism (Feb); 4-H (Jul); Answer Book (Jun); Fashion (Mar); Garden (May); Gift Guide (Nov); Cookbook (Oct); Home Improvement (Sept).
Special Weekly Sections: Health (Fri); School (Mon); Kids Page (S); Auto (Sat); Entertainment (Thur).
Magazines: Sunday Color Comics Continental (Other); USA WEEKEND Magazine (S).
Pub....Chuck Wells
Administrative Mgr. ....Charlotte Patrick
Adv. Dir., Sales/Mktg..............Sharon Shumate
Adv. Mgr., Classified...................Jane Hoffman
Ed...Bob Gustin
Assoc. Ed............................Harry McCawley
News Ed...Joe Gill
Newsroom Coord.......................Jane Peabody
Systems Mgr. ....Terry Clark
Prodn. Dir..............................Neil Thompson
Prodn. Mgr., Post Press...............Wally Veluzat
Press Supvr...............................Randy Reeves
Market Information: TMC.
Mechanical available: Offset; Black and 3 ROP colors; insert accepted - product sampling bags; page cutoffs - 22 3/4.
Mechanical Specifications: Type page 13 x 21 1/2; E - 6 cols, 2 1/16, 1/8 between; A - 6 cols, 2 1/16, 1/8 between; C - 9 cols, 1 3/8, 1/16 between.
Commodity Consumption: Avg. Page Number Per Issue - Daily 24; Avg. Page Number Per Issue - Plates Used 30160; Avg. Page Number Per Issue - Saturday 30; Avg. Page Number Per Issue - Sunday 36; widths 27 1/2; Newsprint Used - Short Tons 3120; Printing Ink Used - Black 27519; Pri
Equipment; Editorial Hardware – 8-Gateway/P200, 22-IBM/486-33, 2-Novell/SFt3-ALR, 10-Gateway/PIII 500, 22-Gateway/Celerah 350, 2-HP/LC2000 NT/SQL; Editorial Equipment – APP/Power Mac 7100, APP/Mac 8100-100, APP/Power Mac, 5-APP/Mac G3; Editorial Printers – 1-Panasonic/KX P1595, 1-APP/Mac LaserWr CLASSIFIED: Front-end Software – PPI, ACT, Classified.; Classified Hardware – 9-HP/PC, 9-Gateway/Celeron 350; Classified Printers – HP/4M Plus DISPLAY: Ad make-up applications – QPS/QuarkXPress 3.332; Layout Software – Mk/Ad Director, APP/Mac.; Display Hardware – 12-APP/Mac; Display Printers – 1-HP/4MV, 2-HP/LaserJet 5000, 2-AG/Selectset 5000/MON RIP, Pre Press/Panther Pro 62, Pre Press/Panther RIP PRODUCTION: Pagination Software – ACT/V2, ACT/V04, ACT/V003.; Production Equipment – TI/OmniPage 5.0, APP/Mac, Pre Press/Panther Pro 62, Pre Press/Panther RIP, Pre Press/Panther Imposer; Cameras – 1-C/Spartan II; Scanners – 1-ECR/1030, 3-Umax, 1-Lf/AP Leafscan 45, 3-Kk/2035 PRESSROOM: Line 1 – 12-DGM/850 single width 1998; Press Drives – 3-Fin/150 HP Drive 1998; Folders – 1, 1-1998; Pasters – Jun-98; Reels and Stands – 2-G/Stands 1998; Press control system – Smith/Spray Bars, 1998. MAILROOM: Counter stackers – 2-HI/Olympian, HI/Rima; Inserters and stuffers – 1-S/1472; Bundle tying machines – 2-Sterling/MR45, 1-OVL/410.; Audio Hardware – Info-Connect/Pottsville Republican, New Horizons/Info-Connect, Gateway/P200 BUSINESS COMPUTERS: Business Software – PBS/MediaPlus; Business Hardware – MS/NT Server 4.0, ALR/Evolution, HP/LC2000 Exchange

CONNERSVILLE

CONNERSVILLE NEWS-EXAMINER

406 Central Ave., Connersville, Ind., 47331-0287; gen tel (765) 825-0581; adv tel (765) 825-0585; ed tel (765) 825-0588; gen fax (765) 825-4599; adv fax (765) 825-4599; ed fax (765) 825-4599; gen e-mail newsexaminer@newsexaminer.com; web site www.newsexaminer.com
Published: Mon, Tues, Wed, Thur, Fri, Sat
Weekday Frequency: m
Circulation: 7,390; 7,390(sat)
Last Audit: December 4, 2009
Price: 8.25/mo (city), $8.50/mo (motor routes); 144.00, $99.00/yr (city), $102.00/yr (motor routes).
Advertising: Open inch rate $18.85
News services: AP.
Politics: Independent-Republican.
Not Published: New Year; Memorial Day; Independence Day; Labor Day; Thanksgiving; Christmas.
Special Editions: Home Improvement (Apr); Back-to-School (Aug); Christmas Greetings (Dec); Bridal (Jan); TV (Mar); Cookbook Magazine (Nov); Car Care (Oct).
Special Weekly Sections: Church Page (Fri); Best Food Day (Mon); Best Real Estate Days (Thur).
Magazines: Valley View (Quarterly); USA WEEKEND Magazine (Sat).
Gen. Mgr...Joy Pears
Adv. Mgr..Joy Pierce
Circ. Mgr. ....Bill Wulff
Online Ed......................................Gary Hufferd
Sports Ed....................................Mike Moffett
Online Mgr...........................Donald Schneider
Market Information: Split run; TMC; Zoned editions.
Mechanical available: Offset; Black and 3 ROP colors; insert accepted - free standing; page cutoffs - 22 3/4.
Mechanical Specifications: Type page 13 x 21; E - 6 cols, 2 1/16, 1/8 between; A - 6 cols, 2 1/16, 1/8 between; C - 9 cols, 1 5/16, 1/8 between.
Commodity Consumption: Avg. Page Number Per Issue - Daily 18; Avg. Page Number Per Issue - Plates Used 12000; Avg. Page Number Per Issue - Saturday 18; widths 27 1/2; Newsprint Used - Metric Tons 300; Printing Ink Used - Black 9209; Printing Ink Used - Color 614; Printing Ink
Equipment EDITORIAL: Front-end Software – QPS/QuarkXPress 3.32, Adobe/Photoshop 3.0.; Editorial Hardware – 1-IBM, 2-APP/Mac PowerBook 150, 5-APP/Power Mac 4400, 5-Umax/C600 CLASSIFIED: Front-end Software – Baseview.; Classified Hardware – 4-APP/Mac IIci, APP/Mac Quadra 630; Classified Equipment – Iomega/100 MB Zip Drive; Classified Printers – APP/Mac LaserWriter II, Okidata/Microline 32, APP/Mac Stylewriter DISPLAY: Ad make-up applications – QPS/QuarkXPress 3.32; Layout Software – 2-APP/Mac SE.; Display Hardware – APP/Mac Quadra 630, 4-APP/Power Mac 7300, APP/Power Mac 7500, APP/Power Mac 8100, APP/Power Mac 7100, APP/Power Mac 9500, APP/Mac G3, APP/Power Mac; Display Printers – HP/LaserJet 4V, Stylewriter PRODUCTION: Pagination Software – APP/Mac, QPS.; Production Equipment – MON/RIP Express 1.02, Monotype/ImageMaster 1000; Cameras – 1-SCREEN PRESSROOM: Line 1 – 6-G/Suburban single width 1960; Line 2 – 4-G/Community single width 1973; Folders – G/SSC, G/SC; Pasters – 1; Reels and Stands – 6-G/Suburban Rollstand. MAILROOM: Counter stackers – 1/Mid America Graphics, 1-/BG; Bundle tying machines – 1-Bu/String, 1-Bu/Strap; Addressing machine – 1-/Mk; Other equipment –Challenge/30 Trimmer, Bostitch/Saddle Stitcher. BUSINESS COMPUTERS: Business Software – IBM/AS-400, Baseview; Business Hardware – IBM/AS-400, Baseview

CONNERSVILLE PUBLISHING CO., INC.

406 Central Ave., Connersville, Ind., 47331-0287; gen tel (765) 825-0581; gen fax (765) 825-4599; gen e-mail newsexaminer@newsexaminer.com; web site www.newsexaminer.com

CRAWFORDSVILLE

JOURNAL REVIEW

119 N. Green St., Crawfordsville, Ind., 47933-1708; gen tel (765) 362-1200; adv tel (765) 362-1200; ed tel (765) 362-1201; adv fax (765) 364-5428; ed fax (765) 364-5424; adv e-mail sstorie@jrpress.com; ed e-mail jheater@jrpress.com; web site www.journalreview.com
Published: Mon, Tues, Wed, Thur, Fri, Sat
Weekday Frequency: m
Circulation: 6,650; 6,650(sat)
Last Audit: September 30, 2009
Price: 13.00/mo; 139.00/yr.
Advertising: Open inch rate $15.90
News services: AP.
Politics: Independent. **Established:** 1841
Not Published: New Year; Christmas.
Special Editions: Home Improvement (Apr); Fall Sports Preview (Aug); Caroling Song Book (Dec); Wedding Planner (Feb); Wedding Planner (Jul); Strawberry Festival (Jun); Area Golf Guide (Mar); Indy 500 (May); Basketball (Nov); Home Improvement (Oct); Fall Activity Guide (Sep
Special Weekly Sections: Church (Sat); Best Food Day (Tues).
Magazines: Montgomery County Directory (Annually); Friends and Family (Monthly); USA WEEKEND Magazine (Sat).
Pub....Sean Smith
Mng. Ed....Jay Heater
Sports Ed.....................................Matt Wilson
Prodn. Mgr., Composing Room.....Lauri Shillings
Prodn. Foreman, Lead Pressman.Ronald Cooley
Market Information: TMC.
Mechanical available: Offset; Black and 3 ROP colors; insert accepted; page cutoffs - 22 3/4.
Mechanical Specifications: Type page 13 x 21 1/2; E - 6 cols, 2 1/16, 1/8 between; A - 6 cols, 2 1/16, 1/8 between; C - 9 cols, 1 11/32, 1/8 between.
Commodity Consumption: Avg. Page Number Per Issue - Daily 23; Avg. Page Number Per Issue - Plates Used 7550; Avg. Page Number Per Issue - Saturday 32; widths 27 1/2; Newsprint Used - Metric Tons 530; Printing Ink Used - Black 12500; Printing Ink Used - Color 1750; Printing Ink
Equipment EDITORIAL: Front-end Software – Baseview 3.0.; Editorial Hardware – APP/Mac; Editorial Printers – GCC/SelectPress 600, Epson CLASSIFIED: Front-end Software – Baseview/Class Manager Plus.; Classified Hardware – APP/Mac; Classified Printers – Epson DISPLAY: Ad make-up applications – Multi-Ad 3.8, Multi-Ad/Creator 2.0; Layout Software – 4-APP/Mac.; Display Hardware – 1-APP/Mac G3, 4-APP/Mac 7300; Display Printers – APP/Mac LaserWriter, QMS/860 PRODUCTION: Pagination Software – QPS/QuarkXPress 3.32.; Production Equipment – APP/Mac, GCC/Select Press 600, QMS/860 Print System; Cameras – 1-B; Scanners – Umax/Powerlook II, Nikon/Film PRESSROOM: Line 1 – 9-HI/V-15D 1981; Press Drives – HI/Cutler Hammer; Folders – 1; Reels and Stands – 7; Inserters and stuffers – KAN/480; Bundle tying machines – MLN, Bu. BUSINESS COMPUTERS: Business Software – Great Plains, AR Works; Business Hardware – 4-HP

DECATUR

DECATUR DAILY DEMOCRAT

141 S. Second St., Decatur, Ind., 46733-5001; gen tel (260) 724-2121; gen fax (260) 724-7981; gen e-mail dailydemo@decaturdailydemocrat.com; adv e-mail advertising@decaturdailydemocrat.com; ed e-mail editorial@decaturdailydemocrat.com; web site www.decaturdailydemocrat.com
Group: Horizon Publications
Published: Mon, Tues, Wed, Thur, Fri, Sat
Weekday Frequency: e
Saturday Frequency: m
Circulation: 5,000; 5,000(sat)
Last Audit: Sworn September 29, 2001
Price: 2.25/wk; 9.00/mo; 115.00/yr.
Advertising: Open inch rate $12 .54
Insert rate: $47M
News services: AP.
Politics: Independent. **Established:** 1857
Advertising not accepted: Y
Not Published: New Year; Memorial Day; Independence Day; Labor Day; Thanksgiving; Christmas.
Own facility?: Y
Special Editions: Basketball (Feb); Christmas Opening (Nov); Callithumpian (Oct).
Special Weekly Sections: Business News (Sat); Best Food Day (Mon); Church Page (Sat); Agri-News (Thur); School Scene (Wed).
Magazines: Weekly TV Section (Fri); American Profile (Sat)
Broadcast Affiliations: None
Profile: independent
Pub...Ronald Storey
Bus. Mgr. ....Ruth Hernadez
Adv. Mgr., Classified ....Ita Mari Long
Circ. Mgr. ....Ryan Green
Mng. Ed...........................Robert W. Shraluka
Features Ed. ....J. Swygart
Lifestyle Ed...............................Kristen Baron
Sports Ed...............................James Hopkins
Market Information: TMC.
Mechanical available: Offset; Black and 3 ROP colors; insert accepted - all inserts accepted; page cutoffs - 22 3/4.
Mechanical Specifications: Type page 13 x 21 1/2; E - 6 cols, 2 1/8, 1/8 between; A - 6 cols, 2 1/8, 1/8 between; C - 6 cols, 2 1/8, 1/8 between.
Commodity Consumption: er Per Issue - Daily 16; Avg. Page Number Per Issue - Plates Used 3700; Avg. Page Number Per Issue - Saturday 20; widths 27 1/2; Newsprint Used -

Short Tons 212; Printing Ink Used - Black 8500; Printing Ink Used - Color 680; Printing Ink Us

Equipment EDITORIAL: Front-end Software – Baseview/NewsEdit.; Editorial Hardware – 4-APP/Mac Quadra 605, APP/Mac Quadra 630, 2-APP/Mac Quadra 610, APP/Mac Quadra 650; Editorial Printers – APP/Mac LaserWriter 630 Pro, APP/Mac LaserWriter 16-1600 PS CLASSIFIED: Front-end Software – Claris/FileMaker Pro.; Classified Hardware – APP/Mac Quadra 610 PRODUCTION: Pagination Software – QPS/QuarkXPress 3.31.; Production Equipment – 2-APP/Power Mac, 1-APP/Mac Pro 630; Cameras – 1-R/400; Scanners – 3-Microtek PRESSROOM: Line 1 – 8-G/Community (2 stacks); Folders – 1; Bundle tying machines – 1-Bu/162X

Delivery method: Newsstand, Private Carrier, Racks

ELKHART

THE ELKHART TRUTH

421 S. Second St., Elkhart, Ind., 46516; gen tel (574) 294-1661; adv tel (574) 294-1661; ed tel (574) 296-5805; gen fax (574) 294-4014; adv fax (574) 293-3302; ed fax (574) 294-3895; gen e-mail newsroom@etruth.com; adv e-mail malexander@etruth.com; ed e-mail ghalling@etruth.com; web site www.etruth.com

Published: Mon, Tues, Wed, Thur, Fri, Sat, Sun
Weekday Frequency: m
Saturday Frequency: m
Circulation: 20,524; 20,524(sat); 23,715(sun)
Last Audit: ABC September 30, 2011
Price: 11.59/mo (carrier); 137.00/yr (carrier).
Advertising: Open inch rate $38
News services: AP, SHNS, MCT
Politics: Independent. **Established:** 1889
Own facility?: Y
Special Editions: Spring Car Care (Apr); Healthy Living (May & October); Business & Industry (Feb); Brides (Jan); 4-H Fair (Jul); Best of Elkhart (March); Fall Home Improvement (Sept).
Special Weekly Sections: Weekend Projects (Fri); A&E (Thurs); Faith (Sat); Food (Mon.); Health & Fitness (Wed); TV (Fri)
Magazines: USA WEEKEND Magazine (Sat).
Broadcast Affiliations: WBYT-FM South Bend, IN; WTRC Elkhart, IN; WBYR-FM/WFWI-FM/WQHK-FM/AM Fort Wayne, IN; WAOR-FM South Bend, IN.

Publisher .... Brandon Erlacher
Controller .... Jeff Laderer
Mng. Ed. .... Gregory Halling
Fun Writer .... Marshall King
Sports Ed. .... Bill Beck
Prodn. Mgr., Pressroom .... John Platt
Managing Editor .... Halling Greg
Audience Development Director .... Doug McAvoy
Data Processing Mgr. .... Darrick King

Market Information: ADS; Split run; TMC.
Mechanical available: Web Offset; Black and 3 ROP colors; insert accepted - card stock, single sheets, quarter folded; page cutoffs - 22 3/4.
Mechanical Specifications: Type page 10 x 21 1/2; E - 5 cols, 1.9, 1/8 between; A - 5 cols, 1.9, 1/8 between; C - 6 cols, 1.5625, 1/8 between.
Commodity Consumption: Avg. Page Number Per Issue - Daily 35; Avg. Page Number Per Issue - Plates Used 32900; Avg. Page Number Per Issue - Sunday 76; widths 50; Newsprint Used - Metric Tons 2580; Newsprint Used - Short Tons 2840; Printing Ink Used - Black 47750; Printing Ink U
Equipment EDITORIAL: Front-end Software – Saxotech/InDesign; Editorial Hardware – APP/Mac; Editorial Printers – HP/Laserjet 8100 N, NewGen CLASSIFIED: Front-end Software – DTI/Class Manager Pro, QPS/QuarkXPress.; Classified Hardware – APP/Mac; Classified Printers – APP/Mac LaserWriter DISPLAY: Ad make-up applications – DTI/Ad Manager Pro; Layout Software – MEI/ALS.; Display Hardware – APP/Mac; Display Printers – HP/Laserjet 8150N, HP/Color Laserjet SM PRODUCTION: Pagination Software – QPS/QuarkXPress 4.11.; Production Equipment – Caere/OmniPage 8.0, AG/PPG Rips; Scanners – Umax AG, Kk/Slides PRESSROOM: Line 1 – 5-HI/N1650 1973; Press Drives – GE/200 h.p., ASEA/200 h.p.; Folders – 2-HI/2:1; Reels and Stands – 4-HI/Registron Reel Stand 1973; Press control system – BII/Bender, 4-BII/Register Board; Press registration system – USA/Copy. MAILROOM: Counter stackers – 2/MRS, 1-/QWI; Inserters and stuffers – 6-Mc/N660, 2-Mc/N660, 8-Mc/N660; Bundle tying machines – 2-/Power Strap; Addressing machine – 1-/KR. BUSINESS COMPUTERS: Business Software – G/Dynamics; Business Hardware – Dell
Delivery method: Newsstand, Private Carrier, Racks

TRUTH PUBLISHING CO., INC.

Communicana Bldg., Elkhart, Ind., 46515; gen tel (574) 294-1661; gen fax (574) 294-4014
Politics: 1889

ELWOOD

ELWOOD CALL-LEADER

317 S. Anderson St., Elwood, Ind., 46036-2018; gen tel (765) 552-3355; adv tel (765) 552-3355; ed tel (765) 552-3355; gen fax (765) 552-3358; adv fax (765) 552-3358; ed e-mail elpub@elwoodpublishing.com; web site www.elwoodpublishing.com

Published: Mon, Tues, Wed, Thur, Fri, Sat, Sun
Weekday Frequency: e
Saturday Frequency: m
Circulation: 3,081; 3,081(sat)
Last Audit: October 10, 2003
Price: 7.00/mo (carrier), $8.00/mo (motor route); 97.40,$ 75.60/yr (carrier), $86.40/yr (motor route).
Advertising: Open inch rate $9.00
News services: AP.
Politics: Independent.
Not Published: New Year; Memorial Day; Independence Day; Labor Day; Thanksgiving; Christmas.
Special Editions: Farm & Garden (Apr); Fair Wrap-up (Aug); Cookbook (Feb); Mature Years (Jan); Welcome to Elwood (Jun); Spring Opening (Mar); Spring Home Improvement (May); Christmas Opening (Nov); Fall Brides (Oct); Frankton Heritage Days Festival (Sept).
Special Weekly Sections: Best Food Day (Mon).
Magazines: What's On TV (Fri); The Mini-Page for Kids (Tues).

Adv. Dir. .... Michael Brown
Adv. Dir .... Robert L. Nash
News Ed. .... Saundra Burton
Sports Ed. .... Ed Hamilton
Prodn. Mgr., Pre Press .... Chris Idlewine
Prodn. Mgr., Pressroom .... Randy Bayne

Market Information: TMC.
Mechanical available: Web Offset; Black and 3 ROP colors; insert accepted; page cutoffs - 22 3/4.
Mechanical Specifications: Type page 13 x 21 1/2; E - 6 cols, 2 1/16, 1/8 between; A - 6 cols, 2 1/16, 1/8 between; C - 8 cols, 1 1/2, 3/20 between.
Commodity Consumption: Avg. Page Number Per Issue - Daily 10; Avg. Page Number Per Issue - Plates Used 2150; widths 13 3/4; Newsprint Used - Metric Tons 90; Newsprint Used - Short Tons 98; Printing Ink Used - Black 2880; Printing Ink Used - Color 360; Printing Ink Used - Pages
Equipment EDITORIAL: Front-end Software – Mk/Mycro-Comp.; Editorial Hardware – Mk/1100 CLASSIFIED: Front-end Software – Mk/Mycro-Comp.; Classified Hardware – Mk/1100; Production Equipment – 2-APP/Mac LaserWriter II NT/NTX; Cameras – 1-R/Commodore. PRESSROOM: Line 1 – 4-G/Community; Folders – 1; Bundle tying machines – 2/Malow; Addressing machine – 2-/Am.; Business Hardware – 1-BS/B-20, 1-RSK/TRS 80 model 4

ELWOOD PUBLISHING CO., INC.

317 S. Anderson St., Elwood, Ind., 46036-2018; gen tel (765) 552-3355; gen fax (765) 552-3358; gen e-mail elpub@elwoodpublishing.com; web site www.elwoodpublishing.com

Pub. Bob Nash

EVANSVILLE

EVANSVILLE COURIER & PRESS

300 E. Walnut St., Evansville, Ind., 47713; gen tel (812) 424-7711; adv tel (812) 464-7582; ed tel (812) 461-0799; gen fax (812) 464-7487; adv fax (812) 464-7487; ed fax (812) 422-8196; gen e-mail eccnewmedia@courierpress.com; adv e-mail hedged@courierpress.com; ed e-mail stewartm@courierpress.com; web site www.courierpress.com

Published: Mon, Tues, Wed, Thur, Fri, Sat, Sun
Weekday Frequency: m
Saturday Frequency: m
Circulation: 51,338; 53,305(sat); 72,818(sun)
Last Audit: ABC September 30, 2011
Price: 17.60/mo; 208.00/yr.
Advertising: Open inch rate $111.00
Insert rate: $50.28 2 tab Sunday
News services: AP, NYT, SHNS.
Politics: Independent. **Established:** 1845
Not Published: None
Own facility?: Y
Special Editions: Visitor Guide (Apr); Progress (Aug); Coupon Book (Dec); Healthwise (Feb); Internet Directory (Jan); Progress (Jul); Coupon Book (Mar); Coupon Book (May); Christmas Gift Guide (Nov); New Car Guide (Oct); Home & Garden (Sept).
Special Weekly Sections: TV Book, West, Warrick
Magazines: Access (Fri); Parade (S).

Pres./Pub. .... Jack Pate
HR Dir. .... Thomas Mominee
Dir., Mktg. .... Kathryn Gieneart
Editor .... Mizell Stewart III
Advertising Director .... Dave Hedge
I.T. Director .... Krista McDivitt
Director/Circulation Sales .... Steve Traud
Finance Director .... Bill Anthony
Dir., Finance .... Michael Hales
Credit Mgr. .... Jeffrey S. Harden
Adv. Sr. Mgr., Retail Sales .... Kevin Kalebjian
Adv. Mgr., Retail Sales .... Ron Obermeier
Mgr., Mktg. Servs. .... Carolyn Franklin
Asst. Mng. Ed., News .... Kathleen Wagner
Editorial Page Ed. .... Chuck Leach
Entertainment Ed. .... Roger McBain
Features Ed. .... Linda Negro
Asst. Features Ed. .... Anne Schleper
Librarian .... Roseann Derk
Metro Ed. .... Charlene Tolbert
New Media Ed. .... Jim Beck
Sports Ed. .... Tim Ethridge
Asst. Sports Ed. .... Tim Kaiser
Television Ed. .... Rebecca Coudret

Market Information: ADS; Split run; TMC; Zoned editions.
Mechanical available: Flexo; Black and 3 ROP colors; insert accepted; page cutoffs - 22 1/32.
Mechanical Specifications: Type page 12 x 21 1/8; E - 6 cols, 2 1/16, 1/6 between; A - 6 cols, 2 1/16, 1/6 between; C - 10 cols, 1 1/4, 1/6 between.
Commodity Consumption: Avg. Page Number Per Issue - Daily 38; Avg. Page Number Per Issue - Plates Used 152240; Avg. Page Number Per Issue - Saturday 46; Avg. Page Number Per Issue - Sunday 88; widths 13 3/8; Newsprint Used - Metric Tons 11274; Printing Ink Used - Black 384532;
Equipment EDITORIAL: Front-end Software – Mediaware; Editorial Hardware – Wyse Thin Clients, Dell laptops; Editorial Printers – LaserJets CLASSIFIED: Front-end Software – Brainworks; Classified Hardware – Wyse Thin Clients, Dell laptops; Classified Printers – HP/LaserJets, Ricoh MFP DISPLAY: Ad make-up applications – Mediaware - Saxotech; Layout Software – APP/Mac, MEI.; Display Hardware – APP/Mac G3, Dell 24 Widescreen; Display Printers – LaserJets PRODUCTION: Pagination Software – QPS 1.12, AT/Class P; Production Equipment – Scitex/Dolev 800, Scitex/Dolev 450, Scitex/Dolev 4 Press, III/Laser; Cameras – Pager, Nu Arc SSTE-2024-C; Scanners – Scitex/Smart, Scitex/Smart 2, AG/Arcus II, 5-Kodak/RFS 2035, HP/ScanJet 40, AG Duoscan T1200 PRESSROOM: Line 1 – MOT/Flexo double width 1989, 12; Folders – 2-MOT/2:1, 1-MOT/3:2; Pasters – MOT/Auto; Reels and Stands – 12 MAILROOM: Counter stackers – 2-HL/Monitor HT, 2-HL/Monitor HT II, 4/RIMA, QWI, 1-/QUIPP, TMSI; Inserters and stuffers – 2-Heidelberg/2299, NP-2299; Bundle tying machines – Power Strap, Power Strap/PSN6E, 4-/Power Strap/PSN6, 1-/Power Strap/PSN6E, 3-/Pow AUDIO: Audio Software – US Telephony; Audio Hardware – VNN, PEP, PC 486 BUSINESS COMPUTERS: Business Software – Word, Excel, Access, Outlook, Mediaware, Brainworks; Business Hardware – Wyse Thin Clients, Dell laptops
Delivery method: Mail, Newsstand, Private Carrier, Racks

FORT WAYNE

THE JOURNAL GAZETTE

600 W. Main St., Fort Wayne, Ind., 46802; gen tel (260) 461-8773; ed tel (260) 461-8113; gen fax (260) 461-8648; ed fax (260) 461-8648; gen e-mail jgnews@jg.net; ed e-mail jgnews@jg.net; web site www.journalgazette.net

Published: Mon, Tues, Wed, Thur, Fri, Sat, Sun
Weekday Frequency: m
Saturday Frequency: m
Circulation: 56,187; 74,427(sat); 102,861(sun)
Last Audit: ABC September 30, 2011
Price: 3.30/wk; 176.80/yr.
Advertising: Open inch rate $194.18
News services: AP, SHNS, LAT-WP, VNU, TMS.
Politics: Independent.
Note: For detailed production and mechanical information, see Fort Wayne Newspapers Inc. listing.
Special Editions: Home & Lawn (Apr); Health Career Expo (Feb); Big Boys Tech & Toys Show (Jan); Back to School (Jul); Home Furnishings (Mar); Indy 500 (May); Holiday Shopping Guide (Nov); Directions (Oct); Parade of Homes (Sept).
Special Weekly Sections: Entertainment (Fri); Solutions (Mon); Entertainment/Restaurants/Theatres (Other); Garden (S); Religion (Sat); Politics (Tues); Food/Best Food Day (Wed).
Magazines: Parade (S).
Broadcast Affiliations: WPTA.

Vice Pres./Pub. .... Julie Inskeep
Sec./Treasurer .... Jerry D. Fox
Ed. .... Craig Klugman
Mng. Ed. .... Sherry Skufca
Asst. Mng. Ed., Metro .... Tom Germuska
Bus. Ed. .... Lisa Green
Design Ed. .... Jim Touvell
Editorial Page Ed. .... Tracy Warner
Features Ed. .... Terri Richardson
News Technology Mgr. .... Tom Pellegrene
Sports Ed. .... Mark Jaworski
Systems Ed. .... Paul Wagner

Market Information: ADS; TMC; Zoned editions.
Mechanical available: Flexo, Letterpress; Black and ROP colors; insert accepted; page cutoffs - 23 9/16.
Mechanical Specifications: Type page 13 x 22; E - 6 cols, between; A - 6 cols, between; C - 10 cols, between.
Equipment EDITORIAL: Front-end Software – CCI.; Editorial Hardware – IBM; Editorial Equipment – APP/Mac; Editorial Printers – HP/LaserJet CLASSIFIED: Front-end Software – III/Tecs 2.; Classified Hardware – Dell DISPLAY: Ad make-up applications – Multi-Ad/Creator; Layout Software – CJ.; Display Hardware – APP/Mac BUSINESS COMPUTERS: Business Software – WordPerfect, Quattro; Business Hardware – HP/3000-967

THE NEWS-SENTINEL
600 W. Main St., Fort Wayne, Ind., 46802; gen tel (260) 461-8222; gen fax (260) 461-8817; gen e-mail ns@news-sentinel.com; web site www.news-sentinel.com
Group: Ogden Newspapers
Published: Mon, Tues, Wed, Thur, Fri, Sat
Weekday Frequency: e
Saturday Frequency: e
Circulation: 18,118; 18,638(sat)
Last Audit: ABC September 30, 2011
Price: 2.05/wk; 93.60/yr.
Advertising: Open inch rate $174.78
News services: AP
Politics: Independent.
Note: For detailed production and mechanical information, see Fort Wayne Newspapers Inc. listing.
Advertising not accepted: Y
Not Published: Sunday
Special Editions: Home & Lawn (Apr); Health Career Expo (Feb); Big Boys Tech & Toys Show (Jan); Back-to-School (Jul); Town & Country (Mar); Indy 500 (May); Holiday Shopping Guide (Nov); Diner's Guide (Oct); Parade of Homes (Sept).
Special Weekly Sections: Business Monday; Features/food section (Tues); Neighbors (Wed,Sat); Ticket!/entertainment (Thurs); TV listings (Sat).
Magazines: Summit City Savings (Sat).
CEO/President/Publisher...Michael J. Christman
Sr. Ed...Kerry Hubartt
Asst. Metro/Bus. Ed.............Lisa Esquivel Long
Editorial Page Ed.............................Leo Morris
Multimedia Ed................Laura Weston-Elchert
Digital Content Director/News Ed......Caleb Cook
Metro Ed......................................Elbert Starks
Features Ed...............................Kevin Kilbane
Sports Ed..Tom Davis
Design Ed.....................................Brad Saleik
Market Information: ADS
Mechanical available: Flexo, Letterpress; Black and ROP colors; insert accepted; page cutoffs - 23 9/16.
Mechanical Specifications: Type page 13 x 22; E - 6 cols, 2 1/16, 1/8 between; A - 6 cols, 2 1/16, 1/8 between; C - 10 cols, 1 1/4, 1/16 between.
Equipment EDITORIAL: Front-end Software – III/Tecs 2.; Editorial Hardware – Dell; Editorial Printers – Epson, HP/LaserJet CLASSIFIED: Front-end Software – III/Tecs 2.; Classified Hardware – Dell; Classified Printers – Epson, HP/LaserJet
Delivery method: Newsstand, Private Carrier, Racks

FRANKFORT

THE TIMES
251 E. Clinton St., Frankfort, Ind., 46041; gen tel (765) 659-4622; adv tel (765) 659-4622; ed tel (765) 659-4622; gen fax (765) 654-7031; adv fax (765) 654-7031; ed fax (765) 654-7031; adv e-mail adv@ftimes.com; ed e-mail news@ftimes.com; web site www.ftimes.com
Group: Paxton Media Group
Published: Mon, Tues, Wed, Thur, Fri, Sat
Weekday Frequency: m
Saturday Frequency: m
Circulation: 4,694; 4,694(sat)
Last Audit: Sworn September 30, 2004
Price: 13.35/week
Advertising: Open inch rate $20.91
Insert rate: Single sheet $45/m daily; $49/m Weekend
News services: AP.
Politics: Independent. **Established:** 1894
Not Published: Sunday
Own facility?: Y
Special Editions: Back to School (Aug); Spring Home Improvement (April) Fall Home Improvement (Fall); Father's Day (Jun); Mother's Day (May); 4-H Tab (Other); Fall Farm (Sept) Fall Gridiron (Aug) Spring Farm (Spring).
Magazines: USA WEEKEND Magazine (Fri).
Publisher............................Sharon Bardonner
Circulation Director..................Amanda Marcel
Classified/Retail Inside Sales...........Angie Hale
Accounting Clerk..................Joann Spaulding
Pub...Terry Ward
Adv. Dir.......................................Thaya Sterrett
Circ. Mgr...Linda Clark
Mng. Ed.....................................Brian Peloza
Prodn. Mgr............................Ken Koppelmann
Market Information: TMC 2,000 rack distribution
Mechanical available: Offset; Black and 3 ROP colors; insert accepted - single sheets, booklets; page cutoffs - 22 3/4.
Mechanical Specifications: Type page 10 x 21 1/2; E - 6 cols, 4.587, 1/8 between; A - 6 cols, 1.587, 1/8 between
Commodity Consumption: Avg. Page Number Per Issue - Daily 13.6; Avg. Page Number Per Issue - Plates Used 3013; widths 25; Newsprint Used - Metric Tons 510; Printing Ink Used - Black 3175; Printing Ink Used - Color 1160; Printing Ink Used - Pages Printed 4150.
Equipment EDITORIAL: Front-end Software – Falcon; InDesign; Editorial Hardware – PC CLASSIFIED: Front-end Software – MediaSpan; Classified Hardware – PC DISPLAY: Ad make-up applications – MediaSpan; Display Hardware – PC PRODUCTION: Pagination Software – InDesign PRESSROOM: Line 1 – Print at Chronicle-Tribune, Marion, IN MAILROOM: Counter stackers – Insert at Chronicle-Tribune, Marion, IN BUSINESS COMPUTERS: Business Software – MediaSpan; Business Hardware – PC
Zip Codes served: 46041; 46065; 46035; 46050; 46039; 46057; 46067; 46058
Delivery method: Mail, Newsstand, Private Carrier, Racks

FRANKLIN

DAILY JOURNAL
2575 N. Morton St., Franklin, Ind., 46131; gen tel (317) 736-7101; adv tel (317) 736-2750; ed tel (317) 736-2749; gen fax (317) 736-2759; adv fax (317) 736-2713; ed fax (317) 736-2766; gen e-mail publisher@dailyjournal.net; ed e-mail editor@dailyjournal.net; web site www.dailyjournal.net
Published: Mon, Tues, Wed, Thur, Fri, Sat
Weekday Frequency: m
Saturday Frequency: m
Circulation: 14,201; 15,605(sat)
Last Audit: September 30, 2009
Price: 10.95/mo; 131.40/yr.
Advertising: Open inch rate $21.91
News services: AP, SHNS.
Politics: Independent.
Not Published: Christmas.
Special Editions: American Home Week (Apr); Back to School (Aug); Worship Directory (Dec); Wedding Planner (Jan); Johnson County 4-H Fair (Jul); Junior Journal (Mar); Salute (May); Coupons Plus (Monthly); Holiday Gift Guide (Nov); Health Guide (Oct); Family (Quarterly); Yo
Special Weekly Sections: School Page (Mon); Business Pages (Sat); Best Food Day (Wed).
Magazines: Parade (Sat).
Pub....Chuck Wells
Adv. Dir.................................Christina Cosner
Circ. Dir.......................................Steve Hood
Ed...Scarlet Syse
Asst. Mng. Ed.......................Michele Holtkamp
Features Writer...........................Ryan Trares
Sports Ed.....................................Rick Morwick
Mgmt. Info Servs. Mgr.................Mike Brogdon
Mechanical available: Offset; Black and 3 ROP colors; insert accepted; page cutoffs - 22 3/8.
Mechanical Specifications: Type page 11 5/8 x 21 5/8; E - 6 cols, 2 5/6, 1/8 between; A - 6 cols, 2 5/6, 1/8 between; C - 9 cols, between.
Commodity Consumption: Avg. Page Number Per Issue - Daily 21; Avg. Page Number Per Issue - Plates Used 12000; Avg. Page Number Per Issue - Saturday 30; widths 25; Newsprint Used - Short Tons 613; Printing Ink Used - Black 21850; Printing Ink Used - Color 4650; Printing Ink Use
Equipment EDITORIAL: Front-end Software – QPS/QuarkXPress 4.11, Microsoft/Word 2.0.; Editorial Hardware – 10-PC, 2-APT/PC file-servers, 12-PC, MS 2000 Server; Editorial Equipment – Umax/Power Look IV, AP/Mac G4; Editorial Printers – ECR/VR 36, ECR/4550 CLASSIFIED: Front-end Software – QPS/QuarkXPress 4.11, ACT.; Classified Hardware – 4-PC, 1-MS 2000 Server; Classified Printers – Lexmark T520 DISPLAY: Ad make-up applications – Multi-Ad/Creator 4.0, CNI/Ad Database; Layout Software – Multi-Ad, CNI/Ad Database.; Display Hardware – 5-AP/Mac G4; Display Printers – ECR/VR 36, Laserwriter 16/600 PRODUCTION: Pagination Software – APT, QPS/QuarkXPress 4.11.; Production Equipment – APP/Mac LaserWriter II NT, ECR/VR 36, Unity/1200 XLO, APP/Mac LaserWriter IIg, ECR/4550; Scanners – Umax/Power Look III; Reels and Stands – 9-G/Roll Stand. MAILROOM: Counter stackers – BG/105, Rima/RS 2517; Inserters and stuffers – 2-KAN/420; Bundle tying machines – 3/Bu, 1-/MLN; Wrapping singles – Power Strap/Bottom Wrap.

GOSHEN

THE GOSHEN NEWS
114 S. Main St., Goshen, Ind., 46526; gen tel (574) 533-2151; adv tel (574) 533-2151; ed tel (574) 533-2151; gen fax (574) 533-0839; adv fax (574) 533-0839; ed fax (574) 534-8830; adv e-mail advertising@goshennews.com; ed e-mail news@goshennews.com; web site www.goshennews.com
Group: CNHI
Published: Mon, Tues, Wed, Thur, Fri, Sat, Sun
Weekday Frequency: m
Saturday Frequency: m
Circulation: 12,500; 12,500(sat); 12,500(sun)
Last Audit: Sworn September 30, 2008
Price: 10.50/mo.
Advertising: Open inch rate $26.80
News services: AP.
Politics: Independent.
Own facility?: Y
Special Editions: Car Care Tab (Fall); Fall & Winter Sports Tab (Other); Home Improvement (Spring).
Special Weekly Sections: Viewer's Choice (TV Listings) (Fri); Food Section (full color recipes on front cover) (Tues).
Magazines: Parade (S).
Pub.................................James D. Kroemer
Bus. Mgr...............................Pam McCarney
Circ. Dir.....................................Rick Carlson
Ed....................................Michael Wanbaugh
City Ed................................Roger Schneider
Lifestyle Ed...........................Monica Joseph
Prodn. Mgr., Systems............Richard Leinbach
Advertising director
Stacey Ramsey
Sports Editor............................David Vantress
Sports Ed.......................................Stu Swartz
Market Information: TMC.
Mechanical available: Offset; Black and 3 ROP colors; insert accepted; page cutoffs - 22 3/4.
Mechanical Specifications: Type page 11 1/8 x 21 1/2; E - 6 cols, 1 3/4, 1/8 between; A - 6 cols, 1 3/4, 1/8 between; C - 9 cols, 1 1/8, 1/8 between.
Commodity Consumption: Avg. Page Number Per Issue - Daily 25; Avg. Page Number Per Issue - Plates Used 8500; widths 25; Newsprint Used - Metric Tons 750; Printing Ink Used - Black 30000; Printing Ink Used - Color 1800; Printing Ink Used - Pages Printed 8500.
Equipment EDITORIAL: Front-end Software – In-Copy, InDesign; Editorial Hardware – PC CLASSIFIED: Front-end Software – Mk.; Classified Hardware – Mk, Baseview DISPLAY: Ad make-up applications – Scan, Multi-Ad/Creator; Display Hardware – APP/Mac BUSINESS COMPUTERS: Business Software – Vision Data; Business Hardware – DEC, PC

NEWS PRINTING CO., INC.
PO Box 569, Goshen, Ind., 46527-0569; gen tel (574) 533-2151; gen fax (574) 533-0839; gen e-mail news@goshennews.com; web site www.goshennews.com

GREENCASTLE

BANNER-GRAPHIC
100 N. Jackson St., Greencastle, Ind., 46135; gen tel (765) 653-5151; gen fax (765) 653-2063; web site www.banner-graphic.com
Published: Mon, Wed, Thur, Fri, Sat
Weekday Frequency: e
Saturday Frequency: e
Circulation: 5,129; 5,129(sat)
Last Audit: September 30, 2007
Price: 7.60/mo; 108.00/yr.
Advertising: Open inch rate $18.00(e-mon)
News services: AP.
Politics: Independent.
Advertising not accepted: Material not considered in best interests of readers.
Not Published: New Year; Memorial Day; Independence Day; Labor Day; Thanksgiving; Christmas.
Special Weekly Sections: NASCAR (Fri); Senior Citizens (Thur); Farm News (Wed).
Magazines: Relish (Monthly); USA WEEKEND Magazine (Sat); American Profile (Weekly).
Broadcast Affiliations: WTRC & WYEZ (FM) Elkhart, INWMEE & WMEF (FM) Fort Wayne, IN; WCUZ & WFFX (FM) Grand Rapids, MI; WCKY & WWEZ (FM) Cincinnati, OH.
Pub...Randy E. List
Gen. Mgr.....................................Daryl Taylor
Adv. Mgr....John York
Circ. Mgr.............................Becky Underwood
Ed...Jamie Barrand
Asst. Ed.................................Jared Jernagan
Sports Ed.................................Caine Gardner
Market Information: TMC.
Mechanical available: Offset; Black and 3 ROP colors; insert accepted; page cutoffs - 22 3/4.
Mechanical Specifications: Type page 13 x 21; E - 6 cols, 2 1/16, 1/8 between; A - 6 cols, 2 1/16, 1/8 between; C - 8 cols, 1 3/4, 1/8 between.
Commodity Consumption: Avg. Page Number Per Issue - Daily 12; Avg. Page Number Per Issue - Plates Used 4700; widths 13 3/4; Newsprint Used - Short Tons 161; Printing Ink Used - Black 4700; Printing Ink Used - Color 180; Printing Ink Used - Pages Printed 3920.
Equipment EDITORIAL: Front-end Software – Baseview. CLASSIFIED: Front-end Software – Baseview. DISPLAY: Ad make-up applications – Multi-Ad/Creator.; Production Equipment – Nu/Flip Top; Cameras – LE, R/500. PRESSROOM: Line 1 – 5-G/Community 1977; Folders – 1-G/2:1.; Bundle tying machines – 2/BN; Addressing machine – 1-/Wm.

BANNER-GRAPHIC, INC.
100 N. Jackson St., Greencastle, Ind., 46135; gen tel (765) 653-5151; gen fax (765) 653-2063
Politics: 1925

GREENFIELD

DAILY REPORTER
22 W. New Rd., Greenfield, Ind., 46140-1090; gen tel (317) 462-5528; adv tel (317) 467-6000; ed tel (317) 467-6022; gen fax (317) 467-6017; adv fax (317) 467-6009; ed fax (317) 467-6017; gen e-mail circ@greenfieldreporter.com; bizmgr@greenfieldreporter.com; adv e-mail advert@greenfieldreporter.com; ed e-mail edit@greenfieldreporter.com; web site

www.greenfieldreporter.com
Group: Home News Enterprises
Published: Tues, Wed, Thur, Fri, Sat
Weekday Frequency: e
Saturday Frequency: m
Circulation: 8,729; 8,729(sat)
Last Audit: September 30, 2009
Price: 9.50/mo; 109.00/yr.
Advertising: Open inch rate $13.94
News services: AP, NEA.
Politics: 1908
Advertising not accepted: Y
Not Published: New Year; Independence Day; Veterans Day; Thanksgiving; Christmas.
Own facility?: Y
Special Editions: Car Care (Apr); Back-to-School (Aug); Last Minute Gift Ideas (Dec); Meet Your Merchants (Feb); Proms (Jan); 4-H Fair (Jul); 4-H Handbook (Jun); Spring Sports (Mar); Indy 500 Preview (May); Winter Sports (Nov); Car Care (Oct); Riley Festival (Sept).
Special Weekly Sections: Real Estate (Sat); Business News (Thur); Education (Tues); Ag (Wed).
Magazines: Parade (Sat).
Pub./Vice Pres. ....Randall Shields
Admin. Mgr. ....Debby Brooks
Adv. Dir. ....John Senger
Adv. Mgr., Commercial Sales ....Carrie Lacy
Adv. Mgr., Classified ....Sue Engle
Ed. ....David Hill
Mng. Ed. ....Karen Crawford
Photo Ed. ....Tom Russo
Sports Ed. ....Brian Harmon
Prodn. Dir. ....Larry Ham
Prodn. Mgr., Pre Press ....Jim Steele
Circ Dir. ....David Koenig
Prodn. Mgr., Post Press ....Keith Butler
Market Information: TMC; Zoned editions.
Mechanical available: Offset; Black and 3 ROP colors; insert accepted - max. size 11 x 13; page cutoffs - 22 3/4.
Mechanical Specifications: Type page 11 1/2 x 21 1/2; E - 6 cols, 1 3/4, 1/8 between; A - 6 cols, 1 3/4, 1/8 between; C - 9 cols, 1 3/16, 1/16 between.
Commodity Consumption: Avg. Page Number Per Issue - Daily 18.3; widths 50; Printing Ink Used - Pages Printed 5616.
Equipment EDITORIAL: Front-end Software – APT; Editorial Hardware – PC CLASSIFIED: Front-end Software – APT; Classified Hardware – PC; Display Hardware – Mac PRODUCTION: Pagination Software – APT; Production Equipment – Kreo PRESSROOM: Line 1 – 19-G/Community; Line 2 – 13-G/Community; Press Drives – 4-Fin/75 h.p., 2-Fin/125 hp; Folders – 3-G/Community SSC; Pasters – 6-Enkel/Zero Speed Splicer 1990; Press control system – Fin/Control System 1994. MAILROOM: Counter stackers – Rima/25 105, GMA 2000; Inserters and stuffers – GMA; Bundle tying machines – 1-MLN/Spirit, 2-Bu/BT-18, 1-Bu/BT-18. BUSINESS COMPUTERS: Business Software – APT; Business Hardware – PC
Zip Codes served: 46140,46040,46163,46227
Delivery method: Mail, Private Carrier, Racks

GREENSBURG

GREENSBURG DAILY NEWS

135 S. Franklin St., Greensburg, Ind., 47240; gen tel (812) 663-3111; gen fax (812) 663-2985; ed fax (812) 662-7552; gen e-mail adam.huening@greensburgdailynews.com; web site www.greensburgdailynews.com
Group: U.S. Suburban Press, Inc.
Published: Mon, Tues, Wed, Thur, Fri, Sat
Weekday Frequency: e
Circulation: 5,569; 5,569(sat)
Last Audit: September 29, 2003
Price: 2.00/wk; 8.67/mo; 118.00/yr.
Advertising: Open inch rate $15.85
News services: AP.
Not Published: Christmas.
Special Editions: Spring Spectacular (Apr); Parade of Honor (Aug); Carol Book/Holiday Cookbook (Dec); Chamber of Commerce Tab (Feb); Tax Tips Tab (Jan); After Fair Tab (Jul); Mini Progress (Jun); Ag Week Tab (Mar); Mother's Day Gang Page (May); Basketball (Nov); Say Nope t
Special Weekly Sections: Church News (Fri); School News (Sat); Pastimes (Thur); Commerce News (Tues); Agri-News (Wed).
Magazines: Relish (Monthly); American Profile (Weekly).
Regl. Pub. ....Laura Welborn
Adv. Dir., Regl. ....Keith Wells
Regl. Mng. Ed ....Kevin L. Green
News Ed. ....Adam Huening
Sports Ed. ....Aaron Kirchoff
Dir., Info Servs./Tech ....Denver Sullivan
Prodn. Dir., Graphic Arts ....Susan Peters
Prodn. Mgr., Mailroom ....Lisa Huff
Market Information: TMC.
Mechanical available: Offset; Black and 3 ROP colors; insert accepted - all; page cutoffs - 23.
Mechanical Specifications: Type page 13 x 21 1/2; E - 6 cols, 2 1/16, 1/8 between; A - 6 cols, 2 1/16, 1/8 between; C - 8 cols, 1 7/16, 1/8 between.
Commodity Consumption: Avg. Page Number Per Issue - Daily 14.5; Avg. Page Number Per Issue - Plates Used 4000; Avg. Page Number Per Issue - Saturday 14.5; widths 27; Newsprint Used - Short Tons 385; Printing Ink Used - Black 7430; Printing Ink Used - Color 1760; Printing Ink U
Equipment EDITORIAL: Front-end Software – QPS/QuarkXPress.; Editorial Hardware – APP/Mac; Editorial Equipment – Umax/12 x 12 scanner, 3-Microtek/CD 300 Drives, Polaroid/SprintScan 35; Editorial Printers – 1-NewGen/Imager 12 Plus, 2-APP/Mac LaserWriter IIg, HP/4 MV CLASSIFIED: Front-end Software – Baseview/Class Manager Plus.; Classified Hardware – APP/Mac SE30; Classified Printers – APP/Mac LaserWriter; Production Equipment – 1-Nat, 2-APP/Mac LaserWriter IIg, HP/4MV; Cameras – 1-CL; Scanners – Equipment ☐ QPS/QuarkXPress. PRESSROOM: Line 1 – 1-G 1981; Line 2 – 5-G/Community single width 1973, 1-G/Community single width 1992; Folders – 1; Bundle tying machines – 1/Bu; Addressing machine – 2-Wm/Labels.; Audio Hardware – 1-Recordak/MPE BUSINESS COMPUTERS: Business Software – Microsoft/Excel, Word processing; Business Hardware – PC 486-DXZ-50, PC 486-DX2-66

HARTFORD CITY

NEWS-TIMES

123 S. Jefferson St., Hartford City, Ind., 47348; gen tel (765) 348-0110; gen fax (765) 348-0112; gen e-mail newstimes@comcast.net; web site www.hartfordcitynewstimes.com
Published: Mon, Tues, Wed, Thur, Fri, Sat
Weekday Frequency: m
Circulation: 1,473; 1,473(sat)
Last Audit: September 30, 2003
Price: 2.20/wk (in county); 9.45/mo (in county); 105.00/yr (in county).
Advertising: Open inch rate $7.45
News services: AP.
Politics: Independent.
Not Published: New Year; Memorial Day; Independence Day; Labor Day; Thanksgiving; Christmas.
Special Editions: Spring Car Care (Apr); Progress (Feb); New Year's Baby (Jan); 4-H (Jul); Home & Garden (Mar); Graduation (May); Christmas Tab (Nov); Fall Home Yard Garden (Oct).
Pub. ....Cynthia Payne
Adv. Mgr. ....Tammy Roach
Mng. Ed. ....Danny Careins
Photographer ....Don Rogers
Market Information: TMC.
Mechanical available: Offset; Black and 3 ROP colors; insert accepted; page cutoffs - 22 1/2.
Mechanical Specifications: Type page 13 x 21 1/2; E - 6 cols, 2, 1/6 between; A - 6 cols, 2, 1/6 between; C - 8 cols, 2, 1/6 between.
Commodity Consumption: Avg. Page Number Per Issue - Daily 12; widths 27 1/2.
Equipment EDITORIAL: Front-end Software – Microsoft/Word 4.0.; Editorial Hardware – 2-APP/Mac Classic II, 1-APP/Mac Plus, APP/Mac Quadra 630, 1-APP/Mac Quadra 630; Editorial Printers – APP/Mac LaserWriter II NT CLASSIFIED: Front-end Software – Microsoft/Word 4.0, Multi-Ad.; Classified Hardware – 1-APP/Mac Plus, 2-APP/Mac SE30, 2-APP/Mac II; Classified Printers – APP/Mac LaserWriter II NT, APP/Mac LaserWriter Pro DISPLAY: Ad make-up applications – Multi-Ad; Display Hardware – 1-APP/Mac LC, 2-APP/Mac SE, 3-APP/Mac Radius Full Page Display; Display Printers – APP/Mac LaserWriter II NTX; Production Equipment – Nu/Flip Top; Cameras – SCREEN/Companica 680C.; Bundle tying machines – Bu.; Business Hardware – Arche Triumph/386SX

HUNTINGTON

HUNTINGTON HERALD-PRESS

7 N. Jefferson St., Huntington, Ind., 46750; gen tel (260) 356-6700; adv tel (260) 356-6700; ed tel (260) 356-6700; gen fax (260) 356-9026; adv fax (260) 356-9026; ed fax (260) 356-9026; adv e-mail hpads@h-ponline.com; ed e-mail hpnews@h-ponline.com; web site www.h-ponline.com
Published: Mon, Tues, Wed, Thur, Fri, Sun
Weekday Frequency: e
Circulation: 6,364; 6,364(sun)
Last Audit: October 1, 2002
Price: 2.00/wk; 26.00/13wk, $52.00/26wk, $98.80/52wk.
Advertising: Open inch rate $12.30
News services: AP.
Politics: Independent-Republican.
Not Published: Christmas.
Special Editions: Spring Home & Garden II (Apr); Markle Wildcat Days (Aug); Gift Hang-Up (Dec); Huntington County Landmarks (Feb); Girl's Basketball Sectional (Jan); Andrews Summer Festival (Jul); Heritage Days (Jun); Farm (Mar); Golf Guide (May); Holiday Charm (Nov); Nati
Special Weekly Sections: Church Page (Fri); Best Food Days (S); Business (Thur); Business Page (Tues); Farm Page (Wed).
Magazines: Comics (S).
Pub. ....Andy Eads
Adv. Mgr., Classified ....Brenda Ross
Online Adv. Mgr. ....June Whittamore
Ed. ....Rebekah Sandlin
City Ed ....Rebekah Meyer
Sports Ed ....Sean Giggy
Market Information: Split run; TMC; Zoned editions.
Mechanical available: Offset; Black and 3 ROP colors; insert accepted; page cutoffs - 21.
Mechanical Specifications: Type page 13 x 21; E - 6 cols, 2 1/16, 1/8 between; A - 6 cols, 2 1/16, 1/8 between; C - 8 cols, 1 3/8, 1/16 between.
Commodity Consumption: Avg. Page Number Per Issue - Daily 14; Avg. Page Number Per Issue - Plates Used 4584; Avg. Page Number Per Issue - Sunday 25; widths 27 1/2; Newsprint Used - Short Tons 265; Printing Ink Used - Black 9800; Printing Ink Used - Color 600; Printing Ink Used
Equipment EDITORIAL: Front-end Software – Baseview/NewsEdit, QPS/QuarkXPress, Adobe/Photoshop, Aldus/FreeHand, Multi-Ad.; Editorial Hardware – 3-APP/Power Mac; Editorial Printers – APP/Mac LaserWriter NT, 2-APP/Mac LaserWriter NTX CLASSIFIED: Front-end Software – Baseview/Class Manager.; Classified Hardware – APP/Power Mac; Classified Printers – APP/Mac LaserWriter NTX DISPLAY: Ad make-up applications – QPS/QuarkXPress, Multi-Ad, Aldus/FreeHand, Adobe/Illustrator, Baseview/Display Manager.; Display Hardware – 2-APP/Power Mac; Display Printers – APP/Mac LaserWriter II NTX PRODUCTION: Pagination Software – QPS/QuarkXPress 3.32.; Production Equipment – TI/OmniPage 2.0, Mk/MSF 300, Kk/35mm Scanner; Cameras – 1-B/Caravelle; Scanners – 3-HP, HP/ScanJet, 2-Microtek/Flatbed, HP/ScanJet 5P PRESSROOM: Line 1 – 2-G/Urbanite 1967, 1-G/Urbanite (3 color) 1967.; Inserters and stuffers – KAN/320 5 stations; Bundle tying machines – Dynaric. BUSINESS COMPUTERS: Business Software – Dynamics (Great Plains); Business Hardware – Dell PC

INDIANAPOLIS

THE INDIANAPOLIS STAR

307 N. Pennsylvania St., Indianapolis, Ind., 46204; gen tel (317) 444-4000; adv tel (317) 444-7000; ed tel (317) 444-6170; gen fax (317) 444-7100; adv fax (317) 444-7300; ed fax (317) 444-8616; adv e-mail indyadvertising@indystar.com; ed e-mail stareditor@indystar.com; web site www.indystar.com
Published: Mon, Tues, Wed, Thur, Fri, Sat, Sun
Weekday Frequency: m
Saturday Frequency: m
Circulation: 171,662; 158,917(sat); 313,057(sun)
Last Audit: ABC September 30, 2011
Price: 3.60/wk (4 day=thur-S/fri-mon), $1.95/wk (S only).
Advertising: National Sunday Open inch rate $406.00
News services: AP.
Politics: Independent. **Established:** 1903
Own facility?: Y
Special Editions: Pro & College Football (Aug); Final Four (Mar); 500-Mile Auto Race Souvenir (May); Voter's Guide (Nov); Pro Basketball (Oct).
Special Weekly Sections: Indy Living (S); Taste (Wed); Colts Weekly (Weekly).
Magazines: USA WEEKEND Magazine (S).
Broadcast Affiliations: WTHR-TV Indianapolis, IN.
Vice Pres., Finance ....J. Bruce Klink
Sales & Marketing, Vice Pres. ...Patrick Peregrin
Adv. Dir., Display ....John Cherba
Adv. Dir., Opns. ....Lisa Hite-Wadler
Brand Mgr. ....Jennifer Gombach
Circ. Mgr., Mktg./Admin. ....Bryan Sturgeon
Vice Pres./Ed. ....Dennis R. Ryerson
Mng. Ed. ....Jennifer Green
Asst. Mng. Ed., Bus. ....Steve Berta
Asst. Mng. Ed., Visuals ....Scott Goldman
Assoc. Ed. ....Russell B. Pulliam
Asst. Editorial Page Ed./copydesk Ed. Tim Swarens
Features Wire Ed. ....Harold Wiley
Photography Dir. ....Mike Fender
Suburban Ed. ....Kevin Morgan
Prodn & IT, Vice Pres. ....Bill Bolger
Class Adv Director ....Yasha Holmes
Pres./Pub. ....Michael Kane
Circ Dir., Home Delivery/Transportation John Anderson
Exec. Ed. ....Juli Metzger
Prodn. Dir., Printing/Packaging Gilbert Escobedo
Market Information: TMC; Zoned editions.
Mechanical available: Offset; Black and 4 ROP colors; insert accepted; page cutoffs - 21 1/2.
Mechanical Specifications: Type page 10 x 20 1/2; E - 6 cols, 1 1/2, 5/32 between; A - 6 cols, 1 1/2, 5/32 between; C - 10 cols, 29/32, 1/16 between.
Commodity Consumption: Avg. Page Number Per Issue - Daily 73; Avg. Page Number Per Issue - Plates Used 815000; Avg. Page Number Per Issue - Sunday 165; widths 50; Newsprint Used - Metric Tons 42455; Printing Ink Used - Black 700000; Printing Ink Used - Color 720000; Printing I
Equipment EDITORIAL: Front-end Software – CCI 6.0.; Editorial Hardware – AT, Compaq; Editorial Printers – 25-Epson, TI, NEC, HP/LaserPrinter, HP/DeskJet CLASSIFIED: Front-end Software – AT/Enterprise 1.7xml, AT/Classified 1.7xml, AT/Retail 1.7xml, AT/Preprints 1.7xml.; Classified Hardware – AT/Enterprise 205-seat, Compaq, 2-Sun/E4500; Classified Equipment – AT/Classified, AT/Pagination, IBM/RISC 6000; Classified Printers – 8-HP/LaserJet DISPLAY: Ad make-up applications – DPS AdTracker/Adobe Creative Suite 4; Layout Software – MEI/ALS 4.2.; Display Hardware – iMac 27, 2-Sun/Ultra 3000; Display Printers – Canon

ImageRunner C4080 PRODUCTION: Pagination Software – CCI 6.0.; Production Equipment – 3-Creo/Trendsetter 200, 1-ICG/3601; Scanners – 2-Creo/IQSmart2 PRESSROOM: Line 1 – 7-MAN/Geoman 75; Line 2 – 7-MAN/Geoman 75; Line 3 – 7-MAN/Geoman 75; Line 4 – 3-MAN/Geoman 75; Press Drives – MAN Roland; Folders – 1-MAN/Quarterfold, 7-MAN/2:5:5 Jaw; Reels and Stands – 24-MAN/CD13 RTP; Press control system – MAN/PECOM MAILROOM: Counter stackers – 7-HPS/Dual carrier, 5-Prim/Hail Commmercial, 3/Gammerler, 14-/QWI 401, 2-/HT, 2-QWI/501C; Inserters and stuffers – 2-HI/1472P, 1-Na/NP2299, 1-Na/NP 630; Bundle tying machines – 29-/Dynaric; Wrapping singles – Addressing machine □ 2-/AVY, 4-QP/Vipers 97, AUDIO: Audio Software – QNX; Audio Hardware – IT Network, 3-PC 486, Brite Voice Systems/60-line BUSINESS COMPUTERS: Business Software – ESA, DUS/VSE; Business Hardware – IBM/ES9000-170, IBM/AS-400

Delivery method: Mail, Newsstand, Private Carrier, Racks

JASPER

THE HERALD

216 E. Fourth St., Jasper, Ind., 47547-0031; gen tel (812) 482-2424; adv tel (812) 482-2424; ed tel (812) 482-2626; gen fax (812) 482-4104; adv fax (812) 634-7142; ed fax (812) 482-5241; gen e-mail news@dcherald.com; adv e-mail ads@dcherald.com; ed e-mail news@dcherald.com; web site www.duboiscountyherald.com

Published: Mon, Tues, Wed, Thur, Fri, Sat
Weekday Frequency: e
Saturday Frequency: m
Circulation: 11,240; 11,240(sat)
Last Audit: Sworn September 26, 2003
Price: 15.00/mo (carrier), $12.00/mo (motor route).
Advertising: Open inch rate $15.00
News services: AP, CNS.
Politics: 1895
Not Published: New Year; Memorial Day; Independence Day; Labor Day; Thanksgiving; Christmas.
Own facility?: Y
Special Editions: Home, Lawn & Garden (Apr); Christmas Greetings (Dec); Boys Basketball Sectional (Feb); Brides & Weddings (Jan); 4-Fair Kick-off (Jul); Senior Citizen Salute (Jun); Boys Basketball Sectional (Mar); Graduation (May); Christmas Opening (Nov); Winter Car Care
Special Weekly Sections: Religion (Fri); Science (Mon); Travel (Thur); Business (Tues).
Magazines: USA WEEKEND Magazine (Sat).
Co-president; co-publisher......Dan E. Rumbach
Controller/Treasurer......Mark Fierst
Mgr., HR......Mike Mazur
Subscriber Services manager......Keith Milton
City Ed.......Martha Rasche
Co-president; co-publisher; editor John A. Rumbach
People Ed.......Janet Epple
Wire Ed.......Dawn Mazur
Prodn. Mgr.......Mike Oser
Managing Editor......Justin Rumbach
Advertising Director......Tom Stephens
Distribution Manager......Dan Hoppenjans
Market Information: Split run; @RecordBody:**Mechanical available:** Offset; Black and 3 ROP colors; insert accepted - subject to approval; page cutoffs - 17 1/2.
Mechanical Specifications: Type page 10 3/16 x 16; E - 5 cols, 1 7/8, 1/8 between; A - 5 cols, 1 7/8, 1/8 between; C - 6 cols, 1 1/2, 1/8 between.
Commodity Consumption: Avg. Page Number Per Issue - Daily 37.59; Avg. Page Number Per Issue - Plates Used 5065; widths 35; Newsprint Used - Metric Tons 600; Printing Ink Used - Black 16246; Printing Ink Used - Color 2553; Printing Ink Used - Pages Printed 11540.
Equipment EDITORIAL: Front-end Software – QPS/QuarkXPress 6.5, Baseview/NewsEdit Pro IQUE, Adobe/Photoshop CS.; Editorial Hardware – 19-APP/Mac; Editorial Printers – Xerox Phaser 5500, APP/Mac HP Laserjet CLASSIFIED: Front-end Software – Baseview.; Classified Hardware – 2-APP/Mac DISPLAY: Ad make-up applications – Multi-Ad/Creator, Baseview/PMP; Layout Software – Mk/Managing Editor AdForce.; Display Hardware – 6-APP/Mac; Display Printers – Xerox Phaser 5500 PRODUCTION: Pagination Software – QPS/QuarkXPress, MediaSpan.; Production Equipment – Kodak CTP; Cameras – DSA; Scanners – 1-AG/Arcus 2 PRESSROOM: Line 1 – 6-G/with hump single width 1974; Line 2 – 1-G/Color single width. MAILROOM: Counter stackers – 1/Gammerler STC70; Inserters and stuffers – KAN/480, Kan/4-Bay/Multi-Feeder; Bundle tying machines – 3-Bu/60-71; Addressing machine – 1-Am/57; Other equipment – BG/109 Count-O-Veyor. BUSINESS COMPUTERS: Business Software – MSSI; Business Hardware – Novell/Network
Delivery method: Mail, Newsstand, Private Carrier, Racks

JEFFERSONVILLE

THE EVENING NEWS

221 Spring St., Jeffersonville, Ind., 47130; gen tel (812) 283-6636; gen fax (812) 284-7081; gen e-mail evennews@newsandtribune.com; web site www.newsandtribune.com

Published: Mon, Tues, Wed, Thur, Fri, Sat
Weekday Frequency: e
Circulation: 7,152; 7,152(sat)
Last Audit: September 30, 2004
Price: 8.50/mo; 98.00/yr.
News services: AP, NEA, Scripps Howard.
Politics: Independent-Democrat.
Note: The Jeffersonville Evening News (e) has a combination rate of $23.62 with the New Albany Tribune (eS). Individual newspaper rates not made available.
Special Editions: Spring Fashion (Apr); Back-to-School (Aug); Christmas Style (Dec); Basketball (Feb); Cookbook (Jan); Travel (Jun); Progress (Mar); Bridal (May); Thanksgiving (Nov); New Car Preview (Oct); Football (Sept).
Magazines: TV News/Golden Opportunity (Monthly).
Bus. Mgr.......Elizabeth Newland
Circ. Mgr.......Mike Massek
Exec. Ed.......Steve Kozarovich
Educ. Ed.......Brenda Dorman
Lifestyle Ed.......Amy Huffman
Photo Ed.......C.E. Branham
Sports Ed.......Kevin Harris
Telecom Mgr.......Doug Duvall
Prodn. Foreman, Composing......Brandy Jones
Prodn. Foreman, Composing......Harry Fox
Prodn. Foreman, Press......John Vissing
Market Information: TMC.
Mechanical available: Offset; Black and 3 ROP colors; insert accepted; page cutoffs - 21 1/2.
Mechanical Specifications: Type page 13 x 21 1/2; E - 6 cols, 2, 1/12 between; A - 6 cols, 2, 1/8 between; C - 9 cols, 1 1/3, 1/12 between.
Commodity Consumption: Avg. Page Number Per Issue - Daily 16; Avg. Page Number Per Issue - Plates Used 6000; Avg. Page Number Per Issue - Saturday 20; widths 27 1/2; Newsprint Used - Short Tons 640; Printing Ink Used - Black 17000; Printing Ink Used - Color 1800; Printing Ink
Equipment EDITORIAL: Front-end Software – QPS/QuarkXPress, Baseview/NewsEdit.; Editorial Hardware – APP/Mac Quadra 800; Editorial Printers – LaserMaster/Unity 1200XL, APP/Mac LaserWriter IIg CLASSIFIED: Front-end Software – QPS/QuarkXPress, Baseview/NewsEdit.; Classified Hardware – APP/Mac Quadra 800; Classified Printers – LaserMaster/Unity 1200XL, APP/Mac LaserWriter IIg PRODUCTION: Pagination Software – QPS/QuarkXPress 3.3.; Production Equipment – TI/OmniPage 2.1, LaserMaster/Unity 1200 XLO; Cameras – SCREEN/C-690-C; Scanners – Umax/840 PRESSROOM: Line 1 – 19-G/Urbanite IF 6507; Line 2 – 20-G/Urbanite IF 6507; Line 3 – 21-G/Urbanite IF 6507; Line 4 – 22-G/Urbanite IF 6507; Line 5 – 23-G/Urbanite IF 6507; Folders – G/U-1280-1D29054; Reels and Stands – 1-G/2 Tier, 1-G/3 Tier; Press control system – 2 MAILROOM: Counter stackers – BG; Inserters and stuffers – Mc/60-40; Bundle tying machines – 2/Bu; Addressing machine – Wm. BUSINESS COMPUTERS: Business Software – Vision Data; Business Hardware – DEC/VT320

NEWS AND JOURNAL, INC.

221 Spring St., Jeffersonville, Ind., 47130; gen tel (812) 283-6636; gen fax (812) 284-7080; gen e-mail evennews@news-tribune.net; web site www.news-tribune.net

Published: Mon, Tues, Wed, Thur, Fri, Sat, Sun
Price: 98.00/yr.
Advertising: Open inch rate $21.00

KENDALLVILLE

THE NEWS-SUN

102 N. Main St., Kendallville, Ind., 46755; gen tel (260) 347-0400; gen fax (260) 347-7281; adv fax (260) 347-7282; ed fax (260) 347-2693; gen e-mail info@kpcnews.net; ed e-mail terryh@kpcnews.net; web site www.thenewssunonline.com

Group: KPC Media Group Inc.
Published: Mon, Tues, Wed, Thur, Fri, Sat, Sun
Weekday Frequency: m
Saturday Frequency: m
Circulation: 8,039; 8,039(sat); 7,555(sun)
Last Audit: ABC September 30, 2011
Price: 162.00/yr.
Advertising: Open inch rate $17.30
News services: AP.
Politics: 1859
Not Published: New Year; Memorial Day; Independence Day; Labor Day; Christmas.
Own facility?: Y
Special Editions: Look at Lagrange (Apr); Wedding Planner (Aug); Wedding Planner (Feb); Noble County Answer Book (Jan); Noble Co. 4-H Scrapbook (Jul); Sectional Basketball Preview (Mar); Graduation (May); Basketball Preview (Nov); Apple Festival (Oct); ACD Festival (Sept).
Special Weekly Sections: Church Page (Fri); Business Page (Other); Homes To Own (S); Agri-Business Page (Sat); Outdoor Life (Thur).
Magazines: USA WEEKEND Magazine (S); American Profile (Weekly).
Pres./CEO/Pub.......Terry Housholder
CFO......Donna Scanlon
Mgr., HR......Nancy Sible
Adv. Vice Pres., Sales/Mktg......Bret Jacomet
Adv. Dir.......Karen Bloom
Circ. Dir.......Bruce Hakala
Senior Reporter......Matt Getts
Prodn. Mgr., Composing......Jane Minick
GM/VP Sales Mktg......Don Cooper
Sports Editor......James Fisher
executive editor......David Kurtz
Market Information: ADS; TMC.
Mechanical available: Offset; Black and 3 ROP colors; insert accepted - product samples; page cutoffs - 22 3/4.
Mechanical Specifications: Type page 11 1/2 x 21 1/2; E - 6 cols, 1 3/4, 1/8 between; A - 6 cols, 1 3/4, 1/8 between; C - 9 cols, 1 3/4, 1/8 between.
Commodity Consumption: Avg. Page Number Per Issue - Daily 16; Avg. Page Number Per Issue - Plates Used 15000; Avg. Page Number Per Issue - Saturday 24; widths 25; Newsprint Used - Metric Tons 1083; Newsprint Used - Short Tons 1193; Printing Ink Used - Black 6000; Printing Ink
Equipment EDITORIAL: Front-end Software – Baseview, QPS/QuarkXPress.; Editorial Hardware – 12-APP/Mac; Editorial Equipment – 6-RSK/TRS 80 Model 100; Editorial Printers – 2-APP/Mac LaserWriter CLASSIFIED: Front-end Software – Baseview, QPS/QuarkXPress.; Classified Hardware – 3-APP/Mac; Classified Printers – 2-APP/Mac LaserWriter DISPLAY: Ad make-up applications – QPS/QuarkXPress, Multi-Ad.; Display Hardware – 9-APP/Mac; Display Printers – 2-APP/Mac LaserWriter PRODUCTION: Pagination Software – QPS/QuarkXPress 4.0.; Production Equipment – Caere/OmniPage 6.0, AG/Imagesetter 1200; Cameras – 1-B; Scanners – 1-Kk, 4-AG PRESSROOM: Line 1 – 4-G/Floor SSC Units 1988, 1-Stalk/Pathfinder 1988; Line 2 – 2-G/4-High 1991; 1999; Line 3 – 2; Pasters – 2 MAILROOM: Counter stackers – 1/The Stacker Machine Co/S-N 316-19; Inserters and stuffers – 1-KAN/5 pocket, KAN/Twin Stacker, MM/Saddle Binds-5 Pocket, 1-Challenge/Single Knife; Bundle tying machines – It; Other equipment – Mm. BUSINESS COMPUTERS: Business Software – Baseview/Ad Manager Pro 2.02, Dynamics/Great Plains, Baseview/Circulation Pro 1.8.0; Business Hardware – 1-Covircint/580
Delivery method: Mail, Newsstand, Private Carrier, Racks

KOKOMO

KOKOMO TRIBUNE

300 N. Union St., Kokomo, Ind., 46901; gen tel (765) 459-3121; ed tel (765) 454-8584; gen fax (765) 456-3815; adv fax (765) 456-3815; ed fax (765) 854-6733; web site www.kokomotribune.com

Published: Mon, Tues, Wed, Thur, Fri, Sat, Sun
Weekday Frequency: m
Saturday Frequency: m
Circulation: 20,100; 20,100(sat); 20,544(sun)
Last Audit: September 30, 2008
Price: 3.00/wk, $3.25/wk (motor route); 13.00/mo; 156.00/yr.
Advertising: Open inch rate $45.90
News services: AP.
Politics: Independent.
Magazines: Relish (Monthly); TV Update (Other); Parade (S).
Pub.......Robyn McCloskey
Adv. Dir.......Kristin Johnson
Circ. Dir.......Robin Harper
Lifestyle Ed.......Erin Schultz
News Ed.......Misty Knisley
Photo Ed.......Tim Bath
Sports Ed.......Dave Kitchell
Mgmt. Info Servs. Mgr.......Jim Smith
Market Information: ADS; TMC; Zoned editions.
Mechanical available: Offset; Black and 3 ROP colors; insert accepted - any; page cutoffs - 22 3/4.
Mechanical Specifications: Type page 13 x 21 1/2; E - 6 cols, 2 1/16, 1/8 between; A - 6 cols, 2 1/16, 1/8 between; C - 9 cols, 1 3/8, 1/16 between.
Commodity Consumption: Avg. Page Number Per Issue - Daily 28; Avg. Page Number Per Issue - Sunday 176; widths 54; Newsprint Used - Metric Tons 1800.
Equipment EDITORIAL: Front-end Software – Baseview 3.1.8.; Editorial Hardware – APP/Mac 73; Editorial Equipment – APP/Mac; Editorial Printers – GCC CLASSIFIED: Front-end Software – AT.; Classified Hardware – APP/Mac G3; Classified Equipment – Umax, Epson/Scanner; Classified Printers – GCC DISPLAY: Ad make-up applications – QPS/QuarkXPress 4.x; Layout Software – Baseview.; Display Hardware – APP/Mac G3; Display Printers – GCC, Tektronix; Production Equipment – QPS/QuarkXPress 4.x, Baseview/NewsEdit Pro-Que 3.1.x.; Bundle tying machines – 2-Signode/MLN-2A Strapper; Addressing machine – Nikor Mark-Model-20.; Business Hardware – 1-DEC/1170

LA PORTE

HERALD-ARGUS

701 State St., La Porte, Ind., 46350-3328; gen tel (219) 362-2161; gen fax (219) 362-2166; gen e-mail ha@heraldargus.com; adv e-mail display@heraldargus.com; ed e-mail editorial@heraldargus.com; web site www.heraldargus.com

Published: Mon, Tues, Wed, Thur, Fri, Sat
Weekday Frequency: e
Saturday Frequency: e
Circulation: 8,397; 7,072(sat)
Last Audit: ABC September 30, 2011
Price: 2.45/wk (carrier); 11.70/mo (motor route); 108.00/yr (carrier),168.00/yr (mail).
Advertising: Open inch rate $15.46
News services: AP, SHNS.
Politics: Independent-Republican.
Not Published: New Year; Memorial Day; Independence Day; Labor Day; Thanksgiving; Christmas.
Special Editions: Home Improvement/Gardening (Apr); Finance (Feb); Farm (Mar); Christmas (Nov); Car Care (Oct).
Special Weekly Sections: Senior (Fri); Best Food Day (Mon); Religion (Sat); Homes (Thur); Agriculture (Tues); Business/Industry (Wed).
Magazines: TV Viewer (television listings) (Sat); American Profile (Weekly).
Pub. ....Patrick Kellar
Adv. Dir. ....Brad Reisig
Circ. Mgr. ....Julie McKiel
Exec. Ed. ....Chris Schable
Features Ed. ....Lisa Mayes
Sports Ed. ....Adam Parkhouse
Mechanical available: Offset; Black and 3 ROP colors; insert accepted; page cutoffs - 22 3/4.
Mechanical Specifications: Type page 13 x 21 1/2; E - 6 cols, 2 1/16, 1/8 between; A - 6 cols, 2 1/16, 1/8 between; C - 9 cols, 1 3/8, 1/16 between.
Commodity Consumption: Avg. Page Number Per Issue - Daily 24; Avg. Page Number Per Issue - Plates Used 10100; widths 27 1/2; Newsprint Used - Metric Tons 514; Newsprint Used - Short Tons 566; Printing Ink Used - Black 10653; Printing Ink Used - Color 1150; Printing Ink Used -
Equipment EDITORIAL: Front-end Software – Dewar/Disc Net, FSI.; Editorial Hardware – Dewar/Sys II, DTK; Editorial Equipment – 16-Dewar/Discribe, 16-DTK CLASSIFIED: Front-end Software – Dewar/Disc Net.; Classified Hardware – Dewar/Sys II; Classified Equipment – 5-Dewar/Discribe; Layout Software – 2-Dewar/Sys IV.; Display Hardware – 2-Dewar/AST PRODUCTION: Pagination Software – FSI, QPS/QuarkXPress 3.32.; Production Equipment – 1-MON/PaperMaster 2, 1-MON/ImageMaster 1000, 3-MON/Image Master 1500; Cameras – 1-Nu/2024-V, 1-R/580; Scanners – Nikon/ScanTouch 8 1/2 x 14 PRESSROOM: Line 1 – 6-G/Urbanite, 1-G/3-Color single width; Press Drives – 2; Folders – 1-G/Universal 1963; Reels and Stands – Jun-72; Press control system – 1995; Bundle tying machines – 1-Bu/String Tyer, 1-MLN/EE.; Business Hardware – DTK/Pentium-100

LA PORTE PUBLISHING LLC
701 State St., La Porte, Ind., 46350-3328; gen tel (219) 362-2161; gen fax (219) 362-2166

LAFAYETTE

FEDERATED PUBLICATIONS, INC.
217 N. 6th St., Lafayette, Ind., 47901-1448; gen tel (765) 423-5511; gen fax (765) 742-5633

JOURNAL AND COURIER
217 N. Sixth St., Lafayette, Ind., 47901-1448; gen tel (765) 423-5511; adv tel (765) 423-5512; ed tel (765) 423-5511; gen fax (765) 742-5633; adv fax (765) 742-5633; ed fax (765) 420-5246; gen e-mail jconline@journalandcourier.com; adv e-mail jholm@journalandcourier.com; ed e-mail jdoll@journalandcourier.com; web site www.jconline.com
Published: Mon, Tues, Wed, Thur, Fri, Sat, Sun
Weekday Frequency: m
Saturday Frequency: m
Circulation: 26,658; 26,658(sat); 36,420(sun)
Last Audit: ABC September 30, 2011
Price: 3.95/wk; 205.40/yr.
Advertising: Open inch rate $57.87
News services: AP, GNS, LAT-WP.
Politics: Independent.
Special Editions: Bragging Rights (Apr); Community Connections (Aug); Builders Showcase (Every other month); Football Saturday (Fall); Grading Our Schools (Jan); Spring Home Improvement (Mar); Schools of Greater Lafayette (May); Coupon Express (Monthly); Profiles (Oct).
Special Weekly Sections: TGIF (Fri); Food & Drink (Mon); Life (S); Homes (Sat); Diversion (Thur); Health & Fitness (Tues); Relate (Wed).
Magazines: USA WEEKEND Magazine (Sat).
Pres./Pub. ....Gary Suisman
Controller ....Chris Deno
Bus. Consultant ....Iris Hayden
Adv. Dir. ....Jim Holm
Adv. Mgr., Classified ....Becky Taylor
Adv. Mgr., Retail ....Sharon Bardonner
Dir., Market Devel. ....Nancy Jo Trafton
Circ. Dir. ....Mick Siemers
Exec. Ed. ....Julie Doll
Mng. Ed. ....Henry Howard
Copy Ed. ....Bob Bloom
Editorial Page Ed. ....Linda Kirchubel
Enterprise Ed. ....Dave Smith
Features Ed. ....Julie McClure
Librarian ....Jackie Cummings
Local/Regl. Ed. ....Dave Bangert
Sports Ed. ....Jim Stafford
Dir., Information Sys. ....Gary Love
Online Mgr. ....Joe Younquist
Opns. Dir. ....Travis Komidar
Market Information: TMC.
Mechanical available: Letterpress; Black and 3 ROP colors; insert accepted - Sample-packs and We-Prints; page cutoffs - 22 3/4.
Mechanical Specifications: Type page 13 x 21 1/2; E - 6 cols, 2 1/8, 1/8 between; A - 6 cols, 2 1/8, 1/8 between; C - 9 cols, 1 3/8, 1/8 between.
Commodity Consumption: Avg. Page Number Per Issue - Daily 30; Avg. Page Number Per Issue - Plates Used 51866; Avg. Page Number Per Issue - Saturday 36; Avg. Page Number Per Issue - Sunday 48; widths 54; Newsprint Used - Metric Tons 3466; Printing Ink Used - Black 121950; Print
Equipment EDITORIAL: Front-end Software – Baseview/NewsEdit Pro.; Editorial Hardware – 47-APP/Mac, 32-APP/Mac Server; Editorial Equipment – APP/Mac G4, APP/E-Mac; Editorial Printers – DEC/LA 180, OCE/Proof Express CLASSIFIED: Front-end Software – Mactive 2.16.50.; Classified Hardware – IBM/Server, Dell/Workstations; Classified Printers – HP/8150N DISPLAY: Ad make-up applications – Multi-Ad; Layout Software – APP/Mac.; Display Hardware – APP/Mac, 9-APP/Mac; Display Printers – 1-Linotype-Hell/Linotronic 530, 2-Pre Press/Panther 46H5 PRODUCTION: Pagination Software – Baseview.; Production Equipment – 1-Lf, 2-Panther/PrePress; Scanners – Kk/CoolScan PRESSROOM: Line 1 – 6-G/Mark (2 half decks; 1 hump) 1959; Folders – G/2:1; Press registration system – K&F/Pin Registration. MAILROOM: Counter stackers – HL, 1/QWI; Inserters and stuffers – 1-HI/1472; Bundle tying machines – Dynaric; Addressing machine – Ch.; Audio Hardware – Octel; Business Hardware – 1-IBM/AS-400 F35

LEBANON

LEBANON NEWSPAPERS, INC.
117 E. Washington, Lebanon, Ind., 46052; gen tel (765) 482-4650; gen fax (765) 482-4652; gen e-mail kristin.jhonson@reporter.net

THE REPORTER
117 E. Washington St., Lebanon, Ind., 46052; gen tel (765) 482-4650; adv tel (765) 482-4650; ed tel (765) 482-4650; gen fax (765) 482-4652; adv fax (765) 482-4652; ed fax (765) 482-4652; ed e-mail news@reporter.net; web site www.reporter.net
Published: Mon, Tues, Wed, Thur, Fri, Sat
Weekday Frequency: m
Circulation: 5,264; 5,264(sat)
Last Audit: September 30, 2003
Price: 1.80/wk.
Advertising: Open inch rate $10.50
News services: AP.
Politics: Independent-Republican. **Established:** 1891
Not Published: New Year; Thanksgiving; Christmas.
Special Editions: Auto-Home Show (Apr); Christmas Greetings (Dec); Brides (Feb); County 4-H Fair (Jul); 500 Specials (May); Christmas Opening (Nov).
Special Weekly Sections: Business Page (Fri); Shopper's Extra (Thur); Farm Pages (Tues); Best Food (Wed).
Magazines: TV Times (Sat); American Profile (Weekly).
Adv. Mgr. ....Rick Whiteman
Circ. Mgr. ....Kathy Armmold
Mng. Ed. ....Marda Johnson
Ed. ....Greta Sanderson
Farm Ed. ....Rod Rose
Mechanical available: Offset; Black and 3 ROP colors; insert accepted; page cutoffs - 22 3/4.
Mechanical Specifications: Type page 13 x 21; E - 6 cols, 2 1/16, 1/8 between; A - 6 cols, 2 1/16, 1/8 between; C - 6 cols, 2 1/16, 1/8 between.
Commodity Consumption: Avg. Page Number Per Issue - Daily 14; Avg. Page Number Per Issue - Plates Used 2500; widths 28; Newsprint Used - Short Tons 250; Printing Ink Used - Black 7500; Printing Ink Used - Color 100; Printing Ink Used - Pages Printed 5000.
Equipment EDITORIAL: Front-end Software – Baseview/NewsEdit 3.1.; Editorial Hardware – 10-APP/Mac; Editorial Equipment – Fotovix, Fuvix/FV-7; Editorial Printers – 2-APP/Mac CLASSIFIED: Front-end Software – Baseview/Class Manager.; Classified Hardware – 1-APP/Mac; Classified Printers – 1-APP/Mac DISPLAY: Ad make-up applications – Multi-Ad/Creator; Layout Software – 1-APP/Mac.; Display Printers – 1-APP/Mac LaserPrinter PRODUCTION: Pagination Software – QPS/QuarkXPress 2.12, QPS/QuarkXPress 3.2.; Production Equipment – Caere/OmniPage Pro, 1-Printware, 1-Linotype-Hell/Linotronic, 1-Pre Press/Panther Pro 36; Cameras – 1-B/Caravel; Scanners – 1-AG/COM, 2-AG, 1-Nikon/Coolscan, 1-Polaroid/SprintScan, 1-Umax PRESSROOM: Line 1 – 7-G/Community; Folders – 1; Bundle tying machines – 1/Dynaric; Addressing machine – Wm.; Business Hardware – IBM

LINTON

THE EVENING WORLD
79 S. Main St., Linton, Ind., 47441; gen tel (812) 847-4487; adv tel (812) 847-4487; ed tel (812) 847-4487; gen fax (812) 847-9513; adv fax (812) 847-9513; ed fax (812) 847-9513; gen e-mail cpruett@dailycitizen.com; adv e-mail clehman@dailycitizen.com; web site www.dailycitizen.com
Published: Mon, Tues, Wed, Thur, Fri
Weekday Frequency: e
Circulation: 2,178
Last Audit: September 18, 2003
Price: 6.75/mo; 77.40/yr.
Advertising: Open inch rate $9.90
News services: AP.
Politics: Democrat.
Not Published: Memorial Day; Independence Day; Labor Day; Thanksgiving; Christmas.
Pub. ....Randy List
Adv. Mgr. ....Christy Lehman
Adv. Mgr., Classified ....Kelley Clampitt
Circ. Mgr. ....Laura Faulk
Ed. ....Chris Pruett
Sports Ed. ....Paul Wilcoxen
Market Information: TMC.
Mechanical available: Offset; Black and 3 ROP colors; insert accepted; page cutoffs - 22 3/4.
Mechanical Specifications: Type page 13 x 21 1/2; E - 6 cols, 2 1/16, 1/8 between; A - 6 cols, 2 1/16, 1/8 between; C - 9 cols, 1 1/2, 1/8 between.
Commodity Consumption: Avg. Page Number Per Issue - Daily 10; Avg. Page Number Per Issue - Plates Used 1664; widths 28; Newsprint Used - Short Tons 165; Printing Ink Used - Black 2000; Printing Ink Used - Color 50.
Equipment EDITORIAL: Front-end Software – Claris/MacWrite.; Editorial Hardware – APP/Macs; Editorial Equipment – Smith-Corona/; Editorial Printers – APP/Mac LaserWriter CLASSIFIED: Front-end Software – Claris/MacWrite, Microsoft/Word.; Classified Hardware – APP/Macs; Classified Equipment – 3-Ro; Classified Printers – APP/Mac ImageWriter II DISPLAY: Ad make-up applications – QPS/QuarkXPress; Display Hardware – APP/Mac IIci; Display Printers – LaserMaster/1000, APP/Mac LaserWriter 8500; Production Equipment – 1-B; Cameras – 1-R; Scanners – HP/Flatbed. PRESSROOM: Line 1 – 4-G/Community; Line 2 – 1-ABD/360; Folders – G/C. BUSINESS COMPUTERS: Business Software – Peachtree; Business Hardware – APP/Mac LCII

GREENE COUNTY DAILY WORLD
79 S. Main St., Linton, Ind., 47441; gen tel (812) 847-4487; gen fax (812) 847-9513; gen e-mail cpruett@dailycitizen.com; adv e-mail christy_lehman@hotmail.com; ed e-mail cpruett79@hotmail.com; web site www.gcdailyworld.com
Published: Tues, Wed, Thur, Fri, Sat
Weekday Frequency: e
Saturday Frequency: m
Circulation: 2,979; 2,979(sat)
Last Audit: September 29, 2003
Price: 7.00/mo; 93.00/yr.
Advertising: Open inch rate $10.50
News services: AP.
Politics: Independent. **Established:** 1900
Advertising not accepted: Vending machine.
Not Published: New Year; Memorial Day; Labor Day; Thanksgiving; Christmas.
Special Weekly Sections: Greene-Sullivan Weekender (S).
Magazines: Relish (Monthly).
Pub. ....Randy List
Adv. Dir. ....Christy Lehman
Circ. Mgr. ....Laura Faulk
Online Ed. ....Chris Pruett
Sports Ed. ....BJ Hargis
Prodn. Foreman ....Mike Miller
Market Information: Split run; TMC; Zoned editions.
Mechanical available: Offset; Black and 4 ROP colors; insert accepted; page cutoffs - 22 3/4.
Mechanical Specifications: Type page 12 1/4 x 21; E - 6 cols, 1 7/8, 1/8 between; A - 6 cols, 1 7/8, 1/8 between; C - 8 cols, 1 3/4, 1/8 between.
Commodity Consumption: Avg. Page Number Per Issue - Daily 41.
Equipment; Production Equipment – 1-Nu, 1-COM/4961TL, 1-COM/7200, 1-COM/7200L; Cameras – 1-LE/500.; Line 2 – 3-HI/V-15A; Folders – 1; Addressing machine – 1/Am.; Business Hardware – PBS

LOGANSPORT

PHAROS-TRIBUNE
517 E. Broadway Ave., Logansport, Ind., 46947; gen tel (574) 722-5000; adv tel (574) 722-5177; ed tel (574) 732-5155; gen fax (574) 732-5080; adv fax (574) 732-5050; ed fax (574) 732-5070; gen e-mail ptnews@pharostribune.com; adv e-mail chris.ford@pharostribune.com; ed e-mail kelly.hawes@pharostribune.com; web site www.pharostribune.com
Published: Mon, Tues, Wed, Thur, Fri, Sat, Sun
Saturday Frequency: m
Circulation: 9,303; 8,766(sat); 9,481(sun)
Last Audit: September 30, 2006

Price: 2.65/wk; 11.48/mo; 137.80/yr.
Advertising: Open inch rate $18.90
News services: AP, MCT.
Politics: Independent. **Established:** 1844
Advertising not accepted: Work-at-home job opportunities.
Special Editions: Football (Aug); 4-H (Jul); Winter Sports (Nov).
Special Weekly Sections: Religion (Fri); Senior Living (S).
Magazines: Parade (S).
Pub. ....Robyn McCloskey
Gen. Mgr....Kim Dillon
HR...Sandra Forrest
Adv. Dir. ....Chris Ford
District Sales Mgr. ....Heather James
Dir., Mktg..............................Stefani Closson
Circ. Mgr................................Jack Hutcheson
Customer Serv. Mgr. ....Becky Hirschler
Mng. Ed. ....Kelly Hawes
Editorial Page Ed.........................David Kitchell
Sports Ed......................................Beau Wicker
Prodn. Graphic Artist ....Amy Newcom
Prodn. Mgr., Pre/Post Press...........Randy Houle
Prodn. Mgr., Pre Press ....Rich Cox
Market Information: TMC.
Mechanical available: Offset; Black and 3 ROP colors; insert accepted; page cutoffs - 22 3/4.
Mechanical Specifications: Type page 13 x 21 1/2; E - 6 cols, 2 1/16, 1/8 between; A - 6 cols, 2 1/16, 1/8 between; C - 6 cols, 2 1/16, 1/8 between.
Commodity Consumption: Avg. Page Number Per Issue - Daily 20; Avg. Page Number Per Issue - Plates Used 18592; Avg. Page Number Per Issue - Sunday 28; widths 34; Newsprint Used - Metric Tons 600; Newsprint Used - Short Tons 667; Printing Ink Used - Black 19530; Printing Ink Use
Equipment EDITORIAL: Front-end Software – Baseview.; Editorial Hardware – Sun; Editorial Equipment – Lf/AP Leaf Picture Desk, Lf/Leafscan 35; Editorial Printers – 2-APP/Mac LaserWriter II NTX, 2-Copal/Dash 600 CLASSIFIED: Front-end Software – Atex.; Classified Hardware – Sun, NCD; Classified Printers – HP/LaserJet, Copal/Dash 600 DISPLAY: Ad make-up applications – Adobe/InDesign; Layout Software – ALS.; Display Hardware – APP/Mac II; Display Printers – 2-APP/Mac LaserWriter II NTX, 2-Copal/Dash 600 PRODUCTION: Pagination Software – QPS/QuarkXPress 4.11.; Production Equipment – TI/OmniPage 2.12, 1-AG/Focus Color Plus; Scanners – Horizon PRESSROOM: Line 1 – 19-G/SSC 1984.; Inserters and stuffers – 4/MM; Bundle tying machines – 1-/MLN, OVL/415. BUSINESS COMPUTERS: Business Software – Vision Data, ADP; Business Hardware – 1-Sun/4-110, 1-Sun/SLC, 1-Compaq/Prolinca 3/25

MADISON

THE MADISON COURIER

310 Courier Sq., Madison, Ind., 47250; gen tel (812) 265-3641; gen fax (812) 273-6903; adv e-mail mcadv@madisoncourier.com; ed e-mail etompkin@madisoncourier.com; web site www.madisoncourier.com
Published: Mon, Tues, Wed, Thur, Fri, Sat, Sun
Weekday Frequency: e
Saturday Frequency: m
Circulation: 8,848; 8,848(sat)
Last Audit: October 12, 2004
Price: 7.15/mo (carrier), $7.50/mo (auto); 78.10/yr (carrier), $82.00/yr (auto).
Advertising: Open inch rate $10.50
News services: AP, NEA.
Politics: Republican. **Established:** 1837
Not Published: New Year; Memorial Day; Independence Day; Labor Day; Thanksgiving; Christmas.
Special Editions: Home and Car Improvement Tab (Apr); Year-End Tab (Dec); Tax Tab (Feb); Wedding Tab (Jan); 4-H Fair Tab (Jul); Cookbook (Jun); Lawn & Garden Tab (Mar); Graduation Tab (May); Basketball Preview Tab (Nov); Chautauqua Tab (Sept).
Magazines: American Profile (Weekly).
Pres./Pub...............................Jane W. Jacobs
Adv. Mgr. ....Mark McKee
Circ. Mgr.....................................Curt Jacobs
Editorial Page Ed. ....Elliot Tompkin
News Ed.................................Mark Campbell
Sports Ed. ....David Campbell
New Media Dir................................Robin Cull
Prodn. Mgr. ....Jack Ulery
Prodn. Mgr., Mailroom..............William Jacobs
Mechanical available: Offset; Black and 3 ROP colors; insert accepted - single sheet, booklets, samples; page cutoffs - 22 3/4.
Mechanical Specifications: Type page 13 x 21 1/2; E - 6 cols, 2 1/16, 1/8 between; A - 6 cols, 2 1/16, 1/8 between; C - 8 cols, 1 1/2, 1/8 between.
Commodity Consumption: Avg. Page Number Per Issue - Daily 16; Avg. Page Number Per Issue - Plates Used 2397; widths 27 1/2; Newsprint Used - Short Tons 358; Printing Ink Used - Black 6750; Printing Ink Used - Color 1000; Printing Ink Used - Pages Printed 5892.
Equipment EDITORIAL: Front-end Software – Baseview, Ethernet.; Editorial Hardware – 9-APP/Power Mac 7200, 3-APP/Power Mac G3; Editorial Equipment – 1-RSK/Tandy portable Model 100, 3-APP/Power Mac 7200-120 for remote office; Editorial Printers – 1-APP/Mac LaserWriter II NT CLASSIFIED: Front-end Software – Baseview.; Classified Hardware – 3-APP/Power Mac G3; Classified Printers – 1-APP/Mac ImageWriter II NT DISPLAY: Ad make-up applications – DTI, QPS/QuarkXPress 3.32, Multi-Ad/Creator; Layout Software – COM/One System, 1-APP/Mac 7600.; Display Hardware – 3-APP/Mac G3, 4-APP/iMac G3; Display Printers – APP/Mac LaserWriter II NT, 1-Dataproducts/Typhoon 8 PRODUCTION: Pagination Software – QPS/QuarkXPress 4.0.; Production Equipment – 1-Nu, Pre Press/Panther, Pre Press/Panther 34P; Cameras – R/400; Scanners – 1-Nikon/LS 1000, Epson 1600 PRESSROOM: Line 1 – 6-KP/News King; Reels and Stands – 6; Press control system – 1; Inserters and stuffers – KAN/4 Station; Bundle tying machines – 2/Bu.; Audio Hardware – Zimmer Interactive; Business Hardware – 4-TI/1505

MARION

CHRONICLE-TRIBUNE

610 S. Adams St., Marion, Ind., 46953; gen tel (765) 664-5111; gen fax (765) 664-6292; adv fax (765) 664-0729; ed fax (765) 668-4256; gen e-mail ctreport@att.net; web site www.chronicle-tribune.com
Published: Mon, Tues, Wed, Thur, Fri, Sat, Sun
Weekday Frequency: m
Saturday Frequency: m
Circulation: 11,793; 11,759(sat); 14,034(sun)
Last Audit: September 30, 2009
Price: 3.40/wk; 14.73/mo; 176.80/yr.
Advertising: Open inch rate $41.04
News services: AP, GNS.
Politics: Independent.
Special Editions: Football Preview (Aug); Medical Directory (Feb); Bridal Tab (Jan); Senior Citizens (Jul); Progress (Mar); Women's Expo (Oct); Crossword Puzzle (Semi-yearly).
Special Weekly Sections: Travel (Fri); Best Food Day (Mon); Business (S); Business (Sat); Home (Thur); Kids Zone (Tues); Relationships (Wed).
Magazines: Northern Neighbors (S).
Pub. ....Niel Ronquist
Finance Mgr. ....Ruth Ann Barnes
Circ. Dir. ....Linda Kozlowski
Photo Ed. ....Jeff Morehead
Dir., Systems...............................Gary Stoffer
Market Information: TMC.
Mechanical available: Offset; Black and 3 ROP colors; insert accepted - 4x 5 cards to 11 3/8 x 13 3/4 products; page cutoffs - 22 3/4.
Mechanical Specifications: Type page 11 5/8 x 21 1/2; E - 7 cols, 1 2/3, between; A - 6 cols, 2 1/16, 1/8 between; C - 9 cols, 1 3/8, 1/16 between.
Commodity Consumption: Avg. Page Number Per Issue - Daily 18; Avg. Page Number Per Issue - Sunday 46; widths 12 1/2; Newsprint Used - Metric Tons 999; Newsprint Used - Short Tons 1101; Printing Ink Used - Black 25200; Printing Ink Used - Color 11960; Printing Ink Used - Pages
Equipment EDITORIAL: Front-end Software – APT 2.006.004.; Editorial Hardware – IBM; Editorial Printers – HP/8550, HP/8000, HP/4MV CLASSIFIED: Front-end Software – APT 2.006.004.; Classified Hardware – IBM; Classified Equipment – Accuset/1000 Imagesetters; Classified Printers – HP/4MV, HP/8000 DISPLAY: Ad make-up applications – Multi-Ad/Creator; Layout Software – APP/Mac.; Display Hardware – APP/Mac; Display Printers – HP/4MV, HP/8000 PRODUCTION: Pagination Software – QPS/QuarkXPress 4.10.; Production Equipment – 2-MON/1000 Imagesetter, Nu/Flip Top FT40APRNS; Cameras – 1-C/Spartan III; Scanners – Howtek/D7500, Microtek PRESSROOM: Line 1 – 12-G/Urbanite 845 single width 1970; Line 2 – 6-G/Urbanite 557 single width 1974; Pasters – 7; Press control system – Fin/Drive Sys. MAILROOM: Counter stackers – 1-HL/Monitor HI II, 2-HI/RS30; Inserters and stuffers – 1-Mc/660-20; Bundle tying machines – 1-MLN/2A, OVL/415, Bu/String; Wrapping singles – Manual; Addressing machine – Ch/596-985.; Business Hardware – Time Mgt Sys, IBM/AS-400

CHRONICLE TRIBUNE

610 S. Adams St., Marion, Ind., 46952; web site www.chronicle-tribune.com
Published: Mon, Tues, Wed, Thur, Fri, Sat, Sun
Weekday Frequency: m
Saturday Frequency: m
Circulation: 12,238; 12,238(sat); 14,637(sun)
Last Audit: ABC September 30, 2011

MARTINSVILLE

THE REPORTER-TIMES

60 S. Jefferson St., Martinsville, Ind., 46151; gen tel (765) 342-3311; adv tel (800) 804-8420; ed tel (765) 342-3311; gen fax (765) 342-1446; gen e-mail reporter@reportert.com; adv e-mail adsrvs@reportert.com; web site www.reporter-times.com
Group: U.S. Suburban Press, Inc.
Published: Mon, Tues, Wed, Thur, Fri, Sat
Weekday Frequency: e
Circulation: 4,714; 4,714(sat); 40,171(sun)
Last Audit: September 30, 2008
Price: 10.40/mo; 113.55/yr.
Advertising: Open inch rate $13.89
News services: AP.
Politics: Independent. **Established:** 1889
Note: This publication shares a joint Sunday edition with the Bedford (IN) Times-Mail (mS) and the Bloomington (IN) Herald-Times (mS).
Advertising not accepted: Brokered; Advertising that requires investment.
Not Published: New Year; Memorial Day; Independence Day; Labor Day; Christmas.
Special Editions: Football Preview (Aug); Last Minute Gifts (Dec); Boy Scout Page (Feb); Father's Day (Jun); Girl Scout Page (Mar); Graduation (May); Christmas Kick-Off (Nov); Fall Festival Program (Oct); Customer Appreciation Days (Sept).
Special Weekly Sections: NASCAR (Fri); Church (Sat); Health (Tues).
Magazines: TV Times (Sat).
Profile: The Reporter-Times is a daily newspaper covering Morgan County, IN.
Pub........................................Mayer Maloney
Sr. Vice Pres., Newspaper Opns. Charles V. Pittman
Adv. Mgr....................................Karen DeWitt
Circ. Dir......................................Tim D. Smith
Mng. Ed. ....Brian Culp
News Ed...............................Ronald Hawkins
Sports Ed....................................Steve Page
Sunday Ed.....................................A.J. Nelson
IT Mgr.....................................Tom Callahan
Market Information: TMC.
Mechanical available: Offset; Black and 3 ROP colors; insert accepted - all; page cutoffs - 22 3/4.
Mechanical Specifications: Type page 13 x 21 1/2; E - 6 cols, 2, 1/8 between; A - 6 cols, 2, 1/8 between; C - 9 cols, 1 5/16, 1/16 between.
Commodity Consumption: Avg. Page Number Per Issue - Daily 15; Avg. Page Number Per Issue - Saturday 13.
Equipment; Editorial Hardware – APP/Mac; Editorial Printers – APP/Mac LaserWriter. PRESSROOM: Line 1 – 7-G/Community (color unit); Folders – 1-G/2:1.; Bundle tying machines – 2/Bu.; Business Hardware – Software ☐ Baseview

MERRILLVILLE

POST-TRIBUNE

1433 E. 83rd Ave., Merrillville, Ind., 46410-6307; gen tel (219) 648-3000; adv tel (219) 648-3171; ed tel (219) 648-3158; gen fax (219) 648-3246; adv fax (219) 648-2187; ed fax (219) 648-3234; adv e-mail ads@post-trib.com; ed e-mail editor@post-trib.com; web site www.post-trib.com
Published: Mon, Tues, Wed, Thur, Fri, Sat, Sun
Weekday Frequency: m
Saturday Frequency: m
Circulation: 52,106; 50,326(sat); 53,517(sun)
Last Audit: September 30, 2009
Price: 3.00/wk; 156.00/yr.
Advertising: Open inch rate $100.92
News services: AP, MCT, LAT-WP.
Politics: Independent.
Special Editions: Golf Section (Apr); Quickly (Aug); Festival of Lights (Dec); Pride of Hobart/Lake Station (Feb); New Year New You (Jan); Healthy Life Magazine (Jul); Weightlifting (Jun); Pride of Gary (Mar); Festival of Homes/Home Improvement (May); Merrillville Chamber
Special Weekly Sections: Weekend (Fri); High Profile (Mon); TV (S); Families (Thur); Health & Fitness (Tues); Food (Wed).
Magazines: USA WEEKEND Magazine (S).
Pub. ....Lisa Tatina
Adv. Supvr., Retail ....Rich Cains
Exec. Ed. ....Paulette Haddix
Porter County Ed. ....Carole Carlson
Sports Ed. ....Jeff Majeske
Mgmt. Info Servs. Mgr. ....Doug Bogart
Telecom Mgr..........................Richard McGhee
Market Information: Split run; TMC; Zoned editions.
Mechanical available: Offset; Black and 3 ROP colors; insert accepted - other inserts on request; page cutoffs - 22.
Mechanical Specifications: Type page 13 x 21; E - 6 cols, 2 1/16, 1/8 between; A - 6 cols, 2 1/16, 1/8 between; C - 10 cols, 1 1/4, 1/16 between.
Commodity Consumption: Avg. Page Number Per Issue - Daily 40; Avg. Page Number Per Issue - Plates Used 96000; Avg. Page Number Per Issue - Sunday 92; widths 54; Newsprint Used - Metric Tons 7500; Printing Ink Used - Black 180000; Printing Ink Used - Color 35000; Printing Ink U
Equipment EDITORIAL: Front-end Software – QPS.; Editorial Hardware – APP/iMac workstations CLASSIFIED: Front-end Software – AT/IAS, Mactive.; Classified Hardware – AT/IAS, Dell/PII 350 DISPLAY: Ad make-up applications – QPS/QuarkXPress 3.3, Adobe/Photoshop 3.0, Adobe/Illustrator 5.5; Layout Software – CJ, HP.; Display Hardware – APP/Mac PRODUCTION: Pagination Software – MEI/ALS 1.7.; Production Equipment – Caere Omni Page Pro 8.0, 1-MON/Laserpress, 1-MON/News Express; Cameras – 1-C/Spartan III, 2-C/Marathon; Scanners – 1-ECR/Autokon, 2-Lf/Leafscan 35, Scanview/Scanmate 4000 PRESSROOM: Line 1 – 3-PEC/Eagle 3 Color, 6-PEC/Spectrum B&W; Folders – 2; Pasters – 6-G/Automatic, 3-PEC/Automatic; Reels and Stands – 9-G/Mark II; Press control system – TKS/TMPC. MAILROOM: Counter stackers – 2-QWI/3000, 2-Id/440, 2-QWI/200; Inserters and stuffers –

1-GMA/14-72p, 1-S/48p; Bundle tying machines – 2-MLN/2A, 2-MLN/News 90; Addressing machine – 2/Ch, VideoJet Ink Jet Printer; Other equipment –MM with quarter folder.; Business Hardware – HP/3000-947

MICHIGAN CITY

NEWS DISPATCH

121 W. Michigan Blvd., Michigan City, Ind., 46360; gen tel (219) 874-7211; gen fax (219) 872-8511; adv fax (219) 878-4487; ed fax (219) 872-8511; gen e-mail news@thenewsdispatch.com; adv e-mail ads@thenewsdispatch.com (retail); classifieds@thenewsdispatch.com (classified); ed e-mail news@thenewsdispatch.com; web site www.thenewsdispatch.com

Published: Mon, Tues, Wed, Thur, Fri, Sat, Sun
Weekday Frequency: m
Saturday Frequency: m
Circulation: 8,628; 8,628(sat); 9,275(sun)
Last Audit: September 30, 2009
Price: 12.25/mo; 179.40/yr.
Advertising: Open inch rate $22.30
News services: AP.
Politics: Independent.
Not Published: New Year; Memorial Day; Labor Day; Christmas.
Special Editions: Real Estate Guide (Monthly).
Special Weekly Sections: Book Review (Fri); Business (S); Real Estate (Sat); Best Food Day (Wed).
Magazines: USA WEEKEND Magazine (S); TV Listings (own, local newsprint) (Sat).
Pub. .... Patrik Kellar
Adv. Dir. .... Isis Leon-Cains
Adv. Mgr., Nat'l Rep. .... Cindy Galligan
Education/Lifestyles Columnist Deborah Sederberg
Entertainment Ed. .... Andrew Tallackson
Harbor Country News Ed. .... Dave Johnson
Lifestyle Ed. .... Kristin Miller
News Ed. .... David Hawk
Market Information: ADS; TMC; Zoned editions.
Mechanical available: Offset; Black and 3 ROP colors; insert accepted; page cutoffs - 22 3/4.
Mechanical Specifications: Type page 11 5/8 x 21 1/2; E - 6 cols, 1 5/6, 1/8 between; A - 6 cols, 1 5/6, 1/8 between; C - 9 cols, 1 1/6, 1/8 between.
Commodity Consumption: Avg. Page Number Per Issue - Daily 26; Avg. Page Number Per Issue - Sunday 36; widths 13 3/4; Newsprint Used - Metric Tons 750; Printing Ink Used - Black 20000; Printing Ink Used - Color 3800.
Equipment EDITORIAL: Front-end Software – Baseview, QPS/QuarkXPress 3.32, Baseview/NewsEdit.; Editorial Hardware – APP/Mac; Editorial Printers – 2-APP/Mac LaserWriter II NTX, HP/4MV, QMS/860, Tektronix/300X CLASSIFIED: Front-end Software – Baseview/Class Manager Pro.; Classified Hardware – APP/Mac; Classified Printers – 2-APP/Mac LaserWriter IINTX, HP/4MV, QMS/860, Tektronix/300X DISPLAY: Ad make-up applications – Managing Editor/ALS, QPS/QuarkXPress; Layout Software – APP/Mac.; Display Hardware – APP/Mac; Display Printers – 2-APP/Mac LaserWriter II NTX, HP/4MV, QMS/860, Tektronix/300x PRODUCTION: Pagination Software – QPS/QuarkXPress 3.32.; Production Equipment – Caere/OmniPage, AG/Rapline 17; Cameras – R; Scanners – Visioneer/Paperport, Nikon/Super Coolscan, Lf/AP Leafscan 35, AG/StudioScan II, Hp/ScanJet HC, AG/Studio Star PRESSROOM: Line 1 – 8-G/Urbanite (3 color) 1972; Folders – G/Half & Quarter; Reels and Stands – 8-G/Reel Stand. MAILROOM: Counter stackers – BG/110HB; Inserters and stuffers – 3-KAN/320; Bundle tying machines – MLN.; Audio Hardware – Software □ SMS/Stauffer Gold; Business Hardware – Baseview

MONTICELLO

HERALD JOURNAL

114 S. Main St., Monticello, Ind., 47960; gen tel (574) 583-5121; gen fax (574) 583-4241; web site newsbug.info/monticello_herald_journal

Published: Mon, Tues, Wed, Thur, Fri, Sat
Weekday Frequency: m
Saturday Frequency: m
Circulation: 5,100; 5,100(sat)
Last Audit: September 30, 2002
Price: 9.00/mo; $104/yr; $34/3mo, $104/6mo.
Advertising: Open inch rate $15.00
News services: AP.
Politics: Republican.
Not Published: New Year; Memorial Day; Independence Day; Labor Day; Thanksgiving; Christmas.
Own facility?: Y
Special Weekly Sections: TV (Fri); Best Food Day (Thurs); Business & Financial (Sat); Best Food Day (Thur); Senior Citizens (Tues); Self Help (Wed).
Gen. Mgr. .... Karen Frankscoviak
Circ. Dir. .... Greg Perrotto
Mng. Ed. .... Katie Duffey
Market Information: TMC.
Mechanical available: Offset; Black and 3 ROP colors; insert accepted; page cutoffs - 22 3/4.
Mechanical Specifications: Type page 13 x 21 1/2; E - 6 cols, 1 5/6, 1/8 between; A - 6 cols, 1 5/6, 1/8 between; C - 9 cols, 1 5/16, 1/8 between.
Commodity Consumption: Avg. Page Number Per Issue - Daily 10; Avg. Page Number Per Issue - Plates Used 6000; widths 34; Newsprint Used - Short Tons 99; Printing Ink Used - Black 5820; Printing Ink Used - Color 2600; Printing Ink Used - Pages Printed 3200.
Equipment EDITORIAL: Front-end Software – APT 4.0.; Editorial Hardware – Dell/PC; Editorial Printers – APP/Mac LaserWriter II CLASSIFIED: Front-end Software – APT 4.0.; Classified Hardware – Dell/PC; Classified Printers – APP/Mac LaserWriter II; Layout Software – APP/Mac.; Display Hardware – Quark, Ad Builder; Display Printers – APP/Mac LaserWriter II; Production Equipment – 1-Nu/Flip Top FT40UPNS, SCREEN; Cameras – LE, R. PRESSROOM: Line 1 – 5-G/Community 1963.
Delivery method: Mail, Newsstand, Racks

MUNCIE

THE STAR PRESS

345 S. High St., Muncie, Ind., 47305; gen tel (765) 213-5700; adv tel (765) 213-5711; ed tel (765) 747-5754; gen fax (765) 213-5703; adv fax (765) 213-5937; ed fax (765) 213-5858; ed e-mail news@muncie.gannett.com; web site www.thestarpress.com

Published: Mon, Tues, Wed, Thur, Fri, Sat, Sun
Weekday Frequency: m
Saturday Frequency: m
Circulation: 21,117; 21,117(sat); 27,959(sun)
Last Audit: ABC September 30, 2011
Price: 3.45/wk; 169.00/yr.
Advertising: Open inch rate $42.88
News services: AP, MCT, SHNS, GNS.
Politics: Independent.
Special Weekly Sections: Best Food (Thur).
Magazines: TV Week (S).
Dir., Finance .... Steve Lam
Adv. Dir .... Mary Young
Dir., Mktg./Servs. .... Tom Roghrock
Circ. Dir. .... Tim Alexander
Mng. Ed. .... Lisa Nellessen-Lara
Exec. Ed. .... Gene Williams
Arts/Entertainment Reporter .... Michelle Kinsey
Bus./Finance Ed. .... Brian Royseon
Design Ed. .... Kara Stmyer
Editorial Page Ed. .... Jeff Ward
Features Ed. .... Deb Sorrell
Metro Ed. .... Douglas Walker
Asst. Metro Ed. .... Robin Gibson
Sports Ed. .... Greg Fallon
Dir., Info Servs. .... Ron Daugherty
Webmaster .... Phil Beebe
Market Information: ADS; Split run; TMC; Zoned editions.
Mechanical available: Letterpress; Black and 3 ROP colors; insert accepted; page cutoffs - 22 3/4.
Mechanical Specifications: Type page 13 x 21 3/8; E - 6 cols, 2, 1/6 between; A - 6 cols, 2, 1/6 between; C - 9 cols, 1 3/8, 1/16 between.
Commodity Consumption: Avg. Page Number Per Issue - Daily 28; Avg. Page Number Per Issue - Plates Used 23600; Avg. Page Number Per Issue - Sunday 56; widths 41 3/4; Newsprint Used - Metric Tons 2600; Printing Ink Used - Black 49000; Printing Ink Used - Color 21000; Printing In
Equipment EDITORIAL: Front-end Software – DTI 4.3.; Editorial Hardware – APP/Mac, Sun; Editorial Equipment – HP/1020 Platter; Editorial Printers – APP/Mac LaserPrinter, HPM, Lexmark CLASSIFIED: Front-end Software – Baseview.; Classified Hardware – APP/Mac; Classified Printers – HP/4050 DISPLAY: Ad make-up applications – DTI/311 4.3; Layout Software – DTI 4.3.; Display Hardware – Sun/Servers, APP/Macs; Display Printers – APP/Mac LaserPrinter PRODUCTION: Pagination Software – DTI/Speed Planner 3.1.; Production Equipment – 2-AG/Select 7000, 1-AG/Avantra 25; Cameras – Kl; Scanners – AG/Flatbed PRESSROOM: Line 1 – 6-G/double width 1964. MAILROOM: Counter stackers – 2/QWI; Bundle tying machines – 2-/Power Strap; Wrapping singles – Manual; Addressing machine – Manual, Topping.; Audio Hardware – Software □ Brite BUSINESS COMPUTERS: Business Software – PBS, SBS, Cyborg; Business Hardware – 2-Sun/Ultra 10, Sun/Sparc 20

MUNSTER

NORTHWEST INDIANA NEWSPAPERS, INC.

601 45th Ave., Munster, Ind., 46321; gen tel (219) 933-3200; gen fax (219) 932 3249

THE TIMES

601 W. 45th Ave., Munster, Ind., 46321; gen tel (219) 933-3200; adv tel (219) 933-3255; ed tel (219) 933-3223; gen fax (219) 933-3249; adv fax (219) 933-3332; ed fax (219) 933-3249; gen e-mail comments@nwitimes.com; adv e-mail classifieds@nwitimes.com; ed e-mail letters@nwitimes.com; newstips@nwitimes.com; web site www.nwi.com

Published: Mon, Tues, Wed, Thur, Fri, Sat, Sun
Weekday Frequency: m
Saturday Frequency: m
Circulation: 86,894; 84,586(sat); 91,701(sun)
Last Audit: ABC September 30, 2011
Price: 4.15/wk; 17.98/mo; 120.00/yr.
Advertising: Open inch rate $90.70
News services: AP, CNS.
Politics: Independent. **Established:** 1906
Special Editions: Home Improvement/Lawn & Garden (Apr); Football (Aug); Christmas Gift Guide (Dec); Best of the Region (Feb); Bridal (Jan); Newspapers in Education (Mar); Basketball (Nov); Regional (Oct).
Special Weekly Sections: On the Go (Fri); Your Money (Mon); Forum (S); Religion (Sat); Living (Thur); INK-Issues and News for Kids (Tues); Food (Wed).
Magazines: Color Comics (S).
Pub. .... Bill Masterson
Gen. Mgr., Portage .... Robert Blaszkiewicz
Retail Adv. Mgr., Valparaiso .... Debbie Anselm
Exec. Ed. .... William Nangle
Mng. Ed., News .... Paul Mullaney
Prodn. Foreman, Systems Admin. ..... Mike Gower
Market Information: Split run; TMC; Zoned editions.
Mechanical available: Offset; Black and 3 ROP colors; insert accepted - envelope, card; page cutoffs - 21.
Mechanical Specifications: Type page 13 x 21; E - 6 cols, 2 3/100, 1/6 between; A - 6 cols, 2 3/100, 1/6 between; C - 10 cols, 1 1/4, 1/6 between.
Commodity Consumption: Avg. Page Number Per Issue - Daily 56; Avg. Page Number Per Issue - Plates Used 216000; Avg. Page Number Per Issue - Sunday 96; widths 41 1/4; Newsprint Used - Metric Tons 12960; Newsprint Used - Short Tons 28571; Printing Ink Used - Black 200000; Printi
Equipment EDITORIAL: Front-end Software – Sun/Lotus Notes.; Editorial Hardware – 12-Sun/Sparc, 80-PC; Editorial Printers – HP/Laser, Iptech/RIP CLASSIFIED: Front-end Software – Vision Data.; Classified Hardware – 7-Sun/Sparc, 14-NCD, 6-Sun/Sparc, 2-NCD, 5-PC; Classified Printers – APP/Mac Laser DISPLAY: Ad make-up applications – QPS/QuarkXPress; Layout Software – SCS/Layout 8000, MIE.; Display Hardware – 40-APP/Mac; Display Printers – Iptech/RIP PRODUCTION: Pagination Software – QPS/QuarkXPress 4.11.; Production Equipment – 2-ECR/Pelbox Full-page, 2-APP/Mac Laser, Hyphen/3100, Epson/836XL; Cameras – WL/Digital Camera, Nikon/D1; Scanners – 4-Epson/836XLT, Iptech/RIP PRESSROOM: Line 1 – 8-G/Headliner double width 1989; Line 2 – 8-G/Urbanite single width. MAILROOM: Counter stackers – 3/MM, 1-MM/388, 3-MM/310, 1-/HL; Inserters and stuffers – 4-MM/308, GMA/SLS 2000; Bundle tying machines – 3-/MLN, 2-/OVL, 1-/Sterling, Dynaric; Wrapping singles – 2-KP/KJ; Mailroom control system – GMA/SAM; Addressing machine – 2-/Bar; Business Hardware – Sun/4, COM, 10-PC

NEW ALBANY

TRIBUNE

303 Scribner Dr., New Albany, Ind., 47150; gen tel (812) 944-6481; adv tel (812) 206-2133; ed tel (812) 944-6481; gen fax (812) 206-4598; adv fax (812) 206-4600; ed fax (812) 206-4598; gen e-mail info@newsandtribune.com; web site www.newsandtribune.com

Published: Tues, Wed, Thur, Fri, Sun
Weekday Frequency: e
Circulation: 13,054; 9,854(sun)
Last Audit: September 30, 2005
Price: 2.50/wk; 150.00/yr.
Advertising: Open inch rate $25.73
News services: AP.
Politics: Independent.
Note: The New Albany Tribune (eS) has a combination rate of $23.62 with the Jeffersonville Evening News (e). Individual newspaper rates not made available.
Not Published: Christmas.
Magazines: Color Comics (S).
Gen. Mgr. .... Angela Clark
Circ. Mgr. .... Angie Troncin
Exec. Ed. .... Steve Kozarovich
Mng. Ed. .... Shea Van Hoy
Regl. Ed. .... Chris Morris
Sports Ed. .... Mike Hutsell
Prodn. Mgr. .... Harry Fox
Prodn. Mgr. .... Brandi Jones
Market Information: TMC.
Mechanical available: Offset; Black and 1 ROP colors; insert accepted; page cutoffs - 21 1/2.
Mechanical Specifications: Type page 13 x 21 1/2; E - 6 cols, 2 1/16, 1/8 between; A - 6 cols, 2 1/16, 1/8 between; C - 9 cols, 1 5/16, 1/8 between.
Commodity Consumption: Avg. Page Number Per Issue - Daily 38; Avg. Page Number Per Issue - Sunday 86; widths 27 1/2; Newsprint Used - Short Tons 480; Printing Ink Used - Black 22000; Printing Ink Used - Color 400; Printing Ink Used - Pages Printed 5500.
Equipment; Editorial Hardware – 1-COM/One.; Classified Hardware – 1-COM/One.; Production Equipment – 1-LE; Cameras – 1-LE. PRESSROOM: Line 1 – 8-G; Folders – 1-G/2:1.; Bundle tying machines – 1/Bu; Addressing machine – 1-/Am.; Business Hardware – 2-Auto Tape/9100

NEW CASTLE

THE COURIER-TIMES

201 S. 14th St., New Castle, Ind., 47362; gen tel (765) 529-1111; gen fax (765) 529-1731; adv e-mail shart@thecouriertimes.com; web site www.thecouriertimes.com
Published: Mon, Tues, Wed, Thur, Fri, Sat
Weekday Frequency: m
Circulation: 9,166; 9,166(sat)
Last Audit: September 30, 2003
Price: 2.50/wk; 130.00/yr.
Advertising: Open inch rate $17.00
News services: AP.
Politics: Independent.
Not Published: Christmas.
Special Editions: Travel Guide (Apr); Toolbox (Aug); End-of-Year Clearance (Dec); Progress (Feb); Bridal Tab (Jan); 4-H Tab (Jul); Faces & Places Tab (Jun); Car Care (Mar); Graduation Tab (May); Basketball (Nov); Silver Salute (Oct); Fall Fashion (Sept).
Magazines: USA WEEKEND Magazine (Sat).
Pub. .... Tina West
Bus. Mgr. .... Chris Foreman
Adv. Mgr. .... Scott Hart
Circ. Dir. .... Teresa Blake
Mng. Ed. .... Randy Rendfeld
Neighbors Ed. .... Donna Cronk
News Ed. .... John Hodge
Sports Ed. .... Jeremy Hines
Mechanical available: Web Offset; Black and 3 ROP colors; insert accepted; page cutoffs - 22 3/4.
Mechanical Specifications: Type page 13 x 21 1/2; E - 6 cols, 2 1/16, 1/8 between; A - 6 cols, 2 1/16, 1/8 between; C - 9 cols, 1 3/8, 1/16 between.
Commodity Consumption: Avg. Page Number Per Issue - Daily 20; widths 13 1/2; Newsprint Used - Metric Tons 620.
Equipment; Editorial Hardware – 1-APP/Power Mac 9500, 1-APP/Power Mac 8150, 1-APP/Power Mac 8100, 3-APP/Power Mac 7100, 4-APP/Power Mac 6100, 5-APP/Mac Quadra 630, 1-APP/Mac Quadra 605, 2-APP/Mac PowerBook 150, 2-APP/Mac PowerBook 190, 1-APP/Mac II; Editorial Printers – Xante/Accel-A-W CLASSIFIED: Front-end Software – Baseview, Ad Manager Pro.; Classified Hardware – 4-APP/iMAC, GCC/Elite 12/600; Classified Printers – Okidata/3410 DISPLAY: Ad make-up applications – QPS/QuarkXPress 3.32.; Display Hardware – 1-APP/Power Mac 7300, 2-APP/Power Mac G3, 1-APP/Mac IIci, 1-APP/Mac Color Classic; Display Printers – QMS/860, APP/Mac LaserPrinter II, APP/Mac Laser Writer 8500 PRODUCTION: Pagination Software – QPS/QuarkXPress 3.32.; Production Equipment – Caere/OmniPage 6.0; Cameras – 1-R/580; Scanners – AG/Studio STM, Microtek/ScanMaster IIXE, Minolta/Quick Scan 35, Nikon/Coolscan 2000 PRESSROOM: Line 1 – 5-G/Urbanite 1990; Press Drives – Fin/120hp; Folders – 1 MAILROOM: Counter stackers – 1-BG/Count-O-Veyor 108; Bundle tying machines – 1-Bu/20, 1-Bu/String Tyer, 1-Bu/Tape Wrapper; Addressing machine – 1-Am/6341B. AUDIO: Audio Software – SMS/Stauffer Gold Audiotext System; Audio Hardware – Samsung/Deskmaster 486/33P; Business Hardware – IBM/AS-400

NOBLESVILLE

THE NOBLESVILLE DAILY TIMES

152 S. Ninth St., Noblesville, Ind., 46061-0579; gen tel (317) 770 7777; gen fax (317) 770-5770; ed e-mail rhansen@noblesvilledaily.com; web site www.noblesvilledailytimes.com
Published: Mon, Tues, Wed, Thur, Fri, Sat
Weekday Frequency: m
Price: 77.00/yr.
Advertising: Open inch rate $14.25
Note: This publication switched to an (m-mon to sat) publishing plan from a weekly (thur) publishing plan on June 2, 2003.
Own facility?: Y
Special Editions: American Profile (Weekly).
Pub. .... Terry L. Coomer
Bus. Mgr. .... Chuck Turean
Adv. Dir. .... Jeff Stutesman
Circ. Mgr. .... Lisa Garrett
Ed. .... George Piper

PERU

THE PERU TRIBUNE

26 W. Third St., Peru, Ind., 46970; gen tel (765) 473-6641; gen fax (765) 472-4438; gen e-mail rmitchell@paxtonmedia.com; web site www.perutribune.com
Published: Mon, Tues, Wed, Thur, Fri, Sat
Weekday Frequency: m
Circulation: 6,700; 6,700(sat)
Last Audit: March 25, 2010
Price: 13.75/mo; 161.00/yr.
Advertising: Open inch rate $20.70
News services: AP.
Politics: Independent. **Established:** 1921
Not Published: Christmas.
Special Editions: Business Expo (Apr); This is Miami County (Aug); Christmas Gift Guides (Dec); Girls Basketball (Feb); Soil & Water (Jan); Circus (Jul); Softball Pages (Jun); Spring Farm (Mar); Mother's Day (May); Christmas Opening (Nov); Shopping with Santa (Oct); Fall F
Special Weekly Sections: Business Page (Mon); Milestones (Weddings, Engagements, etc) (Sat); Food Page (Thur); School Page (Wed).
Magazines: Calendar (Annually); Channel Changer (Sat).
Pub. .... Randy Mitchell
Bus. Mgr. .... Patricia Nelson
Adv. Dir. .... Michelle Boswell
Circ. Supvr. .... Eric Steg
Mng. Ed. .... Aaron Turner
News Ed. .... Laurie Kietaber
Sports Ed. .... Austan Kas
Sports Ed. .... Chris Butcher
Market Information: ADS; TMC.
Mechanical available: Offset; Black and 3 ROP colors; insert accepted - single sheets, DOO sizes; page cutoffs - 22 3/4.
Mechanical Specifications: Type page 10 1/8 x 21 1/2; E - 6 cols, 1 5/8, 1/8 between; A - 6 cols, 1 5/8, 1/8 between; C - 9 cols, 1 1/16, 1/8 between.
Commodity Consumption: Avg. Page Number Per Issue - Daily 14; Avg. Page Number Per Issue - Saturday 16; widths 21; Newsprint Used - Metric Tons 345; Printing Ink Used - Black 6558; Printing Ink Used - Color 1380; Printing Ink Used - Pages Printed 6123.
Equipment EDITORIAL: Front-end Software – Baseview/NewsEdit 3.1, QPS/QuarkXPress 3.3.; Editorial Hardware – APP/Mac; Editorial Printers – APP/Mac LaserWriters; Classified Hardware – 2-HI/Micro-Store. DISPLAY: Ad make-up applications – Multi-Ad/Creator 3.5; Layout Software – APP/Mac.; Display Printers – APP/Mac LaserWriter, Xante PRODUCTION: Pagination Software – QPS/QuarkXPress.; Production Equipment – Multi-Ad/Creator 3.5, 2-APP/Mac PRESSROOM: Line 1 – 4-G/Urbanite; Folders – 1-G/2:1; Pasters – 2; Bundle tying machines – 1/Bu, 1-/Plastic Strap; Addressing machine – 1-/WM. AUDIO: Audio Software – SMS/Stauffer Gold; Audio Hardware – SMS, IBM; Business Hardware – IBM/AS-400

PLYMOUTH

PILOT NEWS

214 N. Michigan St., Plymouth, Ind., 46563; gen tel (574) 936-3101; gen fax (574) 936-3844; gen e-mail news@thepilotnews.com; adv e-mail ads@thepilotnews.com; ed e-mail pilot@thepilotnews.com; web site www.thepilotnews.com
Published: Mon, Tues, Wed, Thur, Fri, Sat, Sun
Weekday Frequency: e
Saturday Frequency: m
Circulation: 6,227; 6,227(sat)
Last Audit: September 30, 1998
Price: 90.00/yr (carrier), $96.00/yr (auto), $114.00/yr (mail).
Advertising: Open inch rate $11.75
News services: AP, SHNS.
Politics: Independent-Republican. **Established:** 1851
Not Published: New Year; Memorial Day; Independence Day; Labor Day; Thanksgiving; Christmas.
Magazines: TV Week (Sat); American Profile (Weekly).
Pub. .... Rick A. Kreps
Gen. Mgr. .... Jerry Bingle
Adv. Mgr., Mktg. .... Cindy Stockton
Mng. Ed. .... Maggie Nixon
Sports Ed. .... Dee Grenert
Prodn. Foreman, Composing .... Greg Hildebrand
Market Information: TMC.
Mechanical available: Offset; Black and 3 ROP colors; insert accepted; page cutoffs - 22 3/4.
Mechanical Specifications: Type page 13 x 21 1/2; E - 6 cols, 2 1/16, 1/8 between; A - 6 cols, 2 1/16, 1/8 between; C - 10 cols, 1 3/8, 1/16 between.
Commodity Consumption: Avg. Page Number Per Issue - Daily 12; Avg. Page Number Per Issue - Plates Used 5057; Avg. Page Number Per Issue - Saturday 16; widths 28; Newsprint Used - Short Tons 385; Printing Ink Used - Black 8713; Printing Ink Used - Color 1500; Printing Ink Used
Equipment EDITORIAL: Front-end Software – Baseview.; Editorial Hardware – APP/Mac CLASSIFIED: Front-end Software – Baseview.; Classified Hardware – APP/Mac DISPLAY: Ad make-up applications – QPS/QuarkXPress.; Display Hardware – APP/Mac PRODUCTION: Pagination Software – QPS/QuarkXPress 3.3.; Production Equipment – HP/Laserjet 4, Xante/Accel-a-Writer; Cameras – 1-B/Caravel; Bundle tying machines – 1/Bu; Addressing machine – El/3101.

PORTLAND

THE COMMERCIAL REVIEW

309 W. Main St., Portland, Ind., 47371; gen tel (260) 726-8141; ed tel (260) 726-8142; gen fax (260) 726-8143; adv fax (260) 726-8143; ed fax (260) 726-8143; adv e-mail cr.ads@comcast.net; ed e-mail cr.news@comcast.net; web site www.thecr.com
Published: Mon, Tues, Wed, Thur, Fri, Sat, Sun
Weekday Frequency: e
Saturday Frequency: m
Circulation: 4,813; 4,813(sat)
Last Audit: October 1, 2003
Price: 6.75/mo (city), $7.45/mo (motor route); 74.00/yr (city), $83.00/yr (motor route/mail).
Advertising: Open inch rate $9.00
News services: AP.
Politics: Republican. **Established:** 1871
Not Published: New Year; Memorial Day; Independence Day; Labor Day; Thanksgiving; Christmas.
Special Editions: Spring Sports (Apr); Engine and Tractor Show (Aug); Christmas Greetings (Dec); New Cars (Feb); Brides (Jan); Swiss Days (Jul); Seniors (Jun); Spring Home Improvement (Mar); Graduation (May); Winter Sports (Nov); Harvest (Oct); Fall Home Improvement (Sept)
Magazines: American Profile (Sat).
Chrmn./Pres./Pub. .... John C. Ronald
Bus. Mgr. .... Julie Swoveland
Adv. Mgr., Classified .... Kim Snowden
Adv. Mgr., Promo. .... Jeanne Lutz
News Ed. .... Mike Snyder
Society Ed. .... Virginia Cline
Sports Ed. .... Raymond Cooney
Prodn. Supt. .... Dave Marchand
Prodn. Foreman, Composing .... Brian Todd
Prodn. Foreman, Pressroom ...... James Ridgway
Market Information: TMC.
Mechanical available: Offset; Black and 3 ROP colors; insert accepted; page cutoffs - 22.
Mechanical Specifications: Type page 13 x 21 1/4; E - 6 cols, 2 1/16, 1/8 between; A - 6 cols, 2 1/16, 1/8 between; C - 8 cols, 1 1/2, 1/16 between.
Commodity Consumption: Avg. Page Number Per Issue - Daily 12.6; Avg. Page Number Per Issue - Plates Used 2000; widths 14; Newsprint Used - Short Tons 200; Printing Ink Used - Black 5400; Printing Ink Used - Color 850; Printing Ink Used - Pages Printed 3870.
Equipment EDITORIAL: Front-end Software – Baseview, QPS/QuarkXPress.; Editorial Hardware – APP/Mac; Editorial Printers – APP/Mac CLASSIFIED: Front-end Software – Baseview.; Classified Hardware – APP/Mac; Classified Printers – APP/Mac DISPLAY: Ad make-up applications – QPS/QuarkXPress.; Display Hardware – APP/Mac; Display Printers – APP/Mac LaserPrinter; Production Equipment – APP/Mac LaserPrinters, 1-B/30x40; Cameras – 1-R/20x24; Scanners – HP/ScanJet. PRESSROOM: Line 1 – 5-G/Community (DEV Horizon Stack Unit); Folders – 1 BUSINESS COMPUTERS: Business Software – Great Plains; Business Hardware – IBM/PC-AT

GRAPHIC PRINTING CO., INC.

309 W. Main St., Portland, Ind., 47371; gen tel (260) 726-8141; gen fax (260) 726-8143; adv e-mail cr.ads@comcast.net; ed e-mail cr.news@comcast.net; web site thecr.com
Published: Mon, Tues, Wed, Thur, Fri, Sat
Weekday Frequency: e
Saturday Frequency: m
Price: $0.50 newstand price
Politics: 1891
Advertising not accepted: N
Not Published: New years, Memorial day, July 4th, Labor Day, Tahnksgiving, Christmas
Own facility?: Y
Zip Codes served: 47371, 47326, 47369, 47336, 47373, 45846
Delivery method: Mail, Newsstand, Private Carrier, Racks

PRINCETON

PRINCETON DAILY CLARION

100 N. Gibson St., Princeton, Ind., 47670-0030; gen tel (812) 385-2525; gen fax (812) 386-6199; gen e-mail gblack@pdclarion.com; ed e-mail andrea@pdclarion.com; web site www.pd-clarion.com
Group: Brehm Communications
Published: Mon, Tues, Wed, Thur, Fri
Weekday Frequency: m
Circulation: 6,300
Last Audit: Sworn October 2, 2001
Price: 8.20/mo; 86.00/yr.
Advertising: Open inch rate $13.50
Insert rate: $40/M
News services: AP.
Politics: . **Established:** 1846
Not Published: New Year; Memorial Day; Independence Day; Labor Day; Thanksgiving; Christmas.
Own facility?: Y
Special Weekly Sections: Entertainment Page (Fri); Best Food Day (Mon); Business Page (Thur); Farm Page (Tues).
Pub. .... Gary Blackburn
Bus. Mgr. .... Marietta Nelson
Ed. .... Andrea Howe
Prodn. Mgr. .... Mark Armstrong
ad manager .... Lori Martin
Market Information: ADS; TMC.
Mechanical available: Offset; Black and 3 ROP colors; insert accepted; page cutoffs - 22 3/4.
Mechanical Specifications: Type page 12 x 21 1/2; E - 6 cols, 1 7/10, 1/6 between; A - 6 cols, 1 7/10, 1/6 between; C - 8 cols, 1 1/4, 1/6 between.
Commodity Consumption: Avg. Page Number Per Issue - Daily 14; widths 30; Newsprint Used - Short Tons 795.
Equipment EDITORIAL: Front-end Software – Baseview.; Editorial Hardware – APP/Macs; Ed-

itorial Printers – Pre Press/Panther CLASSIFIED: Front-end Software – Baseview.; Classified Hardware – APP/Macs DISPLAY: Ad make-up applications – Multi-Ad/Creator.; Display Hardware – APP/Mac PRODUCTION: Pagination Software – QPS/QuarkXPress.; Production Equipment – APP/Mac LaserWriters, Pre Press/Kodak CTP PRESSROOM: Line 1 – 8-G/Community.; Inserters and stuffers – 4/KAN; Bundle tying machines – .; Business Hardware – Qantel

Delivery method: Mail, Newsstand, Private Carrier, Racks

RENSSELAER

REPUBLICAN

117 N. Van Rensselaer St., Rensselaer, Ind., 47978; gen tel (219) 866-5111; gen fax (219) 866-3775; ed e-mail editor@rensselaerrepublican.com; web site www.myrepublican.info

Published: Mon, Tues, Wed, Thur, Fri, Sat
Weekday Frequency: m
Circulation: 2,049; 2,049(sat)
Last Audit: September 30, 2003
Price: 1.60/wk; 110.00/yr.
Advertising: Open inch rate $12.00
News services: AP.
Politics: Republican. **Established:** 1866
Not Published: New Year; Memorial Day; Independence Day; Labor Day; Thanksgiving; Christmas.
Special Editions: Football Preview (Aug); Spring Bridal (Feb); Business Established (Jan); Progress (Jun); Ag Day (Mar); Auto News (Monthly); Christmas Tab (Nov); Fall Home Improvement (Sept).
Special Weekly Sections: Church Page (Fri); Youth on the Move (Mon); Farm (Sat); Best Food Day (Thur); Business News (Tues); Farm (Wed).
Magazines: Final Score (school year) (Monthly); Farm Focus (newsprint tab) (Other).
Pub. .... Don L. Hurd
Exec. Ed. .... Clayton Doty
Sports Ed. .... Harley Tomlinson
Prodn. Mgr. .... Misty Longstreth
Market Information: TMC; Zoned editions.
Mechanical available: Offset; Black and 2 ROP colors; insert accepted; page cutoffs - 22 3/4.
Mechanical Specifications: Type page 13 x 21 1/2; E - 6 cols, 2, 1/4 between; A - 6 cols, 2, 1/4 between; C - 9 cols, 1/4 between.
Commodity Consumption: Avg. Page Number Per Issue - Daily 12; Avg. Page Number Per Issue - Plates Used 6024; Avg. Page Number Per Issue - Saturday 12; widths 27 1/2; Newsprint Used - Short Tons 210; Printing Ink Used - Black 10800; Printing Ink Used - Color 750; Printing Ink U
Equipment EDITORIAL: Front-end Software – Baseview/NewsEdit 3.25, QPS/QuarkXPress 3.2.; Editorial Hardware – 2-APP/Mac 610, 9-APP/Mac LC II; Editorial Printers – APP/Mac LaserWriter Pro, APP/Mac LaserWriter IIg CLASSIFIED: Front-end Software – Mk/Newscraft.; Classified Hardware – 2-Ultra/486D-40; Classified Printers – 2-Epson/LQ 1170 DISPLAY: Ad make-up applications – Multi-Ad 3.8, Adobe/Photoshop 2.5.1, QPS/QuarkXPress 3.2, Broderbund/Typestyler 2.0; Display Hardware – 3-APP/Mac Quadra; Display Printers – APP/Mac LaserWriter 16 600 PS, APP/Mac LaserWriter Pro 630 PRODUCTION: Pagination Software – QPS/QuarkXPress 3.2.; Production Equipment – Nu/FT40V2UP; Cameras – SCREEN/680-C; Scanners – Microtek/ScanMaker IIsp, Microtek/ScanMaker IIIxe PRESSROOM: Line 1 – 5-HI/V-15D single width 1994; Folders – HI/JF-25; Reels and Stands – 5 MAILROOM: Counter stackers – BG/Count-O-Veyor 08; Bundle tying machines – 1-EAM-Mosca/Strapper, 1/Miller-Bevco/Strapper; Addressing machine – 2-/Address-matic. BUSINESS COMPUTERS: Business Software – Lotus 1-2-3, Microsoft/Excel, Microsoft/Office, Listmaster; Business Hardware – 1-PC 386, 1-PC 486, APP/Mac LC III

RICHMOND

PALLADIUM-ITEM

1175 N. A St., Richmond, Ind., 47374; gen tel (765) 962-1575; adv tel (765) 973-4422; ed tel (765) 962-1575; gen fax (765) 973-4570; adv fax (765) 973-4440; ed fax (765) 973-4570; web site www.pal-item.com

Published: Mon, Tues, Wed, Thur, Fri, Sat, Sun
Weekday Frequency: m
Saturday Frequency: m
Circulation: 9,865; 9,865(sat); 15,654(sun)
Last Audit: ABC September 30, 2011
Price: 3.25/wk; 169.00/yr.
Advertising: Open inch rate $50.05
News services: AP, GNS.
Politics: 1831
Special Editions: Progress (Apr); Newcomer's Community Guide (Aug); Bridal (Feb); Farm (Jan); Home Improvement (Jul); Home Improvement (Jun); Racing (May); Home Improvement (Sept).
Special Weekly Sections: Education (Mon); Automotive Sunday (S); Business (Sat); Entertainment (Thur); Farm (Wed).
Magazines: USA WEEKEND Magazine (S).
Bus. Mgr. .... Mike Chamberlain
Adv. Dir. .... Paige O'Neal
Adv. Mgr., Classified Sales .... Johnny Martinez
Circ. Dir. .... Cheryl Joyce
Exec. Ed. .... Micket Johnson
Asst. Mng. Ed. .... Brian Guth
Editorial Page Ed. .... Dale McConnaughay
Prodn. Mgr., Distr. .... David Davis
Sports Ed. .... Josh Chapin
Market Information: TMC.
Mechanical available: Offset; Black and 3 ROP colors; insert accepted - single sheets; page cutoffs - 22.
Mechanical Specifications: Type page 11 63/100 x 21; E - 6 cols, 2 1/16, 1/8 between; A - 6 cols, 1 5/6, 1/8 between; C - 9 cols, 1 6/25, 1/8 between.
Commodity Consumption: Avg. Page Number Per Issue - Daily 20; Avg. Page Number Per Issue - Plates Used 38400; Avg. Page Number Per Issue - Sunday 61; widths 27 1/4; Newsprint Used - Metric Tons 1200; Printing Ink Used - Black 32000; Printing Ink Used - Color 12000; Printing In
Equipment EDITORIAL: Front-end Software – Microsoft/Windows 95, Microsoft/Word, QPS/QuarkXPress.; Editorial Hardware – APT; Editorial Printers – HP CLASSIFIED: Front-end Software – APT.; Classified Hardware – APT; Classified Printers – HP DISPLAY: Ad make-up applications – Multi-Ad/Creator 4.04, QPS/QuarkXPress 4.1, Adobe/Illustrator, Adobe/PhotoShop 5.0; Layout Software – CNI.; Display Hardware – CNI; Display Printers – GCC PRODUCTION: Pagination Software – QPS/QuarkXPress.; Production Equipment – 3-Nu/Flip Top FT4OV6UPNS, 1-Anitec; Cameras – C/Spartan III; Scanners – 2-GEI/Copydot 1000, Lf/Leafscan 35, Umax/8 PRESSROOM: Line 1 – 18-G/Urbanite single width 1984; Line 2 – 4-HI/V15A-6%; Folders – 2; Reels and Stands – G/2-Arm RTP. MAILROOM: Counter stackers – 1-PPK/Ministack, 2/MM, 2-QWI/350, QWI/GC610; Inserters and stuffers – 1-MM/EM 101, 1-GMA/SLS 1000; Bundle tying machines – 3-/MLN, 1-Sa/Twine, Power Strap, OVL; Wrapping singles – 1-/Sa; Addressing machine – 1-/Barstrom, 1-/Ch.; Business Hardware – IBM/AS-400

ROCHESTER

THE ROCHESTER SENTINEL

118 E. Eighth St., Rochester, Ind., 46975; gen tel (574) 223-2111; adv tel (574) 224-5323; ed tel (574) 223-2111; gen fax (574) 223-5782; adv fax (574) 223-5782; ed fax (574) 223-5782; adv e-mail ads@rochsent.com; ed e-mail news@rochsent.com; web site www.rochsent.com

Published: Mon, Tues, Wed, Thur, Fri, Sat, Sun
Weekday Frequency: e
Saturday Frequency: m
Circulation: 3,761; 3,761(sat)
Last Audit: October 1, 2004
Price: 13.00/mo (foot carrier); 135.00/yr(foot carrier); 13.50/mo(moto carrier) 141.00/yr(moto carrier).
Advertising: Open inch rate $9.88
News services: AP, CNS, TMS.
Politics: Independent. **Established:** 1850
Not Published: New Year; Memorial Day; Independence Day; Labor Day; Thanksgiving; Christmas.
Special Editions: Financial (Apr); High School Football (Aug); Year-in-Review (Dec); Basketball (Feb); Taxes (Jan); 4-H Fair (Jul); Home, Lawn, Garden (Mar); Graduates (May); Christmas Shopping (Nov); New Car Showing (Oct); Senior Lifestyle (Sept).
Special Weekly Sections: TV Guide (Sat).
Magazines: American Profile (Sat).
Pres. .... Jack K. Overmyer
Vice Pres./Treasurer .... Margery H. Overmyer
Pub. .... Sarah Overmyer Wilson
Adv. Dir. .... Karen Vojtasek
Circ. Mgr. .... Gary Roe
Ed. .... William S. Wilson
Lifestyles Ed. .... Rhonda Johnson
News Ed. .... Christina Seiler
Photo Dept. Mgr. .... Michael Kenny
Sports Ed. .... Val Tsoutsouris
Market Information: TMC.
Mechanical available: Offset; Black and 3 ROP colors; insert accepted; page cutoffs - 22 1/2.
Mechanical Specifications: Type page 13 x 21 1/2; E - 6 cols, 2 1/6, 1/6 between; A - 6 cols, 2 1/6, 1/6 between; C - 6 cols, 2 1/6, 1/6 between.
Commodity Consumption: Avg. Page Number Per Issue - Daily 12; Avg. Page Number Per Issue - Plates Used 3000; widths 27 1/2; Newsprint Used - Short Tons 200; Printing Ink Used - Black 5700; Printing Ink Used - Color 200; Printing Ink Used - Pages Printed 3800.
Equipment EDITORIAL: Front-end Software – QPS/QuarkXPress 3.3, Freedom Systems Intergrator/Vanguard Edi; Editorial Hardware – 3-APP/Power Mac, 5-APP/iMac; Editorial Equipment – 2-APP/Mac PowerBook, APP/Power Mac 7200 File Server, APP/Mac Quadra 610 Wire Server, Scanners; Editorial Printers – Xante/Accel-a-Writer 36 CLASSIFIED: Front-end Software – Baseview/Ad Pro.; Classified Hardware – 1-APP/Mac DISPLAY: Ad make-up applications – Multi-Ad/Creator; Layout Software – QPS/QuarkXPress.; Display Hardware – 2-APP/iMac; Display Printers – 1-QMS/LaserWriter 600 dpi PRODUCTION: Pagination Software – QPS/QuarkXPress 3.3.; Scanners – Nikon; Line 4 – 1-HI/Cotrell V-15A Offset 1977.; Bundle tying machines – 1-Bu/169D. BUSINESS COMPUTERS: Business Software – Baseview/Ad Pro, Peachtree: Accts Payable, AR Works; Business Hardware – HP/Pavilion, APP/Mac G-3

THE SENTINEL CORP.

118 E. 8th St., Rochester, Ind., 46975; gen tel (574) 223-2111; gen fax (574) 223-5782; gen e-mail karenv@rochsent.com; web site www.rochsent.com

Published: Mon, Tues, Wed, Thur, Fri, Sat, Sun
Price: 117.00/yr.
Advertising: Open inch rate $7.44

RUSHVILLE

RUSHVILLE NEWSPAPERS, INC.

219 N. Perkins St., Rushville, Ind., 46173; gen tel (765) 932-2222; gen fax (765) 932-4358

RUSHVILLE REPUBLICAN

126 S. Main St., Rushville, Ind., 46173-0189; gen tel (765) 932-2222; gen fax (765) 932-4358; gen e-mail rushvillerepublican@rushvillerepublican.com ; web site www.rushvillerepublican.com

Group: U.S. Suburban Press, Inc.
Published: Mon, Tues, Wed, Thur, Fri, Sat
Weekday Frequency: e
Circulation: 3,682; 3,682(sat)
Last Audit: October 1, 2001
Price: 8.88/mo; 110.00/yr (carrier), $112.00/yr (mail, in county), $118.00/yr (mail, out of county).
Advertising: Open inch rate $13.65
News services: AP.
Politics: Independent. **Established:** 1840
Not Published: Memorial Day; Independence Day; Labor Day; Thanksgiving; Christmas.
Special Editions: Football (Aug); Progress (Feb); Rush County Fair (Jul); Farm Fest (Mar); Graduation (May); Christmas Opening (Nov); Women in Business (Oct); Home Improvement (Sept).
Special Weekly Sections: Church (Fri); Agriculture (Mon); School (Thur).
Magazines: Relish (Monthly); American Profile (Weekly).
Adv. Mgr. .... Marilyn Land
Mng. Ed. .... Kevin Green
Sports Ed. .... Aaron Kirchoff
Graphic Arts Dir. .... Susan Peters
Market Information: TMC.
Mechanical available: Offset; Black and 3 ROP colors; insert accepted; page cutoffs - 21 1/2.
Mechanical Specifications: Type page 13 x 21 1/2; E - 6 cols, 2 1/16, 1/8 between; A - 6 cols, 2 1/16, 1/8 between; C - 8 cols, 1 17/32, 1/8 between.
Commodity Consumption: Avg. Page Number Per Issue - Daily 12.
Equipment EDITORIAL: Front-end Software – QPS/QuarkXPress 2.12, Baseview/NewsEdit.; Editorial Hardware – 4-APP/Mac; Editorial Printers – APP/Mac LaserPro 630, APP/Mac LaserWriter, APP/Mac LaserWriter Plus CLASSIFIED: Front-end Software – Baseview/Class Manager, QPS/QuarkXPress 3.0.; Classified Hardware – APP/Mac SE30, APP/Mac IIsi, APP/Mac ImageWriter; Classified Printers – APP/Mac LaserWriter; Layout Software – APP/Mac SE30.; Display Hardware – Printers □ APP/Mac LaserWriter; Display Printers – Software □ Multi-Ad/Creator PRODUCTION: Pagination Software – QPS/QuarkXPress, Adobe/Photoshop.; Production Equipment – Caere/OmniPage, Microtek/ScanMaker II Flatbed; Cameras – 1-Nu PRESSROOM: Line 1 – G.; Bundle tying machines – 2/Bu; Addressing machine – ATT.

SEYMOUR

THE TRIBUNE

100 St. Louis Ave., Seymour, Ind., 47274; gen tel (812) 522-4871; adv tel (812) 523-7052; ed tel (812) 523-7051; gen fax (812) 523-0907; adv fax (812) 522-7691; ed fax (812) 522-3371; gen e-mail tribune@tribtown.com; adv e-mail advertising@tribtown.com; ed e-mail news@tribtown.com; web site www.tribtown.com

Group: Freedom Communications
Published: Mon, Tues, Wed, Thur, Fri, Sat
Weekday Frequency: All day
Saturday Frequency: All day
Circulation: 8,951; 8,951(sat)
Last Audit: October 1, 2003
Price: $4.15/wk; $171.60/yr.
News services: AP, Freedom Wire, Knight Ridder
Politics: Independent. **Established:** 1877
Not Published: Sunday
Own facility?: Y
Pub. .... Richard Davis
Bus./HR Mgr. .... Hue Cunningham
Adv. Dir. .... Scott Embry
Circ. Dir. .... Tom Kesterson
Ed. .... Dan Davis
Commun./Copy Ed. .... Joanne Persinger
Page Ed. .... Michael Brabley
Sports Ed. .... Zach Spicer

Equipment PRESSROOM: Line 1 – 4-G/Urbanite (retired)

SHELBYVILLE

THE SHELBYVILLE NEWS

123 E. Washington St., Shelbyville, Ind., 46176; gen tel (317) 398-6631; gen fax (317) 398-0194; gen e-mail shelbynews@shelbynews.com; web site www.shelbynews.com
Group: U.S. Suburban Press, Inc.
Published: Mon, Tues, Wed, Thur, Fri, Sat, Sun
Weekday Frequency: e
Saturday Frequency: m
Circulation: 8,315; 8,315(sat)
Last Audit: September 30, 2006
Price: 13.25/mo; 149.00/yr .
Advertising: Open inch rate $17.00
News services: AP Graphics, MCT, NEA, SHNS, AP.
Politics: Independent. **Established:** 1947
Not Published: Christmas.
Special Editions: Home & Garden (Apr); Santa Letters and Coloring Book (Dec); Girls Sectional Preview (Feb); Health & Fitness (Jan); Back-to-School (Jul); Shelby County Fair (Jun); Car Care (May); Holiday Gift Guide (Nov); Home Improvement (Oct); Shelby County Profiles (Se
Magazines: USA WEEKEND Magazine (Sat).
Pub. .... Rachael Raney
Bus. Mgr. .... Chris Foreman
Adv. Dir. .... Jody Street
Asst. Ed. .... Mark Swincher
Chief Photographer .... Dayla Thurston
Sports Ed. .... Jeff Brown
Market Information: TMC.
Mechanical available: Offset; Black and 3 ROP colors; insert accepted; page cutoffs - 22 3/4.
Mechanical Specifications: Type page 10 1/8 x 21 1/2; E - 6 cols, 1 19/32, 1/8 between; A - 6 cols, 1 5/6, 1/8 between; C - 9 cols, 1 13/32, 1/8 between.
Commodity Consumption: Avg. Page Number Per Issue - Daily 20; Avg. Page Number Per Issue - Plates Used 5400; Avg. Page Number Per Issue - Saturday 20; widths 25; Newsprint Used - Short Tons 483; Printing Ink Used - Black 15109; Printing Ink Used - Color 2500; Printing Ink Used
Equipment EDITORIAL: Front-end Software – Baseview.; Editorial Hardware – Baseview, APP/Mac; Editorial Printers – Lexmark/Optra RN Plus CLASSIFIED: Front-end Software – Baseview.; Classified Hardware – Baseview, APP/Mac; Classified Printers – Lexmark/Optra DISPLAY: Ad make-up applications – QPS, Multi-Ad/Creator, Aldus/Freehand, Adobe/Photoshop, Adobe/Illustrator; Layout Software – Multi-Ad/ALS 2.0.2.; Display Hardware – APP/Power Macs; Display Printers – Lexmark/Optra Rnt PRODUCTION: Pagination Software – QPS/QuarkXPress 4.1.; Production Equipment – Caere/OmniPage Pro 6, 2-Harlequin/RIP, Pre Press/Panther Pro 46 with Ap Power Mac 8500 PC RIP, Kk/RFS; Cameras – SCREEN/C680-C; Scanners – Kk/RFS 2035, AG/Arcus, Umax/PowerBook, Nikon/LS1000 PRESSROOM: Line 1 – 8-G/SC, 1-G/SSC UOP single width; Line 2 – 2-G/SSC single width; Line 3 – 1-G/SSC UOP single width; Folders – 2-G/2:1; Pasters – 2-Butler/Automatic. MAILROOM: Counter stackers – 2-BG/105; Inserters and stuffers – 6-KAN/320, 7-KAN/760; Bundle tying machines – 3/Bu. BUSINESS COMPUTERS: Business Software – Great Plains, Baseview; Business Hardware – APP/Mac, Baseview

SOUTH BEND

SOUTH BEND TRIBUNE

225 W. Colfax Ave., South Bend, Ind., 46626; gen tel (574) 235-6161; adv tel (574) 235-6389 (retail); ed tel (574) 235-6161; gen fax (574) 236-1765; adv fax (574) 239-2648; ed fax (574) 236-1765; gen e-mail sbt-news@sbtinfo.com; adv e-mail classifieds@sbtinfo.com; csmith@sbtinfo.com; ed e-mail letters@sbtinfo.com; web site www.southbendtribune.com
Group: Metro Newspaper Advertising Services, Inc.
Published: Mon, Tues, Wed, Thur, Fri, Sat, Sun
Weekday Frequency: m
Saturday Frequency: m
Circulation: 62,107; 67,622(sat); 80,542(sun)
Last Audit: ABC September 30, 2011
Price: 11.80/mo; 130.32/yr.
Advertising: Open inch rate $88.56
News services: AP, SHNS, PR Newswire.
Politics: Independent.
Not Published: Christmas.
Special Weekly Sections: Faith (Fri); Food Focus (Mon); Automotion (S); Farming (Sat); Family (Tues); Our Health (Wed).
Magazines: TV Magazine (S).
Vice Pres./Gen. Mgr. .... Steve Funk
Vice Pres., Admin. .... Ed Henry
Controller .... Mark Hocker
Mgr., HR .... Racquel Harris
Purchasing Agent .... Leslie Winey
Adv. Dir. .... Carol Smith
Adv. Dir., Flagship .... Mike Pozzi
Adv. Mgr., Classified .... Mary Zenor
Circ. Dir., Subscriber Servs./Alternate Delivery Kevin Shaw
Circ. Mgr., East Zone .... Bob Emerson
Circ. Mgr., Opns. .... Pam Bishop
Circ. Mgr., Sales/Retention .... Terry Bauer
Circ. Mgr., Transportation .... Frank Rice
Circ. Asst., Subscriber Servs./Training Mgr. Tom Myers
Ed. .... David Ray
Mng. Ed. .... Tim Harmon
Editorial Page Ed. .... Gayle Dantzler
Asst. Editorial Page Ed. .... Alesia Redding
Features Ed. .... Chris Benninghoff
Market Information: ADS; Split run; TMC; Zoned editions.
Mechanical available: Anilox Keyless Offset; Black and 3 ROP colors; insert accepted; page cutoffs - 21 3/16.
Mechanical Specifications: Type page 13 x 22 1/4; E - 6 cols, 2 1/16, 1/8 between; A - 6 cols, 2 1/16, 1/8 between; C - 10 cols, 1 3/16, 1/16 between.
Commodity Consumption: Avg. Page Number Per Issue - Daily 48; Avg. Page Number Per Issue - Plates Used 72540; Avg. Page Number Per Issue - Sunday 114; widths 55; Newsprint Used - Metric Tons 10886; Newsprint Used - Short Tons 12000; Printing Ink Used - Black 440000; Printing I
Equipment EDITORIAL: Front-end Software – Dewar.; Editorial Hardware – Compaq/Alpha-NT CLASSIFIED: Front-end Software – Compuclass.; Classified Hardware – Compaq/Alpha-NT DISPLAY: Ad make-up applications – AD-Tracker; Layout Software – AD-Tracker.; Display Hardware – 8-APP/Mac, 3-PC, Compaq/Alpha-NT; Display Printers – V/600dpi, X/VP300 Proofer, III/VP600 Proofer, Tektronix/Phaser 300, color proofer, HP/755 PRODUCTION: Pagination Software – Dewar.; Production Equipment – 3-III/3850 Negative Output Devices, 2-Linotype-Hell/Lino 530; Cameras – 2-C/Marathon, 1-K/v241; Scanners – 1-III/Infoscan 3725, 1-ScanView/ScanMate 5000, Horizon/Flatbed PRESSROOM: Line 1 – 20-KBA/Anilox Keyless Offset double width 1994; Folders – 1-KBA/gear, 2-KBA/jaw; Reels and Stands – Aug-94; Press control system – 1994 MAILROOM: Counter stackers – 6-S; Inserters and stuffers – 2-Fg/Drum 6:1, HI 630 13:1; Bundle tying machines – 6-MVP/5000, 6-MVP/2000; Other equipment –Mc.; Audio Hardware – Brite BUSINESS COMPUTERS: Business Software – GEAC, CIS 7.05, AIM 8.02H; Business Hardware – 1-DEC/VAX 4000-300, 1-DEC/VAX 400-705

SPENCER

SPENCER EVENING WORLD

114 E. Franklin St., Spencer, Ind., 47460; gen tel (812) 829-2255; gen fax (812) 829-4666; ed e-mail editor@spencereveningworld.com; web site www.spencereveningworld.com
Published: Mon, Tues, Wed, Thur, Fri
Weekday Frequency: m
Circulation: 3,590
Last Audit: September 30, 2003
Price: 52.00/yr.
Advertising: Open inch rate $5.00
Politics: Democrat. **Established:** 1927
Not Published: New Year; Memorial Day; Independence Day; Labor Day; Thanksgiving; Christmas.
Dir., Publications .... Tom Gillaspy
Gen. Mgr. .... John A. Gillaspy
Editor .... Travis Curry
Prodn. Mgr. .... Philip Gillaspy
Circulation, Ad Sales .... Kim Bray
Circ. Dir. .... Kin Bray
Market Information: TMC.
Mechanical available: Offset; Black and 2 ROP colors; insert accepted; page cutoffs - 22 3/4.
Mechanical Specifications: Type page 15 1/8 x 21; E - 7 cols, 2 1/16, 1/8 between; A - 7 cols, 2 1/16, 1/8 between; C - 7 cols, 2 1/16, 1/8 between.
Commodity Consumption: Avg. Page Number Per Issue - Daily 8; widths 32.
Equipment; Production Equipment – 2-APP/Mac Laser, 1-B/2500; Cameras – 1-K/240, 1-R; Scanners – Microtek. PRESSROOM: Line 1 – 4-G/Community.; Bundle tying machines – 1-Bu/29480; Addressing machine – 1-El/300; Other equipment –CH.

SULLIVAN

THE SULLIVAN DAILY TIMES

115 W. Jackson St., Sullivan, Ind., 47882-0130; gen tel (812) 268-6356; gen fax (812) 268-3110; gen e-mail publisher@sullivan-times.com; web site www.sullivan-times.com
Published: Mon, Tues, Wed, Thur, Fri
Weekday Frequency: e
Circulation: 4,115
Last Audit: September 30, 2003
Price: 1.15/wk (carrier); 6.00/mo (motor route); 63.00/yr (mail).
Advertising: Open inch rate $9.00
News services: AP.
Politics: Democrat.
Not Published: New Year; Memorial Day; Independence Day; Labor Day; Thanksgiving; Christmas.
Special Editions: Home & Garden (Apr); Sports (Aug); Christmas (Dec); Ag Tab (Feb); Ag Tab (Jan); Ag Tab (Mar); Dollar Days (May); Christmas (Nov); Home & Garden (Oct).
Special Weekly Sections: Religion (Fri); Agriculture (Mon); Nostalgia (Thur); Business (Tues); Opinion (Wed).
Magazines: Senior (Citizen) Informant (Monthly); TV Times (Thur).
Gen. Mgr. .... Tom P. Gettinger
Bus. Mgr. .... Patricia Morgan
Circ. Mgr. .... Tina Baker
Mng. Ed. .... Nancy P. Gettinger
Sports Ed. .... Rick Curl
Prodn. Mgr. .... John McMillikan
Mechanical available: Offset; Black and 2 ROP colors; insert accepted; page cutoffs - 21.
Mechanical Specifications: Type page 13 3/8 x 21; E - 6 cols, 2 1/12, 1/6 between; A - 6 cols, 2 1/12, 1/6 between; C - 6 cols, 2 1/12, 1/6 between.
Commodity Consumption: Avg. Page Number Per Issue - Daily 10; Avg. Page Number Per Issue - Plates Used 1400; widths 28; Newsprint Used - Metric Tons 1120; Printing Ink Used - Black 1056; Printing Ink Used - Color 10; Printing Ink Used - Pages Printed 50000.
Equipment EDITORIAL: Front-end Software – SunType, QPS/QuarkXPress, Adobe/Photoshop.; Editorial Hardware – 4-APP/iMac, PC 486, PC 386 DX; Editorial Printers – Xante/11x17 CLASSIFIED: Front-end Software – SunType, QPS/QuarkXPress, Adobe/Photo-Shop.; Classified Hardware – 5-Pentium/PC DISPLAY: Ad make-up applications – Advent/3B2, Archetype/Corel Draw, QPS/QuarkXPress, Adobe/Photoshop; Layout Software – APP/Power Mac 7100, APP/Power-Mac 7100.; Display Hardware – APP/Mac 8000, APP/Mac Scanner; Display Printers – Xante/11x17 PRODUCTION: Pagination Software – QPS/QuarkXPress, Adobe/PhotoShop.; Cameras – R/500; Scanners – APP/Mac PRESSROOM: Line 1 – 4-HI/V-15A 1973; Folders – HI/J-7.; Bundle tying machines – Sa. BUSINESS COMPUTERS: Business Software – Synaptic/Micro Solutions; Business Hardware – PC 386 DX, PC 286

TERRE HAUTE

THE TRIBUNE STAR

222 S. Seventh St., Terre Haute, Ind., 47807; gen tel (812) 231-4200; adv tel (812) 231-4215; ed tel (812) 231-4200; gen fax (812) 231-4347; adv fax (812) 231-4234; ed fax (812) 231-4321; gen e-mail community@tribstar.com; adv e-mail advertising@tribstar.com; web site www.tribstar.com; www.terrehauteliving.com
Published: Mon, Tues, Wed, Thur, Fri, Sat, Sun
Weekday Frequency: m
Saturday Frequency: m
Circulation: 21,479; 21,479(sat); 24,767(sun)
Last Audit: September 30, 2009
Advertising: Open inch rate $50.55
News services: AP, MCT.
Politics: Independent.
Special Weekly Sections: Entertainment (Fri); Best Food Day (Mon); Religion (Sat); Education (Wed).
Magazines: Terre Haute Living (Every other month); Valley Homes Tab (Fri); Parade (S).
Pub. .... William (B.J.) Riley
Adv. Dir. .... Robert Miller
Adv. Mgr., Retail .... Tanya Wilhoyte
Mktg. Dir. .... Courtney Zellars
Circ. Mgr., Single Copy .... Kyle Poorman
Ed. .... Max Jones
Columnist .... Mark Bennett
News Ed. .... Susan Duncan
Online Ed. .... Sheila K. Ter Meer
Sports Ed. .... Todd Golden
Prodn. Dir. .... Brian Lane
Prodn. Supt., Press .... Terry Lambert
Prodn. Foreman, Composing .... David Bonham
Market Information: ADS; TMC.
Mechanical available: Offset; Black and 3 ROP colors; insert accepted; page cutoffs - 22 3/4.
Mechanical Specifications: Type page 11 3/4 x 21 1/2; E - 6 cols, 1 5/6, 1/8 between; A - 6 cols, 1 5/6, 1/8 between; C - 9 cols, 1 5/6, 1/16 between.
Commodity Consumption: Avg. Page Number Per Issue - Daily 34; Avg. Page Number Per Issue - Plates Used 35750; Avg. Page Number Per Issue - Sunday 114; widths 12 1/2; Newsprint Used - Short Tons 3300; Printing Ink Used - Black 86500; Printing Ink Used - Color 13500; Printing In
Equipment EDITORIAL: Front-end Software – CText/AFM, Baseview, Baseview/NewsEdit Pro I Que.; Editorial Hardware – DEC, APP/Mac CLASSIFIED: Front-end Software – CText/Classified Advertising System, Baseview/Ad Manager Pro.; Classified Hardware – DEC, APP/MAC DISPLAY: Ad make-up applications – Managing Editor/ALS, QPS/QuarkXPress; Layout Software – APP/Mac.; Display Hardware – APP/Mac PRODUCTION: Pagination Software – QPS/QuarkXPress.; Production Equipment – X, Pre Press/Panther Pro, Pre Press/Panther Pro 46; Cameras – 1-B/1822, 1-LC/21121; Scanners – 1-Lf/Leafscan 35, 1-Sharp/JX600, 2-Nikon/Super Coolscan, 2-Polaroid/SprintScan 35 PRESSROOM: Line 1 – 10-G/Urbanite 1978; Folders – 2; Pasters – 3; Reels and Stands – 4 MAILROOM: Counter stackers – 2-Id/2000; Inserters and stuffers – 1-GMA/SLS 1000, 1-GMA/SLS 2000 12:1; Bundle tying machines – 2-Dynaric/NP2; Addressing machine – 1/Ch.; Audio Hardware – Software ☐ Zimmers Interactive BUSINESS COMPUTERS:

Business Software – PBS; Business Hardware – HP/9000

TRIBUNE-STAR PUBLISHING CO., INC.
222 S 7th St., Terre Haute, Ind., 47808-0149; gen tel (812) 231-4200; gen fax (812) 231-4234
Published: Mon, Tues, Wed, Thur, Fri, Sat, Sun
Weekday Frequency: m
Saturday Frequency: m
Circulation: 20,093; 20,093(sat); 23,978(sun)
Last Audit: ABC September 30, 2011

TIPTON

TIPTON COUNTY TRIBUNE
116 S. Main St., Ste. A, Tipton, Ind., 46072; gen tel (765) 675-2115; adv tel (765) 675-2115; ed tel (765) 675-2115; adv fax (765) 675-4147; ed fax (765) 675-4147; gen e-mail tiptontribune@elwoodpublishing.com; web site www.elwoodpublishing.com
Published: Mon, Tues, Wed, Thur, Fri, Sat, Sun
Weekday Frequency: e
Saturday Frequency: m
Circulation: 2,816; 2,816(sat)
Last Audit: September 30, 2000
Price: 7.00/mo (carrier), $8.00/mo (motor route); 108.00, $75.60/yr (carrier).
Advertising: Open inch rate $9.00
News services: AP.
Politics: Independent.
Not Published: New Year; Memorial Day; Independence Day; Labor Day; Thanksgiving; Christmas.
Special Editions: Farm & Garden (Apr); Football Preview (Aug); Mature Years (Jan); Mature Years (Jul); Spring Brides (Mar); Spring Home Improvement (May); Christmas Opening (Nov); Fall Home Improvement (Oct).
Magazines: What's On TV (Fri); The Mini-Page (Tues).
Pub. ....Robert L. Nash
Asst. Pub ....Brian Barnes
Adv. Mgr. ....Mike Brown
News Ed. ....Jackie Henry
Sports Ed. ....Michelle Garmon
Prodn. Mgr., Pre Press ....Chris Idlewine
Prodn. Mgr., Pressroom ....Randy Bayne
Market Information: ADS; TMC.
Mechanical available: Web Offset; Black and 3 ROP colors; insert accepted; page cutoffs - 22 3/4.
Mechanical Specifications: Type page 13 x 21 1/2; E - 6 cols, 2 1/16, 1/8 between; A - 6 cols, 2 1/16, 1/8 between; C - 8 cols, 1 1/2, 1/32 between.
Commodity Consumption: Avg. Page Number Per Issue - Daily 10; Avg. Page Number Per Issue - Plates Used 2150; Avg. Page Number Per Issue - Saturday 10; widths 27 1/2; Newsprint Used - Metric Tons 65; Newsprint Used - Short Tons 72; Printing Ink Used - Black 2160; Printing Ink U
Equipment EDITORIAL: Front-end Software – Mk/Mycro-Comp.; Editorial Hardware – Mk/1100 CLASSIFIED: Front-end Software – Mk/Mycro-Comp.; Classified Hardware – Mk/1100; Layout Software – 2-APP/Mac SE.; Production Equipment – 2-APP/Mac LaserWriter II NT/NTX; Cameras – 1-R/Commodore. PRESSROOM: Line 1 – 4-G/Community; Folders – 1; Bundle tying machines – 1/Malow, 1-/Bu.; Business Hardware – 1-Bs/B-20, 1-RSK/TRS 80 model 4

VINCENNES

VINCENNES SUN-COMMERCIAL
702 Main St., Vincennes, Ind., 47591; gen tel (812) 886-9955; adv tel (812) 886-9955; ed tel (812) 886-9955; gen fax (812) 885-2235; adv fax (812) 885-2237; ed fax (812) 885-2237; gen e-mail vscnews@suncommercial.com; adv e-mail retail@suncommercial.com; classified@suncommercial.com; circulation@suncommercial.com; ed e-mail newstip@suncommercial.com; web site www.suncommercial.com
Published: Mon, Tues, Wed, Thur, Fri, Sun
Weekday Frequency: e
Circulation: 8,841; 10,605(sun)
Last Audit: September 30, 2007
Price: 3.15/wk; 12.25/mo; 147.00/yr.
Advertising: Open inch rate $24.12
News services: AP.
Politics: Independent. **Established:** 1931
Special Editions: County Fair (Aug); Basketball (Feb); Farm (Mar).
Special Weekly Sections: Real Estate (S); Best Food Day (Wed).
Magazines: USA WEEKEND Magazine (S).
Pub. ....Vickie K. Palmer
Adv. Dir. ....Shanon O'Toole
Circ. Mgr. ....George Roark
Asst. Ed ....Dave Staver
Editorial Page Ed. ....Gayle Robbins
Women's Ed. ....Susan Wright
Market Information: TMC.
Mechanical available: Offset; Black and 3 ROP colors; insert accepted; page cutoffs - 22 3/4.
Mechanical Specifications: Type page 11 5/8 x 21; E - 6 cols, 2 1/16, 1/8 between; A - 6 cols, 2 1/16, 1/8 between; C - 9 cols, 1 3/8, 1/16 between.
Commodity Consumption: Avg. Page Number Per Issue - Daily 24; Avg. Page Number Per Issue - Plates Used 9500; Avg. Page Number Per Issue - Sunday 44; widths 28; Newsprint Used - Metric Tons 780; Newsprint Used - Short Tons 860; Printing Ink Used - Black 16500; Printing Ink Used
Equipment EDITORIAL: Front-end Software – Baseview/NewsEdit, Baseview/Wire Manager.; Editorial Hardware – APP/Mac; Editorial Equipment – SCS/Linx CLASSIFIED: Front-end Software – Baseview/Class Manager Plus.; Classified Hardware – APP/Mac DISPLAY: Ad make-up applications – Multi-Ad/Creator, QPS/QuarkXPress 3.1.; Display Hardware – APP/Mac; Production Equipment – 1-Nat/330, Nikon, Adobe/Photoshop; Cameras – 1-R/500. PRESSROOM: Line 1 – 5-G/Urbanite (2 balloon formers) 1968; Folders – 1; Inserters and stuffers – Manual; Bundle tying machines – Bu. BUSINESS COMPUTERS: Business Software – In-house; Business Hardware – 1-IBM/Sys 36

WABASH

WABASH PLAIN DEALER
123 W. Canal St., Wabash, Ind., 46992; gen tel (260) 563-2131; gen fax (260) 563-0816; adv e-mail ads@wabashplaindealer.com; ed e-mail news@wabashplaindealer.com; web site www.wabashplaindealer.com
Published: Mon, Tues, Wed, Thur, Fri, Sat
Weekday Frequency: m
Circulation: 6,108; 6,108(sat)
Last Audit: September 30, 2007
Price: 11.30/mo; 135.00/yr.
Advertising: Open inch rate $16.44
News services: AP.
Politics: Independent. **Established:** 1859
Not Published: Christmas.
Special Editions: Spring Lawn Care (Apr); High School Football Kick-Off (Aug); Holiday Lifestyles (Dec); Valentine's Day (Feb); January Clearance (Jan); Wabash County 4-H Fair (Jul); Summer Bride (Jun); Wabash Valley Farmer (Mar); Health Care (May); Home Furnishings (Nov);
Special Weekly Sections: Business (Mon); Channel Changer TV Listings (Sat); Dollars & Cents (Tues); Community (Wed).
Magazines: USA WEEKEND Magazine (Sat).
Pub. ....Randy Mitchell
Bus. Office Mgr. ....Trish Nelson
Adv. Mgr. ....Kerry Davis
Circ. Mgr., Single Copy ....Andy Denith
Online Ed. ....Joseph Slacian
Sports Ed ....Josh Sigler
Market Information: ADS; TMC.
Mechanical available: Offset; Black and 3 ROP colors; insert accepted; page cutoffs - 22 3/4.
Commodity Consumption: Avg. Page Number Per Issue - Daily 14; Avg. Page Number Per Issue - Plates Used 4800; Avg. Page Number Per Issue - Saturday 16; widths 25; Newsprint Used - Metric Tons 229; Printing Ink Used - Black 1500; Printing Ink Used - Color 1000.
Equipment EDITORIAL: Front-end Software – QPS/QuarkXPress.; Editorial Hardware – APP/Mac CLASSIFIED: Front-end Software – Baseview.; Classified Hardware – APP/Mac; Classified Printers – APP/Mac DISPLAY: Ad make-up applications – QPS/QuarkXPress, Multi-Ad.; Display Hardware – APP/Mac PRODUCTION: Pagination Software – QPS/QuarkXPress.; Production Equipment – 2-Nu, 1-ECR; Cameras – 1-R PRESSROOM: Line 1 – 4-G/Urbanite; Folders – 1, 1-G/Quarter. MAILROOM: Counter stackers – 1/BG; Bundle tying machines – 3-/Bu.

WARSAW

REUB WILLIAMS & SONS, INC.
Times Bldg. conner st., Warsaw, Ind., 46581; gen tel (574) 267-3111; gen fax (574) 268-1300; gen e-mail tuzas@earthlink.net

TIMES-UNION
Times Bldg., Warsaw, Ind., 46581-1448; gen tel (574) 267-3111; gen fax (574) 267-7784; adv fax (574) 268-1300; ed fax (574) 267-7784; gen e-mail news@timesuniononline.com; web site www.timesuniononline.com
Published: Mon, Tues, Wed, Thur, Fri, Sat
Weekday Frequency: e
Saturday Frequency: m
Circulation: 10,235; 10,235(sat)
Last Audit: September 30, 2009
Price: 13.00/mo (mail out of county); 143.00/yr (mail out of county).
Advertising: Open inch rate $13.10
News services: AP, AP Laserphoto, MCT, NEA, SHNS.
Politics: Independent-Republican. **Established:** 1854
Not Published: New Year; Memorial Day; Independence Day; Labor Day; Thanksgiving; Christmas.
Special Editions: Home Improvement (Apr); Holiday Wrap-Up (Dec); Girls' Sectional Preview (Feb); Halftimes (Jan); Customer Appreciation Week (Jul); Father's Day (Jun); Agriculture (Mar); Mother's Day (May); Holiday Gift Guide (Nov); Fall Bridal (Oct); Home Improvement (Sep
Special Weekly Sections: Outdoors (Sat); Leisure (Thur); Farm Page (Wed).
Magazines: USA WEEKEND Magazine (Sat).
Pub. ....M.L. Hartle
Comptroller/Credit Mgr. ....Dennis Plummer
Adv. Mgr./Dir., Special Editions ....William Hays
General Manager ....Gary Gerard
Business, Farm, County Government Dan Riordin
Lifestyle, Religion ....Vicki Taylor
Copy Editor, Education Ed. ....David Slone
Consultant ....Norm Hagg
Police, Courts Ed. ....Aaron Organ
City Govt., Politics Ed. ....Jennifer Peryam
Online Ed. ....Jordan Fouts
Sports Ed. ....Dale Hubler
Sports Writer ....Anthony Gadson
Market Information: TMC.
Mechanical available: Offset; Black and 3 ROP colors; insert accepted - all; page cutoffs - 21.
Mechanical Specifications: Type page 11 5/8 x 21; E - 6 cols, 1 5/6, 1/8 between; A - 6 cols, 1 5/6, 1/8 between; C - 9 cols, 1 1/6, 1/8 between.
Commodity Consumption: Avg. Page Number Per Issue - Daily 24; Avg. Page Number Per Issue - Plates Used 10200; Avg. Page Number Per Issue - Saturday 50; widths 12 1/2; Newsprint Used - Short Tons 600; Printing Ink Used - Black 19500; Printing Ink Used - Color 4000; Printing Ink
Equipment EDITORIAL: Front-end Software – QPS/QuarkXPress 4.1, Adobe/Photoshop.; Editorial Hardware – 15-Mac, 2-Mac G4, 1-Mac G3; Editorial Equipment – Pre Press/Panther Pro Imagesetter 46; Editorial Printers – APP/Mac LaserWriter II, Xante/G3 CLASSIFIED: Front-end Software – Baseview.; Classified Hardware – 4-iMac; Classified Printers – Pre Press/Panther Pro Imagesetter 46 DISPLAY: Ad make-up applications – Multi-Ad/Creator, Aldus/FreeHand 8.0.; Display Hardware – 6-Mac; Display Printers – Xante 3E PRODUCTION: Pagination Software – QPS/QuarkXPress 4.1, Adobe/Photoshop 5.5.; Production Equipment – 1-Nu/Ultra-Plus; Cameras – 1-Nu/2024SST PRESSROOM: Line 1 – 6-G/Urbanite 1974; Folders – 1 MAILROOM: Counter stackers – 1-Rima-Harris/RS-2510; Inserters and stuffers – MM/227E 5-into-1; Bundle tying machines – 2/Bu; Addressing machine – 1-/Am, 1-/El.; Business Hardware – IBM

WASHINGTON

THE WASHINGTON TIMES-HERALD
102 E. Van Trees St., Washington, Ind., 47501; gen tel (812) 254-0480; adv tel (812) 254-0480; ed tel (812) 254-0480; gen fax (812) 254-7517; adv fax (812) 254-7517; ed fax (812) 254-7517; web site www.washtimesherald.com
Published: Mon, Tues, Wed, Thur, Fri, Sat, Sun
Weekday Frequency: e
Saturday Frequency: m
Circulation: 8,768; 8,768(sat)
Last Audit: March 31, 2003
Price: 8.50/mo; 102.00/yr.
Advertising: Open inch rate $13.00
News services: AP.
Politics: Independent. **Established:** 1867
Advertising not accepted: Mail order.
Not Published: New Year; Memorial Day; Independence Day; Labor Day; Thanksgiving; Christmas.
Special Editions: Farm Review & Forecast (Apr); Back-to-School (Aug); Christmas (Dec); Customer Appreciation (Jan); Progress (Jul); Basketball (Mar); Basketball (Nov); Sidewalk Sale Days (Sept).
Special Weekly Sections: Church Page (Fri); Food (Mon); Agriculture Page (Sat); Area News (Thur); Business Page (Tues); IRS Income Tax (Wed).
Magazines: American Profile (Sat).
Pub. ....Ron Smith
Bus. Mgr. ....Ellen Pride
Adv. Dir. ....Stacey Ramsey
Circ. Mgr. ....Laura Theine
Circ. Dir. ....Scott Sullivan
Editorial Page Ed. ....Melody Brunson
Food/Society Ed. ....Shannon Graber
News Ed. ....Pat Morrison
Sports Ed. ....Todd Lancaster
Asst. Sports Ed. ....Mike Myers
Photographer ....Kelly Overton
Market Information: TMC.
Mechanical available: Offset; Black and 3 ROP colors; insert accepted; page cutoffs - 22 3/4.
Mechanical Specifications: Type page 13 x 21 1/2; E - 6 cols, 2 1/16, 1/8 between; A - 6 cols, 2 1/16, 1/8 between; C - 8 cols, 1 1/2, 1/8 between.
Commodity Consumption: Avg. Page Number Per Issue - Daily 16; Avg. Page Number Per Issue - Plates Used 2500-3000; Avg. Page Number Per Issue - Saturday 24; widths 24; Newsprint Used - Metric Tons 325; Printing Ink Used - Black 10200; Printing Ink Used - Color 1040; Printing In
Equipment EDITORIAL: Front-end Software – Baseview, Adobe/Photoshop, Multi-Ad/Creator II.; Editorial Hardware – 1-Mk/1100, APP/Mac; Editorial Printers – APP/Mac LaserWriter II, Xante/Accel-a-Writer 8200 (1200 dpi), Epson/Stylus Color 3000 Printer CLASSIFIED: Front-end Software – Baseview.; Classified Hardware – APP/Mac; Classified Printers – Xante/Accel-a-Writer 8200 (1200 dpi) DISPLAY: Ad make-up applications – Multi-Ad/Creator II, Adobe/Photoshop, AP/AdSend; Layout Software – APP/Mac IIsi.; Display Printers – Xante Accel-a-Writer 8200 (1200 dpi) PRODUCTION: Pagination Software – Baseview.; Production

Equipment – 1-Nu/Flip Top 40M, 1-M/314, C/T-45; Cameras – 1-LE/R 500 PRESSROOM: Line 1 – 8-HI/Cotrell 15A; Line 2 – 1-ATF/Chief 15; Line 3 – 1-Townsend/T-51 Color; Folders – 2; Bundle tying machines – 2-Bu/Package Tie; Addressing machine – Mailing Machine Systems.; Business Hardware – Software ☐ Vision Data

WINCHESTER

THE NEWS-GAZETTE

224 W. Franklin St., Winchester, Ind., 47394; gen tel (765) 584-4501; gen fax (765) 584-3066; gen e-mail ngeditor@comcast.net; web site www.winchesternewsgazette.com
Published: Mon, Tues, Wed, Thur, Fri, Sat, Sun
Weekday Frequency: e
Saturday Frequency: m
Circulation: 3,700; 3,700(sat)
Last Audit: March 31, 2001
Price: 8.80/mo; 146.00/yr.
Advertising: Open inch rate $9.20
News services: AP.
Politics: Independent.
Not Published: New Year; Memorial Day; Independence Day; Labor Day; Thanksgiving; Christmas.
Special Weekly Sections: Church (Fri); Farm (Sat); Business Salute (Tues).
Magazines: American Profile (Weekly).
Pub. .... Kami Shinn
Circ. Mgr. .... Dawn Lowe
Sports Ed. .... Rick Reed
Market Information: TMC; Zoned editions.
Mechanical available: Offset; Black and 3 ROP colors; insert accepted; page cutoffs - 22 3/4.
Mechanical Specifications: Type page 13 x 21 1/2; E - 6 cols, 2 1/14, 1/8 between; A - 6 cols, 2 1/14, 1/8 between; C - 10 cols, 1 1/5, 1/6 between.
Commodity Consumption: Avg. Page Number Per Issue - Daily 10; Avg. Page Number Per Issue - Plates Used 4284; widths 28; Newsprint Used - Short Tons 160; Printing Ink Used - Black 19500; Printing Ink Used - Color 3000; Printing Ink Used - Pages Printed 3600.
Equipment EDITORIAL: Front-end Software – QPS/QuarkXPress, Baseview.; Editorial Hardware – APP/Mac 605, APP/Mac 610, APP/Power Mac 7200; Editorial Printers – APP/Mac LaserWriter Pro 630 CLASSIFIED: Front-end Software – Baseview.; Classified Hardware – APP/Mac 605; Classified Printers – APP/Mac LaserWriter Pro 630; Layout Software – Multi-Ad, QPS/QuarkXPress, Adobe/Photoshop.; Display Hardware – APP/Mac 610; Display Printers – APP/Mac LaserWriter Pro 630; Production Equipment – Nu/Flip Top; Cameras – R/500. PRESSROOM: Line 1 – 5-G/Community 1973; Folders – 1; Bundle tying machines – 2-Bu/String Tyer; Addressing machine – 2/Am.; Business Hardware – Software ☐ Microsoft/Office, Listmaster

IOWA

AMES

THE TRIBUNE

317 Fifth St., Ames, Iowa, 50010; gen tel (515) 232-2160; gen fax (515) 232-2364; gen e-mail tribune@amestrib.com; adv e-mail advertising@amestrib.com; ed e-mail news@amestrib.com; web site www.amestrib.com
Published: Tues, Wed, Thur, Fri, Sat
Weekday Frequency: e
Saturday Frequency: m
Circulation: 9,025; 13,736(sat)
Last Audit: Sworn N/A
Price: 2.85/wk; 133.36/yr.
Advertising: Open inch rate $24.98
News services: AP, CNS, NEA, NYT, TMS.
Politics: Independent.
Not Published: Christmas.
Special Editions: Engagement Album (); University (Aug); Annual Update (Feb); Home (Mar); Facets (Monthly); Game Day (Other); Agri-Times (Quarterly).
Special Weekly Sections: Church (Fri); TV Times (S); Homefinder (Sat); Entertainment (Thur); Best Food Day (Wed).
Magazines: Relish (Monthly); Parade (S).
Pub. .... John Goossen
Adv. Dir. .... John Greving
Circ. Dir. .... Daniel Cronin
Ed. .... Alexandra Hayne
Bus. Ed. .... Todd Purras
Systems Mgr. .... Tyson Dohse
Prodn. Mgr. .... Dawn Roof
Prodn. Mgr., Mailroom .... Luke Williams
Prodn. Mgr., Pressroom .... Larry Thede
Market Information: ADS; Split run; TMC; Zoned editions.
Mechanical available: Offset; Black and 3 ROP colors; insert accepted; page cutoffs - 22 3/4.
Mechanical Specifications: Type page 13 x 21 1/2; E - 6 cols, 2 1/16, 1/8 between; A - 6 cols, 2 1/16, 1/8 between; C - 9 cols, 1 1/4, 3/16 between.
Commodity Consumption: Avg. Page Number Per Issue - Daily 32; Avg. Page Number Per Issue - Plates Used 48300; Avg. Page Number Per Issue - Sunday 32; widths 25; Newsprint Used - Short Tons 1800; Printing Ink Used - Black 27967; Printing Ink Used - Color 25088; Printing Ink Use
Equipment EDITORIAL: Front-end Software – Microsoft/Word, QPS/QuarkXPress.; Editorial Hardware – APP/Mac; Editorial Printers – HP CLASSIFIED: Front-end Software – Baseview.; Classified Printers – HP DISPLAY: Ad make-up applications – QPS/QuarkXPress; Layout Software – 8-APP/Mac Laser Output.; Display Hardware – APP/Mac; Production Equipment – 5-APP/Mac LaserWriter, Pre Press/Panther Plus Imagesetter 46; Cameras – 1-R; Scanners – 1-APP/Mac. PRESSROOM: Line 1 – 6-G/Urbanite; Folders – 1; Inserters and stuffers – 8-KAN/480; Bundle tying machines – 1/Ca; Addressing machine – 1-St/1620 QFL. BUSINESS COMPUTERS: Business Software – OSAS 6.05, Synaptic 4.06; Business Hardware – 8-IBM, 11-Dell

ATLANTIC

ATLANTIC NEWS-TELEGRAPH

410 Walnut St., Atlantic, Iowa, 50022; gen tel (712) 243-2624; adv tel (712) 243-2624; ed tel (712) 243-2624; gen fax (712) 243-4988; adv fax (712) 243-4988; ed fax (712) 243-4988; gen e-mail news@ant-news.com; adv e-mail ant@ant-news.com; ed e-mail news@ant-news.com; web site www.atlanticnewstelegraph.com
Published: Mon, Tues, Wed, Thur, Fri, Sat, Sun
Weekday Frequency: e
Saturday Frequency: m
Circulation: 3,398; 3,398(sat)
Last Audit: October 1, 2002
Price: 11.00/mo; 139.00/yr; 34.75.00/13wk.
Advertising: Open inch rate $10.50
News services: AP.
Politics: Independent-Republican. **Established:** 1871
Not Published: New Year; Memorial Day; Independence Day; Labor Day; Thanksgiving; Christmas.
Special Editions: Beauty/Cosmetology (Annually); Education (Apr); Wedding (Aug); Wedding (Jan); Graduation (May); Real Estate (Monthly); Health (Quarterly).
Special Weekly Sections: Entertainment (Thur).
Magazines: Atlantic Farm (Monthly); American Profile (Weekly).
Broadcast Affiliations: ABC; NBC; CBS-Omaha.
Pub. .... Connie Collins
Circ. Dir. .... Deb Baker
Ed. .... Jeff Lundquist
Sports Ed. .... Drew Herron
Market Information: ADS; TMC.
Mechanical available: Offset; Black and 4 ROP colors; insert accepted - free samples; page cutoffs - 22 3/4.
Mechanical Specifications: Type page 13 1/8 x 21 1/2; E - 6 cols, 2 1/16, 1/8 between; A - 6 cols, 2 1/16, 1/8 between; C - 6 cols, 2 1/16, 1/8 between.
Commodity Consumption: Avg. Page Number Per Issue - Daily 12; Avg. Page Number Per Issue - Saturday 12; widths 27 1/2; Newsprint Used - Short Tons 410; Printing Ink Used - Black 5000; Printing Ink Used - Color 4000.
Equipment; Editorial Hardware – 1-APP/Mac.; Classified Hardware – 1-APP/Mac.; Production Equipment – 1-Ic; Cameras – 1-Nu; Scanners – APP/Mac One, 1-APP/Mac LaserPrinter Scanner. PRESSROOM: Line 1 – 6-G; Folders – 1-G/2:1.; Bundle tying machines – 3/Bu.; Business Hardware – IBM

BOONE

BOONE NEWS-REPUBLICAN

2136 Mamie Eisenhower St., Boone, Iowa, 50036; gen tel (515) 432-1234; adv tel (515) 432-1234; ed tel (515) 432-1234; gen fax (515) 432-7811; adv fax (515) 432-7811; ed fax (515) 432-7811; gen e-mail news@newsrepublican.com; ed e-mail boonenews@fbx.com; web site www.newsrepublican.com
Published: Mon, Wed, Thur, Fri, Sat
Weekday Frequency: e
Saturday Frequency: m
Circulation: 2,478; 8,200(sat)
Last Audit: September 30, 2005
Price: 8.50/mo; 90.00/yr.
Advertising: Open inch rate $8.85
News services: AP.
Politics: Independent.
Not Published: New Year; Memorial Day; Independence Day; Labor Day; Thanksgiving; Christmas.
Special Editions: Salute to Working Women (Apr); Football Preview (Aug); Home For The Holidays (Dec); Boone Tourism Guide (Feb); Chamber of Commerce (Jan); Real Estate Guide (Jul); Fair (Jun); Boone Tourism Guide (Mar); Real Estate Guide (May); Moonlight Madness (Nov); Rea
Special Weekly Sections: Church Page (Fri); Entertainment (Thur); Engagement/Weddings (Tues).
Magazines: American Profile (Weekly).
Pub. .... Claudia Lovin
Adv. Mgr. .... Susan E. Tolan
Sports Ed. .... Mo Kelley
Market Information: ADS; TMC.
Mechanical available: Offset; Black and 3 ROP colors; insert accepted - subject to approval; page cutoffs - 22 3/4.
Mechanical Specifications: Type page 13 x 21 1/2; E - 6 cols, 2 1/16, 1/8 between; A - 6 cols, 2 1/16, 1/8 between; C - 9 cols, 1 1/3, 1/8 between.
Commodity Consumption: Avg. Page Number Per Issue - Daily 9; Avg. Page Number Per Issue - Plates Used 2000; widths 14; Newsprint Used - Short Tons 152; Printing Ink Used - Black 6000; Printing Ink Used - Color 400; Printing Ink Used - Pages Printed 3200.
Equipment EDITORIAL: Front-end Software – Mk/550.; Editorial Hardware – 5-Mk/Newswriter; Editorial Printers – 1-APP/Mac LaserWriter Pro 630; Classified Hardware – 1-APP/Mac Quadra 610; Classified Equipment – App/Mac 610; Classified Printers – HP/8100, HP/400. DISPLAY: Ad make-up applications – Aldus/PageMaker 6.5.; Display Hardware – 1-APP/Mac 7200, 1-APP/Mac 8600, Compaq 5700 PC; Display Printers – 1-HP/8100; Production Equipment – Nu, Mk/Touchwriter, 2-APP/Mac, HP/8100, HP/4000N; Cameras – N; Scanners – HP/6200C. PRESSROOM: Line 1 – 1972; Bundle tying machines – 1-Yamada/TM 36; Addressing machine – 3/Wm.; Business Hardware – 2-Compaq/Prosigmia, 1-Sun/Ultra 10

BURLINGTON

BURLINGTON HAWK EYE CO.

800 S. Main, Burlington, Iowa, 52601; gen tel (319) 754-8461; gen fax (319) 754-6824; gen e-mail sdelaney@thefawkeye.com; web site www.thehawkeye.com
Published: Mon, Tues, Wed, Thur, Fri, Sat, Sun
Circulation: 17,300; 17,300(sat); 17,300(sun)
Last Audit: Sworn December 31, 2010
Price: 135.00/yr.
Advertising: Open inch rate $17.42
Politics: 1865

THE HAWK EYE

800 S. Main St., Burlington, Iowa, 52601; gen tel (319) 754-8461; adv tel (319) 754-8463 (class); ed tel (319) 754-8461; gen fax (319) 754-6824; adv fax (319) 754-6824; ed fax (319) 754-6824; gen e-mail news@thehawkeye.com; adv e-mail advertising@thehawkeye.com; ed e-mail letters@thehawkeye.com; web site www.thehawkeye.com
Published: Mon, Tues, Wed, Thur, Fri, Sat, Sun
Weekday Frequency: m
Saturday Frequency: m
Circulation: 18,777; 18,777(sat); 19,980(sun)
Last Audit: September 30, 2008
Price: 10.50/mo (carrier), $11.50/mo (motor route); 135.00/yr (carrier), $150.00/yr (motor route).
Advertising: Open inch rate $21.98
News services: AP.
Politics: Independent.
Special Editions: Progress (Feb); Progress (Mar); Guide to Hawk Eye Land (May).
Special Weekly Sections: Education (Mon); Mutual Funds & Stocks (S); Religion (Sat); Entertainment (Thur); Health (Tues); Best Food Day (Wed).
Magazines: Relish (Monthly); TV Section (S); Home Magazine (Sat); American Profile (Weekly).
Bus. Mgr. .... LeDonna Kitsch
Mgr., HR .... Jan Jaeger
Adv. Dir. .... Janet Stottmeister
Adv. Mgr., Classified .... Laurie Trautner
Adv. Coord., Major Accts .... Cheryl Newell
Circ. Mgr. .... Tom Seibert
Mng. Ed. .... Dale Alison
Ed. .... Steve Delaney
Bus. Ed. .... Mike Augusburger
Features Ed. .... Criss Roberts
News Ed. .... Randy Miller
Photo Dept. Mgr. .... John Gaines
Sports Ed. .... John Bohenkamp
Prodn. Mgr., Systems .... Tony Miller
Prodn. Mgr., Packaging .... Steve Deggendorf
Prodn. Supt. .... Tom Lingenfelter
Market Information: TMC.
Mechanical available: Offset; Black and 3 ROP colors; insert accepted; page cutoffs - 22 3/4.
Mechanical Specifications: Type page 11 63/100 x 21 1/2; E - 6 cols, 1 5/6, 1/8 between; A - 6 cols, 1 5/6, 1/8 between; C - 8 cols, 1 19/50, 4/50 between.
Commodity Consumption: Avg. Page Number Per Issue - Daily 20; Avg. Page Number Per Issue - Plates Used 14918; Avg. Page Number Per Issue - Saturday 18; Avg. Page Number Per Issue - Sunday 44; widths 27 1/2; Newsprint Used - Metric Tons 1113; Printing Ink Used - Black 25638; Pr
Equipment EDITORIAL: Front-end Software – Baseview/News Edit Pro IQue 3.1.8.; Editorial Hardware – APP/Mac; Editorial Printers – HP/5000, 2-HP/4000, HP/750C Plus CLASSIFIED: Front-end Software – Baseview.; Classified Hardware – 4-APP/Mac G3, APP/Mac 7350 ASIP Server; Classified Printers – HP/6 MP DISPLAY: Ad make-up applications – Multi-Ad/Creator 4.0.1; Layout Software – MEI/ALS 2.0.; Display Hardware – 3-APP/Mac 7500-100, 3-APP/Mac G3, 2-Umax/C500, 1-APP/Mac 8100, 2-APP/Mac Q 650; Display Printers – Epson/740 PRODUCTION: Pagination Software – QPS/QuarkXPress 4.11.; Production Equipment – Nat/Subtractive 33-1, 1-Nu/Flip Top FT40URNS, 2-Carnfeldt/RA; Cameras – 1-R; Scanners – 1-Umax/Vista 58, 7-

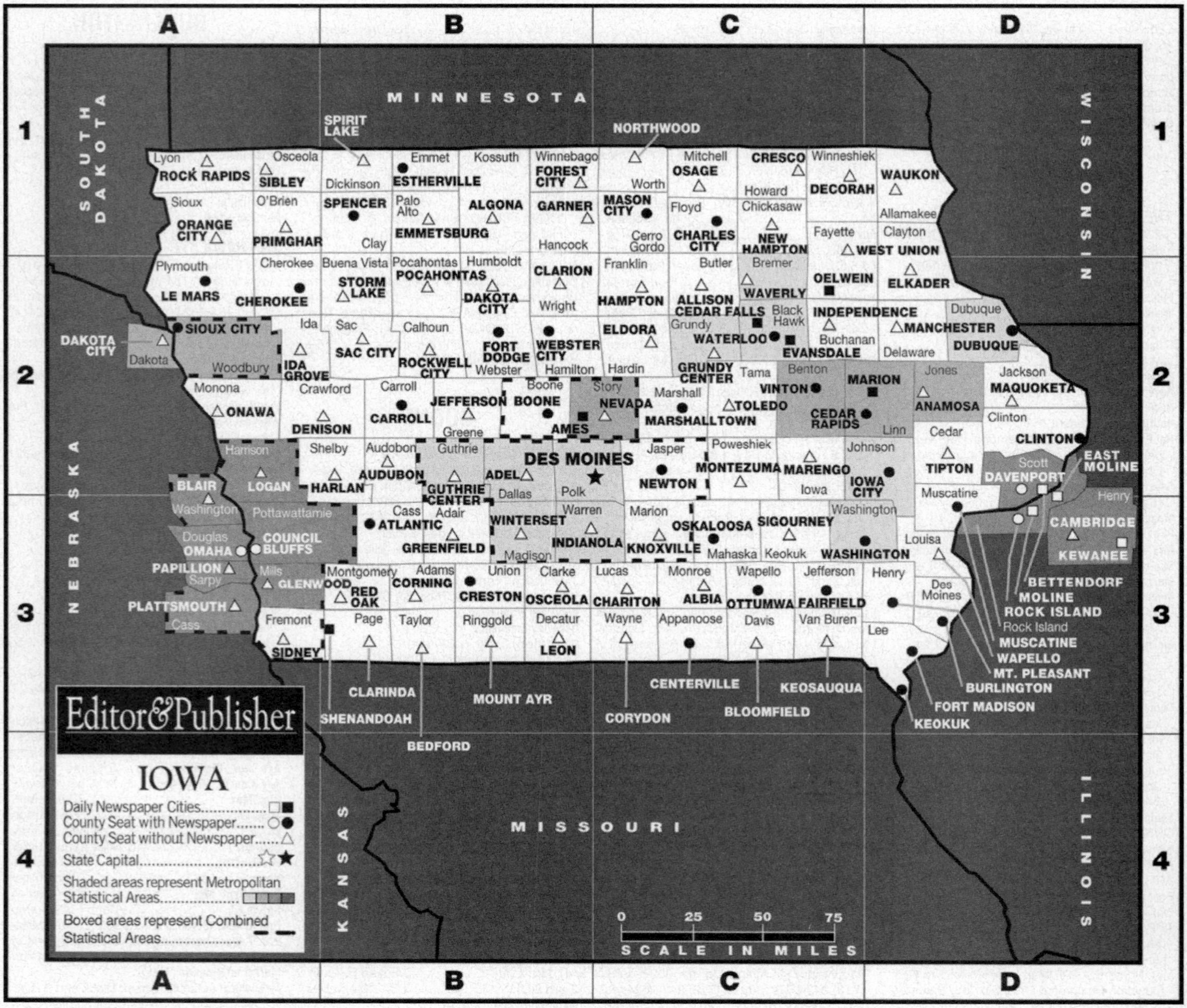

Umax/Flatbed PRESSROOM: Line 1 – 6-G/1008 single width (2 formers); Folders – 1; Reels and Stands – Roll/Stands. MAILROOM: Counter stackers – Id/660, QWI/400; Inserters and stuffers – MM (6 inserter, auto eject); Bundle tying machines – Sterling/MR50; Other equipment –Ideal/Plastic Wrap, QWI/Press Conveyor.; Business Hardware – Data Sciences

CARROLL

DAILY TIMES HERALD

508 N. Court St., Carroll, Iowa, 51401; gen tel (712) 792-3573; gen fax (712) 792-5218; gen e-mail general@carollspaper.com; web site www.carollspaper.com

Published: Mon, Tues, Wed, Thur, Fri
Weekday Frequency: e
Circulation: 6,321
Last Audit: October 9, 2003
Price: 1.35/wk; 7.35/mo; 90.00/yr.
Advertising: Open inch rate $8.00
News services: AP.
Politics: Independent. **Established:** 1868
Not Published: New Year; Memorial Day; Independence Day; Labor Day; Thanksgiving; Christmas.
Special Editions: Chamber (Other).
Magazines: TV Magazine (Fri); American Profile (Weekly).
Pres./Pub./Treasurer..............James B. Wilson
Gen. Mgr.....................................Anne Wilson
Adv. Mgr., Retail...............................Tom Burns
Circ. Mgr....................................Daniel Haberl
News Ed.......................................Larry Devine
Online Ed.......................................Doug Burns
Sports Ed.................................Ashley Schable
Prodn. Foreman, Press..................Tim Bohling
Market Information: TMC; Zoned editions.
Mechanical available: Offset; Black and 3 ROP colors; insert accepted; page cutoffs - 21 1/2.
Mechanical Specifications: Type page 12 1/2 x 21; E - 6 cols, 1 5/6, 1/6 between; A - 6 cols, 1 5/6, 1/6 between; C - 8 cols, 1 1/3, 1/6 between.
Commodity Consumption: Avg. Page Number Per Issue - Daily 14; widths 28; Newsprint Used - Short Tons 279.
Equipment EDITORIAL: Front-end Software – Microsoft/Word 6.0.1.; Editorial Hardware – APP/Mac; Editorial Printers – APP/Mac LaserWriter; Classified Hardware – APP/Mac; Classified Printers – APP/Mac LaserWriter. DISPLAY: Ad make-up applications – Adobe/PageMaker 6.0, Adobe/Photoshop 6.0, Microsoft/Word 6.0.1; Layout Software – APP/Mac.; Display Printers – APP/Mac LaserWriter; Production Equipment – APP/Mac LaserWriter; Cameras – 1-Nu/SST 1923. PRESSROOM: Line 1 – 6-HI/Cotrell V-15A; Folders – 1-G/2:1.; Bundle tying machines – 1-MM/Strap-Tyer.; Business Hardware – Synaptic/Circulation Sys

CEDAR RAPIDS

THE GAZETTE

500 3rd Ave. SE, Cedar Rapids, Iowa, 52401-1608; gen tel (319) 398-8333; adv tel (319) 398-8222; ed tel (319) 398-8313; adv fax (319) 398-5848; ed fax (319) 398-5846; gen e-mail gazettenewsroom@gazcomm.com; adv e-mail advertise@sourcemedia.net; ed e-mail editorial@thegazette.com; web site www.thegazette.com

Published: Mon, Tues, Wed, Thur, Fri, Sat, Sun
Weekday Frequency: m
Saturday Frequency: m
Circulation: 47,476; 55,926(sat); 61,374(sun)
Last Audit: ABC September 30, 2011
Price: 4.95/wk; 236.95/yr.
Advertising: Open inch rate $72.30
News services: AP, LAT-WP, MCT.
Politics: Independent. **Established:** 1883
Own facility?: Y
Special Editions: College/Pro & Prep Football Guide (Aug); New Baby News (Feb); Stocks & Business Review (Jan); Freedom Festival Guide (Jun); Spring Car Care (Mar); Explore (May); College Guide (Sept).
Special Weekly Sections: Milestones (S); TV Vision (Sat); Hoopla (Thur).
Magazines: Dash(Monthly); Parade (S); @RecordBody:**Broadcast Affiliations:** KCRG.
Profile: The Gazette Company is a Cedar Rapids based independently-owned media organization. Its subsidiary Gazette Communications, Inc. publishes The Gazette newspaper, local shoppers, and does commercial printing. It also has numerous sites online and direct mar
Chrmn....Joe Hladky
Pres...Chuck Peters
Vice Pres./Treasurer..................Ken Slaughter
Editor..Lyle Muller
Columnist...................................Dave Rasdal
Opinion Page Ed.....................Jeff Tecklenburg

Publisher....Tim McDougall
Product Director....Steve Lorenz
Managing Editor....Annette Schulte
Columnist....Todd Dorman
Columnist....Jennifer Hemmingsen
Pub./Vice Pres./Gen. Mgr., Gazette Communications Dave Storey
Sec.....Elizabeth T. Barry
Dir., Market Research/Adv. Servs.....Jeff Wolff
Circ. Systems Admin.....Ted Fries
Ed.....Steve Buttry
Automotive Columnist....Tim Banse
Columnist....Mike Deupree
Community Ed.....Diana Nolen
George Ford
Iowa Ed.....Mary Sharp
Online Ed.....Kathy Alter
Outdoors Writer....Orlan Love
Picture Ed.....Rollin Banderob
Market Information: TMC
Mechanical available: Offset; Black and 3 ROP colors; insert accepted - preprinted tab, booklets, single sheet; page cutoffs - 20.
Mechanical Specifications: Type page 11 5/8 x 20; E - 6 cols, 2, between; A - 6 cols, 2, between; C - 6 cols, 1 1/3, 2/3 between.
Equipment; Editorial Hardware – HP; Editorial Equipment – Saxotech and In Design; Editorial Printers – HP CLASSIFIED: Front-end Software – Atex; Classified Hardware – HP; Classified Equipment – Quest/Page Pair, Mindset Live Pag; Classified Printers – HP/LaserJet, DISPLAY: Ad make-up applications – In Design; Display Hardware – PC; Display Printers – HP; Production Equipment – Kodak CTP PRESSROOM: Line 1 – 9-G/Universal 70 single width (8-four towers)(1-5 high tower) 1999; Folders – 1-G/J233 double width 1999, 3-G/J233 single width 1999; Pasters – Enkel/Universal, 14-Enkel/Autoweb; Reels and Stands – Enkel/Megtec; Press control system – Honeywell/P MAILROOM: Counter stackers – HI/Olympian, 2-QWI/350, 2-Rima/SN 2510, 3-Rima/SL 3010, 1-Rima/105; Inserters and stuffers – 2-GMA/SLS2000; Bundle tying machines – GMA/Combi Stacks; Mailroom control system – GMA/SAM; Addressing machine – 2/Dm, 2-/Videojet Systems BUSINESS COMPUTERS: Business Software – Oracle, Microsoft/Windows, DSI; Business Hardware – 4-Sun/Sparc 1000, Alpha/2000
Delivery method: Mail, Newsstand, Private Carrier, Racks

CENTERVILLE

AD EXPRESS & DAILY IOWEGIAN

201 N. 13th St., Centerville, Iowa, 52544; gen tel (641) 856-6336; adv tel (641) 856-6336; ed tel (641) 856-6336; gen fax (641) 856-8118; adv fax (641) 856-8118; ed fax (641) 856-8118; gen e-mail iowegianpublisher@mchsi.com; web site www.dailyiowegian.com
Published: Mon, Tues, Wed, Thur, Fri
Weekday Frequency: m
Circulation: 2,806
Last Audit: December 3, 2009
Price: 64.00/yr.
Advertising: Open inch rate $9.60
News services: AP.
Politics: Independent.
Not Published: New Year; Washington's Birthday; Memorial Day; Independence Day; Labor Day; Veteran's Day; Thanksgiving; Christmas.
Special Editions: Farm (Apr); Progress (Feb); Outdoor Recreation (Jun); Fall-Winter Sports Tab (Nov); Farm (Oct); Fall-Winter Sports Tab (Sept).
Magazines: Relish (Monthly); American Profile (Weekly).
Circ. Mgr.....Becky Maxwell
Mng. Ed.....Michael Schaffer
Society Ed.....Kristal Fowler
Market Information: TMC.
Mechanical available: Offset; Black and 3 ROP colors; insert accepted; page cutoffs - 22 3/4.
Mechanical Specifications: Type page 12 x 21 1/2; E - 6 cols, 1 7/8, 1/8 between; A - 6 cols, 1 7/8, 1/8 between; C - 6 cols, 1 7/8, 1/8 between.
Commodity Consumption: Avg. Page Number Per Issue - Daily 12; widths 34; Printing Ink Used - Black 5000; Printing Ink Used - Color 300.
Equipment EDITORIAL: Front-end Software – QPS, Baseview.; Editorial Hardware – APP/Mac; Editorial Printers – APP/Mac LaserWriter, Xante/Accel-a-Writer; Classified Hardware – APP/Mac; Layout Software – APP/Mac.; Production Equipment – Nu; Cameras – Acti. PRESSROOM: Line 1 – G/Community; Line 2 – G/Community; Line 3 – G/Community; Line 4 – G/Community.; Business Hardware – HP/2000

CHARLES CITY

CHARLES CITY PRESS

801 Riverside Dr., Charles City, Iowa, 50616; gen tel (641) 228-3211; adv tel (641) 228-3211; ed tel (641) 228-3211; gen fax (641) 228-2641; adv fax (641) 228-2641; ed fax (641) 228-2641; adv e-mail ads@charlescitypress.com; ed e-mail editor@charlescitypress.com; web site www.charlescitypress.com
Group: Hallmark Integrated Media, Inc.
Published: Mon, Tues, Wed, Thur, Fri
Weekday Frequency: All day
Circulation: 2,970
Last Audit: Sworn October 1, 2003
Price: 12.00/mo; 112.00/yr.
Advertising: Open inch rate $14.68
News services: INA, AP.
Politics: Independent. **Established:** 1896
Not Published: New Year; Memorial Day; Independence Day; Labor Day; Thanksgiving; Christmas.
Own facility?: Y
Special Editions: Agriculture (Feb); Agriculture (Jan); Agriculture (Jul); Beef (May); Pork (Oct).
Pub./President/Owner....Gene A. Hall
Circ. Mgr.....Terri Lawless
Mng. Ed.....Joel Gray
Weekend Ed.....Mark Wicks
Prodn. Foreman, Press....Carrie Schmidt
Market Information: ADS; TMC.
Mechanical available: Offset; Black and 3 ROP colors; insert accepted; page cutoffs - 22 1/2.
Mechanical Specifications: Type page 11 1/2 x 21 1/2; E - 6 cols, 1 3/4, 1/6 between; @RecordBody:**Commodity Consumption:** A0vg. Page Number Per Issue - Daily 14; Avg. Page Number Per Issue - Plates Used 14000; widths 25; Newsprint Used - Metric Tons 350; Pri4nting Ink Used - Black 1200; Printing Ink Used - Color 900; Printing Ink Used - Pages Printed 9400.
Equipment EDITORIAL: Front-end Software – Quark, Baseview; Editorial Hardware – APP/Mac ; Editorial Printers – APP/Mac LaserWriter Plus CLASSIFIED: Front-end Software – Quark; Classified Hardware – APP/Mac DISPLAY: Ad make-up applications – Multi-Ad/Creator, QPS.; Display Hardware – APP/Mac, APP/Mac ; Display Printers – APP/Mac LaserWriter PRESSROOM: Line 1 – 13-G/Community 1984; Folders – 1-G/SC, 1-G/Community. MAILROOM: Counter stackers – BG/Count-O-Veyor; Bundle tying machines – Bu; Wrapping singles – El.; Addressing machine – VideoJet; Other equipment –Kodak CTP
Zip Codes served: 50616
Delivery method: Mail, Newsstand, Racks

CHEROKEE

CHRONICLE TIMES

Times Bldg., 111 S. 2nd St., Cherokee, Iowa, 51012; gen tel (712) 225-5111; adv tel (712) 225-5111; ed tel (712) 225-5111; gen fax (712) 225-2910; adv fax (712) 225-2910; ed fax (712) 225-2910; adv e-mail ads@ctimes.biz; ed e-mail editor@ctimes.biz; web site www.chronicletimes.com
Published: Mon, Wed, Thur, Fri
Weekday Frequency: m
Circulation: 2,389
Price: 10.00/mo; 82.00/yr.
Advertising: Open inch rate $10.50
News services: AP.
Politics: 1870
Not Published: New Year; Independence Day; Thanksgiving; Christmas.
Special Editions: Home Improvement (Apr); Back-to-School (Aug); Progress (Feb); Fair (Jul); Farm (Mar); Rodeo (May); Winter Sports (Nov); Winter Fashion (Oct); Car Care (Sept).
Special Weekly Sections: Religion (Sat); Business (Thur).
Magazines: Relish (Monthly).
Co-Assoc. Pub.....Paul Struck
Adv. Mgr.....Troy Valentine
Adv. Mgr.....Rhonda Fassler
Adv. Mgr.....Chris Reed
Sports Ed.....Dan Whitney
Market Information: TMC.
Mechanical available: Offset; Black and 3 ROP colors; insert accepted; page cutoffs - 22 3/4.
Mechanical Specifications: Type page 13 x 21 1/2; E - 6 cols, 2 1/16, 1/8 between; A - 6 cols, 2 1/16, 1/8 between; C - 6 cols, 2 1/16, 1/8 between.
Commodity Consumption: Avg. Page Number Per Issue - Daily 12.
Equipment; Production Equipment – 2-APP/Mac LaserWriter, 1-APP/Mac LaserPrinter; Cameras – SCREEN/250.

CLINTON

CLINTON HERALD

221 6th Ave. S., Clinton, Iowa, 52733-2961; gen tel (563) 242-7101; adv tel (563) 242-7101; ed tel (563) 242-7101; gen fax (563) 242-3854; adv fax (563) 242-7145; ed fax (563) 242-7145; adv e-mail senright@clintonherald.com; ed e-mail cbielema@clintonherald.com; web site www.clintonherald.com
Published: Mon, Tues, Wed, Thur, Fri, Sat
Weekday Frequency: e
Saturday Frequency: e
Circulation: 9,688; 9,688(sat)
Last Audit: ABC September 30, 2011
Price: 8.50/mo; 87.00/yr; 24.00/3mo.
Advertising: Open inch rate $16.72
News services: AP.
Politics: Independent. **Established:** 1856
Not Published: Independence Day; Christmas.
Special Editions: Holiday Gift Guides (Dec); Health & Fitness (Feb); Brides & Weddings (Jan); Riverboat Days (Jun); Home Improvement/Yard & Garden (Mar); Art in the Park (May); Christmas Open House (Nov); Bazaar (Sept).
Special Weekly Sections: Church Page (Fri); Best Food Day (Wed).
Magazines: USA WEEKEND Magazine (Sat); TV Tab (Thur); American Profile (Weekly).
Chrmn.....Harvey Brock
Pub....Don Richlen
Bus. Mgr.....Marge Garrison
Adv. Dir.....Wayne Larkey
Adv. Mgr., Classified....Sherri Enright
Ed.....Charlene Bielema
Photo Dept. Mgr.....Jerry Dahl
Prodn. Mgr.....David Bidrawn
Market Information: TMC.
Mechanical available: Offset; Black and 3 ROP colors; insert accepted; page cutoffs - 22 3/4.
Mechanical Specifications: Type page 11 3/5 x 21 1/2; E - 6 cols, 1 4/5, 1/8 between; A - 6 cols, 1 4/5, 1/8 between; C - 9 cols, 1 1/5, 1/16 between.
Commodity Consumption: Avg. Page Number Per Issue - Daily 22; Avg. Page Number Per Issue - Plates Used 9100; widths 25; Printing Ink Used - Black 32611; Printing Ink Used - Color 3500; Printing Ink Used - Pages Printed 9444.
Equipment; Editorial Hardware – Dewar, 14-PC 286 Workstation, 11-IBM.; Classified Hardware – Dewar, 3-PC 286 Workstation; Classified Equipment – 5-IBM.; Production Equipment – 2-Nu; Cameras – 1-C. PRESSROOM: Line 1 – 4-G/Urbanite; Folders – 1-G/2:1; Pasters – Butler/Automatic. MAILROOM: Counter stackers – 1-BG/108, 1-Id/CS202; Inserters and stuffers – 1/MM; Bundle tying machines – 2-MLN/ML1; Wrapping singles – 1-St/510; Addressing machine – 1-St/1200.; Business Hardware – 1-Hw/L62

COUNCIL BLUFFS

THE DAILY NONPAREIL

535 W. Broadway, Ste. 300, Council Bluffs, Iowa, 51502; gen tel (712) 328-1811; gen fax (712) 325-5776; gen e-mail mhoffman@nonpareilonline.com; adv e-mail advertising@nonpareilonline.com; ed e-mail editorial@nonpareilonline.com; web site www.nonpareilonline.com; www.swiowanews.com
Published: Tues, Wed, Thur, Fri, Sat, Sun
Weekday Frequency: e
Saturday Frequency: e
Circulation: 11,564; 11,564(sat); 13,719(sun)
Last Audit: ABC September 30, 2011
Price: 2.00/wk; 119.00/yr; 8.00/4wk.
Advertising: Open inch rate $27.50
News services: AP.
Politics: Independent. **Established:** 1849
Not Published: Christmas; If holiday falls on Sunday, Monday edition will not be published.
Special Editions: Outdoor Living (Apr); Back-to-School (Aug); Presidents' Day Sale (Feb); Working Women (Jul); Spring Car Care (Mar); New Car Care (Oct); Golden Years (Sept).
Special Weekly Sections: Church News (Fri); Business and Farm (S); TV Preview Magazine (Sat); Diversions Magazine (Thur); Best Food Day (Tues).
Magazines: USA WEEKEND Magazine (S); American Profile (Weekly).
Pub....Tom Schmitt
Comptroller....Amy McKay
Adv. Dir.....Dan Collin
Adv. Mgr., Classified....Jaimi Miller
Adv. Mgr., Retail....Cindy Bunten
Asst. Mng. Ed.....Courtney Brummer
Editorial Page Ed.....Jon Leu
Religion Ed.....Kim Bousquet
Sports Ed.....Kevin White
Internet Coord./New Media Ed...Marsha Hoffman
Market Information: ADS; TMC.
Mechanical available: Offset; Black and 3 ROP colors; insert accepted; page cutoffs - 22 3/4.
Mechanical Specifications: Type page 12 1/2 x 21 1/2; E - 6 cols, 2 1/16, 1/8 between; A - 6 cols, 2 1/16, 1/8 between; C - 9 cols, 1 3/8, 1/16 between.
Commodity Consumption: Avg. Page Number Per Issue - Daily 18; Avg. Page Number Per Issue - Plates Used 7000; Avg. Page Number Per Issue - Sunday 40; widths 30; Newsprint Used - Short Tons 925; Printing Ink Used - Black 25000; Printing Ink Used - Color 5000; Printing Ink Used -
Equipment EDITORIAL: Front-end Software – FSI.; Editorial Hardware – 15-APP/Mac 2200, 4-APP/Mac 8500; Editorial Equipment – Lf/AP Leaf Picture Desk, APP/Mac Quadra; Editorial Printers – 2-Pre Press/Panther Pro 36, HP/LaserJet 4MV; Classified Hardware – 4-Cx. DISPLAY: Ad make-up applications – Aldus/FreeHand 3.1, Aldus/PageMaker 5.0, QPS/QuarkXPress 3.3, Broderbund/Typestyler 2.1, Ofoto 2.0; Display Hardware – 5-APP/Mac 7200; Display Printers – APP/Mac Pro 630, HP/LaserJet 4MV, 2-Pre Press/Panther Pro 36 PRODUCTION: Pagination Software – QPS/QuarkXPress 3.3, FSI.; Production Equipment – Caere/OmniPage 3.0, HP/4MV, 2-Pre Press/Panther Pro 36; Cameras – 1-SCREEN; Scanners – APP/Mac Scanners PRESSROOM: Line 1 – 8-G/Community (3-Color Unit & 1-Stack

Unit). MAILROOM: Counter stackers – 1-Toledo/Scale #1938; Inserters and stuffers – 1-Mandelli/Star 100 (paper cutter); Bundle tying machines – 1-MLN/Spirit, 1-MLN/SP 300; Mailroom control system – MM/1511 Stitcher-Trimmer; Addressing machine – 1-Ch/595. BUSINESS COMPUTERS: Business Software – Newzware; Business Hardware – 1-NCR/I9020

CRESTON

CRESTON NEWS ADVERTISER

503 W. Adams St., Creston, Iowa, 50801; gen tel (641) 782-2141; gen fax (641) 782-6628; gen e-mail cna@crestonnews.com; adv e-mail advertising@crestonnews.com; ed e-mail editor@crestonnews.com; web site www.crestonnewsadvertiser.com

Published: Mon, Tues, Wed, Thur, Fri
Weekday Frequency: e
Circulation: 5,492
Price: 99.00/yr.
Advertising: Open inch rate $11.54
News services: AP.
Politics: Independent.
Not Published: New Year; Memorial Day; Independence Day; Labor Day; Thanksgiving; Christmas.
Special Editions: Car Care (Apr); Wedding (Jan); Progress (Mar); Beef (May); Pre-Christmas (Nov); Car Care (Oct).
Special Weekly Sections: TV & Entertainment (Fri); Church Page (Thur); Best Food Day (Tues); Farm Page (Wed).
Magazines: American Profile (Fri); Relish (Monthly).
Pub. ....Rich Paulsen
Office Mgr. ....Rose Henry
Adv. Dir. ....Chris Dorsey
News Ed. ....Stephani Finley
Sports Ed. ....Larry Peterson
Systems Administrator ....Dorine Peterson
Prodn. Mgr. ....Kevin Lindley
Market Information: TMC.
Mechanical available: Offset; Black and 3 ROP colors; insert accepted; page cutoffs - 22 3/4.
Mechanical Specifications: Type page 13 x 21 1/2; E - 6 cols, 2, 1/6 between; A - 6 cols, 2, 1/6 between; C - 9 cols, 1 3/10, 3/20 between.
Commodity Consumption: Avg. Page Number Per Issue - Daily 20; Avg. Page Number Per Issue - Plates Used 4400; widths 27 1/2; Newsprint Used - Short Tons 397; Printing Ink Used - Black 9490; Printing Ink Used - Color 500; Printing Ink Used - Pages Printed 5100.
Equipment EDITORIAL: Front-end Software – Baseview/NewsEdit, Baseview/QXEdit.; Editorial Hardware – APP/Mac, APP/iMac; Editorial Equipment – Polaroid/SprintScan, AG/Flatbed Scanner; Editorial Printers – APP/Mac LaserWriter CLASSIFIED: Front-end Software – Baseview/Class Manager Pro, Claris/Hypercard.; Classified Hardware – APP/Mac; Classified Printers – APP/Mac LaserWriter DISPLAY: Ad make-up applications – QPS/QuarkXPress 4.04.; Display Hardware – APP/Mac G4; Display Printers – APP/Mac LaserWriter PRODUCTION: Pagination Software – Baseview 3.15.; Production Equipment – Text-Bridge; Cameras – B/Caravelle; Scanners – APP/Mac Scanner, APP/Mac, AG PRESSROOM: Line 1 – G/Community single width 1965; Line 2 – G/Community single width 1965; Line 3 – G/Community single width 1965; Line 4 – G/Community single width 1965; Line 5 – G/Community single width 1976; Line 6 – G/Community single width 1976.; Bundle tying machines – Bu. BUSINESS COMPUTERS: Business Software – Vision Data; Business Hardware – Digital/Prioris XL 6200

CRESTON PUBLISHING CO.

503 W. Adams St., Creston, Iowa, 50801; gen tel (641) 782-2141; gen fax (641) 782-6628

DAVENPORT

QUAD-CITY TIMES

500 E. 3rd St., Davenport, Iowa, 52801-1708; gen tel (563) 383-2200; adv tel (563) 383-2296; ed tel (563) 383-2320; gen fax (563) 383-2433; adv fax (563) 322-6733; ed fax (563) 383-2370; gen e-mail qctimes@qctimes.com; adv e-mail retail@qctimes.com; ed e-mail newsroom@qctimes.com; web site www.qctimes.com

Published: Mon, Tues, Wed, Thur, Fri, Sat, Sun
Weekday Frequency: m
Saturday Frequency: m
Circulation: 45,360; 46,353(sat); 59,482(sun)
Last Audit: ABC September 30, 2011
Price: 4.50/wk; 18.53/mo; 234.00/yr.
Advertising: Open inch rate $101.37
News services: AP, CNA, Associations, Inc..
Politics: 1890
Special Editions: Answer Book (Other); Spring Fashion (Spring); Summer Fun (Summer).
Special Weekly Sections: Home (S); GO! (Thur); Best Food Day (Wed).
Magazines: Relish (Monthly); Parade (S).
Pub. ....Julie Bechtel
Controller ....Carol McCormick
Dir., HR ....Andrew Wall
Adv. Dir. ....Keely Byars
Adv. Mgr., Classified ....Steve Jameson
Circ./Mktg. Dir. ....Stacey Molony-Klimek
Exec. Ed. ....Jan Touney
Bus. Ed. ....Deborah Brasier
Online Dir. ....Tim D'Avis
Opns. Dir. ....Eric Schult
Market Information: TMC; Zoned editions.
Mechanical available: Offset; Black and 3 ROP colors; insert accepted; page cutoffs - 22.
Mechanical Specifications: Type page 9 29/32 x 20 7/8; E - 6 cols, 1 9/16, 3/32 between; A - 6 cols, 1 9/16, 3/32 between; C - 6 cols, 1 9/16, 3/32 between.
Commodity Consumption: Avg. Page Number Per Issue - Daily 40; Avg. Page Number Per Issue - Plates Used 62000; Avg. Page Number Per Issue - Sunday 88; widths 41; Newsprint Used - Metric Tons 6404; Printing Ink Used - Black 265500; Printing Ink Used - Color 47250; Printing Ink U
Equipment EDITORIAL: Front-end Software – CText/Dateline, CText/Expressline.; Editorial Hardware – Gateway/P155; Editorial Printers – HP/LaserJet CLASSIFIED: Front-end Software – CText/AdVision.; Classified Hardware – Gateway/P155; Classified Printers – HP/LaserJet DISPLAY: Ad make-up applications – QPS/QuarkXPress 4.0, Adobe/Photoshop 4.0; Layout Software – SCS/Layout 8000.; Display Hardware – APP/Mac; Display Printers – HP/LaserJet PRODUCTION: Pagination Software – CText/ALPS.; Production Equipment – 2-AU/APS-800, 2-AU/APS-108; Cameras – 1-C/19, 1-Nu/19; Scanners – Howtek/2500 PRESSROOM: Line 1 – 26-G/Colorliner 1990; Line 2 – 10-G/Community 1976, 18-G/Community; Line 3 – 28-G/Colorliner; Folders – 6-G/3:2, 2-G/SSC 1995; Reels and Stands – 8 MAILROOM: Counter stackers – 4-QWI/400; Inserters and stuffers – 1-MM/227, 2-HI/1372 w/Icon System; Bundle tying machines – 1-MLN/MLN2A, 1-MLN/MLN2, 2-Dynaric/1500; Mailroom control system – HI; Addressing machine – 2/CH; Other equipment –MM/Stitcher-Trimmer.; Business Hardware – IBM/AS-400

DENISON

DENISON BULLETIN AND REVIEW

1410 Broadway, Denison, Iowa, 51442; gen tel (712) 263-2122; gen fax (712) 263-8484; gen e-mail editor@bulletinreview.com; adv e-mail ads@bulletinreview.com; web site www.dbrnews.com

Published: Mon, Tues, Wed, Fri
Weekday Frequency: e
Circulation: 3,650
Last Audit: Sworn N/A
Advertising: Open inch rate $9.25
Insert rate: $54.00/M.
Politics: 1867
Own facility?: Y
Pub. ....Greg Wehle
Circ. Mgr. ....Jackie Gallagher
Ed. ....Gordon Wolf
Prodn. Mgr. ....Bonnie Hill
Mechanical Specifications: Type page 10.25x 21 1/2; E - 6 cols, 2 1/8, 1/10 between; A - 6 cols, 2 1/18, 1/10 between; C - 8 cols, 1 1/2, 1/10 between.
Zip Codes served: We serve over 130 communities each week

DES MOINES

THE DES MOINES REGISTER

715 Locust St., Des Moines, Iowa, 50309; gen tel (515) 284-8000; adv tel (515) 284-8043; ed tel (515) 284-8201; adv fax (515) 286-2530; ed fax (515) 284-2540; ed e-mail letters@news.dmreg.com; web site www.desmoinesregister.com

Group: Newspapers First, Inc.
Published: Mon, Tues, Wed, Thur, Fri, Sat, Sun
Weekday Frequency: m
Saturday Frequency: m
Circulation: 105,151; 114,689(sat); 216,648(sun)
Last Audit: ABC September 30, 2011
Price: 1.75/wk (m), $1.75/wk (S); 7.00/mo (m), $7.00/mo (S); 91.00/yr (m), $91.00/yr (S).
Advertising: Open inch rate $341.25
News services: AP, LAT-WP, MCT, NYT, GNS, Bloomberg.
Politics: Independent.
Note: The advertising rate for The Des Moines Register automatically includes insertion in the Iowa City Press-Citizen (m).
Special Editions: Fashion (Aug); Wedding (Jan); RAGBRAI (Jul); Fashion (Mar); Vacation Iowa (May); Fashion (Nov); College Guide (Oct).
Special Weekly Sections: Metro Real Estate (Fri); Work & Money (Mon); Iowa Life (S); Home and Garden (Sat); Datebook (Thur); Around Town (Wed).
Magazines: USA WEEKEND Magazine (S).
Pres./Pub./Gen. Mgr. ....Laura Hollingsworth
Vice Pres., HR ....Joyce M. Ray
Vice. Pres. Finance ....Julie Harvey
Vice. Pres. Adv. ....Kevin Hall
Vice. Pres. Marketing ....Susan Patterson Plank
Vice Pres., Circ. ....Rick Bell
Circ. Mgr., Opns. ....Joe Grochala
Ed ....Carolyn Washburn
Mng. Ed. ....Randy Brubaker
Asst. Mng. Ed., Sports ....Bryce Miller
Bus. Ed. ....Lynn Hicks
Editorial Page Ed ....Linda Fandel
Entertainment Ed. ....Joe Hawkins
Health/Medical Reporter ....Tony Leys
Sr. Ed., Magazine ....Vicki Ashwill
News Ed. ....Randy Evans
Market Information: Split run; TMC; Zoned editions.
Mechanical available: Cold Web Offset; Black and 3 ROP colors; insert accepted; page cutoffs - 21 1/2.
Mechanical Specifications: Type page 11 1/2 x 20 1/2; E - 6 cols, 2 1/16, 1/8 between; A - 6 cols, 2 1/16, 1/8 between; C - 10 cols, 1 3/16, 1/8 between.
Commodity Consumption: Avg. Page Number Per Issue - Daily 44; Avg. Page Number Per Issue - Saturday 48; Avg. Page Number Per Issue - Sunday 110; widths 50; Newsprint Used - Metric Tons 23400; Newsprint Used - Short Tons 25800.
Equipment EDITORIAL: Front-end Software – DTI/Speedplanner, DTI/Pagespeed, DTI/Speedwriter.; Editorial Hardware – Sun/3000; Editorial Equipment – APP/Mac; Editorial Printers – APP/Mac LaserWriter, HP/LaserJet, QMS CLASSIFIED: Front-end Software – DTI/Classpeed 5.0.1.; Classified Hardware – Sun/420; Classified Equipment – ROLM, ACD; Classified Printers – QMS, HP/Laserjet DISPLAY: Ad make-up applications – DTI/AdSpeed, DTI/Speedplanner; Display Hardware – APP/Macs, Sun/630S, Sun/3000; Display Printers – 2-QMS, Epson/Stylus, HP/LaserJet PRODUCTION: Pagination Software – DTI 4.3.; Production Equipment – 2-III/3850 Grafix Color Imager, 1-Aii 3850 Wide; Scanners – Horizon/Color, AGFA-T2000, PURUP-ESKOFOT 2024, Umax Mirage II, Umax Powerlook III, Kodak Pro 3570 PRESSROOM: Line 1 – Jun-00; Line 2 – Jun-00; Folders – 3, 2; Pasters – 15 MAILROOM: Counter stackers – 9-QWI/401, 4-QWI/351, 2-BG/STC70; Inserters and stuffers – 2-HI/NP632-30; Bundle tying machines – 13-Sterling/NS50, 2-Sterling/NS45; Mailroom control system – 1-HI/PRIMA, 1-QWI/BDS; Addressing machine – 1-AVY/Labeler 5209, 1-KAN/600. BUSINESS COMPUTERS: Business Software – Microsoft/Office; Business Hardware – 1-IBM AS/-400, 1-IBM AS/-400

DUBUQUE

TELEGRAPH HERALD

801 Bluff St., Dubuque, Iowa, 52001-4647; gen tel (563) 588-5611; adv tel (563) 588-5617; ed tel (563) 588-5671; gen fax (563) 588-5739; adv fax (563) 588-3834; ed fax (563) 588-5745; gen e-mail thonline@wcinet.com; web site www.thonline.com

Published: Mon, Tues, Wed, Thur, Fri, Sat, Sun
Weekday Frequency: m
Saturday Frequency: m
Circulation: 25,994; 25,994(sat); 30,903(sun)
Last Audit: ABC September 30, 2011
Price: 4.65/wk; 19.95/mo; 243.36/yr.
Advertising: Open inch rate $38.74
News services: AP, MCT.
Politics: . **Established:** 1836
Advertising not accepted: Y
Own facility?: Y
Special Editions: Her Magazine (8X/year); Fair (Aug); Last Minute Gift Guide (Dec); Baby Register (Feb); Chronology (Jan); Senior Living (quarterly); Home Builders Show (Mar); Those We Remember (May); Holiday Food & Entertaining (Nov); College Fair (Oct); Him Magazine (8X/year), My Vacationland (May, Sept.), Real Estate Magazine (monthly),
Special Weekly Sections: Your Neighbors (Saturday); Health/Fitness (Mon); Technology (S); Religion (Sat); Arts & Entertainment (Thur); Family (Tues); Food (Wed).
Magazines: Dash (Monthly); Parade (S).
Spry (Monthly)
USA Weekend (F)
Broadcast Affiliations: WHBY-AM/WAPL-FM Appleton, WI; WKSZ-FM/WZOR-FM Green Bay, WI.
Treasurer ....Grady Ivy
Pub. ....James F. Normandin
Dir., Promo. ....Diane Mohr
Circ. Mgr. ....Mike Newland
City Ed. ....Ken Brown
Copy Ed. ....Gary Dura
Editorial Page Ed. ....Brian Cooper
Features Ed. ....Jim Swenson
News Ed. ....Monty Gilles
Photo Mgr. ....Dave Kettering
Sports Ed. ....Jim Leitner
Prodn. Mgr., Pressroom ....Jim Thiltgen
Business Manager ....Libby Burkhart
Market Information: TMC.
Mechanical available: Offset; Black and 3 ROP colors; insert accepted - single sheet, 60 lbs. min.; page cutoffs - 22 3/4.
Mechanical Specifications: Type page 12 1/2 x 21 3/4; E - 6 cols, 1 5/6, 1/8 between; A - 6 cols, 1 5/6, 1/8 between; C - 9 cols, 1 3/16, 1/8 between.
Commodity Consumption: Avg. Page Number Per Issue - Daily 31; Avg. Page Number Per Issue - Plates Used 48000; Avg. Page Number Per Issue - Saturday 31; Avg. Page Number Per Issue - Sunday 66; widths 50; Newsprint Used - Metric Tons 2175; Printing Ink Used - Black 66000; Printi
Equipment EDITORIAL: Front-end Software – Dewar/View, Microsoft/Word 6.0, QPS/QuarkXPress 3.3.; Editorial Hardware – DEC/486 workstations, DEC/VAX 105A servers; Editorial

Printers – QMS/860, APP/Mac LaserPro 630 CLASSIFIED: Front-end Software – Mactive.; Classified Hardware – Compaq/Proliant 5000, Microsoft/NT 4.0, SQL/Server 4.5; Classified Equipment – Compaq/Deskpro 2000 Workstations; Classified Printers – HP/LaserJet 5M DISPLAY: Ad make-up applications – QPS/QuarkXPress 4.01, Adobe/Illustrator 8.0, Adobe/Photoshop 5.5; Layout Software – MEI/ALS.; Display Hardware – APP/Mac G3, CSI, CJ, 2-Alpha 3305, AU/Oman; Display Printers – QMS/860, Canon/700 Color Laser, AU/Typhoon PRODUCTION: Pagination Software – QPS/QuarkXPress 3.3.; Production Equipment – Caere/OmniPage 5.0, 1-Nu/Flip Top (2pg), Adobe/Photoshop 5.0, 4-APP/Mac G3; Cameras – 1-R, 1-C; Scanners – Sharp/Flatbed scanner, ECR/Autokon 1000DE, AG/Horizon Plus, 5-AG/Arcus II PRESSROOM: Line 1 – 4-G/Metro (2 Half decks) 1965; Press Drives – 1965; Folders – 1-G/2:1 1965; Pasters – Apr-65; Reels and Stands – 4-1965. MAILROOM: Counter stackers – 2-QWI, HI/Olympian; Inserters and stuffers – 1-SLS/1000 14:1; Bundle tying machines – 1-Samuel, 1/MLN, Si/LB-News 3000; Addressing machine – 1-Ch/4-Up.; Audio Hardware – Interactive Media, Cedar Rapids, IA BUSINESS COMPUTERS: Business Software – DTI/:Adv, Mactive 11.1.x :Circ, DSG/UtilPro 4.5 :Payroll/HR, Epicor/Platinum SQL 4.Za :Accts Payable; Business Hardware – 2-DEC/Compaq 4000-101A cluster

Delivery method: Mail, Newsstand, Private Carrier, Racks

ESTHERVILLE

ESTHERVILLE DAILY NEWS

10 N. Seventh St., Estherville, Iowa, 51334; gen tel (712) 362-2622; adv tel (712) 362-2622; ed tel (712) 362-2622; gen fax (712) 362-2624; adv fax (712) 362-2624; ed fax (712) 362-2624; gen e-mail production@esthervilledailynews.com; ed e-mail editor@esthervilledailynews.com; web site www.esthervilledailynews.com

Published: Tues, Wed, Thur, Fri, Sat
Weekday Frequency: m
Circulation: 2,282; 2,282(sat)
Last Audit: March 31, 2006
Price: 6.00/mo; 65.00/yr; 16.00/3mo, $31.00/6mo.
Advertising: Open inch rate $9.81
News services: AP.
Politics: Independent.
Not Published: New Year; Memorial Day; Independence Day; Labor Day; Thanksgiving; Christmas.
Special Weekly Sections: Farm (Sat); Religion (Thur); Business (Wed).
Magazines: TV Update (Thur).
Pub. .... Glen Caron
Bus. Mgr. .... Tonya Cole
Adv. Dir. .... Dar Isaackson
Sports Ed. .... David Swartz
Prodn. Mgr., Composing .... Theresa Odom
Market Information: ADS; TMC.
Mechanical available: Offset; Black and 3 ROP colors; insert accepted.
Mechanical Specifications: Type page 13 x 21 1/2; E - 6 cols, 2 1/16, 1/8 between; A - 6 cols, 2 1/16, 1/8 between; C - 6 cols, 2, 1/16 between.
Commodity Consumption: Avg. Page Number Per Issue - Daily 8.
Equipment EDITORIAL: Front-end Software – WriteNow.; Editorial Hardware – APP/Mac Classic; Editorial Equipment – 7-COM/MDT 350; Editorial Printers – APP/Mac LaserWriter II CLASSIFIED: Front-end Software – QPS/QuarkXPress.; Classified Hardware – 2-APP/Mac LC; Classified Printers – APP/Mac LaserWriter II DISPLAY: Ad make-up applications – QPS/QuarkXPress.; Display Hardware – 2-APP/Mac LC; Display Printers – APP/Mac LaserWriter II; Production Equipment – APP/Mac LaserWriter II.

FAIRFIELD

THE FAIRFIELD LEDGER

112 E. Broadway, Fairfield, Iowa, 52556-0110; gen tel (641) 472-4129; adv tel (641) 472-4130; ed tel (641) 472-2116; gen fax (641) 472-1916; gen e-mail ffledger@lisco.com; web site www.ffledger.com

Published: Mon, Tues, Wed, Thur, Fri
Weekday Frequency: e
Circulation: 3,194
Last Audit: October 1, 2003
Price: 1.75/wk (carrier); 95.00/yr.
Advertising: Open inch rate $10.35
News services: AP.
Politics: Independent. **Established:** 1849
Not Published: New Year; Memorial Day; Independence Day; Labor Day; Thanksgiving; Christmas.
Special Editions: Home Improvement (Apr); Back-to-School (Aug); Bridal (Feb); Faces & Places (Jan); Fiesta Days (Jul); Parsons College Reunion (Jun); Conservation (Mar); Beef Month (May); Pork Month (Oct).
Special Weekly Sections: Religion (Fri); Business (Thur); Best Food Day (Tues); Farm Page (Wed).
Magazines: American Profile (Weekly).
Office Mgr. .... Marcia Weller
Adv. Mgr. .... Gene Luedtke
Adv. Mgr., Classified .... Sherry Tipp
Circ. Mgr. .... Lisa Metcalf
Ed. .... Jeff Wilson
City Ed. .... Vicki Tillis
Society Ed. .... Sherry Manley
Market Information: TMC; Zoned editions.
Mechanical available: Offset; Black and 3 ROP colors; insert accepted; page cutoffs - 22 3/4.
Mechanical Specifications: Type page 13 x 21 1/2; E - 6 cols, 2 1/16, 1/8 between; A - 6 cols, 2 1/16, 1/8 between; C - 8 cols, 1 1/2, 1/8 between.
Commodity Consumption: Avg. Page Number Per Issue - Daily 12; widths 28; Newsprint Used - Short Tons 190; Printing Ink Used - Black 5400; Printing Ink Used - Color 1000; Printing Ink Used - Pages Printed 5154.
Equipment: Editorial Hardware – Mk.; Layout Software – 2-Page Monitor, 1-APP/Mac II.; Production Equipment – 1-Nu; Cameras – 1-K/241. PRESSROOM: Line 1 – 5-G/Community; Folders – 1-G/Community, 1-G/Gregg Plow.; Bundle tying machines – 1/Sa; Addressing machine – St/1600.; Business Hardware – Tandy/3000

FORT DODGE

THE MESSENGER

713 Central Ave., Fort Dodge, Iowa, 50501-0659; gen tel (515) 573-2141; gen fax (515) 573-2148; adv fax (515) 573-2136; ed fax (515) 574-4529; adv e-mail admgr@messengernews.net; ed e-mail editor@messengernews.net; web site www.messengernews.net

Published: Mon, Tues, Wed, Thur, Fri, Sat, Sun
Weekday Frequency: m
Saturday Frequency: m
Circulation: 13,553; 13,553(sat); 15,818(sun)
Last Audit: ABC September 30, 2011
Price: 3.60/wk; 14.35/mo.; .172.20/yr; 89.85/6 mo.
News services: AP.
Politics: Independent-Republican. **Established:** 1856
Note: National advertising is sold in combination with the Webster City Daily Freeman-Journal (e) for $47.70 individual newspaper rates not made available.
Own facility?: Y
Special Editions: Bridal Guide (Jan); Progress Edition (Feb); Crime Prevention (Feb); Home & Garden Show (Mar); Golf Directory (Apr); Visitors Guide (May); Hometown Pride (June); Wedding Planner (July); Little League tab (July); Girls Sate Softball Tournament (July); Football Preview (Aug); All About Home (Sep); Winter Sports (Nov); Christmas Countdown (Nov); Holiday Showcase (Dec); Senior's tab (monthly); Business Review (monthly); Real Estate Buyer's Guide (monthly)
Special Weekly Sections: Education Page (Mon); Business (S); Religion (Sat); Best Food Day (Wed).
Magazines: Parade (S).
Pub. .... Larry D. Bushman
Adv. Mgr., Classified .... Jean Warg
Adv. Mgr., Retail .... Charlene Peterson
Circ. Dir. .... Grant Gibbons
Mng. Ed. .... Barbara Wallace Hughes
Ed. Emer. .... Walter B. Stevens
Editorial Page Ed. .... Terry Dwyer
Farm Ed .... Larry Kershner
Prodn Sup .... Michelle Colshan
Lifestyle Ed. .... Sandy Mickelson
Sports Ed. .... Eric Pratt
Data Processing Mgr. .... Rex Lee
Online Mgr .... Regina Smith
Advertising Director .... David Jakeman
Adv. Dir. .... David Jacobson
Market Information: TMC.
Mechanical available: Offset; Black and 3 ROP colors; insert accepted; page cutoffs - 22 3/4.
Mechanical Specifications: Type page 11 1/106 x 21 1/2; E - 6 cols, 1 3/4, 1/16 between; A - 6 cols, 1 3/4, 1/16 between; C - 9 cols, 1 1/4, 1/16 between.
Commodity Consumption: Avg. Page Number Per Issue - Daily 28; Avg. Page Number Per Issue - Plates Used 16500; Avg. Page Number Per Issue - Sunday 62; widths 24; Newsprint Used - Short Tons 1398; Printing Ink Used - Black 30500; Printing Ink Used - Color 19000; Printing Ink Use
Equipment EDITORIAL: Front-end Software – QPS/QuarkXPress 4.1, Adobe/Photoshop 7.0.; Editorial Hardware – MS Windows 2003; IMAC G6; Editorial Printers – 1-HP LaserJet 5100; Classified Hardware – MS Windows 2003; Classified Printers – 1-LaserJet 2035n DISPLAY: Ad make-up applications – Multi-Ad/Creator 8; Layout Software – ALS/Page Director 4.1.7.; Display Printers – HP LaserJet 5000 PRODUCTION: Pagination Software – QPS/QuarkXPress 8; Production Equipment – HP 5500n Printer; HP 5550n Printer; Scanners – Epson V330 Scanner PRESSROOM: Line 1 – 14-G; Press Drives – 2-Fin/100 h.p.; Folders – 1-G/3:2, 1-G/SSC, 1-G/SSC/Quarter Folder; Pasters – 8-Martin/EC Splicer. MAILROOM: Counter stackers – 2-BG/108, HI/HT II, 1-HI/RS25; Inserters and stuffers – HI/1372, Muller 227 6/1; Bundle tying machines – 3/Bu; Wrapping singles – 1-Power Strap; Addressing machine – KR/Inkjet; Other equipment –Ruline/Glue-Trimmer, MM/Stitcher-Trimme; Business Hardware – NCR
Delivery method: Mail, Newsstand, Private Carrier, Racks

FORT MADISON

FORT MADISON DAILY DEMOCRAT

1226 Ave. H, Fort Madison, Iowa, 52627-0160; gen tel (319) 372-6421; adv tel (319) 372-6421; ed tel (319) 372-6421; gen fax (319) 372-3867; adv fax (319) 372-3867; ed fax (319) 372-3867; gen e-mail publisher@dailydem.com; adv e-mail advertising@dailydem.com; ed e-mail editor@dailydem.com; web site www.dailydem.com

Published: Mon, Tues, Wed, Thur, Fri
Weekday Frequency: e
Circulation: 4,847
Price: $83.20/yr; $7.00/4wk, $21.00/12wk, $39.60/24wk.
Advertising: Open inch rate $15.50
Insert rate: $54.60 per 1000 net
News services: AP.
Politics: Independent. **Established:** 1868
Note: Democrat Co. is owned by Brehm Communications Inc. Through it's subsidiaries, Democrat Co., Gull Communications, Hi-Desert Publishing Co., Inc., News West Publishing Company Inc., Penny Power Publications Inc., Placer Community Newspapers, Inc. and Princ
Not Published: New Year; Memorial Day; Independence Day; Labor Day; Thanksgiving; Christmas.
Own facility?: Y
Special Editions: Vacation (Apr); Tri-State Rodeo (Aug); Bridal Tab (Jan); Fair Tab (Jul); Bridal Tab (Jun); Graduation (May); Progress (Oct); Home Improvement (Sept).
Special Weekly Sections: Religion (Fri); Weekend Sports Wrap-Up (Mon); Entertainment (Thur); Farm Page (Tues); Business Page (Wed).
Magazines: American Profile (Mon).
Profile: Daily newspaper, central printing plant
Pub. .... Gary Milks
Bus. Mgr. .... Mary Older
Online Ed. .... Robin Delaney
Sports Ed. .... Chris Faulkner
Data Processing Mgr. .... Theresa Stolley
Prodn. Mgr. .... Tracy Burris
Prodn. Mgr., Composing .... Lee Vandenberg
Prodn. Mgr., Mailroom .... Sue Menke
Market Information: TMC.
Mechanical available: Offset; Black and 3 ROP colors; insert accepted; page cutoffs - 22 3/4.
Mechanical Specifications: Type page 11 5/8 x 21 1/2; E - 6 cols, 1 5/6, 1/8 between; A - 6 cols, 1 5/6, 1/8 between; C - 6 cols, 1 5/6, 1/8 between.
Commodity Consumption: Avg. Page Number Per Issue - Daily 24; Avg. Page Number Per Issue - Plates Used 15000; widths 34; Newsprint Used - Metric Tons 715; Printing Ink Used - Black 20000; Printing Ink Used - Color 2000; Printing Ink Used - Pages Printed 4700.
Equipment EDITORIAL: Front-end Software – DragX, QPS/QuarkXPress, Baseview/Qtools, Baseview/NewsEdit Pro.; Editorial Hardware – 1-APP/Mac 7100, APP/Mac Quadra 630; Editorial Printers – 1-COM/8400, NewGen/Laser Printer, Pre Press/Panther Plus Imagesetter CLASSIFIED: Front-end Software – Baseview/Class Manager.; Classified Hardware – APP/Mac Quadra 630; Classified Equipment – Okidata/320 Microline Printer; Classified Printers – COM/8400 DISPLAY: Ad make-up applications – QPS/QuarkXPress, Baseview, Adobe/Photoshop, Multi-Ad/Creator; Layout Software – 1-APP/Power Mac 7100.; Display Hardware – APP/Mac; Display Printers – COM/8400, Pre Press/Panther Plus Imagesetter PRODUCTION: Pagination Software – QPS/QuarkXPress, Baseview/Qtools, DragX.; Production Equipment – 1-Nu, Pre Press/Panther Plus, Kodak CTP; Cameras – Acti; Scanners – Lf/Leafscan 35, Umax/PowerLook, Nikon/LS1000 PRESSROOM: Line 1 – 10-G/Community; Folders – 1; Pasters – BG/Acumeter.; Inserters and stuffers – KAN/320 4:1; Bundle tying machines – Bu, MLN/Strappers; Addressing machine – Wm; Other equipment –Challenge/3 Knife Trimmer. BUSINESS COMPUTERS: Business Software – Quatro Pro 4.0, Word Perfect 5.1, Microsoft/Windows 3.1; Business Hardware – Qantel, SBS
Delivery method: Mail, Newsstand, Private Carrier, Racks

IOWA CITY

IOWA CITY PRESS-CITIZEN

1725 N. Dodge St., Iowa City, Iowa, 52245; gen tel (319) 337-3181; gen fax (319) 466-7645; adv fax (319) 339-5953; adv e-mail classified@press-citizen.com; advertising@press-citizen.com; web site www.press-citizen.com

Published: Mon, Tues, Wed, Thur, Fri, Sat
Weekday Frequency: m
Saturday Frequency: m
Circulation: 9,718; 12,080(sat)
Last Audit: ABC September 30, 2011
Price: 10.00/4wk, $32.50/13wk.
Advertising: Open inch rate $41.64
News services: AP, GNS, LAT-WP, News America.
Politics: Independent.

Note: On Sundays, readers receive the Sunday state edition of the Des Moines Register wrapped in a full local news section provided by the Iowa City Press-Citizen. See the Des Moines Register listing for Sunday circulation and advertising rates.
Special Editions: Spring Homes (Apr); The Key (Aug); Holiday Guide II (Dec); Bridal (Feb); Chamber Annual Report (Jan); Best of Area (Jul); Go Play (Jun); KXIC Home Show (Mar); Holiday Guide I (Nov); Welcome Home Iowa City (Oct); Go Play (Sept).
Special Weekly Sections: Church News (Fri); Channels (Sat); Outdoor/Recreation (Thur); Life (Wed).
Magazines: USA WEEKEND Magazine (Sat).
Adv. Mgr., Classified .... Shawn Reineke
Dir., Mktg. Serv. .... Dan Brown
Mng. Ed. .... Jim Lewers
Asst. Ed. .... Tricia Dewall
City Ed. .... Greg Smith
News Ed. .... Emily Hagemann
Photo Ed. .... Dan Williamson
Sports Ed. .... Ryan Suchomel
AS400 Analyst .... Jim Tvedte
Online Ed. .... Patrick Riepe
Prodn. Mgr., Pre Press .... Chris Hayes
Market Information: TMC.
Mechanical available: Offset; Black and 3 ROP colors; insert accepted; page cutoffs - 22 3/4.
Mechanical Specifications: Type page 11 5/8 x 21 1/2; E - 6 cols, 1 5/16, 1/8 between; A - 6 cols, 1 5/16, 1/8 between; C - 9 cols, 1 1/6, 1/8 between.
Commodity Consumption: Avg. Page Number Per Issue - Daily 28; Avg. Page Number Per Issue - Plates Used 14351; Avg. Page Number Per Issue - Saturday 40; widths 24; Newsprint Used - Metric Tons 1756; Newsprint Used - Short Tons 1936; Printing Ink Used - Black 25520; Printing Ink
Equipment; Editorial Hardware – 1-APT.; Classified Hardware – 1-APT. DISPLAY: Ad make-up applications – QPS/QuarkXPress, Adobe/Photoshop, Adobe/PageMaker, Adobe/Illustrator, Macromedia/Freehand; Display Printers – HP/LaserJet 4MV PRODUCTION: Pagination Software – ProImage/NewsWay.; Production Equipment – KPG; Cameras – Scanners □ Diadem/200S Direct Screen; Scanners – Diadem/200S Direct Screen PRESSROOM: Line 1 – 14-G/Urbanite 1000 Series; Folders – 1; Press control system – G. MAILROOM: Counter stackers – QWI/400, QWI/500, QWI/501; Inserters and stuffers – HI/1372; Bundle tying machines – 1-Dynaric/1500, 1/MLN; Wrapping singles – QWI/Underwrap; Other equipment – MM/1509 Minuteman.; Business Hardware – IBM/AS-400

KEOKUK

DAILY GATE CITY

1016 Main St., Keokuk, Iowa, 52632; gen tel (319) 524-8300; gen fax (319) 524-4363; gen e-mail gatecity@dailygate.com; adv e-mail advertising@dailygate.com; web site www.dailygate.com
Published: Mon, Tues, Wed, Thur, Fri
Weekday Frequency: e
Circulation: 5,500
Last Audit: January 2, 2008
Price: 80.00/yr.
Advertising: Open inch rate $15.45
News services: AP.
Politics: Independent. **Established:** 1847
Not Published: New Year; Memorial Day; Independence Day; Labor Day; Thanksgiving; Christmas.
Special Editions: Lawn & Garden (Apr); Labor Day (Aug); Chronology (Dec); Progress (Feb); Bridal (Jan); Estate (Jun); Spring Car Care (Mar); Newcomers & Vacation (May); Winter Sports (Nov); Woman (Oct); Fall Home Improvement (Sept).
Magazines: TV Magazine (Fri); American Profile (Weekly).
Pub. .... Mark Smidt
Adv. Dir. .... Doug Shipman
Adv. Asst. .... Mary Holmes
Circ. Mgr. .... Diane Bolton
Mng. Ed. .... Steve Dunn
Sports Ed. .... Brad Cameron
Prodn. Mgr. .... Judy Nagel
Market Information: ADS; TMC.
Mechanical available: Offset; Black and 3 ROP colors; insert accepted; page cutoffs - 22 3/4.
Mechanical Specifications: Type page 13 1/4 x 21 1/2; E - 6 cols, 2 1/16, 1/16 between; A - 8 cols, 1 1/2, 1/8 between; C - 8 cols, 1 1/2, 1/8 between.
Commodity Consumption: Avg. Page Number Per Issue - Daily 14; widths 27 1/2; Newsprint Used - Short Tons 500.
Equipment EDITORIAL: Front-end Software – Baseview.; Editorial Hardware – APP/Mac CLASSIFIED: Front-end Software – Baseview.; Classified Hardware – APP/Mac; Layout Software – 3-APP/Power Mac 7100.; Display Hardware – APP/Mac; Display Printers – Xante/8200 PRODUCTION: Pagination Software – Baseview.; Production Equipment – Xante/8200, Adobe/Photoshop; Cameras – 1-R/24580; Bundle tying machines – MLN/2EE.; Business Hardware – Qantel

LE MARS

LE MARS DAILY SENTINEL

41 1st Ave. NE, Le Mars, Iowa, 51031; gen tel (712) 546-7031; gen fax (712) 546-7035; gen e-mail sentinel@lemarscomm.net; adv e-mail mjost@lemarscomm.net; web site www.lemarssentinel.com
Published: Mon, Tues, Wed, Thur, Fri
Weekday Frequency: e
Circulation: 2,584
Last Audit: Sworn October 10, 2002
Price: 97.50/yr.
Advertising: Open inch rate $12.85
Insert rate: 80/1000
News services: AP.
Politics: Independent. **Established:** 1870
Not Published: Legal holidays.
Own facility?: Y
Special Editions: Visitor's Guide (Apr); Back-to-School (Aug); Holiday (Dec); Pride in Plymouth Co. (Feb); Bridal (Jan); County Fair (Jul); Summer Sports (Jun); Homes n' Style (Mar); Grad Tab (May); Homes n' Style (Sept).
Special Weekly Sections: NASCAR (Fri); Agriculture (Thur); Cooking (Tues); Business (Wed).
Magazines: Relish (Monthly); American Profile (Weekly). Athlon Sports monthly
Pub. .... Tom Stangl
Mktg. Dir. .... Monte Jost
Lifestyles Ed. .... Beverly Van Buskirk
Data Processing Mgr. .... Judy Barnable
Composition Mgr. .... Shannon Jost
Market Information: TMC.
Mechanical available: Offset; Black and 3 ROP colors; insert accepted; page cutoffs - 21 1/2.
Mechanical Specifications: Type page 13 x 21 1/2; E - 6 cols, 2 1/16, 1/8 between; A - 6 cols, 2 1/16, 1/8 between; C - 6 cols, 2 1/16, 1/8 between.
Commodity Consumption: Avg. Page Number Per Issue - Daily 16; Avg. Page Number Per Issue - Plates Used 8000; widths 14; Newsprint Used - Short Tons 350; Printing Ink Used - Black 4500; Printing Ink Used - Color 500.
Equipment EDITORIAL: Front-end Software – APP/Mac, QPS/QuarkXPress 6.0.; Editorial Hardware – APP/Mac; Editorial Equipment – Konica, Imagesetter; Editorial Printers – APP/Mac LaserWriters, QMS/860, NewGen/DesignXpress CLASSIFIED: Front-end Software – QPS/QuarkXPress 6.0.; Classified Hardware – APP/Mac, CAMS; Classified Printers – APP/Mac LaserWriters DISPLAY: Ad make-up applications – QPS/QuarkXPress 6.0.; Display Hardware – APP/Mac; Display Printers – APP/Mac LaserWriter; Production Equipment – SL/GNS-28; Cameras – 1-SCREEN/C-240-D, Kyoto/Japan; Scanners – Polaroid. PRESSROOM: Line 1 – 6-G/Community; Folders – 1; Reels and Stands – 5-G/Community Stand.; Bundle tying machines – Malow/50, Bu; Addressing machine – Miller/Bevco 285.; Business Hardware – 4-Gateway/2000, Compaq, Compaq
Delivery method: Mail, Private Carrier, Racks

MARSHALLTOWN

TIMES-REPUBLICAN

135 W. Main St., Marshalltown, Iowa, 50158-1300; gen tel (641) 753-6611; gen fax (641) 753-8813; gen e-mail trpub@timesrepublican.com; adv e-mail tradv@timesrepublican.com; ed e-mail news@timesrepublican.com; web site www.timesrepublican.com
Group: The Nutting Company
Published: Mon, Tues, Wed, Thur, Fri, Sat, Sun
Weekday Frequency: e
Saturday Frequency: m
Circulation: 8,180; 8,180(sat); 8,678(sun)
Last Audit: ABC September 30, 2011
Price: 3.00/wk (carrier), $3.25/wk (mt. rt/mail); 12.20 /mo (carrier), $13.20 /mo (mt. rt/mail); 146.55/yr (carrier), $158.20/yr (mail/mt. rt).
Advertising: Open inch rate $23.80
Insert rate: $36 and up
News services: AP.
Politics: Independent. **Established:** 1856
Own facility?: Y
Special Editions: Seniors Tab (Apr); Football Contest (Aug); Holiday Greetings (Dec); Agri-Business (Feb); Bridal Tab (Jan); Little League Review (Jul); Outdoors (Jun); Home Improvement (Mar); Health Tab (May); Business Magazine (Monthly); Christmas Countdown (Nov); NFL &
Special Weekly Sections: Best Food Day (S); Religion (Sat); Best Food Day (Wed).
Magazines: Parade (S).
Pub. .... Mike Schlesinger
Marketing Director .... Denise Kemp
Circ. Dir. .... Randy Cutright
Copy Ed. .... Wes Burns
Educ. Reporter .... Andrew Potter
Reporter .... Ken Black
Managing Editor .... Abigail McWilliam
Sports Ed. .... Ross Thede
Television/Film Ed. .... Pam Rogers
IT Dir. .... Steve Plain
Prodn. Mgr., Press .... Clayton Steil
Adv. Dir. .... Diane Bryant
Market Information: ADS; TMC.
Mechanical available: Offset; Black and 3 ROP colors; insert accepted - all, no brokered group ads; page cutoffs - 22 3/4.
Mechanical Specifications: Type page 10 x 21 1/2; E - 6 cols, 1 1/2, 1/4 between; A - 6 cols, 1 1/2, 1/4 between; C - 9 cols, 1, 1/8 between.
Commodity Consumption: Avg. Page Number Per Issue - Daily 19; Avg. Page Number Per Issue - Plates Used 40000; Avg. Page Number Per Issue - Saturday 24; Avg. Page Number Per Issue - Sunday 50; widths 25; Newsprint Used - Short Tons 2000; Printing Ink Used - Black 60000; Printin
Equipment; Editorial Hardware – G-5s; Classified Hardware – Dell DISPLAY: Ad make-up applications – Multi-Ad/Creator, QPS/QuarkXPress; Layout Software – G-5s; Production Equipment – ECRM - CTP PRESSROOM: Line 1 – 8-G/Community (upper former) 1988; Line 2 – 8-G/Community (upper former) 1988 MAILROOM: Counter stackers – HI; Bundle tying machines – EAM-Mosca/Automatic, MLN; Wrapping singles – QWI; Addressing machine – Ch.; Business Hardware – Dell
Zip Codes served: 50005; 50051; 50056; 50078; 50106; 50112; 50120; 50122; 50141; 50142; 50148; 50158; 50163; 50173; 50234; 50239; 50247; 50258; 50269; 50278; 50609; 50621; 50627; 50632; 50635; 50637; 50638; 50680; 52339; 52342

MASON CITY

GLOBE-GAZETTE

300 N. Washington Ave., Mason City, Iowa, 50401; gen tel (641) 421-0500; adv tel (641) 421-0546; ed tel (641) 421-0524; gen fax (641) 421-7108; adv fax (641) 421-7108; ed fax (641) 421-7108; adv e-mail adservices@globegazette.com; ed e-mail news@globegazette.com; web site www.globegazette.com
Published: Mon, Tues, Wed, Thur, Fri, Sat, Sun
Weekday Frequency: m
Saturday Frequency: m
Circulation: 14,049; 14,049(sat); 18,380(sun)
Last Audit: ABC September 30, 2011
Price: 3.90/wk; 16.90/mo; 198.00/yr.
Advertising: Open inch rate $32.45
News services: AP.
Politics: Independent. **Established:** 1893
Not Published: Christmas.
Special Editions: Builder's Tour (Apr); Fall Fashion Show (Aug); Gifts (Dec); All About Love (Feb); Health & Fitness (Jan); Economic Report (Jul); Grilling Made Easy (Jun); Do it Yourself (Mar); Lawn & Garden (May); North Iowa Farmer (Monthly); High School Winter Sports (N
Special Weekly Sections: Outdoors (Fri); Teens (Mon); Business (S); Religion (Sat); Entertainment (Thur); Food/Grocery (Tues); Home & Health (Wed).
Magazines: Relish (Monthly); Parade (S); American Profile (Weekly).
Controller .... Linda Halfman
Adv. Mgr., Classified .... Amy Stoeffler
Adv. Mgr., Display .... Greg Wilderman
Mktg. Mgr. .... Ruth Miller
Circ. Mgr. .... Jeff Binstock
Ed. .... Joe Buttweiler
City Ed. .... Jane Reynolds
Editorial Page Ed. .... Bob Steenson
Editorial Page Ed. .... Tom Thomas
Librarian .... Judy Delperdang
Lifestyle Ed. .... Karen Jacobs
Online Ed. .... Olivia Ostrander
Reporter .... Jan Horgen
Sports Ed. .... Kirk Hard Castle
Data Processing Mgr. .... Terry Balek
Prodn. Coord., New Media .... Howard Query
Prodn. Supvr., Pre Press .... Lisa Ahrens
Prodn. Supvr., Pressroom .... Rob Curly
Market Information: ADS; Split run; TMC.
Mechanical available: Letterpress; Black and 3 ROP colors; insert accepted - self-adhesive notes, samples; page cutoffs - 22.
Mechanical Specifications: Type page 12 x 21; E - 6 cols, 2 1/16, 1/8 between; A - 6 cols, 2 1/16, 1/8 between; C - 9 cols, 1 3/8, 1/16 between.
Commodity Consumption: Avg. Page Number Per Issue - Daily 24; Avg. Page Number Per Issue - Plates Used 19637; Avg. Page Number Per Issue - Sunday 60; widths 35; Newsprint Used - Metric Tons 1280; Newsprint Used - Short Tons 1411; Printing Ink Used - Black 28000; Printing Ink U
Equipment EDITORIAL: Front-end Software – MS/NT 4.0.; Editorial Hardware – 2-IBM/RS 6000, Compaq/Proliant Server 2500; Editorial Printers – HP; Classified Hardware – 2-IBM/RS 6000; Classified Printers – HP. DISPLAY: Ad make-up applications – QPS/QuarkXPress 4.02; Layout Software – MEI/ALS.; Display Hardware – APP/Mac; Display Printers – HP PRODUCTION: Pagination Software – QPS/QuarkXPress 3.32.; Production Equipment – 2-Pre Press/Panther Pro-46, APP/Mac Preserver; Cameras – 1-R/480, 1-C/Spartan II, ECR/Autokon 1000; Scanners – AG/Argus II PRESSROOM: Line 1 – 8-KBA/Mot-Colormax 5W with CIC single width; Folders – 1-G/SSC, 1.; Inserters and stuffers – 1-MM/227E 5:1; Bundle tying machines – 2-MLN/ML2EE; Addressing machine – 1-Ch/595-596.; Business Hardware – 1-IBM/AS-400

MOUNT PLEASANT

MT. PLEASANT NEWS

215 W. Monroe St., Mount Pleasant, Iowa, 52641; gen tel (319) 385-3131; gen fax (319) 385-8048; gen e-mail news@mp-news.net; adv e-mail adv@mpnews.net; ed e-mail news@mpnews.net; web site www.mpnews.net

Published: Mon, Tues, Wed, Thur, Fri
Weekday Frequency: e
Circulation: 2,668
Last Audit: October 1, 2003
Price: 94.00/yr (in state), $125.00/yr (out-of-state); 26.00/3mo (carrier), $30.50/3mo (out-of-county).
Advertising: Open inch rate $9.43
News services: AP.
Politics: Independent. **Established:** 1878
Not Published: New Year; Memorial Day; Independence Day; Labor Day; Thanksgiving; Christmas.
Special Editions: Home Improvement (Apr); Senior Citizen (Aug); Basketball (Dec); Brides (Jan); Fair (Jul); Little League/Softball (Jun); Agriculture (Mar); Summer Fun (May); Christmas Showcase (Nov); Chamber of Commerce (Oct); Senior Lifestyle (Sept).
Special Weekly Sections: Entertainment (Fri); Business (Mon); Education (Thur); Agriculture (Tues); Editorial Page (Wed).
Magazines: American Profile (Mon).
Pub. ....Bill Gray
Design Dept. Mgr. ....Brad Jackson
News Ed. ....Jeff Hunt
Market Information: ADS; TMC.
Mechanical available: Offset; Black and 3 ROP colors; insert accepted - any; page cutoffs - 22 5/8.
Mechanical Specifications: Type page 13 x 21 1/2; E - 6 cols, 2 1/16, 1/8 between; A - 6 cols, 2 1/16, 1/8 between; C - 8 cols, 1 7/16, 1/8 between.
Commodity Consumption: Avg. Page Number Per Issue - Daily 10; Avg. Page Number Per Issue - Plates Used 2811; widths 28; Newsprint Used - Short Tons 111; Printing Ink Used - Black 3905; Printing Ink Used - Color 850; Printing Ink Used - Pages Printed 4000.
Equipment; Editorial Hardware – 1-APP/Power Mac, 1-APP/Mac G3, 1-APP/iMac.; Classified Hardware – 1-APP/Power Mac.; Layout Software – 2-APP/Mac G3, APP/Mac Quadra 650. PRODUCTION: Pagination Software – QPS/QuarkXPress 4.0.; Production Equipment – 1-Nat/250; Cameras – 1-Nu; Scanners – APP/Mac PRESSROOM: Line 1 – 4-G/Community; Folders – 1; Bundle tying machines – 1/Bu; Addressing machine – 2-/Wm.; Business Hardware – IBM

MUSCATINE

MUSCATINE JOURNAL

301 E. Third St., Muscatine, Iowa, 52761; gen tel (563) 263-2331; gen fax (563) 262-8042; gen e-mail news@muscatinejournal.com; adv e-mail sales@muscatinejournal.com; ed e-mail news@muscatinejournal.com; web site www.muscatinejournal.com

Group: Metro Suburbia, Inc./Newhouse Newspapers
Published: Mon, Tues, Wed, Thur, Fri, Sat
Weekday Frequency: m
Saturday Frequency: m
Circulation: 5,834; 5,804(sat)
Last Audit: ABC September 30, 2011
Price: 2.44/wk; 10.60/mo; 121.75/yr.
Advertising: Open inch rate $16.80
News services: AP, DF, TMS.
Politics: Independent. **Established:** 1840
Not Published: New Year; Christmas.
Special Editions: Spring Car Care (Apr); Back-to-School (Aug); Gift Guide (Dec); Answer Book (Jul); Little League (Jun); Gift Guide (Nov); Car Care (Oct); Find it in Muscatine (Sept).
Special Weekly Sections: Faith (Fri); Work & Money (Sat); Etcetera (Thur); Outside (Tues); Friends & Family (Wed).
Magazines: Primetime (Sat).
Pub. ....Bob Blackman
Circ. Mgr. ....Brenda Ver Steegh
Ed. ....Chris Steinbach
Features Ed. ....Ann Phillips
News Ed. ....Rusty Schrader
Sports Ed. ....Matt Coss
Market Information: ADS; TMC.
Mechanical available: Offset; Black and 3 ROP colors; insert accepted; page cutoffs - 20 1/2.
Mechanical Specifications: Type page 11 3/5 x 20 1/2; E - 6 cols, 1 4/5, 1/8 between; A - 6 cols, 1 4/5, 1/8 between; C - 9 cols, 1 3/8, 1/16 between.
Commodity Consumption: Avg. Page Number Per Issue - Daily 22; Avg. Page Number Per Issue - Plates Used 8500; Avg. Page Number Per Issue - Saturday 28; widths 34; Newsprint Used - Metric Tons 600; Printing Ink Used - Black 24700; Printing Ink Used - Color 800; Printing Ink Used
Equipment EDITORIAL: Front-end Software – Baseview.; Editorial Hardware – APP/Mac; Editorial Equipment – APP/Mac IIsi, AP/GraphicsNet, Lf/AP Leaf Picture Desk, Lf/Negative Scanner; Editorial Printers – HP 551 CLASSIFIED: Front-end Software – Baseview.; Classified Hardware – APP/Mac; Classified Printers – HP 8150 DISPLAY: Ad make-up applications – QPS/QuarkXPress; Layout Software – APP/Mac, QPS/QuarkXPress.; Display Hardware – APP/Mac; Display Printers – HP/5MV, HP/8000 DN, HP/8150 DN PRODUCTION: Pagination Software – Baseview.; Production Equipment – Lf/AP Leaf Picture Desk, AG/Rapiline 17; Scanners – APP/Mac One Scanner, HP/ScanJet; Bundle tying machines – 1-MLN/Spirit-Strapper. BUSINESS COMPUTERS: Business Software – IBM/AS-400, Lee Business System, Microsoft/Office 2000; Business Hardware – IBM/AS-400, Remote access via T-1, PC Workstations

NEWTON

NEWS PRINTING CO.

200 First Ave. E, Newton, Iowa, 50208; gen tel (641) 792-3121; gen fax (641) 791-7104

NEWTON DAILY NEWS

200 1st Ave. E, Newton, Iowa, 50208-0967; gen tel (641) 792-3121; gen fax (641) 791-7104; adv e-mail advertising@newtondailynews.com; ed e-mail newsroom@newtondailynews.com; web site www.newtondailynews.com

Published: Mon, Tues, Wed, Thur, Fri
Weekday Frequency: e
Circulation: 5,476
Last Audit: September 20, 2001
Price: 1.65/wk; 8.00/mo; 81.00/yr.
Advertising: Open inch rate $13.50
News services: AP, CNS, MCT, NEA, TMS.
Politics: 1902
Not Published: New Year; Memorial Day; Independence Day; Labor Day; Thanksgiving; Christmas.
Special Editions: Progress Edition (Feb); Spring Bridal (Jan); Business Showcase (Nov); Local Business Women (Oct); Fall Football (Sept).
Special Weekly Sections: TV Digest (Fri).
Magazines: Relish (Monthly); American Profile (Thur).
Pub ....Jim Nelson
Bus. Mgr. ....Brenda Lamb
Adv. Dir. ....Mark Drudge
Ed. ....Andy Karr
Prodn. Mgr. ....Kelly Vest
Prodn. Mgr. ....John DeGrado
Prodn. Mgr., Commercial Printing Chris Basinger
Prodn. Supvr., Composing Room Mari Jo DeGrado
Market Information: TMC.
Mechanical available: Offset; Black and 3 ROP colors; insert accepted; page cutoffs - 22 3/4.
Mechanical Specifications: Type page 12 1/2 x 21 1/2; E - 6 cols, 1 7/8, 1/8 between; A - 6 cols, 1 7/8, 1/8 between; C - 9 cols, 1 1/4, 1/16 between.
Commodity Consumption: Avg. Page Number Per Issue - Daily 14; Avg. Page Number Per Issue - Plates Used 4758; widths 25; Newsprint Used - Short Tons 156; Printing Ink Used - Black 4800; Printing Ink Used - Color 900; Printing Ink Used - Pages Printed 4662.
Equipment EDITORIAL: Front-end Software – QPS/QuarkXPress 4.1, Microsoft/Word.; Editorial Hardware – APP/Mac; Editorial Printers – APP/Mac LaserWriter Plus CLASSIFIED: Front-end Software – Baseview.; Classified Hardware – APP/iMac; Layout Software – Adforce.; Display Hardware – iMac/G4 PRODUCTION: Pagination Software – QuarkXPress 4.1.; Production Equipment – 1-Nu, APP/Mac, Konica/5100T 5.3, Konica/3100S 5.1; Cameras – 1-Kk PRESSROOM: Line 1 – 6-G/Suburban 1969. MAILROOM: Counter stackers – 1/BG; Bundle tying machines – 3-Bu, 3-Strapmatic; Addressing machine – KR.; Business Hardware – 2-BI, ATT

OELWEIN

THE OELWEIN DAILY REGISTER

25 First St. SE, Oelwein, Iowa, 50662; gen tel (319) 283-2144; gen fax (319) 283-3268; gen e-mail news@oelweindailyregister.com; adv e-mail ads@oelweindailyregister.com; ed e-mail editor@oelweindailyregister.com; web site www.oelweindailyregister.com

Published: Mon, Tues, Wed, Thur, Fri, Sat
Weekday Frequency: All day
Saturday Frequency: All day
Circulation: 2,354; 2,354(sat)
Price: 149.00/yr.
Advertising: Open inch rate $18.60
News services: AP.
Politics: 1881
Not Published: New Year; Memorial Day; Independence Day; Labor Day; Thanksgiving; Christmas.
Own facility?: Y
Special Editions: Husky (Apr); Pigskin Preview (Aug); Christmas Promotions (Dec); Soil Conservation (Feb); Bridal (Jan); Summer Sports (Jul); Father's Day (Jun); Update (Mar); Graduation (May); Christmas Open House (Nov); Fire Prevention (Oct); Fall-Tourism (Sept).
Special Weekly Sections: Weekly TV (Fri); Agriculture Edition (Wed).
Pub. ....Deb Weigel
Circ. Mgr. ....Sue Hosto
Mng. Ed. ....Jack Swanson
City Ed. ....Deb Kunkle
Prodn. Mgr. ....David Gelhausen
Market Information: TMC.
Mechanical available: Offset; Black and 3 ROP colors; insert accepted; page cutoffs - 22 3/4.
Mechanical Specifications: Type page 12 x 21 1/2; E - 6 cols, 1 7/8, 1/6 between; A - 6 cols, 1 7/8, 1/6 between; C - 9 cols, 1 1/2, 1/12 between.
Commodity Consumption: Avg. Page Number Per Issue - Daily 12; widths 26 1/2.
Equipment; Production Equipment – 2-COM/Unisetter, 1-COM/Area Unified Composer. PRESSROOM: Line 1 – 7-G/C901; Folders – 2; Bundle tying machines – 1/Bu, 1-/Sa, 1-Malow/MC-50; Addressing machine – 1-SC/labeler.

OSKALOOSA

OSKALOOSA HERALD

1901 A Ave. W., Oskaloosa, Iowa, 52577-0530; gen tel (641) 672-2581; ed tel (641) 672-2581; gen fax (641) 672-2294; adv fax (641) 673-8226; ed fax (641) 672-1264; adv e-mail oskyclass@oskyherald.com; ed e-mail oskynews@oskyherald.com; web site www.oskaloosaherald.com

Published: Mon, Tues, Wed, Thur, Fri
Weekday Frequency: e
Circulation: 3,381
Last Audit: September 30, 2005
Price: 8.00/mo (in county); 88.00/yr.
Advertising: Open inch rate $9.45
News services: NEA, INA, AP.
Not Published: New Year; Martin Luther King Jr.'s Birthday; President's Day; Memorial Day; Independence Day; Labor Day; Columbus Day; Veteran's Day; Thanksgiving; Christmas.
Special Editions: Progress (Mar).
Special Weekly Sections: TV Listings (Fri); Business (Wed).
Magazines: Relish (Monthly); American Profile (Weekly).
Pub. ....Tim Kurtz
Bus. Mgr. ....Connie Sanders
Adv. Dir. ....Deb Van Engelenhoven
Circ. Mgr. ....Connie Davis
Ed. ....Duane Nollen
Market Information: TMC.
Mechanical available: Offset; Black and 3 ROP colors; insert accepted - all; page cutoffs - 22 3/4.
Mechanical Specifications: Type page 13 x 21 1/2; E - 6 cols, 2 1/16, 1/8 between; A - 6 cols, 2 1/16, 1/8 between; C - 6 cols, 2 1/16, 1/16 between.
Commodity Consumption: Avg. Page Number Per Issue - Daily 12; Printing Ink Used - Black 6000.
Equipment EDITORIAL: Front-end Software – QPS.; Editorial Hardware – APP/Mac; Classified Hardware – APP/Mac.; Layout Software – APP/Mac.; Production Equipment – 1-Nu/Flip Top FT40L, LE/24AQ; Cameras – Acti/S 25; Scanners – APP/Mac. PRESSROOM: Line 1 – 6-WPC/Web Leader.; Bundle tying machines – 1-Bu/182XE4, 1-Sa/SR2CTAN; Addressing machine – 1-Am/1950B.; Business Hardware – IBM

OTTUMWA

MONEY SAVER

213 E. Second St., Ottumwa, Iowa, 52501; gen tel (641) 684-4611; adv tel 641-683-5381; gen fax (641) 684-7834; adv fax 641-683-4118; adv e-mail mtews@ottumwacourier.com; web site www.ottumwacourier.com

Published: Mon, Tues, Wed, Thur, Fri, Sat
Weekday Frequency: m
Saturday Frequency: m
Circulation: 11,210; 10,380(sat)
Last Audit: Sworn N/A
Advertising: Open inch rate $20.25
Insert rate: $48.00/M; Single-sheet rate.
News services: CNHI - AP
Politics: 1848
Not Published: Sunday
Own facility?: Y
Special Weekly Sections: TV, Shopper
Publisher ....Martin Cody
Ed. ....Jeff Hutton
Mechanical Specifications: Type page 10.125 x 21; E - 6 cols, 1.583, .077 between; A - 6 cols, 1.583, .077 between.
Equipment CLASSIFIED: Front-end Software – Baseview - AdManager Pro; Classified Hardware – Mac OSX PRESSROOM: Line 1 – GOSSURBANITE; Press Drives – 100 HP WESTINGHOUSE; Folders – 1-2:1 U850; Pasters – MANUAL PASTERS; Reels and Stands – 4 DECK REELSTAND; Press control system – FINCOR; Press registration system – DUARTE PIN SYSTEM MAILROOM: Counter stackers – QUIPP; Inserters and stuffers – MUELLER-RANSA; Bundle tying machines – DYNARIC; Mailroom control system – ALLEN BRADLEY - SPECIALTY EQUIPMENT
Zip Codes served: 52501

THE OTTUMWA COURIER

213 E. Second St., Ottumwa, Iowa, 52501-2902; gen tel (641) 684-4611; adv tel (641) 683-5349; ed tel (641) 683-5365; gen fax (641) 684-7834; adv fax (641) 683-4118; ed

fax (641) 684-7326; adv e-mail addirector@ottumwacourier.com; ed e-mail news@ottumwacourier.com; web site www.ottumwacourier.com
Group: Community Newspaper Holdings, Inc.
Published: Mon, Tues, Wed, Thur, Fri, Sat
Weekday Frequency: m
Saturday Frequency: m
Circulation: 11,051; 10,674(sat)
Last Audit: ABC September 30, 2011
Price: 75 cents/M-F newsstand; $1.50 Saturday newsstands
Advertising: Open inch rate $23.31
News services: AP.
Politics: Independent. **Established:** 1848
Not Published: Christmas.
Own facility?: Y
Special Editions: Spring Home Improvement 1 (Apr); Bridal Tab (Feb); Home Expo (Mar); Salute to Graduates (May); Fall Sports Preview (Sept).
Special Weekly Sections: TV & Entertainmentr (Fri); Business (Mon); Saturday Extra (Sat); Outdoor Sports (Thur); Food (Thur).
Magazines: Relish (Monthly); American Profile (Weekly); Parade (Weekly)
Pub. ....Martin Cody
Business Manager ....Connie Sanders
Adv. Dir. ....Monica Tews
Circ. Dir. ....Doug Techel
Editor ....Jeff Hutton
Sports Ed. ....James Grob
Prodn. Supvr., Mailroom ....Amy Haines
Prodn. Mgr., Pressroom ....Nick Workman
Creative Services manager ....Grettel Meixner
Market Information: ADS; Split run; TMC.
Mechanical available: Offset; Black and 3 ROP colors; insert accepted; page cutoffs - 22 3/4.
Mechanical Specifications: Type page 13 x 21 1/2; E - 6 cols, 2 1/16, 1/6 between; A - 6 cols, 2 1/16, 1/6 between; C - 9 cols, 1 3/8, 1/16 between.
Commodity Consumption: Avg. Page Number Per Issue - Daily 22; Avg. Page Number Per Issue - Plates Used 10000; widths 27 1/2; Newsprint Used - Metric Tons 750; Printing Ink Used - Black 25980; Printing Ink Used - Color 4261; Printing Ink Used - Pages Printed 7100.
Equipment EDITORIAL: Front-end Software – Baseview/Ne; Editorial Hardware – 2-APP/Mac 8550 Workgroup Server, 1-APP/Mac 7250 Workgroup Server, 11-Motorola/StarMax 3800-180, 6-Motorola/StarMax 4000-200; Editorial Equipment – Microtek/ScanMaker, Polaroid/SprintScan, Lf/AP Leaf Picture Desk; Editorial Printers – HP/6MP CLASSIFIED: Front-end Software – Baseview/Class Manager Pro.; Classified Hardware – 1-APP/Mac 8550 Workgroup Server, 5-APP/Mac 7200-120; Classified Printers – HP/5MP DISPLAY: Ad make-up applications – Multi-Ad/Creator 4.0, Aldus/Freehand 8.0, Aldus/PageMaker 6.5, QPS/QuarkXPress; Display Hardware – 2-Motorola/StarMax 4000-200, Motorola/StarMax 3000-180, 3-APP/Power Mac 7600; Display Printers – QMS/PS-410, HP/LaserJet IIIsi, Unity/LaserMaster 1800, HP/455 Ca PRODUCTION: Pagination Software – QPS/QuarkXPress 3.32, Adobe/PageMaker 5.0.; Production Equipment – Digi-Colour, Caere/OmniPage Direct, Adobe/Photoshop 5.0; Cameras – 1-C/Spartan II, 1-SCREEN; Scanners – HP/ScanJet Plus, HP/ScanJet IIp, 2-Microtek III, Polaroid/SprintScan PRESSROOM: Line 1 – 5-G/Urbanite 850 1971; Folders – 1-G/2:1; Reels and Stands – 1, 9. MAILROOM: Counter stackers – 1-HL/Monitor; Inserters and stuffers – MM/227E 5:1; Bundle tying machines – 1/Cyclops, 1-/MLN, 1-Dynaric/NP1500; Wrapping singles – 1-Id/Bottom Wrapper; Addressing machine – 1-Ch/582N, 1-VideoJet/569 Labeler; Other equipment –1-Ch/552 AUDIO: Audio Software – LNS/Voice Response; Audio Hardware – Apex/Unix Server BUSINESS COMPUTERS: Business Software – Microsoft/Excel, Microsoft/Word PC Support, WordPerfect, Microsoft/Access; Business Hardware – IBM/AS-400, 4-Gateway/166, Corporate WAN
Delivery method: Mail, Newsstand, Private Carrier

SHENANDOAH

VALLEY NEWS TODAY

617 W. Sheridan Ave., Shenandoah, Iowa, 51601-1707; gen tel (712) 246-3097; gen fax (712) 246-3099; gen e-mail editorial@valleynewstoday.com; adv e-mail ads@valleynewstoday.com; web site www.valleynewstoday.com
Published: Tues, Wed, Thur, Fri, Sun
Weekday Frequency: e
Circulation: 2,432; 3,196(sun)
Last Audit: September 28, 2001
Price: 86.00/yr.
Advertising: Open inch rate $7.20
News services: Iowa Media Link.
Special Editions: Spring Sports (Apr); Back-to-School (Aug); Christmas Gift Booklet (Dec); Progress (Feb); Health (Jan); Southwest Iowa Fairs (Jul); Summer Sports (Jun); Gardening (Mar); Beef (May); Christmas Kick-Off (Nov); Fall Home Improvement (Sept).
Pub. ....David Gustafson
Acct. Exec. ....Mark Anderson
Acct. Exec. ....Rhonda Byers
Acct. Exec. ....Richard Perala
Circ. Mgr. ....Kimberly Kellison
Ed. ....Kevin Slater
Market Information: Split run; TMC.
Mechanical available: Offset; Black and 3 ROP colors; insert accepted; page cutoffs - 22 5/8.
Mechanical Specifications: Type page 13 x 21 1/2; E - 6 cols, 2, 1/6 between; A - 6 cols, 2, 1/6 between; C - 6 cols, 2, 1/6 between.
Commodity Consumption: Avg. Page Number Per Issue - Daily 14; Avg. Page Number Per Issue - Plates Used 2200; Avg. Page Number Per Issue - Saturday 32; widths 28; Newsprint Used - Short Tons 200; Printing Ink Used - Black 9000; Printing Ink Used - Color 1500; Printing Ink Used
Equipment EDITORIAL: Front-end Software – Microsoft/Word.; Editorial Hardware – APP/Mac; Editorial Printers – APP/Mac LaserWriter Pro 600, Lexmark/1200 CLASSIFIED: Front-end Software – Microsoft/Word.; Classified Hardware – APP/Mac DISPLAY: Ad make-up applications – Aldus/PageMaker.; Display Hardware – APP/Mac; Display Printers – APP/Mac LaserWriter Pro 800; Scanners – HP.; Business Hardware – Avis/500

VALLEY PUBLICATIONS

702 W. Sheridan Ave., Shenandoah, Iowa, 51601; gen tel (712) 246-3097; gen fax (712) 246-3099; gen e-mail editorial@valleynewstoday.com
Published: Mon, Tues, Wed, Thur, Fri, Sat, Sun
Price: 86.00/yr.
Advertising: Open inch rate $9.09

SIOUX CITY

SIOUX CITY JOURNAL

515 Pavonia St., Sioux City, Iowa, 51101-2245; gen tel (712) 293-4250; adv tel (712) 293-4325; ed tel (712) 293-4224; gen fax (712) 279-5099; adv fax (712) 279-5099; ed fax (712) 279-5059; adv e-mail adv@siouxcityjournal.com; web site www.siouxcityjournal.com
Group: Metro Newspaper Advertising Services, Inc.
Published: Mon, Tues, Wed, Thur, Fri, Sat, Sun
Weekday Frequency: m
Saturday Frequency: m
Circulation: 33,837; 33,837(sat); 38,114(sun)
Last Audit: ABC September 30, 2011
Price: 14.50/mo (carrier); 188.50/yr (carrier).
Advertising: Open inch rate $56.50
News services: AP.
Politics: Independent.
Not Published: New Year; Christmas.
Special Editions: Progress (Mar).
Special Weekly Sections: TV Log (Fri); Auto (S); Home Improvement (Sat); Health (Thur); Food (Wed).
Magazines: USA WEEKEND Magazine (S); American Profile (Weekly).
Pub. ....Ron Peterson
Controller ....Sue Stusse
Adv. Dir. ....Gary Miller
Ed. ....Mitch Pugh
Mng. Ed., Sports ....Jeff Tobin
City Ed. ....Barbara Walker
Opinion Ed. ....Mike Gors
Librarian ....Janet Lubsen
Music Ed. ....Bruce Miller
News Ed., Night ....Jim Jenkins
Photo Dept. Mgr. ....Tim Hynds
Society/Women's Ed. ....Tim Gallagher
Sports Ed. ....Terry Hersom
Mgmt. Info Servs. Mgr. ....Mark Schmith
Online Mgr. ....Rob Kritzer
Prodn. Foreman, Mailroom Brad Christopherson
Market Information: ADS; Split run; TMC; Zoned editions.
Mechanical available: Offset; Black and 3 ROP colors; insert accepted; page cutoffs - 22 3/4.
Mechanical Specifications: Type page 11 1/2 x 21 1/2; E - 6 cols, 1 3/4, 1/8 between; A - 6 cols, 1 3/4, 1/8 between; C - 9 cols, 1 1/16, 1/8 between.
Commodity Consumption: Avg. Page Number Per Issue - Daily 36; Avg. Page Number Per Issue - Plates Used 13000; Avg. Page Number Per Issue - Saturday 40; Avg. Page Number Per Issue - Sunday 60; widths 25; Newsprint Used - Metric Tons 3000; Newsprint Used - Short Tons 881546; Pri
Equipment EDITORIAL: Front-end Software – Lotus/Notes, QPS/QuarkXPress, News Engine.; Editorial Hardware – COM/Intrepid 48, APP/Mac; Editorial Printers – NewGen, HP, Pre Press/Panther Imagesetter 36 CLASSIFIED: Front-end Software – APT.; Classified Hardware – COM/Intrepid 48, APP/Mac; Classified Printers – NewGen DISPLAY: Ad make-up applications – QPS/QuarkXPress 3.0, Multi-Ad/Creator; Layout Software – APP/Mac G4, MEI.; Display Hardware – APP/Mac G4; Display Printers – NewGen, Pre Press/Panther Pro Imagesetter 36; Production Equipment – 2-NewGen, Pre Press/Panther Pro Imagesetter 36; Scanners – Panasonic/Image Scanner 16. PRESSROOM: Line 1 – 14-G/Urbanite (6 Stacked). MAILROOM: Counter stackers – 3-QWI; Inserters and stuffers – GMA; Bundle tying machines – QWI; Addressing machine – Kk. BUSINESS COMPUTERS: Business Software – Baseview; Business Hardware – APP/Mac G3

SIOUX CITY NEWSPAPERS, INC.

515 Pavonia St., Sioux City, Iowa, 51101; gen tel (712) 293-4244; gen fax (712) 279-5099

SPENCER

THE DAILY REPORTER

310 E. Milwaukee St., Spencer, Iowa, 51301; gen tel (712) 262-6610; gen fax (712) 262-3044; adv e-mail advertising@spencerdailyreporter.com; ed e-mail news@spencerdailyreporter.com; web site www.spencerdailyreporter.com
Published: Tues, Wed, Thur, Fri, Sat
Weekday Frequency: m
Circulation: 4,004; 3,852(sat)
Last Audit: March 31, 2004
Price: 6.50/mo; 80.00/yr.
Advertising: Open inch rate $8.05
News services: AP, NEA.
Politics: Independent.
Not Published: New Year; Memorial Day; Independence Day; Labor Day; Thanksgiving; Christmas.
Special Weekly Sections: Religion (Fri); TV (Thur); Best Food Day (Wed).
Magazines: Relish (Monthly); TV Update (Thur); American Profile (Weekly).
Pub ....Paula Buenger
Adv. Dir. ....Janelle Madison
Ed. ....Randy Cauthron
Design Ed. ....Skyler Sebby
Sports Ed. ....Jeff Hasselmann
Market Information: Split run; TMC; Zoned editions.
Mechanical available: Offset; Black and 3 ROP colors; insert accepted - any; page cutoffs - 22 5/8.
Mechanical Specifications: Type page 13 x 21 1/2; E - 6 cols, 2 1/16, 1/8 between; A - 6 cols, 2 1/16, 1/8 between; C - 6 cols, 2 1/16, 1/8 between.
Commodity Consumption: Avg. Page Number Per Issue - Daily 10; widths 27; Newsprint Used - Short Tons 650; Printing Ink Used - Black 10000; Printing Ink Used - Color 3000; Printing Ink Used - Pages Printed 12.
Equipment; Editorial Hardware – Mk.; Classified Hardware – Mk.; Layout Software – 4-APP/Mac.; Production Equipment – Nat/A-250; Cameras – SCREEN/Companica; Scanners – Gam. PRESSROOM: Line 1 – 5-G/Community.; Bundle tying machines – Bu; Addressing machine – Am.; Business Hardware – APP/Mac

VINTON

CEDAR VALLEY DAILY TIMES

108 E. Fifth St., Vinton, Iowa, 52349-1759; gen tel (319) 472-2311; gen fax (319) 472-4811; adv e-mail ads@cedarvalleydailytimes.com; ed e-mail editor@cedarvalleydailytimes.com; web site www.cedarvalleydailytimes.com
Published: Mon, Tues, Wed, Thur, Fri
Weekday Frequency: m
Circulation: 2,000
Last Audit: March 31, 2007
Price: 89.00/yr (carrier), $79.00/yr (mail).
Advertising: Open inch rate $13.60
News services: LAT-WP, Iowa Newspaper Media Link.
Politics: Independent. **Established:** 1886
Not Published: New Year; Memorial Day; Independence Day; Labor Day; Thanksgiving; Christmas.
Pub. ....Deb Weigel
News Ed. ....John Jensen
Sports Ed. ....Brett Myers
Mechanical available: Offset; Black and 3 ROP colors; insert accepted - most; page cutoffs - 21.
Mechanical Specifications: Type page 12 1/4 x 21; E - 6 cols, 1 11/12, 1/6 between; A - 6 cols, 1 11/12, 1/6 between; C - 6 cols, 1 11/12, 1/6 between.
Commodity Consumption: Avg. Page Number Per Issue - Daily 10-16; Avg. Page Number Per Issue - Plates Used 5200; widths 34; Newsprint Used - Short Tons 250; Printing Ink Used - Black 7500; Printing Ink Used - Color 200.
Equipment EDITORIAL: Front-end Software – Adobe/PageMaker 6.5.; Editorial Hardware – COM; Classified Hardware – APP/Mac. DISPLAY: Ad make-up applications – Aldus/PageMaker 6.5, Multi-Ad 4.01; Layout Software – APP/Mac G3. PRODUCTION: Pagination Software – Aldus/PageMaker 6.5.; Production Equipment – 2-V/430; Cameras – 1-B/17423; Scanners – HP MAILROOM: Counter stackers – 1-BG/Count-O-Veyor; Bundle tying machines – 2/Bu; Addressing machine – 1-Am/500.

WASHINGTON

THE WASHINGTON EVENING JOURNAL

111 N. Marion Ave., Washington, Iowa, 52353-1728; gen tel (319) 653-2191; gen fax (319) 653-7524; gen e-mail pub@washjrnl.com; adv e-mail adv@washjrnl.com; ed e-mail news@washjrnl.com; web site www.washjrnl.com
Published: Mon, Tues, Wed, Thur, Fri
Weekday Frequency: e
Circulation: 3,462
Last Audit: September 28, 2004
Price: 102.00/yr.
Advertising: Open inch rate $10.35
News services: AP.
Politics: Independent.
Not Published: New Year; Memorial Day; Inde-

pendence Day; Labor Day; Thanksgiving; Christmas.
Special Editions: Christmas (Dec); Fall Opening (Fall); Beef Issue (May); Pork Production (Oct); Spring Opening (Spring).
Special Weekly Sections: Week in Review (Fri); Business (Mon); Farm Page (Thur); Best Food Day (Tues).
Magazines: American Profile (Mon); Relish (Monthly).
Circ. Dir. ....Kim Stout
Ed. ....Darwin K. Sherman
Sports Ed. ....Travis Brown
Prodn. Mgr. ....Steve Dunbar
Market Information: ADS; Split run; TMC.
Mechanical available: Offset; Black and 3 ROP colors; insert accepted; page cutoffs - 22 3/4.
Mechanical Specifications: Type page 13 x 21 1/2; E - 6 cols; 2 1/16, 1/16 between; A - 6 cols, 2 1/16, 1/16 between; C - 8 cols, 1 9/16, 1/8 between.
Commodity Consumption: Avg. Page Number Per Issue - Daily 10; widths 13 3/4; Newsprint Used - Metric Tons 140; Printing Ink Used - Pages Printed 2540.
Equipment EDITORIAL: Front-end Software – Microsoft/Word.; Editorial Hardware – APP/Mac; Editorial Printers – APP/Mac LaserWriter II NT 630 CLASSIFIED: Front-end Software – Microsoft/Word, Aldus/PageMaker.; Classified Hardware – APP/Mac DISPLAY: Ad make-up applications – Aldus/PageMaker, Multi-Ad/Creator.; Display Hardware – APP/Mac; Display Printers – APP/Mac LaserWriter II NT 630; Production Equipment – APP/Mac NT. PRESSROOM: Line 1 – HI/V-15A 1972. BUSINESS COMPUTERS: Business Software – BMF; Business Hardware – PC

INLAND MEDIA COMPANY, INC..

111 N. Marion Ave., Washington, Iowa, 52353; gen tel (319) 653-2191; gen fax (319) 653-7524; web site www.washjrnl.com
Published: Mon, Tues, Wed, Thur, Fri
Weekday Frequency: e
Advertising: Open inch rate $8.21
Own facility?: Y

WATERLOO

THE COURIER

501 Commercial St., Waterloo, Iowa, 50704; gen tel (800) 798-1717; adv tel (319) 291-1497; ed tel (319) 291-1460; gen fax (319) 291-1569; ed fax (319) 291-2069; web site www.wcfcourier.com
Published: Mon, Tues, Wed, Thur, Fri, Sun
Weekday Frequency: e
Saturday Frequency: m
Circulation: 37,994; 39,229(sat); 44,950(sun)
Last Audit: ABC September 30, 2011
Price: 3.88/wk; 215.80/yr.
Advertising: Open inch rate $39.60
News services: AP.
Politics: Independent.
Special Weekly Sections: Friday (weekend) (Fri); Fashion (Mon); Travel Pages (S); People (Thur); Food (Tues); Arts (Wed).
Magazines: Relish (Monthly); TV Showtime (S).
Pub ....David Braton
Controller ....Barbara Anderson
Admin. Asst. ....Brenda Douglass
Adv. Mgr., Classified ....Sharon Jordan
Mktg. Dir. ....Angela Dark
Ed. ....Nancy Raffensperger-Newhoff
Community Desk Ed. ....Catherine Kittrell
Lifestyles Ed. ....Melody Parker
News Ed. ....Pat Kinney
Asst. News Ed. ....Doug Hines
Online Ed. ....Michelle Gebhardt
Regl. Ed. ....Jim Stanton
Sports Ed. ....Doug Newhoff
Prodn. Foreman, Composing ....Larry Orth
Prodn. Foreman, Mailroom ....Greg Schmitz
Market Information: Split run; TMC; Zoned editions.
Mechanical available: Offset; Black and 3 ROP colors; insert accepted; page cutoffs - 22 3/4.
Mechanical Specifications: Type page 13 x 21 1/2; E - 6 cols, 2 1/8, 1/6 between; A - 6 cols, 2 1/8, 1/6 between; C - 9 cols, 1 3/8, 1/6 between.
Commodity Consumption: Avg. Page Number Per Issue - Daily 36; Avg. Page Number Per Issue - Plates Used 20500; Avg. Page Number Per Issue - Sunday 82; widths 13 3/4; Newsprint Used - Metric Tons 3750; Printing Ink Used - Black 120000; Printing Ink Used - Color 12000; Printing I
Equipment EDITORIAL: Front-end Software – Arbortext, QPS/QuarkXPress.; Editorial Hardware – Sun; Editorial Printers – ECR/Pelbox, APP/Mac LaserWriters CLASSIFIED: Front-end Software – Unify, Vision Data/Island Write.; Classified Hardware – Sun; Classified Printers – APP/Mac LaserWriters, ECR/Pelbox DISPLAY: Ad make-up applications – QPS/QuarkXPress; Layout Software – SCS.; Display Hardware – APP/Mac; Display Printers – APP/Mac LaserWriters, ECR/Pelbox PRODUCTION: Pagination Software – QPS.; Production Equipment – 2-ECR/Autokon Pelbox, AG; Cameras – B; Scanners – Lf, AG/Horizon PRESSROOM: Line 1 – 5 MAILROOM: Counter stackers – 3-Id/440; Inserters and stuffers – 2-MM/308; Bundle tying machines – 2-MLN/Hi speed; Addressing machine – 1/KR. BUSINESS COMPUTERS: Business Software – Vision Data, Access Technology; Business Hardware – 1-Sun/Sparc

WEBSTER CITY

THE DAILY FREEMAN-JOURNAL

720 Second St., Webster City, Iowa, 50595; gen tel (515) 832-4350; gen fax (515) 832-2314; gen e-mail mfertig@freemanjournal.net; adv e-mail advertising@freemanjournal.net; ed e-mail editor@freemanjournal.net; web site www.webstercitynews.com
Published: Mon, Tues, Wed, Thur, Fri
Weekday Frequency: e
Circulation: 2,327
Last Audit: ABC September 30, 2011
Price: 67.60/yr.
News services: AP.
Politics: Independent-Republican.
Note: Advertising is sold in combination with the Fort Dodge Messenger (mS) for $43.22. Individual newspaper rates not made available.
Not Published: New Year; Memorial Day; Independence Day; Labor Day; Thanksgiving; Christmas.
Mgr., Mktg./Promo. ....Michael A. Fertig
Circ. Mgr. ....Grant Gibbon
Ed. ....Lori Berglund
Sports Ed. ....Troy Banning
Prodn. Mgr. ....Randy Smith
Market Information: TMC.
Mechanical available: Offset; Black and 3 ROP colors; insert accepted; page cutoffs - 22 3/4.
Mechanical Specifications: Type page 13 x 21 1/2; E - 6 cols, 2 1/16, 1/8 between; A - 6 cols, 2 1/16, 1/8 between; C - 9 cols, 1 5/16, 1/8 between.
Commodity Consumption: Avg. Page Number Per Issue - Daily 12; Avg. Page Number Per Issue - Plates Used 3455; widths 25; Newsprint Used - Short Tons 96; Printing Ink Used - Black 1520; Printing Ink Used - Color 650; Printing Ink Used - Pages Printed 2570.
Equipment: Editorial Hardware – 2-APP/Mac G3, APP/Power Mac, 2-APP/Mac G4; Editorial Printers – ECR/108, ECR/1500, Konica/Jetsetter.; Classified Hardware – APP/Mac G3. PRODUCTION: Pagination Software – QPS.; Production Equipment – 1-Nu, 2-Pako, APP/Mac, ECR/6200; Cameras – 1-Spartan II Flatbed Scanner PRESSROOM: Line 1 – 14-G/Suburban; Press Drives – 2-HP/100; Folders – 1-G/Urbanite, 1. MAILROOM: Counter stackers – 2-HI/RS 25; Inserters and stuffers – HI; Bundle tying machines – 2/Bu; Addressing machine – 2-/Ch; Other equipment –MM Stitcher-Trimmer.

OGDEN NEWSPAPERS, INC.

720 Second St., Webster City, Iowa, 50595; gen tel (515) 832-4350; gen fax (515) 832-2314

KANSAS

ABILENE

ABILENE REFLECTOR-CHRONICLE

303 N. Broadway, Abilene, Kan., 67410; gen tel (785) 263-1000; adv tel (785) 263-1000; ed tel (785) 263-1000; gen fax (785) 263-1645; adv fax (785) 263-1645; ed fax (785) 263-1645; gen e-mail publisher@abilene-rc.com; adv e-mail advertising@abilene-rc.com; ed e-mail news@abilene-rc.com; web site www.abilene-rc.com
Group: Kansas Press Association
Published: Mon, Tues, Wed, Thur, Fri, Sat, Sun
Weekday Frequency: e
Saturday Frequency: m
Circulation: 3,935; 3,935(sat)
Last Audit: September 30, 2001
Price: 7.00/mo; 81.00/yr.
Advertising: Open inch rate $7.50
News services: AP.
Politics: Republican.
Not Published: New Year; Memorial Day; Independence Day; Labor Day; Thanksgiving; Christmas.
Special Editions: Christmas (Dec); Fall Home Tour Tab (Fall); Graduation (May); Wrestling (Other).
Magazines: American Profile (Fri).
Adv. Mgr. ....Janelle Gantenbein
Circ. Mgr. ....Daniel Vanderburg
Editorial Page Ed. ....Dave Bergmeier
News Ed ....Carla Strand
Market Information: TMC; Zoned editions.
Mechanical available: Offset; Black and 3 ROP colors; insert accepted; page cutoffs - 21 1/2.
Mechanical Specifications: Type page 12 1/2 x 21 1/2; E - 6 cols, 1 7/8, 1/8 between; A - 6 cols, 1 7/8, 1/8 between; C - 6 cols, 1 7/8, 1/8 between.
Commodity Consumption: Avg. Page Number Per Issue - Daily 12; Avg. Page Number Per Issue - Plates Used 2800; widths 14; Newsprint Used - Short Tons 135; Printing Ink Used - Black 10 barrels; Printing Ink Used - Pages Printed 3250.
Equipment EDITORIAL: Front-end Software – QPS/QuarkXPress. CLASSIFIED: Front-end Software – Microsoft/Word, QPS/QuarkXPress.; Classified Equipment – 2-IBM/Typewriter DISPLAY: Ad make-up applications – QPS/QuarkXPress; Layout Software – QPS/QuarkXPress.; Production Equipment – 1-Nat/A-250; Cameras – 1-Acti. PRESSROOM: Line 1 – 4-G; Folders – 1-G/2:1.; Bundle tying machines – 1/Sa; Addressing machine – 1-/Am.

REFLECTOR CHRONICLE PUBLISHING CORP.

303 N. Broadway, Abilene, Kan., 67410; gen tel (785) 263-1000; gen fax (785) 263-1645

ARKANSAS CITY

ARKANSAS CITY TRAVELER

200 E. 5th Ave., Arkansas City, Kan., 67005; gen tel (620) 442-4200; adv tel (620) 442-4200; ed tel (620) 442-4200; gen fax (620) 442-7483; adv fax (620) 442-7483; ed fax (620) 442-7483; gen e-mail news@arkcity.net; arkcity@arkcity.net; ed e-mail traveler@horizon.hit.net; web site www.arkcity.net
Group: Kansas Press Association
Published: Mon, Tues, Wed, Thur, Fri, Sat, Sun
Weekday Frequency: e
Saturday Frequency: m
Circulation: 4,832; 4,832(sat)
Last Audit: September 22, 2001
Price: 7.02/mo; 75.05/yr.
Advertising: Open inch rate $8.88
News services: AP.
Politics: Independent. **Established:** 1870
Not Published: New Year; Independence Day; Christmas.
Special Weekly Sections: Health (Fri); Education (Mon); Weddings/Engagements (Sat); Farm Page (Thur); Business (Tues); Food (Wed).
Magazines: USA WEEKEND Magazine (Sat).
Pub. ....Dave Seaton
Bus. Mgr. ....Susie Kincaid
Society Ed. ....Jean Crowley
Prodn. Mgr., Pre Press ....Kay Batdorf
Market Information: Split run; TMC; Zoned editions.
Mechanical available: Offset; Black and 3 ROP colors; insert accepted - all.
Mechanical Specifications: Type page 13 x 21 1/2; E - 6 cols, 2, 3/16 between; A - 6 cols, 2, 3/16 between; C - 6 cols, 2, 3/16 between.
Commodity Consumption: Avg. Page Number Per Issue - Daily 12; widths 28; Newsprint Used - Short Tons 322; Printing Ink Used - Pages Printed 4340.
Equipment: Editorial Hardware – APP/Mac, 3-APP/Mac IIsi, 5-APP/Mac Classic, 6-APP/Mac SE, 1-APP/Mac IIci; Editorial Equipment – SMS/Stauffer Gold, APP/Mac SE Super Drive.; Classified Hardware – 1-APP/Mac; Classified Printers – APP/Mac LaserPrinter.; Display Printers – APP/Mac LaserWriter II, APP/Mac LaserWriter II NTX.; Production Equipment – APP/Mac LaserWriter II, APP/Mac LaserWriter II NTX; Cameras – 1-B, Acti. PRESSROOM: Line 1 – 7-G/Community; Folders – 1; Bundle tying machines – 1/Sa; Addressing machine – 2-/Am.; Business Hardware – ATT

ATCHISON

ATCHISON GLOBE

1015-25 Main St., Atchison, Kan., 66002; gen tel (913) 367-0583; adv tel (913) 367-0583; ed tel (913) 367-0583; gen fax (913) 367-7531; adv fax (913) 367-7531; ed fax (913) 367-7531; gen e-mail globe@npgco.com; adv e-mail christym@npgco.com; ed e-mail aglobe@journey.com; web site www.atchisondailyglobe.com
Published: Mon, Tues, Wed, Thur, Fri, Sat, Sun
Weekday Frequency: e
Saturday Frequency: m
Circulation: 3,293; 3,293(sat)
Last Audit: October 1, 2003
Price: 8.00/mo (carrier), $9.20/mo (mail); 99.00/yr (carrier), $96.00/yr (mail).
Advertising: Open inch rate $13.40
News services: AP.
Politics: Independent.
Not Published: New Year; Memorial Day; Independence Day; Labor Day; Thanksgiving; Christmas.
Pub. ....Chris Wessel
Office Mgr. ....Marilyn Andre
Adv. Mgr. ....Christy McKibben
Circ. Mgr. ....Sarah Griffin
Mng. Ed. ....Dan Galbraith
Design Ed. ....Scott Johnson
Lifestyles Ed. ....Kimberly Geffert
News Ed. ....Angela Holmes
Sports Ed. ....Josh Pound
Prodn. Foreman, Paste-Up ....Rita Jones
Market Information: TMC.
Mechanical available: Offset; Black and 3 ROP colors; insert accepted; page cutoffs - 22 3/4.
Mechanical Specifications: Type page 13 x 21 1/2; E - 6 cols, 2 1/16, 1/8 between; A - 6 cols, 2 1/16, 1/8 between; C - 8 cols, 1 1/2, 1/8 between.
Commodity Consumption: Avg. Page Number Per Issue - Daily 12; widths 27 1/2; Newsprint Used - Short Tons 220; Printing Ink Used - Pages Printed 3963.

Equipment EDITORIAL: Front-end Software – Microsoft/Word.; Editorial Hardware – APP/Mac; Editorial Printers – 2-APP/Mac LaserWriter Plus CLASSIFIED: Front-end Software – CAMS.; Classified Hardware – APP/Mac; Classified Printers – APP/Mac LaserWriter Plus DISPLAY: Ad make-up applications – Multi-Ad/Creator; Layout Software – APP/Mac.; Display Hardware – APP/Mac; Display Printers – APP/Mac LaserWriter Plus; Production Equipment – Nu/UP; Cameras – SCREEN/Companica 680 C. PRESSROOM: Line 1 – 5-HI/V-15A 1977.; Bundle tying machines – OVL. BUSINESS COMPUTERS: Business Software – Lotus 1-2-3; Business Hardware – MIS 486

AUGUSTA

AUGUSTA DAILY GAZETTE

204 E. Fifth St., Augusta, Kan., 67010-0009; gen tel (316) 775-2218; gen fax (316) 775-3220; adv e-mail advmgr@augustagazette.com; ed e-mail mmcdermott@augustagazette.com; web site www.augustagazette.com

Group: Kansas Press Association
Published: Mon, Tues, Wed, Thur, Fri
Weekday Frequency: e
Circulation: 2,247
Last Audit: September 23, 2003
Price: 7.40/mo (carrier); 84.40/yr.
Advertising: Open inch rate $8.75
News services: AP.
Politics: Independent.
Note: For printing and production information see the El Dorado Times listing.
Not Published: New Year; Presidents' Day; Memorial Day; Independence Day; Labor Day; Thanksgiving; Christmas.
Special Editions: Women's (Apr); Get Ready for School (Aug); Christmas (Dec); Yearly Review (Jan); Spring Opening (May); Progress (Nov); Football (Sept).
Magazines: American Profile (Weekly).
Pub. .... Kent Bush
Adv. Dir. .... Amber Jackson
Circ. Mgr. .... Ron Boyer
Ed. .... Michael McDermott
Graphics Ed./Art Dir. .... Rhonda Zinn
Life Style Ed. .... Belinda Larson
Sports Ed. .... John Curtis
Market Information: Split run; TMC.
Mechanical available: Offset; Black and 2 ROP colors; insert accepted; page cutoffs - 22 3/4.
Mechanical Specifications: Type page 13 x 21; E - 6 cols, 2 3/4, 1/8 between; A - 6 cols, 2 3/4, 1/8 between; C - 6 cols, 2 3/4, 1/8 between.
Commodity Consumption: Avg. Page Number Per Issue - Daily 8; Avg. Page Number Per Issue - Plates Used 2058; widths 12 1/2; Newsprint Used - Short Tons 217; Printing Ink Used - Black 6607; Printing Ink Used - Color 1076; Printing Ink Used - Pages Printed 1804.
Equipment; Editorial Hardware – Mk; Editorial Printers – APP/Mac LaserPrinter. PRESSROOM: Line 1 – 1-ATF/Chief 17, 1-ATF/Chief 117; Line 2 – SLN/17x22.; Bundle tying machines – Bu.; Business Hardware – IBM, Quickbook

CHANUTE

CHANUTE PUBLISHING CO.

PO Box 559, Chanute, Kan., 66720; gen tel (620) 431-4100; gen fax (620) 431-2635; gen e-mail publisher@chanute.com; adv e-mail adreps@chanute.com; ed e-mail news@chanute.com; web site www.chanute.com

Group: Kansas Newspapers, LLC
Published: Tues, Wed, Thur, Fri, Sat
Weekday Frequency: m
Saturday Frequency: m
Circulation: 3,900; 3,900(sat)
Politics: 1892
Not Published: Sunday, Monday
Own facility?: Y
Profile: 5-day daily community newspaper
Delivery method: Mail, Newsstand, Private Carrier, Racks

THE CHANUTE TRIBUNE

18 S. Evergreen Ave., Chanute, Kan., 66720; gen tel (620) 431-4100; gen fax (620) 431-2635; gen e-mail office@chanute.com; adv e-mail adreps@chanute.com; web site www.chanute.com

Group: Kansas Press Association
Published: Tues, Wed, Thur, Fri, Sat
Weekday Frequency: e
Saturday Frequency: m
Circulation: 4,359; 4,359(sat)
Last Audit: September 24, 2003
Price: 84.46/yr.
Advertising: Open inch rate $8.28
News services: AP.
Politics: Independent. **Established:** 1892
Not Published: New Year; Memorial Day; Independence Day; Labor Day; Thanksgiving; Christmas.
Special Editions: Basketball (Apr); Back-to-School (Aug); Holiday Recipe (Dec); Tax Tab (Feb); Bridal Tab (Jan); Medical Tab (Jul); Summer Fun (Jun); Football (Sept).
Special Weekly Sections: Family (Fri); Agriculture (Mon); Anniversaries (Sat); Education (Thur); Community News (Tues); Seniors (Wed).
Magazines: This Week (local, newsprint) (Sat); American Profile (Wed); USA WEEKEND Magazine (Weekly).
Pub. .... Shanna Guiot
Display Adv. Rep. .... Andrea Evans
Display Adv. Rep. .... Dianna Litzel
Circ. Mgr. .... Amy Jensen
Mng. Ed. .... Stu Butcher
Asst. Mng. Ed. .... Melissa Smith
Market Information: TMC.
Mechanical available: Offset; Black and 3 ROP

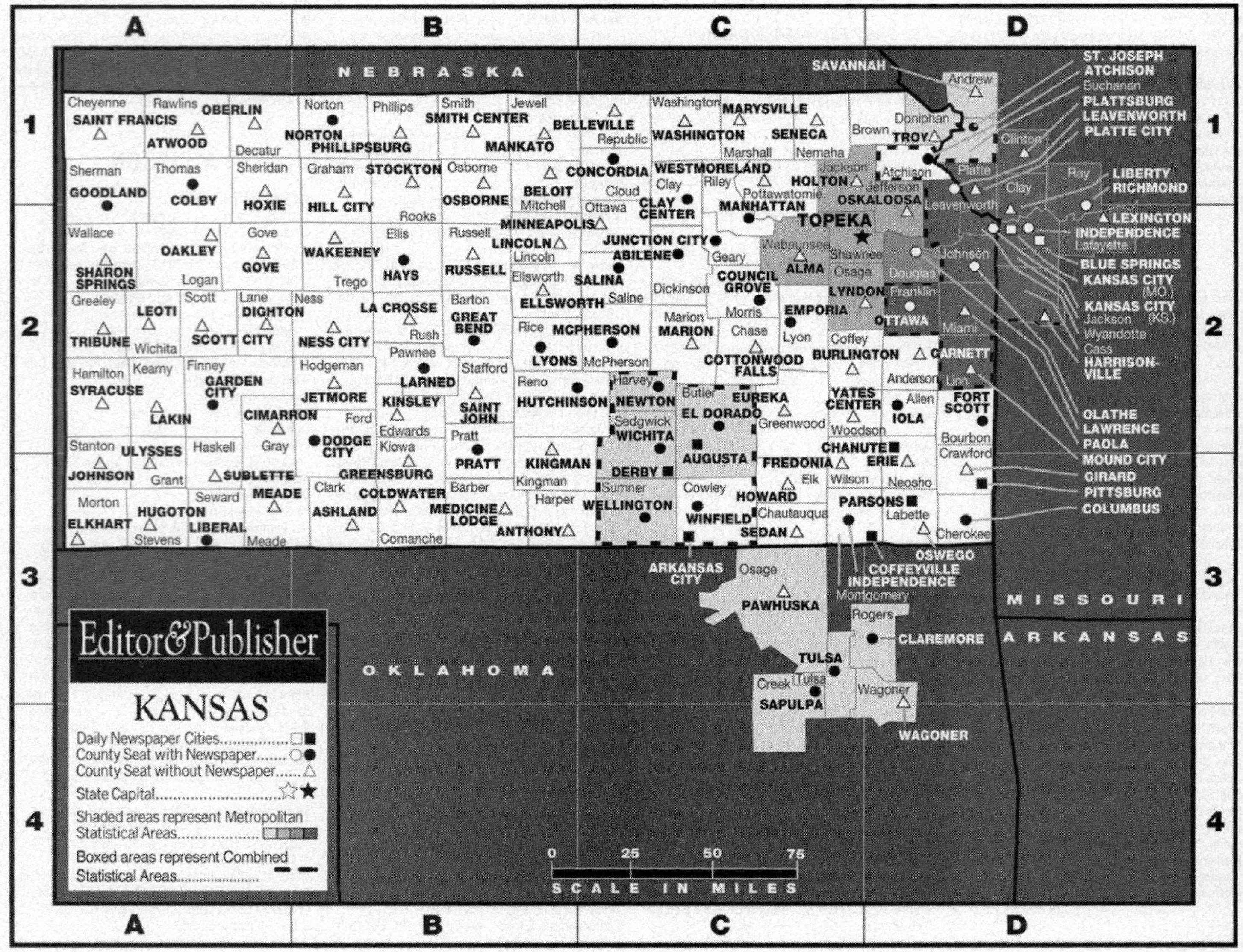

colors; insert accepted; page cutoffs - 22 3/4.
Mechanical Specifications: Type page 11 5/8 x 21 1/2; E - 6 cols, 1 5/6, 1/8 between; A - 6 cols, 1 5/6, 1/8 between; C - 8 cols, 1 3/8, 1/16 between.
Commodity Consumption: Avg. Page Number Per Issue - Daily 12; widths 25.
Equipment EDITORIAL: Front-end Software – FSI 1.3.0.; Editorial Hardware – AP/Mac; Editorial Printers – Xante CLASSIFIED: Front-end Software – Baseview 4.0.; Classified Hardware – AP/Mac; Classified Printers – Xante PRODUCTION: Pagination Software – Quark 4.0.; Production Equipment – Xante/8200, Xante/G3; Business Hardware – Icanon/Newzware

CLAY CENTER

THE CLAY CENTER DISPATCH

805 Fifth St., Clay Center, Kan., 67432-0519; gen tel (785) 632-2127; gen fax (785) 632-6526; gen e-mail dispatch@claycenter.com; adv e-mail addesk@claycenter.com; ed e-mail social@claycenter.com; web site www.claycenter.com
Group: Kansas Press Association
Published: Mon, Tues, Wed, Thur, Fri
Weekday Frequency: e
Circulation: 3,200
Last Audit: March 31, 2008
Price: 67.25/yr.
Advertising: Open inch rate $6.90
News services: AP.
Politics: Independent.
Advertising not accepted: Liquor.
Not Published: New Year; Memorial Day; Independence Day; Labor Day; Columbus Day; Veteran's Day; Thanksgiving; Christmas.
Special Editions: Home & Garden (Apr); Back-to-School (Aug); F.F.A. (Feb); Social Security/Tax (Jan); Fair Preview Tab (Jul); Car Care (Mar); Graduation (May); Christmas (Nov); Car Care (Oct); Rodeo (Sept).
Adv. Dir.................................Hilary Thompson
Circ. Mgr.................................McKenna Porter
Editorial Page Ed.................Harry E. Valentine
Sports Ed. ....Dave Berggren
Prodn. Supt./Foreman, Composing .....Aaron Bull
Market Information: TMC.
Mechanical available: Offset; Black and 3 ROP colors; insert accepted; page cutoffs - 22 3/4.
Mechanical Specifications: Type page 13 x 21; E - 6 cols, 2 1/16, 1/8 between; A - 6 cols, 2 1/16, 1/8 between; C - 6 cols, 2 1/16, 1/8 between.
Commodity Consumption: Avg. Page Number Per Issue - Daily 9; widths 14; Newsprint Used - Short Tons 80.
Equipment; Editorial Hardware – PC; Editorial Printers – HP/LaserJet.; Classified Hardware – PC; Classified Printers – HP/LaserJet.; Layout Software – Archetype/Corel Draw.; Display Hardware – PC; Production Equipment – HP; Cameras – 1-K/240V. PRESSROOM: Line 1 – G/Community; Folders – 1-G/3:1.; Addressing machine – 1/Ch.; Business Hardware – Epson/386, Acer/486, Nobilis-Pentium

COFFEYVILLE

THE COFFEYVILLE JOURNAL

8th & Elm St., Coffeyville, Kan., 67337-0849; gen tel (620) 251-3300; adv tel (620) 251-3300; gen fax (620) 251-1905; adv fax (620) 251-1905; adv e-mail advertising@cj.kscoxmail.com
Group: Kansas Press Association
Published: Tues, Wed, Thur, Fri, Sun
Weekday Frequency: m
Circulation: 4,103; 4,103(sun)
Last Audit: September 30, 2003
Price: 6.70/mo; 77.70/yr.
Advertising: Open inch rate $9.50
News services: AP.
Politics: Independent. **Established:** 1875
Advertising not accepted: Vending machine routes; Work at home; Astrology.
Special Editions: Fair (Aug); Recipe (Mar); Graduation (May); Fashion (Sept).
Magazines: TV Watch (own) (S); American Profile (Weekly).
Pub.......................................Kirk Clinkscales
Ed....Jim Butcher
Market Information: TMC.
Mechanical available: Offset; Black and 3 ROP colors; insert accepted; page cutoffs - 22 3/4.
Mechanical Specifications: Type page 13 x 21 1/2; E - 6 cols, 2 1/16, 1/8 between; A - 6 cols, 2 1/16, 1/8 between; C - 9 cols, 1 3/8, 1/8 between.
Commodity Consumption: Avg. Page Number Per Issue - Daily 10; Avg. Page Number Per Issue - Plates Used 5600; Avg. Page Number Per Issue - Sunday 22; widths 27; Newsprint Used - Short Tons 225; Printing Ink Used - Black 8700; Printing Ink Used - Color 775; Printing Ink Used - P
Equipment; Editorial Hardware – 2-DEC/PDP 11-34, Hx/Hs 46.; Classified Hardware – 1-Hx.; Layout Software – 1-Hx.; Production Equipment – 2-COM/Universal Videosetter; Cameras – 1-R/480. PRESSROOM: Line 1 – 6-HI/Cotrell V-22; Folders – 1-HI/2:1. MAILROOM: Counter stackers – HI/RS 25; Bundle tying machines – 2/Bu.; Business Hardware – DPT

COLBY

COLBY FREE PRESS

155 W. Fifth St., Colby, Kan., 67701; gen tel (785) 462-3963; adv tel (785) 462-3963; ed tel (785) 462-3963; gen fax (785) 462-7749; adv fax (785) 462-7749; ed fax (785) 462-7749; gen e-mail free.press@nwkansas.com; adv e-mail colby.ads@nwkansas.com; ed e-mail colby.editor@nwkansas.com; web site www.nwkansas.com
Group: Nor'West Newspapers
Published: Mon, Wed, Thur, Fri
Weekday Frequency: e
Circulation: 1,588
Last Audit: Sworn October 1, 2001
Price: $85/$95 yr/.75/issue
Advertising: Open inch rate $7.95
Insert rate: $70-$100m
News services: AP.
Politics: Independent. **Established:** 1888
Advertising not accepted: Y
Not Published: New Year; Independence Day; Thanksgiving; Christmas.
Own facility?: N
Profile: Daily community newspaper serving Thomas and surrounding counties.
publisher.........................Sharon Friedlander
Market Information: TMC.
Mechanical available: Offset; Black and 2 ROP colors; insert accepted; page cutoffs - 21 1/2.
Mechanical Specifications: Type page 13 x 21 1/2; E - 6 cols, 2 1/16, 1/8 between; A - 6 cols, 2 1/16, 1/8 between; C - 6 cols, 2 1/16, 1/8 between.
Equipment EDITORIAL: Front-end Software – inDesign, neoOffice, PhotoShop; Editorial Hardware – Apple Mac; Classified Hardware – 1-APP/Mac.; Layout Software – 1-APP/Mac. PRESSROOM: Line 1 – none; Business Hardware – IBM/AT, IBM/PC-2
Zip Codes served: 677
Delivery method: Mail, Newsstand, Private Carrier, Racks

COLUMBUS

CHEROKEE COUNTY NEWS-ADVOCATE

114 S. Kansas, Columbus, Kan., 66725; gen tel (620) 429-2773; gen fax (620) 429-3223; gen e-mail colodv@colombus-ks.com; web site www.columbusdailyadv.com
Group: American Consolidated Media
Published: Wed
Weekday Frequency: m
Circulation: 3,300
Last Audit: Sworn September 27, 2001
Price: 29.00 year 14.50 6 mo 7.25 3 months
Advertising: Open inch rate $5.50
Insert rate: 60.00 cpm
News services: AP.
Politics: 1874
Not Published: New Year; Memorial Day; Independence Day; Labor Day; Thanksgiving; Christmas.
Own facility?: N
Special Editions: Christmas (Dec); Fair (Jul); Graduation (May); Car Care (Oct).
Publisher..........................Chris Zimmerman
Commodity Consumption: Avg. Page Number Per Issue - Daily 8; Avg. Page Number Per Issue - Plates Used 1200; widths 27 1/2; Newsprint Used - Short Tons 45; Printing Ink Used - Black 275; Printing Ink Used - Pages Printed 1800.
Equipment EDITORIAL: Front-end Software – QPS/QuarkXPress.; Editorial Hardware – 4-APP/Mac; Editorial Printers – HP/LaserJet II, HP/LaserJet III, HP/LaserJet 4MV; Classified Hardware – Pentium/PC.; Layout Software – Aldus/PageMaker.; Display Hardware – PC Pentium; Display Printers – HP/LaserJet 4MV; Production Equipment – B; Cameras – Acti; Scanners – Microtek, Umax. PRESSROOM: Line 1 – 2; Addressing machine – Automecha/Accufast PUM. BUSINESS COMPUTERS: Business Software – ListMaster, Interlink-Subscriptions; Business Hardware – Pentium/PC

CONCORDIA

CONCORDIA BLADE-EMPIRE

510 Washington St., Concordia, Kan., 66901; gen tel (785) 243-2424; gen fax (785) 243-4407; gen e-mail bladeempire@nckcn.com; web site www.bladeempire.com
Group: Kansas Press Association
Published: Mon, Tues, Wed, Thur, Fri
Weekday Frequency: e
Circulation: 2,357
Last Audit: September 28, 2001
Price: 98.00/yr.
Advertising: Open inch rate $5.20
News services: AP.
Politics: Independent. **Established:** 1904
Not Published: New Year; Memorial Day; Independence Day; Labor Day; Thanksgiving; Christmas.
Bus. Mgr. ....John Hamel
Circ. Dir. ....Denise Lahodery
Ed...Brad Lowell
Sports Ed...Jim Lowell
Women's Ed. ....Sharon Coy
Prodn. Mgr., Pressroom ....Lou Collins
Mechanical available: Offset; Black and 3 ROP colors; insert accepted; page cutoffs - 22 1/2.
Commodity Consumption: Avg. Page Number Per Issue - Daily 16.
Equipment EDITORIAL: Front-end Software – Mk/Mycro-Comp AdWriter.; Editorial Hardware – Mk CLASSIFIED: Front-end Software – Mk/Mycro-Comp AdWriter.; Classified Hardware – Mk; Production Equipment – 1-Nu; Cameras – DAI. PRESSROOM: Line 1 – 4-1968.; Bundle tying machines – Bu.; Business Hardware – RSK/Tandy

COUNCIL GROVE

COUNCIL GROVE REPUBLICAN

208 W. Main St., Council Grove, Kan., 66846; gen tel (620) 767-5123; gen fax (620) 767-5124; gen e-mail cgnews@cgtelco.net; web site www.councilgrove.com
Group: Kansas Press Association
Published: Mon, Tues, Wed, Thur, Fri
Weekday Frequency: e
Circulation: 2,150
Price: 4.60/mo (news carrier); 51.98/yr (county), $65.98/yr (state), $75.98/yr (out-of-state).
Advertising: Open inch rate $5.11
News services: AP.
Politics: Republican. **Established:** 1876
Not Published: New Year; Memorial Day; Independence Day; Labor Day; Thanksgiving; Christmas.
Special Editions: Tourism (Apr); Bridal (Feb); Soil Conservation (Jan); County Fair (Jul); Historical Festival (Jun).
Adv. Dir. ....Becky Evans
Circ. Mgr. ....Christy Jimerson
Ed. ....Craig A. McNeal
Mechanical available: Offset; Black and 3 ROP colors; insert accepted; page cutoffs - 22 3/4.
Mechanical Specifications: Type page 15 3/16 x 21 1/2; E - 7 cols, 2 1/12, 1/6 between; A - 7 cols, 2 1/12, 1/6 between; C - 7 cols, 2 1/12, 1/6 between.
Commodity Consumption: Avg. Page Number Per Issue - Daily 6; widths 33; Printing Ink Used - Pages Printed 1316.
Equipment EDITORIAL: Front-end Software – Microsoft/Word 3.0.; Editorial Hardware – 3-APP/Mac; Editorial Printers – APP/Mac LaserWriter II NT CLASSIFIED: Front-end Software – Microsoft/Word 6.0, Aldus/PageMaker 5.0.; Classified Hardware – 1-APP/Power Mac Performa; Classified Printers – APP/Mac LaserWriter 16/600 PS DISPLAY: Ad make-up applications – Aldus/PageMaker 5.0.; Display Hardware – 1-APP/Power Mac Performa; Display Printers – APP/Mac LaserWriter 16/600 PS; Production Equipment – 1-APP/Mac LaserWriter II NT, APP/Mac LaserWriter 16/600 PS.; Addressing machine – Ap/Mac ImageWriter II; Other equipment –Premier/Quick Pick Label Dispenser.

DODGE CITY

DODGE CITY DAILY GLOBE

705 Second St., Dodge City, Kan., 67801; gen tel (620) 225-4151; adv tel (620) 225-4151; ed tel (620) 225-4151; gen fax (620) 225-4154; adv fax (620) 225-4154; ed fax (620) 225-4154; gen e-mail dcnews@dodgeglobe.com; web site www.dodgeglobe.com
Group: Kansas Press Association
Published: Mon, Tues, Wed, Thur, Fri, Sat
Weekday Frequency: m
Circulation: 9,700; 9,700(sat)
Last Audit: March 31, 1998
Price: 2.00/wk; 126.28/yr.
Advertising: Open inch rate $9.40
News services: AP.
Politics: Independent.
Not Published: Memorial Day; Independence Day; Labor Day; Christmas.
Special Editions: Progress (Feb); Bridal Tab (Jan); Bridal Tab (Jul); City Guide (Jun); Tourist Tab (Mar); Christmas Kick-Off (Thanksgiving Day) (Nov); Senior Citizens (Oct); Fall Fashion (Sept).
Special Weekly Sections: Youth Page (Fri); Seniors (Mon); Business Page (Sat); Health Page (Tues); Best Food Day (Wed).
Magazines: USA WEEKEND Magazine (Fri); Relish (Monthly).
Bus. Mgr./Personnel Mgr. ....Debbie Eddy
Display Adv. Mgr. ....Darrel Adams
Classified Adv. Mgr. ....Rebecca Gerber
Circ. Mgr...................................Patricia O'Neal
News Ed. ....Gene Lehmann
Website Mgr................................Shawn Cannon
Prodn. Foreman, Mailroom ....Roger Hedgecoth
Prodn. Foreman, Pressroom ....Edward O'Neil
Market Information: TMC.
Mechanical available: Offset; Black and 3 ROP colors; insert accepted; page cutoffs - 22 3/4.
Mechanical Specifications: Type page 11 1/4 x 21 1/2; E - 6 cols, 1 7/8, 1/16 between; A - 6 cols, 1 7/8, 1/16 between; C - 6 cols, 1 7/8, 1/16 between.
Commodity Consumption: Avg. Page Number Per Issue - Daily 18; Avg. Page Number Per

Issue - Plates Used 6000; Avg. Page Number Per Issue - Saturday 24; widths 25; Newsprint Used - Short Tons 475; Printing Ink Used - Black 10400; Printing Ink Used - Color 1650; Printing Ink Used

Equipment EDITORIAL: Front-end Software – Baseview, QPS/QuarkXPress.; Editorial Hardware – 6-APP/iMac, 3-APP/Mac SE, 4-APP/Mac Classic, 2-APP/Mac Quadra 610, APP/Mac 4400, APP/Mac 7600; Editorial Printers – APP/Mac LaserWriter NTX, MON, HP/LaserJet CLASSIFIED: Front-end Software – Baseview.; Classified Hardware – APP/Mac G3; Classified Printers – APP/Mac LaserWriter NTX DISPLAY: Ad make-up applications – Aldus/PageMaker, Aldus/FreeHand, QPS/QuarkXPress; Layout Software – APP/Mac.; Display Hardware – 4-APP/Mac G3, APP/Mac 7600, APP/Mac 4400; Production Equipment – APP/Mac LaserWriter NTX, APP/Mac LaserWriter NT, MON, HP/LaserJet 4MV. PRESSROOM: Line 1 – 7-G/Community 1976; Folders – 1; Inserters and stuffers – KAN/480; Addressing machine – Ch/705. AUDIO: Audio Software – SMS/Stauffer Gold; Audio Hardware – Samsung/486 BUSINESS COMPUTERS: Business Software – SMS/Business Software, Unix; Business Hardware – Epson/486, Unix, Wyse/terminals

EL DORADO

THE EL DORADO TIMES

114 N. Vine St., El Dorado, Kan., 67042; gen tel (316) 321-1120; gen fax (316) 321-7722; adv e-mail advertising@eldoradotimes.com; ads@eldoradotimes.com; web site www.eldoradotimes.com

Group: Kansas Press Association
Published: Mon, Tues, Wed, Thur, Fri
Weekday Frequency: e
Circulation: 3,396
Last Audit: September 25, 2002
Price: 10.66/mo; 106.80/yr.
Advertising: Open inch rate $8.75
News services: AP.
Politics: Independent.
Advertising not accepted: Abortion; Investments.
Not Published: New Year; Memorial Day; Independence Day; Labor Day; Thanksgiving; Christmas.
Magazines: TV Section (Thur); American Profile (Weekly).
Pub. ....Kent Bush
Display Adv. Mgr. ....Michelle Griffith
Classified Adv. Mgr. ....Heidi Dupuy
Circ. Mgr. ....Genie Reed
News Ed. ....Julie Clements
Sports Ed. ....Dammon Alexander
Prodn. Mgr. ....Justin Jacobucci
Market Information: ADS; TMC.
Mechanical available: Offset; Black and 3 ROP colors; insert accepted; page cutoffs - 22 3/4.
Mechanical Specifications: Type page 13 x 21 1/2; E - 6 cols, 2 1/16, 1/8 between; A - 6 cols, 2 1/16, 1/8 between; C - 6 cols, 2 1/16, 1/8 between.
Commodity Consumption: Avg. Page Number Per Issue - Daily 12; Avg. Page Number Per Issue - Plates Used 9600; widths 28; Newsprint Used - Short Tons 414; Printing Ink Used - Pages Printed 3881.
Equipment EDITORIAL: Front-end Software – QPS 3.2.; Editorial Hardware – APP/Mac; Editorial Printers – APP/Mac LaserPrinter CLASSIFIED: Front-end Software – QPS 3.2.; Classified Hardware – APP/Mac; Classified Printers – APP/Mac LaserPrinter DISPLAY: Ad make-up applications – QPS/QuarkXPress.; Display Hardware – APP/Mac II; Display Printers – APP/Mac LaserWriter; Production Equipment – 1-B/MP2; Cameras – 1-Acti/225. PRESSROOM: Line 1 – 6-HI/Cotrell V-25 & V-22; Folders – 1 MAILROOM: Counter stackers – 1/BG; Bundle tying machines – 1-/Bu; Wrapping singles – 1-/Bu; Addressing machine – 1-Am/6381, 1-/KR. BUSINESS COMPUTERS: Business Software – NoMads 7.55; Business Hardware – IBM/386

EMPORIA

THE EMPORIA GAZETTE

517 Merchant St., Emporia, Kan., 66801; gen tel (620) 342-4800; adv tel (620) 342-4803; ed tel (620) 342-4805; gen fax (620) 342-8108; adv fax (620) 342-8108; ed fax (620) 342-8108; gen e-mail newsroom@emporiagazette.com; web site www.emporiagazette.com

Group: Kansas Press Association
Published: Mon, Tues, Wed, Thur, Fri, Sat
Weekday Frequency: e
Circulation: 6,355; 6,355(sat)
Last Audit: September 30, 2009
Price: 7.25/mo (carrier), $9.90/mo (mail); 90.39/yr (carrier), $118.80/yr (mail).
Advertising: Open inch rate $10.56
News services: AP, NYT, Kansas Press Assoc.
Politics: Independent.
Advertising not accepted: Astrology.
Not Published: New Year; Memorial Day; Independence Day; Labor Day; Christmas.
Special Editions: Spring Car Care (Apr); Back-to-School (Aug); New Year's Greetings (Dec); Get Away Emporia (Jan); Ads By Kids (Mar); Coloring Book (May); Christmas Gift Guide (Nov); Fall Car Care (Oct); La Voz Latina (Spanish) (Quarterly); Football (Sept).
Special Weekly Sections: Weekend Business (Sat).
Magazines: TV Week (Sat).
Pres. ....Paul David Walker
Circ. Mgr. ....Brenda Armitage
Gen. Mgr. ....Ray J. Beals
Adv. Mgr., Display/Nat'l ....Jay Wilson
Circ. Mgr. ....Melissa Heinitz
Mng. Ed. ....Gwen Larson
Editorial Page Ed. ....Patrick S. Kelley
Travel Ed. ....Barbara White Walker
Online Mgr. ....Christopher White Walker
Prodn. Mgr. ....Dallas Sedgwick
Mgr., Distr. ....Larry Leaver
Mechanical available: Offset; Black and 3 ROP colors; insert accepted - single sheets, 8 1/2 x 11 min.; page cutoffs - 22 3/4.
Mechanical Specifications: Type page 13 x 21; E - 6 cols, 2 1/16, 1/8 between; A - 6 cols, 2 1/16, 1/8 between; C - 6 cols, 2 1/16, 1/8 between.
Commodity Consumption: Avg. Page Number Per Issue - Daily 23; Avg. Page Number Per Issue - Plates Used 4200; widths 27 1/2; Newsprint Used - Short Tons 420; Printing Ink Used - Black 13000; Printing Ink Used - Color 350; Printing Ink Used - Pages Printed 7450.
Equipment EDITORIAL: Front-end Software – QPS/QuarkXPress, FSI.; Editorial Hardware – APP/Power Mac 7200-120; Editorial Printers – 2-Select Press/600 CLASSIFIED: Front-end Software – FSI, Advance Sales.; Classified Hardware – APP/Power Mac 7200-120; Classified Printers – HP/LaserJet 5P DISPLAY: Ad make-up applications – FSI; Layout Software – FSI, ROP Layout, Advance Pro (for booking ads).; Display Hardware – APP/Power Mac 7200-120 PRODUCTION: Pagination Software – QPS/QuarkXPress/with FSI extensions.; Production Equipment – Text Bridge, Burgess/Light Source; Cameras – 1-Acti/183; Scanners – Umax/PowerBook 2000, 2-Umax/PowerBook II, Nikon/Coolscan II, APP/Color one 600-27, 2-Umax Mirage IIse PRESSROOM: Line 1 – 7-G/Community single width 1974; Folders – 1; Inserters and stuffers – 5-KAN/480; Bundle tying machines – 2-Bu/23; Addressing machine – 1-KAN/Labeler. BUSINESS COMPUTERS: Business Software – SMS; Business Hardware – IBM/340

WHITE CORP., INC.

517 Merchant St., Emporia, Kan., 66801; gen tel (620) 342-4800; gen fax (620) 342-8108; web site http://www.emporiagazette.com/

FORT SCOTT

THE FORT SCOTT TRIBUNE

12 E. Wall St., P.O. Box 150, Fort Scott, Kan., 66701-0150; gen tel (620) 223-1460; adv tel (620) 223-1460; ed tel (620) 223-1462; gen fax (620) 223-1469; adv fax (620) 223-1469; gen e-mail editor@fstribune.com; adv e-mail advertising@fstribune.com; web site www.fstribune.com

Group: Rust Publishing MO-KS, LLC
Kansas Press Association
Published: Tues, Wed, Thur, Fri, Sat
Weekday Frequency: m
Saturday Frequency: m
Circulation: 3,289; 3,289(sat)
Last Audit: October 1, 2003
Price: 7.55/mo; 85.00/yr.
Advertising: Open inch rate $9.85
News services: AP.
Politics: 1884
Not Published: New Year; Memorial Day; Independence Day; Labor Day; Veteran's Day; Thanksgiving; Christmas.
Own facility?: Y
Special Editions: Back-to-School (Aug); Basketball (Dec); Wedding (Jan); Fair (Jul); Good Ol' Days (Jun); Home Show (Mar); Graduation (May); Car Care (Oct); Football (Sept).
Special Weekly Sections: Church (Fri); Business (Thur); Senior Page (Tues)
Publisher ....Julie Righter
Adv. Dir. ....Lorie Harter
Sports Ed. ....Scott Nuzum
Managing Editor ....Ruth Campbell
Circ. Mgr. ....Betty Righter
Market Information: TMC.
Mechanical available: Offset; Black and 1 ROP colors; insert accepted; page cutoffs - 22 3/4.
Mechanical Specifications: Type page 13 x 21; E - 6 cols, 2 1/16, 1/8 between; A - 6 cols, 2 1/16, 1/8 between; C - 8 cols, 1 1/2, 1/8 between.
Commodity Consumption: Avg. Page Number Per Issue - Daily 11; Avg. Page Number Per Issue - Plates Used 2500; widths 27 1/2; Newsprint Used - Short Tons 122; Printing Ink Used - Black 3200; Printing Ink Used - Color 150; Printing Ink Used - Pages Printed 4389.
Equipment; Editorial Hardware – APP/Mac; Editorial Equipment – APP/Mac Scanner, 5-APP/Mac, 1-Radius; Editorial Printers – APP/Mac LaserWriter II.; Classified Hardware – APP/Mac; Classified Equipment – 1-APP/Mac, 1-Radius/Monitor; Classified Printers – APP/Mac LaserWriter II.; Production Equipment – B/Ultra-Lite 1500, LE/Line 17; Cameras – 1-Acti.; Bundle tying machines – 1-Bu/BT-17; Addressing machine – Compudyne/486SX-25. BUSINESS COMPUTERS: Business Software – Listmaster Systems (Omaha, NE); Business Hardware – 1-Compudyne/386DN-25, 1-Compudyne/486DN
Delivery method: Mail, Racks

GARDEN CITY

THE GARDEN CITY TELEGRAM

310 N. Seventh St., Garden City, Kan., 67846; gen tel (620) 275-8500; gen fax (620) 275-5165; gen e-mail riggs@gctelegram.com; adv e-mail advertising@gctelegram.com; ed e-mail newsroom@gctelegram.com; web site www.gctelegram.com

Group: Kansas Press Association
Published: Mon, Tues, Wed, Thur, Fri, Sat, Sun
Weekday Frequency: e
Saturday Frequency: m
Circulation: 7,432; 7,966(sat)
Last Audit: March 31, 2008
Price: 8.11/mo; 102.26/yr.
Advertising: Open inch rate $14.88
News services: AP, Harris.
Politics: Independent. **Established:** 1906
Not Published: New Year; Memorial Day; Independence Day; Labor Day; Thanksgiving; Christmas.
Special Weekly Sections: Weddings/Engagements (Sat); Farm Pages (Thur); Best Food Day (Wed).
Magazines: USA WEEKEND Magazine (Sat).
Bus./HR Mgr. ....Marisa Perez
Adv. Dir. ....Charity Ochs
Classifieds Mgr. ....Sharynn Bowman
Circ. Mgr. ....Jeremy Banwell
Bus. Ed. ....Brett Riggs
Editorial Page Ed. ....Dena Sattler
Photo Dept. Mgr. ....Brad Nading
Market Information: TMC.
Mechanical available: Offset; Black and 3 ROP colors; insert accepted - we prints-Telegram prints; page cutoffs - 22 3/4.
Mechanical Specifications: Type page 13 x 21 1/2; E - 6 cols, 2 1/8, 3/8 between; A - 6 cols, 2 1/8, 3/8 between; C - 8 cols, 1 1/2, 1/16 between.
Commodity Consumption: Avg. Page Number Per Issue - Daily 22; Avg. Page Number Per Issue - Plates Used 8700; widths 13 3/4; Newsprint Used - Metric Tons 480; Printing Ink Used - Black 11700; Printing Ink Used - Color 1560; Printing Ink Used - Pages Printed 6490.
Equipment EDITORIAL: Front-end Software – Baseview/NewsEdit IQUE, QP; Editorial Hardware – APP/Mac Centris 610, APP/Mac Centris 650, APP/Mac Centris 660, APP/Mac Centris 800, APP/Mac Quadra 610, APP/Mac Quadra 650, APP/Mac Quadra 660, APP/Mac Quadra 800; Editorial Printers – NewGen/1200B, ECR/Pelbox VR 36 CLASSIFIED: Front-end Software – Multi-Ad/Creator, QPS/QuarkXPress, Baseview.; Classified Hardware – APP/Mac Centris 610s, APP/Mac Quadra 800, 2-COM; Classified Printers – NewGen/1200B Laser Printer DISPLAY: Ad make-up applications – Multi-Ad/Creator, QPS/QuarkXPress, Base; Display Hardware – APP/Mac IIsx, APP/Mac Centris 610, APP/Mac Centris 650, APP/Mac Centris 800, APP/Mac Quadra 610, APP/Mac Quadra 650, APP/Mac Quadra 800, APP/Power Mac G3; Display Printers – NewGen/1200B Laser Printer PRODUCTION: Pagination Software – QPS/QuarkXPress 3.3.; Production Equipment – Caere/OmniPage Pro, Adobe/Photoshop, APP/Power Mac 7100; Cameras – 1-R/580 PRESSROOM: Line 1 – 8-G/SC 578; Folders – 1; Inserters and stuffers – KAN/480; Bundle tying machines – 1-Bu/66858, 1-Bu/32133; Addressing machine – 1-Am/1900, 1/Ch. AUDIO: Audio Software – SMS/Stauffer Gold Audiotext SGA 2a; Audio Hardware – Epson/Tower 3000 BUSINESS COMPUTERS: Business Software – Microsoft/Office, Microsoft/Windows, Informix/Smart II; Business Hardware – 3-DEC/PC LPV 433 DX, 6-TI/DSI Digital Venturis

TELEGRAM PUBLISHING CO.

310 N. 7th St., Garden City, Kan., 67846; gen tel (620) 275-8500; gen fax (620) 275-5165; adv e-mail advetising@gctelegram.com; web site www.gctelegram.com

Published: Mon, Tues, Wed, Thur, Fri, Sat, Sun
Price: 102.26/yr.
Advertising: Open inch rate $10.6

GOODLAND

GOODLAND PUBLISHING CO.

1205 Main St., Goodland, Kan., 67735; gen tel (785) 899-2338; gen fax (785) 899-6186; web site www.nwkansas.com

Price: 76.00/yr.
Advertising: Open inch rate $8.85 (classified)
Politics: 1932

GREAT BEND

GREAT BEND TRIBUNE

2012 Forest St., Great Bend, Kan., 67530-0228; gen tel (620) 792-1211; adv tel (620) 792-1211; ed tel (620) 792-1211; gen fax (620) 792-3441; adv fax (620) 792-3441; ed

fax (620) 792-8381; gen e-mail email@gbtribune.com; adv e-mail advertising@gbtribune.com; ed e-mail dhogg@gbtribune.com; web site www.gbtribune.com
Group: Morris Multimedia
Published: Tues, Wed, Thur, Fri, Sun
Weekday Frequency: m
Circulation: 6,282; 6,134(sun)
Last Audit: Sworn September 30, 2006
Price: 10.27/mo; 111.60/yr.
Advertising: Open inch rate $12.06
News services: AP.
Politics: Independent. **Established:** 1876
Not Published: Christmas.
Special Editions: Spring Opening (Mar); Christmas Shopping (Nov).
Special Weekly Sections: Church Page (Fri); Health (S); 50+ (Thur); Food Day (Wed).
Pub. ....Mary Hoisington
Mng. Ed. ....Dale Hogg
City Ed. ....Charles Smith
Online Mgr. ....Janet Dayton
Prodn. Foreman, Mailroom.............Jill Johnson
Prodn. Mgr., Pre Press.................Karma Byers
Market Information: TMC; Zoned editions.
Mechanical available: Offset; Black and 3 ROP colors; insert accepted - all; page cutoffs - 22 1/2.
Mechanical Specifications: Type page 12 x 21 1/2; E - 6 cols, 2, 1/8 between; A - 6 cols, 2, 1/8 between; C - 8 cols, 1 3/8, 1/8 between.
Commodity Consumption: Avg. Page Number Per Issue - Daily 17; Avg. Page Number Per Issue - Plates Used 3282; Avg. Page Number Per Issue - Sunday 34; widths 12 1/2; Newsprint Used - Short Tons 400; Printing Ink Used - Black 7800; Printing Ink Used - Color 1500; Printing Ink Use
Equipment EDITORIAL: Front-end Software – adobe creative sweek; Editorial Hardware – IBM/PC; Editorial Printers – hp; Classified Hardware – APP/Mac; Classified Printers – HP PRODUCTION: Pagination Software – Adobe Creative Suite; Production Equipment – MAC G3/ Pre Press/Panther Imagesetter; Cameras – 1-Op; Scanners – APP/Mac LC III PRESSROOM: Line 1 – 8-G/Community. MAILROOM: Counter stackers – BG/Count-O-Veyor; Bundle tying machines – 2-Bu/Tyer; Addressing machine – KR.; Audio Hardware – SMS BUSINESS COMPUTERS: Business Software – MAS 90; Business Hardware – IBM/PC
Delivery method: Mail, Newsstand, Private Carrier, Racks

HAYS

THE HAYS DAILY NEWS

507 Main St., Hays, Kan., 67601-4228; gen tel (785) 628-1081; gen fax (785) 628-8186; adv e-mail advertising@dailynews.net; ed e-mail newsroom@dailynews.net; web site www.hdnews.net
Group: Kansas Press Association
Published: Mon, Tues, Wed, Thur, Fri, Sun
Weekday Frequency: e
Circulation: 11,000; 11,300(sun)
Last Audit: Sworn March 31, 2007
Price: 11.98/mo; 135.20/yr.
Advertising: Open inch rate $16.65
Insert rate: $940 Flat Rate
News services: AP, Harris.
Politics: Independent. **Established:** 1929
Not Published: Memorial Day; Labor Day.
Own facility?: Y
Special Editions: College (Aug); Christmas & New Years Greetings (Dec); Bridal Fair (Feb); Sidewalk Bazaar (Jul); Wild West Festival (Jun); Travel & Tourism (May); Christmas (Nov); Area Football (Sept).
Special Weekly Sections: Church Services (Fri); Real Estate (S); Best Food Day (Tues); Generations (Wed).
Magazines: Das Haus (Every other month); TV Guide (Fri); USA WEEKEND Magazine (S). Sports Ink published every month the last Thursday
Bus. Mgr. ....Janice Tinkel
Adv. Dir. ....Mary Karst
Circ. Mgr. ....Robert Wiegel
Ed. ....Pat Lowry
Mng. Ed. ....Ron Fields
Photo Ed..................................Steve Hausler
Sports Ed.............................Randy Gonzales
Asst. Sports Ed...........................Nick Schwien
Editorial Writer ....Pat Lowrey
Prodn. Mgr., Opns........................Steve Ruder
Market Information: TMC.
Mechanical available: Offset; Black and 3 ROP colors; insert accepted - all; page cutoffs - 22 3/4.
Mechanical Specifications: Type page 10 5/16 x 21 1/2; E - 6 cols, 1 17/32, 1/8 between; A - 6 cols, 1 17/32, 1/8 between; C - 8 cols, 1 3/16, 3/32 between.
Commodity Consumption: Avg. Page Number Per Issue - Daily 20; Avg. Page Number Per Issue - Plates Used 29998; Avg. Page Number Per Issue - Sunday 45; widths 10 5/16; Newsprint Used - Short Tons 735.782; Printing Ink Used - Black 20798; Printing Ink Used - Color 4712; Printing
Equipment EDITORIAL: Front-end Software – FSI/Edit, QPS/QuarkXPress 3.3.; Editorial Hardware – APP/Mac CLASSIFIED: Front-end Software – QPS/QuarkXPress 3.3, FSI/Advance Pro.Indesign 3; Classified Hardware – APP/Mac; Classified Printers – Epson, Epson/LQ 1170 DISPLAY: Ad make-up applications – Microsoft/Word, QPS/QuarkXPress 3.3; Layout Software – Mu; Display Hardware – 1-APP/Mac Classic, 1-APP/Power Mac, 1-APP/Mac Quadra 650, 1-APP/Power Mac; Display Printers – Design Express/6, GCC/Elite XL600 PRODUCTION: Pagination Software – QPS/QuarkXPress 3.3. Indesign 3; Production Equipment – Caere/OmniPage 5.0, ECR/VR36, Elite XL 20/60; Cameras – 1-R/580; Scanners – 2-Lf/Leafscan 35, Microtek/II HR PRESSROOM: Line 1 – 8-G/SC 650 Single width 1974; Folders – 1-G/3:2.; Inserters and stuffers – 1-KAN/480 (6 station), KAN/Multi-feeder (4 station); Bundle tying machines – Mc/40 String Tyer, Transpak/A-72 Strapper; Addressing machine – Videojet/Excel inkjet printer. BUSINESS COMPUTERS: Business Software – Microsoft/Office, Newzware; Business Hardware – TI/941

HIAWATHA

HIAWATHA WORLD

607 Utah St., Hiawatha, Kan., 66434; gen tel (785) 742-2111; gen fax (785) 742-2276; ed e-mail world@npgco.com
Published: Tues, Fri
Circulation: 2,300
Last Audit: Estimate January 21, 2005
Price: 52.58/yr.
Advertising: Open inch rate $6.50
Politics: Republican.
Own facility?: Y
Adv. Mgr. ....Bobi Dozier
Circ. Mgr. ....Dan Glynn
Mechanical Specifications: Type page 13 x 21; E - 6 cols, 2 1/16, 1/8 between; A - 6 cols, 2 1/16, 1/8 between; C - 6 cols, 2 1/16, 1/8 between.

HUTCHINSON

THE HUTCHINSON NEWS

300 W. 2nd Ave., Hutchinson, Kan., 67501-5211; gen tel (620) 694-5700; adv tel (620) 694-5700; ed tel (620) 694-5700; gen fax (620) 694-5799; adv fax (620) 662-4186; ed fax (620) 662-4186; gen e-mail rchristner@harrisbusiness.com; adv e-mail lshea@hutchnews.com; ed e-mail jmont@hutchnews.com; web site www.hutchnews.com
Group: Harris Ent, Inc
Kansas Press Association
Published: Mon, Tues, Wed, Thur, Fri, Sat, Sun
Weekday Frequency: m
Saturday Frequency: m
Circulation: 31,095; 31,095(sat); 33,472(sun)
Last Audit: Sworn December 30, 2010
Price: 14.35/mo (carrier); 154.46/yr (carrier).
Advertising: Open inch rate $26.75
Insert rate: $55/m
News services: AP, SHNS, TMS
Politics: Independent. **Established:** 1872
Own facility?: Y
Special Editions: Reno Co. Homes (Monthly); Better Health & Living (Quarterly).
Special Weekly Sections: TV Mag (S)
Magazines: USA WEEKEND Magazine (S), Athlon Sports (Monthly)
Profile: Daily newspaper serving 40 counties in south-central and south-western Kansas.
HR Dir.....................................Rex Christner
Adv. Dir. ....Leslie Shea
Adv. Supvr., Sales......................Darren Werth
Circ. Mgr., Opns...........................Debbie Irwin
Ed./Pub..............................John Montgomery
Mng. Ed. ....Mary Rintoul
News Ed....................................Jason Probst
Reporter..John Green
Prodn. Mgr. ....Gregg Beals
Prodn. Mgr., Pressroom ....Mike Heim
Prodn. Mgr., Packaging/Distribution Jeremy Coen
Market Information: Zoned editions.
Mechanical available: Offset; Black and 3 ROP colors; insert accepted - Tab-ons; page cutoffs - 21 1/2.
Mechanical Specifications: Type page 11 3/4 x 21 1/2; E - 6 cols, 1 4/5, 1/7 between; A - 6 cols, 1 4/5, 1/7 between; C - 9 cols, 1 1/5, 1/7 between.
Commodity Consumption: Avg. Page Number Per Issue - Daily 27; Avg. Page Number Per Issue - Plates Used 24450; Avg. Page Number Per Issue - Saturday 48; Avg. Page Number Per Issue - Sunday 56; widths 25; Newsprint Used - Metric Tons 2128; Printing Ink Used - Black 46350; Printi
Equipment EDITORIAL: Front-end Software – APT/ACT 3.05, QPS 5.0.; Editorial Hardware – Dell/Pentium Server NT 40, 30-PC; Editorial Printers – HP/Laserjet 8000N 1999 CLASSIFIED: Front-end Software – APT/ACT 3.05.; Classified Hardware – Dell/Pentium Server NT 4.0; Classified Printers – HP/Laserjet 4v DISPLAY: Ad make-up applications – Adobe/Illustrator 9.0, QPS 4.0, Adobe/Photoshop 6.0; Layout Software – APT.; Display Hardware – Pentium Dell Server NT, Umax/Scanners, Dell/PC's; Display Printers – HP/Laserjet 8000N PRODUCTION: Pagination Software – QPS/QuarkXPress 5.0, APT/ACT 3.05.; Production Equipment – 1-Nu/FT40UPNS, Adobe/Photoshop, 2-3850 Sierra Imager, III/3850 15 Imager, HP/Laserjet 8000N PRESSROOM: Line 1 – 8-G/1018-4-72; Press Drives – 2, 2-150 HP/Electic Motors; Folders – 1-G/1018 Folder w/upper Former; Reels and Stands – 8 MAILROOM: Counter stackers – HL/DC, HL/Monitor; Inserters and stuffers – 1-MM/227E, GMA/SLS 1000A; Bundle tying machines – 1-Sterling/MR45CH, 2-MLN/2EE; Addressing machine – 1-KR/221 227. BUSINESS COMPUTERS: Business Software – Microsoft/Office XP Pro, Newzware; Business Hardware – 1-Dell/Poweredge 2500
Zip Codes served: over 100
Delivery method: Mail, Newsstand, Private Carrier, Racks

INDEPENDENCE

INDEPENDENCE DAILY REPORTER

320 N. 6th St., Independence, Kan., 67301; gen tel (620) 331-3550; gen fax (620) 331-3550; adv e-mail ads@dreporter.com
Group: Kansas Press Association
Published: Mon, Tues, Wed, Thur, Fri, Sun
Weekday Frequency: e
Circulation: 6,654; 6,654(sun)
Last Audit: September 23, 2001
Price: 99.95/yr.
Advertising: Open inch rate $7.85
News services: AP.
Politics: Independent.
Advertising not accepted: Mail order.
Not Published: Independence Day; Christmas.
Sec./Treasurer ....Kristin Meyer
Controller/Credit Mgr. ....Tracy Harder
Mgr., Promo............................Steve McBride
Circ. Dir. ....James Tracy
Amusements Ed. ....Georgia High
Aviation Ed...........................Doug Armbruster
Bus./Finance Ed....................Herbert A. Meyer
Educ./School Ed. ....Greg Lower
Society/Women's Ed. ....Taina Copeland
Sports Ed. ....Brian Thomas
Travel Ed............................Herbert A. Meyer
Market Information: Split run.
Mechanical available: Offset; Black and 3 ROP colors; insert accepted; page cutoffs - 22 3/4.
Mechanical Specifications: Type page 13 x 21; E - 6 cols, 2 1/16, 1/8 between; A - 6 cols, 2 1/16, 1/8 between; C - 6 cols, 2 1/16, 1/8 between.
Commodity Consumption: Avg. Page Number Per Issue - Daily 20; Avg. Page Number Per Issue - Plates Used 3600; Avg. Page Number Per Issue - Sunday 60; widths 27 1/2; Newsprint Used - Short Tons 220; Printing Ink Used - Black 4536; Printing Ink Used - Color 577; Printing Ink Used
Equipment EDITORIAL: Front-end Software – Mk/1100, FSI/Vanguard System.; Editorial Hardware – Mk/1100, 7-APP/Mac Quadra 630 CLASSIFIED: Front-end Software – Mk/1100, FSI/Vanguard System.; Classified Hardware – Mk/1100, 3-APP/Mac Quadra 630; Production Equipment – 2-APP/Mac LaserWriter II; Cameras – 1-Acti/183. PRESSROOM: Line 1 – 6-G/SC 1973.; Inserters and stuffers – 1-DG/320; Bundle tying machines – 1-Malow/51; Wrapping singles – 2-St/510W. BUSINESS COMPUTERS: Business Software – Unix, R&D Systems; Business Hardware – 5-Unix/U5000-30C

THE REPORTER PUBLISHING CO., INC.

320 N. 6th St., Independence, Kan., 67301; gen tel (620) 331-3550; gen fax (620) 331-3550 ext 164

IOLA

IOLA REGISTER

302 S. Washington Ave., Iola, Kan., 66749; gen tel (620) 365-2111; gen fax (620) 365-6289; adv e-mail registerdisplay@gmail.com; ed e-mail editorial@iolaregister.com; web site www.iolaregister.com
Group: Kansas Press Association
Published: Mon, Tues, Wed, Thur, Fri, Sat, Sun
Weekday Frequency: e
Saturday Frequency: m
Circulation: 3,750; 3,750(sat)
Last Audit: October 8, 2003
Price: 7.76/mo; 72.42/yr.
Advertising: Open inch rate $8.00
News services: AP.
Politics: Independent-Republican.
Advertising not accepted: 900 numbers.
Not Published: New Year; Memorial Day; Independence Day; Labor Day; Thanksgiving; Christmas.
Special Editions: Fair (Aug); Sports Tab (Dec); Fair (Jun); Spring (Mar); Business & Professional Tab (Oct); Sports Tab (Sept).
Special Weekly Sections: Farm Page (Mon); TV Guide (Thur); Best Food Day (Tues).
Office Mgr. ....Glenda Aikins
Adv. Mgr. ....Mark L. Hastings
Adv. Mgr., Classified....................Pam Holland
Circ. Mgr...................................Gita Johnson
Action Line Ed. ....Richard Luken
Editorial Page Ed..........................Susan Lynn
Graphics Ed./Art Dir. ....Sara Weide
Health/Medical Ed...................Jenelle Johnson
Nat'l Ed. ....Emerson E. Lynn
News Ed.....................................Bob Johnson
Online Ed..................................David Gilham
Photo Ed................................Jocelyn Sheets
Market Information: TMC.
Mechanical available: Offset; Black and 1 ROP colors; insert accepted; page cutoffs - 21 1/2.
Mechanical Specifications: Type page 13 x 21 1/2; E - 6 cols, 2 1/16, 3/16 between; A - 6 cols, 2 1/16, 3/16 between; C - 8 cols, 2

1/16, 3/16 between.
Commodity Consumption: Avg. Page Number Per Issue - Daily 16; Avg. Page Number Per Issue - Saturday 8; widths 27 1/2; Newsprint Used - Short Tons 160; Printing Ink Used - Black 5000; Printing Ink Used - Color 200; Printing Ink Used - Pages Printed 4576.
Equipment EDITORIAL: Front-end Software – Baseview, QPS/QuarkXPress, Microsoft/Word.; Editorial Hardware – APP/Mac 7600, APP/Mac 9600, APP/Mac G3, APP/Mac G4; Editorial Printers – Xante, HP/4000 DISPLAY: Ad make-up applications – APP/Mac Sys 8.0, APP/Mac Sys 7.5, Adobe/Photoshop, Multi-Ad/Creator.; Display Hardware – APP/Mac G3, APP/Mac 7600; Display Printers – Xante; Production Equipment – LE/LD18; Cameras – Acti/183. PRESSROOM: Line 1 – HI/Cotrell V-15A; Press control system – 1972 BUSINESS COMPUTERS: Business Software – Microsoft/Windows 95, Pachioli/Works; Business Hardware – 3-SAMTRON/SM-460

THE IOLA REGISTER PUBLISHING CO.
302 S. Washington Ave., Iola, Kan., 66749-3255; gen tel (620) 365-2111; gen fax (620) 365-6289

JUNCTION CITY

THE DAILY UNION
222 W. Sixth St., Junction City, Kan., 66441-0129; gen tel (785) 762-5000; adv tel (785) 762-5000; ed tel (785) 762-5000; gen fax (785) 762-4584; adv fax (785) 762-4584; ed fax (785) 762-4584; adv e-mail adv.mgr@thedailyunion.net; ed e-mail m.editor@thedailyunion.net; web site thedailyunion.net
Published: Tues, Wed, Thur, Fri, Sat
Weekday Frequency: m
Saturday Frequency: m
Circulation: 3,500; 4,050(sat)
Last Audit: Sworn September 30, 2009
Price: 9.50/mo; 108.00/yr.
Advertising: Open inch rate $10.40
News services: AP, CNS, TMS.
Politics: Independent. **Established:** 1861
Not Published: New Year; Memorial Day; Independence Day; Labor Day; Thanksgiving; Christmas.
Own facility?: Y
Special Editions: A-Z Page (Aug); Christmas Greetings (Dec); Outlook (Feb); Bridal (Jan); JC Guide (Jul); Spring Home & Garden (Mar); Gift Guide (Nov); Design an Ad (Oct); Football (Sept).
Special Weekly Sections: Faith (Fri); Wedding Page (S); Lifestyle (Thur); Food (Tues).
Magazines: TV Channel Cues (local, newsprint) (S).
Pres./ceo ....John Grey Montgomery
Office Mgr./Purchasing Agent ....Penny Nelson
Editorial Page Ed. ....Tom Throne
Market Information: TMC.
Mechanical available: Offset; Black and 3 ROP colors; insert accepted; page cutoffs - 22 3/4.
Mechanical Specifications: Type page 13 x 21 1/2; E - 6 cols, 2 1/16, 1/8 between; A - 6 cols, 2 1/16, 1/8 between; C - 6 cols, 2 1/16, 1/8 between.
Commodity Consumption: Avg. Page Number Per Issue - Daily 15; Avg. Page Number Per Issue - Plates Used 4450; Avg. Page Number Per Issue - Sunday 39; widths 34; Newsprint Used - Short Tons 270; Printing Ink Used - Black 10949; Printing Ink Used - Color 3880; Printing Ink Used -
Equipment EDITORIAL: Front-end Software – Baseview.; Editorial Hardware – 14-Power Computing/180, 3-Power Computing/225, 1-APP/iMac G3 CLASSIFIED: Front-end Software – Baseview.; Classified Hardware – 1-Power Computing/180, APP/iMac G3; Classified Printers – 2-Tally/T-6050 DISPLAY: Ad make-up applications – Multi-Ad/Creator 4.0, QPS/QuarkXPress 4.1, Adobe/Photoshop 6.0, Adobe/Illustrator 8.0, Adobe/Acrobat 5.0; Display Hardware – 1-APP/Mac 8500, 2-APP/Mac 7100, 2-Power Computing/150, 2-APP/Mac G3, 1-APP/Mac G4; Display Printers – HP/4MV, 1-Epson 3000, 1-QMS/2060 PRODUCTION: Pagination Software – Baseview.; Production Equipment – 1-Nu, 1-QMS/2060 LaserWriter, 1-Pre Press/Panther Pro 46 Imagesetter; Cameras – 1-Acti; Scanners – 4-Microtek/Scanner, 1-Poloroid/Sprint Scan 35 PRESSROOM: Line 1 – 6-G/Community; Folders – 1-G/Suburban.; Inserters and stuffers – 1-KAN/760; Bundle tying machines – 1/Bu, 2-Malow/MC Straptyer. BUSINESS COMPUTERS: Business Software – Baseview; Business Hardware – 6-APP/iMac G3, 1-Power Computing/180, 1-Power Computing/150
Delivery method: Mail, Newsstand, Racks

MONTGOMERY COMMUNICATION, INC.
222 W. Sixth St., Junction City, Kan., 66441; gen tel (785) 762-5000; gen fax (785) 762-4584

KANSAS CITY

KANSAS CITY KANSAN
7815 Parallel Pkwy., Kansas City, Kan., 66112; gen tel (913) 371-4300; adv tel (913) 371-4300; ed tel (913) 371-4300; gen fax (913) 342-8620; ed fax (913) 342-8620; adv e-mail retail@kansascitykansan.com; ed e-mail news@kansascitykansan.com; web site www.kansascitykansan.com
Group: Kansas Press Association
Published: Tues, Wed, Thur, Fri, Sat
Weekday Frequency: e
Saturday Frequency: m
Circulation: 8,000; 8,065(sat)
Last Audit: September 30, 2001
Price: 74.63/yr; 23.55/3mo.
Advertising: Open inch rate $8.85
News services: AP.
Politics: Independent.
Not Published: Memorial Day; Labor Day; Christmas.
Special Editions: Bank Statement (Apr); Coupon Pages (Aug); Christmas Gift Guide 2 (Dec); KCK Chamber of Commerce Tab (Feb); Bank Statement (Jan); Seniors' Tab (Jul); Father's Day (Jun); Spring Automotive (Mar); Summer Education Guide (May); Christmas Gift Guide 1 (Nov); L
Magazines: TV This Week in Wyandotte County (Sat).
Circ. Mgr. ....Drew Savage
Mng. Ed. ....Matt Kelsey
Sports Ed.................................Jeremy Banks
Market Information: TMC.
Mechanical available: Offset; Black and 3 ROP colors; insert accepted; page cutoffs - 21 1/2.
Mechanical Specifications: Type page 12 3/4 x 21 1/2; E - 6 cols, 2, 1/4 between; A - 6 cols, 2, 1/4 between; C - 9 cols, 1 5/16, 1/6 between.
Commodity Consumption: Avg. Page Number Per Issue - Daily 12; Avg. Page Number Per Issue - Sunday 20.
Equipment EDITORIAL: Front-end Software – Microsoft/Word, QPS/QuarkXPress.; Editorial Hardware – APP/Mac, APP/Mac G3, APP/iMac; Editorial Printers – 2-Dataproducts/LZR 1560 CLASSIFIED: Front-end Software – Baseview 2.0.3.; Classified Hardware – APP/Mac, APP/iMac, APP/Mac G3; Classified Printers – Dataproducts/LZR 1560, Okidata/Microline 591 DISPLAY: Ad make-up applications – QPS/QuarkXPress 3.2, Multi-Ad/Creator 4.0, Adobe/Photoshop 5.0; Layout Software – APP/iMac, APP/Mac G3.; Display Hardware – APP/Mac; Display Printers – Dataproducts/LZR 1560, Xante Accel-A-Writer 8200 PRODUCTION: Pagination Software – QPS/QuarkXPress 3.2, Microsoft/Word 5.0.; Production Equipment – OmniPage LE 5.1; Cameras – DAI, Olympus/Digital Cameras, Kk; Scanners – Microtek/ScanMaker, AG/Argus II, Nikon/LS-2000, Polaroid/Sprint Scan 35 PRESSROOM: Line 1 – 5-G/Urbanite.; Inserters and stuffers – KAN/480; Bundle tying machines – MLN. BUSINESS COMPUTERS: Business Software – BMF; Business Hardware – 3-IBM/PC

LARNED

THE TILLER & TOILER
115 W. Fifth St., Larned, Kan., 67550; gen tel (620) 285-3111; gen fax (620) 285-6062; gen e-mail tiller@star.kscoxmail.com
Published: Mon, Tues, Wed, Thur, Fri
Weekday Frequency: e
Circulation: 1,434
Last Audit: October 1, 2001
Price: 61.94/yr (in county).
Advertising: Open inch rate $4.25
News services: AP.
Politics: Republican.
Not Published: New Year; Memorial Day; Independence Day; Labor Day; Thanksgiving; Day after Thanksgiving; Christmas.
Pres. ....Marshall Settle
Pub. ....John M. Settle
Adv. Rep. ....Bryan Martin
Adv. Rep. ....Paula Settle
Circ. Mgr. ....Shirley Strassburg
Mng. Ed. ....Dennis Martin
Sports Ed. ....Mark Zwink
Online Mgr. ....Lisa Springer
Prodn. Mgr., Pressroom ....Bob Crawford
Market Information: TMC.
Mechanical available: Offset; Black and 3 ROP colors; insert accepted.
Mechanical Specifications: Type page 12 7/8 x 21 1/2; E - 6 cols, 2 1/16, 1/8 between; A - 6 cols, 2 1/16, 1/8 between; C - 6 cols, 2 1/16, 1/8 between.
Commodity Consumption: Avg. Page Number Per Issue - Daily 12.
Equipment; Production Equipment – 4-P, 2-COM, 1-F; Cameras – 1-DAI. PRESSROOM: Line 1 – 3-HI/Cotrell.; Addressing machine – 1/Am.

LAWRENCE

THE WORLD CO.- LAWRENCE, KAN., JOURNAL-WORLD
609 New Hampshire St., P.O. Box 888, Lawrence, Kan., 66044; gen tel (785) 843-1000; adv tel (785) 832-7111; ed tel (785) 832-7154; gen fax (785) 843-1922; adv fax (785) 843-1922; ed fax (785) 843-4512; gen e-mail news@ljworld.com; adv e-mail scantrell@ljworld.com; ed e-mail news@ljworld.com; web site www.ljworld.com
Group: The World Company
Published: Mon, Tues, Wed, Thur, Fri, Sat, Sun
Weekday Frequency: m
Saturday Frequency: m
Circulation: 27,813; 27,813(sat); 28,630(sun)
Last Audit: ABC September 30, 2011
Price: $210.89/yr
Advertising: Open rates w/4C: Page $4330, 1/2 page $2164, 1/4 pg $1100, 1/8 pg $550
Insert rate: $39 CPM single sheet
News services: AP
Politics: Independent. **Established:** 1891
Own facility?: Y
Special Editions: Only in Lawrence (Apr); Kansas University (Aug); KU Basketball (Oct); Holiday Gift Guide (Nov).
Special Weekly Sections: Go!, Hometown Lawrence (real estate)
Magazines: USA Weekend, Sun; Spry, Mon.; Relish, Wed.; American Profile, Sat.
Broadcast Affiliations: None
CFO.......................................Tom Hornbaker
COO.....................................Suzanne Schlicht
Pres., Newspapers Div............Dolph C. Simons
Pres., Electronics Div.....................Dan Simons
Pres., Mediaphormedia ....Dan Cox
Special Projects Dir........................Ralph Gage
Chairman................................Dolph Simons
Circ. Mgr. ....Chris Bell
Editor and Chairman ....Dolph C. Simons
Mng. Ed.............................Dennis Anderson
Marketing Director ....Monica Taylor
Community Editor.............Caroline Trowbridge
Editorial Page Ed...........................Ann Gardner
Editor ....Dolph Simons
Sports Ed.....................................Tom Keegan
IT Dir.......................................Brad Fanshier
Director of Media Strategies ....Jane Stevens
Vice President of Sales and Marketing Susan Cantrell
Community Editor.............Caroline Trowbridge
Editorial Page Editor ....Ann Gardner
COO ....Suzanne Schlicht
Sports Editor................................Tom Keegan
Director of Market Strategies.....Edwin Rothrock
Marketing Director ....Monica Taylor
Entertainment Editor ....Trevan McGee
Production Director...................Ed Ciambrone
Production Manager-Distribution....Rich Salierno
Production Manager-prepress ....David Burton
Production Manager-Press.................Gary Post
Business Editor......................Chad Lawhorn
President, Mediaphormedia LLC ....Dan Cox
Market Information: TMC, electronic edition, online business directory, operate database, ADS
Mechanical available: Offset; Black and 3 ROP colors; insert accepted; page cutoffs - 22.
Mechanical Specifications: Type page 11 1/3 x 20 5/6; E - 6 cols, 1 7/8, 1/8 between; A - 6 cols, 1 7/8, 1/8 between; C - 9 cols, 1 1/8, 1/16 between.
Commodity Consumption: Newsprint 1079 short tons; widths 24-in., 25-in., 31-in.; black ink 17,791 lbs., color inks, 18,754 lbs., single pages printed, 12,170, average pages per issue, 27 (d), 48 (Sat), 50 (Sun); single plates used 48,890.
Equipment EDITORIAL: Front-end Software – Baseview/NewsEdit.; Editorial Hardware – MAC; Editorial Printers – HP 1050C CLASSIFIED: Front-end Software – Advanced Publishing Technology; Classified Hardware – Dell, HP, IBM DISPLAY: Ad make-up applications – Mediaspan Production Manager Pro; Display Hardware – MAC PRODUCTION: Pagination Software – alphaQuest Print Xpress; Production Equipment – alfaQuest CTP, two lines; Cameras – 1-B PRESSROOM: Line 1 – Goss Urbanite, 18 units; Line 2 – Goss Urbanite 12 units; Press Drives – Fincor; Folders – Goss; Pasters – Enkel Autoweb MAILROOM: Counter stackers – Quipp; Inserters and stuffers – Muller 227, 308, and GMA SLS100A; Bundle tying machines – Signode, Dynaric and Oval; Addressing machine – Cheshire; Other equipment –Profitpackaging front-page label applicator BUSINESS COMPUTERS: Business Software – Great Plains; Business Hardware – Dell, HP, IBM
Zip Codes served: 66025, 66044, 66045, 66046, 66047, 66049, 66050, 66066
Delivery method: Mail, Newsstand, Private Carrier, Racks

LEAVENWORTH

THE LEAVENWORTH TIMES
422 Seneca St., Leavenworth, Kan., 66048; gen tel (913) 682-0305; adv tel (913) 682-0305; ed tel (913) 682-0305; gen fax (913) 682-1114; adv fax (913) 682-1114; ed fax (913) 682-1114; gen e-mail ltimes@sbcglobal.net; adv e-mail ltimesad@sbcglobal.net; ed e-mail ltimesed@sbcglobal.net; web site www.leavenworthtimes.com
Group: Kansas Press Association
Published: Tues, Wed, Thur, Fri, Sat
Weekday Frequency: e
Saturday Frequency: m
Circulation: 5,608; 6,318(sat)
Last Audit: March 31, 2006
Price: 10.55/mo; 121.51/yr.
Advertising: Open inch rate $15.50
News services: AP, DJ.
Politics: Independent. **Established:** 1857
Not Published: New Year; Memorial Day; Independence Day; Labor Day; Christmas.
Magazines: USA WEEKEND Magazine (S).
Pub..Tim Larson
Adv. Dir. ....Meredith Timmons
Circ. Dir. ....Barbara Daniels
Mng. Ed.......................................Scott Lowder
Sports Ed....................................Sara Mettlen
Prodn. Foreman..........................Tina Everrett
Mechanical available: Offset; Black and 3 ROP colors; insert accepted - free-standing cards;

page cutoffs - 22 3/4.
Mechanical Specifications: Type page 11 9/16 x 21 1/2; E - 6 cols, 1 13/16, 1/8 between; A - 6 cols, 1 13/16, 1/8 between; C - 9 cols, 1 3/16, 1/8 between.
Commodity Consumption: Avg. Page Number Per Issue - Daily 14; Avg. Page Number Per Issue - Sunday 22; widths 34.
Equipment EDITORIAL: Front-end Software – Baseview.; Editorial Hardware – APP/Mac; Editorial Equipment – Pre Press/Panther Pro 36; Editorial Printers – HP/LaserJet 4MV CLASSIFIED: Front-end Software – CAMS.; Classified Hardware – APP/iMac; Classified Printers – APP/Mac 12-640 DISPLAY: Ad make-up applications – Multi-Ad/Creator, APP/Mac System 9; Layout Software – APP/Mac.; Display Printers – HP/LaserJet 4MV PRODUCTION: Pagination Software – QPS/QuarkXPress 4.1.; Production Equipment – Caere/OmniPage 7.0, 1-COM/8400, 2-APP/Mac; Cameras – 1-Nu PRESSROOM: Line 1 – 8-G/Community; Folders – 1-G/quarter folder, 1. MAILROOM: Counter stackers – BG/Count-O-Veyor; Bundle tying machines – 2-Malow/Strap-Tyer, 1/Strapack; Addressing machine – 1-/Am. BUSINESS COMPUTERS: Business Software – Nomads/ListMaster; Business Hardware – PC

LIBERAL

SOUTHWEST DAILY TIMES

16 S. Kansas Ave., Liberal, Kan., 67901-3732; gen tel (620) 624-2541; adv tel (620) 624-2541; ed tel (620) 624-2541; gen fax (620) 624-0735; adv fax (620) 624-0735; ed fax (620) 624-0735; adv e-mail ads@swdtimes.com; ed e-mail editor@swdtimes.com; web site www.swdtimes.com
Group: Kansas Press Association
Published: Tues, Wed, Thur, Fri, Sun
Weekday Frequency: m
Circulation: 4,250; 4,500(sun)
Price: 8.25/mo; 110.00/yr.
Advertising: Open inch rate $13.00
News services: AP.
Politics: Independent.
Special Editions: Life & Times (Mar); Life & Times (Sept).
Special Weekly Sections: Entertainment (Fri); Leisure Times (S); Farm & Ranch (Thur); Business Day (Tues); Best Food Day (Wed).
Magazines: FYI (S).
Pub. ....Jim Gutzmer
Bus. Mgr. ....Amber Austin
Mng. Ed. ....Tony Hernandez
Sports Ed. ....Eric Viccaro
Prodn. Mgr. ....Katie Taylor
Mailroom Mgr. ....Esperanza Nunez
Market Information: Split run; TMC; Zoned editions.
Mechanical available: Offset; Black and 3 ROP colors; insert accepted - cards, catalogs; page cutoffs - 21 1/2.
Mechanical Specifications: Type page 12 1/2 x 20; E - 6 cols, 2, 1/8 between; A - 6 cols, 2, 1/8 between; C - 9 cols, 1 5/16, 1/16 between.
Commodity Consumption: Avg. Page Number Per Issue - Daily 20; Avg. Page Number Per Issue - Plates Used 3500; Avg. Page Number Per Issue - Sunday 36; widths 27; Newsprint Used - Short Tons 420; Printing Ink Used - Color 400; Printing Ink Used - Pages Printed 6254.
Equipment EDITORIAL: Front-end Software – Baseview/NewsEdit, QPS/QuarkXPress 3.31, Adobe/Photoshop 2.5.1.; Editorial Hardware – 7-APP/Power Mac; Editorial Equipment – 2-Flatbed Scanners, Lf/Leafscan Negative Scanner, Pre Press/Panther Imagesetter; Editorial Printers – 2-Elite/XL 608 600 DPI CLASSIFIED: Front-end Software – Baseview/Class Manager.; Classified Hardware – 1-APP/Mac SE, 1-APP/Mac SE30, APP/Mac LC III; Classified Equipment – Printers □ APP/Mac ImageWriter II DISPLAY: Ad make-up applications – Aldus/PageMaker, Broderbund/TypeStyler, QPS/QuarkXPress, Adobe/Photoshop 2.5, AP AdSend; Display Hardware – 1-APP/Mac Classic, 2-APP/Mac II, 1-APP/Mac Classic, APP/Mac Centris 660AV; Display Printers – Pre Press/Panther ImageSetter PRODUCTION: Pagination Software – QPS/QuarkXPress 3.31.; Production Equipment – Caere/OmniPage 2.1, 1-Pre-Press/ImageSetter, Konica/7200; Cameras – Acti/Horizontal Full Frame; Scanners – Relisys/Color Scan, 1-Lf/Leafscan 35mm Negative Scanner PRESSROOM: Line 1 – 5-WPC/Atlas (1-Quadra color;; Folders – 1 MAILROOM: Counter stackers – 1-KAN/4 station; Bundle tying machines – 2/Bu; Other equipment –Bostich/Stitcher.; Business Hardware – 7-HP/Pentium II

LYONS

THE LYONS NEWS

210 W. Commercial St., Lyons, Kan., 67554; gen tel (620) 257-2368; gen fax (620) 257-2369; adv fax (620) 257-2369; ed fax (620) 257-2369; gen e-mail admin@ldn.kscoxmail.com; adv e-mail advertising@ldn.kscoxmail.com
Published: Tues, Fri
Circulation: 2,321
Last Audit: Sworn
Advertising: Open inch rate $5.55
Politics: Independent. **Established:** 1906
Publisher ....David Seattle
Office Manager ....Anita Settle
News Editor ....Janna Splitter
Advertising ....Jacque Modrow
Ed. ....Jim Misunas
Circ. Dir. ....Cindy Moore
Sports Ed. ....Linda Sunley
Mechanical Specifications: Type page 13 x 21; E - 6 cols, 2, 1/8 between; A - 6 cols, 2, 1/8 between; C - 6 cols, 2, 1/8 between.

MANHATTAN

THE MANHATTAN MERCURY

318 N. Fifth St., Manhattan, Kan., 66502; gen tel (785) 776-2200; adv tel (785) 776-2200; ed tel (785) 776-2300; gen fax (785) 776-8807; adv fax (785) 776-8807; ed fax (785) 776-8807; adv e-mail adv@themercury.com; ed e-mail news@themercury.com; web site www.themercury.com
Group: Kansas Press Association
Published: Mon, Tues, Wed, Thur, Fri, Sun
Weekday Frequency: e
Circulation: 8,300; 9,804(sun)
Last Audit: September 30, 2009
Price: 126.00/yr (carrier).
Advertising: Open inch rate $13.83
News services: AP, NYT, LAT-WP, SHNS.
Politics: Independent.
Not Published: New Year; Labor Day; Christmas.
Special Editions: Spring Fix-Up (Apr); KSU (Aug); Weddings/Brides (Feb); Financial Planning (Jan); Senior Citizens (Monthly); Homes (Quarterly); Guide to Manhattan (Sept).
Special Weekly Sections: Cars (Fri); Food & Drink (Tues).
Magazines: Parade (S).
Broadcast Affiliations: KMAN; KMKF; KXBZ.
Gen. Mgr. ....Ned M. Seaton
Circ. Mgr. ....Bonnie Raglin
Ed. in Chief ....Edward L. Seaton
Exec. Ed. ....Bill Felber
Editorial Page Ed. ....Walter Braun
Photo Ed. ....Rod Mikinski
Sports Ed. ....Josh Kinder
Online Mgr. ....Ned Seaton
Prodn. Coord., Systems ....Brian Carter
Market Information: ADS; TMC.
Mechanical available: Offset; Black and 3 ROP colors; insert accepted - all; page cutoffs - 22 3/4.
Mechanical Specifications: Type page 13 x 21 1/2; E - 6 cols, 2 1/16, 1/8 between; A - 6 cols, 2 1/16, 1/8 between; C - 6 cols, 2 1/16, 1/8 between.
Commodity Consumption: Avg. Page Number Per Issue - Daily 22; Avg. Page Number Per Issue - Plates Used 23300; Avg. Page Number Per Issue - Sunday 52; widths 14; Newsprint Used - Short Tons 750; Printing Ink Used - Black 22000; Printing Ink Used - Color 3000; Printing Ink Used
Equipment EDITORIAL: Front-end Software – Mk/Page, QPS/QuarkXPress.; Editorial Hardware – 1-Mk/1100 Plus, IBM, 14-RSK/TRS 80-100, 4-APP/Mac, 10-Mk; Editorial Printers – APP/Mac LaserWriter NTX, TI, HP/LaserJet, Xante/Accel-A-Writer CLASSIFIED: Front-end Software – Baseview/Ad Manager Pro.; Classified Hardware – 5-APP/Mac; Classified Equipment – IBM; Classified Printers – APP/Mac LaserWriter NTX, TI, HP/LaserJet DISPLAY: Ad make-up applications – QPS/QuarkXPress, Adobe/Acrobat; Layout Software – Baseview.; Display Hardware – 1-APP/Mac; Display Printers – HP/LaserJet PRODUCTION: Pagination Software – QPS/QuarkXPress 3.21.; Production Equipment – Caere/OmniPage Pro 5.0, HP/4MV; Cameras – 1-R/580; Scanners – Umax/UG80, 1-KK/RFS 2035, 1-Umax/Powerbook II, Umax/Mirage II PRESSROOM: Line 1 – 6-HI/845 1970; Folders – 1-HI/2:1; Reels and Stands – 1; Press control system – Haley/Controller 1970. MAILROOM: Counter stackers – 1-BG/Count-O-Veyor 107; Inserters and stuffers – 5-KAN/480; Bundle tying machines – 1-Bu/Constellation K101; Addressing machine – 1/KAN. BUSINESS COMPUTERS: Business Software – Quickbooks; Business Hardware – APP/Mac

SEATON PUBLISHING CO., INC.

318 N. Fifth St., Manhattan, Kan., 66502; gen tel (785) 776-2200; gen fax (785) 776-8807; ed e-mail editor@themercury.com; web site www.themercury.com
Politics: 1859

MCPHERSON

MCPHERSON SENTINEL

301 S. Main St., McPherson, Kan., 67460-0926; gen tel (620) 241-2422; gen fax (620) 241-2425; gen e-mail sentinel@mcphersonsentinel.com; adv e-mail joni.regnier@mcphersonsentinel.com; ed e-mail news@mcphersonsentinel.com; web site www.mcphersonsentinel.com
Group: Kansas Press Association
Published: Tues, Wed, Thur, Fri, Sat
Weekday Frequency: e
Saturday Frequency: e
Circulation: 4,200; 4,200(sat)
Last Audit: Sworn October 1, 2003
Price: 14.88/mo; 135.40/yr.
Advertising: Open inch rate $14.50
Insert rate: $70.00
News services: AP.
Politics: Independent.
Not Published: New Year; Memorial Day; Independence Day; Labor Day; Thanksgiving; Christmas,Sundays and Monday.
Own facility?: Y
Special Editions: Back-to-School (Aug); Christmas (Dec); Soil Conservation (Jan); 4-H & County Fair (Jul); Christmas (Nov); Football (Sept).
Special Weekly Sections: This Week on TV (Fri).
Magazines: American Profile (Sat).
Adv. Dir. ....Joni Regnier
Adv. Dir., Classified ....Linda Born
Ed. ....Katie Stockstill
Sports Ed. ....Steve Sell
Prodn. Mgr., Pressroom ....Richard Henson
Publisher ....Randy Mitchell
Circulation Manager ....Jamie Fisher
Controller ....Shelly Drake
Mailroom Manager ....Linda Brown
Pub. ....Ken Knepper
Bus. Mgr. ....Melanie Hanson
Circ. Mgr. ....Barb Herl
Prodn. Mgr. ....Janell Dreiling
Market Information: TMC.
Mechanical available: Offset; Black and 3 ROP colors; insert accepted; page cutoffs - 21 1/2.
Mechanical Specifications: Type page 11 x 21 1/2; E - 6 cols, 1 3/4, 1/6 between; A - 6 cols, 1 3/4, 1/6 between; C - 6 cols, 1 3/4, 1/6 between.
Commodity Consumption: Avg. Page Number Per Issue - Daily 14; Avg. Page Number Per Issue - Plates Used 10000; Avg. Page Number Per Issue - Saturday 14; widths 12 1/2; Newsprint Used - Short Tons 244; Printing Ink Used - Black 2700; Printing Ink Used - Color 150; Printing Ink U
Equipment EDITORIAL: Front-end Software – Adobe/Photoshop 3.0, QPS/QuarkXPress 7.53, Baseview.; Editorial Hardware – APP/Mac; Editorial Equipment – Umax/S-6E Flatbed Scanner, Polaroid/Sprint Scan 35; Editorial Printers – Xante/Accel-A-Writer 3G CLASSIFIED: Front-end Software – Baseview.; Classified Hardware – APP/Mac; Classified Printers – APP/Mac LaserWriter II DISPLAY: Ad make-up applications – QPS/QuarkXPress 7.5; Display Hardware – APP/Mac G3, APP/Mac G4; Display Printers – Xante/Accel-A-Writer 3G; Production Equipment – Nu/Flip Top FT4OUPNS; Cameras – Acti. PRESSROOM: Line 1 – 5-G/Community 1974; Line 2 – 1-G/Community 1995.; Bundle tying machines – 1/Marlo, Miller-Bevco/Strapper.
Zip Codes served: 67460

NEWTON

THE NEWTON KANSAN

121 W. Sixth St., Newton, Kan., 67114-2117; gen tel (316) 283-1500; gen fax (316) 283-2471; adv e-mail advertising@thekansan.com; web site www.thekansan.com
Group: Kansas Press Association
Published: Mon, Tues, Wed, Thur, Fri, Sat, Sun
Weekday Frequency: e
Saturday Frequency: m
Circulation: 7,513; 7,513(sat)
Last Audit: September 30, 2007
Price: 8.50/mo; 113.95/yr.
Advertising: Open inch rate $15.76
News services: AP.
Politics: Independent.
Advertising not accepted: Cigarette.
Not Published: New Year; Memorial Day; Independence Day; Labor Day; Thanksgiving; Christmas.
Special Editions: Bridal Tab (Jan); Welcome to Harvey County (Jun); Home Improvement (Mar); Christmas Kick-Off (Nov); Holiday Creations-Including Cookbook (Oct); Living Well (Quarterly).
Special Weekly Sections: Religion Page (Fri); Business Page (Sat); Farm Page (Thur).
Magazines: Relish (Monthly); USA WEEKEND Magazine (Sat).
Mktg./Customer Serv. ....Patrick Frantum
Editorial Page Ed. ....Christian Wyrick
Educ./Features Ed. ....Chad Frey
Food/Lifestyle Ed. ....Wendy Nugent
News Ed. ....Christina Janney
Data Processing Mgr. ....Shelly Drake
Audiotex Mgr. ....Mark Schnabel
Prodn. Supvr., Pressroom ....Ken Driskill
Market Information: ADS; TMC.
Mechanical available: Offset; Black and 3 ROP colors; insert accepted; page cutoffs - 22 3/4.
Mechanical Specifications: Type page 13 x 21 1/2; E - 6 cols, 2 1/2, 1/6 between; A - 6 cols, 2 1/2, 1/6 between; C - 6 cols, 2 1/2, 1/6 between.
Commodity Consumption: Avg. Page Number Per Issue - Daily 15.3; Avg. Page Number Per Issue - Plates Used 3300; widths 25; Newsprint Used - Short Tons 320; Printing Ink Used - Black 6000; Printing Ink Used - Color 1200; Printing Ink Used - Pages Printed 4690.
Equipment EDITORIAL: Front-end Software – Adobe/Photoshop 5.5, QPS/QuarkXPress 3.32,; Editorial Hardware – 1-APP/Mac G3, APP/Mac G4, 2-APP/Mac Power PC 4400-200, 4-APP/Mac Power PC 7300-80; Editorial Equipment – 2-APP/Mac Quadra 650, Nikon/Film Scanner, Nikon/Scantouch Flatbed; Editorial

Printers – MON/Imagesetter CLASSIFIED: Front-end Software – QPS/QuarkXPress, Baseview/Classified, Adobe/Photoshop 5.0, Adobe/Acrobat 5.0.; Classified Hardware – 1-APP/iMac 333; Classified Printers – APP/Mac Imagewriter, APP/Mac LaserWriter 16-600 PS DISPLAY: Ad make-up applications – QPS/QuarkXPress 4.0, Multi-Ad/Creator 4.0, Adobe/Photoshop 5.5, Adobe/Acrobat 4.0; Layout Software – Ad Force II.; Display Hardware – 2-APP/Mac G3, 1-Power PC/7300-180, 1-Power PC/7200-120, APP/Mac G3; Display Printers – 1-MON/Imagesetter, HP/LaserWriter 4050 PRODUCTION: Pagination Software – QPS/QuarkXPress 4.1.; Production Equipment – OmniPage, APP/Mac G3, APP/Mac G4; Cameras – DAI/DS; Scanners – Umax/Astra 4000LS, Nikon/Color Film Scanner, Nikon/Scantouch Flatbed PRESSROOM: Line 1 – 7-G/Single Width 1972; Folders – 1-G/SC.; Bundle tying machines – 2/Bu; Addressing machine – 1-/Ch. BUSINESS COMPUTERS: Business Software – PBS; Business Hardware – Gateway

NORTON

HAYNES PUBLISHING COMPANY

215 S. Kansas St., Norton, Kan., 67654; gen tel (785) 877-3361; gen fax (785) 877-3732; gen e-mail nortontelegram@nwkansas.com; adv e-mail dpaxton@nwkansas.com; web site www.nwkansas.com

Published: Mon, Tues, Fri
Weekday Frequency: e
Circulation: 1,600
Insert rate: .07 Mon / .08 Tues or Fri
Not Published: Sun, Wed, Thurs, Sat
Own facility?: Y
Delivery method: Mail, Private Carrier, Racks

OBERLIN

NOR'WEST NEWSPAPERS

170 S. Penn Ave., Oberlin, Kan., 67749; gen tel (785) 475-2206; gen fax 785-475-2800; web site www.nwkansas.com

Group: Haynes Publishing Co.
Published: Mon, Tues, Fri
Weekday Frequency: e
Circulation: 2,004
Last Audit: Sworn October 4, 2002
Price: $1/issue
Advertising: Open inch rate $7.95
Insert rate: $70-$100m
News services: AP
Politics: 1993
Advertising not accepted: N
Own facility?: Y
Profile: daily and weekly newspapers, shoppers serving Northwest Kansas
Circ. Mgr./office manager..............Sheila Smith
Society Ed./composition...............Pat Schiefen
Editor/general manager......................Tom Betz
advertising representative..............Jeff Dreiling
advertising representative............Lisa McNeely
ad designer/traffic manager.......Jessica Corbin
president.................................Steve Haynes
Market Information: rural, farm and ranch
Mechanical Specifications: Type page 12 x 21 1/2; E - 6 cols, 2, 1/8 between; A - 6 cols, 2, 1/8 between; C - 6 cols, 2, 1/8 between.
Equipment; Editorial Hardware – Mac PRESSROOM: Line 1 – 6 units Harris/Fairchild V15; Press Drives – Harris; Folders – Harris; Reels and Stands – three; Press control system – Harris; Press registration system – manual; Bundle tying machines – 2; Addressing machine – 1
Zip Codes served: 67700-99
Delivery method: Mail, Newsstand, Private Carrier, Racks

OLATHE

THE OLATHE NEWS

PO Box 130, Olathe, Kan., 66051-0130; gen tel (913) 764-2211; web site www.theolathenews.com/

OTTAWA

THE OTTAWA HERALD

104 S. Cedar St., Ottawa, Kan., 66067; gen tel (785) 242-4700; adv tel (785) 242-4700; ed tel (785) 242-4700; gen fax (785) 242-9420; adv fax (785) 242-9420; ed fax (785) 242-9420; gen e-mail news@ottawaherald.com; adv e-mail advertising@ottawaherald.com; ed e-mail letters@ottawaherald.com; web site www.ottawaherald.com

Group: Kansas Press Association
Published: Tues, Wed, Thur, Fri, Sat
Weekday Frequency: m
Saturday Frequency: m
Circulation: 4,500; 4,750(sat)
Last Audit: Sworn October 1, 2001
Price: 9.55/mo; 98.64/yr.
Advertising: Open inch rate $10.56
News services: AP, Harris News Service.
Politics: Independent.
Not Published: New Year; Memorial Day; Independence Day; Labor Day; Thanksgiving; Christmas.
Own facility?: N
Special Editions: Football (Aug); Christmas Gift Guides (Dec); Progress (Feb); Christmas Gift Guides (Nov).
Special Weekly Sections: Health (Fri); Farm (Mon); Real Estate (Sat); Society (Weddings/Engagements) (Wed).
Magazines: American Profile (Sat); USA WEEKEND Magazine (Weekly).
Editorial Page Ed....................Jeanny J. Sharp
Features Ed.................................Tommy Felts
Online Ed. ....Gordon Billingsley
Sports Ed.......................................Greg Mast
Data Processing Mgr.....................Kathy Miller
Prodn. Coord., Adv. Servs..............Patty Sheler
Marketing Director.......................Linda Brown
Advertising Director....................Laurie Blanco
Prodn. Mgr...................................Tim Millbern
Prodn. Mgr., Mailroom.....................Eva Myers
Market Information: TMC.
Mechanical available: Offset; Black and 3 ROP colors; insert accepted; page cutoffs - 22 3/4.
Mechanical Specifications: Type page 12 13/16 x 21 1/2; E - 6 cols, 2, 3/16 between; A - 6 cols, 2, 3/16 between; C - 6 cols, 1 15/16, 3/16 between.
Commodity Consumption: Avg. Page Number Per Issue - Daily 12; Avg. Page Number Per Issue - Plates Used 10495; Avg. Page Number Per Issue - Saturday 16; widths 27; Newsprint Used - Metric Tons 328.4; Printing Ink Used - Black 11105; Printing Ink Used - Color 900; Printing Ink U
Equipment EDITORIAL: Front-end Software – InDesign, InCopy; Editorial Hardware – APP/Mac APP/Mac G4, APP/Mac 7200, APP/Mac 7100, APP/Mac 7500; Editorial Printers – APP/Mac LaserWriter NTX, Xante/Accel-a-writer, HP/LaserJet 4V CLASSIFIED: Front-end Software – ; Classified Hardware – APP/Mac ; Classified Printers – APP/Mac LaserWriter II, Epson/740; Layout Software – Other Equipment ☐ CD; Display Hardware – APP/Power Mac 7600, APP/Power Mac 7100, APP/Power Mac 7200; Display Printers – APP/Mac LaserWriter Plus, Xante/Accel-a-writer, Epson/740 PRODUCTION: Pagination Software – QPS/QuarkXPress.; Production Equipment – Caere/OmniPage Direct, Xante/Accel-A-Writer, HP/LaserJet 4V; Scanners – Microtek/Scanner, Linotype-HEII, Poloroid/SprintScan 35 BUSINESS COMPUTERS: Business Software – Microsoft/Office, Newzware; Business Hardware – 5-PC
Zip Codes served: 66006, 66033, 66042, 66044, 66067, 660632, 66076, 66078, 66079, 66080, 66092, 66095, 66510
Delivery method: Mail, Newsstand, Racks

PARSONS

PARSONS PUBLISHING CO.

220 S. 18th St., Parsons, Kan., 67357; gen tel (620) 421-2000; gen fax (620) 421-2217; web site www.parsonssun.com; www.parsonssun.com

PARSONS SUN

220 S. 18th St., Parsons, Kan., 67357-0836; gen tel (620) 421-2000; ed tel (620) 421-2000; gen fax (620) 421-2217; adv fax (620) 421-2217; ed fax (620) 421-2217; adv e-mail display@parsonssun.com; ed e-mail editor@parsonssun.com; web site www.parsonssun.com

Group: Kansas Press Association
Published: Mon, Tues, Wed, Thur, Fri, Sat, Sun
Weekday Frequency: e
Saturday Frequency: m
Circulation: 5,420; 5,420(sat)
Last Audit: September 25, 2003
Price: 108.51/yr; 29.20/3mo.
Advertising: Open inch rate $11.00
News services: AP, Harris.
Politics: Independent. **Established:** 1871
Not Published: New Year; Memorial Day; Independence Day; Labor Day; Thanksgiving; Christmas.
Special Editions: Spring Home Improvement (Apr); Back-to-School (Aug); Basketball (Dec); Senior Lifestyles (Every other month); Community (Feb); Tax & Financial Planning (Jan); Fair Tab (Jul); Why My Dad's the Greatest (Jun); Agriculture (Mar); Outdoor Living (May); Recipe
Special Weekly Sections: TV Scene (Fri); Business (Mon); Best Food Day (Wed).
Magazines: American Profile (Weekly).
Circ. Mgr. ....Amy Jensen
Asst. Mng. Ed. ....Jamie Willey
Editorial Page Ed...........................Ray Nolting
Mgmt. Info Servs. Mgr. ....Shanna Guiot
Prodn. Supt., Presses ....Rusty Furan
Market Information: TMC.
Mechanical available: Offset; Black and 3 ROP colors; insert accepted - any; page cutoffs - 22 3/4.
Mechanical Specifications: Type page 13 x 21; E - 6 cols, 2 1/16, 1/8 between; A - 6 cols, 2 1/16, 1/8 between; C - 6 cols, 2 1/16, 1/8 between.
Commodity Consumption: Avg. Page Number Per Issue - Daily 14; Avg. Page Number Per Issue - Plates Used 2904; Avg. Page Number Per Issue - Saturday 16; widths 30; Newsprint Used - Metric Tons 342; Printing Ink Used - Black 5700; Printing Ink Used - Color 8500; Printing Ink Used
Equipment EDITORIAL: Front-end Software – Aldus/FreeHand, QPS, Multi-Ad/Creator, Baseview, Adobe/Photoshop, QPS/QuarkXPress.; Editorial Hardware – APP/Mac; Editorial Printers – Xante/3G, Xante/8200 CLASSIFIED: Front-end Software – Baseview.; Classified Hardware – APP/Mac; Classified Printers – Okidata, Xante/3G, Xante/8200 DISPLAY: Ad make-up applications – QPS, Baseview, Multi-Ad/Creator, Adobe/Photoshop; Layout Software – Baseview.; Display Hardware – APP/Mac, 1998-APP/Mac; Display Printers – APP/Mac LaserWriter II, Xante/8200 PRODUCTION: Pagination Software – Baseview 2.05.; Production Equipment – Nu, NuArc Nu; Cameras – 1-Acti; Scanners – APP/Mac One, APP/Mac, Umax/UC1260 PRESSROOM: Line 1 – 7-G; Folders – 1-G/2:1.; Inserters and stuffers – MM; Bundle tying machines – 2/Bu. BUSINESS COMPUTERS: Business Software – Microsoft/Excel, Microsoft/Word; Business Hardware – DSI/PaperTrak

PITTSBURG

THE MORNING SUN

701 N. Locust St., Pittsburg, Kan., 66762-0570; gen tel (620) 231-2600; adv tel (620) 231-2600; ed tel (620) 231-2600; gen fax (620) 231-0645; adv fax (620) 231-0645; ed fax (620) 231-0645; adv e-mail cindy.rushton@morningsun.net; ed e-mail stephen.wade@morningsun.net; web site www.morningsun.net

Published: Mon, Tues, Wed, Thur, Fri, Sat, Sun
Weekday Frequency: m
Saturday Frequency: m
Circulation: 10,312; 10,312(sat); 9,300(sun)
Last Audit: October 1, 2003
Price: 1.04/mo; 121.57/yr.
Advertising: Open inch rate $15.30
News services: AP.
Politics: Independent.
Not Published: Christmas.
Special Weekly Sections: Business Page (Other); Bridal Pages (S); Church Page (Sat); Best Food Day (Wed).
Magazines: Relish (Monthly); USA WEEKEND Magazine (S); American Profile (Sat).
Broadcast Affiliations: NBC; ABC; CBS; Fox.
Bus. Mgr. ....Kaycie Brown
Adv. Dir. ....Cindy Rushton
Circ. Dir. ....Mike Dalton
Mng. Ed. ....Stephen Wade
Features Ed. ....Nikki Patrick
News Ed.......................................Jacob Brower
Online Dir. ....Brandon Belew
Prodn. Mgr., Pre Press................Jeremy Parvin
Market Information: TMC.
Mechanical available: Offset; Black and 3 ROP colors; insert accepted; page cutoffs - 22 3/4.
Mechanical Specifications: Type page 11 1/2 x 21 1/2; E - 6 cols, 2 1/16, 1/8 between; A - 6 cols, 2 1/16, 1/8 between; C - 9 cols, 1 1/4, 1/8 between.
Commodity Consumption: Avg. Page Number Per Issue - Daily 16; Avg. Page Number Per Issue - Saturday 24; Avg. Page Number Per Issue - Sunday 32; widths 12 1/2; Newsprint Used - Metric Tons 382.
Equipment; Layout Software – APP/Mac.; Production Equipment – 1-B/500-255; Cameras – 1-B/Commodore 241305. PRESSROOM: Line 1 – 5-G/Urbanite; Folders – 1-G/2:1.; Inserters and stuffers – 1-MM/5 heads; Bundle tying machines – 1-MLN/ML2EE; Addressing machine – 1/Ch; Other equipment –MM/Minuteman.; Business Hardware – ATT/WGS

PITTSBURG PUBLISHING CO.

701 N. Locust St., Pittsburg, Kan., 66762; gen tel (620) 231-2600; gen fax (620) 231-0645

Politics: 1887

PRATT

THE PRATT TRIBUNE

320 S. Main St., Pratt, Kan., 67124; gen tel (620) 672-5511; gen fax (620) 672-5514; gen e-mail publisher@pratttribune.com; web site www.pratttribune.com

Group: Kansas Press Association
Published: Mon, Tues, Wed, Thur, Fri
Weekday Frequency: e
Circulation: 2,000
Last Audit: March 31, 2008
Price: 109.00/yr.
Advertising: Open inch rate $11.19
News services: Papert (Landon).
Politics: Independent.
Not Published: New Year; Memorial Day; Independence Day; Labor Day; Thanksgiving; Christmas.
Special Editions: Home Improvement (Apr); Back-to-School (Aug); Christmas Gift Guide (Dec); Progress (Feb); 1/2 Day Sale (Jan); 4-H Fair Results (Jul); 4-H Sale (Jun); City-Farm Festival (Mar); Mother's Day (May); Christmas (Nov); Hunting (Oct); Senior Citizens (Sept).
Special Weekly Sections: Outdoors (Fri); Business (Mon); Kids (Thur); Farm (Tues); Seniors (Wed).
Magazines: Total TV (Tues); American Profile (Weekly).
Pub...Keith Lippoldt
Adv. Mgr. ....Laurie Anderson
Circ. Mgr.....................................Karen Rhone
Mng. Ed. ....Conrad Easterday

Market Information: Split run; TMC.
Mechanical available: Offset; Black and 3 ROP colors; insert accepted; page cutoffs - 22 3/4.
Mechanical Specifications: Type page 13 3/4 x 21 1/2; E - 6 cols, 2 1/16, 1/8 between; A - 6 cols, 2 1/16, 1/8 between; C - 8 cols, 2 1/16, 1/8 between.
Commodity Consumption: Avg. Page Number Per Issue - Daily 12.
Equipment; Editorial Hardware – 6-Mk.; Classified Hardware – 1-Mk.; Production Equipment – 3-COM; Cameras – 1-R. PRESSROOM: Line 1 – 4-G/Community.; Folders – 2; Bundle tying machines – 1/Bu; Addressing machine – 1-/Am.; Business Hardware – 1-Bs

SALINA

THE SALINA JOURNAL

333 S. Fourth St., Salina, Kan., 67401; gen tel (785) 823-6363; adv tel (785) 823-6363; ed tel (785) 823-6363; gen fax (785) 823-3207; adv fax (785) 823-3207; ed fax (785) 827-6363; adv e-mail knorwood@salina.com; web site www.salina.com
Group: Kansas Press Association
Published: Mon, Tues, Wed, Thur, Fri, Sat
Weekday Frequency: m
Saturday Frequency: m
Circulation: 24,124; 24,934(sun)
Last Audit: Sworn December 30, 2010
Price: 4.00/wk; 16.00/mo; 168.00/yr.
Advertising: Open inch rate $31.00
News services: AP, NYT, Cox News Service, SHNS, Harris.
Politics: Independent. **Established:** 1871
Special Editions: Guide to Salina (Aug); Christmas Gift Guide (Dec); Progress (Feb); Bridal (Jan); Back-to-School (Jul); River Festival (Jun); Progress (Mar); Travel (May); Christmas Gift Guide (Nov); Football (Sept).
Special Weekly Sections: Encore/Entertainment (Fri); Neighbors (Mon); Church (Sat); Home/Garden (Thur); Best Food Day (Wed).
Magazines: Dream Homes (Quarterly); USA WEEKEND Magazine (S); TV Week (TV Listings) (Sat).
Pub.....Tom Bell
Bus./HR Dir.....Jacki Ryba
Adv. Mgr.....Kim Norwood
Circ. Dir.....Bob Spessard
Circ. Mgr.....Mollie Purcell
Exec. Ed.....Ben Wearing
Deputy Ed.....Sharon Montague
Chief Photograher....Tom Dorsey
Society Ed.....Gary Demuth
Sports Ed.....Bob Davidson
Systems Mgr.....Bob Kelly
Webmaster....Tami Corn
Prodn. Dir.....Dave Atkinson
Market Information: Split run; TMC; Zoned editions.
Mechanical available: Offset; Black and 3 ROP colors; insert accepted; page cutoffs - 22 3/4.
Mechanical Specifications: Type page 12 x 21 1/2; E - 6 cols, 1 7/8, 1/8 between; A - 6 cols, 1 7/8, 1/8 between; C - 9 cols, 1 1/4, 1/16 between.
Commodity Consumption: Avg. Page Number Per Issue - Daily 30; Avg. Page Number Per Issue - Plates Used 69368; Avg. Page Number Per Issue - Sunday 53; widths 25; Newsprint Used - Metric Tons 2104; Printing Ink Used - Black 45531; Printing Ink Used - Color 17280; Printing Ink Us
Equipment EDITORIAL: Front-end Software – QPS/Q-Edit, 3-LiveWire.; Editorial Hardware – 12-APP/Mac G4, 3-Pentium/File Server, 3-Microsoft/Windows NT, 16-APP/iMac; Editorial Printers – HP/4MV, APP/Mac 12/640 PS CLASSIFIED: Front-end Software – Baseview.; Classified Hardware – APP/Mac Servers IP; Classified Printers – Okidata/393, HP/DeskJet DISPLAY: Ad make-up applications – Multi-Ad/Creator, QPS/QuarkXPress 4.1.1, Adobe/Acrobat, Adobe/Illustrator, Adobe/Photoshop; Layout Software – Pentium/NT Serv; Display Hardware – APP/Mac Quadra 950, 8-APP/Mac G3; Display Printers – 2-Epson/Stylus 3000, HP/4000, HP/4MV PRODUCTION: Pagination Software – QPS/QuarkXPress 4.1.1, QED.; Production Equipment – 2-XIT, 1-Nu/Flip Top FT40APRNS; Scanners – 2-AG/Arcus Scanner PRESSROOM: Line 1 – 3-G/Urbanite (color), 5-G/Urbanite (black); Press Drives – 2; Folders – 1-G/2:1; Reels and Stands – 6, 2-G/Stands, 2-G/Rolls. MAILROOM: Counter stackers – QWI; Inserters and stuffers – HI/1472-13 head; Bundle tying machines – MLN; Wrapping singles – MLN; Addressing machine – MM. BUSINESS COMPUTERS: Business Software – PaperTrack; Business Hardware – Data Sciences, HP

TOPEKA

THE TOPEKA CAPITAL-JOURNAL

616 SE Jefferson St., Topeka, Kan., 66607; gen tel (785) 295-1111; adv tel (785) 295-1111; ed tel (785) 295-1111; gen fax (785) 295-1230; adv fax (785) 295-1261 (Display); ed fax (785) 295-1230; web site www.cjonline.com
Published: Mon, Tues, Wed, Thur, Fri, Sat, Sun
Weekday Frequency: m
Saturday Frequency: m
Circulation: 33,425; 34,217(sat); 41,344(sun)
Last Audit: ABC September 30, 2011
Price: 13.00/mo (carrier), $16.91/mo (mail); 156.00/yr (carrier), $203.00/yr (mail).
Advertising: Open inch rate $99.43
News services: SHNS, AP, LAT-WP.
Special Editions: Cooking School (Apr); Pathways to Good Living (Aug); H.S. Basketball Tab (Dec); Grow Topeka (Feb); Campus Guides (Jan); Customer Appreciation (Jul); Manufactured Homes (Jun); Estate Planning (Mar); KS Outdoors (May); Prosper (Monthly); Pathways to Good Li
Special Weekly Sections: Weekender (Fri); Government (Mon); Real Estate (S); Religion (Sat); Heartland (Thur); Good Taste (Wed).
Magazines: Relish (Monthly); USA WEEKEND Magazine (S).
Pub.....Mark E. Nusbaum
Dir., HR....Heather Johanning
Adv. Dir.....Bob Barth
Sports Ed.....Eric Turner
City Ed.....Fred Johnson
Editorial Page Ed.....Mike Hall
Features Ed.....Tomari Quinn
Librarian....Patricia Johnston
News Ed.....Wayne Stewart
Exec. Sports Ed.....Kurt Caywood
Online Mgr.....Phil Thompson
Prodn. Foreman, Pressroom (Night) Mike Morgan
Prodn. Mgr., Mailroom....Ron Beavers
Prodn. Supt., Press....Brad Arthurs
Market Information: TMC; Zoned editions.
Mechanical available: Offset; Black and 3 ROP colors; insert accepted - cards; page cutoffs - 23 9/16.
Mechanical Specifications: Type page 11 5/8 x 22 3/4; E - 6 cols, 2 1/16, 1/8 between; A - 6 cols, 2 1/16, 1/8 between; C - 10 cols, 1 1/16, 3/32 between.
Commodity Consumption: Avg. Page Number Per Issue - Daily 40; Avg. Page Number Per Issue - Plates Used 62525; Avg. Page Number Per Issue - Saturday 48; Avg. Page Number Per Issue - Sunday 64; widths 37 1/2; Newsprint Used - Metric Tons 5171; Newsprint Used - Short Tons 5700; P
Equipment EDITORIAL: Front-end Software – Adobe/Photoshop, DTI 4.3.; Editorial Hardware – APP/Mac; Editorial Printers – HP CLASSIFIED: Front-end Software – DTI 4.3.; Classified Hardware – APP/Mac; Classified Printers – HP DISPLAY: Ad make-up applications – Adobe/Illustrator, DTI; Layout Software – DTI.; Display Hardware – APP/Mac; Display Printers – HP PRODUCTION: Pagination Software – QPS/QuarkXPress 3.3, DT.; Production Equipment – 2-Nu/Flip Top; Scanners – HP/ScanJet IIcx PRESSROOM: Line 1 – 8-Goss/HO-1991, 2-G/Color half decks double width 1963, 1, 7, 5; Folders – 1; Press registration system – Pin/Registration. MAILROOM: Counter stackers – 4/TMSI; Inserters and stuffers – 2-/GMA1000 - 18 Lead; Bundle tying machines – 4-/DiNaric; Wrapping singles – 4-/Bu; Addressing machine – 1-KAN 600/650 with QTR Folder. AUDIO: Audio Software – Morris Information Services; Audio Hardware – Morris Information Services, PC BUSINESS COMPUTERS: Business Software – Unix, Claris Financials; Business Hardware – 1-IBM/RS 6000

WELLINGTON

WELLINGTON DAILY NEWS

113 W. Harvey Ave., Wellington, Kan., 67152-0368; gen tel (620) 326-3326; gen fax (620) 326-3290; adv e-mail advertising@wellingtondailynews.com; web site www.wgtndailynews.com
Group: Kansas Press Association
Published: Wed
Weekday Frequency: e
Circulation: 2,100
Last Audit: Sworn September 30, 2007
Price: 58.24/yr; 14.56/3mo.
Advertising: Open inch rate $12.00
Insert rate: 70.00
News services: AP.
Politics: 1901
Not Published: New Year; Memorial Day; Independence Day; Labor Day; Thanksgiving; Christmas.
Own facility?: Y
Special Editions: Football Tab (Aug); Spring Tab (Mar); Christmas Tab (Nov); Fall Tab (Sept).
Special Weekly Sections: TV Guide (Fri).
Magazines: American Profile (Tues).
Circ. Mgr.....Terry Herl
Publisher....Randy Mitchell
Controller....Shelly Drake
managing Editor....Nate Jones
Pub.....Richard A. Horn
Adv. Mgr.....Amy Collins
Adv., Classified/Legal....Erika White
Ed.....Dustey Sansler
Lifestyle Ed.....Teresa Lee
Mechanical available: Offset; Black and 2 ROP colors; insert accepted; page cutoffs - 21 1/2.
Mechanical Specifications: Type page 13 x 21 1/2; E - 6 cols, 2, 1/8 between; A - 6 cols, 2, 1/8 between; C - 6 cols, 2, 1/8 between.
Commodity Consumption: Avg. Page Number Per Issue - Daily 10; Avg. Page Number Per Issue - Plates Used 1270; widths 28; Newsprint Used - Short Tons 100; Printing Ink Used - Black 2200; Printing Ink Used - Color 50; Printing Ink Used - Pages Printed 2540.
Equipment EDITORIAL: Front-end Software – Baseview/NewsEdit, QPS/QuarkXPress.; Editorial Hardware – 3-APP/Mac G4, APP/Mac IIci, 3-APP/Mac G3; Editorial Printers – Xante/Accel-a-Writer 3G; Classified Hardware – APP/Mac G3; Classified Printers – Xante/Accel-a-Writer 3G. DISPLAY: Ad make-up applications – QPS/QuarkXPress, Aldus/PageMaker; Layout Software – APP/Mac G4.; Display Hardware – Printers Â□ Xante/Accel-a-Writer 3G; Cameras – SCREEN.; Inserters and stuffers – Manual; Bundle tying machines – Manual; Addressing machine – Dispensa-matic.
Zip Codes served: 67152
Delivery method: Mail

WICHITA

THE WICHITA EAGLE

825 E. Douglas, Wichita, Kan., 67202; gen tel (316) 268-6000; adv tel (316) 268-6377; ed tel (316) 268-6351; gen fax (316) 268-6395; adv fax (316) 268-6234; ed fax (316) 268-6627; ed e-mail wenews@wichitaeagle.com; web site www.kansas.com
Group: McClatchy Company
Kansas Press Association
Published: Mon, Tues, Wed, Thur, Fri, Sat, Sun
Weekday Frequency: m
Saturday Frequency: m
Circulation: 67,003; 76,484(sat); 100,199(sun)
Last Audit: ABC September 30, 2011
Price: 3.69/wk; 16.03/mo; 191.88/yr (carrier), $235.04/yr (mail).
Advertising: Open inch rate $182.25
News services: AP, MCT, WP/BLOOM
Politics: 1872
Own facility?: Y
Special Editions: Voter's Guide (Apr); Wine Festival (Aug); Economic Outlook (Oct); Brides Guide (Jan); Reader' Choice (July); Summer Activities (May); Woofstock (Oct)
Special Weekly Sections: Business (Tue-Sun); Health (Tues)
Magazines: Parade (S)
Broadcast Affiliations: KWCH Channel 12.
Vice Pres., Finance....Dale Seiwert
Editor/Vice Pres., News....Sherry Chisenhall
Investigations Editor....Jean Hays
Deputy Ed., News....Tom Shine
Deputy Ed., News Desk....Michael Roehrman
Metro Ed.....Marcia Werts
Night city editor....Kevin McGrath
Opinion Ed.....Phillip Brownlee
Sports Ed.....Kirk Seminoff
Asst. Sports Ed.....Tom Seals
Pres. and publisher....Kim Nussbaum
VP/Operations....Cindy Trenary
Circulation Director....Lindsey Schaefer
Pres./Pub.....Pam Siddall
Vice Pres., HR....Micki Debbrecht
Asst. to the Pub.....Janice Trammell
Deputy Ed., Interactive....Nick Jungman
Bus. Ed.....Dan Loving
Features Ed.....Lori Linenberger
Prodn. Mgr., Bldg.....Jim Hollaway
Market Information: ADS; Split run; TMC; Zoned editions.
Mechanical available: Flexo; Black and 3 ROP colors; insert accepted; page cutoffs - 21.
Mechanical Specifications: Type page 12 x 21; E - 6 cols, 1 3/16, 1/6 between; A - 6 cols, 1 3/16, 1/6 between; C - 10 cols, 1 1/8, 1/12 between.
Commodity Consumption: Avg. Page Number Per Issue - Daily 40; Avg. Page Number Per Issue - Plates Used 96275; Avg. Page Number Per Issue - Saturday 58; Avg. Page Number Per Issue - Sunday 108; widths 12 1/2; Newsprint Used - Metric Tons 12360; Printing Ink Used - Black 356000;
Equipment EDITORIAL: Front-end Software – Dewar/View.; Editorial Hardware – HP/Desktop PCs, MS/Windows NT; Editorial Equipment – Lf/AP Leaf Picture Desk; Editorial Printers – HP/LaserJet CLASSIFIED: Front-end Software – AT/Enterprise.; Classified Hardware – HP/Desktop PCs, Sun/Servers; Classified Equipment – Edgil/EdgCapture Credit Card Authorization Server; Classified Printers – HP/LaserJet DISPLAY: Ad make-up applications – Multi-Ad/Creator 4.0.3; Layout Software – AT/Architect.; Display Hardware – APP/Mac G4, APP/Mac G3; Display Printers – Canon, OCE, HP/750C, Xante/Color Laser PRODUCTION: Pagination Software – Ad Manager.; Production Equipment – 2-III/3850, Adobe/Photoshop 4.0; Cameras – 1-C/Marathon; Scanners – ECRM, Arcus II, Agfa/Duoscan PRESSROOM: Line 1 – 10-KBA/Colormax II 2002; Folders – 3; Pasters – 14 MAILROOM: Counter stackers – 4-QWI/300, 2-QWI/350, 3-QWI/400; Inserters and stuffers – 3-S/72P; Bundle tying machines – 6-Dynaric/NP-2; Wrapping singles – 2-OVL/415; Addressing machine – 1/KAN; Other equipment –1-/KAN.; Audio Hardware – Gem 2 Inc. BUSINESS COMPUTERS: Business Software – CIS 3.02:Payroll, CIS 6.05.A, GEAC/Payroll 3.02C, Mediastream/CIS 6.05B; Business Hardware – HP/3000-KS/969

WINFIELD

WINFIELD DAILY COURIER

201 E. Nineth St., Winfield, Kan., 67156; gen tel (620) 221-1050; gen fax (620) 221-1101; gen e-mail courier@winfieldcourier.com; adv e-mail advertising@winfieldcourier.com; ed

e-mail editorial@winfieldcourier.com; web site www.winfieldcourier.com
Group: Kansas Press Association
Published: Mon, Tues, Wed, Thur, Fri, Sat, Sun
Weekday Frequency: e
Saturday Frequency: m
Circulation: 4,522; 4,522(sat)
Last Audit: September 30, 2008
Price: 5.69/mo; 63.80/yr (carrier/mail).
Advertising: Open inch rate $9.31
News services: AP, LAT-WP.
Politics: Independent.
Not Published: New Year; Independence Day; Christmas.
Special Editions: Health Care (Apr); Cowley County Fair (Aug); Achievement (Feb); Spring Clean Up Tab (Mar); Kanza (May); Cowley County Farmer-Rancher (Monthly); Getting Ready for Winter (Oct); Football Tab (Sept).
Magazines: USA WEEKEND Magazine (Sat).
Gen. Mgr.....................Lloyd Craig
Adv. Mgr., Classified..........Marsha Wesseler
Circ. Mgr.....................Wes Townsley
Mng. Ed....................Roy Graber
Editorial Page Ed...........Frederick D. Seaton
Features Ed.....................Judy Zaccaria
Sports Ed.....................Joey Salkoff
Market Information: TMC.
Mechanical available: Offset; Black and 3 ROP colors; insert accepted - will consider any requests; page cutoffs - 22.
Mechanical Specifications: Type page 13 x 21; E - 6 cols, 2 1/16, 1/8 between; A - 6 cols, 2 1/16, 1/8 between; C - 8 cols, 1 1/2, 1/8 between.
Commodity Consumption: Avg. Page Number Per Issue - Daily 12; Avg. Page Number Per Issue - Plates Used 2177; Avg. Page Number Per Issue - Saturday 12; widths 13 3/4; Newsprint Used - Metric Tons 184; Printing Ink Used - Black 4400; Printing Ink Used - Color 500; Printing Ink U
Equipment EDITORIAL: Front-end Software – FSI, Multi-Ad/Creator, QPS/QuarkXPress.; Editorial Hardware – 9-Mk; Editorial Equipment – APP/Mac One Scanner, Nikon/Negative Scanner, 2-Umax/Flatbed Scanner; Editorial Printers – LaserMaster/, Xante/Accel-A-Writer, APP/Mac G3 Imagesetter, ECR CLASSIFIED: Front-end Software – BMF.; Classified Hardware – IBM; Classified Printers – Epson/DFX-5000, Epson/LQ-1070 DISPLAY: Ad make-up applications – FSI; Layout Software – Multi-Ad/Creator, Aldus/PageMaker, Canvas, QPS/QuarkXPress.; Display Hardware – APP/Power Mac; Display Printers – LaserMaster, APP/Mac PS PRODUCTION: Pagination Software – QPS/QuarkXPress 3.3.; Production Equipment – 1-B, 1-Kk/Ektamatic; Cameras – 1-Acti; Scanners – Umax, Nikon PRESSROOM: Line 1 – 4-G/Community.; Inserters and stuffers – 1-KAN/3 Station; Bundle tying machines – 1/Miller-Bevco; Addressing machine – 2-Am/1900. AUDIO: Audio Software – TCS; Audio Hardware – Tele Computer Service, 1-IBM BUSINESS COMPUTERS: Business Software – BMF; Business Hardware – Cumulus/PC, IBM

WINFIELD PUBLISHING CO., INC.

201 E. 9th St., Winfield, Kan., 67156; gen tel (620) 221-1050; gen fax (620) 221-1101; gen e-mail courier@winfieldcourier.com
Published: Mon, Tues, Wed, Thur, Fri, Sat, Sun
Price: 80.40.
Advertising: Open inch rate $6.76

KENTUCKY

ASHLAND

ASHLAND PUBLISHING CO.

226 17th St., Ashland, Ky., 41105-0311; gen tel (606) 326-2600; gen fax (606) 329-2679; gen e-mail eepriess@dailyindependant.com; web site www.dailyindependant.com
Published: Mon, Tues, Wed, Thur, Fri, Sat, Sun
Price: 189.00/yr.
Advertising: Open inch rate $26.11

THE DAILY INDEPENDENT

224 17th St., Ashland, Ky., 41101; gen tel (606) 326-2600; adv tel (606) 326-2602; ed tel (606) 326-2672; adv fax (606) 326-2680; ed fax (606) 326-2678; adv e-mail adservices@dailyindependent.com; web site www.dailyindependent.com
Published: Mon, Tues, Wed, Thur, Fri, Sat, Sun
Weekday Frequency: m
Saturday Frequency: m
Circulation: 13,861; 13,861(sat); 15,309(sun)
Last Audit: ABC September 30, 2011
Price: 3.65/wk (carrier); 15.80/mo (carrier); 189/yr (carrier).
Advertising: Open inch rate $31.26
News services: AP, ONS, SHNS.
Politics: Independent. **Established:** 1896
Not Published: Christmas.
Special Editions: Design-An-Ad (Apr); ACC Tab (Aug); Girls Basketball (Dec); Parents & Kids (Feb); Taxes & Investing (Jan); Primetime (Jul); Carter County Salute (Jun); Entertainment (Mar); Greenup County Salute (May); Boys Basketball (Nov); Insight (Oct); Entertainment (S
Special Weekly Sections: Best Food Day (S); Best Food Day (Wed).
Magazines: Relish (Monthly); Parade (S).
Pub.....................Eddie Blakeley
Controller....................Lisa Callihan
Adv. Dir.....................Nikki Clay
Circ. Dir.....................Edward Speaks
Ed.....................Michael D. Reliford
Mng. Ed.....................Mark Maynard
Lifestyles Ed.....................Lee Ward
Opinion Page Ed.....................John Cannon
Photo Dept. Mgr.....................John Flavell
Prodn. Mgr., Mailroom..........Bengy Barrett
Prodn. Mgr., Pressroom..........Steve Reliford
Market Information: ADS; Split run; TMC.
Mechanical available: Offset; Black and 3 ROP colors; insert accepted; page cutoffs - 22 3/4.
Mechanical Specifications: Type page 13 x 21; E - 6 cols, 2 1/16, 1/8 between; A - 6 cols, 2 1/16, 1/8 between; C - 8 cols, 1 9/16, 1/16 between.
Commodity Consumption: Avg. Page Number Per Issue - Daily 28; Avg. Page Number Per Issue - Plates Used 12500; Avg. Page Number Per Issue - Saturday 16; Avg. Page Number Per Issue - Sunday 68; widths 27 1/2; Newsprint Used - Metric Tons 1490; Newsprint Used - Short Tons 1719; P
Equipment EDITORIAL: Front-end Software – Dewar.; Editorial Hardware – IBM; Editorial Equipment – Pagination Terminals; Editorial Printers – HP/LaserJet CLASSIFIED: Front-end Software – Atex, Dewar.; Classified Hardware – IBM; Classified Printers – APP/Mac LaserWriter IIg, HP/LaserJet DISPLAY: Ad make-up applications – Managing Editor/ALS 2.5; Layout Software – MEI/ALS 2.5.; Display Hardware – IBM, APP/Mac IIsi; Display Printers – HP/LaserJet PRODUCTION: Pagination Software – Dewar/View 2.0.; Production Equipment – Caere/OmniPage 2.0, AU/APS-6-84-ACS, AU/APS-6600 Plain Paper; Cameras – 1-Nu, 1-B, 1-LE; Scanners – Lf/Leafscan 35 PRESSROOM: Line 1 – 7-HI/Cotrell 845 1970; Folders – 1-HI/2:1. MAILROOM: Counter stackers – 2/HL; Inserters and stuffers – 1-/GMA; Bundle tying machines – Power Strap/PSN-6E.; Business Hardware – IBM/AS-400 D80

BOWLING GREEN

DAILY NEWS

813 College St., Bowling Green, Ky., 42101; gen tel (270) 781-1700; adv tel (270) 783-3233; ed tel (270) 783-3235; gen fax (270) 781-0726; adv fax (270) 783-3221; ed fax (270) 783-3237; gen e-mail dnews@bgdailynews.com; adv e-mail advertising@bgdailynews.com; ed e-mail dnews@bgdailynews.com; web site www.bgdailynews.com
Published: Mon, Tues, Wed, Thur, Fri, Sat, Sun
Weekday Frequency: e
Saturday Frequency: m
Circulation: 18,442; 23,911(sun)
Last Audit: ABC September 30, 2011
Price: 3.11/wk; 13.46/mo; 145.00/yr.
Advertising: Open inch rate $30.57
Insert rate: 64.00/m;single-
News services: AP.
Politics: Independent. **Established:** 1854
Not Published: Independence Day; Labor Day; Thanksgiving; Christmas.
Own facility?: Y
Special Editions: Home & Garden Tab (Apr); Pets on Parade (Aug); Holiday Gift Guide (Dec); Financial Tab (Feb); Back to School Tab (Jul); Soap Box Derby Tab (May); High School Basketball Tab (Nov); Industry Appreciation Tab (Oct); House to Home (Quarterly); Better Health &
Special Weekly Sections: TV This Week (Sat).
Magazines: Relish (Monthly); Parade (S); American Profile (Weekly).
Broadcast Affiliations: WKCT-AM; WDNS-FM.
Pub./Pres.....................John Gaines
Adv. Mgr.....................Mark Mahagan
Adv. Mgr., Classified....................Julie Dickens
Adv. Mgr., Nat'l....................Joanie Davis
Mgr., Promo.....................Scott Gaines
Circ. Mgr.....................Troy Warren
Mgr., Educ. Serv.....................Sharyre Noel
Managing Editor....................Andy Dennis
City Ed.....................Daniel Pike
Editorial Page Ed.....................Steve Gaines
Living/Lifestyle Ed.....................Alyssa Harvey
Asst. Mgr./Photo Editor....................Joe Imel
Online Mgr.....................Chris Houchens
Prodn. Mgr.....................Larry Simpson
Mailroom Mgr.....................George Stewart
Prodn. Mgr., Pressroom....................Glen Spear
Co-Owner....................Mary Gaines
Photo Ed.....................Joe Imel
Market Information: ADS; TMC.
Mechanical available: Offset; Black and 3 ROP colors; insert accepted; page cutoffs - 22 3/4.
Mechanical Specifications: Type page 11 5/8 x 21; E - 6 cols, 1 4/5, 1/8 between; A - 6 cols, 1 4/5, 1/8 between; C - 9 cols, 1 1/5, 1/10 between.
Commodity Consumption: Avg. Page Number Per Issue - Daily 24; Avg. Page Number Per Issue - Plates Used 36000; Avg. Page Number Per Issue - Saturday 34; Avg. Page Number Per Issue - Sunday 68; widths 13 3/4; Newsprint Used - Short Tons 1596; Printing Ink Used - Black 33200; Pri
Equipment EDITORIAL: Front-end Software – MediaSpan; Editorial Hardware – APP/Mac, 1-G/3, 10-IMAC, 13-G/4; Editorial Printers – 1-HP/5100 CLASSIFIED: Front-end Software – FSI/Brainworks.; Classified Hardware – WINDOWS
; Classified Equipment – BRAINWORKS; Classified Printers – HP/2200; Layout Software – Baseview/Ad Force, 1-APP/Mac G4, 2-Imac. PRODUCTION: Pagination Software – CTP-PRESTILIGENCE ; Production Equipment – Mac/CTP-Screen; Cameras – 1-C/Spartan III PRESSROOM: Line 1 – 9-G/Urbanite single width; Press Drives – 2-Cutter Hammer; Folders – 1-G/Urbanite; Reels and Stands – 8- MAILROOM: Counter stackers – 3 QUIPP 400; Inserters and stuffers – 1 Muller Tandem 227 10 into 1, 1 K&M Titan 12 into 1 ; Bundle tying machines – 3-Samuel; Wrapping singles – N/A; Mailroom control system – K&M; Addressing machine – PROFIT PKGING-P3 LABLER BUSINESS COMPUTERS: Business Software – Brainworks; Business Hardware – Microsoft/Windows 98, A-Open, Compaq
Zip Codes served: 42101,42102,42103,42104
Delivery method: Mail, Newsstand, Private Carrier, Racks

CORBIN

TIMES-TRIBUNE

201 N. Kentucky St., Corbin, Ky., 40701; gen tel (606) 528-2464; gen fax (606) 528-9850; adv fax (606) 528-1335; ed fax (606) 528-9850; adv e-mail advertising@thetimestribune.com; ed e-mail newsroom@thetimestribune.com; web site www.thetimestribune.com
Published: Mon, Tues, Wed, Thur, Fri, Sat
Weekday Frequency: e
Circulation: 6,166; 6,166(sat)
Last Audit: October 8, 2002
Price: 9.00/mo; 108.00/yr.
Advertising: Open inch rate $14.74
News services: AP.
Not Published: New Year; Memorial Day; Independence Day; Labor Day; Christmas.
Special Weekly Sections: Church Page (Sat); Business (Tues); Best Food Day (Wed).
Magazines: TV Guide (Sat); American Profile (Weekly).
Pub.....................Bill Hanson
Circ. Dir.....................Ernie Horn
Community Ed.....................Bobbie Poynter
Editorial Page Ed...........Samantha Swindler
Graphics Ed....................Heather Ponder
Sports Ed.....................Les Dixon
Data Processing Mgr.....................Paula Jones
Composing Mgr...........Rebecca Lawson
Market Information: TMC.
Mechanical available: Offset; Black and 3 ROP colors; insert accepted; page cutoffs - 22 3/4.
Mechanical Specifications: Type page 13 x 21 1/2; E - 6 cols, 2 1/16, 1/8 between; A - 6 cols, 2 1/16, 1/8 between; C - 9 cols, 1 3/8, 1/8 between.
Commodity Consumption: Avg. Page Number Per Issue - Daily 16; Avg. Page Number Per Issue - Plates Used 6000; Avg. Page Number Per Issue - Saturday 16; widths 27 1/2; Newsprint Used - Short Tons 450; Printing Ink Used - Black 4000; Printing Ink Used - Pages Printed 4646.
Equipment EDITORIAL: Front-end Software – Mk, Aldus/FreeHand, Adobe/Photoshop, QPS/QuarkXPress, Aldus/PageMaker, Multi-Ad/Creator.; Editorial Hardware – Mk, APP/Mac IIci, APP/Mac IIcx; Editorial Printers – 2-APP/Mac LaserWriter, 2-Tegra/Varityper VT600W, 1-Tegra/Varityper 4990T Imagesetter CLASSIFIED: Front-end Software – Mk.; Classified Hardware – Mk; Classified Printers – 2-APP/Mac LaserWriter DISPLAY: Ad make-up applications – Mk, Aldus/FreeHand, Adobe/Photoshop, QPS/QuarkXPress, Aldus/PageMaker, Multi-Ad/Creator; Layout Software – Multi-A; Display Hardware – Mk, APP/Mac IIcx, APP/Mac IIci; Display Printers – 2-APP/Mac LaserWriter, 2-Tegra/Varityper VT600W, 1-Tegra/Varityper 4990T Imagesetter; Production Equipment – Caere/OmniPage; Cameras – 1-Nu, 1-SCREEN/680C; Scanners – Lf/Leafscan 35, AVR. PRESSROOM: Line 1 – 4-G/Community 1970; Line 2 – 2-G/Community 1980.; Bundle tying machines – Strapex; Addressing machine – Ch.; Business Hardware – ListMasters

COVINGTON

SCRIPPS HOWARD, INC.

421 Madison Ave., Covington, Ky., 41011; gen tel (859) 292-2600; gen fax (859) 291-2525

DANVILLE

THE ADVOCATE-MESSENGER

330 S. Fourth St., Danville, Ky., 40422; gen tel (859) 236-2551; adv tel (859) 236-2551; ed tel (859) 236-2551; gen fax (859) 236-9566; adv fax (859) 236-9566; ed fax (859) 236-9566; gen e-mail advocate@amnews.com; adv e-mail advertising@amnews.com; ed e-mail newsdepart-

ment@amnews.com; web site www.amnews.com
Published: Sun
Circulation: 8,214; 9,913(sun)
Last Audit: September 30, 2008
Price: 12.50/mo (carrier/motor route); 121.00/yr.
Advertising: Open inch rate $19.50
News services: AP.
Politics: Independent.
Not Published: New Year; Memorial Day; Independence Day; Labor Day; Christmas.
Special Editions: Football Preview (Aug); Season's Greetings (Dec); Brass Band Festival (Jun); Basketball Preview (Nov).
Special Weekly Sections: Church Page (Fri); Tec Know Page (Mon); Business Page (S); Country Life Page (Tues); Seasonings (Wed).
Magazines: Parade (S); American Profile (Weekly).
Chrmn. .... Mary Schurz
Bus. Mgr. .... Renita Cox
Adv. Mgr. .... Bradley Toy
Adv. Mgr., Nat'l .... Jerry Dunn
Circ. Dir. .... Jill Sinclair
Mng. Ed. .... John Nelson
Ed. .... Scott C. Schurz
Copy Ed. .... Todd Kleffman
Features Ed. .... Emily Morse-Toadvine
News Ed. .... Vicki Stevens
Sports Ed. .... Larry Vaught
Info. Tech. Dir. .... James Morris
Prodn. Foreman, Press .... Troy Maddox
Prodn. Mgr., Mailroom .... Jesse DuVall
Market Information: TMC.
Mechanical available: Offset; Black and 3 ROP colors; insert accepted; page cutoffs - 22 3/4.
Mechanical Specifications: Type page 13 3/4 x 21 1/2; E - 6 cols, 2 1/16, 1/8 between; A - 6 cols, 2 1/16, 1/8 between; C - 9 cols, 1 3/8, 1/16 between.
Commodity Consumption: Avg. Page Number Per Issue - Daily 23; Avg. Page Number Per Issue - Plates Used 9207; Avg. Page Number Per Issue - Sunday 66; widths 27 1/2; Newsprint Used - Short Tons 634; Printing Ink Used - Black 15700; Printing Ink Used - Color 3452; Printing Ink Us
Equipment EDITORIAL: Front-end Software – Baseview/NewsEdit.; Editorial Hardware – APP/Mac CLASSIFIED: Front-end Software – Baseview/Class Manager Pro 1.0.7.; Classified Hardware – APP/Mac DISPLAY: Ad make-up applications – QPS/QuarkXPress 4.0; Layout Software – ALS.; Display Hardware – APP/Mac; Display Printers – Ultra PRODUCTION: Pagination Software – QPS/QuarkXPress 4.11.; Production Equipment – 2-APP/Mac LaserPrinters, 3-Ultra/94 Imagesetter; Cameras – 1-LE, 1-R; Scanners – Data Copy/730 GS, Microtek/Scanmaker E6 PRESSROOM: Line 1 – 5-MAN/Uniman 4x2 (half color decks) 1985; Press Drives – Reliance/Max Pac Plus; Folders – 1 MAILROOM: Counter stackers – 2-HI/Graphics Model 2512; Inserters and stuffers – MM/227E; Bundle tying machines – 1-Bu/AS210A, 1-Akebono/515A; Mailroom control system – HL/Conveyor; Addressing machine – KR/515 Base w/211 Head; Other equipment –Accuwrap/25 Bottom Wr BUSINESS COMPUTERS: Business Software – PBS, Lotus/Release 5, Ad Management 3.0; Business Hardware – Great Plains Dynamic IBM/RISC Sys 6000 CIO, Microsoft/Windows NT Server

ELIZABETHTOWN

THE NEWS ENTERPRISE

408 W. Dixie Ave., Elizabethtown, Ky., 42701; gen tel (270) 769-1200; ed tel (270) 769-2312; gen fax (270) 765-7318; adv fax (270) 769-5950; ed fax (270) 769-6965; gen e-mail ne@thenewsenterprise.com; web site www.thenewsenterprise.com
Published: Mon, Tues, Wed, Thur, Fri, Sun
Weekday Frequency: m
Circulation: 13,735; 18,903(sun)
Last Audit: ABC September 30, 2011

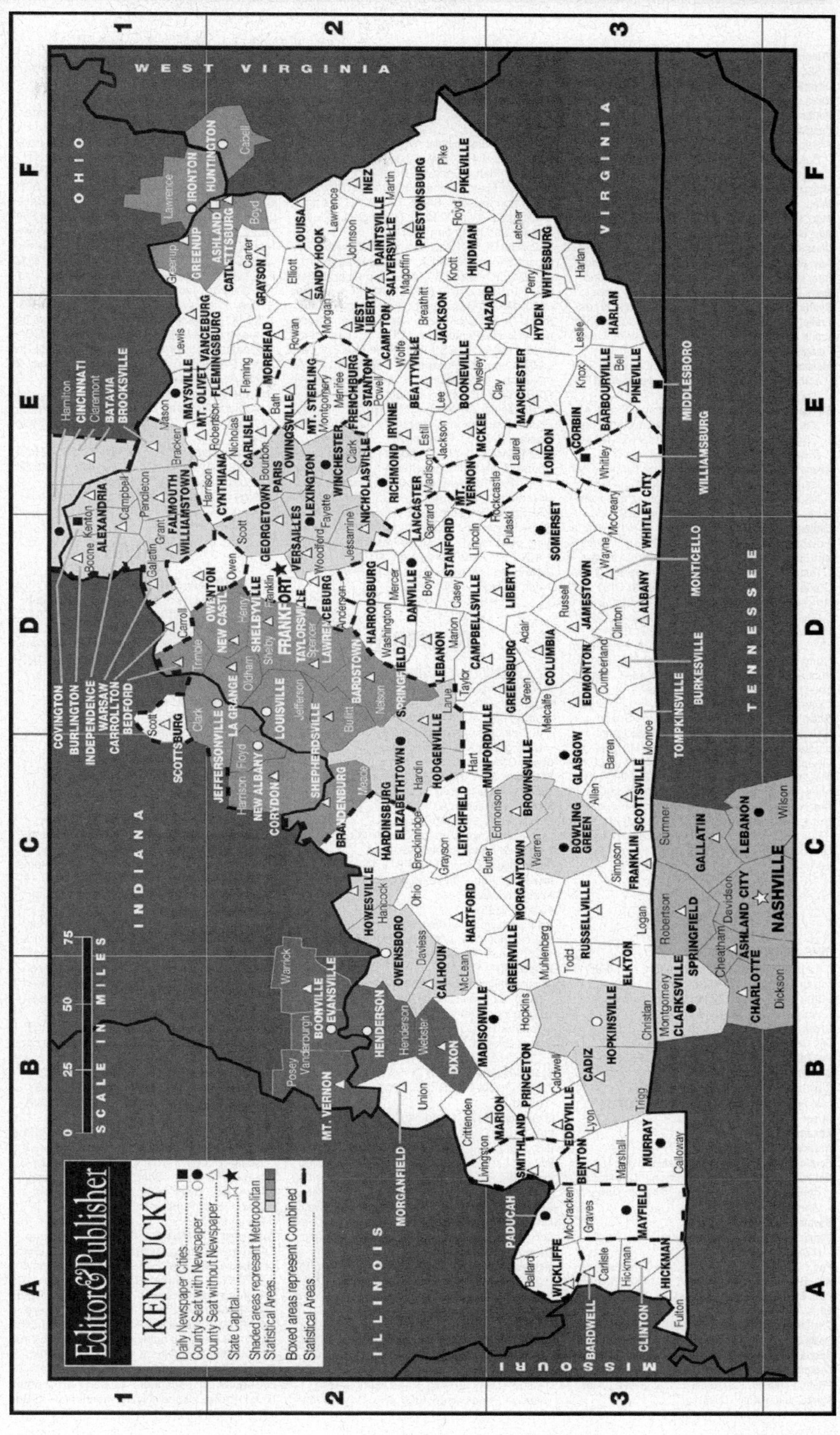

Price: 9.50/mo; 97.00/yr; 26.00/3mo, $50.00/6mo.
Advertising: Open inch rate $26.66
News services: AP.
Politics: Independent. **Established:** 1974
Special Weekly Sections: Entertainment (Fri); Senior Living (Mon); Business Pages (S); Best Food Day (Thur); Farm Pages (Tues); Real Estate (Wed).
Magazines: Relish (Monthly); Parade (S).
Pub....Chris Ordway
Mgr., Bus. Office...Carol Underdonk
Adv. Mgr....Larry Jobe
Classifed Adv. Mgr....Michelle McGuffin
Adv. Graphic Design Team Leader...Lydia Leasor
Circ. Mgr....Portia Oldham
News Ed....Jeff D'Alessio
Sports Ed....Chuck Jones
Prodn. Mgr., Admin....David Dickens
Prodn. Press Team Leader...Charles Love
Market Information: TMC.
Mechanical available: Offset; Black and 4 ROP colors; insert accepted - all; page cutoffs - 22 3/4.
Mechanical Specifications: Type page 11 5/8 x 21 1/2; E - 6 cols, 1 5/6, 1/8 between; A - 6 cols, 1 5/6, 1/8 between; C - 8 cols, 1 1/2, 1/8 between.
Commodity Consumption: Avg. Page Number Per Issue - Daily 30; Avg. Page Number Per Issue - Plates Used 20000; Avg. Page Number Per Issue - Sunday 60; widths 27 1/2.
Equipment: Editorial Hardware – CText; Editorial Equipment – 1-Turbo/XT, 2-Dell/220, SCS/Layout 8000. CLASSIFIED: Front-end Software – CText, Novell 4.0.; Classified Hardware – CText; Classified Printers – C.Itoh/CI 5000 DISPLAY: Ad make-up applications – SCS/Layout 8000 6.08; Layout Software – 11-APP/Mac II.; Display Hardware – Dell/220; Display Printers – HP/LaserJet IVP PRODUCTION: Pagination Software – QPS/QuarkXPress 3.31 R5.; Production Equipment – 2-VHreSetter/94E, PageScan/3, APP/Mac LaserWriter II NTX, Compaq/LaserWriter; Cameras – DST/240C; Scanners – Kk/2035RFS, Microtek/Scanmaker IIXE PRESSROOM: Line 1 – 11-G/Community single width; Folders – 1-KP/2:1. MAILROOM: Counter stackers – 2/BG, 1-MM/310-20, 1-MM/231; Inserters and stuffers – 3-/MM; Bundle tying machines – 3-/Bu, 3-/MLN; Addressing machine – 1-/Ch, 1-/KR.; Audio Hardware – Brite, Brite BUSINESS COMPUTERS: Business Software – Lotus, Microsoft/Works 3.1; Business Hardware – 8-IBM/5251 terminal, Papertrak

FRANKFORT

THE STATE JOURNAL

1216 Wilkinson Blvd., Frankfort, Ky., 40601; gen tel (502) 227-4556; gen fax (502) 227-2831; adv e-mail llynch@state-journal.com; web site www.state-journal.com
Group: ????
Dix Communications
Published: Mon, Tues, Wed, Thur, Fri, Sun
Weekday Frequency: All day
Circulation: 9,000; 9,500(sun)
Last Audit: Sworn September 30, 2009
Price: 11.00/mo; 132.00/yr.
Advertising: Open inch rate $13.00
News services: AP, NYT.
Politics: Independent. **Established:** 1902
Not Published: New Year; Memorial Day; Independence Day; Labor Day; Thanksgiving; Christmas.
Own facility?: Y
Magazines: Main Street (S); American Profile (Weekly).
Pub....Ann Dix Maenza
Adv. Dir....Lloyd Lynch
Circ. Mgr....Rick Kuiper
Ed....Carlton West
City Ed....Ron Herron
News Ed....Karen Henderson
Sports Ed....Linda Youkin
Composing Dir....Linda Roberts
Prodn. Foreman, Pressroom...Steve Estes
Market Information: TMC.
Mechanical available: Offset; Black and 3 ROP colors; insert accepted - all; page cutoffs - 21 1/2.
Mechanical Specifications: Type page 13 x 21 1/2; E - 6 cols, 2, 1/9 between; A - 6 cols, 2, 1/9 between; C - 8 cols, 1 1/2, 1/9 between.
Commodity Consumption: Avg. Page Number Per Issue - Daily 20; Avg. Page Number Per Issue - Plates Used 10135; Avg. Page Number Per Issue - Sunday 58; widths 14; Newsprint Used - Short Tons 700; Printing Ink Used - Black 23250; Printing Ink Used - Color 3350; Printing Ink Used
Equipment EDITORIAL: Front-end Software – Microsoft/Word, PowerSh; Editorial Hardware – APP/Mac Quadra 950, APP/Mac Quadra 840, 11-APP/Power Mac 6100, 1-APP/Power Mac 8100, 1-APP/Mac Quadra 700; Editorial Equipment – Lf/AP Leaf Picture Desk, 2-Nikon/Scanner; Editorial Printers – 1-APP/Mac LaserPrinter IIg, 1-TI/810 CLASSIFIED: Front-end Software – Mk.; Classified Hardware – 3-Mk DISPLAY: Ad make-up applications – Aldus/PageMaker, QPS/QuarkXPress; Layout Software – APP/Mac IIci, APP/Power Mac 6100. PRODUCTION: Pagination Software – QPS/QuarkXPress 3.31.; Production Equipment – 2-APP/Mac ci, 1-XIT/Clipper, 2-APP/Mac LaserPrinter, 3-QMax/Imagesetter, 4-APP/Power Mac 7100, 1-APP/Power Mac 8100; Cameras – 2-B/Vertical; Scanners – 2-Nikon/Scanner PRESSROOM: Line 1 – 8-G/Community (color deck).; Inserters and stuffers – 3/MM; Bundle tying machines – 2-/Bu; Addressing machine – 1-/KR.; Business Hardware – APT
Delivery method: Mail, Newsstand, Private Carrier, Racks

GLASGOW

GLASGOW DAILY TIMES

100 Commerce Dr., Glasgow, Ky., 42141; gen tel (270) 678-5171; gen fax (270) 678-5052; adv fax (270) 678-3372; adv e-mail dtimesad@glasgowdailytimes.com; web site www.glasgowdailytimes.com
Group: CNHI
Published: Mon, Tues, Wed, Thur, Fri, Sat
Weekday Frequency: All day
Saturday Frequency: All day
Circulation: 7,541; 8,513(sat)
Last Audit: Sworn September 30, 2009
Price: 9.00/mo (in-state); 99.00/yr.
Advertising: Open inch rate $13.44
Insert rate: Varies by page count
News services: AP.
Politics: 1865
Not Published: New Year; Memorial Day; Independence Day; Labor Day; Thanksgiving; Christmas. Postal Holidays
Own facility?: Y
Special Editions: Spring Home Improvement (Apr); Sidewalk Days (Aug); Christmas Greetings (Dec); Tax Preparation (Feb); Today's Bride (Jun); Times Community Review (Mar); Car Care (May); Tobacco (Nov); Car Care (Oct); Senior Citizens Tab (Sept).
Special Weekly Sections: TV Screen (Sat); Church (S); Farming (Thur); Best Food Day (Wed).
Magazines: Relish (Monthly); Parade (S).
Pub....Keith Ponder
Bus. Mgr....Sonya Turner
Ed....James Brown
Prodn. Dir....Chuck Roberts
Mailroom Mgr....Mary Pike
General Manager...Scotty Maxwell
Adv. Dir....Amy Lee
Circ. Mgr....Leslie McAlpin
Market Information: TMC.
Mechanical available: Offset; Black and 3 ROP colors; insert accepted; page cutoffs - 21 1/2.
Mechanical Specifications: Type page 13 x 21 1/2; E - 6 cols, 2 1/16, 1/8 between; A - 6 cols, 2 1/16, 1/8 between; C - 8 cols, 1 5/16, 1/8 between.
Commodity Consumption: Avg. Page Number Per Issue - Daily 20; Avg. Page Number Per Issue - Plates Used 4000; Avg. Page Number Per Issue - Sunday 28; widths 27; Newsprint Used - Metric Tons 425; Printing Ink Used - Black 12000; Printing Ink Used - Color 1200.
Equipment EDITORIAL: Front-end Software – APP/Mac Sys 7.5, Baseview/NewsEdit Pro 2.1.2, QPS/QuarkXPress 3.32.; Editorial Hardware – APP/Power Mac; Editorial Equipment – IBM/Selectric; Editorial Printers – 1-APP/Mac LaserWriter IIg, Xante/Accel-a-Writer 8200 CLASSIFIED: Front-end Software – Baseview/Class Manager Pro 1.0.5B, APP/Mac System 7.5.2.; Classified Hardware – APP/Power Mac; Classified Printers – Okidata/Pacemark 3410 DISPLAY: Ad make-up applications – Ad Force 1.0, Adobe; Layout Software – 1-APP/Power Mac 7200-90 with Ad Force 1.0, Adobe.; Display Hardware – APP/Power Mac 7200-90; Display Printers – 1-APP/Mac IIg, Xante/Accel-a-Writer 8200 PRODUCTION: Pagination Software – Baseview/NewsEdit Pro 21.2.; Production Equipment – APP/Mac, 2-Xante/Accel-a-Writer 8200; Cameras – 1-B; Scanners – 2-Epson/ESI 200C, 1-Polaroid/SprintScan 35; Business Hardware – 1-Unisys, 3-Link/Console, Brain Works, Baseview
Zip Codes served: 42717; 42722; 42127; 42129; 42133; 42141; 42746; 42152; 42749; 42759; 42765; 42160; 42171; 42166; 42167
Delivery method: Mail, Newsstand, Racks

HARLAN

THE HARLAN DAILY ENTERPRISE

1548 S. Hwy. 421, Harlan, Ky., 40831; gen tel (606) 573-4510; gen fax (606) 573-0042; gen e-mail paper@harlanonline.net; adv e-mail advertising@harlanonline.net; ed e-mail editor@harlanonline.net; web site www.harlandaily.com
Published: Mon, Tues, Wed, Thur, Fri, Sat
Weekday Frequency: m
Circulation: 6,904; 6,904(sat)
Last Audit: September 29, 2001
Price: 7.25/mo; 93.00/yr.
Advertising: Open inch rate $13.48
News services: Landon Media Group.
Politics: Independent.
Not Published: Christmas.
Special Editions: Home Improvement (Apr); Christmas Greetings (Dec); Harlan County Heritage Tab (Feb); Christmas Shopping Guide (Nov); Fall Car Care Tab (Oct); Home Improvement (Sept).
Magazines: USA WEEKEND Magazine (Sat); American Profile (Weekly).
Pub....Pat Lay
Adv. Mgr....Wylene Miniard
Circ. Mgr....Ame Massingald
Mng. Ed....John Henson
News Ed....Debbie Caldwell
Sports Ed....John Middleson
Market Information: TMC.
Mechanical available: Offset; Black and 3 ROP colors; insert accepted - catalogs; page cutoffs - 22 1/2.
Mechanical Specifications: Type page 13 x 21 1/2; E - 6 cols, 2 1/16, 1/8 between; A - 6 cols, 2 1/16, 1/8 between; C - 8 cols, 1 3/4, 1/16 between.
Commodity Consumption: Avg. Page Number Per Issue - Daily 14; Avg. Page Number Per Issue - Plates Used 2503; widths 27 1/2; Newsprint Used - Short Tons 330; Printing Ink Used - Black 9680; Printing Ink Used - Color 4804; Printing Ink Used - Pages Printed 4382.
Equipment EDITORIAL: Front-end Software – QPS/QuarkXPress, Baseview/NewsEdit.; Editorial Hardware – 6-APP/Mac; Editorial Equipment – APP/Mac Scanner; Editorial Printers – 2-APP/Mac LaserWriter II CLASSIFIED: Front-end Software – Fox.; Classified Hardware – 1-APP/Mac; Classified Printers – Okidata DISPLAY: Ad make-up applications – Multi-Ad/Creator.; Display Hardware – 2-APP/Mac; Production Equipment – 1-Nu; Cameras – 1-C/Spartan III; Scanners – Ca/Sharpshooter Densi-Probe.; Bundle tying machines – 2/Bu; Addressing machine – KR.; Business Hardware – IBM/Sys 36, IBM/PC

HENDERSON

THE GLEANER

455 Klutey Park Plz., Henderson, Ky., 42419-0004; gen tel (270) 827-2000; adv tel (270) 831-8303; gen fax (270) 827-2765; adv fax (270) 827-2765; gen e-mail saustin@thegleaner.com; adv e-mail ads@thegleaner.com; ed e-mail news@thegleaner.com; web site www.thegleaner.com
Published: Tues, Wed, Thur, Fri, Sat, Sun
Weekday Frequency: m
Saturday Frequency: m
Circulation: 9,678; 9,678(sat); 10,845(sun)
Last Audit: ABC September 30, 2011
Price: 11.95/mo; 131.45/yr.
Advertising: Open inch rate $17.09
News services: AP.
Politics: 1885
Special Editions: Do-It-Yourself (Apr); Football Tab (Aug); Fair (Jul); Lawn & Garden (Mar); Holiday Entertaining (Nov).
Special Weekly Sections: NASCAR (Fri); Business (S); Farm (Sat); Health (Thur); Gleaner Jr. (Tues).
Magazines: Parade (S).
Pub....Steve Austin
Circ. Mgr....Lori Bush
Ed....David Dixon
Graphics Ed./Art Dir....Mike Moore
Health/Medical Ed....Judy Jenkins
Lifestyle Ed....Donna Stinnett
News Ed....Doug White
Photo Ed....Mike Lawrence
Religion Ed....Frank Boyett
Science/Technology Ed....Chuck Stinnett
Market Information: Split run; TMC.
Mechanical available: Offset; Black and 3 ROP colors; insert accepted - any; page cutoffs - 22 3/4.
Mechanical Specifications: Type page 13 x 21 1/2; E - 6 cols, 2 1/16, 1/8 between; A - 6 cols, 1 5/6, 1/8 between; C - 9 cols, 1 1/2, 1/16 between.
Commodity Consumption: Avg. Page Number Per Issue - Daily 28; Avg. Page Number Per Issue - Plates Used 26300; Avg. Page Number Per Issue - Sunday 49; widths 24 7/8; Newsprint Used - Short Tons 1915; Printing Ink Used - Black 47101; Printing Ink Used - Color 21380; Printing Ink
Equipment: Editorial Hardware – 1-HI; Editorial Equipment – Lf/AP Leaf Picture Desk, 20-HI.; Classified Hardware – 5-FSI.; Layout Software – 1-HI/8600.; Production Equipment – 1-ECR, 1-ECR; Cameras – 1-SCREEN. PRESSROOM: Line 1 – 11 MAILROOM: Counter stackers – Gammerler/KL 507; Inserters and stuffers – 6-MM/227; Bundle tying machines – 2/Sterling; Addressing machine – 2-/Wm, 1-/KAN; Other equipment –1-/MM, Gammerler/RS 11.; Business Hardware – TI/1500

HOPKINSVILLE

KENTUCKY NEW ERA

1618 E. Ninth St., Hopkinsville, Ky., 42241; gen tel (270) 886-4444; adv tel (270) 887-3270; ed tel (270) 887-3230; gen fax (270) 887-3222; adv fax (270) 887-3222; ed fax (270) 887-3222; gen e-mail editor@kentuckynewera.com; adv e-mail ads@kentuckynewera.com; ed e-mail editor@kentuckynewera.com; web site www.kentuckynewera.com
Published: Mon, Tues, Wed, Thur, Fri, Sat
Weekday Frequency: e
Saturday Frequency: m
Circulation: 10,000; 10,500(sat)
Last Audit: Sworn September 30, 2009
Price: 14.00/mo; 168.00/yr.
Advertising: Open inch rate $30.58
News services: AP, TMS.
Politics: 1869
Not Published: New Year; Independence Day;

Labor Day; Thanksgiving; Christmas.
Own facility?: Y
Special Editions: Please call our advertising department for a full list of special sections published monthly and yearly.
Special Weekly Sections: University of Kentucky Sports Page (Fri); Tax Tips (weekly, Jan-Apr) (Other); Outdoor Page (Sat); Farm Page (Thur); Best Food Day (Wed); Homes and Building Tips (Apr.-Jan.) (Weekly).
Magazines: Relish (Monthly); USA WEEKEND Magazine (Sat); American Profile (Weekly), Spry (Monthly), Athlon Sports (Monthly)
Pres./Gen. Mgr. ....Charles A. Henderson
Publisher ....Taylor Wood Hayes
Bus. Mgr. ....Sheryl Ellis
Adv. Mgr. ....Ted Jatczak
Classified Manager ....Nancy Reece
Circulation Director ....Tony Henson
Editor....................................Jennifer Brown
Lifestyles Editr ....Dennis Oneil
Web Publisher............................Dan Stahl
Production Manager ....Chris Hollis
Sports Editor ....Joe Wilson
Photographer / Copy Desk Chief.........Dana Long
Market Information: TMC.
Mechanical available: Offset; Black and 3 ROP colors; insert accepted; page cutoffs - 22 3/4.
Mechanical Specifications: Type page 11 5/8 x 21 1/2; E - 6 cols, 1/8 between; A - 6 cols, 1/8 between; C - 9 cols, 1/8 between.
Commodity Consumption: Avg. Page Number Per Issue - Daily 24; Avg. Page Number Per Issue - Plates Used 14400; Avg. Page Number Per Issue - Saturday 40; widths 25; Newsprint Used - Short Tons 1200; Printing Ink Used - Black 27145; Printing Ink Used - Color 6600; Printing Ink Us
Equipment EDITORIAL: Front-end Software – APT, ACT.; Editorial Hardware – APT; Editorial Equipment – 1-Ultra/4000 Imagesetter, 1-Ultra/5400 Imagesetter, 1-Konica/Image Setter, Konica/EV Jetsetter; Editorial Printers – 6-HP, 4-HP/5000N CLASSIFIED: Front-end Software – Vision Data; Classified Hardware – Dell; Classified Printers – HP DISPLAY: Ad make-up applications – QPS/QuarkXPress 4.0, Aldus/FreeHand 7.0, Adobe/Photoshop 4.0; Layout Software – QPS/QuarkXPress. Adobe Indesign; Display Hardware – Dell; Display Printers – HP Laser PRODUCTION: Pagination Software – QPS/QuarkXPress 4.0.; Production Equipment – 1-Nu/Flip Top, 1-Nat/26, 1-Konica/EV Jetsetter; Scanners – 1-HP/Scanner, 4-Microtek/ScanMaker II 5P PRESSROOM: Line 1 – 7-G/Urbanite U864 (Upper former) 1971; Inserters and stuffers – 8-KAN/480; Bundle tying machines – 2/OVL, 1-/OVL; Wrapping singles – 4-/Dri wrap; Addressing machine – 1-St/mailing label, 6-/Wm. BUSINESS COMPUTERS: Business Software – Vision Data; Business Hardware – Dell
Zip Codes served: 42240,42262,42234,42286,42223,42211,42220,42221,42236,42241,42254,42266,42445,42280,42220,42204,42216
Delivery method: Newsstand, Private Carrier, Racks

LEXINGTON

LEXINGTON HERALD-LEADER

100 Midland Ave., Lexington, Ky., 40508-1999; gen tel (859) 231-3100; adv tel (859) 231-3150; ed tel (859) 231-3200; gen fax (859) 231-3454; adv fax (859) 231-3494; ed fax (859) 231-9738; gen e-mail hlnews@herald-leader.com; ed e-mail hleditorial@herald-leader.com; web site www.kentucky.com
Group: Newspapers First, Inc.
Published: Mon, Tues, Wed, Thur, Fri, Sat, Sun
Weekday Frequency: m
Saturday Frequency: m
Circulation: 89,050; 90,584(sat); 117,980(sun)
Last Audit: ABC September 30, 2011
Price: 4.60/wk; 19.95/mo; 239.40/yr; 59.85/13wk, $119.70/26wk.
Advertising: Open inch rate $202.59
News services: AP, NYT, MCT, LAT-WP.
Special Editions: Golf (Apr); Technology in the Medical Field (Aug); Get Healthy (Dec); Jessamine Co. (Feb); Bluegrass Buys (Jan); Life Begins at 50 (Jul); Lexingtonian (Jun); From House to Home (Mar); Health & Healing (May); Downtown for the Holidays (Nov); Hamburg Living
Special Weekly Sections: Weekender (Fri); Business Monday (Mon); Arts & Life (S); Faith & Values (Sat); Free Time (Thur); Health & Family (Tues); Communities (Wed).
Magazines: Parade (S).
Pub./Pres. ....Timothy M. Kelly
CFO ....Sheila Vose
Vice Pres., HR/Community Rel. ....Michael Wells
Adv. Dir. ....Waynes Snow
Circ. Dir...............................Nelson Fonticiella
Sr. Circ. Mgr. ....Julie Achauer
Ed....Peter Baniak
Asst. Mng. Ed., Local News ....Tom Caudill
Cartoonist...Joel Pett
Editorial Page Ed. ....Vanessa Gallman
Photo Dir. ....Ron Garrison
Sports Ed......................................Gene Abell
Prodn. Vice Pres., Opns. ....David Stone
Prodn. Mgr., Bus. Systems..........Mike Serraglio
Prodn. Mgr., Customer Serv......Mary Ann Hatton
Prodn. Mgr., Facility/Environmental Deborah Taylor
Prodn. Mgr., Pre Press ....Joel Allen
Prodn. Mgr., Pressroom ....John Royse
Prodn. Mgr., Systems Opns. ....John Clemons
Market Information: ADS; Split run; TMC; Zoned editions.
Mechanical available: Offset; Black and 3 ROP colors; insert accepted - cata books for topping; page cutoffs - 22 3/4.
Mechanical Specifications: Type page 13 x 21 1/2; E - 6 cols, 2 1/16, 1/8 between; A - 6 cols, 2 1/16, 1/8 between; C - 10 cols, 1 1/4, 1/16 between.
Commodity Consumption: Avg. Page Number Per Issue - Daily 59; Avg. Page Number Per Issue - Plates Used 163800; Avg. Page Number Per Issue - Sunday 148; widths 54; Newsprint Used - Metric Tons 19570; Newsprint Used - Short Tons 20470; Printing Ink Used - Black 371280; Printing
Equipment EDITORIAL: Front-end Software – QPS, 2-HP/1050C Proofer, 2-HP/2000 Proofer, OCE/9400.; Editorial Hardware – 6-AT/Series 6, 112-APP/Mac; Editorial Printers – Linotype-Hell/Lino 530, LaserMaster/Unity, CSI/Newsjet CTP with Plate Q CLASSIFIED: Front-end Software – Cybergraphics 5.0, Caere/OmniPage.; Classified Hardware – 2-DEC/VAX 4000-60; Classified Equipment – APP/Mac, HP/Scanner; Classified Printers – Linotype-Hell/Linotype 530 DISPLAY: Ad make-up applications – Multi-Ad/Creator; Layout Software – Mk/Ad Director, MEI/ALS.; Display Hardware – APP/Mac; Display Printers – Linotype-Hell/Linotype 530, LaserMaster/Unity, CSI/Firescript PRODUCTION: Pagination Software – QPS/QuarkXPress 4; Production Equipment – 2-Linotype-Hell/Linotype 530, RIP 50XMO, 1-CSI/Newsjet Plotter with Firescript RIP, HP/Laserwriter 600; Cameras – 1-C/Pager, 1-C/Spartan III; Scanners – APP/Mac, 2-Microtek/600ZS, ECR/Autokon 4000, 2-Howtek/D4000 PRESSROOM: Line 1 – 7-G/Metro (3 half decks); Line 2 – 7-G/Metro (3 half decks); Folders – 3-G/Imperial 3:2; Pasters – 14-G/Digital; Reels and Stands – 14-G/Reels; Press control system – G/PCS; Press registration system – Standard/Pin Register. MAILROOM: Counter stackers – 1/QWI, 2-/MM, 4-Id/2100, Gammerler; Inserters and stuffers – 2-/Fg; Bundle tying machines – 5-MLN/HS, 1-MLN/EE, 1-/Bu, 2-Dynaric/NPZ; Wrapping singles – 4-/QWI; Addressing machine – 2-KAN/AVY Labeler; Other equipment –2-HI/Sadddle St; Business Hardware – 1-HP/3000 Series 955

LOUISVILLE

THE COURIER-JOURNAL

525 W. Broadway, Louisville, Ky., 40202; gen tel (502) 582-4011; adv tel (502) 582-4708; ed tel (502) 582-4691; adv fax (502) 582-7111; ed fax (502) 582-4200; web site www.courier-journal.com
Published: Mon, Tues, Wed, Thur, Fri, Sat, Sun
Weekday Frequency: m
Saturday Frequency: m
Circulation: 142,801; 151,371(sat); 257,611(sun)
Last Audit: ABC September 30, 2011
Price: 19.00/mo; 228.00/yr.
Advertising: Open inch rate $397.11
News services: AP, NYT, LAT-WP, GNS, Dow Jones.
Politics: Independent-Democrat. **Established:** 1868
Special Editions: Thunder Preview (Apr); Used Car Guide (Aug); Be Heathly Kentuckiana (Feb); Parent's Survival Guide (Jul); Savvy Home Buyer (Mar); Be Healthy Kentuckiana (May); Be Healthy Kentuckiana (Nov); Tour of Homes-2nd Edition (Oct); On Course (Sept).
Special Weekly Sections: Weekend (Fri); Real Estate (S); Scene (Sat); Family (Thur); Health (Tues); Food (Wed).
Magazines: Her Scene (Quarterly); TV Week & Cable Guide (S); USA WEEKEND Magazine (Sat).
Pres./Pub.................................Arnold Garson
Exec. Ed./Vice Pres., News.........Bennie L. Ivory
Mng. Ed........................................Jean Porter
Editorial Page Ed.....................Stephen Ford
Editorial Writer................................Pam Platt
Food Ed.......................................Ron Mikulak
Metro Ed. ....Mike Trautman
Music Critic..............................Jeffrey Puckett
Opns. News Mgr......................James Kirchner
Opinion Pages Ed. ....Keith Runyon
Religion Writer.............................Peter Smith
Sports Ed. ....Harry Bryan
Suburban Ed...............................Veda Morgan
Washington Bureau ....James Carroll
Market Information: Split run; TMC; Zoned editions.
Mechanical available: Offset; Black and 3 ROP colors; insert accepted - samples; page cutoffs - 21.
Mechanical Specifications: Type page 11 x 20; E - 6 cols, 1 13/16, 1/8 between; A - 6 cols, 1 13/16, 1/8 between; C - 10 cols, 1 1/20, 1/8 between.
Commodity Consumption: Avg. Page Number Per Issue - Daily 54; Avg. Page Number Per Issue - Sunday 132; widths 25; Newsprint Used - Metric Tons 33800; Printing Ink Used - Black 52800; Printing Ink Used - Pages Printed 27581.
Equipment EDITORIAL: Front-end Software – AT 4.7.6.; Editorial Hardware – 6-AT/JII; Editorial Printers – Florida Data/Line Printer, GE/Proofer CLASSIFIED: Front-end Software – AT 4.7.6.; Classified Hardware – 2-AT; Classified Printers – HP/4MV Laserjet DISPLAY: Ad make-up applications – III 9.3.3.35; Layout Software – Baseview, Ad Manager AII.; Display Hardware – APP/Mac, Sun/Ultra II; Display Printers – GE/Proofer, HP/755 CM PRODUCTION: Pagination Software – AT/Press 2 GO.; Production Equipment – 3-III/3810, 3-AII/3850; Cameras – 2-C/Pager II PRESSROOM: Line 1 – 7-G/Mark I 1948, 2-KBA/MOT 5 color DW 1992; Line 2 – 7-G/Mark I 1948, 2-KBA/MOT 5 color DW 1992; Line 3 – 6-H/Color Convertible 1953, 2-KBA/MOT 5 color DW 1992; Line 4 – 7-G/Mark II 1968, 2-KBA/MOT 5 color DW 1992; Folders – 3-G/3:2, 1-H/2:1. MAILROOM: Counter stackers – 3-QWI/SJ201, 4-QWI/301B, 3/QWI 401; Inserters and stuffers – 3-HI/72P, 1-/HI 630; Bundle tying machines – 2-EAM-Mosca/RO-TA-500PA, 2-/Power Strap/PSN-5, 1-/Power Strap/PSN-6, 3-MLN/2A, 6-Samuel/NT30 Strappers, 3-Samuel/NT30; Addressing machine – Addressing

MADISONVILLE

THE MESSENGER

221 S. Main St., Madisonville, Ky., 42431; gen tel (270) 824-3300; adv tel (270) 824-3262; ed tel (270) 824-3224; gen fax (270) 821-6855; adv fax (270) 821-6855; ed fax (270) 825-3733; gen e-mail newsroom@the-messenger.com; adv e-mail dlittlepage@the-messenger.com; ed e-mail letters@the-messenger.com; web site www.the-messenger.com
Published: Tues, Wed, Thur, Fri, Sat, Sun
Weekday Frequency: m
Circulation: 7,422; 7,422(sat); 7,352(sun)
Last Audit: September 30, 2008
Price: 13.75/mo; 162.00/yr.
Advertising: Open inch rate $19.10
News services: AP.
Politics: Independent. **Established:** 1914
Advertising not accepted: NC-17 movies; Exotic dancing.
Special Editions: Football (Aug); Christmas Sections (Dec); Bridal Tour (Jan); Fair Tab (Jul); Christmas Sections (Nov); Women in Business (Oct); Progress (Sept).
Special Weekly Sections: Pennyrile Plus (Wed).
Magazines: USA WEEKEND Magazine (S).
Pub. ....Rick Welch
Bus. Mgr. ....Angie York
Adv. Dir. ....Deborah Littlepage
Circ. Dir. ....Cindy Ashby
Exec. Ed.......................................Tom Clinton
Sports Ed. ....Forrest Rutherford
Sports Ed. ....Nick Brockman
Market Information: ADS; TMC.
Mechanical available: Offset; Black and 3 ROP colors; insert accepted; page cutoffs - 22 3/4.
Mechanical Specifications: Type page 11 13/16 x 21 1/4; E - 6 cols, 1 13/16, 1/8 between; A - 6 cols, 1 13/16, 1/8 between; C - 9 cols, 1 1/8, 1/8 between.
Commodity Consumption: Avg. Page Number Per Issue - Daily 20; Avg. Page Number Per Issue - Plates Used 3150; Avg. Page Number Per Issue - Saturday 16; Avg. Page Number Per Issue - Sunday 32; widths 12 1/2; Newsprint Used - Short Tons 525; Printing Ink Used - Black 15000; Print
Equipment; Editorial Hardware – 14-AT/5000, APP/Power Mac; Editorial Equipment – 3-APP/Mac SE, Lf/AP Leaf Picture Desk; Editorial Printers – Software □ QPS/QuarkXPress.; Classified Hardware – 4-AT/5000. DISPLAY: Ad make-up applications – Multi-Ad/Creator, Broderbund/TypeStyler, Claris/MacDraw Pro, Adobe/Photoshop, Adobe/Illustrator; Display Printers – APP/Mac LaserWriter 650, Dataproducts/LZR1560, ECR/Imagesetter; Production Equipment – 2-COM/8400, ECR/Imagesetter; Cameras – 1-Nu. PRESSROOM: Line 1 – 8-G/Community.; Inserters and stuffers – KAN/480; Bundle tying machines – 1-Si/LB.; Business Hardware – Baseview

MAYFIELD

THE MAYFIELD MESSENGER

201 N. Eighth St., Mayfield, Ky., 42066; gen tel (270) 247-5223; ed tel (270) 247-1515; gen fax (270) 247-6336; gen e-mail mayfieldmessenger@newwavecomm.net
Group: Kentucky Press Service, Inc.
Published: Mon, Tues, Wed, Thur, Fri
Weekday Frequency: e
Circulation: 5,000
Last Audit: Sworn September 30, 2005
Price: 7.00/mo; 78.00/yr.
Advertising: Open inch rate $8.10
News services: AP.
Politics: Independent.
Not Published: New Year; Independence Day; Thanksgiving; Christmas.
Own facility?: Y
Pub....Eric Hoffman
Bus. Mgr. ....Carolyn Williams
Adv. Dir. ....Susan B. Seay
Adv. Mgr., Classified ....Zina Smith
Circ. Mgr.......................................Mike Clark
Prodn. Supt. ....Dave Robertson
Market Information: TMC.
Mechanical available: Offset; Black and 3 ROP colors; insert accepted - free-standing inserts; page cutoffs - 22 3/4.
Mechanical Specifications: Type page 12 7/8 x 21

1/2; E - 6 cols, 2 1/16, 1/8 between; A - 6 cols, 2 1/16, 1/8 between; C - 9 cols, 1 1/2, 1/16 between.
Commodity Consumption: Avg. Page Number Per Issue - Daily 20; Avg. Page Number Per Issue - Plates Used 6000; widths 27 1/2; Newsprint Used - Short Tons 300; Printing Ink Used - Black 10000; Printing Ink Used - Color 400; Printing Ink Used - Pages Printed 6500.
Equipment EDITORIAL: Front-end Software – Baseview/NewsEdit Pro, DragX, QPS/QuarkXPress.; Editorial Hardware – 3-APP/Mac 7200 with CD-Rom, 3-APP/Mac 7500 with CD-Rom, 1-APP/Mac PowerBook 540c; Editorial Printers – 2-APP/Mac LaserWriter, 1-NewGen/Image Plus 11 x 17; Classified Hardware – 1-APP/Mac Performa 425, 1-APP/Mac 7200 with CD-Rom; Classified Printers – 1-APP/Mac LaserPrinter.; Display Hardware – 3-APP/Mac 7500 with CD-Rom; Display Printers – Software ◻ Multi-Ad/Creator; Production Equipment – 2-Nu; Cameras – 1-B. PRESSROOM: Line 1 – 7-G/Community; Folders – 1-G/SC.; Bundle tying machines – 2/Bu; Addressing machine – 1-/Am.; Business Hardware – 1-APP/Mac SE, 1-APP/Mac, 2-IBM

MESSENGER NEWSPAPERS, INC.
201 N. 8th St., Mayfield, Ky., 42066; gen tel (270) 247-5223; gen fax (270) 247-6336

MAYSVILLE

THE LEDGER INDEPENDENT
120 Limestone St., Maysville, Ky., 41056; gen tel (606) 564-9091; gen fax (606) 564-6893; gen e-mail ponto@maysvilleky.net; web site www.maysville-online.com
Published: Mon, Tues, Wed, Thur, Fri, Sat
Weekday Frequency: m
Saturday Frequency: m
Circulation: 6,697; 7,305(sat)
Last Audit: ABC September 30, 2011
Price: 2.25/wk; 9.00/mo; 117.00/yr (carrier), $148.20/yr (mail).
Advertising: Open inch rate $18.57
News services: AP.
Politics: Independent. **Established:** 1968
Not Published: Christmas.
Special Editions: Car Care (Apr); Back-to-School (Aug); Christmas Greetings (Dec); Cookbook (Feb); Income Tax Guide (Jan); Dairy Month (Jun); Basketball (Mar); Homemakers (May); Basketball (Nov); 4-H (Oct); Car Care (Sept).
Special Weekly Sections: Food (Mon); Lifestyles/TV (Sat); Home and Garden (Thur); Food (Tues); Food (Wed).
Magazines: Relish (Monthly); Parade (Weekly).
Pub....Robert L. Hendrickson
Controller....Kellie Cracraft
Adv. Mgr.....Patricia Moore
Circ. Mgr.....Marsha Fritz
Ed....Mary Ann Kerns
Market Information: ADS; TMC.
Mechanical available: Offset; Black and 3 ROP colors; insert accepted; page cutoffs - 22 3/4.
Mechanical Specifications: Type page 13 x 21 1/2; E - 6 cols, 2 1/16, 1/8 between; A - 6 cols, 2 1/16, 1/8 between; C - 8 cols, 1 1/2, 1/8 between.
Commodity Consumption: Avg. Page Number Per Issue - Daily 20; widths 27 1/2; Newsprint Used - Short Tons 625; Printing Ink Used - Pages Printed 6500.
Equipment EDITORIAL: Front-end Software – Lotus/Notes.; Editorial Hardware – CText; Classified Hardware – CText.; Layout Software – DEC/Layout 8000.; Production Equipment – 1-B, V/VT-600; Cameras – 1-DAI. PRESSROOM: Line 1 – 10-G/Community; Folders – 1-HI/Cotrell. MAILROOM: Counter stackers – 1/BG; Inserters and stuffers – MM; Bundle tying machines – MLN; Addressing machine – 1-/Ch.; Business Hardware – 2-ATT, BI, ATT/7300

MAYSVILLE NEWSPAPERS, INC.
PO Box 518, Maysville, Ky., 41056; gen tel (606) 564-9091; gen fax (606) 564-6893

MIDDLESBORO

MIDDLESBORO DAILY NEWS
120 N. 11th St., Middlesboro, Ky., 40965; gen tel (606) 248-1010; gen fax (606) 248-7614; web site www.middlesborodailynews.com
Group: Kentucky Press Service, Inc.
Published: Mon, Tues, Wed, Thur, Fri, Sat, Sun
Weekday Frequency: e
Saturday Frequency: m
Circulation: 5,873; 5,873(sat)
Last Audit: October 1, 2004
Price: 8.25/mo; 99.00/yr.
Advertising: Open inch rate $15.92
News services: AP.
Politics: Independent.
Not Published: New Year; Memorial Day; Independence Day; Labor Day; Thanksgiving; Christmas.
Special Editions: Chamber of Commerce Membership Directory (Apr); Football (Aug); Letters to Santa (Dec); Progress (Feb); I'm Proud to be an American (Jul); Like Father Like Son (Jun); Home Improvement (Mar); Graduation (May); Caroling Book (Nov); Fall Festival (Oct); Read
Special Weekly Sections: Religion Page (Fri); Business Page (Thur).
Magazines: USA WEEKEND Magazine (Sat); American Profile (Tues).
Pub....Tom Spargur
Adv. Dir.....Pat Cheek
Circ. Mgr.....Lisa Gray
News Ed....Brandy Calvert
Sports Ed.....Jay Compton
Teen-Age/Youth Ed.....Donna Greene
Market Information: TMC.
Mechanical available: Offset; Black and 3 ROP colors; insert accepted; page cutoffs - 22 3/4.
Mechanical Specifications: Type page 11 5/8 x 21 1/2; E - 6 cols, 1 13/16, 1/8 between; A - 6 cols, 1 13/16, 1/8 between; C - 9 cols, 1 13/16, 1/8 between.
Commodity Consumption: widths 27 1/2.
Equipment EDITORIAL: Front-end Software – Baseview.; Editorial Hardware – APP/Mac; Editorial Printers – APP/Mac LaserPrinter CLASSIFIED: Front-end Software – Baseview.; Classified Hardware – APP/Mac; Classified Printers – APP/Mac LaserPrinter DISPLAY: Ad make-up applications – Baseview; Display Hardware – 2-APP/Mac; Display Printers – APP/Mac LaserPrinter PRODUCTION: Pagination Software – QPS/QuarkXPress.; Production Equipment – APP/Mac; Cameras – Acti PRESSROOM: Line 1 – 6-G/Community 1971.; Bundle tying machines – 3/Bu.; Business Hardware – IBM/Sys 36

MURRAY

THE MURRAY LEDGER & TIMES
1001 Whitnell Ave., Murray, Ky., 42071-0018; gen tel (270) 753-1916; adv tel (270) 753-1916; ed tel (270) 753-1916; gen fax (270) 753-1927; gen e-mail mlt@murrayledger.com; adv e-mail ads@murrayledger.com; ed e-mail editor@murrayledger.com; web site www.murrayledger.com
Published: Mon, Tues, Wed, Thur, Fri, Sat
Weekday Frequency: m
Saturday Frequency: m
Circulation: 7,459; 7,459(sat)
Last Audit: September 30, 2004
Price: $105/year local
Advertising: Open inch rate $10.50
News services: AP, TMS.
Politics: Independent.
Not Published: New Year; Memorial Day; Independence Day; Labor Day; Thanksgiving; Christmas.
Own facility?: Y
Special Editions: Home Improvement (Apr); Back-to-School (Aug); In Our Backyard Magazine (June & Dec); Brides (Jan); Brides (Jun); Car Care (May); Fall Home Improvement (Oct); Homecoming (Sept).
Special Weekly Sections: Church Page (Fri); Farm Page (Mon); Outdoor Page (Sat); Arts & Entertainment (Thur); Education Page (Tues); Best Food Day (Wed).
Pub.....Alice Rouse
Mng. Ed....Greg Travis
Market Information: ADS; TMC.
Mechanical available: Offset; Black and 3 ROP colors; insert accepted - all; page cutoffs - 21.
Mechanical Specifications: Type page 12 1/2 x 21 1/2; E - 6 cols, 1 5/6, 1/8 between; A - 6 cols, 1 5/6, 1/8 between; C - 9 cols, 1 1/4, 1/16 between.
Commodity Consumption: Avg. Page Number Per Issue - Daily 16; Avg. Page Number Per Issue - Plates Used 8000; widths 25; Newsprint Used - Short Tons 550; Printing Ink Used - Black 12000; Printing Ink Used - Color 500; Printing Ink Used - Pages Printed 6076.
Equipment EDITORIAL: Front-end Software – Baseview/NewsEdit Pro, QPS/QuarkXPress 4.0.; Editorial Hardware – APP/Mac; Editorial Printers – Xante/8200 CLASSIFIED: Front-end Software – Baseview/Ad Manager Pro.; Classified Hardware – APP/Mac G3; Classified Printers – Okidata, Xante/Accel-A-Writer DISPLAY: Ad make-up applications – QPS/QuarkXPress 4.0, Adobe/Photoshop 4.0; Layout Software – APP/Mac.; Display Hardware – APP/Mac; Display Printers – Xante/8200 PRODUCTION: Pagination Software – QPS/QuarkXPress 6.1.; Production Equipment – 13-APP/Mac G5, Xante/Accel-A-Writer 8200; Cameras – 1-DAI/Vertical PRESSROOM: Line 1 – 8-G/Community (upper former) 1981; Folders – 1 MAILROOM: Counter stackers – 1/KAN; Inserters and stuffers – 2-/Bu; Wrapping singles – 1-/Ch; Addressing machine – 1 BUSINESS COMPUTERS: Business Software – MSSI; Business Hardware – AcerView 54E
Delivery method: Mail, Newsstand, Private Carrier, Racks

MURRAY NEWSPAPERS, INC.
1001 Whitnell Ave., Murray, Ky., 42071; gen tel (270) 753-1916; gen fax (270) 753-1927; gen e-mail mlt@murrayledger.com; adv e-mail ads@murrayledger.com; ed e-mail editor@murrayledger.com; web site www.murrayledger.com
Published: Mon, Tues, Wed, Thur, Fri, Sat
Weekday Frequency: m
Saturday Frequency: m
News services: AP
Politics: 1879
Advertising not accepted: N
Not Published: Sunday
Own facility?: Y
Delivery method: Mail, Newsstand, Private Carrier, Racks

OWENSBORO

MESSENGER-INQUIRER
1401 Frederica St., Owensboro, Ky., 42301; gen tel (270) 926-0123; adv tel (270) 691-7239; ed tel (270) 926-0123; gen fax (270) 685-3446; adv fax (270) 691-7244; ed fax (270) 686-7868; adv e-mail fmurry@messenger-inquirer.com; achinn@messenger-inquirer.com; web site www.messenger-inquirer.com
Published: Mon, Tues, Wed, Thur, Fri, Sat, Sun
Weekday Frequency: m
Saturday Frequency: m
Circulation: 21,701; 21,701(sat); 24,978(sun)
Last Audit: ABC September 30, 2011
Price: 3.22/wk; 13.95/mo; 159.10/yr (d & S).
Advertising: Open inch rate $44.28
News services: AP, MCT.
Politics: Independent.
Special Editions: Spring Improvements (Apr); Holiday Greetings (Dec); Home & Garden Show (Feb); Coupon Quarterly (Jan); Made in our Backyard (Jul); Southern Living Cooking School (Jun); Prime (Mar); Bar-B-Q Festival (May); Holiday Entertainments & Gifts (Nov); Voter's Guid
Special Weekly Sections: Entertainment (Fri); Style (S); Sports Weekend (Sat); Health (Thur); Community (Tues); Education (Wed).
Magazines: USA WEEKEND Magazine (S).
Pub.....Bob Morris
Controller....Angie York
Adv. Dir.....Faye Murry
Adv. Mgr., Display....Yvette Wilson
Adv. Mgr., Servs.....Barbara Smith
Circ. Dir.....Barry Carden
Circ. Mgr., Home Delivery....Tom Greer
Circ. Mgr., Mktg.....Robin Byars
Ed.....Dan Heckel
Mng. Ed., McLean Co.....Matthew Francis
Sr. Copy Ed.....Owen Covington
Copy Ed.....Eugene Embry
Copy Ed.....Mary Kissel
Copy Ed.....Jamie Madigan
Librarian....Sherri Heckel
News Ed.....Hunter Reigler
Photo Ed.....Robert Bruck
Sports Copy Ed.....Harold Martin
Sports Ed.....Jim Pickens
Market Information: Split run; TMC.
Mechanical available: Offset; Black and 3 ROP colors; insert accepted - sizes up to 14 x 10 1/2 large; 5 x 7 small; page cutoffs - 22 3/4.
Mechanical Specifications: Type page 13 x 21; E - 5 cols, 2 1/16, 1/6 between; A - 6 cols, 2 1/16, 1/6 between; C - 10 cols, 1 1/4, 1/6 between.
Commodity Consumption: Avg. Page Number Per Issue - Daily 33.9; Avg. Page Number Per Issue - Plates Used 32004; Avg. Page Number Per Issue - Sunday 83.9; widths 41 1/4; Newsprint Used - Metric Tons 2914; Printing Ink Used - Black 72281; Printing Ink Used - Color 16710; Printin
Equipment: Editorial Hardware – 5-APP/Power Mac G3 400 Mhz, 32-APP/I-Mac, 9-APP/Power Mac G3 300 Mhz; Editorial Equipment – 1-Lf/AP Leaf Picture Desk, 5-Cascade/OPI Server, Sun/Sparc 20, Cascade/Dataflow Server; Editorial Printers – 1-Lf/AP Leaf Picture Desk, 1-Cascade/OPI Server, Ultra 2, Casca CLASSIFIED: Front-end Software – Baseview/AppleShare IP 6.0, Baseview/Ad Manager Pro 2.0.6, AR Module, Baseview/Class Flow 2.2.1.; Classified Hardware – 11-APP/Power Mac G3 300, OS 8.5.1 DISPLAY: Ad make-up applications – QPS/QuarkXPress, Adobe/Illustrator; Layout Software – Mk/Managing Editor, Mk/Ad Director. PRODUCTION: Pagination Software – QPS/QuarkXPress 4.0.4.; Production Equipment – 1-Douthitt, Hyphen/Imagesetter 3100, 2-Xante/Accel-a-Writer 8300; Cameras – 1-C/Spartan, 1-SCREEN/Vertical; Scanners – ECR/8400 Line & halftone camera, 1-Howtek/D-400 drum scanner, AG/Arcus II PRESSROOM: Line 1 – 4-G/Metro 3033 double width 1968; Folders – 1-G/2:1 double width; Pasters – 3-G/Auto; Reels and Stands – 4 MAILROOM: Counter stackers – 1-HL/stackpack, 1-HL/Monitor, 1-Id/550, 1-HL/Dual Carrier, 1/QWI; Inserters and stuffers – 1-S/848, 1-13/72; Bundle tying machines – 2-/Power Strap/PSN6, 1-MLN/ML2EE; Mailroom control system – K&M/Image PC Packaging System; Addressing machine – Addressing BUSINESS COMPUTERS: Business Software – CJ/AIM; Business Hardware – HP/937LX

PADUCAH

THE PADUCAH SUN
408 Kentucky Ave., Paducah, Ky., 42003; gen tel (270) 575-8600; adv tel (270) 575-8750; ed tel (270) 575-8650; gen fax (270) 575-8780; adv fax (270) 575-8771; ed fax (270) 442-7859; ed e-mail news@paducahsun.com; web site www.paducahsun.com
Group: Kentucky Press Service, Inc.
Published: Mon, Tues, Wed, Thur, Fri, Sat, Sun
Weekday Frequency: m
Saturday Frequency: m
Circulation: 19,618; 19,618(sat); 22,473(sun)

Last Audit: ABC September 30, 2011
Price: 15.00/mo; 210.00/yr.
Advertising: Open inch rate $34.14
News services: AP, MCT.
Politics: 1896
Special Editions: Quilt Show (Apr); Newspapers in Education Advertising Kick-Off (Aug); Holiday Greetings (Dec); NASCAR (Feb); Brides (Jan); Fall Fashion (Jul); The Crimestopping Handbook (Jun); Spring Outdoors (Mar); Lakeland (May); House Call (Monthly); Holiday Gift Guid
Special Weekly Sections: Church (Fri); Health (Mon); Books (S); Outdoor (Sat); Food Day (Tues); Outdoor (Wed).
Magazines: USA WEEKEND Magazine (S); Posh (Semi-monthly).
Broadcast Affiliations: WPSD-TV, NBC.
Controller.................................Jamie Paxton
Gen. Mgr..................................Gary Adkisson
Adv. Mgr., Retail..........................Becky Smith
Circ. Asst. Mgr...............................Judy Lynch
Ed..Jim Paxton
Mng. Ed..................................Duke Conover
Bus./Finance Ed.............................Joe Walker
Editorial Page Ed........................Mac Thrower
Entertainment/Amusements Ed.......C.D. Bradley
Farm/Agriculture Ed............................Ron Clark
Home Furnishings Ed.........Leigh Landini Wright
Nat'l Ed...Chris Ash
News Ed..................................Mark Hultman
Online Ed..........................Crystal Shackelford
Photo Ed..............................Barkley Thielman
Political/Gov't Ed.......................Bill Bartleman
Market Information: Split run; TMC; Zoned editions.
Mechanical available: Offset; Black and 3 ROP colors; insert accepted; page cutoffs - 21 1/4.
Mechanical Specifications: Type page 13 1/8 x 21 1/4; E - 6 cols, 1 5/6, 1/8 between; A - 6 cols, 1 5/6, 1/8 between; C - 9 cols, 1 5/8, 1/8 between.
Commodity Consumption: Avg. Page Number Per Issue - Daily 28; Avg. Page Number Per Issue - Plates Used 25750; Avg. Page Number Per Issue - Sunday 48; widths 25; Newsprint Used - Short Tons 5000; Printing Ink Used - Black 17000; Printing Ink Used - Color 6000; Printing Ink Used
Equipment EDITORIAL: Front-end Software – DTI, APP/Mac Sys 8.1.; Editorial Hardware – 2-Sun/Sparc 5, 1-Sun/Sparc Ultra; Editorial Equipment – HP/1600CM Color Printer; Editorial Printers – QMS/1660, APP/Mac LaserWriter 16-600, 2-ECR/4550, MON/2000 CLASSIFIED: Front-end Software – Multi-Ad, Baseview, Baseview/Ad Manager Pro.; Classified Hardware – 4-APP/Mac 4400; Classified Equipment – APP/Mac 9650-233 fileserver; Classified Printers – APP/Mac Personal LaserWriter, APP/Mac Imagewriter; Layout Software – SII, MEI.; Display Hardware – Sun/Sparc; Display Printers – APP/Mac LaserWriter; Production Equipment – Caere/OmniPage, Publish Pac, Adobe/Photoshop 4.0, ECR 1085, Textroix Phaser 740; Cameras – C/Spartan II, AG/20 x 24, Kk Ap Digital Camera; Scanners – 2-Polaroid/SprintScan 35, Microtek/IIXE, Dest, Nikon/3510AF, Microtek/IISP, 2-Microtek/Scanma PRESSROOM: Line 1 – 10-G/Urbanite; Folders – G/Urbanite. MAILROOM: Counter stackers – 2/Id, 1-/S; Inserters and stuffers – 1-/HI; Bundle tying machines – 2-/Bu, 1-Id. BUSINESS COMPUTERS: Business Software – Great Plains, Baseview; Business Hardware – APP/Mac LAN, Microsoft/Windows NT

PIKEVILLE

THE APPALACHIAN NEWS-EXPRESS

129 Caroline Ave., Pikeville, Ky., 41501-1101; gen tel (606) 437-4054; gen fax (606) 437-4246; ed e-mail news@news-expressky.com; web site www.news-expressky.com
Published: Wed, Fri, Sat
Circulation: 11,000
Last Audit: Estimate January 21, 2005
Price: 11.50/mo; 99.00/yr; 34.00/3mo, $59.00/6mo.
Advertising: Open inch rate $9.40
Magazines: American Profile (Weekly).
Pub...................................Jeff Vanderbeck
Office Mgr.....................................Lisa Moore
Adv. Dir.......................................Mike Davis
Ed...Jerry Boggs
Everyday Living Ed........................Nancy Goss
Sports Ed....................................Randy White
Prodn. Mgr...............................Tina Gayheart
Mechanical Specifications: Type page 12 x 21 1/2; E - 6 cols, 1 5/6, 1/4 between; A - 6 cols, 1 5/6, 1/4 between; C - 9 cols, 1 1/6, 1/4 between.
Equipment; Layout Software – QPS/QuarkXPress 4.0, Adobe/Photoshop 3.0. PRESSROOM: Line 1 – 6-G/Community color hump.

RICHMOND

THE RICHMOND REGISTER

380 Big Hill Ave., Richmond, Ky., 40475; gen tel (859) 623-1669; adv tel (859) 624-6681; gen fax (859) 623-2337; ed fax (859) 623-7408; gen e-mail news@richmondregister.com; ed e-mail editor@richmondregister.com; web site www.richmondregister.com
Group: Kentucky Press Service, Inc.
Published: Mon, Tues, Wed, Thur, Fri, Sat, Sun
Weekday Frequency: e
Saturday Frequency: e
Circulation: 4,992; 4,992(sat); 5,337(sun)
Last Audit: ABC September 30, 2011
Price: 8.00/mo; 120.00/yr.
Advertising: Open inch rate $12.96(m-fri)
News services: AP.
Politics: Independent. **Established:** 1808
Not Published: Christmas.
Special Weekly Sections: Real Estate (Fri); Health & Fitness (Mon); TV Supplement (Sat); Outdoors (Thur); Food (Wed).
Magazines: USA WEEKEND Magazine (S).
Pub.......................................Nicholas Lewis
Adv. Dir....................................Sherrie Hawn
Circ. Mgr....................................Cecil Foster
Ed...Lorie Love
Sports Ed............................Nathan Hutchison
Market Information: TMC; Zoned editions.
Mechanical available: Offset; Black and 3 ROP colors; insert accepted; page cutoffs - 23.
Mechanical Specifications: Type page 13 x 21 1/2; E - 6 cols, 2 1/16, 1/8 between; A - 6 cols, 2 1/16, 1/8 between; C - 9 cols, 1 3/8, 1/16 between.
Commodity Consumption: Avg. Page Number Per Issue - Daily 16; widths 13 3/4; Newsprint Used - Short Tons 550.
Equipment EDITORIAL: Front-end Software – HI/Compuedit, HI/1420.; Editorial Hardware – 6-Mk/4003; Classified Hardware – 2-Mk/4010.; Layout Software – Mk/Ad Comp.; Production Equipment – 2-COM/2961HS, 1-COM/Unisetter, 1-M/101; Cameras – 1-R/500. PRESSROOM: Line 1 – 6-G/Community; Folders – 2-G/2:1.; Inserters and stuffers – MM/3 bay; Bundle tying machines – 1/MLN, 1-MLN/MLIEE; Addressing machine – 1-Am/1900.

SOMERSET

THE COMMONWEALTH-JOURNAL

110-112 E. Mt. Vernon St., Somerset, Ky., 42502; gen tel (606) 678-8191; gen fax (606) 679-9225; adv fax (606) 679-4866; gen e-mail jmcneely@somerset-kentucky.com; web site www.somerset-kentucky.com
Published: Tues, Wed, Thur, Fri, Sat, Sun
Weekday Frequency: m
Circulation: 9,741; 9,741(sat); 9,914(sun)
Last Audit: March 31, 2007
Price: 7.50/mo (carrier); 90.00/yr (home delivery).
Advertising: Open inch rate $14.77
News services: AP, NEA.
Politics: Independent.
Not Published: Christmas.
Special Editions: Baby Week (Apr); High School Football (Aug); Christmas Songbook (Dec); Winter Clearance (Feb); Chamber Annual Report (Jan); Back-to-School (Jul); Summer Clearance (Jun); Agriculture Week (Mar); Grads (May); Regional Basketball Preview (Nov); Professional
Special Weekly Sections: Business (S); Best Food Days (Wed).
Magazines: Relish (Monthly); Parade (S).
Pub.......................................Jack McNeely
Bus. Mgr................................Shannon King
Adv. Dir................................Mike Hornback
Circ. Mgr.....................................Jim Girdler
Grp. Ed............................Ken Shmidheiser
News Ed...Jeff Neal
Sports Ed.............................Steve Cornelius
Market Information: ADS; TMC.
Mechanical available: Offset; Black and 3 ROP colors; insert accepted - half-fold, quarter-fold; page cutoffs - 22 3/4.
Mechanical Specifications: Type page 13 x 21 1/2; E - 6 cols, 2 1/16, 1/8 between; A - 6 cols, 2 1/16, 1/8 between; C - 10 cols, 1 3/16, 1/12 between.
Commodity Consumption: Avg. Page Number Per Issue - Daily 20; Avg. Page Number Per Issue - Plates Used 7020; Avg. Page Number Per Issue - Sunday 36; widths 27 1/2; Newsprint Used - Short Tons 440; Printing Ink Used - Black 24000; Printing Ink Used - Color 2600; Printing Ink Us
Equipment EDITORIAL: Front-end Software – QPS/QuarkXPress.; Editorial Hardware – APP/Mac Quadra 650, APP/Mac Quadra 610, APP/Mac Quadra 605; Editorial Printers – HP/LaserJet; Classified Hardware – Equipment □ 2-APP/Mac Quadra 605.; Layout Software – 2-APP/Mac Quadra 650.; Display Printers – 1-APP/Mac LaserWriter; Production Equipment – 2-APP/Mac Quadra 650; Cameras – 1-BKY/Omega 20x24. PRESSROOM: Line 1 – 6-G/Community SC157; Folders – 1 MAILROOM: Counter stackers – 4/MM; Inserters and stuffers – 4-/MM; Bundle tying machines – 2-Felins/Paktyer F10-F12; Addressing machine – 2-Am/1800-1900.; Business Hardware – Vision Data/486

WINCHESTER

THE WINCHESTER SUN

20 Wall St., Winchester, Ky., 40391; gen tel (859) 744-3123; adv tel (859) 355-1221; ed tel (859) 355-1222; gen fax (859) 745-0638; adv fax (859) 745-0638; ed fax (859) 745-0638; adv e-mail advertising@winchestersun.com; ed e-mail news@winchestersun.com; web site www.winchestersun.com
Group: Kentucky Press Service, Inc.
Published: Mon, Tues, Wed, Thur, Fri, Sat, Sun
Weekday Frequency: e
Saturday Frequency: m
Circulation: 7,209; 7,209(sat)
Last Audit: October 1, 2002
Price: 10.00/mo; 120.00/yr.
Advertising: Open inch rate $11.70
News services: AP.
Politics: Conservative. **Established:** 1878
Not Published: New Year; Memorial Day; Independence Day; Labor Day; Thanksgiving; Christmas.
Special Editions: Back-to-School (Aug); Holiday Greetings (Dec); Parade of Babies (Jan); Year In Review (Jul); Kids Today (Jun); Spring Home Improvement (Mar); Seniors Graduation (May); Holiday Gift Guide (Nov); Holiday Bazaars (Oct); Literacy (Sept).
Special Weekly Sections: Health & Fitness (Mon); Church (Sat); Business (Wed).
Magazines: Relish (Monthly); American Profile (Weekly).
Pub........................................Dave Eldridge
Sec...Linda Dupue
Adv. Mgr......................................Cindy Juett
Circ. Dir......................................Bob Martin
Mng. Ed..................................Randy Patrick
Sports Ed..................................Keith Taylor
Market Information: TMC; Zoned editions.
Mechanical available: Offset; Black and 3 ROP colors; insert accepted; page cutoffs - 22 3/4.
Mechanical Specifications: Type page 11 x 21 1/2; E - 6 cols, 1 11/16, 1/8 between; A - 6 cols, 1 11/16, 1/8 between; C - 8 cols, 1 3/16, 1/8 between.
Commodity Consumption: Avg. Page Number Per Issue - Daily 16; Avg. Page Number Per Issue - Plates Used 6080; widths 27; Newsprint Used - Short Tons 882; Printing Ink Used - Black 26536; Printing Ink Used - Color 8550; Printing Ink Used - Pages Printed 12159.
Equipment EDITORIAL: Front-end Software – Baseview/NewsEdit 3.2.5, QPS/QuarkXPress 3.3.; Editorial Hardware – 9-APP/Mac; Editorial Printers – Compaq CLASSIFIED: Front-end Software – Multi-Ad/CAMS.; Classified Hardware – 2-APP/Mac; Classified Printers – Okidata/Microline 321 DISPLAY: Ad make-up applications – Vision Data 6.3.; Display Printers – Epson/DFX 5000 PRODUCTION: Pagination Software – QPS/QuarkXPress.; Production Equipment – 4-APP/Mac, Uni-Setter 94E; Cameras – 1-LE; Scanners – 3-Microtek/Scanmaker IIxe PRESSROOM: Line 1 – 7, 2; Folders – 2 MAILROOM: Counter stackers – Stacker/652; Inserters and stuffers – MM, KAN/480; Bundle tying machines – 2/Bu; Addressing machine – 1-/KR, KR/1090 Inline Mailtable & Electric Head; Other equipment –2-Ap/Mac Quadra 630, Baseview/Circulation Pro 1.9.2, Ap/Mac Laser BUSINESS COMPUTERS: Business Software – Payroll: Vision Data, APGL; Business Hardware – Compaq

LOUISIANA

ABBEVILLE

ABBEVILLE MERIDIONAL

318 N. Main St., Abbeville, La., 70510; gen tel (337) 893-4223; adv tel (337) 893-4223; ed tel (337) 893-4223; gen fax (337) 898-9022; adv fax (337) 898-9022; ed fax (337) 898-9022; gen e-mail abbmerid@bellsouth.net; adv e-mail abbmerid@bellsouth.net; ed e-mail abbmerid@bellsouth.net; web site www.abbevillenow.com
Published: Tues, Wed, Thur, Fri, Sun
Weekday Frequency: m
Circulation: 5,379; 5,379(sun)
Last Audit: September 30, 2003
Price: 7.00/mo; 84.00/yr.
Advertising: Open inch rate $9.50
News services: AP, NEA.
Politics: Independent. **Established:** 1856
Special Editions: Progress (Apr); Football (Aug); Newcomer (Feb); Bridal (Jan); Back To School (Jul); Substance Abuse (Jun); Home Improvement (Mar); Graduation (May); Christmas Gift Guide (Nov); Giant Omelette Festival (Oct); Women's Tab (Sept).
Special Weekly Sections: Bridal (S).
Magazines: Parade (S).
Broadcast Affiliations: KATC (ABC); KLFY (CBS); KADN (FOX).
Mgr., Mktg./Promo....................Kathy Cormier
Circ. Mgr.................................Cindy Nicholas
Mng. Ed.....................................Justin Martin
Lifestyles Ed.................................Jeff Nemez
Market Information: TMC.
Mechanical available: Offset; Black and 3 ROP colors; insert accepted; page cutoffs - 22 7/8.
Mechanical Specifications: Type page 11 11/16 x 21 1/2; E - 6 cols, 1 4/5, 1/8 between; A - 6 cols, 1 4/5, 1/16 between; C - 9 cols, 1 3/20, 1/8 between.
Commodity Consumption: Avg. Page Number Per Issue - Daily 14; Avg. Page Number Per Issue - Plates Used 11940; Avg. Page Number Per Issue - Sunday 24; widths 25;

Newsprint Used - Short Tons 260; Printing Ink Used - Black 5915; Printing Ink Used - Color 800; Printing Ink Used -

Equipment; Editorial Hardware – Mk; Editorial Equipment – 9-COM.; Classified Hardware – Mk; Classified Equipment – 1-COM.; Layout Software – APP/Mac.; Production Equipment – 2-APP/Mac LaserWriter; Cameras – SCREEN/Companica Horizontal. PRESSROOM: Line 1 – 6-KP/News King.; Bundle tying machines – 1/Bu; Addressing machine – IBM/Sys (with printer for labeling).; Business Hardware – PC

ALEXANDRIA

THE TOWN TALK

1201 Third St., Alexandria, La., 71301; gen tel (318) 487-6397; adv tel (318) 487-6391; ed tel (318) 487-6370; gen fax (318) 487-2950; adv fax (318) 487-2985; ed fax (318) 487-6488; gen e-mail editor@thetowntalk.com; adv e-mail advertising@thetowntalk.com; ed e-mail editor@thetowntalk.com; web site www.thetowntalk.com

Group: Gannett
Published: Mon, Tues, Wed, Thur, Fri, Sat, Sun
Weekday Frequency: m
Saturday Frequency: m
Circulation: 20,883; 20,883(sat); 28,792(sun)
Last Audit: ABC September 30, 2011
Price: 15.60/mo; 187.20/yr, $20.50/mo (mail)
Advertising: Open inch rate $45.70
Insert rate: Full run card stock $59 CPM
News services: AP, SHNS, GNS.
Politics: 1883
Own facility?: Y
Special Editions: Football (Aug)
Special Weekly Sections: Weekend (Fri); Amusement Page (S); Church (Sat); Shopper's Marketplace (Wed).
Magazines: USA WEEKEND Magazine (S).
Profile: The first issue of The Town Talk was published March 17, 1883. The Town Talk has been published on a daily basis with the exception of a brief period of time when it was published as a weekly product. Started as a family-owned paper, The Town Talk was purchased by Gannett in 2001.

Pres./Pub. ....William E. Humphrey
Adv. Dir. ....William C. Heirtzler
Exec. Ed. ....Paul V. Carty
Audience Development Director..........Jim Smilie
Production Director......................Ross Doland
Asst. Managing Editor...............John Marcase
Asst. Managing Editor............Richard Sharkey
Advertising Sales Manager........Terry Broussard
Classified Sales Supervis......Harold Constance
Advertising Services Manager...Da'Shaun Baker
Controller.......................................Jim Myers
Dir., Personnel.........................Joy L. Williford
Mktg. Mgr.....................................Gina Turner
Circ. Mgr., Single Copy...............Shari Bedoya
Circ. Mgr........................................Joel Staub
Deputy Dir................................Sean McCrory
Features Ed..........................LeCrete Robinson
Multimedia Ed.......................Melissa Gregory
Sports Ed.................................Randy Benson
Dir., Information Servs..................John Choate
Prodn. Dir...............................Dorothy Sasser
Prodn. Mgr.................................Scott Neville
Market Information: TMC.
Mechanical available: Offset; Black and 3 ROP colors; insert accepted; page cutoffs - 22.
Mechanical Specifications: Type page 11 5/8 x 21; E - 6 cols, 1 13/16, 1/8 between; A - 6 cols, 1 13/16, 1/8 between; C - 9 cols, 1 13/16, 1/16 between.
Commodity Consumption: Avg. Page Number Per Issue - Daily 36; Avg. Page Number Per Issue - Plates Used 44230; Avg. Page Number Per Issue - Saturday 36; Avg. Page Number Per Issue - Sunday 60; widths 25; Newsprint Used - Metric Tons 3270; Printing Ink Used - Black 49980; Printi

Equipment EDITORIAL: Front-end Software – MS Windows; Harris; Adobe InDesign; Editorial Hardware – PCs CLASSIFIED: Front-end Software – MS Windows; Mactive; Classified Hard-

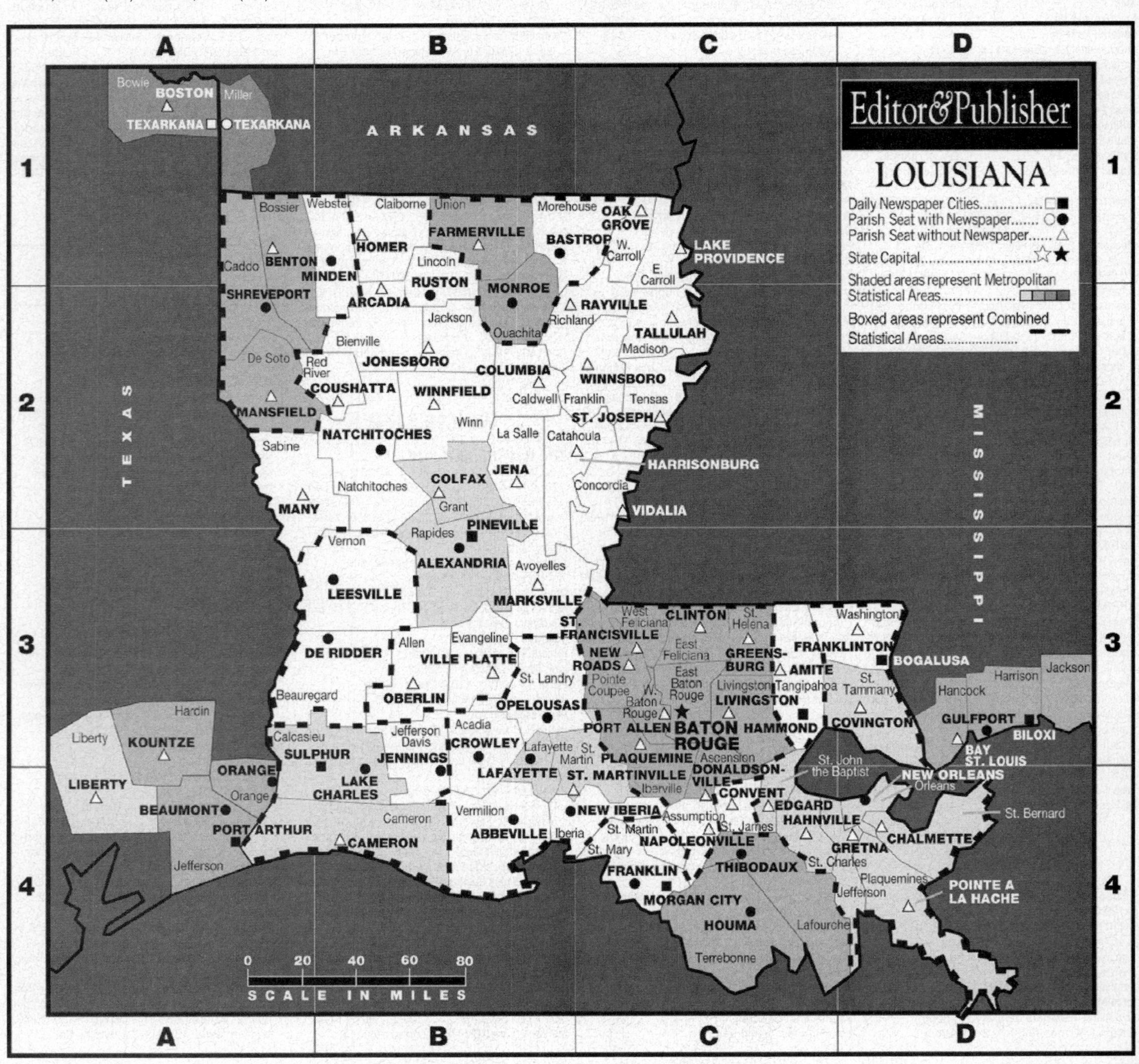

ware – PCs DISPLAY: Ad make-up applications – MS Windows; Adobe InDesign; Display Hardware – PCs; Production Equipment – 2 Agfa 3850 ImageSetters PRESSROOM: Line 1 – Manroland Uniset 70; Folders – 2-manroland 3:2; Pasters – 10 Enkel Reel Stands MAILROOM: Counter stackers – 2-QWI/501; 1-QWI/400; Inserters and stuffers – 2-SLS1000; Bundle tying machines – 4 oval strappers; Other equipment –In-Line Sticky Note Applicator BUSINESS COMPUTERS: Business Software – MS Windows; Genysis; Business Hardware – PCs
Delivery method: Mail, Newsstand, Private Carrier, Racks

BASTROP

BASTROP DAILY ENTERPRISE

119 E. Hickory St., Bastrop, La., 71220; gen tel (318) 281-4421; adv tel (318) 281-4421; ed tel (318) 281-2691; gen fax (318) 283-1699; web site www.bastropenterprise.com
Published: Tues, Wed, Thur, Fri, Sat
Weekday Frequency: m
Circulation: 4,241; 4,241(sat)
Last Audit: March 31, 2006
Price: 6.00/mo.
Advertising: Open inch rate $11.00
Politics: Independent.
Not Published: New Year; Independence Day; Labor Day; Thanksgiving; Christmas.
Special Editions: Pride (Apr); Bridal (Feb); Newcomer Guide (Jul); Graduation (May); Gift Guide (Nov); Quarterly (Oct); Gin Whistle (Sept).
Special Weekly Sections: Farm (Thur); Food (Wed).
Magazines: American Profile (Weekly).
Pub. ....Jerry Pye
Display Adv. Mgr. ....Lydia Crow
Classified Adv. Mgr. ....Melissa Moore
Circ. Mgr. ....Ricky Shaw
News Ed. ....Dee Tubbs
Sports Ed. ....Marq Mitcham
Prodn. Mgr. ....Steve Loock
Market Information: TMC.
Mechanical available: Offset; Black and 3 ROP colors; insert accepted - any; page cutoffs - 22 3/4.
Mechanical Specifications: Type page 13 x 21; E - 6 cols, 2 1/16, 1/8 between; A - 6 cols, 2 1/16, 1/8 between; C - 9 cols, 1 5/16, 1/8 between.
Commodity Consumption: Avg. Page Number Per Issue - Daily 14; Avg. Page Number Per Issue - Plates Used 4200; widths 27 1/2; Newsprint Used - Short Tons 220; Printing Ink Used - Black 6000; Printing Ink Used - Color 1000; Printing Ink Used - Pages Printed 4000.
Equipment; Editorial Hardware – Mk.; Classified Hardware – Mk.; Layout Software – APP/Mac.; Production Equipment – APP/Mac LaserWriter, 1-B; Cameras – 1-C/Model T, 1-CL. PRESSROOM: Line 1 – 5-G/Suburban.; Inserters and stuffers – 1/KR; Bundle tying machines – 2-/Bu; Addressing machine – 3-/Dispensa-Matic. BUSINESS COMPUTERS: Business Software – Word Processing; Business Hardware – 2-RSK/II-TRS-80

BASTROP NEWSPAPERS, INC.

PO Box 311, Bastrop, La., 71220; gen tel (318) 281-4421; gen fax (318) 283-1699

BATON ROUGE

THE ADVOCATE

7290 Bluebonnet Blvd., Baton Rouge, La., 70810-5494; gen tel (225) 383-1111; adv tel (225) 388-0262; ed tel (225) 383-1111; gen fax (225) 388-0348; adv fax (225) 388-0348; ed fax (225) 388-0371; adv e-mail srunnels@theadvocate.com; ed e-mail credman@theadvocate.com; web site www.theadvocate.com
Published: Mon, Tues, Wed, Thur, Fri, Sat, Sun
Weekday Frequency: m
Saturday Frequency: m
Circulation: 75,809; 82,005(sat); 102,240(sun)
Last Audit: ABC September 30, 2011
Price: 3.91/wk; 16.95/mo; 193.23/yr.
Advertising: Open inch rate $75.09
News services: AP, MCT-LAT.
Politics: Independent. **Established:** 1842
Special Weekly Sections: Wheels (Fri); Business (S); Food (Thur).; Fun (weekly entertainment tab), Fri.; Magazine (weekly arts & culture section), Sun.
Magazines: Entertainment FUN (Fri); Parade (S).
Broadcast Affiliations: WBRZ-TV Baton Rouge, LA; KRGV-TV Weslaco, TX.
Pub. ....David C. Manship
CFO ....Ralph Bender
CTO ....Richard Shurley
HR Dir. ....Candace Martin
Adv. Dir. ....Sheila Runnels
Classified Adv./Bus. Dev. Mgr. ....Art de la Torre
Mktg. Dir. ....Linda Wunstel
Mktg. Mgr. ....Charlene Robert
Circ. Dir. ....Dean Blanchard
Exec. Ed. ....Carl Redman
Mng. Ed. ....Fred Kalmbach
News Features Editor ....Greg Langley
Editorial Page Ed. ....Bill Bankston
Librarian ....Judy Jumonville
Metro Ed. ....Vicki Ferstel
Online Ed. ....Paul Walters
People Ed. ....Madelyn Lamb
Photo Dept. Mgr. ....John Ballance
Production Director ....Bret Dupre
Asst. Production Director ....Sterling Rabalais
Asst. Mng. Ed., Features ....Arthur J. Adams
Entertainment/TV Ed. ....Greg Langley
Market Information: ADS; TMC; Zoned editions.
Mechanical available: Offset; Black and 3 ROP colors; insert accepted; page cutoffs - 21.
Mechanical Specifications: Type page 11 1/8 x 20; E - 6 cols, 1 3/4, 1/8 between; A - 6 cols, 1 3/4, 1/8 between; C - 9 cols, 1 1/8, 1/8 between.
Commodity Consumption: Avg. Page Number Per Issue - Daily 57; Avg. Page Number Per Issue - Plates Used 91950; Avg. Page Number Per Issue - Saturday 60; Avg. Page Number Per Issue - Sunday 116; widths 12; Newsprint Used - Short Tons 15435; Printing Ink Used - Black 314500; Prin
Equipment EDITORIAL: Front-end Software – AT/DewarView 2.1.; Editorial Hardware – HP Clustered Servers CLASSIFIED: Front-end Software – Computext/CompuClass.; Classified Hardware – HP Clustered Servers DISPLAY: Ad make-up applications – QPS/QuarkXPress, Multi-Ad/Creator; Layout Software – MEI-ALS/Layout. PRODUCTION: Pagination Software – Dewar/Pagination 1.41.
Circulation: Atex World Class; Production Equipment – 2-Agfa Advantage DL imagers, 2-Agfa VSP 85-S processors, 1-Nela plate punch & bender PRESSROOM: Line 1 – 1-manroland Regioman; Folders – 2-G/3:2; Pasters – 8; Reels and Stands – 8; Press control system – PECOM - 3 stations MAILROOM: Counter stackers – 6-Quipp 501, 3-Schur palletizers; Inserters and stuffers – 2-GMA/SLS 3000; Bundle tying machines – 7-Dynaric/NP-2; Wrapping singles – 1-Dynaric/DFII; Other equipment –3-Accraply Post-It Note, 1-Muller Martini Bravo Plus stitcher trimmer. BUSINESS COMPUTERS: Business Software – A/R: Atex-AIM, A/P-G/L:Epicor, P/R:Sage-Abra; Business Hardware – Dell VM Servers

BOGALUSA

DAILY NEWS

525 Avenue V, Bogalusa, La., 70427; gen tel (985) 732-2565; gen fax (985) 732-4006; adv e-mail dnadvertising@edailynews.info; ed e-mail edit@edailynews.info; web site www.edailynews.info
Published: Mon, Tues, Wed, Thur, Fri, Sun
Weekday Frequency: e
Circulation: 5,195; 5,195(sun)
Last Audit: June 30, 2004
Price: 8.50/mo; 101.97/yr.
Advertising: Open inch rate $10.49
News services: AP.
Politics: Independent.
Not Published: Independence Day; Labor Day.
Special Editions: Progress (Apr); Mardi Gras (Feb); Progress (May); Parish Fair (Oct).
Special Weekly Sections: TV Focus (Fri); Best Food Days (S); Best Food Days (Wed).
Magazines: TV Update (Fri); USA WEEKEND Magazine (S).
Pub. ....John H. Walker
Adv. Dir. ....Tracy McKeithen
Adv. Mgr., Classified ....Debbie Doty
Circ. Dir. ....Amelia LeBlue
Prodn. Mgr. ....Cindy Slocum
Market Information: TMC.
Mechanical available: Offset; Black and 3 ROP colors; insert accepted; page cutoffs - 22 3/4.
Mechanical Specifications: Type page 13 x 21 1/2; E - 6 cols, 2, 1/6 between; A - 6 cols, 2, 1/6 between; C - 9 cols, between.
Commodity Consumption: Avg. Page Number Per Issue - Daily 18; Avg. Page Number Per Issue - Plates Used 7300; Avg. Page Number Per Issue - Sunday 32; widths 27; Newsprint Used - Short Tons 500; Printing Ink Used - Black 15000; Printing Ink Used - Color 600; Printing Ink Used -
Equipment; Editorial Hardware – Mk; Editorial Printers – APP/Mac LaserWriter II.; Classified Hardware – Mk; Classified Printers – APP/Mac LaserWriter II. DISPLAY: Ad make-up applications – QPS/QuarkXPress.; Display Hardware – APP/Mac IIci; Display Printers – NewGen/Turbo PS 800; Production Equipment – APP/Mac LaserWriter, APP/Mac LaserWriter II; Scanners – Microtek/Scanmaker 600Z. PRESSROOM: Line 1 – 8-WPC/Atlas 1991; Line 2 – 7-WPC/Atlas; Press Drives – Folders Â□ 1-WPC/Marc 25, 1-WPC/Atlas, 1-WPC/Gate; Reels and Stands – Press control system Â□ 2. MAILROOM: Counter stackers – 1-BG/Count-O-Veyor, 1/Mid America Graphics; Bundle tying machines – .; Business Hardware – DEC/Micro VAX

CROWLEY

THE CROWLEY POST-SIGNAL

602 N. Parkerson Ave., Crowley, La., 70526; gen tel (337) 783-3450; gen fax (337) 788-0949; gen e-mail editor.crowley@lsnweb.com; adv e-mail cpsads@bellsouth.net; ed e-mail cpsnews@bellsouth.net; web site www.crowleypostsignal.com
Published: Tues, Wed, Thur, Fri, Sun
Weekday Frequency: m
Circulation: 4,476; 4,476(sun)
Last Audit: September 29, 2002
Price: 90.00/yr; 22.50/3mo.
Advertising: Open inch rate $9.50
News services: AP, NEA.
Politics: Conservative.
Special Editions: National DARE Day (Apr); Drive Safely Page (Aug); Acadia Parish First Baby (Dec); Vo-Tech Education Week (Feb); Honor Roll (Jan); Rice Field Day (Jul); Flag Day (Jun); Home Improvement (Mar); Iota Graduation Page (May); Pharmacy Week (Nov); National 4-H W
Magazines: Parade (S).
Circ. Mgr. ....Casey Saulk
City Ed. ....Harold Gonzales
Sports Ed. ....Chris Quebedeaux
Prodn. Dept. Mgr. ....Kathy Duncan
Market Information: ADS; TMC.
Mechanical available: Offset; Black and 4 ROP colors; insert accepted; page cutoffs - 21 1/2.
Mechanical Specifications: Type page 13 x 21 1/2; E - 6 cols, 1 3/4, 1/8 between; A - 6 cols, 1 3/4, 1/8 between; C - 6 cols, 1 3/4, 1/8 between.
Commodity Consumption: Avg. Page Number Per Issue - Daily 18; Avg. Page Number Per Issue - Sunday 28; widths 25.
Equipment; Bundle tying machines – 1-Wilton/Stra Pack; Addressing machine – 2/Dispensa-Matic.

DE RIDDER

BEAUREGARD DAILY NEWS

903 W. First St., De Ridder, La., 70634; gen tel (337) 462-0616; gen fax (337) 463-5347; gen e-mail bdnews@cox-internet.com; web site www.deridderdailynews.com
Published: Tues, Wed, Thur, Fri, Sun
Weekday Frequency: m
Circulation: 13,500; 13,500(sun)
Last Audit: March 31, 2001
Price: 93.00/yr.
Advertising: Open inch rate $13.46
News services: AP, NEA.
Special Editions: Football (Aug); Bridal (Feb); Income Tax (Jan); Business Review (Jul); Christmas Carol Song Book (Nov); Holiday Cookbook (Oct); Home Improvement (Sept).
Magazines: Color Comics (S).
Pub. ....Beaux Victor
Adv. Mgr. ....Cindy Sherman
Ed. ....William Wadsack
Market Information: TMC.
Mechanical available: Web Offset; Black and 3 ROP colors; insert accepted; page cutoffs - 22 3/4.
Mechanical Specifications: Type page 13 x 21; E - 6 cols, 2 1/16, 1/8 between; A - 6 cols, 2 1/16, 1/8 between; C - 8 cols, 1 7/16, 1/8 between.
Commodity Consumption: Avg. Page Number Per Issue - Daily 18; Avg. Page Number Per Issue - Sunday 28.
Equipment; Editorial Hardware – Mk/1100 Plus, APP/Mac; Editorial Equipment – 5-Mk.; Classified Hardware – 2-Mk/Plus II; Classified Equipment – Mk.; Layout Software – 1-Mk/Ad Touch, APP/Mac.; Display Hardware – Other Equipment Ã□Â□ 1-Mk; Production Equipment – 2-APP/Mac LaserPrinter; Cameras – Portage/DPS 80, Argyle/23.

FRANKLIN

THE FRANKLIN BANNER-TRIBUNE

115 Wilson St., Franklin, La., 70538-0566; gen tel (337) 828-3706; gen fax (337) 828-2874; adv e-mail admanager@banner-tribune.com; ed e-mail editor@banner-tribune.com; web site www.banner-tribune.com
Published: Mon, Tues, Wed, Thur, Fri
Weekday Frequency: e
Circulation: 3,351
Last Audit: October 1, 2002
Price: 69.69/yr; 20.80/3mo, 37.44/6mo.
Advertising: Open inch rate $7.40
News services: AP.
Politics: Independent.
Not Published: New Year; Christmas.
Special Editions: Profile (Apr); Football (Aug); Christmas (Dec); Bridal (Jan); Drug Free (Oct).
Adv. Mgr. ....Debbie Von Werder
Adv. Mgr., Classified ....Judy Touchet
Circ. Mgr. ....Debbie Billiot
Mng. Ed. ....Vanessa Pritchett
Lifestyles Ed. ....Michelle Baker
Sports Ed. ....Anthony Mitchell
Data Processing Mgr. ....Judith Touchet
Online Mgr. ....Allan Von Werder
Market Information: TMC.
Mechanical available: Offset; Black and 3 ROP colors; insert accepted - all; page cutoffs - 22 3/4.
Mechanical Specifications: Type page 13 x 21; E - 6 cols, 2, 1/6 between; A - 6 cols, 2, 1/6 between; C - 8 cols, 1 1/2, 1/8 between.
Commodity Consumption: Avg. Page Number Per Issue - Daily 20; Avg. Page Number Per Issue - Plates Used 2400; widths 29; Newsprint Used - Metric Tons 100; Printing Ink Used - Black 2000; Printing Ink Used - Color 150; Printing Ink Used - Pages Printed 3000.

Equipment EDITORIAL: Front-end Software – COM/RTR Edit.; Editorial Hardware – COM/One Sys; Editorial Equipment – Panasonic; Editorial Printers – 2-NewGen/Turbo Laser CLASSIFIED: Front-end Software – COM/RTR Translator III.; Classified Hardware – COM/One Sys DISPLAY: Ad make-up applications – Archetype/Corel Draw.; Display Hardware – PC 486, PC 486 (with CD-Rom); Display Printers – 2-NewGen/Turbo Laser; Production Equipment – 2-NewGen/600B Laser Printer. PRESSROOM: Line 1 – 2-G/Suburban; Folders – 1 BUSINESS COMPUTERS: Business Software – In-house; Business Hardware – 2-PC 386

HAMMOND

THE DAILY STAR

725 S. Morrison Blvd., Hammond, La., 70403; gen tel (985) 254-7827; gen fax (985) 542-0242; adv fax (985) 542-5292; adv e-mail advertisingdir@hammondstar.com; ed e-mail news@hammondstar.com; editor@hammondstar.com; web site www.hammondstar.com

Published: Tues, Wed, Thur, Fri, Sat, Sun
Weekday Frequency: m
Circulation: 9,595; 9,595(sat); 11,186(sun)
Last Audit: September 30, 2008
Price: 138.32/yr; 10.64/4wk.
Advertising: Open inch rate $22.50
News services: AP.
Politics: Independent.
Not Published: New Year; Memorial Day; Independence Day; Labor Day; Thanksgiving; Christmas.
Special Editions: Strawberry Festival (Apr); Football (Aug); Basketball Tourney (Dec); Profile Progress (Feb); Medical (Jul); Kids Beat (Mar).
Special Weekly Sections: Church (Fri); Business (S); Best Food Days (Wed).
Magazines: Bon Temps (Fri); USA WEEKEND Magazine (S).
Pub. .... Keenan Gingles
Bus. Mgr. .... Joseph P. Davis
Adv. Mgr. .... Debi Manasco
Circ. Mgr. .... Willam Calcut
City Ed. .... Joan Davis
Photo Ed. .... Lillian K. Mirando
Sports Ed. .... John Lenz
Prodn. Mgr. .... Art Graziano
Market Information: TMC.
Mechanical available: Offset; Black and 3 ROP colors; insert accepted; page cutoffs - 22 3/4.
Mechanical Specifications: Type page 13 x 21 1/2; E - 6 cols, 2, 1/6 between; A - 6 cols, 2, 1/6 between; C - 9 cols, 1 2/5, 1/8 between.
Commodity Consumption: Avg. Page Number Per Issue - Daily 18; Avg. Page Number Per Issue - Plates Used 36000; Avg. Page Number Per Issue - Sunday 38; widths 27 1/2; Newsprint Used - Metric Tons 1536; Printing Ink Used - Black 29364; Printing Ink Used - Color 3360; Printing Ink
Equipment EDITORIAL: Front-end Software – Baseview, QPS/QuarkXPress.; Editorial Hardware – APP/Mac; Editorial Equipment – HP/ScanJet 2C, CD-Rom; Editorial Printers – 2-Compaq/PageMarq 20 CLASSIFIED: Front-end Software – Baseview/Class Manager.; Classified Hardware – APP/Mac; Classified Printers – Okidata, APP/Mac LaserWriter DISPLAY: Ad make-up applications – Broderbund/Typestyler 2.0, Multi-Ad/Creator, QPS/QuarkXPress, Aldus/FreeHand; Layout Software – APP/Mac 4400, APP/Mac Quadra 650, APP/Powe; Display Hardware – APP/Mac; Display Printers – 2-Compaq/Page Marq 20 PRODUCTION: Pagination Software – QPS/QuarkXPress 3.31.; Production Equipment – MON/1270 Imagesetter, Douthitt/3040; Cameras – Acti/Horizontal, AG/Rapiline 17; Scanners – HP/ScanJet 2C PRESSROOM: Line 1 – 7-G/Urbanite, 1-G/Urbanite (color unit) 1983; Folders – 1-G/2:1. MAILROOM: Counter stackers – 1-BG/Count-O-Veyor, HH/3017S; Bundle tying machines – 1-MLN/Strapper, 1-MLN/Strapper; Other equipment –Ideal/Shrink wrapper & Tunnel. BUSINESS COMPUTERS: Business Software – Microsoft/Windows, Microsoft/Excel, Microsoft/Word; Business Hardware – Microsoft/Windows NT

HOUMA

THE COURIER

3030 Barrow St., Houma, La., 70360; gen tel (985) 850-1100; adv tel (985) 857-2270; ed tel (985) 857-2200; gen fax (985) 850-1116; adv fax (985) 857-2229; ed fax (985) 857-2244; ed e-mail news@houmatoday.com; web site www.houmatoday.com

Published: Mon, Tues, Wed, Thur, Fri, Sat, Sun
Weekday Frequency: e
Saturday Frequency: e
Circulation: 12,324; 20,887(sat); 16,094(sun)
Last Audit: ABC September 30, 2011
Price: 3.12/wk; 13.50/mo; 162.00/yr.
News services: AP, NYT.
Politics: 1878
Own facility?: Y
Special Editions: Bayou Gourmet Cookbook (Apr); Football Tab (Aug); Christmas Greetings (Dec); Mardi Gras Tab (Feb); Tax Guide (Jan); Graduation (May); Bridal (Oct); Oil & Industry (Sept).
Special Weekly Sections: Big Fun on the Bayou (Fri); Health & Fitness (Mon); Louisiana Style (S); Outdoors (Thur); Home & Family (Tues); Bon Appetit (Wed).
Magazines: Big Fun on the BAYOU (Fri); Parade (S).
Publisher .... H. Miles Forrest
Controller .... Darlene Rodrigue
Inside Sales / Class Manager .... Marian Long
Advertising Director .... Robin Conerly
Executive Editor .... Keith Magill
City Editor .... Dee Dee Thurston
Lifestyles Editor .... Shane Thibodeaux
Sports Editor .... Brent St. Germain
Operations Manager .... Mark Gray
Packaging / Circulation Manager Lawrence Knoblock
Market Information: ADS; TMC.
Mechanical available: Offset; Black and 3 ROP colors; insert accepted - zoned inserts; page cutoffs - 22.
Mechanical Specifications: Type page 11 x 22; E - 6 cols, 1.708, 11 pts. between; A - 6 cols, 1.708, 11 pts. between; C - 9 cols, 1.126, 11 pts. between.
Commodity Consumption: Avg. Page Number Per Issue - Daily 26; Avg. Page Number Per Issue - Plates Used 45000; Avg. Page Number Per Issue - Sunday 60; widths 24.0; Newsprint Used - Short Tons 3000; Printing Ink Used - Black 48000; Printing Ink Used - Color 7800; Printing Ink
Equipment EDITORIAL: Front-end Software – ATS; Editorial Equipment – PC's; Editorial Printers – Xerox CLASSIFIED: Front-end Software – ATS; Classified Hardware – IBM Compatable; Classified Equipment – PC's DISPLAY: Ad make-up applications – Xpance; SalesForce; Display Hardware – 6-APP/Mac; Display Printers – Xerox 325 copier / printer PRODUCTION: Pagination Software – Presstelligence; Production Equipment – 2 Agfa Advantage X PRESSROOM: Line 1 – DGM 440 44 page with 28 pages of Color (7 towers 4 mono units); Press Drives – Rex Roth; Folders – DGM 440 & Goss SSC; Pasters – Martin ; Reels and Stands – Martin; Press control system – DGM with Perretta ink controls; Press registration system – Quad Tec MAILROOM: Counter stackers – 3-Id/660; Inserters and stuffers – GMA/SLS 1000; Bundle tying machines – 1/Bu, 2-MLN/2; Addressing machine – 2-/El, KR/211; Other equipment –MLN/Stitcher-Trimmer.
Delivery method: Mail, Newsstand, Private Carrier, Racks

JENNINGS

JENNINGS DAILY NEWS

238 Market St., Jennings, La., 70546; gen tel (337) 824-3011; gen fax (337) 824-3019; gen e-mail jdnpublisher@bellsouth.net; adv e-mail jdnadvertising@bellsouth.net; ed e-mail jdneditor@bellsouth.net; web site www.jenningsdailynews.net

Published: Tues, Wed, Thur, Fri, Sun
Weekday Frequency: e
Circulation: 4,816; 4,816(sun)
Last Audit: September 30, 2003
Price: 7.50/mo; 90.00/yr.
Advertising: Open inch rate $15.30
News services: AP.
Politics: Independent. **Established:** 1896
Advertising not accepted: 900 numbers.
Special Editions: Pride in Business (Apr); Football (Aug); Home Buyer's Guide (Every other month); Business Focus (Feb); Income Tax (Jan); Rice Harvest (Jul); Pride in Business (Jun); Spring Lawn & Garden (Mar); Pride in Business (May); Drug Awareness (Nov); Christmas Head
Magazines: Market Street Trader (Wed).
Pub. .... Dona H. Smith
Adv. Dir. .... Christine Touchet
Circ. Mgr. .... Sandra Miller
News/Family/Living Ed. .... Rebecca Chaisson
Prodn. Foreman, Pressroom .. Wilfred Broussard
Market Information: TMC.
Mechanical available: Offset; Black and 3 ROP colors; insert accepted - all; page cutoffs - 21 1/2.
Mechanical Specifications: Type page 13 x 21 1/2; E - 6 cols, 2 1/16, 1/8 between; A - 6 cols, 2 1/16, 1/8 between; C - 8 cols, 1 1/2, 1/8 between.
Commodity Consumption: Avg. Page Number Per Issue - Daily 12; Avg. Page Number Per Issue - Plates Used 2500; Avg. Page Number Per Issue - Sunday 18; widths 27; Newsprint Used - Short Tons 300; Printing Ink Used - Black 7000; Printing Ink Used - Color 750; Printing Ink Used - P
Equipment EDITORIAL: Front-end Software – QPS/QuarkXPress 4.0, Adobe/InDesign.; Editorial Hardware – APP/Mac G4; Editorial Equipment – Minolta/Quick Scan Negative Scanner, Abaton/Flatbed Scanner; Editorial Printers – HP/5100 Series CLASSIFIED: Front-end Software – Baseview/Class Manager.; Classified Hardware – APP/Mac G4; Classified Printers – HP/5100 Series, Okidata/Microline 320 Turbo; Layout Software – APP/Mac G4.; Display Hardware – Printers □ HP/5100 Series; Display Printers – Software □ Adobe/PageMaker 6.5, Adobe/InDesign, Quark 4.0; Production Equipment – 1-Nu/Flip Top FT40, APP/Mac Pro Edit 600; Cameras – Scanners □ Minolta/Negative scanner. PRESSROOM: Line 1 – 4-HI/Cotrell V-15A.; Addressing machine – IBM/486.

NEWSPAPER SERVICE CO., INC.

238 Market St., Jennings, La., 70546; gen tel (337) 824-3011; gen fax (337) 824-3019

LAFAYETTE

THE DAILY ADVERTISER

1100 Bertrand Dr., Lafayette, La., 70506; gen tel (337) 289-6300; adv tel (337) 289-6300; ed tel (337) 289-6397; gen fax (337) 289-6443; adv fax (337) 289-6466; ed fax (337) 289-6443; adv e-mail advertise@theadvertiser.com; ed e-mail editorial@theadvertiser.com; web site www.theadvertiser.com

Published: Mon, Tues, Wed, Thur, Fri, Sat
Weekday Frequency: m
Saturday Frequency: m
Circulation: 29,374; 29,374(sat); 42,829(sun)
Last Audit: ABC September 30, 2011
Price: 11.75/mo, $8.25/mo (wknd); 141.00/yr.
Advertising: Open inch rate $81.62
News services: AP, NYT, GNS.
Special Editions: Homes by Design (Apr); Back-to-School/Fall Fashion (Aug); Launching a New Millenium (Dec); Mardi Gras Tab (Feb); Technology for the Millennium (Jul); 3rd Annual Cookbook (Jun); Bridal/Spring Fashion (Mar); Acadiana Yearbook (May); Holiday Giver's Guide (N
Special Weekly Sections: Wheels (S); TV Week (Sat); Church Page (Weekly).
Magazines: USA WEEKEND Magazine (S).
Pres./Pub. .... Leslie J. Hurst
Dir., Mktg .... Blake Spivak
Circ. Dir. .... Robert Binkley
Exec. Ed. .... Denise Richter
Photography Ed. .... Peter Piazza
Prodn. Dir. .... Ross Doland
Market Information: ADS; TMC; Zoned editions.
Mechanical available: Offset; Black and 3 ROP colors; insert accepted - any; page cutoffs - 21 1/2.
Mechanical Specifications: Type page 11 1/2 x 20 1/2; E - 6 cols, 1 3/4, between; A - 6 cols, 1 5/6, between; C - 9 cols, 1 3/16, between.
Commodity Consumption: Avg. Page Number Per Issue - Daily 40; Avg. Page Number Per Issue - Plates Used 57600; Avg. Page Number Per Issue - Saturday 48; Avg. Page Number Per Issue - Sunday 104; widths 25; Newsprint Used - Short Tons 57600; Printing Ink Used - Black 89600.
Equipment EDITORIAL: Front-end Software – QPS/QuarkXPress 3.32, Baseview/NewsEdit Pro IQUE.; Editorial Hardware – APP/Mac; Editorial Printers – HP/LaserJet 5si/MX, Postscript, HP/DeskJet 750C Plus, V/3000-5300B, Pre Press/Panther Pro 46HS, 2-Konica/Jetsetter 6200 CLASSIFIED: Front-end Software – Baseview/Ad Manager Pro 2.0.6.; Classified Hardware – APP/Mac; Classified Printers – HP/Laser Jet 8100N DISPLAY: Ad make-up applications – QPS/QuarkXPress 4, Adobe/Photoshop 5.5, Adobe/Illustrator 8; Layout Software – APP/Mac.; Display Hardware – APP/Mac G4; Display Printers – HP/LaserJet 5si/MX, Postscript PRODUCTION: Pagination Software – QPS/QuarkXPress 4.11, Baseview/Drag X.; Production Equipment – Caere/OmniPage, LE/220-QT, 2-Colenta/Online Processors, 2-Glunz & Jensen; Cameras – COM/680C; Scanners – Kk/RFS 2035, 3-Nikon/Super Coolscan PRESSROOM: Line 1 – MAN/Roland uriset 70 32 couples 1999; Folders – G/U 1320; Pasters – 8-Cary/Pasters, 10; Press registration system – Duarte/Pin System. MAILROOM: Counter stackers – 4/Compass 180; Inserters and stuffers – GMA/SLS 1000; Bundle tying machines – 4-/Samuel; Wrapping singles – Id; Mailroom control system – GMA; Addressing machine – KAN; Other equipment –MM. BUSINESS COMPUTERS: Business Software – Unix; Business Hardware – PBS

LAKE CHARLES

AMERICAN PRESS

4900 Hwy. 90 E., Lake Charles, La., 70615; gen tel (337) 433-3000; adv tel (337) 494-4047; ed tel (337) 494-4072; gen fax (337) 494-4008; adv fax (337) 494-4008; ed fax (337) 494-4070; gen e-mail news@americanpress.com; adv e-mail cperkins@americanpress.com; web site www.americanpress.com

Published: Mon, Tues, Wed, Thur, Fri, Sat, Sun
Weekday Frequency: m
Saturday Frequency: m
Circulation: 30,439; 30,439(sat); 36,589(sun)
Last Audit: ABC September 30, 2011
Price: 10.50/mo; 121.00/yr.
Advertising: Open inch rate $35.30
News services: AP.
Politics: Independent.
Special Editions: Home Improvement (Apr); Back-to-School (Aug); Brides (Feb); Mardi Gras (Jan); Contraband Days (May); Christmas Gift Guide (Nov); Football (Sept).
Special Weekly Sections: Marquee (Fri); Face to Face (Mon); Face to Face (Tues).
Magazines: Parade (S); Focus (Sat).
Pub. .... Thomas B. Shearman
Bus. Mgr. .... Anita Tinsley
Classified Adv. Mgr. .... Connie Perkins
Adv. Mgr., Retail/Nat'l .... Gen Ducas

Ed. ....Brett Dower
Mng. Ed...............................Bobby Dower
Entertainment Ed...............................Gail Norris
Living Ed. ....Pamela Seal
Sports Ed...............................Scooter Hobbs
Webmaster ....Roger Demary
Prodn. Mgr., Distr. Ctr...............................Linda Walker
Prodn. Mgr., Computer..............................Gary Fletcher
Prodn. Foreman, Pressroom..........G.J. Johnson
Market Information: TMC.
Mechanical available: Offset; Black and 3 ROP colors; insert accepted; page cutoffs - 22 3/4.
Mechanical Specifications: Type page 13 x 22; E - 6 cols, 2 1/16, 1/8 between; A - 6 cols, 2 1/16, 1/8 between; C - 10 cols, 1 1/6, 1/6 between.
Commodity Consumption: Avg. Page Number Per Issue - Daily 39; Avg. Page Number Per Issue - Plates Used 24000; Avg. Page Number Per Issue - Sunday 60; widths 55; Newsprint Used - Short Tons 3409; Printing Ink Used - Black 43080; Printing Ink Used - Color 28644; Printing Ink Use
Equipment EDITORIAL: Front-end Software – SII, QPS/QuarkXPress.; Editorial Hardware – Tandem, APP/Mac CLASSIFIED: Front-end Software – Baseview.; Classified Hardware – APP/Mac; Layout Software – Baseview/Ad Manager Pro.; Display Hardware – APP/Mac; Display Printers – Software Baseview/Ad Manager Pro PRODUCTION: Pagination Software – QPS/QuarkXPress.; Production Equipment – V, Sharp/600; Cameras – C/Spartan III; Scanners – HP, APP/Mac, Sharp, Lf/Leafscan 35 PRESSROOM: Line 1 – 8-HI/1660 1982; Pasters – 7-MEG/2-ARM 1982. MAILROOM: Counter stackers – 3-QWI/300; Inserters and stuffers – 2-S/72P; Bundle tying machines – 3/Dynaric; Addressing machine – 1-/Ch; Other equipment –QWI Conveyor System. BUSINESS COMPUTERS: Business Software – CJ, Baseview, Great Plains Dynamics; Business Hardware – Gateway, APP/Mac

LEESVILLE

THE LEESVILLE DAILY LEADER

206 E. Texas St., Leesville, La., 71446; gen tel (337) 239-3444; gen fax (337) 238-1152; gen e-mail ldleader@cebridge.net; web site www.leesvilledailyleader.com
Published: Tues, Wed, Thur, Fri, Sun
Weekday Frequency: m
Circulation: 3,794; 3,794(sun)
Last Audit: September 28, 2001
Price: 93.00/yr.
Advertising: Open inch rate $13.46
News services: AP.
Special Editions: Secretaries Week (Apr); Real Estate Page (Aug); Christmas Gift Guide & Santa's Letters (Dec); Valentine's Special (Feb); Dollar Days (Jan); Car Care (Jul); Travel Guide (Jun); Business Card (Mar); Arts & Crafts (May); Thanksgiving Specials (Nov); Columbus
Display Adv...............................Teresa Laurie
Circ. Dir. ....Destiny Jefferson
Ed...............................Brian Trahan
Sports Ed. ....Daniel Green
Market Information: TMC.
Mechanical available: Offset; Black and 3 ROP colors; insert accepted; page cutoffs - 22 3/4.
Mechanical Specifications: Type page 12 1/2 x 21; E - 6 cols, 2 1/16, 1/8 between; A - 6 cols, 2 1/16, 1/8 between; C - 8 cols, 1 1/2, 1/8 between.
Commodity Consumption: Avg. Page Number Per Issue - Daily 16; Avg. Page Number Per Issue - Plates Used 9000; Avg. Page Number Per Issue - Sunday 20; widths 27 1/2; Newsprint Used - Short Tons 900; Printing Ink Used - Black 71000; Printing Ink Used - Color 1000.
Equipment; Editorial Hardware – 5-Mk.; Classified Hardware – 2-Mk.; Layout Software – APP/Mac. PRODUCTION: Pagination Software – APP/Mac.; Production Equipment – HP PRESSROOM: Line 1 – 3-WL/Color Quad; Line 2 – 5-WL/Regular.

MINDEN

MINDEN PRESS-HERALD

203 Gleason St., Minden, La., 71055; gen tel (318) 377-1866; gen fax (318) 377-1895; gen e-mail jbeavers@press-herald.com; web site www.nwlanews.com
Published: Mon, Tues, Wed, Thur, Fri
Weekday Frequency: e
Circulation: 5,003
Last Audit: September 27, 2001
Price: 8.00/mo; 96.00/yr.
Advertising: Open inch rate $8.50
News services: AP.
Politics: Independent.
Special Editions: Car Care (Fall); Car Care (Spring).
Magazines: American Profile (Weekly).
Pres./Gen. Mgr...............................Nila Johnson
Circ. Dir...............................Shwana Willis
Art Dir...............................Shelly Moesch
Sports Ed. ....Gregg Parks
Online Mgr...............................Josh Beavers
Prodn. Dir. ....Dennis Philebar
Karin Kirkley
Market Information: TMC.
Mechanical available: Offset; Black and 3 ROP colors; insert accepted; page cutoffs - 21.
Mechanical Specifications: Type page 13 1/16 x 21; E - 6 cols, 2 1/16, 1/8 between; A - 6 cols, 2 1/16, 1/8 between; C - 9 cols, 1 3/8, 1/8 between.
Commodity Consumption: Avg. Page Number Per Issue - Daily 16; Avg. Page Number Per Issue - Plates Used 6500; widths 27 1/2; Newsprint Used - Short Tons 450; Printing Ink Used - Black 17000; Printing Ink Used - Color 5200; Printing Ink Used - Pages Printed 6200.
Equipment EDITORIAL: Front-end Software – QPS 3.3.; Editorial Hardware – APP/Mac; Editorial Printers – HP/4MV CLASSIFIED: Front-end Software – BMF.; Classified Hardware – PC; Display Hardware – APP/Mac.; Production Equipment – 1-Nu/Flip Top; Cameras – 1-Argyle/23-G23. PRESSROOM: Line 1 – 6-WPC/Leader; Folders – 1; Bundle tying machines – 1-Felins/Pack Tyer; Addressing machine – Wm.; Business Hardware – IBM/Sys 36 PC LINV

MONROE

THE NEWS-STAR

411 N. Fourth St., Monroe, La., 71210-1502; gen tel (318) 322-5161; adv tel (318) 362-0200; ed tel (318) 362-0261; gen fax (318) 362-0311; adv fax (318) 362-0225; ed fax (318) 362-0273; gen e-mail dpetty@monroe.gannett.com; web site www.thenewsstar.com
Published: Mon, Tues, Wed, Thur, Fri, Sat, Sun
Weekday Frequency: m
Saturday Frequency: m
Circulation: 24,227; 21,882(sat); 28,516(sun)
Last Audit: ABC September 30, 2011
Price: 14.35/mo; 172.20/yr (carrier), $185.40/yr (mail).
Advertising: Open inch rate $97.39
News services: AP, GNS, MCT, LAT-WP.
Politics: Independent.
Special Weekly Sections: Auto (Fri); Travel (S); Best Food Edition (Wed).
Magazines: This Week (Fri); USA WEEKEND Magazine (S).
Pres./Pub. ....David B. Petty
Adv. Dir...............................Brad Lackey
Gen. Sales Mgr. ....Debbie Coplen
Mng. Ed. ....Ken Stickney
Asst. Mng. Ed., Local..............Eleanor Rushing
Asst. Mng. Ed., Online/Sports...........Nick Delso
Accent Ed. ....Hope Young
Multimedia Ed...............................Fred Phillips
News Ed...............................Mark Henderson
Photography Ed...............................Margaret Croft
Prodn. Dir...............................Doug Nobles
Market Information: ADS; TMC; Zoned editions.
Mechanical available: Letterpress; Black and 3 ROP colors; insert accepted; page cutoffs - 22 1/2.
Mechanical Specifications: Type page 13 1/12 x 22 1/2; E - 6 cols, 2, 1/6 between; A - 6 cols, 2, 1/6 between; C - 9 cols, 1 7/18, 1/2 between.
Commodity Consumption: Avg. Page Number Per Issue - Daily 32; Avg. Page Number Per Issue - Plates Used 55200; Avg. Page Number Per Issue - Sunday 72; widths 27; Newsprint Used - Short Tons 3375; Printing Ink Used - Black 68000; Printing Ink Used - Color 9800; Printing Ink Used
Equipment EDITORIAL: Front-end Software – APT.; Editorial Hardware – PC; Editorial Equipment – 42-PC, 6-APP/Mac; Editorial Printers – 1-AU/LZR-1200 Laser Printer, 1-HP/LaserJet 8000 CLASSIFIED: Front-end Software – APT.; Classified Hardware – PC; Classified Equipment – 14-PC; Classified Printers – HP/LaserJet 8000; Layout Software – COM.; Display Hardware – 2-APP/Mac Quadra 840 AV, 2-APP/Mac Quadra 610, 1-APP/Mac Quadra 950 fileserver; Display Printers – AU/APS-6-84-ACS, AU/APS-1560 LaserPrinter PRODUCTION: Pagination Software – QPS/QuarkXPress 4.03, QPS/QuarkXPress 3.32.; Production Equipment – AU/3850 Sierra with LE Processor, 2-LE/APS-36, 2-P/EL26, 1-C/P66F; Cameras – 1-C/Spartan III, 1-C/Newspager; Scanners – 1-ECR/Autokon PRESSROOM: Line 1 – 8-G/Mark I Letterpress 2138 Double Width (3 half-deck); Folders – 1-G/Double; Press control system – 8-Fin/3122 60hp DC drives; Press registration system – WL/Magnetic Saddles. MAILROOM: Counter stackers – 2-HL/HT, 1-Id/NS440; Inserters and stuffers – 1-HI/NP 624; Bundle tying machines – MLN; Wrapping singles – Id. BUSINESS COMPUTERS: Business Software – IBM/AS-400 F10; Business Hardware – IBM/AS-400 F10

MORGAN CITY

THE DAILY REVIEW

1014 Front St., Morgan City, La., 70380; gen tel (985) 384-8370; adv tel (985) 384-8370; ed tel (985) 384-8370; gen fax (985) 384-4255; adv fax (985) 384-4255; ed fax (985) 384-4255; adv e-mail advertising@daily-review.com; ed e-mail news@daily-review.com; web site www.daily-review.com
Published: Mon, Tues, Wed, Thur, Fri
Weekday Frequency: e
Circulation: 5,946
Last Audit: September 30, 2002
Price: 54.00/yr (local), $103.00/yr (mail).
Advertising: Open inch rate $8.12
News services: AP.
Politics: Independent.
Not Published: New Year; Christmas.
Special Editions: Progress (Apr); Energy Coastal (Dec); Chamber of Commerce (Jan); Dixie Youth-Little League Baseball (Jul); Drug Free Tab (Oct); Shrimp & Petroleum Festival-Oil/Seafood (Sept).
Special Weekly Sections: Real Estate (Fri).
Assoc. Pub./Gen. Mgr...................Andy Shirley
Adv. Mgr. ....Charles Lejeune
Mng. Ed...............................Ted McManus
News Ed...............................Steve Shirley
Sports Ed...............................Jon Martin
Online Mgr...............................Jack Rankin
Prodn. Mgr...............................Carol LeBlanc
Market Information: TMC.
Mechanical available: Offset; Black and 3 ROP colors; insert accepted - 8 1/2 x 11 card or single sheet; page cutoffs - 22 15/16.
Mechanical Specifications: Type page 13 x 21 1/2; E - 6 cols, 2 1/16, 1/8 between; A - 6 cols, 2 1/16, 1/8 between; C - 8 cols, 1 1/2, 1/8 between.
Commodity Consumption: Avg. Page Number Per Issue - Daily 16; Avg. Page Number Per Issue - Plates Used 3000; widths 28; Newsprint Used - Short Tons 450; Printing Ink Used - Black 1120; Printing Ink Used - Color 40; Printing Ink Used - Pages Printed 4980.
Equipment EDITORIAL: Front-end Software – APT/ACT.; Editorial Hardware – Microsoft/Windows NT 4; Editorial Equipment – Xante; Editorial Printers – NewGen/Laser PS 840E, Dupont, ECR/Knock Out Imagesetter CLASSIFIED: Front-end Software – APT/ACT.; Classified Hardware – Microsoft/Windows NT 4; Classified Printers – NewGen/Laser PS-840E, Dupont, ECR/Knock Imagesetter; Display Hardware – Other ÃÂÃÂ 2-Gateway/Pentium 2, APT.; Production Equipment – 3-Nu, 2-NewGen/Turbo PS-840E; Cameras – Acti/Tech; Scanners – Panasonic, Microtek. PRESSROOM: Line 1 – 12-G; Folders – 1, 1-G/Urbanite.; Business Hardware – DEC

NATCHITOCHES

NATCHITOCHES TIMES

904 Hwy. 1 S., Natchitoches, La., 71457; gen tel (318) 352-5501; gen fax (318) 352-7842; gen e-mail nattimes@wnonline.net; adv e-mail advertising@natchitochestimes.com; ed e-mail news@natchitochestimes.com; web site www.natchitochestimes.com
Published: Tues, Wed, Thur, Fri, Sat
Weekday Frequency: m
Circulation: 4,805; 4,805(sat)
Last Audit: September 26, 2001
Price: 6.50/mo; 65.00/yr.
Advertising: Open inch rate $9.75
News services: AP.
Politics: 1903
Not Published: Christmas Day.
Special Editions: Bridal (Jun).
Pres./Pub. ....Lovan Thomas
Mgr., Mktg./Promo. ....Steve Clowell
Circ. Mgr. ....Jerry Hooper
Ed...............................Carolyn Roy
Prodn. Mgr...............................Ernie Davis
Systems Mgr. ....Dennis Doll
Market Information: ADS; TMC.
Mechanical available: Offset; Black and ROP colors; insert accepted - Sticky notes; page cutoffs - 22 3/4.
Mechanical Specifications: Type page 13 x 21; A - 6 cols, 2, between.
Commodity Consumption: Avg. Page Number Per Issue - Daily 18; widths 27 1/2; Printing Ink Used - Pages Printed 23400.
Equipment EDITORIAL: Front-end Software – QPS/QuarkXPress.; Editorial Hardware – APP/Power Mac, Linotype-Hell/Linotron 190; Editorial Printers – APP/Mac LaserWriter 810 CLASSIFIED: Front-end Software – Multi-Ad.; Production Equipment – Linotype-Hell/Linotron 190. PRESSROOM: Line 1 – 10-G.

NEW IBERIA

THE DAILY IBERIAN

926 E. Main St., New Iberia, La., 70560; gen tel (337) 365-6773; adv tel (337) 365-6773; ed tel (337) 365-6773; gen fax (337) 367-9640; adv fax (337) 367-9640; ed fax (337) 367-9640; gen e-mail dailyiberian@bellsouth.net; adv e-mail iberianads@bellsouth.net; ed e-mail dailyiberian@bellsouth.net; web site www.iberianet.com
Published: Mon, Tues, Wed, Thur, Fri, Sun
Weekday Frequency: e
Circulation: 11,575; 12,281(sun)
Last Audit: September 30, 2011
Price: 8.50/mo; 102.00/yr (carrier), $143.52/yr (mail).
Advertising: Open inch rate $18.99
News services: AP.
Politics: Independent.
Not Published: New Year; Christmas.
Special Editions: HS Graduation (Apr); Estate Planning (Aug); Gift Guide (Dec); Newcomer's Guide (Feb); Bridal (Jan); Focus on Women (Jul); Father's Day (Jun); Home & Garden (Mar); Mother's Day (May); Gift

Guide (Nov); Farm (Oct); Cookbook (Sept).
Special Weekly Sections: Church Page (Fri); Business (S); Business News (Thur); Health News (Tues); Food (Wed).
Magazines: TV Listings (Fri); USA WEEKEND Magazine (S).
Bus. Mgr...............................Amanda Seneca
Adv. Mgr...Alan Rini
Circ. Dir.....................................John Poirier
Ed....Jeff Zeringue
City Ed..................................Stephen Hemelt
Living/Lifestyle Ed.............................Bill Smith
Sr. News. Ed./Outdoor Ed..........Don Shoopman
Photo Ed....Lee Ball
Sports Ed..................................Chris Landry
Audiotex Mgr............................Will Chapman
Prodn. Mgr................................Jerry Sexton
Prodn. Mgr., Mailroom.................Sherry Jeske
Market Information: ADS; TMC; Zoned editions.
Mechanical available: Offset; Black and 3 ROP colors; insert accepted; page cutoffs - 22 3/4.
Mechanical Specifications: Type page 11 5/8 x 21 1/2; E - 6 cols, 1 3/4, 3/16 between; A - 6 cols, 1 3/4, 3/16 between; C - 9 cols, 1 5/16, between.
Commodity Consumption: Avg. Page Number Per Issue - Daily 20; Avg. Page Number Per Issue - Plates Used 5276; Avg. Page Number Per Issue - Sunday 36; widths 22 3/4; Newsprint Used - Short Tons 864; Printing Ink Used - Black 17740; Printing Ink Used - Color 1000; Printing Ink Us
Equipment EDITORIAL: Front-end Software – AppleShare 6.3, QPS/QuarkXPress 4.01, Microsoft/Word 6.0.; Editorial Hardware – APP/Mac, APP/Mac G4; Editorial Equipment – 2-Nikon/Scanner, 2-AG/Flat Bed Scanner; Editorial Printers – Xante/8300-1200 DPI, ECR/8600 Imagesetter CLASSIFIED: Front-end Software – Baseview.; Classified Hardware – Baseview, 1-APP/Mac G3, 2-APP/Power Mac; Classified Equipment – APP/Mac LaserWriter NTF; Classified Printers – Xante/Accel-A-Writer 8200, Okidata/Pacemark 3410 DISPLAY: Ad make-up applications – Aldus/PageMaker 5.0, Multi-Ad/Creator 4.0, Lotus, QPS/QuarkXPress 4.04, Adobe/Photoshop 3.0, Adobe/Photoshop 4.0; Display Hardware – APP/Mac G4, 3-APP/Mac G3 300, Motorola/3000-200; Display Printers – APP/Mac, Xante/8300 PRODUCTION: Pagination Software – QPS/QuarkXPress 4.04.; Production Equipment – Caere/OmniPage 2.1, APP/Mac LaserWriter NT, APP/Mac LaserWriter NTX, APP/Mac LaserWriter, WDS, APP/Mac Asante, 2-Xante/8300, 1-ECR/Imagesetter; Cameras – Acti/183; Scanners – APP/Mac Scanner PRESSROOM: Line 1 – 5-G/Urbanite; Press Drives – 1; Folders – G/Urbanite U521. MAILROOM: Counter stackers – MRS; Bundle tying machines – MLN. AUDIO: Audio Software – New Horizons Group; Audio Hardware – New Horizons Group; Business Hardware – Vision Data

WICK COMMUNICATIONS CO.

PO Box 9290, New Iberia, La., 70562-9290; gen tel (337) 365-6773; gen fax (337) 367-9640

NEW ORLEANS

THE TIMES PICAYUNE

3800 Howard Ave., New Orleans, La., 70125-1429; gen tel (504) 826-3179; adv tel (504) 826-3075; ed tel (504) 826-3300; gen fax (504) 826-3636; adv fax (504) 826-3800; ed fax (504) 826-3007; gen e-mail citydesk@timespicayune.com; letters@timespicayune.com; adv e-mail ads@timespicayune.com; ed e-mail editor@timespicayune.com; photos@timespicayune.com; web site www.nola.com; www.timespicayune.com
Published: Mon, Tues, Wed, Thur, Fri, Sat, Sun
Weekday Frequency: m
Saturday Frequency: m
Circulation: 135,716; 134,437(sat); 155,435(sun)
Last Audit: ABC September 30, 2011
Price: $13.00/mo (mS), $7.50/mo (m), $9.00/mo (S); $156.00/yr.
Advertising: Open inch rate $186.00
News services: Metro Suburbia Inc./Newhouse Newspapers.
Politics: Independent. **Established:** 1837
Special Editions: Jazz Fest-Weekend 1 (Apr); Mardi Gras Tabloid (Feb); Wedding Book (Jan); Essence Fest (Jun); Jazz Fest-Weekend 2 (May).
Special Weekly Sections: Weekend Entertainment (Fri); Travel Feature (S); Real Estate/Home Interiors Tab (Sat); Best Food Day (Thur).
Magazines: WISH (Monthly); Parade (S).
Publisher................................Ashton Phelps
Vice Pres./Gen. Mgr......................Ray Massett
Vice Pres./Bus. Mgr....................David Francis
Vice Pres., HR...............................Beth Adams
Vice Pres., Adv................................Kelly Rose
Adv. Mgr., Auto..............................Dave Usner
Adv. Mgr., Classified...................Sara Barnard
Vice Pres., Mktg........................Renee Bigelow
Vice Pres., Circ.............................Phil Ehrhardt
Ed....Jim Amoss
Mng. Ed.......................................Peter Kovacs
Mng. Ed...Dan Shea
Online Ed............................Lynn Cunningham
Bus. Ed...Kim Quillen
Vice Pres./Circ. Dir.....................Philip Ehrhardt
Vice Pres., Purchasing...........Wayne Benjamin
Adv. Asst. Dir....................Bryan Schexnayder
Adv. Mgr., Creative Servs.................Liz Gruder
Adv. Mgr., Real Estate............JoAnn Chiasson
City Ed...David Meeks
Columnist..................................Lolis Eric Elie
Market Information: Split run; TMC; Zoned editions.
Mechanical available: Offset; Black and 3 ROP colors; insert accepted - min. 3 x 5; page cutoffs - 22 1/16.
Mechanical Specifications: Type page 11 5/8 x 21; E - 6 cols, 1 3/4, 1/8 between; A - 6 cols, 1 3/4, 1/8 between; C - 10 cols, 1 1/16, 1/16 between.
Commodity Consumption: widths 49 7/8.
Equipment EDITORIAL: Front-end Software – HI.; Editorial Hardware – 6-Sun/Sparc Ultra; Editorial Printers – 20-HP/4000, 10-HP CLASSIFIED: Front-end Software – HI/Metro CASH.; Classified Hardware – 2-Intel/XLXBASE 8TE 8F Fileservers; Classified Printers – 4-Epson/DFX-5000, 3-Epson/LX810, 3-Epson/LX3000 DISPLAY: Ad make-up applications – HI/Pagination System, Sun/Conton Scanner software, APP/Mac, Deltagraph, Timer/AI-95OX; Display Hardware – Sun/Ultra, APP/Mac Quadra, Timer/AI-95OX; Display Printers – Mercury/N1000 Instant Printer, APP/Mac LaserWriter Plus, HP/LaserWriter; Production Equipment – 4-AU/APG, 5-WL, 5-WL, 7-WL; Cameras – 2-C/Newspager; Scanners – Equipment ☐ HI 2.5. PRESSROOM: Line 1 – 10-G/HO; Line 2 – 9-G/HO; Line 3 – 11-G/HO; Line 4 – 11-G/HO; Line 5 – 11-G/HO; Folders – 2-G/3:2, 6-H/3:2, 2-H/2:1; Pasters – 11-G/Static Belt, 27-H/Running Belt; Reels and Stands – 11-G/Static Belt, 27-H/Running Belt; Press control system – G/M MAILROOM: Counter stackers – 2-Rima/RS25, 3-Rima/RS3017, 14-HI/Olympian; Inserters and stuffers – 3-HI/1372R, 2-HI/1472, 1-HI/2299; Bundle tying machines – 5-Dynaric/NPI, 9-Dynaric/NP2, 9-Dynaric/DF-20, 2-OVL/415; Mailroom control system – Heidleburg/ICN 300, Icon/ BUSINESS COMPUTERS: Business Software – PDS, HITEC; Business Hardware – IBM/MP3000 H30, Novell/Network

OPELOUSAS

THE DAILY WORLD

1206 Heather Dr., Opelousas, La., 70570-2389; gen tel (337) 942-4971; adv tel (337) 942-4971; ed tel (337) 942-4971; gen fax (337) 943-7067; adv fax (337) 943-7067; ed fax (337) 943-7067; ed e-mail news@dailyworld.com; web site www.dailyworld.com
Published: Mon, Tues, Wed, Thur, Fri, Sun
Weekday Frequency: m
Circulation: 5,669; 7,060(sun)
Last Audit: ABC September 30, 2011
Price: 8.50/mo.
Advertising: Open inch rate $31.58
News services: AP.
Politics: Independent.
Not Published: Christmas.
Special Editions: Brides (Apr); Football Roundup (Aug); Progress (Feb); Woman's World (Jul); Father's Day (Jun); Home Improvement (Mar); Real Estate Magazine (Monthly); Fall Car Care (Nov); Cooking (Oct).
Special Weekly Sections: Church Page (Fri); Farm Page (Mon); Business (S); Acadiana TV Listings (Thur); Medical Page (Tues); Food Page (Wed).
Magazines: USA WEEKEND Magazine (S).
Pres./Pub...............................Leslie J. Hurst
Classified Adv. Mgr...................Allison Graham
Circ. Dir...................................Bobby Binkley
Sports Ed...................................Christy Smith
Prodn. Mgr...................................Ross Doland
Market Information: TMC; Zoned editions.
Mechanical available: Offset; Black and 3 ROP colors; insert accepted; page cutoffs - 23 1/2.
Mechanical Specifications: Type page 13 x 21 1/2; E - 6 cols, 2 1/16, 3/16 between; A - 6 cols, 2 1/16, 3/16 between; C - 9 cols, 1 3/8, 1/8 between.
Commodity Consumption: Avg. Page Number Per Issue - Daily 22; Avg. Page Number Per Issue - Plates Used 7950; Avg. Page Number Per Issue - Sunday 34; widths 27 1/2; Newsprint Used - Short Tons 750; Printing Ink Used - Black 24000; Printing Ink Used - Color 4000; Printing Ink Us
Equipment EDITORIAL: Front-end Software – Baseview 2.1.; Editorial Hardware – 2-AT/5000, IBM, APP/Power Mac; Editorial Equipment – 21-AT; Classified Hardware – 1-AT/5000; Classified Equipment – 4-AT, IBM.; Layout Software – 1-AT. PRODUCTION: Pagination Software – Baseview 2.1, QPS/QuarkXPress.; Production Equipment – Pre Press/Panther Pro, 2-Pre Press/Panther Plus, 1-Nu/52; Cameras – 1-C/Spartan II PRESSROOM: Line 1 – 8-G/Community 1993; Folders – 2 MAILROOM: Counter stackers – BG/Count-O-Veyor; Inserters and stuffers – KAN/4into1; Bundle tying machines – 1/Bu, 1-/Power Strap; Addressing machine – 1-/Ch.; Business Hardware – DPT/8200, IBM/3600, IBM/PC-Model 50, IBM/PC-Model 25

RUSTON

RUSTON DAILY LEADER

212 W. Park Ave., Ruston, La., 71270; gen tel (318) 255-4353; gen fax (318) 255-4006; gen e-mail newsroom@rustonleader.com; web site www.rustonleader.com
Group: ????
Published: Mon, Tues, Wed, Thur, Fri, Sun
Weekday Frequency: e
Circulation: 4,963; 5,438(sun)
Last Audit: Sworn October 6, 2003
Price: 12.50/mo; 138.00/yr.
Advertising: Daily Open inch rate $11.00, Sunday Rate $11.75
Insert rate: $60/M, Contract $40-50/M
News services: AP.
Politics: Independent. **Established:** 1894
Advertising not accepted: Y
Not Published: Christmas, Labor Day
Own facility?: Y
Special Editions: Living Well Magazine (Slick) Quarterly; Mother's Day Salute (Apr); Football (Aug); Pride Series (April, May June); Christmas Greetings (Dec); Financial Focus (Feb); Progress (Jan); Anniversary (Jun); Graduation (May); Christmas Gift Guide (Nov); Welcome Edition for LA Tech (Sept), Peach Festival Editions (June).
Magazines: Parade (S), Living Well (S) quarterly
Broadcast Affiliations: KIX-FM; KPCH-FM Ruston, LA.
Advertising Manager............Jeanie McCartney
Publisher...Rick Hohlt
Exec. Sports Ed...............................O.K. Davis
General Manager...........................Cody Richard
Asst. Advertising Manager..............Adam Hohlt
Editor..Laura Bond
Circulation Manager.........Caskey Schexnyder
News Editor.............................Scott Boatright
Mechanical available: Offset; Black and 3 ROP colors; insert accepted; page cutoffs - 21 1/2.
Mechanical Specifications: Type page 10.5 x 21 1/2; E - 6 cols, 1.792, 1/8 between.
Commodity Consumption: Avg. Page Number Per Issue - Daily 16; Avg. Page Number Per Issue - Sunday 24; widths 12 1/2; Newsprint Used - Metric Tons 298; Printing Ink Used - Black 1400; Printing Ink Used - Color 725; Printing Ink Used - Pages Printed 5300.
Equipment EDITORIAL: Front-end Software – InDesign; Editorial Hardware – APP/Mac CLASSIFIED: Front-end Software – Baseview/Class Manager.; Classified Hardware – APP/Mac DISPLAY: Ad make-up applications – Aldus/PageMaker; Layout Software – APP/Mac SE, APP/Mac Plus.; Display Hardware – APP/Mac; Production Equipment – 1-Nat; Cameras – 1-AG; Scanners – Abaton/Scanner. PRESSROOM: Line 1 – 7 Unit Goss Community; Folders – 1; Press registration system – CTP; Bundle tying machines – 2/Bu; Addressing machine – 1-/Am.; Business Hardware – 1-RSK/80
Zip Codes served: 71270, 71222, 71241, 71260, 71201, 71277, 71280, 71225, 71235
Delivery method: Mail, Newsstand, Private Carrier, Racks

RUSTON PUBLISHERS, INC.

212 W. Park Ave., Ruston, La., 71270; gen tel (318) 255-4353; gen fax (318) 255-4006

SHREVEPORT

THE SHREVEPORT TIMES

222 Lake St., Shreveport, La., 71130; gen tel (318) 459-3200; adv tel (318) 459-3323; ed tel (318) 459-3233; gen fax (318) 459-3301; adv fax (318) 459-3392; ed fax (318) 459-3301; web site www.shreveporttimes.com
Group: Gannett Co., Inc.
Metro Newspaper Advertising Services, Inc.
Published: Mon, Tues, Wed, Thur, Fri, Sat, Sun
Weekday Frequency: m
Saturday Frequency: m
Circulation: 38,216; 38,216(sat); 52,838(sun)
Last Audit: ABC September 30, 2011
Price: 17.98/mo; 215.76/yr.
Advertising: Open inch rate $103.00
News services: AP, GNS.
Politics: 1871
Not Published: N/A
Own facility?: Y
Special Editions: Independence Bowl (Dec); Home Products Show (Feb); Outlook (Jan); Parade of Homes (Jun); Red River Revel (Sept).
Special Weekly Sections: Preview (Entertainment) (Fri); Travel (S); Automotive (Sat); Food (Wed).
Magazines: USA WEEKEND Magazine (S).
Broadcast Affiliations: N/A
Pub...Pete Zanmiller
HR Business Partner....................Arlene Adger
Controller...................................Mary Hanisee
Adv. Mgr., Telemktg......................Jackie Jones
Operations. Dir.............................Kevin Welsh
Exec. Ed....Africa Price
Editorial Page Ed.........................Craig Durrett
Fashion Ed................................Margaret Martin
Local Ed........................................Velda Hunter
News Ed.......................................Curtis Heyen
Online Ed.................................Scott Anderson
Features Ed................................Kathie Rowell
Adv. Key Acct Mngr...................Rick Thurman
Adv. Local Territory Manager.....Angela Haacker
Digital Sales Manager................Adrian Soyars
IT Director....................................Cilla Trenado
Production Operations Manager...Michael Griffin
Circ. Mgr......................................David Kirby
Circ. Mgr., Single Copy....................Amy Heirs
Community Ed........................Sherry Shepherd
Market Information: TMC; Zoned editions.

Mechanical available: Offset; Black and 3 ROP colors; insert accepted; page cutoffs - 18.5.
Mechanical Specifications: Type page 10 x 17.25; E - 6 cols, 1.54, .17 between; A - 6 cols, 1.54, .17 between; C - 6 cols, 1.54, .16 between.
Commodity Consumption: Avg. Page Number Per Issue - Daily 42; Avg. Page Number Per Issue - Sunday 90; widths 41; Newsprint Used - Short Tons 9809; Printing Ink Used - Black 98336; Printing Ink Used - Color 37833; Printing Ink Used - Pages Printed 17554.
Equipment EDITORIAL: Front-end Software – SII/Guardian 90.; Editorial Hardware – SII/CLX 840; Editorial Printers – Tandem/5212, APP/Mac LaserWriter II NT CLASSIFIED: Front-end Software – Mactive.; Classified Hardware – PC-based; Classified Printers – PC Desktop; Layout Software – CS5.; Display Hardware – PC PRODUCTION: Pagination Software – QPS/QuarkXPress 3.31.; Production Equipment – AU/APS6-108S, P/OL260; Scanners – Lf/Leafscan 35, AG, AG/Arcus PRESSROOM: Line 1 – 4 towers Wifag OF790 (double width) 1991; Folders – 2 Wifag 5:3.; Pasters – 6 Wifag w-arm auto pasters MAILROOM: Counter stackers – 2/quipp packman; 2/Gammerler; 1/Quipp 400; Inserters and stuffers – 1/G 2299; Bundle tying machines – 3/Dynaric.; Mailroom control system – 1/Miracom ; Addressing machine – 1/Videojet; Other equipment –2/Accraply labelers; BUSINESS COMPUTERS: Business Software – Microsoft/Office 2000
Zip Codes served: 71001, 71003, 71006, 71007, 71009, 71018, 71019, 71023, 71024, 71027, 71028, 71030, 71032, 71033, 71037, 71038, 71039, 71040, 71044, 71047, 71049, 71051, 71052, 71055, 71060, 71061, 71063, 71064, 71065, 71067, 71068, 71071, 71072, 71073, 71075, 71078, 71082, 71101, 71103, 71104, 71105, 71106, 71107, 71108, 71109, 71110, 71111, 71112, 71115, 71118, 71119, 71129, 71251, 71270, 71411, 71419, 71429, 71449, 71457, 75633, 75639, 75670, 75672, 75692
Delivery method: Mail, Newsstand, Private Carrier, Racks

SLIDELL

SLIDELL SENTRY-NEWS

364B Pontchartrain Dr., Slidell, La., 70458; gen tel (985) 643-4918; gen fax (985) 643-4966; gen e-mail sentryedit@wickscommunications.com; web site www.slidellsentry.com
Group: U.S. Suburban Press, Inc.
Published: Tues, Wed, Thur, Fri, Sat, Sun
Weekday Frequency: m
Circulation: 4,541; 4,541(sat); 4,661(sun)
Last Audit: September 30, 2003
Price: 8.75/mo.
Advertising: Open inch rate $9.90
News services: AP, NEA.
Not Published: Independence Day; Labor Day.
Special Editions: Football (Aug); Med Fax (Health Care) (Jan); Back-to-School (Jul); Graduation Tab (Jun); Home & Garden (Mar); Progress (May); Cookbook (Nov).
Special Weekly Sections: Spotlight (S); Church Page (Sat); Spotlight (Thur); Spotlight (Tues); Spotlight (Wed).
Magazines: Tempo (Leisure & Entertainment) (Fri); Broker East (Real Estate) (S).
Pub. .... Terry Maddox
Bus. Mgr. .... Ann McGehee
Adv. Mgr., Retail .... Mary Christopher
Adv. Mgr., Classified .... Debbie Simmons
Circ. Mgr. .... Brett Bridges
Mng. Ed. .... Shell Armstrong
Amusements Ed. .... John Perkins
Lifestyles Ed. .... Betsy Swenson
Sports Ed. .... David Perdum
Prodn. Mgr. .... Jane Cranford
Market Information: Split run; TMC.
Mechanical available: Offset; Black and 3 ROP colors; insert accepted; page cutoffs - 21 1/2.
Mechanical Specifications: Type page 13 x 21 1/2; E - 6 cols, 2 1/16, 1/8 between; A - 6 cols, 2 1/16, 1/8 between; C - 8 cols, 1 9/16, 1/16 between.
Equipment; Editorial Hardware – Mk; Editorial Printers – APP/Mac.; Classified Hardware – Mk; Classified Printers – APP/Mac.; Display Hardware – APP/Mac; Display Printers – NewGen.; Production Equipment – 8-COM/UTS; Cameras – Argyle/23. PRESSROOM: Line 1 – 4-KP/News King.; Bundle tying machines – 2/Bu; Addressing machine – Am.; Business Hardware – 2-IBM

SULPHUR

SOUTHWEST DAILY NEWS

716 E. Napoleon St., Sulphur, La., 70663-3402; gen tel (337) 527-7075; adv tel (337) 527-7075; ed tel (337) 527-7075; gen fax (337) 528-9557; adv fax (337) 528-9557; ed fax (337) 528-9557; adv e-mail swtdaily@yahoo.com; ed e-mail sdneditorial@yahoo.com; web site www.sulphurdailynews.com
Published: Tues, Wed, Thur, Fri, Sun
Weekday Frequency: m
Circulation: 4,631; 4,631(sun)
Last Audit: September 27, 2001
Price: 98.05/yr.
Advertising: Open inch rate $10.50
News services: AP.
Special Editions: Secretaries' Day (Apr); Labor Day Specials (Aug); Last Minute Gifts (Dec); Valentine's Day Specials (Feb); New Year's Greetings (Jan); School Supply List Pages (Jul); Father's Day Specials (Jun); Business Review (Mar); Mother's Day Specials (May); Turkeyo
Magazines: TV Weekend (Fri).
Pub. .... Suzanne Peveto
Adv. Dir. .... Jill Humphrey
Ed. .... Marilyn Monroe
Sports Ed. .... Rodrick Anderson
Market Information: TMC.
Mechanical available: Offset; Black and 3 ROP colors; insert accepted; page cutoffs - 22 3/4.
Mechanical Specifications: Type page 13 x 21; E - 6 cols, 2 1/16, 1/8 between; A - 6 cols, 2 1/16, 1/8 between; C - 8 cols, 1 1/2, 1/8 between.
Commodity Consumption: Avg. Page Number Per Issue - Daily 18; Avg. Page Number Per Issue - Plates Used 9000; Avg. Page Number Per Issue - Sunday 22; widths 27 1/2; Newsprint Used - Short Tons 950; Printing Ink Used - Black 22000; Printing Ink Used - Color 3000.
Equipment EDITORIAL: Front-end Software – QPS, Adobe/Illustrator, Adobe/Photoshop.; Editorial Hardware – Mk, APP/Mac; Classified Hardware – Mk. DISPLAY: Ad make-up applications – APP/Mac; Layout Software – APP/Mac.; Display Hardware – APP/Mac PRODUCTION: Pagination Software – Mk/Page Director.; Production Equipment – Caere/OmniPage, QMS/860; Cameras – Kk; Scanners – Nikon, HP/ScanJets PRESSROOM: Line 1 – 3-WL/Color Quad; Line 2 – 5-WL/Regular. MAILROOM: Counter stackers – BG; Bundle tying machines – OVL; Addressing machine – Ch. BUSINESS COMPUTERS: Business Software – MSSI; Business Hardware – HP

THIBODAUX

THE DAILY COMET

104 Hickory St., Thibodaux, La., 70301-2008; gen tel (985) 448-7600; adv tel 985-857-2270; ed tel (985) 448-7612; gen fax (985) 448-7606; adv fax 985-448-7606; ed fax 985-448-7606; ed e-mail news@dailycomet.com; web site www.dailycomet.com
Published: Mon, Tues, Wed, Thur, Fri, Sat, Sun
Weekday Frequency: m
Saturday Frequency: m
Circulation: 11,224; 11,224(sat); 11,475(sun)
Last Audit: ABC September 30, 2011
Price: 12.00/mo; 144.00/yr (carrier).
News services: AP, NYT.
Politics: 1888
Note: The Thibodaux Daily Comet (e) has a combination rate of $45.05 with the Houma Courier (eS). Individual newspaper rates not made available.
Own facility?: N
Special Editions: Back-to-School (Aug); Wedding (Feb); FYI (Jan); Wedding (Jul); Graduation (May); Christmas Opening (Nov); Football (Sept).
Special Weekly Sections: Religion Page (Fri); Bridal Announcements (Mon); Mes Amis (Thur); Health Page (Tues); Best Food Day (Wed).
Magazines: USA WEEKEND Magazine (Fri).
Pub. .... H. Miles Forrest
Controller .... Darlene Rodrigue
Inside Sales Manager .... Marian Long
Advertising Director .... Robin Conerly
Executive Editor .... Keith Magill
City Editor .... Robert Zullo
Editorial Page Editor .... Mike Gorman
Sports Ed. .... Brent St. Germain
Operations Manager .... Mark Gray
Market Information: TMC.
Mechanical available: Offset; Black and 3 ROP colors; insert accepted; page cutoffs - 22.75
Mechanical Specifications: Type page 11 x 22; E - 6 cols, 1.708, 11 pts. between; A - 6 cols, 1.708, 11 pts. between; C - 9 cols, 1.126, 11 pts. between.
Commodity Consumption: Avg. Page Number Per Issue - Daily 24; Avg. Page Number Per Issue - Plates Used 16790; widths 27 1/2; Newsprint Used - Metric Tons 900; Printing Ink Used - Black 22440; Printing Ink Used - Pages Printed 7300.
Equipment EDITORIAL: Front-end Software – ATS CLASSIFIED: Front-end Software – ATS DISPLAY: Ad make-up applications – Xpance; SalesForce BUSINESS COMPUTERS: Business Software – PBS
Delivery method: Mail, Newsstand, Private Carri

MAINE

AUGUSTA

KENNEBEC JOURNAL

274 Western Ave., Augusta, Maine, 04330; gen tel (207) 623-3811; adv tel (207) 623-3811; ed tel (207) 623-3811; gen fax (207) 621-5621; adv fax (207) 623-0614; ed fax (207) 623-2220; gen e-mail kjedit@centralmaine.com; adv e-mail cmnclass@centralmaine.com; ed e-mail kjedit@centralmaine.com; web site www.kjonline.com
Published: Mon, Tues, Wed, Thur, Fri, Sat, Sun
Weekday Frequency: m
Saturday Frequency: m
Circulation: 11,224; 12,862(sat); 11,475(sun)
Last Audit: ABC September 30, 2011
Price: 3.50/wk (carrier & motor route); 14.95/mo (home delivery); 171.60/yr (home delivery).
News services: AP, NYT, LAT-WP, SHNS.
Politics: 1825
Note: The Augusta Kennebec Journal (mS) has a combination rate of $56.86 (m-mon to sat) and $59.65 (S) with the Waterville Morning Sentinel (mS). Individual newspaper rates not made available.
Not Published: Christmas Day.
Special Editions: Spring Scouting (Apr); College Bound (Aug); Winter Scouting (Dec); Baby Parade (Feb); Maine Manufacturing Housing (Jan); Old Hallowell Days (Jul); Winslow 4th of July (Jun); Medical Journal (Mar); Brides & Grooms (May); Winter in Maine (Nov); Old Hallowel
Special Weekly Sections: What's Happening (entertainment) (Fri); What's on TV (S).
Magazines: USA WEEKEND Magazine (S).
Broadcast Affiliations: WMTW.
Adv./Promo. Dir. .... Cindy Stevens
Adv. Mgr., Classified Sales .... Rick DeBruin
Adv. Mgr., Retail Sales .... Larry Rioux
Circ. Mgr., Sales/Retention ... Charlene McGraw
Circ. Mgr., Single Copy .... Lew Strout
Ed. .... Richard L. Connor
Community Ed. .... Tedda Henry
Editorial Page Ed. .... Bill Thompson
Features Ed. .... Patty Ammons
Opinion Page Ed. .... Naomi Stalit
Sports Ed. .... Ben Sturtevant
Prodn. Dir., Opns. .... Dick Boyer
Market Information: Split run; TMC.
Mechanical available: Offset; Black and 3 ROP colors; insert accepted - product samples; page cutoffs - 22 3/4.
Mechanical Specifications: Type page 13 x 21 1/2; E - 6 cols, 2 1/16, 1/8 between; A - 6 cols, 2 1/16, 1/8 between; C - 9 cols, 1 3/8, 1/16 between.
Commodity Consumption: Avg. Page Number Per Issue - Daily 30; Avg. Page Number Per Issue - Plates Used 32648; Avg. Page Number Per Issue - Saturday 36; Avg. Page Number Per Issue - Sunday 48; widths 25; Newsprint Used - Short Tons 1512; Printing Ink Used - Black 34620; Printin
Equipment EDITORIAL: Front-end Software – SCS.; Editorial Hardware – SCS, Dell/Pentium PCs; Editorial Printers – HP/LaserPrinter, Xante/8300 CLASSIFIED: Front-end Software – SCS.; Classified Hardware – Dell/Pentium PCs; Classified Printers – HP/LaserPrinter DISPLAY: Ad make-up applications – Multi-Ad/Creator, QPS/QuarkXPress 3.31; Layout Software – SCS/Layout 8000.; Display Hardware – SCS, APP/Power Macs; Display Printers – Xante/8300 PRODUCTION: Pagination Software – QPS/QuarkXPress 3.31, SCS.; Production Equipment – 2-AG/Avantra 25, 2-Nu/FT40; Cameras – 1-C/Spartan II, 2-AG/RPS; Scanners – Howtek, Scan/Master 2500 PRESSROOM: Line 1 – 14-G/Urbanite; Line 3 – 2-D&R/(on Press Glue Sys); Press Drives – 4-HP/100; Folders – 2-G/Urbanite, 2-G/Quarterfolder; Pasters – 6-KTI/Splicers. MAILROOM: Counter stackers – 1-Gammerler/STC 70, 1-HL/Monitor, 1-HI/RS25, 2-Powerstrap/PSN-6C, 2-TMSI/Compass180; Inserters and stuffers – 1-HI/1372; Bundle tying machines – 2-It/SX 500, 1-Dynarc/NP2; Mailroom control system – HI/Stacker Program 009; Addressing machine – Addressing mac; Audio Hardware – Texas Micro/PC BUSINESS COMPUTERS: Business Software – Microsoft/Excel, Microsoft/Word, CJ; Business Hardware – IBM/4331 II, DEC/VAX 3100, Dell/Pentium

BANGOR

BANGOR DAILY NEWS

491 Main St., Bangor, Maine, 04402-1329; gen tel (207) 990-8000; adv tel (207) 990-8260; ed tel (207) 990-8030; gen fax (207) 941-9476; adv fax (207) 941-0885; ed fax (207) 941-9476; gen e-mail bdnmail@bangordailynews.net; adv e-mail advertising@bangordailynews.net; ed e-mail bdnnews@bangordailynews.net; web site www.bangornews.com
Published: Mon, Tues, Wed, Thur, Fri, Sat, Sun
Weekday Frequency: m
Saturday Frequency: m
Circulation: 47,474; 56,065(sat); 56,065(sun)
Last Audit: ABC September 30, 2011
Price: 3.30/wk (carrier, motor route); 221.00/yr (mail).
Advertising: Open inch rate $95.68(wknd)
News services: AP, LAT-WP.
Politics: Independent.
Special Editions: Bangor Spring Home Show (Apr); Home Furnishings: Trends & Styles (Aug); High School Basketball (Dec); Eastern Agency On Aging-Life Times (Feb); Photographs of the Year: The Best From Our Pages (Jan); Planning Your Wedding (Jul); Experience Maine (Jun); Do
Special Weekly Sections: Maine Style (S).

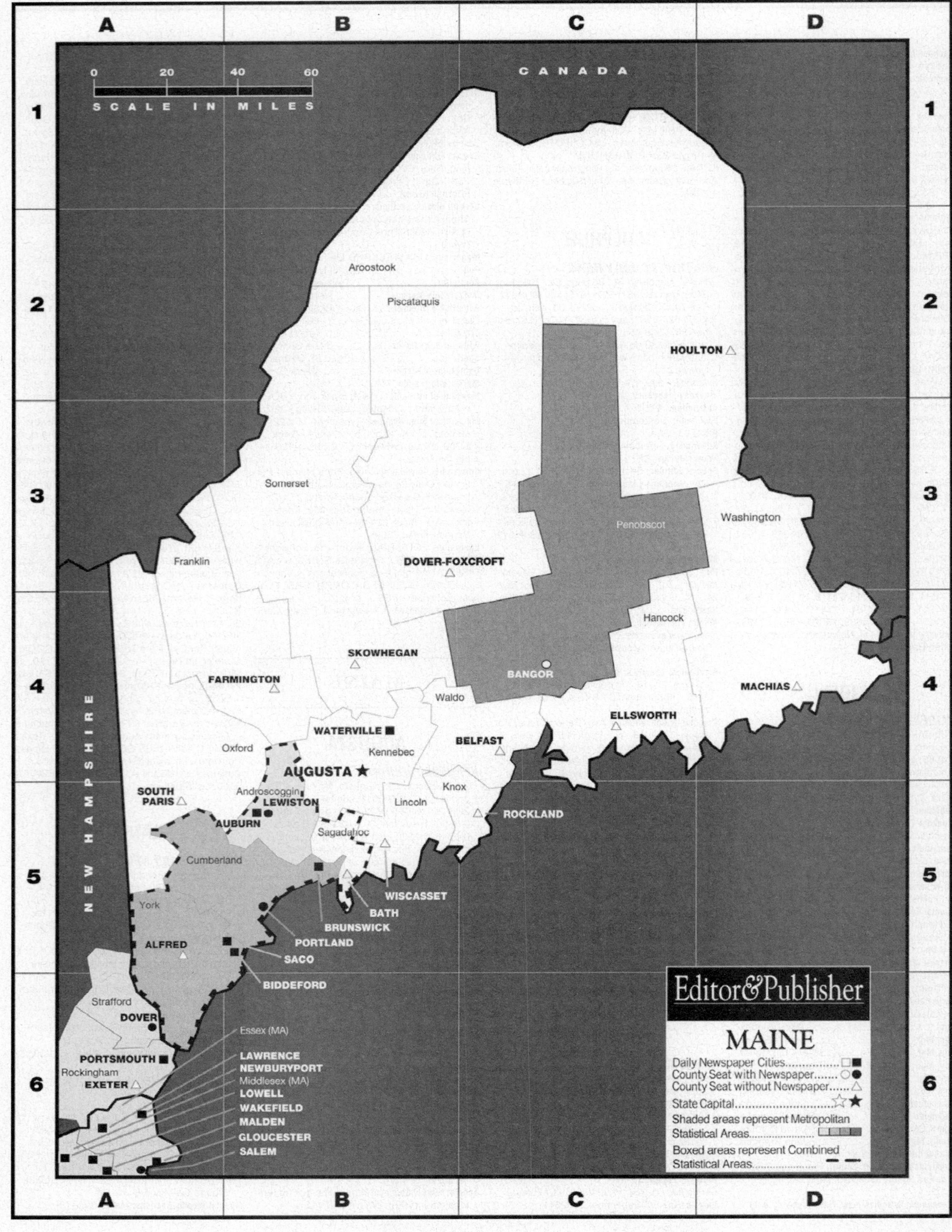
A
B
C
D
1
2
3
4
5
6
0
20
40
60
SCALE IN MILES
CANADA
NEW HAMPSHIRE
Aroostook
Piscataquis
HOULTON
Somerset
Penobscot
Washington
Franklin
DOVER-FOXCROFT
Hancock
SKOWHEGAN
BANGOR
FARMINGTON
MACHIAS
Waldo
ELLSWORTH
WATERVILLE
Oxford
Kennebec
BELFAST
AUGUSTA
SOUTH PARIS
Androscoggin
LEWISTON
Knox
Lincoln
ROCKLAND
AUBURN
Sagadahoc
Cumberland
WISCASSET
York
BATH
BRUNSWICK
PORTLAND
ALFRED
SACO
BIDDEFORD
Strafford
DOVER
Essex (MA)
PORTSMOUTH
LAWRENCE
NEWBURYPORT
Rockingham
Middlesex (MA)
EXETER
LOWELL
WAKEFIELD
MALDEN
GLOUCESTER
SALEM
Editor&Publisher
MAINE
Daily Newspaper Cities
County Seat with Newspaper
County Seat without Newspaper
State Capital
Shaded areas represent Metropolitan Statistical Areas
Boxed areas represent Combined Statistical Areas

Magazines: Color Comics (S); USA WEEKEND Magazine (Sat); Food (Wed).
Vice Pres., Admin. ....Robert W. Stairs
HR Mgr. ....Jennifer Holmes
Controller ....Timothy Reynolds
Adv. Mgr., Sales ....Betch Grant
Adv. Mgr., Sales ....J. Michael Kearney
Dir., Mktg. Servs. ....Elizabeth Hansen
Circ. Dir./Home Delivery Mgr. ....Jim Hayes
Circ. Mgr., Customer Serv. ....Todd Mc Cloud
Circ. Mgr., Sales/Mktg. ....Harth Horne
Ed. ....Richard J. Warren
Asst. Ed. ....Dale Mc Garrigle
Bus. Ed. ....Micheal J. Dowd
Copy Desk Ed. ....Greg McManus
Editorial Page Ed. ....Susan Young
Graphics/Design Ed. ....Eric Zelz
Librarian ....Charles Campo
News Ed. ....Rick Levasseur
Photo Ed. ....Scott Haskell
Market Information: Split run; TMC; Zoned editions.
Mechanical available: Flexography; Black and 3 ROP colors; insert accepted - free standing, single sheet, product samples; page cutoffs - 22.
Mechanical Specifications: Type page 11 5/8 x 21; E - 6 cols, 1 5/6, 1/8 between; A - 6 cols, 1 5/6, 1/8 between; C - 9 cols, 1 3/8, 3/32 between.
Commodity Consumption: Avg. Page Number Per Issue - Daily 36; Avg. Page Number Per Issue - Plates Used 55340; Avg. Page Number Per Issue - Saturday 71; widths 49; Newsprint Used - Metric Tons 5100; Printing Ink Used - Black 119105; Printing Ink Used - Color 125739; Printing In
Equipment EDITORIAL: Front-end Software – AT/Dewarview (2000).; Editorial Hardware – 2-IBM/Netfinity 5500, IBM/PC; Editorial Equipment – PC Bureau Dial-up Network; Editorial Printers – HP/Laserjet, X/Docuprint N32 CLASSIFIED: Front-end Software – Unisys/AD Center, Informatel/AdPlacer.; Classified Hardware – 2-Dell/Poweredge 4200, 18-IBM/Aptiva; Classified Printers – 1-HP/Laserjet 4000, HP/Laserjet 6P, HP/Laserjet 4MV DISPLAY: Ad make-up applications – Multi Ad/Creator, QPS/QuarkXPress; Layout Software – MEI/ALS, 6-APP/Mac.; Display Hardware – 9-APP/MAC; Display Printers – 1-Canon/2100, 1-HP/Laserjet 4, 1-Docuprint N32 PRODUCTION: Pagination Software – AT/Pagemaker, QPS/QuarkXPress.; Production Equipment – 1-LaserMaster/1200, 2-SelectSet/5000, 2-Rapid, 1-Avantra/25; Scanners – 1-AG/Arcus II, 1-AG/Duoscan PRESSROOM: Line 1 – 8-H/PEC (double width flexo); Folders – 1-H/3:2. MAILROOM: Counter stackers – 4/HL, 1-Id/4400; Inserters and stuffers – 1-HI/1472, 1-GMA/SLS 1000; Bundle tying machines – 1-/Power Strap/PSN5, 4-/Power Strap/PSN6, 1-Samuel/NT 40; Wrapping singles – 6-Monarch/Bottom wrap; Addressing machine – 1-KAN/Labeling System BUSINESS COMPUTERS: Business Software – In-house, Accts Receivable; Business Hardware – IBM/AS-400

BANGOR PUBLISHING CO.

491 Main St., Bangor, Maine, 04402-1329; gen tel (207) 990-8000; gen fax (207) 941-9476

BIDDEFORD

JOURNAL TRIBUNE

457 Alfred St., Biddeford, Maine, 04005; gen tel (207) 282-1535; gen fax (207) 282-3138; gen e-mail emailads@journaltribune.com; adv e-mail mpassmore@journaltribune.com; ed e-mail jtcommunity@journaltribune.com; web site www.journaltribune.com
Published: Mon, Tues, Wed, Thur, Fri, Sat
Weekday Frequency: e
Saturday Frequency: m
Circulation: 6,676; 7,476(sat)
Last Audit: Sworn September 30, 2009
Price: 130.00/yr (carrier), $160.00/yr (mail).
Advertising: $14.25
Insert rate: $50
News services: AP, SHNS.
Politics: Independent.
Not Published: New Year; Memorial Day; Independence Day; Labor Day; Christmas.
Own facility?: Y
Magazines: USA WEEKEND Magazine (Sat).
General Manager ....Michelle Passmore
Mechanical available: Offset; Black and 3 ROP colors; insert accepted; page cutoffs - 22 3/4.
Mechanical Specifications: Type page 13 x 21 1/2; E - 6 cols, 2 1/16, 1/8 between; A - 6 cols, 2 1/16, 1/8 between; C - 9 cols, 1 3/8, 1/16 between.
Commodity Consumption: Avg. Page Number Per Issue - Daily 28; Avg. Page Number Per Issue - Plates Used 8000; Avg. Page Number Per Issue - Saturday 40; widths 32; Newsprint Used - Short Tons 780; Printing Ink Used - Black 24050; Printing Ink Used - Color 1100; Printing Ink Used
Equipment EDITORIAL: Front-end Software – Baseview/NewsEdit Pro.; Editorial Hardware – Ik/Minitek I, 1-APP/Mac SE, 1-APP/Mac IIcx, 2-APP/Mac G3, 2-APP/Mac 6100; Classified Hardware – Ik/Minitek I; Classified Printers – NewGen/Turbo 600, Design Express lo, 6-Micro Laser 600.; Layout Software – 5-APP/Mac IIcx, 3-APP/Mac SE, 1-NewGen/630, 1-NewGen/660, 2-APP/Power Mac 6100, 1-APP/Mac LC 520.; Display Printers – 1-APP/Mac, Micro Laser 600 PRODUCTION: Pagination Software – QPS/QuarkXPress 4.0.; Production Equipment – ECR/VRL 36, DAI/LD-260-L; Cameras – 1-R/5000; Scanners – Umax, APP/Mac PRESSROOM: Line 1 – 6-G/U 553; Folders – 1; Inserters and stuffers – 1-MM/227; Bundle tying machines – 2/Sa, 1-/MLN; Addressing machine – 1-Ch/525E.; Business Hardware – 1-TI/690
Zip Codes served: 04005, 04072, 04073, 04083, 04054, 04063, 04027, 04074, 03907, 04087, 04030, 04005, 04042, 04093, 04004, 04038, 04048, 04095, 04076, 04001, 03906, 04002, 04046, 04094, 04046, 04090, 04043, 04002, 04064, 04014, 04042, 04061, 04006
Delivery method: Newsstand, Private Carrier, Racks

BRUNSWICK

BRUNSWICK PUBLISHING CO.

3 Buisness Pkwy., Brunswick, Maine, 04011; gen tel (207) 729-3311; gen fax (207) 729-5728; gen e-mail news@timesrecord.com; web site www.timesrecord.com
Price: 12.35/mo; 124.70/yr.
Advertising: Open inch rate $13.25

THE TIMES RECORD

3 Business Pkwy., Brunswick, Maine, 4011; gen tel (207) 729-3311; adv tel (207) 729-3311; ed tel (207) 729-3311; gen fax (207) 729-5728; adv fax (207) 725-8619; ed fax (207) 721-3151; gen e-mail adsales@timesrecord.com; adv e-mail adsales@timesrecord.com; ed e-mail letters@timesrecord.com; web site www.timesrecord.com
Published: Mon, Tues, Wed, Thur, Fri
Weekday Frequency: e
Circulation: 8,490
Last Audit: September 30, 2009
Price: 2.25/wk (carrier), $2.40/wk (auto); 103.30/yr (carrier), $110.55/yr (auto).
Advertising: Open inch rate $15.75
News services: AP, NYT.
Politics: Democrat.
Advertising not accepted: Tobacco.
Not Published: New Year; Memorial Day; Independence Day; Labor Day; Thanksgiving; Christmas.
Special Editions: Home & Garden (Apr); Back-to-School (Aug); Year In Review (Dec); Automotive (Feb); Money (Jan); Saltwater Fishing (Jul); Newspapers in Education (Mar); Summer Lifestyles (May); Holiday Gift Guide (Nov); Car Care (Oct); Home Improvement (Sept).
Special Weekly Sections: Living (Fri); Best Food Day (Mon); Sights & Sounds (Thur); Milestones (Weddings & Engagements) (Tues); Business (Wed).
Magazines: Real Estate Extra (Fri).
Pub ....Chris Miles
Office Mgr. ....Stacy White
Adv. Dir. ....Michelle Passmore
Circ. Mgr. ....George Reichert
Bus./Wire Ed. ....Robert Long
Community Ed. ....Elizabeth Lardie
Features Ed. ....Jonathan White
Kids Ed. ....Daryl Madore
Opinion Page Ed. ....Jim McCarthy
Photo Ed. ....Troy Bennett
Sports Ed. ....George Almasi
Webmaster ....Joseph Keelan
Prodn. Mgr., Mailroom ....Glenda Grant
Prodn. Mgr., Pre Press/Post Press ....Jeff Hewett
Prodn. Mgr., Press room ....Russell Libbey
Market Information: TMC.
Mechanical available: Offset; Black and 2 ROP colors; insert accepted; page cutoffs - 22 3/4.
Commodity Consumption: Avg. Page Number Per Issue - Daily 28; Avg. Page Number Per Issue - Plates Used 4070; widths 28; Newsprint Used - Short Tons 850; Printing Ink Used - Black 22200; Printing Ink Used - Color 2780; Printing Ink Used - Pages Printed 7085.
Equipment EDITORIAL: Front-end Software – Baseview/Server IQUE.; Editorial Hardware – APP/Mac; Editorial Equipment – 2-Linotype-Hell/L530 Imagesetter with Ultra Rip 4.5; Editorial Printers – 1-MON, HP/5000 CLASSIFIED: Front-end Software – Caere/OmniPage Plus, Baseview.; Classified Hardware – APP/Mac; Classified Printers – HP/5000 DISPLAY: Ad make-up applications – QPS/QuarkXPress 3.32; Layout Software – APP/Mac, QPS/QuarkXPress.; Display Hardware – APP/Mac; Display Printers – Compaq/PageMarq 20, HP/8000, 2-Linotype-Hell/L530 Imagesetter with RIP 4.5 PRODUCTION: Pagination Software – QPS/QuarkXPress 4.10.; Production Equipment – 2-L/530, LE/PC 1800, LE/Excel 26; Cameras – C/Spartan III; Scanners – AG/Arcus Scanner, 1-APP/Mac PRESSROOM: Line 1 – G/Community (2-4HI, 1-2HI) (single width) 1985; Line 2 – G/Community (6, 1 VOP) (single width) 1980; Line 3 – DGM/430 (1-4HI) (single width) 1999; Press Drives – Fin/Digital Drive; Folders – 2-G/SSC, 1; Pasters – 3-Enkel/OSpud. MAILROOM: Counter stackers – 3-Gammler/KL 503/1; Inserters and stuffers – 1-MM/227E; Bundle tying machines – 4-EAM-Mosca/Rom, 1-Si/LB-2000; Addressing machine – 1-Ch/539, KR/512; Other equipment –1-Gammler/RSI-II Trimmer, 1-AGE/Trimmer. BUSINESS COMPUTERS: Business Software – Vision Data; Business Hardware – Sun/4-110

LEWISTON

SUN JOURNAL

104 Park St., Lewiston, Maine, 04240; gen tel (207) 784-5411; gen fax (207) 777-3436; adv fax (207) 784-5955; ed fax (207) 777-3436; adv e-mail brioux@sunjournal.com; ed e-mail editor@sunjournal.com; web site www.sunjournal.com
Published: Mon, Tues, Wed, Thur, Fri, Sat, Sun
Weekday Frequency: m
Saturday Frequency: m
Circulation: 27,051; 27,051(sat); 27,548(sun)
Last Audit: Sworn September 30, 2009
Price: 4.15/wk; 191.00/yr.
Advertising: Open inch rate $30.15 daily, $31.66 Sunday
Insert rate: $50/M
News services: AP, CSM, MCT.
Politics: Independent. **Established:** 1861
Not Published: Christmas.
Own facility?: Y
Special Editions: January
□ Healthy Living: January 14, 2011
Featuring quality of life information.
□ Women□s Journal: January 23, 2011
An in-depth feature on current women□s issues and interests.
February
□ Home Furnishings: February 4, 2011
Info on ideas and trends in home decor.
□ Spring Wedding Guide: February 6, 2011
Complete info for planning a wedding from beginning to end.
□ Presidents Day: February 12, 2011
Features dealer information, options and highlights of 2011 vehicles.
March
□ Spring Home Improvement: March 11, 2011
Full of articles and information for every area of the home.
□ Western ME Builders Guide: March 12, 2011
Featuring great ideas for the home and office.
□ The Men□s Issue : March 18, 2011
Created and designed with men□s interests in mind.
□ Spring Car Care: March 25, 2011
Helpful hints and expert advice pertaining to your car.
April
□ Landscaping and Gardening: April 8, 2011
Info for green thumbs, gardeners and homeowners.
□ Profile: April 9, 2011
An in-depth look at the Central Maine business scene.
□ College Bound: April 15, 2011
Financial aid information, college selection, and career choices.
□ Senior Living: April 24, 2011
Designed, researched and written for mature readers.
May
□ Summer in Maine: May 9, 2011
Find summer getaways and events all in one supplement.
□ Graduation: May 20, 2011
Includes photos of top students, lists of senior class members, and graduation ceremony information.
June
□ Women□s Journal: June 18, 2011
An in-depth feature on current women□s issues and interests.
July
August
□ Our Town: August 5, 2011
Two editions provide essential information on education, community, government, economy, sports and recreation.
□ Balloon Festival: August 14, 2011
Provides an entertainment schedule, official map, vendor list, photos of participating balloons, lists of launch sites and exhibits.
□ Money: August 14, 2011
Loaded with financial advice for saving and spending wisely.
□ Fall Wedding Guide: August 28, 2011
Complete info for planning a wedding from beginning to end.
September
□ Fall Sports: September 2, 2011
Schedules, photos and roundups of high school fall sports.
□ Fall Home Improvement: September 9, 2011
Full of articles and information for every area of the home.
□ Hunting in Maine: September 17, 2011
Includes articles on hunting techniques and more.
□ Fall Car Care: September 23, 2011
Helpful hints and expert advice

on preparing vehicles for winter.
October
□ Choices: October 9, 2011 (TBA)
Restaurants, bars and local hot spots share menus, specialty items and unique offerings.
□ Family: October 10, 2010
Topics for families, all generations included.
November
□ Veterans Day:
November 11, 2010
Personal stories from our service men and women.
□ Western ME Holiday Series (5):
November 25, December 2, 9, 16, 20, 2010
□ NEW Holiday Features Series (4): November 18, 25, December 2, 9, 2010 (Dates TBA)
Gift ideas, recipes, Santa letters, and songbook.
December
□ Winter Sports:
December 3, 2010
Schedules, photos and roundups of high school winter sports.
□ Winter in Maine:
December 5, 2010
Coverage of all types of winter recreation.
□ Season□s Greetings:
December 24, 2010
Merchants thank and wish customers well in the holiday season.
□ Business Review:
December 31, 2010
A review of the longevity and services of local businesses.

Special Weekly Sections: Economy/Business (S).
Magazines: Relish (Monthly); PARADE Magazine (S); American Profile (Weekly), Spry (Monthly), Decathalon Sports (Monthly).
Pres./Pub...........................James R. Costello
Vice Pres. Adv./Mktg.........Stephen M. Costello
Vice Pres., HR......................Maureen Wedge
Adv. Mgr...................................Jody Jalbert
Circ. Dir................................Mike Theriault
Exec. Ed...................................Rex Rhoades
Mng. Ed., Day...............................Judy Meyer
Mng. Ed., Night............................Peter Phelan
Nat'l Ed...........................Heather McCarthy
Photo Ed............................Russell Dillingham
Regl. Ed.....................................Scott Thistle
Sports Ed................................Steve Sherlock
Travel Ed...................................Ursula Albert
Vice Pres., Technology..............David Costello
Vice Pres., Operations.............James Costello
Treasurer................................Edward Snook
Treasurer...........................Edward M. Snook
Vice Pres./Bus. Mgr.............James A. Thornton
Community News.......................Danielle Libby
Market Information: Zoned editions.
Mechanical available: Offset; Black and 3 ROP colors; insert accepted; page cutoffs - 22 3/4.
Mechanical Specifications: Type page 11 3/5 x 21; E - 6 cols, 1 4/5, 1/8 between; A - 6 cols, 1 4/5, 1/8 between; C - 9 cols, 1 1/5, 1/16 between.
Commodity Consumption: Avg. Page Number Per Issue - Plates Used 36500; Avg. Page Number Per Issue - Sunday 102; widths 27; Newsprint Used - Short Tons 4500; Printing Ink Used - Black 76000; Printing Ink Used - Color 10000.
Equipment EDITORIAL: Front-end Software – MS/NT, QPS/QuarkXPress, Microsoft/Word 7.0.; Editorial Hardware – 3-PC Server; Editorial Equipment – APP/Mac Plus Agaton Scanner, CD, 3-HP/11x17; Editorial Printers – 2-AU/APS2000, 11x17, 3-AG/Accuset 1500 CLASSIFIED: Front-end Software – PPI; Classified Hardware – PC; Classified Printers – HP/11x17 DISPLAY: Ad make-up applications – In-design, Xpance, Photoshop; Display Hardware – PC; Display Printers – HP/11x17 PRODUCTION: Pagination Software – ACI.; Production Equipment – AG/Accuset 1500, AG/660 Rapid Access, C/Rapid Access; Cameras – 1-R/481, 1-R/432; Scanners – ECR/Autokon 1000, AG/RPS 20 x 24, 1-CD/625E Scanner PRESSROOM: Line 1 – 15-G/Urbanite 1283; Press Drives – 2; Folders – 1-G/2:1; Pasters – 6; Press control system – Fincore MAILROOM: Counter stackers – 3-QWI/SJ200; Inserters and stuffers – 1-HI/1372
1-SLS 1000; Bundle tying machines – 1/MLN, 2-/AHS, 1-MLN/MLIEE, 1-MLN/Spirit.; Mailroom control system – Burt; Addressing machine – Micro Ink-jet
Delivery method: Mail, Newsstand, Private Carrier, Racks

PORTLAND

PORTLAND PRESS HERALD/MAINE SUNDAY TELEGRAM

One City Center, Portland, Maine, 04101; gen tel (207) 791-6600; adv tel (207) 791-6200; ed tel (207) 791-6320; adv fax (207) 791-6925; ed fax (207) 791-6920; web site www.pressherald.com
Published: Mon, Tues, Wed, Thur, Fri, Sat, Sun
Weekday Frequency: m
Saturday Frequency: m
Circulation: 52,323; 50,289(sat); 82,300(sun)
Last Audit: ABC September 30, 2011
Price: 4.10/wk; 16.95/mo; 149.25/yr.
Advertising: Open inch rate $57.55
News services: AP, LAT-WP, Tribune Media, Universal Press, King Features, United Media, CSM, CQ.
Politics: Independent.
Special Editions: 50 Plus (Apr); Vacationland (Aug); National Engineers Week (Feb); Wedding Planner (Jan); People's Choice, Seniority (Jul); Vacationland (Jun); Death and Dying (Mar); Vacationland (May); Holiday Gift Guide (Nov); Home Furnishings (Oct); Fall Home Improveme
Special Weekly Sections: Business Friday (Fri); On Screen (S); Religion & Values (Sat); GO (Thur); Business (Tues); Food & Health (Wed).
Magazines: Parade (S); American Profile (Weekly).
Deputy Mng. Ed., Online/Multimedia Angela Muhs
Ed..................................Richard L. Connor
Ed...Rod Harmon
Dir., HR...............................Karen Dobbyn
Prodn. Mgr., Pressroom/Distr.....Keith Toothaker
VP & Executive Editor..................Scott Wasser
Vice Pres...........................Jeannine A. Guttman
Classified Adv. Mgr.............Jennifer Sorenson
Retail Adv. Mgr.............................Anton Kaufer
Acting Circ. Dir.............................Mark Berry
Deputy Mng. Ed., Opns./Sports........Don Coulter
Dir., Opns...............................Steven Infinger
Prodn. Mgr., Pressroom..............Mark Bragdon
Market Information: ADS; Split run; TMC; Zoned editions.
Mechanical available: Flexographic; Black and 3 ROP colors; insert accepted - all; page cutoffs - 22.
Mechanical Specifications: Type page 11 5/8 x 21; E - 6 cols, 1 5/6, 1/8 between; A - 6 cols, 1 5/6, 1/8 between; C - 10 cols, 1 1/16, 3/16 between.
Commodity Consumption: Avg. Page Number Per Issue - Daily 40; Avg. Page Number Per Issue - Plates Used 100000; Avg. Page Number Per Issue - Sunday 120; widths 49; Newsprint Used - Metric Tons 9979; Newsprint Used - Short Tons 11000; Printing Ink Used - Black 261000; Printing I
Equipment EDITORIAL: Front-end Software – DTI 4.2.3.; Editorial Hardware – 2-Sun/3000e, 160-APP/Mac PPC; Editorial Printers – 6-HP/4000, 2-AII/2500, 1-AII/1055, AII/APS 2000, 2-HP/1055 CLASSIFIED: Front-end Software – DTI 4.2.3.; Classified Hardware – 2-Sun/3000e, 54-APP/Mac PPC; Classified Printers – 3-HP/4000, 1-AII/2500, 2-HP/2500 DISPLAY: Ad make-up applications – QPS/QuarkXPress, Multi-Ad, Macromedia/Freehand, Adobe/Photoshop, DTI; Layout Software – DTI.; Display Hardware – 2-Sun/3000e; Display Printers – 2-HP/XL 3000, 1-HP/755 CM, 2-HP/4000 PRODUCTION: Pagination Software – DTI/PlanBuilder 4.2.3.; Production Equipment – 2-MacDermit CTP, 2-NAPP/Flex Processor Unit; Scanners – ECR, 7-HP/3C, 2-Kk/2035, 1-Howtek PRESSROOM: Line 1 – 6-G/Flexoliner 1989; Line 2 – 6-G/Flexoliner 1989; Folders – 2-G/160 Page Sovereign, G/Double Delivery; Pasters – 12-G/CT 50; Reels and Stands – 12-G/Reels; Press registration system – 4-Web/Press Controls. MAILROOM: Counter stackers – 6-HL/HT2, 1/QWI; Inserters and stuffers – 1-HI/2299, 1-HI/1372; Bundle tying machines – 10-OVL/JP40, 2-/MLN, 1-/Dynaric; Wrapping singles – Altek/Skid Stretch Wrap Machine; Mailroom control system – HL/Dock console; Addressing machine – Addressing machine BUSINESS COMPUTERS: Business Software – Microsoft/Office 4.3, Great Plains Dynamics C/S; Business Hardware – Digital Alpha Servers

WATERVILLE

MORNING SENTINEL

31 Front St., Waterville, Maine, 4901; gen tel (207) 873-3341; gen fax (207) 861-9223; adv fax (207) 861-9222; ed fax (207) 861-9191; web site www.onlinesentinel.com
Group: MaineToday Media
Published: Mon, Tues, Wed, Thur, Fri, Sat, Sun
Weekday Frequency: m
Saturday Frequency: m
Circulation: 15,434; 15,434(sat); 15,957(sun)
Last Audit: September 30, 2009
News services: AP, LAT-WP, SHNS.
Politics: Independent.
Note: The Waterville Morning Sentinel (mS) has a combination rate of $56.86 (m-mon to sat) and $59.65 (S) with the Augusta Kennebec Journal (mS). Individual newspaper rates not made available.
Own facility?: Y
Special Editions: Spring Scouting (Apr); Skowhegan Fair (Aug); Holiday Shopping Guide II (Dec); Family Expo (Feb); Bridal (Jan); Pre-Owned Autos/Trucks/SUVs (Jul); Graduation (Jun); Maine Paper Expo (Mar); Start Your Engines (May); Holiday Shopping Guide I (Nov); Fall Home
Special Weekly Sections: What's Happening (entertainment) (Fri); What's on TV (S).
Magazines: USA WEEKEND Magazine (S).
HR Dir.......................................Karen Dobbyn
Adv. Mgr., Classified Sales........Michael Hersey
Richard L. Connor
Editorial Page Ed.......................Bill Thompson
Deputy Sports Ed.......................Gary Hawkins
Managing Editor................................Jim Evans
Editor and Publisher.................Antony Ronzio
Mechanical available: Offset; Black and 3 ROP colors; insert accepted - product samples; page cutoffs - 22 3/4.
Mechanical Specifications: Type page 13 x 21 1/2; E - 6 cols, 2 1/32, 5/32 between; A - 6 cols, 2 1/32, 5/32 between; C - 9 cols, 1 5/16, 1/16 between.
Commodity Consumption: Avg. Page Number Per Issue - Daily 30; Avg. Page Number Per Issue - Plates Used 35400; Avg. Page Number Per Issue - Saturday 36; Avg. Page Number Per Issue - Sunday 48; widths 27 1/2; Newsprint Used - Short Tons 1872; Printing Ink Used - Black 42420; Pri
Equipment EDITORIAL: Front-end Software – SCS.; Editorial Hardware – 3-Dell; Editorial Printers – HP/LaserPrinters CLASSIFIED: Front-end Software – SCS.; Classified Hardware – Dell/Pentium PCs; Classified Printers – HP/LaserPrinter DISPLAY: Ad make-up applications – Multi-Ad/Creator 4.0.1; Layout Software – SCS/Layout 8000.; Display Hardware – 5-PC; Display Printers – HP, C.Itoh, Dataproducts/LZR1560 PRODUCTION: Pagination Software – SCS, QPS/QuarkXPress 3.31.; Production Equipment – Dataproducts/L2R2080 Laser printer, Graham; Cameras – 1-C/Spartan III; Scanners – HP, Howtek/Scan-Master 2500 PRESSROOM: Line 1 – G/Urbanite; Line 2 – 1, 3; Line 3 – 1 MAILROOM: Counter stackers – 1-HI/R525, 3-H/4 Monitor, Gammerter/STC 70; Inserters and stuffers – 1-HI/1372; Bundle tying machines – 2-IT/SX 500, 2/Power Strap/PSN 65; Wrapping singles – Mailroom control system Â□ HI/Stacker Program 009; Addressing machine – 1-Domino/Amjet Jerray BUSINESS COMPUTERS: Business Software – Microsoft/Word, Microsoft/Excel, CJ; Business Hardware – Dell/486
Delivery method: Mail, Newsstand, Private Carrier, Rackser, Racks

MARYLAND

ANNAPOLIS

THE CAPITAL

2000 Capital Dr., Annapolis, Md., 21401; gen tel (410) 268-5000; adv tel (410) 268-7000; ed tel (410) 268-5000; gen fax (410) 268-4643; adv fax (410) 280-5974; ed fax (410) 280-5953; ed e-mail capletts@capital-gazette.com; web site www.hometownannapolis.com
Published: Mon, Tues, Wed, Thur, Fri, Sat, Sun
Weekday Frequency: e
Saturday Frequency: e
Circulation: ; 38,048(sun)
Last Audit: ABC September 30, 2011
Price: 2.75/wk; 12.50/mo; 159.44/yr.
Advertising: Open inch rate $39.71
News services: AP, MCT.
Politics: Independent. **Established:** 1884
Not Published: New Year; Memorial Day; Independence Day; Labor Day; Christmas (unless holiday falls on a Sunday).
Special Editions: Home & Garden (Apr); Football (Aug); Gift Guide (Dec); Real Estate (May); Real Estate (Oct); Home & Garden (Sept).
Special Weekly Sections: Annapolis (Fri); Commercial, Industrial & Business Real Estate (S); Stock Home & Real Estate (Sat); Food (Wed).
Magazines: Relish (Monthly); USA WEEKEND Magazine (S).
CFO...Charles Feeney
Circ. Dir.......................................Rob Pryor
Exec. Ed.................................Tom Marquardt
Asst. City Ed...............................John Wilfong
Editorial Page Ed..................Gerald Fischman
Environmental Ed..............................Pim Wood
Graphics Ed................................Loretta Haring
News Ed....................................Mark Murphy
Online Ed...................................Brian Henley
Political/Gov't Ed.....................Stuart Samuels
Sports Ed...................................Gerry Jackson
Travel Ed......................................Kathy Flynn
Online Mgr...............................Nick Lundskow
Prodn. Mgr...............................William Hope
Prodn. Mgr., Distr.............................Don White
Mechanical available: Offset; Black and 3 ROP colors; insert accepted; page cutoffs - 22.
Mechanical Specifications: Type page 11 7/8 x 21; E - 6 cols, 2 1/16, 1/8 between; A - 6 cols, 2 1/16, 1/8 between; C - 9 cols, 1 3/8, 1/16 between.
Commodity Consumption: Avg. Page Number Per Issue - Daily 36; Avg. Page Number Per Issue - Plates Used 70374; Avg. Page Number Per Issue - Saturday 52; Avg. Page Number Per Issue - Sunday 78.7; widths 50; Newsprint Used - Metric Tons 5718; Newsprint Used - Short Tons 6304; Pri
Equipment EDITORIAL: Front-end Software – Cybergraphics.; Editorial Hardware – 86-DEC/VAX 6000; Editorial Equipment – 1-HP/ScanJet; Editorial Printers – 4-Panasonic/2624 CLASSIFIED: Front-end Software – Cybergraphics.; Classified Hardware – 35-DEC/VAX 6000 Terminals; Classified Printers – 2-Panasonic/2624, 2-TI/850; Layout Software – SCS/Layout 8000.; Display Hardware – DEC/VAX 6000; Display Printers – 4-HP/LaserJet IV PRODUCTION: Pagination Software – Cybergraphics.; Production Equipment – 2-Nu/631, 1-AG; Cameras – 1-C/Spartan III; Scanners – 2-ECR/Autokon 1000, 1-ECR/Au-

tokon 2040, 4-AG/Argus II PRESSROOM: Line 1 – 5-G/Headliner Offset double width (3 color decks); Folders – 3-G/2:1; Pasters – 5-G/RTP. MAILROOM: Counter stackers – 4/RKW, 1-/HL, 2-/QWI; Inserters and stuffers – 1-HI/1372; Bundle tying machines – 4-MLN/2A; Mailroom control system – ARS/272; Addressing machine – 2-KR/15W-211 Head. BUSINESS COMPUTERS: Business Software – Data Sciences, Neasi Weber Ad Marc, Mcba; Business Hardware – 2-DEC/VAX 6000

BALTIMORE

THE BALTIMORE SUN

501 N. Calvert St., Baltimore, Md., 21278; gen tel (410) 332-6000; adv tel (410) 332-6300; ed tel (410) 332-6221; gen fax (410) 332-6670; adv fax (410) 332-6084; ed fax (410) 332-6977; web site www.baltimoresun.com

Published: Mon, Tues, Wed, Thur, Fri, Sat, Sun
Weekday Frequency: m
Saturday Frequency: m
Circulation: 170,510; 251,947(sat); 314,253(sun)
Last Audit: ABC September 30, 2011
Price: 3.94/wk; 17.08/mo; 204.88/yr.
Advertising: Open inch rate $365.00
News services: Tribune Newspaper Network, RN, MCT, NYT, DJ, LAT-WP, AFP.
Politics: Independent.
Special Editions: Preakness Wrap-Up (Apr); Our Future/Carroll Schools (Aug); High Tech Education (Dec); Health Today (Every other month); College Goal Sunday Program (Feb); Career Builder XL II (Jan); Ravens Training Camp (Jul); A.A. Co. Residents Guide (Jun); Credit Union
Special Weekly Sections: Welcome Home (Wed).
Magazines: Parade (S).

Pres./Pub./CEO ..... Timothy Ryan
Vice Pres./CFO ..... Rich Goldstein
Vice Pres./Gen. Mgr. ..... John Patinella
Dir., Budgets/Finance Planning .. Barbara Ireland
Controller ..... Erik Smist
Exec. Dir., Retail Sales ..... Mike Beatty
Dir., Nat'l Adv. ..... Harvey Hill
Adv. Dir., Sales Devel./Target Mktg. Deborah Bennett
Adv. Dir., Major Retail/Food ..... Marty Padden
Adv. Dir., Local Retail/Multimedia/Creative Annie Hager
Dir., Classified Adv. ..... William Janus
Vice Pres., Mktg. ..... Timothy Thomas
Circ. Dir., Mktg./Retail Sales ..... Gary Olszewski
Circ. Mgr., Distr./Fleet ..... Joe Salamone
Ed./Sr. Vice Pres. ..... Montgomery Cook
Deputy Mng. Ed., Metro ..... Sandy Banisky
Deputy Mng. Ed., News ..... Paul Moore
Asst. Mng. Ed., Bus. ..... Bernie Kohn
Asst. Mng. Ed., Graphics Michelle Deal Zimmerman
Asst. Mng. Ed., Photo ..... Jim Preston

Market Information: ADS; TMC; Zoned editions.
Mechanical available: Offset; Black and 3 ROP colors; insert accepted - all; page cutoffs - 22.
Mechanical Specifications: Type page 11 5/8 x 20 3/4; E - 6 cols, 1 13/16, 1/8 between; A - 6 cols, 1 13/16, 1/8 between; C - 10 cols, 1 1/16, 1/8 between.
Commodity Consumption: Avg. Page Number Per Issue - Daily 75; Avg. Page Number Per Issue - Plates Used 590000; Avg. Page Number Per Issue - Saturday 72; Avg. Page Number Per Issue - Sunday 180; widths 49 7/8; Newsprint Used - Metric Tons 52200; Printing Ink Used - Black 871355
Equipment EDITORIAL: Front-end Software – HI/NME 4.7, HI/NMP 4.7, QPS/QuarkXPress 4.1, Adobe/Phot; Editorial Hardware – HI, 3-Sun/5500, 400-IBM, 60-APP/Mac; Editorial Equipment – 2-AP/Preserver; Editorial Printers – HP/2500, HP/1050, Xante/Accel-a-Writer 3G, Xante/Color Laser, HP/LaserJet 4050N, HP/5SI, OCE/Proofer CLASSIFIED: Front-end Software – SII/Czar II, Scoop, A151 Fax Action, SII/SCP 1.7n.; Classified Hardware – SII/Tandem K2000, Sun/Ultra 3000; Classified Equipment – 1-TDD-TYY C-Phone 1-A; Classified Printers – HP/2500, HP/1050, Xante/Accel-a-Writer 3G, Xante/Color Laser, HP/LaserJet 4050N, HP/5SI DISPLAY: Ad make-up applications – Managing Editor/ALS 3.0, SII/Coyote3, QPS/QuarkXPress 4.1, Adobe/Photoshop 5.5, A; Display Hardware – 75-APP/Mac, 120-IBM, IBM/Mainframe, Sun/Ultra 3000; Display Printers – HP/2500, HP/1050, Xante/Accel-a-Writer 3G, Xante/Color Laser, HP/LaserJet 4050N, HP/5SI PRODUCTION: Pagination Software – HI/NMP 4.7.; Production Equipment – 5-III/3850, 1-WL/3, Umax/D-16L Flat Bed, 1-ECR/Stingray, 9-Flat Bed Scanners, Nikon/Cool Scan; Scanners – 2-Eskofot PRESSROOM: Line 1 – 12-G/Colorliner double width; Line 2 – 12-G/Colorliner double width; Line 3 – 12-G/Colorliner double width; Line 4 – 12-G/Colorliner double width; Folders – 3-G/Double 3:2, 1-G/Single 3:2; Reels and Stands – 48-CT/50 Reels. MAILROOM: Counter stackers – 2/Stackpack, 2-/Gammerler, 20-HL/HT II, 12-/QUI; Inserters and stuffers – 1-GMA/SLS 2000 12:2, 2-GMA/SLS 2000 20:2, 2-GMA/SLS 2000 26:2; Bundle tying machines – 32-/Power Strap (5,6,6E), 17-/Dynaric; Wrapping singles – 3-HL/Monarch, 20 AUDIO: Audio Software – Audiotext 2500; Audio Hardware – Micro Voice Systems, VNN, Audiotext 2500 BUSINESS COMPUTERS: Business Software – Users Sierra Group, GEAC/Smart Stream, GEAC/Smart Stream 4.1; Business Hardware – IBM/9672 R52, IBM/OS 390 2.9

CAMBRIDGE

THE DAILY BANNER

1000 Goodwill Ave., Cambridge, Md., 21613-0580; gen tel (410) 228-3131; gen fax (410) 228-6547; gen e-mail banrnews@newszap.com; adv e-mail ad-sales@newszap.com; adsupport@newszap.com

Published: Mon, Tues, Wed, Thur, Fri, Sat, Sun
Weekday Frequency: e
Saturday Frequency: m
Circulation: 3,561; 3,561(sat)
Last Audit: June 30, 2004
Price: 78.00/yr (local), $95.00/yr (outside local area).
Advertising: Open inch rate $19.56
News services: AP.
Politics: Independent. **Established:** 1897
Profile: The Eastern Shore's oldest daily newspaper dominates the market in Maryland's largest county, Dorchester County. The Daily Banner is located in Cambridge, the center of the country's population as well as its business and cultural hub.

Adv. Dir., Regl. ..... Pat Lee
Circ. Mgr. ..... Jason Coffman
Chief Ed. ..... Andrew West

Market Information: Split run; TMC.
Mechanical available: Offset; Black and full color ROP colors; insert accepted - Max 11X10, Min 6 1/4X7; page cutoffs - 21.
Mechanical Specifications: Type page 11 5/8 x 20; E - 6 cols, 1 5/6, 1/6 between; A - 6 cols, 1 5/6, 1/6 between; C - 9 cols, 1 3/16, 1/16 between.
Commodity Consumption: Avg. Page Number Per Issue - Daily 20; widths 27 1/2; Newsprint Used - Short Tons 325; Printing Ink Used - Black 24000; Printing Ink Used - Color 1000; Printing Ink Used - Pages Printed 5200.
Equipment EDITORIAL: Front-end Software – QPS/QuarkXPress 3.3.2, Maco/S 7.5.2, WriteNow 4.0.; Editorial Hardware – APP/Mac SE, APP/Mac II, APP/Power Mac; Editorial Printers – APP/Mac LaserWriter Pro 810 CLASSIFIED: Front-end Software – Baseview/Class Ads.; Classified Hardware – APP/Mac SE, APP/Mac II; Layout Software – APP/Mac. PRO-

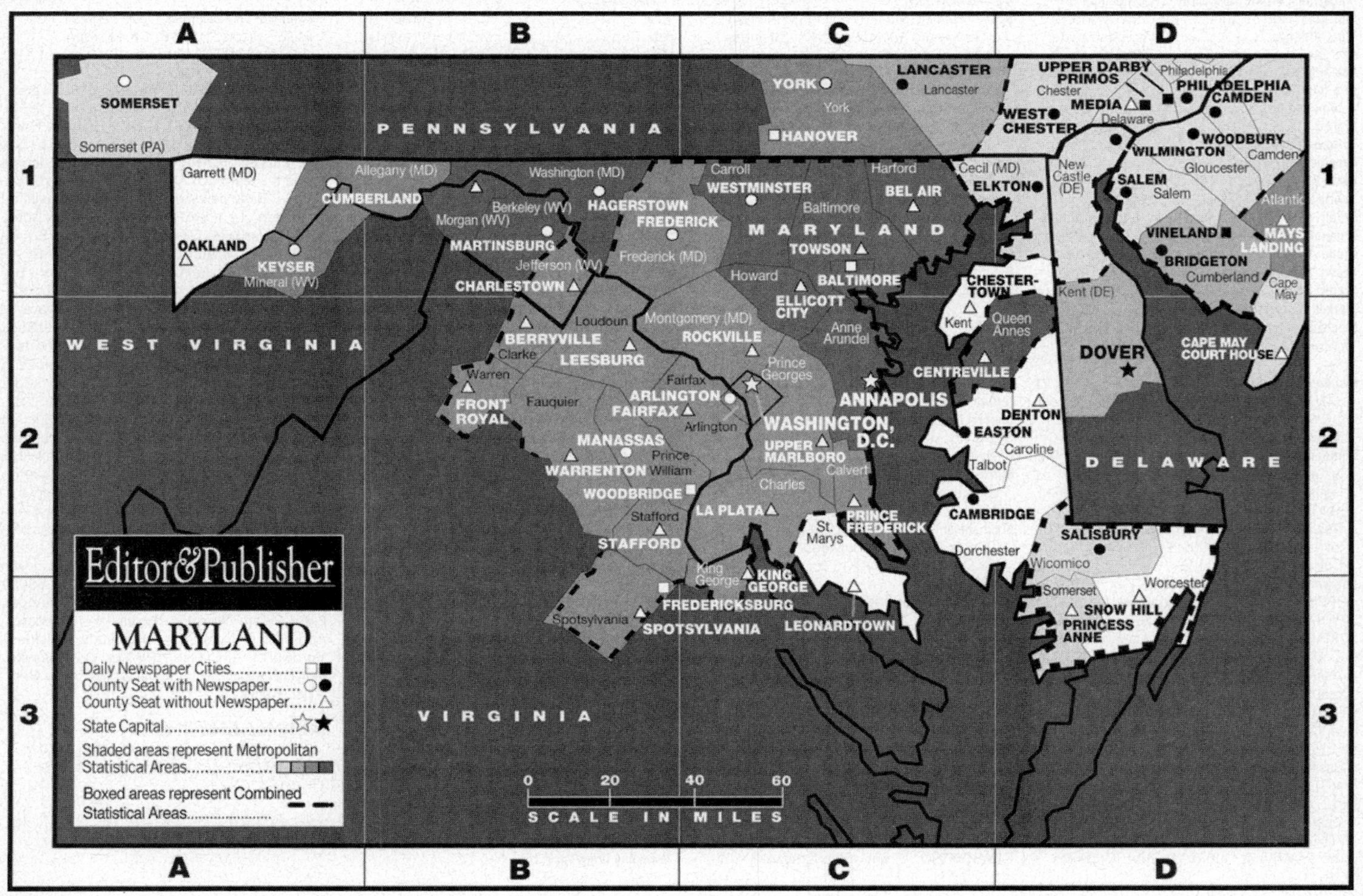

DUCTION: Pagination Software – QPS/QuarkXPress 3.3.2.; Production Equipment – 1-Nu/Flip Top FT40UP, 2-APP/Mac LaserWriter Pro 810, S, N/104; Cameras – 1-R/400 PRESSROOM: Line 1 – 5-G/Community; Folders – 2; Inserters and stuffers – 1-MM/EM 102; Bundle tying machines – 2-Bu/18; Addressing machine – 2-El/Dymatic 3301.; Business Hardware – 3-DEC/VT220

CUMBERLAND

THE CUMBERLAND TIMES-NEWS

19 Baltimore St., Cumberland, Md., 21501; gen tel (301) 722-4600; adv tel (301) 722-4600; ed tel (301) 722-4600; gen fax (301) 722-4870; adv fax (301) 722-4870; ed fax (301) 722-5270; gen e-mail ctn@times-news.com; adv e-mail sstouffer@mindspring.com; ed e-mail jpalderton@mindspring.com; jpalderton@times-news.com; web site www.times-news.com

Published: Mon, Tues, Wed, Thur, Fri, Sat, Sun
Weekday Frequency: m
Saturday Frequency: m
Circulation: 23,419; 23,419(sat); 25,472(sun)
Last Audit: ABC September 30, 2011
Price: 9.00/mo; 108.00/yr.
Advertising: Open inch rate $44.43
News services: AP.
Politics: Independent.
Not Published: Day after New Year; Memorial Day; Independence Day; Labor Day; Day after Thanksgiving; Day after Christmas.
Special Editions: Back-to-School (Aug); Bridal Tab (Feb); Tax Tips Tab (Jan); Progress (Mar); Home Improvement (May); Sports Magazine (Monthly); Car Care Tab (Oct); Home Improvement (Sept).
Special Weekly Sections: Food (S); Real Estate (Sat); Automotive (Thur); Food (Wed).
Magazines: Relish (Monthly); Parade (S).
Pub./Gen. Mgr. ....Ronald Monahan
Mgr., Finance ....Thomas Snyder
Adv. Dir. ....Jennifer James
Adv. Mgr., Classified ....Cindy Hopkins
Circ. Mgr. ....George J. Griffin
Automotive Ed. ....Robert Likens
City Ed. ....Debra Meyer
Editorial Page Ed. ....Jan Alderton
Graphics Ed./Art Dir. ....Jeremy Warnick
News Ed. ....John Smith
Sports Ed. ....Michael Burke
Prodn. Mgr., Mailroom/Post Press George Griffin
Prodn. Mgr., Pre Press/Pressroom ....Gus Bell
Prodn. Mgr., Pressroom ....James Bell
Prodn. Mgr., Systems ....Robert McDonald
Prodn. Supvr., Plant Maintenance .....James Huff
Market Information: TMC.
Mechanical available: Offset; Black and 3 ROP colors; insert accepted; page cutoffs - 22 3/4.
Mechanical Specifications: Type page 11 5/8 x 21 1/2; E - 6 cols, 1 5/6, 1/8 between; A - 6 cols, 1 5/6, 1/8 between; C - 9 cols, 1 1/4, 1/16 between.
Commodity Consumption: Avg. Page Number Per Issue - Daily 28; Avg. Page Number Per Issue - Plates Used 30000; Avg. Page Number Per Issue - Sunday 48; widths 50; Newsprint Used - Short Tons 2700; Printing Ink Used - Black 43000; Printing Ink Used - Color 4000.
Equipment; Editorial Hardware – PC, APP/iMac, APP/Mac G3; Editorial Equipment – 14-COM, APP/Mac Quadra 950, X/1200 R Scanner, Lf/AP Leaf Picture Desk, Lf/Leafscan 35; Editorial Printers – Genicom, Tegra/4000, Pre Press/Panther Pro, V/5100, DEC/1152, Xante/36, Pre Press/Panther Pro 36, Pre Press/ CLASSIFIED: Front-end Software – COM/One Sys, CText, Baseview/Ad Manger Pro.; Classified Hardware – PC, APP/iMac, APP/Mac G3; Classified Equipment – 4-COM; Classified Printers – Genicom, Tegra/4000, Pre Press/Panther Pro, V/5100, DEC/1152, Xante/36, Pre Press/Panther Pro 36, Pre Press/Panther Pro 46 DISPLAY: Ad make-up applications – CText, Multi-Ad/Creator 4.0.6; Layout Software – SCS/Layout 8000, ALS 2.5, MEI/ALS.; Display Hardware – PC, APP/iMac; Display Printers – DEC/Laser 1152, Pre Press/Panther Pro 46, Pre Press/Panther Pro 36, Xante/36 PRODUCTION: Pagination Software – QPS/QuarkXPress 3.12, QPS/QuarkXPress 3.1.; Production Equipment – 1-Nu/Flip Top FT40V4UP, 2-V/5100, 1-V/4000, 1-V/5300E; Cameras – 1-C/Spartan II; Scanners – Sharp/Color, X/B-W PRESSROOM: Line 1 – 8-G/Cosmo, 1-G/Cosmo Press-5units-#3543 1979; Reels and Stands – 5, 10. MAILROOM: Counter stackers – 1-Id/2000; Inserters and stuffers – GMA/8 pocket, GMA/SLS 1000; Bundle tying machines – 1-MLN/NPS 80, OVL/JP-40, MLN/2EE, Power Strap/PSNG, PS/5; Addressing machine – KR; Other equipment –MM/stitcher. BUSINESS COMPUTERS: Business Software – Newzware; Business Hardware – IBM/Sys 36, M/8, K/9000

THE TIMES & ALLEGANIAN CO.

19 Baltimore St., Cumberland, Md., 21502; gen tel (301) 722-4600; gen fax (301) 724-6222

EASTON

THE STAR-DEMOCRAT

29088 Airpark Dr., Easton, Md., 21601; gen tel (410) 822-1500; adv tel (410) 770-4040; ed tel (410) 770-4010; gen fax (410) 770-4011; adv fax (410) 770-4048; ed fax (410) 770-4019; web site www.stardem.com

Published: Mon, Tues, Wed, Thur, Fri, Sun
Circulation: 15,284; 16,326(sun)
Last Audit: September 30, 2009
Price: 26.46/3mo; 101.43/yr.
Advertising: Open inch rate $24.95
News services: AP.
Politics: Independent.
Not Published: New Year; Christmas.
Own facility?: Y
Special Editions: Healthy Living (Monthly), Chesapeake 360, (Quarterly). Business Ledger (Quarterly)
Special Weekly Sections: Church Page (Fri); Weekend (Friday) Family Page (Mon); Life on the Shore (S); Life on the Shore (Wed).
Magazines: Relish (Monthly); USA WEEKEND Magazine (S); American Profile (Weekly).
Profile: Community newspaper and commercial printing company serving Maryland's Eastern Shore.
Gen. Mgr. ....David Fike
Adv. Mgr. ....Konrad La Prade
Mktg. Mgr. ....Kevin A. Fike
Distr. Mgr. ....Louis Walls
Exec. Ed. ....Denise Riley
Mng. Ed. ....Barbara Sauers
Bus. Ed. ....Chris Knauss
Community Ed. ....Katie Sullivan
Chief Copy Ed. ....John Griep
Entertainment Ed. ....Greg Maki
Online Ed. ....Richard Polk
Special Sections Ed. ....David Everman
Sports Ed. ....William Haufe
Composition Mgr. ....Shirley Jackson
Mechanical available: Offset; Black and 3 ROP colors; insert accepted; page cutoffs - 22 3/4.
Mechanical Specifications: Type page 12 x 21; E - 6 cols, 1 7/8, 1/10 between; A - 6 cols, 1 7/8, 1/10 between; C - 9 cols, 1 3/16, 1/10 between.
Commodity Consumption: Avg. Page Number Per Issue - Daily 25; Avg. Page Number Per Issue - Plates Used 5463; Avg. Page Number Per Issue - Sunday 36; widths 25 1/2; Newsprint Used - Short Tons 550; Printing Ink Used - Black 15000; Printing Ink Used - Color 2500; Printing Ink Us
Equipment EDITORIAL: Front-end Software – QPS/QuarkXPress 4.04, Microsoft/Windows.; Editorial Hardware – APP/Mac, APP/Mac G3, APP/Mac G4; Editorial Equipment – APP/Mac Scanner, Sun/Sparc, Sun/Sparc Station, AP/Satellite Data Sys, Lf/AP Leaf Picture Desk; Editorial Printers – APP/Mac Laser, HP/55I CLASSIFIED: Front-end Software – Brainworks/Classified.; Classified Hardware – APP/Mac, PC; Classified Printers – APP/Mac Laser, Birmy/Page Scan 3, HP/55I, HP/400 DISPLAY: Ad make-up applications – QPS/QuarkXPress 4.04; Layout Software – MEI/ALS.; Display Hardware – APP/Mac; Display Printers – APP/Mac Laser, HP/55I; Production Equipment – Amerigraph/Magnum. PRESSROOM: Line 1 – 1-DGM/430; Line 2 – 14-G/Community; Folders – 2-G/SSC; Press control system – Fin. MAILROOM: Counter stackers – QWI/400, Newstech, SLS/1000; Bundle tying machines – 4-Dynaric; Addressing machine – 1-Ch/Labeler, 2-Videojet/4000. BUSINESS COMPUTERS: Business Software – ICIS, Lotus, Prologic/PR, Xenix, Aware; Business Hardware – TI/990, AST/386, AST/286
Zip Codes served: 21601
Delivery method: Mail, Newsstand, Private Carrier, Racks

ELKTON

CECIL WHIG

601 N. Bridge St., Elkton, Md., 21921; gen tel (410) 398-3311; gen fax (410) 398-4044; web site www.cecilwhig.com

Group: U.S. Suburban Press, Inc.
Published: Mon, Tues, Wed, Thur, Fri
Weekday Frequency: m
Circulation: 12,163
Last Audit: September 30, 2008
Price: 79.00/yr.
Advertising: Open inch rate $22.90
News services: AP, U.S. Suburban Press Inc..
Politics: Independent. **Established:** 1841
Not Published: New Year; Christmas.
Special Editions: Pulse (Jan); Home Improvement (Mar); Home Improvement (Sept).
Special Weekly Sections: TV (Fri); Accent Feature (Wed).
Magazines: Relish (Monthly); American Profile (Weekly).
Pub. ....David Fike
Adv. Dir. ....Edward Hoffman
Adv. Dir. ....Harry Poter
Delivery Supvr. ....Mary Ferguson
Circ. Dir. ....Bill Sims
Mng. Ed ....Michael Bullard
Features Ed ....Cady Ciamaricone
Sports Ed ....John Davis
Prodn. Mgr., Pre Press ....Stephanie Solomon
Market Information: TMC; Zoned editions.
Mechanical available: Offset; Black and ROP colors.
Commodity Consumption: Avg. Page Number Per Issue - Daily 24.
Equipment EDITORIAL: Front-end Software – QPS/QuarkXPress, Claris/MacWrite II.; Editorial Hardware – Mk, APP/Mac; Classified Hardware – Mk. DISPLAY: Ad make-up applications – Multi-Ad/Creator, QPS/QuarkXPress, APP/Mac Write II; Layout Software – Mk, APP/Mac.; Display Hardware – APP/Mac; Display Printers – Birmy/RIPs, Ultre, Canon/11x17; Production Equipment – Nu/Flip Top; Cameras – Photo Ace/260 D. PRESSROOM: Line 1 – 18-G/Community (One Line; 3 Power Drives); Folders – 2 MAILROOM: Counter stackers – 2/MM; Inserters and stuffers – MM/227; Bundle tying machines – MLN/MLEE; Addressing machine – Ch/4UP (One Line, one off-line).

FREDERICK

THE FREDERICK NEWS-POST

351 Ballenger Centre Dr., Frederick, Md., 21703; gen tel (301) 662-1177; adv tel (301) 662-1162; ed tel (301) 662-1178; gen fax (301) 682-7831; adv fax (301) 698-5206 (display); ed fax (301) 662-8299; gen e-mail info@fredericknewspost.com; adv e-mail classifieds@fredericknewspost.com; web site www.fredericknewspost.com

Group: Randall Family, LLC
U.S. Suburban Press, Inc.
Published: Tues, Wed, Thur, Fri, Sat, Sun
Weekday Frequency: m
Saturday Frequency: m
Circulation: 33,082; 33,082(sat); 34,602(sun)
Last Audit: ABC September 30, 2011
Price: 10.99/mo (carrier); 148.4/yr (carrier).
News services: AP, SHNS, CNS, MCT, TMS.
Politics: none. **Established:** 1883
Own facility?: Y
Special Editions: Frederick Keys Orioles Supplement (Pullout) (Apr); Fall Football Guide (Aug); Holiday Gift Guide (Dec); Wedding Planner (Jan); Hello Frederick County (Jul); Progress (Mar); Spring Automotive (May); Holiday Magazine (Nov); Fall Automotive (Oct); Health & F
Special Weekly Sections: Lifestyle (Fri); Farm (Mon); Comics (S); Auto (Sat); Home & Family (Thur); Health & Fitness (Tues); Food (Wed).
Magazines: Relish (Monthly); USA WEEKEND Magazine (S); TV Week (Sat); American Profile (Wed).
President ....Myron W. Randall
CFO ....Edmond B. Gregory
Adv. Mgr. ....Connie Hastings
Adv. Mgr., Classified ....Dawn Routzahn
Circ. Mgr. ....Kerry Turner
Circ. Mgr., Customer Serv. .Rebecca Ketterman
Publisher ....Geordie Wilson
Mng. Ed. ....Terry Headlee
Asst. Mg. Ed. ....Rob Walters
Features Ed. ....Sue Guynn
Chief Photographer/Photo Ed. ....Sam Yu
Sports Ed. ....Josh Smith
Dir., Internet Servs. ....Audrey Covington
Prodn. Dir., Opns. ....Will Randall
Dir., HR ....Diane Wardenfelt
Circ. Asst. Dir. ....Joseph O'Toole
Asst. Mng. Ed. ....Nancy Luse
Bus. Ed. ....Ed Waters
Sr. Web Application Developer Michael Appenzeller
Market Information: Split run; TMC.
Mechanical available: Offset; Black and 3 ROP colors; insert accepted - all; page cutoffs - 21.
Mechanical Specifications: Type page 11 1/2 x 21; E - 6 cols, 1 13/16, 1/8 between; A - 6 cols, 1 13/16, 1/8 between; C - 9 cols, 1 1/8, 1/8 between.
Equipment EDITORIAL: Front-end Software – Baseview/NewsEditPro IQue 3.5.3, QPS/QuarkXPress 4.1.1, DD.; Editorial Hardware – 12-APP/eMac, 24-APP/PowerMac G4, 6-APP/iBook, 5-APP/PowerBook G4; Editorial Printers – Xerox CLASSIFIED: Front-end Software – Baseview/Advertising Pro; Classified Hardware – 8-APP/eMac, 3-APP/iBook, APP/PowerBook G4, IMac; Classified Equipment – 2-ECR/Autokon; Classified Printers – Xerox DISPLAY: Ad make-up applications – Baseview/Advertising Pro 2.1.x, Baseview/ProductionManagerPro 1.9; Display Hardware – 7-APP/iBook, 3-APP/iMac, 2-APP/PowerBook G4, 2-APP/PowerMac G4; Display Printers – Xerox/ColorCube PRODUCTION: Pagination Software – QuarkXPress, Baseview/NewsEditPro IQue, Baseview/Classflow, MEI/ALS 4.2, Baseview/ProductionManagerPro; Production Equipment – 1-Nat/A-250, 4-Multi-Ad; Scanners – Epson/Expression 1640XL, Microtek/Artix 2020 PRESSROOM: Line 1 – 6-TKS Colortop 4000; Press Drives – shaftless; Folders – 2-TKS 3:2:2 (1 with quarter fold); Pasters – 9-Megtec; Press control system – TKS; Press registration system – QTI MAILROOM: Counter stackers – 3-QWI/501, 1-QWI/401; Inserters and stuffers – GMA/SLS 2000 12:2, SLS3000 24:2; Bundle tying machines – 3-DynaricViper, 2-/PackMan; Wrapping singles – 1-HL/Monarch; Addressing machine – KirkRudy; Business Hardware – APP/iMac, APP/Mac G4, Baseview
Delivery method: Mail, Newsstand, Private Carrier, Racks

RANDALL FAMILY, LLC

200 E. Patrick St., Frederick, Md., 21701; gen tel (301) 662-1177; gen fax (301) 682-7831

HAGERSTOWN

THE HERALD-MAIL

100 Summit Ave., Hagerstown, Md., 21740; gen tel (301) 733-5131; adv tel (301) 733-5131, ext. 2500; ed tel (301) 733-5131, ext. 2300; gen fax (301) 733-7264; adv fax (301) 733-7264; ed fax (301) 714-0245; gen e-mail news@herald-mail.com; adv e-mail advertising@herald-mail.com; ed e-mail opinion@herald-mail.com; web site www.herald-mail.com
Group: Schurz Communications Inc.
Published: Mon, Tues, Wed, Thur, Fri, Sat, Sun
Weekday Frequency: m
Saturday Frequency: m
Circulation: 25,677; 25,677(sat); 31,806(sun)
Last Audit: ABC September 30, 2011
Price: 75 cents daily; $1.50 daily
Advertising: Open inch rate $28.87
News services: AP
Not Published: Christmas
Special Weekly Sections: Money (S); Weekend (Thur); Farm Page (Tues); Food Pages & Recipes (Wed).
Magazines: Relish (Monthly); Parade (S).
IT Director .... Brian Taylor
Controller .... Kim Reno
Advertising Director .... Brittney Hamilton
Digital Director .... Liz Thompson
Executive Editor .... Jake Womer
Sports Editor .... Mark Keller
Production and pagination manager . Brian Sease
Circulation Director .... Brian Tedrick
President and Publisher .... Andy Bruns
Market Information: ADS; TMC.
Mechanical available: Offset; Black and 3 ROP colors; insert accepted - Product Samples/Donation Bags; page cutoffs - 21 1/2.
Mechanical Specifications: Type page 12 x 21 1/2; E - 6 cols, 1 5/6, 1/8 between; A - 6 cols, 1 5/6, 1/8 between; C - 9 cols, between.
Equipment EDITORIAL: Front-end Software – Baseview.; Editorial Hardware – APP/iMac, APP/Mac G4, Mac Mini, MacBooks; Editorial Printers – Savin PRODUCTION: Pagination Software – Baseview/NewsEdit Pro IQue 3+, InDesign CS2; Production Equipment – Nat, Nu; Cameras – Scanners Â☐ Epson Expression Umax Powerlook III; Press control system – 2, 2.
Zip Codes served: 21740

SALISBURY

THE DAILY TIMES

618 Beam St., Salisbury, Md., 21801; gen tel (410) 749-7171; gen fax (410) 543-8736; adv fax (410) 543-8736; ed fax (410) 749-7290; gen e-mail gbassett@dmg.gannett.com; web site www.delmarvanow.com
Group: Delmarva Media Group/Gannett Co. Inc.
Published: Mon, Tues, Wed, Thur, Fri, Sat, Sun
Weekday Frequency: m
Saturday Frequency: m
Circulation: 23,460; 17,210(sat); 23,460(sun)
Last Audit: ABC September 30, 2011
Price: 2.85/wk; 12.39/mo; 148.60/yr.
News services: AP, NEA.
Politics: 1886
Advertising not accepted: N
Own facility?: N
Special Editions: Visitor's Guide (Apr); Health Guide (Feb); Eastern Shore Real Estate (Monthly); Visitor's Guide (Sept).
Special Weekly Sections: Go! (Fri); Best Food Days (S); TV (Sat); Best Food Days (Wed).
Adv. Dir. .... Rob Scott
Circ. Mgr. .... Nikki LaVigne
Gen. Mgr & Exec. Ed. .... Greg Bassett
Operations Dir. .... Ron Smith
Bus. Mgr. .... Anne O'Connell
Controller .... Judy Petroff
HR .... Denise Stypinski
Bus. Ed. .... Gwenn Garland
City Ed. .... Joe Carmi
Sports Ed. .... Ben Penserga
Style Ed. .... Cindy Robinson
Prodn. Dir. .... Ray DeGroff
Commodity Consumption: Avg. Page Number Per Issue - Daily 30; Avg. Page Number Per Issue - Plates Used 29851; Avg. Page Number Per Issue - Saturday 28; Avg. Page Number Per Issue - Sunday 58; widths 54; Newsprint Used - Short Tons 2600; Printing Ink Used - Black 6700; Printing
Equipment; Other equipment –MM/1529.
Delivery method: Mail, Newsstand, Private Carrier, Racks

WESTMINSTER

CARROLL COUNTY TIMES

201 Railroad Ave., Westminster, Md., 21157; gen tel (410) 848-4400; adv tel (410) 848-4400; ed tel (410) 857-7878; adv fax (410) 857-1176; web site www.carrollcounty-times.com
Group: U.S. Suburban Press, Inc.
Published: Mon, Tues, Wed, Thur, Fri, Sat, Sun
Weekday Frequency: m
Saturday Frequency: m
Circulation: 22,715; 22,715(sat); 24,796(sun)
Last Audit: ABC September 30, 2011
Price: 11.00/mo; 94.50/yr.
Advertising: Open inch rate $25.97
News services: AP, GNS, SHNS.
Politics: Independent. **Established:** 1911
Not Published: Christmas.
Special Editions: CCT & CCTX (Aug); Mt. Airy Shopper (Dec); Bridal Guide (Jan); Ravens Practice Guide (Jul); CCT & CCTX (Jun); Holiday Lifestyles (Nov); Fall Home Improvement (Oct); Wine Festival (Sept).
Special Weekly Sections: Homes (Fri); Carroll Life (S); School Page (Thur); Best Food Day (Wed).
Magazines: Relish (Monthly); USA WEEKEND Magazine (S); American Profile (Weekly).
Pub. .... Patricia Richardson
Adv. Dir. .... Charles W. Baker
Circ. Dir. .... Michael Memphis
Editorial Page Ed. .... Jim Lee
Librarian .... Robin Sealover
Sports Ed. .... Bob Blubaugh
Prodn. Dir. .... Greg Linard
Prodn. Mgr. .... Kevin Coutts
Prodn. Mgr., Mailroom/Post Press .. Sandra Rose
Prodn. Mgr., Pre Press .... Ray Cone
Prodn. Mgr., Pressroom .... Ron McGee
Market Information: TMC; Zoned editions.
Mechanical available: Offset; Black and 3 ROP colors; insert accepted; page cutoffs - 22 3/4.
Mechanical Specifications: Type page 13 x 21 1/2; E - 6 cols, 2 1/16, 1/8 between; A - 6 cols, 2 1/16, 1/8 between; C - 6 cols, 2 1/16, 1/8 between.
Commodity Consumption: Avg. Page Number Per Issue - Daily 38; Avg. Page Number Per Issue - Sunday 52; widths 27 1/4; Newsprint Used - Short Tons 1837; Printing Ink Used - Black 47524; Printing Ink Used - Color 12650; Printing Ink Used - Pages Printed 12298.
Equipment EDITORIAL: Front-end Software – CText/AFM Editorial System, QPS 3.3.; Editorial Hardware – Novell, Dell/Pentium II; Editorial Printers – HP/LaserJet IV, Avantra/25xT Imagesetter CLASSIFIED: Front-end Software – APT/Classified System.; Classified Hardware – Compaq/Proliant, Dell/Pentium III, Microsoft/Windows NT 4.0; Classified Printers – 2-AG, HP/LaserJet 4050 TN, Avantra/25xT Imagesetter DISPLAY: Ad make-up applications – Multi-Ad/Creator 4.01; Display Hardware – 13-APP/Mac, 2-APP/Power Mac 7100, APP/Power Mac 7300, APP/Mac G3; Display Printers – HP/LaserJet, ECR/Pelbox 3850, ECR/Pelbox 1245CX, AG, Avantra/25xT, HP/LaserJet 8000 PRODUCTION: Pagination Software – APT/Classified System with QuarkXPress 3.32.; Production Equipment – WL, Teaneck, Konica/OL Conveyor System; Cameras – C/Spartan III, AG/2024; Scanners – AG/Arcus II, Umax/Astra 2400S, Scitex/Smart 342L, 2-Umax/Powerlook II, HP/ScanJet 4C PRESSROOM: Line 1 – 9-G/Super Community; Line 2 – 5-G/Community; Line 3 – 10-G/Urbanite; Folders – 4; Pasters – 6, 1; Reels and Stands – Mill/Stands. MAILROOM: Counter stackers – 2-HI/RS-3010, 1-HI/RS, LD, 1-BG/Count-O-Veyor 1055MM; Inserters and stuffers – 1-MM/7:1, 1-HI/1372 (Dual Delivery Lines), 1-MM/Stacker, 2-Id/Stacker; Bundle tying machines – 2/Bu, 2-/OVL, 1-OVL/Semi-automatic, 1-Ty/Tech; Addressing machine – Addressing ma BUSINESS COMPUTERS: Business Software – Microsoft/DOS 310, Microsoft/Works, Microsoft/Office, Lotus, Corel/Word Perfect 6.1, Microsoft/Windows 95; Business Hardware – IBM/Sys 36, 3-Convergent/AWS, PC 386, PC 486, PC 586

MASSACHUSETTS

ATHOL

ATHOL DAILY NEWS

225 Exchange St., Athol, Mass., 1331; gen tel (978) 249-3535; adv tel (978) 249-3535; gen fax (978) 249-9630; gen e-mail adn@atholdailynews.com; web site www.atholdailynews.com
Published: Mon, Tues, Wed, Thur, Fri, Sat, Sun
Weekday Frequency: e
Saturday Frequency: m
Circulation: 4,661; 4,661(sat)
Last Audit: September 30, 2003
Price: 2.40/wk; 9.10/mo; 135.00/yr (carrier).
Advertising: Open inch rate $7.60
News services: AP.
Politics: Independent-Republican.
Not Published: New Year; Memorial Day; Independence Day; Labor Day; Thanksgiving; Christmas.
Special Editions: River Rat Review (Apr); First Baby Contest (Dec); Boy Scout Page (Feb); Bridal Supplement (Jan); Graduation Pages (Jun); Graduation Pages (May); Thanksgiving Greetings (Nov); Fire Prevention (Oct); Football Pages (Sept).
Special Weekly Sections: Amusements (Fri); Best Food Day (Mon); Quabbin Times (Sat).
Adv. Dir. .... Daniel Mahoney
Dir., Mktg./Promo. .... Richard J. Chase
Circ. Mgr. .... Betty Jacques
Mng. Ed. .... Deborah Porter
Real Estate Ed. .... Barney B. Cummings
Opns. Dir./Prodn. Supt. .... Robert A. Perkins
Market Information: TMC.
Mechanical available: Offset; Black and 3 ROP colors; insert accepted - single sheet 8 1/2 x 11 minimum; page cutoffs - 22 3/4.
Mechanical Specifications: Type page 13 x 21; E - 6 cols, 2 1/16, 1/4 between; A - 6 cols, 2 1/16, 1/4 between; C - 8 cols, 1 1/2, 1/8 between.
Commodity Consumption: Avg. Page Number Per Issue - Daily 14; Avg. Page Number Per Issue - Plates Used 3684; widths 28; Newsprint Used - Short Tons 280; Printing Ink Used - Black 12000; Printing Ink Used - Color 1300; Printing Ink Used - Pages Printed 7368.
Equipment EDITORIAL: Front-end Software – Baseview.; Editorial Hardware – APP/Mac; Editorial Printers – MON/PageScan, GCC CLASSIFIED: Front-end Software – Baseview.; Classified Hardware – APP/Mac; Layout Software – APP/Mac.; Display Hardware – Vision Data; Production Equipment – 1-Nu; Cameras – 1-Nu/20 x 24. PRESSROOM: Line 1 – 4-G.; Bundle tying machines – 1/Strapex; Addressing machine – 1-RSK/TRS 80, Vision Data/Circ Sys, 1-/Ch.; Business Hardware – RSK/TRS-80, Vision Data/Business Sys, APP/Mac Desktop Pub Sys

ATTLEBORO

THE SUN CHRONICLE

34 S. Main St., Attleboro, Mass., 02703-0600; gen tel (508) 222-7000; adv tel (508) 222-7000; ed tel (508) 222-7000; gen fax (508) 226-0456; adv fax (508) 236-0461; ed fax (508) 236-0462; adv e-mail news@thesunchronicle.com; web site www.thesunchronicle.com
Published: Mon, Tues, Wed, Thur, Fri, Sat, Sun
Weekday Frequency: m
Saturday Frequency: m
Circulation: 14,245; 16,026(sat); 15,258(sun)
Last Audit: ABC September 30, 2011
Price: 4.00/wk (home delivery); 15.75/mo (home delivery); 195.00 (home delivery)/yr.
Advertising: Open inch rate $18.75
Insert rate: 57/m
News services: AP
Politics: 1971
Advertising not accepted: Y
Not Published: New Year; Independence Day; Thanksgiving; Christmas.
Own facility?: Y
Special Editions: Lawn and Garden (Apr); Doing Busines with Your Neighbors (Aug); Last Chance Gift Guide (Dec); Weddings (Feb); Your Home (Jan); Emergency Guide (Jul); Living Here (Jun); Recycling Guide (Mar); Mother's Day Pictorial (May); Early Holiday Gift Guide (Nov); D
Special Weekly Sections: Pets(Mon); Teens (Tues); Best Food Day (Wed), entertainment (Thurs).
Magazines: Relish (Monthly); USA WEEKEND Magazine (S); American Profile (Weekly).
Pub. .... Oreste D'Arconte
Bus. Mgr. .... Antonio H. DaRosa
Mktg./Promo. Mgr. .... Ray Lacaillade
Ed. .... Mike Kirby
Asst. Mng. Ed., Features .... Ken Ross
Asst. Mng. Ed., News .... Craig Borges
Editorial Page Ed. .... Mark Flanagan
Politics Reporter .... Jim Hand
Sports Ed. .... Dale Ransom
Sports Ed., Sunday .... Andrew Bryce
Sunday Ed. .... Tom Reilly
General Manager .... Jeff Peterson
Market Information: Split run; TMC;
Mechanical available: Offset; Black and 4 ROP colors; insert accepted; page cutoffs - 22 3/4.
Mechanical Specifications: Type page 13 x 21 1/2; E - 6 cols, 2 1/16, 1/8 between; A - 6 cols, 2 1/16, 1/8 between; C - 9 cols, 1 3/8, 1/16 between.
Commodity Consumption: Avg. Page Number Per Issue - Daily 32.8; Avg. Page Number Per Issue - Plates Used 18500; Avg. Page Number Per Issue - Sunday 81.3; widths 25; Newsprint Used - Metric Tons 2100; Printing Ink Used - Black 40000; Printing Ink Used - Color 7000; Printing Ink
Equipment EDITORIAL: Front-end Software – CText/Dateline, Microsoft/Windows NT.; Editorial Hardware – Novell/Netserver; Editorial Equipment – AU/APS 6-84 ACS, Imagesetters; Editorial Printers – Typhoon/800 dpi, Hyphen/600 dpi CLASSIFIED: Front-end Software – CText/OS-2 Advision.; Classified Hardware – Novell/Netserver; Classified Printers – 2-Typhoon/800 dpi DISPLAY: Ad make-up applications – QuarkXPress, Microsoft/Windows NT; Layout Software – 3-PC, Layout/8000.; Display Hardware – PC fileserver; Display Printers – Hyphen/600 dpi, Typhoon/800 dpi, 2-AU/APS 6/84 PRODUCTION: Pagination Software – QPS/QuarkXPress 3.1.; Production Equipment – 2-AU/APS 6/84 ACS, 3-APP/Mac LaserWriter NTX, Hyphen/600 dpi, Typhoon/800 dpi PRESSROOM: Line 1 – 10-G/Urbanite; Folders – 1 MAILROOM: Counter stackers – 2-HL/Monitor II; Inserters and stuffers – GMA/SLS 1000 (10 pockets); Bundle tying machines – 1/MLN, 2-MLN/ML2EE, Power Strap.; Other equipment –stitcher-trimmer BUSINESS COMPUTERS: Business Software – GEAC/Vision Shift; Business Hardware – HP/3000 Model 927
Delivery method: Mail, Newsstand, Private Carrier, Racks

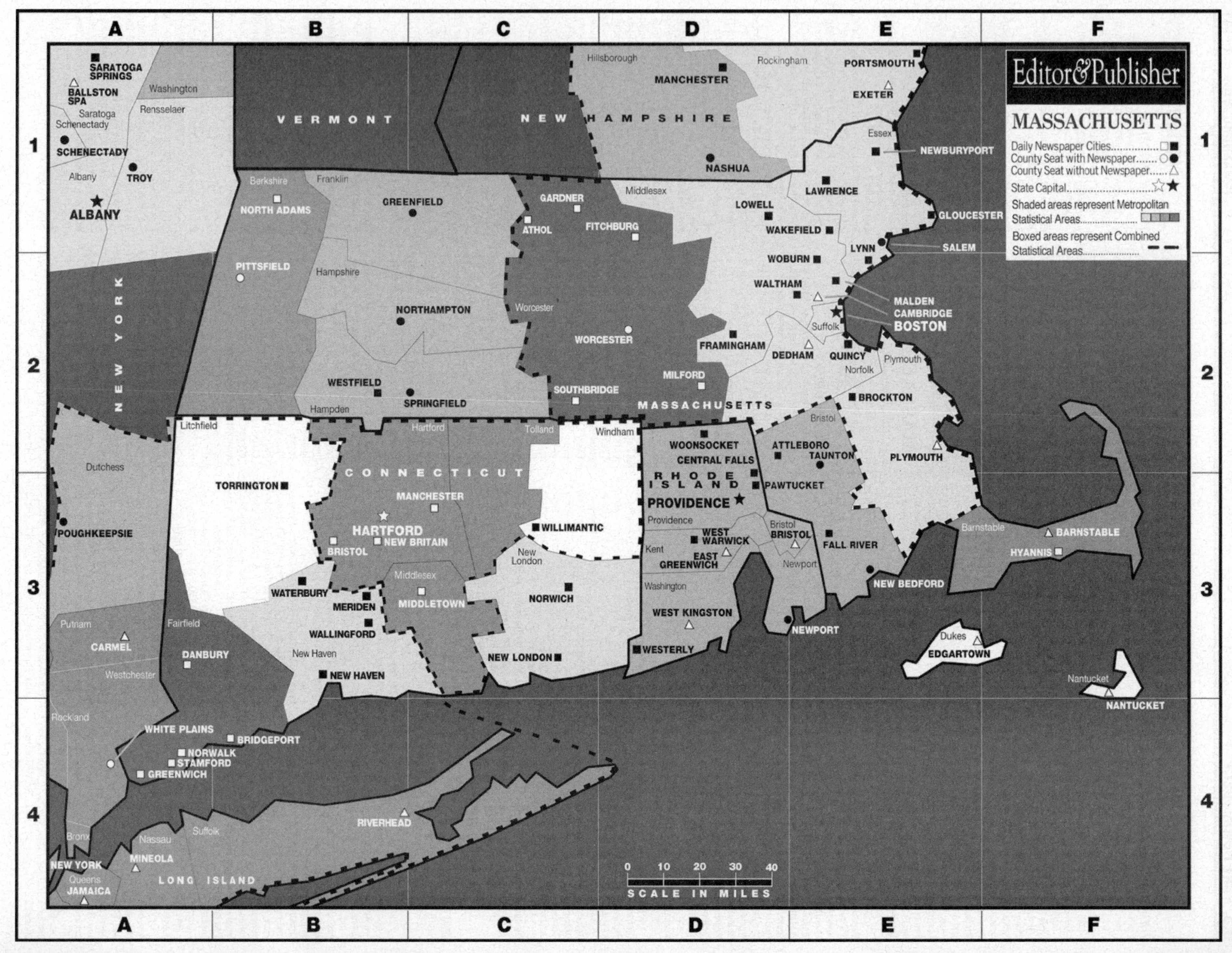

Editor&Publisher
MASSACHUSETTS
Daily Newspaper Cities
County Seat with Newspaper
County Seat without Newspaper
State Capital
Shaded areas represent Metropolitan Statistical Areas
Boxed areas represent Combined Statistical Areas
VERMONT
NEW HAMPSHIRE
NEW YORK
MASSACHUSETTS
CONNECTICUT
RHODE ISLAND
LONG ISLAND
SARATOGA SPRINGS
BALLSTON SPA
Saratoga
Schenectady
SCHENECTADY
TROY
Albany
ALBANY
Washington
Rensselaer
Berkshire
Franklin
NORTH ADAMS
GREENFIELD
PITTSFIELD
Hampshire
NORTHAMPTON
WESTFIELD
SPRINGFIELD
Hampden
GARDNER
ATHOL
FITCHBURG
Worcester
WORCESTER
SOUTHBRIDGE
MILFORD
Hillsborough
MANCHESTER
NASHUA
Rockingham
PORTSMOUTH
EXETER
Essex
NEWBURYPORT
LAWRENCE
Middlesex
LOWELL
WAKEFIELD
WOBURN
WALTHAM
LYNN
SALEM
GLOUCESTER
MALDEN
CAMBRIDGE
BOSTON
Suffolk
FRAMINGHAM
DEDHAM
QUINCY
Norfolk
Plymouth
BROCKTON
Bristol
ATTLEBORO
TAUNTON
PLYMOUTH
PAWTUCKET
FALL RIVER
NEW BEDFORD
Barnstable
BARNSTABLE
HYANNIS
Dukes
EDGARTOWN
Nantucket
NANTUCKET
Litchfield
TORRINGTON
Hartford
Tolland
Windham
MANCHESTER
HARTFORD
NEW BRITAIN
BRISTOL
WILLIMANTIC
New London
NORWICH
NEW LONDON
Middlesex
MIDDLETOWN
WATERBURY
MERIDEN
WALLINGFORD
New Haven
NEW HAVEN
WOONSOCKET
CENTRAL FALLS
PROVIDENCE
Providence
Kent
WEST WARWICK
EAST GREENWICH
BRISTOL
Newport
NEWPORT
Washington
WEST KINGSTON
WESTERLY
Dutchess
POUGHKEEPSIE
Putnam
CARMEL
Fairfield
DANBURY
Westchester
Rockland
WHITE PLAINS
BRIDGEPORT
NORWALK
STAMFORD
GREENWICH
RIVERHEAD
Bronx
Nassau
Suffolk
NEW YORK
MINEOLA
Queens
JAMAICA
0 10 20 30 40
SCALE IN MILES

BEVERLY

THE SALEM NEWS

32 Dunham Road, Beverly, Mass., 01915; gen tel (978) 922-1234; gen fax (978) 927-4330; web site www.salemnews.com

Group: CNHI
Published: Mon, Tues, Wed, Thur, Fri, Sat
Weekday Frequency: e
Saturday Frequency: e
Circulation: 10,087; 10,087(sat)
Last Audit: ABC September 30, 2011

BOSTON

THE BOSTON GLOBE

135 Morrissey Blvd., Boston, Mass., 2125; gen tel (617) 929-2000; adv tel (617) 929-2100; ed tel (617) 929-2000; gen fax (617) 929-3318; adv fax (617) 929-3481; ed fax (617) 929-3186; gen e-mail pr@globe.com; adv e-mail advertising@globe.com; ed e-mail news@globe.com; web site www.boston.com

Published: Mon, Tues, Wed, Thur, Fri, Sat, Sun
Weekday Frequency: m
Saturday Frequency: m
Circulation: 205,939; 208,562(sat); 360,186(sun)
Last Audit: ABC September 30, 2011
Price: 6.75/wk, $7.00/wk (AOZ); 27.00/mo; 351.00/yr.
Advertising: Open inch rate $685.00
News services: AP, DJ, LAT-WP, MCT, RN.
Politics: Independent.
Special Editions: Cape Cod Distinctive Homes (Apr); College Football Preview (Aug); Continuing Education (Dec); Florida (Feb); Valentine's Day Restaurants (Jan); NHIS NASCAR (Jul); Cape Cod Distinctive Shopping (Jun); Health and Hospitals (Mar); Mother's Day Restaurants (M
Special Weekly Sections: Real Estate (S); Life At Home (Thur); Health/Science (Tues); Food (Wed).
Magazines: Parade (S).
Pub. .... P. Steven Ainsley
Pres. .... Chris Mayer
Sr. Vice Pres./CFO/Treasurer .... George Barrios
Sr. Vice Pres., Employee Rel. Gregory L. Thornton
Vice Pres., Employee Rel. .... Harriet E. Gould
Vice Pres., HR .... Christopher Hall
Dir., Benefits .... Stephen J. Behenna
Mng. Dir., Pdct. Innovation .... Lucy Bartholomay
Chief Adv. Officer .... Samuel P. Martin
Adv. Vice Pres., Nat'l/Retail .... Lauren Chacon
Adv. Vice Pres., Recruitment/Auto/Real Estate/Travel Lisa DeSisto
Adv. Dir., Cross Media Sales .. Michael Flanagan
Adv. Dir., Opns. .... Richard Masotta
Adv. Dir., Retail .... Peter Ockerbloom
Adv. Dir., Serv. .... Thomas P. Folan
Adv. Div. Mgr., Amusement .... Elizabeth Sucher
Adv. Div. Mgr., Automotive .... John Birolini
Adv. Div. Mgr., City Weekly Mark Joseph Sullivan
Adv. Div. Mgr., Commun. .... Theresa Ricciardi
Adv. Div. Mgr., Cor. .... Donna Rice
Market Information: ADS; Split run; TMC; Zoned editions.
Mechanical available: Offset; Black and 3 ROP colors; insert accepted - product samples; page cutoffs - 22.
Mechanical Specifications: Type page 12 1/2 x 22; E - 6 cols, 1 5/6, 1/8 between; A - 6 cols, 1 5/6, 1/8 between; C - 10 cols, 1, 1/16 between.
Commodity Consumption: Avg. Page Number Per Issue - Daily 93; Avg. Page Number Per Issue - Plates Used 824000; Avg. Page Number Per Issue - Saturday 99; Avg. Page Number Per Issue - Sunday 244; widths 50; Newsprint Used - Metric Tons 130249; Newsprint Used - Short Tons 130000;
Equipment EDITORIAL: Front-end Software – CCI.; Editorial Hardware – SUN 6800; Editorial Equipment – Reporter System News Engin; Editorial Printers – HP CLASSIFIED: Front-end Software – ATEX IAS.; Classified Hardware – PDP 11; Classified Equipment – Edgil/credit card processing, MCT/AdFax, MCT/AdFast, Ad Express, AP/AdSend, Cascade/DataFlow; Classified Printers – HP DISPLAY: Ad make-up applications – Cx, AT; Layout Software – 6-IBM/RS 6000-320 at class page, 5-Cx/360, 3-Cx/380, 3-Cx/Sparc IFC, APP/Mac, Cascade/Image, Data Flow.; Display Hardware – ATEX PDP 11; Display Printers – AII, AU/Oman direct to plate PRODUCTION: Pagination Software – AT/Ed Page 1.7, Press To Go, AT/Architect.; Production Equipment – TextBridge, 5-Jensen PRESSROOM: Line 1 – 10-G/Metroliner, 2-G/Metro Color (4/4-color tower); Line 2 – 10-G/Metroliner, 2-G/Metro Color (4/4-color tower); Line 3 – 10-G/Metroliner, 2-G/Metro Color (4/4 color tower); Line 4 – 10-G/Metroliner, 2-G/Metro Color (4/4 color tower); Line 5 – 10 MAILROOM: Counter stackers – 21-QWI/301, 6-HL/Dual Carriers, 16/QWI; Inserters and stuffers – 15-MM/6:1, 3-GMA/Alphaliner 14:1, 1-GMA/Alphaliner 6:1, 3-GMA/SLS 1000 28:2, 15-GMA/SLS 1000 6:1, 2-GMA/SLS 2000 8:1; Bundle tying machines – Dynaric/30, Power Strap/13; Audio Hardware – Micro Voice; Business Hardware – 1-DEC/VAX 7840, 1-DEC/VAX 7740, 2-DEC/VAX 6620, 1-DEC/VAX 6420, 3-DEC/Alpha 2000, 3-DEC/VAX 4000, 2-DEC/Alpha 4000

BOSTON HERALD

One Herald Sq., Boston, Mass., 02118-2297; gen tel (617) 426-3000; adv tel (617) 619-6601; ed tel (617) 619-6400; adv fax (617) 619-6160; ed fax (617) 619-6450; gen e-mail letterstotheeditor@bostonherald.com; adv e-mail natadv@bostonherald.com; web site www.bostonherald.com

Group: Metro Newspaper Advertising Services, Inc.
Published: Mon, Tues, Wed, Thur, Fri, Sat, Sun
Weekday Frequency: m
Saturday Frequency: m
Circulation: 113,798; 93,281(sat); 85,828(sun)
Last Audit: ABC September 30, 2011
Price: 4.25/wk; 18.60/mo (d, mail), $28.20/mo (dS, mail).
Advertising: Open inch rate $386.60
News services: AP, RN, Business Wire, DJ, TMS.
Politics: Independent.
Special Editions: Careers Extra (Monthly); Health (Semi-yearly).
Special Weekly Sections: Scene (Fri); Business Extra (Mon); Sports Pull-Out (S); Super Saturday Classifieds (Sat); Travel (Thur); Tuesday Business (Tues); Food (Wed).
Magazines: USA WEEKEND Magazine (S).
Owner/Pres./Pub. .... Patrick J. Purcell
Vice Pres., Finance .... Jeffrey Magram
Adv. Dir., Classified .... Joseph J. LoPilato
Adv. Dir., Display .... Scott Whalen
Adv. Mgr., Classified .... Beth O'Grady
Adv. Mgr., Display .... Patrick Purcell
Adv. Mgr., Market Research .... Dianne Chin
Circ. Vice Pres. .... John Hoarty
Circ. Asst. Dir. .... James DeSalvo
Circ. Mgr., Home Delivery .... Gerald Sher
Circ. Mgr., Mktg. .... Carol Conry
Circ. Mgr., Single Copy Sales .... John Palmer
Circ. Coord. .... Arthur Vachon
Ed. in Chief .... Kevin R. Convey
Deputy Mng. Ed., Features .... Sandra Kent
Deputy Bus. Ed. .... Frank Quaratiello
Sr. Exec. City Ed. .... Eric Convey
Exec. City Ed. .... Jen Miller
Design/Prodn. Ed. .... Jim Potter
Editorial Page Ed. .... Shelly Cohen
Market Information: Split run.
Mechanical available: Letterpress (direct); Black and 3 ROP colors; insert accepted; page cutoffs - 22 3/4.
Mechanical Specifications: Type page 10 1/2 x 13 1/4; E - 5 cols, 2, 1/8 between; A - 5 cols, 2, 1/8 between; C - 9 cols, 1 1/20, 1/8 between.
Commodity Consumption: Avg. Page Number Per Issue - Daily 104; Avg. Page Number Per Issue - Plates Used 350000; Avg. Page Number Per Issue - Sunday 168; widths 28; Newsprint Used - Metric Tons 45000; Printing Ink Used - Black 1100000; Printing Ink Used - Color 28000; Printing
Equipment EDITORIAL: Front-end Software – Atex 4.0.; Editorial Hardware – AT/9000; Editorial Equipment – 124-AT/Terminal, APP/Mac Radius, APP/Mac IIfx, APP/Super Mac, APP/Mac, 10-PC 486, 22-APP/Mac; Editorial Printers – 2-Panasonic/1180, 5-Canon/Laser, 3-LaserMaster/1800 DAF, 4-QMS/860 CLASSIFIED: Front-end Software – Unisys/Ad Manager 3.0.; Classified Hardware – Sun/E450; Classified Equipment – 40-PC Clients; Classified Printers – Panasonic/1180, 1-C.Itoh/8000, 2-HP/DeskJet 520, 1-HP/LaserJet IIP, 1-PAN/KXP-1826, 1-PAN/KXP-1624, 1-PAN/KXP-2124 DISPLAY: Ad make-up applications – NPSI/Classpag; Layout Software – MEI/ALS.; Display Hardware – 15-APP/Mac PRODUCTION: Pagination Software – ESE/Editorial News Layout.; Production Equipment – 3-Na/Titan III, 1-AG/25, 1-AG/25S, 1-AG/25XT; Cameras – Scanners □ 3-AG/Duoscan, 2-Kk/RF 52000, 1-Nikon/Super Coolscan, 4-Polaroid/Slide, 1-Tecsa/Copy Dot Scanner PRESSROOM: Line 1 – 17-H/Color Convertible 1958; Line 2 – 12-H/Color Convertible 1958; Line 4 – H/Color Convertible 1958; Line 5 – H/Color Convertible 1958; Line 6 – H/Color Convertible 1958; Line 7 – 7; Press Drives – 5, J&K/Power Conversion; Folders – 5-H/3:2 MAILROOM: Counter stackers – 5/HL, 8-QWI/351; Inserters and stuffers – S/NP630 26:1; Bundle tying machines – 5-MLN/2A, 10-/Dynaric; Wrapping singles – 2-Id, 3-/PS, 7-/HI. BUSINESS COMPUTERS: Business Software – Lawson:; Business Hardware – 1-Microsoft/NT CS System, 2-Unix C/S Systems, 1-Unix/SCO, 1-Unisys Advtg. System

THE CHRISTIAN SCIENCE MONITOR

210 Massachusetts Ave., Boston, Mass., 02115-3012; gen tel (617) 450-2000; adv tel (617) 450-2644; ed tel (617) 450-2305; adv fax (617) 450-2668; ed e-mail readercomment@csmonitor.com; web site www.csmonitor.com

Published: Sun
Weekday Frequency: m
Circulation: 52,214; 80,000(sun)
Last Audit: September 30, 2008
Price: 189.00/yr.
News services: RN, AP, CQ, DJ, LAT-WP, NYT, TMS, Federal News Service, Universal Press Sydnicate.
Politics: Independent. **Established:** 1908
Note: Effective March 27, 2009, The Christian Science Monitor shifted from daily (M-F) print to weekly print with a strong emphasis on its website, CSMonitor.com. It also publishes a subscriber-supported Daily News Briefing delivered via e-mail and is available in digital forms directly or via e-readers such as the Kindle and Nook.
Advertising not accepted: N
Own facility?: Y
Special Editions: Future Focus (quarterly)
Profile: Founded by Mary Baker Eddy in 1908, the Monitor is an international daily newspaper with a stated goal of injuring no man and blessing all mankind
Mng. Pub. .... Jonathan D. Wells
Adv. Dir. .... Bob Hanna
Ed. .... John Yemma
Mng. Ed. .... Marshall Ingwerson
Book Ed. .... Marjorie Kehe
Chief Editorial Writer .... Clayton Jones
Graphics Ed./Art Dir. .... John Kehe
Online Editor .... David Scott
Nat'l News Ed. .... Cheryl Sullivan
Business Editor .... Laurent Belsie
Int'l News Editor .... Amelia Newcomb
Weekly Editor .... Clay Collins
Photo Editor .... Alfredo Sosa
Circ. Dir. .... Brook Holmberg
Ed. at Large .... Richard C. Bergenheim
Mng. Ed., csmonitor.com .... Karla Vallance
Assoc. Ed., csmonitor.com .... Deborah Bloom
Back Page Ed. .... Scott Armstrong
Bus./Finance Ed. .... Vic Roberts
Cairo Bureau Chief .... Dan Murphy
Columnist .... Marilyn Gardner
Features Ed. .... Owen Thomas
Home Forum Ed. .... Judy Lowe
Market Information: Split run.
Mechanical available: Offset; Black and 3 ROP colors; insert accepted - stuffers; page cutoffs - 12 3/4.
Mechanical Specifications: Type page 10 7/16 x 13 7/8; E - 5 cols, 1 5/6, 1/8 between; A - 5 cols, 1 5/6, 1/8 between; C - 5 cols, between.
Commodity Consumption: Avg. Page Number Per Issue - Daily 20; Avg. Page Number Per Issue - Plates Used 23296; widths 13 3/4; Newsprint Used - Metric Tons 780; Printing Ink Used - Black 46800; Printing Ink Used - Color 46800; Printing Ink Used - Pages Printed 5824.
Equipment EDITORIAL: Front-end Software – QPS/QuarkXPress 4.11, QPS/Copydesk 2.1.; Editorial Hardware – 150-APP/Mac; Editorial Equipment – Umax/Scanner, Kodak/Professional RFS 3470 Scanner, Nikon/LS-3510 Scanner; Editorial Printers – HP/LaserJet, HP/Color LaserJet, HP/DeskJet; Layout Software – QPS/QuarkXPress. PRODUCTION: Pagination Software – AII/Plate Room Manager 2.6, AII/Page Pair.; Production Equipment – AG, AII/3850 CTP; Scanners – Scitex/Eversmart, X
Delivery method: Mail

FALL RIVER

THE HERALD NEWS

207 Pocasset St., Fall River, Mass., 02722-3010; gen tel (508) 676-8211; gen fax (508) 676-2588; adv fax (508) 676-2588; ed fax (508) 676-2566; adv e-mail ads@heraldnews.com; ed e-mail editor@heraldnews.com; news@heraldnews.com; web site www.heraldnews.com

Published: Mon, Tues, Wed, Thur, Fri, Sat, Sun
Weekday Frequency: m
Saturday Frequency: m
Circulation: 14,804; 16,547(sat); 15,719(sun)
Last Audit: ABC September 30, 2011
Price: 3.70/wk; 215.00/yr.
Advertising: Open inch rate $46.02
News services: AP.
Politics: Independent. **Established:** 1872
Note: The Herald News also prints the Taunton Daily Gazette.
Special Editions: Home & Garden (Apr); Fall River Celebrates America (Aug); Hockey & Basketball Preview (Dec); Auto (Feb); Super Bowl (Jan); Business Review (Jul); Bridal (Jun); Progress (Mar); Home & Garden (May); County Kids (Monthly); Christmas in Fall River (Nov); Home
Special Weekly Sections: Friday (Entertainment Guide) (Fri); Lifestyle (S); Real Estate Guide (Sat); Wheels (Tues); Best Food Day (Wed).
Magazines: Comics (S).
Pub. .... Sean Burke
Adv. Dir. .... Thomas Booth
Circ. Dir. .... Thomas Amato
Ed. in Chief .... Lisa Strattan
Mng. Ed. .... Jon Root
City Ed. .... Scott Dolan
Editorial Page Ed. .... Patrick Luce
Features Ed. .... Lynne Sullivan
Life Ed. .... Carla Dempsey
News Ed. .... Michael Pacheco
Sports Ed. .... Michael Thomas
Prodn. Dir. .... Michael Niland
Prodn. Mgr., Pre Press .... Eric Rivas
Market Information: TMC.
Mechanical available: Offset; Black and 3 ROP colors; insert accepted; page cutoffs - 22 3/4.
Mechanical Specifications: Type page 12 x 21 1/2; E - 6 cols, 2, 1/8 between; A - 6 cols, 2, 1/8 between; C - 9 cols, 2 3/4, 1/12 between.
Commodity Consumption: Avg. Page Number Per Issue - Daily 34; Avg. Page Number Per Issue - Plates Used 31220; Avg. Page Number Per Issue - Sunday 64; widths 12 1/2; Newsprint Used - Short Tons 3128; Printing Ink Used - Black 67254; Printing Ink Used - Color 15665; Printing Ink
Equipment EDITORIAL: Front-end Software – Dewar/View.; Editorial Hardware – Dewar/Information System, PC Network; Editorial Printers – MON CLASSIFIED: Front-end Software – Dewar/Sys IV.; Classified Hardware – Dewar/Information System, PC Network DISPLAY: Ad

make-up applications – Multi-Ad/Creator; Layout Software – Dewar.; Display Hardware – APP/Mac Centris 650; Display Printers – MON PRODUCTION: Pagination Software – Dewar/View, QPS.; Production Equipment – 2-MON/ExpressMaster 1200, 1-MON/PaperMaster 600; Cameras – 1-C/Spartan III; Scanners – Lf/Leafscan 35 PRESSROOM: Line 1 – 9-G/Urbanite single width; Folders – G/Urbanite 2:1; Pasters – 8-Jardis/Automatic 4540. MAILROOM: Counter stackers – 2-HL/Monitor, 1-MM/CN70 (388); Inserters and stuffers – GMA/SLS 1000A 10:1; Bundle tying machines – 4-MLN/EE, 1-MLN/2A; Addressing machine – 1-Ch/515010.; Audio Hardware – Method Five BUSINESS COMPUTERS: Business Software – INSI; Business Hardware – 1-Bs/92, IBM/AS-400

NORTHEAST PUBLISHING, INC.

207 Pocasset St., Fall River, Mass., 02722-3010; gen tel (508) 676-8211; gen fax (508) 673-3375; web site www.heraldnews.com

FITCHBURG

SENTINEL & ENTERPRISE

808 Main St., Fitchburg, Mass., 01420; gen tel (978) 343-6911; adv tel (978) 343-6911; ed tel (978) 343-6911; gen fax (978) 342-1158; adv fax (978) 345-8421; ed fax (978) 342-1158; gen e-mail news@sentinelandenterprise.com; adv e-mail advertising@mediaonene.com; ed e-mail news@sentinelandenterprise.com; web site www.sentinelandenterprise.com

Published: Mon, Tues, Wed, Thur, Fri, Sat, Sun
Weekday Frequency: m
Saturday Frequency: m
Circulation: 14,607; 14,580(sat); 17,108(sun)
Last Audit: ABC September 30, 2011
Price: 2.75/wk; 165.00/yr.
Advertising: Open inch rate $28.00
News services: AP, SHNS, TMS.
Politics: Independent. **Established:** 1838
Not Published: Christmas.
Special Editions: Back-to-School (Aug); Holiday Gift Guides (Dec); Washington's Birthday (Feb); Bride & Groom (Jan); Longso Bike Race (Jul); Spring Home Improvement (Mar); Graduation (May); Thanksgiving Sports (Nov); Fall Car Care (Oct); Fall Home Improvement (Sept).
Special Weekly Sections: Auto (Thur); Gallery of Homes (Wed); TV Week (Weekly).
Magazines: USA WEEKEND Magazine (S).
Pub.......Sean McDonald
Circ. Mgr.......Dennis West
Ed.......Jeff McMenemy
Sports Ed.......Ross Edwards
Prodn. Mgr., Graphics......Karen Fioretti
Market Information: ADS; Split run; TMC.
Mechanical available: Offset; Black and 3 ROP colors; insert accepted - single sheet; page cutoffs - 20 1/2.
Mechanical Specifications: Type page 13 x 21 1/2; E - 6 cols, 2 1/16, 1/8 between; A - 6 cols, 2 1/16, 1/8 between; C - 9 cols, 1 3/8, 1/16 between.
Commodity Consumption: Avg. Page Number Per Issue - Daily 28; Avg. Page Number Per Issue - Plates Used 9744; Avg. Page Number Per Issue - Sunday 40; widths 25; Newsprint Used - Metric Tons 1668; Printing Ink Used - Black 26158; Printing Ink Used - Color 3350; Printing Ink Used
Equipment EDITORIAL: Front-end Software – CText, Baseview/NewsEdit Pro.; Editorial Hardware – CText, APP/Mac; Editorial Equipment – HP/Laser Printer; Editorial Printers – Pre Press/Panther CLASSIFIED: Front-end Software – PPI.; Classified Hardware – CText, Microsoft/Windows NT; Classified Printers – Pre Press/Panther DISPLAY: Ad make-up applications – QPS/QuarkXPress, Adobe/Photoshop; Layout Software – Layout/8000.; Display Hardware – APP/Power Mac; Display Printers – Pre Press/Panther, HP/LaserJet 4VMV, HP/LaserJet 4Plus PRODUCTION: Pagination Software – QPS/QuarkXPress.; Production Equipment – Pre Press/Panther, HP/LaserJet 4Plus, HP/LaserJet 4VMV; Cameras – LE/121; Scanners – Nikon, Polaroid PRESSROOM: Line 1 – 8-G/Urbanite; Line 2 – 6-MAN; Folders – 1-G/2:1, MR/2:1; Press control system – Thin Core; Press registration system – Duarte. MAILROOM: Counter stackers – S/J4109-2200-2, QWI/300-4; Inserters and stuffers – K&M/1372-2; Bundle tying machines – OVL, Dynaric; Addressing machine – KR; Other equipment –MM. AUDIO: Audio Software – U.S. Telecom 4.31; Audio Hardware – ITN, Texax Micro BUSINESS COMPUTERS: Business Software – PBS/MediaPlus; Business Hardware – PBS

FRAMINGHAM

METROWEST DAILY NEWS

33 New York Ave., Framingham, Mass., 01701-9157; gen tel (508) 626-3800; adv tel (508) 626-3835; ed tel (508) 626-4415; gen fax (508) 626-3900; ed fax (508) 626-4400; gen e-mail metrowest@cnc.com; ed e-mail mdnletters@cnc.com; web site www.metrowestdailynews.com; www.townonline.com

Published: Mon, Tues, Wed, Thur, Fri, Sat, Sun
Weekday Frequency: m
Saturday Frequency: m
Circulation: 18,087; 16,522(sat); 22,314(sun)
Last Audit: ABC September 30, 2011
Price: 4.25/wk; 221.00/yr (carrier), $286.00/yr (mail).
Advertising: Open inch rate $43.95
News services: AP, SHNS.
Politics: Independent. **Established:** 1897
Special Editions: Spring Home & Garden (Apr); Back-to-School/College (Aug); Last Minute Gift Guide (Dec); Presidents' Day (Feb); Weddings (Jan); Community Guides (Jul); MetroWest Community Guide (Jun); Business (Mar); Health & Lifestyles (May); Holiday Gift Guide (Nov); In
Special Weekly Sections: Autoweekly (Fri); MetroWest Business Journal (Mon); Expanded Entertainment (S); Mutual Fund Listing (Sat); MetroWest Weekend (Thur); Health and Environment (Tues); Best Food Day (Wed).
Magazines: USA WEEKEND Magazine (S).
Profile: Daily newspaper
Pub.......Perk Davis
Adv. Vice Pres.......Mark Cohen
Vice Pres., Promo......Robin Lorenzen
Circ. Dir.......Linda Vahey Steele
Circ. Mgr., Transportation......Gary Burnell
Mng. Ed.......Chris Biondi
Bus. Ed.......Greg Turner
Editorial Page Ed.......Rick Holmes
Features Ed.......Nancy Olesin
News Ed.......Richard Lodge
Photo Dept. Mgr.......Art Illman
Sports Ed.......Craig Larson
Data Processing Mgr.......Barbara Ball
Site Mgr.......John Perron
Telecom Mgr.......Kenneth Haggerty
Opns. Dir., Distr./Post Press......Todd Fitzgerald
Market Information: ADS; Split run; TMC; Zoned editions.
Mechanical available: Offset; Black and 3 ROP colors; insert accepted; page cutoffs - 21 1/2.
Mechanical Specifications: Type page 11 3/4 x 21; E - 6 cols, 2 1/16, 1/8 between; A - 6 cols, 2 1/16, 1/8 between; C - 9 cols, 1 3/8, 1/16 between.
Commodity Consumption: Avg. Page Number Per Issue - Daily 36; Avg. Page Number Per Issue - Plates Used 266000; Avg. Page Number Per Issue - Saturday 36; Avg. Page Number Per Issue - Sunday 76; widths 24 1/4; Newsprint Used - Short Tons 16000; Printing Ink Used - Black 320000;
Equipment EDITORIAL: Front-end Software – III/Editorial System, Microsoft/Windows 95.; Editorial Hardware – Pentium/PC 586, PC 486; Editorial Equipment – Microcom/Modems, US Robotics/Modems; Editorial Printers – HP/LaserJet 4MV CLASSIFIED: Front-end Software – III/Classified Software.; Classified Hardware – PC 486; Classified Equipment – Microcom/Modems; Classified Printers – HP/LaserJet 4MV; Layout Software – 2-HI/2002, 2-HI/2220, 2-HI/1420, 1-COM/MDT 350, 2-HI/1250, 2-Vecra. PRODUCTION: Pagination Software – QPS/QuarkXPress 3.3.; Production Equipment – 3-Graham, 2-CK Optical/5%; Cameras – 2-Image Maker/506A, 2-C/Newspager; Scanners – 3-Kk/2035 Film Scanner, 1-AG/Arcus Plus Color Scanner, 1-Autokon/Flatbed Scanner PRESSROOM: Line 1 – 12-G/Urbanite single width 1979; Line 2 – 12-G/Urbanite single width 1979; Line 3 – 1-G/HV single width 1979; Press Drives – 3; Folders – 2-G/Urbanite 1000 Series w 1/4 Folders, 1-G/HV Signature Folder; Pasters – 20-G/Automatic 2 arm; Reels and Stands – Reels and St MAILROOM: Counter stackers – 4-HL/Monitor, 2/Compass, 1-/RIMA; Inserters and stuffers – 1-GMA/Alpaliner, 1-GMA/SLS 1000; Bundle tying machines – 6-/MLN; Addressing machine – 3-Domino/Ink Jet Printer. BUSINESS COMPUTERS: Business Software – Microsoft/Windows 95; Business Hardware – Sun/Sparc Station 20-Unix, 2-Axiom/Netware 4.11

GARDNER

THE GARDNER NEWS

309 Central St., Gardner, Mass., 1440; gen tel (978) 632-8000; adv tel (978) 632-9240; ed tel (978) 632-8000; gen fax (978) 630-2231; adv fax (978) 630-2231; ed fax (978) 630-5410; gen e-mail businessoffice@thegardnernews.com; adv e-mail ads@thegardnernews.com; ed e-mail editorialdept@thegardnernews.com; web site www.thegardnernews.com

Published: Mon, Tues, Wed, Thur, Fri, Sat
Weekday Frequency: e
Saturday Frequency: e
Circulation: 4,900; 4,900(sat)
Last Audit: ABC September 30, 2011
Price: 156.00/yr.
Advertising: Open inch rate $10.05
News services: AP.
Politics: Independent.
Not Published: New Year; Memorial Day; Independence Day; Labor Day; Thanksgiving; Christmas.
Special Weekly Sections: Lifestyle (Sat); Lifestyle (Thur); Business (Tues); Lifestyle (Wed).
Pub.......Alberta Bell
Acct. Servs. Mgr.......Pam Hebert
Circ. Dir.......Crystal Kingsbury
Mng. Ed.......Daniel Kittredge
Sports Ed.......Tom Trainque
Prodn. Mgr.......Joanna Deizeium
Prodn. Mgr., Pressroom......Cornelius Harris
Mechanical available: Offset; Black and 2 ROP colors; insert accepted; page cutoffs - 22 1/4.
Mechanical Specifications: Type page 12 5/8 x 21 1/4; E - 7 cols, 1 5/8, 1/6 between; A - 7 cols, 1 5/8, 1/6 between; C - 7 cols, 1 5/8, 1/6 between.
Commodity Consumption: Avg. Page Number Per Issue - Daily 16; Avg. Page Number Per Issue - Plates Used 2600; widths 28; Newsprint Used - Short Tons 306; Printing Ink Used - Pages Printed 4960.
Equipment EDITORIAL: Front-end Software – COM/One System.; Editorial Hardware – 4-COM/Intrepid 4, COM/Power Editors-28A CLASSIFIED: Front-end Software – Baseview/Class Manager.; Classified Hardware – 4-APP/Mac LC 4-40; Classified Equipment – 1-IBM/Selectric III; Classified Printers – 1-APP/Mac ImageWriter II, 1-Okidata/293, 1-NEC/90 LaserPrinter DISPLAY: Ad make-up applications – APP/Mac with Multi-Ad.; Display Hardware – 3-APP/Mac ci 8-160; Display Printers – 2-NEC/90 LaserPrinter; Production Equipment – Nu/Flip Top FT40UNS; Cameras – Acti/Process; Scanners – Typist/3.0, Konica, ECR/Autokon 1040. PRESSROOM: Line 1 – KP/Color King F-11; Line 2 – KP/Color King F-11; Line 3 – KP/Color King F-11; Line 4 – KP/Color King F-11; Folders – 1; Bundle tying machines – 1-Akebono/Oval Strapping. BUSINESS COMPUTERS: Business Software – Armor/Premier; Business Hardware – 1-Samsung/Monochrome Display Monitor, 1-IBM/PC

GLOUCESTER

GLOUCESTER DAILY TIMES

36 Whittemore St., Gloucester, Mass., 01930; gen tel (978) 283-7000; adv tel (978) 283-7000; ed tel (978) 283-7000; gen fax (978) 282-4397; adv fax (978) 282-4397; ed fax (978) 282-4397; gen e-mail gdp@ecnnews.com; web site www.gloucestertimes.com; www.northshoreonline.com

Group: CNHI
Published: Mon, Tues, Wed, Thur, Fri, Sat
Weekday Frequency: e
Saturday Frequency: e
Circulation: 8,055; 8,055(sat)
Last Audit: ABC September 30, 2011
Price: $.75day/$3.50 wk
Advertising: Open inch rate $25.80
News services: AP, ONS.
Politics: Independent.
Not Published: Christmas.
Special Editions: Spring Home Improvement (Apr); Washington's Birthday Auto (Feb); Business Update (Jan); Guide to the North Shore (Jun); Spring Bride (Mar); Spring Real Estate Review (May); Fall Home & Garden (Oct); Fall Fashions (Sept).
Special Weekly Sections: Food (Wed).
Magazines: USA WEEKEND Magazine (Fri); Relish (Monthly).
Publisher......Al Getler
Adv. Dir., Retail......Timothy E. Brady
Directr of Circulation......Steve Milone
Editor......Ray Lamont
Market Information: TMC.
Mechanical available: Offset; Black and 3 ROP colors; insert accepted - any; page cutoffs - 21.
Mechanical Specifications: Type page 11 1/2 x 21; E - 6 cols, 1 13/16, 5/16 between; A - 6 cols, 1 13/16, 5/16 between; C - 9 cols, 1 7/32, 3/22 between.
Commodity Consumption: Avg. Page Number Per Issue - Daily 32; Avg. Page Number Per Issue - Plates Used 4728; widths 50; Newsprint Used - Metric Tons 877; Printing Ink Used - Black 10835.
Equipment EDITORIAL: Front-end Software – Mediaspan; Editorial Hardware – Mediaspan; Editorial Printers – QMS/860 CLASSIFIED: Front-end Software – APT; Classified Hardware – APT DISPLAY: Ad make-up applications – APT; Layout Software – MEI/ALS 7.0; Display Hardware – APP/Mac, PC; Display Printers – HP/ Laser Jet 4 Plus PRODUCTION: Pagination Software – Adobe
InDesign; Production Equipment – Agfa Advantage Imagesetters; Cameras – Kodak
Cannon; Scanners – ECR/100
Epson/636
Polaroid/Sprint S PRESSROOM: Line 1 – 8-G/Metro (3 color decks); Folders – 1-G/Double 2:1 MAILROOM: Counter stackers – Goss Olympian; Inserters and stuffers – 4 wo
Goss 630 inserters; Mailroom control system – Omnizone; Addressing machine – Domino; Business Hardware – IBM/AS-400
Delivery method: Newsstand, Private Carrier, Racks

GREENFIELD

THE RECORDER

14 Hope St., Greenfield, Mass., 01302; gen tel (413) 772-0261; adv tel (413) 772-0261; ed tel (413) 772-0261; gen fax (413) 772-2906; adv fax (413) 774-5511; ed fax (413) 774-5020; gen e-mail info@recorder.com; adv e-mail ads@recorder.com; ed e-mail letters@recorder.com; news@recorder.com; web site http://www.recorder.com/

Published: Mon, Tues, Wed, Thur, Fri, Sat
Weekday Frequency: m

Saturday Frequency: m
Circulation: 11,500; 11,500(sat)
Last Audit: ABC September 30, 2011
Price: 12.00/mo; 144.00/yr.
Advertising: Open inch rate $22.22
News services: AP, LAT-WP.
Politics: Independent.
Not Published: Christmas.
Special Editions: Business (Apr); Back-to-School (Aug); Holiday Recipes (Dec); Finance (Feb); Bridal (Jan); Summer Tourism (Jun); First Snow (Nov); Winter Tourism (Oct); Fall Tourism (Sept).
Special Weekly Sections: Rental Property Page (Fri); Child Services (Mon); Home & Garden (Sat); Arts/Entertainment (Thur); Classes, Courses & Workshops (Tues).
Magazines: Relish (Monthly); USA WEEKEND Magazine (Sat); American Profile (Weekly).
Broadcast Affiliations: WFSB (CBS) Hartford, CT; WCVB (ABC) Boston; WHDH (CBS) Boston; WBZ (NBC) Boston; WGGB (ABC) Springfield, MA; WWLP (NBC) Springfield, MA; WGBY (PBS).
Pub. .... Dennis Skoglund
Controller .... Jeff Morse
Bus. Mgr. .... Pat Maleno
Adv. Dir. .... Richard Fahey
Adv. Mgr., Classified .... Jeanne Martin
Circ. Dir. .... Kevin Lamagdelaine
Editorial Bd .... Kay Berenson
Editorial Bd. .... Timothy A. Blagg
Mng. Ed. .... George Forcier
Books Ed .... Adam Orth
Bus. Ed .... Bob York
Copy Desk Chief .... Greg Taylor
Editorial Page Ed. .... Justin Abelson
Market Information: ADS; TMC.
Mechanical available: Offset; Black and 3 ROP colors; insert accepted - all; page cutoffs - 22 3/4.
Mechanical Specifications: Type page 13 x 21 3/8; E - 6 cols, 2 1/2, 1/6 between; A - 6 cols, 2 1/2, 1/6 between; C - 9 cols, 1 5/16, 3/32 between.
Commodity Consumption: Avg. Page Number Per Issue - Daily 27; Avg. Page Number Per Issue - Plates Used 10000; widths 27 1/2; Newsprint Used - Metric Tons 849; Newsprint Used - Short Tons 936; Printing Ink Used - Black 19586; Printing Ink Used - Color 3672; Printing Ink Used -
Equipment EDITORIAL: Front-end Software – Atex/Prestige.; Editorial Hardware – Pentium; Editorial Equipment – Pre Press/Panther Pro 36; Editorial Printers – Epson, HP CLASSIFIED: Front-end Software – Baseview.; Classified Hardware – 5-APP/Mac; Classified Printers – APP/Laser Writer DISPLAY: Ad make-up applications – Multi/Ad Creator; Layout Software – MEI/ALS.; Display Hardware – Macintosh; Display Printers – Xante/Accel-a-Writer 3G PRODUCTION: Pagination Software – Atex Prestige.; Production Equipment – 2-Pre Press/Panther Pro 36, Nu; Cameras – C/Spartan I; Scanners – Nikon/LS 1000, Pixel-Craft/8200 PRESSROOM: Line 1 – 5-G/Urbanite 1966, DEV/2400 1984; Line 2 – 1-G/(3-color unit) 1996; Press Drives – Feb-95; Folders – 1-G/Urbanite 1966; Press control system – 1-1995. MAILROOM: Counter stackers – 2/QWI; Inserters and stuffers – HI/624; Bundle tying machines – Strapex, Dynaric; Addressing machine – KR.; Business Hardware – HP/3000

HYANNIS

CAPE COD TIMES

319 Main St., Hyannis, Mass., 02601; gen tel (508) 775-1200; adv tel (508) 775-1200; ed tel (508) 775-1200; gen fax (508) 771-3292; adv fax (508) 775-7337; ed fax (508) 771-3292; gen e-mail news@capecodonline.com; adv e-mail advertising@capecodonline.com; ed e-mail news@capecodonline.com; web site www.capecodonline.com
Published: Mon, Tues, Wed, Thur, Fri, Sat, Sun
Weekday Frequency: m
Saturday Frequency: m
Circulation: 40,461; 45,353(sat); 46,127(sun)
Last Audit: ABC September 30, 2011
Price: 6.79/wk
Advertising: Modular Rates
News services: AP, DJ, ONS, NYT, LAT-WP.
Politics: Independent. **Established:** 1936
Not Published: Christmas (except Sunday).
Special Editions: Home & Garden, Gift Guide, Presidents' Day Auto, Summer Guide, Classroom Times, Rising Stars, Your Home
Special Weekly Sections: Outdoors (Fri); Golf Monday (summer) (Mon); At Home (S); Arts & Entertainment (Sat); Health & Fitness (Thur); Health & Science (Tues); Food (Wed).
Magazines: CapeWeek Magazine (Fri); Prime Time (Monthly); Cape Cod View (Other); Parade (S).
Pres./Pub. .... Peter D. Meyer
Controller .... David Hundt
Mgr., HR .... Stacia Plumb
Bldg. Mgr. .... Scott Freeman
Adv. Dir. .... Kathleen McMahon
Adv. Mgr. .... Lisa Maiden
Adv. Mgr. .... Jeffrey Rixon
Classified Adv. Mgr. .... April Miller
Cape Cod View/Primetime Mgr. ..... Sean Randall
Sales Mktg./Collateral Mgr. .... Karen Ryder
Member Servs. Dir. .... Robert Sypek
Member Servs. Mgr. .... Joseph Allen
Member Servs. Systems Mgr. .... Leith Young
Ed. .... Paul Pronovost
Entertainment Ed. .... Tim Miller
Market Information: Split run; TMC.
Mechanical available: Offset; Black and 3 ROP colors; insert accepted; page cutoffs - 22 3/4.
Mechanical Specifications: Type page 13 x 21 1/2; E - 6 cols, 2, 1/3 between; A - 6 cols, 2 1/16, 1/3 between; C - 9 cols, 1 2/5, 1/6 between.
Commodity Consumption: Avg. Page Number Per Issue - Daily 43; Avg. Page Number Per Issue - Plates Used 50000; Avg. Page Number Per Issue - Sunday 88; widths 55; Newsprint Used - Metric Tons 5554; Printing Ink Used - Black 126000; Printing Ink Used - Color 22200; Printing Ink U
Equipment EDITORIAL: Front-end Software – AT, Dewar/View.; Editorial Hardware – PC, 80-IBM/350; Editorial Printers – HP/Laser, 4-HP/4MV, 5-HP/Si CLASSIFIED: Front-end Software – Enterprise.; Classified Hardware – 27-IBM/PL 300; Classified Printers – APP/Mac Laser 5000N DISPLAY: Ad make-up applications – QPS/QuarkXPress 3.2; Layout Software – APP/Mac, ALS.; Display Hardware – IBM/al350, IBM/Pl 500; Display Printers – HP/Laser, 2-HP/Laser 5000N PRODUCTION: Pagination Software – QPS/QuarkXPress.; Production Equipment – Cx, III/3850, III/3850; Cameras – C/Spartan; Scanners – 2-ECR/Autokon PRESSROOM: Line 1 – 12-G/Metro 1988; Folders – 2-G/3:2; Pasters – 11-G/RTP. MAILROOM: Counter stackers – 3/HL, 1-/HL; Inserters and stuffers – 2-GMA/6:1, 1-GMA/14:1; Bundle tying machines – 4-/OVL; Addressing machine – 1-/Ch; Other equipment –MM/4HD.
Delivery method: Mail, Newsstand, Private Carrier, Racks

LOWELL

THE SUN

491 Dutton St., Lowell, Mass., 01854; gen tel (978) 458-7100; adv tel (978) 970-4721; ed tel (978) 970-4667; gen fax (978) 970-4800; adv fax (978) 970-4723; ed fax (978) 970-4600; adv e-mail advertising@lowellsun.com; ed e-mail backtalk@lowellsun.com; web site www.lowellsun.com
Published: Mon, Tues, Wed, Thur, Fri, Sat, Sun
Weekday Frequency: e
Saturday Frequency: m
Circulation: 42,899; 33,638(sat); 47,897(sun)
Last Audit: ABC September 30, 2011
Price: 3.60/wk; 187.20/yr.
Advertising: Open inch rate $54.30
News services: AP, SHNS, NEA, MCT.
Politics: Independent. **Established:** 1878
Own facility?: Y
Special Editions: Home & Garden/Home Improvement (Apr); Summer Auto (Aug); Christmas Gift Guide (Dec); Bridal (Feb); Local Heroes (Jan); Folk Festival (Jul); Summer Living (Jun); Spring Auto (Mar); Women in Business (May); Holiday Happenings (Nov); Fall Auto (Oct); A Day i
Special Weekly Sections: Color Comics (S); Restaurant Guide (Sat); Stepping Out (Thur); Food (Wed).
Magazines: USA WEEKEND Magazine (S).
Pres./Pub. .... Mark O'Neil
CFO .... John Habbe
Adv. Mgr., New Media .... Andrea Mendes
Circ. Mgr., Alternate Delivery Maureen Sylvester
Circ. Mgr., Home Delivery .... Gary Wright
Circ. Mgr., Systems .... Tom Gauthier
Circ. Mgr., Telemktg./Promo. . Shelley Laurencio
Ed. .... James Campanini
Mng. Ed. .... Charles St. Amand
Asst. Mng. Ed., Local News .... Kris Pisarik
Asst. Mng. Ed., Local News-Weekend Tom Zuppa
Automotive Ed. .... Nick Caraganis
Bus. Ed. .... Dan O'Brien
City Ed. .... Chris Scott
Columnist/Copy Ed. .... Dan Phelps
Copy Ed. .... Bruce Phillips
Copy Ed. .... Matt Spencer
Lifestyle Copy Ed. .... Joanne Deegan
VP Advertising .... Scott Rosenburgh
VP Circulation .... Mike Sheehan
Director Of Operations .... Bill Walker
Chrmn. .... Kendall M. Wallace
Editorial Page Ed. .... Sharon Flaherty
Market Information: ADS; Split run; TMC; Zoned editions.
Mechanical available: DiLitho; Black and 3 ROP colors; insert accepted - spadea; page cutoffs - 21 1/2.
Mechanical Specifications: Type page 12 x 21 1/2; E - 6 cols, 1 9/10, 1/8 between; A - 6 cols, 1 9/10, 1/16 between; C - 9 cols, 1 1/5, 1/8 between.
Commodity Consumption: Avg. Page Number Per Issue - Daily 44; Avg. Page Number Per Issue - Plates Used 57000; Avg. Page Number Per Issue - Saturday 32; Avg. Page Number Per Issue - Sunday 120; widths 37 1/2; Newsprint Used - Metric Tons 4000; Printing Ink Used - Black 106000;
Equipment EDITORIAL: Front-end Software – QPS/QuarkXPress, Baseview/Qtools, Baseview/QXedit, Baseview/NewsEdit, APP/Appleshare & Windows NT Network.; Editorial Hardware – 1-APP/Mac LAN and WAN; Editorial Printers – HP/4MV, HP/5000N; Classified Hardware – PPI/System; Classified Equipment – Printers ÂD V/5100 Typesetter; Classified Printers – Software ÂD Microsoft/Windows NT. DISPLAY: Ad make-up applications – Multi-Ad/Creator, QPS/QuarkXPress 4.1; Layout Software – 8-APP/Mac.; Display Hardware – 8-APP/Mac; Display Printers – HP 5000/N PRODUCTION: Pagination Software – QPS/QuarkXPress 4.1, Baseview/Qtools, Baseview/QXedit.; Production Equipment – Mk, Caere/OmniPage Professional, Adobe/Photoshop; Cameras – AG PRESSROOM: Line 1 – 6-MAN, H/double width; Line 2 – 8-G/Urbanite single width; Press Drives – GE/Tenetrol; Folders – H/2:1 1967; Press control system – GE/SCR. MAILROOM: Counter stackers – 4-QWI/300; Bundle tying machines – 2-Dynaric; Addressing machine – 2-KR.; Business Hardware – IBM/AS-400 Advanced 36
Delivery method: Mail, Newsstand, Private Carrier, Racks

LYNN

THE DAILY ITEM

38 Exchange St., Lynn, Mass., 1903; gen tel (781) 593-7700; gen fax (781) 581-3178; adv fax (781) 581-3178; ed fax (781) 598-2891; gen e-mail contactus@itemlive.com; adv e-mail advertising@itemlive.com; ed e-mail news@itemlive.com; web site www.itemlive.com
Published: Mon, Tues, Wed, Thur, Fri, Sat
Weekday Frequency: m
Saturday Frequency: m
Circulation: 11,650; 11,480(sat)
Last Audit: September 30, 2009
Price: 2.50/wk; 10.80/mo; 109.20/yr.
Advertising: Open inch rate $35.80
News services: AP, SHNS.
Politics: Independent.
Advertising not accepted: Tobacco.
Not Published: Independence Day; Christmas.
Special Editions: Spring Home Improvement (Apr); Back-to-School (Aug); Holiday Songbook (Dec); Washington's Birthday Auto (Feb); Brides Tab (Jan); 101 Things For Kids To Do (Jun); Progress (Mar); Spring Car Care (May); New Car Preview (Nov); Business & Professional Womem (
Special Weekly Sections: Home (Mon); Travel (Sat); Dining Out (Thur); Home (Tues); Food (Wed).
Pres./Pub./Dir. .... Peter H. Gamage
Gen. Mgr. .... Phil Ouellette
Controller .... Lori Towne
Mgr., Educ. Serv. .... Jacqueline Lauber
Adv. Dir. .... Tara Cleary
Adv. Coord. .... Paula Smith
City Ed. .... Jill Gadsby
News Ed .... Hank Collins
Sports Ed .... Stephen Krause
Mgr., Info Servs./Online Mgr. .... Ralph Nelson
Prodn. Foreman, Composing .... Martin Dullea
Prodn. Foreman, Composing .... John Winslow
Mechanical available: Black and 3 ROP colors; insert accepted - any; page cutoffs - 21 1/4.
Mechanical Specifications: Type page 13 x 21; E - 6 cols, 2 1/16, 1/8 between; A - 6 cols, 2 1/16, 1/8 between; C - 9 cols, 1 5/16, 1/8 between.
Commodity Consumption: Avg. Page Number Per Issue - Daily 28; Avg. Page Number Per Issue - Saturday 24; widths 55.
Equipment EDITORIAL: Front-end Software – Microsoft/Windows 98, Microsoft/Office 2000, QPS/QuarkXPress 4.1.; Editorial Hardware – Gateway; Editorial Equipment – Polaroid/SprintScan; Editorial Printers – Lexmark/Optra LXI Plus Printer CLASSIFIED: Front-end Software – Sparrow Information Systems/Intertext.; Classified Hardware – AST/Bravo MS 4.66d Terminals DISPLAY: Ad make-up applications – Adobe/Illustrator, Adobe/Streamline, Adobe/Photoshop, Macromedia/Freehand, AP AdSend, Multi-Ad/Creator, QPS/QuarkXPress; Display Hardware – Power Mac, MS/NT Server, Gateway; Display Printers – 1-APP/Mac LaserWriter PRODUCTION: Pagination Software – QPS/QuarkXPress 3.32, MEI/ALS 3.0.; Production Equipment – 1-Gateway/P6 NT Server on Xytron/RIP, 1-Gateway/P5, 1-ScanJet/Scanner PRESSROOM: Line 1 – 5-H/Color Convertible. BUSINESS COMPUTERS: Business Software – CAS; Business Hardware – Newzware

HASTINGS & SONS PUBLISHING CO.D/B/A THE DAILY ITEM

38 Exchange St., Ste 38, Lynn, Mass., 01901-1425; gen tel (781) 593-7700; adv tel 7815937700; ed tel 7815937700; oth tel 7815937700; gen fax (781) 581-3178; web site itemlive.com
Group: Hastings & Sons Publishing Co.
Published: Mon, Tues, Wed, Thur, Fri, Sat
Weekday Frequency: m
Saturday Frequency: m
Circulation: 13,316; 12,919(sat)
Price: 130.00/yr.
Advertising: Open inch rate $31.45
News services: AP, SHNS
Politics: 1877
Advertising not accepted: N
General Manager .... Phil Ouellette
Equipment EDITORIAL: Front-end Software – Microsoft; Editorial Equipment – Desktop/Laptops CLASSIFIED: Front-end Software – NewzWare; Classified Equipment – Icanon; Cameras – Canon
Delivery method: Mail, Newsstand, Private Carrier, Racks

MALDEN

THE EVENING NEWS-MERCURY

277 Commercial St., Malden, Mass., 2148; gen tel (781) 321-8000; gen fax (781) 321-8008; gen e-mail editor@maldennews.com

Published: Mon, Tues, Wed, Thur, Fri
Weekday Frequency: e
Circulation: 13,800
Last Audit: September 30, 2006
Price: 13.00/mo; 121.00/yr.
Advertising: Open inch rate $20.00
News services: Landon Media Group, U.S. Suburban Press Inc..
Politics: Independent.
Not Published: New Year; Memorial Day; Independence Day; Labor Day; Columbus Day; Thanksgiving; Christmas.
Special Editions: Home & Car Care (Apr); Holiday Recipe (Dec); Bridal (Feb); Progress (Jan); Social Security (Jul); Money (Mar); Holiday Recipe (Nov); Chamber of Commerce (Oct); Golf (Sept).
Special Weekly Sections: Tempo (Thur).
Pub. ....Daniel J. Horgan
Adv. Mgr., Sales ....Jim Horgan
Circ. Mgr. ....Nicole Caron
Sports Ed. ....Stephen Freker
Market Information: TMC.
Mechanical available: Offset; Black and 3 ROP colors; insert accepted - single card stock, all tab or standard-size insert; page cutoffs - 22 3/4.
Mechanical Specifications: Type page 13 x 21 1/2; E - 6 cols, 2 1/16, 1/8 between; A - 6 cols, 2 1/16, 1/8 between; C - 9 cols, 1 3/8, 1/8 between.
Commodity Consumption: Avg. Page Number Per Issue - Daily 28; widths 28; Newsprint Used - Short Tons 710; Printing Ink Used - Black 19400; Printing Ink Used - Color 180.
Equipment; Editorial Hardware – 26-COM/Intrepid.; Classified Hardware – 26-COM/Intrepid.; Production Equipment – 2-COM/8400, 2-COM/Lasermaster 1200; Cameras – 1-Nu/Horizontal, 1-K/Vertical. PRESSROOM: Line 1 – 6-HI/V-15A; Folders – 1; Inserters and stuffers – 1-S/24P; Bundle tying machines – 2/Sa; Addressing machine – 1-/Am.; Business Hardware – Compaq/386, Accpac

MILFORD

MILFORD DAILY NEWS

159 S. Main St., Milford, Mass., 01757-0160; gen tel (508) 473-1111; adv tel (800) 624-7355; ed tel (508) 634-7522; gen fax (508) 634-7514; gen e-mail milford@cnc.com; web site www.milforddailynews.com

Group: U.S. Suburban Press, Inc.
Published: Mon, Tues, Wed, Thur, Fri, Sat, Sun
Weekday Frequency: m
Saturday Frequency: m
Circulation: 5,892; 7,144(sat); 6,227(sun)
Last Audit: ABC September 30, 2011
Price: 2.70/wk (home delivery); 221.00/yr.
Advertising: Open inch rate $17.55
News services: NYT, AP.
Not Published: New Year; Memorial Day; Independence Day; Labor Day; Christmas.
Special Editions: Secretaries' Week Pages (Apr); Pawtucket Red Sox Night (Aug); Christmas Cards (Dec); Spring Bridal Tab (Feb); Tax Column (Jan); Sidewalk Sale Days (Jul); Father's Day Page (Jun); Physical Fitness Page (Mar); Summer Fun Tab (May); Gift Spotter (Nov); Fall
Special Weekly Sections: Bridal Registry (Mon).
Magazines: Sports Extra (tab) (Fri); USA Weekender (Sat).
Pub. ....Kirk Davis
Office Mgr. ....Marilyn Comastra
Display Adv. Mgr. ....Cheryl Robinson
Online Adv. Mgr......................Christopher Eck
Circ. Mgr. ....Linda Vahey
Exec. Ed. ....Richard Lodge
Mng. Ed. ....Bethany Edwards
Entertainment Ed. ....Jenifer Lipson
Asst. News Ed ....Heather Mc Carron
Sports Ed....................................Art Davidson
Website Mgr. ....Nicole Simmons
Prodn. Foreman, Composing............Bob Skerry
Mechanical available: Offset; Black and 3 ROP colors; insert accepted - min size 5 x 8; page cutoffs - 21 1/2.
Mechanical Specifications: Type page 13 x 21 1/2; E - 6 cols, 2 1/16, 1/8 between; A - 6 cols, 2 1/16, 1/8 between; C - 9 cols, 1 3/8, 1/16 between.
Equipment EDITORIAL: Front-end Software – III 3.9.; Editorial Hardware – 25-PC; Editorial Equipment – 18-RSK/TRS 80 Model 100, RSK/TRS 80 Model 200, Lf/Leafscan 35; Editorial Printers – Toshiba/P351 SQ, APP/Mac LaserWriter, 2-QMS/860, HP/4M Plus CLASSIFIED: Front-end Software – III 3.9.; Classified Hardware – 4-PC; Classified Printers – Toshiba/P351 SX DISPLAY: Ad make-up applications – DTI/AdSpeed, QPS/QuarkXPress.; Display Hardware – 10-APP/Mac; Display Printers – 2-APP/Mac LaserWriter, 2-QMS/860, HP/4MV, HP6 PRODUCTION: Pagination Software – QPS/QuarkXPress 3.3, Microsoft/Windows, APP/Mac.; Production Equipment – 2-QMS/860, AG, ECR/VL 36 Imagesetter; Cameras – 1-R, 1-LE/R, AG/RPS 6100S; Scanners – Lf/Leafscan 35, Microtek, HP/Scanner BUSINESS COMPUTERS: Business Software – DSI; Business Hardware – TI/990-12R

NEEDHAM

WALTHAM NEWS TRIBUNE

254 Second Ave., Needham, Mass., 02494; gen tel (781) 398-8002; gen e-mail newstribune@wickedlocal.com; web site www.wickedlocal.com/waltham

Group: GateHouse Media Inc.
Published: Fri
Weekday Frequency: m

NEW BEDFORD

THE STANDARD-TIMES

25 Elm St., New Bedford, Mass., 2740; gen tel (508) 997-7411; adv tel (508) 997-0011; ed tel (508) 979-4450; gen fax (508) 979-4541; adv fax (508) 977-4585 (classified); ed fax (508) 997-7491; ed e-mail newsroom@s-t.com; web site www.southcoasttoday.com

Published: Mon, Tues, Wed, Thur, Fri, Sat, Sun
Weekday Frequency: m
Saturday Frequency: m
Circulation: 22,814; 26,433(sat); 24,615(sun)
Last Audit: ABC September 30, 2011
Price: 2.50/wk (d), $1.70/wk (S), $3.30/wk (dS); 14.30/mo; 191.88/yr.
Advertising: Open inch rate $70.25
News services: AP, NYT, DJ, ONS.
Politics: Independent.
Special Editions: Spring Auto Service (Apr); Health & Medicine (Aug); Last Minute Gift Guide (Dec); Washington's Birthday Auto (Feb); Parenting (Jan); Parenting (Jul); Seniors (Jun); Spring Home & Garden (Mar); Seaside Summer Recreation (May); Holiday Planner (Nov); Fall A
Special Weekly Sections: Sports Monday (Mon); At Home (S); Real Estate Today Tab (Sat).
Magazines: Relish (Monthly); TV Update (S).
Controller ....Jenna McDonnell
Dir., HR ....Joel E. Burns
Adv. Asst. Dir. ....Theresa Pereira
Dir., Sales/Mktg. ....Sheila Parker
Dir., Educational Servs................Jean Bessette
Mgr., Sales/Mktg. Servs. Kathleen Winterbottom
Circ. Dir.................................Brian Stephens
Ed....Robert V. Unger
Mng. Ed.................Mary Wessling-Harrington
Central Bureau Chief........Sue Pawlak-Seaman
Editorial Page Ed.................Stephen F. Urbon
Environmental Ed......................Monica Allen
Asst. Features Ed. ....Joanna McQuillen Weeks
Health Ed. ....Anne Humphrey
Librarian.....................................Gail Couture
Online Ed. ....Michael Connery
Photo Ed........................................Jack Iddon
Market Information: Split run; TMC; Zoned editions.
Mechanical available: Offset; Black and 3 ROP colors; insert accepted - single sheets, catabooks; page cutoffs - 22 3/4.
Mechanical Specifications: Type page 13 x 21 1/2; E - 6 cols, 2 1/16, 1/8 between; A - 6 cols, 2 1/16, 1/8 between; C - 9 cols, 1 3/8, 1/16 between.
Commodity Consumption: Avg. Page Number Per Issue - Daily 32; Avg. Page Number Per Issue - Plates Used 56000; Avg. Page Number Per Issue - Sunday 78; widths 41 1/8; Newsprint Used - Metric Tons 3520; Printing Ink Used - Black 60170; Printing Ink Used - Color 18086; Printing In
Equipment EDITORIAL: Front-end Software – Dewar/Unixaix Network.; Editorial Hardware – 45-Dell/486 66mhz; Editorial Printers – 2-HP/4M, 1-HP/44 Color Plotter, 1-NewGen/11x17 Laser Printer CLASSIFIED: Front-end Software – AT/Enterprise.; Classified Hardware – IBM/RS 6000, 20-PC; Classified Printers – HP/4M 4V DISPLAY: Ad make-up applications – Microsoft/Windows, QPS/QuarkXPress, Adobe/Photoshop, Dewar/View, Sybase.; Display Hardware – PC; Display Printers – 2-HP/4M, 4-HP/4M 4V PRODUCTION: Pagination Software – QPS/QuarkXPress 3.3.; Production Equipment – 1-Wing Lynch/Color, 1-Lf/Leafscan 45; Cameras – 1-C/Spartan III, 1-C/Marathon; Scanners – 1-ECR/Autokon 1000DE PRESSROOM: Line 1 – 8-G/Metro double width (3 process Color Units); Folders – 2; Pasters – 8; Reels and Stands – 8 MAILROOM: Counter stackers – 2/QWI; Inserters and stuffers – 1-GMA/SLA 100 (8 stations), 1-GMA/SLS 1000A 6:1; Bundle tying machines – 2-MLN/MLN2; Addressing machine – 1-/KR. BUSINESS COMPUTERS: Business Software – INSI, Software Plus, Computer Associates, Lawson; Business Hardware – IBM/AS-400

NEWBURYPORT

THE DAILY NEWS

23 Liberty St., Newburyport, Mass., 1950; gen tel (978) 462-6666; adv tel (978) 462-6666; ed tel (978) 462-6666; gen fax (978) 465-8505; adv fax (978) 465-9612; ed fax (978) 462-8505; ed e-mail jmacone@ecnnews.com; web site www.newburyport-news.com

Published: Mon, Tues, Wed, Thur, Fri, Sat, Sun
Weekday Frequency: e
Saturday Frequency: m
Circulation: 10,973; 10,973(sat)
Last Audit: September 30, 2009
Price: 173.00/yr.
Advertising: Open inch rate $25.80
News services: AP, ONS.
Politics: Independent.
Not Published: New Year; Memorial Day; Independence Day; Labor Day; Christmas.
Special Editions: Auto Showcase (Apr); Back-to-School (Aug); Christmas Gift Guide (Dec); Presidents' Day (Feb); Pulse (Jan); Guides to The North Shore (May); Traditions (Nov); Year End Clearance (Oct); Fall Home Improvement (Sept).
Special Weekly Sections: Food (Wed).
Magazines: USA WEEKEND Magazine (Fri).
Profile: The Daily News is one of three daily newspapers that comprise Essex County Newspapers, which serves the communities to the north of Greater Boston
Adv. Mgr. ....Catherine Giannonccaro
Home Delivery Mgr......................Judy Sullivan
Ed....John Macone
City Ed.......................................Will Courtney
Features Ed......................Sonya Vartabedian
Night Ed. ....Merrily Buchs
Sports Ed. ....Dan Guttenplan
IT/Prodn. Dir. ....John Gregory
Vice Pres., Opns. ....Jim Saozone
Market Information: TMC.
Mechanical available: Offset; Black and 3 ROP colors; insert accepted; page cutoffs - 22 3/4.
Mechanical Specifications: Type page 11 1/2 x 21; E - 6 cols, 1 13/16, 5/16 between; A - 6 cols, 1 13/16, 5/16 between; C - 9 cols, 1 7/32, 3/32 between.
Commodity Consumption: Avg. Page Number Per Issue - Daily 32; Avg. Page Number Per Issue - Plates Used 5304; widths 50; Newsprint Used - Metric Tons 984; Printing Ink Used - Black 12155.
Equipment EDITORIAL: Front-end Software – QPS/QuarkXPress.; Editorial Hardware – PC; Classified Hardware – AT. DISPLAY: Ad make-up applications – QPS/QuarkXPress, Archetype/Designer; Layout Software – PC.; Display Hardware – PC Network PRODUCTION: Pagination Software – QuarkXpress 4.0.; Production Equipment – Nu-Arc; Scanners – Epson; Business Hardware – IBM/AS400

NORTH ADAMS

NEW ENGLAND NEWSPAPERS, INC.

124 American Legion Dr., North Adams, Mass., 01247; gen tel (413) 663-3741 ext 270; gen fax (413) 662-2792

NORTH ADAMS TRANSCRIPT

124 American Legion Dr., North Adams, Mass., 1247; gen tel (413) 663-3741; adv tel (413) 663-3741; ed tel (413) 663-3741; gen fax (413) 662-2792; ed e-mail news@thetranscript.com; web site www.thetranscript.com

Group: Metro Suburbia, Inc./Newhouse Newspapers
Published: Mon, Tues, Wed, Thur, Fri, Sat, Sun
Weekday Frequency: e
Saturday Frequency: m
Circulation: 4,877; 5,703(sat); 5,703(sun)
Last Audit: ABC September 30, 2011
Price: 2.45/wk (carrier), $2.65/wk (auto); 10.62/mo (carrier), $10.90/mo (auto); 116.44/yr (carrier), $130.10 (auto).
News services: AP.
Politics: Independent. **Established:** 1843
Note: Advertising is sold in combination with the Pittsfield Berkshire Eagle (mS) for $51.70(d) and $53.80(S). Individual newspaper rates not made available.
Not Published: New Year; Memorial Day; Independence Day; Labor Day; Christmas.
Special Weekly Sections: Arts (Fri); Churches (Sat); Outdoors (Thur); Consumer (Fashion) (Tues).
Magazines: USA WEEKEND Magazine (Sat); American Profile (Weekly).
Bus. Mgr. ....Catherine Wandrei
Adv. Dir....................................Bob Chapman
Circ. Dir....................................Kim Alexander
Ed....Glenn Drohan
City Ed...........................Margaret R. Buttons
Editorial Page Ed. ....Kevin Moran
Sports Ed. ....Scott Barrett
Market Information: Split run; TMC.
Mechanical available: Offset; Black and 3 ROP colors; insert accepted; page cutoffs - 22 3/4.
Mechanical Specifications: Type page 13 x 21 1/2; E - 6 cols, 2 1/16, 1/8 between; A - 6 cols, 2 1/16, 1/8 between; C - 9 cols, 1 3/8, 1/16 between.
Commodity Consumption: Avg. Page Number Per Issue - Daily 18; Avg. Page Number Per Issue - Plates Used 3700; widths 25; Newsprint Used - Short Tons 316; Printing Ink Used - Black 18000; Printing Ink Used - Color 500.
Equipment EDITORIAL: Front-end Software – Baseview.; Editorial Hardware – APP/Mac G4, APP/iMac; Classified Hardware – Dell/Pentium Network.; Production Equipment – 1-Anitec/526, 1-Nu; Cameras – 1-AG/3000, 1-AG/RPS 2024, 1-Acti/Horizontal. PRESSROOM: Line 1 – 8-G/Community 1980; Folders – G/SC, G/(with upper former). MAILROOM: Counter stackers – 1-BG/Count-O-Veyor; Bundle tying machines – 2-CYP/RO-500-N-S, 1-Akebono/Oval Strapping.; Business Hardware – GEAC

NORTH ANDOVER

THE EAGLE-TRIBUNE

100 Turnpike St., North Andover, Mass., 01845-5033; gen tel (978) 946-2000; adv tel (978) 946-2000; ed tel (978) 946-2000; gen fax (978) 685-1588; adv fax (978) 685-1588; ed fax (978) 687-6045; gen e-mail news@eagletribune.com; adv e-mail adv@eagletribune.com; ed e-mail news@eagletribune.com; web site www.eagletribune.com

Group: CNHI
Published: Mon, Tues, Wed, Thur, Fri, Sat, Sun
Weekday Frequency: e
Saturday Frequency: e
Circulation: 76,135; 76,135(sat); 38,725(sun)
Last Audit: ABC September 30, 2011
Price: $4.50/wk; 210.00/yr.
Advertising: Open inch rate $50.40
Insert rate: $60.00/m
News services: AP, SHNS.
Politics: 1867
Not Published: Christmas.
Own facility?: Y
Special Editions: Easter Church Pages (Apr); Health & Fitness (Aug); Parent! (Feb); Accent on Finance (Jan); Parent! (Jun); Real Estate Review (Mar); Real Estate Review (Nov); Columbus Day Auto Weekend (October) Where we Live (June)
Special Weekly Sections: Entertainment
Magazines: USA WEEKEND Magazine (S).
Pub. ....Al Getler
Credit Mgr. ....Allen Naffah
Adv. Dir. ....Timothy E. Brady
Circ. Vice Pres. ....Steve Milone
Circ. Mgr., Sales ....Steven Baskin
Editor ....Alan White
Features Editor ....Tracey Rauh Solomon
Director of IT ....John Gregory
Director of Operations ....James Falzone
Director of Humas Resources ....Laurie DAmore
Market Information: TMC; Zoned editions.
Mechanical available: Offset; Black and 3 ROP colors; insert accepted; page cutoffs - 22 3/4.
Mechanical Specifications: Type page 11 1/16 x 21 1/2; E - 6 cols, 1 5/6, 1/8 between; A - 6 cols, 1 5/6, 1/8 between; C - 10 cols, 1 1/16, 1/16 between.
Commodity Consumption: Avg. Page Number Per Issue - Daily 22; Avg. Page Number Per Issue - Plates Used 98799; Avg. Page Number Per Issue - Saturday 26; Avg. Page Number Per Issue - Sunday 86; widths 50; Newsprint Used - Short Tons 5800; Printing Ink Used - Black 105480; Printi
Equipment EDITORIAL: Front-end Software – Mediaspan; Editorial Hardware – Mediaspan; Editorial Printers – QMS/860 CLASSIFIED: Front-end Software – APT; Classified Hardware – APT; Classified Printers – Epson/LaserWriter DISPLAY: Ad make-up applications – APT; Layout Software – MEI/ALS 7.0.; Display Hardware – APP/Mac, PC; Display Printers – HP/LaserJet 4 Plus PRODUCTION: Pagination Software – Adobe, InDesign; Production Equipment – Agfa Advantage Imagesetters; Cameras – Kodak, Cannon; Scanners – ECR/1000, Epson/636, Polaroid/SprintScan PRESSROOM: Line 1 – 8-G/Metro (3 color decks); Folders – 1-G/Double 2:1. MAILROOM: Counter stackers – Goss Olympian; Inserters and stuffers – 7wo, Goss 630 inserters; Bundle tying machines – 4/Power Strap; Mailroom control system – Omnizone; Addressing machine – Domino BUSINESS COMPUTERS: Business Software – INSI; Business Hardware – IBM/AS-400
Zip Codes served:
01810,01825,01830,01832,01833,01834,01835,01840,01841,01843,01844,01845,01850,01860,01864,01876,01887,01913,01921,01949,01950,01952,01985,03036,03038,03053,03076,03079,03087,03811,03819,03826,03827,03841,03842,03848,03858,03865,03873,03874,
Delivery method: Mail, Newsstand, Private Carrier, Racks

NORTHAMPTON

DAILY HAMPSHIRE GAZETTE

115 Conz St., Northampton, Mass., 01061-0299; gen tel (413) 584-5000; adv tel (413) 584-5000; ed tel (413) 585-5250; gen fax (413) 585-5299; adv fax (413) 585-5293; adv e-mail sales@gazettenet.com; ed e-mail newsroom@gazettenet.com; web site www.gazettenet.com

Published: Mon, Tues, Wed, Thur, Fri, Sat
Weekday Frequency: m
Saturday Frequency: m
Circulation: 15,572; 16,978(sat)
Last Audit: ABC September 30, 2011
Price: 2.70/wk; 10.80/mo; 128.50/yr.
Advertising: Open inch rate $22.44
News services: AP, LAT-WP.
Politics: Independent. **Established:** 1786
Not Published: Christmas; New Year.
Special Editions: Spring Home & Garden (Apr); Back-to-School (Aug); Wine (Dec); Business & Industry (Feb); Summer Guide (Jun); Spring Fashion (Mar); Create-An-Ad (May); Christmas Shopping Bag (Nov); Auto (Oct); Valley Almanac (Sept).
Special Weekly Sections: Real Estate (Fri); Automotive (Sat); Home & Garden (Thur); Health (Tues); Lifestyle Features (Wed).
Magazines: Television (weekly TV log) (Sat).
Pres./Pub. ....Aaron Julien
Adv. Dir. ....Mark Iacuessa
Adv. Mgr., Retail ....Dave Permutter
Adv. Prodn. Mgr. ....Rita Turcotte
Adv. Mgr., Classified ....David A. Sikop
Circ. Dir. ....Dennis Skoglund
Circ. Asst. Mgr. ....Mark Galant
Ed. ....James T. Foudy
Mng. Ed., Features ....Debra Scherban
Mng. Ed., News ....Larry Parnass
Librarian ....Nancy Rhodes
Religion Ed. ....Deb Oakley
Sports Ed. ....Stanley Moulton
Online/New Media Mgr. ....Gerry LeBlanc
Info Servs. Mgr. ....Paris Finley
Prodn. Mgr., Distr. Ctr. ....Robert Diemand
Prodn. Mgr., Distr. Ctr. ....Chris Kostek
Prodn. Mgr., Pressroom ....John Raymer
Market Information: Split run; TMC.
Mechanical available: Offset; Black and 3 ROP colors; insert accepted - product samples; page cutoffs - 22 3/4.
Mechanical Specifications: Type page 11 5/8 x 21 1/2; E - 6 cols, 1 5/6, 1/8 between; A - 6 cols, 1 5/6, 1/8 between; C - 9 cols, 1 1/4, 1/8 between.
Commodity Consumption: Avg. Page Number Per Issue - Daily 41.5; Avg. Page Number Per Issue - Plates Used 26254; widths 25; Newsprint Used - Short Tons 1608; Printing Ink Used - Black 41300; Printing Ink Used - Color 1200; Printing Ink Used - Pages Printed 12775.
Equipment EDITORIAL: Front-end Software – APT/ACT 2.06, Microsoft/Word 6.0.; Editorial Hardware – Dell/Poweredge 1300, 60-PC Workstation, 2-Compaq/Proliant 1600; Editorial Printers – X, 1-Xerox/NP32 CLASSIFIED: Front-end Software – APT/ACT 2.06, QPS/QuarkXPress 3.32.; Classified Hardware – 6-PC Workstation, Compaq/Proliant 1600; Classified Printers – HP, X DISPLAY: Ad make-up applications – Ad Tracking, APT/ACT, Adobe/Photoshop, QPS/QuarkXPress 4.0, Adobe/Illustrator; Layout Software – Compaq/Proliant 1600.; Display Hardware – 20-PC Workstation; Display Printers – HP, X PRODUCTION: Pagination Software – QPS/QuarkXPress 3.32, APT/ACT 2.06.; Production Equipment – AP Server; Scanners – Microtek/Scanmaker 3 PRESSROOM: Line 1 – 11-G/Urbanite single width (3-color satellite unit); Press Drives – 2, 100-HP/Westinghouse, 100-HP/GE; Folders – 1-G/Urbanite; Reels and Stands – 2-G/3-High Stands; Press registration system – Duarte/Pin Register System. MAILROOM: Counter stackers – 3/QWI; Inserters and stuffers – 1-GMA/SLS 1000 12:2; Bundle tying machines – 2-Dynaric/SSB 70; Mailroom control system – Linc/Packaging Line Control System, Address/Linc, Stack/Line, Key/Line; Addressing machine – 2-/Ch, Address/Linc I AUDIO: Audio Software – New Horizons/Info-Connect; Audio Hardware – Choice Content BUSINESS COMPUTERS: Business Software – DSI; Business Hardware – 1-DEC/Prioris HX 590 System, Papertrack/2000

H S GERE & SONS, INC.

115 Conz St., Northampton, Mass., 01061; gen tel (413) 584-5000; gen fax (413) 585-5222; gen e-mail products@gazettenet.com; web site www.gazettenet.com

Price: 128.50/yr.
Advertising: Open inch rate $17.63

NORWOOD

THE DAILY NEWS TRANSCRIPT

1091 Washington St, Norwood, Mass., 02062; gen tel (781) 433-8307; web site www.dailynewstranscript.com

Group: GateHouse Media Inc.

PITTSFIELD

THE BERKSHIRE EAGLE

75 S. Church St., Pittsfield, Mass., 01201-6157; gen tel (413) 447-7311; adv tel (413) 447-7311; ed tel (413) 447-7311; gen fax (413) 442-7611; adv fax (413) 449-3419; ed fax (413) 499-3419; ed e-mail news@berkshireeagle.com; web site www.berkshireeagle.com

Published: Mon, Tues, Wed, Thur, Fri, Sat, Sun
Weekday Frequency: m
Saturday Frequency: m
Circulation: 24,657; 25,806(sat); 27,873(sun)
Last Audit: ABC September 30, 2011
Price: 14.73/mo, $20.63/mo (mail); 176.68/yr, 247.50/yr (mail).
News services: AP, NYT, TMS.
Politics: Independent.
Note: Advertising is sold in combination with the North Adams Transcript (eS) for $51.70(d) & $53.80(S). Individual newspaper rates not made available.
Not Published: Christmas.
Special Editions: Spring Home Improvement (Apr); Think Kids II (Aug); Letters to Santa (Dec); Think Kids I (Feb); Health Quarterly (Jan); Pittsfield Community Guide (Jul); Wedding Planner II (Jun); Health Quarterly (Mar); South County Community Guide (May); Holiday Gift Gu
Special Weekly Sections: This Weekend/Outdoors (Fri); Health & Science (Mon); Wall Street Journal Sunday (S); Homes (Sat); The 413 (Thur); e-Life (Tues); Food, etc. (Wed).
Magazines: USA WEEKEND Magazine (S); Berkshires Week (June-Oct) (Thur).
Broadcast Affiliations: WRGB-CBS.
Pres./Pub. ....Andrew Mick
Controller ....Frank McKenna
Dir., Systems ....William Macfarlane
Mgr., HR ....Alinda Shank
Adv. Mgr. ....Robert Chapman
Adv. Supvr., Sales ....Robbie Brassard
Adv. Mgr., Interactive Sales ....Raymond Arroyo
Mng. Ed. ....Kevin Moran
Berkshires Week Ed. ....Katherine Abbott
Editorial Page Ed. ....William Everhart
Entertainment Ed. ....Jeffrey Borak
Features Ed. ....Charles Bonenti
Sports Ed. ....Matthew Strague
Exec. Ed. ....Tim Farkas
Market Information: TMC.
Mechanical available: Offset; Black and 3 ROP colors; insert accepted - product samples; page cutoffs - 22 3/4.
Mechanical Specifications: Type page 11 1/2 x 21 1/2; E - 6 cols, 1 5/6, 1/8 between; A - 6 cols, 1 5/6, 1/8 between; C - 9 cols, 1 1/5, 1/16 between.
Commodity Consumption: Avg. Page Number Per Issue - Daily 39; Avg. Page Number Per Issue - Plates Used 36000; Avg. Page Number Per Issue - Sunday 86; widths 12 1/2; Newsprint Used - Metric Tons 2690; Printing Ink Used - Black 84000; Printing Ink Used - Color 32400; Printing In
Equipment EDITORIAL: Front-end Software – HP/5000, Baseview/Newsedit Pro.; Editorial Hardware – Mac/G3, Mac/G4 CLASSIFIED: Front-end Software – PPI/Unisys.; Classified Hardware – NT/Servers; Classified Printers – HP/5000 DISPLAY: Ad make-up applications – Multi-Ad 7.0; Layout Software – CLS/ALS.; Display Hardware – Mac/XServer, GH; Display Printers – HP/5000 PRODUCTION: Pagination Software – Baseview.; Production Equipment – ECRM 6.2, Adobe/Photoshop; Scanners – Epson/2400 PRESSROOM: Line 1 – 13-G/Urbanite; Folders – G/Urbanite, Hantscho/F10W839; Pasters – 8-Enkel/Auto Paster. MAILROOM: Counter stackers – 3-TMST/Compass; Inserters and stuffers – GMA/SLS 1000 8:1; Bundle tying machines – 3-Samuel/Power Strap, Bu; Wrapping singles – Mailroom control system ☐ Prism; Addressing machine – Ch; Other equipment –MM/4-Pocket Stitcher-Trimmer.; Business Hardware – DEC/Micro VA 3600, HP/3000 MPE/IX

QUINCY

THE PATRIOT LEDGER

400 Crown Colony Dr., Quincy, Mass., 02169; gen tel (617) 786-7000; adv tel (617) 786-7100 (class); ed tel (617) 786-7026; gen fax (617) 786-7120; adv fax (617) 786-7092 (class); ed fax (617) 786-7025; gen e-mail newsroom@ledger.com; adv e-mail ads@ledger.com; classads@ledger.com; web site www.patriotledger.com

Published: Mon, Tues, Wed, Thur, Fri, Sat, Sun
Weekday Frequency: e
Saturday Frequency: m
Circulation: 38,326; 45,344(sat); 45,344(sun)
Last Audit: ABC September 30, 2011
Price: 3.50/wk; 187.00/yr; 86.45/6mo.
Advertising: Open inch rate $64.48
News services: NYT, AP, SHNS, TMS.
Politics: 1837
Special Editions: Jobs & Education: Education Focus (Apr); Your Community (Aug); Jobs & Education (Dec); Coupon Book (Feb); Superbowl (Jan); Jobs & Education II (Jul); Advice for the Experts (Jun); South Shore Women II (Mar); Career Connection I (May); South Shore Women VI
Special Weekly Sections: Housing Extra (Real Estate Section) (Fri); Lifestyle (Mon); Home (Sat); Get Out (Thur); Health/Science (Tues); Food (Wed).
Magazines: USA WEEKEND Magazine (Sat).
Pub. ....Kirk Davis
Vice Pres., Finance ....James Piasecki
Exec. Office Mgr. ....Gayle Sheehan
Mgr., HR ....Cyndi Papile
Vice Pres., Adv./Mktg. ....Ed Feldman
Adv. Dir., Classifieds-South of Boston Media Group Linda Siemers
Adv. Mgr., Opns./Classified ....Helen Taylor
Adv. Mgr., Opns./Retail ....Edward J. Siemers
Mgr., Mktg./Promo. ....Elaine Quinn
Vice Pres., Circ. ....Paul Selicissimo
Ed. ....Chazy Dowaliby
Mng. Ed. ....Terry Ryan
Bus. Ed. ....Jon Chesto
City Ed. ....Greg Botelho
Editorial Page Ed. ....John Murphy
Electronic Library Info Systems Mgr. Linda Chapman
Features Ed. ....Dana Barbuto
Local News Ed. ....Linda Shepherd
Online Ed. ....Ken Johnson
Photo/Graphics Ed. ....Jennifer Wagner
Market Information: TMC; Zoned editions.
Mechanical available: Letterpress (direct); Black and 3 ROP colors; insert accepted; page cutoffs - 23 9/16.
Mechanical Specifications: Type page 13 x 22; E - 6 cols, 2, 1/8 between; A - 6 cols, 2, 1/8 between; C - 9 cols, 1 3/8, 3/4 between.
Commodity Consumption: Avg. Page Number Per Issue - Daily 47; Avg. Page Number Per

Issue - Plates Used 28764; Avg. Page Number Per Issue - Saturday 97; widths 40 1/2; Newsprint Used - Metric Tons 7238; Printing Ink Used - Black 296537; Printing Ink Used - Color 22086; Printing

Equipment; Editorial Hardware – 2-Dell/6300 PowerEdge, 1-Dell/4300, 3-Dell/6400GX1, 1-AP/IBM Photo Server, 74-Dell/Optiplex PC, 16-Dell/Inspiron, 6-APP/Mac G3/G4; Editorial Equipment – 1-HP/Scanjet 6300C, 1-Epson/Expression 836XL, 2-Nikon/CoolScan; Editorial Printers – 1-HP/4050, 3-HP/5000, 1-HP CLASSIFIED: Front-end Software – SCS/AdMax, SCS/ClassPag.; Classified Hardware – 1-Dell/6300 PowerEdge, 2-Dell/2300 PowerEdge, 27-Dell/Optiplex PC; Classified Printers – 1-HP/4050, 1-HP/8000, 1-Citoh/SQE DISPLAY: Ad make-up applications – SCS/AdMax, SCS/AdTrack, SCS/Layout, Multi-Ad/Creator, Adobe/Photoshop, Adobe/Illus; Display Hardware – 1-Dell/6300 PowerEdge, 2-Dell/4300 PowerEdge, 17-Optiplex PC, 10-APP/Mac G3/G4, 1-Dell/Inspiron; Display Printers – 3-HP/4050, 2-QMS/2560, 1-QMS-Minolta/6100 PRODUCTION: Pagination Software – Tera/Good News 3.; Production Equipment – 2-Na/Starlite, Konica/4550 Imagesetter, Konica/6200 Imagesetter; Cameras – 1-C/Pager, 1-R/432 Mic II, 1-AG/RPS 2024 Automatic PRESSROOM: Line 1 – 8-H/Colormatic double width 1987; Press Drives – 5-PEC/Custom Made 100 h.p.; Folders – 2; Press control system – PEC/Bond; Press registration system – Kiam/3-Color Registration System. MAILROOM: Counter stackers – 2-HL/HT-2, 3-HL/Monitor; Inserters and stuffers – 2-GMA/SLS 1000 8:1; Bundle tying machines – 4-OVL/JP-80, 1-OVL/Constellation, 1-MLN/WorldNews; Wrapping singles – 2-HL/Bottom Wrap; Addressing machine – 1-IBM/AS 400.; Business Hardware – 1-IBM/AS-400 Model 9402, SCS/AdMax

RANDOLPH

THE ENTERPRISE

15 Pacella Park Dr., Randolph, Mass., 02368-1700; gen tel (508) 586-6200; adv tel (508) 638-5580; ed tel (508) 427-4054; gen fax (508) 427-4949; adv fax (508) 638-5570; ed fax (508) 427-4027; gen e-mail mypaper@enterprisenews.com; adv e-mail retailadv@enterprisenews.com; classifieds@enterprisenews.com; ads@enterprisenews.com; salesteam@wickedlocal.com; ed e-mail newsroom@enterprisenews.com; letters@enterprisenews.com; web site www.enterprisenews.com

Published: Mon, Tues, Wed, Thur, Fri, Sun
Weekday Frequency: e
Circulation: 22,068; 25,265(sat); 24,983(sun)
Last Audit: ABC September 30, 2011
Price: 3.90/wk; 15.60/mo; 202.30/yr.
Advertising: Open inch rate $46.08
News services: AP, LAT-WP, SHNS.
Politics: Independent. **Established:** 1880
Not Published: Christmas.
Special Editions: Education (Apr); Coupon Book (Aug); Chronology Pages/Year in Review (Dec); Living Well (Every other month); Coupon Book (Feb); Golfers Corner (Jul); How to Guide (Jun); Progress (Mar); Professional Profiles (May); Gift Guide (Nov); Coupon Book (Oct); Foot
Special Weekly Sections: Style (Fri); Next (Mon); Travel (S); Family Life (Sat); Mind & Body (Thur); Mind & Body (Tues); Good Taste (Wed).
Magazines: USA WEEKEND Magazine (S).
Pub. ....Rick Daniels
Controller ....Rita J. Holloway
Adv. Dir., Retail ....Michael Harwood
Adv. Mgr., Classified ....Linda Siemers
Adv. Coord., Nat'l/Preprint ....Jennifer Picardi
Dir., Online Sales ....Chris Eck
Circ. Mgr. ....Scott Murdoch
Circ. Coord., Newspapers in Educ. Cheryl Showstack
Ed. ....Chazy Dowaliby
Mng. Ed. ....Steven Damish
Editorial Page Ed. ....Gary Finkelstein
Librarian ....Beth Rose
Asst. Metro Ed. ....Marilyn Hancock
Online Ed. ....Ken Johnson
Online Sports Ed. ....Ken Lechtanski
Photo Dir./Ed. ....Craig Murray
Radio/Television Ed. ....Martha Raber
Sports Ed. ....Mark Torpey
Market Information: Split run; TMC; Zoned editions.
Mechanical available: Letterpress and Flexo combined; Black and 3 ROP colors; insert accepted - samples; page cutoffs - 22 3/4.
Mechanical Specifications: Type page 13 x 21; E - 6 cols, 2 1/16, 1/8 between; A - 6 cols, 2 1/16, 1/8 between; C - 9 cols, 1 3/8, 1/16 between.
Commodity Consumption: Avg. Page Number Per Issue - Daily 40; Avg. Page Number Per Issue - Plates Used 38080; Avg. Page Number Per Issue - Sunday 80; widths 41 1/4; Newsprint Used - Metric Tons 3746; Printing Ink Used - Black 97237; Printing Ink Used - Color 40702; Printing In
Equipment; Editorial Hardware – 2-Dell/6400 Application Server, 1-Dell/4400 Library Server, 2-Dell/GX1 AP Wire Service, 2-Dell/GX1 Primary & Secondary Domain Name Controllers, 1-Dell/GX110 Terminal Server, 45-Dell/Optiplex/GX1 workstation, 6-APP/Mac workstation, 3-APP/iMac, 3 CLASSIFIED: Front-end Software – SCS/Admax-Classified, Microsoft/Office 2000, Adobe/Photoshop.; Classified Hardware – 1-Dell/6300 Application Server, AT/SYSDECO-Classified Pagination Server, 11-Dell/GX1 Workstation; Classified Equipment – HP/Flatbed Scanner; Classified Printers – 1-HP/8000, HP/4050 DISPLAY: Ad make-up applications – SCS; Display Hardware – 1-Dell/6300 Application Server, 1-Dell/4300 Application Server, 1-Dell/2300 Application Server, 7-APP/Mac G3 workstation, 10-Dell/GX1 Workstation, Umax/Page Scanner; Display Printers – 1-HP/8000, HP/4050, 1-HP/LaserJet 4MV, 1-Epson/3000 PRODUCTION: Pagination Software – Tera/GN3-Fred.; Production Equipment – Na/Systems Flexo Processor, 2-MON/RipExpress RIP, 2-ECR/PelBox 108C, 1-III/3850, Konica/RIP; Cameras – 1-C/Spartan III, 1-P/Pager; Scanners – 1-ECR/Autokon 1000, X/7650, Umax PRESSROOM: Line 1 – G/Mark I (double width) 1960; Line 2 – MAN/Flexoman (double width) 1989; Line 3 – MAN/Flexoman (w/hump) (double width) 1989; Line 4 – G/Mark I (double width) 1960; Line 5 – G/Mark I (double width) 1960; Line 6 – MAN/Flexoman (double width) 1989 MAILROOM: Counter stackers – 2-QWI/Sport; Inserters and stuffers – 1-GMA/SLS 1000; Bundle tying machines – 1-OVL/JP-80, 1-OVL/JP-80, 2-OVL/Strapmaster; Wrapping singles – Addressing machine ÂD 2-VideoJet/Series 270.; Audio Hardware – Tele-Publishing Inc BUSINESS COMPUTERS: Business Software – CJ, Southware/Accounting Systems, Geac/Circulation Systems, SCS/ADMAX-Billing; Business Hardware – DEC/VAX 4100, Microsoft/Windows NT, CI/1000 Sge Printer, HP/4050, Dell/GX1 workstation, Mac/O/S, SCO/Unix

SOUTHBRIDGE

SOUTHBRIDGE EVENING NEWS

25 Elm St., Southbridge, Mass., 01550; gen tel (508) 764-4325; adv tel (508) 764-4325; ed tel (508) 764-4325; gen fax (508) 764-8015; adv fax (508) 764-8102; ed fax (508) 764-8015; ed e-mail news@sbnews.com; web site www.southbridgeeveningnews.com

Group: Stonebridge Press
Published: Mon, Tues, Wed, Thur, Fri
Weekday Frequency: All day
Circulation: 4,500
Last Audit: Sworn March 31, 2008
Price: 2.75/wk; 6.20/mo; 110.00/yr.
Advertising: Open inch rate $15.05
News services: AP.
Politics: 1923
Not Published: New Year; Memorial Day; Independence Day; Labor Day; Thanksgiving; Christmas.
Own facility?: Y
President & Publisher ....Frank Chilinski
Adv. Sales Exec. ....Jean Ashton
Exec. Ed. ....Walter Bird
Mechanical available: Offset; Black and 3 ROP colors; insert accepted; page cutoffs - 17.
Mechanical Specifications: Type page 9 5/8 x 16; E - 6 cols, 1 1/2, 3/16 between; A - 6 cols, 1 1/2, 1/10 between; C - 7 cols, 1 3/8, 1/10 between.
Commodity Consumption: Avg. Page Number Per Issue - Daily 24; Avg. Page Number Per Issue - Plates Used 1530; widths 14; Newsprint Used - Short Tons 181; Printing Ink Used - Black 8190; Printing Ink Used - Color 156; Printing Ink Used - Pages Printed 6120.

STONEBRIDGE PRESS, INC.

25 Elm St., Southbridge, Mass., 01550; gen tel (508) 764-4325; gen fax (508) 764-8102; gen e-mail fchilinski@stonebridgepress.com; web site www.stonebridgepress.com

Published: Mon, Tues, Wed, Thur, Fri
Weekday Frequency: All day
Circulation: 4,200
Politics: 1922
President & Publisher ....Frank Chilinski
Adv. Mgr. ....Jean Ashton
Delivery method: Mail, Newsstand, Private Carrier, Racks

SPRINGFIELD

THE REPUBLICAN

1860 Main St., Springfield, Mass., 01103; gen tel (413) 788-1000; adv tel (413) 788-1250; ed tel (413) 788-1200; gen fax (413) 788-1199; adv fax (413) 788-1199; ed fax (413) 788-1301; ed e-mail news@repub.com; web site www.repub.com

Published: Mon, Tues, Wed, Thur, Fri, Sat, Sun
Weekday Frequency: m
Saturday Frequency: m
Circulation: 57,349; 41,644(sat); 101,471(sun)
Last Audit: ABC September 30, 2011
Advertising: Open inch rate $105.71
News services: AP, NYT, LAT-WP, NNS.
Politics: Independent. **Established:** 1824
Special Editions: Back-to-School (Aug); Presidents' Day Auto (Feb); Outlook (Jan); Home Show (Mar); Fall Home Improvement (Sept).
Special Weekly Sections: Movies (Fri); Parenting (Mon); TV Time (S); Weekend (Thur); Unlisted for Teens (Tues); Best Food Day (Wed).
Magazines: Leisure Time (S).
Pub./CEO ....Larry A. McDermott
Asst. to Pub. ....Robyn A. Newhouse
Vice Pres./Gen. Mgr. ....Frederick Fedesco
Controller ....David B. Evans
Dir., HR ....Judith C. Fraser
Adv. Dir. ....Mark French
Adv. Mgr., Classified ....Marysue Mooney
Adv. Mgr., Major Accts ....Rita J. Martin
Adv. Servs. Mgr. ....Gregory Robinson
Mktg. Dir. ....Maureen Sullivan
Exec. Ed. ....Wayne E. Phaneuf
Mng. Ed., Lifestyle ....Ray Kelly
Mng. Ed., Special Projects ....Cynthia Simson
Bus. Ed ....James Kinney
City Ed., Day ....Steve Smith
City Ed., Night ....Lu Feorino
Photo Ed. ....Dale Ruff
Sports Ed ....Joe Deburro
IT Mgr. ....Rob Chapin
Market Information: ADS; Split run; TMC; Zoned editions.
Mechanical available: Offset; Black and 3 ROP colors; insert accepted - BFD inserts; page cutoffs - 21.
Mechanical Specifications: Type page 11 5/8 x 20 1/4; E - 6 cols, 1 5/6, 1/8 between; A - 6 cols, 1 5/6, 1/8 between; C - 10 cols, 1 7/100, 1/16 between.
Commodity Consumption: Avg. Page Number Per Issue - Daily 44; Avg. Page Number Per Issue - Plates Used 120000; Avg. Page Number Per Issue - Sunday 134; widths 50; Newsprint Used - Short Tons 12445; Printing Ink Used - Black 166497; Printing Ink Used - Color 135120.
Equipment EDITORIAL: Front-end Software – HI/Newsmaker Editorial.; Editorial Hardware – Dell; Editorial Printers – 2-HP/Designjet 2500 CLASSIFIED: Front-end Software – Mactive 2.24.; Classified Hardware – Dell; Classified Printers – Dataproducts DISPLAY: Ad make-up applications – QPS/QuarkXPress; Layout Software – Mactive/PGL.; Display Hardware – Mactive PRODUCTION: Pagination Software – HI/Newsmaker, Mactive/PGL, Proimage/Newsway.; Production Equipment – Adobe/Photoshop, APP/Mac Desktop PRESSROOM: Line 1 – 5-MAN/Regioman (8 couples); Press Drives – Bammueller; Folders – 2; Reels and Stands – 6-MAN/CD 13. MAILROOM: Counter stackers – 5-QWI/400, 2-QWI/300, 1-Gammerler/KL 503; Inserters and stuffers – 1-SLS/3000 28:2, 2-SLS/3000 14:2; Bundle tying machines – 3/Strapex, 6-/Dynaric; Wrapping singles – 6-/QWI; Addressing machine – 3-Ch/525E Labeler; Other equipment –1- BUSINESS COMPUTERS: Business Software – AP, GL, Platinum, Ultipro Payroll System; Business Hardware – 2-Dell, IBM/AS-400, Power Edge/4200

TAUNTON

TAUNTON DAILY GAZETTE

5 Cohannet St., Taunton, Mass., 02780-0111; gen tel (508) 880-9000; adv tel (508) 880-9000; ed tel (508) 880-9000; gen fax (508) 967-3109; adv fax (508) 967-3101; ed fax (508) 967-3101; adv e-mail composing@tauntongazette.com; ed e-mail newsroom@tauntongazette.com; web site www.tauntongazette.com

Published: Mon, Tues, Wed, Thur, Fri, Sat, Sun
Weekday Frequency: m
Saturday Frequency: m
Circulation: 6,566; 7,518(sat); 7,289(sun)
Last Audit: ABC September 30, 2011
Price: 3.30/wk; 171.00/yr.
Advertising: Open inch rate $29.57
News services: AP.
Politics: Independent.
Special Editions: Springs Looking Good (Apr); Back-to-School (Aug); Procrastinator's Guide (Dec); Presidents' Day (Feb); Bridal Guide (Jan); Best of Best (Jul); Cape Road (Jun); Winter Wipe Out (Mar); Design an Ad (May); Coupons (Monthly); Christmas Gift (Nov); Trick or Tr
Special Weekly Sections: Look at Area Business (Fri); Professional Directory (Mon); Real Estate (Sat); Look at Area Business (Tues); Food Page (Wed).
Magazines: Coupons Tab (Monthly); USA WEEKEND Magazine (S).
Pub. ....Sean Burke
Vice Pres., Adv. ....Mark Cohen
Adv. Mgr. ....Jordon Tessier
Online Adv. Mgr. ....Chris Eck
Circ. Mgr. ....Doug Fredericks
Mng. Ed. ....Dino Ciliberti
Lifestyles Ed. ....Leeann Hubbard
Sports Ed. ....Steve Sanchez
Website Mgr. ....Anne Eisenmenger
Market Information: ADS; TMC.
Mechanical available: Offset; Black and 3 ROP colors; insert accepted - all; page cutoffs - 22 3/4.
Mechanical Specifications: Type page 12 x 21 1/2; E - 6 cols, 1 7/8, 3/16 between; A - 6 cols, 1 7/8, 3/16 between; C - 9 cols, 1 1/4, 1/8 between.
Commodity Consumption: Avg. Page Number Per Issue - Daily 26; Avg. Page Number Per Issue - Plates Used 8541; Avg. Page Number Per Issue - Saturday 28; Avg. Page Number Per Issue - Sunday 38; widths 12 1/2; Newsprint Used - Short Tons 897; Printing Ink Used - Pages Printed 1136
Equipment EDITORIAL: Front-end Software – Mk, APP/Mac, Baseview.; Editorial Hardware – Mk, APP/Mac; Editorial Printers – Okidata,

HP/HMV CLASSIFIED: Front-end Software – AT.; Classified Hardware – Mk, APP/Mac; Classified Printers – HP DISPLAY: Ad make-up applications – NewzWare; Layout Software – Mk/MasterPlanner.; Display Hardware – HP; Display Printers – HP PRODUCTION: Pagination Software – QPS/QuarkXPress 4.0.; Production Equipment – Nu; Cameras – SCREEN, R, C/Spartan 3; Scanners – Epson, Nikon/Super Coolscan PRESSROOM: Line 1 – 9-G/Urbanite single width; Pasters – 8-Jardis/Ebway; Press registration system – Duarte/Pin Registration System. MAILROOM: Counter stackers – 3/Hall; Inserters and stuffers – GMA/SLS 1000; Bundle tying machines – MLN/ML2E, Signode/MLN 2A; Wrapping singles – 3-Hall/Monarch; Addressing machine – CH/525. BUSINESS COMPUTERS: Business Software – Microsoft/Excel 7, Lotus 5.0, Newzware; Business Hardware – CCPS

WAKEFIELD

WAKEFIELD DAILY ITEM

26 Albion St., Wakefield, Mass., 1880; gen tel (781) 245-0080; gen fax (781) 246-0061; ed e-mail news@wakefielditem.com; web site www.wakefielditem.com

Published: Mon, Tues, Wed, Thur, Fri
Weekday Frequency: e
Circulation: 4,556
Last Audit: March 31, 2007
Price: 1.90/wk (home delivery); 216.00/yr (mail).
Advertising: Open inch rate $20.00
News services: AP.
Politics: Independent.
Not Published: New Year; Memorial Day; Independence Day; Labor Day; Thanksgiving; Christmas.
Special Editions: Mother's Day Page (Apr); Back-to-School (Aug); New Baby (Dec); Valentine's Page (Feb); Bridal Supplement (Jan); 4th of July (Jul); Father's Day Page (Jun); Easter Page (Mar); Graduation Pages (May); Thanksgiving Day (Nov); Columbus Day (Sept).

Gen. Mgr. ....Glenn Dolbeare
Adv. Mgr. ....Phil Simonson
Adv. Mgr., Classified ....Marcia Perry
Circ. Mgr. ....Thomas Tine
Ed. ....Peter Rossi
Asst. Ed. ....Robert Burgess
School Ed. ....Gail Lowe
Sports Ed. ....Jim Southmayd

Mechanical available: Offset; Black.
Mechanical Specifications: Type page 13 x 21; E - 6 cols, 2 1/16, 1/8 between; A - 9 cols, 1 1/4, 1/8 between; C - 9 cols, 1 1/4, 1/8 between.
Commodity Consumption: Avg. Page Number Per Issue - Daily 16.
Equipment EDITORIAL: Front-end Software – Baseview/NewsEdit.

WESTFIELD

THE WESTFIELD NEWS

62-64 School St., Westfield, Mass., 01085; gen tel (413) 562-4181; gen fax (413) 562-4185; gen e-mail newsroom@wenpub.com

Group: The Westfield News Group LLC
Published: Mon, Tues, Wed, Thur, Fri, Sat
Weekday Frequency: e
Saturday Frequency: m
Circulation: 5,300; 5,300(sat)
Last Audit: March 31, 2008
Price: 12.00/mo (in county), $9.00/mo (mail); 125.00/yr.
News services: AP.
Not Published: New Year; Memorial Day; Independence Day; Labor Day; Thanksgiving; Christmas.
Own facility?: Y

Gen. Mgr./Bus. Mgr. ....Marie Brazee
Adv. Dir. ....Martha Baillargeon
Ed. ....Dan Moriarty
Enfield Ed. ....Jeff Hanouille
Longmeadow Ed. ....Hope Tremblay
Sports Reporter ....Chris Putz
President ....Patrick Berry
Pres. ....Joe L. Allbritton
City Ed. ....Dave Canton

Market Information: TMC.
Commodity Consumption: Avg. Page Number Per Issue - Daily 20
Equipment; Production Equipment – APP/Mac; Cameras – AG/1600; Bundle tying machines – 2/Bu
Delivery method: Mail, Newsstand, Private Carrier, Racks

WOBURN

DAILY TIMES CHRONICLE

1 Arrow Dr., Woburn, Mass., 1801; gen tel (781) 933-3700; adv tel (781) 933-3700; ed tel (781) 933-3700; gen fax (781) 932-3321; adv fax (781) 932-3321; ed fax (781) 932-3321; gen e-mail news@woburnonline.com; adv e-mail woburnads@rcn.com; ed e-mail news@woburnonline.com; web site www.homenewshere.com

Published: Mon, Tues, Wed, Thur, Fri
Weekday Frequency: e
Circulation: 10,872
Last Audit: September 30, 2007
Price: 2.25/wk; 10.00/mo; 122.50/yr.
Advertising: Open inch rate $20.00
News services: AP, NEA.
Politics: Independent. **Established:** 1901
Not Published: New Year; Memorial Day; Independence Day; Labor Day; Thanksgiving; Christmas.
Special Editions: Spring Home Improvement (Apr); Pre-Season Football (Aug); Christmas (Dec); Your Health (Feb); Graduation (Jun); Social Security (Mar); Spring Home Improvement (May); Fall Home Improvement (Nov); Fall Home Improvement (Oct); Bridal (Sept).
Special Weekly Sections: Bridal Directory (Fri); Medical Directory (Mon); Business Guide (Thur); Business Guide (Tues); Medical Directory (Wed).
Magazines: Middlesex East (Wed).

Pres./Pub./Treasurer/Personnel Mgr. Peter M. Haggerty
Office Mgr./Purchasing Agent ....Joel Haggerty
Controller ....Christopher Campbell
Adv. Dir. ....Thomas Kirk
Mgr., Promo ....Mark J. Haggerty
Circ. Mgr. ....Peter Curran
Ed ....James D. Haggerty
City Ed. ....Gordon Vincent
Film/Theater Ed. ....Michael Haggerty
Nat'l Ed. ....James D. Haggerty
News Ed. ....James D. Haggerty
News Ed., Burlington ....John White
News Ed., Winchester ....Chris Connelly
Social Ed. ....Melissa Finn
Sports Ed. ....Steve Algeri
Prodn. Mgr. ....Jay M. Haggerty
Prodn. Mgr., Pressroom ....Lance Jonsson

Market Information: ADS; Split run; TMC; Zoned editions.
Mechanical available: Offset; Black and 3 ROP colors; insert accepted; page cutoffs - 21.
Mechanical Specifications: Type page 11 5/8 x 21; E - 6 cols, 1 4/5, 1/8 between; A - 6 cols, 1 4/5, 1/16 between; C - 9 cols, 1 3/20, 1/8 between.
Commodity Consumption: Avg. Page Number Per Issue - Daily 36; Avg. Page Number Per Issue - Plates Used 10250; widths 28; Newsprint Used - Short Tons 825; Printing Ink Used - Black 23200; Printing Ink Used - Color 1700; Printing Ink Used - Pages Printed 9706.
Equipment EDITORIAL: Front-end Software – Baseview.; Editorial Hardware – 5-APP/iMac; Editorial Equipment – Okidata/Doc-IT 4000 Scanner; Editorial Printers – 2-HP/LaserJet 4 CLASSIFIED: Front-end Software – Baseview.; Classified Hardware – 6-APP/iMac DISPLAY: Ad make-up applications – Baseview; Layout Software – 2-APP/Power Mac 7100-80, 4-APP/iMac G4.; Display Hardware – Konica/2100 Turbo EV-Jetsetter; Display Printers – HP/LaserJet 5000N; Production Equipment – 1-BKY, 1-Ca; Cameras – 2-DSA. PRESSROOM: Line 1 – 8-G/Community 1975.; Inserters and stuffers – MM; Bundle tying machines – 1/CYP, 2-/Sa; Wrapping singles – Am; Addressing machine – 2-Am/1800.; Business Hardware – 6-Vision Data

WORCESTER

TELEGRAM & GAZETTE

20 Franklin St., Worcester, Mass., 01615-0012; gen tel (508) 793-9100; adv tel (508) 793-9200; ed tel (508) 793-9245; gen fax (508) 793-9313; adv fax (508) 767-9512; ed fax (508) 793-9281; gen e-mail info@telegram.com; adv e-mail advertise@telegram.com; ed e-mail newstips@telegram.com; web site www.telegram.com

Published: Mon, Tues, Wed, Thur, Fri, Sat, Sun
Weekday Frequency: m
Saturday Frequency: m
Circulation: 76,456; 73,563(sat); 83,237(sun)
Last Audit: ABC September 30, 2011
Price: 21.75/mo; 252.20/yr.
Advertising: Open inch rate $133.36
News services: AP, NYT, Bloomberg.
Politics: Independent.
Special Editions: Banking & Finance (Apr); Parenting (Aug); Christmas Gifts (Dec); Business Review (Feb); Educational Showcase (Jan); Summer Book (Jun); Health & Hospital (Mar); Health & Fitness (May); New Cars (Nov); Health & Hospital (Oct); Fall Home Improvement (Sept).
Special Weekly Sections: Travel (S); Time Out (Thur).
Magazines: Parade (S).

Pub. ....Bruce Gautley
Dir., Finance ....Natalie Bradely
Dir., HR ....Victor A. Dinardo
Personnel Mgr. ....Dana Dover
Credit Mgr. ....Robert L. Meunier
Adv. Mgr., Display ....Reinhold Wolfram
Adv. Mgr., Nat'l ....Karen A. Aloia
Dir., Mktg./New Bus. Devel. ....Nancy Cahalen
Dir., Research ....Averil Capers
Circ. Dir. ....Anthony J. Simollardes
Circ. Mgr., Field Opns. ....John O'Brien
Circ. Mgr., Sales/Mktg. ....Katharine A. Silvestri
Circ. Mgr., Single Copy Sales ....Dana Robbins
Mng. Ed. ....Leah Lamson
Mng. Ed. ....Anne N. Esposito
Editorial Page Ed. ....George R. French
Educ. Ed ....Clive McFarlane
Educ. Ed. ....Mark Melady
Environmental Ed. ....John J. Monahan
Features Ed. ....Karen Webber

Market Information: ADS; Split run; TMC; Zoned editions.
Mechanical available: Flexography; Black and 3 ROP colors; insert accepted - partials d & S; page cutoffs - 22.
Mechanical Specifications: Type page 11 5/8 x 21; E - 6 cols, 1 5/6, 1/8 between; A - 6 cols, 1 5/6, 1/8 between; C - 9 cols, 1 3/8, 1/8 between.
Commodity Consumption: Avg. Page Number Per Issue - Daily 44; Avg. Page Number Per Issue - Plates Used 159193; Avg. Page Number Per Issue - Sunday 124; widths 50; Newsprint Used - Metric Tons 12800; Newsprint Used - Short Tons 13999; Printing Ink Used - Black 304636; Printing
Equipment; Editorial Hardware – 2-Sun/V480, 2-Sun/V120, sola*, Sun/Solaris 5.9; Editorial Printers – Epson/DFX 5000, HP/2100TN, Xante/Accel-A-Writer. CLASSIFIED: Front-end Software – Enterprise 1.4.8304.; Classified Hardware – 2-Compaq/ML350, NEC/P300; Classified Printers – Lexmark/1260, Epson/DFX-5000; Layout Software – 4-Cx, APP/Mac, SCS/Layout 8000, SCC/Layout 8000 (10), QWS.; Display Printers – Cihon/5000 Dot Matrix; Production Equipment – 1-ECR/3850, 1-ECR/9100, 6-Xante/Laser Printer 8200; Scanners – 3-Umax PowerLook, 3-Eskoscan/Full Page Scanners. PRESSROOM: Line 1 – 7-G/Flexoliner double width 1991; Line 2 – 7-G/Flexoliner double width 1991; Folders – 2-Sovereign/3:2, 1-G/3:2 double, 1-G/3:2 single; Pasters – 14-G/CT50; Reels and Stands – 14 MAILROOM: Counter stackers – 8-HL/HT II, 2/Quipp 501; Inserters and stuffers – 4-/GMA, 2-GMA/SLS 1000 28:2, 2-GMA/SLS 1000 16:2; Bundle tying machines – 12-Dynaric/NP2; Mailroom control system – GMA/SAM; Addressing machine – Ch/523, Videojet/Ink Jet 4000, Scitex.; Business Hardware – 1-DEC/VAX 4000-100, 1-IBM/AS-400

MICHIGAN

ADRIAN

THE DAILY TELEGRAM

133 N. Winter St., Adrian, Mich., 49221; gen tel (517) 265-5111; adv tel (517) 265-5111; ed tel (517) 265-5111; gen fax (517) 263-4152; adv fax (517) 265-3030; ed fax (517) 263-4152; adv e-mail Shawn winter <shawn@telegramadvertising.com>; ed e-mail editor@lenconnect.com; web site www.lenconnect.com

Group: GateHouse Media, Inc.
Published: Mon, Tues, Wed, Thur, Fri, Sat, Sun
Weekday Frequency: e
Saturday Frequency: m
Circulation: 13,137; 13,770(sat); 15,385(sun)
Last Audit: ABC September 30, 2011
Price: Carrier:3.81/wk 16.50mo. Motor route; $3.98 per week, $17.50 per mo. $192.00/yr.
Advertising: Open inch rate $26.50
News services: GateHouse Media, Inc.
Politics: 1892
Not Published: New Year; Memorial Day; Independence Day; Labor Day; Thanksgiving; Christmas.
Own facility?: Y
Special Weekly Sections: Entertainment TV Log (Fri); Outdoor Page (S); Church Page (Sat).
Magazines: Parade (S).

Pub. ....Paul J. Heidbreder
Adv. Dir. ....Deb Werner
News Ed. ....Dave Panian
Photo Ed. ....Lad Strayer
Sports Ed. ....Mark Lenz
Travel Ed. ....Marge Furgason
Prodn. Mgr., Composing ....Bruce Banks
Prodn. Mgr., Pressroom ....Royce Ohlinger
Prodn. Mgr., Distr. ....Jeff Stahl
Prodn. Mgr., Mailroom ....Boe Tason

Market Information: ADS; TMC.
Mechanical available: Offset; Black and 3 ROP colors; insert accepted - front page self-adhesive notes; page cutoffs - 22 3/4.
Mechanical Specifications: Type page 13 1/16 x 21 1/2; E - 6 cols, 1 7/8, 1/8 between; A - 6 cols, 1 7/8, 1/8 between; C - 9 cols, 1/8 between.
Equipment EDITORIAL: Front-end Software – QPS/QuarkXPress, Media Span IQ/NewsEdit.; Editorial Hardware – APP/Mac CLASSIFIED: Front-end Software – Media Span.; Classified Hardware – APP/Mac; Classified Equipment – App/Mac DISPLAY: Ad make-up applications – QPS/QuarkXPress, Adobe/Photoshop, Multi-Ad/Creator, Media Span; Layout Software – APP/Mac.; Production Equipment – ECRM/CTP PRESSROOM: Line 1 – 9-G/Community (3 color decks; 2 formers); Press Drives – 2; Folders – 1-G/55C. MAILROOM: Counter stackers – 2-HL/Monitor; Inserters and stuffers – Titan/12:1; Bundle tying machines – Sa; Addressing machine – Prism.; Business Hardware – PC

ALPENA

THE ALPENA NEWS

130 Park Pl., Alpena, Mich., 49707; gen tel

(989) 354-3111; adv tel (989) 354-3111; ed tel (989) 354-3111; gen fax (989) 354-2096; adv fax (989) 354-2096; ed fax (989) 354-2096; adv e-mail alpenaads@thealpenanews.com; ed e-mail newsroom@thealpenanews.com; web site www.thealpenanews.com

Published: Mon, Tues, Wed, Thur, Fri, Sat
Weekday Frequency: m
Saturday Frequency: m
Circulation: 9,114; 9,114(sat)
Last Audit: ABC September 30, 2011
Price: 1.95/wk; 7.80/mo; 133.00/yr.
Advertising: Open inch rate $23.50
News services: AP, NEA.
Politics: Independent. **Established:** 1899
Not Published: New Year; Christmas.
Special Editions: Gardening and Outdoor (Apr); Back-to-School (Aug); Bridal (Feb); Home Improvement (Mar); Car Care (May); Deer Hunting (Nov); Car Care (Oct); Football (Sept).
Special Weekly Sections: Entertainment (Fri); Entertainment (Sat); Real Estate Section (Thur).
Magazines: USA WEEKEND Magazine (Sat).
Personnel Mgr. ....Bill Speer
Adv. Mgr. ....Laura Lancewicz
Features Ed. ....Diane Speer
Online Ed. ....Steve Murch
Sports Ed. ....Chris Dombrowlowski
Data Processing Mgr. ....Kathryn Burton
Prodn. Mgr. ....Sue Fryske
Prodn. Mgr., Pre Press ....Ken Pokorzynski
Prodn. Foreman, Pressroom ....Jim Brown
Market Information: ADS; TMC; Zoned editions.
Mechanical available: Offset; Black and 3 ROP colors; insert accepted; page cutoffs - 22 3/4.
Mechanical Specifications: Type page 12 x 21 1/2; E - 6 cols, 1 7/8, 1/8 between; A - 6 cols, 1 7/8, 1/8 between; C - 8 cols, 1 3/8, 1/16 between.
Commodity Consumption: Avg. Page Number Per Issue - Daily 16; Avg. Page Number Per Issue - Plates Used 13410; Avg. Page Number Per Issue - Saturday 26; widths 27; Newsprint Used - Short Tons 598; Printing Ink Used - Black 13600; Printing Ink Used - Color 5250; Printing Ink Use
Equipment EDITORIAL: Front-end Software – Baseview, Write-Now, QPS/QuarkXPress, Aldus/FreeHand, Adobe/Photoshop.; Editorial Hardware – APP/Mac; Editorial Printers – HP/4MV CLASSIFIED: Front-end Software – Baseview.; Classified Hardware – 2-APP/Mac LC DISPLAY: Ad make-up applications – Aldus, QPS, Multi-Ad, Aldus/FreeHand, Adobe/Photoshop; Layout Software – APP/Power Mac.; Display Hardware – Printers ☐ HP/4MV PRODUCTION: Pagination Software – QPS/QuarkXPress 4.04, QPS/QuarkXPress 3.32.; Production Equipment – 1-LE/LD-18, 1-Nu/Flip Top FT40V6UP; Cameras – 1-R/580 PRESSROOM: Line 1 – 6-G/U 911; Folders – 1; Bundle tying machines – 1/Sa, 2-/MLN; Addressing machine – 1-/St.; Business Hardware – 1-IBM/34

ALPENA NEWS PUBLISHING CO.

130 Park Pl., Alpena, Mich., 49707; gen tel (989) 354-3111; gen fax (989) 354-2096; gen e-mail newsroom@thealpenanews.com; adv e-mail alpenaads@thealpenanews.com; ed e-mail smurch@thealpenanews.com; web site www.thealpenanews.com

Published: Mon, Tues, Wed, Thur, Fri, Sat
Weekday Frequency: m
Saturday Frequency: m
Circulation: 9,255; 10,154(sat)
Price: 153.40/yr.
Advertising: Open inch rate $17.20
Politics: 1899
Not Published: Sunday

Own facility?: Y
Delivery method: Private Carrier

BAD AXE

THE HURON DAILY TRIBUNE

211 N. Heisterman St., Bad Axe, Mich., 48413; gen tel (989) 269-6461; adv tel (989) 269-6461; ed tel (989) 269-6461; gen fax (989) 269-9893; adv fax (989) 269-2691; ed fax (989) 269-9435; gen e-mail tribune@hearstnp.com; hdt_news@hearstnp.com; adv e-mail vyaroch@hearstnp.com; ed e-mail kniebel@hearstnp.com; web site www.michigansthumb.com
Group: U.S. Suburban Press, Inc.
Published: Mon, Tues, Wed, Thur, Fri, Sun
Weekday Frequency: e
Circulation: 6,461; 7,254(sun)
Last Audit: September 30, 2007
Price: 2.40/wk; 10.40/mo; 115.20/yr; 28.80/12wk.
Advertising: Open inch rate $21.25
News services: AP.
Politics: Independent.
Not Published: New Year; Memorial Day; Independence Day; Labor Day; Thanksgiving; Christmas.
Special Editions: Golf (Apr); Real Estate Guides (Aug); Holiday Gift Guide (Dec); Real Estate Guides (Feb); Progress (Jan); Real Estate Guides (Jul); Real Estate Guides (Jun); Traveler (May); Holiday Gift Guide (Nov); Home Improvement (Sept).
Magazines: Thumb Farmer (Monthly); USA WEEKEND Magazine (S).
Pub. ....Jan Stoeckle
Controller ....Marilyn Wiley
Adv. Dir. ....Victoria Yaroch
Circulation Dir. ....Gerald Ives
Ed ....Kelly L. Jerome
Features Ed. ....Kelly L. Niebel
Sports Ed. ....Mike Bogan
Digital Media Dir. ....Aileen Prill
Prodn. Mgr. ....Jerry Gibbard
Market Information: TMC.
Mechanical available: Offset; Black and 3 ROP colors; insert accepted - subject to approval; page cutoffs - 22 3/4.
Mechanical Specifications: Type page 13 x 21 1/2; E - 6 cols, 2 1/16, 1/8 between; A - 6 cols, 2 1/16, 1/8 between; C - 9 cols, 1 3/8, 1/16 between.
Commodity Consumption: Avg. Page Number Per Issue - Daily 20; Avg. Page Number Per Issue - Plates Used 8900; widths 27; Newsprint Used - Short Tons 851; Printing Ink Used - Black 24480; Printing Ink Used - Color 2680; Printing Ink Used - Pages Printed 5004.
Equipment EDITORIAL: Front-end Software – Baseview/NewsEdit 3.3, Baseview.; Editorial Hardware – APP/Mac; Editorial Equipment – APP/Mac Scanner, Lf/AP Leaf Picture Desk, APP/Power Mac, APP/Power Mac/7100 Photo Desk; Editorial Printers – APP/Mac LaserWriter II, APP/Mac LaserWriter 810, AG/Imagesetter 800 CLASSIFIED: Front-end Software – Baseview, Mk/Class Manager 3.2.; Classified Hardware – APP/Mac; Classified Equipment – APP/Mac Scanner; Classified Printers – APP/Mac LaserWriter II DISPLAY: Ad make-up applications – QPS/QuarkXPress 3.3; Layout Software – Ad Director.; Display Hardware – APP/Power Mac, APP/Power Mac PC 7100; Display Printers – APP/Mac LaserWriter II, APP/Mac LaserWriter 810 PRODUCTION: Pagination Software – AG, QPS/QuarkXPress 4.0.; Production Equipment – AG/800 Imagesetter, Power PC/8100; Cameras – C/Spartan III, C/Marathon; Scanners – Umax, Nikon PRESSROOM: Line 1 – 9-KP/News King; Folders – 1; Pasters – BG/Acumeter.; Inserters and stuffers – KAN; Bundle tying machines – 2/Bu; Addressing machine – Ch.; Audio Hardware – AP StockQuote, ITN BUSINESS COMPUTERS: Business Software – Discus; Business Hardware – AdMark

BATTLE CREEK

BATTLE CREEK ENQUIRER

77 E. Michigan Ave., Suite 101, Battle Creek, Mich., 49017-3002; gen tel (269) 964-7161; adv tel (269) 966-0572; ed tel (269) 966-0672; gen fax (269) 964-0299; adv fax (269) 964-8242; ed fax (269) 964-0299; web site battlecreekenquirer.com
Group: Gannett Co. Inc.
Published: Mon, Tues, Wed, Thur, Fri, Sat, Sun
Weekday Frequency: m
Saturday Frequency: m
Circulation: 15,275; 17,133(sat); 23,000(sun)
Last Audit: ABC September 30, 2011
Price: 3.25/wk; 13.00/mo (carrier); 182.00/yr.
News services: AP, GNS.
Politics: 1900
Own facility?: N
Special Editions: Wedding Planner (Jan); Senior Connections (Jan, Mar, May, Jul, Nov) Progress (Feb); Homezone (Mar); Homebuyer Guide (Mar); Golf (April); Outdoors (Apr, Sep); Travel (May); Airshow (June); Big Summer Deals (June); Grad section (June); Resident Resource (Jul); Back to School (Jul); Football (Aug); Kidvertising (Oct); Holiday (Nov); Basketball (Dec).
Special Weekly Sections: WOW (What's On Weekends) (Fri).
Magazines: USA WEEKEND Magazine (Fri).
Circ. Mgr., Home Delivery ....Merrie Shina
General Manage and Executive Editor Michael McCullough
Assistant managing editor ....Bob Warner
Photo editor ....John Grap
Managing Editor ....Eric Greene
Sports Editor ....Bill Broderick
Assistant managing editor ....Charles Carlson
Opinion Page Editor ....Steve Smith
Digital Editor ....Bill Miller
Features Editor ....Annie Kelley
Mechanical available: Offset; Black and 3 ROP colors; insert accepted - zoned;
Equipment PRODUCTION: Pagination Software – Newsgate/CCI
Zip Codes served: 49017; 49015; 49037; 49014; 49020; 49021; 49046; 49050; 49058; 49060; 49073;49076; 49096; 49033; 49068; 49224; 49245; 49092; 49011; 49028; 49029; 49036; 49040; 49051; 49082; 49089; 49094; 49012; 49034; 49053;
Delivery method: Mail, Newsstand, Private Carrier, Racks

BAY CITY

THE BAY CITY TIMES

311 Fifth St., Bay City, Mich., 48708-58530; gen tel (989) 895-8551; adv tel (989) 894-9661; ed tel (989) 894-9630; gen fax (989) 895-5910; adv fax (989) 895-5910; ed fax (989) 893-0649; gen e-mail newsroom@bc-times.com; adv e-mail corr@bc-times.com; ed e-mail newsroom@bc•times.com; web site www.mlive.com
Group: Metro Suburbia, Inc./Newhouse Newspapers
Published: Thur, Fri, Sun
Circulation: 33,486
Last Audit: ABC September 30, 2011
Price: 12.00/mo (carrier), $12.50/mo (motor route), $15.00/mo (mail); 144.00/yr.
Advertising: Open inch rate $38.27
News services: AP, LAT-WP, NNS.
Politics: 4. **Established:** 1873
Special Editions: Catching ZZZ's (Apr); Football Tab (Aug); Last Minute Gifts (Dec); Everyday Money (Feb); Weddings (Jan); Salute to Bay Area Business (Jul); For Your Wedding (Jun); Women's Expo (Mar); Health Care (May); Five Star Favorites (Nov); Fall Care Care (Sept).
Special Weekly Sections: Outdoor Pages (Fri); Food (Mon); Farm Pages (S); Anniversaries (Sat); Weekend Scene Magazine (Thur); Kids Pages (Tues); Homestyle (Wed).
Magazines: Parade (S).
Pub. ....Matt Sharp
Controller ....Gary L. Weiss
Adv. Dir. ....Cynthia A. Orr
Adv. Nat'l Classified Mgr. ....Denise Taglauer
Mgr., Mktg./Promo. ....Cynthia Orr
Circ. Dir. ....Vincent Cone
Circ. Mgr. ....Michael Krygier
Ed. ....John P. Hiner
Bus. Ed. ....Rob Clark
Editorial Page Ed. ....Clark M. Hughes
Educ. Ed. ....Patti Brandt
Librarian ....Ann Sauve
Lifestyle Ed. ....Carol Zedaker
Metro Ed. ....Kelly Adrian Frick
News Ed. ....Dave Shane
Political/Gov't Ed. ....Jeff Kart
Market Information: Split run; TMC; Zoned editions.
Mechanical available: Offset; Black and full color ROP colors; insert accepted; page cutoffs - 20.
Mechanical Specifications: Type page 11 5/8 x 20 1/4; E - 6 cols, 1 5/6, between; A - 6 cols, 1 5/6, between; C - 10 cols, 1 1/16, between.
Commodity Consumption: Avg. Page Number Per Issue - Daily 27; Avg. Page Number Per Issue - Plates Used 48000; Avg. Page Number Per Issue - Saturday 27; Avg. Page Number Per Issue - Sunday 68; widths 41; Newsprint Used - Metric Tons 2496; Printing Ink Used - Black 67334; Printi
Equipment EDITORIAL: Front-end Software – Baseview.; Editorial Hardware – Apple; Editorial Equipment – APP/Mac; Editorial Printers – HP/LaserJet II CLASSIFIED: Front-end Software – AT 4.4.10.; Classified Hardware – AT/9000 DISPLAY: Ad make-up applications – QPS/QuarkXPress 4.11, Multi-Ad/Creator 6.5, Adobe/Photoshop 7.0, Baseview/PMP.; Display Hardware – APP/Mac, Dell/486 PC, Dell/NT 2400, Harlequin 5.x, Sun/Sparc 20 RIP Express 3000; Display Printers – HP/4 MV, HP/5000N PRODUCTION: Pagination Software – Baseview.; Production Equipment – AP; Scanners – 2-AG/Duoscan T1200; Folders – 2; Pasters – 5 MAILROOM: Counter stackers – Flexi Roll Buffer; Inserters and stuffers – 2/SLS 3000, 5-/AU PP 500; Bundle tying machines – Dyneric. BUSINESS COMPUTERS: Business Software – PBS, Solaris/OS, SBS; Business Hardware – 1-Sun/Ultra Sparc 140, 1-Sun/Sparc 20, 1-Sun/Ultra 200 E

BIG RAPIDS

THE PIONEER - BIG RAPIDS

115 N. Michigan Ave., Big Rapids, Mich., 49307; gen tel (231) 796-4831; adv tel (231) 592-8365; ed tel (231) 592-8360; gen fax (231) 796-1152; gen e-mail pioneer@pioneergroup.com; adv e-mail advertising@pioneergroup.net; ed e-mail dclark@pioneergroup.com; web site www.bigrapidsnews.com
Published: Mon, Tues, Wed, Thur, Fri, Sat
Weekday Frequency: m
Circulation: 5,221; 5,221(sat)
Last Audit: October 1, 2002
Price: 9.95/mo; 107.50/yr; 56.75/6mo, $29.25/3mo.
Advertising: Open inch rate $14.75
News services: AP.
Politics: Independent.
Not Published: New Year; Memorial Day; Independence Day; Labor Day; Thanksgiving; Christmas.
Special Editions: Recreation (Apr); Ferris State University Orientation Welcome (Aug); Songbook (Dec); Car Care Tab (Fall); Bridal Issue (Jan); Sidewalk Sales (Jul); Progress (Jun); Graduation (May); Christmas Gift Guide (Nov); Soil Conservation (Sept); Car Care Tab (Sprin
Special Weekly Sections: Eye on Entertainment (Sat).
Magazines: USA WEEKEND Magazine (Sat); American Profile (Tues).
CFO ....Sharon Doxee
Pub. ....John Norton
HR Mgr. ....Patti Wilson
Adv. Mgr. ....Sharon Frederick
Editorial Page Ed. ....Dave Clark
Sports Ed. ....Zeke Jennings
Mgmt. Info Servs. Mgr. ....Kris Keusch
Prodn. Mgr., Distr. ....Sue Vellanti
Press. Mgr. ....Robert Kaminski
Gen. Mgr., Printing ....Cheryl Rosen
Market Information: ADS; TMC; Zoned editions.
Mechanical available: Offset; Black and 3 ROP colors; insert accepted - all; page cutoffs - 21.
Mechanical Specifications: Type page 12 x 21 1/2; E - 6 cols, 2, 1/6 between; A - 6 cols, 1 3/8, 7/16 between; C - 6 cols, 1 3/8, 7/16 between.
Commodity Consumption: Avg. Page Number Per Issue - Daily 16; Avg. Page Number Per Issue - Plates Used 14000; widths 25; Newsprint Used - Short Tons 700; Printing Ink Used - Black 16000; Printing Ink Used - Color 2000; Printing Ink Used - Pages Printed 16848.
Equipment EDITORIAL: Front-end Software – Baseview/NewsEdit Pro 2.2.2.; Editorial Hardware – APP/Mac, Poweruser/fileserver; Editorial Equipment – 9-APP/Mac, 1-APP/Mac II; Editorial Printers – Xante, ECR/Imagesetter, X/Color Laser CLASSIFIED: Front-end Software – APP/Power Mac, Baseview/Ad Manager Pro.; Classified Hardware – APP/Mac, Poweruser/fileserver; Classified Equipment – 2-APP/Mac, Xante, ECR/Imagesetter; Classified Printers – ECR/Imagesetter; Layout Software – APP/Power Macs.; Display Hardware – APP/Power Mac, Baseview/Ad Manager Pro; Display Printers – Xante/Accel-a-Writer 8100 PRODUCTION: Pagination Software – QPS/QuarkXPress 3.2.; Production Equipment – 2-APP/Mac LaserWriter II, 1-Nu/FT40LNS; Cameras – 1-AG/RPS 2024S, 1-LE/480; Scanners – 1-AG/Studio Star, 1-Polaroid/SprintScan Plus PRESSROOM: Line 1 – 2-4/HI, 2-2/HI, 2, 2-HI/JF-35 Folders; Line 2 – 1-4/HI, 2-2/HI, 2, HI/JF-35 Folder single width; Press Drives – 30, 100, GE/Motor Drive; Folders – 1-HI/JF7, 1-HI/JF-35; Pasters – 4-Martin/EC Plus zero speed; Reels and Stands – 5 MAILROOM: Counter stackers – Rima, RS/25; Inserters and stuffers – KAN/480 6:1; Bundle tying machines – 2-Bu/String Tyers, 1-Mosca/Strapper; Addressing machine – Wm. BUSINESS COMPUTERS: Business Software – Great Plains, Baseview; Business Hardware – Microsoft/Windows NT 4.0, APP/Power Mac Work Group 8550

CADILLAC

CADILLAC NEWS

130 N. Mitchell St., Cadillac, Mich., 49601-0640; gen tel (231) 775-6565; adv tel (231) 775-6565; ed tel (231) 775-6564; gen fax (231) 775-8790; gen e-mail customerservice@cadillacnews.com; adv e-mail psorger@cadillacnews.com; ed e-mail mseward@cadillacnews.com; web site www.cadillacnews.com
Published: Mon, Tues, Wed, Thur, Fri, Sat
Weekday Frequency: m
Saturday Frequency: m
Circulation: 10,175; 10,175(sat)
Last Audit: September 27, 2003
Price: 10.74/mo; 138.00/yr.
Advertising: Open inch rate $26.05
News services: AP.
Politics: Independent. **Established:** 1872
Not Published: New Year; Martin Luther King Jr. Day; Presidents' Day; Memorial Day; Independence Day; Labor Day; Columbus Day; Veteran's Day; Thanksgiving; Christmas.
Own facility?: Y
Special Editions: Spring Home Improvement (Apr); Brides & Weddings (Aug); Christmas Gift Guide (Dec); Home Show (Feb); Generations (50+) (Jan); Summer Recreation II (Jun); Progress (Mar); Summer Recreation I (May); Hunting Guide (Nov); Generations (50+) (Oct); Fall Home Im
Special Weekly Sections: Church (Fri); Outdoors (Sat); Entertainment (Thur); Seniors (Tues); Family (Wed).
Magazines: USA WEEKEND Magazine (Sat);

American Profile (Weekly).
Pres./Pub. ......T. Chris Huckle
Mgr., Bus./Personnel ......Sandy Smith
Adv. Leader ......Pat Sorger
Editorial Page Ed. ......Matthew Seward
Sports Ed. ......Marc Vieau
Prodn. Leader ......Ken Koch
Market Information: TMC; Zoned editions.
Mechanical available: Offset; Black and 3 ROP colors; insert accepted; page cutoffs - 22 3/4.
Mechanical Specifications: Type page 10 3/8 x 21 1/2; E - 6 cols, 2 1/16, 1/8 between; A - 6 cols, 2 1/16, 1/8 between; C - 6 cols, 2 1/16, 1/8 between.
Commodity Consumption: widths 28.
Equipment EDITORIAL: Front-end Software – Woodwing/InDesign CLASSIFIED: Front-end Software – Baseview/Classified, Baseview/Ad Manager Pro.; Classified Hardware – Mac; Classified Printers – Xerox DISPLAY: Ad make-up applications – Multi-Ad/Creator; Layout Software – MEI/ALS.; Display Hardware – Mac PRESSROOM: Line 1 – 6-HI/V-15A (Upper Former) 1969.; Inserters and stuffers – KAN/760 (6 Station); Bundle tying machines – Bu; Addressing machine – Domino/Ink Jet.; Audio Hardware – Mac BUSINESS COMPUTERS: Business Software – Baseview; Business Hardware – APP/Mac
Delivery method: Mail

CHEBOYGAN

CHEBOYGAN DAILY TRIBUNE

308 N. Main St., Cheboygan, Mich., 49721-1545; gen tel (231) 627-7144; gen fax (231) 627-5331; adv e-mail nancy@cheboygantribune.com; ads@cheboygantribune.com; web site www.cheboygannews.com
Published: Mon, Tues, Wed, Thur, Fri
Weekday Frequency: m
Circulation: 4,864
Last Audit: October 3, 2001
Price: 103.00/yr; 40.00/3mo, $60.00/6mo.
Advertising: Open inch rate $15.40
News services: AP.
Not Published: All legal holidays.
Special Editions: Home Improvement (Apr); Design an Ad (Feb); Home Improvement (Mar).
Special Weekly Sections: Real Estate (Fri); Schools (Mon); Food (Thur); Business (Tues); Weddings (Wed).
Magazines: American Profile (Weekly).
Pub. ......Gary Lamberg
Adv. Mgr. ......Nancy Kidder
Classified Mgr. ......Tina Gonser
Circ. Mgr. ......Mary Whaley
Ed. ......Michael Eads
Sports Ed. ......John Adams
Prodn. Mgr., Pressroom ......Jerry Pond
Prodn. Mgr., Mailroom ......Donetta Carney
Market Information: ADS; TMC.
Mechanical available: Offset; Black and 2 ROP colors; insert accepted; page cutoffs - 21 1/2.
Mechanical Specifications: Type page 12 1/2 x 21; E - 6 cols, 2 1/16, 1/8 between; A - 6 cols, 2 1/16, 1/8 between; C - 6 cols, 2 1/16, 1/8 between.
Commodity Consumption: Avg. Page Number Per Issue - Daily 12; Avg. Page Number Per Issue - Plates Used 2700; widths 25; Newsprint Used - Short Tons 250; Printing Ink Used - Black 6000; Printing Ink Used - Color 375; Printing Ink Used - Pages Printed 3640.
Equipment EDITORIAL: Front-end Software – QPS/QuarkXPress 3.3, Macromedia/Freehand, Baseview/NewsEdit.; Editorial Hardware – APP/Mac; Editorial Printers – LaserWriter 16/600; Classified Hardware – APP/Mac; Classified Printers – Xante 3G. DISPLAY: Ad make-up applications – Aldus/Freehand 5.5, QPS/QuarkXPress; Layout Software – 3-APP/Power Mac 7200-120.; Display Printers – Laserwriter 16/6000 PS; Production Equipment – 1-Nu; Cameras – 2-K. PRESSROOM: Line 1 – 5-G/Community single width; Folders – 1; Bundle tying machines – Bu, Malow; Addressing machine – Am.; Business Hardware – PC

COLDWATER

THE DAILY REPORTER

15 W. Pearl St., Coldwater, Mich., 49036; gen tel (517) 278-2318; gen fax (517) 278-6041; adv fax (517) 278-6041; ed fax (517) 278-6041; gen e-mail dferro@thedailyreporter.com; ed e-mail editor@thedailyreporter.com; web site www.thedailyreporter.com
Published: Mon, Tues, Wed, Thur, Fri, Sat
Weekday Frequency: m
Circulation: 5,316; 5,316(sat)
Last Audit: October 1, 2001
Price: 9.35/mo; 110.00/yr, $180.00/yr (mail).
Advertising: Open inch rate $10.25
News services: AP, LAT-WP.
Politics: Independent.
Not Published: New Year; Memorial Day; Independence Day; Labor Day; Thanksgiving; Christmas.
Special Weekly Sections: TV Listing (Sat); NASCAR (Thur).
Magazines: American Profile (Weekly).
Adv. Dir. ......David R. Ferro
Circ. Dir. ......Craig Sours
Online Ed. ......Heather Jeffrey
Prodn. Mgr., Composing ......Carla Ludwick
Market Information: TMC.
Mechanical available: Offset; Black and 3 ROP colors; insert accepted - 8 x 11 1/2 & over; page cutoffs - 21 1/2.
Mechanical Specifications: Type page 11 3/4 x 21 5/8; E - 6 cols, 1/6 between; A - 6 cols, 1/6 between; C - 9 cols, 1/6 between.
Commodity Consumption: widths 25.
Equipment EDITORIAL: Front-end Software – Adobe/Photoshop 4.0, Macromedia/Freehand 7.0, QPS/QuarkXPress 4.04, Baseview.; Editorial Hardware – APP/Mac; Editorial Printers – APP/Mac LaserWriter, Xante/Accel-a-Writer 8300, Epson/5200 Color CLASSIFIED: Front-end Software – Baseview.; Classified Hardware – APP/Mac; Classified Printers – Okidata DISPLAY: Ad make-up applications – Multi-Ad/Creator 4.0, QPS/QuarkXPress 4.04; Layout Software – Baseview.; Display Hardware – APP/Power Mac; Display Printers – APP/Mac Laser, Xante/Accel-a-Writer 8300, Epson/5200 Color PRODUCTION: Pagination Software – QPS/QuarkXPress 4.04.; Production Equipment – Caere/OmniPage, Nikon/Scan; Scanners – Umax; Business Hardware – Vision Data

INDEPENDENT MEDIA GROUP

15 W. Pearl St., Coldwater, Mich., 49036; gen tel (517) 278-2318; gen fax (517) 278-6041

DETROIT

DETROIT FREE PRESS

600 W. Fort St., Detroit, Mich., 48226-3138; gen tel (313) 222-6400; adv tel (586) 977-7500; ed tel (313) 222-6600; gen fax (313) 222-5981; ed fax (313) 222-5981; gen e-mail city@freepress.com; business@freepress.com; ed e-mail city@freepress.com; web site www.freep.com
Published: Mon, Tues, Wed, Thur, Fri, Sat, Sun
Weekday Frequency: m
Saturday Frequency: m
Circulation: 234,579; 219,755(sat); 639,350(sun)
Last Audit: ABC September 30, 2011
Advertising: Open inch rate $777.00
News services: AP, NYT, RN, DJ, GNS.
Politics: Independent.
Note: Effective March 30, 2009, the Detroit Fee Press will cease daily print publication, and will publish Thursdays, Fridays and Sundays. For detailed mechanical specifications, advertising, circulation, production and other business office personnel, see Detr
Special Weekly Sections: Weekend (Fri); The Money Report (Mon); The Puck (Thur); Body & Mind (Tues).
Magazines: USA WEEKEND Magazine (S).
Administrative Mgr. ......Grace Bennett
Ed. ......Paul Anger
Exec. Ed. ......Caesar Andrews
Deputy Mng. Ed. ......Dale Parry
Deputy Mng. Ed. ......Dave Robinson
Deputy Mng. Ed. ......Jeff Taylor
Deputy Mng. Ed ......Julie Topping
Deputy Mng. Ed., Online ......Nancy Andrews
Asst. Mng. Ed., Features ......Sharon Wilmore
Asst. Mng. Ed., Presentation ......Steve Dorsey
Asst. Mng. Ed., Web ......Nancy Laughlin
Editorial Page Ed. ......Ron Dzwonkowski
Bus. Ed. ......Randy Essex
Copy Desk Chief ......Alex Cruden
Features Ed. ......Tina Croley
Library Dir ......Alice Pepper
Metro Ed. ......Jim Wilhelm
Deputy Metro Ed. ......Bob Campbell
Deputy Metro Ed. ......Todd Spangler
Market Information: Zoned editions.
Equipment; Audio Hardware – City Line, VNN, Brite Voice Systems

THE DETROIT NEWS

615 W. Lafayette Blvd., Detroit, Mich., 48226; gen tel (313) 222-2300; adv tel (313) 222-2700; ed tel (313) 222-2300; gen fax (313) 222-2335; ed fax (313) 222-2335; gen e-mail editor@detroitnews.com; ed e-mail letters@detroitnews.com; web site www.detroitnews.com
Group: MediaNews Group
Published: Mon, Tues, Wed, Thur, Fri, Sat
Weekday Frequency: m
Saturday Frequency: m
Circulation: 139,128; 128,571(sat)
Last Audit: ABC September 30, 2011
Advertising: Open National inch rate $522.00
News services: AP, DJ, NYT, SHNS, Bloomberg, McClatchy.
Politics: 1873
Note: Effective Mar. 30, 2009, The Detroit News will provide home delivery on Thursday and Friday. It will be available only at newsstands on Mon., Tues., Wed. and Sat.
Special Editions: Tiger Baseball (Apr); Michiganians of the Year (May) ; Auto Show (Jan); Rosa Parks Scholars (Jun); NBA/Pistons (Nov); NHL/Red Wings (Oct); Prep Football (Aug); College football (Aug); NFL (Sept).
Magazines: USA Weekend (S).
Editor and Publisher ......Jonathan Wolman
Managing Editor ......Don Nauss
Asst. Managing Editor ......Michael Brown
Online Content Dir. ......Pam Shermeyer
Arts/Entertainment Ed. ......Leslie Green
City Ed., Night ......Chris Rizk
Deputy Metro Editor ......Maryann Struman
Business Editor ......Joanna Firestone
Presentation Editor ......Richard Epps
Auto Editor ......Alan Derringer
Asst. Managing Editor ......Felecia Henderson
Asst. Managing Editor ......Walter Middlebrook
Editorial Page Editor ......Nolan Finley
Deputy Managing Editor ......Gary Miles
Sports Editor ......Phil Laciura
Market Information: Zoned editions.
Equipment AUDIO: Audio Software –

DOWAGIAC

DOWAGIAC DAILY NEWS

205 Spaulding St., Dowagiac, Mich., 49047-0030; gen tel (269) 782-2101; gen fax (269) 782-5290; gen e-mail leader.news@leaderpub.com; web site www.dowagiacnews.com
Published: Mon, Tues, Wed, Thur, Fri
Weekday Frequency: e
Circulation: 1,586
Last Audit: September 30, 2007
Advertising: Open inch rate $12.80
News services: American Newspaper Representatives Inc..
Politics: Independent.
Note: For detailed production information, see the Niles Daily Star listing.
Not Published: New Year; Memorial Day; Independence Day; Labor Day; Christmas.
Special Editions: College (Aug); Bridal (Feb); Summer Fun (Jul); Home Improvement (Mar); Waterfront (May); Welcome to the Neighborhood (Monthly); Cookbook (Nov); Waterfront (Sept).
Special Weekly Sections: TV (Fri).
Magazines: F.Y.I. (June) (Annually).
Gen. Mgr. ......Bryan Clapper
Adv. Dir. ......Kevin Smith
Distr. Mgr. ......Rick Lott
Mng. Ed. ......John Eby
Sports Ed. ......Scott Novak
Prodn. Mgr., Pressroom ......Bob Bell
Market Information: Split run; TMC; Zoned editions.
Mechanical available: Offset; Black and 3 ROP colors; insert accepted - all; page cutoffs - 22 3/4.
Mechanical Specifications: Type page 13 1/8 x 21 1/2; E - 8 cols, 1 1/2, 1/6 between; A - 8 cols, 1 1/2, 1/6 between; C - 8 cols, 1 1/2, 1/6 between.
Equipment EDITORIAL: Front-end Software – QPS/QuarkXPress, Microsoft/Write.; Editorial Hardware – APP/Mac; Editorial Printers – HP/4MV CLASSIFIED: Front-end Software – Baseview.; Classified Hardware – APP/Mac; Classified Printers – HP/4MV DISPLAY: Ad make-up applications – DTI/AdSpeed; Layout Software – QPS/QuarkXPress.; Display Hardware – APP/Mac; Production Equipment – QPS/QuarkXPress. PRESSROOM: Line 1 – 10-KP/News King single width.

ESCANABA

DAILY PRESS

600 Ludington St., Escanaba, Mich., 49829; gen tel (906) 786-2021; adv tel (906) 786-2021; ed tel (906) 786-2021; gen fax (906) 786-3752; adv fax (906) 786-3752; ed fax (906) 786-9006; ed e-mail news@dailypress.net; web site www.dailypress.net
Published: Mon, Tues, Wed, Thur, Fri, Sat, Sun
Weekday Frequency: e
Saturday Frequency: m
Circulation: 7,214; 8,158(sat); 7,873(sun)
Last Audit: ABC September 30, 2011
Price: 3.05/wk; 13.20/mo; 151.40/yr.
Advertising: Open inch rate $24.65
News services: AP.
Politics: Independent.
Not Published: New Year; Thanksgiving; Christmas.
Special Editions: Spring Fashion (Apr); Fall Back-to-School (Aug); Bride & Groom (Jan); Fashion (Sept).
Magazines: USA WEEKEND Magazine (Sat).
Bus. Mgr. ......Connie Ettenhofer
Adv. Mgr. ......Ann Troutman
Circ. Mgr. ......Dennis Bowen
Features Ed. ......Julian Jameson
Political/Gov't Ed. ......Brian Rowell
Prodn. Foreman, Pressroom ......Jessica Koth
Publisher ......McDonald Dan
Market Information: TMC.
Mechanical available: Offset; Black and 3 ROP colors; insert accepted - small booklets; page cutoffs - 22 3/4.
Mechanical Specifications: Type page 11 3/4 x 21 1/2; E - 6 cols, 1 3/4, 1/6 between; A - 6 cols, 1 3/4, 1/6 between; C - 9 cols, 1 3/8, 1/8 between.
Commodity Consumption: Avg. Page Number Per Issue - Daily 16; widths 24; Newsprint Used - Short Tons 800.
Equipment; Editorial Hardware – Mk; Editorial Equipment – 4-Panasonic; Editorial Printers – TI/KSR Omni Printer.; Classified Hardware – Mk; Classified Printers – 2-V.; Layout Software – Mk.; Production Equipment – 1-LE; Cameras – 1-Nu/SST 20 x 24. PRESSROOM: Line 1 – 9-G/Community (Color head); Folders – 2; Bundle tying machines – 2-Bu/Strapper, MLN/Spirit-Strapper; Addressing machine – SAC/JR.; Business Hardware – ATT

FLINT

THE FLINT JOURNAL

200 E. First St., Flint, Mich., 48502-1925; gen tel (810) 766-6100; adv tel (810) 766-6200; ed tel (810) 766-6326; gen fax (810) 767-9480; adv fax (810) 767-8922; ed fax (810) 767-7518; gen e-mail fj@flintjournal.com; adv e-mail kkoviel@boothmichigan.com; ed e-mail fj@flintjournal.com; web site www.flintjournal.com

Group: Metro Suburbia, Inc./Newhouse Newspapers
Published: Tues, Thur, Fri, Sun
Weekday Frequency: e
Saturday Frequency: m
Circulation: 46,980; 74,876(sat); 68,611(sun)
Last Audit: ABC September 30, 2011
Price: 2.65/wk; 11.49/mo; 137.88/yr.
Advertising: Open inch rate $74.88
News services: AP, NYT, LAT-WP, NNS.
Politics: Independent.
Special Editions: Golf (Apr); HS Football Preview (Aug); Wrap (Dec); Black History Month (Feb); Weddings (Jan); Business Profiles (Jun); The Answer Book (Mar); Home & Yard (May); Wrap (Nov); Senior Health Expo (Oct); Life & Legacy (Sept).
Special Weekly Sections: The Entertainer (Fri); Technology-Tempo (Mon); Viewpoint (S); Religion (Sat); Wheels (Thur); Food-Tempo (Tues); Education (Wed).
Magazines: Color Comics (S); Coupon Books (Wed).
Pub. .... Matt Sharp
Adv. Dir. .... Mary Alexander
Adv. Mgr., Retail Sales Initiatives Wendy Brimley
Adv. Coord., Pre Print .... Nancy Zbiciak
Circ. Mktg. Mgr. .... Mike Pastorino
Community Ed. .... Marjory Raymer
Food Writer .... Ron Krueger
Home Section Ed .... Jennifer Walkling
Info. Systems Mgr. .... Michael Van Hine
New Media/Online Mgr. Mary Ann Chick Whiteside
Opns. Dir. .... Robert D. White
Prodn. Mgr. .... Dave Roberts
Prodn. Asst. Mgr., Pressroom .... Lonnie Davis
Market Information: Split run; TMC.
Mechanical available: Offset; Black and 3 ROP colors; insert accepted - zoned pre-prints, minis; page cutoffs - 21.
Mechanical Specifications: Type page 11 5/8 x 20; E - 6 cols, 1 5/6, 1/8 between; A - 6 cols, 1 5/6, 1/8 between; C - 10 cols, 1 1/8, 1/8 between.
Commodity Consumption: Avg. Page Number Per Issue - Daily 43; Avg. Page Number Per Issue - Plates Used 75080; Avg. Page Number Per Issue - Saturday 43; Avg. Page Number Per Issue - Sunday 96; widths 50; Newsprint Used - Metric Tons 9444; Printing Ink Used - Black 168530; Print
Equipment; Editorial Hardware – Software ☐ Baseview/NewsEdit Pro. CLASSIFIED: Front-end Software – Mactive 2.22.; Layout Software – Multi-Ad/Creator.; Display Hardware – B/S 360 PRODUCTION: Pagination Software – Baseview, Adobe/InDesign.; Production Equipment – Lf/AP Leaf Picture Desk, Adobe/Photoshop PRESSROOM: Line 1 – MAN/Roland Regioman; Press Drives – Baumuller; Folders – 1-MAN/Double-out 64 pg.; Pasters – Reels and Stands ☐ 4-MAN/CD13; Press control system – PECOM. MAILROOM: Counter stackers – 4-QWI/501, 1-QWI/400, 2-HL/Dual Carrier; Inserters and stuffers – 2-GMA/SLS3000; Bundle tying machines – 5-Dynaric/4. AUDIO: Audio Software – PC based; Audio Hardware – Voice News Network BUSINESS COMPUTERS: Business Software – In-house, PBS 2.5, SBS, Newsprint: SCS; Business Hardware – Sun/Sparc 2, Sun/Ultra 170

GRAND HAVEN

GRAND HAVEN TRIBUNE

101 N. Third St., Grand Haven, Mich., 49417; gen tel (616) 842-6400; adv tel (616) 842-7180; ed tel (616) 842-8790; gen fax (616) 842-9584; adv fax (616) 842-9584; ed fax (616) 842-9584; adv e-mail ads@grandhaventribune.com; web site www.grandhaventribune.com

Published: Mon, Tues, Wed, Thur, Fri, Sat
Weekday Frequency: e
Saturday Frequency: e
Circulation: 8,813; 8,813(sat)
Last Audit: ABC September 30, 2011
Price: 2.00/wk (carrier), $2.05/wk (motor route); 115.00yr (in county), $138.00/yr (other points).
Advertising: Open inch rate $18.68
News services: AP.
Politics: Independent. **Established:** 1885
Not Published: New Year; Memorial Day; Independence Day; Labor Day; Thanksgiving; Christmas.
Special Editions: Boating (Apr); Coast Guard (Aug); Winter Sports (Dec); Bridal (Jan); Progress (Mar); Education (May); New Cars (Nov); Arts (Sept).
Special Weekly Sections: Best Food Day (Mon); Church (Sat); Business (Thur).
Magazines: USA WEEKEND Magazine (Sat).
Pub./Vice Pres. .... Paul Bedient
Treasurer .... Alice W. Rau
Adv. Dir. .... Rob Francis
Circ. Dir. .... Ken Metzdorf
Mng. Ed. .... Len Painter
News Ed. .... Becky Vargo
Sports Ed. .... Matt DeYoung
Press Foreman/Supvr. .... Jerry Grimminck
Market Information: TMC.
Mechanical available: Offset; Black and 3 ROP colors; insert accepted; page cutoffs - 22 1/2.
Mechanical Specifications: Type page 13 x 21 1/2; E - 6 cols, 2 1/16, 1/8 between; A - 6 cols, 2 1/16, 1/8 between; C - 8 cols, 1 7/8, 1/8 between.
Commodity Consumption: Avg. Page Number Per Issue - Daily 18; widths 11 1/4; Newsprint Used - Short Tons 391; Printing Ink Used - Black 11000; Printing Ink Used - Pages Printed 5700.
Equipment EDITORIAL: Front-end Software – Baseview.; Editorial Hardware – 2-CD/2330, 15-APP/Mac; Editorial Printers – HP/LaserJet CLASSIFIED: Front-end Software – Vision Data.; Classified Hardware – 3-Sun; Classified Printers – HP/LaserJet DISPLAY: Ad make-up applications – Adobe/PageMaker, QPS/QuarkXPress, Adobe/Photoshop.; Display Hardware – APP/Mac G4; Display Printers – Xante; Production Equipment – 1-Nat/Super A-250; Cameras – 1-SCREEN/650C. PRESSROOM: Line 1 – 5-G/Urbanite; Inserters and stuffers – KAN/480; Bundle tying machines – 1-Sa/BM1A. AUDIO: Audio Software – Infoconnect 4.30b; Audio Hardware – Northgate/486; Business Hardware – 1-Unisys/5000

GRAND RAPIDS

THE GRAND RAPIDS PRESS

155 Michigan St. NW, Grand Rapids, Mich., 49503-2302; gen tel (616) 222-5400; adv tel (616) 222-5600; ed tel (616) 222-5508; gen fax (616) 222-5409; adv fax (616) 222-5206; ed fax (616) 222-5269; web site www.mlive.com/grpress

Group: Metro Suburbia, Inc./Newhouse Newspapers
Published: Mon, Tues, Wed, Thur, Fri, Sat, Sun
Weekday Frequency: e
Saturday Frequency: m
Circulation: 92,842; 106,376(sat); 152,231(sun)
Last Audit: ABC September 30, 2011
Price: 16.00/mo (carrier); 432.00/yr (mail out of state).
Advertising: Open inch rate $102.00
News services: AP, NYT, SHNS, NNS, TMS.
Politics: Independent. **Established:** 1892
Special Editions: Golf (Apr); High School Football (Aug); Home Expo (Feb); International Auto Show (Jan); Lakeshore Living (Jun); Home & Garden (Mar); Parade of Homes (May); Lakeshore Holidays (Nov); Grand Rapids Griffins-IHL Hockey (Oct); On Stage-Entertainment/Arts (Sept
Special Weekly Sections: Home and Garden (S); Outdoors (Sat); Weekend (Thur).
Magazines: Parade (S).
Pub. .... Danny R. Gaydou
Gen. Mgr. .... Steven Westphal
Dir., Finance/HR .... Michael P. Ply
Mgr., HR .... Marietta Foley
Adv. Dir., Sales .... Julie Cullen
Adv. Mgr., Classified .... Michelle Covington
Adv. Mgr., Prodn. .... Mike Van Dusen
Adv. Coord., Interactive Sales .... Erin Jones
Mgr., Mktg./Promo. .... Mary Oudsema
Circ. Dir. .... Martha Hines
Circ. Mgr., Sales/Mktg. .... Brook Powers
Circ. Mgr., Single Copy .... Alecia Hawkins
Circ. Opns. Mgr. .... Jon Vanzomeren
Ed. .... Paul M. Keep
Books Ed. .... Sue Thoms
Bus. Ed. .... Nancy Crawley
Editorial Page Ed. .... Ed Golder
Entertainment Ed. .... John Gonzalez
Food Ed. .... Linda Odette
Market Information: TMC; Zoned editions.
Mechanical available: Offset; Black and 3 ROP colors; insert accepted - spadea; page cutoffs - 21.
Mechanical Specifications: Type page 10 7/8 x 19 1/2; E - 6 cols, 1 23/32, 3/32 between; A - 6 cols, 1 23/32, 3/32 between; C - 10 cols, 1 1/16, 1/32 between.
Commodity Consumption: Avg. Page Number Per Issue - Daily 60; Avg. Page Number Per Issue - Plates Used 240000; Avg. Page Number Per Issue - Saturday 64; Avg. Page Number Per Issue - Sunday 175; widths 37 1/2; Newsprint Used - Metric Tons 23609; Printing Ink Used - Black 768000
Equipment EDITORIAL: Front-end Software – HI/Newsmaker Editorial 3.4.; Editorial Hardware – HI/XP-21 Server (3.5); Editorial Printers – 2-XIT/Laser Printer CLASSIFIED: Front-end Software – Mactive/Ad Base.; Classified Hardware – Sun/E450, A-5200 Disk ARRAVS; Classified Equipment – 50-Dell/PC; Classified Printers – HP/2100 DISPLAY: Ad make-up applications – Xpance, Basys/Print CTP; Layout Software – PPI.; Display Hardware – 28-APP/Mac G3 & G4; Display Printers – 4-Xante PRODUCTION: Pagination Software – HI/NME 1.6.6.2 (40 stations), HI/NMP.; Production Equipment – 2-Anacoil, 2-Glunz & Jensen; Scanners – 3-AG/Horizons Plus PRESSROOM: Line 1 – MAN/Geoman (64 couples); Press Drives – Baumueller; Folders – 2-MAN; Pasters – 12-MAN; Reels and Stands – 12-MAN; Press control system – MAN; Press registration system – Graphic Control. MAILROOM: Counter stackers – 10-QWI/500; Inserters and stuffers – 3-GMA/SLS 3000 (30:2); Bundle tying machines – 13/Dynaric; Wrapping singles – 5-Dynaric/Single tyer; Mailroom control system – GMA/SAM; Addressing machine – 2-Ch/Labeler; Other equipment –9-PMI/Pla BUSINESS COMPUTERS: Business Software – SBS 4.6.5, PBS 3.OB; Business Hardware – Sun/Sparc 20, Sun/E 450

GREENVILLE

THE DAILY NEWS

109 N. Lafayette St., Greenville, Mich., 48838; gen tel (616) 754-9301; adv tel (616) 754-9301; ed tel (616) 754-9301; gen fax (616) 754-8559; adv fax (616) 754-8559; ed fax (616) 754-8559; gen e-mail info@staffordgroup.com; web site www.thedailynews.cc

Published: Mon, Tues, Wed, Thur, Fri, Sat, Sun
Weekday Frequency: e
Saturday Frequency: m
Circulation: 7,754; 8,406(sat)
Last Audit: September 30, 2008
Price: 8.95/mo (carrier); 129.00/yr.
Advertising: Open inch rate $14.50
News services: AP.
Politics: Independent.
Not Published: New Year; Memorial Day; Independence Day; Labor Day; Thanksgiving; Christmas.
Special Editions: Spring Sports (Aug); Advanced Christmas (Oct).
Special Weekly Sections: TV Guide (Fri); Business Page (Mon); Home (Sat); Leisure Page (Thur); Food Page (Tues); Agriculture Page (Wed).
Magazines: USA WEEKEND Magazine (Sat).
Pres./Gen. Mgr., Publications .... Rob Stafford
Circ. Dir .... Carol Pettengill
News Ed. .... Darrin Clark
Asst. News Ed. .... Ryan Jeltema
Chief Photographer .... Greg Dekraker
Sports Ed. .... John Raffel
Mgmt. Info Servs. Mgr. .... John Frizzo
Prodn. Mgr. .... Jeff Morris
Market Information: ADS; TMC.
Mechanical available: Offset; Black and 3 ROP colors; insert accepted; page cutoffs - 22 3/4.
Mechanical Specifications: Type page 13 3/4 x 21; E - 6 cols, 2 1/18, between; A - 6 cols, 2 1/18, between; C - 6 cols, 2 1/18, between.
Commodity Consumption: Avg. Page Number Per Issue - Daily 18; Avg. Page Number Per Issue - Plates Used 3245; Avg. Page Number Per Issue - Saturday 22; widths 25; Newsprint Used - Short Tons 420; Printing Ink Used - Black 9900; Printing Ink Used - Color 1600; Printing Ink Used
Equipment; Editorial Hardware – 1-APP/Mac 8150 Workgroup Server, 4-APP/Power Mac 7100-80, 1-Power Computing/210, 7-APP/Mac Performa 638CD, APP/Mac LC III; Editorial Equipment – Minolta/RP605Z microfilm reader, Kk/35 mm Film Scanner, Nikon/LS 1000 Film Scanner; Editorial Printers – APP/Mac LaserW CLASSIFIED: Front-end Software – Baseview/Class Flow 2.2.5, QPS/QuarkXPress 3.32, Baseview/Class Manager Pro.; Classified Hardware – 1-APP/Mac 8150 Workgroup Server; Classified Printers – APP/Mac LaserWriter IIg, Okidata/Line Printer; Display Hardware – APP/Mac 8550-200 Workgroup Server, 2-APP/Mac 7500, 1-APP/Mac 7100, 1-APP/Mac4400, 2-APP/Mac 6100, 1-APP/Mac Centris 650, 1-Power Computing/Pro 210, 1-APP/Mac IIsi, 1-APP/Mac IIcx, 1-APP/Mac LCII; Display Printers – 1-QMS/860, 1-GCC/Elite XL 1208, APP/M; Production Equipment – Caere/OmniPage Pro 7.0, 1-APP/Mac 9600-200, Tektronix/Phaser 300X Color Printer; Cameras – COM/6700; Scanners – HSD/Scan-X Pro, Kk/35mm rapid film scanner. PRESSROOM: Line 1 – 8-G/Community SSC (1-4-high) 1986; Folders – 1-G/SSC; Reels and Stands – 1-FBWAY/HS-35000.; Bundle tying machines – 1/MLN, 1-/Bu; Addressing machine – 1-/KR; Other equipment –MM/5-Pocket Saddle Stitcher. AUDIO: Audio Software – New Horizons/Info-Connect; Audio Hardware – TMS, AP, TI/Micro 486 Series BUSINESS COMPUTERS: Business Software – Great Plains; Business Hardware – Microsoft/Windows NT, HP/133 DL Server

HILLSDALE

HILLSDALE DAILY NEWS

33 McCollum St., Hillsdale, Mich., 49242; gen tel (517) 437-7351; gen fax (517) 437-3963; web site www.hillsdale.net

Published: Mon, Tues, Wed, Thur, Fri, Sat, Sun
Weekday Frequency: e
Saturday Frequency: m
Circulation: 7,285; 7,285(sat)
Last Audit: October 19, 2001
Price: 7.75/mo; 76.00/yr.
Advertising: Open inch rate $12.00
News services: AP.
Politics: Independent.
Not Published: New Year; Memorial Day; Independence Day; Labor Day; Thanksgiving; Christmas.
Special Editions: Classified Promotion (Apr); Jonesville Sidewalk Sales (Aug); New Year's Baby Promotion (Dec); Valentine's Promotion (Feb); Progress (Jan); Hillsdale Sidewalk Days (Jul); Silver Salute Tab (Jun); Health & Fitness Tab (Mar); Memoriams

(May); Pre-Christmas (
Special Weekly Sections: TV Key (Fri).
Magazines: Relish (Monthly); USA WEEKEND Magazine (Sat); American Profile (Weekly).
Pub. ....David Ferro
Adv. Mgr. ....Tony Vanburen
Circ. Mgr. ....RoxAnne Morgret
Ed. ....Jim Pruitt
News Ed. ....Thomas Marcetti
Sports Ed. ...................................R.J. Walters
Market Information: ADS; TMC.
Mechanical available: Offset; Black and 3 ROP colors; insert accepted; page cutoffs - 22 3/4.
Mechanical Specifications: Type page 13 1/16 x 21 1/2; E - 6 cols, 2 1/16, 1/8 between; A - 6 cols, 2 1/16, 1/8 between; C - 8 cols, 1 7/8, 1/8 between.
Commodity Consumption: Avg. Page Number Per Issue - Daily 14; Avg. Page Number Per Issue - Plates Used 4000; Avg. Page Number Per Issue - Saturday 12; widths 34; Newsprint Used - Short Tons 319; Printing Ink Used - Black 10000; Printing Ink Used - Color 1200; Printing Ink Used
Equipment EDITORIAL: Front-end Software – Baseview/NewsEdit.; Editorial Hardware – APP/Mac; Editorial Printers – APP/Mac LaserWriter NTX CLASSIFIED: Front-end Software – Baseview/Classified.; Classified Hardware – APP/Mac; Classified Printers – APP/Mac LaserWriter NTX DISPLAY: Ad make-up applications – QPS/QuarkXPress, Multi-Ad/Creator; Display Hardware – APP/Mac; Display Printers – APP/Mac LaserWriter 630; Production Equipment – APP/Mac LaserWriter 600, Adobe/Photoshop; Cameras – SCREEN/250; Scanners – APP/Mac Scanner, Nikon/Photo, Microtek/Scanmaker II. PRESSROOM: Line 1 – 5-G/Community; Folders – 1; Bundle tying machines – MLN/1100, 1/MLN, 1-/Strapex; Addressing machine – Ch/705, Automecha/AccuFast PL. BUSINESS COMPUTERS: Business Software – Unix/SCO U-386, SMS; Business Hardware – HP, 4-ATT/610

HOLLAND

THE HOLLAND SENTINEL

54 W. Eighth St., Holland, Mich., 49423; gen tel (616) 546-4200; adv tel (616) 392-2311; ed tel (616) 392-2311; gen fax (616) 392-3526; adv fax (616) 392-3526; ed fax (616) 393-6710; gen e-mail newsroom@hollandsentinel.com; web site www.hollandsentinel.com
Group: Metro Newspaper Advertising Services, Inc.
Published: Mon, Tues, Wed, Thur, Fri, Sat, Sun
Weekday Frequency: m
Saturday Frequency: m
Circulation: 16,974; 16,499(sat); 18,268(sun)
Last Audit: ABC September 30, 2011
Price: 11.25/mo; 132.00/yr.
Advertising: Open inch rate $15.23
News services: AP, MCT.
Politics: Independent. **Established:** 1896
Special Editions: Spring Car Care (Apr); Hope College (Aug); Last Minute Gifts (Dec); Taxes (Feb); Brides (Jan); Parade of Homes (Jun); Holland Home Show (Mar); Tulip Time (May); Coupon Tab (Monthly); Song Book (Nov); Dream Homes (Oct); Women in Business (Sept).
Special Weekly Sections: Religion (Fri); In Step (Mon); Home (S); TV Today (Sat); Haps (Thur); Education (Wed).
Magazines: Relish (Monthly); USA WEEKEND Magazine (S); American Profile (Weekly).
Pub. ....Pete Esser
Bus. Mgr. ....Jennifer Kartes
Adv. Mgr. ....Janet Johnson
Circ. Mgr. ....Steve Kenemer
Ed. ....Pamela Fisher
Community Content Team Leader .....Lori Timmer
News Team Leader ....Jim Hayden
News Team Asst. Leader ....Roel Garcia
Photo/Video Team Leader..........Dennis Geppert
Presentation Team Leader............Krista Babbitt
Sports Team Leader ....Alan Babbitt

Prodn. Mgr., Pre Press ....Jerry Raab
Market Information: ADS; TMC.
Mechanical available: Offset; Black and 3 ROP colors; insert accepted; page cutoffs - 22 3/4.
Mechanical Specifications: Type page 11 5/8 x 21 1/2; E - 6 cols, 1 5/6, 1/8 between; A - 6 cols, 1 5/6, 1/8 between; C - 9 cols, 1 3/16, 1/8 between.
Commodity Consumption: Avg. Page Number Per Issue - Daily 36; Avg. Page Number Per Issue - Sunday 54; widths 13 3/4; Newsprint Used - Metric Tons 1569; Printing Ink Used - Black 28800.
Equipment EDITORIAL: Front-end Software – Baseview/NewsEdit Pro IQUE 3.1.8.; Editorial Hardware – APP/Power Mac, APP/Mac G3/300; Editorial Equipment – Epson/636 Flatbed Scanner, Nikon/Film Scanner; Editorial Printers – APP/Mac LaserWriter II NTX CLASSIFIED: Front-end Software – Baseview.; Classified Hardware – APP/Power Mac 233; Classified Printers – APP/Mac LaserWriter II NTX; Layout Software – ALS(Version 2.5).; Display Hardware – Printers ☐ APP/Mac LaserWriter II NTX; Production Equipment – Nat, 2-MON/1270; Cameras – R; Scanners – Epson, Microtek, HP. PRESSROOM: Line 1 – 10-G/Urbanite; Folders – 1 MAILROOM: Counter stackers – 2/HL; Inserters and stuffers – 1-HI/NP 848; Bundle tying machines – 1-Signode, 1-Sterling/MR45CH; Addressing machine – 1-/Ch. AUDIO: Audio Software – Ad/Que Filemaker Pro 5.0; Audio Hardware – SMS BUSINESS COMPUTERS: Business Software – Clarus; Business Hardware – Pc

HOUGHTON

THE DAILY MINING GAZETTE

206 Shelden Ave., Houghton, Mich., 49931; gen tel (906) 482-1500; adv tel (906) 483-2211; gen fax (906) 482-2726; gen e-mail gazette@mininggazette.com; adv e-mail gazetteadv@mininggazette.com; web site www.mininggazette.com
Published: Mon, Tues, Wed, Thur, Fri, Sat
Weekday Frequency: e
Saturday Frequency: m
Circulation: 7,552; 7,845(sat)
Last Audit: ABC September 30, 2011
Price: 10.15/mo (carrier), $12.50/mo (mail); 136.00/yr.
Advertising: Open inch rate $21.86
News services: AP, Thomson Newspapers Inc..
Politics: Independent. **Established:** 1858
Not Published: New Year; Thanksgiving; Christmas.
Special Weekly Sections: Children Today (Fri); Best Food Day (Mon); Business Page (Sat); Outdoors (Wed).
Magazines: TV Update Magazine (Fri); USA WEEKEND Magazine (Sat).
Pub. ....Michael Scott
Adv. Dir. ....Yvonne Robillard
Circ. Mgr. ....Jennifer Biekkola
City Ed. ....Samantha Voigt
News Ed. ....Mark Wilcox
Sports Ed. ....Pete Pietrangelo
Market Information: ADS; TMC.
Mechanical available: Offset; Black and 3 ROP colors; insert accepted - up to 11 x 13; page cutoffs - 21.
Mechanical Specifications: Type page 13 x 21 1/2; E - 6 cols, 2, 1/6 between; A - 6 cols, 2, 1/6 between; C - 9 cols, 1 1/3, 1/6 between.
Commodity Consumption: Avg. Page Number Per Issue - Daily 16; widths 27 1/2.
Equipment EDITORIAL: Front-end Software – Mk.; Editorial Hardware – Mk/1100 Plus; Editorial Printers – TI/810 CLASSIFIED: Front-end Software – Mk.; Classified Hardware – Mk/1100 Plus; Classified Printers – TI/810 DISPLAY: Ad make-up applications – QPS/QuarkXPress, Multi-Ad/Creator 3.5; Layout Software – APP/Mac.; Display Hardware – APP/Mac IIsi; Display Printers – APP/Mac LaserWriter II; Production Equipment – Lf, Lf; Cameras – COM/680C. PRESSROOM: Line 1 – 8-G/Offset 1980.; Bundle tying machines – 4/Bu; Addressing machine – PC.; Audio Hardware – PC BUSINESS COMPUTERS: Business Software – Q&A, Lotus, Microsoft/Windows; Business Hardware – 6-IBM/PC network

HOWELL

THE LIVINGSTON COUNTY DAILY PRESS & ARGUS

323 E. Grand River Ave., Howell, Mich., 48843; gen tel (517) 548-2000; gen fax (517) 548-3005; web site www.livingstondaily.com
Published: Mon, Tues, Wed, Thur, Fri, Sun
Weekday Frequency: m
Circulation: 11,965; 16,859(sun)
Last Audit: ABC September 30, 2011
Advertising: Open inch rate $35.14
Own facility?: Y
Magazines: USA WEEKEND Magazine (S); American Profile (Weekly).
Gen. Mgr. ....Richard Perlberg
Circ. Dir. ....Mary Scott
Mng. Ed. ....Maria Stuart
Sports Ed. ....Tim Robinson

IONIA

SENTINEL-STANDARD

114 N. Depot St., Ionia, Mich., 48846; gen tel (616) 527-2100; adv tel (616) 527-2100; ed tel (616) 527-2100; gen fax (616) 527-6860; adv fax (616) 527-6860; ed fax (616) 527-6860; gen e-mail publisher@sentinel-standard.com; adv e-mail advertising@sentinel-standard.com; ed e-mail newsroom@sentinel-standard.com; web site www.sentinel-standard.com
Published: Tues, Wed, Thur, Fri, Sat
Weekday Frequency: m
Circulation: 2,883; 2,883(sat)
Last Audit: September 24, 2003
Price: 10.00/mo; 99.00/yr.
Advertising: Open inch rate $12.50
News services: AP.
Politics: Independent.
Magazines: American Profile (Weekly).
Pub. ....Cindy Conrad
Circ. Mgr. ....Vicki Jockheck
Weekend Ed. ....Amanda Cairo
Prodn., Composition ....Pat Schoonmaker
Market Information: Split run; TMC; Zoned editions.
Mechanical available: Offset; Black and 4 ROP colors; insert accepted; page cutoffs - 22.
Mechanical Specifications: Type page 12 x 22; E - 6 cols, 1 5/16, 1/8 between; A - 6 cols, 1 5/16, 1/8 between; C - 8 cols, 1 7/8, 1/8 between.
Commodity Consumption: Avg. Page Number Per Issue - Daily 12; Avg. Page Number Per Issue - Plates Used 5000; Avg. Page Number Per Issue - Saturday 10; widths 25; Newsprint Used - Short Tons 224; Printing Ink Used - Black 9450; Printing Ink Used - Pages Printed 21360.
Equipment EDITORIAL: Front-end Software – QPS/QuarkXPress, Baseview/NewsEdit Pro.; Editorial Hardware – 1-APP/Mac Quadra 630, 2-APP/Power Mac 6100-60, APP/iMac, 2-APP/Mac G3; Editorial Printers – 1-APP/Mac LaserWriter 16-600 PS CLASSIFIED: Front-end Software – Baseview.; Classified Hardware – APP/Mac G3; Classified Printers – APP/Mac LaserWriter; Layout Software – Multi-Ad/Creator.; Display Hardware – APP/Mac IIvx; Display Printers – HP/Laser PRODUCTION: Pagination Software – QPS/QuarkXPress 3.3.; Production Equipment – 1-Nat, 1-C; Cameras – 1-B PRESSROOM: Line 1 – 4-HI/V-15A; Folders – 1; Inserters and stuffers – 1-MM/227E (4 station); Bundle tying machines – 1/Sa, 1-/Bu.; Business Hardware – 2-Dell, 2-Packard Bell/Legend 401CD

IRON MOUNTAIN

THE DAILY NEWS

215 E. Ludington St., Iron Mountain, Mich., 49801; gen tel (906) 774-2772; adv tel (906) 774-2772; ed tel (906) 774-2772; gen fax (906) 774-7660; adv fax (906) 774-9545; ed fax (906) 774-1285; gen e-mail bjohnson@ironmountaindailynews.com; adv e-mail advertising@ironmountaindailynews.com; ed e-mail news@ironmountaindailynews.com; web site www.ironmountaindailynews.com
Group: Ogden Publishing
Published: Mon, Tues, Wed, Thur, Fri, Sat
Weekday Frequency: e
Saturday Frequency: e
Circulation: 7,912; 8,682(sat)
Last Audit: ABC September 30, 2011
Price: 3.25/wk (carrier); 14.00/mo; 168.00/yr.
Advertising: Open inch rate $17.90
Insert rate: $57 per thousand
News services: AP, TMS.
Politics: Independent. **Established:** 1921
Advertising not accepted: N
Not Published: New Year; Thanksgiving; Christmas.
Special Editions: Logging Today (Apr); Vacation Guide (Aug); Christmas (Dec); Ski Jumping (Feb); Bride (Jan); Rodeo (Jul); Vacation Guide (Jun); Baby (Mar); Graduation (May); Cookbook (Nov); Hunting (Oct); Drug Coloring Book (Other); Logging Today (Sept).
Special Weekly Sections: TV Preview (Fri); Food (Mon); Business (Sat); Health (Thur); Business (Tues).
Magazines: USA WEEKEND Magazine (Sat).
Pub. ....Robert J. Johnson
Adv. Dir. ....Traci Charette
Adv. Mgr., Classified ....Carrie Hyska
Bus./Finance Ed. ....Linda Lobeck
Editorial Page Ed. ....Blaine Hyska
Entertainment/Amusements Ed. Marguerite Lanthier
Lifestyles Ed. ....Terri Castelaz
News Ed. ....Jim Anderson
Photo Ed. ....Theresa Peterson
Sports Ed. ....Burt Angeli
Online Mgr. ....Maggie Lanthier
Circulation Sales and Marketing Director Rebekah Rose
Prodn. Mgr., Mailroom ....Sally Johnson
Prodn. Mgr., Pressroom ....Jeff Schwaller
Prodn. Supvr., Graphics ....Joe Edlebeck
Market Information: TMC.
Mechanical available: Offset; Black and 3 ROP colors; insert accepted - all; page cutoffs - 22 3/4.
Mechanical Specifications: Type page 11 3/4 x 21 1/2; E - 6 cols, 1 3/4, 1/8 between; A - 6 cols, 1 3/4, 1/8 between; C - 9 cols, 1 1/0, 1/9 between.
Commodity Consumption: Avg. Page Number Per Issue - Daily 22; Avg. Page Number Per Issue - Saturday 24; widths 24; Printing Ink Used - Pages Printed 7120.
Equipment EDITORIAL: Front-end Software – QuarkXpress, Adobe Creative Suite; Editorial Hardware – iMac; Editorial Equipment – iMac; Editorial Printers – HP CLASSIFIED: Front-end Software – Microsoft Office; Classified Hardware – iMac, Dell, HP; Classified Printers – HP DISPLAY: Ad make-up applications – Multi-Ad/Creator 8, Adobe/Illustrator; Layout Software – iMac; Display Hardware – iMac, HP; Display Printers – HP Laserjet PRESSROOM: Line 1 – 11-G/Community single width; Folders – 2, 1-G/Community SSC, 1-SC/Community. MAILROOM: Counter stackers – 1-Baldwin/Coun-O-Stacker; Inserters and stuffers – 1-MM/6 pocket & head; Bundle tying machines – 2-Mosca/Rom-P2, 1/Bu; Other equipment – 1-MM/Minuteman.; Business Hardware – APP/Mac, IBM
Delivery method: Mail, Newsstand, Private Carrier, Racks

IRONWOOD

THE DAILY GLOBE

118 E. McLeod Ave., Ironwood, Mich., 49938-0548; gen tel (906) 932-2211; adv tel (906) 932-2211; ed tel (906) 932-2211; gen fax (906) 932-5358; adv fax (906) 932-5358; ed fax (906) 932-5358; adv e-mail globeads@chartermi.net; ed e-mail globe-news@charterinternet.com; web site www.yourdailyglobe.com

Published: Mon, Tues, Wed, Thur, Fri, Sat
Weekday Frequency: m
Circulation: 6,498; 6,498(sat)
Last Audit: November 19, 2004
Price: 11.75/wk (carrier); 31.50/mo (carrier); 129.00/yr (carrier).
Advertising: Open inch rate $11.46
News services: AP, LAT-WP.
Politics: Independent.
Not Published: New Year; Memorial Day; Independence Day; Labor Day; Thanksgiving; Christmas.
Special Editions: Home Improvement (Apr); County Fair (Aug); Christmas Gift Guide (Dec); Progress (Feb); Winter Fun Guide (Jan); Home Builders (Mar); Summer Fun Guide (May); Senior Sentinel (Monthly); Deer Hunting (Nov); Winter Fun Guide (Oct); Our Towns (Sept).
Special Weekly Sections: Business (Fri); Business (Sat); Business (Thur); Business (Tues); Business (Wed).
Magazines: TV Entertainment (local) (Fri); American Profile (Tues).
Pub. ....Joe Karius
Circ. Mgr. ....Kathy Dishaw
Mng. Ed. ....Phil Watson
Market Information: ADS; TMC.
Mechanical available: Offset; Black and 4 ROP colors; insert accepted; page cutoffs - 22 3/4.
Mechanical Specifications: Type page 13 x 21 1/2; E - 6 cols, 2 1/16, 1/8 between; A - 6 cols, 2 1/16, 1/8 between; C - 9 cols, 1 3/8, 1/16 between.
Commodity Consumption: Avg. Page Number Per Issue - Daily 18; Avg. Page Number Per Issue - Plates Used 6900; Avg. Page Number Per Issue - Saturday 18; widths 27; Newsprint Used - Short Tons 425; Printing Ink Used - Black 5900; Printing Ink Used - Color 950; Printing Ink Used -
Equipment EDITORIAL: Front-end Software – Adobe/Photoshop, QPS/QuarkXPress.; Editorial Hardware – 9-APP/Mac; Editorial Equipment – Pre Press/Panther Vorityper; Editorial Printers – 2-QMS/11x17 CLASSIFIED: Front-end Software – 2-Baseview.; Classified Hardware – APP/Mac; Classified Printers – 1-QMS/Nx17 DISPLAY: Ad make-up applications – QPS/QuarkXPress, Adobe/Photoshop; Display Hardware – APP/Mac; Display Printers – 1-QMC/11x17 PRODUCTION: Pagination Software – QPS/QuarkXPress 5.0, Macromedia/Freehand, Adobe/Photoshop 6.; Production Equipment – 1-Nu; Cameras – 1-Co/Horizontal 25 CS; Scanners – Epson, Umax, Polariod/Sprintscan PRESSROOM: Line 1 – 8-G/Community; Folders – 1-G/2:1.; Inserters and stuffers – Kan 3:1; Bundle tying machines – 3/Bu; Addressing machine – 1-Miller/Bevco 285.

DAILY GLOBE, INC.

118 E. McLeod Ave., Ironwood, Mich., 49938; gen tel (906) 932-2211; gen fax (906) 932-5358; web site www.ironwooddaily-globe.com

Price: 123.15/yr.
Advertising: Open inch rate $11.46
Insert rate: 55.00 M
Politics: 1919
Not Published: Sunday
Publisher ....Lisa Ursini

JACKSON

THE JACKSON CITIZEN PATRIOT

214 S Jackson St, Jackson, Mich., 49201-2267; gen tel (517) 787-2300; adv tel (517) 787-2300; ed tel (517) 768-4910; gen fax (517) 768-4812; adv fax (517) 787-4053; ed fax (517) 787-9711; ed e-mail jcpnews@cit-pat.com; web site http://www.mlive.com

Group: Advance Publications
Metro Suburbia, Inc./Newhouse Newspapers
Published: Mon, Tues, Wed, Thur, Fri, Sat, Sun
Weekday Frequency: e
Saturday Frequency: e
Circulation: 22,490; 25,962(sat); 28,280(sun)
Last Audit: ABC September 30, 2011
Price: 16.60/mo
News services: AP, MCT
Politics: 1837
Own facility?: Y
Special Weekly Sections: In Town & Around Entertainment guide, Thursdays; TV magazine, Friday
Magazines: Parade (S); TV Mag (Fri).
Pub. ....Sandy Petykiewicz
Adv. Dir. ....Margaret Parshall
Adv. Sales Mgr. ....Mike La Rocque
Distribution Mgr. ....Jeff Crowell
Assoc. Ed. Online/Print Production ....Jerry Sova
Pre Press Supvr. ....Eric White
Associate Editor/Content
Sara Scott
Controller ....Dale Phillips
Circ. Mgr. ....Sandy Eisele
Ed. ....Eileen Lehnert
Features Ed. ....John Piper
Librarian ....Susanne Weible
Metro Ed. ....Tom Perrin
Online Ed. ....Jamie Iseler
Sports Ed. ....Chris Iott
TV Magazine ....Sherri Cauthon
Market Information: ADS; TMC; Zoned editions.
Mechanical available: Offset; Black and 3 ROP colors; insert accepted - any; page cutoffs - 22 3/4.
Mechanical Specifications: Type page 13 x 21 3/4; E - 6 cols, 2 1/16, 1/8 between; A - 6 cols, 2 1/16, 1/8 between; C - 10 cols, 1 1/4, 1/16 between.
Equipment EDITORIAL: Front-end Software – Photoshop, InDesign; Editorial Hardware – APP/Mac DISPLAY: Ad make-up applications – InDesign; Display Hardware – APP/Mac BUSINESS COMPUTERS: Business Software – Booth Computer Division, PBS, Word, Microsoft/Windows, ; Business Hardware – MacIntosh, Dell
Zip Codes served: 49201, 49202, 49203, 49234, 49230
Delivery method: Mail, Newsstand, Private Carrier, Racks

KALAMAZOO

KALAMAZOO GAZETTE

401 S. Burdick St., Kalamazoo, Mich., 49007; gen tel (269) 345-3511; gen fax (269) 388-8427

Group: Metro Suburbia, Inc./Newhouse Newspapers
Published: Mon, Tues, Wed, Thur, Fri, Sat, Sun
Last Audit: N/A
Advertising: Open inch rate $16.90
Ed. ....Rebecca Pierce

LANSING

LANSING STATE JOURNAL

120 E. Lenawee St., Lansing, Mich., 48919; gen tel (517) 377-1000; ed tel (517) 377-1112; adv fax (517) 482-5476; ed fax (517) 377-1298; adv e-mail sking@lsj.com; web site www.lansingstatejournal.com

Group: Metro Suburbia, Inc./Newhouse Newspapers
Published: Mon, Tues, Wed, Thur, Fri, Sat, Sun
Weekday Frequency: m
Saturday Frequency: m
Circulation: 42,610; 45,945(sat); 65,583(sun)
Last Audit: ABC September 30, 2011
Price: 195.00/yr.
Advertising: Open inch rate $131.62
News services: AP, GNS.
Special Editions: Welcome (Aug); Bride (Jan); Parade of Homes (Jun); Stoneworks (Mar); Vacation Escapes (May); Wishbook (Nov); College Football (Sept).
Special Weekly Sections: Business Monday (Mon); Sunday Real Estate Advertising (S); What's On (Thur); Greater Lansing Real Estate Weekly (Wed).
Magazines: USA WEEKEND Magazine (S).
Pres./Pub. ....Brian Priester
Controller ....David Davies
Accts. Mgr. ....Kathi Waters
Dir., HR ....Melissa Alford
Adv. Dir. ....Stacia King
Dir., Market Devel. ....Kevin McFatridge
Mktg. Mgr. ....Ramon Brown
Circ. Dir. ....Linda Argue
Exec. Ed. ....Mickey Hirten
Mng. Ed. ....Stephanie Angel
Asst. City Ed. ....Jason Cody
Asst. City Ed., Night ....David McClendum
Editorial Page Ed ....Derek Melot
Entertainment Ed. ....Mike Hughes
Features Ed. ....Robin Swartz
News Ed. ....Cindy Hudson
Online News Ed. ....Suzanne Salay
Political/Gov't Ed. ....Chris Andrews
Sports Ed. ....Mark Meyer
Prodn. Dir. ....Rick Wagoner
Market Information: Split run; TMC.
Mechanical available: Offset; Black and 3 ROP colors; insert accepted; page cutoffs - 23 9/16.
Mechanical Specifications: Type page 11 5/8 x 22; E - 6 cols, 1 5/6, 1/8 between; A - 6 cols, 1 5/6, 1/8 between; C - 10 cols, 1 1/8, 1/16 between.
Commodity Consumption: Avg. Page Number Per Issue - Daily 36; Avg. Page Number Per Issue - Plates Used 47600; Avg. Page Number Per Issue - Sunday 90; widths 27 1/2; Newsprint Used - Short Tons 7208; Printing Ink Used - Black 235000; Printing Ink Used - Color 20000; Printing In
Equipment; Editorial Hardware – AT.; Classified Hardware – 34-AT; Classified Equipment – 16-DEC. DISPLAY: Ad make-up applications – APP/Mac, Multi-Ad/Creator, QPS/QuarkXPress, Adobe/Photoshop; Layout Software – AT/Architect.; Display Hardware – APP/Macs, AT; Display Printers – Linotype-Hell/Linotronic Imagesetter; Production Equipment – 1-He/200, 1-LE/LD18; Cameras – 1-C/Newspaper II, 1-C/Spartan II. PRESSROOM: Line 1 – TKS/Offset (9 units; 5 half decks); Press Drives – SCR/DC-55-KW; Folders – 1-TKS/3:2 Double Delivery; Pasters – 3-ARM/RTP. MAILROOM: Counter stackers – 3-QWI/300, 2-Id/660; Inserters and stuffers – 1-HI/WP 630 (27 Head); Bundle tying machines – 2/Power Strap/PSN 6, 3-/Power Strap/PSN 6-E; Wrapping singles – Hand; Addressing machine – Ch/525E.; Business Hardware – IBM/Sys 38

LUDINGTON

DAILY NEWS

202 N. Rath Ave., Ludington, Mich., 49431-0340; gen tel (231) 845-5181; adv tel (231) 845-5181; ed tel (231) 845-5182; gen fax (231) 843-4011; gen e-mail ldn@ludingtondailynews.com; web site www.ludingtondailynews.com

Group: Shoreline Media, Inc.
Published: Mon, Tues, Wed, Thur, Fri, Sat
Weekday Frequency: e
Saturday Frequency: e
Circulation: 7,002; 7,002(sat)
Last Audit: ABC September 30, 2011
Price: 181.95/yr, $278.55/yr (mail).
Advertising: Open inch rate $14.95
Insert rate: variable
News services: AP.
Politics: Independent.
Not Published: New Year; Memorial Day; Independence Day; Labor Day; Thanksgiving; Christmas.
Own facility?: Y
Special Editions: Local Sports (Apr); Back-to-School (Aug); Christmas Catalogue (4 times) (Dec); Bridal (Feb); Graduation (Jun); Progress (Mar); Lake Winds (May); Christmas Opener (Nov); Home Care/Car Care (Oct); Local Sports (Sept).
Special Weekly Sections: TV Week (Fri); Best Food Day (Mon); Youth (Sat); Outdoor (Thur); Bridal (Tues); Business (Wed).
Magazines: American Profile (Weekly). Relish (weekly)
Pres. ....David R. Jackson
Pub. ....Jeffrey N. Evans
Vice Pres. ....William R. Jackson
Treasurer ....Susan L. McDuffee
Adv. Mgr. ....John Walker
Circ. Mgr. ....Julie Payment
Mng. Ed. ....Steve Begnoche
News Ed. ....Patti Klevorn
Religion Ed. ....Mark Steigenga
Sports Ed. ....Lloyd Wallace
Wire Ed. ....Stephen Begnoche
Online Mgr. ....Mark Eisenlohr
Prodn. Mgr./Foreman ....Jeffrey Evans
Prodn. Mgr., Mailroom ....Chris Ashprat
Prodn. Supvr., Pressroom ....Bob Grabowski
Lora Grabowski
Bus. Mgr. ....Alan H. Nichols
Market Information: ADS; TMC.
Mechanical available: Offset; Black and 3 ROP colors; insert accepted; page cutoffs - 22 3/4.
Mechanical Specifications: Type page 13 x 21 1/2; E - 6 cols, 2 1/12, 1/6 between; A - 6 cols, 2 1/12, 1/6 between; C - 6 cols, 2 1/12, 1/6 between.
Commodity Consumption: Avg. Page Number Per Issue - Daily 22.5; Avg. Page Number Per Issue - Plates Used 3940; widths 27 1/2; Newsprint Used - Metric Tons 310; Printing Ink Used - Black 7068; Printing Ink Used - Color 1600; Printing Ink Used - Pages Printed 6885.
Equipment EDITORIAL: Front-end Software – Baseview, QPS/QuarkXPress.; Editorial Hardware – 12-APP/Mac; Editorial Printers – 2-APP/Mac, NewGen/Imager Plus 12 CLASSIFIED: Front-end Software – Baseview.; Classified Hardware – APP/Mac; Classified Printers – APP/Mac, NewGen/Imager, HP/LaserJet 4MV DISPLAY: Ad make-up applications – Aldus/PageMaker, Multi-Ad, QPS/QuarkXPress, Adobe/Illustrator, Adobe/Photoshop, Macromedia/Freehand, Streamline; Display Hardware – APP/Mac; Display Printers – APP/Mac, HP/LaserJet 4MV PRODUCTION: Pagination Software – QPS/QuarkXPress 3.31, Adobe/PageMaker 6.0.; Production Equipment – ECR/ScriptWriter; Scanners – Umax/Mirage, HP/ScanJet PRESSROOM: Line 1 – 12-G/Community 1972; Folders – G/Community.; Inserters and stuffers – KAN/4 station; Bundle tying machines – MLN, Bu, Malow. AUDIO: Audio Software – New Horizons/Info-Connect; Audio Hardware – TMS, IBM BUSINESS COMPUTERS: Business Software – INSI, Lotus, WordPerfect, Query; Business Hardware – IBM/Sys 36, IBM/PC
Delivery method: Private Carrier

MANISTEE

J B PUBLISHING CO.

75 W. Maple St., Manistee, Mich., 49660; gen tel (231) 723-3592; gen fax (231) 723-4733; web site www.jbpublications.com

Price: 129.00/yr.
Advertising: Open inch rate $10.25

MANISTEE NEWS-ADVOCATE

75 Maple St., Manistee, Mich., 49660; gen tel (231) 723-3592; gen fax (231) 723-4733; gen e-mail advocate@pioneergroup.com; adv e-mail advertising@pioneergroup.com; ed e-mail stories@pioneergroup.com; web site www.manisteenews.com

Published: Mon, Tues, Wed, Thur, Fri, Sat
Weekday Frequency: m
Circulation: 4,928; 4,928(sat)
Last Audit: November 19, 2004
Price: 9.00/mo; 129.00/yr.
Advertising: Open inch rate $11.50

News services: AP.
Politics: Independent.
Not Published: New Year; Memorial Day; Independence Day; Labor Day; Thanksgiving; Christmas.
Special Editions: Spring Sports (Apr); Christmas Opening (Dec); Forest Festival (Jun); Bridal (Mar); Hunting (Oct); Fall Sports (Sept).
Special Weekly Sections: Religion (Fri); Business (Mon); Seniors (Sat); Outdoors (Thur); Lifestyles (Tues).
Magazines: USA WEEKEND Magazine (Sat); American Profile (Weekly).
Pub. ....Marilyn Barker
Circ. Mgr. ....Aaron Dekuiper
Religion Ed ....David Barber
Sports Ed. ....Mathew Wendzl
Prodn. Mgr., Pressroom ....Sheryl Rossen
Market Information: ADS; Split run; TMC.
Mechanical available: Offset; Black and 3 ROP colors; insert accepted - all; page cutoffs - 22 1/2.
Mechanical Specifications: Type page 13 1/2 x 21 3/4; E - 6 cols, 2 1/16, 1/8 between; A - 6 cols, 2 1/16, 1/8 between; C - 9 cols, 1 3/8, 1/8 between.
Commodity Consumption: Avg. Page Number Per Issue - Daily 32; Avg. Page Number Per Issue - Plates Used 2850; widths 14; Newsprint Used - Short Tons 585; Printing Ink Used - Pages Printed 3950.
Equipment EDITORIAL: Front-end Software – Aldus/PageMaker, QPS/QuarkXPress, Baseview/NewsEdit Pro.; Editorial Hardware – 9-APP/Mac; Editorial Printers – HP, QMS CLASSIFIED: Front-end Software – Baseview.; Classified Hardware – 3-APP/Mac; Classified Equipment – 2-APP/Mac; Classified Printers – QMS DISPLAY: Ad make-up applications – Baseview/Ad Manager; Layout Software – 3-APP/Mac.; Display Hardware – Printers ☐ QMS PRODUCTION: Pagination Software – Adobe/Pagemaker 6.5, Adobe/Photoshop 4.0.; Production Equipment – 1-Nu, ECR/Scriptsetter; Scanners – AG, Polaroid PRESSROOM: Line 1 – 7-HI/Cotrell 15A; Folders – 1-HI/2:1.; Inserters and stuffers – KAN/7:1; Bundle tying machines – Sa; Addressing machine – Wm.; Business Hardware – 3-IBM

MARQUETTE

THE MINING JOURNAL

249 W. Washington St., Marquette, Mich., 49855; gen tel (906) 228-2500; adv tel (906) 228-2500; ed tel (906) 228-2500; gen fax (906) 228-5556; adv fax (906) 228-3273; ed fax (906) 228-2617; web site www.miningjournal.net
Group: Nutting Newspapers of Michigan Inc
Published: Mon, Tues, Wed, Thur, Fri, Sat, Sun
Weekday Frequency: e
Saturday Frequency: e
Circulation: 12,138; 13,456(sat); 14,509(sun)
Last Audit: ABC September 30, 2011
Price: 182.00/yr (carrier), $171.60 (motor route), $195.00/yr (mail).
Advertising: Open inch rate $32.18 Natl rate
Insert rate: see rate card
News services: AP,
Politics: Independent. **Established:** 1846
Not Published: New Year; Thanksgiving; Christmas.
Own facility?: Y
Special Editions: Bridal (Feb); Spring Home Improvement (Mar); Lawn & Garden (May); Cookbook (Nov); Fall Car Care (Oct).
Special Weekly Sections: Outdoor Page (S); Builders Page (Thur).
Magazines: TV Week (Sat); Parade (S).
Pub. ....James A. Reevs
Circ. Mgr. ....Jerry Newhouse
Mng. Ed. ....Bud Sargent
Deputy Mng. Ed. ....Dave Schneider
Lifestyle Ed. ....Diane Biery
News Ed. ....Dan Weingerten
Advertising Director ....Jim Parks
Creative Services Manager ....Dave Bond
Sports Editor ....Matt Wellens
Market Information: TMC.
Mechanical available: Offset; Black and 3 ROP colors; insert accepted; page cutoffs - 22 3/4.
Mechanical Specifications: Type page 11 x 21 1/2; E - 6 cols, 1.583
Commodity Consumption: Avg. Page Number Per Issue - Daily 22; Avg. Page Number Per Issue - Plates Used 6400; Avg. Page Number Per Issue - Sunday 54; widths 27 1/2; Newsprint Used - Short Tons 1000; Printing Ink Used - Black 35000; Printing Ink Used - Color 3000; Printing Ink U
Equipment EDITORIAL: Front-end Software – Mk/Mycro-Comp Touchwriter.; Editorial Hardware – Mac's; Editorial Printers – V/4990 Laser-Printer, Konica/2100 EV Jetsetter; Classified Hardware – Mac's; Layout Software – COM/MCS 100, 3-APP/Mac Centris 650, 1-APP/Mac IIcx.; Production Equipment – 1-Nu/Flip Top FT40UPNS, APP/Mac Scanner-DTP; Cameras – 1-SCREEN/Auto Companica 690C. PRESSROOM: Line 1 – 8; Folders – 1; Bundle tying machines – 2-MLN/ML1EE, 1-MLN/Spirit; Addressing machine – 1/Wm.; Business Hardware – Anzio

MIDLAND

MIDLAND DAILY NEWS

124 S. McDonald St., Midland, Mich., 48640; gen tel (989) 835-7171; adv tel (989) 835-7171; ed tel (989) 835-7171; gen fax (989) 835-9151; adv fax (989) 835-8591; ed fax (989) 835-6991; gen e-mail mdnletters@mdn.net; web site www.ourmidland.com
Group: U.S. Suburban Press, Inc.
Published: Mon, Tues, Wed, Thur, Fri, Sat, Sun
Weekday Frequency: e
Saturday Frequency: e
Circulation: 11,541; 11,933(sat); 14,645(sun)
Last Audit: ABC September 30, 2011
Price: 2.66/wk; 10.64/mo; 137.76/yr.
Advertising: Open inch rate $33.00
News services: AP, NYT, HN.
Politics: Independent.
Special Editions: Envision (Feb); Envision (Mar).
Special Weekly Sections: Midland Living & Entertainment (Fri); Best Food Day (Mon); Science Page (S); Church Page (Sat); Agriculture (Thur); Arts Page (Wed).
Magazines: Color Comics (S); USA WEEKEND Magazine (Sat).
Pub ....Jenny Anderson
Adv. Dir., Retail ....Kevin Prior
Adv. Mgr., Online Sales ....Erik Barnard
Circ./Distr. Mgr. ....Gary Wamsley
Ed. ....John H. Telfer
Editorial Page Ed ....Ralph E. Wirtz
Lifestyle Ed. ....Lori Qualls
Photo Ed. ....Ryan Wood
Sports Ed. ....Chris Stevens
Prodn. Mgr., Post Press ....Tim Newman
Market Information: ADS; Split run; TMC.
Mechanical available: Offset; Black and 3 ROP colors; insert accepted; page cutoffs - 22 3/4.
Mechanical Specifications: Type page 13 x 21 1/2; E - 6 cols, 2 1/16, 1/8 between; A - 6 cols, 2 1/16, 1/8 between; C - 9 cols, 1 1/2, 1/16 between.
Commodity Consumption: Avg. Page Number Per Issue - Daily 26; Avg. Page Number Per Issue - Plates Used 26000; Avg. Page Number Per Issue - Sunday 60; widths 27; Newsprint Used - Short Tons 1120; Printing Ink Used - Black 35000; Printing Ink Used - Color 5980; Printing Ink Used
Equipment EDITORIAL: Front-end Software – Baseview/NewsEdit 1.12, QPS/QuarkXPress 3.31.; Editorial Hardware – 4-APP/Mac Quadra 650, 10-APP/Mac Quadra 605, 2-Umax/5900; Editorial Equipment – 2-Accuset/1500 Imagesetter; Editorial Printers – 1-APP/LaserJet 2100M, 1-APP/Mac LaserWriter Pro 630 CLASSIFIED: Front-end Software – Baseview/Class Manager 3.3.4.; Classified Hardware – 5-APP/Mac Quadra 105, 2-APP/Power Mac 7300; Classified Equipment – Printers ☐ 1-APP/LaserJet 2100M DISPLAY: Ad make-up applications – QPS/QuarkXPress 4.04, Adobe/Photoshop 5.5; Layout Software – ALS (version 2.1.1).; Display Hardware – 2-APP/Mac 7300, 2-Umax 5900, APP/Power Mac 5100, 1-APP/Mac, 2-APP/iMac G3; Display Printers – 2-HP/LaserJet 4M PRODUCTION: Pagination Software – QPS/QuarkXPress 3.3.2, QPS/QuarkXPress 4.04.; Production Equipment – 1-Neg, 1-APP/Mac 8500-132; Cameras – 1-C/Spartan III, AG/RPS6100S; Scanners – 1-Nikon/35mm, Epson/800C Flatbed, 1-Nikon/1000 35mm, 1-AG/Arcus II Flatbed PRESSROOM: Line 1 – 8-G/Urbanite single width 1984; Folders – 1; Reels and Stands – 2 MAILROOM: Counter stackers – HL/Monitor; Inserters and stuffers – S/P48; Bundle tying machines – OVL; Other equipment –HI/Bottom Wrap.; Audio Hardware – Brite Voice Systems; Business Hardware – IBM/AS-400

MONROE

THE MONROE EVENING NEWS

20 W. First, Monroe, Mich., 48161; gen tel (734) 242-1100; adv tel (734) 242-1100; ed tel (734) 242-1100; gen fax (734) 242-3175; adv fax (734) 242-3175; ed fax (734) 242-0937; adv e-mail ads@monroenews.com; ed e-mail newsmail@monroenews.com; web site www.monroenews.com
Group: The Monroe Publishing Company
Published: Mon, Tues, Wed, Thur, Fri, Sat, Sun
Weekday Frequency: e
Saturday Frequency: e
Circulation: 17,350; 18,910(sat); 41,906(sun)
Last Audit: ABC September 30, 2011
Price: 174.72/year
Advertising: Sunday Open Inch: $25.21; Daily Open Inch: $23.26
Insert rate: Call for rates
News services: AP
Politics: Independent. **Established:** 1825
Advertising not accepted: Y
Not Published: Thanksgiving Day, Christmas Day, New Year's Day and Independence Day
Own facility?: Y
Special Editions: Fair Premium Guide (Apr); Fall Sports (Aug); High School Basketball (Dec); Auto Showcase (Jan); Monroe County Fair (Jul); Business Profiles (Jun); Bedford Business Association (Mar); Medical Directory (May).
Special Weekly Sections: Farm (Fri); Best Food Day (Mon); Business (S); Living (Thur); Health (Tues).
Magazines: Relish (Monthly); Monroe Magazine (Quarterly); Parade (S).
Pres./Pub ....Lonnie Peppler-Moyer
CFO ....Jay Hollon
Sec./HR Dir. ....Shirley Hyden
Adv. Dir., Sales ....Jeanine Bragg
Circ. Mgr. ....Dave Zewicky
Ed. ....Deborah Saul
Creative Serv./Alt Pub Mgr. ....Jim Dombrowski
Bus. Ed ....Charles Slat
Editorial Page Ed. ....Deb Saul
Local Ed. ....Doug Donnelly
Presentation Ed. ....Stacy Sominski
Sports Ed. ....Ron Montri
New Media Mgr., Web ....Rob Gorczyca
Opns. Dir., Systems ....Trent Langton
Prodn. Mgr., Distr. ....Kevin Gosset
Pressroom Foreman ....Dale Hill
Market Information: TMC.
Mechanical available: Offset; Black and 3 ROP colors; insert accepted - self-adhesive notes, product samples; page cutoffs - 22 3/4.
Mechanical Specifications: Type page 11 5/8 x 21; E - 6 cols, 2, 1/6 between; A - 6 cols, 2, 1/8 between; C - 9 cols, 1 1/5, 1/9 between.
Commodity Consumption: Avg. Page Number Per Issue - Daily 27; Avg. Page Number Per Issue - Plates Used 24200; Avg. Page Number Per Issue - Sunday 34; widths 25; Newsprint Used - Metric Tons 1484; Printing Ink Used - Black 29650; Printing Ink Used - Color 9000; Printing Ink Use
Equipment EDITORIAL: Front-end Software – Saxotech; Editorial Hardware – PC Based; Editorial Printers – Xante/Accel-a-writer CLASSIFIED: Front-end Software – DTI; Classified Hardware – PC Based DISPLAY: Ad make-up applications – Adobe Indesign; Display Hardware – Macintosh Based; Display Printers – Xante/Accel-a-Writer, X/Phaser 1235 PRODUCTION: Pagination Software – Adobe Indesign; Production Equipment – PC Based; Cameras – LE; Scanners – Kk, Microtek/ScanMaker II, HP/ScanJet 4C, Graphic Enterprise/Tesca 18x24 PRESSROOM: Line 1 – Web Atlas; Line 2 – Web Atlas MAILROOM: Counter stackers – Comet; Inserters and stuffers – Harris 1372; Bundle tying machines – 1-/OUL, 3-MLN/MLEE, 2-MLN/HSMLN 2A; Mailroom control system – GMA/WinLincs; Other equipment –MM/1550 Presto Saddle Stitcher. BUSINESS COMPUTERS: Business Software – Microsoft Dynamics DTI; Business Hardware – PC Based
Delivery method: Mail, Newsstand, Private Carrier, Racks

MOUNT CLEMENS

THE DAILY TRIBUNE

100 Macomb Daily Dr., Mt. Clemens, Mich., 48043; gen tel (888) 622-6629; gen fax (586) 469-4711; web site www.dailytribune.com
Published: Wed, Thur, Fri, Sun
Weekday Frequency: e
Circulation: 5,594; 6,166(sun)
Last Audit: ABC September 30, 2011
Price: 2.25/wk (carrier); 9.00/mo.
Advertising: Open inch rate $72.03
News services: AP, U.S. Suburban Press Inc..
Politics: Independent. **Established:** 1902
Special Editions: Home Improvement (Apr); Woodward Dream Cruise (Aug); Holiday Magic (Dec); Progress (Feb); Auto Show (Jan); Spring Home Improvement (Mar); Home Improvement (May); Holiday Gifting (Nov); Home Interior (Oct); Fall Home Improvement (2 times) (Sept).
Special Weekly Sections: Entertainment (Fri); Food (Mon); Auto (S); Real Estate (Thur); Schools (Tues).
Magazines: Parade (S).
Pub. ....Jerry Bammel
Circ. Mgr. ....Mike Muszall
Exec. Ed. ....Richard Kelley
Sports Ed. ....George Pohly
Market Information: ADS; TMC; Zoned editions.
Mechanical available: Offset; Black and 3 ROP colors; insert accepted - card stock; page cutoffs - 21 1/2.
Mechanical Specifications: Type page 13 x 21 1/2; E - 6 cols, 2 1/16, 1/8 between; A - 6 cols, 2 1/16, 1/8 between; C - 10 cols, 1 3/8, 1/16 between.
Commodity Consumption: Avg. Page Number Per Issue - Daily 28; Avg. Page Number Per Issue - Plates Used 51600; Avg. Page Number Per Issue - Sunday 50; widths 55; Newsprint Used - Metric Tons 5443; Newsprint Used - Short Tons 6000; Printing Ink Used - Black 145284; Printing Ink
Equipment EDITORIAL: Front-end Software – WordPerfect 6.0.; Editorial Hardware – 18-PC 486-80; Classified Hardware – 2-HAS/Magician.; Layout Software – SCS/Layout 8000.; Display Hardware – APP/Mac; Display Printers – Software ☐ QPS/QuarkXPress 3.31; Production Equipment – AU/APS 6-108S; Cameras – 1-C/Marathon. PRESSROOM: Line 1 – 8-G/Cosmo Offset; Reels and Stands – 8 MAILROOM: Counter stackers – 1-St/251, 2-Id/440; Inserters and stuffers – 1/MC, 8-St/PK; Bundle tying machines – 2-MLN/ML2EE.; Business Hardware – IBM/AS-400

THE MACOMB DAILY

100 Macomb Daily Dr., Mount Clemens, Mich., 48043; gen tel (586) 469-4510; adv tel (586) 469-4510; ed tel (586) 469-4510; gen fax (586) 469-4512; adv fax (586) 469-4711; ed fax (586) 469-2892; adv e-mail roger.hages@macombdaily.com; ed e-mail ken.kish@macombdaily.com; web site

www.macombdaily.com
Group: Journal Register Company
Published: Mon, Tues, Wed, Thur, Fri, Sat, Sun
Weekday Frequency: m
Saturday Frequency: m
Circulation: 50,273; 41,442(sat); 64,074(sun)
Last Audit: ABC September 30, 2011
Price: $4.30/wk (carrier); @RecordBody:**Advertising:** $70.52 (Sunday open rate)
News services: AP
Politics: 1841
Advertising not accepted: Y
Own facility?: N
Special Editions: January: Brides & Grooms, Social Security, North American Auto Show February: WaterWays/Detroit Boat Show March: Choices in Education, Macomb on the Move/Quality of Life, Macomb on the Move/Made in Michigan April: Macomb on the Move/Education, Spring Golf May: Macomb on the Move/Business & Industry, Travels June: Best of the Best, Brides & Grooms August: Macomb Preps September: Waterways, Travels October: Choices in Education, November: Holiday Ideas December Last Minute Gift Guide, Holiday Wrap, Holiday Greetings to the Troops
Special Weekly Sections: Homes (Sunday); Marquee/Entertainment (Friday); Health (Tues); Lifelines (Sunday) Homefront (Sunday) Wheels (Thur. & Sun.)
Magazines: Parade (S).
Promotions Manager .... Myra Kieffer
Circ. Dir. .... Mike Muszall
Lifestyles Editor .... Niky Hachigian
Mng. Ed., News .... Ken Kish
Features/Entertainment Ed. .... Debbie Komar
Photo Dept. Mgr. .... Dave Posavetz
Sports Ed. .... George Pohly
Data Processing Mgr. .... Jeff Clark
Executive Editor
Richard Kelley
Publisher .... Jerry Bammel
Advertising Director
Roger Hages
Classified Manager .... Kathy Bean
VP of Finance, General Manager ... Jerry Bammel
VP of Operations, Production Director . Pat Eagan
Director of Digital Sales .... Sarah Probert
Market Information: TMC; Zoned editions.
Mechanical available: Offset; Black and 3 ROP colors; insert accepted - card stock, books; page cutoffs - 20.
Mechanical Specifications: Broadsheet page - 6 columns (9.89) x 20; column gutter 8 pts.; page gutter 80 pts.; page margins 40 pts.
Commodity Consumption: Avg. Page Number Per Issue - Daily 40; Avg. Page Number Per Issue - Plates Used 97500; Avg. Page Number Per Issue - Saturday 26; Avg. Page Number Per Issue - Sunday 88; widths 27; Newsprint Used - Metric Tons 5352; Newsprint Used - Short Tons 5900; Print
Equipment DISPLAY: Ad make-up applications – Adobe InDesign; Layout Software – SCS/Layout 8000, PC Workstations.; Pasters – 8; Mailroom control system – Burt Technologies
Zip Codes served: 48065, 48005, 48062, 48095, 48094, 48096, 48050, 48048, 48316, 48317, 48314, 48315, 48313, 48312, 48310, 48089, 48088, 48091, 48092, 48093, 48015, 48026, 48021, 48080, 48081, 48082, 48035, 48036, 48038, 48043, 48045, 48042, 48044, 48051, 48047
Delivery method: Newsstand, Private Carrier, Racks

MOUNT PLEASANT

MORNING SUN

711 W. Pickard St., Mount Pleasant, Mich., 48804-0447; gen tel (989) 779-6000; adv tel (989) 779-6110; ed tel (989) 779-6050; gen fax (989) 776-6012; adv fax (989) 779-6101; ed fax (989) 779-6051; gen e-mail news@michigannewspapers.com; adv e-mail dnegus@michigannewspapers.com; ed e-mail news@michigannewspapers.com; web site www.themorningsun.com
Published: Mon, Tues, Wed, Thur, Fri, Sat, Sun
Weekday Frequency: m
Saturday Frequency: m
Circulation: 8,073; 7,906(sat); 9,362(sun)
Last Audit: ABC September 30, 2011
Price: 4.50/wk
Advertising: Open inch rate $17.35-daily, $18.25-Sunday
Insert rate: $50/M single sheet
News services: AP.
Special Editions: Yard & Garden (Apr); Football Preview (Aug); Basketball Tab (Dec); Progress (Feb); Bridal Tab (Jan); Bridal Tab (Jul); Home Show (Mar); Highland Festival (May); Thanksgiving Day (Nov); Car Care (Oct); Fall Yard and Garden (Sept).
Special Weekly Sections: Dining (Fri); Health Lifestyles (Thur); Golf (Tues).
Magazines: Parade (S).
Pub. .... Al Frattura
Adv. Dir. .... Don Negus
Adv. Mgr., Classified .... Donna Pung
Circ. Dir. .... Cristine Fox
Exec. Ed. .... Rick Mills
Mng. Ed., Alma .... Linda Gittleman
Photo Ed., Mt. Pleasant .... Lisa Yanick
Sunday Ed. .... Mindy Norton
Director of Sales & Marketing .... Tammy Fisher
Mng. Ed. .... Steve Coon
Mgmt. Info Servs. Mgr. .... Jessica Stroud
Prodn. Mgr., Mailroom .... Matt Field
Prodn. Mgr., Composing .... Cindy McClain
Prodn. Mgr., Pre Press .... Jerry Stahl
Market Information: ADS; TMC; Zoned editions.
Mechanical available: Offset; Black and 3 ROP colors; insert accepted; page cutoffs - 22.
Mechanical Specifications: Type page 13 x 21; E - 6 cols, 2 1/16, 1/8 between; A - 8 cols, 3 1/5, 1/8 between; C - 8 cols, 1 1/2, 1/8 between.
Commodity Consumption: Avg. Page Number Per Issue - Daily 13; Avg. Page Number Per Issue - Plates Used 3932; Avg. Page Number Per Issue - Sunday 29; widths 13 3/4; Newsprint Used - Short Tons 536; Printing Ink Used - Black 19546; Printing Ink Used - Color 3666; Printing Ink Us
Equipment EDITORIAL: Front-end Software – Alfa; Editorial Printers – HP/4P, HP/5P CLASSIFIED: Front-end Software – PBS/AdPlus.; Classified Hardware – Compaq/PL 1500; Classified Printers – 1-Epson/DFX-8000 DISPLAY: Ad make-up applications – QPS/QuarkXPress 4.0, Adobe/Photoshop 5.0, Adobe/Illustrator 7.0; Layout Software – PBS/AdPlus, PBS/AdPlacer.; Display Hardware – 13-APP/Mac; Display Printers – 2-HP/5000, 1-NewGen/Imager Plus 12, 1-HP/4V, 1-AG/Accuset 1000, 1-Scitex/Dolev 400 PRODUCTION: Pagination Software – PBS/AdPlacer.; Cameras – 1-B/4000, 1-Nu/VIC-1418, 1-TogeeMD/480, 1-Acti/253; Scanners – 1-AG/Arcus Plus, AG/Horizon Flatbed PRESSROOM: Line 1 – 14-G/Community (2 Path finder color decks); Line 2 – 10-G/Community. MAILROOM: Counter stackers – 2/BG; Inserters and stuffers – 1-K&M/1472, 3-MM; Bundle tying machines – 6-/Bu; Other equipment –2-MM.; Business Hardware – Compaq/PL 1500
Delivery method: Private Carrier, Racks

MUSKEGON

THE MUSKEGON CHRONICLE

981 Third St., Muskegon, Mich., 49443-0059; gen tel (231) 722-3161; adv tel (231) 725-6315; ed tel (231) 725-6342; gen fax (231) 728-3330; adv fax (231) 726-3434; ed fax (231) 722-2552; gen e-mail muprod@muskegonchronicle.com; ed e-mail jstephenson@muskegonchronicle.com; web site www.mlive.com
Group: Metro Suburbia, Inc./Newhouse Newspapers
Published: Mon, Tues, Wed, Thur, Fri, Sat, Sun
Weekday Frequency: e
Saturday Frequency: m
Circulation: 28,574; 30,638(sat); 35,791(sun)
Last Audit: ABC September 30, 2011
Price: 11.75/mo (carrier), $11.50/mo (auto).
Advertising: Open inch rate $57.65
News services: AP, NNS.
Politics: Independent. **Established:** 1857
Special Editions: Spring Sports (Apr); Football (Aug); Winter Sports (Dec); Home Show (Feb); Living Here (Jan); Personal Safety (Jul); Senior Lifestyles (Jun); Today's Living (Mar); Pet Care (May); Home for the Holidays (Nov); Full Cruisin' (Oct); Parade of Homes (Sept).
Special Weekly Sections: Church Pages (Fri); Best Food Day (Mon); Stock Market (S); Kids Pages (Sat); Venture Outdoors (Thur); Wheels (Wed).
Magazines: Parade (S).
Broadcast Affiliations: WZZM (ABC); WWMT (CBS); WOOD (NBC).
Gen. Mgr. .... Steve Westphal
Controller .... Kimberly A. Ahrens
Adv. Dir., Nat'l Sales .... Sheila Reinecke
Mktg. Mgr. .... Tom Schaub
Mktg. Promo. Mgr. .... Chris Zahrt
Circ. Mgr., Zone .... Joel Seifert
Circ. Supvr., Pre Print .... Michele Faust
Ed. .... Cindy Fairfield
Bus./Finance Ed. .... Dave Alexander
City Ed. .... Jerry Morlock
Editorial Page Ed. .... David Kolb
Librarian .... Mary Franklin
News Ed .... Paula Holmes-Greeley
Online Ed. .... Lee Lupo
Sports Ed. .... Tom Kendra
Market Information: Split run; TMC; Zoned editions.
Mechanical available: Offset; Black and 3 ROP colors; insert accepted; page cutoffs - 21 1/2.
Mechanical Specifications: Type page 11 7/8 x 20 5/8; E - 6 cols, 1 7/8, 1/8 between; A - 6 cols, 1 7/8, 1/8 between; C - 10 cols, 1 1/10, 1/18 between.
Commodity Consumption: Avg. Page Number Per Issue - Daily 30; Avg. Page Number Per Issue - Plates Used 48000; Avg. Page Number Per Issue - Sunday 73; widths 25; Newsprint Used - Short Tons 4187; Printing Ink Used - Black 117755; Printing Ink Used - Color 22557; Printing Ink Us
Equipment EDITORIAL: Front-end Software – Baseview/News Edit Pro 3.23.; Editorial Hardware – 2-Mac/G3; Editorial Equipment – APP/Mac G3 Tranporter, 1-APP/Mac PC 8100/80 Wire Feed, 2-APP/Mac Webster Server; Editorial Printers – GCC/Elite XL 20/600, 2-HP/4050 Laser CLASSIFIED: Front-end Software – Mactive.; Classified Hardware – DEC/PDP 11-34, AT/J-11; Classified Equipment – Sharp/FO551 Fax, 2-ClassPage Pagination Stations; Classified Printers – 1-Okidata/395 DISPLAY: Ad make-up applications – Baseview/PMP.; Display Hardware – APP/Mac G3/450 PRODUCTION: Pagination Software – All/Oman/Page Pair.; Production Equipment – APP/Mac G4 Photoserver, SST/Imagesetter; Cameras – 2-3850 Online Processors; Scanners – Opal/Ultra, 3-Umax/Flatbed PRESSROOM: Line 1 – 25-G/Magnum (5 towers); Press Drives – Allen Bradley; Folders – 2-Universal, 2-SSC; Pasters – Meg-Tec/2-arm reels; Press control system – Allen Bradley; Press registration system – Quad Tec. MAILROOM: Counter stackers – 1-HL/Monitor, 1-HL/HT, 1-HL/HT, 1-HL/Dual Corrior, 1-QWI/DC; Inserters and stuffers – 1-GMA/SLS 1000, 1-GMA/SLS 1000A; Bundle tying machines – 1-Dynaric/NP2, 1-MLN/Strapper, 1-Dynaric/NP2; Wrapping singles – 1-Bu/String Tyer; Addressing machine – Addressing; Audio Hardware – New Horizon Group, 20 Line PC System/NT Based; Business Hardware – 2-TI/990

NILES

NILES DAILY STAR

217 N. 4th St., Niles, Mich., 49120-2301; gen tel (269) 683-2101; adv tel (269) 687-7720; gen fax (269) 683-2175; adv e-mail kevin.smith@leaderpub.com; web site www.nilesstar.com; www.leaderpub.com
Published: Mon, Tues, Wed, Thur, Fri, Sat, Sun
Weekday Frequency: e
Saturday Frequency: m
Circulation: 2,361; 2,361(sat)
Last Audit: August 30, 2004
Advertising: Open inch rate $12.80
Politics: Independent.
Not Published: New Year; Memorial Day; Independence Day; Labor Day; Christmas.
Magazines: F.Y.I. (June) (Annually).
Pub. .... Bryan Clapper
Adv. Dir. .... Kevin Smith
Distr. Mgr. .... Rick Lott
Assoc. Ed. .... Marcia Steffens
Sports Ed. .... Scott Novak
Prodn. Mgr., Pressroom .... Bob Bell
Market Information: TMC.
Mechanical available: Offset; Black and 3 ROP colors; insert accepted - all; page cutoffs - 22 5/8.
Mechanical Specifications: Type page 13 1/4 x 21 1/2; E - 8 cols, 1 1/2, 1/6 between; A - 8 cols, 1 1/2, 1/6 between; C - 8 cols, 1 1/2, 1/6 between.
Commodity Consumption: Avg. Page Number Per Issue - Daily 13; Avg. Page Number Per Issue - Plates Used 7200; widths 15; Newsprint Used - Short Tons 1040; Printing Ink Used - Black 22800; Printing Ink Used - Color 4100.
Equipment EDITORIAL: Front-end Software – QPS/QuarkXPress 4.0.; Editorial Hardware – APP/Mac CLASSIFIED: Front-end Software – Baseview.; Classified Hardware – APP/Mac; Layout Software – APP/Mac.; Production Equipment – Caere/OmniPage. PRESSROOM: Line 1 – 10-KP/News King single width; Folders – 2 MAILROOM: Counter stackers – 1-BG/Count-O-Veyor 108; Inserters and stuffers – MM/3 Station; Bundle tying machines – 3/Bu, 1-/Sa, 1-/MLN; Addressing machine – Dispensa-Matic.; Business Hardware – 1-IBM/5364-PC Sys 36, 2-IBM/5150, 2-RSK/1000TL2

OWOSSO

THE ARGUS-PRESS

201 E. Exchange St., Owosso, Mich., 48867; gen tel (989) 725-5136; gen fax (989) 725-6376; gen e-mail argus@chartermi.net; web site www.argus-press.com
Published: Mon, Tues, Wed, Thur, Fri, Sat, Sun
Saturday Frequency: m
Circulation: 11,249; 11,249(sat); 11,249(sun)
Last Audit: October 3, 2003
Price: 10.50/mo; 105.00/yr.
Advertising: Open inch rate $21.75
News services: AP, AP Graphics Net.
Politics: Independent. **Established:** 1854
Not Published: New Year; Memorial Day; Independence Day; Labor Day; Thanksgiving; Christmas.
Special Editions: Best of Shiawassee (Annually); Christmas Gift Guide (Dec); Fall Car Care (Fall).
Magazines: Color Comics (S).
Pub. .... Thomas E. Campbell
Adv. Dir. .... Michael Kruszkowski
Dir., Mktg./Promo .... Catherine Campbell
Circ. Mgr. .... Katrina Silvers
Ed. .... Richard E. Campbell
News Ed .... Daniel Basso
Prodn. Mgr., Mailroom .... Lester Dibean
Prodn. Mgr., Pre Press .... Julie Anderson
Market Information: TMC.
Mechanical available: Offset; Black and 3 ROP colors; insert accepted - subject to approval; page cutoffs - 21 1/2.
Mechanical Specifications: Type page 13 x 21 1/2; E - 6 cols, 2 1/16, 1/8 between; A - 6 cols, 2 1/16, 1/8 between; C - 9 cols, 1 3/8, 1/16 between.
Commodity Consumption: Avg. Page Number Per Issue - Daily 16; Avg. Page Number Per Issue - Plates Used 9000; Avg. Page Number Per Issue - Saturday 16; Avg. Page Number Per Issue - Sunday 32; widths 27 1/2; Newsprint Used - Short Tons 600; Printing Ink Used - Black 20000; Print
Equipment EDITORIAL: Front-end Software – Baseview/NewsEdit Pro, QPS/QuarkXPress.; Editorial Hardware – APP/Power Mac 7300, APP/Mac G4; Editorial Equipment –

Nikon/Coolscan; Editorial Printers – APP/Mac Laser Writer 8500 CLASSIFIED: Front-end Software – Baseview/Ad Manager Pro.; Classified Hardware – APP/Power Mac 7300; Production Equipment – AG/Accuset 1500; Cameras – DSA; Scanners – Equipment Â QPS/QuarkXPress 4.0. PRESSROOM: Line 1 – 5-G/Urbanite 1964.; Inserters and stuffers – 8-KAN/480; Bundle tying machines – EAM-Mosca; Addressing machine – Ch. BUSINESS COMPUTERS: Business Software – BMF; Business Hardware – Acer/PC

PETOSKEY

NORTHERN MICHIGAN REVIEW, INC.

319 State St., Petoskey, Mich., 49770-2746; gen tel (231) 347-2554; gen fax (231) 347-6833; gen e-mail petoskeynews@petoskeynews.com; ed e-mail petoskeynews@petoskeynews.com; web site www.petoskeynews.com
Group: Schurz Communications
Published: Mon, Tues, Wed, Thur, Fri, Sat
Pres....Ken Winter

PETOSKEY NEWS-REVIEW

319 State St., Petoskey, Mich., 49770-0528; gen tel (231) 347-2544; adv tel (231) 439-9310; ed tel (231) 439-9302; gen fax (231) 347-6833; adv fax (231) 347-0669; ed fax (231) 347-5461; gen e-mail petoskeynews@petoskeynews.com; adv e-mail clyons@petoskeynews.com; ed e-mail kstanley@petoskeynews.com; web site www.petoskeynews.com
Group: U.S. Suburban Press, Inc.
Published: Mon, Tues, Wed, Thur, Fri
Weekday Frequency: e
Circulation: 8,994
Last Audit: March 31, 2008
Price: 2.85/wk (carrier); 11.40/mo (mail); 133.40/yr.
Advertising: Open inch rate $20.40(e-fri)
News services: AP, U.S. Suburban Press Inc..
Politics: Independent.
Advertising not accepted: NC-17 movies & materials; Tobacco & cigarettes.
Not Published: New Year; Memorial Day; Independence Day; Labor Day; Thanksgiving; Christmas.
Special Editions: Summer Guide (Apr); Football Preview (Aug); Christmastime Memories (Dec); Parenting Awareness (Feb); East Jordan Snow Blast (Jan); Petoskey Sidewalk Sales (Jul); Welcome Back Resorters (Jun); Your Home (Mar); Dining Guide (May); Homes (Monthly); Winter Gu
Special Weekly Sections: Real Estate (Fri); Food (Mon); NASCAR (Thur); Health (Tues); Outdoor (Wed).
Magazines: Parade (Fri).
Profile: The Petoskey News-Review has been locally owned and printed for the past 128 years. The Monday-Friday newspaper is distributed in Charlevoix county, an area known as a summer and winter vacation and resort destination. The company also publishes the Super
Pres./Pub.................................Doug Caldwell
Adv. Mgr., Retail ....Christy Lynos
Circ. Mgr...Carl Lyons
Circ. Mgr., Promo........................Dena Sydow
Online Ed. ....Kendall Stanley
People Ed. ....Babette Stenuis
Religion Ed. ....Deb McGuiness
Sports Ed.................................Andy Sneddon
Wire Ed. ....Neil Stilwell
Prodn. Mgr. ....Paul Gunderson
Market Information: ADS; TMC.
Mechanical available: Offset; Black and 3 ROP colors; insert accepted - one page flyers, catalog size; page cutoffs - 22 3/4.
Mechanical Specifications: Type page 11 5/8 x 21 1/2; E - 6 cols, 1 5/6, 1/8 between; A - 6 cols, 1 5/6, 1/8 between; C - 6 cols, 1 5/6, 1/8 between.
Commodity Consumption: Avg. Page Number Per Issue - Daily 33; Avg. Page Number Per Issue - Plates Used 7500; widths 25; Newsprint Used - Short Tons 675; Printing Ink Used - Black 16900; Printing Ink Used - Color 3400; Printing Ink Used - Pages Printed 7986.
Equipment EDITORIAL: Front-end Software – Adobe/InDesign CSI, Baseview/NewsEdit Pro.; Editorial Hardware – APP/Mac; Editorial Printers – APP/Mac 8500, ECR/VRL 36HS CLASSIFIED: Front-end Software – Baseview/Ad Manager Pro.; Classified Hardware – APP/Mac; Classified Printers – ECR/VRL 36HS DISPLAY: Ad make-up applications – QPS/QuarkXPress; Layout Software – Adobe/InDesign CSI.; Display Hardware – APP/Mac; Display Printers – APP/Mac LaserWriter 8500, ECR/VRL 36HS Scriptsetter PRODUCTION: Pagination Software – Adobe/InDesign CSI.; Production Equipment – ECR/VRL 36HS Scriptsetter, Panther/Pro 62; Scanners – Mycro-Tek/9900XL PRESSROOM: Line 1 – 8-G/Community single width, 2-DGM/4 Highs 2000; Line 4 – G 2000; Folders – 1-G/SSC. MAILROOM: Counter stackers – BG/205; Bundle tying machines – 1/Bu, 2-Mosca/Strapper. BUSINESS COMPUTERS: Business Software – PBS; Business Hardware – DEC/1000A 4-233 Alpha Server

PONTIAC

THE OAKLAND PRESS

48 W. Huron St., Pontiac, Mich., 48342; gen tel (248) 332-8181; adv tel (248) 745-4595; ed tel (248) 745-4619; gen fax (248) 332-8885; adv fax (248) 332-1657; ed fax (248) 332-8885; gen e-mail vop@oakpress.com; adv e-mail teresa.goodrich@oakpress.com; ed e-mail glenn.gilbert@oakpress.com; web site www.theoaklandpress.com
Group: U.S. Suburban Press, Inc.
Published: Mon, Tues, Wed, Thur, Fri, Sat, Sun
Weekday Frequency: m
Saturday Frequency: m
Circulation: 65,211; 62,660(sat); 78,541(sun)
Last Audit: ABC September 30, 2011
Price: 3.25/wk; 169.00/yr; 84.25/6mo, 16.25/5wk.
Advertising: Open inch rate $109.74
News services: AP, LAT-WP, SHNS, NYT, TMS.
Politics: Independent. **Established:** 1844
Special Editions: Religious Directory (Apr); Salute to Business (Aug); Tis the Season (Dec); Senior Living (Feb); No Ordinary Sale (Jan); Concours d'Elegance (Jul); Senior Living (Jun); Spring Home & Garden/Cobo (Mar); MI Vacation Guide (May); Lagniappe (Nov); College Guid
Special Weekly Sections: Marquee Entertainment Tab (Fri); Food (Mon); Real Estate (S); Building (Sat); Health (Thur); Youth & Teen (Tues); Real Estate (Wed).
Magazines: Parade (S).
Pub. & Sr. Vice Pres., Michigan Papers Kevin Haezebroeck
Adv. Dir. ....Teresa Goodrich
Adv. Mgr., Automotive ....Mark Reitenga
Adv. Mgr., New Media ....Racine Purdy
Dir., Mktg...............................Kimberly Klein
Vice Pres., Circ. ....Jeff Schell
Circ. Mgr., Home Delivery ....Dwight Major
Circ. Mgr., Single Copy..................Tina Graves
Exec. Ed.....................................Glenn Gilbert
Automotive Ed.......................Joseph Szczesny
Editorial Asst. ....Leah English
Local News Ed. ....Julie Jacobson
Metro Ed., Community/Sunday ....Lee Dryden
Metro Ed., Nights.............................Gary Gould
Metro Ed., Projects ....Al Adler
News Ed....Kathy Gay
Photo Ed................................Tim Thompson
Sports Ed.......................................Jeff Kuehn
Travel Ed...............................Roger Wingelaar
Market Information: ADS; Split run; TMC; Zoned editions.
Mechanical available: Headliner Offset; Black and 3 ROP colors; insert accepted - 7 hm books; page cutoffs - 22 1/4.
Mechanical Specifications: Type page 13 1/4 x 21; E - 6 cols, 1 3/4, 1/8 between; A - 6 cols, 1 3/4, between; C - 10 cols, 1 3/16, 1/8 between.
Commodity Consumption: Avg. Page Number Per Issue - Daily 48; Avg. Page Number Per Issue - Plates Used 24300; Avg. Page Number Per Issue - Sunday 104; widths 50; Newsprint Used - Metric Tons 12534; Newsprint Used - Short Tons 13787; Printing Ink Used - Black 318534; Printing I
Equipment EDITORIAL: Front-end Software – Baseview/Client Server 2.2.; Editorial Hardware – 2-APP/Mac 9500, Main/Back-up Server; Editorial Equipment – 1-APP/Mac 950 with Wire Manager, 1-APP/Mac 6100; Editorial Printers – 10-HP/DeskWriters CLASSIFIED: Front-end Software – CompuClass/Computext.; Classified Hardware – Pentium/PC-100, Pentium/II, Gateway, Compaq, Microsoft/Windows NT DISPLAY: Ad make-up applications – Managing Editor/ALS 2.0; Layout Software – Mk/Managing Editor.; Display Hardware – IBM/J50-RISC6000, APP/Mac G3, Radius/ZOE Monitor; Display Printers – 1-APP/Mac II NTX PRODUCTION: Pagination Software – QPS/QuarkXPress, AU, AU/OMAN OPI.; Production Equipment – 2-ECR/3850, 3-XIT/Clipper Plain Paper 11 x 17, Aii/3850 Imagesetter; Cameras – C/Spartan III; Scanners – AG/Flatbed Scanner, Kk/Transparency Film Scanner PRESSROOM: Line 1 – 10-G/Headliner Offset double width; Folders – 1-G/3:2; Reels and Stands – 10-Reels/Stands; Press control system – G/MPCS. MAILROOM: Counter stackers – 3-QWI/300, 1-Id/2000; Inserters and stuffers – 1/AM Graphics/NP 630, 24-/Hopper; Bundle tying machines – 6-/NP2, Dynarics; Mailroom control system – Burt Technologies. BUSINESS COMPUTERS: Business Software – PBS/MediaPlus 3.0, Word Processing, PBS 3.0, SBS 3.0; Business Hardware – IBM/J50 RISC 6000, 1-IBM/590 RISC 6000

PORT HURON

TIMES HERALD

911 Military St., Port Huron, Mich., 48061-5009; gen tel (810) 985-7171; adv tel (810) 985-7171; ed tel (810) 989-6257; adv fax (810) 989-6293; ed fax (810) 989-6294; gen e-mail tmshrld@ic.net; web site www.thetimesherald.com
Published: Mon, Tues, Wed, Thur, Fri, Sat, Sun
Weekday Frequency: m
Saturday Frequency: m
Circulation: 16,977; 19,257(sat); 28,451(sun)
Last Audit: ABC September 30, 2011
Advertising: Open inch rate $67.20
News services: AP, GNS.
Politics: Independent.
Special Editions: Golf (Apr); Football (Aug); Blue Water Winter Guide (Fall); Woman's Day Expo (Feb); Mackinac (Jul); Almanac (Mar); Graduation (May); Gift Guide His and Hers (Nov); Bridal (Semi-yearly); Emergency Services Guide (Sept); Blue Water Summer Guide (Spring).
Special Weekly Sections: Living (S); Religion (Sat).
Magazines: Savvy (Every other month); B2B (Monthly); USA WEEKEND Magazine (Sat).
Adv. Dir...................................Lorinda Driscoll
Sr. Adv. Sales Mgr. ....Pam Ford
Circ. Opns. Mgr. ....Sheri Guske
Mng. Ed....................................Judith McLean
Editorial Page Ed...........................Tom Walker
Graphics Ed. ....Michael Eckert
Prodn. Mgr............................Shawn Bumeder
Prodn. Mgr., Mailroom ....Dave Lyon
Pre Press Mgr. ....Bill Cusac
Market Information: ADS; Split run; TMC.
Mechanical available: Offset; Black and 3 ROP colors; insert accepted; page cutoffs - 22 3/4.
Mechanical Specifications: Type page 10 x 21.5; E - 6 cols, 1.583, 0.069 between; A - 6 cols, 1.583, 0.069 between; C - 9 cols, 1.063, 0.069 between.
Commodity Consumption: Avg. Page Number Per Issue - Daily 30; Avg. Page Number Per Issue - Plates Used 47272; Avg. Page Number Per Issue - Saturday 36; Avg. Page Number Per Issue - Sunday 80; widths 12 1/2; Newsprint Used - Metric Tons 2690; Newsprint Used - Short Tons 2965; P
Equipment EDITORIAL: Front-end Software – APT.; Editorial Hardware – Compaq/Server, PC Workstation, Pentium/PC II; Editorial Equipment – GMTI/DigiCol Archive; Editorial Printers – HP CLASSIFIED: Front-end Software – APT.; Classified Hardware – Compaq/Server, PC Workstation; Classified Printers – HP/GMP DISPLAY: Ad make-up applications – QPS/QuarkXPress 3.3, Adobe/Photoshop 4.0, Adobe/Illustrator 7.0; Layout Software – 4-Advanced Publishing Technology (Layout 8000).; Display Hardware – 1-Compaq/Server PRODUCTION: Pagination Software – Advanced Publishing Technology 2.6.; Production Equipment – 2-Nat/A250, 2-MON/4500, 2-PaperMaster 600; Cameras – 1-C/Spartan III; Scanners – Lf/Leafscan 35, Nikon/Coolscan, Microtek/ScanMaker IIXE PRESSROOM: Line 1 – 18-G/Urbanite 1980; Folders – 2, 1-G/Quarter on-line; Pasters – 9-G/RTP. MAILROOM: Counter stackers – 2-QWI/300, 1-QWI/1000, 1/Fg, 1-/Grammerver 507; Inserters and stuffers – 1-GMA/1000; Bundle tying machines – 2-MLN/MLN2A, 2-MLN/Spirit; Addressing machine – 2-/Ch, 1-Barstrom/on-line 1up labeler; Other equipment –MM.

SAINT JOSEPH

THE HERALD-PALLADIUM

3450 Hollywood Rd., Saint Joseph, Mich., 49085; gen tel (269) 429-2400; adv tel (269) 429-2400; ed tel (269) 429-2400; gen fax (269) 429-7661; adv fax (269) 429-7661; ed fax (269) 429-4398; adv e-mail advertising@theh-p.com; ed e-mail localnews@theh-p.com; web site www.theh-p.com
Published: Mon, Tues, Wed, Thur, Fri, Sat, Sun
Weekday Frequency: m
Saturday Frequency: m
Circulation: 16,420; 16,420(sat); 19,528(sun)
Last Audit: Sworn September 30, 2009
Price: 25.00/4 weeks/ $300 annually
Advertising: Open inch rate $31.46
News services: AP, NEA, SHNS, LAT-WP.
Own facility?: Y
Special Editions: Tour Guide (Apr); Berrien County Youth Fair (Aug); Basketball Preview (Dec); Spring Brides (Feb); Glad-Peach Festival (Jul); Golden Years (Jun); Spring Car Care (Mar); Graduation Tab (May); Living in the Southwest (Monthly); Holiday Recipe/Craft Guide (No
Special Weekly Sections: Weekend Entertainment (Thur).
Magazines: USA WEEKEND Magazine (Sat).
Publisher..................................David Holgate
Controller....................................Robby Estes
Mgr., Opns......................................Larry Hall
City Ed.......................................Jim Dalgleish
Editorial Page Ed..........................Dale Brewer
Metro Ed. ....Ted Hartzell
News Ed....................................Steve Jewell
Online Ed....................................Dave Brown
Photo Ed.......................................John Madill
Sports Ed................................Jason Mitchell
Systems Mgr............................John Schaffer
Prodn. Mgr., Pressroom ...Gary Vanlandingham
Market Information: TMC.
Mechanical available: Offset; Black and 3 ROP colors; insert accepted; page cutoffs - 22 3/4.
Mechanical Specifications: Type page 13 x 21 1/2; E - 6 cols, 2 1/16, 1/8 between; A - 6 cols, 2 1/16, 1/8 between; C - 9 cols, 1 15/16, 1/8 between.
Commodity Consumption: Avg. Page Number Per Issue - Daily 30; Avg. Page Number Per Issue - Plates Used 39664; Avg. Page Number Per Issue - Sunday 64; widths 27 1/2; Newsprint Used - Short Tons 2550; Printing Ink Used - Black 92621; Printing Ink Used - Color 20580; Printing Ink
Equipment EDITORIAL: Front-end Software – QPS/QuarkXPress, Baseview/NewsEdit IQUE 3.02.; Editorial Hardware – APP/Mac; Editorial Equipment – 1-APP/Mac IIci, 4-TM, 9-RSK, 5-

Falcon, APP/Mac Quadra 800 CLASSIFIED: Front-end Software – Baseview/ClassFlow 2.0.; Classified Hardware – APP/Mac DISPLAY: Ad make-up applications – Multi-Ad/Creator 3.8, QPS/QuarkXPress 3.32; Display Hardware – APP/Mac; Production Equipment – 1-Nu/Flip Top FT40, 1-SCREEN/LD281Q, 1-V/1200; Cameras – 1-C/Spartan II. PRESSROOM: Line 1 – 4-G/Cosmo double width 1978, 2-1990; Pasters – 4-G/Automatic. MAILROOM: Counter stackers – 1-Id/NS440, 2-Id/Marathoner; Inserters and stuffers – 2-Mc/660; Bundle tying machines – 2-Dynaric/NP2. BUSINESS COMPUTERS: Business Software – Baseview; Business Hardware – 2-HP/9000

SAULT SAINTE MARIE

THE EVENING NEWS

109 Arlington St., Sault Sainte Marie, Mich., 49783; gen tel (906) 632-2235; gen fax (906) 632-1222; gen e-mail enoffice@sooeveningnews.com; adv e-mail ensales@sooeveningnews.com; ed e-mail edit@sooeveningnews.com; web site www.sooeveningnews.com

Published: Mon, Tues, Wed, Thur, Fri, Sun
Weekday Frequency: e
Circulation: 6,772; 6,772(sun)
Last Audit: September 28, 2001
Price: 3.00/wk; 12.00/mo; 193.00/yr.
Advertising: Open inch rate $17.00
News services: AP.
Politics: Independent.
Not Published: New Year; Memorial Day; Independence Day; Labor Day; Thanksgiving; Christmas.
Special Editions: Fall Sports (Aug); Christmas (Dec); Taxes (Feb); Progress (Jan); Graduation (Jun); Vacation Guide (May); Christmas (Nov).
Magazines: TV (Fri); American Profile (Weekly).
Pub....................Howard A. Kaiser
Circ. Mgr.....................Kate Hoornstra
Ed. in Chief....................Kenn Filkins
Prodn. Mgr.....................Wayne McCuaig
Market Information: TMC.
Mechanical available: Offset; Black and 3 ROP colors; insert accepted; page cutoffs - 22 3/4.
Mechanical Specifications: Type page 13 x 21; E - 6 cols, 2 1/16, 1/8 between; A - 6 cols, 2 1/16, 1/8 between; C - 9 cols, 1 3/8, 1/16 between.
Commodity Consumption: Avg. Page Number Per Issue - Daily 14; Avg. Page Number Per Issue - Plates Used 5116; Avg. Page Number Per Issue - Sunday 32; widths 13 3/4; Newsprint Used - Short Tons 600; Printing Ink Used - Black 24000; Printing Ink Used - Color 500; Printing Ink Use
Equipment; Editorial Hardware – APP/Mac.; Classified Hardware – PC Designs. DISPLAY: Ad make-up applications – APP/Mac IIsi; Layout Software – PC Designs.; Production Equipment – 5-COM; Scanners – 2-COM. PRESSROOM: Line 1 – 7-HI/V-15A; Folders – HI/JF-7.; Bundle tying machines – 2/MLN; Addressing machine – 1-/Am.; Business Hardware – PC Designs

STURGIS

STURGIS JOURNAL

209 John St., Sturgis, Mich., 49091; gen tel (269) 651-5407; gen fax (269) 651-2296; gen e-mail newsroom@sturgisjournal.com; web site www.sturgisjournal.com

Published: Mon, Tues, Wed, Thur, Fri, Sat
Weekday Frequency: m
Saturday Frequency: m
Circulation: 6,320; 6,850(sat)
Last Audit: September 30, 2004
Price: 7.90/mo; 94.80/yr.
Advertising: Open inch rate $12.50
News services: AP.
Politics: Independent.
Not Published: New Year; Memorial Day; Independence Day; Labor Day; Thanksgiving; Christmas; President's day; Columbus day; Veterans day.
Special Weekly Sections: Best Food Day (Mon); Church Page (Sat); Dining & Entertainment (Thur).
Magazines: TV Section (Mon-fri); American Profile (Weekly).
Pub.....................Daniel J. Tollefson
Bus. Mgr.....................Gwen Donmyer
Display Adv. Mgr.....................Brenda Kane
Classified Adv. Mgr....................Laurie Blosser
Circ. Mgr.....................Jaymes MacDonald
Ed.....................Candice Phelps
Features Ed.....................Dennis Volkert
Sports Ed.....................Corky Emrick
Prodn. Mgr.....................Mark Sears
Prodn. Mgr., Distr.....................Sheila Larsen
Market Information: TMC.
Mechanical available: Offset; Black and 3 ROP colors; insert accepted; page cutoffs - 22 7/10.
Mechanical Specifications: Type page 13 x 21 1/2; E - 6 cols, 2 1/16, 1/8 between; A - 6 cols, 2 1/16, 1/8 between; C - 9 cols, 1 3/8, 1/16 between.
Commodity Consumption: Avg. Page Number Per Issue - Daily 16; Avg. Page Number Per Issue - Plates Used 5200; widths 27; Newsprint Used - Short Tons 310; Printing Ink Used - Black 8710; Printing Ink Used - Color 580; Printing Ink Used - Pages Printed 5410.
Equipment; Editorial Hardware – APP/Mac.; Classified Hardware – 3-Big Screen/S, 3-APP/Mac one double.; Layout Software – APP/Mac.; Production Equipment – Pre Press/Panther Pro, 1-LE; Cameras – 1-R/Horizontal. PRESSROOM: Line 1 – 7-G/Community; Line 2 – 7-G/SC665; Folders – 1; Bundle tying machines – 1/Bu, 1-/Sa, 1-/MLN; Addressing machine – 1-/Am, KR.; Business Hardware – 4-NCR

THREE RIVERS

THREE RIVERS COMMERCIAL-NEWS

124 N. Main St., Three Rivers, Mich., 49093; gen tel (269) 279-7488; adv tel (269) 273-9158; ed tel (269) 279-7488; gen fax (269) 279-6007; adv fax (269) 279-6007; ed fax (269) 279-6007; ed e-mail newsroom@threeriversnews.com; web site www.threeriversnews.com

Published: Mon, Tues, Wed, Thur, Fri, Sat, Sun
Weekday Frequency: e
Saturday Frequency: m
Circulation: 3,043; 3,043(sat)
Last Audit: September 30, 2001
Price: 6.00/mo; 72.00/yr, $86.00/yr (in county).
Advertising: Open inch rate $10.75
News services: AP.
Politics: Independent.
Not Published: New Year; Memorial Day; Independence Day; Labor Day; Thanksgiving; Christmas.
Special Editions: Spring Car Care (Apr); Football Preview (Aug); Gift Certificate Page (Dec); White Sale (broadsheet) (Feb); The Way We Were (Jan); Michigan Medical Society (Jul); The Way We Were (Jun); NCAA Basketball (grid) (Mar); Graduation (May); Gift Guide (Nov); Fair
Magazines: American Profile (Weekly).
Pub....................Dirk Milliman
Pub....................Penelope Faber Milliman
Circ. Mgr.....................Deb Smith
Mng. Ed.....................Elena Hines
Market Information: TMC.
Mechanical available: Offset; Black and 3 ROP colors; insert accepted - any; page cutoffs - 22 3/4.
Mechanical Specifications: Type page 12 3/4 x 21 1/2; E - 6 cols, 2, 1/6 between; A - 8 cols, 1 1/2, 1/9 between; C - 8 cols, 1 1/2, 1/9 between.
Commodity Consumption: Avg. Page Number Per Issue - Daily 12; Avg. Page Number Per Issue - Plates Used 1872; widths 27 1/2; Newsprint Used - Short Tons 225; Printing Ink Used - Black 1600; Printing Ink Used - Color 500; Printing Ink Used - Pages Printed 3744.
Equipment EDITORIAL: Front-end Software – Mk/1100.; Editorial Hardware – 3-Mk/1100 Plus, 2-COM; Classified Hardware – 1-Mk/1100 Plus.; Production Equipment – 1-COM/8400, 1-COM/Trendsetter; Cameras – 1-B/Caravelle, 1-Cl. PRESSROOM: Line 1 – 5-HI/Cotrell V-15A; Folders – 1; Bundle tying machines – 2/Bu; Addressing machine – 1-/Am.; Business Hardware – Compaq/Deskpro

TRAVERSE CITY

RECORD-EAGLE

120 W. Front St., Traverse City, Mich., 49684-2202; gen tel (231) 946-2000; adv tel (231) 946-2000; ed tel (231) 946-2000; gen fax (231) 946-8273; adv fax (231) 946-8273; ed fax (231) 946-8632; gen e-mail editor@record-eagle.com; ed e-mail bthomas@record-eagle.com; web site www.record-eagle.com

Published: Mon, Tues, Wed, Thur, Fri, Sat, Sun
Weekday Frequency: m
Saturday Frequency: m
Circulation: 22,029; 22,855(sat); 29,722(sun)
Last Audit: ABC September 30, 2011
Price: 3.40/wk; 13.60/mo; 162.75/yr.
Advertising: Open inch rate $30.00
News services: AP, DJ, ONS, MCT, LAT-WP.
Politics: Independent. **Established:** 1858
Special Editions: Spring Guide (Apr); Autumn Guide (Aug); Holiday Gift Guide (Dec); Winter Home (Jan); Mid Summer Home (Jul); Summer Guide (Jun); Bridal (Mar); Lawn & Garden (May); Coupon Savings (Monthly); Ski Directory (Nov); Autumn Guide (Oct); Wine (Other); Summer Guid
Special Weekly Sections: Arts & Entertainment (Fri); Food (Mon); Business (S); Faith (Sat); Our Town (Thur); Education (Tues); Business (Wed).
Magazines: Parade (S).
Profile: Daily and Sunday newspaper with online service and commercial printing operation, serving 13 counties of northwest lower Michigan.
Adv. Mgr.....................Tom Wyatt
Adv. Mgr., Classified....................Jeana Daenzer
Adv. Mgr., Special Projects....................Dan Roach
Mktg. Dir.....................Maia Conway
Circ. Mgr.....................Steve Knape
Exec. Ed.....................Bill Thomas
Assoc. Ed.....................Marta Hepler Drahos
Bus. Ed.....................Bill O'Brien
Editorial Page Ed....................Dave Miller
Features Ed....................Kathy Gibbons
News Ed.....................Mike Tyree
Regl. Ed....................Loraine Anderson
Sports Ed....................Denny Chase
Prodn. Dir.....................Michelle Mulliner
Prodn. Mgr., Mailroom....................Monica Stanley
Market Information: ADS; TMC.
Mechanical available: Offset; Black and 3 ROP colors; insert accepted - sample bags, envelopes; page cutoffs - 21.
Mechanical Specifications: Type page 11 3/4 x 21 1/2; E - 6 cols, 1 7/8, 1/8 between; A - 6 cols, 1 7/8, 1/8 between; C - 9 cols, 1 1/5, 1/5 between.
Commodity Consumption: Avg. Page Number Per Issue - Daily 32; Avg. Page Number Per Issue - Plates Used 14000; Avg. Page Number Per Issue - Saturday 36; Avg. Page Number Per Issue - Sunday 66; widths 25; Newsprint Used - Metric Tons 2600; Printing Ink Used - Black 62000; Printi
Equipment EDITORIAL: Front-end Software – Microsoft/Windows 95, Microsoft/Word 7.0, Dewar/View, Adobe/Photoshop, QPS/QuarkXPress.; Editorial Hardware – 41-PC P133, 2-IBM/RS 6000 Server; Editorial Printers – 2-Okidata/320, 3-HP/4MV, 1-HP/5SI MX CLASSIFIED: Front-end Software – Dewar/Sys II.; Classified Hardware – Dewar/Sys II; Classified Printers – Okidata/320 DISPLAY: Ad make-up applications – QPS/QuarkXPress; Layout Software – PCs, QPS/QuarkXPress.; Display Hardware – 7-PC P166; Display Printers – 2-Okidata/320, 3-HP/4MV, 1-HP/5SI MX PRODUCTION: Pagination Software – Dewar/View.; Production Equipment – Caere/OmniPage Pro, 1-Tegra/Varityper 5510, 2-MON/Imagesetter; Scanners – HP/ScanJet PRESSROOM: Line 1 – 5-1992. MAILROOM: Counter stackers – 3/QWI; Inserters and stuffers – 14-GMA/SLS 1000; Bundle tying machines – 3-/Power Strap; Other equipment –MM.; Audio Hardware – ITN; Business Hardware – IBM/AS-400, APP/Mac

MINNESOTA

ALBERT LEA

ALBERT LEA TRIBUNE

808 W. Front St., Albert Lea, Minn., 56007; gen tel (507) 373-1411; adv tel (507) 379-3427; ed tel (507) 379-3433; gen fax (507) 373-0333; ed e-mail news@albertleatribune.com; web site www.albertleatribune.com

Published: Mon, Tues, Wed, Thur, Fri, Sat, Sun
Weekday Frequency: e
Circulation: 6,315; 6,315(sun)
Last Audit: October 1, 2003
Price: 10.50/mo; 129.00/yr.
Advertising: Open inch rate $17.85
News services: AP.
Politics: Independent. **Established:** 1897
Not Published: New Year; Memorial Day; Independence Day; Labor Day; Christmas.
Special Editions: Sports (Apr); Fair (Aug); Progress (Feb); Pork (Jan); Albert Lea Guide (Jun); Health/Wellness (Mar); Wedding (May); Sports (Nov); Car Care (Oct); Seniors (Quarterly).
Special Weekly Sections: Religion (Fri); Lifestyles (S); Entertainment (Wed).
Magazines: Relish (Monthly); Parade (S).
Pub.....................Scott Schmeltzer
Acct. Mgr.....................Lisa Foley
Adv. Dir.....................Crystal Miller
Circ. Mgr.....................Jim Gold
Mng. Ed.....................Tim Engstrom
Lifestyles Reporter....................Geri McShane
Sports Ed.....................Nick Gerhardt
Market Information: ADS; TMC.
Mechanical available: Offset; Black and 3 ROP colors; insert accepted; page cutoffs - 22 3/4.
Mechanical Specifications: Type page 13 x 21 1/2; E - 6 cols, 2 1/16, 1/8 between; A - 6 cols, 2 1/16, 1/8 between; C - 10 cols, 1 3/8, 1/8 between.
Commodity Consumption: Avg. Page Number Per Issue - Daily 14; Avg. Page Number Per Issue - Plates Used 3900; Avg. Page Number Per Issue - Sunday 26; widths 27 1/2; Newsprint Used - Short Tons 274; Printing Ink Used - Black 4500; Printing Ink Used - Color 300; Printing Ink Used
Equipment EDITORIAL: Front-end Software – CD, Baseview, QPS/QuarkXPress.; Editorial Hardware – CD, APP/Mac G4; Editorial Printers – NEC/SilentWriter, LaserMaster/ CLASSIFIED: Front-end Software – CD, Baseview.; Classified Hardware – APP/Mac G4; Classified Printers – NEC/SilentWriter, LaserMaster DISPLAY: Ad make-up applications – QPS/QuarkXPress; Layout Software – QPS/QuarkXPress.; Display Hardware – 2-APP/Mac Centris; Production Equipment – APP/Mac, Nat; Scanners – 2-COM/Unisetter 070, DTI/1200, APP/Mac, LaCie, Microtek. BUSINESS COMPUTERS: Business Software – Quicken, PBS; Business Hardware – IBM, TI/LaserWriters

AUSTIN

AUSTIN DAILY HERALD

310 NE Second St., Austin, Minn., 55912; gen tel (507) 433-8851; gen fax (507) 437-8644; ed e-mail newsroom@austindailyher-

ald.com; web site www.austindailyherald.com
Published: Mon, Tues, Wed, Thur, Fri, Sun
Weekday Frequency: e
Circulation: 6,536; 6,536(sun)
Last Audit: September 26, 2002
Price: 2.05/wk; 101.60/yr.
Advertising: Open inch rate $18.50
News services: AP.
Politics: Independent. **Established:** 1891
Advertising not accepted: Mail order; Vending machine.
Not Published: New Year; Memorial Day; Independence Day; Labor Day.
Special Editions: Barrow Show (Other).
Special Weekly Sections: Lifestyles (S).
Magazines: Relish (Monthly); Parade (S).
Adv. Dir. ....Jana Gray
News Ed. ....David Richards
Sports Ed. ....Rocky Hulne
Market Information: Split run; TMC.
Mechanical available: Offset; Black and 3 ROP colors; insert accepted; page cutoffs - 22 3/4.
Mechanical Specifications: Type page 13 x 21 1/2; E - 6 cols, 2, 1/8 between; A - 6 cols, 2, 1/8 between; C - 9 cols, 2, 1/8 between.
Equipment EDITORIAL: Front-end Software – QPS/QuarkXPress, Adobe/Photshop, Baseview/News Edit Pro.; Editorial Hardware – APP/Power Mac; Editorial Printers – PrePress/Panther Pro Imagesetter CLASSIFIED: Front-end Software – Baseview/News Edit Pro.; Classified Hardware – 1-APP/Mac; Classified Printers – HP DISPLAY: Ad make-up applications – QPS/QuarkXPress, Adobe/Illustrator, Adobe/PhotoShop.; Display Hardware – APP/Mac; Display Printers – HP/Imagesetter PRODUCTION: Pagination Software – QPS/QuarkXPress 4.0.; Production Equipment – Digi-Colour; Cameras – R, LE PRESSROOM: Line 1 – 8-G/Community 1976.; Bundle tying machines – 2-Bu/Tyer.

BEMIDJI

DAILY PIONEER

1320 Neilson Ave. S.E., Bemidji, Minn., 56619; web site bemidjipioneer.com
Published: Sun
Circulation: ; 9,401(sun)
Last Audit: September 30, 2010Steve Wagner

THE PIONEER

1320 Neilson Ave. SE, Bemidji, Minn., 56601; gen tel (218) 333-9200; adv tel (218) 333-9200; ed tel (218) 333-9200; adv fax (218) 333-9819; ed fax (218) 333-9820; gen e-mail jmail@bemidjipioneer.com; adv e-mail jmail@bemidjipioneer.com; ed e-mail news@bemidjipioneer.com; web site www.bemidjipioneer.com
Published: Tues, Wed, Thur, Fri, Sat, Sun
Weekday Frequency: m
Circulation: 8,674; 8,674(sat); 10,036(sun)
Last Audit: March 31, 2008
Price: 8.00/wk; 11.00/mo; 132.00/yr.
Advertising: Open inch rate $18.80
News services: AP, NEA.
Politics: Independent. **Established:** 1896
Not Published: Christmas (unless falls on Wed or Sun).
Special Editions: Last Minute Gift Guide (Other).
Special Weekly Sections: Outdoors (Fri); Best Food Day (S); Community (Wed).
Magazines: Relish (Monthly); Parade (S).
Pub ....Dennis Doeden
Bus. Mgr. ....Tammie Richter
Adv. Dir., Display/Classified ....Jeff Halverson
Circ. Dir. ....Tedd Wisner
Ed. ....Molly Miron
Photo Ed. ....Monte Draper
Political Ed. ....Brad Swenson
Sports Ed. ....Jim Carrington
Composing Mgr./System Admin. ....Bonnie Cook
Prodn. Mgr. ....Tim Roline
Market Information: TMC.
Mechanical available: Offset; Black and 3 ROP colors; insert accepted - free-standing cards & envelopes; page cutoffs - 22 3/4.
Mechanical Specifications: Type page 11 5/8 x 21 1/2; E - 6 cols, 1 5/6, 1/8 between; A - 6 cols,

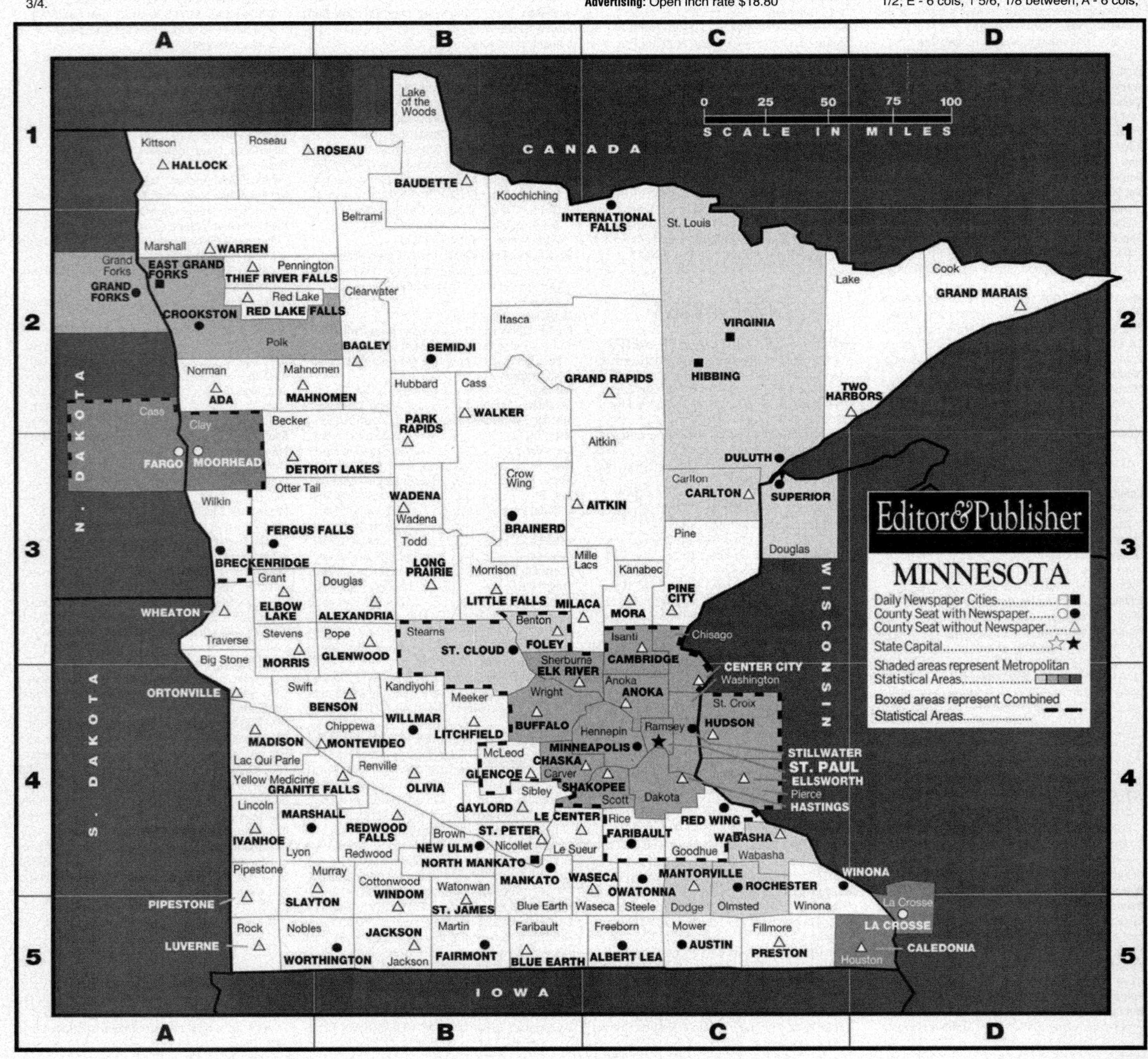

1 5/6, 1/8 between; C - 10 cols, 1 1/4, 1/16 between.
Commodity Consumption: Avg. Page Number Per Issue - Daily 14; Avg. Page Number Per Issue - Plates Used 15600; Avg. Page Number Per Issue - Sunday 26; widths 30; Newsprint Used - Short Tons 455; Printing Ink Used - Black 17000; Printing Ink Used - Color 1430; Printing Ink Used
Equipment EDITORIAL: Front-end Software – APT/ACT.; Editorial Hardware – Microsoft/Windows XP, Dell; Editorial Equipment – Polaroid/Slide Scanner; Editorial Printers – Dataproducts/Typhoon 16 CLASSIFIED: Front-end Software – APT/ACT.; Classified Hardware – Microsoft/Windows XP, Dell; Classified Printers – HP/LaserJet 4000 DISPLAY: Ad make-up applications – QPS/QuarkXPress 4.1; Display Hardware – Microsoft/Windows XP, Dell, APP/Mac; Display Printers – Dataproducts/Typhoon 16 PRODUCTION: Pagination Software – Adobe/Photoshop 5.5, QPS/QuarkXPress 4.1.; Production Equipment – 1-Nat/340; Cameras – 1-B/1822, Epson; Scanners – 2-Umax/Powerlook II, Microtek/Scanners, Polaroid/Slide Scanner PRESSROOM: Line 1 – 9-G/Community C-1378; Folders – G/Community.; Bundle tying machines – 1-Bu/20000, 1-MLN/ML2EE. BUSINESS COMPUTERS: Business Software – Microsoft/Windows XP, Citrix, Microsoft/Excel; Business Hardware – Dell, Microsoft/Windows XP

BRAINERD

BRAINERD DISPATCH

506 James St., Brainerd, Minn., 56401-0974; gen tel (218) 829-4705; gen fax (218) 825-8170; adv fax (218) 829-7735; ed fax (218) 829-0211; web site www.brainerddispatch.com
Group: Metro Newspaper Advertising Services, Inc.
Published: Mon, Tues, Wed, Thur, Fri, Sun
Weekday Frequency: m
Circulation: 11,088; 15,969(sun)
Last Audit: ABC September 30, 2011
Price: 125.00/yr.
Advertising: Open inch rate $16.50
News services: AP, LAT-WP.
Not Published: Saturday
Own facility?: Y
Special Editions: Golf Guide (Apr); Senior Class (monthly); Weddings North (Feb); Up North Autos; Christmas Catalog (Nov); Her Voice (Qtr): Health Watch (Qtr); Outdoors Traditions (Qtr); We are 181 (Spr & Fall)
Special Weekly Sections: Housing Page (Fri); TV Week (S); Entertainment (Thur); Neighbors (Wed).
Magazines: Relish (Monthly); USA WEEKEND; Parade Magazine (S); American Profile (Weekly).
Controller/HR Dir.............................Kari Lake
Adv. Dir.............................Tim Bogenschutz
Adv. Mgr., Classified............................Susie Alters
Circ. Dir.............................John Gagliano
Ed.............................Roy Miller
Assoc. Ed.............................Mike O'Rourke
Photographer............................Steve Kohls
Sports Ed.............................Mike Bialka
Online Mgr.............................Denton Newman
IT Mgr.............................Jason Walkowiak
Prodn. Coord.............................Dianna Kiehlbauch
VP of Revenue Development........Sam Swanson
Distribution Manager............................Jamie Olson
Marketing Coordinator............................Nikki Lyter
Market Information: TMC.
Mechanical available: Offset; Black and 3 ROP colors; insert accepted; page cutoffs - 22 3/4.
Mechanical Specifications: Type page 11 5/8 x 21 1/2; E - 6 cols, 1 3/4, 1/4 between; A - 6 cols, 1 3/4, 1/4 between; C - 6 cols, 1 3/4, 1/4 between.
Commodity Consumption: Avg. Page Number Per Issue - Daily 22; Avg. Page Number Per Issue - Plates Used 9000; Avg. Page Number Per Issue - Sunday 56; widths 12 7/16; Newsprint Used - Metric Tons 1400; Printing Ink Used - Black 22000; Printing Ink Used - Color 6000; Printing Ink
Equipment; Cameras – D PRESSROOM: Line 1 – 8-G/Community (balloon) 1978; Folders – 1-G/SSC; Press registration system – Duarte. MAILROOM: Counter stackers – BG; Inserters and stuffers – MM/4; Bundle tying machines – 2/MLN; Addressing machine – Ch/525E.
Delivery method: Mail, Newsstand, Private Carrier, Racks

CROOKSTON

CROOKSTON DAILY TIMES

124 S. Broadway St., Crookston, Minn., 56716; gen tel (218) 281-2730; adv tel (218) 281-2730; ed tel (218) 281-2730; gen fax (218) 281-7234; adv fax (218) 281-7234; ed fax (218) 281-7234; ed e-mail editor@crookstontimes.com; web site www.crookstontimes.com
Published: Mon, Tues, Wed, Thur, Fri
Weekday Frequency: e
Circulation: 1,769
Last Audit: September 25, 2002
Price: 1.90/wk (in state); 24.70/mo (in state); 94.00/yr (in state).
Advertising: Open inch rate $13.05
News services: AP.
Politics: Independent. **Established:** 1885
Magazines: American Profile (Weekly).
Pub.............................Randal Hultgren
Adv. Mgr.............................Calvin Anderson
Circ. Mgr............................Carl Melbye
News Ed.............................Mike Christopherson
Sports Ed.............................Derek Martin
Women's Ed.............................Jannelle Brekken
Prodn. Mgr.............................Lynn Oaks
Market Information: TMC; Zoned editions.
Mechanical available: Offset; Black and 4 ROP colors; insert accepted; page cutoffs - 21 1/2.
Mechanical Specifications: Type page 13 x 21 1/2; E - 6 cols, 2 1/16, 1/8 between; A - 6 cols, 2 1/16, 1/8 between; C - 6 cols, 2 1/16, 1/8 between.
Commodity Consumption: Avg. Page Number Per Issue - Daily 10; Avg. Page Number Per Issue - Plates Used 1650; widths 28; Newsprint Used - Short Tons 300; Printing Ink Used - Black 600; Printing Ink Used - Color 100; Printing Ink Used - Pages Printed 3300.
Equipment; Editorial Hardware – Mk; Editorial Printers – APP/Mac LaserWriter Plus. DISPLAY: Ad make-up applications – Aldus/PageMaker.; Display Hardware – APP/Mac; Display Printers – APP/Mac Laser; Production Equipment – LE; Cameras – B. PRESSROOM: Line 1 – 5-G/Community 1980; Folders – 1-G/2:1.; Bundle tying machines – 1/Marlow; Addressing machine – DEC/Line Printer. BUSINESS COMPUTERS: Business Software – Nomads/Listmaster; Business Hardware – 1-Corsair/120 mp

DULUTH

DULUTH NEWS TRIBUNE

424 W. First St., Duluth, Minn., 55802; gen tel (218) 723-5281; adv tel (218) 723-5225; ed tel (218) 723-5300; gen fax (218) 723-5339; adv fax (218) 723-5295; ed fax (218) 720-4120; adv e-mail advert@duluthnews.com; ed e-mail letters@duluthnews.com; web site www.duluthsuperior.com; www.duluthnewstribune.com
Group: Metro Newspaper Advertising Services, Inc.
Published: Mon, Tues, Wed, Thur, Fri, Sat, Sun
Weekday Frequency: m
Saturday Frequency: m
Circulation: 32,631; 32,631(sat); 49,257(sun)
Last Audit: Sworn September 30, 2010
Price: 3.48/wk (carrier); 13.92/mo (carrier); 180.96/yr (carrier).
Advertising: Open inch rate $95.00
News services: AP, MCT, NYT, LAT-WP.
Politics: Independent. **Established:** 1869
Special Editions: Builders & Remodelers (Apr); Back to School (Aug); Gift Guide (Dec); Boat, Sports and Travel (Feb); Wedding Planner (Jan); Outlook Progress (Mar); Spring Living (May); Healthy Living (Nov); Northland Winter Visitor (Oct); Northern Hunter (Sept).
Special Weekly Sections: WAVE (Fri); Travel (S); Home & Garden (Sat); Taste (Thur).
Magazines: Relish (Monthly); Parade (S).
Pub.............................Ken Browall
Adv. Dir.............................Roz Randorf
Adv. Mgr., Market Devel.....Erin Pollard Makela
Adv. Mgr., Sales Devel...............Gene Pelletier
Circ. Mgr.............................Tim McLoughin
Exec. Ed.............................Rob Karwath
Editorial Page Ed.............................Chuck Frederick
Multimedia Ed.............................Jimmy Bellamy
News Ed.............................Craig Gustafson
Sports Ed.............................Rick Lubbers
Prodn. Mgr.............................Mike Farmer
Prodn. Mgr., Post Press..........Frank Grandson
Prodn. Foreman, Pressroom..................Jim Hill
Market Information: Split run; TMC; Zoned editions.
Mechanical available: Flexographic; Black and 3 ROP colors; insert accepted; page cutoffs - 22 3/4.
Mechanical Specifications: Type page 11 5/8 x 21; E - 6 cols, 1 13/16, 1/8 between; A - 6 cols, 1 13/16, 1/16 between; C - 10 cols, 1 13/16, 1/8 between.
Commodity Consumption: Avg. Page Number Per Issue - Daily 40; Avg. Page Number Per Issue - Plates Used 72000; Avg. Page Number Per Issue - Saturday 56; Avg. Page Number Per Issue - Sunday 108; widths 37 1/2; Newsprint Used - Metric Tons 6804; Printing Ink Used - Black 234239;
Equipment EDITORIAL: Front-end Software – HI/Newsmaker Editorial 2.6.; Editorial Hardware – Sun/Sparc 51, PCs; Editorial Printers – 1-HP/LaserJet IV, 2-Epson/LQ 550, 1-HP/LaserJet 5si/MX, 1-HP/DesignJet 755CM CLASSIFIED: Front-end Software – HI/CASH.; Classified Hardware – 2-Pentium/Servers, 20-Pentium/PC; Classified Printers – 1-HP/LaserJet 5si/MX, 1-HP/LaserJet 5si/MX, 1-Epson/Dot Matrix DISPLAY: Ad make-up applications – HI/Dash, QPS/QuarkXPress; Layout Software – GEAC/Layout 5.0.1 E.; Display Hardware – 2-Sun/Sparc 51; Display Printers – 1-HP/LaserJet 5si/MX, 1-HP/DesignJet 755 CM PRODUCTION: Pagination Software – HI/PLS 2.0.; Production Equipment – 3-AII/APS6-108c, AG/Avontra 30, Na/FP II; Scanners – Lf, X/7650, 1-Howtek/D4000, AG PRESSROOM: Line 1 – 1-MOT/Color Max (Flexo); Line 2 – 1-MOT/FX4 Flexo; Line 3 – 1-MOT/FX4 Flexo (w/half deck & 2 color tower) 1990; Line 4 – 2-MOT/FX4 Flexo (with half deck); Press Drives – PEC/Bond; Folders – G/2:1; Press control system – PEC/James Bond, PEC/Bond. MAILROOM: Counter stackers – 1-Id/660, 5-QWI/200; Inserters and stuffers – 1-MM/308-208 Biliner, 1-HI/Stuffing Machine 1372; Bundle tying machines – 2/Power Strap, 1-/Dynaric; Wrapping singles – 1-/Ca, 1-/Maylo; Mailroom control system – 1-Prism/Insert Management BUSINESS COMPUTERS: Business Software – GEAC, CIS, AIM, Microsoft/Office Pro; Business Hardware – 1-HP/3000-947

FAIRMONT

SENTINEL

64 Downtown Plz., Fairmont, Minn., 56031; gen tel (507) 235-3303; gen fax (507) 235-3718; gen e-mail news@fairmontsentinel.com; adv e-mail ads@fairmontsentinel.com; web site www.fairmontsentinel.com
Published: Mon, Tues, Wed, Thur, Fri, Sat
Weekday Frequency: m
Saturday Frequency: m
Circulation: 5,423; 5,682(sat)
Last Audit: ABC September 30, 2011
Price: 3.20/wk; 12.80/mo (carrier); 124.00/yr (carrier).
Advertising: Open inch rate $24.30
News services: AP.
Politics: 1874
Not Published: New Year; Independence Day; Thanksgiving; Christmas.
Own facility?: Y
Special Weekly Sections: TV Book (Fri).
Magazines: USA WEEKEND Magazine (Sat).
Pub.............................Gary Andersen
Adv. Dir.............................Kathy Ratcliff
Circ. Dir.............................Kyle Tromanhauser
Court Reporter............................Jennifer Brookens
Sports Ed.............................Charlie Sorrells
Data Processing Mgr.............................Lee Smith
Composition Supvr.............................Lisa Thate
Market Information: ADS; TMC.
Mechanical available: Offset; Black and 3 ROP colors; insert accepted; page cutoffs - 18 1/2.
Mechanical Specifications: Type page 13 x 21 1/2; E - 6 cols, 1 43/50, 1/8 between; A - 6 cols, 1 43/50, 1/8 between; C - 9 cols, 1 19/100, 1/16 between.
Commodity Consumption: Avg. Page Number Per Issue - Daily 20; Printing Ink Used - Pages Printed 5800.
Equipment; Editorial Hardware – APP/Mac Pagination Network, 10-APP/Mac PPC 7100-80.; Classified Hardware – 2-APP/PPC 7100/80. DISPLAY: Ad make-up applications – QPS; Layout Software – APP/Mac, Multi-Ad/Creator.; Display Hardware – APP/Mac LC, APP/Mac Quadra, APP/Mac Centris, APP/Power Mac 6100, APP/Mac Server; Display Printers – QMS/860 PRODUCTION: Pagination Software – QPS/QuarkXPress 3.31.; Production Equipment – APP/Mac Laser, OCU; Cameras – 1-B; Scanners – Nikon/Coolscan 35mm; Business Hardware – NCR

FARIBAULT

FARIBAULT DAILY NEWS

514 Central Ave., Faribault, Minn., 55021; gen tel (507) 333-3100; adv tel (507) 333-3120; ed tel (507) 333-3131; gen fax (507) 333-3102; ed fax (507) 333-3103; ed e-mail jagliatta@faribault.com; web site www.faribault.com
Group: Huckle Media
Published: Tues, Wed, Thur, Fri, Sat, Sun
Weekday Frequency: m
Circulation: 6,235; 6,235(sat); 6,235(sun)
Price: 138.00/yr; 37.50/3mo.
Advertising: Open inch rate $16.25
News services: AP.
Politics: Independent. **Established:** 1914
Advertising not accepted: N
Not Published: New Year; Memorial Day; Independence Day; Labor Day; Christmas.
Special Editions: Spring Sports (Apr); Christmas Song Book (Dec); Brides (Jan); Rice County Fair (Jul); Heritage Festival (Jun); Community Profile (Mar); Senior Lifestyles (May); Winter Sports Preview (Nov); How to Guide (Oct); Home & Garden (Sept).
Magazines: Relish (Monthly); Parade (S); American Profile (Weekly).
Controller............................Kevin Haekenkamp
Circ. Mgr............................Daniel Walock
Mng. Ed.............................William Dillon
Prodn. Mgr.............................Roger Stolley
Publisher............................Steven Pope
Ed.............................Paula Patton
Market Information: ADS; TMC.
Mechanical available: Offset; Black and 4 ROP colors; insert accepted - free standing; page cutoffs - 22 3/4.
Mechanical Specifications: Type page 11 5/8 x 21 1/2; E - 6 cols, 1 5/6, 1/8 between; A - 6 cols, 1 5/6, 1/8 between; C - 6 cols, 1 5/6, 1/8 between.
Commodity Consumption: Avg. Page Number Per Issue - Daily 18; Avg. Page Number Per Issue - Plates Used 15000; Avg. Page Number Per Issue - Sunday 22; widths 25; Newsprint Used - Metric Tons 900; Newsprint Used - Short Tons 1500; Printing Ink Used - Black 15000; Printing Ink Us
Equipment EDITORIAL: Front-end Software –

Baseview/NewsEdit Pro IQUE 4.0.4b5, Adobe/InDesign CS 2.0. CLASSIFIED: Front-end Software – Baseview/Ad Manager Pro 1.9.1.77.; Display Hardware – Software □ Adobe/InDesign CS 2.0.; Production Equipment – 1-Kk/Trendsetter 50, 1-Kk/Trendsetter 100. PRESSROOM: Line 1 – 16-G/Community Single Width; Folders – DGM/1030; Press control system – Fin. MAILROOM: Counter stackers – 1-KAN/Newstac; Inserters and stuffers – 1-KAN/480 Station Inserter 12:1; Bundle tying machines – 3-Si/LB2000, 1-Si/LB2330 Auto Strapper; Addressing machine – 1-Domino/Jet-A-Ray; Other equipment –MM/Trimmer Stitcher-4 pocket.

Delivery method: Mail, Newsstand, Private Carrier, Racks

FERGUS FALLS

FERGUS FALLS DAILY JOURNAL

914 E. Channing Ave., Fergus Falls, Minn., 56537; gen tel (218) 736-7511; adv tel (218) 736-7511; ed tel (218) 736-7511; gen fax (218) 736-5919; adv fax (218) 736-5919; ed fax (218) 736-5919; adv e-mail display.advertising@fergusfallsjournal.com; ed e-mail newsroom@fergusfallsjournal.com; web site www.fergusfallsjournal.com

Published: Mon, Tues, Wed, Thur, Fri, Sat, Sun
Weekday Frequency: e
Saturday Frequency: m
Circulation: 8,414; 8,414(sat)
Last Audit: September 30, 2002
Price: 10.95/mo; 131.40/yr.
Advertising: Open inch rate $17.29
News services: AP.
Politics: 1873
Not Published: New Year; Memorial Day; Independence Day; Labor Day; Thanksgiving; Christmas.
Special Editions: Resorter (Aug); Christmas Gift Guide 3 (Dec); Profile (Feb); Chamber Tab (Jan); Crazy Days (Jul); Summer Fun Guide (Jun); Home & Health (Mar); Resorter (May); Christmas Gift Guide 1 (Nov); BPW (Oct); F.Y.I. (Sept).
Special Weekly Sections: Business (Mon); Lifestyle (Sat); Education (Tues); Food (Wed).
Magazines: USA WEEKEND Magazine (Sat); TV Journal (Thur).
Pub ....David D. Churchill
Adv. Mgr., Classified ....Joel Myhre
News Ed. ....Debbie Irmen
Prodn. Foreman, Pressroom ....Jeff Schreiber
Prodn. Mgr., Distr./Mailroom ....Connie Knapp
Prodn. Mgr., Pre Press ....Deb Erikson
Market Information: Split run; TMC; Zoned editions.
Mechanical available: Web-Offset; Black and 3 ROP colors; insert accepted; page cutoffs - 22 3/4.
Mechanical Specifications: Type page 13 x 21 1/2; E - 6 cols, 2 1/16, 1/8 between; A - 6 cols, 2 1/16, 1/8 between; C - 9 cols, 1 1/3, 1/8 between.
Commodity Consumption: Avg. Page Number Per Issue - Daily 14; Avg. Page Number Per Issue - Saturday 18; widths 27 1/2; Newsprint Used - Short Tons 350; Printing Ink Used - Pages Printed 3890.
Equipment EDITORIAL: Front-end Software – QPS/QuarkXPress 4.1.; Editorial Hardware – APP/Power Mac, APP/Mac G4, APP/iMac; Editorial Printers – HP/4MV CLASSIFIED: Front-end Software – Baseview.; Classified Hardware – 3-APP/Mac, APP/Power Mac; Classified Printers – APP/LaserWriter 630 DISPLAY: Ad make-up applications – PBS 3.0.; Display Hardware – 1-PC, 1-APP/Mac PRODUCTION: Pagination Software – QPS/QuarkXPress.; Production Equipment – Nat/A-250; Cameras – SCREEN/Vertical, SCREEN/Horizontal PRESSROOM: Line 1 – 7-G/Community, 1-G/Colorliner.; Bundle tying machines – 1/Bu, 1-/Gd; Addressing machine – 1-/Ch. BUSINESS COMPUTERS: Business Software – RPG/II; Business Hardware – 3-IBM/VP 486-33 SX

HIBBING

THE DAILY TRIBUNE

2142 1st Ave., Hibbing, Minn., 55746-0038; gen tel (218) 262-1011; adv tel (218) 268-1011; ed tel (218) 262-1011; gen fax (218) 262-4318; adv fax (218) 262-4318; ed fax (218) 262-4318; gen e-mail tribune@hibbingmn.com; adv e-mail ads@hibbingmn.com; ed e-mail tribune@hibbingmn.com; web site www.hibbingmn.com

Published: Mon, Tues, Wed, Thur, Fri, Sat, Sun
Weekday Frequency: m
Saturday Frequency: m
Circulation: 4,519; 4,519(sat); 4,973(sun)
Last Audit: March 31, 2008
Price: 138.00/yr; 15.96/6wk, $34.50/13wk, $69.16/26wk.
Advertising: Open inch rate $18.64
News services: AP.
Politics: Independent. **Established:** 1897
Note: The Daily Tribune is printed by the Mesabi Publishing Co. at the Mesabi Daily News in Virginia, MN.
Not Published: New Year; Memorial Day; Independence Day; Labor Day; Thanksgiving; Christmas.
Special Editions: Home Improvement (Apr); Back-to-School (Aug); Progress (Feb); Bridal (Jan); Christmas (Nov); Car Fix-up (Sept).
Special Weekly Sections: TV Week (S); Churches (Sat).
Magazines: Relish (Monthly); American Profile (S).
Family Ed. ....Sue Hancock
Sports Ed. ....Gary Giombetti
Online. Ed. ....Wanda Moeller
Market Information: TMC.
Mechanical available: Offset; Black and 3 ROP colors; insert accepted; page cutoffs - 21 1/2.
Commodity Consumption: Avg. Page Number Per Issue - Daily 16; Avg. Page Number Per Issue - Plates Used 9788; Avg. Page Number Per Issue - Saturday 20; Avg. Page Number Per Issue - Sunday 32; Printing Ink Used - Pages Printed 8229.
Equipment EDITORIAL: Front-end Software – Baseview.; Editorial Hardware – APP/Power Mac G3; Editorial Equipment – Lf/AP Leaf Picture Desk, AP/Graphics; Editorial Printers – HP/Laserjet 5000N, HP/LaserJet 8100N CLASSIFIED: Front-end Software – Baseview.; Classified Hardware – APP/Mac G3; Classified Printers – HP/Laserjet 5000N, HP/LaserJet 8100N DISPLAY: Ad make-up applications – QPS/QuarkXPress; Layout Software – Multi-Ad/Creator, QPS/QuarkXPress.; Display Hardware – 3-APP/Mac G3; Display Printers – HP/Laserjet 5000N, HP/LaserJet 8100N PRODUCTION: Pagination Software – Baseview/NewsEdit Pro.; Production Equipment – HP/Laserjet 5000N; Cameras – B/30x 40; Scanners – Nikon/LS-2000; Inserters and stuffers – 1-KAN/320-402; Bundle tying machines – 2/Bu; Wrapping singles – 1-/Bu; Addressing machine – 1-/Am. BUSINESS COMPUTERS: Business Software – Vision Data; Business Hardware – Packard Bell

HTC, INC.

2142 1st Ave., Hibbing, Minn., 55746; gen tel (218) 262-1011; gen fax (218) 262-4318

Price: 160.00/yr.
Advertising: Open inch rate $9.50

INTERNATIONAL FALLS

THE DAILY JOURNAL

1602 Hwy. 71, International Falls, Minn., 56649; gen tel (218) 285-7411; adv tel (218) 285-7411; ed tel (218) 285-7411; gen fax (218) 285-7206; adv fax (218) 285-7206; ed fax (218) 285-7206; adv e-mail mickie@ifallsdailyjournal.com; ed e-mail laurel@ifallsdailyjournal.com; web site www.ifallsdailyjournal.com

Published: Mon, Tues, Wed, Thur, Fri
Weekday Frequency: e
Circulation: 3,703
Last Audit: September 8, 2003
Price: 7.20/mo; 85.00/yr.
Advertising: Open inch rate $10.65
News services: AP.
Not Published: New Year; Memorial Day; Independence Day; Labor Day; Thanksgiving; Christmas.
Special Editions: Body & Mind (Quarterly).
Special Weekly Sections: Business Page (Tues); TV Guide (Wed).
Magazines: Relish (Monthly).
Pub. ....Rob Davenport
Adv. Mgr. ....Mickie Olson
Circ. Mgr. ....Dana Hartje
Ed. ....Laurel Beager
Market Information: ADS; Split run; TMC.
Mechanical available: Offset; Black and 3 ROP colors; insert accepted; page cutoffs - 21 1/2.
Mechanical Specifications: Type page 13 x 21 1/2; E - 6 cols, 2 1/16, 1/8 between; A - 6 cols, 2 1/16, 1/8 between; C - 8 cols, 1 1/2, 1/8 between.
Commodity Consumption: Avg. Page Number Per Issue - Daily 14; widths 14; Newsprint Used - Short Tons 160; Printing Ink Used - Black 3450; Printing Ink Used - Color 230.
Equipment EDITORIAL: Front-end Software – NewsEdit/Pro.; Editorial Hardware – APP/Mac; Editorial Printers – APP/Mac CLASSIFIED: Front-end Software – Baseview.; Classified Hardware – APP/Mac DISPLAY: Ad make-up applications – QPS/QuarkXPress; Layout Software – APP/Mac.; Display Hardware – APP/Mac; Display Printers – APP/Mac LaserPrinter; Production Equipment – APP/Mac; Cameras – SCREEN/Companica 690E; Scanners – APP/Mac, HP. PRESSROOM: Line 1 – 6-G/Community.; Bundle tying machines – Bu; Addressing machine – KR. BUSINESS COMPUTERS: Business Software – MSSI, Quattro/Pro; Business Hardware – IBM/PS-2 Model 50

MANKATO

THE FREE PRESS

418 S. 2nd St., Mankato, Minn., 56001-3287; gen tel (507) 625-4451; adv tel (507) 344-6364; ed tel (507) 344-6397; gen fax (507) 625-1149; adv fax (507) 625-1149; ed fax (507) 388-4355; adv e-mail advertising@mankatofreepress.com; ed e-mail editor@mankatofreepress.com; web site www.mankatofreepress.com

Published: Mon, Tues, Wed, Thur, Fri, Sat, Sun
Weekday Frequency: m
Saturday Frequency: m
Circulation: 20,481; 20,481(sat); 20,512(sun)
Last Audit: September 30, 2009
Price: 3.05/wk; 166.00/yr; 12.20/4wk.
Advertising: Open inch rate $24.73
Insert rate: $53.88/M.
News services: AP.
Politics: Independent. **Established:** 1887
Not Published: Christmas.
Special Editions: Spring Spectator (Apr); Financial Planning (Feb); Senior Citizens (Jan); Senior Citizens (Jul); Meet Your Area Business People (Jun); Mother's Day (May); Holiday Gift Guide (Nov); Senior Citizens (Oct); Fall Improvement (Sept).
Special Weekly Sections: Religion (Fri); Business & Financial (Mon); Wedding/Engagement (S); Home & Garden (Sat); Arts & Entertainment (Thur); Food (Tues).
Magazines: Parade (Fri).
Pub. ....Jim Santori
Adv. Dir. ....David Habrat
Circ. Dir. ....Denise Zernechel
Mng. Ed. ....Joe Spear
Features Ed. ....Amanda Dyslin
News Ed., Day ....Kathy Vos
News Ed., Night ....Doug Wolter
Sports Ed. ....Jim Rueda
Prodn. Dir. ....Glen Asleson
Prodn. Foreman, Pressroom ....Lon Youngerberg
Market Information: TMC.
Mechanical available: Offset; Black and 3 ROP colors; insert accepted - half-tab, free-standing cards; page cutoffs - 22 3/4.
Mechanical Specifications: Type page 11 5/8 x 21 1/2; E - 6 cols, 1 7/8, 1/8 between; A - 6 cols, 1 7/8, 1/8 between; C - 9 cols, 1 3/16, 1/8 between.
Commodity Consumption: Avg. Page Number Per Issue - Daily 27; Avg. Page Number Per Issue - Plates Used 12000; Avg. Page Number Per Issue - Sunday 28; widths 25; Newsprint Used - Metric Tons 1338; Printing Ink Used - Black 30000; Printing Ink Used - Color 5000; Printing Ink Use
Equipment EDITORIAL: Front-end Software – Dewar/View, QPS/QuarkXPress, Adobe/Photoshop.; Editorial Hardware – 29-IBM/350; Editorial Equipment – 1-Lf/AP Leaf Picture Desk, 1-APP/Power Mac 7100; Editorial Printers – HP/4 MV, HP/5Si, HP/2500CP CLASSIFIED: Front-end Software – AT/Enterprise.; Classified Hardware – 8-IBM/300 PL; Classified Printers – HP/4MV DISPLAY: Ad make-up applications – Managing Editor/Ad Dummy, Multi-Ad/Creator, QPS/QuarkXPress, Adobe/Photoshop, Adobe/Illustrator; Layout Software – 7-IBM/350.; Display Hardware – Dewar, 1-APP/Power Mac 8500, APP/Mac G3, APP/Power Mac 6100; Display Printers – HP/5Si PRODUCTION: Pagination Software – Dewar/View, QPS/QuarkXPress.; Production Equipment – 2-AG/Accuset 1500, 1-ECR/4550 JetSetter; Cameras – C/Spartan III; Scanners – 1-ECR/Autokon 1030N PRESSROOM: Line 1 – 6-G/Urbanite 1969; Line 2 – 2-G/Urbanite 1999; Folders – 1 MAILROOM: Counter stackers – Id/2200, Id/Olympian, TMS I; Inserters and stuffers – GMA/SLS 1000R; Bundle tying machines – 3-MLN/MLNEE, 1-MLN/2EE, 2-MLN/IEE, 1/Power Strap/Newstyer 2000, Power Strap/P-250 A; Addressing machine – 1-/Ch, 1-/KR.; Business Hardware – 1-IBM/AS-400

MARSHALL

INDEPENDENT

508 W. Main St., PO Box 411, Marshall, Minn., 56258; gen tel (507) 537-1551; gen fax (507) 537-1557; gen e-mail independent@marshallindependent.com; adv e-mail adcomp@marshallindependent.com; ed e-mail news@marshallindependent.com; web site www.marshallindependent.com

Group: Ogden Newspapers of MN Inc
Published: Mon, Tues, Wed, Thur, Fri, Sat
Weekday Frequency: m
Saturday Frequency: m
Circulation: 5,970; 6,097(sat)
Last Audit: ABC September 30, 2011
Price: 15.20/mo; 153.40/yr.
Advertising: Open inch rate $21.50
Insert rate: $44/M -single sheet
News services: AP.
Politics: Independent. **Established:** 1874
Not Published: Memorial Day; Labor Day; Christmas.
Own facility?: Y
Special Editions: Lawn & Garden (Apr); Back-to-School (Aug); Spring Bridal (Feb); Pork Products Tab (Jan); Crazy Days (Jul); Graduation (May); Cookbook (Nov); Fall Car Care (Oct).
Special Weekly Sections: Church News (Fri); Business (Mon); Weddings (Sat); Farm Focus (Thur); Best Food Day (Wed).
Magazines: USA WEEKEND Magazine (Sat).
Pub. ....Russell D. Labat
Bus. Mgr. ....Jane Sovell
Adv. Mgr. ....Tara Brandl
Circ. Mgr. ....Julie Dobrenski
News Ed. ....Per Peterson
Prodn. Mgr., Pre Press ....Deb Johnson
Prodn. Mgr., Pressroom ....Terry Zinnel
Market Information: TMC; Zoned editions.
Mechanical available: Offset; Black and 3 ROP colors; insert accepted; page cutoffs - 22 3/4.
Mechanical Specifications: Type page 10 x 21 1/2; E - 6 cols, 1 19/32, 1/8 between; A - 6 cols, 1 19/32, 1/8 between; C - 9 cols, 1 1/32, 1/8 between.
Commodity Consumption: Avg. Page Number Per

Issue - Daily 22; Avg. Page Number Per Issue - Plates Used 11450; widths 32; Newsprint Used - Short Tons 515.14; Printing Ink Used - Black 11828; Printing Ink Used - Color 3760; Printing Ink Used - Pages Printed 7316.
Equipment EDITORIAL: Front-end Software – Quark; Editorial Printers – Canon, HP CLASSIFIED: Front-end Software – Quark; Classified Hardware – Power IMacs's; Classified Printers – Canon, HP PRODUCTION: Pagination Software – QuarkXPress ; Production Equipment – CTP; Cameras – CTP PRESSROOM: Line 1 – 6-G/Community; Folders – 1 MAILROOM: Counter stackers – BG/Count-O-Veyor 108; Inserters and stuffers – MM; Bundle tying machines – 1-/Mosca; Addressing machine – 1-KR/215, 1-KR/211-215.; Business Hardware – 1-NCR
Delivery method: Mail, Newsstand, Private Carrier, Racks

MINNEAPOLIS

STAR TRIBUNE

425 Portland Ave., Minneapolis, Minn., 55488; gen tel (612) 673-4000; adv tel (612) 673-7777; ed tel (612) 673-4823; ed fax (612) 673-4359; web site www.startribune.com
Published: Mon, Tues, Wed, Thur, Fri, Sat, Sun
Weekday Frequency: m
Saturday Frequency: m
Circulation: 298,147; 262,333(sat); 543,633(sun)
Last Audit: ABC September 30, 2011
Advertising: Retail open rate: $298/inch Sun.; $181/inch daily
News services: Associated Press, New York Times Service, McClatchy Tribune Information Service, Washington Post/Bloomberg Service, Scripps Howard News Service, Bloomberg, Dow Jones Information Service
Special Editions: Homes magazine (monthly); Balance (January);
MN Explorer (March, August, November);
Golden Gavel (March & September);
The Good Life (Mar., Apr., Aug., Sept.);
Drive (Spring/Fall);
Top Workplaces (June);
State Fair preview (Aug.);
College Fair Guide (Oct.);
Charitable Giving Guide (Nov.);
Holiday Gift Guide (Nov.)
Special Weekly Sections: Sun.: Business+Money, Travel, Opinion Exchange, Homes Sunday, Comics, Twin Cities+Life, Dakota County, StribExpress; Mon.: Business Insider; Wed.: Variety H+G, North Extra, West Extra, South Extra; Thurs.: Taste, Vita.mn; Sat.: Twin Cities Values
Magazines: Parade (Sun.);
TV Week Lite (Fri. Single Copy); DASH (Monthly)
Publisher and CEO..........Michael Klingensmith
Sr. Vice Pres., Opns................Kevin Desmond
Sr. Vice Pres., Circ...........Steven H. Alexander
Vice Pres./Controller and Treasurer Chuck Brown
Adv. Vice Pres., Sales...............Paul Kasbohm
Creative Director...................Jane Messenger
Dir., Sales Mktg./Research......Dave Gundersen
Circ. Vice Pres...........................Cindy Doege
Ed./Sr. Vice Pres........................Nancy Barnes
Ed./VP Editorial Pages................Scott Gillespie
Mng. Ed., News........................Rene Sanchez
Mng. Ed., Presentation/Innovation...Cory Powell
Asst. Mng. Ed., Admin...................Bob Schafer
Asst. Mng. Ed., Continuous News.....Terry Sauer
Director of Marketing..................Steve Yaeger
Chief Revenue Officer....................Jeff Griffing
VP, Consumer Marketing................Rob Gursha
Managing Editor, Operations.....Duchesne Drew
Sr. VP Digital..............................Jim Bernard
Sr. V.P. General Counsel...........Randy Lebedoff
V.P. National Sales...........................Ray Faust
Vice President, HR...................Adrienne Sirany
Market Information: Split run; TMC; Zoned editions.
Mechanical available: Offset; Black and 3 ROP colors; insert accepted - free standing, bags; page cutoffs - 22 1/16.
Mechanical Specifications: Type page 11 1/2 x 21; E - 6 cols, 1 3/4, 1/6 between; A - 6 cols, 1 3/4, 1/6 between; C - 10 cols, 1 1/16, 1/12 between.
Commodity Consumption: Plates Used: 350,000/yr.; Width: 24; Newsprint Used □ 28,000 metric tons/yr.; Printing Ink Used: Black 1630000
Equipment PRESSROOM: Line 1 – 11-G/Headliner Offset (6 half decks) 1987; Line 2 – 11-G/Headliner Offset (6 half decks) 1987; Line 3 – 11-G/Headliner Offset (6 half decks) 1987; Line 4 – 11-G/Headliner Offset (6 half decks) 1987; Line 5 – 11-G/Headliner Offset (6 half decks) 1987 MAILROOM: Counter stackers – 14 Quipp Model 400; 1 Quipp Model 500; 9 Ferag stackers
; Inserters and stuffers – 3 Ferag 16:1 Rollstream/Drums; 1 Ferag 6-unit disk pool; 1 Ferag 8-unit disk pool; 2 Heidelberg NP-632s
; Wrapping singles – 2 Schur palletizer; 1 Windab shrinkwrapper;
7 Dynaric Model 3000 strappers; 18 Dynaric Model 4000 strappers
; Other equipment –Sticky Note Applicators: 5 Accraply applicators

NEW ULM

THE JOURNAL

303 N. Minnesota St., New Ulm, Minn., 56073-0487; gen tel (507) 359-2911; gen fax (507) 359-7362; adv e-mail ads@nujournal.com; ed e-mail editor@nujournal.com; web site www.nujournal.com
Published: Mon, Tues, Wed, Thur, Fri, Sat, Sun
Weekday Frequency: m
Saturday Frequency: m
Circulation: 6,955; 6,955(sat); 7,520(sun)
Last Audit: ABC September 30, 2011
Price: 13.00/mo; 156.00/yr.
Advertising: Open inch rate $24.80
News services: AP.
Politics: Independent. **Established:** 1898
Not Published: New Year; Independence Day; Thanksgiving; Christmas.
Special Editions: Medical Directory (Annually); Fall Car Care (Fall); Presidents' Day Coupon (Feb); January Thaw (Jan); Shamrock Days (Mar); Graduation Tab (May); Christmas Kick-Off (Nov); Spring Car Care (Spring); Winter Sports (Winter).
Special Weekly Sections: Agri-Business (Fri); Lifestyle (S); Church News (Sat); Best Food Day (Tues).
Magazines: Parade (S).
Pub...Bruce Fenske
Circ. Mgr....................................Steve Grosam
City Reporter................................Ron Larsen
Features Ed............................Kevin Sweeney
News Ed....................................Donna Weber
Regl. Reporter................................Fritz Bush
Sports Ed..............................Jeremy Behnke
Mgr., Mgmt. Info Servs...........Debbie Dubberly
Online Mgr...........................Kremena Tordova
Prodn. Supt.................................Kris Wilfahrt
Market Information: TMC.
Mechanical available: Offset; Black and 3 ROP colors; insert accepted; page cutoffs - 21 1/2.
Mechanical Specifications: Type page 10 x 21 1/2; E - 6 cols, 1/8 between; A - 6 cols, 1/8 between; C - 9 cols, 1/16 between.
Commodity Consumption: Avg. Page Number Per Issue - Daily 19; Avg. Page Number Per Issue - Sunday 24; widths 20; Printing Ink Used - Pages Printed 5906.
Equipment EDITORIAL: Front-end Software – QPS/QuarkXPress 4.0.; Editorial Hardware – 10-APP/Mac 7100; Editorial Equipment – Polaroid/Film Scanner, 2-APP/Mac PC 6100, 1-APP/Mac PC 7100; Editorial Printers – HP; Classified Hardware – 2-APP/Mac 7100; Classified Printers – HP. DISPLAY: Ad make-up applications – Multi-Ad/Creator II; Layout Software – 1-APP/Power Mac G3, 3-APP/Mac G4. PRODUCTION: Pagination Software – QPS/QuarkXPress 4.0.; Production Equipment – 2-HP/LaserPrinter; Business Hardware – NCR/Tower

OWATONNA

OWATONNA PEOPLE'S PRESS

135 W. Pearl St., Owatonna, Minn., 55060-0346; gen tel (507) 451-2840; adv tel (507) 444-2386; ed tel (509) 444-2379; gen fax (507) 444-2382; adv fax 507-444-2382; ed fax (507) 451-6020; adv e-mail densley@owatonna.com; ed e-mail jjackson@owatonna.com; web site www.owatonna.com
Published: Tues, Wed, Thur, Fri, Sat, Sun
Weekday Frequency: m
Saturday Frequency: m
Circulation: 6,389; 6,389(sat); 6,493(sun)
Last Audit: Sworn September 30, 2009
Price: 39.00/12wk; $142.50/48wk.
Advertising: Open inch rate $18.70
News services: AP.
Politics: Independent. **Established:** 1874
Not Published: New Year; Memorial Day; Independence Day; Labor Day; Christmas.
Own facility?: Y
Special Editions: Spring Sports (Apr); Steele County Fair (Aug); Park & Rec (Feb); Bridal (Jan); Park & Rec (Jul); Bridal (Jun); Portraits (Mar); Graduation (May); Christmas Kick-Off (Nov); Welcome Guide (Oct); Home & Garden (Sept).
Magazines: Relish (Monthly); Parade (S); American Profile (Weekly).
Controller.........................Kevin Haekenkamp
Advertising Director..................Debbie Ensley
Circ. Mgr...................................Carol Harvey
Mng. Ed.................................Jeffrey Jackson
Publisher/Editor........................Ronald Ensley
Prodn. Mgr................................Roger Stolley
Market Information: ADS; TMC.
Mechanical available: Offset; Black and 4 ROP colors; insert accepted - free standing; page cutoffs - 22 3/4.
Mechanical Specifications: Type page 10 2/5 x 21 1/2; E - 6 cols, 1 16/25, 1/8 between; A - 6 cols, 1 16/25, 1/8 between; C - 6 cols, 1 16/25, 1/8 between.
Commodity Consumption: Avg. Page Number Per Issue - Daily 24; Avg. Page Number Per Issue - Sunday 32; widths 25; Newsprint Used - Metric Tons 900; Newsprint Used - Short Tons 1500; Printing Ink Used - Black 15000; Printing Ink Used - Color 3000.
Equipment EDITORIAL: Front-end Software – Baseview/NewsEdit Pro IQUE 4.0.4b5, Adobe/InDesign 2.0.; Editorial Hardware – 4-APP/Power Mac G4, 1-APP/iMac, 1-APP/Power Mac G5, 2-APP/eMac; Classified Hardware – Software Â□ Baseview/Ad Manager Pro 1.9.1.77. DISPLAY: Ad make-up applications – Adobe/InDesign CS 2.0.; Display Hardware – 3-APP/Power Mac G4, 1-APP/Power Mac G5; Display Printers – HP/Color Laserjet Printer, QMS/2060 Printer PRODUCTION: Pagination Software – Prinergy, Integis, Pit Stop, QPS/QuarkXPress 6.1.; Production Equipment – 1-ECR/36 HS, 1-Kk/Trendsetter 100, 2-APP/Mac G3 PRESSROOM: Line 1 – 16-G/Community single width; Folders – DGM/1030; Pasters – Jardis; Press control system – Fin. MAILROOM: Counter stackers – KAN/Newstac; Inserters and stuffers – KAN/480 Station Inserter12:1; Bundle tying machines – 3-Si/LB2000, 1-Si/LB2330 Auto Strapper; Addressing machine – 1-Domino/Jet-A-Ray; Other equipment –MM/Trimmer Stitcher-4 pocket. BUSINESS COMPUTERS: Business Software – Windows 97; Business Hardware – PC's
Delivery method: Mail, Newsstand, Private Carrier, Racks

RED WING

REPUBLICAN EAGLE

2760 N. Service Dr., Red Wing, Minn., 55066; gen tel (651) 388-8235; adv tel (651) 388-8235; ed tel (651) 388-8235; gen fax (651) 388-3404; adv fax (651) 388-3404; ed fax (651) 388-3404; gen e-mail news@republican-eagle.com; ed e-mail letters@republican-eagle.com; web site www.republican-eagle.com
Published: Tues, Wed, Thur, Fri, Sat
Weekday Frequency: e
Saturday Frequency: m
Circulation: 5,824; 5,824(sat)
Last Audit: March 31, 2008
Price: 10.25/mo (carrier); 104.00/yr (carrier).
Advertising: Open inch rate $12.35
News services: AP.
Politics: Independent. **Established:** 1857
Not Published: New Year; Memorial Day; Independence Day; Labor Day; Thanksgiving; Christmas.
Special Editions: Home Improvement (Apr); County Fair (Aug); Last Minute Gift Guide (Dec); Wedding (Jan); Progress (Mar); Graduation (May); Christmas Catalog (Nov); Red Wing Business People (Oct); Home Improvement (Sept).
Magazines: Parade (S); TView (Weekly).
Pub...Steve Messick
Gen. Mgr.................................Michael Keuhn
News Ed.................................Anne Jacobson
Prodn. Mgr...................................Terry Meier
Market Information: ADS; TMC.
Mechanical available: Offset; Black and 3 ROP colors; insert accepted - zoned; page cutoffs - 22 3/4.
Mechanical Specifications: Type page 13 x 21 1/2; E - 6 cols, 2 1/16, 1/8 between; A - 6 cols, 2 1/16, 1/8 between; C - 8 cols, between.
Commodity Consumption: Avg. Page Number Per Issue - Daily 14; Avg. Page Number Per Issue - Plates Used 22880; Avg. Page Number Per Issue - Saturday 22; widths 28; Newsprint Used - Short Tons 2100; Printing Ink Used - Black 46691; Printing Ink Used - Color 1935; Printing Ink Us
Equipment EDITORIAL: Front-end Software – Baseview/NewsEdit, QPS/QuarkXPress, Adobe/Photoshop. CLASSIFIED: Front-end Software – Baseview/Class Manager Plus, QPS/QuarkXPress. DISPLAY: Ad make-up applications – Multi-Ad/Creator, Macromedia/Freehand, Adobe/Pagemaker, Adobe/Photoshop. PRODUCTION: Pagination Software – QPS/QuarkXPress; Production Equipment – Konica/EV Jetsetter 4500, APP/Mac LaserWriter 8500, NewGen/12Xf Imager Plus, Konica/4550 Ev JetSetter; Cameras – R/475, Screen/Rollmatic 475-D; Scanners – Lf/Leafscan 35, HP/ScanJet 4C, Nikon/LS1000 Super Coolscan PRESSROOM: Line 1 – 8-G/Community 1988, 1-G/SSC four high 1996; Press Drives – 2-Fin/75 h.p., 1-Fin/60 h.p.; Folders – 2-G/SSC; Pasters – 1 MAILROOM: Counter stackers – 1-BG/105, 1-BG/109; Inserters and stuffers – KR/512; Bundle tying machines – 2/Bu, 2-EAM-Mosca/Rom; Addressing machine – 2-KR/211.

ROCHESTER

POST-BULLETIN

18 1st Ave. SE, Rochester, Minn., 55903-6118; gen tel (507) 285-7600; adv tel (507) 285-7716; ed tel (507) 285-7700; adv fax (507) 285-7666; ed fax (507) 285-7772; gen e-mail news@postbulletin.com; adv e-mail advertising@postbulletin.com; ed e-mail news@postbulletin.com; web site www.postbulletin.com
Published: Mon, Tues, Wed, Thur, Fri, Sat
Weekday Frequency: e
Circulation: 44,631
Last Audit: September 30, 2006
Price: 3.05/wk; 143.60/yr; 39.65/13wk.
Advertising: Open inch rate $53.84(wknd)
News services: AP, NYT, MCT.
Politics: Independent.
Advertising not accepted: Tobacco.
Special Editions: Boomer (Apr); Education (Aug); Last Minute Gift Catalog (Dec); Rochester Area Builders Home Show (Feb); Weddings (Jan); Honor Roll (Jul); Rochesterfest (Jun); Employment (Mar);

Spring Home & Garden (May); Home for the Holidays (Nov); Drive Magazine (Oct);
Special Weekly Sections: Real Estate Marketplace (Fri); Seniors (Mon); Travel (Sat); Prevue (Thur); Teen Beat (Tues); Food (Wed).
Magazines: Homefinder (Monthly); USA WEEKEND Magazine (Sat); American Profile (Weekly).
Pub. ....Randy Chapman
Dir., HR ....Carmen Kyllo
Bus. Mgr. ....Chris Blade
Adv. Mgr., Classified ....Sue Lovejoy
Dir., Promo. ....John Withers
Circ. Mgr. ....Todd Heroff
Circ. Mgr., Customer Serv. ....Carla Severson
Ed ....Robert Hill
Mng. Ed. ....Jay Furst
City Ed. ....Randi Kallas
Editorial Page Ed. ....Greg Sellnow
Environmental/Ecology Ed. ....John Weiss
Lifestyle Ed. ....Janice McFarland
Sports Ed. ....Craig Swalboski
Dir., Tech. Servs. ....Victor Denny
Dir., Internet Servs. ....G. Mark Kelm
Prodn. Dir., Opns. ....Jeffrey Lansing
Market Information: Split run; TMC; Zoned editions.
Mechanical available: Offset; Black and 3 ROP colors; insert accepted; page cutoffs - 22.
Mechanical Specifications: Type page 13 x 21; E - 6 cols, 2 1/16, 1/8 between; A - 6 cols, 2 1/16, 1/8 between; C - 8 cols, 1 9/16, 1/16 between.
Commodity Consumption: Avg. Page Number Per Issue - Daily 50; Avg. Page Number Per Issue - Plates Used 77800; widths 50; Newsprint Used - Metric Tons 4200; Printing Ink Used - Black 100000; Printing Ink Used - Color 55970; Printing Ink Used - Pages Printed 15614.
Equipment EDITORIAL: Front-end Software – Baseview.; Editorial Hardware – APP/Mac; Editorial Printers – HP CLASSIFIED: Front-end Software – Baseview.; Classified Hardware – APP/Mac; Classified Printers – HP DISPLAY: Ad make-up applications – QPS/QuarkXPress, Adobe/Illustrator, Adobe/Photoshop; Layout Software – Mk/Ad Director.; Display Hardware – APP/Mac; Display Printers – 2-AG/SelectSet 5000, 1-AG/9400PS PRODUCTION: Pagination Software – QPS 3.11, QPS 4.0.; Production Equipment – 2-Polaroid/Sprintscant, 1-Devotec/DE; Scanners – Polaroid/Sprintscant, Umax, Nikon, AG PRESSROOM: Line 1 – 5-G/Headliner Offset (3 decks) double width 1988; Folders – G/2:1. MAILROOM: Counter stackers – 3-QWI/500, 1-QWI/401; Inserters and stuffers – GMA/3000 20:2, GMA/10 Heads; Bundle tying machines – Ovalstrapping; Wrapping singles – Mosca; Mailroom control system – GMA/SAM; Addressing machine – KR, Prism; Other equipment –4-MM/Si; Audio Hardware – Brite, PC BUSINESS COMPUTERS: Business Software – IBM/AS-400, Microsoft/Office, Abra Suite, PBS; Business Hardware – IBM/AS-400 720-2062, PCs, Sun/Enterprise

SAINT CLOUD

ST. CLOUD NEWSPAPERS, INC.

3000 N. 7th St., Saint Cloud, Minn., 56302; gen tel (320) 255-8700; gen fax (320) 255-8775
Price: 197.60/yr.
Advertising: Open inch rate $8.50
Politics: 1861

ST. CLOUD TIMES

3000 N. Seventh St., Saint Cloud, Minn., 56303; gen tel (320) 255-8700; ed tel (320) 255-8776; gen fax (320) 255-8775; adv fax (320) 255-8773; adv e-mail classifieds@stcloudtimes.com; ed e-mail newsroom@stcloudtimes.com; web site www.sctimes.com
Published: Mon, Tues, Wed, Thur, Fri, Sat, Sun
Weekday Frequency: m
Saturday Frequency: m
Circulation: 20,710; 24,776(sat); 31,261(sun)
Last Audit: ABC September 30, 2011
Price: 3.50/wk (carrier); 15.17/mo (carrier); 182.00/yr (carrier).
Advertising: Open inch rate $90.28
News services: AP, GNS.
Politics: Independent. **Established:** 1861
Special Editions: Lawn & Garden (Apr); Christmas Gift Guide (Dec); Bridal (Jan); Bridal (Jul); Home Times (Semi-monthly); Football (Sept).
Special Weekly Sections: Techetera (Mon); Travel Page (S); Weddings/Engagements (Sat); Up Next (Thur).
Magazines: USA WEEKEND Magazine (Fri); Weekend Plus (Entertainment Section) (Thur).
Pres./Pub. ....Bill Albrecht
Adv. Mgr., Classified ....Celeste P. Simon
Adv. Mgr., Online Devel. ....Julie Schlagheck
Adv. Mgr., Territory Retail Sales Marilyn Birkland
Mktg. Devel. Dir. ....Dennis Host
Circ. Sales Mgr. ....Tom Steve
Circ. Asst. Mgr. ....Kathryn R. Andersen
Mng. Ed. ....John L. Bodette
Asst. Mng. Ed. ....Mike Knaak
Editorial Page Ed. ....Randy Krebs
Photo Dept. Mgr. ....David Schwarz
Topics Ed. ....Noreen Kaluza
Opns. Dir. ....Geary J. Yaeger
Prodn. Mgr., Mailroom ....Allen Jungels
Bldg. Serv. Mgr. ....Mark Hessler
Market Information: Split run; TMC.
Mechanical available: Offset; Black and 3 ROP colors; insert accepted; page cutoffs - 22 3/4.
Mechanical Specifications: Type page 11 5/8 x 21 1/2; E - 6 cols, 1 5/6, 1/8 between; A - 6 cols, 1 5/6, 1/8 between; C - 9 cols, 1 7/25, 1/16 between.
Commodity Consumption: Avg. Page Number Per Issue - Daily 38; Avg. Page Number Per Issue - Plates Used 126000; Avg. Page Number Per Issue - Sunday 83; widths 37 1/2; Newsprint Used - Metric Tons 2783; Newsprint Used - Short Tons 3068; Printing Ink Used - Black 42324; Printing
Equipment EDITORIAL: Front-end Software – SII.; Editorial Hardware – Tandem/KI 22; Editorial Equipment – 40-PC, 30-APP/Mac; Editorial Printers – HP/LaserJet 8000N, QMS/2060 FX, HP/LaserJet 4050N, Epson/Stylus Photo 750; Classified Hardware – IBM/X345; Classified Equipment – 13-PC; Classified Printers – HP/4050, HP/5M, HP/4L. DISPLAY: Ad make-up applications – Multi-Ad/Creator 4.0; Layout Software – MEI/ALS.; Display Hardware – 11-APP/Mac G3; Display Printers – HP/LaserJet 8000N, HP/LaserJet 8550N, HP/DesignJet 2500, HP/DesignJet 1050C PRESSROOM: Line 1 – 8-HI/1650 1974; Press Drives – Haley/Control (4 GE Drive Motors); Folders – 2-HI/2:1; Pasters – 5-Registron/3 arm RTP.; Bundle tying machines – 2-Dynaric.; Business Hardware – IBM/AS-400

SAINT PAUL

NORTHWEST PUBLICATIONS, INC.

345 Cedar St., Saint Paul, Minn., 55101; gen tel (651) 222-5011; gen fax (651) 228-5308

ST. PAUL PIONEER PRESS

345 Cedar St., Saint Paul, Minn., 55101; gen tel (651) 222-1111; ed tel (651) 228-5490; gen fax (651) 228-5308; adv fax (651) 228-5268; ed fax (651) 228-5500; gen e-mail infodesk@pioneerpress.com; ed e-mail letters@pioneerpress.com; web site www.twincities.com
Group: Metro Newspaper Advertising Services, Inc.
Published: Mon, Tues, Wed, Thur, Fri, Sat, Sun
Weekday Frequency: m
Saturday Frequency: m
Circulation: 188,081; 165,897(sat); 252,796(sun)
Last Audit: ABC September 30, 2011
Price: 4.00/wk; 17.33/mo; 208.00/yr.
Advertising: Open inch rate $243.74
News services: AP, MCT, LAT-WP, The Newspaper Network (TNN).
Politics: Independent.
Special Editions: Travel Guides (March and August); Live to Age Well (March, August and November); Worship Directory (April and December); Higher Education (July and December); State Fair (August); Vikings Season Preview (September); Arts previews (March, September and November); Breast Cancer Awareness (October); Non Profit Giving Guide (November); Golf Guide (Apr); Home & Lifestyle (Aug); Ski (Dec); Winter Carnival (Jan); Home & Lifestyle (Jul); Summer Fun Guide (Jun); Summer Camp for Kids (Mar); Home & Lifestyle (Oct)
Special Weekly Sections: Fall Gardening (Sept-Oct) (Other); Showtime (S).
Magazines: Parade (S).
Profile: The Pioneer Press, Minnesota's First Newspaper and a three-time winner of journalism's highest honor, the Pulitzer Prize, serves readers and advertisers in the Twin Cities' East Metro region and western Wisconson. A distinctive attitude and a commitment
Pres./Pub. ....Guy Gilmore
Credit Mgr. ....Dawn Lindgren
Commun. Mgr. ....Pat Effenberger
Vice Pres., Adv. ....Greg Mazanec
Adv. Dir., Classified ....Dee Mccants
Vice Pres., Circ. ....Andrew Mok
Dir., Mktg. ....Lori Swanson
Dir., Market Research/Info. ....Jean Pearson
Editor ....Mike Burbach
Vice Pres. Production ....Kevin Garris
CFO ....Neil Mullen
Market Information: Split run; TMC; Zoned editions.
Mechanical available: Offset; Black and 3 ROP colors; insert accepted - self-adhesive notes, paper bags, product samples; page cutoffs - 22.
Mechanical Specifications: Type page 11 1/2 x 21; E - 5 cols, 1 11/16, 3/16 between; A - 6 cols, 2 1/16, 3/16 between; C - 10 cols, 1 1/8, between.
Commodity Consumption: Avg. Page Number Per Issue - Daily 52; Avg. Page Number Per Issue - Plates Used 254584; Avg. Page Number Per Issue - Saturday 52; Avg. Page Number Per Issue - Sunday 140; widths 18 3/4; Newsprint Used - Metric Tons 28536; Newsprint Used - Short Tons 3145
Equipment PRESSROOM: Line 1 – 6-G/Metroliner Double Width; Line 2 – 6-G/Metroliner Double Width; Line 3 – 6-G/Metroliner Double Width; Folders – 3-G/3:2 single. MAILROOM: Counter stackers – 7-Quipp, 5-HL/Monitor; Inserters and stuffers – 2-Dynaric/NP

STILLWATER

STILLWATER GAZETTE

1931 Curve Crest Blvd., Stillwater, Minn., 55082-6063; gen tel (651) 439-3130; adv tel (651) 796-1116; ed tel (651) 439-3130; gen fax (651) 439-4713; adv fax (651) 439-4713; ed fax (651) 439-4713; gen e-mail gazette@acnpapers.com; web site www.stillwatergazette.com
Published: Mon, Tues, Wed, Thur, Fri
Weekday Frequency: e
Circulation: 3,341
Last Audit: September 29, 2003
Price: 99.50/yr.
Advertising: Open inch rate $13.75
News services: AP.
Politics: Independent. **Established:** 1870
Not Published: New Year; Memorial Day; Independence Day; Labor Day; Thanksgiving; Christmas.
Special Editions: Community Volunteers Sponsor Page (Apr); Football Tab (Aug); Holiday Lighting Contest (Dec); Presidents' Day Sponsor Page (Feb); Jaycees' Sponsor Page (Jan); Lumberjacks' Days Tab (Jul); Graduation (Jun); Spring Sports Tab (Mar); Memorial Day Sponsor Page
Special Weekly Sections: Valley Life (Wed).
Magazines: USA WEEKEND Magazine (Fri).
Pub. ....Mark Berriman
Adv. Mgr., Classified ....Cindy Leman
Adv. Acct. Exec. ....Pam Ekhaml
Adv. Acct. Exec. ....Doug Lacher
Adv. Acct. Exec. ....Elizabeth Wallen
Circ. Mgr. ....David Mooney
Mng. Ed. ....Micki Adams
Sports Ed. ....Stuart Groskreutz
Prodn. Mgr. ....Seanne Hagemeyer
Market Information: TMC.
Mechanical available: Offset; Black and 1 ROP colors; insert accepted - must be 1/4 folded, no catalogs; page cutoffs - 21 5/8.
Mechanical Specifications: Type page 13 x 21 1/2; E - 6 cols, 2 1/16, 1/8 between; A - 6 cols, 2 1/16, 1/8 between; C - 9 cols, 1 3/8, 1/16 between.
Commodity Consumption: Avg. Page Number Per Issue - Daily 12; Avg. Page Number Per Issue - Plates Used 2400; widths 28; Newsprint Used - Short Tons 210; Printing Ink Used - Pages Printed 4020.
Equipment; Editorial Hardware – CText.; Classified Hardware – Baseview. DISPLAY: Ad make-up applications – Aldus/PageMaker; Layout Software – APP/Mac.; Production Equipment – 1-Nu/FT40L; Cameras – 1-B/1822. PRESSROOM: Line 1 – 4-HI/V-15A; Folders – 1; Bundle tying machines – 1/Bu; Addressing machine – 1-/Am.

VIRGINIA

MESABI DAILY NEWS

704 7th Ave. S., Virginia, Minn., 55792; gen tel (218) 741-5544; adv tel (218) 741-5544; ed tel (218) 741-5544; gen fax (218) 741-1005; adv fax (218) 749-1836; ed fax (218) 741-1005; gen e-mail mdn@virginiamn.com; adv e-mail mdnprod@mx3.com; ed e-mail mdnedit@virginiamn.com; web site www.virginiamn.com
Group: U.S. Suburban Press, Inc.
Published: Mon, Tues, Wed, Thur, Fri, Sat, Sun
Weekday Frequency: m
Saturday Frequency: m
Circulation: 9,143; 9,143(sat); 10,488(sun)
Last Audit: March 31, 2008
Price: 3.05/wk; 158.60/yr.
Advertising: Open inch rate $17.69
News services: AP, NEA, TMS.
Politics: Independent.
Special Editions: Car Tab (Apr); 4-Gift Guides (Dec); Hockey Tab (Feb); Area Baby Album (Jan); Sidewalk Days (Jul); Outdoor Land of Loon (Jun); Year-End (Mar); Home Improvement (May); Thanksgiving Spectacular (Nov); Car Tab (Oct); Health Pulse (Quarterly); Visitors Guide (
Special Weekly Sections: Food (S); Churches (Sat); Food (Wed).
Magazines: Relish (Monthly); USA WEEKEND Magazine (S); American Profile (Weekly).
Adv. Dir. ....Christopher Knight
Regl. Ed. ....Charles Ramsey
Market Information: Split run; TMC; Zoned editions.
Mechanical available: Offset; Black and 3 ROP colors; insert accepted; page cutoffs - 20.
Mechanical Specifications: Type page 13 x 21 1/2; E - 6 cols, 1 5/6, 5/16 between; A - 6 cols, 1 5/6, 5/16 between; C - 9 cols, 1 1/6, 5/16 between.
Commodity Consumption: Avg. Page Number Per Issue - Daily 24; Avg. Page Number Per Issue - Plates Used 24000; Avg. Page Number Per Issue - Sunday 36; widths 25; Newsprint Used - Short Tons 2000; Printing Ink Used - Black 24000; Printing Ink Used - Color 5000; Printing Ink Used
Equipment EDITORIAL: Front-end Software – APP/Mac, Baseview.; Editorial Hardware – 18-APP/Mac; Editorial Printers – 1-APP/Mac LaserWriter NTX, 2-HP/8000N, 1-AG/25SX, 1-AG/Accuset 1000 CLASSIFIED: Front-end Software – Baseview.; Classified Hardware – Printers □ 1-APP/Mac LaserWriter NTX, 2-HP/8000N, 1-Ag/Accuset 1000, 1-AG/25SX DISPLAY: Ad make-up applications – Multi-Ad, QPS/QuarkXPress, Aldus/FreeHand; Layout Software – 4-APP/Power Mac G-3, 1-

APP/Power Mac 9500.; Display Printers – 2-HP/8000N, 1-MON/1000, 1-AG/255X PRODUCTION: Pagination Software – QPS/QuarkXPress, Baseview.; Production Equipment – Caere/OmniPage, MON/1000; Cameras – 1-B; Scanners – AG/Arcus, 2-Umax 1200S PRESSROOM: Line 1 – 8-G/Urbanite; Folders – 1-G/2:1. MAILROOM: Counter stackers – 1/HL; Inserters and stuffers – 6-KAN/660; Bundle tying machines – 1-Sterling/MR40, 1-Sterling/SSM-Mini; Wrapping singles – 2-/Bu; Addressing machine – 1-/KAN.; Business Hardware – 1-IBM/Risc 6000

WILLMAR

WEST CENTRAL TRIBUNE

2208 SW Trott Ave., Willmar, Minn., 56201; gen tel (320) 235-1150; gen fax (320) 235-6769; adv e-mail wctads@wctrib.com; web site www.wctrib.com

Published: Mon, Tues, Wed, Thur, Fri, Sat
Weekday Frequency: m
Saturday Frequency: m
Circulation: 14,063; 14,063(sat)
Last Audit: Sworn September 30, 2010
Price: 2.191/wk (carrier), $2.31/wk (mail); 10.00/mo (carrier), $10.55/mo (mail); 115.00/yr.
Advertising: Open inch rate $21.57
News services: AP.
Politics: Independent. **Established:** 1895
Not Published: New Year; Memorial Day; Independence Day; Labor Day; Thanksgiving; Christmas.
Special Editions: Earth Day (Apr); Fall Football Preview (Aug); Holiday (Dec); Bridal I (Feb); Willmar Mid Summer (Jul); City Festival (Jun); Agriculture (Mar); Mother's Day (May); Holiday Greetings (Nov); Health Services Directory (Oct); Fall Home Improvement (Sept).
Special Weekly Sections: Business (Tues).
Magazines: Parade (S).
Pub...................................Steven Ammerman
Bus. Mgr. ....Lila Rekedal
Adv. Dir. ....Jan Queenan
Mktg. Dir. ....Kerry Gislason
Ed. ....Kelly Boldan
Assoc. Ed........................................Gary Miller
Copy Ed. ....Dan Burdett
Farm Ed. ....David Little
Features Ed. ....Sharon Bomstad
News Ed. ....Susan Lunneborg
Photo Dept. Mgr. ....Bill Zimmer
Sports Ed. ....Scott Thoma
Women's Ed....................................Anne Polta
Market Information: TMC.
Mechanical available: Offset; Black and 3 ROP colors; insert accepted - print & deliver program; page cutoffs - 22 3/4.
Mechanical Specifications: Type page 11 9/16 x 21; E - 6 cols, 1 13/16, 1/8 between; A - 6 cols, 1 13/16, 1/8 between; C - 8 cols, 1 13/16, 1/8 between.
Commodity Consumption: Avg. Page Number Per Issue - Daily 26; Avg. Page Number Per Issue - Plates Used 5539; Avg. Page Number Per Issue - Saturday 22; widths 27 1/2; Newsprint Used - Metric Tons 815; Printing Ink Used - Black 25730; Printing Ink Used - Color 1080; Printing Ink
Equipment EDITORIAL: Front-end Software – APT.; Editorial Hardware – Micron/workstation, Dell, Compaq/Server; Editorial Equipment – APP/Mac G4; Editorial Printers – AU/APS2000, AU/Imagesetter, Epson/Color Proofer, HP CLASSIFIED: Front-end Software – APT.; Classified Hardware – Dell, Micron/Workstation, Compaq; Classified Printers – AU/APS2000, Au/Imagesetter, HP/4m DISPLAY: Ad make-up applications – APT; Layout Software – APT.; Display Hardware – Micron/Workstations, Dell, Compaq; Display Printers – APD/2000 PRODUCTION: Pagination Software – APT.; Production Equipment – Wordlinx 2.1, AU/108C; Cameras – 2-C/Spartan III; Scanners – 3-Umax/PowerLook PRESSROOM: Line 1 – BG/Dampening System, 8-G/Community; Folders – 1-G/SCI, G/SSC.; Bundle tying machines – OVL; Addressing machine – Ch/596. BUSINESS COMPUTERS: Business Software – Collier-Jackson Inc; Business Hardware – DEC/VAX 6410, DEC/2100A Alpha

WINONA

WINONA DAILY NEWS

601 Franklin St., Winona, Minn., 55987; gen tel (507) 453-3500; adv tel (507) 453-3560; ed tel (507) 453-3510; gen fax (507) 454-1440; adv fax (507) 454-1440; ed fax (507) 453-3517; adv e-mail sales@winonadailynews.com; ed e-mail news@winonadailynews.com; web site www.winonadailynews.com

Group: Metro Suburbia, Inc./Newhouse Newspapers
Published: Mon, Tues, Wed, Thur, Fri, Sat, Sun
Weekday Frequency: m
Saturday Frequency: m
Circulation: 9,240; 10,283(sat); 10,351(sun)
Last Audit: ABC September 30, 2011
Price: 3.10/wk; 157.00/yr.
Advertising: Open inch rate $23.95
News services: AP, Landon Media Group, Lee National Sales Group.
Politics: Independent. **Established:** 1855
Special Editions: Golf Guide (Apr); Back-to-School/Campus (Aug); Christmas (Dec); Home Improvement (Feb); Bridal Showcase (Jan); Bowling Review (Jun); Academic Excellence (Mar).
Special Weekly Sections: Lifestyle (S); TV (Sat); Entertainment (Thur); Food (Wed).
Magazines: Parade (S); American Profile (Weekly).
Pub..................................Rusty Cunningham
Adv. Dir. ....Thomas Kelly
Adv. Mgr., Classified.................Vicky Peterson
Ed....Darrell Ehrlink
City Ed. ....Matt Christensen
Online Ed. ....Jerome Christenson
Market Information: TMC.
Mechanical available: Offset; Black and 3 ROP colors; insert accepted - self-adhesive notes, poly bags; page cutoffs - 22 3/4.
Mechanical Specifications: Type page 11 5/8 x 21 1/2; E - 6 cols, 1 5/6, 1/8 between; A - 6 cols, 1 5/6, 1/8 between; C - 9 cols, 1 1/5, 1/16 between.
Commodity Consumption: Avg. Page Number Per Issue - Daily 20; Avg. Page Number Per Issue - Plates Used 14000; Avg. Page Number Per Issue - Sunday 40; widths 27 1/4; Newsprint Used - Metric Tons 820; Printing Ink Used - Black 19000; Printing Ink Used - Color 2000; Printing Ink
Equipment EDITORIAL: Front-end Software – CText/Dateline OS-2 3.00.; Editorial Hardware – 14-Gateway/2000 P5-90, 2-Gateway/2000 P5-100; Editorial Equipment – 1-APP/Power Mac 8500-180, 1-Nikon/Scanner, 1-APP/Mac IIci, 1-APP/Mac Classic; Editorial Printers – 2-HP/5Si, 1-HP/4Si, 1-APP/Mac LaserWriter IIf CLASSIFIED: Front-end Software – CText/Advision OS-2 3.00.; Classified Hardware – 3-Gateway/2000 P5-90 DISPLAY: Ad make-up applications – Multi-Ad/Creator, Aldus/FreeHand, Adobe/Photoshop, Adobe/TypeStyler, Kwick Query, Watch It; Layout Software – 4-APP/Power Mac, 1-APP/Mac Quadra 950.; Display Printers – 1-HP/4MV, 1-HP/4M Plus; Production Equipment – 2-HP/5Si; Cameras – 1-B. PRESSROOM: Line 1 – 5-G/Urbanite; Folders – 1-G/2:1. MAILROOM: Counter stackers – Hall Monitor; Inserters and stuffers – HI 1372; Bundle tying machines – Dynaric/Strapper, SMS/Stauffer Gold; Addressing machine – 1-Ch/525E. BUSINESS COMPUTERS: Business Software – Custom Software; Business Hardware – IBM/AS-400

WORTHINGTON

THE DAILY GLOBE

300 11th St., Worthington, Minn., 56187; gen tel (507) 376-9711; adv tel (507) 376-9711; ed tel (507) 376-9711; gen fax (507) 376-5202; adv fax (507) 376-5202; ed fax (507) 376-5202; adv e-mail dgcompostion@dglobe.com; ed e-mail dgnews@dglobe.com; web site www.dglobe.com

Published: Mon, Tues, Wed, Thur, Fri, Sat
Weekday Frequency: m
Circulation: 8,229; 8,229(sat)
Last Audit: Sworn September 30, 2010
Price: 10.45/mo (carrier), $11.70/mo (mail); 122.85/yr (carrier), $132.00/yr (mail).
Advertising: Open inch rate $21.14
News services: AP.
Politics: Independent. **Established:** 1872
Not Published: New Year; Memorial Day; Independence Day; Labor Day; Thanksgiving; Christmas.
Special Editions: Home Improvement (Apr); Real Estate Guide (Every other month); Builders (Fall); Bridal Tab (Jan); Bridal Tab (Jun); Progress Annual Report (Mar); Active Life (Quarterly); Builders (Spring).
Special Weekly Sections: Dining & Entertainment (Fri); Business (Mon); Education (Sat); Religion (Thur); Agriculture (Tues); Seniors (Wed); Lifestyles (Weekly).
Magazines: TV Pre-Vu (Fri); Relish (Monthly); Parade (S); American Profile (Sat).
Pub. ....Joni Harms
Bus. Mgr. ....Anita Holmes
Adv. Supvr., Classified...............Sheila Kluever
Circ. Mgr....................................Denise Erwin
Mng. Ed. ....Ryan McGaughey
Lifestyle Ed.............................Beth Namanny
Sports Ed. ....Aaron Hagen
Prodn. Mgr., Composing ....Cindy Ramert
Prodn. Foreman, Pressroom..............Rob Muck
Market Information: TMC.
Mechanical available: Offset; Black and 3 ROP colors; insert accepted; page cutoffs - 21.
Mechanical Specifications: Type page 11 5/8 x 21; E - 6 cols, 1 7/8, 1/8 between; A - 6 cols, 1 7/8, 1/8 between; C - 9 cols, 1 1/4, 1/8 between.
Commodity Consumption: widths 27.
Equipment EDITORIAL: Front-end Software – ACT 2.06.004.; Editorial Equipment – 4-APP/Mac; Editorial Printers – Data Products/Typhoon 16, Epson/1270 CLASSIFIED: Front-end Software – ACT 2.06.004.; Classified Equipment – Printers Â Dataproducts/Typhoon 16, HP DISPLAY: Ad make-up applications – QPS/QuarkXPress 4.0; Layout Software – APP/Mac.; Display Hardware – 3-APP/Mac IIci; Display Printers – Data Products/Typhoon 16, Epson/1270 PRODUCTION: Pagination Software – QPS/QuarkXpress 4.0.; Production Equipment – Nu/Flip Top FT40V6UPNS, 2-Glunz & Jensen/Online Processor; Cameras – SCREEN; Scanners – 3-Umax/Powerlook 2 PRESSROOM: Line 1 – 11-HI/V15 SingleWidth 1999; Folders – 2, HI/JF-7, HI/JF-25. MAILROOM: Counter stackers – Tiger; Inserters and stuffers – Manual; Bundle tying machines – 2/Akebono; Addressing machine – KR; Other equipment –MM/Sticher-Trimmer.; Audio Hardware – Computer/Ads-on-call BUSINESS COMPUTERS: Business Software – Microsoft/Office, Microsoft/Windows 95, Microsoft/Windows 98, Microsoft/Excell 2000, Citrix/Great Plains Postaboft Geac; Business Hardware – 10-Micron PC, 1-Dell PC

MISSISSIPPI

BILOXI

GULF PUBLISHING CO., INC.

205 DeBuys Rd., Gulfport, Miss., 39507; gen tel (228) 896-2100; gen fax (228) 896-2362

THE SUN HERALD

205 DeBuys Rd., Gulfport, Miss., 39507-2837; gen tel (228) 896-2100; adv tel (228) 896-2400; ed tel (228) 896-2301; gen fax (228) 896-2362; adv fax (228) 896-2362; ed fax (228) 896-2104; gen e-mail maildrop@sunherald.com; ed e-mail news@sunherald.com; web site www.sunherald.com

Published: Mon, Tues, Wed, Thur, Fri, Sat, Sun
Weekday Frequency: m
Saturday Frequency: m
Circulation: 31,834; 31,408(sat); 39,900(sun)
Last Audit: ABC September 30, 2011
Price: 14.00/mo, $11.00/mo (m); 159.60/yr.
Advertising: Open inch rate $65.68
News services: AP, MCT, SHNS.
Politics: Independent.
Special Editions: Guide to Gulf Coast Living (Apr); Football (Aug); Attractions (Feb); Annual Progress (Jan); Wellness/Healthcare Directory (Jul); Nike Classic (Mar); Home & Products Show (May); Auto Showroom (Nov); Annual Salute to the Military (Oct); NIE Literacy (Sept).
Special Weekly Sections: Marquee (Fri); Youth (Mon); TV Week (S); Home & Garden (Thur); Casino Entertainment (Tues); Coupon Shopper (Wed).
Magazines: Parade (S).
Pres./Pub.......................................Glen Nardi
CFO..Flora Point
HR Mgr. ....Wanda Howell
Coord., Credit...............................Faye Taylor
Mktg. Dir. ....John McFarland
Circ. Dir. ....Gary Raskett
Exec. Ed. ....Stan Tiner
Editorial Dir. ....Marie Harris
Entertainment Ed.........................Jean Prescott
Features Ed. ....Scott Hawkins
Local News Ed........................Kate Magandy
Outdoors Ed. ....Al Jones
Photo Ed.......................................Drew Tarter
Special Sections Mgr.................Dorothy Wilson
Sports Ed. ....Doug Barber
Data Processing Mgr...................Carole Brown
Prodn. Mgr., Composing ....Gary Rachuba
Prodn. Mgr., Distr...........................Randy Seib
Prodn. Mgr., Pressroom..................Dean Cook
Mechanical available: Offset; Black and 3 ROP colors; insert accepted - product samples; page cutoffs - 21.
Mechanical Specifications: Type page 13 x 21; E - 6 cols, 2 1/16, 1/8 between; A - 6 cols, 2 1/16, 1/8 between; C - 10 cols, 1 3/8, 1/16 between.
Commodity Consumption: Avg. Page Number Per Issue - Daily 51.0; Avg. Page Number Per Issue - Plates Used 60000; Avg. Page Number Per Issue - Sunday 142.0; widths 40 1/2; Newsprint Used - Metric Tons 7070; Printing Ink Used - Black 109965; Printing Ink Used - Color 86233; Print
Equipment EDITORIAL: Front-end Software – DTI/Client Software.; Editorial Hardware – Sun; Editorial Printers – HP/LaserJet 8000N CLASSIFIED: Front-end Software – Genera 4.6.; Classified Hardware – Cybergraphics, Cybersell; Classified Printers – HP/LaserJet 2100TN DISPLAY: Ad make-up applications – CJ 8.02H; Layout Software – CJ.; Display Hardware – HP; Display Printers – HP PRODUCTION: Pagination Software – DTI Ultra Enterprise 450.; Production Equipment – Visioneer, Au/3850 Imager, 1-Konica/66 RA, 2-Konica/550; Cameras – 1-C/Pager; Scanners – 1-Howtek/4000 Desktop, 1-Howtek/2500 Flatbed, AG/Arcus II Flatbed, Aii/3750 PRESSROOM: Line 1 – 6-G/Headliner Offset double width 1987; Folders – 1-G/3:2 1987; Pasters – 6/RTP; Reels and Stands – CT/50; Press control system – G/MCC-MPCS. MAILROOM: Counter stackers – 1-QWI/400, 2-QWI/350; Inserters and stuffers – 1-Harris 8/48, 1-HI/1572, 1-HI 8/48; Bundle tying machines – 3-Dynaric/1500, 1-OVL/JP-80, 1/Dynaric Q52000; Wrapping singles – 2-/QWI, 2-Id/6113, Viper; Addressing machine – 1-/Ch, 1-Ch/5 BUSINESS COMPUTERS: Business Software – CJ; Business Hardware – HP/3000-937

BROOKHAVEN

DAILY LEADER

128 N. Railroad Ave., Brookhaven, Miss., 39602; gen tel (601) 833-6961; adv tel 601-833-6961; ed tel 601-833-6961; gen fax (601) 833-6714; adv fax 601-823-5853; ed fax 601-833-6714; adv e-mail advertising@dailyherald.com; ed e-mail mcoleman@dailyleader.com; web site www.dailyleader.com

Group: Southwest Publishers Inc
Published: Tues, Wed, Thur, Fri, Sun
Weekday Frequency: e
Circulation: 7,800; 6,200(sun)
Last Audit: ABC September 30, 2011
Price: 10.00/mo.
Advertising: Open inch rate $12.89
Insert rate: CPM based on page Qty
News services: AP.
Politics: 1883
Advertising not accepted: Y
Not Published: New Year; Independence Day; Labor Day; Thanksgiving; Christmas.
Own facility?: Y
Special Editions: FOCUS Magazine - quarterly
Brides Magazine - annually
Gridiron Magazine - annually
Special Weekly Sections: Church Page (Fri); TV Guide (S); Outdoors Page (Thur); Best Food Day (Wed).
Magazines: Parade (S). Relish (m)
Profile: Community daily newspaper serving Southwest Mississippi
Exec. Vice Pres./Sec./Treasurer ..Amy A. Jacobs
Dir., Mktg./Promo......................Glynna Broxon
Mng. Ed....................................Matt Coleman
Editorial Page Ed.................William O. Jacobs
Sports Ed...Tom Goetz
Prodn. Mgr., Pressroom ....Malcom Stewart
Market Information: TMC.
Mechanical available: Offset; Black and 3 ROP colors; insert accepted; page cutoffs - 21 1/2.
Mechanical Specifications: Type page 13 x 21 1/2; E - 6 cols, 2 1/16, 1/8 between; A - 6 cols, 2 1/16, 1/8 between; C - 6 cols, 2 1/16, 1/8 between.
Commodity Consumption: Avg. Page Number Per Issue - Daily 16; Avg. Page Number Per Issue - Plates Used 3900; Avg. Page Number Per Issue - Sunday 24; widths 27 1/2; Newsprint Used - Short Tons 300; Printing Ink Used - Black 9500; Printing Ink Used - Color 1000; Printing Ink Use
Equipment EDITORIAL: Front-end Software – MS Word, InDesign; Editorial Hardware – Imac CLASSIFIED: Front-end Software – Mk, Baseview.; Classified Hardware – Imac DISPLAY: Ad make-up applications – InDesign; Layout Software – APP/Mac.; Display Hardware – iMac; Display Printers – APP/Mac LaserWriter II PRODUCTION: Pagination Software – InDesign; Production Equipment – BaysPrint; Scanners – APP/Mac Scanner PRESSROOM: Line 1 – KP/News King 1988; Line 2 – KP/News King 1988; Line 3 – KP/News King 1988; Line 4 – KP/News King 1988; Line 5 – KP/News King 1988; Line 6 – KP/News King 1996; Line 7 – KP/News King 1994; Line 8 – KP/News King 1996; Folders – KP/KJ-8.; Bundle tying machines – Sivaron; Addressing machine – Cheshire BUSINESS COMPUTERS: Business Software – Vision Data; Business Hardware – PC
Zip Codes served: 39601,39629,39662,39191,39654,39665,39641,39647,39668,39644,39666
Delivery method: Private Carrier, Racks

SOUTHWEST PUBLISHERS, INC.

PO Box 551, Brookhaven, Miss., 39602; gen tel (601) 833-6961; gen fax (601) 833-6714; adv fax (601) 823-5853; gen e-mail news@dailyleader.com; adv e-mail classified@dailyleader.com; web site www.dailyleader.com

Published: Tues, Wed, Thur, Fri, Sun
Weekday Frequency: e
Circulation: 5,826; 5,931(sun)
Insert rate: $50/1000 single Sheet
Politics: 1883

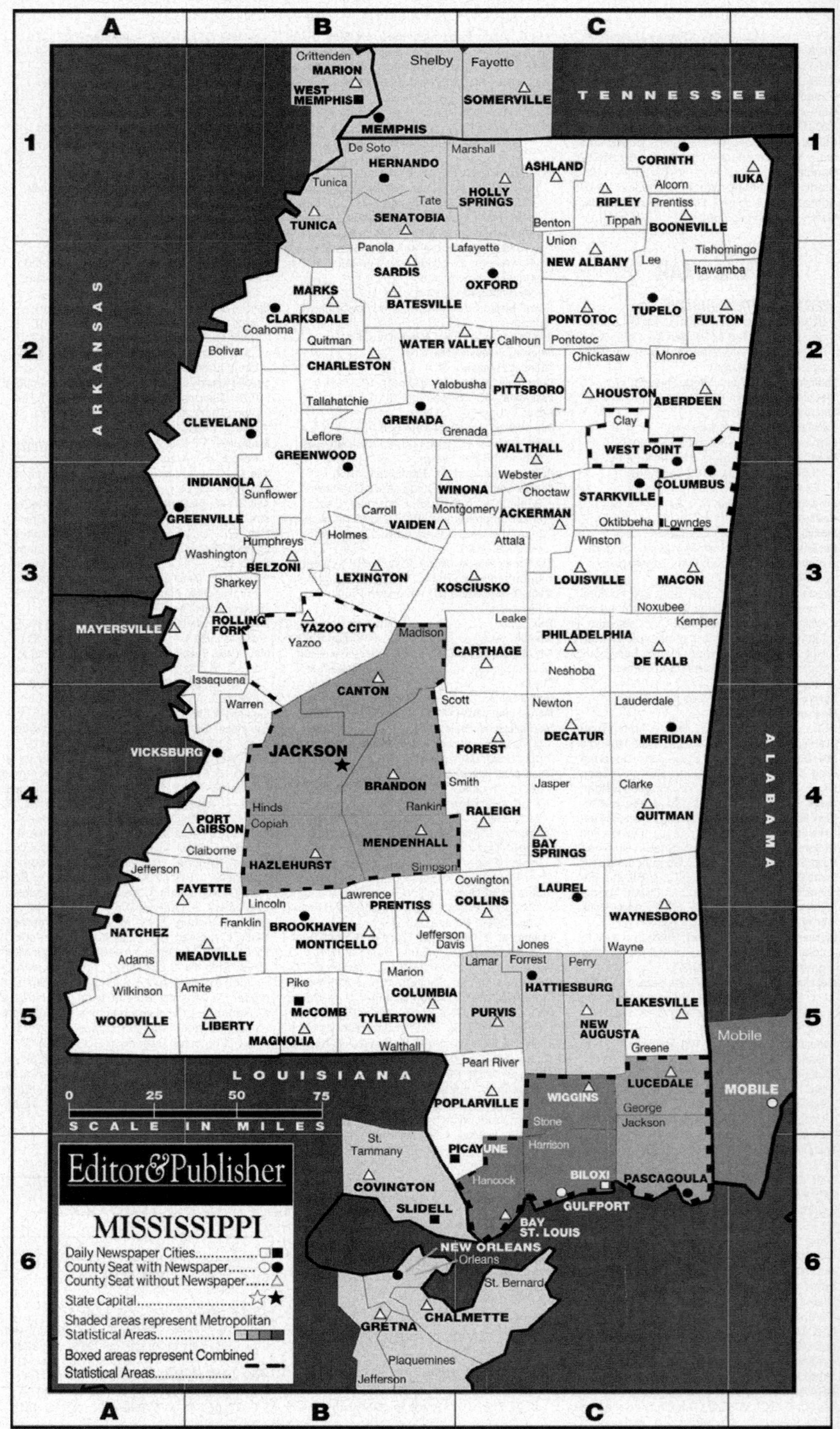

Not Published: Monday, Saturday
Own facility?: Y
Equipment; Classified Hardware – MacIntosh; Classified Equipment – Media Span; Classified Printers – Lexmark & Okidata; Press Drives – 75 HP; Folders – K-J8 MAILROOM: Counter stackers – 2 BUSINESS COMPUTERS: Business Software – Vision Data; Business Hardware – Varied
Zip Codes served: 39601, 39629, 39662, 39191, 39654, 39665, 39641, 39647, 39668
Delivery method: Mail, Newsstand, Private Carrier

CLARKSDALE

THE CLARKSDALE PRESS REGISTER

123 E. Second St., Clarksdale, Miss., 38614-1119; gen tel (662) 627-2201; adv tel (662) 627-2201; ed tel (662) 627-2201; gen fax (662) 624-5125; adv fax (662) 624-5125; ed fax (662) 624-5125; web site www.press-register.com
Published: Tues, Wed, Thur, Fri, Sun
Weekday Frequency: e
Circulation: 5,200; 5,200(sun)
Last Audit: September 29, 2005
Price: 10.00/mo.
Advertising: Open inch rate $10.55
News services: AP.
Politics: Independent.
Special Editions: Economic Profile (Apr); Back-to-School (Aug); Christmas Gift Guide (Dec); Thanksgiving/Christmas Kick-Off (Nov); Women in Business (Oct).
Magazines: Parade (S); Entertainment Tab (Sat).
Pub. ....Jay Strasner
Office Mgr. ....Sandy Hite
Adv. Dir. ....Brenda Keller
Ed. ....Patricia Hymel
Mechanical available: Offset; Black and 3 ROP colors; insert accepted - standing cards, catalogs; page cutoffs - 21 1/2.
Mechanical Specifications: Type page 13 x 21 1/2; E - 6 cols, 2 1/16, 1/8 between; A - 6 cols, 2 1/16, 1/8 between; C - 8 cols, 1 1/2, 1/8 between.
Commodity Consumption: Avg. Page Number Per Issue - Daily 14; widths 14; Newsprint Used - Short Tons 300.
Equipment EDITORIAL: Front-end Software – QPS/QuarkXPress.; Editorial Hardware – 7-IBM; Editorial Equipment – Lf/AP Leaf Picture Desk; Editorial Printers – Xante/3G CLASSIFIED: Front-end Software – Synaptic.; Classified Hardware – 2-IBM; Classified Printers – Xante/3G DISPLAY: Ad make-up applications – QPS/QuarkXPress; Layout Software – 1-IBM/8507 Terminal.; Display Printers – Xante 3G; Production Equipment – 1-B, 1-Kodamatic/425 Processor; Cameras – 1-B; Scanners – Equipment □ QPS/QuarkXPress 3.32. PRESSROOM: Line 1 – 6-KP/Daily King; Reels and Stands – 6; Inserters and stuffers – 1/St; Bundle tying machines – 3-/Bu; Addressing machine – 1-/PB.; Business Hardware – 1-ATT/Unix

DELTA PRESS PUBLISHING CO.

123 E. 2nd St., Clarksdale, Miss., 38614; gen tel (662) 627-2201; gen fax (662) 624-5125

CLEVELAND

THE BOLIVAR COMMERCIAL

821 N. Chrisman Ave., Cleveland, Miss., 38732; gen tel (662) 843-4241; adv tel (662) 843-4241; ed tel (662) 843-4241; gen fax (662) 843-1830; adv fax (662) 843-1830; ed fax (662) 843-1830; adv e-mail david.laster@bolivarcommercial.com; ed e-mail denise.strub@bolivarcommercial.com; web site www.bolivarcom.com
Published: Mon, Tues, Wed, Thur, Fri
Weekday Frequency: e
Circulation: 6,205
Last Audit: September 30, 2008
Price: 78.00/yr.
Advertising: Open inch rate $9.95
News services: AP.
Politics: Independent.
Not Published: New Year; Independence Day; Labor Day; Thanksgiving; Christmas.
Special Editions: Crosstie Arts Festival (Apr); Football (Aug); Christmas Gift Guide (Dec); Valentine (Feb); Delta Agriculture Expo (Jan); Back-to-School (Jul); Summer/Outdoor (Jun); Italian Festival of Mississippi (Mar); Nurses' Week (May); Light Up Your Holidays (Nov); B
Special Weekly Sections: Business (Fri); Sports Wrap-up (Mon); Best Food Day (Wed).
Magazines: American Profile (Weekly).
Pub. ....Mark Williams
Adv. Mgr. ....David Laster
Circ. Mgr. ....Curtis Peepleas
Mng. Ed. ....Denise Strub
Sports Ed. ....Andy Collier
Prodn. Mgr. ....Sharon Clinton
Head Pressman ....Spencer Haywood
Market Information: Split run; TMC; Zoned editions.
Mechanical available: Offset; Black and 1 ROP colors; insert accepted; page cutoffs - 22 3/4.
Mechanical Specifications: Type page 13 x 21 1/2; E - 6 cols, 2 1/16, 1/8 between; A - 6 cols, 2 1/16, 1/8 between; C - 8 cols, 1 1/2, 1/8 between.
Commodity Consumption: Avg. Page Number Per Issue - Daily 14; Avg. Page Number Per Issue - Plates Used 3640; widths 27 1/2; Newsprint Used - Short Tons 240; Printing Ink Used - Black 4750; Printing Ink Used - Color 150; Printing Ink Used - Pages Printed 3664.
Equipment EDITORIAL: Front-end Software – Baseview.; Editorial Hardware – 8-APP/Mac Quadra 605; Editorial Printers – NewGen/1200 Turbo Laser CLASSIFIED: Front-end Software – Baseview.; Classified Hardware – 1-APP/Mac Quadra DISPLAY: Ad make-up applications – QPS/QuarkXPress, Adobe/Photoshop.; Display Hardware – 3-APP/Mac Quadra 650 PRODUCTION: Pagination Software – Baseview.; Production Equipment – 1-Amerigraph, Polaroid; Cameras – 1-B; Scanners – 1-HP, Polaroid PRESSROOM: Line 1 – 5-G/Community; Folders – 1 MAILROOM: Counter stackers – Systems Technology Inc.; Bundle tying machines – 1/MLN; Mailroom control system – RSK/4025 LX; Addressing machine – 2-/Dispensa-Matic/16. BUSINESS COMPUTERS: Business Software – PBS; Business Hardware – DEC/XL-466, 2-Genicom/3840P Printer

COLUMBUS

THE COMMERCIAL DISPATCH

516 Main St., Columbus, Miss., 39703-0511; gen tel (662) 328-2424; adv tel (662) 328-2427; ed tel (662) 328-2471; gen fax (662) 329-8937; adv fax (662) 329-1521; ed fax (662) 329-8937; gen e-mail letters@cdispatch.com; adv e-mail artist@cdispatch.com; ed e-mail letters@cdispatch.com; web site www.cdispatch.com
Published: Mon, Tues, Wed, Thur, Fri, Sun
Weekday Frequency: e
Circulation: 13,338; 13,997(sun)
Last Audit: March 31, 2008
Price: 9.00/mo.
Advertising: Open inch rate $14.85
News services: AP, LAT-WP.
Politics: Independent. **Established:** 1879
Special Editions: Football Preview (Aug); Health & Fitness (Feb); Money & Taxes (Jan); FYI (Jun); Home & Garden (Mar); Salute to Family Owned Business (May); Back to School (Sept).
Special Weekly Sections: Religion & Church Directory (Fri); What's on TV Tab (S); Best Food Day (Wed).
Magazines: Parade (S).
Broadcast Affiliations: WCBI-TV.
Gen. Mgr. ....Birney Imes
Bus. Mgr./Controller ....Terri Collums
Adv. Mgr. ....Hye Coleman
Asst. Adv. Dir. ....Samantha Williamson
Circ. Dir. ....Bobby Tingle
Mng. Ed. ....Steve Mullen
Lifestyle Ed. ....Jan Swoope
News Ed. ....Garthia Elena Burnett
Sports Ed. ....Adam Minichino
Asst. Sports Ed. ....Danny P. Smith
Prodn. Mgr. ....Jeff Lipsey
Pre Press Mgr. ....Tina Perry
Market Information: TMC.
Mechanical available: Offset; Black and 3 ROP colors; insert accepted - pocket-book or single card; page cutoffs - 21 1/2.
Mechanical Specifications: Type page 13 x 21 1/2; E - 6 cols, 2 1/16, 1/8 between; A - 6 cols, 2 1/16, 1/8 between; C - 9 cols, 1 3/8, 1/8 between.
Commodity Consumption: Avg. Page Number Per Issue - Daily 26; Avg. Page Number Per Issue - Sunday 50; widths 25; Newsprint Used - Short Tons 970; Printing Ink Used - Black 20500; Printing Ink Used - Color 2100; Printing Ink Used - Pages Printed 8542.
Equipment EDITORIAL: Front-end Software – QPS/QuarkXPress, Synaptic.; Editorial Hardware – L; Editorial Printers – APP/Mac Laser-Writer II CLASSIFIED: Front-end Software – Baseview.; Classified Hardware – APP/iMac, APP/Mac G3; Classified Equipment – 3-AST/Bravo-286; Classified Printers – HP/Laser-Jet 4V, APP/Mac Laser Writer 8500 DISPLAY: Ad make-up applications – QPS/QuarkXPress, Aldus/PageMaker, QPS/QuarkXPress 4.0, Adobe/Illustrator 8.0, Adobe/Photoshop 5.5; Display Hardware – APP/Mac G3; Display Printers – APP/Mac Laser Writer 8500, HP DeskJet 1220S PRODUCTION: Pagination Software – QPS/QuarkXPress.; Production Equipment – APP/Mac LaserWriter II; Cameras – Acti/225; Scanners – Microtek, Nikon/Flatbed, AG/Argus 2 PRESSROOM: Line 1 – 7-G/501(1), G/Urbanite. MAILROOM: Counter stackers – HL/Monitor; Inserters and stuffers – MM/227S 6:1; Bundle tying machines – 1-Sterling/GR40.; Business Hardware – IBM/Sys 400, APP/Mac LaserWriter

CORINTH

THE DAILY CORINTHIAN

1607 S. Harper Rd., Corinth, Miss., 38834; gen tel (662) 287-6111; gen fax (662) 287-3525; gen e-mail news@dailycorinthian.com; ed e-mail advertising@dailycorinthian.com; web site www.dailycorinthian.com
Published: Tues, Wed, Thur, Fri, Sat, Sun
Weekday Frequency: m
Circulation: 6,113; 6,113(sat); 6,186(sun)
Last Audit: September 30, 2008
Price: 10.00/mo; 120.00/yr.
Advertising: Open inch rate $16.95
News services: AP.
Politics: Independent.
Not Published: Christmas.
Special Editions: Bridal Tab (Apr); Back-to-School (Aug); Progress (Feb); Chamber Directory (Jan); Homemakers School (Mar); Tour Guide (May); Christmas Guide (Nov).
Special Weekly Sections: Church Page (Fri).
Magazines: USA WEEKEND Magazine (S).
Pub. ....Reese Terry
Bus. Mgr. ....Beth Cossett
Circ. Dir. ....Amy Mercer
News Ed. ....Wax Stein
Prodn. Foreman, Pressroom ....Wayne Hodges
Market Information: TMC.
Mechanical available: Offset; Black and 3 ROP colors; insert accepted; page cutoffs - 21.
Mechanical Specifications: Type page 13 x 21; E - 6 cols, 1 4/5, 1/8 between; A - 6 cols, 1 4/5, 1/8 between; C - 9 cols, 1 9/20, 1/8 between.
Commodity Consumption: Avg. Page Number Per Issue - Daily 22; Avg. Page Number Per Issue - Plates Used 10800; Avg. Page Number Per Issue - Saturday 20; Avg. Page Number Per Issue - Sunday 26; widths 25; Newsprint Used - Short Tons 339; Printing Ink Used - Black 15300; Printing
Equipment EDITORIAL: Front-end Software – Baseview/NewsEdit Pro, QPS/QuarkXPress 3.32.; Editorial Hardware – APP/Mac; Editorial Equipment – 8-Dewar/Disc Net CLASSIFIED: Front-end Software – Ad Manager Pro 2.0.6.; Classified Hardware – APP/Mac; Classified Equipment – APP/Mac DISPLAY: Ad make-up applications – Multi-Ad/Creator, QPS/QuarkX-Press 3.32.; Display Hardware – 4-APP/Mac G3; Display Printers – Xante/8200, Xerox/Phaser 740 Color PRODUCTION: Pagination Software – QPS/QuarkXPress 3.32.; Production Equipment – 1-Nu/Plate Burner, Xante/Accel-a-Writer 3G; Cameras – 1-B/Caravel; Scanners – 2-Microtek/ScanMaker II XE Flatbed, Nikon/Coolscan-Polaroid/Sprint Scan, Microtek 9600 XL Flatbed PRESSROOM: Line 1 – 7-G/Community 1982.; Inserters and stuffers – KAN/480; Bundle tying machines – MLN/Strapper.; Audio Hardware – Software □ AP Stockquote Hotline BUSINESS COMPUTERS: Business Software – INSI; Business Hardware – APP/Mac

PAXTON MEDIA

1607 S. Harper Rd., Corinth, Miss., 38834; gen tel (662) 287-6111; gen fax (662) 287-3525

GREENVILLE

DELTA DEMOCRAT PUBLISHING CO., INC.

988 N Broadway Dr, Greenville, Miss., 38702; gen tel (662) 335-1155; gen fax (662) 335-2860
Published: Mon, Tues, Wed, Thur, Fri, Sun
Weekday Frequency: e

DELTA DEMOCRAT TIMES

988 N. Broadway, Greenville, Miss., 38701-2349; gen tel (662) 335-1155; adv tel (662) 378-0741; gen fax (662) 335-2860; ed fax (662) 378-0777; gen e-mail ddtnews@ddtonline.com; web site www.ddtonline.com
Published: Mon, Tues, Wed, Thur, Fri, Sun
Weekday Frequency: e
Circulation: 6,071; 7,211(sun)
Last Audit: ABC September 30, 2011
News services: AP.
Politics: Libertarian.
Special Editions: Fall Football (Aug); Bridal (Feb); Back-to-School (Jul); Our Town (Mar); Holiday Shopping Guide (Nov).
Special Weekly Sections: Church Page (Fri); Business (Mon); Entertainment (Thur); Business News & Views (Tues); Best Food Day (Wed).
Magazines: Color Comics (S).
Market Information: ADS; TMC.
Mechanical available: Offset; Black and 3 ROP colors; insert accepted - booklets; page cutoffs - 22 3/4.
Mechanical Specifications: Type page 13 x 21 1/2; E - 6 cols, 2 1/16, 1/8 between; A - 6 cols, 2 1/16, 1/8 between; C - 8 cols, 1 1/2, 1/16 between.
Commodity Consumption: Avg. Page Number Per Issue - Daily 14; Avg. Page Number Per Issue - Sunday 40; widths 13 1/2; Newsprint Used - Metric Tons 650; Newsprint Used - Short Tons 720.

GREENWOOD

THE GREENWOOD COMMONWEALTH

329 Hwy. 82 W., Greenwood, Miss., 38930; gen tel (662) 453-5312; gen fax (662) 453-2908; gen e-mail commonwealth@gwcommonwealth.com; web site www.gwcommonwealth.com
Published: Mon, Tues, Wed, Thur, Fri, Sun
Weekday Frequency: e
Circulation: 6,053; 6,389(sun)
Last Audit: ABC September 30, 2011

Price: 11.00/mo; 126.00/yr.
Advertising: Open inch rate $14.90
News services: AP.
Politics: Independent. **Established:** 1896
Not Published: Independence Day; Labor Day.
Special Editions: Football (Aug); Christmas Greetings (Dec); Profile (Feb); Health and Fitness (Jul); Families in Business (Mar); Farming (May); Christmas Gift Guide (Nov); People's Choice (Oct).
Special Weekly Sections: Religion (Fri); Color Comics (S).
Magazines: Leflore Illustrated Weddings (Annually); Parade (S); Leflore Illustrated (Semi-yearly).
Bus. Mgr.........Eddie Ray
Adv. Mgr.........Larry Alderman
Circ. Mgr.........Shirley Cooper
Mng. Ed.........Charles Corder
Editorial Page Ed.........Tim Kalich
Lifestyles Ed.........Andrea Hall
Sports Ed.........Bill Burrus
Market Information: TMC.
Mechanical available: Offset; Black and 3 ROP colors; insert accepted - all; page cutoffs - 22 3/4.
Mechanical Specifications: Type page 11 x 21 1/2; E - 6 cols, 1 3/4, 1/8 between; A - 6 cols, 1 3/4, 1/8 between; C - 8 cols, 1 1/4, 1/8 between.
Commodity Consumption: Avg. Page Number Per Issue - Daily 14; Avg. Page Number Per Issue - Plates Used 5500; Avg. Page Number Per Issue - Sunday 30; widths 28; Newsprint Used - Short Tons 260; Printing Ink Used - Black 81000; Printing Ink Used - Color 1.340; Printing Ink Used
Equipment; Editorial Hardware – 1-PC Warehouse/Pent 100, 4-PC Warehouse/System 486, 1-Princeton/Monitor, 1-HP/Pavilion Pent 200, 1-Plus Data/Pent 133, 3-Optiquest/Q71 Monitor, 2-Optiquest/Q51 Monitor, 1-Gateway/GP7 Pentium 111-600, 1-Pentium/111-733, 1-Gateway/GP7 Pentium III CLASSIFIED: Front-end Software – Sun/Suntype Classified System 4.1.; Classified Hardware – 1-Compaq/Deskpro 2000, 1-Optiquest/Q71; Classified Printers – NewGen/Turbo PS800P DISPLAY: Ad make-up applications – QPS/QuarkXPress 3.32, QPS/QuarkXpress 4.1, Adobe/Live Motion, A; Display Hardware – 1-PC Warehouse Pent 100, 1-PC Warehouse System 486, 1-Compaq Presario 366 Pent, 3-Optiquest/Q71, 2-Gateway GP7, Pentium 111/667, 1-Optiquest/Q51; Display Printers – Xante/8200W PRODUCTION: Pagination Software – QPS/QuarkXPress 3.32.; Production Equipment – 1-Amerigraph/Magnum Platemaker, Xante/Laser 8200W, ECR/Scriptwriter VRL 36; Cameras – 1-R/580; Scanners – HP/ScanJet 4C, Polaroid/SprintScan 4000 PRESSROOM: Line 1 – 6-KP/News King (colorking) 1970; Folders – 1-KP/K-6. MAILROOM: Counter stackers – 14-KAN/Quadra Cart; Inserters and stuffers – 5-KAN/320; Bundle tying machines – CYP/Rotan 500N, MLN/SP300; Addressing machine – KR/215. BUSINESS COMPUTERS: Business Software – Vision Data, AccPac BPI-GL; Business Hardware – Compaq/Proliant 800, 1-Maxum/486, HP/Pavilion

GRENADA

THE DAILY STAR

50 Corporate Row, Grenada, Miss., 38901-2823; gen tel (662) 226-4321; gen fax (662) 226-8310; gen e-mail dailystar@grenadastar.com; ed e-mail editor@grenadastar.com; web site www.grenadastar.com
Published: Mon, Tues, Wed, Thur, Fri
Weekday Frequency: e
Circulation: 5,776
Last Audit: September 30, 2001
Price: 8.75/mo; 107.00/yr.
Advertising: Open inch rate $9.00
News services: AP.
Politics: Independent.
Advertising not accepted: Abortion; Adoption; 900 numbers; Envelope stuffers.
Not Published: New Year; Memorial Day; Independence Day; Labor Day; Thanksgiving; Christmas.
Special Editions: Back-to-School (Aug); Christmas Greetings (Dec); Brides (Feb); Tax Tips (Jan); Progress (Jun); Spring Fashion (Mar); Graduation (May); Thanksgiving (Nov); Basketball (Oct); Fall Fashion (Sept).
Magazines: American Profile (Weekly).
Pub.........Joseph B. Lee
Sec./Treasurer........Brenda R. Lee
Gen. Mgr.........Fred Adams
Lifestyle Ed.........Nannette Lascer
Sports Ed.........Chuck Hathcock
Creative Servs. Mgr.........Musset McPhail
Data Processing Mgr.........Stephanie Dees
Market Information: Split run; TMC; Zoned editions.
Mechanical available: Offset; Black and 3 ROP colors; insert accepted; page cutoffs - 22 3/4.
Mechanical Specifications: Type page 13 x 21 1/2; E - 6 cols, 2 1/16, 1/8 between; A - 6 cols, 2 1/16, 1/8 between; C - 6 cols, 2 1/16, 1/8 between.
Commodity Consumption: Avg. Page Number Per Issue - Daily 16.
Equipment EDITORIAL: Front-end Software – QPS, Microsoft/Word.; Editorial Hardware – ACT, APP/Mac, Gateway/2000; Editorial Printers – Xante CLASSIFIED: Front-end Software – Synaptic.; Classified Hardware – PC DISPLAY: Ad make-up applications – QPS/QuarkXPress 3.32; Layout Software – QPS/QuarkXPress, Adobe/Photoshop.; Display Hardware – APP/Mac, PC, Gateway/2000; Display Printers – Xante/Accel-a-Writer PRODUCTION: Pagination Software – QPS/QuarkXPress 3.31.; Production Equipment – Caere/OmniPage Pro 6.0; Cameras – C/Spartan III; Scanners – Umax PRESSROOM: Line 1 – 6-KP/News King 1968.; Business Hardware – Software □ Synaptic

HATTIESBURG

HATTIESBURG AMERICAN

825 N. Main St., Hattiesburg, Miss., 39401; gen tel (601) 582-4321; ed tel (601)584-3070; gen fax (601) 584-3075; adv fax (601)584-3074; ed fax (601) 584-3130; gen e-mail tfowler@hattiesburgamerican.com; web site www.hattiesburgamerican.com
Group: The Gannett Company
Published: Mon, Tues, Wed, Thur, Fri, Sat, Sun
Weekday Frequency: e
Saturday Frequency: m
Circulation: 11,560; 14,094(sat); 16,377(sun)
Last Audit: ABC September 30, 2011
Price: 15.50/mo; 186/yr.
News services: AP, GNS.
Politics: Independent.
Note: The Hattiesburg American is printed at the Clarion Ledger located at 201 S. Congress Street, Jackson, MS.
Own facility?: Y
Special Editions: Bridal (Jan)
Progress Ed (Jan)
Newcomers (June)
Football (Aug)
Magazines: American Homes Guide (Monthly); USA WEEKEND Magazine (S).
Circ. Mgr.........Rosalind Cooley
Metro Ed.........Erin Kosnac
Online Ed.........Lici Beveridge
Asst. Sports Ed.........Alan Hinton
Mgr., Bus. Systems........Sherri McCain
Market Information: TMC.
Mechanical available: Offset; Black and 3 ROP colors; insert accepted; page cutoffs - 21 1/2.
Mechanical Specifications: Type page 13 x 21 1/2; E - 6 cols, 2 1/16, 1/8 between; A - 6 cols, 2 1/16, 1/8 between; C - 9 cols, 1 5/16, 1/8 between.
Commodity Consumption: Avg. Page Number Per Issue - Daily 26; Avg. Page Number Per Issue - Plates Used 21762; Avg. Page Number Per Issue - Sunday 69; widths 27 1/4; Newsprint Used - Short Tons 2097; Printing Ink Used - Black 43260; Printing Ink Used - Color 25507; Printing Ink
Equipment; Classified Hardware – Mactive; Reels and Stands – ; Business Hardware – IBM/AS-400
Zip Codes served:
39401,39402,39465,39455,39474
Delivery method: Mail, Newsstand, Private Carrier, Racks

HERNANDO

DESOTO TIMES TODAY

315 Losher St., Hernando, Miss., 38632; gen tel (662) 429-6397; gen fax (662) 429-5229; adv e-mail edalecross@desototimes.com; ed e-mail editor@desototimes.com; web site www.desototimes.com
Published: Tues, Wed, Thur, Fri, Sat
Weekday Frequency: m
Circulation: 7,810; 7,810(sat)
Last Audit: September 30, 2001
Price: 9.00/mo; 108.00/yr.
Advertising: Open inch rate $11.35
News services: AP.
Not Published: New Year; Independence Day; Thanksgiving; Christmas.
Special Editions: Home (Apr); Football (Aug); Gift Guide (Dec); Weddings (Feb); Education (Jul); Visitor's Guide (Jun); Home (Mar); Graduation (May); Gift Guide (Nov); Cars (Oct).
Special Weekly Sections: Time for Weekend (Fri); Church (Sat); Food (Wed).
Pub.........Brian Bloom
Adv. Dir.........Dale Cross
Ed.........Curt Middleton
Market Information: ADS; TMC.
Mechanical available: Offset; Black and ROP colors; insert accepted; page cutoffs - 21.
Mechanical Specifications: Type page 13 x 21; E - 6 cols, 2 3/100, 1/6 between; A - 6 cols, 2 3/100, 1/6 between; C - 8 cols, 1 1/2, 1/6 between.
Equipment EDITORIAL: Front-end Software – Baseview/News Edit.; Editorial Hardware – APP/Mac CLASSIFIED: Front-end Software – Baseview/Ad Manager Pro.; Classified Hardware – APP/Mac DISPLAY: Ad make-up applications – QPS/QuarkXPress; Layout Software – APP/Mac.; Display Hardware – Baseview/Ad Manager Pro PRODUCTION: Pagination Software – QPS/QuarkXPress.; Production Equipment – Pre Press/Panther Plus

JACKSON

THE CLARION-LEDGER

201 S. Congress St., Jackson, Miss., 39201-4202; gen tel (601) 961-7000; adv tel (601) 961-7142; ed tel (601) 961-7330; adv fax (601) 961-7155; ed fax (601) 961-7211; web site www.clarionledger.com
Group: Gannett
Published: Mon, Tues, Wed, Thur, Fri, Sat, Sun
Weekday Frequency: m
Saturday Frequency: m
Circulation: 59,166; 60,786(sat); 74,744(sun)
Last Audit: ABC September 30, 2011
Price: 16.75/mo; 201.00/yr.
News services: AP, NYT, GNS, NNA, Independent Press.
Politics: Independent. **Established:** 1837
Note: The Jackson Clarion-Ledger (mS) has a combination rate of $180.35(mon to fri), $180.35(sat) and $217.66(S) with the Hattiesburg American (eS). Individual newspaper rates not made available.
Advertising not accepted: Y
Own facility?: Y
Special Editions: College Football (Aug); FYI (Jun); Week on the Water (May); Tour of Homes (Oct); Tis the Season Holiday Gift Guide (Nov & Dec.)
Special Weekly Sections: Autos (Fri); e-tech (Mon); Perspective (S); Religion (Sat); Mississippi Weekend (Thur); Heath Scene (Tues); Food (Wed).
Magazines: USA WEEKEND Magazine (S).
VIP Magazine
Broadcast Affiliations: TV-WLBT, WAPT, WJTV, WDBD.
Dir., Finance........Joe Williams
Credit Mgr.........Carolyn Allen
Adv. Dir.........Roland Weeks
Adv. Pre Prints........Beverly Bennett
Circ. Mgr.........Vera Bridges
Circ. Mgr., Single Copy........Chris Hutchinson
Bus. Ed.........Kevin Richardson
Editorial Cartoonist........Marshall Ramsey
Editorial Page Ed.........David Hampton
Assistant Managing Editor/Multimedia Earnest Hart
Asst. Managing Editor/News & Business Debbie Skipper
Metro Ed.........Grace Simmons Fisher
Publisher........Leslie Hurst
Sales and Marketing Manager....Mary Ann Kirby
Market Information: Split run; TMC; Zoned editions.
Mechanical available: Offset; Black and 4 ROP colors; insert accepted - print & deliver, samples; page cutoffs - 22.
Mechanical Specifications: Type page 11 1/8 x 21; E - 6 cols, 1 3/4, 1/8 between; A - 6 cols, 1 3/4, 1/8 between; C - 10 cols, 1.063, .0556 between.
Commodity Consumption: Avg. Page Number Per Issue - Daily 54; Avg. Page Number Per Issue - Plates Used 134000; Avg. Page Number Per Issue - Sunday 122; widths 27; Newsprint Used - Short Tons 15429; Printing Ink Used - Black 283200; Printing Ink Used - Color 136000; Printing In
Equipment EDITORIAL: Front-end Software – QPS 1.12.; Editorial Hardware – QPS CLASSIFIED: Front-end Software – DTI/ClassSpeed 4.2.2.; Classified Hardware – DELL PC; Classified Printers – HP, CANON DISPLAY: Ad make-up applications – AD TEACHER/INDESIGN; Layout Software – MEI/ALS. MACTIVE PGL; Display Hardware – DELL PC; Display Printers – QMS/860, AU/Broadsheet, HP/650C, Tektronix/780, CANON, XANTE PRODUCTION: Pagination Software – QPS.; Production Equipment – APP/Server, Graham, 1-K/550; Cameras – 1-C/Spartan; Scanners – 6-Umax/UC-1260 Flatbed, 2-Tecsa/TS2470, 2-AG/Argus 2, 1-Linotype-Hell/Opal Ultra PRESSROOM: Line 1 – 8-G/Metroliner (double width) 1982; Line 2 – 8-G/Metroliner (double width) 1995; Folders – 2-1982, 2-1995; Pasters – G/3-arm RTP. MAILROOM: Counter stackers – 3-Id, 6/QWI; Inserters and stuffers – 2-S/1372P, 1-NP/630; Bundle tying machines – 2-MLN/News 90, 4-/Sterlings, 2-/OVL; Other equipment –MM/Stitcher-Trimmer.; Audio Hardware – Meridian Mail; Business Hardware – IBM AS/400

LAUREL

LAUREL LEADER-CALL

130 Beacon St., Laurel, Miss., 39440; gen tel (601) 428-0551; gen fax (601) 426-3550; adv e-mail ad1@laurelleadercall.com; ed e-mail editor@laurelleadercall.com; web site www.leadercall.com
Group: CNHI
Published: Tues, Wed, Thur, Sun
Weekday Frequency: m
Saturday Frequency: m
Circulation: 7,636; 7,636(sat); 7,454(sun)
Last Audit: March 31, 2008
Price: 6.95/mo; 75.00/yr.
Advertising: Open inch rate $12.50
News services: AP.
Politics: 1911
Not Published: New Year; Independence Day; Labor Day; Christmas.
Own facility?: Y
Special Weekly Sections: TV Entertainment (Sat); Best Food Day (Wed).
Magazines: Relish (Monthly); Parade (S).
Business Manager........Skippy Hiha
Circ. Mgr.........Lisa Miller
Ed.........Rob Sigler
Publisher........Mitchell Lynch
Mechanical available: Offset; Black and 3 ROP

colors; insert accepted; page cutoffs - 22 3/4.
Mechanical Specifications: Type page 13 x 21 1/2; E - 6 cols, 2 1/16, 1/8 between; A - 6 cols, 2 1/16, 1/8 between; C - 9 cols, 1 3/8, 1/16 between.
Commodity Consumption: Avg. Page Number Per Issue - Daily 16.
Equipment; Editorial Hardware – APP/Mac.; Classified Hardware – APP/Mac.; Display Hardware – APP/Mac.; Production Equipment – 2-APP/Mac LaserPrinter; Cameras – 1-R/500. PRESSROOM: Line 1 – 8-G/Community SFC; Folders – 1; Bundle tying machines – 1/Ms; Addressing machine – 1-Am/4000EP.
Delivery method: Mail, Newsstand, Private Carrier, Racks

MCCOMB

ENTERPRISE-JOURNAL

112 Oliver Emmerich Dr., McComb, Miss., 39648-6330; gen tel (601) 684-2421; gen fax (601) 684-0836; adv e-mail advertising@enterprise-journal.com; ed e-mail news@enterprise-journal.com; web site www.enterprise-journal.com
Published: Mon, Tues, Wed, Thur, Fri, Sun
Weekday Frequency: e
Circulation: 9,629; 10,456(sun)
Last Audit: September 30, 2009
Price: 10.00/mo; 120.00/yr.
Advertising: Open inch rate $18.38
News services: AP.
Politics: Independent.
Not Published: New Year; Independence Day; Labor Day; Christmas.
Special Editions: Graduation (Apr); Football (Aug); Christmas Greetings (Dec); Brides (Jan); Back-to-School (Jul); Perspective (Mar); Kids Design-Ad (May); Songbook (Nov); Recipe (Oct); Outdoor (Sept).
Special Weekly Sections: TV Log (S); Best Food Day (Wed).
Magazines: Parade (S).
Purchasing Agent....................Mitch Lambuth
Adv. Mgr.....................Lauren Devereaux
Circ. Dir.....................Tammy Britt
Ed....................Jack Ryan
News Ed.....................Matt Williamson
Prodn. Mgr.....................Keith Hux
Press Mgr.....................Joel Anderson
Market Information: TMC.
Mechanical available: Offset; Black and 3 ROP colors; insert accepted; page cutoffs - 22 3/4.
Mechanical Specifications: Type page 13 x 21 1/2; E - 6 cols, 2, 1/8 between; A - 6 cols, 2, 1/8 between; C - 8 cols, 1 1/2, 1/8 between.
Commodity Consumption: Avg. Page Number Per Issue - Daily 17; Avg. Page Number Per Issue - Plates Used 12000; Avg. Page Number Per Issue - Sunday 38; widths 28; Newsprint Used - Metric Tons 661; Newsprint Used - Short Tons 600; Printing Ink Used - Black 23000; Printing Ink Use
Equipment EDITORIAL: Front-end Software – QPS/QuarkXPress.; Editorial Hardware – PC; Editorial Printers – 2-Xante CLASSIFIED: Front-end Software – Mk, Synaptic.; Classified Hardware – Mk, Compaq DISPLAY: Ad make-up applications – QPS/QuarkXPress.; Display Hardware – IBM/PC PRODUCTION: Pagination Software – QPS/QuarkXPress.; Production Equipment – PC, 1-Nu/Subtractive Plate Processor, Konica/EV Jetsetter; Cameras – C/Spartan II; Scanners – 1-Polaroid, 2-HP, 1-HP/6100 C Flatbed PRESSROOM: Line 1 – Aug-87; Folders – 1, 1-KP/JK8. MAILROOM: Counter stackers – 2-BG/Count-O-Veyor; Inserters and stuffers – MM; Bundle tying machines – 2/MLN; Addressing machine – 1-/KR. BUSINESS COMPUTERS: Business Software – Unix, Vision Data, Accpac BPI; Business Hardware – Compaq

MERIDIAN

THE MERIDIAN STAR

814 22nd Ave., Meridian, Miss., 39301; gen tel (601) 693-1551; adv tel (601) 693-1551; ed tel (601) 693-1551; gen fax (601) 485-1275; adv fax (601) 485-1229; ed fax (601) 485-1275; web site www.meridianstar.com
Group: Mississippi Press Services, Inc.
Published: Mon, Tues, Wed, Thur, Fri, Sat, Sun
Weekday Frequency: m
Saturday Frequency: m
Circulation: 11,568; 11,568(sat); 13,255(sun)
Last Audit: September 30, 2009
Price: 12.00/mo; 131.40/yr.
Advertising: Open inch rate $31.13
News services: AP.
Politics: Independent-Conservative.
Not Published: Christmas.
Special Editions: EMCC Salute (Apr); Bands & Cheerleaders (Aug); Christmas Greetings (Dec); Profile (Feb); Tanning Page (Jan); FYI (Jul); State Games Tab (Jun); Spring Lawn & Garden (Mar); Jimmie Rogers Days (May); Christmas Early Bird Buys (Nov); Who's The Best (Oct); Fal
Special Weekly Sections: TV Viewing (Fri); Best Food Day (Wed).
Magazines: Relish (Monthly); Parade (S); American Profile (Weekly).
Pub.....................Crystal Dupre
Adv. Dir.....................Renae Alexander
Photo Dept. Mgr.....................Paula Merritt
Teen-Age/Youth Ed.....................Ida Brown
Prodn. Mgr., Pressroom....................Joey Poe
Prodn. Mgr., Composing......Jennifer Hammond
Market Information: ADS; TMC.
Mechanical available: Offset; Black and 3 ROP colors; insert accepted; page cutoffs - 22 3/4.
Mechanical Specifications: Type page 13 1/4 x 21 1/2; E - 6 cols, 2, 1/6 between; A - 6 cols, 2, 1/6 between; C - 9 cols, 1 1/2, 1/6 between.
Commodity Consumption: Avg. Page Number Per Issue - Daily 28; Avg. Page Number Per Issue - Plates Used 29000; Avg. Page Number Per Issue - Sunday 40; widths 27; Newsprint Used - Short Tons 3900; Printing Ink Used - Black 99000; Printing Ink Used - Color 20500; Printing Ink Use
Equipment EDITORIAL: Front-end Software – APP/Mac.; Editorial Hardware – APP/Mac; Editorial Printers – APP/Mac LaserWriter II NTX, V CLASSIFIED: Front-end Software – Vision Data, Baseview.; Classified Hardware – Vision Data; Classified Printers – APP/Mac LaserWriter II NTX DISPLAY: Ad make-up applications – Aldus/PageMaker; Layout Software – APP/Mac.; Display Hardware – APP/Mac, APP/Mac II NTX; Production Equipment – 1-Nu, V/Imagesetter; Cameras – C/Spartan III. PRESSROOM: Line 1 – 9-G/Urbanite 1975. MAILROOM: Counter stackers – 2/HL; Inserters and stuffers – 1-/MM 4:1, 1-/KAN (6:1); Bundle tying machines – 4-/MLN; Addressing machine – El.; Business Hardware – Software ☐ Vision Data

NATCHEZ

THE NATCHEZ DEMOCRAT

503 N. Canal St., Natchez, Miss., 39120; gen tel (601) 442-9101; adv tel (601) 442-9101; ed tel (601) 442-9101; gen fax (601) 442-7315; adv fax (601) 442-7315; ed fax (601) 442-7315; gen e-mail newsroom@natchezdemocrat.com; web site www.natchezdemocrat.com
Group: Mississippi Press Services, Inc.
Published: Mon, Tues, Wed, Thur, Fri, Sat, Sun
Weekday Frequency: m
Saturday Frequency: m
Circulation: 8,428; 8,428(sat); 8,536(sun)
Last Audit: September 30, 2005
Price: 13.00/mo (home delivery).
Advertising: Open inch rate $22.36
News services: AP.
Politics: Independent.
Special Editions: Profile (Feb); Natchez & Its Neighbors (Jul); Spring Pilgrimage (Mar); Fall Pilgrimage (Oct).
Special Weekly Sections: Real Estate Preview (Fri); Business/Financial (S); Religion (Sat); Best Food Day (Wed).
Magazines: USA WEEKEND Magazine (S).
Pres.....................Todd H. Carpenter
Pub.....................Kevin Cooper
Bus. Mgr.....................Cassie Strickland
Adv. Mgr.....................Ryan Richardson
Mng. Ed.....................Julie Finley
Sports Ed.....................Jeff Edwards
Prodn. Mgr.....................Johnnie Griffin
Market Information: ADS; TMC; Zoned editions.
Mechanical available: Offset; Black and 3 ROP colors; insert accepted; page cutoffs - 22 3/4.
Mechanical Specifications: Type page 13 x 21 1/2; E - 6 cols, 2 1/16, 1/8 between; A - 6 cols, 2 1/16, 1/8 between; C - 9 cols, 1 3/8, 1/16 between.
Commodity Consumption: Avg. Page Number Per Issue - Daily 20; Avg. Page Number Per Issue - Plates Used 10000; Avg. Page Number Per Issue - Sunday 40; widths 13 3/4; Newsprint Used - Short Tons 775; Printing Ink Used - Black 45000; Printing Ink Used - Color 4500; Printing Ink U
Equipment EDITORIAL: Front-end Software – QPS/QuarkXPress.; Editorial Hardware – 8-APP/Power Mac; Editorial Printers – 2-Xante/8200, 1-QMS/860 CLASSIFIED: Front-end Software – Baseview.; Classified Hardware – 3-APP/Mac Quadra 630; Classified Printers – Xante/8200; Layout Software – 2-APP/Power Mac.; Display Hardware – Printers ☐ 2-Xante/8200, 1-QMS/860 PRODUCTION: Pagination Software – QPS/QuarkXPress.; Production Equipment – 1-Nu; Cameras – 1-C PRESSROOM: Line 1 – 10-KP/News King; Folders – 1-KP/Balloon former; Reels and Stands – 8 MAILROOM: Counter stackers – 1-BG/Count-O-Veyor; Bundle tying machines – 1/Md; Addressing machine – 2-/El, 2-/Am.; Business Hardware – 2-RSK

NATCHEZ NEWSPAPERS, INC.

503 N. Canal St., Natchez, Miss., 39120; gen tel (601) 442-9101; gen fax (601) 442-7315; gen e-mail publisher@natchezdemocrat.com; adv e-mail ads@natchezdemocrat.com; ed e-mail newsroom@natchezdemocrat.com; web site www.natchezdemocrat.com
Group: Boone Newspapers Inc.
Published: Mon, Tues, Wed, Thur, Fri, Sat, Sun
Weekday Frequency: m
Saturday Frequency: m
Circulation: 66,500; 9,500(sat); 9,500(sun)
Last Audit: Sworn
News services: AP, MCT
Politics: 1865
Advertising not accepted: Y
Not Published: None
Own facility?: Y
Publisher....................Kevin Cooper
Pub....................Todd Carpenter
Ed.....................Kari Whipple
Delivery method: Mail, Newsstand, Private Carrier, Racks

OXFORD

THE OXFORD EAGLE

916 Jackson Ave., Oxford, Miss., 38655; gen tel (662) 234-4331; gen fax (662) 234-4351; adv e-mail classified@oxfordeagle.com; ed e-mail news@oxfordeagle.com; web site www.oxfordeagle.com
Group: Mississippi Press Services, Inc.
Published: Mon, Tues, Wed, Thur, Fri
Weekday Frequency: e
Circulation: 5,016
Last Audit: October 1, 2002
Price: 5.75/mo; 69.00/yr; 17.20/3mo.
Advertising: Open inch rate $9.25
News services: AP.
Not Published: New Year; Independence Day; Labor Day; Day after Thanksgiving; Christmas.
Special Weekly Sections: School News (Fri); Business/Finance Page (Mon); Farm/Home Page (Thur); Newcomers (Tues); Food Day (Wed).
Magazines: American Profile (Weekly).
Pres./Pub.....................Tim Phillips
Pres./Pub.....................Rita Vasilyev
Adv. Dir.....................Brian Roy
Circ. Mgr.....................Belinda Jones
Ed....................Don Whitten
News Ed.....................Jon Scott
Photo Ed.....................Bruce Newman
Sports Ed.....................John Davis
Head Pressman....................Eddie Lance
Market Information: TMC.
Mechanical available: Offset; Black and 3 ROP colors; insert accepted; page cutoffs - 22 3/4.
Mechanical Specifications: Type page 13 1/8 x 21; E - 6 cols, 2 1/16, 1/8 between; A - 6 cols, 2 1/16, 1/8 between; C - 8 cols, 1 1/2, 1/8 between.
Commodity Consumption: Avg. Page Number Per Issue - Daily 17; Avg. Page Number Per Issue - Plates Used 3240; widths 28; Newsprint Used - Short Tons 315; Printing Ink Used - Black 15000; Printing Ink Used - Color 210; Printing Ink Used - Pages Printed 3120.
Equipment EDITORIAL: Front-end Software – Baseview/NewsEdit.; Editorial Hardware – COM CLASSIFIED: Front-end Software – Baseview/Class Manager.; Classified Hardware – COM; Layout Software – COM.; Production Equipment – 1-COM/CRT; Cameras – 1-R. PRESSROOM: Line 1 – 6-G/Community (upper folder).; Bundle tying machines – 2/Felins; Addressing machine – 1-/Am. BUSINESS COMPUTERS: Business Software – Word processing; Business Hardware – 1-RSK/16B, 1-RSK/DT 100, 2-RSK/100

PASCAGOULA

THE MISSISSIPPI PRESS

PO Box 849, Pascagoula, Miss., 39568-0849; gen tel (228) 762-1111; adv tel (228) 762-1111; ed tel (228) 934-1424; gen fax (228) 934-1454; adv fax (228) 934-1454; ed fax (228) 934-1474; gen e-mail msnews@themississippipress.com; adv e-mail pressads@themississippipress.com; web site www.gulflive.com
Published: Wed, Thur, Fri, Sun
Weekday Frequency: m
Circulation: 15,050; 14,252(sun)
Last Audit: September 30, 2008
Price: 9.00/mo; 108.00/yr.
Advertising: Open inch rate $33.79
News services: AP, NNS, SHNS, TMS.
Politics: Independent.
Special Editions: Football (Aug); Black History Month (Feb); Back to School (Jul); Newspaper In Education (Mar); Mother's Day (May); Homes & More (Monthly); Christmas Guide (Nov); Peter Anderson Art Festival (Oct); Home & Garden Show (Sept).
Special Weekly Sections: Fishing (Fri); Health (S); Religion (Sat); Entertainment/TV (Thur).
Pub.....................Wanda Heary Jacobs
Pub.....................Gareth Clary
Adv. Mgr.....................Roy May
Features Ed.....................Susan Ruddiman
Market Information: Split run; TMC; Zoned editions.
Mechanical available: Offset; Black and 3 ROP colors; insert accepted - mini, flexi, spadea; page cutoffs - 22 3/4.
Mechanical Specifications: Type page 11 5/8 x 21 1/2; E - 6 cols, 1 13/16, 1/8 between; A - 6 cols, 1 13/16, 1/8 between; C - 10 cols, 1 1/16, 1/8 between.
Commodity Consumption: Avg. Page Number Per Issue - Daily 32; Avg. Page Number Per Issue - Plates Used 20000; Avg. Page Number Per Issue - Sunday 48; widths 12 1/2; Newsprint Used - Metric Tons 1002; Newsprint Used - Short Tons 1104; Printing Ink Used - Black 25000; Printing I
Equipment EDITORIAL: Front-end Software – Baseview.; Editorial Hardware – 5-APP/Mac

(with file server); Editorial Equipment – Scenic-Soft/OPI Color Central 2,2; Editorial Printers – AU/3850, AU/108C CLASSIFIED: Front-end Software – Baseview, QPS.; Classified Hardware – 6-APP/Super Mac C-500, 2-APP/iMac; Classified Printers – QMS/Laserwriter, APP/Mac LaserWriter Pro DISPLAY: Ad make-up applications – Baseview, QPS; Layout Software – Baseview/Ad Manager.; Display Hardware – 6-APP/Mac G3; Display Printers – 1-New-Gen/600 PRODUCTION: Pagination Software – QPS 4.0, Mk/Managing Editor.; Production Equipment – Nu Plate Burner, AU/3850, Lf/AP Leaf Picture Desk; Cameras – SCREEN/270-D; Scanners – Lf/Leafscan, Microtek, Nikon/LS 2000 PRESSROOM: Line 1 – 1-G/Urbanite 1013 single width (8 stacked units, 1 full color); Press registration system – KFM/Pin Registration System. MAILROOM: Counter stackers – 5-HL; Inserters and stuffers – 1-MM/227, 1-HI/1872; Bundle tying machines – 1-Bu/68950, 2-Si/MLN2A.; Business Hardware – 6-Compaq/Proline 450, 2-Compaq/Desk Pro

MISSISSIPPI PRESS REGISTER, INC.

405 Delmas Ave., Pascagoula, Miss., 39568-0849; gen tel (228) 934-1400; gen fax (228) 934-1473

PICAYUNE

PICAYUNE ITEM

17 Richardson Ozona Rd., Picayune, Miss., 39466; gen tel (601) 798-4766; adv tel (601) 798-4766; ed tel (601) 798-4766; gen fax (601) 798-8602; adv fax (601) 798-8602; ed fax (601) 798-8602; gen e-mail item@picayuneitem.com; web site www.picayuneitem.com

Group: Mississippi Press Services, Inc.
Published: Tues, Wed, Thur, Fri, Sun
Weekday Frequency: e
Circulation: 4,377; 5,369(sun)
Last Audit: March 31, 2008
Price: 6.00/mo; 72.00/yr.
Advertising: Open inch rate $14.89
News services: AP, NEA.
Politics: Independent.
Advertising not accepted: Liquor.
Special Editions: Pearl River County Today (Other).
Special Weekly Sections: Entertainment (S); Farm (Wed).
Magazines: Relish (Monthly); Profile Sunday Magazine (S); River County Football (Thur).
Pub. .... Tom Andrews
Adv. Dir. .... Mary Weems
Circ. Dir. .... Annett Webber
Mng. Ed. .... Will Sullivan
Sports Ed. .... Curtis Rockwell
Prodn. Foreman, Pressroom .... Steven Ellis
Market Information: TMC.
Mechanical available: Offset; Black and 3 ROP colors; insert accepted; page cutoffs - 22 3/4.
Commodity Consumption: Avg. Page Number Per Issue - Daily 24; Avg. Page Number Per Issue - Plates Used 3380; Avg. Page Number Per Issue - Sunday 48; widths 25; Newsprint Used - Metric Tons 180; Printing Ink Used - Black 6570; Printing Ink Used - Color 400; Printing Ink Used -
Equipment; Editorial Hardware – 5-Mk; Editorial Printers – 2-APP/Mac LaserWriter.; Classified Hardware – 2-Mk. DISPLAY: Ad make-up applications – QPS/QuarkXPress 4.0; Layout Software – 3-APP/Mac.; Display Printers – 1-APP/Mac LaserWriter II NTX, Dataproducts/LZR 1560 PRODUCTION: Pagination Software – Baseview.; Production Equipment – 2-APP/Mac LaserWriter II NTX; Cameras – Goerz/J72; Scanners – APP/Mac Scanner PRESSROOM: Line 1 – 4; Folders – 1 MAILROOM: Counter stackers – 1/BG; Bundle tying machines – 1-/Bu; Addressing machine – Automecha/Accufast.; Business Hardware – Unisys

STARKVILLE

STARKVILLE DAILY NEWS

304 E. Lampkin St., Starkville, Miss., 39759; gen tel (662) 323-1642; gen fax (662) 323-6586; gen e-mail sdnews@bellsouth.net; adv e-mail sdnads@bellsouth.net; ed e-mail sdneditor@bellsouth.net; web site www.starkvilledailynews.com

Group: Mississippi Press Services, Inc.
Published: Mon, Tues, Wed, Thur, Fri, Sat, Sun
Weekday Frequency: m
Saturday Frequency: m
Circulation: 7,071; 7,071(sat); 7,071(sun)
Last Audit: October 1, 2004
Price: 10.00/mo; 86.00/yr.
Advertising: Open inch rate $13.72
News services: AP.
Politics: Independent.
Note: For detailed production information, see West Point Daily Times Leader.
Advertising not accepted: NC-17 movies.
Not Published: New Year; Memorial Day; Independence Day; Labor Day; Thanksgiving; Christmas.
Special Editions: Bulldog Weekend (Apr); Welcome Back Miss. State (Aug); Progress (Feb); Christmas Gift Guide (Nov).
Special Weekly Sections: Entertainment (Fri); Weddings (S); Religion (Sat); Agriculture (Thur); Business (Tues); Education (Wed).
Magazines: American Profile (S).
Bus. Mgr. .... Marcia Deaton
Creative Dir. .... Larry Bost
Mgr., Mktg./Promo. .... Don Norman
Educ. Ed. .... Shea Staskowski
Online Ed. .... Brian Hawkins
Market Information: TMC.
Mechanical available: Offset; Black and 3 ROP colors; insert accepted; page cutoffs - 22 3/4.
Mechanical Specifications: Type page 10 x 21 1/2; E - 6 cols, 1 9/16, 1/8 between; A - 6 cols, 1 9/16, 1/8 between; C - 9 cols, 1 1/32, 1/8 between.
Commodity Consumption: Avg. Page Number Per Issue - Daily 14; Avg. Page Number Per Issue - Plates Used 4000; Avg. Page Number Per Issue - Saturday 12; Avg. Page Number Per Issue - Sunday 20; widths 24; Newsprint Used - Short Tons 350; Printing Ink Used - Black 10000; Printing
Equipment EDITORIAL: Front-end Software – Baseview.; Editorial Hardware – APP/Power Mac, APP/Mac Quadra 605, APP/Mac G3, APP/Mac G4; Editorial Printers – APP/Mac LaserWriter II, GCC/Elite XL CLASSIFIED: Front-end Software – Baseview.; Classified Hardware – APP/Mac Quadra 605 DISPLAY: Ad make-up applications – QPS/QuarkXPress 4.2; Display Hardware – APP/Mac Quadra 660, APP/Mac Quadra 650, Umax, APP/Power Mac, APP/Mac G3, APP/Mac G4; Display Printers – GCC/Elite XL; Production Equipment – QPS/QuarkXPress 4.2.; Business Hardware – PC

TUPELO

JOURNAL PUBLISHING COMPANY

1242 S. Green St., Tupelo, Miss., 38804; gen tel (662) 842-2611; gen fax (662) 842-2233; gen e-mail clay.foster@journalinc.com; web site www.nems360.com

Group: Journal, Inc.
Politics: 1870
Note: Journal Publishing Company owns these weekly publications: Pontotoc Progress, Monroe Journal, Chickasaw Journal, Chickasaw Shopper, Southern Sentinel, New Albany News Exchange, Southern Advocate, Itawamba County Times, Times Plus
Associate Publisher - Human Resources/Community Newspapers .... Charlotte Wolfe
CEO/Publisher/President .... Clay Foster

JOURNAL PUBLISHING COMPANY

1242 S. Green St., Tupelo, Miss., 38804-6301; gen tel (662) 842-2611; adv tel (662) 842-2614; ed tel (662) 842-2612; gen fax (662) 842-2233; adv fax (662) 620-8301; ed fax (662) 842-2233; gen e-mail questions@journalinc.com; adv e-mail richard.crenshaw@journalinc.com; ed e-mail lloyd.gray@journalinc.com; web site www.nems360.com

Group: Journal, Inc.
Published: Mon, Tues, Wed, Thur, Fri, Sat, Sun
Weekday Frequency: m
Saturday Frequency: m
Circulation: 33,380; 33,988(sat); 34,861(sun)
Last Audit: Sworn September 30, 2009
Price: $11/mo; $128/yr; $33/3mo, $66/6mo.
Advertising: $23.43 Modular Rate per inch
Insert rate: $42.25/1000 Single Full (weekday) Zoned add 12%
News services: AP, MCT.
Politics: 1870
Advertising not accepted: N
Not Published: Christmas
Own facility?: Y
Special Editions: Business Journal (1 each month); Healthly Living (Jan); North MS Health Journal Magazine (Mar & Aug); Spring Fashion (Mar); Blue Suede Cruise (Apr); Gum Tree Writing (May); The Source Magazine (May); Memorial Day (May); Graduation (May); Young at Heart (June); How To Guide (June); Election tab (July); Back to School (July); Traveler Magazine (Aug); High School Football (Aug); Fall Brides (Aug); College Football (Aug); Fall Home Improvement (Sept); Fall Fashion (Sept); Marching Band Festival (Oct); Breast Cancer Awareness (Oct); Women at Work (Oct); Taste of the Season Cookbook (Nov); Holiday Gift Guide (Nov); @RecordBody:**Special Weekly Sections:** Religion (Sat); Food (Wed)
Magazines: Relish (Monthly); Parade (Sunday)
Profile: Northeast Mississippi Daily Journal
Director of Finance .... Rosemary Jarrell
Advertising and Marketing Director Richard Crenshaw
Classified Advertising Manager .... Cindy Carr
CEO/Publisher/President .... Clay Foster
Executive Editor .... Lloyd Gray
Editorial Page Editor .... Joe Rutherford
Lifestyles Editor .... Leslie Criss
Radio/Television Ed. .... Judy Putt
Circulation - Sales Manager .... Alisha Wilson
Circulation - Delivery Manager Michael King
Associate Publisher - Human Resources/Community Newspapers .... Charlotte Wolfe
Interactive Director .... Michael Duran
Market Information: TMC; Zoned editions.
Mechanical available: Offset; Black and 3 ROP colors; insert accepted - all; page cutoffs - 22 3/4.
Mechanical Specifications: Type page 13 x 21 1/2; E - 6 cols, 2 1/16, 1/8 between; A - 6 cols, 2 1/16, 1/8 between; C - 8 cols, 1 1/2, 1/8 between.
Commodity Consumption: Avg. Page Number Per Issue - Daily 30; Avg. Page Number Per Issue - Plates Used 47,695; Avg. Page Number Per Issue - Sunday 62; widths 27 1/2; Newsprint Used - Short Tons 3,226; Printing Ink Used - Black 75,505; Printing Ink Used - Color 43,244
Equipment EDITORIAL: Front-end Software – NewsEdit; IQweb; Editorial Hardware – 35-APP/Mac; Editorial Printers – HP CLASSIFIED: Front-end Software – Brainworks, AdPerks, Windows XP; Classified Hardware – Dell; Classified Printers – HP4250 Laserjet DISPLAY: Ad make-up applications – Multi-Ad/Creator; Layout Software – SCS/Layout 8000; Display Hardware – APPLE/MAC; Display Printers – HP8150, HP4700 Color PRODUCTION: Pagination Software – NewsExtremes; QPS/QuarkXpress 6.50; Photoshop; Production Equipment – 2 - Kodak NewsSetter TH100; Scanners – 1 - Epson 1640XL; 1 - Scanmaker 9800XL PRESSROOM: Line 1 – 12-G/Urbanite U1366 1990; Press Drives – 1990; Folders – 1-G/U-1366 1990, 1-G/SU-1708 1990; Pasters – 8 MAILROOM: Counter stackers – 1 HL/Monitor; 3 TMSI-Compass; 1 TMSI4500; Inserters and stuffers – 2 - SLS3000; Bundle tying machines – 4 - Dynaric NP3000; Wrapping singles – ; Addressing machine – Scitex 120 BUSINESS COMPUTERS: Business Software – Brainworks (AR); Navision (GL,PR,AP); Windows XP; Business Hardware – Dell
Zip Codes served: 38603 to 38915
Delivery method: Mail, Newsstand, Private Carrier, Racks

NORTHEAST MISSISSIPPI

1242 South Green St., Tupelo, Miss., 38804; gen tel 662-842-2611; web site www.djournal.com

Published: Mon, Tues, Wed, Thur, Fri, Sat, Sun
Weekday Frequency: m
Saturday Frequency: m
Circulation: 33,583; 33,723(sat); 35,439(sun)
Last Audit: ABC September 30, 2011

VICKSBURG

THE VICKSBURG POST

1601 F N. Frontage Rd., Vicksburg, Miss., 39180; gen tel (601) 636-4545; adv tel (601) 636-4545; ed tel (601) 636-4545; gen fax (601) 619-0133; adv fax (601) 634-0897; ed fax (601) 634-0897; gen e-mail sysadmin@vicksburgpost.com; adv e-mail ads@vicksburgpost.com; ed e-mail post@vicksburgpost.com; web site www.vicksburgpost.com

Published: Mon, Tues, Wed, Thur, Fri, Sat, Sun
Saturday Frequency: m
Circulation: 10,809; 10,809(sat); 11,562(sun)
Last Audit: September 30, 2011
Price: 13.00/mo; 156.00/yr.
Advertising: Open inch rate $17.78
News services: AP.
Politics: Independent. **Established:** 1883
Not Published: Christmas.
Special Editions: Home Improvement (Apr); High School Football (Aug); Last Minute Gift Guide (Dec); African American History (Feb); Brides (Jan); Family-Owned Business (Jun); Industry (Mar); Car Care (May); Health Services Directory (Nov); Home Improvement (Oct); College F
Special Weekly Sections: TV (S); Religion (Sat); Education (Wed).
Magazines: Parade (S).
Broadcast Affiliations: WAPT-ABC; WJTV-CBS; WLBT-NBC.
Gen. Mgr. .... Jimmy Clark
Admin. Mgr. .... Sandra Bernier
Adv. Dir. .... Barney Partridge
Circ. Dir. .... Becky Chandler
Ed. .... Louis P. Cashman
Exec. Ed .... Charles D. Mitchell
Mng. Ed. .... Karen Gamble
Asst. Mng. Ed., News .... Misty McDermitt
Asst. Mng. Ed., Photo .... Brian Loden
Asst. Mng. Ed., Sports .... Steve Wilson
Presentation Ed. .... Mary Kittrell
Prodn. Foreman, Pressroom .... Bobby Childers
Market Information: TMC.
Mechanical available: Offset; Black and 3 ROP colors; insert accepted; page cutoffs - 22 3/4.
Mechanical Specifications: Type page 13 x 21; E - 6 cols, 2 1/16, 1/8 between; A - 6 cols, 2 1/16, 1/8 between; C - 8 cols, 1 3/8, 1/16 between.
Commodity Consumption: Avg. Page Number Per Issue - Daily 26; Avg. Page Number Per Issue - Plates Used 11000; Avg. Page Number Per Issue - Sunday 44; widths 27 1/2; Newsprint Used - Short Tons 1200; Printing Ink Used - Black 27450; Printing Ink Used - Color 550; Printing Ink U
Equipment EDITORIAL: Front-end Software – FSI, QPS.; Editorial Hardware – 30-APP/Mac; Editorial Printers – 3-Xante CLASSIFIED: Front-end Software – FSI, QPS.; Classified Hardware – 2-APP/Mac; Classified Printers – 2-Xante; Layout Software – FSI, QPS.; Display Hardware – 6-APP/Mac, 6-APP/Mac; Display Printers – 2-Xante, HP PRODUCTION: Pagination Software – FSI.; Production Equipment – 2-Nu; Cameras – 1-R; Scanners – 2-Nikon/Coolscan PRESSROOM: Line 1 – 8-G/Urbanite; Folders – 1; Bundle tying machines – 2/MLN.; Business

Hardware – 1-DEC/11-21, 5-DEC/101

VICKSBURG PRINTING & PUBLISHING CO.

1601 F North Frontage Rd., Vicksburg, Miss., 39180; gen tel (601) 636-4545; gen fax (601) 634-0897

WEST POINT

DAILY TIMES LEADER

221 E. Main St., West Point, Miss., 39773; gen tel (662) 494-1422; adv tel (662) 494-1422; ed tel (662) 494-1353; gen fax (662) 494-1414; adv fax (662) 494-1414; gen e-mail sdnpub@bellsouth.net; adv e-mail dtlads@bellsouth.net

Published: Tues, Wed, Thur, Fri, Sun
Weekday Frequency: m
Circulation: 2,758; 2,758(sun)
Last Audit: September 30, 2007
Price: 9.00/mo; 74.00/yr.
Advertising: Open inch rate $9.90
News services: AP.
Politics: Independent.
Advertising not accepted: Dating material.
Not Published: New Year; Memorial Day; Independence Day; Labor Day; Thanksgiving; Christmas.
Special Editions: Progress (Feb); Gift Guide (Nov); Prairie Arts Festival (Sept).
Special Weekly Sections: TV Guide (S).
Magazines: TeleVisions (combined insertion with Starkville Daily News) (Other); Tuned In (S); American Profile (Weekly).
Pub. ....Don Norman
Circ. Clerk....................Natasha Watson
Ed. ....Jeannetta Edwards
Sports Ed. ....Kenneth Mister
Market Information: TMC.
Mechanical available: Offset; Black and 3 ROP colors; insert accepted - Post It's; page cutoffs - 22 3/4.
Mechanical Specifications: Type page 11 5/8 x 21 1/2; E - 6 cols, 3 3/4, 1/8 between; A - 6 cols, 3 3/4, 1/8 between; C - 9 cols, 1 3/8, 1/8 between.
Commodity Consumption: Avg. Page Number Per Issue - Daily 12; Avg. Page Number Per Issue - Sunday 16; widths 25; Newsprint Used - Short Tons 392; Printing Ink Used - Black 8935.
Equipment EDITORIAL: Front-end Software – Baseview.; Editorial Hardware – IMACS; Editorial Printers – APP/Mac LaserWriter CLASSIFIED: Front-end Software – Baseview.; Classified Hardware – IMACS; Layout Software – APP/Power Mac G3, IMACS.; Display Hardware – APP/Mac Radius; Display Printers – APP/Mac Laser Writer, GCC/Elite XL PRODUCTION: Pagination Software – QPS/QuarkXPress 4.24.; Production Equipment – APP/Mac LaserWriter II; Cameras – Konica PRESSROOM: Line 1 – 6-G/Community. MAILROOM: Counter stackers – BG; Bundle tying machines – Strapping.; Business Hardware – PC

MISSOURI

BOONVILLE

BOONVILLE DAILY NEWS

412 E. High St., Boonville, Mo., 65233; gen tel (660) 882-5335; gen fax (660) 882-2256; gen e-mail news@boonvillenews.com; web site www.boonvilledailynews.com

Group: Missouri Press Service, Inc.
Published: Mon, Tues, Wed, Thur, Fri
Weekday Frequency: e
Circulation: 2,484
Last Audit: September 30, 2007
Price: 102.60/yr.
Advertising: Open inch rate $10.44
News services: AP.
Politics: Independent.
Not Published: New Year; Memorial Day; Independence Day; Labor Day; Thanksgiving; Christmas.
Special Weekly Sections: Agriculture (Thur); Business (Wed).
Magazines: Boonville Cable View (TV Guide) (Fri); American Profile (Weekly).
Pub. ....Deborah Marshall
Circ. Dir. ....Lisa Glasscock
Display Adv. Mgr. ....Mike Kellner
Sports Ed. ....Chris Bowie
Market Information: TMC.
Mechanical available: Offset; Black and 3 ROP colors; insert accepted; page cutoffs - 22 3/4.
Mechanical Specifications: Type page 13 x 21; E - 6 cols, 2 1/16, 1/8 between; A - 6 cols, 2 1/16, 1/8 between; C - 6 cols, 2 1/16, 1/8 between.
Commodity Consumption: Avg. Page Number Per Issue - Daily 12; Avg. Page Number Per Issue - Plates Used 3000; widths 27 1/2; Newsprint Used - Short Tons 200; Printing Ink Used - Black 6500; Printing Ink Used - Color 700; Printing Ink Used - Pages Printed 3200.
Equipment EDITORIAL: Front-end Software – QPS/QuarkXPress (3.32).; Editorial Hardware – APP/Mac Plus, APP/Mac Classic, APP/Power Mac; Editorial Printers – 1-APP/Mac LaserPrinter, 1-APP/Mac LaserWriter 360, 1-HP/4MV CLASSIFIED: Front-end Software – QPS/QuarkXPress 3.32.; Classified Hardware – APP/Mac SE, 1-APP/Power Mac; Classified Printers – APP/Mac LaserWriter 12-640 DISPLAY: Ad make-up applications – QPS/QuarkXPress 3.32.; Display Hardware – APP/Power Mac; Display Printers – APP/Mac LaserWriter 12-640 PRODUCTION: Pagination Software – QPS/QuarkXPress 3.32.; Production Equipment – Nu, 1-APP/Mac LaserPrinter; Cameras – SCREEN PRESSROOM: Line 1 – 4-G/Community; Folders – 1 MAILROOM: Counter stackers – BG; Bundle tying machines – 3/Bu; Addressing machine – 2-/Dispensa-Matic/16.; Business Hardware – IBM, AT

THE WEEKLY

412 High St., Boonville, Mo., 65233; gen tel (660) 882-5335; gen fax (660) 882-2256; gen e-mail news@boonvilledailynews.com; web site www.boonvilledailynews.com

Published: Tues, Wed, Thur, Fri
Weekday Frequency: e
Circulation: 3,625
Last Audit: Sworn N/A
Price: 28.00/yr.
Advertising: Open inch rate $10.00
Insert rate: $60.00/M.
Politics: 1911
Own facility?: Y
Adv. Mgr. ....Deborah Marshall
Ed. ....Teresa Kreba

BRANSON

BRANSON TRI-LAKES DAILY NEWS

200 Industrial Park Dr., Hollister, Mo., 65672; gen tel (417) 334-3161; adv tel (417) 334-3161; ed tel (417) 334-3161; oth tel 2564900935; gen fax (417) 334-4299; adv fax (417) 334-8275; ed fax (417) 335-3933; gen e-mail publisher@bransontrilakesnews.com; adv e-mail publisher@bransontrilakesnews.com; ed e-mail publisher@bransontrilakesnews.com; web site www.bransontrilakesnews.com

Group: Missouri Press Service, Inc.
Published: Tues, Wed, Thur, Fri, Sat
Weekday Frequency: m
Circulation: 11,170; 11,170(sat)
Last Audit: September 22, 2001
Price: 50.00/yr.
Advertising: Open inch rate $15.00
Insert rate: $60M
Politics: 1892
Not Published: New Year; Independence Day; Thanksgiving; Christmas; Veteran's Day.
Own facility?: Y
Special Editions: Brides (Apr); Rodeo (Aug); Christmas Greetings (Dec); Homecoming (Feb); Taney County Fair (Jul); Safe Boating (Jun); Memorial Day Sale (May); Football (Oct); Fall Home Improvement (Sept).
Special Weekly Sections: Endearments (Sat); Education (Thur); Grocery (Wed).
Magazines: Branson TV Take One (TV/Entertainment) (Fri); Ozark Mountain Visitor (Tourist tab) (Monthly).
Pub. ....Mike Schuver
Sports Ed. ....Pat Dailey
Market Information: TMC.
Mechanical available: Offset; Black and 3 ROP colors; insert accepted; page cutoffs - 21.
Mechanical Specifications: Type page 11 1/2 x 21; E - 6 cols, 1 13/16, 1/8 between; A - 6 cols, 1 13/16, 1/8 between; C - 6 cols, 1 13/16, 1/8 between.
Equipment EDITORIAL: Front-end Software – Baseview/NewsEdit, Baseview/Wire Manager.; Editorial Hardware – APP/Mac G3; Editorial Printers – APP/Mac LaserPrinter CLASSIFIED: Front-end Software – Baseview/Class Manager.; Classified Hardware – APP/iMac, 2-APP/Mac Classic II; Classified Printers – APP/Mac LaserPrinter DISPLAY: Ad make-up applications – Baseview/Ad Manager, QPS/QuarkXPress; Display Hardware – APP/Mac G3; Display Printers – APP/Mac LaserWriter IIg; Production Equipment – Caere/OmniPage; Cameras – LE; Scanners – Ofoto, APP/Mac One Scanner. PRESSROOM: Line 1 – 12-G/Community 1996. MAILROOM: Counter stackers – KAN; Inserters and stuffers – KAN/480 5:1; Bundle tying machines – Bu; Addressing machine – KAN; Other equipment – mcCain Stitcher-Trimmer.; Business Hardware – 5-PC, MSSI
Zip Codes served: 65672
Delivery method: Mail, Newsstand, Racks

BROOKFIELD

LINN COUNTY LEADER

107-109 N. Main St., Brookfield, Mo., 64628; gen tel (660) 258-7237; gen fax (660) 258-7238; gen e-mail honey@shighway.com; web site www.linncountyleader.com

Published: Mon, Wed, Fri
Circulation: 3,300
Last Audit: Estimate February 23, 2005
Price: 75.00/yr.
Advertising: Open inch rate $7.00
Politics: Independent. **Established:** 2004
Pub ....Rod Dixon
Circ. Mgr. ....Monica Graves

CAMDENTON

LAKE SUN LEADER

918 N. State Hwy. 5, Camdenton, Mo., 65020; gen tel (573) 346-2132; adv tel (573) 346-2132; ed tel (573) 346-2132; gen fax (573) 346-4508; adv fax (573) 346-4508; ed fax (573) 346-4045; ed e-mail business@lakesunleader.com; web site www.lakesunleader.com

Published: Mon, Tues, Wed, Thur, Fri
Weekday Frequency: m
Circulation: 4,370
Last Audit: October 21, 2003
Price: 102.95/yr; 41.95/4mo,57.65/6mo,75.15/8mo.
Advertising: Open inch rate $9.30(m-fri)
News services: AP.
Politics: Independent.
Not Published: New Year; Thanksgiving; Christmas.
Magazines: American Profile (Weekly).
Pub. ....John Tucker
Gen. Mgr. ....Lisa Miller
Circ. Mgr. ....Debbie Hyman
Ed. ....David Schiefelbein
Prodn. Mgr. ....Peggy Trinkle
Market Information: Split run; TMC; Zoned editions.
Mechanical available: Offset; Black and 2 ROP colors; insert accepted.
Mechanical Specifications: Type page 13 x 21 1/2; E - 6 cols, 2 1/16, 1/8 between; A - 6 cols, 2 1/16, 1/8 between; C - 6 cols, 2 1/16, 1/8 between.
Commodity Consumption: Avg. Page Number Per Issue - Daily 18; Avg. Page Number Per Issue - Plates Used 5300; widths 27 1/2; Newsprint Used - Short Tons 520; Printing Ink Used - Black 15620; Printing Ink Used - Color 2160; Printing Ink Used - Pages Printed 5200.
Equipment; Editorial Hardware – APP/Mac; Editorial Equipment – IBM, HP.; Classified Equipment – COM/MCS.; Display Hardware – APP/Mac.; Production Equipment – HP/LaserJet; Scanners – DSA. MAILROOM: Counter stackers – KAN/320; Bundle tying machines – Bu; Addressing machine – Ch.; Business Hardware – IBM/Sys 36, AmDek/Sys 286A

CAPE GIRARDEAU

CONCORD PUBLISHING HOUSE, INC.

301 Broadway, Cape Girardeau, Mo., 63701; gen tel (573) 335-6611; gen fax (573) 339-0815

SOUTHEAST MISSOURIAN

301 Broadway, Cape Girardeau, Mo., 63701; gen tel (573) 335-6611; adv tel (573) 335-6611 ext 170; ed tel (573) 335-6611 ext 252; gen fax (573) 334-9258; adv fax (573) 339-0815; ed fax (573) 334-7288; gen e-mail jrust@semissourian.com; adv e-mail advertising@semissourian.com; ed e-mail letters@semissourian.com; web site www.semissourian.com

Published: Mon, Tues, Wed, Thur, Fri, Sat, Sun
Weekday Frequency: m
Saturday Frequency: m
Circulation: 13,234; 12,945(sat); 16,103(sun)
Last Audit: September 30, 2009
Price: 13.50/mo; 148.50/yr (carrier).
Advertising: Open inch rate $21.40
News services: AP.
Politics: Independent. **Established:** 1904
Not Published: New Year(unless on Sun); Memorial Day; Independence Day; Labor Day; Christmas(unless on Sun).
Special Editions: University Tab (Apr); Back-to-School (Aug); Traditional Christmas (Dec); Progress (Feb); Bridal (Jan); Vacations (Jun); Lawn & Garden (Mar); Vacations (May); Best of the Season (Nov); Newcomer's Guide (Oct); Fall Home Improvement & Decorating (Sept).
Special Weekly Sections: Business (Mon); Travel (S); Health (Sat); Arts & Leisure (Thur); Learning (Tues); Food (Wed).
Magazines: 1st Sunday (Monthly); Parade (S).
Pub. ....Jon K. Rust
Assoc. Pub. ....Jim Maxwell
CFO ....Richard Caldwell
Adv. Dir. ....Gera Legrand
Circ. Dir. ....Mark Kneer
Ed. ....R. Joe Sullivan
Mng. Ed. ....Bob Miller
Sports Ed. ....Toby Carrig
Data Processing Mgr. ....Brad Hollerbach
Prodn. Coord. ....John Renaud
Prodn. Supvr. ....Steve Rose
Market Information: ADS; TMC; Zoned editions.
Mechanical available: Offset; Black and 3 ROP colors; insert accepted - card 80 lb. stock; page cutoffs - 21 1/2.
Mechanical Specifications: Type page 11 5/8 x 20 3/4; E - 6 cols, 1 5/6, 1/8 between; A - 6 cols, 1 5/6, 1/8 between; C - 9 cols, 1 5/6, 1/8 between.
Commodity Consumption: Avg. Page Number Per Issue - Daily 28; Avg. Page Number Per Issue - Plates Used 30000; Avg. Page Number Per Issue - Sunday 60; widths 25; Newsprint Used - Metric Tons 2500; Printing Ink Used - Black 100000; Printing Ink Used - Color 30000; Printing Ink U
Equipment EDITORIAL: Front-end Software – Baseview, QPS/QuarkXPress 4.1, Adobe/Pho-

toshop 6.0, Aldus/FreeHand 7.; Editorial Hardware – 30-APP/Mac; Editorial Printers – 2-HP/8000 CLASSIFIED: Front-end Software – Baseview/Ad Manager.; Classified Hardware – 5-APP/Mac; Classified Printers – HP/5si DISPLAY: Ad make-up applications – Multi-Ad/Creator 6, Adobe/Photoshop CS, Adobe/Illustrator CS, QPS/QuarkXPress 4.1; Layout Software – MEI/AdForce.; Display Hardware – 16-APP/Mac, 1-IBM; Display Printers – HP/8000; Production Equipment – Caere/OmniPage, HP/8000(G), HP/DesignJet 2500; Cameras – R; Scanners – 2-Polaroid/SprintScan, 3-Epson/1200C. PRESSROOM: Line 1 – 5-WPC/Leader (1-Quad color); Line 2 – 6-WPC/Leader; Folders – 2-WPC/2:1.; Inserters and stuffers – 2-KAN/480; Bundle tying machines – 1-Sa/EM9142, 1-Sa/ML2EE, 1/MLN; Wrapping singles – 4-/Bu; Addressing machine – Ch/labeler. BUSINESS COMPUTERS: Business Software – Synaptic, Macola, Synaptic/AR; Business Hardware – 12-IBM Clone

CARTHAGE

THE CARTHAGE PRESS

800 W. Central, Carthage, Mo., 64836-0678; gen tel (417) 358-2191; gen fax (417) 358-7428; gen e-mail news@carthagepress.com; adv e-mail advertising2@carthagepress.com; ed e-mail news@carthagepress.com; web site www.carthagepress.com

Group: Gatehouse Media
Published: Tues, Wed, Thur, Fri, Sun
Weekday Frequency: m
Circulation: 2,100; 2,400(sun)
Last Audit: Sworn September 23, 2002
Price: 13.00/mo; 115.00/yr.
Advertising: Open inch rate $11.00
Insert rate: 50.00 cpm
News services: AP.
Politics: Independent. **Established:** 1884
Not Published: Christmas, Thanksgiving, Independence Day
Special Editions: Easter Dining Guide (Apr); Home Guide (Aug); Last Minute Gift Guide (Dec); Restaurants & Entertainment (Feb); Chamber Tab (Jan); Independence Day (Jul); Flag Day Sponsor (Jun); St. Patrick's Day (Mar); Jasper/Lockwatch Graduation (May); We Want Your Busin
Special Weekly Sections: Business Page (Sun); Church Page (Sat); Farm (Thur); Food (Tues); School Page (Wed).
Magazines: American Profile (Weekly).
Mng. Ed. .... John Hacker
Publisher .... Steve Boggs
Ad Director .... Kelley Young
Market Information: TMC.
Mechanical available: Offset; Black and 3 ROP colors; insert accepted - card stock; page cutoffs - 22 3/4.
Mechanical Specifications: Type page 13 x 21 1/2; E - 6 cols, 2 1/16, 1/8 between; A - 6 cols, 2 1/16, 1/8 between; C - 9 cols, 1 5/8, 1/8 between.
Commodity Consumption: Avg. Page Number Per Issue - Daily 12; widths 27 1/2.
Equipment: Editorial Hardware – Mac 10.5.8; Classified Hardware – Mk/1100 Plus. DISPLAY: Ad make-up applications – QPS/QuarkXPress.; Display Hardware – APP/Mac; Folders – 2; Bundle tying machines – 1/Bu
Delivery method: Newsstand, Private Carrier, Racks

CHILLICOTHE

CHILLICOTHE NEWSPAPERS, INC.

818 Washington, Chillicothe, Mo., 64601; gen tel (660) 646-2411; gen fax (660) 646-2028

Price: 88.00/yr.
Advertising: Open inch rate $7.55
Politics: 1860

CONSTITUTION-TRIBUNE

818 Washington St., Chillicothe, Mo., 64601; gen tel (660) 646-2411; adv tel (660) 646-2411; ed tel (660) 646-2411; gen fax (660) 646-2028; adv fax (660) 646-2028; ed fax (660) 646-2028; gen e-mail ctnews@chillicothenews.com; adv e-mail andrea@chillicothe.townnews.com; web site www.chillicothenews.com

Published: Mon, Tues, Wed, Thur, Fri
Weekday Frequency: e
Circulation: 3,461
Last Audit: September 30, 2002
Price: 12.87/mo; 110.44/yr.
Advertising: Open inch rate $7.75
News services: AP.
Politics: Independent. **Established:** 1860
Not Published: New Year; Memorial Day; Independence Day; Labor Day; Thanksgiving; Christmas.
Pub./Purchasing Agent .... Rod Dixon
Bus. Mgr. .... Mardy Moore
Adv. Dir. .... Andrea Graves
Circ. Mgr. .... Jenetta Cramner
City Ed. .... Laura Schuler
News Ed. .... Catherine Stortz
Political/Gov't Ed. .... Cathy Ripley
Sports Ed. .... Paul Sturm
Prodn. Supvr., Press .... Eddie Melte
Market Information: ADS; TMC; Zoned editions.
Mechanical available: Offset; Black and 2 ROP

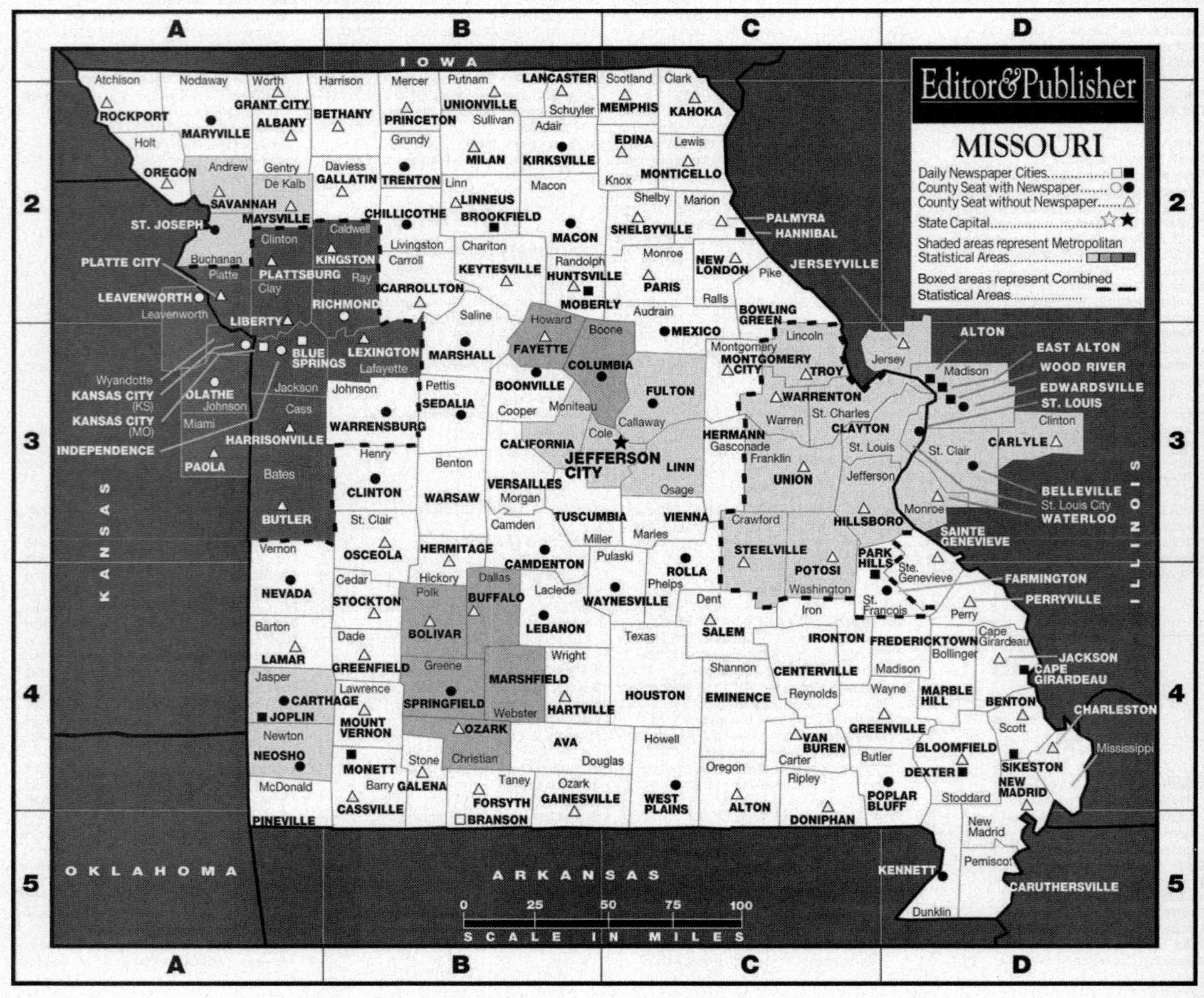

colors; insert accepted - 1-page flyers; page cutoffs - 21 1/2.
Mechanical Specifications: Type page 13 1/2 x 21 1/2; E - 6 cols, 2 1/16, 1/8 between; A - 6 cols, 2 1/16, 1/8 between; C - 6 cols, 2 1/16, 1/8 between.
Commodity Consumption: Avg. Page Number Per Issue - Daily 12; Avg. Page Number Per Issue - Plates Used 4019; widths 27 1/2; Newsprint Used - Short Tons 315; Printing Ink Used - Black 5700; Printing Ink Used - Color 801; Printing Ink Used - Pages Printed 4685.
Equipment; Editorial Hardware – 6-CText; Editorial Equipment – CText/Fileserver, CText/AP Wire receiver.; Layout Software – 3-APP/Mac Plus.; Production Equipment – 2-APP/Mac LaserWriter, 1-COM; Cameras – 1-Nu. PRESSROOM: Line 1 – 4-G/Community.; Bundle tying machines – 1/Malow, 1-/Bu; Addressing machine – 3-/Rp.

CLINTON

THE CLINTON DAILY DEMOCRAT

212 S. Washington St., Clinton, Mo., 64735; gen tel (660) 885-2281; gen fax (660) 885-2265
Published: Mon, Tues, Wed, Thur, Fri
Weekday Frequency: e
Circulation: 4,150
Price: 3.75/mo (carrier); 78.00/yr .
Advertising: Open inch rate $6.75
News services: NEA.
Politics: Democrat. **Established:** 1868
Not Published: New Year; Memorial Day; Independence Day; Labor Day; Thanksgiving; Christmas.
Special Weekly Sections: Church News (Fri); Conservation/Outdoors (Thur).
Gen. Mgr. ....Daniel B. Miles
Sports Ed. ....Jim Lawson
Prodn. Mgr. ....Mike Gregory
Market Information: TMC.
Mechanical available: Offset; Black and 2 ROP colors; insert accepted; page cutoffs - 22 1/2.
Mechanical Specifications: Type page 13 x 21 1/2; E - 6 cols, 2 1/16, 1/8 between; A - 6 cols, 2 1/16, 1/8 between; C - 6 cols, 2 1/16, 1/8 between.
Commodity Consumption: Avg. Page Number Per Issue - Daily 14; widths 28.
Equipment; Editorial Hardware – 1-IBM, 1-Ro.; Classified Equipment – 1-Ro, 1-IBM.; Layout Software – 1-COM/7200, 1-COM/Mark IV.; Production Equipment – 1-HA, 1-EK.; Bundle tying machines – 1/Malow; Addressing machine – 1-Am/Mail 5.; Business Hardware – APP/Mac

DEMOCRAT PUBLISHING CO., INC.

212 S. Washington, Clinton, Mo., 64735; gen tel (660) 885-2281; gen fax (660) 885-2265

COLUMBIA

COLUMBIA DAILY TRIBUNE

101 N. 4th St., Columbia, Mo., 65201-4416; gen tel (573) 815-1500; adv tel (573) 815-1800; ed tel (573) 815-1700; oth tel (573) 815-1600; gen fax (573) 815-1701; adv fax (573) 815-1801; ed fax (573) 815-1701; oth fax (573) 815-1601; gen e-mail circmail@columbiatribune.com; adv e-mail displayad@columbiatribune.com; ed e-mail editor@columbiatribune.com; web site www.columbiatribune.com
Group: Tribune Publishing Company, DBA Columbia Daily Tribune
Published: Mon, Tues, Wed, Thur, Fri, Sat, Sun
Weekday Frequency: e
Saturday Frequency: m
Circulation: 19,958; 24,522(sun)
Last Audit: ABC September 30, 2011
Price: $3.23 per week; $14.00 per month; $155.00 per year
Advertising: Open inch rate $23.50
Insert rate: Open full run begins at $71.00 per M
News services: AP, McClatchy, TMS
Politics: Independent. **Established:** 1901
Not Published: New Year; Memorial Day; Independence Day; Labor Day; Thanksgiving; Christmas
Special Weekly Sections: Ovation (S); Pulse (S); Saturday Business Magazine (Sat); GO! (Thur); Food (Wed).
Magazines: USA WEEKEND Magazine (Sat).
Profile: The Columbia Daily Tribune is an independently owned newspaper, established in Mid-Missouri in 1901. The Tribune offers professional advertising services, including zoning for pre-print advertising, in a strong growth market. Our commercial division, Trib
Treasurer/Publisher ....Vicki S. Russell
Chief Financial Officer.........................Jeff Moe
Vice President of Sales.............Les Borgmeyer
Adv. Mgr., Classified..................Wheeler Ruby
Adv. Major Acct./Pre Print Coord. ....Jill Gates
Mktg./Promo. Mgr. ....Linda Hays
Circ. Dir....Dirk Dunkle
Circ. Mgr., Educ./Promos. Coord. Shannon Arthur
Circ. Info Systems Mgr. ....Ron Allen
City Ed.......................................Lora Wegman
Copy Chief ....Chip Price
Managing Editor/Editorial Page Ed. Jim Robertson
Editorial Writer.......................Henry J. Waters
IT Director....................................Drew Myers
Market Information: TMC.
Mechanical available: Offset; Black and 4 ROP colors; insert accepted; page cutoffs - 22.
Mechanical Specifications: Type page 11 3/8 x 21; E - 6 cols, 1 3/4, 1/6 between; A - 6 cols, 1 3/4, 1/6 between; C - 7 cols, 1 9/16, 1/12 between.
Commodity Consumption: Avg. Page Number Per Issue - Daily 30; Avg. Page Number Per Issue - Plates Used 30000; Avg. Page Number Per Issue - Saturday 42; Avg. Page Number Per Issue - Sunday 64; widths 13 1/2; Newsprint Used - Short Tons 2151; Printing Ink Used - Black 53775; Pri
Equipment PRESSROOM: Line 1 – 20 unit DGM 430 (22 3/4 x 35) with two folders
DGM 1030 combination folder
DGM 1035 combination folder
; Line 2 – 48 unit Goss Universal 45 (22 x 35) 2- 1:3:3 jaw folders with upper formers, q-fold and crosshead
perf; Press Drives – Allen Bradley drives with drive shaft; Folders – DGM 1030 combination folder with q-fold and crosshead perf
DGM 1035 combination folder with q-fold and crosshead perf
Universal 2 1:3:3 jaw folder with uppper former; q-fold and crosshead perf; Pasters – Universal press has AMAL AR60C splicers; Press registration system – Universal is equipped with I-Tech Registration System MAILROOM: Counter stackers – Gammerler STC70 stackers on all press lines; Inserters and stuffers – GMA SLS1000 inserter-12 into 1
Muller Martini 227 inserter-16 into 1 with CS-10 Muller stacker
Muller Martini 227 inserter-4 into 1 with Rima RS counter stacker; Bundle tying machines – Signode LB-2330 tying machine
Signode LB-2000 tying machine
Signode LBX-2000 tying machine; Wrapping singles – Arpac 55G1-200 bundle shrinkwrapper; Addressing machine – 3 - Domino JetArray in-line and off-line with Rima (Harris) RS12 counter stackers; Other equipment –P3 applicator; Challenge Drill;Heidelberg q-folder
Zip Codes served: 65203,65202,65201,65010,65240,65255,65233,65251,65270,65279,65248,65265,65284,65256,65039,65254,65243,65274,65231,65230,65259,65287,65262,65043,65211,65278,65216,65250,65285,65109,65101,65063
Delivery method: Mail, Newsstand, Private Carrier, Racks

COLUMBIA MISSOURIAN

221 S Eighth Street, Columbia, Mo., 65201; gen tel (573) 882-5700; adv tel (573) 882-5748; ed tel (573) 882-5720; gen fax (573) 884-5293; adv fax (573) 884-5293; ed fax (573) 882-5702; adv e-mail advertising@columbiamissourian.com; ed e-mail editor@diqmo.org; web site www.columbiamissourian.com; www.mymissourian.com
Group: Missouri Press Association
Published: Tues, Wed, Thur, Fri, Sun
Weekday Frequency: m
Circulation: 6,008; 6,010(sun)
Last Audit: Sworn March 31, 2007
Price: 9.50/mo(carrier); 88.50/yr(carrier).
Advertising: Open inch rate $8.20
Insert rate: $43 per 1,000
News services: AP, LAT-WP, NYT, SHNS, TMS.
Politics: Independent. **Established:** 1908
Not Published: Dec. 26.
Special Editions: Progress (Growth of Columbia); Tourism (State of MO); Collegetowne; Welcome Back; Tiger Kickoffs (Mizzou Football); Homecoming (Mizzou Tigers); Tiger Tipoffs (Mizzou Basketball)
Special Weekly Sections: Entertainment (Fri); Ideas (S); Best Food Day (Wed).
Magazines: Parade (S); VOX (Thur).
General Manager ....Dan Potter
Advertising Director ....Jack Swartz
Executive Editor........................Tom Warhover
Production Manager.....................Bruce Moore
Photo Dir.....................................Todd Winge
Market Information: Zoned editions
Mechanical available: Offset; Black and 4 ROP colors; insert accepted; page cutoffs - 20.5 inches
Mechanical Specifications: Broadsheet (ROP) Page Size: 11.625□ x 20.5□
6 col = 11.625□
5 col = 9.25□
4 col = 7.375□
3 col = 5.5□
2 col = 3.625□
1 col = 1.75□
Tab Page Size (VOX, Special Sections):
Full Page = 9.75□ x 11□
1/2 pg Hor = 9.75□ x 5.417□
1/2 pg Ver = 4.79□ x 11□
1/4 pg Hor = 4.79□ x 5.417□
1/4 pg Ver = 2.3125□ x 11□
1/8 pg Hor = 4.79□ x 2.625□
1/8 pg Ver = 2.3125□ x 5.417□
1/16 pg = 2.3125□ x 2.625□
Commodity Consumption: Avg. Page Number Per Issue - Daily 16; Avg. Page Number Per Issue - Plates Used 14500; Avg. Page Number Per Issue - Sunday 49; widths 30; Newsprint Used - Short Tons 1010; Printing Ink Used - Black 33500; Printing Ink Used - Color 3000; Printing Ink Used
Equipment; Editorial Hardware – 2-HAS/HS-55, IBM; Editorial Equipment – 26-IBM/PC, 7-HAS/Edit 3, 3-HAS/Edit 8, 2-HAS/Magician Layout, 2-HAS/NewsPro.; Editorial Printers – Ricoh; Classified Equipment – 2-HAS/Edit 8.; Display Hardware – 5-APP/Mac.; Display Printers – Ricoh; Scanners – Dest/PC Scan. PRESSROOM: Line 1 – N/A; Folders – 2 MAILROOM: Counter stackers – N/A
Zip Codes served: 65010, 65201, 65202, 65203, 65211, 65212, 65215, 65039, 65240, 65251, 65255, 65256
Delivery method: Mail, Newsstand, Private Carrier, Racks

MISSOURIAN PUBLISHING ASSOCIATION

221 S. Eighth St., Columbia, Mo., 65201; gen tel (573) 882-5700; gen fax (573) 884-5293
Price: 88.50/yr.
Advertising: Open inch rate $7.40
Politics: 1908

DEXTER

THE DAILY STATESMAN

133 S. Walnut St., Dexter, Mo., 63841; gen tel (573) 624-4545; gen fax (573) 624-7449; ed fax (573) 624-7449; gen e-mail bgreer@dailystatesman.com; ed e-mail nhyslop@dailystatesman.com; web site www.dailystatesman.com
Group: Rust Communications Co., Inc.
????
Published: Tues, Wed, Thur, Fri, Sun
Weekday Frequency: e
Circulation: 3,300; 3,150(sun)
Last Audit: Sworn September 30, 2005
Price: 9.00/mo; 91.00/yr.
Advertising: Open inch rate $12.24
News services: AP, NEA.
Politics: Independent. **Established:** 1879
Not Published: New Year; Memorial Day; Independence Day; Labor Day; Thanksgiving; Christmas.
Own facility?: Y
Special Editions: Spring Fashion (Apr); Progress (Feb); Fall Fashion (Sept).
Magazines: Farm Monthly (Feb-Nov) (Monthly); Southeast Missouri Farmer (Feb-Nov) (Other); Parade (S).
Pub. ....Bud Hunt
Adv. Mgr....................................Betty Watkins
Ed..Noreen Hyslop
Prodn. Foreman, Composing.......Marilyn Tucker
Ad manager...............................Betty Watkins
Assistant Publisher ....Bobby Greer
Circ. Clerk ....Melissa Copeland
Market Information: Split run; TMC; Zoned editions.
Mechanical available: Offset; Black and 3 ROP colors; insert accepted.
Mechanical Specifications: Type page 13 x 22 1/2; E - 6 cols, 2 1/16, 1/8 between; A - 6 cols, 2 1/16, 1/8 between; C - 8 cols, 1 1/2, 1/8 between.
Commodity Consumption: Avg. Page Number Per Issue - Daily 28.
Equipment; Editorial Hardware – 1-COM/MDT 350.; Classified Hardware – 1-COM/MDT 350.; Production Equipment – 1-COM/4961, 1-COM/2961; Cameras – 1-Acti/140.; Bundle tying machines – 1/Strap Tyer

FULTON

THE FULTON SUN

115 E. 5th St., Fulton, Mo., 65251; gen tel (573) 642-7272; gen fax (573) 642-0656; adv e-mail display@fultonsun.com; ed e-mail news@fultonsun.com; web site www.fultonsun.com
Published: Tues, Wed, Thur, Fri, Sun
Weekday Frequency: m
Circulation: 3,600; 4,300(sun)
Last Audit: Sworn October 3, 2002
Price: 65.00/yr.
Advertising: Open inch rate $8.55(m-wed)
News services: AP.
Politics: Independent. **Established:** 1875
Not Published: New Year; Memorial Day; Independence Day; Labor Day; Thanksgiving; Christmas.
Special Editions: Customer Appreciation (Apr); Christmas Greetings (Dec); Women in Business (Jun); Graduation (May); Favorite Recipes (Oct); Senior Style (Quarterly); Sports Preview (Semi-yearly).
Special Weekly Sections: Food (Wed).
Magazines: Parade (S).
Ed....Karen Atkins
Sports Ed.....................................Ryan Boland
Prodn. Mgr., Pre Press..............Karen Kuzinski
Marketing Manager...................Pati McDonald
Adv. Mgr., Display ....Andy Palmer
Adv. Mgr., Classified ....Kylie Wingragh
Circ. Mgr. ....Anessa Wheat
Market Information: TMC.
Mechanical available: Offset; Black and 3 ROP colors; insert accepted; page cutoffs - 21 1/2.
Mechanical Specifications: Type page 13 x 21; E - 6 cols, 2 1/16, 1/8 between; A - 6 cols, 2 1/16, 1/8 between; C - 9 cols, 1 3/8, 1/16 between.
Commodity Consumption: Avg. Page Number Per Issue - Daily 14.
Equipment EDITORIAL: Front-end Software – Baseview.; Editorial Hardware – Printers □ APP/Mac LaserWriter NTX, APP/Mac LaserWriter Pro, Xante/8300 CLASSIFIED: Front-end Software – Baseview. DISPLAY: Ad make-up applications – Multi-Ad, Baseview; Layout Software – Multi-Ad.; Display Hardware – Software

☐ Multi-Ad, Baseview; Production Equipment – APP/Mac LaserWriter Pro; Cameras – R. PRESSROOM: Line 1 – 4-G/Community 1991; Folders – 1 MAILROOM: Counter stackers – 1-BG/Count-O-Veyor; Bundle tying machines – 1/Bu.

HANNIBAL

HANNIBAL COURIER-POST

200 N. 3rd, Hannibal, Mo., 63401; gen tel (573) 221-2800; adv tel (573) 221-2800; ed tel (573) 221-2800; gen fax (573) 221-1568; adv fax (573) 221-1568; ed fax (573) 221-5800; adv e-mail advertising@courierpost.com; ed e-mail newsroom@courierpost.com; web site www.hannibal.net

Group: Missouri Press Service, Inc.
Published: Mon, Tues, Wed, Thur, Fri, Sat
Weekday Frequency: m
Saturday Frequency: m
Circulation: 7,301; 7,023(sat)
Last Audit: September 30, 2008
Price: 10.50/mo (city), $11.50/mo (rural); 114.62/yr.
Advertising: Open inch rate $15.30
News services: AP, Morris News Service.
Politics: Independent. **Established:** 1838
Advertising not accepted: Cigarettes; advertisements in poor taste or of questionable credibility.
Not Published: Christmas.
Special Editions: Visitor's Guide (Aug); Progress (Feb); Progress (Jan); Visitor's Guide (Jul); Visitor's Guide (Jun); Progress (Mar); Visitors Guide (May).
Special Weekly Sections: Real Estate (Fri); Arts (Sat); Education (Thur); Business (Tues); Health (Wed).
Magazines: Relish (Monthly); USA WEEKEND Magazine (Sat); American Profile (Tues).
Broadcast Affiliations: KHQA-TV (CBS); WGEM-TV (NBC); WEWB-TV (WB).
Pub. .... John R. Whitaker
Controller/Dir., HR .... Janet Willett
Dir., Sales/Mktg. .... Tina Kopecky
Circ. Dir. .... Ron Schott
Ed. .... Mary Lou Montgomery
Mng. Ed. .... Don Krause
Technology Dir. .... Ryan Strubinger
Market Information: TMC.
Mechanical available: Offset; Black and 3 ROP colors; insert accepted - bags; page cutoffs - 22 3/4.
Mechanical Specifications: Type page 11 5/8 x 21 1/2; E - 6 cols, 1 13/16, 1/8 between; A - 6 cols, 1 13/16, 1/8 between; C - 9 cols, 1 1/8, 1/8 between.
Commodity Consumption: Avg. Page Number Per Issue - Daily 15; Avg. Page Number Per Issue - Plates Used 8850; Avg. Page Number Per Issue - Saturday 29; widths 27; Newsprint Used - Metric Tons 339; Printing Ink Used - Black 6500; Printing Ink Used - Color 300; Printing Ink Used
Equipment EDITORIAL: Front-end Software – QPS/QuarkXPress 4.1, Baseview.; Editorial Hardware – 6-APP/G-4, 2-PC/Power; Editorial Equipment – 2-APP/Mac Flatbed scanners, 1-Nikon/LS-1000 Scanner, 1-Phototherm/Automatic Film Processor; Editorial Printers – APP/Mac 16/600 CLASSIFIED: Front-end Software – Baseview.; Classified Hardware – 2-APP/G-4; Classified Printers – HP/4000, APP/Mac LaserWriter 630 Pro, HP/4MV, HP/Laser Jet 4050 DISPLAY: Ad make-up applications – Multi-Ad/Creator, QPS/QuarkXPress, QPS/QuarkXpress 5.2; Layout Software – Multi-Ad.; Display Hardware – 4-APP/Mac ViewSonic 2-page displays; Display Printers – HP/4MV, HP/LaserJet 4000, HP/8550N Color Printer PRODUCTION: Pagination Software – Quark 4.1, Quark 5.2.; Production Equipment – Nu/Flip Top FT40VGUPNS, Pre Press/Panther RIP, Pre Press/Set 1000/Harlequin Navigator, AG/Accuset 1000; Cameras – 1-R/500; Scanners – Epson PRESSROOM: Line 1 – 9-G/Community single width 1968; Folders – G/Quarter.; Bundle tying machines – MLN; Addressing machine – 1/Ch. BUSINESS COMPUTERS: Business Software – Unix/SCO 4.2; Business Hardware – Digital Venturis

INDEPENDENCE

THE EXAMINER

410 S. Liberty St., Independence, Mo., 64050; gen tel (816) 254-8600; adv tel (816) 350-6336; ed tel (816) 350-6365; gen fax (816) 836-3805; adv fax (816) 836-3805; ed fax (816) 254-0211; web site www.examiner.net

Published: Mon, Tues, Wed, Fri
Weekday Frequency: e
Saturday Frequency: m
Circulation: 10,531
Last Audit: Sworn September 30, 2010
Price: 8.37/mo; 104.00/yr.
News services: AP, SHNS.
Politics: Democrat. **Established:** 1898
Note: Advertising is sold in combination with the Blue Springs Examiner (e) for $30.55 - (d). Individual newspaper rates not made available.
Not Published: New Year; Memorial Day; Independence Day; Labor Day; Christmas.
Special Editions: Spring Car Care (Apr); Senior Citizens (Aug); Holiday Gift Guide (Dec); Review & Forecast (Feb); Tourist Guide (Jan); Guide to Independence (Jun); Health & Fitness (Mar); Spring Parade of Homes (May); Christmas Opening (Nov); Car Care (Oct); Fall Parade o
Special Weekly Sections: TV (Fri).
Magazines: Relish (Monthly); USA WEEKEND Magazine (Sat).
Profile: Local community daily newspaper serving Eastern Jackson County, Missouri.
Gen. Mgr. .... Dale Brendel
Bus. Mgr. .... Sharon Hall
Dir., Mktg. .... Sandy Turner
Editorial Page Ed. .... Jeff Fox
Prodn. Mgr. .... Paul Hunting
Market Information: TMC.
Mechanical available: Offset; Black and 3 ROP colors; insert accepted - all; page cutoffs - 22 3/4.
Mechanical Specifications: Type page 13 x 21 1/2; E - 6 cols, 2 1/16, 1/8 between; A - 6 cols, 2 1/16, 1/8 between; C - 8 cols, 1 1/2, 1/8 between.
Commodity Consumption: Avg. Page Number Per Issue - Daily 24; Avg. Page Number Per Issue - Plates Used 8216; Avg. Page Number Per Issue - Saturday 40; widths 25; Newsprint Used - Short Tons 914; Printing Ink Used - Black 21463; Printing Ink Used - Color 3911; Printing Ink Used
Equipment EDITORIAL: Front-end Software – Baseview/Editorial System.; Editorial Hardware – 26-APP/Mac; Editorial Equipment – SMS/Library System; Editorial Printers – MON/270, Pre Press/Panther 46 CLASSIFIED: Front-end Software – Baseview.; Classified Hardware – 8-APP/Mac Performa 630; Classified Printers – MON/Express Master 1270 DISPLAY: Ad make-up applications – Adobe/Photoshop, QPS/QuarkXPress 3.32, Adobe/Illustrator; Layout Software – 1-APP/Power Mac with Ad Director.; Display Hardware – APP/Mac; Display Printers – APP/Mac, APP/Mac LaserWriter Pro PRODUCTION: Pagination Software – QPS/QuarkXPress 4.0, Baseview/Editorial Systems.; Production Equipment – MON/Imagesetter, Nu/40V6U, Panther 46; Cameras – 1-B PRESSROOM: Line 1 – 7-G/Urbanite; Folders – 1-G/Urbanite, 1-G/Suburban. MAILROOM: Counter stackers – 1-Id; Inserters and stuffers – 1-HI/NP 848; Bundle tying machines – 1/MLN; Addressing machine – 1-/KR. AUDIO: Audio Software – SMS/Stauffer Gold; Audio Hardware – AP, SMS/Epson Action Tower 3000; Business Hardware – 1-ATT/6386E-WGS

JEFFERSON CITY

NEWS TRIBUNE

210 Monroe St., Jefferson City, Mo., 65101; gen tel (573) 636-3131; adv tel 573-761-0228; ed tel 573-761-0240; adv fax (573) 636-7035; ed fax (573) 636-0235; gen e-mail news@newstribune.com; adv e-mail display@newstribune.com; ed e-mail editor@newstribune.com; web site www.newstribune.com

Group: WEHCO Media
Published: Mon, Tues, Wed, Thur, Fri, Sat, Sun
Weekday Frequency: m
Saturday Frequency: m
Circulation: 17,706; 17,706(sat); 21,554(sun)
Last Audit: Sworn September 30, 2008
Price: 8.50/mo (carrier), $9.80/mo (mail); 90.00/yr (carrier), $98.00/yr (mail).
Advertising: Open inch rate $14.30(daily); $15.80 (Sunday)
Insert rate: 2tab-$50/$51; 4tab-$52/$53; 8tab-$54/$55; 12tab-$56/$57; 16tab-$59/$60; 20tab-$61/$62; 24tab-$64/$65; 28tab-$66/$67; 32tab-$68/$69
News services: AP.
Politics: Independent.
Not Published: New Year; Memorial Day; Independence Day; Labor Day; Thanksgiving; Christmas.
Own facility?: Y
Special Editions: Active Times (monthly); Escape (Thursday); Styles (Sunday); Health (Tuesday); Flavors (Wednesday); TV Week (Friday); Church Page (Friday); Real Estate (Friday); Home Living (quarterly)
Special Weekly Sections: Business (daily); Health (Tuesday); Flavor (Wednesday); Escape (Thursday); Style (Sunday)
Magazines: Parade (S).
Publisher .... Walter E. Hussman
Gen. Mgr. .... Mike Vivion
Advertising Manager .... Jane Haslag
Mng. Ed. .... Gary Castor
Sports Ed. .... Tom Rackers
Prodn. Mgr., Pressroom .... Mark Wiethaupt
Circ. Mgr. .... Michael Johns
Mechanical available: Offset; Black and 3 ROP colors; insert accepted; page cutoffs - 20.25.
Mechanical Specifications: Type page 11 5/8 x 20 1/4; E - 6 cols, 2 1/16, 1/8 between; A - 6 cols, 2 1/16, 1/8 between; C - 6 cols, 2 1/16, 1/8 between.
Commodity Consumption: Avg. Page Number Per Issue - Daily 28.8; Avg. Page Number Per Issue - Sunday 64; widths 25; Newsprint Used - Short Tons 1800; Printing Ink Used - Pages Printed 12178.
Equipment EDITORIAL: Front-end Software – Baseview.; Editorial Hardware – APP/Mac; Editorial Printers – Copiers CLASSIFIED: Front-end Software – PBS-DTI; Classified Hardware – PBS-DTI; Classified Printers – Copiers; Layout Software – Multi-Ad, QPS/QuarkXPress.; Display Hardware – APP/Mac PRODUCTION: Pagination Software – InDesign; Production Equipment – Computer to Plate; Cameras – 1-R PRESSROOM: Line 1 – 7-G/U 909; Folders – 1 MAILROOM: Counter stackers – Quipp 440; Inserters and stuffers – HI, GMA/1000; Bundle tying machines – Quipp; Addressing machine – 1/Ch. BUSINESS COMPUTERS: Business Software – PBS; Business Hardware – PBS-Sun
Zip Codes served: 65001, 65010, 65013, 65014, 65016, 65018, 65023, 65024, 65026, 65032, 65035, 65039, 65043, 65046, 65048, 65049, 65051, 65053, 65054, 65058, 65059, 65061, 65063, 65066, 65074, 65075, 65076, 65080, 65081, 65082, 65084, 65085, 65101, 65109, 65251, 65086, 65582
Delivery method: Mail, Newsstand

NEWS TRIBUNE CO.

210 Monroe St., Jefferson City, Mo., 65102; gen tel (573) 636-3131; gen fax (573) 636-7035

Price: 96.00/yr.
Advertising: Open inch rate $7.90

JOPLIN

THE JOPLIN GLOBE

117 E. Fourth St., Joplin, Mo., 64801; gen tel (417) 623-3480; adv tel (417) 781-5500; gen fax (417) 623-8450; adv fax (417) 623-8598; ed fax (417) 623-8598; gen e-mail emailads@joplinglobe.com; adv e-mail tholder@joplinglobe.com; ed e-mail cstark@joplinglobe.com; web site www.joplinglobe.com

Group: Missouri Press Service, Inc.
Published: Mon, Tues, Wed, Thur, Fri, Sat, Sun
Weekday Frequency: m
Saturday Frequency: m
Circulation: 23,374; 22,605(sat); 28,863(sun)
Last Audit: ABC September 30, 2011
Price: 15.95/mo (carrier); 171.40/yr.
Advertising: Open inch rate $49.20
News services: AP.
Politics: Independent. **Established:** 1896
Special Editions: Silver Enquirer (Monthly); Grace Magazine (Quarterly).
Special Weekly Sections: Entertainment (Fri); Sports Monday (Mon); Neighbors (Thur); Business Tuesday (Tues); Best Food (Wed).
Magazines: Parade (S).
Pub./Pres. .... Daniel P. Chiodo
Controller .... Tim Robinson
Credit Mgr. .... Amber Severns
Adv. Dir. .... Tim Holder
Adv. Supvr., Classified .... Sharon Fitzjohn
Ed. .... Carol Stark
City Ed. .... Micheal Stair
Editorial Page Ed. .... Clair Goodwin
Metro Ed. .... Andy Ostemeyer
Sports Ed. .... Jim Henry
Online Mgr. .... John Cruzan
Prodn. Dir. .... David Starchman
Market Information: ADS; TMC.
Mechanical available: Offset; Black and 3 ROP colors; insert accepted; page cutoffs - 22 3/4.
Mechanical Specifications: Type page 13 x 21 3/4; E - 6 cols, 2 1/16, 1/8 between; A - 6 cols, 2 1/16, 1/8 between; C - 6 cols, 2 1/16, 1/8 between.
Commodity Consumption: Avg. Page Number Per Issue - Daily 28; Avg. Page Number Per Issue - Plates Used 30000; Avg. Page Number Per Issue - Sunday 62; widths 27 1/2; Newsprint Used - Metric Tons 2498; Printing Ink Used - Black 75000; Printing Ink Used - Color 12000; Printing In
Equipment EDITORIAL: Front-end Software – AT.; Editorial Hardware – IBM/RS 6000; Editorial Printers – HP/5, HP/4 CLASSIFIED: Front-end Software – AT, Enterprise.; Classified Hardware – IBM/RS 6000; Classified Printers – HP/4; Layout Software – IBM/PC.; Production Equipment – AmeriGraph/Magnum 453 Seds, Southern Litho/GNS 39, W/30 D; Cameras – 1-C, 1-R; Scanners – ECR/1000DE, ECR/1030C. PRESSROOM: Line 1 – 5-G/Headliner Unit (2 color decks) 1986; Folders – 2-G/2:1; Pasters – G/Automatic 1986; Reels and Stands – 1986; Press control system – PEC/Bond Drive 1985. MAILROOM: Counter stackers – 2/QWI, 1-/QWI; Inserters and stuffers – MM/227 2:1; Bundle tying machines – 2-Si/Snl; Wrapping singles – Bann/Tyer; Addressing machine – 1-/Ch; Other equipment –MM/Stitcher-Trimmer.; Business Hardware – IBM/AS-400

KANSAS CITY

THE KANSAS CITY STAR

1729 Grand Blvd., Kansas City, Mo., 64108-1413; gen tel (816) 234-4100; adv tel (816) 234-4150; ed tel (816) 234-4636; gen fax (816) 234-4100; adv fax (816) 234-4101; gen e-mail starinfo@kcstar.com; web site www.kansascity.com

Group: Missouri Press Service, Inc.
Published: Mon, Tues, Wed, Thur, Fri, Sat, Sun
Weekday Frequency: m
Saturday Frequency: m
Circulation: 199,222; 204,919(sat); 300,450(sun)
Last Audit: ABC September 30, 2011

Price: 17.00/mo (KS & MO).
Advertising: Open inch rate $583.00
News services: AP, MCT, NYT.
Politics: Independent.
Special Editions: Lawn, Garden & Home (Apr); Diaper Days II (Aug); Holiday Religion (Dec); Remodeling & Decorating Expo (Feb); American Heart Association (Jan); Active Times (Jul); Progress (Jun); Recycling (Mar); Lawn, Garden & Home (May); The Star Gift Guide I (Nov); The
Special Weekly Sections: Preview (Fri); Sports Extra (Mon); Money Wise (S); Faith (Sat); Business (Tues); Food (Wed).
Magazines: Parade (S).
Pres./Pub. ....Mark Zieman
Finance/Accounting Mgr. ....Bryan Harbison
Adv. Vice Pres. ....Tim Doty
Adv. Dir., Retail/Suburban Opns.........Steve Curd
Circ. Vice Pres. ....Chris Christian
Circ. Mgr., Alternative Delivery..........Keith Tede
Ed...Mike Fannin
Mng. Ed., Local/Nat'l ....Steve Shirk
Asst. Mng. Ed. ....Tom Dolphens
Asst. Mng. Ed., Kansas ....Michael Nelson
Arts Ed.......................................Alice Thorson
Books Ed. ....John M. Eberhart
Cartoonist......................................Lee Judge
Columnist..................................Jerry Heaster
Columnist...........................Rhonda Lokeman
Columnist............................Tom McClanahan
Editorial Page Ed. ....Miriam Pepper
Deputy Editorial Page Ed.................Steve Winn
Asst. Editorial Page Ed. ....Laura Scott
Editorial Writer/Columnist ....Yael Abouhalkah
Market Information: ADS; Split run; TMC; Zoned editions.
Mechanical available: Converted Letterpress to Offset; Black and 3 ROP colors; insert accepted; page cutoffs - 23 9/16.
Mechanical Specifications: Type page 13 x 22 1/4; E - 6 cols, 2 1/16, 1/8 between; A - 6 cols, 2 1/16, 1/8 between; C - 10 cols, 1 3/16, 1/16 between.
Commodity Consumption: Avg. Page Number Per Issue - Daily 69; Avg. Page Number Per Issue - Plates Used 498480; Avg. Page Number Per Issue - Saturday 93; Avg. Page Number Per Issue - Sunday 195; widths 27 3/8; Newsprint Used - Short Tons 66000; Printing Ink Used - Black 1417060
Equipment EDITORIAL: Front-end Software – Dewar/Disc System IV, QPS/QuarkXPress 3.3.; Editorial Hardware – 240-Novell/PC, 25-APP/Mac, APP/Power Mac; Editorial Equipment – Lf/AP Leaf Picture Desk, APP/Mac; Editorial Printers – Epson/LaserPrinter, HP/LaserPrinter, QMS/Laser Printers; Classified Hardware – DEC/VAX; Classified Equipment – HDS, Northern Telephones.; Display Hardware – 1-APP/Mac IIx, 8-APP/Mac IIcx, 8-APP/Mac ci, 1-APP/Mac IIfx, 2-APP/Mac Quadra 700, 1-APP/Mac Quadra 650, 4-APP/Mac Quadra 800, APP/Mac Centris 650, 1-APP/Mac SE, 2-APP/Mac Power PC 7100, 2-APP/Mac Quadra 900, 5-APP/Mac Plus, 2-PC 486, 1-PC 386; Production Equipment – 2-WL/Lith-X-Pozer III, 2-AU/7000 Imagesetters, 2-AU/APS-108 FC Imagesetters, 1-AU/APS-3850 SST; Cameras – 2-C/Newspager; Scanners – 1-ECR/2045C, 1-Scitex/Smart 2045C, 1-Scitex/Smart 342, 2-AG/Horizon Plus, 3-Umax/PowerLook II, 2-Kk/3570, 2-Kk/ PRESSROOM: Line 1 – 10-H/Colormatic converted offset 1966; Line 2 – 10-H/Colormatic converted offset 1967; Line 3 – 10-H/Colormatic converted offset 1968; Line 4 – 15-H/Colormatic converted offset 1969; Folders – 9-H; Reels and Stands – 45-MAN. MAILROOM: Counter stackers – 11-HL/Monitor II; Inserters and stuffers – 5-HI/1372; Bundle tying machines – 11-Dynamic/Tying Machines NT-2; Addressing machine – 2-Ch. AUDIO: Audio Software – Mk/StarTouch, Brite Voice Systems, PEP; Audio Hardware – PC 486, Unix; Business Hardware – PCs, DEC/VAX

THE OLATHE NEWS

1729 Grand Blvd, Kansas City, Mo., 64108; gen tel (913) 764-2211; adv tel (816) 234-4000; ed tel 816-234-7738; oth tel 816-234-4407; ed e-mail respinoza@kcstar.com; web site www.theolathenews.com
Group: KANSAS CITY STAR MCCLATCHY
Published: Wed, Sat
Weekday Frequency: m
Saturday Frequency: m
Circulation: 14,708; 17,182(sat)
Last Audit: Sworn September 30, 2007
Price: 5.43
Politics: Independent. **Established:** 1960
Advertising not accepted: Y
Own facility?: Y
EDITOR........................RICHARD ESPINOZA
FINANCIAL ANALYST/ CIRCULATIONGINGER HOUSE
RETAIL ADVERTISING ....CIANI RON
CLASSIFIED CALL CENTER MANAGERANDERSON DEBORAH
Equipment; Reels and Stands – 5
Zip Codes served: 66061,66062,66030,66083,66018
Delivery method: Mail, Newsstand, Private Carrier

KENNETT

THE DAILY DUNKLIN DEMOCRAT

203 First St., Kennett, Mo., 63857; gen tel (573) 888-4505; adv tel (573) 888-4505; ed tel (573) 888-4505; gen fax (573) 888-5114; adv fax (573) 888-5114; ed fax (573) 888-5114; gen e-mail bhunt@dddnews.com; ed e-mail ganderson@dddnews.com; web site www.dddnews.com
Published: Tues, Wed, Thur, Fri, Sun
Weekday Frequency: e
Circulation: 3,500; 3,600(sun)
Last Audit: Sworn October 1, 2003
Price: 7.50/mo; 90.00/yr (mail, city), $108.00/yr (mail, outside city).
Advertising: Open inch rate $11.85
News services: AP.
Politics: Independent-Liberal. **Established:** 1888
Advertising not accepted: Y
Not Published: New Year; Memorial Day; Independence Day; Labor Day; Thanksgiving; Christmas.
Special Editions: Progress (Mar). Newcomer's (Jul)
Special Weekly Sections: Church (Fri); Agriculture (S); Food Pages (Thur); Food Pages (Tues); Business Page (Wed).
Magazines: Relish (Monthly); Parade (S); American Profile (Weekly).
Office Mgr................................Debbie Wright
Mgr., Mktg./Promo. ....Bud Hunt
Circ. Dir. ....Randy Hindman
Mng. Ed............................Deanna Coronado
Sports Ed. ....Mike Buhler
Prodn. Mgr., Pressroom.............John Emerson
Market Information: Split run; TMC; Zoned editions.
Mechanical available: Offset; Black and 3 ROP colors; insert accepted; page cutoffs - 23.
Mechanical Specifications: Type page 11 5/8 x 21; E - 6 cols, 1 5/6, 1/8 between; A - 6 cols, 1 5/6, 1/8 between; C - 9 cols, 1 1/6, 1/8 between.
Commodity Consumption: Avg. Page Number Per Issue - Daily 16; Avg. Page Number Per Issue - Sunday 74; widths 25; Newsprint Used - Short Tons 242; Printing Ink Used - Black 2150; Printing Ink Used - Color 918; Printing Ink Used - Pages Printed 10286.
Equipment EDITORIAL: Front-end Software – Baseview/NewsEdit Pro.; Editorial Hardware – APP/iMac; Editorial Printers – HP/8000; Production Equipment – 3M. PRESSROOM: Line 1 – 8-G/Community.; Inserters and stuffers – 2-KAN/320; Bundle tying machines – .; Business Hardware – 1-IBM
Delivery method: Mail, Newsstand, Private Carrier, Racks

KIRKSVILLE

KIRKSVILLE DAILY EXPRESS

110 E. McPherson St., Kirksville, Mo., 63501; gen tel (660) 665-2808; gen fax (660) 665-2608; gen e-mail kvnews@sbcglobal.net; fredaily@swbell.net; web site www.kirksvilledailyexpress.com
Published: Mon, Tues, Wed, Thur, Fri, Sun
Weekday Frequency: e
Circulation: 4,263; 4,263(sun)
Last Audit: September 27, 2004
Price: 124.80/yr.
Advertising: Open inch rate $9.90
News services: AP.
Politics: Independent. **Established:** 1901
Not Published: New Year; Memorial Day; Independence Day; Labor Day; Thanksgiving; Christmas.
Special Editions: Progress (Jul).
Special Weekly Sections: TVisions (Thur).
Magazines: American Profile (S).
Pub./Bus. Mgr. ....Larry W. Freels
Adv. Mgr. ....George Wriedt
Adv. Mgr., Classified.................Carole Murphy
Mng. Ed..............................Jason Hunsicker
Sports Ed. ....Adam Harringa
Market Information: Split run; TMC.
Mechanical available: Offset; Black and 3 ROP colors; insert accepted; page cutoffs - 22 3/4.
Mechanical Specifications: Type page 11 2/3 x 21; E - 6 cols, 1 15/16, 5/32 between; A - 6 cols, 1 15/16, 5/32 between; C - 6 cols, 1 15/16, 5/32 between.
Commodity Consumption: Avg. Page Number Per Issue - Daily 12; Avg. Page Number Per Issue - Plates Used 8250; Avg. Page Number Per Issue - Sunday 24; widths 13 3/4; Newsprint Used - Short Tons 340; Printing Ink Used - Black 8500; Printing Ink Used - Color 600; Printing Ink Used
Equipment EDITORIAL: Front-end Software – APP/Mac.; Editorial Hardware – APP/Mac CLASSIFIED: Front-end Software – Baseview.; Classified Hardware – 6-APP/Mac; Classified Equipment – CD-Rom; Classified Printers – 3-APP/Mac LaserPrinter DISPLAY: Ad make-up applications – QPS/QuarkXPress 6.1; Layout Software – QPS/QuarkXPress 6.1.; Production Equipment – 1-Nu/Double Flip Top; Cameras – 1-R/400; Scanners – 4-Scanmaker/X6EL. PRESSROOM: Line 1 – 6-G/Community 1970; Folders – 1; Bundle tying machines – 2/Bu; Addressing machine – 1-Miller/Bevco/LS-385.; Business Hardware – RSK/12, 1-IBM/AT

KIRKSVILLE PUBLISHING CO.

110 E. McPherson St., Kirksville, Mo., 63501; gen tel (660) 665-2808; gen fax (660) 665-2608

LEBANON

THE LEBANON DAILY RECORD

100 E. Commercial St., Lebanon, Mo., 65536; gen tel (417) 532-9131; gen fax (417) 532-8140; gen e-mail editor@lebanondailyrecord.com; adv e-mail ldrclass@lebanondailyrecord.com (Classified); adsales@lebanondailyrecord.com (Retail); ed e-mail editor@lebanondailyrecord.com; web site www.lebanondailyrecord.com
Group: Lebanon Publishing Company, Inc.
Published: Mon, Tues, Wed, Thur, Fri, Sun
Weekday Frequency: e
Circulation: 13,576; 5,192(sun)
Last Audit: Sworn October 1, 2001
Price: 84.70/yr; 25.78/3mo, $51.46/6mo.
Advertising: Open inch rate $9.80
News services: AP.
Politics: Republican. **Established:** 1934
Not Published: New Year; Memorial Day; Independence Day; Labor Day; Thanksgiving; Christmas.
Own facility?: Y
Special Editions: Back-to-School (Aug); Progress (Feb); Fair Tab (Jul); Hillbilly Days (Jun); Senior Living (Monthly); Winter Sports (Nov).
Special Weekly Sections: Outdoors (Thur); Agriculture (Tues).
Magazines: Senior Living (Monthly); American Profile (Weekly).
Pres./Pub.............................Dalton C. Wright
CFO/Bus. Mgr. ....Phyllis Wilson
Adv. Mgr. ....Rene Barker
Circ. Mgr. ....Helen Davis
Ed. ....Julie Crawford
Sports Ed.....................................Matt Wilson
Audiotex Mgr...........................Beth Durreman
Market Information: ADS; TMC.
Mechanical available: Offset; Black and 3 ROP colors; insert accepted; page cutoffs - 22 3/4.
Mechanical Specifications: Type page 13 x 21 1/2; E - 6 cols, 2, 1/6 between; A - 6 cols, 2, 1/6 between; C - 6 cols, 2, 1/6 between.
Commodity Consumption: Avg. Page Number Per Issue - Daily 12; Avg. Page Number Per Issue - Plates Used 6700; Avg. Page Number Per Issue - Sunday 16; widths 27 1/2; Newsprint Used - Short Tons 290; Printing Ink Used - Black 1400; Printing Ink Used - Color 1800; Printing Ink Use
Equipment EDITORIAL: Front-end Software – Adobe/PageMaker 6.5, Adobe/Photoshop 3.0.; Editorial Hardware – APP/Power Mac/G4/TMac, APP/Mac; Editorial Printers – HP/5000 CLASSIFIED: Front-end Software – Multi-Ad/CAMS.; Classified Hardware – APP/Mac DISPLAY: Ad make-up applications – Adobe/PageMaker 6.5, Multi-Ad/Creator 4.0, Adobe/Photoshop 3.05, QPS/QuarkXPress; Layout Software – APP/Mac.; Display Hardware – APP/Mac; Display Printers – APP/Mac LaserWriter 16-600, New-Gen/Imager Plus 12xf PRODUCTION: Pagination Software – Adobe/PageMaker 6.5, Multi-Ad/Creator, Adobe/Photoshop, QPS/QuarkXPr; Production Equipment – APP/Mac LaserWriter 4-600, APP/Mac LaserWriter 161600, NewGen/Imager Pro; Cameras – Umax/5-8, Polaroid/SprintScan Neg Scanners – Nu/Horizontal SSTE2024; Scanners – PRESSROOM: Line 1 – 4-G/Community 1964; Line 2 – 4-G/Community 1992. MAILROOM: Counter stackers – BG; Bundle tying machines – 2/Bu; Addressing machine – KR/215. BUSINESS COMPUTERS: Business Software – DAC/Easy, Lotus 1-2-3, Quattro/Pro; Business Hardware – 3-PC 386
Delivery method: Mail, Newsstand, Private Carrier, Racks

MACON

MACON CHRONICLE-HERALD

204 W. Bourke St., Macon, Mo., 63552; gen tel (660) 385-3121; gen fax (660) 385-3082; gen e-mail chnews@centurytel.net; web site www.maconch.com
Group: Missouri Press Service, Inc.
Published: Tues, Wed, Thur, Fri
Weekday Frequency: e
Circulation: 2,301
Last Audit: September 26, 2003
Price: 130.79/yr.
Advertising: Open inch rate $8.55
News services: AP.
Politics: Independent.
Not Published: New Year; Memorial Day; Independence Day; Labor Day; Thanksgiving; Christmas.
Special Editions: Bridal (Apr); Farmer Appreciation (Aug); Christmas Wrap-up (Dec); Recipe (Feb); Year-in-Review (Jan); Summer Baseball (Jun); Chamber of Commerce Tab (Mar); Graduation (May); Basketball (Nov); FFA Appreciation (Oct); Football (Sept).
Magazines: TV Guide (Fri).
Pub...Pat Quinly
Mgr., Mktg./Promo......................Chuck Kindle
Circ. Dir....................................Kevin Britton
Ed....Terri Hackett
Sports Ed...Chris Ray
Market Information: Split run; TMC; Zoned editions.
Mechanical available: Offset; Black and 3 ROP colors; insert accepted; page cutoffs - 22 3/4.
Mechanical Specifications: Type page 11 5/8 x 21; E - 6 cols, 2, 1/6 between; A - 6 cols, 2, 1/6 between; C - 6 cols, 2, 1/6 between.

Commodity Consumption: Avg. Page Number Per Issue - Daily 12; Avg. Page Number Per Issue - Plates Used 2500; widths 27 1/2; Newsprint Used - Short Tons 300; Printing Ink Used - Black 6500; Printing Ink Used - Color 400; Printing Ink Used - Pages Printed 20000.
Equipment EDITORIAL: Front-end Software – Aldus/PageMaker.; Editorial Hardware – APP/Mac; Editorial Printers – APP/Mac LaserWriter II CLASSIFIED: Front-end Software – Aldus/PageMaker.; Classified Hardware – APP/Mac; Classified Printers – APP/Mac LaserWriter DISPLAY: Ad make-up applications – Aldus/PageMaker.; Display Hardware – APP/Mac; Display Printers – APP/Mac LaserWriter II; Production Equipment – LE; Cameras – R. PRESSROOM: Line 1 – 6-KP/News King 475 1966.; Bundle tying machines – Bu.

MARSHALL

THE MARSHALL DEMOCRAT-NEWS

121 N. Lafayette St., Marshall, Mo., 65340; gen tel (660) 886-2233; adv tel (660) 886-2233; gen fax (660) 886-8544; adv fax (660) 886-8544; gen e-mail shellyarth@socket.net; ed e-mail marshalleditor@socket.net; web site www.marshallnews.com
Published: Mon, Tues, Wed, Thur, Fri
Weekday Frequency: e
Circulation: 3,125
Last Audit: September 29, 2004
Price: 7.78/mo; 99.00/yr; 40.70/6mo.
Advertising: Open inch rate $8.32
News services: AP.
Politics: Independent. **Established:** 1879
Advertising not accepted: Investments requested.
Not Published: New Year; Memorial Day; Independence Day; Labor Day; Thanksgiving; Christmas.
Special Weekly Sections: Religion (Fri); Business (Thur); Health (Tues); Food (Wed).
Magazines: TV Preview (Fri); Relish (Monthly).
Pub. ....Shelly Arth
Adv. Mgr. ....Mike Davis
Circ. Mgr. ....Pat Morrow
Ed. ....Eric Crump
Sports Ed. ....Chris Allen
Prodn. Mgr. ....Jessica Wise
Market Information: TMC.
Mechanical available: Offset; Black and 3 ROP colors; insert accepted; page cutoffs - 21 1/2.
Mechanical Specifications: Type page 13 x 21 1/2; E - 6 cols, 2 1/16, 1/8 between; A - 6 cols, 2 1/16, 1/8 between; C - 6 cols, 2 1/16, 1/8 between.
Commodity Consumption: Avg. Page Number Per Issue - Daily 10; Avg. Page Number Per Issue - Plates Used 2000; widths 28; Newsprint Used - Short Tons 204; Printing Ink Used - Black 5400; Printing Ink Used - Color 200; Printing Ink Used - Pages Printed 3100.
Equipment; Editorial Hardware – 8-APP/Mac; Editorial Printers – 1-APP/Mac.; Classified Hardware – 1-APP/Mac.; Display Hardware – 2-APP/Mac; Display Printers – 1-APP/Mac.; Production Equipment – 1-Nu; Cameras – 1-R/500, LE; Scanners – Gam/Digital Densitometer. PRESSROOM: Line 1 – 5-KP/News King 1976.; Bundle tying machines – 1/Bu; Wrapping singles – Addressing machine ☐ 1-/Ch.; Business Hardware – 1-Packard Bell, 2-Acros

THE MARSHALL PUBLISHING CO.

121 N. Lafayette St., Marshall, Mo., 65340; gen tel (660) 886-2233; gen fax (660) 886-8544
Price: 99.00/yr.
Advertising: Open inch rate $7.64
Politics: 1879

MARYVILLE

THE MARYVILLE DAILY FORUM

111 E. Jenkins St., Maryville, Mo., 64468; gen tel (660) 562-2424; gen fax (660) 562-2823; ed e-mail newsroom@asde.net; web site www.maryvilledailyforum.com
Published: Mon, Tues, Wed, Thur, Fri
Weekday Frequency: m
Circulation: 3,500
Last Audit: March 31, 2006
Price: 7.75/mo; 90.00/yr.
Advertising: Open inch rate $8.60
News services: AP.
Politics: Independent. **Established:** 1869
Not Published: New Year; Independence Day; Thanksgiving; Christmas.
Special Editions: Real Estate (Aug); Holiday Gift Guide (Dec); Progress (Jan); Newcomers (Jul); Fair (Jun); Spring Home Improvement (Mar); Real Estate (May); Fall Sports (Football) (Sept).
Special Weekly Sections: Religion (Fri); Television (Thur).
Magazines: American Profile (S); TV Forum (Thur).
Pub ....Phil Cobb
Bus. Mgr. ....Dede Linville
Sports Ed. ....Charlie Slenker
Prodn. Mgr., Pressroom ....Todd Puckett
Prodn. Mgr., Composing ....Gary Darling
Market Information: TMC.
Mechanical available: Offset; Black and 2 ROP colors; insert accepted; page cutoffs - 21 1/2.
Mechanical Specifications: Type page 13 x 21 1/2; E - 6 cols, 2 1/16, 1/8 between; A - 6 cols, 2 1/16, 1/8 between; C - 6 cols, 2 1/16, 1/8 between.
Commodity Consumption: Avg. Page Number Per Issue - Daily 12; Avg. Page Number Per Issue - Plates Used 9600; Avg. Page Number Per Issue - Sunday 16; widths 27 1/2; Newsprint Used - Short Tons 580; Printing Ink Used - Black 8400; Printing Ink Used - Color 2100; Printing Ink Use
Equipment EDITORIAL: Front-end Software – Aldus/PageMaker 4.0.; Editorial Hardware – 4-APP/Mac Plus, 1-APP/Mac SE30, 1-APP/Mac LC II, 2-APP/iMac; Editorial Equipment – APP/Mac Scanner; Editorial Printers – APP/Mac LaserWriter, HP/2000N CLASSIFIED: Front-end Software – Baseview.; Classified Hardware – 1-APP/iMac; Classified Printers – HP/2000N DISPLAY: Ad make-up applications – QPS/QuarkXPress.; Display Hardware – 1-APP/iMac; Display Printers – APP/Mac LaserWriter II NT; Production Equipment – Graham/S 3-27, DAI/LD-1800A; Cameras – B/Gammamatic. PRESSROOM: Line 1 – 6-G/Community 1978.; Bundle tying machines – Bu/182, Malow/Strap-tyer; Wrapping singles – Strap-Matic/202A. BUSINESS COMPUTERS: Business Software – Quick Book Pro; Business Hardware – Cougar Mountain, MSSI

MEXICO

MEXICO LEDGER

300 N. Washington St., Mexico, Mo., 65265-0008; gen tel (573) 581-1111; gen fax (573) 581-2029; adv e-mail display@mexicoledger.com; ed e-mail news@mexicoledger.com; web site www.mexicoledger.com
Group: Missouri Press Service, Inc.
Published: Mon, Tues, Wed, Thur, Fri
Weekday Frequency: e
Circulation: 7,000
Last Audit: March 31, 2006
Price: 12.00/mo; 125.00/yr.
Advertising: Open inch rate $12.50
News services: AP, SHNS.
Politics: Independent. **Established:** 1855
Not Published: New Year; Memorial Day; Independence Day; Labor Day; Thanksgiving; Christmas.
Special Editions: Home Improvement (Apr); Football (Aug); Progress (Feb); Hometown (Jun); Car Care (Mar); Christmas Kick-Off (Nov); Back-to-School (Oct).
Special Weekly Sections: Church Page (Fri); Best Food Day (Mon); TV Tab (Sat); Farm Page (Thur); Best Food Day (Tues); Financial/Business Page (Wed).
Magazines: Relish (Monthly); American Profile (Sat).
Broadcast Affiliations: ABC; NBC; CBS.
Pub. ....Joe May
Mgr., Mktg./Promo. ....Martin Keller
Political/Gov't Ed. ....Janeen Sims
Religion Ed. ....Brenda Fike
Market Information: Split run; TMC.
Mechanical available: Offset; Black and 3 ROP colors; insert accepted; page cutoffs - 21 1/2.
Mechanical Specifications: Type page 13 x 21 1/2; E - 6 cols, 2, 1/12 between; A - 6 cols, 2, 1/12 between; C - 7 cols, 2, 1/12 between.
Commodity Consumption: Avg. Page Number Per Issue - Daily 14; widths 13 3/4; Newsprint Used - Short Tons 500; Printing Ink Used - Black 6000; Printing Ink Used - Color 570; Printing Ink Used - Pages Printed 4288.
Equipment EDITORIAL: Front-end Software – QPS/QuarkXPress, Multi-Ad/Creator, Adobe/Photoshop, Adobe/PageMaker.; Editorial Hardware – 11-APP/Mac; Editorial Equipment – APP/Mac; Editorial Printers – HP/4V, HP/5000 CLASSIFIED: Front-end Software – Cx.; Classified Hardware – 1-APP/Mac Performa 6300; Classified Printers – Ap DISPLAY: Ad make-up applications – Multi-Ad/Creator, Aldus/PageMaker; Layout Software – 2-APP/Power Mac 7200-90.; Display Printers – HP/5000 PRODUCTION: Pagination Software – QPS/QuarkXPress.; Production Equipment – 1-Nu; Cameras – 1-R/580, 1-SCREEN/680C; Scanners – Lf/Leafscan, APP/Mac Scanner PRESSROOM: Line 1 – 7-G/Community; Folders – 1; Bundle tying machines – 1/Bu; Wrapping singles – 1-Sa/SM; Addressing machine – 1-/Ch. BUSINESS COMPUTERS: Business Software – Microsoft/Windows 98, QuickBooks, Excel Microsoft/Excel, Lotus 1-2-3, Microsoft/Word; Business Hardware – Maxtech/ChipTex

MOBERLY

MOBERLY MONITOR-INDEX & EVENING DEMOCRAT

218 N. Williams St., Moberly, Mo., 65270; gen tel (660) 263-4123; adv tel (660) 263-4123; ed tel (660) 263-4123; gen fax (660) 263-3626; adv fax (660) 263-3626; ed fax (660) 263-3626; adv e-mail advertising@moberlymonitor.com; ed e-mail news@moberlymonitor.com; web site www.moberlymonitor.com
Published: Mon, Tues, Wed, Thur, Fri, Sun
Weekday Frequency: e
Circulation: 5,342; 5,342(sun)
Last Audit: October 1, 2001
Price: 8.00/mo (carrier), $9.00/mo (mail); 108.00/yr (carrier), $120.00/yr (mail); 24.00/3mo, $48.00/6mo (carrier); $30.00/3mo, $60.00/6mo (mail).
Advertising: Open inch rate $15.75
News services: AP, NEA, TMS.
Politics: Independent. **Established:** 1869
Advertising not accepted: Adoption.
Not Published: New Year; Memorial Day; Independence Day; Labor Day; Thanksgiving; Christmas.
Special Editions: Chamber Tab (Apr); Back-to-School (Aug); Christmas Greetings (Dec); Valentine Hearts (Feb); Bridal (Jan); County Fairs (Jul); Spring Bridal (Jun); Progress (Mar); Graduation (May); Cookbook (Nov); Fall Fashion (Sept).
Special Weekly Sections: Church Guide (Fri); Business Page (Thur); Best Food Day (Tues).
Magazines: Business Review (Fri); 50 Something (Monthly); American Profile (S); Youth Today (Tues).
Broadcast Affiliations: KMOU; KMIZ.
Pub ....Bob Cunningham
Bus. Mgr. ....Debbie Lowery
Division Mgr. ....Gene Hall
Adv. Mgr., Classified ....Nancy Bartollacci
Mgr., Mktg./Promo. ....Judy Orton
Circ. Mgr. ....Tammy Bradds
Entertainment/Amusements Ed. Debbie Fitzpatrick
Environmental Ed. ....Charles Embree
Features Ed. ....Deborah Fitzpatrick
Lifestyle Ed. ....Connie Duvall
Nat'l Ed. ....Ruth Carr
Market Information: Split run; TMC; Zoned editions.
Mechanical available: Offset; Black and 3 ROP colors; insert accepted; page cutoffs - 22 3/4.
Mechanical Specifications: Type page 13 x 21 1/2; E - 6 cols, 2 1/16, 1/5 between; A - 6 cols, 2 1/16, 1/5 between; C - 8 cols, 1 1/2, 1/5 between.
Commodity Consumption: Avg. Page Number Per Issue - Daily 14; Avg. Page Number Per Issue - Plates Used 2900; Avg. Page Number Per Issue - Sunday 36; widths 27 1/2; Newsprint Used - Short Tons 280; Printing Ink Used - Black 10430; Printing Ink Used - Color 400; Printing Ink Use
Equipment EDITORIAL: Front-end Software – Mk, QPS/QuarkXPress, Baseview, Brainworks.; Editorial Hardware – Mk, APP/Mac; Editorial Equipment – Epson/Film Scanner, APP/Mac Scanner; Editorial Printers – NewGen/Oversize, APP/Mac, APP/Mac LaserWriter Pro, NewGen/DesignXpress, Xante/Accel-A-Writer CLASSIFIED: Front-end Software – Baseview, Fox, Aldus, QPS/QuarkXPress.; Classified Hardware – APP/Mac; Classified Equipment – APP/Mac Scanner; Classified Printers – NewGen/DesignXpress 17 DISPLAY: Ad make-up applications – Multi-Ad/Creator, Aldus/FreeHand, QPS/QuarkXPress, Baseview, Brainworks; Layout Software – Baseview; Display Hardware – APP/Mac; Display Printers – APP/Mac LaserWriter Pro, NewGen/DesignXpress 17 PRODUCTION: Pagination Software – Baseview.; Production Equipment – 1-Nu, APP/Power Mac 64; Cameras – Acti; Scanners – APP/Mac, Epson/Film Scanner PRESSROOM: Line 1 – 6-Unit/Community; Folders – G/Suburban.; Bundle tying machines – StrapMatic 202A; Addressing machine – Wm, MB-45/Labeling Machine. BUSINESS COMPUTERS: Business Software – QuarkXPress 7.0, Baseview, Brainworks, SSPS System; Business Hardware – Mk, APP/Mac

MONETT

THE MONETT TIMES

505 Broadway, Monett, Mo., 65708-0040; gen tel (417) 235-3135; gen fax (417) 235-8852; adv e-mail classifieds@monett-times.com; advertising@monett-times.com; ed e-mail editor@monett-times.com; editor@monett-times.com; web site www.monett-times.com
Group: Missouri Press Service, Inc.
Published: Mon, Tues, Wed, Thur, Fri
Weekday Frequency: e
Circulation: 3,976
Last Audit: October 1, 2001
Price: 40.00/yr.
Advertising: Open inch rate $8.10
News services: AP.
Politics: Republican. **Established:** 1908
Not Published: New Year; Memorial Day; Independence Day; Labor Day; Thanksgiving; Christmas.
Special Editions: Christmas (Dec); Progress (Feb); Football (Oct); Basketball (Other).
Magazines: American Profile (Weekly).
Pub. ....Lisa Craft
Circ. Dir. ....Melissa Leech
Mng. Ed. ....Murray Bishoff
Sports Ed. ....Charles F. Brady
Prodn. Mgr. ....Allen Adkins
Market Information: TMC.
Mechanical available: Offset; Black and 3 ROP colors; insert accepted; page cutoffs - 22 3/4.
Mechanical Specifications: Type page 13 x 21 1/2; E - 6 cols, 2, 1/4 between; A - 6 cols, 2, 1/4 between; C - 6 cols, 2, 1/4 between.
Commodity Consumption: Avg. Page Number Per Issue - Daily 8; Avg. Page Number Per Issue - Plates Used 4000; widths 28; Newsprint

Used - Short Tons 100; Printing Ink Used - Pages Printed 2300.

Equipment EDITORIAL: Front-end Software – Microsoft/Word, Aldus/PageMaker, Microsoft/Windows.; Editorial Hardware – APP/Power Mac; Editorial Printers – APP/Mac LaserWriter CLASSIFIED: Front-end Software – Microsoft/Word, Aldus/PageMaker, Microsoft/Windows.; Classified Hardware – APP/Power Mac SE; Classified Printers – APP/Mac LaserWriter DISPLAY: Ad make-up applications – Aldus/PageMaker; Layout Software – APP/Power Mac.; Display Printers – APP/Mac LaserWriter, LaserMaster/1200 dpi; Production Equipment – APP/Power Mac, Adobe/Photoshop; Cameras – CL; Scanners – 1-LaCie, Minolta. PRESSROOM: Line 1 – 4-WPC/Quadra Color 1995; Folders – 1; Bundle tying machines – 2/Bu.; Business Hardware – DEC/PC XL 466D2

NEOSHO

NEOSHO DAILY NEWS

1006 W. Harmony St., Neosho, Mo., 64850; gen tel (417) 451-1520; gen fax (417) 451-6408; adv e-mail advertising@neoshodailynews.com; ed e-mail editor@neoshodailynews.com; web site www.neoshodailynews.com

Group: Missouri Press Service, Inc.
Published: Mon, Tues, Wed, Thur, Fri, Sun
Weekday Frequency: e
Circulation: 3,474; 3,892(sun)
Last Audit: March 31, 2001
Price: 9.42/mo; 104.44/yr.
Advertising: Open inch rate $9.25
News services: AP.
Politics: 1905
Not Published: New Year; Memorial Day; Independence Day; Labor Day; Thanksgiving; Christmas.
Special Editions: City-Wide Garage Sale (Apr); Back-to-School (Aug); Christmas Greetings (Dec); Year of Progress (Feb); Babies of Last Year (Jan); Fair Tabs (Jul); Lawn & Garden (Mar); Graduation (May); Holiday Gift Guide (Nov); Our Town (Oct).
Special Weekly Sections: Health (Mon); TV Guide & Entertainment (S); Business (Tues); Food (Wed).
Magazines: American Profile (Weekly).
Pub. .... Rick Rogers
Circ. Mgr. .... Tena Mathews
Sports Ed. .... Cody Thoren
Online Mgr./Mgmt. Info Servs. Mgr. ...... John Ford
Prodn. Mgr., Pressroom .... James Abruzzo
Market Information: TMC.
Mechanical available: Offset; Black and 3 ROP colors; insert accepted; page cutoffs - 22 3/4.
Mechanical Specifications: Type page 11 5/8 x 21 1/2; E - 6 cols, 2 1/16, 1/8 between; A - 6 cols, 2 1/16, 1/8 between; C - 6 cols, 2 1/16, 1/8 between.
Commodity Consumption: Avg. Page Number Per Issue - Daily 12; Avg. Page Number Per Issue - Plates Used 1100; Avg. Page Number Per Issue - Sunday 20; widths 25; Newsprint Used - Short Tons 156; Printing Ink Used - Black 1500; Printing Ink Used - Color 500; Printing Ink Used - P
Equipment EDITORIAL: Front-end Software – Baseview.; Editorial Hardware – APP/Mac; Editorial Equipment – Pre Press/Panther Pro Imagesetter CLASSIFIED: Front-end Software – CAMS.; Classified Hardware – APP/Mac; Classified Printers – APP/Mac ImageWriter PRODUCTION: Pagination Software – QPS/QuarkXPress, Pre Press/Imagesetter.; Production Equipment – APP/Mac LaserWriter Select, APP/Mac, HP/LaserJet 4MV, 2-Pre Press Panther Pro Imagesetter; Cameras – R; Scanners – 2-Microtek/EM6 PRESSROOM: Line 1 – 9-G/Community 1971; Folders – 1-G/Community, 1-G/SC 1971; Press registration system – 2 MAILROOM: Counter stackers – 1/BG; Bundle tying machines – 2-/Miller-Bevco. BUSINESS COMPUTERS: Business Software – Nomads, QuickBooks; Business Hardware – PC

NEVADA

THE NEVADA DAILY MAIL

131 S. Cedar St., Nevada, Mo., 64772; gen tel (417) 667-3344; adv tel (417) 667-3344; ed tel (417) 667-3344; oth tel (417) 667-3344; gen fax (417) 667-7475; adv fax (417) 667-7475; ed fax (417) 667-7475; gen e-mail composing@nevadadailymail.com; adv e-mail advertising@nevadadailymail.com; ed e-mail editorial@nevadadailymail.com; web site www.nevadadailymail.com

Group: Rust Communications
Published: Tues, Wed, Thur, Fri
Weekday Frequency: m
Circulation: 2,300
Last Audit: Sworn September 30, 2007
Price: 8.00/mo; 79.00/yr.
Advertising: Open inch rate $9.85
Insert rate: Call for rates
News services: AP, NEA.
Politics: Democrat. **Established:** 1883
Not Published: New Year; Memorial Day; Independence Day; Labor Day; Veterans Day; Thanksgiving; Christmas.
Own facility?: Y
Special Editions: Back-to-School (Aug); Christmas Shoppers (Dec); Brides (Jan); Home Improvement (Mar); Graduation (May); Puzzle Pages (Monthly); Home Improvement (Oct).
Special Weekly Sections: Senior (Thurs); Youth (Sat)
Magazines: SHE
AGELESS
Broadcast Affiliations: none
Profile: daily newspaper
Pub. .... Julie Simpson
Bus. Mgr. .... Lois McMillan
Adv. Dir. .... Lorie Harter
Ed. .... Lynn Wade
Lifestyles Ed. .... Sharyon Duke
Prodn. Mgr. .... Chris Jones
Market Information: TMC.
Mechanical available: Offset; Black and 3 ROP colors; insert accepted; page cutoffs - 21.
Mechanical Specifications: Type page 13 x 21; E - 6 cols, 2 1/16, 1/8 between; A - 6 cols, 2 1/16, 1/8 between; C - 6 cols, 2 1/16, 1/8 between.
Commodity Consumption: Avg. Page Number Per Issue - Daily 12; Avg. Page Number Per Issue - Plates Used 3800; Avg. Page Number Per Issue - Sunday 20; widths 27; Newsprint Used - Metric Tons 342; Newsprint Used - Short Tons 310; Printing Ink Used - Black 5400; Printing Ink Used
Equipment; Editorial Hardware – COM/UTS, APP/Mac. DISPLAY: Ad make-up applications – QPS/QuarkXPress 4.1.; Production Equipment – CTP PRESSROOM: Line 1 – 5-G/Community; Folders – 1; Bundle tying machines – 1/Bu, 1-/St; Wrapping singles – 2-/Sa
Delivery method: Mail, Newsstand, Racks

RUST COMMUNICATIONS

131 S. Cedar, Nevada, Mo., 64772; gen tel (417) 667-3344; gen fax (417) 667-7475

Price: 79.00/yr.
Advertising: Open inch rate $10.00
Politics: 1883

PARK HILLS

DAILY JOURNAL

1513 St. Joe Dr., Park Hills, Mo., 63601; gen tel (573) 431-2010; gen fax (573) 431-7640; adv e-mail advertising@dailyjournalonline.com; ed e-mail editorial@dailyjournalonline.com; web site www.dailyjournalonline.com

Group: Lee Enterprises
Published: Mon, Tues, Wed, Thur, Fri, Sat
Weekday Frequency: e
Saturday Frequency: m
Circulation: 6,915; 6,915(sat); 7,279(sun)
Last Audit: September 30, 2009
News services: NEA, AP, TMS.
Politics: Independent. **Established:** 1935
Not Published: New Year; Memorial Day; Independence Day; Labor Day; Christmas.
Own facility?: Y
Special Editions: see website
Pub. .... Gary Berblinger
Adv. Dir. .... Andy Raley
Health/Medical Ed. .... Renee Stacy
Sports Ed. .... Donn Adamson
Wire Ed. .... Sherry Greminger
Circulation Manager
Angel King
Market Information: TMC.
Mechanical available: same as daily, see website
Equipment; Line 2 – 1
Delivery method: Mail, Newsstand, Private Carrier, Racks

POPLAR BLUFF

DAILY AMERICAN REPUBLIC

208 Poplar St., Poplar Bluff, Mo., 63901; gen tel (573) 785-1414; adv tel (573) 785-1414; gen fax (573) 785-2706; adv e-mail caradv@imsinternet.net; web site www.darnews.com

Published: Mon, Tues, Wed, Thur, Fri, Sun
Weekday Frequency: e
Circulation: 10,106; 11,162(sun)
Last Audit: September 30, 2009
Price: 9.00/mo; 110.00/yr.
Advertising: Open inch rate $17.10
News services: AP, NYT.
Politics: Independent. **Established:** 1895
Not Published: New Year; Memorial Day; Independence Day; Labor Day; Thanksgiving; Christmas.
Magazines: TV Update (Other); Parade (S).
Pub. .... Don Schrieber
Bus. Mgr./Controller .... Rachel Coleman
Adv. Dir. .... Joe Jordan
Circ. Dir. .... Gary Richard
Agriculture Ed. .... Stan Berry
Lifestyle Ed. .... Michele Friedrich
News Ed. .... Barbara Horton
Religion Ed. .... Dorothy Carlson
Sports Ed. .... Brian Rosener
Prodn. Foreman, Pressroom .... Randy Graves
Market Information: TMC; Zoned editions.
Mechanical available: Offset; Black and 2 ROP colors; insert accepted - product samples; page cutoffs - 22 3/4.
Mechanical Specifications: Type page 13 x 21 1/2; E - 6 cols, 2 1/16, 1/8 between; A - 6 cols, 2 1/16, 1/8 between; C - 6 cols, 2 1/16, 1/8 between.
Commodity Consumption: Avg. Page Number Per Issue - Daily 23; Avg. Page Number Per Issue - Sunday 48; widths 27; Newsprint Used - Short Tons 750.
Equipment; Editorial Hardware – 1-COM/UTS, 1-RSK/TRS 80-100.; Classified Hardware – 1-COM/UC.; Layout Software – 2-COM/Advantage I.; Production Equipment – 1-COM/8600, 1-COM/Unisetter, 2-COM/7200; Cameras – 1-B/4000. PRESSROOM: Line 1 – 5-G/Urbanite; Folders – 1-G/2:1.; Bundle tying machines – 1/Malow; Addressing machine – RSK/TRS 80.; Business Hardware – 1-RSK/TRS 80-16B

RICHMOND

THE DAILY NEWS

204 W. North Main St., Richmond, Mo., 64085; gen tel (816) 776-5454; adv tel (816) 776-5454; ed tel (816) 776-5454; adv fax (816) 470-6397; gen e-mail news@richmond-dailynews.com; adv e-mail ads@richmond-dailynews.com; web site www.richmond-dailynews.com

Published: Mon, Tues, Wed, Thur, Fri
Weekday Frequency: e
Circulation: 2,100
Last Audit: September 30, 2008
Price: 6.50/mo; 66.00/yr.
Advertising: Open inch rate $5.40
Politics: Independent. **Established:** 1914
Not Published: New Year; Memorial Day; Independence Day; Labor Day; Thanksgiving; Christmas.
Special Editions: Spring Home Improvement Guide (Apr); Sidewalk Days (Aug); Greetings and Letters to Santa (Dec); Pharmacy Tab (Mar); Mushroom Festival Guide (May); Coupon Clipper (Monthly); Christmas Gift Guide (Nov); Fall Car Care (Oct); Agri-Business Tab (Sept).
Special Weekly Sections: Religion (Thur); Agriculture (Tues).
Pub. .... JoEllen Black
Adv. Sales .... Sandra Alder
Adv. Sales .... Marie King
Ed. .... Dennis Sharkey
Composing Mgr. .... Karen Payne
Market Information: TMC.
Mechanical available: Offset; Black and 3 ROP colors; insert accepted - must be labelled as supplement to Daily News; page cutoffs - 22 3/4.
Mechanical Specifications: Type page 12 1/4 x 21 1/2; E - 4 cols, 2 31/32, 1/8 between; A - 7 cols, 1 5/8, 1/8 between; C - 7 cols, 1 5/8, 1/8 between.
Commodity Consumption: Avg. Page Number Per Issue - Daily 9; Avg. Page Number Per Issue - Plates Used 4800; widths 13 1/2; Newsprint Used - Short Tons 120; Printing Ink Used - Black 9000; Printing Ink Used - Color 400; Printing Ink Used - Pages Printed 2400.
Equipment EDITORIAL: Front-end Software – QPS/QuarkXPress 4.0.; Editorial Hardware – 5-Macintosh/iMac; Editorial Printers – APP/Mac LaserWriter IIF, APP/Mac Laserwriter Select, GCC/Elite XL 20/600; Classified Hardware – 1-Macintosh/iMac; Classified Printers – APP/Mac LaserWriter IIF. DISPLAY: Ad make-up applications – Adobe/InDesign 2.0; Layout Software – 2-APP/Mac G-3.; Display Printers – GCC/Elite XL 20/600, APP/Mac LaserWriter IIF, APP/LaserWriter Select 360; Production Equipment – 1-Nu; Cameras – 1-R/400; Scanners – Umax/2400, Nikon/CoolScan III. PRESSROOM: Line 1 – 5-G/Community; Pasters – Press Drive Ã□Â□Ã□Â□Ã□Â□Ã□Â□Ã□Â□Ã□Â□Ã□Â□Ã□Â□Ã□Â□Ã□Â□Ã□Â□Ã□Â¯Ã□Â□Ã□Â□Ã□Â□Ã□Â¿ Ã□Â□Ã□Â□Ã□Â□Ã□Â½ 1-HP/30; Reels and Stands – 5 MAILROOM: Counter stackers – 1-BG/Count-O-Veyor; Bundle tying machines – 2/Bu.; Business Hardware – IBM/5120

ROLLA

ROLLA DAILY NEWS

101 W. Seventh St., Rolla, Mo., 65401; gen tel (573) 364-2468; ed tel (573) 341-5222; gen fax (573) 341-5847; adv fax (573) 364-6107; gen e-mail rdnnews@gmail.com; web site www.therolladailynews.com

Group: Missouri Press Service, Inc.
Published: Mon, Tues, Wed, Thur, Fri, Sat
Weekday Frequency: m
Circulation: 4,875; 4,875(sat)
Last Audit: October 1, 2003
Price: 92.10/yr.
Advertising: Open inch rate $15.55
News services: AP.
Politics: Independent.
Note: This publication is printed at the Waynesville Daily Guide, St. Robert.
Not Published: New Year; Memorial Day; Independence Day; Labor Day; Thanksgiving; Christmas.
Special Editions: Fashion (Apr); Back-to-School (Aug); Car Care (Dec); Newcomers (Feb); Bridal (Jan); Progress (Jul); Lawn & Garden (Mar); Christmas (Nov); Car Care (Oct); Welcome Back Students (College) (Sept).
Magazines: TV (Every other week); Features/Living (S); American Profile (Weekly).
Pub. .... Floyd Jernigan
Adv. Dir. .... Alissa Martin
Circ. Mgr. .... Kelly Wallis
Ed. .... Alan Gerstenecker
Market Information: ADS; TMC.
Mechanical available: Offset; Black and 4 ROP

colors; insert accepted; page cutoffs - 21.
Mechanical Specifications: Type page 13 3/4 x 21; E - 6 cols, 2, 1/8 between; A - 6 cols, 2, 1/8 between; C - 6 cols, 2, 1/8 between.
Commodity Consumption: Avg. Page Number Per Issue - Daily 12; Avg. Page Number Per Issue - Sunday 40.
Equipment EDITORIAL: Front-end Software – TC.; Editorial Equipment – Rem; Editorial Printers – APP/Mac LaserWriter II CLASSIFIED: Front-end Software – TC.; Classified Printers – Epson DISPLAY: Ad make-up applications – QPS/QuarkXPress; Display Hardware – 3-APP/Mac SE; Display Printers – APP/Mac LaserWriter II; Production Equipment – 1-Nat/A-250; Cameras – 1-Acti/183.; Bundle tying machines – 1-Strapper/Transpak, S/323; Addressing machine – 1/Ch.; Business Hardware – 2-Amdek/268A, Nomad

SAINT JOSEPH

ST. JOSEPH NEWS-PRESS

825 Edmond St., Saint Joseph, Mo., 64501; gen tel (816) 271-8500; adv tel (816) 271-8527; ed tel (816) 271-8500; gen fax (816) 271-8692; adv fax (816) 271-8696; ed fax (816) 271-8692; adv e-mail tweddle@npgco.com; ed e-mail editorial@npgco.com; web site www.stjoe-news-press.com
Group: Missouri Press Service, Inc.
Published: Mon, Tues, Wed, Thur, Fri, Sat, Sun
Weekday Frequency: m
Saturday Frequency: m
Circulation: 25,681; 29,189(sat); 30,071(sun)
Last Audit: ABC September 30, 2011
Price: 14.78/mo; 185.00/yr.
Advertising: Open inch rate $55.00
News services: AP, MCT.
Politics: Independent. **Established:** 1845
Special Editions: Good News In Education (Apr); Football (Aug); Holiday Songbook (Dec); Business Journal (Feb); Brides (Jan); Around St. Joseph (Jul); Progress (Mar); Young At Heart (Monthly); Gift Guide (Nov); Cookbook (Oct); Your Money Matters (Quarterly); Fall Home Impr
Special Weekly Sections: Off Hours (Fri); Business/Financial (S); Consumer's Guide (Sat); Best Food Day (Wed).
Magazines: Parade (S).
Bd. Chrmn./Treasurer..................Hank Bradley
Pres./Pub.............................David R. Bradley
Vice Pres., Finance/Sec............Lyle Leimkuhler
Controller....................................Bruce Kneib
Gen. Mgr................................Lee M. Sawyer
Adv. Dir....Tim Weddle
Mktg. Dir.......................................Carole Dunn
Circ. Dir........................................Kevin Smith
Circ. Mgr., Customer Serv. ....Paul Spohr
Ed. ....David R. Bradley
Exec. Ed. ....Dennis Ellsworth
City Ed. ....Steve Booher
Features Ed............................Jessica Deltaven
Photo Ed. ....Eric Keith
Market Information: TMC.
Mechanical available: Offset; Black and 3 ROP colors; insert accepted; page cutoffs - 21.
Mechanical Specifications: Type page 13 x 20; E - 6 cols, 2 1/16, 1/8 between; A - 6 cols, 2 1/16, 1/8 between; C - 9 cols, 1 3/8, 1/16 between.
Commodity Consumption: Avg. Page Number Per Issue - Daily 29; Avg. Page Number Per Issue - Plates Used 45000; Avg. Page Number Per Issue - Sunday 46; widths 27; Newsprint Used - Metric Tons 3720; Printing Ink Used - Black 63590; Printing Ink Used - Color 87637; Printing Ink Us
Equipment EDITORIAL: Front-end Software – Quark, METS, Binuscan, Scitex.; Editorial Hardware – 47-Nobilis/450; Editorial Printers – MON CLASSIFIED: Front-end Software – Brainworks.; Classified Hardware – 13-Dell/Dimension 260 1.8GH2; Classified Printers – HP/Deskjet 950 DISPLAY: Ad make-up applications – AG, Adobe/Photoshop, QPS/QuarkXPress, Aldus/FreeHand, Binuscan, Scitex; Display Hardware – APP/Mac G3, APP/Mac G4, APP/Mac G5; Display Printers – HP/Deskjet 1050cer 16 600, X/882T PRODUCTION: Pagination Software – FSI, Preps 3.61.; Production Equipment – Caere/OmniPage, MON/MGS, APP/Mac 8100, APP/Mac 9500 FS; Scanners – 1-ECR/Autokon 2000, PixelCraft, X/7650, Microtek/600 ZS PRESSROOM: Line 1 – 28-G/SSC Magnum single width 1999; Folders – 1-G/Universal 45; Reels and Stands – Enkel; Press registration system – QTI. MAILROOM: Counter stackers – 2-QWI/400; Inserters and stuffers – MM/319 Print Roll, GMA/SLS 2000, GMA/12 Into 2; Bundle tying machines – 2-Dynaric/NP-3; Wrapping singles – 2-Id/Plastic; Addressing machine – 1/Videojet 4000/7000; Other equipment –MM/321 SaddleStit BUSINESS COMPUTERS: Business Software – SBS/Graphical 5.3.1, PBS/AM 3.2, PBS/CM 3.2; Business Hardware – Sun/Sparc Station 20, Dell/E250 Power Edge Dual 450 Mhz Processor

SAINT LOUIS

ST. LOUIS POST-DISPATCH

900 N. Tucker Blvd., Saint Louis, Mo., 63101-1069; gen tel (314) 340-8000; adv tel (314) 340-8500; ed tel (314) 340-8380; adv fax (314) 340-3140; ed fax (314) 340-3050; gen e-mail letters@post-dispatch.com; adv e-mail trees@post-dispatch.com; ed e-mail editorial@post-dispatch.com; web site www.post-dispatch.com; www.stltoday.com
Group: Missouri Press Service, Inc.
Published: Mon, Tues, Wed, Thur, Fri, Sat, Sun
Weekday Frequency: m
Saturday Frequency: m
Circulation: 191,631; 199,914(sat); 332,825(sun)
Last Audit: ABC September 30, 2011
Price: 3.70/wk; 16.03/mo; 192.40/yr.
Advertising: Open inch rate $838.95
News services: AP, MCT, LAT-WP, NYT, RN, SHNS.
Politics: Independent.
Note: This newspaper is published in tabloid format on Saturday.
Special Editions: Lawn, Garden and Home Improvement (Apr); Fall Fashion (Aug); Boat and Sport Show (Feb); Auto Show (Jan); Fair St. Louis (Jun); Spring Fashion (Mar); Top 50 Businesses (May); Christmas Gift Guide (Nov); Dine Out (Oct); Fall Homestyle (Sept).
Special Weekly Sections: Business Plus (Mon); Travel & Leisure (S); Style West (West Zone only) (Thur).
Magazines: Parade (S); Lifestyle (Sat); Get Out (Entertainment) (Thur).
Pub........................................Kevin Mowbray
Credit Mgr................................Kathy Dobson
Purchasing Mgr..........................Teresa Kasate
Asst to Vice Pres., HR...............Connie Albers
Adv. Vice Pres., Sales-Major Accts./Autos/Nat'l/Real Estate............................Denise L. Holman
Adv. Vice Pres., Sales-Recruitment/Classified/Retail Territories/Bus./Health Care ....Jen Wood
Adv. Dir., Admin. ....Dan Kilian
Vice Pres./Dir., Mktg. ....John Maher
Mgr., Consumer Mktg. ....Nancy Long
Circ. Vice Pres./Dir. ....Steve Helm
Ed....Arnie Robbins
Mng. Ed. ....Pam Maples
Asst. Mng. Ed., Projects...........Jean Buchanan
Asst. Mng. Ed., Metro..............Adam Goodman
Asst. Mng. Ed., News...................Steve Parker
Asst. Mng. Ed., Presentation..............Bob Rose
Asst. Mng. Ed., Sports ....Reid Laymance
Books Ed...............................Jane Henderson
Columnist..................................Betty Cuniberti
Commentary Page Ed........................Eric Mink
Market Information: ADS; Split run; TMC; Zoned editions.
Mechanical available: Offset; Black and 3 ROP colors; insert accepted; page cutoffs - 23 9/16.
Mechanical Specifications: Type page 11 3/4 x 22 9/16; E - 6 cols, 2 1/16, 1/8 between; A - 6 cols, 2 1/16, 1/8 between; C - 10 cols, 1 1/2, 1/8 between.
Commodity Consumption: Avg. Page Number Per Issue - Daily 58; Avg. Page Number Per Issue - Plates Used 453050; Avg. Page Number Per Issue - Saturday 88; Avg. Page Number Per Issue - Sunday 122; widths 50; Newsprint Used - Metric Tons 69925.97; Newsprint Used - Short Tons 77079
Equipment EDITORIAL: Front-end Software – 20-HI/Mac Browser.; Editorial Hardware – HI/NMP (3.5.62), HI/NME 3.5, 26-HI/NewsMaker Pagination, 185-HI/NewsMaker Editorial, 4-Sun/Enterprise 4000; Editorial Equipment – 100-IBM/PC CLASSIFIED: Front-end Software – HI/REL 2.1.; Classified Hardware – 2-Sun/Enterprise 4000, 79-HI/AD-Power Client Station DISPLAY: Ad make-up applications – HI/Page Layout Architecture; Display Hardware – 1-APP/Mac Quadra 950, 4-Sun/Sparc 20, 1-Sun/Sparc 5, 2-Sun/Enterprise 4000, 2-Sun/Ultra 2, 5-APP/Mac G3, 3-APP/Mac 8100, 2-APP/Mac 6300; Display Printers – AII/4-6600, 3-Typhoon, 1-HP/8000, 3-HP/2500C PRODUCTION: Pagination Software – HI, NMP (3.5.62), 3-AdPag 3.5.; Production Equipment – TextBridge Pro 9.0, 3-WL/Lith-X-Pozer, 2-Eskofot/26365; Scanners – Epson/636 Scanner, ECR/Autokon 2045, 1-ECR/Autokon 1000 Scanner, 2-X, Scitex/Smartscanner, 2-X/1750, Ik/Digital PRESSROOM: Line 1 – 8-G/Metro 3113 Double Width 1972; Line 2 – 8-G/Metro 3115 Double Width 1972; Line 3 – 8-G/Metro 3114 Double Width 1972; Line 4 – 8-G/Metro 3117 Double Width 1972; Line 5 – 8-G/Metro 3049 Double Width 1968; Line 6 – 8-G/Metro 3116 Double Width 197 MAILROOM: Counter stackers – 2/Sh, 20-/QWI, 3-/Boss; Inserters and stuffers – 3-HI/1372P, 1-HI/1472P, 1-GMA/SLS 28-2; Bundle tying machines – 3-/Power Strap/PSN-6, 18-Sterling/MRCH40; Wrapping singles – 4-/Wrappers-Stretchwrap; Other equipment –4-Alvey/Palletizer; Business Hardware – 16-AT

SEDALIA

THE SEDALIA DEMOCRAT

700 S. Massachusetts Ave., Sedalia, Mo., 65301; gen tel (660) 826-1000; gen fax (660) 826-2413; gen e-mail news@sedaliademocrat.com; adv e-mail theclassifieds@sedaliademocrat.com (classified); advertising@sedaliademocrat.com; ed e-mail news@sedaliademocrat.com; web site www.sedaliademocrat.com
Group: Missouri Press Service, Inc.
Published: Mon, Tues, Wed, Thur, Fri, Sat, Sun
Weekday Frequency: m
Saturday Frequency: m
Circulation: 10,849; 10,849(sat); 9,688(sun)
Last Audit: September 30, 2009
Price: 9.00/mo; 99.20/yr.
Advertising: Open inch rate $17.44
News services: AP.
Politics: Independent. **Established:** 1868
Special Editions: Back-to-School (Aug); Progress (Feb); Tax Guide (Jan); Newcomers (Jun); Farm (Mar).
Special Weekly Sections: Best Food Edition (Wed).
Magazines: Relish (Monthly); TV Week Magazine (S); American Profile (Weekly).
Controller/Purchasing Agent.........Galen Oehrke
Adv. Dir.......................................Bob Midles
Circ. Dir...................................Brandon Grose
Ed. ....Bob Satnan
Sports Ed........................................Kyle Smith
Webmaster/Data Processing Mgr. Richard Desort
Prodn., Commercial Sales............Dave Mullies
Prodn. Mgr., Mailroom............Henry Holtzclaw
Prodn. Foreman, Day..................Allen Cooper
Prodn. Foreman, Pressroom (Day)..John Grimes
Market Information: ADS; TMC.
Mechanical available: Offset; Black and 3 ROP colors; insert accepted; page cutoffs - 22 3/4.
Mechanical Specifications: Type page 11 1/2 x 21 1/2; E - 6 cols, 1 39/50, 1/6 between; A - 6 cols, 1 39/50, 1/6 between; C - 8 cols, 1 29/100, 1/6 between.
Commodity Consumption: Avg. Page Number Per Issue - Daily 18; Avg. Page Number Per Issue - Plates Used 39848; Avg. Page Number Per Issue - Sunday 40; widths 27; Newsprint Used - Short Tons 2006; Printing Ink Used - Black 22966; Printing Ink Used - Color 43458; Printing Ink Use
Equipment EDITORIAL: Front-end Software – Baseview.; Editorial Hardware – APP/Mac 7200-75 PPC, APP/Mac 7200-90 PPC; Editorial Equipment – Lf/AP Leaf Picture Desk; Editorial Printers – GCC/Elite XL808, New Gen/Imager Plus 6, Pre Press/Panther Pro 46 CLASSIFIED: Front-end Software – Baseview, QPS/QuarkXPress.; Classified Hardware – APP/Mac; Classified Printers – C.Itoh/On-Line, Genico/4110, Lexmark, APP/Mac II, NewGen/Imager Plus 6, GCC/Elite XL 808, Okidata/Line Printer, Pre Press/Panther Pro 46 Imagesetter DISPLAY: Ad make-up applications – APP/Mac, Managing Editor/ALS Page Director; Display Hardware – APP/Mac, APP/Mac 8100-100, APP/Mac 7200-90; Display Printers – APP/Mac LaserWriter II, NewGen/Imager Plus 6, GCC/Elite XL 808, Pre Press Panther/Pro 46 PRODUCTION: Pagination Software – QPS/QuarkXPress 3.32.2.; Production Equipment – 1-Nu, Polaroid/SprintScan, Umax/Flatbed, Epson/Flatbed; Cameras – R PRESSROOM: Line 1 – 10-G/Urbanite single width; Line 2 – 12-G/Urbanite single width 1999; Folders – G/Urbanite. MAILROOM: Counter stackers – 1/HL; Inserters and stuffers – 1-/MM; Bundle tying machines – 2-/Ovid; Addressing machine – 1-/Ch. BUSINESS COMPUTERS: Business Software – Southware, Brainworks, Vision Data; Business Hardware – Ram/486 DX66-16mb

SIKESTON

STANDARD DEMOCRAT

205 S. New Madrid St., Sikeston, Mo., 63801; gen tel (573) 471-1137; ed tel (800) 675-6980; gen fax (573) 471-6277; gen e-mail news@standard-democrat.com; web site www.standard-democrat.com
Published: Mon, Tues, Wed, Thur, Fri, Sun
Weekday Frequency: e
Circulation: 5,244; 5,934(sun)
Last Audit: September 30, 2009
Price: 8.40/mo; 85.00/yr.
Advertising: Open inch rate $12.86
News services: AP.
Not Published: New Year; Memorial Day; Independence Day; Labor Day; Thanksgiving; Christmas.
Special Editions: Progress (Feb).
Magazines: Parade (S).
Co-Owner/Gen. Mgr. ....Don Culbertson
Co-Owner/Pub....................Michael L. Jensen
Co-Owner......................................Gary Rust
Adv. Mgr. ....DeAnna Nelson
Circ. Mgr.....................................Merlin Hagy
Food Ed. ....Leonna Heuring
News Ed...Jill Bock
Photo Dept. Mgr..........................Tim Jaynes
Sports Ed.................................David Jenkins
Prodn. Foreman, Press/Camera/Platemaking Gilbert Hutchcraft
Prodn. Foreman, Composing/Paste-Up Carolyn Lee
Market Information: Split run; TMC.
Mechanical available: Offset; Black and 3 ROP colors; insert accepted - card inserts; page cutoffs - 22 3/4.
Mechanical Specifications: Type page 13 x 21 1/2; E - 6 cols, 2 1/16, 1/8 between; A - 6 cols, 2 1/16, 1/8 between; C - 9 cols, 1 3/8, 1/16 between.
Commodity Consumption: Avg. Page Number Per Issue - Daily 23; Avg. Page Number Per Issue - Sunday 67; widths 27 1/2; Newsprint Used - Short Tons 400.
Equipment; Editorial Hardware – 2-COM/UTS, Mk.; Classified Hardware – COM/UTS.; Production Equipment – 2-COM/Universal Videosetter; Cameras – 1-R/400. PRESSROOM: Line 1 – 8-G/Suburban (4 + 4 side by side).; Inserters and stuffers – 1-MM/3 station; Bundle tying machines – 2-Bu/Packaging Machine; Wrapping singles – 7-Sa/EM; Addressing machine – 1-Am/1900.

SPRINGFIELD

SPRINGFIELD NEWS-LEADER

651 Boonville Dr., Springfield, Mo., 65806; gen tel (417) 836-1100; adv tel (417) 836-1107; ed tel (417) 836-1199; gen fax (417) 837-1335; adv fax (417) 836-1147; ed fax (417) 837-1381; ed e-mail letters@springfi.gannett.com; web site www.news-leader.com

Group: Missouri Press Service, Inc.
Published: Mon, Tues, Wed, Thur, Fri, Sat, Sun
Weekday Frequency: m
Saturday Frequency: m
Circulation: 36,144; 44,365(sat); 63,951(sun)
Last Audit: ABC September 30, 2011
Price: 3.50/wk; 182.00/yr.
Advertising: Open inch rate $152.77
News services: AP, GNS, NYT, TMS, LAT-WP.
Politics: Independent. **Established:** 1867
Special Editions: Garden (Apr); Progress (Feb); New Contruction (Jan); New Construction (Jul); Destinations (May); Coupon Clippers (Monthly); Holiday Gift Guide (Nov); New Construction (Oct); Progress (Sept).
Special Weekly Sections: Auto News (Fri); e (Mon); Real Estate (S); Church Pages (Sat); Outdoors (Tues); Best Food Day (Wed).
Magazines: USA WEEKEND Magazine (S).
Broadcast Affiliations: ABC, NBC, CBS/FOX (merged owners), WB, UPN.
Pres./Pub. ....Thomas Bookstaver
HR Dir. ....Debbie Payne
Adv. Bus. Analyst.....................Renee Swaters
Dir., Market Devel. ....Cindy Butner
Circ. Dir....................................David Brown
Circ. Mgr., Single Copy ....Rudy Rinker
Exec. Ed......................................Don Wyatt
Mng. Ed. ....Cheryl Whitsitt
City Ed..Bill Tatum
Graphics Ed...............................John Dengler
Online Ed...........................Gregory Mathews
Photo Ed. ....Dean Curtis
Voices Ed.................................Dave Iseman
Prodn. Dir......................................Tom Tate
Prodn. Mgr., Distr. Ctr. ....Mary Miller
Prodn. Mgr., Pressroom.................Steve Smith
Prodn. Supvr., Composing (Day)...Jo Ann Sneed
Market Information: ADS; TMC.
Mechanical available: Letterpress Direct; Black and 3 ROP colors; insert accepted - flexie single sheets; page cutoffs - 22 3/4.
Mechanical Specifications: Type page 13 x 21 1/2; E - 6 cols, 2 1/16, 1/8 between; A - 6 cols, 2 1/16, 1/8 between; C - 9 cols, 1 3/8, 1/16 between.
Commodity Consumption: Avg. Page Number Per Issue - Daily 38; Avg. Page Number Per Issue - Plates Used 57050; Avg. Page Number Per Issue - Sunday 86; widths 27 1/4; Newsprint Used - Short Tons 8611; Printing Ink Used - Black 183000; Printing Ink Used - Color 44000; Printing In
Equipment EDITORIAL: Front-end Software – AT, QPS/QuarkXPress.; Editorial Hardware – QPS; Editorial Equipment – 70-APP/Power Mac 8500-7200; Editorial Printers – 2-Hyphen/Spectraset 2200, 2-Hyphen/Spectraset 2400 CLASSIFIED: Front-end Software – SII/Pongrass Czar.; Classified Hardware – SII/Synthesis 66; Classified Equipment – QPS, App/Mac System; Classified Printers – Hyphen/Spectraset 2200, Hyphen/Spectraset 2400 DISPLAY: Ad make-up applications – Multi-Ad/Creator, Broderbund/TypeStyler, Adobe/Photoshop, Type/Manager; Layout Software – MEI/ALS, Multi-Ad; Display Hardware – IBM/4500, APP/Mac G4; Display Printers – 4-HP/Plotters, 2-AG/2400, Tektronix/Phaser III, HP/4MV PRODUCTION: Pagination Software – SII/Pongrass Czar.; Production Equipment – AG/2200, Hyphen/Spectraset 2200, Hyphen/Spectraset 2400; Cameras – R/Comet 500; Scanners – 1-Microtek/MRS-600zs, 1-Pro Imager/8000 PixelCraft, 1-Pro Imager/8100 PixelCraft PRESSROOM: Line 1 – 8-G/Mark II Headliner; Folders – 2; Press registration system – G/Web Control Auto Color. MAILROOM: Counter stackers – 3-HL/Monitor, 2-HI/Dual Carrier Stackers, 2-HI/Olympian Stackers; Inserters and stuffers – HI/72P, HI/NP 630 (26 Base/22 Head); Bundle tying machines – 3-MLN/News 90, 2-MLN/1-EE; Wrapping singles – Kraft/Paper, 3-HI/Eclipse Bottomwraps AUDIO: Audio Software – GMTI/Celebro; Audio Hardware – Celebro, HP BUSINESS COMPUTERS: Business Software – Lotus R:5, WordPerfect, Microsoft/Windows; Business Hardware – 1-IBM/AS-400

TRENTON

REPUBLICAN-TIMES

122 E. Eighth St., Trenton, Mo., 64683-0548; gen tel (660) 359-2212; adv tel (660) 359-2212; gen fax (660) 359-4414; adv fax (660) 359-4414; gen e-mail rtimes@lyn.net; adv e-mail rtimes@lyn.net; web site www.republican-times.com

Published: Mon, Tues, Wed, Thur, Fri
Weekday Frequency: e
Circulation: 3,017
Last Audit: October 1, 2002
Price: 54.00/yr.
Advertising: Open inch rate $6.25
News services: AP.
Politics: Independent. **Established:** 1864
Advertising not accepted: Alcoholic beverages.
Not Published: New Year; Memorial Day; Independence Day; Labor Day; Thanksgiving; Christmas.
Special Editions: Spring Outdoors (Apr); Fall Sports (Aug); Graduation (May); Fall Outdoors (Oct).
Special Weekly Sections: TV Guide (Thur).
Adv. Mgr....................................Angela Dugan
Circ. Mgr. ....Donna Wilson
News Ed. ....Diane Raynes
Data Processing Mgr................Wendell Lenhart
Prodn. Dir.....................................Kurt Thorne
Market Information: ADS; TMC.
Mechanical available: Offset; Black and 3 ROP colors; insert accepted; page cutoffs - 21.
Mechanical Specifications: Type page 13 x 21; E - 6 cols, 2 1/16, 1/8 between; A - 6 cols, 2 1/16, 1/8 between; C - 6 cols, 2 1/16, 1/8 between.
Commodity Consumption: Avg. Page Number Per Issue - Daily 10; Avg. Page Number Per Issue - Plates Used 1500; widths 28; Newsprint Used - Metric Tons 120; Printing Ink Used - Black 5000; Printing Ink Used - Color 300; Printing Ink Used - Pages Printed 2700.
Equipment EDITORIAL: Front-end Software – QPS/QuarkXPress.; Editorial Hardware – APP/Power Mac; Editorial Printers – APP/Mac LaserWriter II NTX, HP/LaserJet 4MV CLASSIFIED: Front-end Software – QPS/QuarkXPress.; Classified Hardware – APP/Power Mac; Classified Printers – APP/Power Mac LaserWriter II NTX DISPLAY: Ad make-up applications – QPS/QuarkXPress.; Display Hardware – APP/Power Mac 8100; Display Printers – APP/Mac LaserWriter II NTX, HP/LaserJet 4MV PRODUCTION: Pagination Software – Baseview.; Production Equipment – APP/Mac LaserWriter II NTX, HP/LaserJet 4MR; Cameras – R/Vertical; Scanners – HP/ScanJet 3P, Polaroid/SprintScan 35, Polaroid/SprintScan 35ES PRESSROOM: Line 1 – 4-1970.; Bundle tying machines – Bu, Miller-Bevco/Strapper.; Business Hardware – Pentium/PC

W B ROGERS PRINTING CO., INC.

122 E. 8th St., Trenton, Mo., 64683; gen tel (660) 359-2212; gen fax (660) 359-4414

Published: Mon, Tues, Wed, Thur, Fri, Sat, Sun
Price: 53.36/yr.
Advertising: Open inch rate $6.50

WARRENSBURG

THE DAILY STAR-JOURNAL

135 E. Market St., Warrensburg, Mo., 64093; gen tel (660) 747-8123; gen fax (660) 747-8741; gen e-mail dsjnews@npgco.com; adv e-mail dsjads@npgco.com; web site www.dailystarjournal.com

Published: Mon, Tues, Wed, Thur, Fri
Weekday Frequency: m
Circulation: 4,200
Last Audit: Sworn September 30, 2008
Price: 8.40/mo; 64.59/yr; 21.51/3mo, $35.92/6mo. + tax
Advertising: Open inch rate $11.00
Insert rate: $64.94 cpm & up
News services: AP.
Politics: Independent. **Established:** 1865
Not Published: New Year; Independence Day; Memorial Day; Labor Day; Thanksgiving; Christmas.
Own facility?: Y
Pub....................................William E. James
Adv. Mgr., Promo. ..........................D.J. Lowery
Circ. Dir...................................Kevin D. Quinn
Features Ed. ....Teresa Shane
Sports Ed...............................Corey Edwards
Prodn. Mgr., Pressroom....................Bob Davis
Market Information: TMC.
Mechanical available: Offset; Black and 4 ROP colors; insert accepted; page cutoffs - 21.
Mechanical Specifications: Type page 10.5 x 21
Commodity Consumption: Avg. Page Number Per Issue - Daily 20; Avg. Page Number Per Issue - Plates Used 4000; widths 28; Newsprint Used - Short Tons 404; Printing Ink Used - Black 11800; Printing Ink Used - Color 2800; Printing Ink Used - Pages Printed 5800.
Equipment EDITORIAL: Front-end Software – FSI.; Editorial Hardware – 5-APP/iMac; Editorial Printers – 1-APP/Mac LaserWriter CLASSIFIED: Front-end Software – FSI.; Classified Hardware – 1-Acer; Classified Printers – HP/2100 PRODUCTION: Pagination Software – QPS/QuarkXPress 4.1.; Production Equipment – 1-Nat, 1-APP/Mac G4, 1-APP/Mac; Cameras – 1-DAI PRESSROOM: Line 1 – 1-HI/Cotrell V-15D; Line 2 – 1-Ryobi/11x17; Line 3 – 1-HI/L125C(0).; Inserters and stuffers – KAN/480; Bundle tying machines – 1-Strap Tie/50; Addressing machine – Ch/582N. BUSINESS COMPUTERS: Business Software – PBS/MediaPlus; Business Hardware – 2-IBM/3151
Delivery method: Mail, Racks

THE STAR-JOURNAL PUBLISHING CO.

135 E. Market St., Warrensburg, Mo., 64093; gen tel (660) 747-8123; gen fax (660) 747-8741; adv e-mail ads@dailystarjournal.com

WAYNESVILLE

DAILY GUIDE

108 Holly Dr., Saint Robert, Mo., 65584; gen tel (573) 336-3711; gen fax (573) 336-4640; gen e-mail news@waynesvilledailyguide.com; web site www.waynesvilledailyguide.com

Group: GateHouse Media
Published: Tues, Wed, Thur, Fri, Sat
Weekday Frequency: m
Saturday Frequency: m
Circulation: 852; 892(sat)
Last Audit: Sworn October 1, 1999
Price: 120.00/yr.
Advertising: Open inch rate $8.15
News services: AP.
Politics: Independent. **Established:** 1967
Not Published: New Year; Memorial Day; Independence Day; Labor Day; Thanksgiving; Christmas.
Own facility?: Y
Special Editions: Profiles July
Magazines: Own Newsprint Mag (Fri).
Publisher................................Floyd Jernigan
Market Information: TMC; Zoned editions.
Mechanical available: Offset; Black and 3 ROP colors; insert accepted; page cutoffs - 22 3/4.
Mechanical Specifications: Type page 13 x 21 1/2; E - 6 cols, 2 1/16, 1/8 between; A - 6 cols, 2 1/16, 1/8 between; C - 6 cols, 2 1/16, 1/8 between.
Commodity Consumption: Avg. Page Number Per Issue - Daily 10; Avg. Page Number Per Issue - Plates Used 18000; widths 27 1/2; Newsprint Used - Short Tons 960; Printing Ink Used - Black 23000; Printing Ink Used - Color 2000; Printing Ink Used - Pages Printed 2560.
Equipment EDITORIAL: Front-end Software – Adobe/PageMaker.; Editorial Hardware – APP/Mac; Editorial Printers – APP/Mac LaserWriter 12-640 DISPLAY: Ad make-up applications – Adobe CS/Quark; Display Hardware – Imac; Display Printers – HP; Production Equipment – 1-Nu, 1-AG/Rapid; Cameras – 1-Nu; Scanners – APP/Mac One. PRESSROOM: Line 1 – 7-G/Community (balloon former) 1989; Folders – 1-G/SC, 1-G/Community. MAILROOM: Counter stackers – BG; Inserters and stuffers – Mueller Martini inserter; Addressing machine – 1/Am.; Business Hardware – Dell

WEST PLAINS

WEST PLAINS DAILY QUILL

125 N. Jefferson St., West Plains, Mo., 65775-0110; gen tel (417) 256-9191; gen fax (417) 256-9196; gen e-mail news@westplainsquill.com; adv e-mail ads@centurytel.net; ed e-mail news@westplainsquill.com; web site www.westplainsquill.com

Group: Missouri Press Service, Inc.
Published: Mon, Tues, Wed, Thur, Fri
Weekday Frequency: e
Circulation: 9,109
Last Audit: September 29, 2003
Price: 6.00/mo; 46.54/yr.
Advertising: Open inch rate $11.40
News services: AP.
Politics: Democrat. **Established:** 1902
Not Published: New Year; Memorial Day; Independence Day; Labor Day; Thanksgiving; Christmas.
Special Editions: Recreation (Apr); Football (Aug); Home Improvement (Mar).
Special Weekly Sections: Auctions (Fri); Food (Wed).
Magazines: Kaleidoscope (TV Guide) (Fri).
Bus. Mgr.....................................Judy Collins
Adv. Mgr. ....Carla Bean
Adv. Mgr., Classified.......................Lisa Lonon
Circ. Mgr. ....Lela Hodo
Mng. Ed. ....Jerry P. Womack
Editorial Page Ed. ....Frank L. Martin
Educ. Ed.................................Ron Woolman
Environmental Ed. ....Carol Bruce
Farm Ed....................................Dennis Crider
Fashion Ed...................................Chris White
Mechanical available: Offset; Black and 3 ROP colors; insert accepted; page cutoffs - 21.
Mechanical Specifications: Type page 13 x 21; E - 6 cols, 2, 1/6 between; A - 6 cols, 2, 1/6 between; C - 6 cols, 2, 1/6 between.
Commodity Consumption: Avg. Page Number Per Issue - Daily 14; Avg. Page Number Per Issue - Plates Used 3900; widths 12 1/2; Newsprint Used - Short Tons 2263; Printing Ink Used - Black 6750; Printing Ink Used - Color 1020; Printing Ink Used - Pages Printed 3640.
Equipment EDITORIAL: Front-end Software – Claris/MacWrite II.; Editorial Hardware – 2-APP/Mac G3, 5-APP/Power Mac, 3-APP/Mac G4, 2-APP/Mac 6500; Editorial Equipment – APP/Mac Scanner; Editorial Printers – 3-APP/Mac LaserPrinter CLASSIFIED: Front-end Software – Claris/MacWrite, Aldus/PageMaker.; Classified Hardware – 2-APP/Mac G4; Classified Equipment – APP/Mac Scanner; Classified Printers – APP/Mac LaserPrinter DISPLAY: Ad make-up applications – Aldus/PageMaker, Claris/MacDraw Pro; Display Hardware – APP/Mac; Display Printers – APP/Mac LaserPrinter PRODUCTION: Pagination Software – Adobe/PageMaker, QPS/QuarkXPress.; Production Equipment – 1-Nu; Cameras – B PRESSROOM: Line 1 – May-75; Folders – 1; Bundle tying machines – StraPack; Addressing machine – KAN/500.; Business Hardware – IBM/AS-400e

MONTANA

BILLINGS

BILLINGS GAZETTE

401 N. Broadway, Billings, Mont., 59101; gen tel (406) 657-1200; adv tel (406) 657-1370; ed tel (406) 657-1241; gen fax (406) 657-1207; adv fax (406) 657-1278; ed fax (406) 657-1208; gen e-mail news@billingsgazette.com; ed e-mail speakup@billingsgazette.com; web site www.billingsgazette.com

Group: Montana Newspaper Advertising Service, Inc.
Published: Mon, Tues, Wed, Thur, Fri, Sat, Sun
Weekday Frequency: m
Saturday Frequency: m
Circulation: 37,310; 40,989(sat); 44,689(sun)
Last Audit: ABC September 30, 2011
Price: 4.50/wk; 226.00/yr; 18.00/4wk.
Advertising: Open inch rate $85.70
News services: AP, CNS, MCT, TMS.
Politics: 1885
Special Editions: Car Care (Apr); Montana Fair (Aug); Big Sky State Games (Jul); Answer Book Guide to Billings (Jun); Spring Fashion (Mar); Yellowstone Park Daily (May); Holiday Wish Book (Nov); Fall Car Care (Oct); Hunting (Sept).
Special Weekly Sections: Auto Plus (Fri); Homefront (S); Outdoors (Thur); Best Food Day (Wed).
Magazines: Entertainment Tab (Fri); Relish (Monthly); Parade (S); TV Book (Sat); American Profile (Weekly).
Vice Pres./Pub..................Michael R. Gulledge
Controller.................................Scott Patrick
Adv. Dir., Sales/Mktg...................Dave Worstell
Adv. Mgr., Classified.................Ryan Erosfeau
Circ. Dir. ....Allen Wilson
Ed...Steve Prosinski
Mng. Ed. ....Kristi Angel
Bus./Finance Reporter....................Jan Falstad
Editorial Page Ed.................Pat Bellinghausen
Educ. Reporter............................Laura Tode
Entertainment/Amusements Ed............Jaci Webb
Health/Fitness Ed..................Suzanne Kydland
News Ed. ....Vic Bracht
Photo Chief.......................................Larry Mayer
Political/Gov't Reporter..........James Gransbery
Religion Reporter...............................Sue Olp
Special Projects Ed......................Chris Rubich
Sports Ed...................................Mike Zimmer
Market Information: ADS; TMC; Zoned editions.
Mechanical available: Offset; Black and 3 ROP colors; insert accepted - Adhesive labels; page cutoffs - 22 3/4.
Mechanical Specifications: Type page 11 5/8 x 21 1/2; E - 6 cols, 1 53/64, 3/16 between; A - 6 cols, 1 53/64, 3/16 between; C - 9 cols, 1 11/64, 3/16 between.
Commodity Consumption: Avg. Page Number Per Issue - Daily 34; Avg. Page Number Per Issue - Plates Used 120000; Avg. Page Number Per Issue - Sunday 64; widths 12 1/2; Newsprint Used - Metric Tons 4624; Newsprint Used - Short Tons 5097; Printing Ink Used - Black 82000; Printing
Equipment EDITORIAL: Front-end Software – APT, NT, Microsoft/Word, QPS/QuarkXPress.; Editorial Hardware – Microsoft/Windows NT PS-166; Editorial Printers – Epson/DFX 5000, HP/75 DC, HP/5Simx CLASSIFIED: Front-end Software – CText/AdVision.; Classified Hardware – PC 5-166-OS-2; Classified Printers – HP/5Simx DISPLAY: Ad make-up applications – Adobe/Illustrator, APP/Mac OSX, QPS 5.0; Layout Software – Layout/8000.; Display Hardware – APP/Mac; Display Printers – HP/750C, HP/5Simx PRODUCTION: Pagination Software – APT, QPS/QuarkXPress.; Production Equipment – AU/3850 Laser Imagers, 1-Graham, APP/Mac PRESSROOM: Line 1 – 6-G/Metro offset double width 1967; Press control system – Press Drive ÂD Harland Simon, 7-MOT; Press registration system – KFM. MAILROOM: Counter stackers – 1-QWI/350, 1-QWI/400, 1-QWI/500; Inserters and stuffers – 1-HI/1372; Bundle tying machines – 2/Power Strap, Dynaric; Other equipment –MM/Stitcher-Trimmer, MM/Quarter Folder. BUSINESS COMPUTERS: Business Software – Proprietary; Business Hardware – IBM/Sys 38

MONTANA NEWSPAPER GROUP

401 N. 28th St., Billings, Mont., 59101-1243; gen tel (406) 657-1200; gen fax (406) 657-1350; gen e-mail drussiff@billngsgazette.com; web site www.billingsgazette.com

Published: Mon, Tues, Wed, Thur, Fri, Sat, Sun
Weekday Frequency: m
Saturday Frequency: m
Circulation: 125,450; 74,948(sat); 99,753(sun)
Last Audit: ABC September 30, 2011
Pub...Mike Gullidge
Adv. Dir. ....Dave Worstell
Nat'l Adv. Coord..........................Diana Russiff
Ed...Steve Prosinski

BOZEMAN

BOZEMAN DAILY CHRONICLE

2820 W. College, Bozeman, Mont., 59718; gen tel (406) 587-4491; adv tel (406) 587-4491; ed tel (406) 587-4491; gen fax (406) 587-7995; adv fax (406) 582-2658; ed fax (406) 582-2658; gen e-mail mail@dailychronicle.com; ed e-mail citydesk@dailychronicle.com; web site www.dailychronicle.com

Group: Montana Newspaper Advertising Service, Inc.
Published: Mon, Tues, Wed, Thur, Fri, Sat, Sun
Weekday Frequency: m
Saturday Frequency: m
Circulation: 15,032; 15,032(sat); 15,970(sun)
Last Audit: September 30, 2009
Price: 12.00/mo, $13.00/mo (auto); 144.00/yr, $156.00/yr (auto).
Advertising: Open inch rate $17.82
News services: AP, LAT-WP.
Politics: Independent. **Established:** 1883
Special Editions: Football (Aug); Christmas Cheer (Dec); Spring Home Improvement (Feb); Montana Winter Fair (Jan); Gallatin County Summer Fair (Jul); The Hatch is On (Jun); VISTA (Mar); Explore Yellowstone (May); Christmas Gift Catalog (Nov); Hunting (Oct); Home Improvemen
Special Weekly Sections: Health (Mon); Economy (S); Outdoors (Thur); Lifestyle (Wed).
Magazines: This Week (newsprint) (Fri); Fencelines (Monthly); Parade (S).
Broadcast Affiliations: ABC; NBC; CBS.
Pub./Pres...........................Stephanie Presley
Bus. Mgr. ....Bob Eichenberger
Adv. Dir.....................................Doug Webber
Circ. Dir..................................Steve Buckner
Mng. Ed. ....Nick Ehli
Asst. Mng. Ed............................Karin Ronnow
City Ed. ....Daniel Person
Sports Ed.......................................Tim Dumas
Prodn. Mgr., Mailroom...................Ed Renaud
Market Information: ADS; TMC.
Mechanical available: Offset; Black and 3 ROP colors; insert accepted - most; page cutoffs - 21 1/2.
Mechanical Specifications: Type page 12 1/2 x 21 1/2; E - 6 cols, 2 1/16, 1/8 between; A - 6 cols, 2 1/16, 1/8 between; C - 9 cols, 1 3/8, 1/16 between.
Commodity Consumption: Avg. Page Number Per Issue - Daily 32; Avg. Page Number Per Issue - Saturday 26; Avg. Page Number Per Issue - Sunday 46; widths 12 1/2; Newsprint Used - Metric Tons 925; Printing Ink Used - Pages Printed 10240.
Equipment EDITORIAL: Front-end Software – Baseview/NewsEdit, QPS/QuarkXPress 4.0.; Editorial Hardware – 7-APP/iMac, 2-APP/Mac, 3-APP/Power Mac, 3-APP/Power Mac, 4-APP/Power Mac; Editorial Printers – Hyphen/RIPs, 2-AG/9800 CLASSIFIED: Front-end Software – Baseview/Class Manager Pro.; Classified Hardware – 5-APP/iMac; Classified Printers – Typhoon/20, HP/5simx, Epson/Stylus Pro XL DISPLAY: Ad make-up applications – QPS/QuarkXPress 4.0; Layout Software – Ad Layout System.; Display Hardware – 7-APP/Power Mac; Display Printers – Accuset 1000, Typhoon/20, HP/5sinx, Epson/Stylus Pro XL, HP/1200 C PRODUCTION: Pagination Software – QPS/QuarkXPress 4.0.; Production Equipment – Caere/OmniPage, AG/Studio Scan IIsi; Cameras – 1-K/240, 1-SCREEN; Scanners – 2-Nikon/LS-3510AF, 2-Microtek/ScanMaker E6, AG/Studio Scan IIsi PRESSROOM: Line 1 – 16-2002, 2-G/Community 1976; Folders – 1 MAILROOM: Counter stackers – HI; Inserters and stuffers – 1-MM/227; Bundle tying machines – MLN; Other equipment –1-Mc/2300 XL.; Business Hardware – PBS

BUTTE

THE MONTANA STANDARD

25 W. Granite St., Butte, Mont., 59701; gen tel (406) 496-5500; adv tel (406) 496-5527; ed tel (406) 496-5513; gen fax (406) 496-5551; adv fax (406) 496-5551; ed fax (406) 496-5551; gen e-mail mtstandard@lee.net; ed e-mail editors@mtstandard.com; web site www.mtstandard.com

Published: Mon, Tues, Wed, Thur, Fri, Sat, Sun
Weekday Frequency: m
Saturday Frequency: m
Circulation: 12,432; 13,178(sat); 12,637(sun)
Last Audit: ABC September 30, 2011
Price: 225.90/yr.
Advertising: Open inch rate $33.55
News services: AP, SHNS, MCT, TMS.
Politics: Independent. **Established:** 1876
Special Editions: Fall Sports (Aug); Bridal Tab (Jan); Travel Guide (May); In Business (Quarterly); Hunting Tab (Sept).
Special Weekly Sections: Family Focus (Mon); Real Estate (S); Outdoors (Thur); Three Rivers (Tues); Foods (Wed).
Magazines: Big Sky View (S); Time Out (Sat).
Interim Pub. ....Lynn Lloyd
Retail Adv. Mgr.............................Patti Arntson
Circ. Mgr. ....Steve Biere
Features Ed. ....Carmen Winslow
News Ed.............................Kristie Constantine
Online Ed. ....Gerry O'Brien
Photo Ed. ....Walter Hinick
Sports Ed.....................................Bruce Sayler
Market Information: TMC; Zoned editions.
Mechanical available: Offset; Black and 3 ROP colors; insert accepted - single sheet; page cutoffs - 21 1/2.
Mechanical Specifications: Type page 12 x 21 1/2; E - 6 cols, 2 1/16, 1/8 between; A - 6 cols, 2 1/16, 1/8 between; C - 9 cols, 1 3/8, 1/16 between.
Commodity Consumption: Avg. Page Number Per Issue - Daily 20; Avg. Page Number Per Issue - Sunday 30; widths 27 1/2; Newsprint Used - Metric Tons 1084; Printing Ink Used - Black 20000; Printing Ink Used - Color 10000; Printing Ink Used - Pages Printed 8274.
Equipment EDITORIAL: Front-end Software – CText/Dateline, CText/Expressline.; Editorial Hardware – RSK/600, Novell/Net, Novell/5; Editorial Printers – Pre Press/Panther Pro Imagesetter; Editorial Printers – Pre Press/Panther Pro 46 CLASSIFIED: Front-end Software – CText/Advision.; Classified Hardware – RSK/600, Compaq, Novell/Net; Classified Printers – HP/5Si DISPLAY: Ad make-up applications – Adobe/Photoshop, QPS/QuarkXPress; Layout Software – QPS/QuarkXPress.; Display Hardware – 1-APP/Mac; Display Printers – Pre Press/Panther Plus, Pre Press/VT1200 PRODUCTION: Pagination Software – QPS/Quar; Production Equipment – Caere/OmniPage, 1-Pre Press/VT 1200, 1-Pre Press/Panther Pro 46 Postscript; Cameras – 1-C/Spartan II, 1-Nu/2024V, 1-POS/I Daylight Camera, 1-Nu/Horizontal; Scanners – Lf/Leafscan 35, 1-HP, APP/Mac Quadra, 6-Epson/ES-1200C PRESSROOM: Line 1 – 5-G/Urbanite U849; Line 2 – 6-G/Community; Folders – 2; Inserters and stuffers – 2-MM/227E; Bundle tying machines – 1-Malow/50-S, 1-Malow/50, 1/MLN; Other equipment –Rosback/Stitcher Trimmer, MM/Free Standing Quarter Folder, Pro Cut/Cutter. AUDIO: Audio Software – Sunsoft; Audio Hardware – Lee Enterprises, Unix/Inter-Active; Business Hardware – Gateway/P5 166, IBM/AS-400

GREAT FALLS

GREAT FALLS TRIBUNE

205 River Dr. S., Great Falls, Mont., 59405; gen tel (406) 791-1444; adv tel (406) 791-1440; ed tel (406) 791-1460; gen fax (406) 791-1431; adv fax (406) 791-1436 (Class); ed fax (406) 791-1431; gen e-mail tribcity@greatfallstribune.com; adv e-mail msmith@greatfall.gannett.com (Classified); barnold@greatfall.gannett.com (Retail); ed e-mail tribcity@greatfallstribune.com; web site www.greatfallstribune.com

Group: Metro Newspaper Advertising Services, Inc.
Published: Mon, Tues, Wed, Thur, Fri, Sat, Sun
Weekday Frequency: m
Saturday Frequency: m
Circulation: 26,581; 26,151(sat); 29,818(sun)
Last Audit: ABC September 30, 2011
Price: 4.20/wk; 15.60/mo; 187.20/yr.
Advertising: Open inch rate $64.85
Insert rate: Varies
News services: AP, GNS.
Politics: 1884
Own facility?: Y
Special Editions: Jan: Bridal Guide, What Women Want (WWW)magazine.
Feb: Ag Outlook, Healthy MT magazine, Outlook 20xx.
Mar: Wester Art Roundup, What Women Want, College 101, Guide to Great Falls, Home and Garden Show.
Apr:Newcomers Guide
May:Draw Your Mom, Visit Great Falls,Glacier Gateway, WWW mag., Healthy MT.
June:101 Things to Do in Montana, Draw Your Dad
July: Visit Great Falls, State Fair Preview, WWW mag.,Back to School.
Aug:Healthy MT, Pet Idol, Ag Outlook, Football Preview.
Sept: College 101, Visit Great Falls, Fall Home Guide, WWW mag.
Oct:WWW Expo Guide, Your Health Medical Directory.
Nov:Visit Great Falls, WWW mag., Ag Outlook, Holiday Gift Guides, Healthy MT.
Dec:Visit Great Falls.
also Great Falls Business 6X/yr, fusion 12X/yr, Your Health 12X/yr,Military Retirees Appreciation 2X/yr,
Special Weekly Sections: Hot Ticket (Fri), Health (Tue.), Sunday Life (S); At Home Saturday (Sat); Montana Outdoors (Thur)., Food (Wed.)
Magazines: USA WEEKEND Magazine (S).,relish (T), Spry (T).
Glossy:
What Women Want Magazine
Healthy MT
College 101
Pres./Pub./Editor.......................James Strauss
Acct. Mgr...Viv Hunter
Adv. Dir....Max Smith
Managing Ed............................Gary Moseman
Outdoor Ed...............................Mike Babcock
Production Operations Dir. ....Mike Grafe
Production Mgr., Mailroom................Gene Hieb
Consumer & Business Dev. Director Terry Oyhamburu
Specialty Publication Editor......Amie Thompson
Business Editor...........................Jo Dee Black
Sports Editor..............................Scott Mansch
Circulation Sale Specialist (West Group) Lou Dewaele
Literacy Outreach Coordinator...........Lolly Hader
Adv. Mgr., Classified.......................Katy Kuntz
Bus. Ed....................................Butch Larcombe
Food Ed.......................................Jackie Rice
Sports Ed. ....George Geise
Info Technology Dir. ....Betsy Hoxter

Market Information: ADS; Split run; Zoned editions.
Mechanical available: Offset; Black and 3 ROP colors; insert accepted; page cutoffs - 22 3/4.
Mechanical Specifications: Type page 11 5/8 x 21 1/2; E - 6 cols, 1 5/6, 1/8 between; A - 6 cols, 1 5/6, 1/8 between; C - 9 cols, 1 1/4, 1/16 between.
Commodity Consumption: Avg. Page Number Per Issue - Daily 25; Avg. Page Number Per Issue - Plates Used 34800; Avg. Page Number Per Issue - Sunday 68; widths 25; Newsprint Used - Short Tons 2700; Printing Ink Used - Black 56591; Printing Ink Used - Color 20555; Printing Ink Use
Equipment EDITORIAL: Front-end Software – APT.; Editorial Hardware – APT; Editorial Equipment – Lf/AP Leaf Picture Desk; Editorial Printers – 2 Screen CTP CLASSIFIED: Front-end Software – APT.; Classified Hardware – Mactive DISPLAY: Ad make-up applications – CS-5; Layout Software – APT.; Display Hardware – Mactive, G3; Display Printers – Screen CTP PRODUCTION: Pagination Software – APT.; Production Equipment – 2 Screen CTP; Cameras – Nikon; Scanners – Nikon/LS 1000, Nikon/LS 2000 PRESSROOM: Line 1 – 6-G/Metro (2 color decks) doublewidth 6; Line 2 – 10-Goss Community 5 roll stand; Line 3 – Heidelberg MO 19x25 sheet fed; Folders – 2-G/2:1; Pasters – 6-G/3-Arm RTP.; Press registration system – N/A MAILROOM: Counter stackers – 3-Id/440, 2-QWI/350; Inserters and stuffers – 1472 Harris; Bundle tying machines – 1/OVL, 1-/MLN; Wrapping singles – Manual; Mailroom control system – K&M; Addressing machine – 3-/Wm.; Other equipment –Muler 6:1 saddle stitcher; Audio Hardware – Avaya BUSINESS COMPUTERS: Business Software – IBM, Gannett; Business Hardware – 1-IBM/i5
Delivery method: Mail, Newsstand, Private Carrier, Racks

HAMILTON

RAVALLI REPUBLIC

232 W. Main St., Hamilton, Mont., 59840; gen tel (406) 363-3300; adv tel (406) 363-3300; ed tel (406) 363-3300; gen fax (406) 363-3569; adv fax (406) 363-3569; ed fax (406) 363-1767; ed e-mail editor@ravallirepublic.com; web site www.ravallirepublic.com
Published: Mon, Tues, Wed, Thur, Fri
Weekday Frequency: m
Circulation: 6,345
Last Audit: March 31, 2008
Price: 91.90/yr.
Advertising: Open inch rate $13.00
News services: AP.
Politics: Independent.
Special Editions: School (Aug); Christmas Editions (Dec); Summer Fest (Jul); Agri-Business (Mar); Valley Vista (Tourism Publication) (May); Christmas Editions (Nov); Hunting and Outdoors (Oct).
Special Weekly Sections: Sports (Fri); Business (Mon); Editorial (Thur); Editorial (Tues); People (Wed).
Magazines: Entertainment Connection/TV (Fri).
Broadcast Affiliations: KSVI; KTVQ; KULR.
Bus. Mgr. ....Linda Pollard
Adv. Dir. ....Kristen Bounds
Ed. ....Perry Backus
Copy Ed. ....Clint Burson
Features Reporter ....Sepp Jannotta
Sports Ed. ....David Erickson
Market Information: ADS; TMC.
Mechanical available: Offset; Black and 3 ROP colors; insert accepted; page cutoffs - 22 3/4.
Mechanical Specifications: Type page 13 x 21 1/2; E - 6 cols, 2 1/16, 1/8 between; A - 6 cols, 2 1/16, 1/8 between; C - 9 cols, 2 1/16, 1/8 between.
Commodity Consumption: Avg. Page Number Per Issue - Daily 10; Avg. Page Number Per Issue - Plates Used 1450; widths 27; Newsprint Used - Metric Tons 144; Printing Ink Used - Black 12000; Printing Ink Used - Color 1500; Printing Ink Used - Pages Printed 2730.
Equipment; Editorial Printers – 1-QMS/Laser-Printer. CLASSIFIED: Front-end Software – CText. DISPLAY: Ad make-up applications – Aldus/PageMaker, Ventura, Signature.; Display Hardware – 1-IBM/386, 1-Gateway/486, 2-Gateway/Pentium with CD-Rom; Display Printers – 1-QMS/LaserPrinter; Production Equipment – HP/ScanJet IIc; Cameras – 1-K/241; Scanners – Equipment ☐ Aldus/PageMaker 5.0. PRESSROOM: Line 1 – Folders ☐ 1.; Business Hardware – 2-PC

HAVRE

THE HAVRE DAILY NEWS

119 Second St., Havre, Mont., 59501; gen tel (406) 265-6795; gen fax (406) 265-6798; gen e-mail hdn@havredailynews.com; web site www.havredailynews.com
Group: Montana Newspaper Advertising Service, Inc.
Published: Mon, Tues, Wed, Thur, Fri
Weekday Frequency: e
Circulation: 4,280
Last Audit: September 30, 2003
Price: 129.00/yr.
Advertising: Open inch rate $9.50
News services: AP.
Politics: Independent. **Established:** 1914
Not Published: New Year; Memorial Day; Independence Day; Labor Day; Christmas.
Special Editions: Home & Car Care (Apr); Fair (Aug); Christmas Greetings (Dec); Senior Citizens (Feb); Tax Guide (Jan); Senior Citizens (Jul); Senior Citizens (Jun); Who's Who in Northern Montana (Mar); Tourist Guide (May); Thanksgiving (Nov); Hunting & Fishing Guide (Oct)
Special Weekly Sections: Editorial (Fri); Sports Wrap-up (Mon); Business (Thur); Editorial (Tues); Ranch (Wed).
Magazines: American Profile (Weekly).
Pub. ....Martin Cody

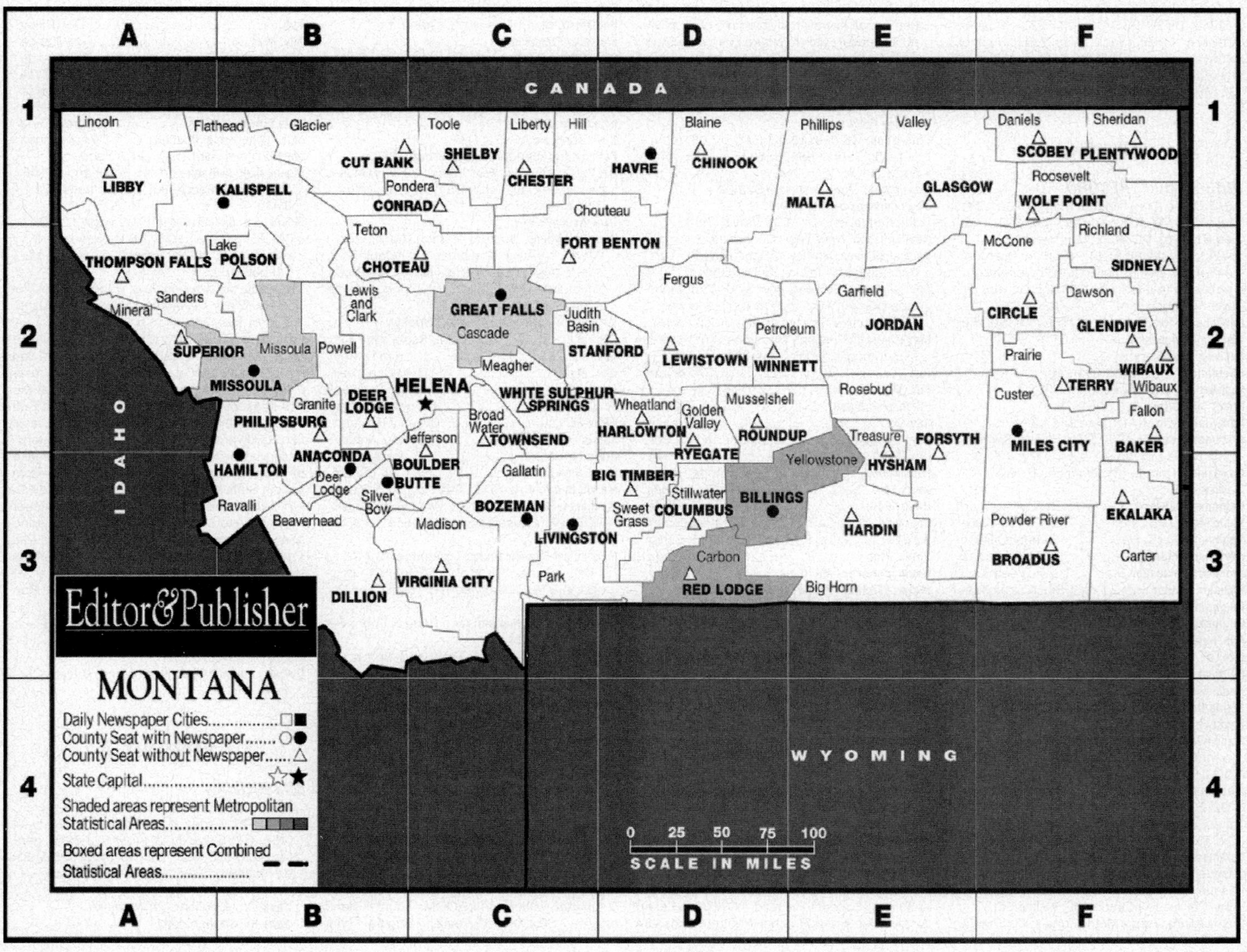

Adv. Mgr. .....Stacy Mantle
Circ. Dir. .....Craig Otterstrom
Mng. Ed. .....John Kelleher
Photo Ed. .....Nikki Carlson
Prodn. Mgr. .....Scott Anderson
Market Information: TMC.
Mechanical available: Offset; Black and 3 ROP colors; insert accepted; page cutoffs - 22 3/4.
Mechanical Specifications: Type page 13 x 21 1/2; E - 6 cols, 2 1/16, 1/8 between; A - 6 cols, 2 1/16, 1/8 between; C - 9 cols, 1 3/8, 1/16 between.
Commodity Consumption: Avg. Page Number Per Issue - Daily 14; Avg. Page Number Per Issue - Plates Used 2795; widths 27; Newsprint Used - Metric Tons 130; Printing Ink Used - Black 3725; Printing Ink Used - Color 300; Printing Ink Used - Pages Printed 4110.
Equipment EDITORIAL: Front-end Software – APP/Mac Sys 7.1, QPS/QuarkXPress 3.31, Baseview/NewsEdit 6.0.; Editorial Hardware – 3-APP/Mac IIci, 4-APP/Mac LC II, 2-APP/Mac 7200; Editorial Printers – Dataproducts/LZR 1560, Typhoon/8 CLASSIFIED: Front-end Software – Baseview/Fox Base Plus 2.01.; Classified Hardware – 1-APP/Mac LC II DISPLAY: Ad make-up applications – APP/Mac System 7.5; Display Hardware – APP/Power Mac 7200-120, APP/Mac II ci; Display Printers – Dataproducts/LZR 1560, Typhoon/8; Production Equipment – Polaroid/SprintScan 35, 1-Typhoon/8; Cameras – 1-K/24; Scanners – Umax/UC630 Color Scanner. PRESSROOM: Line 1 – 4-G/Community; Folders – 1-G/2:1.; Inserters and stuffers – 3-MM/257; Bundle tying machines – 2-Bu/16. BUSINESS COMPUTERS: Business Software – PBS/Media Plus 2.5B; Business Hardware – 1-IBM/386 Compatible, 2-Wyse/370, 1-IBM/486-66 MHz, 1-IBM/Pentium-133 MHz, APP/Mac Performa 6400-180

HELENA

INDEPENDENT RECORD

317 Cruse Ave., Helena, Mont., 59601; gen tel (406) 447-4000; adv tel (406) 447-4008; ed tel (406) 447-4072; gen fax (406) 447-4052; adv fax (406) 447-4052; ed fax (406) 447-4052; gen e-mail irstaff@helenair.com; ed e-mail ireditorial@helenair.com; web site www.helenair.com
Published: Mon, Tues, Wed, Thur, Fri, Sat, Sun
Weekday Frequency: m
Saturday Frequency: m
Circulation: 12,740; 12,393(sat); 13,510(sun)
Last Audit: ABC September 30, 2011
Price: 13.50/mo; 163.50/yr.
Advertising: Open inch rate $45.42
News services: AP, NYT, States News Service, Cox News Service.
Magazines: Parade (S); American Profile (Weekly).
Regional Publisher .....Randy Rickman
Photo Mgr. .....Eliza Wylie
Regional Editor .....Gerry O'Brien
Advertising Manager .....Tonda Meyer
Production Manager .....Lee King
Managing Editor .....Butch Larcombe
Regional Marketing Manager ...Anita Fasbender
Regional Circulation Manager .....Steve Biere
Adv. Mgr. .....Jim Rickman
City Ed. .....Rich Myers
Political Ed. .....John Doran
Radio/Television Ed .....Leah Gilman
Sports/Outdoors Ed. .....Jeff Windmueller
Market Information: ADS; Split run; TMC.
Mechanical available: Offset; Black and ROP colors; insert accepted; page cutoffs - 22 3/4.
Mechanical Specifications: Type page 11 5/8 x 21 1/2; E - 6 cols, 2 1/14, 1/6 between; A - 6 cols, 2 1/14, 1/6 between; C - 9 cols, 1 4/11, 1/6 between.
Commodity Consumption: Avg. Page Number Per Issue - Daily 22; Avg. Page Number Per Issue - Plates Used 11000; Avg. Page Number Per Issue - Sunday 36; widths 34; Newsprint Used - Metric Tons 1000; Printing Ink Used - Black 25000; Printing Ink Used - Color 2700; Printing Ink Use
Equipment EDITORIAL: Front-end Software – CText/Dateline, QPS/QuarkXPress 3.32.; Editorial Hardware – 12-Gateway/P5-166, 6-Gateway/P7-450; Editorial Equipment – APP/Photo Server, IBM; Editorial Printers – 1-Pre Press/Panther Pro, 1-Pre Press/Panther Pro 46 CLASSIFIED: Front-end Software – CText/Advision.; Classified Hardware – 6-Gateway/PIII 1 GH; Classified Printers – Pre Press/Panther Pro, Pre Press/PantherPro 46 DISPLAY: Ad make-up applications – 2-Multi-Ad/Creator, Macromedia/FreeHand, QPS/QuarkXPress 4.0; Layout Software – MEI/ALS.; Display Hardware – 8-APP/Power Mac 7600-120; Display Printers – HP 5000, Epson 2000, HP 4500; Production Equipment – Nu/FT40UPNS; Cameras – 3-Nikon/F2, 1-Nikon/F3; Scanners – APP/Mac Scanner, APP/Mac IIci. PRESSROOM: Line 1 – 8-G/Suburban (balloon former) 1978; Folders – G/Community SC. MAILROOM: Counter stackers – 1-WPC/Quarter folder; Inserters and stuffers – 1/MM; Bundle tying machines – 1-/MLN, 1-/Malow; Addressing machine – 1-/Ch; Other equipment –Rossback/6-head Stitcher-Trimmer. BUSINESS COMPUTERS: Business Software – Microsoft/Windows NT, Microsoft/Office; Business Hardware – Gateway

KALISPELL

DAILY INTER LAKE

727 E. Idaho, Kalispell, Mont., 59901; gen tel (406) 755-7000; gen fax (406) 752-6114; gen e-mail news@dailyinterlake.com; adv e-mail csease@dailyinterlake.com; ed e-mail edit@dailyinterlake.com; web site www.dailyinterlake.com
Published: Mon, Tues, Wed, Thur, Fri, Sat, Sun
Weekday Frequency: m
Saturday Frequency: m
Circulation: 16,029; 16,029(sat); 17,031(sun)
Last Audit: September 30, 2009
Price: 3.75/wk; 186.00/yr.
Advertising: Open inch rate $23.02
News services: AP, LAT-WP.
Politics: Independent. **Established:** 1888
Not Published: New Year; Christmas.
Special Editions: Homes & Real Estate (Monthly); 101 Things To Do (Spring).
Special Weekly Sections: Intertainer (Fri); Montana Life (S); Auto Plus (Sat); Outdoors (Thur); Active Seniors (Tues); Food (Wed).
Magazines: TV Listings Magazine (Fri); Parade (S); American Profile (Weekly).
Pub. .....Tom Kurdy
Bus. Mgr. .....Dorothy Glencross
Purchasing Agent .....Tami Fossen
Adv. Dir. .....Cindy Sease
Adv. Sales Mgr. .....Andrea Call
Circ. Mgr. .....Brant Horn
Features Ed. .....Lynnette Hintze
News Ed. .....Scott Crandell
Online Ed. .....Frank Miele
Sports Ed. .....Dave Lesnick
Wire Ed. .....Mark Esper
Prodn. Mgr. .....Ken Varga
Prodn. Foreman, Mailroom .....T.J. Archer
Prodn. Foreman, Pressroom .....Ed Dickman
Market Information: ADS; TMC.
Mechanical available: Offset; Black and 3 ROP colors; insert accepted - singles sheet, booklets; page cutoffs - 21.
Mechanical Specifications: Type page 11 7/8 x 21; E - 6 cols, 1 7/8, 1/8 between; A - 6 cols, 1 7/8, 1/8 between; C - 9 cols, 1 1/5, 1/8 between.
Commodity Consumption: Avg. Page Number Per Issue - Daily 32; Avg. Page Number Per Issue - Plates Used 13000; Avg. Page Number Per Issue - Sunday 48; widths 25; Newsprint Used - Short Tons 900; Printing Ink Used - Black 35000; Printing Ink Used - Pages Printed 13000.
Equipment EDITORIAL: Front-end Software – Baseview/News Edit, Adobe/Photoshop, Caere/OmniPage.; Editorial Hardware – APP/Mac; Editorial Printers – APP/Mac LaserWriters, Pre Press/Panther Photo Imagesetter CLASSIFIED: Front-end Software – Baseview, Ethernet.; Classified Hardware – APP/Mac; Classified Printers – APP/Mac LaserWriters, APP/Mac ImageWriter DISPLAY: Ad make-up applications – Multi-Ad, Adobe/Illustrator, Microsoft/Excel, QPS/QuarkXPress, Adobe/Photoshop.; Display Hardware – APP/Mac; Display Printers – APP/Mac LaserWriters, LaserMaster/1200, Hyphen/Dash 94EQ Imagesetter, Hyphen/RIP PRODUCTION: Pagination Software – Multi-Ad 4.0.4, Adobe/Photoshop 6.0, Adobe/Acrobat 5.0, Adobe/Illustrator 8.0, QPS/QuarkXPress 4.1, Aldus/Freeha; Production Equipment – Ic/25, APP/Mac 8500, APP/Mac 4400, Panther/Pro 36; Cameras – SCREEN/America 24 vertical; Scanners – 2-Microtek/3002 PRESSROOM: Line 1 – 8-G/Community 1995.; Inserters and stuffers – MM/227; Bundle tying machines – MLN/2EE; Addressing machine – Ch. BUSINESS COMPUTERS: Business Software – Microsoft/Word, Microsoft/Excel; Business Hardware – DEC/Micro VAX, APP/Mac

LIVINGSTON

THE LIVINGSTON ENTERPRISE

401 S. Main St., Livingston, Mont., 59047-4706; gen tel (406) 222-2000; adv tel 800-345-8412; gen fax (406) 222-8580; adv fax 406-222-8580; gen e-mail enterprise@livent.net; adv e-mail ads@livent.net; ed e-mail news@livent.net; web site www.livingstonenterprise.com
Group: Yellowstone Newspapers
Published: Mon, Tues, Wed, Thur, Fri
Weekday Frequency: e
Circulation: 2,604
Last Audit: Sworn September 30, 2004
Price: 11.00/mo
Advertising: Open inch rate $7.85
Insert rate: 245/net
News services: AP.
Politics: Independent. **Established:** 1883
Not Published: New Year; Memorial Day; Independence Day; Labor Day; Thanksgiving; Christmas.
Own facility?: Y
Special Editions: Home & Garden (Apr); Back-to-School (Aug); Christmas Eve (Dec); Fall Sports (Fall); Presidential History Tab (Feb); Bridal Tab (Other); Car Care (Spring); Winter Sport (Winter).
Magazines: American Profile (Weekly).
Controller .....Scott Squillace
Adv. Dir. .....Jim Durfey
Circ. Mgr. .....David Campbell
Publisher .....John Sullivan
Mng. Ed. .....Stephen Matlow
News Ed. .....Dwight Harriman
Sports Editor .....Tom Gersack
Press Foreman .....Luke Miller
Production Manager .....Al Bublitz
Market Information: ADS; TMC; Zoned editions.
Mechanical available: Offset, Web; Black and 3 ROP colors; insert accepted; page cutoffs - 22 3/4.
Mechanical Specifications: Type page 13 x 21 1/4; E - 6 cols, 2 1/16, 1/8 between; A - 6 cols, 2 1/16, 1/8 between; C - 8 cols, 1 1/2, 1/8 between.
Commodity Consumption: Avg. Page Number Per Issue - Daily 14.
Equipment EDITORIAL: Front-end Software – Baseview.; Editorial Hardware – APP/Mac; Editorial Printers – APP/Mac, Pre Press/Panther Pro Imagesetter CLASSIFIED: Front-end Software – Baseview, InDesign; Classified Hardware – APP/Mac DISPLAY: Ad make-up applications – QPS, InDesign; Display Hardware – APP/Mac; Display Printers – APP/Mac LaserWriter, Pre Press/Panther Pro Imagesetter; Production Equipment – APP/Mac LaserWriter, APP/Mac II, APP/Mac IIx, APP/Mac SE, Pre Press/Panther Pro; Cameras – CTP AlphaQuest; Scanners – APP/Mac. PRESSROOM: Line 1 – 4-G/Community, 1-DEV/Color unit, 4-G/High Community; Folders – G/SSC, 1-G/Quarter Folder. MAILROOM: Counter stackers – BG/Count-O-Veyor; Bundle tying machines – 1/Bu, 2-Polychem/PC 500, Plastic Strap; Addressing machine – 1-/Ch; Other equipment –MM/Stitcher-Trimmer. BUSINESS COMPUTERS: Business Software – SBS, BMF; Business Hardware – IBM
Zip Codes served: 59047,59018,59030,59027, 59065, 59082,59086
Delivery method: Mail, Newsstand, Private Carrier, Racks

MILES CITY

MILES CITY STAR

818 Main St., Miles City, Mont., 59301; gen tel (406) 234-0450; gen fax (406) 234-6687; gen e-mail mceditor@midrivers.com; adv e-mail milestar@midrivers.com; ed e-mail mceditor@midrivers.com; web site www.milescitystar.com
Group: Yellowstone Communications Inc.
Published: Mon, Tues, Wed, Thur, Fri
Weekday Frequency: e
Circulation: 2,670
Last Audit: Sworn September 30, 2004
Price: 18.20/mo; 207.50/yr.
Advertising: Open inch rate $7.15
Insert rate: $292
News services: AP.
Politics: 1911
Advertising not accepted: Y
Not Published: New Year; Christmas 4th July Thanksgiving Day; Independence Day; Labor Day; Thanksgiving; Christmas.
Magazines: American Profile (Weekly).
Profile: Community Paper Mon-Friday
Pub. .....Dan Killoy
Adv. Mgr. .....Alan Hauge
Circ. Mgr. .....Jeff Virag
Ed. .....Marla Prell
News Ed. .....Elaine Forman
Sports Ed. .....Josh Samuelson
Data Processing Mgr. .....Sharon Cline
Mgr., Commercial Printing .....Dian Martinez
Market Information: TMC. $507 insert rate
Mechanical available: Offset; Black and 3 ROP colors; insert accepted; page cutoffs - 22 3/4.
Mechanical Specifications: Type page 12 x 21 1/2; E - 6 cols, 2 1/16, 1/8 between; A - 6 cols, 2 1/16, 1/8 between; C - 8 cols, 1 1/2, 1/8 between.
Commodity Consumption: Avg. Page Number Per Issue - Daily 14; widths 24; Newsprint Used - Short Tons 260.
Equipment EDITORIAL: Front-end Software – QPS, Baseview/NewsEdit.; Editorial Hardware – APP/Mac; Editorial Printers – APP/Mac LaserPrinter, LaserMaster/XLO, PrePress/Panther Pro Imagesetter CLASSIFIED: Front-end Software – Baseview/Class Manager Plus.; Classified Hardware – APP/Mac; Classified Printers – LaserMaster/XLO, Okidata DISPLAY: Ad make-up applications – QPS, Metro Laser/CD-Rom; Layout Software – APP/Mac.; Display Hardware – APP/Mac; Display Printers – APP/Mac LaserPrinter, LaserMaster PRODUCTION: Pagination Software – Baseview/NewsEdit.; Production Equipment – APP/Mac, LaserMaster, Adobe/Photosho Indesign; Cameras – 1-K PRESSROOM: Line 1 – 6-G/Community.; Bundle tying machines – 1/Bu String tie
2 Signod strappers; Addressing machine – 1-/Am.; Business Hardware – BFM
Zip Codes served: 59301
Delivery method: Mail, Newsstand, Private Carrier

MISSOULA

MISSOULIAN

500 S. Higgins Ave., Missoula, Mont., 59801-2736; gen tel (406) 523-5200; adv tel (406) 523-5223; ed tel (406) 523-5240; gen fax (406) 523-5221; adv fax (406) 523-5221; ed fax (406) 523-5294; adv e-mail classified@missoulian.com; ed e-mail newsdesk@missoulian.com; web site www.missoulian.com

Published: Mon, Tues, Wed, Thur, Fri, Sat, Sun
Weekday Frequency: m
Saturday Frequency: m
Circulation: 25,966; 25,899(sat); 28,917(sun)
Last Audit: ABC September 30, 2011
Price: $4.40/week, $17.58/month, $208/year
Advertising: Daily Open Rate $65.70, Sunday Open Rate $76.20
Insert rate: Single Sheet $93.30/thousand, rates based on insert size call for rate
News services: AP, NYT.
Politics: Independent. **Established:** 1905
Advertising not accepted: N
Special Editions: Health Fair Tab (January), Missoula's Choice (January), Living Well (Bi-Monthly), Newspapers in Education (March), Montana's Cultural Treasures (March), Uncover Missoula (March), Spring Fasion (April), Montana Designs (April), International Wildlife Film Festival Program/Tab (April/May), Lawn & Garden (April), Graduation (June), Explore the Bitterroot (June), Hot Spots (June), HomeStyle (July), Montana Lyric Opera (July), Chamber of Commerce Directory (July), Missoula Relocation Guide (July), Western Montana Fair (August), MCPS Calendar (August), River City Roots Festival (August), Bear Necessities (August), Grizzly Game Day (Weekly beginning August through College football season), Montana Designs II (September),Fall Fashion (September), Hunting Journal (October), MT CINE International Film Festival (October), Health Resource Guide (October), Brawl of the Wild (November), Holiday Gift Guide (November), Faith Tab (December), Beer & Wine Journal (December), Montana Economic Report (December), Brides & Grooms (December)
Special Weekly Sections: Entertainer (Fri);On TV (S); Health & Fitness (Tues); Best Food Day (Wed).
Magazines: Parade (Sunday), Missoula Magazine (Quarterly), Athlon Sports (Third Tuesday of the Month), Corridor (Monthly),
Publisher....Jim McGowan
Editor....Sherry Devlin
Controller....Annalisa Martin
Market Information: TMC; Zoned editions.
Mechanical available: Offset; Black and 3 ROP colors; insert accepted; page cutoffs - 22 3/4.
Mechanical Specifications: Type page 13 x 21 1/2; E - 6 cols, 2 1/16, 1/8 between; A - 6 cols, 2 1/16, 1/8 between; C - 9 cols, 1 5/16, 1/8 between.
Commodity Consumption: Avg. Page Number Per Issue - Daily 13; Avg. Page Number Per Issue - Sunday 32; widths 27 1/2; Newsprint Used - Metric Tons 2400; Printing Ink Used - Pages Printed 12372.
Equipment; Editorial Hardware – Gateway/P166 Expressline Paginator, 24-Gateway/P166 Dateline Machine, 2-APP/Mac G3, 1-APP/Mac 8500, 1-APP/Mac 7100, 11-CText, 1-DEC/VT-220, 1-APP/Mac fx, 1-APP/Mac Dash, 1-APP/Mac ci, 1-APP/Power Mac 7100; Editorial Equipment – 1-APP/Mac Color One Scanne CLASSIFIED: Front-end Software – CText/Advision, CText/Alps pagination system.; Classified Hardware – 12-Gateway/P166 Advision; Classified Equipment – 1-HP/Scanner; Classified Printers – HP/6MP Postscript Printer DISPLAY: Ad make-up applications – QPS/QuarkXPress 4.0, Aldus/FreeHand 8.0, Adobe/Photoshop 5.0; Layout Software – APP/Mac, QPS/QuarkXPress. PRODUCTION: Pagination Software – CText, QPS/QuarkXPress 3.3.; Production Equipment – APP/iMac, 7-Umax/Astra 12200 Scanner, 1-Pre Press/Panther Pro 46, 1-Pre Press/Panther Pro Imagesetter; Cameras – 1-C/Spartan II, 1-Nu; Scanners – 1-PC 386 PRESSROOM: Line 1 – 9-G; Line 2 – 9-G/Urbanite; Folders – 2, 1-G/Quarter, 2-G/Urbanite 707; Reels and Stands – G/2 stands 3 high. MAILROOM: Counter stackers – 1-Id/Counter Stacker 660, 1-Id/Counter Stacker 2100; Inserters and stuffers – 1-MM/227-0500 E, HI/1372; Bundle tying machines – 2-MLN/Automatic Power Strapping Machines; Addressing machine – 1/AVY, Ch/582 M Base 721 Head; Other equipment –Other equipme; Business Hardware – 2-IBM/Sys 38
Delivery method: Mail, Newsstand, Private Carrier, Racks

NEBRASKA

ALLIANCE

ALLIANCE TIMES-HERALD

114 E. Fourth St., P O BOX G, Alliance, Neb., 69301; gen tel (308) 762-3060; adv tel (308) 762-3060; ed tel (308) 762-3060; gen fax (308) 762-3063; adv fax (308) 762-3063; ed fax (308) 762-3063; gen e-mail athnews@alliancetimes.com; adv e-mail steves@alliancetimes.com; athcomposing@alliancetimes.com; ed e-mail athnews@alliancetimes.com; web site www.alliancetimes.com
Published: Mon, Tues, Wed, Thur, Fri, Sat
Weekday Frequency: e
Saturday Frequency: m
Circulation: 3,028; 3,028(sat)
Last Audit: September 30, 2003
Price: 96.00/yr.
Advertising: Open inch rate $9.75
Insert rate: Varied
News services: AP.
Politics: Independent. **Established:** 1887
Not Published: New Year; ,Independence Day; Memorial Day; Labor Day; Thanksgiving; Christmas.
Own facility?: Y
Special Editions: Spring Home & Garden (Recycling) (Apr); Fair Section-Results (Aug); Letters to Santa and Christmas Greetings (Dec); Business & Industry (Feb); Tax (Jan); Heritage Days Festival (Jul); Spring Ag & Ranch (Mar); Beef (May); Winter Sports (Nov); Fall Ag (Oct)
Special Weekly Sections: Business Page (Other); Farm & Ranch (Thur); Food (Wed).
Pres.....Donald R. Seaton
Exec. Vice Pres./Pub./Sec./Treasurer Fred G. Kuhlman
Vice Pres.....Edward L. Seaton
Adv. Dir.....Steve Stackenwalt
Distr. Mgr.....Chris Nowak
Farm/Web Ed.....John Weare
Lifestyles Ed.....Luayne Weisgerber
Sports Ed.....Tammy Coward
Pressroom Mgr.....Mark Sherlock
Market Information: Split run; TMC.
Mechanical available: Offset; Black and 3 ROP colors; insert accepted; page cutoffs - 21 1/2.
Mechanical Specifications: Type page 14 x 24; E - 6 cols, 1 4/5, 1/8 between; A - 6 cols, 1 4/5, 1/8 between; C - 7 cols, 1 1/2, 1/8 between.
Commodity Consumption: Avg. Page Number Per Issue - Daily 12; Avg. Page Number Per Issue - Plates Used 2300; widths 25; Newsprint Used - Short Tons 110; Printing Ink Used - Black 4200; Printing Ink Used - Color 300; Printing Ink Used - Pages Printed 3584.
Equipment EDITORIAL: Front-end Software – QPS/QuarkXPress, Microsoft/Word.; Editorial Hardware – 7-APP/Mac G5; Editorial Printers – Xante/Accel-a-Writer, HP/LaserJet CLASSIFIED: Front-end Software – Baseview.; Classified Hardware – 1-APP Mac G5; Classified Printers – HP 5000 DISPLAY: Ad make-up applications – Adobe/Photoshop, Microsoft/Word, QPS/QuarkXPress; Layout Software – APP/Mac G5.; Display Hardware – APP/ Mac G5; Display Printers – Xante/Accel-a-Writer; Production Equipment – Xante/Accel-a-Writer; Cameras – R PRESSROOM: Line 1 – 5-G/Community; Folders – 1; Inserters and stuffers – 3/KAN; Bundle tying machines – 1-/Bu. BUSINESS COMPUTERS: Business Software – QuickBooks Pro. 2011; Business Hardware – PC
Delivery method: Mail, Newsstand, Private Carrier, Racks

BEATRICE

BEATRICE DAILY SUN

200 N. Seventh St., Beatrice, Neb., 68310; gen tel (402) 223-5233; adv tel (402) 223-5233; ed tel (402) 223-5233; gen fax (402) 228-3571; adv fax (402) 228-3571; ed fax (402) 228-3571; adv e-mail beatrice.ads@lee.net; ed e-mail beatrice.news@lee.net; web site www.beatricedailysun.com
Group: North Carolina Press Service, Inc.
Published: Mon, Tues, Wed, Thur, Fri, Sat
Weekday Frequency: m
Saturday Frequency: m
Circulation: 5,039; 5,177(sat)
Last Audit: ABC September 30, 2011
Price: 10.00(in town), $9.20(out of town)/mo; 99.95(in town), $96.60(out of town)/yr.
Advertising: Open inch rate $16.46
News services: AP, NEA.
Politics: Independent.
Not Published: New Year; Memorial Day; Independence Day; Labor Day; Thanksgiving; Christmas.
Special Editions: Clean-up (Apr); Back-to-School (Aug); Senior Citizens (Feb); County Fair (Jul); Homestead Days (Jun); Family Business (Mar); Graduation (May); Sports (Nov); 4-H (Oct); Hunting (Sept).
Special Weekly Sections: Farm Page (Fri); Youth (Sat); Religion (Thur); Cooking (Wed).
Magazines: Relish (Monthly); USA WEEKEND Magazine (Sat); American Profile (Weekly).
Regl. Pub.....Jim Ristow
Adv. Mgr.....Tera Sieble
Mng. Ed.....Patrick Ethridge
Sports Ed.....Jane White
Composing Mgr.....Becky Reedy
Market Information: TMC.
Mechanical available: Offset; Black and 3 ROP colors; insert accepted; page cutoffs - 22 3/4.
Mechanical Specifications: Type page 13 x 21 1/2; E - 6 cols, 2, 1/6 between; A - 6 cols, 2, 1/6 between; C - 6 cols, 2, 1/6 between.
Commodity Consumption: Avg. Page Number Per Issue - Daily 18; Avg. Page Number Per Issue - Saturday 24; widths 27 1/2; Newsprint Used - Short Tons 585.
Equipment EDITORIAL: Front-end Software – Baseview/NewsEdit.; Editorial Hardware – 13-APP/Mac Classic II CLASSIFIED: Front-end Software – Multi-Ad/CAMS.; Classified Hardware – 3-APP/Mac LC III DISPLAY: Ad make-up applications – Multi-Ad/Creator 5.1.; Display Hardware – 3-APP/Mac G3, 1-APP/Mac Quadra 950, 1-APP/Power Mac 7200; Display Printers – 2-APP/Mac LaserWriter IIg, 2-HP/4MV; Production Equipment – 1-APP/Mac 6100/66, ECR; Cameras – 1-Nippon/C24DLA; Scanners – Umax/840 PowerLook II, AG/Studio Scan IISI. PRESSROOM: Line 1 – 7-G/Community.; Bundle tying machines – 2/Malow.

COLUMBUS

THE COLUMBUS TELEGRAM

1254 27th Ave., Columbus, Neb., 68601; gen tel (402) 564-2741; adv tel (402) 564-2741; ed tel (402) 564-2741; gen fax (402) 563-7500; adv fax (402) 563-7500; ed fax (402) 563-7500; ed e-mail news@columbustelegram.com; web site www.columbustelegram.com
Group: Lee Enterprises
Published: Mon, Tues, Wed, Thur, Fri, Sun
Weekday Frequency: e
Circulation: 7,638; 8,709(sun)
Last Audit: ABC September 30, 2011
Price: 8.50/mo; 102.00/yr.
Advertising: Open inch rate $26.21
News services: AP, MCT, NEA.
Politics: Independent.
Not Published: Saturday
Special Editions: Senior Salute (Apr); Columbus Day (Aug); Last Minute Gift Idea (Dec); Columbus Home Show (Feb); Bridal (Jan); Farm & Fair (Jul); Father's Day (Jun); Chamber of Commerce (Mar); Ag/Almanac/Beef (May); Christmas Opening (Nov); Power and Progress (Oct); Colle
Special Weekly Sections: Religion/Church (Fri); Top of the Week (Mon); Business (S); Farm (Thur); Senior (Tues); Youth (Wed).
Magazines: Relish (Monthly); USA WEEKEND Magazine (S); American Profile (Wed).
Pub.....Bill Vobejda
Controller....Amy Bell
Adv. Dir.....Ann Blunt
Circ. Dir.....Greg Pehrson
Mng. Ed.....James L. Dean
Copy Desk Chief....Patrick Murphy
Educ. Reporter....Julie Blum
Prodn. Mgr.....Jerry Gaver
Market Information: ADS; TMC.
Mechanical available: Offset; Black and 3 ROP colors; insert accepted; page cutoffs - 21 1/2.
Mechanical Specifications: Type page 12 x 21 1/2; E - 6 cols, 1 7/8, 1/6 between; A - 6 cols, 1 7/8, 1/6 between; C - 9 cols, 1 3/8, 1/6 between.
Commodity Consumption: Avg. Page Number Per Issue - Daily 18; Avg. Page Number Per Issue - Plates Used 6250; Avg. Page Number Per Issue - Sunday 29; widths 25; Newsprint Used - Short Tons 490; Printing Ink Used - Black 18600; Printing Ink Used - Color 6000; Printing Ink Used -
Equipment EDITORIAL: Front-end Software – Baseview.; Editorial Hardware – APP/Mac, Baseview; Editorial Equipment – APP/Mac, Lf/AP Leaf Picture Desk; Editorial Printers – APP/Mac CLASSIFIED: Front-end Software – Baseview.; Classified Hardware – APP/Mac, CText/file-server; Classified Printers – APP/Mac Laser-Printer, C.Itoh/Line Printer; Layout Software – APP/Mac. PRODUCTION: Pagination Software – QPS/QuarkXPress 4.1.; Production Equipment – Caere/OmniPage 5.0, AG/Accuset 1000, HP/LaserJet 4MV, Pre Press/Panther Pro Imagesetter 46 H/S; Cameras – Photo Ace/250D, D, C/250; Scanners – AG/Arcus II PRESSROOM: Line 1 – 9-HI/V-15A 1997; Folders – HI/JF 15. MAILROOM: Counter stackers – BG; Inserters and stuffers – 6-KAN/480; Bundle tying machines – MLN/Spirit, Miller-Bevco/SS 901; Addressing machine – KAN/600. BUSINESS COMPUTERS: Business Software – Vision Data; Business Hardware – DEC/VT 320, DEC/PC, Unix/Platform

FREMONT

FREMONT TRIBUNE

135 N. Main St., Fremont, Neb., 68025; gen tel (402) 721-5000; gen fax (402) 721-8047; gen e-mail tribnews@ftrib.com; web site www.fremontneb.com
Group: North Carolina Press Service, Inc.
Published: Mon, Tues, Wed, Thur, Fri, Sat
Weekday Frequency: e
Saturday Frequency: m
Circulation: 7,398; 7,621(sat)
Last Audit: ABC September 30, 2011
Price: 120.25/yr; 9.25/4wk.
Advertising: Open inch rate $19.00
News services: AP, Lee National Sales Group.
Politics: Independent.
Not Published: New Year; Memorial Day; Independence Day; Labor Day; Christmas.
Special Editions: Bridal Tab (Other).
Special Weekly Sections: Fremont Living (Fri); Church Page (Sat); Agricultural Day (Thur); Business Day (Tues).
Magazines: Relish (Monthly); USA WEEKEND Magazine (Sat); TV Week (Weekly).
Pub.....Bill Vobejda
Controller....Amy Bill
Credit Mgr.....Jessica Noel
Adv. Mgr.....Vincent Laboy
Circ. Dir.....Greg Pehrson
Exec. Ed.....Tracy Buffington
News Ed.....Tammy McKeighan
Sports Ed.....Brent Wasenius

Prodn. Mgr. ....Janelle Prehal
Prodn. Mgr., Press...........................Joe Gaver
Market Information: TMC.
Mechanical available: Offset; Black and 3 ROP colors; insert accepted - coupon envelopes; page cutoffs - 22 3/4.
Mechanical Specifications: Type page 12 1/4 x 21 3/4; E - 6 cols, 1 7/8, 1/8 between; A - 6 cols, 1 7/8, 1/8 between; C - 9 cols, 1 1/4, 1/16 between.
Commodity Consumption: Avg. Page Number Per Issue - Daily 16; Avg. Page Number Per Issue - Plates Used 5000; widths 27; Newsprint Used - Short Tons 500; Printing Ink Used - Black 12000; Printing Ink Used - Color 4700; Printing Ink Used - Pages Printed 6320.
Equipment EDITORIAL: Front-end Software – Baseview.; Editorial Hardware – Baseview, APP/Mac CLASSIFIED: Front-end Software – Baseview.; Classified Hardware – APP/Mac; Layout Software – APP/Mac.; Production Equipment – Panther Pro/46, 1-LE/24BQ; Cameras – 1-C/Spartan III; Scanners – 2-Cp/Alpha. PRESSROOM: Line 1 – 4-HI/V-22-25; Line 2 – 6-HI/V22-25; Folders – 2-HI/2:1. MAILROOM: Counter stackers – 1/PPK; Bundle tying machines – 1-MLN/ML2EES; Addressing machine – 2-Wm/3.; Business Hardware – 1-DEC/1144

GRAND ISLAND

THE GRAND ISLAND INDEPENDENT

422 W. First St., Grand Island, Neb., 68802-1208; gen tel (308) 382-1000; adv tel (308) 382-1000; gen fax (308) 382-8129; adv fax (308) 384-9362; ed e-mail newsdesk@theindependent.com; web site www.theindependent.com
Published: Mon, Tues, Wed, Thur, Fri, Sat, Sun
Weekday Frequency: m
Saturday Frequency: m
Circulation: 17,834; 18,543(sat); 19,573(sun)
Last Audit: ABC September 30, 2011
Price: 12.50/mo EZ Pay (carrier); 138.00/yr.
Advertising: Open inch rate $26.50
Insert rate: $52
News services: AP, SHNS.
Politics: Independent.
Not Published: Christmas (unless a Sunday).
Own facility?: Y
Special Editions: Back-to-School (Aug); Progress and Bridal (Jan); Cooking Show (March) Farm (Mar); Graduation (May); Home Improvement (Monthly); Nebraska State Fair (Aug.); Senior EXPO (Sept); Salute to Women (Oct); Farm (Sept).Christmas Opening (Nov); @RecordBody:**Special Weekly Sections:** Entertainment (Fri); Building Page (Mon); Weddings/Engagements (S); Weekend Sports (Sat); Club Calendar (Thur); City Council (Tues); Lifelines (Wed).
Magazines: Relish (Monthly); TV Week (S); American Profile (Weekly).
Pub./Pres. ....Donald S. Smith
HR Mgr........................................Molly Holcher
Adv. Dir.......................................Sonya Schultz
Adv. Mgr., Retail.........................Kim Sweetser
Assoc. Ed...................................Pete Letheby
Mng. Ed....Jim Faddis
Community Conversation Ed.................Bill Dunn
Creative Dir. ....Lora Ruzicka
Photo Ed...................................Barrett Stinson
Sports Ed. ....Bob Hamar
Women's Ed....................................Terri Hahn
New Media Dir. ....Jack Sheard
Prodn. Dir., Opns. ....John Lilly
IT Manager ....Jody Schweiger
Circulation Director........................Pat Browth
Controller............................Jack Schiefelbein
Info Tech Mgr. ....Josh Kelly
Market Information: TMC.
Mechanical available: Offset; Black and 3 ROP colors; insert accepted - all; page cutoffs - 22 3/4.
Mechanical Specifications: Type page 10 1/2 x 21 1/2; E - 6 cols, 1 5/8, 1/8 between; A - 6 cols, 1 5/8, 1/8 between; C - 8 cols, 1 3/16, 1/8 between.
Commodity Consumption: Avg. Page Number Per

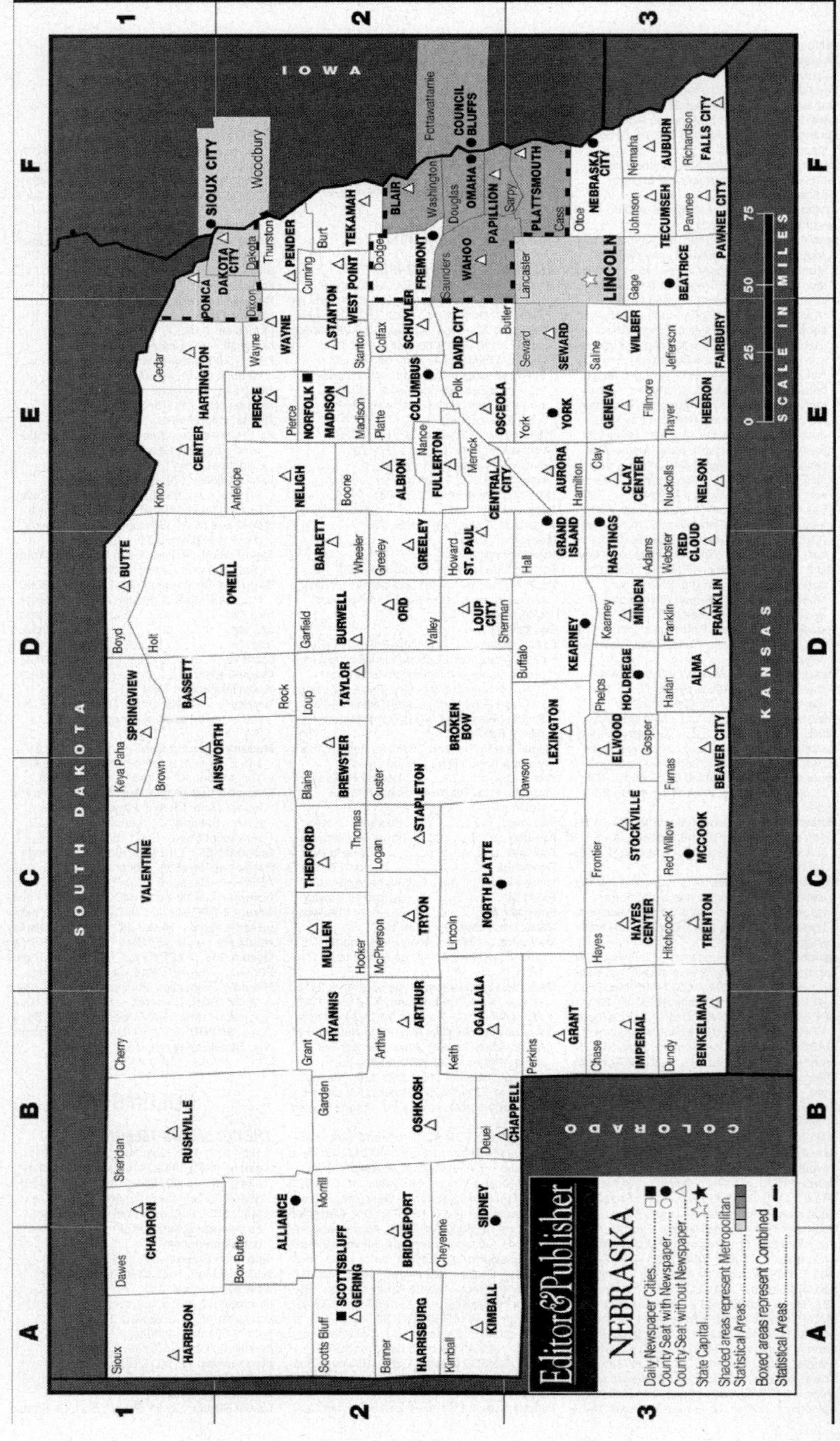

Issue - Daily 30; Avg. Page Number Per Issue - Plates Used 24000; Avg. Page Number Per Issue - Saturday 30; Avg. Page Number Per Issue - Sunday 60; widths 42; Newsprint Used - Short Tons 2050; Printing Ink Used - Black 2850; Printing
Equipment EDITORIAL: Front-end Software – Baseview, QPS/QuarkXPress.; Editorial Hardware – APP/Macs; Editorial Printers – APP/Mac LaserPrinters, V/Imagesetters, 2-Pre Press/Panther Pro CLASSIFIED: Front-end Software – APT; Classified Hardware – APP/Power HP; Classified Printers – APP/Mac LaserWriter DISPLAY: Ad make-up applications – APT/ALS, Multi-Ad/Creator, QPS/QuarkXPress, Adobe/Photoshop; Layout Software – Quadra 880, MEI/ALS.; Display Hardware – 2-APP/Mac G3, 6-APP/Mac G4 PRODUCTION: Pagination Software – InDesign, Multi AD; Production Equipment – Adobe/Photoshop 2.51, 1-Pre Press/Panther 36 PRESSROOM: Line 1 – 10-G/Urbanite double width; Press Drives – 2-Fin/100 h.p.; Folders – 1-G/2:1. MAILROOM: Counter stackers – 1-Id/440, 1-Id/Marathoner; Inserters and stuffers – KM Rotary 14/Pocket; Bundle tying machines – 2-MLN/2A; Addressing machine – 1-KAN/550. AUDIO: Audio Software – Deskmaster; Audio Hardware – Samsung/486-33 BUSINESS COMPUTERS: Business Software – APT; Business Hardware – HP
Delivery method: Mail, Newsstand, Private Carrier, Racks

HASTINGS

HASTINGS TRIBUNE

908 W. Second St., Hastings, Neb., 68902-0788; gen tel (402) 462-2131; adv tel (402) 461-1231; ed tel (402) 462-2131; gen fax (402) 462-2184; adv fax (402) 461-4657; ed fax (402) 462-2184; gen e-mail webmaster@hastingstribune.com; adv e-mail class@hastingstribune.com; ed e-mail tribune@hastingstribune.com; web site www.hastingstribune.com
Group: North Carolina Press Service, Inc.
Published: Mon, Tues, Wed, Thur, Fri, Sat, Sun
Weekday Frequency: e
Saturday Frequency: m
Circulation: 9,617; 9,617(sat)
Last Audit: September 30, 2008
Price: 9.75/mo (carrier); 91.00/yr (carrier); $97.00/yr (motor route).
Advertising: Open inch rate $14.75
News services: AP, NEA, SHNS, TMS.
Politics: Independent. **Established:** 1905
Not Published: New Year; Memorial Day; Independence Day; Labor Day; Thanksgiving; Christmas.
Special Editions: Young at Heart (Apr); Fall Sports (Aug); All I Want For Christmas (Dec); Outlook 1B (Feb); New Kids on the Block (Jan); Hastings Guide (Jul); Spark (Jun); Spring Home Improvement (Mar); Fair Premium (May); Spark (Nov); BPW (Oct); Estate Planning (Sept).
Special Weekly Sections: Youth Page (Mon); Social, Lifestyle Pages (Sat); Best Food Day (Tues).
Magazines: Happenings (Sat); American Profile (Weekly).
Pub. ....Donald R. Seaton
Bus. Mgr./Credit Mgr. ....Donald L. Kissler
Adv. Mgr., Sales ....Wanda Williams
Adv. Servs. ....Carla Carda
Circ. Dir. ....Galen Quick
News Dir. ....Darran Fowler
Asst. News Ed. ....Eric Buderus
Regl. Ed. ....Andrew Raun
Sports Ed. ....Vincent Kuppig
Wire Ed. ....Tami Humphreys
Prodn. Mgr. ....Scott Carstens
Opns. Mgr. ....Doug Edwards
Market Information: TMC; Zoned editions.
Mechanical available: Offset; Black and 3 ROP colors; insert accepted; page cutoffs - 22 3/4.
Mechanical Specifications: Type page 11 1/2 x 21; E - 6 cols, 1 13/16, 1/8 between; A - 6 cols, 1 13/16, 1/8 between; C - 8 cols, 1 5/16, 1/8 between.
Commodity Consumption: Avg. Page Number Per Issue - Daily 20; Avg. Page Number Per Issue - Plates Used 13000; Avg. Page Number Per Issue - Saturday 44; widths 25; Newsprint Used - Short Tons 720; Printing Ink Used - Black 13785; Printing Ink Used - Color 2175; Printing Ink Use
Equipment EDITORIAL: Front-end Software – Baseview/NewsEdit Pro 3.5.4, QPS/QuarkXPress 6.1.; Editorial Hardware – APP/Mac; Editorial Equipment – APP/Mac, Epson/Scanner; Editorial Printers – 2-ECR/Scriptsetter II VR 36, APP/Xante Accel-A-Writer 4 CLASSIFIED: Front-end Software – Baseview/Ad Manager Pro.; Classified Hardware – APP/Mac; Classified Printers – APP/Mac LaserWriter 600, ECR/Scriptsetter II VR36 DISPLAY: Ad make-up applications – Multi-Ad/Creator 7.0.1, QPS/QuarkXPress; Layout Software – APP/Mac.; Display Hardware – 5-APP/Mac; Display Printers – APP/Xante Accel-A-Writer 4, ECR/Scriptsetter II VR36, Epson/3000 PRODUCTION: Pagination Software – QPS/QuarkXPress.; Production Equipment – 2-ECR/Scriptsetter II, IR Imagesetter; Cameras – R/580; Scanners – Nikon/Coolscan PRESSROOM: Line 1 – 6-G/Urbanite 917; Folders – 1, 1-G/Cole Quarter. MAILROOM: Counter stackers – Newstack, Mid America Graphics, KAN; Inserters and stuffers – KAN/480; Bundle tying machines – MLN/MLEE, MLN/2A; Addressing machine – Kan/600 Labeler. BUSINESS COMPUTERS: Business Software – PBS/MediaPlus; Business Hardware – 9-IBM/RISC 6000 (9 terminals)

SEATON PUBLISHING CO.

908 W. 2nd St., Hastings, Neb., 68901; gen tel (402) 462-2131; gen fax (402) 462-2184

HOLDREGE

HOLDREGE DAILY CITIZEN

418 Garfield St., Holdrege, Neb., 68949; gen tel (308) 995-4441; adv tel (308) 995-4441; ed tel (308) 995-4441; gen fax (308) 995-5992; adv fax (308) 995-5992; ed fax (308) 995-5992; gen e-mail holdregecitizennews@yahoo.com
Published: Mon, Tues, Wed, Thur, Fri
Weekday Frequency: e
Circulation: 2,904
Last Audit: September 30, 2005
Price: 3.75/mo; 45.00/yr (carrier), $54.00/yr (mail).
Advertising: Open inch rate $8.00
News services: AP.
Politics: Independent.
Not Published: New Year; Memorial Day; Independence Day; Labor Day; Thanksgiving; Christmas.
Special Weekly Sections: Farm (Mon); Church (Thur); Best Food Day (Wed).
Vice Pres. ....Ruth E. King
Mgr., Mktg./Promo ....Barbara Penrod
Circ. Mgr. ....Julie Horn
Editorial Writer ....Robert D. King
Science Ed. ....Tunney Price
Prodn. Mgr. ....Daniel Jordan
Market Information: TMC.
Mechanical available: Offset; Black and 3 ROP colors; insert accepted - free-standing inserts; page cutoffs - 22 3/4.
Mechanical Specifications: Type page 13 1/4 x 21; E - 6 cols, 2, 1/6 between; A - 6 cols, 2, 1/6 between; C - 8 cols, 1 1/2, 1/6 between.
Commodity Consumption: Avg. Page Number Per Issue - Daily 10; Avg. Page Number Per Issue - Plates Used 2500; widths 30; Newsprint Used - Short Tons 130.5; Printing Ink Used - Black 6500; Printing Ink Used - Color 250; Printing Ink Used - Pages Printed 2640.
Equipment EDITORIAL: Front-end Software – Mk/1100 Plus, Mk/NewsTouch.; Editorial Hardware – 5-Mk; Editorial Equipment – Mk/1100 Plus (2 hard drives); Classified Hardware – Mk. DISPLAY: Ad make-up applications – APP/Mac Scanner, Multi-Ad/Creator, APP/Mac AppleTalk; Layout Software – APP/Mac Radius.; Display Printers – APP/Mac LaserWriter IIf; Production Equipment – APP/Mac LaserWriter; Cameras – D, C/260, SCREEN. PRESSROOM: Line 1 – 4-G/Community 1973.; Bundle tying machines – Bu; Addressing machine – Am.

KEARNEY

KEARNEY HUB

13 E. 22nd St., Kearney, Neb., 68847; gen tel (308) 237-2152; adv tel (308) 233-9701; ed tel (308) 237-2152; gen fax (308) 233-9736; adv fax (308) 233-9736; ed fax (308) 233-9745; gen e-mail news@kearneyhub.com; adv e-mail prepress@kearneyhub.com; web site www.kearneyhub.com
Group: North Carolina Press Service, Inc.
Published: Mon, Tues, Wed, Thur, Fri, Sat
Weekday Frequency: e
Saturday Frequency: m
Circulation: 10,955; 11,731(sat)
Last Audit: ABC September 30, 2011
Price: 9.25/mo; 106.50/yr.
Advertising: Open inch rate $20.75
News services: AP, SHNS.
Politics: Independent. **Established:** 1888
Not Published: Thanksgiving; Christmas.
Special Editions: Home & Decor (Apr); Fair Results (Aug); Home & Decor (Dec); Valentines (Feb); Bridal (Jan); Prime Magazine (Jul); Discover Kearney (Jun); Home & Decor (Mar); Rodeo Nebraska (May); Home & Decor (Nov); Business Profiles (Oct); A Home of Your Own (Sept).
Special Weekly Sections: 50 Plus (Mon); Prep Sports (Sat); Entertainment (Thur); University Report (Tues).
Magazines: Relish (Monthly); USA WEEKEND Magazine (Sat); TV Plus (Thur); American Profile (Weekly).
Pres./Pub ....Steve Chatelain
Adv. Mgr., Sales ....Lori Guthard
Vice Pres., Mktg. ....Julie Speirs
Circ. Mgr. ....Tom Alrich
Ed. ....Stephen Chatelain
Educ. Ed. ....Vicki Rice
Farm/Agriculture Ed. ....Lori Potter
Features Ed. ....Michael Konz
Food/Women's Ed. ....Rick Brown
News Ed. ....Dan Speirs
Regl. Ed. ....Amy Schweitzer
Regl. Ed. ....Tammy Skrdlant
Religion Ed. ....Carol Fettin
Sports Ed. ....Buck Mahoney
Audiotex Mgr ....Dean Buse
Prodn. Mgr. ....Jerry Schmitz
Prodn. Mgr., Distr. ....Ed Szymanski
Market Information: ADS; TMC.
Mechanical available: Offset; Black and 3 ROP colors; insert accepted - min 5 x 7, max 11 x 12 1/2; page cutoffs - 22.
Mechanical Specifications: Type page 11 5/8 x 21; E - 6 cols, 1 5/6, 1/8 between; A - 6 cols, 1 5/6, 1/8 between; C - 9 cols, 1 9/50, 1/8 between.
Commodity Consumption: Avg. Page Number Per Issue - Daily 26; Avg. Page Number Per Issue - Plates Used 9250; widths 25; Newsprint Used - Short Tons 950; Printing Ink Used - Black 17000; Printing Ink Used - Color 2900; Printing Ink Used - Pages Printed 8263.
Equipment EDITORIAL: Front-end Software – APT 2.6.3.; Editorial Hardware – Dell, Intergraph; Editorial Equipment – Pre Press/Panther Pro Imagesetter; Editorial Printers – HP CLASSIFIED: Front-end Software – APT.; Classified Hardware – Dell, Intergraph; Classified Printers – Pre Press/Panther Pro Imagesetter DISPLAY: Ad make-up applications – QPS/QuarkXPress 4.0, Adobe/Photoshop 4.0; Layout Software – PC.; Display Hardware – PC; Display Printers – HP PRODUCTION: Pagination Software – QPS/QuarkXPress 4.03.; Production Equipment – V 4.03, Pre Press/Panther Pro 36; Cameras – 1-SCREEN/C 240; Scanners – Nikon/Super Coolscan, AG/Arcus II, HP/4C PRESSROOM: Line 1 – 13-G/SSC single width (formers) 1990; Folders – 1-G/SSC; Press registration system – Carlson/Ternis. MAILROOM: Counter stackers – QWI/400W; Inserters and stuffers – 1-KAN/480 7:1; Bundle tying machines – 1-MLN/MLN2, 1-Dynamic/D2300; Addressing machine – 1-KAN/600PS labeler.; Audio Hardware – Info-Connect, New Horizons/Info-Connect BUSINESS COMPUTERS: Business Software – Microsoft/Office; Business Hardware – DEC/VAX II

LINCOLN

LINCOLN JOURNAL STAR

926 P St., Lincoln, Neb., 68508-3615; gen tel (402) 472-7300; adv tel (402) 473-7450; ed tel (402) 473-7301; gen fax (402) 473-7414; adv fax (402) 473-7177; ed fax (402) 473-7291; adv e-mail ads@journalstar.com; web site www.journalstar.com
Published: Mon, Tues, Wed, Thur, Fri, Sat, Sun
Weekday Frequency: m
Saturday Frequency: m
Circulation: 59,995; 57,031(sat); 70,819(sun)
Last Audit: ABC September 30, 2011
Price: 3.55/wk; 13.85/mo; 171.60/yr; 14.20/4wk.
Advertising: Open inch rate $78.22
News services: AP, LAT-WP, MCT.
Politics: Independent.
Special Editions: Lincoln Living (Apr); Ultimate Campus Guide (Aug); Last Minute Gift Ideas (Dec); Weddings (Jan); Salute to Lincoln Business (Jul); Lincoln Living (Jun); Girls Basketball (Mar); Lincoln Living (May); Gift Guide (Nov); Lincoln Living (Oct); Inside Football; Bridal Guide (Jan), Seniors/Prime Time (Feb, March, July, Sept); Medical Guide (March)
Special Weekly Sections: Entertainment Pages (Fri); Garden/Home (S); Best Food Day (Wed).
Magazines: L Magazine; Star City Sports
Controller ....Linda Sackshewsky
Adv. Dir. ....Ava Thomas
Circ. Dir. ....Brady Svendgard
Circ. Mgr. ....Matt Kassik
Circ. Mgr., Customer Serv. ....Staci Lunders
Ed. ....Michael Nelson
Book Review Ed. ....George Wright
Bus. Reporter ....Dick Piersol
City Ed. ....Peter Salter
Focus Ed. ....Patty Beutler
Health/Fitness Reporter ....Mark Andersen
Asst. City Ed. ....Shelly Kulhanek
Editorial Page Ed. ....Gordon Winters
Entertainment Reporter ....L. Kent Wolgamott
Entertainment/Culture Reporter ....Jeff Korbelik
Families/Schools/Kids Reporter ....Erin Andersen
Farm/Agribus. Reporter ....Art Hovey
Features Ed. ....Linda Olig
Julie Bechtel
Market Information: ADS; Split run; TMC; Zoned editions.
Mechanical available: Flexo (direct); Black and 3 ROP colors; insert accepted; page cutoffs - 22.
Mechanical Specifications: Type page 12 x 21; E - 6 cols, 2 1/16, 1/8 between; A - 6 cols, 2 1/16, 1/8 between; C - 9 cols, 1 5/16, 1/16 between.
Commodity Consumption: Avg. Page Number Per Issue - Daily 32; Avg. Page Number Per Issue - Plates Used 42000; Avg. Page Number Per Issue - Sunday 84; widths 50; Newsprint Used - Metric Tons 8200; Printing Ink Used - Black 242800; Printing Ink Used - Color 45080; Printing Ink U
Equipment EDITORIAL: Front-end Software – Microsoft/Excel, HI.; Editorial Hardware – 12-PC 486, HI/Newsmaker CLASSIFIED: Front-end Software – HI.; Classified Hardware – CText, 20-APP/Mac Workstation DISPLAY: Ad make-up applications – QPS/QuarkXPress. PRODUCTION: Pagination Software – HI, QPS/QuarkXPress.; Production Equipment – 2-AU/APS-6, 2-LE/LD2600A; Cameras – 2-C/Spartan II; Scanners – Howtek, Nikon PRESSROOM: Line 1 – 1-MAN/Roland Flexo-

man-S 2000; Folders – 2-MAN/Roland. MAILROOM: Counter stackers – 6/QWI; Inserters and stuffers – 2-GMA/SLS 2000; Bundle tying machines – 4-Dynaric/NP-2; Mailroom control system – GMA/SAM; Addressing machine – 2-Scitex/Ink Jet. BUSINESS COMPUTERS: Business Software – Microsoft/Windows NT; Business Hardware – 1-IBM/AS-400

MCCOOK

MCCOOK DAILY GAZETTE

W. First & E Sts., McCook, Neb., 69001; gen tel (308) 345-4500; gen fax (308) 345-7881; ed e-mail editor@mccookgazette.com; web site www.mccookgazette.com

Published: Mon, Tues, Wed, Thur, Fri
Weekday Frequency: e
Circulation: 5,620
Last Audit: March 31, 2008
Price: 7.95/mo; 86.50/yr.
Advertising: Open inch rate $10.95
News services: AP.
Politics: Independent. **Established:** 1911
Not Published: New Year; Memorial Day; Independence Day; Labor Day; Memorial Day; Christmas.
Special Editions: Best Years (Quarterly).
Special Weekly Sections: TV Week (Fri); Farm (Thur); Grocery (Tues).
Magazines: Relish (Monthly); American Profile (Weekly).
Adv. Mgr. .... Sharyn Skiles
Circ. Mgr. .... Marybeth Roschewski
Lifestyle Ed. .... Connie Jo Discoe
News Ed. .... Dawn Cribbs
Sports Ed. .... Steve Kodov
Online/Mgmt. Info Servs. Mgr. ...... Bruce Crosby
Prodn. Mgr., Pressroom .... Dave Mefford
Prodn. Mgr., Pre Press .... Lloyd Shields
Market Information: ADS.
Mechanical available: Offset; Black and 3 ROP colors; insert accepted; page cutoffs - 22 3/4.
Mechanical Specifications: Type page 13 x 21 1/2; E - 6 cols, 2, 1/8 between; A - 6 cols, 2, 1/8 between; C - 6 cols, 2, 1/8 between.
Commodity Consumption: Avg. Page Number Per Issue - Daily 17; Avg. Page Number Per Issue - Plates Used 7000; widths 27; Newsprint Used - Short Tons 350; Printing Ink Used - Black 16000; Printing Ink Used - Color 550; Printing Ink Used - Pages Printed 5302.
Equipment EDITORIAL: Front-end Software – QPS/QuarkXPress, Baseview.; Editorial Hardware – APP/Mac, APP/Power Mac; Editorial Equipment – 2-HI/2221; Editorial Printers – 2-APP/Mac Laser Typesetter CLASSIFIED: Front-end Software – Baseview/Ad Manager Pro.; Classified Hardware – 1-HI, 1-APP/Mac; Classified Equipment – 2-IBM; Layout Software – 3-APP/Mac II AdWriter.; Production Equipment – 2-APP/Mac Laser; Cameras – 1-R/400. PRESSROOM: Line 1 – 6-G/Suburban (2 Stacked units).; Bundle tying machines – 2/Bu; Wrapping singles – 8-/Sa; Addressing machine – 1-LN/25 Auto Mecha. BUSINESS COMPUTERS: Business Software – Nomads, Solomon, Synoptic; Business Hardware – 3-IBM/PC, AT

RUST COMMUNICATIONS

West First & E. Sts., McCook, Neb., 69001; gen tel (308) 345-4500; adv tel 3083454500; ed tel 3083454500; gen fax (308) 345-7881; adv fax 3083457881; ed fax 3083457881; gen e-mail editor@mccookgazette.com; adv e-mail adsales3@mccookgazette.com; ed e-mail editor@mccookgazette.com; web site www.mccookgazette.com

Published: Mon, Tues, Wed, Thur, Fri
Weekday Frequency: e
Circulation: 5,100
Advertising not accepted: Y
Not Published: sat-sun
Own facility?: Y
Delivery method: Mail, Newsstand, Private Carrier, Racks

NEBRASKA CITY

NEBRASKA CITY NEWS-PRESS, INC.

806 Central Ave., Nebraska City, Neb., 68410; gen tel (402) 873-3334; adv tel (402) 873-3334; ed tel (402) 873-3334; gen fax (402) 873-5436; adv fax (402) 873-5436; ed fax (402) 873-5436; adv e-mail kkaufman@ncnewspress.com; ed e-mail editor@ncnewspress.com; web site www.ncnewspress.com

Published: Mon, Tues, Wed, Thur, Fri
Weekday Frequency: e
Circulation: 2,110
Last Audit: September 30, 2003
Price: 7.25/mo; 86.00/yr.
Advertising: Open inch rate $8.65
News services: AP, DF, NEA, TMS.
Politics: Independent. **Established:** 1854
Not Published: New Year; Memorial Day; Independence Day; Labor Day; Thanksgiving; Christmas.
Special Editions: Golf (Apr); County Fair (Aug); Weddings (Feb); Tourism (Jul); Tourism (Mar); Winter Sports (Nov); Home Improvement (Sept).
Magazines: American Profile (Fri).
Pub .... Tim Larson
Adv. Dir. .... Kathy Kaufman
Circ. Mgr. .... Janet Entler
Exec. Ed. .... Tammy Pearson
Sports Ed. .... Kirt Manion
Systems Technologist .... Kim Pierce
Market Information: TMC.
Mechanical available: Offset; Black and 3 ROP colors; insert accepted; page cutoffs - 22 3/4.
Mechanical Specifications: Type page 12 1/4 x 21 1/2; E - 6 cols, 1 7/8, 3/16 between; A - 6 cols, 1 7/8, 3/16 between; C - 6 cols, 1 7/8, 3/16 between.
Commodity Consumption: Avg. Page Number Per Issue - Daily 10; Avg. Page Number Per Issue - Plates Used 2340; widths 26; Newsprint Used - Short Tons 149; Printing Ink Used - Black 3348; Printing Ink Used - Color 307; Printing Ink Used - Pages Printed 3070.
Equipment EDITORIAL: Front-end Software – Quark 5.0.; Editorial Hardware – APP/Mac G3, APP/Mac G4 2000; Editorial Printers – APP/Mac HP5000 CLASSIFIED: Front-end Software – Baseview.; Classified Hardware – APP/Mac G4; Classified Printers – APP/Mac LaserWriter Pro DISPLAY: Ad make-up applications – Adobe/Photoshop 5.0, QPS/QuarkXPress 5.0, Microsoft/Word 5.1; Display Hardware – APP/Mac G3; Display Printers – APP/Mac HP5000 PRODUCTION: Pagination Software – QPS/QuarkXPress 5.0.; Production Equipment – 1-Nu, Scitex; Cameras – B/Vertical PRESSROOM: Line 1 – 4; Line 2 – 4-G; Press Drives – 1; Folders – 1; Press control system – 8-G.; Bundle tying machines – 1/B; Addressing machine – Epson.

GATEHOUSE MEDIA NEBRASKA HOLDINGS

823 Central Ave., Nebraska City, Neb., 68410; gen tel (402) 873-3334; gen fax (402) 873-5436

Published: Tues, Fri
Weekday Frequency: All day
Circulation: 2,200
Advertising not accepted: Y
Own facility?: Y

NORFOLK

NORFOLK DAILY NEWS

525 Norfolk Ave., Norfolk, Neb., 68701; gen tel (402) 371-1020; adv tel (402) 371-1020; ed tel (402) 371-1020; gen fax (402) 371-5802; adv fax (402) 371-5802; ed fax (402) 371-5802; adv e-mail ads@norfolkdailynews.com; ed e-mail editor@norfolkdailynews.com; web site www.norfolkdailynews.com

Published: Mon, Tues, Wed, Thur, Fri, Sat
Weekday Frequency: e
Saturday Frequency: e
Circulation: 14,874; 14,874(sat)
Last Audit: ABC September 30, 2011
Price: 2.00/wk; 9.00/mo; 99.00/yr; 51.50/6mo.
Advertising: Open inch rate $21.00
News services: AP, SHNS.
Politics: Independent-Republican. **Established:** 1888
Not Published: New Year; Memorial Day; Independence Day; Labor Day; Thanksgiving; Christmas.
Special Editions: Agriculture (Apr); Back-to-School (Aug); Christmas Greetings (Dec); Insight (Progress) (Feb); All About Norfolk (Jul); Spring Car Care (Mar); Car Care (Nov); Restaurant (Oct).
Special Weekly Sections: TV Tab (Fri); Farm Pages (Thur); Youth Pages (Tues); Food Pages (Wed).
Magazines: USA WEEKEND Magazine (Sat).
Broadcast Affiliations: Radio WJAG/KEXL.
Pres./Pub. .... Jerry Huse
Gen. Mgr. .... Les Mann
Bus. Mgr. .... Deb Warneke
Adv. Dir. .... Larry Bartscher
Circ. Mgr. .... Missy D. Rech
Ed. .... Kent Warneke
City Ed. .... Grace Petersen
Farm Ed. .... Mary Pat Finn-Hoag
Regl. Ed. .... Greg Wees
Sports Ed. .... Jay Prauner
Prodn. Mgr. .... Mike Jones
Prodn. Foreman, Pressroom .... Jeff Jones
Prodn. Foreman, Mailroom .... Jason Feddern
Market Information: TMC.
Mechanical available: Offset; Black and 3 ROP colors; insert accepted; page cutoffs - 22 3/4.
Mechanical Specifications: Type page 11 3/4 x 21 1/2; E - 6 cols, 1 13/16, 1/8 between; A - 6 cols, 1 13/16, 1/8 between; C - 8 cols, 1 5/16, 1/8 between.
Commodity Consumption: Avg. Page Number Per Issue - Daily 24; Avg. Page Number Per Issue - Plates Used 12717; widths 25; Newsprint Used - Short Tons 1095; Printing Ink Used - Black 19678; Printing Ink Used - Color 6690; Printing Ink Used - Pages Printed 7991.
Equipment EDITORIAL: Front-end Software – Dewar, Novell 3.11, Baseview/NewsEdit Pro IQUE, QPS/QuarkXPress 3.32.; Editorial Hardware – Dewar/Sys IV, APP/Mac II C, 8-Baseview; Editorial Printers – Panasonic/1093, Xante/8300 11x17 CLASSIFIED: Front-end Software – Baseview/Ad Manager Pro.; Classified Hardware – 5-Baseview; Classified Equipment – Xante/8300 11x17; Classified Printers – Okidata/Pacemark 3410, APP/Mac LaserWriter Pro 630 DISPLAY: Ad make-up applications – Dewar, Adobe/Photoshop, Aldus/PageMaker, QPS/QuarkXPress, Multi-Ad; Display Hardware – PC, 2-APP/Power Mac 7100, 2-APP/Mac Quadra; Display Printers – Printware/1217, APP/Mac LaserWriter Pro 630, Pre Press/Panther Imagesetter PRODUCTION: Pagination Software – Baseview/NewsEdit Pro IQ, QPS/QuarkXPress 3.32.; Production Equipment – Caere/OmniPage, Pre Press/7220, Prepress/Panther Plus 46; Cameras – 1-DAI/Vertical, 1-DAI/Horizontal; Scanners – AG/Argus II Scanner PRESSROOM: Line 1 – 8-G/Urbanite 1972; Press control system – 1972 MAILROOM: Counter stackers – 1-Id, 1/Quipp; Inserters and stuffers – KAN/5:1, MM/4:1; Bundle tying machines – 2-/Bu, 1-MLN/2A, 1-/Strapack; Addressing machine – 1-/KAN.; Business Hardware – IBM/AS400, Gateway/Pentium, HP/Pentium

NORTH PLATTE

THE NORTH PLATTE TELEGRAPH

621 N. Chestnut St., North Platte, Neb., 69101; gen tel (308) 532-6000; gen fax (308) 532-9268; gen e-mail publisher@nptelegraph.com; adv e-mail advertising@nptelegraph.com; ed e-mail editor@nptelegraph.com; web site www.nptelegraph.com

Published: Tues, Wed, Thur, Fri, Sat, Sun
Weekday Frequency: m
Saturday Frequency: m
Circulation: 10,150; 11,550(sat); 10,436(sun)
Last Audit: ABC September 30, 2011
Price: 12.55/mo; 121.00/yr.
Advertising: Open inch rate $14.93
News services: AP.
Politics: Independent.
Not Published: Day after Thanksgiving; Christmas.
Special Editions: Real Estate Guide (Monthly).
Special Weekly Sections: TV Week (S).
Magazines: Relish (Monthly); Parade (S); American Profile (Weekly).
Pub. .... Peter Rogers
Bus. Mgr. .... Holli Synder
Dir., Sales (NPC) .... Dee Klein
Circ. Dir. .... Joe Volcek
Exec. Ed. .... Job Vigil
News Ed. .... Sage Merritt
Sports Ed. .... Emily Springer
Prodn. Mgr. .... John Bates
Market Information: ADS; TMC.
Mechanical available: Offset; Black and 3 ROP colors; insert accepted - others, contact for specs; page cutoffs - 22 3/4.
Mechanical Specifications: Type page 11 63/100 x 21 3/4; E - 6 cols, 1 5/6, 1/8 between; A - 6 cols, 1 5/6, 1/8 between; C - 9 cols, 1 5/6, 1/16 between.
Commodity Consumption: Avg. Page Number Per Issue - Daily 20; Avg. Page Number Per Issue - Plates Used 13289; Avg. Page Number Per Issue - Sunday 28; widths 27; Newsprint Used - Metric Tons 842; Printing Ink Used - Black 18982; Printing Ink Used - Color 10668; Printing Ink Use
Equipment EDITORIAL: Front-end Software – Dewar/View 2.0, Dewar, QPS/QuarkXPress 4.04.; Editorial Hardware – 4-Gateway/GP6-400, 2-Gateway/GP6-500; Editorial Equipment – Umax/Mirage IIse, Microsoft/Windows NT Server, 1-Kk/RFS 2035 Plus Film Scanner, 1-Epson/Perfection 1200u; Editorial Printers – HP/SI Mx CLASSIFIED: Front-end Software – ACT.; Classified Hardware – 2-Gateway/GP6-350, 1-Gateway/GP6-333; Classified Equipment – 1-Epson/Perfection 1200u Flatbed Scanner; Classified Printers – 6-HP DISPLAY: Ad make-up applications – DPS/AdTracker, QPS/QuarkXPress 4.11; Layout Software – DPS/AdTracker.; Display Hardware – 1-Gateway/GP6-400 with 21 monitor, 2-Gateway/P-500 with 21 monitor, 2-Dell/800; Display Printers – HP/Si Mx; Production Equipment – Text Bridge/Pro98; Cameras – Acti/225; Scanners – Umax/Mirage IIse. PRESSROOM: Line 1 – 9-HI/V-22 1965. MAILROOM: Counter stackers – TMSI; Inserters and stuffers – 24-HI/6; Bundle tying machines – MLN/MLEE; Addressing machine – Miller/Bevco/1 up Labeler.; Audio Hardware – Business Telecommunication Systems, PC; Business Hardware – Gateway, 8-Gateway/PS-100, 6-E/3200

OMAHA

OMAHA WORLD-HERALD

1314 Douglas St., Ste. 1500, Omaha, Neb., 68102-1848; gen tel (402) 444-1000; adv tel (402) 444-1420; ed tel (402) 444-1304; gen fax (402) 444-1231; adv fax (402) 444-1299; ed fax (402) 444-1231; gen e-mail news@owh.com; web site www.omaha.com

Published: Mon, Tues, Wed, Thur, Fri, Sat, Sun
Weekday Frequency: All day
Saturday Frequency: m
Circulation: 135,282; 133,675(sat); 170,381(sun)
Last Audit: ABC September 30, 2011
Price: 3.64/wk (carrier); 189.28/yr (carrier).
Advertising: Open inch rate $222.00
News services: AP, LAT-WP, MCT, NYT, TV DATA, Tribune Media, Bloomberg.
Politics: 1865
Not Published: none
Own facility?: Y
Special Editions: Welcome Visitors
Live Well Nebraska

Inspired Home
Auto Show 1
Marketplace Rentals
Wedding Essentials
Perspectives 1
Momaha.com Magazine
Perspectives 2
Perspectives 3
Kids Camp
ACEC. Engineers
Auction
College Bound
Lawn, Garden & Home-extra content in Living
Better Business Bureau
7 Reasons to Buy a Home Now!
Metro Values
Storm Chasers
The Look
Worship. Easter
Berkshire Hathaway
Best Places to Work
Spring & Summer Travel
Babies
Super go!
WH Scholars
Taste of Omaha go!
CWS
Offutt Air Show
Football Preview. High School
Football Preview. College
Septemberfest
Big Ten Travel Section
River City Rodeo
Aksarben Coronation
Momaha Pages
Omaha's Favorite Brands
Fall Parade of Homes
Omaha Chamber Book - Extraordinary Opportunities
College Bound. Fair
Architecture
Basketball Preview. College
Holiday Book
Worship. Holiday

Special Weekly Sections: Arts & Travel (S); Religion (Sat); Home/Gardening/Decorating (Thur); Food (Wed).
Magazines: From House To Home (Every other month); Home Guide (Fri); Metro Values (Monthly); Parade (S); Wedding Essentials (Semi-yearly).

Chrmn...................................John Gottschalk
Pub./CEO..............................Terry J. Kroeger
CFO/Sr. Vice Pres....................Duane Polodna
Vice Pres./Gen. Counsel..................Scott Searl
Vice Pres., Opns......................Doug Hiemstra
Finance Dir./Controller.......................Mike Kirk
Dir., Communications.......................Joel Long
Credit Dept. Mgr........................Steven Woods
Mgr., Training..............................Gary Domet
Adv. Dir...................................Thom Kastrup
Adv. Dir., Online/Digital..............Jeff Shabram
Adv. Mgr., Auto Sales....................Brett Snead
Adv. Mgr., Classified...................Larry Etienne
Retail Sales Mgr.............................Lowell Miller
Adv. Mgr., Custom Publishing/Events..Tam Webb
Adv. Mgr., Employment..............Terri Campbell
Adv. Mgr., Local Retail Sales.........Vicki Denker
Adv. Mgr., Major Accts...................Bob Gerken
Adv. Mgr., Real Estate.............Debbie Cavalier
Dir., HR............................Roshelle Campbell
Dir., Marketing............................Rich Warren
Dir., Circulation........................Dennis Cronin
Managing Editor for Digital Development Jeff Carney
Dir., IT..Phil Tomek
Treasurer & Controller............Brenda Draheim
Dir., Production............................Kristy Gerry
VP, News & Content..........................Larry King
VP & General Counsel.....................Scott Searl
Cor. HR Mgr....................................Steve Hoff
Dir., Marketing.............................Rich Warren
Dir., IT..Phil Tomek
Managing Editor for Digital Development Jeff Carney
Treasurer & Controller............Brenda Draheim
Dir., Production............................Kristy Gerry
Dir., Circulation........................Dennis Cronin
VP, News & Content..........................Larry King
Executive Editor............................Mike Reilly
National Advg Acct Exec...............Brandon Bell
Pres/CEO/Pub............................Terry Kroeger
Market Information: ADS; Split run; TMC.
Mechanical available: Offset; Black and 3 ROP colors; inserts accepted - product samples, single sheet fliers; page cutoffs - 22 1/16.
Mechanical Specifications: Type page 11 9/16 x 21 1/4; E - 6 cols, 1 3/4, 5/32 between; A - 6 cols, 1 3/4, 1/16 between; C - 10 cols, 1 1/16, 5/32 between.
Equipment; Editorial Hardware – Dell PE710.VMware; Editorial Equipment – Saxotech CMS / Online CLASSIFIED: Front-end Software – AdbaseE, Mactive, OPI, Xpance; Classified Hardware – Dell PE710.VMware; Layout Software – PPI/Planfag.; Display Printers – 2-MON/ProofExpress PRODUCTION: Pagination Software – AGFA Newsdrive, PPI PlanPag, PPI Pilot; Production Equipment – 2-Agfa/Advantage CLS, 2-K&F VIPB-27 Vision Benders,2-G&J VSP-85S Plate Processors PRESSROOM: Line 1 – Man/Geoman 3/8 Shaftless; Line 2 – 1-Line/18 Towers; Line 3 – 15 4/1 Towers; Line 4 – 3 4/4 Towers; Folders – 3, 1; Pasters – Man/AuroPrep; Reels and Stands – 18; Press control system – Man/PPM-PECOM MAILROOM: Counter stackers – 16-Quipp; Inserters and stuffers – 2-HI/632, 1-HI/632; Wrapping singles – 14-Quipp/3/4 Viper; Mailroom control system – Burt, GE; Addressing machine – 2-Barstrom/In-Line Labeler; Other equipment –Gammler/Commercial Stacker, Palletize BUSINESS COMPUTERS: Business Software – Circ 2000, Mactive, Oracle Financials; Business Hardware – Dell PE710.VMware
Delivery method: Mail, Newsstand, Private Carrier, Racks

SCOTTSBLUFF

STAR-HERALD

1405 Broadway, Scottsbluff, Neb., 69361-3151; gen tel (308) 632-9000; adv tel (308) 632-9020; ed tel (308) 632-9040; gen fax (308) 632-9001; ed fax (308) 632-9003; gen e-mail starherald@starherald.com; web site www.starherald.com
Published: Tues, Wed, Thur, Fri, Sat, Sun
Weekday Frequency: m
Saturday Frequency: m
Circulation: 12,084; 13,623(sat); 12,888(sun)
Last Audit: ABC September 30, 2011
Price: 130.00/yr.
Advertising: Open inch rate $20.10
News services: AP.
Politics: Independent.
Special Weekly Sections: Farm & Ranch (S); TV Week (Sat); Motor News (Wed).
Magazines: Entertainment (Fri); Parade (S); Church & Religious (Sat); Health & Science (Thur); Business News (Tues); Best Food Day (Wed); American Profile (Weekly).

Vice Pres./Pub.............................Jim Holland
Dir., Bus./Personnel Servs........Debbie Flowers
Adv. Dir.................................Doug Southard
Ed........................................Steve Frederick
Sports Ed.....................................Jeff Fielder
Online Mgr................................Jim Mortimore
Prodn. Mgr............................Roger Tollefson
Prodn. Mgr., Distr.......................Richard Knott
Market Information: ADS; TMC.
Mechanical available: Offset; Black and 3 ROP colors; insert accepted - quarter fold, coupon books, alternate delivery; page cutoffs - 21 3/4.
Mechanical Specifications: Type page 10 1/4 x 21 1/2; E - 6 cols, 1 1/2, 1/12 between; A - 6 cols, 1 1/2, 1/12 between; C - 8 cols, 1 3/8, 1/12 between.
Commodity Consumption: Avg. Page Number Per Issue - Daily 20; Avg. Page Number Per Issue - Plates Used 20000; Avg. Page Number Per Issue - Sunday 34; widths 12 1/2; Newsprint Used - Metric Tons 1000; Printing Ink Used - Black 25000; Printing Ink Used - Color 8500; Printing Ink
Equipment EDITORIAL: Front-end Software – Dewar/Disc Net, Adobe/Photoshop.; Editorial Hardware – Dewar/Disc Net, Nar/(Windows base); Editorial Equipment – Lf/AP Leaf Picture Desk (receiver only); Editorial Printers – Okidata, HP/5S1 CLASSIFIED: Front-end Software – GraphX/1.6 Ad taker.; Classified Hardware – GraphX; Classified Printers – Okidata DISPLAY: Ad make-up applications – Archetype/Corel Draw, Adobe/Photoshop, QPS/QuarkXPress; Layout Software – CNI/Ad-tracker, QPS/QuarkXPress.; Display Hardware – IBM/Windows base; Display Printers – Okidata, HP/Laser Color PRODUCTION: Pagination Software – Dewar/View.; Production Equipment – Text/Bridge, LaserMaster/Type, Nat, XIT/HP5 XITron; Cameras – Kk/Image Maker, 1-Acti/SSII; Scanners – Nikon/Neg, Microtek/Flatbed, Umax, HP, Kk/RFS PRESSROOM: Line 1 – 6-HI/845 1972; Line 2 – 4-G/Community 1968 1997; Press Drives – Haley/Control PCL; Folders – HI/Cotrell; Press control system – MHI/PLC. MAILROOM: Counter stackers – 1-BG/107, 1-HL/Monitor, 1-BG/108; Inserters and stuffers – 1-HI/624P; Bundle tying machines – 2-MLN/ML2EE, 1/MLN Sorter-Tyer; Addressing machine – 1-KR/215. BUSINESS COMPUTERS: Business Software – Archetype/Corel Draw, Microsoft/Works, Microsoft/Windows; Business Hardware – Gateways

SIDNEY

SIDNEY SUN-TELEGRAPH

817 12th Ave., Sidney, Neb., 69162-0193; gen tel (308) 254-2818; adv tel (308) 254-2818; ed tel (308) 254-2818; gen fax (308) 254-3925; gen e-mail sidneysun@hamilton.net; adv e-mail ads@sidneysun.com; ed e-mail editor@sidneysun.com; web site www.sidneysuntelegraph.com
Published: Tues, Wed, Thur, Fri, Sat
Weekday Frequency: m
Circulation: 2,450; 2,450(sat)
Last Audit: March 31, 2008
Price: 9.67/mo; 89.00/yr.
Advertising: Open inch rate $11.50
News services: AP, TMS.
Special Editions: Garden (Apr); Home Improvement (Feb); Bridal (Jan); Health (Jul); Senior Scene (Jun); Auto Guide (Mar); Graduation (May); Gift Guide (Nov).
Special Weekly Sections: Automotive (Fri); Food (Tues).
Magazines: Channel Surfer (Fri); American Profile (Weekly).

Gen. Mgr..........................Wayne Baurkemper
Adv. Dir..................................Ramona Koehn
Circ. Mgr...............................Cynthia Klipsel
Ed...Tammy Nelson
Market Information: ADS; Split run; TMC.
Mechanical available: Offset; Black and 3 ROP colors; insert accepted - up to 36 pgs., 13 x 10 max. trim size; page cutoffs - 23.
Mechanical Specifications: Type page 12 x 21 1/2; E - 6 cols, 2, 1/3 between; A - 6 cols, 2, 1/3 between; C - 8 cols, 1/3 between.
Commodity Consumption: Avg. Page Number Per Issue - Daily 12; Avg. Page Number Per Issue - Plates Used 2340; Avg. Page Number Per Issue - Saturday 12; widths 25; Newsprint Used - Short Tons 156; Printing Ink Used - Black 744; Printing Ink Used - Color 280; Printing Ink Used -
Equipment EDITORIAL: Front-end Software – QPS/QuarkXPress 3.32, Baseview/NewsEdit Pro.; Editorial Hardware – 5-APP/Mac G3 on network; Editorial Equipment – 2-Umax/Flatbed Scanner, 1-Kk/Negative Scanner; Editorial Printers – 2-APP/Mac LaserWriter 12640 PS; Classified Hardware – APP/Power Mac 4400; Classified Printers – APP/Mac LaserWriter. DISPLAY: Ad make-up applications – QPS/QuarkXPress 3.32, Adobe/Photoshop, Macromedia/Freehand 8.0; Display Hardware – APP/Power Mac 7300; Display Printers – Xante/Accel-A-Writer Laser 3N 11x17; Production Equipment – Caere/OmniPage Pro 8.0, Dixon/MS 25; Cameras – K/Superbeam 4800; Scanners – Equipment Ð QPS/QuarkXPress 3.32. PRESSROOM: Line 1 – 5-G/Community 1997; Press Drives – RKW/25 h.p. electric 1997; Folders – G/S 1997; Press control system – G/Community 1997; Press registration system – G/Dual-Pin.; Bundle tying machines – Malow/Heavy Duty; Wrapping singles – St/String Tyer. BUSINESS COMPUTERS: Business Software – Microsoft/Windows 98, QuickBooks Pro; Business Hardware – Dell, Pentium II

YORK

YORK NEWS-TIMES

327 Platte Ave., York, Neb., 68467; gen tel (402) 362-4478; adv tel (402) 362-4478; ed tel (402) 362-4478; gen fax (402) 362-6748; adv fax (402) 362-6748; ed fax (402) 362-6748; gen e-mail news@yorknewstimes.com; ed e-mail mwilkinson@yorknewstimes.com; web site www.yorknewstimes.com
Group: North Carolina Press Service, Inc.
Published: Mon, Tues, Wed, Thur, Fri, Sat
Weekday Frequency: m
Circulation: 4,695; 4,695(sat)
Last Audit: September 25, 2001
Price: 7.00/mo; 75.60/yr.
Advertising: Open inch rate $12.50
News services: AP.
Politics: Independent.
Not Published: New Year; Memorial Day; Independence Day; Labor Day; Thanksgiving; Christmas.
Special Weekly Sections: Church Directory/Religion Page (Fri); Regional News (Mon); Prime Time TV Tab (Thur); Best Food Day (Tues); Senior Citizens (Wed).
Magazines: Relish (Monthly); USA WEEKEND Magazine (Sat).

Pub...Greg Awtry
Adv. Sales Mgr............................Kathy Larson
Circ. Mgr........................................Cory Nann
Ed....Steve Moseley
Online Ed.......................................Eric Eckert
Market Information: TMC.
Mechanical available: Offset; Black and 3 ROP colors; insert accepted; page cutoffs - 22 3/4.
Mechanical Specifications: Type page 13 x 21; E - 6 cols, 2 1/12, 1/8 between; A - 6 cols, 2 1/12, 1/8 between; C - 6 cols, 2 1/12, 1/8 between.
Commodity Consumption: Avg. Page Number Per Issue - Daily 13; Avg. Page Number Per Issue - Plates Used 2108; widths 13 1/2; Newsprint Used - Short Tons 180; Printing Ink Used - Black 7510; Printing Ink Used - Color 825; Printing Ink Used - Pages Printed 4200.
Equipment EDITORIAL: Front-end Software – QPS/QuarkXPress, Baseview/NewsEdit.; Editorial Hardware – APP/PowerMac 7600, APP/Mac Server 60; Editorial Equipment – Monotype/ImageSetters, Panther Pro/ImageSetters; Editorial Printers – APP/Mac II NTX, APP/Mac LaserWriter Pro 600, MON, HP/5M CLASSIFIED: Front-end Software – Baseview.; Classified Hardware – APP/Mac Quadra 605, APP/Power Mac 7200; Classified Equipment – Printers ÃŒ APP/Mac LaserWriter Pro 630, HP/LaserJet 5M DISPLAY: Ad make-up applications – Aldus/PageMaker 5.0, QPS/QuarkXPress 3.32; Layout Software – APP/Mac.; Display Hardware – APP/Power Mac 7200, APP/Power Mac 7300; Display Printers – APP/Mac LaserWriter Pro 630, HP/LaserJet 5M; Production Equipment – MON/1270, MON/1270; Cameras – DAI/Screen, C/240-LA; Scanners – Nikon/LS-3510, Microtek/ScanMaker II, APP/Mac One. PRESSROOM: Line 1 – 6-KP/News King (upper former) 1976; Folders – 1-KP/KJ6; Reels and Stands – 6-KP/News King.; Bundle tying machines – Ty-Tech/Model 40 Tyer; Addressing machine – Ch/Mod IV Labeler, Ch/4-up Model 542090. AUDIO: Audio Software – SMS/Stauffer Gold; Audio Hardware – SMS, Samsung BUSINESS COMPUTERS: Business Software – SMS; Business Hardware – NCR/System 3230

NEVADA

CARSON CITY

NEVADA APPEAL

580 Mallory Way, Carson City, Nev., 89701-5360; gen tel (775) 882-2111; adv tel (775) 881-1255; ed tel (775) 882-2111; gen fax (775) 887-2420; adv fax (775) 887-2420; ed fax (775) 887-2420; ed e-mail editor@nevadaappeal.com; web site www.nevadaappeal.com

Published: Tues, Wed, Thur, Fri, Sat, Sun
Weekday Frequency: m
Saturday Frequency: m
Circulation: 11,763; 10,517(sat); 14,478(sun)
Last Audit: Sworn September 30, 2009
Price: 9.00/mo (carrier); 95.00/yr (carrier), 234.00/yr (mail).
Advertising: Open inch rate $28.15
News services: AP.
Politics: Independent.
Advertising not accepted: Y
Not Published: Monday
Special Editions: Deadline Home Improvement (Apr); Deadline Primary Election (Aug); Last Minute Appeal Bonus (Dec); Deadline Customer Appreciation Appeal (Jul); Deadline Father's Day Bonus (Jun); Carson Country (Mar); Deadline Mother's Day Bonus (May); Thanksgiving Gift (N
Special Weekly Sections: Real Estate (Fri); TV Log (S); On the Road (Sat); Food (Wed).
Magazines: Sierra Magazine/Seniors (Monthly); TV Mag (S); American Profile (Weekly).
Pub. ....Niki Gladys
Adv. Mgr. ....Rob Galloway
Circ. Dir. ....Keith Tanoos
Circ. Mgr. ....Lester Fitzhenry
Editorial Page Ed. ....Barry Smith
Entertainment/Amusements Ed. ....Rhonda Costa
Features Ed. ....Teri Vance
Prodn./Opns. Dir. ....Girish Pandit
Prodn. Mgr. ....Betty Jo Heaton
Prodn. Mgr., Pre Press ....Rob Sperry
Editor ....Dennis Noone
Market Information: TMC; Zoned editions.
Mechanical available: Offset; Black and 3 ROP colors; insert accepted - single sheets; page cutoffs - 22 3/4.
Mechanical Specifications: Type page 12 4/5 x 21 1/2; E - 6 cols, 2, 1/6 between; A - 6 cols, 2, 1/6 between; C - 9 cols, 1 1/3, 1/6 between.
Commodity Consumption: Avg. Page Number Per Issue - Daily 31; Avg. Page Number Per Issue - Sunday 68; widths 27 1/2; Newsprint Used - Metric Tons 1170; Printing Ink Used - Black 17500; Printing Ink Used - Color 9050; Printing Ink Used - Pages Printed 13332.
Equipment: Editorial Hardware – 20-APP/Mac.; Classified Hardware – 8-APP/Mac. DISPLAY: Ad make-up applications – QPS/QuarkXPress 4.0, Freehand, Adobe/Illustrator, Adobe/Acrobat, Adobe/Photoshop; Layout Software – 6-APP/Mac.; Display Hardware – APP/Mac; Display Printers – APP/Mac LaserWriter II NTX, APP/Mac Color Printer PRODUCTION: Pagination Software – QPS/QuarkXPress 4.0.; Production Equipment – 1-Amerigraph/Magnum, 2-Graham/Subtractive; Cameras – 1-Hx/150B; Scanners – 1-Hx/150B, 1-CK Optical PRESSROOM: Line 1 – 16-G/Community single width 1996; Folders – 2-G/2:1. MAILROOM: Counter stackers – 2/QWI 200; Inserters and stuffers – 1372-/Valley Remanufacturing; Bundle tying machines – 2-Dynaric/NP3; Mailroom control system – Prism System.; Business Hardware – 2-IBM/PC, Link/MC5 Business ET960
Zip Codes served: 89403, 89410, 89423, 89429, 89447, 89701, 89703, 89704, 89705, 89706
Delivery method: Mail, Newsstand, Private Carrier, Racks

ELKO

ELKO DAILY FREE PRESS

3720 Idaho St., Elko, Nev., 89801; gen tel (775) 738-3118; adv tel (775) 738-3118; ed tel (775) 753-8082; gen fax (775) 738-2215; adv fax (775) 738-2215; ed fax (775) 778-3131; adv e-mail classifieds@elkodaily.com; advertising@elkodaily.com; ed e-mail edit@elkodaily.com; web site www.elkodaily.com

Published: Mon, Tues, Wed, Thur, Fri, Sat, Sun
Weekday Frequency: e
Saturday Frequency: m
Circulation: 5,632; 6,447(sat)
Last Audit: September 30, 2009
Price: 15.00/mo; 125.00/yr.
Advertising: Open inch rate $15.30
News services: AP, TMS.
Politics: Independent. **Established:** 1883
Advertising not accepted: 900 numbers.
Not Published: Christmas.
Special Editions: Home Improvement Guide (Apr); Fall Sports Preview (Aug); Christmas Gift Guide (Dec); Bride's Guide (Feb); Cowboy Poetry Gathering (Jan); Customer Appreciation (Jul); Mining Expo (Jun); Newspapers in Education (Mar); Explore I-80, Nevada Style (May); Chris
Special Weekly Sections: Entertainment & TV Guide (Fri); Society/Events/Business (Sat); Best Food Day (Tues).
Magazines: Relish (Monthly); USA WEEKEND Magazine (Sat).
Circ. Mgr. ....Amy Packham
Mng. Ed. ....Jeff Mullens
Sports Ed. ....Martin Harris
Prodn. Mgr. ....Randy Woodrow
Market Information: TMC.
Mechanical available: Offset; Black and 3 ROP colors; insert accepted; page cutoffs - 22 3/4.
Mechanical Specifications: Type page 11 7/8 x 21 1/2; E - 6 cols, 1 7/8, 1/8 between; A - 6 cols, 1 7/8, 1/8 between; C - 6 cols, 1 7/8, 1/8 between.
Commodity Consumption: Avg. Page Number Per Issue - Daily 19.20; Avg. Page Number Per Issue - Plates Used 7115; Avg. Page Number Per Issue - Saturday 24.50; widths 25; Newsprint Used - Short Tons 550; Printing Ink Used - Black 9000; Printing Ink Used - Color 5000; Printing Ink
Equipment EDITORIAL: Front-end Software – Baseview/NewsEdit Pro 3.2.2.; Editorial Hardware – 1-APP/Mac CLASSIFIED: Front-end Software – Baseview.; Classified Hardware – APP/Mac DISPLAY: Ad make-up applications – Multi-Ad, QPS/QuarkXPress; Layout Software – APP/Mac. PRODUCTION: Pagination Software – QPS/QuarkXPress 4.1.; Production Equipment – Pre Press/Panther, Pre Press/Panther Plus; Cameras – 1-B/2000, 1-Acti PRESSROOM: Line 1 – 7-KP/News King (single); Folders – 1-KP/2:1.; Inserters and stuffers – KAN/6 Station; Bundle tying machines – CyKlop.; Business Hardware – IBM/PC, APP/Mac

FALLON

LAHONTAN VALLEY NEWS & FALLON EAGLE STANDARD

PO Box 1297, Fallon, Nev., 89407-1297; gen tel (775)□423-6041; web site www.lahontanvalleynews.com

Group: Swift Communications
Published: Wed, Fri
Circulation: 3,500

LAHONTAN VALLEY NEWS/FALLON EAGLE STANDARD

562 N. Maine St., Fallon, Nev., 89406-2808; gen tel (775) 423-6041; gen fax (775) 423-0474; gen e-mail news@lahontanvalleynews.com; web site www.lahontanvalleynews.com

Published: Tues, Wed, Thur, Fri, Sun
Weekday Frequency: m
Circulation: 2,938; 3,018(sun)
Last Audit: September 30, 2008
Price: 120.00/yr.
Advertising: Open inch rate $15.50
News services: AP.
Politics: Independent.
Not Published: Federal Holidays.
Special Weekly Sections: TV (Fri).
Magazines: Parade (S); American Profile (Weekly).
Pub. ....Pete Copeland
Adv. Supvr. ....Shannon Burns
Circ. Mgr. ....Keith Sampson
Ed. ....Steve Ranson
Prodn. Mgr. ....Kathi Griffis
Mechanical available: Black and 3 ROP colors; insert accepted.
Mechanical Specifications: Type page 13 x 21 1/2; E - 6 cols, 2 1/16, 1/8 between; A - 6 cols, 2 1/16, 1/8 between; C - 9 cols, 1 5/16, 1/8 between.
Commodity Consumption: Avg. Page Number Per Issue - Daily 12; Avg. Page Number Per Issue - Saturday 12; widths 27 1/2; Newsprint Used - Metric Tons 80; Printing Ink Used - Black 3450; Printing Ink Used - Color 200.
Equipment: Editorial Hardware – COM; Editorial Printers – APP/Mac LaserPrinter.; Classified Hardware – APP/Mac.; Layout Software – APP/Mac.; Display Hardware – Other □ APP/Mac.; Production Equipment – COM; Cameras – Acti. PRESSROOM: Line 1 – 4-KP/News King Offset; Press Drives – Press control system □ CH/Respondor Drive. MAILROOM: Counter stackers – PB; Inserters and stuffers – 4-KAN/620; Bundle tying machines – PAK/Tyer, Felins/F16.; Business Hardware – DA, NCR, IBM

LAS VEGAS

LAS VEGAS REVIEW-JOURNAL

1111 W. Bonanza Rd., Las Vegas, Nev., 89106; gen tel (702) 383-0211; adv tel (702) 383-0388; ed tel (702) 383-0264; gen fax (702) 383-4676; adv fax (702) 383-0389; ed fax (702) 383-4676; ed e-mail letters@lvrj.com; web site www.reviewjournal.com; www.lasvegas.com

Published: Mon, Tues, Wed, Thur, Fri, Sat, Sun
Weekday Frequency: m
Saturday Frequency: m
Circulation: 213,078; 149,045(sat); 186,785(sun)
Last Audit: ABC September 30, 2011
Price: 3.50/wk; 182.00/yr.
Advertising: Open inch rate $253.85
News services: AP, LAT-WP, MCT.
Politics: Independent.
Note: The Las Vegas Review-Journal prints and distributes the Las Vegas Sun as a section of the Review-Journal. The two newspapers are editorially separate.
Special Editions: Guide to Pool & Patio (Apr); Football Preview (Aug); National Finals Rodeo (Dec); Dining Guide (Feb); Super Bowl (Jan); Guide to Pool & Patio (Jul); Dining Guide (Jun); Home and Garden (Mar); Home Furnishings (May); National Family Week (Nov); Las Vegas I
Special Weekly Sections: Neon Entertainment (Fri); Travel (S); Religion (Sat); Taste (Wed).
Magazines: TV Magazine (S).
Pub. ....Sherman Frederick
Gen. Mgr. ....Allan Fleming
Mgr., Bus. Office ....Pat Little
HR Dir. ....Linda Pellegrino
Adv. Dir. ....Bob Brown
Adv. Mgr., Nat'l ....Karen Grover
Adv. Mgr., Sales Devel. ....Gary Plackemeier
Dir., Mktg./Promo. ....H. Dean White
Circ. Dir. ....Ed Parker
Ed. ....Thomas Mitchell
Mng. Ed. ....Charles Zobell
Bus. Ed ....Michael Hiesiger
City Ed. ....Mary Hynes
Editorial Page Ed. ....John Kerr
Features Ed. ....Frank Fertado
Asst. Features Ed ....Pat Morgan
News Ed. ....Mary Greeley
Online Ed. ....Al Gibes
Chief Photographer ....Jeff Scheid
Real Estate Ed. ....Lynn Colliner
Market Information: ADS; Split run; TMC; Zoned editions.
Mechanical available: Offset; Black and 3 ROP colors; insert accepted; page cutoffs - 22.
Mechanical Specifications: Type page 11 3/4 x 21; E - 6 cols, 1 7/8, 1/8 between; A - 6 cols, 1 7/8, 1/8 between; C - 10 cols, 1 1/16, 3/32 between.
Commodity Consumption: Avg. Page Number Per Issue - Daily 82; Avg. Page Number Per Issue - Plates Used 200821; Avg. Page Number Per Issue - Saturday 110; Avg. Page Number Per Issue - Sunday 180; widths 37 1/2; Newsprint Used - Metric Tons 42000; Printing Ink Used - Black 75200
Equipment EDITORIAL: Front-end Software – ESP/2, DTI 4.2.; Editorial Hardware – DTI; Editorial Equipment – APP/Mac, Lf; Editorial Printers – MON/3850 Express Masters, MON/Paper Master CLASSIFIED: Front-end Software – AT/Enterprise 1.4.8.; Classified Hardware – AT/Sysdecoaix RS 6000, Clarion Raid/System; Classified Equipment – MON, MON/MGS OPI System, AT/Pagination; Classified Printers – MON/EM 3850 DISPLAY: Ad make-up applications – DTI/AdSpeed 8.2, CJ/Layout; Layout Software – APP/Mac, CJ.; Display Hardware – APP/Mac, DTI, HP 959KS200, HP/959KS200; Display Printers – XIT/Clippers, MON/3850 Express Masters PRODUCTION: Pagination Software – DTI/Page S; Production Equipment – MON/3850 Express Masters, MON, Futuro, Sharp/Jx-610, Lf/Leafscan 45, Lf/Leafscan 35; Cameras – C/Marathon, B; Scanners – 2-Lf/Leafscan 35, 3-Kk/2035, 1-ECR/Autokon 2045c, 1-Sharp/JX-610, 1-Lf/Leafscan 45, 1-Autokon-1000 PRESSROOM: Line 1 – 8-G/Newsliner Tower double width 1999; Line 2 – 8-G/Newsliner Tower double width 2000; Line 3 – 8-G/Community 1981; Folders – 2, Sovereign/160-Double Folder 3:2; Reels and Stands – 20 MAILROOM: Counter stackers – 12-HI/Olympic, 3-HL/HT, 1-QWI/Sport, 1/MM; Inserters and stuffers – 4-HI/632, 1-/MM; Bundle tying machines – 14-/Dynaric. BUSINESS COMPUTERS: Business Software – CJ 8.02H, Progress 8.2B; Business Hardware – HP/3000-KS 959, HP/9000-KZ 210

LAS VEGAS SUN

2360 Corporate Cir., 3rd Fl., Henderson, Nev., 89074; gen tel (702) 385-3111; adv tel (702) 383-0383; ed tel (702) 385-3111; gen fax (702) 383-7264; adv fax (702) 383-0389; ed fax (702) 383-7264; web site www.lasvegassun.com

Published: Mon, Tues, Wed, Thur, Fri, Sat, Sun
Weekday Frequency: m
Saturday Frequency: m
News services: AP, NYT, SHNS, DJ, GNS.
Politics: 1950
Note: The Las Vegas Sun is distributed as a section of the Las Vegas Review-Journal. See the Review-Journal for information on circulation, advertising rates and production. The Sun remains editorially separate and publishes online content as well.
Broadcast Affiliations: Las Vegas One.
Vice Pres. ....Daniel A. Greenspun
Pub. ....Barbara Greenspun
Adv. Dir., New Media ....Brian Fortney
Ed. ....Brian Greenspun
Mng. Ed. ....Michael J. Kelley
Deputy Mng. Ed. ....Bill Gaspard
Deputy Mng. Ed. ....Drex Heikes
Asst. Mng. Ed., News ....Tom Gorman
Asst. Mng. Ed., News ....Mark Whittington
Dir., Photography ....Mark Damon
Mechanical Specifications: Type page 11 1/2 x 21; E - 6 cols, 1 5/6, 5/36 between; A - 6 cols, 1 5/6, 1/9 between; C - 10 cols, 1 1/24, 1/9 between.
Commodity Consumption: widths 27 1/2.
Equipment EDITORIAL: Front-end Software – Custom Developed, Solaris 2.6, Sun/Sunny Server 1.1.; Editorial Hardware – Sun/Microsys, 4-Sun/1505-80 Server; Editorial Printers – HP/Laser PRODUCTION: Pagination Software – HI/NewsMaker Pagination 3.x.; Production

Equipment – HI/XP-21, APP/NT Server, APP/Photo Desk; Scanners – Sharp/JX-600, Nikon/LS-3510 AF; Business Hardware – 6-Sun/Microsystems 210M, 6-Dell/Server

RENO

RENO GAZETTE-JOURNAL

955 Kuenzli St., Reno, Nev., 89502; gen tel (775) 788-6200; adv tel (775) 788-6238; ed tel (775) 788-6301; adv fax (775) 788-6516; ed fax (775) 788-6458; gen e-mail rgjmail@nevadanet.com; ed e-mail newstips@rgj.com; web site www.rgj.com

Group: Metro Newspaper Advertising Services, Inc.
Published: Mon, Tues, Wed, Thur, Fri, Sat, Sun
Weekday Frequency: m
Saturday Frequency: m
Circulation: 41,164; 38,899(sat); 55,176(sun)
Last Audit: ABC September 30, 2011
Price: 3.25/wk (carrier/motor route); 16.25/mo (carrier/motor route); 195.00/yr (carrier/motor route).
Advertising: Open inch rate $151.44
News services: AP, GNS, LAT-WP, Knight Ridder.
Special Editions: Nevada Living (Apr); Football (Aug); Super Bowl (Jan); Hot August Nights (Jul); Reno Rodeo (Jun); Dining Guide (May); Dining Guide (Nov); Health Source (Oct); National Air Races (Sept).
Special Weekly Sections: Sierra Living (seasonal) (Fri); Technology (Mon); TV Week (S); Homefinder (Sat); Best Bets (Thur); Auto Finder (Wed).
Magazines: USA WEEKEND Magazine (S).
Pub. .... Ted Power
Exec. Ed. .... Beryl Love
Sr. Ed., News/Multimedia .... Mark Lundahl
Calendar Ed. .... Mark Robinson
Columnist .... Lenita Powers
Editorial Page Ed. .... Steve Falcone
Photo Ed. .... Tim Dunn
Television/Movies Reporter .... Forest Hartman
Weekend Ed. .... Michael Martinez
IT Mgr. .... Pat Levy
Prodn. Mgr., Pre Press .... Beth Ptak
Prodn. Mgr., Pressroom .... Joe Morales
Market Information: Split run; TMC; Zoned editions.
Mechanical available: Offset; Black and 3 ROP colors; insert accepted; page cutoffs - 22 3/4.
Mechanical Specifications: Type page 11 5/8 x 21 1/2; E - 6 cols, 1 5/6, 1/8 between; A - 6 cols, 1 5/6, 1/8 between; C - 10 cols, 1, 1/8 between.
Commodity Consumption: Avg. Page Number Per Issue - Daily 58; Avg. Page Number Per Issue - Plates Used 92716; Avg. Page Number Per Issue - Sunday 102; widths 50; Newsprint Used - Metric Tons 11033; Printing Ink Used - Black 224394; Printing Ink Used - Color 127868; Printing In
Equipment EDITORIAL: Front-end Software – CText.; Editorial Hardware – Compaq; Editorial Printers – Autologic CLASSIFIED: Front-end Software – CText.; Classified Hardware – AT, Compaq DISPLAY: Ad make-up applications – Multi-Ad; Layout Software – Layout/8000.; Display Hardware – APP/Mac; Display Printers – AU PRODUCTION: Pagination Software – Ctext.; Production Equipment – 1-LE, Lf/AP Leaf Picture Desk; Cameras – Scanners Â AG/Horizon, Kk, Nikon; Scanners – AG/Horizon, Kk, Nikon PRESSROOM: Line 1 – 7-G/Metro double width (4 Half decks) 1981; Folders – Imperial/3:2; Pasters – G/Automatic; Reels and Stands – G/Automatic, 7-G/3-arm. MAILROOM: Counter stackers – 2/HL, HI; Inserters and stuffers – HI/630; Bundle tying machines – 2-/Dynaric; Mailroom control system – Heidelberg/Prima; Addressing machine – Marconi/InkJet. BUSINESS COMPUTERS: Business Software – Lawson, Cyborg, Genesys; Business Hardware – IBM/AS/400

RENO NEWSPAPERS, INC.

955 Kuenzli, Reno, Nev., 89520; gen tel (775) 788-6200; gen fax (775)788-6521

Published: Mon, Tues, Wed, Thur, Fri, Sat, Sun
Price: 195.00/yr.
Advertising: Open inch rate $15.00

SPARKS

THE DAILY SPARKS TRIBUNE

1002 C St., Sparks, Nev., 89431-4929; gen tel (775) 358-8061; adv tel (775) 358-8061; ed tel (775) 358-8601; gen fax (775) 359-3837; adv fax (775) 359-3837; ed fax (775) 358-3837; gen e-mail tribunenews@sparkstribune.net; web site www.sparkstribune.net

Published: Mon, Tues, Wed, Thur, Fri, Sun
Weekday Frequency: m
Circulation: 5,034; 5,034(sun)
Last Audit: October 1, 2002
Price: 90.00/yr.
Advertising: Open inch rate $20.00
News services: AP.
Politics: Independent.

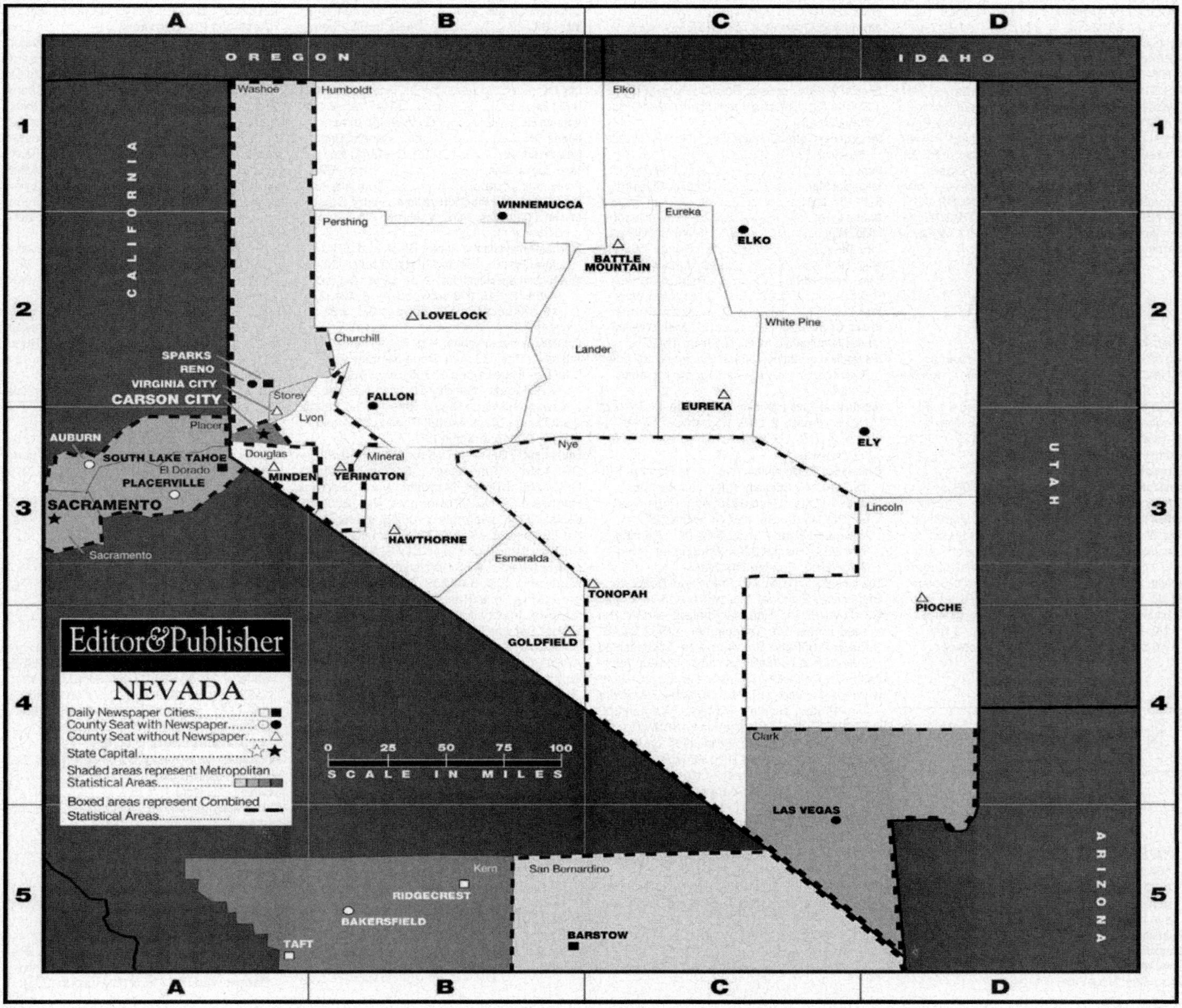

Not Published: New Year; Memorial Day; Independence Day; Labor Day; Thanksgiving; Christmas.
Special Editions: Hometown Christmas (Dec).
Special Weekly Sections: Religion (Fri); Senior Spotlight (Mon); Sports Tab (S); Entertainment (Thur); Business (Tues); Food & Health (Wed).
Magazines: TV Week (S).
Pub. ....Ed Mccaffrey
Adv. Dir. ....Nancy Streets
Circ. Mgr. ....Dave Alexander
Ed. ....Nathan Orme
Mng. Ed. ....Janine Kearney
Sports Ed. ....Dan Eckles
Data Processing Mgr. ....Cindy Mikkelson
Prodn. Foreman, Press/Camera ....Cheryl Bain
Market Information: TMC.
Mechanical available: Offset; Black and 3 ROP colors; insert accepted; page cutoffs - 22 3/4.
Mechanical Specifications: Type page 13 1/2 x 21 1/2; E - 6 cols, 2 1/16, 1/6 between; A - 6 cols, 2 1/16, 1/6 between; C - 7 cols, 1 9/16, 1/6 between.
Commodity Consumption: Avg. Page Number Per Issue - Daily 24; Avg. Page Number Per Issue - Plates Used 9200; widths 27 1/2; Newsprint Used - Metric Tons 412; Printing Ink Used - Black 7200; Printing Ink Used - Color 1200; Printing Ink Used - Pages Printed 8312.
Equipment; Editorial Hardware – APP/Mac Plus, APP/Mac II, APP/Mac SE30; Editorial Printers – HP/4MV. CLASSIFIED: Front-end Software – RSK/Tandy 3000.; Classified Hardware – CText; Classified Printers – HP/4MV; Layout Software – APP/Mac, QPS/QuarkXPress.; Display Printers – HP/4MV; Production Equipment – 1-Nu; Cameras – R; Scanners – APP/Mac. PRESSROOM: Line 1 – 5-G/Community; Folders – 1-G/Community.; Inserters and stuffers – MM; Bundle tying machines – Bu. BUSINESS COMPUTERS: Business Software – PBS/Media; Business Hardware – Tandy/486ei-33, Wyse/60 terminals

WINNEMUCCA

THE HUMBOLDT SUN

1022 S. Grass Valley Rd., Winnemucca, Nev., 89445; gen tel (775) 623-5011; gen fax (775) 623-5243; adv e-mail advertising@humboldtsun.com; ed e-mail editorial@humboldtsun.com; web site www.humboldtsun.com
Published: Tues, Fri
Circulation: 3,650
Last Audit: Sworn November 17, 2008
Advertising: Open inch rate $8.05
Office Mgr. ....Linda Lindeman
Adv. Mgr., Sales ....Holly Rudy-James
Circ. Mgr. ....Sharon Vedis
Ed. ....David Gouger
Prodn. Mgr. ....Terrie Chism
Prodn. Mgr., Press ....Rick Ferro
Mechanical Specifications: Type page 13 x 21 1/2; E - 6 cols, 2, 1/6 between; A - 6 cols, 2, 1/6 between; C - 6 cols, 2, 1/6 between.

NEW HAMPSHIRE

BERLIN

THE BERLIN DAILY SUN

164 Main St., Berlin, N.H., 03570; gen tel (603) 752-5858; gen fax (866) 475-4429; gen e-mail bds@berlindailysun.com; web site www.berlindailysun.com
Published: Mon, Tues, Wed, Thur, Fri
Weekday Frequency: m
Circulation: 8,800
Last Audit: November 18, 2003
Price: 390.00/yr.
News services: AP, Reuters.
Politics: Independent.
Note: For detailed production information, see The Conway Daily Sun.
Pres. ....David N. Danforth
Pub. ....Mark Guerringue
Adv. Mgr., Sales ....Joyce Brothers
Ed. ....Adam Hirshan
Mng. Ed. ....Rose Dodge
Prodn. Mgr. ....Frank Haddy

CLAREMONT

EAGLE PUBLICATIONS, INC.

401 River Rd., Claremont, N.H., 03743; gen tel (603) 543-3100; gen fax (603) 542-9705

EAGLE TIMES

401 River Rd., Claremont, N.H., 03743; gen tel (603) 543-3100; adv tel (603) 543-3100; ed tel (603) 543-3100; gen fax (603) 542-9705; ed e-mail news@tsvmedia.net; web site www.tsvmedia.net
Published: Mon, Tues, Wed, Thur, Fri, Sun
Weekday Frequency: m
Circulation: 7,737; 8,016(sun)
Last Audit: September 30, 2008
Price: 3.80/wk; 15.20/mo; 197.60/yr.
Advertising: Open inch rate $15.85
News services: AP, TMS, Washington Post.
Politics: Independent.
Not Published: New Year; Christmas.
Special Weekly Sections: Religion Page (Fri); Sports (S); Entertainment (Thur); Best Food Day (Wed).
Magazines: Color Comics (S); American Profile (Weekly).
Pub. ....Harvey Hill
Financial Mgr. ....Traci J. Billesimo
Nat'l Adv. Mgr. ....Mary Lizotte
Online Sales ....Alicia Bacon
Mktg. Mgr. ....Melissa Billings
Circ. Dir. ....Randy Yanick
Mng. Ed. ....John Kelleher
Local News Editor ....Patrick O'Grady
IT Dir. ....Alan Wang
Web Coord. ....Kathy Fulcher
Prodn. Coord. ....Mark Walker
Market Information: ADS; Split run; TMC.
Mechanical available: Offset; Black and full color ROP colors; insert accepted; page cutoffs - 22 3/4.
Mechanical Specifications: Type page 12 3/4 x 21 1/2; E - 6 cols, 2 1/16, 1/8 between; A - 6 cols, 2 1/16, 1/8 between; C - 8 cols, 1 9/16, 1/16 between.
Commodity Consumption: Avg. Page Number Per Issue - Daily 26; Avg. Page Number Per Issue - Plates Used 3926; Avg. Page Number Per Issue - Sunday 44; widths 27; Newsprint Used - Short Tons 900; Printing Ink Used - Black 18000; Printing Ink Used - Color 1100; Printing Ink Used -
Equipment EDITORIAL: Front-end Software – Baseview.; Editorial Hardware – 6-APP/Mac G3, 11-APP/Mac; Editorial Printers – MON, Pre Press/Panther Pro Imagesetter, X/N32 CLASSIFIED: Front-end Software – APT.; Classified Hardware – 3-HP DISPLAY: Ad make-up applications – Adobe/PageMaker 6.5; Layout Software – Ad Force, MEI/ALS.; Display Hardware – 3-APP/Mac; Display Printers – Xante/8300 PRODUCTION: Pagination Software – QPS/QuarkXPress 4.0.; Production Equipment – Pre Press/Panther Pro Imagesetter, 2-APP/Mac G3; Cameras – Nu/SSTE2024S-19LT, Nu/VVE-14-18; Scanners – Lf/Leafscan 35, Sharp/JX-450 Color, Sony/UY-S77, Umax/Mirage II PRESSROOM: Line 1 – 8-G/Community SC468 1991. MAILROOM: Counter stackers – Mid America Graphics/News stacker; Bundle tying machines – 2/Sa, 1-/Sterling. BUSINESS COMPUTERS: Business Software – Vision Data; Business Hardware – Sun

CONCORD

CONCORD MONITOR

1 Monitor Dr., Concord, N.H., 03302-1177; gen tel (603) 224-5301; adv tel (603) 224-5301; ed tel (603) 224-5301; gen fax (603) 228-5868; adv fax (603) 228-8238; ed fax (603) 224-8120; gen e-mail news@cmonitor.com; adv e-mail ads@cmonitor.com; ed e-mail letters@cmonitor.com; web site www.concordmonitor.com
Published: Sun
Circulation: 16,138; 16,138(sat); 18,428(sun)
Last Audit: September 30, 2009
Price: 4.25/wk; 221.00/wk.
Advertising: Open inch rate $17.75
News services: AP, CSM, LAT-WP.
Politics: Independent.
Not Published: Christmas.
Special Editions: Speedway Parade (Apr); Belknap County Fair (Aug); Gift Guide (Dec); Auto (Feb); Wedding (Jan); Market Days (Jul); Summer Directory (Jun); Town Meeting (Mar); Gift Guide (Nov); Fall Recreation (Oct); Business Profiles (Sept).
Special Weekly Sections: Entertainment (S); Auctions (Sat); Auctions (Thur); Business (Tues); Food (Wed).
Magazines: USA WEEKEND Magazine (S).
Pub. ....Geordie Wilson
Controller/Co-Gen. Mgr. ....David Sponenberg
Mgr., HR ....Tracie Sponenberg
Adv. Dir. ....Deborah Sanborn
Circ. Dir. ....David Sangiorgio
Exec. Ed. ....Felice Belman
City Ed. ....Hans Schultz
News Ed. ....Ric Tracewski
Opinion Ed. ....Ralph Jimenez
Sports Ed. ....Sandra Smith
New Media Dir. ....Margo Bowie
Tech. Servs. Mgr. ....Ben Allen
Prodn. Mgr., Distr. ....Tom Ahearn
Prodn. Mgr., Pre Press/Pressroom ....Harry Green
Market Information: ADS; Split run; TMC; Zoned editions.
Mechanical available: Flexo; Black and 3 ROP colors; insert accepted; page cutoffs - 22.
Mechanical Specifications: Type page 13 x 21; E - 6 cols, 2 1/16, 1/8 between; A - 6 cols, 2 1/16, 1/8 between; C - 9 cols, 1 3/8, 3/32 between.
Commodity Consumption: Avg. Page Number Per Issue - Daily 36; Avg. Page Number Per Issue - Plates Used 27000; Avg. Page Number Per Issue - Sunday 58; widths 27 1/2; Newsprint Used - Metric Tons 1573; Printing Ink Used - Black 34906; Printing Ink Used - Color 20044; Printing In
Equipment EDITORIAL: Front-end Software – CNI/Agile Teambase Special Edition, QPS/QuarkXPress, Microsoft/Word.; Editorial Hardware – NEC/Powermate Pro 2200x18 seats, NEC/Powermate V100x25 seats; Editorial Equipment – Kante G3; Editorial Printers – Dataproducts/Typhoon 16 CLASSIFIED: Front-end Software – PBS/AdPlacer 7.0.; Classified Hardware – IBM, 8-AZZ/P4 1.8; Classified Printers – 2-Pre Press/Panther Pro 36 DISPLAY: Ad make-up applications – Multi-Ad/Creator 1.6; Layout Software – PBS, Adplacer 7.0.; Display Hardware – 4-APP/Power Mac 7500, 8-APP/G4; Display Printers – Xante/Accel-a-Writer 8200 PRODUCTION: Pagination Software – AGL.; Production Equipment – Na, 2-Pre Press/7225 DB, Epson; Cameras – C/Spartan II; Scanners – ECR/Autokon PRESSROOM: Line 1 – 6-PEC/double width (17 printing couples); Folders – 2-H/3:2. MAILROOM: Counter stackers – HL/Monitor HT II; Inserters and stuffers – GMA/SLS 1000; Bundle tying machines – Dynaric; Wrapping singles – HL/Monarch; Addressing machine – 2-KR/211; Other equipment –MM/Minuteman Stitcher/Trimmer.; Audio Hardware – IBM/486 BUSINESS COMPUTERS: Business Software – CJ; Business Hardware – HP/Micro 3000XE

MONITOR PUBLISHING CO.

PO Box 1177, Concord, N.H., 03302-1177; gen tel (603) 224-5301; gen fax (603) 228-5868

DOVER

FOSTER'S DAILY DEMOCRAT

150 Venture Dr., Dover, N.H., 03820; gen tel (603) 742-4455; adv fax (603) 740-3461; adv e-mail dispatch@fosters.com; ed e-mail letters@fosters.com; web site www.fosters.com
Published: Mon, Tues, Wed, Thur, Fri, Sat, Sun
Weekday Frequency: m
Saturday Frequency: m
Circulation: 15,361; 15,361(sat); 19,721(sun)
Last Audit: September 30, 2009
Price: 8.05/mo (carrier), $11.00/mo (mail).
Advertising: Open inch rate $26.25
News services: AP, NYT.
Politics: Independent. **Established:** 1873
Not Published: New Year; Presidents' Day; Memorial Day; Independence Day; Labor Day; Veteran's Day; Thanksgiving; Christmas.
Own facility?: Y
Special Editions: Bridal Page (Apr); Bridal Page (Aug); Christmas Greetings (Dec); Valentine's Gift Guide (Feb); Weddings (Jan); Parenting (Jul); Dover Chamber of Commerce (Jun); Bridal Page (Mar); Mother's Day Gifts (May); Bridal Page (Nov); Bridal Page (Oct); Bridal Page
Special Weekly Sections: TV Spotlight (Fri); Best Food Day (Sat); Best Food Day (Wed).
Magazines: USA WEEKEND Magazine (S); American Profile (Weekly).
Pres./Pub ....Patrice Foster
Personnel Mgr. ....Cathy Hayward
Controller ....Jennalee Muise
Purchasing Agent ....Lara Sears
Dir., Sales/Mktg. ....Wayne Chick
Circ. Dir. ....James Russell
Ed. ....Theresa Foster
Exec. Ed. ....Rod Doherty
Mng. Ed. ....Mary Pat Rowland
Bus. Ed. ....Jerry Turner
Mgmt. Info Servs. Dir. ....Simeon Broughton
Prodn. Mgr. ....Ray Stockton
Mechanical available: Offset; Black.
Mechanical Specifications: Type page 13 x 21 1/2; E - 6 cols, 2 1/16, 1/8 between; A - 6 cols, 2 1/16, 1/8 between; C - 9 cols, 1 3/8, 1/16 between.
Equipment; Editorial Hardware – 6-AX.; Production Equipment – 7-P, 2-DEC/PDP; Cameras – 1-R, 1-K.; Inserters and stuffers – 1/W; Bundle tying machines – 1-/Sa.
Zip Codes served: 03820
Delivery method: Mail, Newsstand, Private Carrier, Racks

GEORGE FOSTER & CO., INC.

333 Central Ave., Dover, N.H., 03820; gen tel (603) 742-4455; gen fax (603) 740-7079; web site www.fosters.com
Price: 172.90/yr (for seven days in a week); 122.20/yr (for six days in a week).
Advertising: Open inch rate $12.88

HUDSON

THE TELEGRAPH

17 Executive Dr., Hudson, N.H., 03051; gen tel (603) 882-2741; adv tel (603) 594-6555; ed tel (603) 594-6467; gen fax (603) 882-5138; adv fax (603) 882-5138; ed fax (603) 882-2681; gen e-mail news@nashuatelegraph.com; web site www.nashuatelegraph.com
Published: Mon, Tues, Wed, Thur, Fri, Sat, Sun
Weekday Frequency: m
Saturday Frequency: m
Circulation: 20,745; 20,745(sat); 25,352(sun)
Last Audit: September 30, 2009
Price: 3.25/wk; 156.00/yr (carrier).
Advertising: Open inch rate $37.25
News services: AP, LAT-WP.
Politics: Independent. **Established:** 1832
Not Published: Memorial Day; Labour Day; Christmas.
Special Editions: Colossal Classified (Apr); Boomers (Aug); Celebrate New Year's Eve (Dec); Valentine's Day Dining (Feb); The Perfect Wedding (Jan); Graduation (Jun);

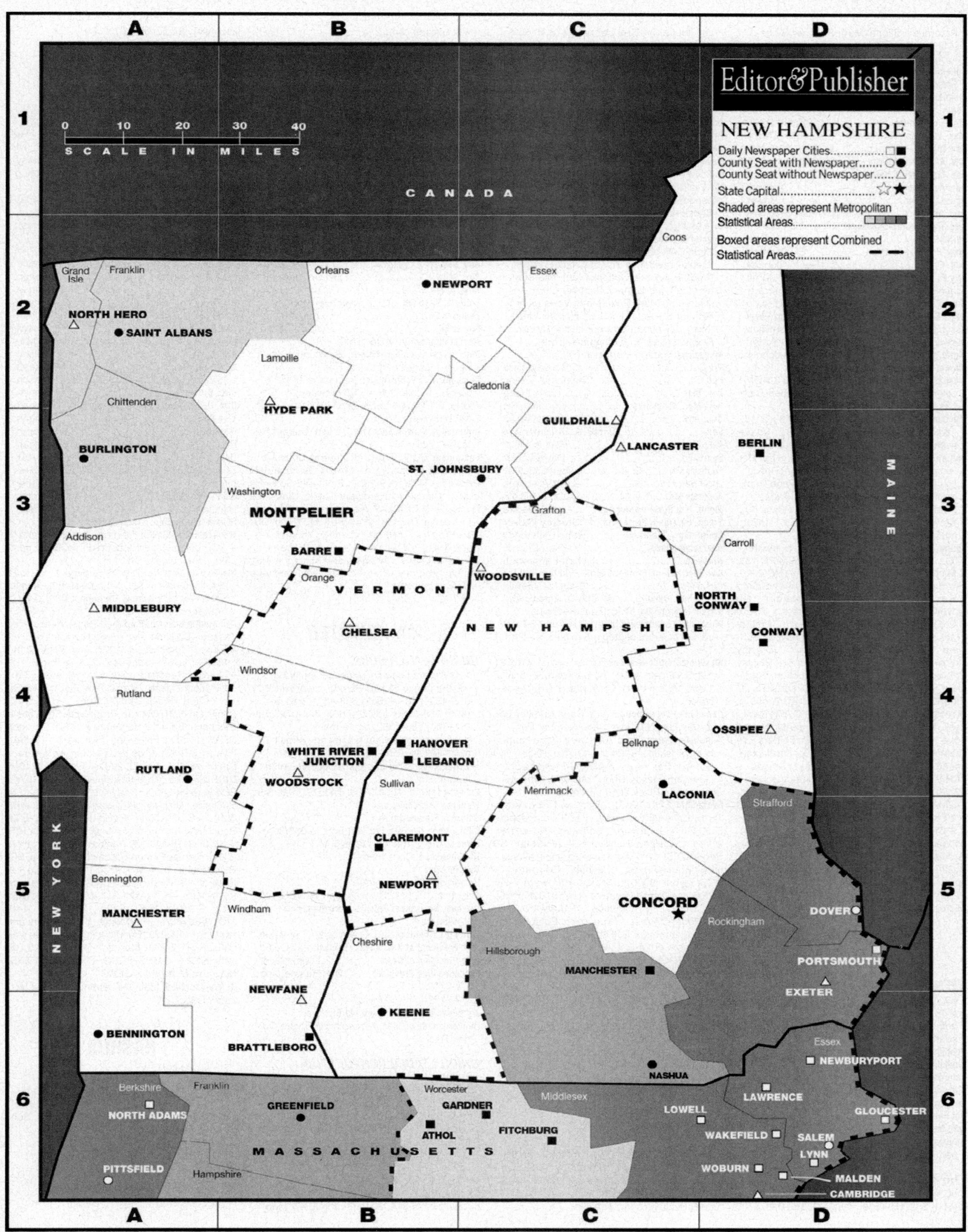

Editor&Publisher
NEW HAMPSHIRE
Daily Newspaper Cities
County Seat with Newspaper
County Seat without Newspaper
State Capital
Shaded areas represent Metropolitan Statistical Areas
Boxed areas represent Combined Statistical Areas
SCALE IN MILES
0 10 20 30 40
CANADA
MAINE
NEW YORK
VERMONT
NEW HAMPSHIRE
MASSACHUSETTS
NEWPORT
NORTH HERO
SAINT ALBANS
HYDE PARK
BURLINGTON
GUILDHALL
LANCASTER
BERLIN
ST. JOHNSBURY
MONTPELIER
BARRE
WOODSVILLE
MIDDLEBURY
CHELSEA
NORTH CONWAY
CONWAY
OSSIPEE
HANOVER
WHITE RIVER JUNCTION
LEBANON
WOODSTOCK
RUTLAND
LACONIA
CLAREMONT
NEWPORT
CONCORD
DOVER
MANCHESTER
PORTSMOUTH
EXETER
NEWFANE
KEENE
BENNINGTON
BRATTLEBORO
NASHUA
NEWBURYPORT
LAWRENCE
NORTH ADAMS
GREENFIELD
GARDNER
ATHOL
FITCHBURG
LOWELL
GLOUCESTER
WAKEFIELD
SALEM
LYNN
PITTSFIELD
WOBURN
MALDEN
CAMBRIDGE

Progress Editions (Mar); Summer Guide (May); Holiday Gift Guide (Nov); Celebtraing Women (Oct); The Perfec
Special Weekly Sections: Religious Pages (Sat); Entertainment Calendar (Thur); Food (Wed).
Magazines: USA WEEKEND Magazine (S).
Pub. ....Terrence L. Williams
Mgr., Accounting ....Donald Smith
Mgr., HR/Vice Pres., Admin. ....Ellin Carroll
Adv. Mgr. ....John Vistorino
Adv. Mgr., Major Accts. ....Diane Locke
Adv. Mgr., Retail Sales ....Shana Brunye
Adv. Asst. Mgr. ....John Armenio
Coord., Promo. ....Jennifer Bower
Circ. Mgr. ....Michael Sheehan
Circ. Mgr., Home Delivery ....Lisa Walker
Ed. in Chief ....Nick Pappas
Mng. Ed., Readership ....Bill Dedman
Bus. Ed. ....Eileen Kennedy
City Ed. ....Jeff Merritt
Editorial Page Ed. ....Claudette Durocher
News Ed. ....David Pierce
Regl. Ed. ....Jonathan Van Fleet
Sports Ed. ....Alan Greenwood
Sunday Ed. ....Marty Karlon
Mgmt. Info Servs. Mgr. Cathleen Babbin-Johnson
Market Information: ADS; TMC.
Mechanical available: Offset; Black and 3 ROP colors; insert accepted - Samples; page cutoffs - 22.
Mechanical Specifications: Type page 13 x 21; E - 6 cols, 2, 1/8 between; A - 6 cols, 2, 1/8 between; C - 9 cols, 1 2/5, 1/12 between.
Commodity Consumption: Avg. Page Number Per Issue - Daily 40; Avg. Page Number Per Issue - Plates Used 18000; Avg. Page Number Per Issue - Saturday 36; Avg. Page Number Per Issue - Sunday 100; widths 50; Newsprint Used - Metric Tons 3653; Printing Ink Used - Pages Printed 1766
Equipment EDITORIAL: Front-end Software – ATS.; Editorial Hardware – 40-Pentium/PC 133, 6-Micron/P400; Editorial Printers – HP/4000, HP/5si, HP/IV CLASSIFIED: Front-end Software – ATS.; Classified Hardware – 18-Novell/P233 4.1; Classified Printers – HP/IV DISPLAY: Ad make-up applications – DPS/Ad-Tracker, QPS/QuarkXPress 4.0; Layout Software – Informatel/Pagination.; Display Hardware – 30-Novell/P200 Server 4.1; Display Printers – HP/IV, HP/850; Production Equipment – 2-P/33-43, Caere/OmniPage Pro, 1-Kk/660; Cameras – Scanners ◻ AG/Arcus II, Mircotek; Scanners – Equipment ◻ ATS/Newsdesk. PRESSROOM: Line 1 – 6-MAN/Uniman 4 x 2 1984; Line 2 – 26-DGM/430; Folders – 2-DGM/1030; Pasters – 5-MEG, Jardis/zero speed FS 5036-11; Reels and Stands – JARIS/JI-150. MAILROOM: Counter stackers – MM/228, 2-QWI/300B; Inserters and stuffers – 1-GMA/SLS 1000 10:1; Bundle tying machines – 2/Power Strap/PSN6E; Addressing machine – 2-Ch/525E. AUDIO: Audio Software – Infoconnect; Audio Hardware – Computer Group/Ads-on-call BUSINESS COMPUTERS: Business Software – Brainworks, Solomon, Ultipro; Business Hardware – 1-Micron/Server P266, Compaq/Server Pro P90, 5-Micron/Server P450, 10-Compaq/P233 Clients

KEENE

KEENE PUBLISHING CORP.

60 West St., Keene, N.H., 03431; gen tel (603) 352-1234; gen fax (603) 352-0437; adv fax (603) 352-9733; web site sentinel-source.com
Published: Mon, Tues, Wed, Thur, Fri, Sat, Sun
Weekday Frequency: All day
Saturday Frequency: m
Circulation: 9,884; 9,884(sat); 10,473(sun)
Politics: 1799
Not Published: 6
Own facility?: Y
Delivery method: Mail, Newsstand, Private Carrier, Racks

THE KEENE SENTINEL

60 West St., Keene, N.H., 03431; gen tel (603) 352-1234; gen fax (603) 352-0437; adv fax (603) 352-9733; ed fax (603) 352-9700; gen e-mail news@keenesentinel.com; web site www.sentinelsource.com
Published: Mon, Tues, Wed, Thur, Fri, Sat, Sun
Weekday Frequency: m
Saturday Frequency: e
Circulation: 9,840; 11,132(sat); 10,539(sun)
Last Audit: ABC September 30, 2011
Price: $183.70 (55)wks
Advertising: Open inch rate $21.00
News services: AP, CNS, LAT-WP, TMS.
Politics: Independent. **Established:** 1799
Not Published: New Year; Memorial Day; Independence Day; Labor Day; Thanksgiving; Christmas.
Own facility?: Y
Special Editions: Home & Garden (Apr); Keene State College (Aug); Last Minute Gift Ideas (Dec); President's Birthday Auto Edition (Feb); Economic Outlook (Jan); Mid-Summer (Jul); Monadnock Summer (Jun); Answerbook (Mar); Pets (May); Vows (June); Monadnock Autumn (Oct.); Holiday Ideas (Nov); @RecordBody:**Special Weekly Sections:** Religion (Sat); Entertainment (Thur).
Magazines: Parade Magazine (S).
Pres. ....James A. Rousmaniere
Pub. ....Thomas M. Ewing
Bus. Mgr. ....Linda Flagg
Adv. Mgr., Classified ....Lorraine Ellis
Circ. Asst. Mgr. ....Paula McMahan
Ed. ....James A. Rousmaniere
Mng. Ed. ....Paul A. Miller
Sports Ed. ....David Lanier
Features Ed. ....Donna Moxley
Local News Ed. ....Cecily Weisburgh
Audiotex Mgr. ....Colin R. Lyle
Mgmt. Info Systems Mgr. ....Chris Carreira
Prodn. Foreman, Pressroom ....Gregory Walker
Prodn. Mgr., Mailroom ....Robert Symonds
Interactive Media ....Ellen Driscoll
Graphics ....Robert Farnsworth
Adv. Mgr., Co-op/Promo. Coord. ....Harry Ahern
Circ. Mgr. ....David McMahan
Dir., Prodn. Opns. ....Joseph D. Antosiewicz
Market Information: TMC; Zoned editions.
Mechanical available: Offset; Black and 3 ROP colors; insert accepted; page cutoffs - 21 1/2.
Mechanical Specifications: Type page 11 3/5 x 21 1/2; E - 6 cols, 1 4/5, 1/8 between; A - 6 cols, 1 4/5, 1/8 between; C - 9 cols, 1 1/5, 1/8 between.
Commodity Consumption: Avg. Page Number Per Issue - Daily 30; Avg. Page Number Per Issue - Plates Used 7000; Avg. Page Number Per Issue - Saturday 40; Avg. Page Number Per Issue - Sunday 57; widths 25; Newsprint Used - Short Tons 957; Printing Ink Used - Black 20000; Printing
Equipment EDITORIAL: Front-end Software – Tera.; Editorial Printers – 1-ECR/Imagesetter CLASSIFIED: Front-end Software – Novell/Network.; Classified Hardware – APP/Mac G3 Server DISPLAY: Ad make-up applications – QPS/QuarkXPress; Layout Software – SCS/Layout 8000.; Display Hardware – 4-APP/Mac; Display Printers – HP/8100N PRODUCTION: Pagination Software – QPS/QuarkXPress.; Production Equipment – Caere/OmniPage, ECR/VRL 36, Konica/9200; Cameras – R/24-580; Scanners – 1-Microtek PRESSROOM: Line 1 – 8-G/Community 1986; Folders – 1 MAILROOM: Counter stackers – HL/Monitor; Inserters and stuffers – HI/848; Bundle tying machines – Dynaric. BUSINESS COMPUTERS: Business Software – PBS/SBS/Brainworks; Business Hardware – IBM, IBM/RS6000
Delivery method: Mail, Newsstand, Private Carrier, Racks

LACONIA

CITIZEN

171 Fair St., Laconia, N.H., 03246; gen tel (603) 524-3800; adv tel (603) 524-3800; ed tel (603) 524-3800; adv fax (603) 524-6702; ed fax (603) 527-3593; gen e-mail news@citizen.com; web site www.citizen.com
Group: Eagle Printing & Publishing. LLC
Published: Mon, Tues, Wed, Thur, Fri, Sat
Weekday Frequency: m
Saturday Frequency: m
Circulation: 6,288; 7,325(sat)
Last Audit: Sworn September 30, 2009
Price: 172.90/yr.
Advertising: Open inch rate $34.88
Insert rate: $50/m
News services: AP.
Politics: Independent.
Advertising not accepted: Y
Own facility?: Y
Special Weekly Sections: BFD (Sat); Weekender (Thur); Money/Business Page (Tues); BFD (Wed).
Publisher ....Harry Hartman
Adv. Dir. ....Mike Masessa
Circ. Mgr. ....Jeff Defrancesco
Mng. Ed. ....Tom Caldwell
Editorial Page Ed. ....Michael Mortensen
Features Ed. ....Krista Marrs
Sports Ed. ....Joe Souza
Market Information: ADS; TMC.
Mechanical available: Offset; Black; insert accepted; page cutoffs - 23.
Mechanical Specifications: Type page 13 x 21 1/2; E - 6 cols, 2 1/14, 1/8 between; A - 6 cols, 2 1/14, 1/8 between; C - 9 cols, 1 1/3, 1/8 between.
Commodity Consumption: Avg. Page Number Per Issue - Daily 30.
Equipment EDITORIAL: Front-end Software – Mk.; Editorial Hardware – MAC/Quark; Editorial Printers – TI CLASSIFIED: Front-end Software – Mk.; Classified Hardware – Mk; Classified Printers – TI DISPLAY: Ad make-up applications – In-Design; Display Hardware – APP/Mac; Display Printers – APP/Mac Laser; Cameras – 1-Nu. PRESSROOM: Line 1 – 16-STD/Pgs ; Line 2 – 16-STD/Pgs ; Inserters and stuffers – MM; Bundle tying machines – .; Business Hardware – CJ/Compuserve

MANCHESTER

UNION LEADER CORP.

100 William Loeb Dr., Manchester, N.H., 03109; gen tel (603) 668-4321; adv tel (603) 668-4321; ed tel (603) 668-4321; gen fax (603) 668-0040; adv fax (603) 624-0727; ed fax (603) 668-0382; gen e-mail publisher@unionleader.com; adv e-mail classified@unionleader.com; ed e-mail writeus@unionleader.com; web site unionleader.com
Published: Mon, Tues, Wed, Thur, Fri, Sat, Sun
Weekday Frequency: m
Saturday Frequency: m
Circulation: 52,119; 30,684(sat); 70,636(sun)
News services: Reuters, WPNS
Not Published: Christmas Day
Own facility?: Y
Broadcast Affiliations: N/A
Pres./Pub. ....Joseph W. McQuaid
Director, Newspaper Sales & Marketing John Whalen
Vice Pres., Finance ....Joyce M. Levesque
Vice President of New Media .Brendan McQuaid
Vice President of News ....Tami Plyler
Executive Vice President ....Dirk Ruemenapp
???? ????
???? ????
Zip Codes served: All New Hampshire
Delivery method: Mail, Newsstand, Private Carrier, Racks

UNION LEADER CORPORATION

100 William Loeb Dr., Manchester, N.H., 03109-5309; gen tel (603) 668-4321; adv tel (603) 668-4321; ed tel (603) 668-4321; gen fax (603) 668-0910; adv fax (603) 624-0727; ed fax (603) 668-0382; gen e-mail publisher@unionleader.com; adv e-mail rascoli@unionleader.com; ed e-mail writeus@unionleader.com; web site www.unionleader.com
Published: Sun
Circulation: 49,314; 29,910(sat); 66,873(sun)
Last Audit: September 30, 2009
Price: 4.00/wk; 10.32/mo; 189.28/yr.
Advertising: Open inch rate $51.15
News services: SHNS, REUTERS, LAT-WP.
Politics: Independent. **Established:** 1946
Not Published: Christmas.
Special Editions: Health & Fitness (Apr); Working Woman (Aug); Holiday Planner (Dec); Washington's Birthday Auto (Feb); Baby Review (Jan); NASCAR Winston Cup (Jul); NH Home Show (Mar); Summer Vacation (May); Home for Holidays (Nov); Dining & Lodging (Oct); Fall House & Hom
Special Weekly Sections: Religion (Fri); Monday's Business (Mon); Get Out! (S); Avenues (Sat); Veterans (Thur); Senior Page (Tues); Flavors (Wed).
Magazines: Parade (S).
Pres./Pub. ....Joseph W. McQuaid
Exec. Vice Pres. ....Dirk F. Ruemenapp
Vice Pres., Finance ....Joyce M. Levesque
Vice Pres., New Media ....Tami Plyler
Vice Pres., HR ....Sharon Ciechon
Adv. Vice Pres. ....Ralph C. Ascoli
Adv. Mgr., Classified ....Charlotte A. Ingalls
Adv. Servs. Mgr. ....Robin Wilson
Adv. Mgr., Retail ....David M. Rousseau
Community Relations Mgr. ....Teresa Robinson
Circ. Dir., Opns. ....Lucien G. Trahan
Circ. Dir., Newspaper Sales/Mktg. John M. Whalen
Vice Pres., News ....Edward C. Domaingue
Mng. Ed., Opns. ....Pat Sheeran
Deputy Mng. Ed., Bus. ....Bill Regan
Deputy Mng. Ed., Sunday ....Vin Sylvia
Editorial Page Dir. ....Andrew Cline
City Ed. ....John Toole
Sunday City Ed. ....James Adams
Columnist ....John DiStaso
Market Information: TMC; Zoned editions.
Mechanical available: Flexographic; Black and 3 ROP colors; insert accepted - samples, post-its; page cutoffs - 22.
Mechanical Specifications: Type page 11 1/2 x 21 1/4; E - 6 cols, 1 5/6, 1/8 between; A - 6 cols, 1 5/6, 1/8 between; C - 9 cols, 1 3/16, 1/8 between.
Commodity Consumption: Avg. Page Number Per Issue - Daily 54; Avg. Page Number Per Issue - Plates Used 71973; Avg. Page Number Per Issue - Saturday 42; Avg. Page Number Per Issue - Sunday 133; widths 25; Newsprint Used - Metric Tons 7812; Printing Ink Used - Black 245000; Prin
Equipment EDITORIAL: Front-end Software – Saxotech; Editorial Hardware – 52-HP desktop CLASSIFIED: Front-end Software – HI/Ad Power, MS/Windows.; Classified Hardware – Dell/PowerEdge 4600, 20-Dell/Optiplex GX605 DISPLAY: Ad make-up applications – GEAC, SCS/Layout 8000; Layout Software – 6-HI/Dash.; Display Hardware – Dell/PG 266-GXA; Production Equipment – 2-CTP PunchGraphix UV-Setter 546, 2-AU/Alpha RIP, 2-HI/XP-21, 8-HI/2100 Pagination Work Station, 2-CTF Server Platform, Konica/K-550 PRESSROOM: Line 1 – 9-MOT/FX4 1990; Folders – 2; Pasters – 9; Reels and Stands – 9; Press control system – 1, 1. MAILROOM: Counter stackers – 2-Id/EDS 660, 1-Id/EDS 440, 1-QWI/SJ100A, 3-HL/Monitor HT; Inserters and stuffers – HI/2299; Bundle tying machines – 3-OVL/JP-80, 2-EAM-Mosca, 3-OVL/JP-40, 3-Dynaric/NP2. BUSINESS COMPUTERS: Business Software – GEAC
Delivery method: Mail, Newsstand, Private Carrier, Racks

NASHUA

TELEGRAPH PUBLISHING CO.

PO Box 1008, Nashua, N.H., 3061; gen tel (603) 882-2741; gen fax (603) 882-5138
Published: Mon, Tues, Wed, Thur, Fri, Sat, Sun
Weekday Frequency: m
Saturday Frequency: m
Circulation: 17,386; 22,796(sun)
Last Audit: ABC September 30, 2011

NORTH CONWAY

THE CONWAY DAILY SUN

64 Seavey St., North Conway, N.H., 3860; gen tel (603) 356-3456; adv tel (603) 356-2999; gen fax (603) 356-8774; ed fax (603) 356-8360; gen e-mail dailysun@conwaydailysun.com; web site www.conwaydailysun.com; www.mount-washingtonvalley.com

Published: Mon, Tues, Wed, Thur, Fri, Sat
Weekday Frequency: m
Circulation: 16,100; 16,100(sat)
Last Audit: November 18, 2003
Advertising: Open inch rate $7.00
News services: AP, RN.
Politics: Independent.
Advertising not accepted: Tobacco.
Not Published: New Year; Labor Day; Thanksgiving; Christmas.
Special Editions: Sports Preview (Apr); Dining Guide (Dec); Economic Review (Feb); Dining Guide (Jul); Sports Preview (May).
Special Weekly Sections: Education (Mon); Real Estate (Sat); Sports (Tues); Business (Wed).
Magazines: Cool News (Fri).
Pres. ....David N. Danforth
Office Mgr. ....Joyce Brothers
Display Adv. Sales Mgr. ....Rick Luksza
Circ. Mgr. ....Mark Guerringue
Ed ....Adam Hirshan
Mng. Ed. ....Bart Bachman
Photography Ed. ....Jamie Gemmiti
Sports Ed. ....Lloyd Jones
Wire/Entertainment Ed. ....Alec Kerr
Prodn. Mgr. ....Frank Haddy
Mechanical available: Offset Web; Black and 1 ROP colors; insert accepted; page cutoffs - 15.
Mechanical Specifications: Type page 10 1/4 x 13 1/2; E - 4 cols, 2 3/4, 1/3 between; A - 6 cols, 1 3/5, 1/6 between; C - 6 cols, 1 3/5, 1/6 between.
Commodity Consumption: Avg. Page Number Per Issue - Daily 32; Avg. Page Number Per Issue - Plates Used 5000; Avg. Page Number Per Issue - Saturday 40; widths 29; Newsprint Used - Metric Tons 500; Printing Ink Used - Pages Printed 7488.
Equipment; Editorial Hardware – 10-APP/Mac; Editorial Equipment – APP/Mac Scanner; Editorial Printers – 2-APP/Mac LaserWriter, 2-HP. CLASSIFIED: Front-end Software – Baseview.; Classified Hardware – 2-APP/Mac Quadra; Layout Software – Aldus/PageMaker, QPS, Adobe/Photoshop, Aldus/FreeHand.; Production Equipment – Kk/42A. PRESSROOM: Line 1 – 5-G/Community Single-width.; Business Hardware – APP/Mac Plus

PORTSMOUTH

PORTSMOUTH HERALD

111 New Hampshire Ave., Portsmouth, N.H., 03801; gen tel (603) 436-1800; adv tel (603) 436-1800; gen fax (603) 427-0550; adv fax (603) 427-0550; ed fax (603) 433-5760; adv e-mail scnadvertising@seacoastonline.com; ed e-mail shaberman@seacoastonline.com; web site www.seacoastonline.com

Published: Mon, Tues, Wed, Thur, Fri, Sat
Weekday Frequency: m
Saturday Frequency: m
Circulation: 9,900; 9,850(sat); 14,941(sun)
Last Audit: ABC September 30, 2011
Price: 3.50/wk; 172.04/yr.
Advertising: Open inch rate $34.00
News services: AP.
Not Published: New Year; Christmas.
Special Editions: Spring Lawn/Garden (Apr); Healthy Living (Aug); Last Minute Gift (Dec); Pres. Auto (Feb); Bridal (Jan); Summer Ports of Call (Jun); St. Pat's Auto (Mar); Mother's Day (May); N.E. Holidays (Nov); Harvest (Oct); Menu Guide (Sept).
Special Weekly Sections: Spotlight Weekly Magazine (Thur); Best Food Day (Wed).
Magazines: R.E. Guide (Monthly); Commercial Real Estate Guide (Quarterly); TV Times (S); Value Zone (Sat); Spotlight Magazine (Thur).
Pub. ....John Tabor
Adv. Dir. ....Linda Holway
Adv. Mgr., Classified/Sales ....Sandra Titus
Circ. Dir. ....Kelvin Parker
Circ. Mgr., Home Delivery ....Dennis Thompson
Circ. Mgr., Retail Sales ....Kevin Marsland
Exec. Ed. ....Howard Altschiller
Editorial Page Ed. ....Shir Haberman
Prodn. Ed. ....Glenn Sabalewski
Sports Ed. ....Ed Flaherty
Sunday Ed. ....Rick Fabrizio
Online Mgr. ....Jeff Raper
Systems Mgr. ....Alana Sullivan
Market Information: ADS; TMC.
Mechanical available: Offset; Black and 3 ROP colors; insert accepted; page cutoffs - 22 3/4.
Mechanical Specifications: Type page 13 x 21 1/2; E - 6 cols, 2 1/16, 1/8 between; A - 6 cols, 2 1/16, 1/8 between; C - 9 cols, 1 3/8, 1/16 between.
Commodity Consumption: Avg. Page Number Per Issue - Daily 36; Avg. Page Number Per Issue - Plates Used 12800; Avg. Page Number Per Issue - Sunday 40; widths 27; Newsprint Used - Metric Tons 909; Newsprint Used - Short Tons 1000; Printing Ink Used - Black 30000; Printing Ink Us
Equipment EDITORIAL: Front-end Software – Dewar/View, QPS/QuarkXPress.; Editorial Hardware – PC; Editorial Printers – Konica/JetSetter CLASSIFIED: Front-end Software – AT/Enterprise, QPS/QuarkXPress.; Classified Hardware – PC; Layout Software – PC.; Display Hardware – QuarkXPress; Display Printers – Konica/JetSetter PRODUCTION: Pagination Software – Classified Pagination 5.4.2.; Production Equipment – 1-Graham; Cameras – SCREEN PRESSROOM: Line 1 – 14-G/Community; Folders – Dauphin/1040, G/55C. MAILROOM: Counter stackers – Remor; Inserters and stuffers – Valley Remanufacturing; Bundle tying machines – 1-OVL/Constellation, 1/CYP. BUSINESS COMPUTERS: Business Software – Microsoft/Excel, Microsoft/Word; Business Hardware – 1-IBM-AS/4

NEW JERSEY

BRIDGETON

BRIDGETON NEWS

100 Commerce St E, Bridgeton, N.J., 08302-2600; gen tel (856) 451-1000; web site www.nj.com

THE NEWS OF CUMBERLAND COUNTY

100 E. Commerce St., Bridgeton, N.J., 08302; gen tel (856) 451-1000; ed tel (856) 451-1003; gen fax (856) 455-0398; adv fax (856) 455-2633; gen e-mail mgray@sjnewsco.com; web site www.nj.com/bridgeton

Published: Mon, Tues, Wed, Thur, Fri, Sat
Weekday Frequency: m
Saturday Frequency: m
Circulation: 5,583; 6,242(sat)
Last Audit: ABC September 30, 2011
Price: 2.30/wk; 119.60/yr; 9.20/4wk, $29.90/13wk, $59.80/6mo.
Advertising: Open inch rate $26.00
News services: AP, NNS.
Politics: Independent. **Established:** 1856
Not Published: Christmas.
Special Editions: Bridal (Apr); Bridal (Aug); Christmas Gift Guides (Dec); Business Review (Jan); Bridal (Jul); Bridal (Jun); Bridal (Mar); Bridal (May); Christmas Gift Guides (Oct); Sportsmen's Jamboree (Sept).
Special Weekly Sections: Real Estate (Fri); Real Estate (Mon); Business (Thur); Food (Wed).
Controller ....Charles MacDonald
Pub. ....Frank Gargano
Adv. Dir. ....James F. DeFillipo
Adv. Mgr., Classified ....Marie Vito
Circ. Dir. ....John Petracci
Librarian ....Sandra Johnson
Music Ed. ....Matt Gray
Night Ed. ....Jack Hummel
Sports Ed. ....Eric Goldstein
Mgmt. Info Servs. Mgr. ..Charles H. MacDonald
Prodn. Mgr., Post Press ....Michael D'Arienzo
Market Information: Zoned editions.
Mechanical available: Offset; Black and 3 ROP colors; insert accepted; page cutoffs - 22 3/4.
Mechanical Specifications: Type page 12 x 21 1/2; E - 6 cols, 1 7/8, 1/8 between; A - 6 cols, 1 7/8, 1/8 between; C - 9 cols, 1 3/16, 1/8 between.
Commodity Consumption: Avg. Page Number Per Issue - Daily 22; Avg. Page Number Per Issue - Plates Used 10000; Avg. Page Number Per Issue - Saturday 16; widths 12 1/2; Newsprint Used - Metric Tons 1810; Printing Ink Used - Black 96300; Printing Ink Used - Color 4500; Printing I
Equipment EDITORIAL: Front-end Software – Baseview/News Edit Pro.; Editorial Hardware – APP/Mac CLASSIFIED: Front-end Software – PPI.; Classified Hardware – 1-PC DISPLAY: Ad make-up applications – CJ; Layout Software – MEI/ALS 2.5.; Display Hardware – HP; Display Printers – HP PRODUCTION: Pagination Software – MEI/CLS 2.7.; Production Equipment – 2-ECR/MAKO Harlequin RIP (VRLHS 36); Cameras – 1-C/Spartan III PRESSROOM: Line 1 – 8-G/Urbanite; Folders – 1 MAILROOM: Counter stackers – 1-BG/105; Inserters and stuffers – 1-HI/1063; Bundle tying machines – 1-Sa/S1100, 2/MLN; Addressing machine – 1-KR w/Q folder.; Business Hardware – HP

CHERRY HILL

COURIER-POST

301 Cuthbert Blvd., Cherry Hill, N.J., 08002-2905; gen tel (856) 663-6000; adv tel (856) 663-7100; ed tel (856) 486-2402; gen fax (856) 663-3190; adv fax (856) 665-5788; ed fax (856) 663-2831; gen e-mail info@courierpostonline.com; web site www.courierpostonline.com

Published: Mon, Tues, Wed, Thur, Fri, Sat, Sun
Weekday Frequency: m
Saturday Frequency: m
Circulation: 50,884; 56,386(sat); 67,743(sun)
Last Audit: ABC September 30, 2011
Price: 3.50/wk; 13.00/mo; 182.00/yr.
Advertising: Open inch rate $192.00
News services: AP, GNS.
Politics: Independent. **Established:** 1875
Special Editions: Pic-a-Home Real Estate Magazine (); Cookbook (Apr); Labor Day Recipe Pages (Aug); End of Month Values (Dec); South Jersey Unlimited (Feb); Luxury Living (Jan); End of Month Values (Jul); Luxury Living (Jun); Luxury Living (Mar); UMD (May); End of Month Va
Special Weekly Sections: Real Estate (Fri); Senior Scoop (Mon); South Jersey Living (S); South Jersey Scene (Sat); Education Express (Tues); Food (Wed).
Magazines: USA WEEKEND Magazine (S).
Pub. ....Walt Lafferty
Dir., HR ....Lori Transmondi
Controller ....Jean Wysocki
Mgr., Retail Adv. ....Joan Mason
Mgr., Classified Adv. ....Loretta Schleifer
Mgr., Nat'l Adv. ....Sophie Falkenstein
Circ. Dir. ....James Gregory
Asst. Mng. Ed., Content ....Joyce Gabriel
Fashion Ed ....Lauretta Stuart
Food Ed. ....Pam Lyons
Living/Lifestyle Ed ....Lisa Atkins
Metro Ed. ....Donna Pipes Jenkins
News Ed. ....Bob Rogers
Photo Ed. ....Ron Karafin
Sports Ed. ....Phil Anastasia
Theater/Music Ed. ....Robert Baxter
Dir., Info Servs. ....Craig Connolly
Dir., Online ....Kim Turberville
Prodn. Opns. Mgr. ....Gary Herman
Market Information: ADS; Split run; TMC; Zoned editions.
Mechanical available: Offset; Black and 3 ROP colors; insert accepted - quarter fold; page cutoffs - 22.
Mechanical Specifications: Type page 12 1/2 x 21 7/16; E - 6 cols, 1 7/8, 1/8 between; A - 6 cols, 1 7/8, 1/8 between; C - 10 cols, 1 3/32, 1/16 between.
Commodity Consumption: Avg. Page Number Per Issue - Daily 62; Avg. Page Number Per Issue - Plates Used 100000; Avg. Page Number Per Issue - Sunday 100; widths 50; Newsprint Used - Short Tons 12295; Printing Ink Used - Black 217600; Printing Ink Used - Color 150233.
Equipment EDITORIAL: Front-end Software – SII/Sys 55, Coyote Layout.; Editorial Hardware – SII/Sys 55; Editorial Equipment – 1-Lf/AP Leaf Picture Desk, 10-APP/Mac; Editorial Printers – HP, Ibon CLASSIFIED: Front-end Software – Ad Base 2.20.; Classified Hardware – Mactive; Classified Printers – HP DISPLAY: Ad make-up applications – DPS; Layout Software – Mactive.; Display Hardware – Mac; Display Printers – HP PRODUCTION: Pagination Software – SII/Coyote Layout.; Production Equipment – 2-KNF, GMTI/Digicol, 2-AU/APS 108C, AU/APS 5000, 1-AU/3850, 2-AU/3850; Scanners – 1-Tesca, 1-Eshofot PRESSROOM: Line 1 – 24-G/Headliner (12 half decks); Folders – 2-G/160-page double delivery; Reels and Stands – G/20 Reels. MAILROOM: Counter stackers – 4/Quipp 401, 1-/Quipp 501; Inserters and stuffers – 2-/AM Graphics, HP/630; Bundle tying machines – 1-/MLN, 3-/Power Strap/Model 5; Mailroom control system – Id; Addressing machine – 2-Barstrom/on-line; Other equipment –5-/Samuel Bott BUSINESS COMPUTERS: Business Software – Lawson, Gensys, Brio IC Verify, Microsoft/Word, Microsoft/Excel, Cyborg, Edywyse, Digicol, Ad Tracker; Business Hardware – 1-IBM/AS-400, 10-Windows NT, 4-Linux, 1-Tandem

GANNETT SATELLITE INFORMATION NETWORK, INC.

301 Cuthbert Blvd., Cherry Hill, N.J., 08002; gen tel (856) 486-2600; gen fax (856) 662-3850; gen e-mail cuserve@courrierpostline.com; adv e-mail classified@courrierpostline.com; web site www.courierpostline.com

Politics: 1875

EAST BRUNSWICK

HOME NEWS TRIBUNE

35 Kennedy Blvd., East Brunswick, N.J., 08816; gen tel (732) 246-5500; ed tel (732) 246-5500; gen fax (732) 565-7223; adv fax (732) 565-7207; ed fax (732) 565-7208; gen e-mail hntmetro@mycentraljersey.com; ed e-mail hntletters@mycentraljersey.com; web site www.mycentraljersey.com

Published: Mon, Tues, Wed, Thur, Fri, Sat, Sun
Weekday Frequency: m
Saturday Frequency: m
Circulation: 31,252; 38,013(sat); 39,372(sun)
Last Audit: ABC September 30, 2011
Price: 3.00/wk.
News services: AP, GNS, Bloomberg.
Politics: 1879
Note: Advertising is sold in combination with The Neptune-Asbury Park Press (mS) for $225.86(d) and $333.79(S). Individual newspaper rates not made available.
Special Editions: Real Estate Showcase (Apr); Bridal (Aug); I Do (Dec); Weddings (Feb); The Guide To Central Jersey (Jun); Spring Home & Garden (Mar); Coupon Book (Monthly); Holiday Gift Guide (Nov); Real Estate Showcase (Oct); Education (Other); This New House (Sept).
Special Weekly Sections: Real Estate (Fri); Sports Monday (Mon); Real Estate (S); Playback (Sat); Primetime (Thur); Home & Garden (Tues); On the Run (Wed).
Magazines: TV Week (S).
Pres./Pub. ....William C. Hidlay
Controller ....Kathy Rasp
Vice Pres., HR ....Michael J. Lorenca

Vice Pres., Adv. ....Sam Siciliano
Vice Pres., Mktg. ....Joseph Cavone
Exec. Ed. ....Charles Paolino
Community Ed. ....Michele J. Kuhn
Editorial Page Ed. ....Philip Hartman
Metro Ed. ....Lois Tommasso
News Ed. ....Todd Bell
Asst. Local Night Ed. ....Nicholas DiGiovanni
Online Ed. ....William Zapcic
Photo Ed. ....Keith Muccilli
Special Sections Ed. ....Anne Bendheim
Sports Ed. ....Jack Genung
Teen Scene Ed. ....Bill Canacci
Vice Pres., Info Servs.........Wayne L. Peragallo
Mgr., Prodn. Systems ....Jim Dundas
Mgr., AS/400 Opns. ....Frank Lewis
Market Information: Split run; TMC; Zoned editions.
Mechanical available: Offset; Black and 3 ROP colors; insert accepted - Post-it note application on A1; page cutoffs - 22 1/25.
Mechanical Specifications: Type page 11 5/8 x 21; E - 6 cols, 1 5/6, 1/8 between; A - 6 cols, 1 5/6, 1/8 between; C - 10 cols, 1 1/10, 5/72 between.
Commodity Consumption: Avg. Page Number Per Issue - Daily 56; Avg. Page Number Per Issue - Plates Used 89811; Avg. Page Number Per Issue - Saturday 50; Avg. Page Number Per Issue - Sunday 108; widths 50; Newsprint Used - Short Tons 9002; Printing Ink Used - Black 150028; Print
Equipment EDITORIAL: Front-end Software – SII.; Editorial Hardware – SII/S4566; Editorial Equipment – 9-HI/NMP, 3-HI/Photo Browser, 96-SII/Coyote 3, 10-APP/Mac Powerbook; Editorial Printers – HP/755C, 2-HP/5000N CLASSIFIED: Front-end Software – SII/Czar II.; Classified Hardware – SII/Sys 66; Classified Printers – Equipment Ã□Â□ SII/Coyote 3 DISPLAY: Ad make-up applications – Adobe/Illustrator 8.0, Multi-Ad/Creator 4.03, Adobe/Photoshop 5.0; Layout Software – SCS/Layout 8000, AU/Ad Manager.; Display Hardware – APP/Mac, AG/Scanner; Display Printers – QMS, HP/5000N; Production Equipment – X, 1-Nu/Flip Top, 3-WL/Lith-X-Pozer III, 1-PrePress/Panther Pro62 Double Truck Imager, 1-AU/SST 3850; Cameras – 1-C/Newspager I; Scanners – 1-Eskofot/2636S, 2-AG/Horizon, 3-AG/Arcus, 3-Kk/2035 Plus, 2-Nikon/Film Scanner, 1-Scitex/Smartscan PRESSROOM: Line 1 – 10-G/Metroliner offset double width 1996; Line 2 – 10-G/Metroliner offset double width 1996; Line 3 – 10-G/Metroliner offset double width 1997; Press Drives – Fin/Digital; Folders – 5-G/3:2; Pasters – 30; Reels and Stands – 30 MAILROOM: Counter stackers – 1-MM/CS310, 11-QWI/SJ530, 2-Boss/Stacker, 2-QWI/SJ100; Inserters and stuffers – 1-S/2299, 4-S/NP630, 1/Philipsburg/4 Station Inserter; Bundle tying machines – 1-Dynaric/SSB79, 6-/Power Strap/PSN-5, 1-/Power Strap/PSN-250, 7-/Power Stra BUSINESS COMPUTERS: Business Software – GN/Genesys, Lawson, Cyborg; Business Hardware – 2-IBM/AS-400

JERSEY CITY

THE JERSEY JOURNAL

30 Journal Sq., Jersey City, N.J., 07306; gen tel (201) 653-1000; adv tel (201) 217-2430; ed tel (201) 653-1000; gen fax (201) 653-1414; adv fax (201) 217-2455; ed fax (201) 653-1414; web site www.thejerseyjournal.com
Published: Mon, Tues, Wed, Thur, Fri, Sat
Weekday Frequency: m
Saturday Frequency: m
Circulation: 19,030; 21,813(sat)
Last Audit: ABC September 30, 2011
Price: 2.25/wk; 120.00/yr; 8.00/4wk.
Advertising: Open inch rate $50.40
News services: AP, MCT, NNS.
Politics: Independent.
Not Published: New Year; Memorial Day; Independence Day; Labor Day; Thanksgiving; Christmas.
Special Editions: Home Sweet Homes Tab (Apr); Women in Business (Aug); Letters to Santa (Dec); President's Pages I & II (Feb); School Guide Pages (Jan); Kids Tab (Jun); Women in Business (Mar); Mother's Day Tab (May); Thanksgiving Day Dine-Out I & II (Nov); Home Improvemen
Special Weekly Sections: Friday Entertainment Guide (Fri); Senior (Thur); Health (Wed).
Magazines: Parade (Sat).
Pub. ....Kendrick Ross
Gen. Mgr. ...............................S.I. Newhouse
Acct. Dept. Mgr. ....John O'Shaughnessy
Adv. Mgr., Retail.........................Tom Pritchard
Ed. in Chief ....Steven Newhouse
Ed. ....Judith Locorriere
Mng. Ed..............................Margaret Schmidt
News Ed...................................Agustin Torres
Sports Ed...............................Ron Zeitlinger
Mgmt. Info Servs. Mgr. ....Andy Savva
Prodn. Dir............................Denise Copeland
Prodn. Mgr., Pre Press..............Gwen Ramsey
Market Information: ADS; Split run; TMC; Zoned editions.
Mechanical available: Offset; Black and 3 ROP colors; insert accepted - sample pouches; page cutoffs - 20 1/2.
Mechanical Specifications: Type page 13 1/4 x 21; E - 6 cols, 2 1/16, 1/8 between; A - 6 cols, 2 1/16, 1/8 between; C - 10 cols, 1 1/4, 1/2 between.
Commodity Consumption: widths 27 1/2; Printing Ink Used - Pages Printed 74000.
Equipment; Editorial Hardware – 45-HI/NewsMaker; Editorial Equipment – HI/XP-21, 15-HI/2100; Editorial Printers – Software □ HI/Newsmaker 3.4. CLASSIFIED: Front-end Software – HI/CASH.; Classified Hardware – 2-UNIX/PC Servers; Classified Printers – Equipment □ 20-PC DISPLAY: Ad make-up applications – HI/NewsMaker 3.4; Layout Software – 5-APP/Mac.; Display Hardware – 2-PC P100; Display Printers – Software □ HI/NewsMaker 3.4 PRODUCTION: Pagination Software – HI/XP-21 3.5.; Production Equipment – 1-AU/3850, 3-AU/APS Soft Pip, 5-HI/Mac Browser, Adobe/Photoshop; Scanners – 3-Umax/Flatbed, 3-Kk/NegScanner MAILROOM: Counter stackers – 1/St; Bundle tying machines – 1-/MLN.; Business Hardware – Icamon/Newzware, 2-Dell/Poweredge

NEPTUNE

ASBURY PARK PRESS

3601 Highway 66, NEPTUNE, N.J., 07754; gen tel 800-822-9770; web site www.app.com
Published: Mon, Tues, Wed, Thur, Fri, Sat, Sun
Weekday Frequency: m
Saturday Frequency: m
Circulation: 104,582; 109,818(sat); 157,723(sun)
Last Audit: ABC September 30, 2011

NEWARK

NEWARK MORNING LEDGER CO.

One Star Ledger Plz., Newark, N.J., 07102-1200; gen tel (973) 392-4141; gen fax (973) 565-0422

THE STAR-LEDGER

55 Court Street, Newark, N.J., 07102-1200; gen tel (973) 392-4141; adv tel (973) 392-5864; ed tel (973) 392-4040; gen fax (973) 643-4641; adv fax (973) 642-6764; ed fax (973) 392-5845; ed e-mail tcurran@starledger.com; web site www.nj.com/starledger
Group: Advance Publications
Published: Mon, Tues, Wed, Thur, Fri, Sat, Sun
Weekday Frequency: m
Saturday Frequency: m
Circulation: 210,586; 181,114(sat); 333,601(sun)
Last Audit: ABC September 30, 2011
Price: 5.25/wk; 15.40/mo; 200.20/yr.

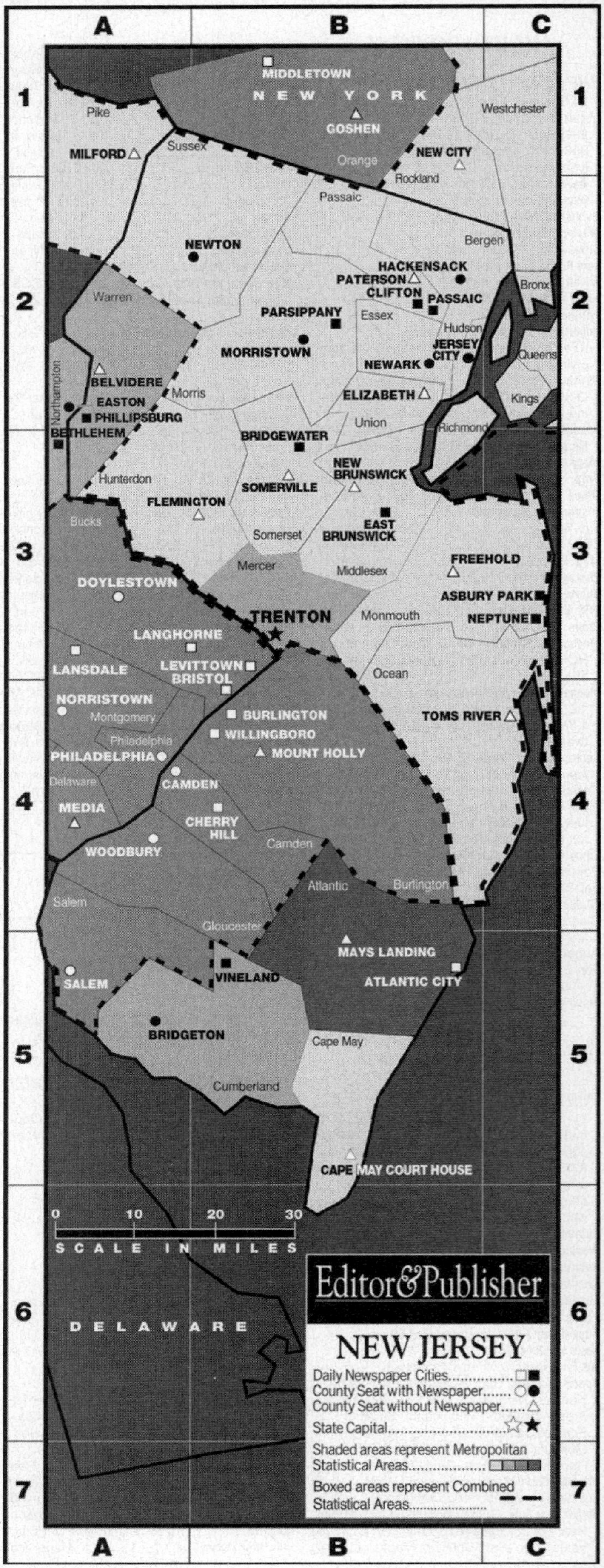

Advertising: Open inch rate $554.32(m-thur)
News services: Metro Suburbia Inc./Newhouse Newspapers, NNS, LAT-WP, DJ, RN, PR Newswire, MCT.
Note: Combination rate for the Star-Ledger/Times of Trenton are valid for select categories of advertising.
Advertising not accepted: N
Own facility?: Y
Special Weekly Sections: Real Estate Marketplace (Fri); Education (S); Home & Garden (Thur); Body Shop (Tues); Savor (Wed).
Magazines: Parade (S).
Inside Jersey (mthly)
Profile: The Star-Ledger is New Jersey's most popular and most honored news source. In 2011, its award winning multimedia newsroom earned a Pulitzer and four NY Emmy awards along with over thirty additional first place awards for writing, photography and videography. The Star-ledger and NJ.com print and digital audiences are unmatched in New Jersey, reaching millions of adults. And now, with the Advance NJ media network, we offer businesses print and digital solutions scalable to any budget, targeted to any audience in the Garden State.
Pub. ....Richard Vezza
Gen. Mgr. ....John F. Dennan
Adv. Dir., Display ....Jay Petrie
Adv. Mgr., Nat'l ....Brian Pfeifer
Director of Marketing. ....Robert C. Provost
Circ. Dir. ....Dennis Carletta
Editor ....Kevin Whitmer
Mng. Ed. ....Steve Liebman
Mng. Ed. ....David Tucker
Assoc. Ed. ....Tom Curran
Editorial Cartoonist ....Drew Sheneman
Editorial Page Ed ....Tom Moran
Deputy Editorial Page Ed ....Daniel Murphy
Advertising Director ....Louis Stancampiano
Market Information: Split run; TMC; Zoned editions.
Mechanical available: Offset; Black and 3 ROP colors; insert accepted - print and deliver program available; page cutoffs - 22.
Mechanical Specifications: Type page 11 5/8 x 21 1/4; E - 6 cols, 1 5/6, 1/8 between; A - 6 cols, 1 5/6, 1/8 between; C - 10 cols, 1 3/16, 1/8 between.
Commodity Consumption: Avg. Page Number Per Issue - Daily 107; Avg. Page Number Per Issue - Plates Used 800000; Avg. Page Number Per Issue - Sunday 193; widths 50; Newsprint Used - Short Tons 130000; Printing Ink Used - Black 2801000; Printing Ink Used - Color 637000; Printing
Equipment EDITORIAL: Front-end Software – HI/XP21, HI/Newsmaker, MON/Postscript RIPS.; Editorial Hardware – Sun/Sparc; Editorial Equipment – 10-HI/8900, 15-APP/Mac, 22-HI/2100; Editorial Printers – 3-MON/Print Express CLASSIFIED: Front-end Software – Mactive 2.20.; Classified Hardware – CSI; Classified Equipment – 2-HI/8900; Layout Software – SCS. PRODUCTION: Pagination Software – HI/XP-21 2.6.; Production Equipment – 1-AGFA/3850, 1-WL/Lith-X-Pozer 3; Scanners – Scitex, 2-AG/Eskofot PRESSROOM: Line 1 – Sep-79; Line 2 – Sep-79; Line 3 – Oct-90; Line 4 – Oct-90; Line 5 – Oct-90; Line 6 – Oct-90; Line 7 – Oct-90; Line 8 – Oct-90; Press Drives – 69; Folders – 11; Pasters – TKS/Automatic. MAILROOM: Counter stackers – 28/HL, 14-/HL; Inserters and stuffers – 2-LS/3000; Bundle tying machines – 22-/Dynaric, 6-/MLN.; Audio Hardware – New Horizons Team, PC BUSINESS COMPUTERS: Business Software – CJ, Microsoft/Office; Business Hardware – HP/Micro XE, HP/927, HP/947, HP/967, HP/969, HP/3000
Delivery method: Mail, Newsstand, Private Carrier, Racks

NEWTON

NEW JERSEY HERALD

2 Spring St., Newton, N.J., 07860; gen tel (973) 383-1500; adv tel (973) 383-1500; ed tel (973) 383-1500; gen fax (973) 383-9284; adv fax (973) 383-9284; ed fax (973) 383-8477; ed e-mail newsroom@njherald.com; web site www.njherald.com
Published: Mon, Tues, Wed, Thur, Fri, Sun
Weekday Frequency: All day
Circulation: 11,220; 17,430(sun)
Last Audit: ABC September 30, 2011
Price: 2.40/wk; 118.56/yr.
Advertising: Open inch rate $31.20
News services: AP, TMS.
Politics: Independent. **Established:** 1829
Not Published: New Year; Memorial Day; Independence Day; Labor Day; Christmas.
Special Editions: Home and Garden (Apr); Back-to-School (Aug); Christmas Gift Guides (Dec); Progress (Feb); White Sale (Jan); Newton Sidewalk Sale (Jul); New Jersey Cardinals (Jun); Expo (Mar); Home & Garden (May); Human Resources (Nov); New Car (Oct); Fall Home Improvemen
Special Weekly Sections: Entertainment (Fri); Business (Mon); Food (S); Best Food Day (Wed).
Magazines: TV Week (S); American Profile (Weekly).
Gen. Mgr. ....Don Cooper
Adv. Dir. ....Mitch Mayer
Promo./Special Projects Mgr. ....Lee Williams
Circ. Dir. ....Mike Lawson
Ed. ....Bruce Tomlinson
Mng. Ed. ....Robert Berczuk
Bus./Entertainment Ed. ....Bob Price
Lifestyle Ed. ....Kathy Stevens
Sports/Night Ed. ....Jim Dente
Pre Press Mgr. ....Jammie Kerr
Pressroom Foreman ....Kurt Smith
Post Press Foreman ....Joe Gilroy
Market Information: TMC.
Mechanical available: Offset; Black and 3 ROP colors; insert accepted; page cutoffs - 22 3/4.
Mechanical Specifications: Type page 13 x 21 1/2; E - 6 cols, 2 1/16, 1/8 between; A - 6 cols, 2 1/16, 1/8 between; C - 9 cols, 1 3/8, 1/16 between.
Commodity Consumption: Avg. Page Number Per Issue - Daily 24; Avg. Page Number Per Issue - Plates Used 14000; Avg. Page Number Per Issue - Saturday 68; widths 12 3/8; Newsprint Used - Metric Tons 1200; Printing Ink Used - Black 23000; Printing Ink Used - Color 7000; Printing Ink
Equipment EDITORIAL: Front-end Software – Baseview/NewsEdit Pro IQUE 3.2.3.; Editorial Hardware – 2-APP/Power Mac G4, 25-APP/Mac G3; Editorial Equipment – 16-AST/286; Editorial Printers – 1-QMS/2425 Ex CLASSIFIED: Front-end Software – Baseview/AdManager Pro 2.0.6.; Classified Hardware – 1-APP/Power Mac G4, 6-APP/iMac G3; Classified Equipment – 7-AST/286; Classified Printers – HP/4050 TN DISPLAY: Ad make-up applications – Baseview Production Manager Pro 1.6; Layout Software – Multi-Ad/Creator II.; Display Hardware – APP/Power Mac G4, 2-APP/Power Mac G3; Display Printers – 1-APP/Mac LaserWriter 16-600 PRODUCTION: Pagination Software – Baseview/NewsEdit Pro IQUE 3.2.3, QPS/QuarkXPress 4.1.; Production Equipment – Adobe/Photoshop, 2-Pre Press/Panther Catara 46 Imagesetter; Cameras – 1-C/Spartan III; Scanners – 2-AG.Duoscan T2000 XL PRESSROOM: Line 1 – 4-G/Urbanite 1973, 4-G/Urbanite 1985; Reels and Stands – 2-G/Stands; Press control system – 2 MAILROOM: Counter stackers – 1-BG/Count-O-Veyor, 1-BG/Count-O-Veyor; Inserters and stuffers – 1-HI/NP 848, 2-HL/Monitor Stacker; Bundle tying machines – 1/MLN, 1-MLN/Spirit; Mailroom control system – Prism; Addressing machine – Domino/Amjet In-line Labeling Syste; Audio Hardware – Tell Me Network BUSINESS COMPUTERS: Business Software – INSI; Business Hardware – IBM/Sys 36B25, IBM/AS400

PARSIPPANY

DAILY RECORD

6 Century Dr., Parsippany, N.J., 07054-0217; gen tel (973) 428-6200; adv tel (973) 428-6551; ed tel (973) 428-6610; gen fax (973) 428-6666; adv fax (973) 428-6529; ed fax (973) 428-6666; gen e-mail newsroom@dailyrecord.com; ed e-mail newsroom@dailyrecord.com; web site www.dailyrecord.com
Published: Mon, Tues, Wed, Thur, Fri, Sat, Sun
Weekday Frequency: m
Saturday Frequency: m
Circulation: 20,855; 24,785(sat); 24,881(sun)
Last Audit: ABC September 30, 2011
Price: 3.10/wk; 12.40/mo; 161.20/yr.
Advertising: Open inch rate $98.00
News services: AP, GNS, Bloomberg, CNS, TMS.
Politics: Independent. **Established:** 1900
Special Editions: Creative Homes (Apr); Family (Aug); Last Minute Gifts (Dec); Bridal (Feb); Coupon Clippers (Jan); Seniors (Jun); Fashion (Mar); Home Improvement (May); Going Shopping (Nov); Coupon Clippers (Oct); High School Football (Sept).
Special Weekly Sections: Real Estate (Fri); Technology (Mon); Real Estate (S); On The Row (Sat); Parisppany Plus (Thur); Business (Tues); Denville/Rockaway Plus (Wed).
Magazines: USA Weekend (S).
Pres./Pub. ....Joseph Cavone
Adv. Dir. ....Bill Ditty
Exec. Ed. ....James A. Flachsenhaar
Mng. Ed. ....Jack Bowie
Editorial Page Ed. ....Fred Snowflack
Features Ed. ....Jim Bohen
Metro Ed. ....Joe Ungaro
News Ed. ....Bill Demarest
Market Information: TMC; Zoned editions.
Mechanical available: Offset; Black and 3 ROP colors; insert accepted; page cutoffs - 22.
Mechanical Specifications: Type page 11 5/8 x 21; E - 6 cols, 1 5/6, 1/8 between; A - 6 cols, 1 5/6, 1/8 between; C - 10 cols, between.
Commodity Consumption: Avg. Page Number Per Issue - Daily 40; Avg. Page Number Per Issue - Plates Used 71890; Avg. Page Number Per Issue - Saturday 36; Avg. Page Number Per Issue - Sunday 104; widths 25; Newsprint Used - Short Tons 5220; Printing Ink Used - Black 98829; Printi
Equipment EDITORIAL: Front-end Software – CNI/Agile.; Editorial Hardware – PCs, APP/Macs; Editorial Equipment – APP/Mac Workstation; Editorial Printers – 2-Postscript/Page-proofer, 3-LaserWriter/ CLASSIFIED: Front-end Software – Intertext/Classified Rev II.; Classified Hardware – PC Network; Classified Equipment – APP/Mac Workstation; Classified Printers – Okidata/3410, NewGen/Postscript Printer DISPLAY: Ad make-up applications – SCS; Layout Software – SCS/Layout 8000.; Display Hardware – PC; Display Printers – APP/Mac LaserWriter PRODUCTION: Pagination Software – QPS/QuarkXPress 4.1, MEI/ALS.; Production Equipment – Caere/OmniPage Pro, 2-C/APS6-108; Scanners – Kk/RFS-2035, HP/3C, 2-Scangraphics/Dot4Dot PRESSROOM: Line 1 – 9; Folders – 1; Pasters – MEG; Reels and Stands – MEG. MAILROOM: Counter stackers – HL/Monitors, 3-HL/Dual Carrier; Inserters and stuffers – HI/1472; Bundle tying machines – 2-Dynaric/N-1, 2-Samuel/NT 30; Addressing machine – Domino/Ink Jet. BUSINESS COMPUTERS: Business Software – Agile Editorial, Microsoft/Office : Company, Gannett Genesys System; Business Hardware – AS400

MORRISTOWN NEWSPAPERS, INC.

800 Jefferson Rd., Parsippany, N.J., 07054-0217; gen tel (973) 428-6200; gen fax (973) 428-6666

PLEASANTVILLE

THE PRESS OF ATLANTIC CITY

1000 W. Washington Ave., P.O. Box 3100, Pleasantville, N.J., 08232-3100; gen tel (609) 272-7000; adv tel (609) 272-7030; ed tel (609) 272-7000; gen fax (609) 272-7040; adv fax 609-272-7059; ed fax (609) 272-7224; gen e-mail acpress@pressofac.com; adv e-mail classad@pressofac.com; ed e-mail newstips@pressofac.com; web site www.pressofatlanticcity.com
Group: South Jersey Publishing Company
Published: Mon, Tues, Wed, Thur, Fri, Sat, Sun
Weekday Frequency: m
Saturday Frequency: m
Circulation: 61,278; 61,278(sat); 74,177(sun)
Last Audit: Sworn September 30, 2009
Price: 5.35/week; 21.67/mon/278.20/yr
Advertising: Open inch rate $53.00 (m), $65.00 (m, t, w), $69.24 (th, f. sa), $86.50 (su)
News services: AP, SHNS, MCT, TMS.
Politics: Independent. **Established:** 1895
Advertising not accepted: N
Not Published: n/a
Own facility?: Y
Special Editions: Clips, Health-The Magazine (Jan); Clips, Bliss Bridal (Feb); Clips, Fore, Health-The Magazine, Celebrate Spring (Mar); Clips, Indulge (Apr); Summer Guide (May); Clips, Health-The Magazine (June); Clips, Best of Press Winners Tab (July); Brendan Borek, Celebrate Ocean City, Fore, Bliss Bridal (Aug); Clips, Home Improvement, Health-The Magazine (Sept); Clips, Indulge, HACAC Education Guide, Holiday 1-Save (Oct); Clips, Holiday 2-Giving, Holiday 3-Celebrate (Nov); Holiday-4 Traditions, Holiday-5 Hurry, Clips (Dec)
Special Weekly Sections: Wellness (Mon); Live (M, T, W, F, Sa); At The Shore (th) Weekly Entertainment; Travel, E-Life, Pets, Taste, Real Estate, Marketplace, Auto (Sun)
Magazines: Parade (S).
Dash (monthly)
Pres./CEO ....John F. Bitzer
Exec. Vice Pres./COO/Pub. ....Keith L. Dawn
Dir., Finance/Admin ....Charles A. Bryant
Dir., HR ....Kathleen J. Leonard
VP Sales & Marketing ....John Celestino
Digital Sales Strategy Manager .Anthony Falduto
Adv. Mgr., Classified ....Larry West
Adv. Mgr., Nat'l/Major ....Michael Falcone
Adv. Mgr., Reg'l ....Conell Carey
Marketing Manager ....Anne Nguyen
NIE Coord. ....Sandy Reed
Circ. Systems & Acquisition/Retention Mgr. Carol Steiger
Circ. Mgr., Sales ....William Muller
Exec. Ed./Content Dir. ....Neill A. Borowski
Deputy Content Dir., Digital ....Steve Warren
Lead Local Content Producer ....Peter Brophy
Local Content Producer/Business ....Kevin Post
Director of Advertising ....Alisha Owens
Special Sections Manager ....David Caywood
Director of Marketing ....Rhona Bronson
Circulation Sales Development Manager Carrie Gill
Lead Local Content Producer/Night .David Turner
Local Content Producer/News ....Scott Cronick
Local Content Producer/Hyperlocal ....Paula Gillis
Local Content Producer/News ....Winfred Keough
Asst. Local Content Producer/Digital ...Dan Good
Local Content Producer/Photo .Vernon Ogrodnek
Local Content Producer/Features ....Steve Cronin
Asst. Entertainment Editor ....Gail Wilson
Entertainment Editor ....Kevin Clapp
Editorial Page Editor ....James Perskie
Librarian ....Martha Zechman
Digital Technical Team Manager ...Guy Pastrana
Local Content Producer/Sports ....Mark Melhorn
IT Manager ....Fred Morgenweck
User Support Manager ....Dave Skeels
Operataions/Pressroom Manager ....Tom Bright
Packaging & Distribution Manager ..Patrick Lowe
PrePress Manager ....Fred Morgenweck
Market Information: Split run; TMC; Zoned editions.
Mechanical available: Flexo; Black and 3 ROP colors; insert accepted; page cutoffs - 22 3/4.
Mechanical Specifications: Type page 11 x 21 1/2; E - 6 cols, 1 5/6, 1/8 between; A - 6 cols, 1 5/6, 1/8 between; C - 10 cols, 1 7/10, 9/10 between.
Commodity Consumption: Avg, daily pages: 34; Avg. Sunday pages: 56; Plates used: 109,211; Width: 47; Newsprint short tons: 5,615; black ink: 125,122; Color ink: 122,144
Equipment EDITORIAL: Front-end Software – Anygraaf/Planner, QPS/QuarkXPress 4.1, Microsoft/Word 6.0 - 10.0.; Editorial Hardware –

Dell Virtual Server 3-2-1 setup; Editorial Equipment – 4-AU/Softpip, 2-Sierra/3850 Wide; Editorial Printers – QMS/860, HP DJ800PS; Classified Hardware – 2-Dell/PowerEdge R610, twin E5640 2.66Ghz processors, 12GB mem, (2) 3TB external RAIDs running ATS AdvisorFlex; Classified Equipment – 3-AU/Grafix rips, 1-Any7graaf OPI system, 2-AU/3850 Sierra Wide; Classified Printers – HP/LaserJe DISPLAY: Ad make-up applications – QPS/QuarkXPress, Microsoft, Anygraaf; Display Hardware – 2-Dell/PowerEdge 2600 2.8 GHz Zeon, 2-Dell/PowerVault 221s w/MS Cluster, MAC/G4/Dell Optiplex; Display Printers – QMS/860, HP/LaserJet 8000N, HP/LaserJet 8100N, QMS/Magicolor 6100, HP/2500C, Xante/CL30 Color Laser PRODUCTION: Pagination Software – QPS/QuarkXPress 4.1, Anygraaf Doris & Planner; Production Equipment – Calera/M-Pro, Au/Sierra 3850 Wide PRESSROOM: Line 1 – 8-H/Colormatic converted to Flexo 1989; Line 2 – 8-H/Colormatic converted to Flexo 1989; Folders – 3-H/3:2; Pasters – 16-H/RTP. MAILROOM: Counter stackers – 2-TMSI/Compass, 4-HL/HT, 2-TMSI/Compass 180; Inserters and stuffers – 2-HI/1472, 1-Titan G-60; Bundle tying machines – 4/Power Strap/PSN 5, 2-NT-440 automatic Strapping Machines, 2-NP/2000, 2-/Samuel Strap Bottom Wrap, 4-/Hall bottom wrap machines; Mailroom control system – 2-/Mailcom Co BUSINESS COMPUTERS: Business Software – GPS/AIM, Platinum/SQL, Excaliber/POS, ADP, GPS/Layout, GPS/Circ; Business Hardware – Dell desktops and notebooks, asst models
Zip Codes served: Atlantic, Cape May and Southern Ocean County
Delivery method: Mail, Newsstand, Private Carrier, Racks

SALEM

TODAY'S SUNBEAM

93 Fifth St., Salem, N.J., 08079; gen tel (856) 935-1500; ed tel (856) 935-1500; gen fax (856) 845-3139; adv fax (856) 935-8161; ed fax (856) 845-3139; gen e-mail tsnews@sjnewsco.com; web site www.nj.com/sunbeam
Published: Mon, Tues, Wed, Thur, Fri, Sat, Sun
Weekday Frequency: m
Saturday Frequency: m
Circulation: 7,526; 6,873(sat); 7,525(sun)
Last Audit: ABC September 30, 2011
Price: 2.20/wk (carrier), $2.30/wk (motor route); 121.70/yr.
Advertising: Open inch rate $26.00
News services: AP, U.S. Suburban Press Inc..
Politics: Independent.
Note: For detailed production information, see the Bridgeton Evening News listing.
Not Published: Christmas (except if it falls on Sunday).
Special Editions: Salem Community College (Apr); Home Guide (Aug); Woodstown Christmas (Dec); Income Tax (Feb); Progress (Jan); Christmas in July (Jul); American Heart Association (Jun); Estate Planning (May); Thanksgiving (Nov); Christmas Gift Guide I (Oct); Home Guide (S
Special Weekly Sections: Real Estate (Wed).
Magazines: Parade (S).
Grp. Gen Mgr. ....Frank Gargano
Pub. ....Ceil Smith
Adv. Dir. ....Janet Schaeffer
Circ. Dir. ....John Petracci
Bus./Finance Ed. ....Tracy Wiggins
City Ed ....Colleen Moore
Nat'l Ed ....Bill Gallo
News Ed ....Bill Gallo
Sports Ed. ....Shawn Leary
Travel Ed. ....John Barna
Women's Ed ....Robin Buoncuore
Data Processing Mgr. ....Edward J. Murray
Market Information: TMC.
Mechanical available: Offset; Black and 3 ROP colors; insert accepted; page cutoffs - 22 3/4.
Mechanical Specifications: Type page 13 x 21 1/2; E - 6 cols, 2 1/16, 1/8 between; A - 6 cols, 2 1/16, 1/8 between; C - 9 cols, 1 1/3, 1/8 between.
Commodity Consumption: Avg. Page Number Per Issue - Daily 24; Avg. Page Number Per Issue - Sunday 32; widths 12 1/2.
Equipment EDITORIAL: Front-end Software – CText.; Editorial Hardware – IBM, PC; Editorial Printers – HP CLASSIFIED: Front-end Software – CText.; Classified Hardware – IBM, PC; Classified Printers – HP BUSINESS COMPUTERS: Business Software – CJ; Business Hardware – HP/3000

SOMERVILLE

COURIER NEWS

92 E. Main St., Ste. 202, Somerville, N.J., 08876-2319; gen tel (908) 243-6600; adv tel (908) 243-6630; ed tel (908) 243-6603; gen fax (908) 243-6651; adv fax (908) 243-6649; ed fax (908) 243-6645; gen e-mail cnmetro@mycentraljersey.com; web site www.mycentraljersey.com
Published: Mon, Tues, Wed, Thur, Fri, Sat, Sun
Weekday Frequency: m
Saturday Frequency: m
Circulation: 19,397; 19,397(sat); 23,560(sun)
Last Audit: September 30, 2009
Price: 3.00/wk; 13.00/mo; 156.00/yr; 39.00/13wk.
Advertising: Open inch rate $110.00
News services: AP, GNS.
Politics: Independent.
Special Editions: What the Holidays Mean to Me (Dec); Forecast (Feb); Graduation Tab (Jun); Tour of Somerville (May); Auto Trend (Monthly); Holiday Gift Guide (Nov); Senior Scoop (Other); Cuisine (Quarterly); NJ House & Home (Semi-monthly); Super Summer Reader (Sept).
Special Weekly Sections: Home Guide (Fri); Destinations (S); Kicks! Weekend Preview (Thur); Community (Wed).
Magazines: USA WEEKEND Magazine (S).
Pres./Pub. ....William C. Hidlay
Adv. Mgr., Ad Servs. ....Judy Coddington
Mng. Ed ....Paul Grzella
Assoc. Ed. ....J. Jefferson Cooke
Digital Ed ....Loren Fisher
Editorial Page Ed. ....Keith Ryzewicz
Market Information: TMC; Zoned editions.
Mechanical available: Offset; Black and 3 ROP colors; insert accepted - samples; page cutoffs - 22 3/4.
Mechanical Specifications: Type page 11 5/8 x 21 1/2; E - 6 cols, 2 1/16, 1/8 between; A - 6 cols, 2 1/16, 1/8 between; C - 10 cols, 1 1/4, 1/16 between.
Commodity Consumption: Avg. Page Number Per Issue - Daily 35; Avg. Page Number Per Issue - Plates Used 51350; Avg. Page Number Per Issue - Sunday 87; widths 50; Newsprint Used - Metric Tons 4727; Printing Ink Used - Black 93827; Printing Ink Used - Color 30288; Printing Ink Us
Equipment EDITORIAL: Front-end Software – SII/Coyote 3002 (000A).; Editorial Hardware – Tandem/Himalaya K200; Editorial Printers – HP/8100N CLASSIFIED: Front-end Software – SII/Coyote 3002 (OOOA), Pongrass (Classified).; Classified Hardware – 17-Tandem/K200; Classified Printers – HP/4000N DISPLAY: Ad make-up applications – Managing Editor/ALS; Layout Software – Managing Editor/ALS 2.5.; Display Hardware – APP/Mac; Display Printers – HP/4050 PRODUCTION: Pagination Software – QPS/QuarkXPress 4.11, Pongrass 3.1.16.; Production Equipment – 2-Anacoil/XPD-32, Epson/Smart Panel; Cameras – 2-C/Marathon; Scanners – Tecsa/TS2470, 2-Epson/836 XL PRESSROOM: Line 1 – 9-H/Lithomatic 60 double width (plus 6 color decks); Press Drives – 9-HP/60, GE/Motors; Folders – 2-H/3:2; Pasters – 9-H/Lithomatic 1972; Reels and Stands – 9-H/Lithomatic 60 1972; Press control system – EDS/Control Master. MAILROOM: Counter stackers – 1-QWI/300, 2-QWI/20, 1/HL; Inserters and stuffers – 1-HI/1472P; Bundle tying machines – 3-/Power Strap, 1-/Power Strap/Manual; Wrapping singles – 2-/QWI; Addressing machine – 2-Ch/539, 2-/Spegram. BUSINESS COMPUTERS: Business Software – Microsoft/Office 97, Microsoft/Access, SQL; Business Hardware – IBM/AS-400, Dell/PC, IBM/Netfinity

TRENTON

THE TIMES

500 Perry St., Trenton, N.J., 08618-3932; gen tel (609) 989-5454; adv tel (609) 989-5452; adv fax (609) 396-5644; ed e-mail news@njtimes.com; web site www.south.nj.com
Published: Mon, Tues, Wed, Thur, Fri, Sat, Sun
Weekday Frequency: m
Saturday Frequency: m
Circulation: 35,413; 34,947(sat); 40,299(sun)
Last Audit: ABC September 30, 2011
Price: 2.95/wk; 11.80/mo; 153.40/yr.
Advertising: Open inch rate $91.14
News services: AP, LAT-WP, NYT, NNS.
Politics: Independent.
Special Editions: Spring Dining Guide (Apr); Fall Special Occasion Planner (Aug); Holiday Dining (Dec); Spring Wedding (Feb); Outlook (Jan); Summer Dining Guide (Jul); Parenting (Jun); Retirement Planning/Nature Living (Mar); Spring Auto (May); Benchmarks (Monthly); Race f
Special Weekly Sections: Entertainment Tab (Fri); Food and Home (S); At Home (Thur); Food and Home (Wed).
Magazines: Parade (S).
Gen. Mgr. ....Michael Newhouse
Controller ....Martin Stewart
Adv. Dir. ....Shiela Montone
Adv. Mgr., Nat'l/Co-Op ....Jonathan Kramer
Mgr., Promo ....Valerie Rushmore
Circ. Asst. Dir. ....Todd Doolittle
Circ. Mgr., Home Delivery ....Ardell Crump
Ed. ....Brian S. Malone
Mng. Ed ....Peter Callas
Editorial Page Ed. ....George Amick
Features Ed. ....Nora O'Dowd
News Ed. ....Ted Quann
Photography Dir. ....Paul Savage
Exec. Sports Ed. ....Jim Gauger
Prodn. Dir., Opns. ....Robert Jarrach
Prodn. Mgr., Pre Press ....Michael Lawson
Prodn. Mgr., Pressroom/Mailroom ....Bill Heider
Prodn. Mgr., Single Copy ....Bob Bruner
Prodn. Mgr., Transportation ....Joseph Kustrup
Market Information: ADS; Split run; TMC; Zoned editions.
Mechanical available: Offset; Black and 3 ROP colors; insert accepted - product sample-custom bags; page cutoffs - 22 3/4.
Mechanical Specifications: Type page 11 5/8 x 21 1/4; E - 6 cols, 1 13/16, 1/8 between; A - 6 cols, 1 13/16, 1/8 between; C - 10 cols, 1 1/8, 5/64 between.
Commodity Consumption: Avg. Page Number Per Issue - Daily 57; Avg. Page Number Per Issue - Plates Used 120000; Avg. Page Number Per Issue - Sunday 177; widths 25; Newsprint Used - Metric Tons 14000; Newsprint Used - Short Tons 14302; Printing Ink Used - Black 276000; Printing
Equipment; Editorial Hardware – AT.; Classified Hardware – AT.; Display Hardware – 5-HI/2100. PRODUCTION: Pagination Software – HI/XP-21.; Production Equipment – 2-AU/APS-6, 2-AU/3850, 1-WL/Lith III; Cameras – 1-C/Marathon, 1-C/NewsPager; Scanners – 1-Eskofot PRESSROOM: Line 1 – 10-G/Metro; Folders – 2-G/3:2; Pasters – 10 MAILROOM: Counter stackers – 3-HL/HT, 1-HL/HT II; Inserters and stuffers – 2-S/72P; Bundle tying machines – 2/MLN, 4-/Dynaric; Addressing machine – 3-/Wm.; Business Hardware – 1-TS/SII, 1-HP/3000

THE TRENTONIAN

600 Perry St., Trenton, N.J., 08618-3934; gen tel (609) 989-7800; adv fax (609) 394-1358; ed fax (609) 393-6072; gen e-mail editor@trentonian.com; web site www.trentonian.com
Published: Mon, Tues, Wed, Thur, Fri, Sat, Sun
Weekday Frequency: m
Saturday Frequency: m
Circulation: 30,275; 25,782(sat); 20,414(sun)
Last Audit: ABC September 30, 2011
Price: 2.30/wk; 9.20/mo; 143.00/yr.
Advertising: Open inch rate $94.71
News services: AP, SNS, MCT.
Politics: Independent.
Special Editions: Trenton Thunder (Apr); NFL Preview (Aug); Gift Guides I, II & III (Dec); Today's Health Care (Feb); Progress (Jan); Family Living (Jul); The Entrepreneurs (Jun); Spring Fashion (Mar); Mother's Day (May); Election Tab (Nov); Women's Health (Oct); Bucks Cou
Special Weekly Sections: Entertainment (Fri); Entertainment (S); Auto (Sat); Best Food Days (Wed).
Magazines: USA WEEKEND Magazine (S).
Pub. ....William T. Murray
Adv. Dir. ....Maggie Ashley
Adv. Mgr., Retail ....Nora Chepl
Adv. Mgr., Classified ....Nancy Seyboth
Circ. Dir. ....Doug Freeman
Ed. ....Aaron Nobel
Online Ed. ....Andria Carter
City Ed. ....Paul Mickle
Editorial Page Ed. ....David Neese
Photo Ed. ....Gregg Slaboda
Sports Ed. ....Matt Osborne
Prodn. Foreman, Mailroom ....John Basile
Prodn. Dir. ....Rocco A. Gallo
Mechanical available: Letterpress (direct)/Flexo; Black and 3 ROP colors; insert accepted - in-house printing; page cutoffs - 14 3/4.
Mechanical Specifications: Type page 10 7/8 x 14 1/4; E - 5 cols, 2 1/16, 1/8 between; A - 5 cols, 2 1/16, 1/8 between; C - 7 cols, 1 3/8, 1/8 between.
Commodity Consumption: Avg. Page Number Per Issue - Daily 64; Avg. Page Number Per Issue - Plates Used 49; Avg. Page Number Per Issue - Saturday 68; Avg. Page Number Per Issue - Sunday 60; widths 45; Newsprint Used - Metric Tons 5.24; Newsprint Used - Short Tons 11.55; Printin
Equipment EDITORIAL: Front-end Software – Dewar/View, QPS/QuarkXPress 3.32.; Editorial Hardware – Dewar/Information System, PC Network; Editorial Printers – HP/5000, APP/Mac Laser Writers CLASSIFIED: Front-end Software – PPI.; Classified Hardware – PC Network; Classified Printers – APP/Mac Laser Writer DISPLAY: Ad make-up applications – Multi-Ad/Creator 4.0, Adobe/Illustrator 5.5, Adobe/Photoshop 4.0, QPS/QuarkXpress 4.0; Layout Software – ALS.; Display Hardware – Epson/Scanner; Display Printers – HP/5000 PRODUCTION: Pagination Software – AT/Dewarview.; Production Equipment – Atm, Harlequin Rips, Burgess; Scanners – Epson PRESSROOM: Line 1 – 6-H/6 letter mono unit (2 decks), 2-H/Flexo mono unit (2 decks); Folders – G/3:2, G/2:1; Pasters – 8; Press control system – PEC/Supervisors. MAILROOM: Counter stackers – 2-HL/HT Monitor; Inserters and stuffers – HI; Bundle tying machines – 1/MSB, 1-MLN/2AHS, 2-MLN/2EE; Wrapping singles – Power Strap/PSN250; Mailroom control system – HI. BUSINESS COMPUTERS: Business Software – INSI; Business Hardware – IBM/AS-400

VINELAND

THE DAILY JOURNAL

891 E. Oak Rd., Vineland, N.J., 08360-

2394; gen tel (856) 691-5000; gen fax (856) 563-5282; ed fax (856) 563-5308; adv e-mail classified@thedailyjournal.com; web site www.thedailyjournal.com
Published: Mon, Tues, Wed, Thur, Fri, Sat
Weekday Frequency: m
Saturday Frequency: m
Circulation: 12,755; 15,492(sat)
Last Audit: ABC September 30, 2011
Price: 3.15/wk (motor route); 164.40/yr (motor route).
Advertising: Open inch rate $54.74
News services: AP, GNS.
Politics: Independent.
Special Weekly Sections: Travel (Weekly).
Magazines: TV Journal (Sat).
Controller....Jean Wysocki
Adv. Dir.....Joseph Calchi
Circ. Dir.....Les Olson
Ed.....Charles W. Nutt
Editorial Page Ed.....John Garrahan
Features Ed.....Lori Jarvis
Local News Ed.....Jason Alt
Metro Ed.....Jerry Staas-Haught
Sports Ed.....Thomas McGurk
Market Information: ADS; TMC.
Mechanical available: Offset; Black and 3 ROP colors; insert accepted; page cutoffs - 21.
Mechanical Specifications: Type page 10 x 21; E - 6 cols, 1 1/4, 1/8 between; A - 6 cols, 1 1/4, 1/8 between; C - 10 cols, 7/8, 1/8 between.
Commodity Consumption: Avg. Page Number Per Issue - Daily 28; Avg. Page Number Per Issue - Plates Used 7176; Avg. Page Number Per Issue - Saturday 28; widths 54; Newsprint Used - Metric Tons 1300; Printing Ink Used - Black 25000; Printing Ink Used - Color 10000; Printing Ink U
Equipment EDITORIAL: Front-end Software – APT/ACT, QPS/QuarkXPress 3.32, Microsoft/Word 97.; Editorial Hardware – APT; Editorial Equipment – Lf/AP Leaf Picture Desk, 2-AG/Studio Scanner, Nikon/LS1000 Coolscan; Editorial Printers – HP, HP/5000 CLASSIFIED: Front-end Software – APT/ACT, QPS/QuarkXPress 3.32, Microsoft/Word 97.; Classified Hardware – APT; Classified Equipment – HP/ScanJet 5s, Eskofot/EskoScan 2636, Teca/EU3000 Scanner; Classified Printers – HP/4MV, HP/5000gn DISPLAY: Ad make-up applications – QPS/QuarkXPress, Adobe/Photoshop, Aldus/FreeHand; Layout Software – 1-APP/Power Mac 7100, 1-APP/Power Mac 8500, 3-APP/Mac G3, 1-APP/Power Mac 7200, 1-APP/Po; Display Hardware – APP/Mac Server, APP/MAC G3; Display Printers – HP/5000 PRODUCTION: Pagination Software – APT, QPS/QuarkXPress 3.32.; Production Equipment – HP/ScanJet 5s, ECR/4550, LE/LD800A, LE/R660; Cameras – C/Marathon, C/Spartan II; Scanners – ECR/Autokon 1000, Scanmate/3000, Eskofot/TecaPage Scanner PRESSROOM: Line 1 – 5-G/Metro double width 1971; Press Drives – Fin/60 HP West; Folders – G/2:1 double. MAILROOM: Counter stackers – QWI/100; Inserters and stuffers – 2-MM/227 5:1; Bundle tying machines – 2/MLN, 2-/Power Strap/Newstyer 2000; Addressing machine – 1-Domino/Ink Jet.; Business Hardware – 1-IBM/AS-400 B30

WEST PATERSON

HERALD NEWS

1 Garret Mountain Plz., West Paterson, N.J., 07424-0471; gen tel (973) 569-7000; adv tel (973) 569-7800; ed tel (973) 569-7100; gen fax (973) 569-7129; adv fax (973) 569-7834; ed fax (973) 569-7129; adv e-mail advertising@northjersey.com; classified@northjersey.com; ed e-mail hncitydesk@northjersey.com; web site www.northJersey.com
Published: Mon, Tues, Wed, Thur, Fri, Sat, Sun
Weekday Frequency: m
Saturday Frequency: m
Price: 3.45/wk; 150.28/yr.
News services: Metro Suburbia Inc..
Politics: Independent. **Established:** 1872
Note: The Herald News is an edition of The Bergen County-Hackensack (NJ) Record, but has its own editorial department. See The Record listing for circulation; advertising rates; special editions; production personnel; commodity consumption; production specifica
Advertising not accepted: Libelous; fraudulent; indecent.
Special Weekly Sections: Bring It (Fri); Entertainment: Primetime (S); Money (Thur); Health (Tues); Food (Wed).
Magazines: TV Book (S).
Dir., Consumer Sales....Bill Lord
Mktg. Dir.....Don Rifkin
Ed.....Stephen McCarthy
Asst. Mng. Ed., Admin.....Doug Clancy
Editorial Page Ed.....Ulysses Rivers
News Ed.....Scott Muller
Dir., Sports....John Balkun
Market Information: TMC.
Mechanical available: Black and ROP colors; insert accepted.
Equipment EDITORIAL: Front-end Software – Agile/Teambase 2.12.20, Microsoft/Word, Microsoft/Windows NT.; Editorial Hardware – Dell/4300; Editorial Printers – Xante/8200, Xante/Accel-a-Writer CLASSIFIED: Front-end Software – DEC/61, Pongrass.; Classified Hardware – CPS/Astrotech 2040 Mainframe DISPLAY: Ad make-up applications – DPS/AdTracker 3.0, QPS/QuarkXPress 4.11, Adobe/Photoshop 5.0, Adobe/Illustrator 8.0, Macromedia/Freehand 9.0, Mactive/Ad Base; Layout Software – ASL.; Display Hardware – Dell/4300, APP/Mac; Display Printers – HP/Laserjet 4000, HP/Laserjet 4050, HP/Laserjet 5000 PRODUCTION: Pagination Software – Agile/Teambase 4.9, QPS/QuarkXPress 4.03.; Production Equipment – AFT/Photoeditor (4.2); Scanners – Nikon/LS 1000 (35 mm), Epson/ES-800C

WILLINGBORO

BURLINGTON COUNTY TIMES

4284 Rte. 130 N., Willingboro, N.J., 08046-2027; gen tel (609) 871-8022; adv tel (609) 871-8085; ed tel (609) 871-8054; gen fax (609) 871-8107; adv fax (609) 871-8145; ed fax (609) 871-0490; web site www.mybctnow.com; www.phillyburbs.com/bct
Group: U.S. Suburban Press, Inc.
Published: Mon, Tues, Wed, Thur, Fri, Sun
Weekday Frequency: m
Saturday Frequency: m
Circulation: 25,233; 27,199(sat); 29,744(sun)
Last Audit: ABC September 30, 2011
Price: 3.50/wk; 14.00/mo; 182.00/yr.
News services: AP, NEA.
Politics: Independent. **Established:** 1958
Note: There is a Greater Philadelphia Newspapers Group combination rate of $239.00(d) & $251.00(S) among the Levittown Bucks County (PA) Courier Times (mS), Doylestown (PA) Intelligencer (mS) & Willingboro Burlington County Times (mS). Individual newspaper rate
Special Editions: Newspapers in Education (Apr); Back-to-School (Aug); Holiday Gifts (Dec); Best of Burlington (Jan); Discover Burlington (Jun); Home & Garden (Mar); Holiday Recipes (Nov); Car Care (Oct); H.S. Sports (Sept).
Special Weekly Sections: To Do (Fri); All About U (Monthly); Wheels (S); At Home (Sat); What's Happening! (Thur).
Magazines: TV Time (S); ToDo (Thur).
Broadcast Affiliations: WWSB-Sarasota, Fl.
Pub.....Mike Scobey
Vice Pres./Dir., Strategy....Stanley M. Ellis
Vice Pres.....Sandra C. Hardy
Vice Pres.....Charles C. Smith
Vice Pres./Sec.....Shirley C. Ellis
Adv. Dir.....Kim Noble
Adv. Team Leader....Lisa Foster
Retail Adv. Mgr.....Brenda C. Cuomo
Classified Adv. Dir.....Cathy Clark
Mktg. Mgr.....Carol Shapcott
Circ. Dir.....Steven F. Todd
Exec. Ed.....Pat Walker
Mng. Ed.....Martha Esposito
Bus. Ed.....Chris Bishop
Editorial Page Ed.....Gretchen Barrett
Entertainment Ed.....Lou Gaul
News Graphics....Mark Perlmutter
Photo Ed.....Rose Shields
Sports Ed.....Wayne Richardson
Systems Mgr.....Jackie White
Market Information: Split run; TMC.
Mechanical available: Offset; Black and 3 ROP colors; insert accepted - product samples; page cutoffs - 21 1/2.
Mechanical Specifications: Type page 11 5/8 x 21 1/2; E - 6 cols, 1 5/6, 3/4 between; A - 6 cols, 1 5/6, 3/4 between; C - 9 cols, 1 3/16, 3/4 between.
Commodity Consumption: Avg. Page Number Per Issue - Daily 38; Avg. Page Number Per Issue - Plates Used 24500; Avg. Page Number Per Issue - Sunday 70; widths 12 1/2; Newsprint Used - Metric Tons 3822; Printing Ink Used - Black 94000; Printing Ink Used - Color 21500; Printing In
Equipment EDITORIAL: Front-end Software – ACI/Open Pgs 1.2, QPS/QuarkXPress.; Editorial Hardware – Compaq/Prolinea PC CLASSIFIED: Front-end Software – Mactive/Admarc.; Classified Hardware – IBM/9672; Classified Printers – IBM/4224 DISPLAY: Ad make-up applications – Multi-Ad/Creator; Layout Software – SCS/Layout 8000.; Display Hardware – Compaq/Deskpro, APP/Power Mac 7600/132, APP/Power Mac 7200/120; Display Printers – HP/II LaserPrinter, 2-QMS/Magicolor, QMS/330 Magicolor CX PRODUCTION: Pagination Software – QPS 3.3.; Production Equipment – W, 1-C; Cameras – C/Marathon, C/Spartan III; Scanners – ECR/Autokon News Graphic System, Dest, Autologic/Monotype PRESSROOM: Line 1 – 7-G/Metro 1968; Folders – 1-G/2:1; Pasters – Reels and Stands ◻ 7-G; Reels and Stands – Press control system ◻ Fin. MAILROOM: Counter stackers – QWI; Inserters and stuffers – GMA/SLS 2000; Bundle tying machines – 1/Power Strap, 2-/MLN, 7-/Dynaric; Addressing machine – Ch.

WOODBURY

THE GLOUCESTER COUNTY TIMES

309 S. Broad St., Woodbury, N.J., 08096; gen tel (856) 845-3300; adv tel (856) 845-3300; ed tel (856) 845-3300; gen fax (856) 845-4318; adv fax (856) 853-7309 (class); ed fax (856) 845-5480; ed e-mail gctimes@sjnewsco.com; web site www.nj.com
Published: Mon, Tues, Wed, Thur, Fri, Sat, Sun
Weekday Frequency: m
Saturday Frequency: m
Circulation: 16,427; 15,423(sat); 19,553(sun)
Last Audit: ABC September 30, 2011
Price: 2.95/wk (motor route), $1.10/wk (sat & S); 138.60/yr; 11.80/4 wk.
Advertising: Open inch rate $43.00
News services: AP, NEA.
Politics: Independent.
Not Published: Christmas (except on Sunday).
Special Editions: Phillies (Apr); Back-to-School (Aug); Holiday Gift Guide II (Dec); Progress (Feb); Spring Bridal (Jan); Guide to Gloucester County (Jul); Best Years (Jun); Spring Lawn & Garden (Mar); Here Comes Summer (May); Holiday Gift Guide I (Nov); New Homes (Oct); E
Special Weekly Sections: Weekender (Fri); Job Locater (Tues).
Magazines: Parade (S).
Vice Pres./Pub.....Frank Gargano
Credit Mgr.....Ellen Cummings
Controller....Charles H. MacDonald
Adv. Mgr., Classified....Marie Vito
Adv. Mgr., Retail....Brad Smith
Circ. Dir.....John Petracci
Travel Ed.....Jim Six
Editorial Page Ed.....Elliot Goldberg
Political/Gov't Ed.....Bryan Arrington
Religion Ed.....Jane Humes
Sports Ed.....Shawn Leary
Sunday Ed.....Glenn Koppelman
Mgr., Info Servs.....Edward J. Murray
Prodn. Dir.....Michael D'Arienzo
Prodn. Facilities....Tom Moore
Prodn. Mgr., Mailroom....Matt Tylutki
Prodn. Foreman, Pressroom....William Gelsinger
Market Information: TMC.
Mechanical available: Offset; Black and 3 ROP colors; insert accepted; page cutoffs - 22 3/4.
Mechanical Specifications: Type page 11 63/100 x 21 1/2; E - 6 cols, 1 5/6, 1/8 between; A - 6 cols, 1 5/6, 1/8 between; C - 9 cols, 1, 1/8 between.
Commodity Consumption: Avg. Page Number Per Issue - Daily 36; Avg. Page Number Per Issue - Sunday 56; widths 12 1/2; Newsprint Used - Metric Tons 1730; Printing Ink Used - Black 90805; Printing Ink Used - Color 9650; Printing Ink Used - Pages Printed 12458.
Equipment EDITORIAL: Front-end Software – CText, Baseview.; Editorial Hardware – APP/Mac CLASSIFIED: Front-end Software – PPI.; Classified Hardware – IBM, PC; Classified Printers – HP DISPLAY: Ad make-up applications – CText, HI; Layout Software – MEI/ALS.; Display Hardware – IBM, PC, HI; Display Printers – HP PRODUCTION: Pagination Software – Baseview/NewsEdit Pro IQUE.; Production Equipment – Nu, 1-APP/Mac 8100-80, 1-APP/Mac Scanner, 1-NewGen/1200 2pi, 1-APP/Mac Printer, 2-ECR/VRL36HS PRESSROOM: Line 1 – 9-G/Urbanite single width 1992; Folders – 1; Reels and Stands – 7-G/Roll stand. MAILROOM: Counter stackers – Id, HL; Inserters and stuffers – AM Graphics/NP 1372; Bundle tying machines – MLN. BUSINESS COMPUTERS: Business Software – CJ/GEAC; Business Hardware – HP/3000

WOODLAND PARK

THE RECORD, HERALD NEWS

1 Garret Mountain Plaza, Woodland Park, N.J., 07424; web site www.northjersey.com
Published: Mon, Tues, Wed, Thur, Fri, Sat, Sun
Weekday Frequency: m
Saturday Frequency: m
Circulation: 146,523; 147,031(sat); 172,660(sun)
Last Audit: ABC September 30, 2011
President./Publisher....Stephen A Borg

NEW MEXICO

ALAMOGORDO

ALAMOGORDO DAILY NEWS

518 24th St., Alamogordo, N.M., 88310; gen tel (575) 437-7120; gen fax (575) 437-7795; adv e-mail adnads@zianet.com; web site www.alamogordonews.com
Group: Texas New Mexico Newspaper Partnership
New Mexico Press Association Display Ad Network
Published: Tues, Wed, Thur, Fri, Sat, Sun
Weekday Frequency: m
Saturday Frequency: m
Circulation: 5,327; 6,098(sun)
Last Audit: ABC September 30, 2011
Price: 8.25/mo.
Advertising: Open inch rate $18.75
News services: AP, CNS.
Politics: Independent. **Established:** 1898
Special Editions: Football (Aug); Christmas (Dec); Back-to-School (Jul); Progress (Mar); Land of Enchantment (May); Holiday Gift Guide (Nov).
Special Weekly Sections: Business (Mon); Food Page (Tues).
Magazines: Relish (Monthly); USA WEEKEND Magazine (S);

Pub. ....Mike Bell
Mng. Ed. ....Michael Johnson
Office Mgr. ....Nanette Gardner
Adv. Dir. ....Lisa Morales
Circ. Mgr. ....Rex Goodin
Market Information: TMC.
Mechanical available: Offset; Black and 3 ROP colors; insert accepted; page cutoffs - 22 3/4.
Mechanical Specifications: Type page 12 1/2 x 21 1/2; E - 6 cols, 2 1/16, 1/8 between; A - 6 cols, 2 1/16, 1/8 between; C - 8 cols, 1 3/8, 1/16 between.
Commodity Consumption: Avg. Page Number Per Issue - Daily 14; Avg. Page Number Per Issue - Sunday 24; widths 25.

ALBUQUERQUE

ALBUQUERQUE JOURNAL

7777 Jefferson St. NE, Albuquerque, N.M., 87109; gen tel (505) 823-7777; adv tel (505) 823-3300; ed tel (505) 823-3800; gen fax (505) 823-3994; adv fax (505) 823-3369; gen e-mail Journal@abqjournal.com; adv e-mail advertising@abqpubco.com; web site www.abqjournal.com
Group: New Mexico Press Association Display Ad Network
Published: Mon, Tues, Wed, Thur, Fri, Sat, Sun
Weekday Frequency: m
Saturday Frequency: m
Circulation: 87,109; 92,512(sat); 113,361(sun)
Last Audit: ABC September 30, 2011
Price: 11.25/mo; 135.00/yr.
Advertising: Open inch rate $133.70
News services: AP, LAT-WP, CSM, MCT, RN.
Politics: Independent. **Established:** 1880
Note: For detailed production and printing information see Albuquerque Publishing Co.
Special Editions: Home and Garden (Apr); Indian Market (Aug); Last Minute Gift Guide (Dec); Bridal (Feb); Home Furnishings (Jul); Senior (Mar); Auto Care (May); Winter Guide (Nov); Balloon Fiesta (Oct); State Fair (Sept).
Special Weekly Sections: Venue (Fri); Business Outlook (Mon); Entertainer (Sat); Business Outlook (Thur).
Magazines: USA WEEKEND Magazine (Fri); Relish (Monthly); Parade (S); American Profile (Tues).
Profile: Largest daily newspaper in New Mexico.
Pres./Pub. ....Thompson H. Lang
Vice Pres. ....William P. Lang
Vice Pres., Finance ....Lowell A. Hare
Ed. ....Kent Walz
Mng. Ed. ....Karen Moses
Bus. Ed. ....Michael Murphy
City Ed. ....Charlie Moore
Editorial Cartoonist ....John Trever
Health/Medical Writer ....Jackie Jadrnak
Librarian ....Chris Mora
Northern Bureau Ed. ....Mark Oswald
Photo Ed. ....Jamie Dispenza
Real Estate Ed. ....Autumn Gray
Science Writer ....John Fleck
State Ed. ....John Robertson
Technology Ed. ....Donn Friedman
Wire Ed. ....Ken Walston
Women's Magazine Ed. ....Carolynn Flynn
Market Information: Split run; Zoned editions.
Mechanical available: Offset; Black and 4 ROP colors; insert accepted; page cutoffs - 21 1/2.
Commodity Consumption: Avg. Page Number Per Issue - Daily 56; Avg. Page Number Per Issue - Sunday 110; widths 50.
Equipment EDITORIAL: Front-end Software – XYQUEST/XyWrite.; Editorial Hardware – HP/486-33 CLASSIFIED: Front-end Software – C-Text.

JOURNAL PUBLISHING CO.

7777 Jefferson NE, Albuquerque, N.M., 87109-4343; gen tel (505) 823-7777; gen fax (505) 823-3994

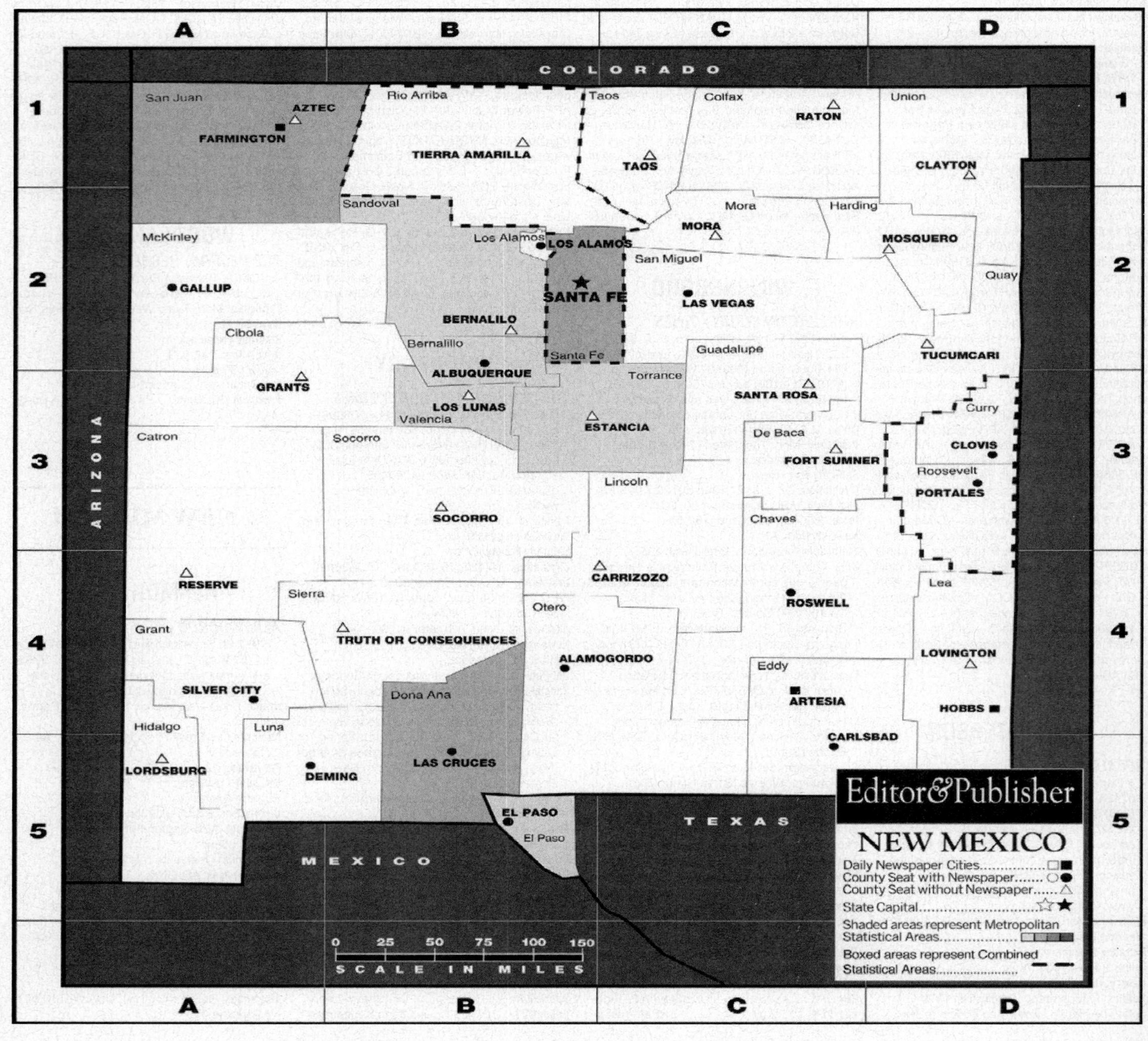

CARLSBAD

CURRENT-ARGUS

620 S. Main St., Carlsbad, N.M., 88220-6243; gen tel (575) 887-5501; gen fax (575) 885-1066; gen e-mail argus@currentargus.com; web site www.currentargus.com
Published: Tues, Wed, Thur, Fri, Sat, Sun
Weekday Frequency: m
Saturday Frequency: m
Circulation: 5,655; 5,655(sat); 5,992(sun)
Last Audit: ABC September 30, 2011
Price: 9.25/mo; 111.00/yr.
Advertising: Open inch rate $18.37
News services: AP.
Politics: Independent.
Not Published: Day after Thanksgiving; Dec. 26.
Special Editions: The Spring (Apr); Back-to-School (Aug); Christmas Greetings (Dec); Valentine's Love Photos (Feb); Chronology (Jan); Western Days (Jul); Our Town (Mar); Newspapers in Schools/Design-An-Ad (May); Christmas Gift Guide (Nov); Retirement (Oct); Football (Sept)
Special Weekly Sections: Best Real Estate Days (Fri); Best Real Estate Days (S); Best Food Day (Wed).
Magazines: TV Spotlight (Fri); USA WEEKEND Magazine (S); American Profile (Weekly).
Pub. ....Rockford M. Hayes
Adv. Dir. ....Larry Hubner
Retail Adv. Mgr. ....Darlene Rushing
District Sales Mgr. ....Georgia Hensley
Mng. Ed. ....Martha Mauritson
Community Ed. ....Christa Hart-Nordstrom
News Ed. ....Tom Schultes
Sports Ed. ....Jeff Keller
Prodn. Mgr. ....Jeff Flores
Market Information: TMC.
Mechanical available: Offset; Black and 3 ROP colors; insert accepted; page cutoffs - 22 1/2.
Mechanical Specifications: Type page 13 x 21 1/2; E - 6 cols, 2 1/16, 1/8 between; A - 6 cols, 2 1/16, 1/8 between; C - 6 cols, 2 1/16, 1/8 between.
Commodity Consumption: Avg. Page Number Per Issue - Daily 18; Avg. Page Number Per Issue - Plates Used 9000; Avg. Page Number Per Issue - Saturday 20; Avg. Page Number Per Issue - Sunday 30; widths 27 1/2; Newsprint Used - Short Tons 381.00; Printing Ink Used - Black 7200; Pri
Equipment EDITORIAL: Front-end Software – XYQUEST/XyWrite, CText.; Editorial Hardware – CText; Editorial Equipment – ECR/Imagesetter; Editorial Printers – APP/Mac LaserPrinters CLASSIFIED: Front-end Software – XYQUEST/XyWrite, CText.; Classified Hardware – CText; Classified Equipment – ECR/Imagesetter; Classified Printers – APP/Mac LaserPrinters DISPLAY: Ad make-up applications – Microsoft/Windows; Layout Software – CText.; Display Hardware – CText/Adept; Display Printers – APP/Mac LaserPrinters; Production Equipment – ECR/Imagesetter; Cameras – Nu/2024 M2 Camera. PRESSROOM: Line 1 – 6-G/Community 1975; Folders – G/Community Quarter.; Inserters and stuffers – KAN/5:1 4086; Bundle tying machines – Bu/Tyer.; Business Hardware – IBM/5363

CLOVIS

CLOVIS NEWS JOURNAL

521 Pile St., Clovis, N.M., 88101; gen tel (575) 763-3431; ed tel (575) 763-6991; gen fax (575) 762-3879; adv fax (575) 762-3879; ed fax (575) 742-1349; adv e-mail CNJAdvertising@cnjonline.com; web site www.cnjonline.com
Group: New Mexico Press Association Display Ad Network
Published: Tues, Wed, Thur, Fri, Sat, Sun
Weekday Frequency: m
Saturday Frequency: m
Circulation: 5,403; 5,403(sat); 6,402(sun)
Last Audit: Sworn September 30, 2009
Price: 15.95/mo (carrier); 174.00/yr (carrier).
Advertising: Open inch rate $12.75
News services: AP.
Politics: Independent. **Established:** 1929
Not Published: Monday
Own facility?: Y
Special Editions: Medical Guide (Apr); Healthy You (Every other month); Home & Garden (Mar); Farm & Ranch (Monthly).
Special Weekly Sections: Just TV (S); The Ticket (Thur).
Magazines: American Profile - Thursday Parade - Sunday
Pub. ....Ray Sullivan
Interim Circulation Director ....Lynn Berry
Ed. ....David Stevens
Mng. Ed. ....Rick White
Info Systems Mgr. ....Paul Tiedemann
Prodn. Mgr. - Freedom Printing ....Daryl Lee
Advertising Director ....Shane Adair
Production Manager ....Jim King
Business Manager ....Teresa McKennon
Human Resources Director ....Joyce Cruce
Adv. Dir. ....Ian Cooke
Circ. Dir. ....Mike Grigg
Market Information: TMC.
Mechanical available: Offset; Black and 3 ROP colors; insert accepted; page cutoffs - 22 3/4.
Mechanical Specifications: Type page 11 3/5 x 21 1/2; E - 6 cols, 1 13/16, 1/8 between; A - 6 cols, 2 13/16, 1/8 between; C - 9 cols, 1 3/16, 1/8 between.
Commodity Consumption: Avg. Page Number Per Issue - Daily 12; Avg. Page Number Per Issue - Plates Used 12100; Avg. Page Number Per Issue - Sunday 32; widths 25; Newsprint Used - Metric Tons 606.40; Printing Ink Used - Black 15619; Printing Ink Used - Color 2538; Printing Ink U
Equipment EDITORIAL: Front-end Software – Baseview.; Editorial Hardware – APP/Mac; Editorial Printers – HP; Classified Hardware – APP/Mac DISPLAY: Ad make-up applications – AdManager Pro 4; Display Hardware – APP/Mac; Display Printers – HP, Ricoh PRODUCTION: Pagination Software – QPS/QuarkXPress 6.5; Production Equipment – App/MAC, Trendsetters; Cameras – R/580; Scanners – Umax Astra 1220U, Canon PRESSROOM: Line 1 – 8-HI/V-15A 1974. Quad Stack Color Press; Inserters and stuffers – 10/Alphaliner; Bundle tying machines – 2-/Bu. BUSINESS COMPUTERS: Business Software – DTI, AR2000, Great Plains; Business Hardware – Dell/HP
Delivery method: Mail, Newsstand, Private Carrier, Racks

DEMING

DEMING HEADLIGHT

219 E. Maple St., Deming, N.M., 88030-4267; gen tel (575) 546-2611; gen fax (575) 546-8116; gen e-mail dheadlight@zianet.com; web site www.demingheadlight.com
Group: New Mexico Press Association Display Ad Network
Published: Mon, Tues, Wed, Thur, Fri
Weekday Frequency: m
Circulation: 3,541
Price: 60.00/yr (mail).
Advertising: Open inch rate $11.85
News services: AP.
Politics: Independent. **Established:** 1881
Not Published: New Year; Memorial Day; Independence Day; Labor Day; Thanksgiving; Christmas.
Special Editions: Duck Race (Aug); Christmas Greetings (Dec); Community Guide (Feb); Life Off the Land (Jul); Medical Tab (Jun); Horizons (Mar); Senior (May); Christmas (Nov); Southwestern Fair (Oct); Mimbres Paguime Connection (Sept).
Magazines: American Profile (Weekly).
Gen. Mgr. ....Wayne Barnard
HR Mgr. ....Judy Luna
Mktg. Consultant ....Monica Gutierrez
Circ. Mgr. ....Barry Webber
Ed. ....Bill Armendariz
Online Ed. ....Jason Gibbs
Market Information: TMC.
Mechanical available: Offset; Black and 3 ROP colors; insert accepted; page cutoffs - 16.
Mechanical Specifications: Type page 10 3/16 x 15 3/4; E - 5 cols, 1 15/16, 1/8 between; A - 5 cols, 1 15/16, 1/8 between; C - 7 cols, 1 5/16, 1/8 between.
Commodity Consumption: Avg. Page Number Per Issue - Daily 16; Avg. Page Number Per Issue - Plates Used 1500; widths 17; Newsprint Used - Metric Tons 115; Printing Ink Used - Black 1620; Printing Ink Used - Color 200; Printing Ink Used - Pages Printed 4160.
Equipment EDITORIAL: Front-end Software – Claris/Works, QPS/QuarkXPress.; Editorial Hardware – APP/Mac; Editorial Equipment – 5-COM; Classified Hardware – GraphX; Classified Equipment – 2-COM; Classified Printers – HP/LaserJet IVsi.; Display Hardware – APP/Mac; Production Equipment – 1-COM/Hd, 2-COM/2-Laser; Cameras – R/Horizontal. PRESSROOM: Line 1 – G/Community; Folders – 1-G/4:1.; Bundle tying machines – Bu; Addressing machine – Dispensa-Matic.; Business Hardware – 3-IBM/PC

FARMINGTON

THE DAILY TIMES

201 N. Allen St., Farmington, N.M., 87499; gen tel (505) 325-4545; adv tel (505) 325-4545; ed tel (505) 325-4545; gen fax (505) 564-4630; adv fax (505) 564-4580; ed fax (505) 564-4630; web site www.daily-times.com
Published: Mon, Tues, Wed, Thur, Fri, Sat, Sun
Weekday Frequency: m
Saturday Frequency: m
Circulation: 14,388; 15,261(sat); 18,001(sun)
Last Audit: ABC September 30, 2011
Price: 9.00/mo; 99.00/yr.
Advertising: Open inch rate $25.30
News services: AP, NYT.
Politics: Independent.
Special Editions: Reader's Choice (Apr); Connie Mack (Aug); Christmas (Dec); Home Expo (Feb); National High School Rodeo (Jul); Freedom Days (Jun); San Juan County Fair (May); Travel Guide (Nov); Parade of Homes (Oct); Health Living (Quarterly); Shiprock Fair (Sept).
Special Weekly Sections: Automotive (Fri); Business (Mon); Lifestyles (S); Explore (Thur); Lifestyles (Wed).
Magazines: Relish (Monthly); USA WEEKEND Magazine (S); American Profile (Weekly).
Pub. ....John Elchert
Adv. Mgr. ....Connie Pruitt
Adv. Coord., Design ....Tonya Birch
Circ. Dir. ....James Whittington
Ed. ....Troy Turner
Sr. Copy Ed. ....Margaret Mathers
Features Ed. ....Debra Mayeux
Online Ed. ....Patrick Hogan
Mgmt. Info Servs. Mgr. ....Leslie Sharpe
Prodn. Dir. ....Cindy Cowan
Market Information: TMC.
Mechanical available: Offset; Black and 3 ROP colors; insert accepted - job shop; page cutoffs - 22 3/4.
Mechanical Specifications: Type page 11 3/4 x 21 1/2; E - 6 cols, 1 5/6, 1/6 between; A - 6 cols, 1 5/6, 1/6 between; C - 9 cols, 1 1/12, 1/6 between.
Commodity Consumption: Avg. Page Number Per Issue - Daily 26; Avg. Page Number Per Issue - Plates Used 16000; Avg. Page Number Per Issue - Sunday 40; widths 12 1/2; Newsprint Used - Metric Tons 1250; Newsprint Used - Short Tons 1375; Printing Ink Used - Black 20000; Printing I
Equipment; Editorial Hardware – 1-APP/Mac PowerBook 520c, 5-APP/Mac Centris 650, 1-APP/Mac Quadra 605, 2-APP/Mac Quadra 610, 4-APP/Mac Quadra 630, 1-APP/Mac Quadra 700, 1-APP/Mac Quadra 900, 2-APP/Mac PowerBook 150, 1-APP/Mac PowerBook 1400CS, 1-APP/Mac PowerBook 3400C, 1-APP; Classified Hardware – 5-APP/iMac; Classified Equipment – 1-Toshiba/Copier 2532 Turbo, 1-Toshiba/Fax TF651 Turbo, 1-Brother/Fax 1850mc, 2-Nikon/Digital; Classified Printers – 1-APP/Mac LaserWriter 12-640 PS, 1-APP/Mac Color Stylewriter 4100, 1-Okidata/Pacemark 3410, 1-HP/Deskwriter 560C, DISPLAY: Ad make-up applications – QPS/QuarkXPress, Adobe/Photoshop, Caere/OmniPage, Baseview, Xante/Accel-a-Writer 8200, Adobe/Acrobat; Layout Software – APP/Mac network.; Display Hardware – 5-APP/Mac G4 PRODUCTION: Pagination Software – QPS/QuarkXPress 5.0.; Production Equipment – 1-Nu/FT40V6 UPNS Plate Burner, 2-APP/Mac G3, 2-APP/Mac 7300, Pre Press/Panther Pro Imagesetter; Scanners – Scitex/Eversmart PRESSROOM: Line 1 – 6-G/Urbanite 1979; Press Drives – 2-HP/100; Folders – 1; Reels and Stands – 2 MAILROOM: Counter stackers – 1-HL/Monitor HT II, 1/MM, 1-HL/Monitor, 1-/BG; Inserters and stuffers – 2-MM/227; Bundle tying machines – 2-OVL/41E, 1-OVL/515, Samuel/NT440; Addressing machine – 1-/KR; Other equipment –1-/Quarter-folder Cashline 552, 1-MM/Stitcher-Tr BUSINESS COMPUTERS: Business Software – Baseview, Dynamics 4.0; Business Hardware – PC Network, 2-AT, 1-Epson/LQ2550, 2-APP/Mac Quadra 610, 1-APP/Mac Centris 660AV, 1-APP/Mac Quadra 630, APP/Power Mac 7200-75

GALLUP

GALLUP INDEPENDENT

500 N. Ninth St., Gallup, N.M., 87301; gen tel (505) 863-6811; gen fax (505) 722-5750; gen e-mail ga11p1nd@cnetco.com; web site www.gallupindependent.com
Group: New Mexico Press Association Display Ad Network
Published: Mon, Tues, Wed, Thur, Fri, Sat
Weekday Frequency: e
Saturday Frequency: e
Circulation: 14,323; 14,323(sat)
Last Audit: ABC September 30, 2011
Price: 9.50/mo; 114.00/yr.
Advertising: Open inch rate $21.00
News services: AP, NYT.
Politics: Independent.
Not Published: New Year; Memorial Day; Independence Day; Labor Day; Thanksgiving; Christmas.
Special Editions: Native Sun (Aug); Native Sun (Jul); Native Sun (Jun); Native Sun (Sept).
Magazines: Relish (Monthly); USA WEEKEND Magazine (Sat); American Profile (Weekly).
Vice Pres./Pub. ....Robert C. Zollinger
Mktg. Mgr. ....Dyanne Valdez
Circ. Mgr. ....Valda Brown
Ed. ....Barry Heifner
Educ. Ed. ....Bill Donaran
Sports Ed. ....Alan Authur
Market Information: TMC; Zoned editions.
Mechanical available: Offset; Black and 3 ROP colors; insert accepted; page cutoffs - 22.
Mechanical Specifications: Type page 13 x 21 1/2; E - 6 cols, 2 1/16, 1/8 between; A - 6 cols, 2 1/16, 1/8 between; C - 7 cols, 1 3/4, 1/8 between.
Commodity Consumption: widths 31 1/2.
Equipment EDITORIAL: Front-end Software – HI.; Editorial Hardware – HI; Editorial Printers – MON CLASSIFIED: Front-end Software – Baseview.; Display Hardware – HI.; Production Equipment – 2-Nu, 1-Nikon/Coolscan 1000, 1-Nikon/Coolscan 2000; Cameras – R/Lens, OH, LE/500; Scanners – Equipment □ HI. PRESSROOM: Line 1 – 24-G/Magnum (6 towers); Folders – Universal. MAILROOM: Counter stackers – 1/Exact Count; Inserters and stuffers – 10-MM/Alphaliner; Bundle tying machines – 2-Wilton/Stra Pack.; Business Hardware – 1-IBM/36

HOBBS

HOBBS NEWS-SUN

201 N. Thorp St., Hobbs, N.M., 88240; gen tel (575) 393-2123; adv tel (575) 391-5408; ed tel (575) 397-4556; gen fax (575) 397-0610; adv fax (575) 397-0610; ed fax (575) 393-5724; gen e-mail hobbsnews@hobbsnews.com; adv e-mail advertise@hobbsnews.com; ed e-mail editor@hobbsnews.com; web site www.hobbsnews.com

Group: New Mexico Press Association Display Ad Network
Published: Tues, Wed, Thur, Fri, Sat, Sun
Weekday Frequency: All day
Saturday Frequency: All day
Circulation: 9,277; 9,277(sat); 9,322(sun)
Last Audit: September 30, 2009
Price: 9.00/mo; 108.00/yr.
Advertising: Open inch rate $15.60
News services: AP, MCT.
Politics: Independent. **Established:** 1928
Own facility?: Y
Special Editions: Back-to-School (Aug); Money & Finance (Jan); Progress Issue (Mar); High School & College Graduation (May); Christmas Gift Guide (Nov); Car Care (Oct); Fall Fashion (Sept).
Special Weekly Sections: Religion (Sat); Education (Thur).
Magazines: Relish (Monthly); Parade (S); American Profile (Weekly).
Vice Pres. ....Thomas B. Shearman
Admin. Asst. ....Dora Montz
Gen. Mgr. ....Kenneth Norris
Circ. Dir. ....Richard Howard
Bus./Finance Writer ....Richard Trout
Design Ed. ....Scott Jones
Editorial Page Ed. ....Daniel Russell
Religion Ed. ....Michelle Fox
Sports Ed. ....Clayton Jones
Prodn. Mgr., Pressroom ....Bennie Gaddy
Market Information: TMC.
Mechanical available: Offset; Black and 3 ROP colors; insert accepted; page cutoffs - 21 1/2.
Mechanical Specifications: Type page 13 x 21 1/2; E - 6 cols, 2 1/16, 1/8 between; A - 6 cols, 2 1/16, 1/8 between; C - 9 cols, 1 5/16, 1/8 between.
Commodity Consumption: Avg. Page Number Per Issue - Daily 20; Avg. Page Number Per Issue - Plates Used 9600; Avg. Page Number Per Issue - Sunday 44; widths 13 3/4; Newsprint Used - Short Tons 585; Printing Ink Used - Black 18000; Printing Ink Used - Color 2400; Printing Ink Us
Equipment EDITORIAL: Front-end Software – Baseview/NewsEdit Pro 3.1.7.; Editorial Hardware – APP/Mac; Editorial Equipment – 2-Pre Press/Panther Pro Imagesetter; Editorial Printers – Tektronix/380, V/5300B, Pre Press/Panther Imagesetter, APP/Mac LaserPrinter Color, Tektronix/Phaser 300, Kk/Full Color CLASSIFIED: Front-end Software – Baseview/Ad Manager Pro 2.06.; Classified Hardware – APP/Mac; Classified Equipment – 2-OS; Classified Printers – Okidata, Imagesetter/II, APP/Mac LaserPrinter, HP/LaserJet DISPLAY: Ad make-up applications – QPS/QuarkXPress 4.1, Multi-Ad, Aldus/FreeHand; Layout Software – APP/Mac.; Display Hardware – APP/Mac; Display Printers – APP/Mac LaserPrinter; Production Equipment – Lf/Leafscan 35, APP/Mac LaserWriter, Imagesetter II, V/5300B, APP/Mac Color LaserWriter, Pre Press/Panther, Tektronix/Phaser 300, APP/Mac Color LaserWriter 12/600 PS; Cameras – 2-AG/NC 2000e, Nikon/D1, Nikon/Coolpix 880, 3-Olympus PRESSROOM: Line 1 – 6-G/Urbanite; Folders – G/1000.; Inserters and stuffers – 1/MM; Bundle tying machines – Wilton/Stra Pack, 1-/OVL. BUSINESS COMPUTERS: Business Software – ADP, Lotus, Zen Write & Calc, WordPerfect 5.1, BMF, Great Plains, Baseview; Business Hardware – BFR, GAT, Standard, IBM

SUN PUBLISHING CORP.

201 N. Thorp, Hobbs, N.M., 88240; gen tel (575) 393-2123; adv tel (575)391-5404; gen fax (575) 393-0275; adv fax (575)397-0610

Published: Tues, Wed, Thur, Fri, Sat, Sun
Own facility?: Y

LAS CRUCES

LAS CRUCES SUN-NEWS

PO Box 1749, Las Cruces, N.M., 88004; gen tel (575) 541-5400; adv tel (575) 541-5426; ed tel (575) 541-5438; gen fax (575) 541-5499; adv fax (575) 541-5499; ed fax (575) 541-5498; web site www.lcsun-news.com

Group: Media News Group
Published: Mon, Tues, Wed, Thur, Fri, Sat, Sun
Weekday Frequency: m
Saturday Frequency: m
Circulation: 22,646; 18,353(sat); 23,917(sun)
Last Audit: ABC September 30, 2011
Price: 10.75/mo; 109.75/yr.
Advertising: Open inch rate $40.59
News services: AP, LAT-WP.
Politics: Independent.
Special Editions: Bridal Tab (Apr); Football Review (Aug); Holiday Preview (Dec); Basketball (Jan); Reader Choices (Jun); Business & Industry (Mar); Discover Greater Las Cruces (May); Mariachi Conference Publication (Oct); Game Day (Sept).
Special Weekly Sections: TV Magazine (Fri); Business Weekly (Mon); Prime Time (Other); Homes Magazine (S).
Magazines: USA WEEKEND Magazine (S); American Profile (Weekly).
Ed. ....Jim Lawitz
Bus. Ed. ....Brook Stockberger
City Ed. ....Brenda Masengill
Online Ed. ....Jason Gibbs
Prodn. Desk Ed. ....Lucas Peerman
Sports Ed. ....Teddy Feinberg
Ad Director ....Heidi Melendrez
Market Information: TMC; Zoned editions.
Mechanical available: Offset; Black and 3 ROP colors; insert accepted - any; page cutoffs - 22 3/4.
Mechanical Specifications: Type page 11 7/8 x 21 1/2; E - 6 cols, 1 7/8, 1/5 between; A - 6 cols, 1 7/8, 1/5 between; C - 9 cols, 1 1/5, 1/5 between.
Commodity Consumption: Avg. Page Number Per Issue - Daily 28; Avg. Page Number Per Issue - Plates Used 1059; Avg. Page Number Per Issue - Saturday 32; Avg. Page Number Per Issue - Sunday 48; widths 25; Newsprint Used - Metric Tons 1400; Printing Ink Used - Black 26555; Printin
Equipment EDITORIAL: Front-end Software – Baseview/NewsEdit Pro IQUE 2.1.3.; Editorial Hardware – APP/Mac; Editorial Printers – LaserMaster/1200 XL, HP/LaserJet IVsi, HP/LaserJet 4MV, ECR/Scriptsetter VRL 36/HS CLASSIFIED: Front-end Software – Baseview/AdManager Pro 2.0.5.; Classified Hardware – APP/Mac; Classified Printers – HP/LaserJet IVsi, HP/LaserJet 4MV DISPLAY: Ad make-up applications – Multi-Ad/Creator 3.8, QPS/QuarkXPress 3.32; Layout Software – 2.02-APP/Mac Page Director ALS.; Display Hardware – APP/Mac; Display Printers – HP/LaserJet IVsi, HP/LaserJet 4MV PRODUCTION: Pagination Software – QPS/QuarkXPress 3.32.; Production Equipment – Caere/OmniPage 3.0, 1-Nu/Flip Top FT40; Cameras – 3-C/Spartan; Scanners – 3-AG/Arcus II, 3-Nikon/LS1000 Film Scanners PRESSROOM: Line 1 – 10-G/U 1187 single width; Press Drives – 2; Folders – 1; Reels and Stands – 6; Press control system – 2; Bundle tying machines – 1/Bu, 1-Ace/50, Strapack/D-52; Addressing machine – 1-El/Communications. BUSINESS COMPUTERS: Business Software – Geac Vision Shift; Business Hardware – PC Network, PC Wintell

LAS VEGAS

LAS VEGAS OPTIC

614 Lincoln Ave., Las Vegas, N.M., 87701-2670; gen tel (505) 425-6796; adv tel (505) 425-6796; gen fax (505) 425-1005; adv fax (505) 425-1005; gen e-mail optic@lasvegasoptic.com; web site www.lasvegasoptic.com

Group: New Mexico Press Association Display Ad Network
Published: Mon, Tues, Wed, Thur, Fri
Weekday Frequency: e
Circulation: 6,049
Last Audit: September 30, 2003
Price: 6.95/mo; 83.40/yr.
Advertising: Open inch rate $11.90(e-fri)
News services: AP.
Politics: Independent.
Not Published: New Year; Independence Day; Labor Day; Thanksgiving; Christmas.
Special Editions: Santa's Workshop (Dec); George Washington (Feb); Fiesta (Jul); Little League (May).
Magazines: Relish (Monthly).
Bookkeeper ....Grace Roybal
Ed. ....Tom McDonald
Mng. Ed. ....David Giuliani
Sports Ed. ....David Wesner
Market Information: ADS; TMC.
Mechanical available: Offset; Black and 1 ROP colors; insert accepted; page cutoffs - 21 1/2.
Mechanical Specifications: Type page 15 1/2 x 22 1/2; E - 6 cols, 2 1/16, 1/8 between; A - 6 cols, 2 1/6, 1/8 between; C - 6 cols, 2 1/6, 1/8 between.
Commodity Consumption: Avg. Page Number Per Issue - Daily 10; widths 27 1/2; Newsprint Used - Metric Tons 120.
Equipment EDITORIAL: Front-end Software – Mk, QPS/QuarkXPress 5.0.; Editorial Hardware – Mk, APP/Mac; Editorial Printers – APP/Mac LaserPrinter CLASSIFIED: Front-end Software – Mk, QPS/QuarkXPress 5.0.; Classified Hardware – Mk, APP/Mac; Classified Printers – APP/Mac LaserPrinter; Production Equipment – 1-Nu, Vastec; Cameras – AG. PRESSROOM: Line 1 – G/Community 1975; Line 2 – G/Community 1975; Line 3 – G/Community 1975; Line 4 – G/Community 1975. BUSINESS COMPUTERS: Business Software – AccPac, Interlink; Business Hardware – 2-PC

LOS ALAMOS

LOS ALAMOS MONITOR

256 D.P. Rd., Los Alamos, N.M., 87544-1268; gen tel (505) 662-4185; gen fax (505) 662-4334; gen e-mail lamonitor@lamonitor.com; adv e-mail laads@lamonitor.com; ed e-mail laeditor@lamonitor.com; web site www.lamonitor.com

Group: New Mexico Press Association Display Ad Network
Published: Tues, Wed, Thur, Fri, Sun
Weekday Frequency: e
Circulation: 4,200; 4,200(sun)
Last Audit: Sworn September 30, 2006
Price: 6.75/mo; 76/yr.
Advertising: Open inch rate $13.29
News services: AP.
Politics: Independent. **Established:** 1963
Advertising not accepted: Y
Not Published: Christmas.
Own facility?: Y
Special Editions: Visitor's Guide (May); Holiday Gift Guide (Nov).
Special Weekly Sections: Religion (Fri); Business (S); Kaleidoscope (Thur).
Magazines: Relish (Monthly); American Profile (S).
Publisher ....Keven Todd
Adv. Sales ....Julie Smith
Circ. Admin. ....Jane Johnson
Mng. Ed. ....Carol Clark
Community Ed. ....Kristen Laskey
Sports Ed. ....Mike Cote
Prodn. Mgr. ....Brian Dunwoody
Prodn. Mgr., IT/Composition ....Rob Lamb
Market Information: TMC.
Mechanical available: Offset; Black and 3 ROP colors; insert accepted - we-prints; page cutoffs - 22 3/4.
Mechanical Specifications: Type page 13 x 21 1/2; E - 6 cols, 1 3/4, 1/8 between; A - 6 cols, 1 3/4, 1/8 between; C - 8 cols, 1 5/16, 1/8 between.
Commodity Consumption: Avg. Page Number Per Issue - Daily 12; Avg. Page Number Per Issue - Sunday 20; widths 25; Newsprint Used - Short Tons 132; Printing Ink Used - Black 4600; Printing Ink Used - Color 200.
Equipment EDITORIAL: Front-end Software – QPS/QuarkXPress.; Editorial Hardware – APP/Mac, APP/Power Mac 7100-66; Editorial Printers – Xante/Accel-a-Writer CLASSIFIED: Front-end Software – Printers □ Xante.; Classified Hardware – AST/Bravo 4-33 DISPLAY: Ad make-up applications – Adobe/Illustrator, Adobe/Photoshop, Multi-Ad/Creator; Layout Software – 1-APP/Mac IIsi, 1-APP/Mac SE, 2-Mk/Ad Comp, 1-Mk/TouchWriter Plus, APP/Mac G-3.; Display Hardware – APP/Mac; Display Printers – 3-APP/Mac LaserPrinter PRODUCTION: Pagination Software – QPS/QuarkXPress, Multi-Ad/CAMS, Multi-Ad/Class Force.; Production Equipment – 1-Nu/Flip Top; Cameras – Nu/2024; Scanners – Nikon PRESSROOM: Line 1 – 5-G/Community; Folders – 1 MAILROOM: Counter stackers – BG/104A; Bundle tying machines – . BUSINESS COMPUTERS: Business Software – Dell/Hard Disc 3165X; Business Hardware – VGA PC, Dell/Hard Disc 3165X
Delivery method: Newsstand, Private Carrier, Racks

LOVINGTON

LOVINGTON LEADER

14 W. Ave. B, Lovington, N.M., 88260-1717; gen tel (505) 396-2844; gen fax (505) 396-5775; gen e-mail leader@leaco.net

Published: Tues, Wed, Thur, Fri, Sun
Weekday Frequency: e
Circulation: 1,495; 1,495(sun)
Last Audit: September 30, 2006
Price: 7.00/mo; 84.00/yr.
Advertising: Open inch rate $7.00
News services: AP.
Politics: Independent.
Advertising not accepted: Liquor; Cigarettes.
Not Published: New Year; Thanksgiving; Christmas.
Special Editions: Car Special (Apr); Buyer's Pages (Aug); Christmas (Dec); All-Stars Sports (Jul); Father's Day Special (Jun); Basketball State Sig Page (Mar); Wildcats Page (May); Wildcat Sig Pages (Nov); Bosses' Week (Oct); Tatum Football (Sept).
Adv. Mgr. ....Joyce Clemens
Ed. ....John Graham
Society Ed. ....Jeanine Graham
Sports Ed. ....Neil Granath
Prodn. Pressman ....Hop Graham
Market Information: TMC.
Mechanical available: Offset; Black and 3 ROP colors; insert accepted; page cutoffs - 22 1/2.
Mechanical Specifications: Type page 13 x 21; E - 6 cols, 2 1/16, 1/8 between; A - 6 cols, 2 1/16, 1/8 between; C - 6 cols, 2 1/16, 1/8 between.
Commodity Consumption: Avg. Page Number Per Issue - Daily 8; Avg. Page Number Per Issue - Plates Used 2600; Avg. Page Number Per Issue - Sunday 16; widths 28; Newsprint Used - Metric Tons 73; Newsprint Used - Short Tons 80; Printing Ink Used - Black 3600; Printing Ink Used - C
Equipment EDITORIAL: Front-end Software – Baseview/NewsEdit.; Editorial Hardware – APP/Mac; Editorial Printers – APP/Mac LaserWriter Select 360, QMS/810 T; Classified Hardware – Wyse. DISPLAY: Ad make-up applications – QPS/QuarkXPress, Adobe/Photoshop; Layout Software – APP/Mac.; Display Printers – OYO/GS-1800 PRODUCTION: Pagination Software – QPS/QuarkXPress, Adobe/Photoshop.; Production Equipment – Caere/OmniPage Pro; Cameras – Nu; Scanners – Umax PRESSROOM: Line 1 – HI/Offset.; Bundle tying machines – 1/BU; Addressing machine – 1-/Am.

WAL-ROY PUBLISHING, INC.

14 W. Ave. B, Lovington, N.M., 88260; gen tel (505) 396-2844; gen fax (505) 396-5775

PORTALES

PORTALES NEWS-TRIBUNE

101 E. First St., Portales, N.M., 88130; gen tel (575) 356-4481; gen fax (575) 356-3630; gen e-mail pnt@yucca.net; web site www.pntonline.com

Group: New Mexico Press Association Display Ad Network
Published: Tues, Wed, Thur, Fri, Sun
Weekday Frequency: e
Circulation: 2,955; 2,955(sun)
Last Audit: September 30, 2007
Price: 5.90/mo; 67.80/yr.
Advertising: Open inch rate $10.25
News services: AP.
Politics: Independent.
Magazines: USA WEEKEND Magazine (S).
Pub. ....Ray Sullivan
Retail Sales Mgr. ....Ian Cook
Sports Ed. ....Dave Wagner
Market Information: TMC.
Mechanical available: Offset; Black and 3 ROP colors; insert accepted; page cutoffs - 22 3/4.
Mechanical Specifications: Type page 13 1/16 x 21 1/2; E - 6 cols, 2 1/16, 1/6 between; A - 6 cols, 2 1/16, 1/6 between; C - 8 cols, 1 1/2, 1/6 between.
Commodity Consumption: Avg. Page Number Per Issue - Daily 32; Avg. Page Number Per Issue - Sunday 60.
Equipment EDITORIAL: Front-end Software – Baseview.; Editorial Hardware – APP/Mac; Editorial Equipment – Pre Press/Panther Plus Imagesetter; Editorial Printers – 2-APP/Mac LaserPrinter CLASSIFIED: Front-end Software – Baseview.; Classified Hardware – APP/Mac; Classified Printers – 1-APP/Mac LaserPrinter; Production Equipment – Mk, APP/Mac Laser-Printers, Pre Press/Panther Plus Imagesetter; Cameras – 1-C/Spartan II; Scanners – 2-APP/Mac Scanner. MAILROOM: Counter stackers – 1/MM; Inserters and stuffers – MM; Bundle tying machines – 1-Bu/TS-210; Addressing machine – 1-Mk/ACE 50.; Business Hardware – IBM

ROSWELL

ROSWELL DAILY RECORD

2301 N. Main St., Roswell, N.M., 88201; gen tel (575) 622-7710; adv tel (575) 622-7710; ed tel (575) 622-7710; gen fax (575) 625-0421; adv fax (575) 625-0421; ed fax (575) 625-0421; gen e-mail admin@roswell-record.com; web site www.roswell-record.com

Group: New Mexico Press Association Display Ad Network
Published: Mon, Tues, Wed, Thur, Fri, Sun
Weekday Frequency: m
Circulation: 11,600; 12,800(sun)
Last Audit: March 31, 2007
Price: 15.00/mo (mail); 180.00/yr (mail).
Advertising: Open inch rate $15.20
News services: AP.
Politics: Independent.
Not Published: Christmas.
Special Editions: Roving Sands (Apr); Sports Tab (Aug); Christmas Time Page (Dec); Valentine's Specials (Feb); Blue Tag Special (Jan); Pet Tab (Jul); Summer Specials (Jun); Mother's Day (May); Pre-Christmas Coupon Book (Nov); Fair Days (Oct); Car Care Tab (Sept).
Special Weekly Sections: Screens (Fri).
Magazines: Vision Magazine (Monthly); USA WEEKEND Magazine (S); American Profile (Weekly).
Pres. ....Robert H. Beck
Pub. ....Charles Fischer
News Ed. ....Andrew Poertner
Online Mgr. ....Adam Jaramillo
Mgr., Mgmt. Info Servs. ....Ann Burns
Mechanical available: Offset; Black and 3 ROP colors; insert accepted; page cutoffs - 22 3/4.
Mechanical Specifications: Type page 13 1/16 x 21 1/2; E - 6 cols, 2 1/16, 1/6 between; A - 6 cols, 2 1/16, 1/6 between; C - 8 cols, 1 1/2, 1/6 between.
Commodity Consumption: Avg. Page Number Per Issue - Daily 24; Avg. Page Number Per Issue - Plates Used 8000; Avg. Page Number Per Issue - Sunday 36; widths 13 3/4; Newsprint Used - Short Tons 660; Printing Ink Used - Black 24000; Printing Ink Used - Color 300; Printing Ink Use
Equipment; Editorial Hardware – APP/Mac Performa 6116 CD-Roms, Polaroid/Sprintscan, AG/Arcus II Scanners; Editorial Equipment – Lf/AP Leaf Picture Desk, Lf/Leafscan, Lf/AP Laserphoto, AG/Arcus II Scanners, Epson/Photo PC 600 Digital Camera; Editorial Printers – APP/Mac LaserPrinters CLASSIFIED: Front-end Software – Baseview/AdManager Pro.; Classified Hardware – APP/iMacs; Classified Printers – APP/Mac Laser Writer 16/600 PS DISPLAY: Ad make-up applications – Baseview; Layout Software – Ad Force.; Display Hardware – Baseview, APP/Mac G3; Display Printers – HP/LaserJet 6MP PRODUCTION: Pagination Software – QPS/QuarkXPress 4.00.; Production Equipment – Caere/OmniPage 2.12, Konica EV Jetsetter 3100S, Xante/Laserprinters; Cameras – 1-C/Spartan II; Scanners – 2-APP/Mac Scanner, 2-AG/Arcus IIs PRESSROOM: Line 1 – 6-G/Urbanite (1 balloon former) single width; Folders – 1 MAILROOM: Counter stackers – 1/MM; Inserters and stuffers – 1-MM/6 Pocket, 1-MM/227 6 Pocket; Bundle tying machines – 1-EAM-Mosca/Rom, 1-ACE/50; Addressing machine – 1-Xenix/System; Other equipment –1-MM/Minuteman Saddle Stitcher.; Business Hardware – Mk/Acer-View, Epson/Printer, BMF/Newspaper System

SANTA FE

THE SANTA FE NEW MEXICAN

202 E. Marcy St., Santa Fe, N.M., 87501; gen tel (505) 983-3303; adv tel (505) 986-3007; ed tel (505) 986-3033; gen fax (505) 995-3875; adv fax (505) 984-1785; ed fax (505) 986-9147; gen e-mail info@sfnewmexican.com; ed e-mail newsroom@sfnewmexican.com; web site www.santafenewmexican.com

Published: Mon, Tues, Wed, Thur, Fri, Sat, Sun
Weekday Frequency: m
Saturday Frequency: m
Circulation: 21,245; 22,616(sat); 22,356(sun)
Last Audit: ABC September 30, 2011
Price: 3.25/wk; 14.08/mo; 152.10/yr.
Advertising: Open inch rate $45.00(m-fri)
News services: AP, NYT, LAT-WP, MCT.
Politics: Independent. **Established:** 1849
Own facility?: Y
Special Editions: Coupon Book (Jan, Mar, Jun, Sep), Enchanting Weddings (Feb), SF Winter Fiesta (Jan), Health Directory (Feb), NM Restaurant Week (Feb), Railrunner (Feb, May, Sep, Dec), Basketball State Tourney (Mar), Kids Summer (Apr), Golf (Apr), Bienvenidos (May), Native Treasures (May), North Stars (Jun), Buckaroo Ball (Jun), International Folk Art (Jun), Spanish Market (Jul), SOFA (Jul), Indian Market (Aug), Fiesta (Aug), Winterlife (Oct), Feliz Navidad (Nov)
Special Weekly Sections: La Voz (Mon)Teen Page (Fri); Health & Science (Mon); Comics (S); Religion (Sat); Outdoors (Thur); Business (Tues); @RecordBody:**Magazines:** Pasatiempo-Weekend Art & Entertainment Magazine (Fri); Vista (Mon); Parade (S); TV Book (Sat).
Pub. ....Robin Martin
Assoc. Pub. ....Ginny Sohn
Credit Mgr. ....Mary Jo Kesler
Opns. Mgr., Classified ....Laura Harding
Circ. Dir. ....Mike Reichard
Mng. Ed. ....Rob Dean
Asst. Mng. Ed. ....Mike Cosgrove
Arts/Entertainment Ed. ....Kristina Melcher
Bus./Finance Ed. ....Bob Quick
City Ed. ....Howard Houghton
Features Ed. ....Bruce Krasnow
Photography Dir. ....Clyde Mueller
Online Ed. ....Hengy Lopez
Prodn. Dir. ....Al Waldron
Prodn. Mgr., Mailroom ....Brian Schultz
Controller ....Robert Romero
Editorial Editor ....Inez Russell Gomez
I.T. Director ....Michael Campbell
Advertising Director ....Tamara Hand
Market Information: ADS
Mechanical available: Offset; Black and 3 ROP colors; insert accepted - pre-sorted A/B; page cutoffs - 22 3/4.
Mechanical Specifications: Type page 11 5/8 x 21 1/3; E - 6 cols, 1 5/6, 1/8 between; A - 6 cols, 1 1/8, 1/8 between; C - 9 cols, 1 3/8, 1/16 between.
Commodity Consumption: Avg. Page Number Per Issue - Daily 32; Avg. Page Number Per Issue - Plates Used 24657; Avg. Page Number Per Issue - Sunday 89; widths 25; Newsprint Used - Metric Tons 2717; Printing Ink Used - Black 55404; Printing Ink Used - Color 16621; Printing Ink Us
Equipment EDITORIAL: Front-end Software – Baseview/News EditPro.; Editorial Hardware – Equipment □ 26-AP/G4; Editorial Printers – HP/LaserJet 4Plus CLASSIFIED: Front-end Software – Baseview/AdManager 4.; Classified Hardware – Baseview/AdManager 4; Classified Equipment – 11-AP/iMac; Classified Printers – 1-HP/5P DISPLAY: Ad make-up applications – QPS/QuarkXPress 4.0; Layout Software – 9-APP/Mac G4.; Display Printers – 1-QMS/860, 1-HP/LaserJet 4MV, 1-MON/Proof Express PRODUCTION: Pagination Software – Adobe InDesign 2.02.; Production Equipment – 2-Pre Press/Panther 46HS with RIP, Adobe/Photoshop PRESSROOM: Line 1 – 9-G/U 870A; Press Drives – 2, 2-HP/200 Baldor Motors; Folders – 1; Reels and Stands – 7-G w/Jardis/Tension Control; Press control system – Ry/Spray Bar System. MAILROOM: Counter stackers – 1-Id, QWI/300, QWI/350; Inserters and stuffers – 1-GMA/SLS 1000 8:1; Bundle tying machines – 1-MLN/Spirit, 1/Power Strap/PSN-6E, 1-Dy/NP3; Mailroom control system – GMA; Addressing machine – 1-GMA/Triton; Other equipment –1-MM/321. BUSINESS COMPUTERS: Business Software – PBS, Sun/SBS; Business Hardware – 2-Sun/Ultra

SILVER CITY

SILVER CITY DAILY PRESS & INDEPENDENT

300 W. Market St., Silver City, N.M., 88062; gen tel (575) 388-1576; gen fax (575) 388-1196; web site www.scdailypress.com

Group: New Mexico Press Association Display Ad Network
Published: Mon, Tues, Wed, Thur, Fri, Sat
Weekday Frequency: e
Circulation: 7,782
Last Audit: September 30, 2002
Price: 2.00/wk (carrier); 77.00/yr (mail, county), $94.00/yr (out of county); 8.00/4wk, $10.00/5wk.
Advertising: Open inch rate $16.25
News services: AP.
Politics: Independent.
Not Published: New Year; Memorial Day; Independence Day; Labor Day; Thanksgiving; Christmas.
Special Weekly Sections: Arts & Entertainment (Thur).
Magazines: TV Guide (Thur).
Circ. Mgr. ....Susie Torres
Ed. in Chief ....Christina Ely
Ed. ....Dean Thompson
Prodn. Mgr., Mailroom ....Mary Ybarra
Market Information: TMC.
Mechanical available: Offset; Black and 3 ROP colors; insert accepted - all; page cutoffs - 21.
Mechanical Specifications: Type page 12 1/2 x 21; E - 6 cols, 2 1/4, 1/8 between; A - 7 cols, 1 5/8, 1/8 between; C - 7 cols, 1 5/8, 1/8 between.
Commodity Consumption: Avg. Page Number Per Issue - Daily 10; widths 28; Newsprint Used - Metric Tons 200; Newsprint Used - Short Tons 180.
Equipment EDITORIAL: Front-end Software – Baseview/Wire Manager.; Editorial Hardware – APP/Mac; Editorial Printers – APP/Mac Laser; Classified Hardware – APP/Mac; Classified Printers – APP/Mac Laser. DISPLAY: Ad make-up applications – Aldus/PageMaker, Claris/MacDraw.; Display Hardware – APP/Mac LC II; Display Printers – APP/Mac Laser PRODUCTION: Pagination Software – Adobe/PageMaker 6.5.; Production Equipment – APP/Mac; Cameras – B/4000 PRESSROOM: Line 1 – 4-KP/News King.
00

SILVER CITY SUN-NEWS

208 W Broadway, Silver City, N.M., 88061; gen tel (505) 538-5893; web site www.scsun-news.com

Group: MediaNews Group Inc

NEW YORK

ALBANY

CAPITAL NEWSPAPERS DIV.

News Plaza, Albany, N.Y., 12212; gen tel (518) 454-5694; gen fax (518) 489-5877 (Admin)

TIMES UNION

645 Albany Shaker Rd., Albany, N.Y., 12211-1158; gen tel (518) 454-5694; adv tel (518) 454-5588; ed tel (518) 454-5420; gen fax (518) 454-5628; adv fax (518) 454-5417; ed fax (518) 454-5628; ed e-mail tuletters@timesunion.com; web site www.timesunion.com

Group: Hearst Corporation
Published: Mon, Tues, Wed, Thur, Fri, Sat, Sun
Weekday Frequency: m
Saturday Frequency: m
Circulation: 65,710; 55,169(sat); 128,001(sun)
Last Audit: ABC September 30, 2011
Price: 6.50/wk (dS); 26.00/mo (dS); 338.00/yr.
Advertising: Open inch rate: Sunday - $144.04; Mon-Wed - $114.21; Thurs-Sat - $121.49
News services: AP, HN, NYT, MCT, Bloomberg, GNS.
Politics: Independent.
Special Editions: Saratoga Style (July); Travers (Aug); College Choices (Apr & Oct); Homeshow (Jan); Golf Guide (Apr)
Special Weekly Sections: Preview (Thur)
Magazines: Life @ Home; Healthy Life; TV Magazine; Explore; VOW Magazine
Pub./CEO ....George R. Hearst
CFO ....Ray Koupal
Dir., Opns./Facilities Planning ....Dan Couto
Adv. Vice Pres. ....Kathleen Hallion
Dir of Audience Development ....Mark Vinciguerra
Ed./Vice Pres. ....Rex Smith
Assoc. Ed. ....Michael V. Spain
Sr. Features Ed. ....Tracy Ormsbee
Sr. Investigations Ed. ....Robert Port
Sr. Local News Ed. ....Teresa Buckley
Opinion Pages Ed. ....Joann M. Crupi
Dir., Technical Servs. ....Charles Hug
Prodn. Mgr. ....Michael Mace
Prodn. Supt., Mailroom ....Richard Casullo
Online Executive Producer ....Paul Block
Mktg. Dir. ....Allison Lauenstein

Art Dir. ....Thomas Palmer
City Ed. ....Susan Mehalack
Features Ed. ....Ruth Fantasia
State Ed. ....Casey Seiler
Interactive Gen. Mgr. ....Patti Hart
Market Information: Split run; Zoned editions.
Mechanical available: Letterpress (direct); Black and 3 ROP colors; insert accepted; page cutoffs - 22 3/4.
Mechanical Specifications: Type page 12 x 21 1/2; E - 6 cols, 1 7/8, 1/8 between; A - 6 cols, 1 7/8, 1/8 between; C - 10 cols, 1 7/8, 1/8 between.
Commodity Consumption: Avg. Page Number Per Issue - Daily 50; Avg. Page Number Per Issue - Sunday 112; widths 50; Newsprint Used - Metric Tons 7500; Printing Ink Used - Black 280,000; Printing Ink Used - Color 40,000
Equipment EDITORIAL: Front-end Software – DTI; Editorial Hardware – Sun CLASSIFIED: Front-end Software – Mactive; Classified Hardware – Sun Cluster DISPLAY: Ad make-up applications – Mactive; Layout Software – DTI, SCS Class Pag.; Display Hardware – Sun Cluster; Production Equipment – 2-AGFA Selectset 25XT
2-AFGA Avantra 20/25 OLP
1-AGFA Phoenix 2250 PRESSROOM: Line 1 – 10-G/Mark II, 4-G/Mark V double width; Folders – 2 MAILROOM: Counter stackers – 8/QWI; Inserters and stuffers – 2-HI/2299 on-line, 1-HI/632, 1 Schur Palitizer; Bundle tying machines – 8-/Dynaric
; Mailroom control system – SAM, 2299 Apsolut 632; Addressing machine – 1-/Ch, 2-/LSI; Other equipment –2-/Barstrom.

AMSTERDAM

THE RECORDER

1 Venner Rd., Amsterdam, N.Y., 12010; gen tel (518) 843-1100; gen fax (518) 843-6580; adv fax (518) 843-1338; ed fax (518) 843-6580; adv e-mail advertising@recordernews.com; ed e-mail news@recordernews.com; web site www.recordernews.com

Published: Mon, Tues, Wed, Thur, Fri, Sat, Sun
Weekday Frequency: m
Saturday Frequency: m
Circulation: 8,116; 8,116(sat); 8,305(sun)
Last Audit: September 30, 2006
Price: 2.50/wk; 154.96/yr.
Advertising: Open inch rate $21.00
News services: LAT-WP, AP, MCT.
Politics: Independent.
Not Published: Christmas.
Special Editions: Pro Baseball Preview (Apr); Summer Projects (Aug); Christmas Gift Guide II (Dec); Year Outlook (Feb); Bridal Book I (Jan); Saratoga Horse Racing (Jul); Bridal Book II (Jun); Cooking Contest (Mar); Christmas Gift Guide I (Nov); Fall Car Care (Oct); Autumn
Special Weekly Sections: Business (Mon); Senior Citizens (S); Best Food Days (Wed).
Magazines: Silver Lining (Monthly); Currents-Arts (S).
Pub. ....Kevin McClary
Adv./Mktg. Dir. ....Brian Krohn
Dir., News Opns. ....Geoff Dylong
Mng. Ed. ....J'Lyn Wimple
Market Information: TMC.
Mechanical available: Offset; Black and 3 ROP colors; insert accepted - samples, cards; page cutoffs - 22 3/4.
Mechanical Specifications: Type page 13 x 21 1/2; E - 6 cols, 2 1/16, 1/8 between; A - 6 cols, 2 1/16, 1/8 between; C - 8 cols, 1 9/16, 1/16 between.
Commodity Consumption: Avg. Page Number Per Issue - Daily 22; Avg. Page Number Per Issue - Plates Used 18000; Avg. Page Number Per Issue - Sunday 54; widths 27 1/2; Newsprint Used - Short Tons 780; Printing Ink Used - Black 20000; Printing Ink Used - Color 1000; Printing Ink U
Equipment; Editorial Hardware – 1-AT/7000; Editorial Equipment – 1-LE/PC 13 Dry Film

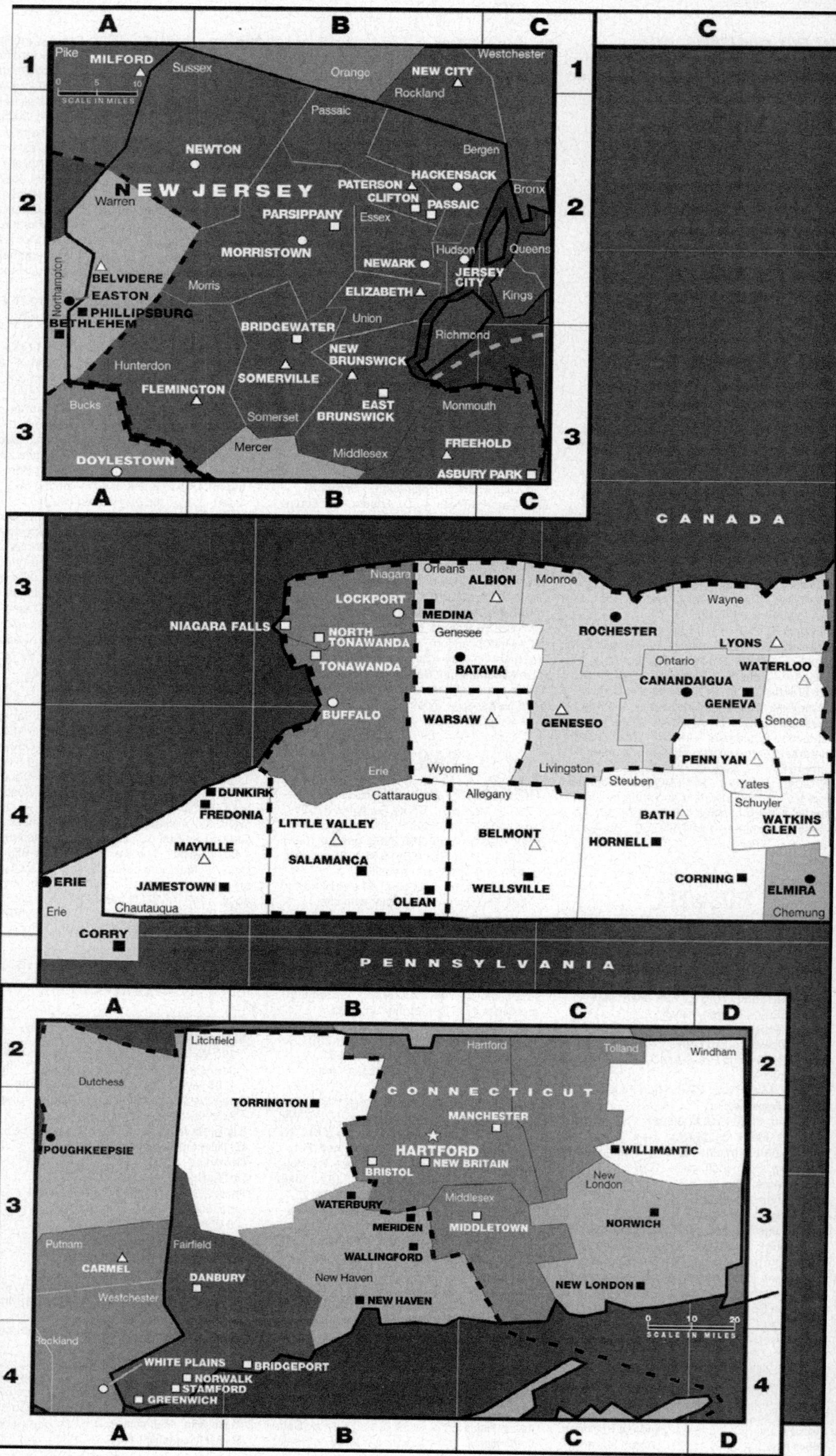

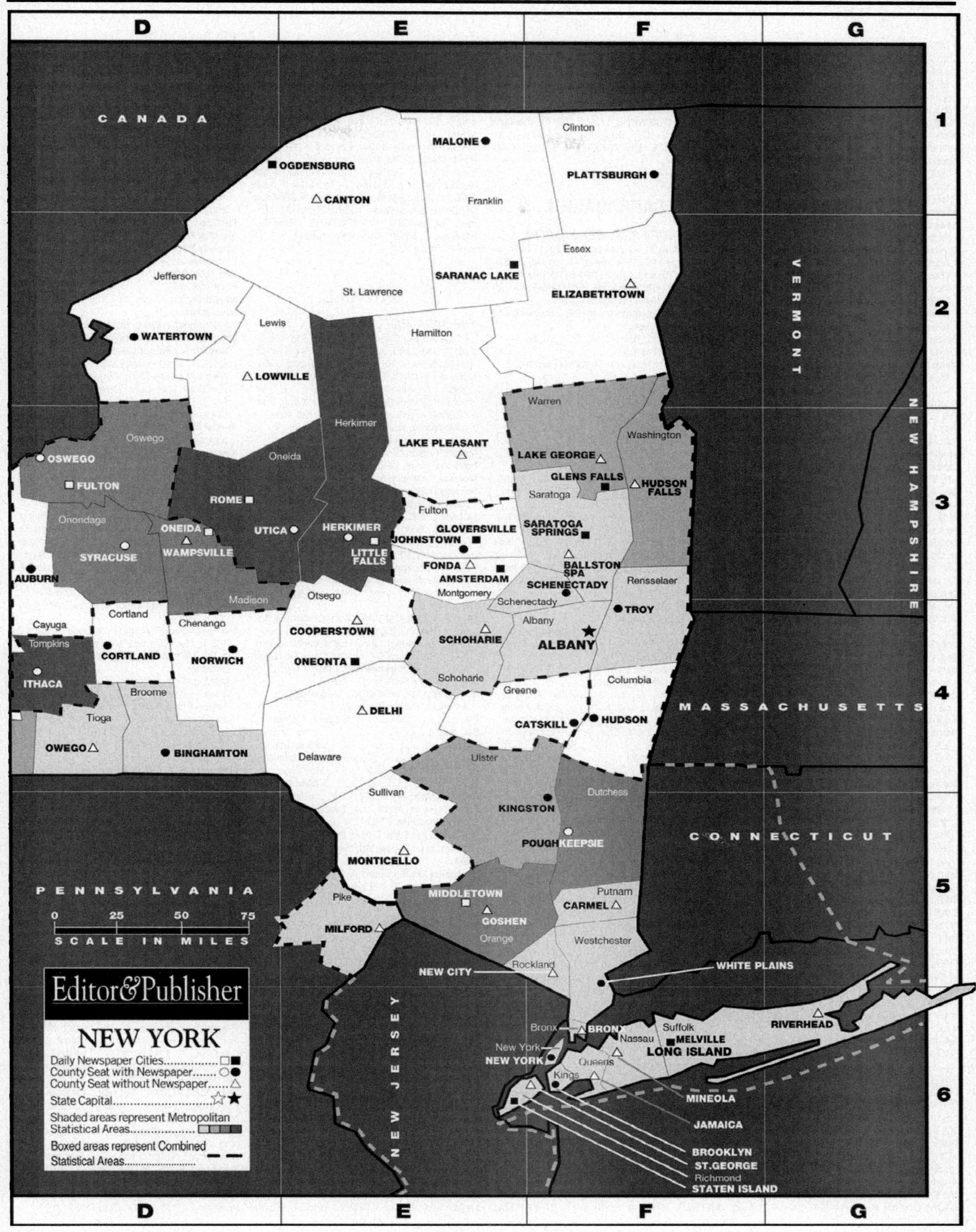
D
E
F
G
1
2
3
4
5
6
CANADA
VERMONT
NEW HAMPSHIRE
MASSACHUSETTS
CONNECTICUT
PENNSYLVANIA
NEW JERSEY
Clinton
MALONE
OGDENSBURG
PLATTSBURGH
CANTON
Franklin
Essex
SARANAC LAKE
Jefferson
St. Lawrence
ELIZABETHTOWN
Lewis
Hamilton
WATERTOWN
LOWVILLE
Warren
Herkimer
Oswego
Washington
LAKE PLEASANT
OSWEGO
Oneida
LAKE GEORGE
GLENS FALLS
HUDSON FALLS
FULTON
Saratoga
ROME
Fulton
Onondaga
HERKIMER
SARATOGA SPRINGS
ONEIDA
UTICA
GLOVERSVILLE
JOHNSTOWN
WAMPSVILLE
SYRACUSE
LITTLE FALLS
FONDA
BALLSTON SPA
AUBURN
AMSTERDAM
SCHENECTADY
Rensselaer
Otsego
Madison
Montgomery
Schenectady
Cortland
TROY
Cayuga
Chenango
COOPERSTOWN
Albany
Tompkins
SCHOHARIE
CORTLAND
NORWICH
ALBANY
ONEONTA
ITHACA
Schoharie
Columbia
Broome
Greene
DELHI
Tioga
HUDSON
CATSKILL
OWEGO
BINGHAMTON
Delaware
Ulster
Sullivan
Dutchess
KINGSTON
POUGHKEEPSIE
MONTICELLO
Putnam
MIDDLETOWN
Pike
CARMEL
GOSHEN
MILFORD
Orange
Westchester
0 25 50 75
SCALE IN MILES
Rockland
NEW CITY
WHITE PLAINS
Editor&Publisher
NEW YORK
Daily Newspaper Cities
County Seat with Newspaper
County Seat without Newspaper
State Capital
Shaded areas represent Metropolitan Statistical Areas
Boxed areas represent Combined Statistical Areas
Bronx
BRONX
Suffolk
RIVERHEAD
Nassau
MELVILLE
New York
LONG ISLAND
NEW YORK
Queens
Kings
MINEOLA
JAMAICA
BROOKLYN
ST.GEORGE
Richmond
STATEN ISLAND

0207; adv fax (716) 849-3409; ed fax (716) 856-4554; gen e-mail webmaster@buffalo.com; web site www.buffalonews.com

Group: New York Newspaper Advertising Service, Inc.
Published: Mon, Tues, Wed, Thur, Fri, Sat, Sun
Weekday Frequency: All day
Saturday Frequency: m
Circulation: 152,074; 165,192(sat); 235,671(sun)
Last Audit: ABC September 30, 2011
Price: 4.50/wk; 234.00/yr.
Advertising: Open inch rate $350.39
News services: AP, MCT, LAT-WP, RN.
Politics: Independent. **Established:** 1880
Special Editions: First Sunday (Apr); Today's Education (Aug); Menus (Dec); Auto Show (Feb); Weddings (Jan); First Sunday (Jul); Horizons (Jun); Buffalo Home Show (Mar); WNY Nurses Assoc. (May); First Sunday (Nov); Bridal Planner (Oct); NFL Preview (Sept).
Special Weekly Sections: The Link (Mon); Pets (Sat); Your Health (Tues); Food (Wed).
Magazines: Gusto (entertainment tab) (Fri); Monday Sports (tab) (Mon); Metro Comics (S); Home Finder (Sat); NEXT (young teens' tab) (Tues).
Pub. .... Stanford Lipsey
Pres. .... Warren T. Colville
Exec. Vice Pres. .... Robert J. Casell
Vice Pres., HR .... Daniel J. Farberman
Chrmn. .... Warren E. Buffett
Adv. Vice Pres./Dir. .... Phillip T. Catanese
Adv. Asst. Dir. .... Sherri Deaton-Callahan
Adv. Mgr., Mktg. Research .... Melissa McCann
Mktg. Vice Pres. .... Dottie Gallagher-Cohen
Promos. Dir. .... Cindy Sterner
Creative Mktg. Mgr. .... Jim Dever
Sr. Creative Servs. Mgr. .... Joe Kirchmyer
Circ. Vice Pres./Dir. .... Rich Williams
Circ. Mgr., Admin. .... Alicia Cheney
Circ. Mgr., Home Delivery .... Mike Benevento
Circ. Mgr., Newspapers in Educ. .... Kelly Asher
Circ. Mgr., Sales .... Thomas R. Heine
Ed. .... Margaret M. Sullivan
Mng. Ed. .... Edward L. Cuddihy
Mng. Ed. .... Gerald Goldberg
Market Information: Split run; TMC; Zoned editions.
Mechanical available: Offset; Black and 3 ROP colors; insert accepted - preprinted tabs, card stock; page cutoffs - 21 1/4.
Mechanical Specifications: Type page 11 5/8 x 20; E - 6 cols, 1 5/6, 1/8 between; A - 6 cols, 1 3/32, 1/8 between; C - 10 cols, 1 1/4, 1/16 between.
Commodity Consumption: Avg. Page Number Per Issue - Daily 56; Avg. Page Number Per Issue - Plates Used 250000; Avg. Page Number Per Issue - Saturday 72; Avg. Page Number Per Issue - Sunday 128; widths 25; Newsprint Used - Metric Tons 50585; Printing Ink Used - Black 1167402; P
Equipment EDITORIAL: Front-end Software – Guardian, OS/C30.9.; Editorial Hardware – SII/Servernet (2000); Editorial Equipment – Lf/AP Leaf Merlin Picture System, 125-Coyote/3 PC Emulation; Editorial Printers – HP/LaserJet 4MV CLASSIFIED: Front-end Software – Guardian, OS/C30.9.; Classified Hardware – SII/Servernet (2000); Classified Equipment – 80-Coyote 3; Classified Printers – HP/LaserJet 4MV DISPLAY: Ad make-up applications – DPS/AdTracker, Adobe/InDesign 2.0; Layout Software – SII/Sys 77, SII/Sails.; Display Hardware – APP/Mac; Display Printers – HP/LaserJet 4MV, GEI/Colorproof XL, GEI/Newsproof PRODUCTION: Pagination Software – SII/Coyote Layout.; Production Equipment – 2-AGFA/3850 CTP, 1-Horizon/Ultra, 1-Lf/Leafscan, 1-Kk/2035; Scanners – 1-AG/Horizon Plus, 1-AG/Horizon Ultra, PixelCraft 2x8100 Scanner, 1-Tecsa/TS2470 PRESSROOM: Line 1 – 7-KBA/Color A Offset double width; Line 2 – 7-KBA/Color A Offset double width; Line 3 – 6-Wd/Metropolitan (4-color deck) double width 1958; Line 4 – 6-Wd/Metropolitan (4-color deck) double width 1958; Line 5 – 6-Wd/Metropolitan (4-color deck) dou MAILROOM: Counter stackers – 8-HPS/Dual Carrier, 3-HPS/Dual Carrier, 3-QWI/501; Inserters and stuffers – 1-AM Graphics/25-head dual delivery inserter, 1-AM Graphics/29-head dual delivery inserter; Bundle tying machines – 9-Dynaric/NP-1, 14-Dynaric/NP-2; Wrapping singles – Wrapping si; Audio Hardware – Newspaper Voice Systems BUSINESS COMPUTERS: Business Software – CJ; Business Hardware – 1-HP/3000-928, 1-HP/3000-918LX, 1-HP/3000-928

CANANDAIGUA

MESSENGER POST NEWSPAPERS

73 Buffalo St., Canandaigua, N.Y., 14424-1085; gen tel (585) 394-0770; adv tel (585) 394-0770; ed tel (585) 394-0770; gen fax (585) 394-6837; adv fax (585) 394-1675; ed fax (585) 394-4160; gen e-mail letters@messengerpostmedia.com; web site www.mpnnow.com

Published: Mon, Tues, Wed, Thur, Fri, Sun
Weekday Frequency: e
Price: 2.65/wk (carrier); 11.48/mo (carrier); 150.00/yr.
Advertising: Open inch rate $17.50
News services: AP, SHNS, LAT-WP.
Politics: Independent.
Note: Messenger Post Newspapers also publishes the Daily Messenger in Canadaigua, New York and one monthly regional guide to arts and antiques.
Not Published: New Year; Memorial Day; Independence Day; Labor Day; Christmas (unless holiday falls on a Sunday).
Special Editions: Homes & Landscapes (Apr); Rx For Good Health (Aug); Holiday Gift Guide (Dec); Interiors (Feb); Wedding Guide (Jan); Summer Homes (Jul); Summer Dining Guide (Jun); Salute to Seniors (Mar); Vacation Guide (May); Holiday Gift Guide (Nov); Rx for Good Health
Special Weekly Sections: Real Estate (Fri); Weddings and Engagements (Mon); Business/Consumer Page (Mon-fri); Stock Page (S); Farm Page (Thur); Seniors Page (Tues); Religion (Wed).
Magazines: Accent on Homes (Fri); TV Viewer (S); Steppin' Out (Thur).
Pub. .... Jim O'Rourke
Vice Pres., Adv. .... Ken Henry
Circ. Dir. .... Keith Witmer
Exec. Ed. .... Rick Jenson
Mng. Ed. .... Kevin M. Frisch
Arts/Entertainment Ed. .... David Willer
Assignment Ed .... Allison Cooper
Assignment Ed. .... Kevin Frisch
City Ed. .... Tim Belknap
Community News Ed. .... Steve Buchiere
Asst. Editorial Page Ed. .... Mike Murphy
Photo Ed. .... Rikki Van Camp
Sports Ed. .... Mike Cutillo
Sunday Ed. .... Margaret Poe
Pub./Gen. Mgr. .... Kathy Hammond
Market Information: ADS; TMC.
Mechanical available: Offset; Black and 3 ROP colors; insert accepted - pocket book style, approved product samples; page cutoffs - 20 1/2.
Mechanical Specifications: Type page 13 x 20 1/2; E - 6 cols, 1 13/16, 1/8 between; A - 6 cols, 1 13/16, 1/8 between; C - 8 cols, 1 3/8, 1/8 between.
Commodity Consumption: Avg. Page Number Per Issue - Daily 26; Avg. Page Number Per Issue - Plates Used 9000; Avg. Page Number Per Issue - Sunday 40; widths 27 1/2; Newsprint Used - Short Tons 1250; Printing Ink Used - Black 45000; Printing Ink Used - Color 6000; Printing Ink U
Equipment EDITORIAL: Front-end Software – APP/Appleworks, QPS/QuarkXPress, Adobe/Photoshop.; Editorial Hardware – APP/Mac G3, HP/NetServers; Editorial Printers – HP/5000 N CLASSIFIED: Front-end Software – Baseview/Ad Manager Pro.; Classified Hardware – HP/NetServers DISPLAY: Ad make-up applications – QPS/QuarkXPress, Aldus/FreeHand, Adobe/Photoshop; Layout Software – MEI/ALS.; Display Hardware – 10-APP/Mac G3/450; Display Printers – 1-QMS/1660, 1-APP/Mac Lasermaster Unity 1200XL, HP 5000 N PRODUCTION: Pagination Software – QPS/QuarkXPress 4.04.; Production Equipment – Textbridge, GRHAM, Wing-Lynch/Model 5, Glunz & Jensen/66; Cameras – Vertical; Scanners – 2-Umax/PowerLook 2000, 3-Kk/Professional 2035 PRESSROOM: Line 1 – 10-G/Community 1994; Folders – 1-G/SSC-8384. MAILROOM: Counter stackers – Id/440; Inserters and stuffers – Am/Sheridan I372P; Bundle tying machines – MLN/Spirit Auto, Bu/Semi-Auto; Addressing machine – Ch/Videojet; Other equipment –Triumph/5221-95 Trimmer. BUSINESS COMPUTERS: Business Software – MSSI; Business Hardware – 11-Intel/Pentium 188

CATSKILL

THE DAILY MAIL

414 Main St., Catskill, N.Y., 12414; gen tel (518) 943-2100; adv tel (518) 828-1616; ed tel (518) 943-2100; gen fax (518) 943-2063; adv fax (518) 828-9437; ed fax (518) 943-2063; gen e-mail publisher@thedailymail.net; adv e-mail classifieds@registerstar.com; ed e-mail editorial@thedailymail.net; web site www.thedailymail.net

Group: Brydson Global Media Sales
Published: Tues, Wed, Thur, Fri
Weekday Frequency: m
Saturday Frequency: m
Circulation: 2,564; 3,231(sat); 2,746(sun)
Last Audit: ABC September 30, 2011
Price: 150.00/yr; 13.00/5wk.
Advertising: Open inch rate $10.93
News services: AP.
Politics: Independent.
Not Published: New Year; Memorial Day; Independence Day; Labor Day; Thanksgiving; Christmas.
Special Editions: Car Care (Apr); Christmas Gift Guide (Dec); Progress Report (Feb); Bridal (Jan); Vacationer (Jun); Home Improvement (Mar); Christmas Gift Guide (Nov); Car Care (Oct); Home Improvement (Sept).
Special Weekly Sections: TV (Sat).
Magazines: USA WEEKEND Magazine (S); American Profile (Weekly).
Pub. .... Roger F. Coleman
Bus. Mgr. .... Tia Scrum
Adv. Dir. .... Pam Geskie
Circ. Dir. .... Joseph Hoffman
Ed. .... Ray Pignone
Sports Ed. .... Mike LaBuff
Data Processing Mgr. .... Phil Finkle
Prodn. Foreman, Press .... Bruce Meiswinkle
Market Information: TMC.
Mechanical available: Offset; Black and 3 ROP colors; insert accepted; page cutoffs - 22 3/4.
Mechanical Specifications: Type page 13 x 21 1/2; E - 6 cols, 2, 1/6 between; A - 6 cols, 2, 1/6 between; C - 10 cols, 1 1/5, 1/12 between.
Commodity Consumption: Avg. Page Number Per Issue - Daily 22; Avg. Page Number Per Issue - Saturday 36; widths 27 1/2; Newsprint Used - Short Tons 600.
Equipment EDITORIAL: Front-end Software – Baseview/NewsEdit Pro.; Editorial Hardware – APP/Mac, APP/Power Mac, APP/Mac G3; Editorial Equipment – AG/1500; Editorial Printers – 3-HP CLASSIFIED: Front-end Software – Baseview.; Classified Hardware – APP/Mac, APP/Power Mac 6100, APP/Power Mac 7100, APP/Mac G3; Classified Equipment – Umax/Scanner; Classified Printers – HP DISPLAY: Ad make-up applications – Multi-Ad/Creator; Layout Software – APP/Mac.; Display Hardware – APP/Mac 7100, APP/Mac G3; Display Printers – APP/Mac LaserPrinter II NT, Compaq/PageMarq 15 PRODUCTION: Pagination Software – QPS/QuarkXPress.; Production Equipment – 3-Laser, HP, 2-AG/Imagesetters; Cameras – Repromaster/2001 PRESSROOM: Line 1 – 13-G/Community; Folders – G/SC.; Inserters and stuffers – I-KAN/5-pocket; Bundle tying machines – 2; Addressing machine – 1/Wm, 1-/X. BUSINESS COMPUTERS: Business Software – PBS; Business Hardware – 2-IBM

CORNING

THE LEADER

34 W. Pulteney, Corning, N.Y., 14830; gen tel (607) 936-4651; gen fax (607) 936-9939; adv fax (607) 962-0782; ed fax (607) 936-9939; web site www.the-leader.com

Published: Mon, Tues, Wed, Thur, Fri, Sat, Sun
Weekday Frequency: m
Saturday Frequency: m
Circulation: 12,818; 12,818(sat); 12,691(sun)
Last Audit: March 31, 2005
Price: 3.50/wk.
Advertising: Open inch rate $24.00
News services: AP.
Politics: Independent. **Established:** 1847
Special Editions: Home Improvement (Apr); September Finger Lakes Fun Book (Aug); Gift Certificates (Dec); Valentine's Day Gifts (Feb); At Home (Jan); August Finger Lakes Fun Book (Jul); July Finger Lakes Fun Book (Jun); People Who Make a Difference (Mar); Corning Classic S
Special Weekly Sections: Flag to Flag Motorsports (Fri); Food (S); Entertainment (Thur).
Magazines: Parade (S); Weekend (Thur).
Pub. .... Dennis Bruen
Opns. Mgr. .... Beth Warren
Adv. Dir. .... Michelle Passmore
Circ. Dir. .... Elmer Kuehner
Mng. Ed. .... Joe Dunning
Features Ed. .... Derek Ek
Online Ed. .... Stella DuPree
Sports Ed. .... Shawn Vargo
Prodn. Foreman, Pressroom .... Jim Jones
Market Information: ADS.
Mechanical available: Offset; Black and 3 ROP colors; insert accepted - spadea; page cutoffs - 22 3/4.
Mechanical Specifications: Type page 11 5/8 x 21 1/2; E - 6 cols, 1 5/6, 1/8 between; A - 6 cols, 1 5/6, 1/8 between; C - 9 cols, 1 3/16, 1/8 between.
Commodity Consumption: Avg. Page Number Per Issue - Daily 24; Avg. Page Number Per Issue - Plates Used 14000; Avg. Page Number Per Issue - Sunday 40; widths 25; Newsprint Used - Metric Tons 1050; Printing Ink Used - Black 26000; Printing Ink Used - Color 7000; Printing Ink Use
Equipment EDITORIAL: Front-end Software – Unix, Microsoft/WindowsNT; Editorial Hardware – 1-APP/Mac Quadra, 9-APP/MacG3; Editorial Equipment – Kodak/Film Scanner, 2-APP/Mac IIci, Lf/AP Leaf Picture Desk; Editorial Printers – 1-ECR/Pelbox 108, 1-APP/Mac LaserWriter, LaserMaster/Unity Turbo XLO, 1-APP/Mac LaserWriter CLASSIFIED: Front-end Software – Vision Data/Classified.; Classified Hardware – 2-Sun/Microsys, Sun/Sparc, 1-Sun/Sparc Station II, 3-Sun/Sparc Station, 1-APP/MacG4; Classified Printers – Lexmark, 2-HP/5000 DISPLAY: Ad make-up applications – QPS/QuarkXPress 4.0, Adobe/Illustrator 8.0, Adobe/Photoshop 4.0; Display Hardware – Sun/Microsys 4-110, 6-APP/Mac II, 1-APP/Mac IIci, 1-APP/Power Mac, 1-APP/MacG4, 3-APP/MacG3; Display Printers – LaserMaster/Unity Turbo XLO, ECR/Pelbox 108, APP/Mac LaserWriter PRODUCTION: Pagination Software – SCS/Linx 3.5.; Production Equipment – Offset, Nu/FT40V 3UPNS; Cameras – 1-K; Scanners – AG/Horizon, AG/Horizon Ultra, APP/Mac Scanner, Kk/Film Scanner PRESSROOM: Line 1 – 1-G/Community. MAILROOM: Counter stackers – 1-BG/Count-O-Veyor, 1-Id, Compass/180; Inserters and stuffers – 1-MM/Tandem heads; Bundle tying machines – 2-MLN/Plastic; Wrapping singles – 1-Id; Addressing machine – 1-Automecha/Accufast; Other equipment –Mc/1800, Hydraulic Baler. BUSINESS COMPUTERS: Business Software – Vision Data, WordPerfect, Access Tech/20-20; Business Hardware – Sun/Micro 4-110, 3-Sun/Sparc SLC

CORTLAND

CORTLAND STANDARD

110 Main St., Cortland, N.Y., 13045-5548; gen tel (607) 756-5665; gen fax (607) 756-5665; gen e-mail admin@cortlandstandard.net; adv e-mail ad-design@cortlandstandard.net; web site www.cortlandstandard.net
Group: New York Newspaper Advertising Service, Inc.
Published: Mon, Tues, Wed, Thur, Fri, Sat
Weekday Frequency: e
Circulation: 10,279; 10,279(sat)
Last Audit: October 1, 2002
Price: 2.10/wk (carrier); 109.20/yr (carrier), $149.50/yr (mail).
Advertising: Open inch rate $15.00
News services: AP.
Politics: Independent.
Not Published: New Year; Memorial Day; Independence Day; Labor Day; Thanksgiving; Christmas.
Special Editions: Senior Scene (Apr); College (Aug); Christmas Greetings (Dec); People Who Make Area Business Run (Feb); Year-in-Review (Jan); High School Graduation (Jun); Bridal (Mar); Summer Sun & Fun (May); Gift Guide (Nov); Car Care (Oct).
Special Weekly Sections: Best Food Day (Mon); Best Food Day (Sat).
Magazines: TV Magazine (Fri).
Vice Pres. ....Ann G. Howe
Pub ....Kevin R. Howe
Bus. Mgr./Gen. Mgr. ....Wayne L. Clark
Adv. Mgr., Classified ....Thomas Shattuck
Adv. Mgr., Retail ....Michael J. Anderson
Circ. Dir. ....Guy C. Ussery
Exec. Ed. ....Sherwood W. Chapman
Mng. Ed. ....Kevin Conlon
Editorial Page Ed. ....Sherwood Chapman
News Ed. ....Michael Welsh
Society/Women's Ed ....Katie Hall
Sports Ed. ....Al Butler
Prodn. Foreman, Composing Stanley Carruthers
Prodn. Foreman, Pressroom ....Raymond Marsh
Market Information: TMC.
Mechanical available: Offset; Black and 2 ROP colors; insert accepted; page cutoffs - 22 3/4.
Mechanical Specifications: Type page 13 1/4 x 21 1/2; E - 6 cols, 2 1/16, 1/8 between; A - 6 cols, 2 1/16, 1/8 between; C - 9 cols, 1 3/8, 1/16 between.
Commodity Consumption: Avg. Page Number Per Issue - Daily 23.68; Avg. Page Number Per Issue - Plates Used 4050; widths 28; Newsprint Used - Short Tons 498; Printing Ink Used - Black 11350; Printing Ink Used - Color 220; Printing Ink Used - Pages Printed 7294.
Equipment EDITORIAL: Front-end Software – Mk/ACE 2.20.; Editorial Hardware – Mk/3000 System; Editorial Printers – Epson/LQ1010 CLASSIFIED: Front-end Software – Mk/NewsTouch, AT/Classified.; Classified Hardware – Mk/3000; Classified Printers – TI/810 DISPLAY: Ad make-up applications – Claris/MacDraw Pro, Aldus/FreeHand 4.0, QPS/QuarkXPress 3.3; Layout Software – APP/Mac Local Talk Network.; Display Hardware – APP/Mac IIcx, APP/Mac IIci; Display Printers – APP/Mac LaserWriter II NT; Production Equipment – Read-it/Pro 3.0A, 2-LaserMaster/Unity 1800-XL Plus; Cameras – 1-Eskofot/6006, 1-B/Commodore 24; Scanners – Applescan. PRESSROOM: Line 1 – 4-G/Urbanite 1968; Folders – 1; Bundle tying machines – 1/MLN. BUSINESS COMPUTERS: Business Software – Vision Data; Business Hardware – Axil/311

DUNKIRK

OBSERVER

8-10 E. 2nd St., Dunkirk, N.Y., 14048-0391; gen tel (716) 366-3000; gen fax (716) 366-3005; ed fax (716) 366-2389; adv e-mail advertising@observertoday.com; ed e-mail editorial@observertoday.com; web site www.observertoday.com
Published: Mon, Tues, Wed, Thur, Fri, Sat, Sun
Weekday Frequency: m
Saturday Frequency: m
Circulation: 8,261; 9,409(sat); 8,779(sun)
Last Audit: ABC September 30, 2011
Price: 2.45/wk (carrier); 10.62/mo; 127.40/yr.
News services: AP, Papert (Landon).
Politics: Independent.
Note: The Dunkirk Observer (mS) has a combination rate of $92.08 with the Jamestown Post-Journal (mS). Individual newspaper rates not made available.
Special Editions: National Secretaries Week/March of Dimes (Apr); Back-to-School (Aug); New Year's Greetings (Dec); Valentine's Sweets & Treats (Feb); Health & Fitness (Jan); Chautauqua County Fair Tab (Jul); Flag Day (Jun); Money Matters (Mar); Spring/Summer Tourism (May)
Magazines: TV Magazine (Fri); Senior Scene Tab (Monthly); USA WEEKEND Magazine (S); Saturday (Tues).
Adv. Dir. ....Meredith V. Patton
Circ. Mgr. ....Shawn Paulus
City Ed. ....Gib Snyder
Publisher ....John D'Agostino
Regl. News Ed. ....Bill Hammond
Sports Ed. ....Craig Harvey
Assistant Managing Editor ....Gregory Bacon
Classified manager ....Joyce Klawon
Market Information: ADS; TMC.
Mechanical available: Offset; Black and 3 ROP colors; insert accepted - all; page cutoffs - 22 1/2.
Mechanical Specifications: Type page 11 3/4 x 21 1/2; E - 6 cols, 1 9/10, 1/8 between; A - 6 cols, 1 9/10, 1/8 between; C - 9 cols, 1 9/10, 1/12 between.
Commodity Consumption: Avg. Page Number Per Issue - Daily 24; Avg. Page Number Per Issue - Plates Used 5320; Avg. Page Number Per Issue - Saturday 28; Avg. Page Number Per Issue - Sunday 44; widths 24; Newsprint Used - Metric Tons 590; Printing Ink Used - Black 14800; Printing
Equipment EDITORIAL: Front-end Software – WriteNow.; Editorial Hardware – 13-APP/Mac Centris 610; Editorial Printers – NewGen/PS480 Laser Printer, HP/4MV CLASSIFIED: Front-end Software – ONI/Class System.; Classified Hardware – 4-APP/Mac Centris 610; Classified Printers – APP/Mac LaserPrinter, 2-HP/2000 DISPLAY: Ad make-up applications – QPS/QuarkXPress, Multi-Ad/Creator, Aldus/FreeHand, Adobe/Photoshop.; Display Hardware – 4-APP/Mac G3 266; Display Printers – HP/4MV PRODUCTION: Pagination Software – QPS/QuarkXPress 3.32.; Production Equipment – ECR/VRL36, BKY/Ascor; Cameras – B, Cannon Pro 70, Nikon/Coolpix 950; Scanners – HP IIcx, Nikon/3510 Scanner, Nikon/LS 1000, 2-Umax/Astra 1200S PRESSROOM: Line 1 – 5-G/Urbanite 1966. MAILROOM: Counter stackers – HL/Monitor; Bundle tying machines – 2/Bu, 1-/Sa. BUSINESS COMPUTERS: Business Software – Western Computer; Business Hardware – 5-Bs/25

ELMIRA

STAR-GAZETTE

201 Baldwin St., Elmira, N.Y., 14902-0285; gen tel (607) 734-5151; adv tel (607) 734-5151; ed tel (607) 734-5151; gen fax (607) 733-4408; adv fax (607) 734-4500; ed fax (607) 733-4408; gen e-mail sgnews@gannett.com; ed e-mail sgnews@gannett.com; web site www.stargazette.com
Group: Gannett Co., Inc.
Published: Mon, Tues, Wed, Thur, Fri, Sat, Sun
Weekday Frequency: m
Saturday Frequency: m
Circulation: 16,114; 16,197(sat); 25,559(sun)
Last Audit: ABC September 30, 2011
Price: 3.50/wk (carrier); 182.00/yr.
News services: AP, GNS
Politics: Independent. **Established:** 1828
Note: Newspapers are printed at the CNY plant located in Johnson City, NY
Special Editions: Outlook (Feb); Home & Garden (spring/fall) Bridal tab (spring) Guide to the Twin Tiers (fall)
Special Weekly Sections: Twin Tiers Homes (Sat.) Time Out (entertainment) (Thurs.)
Magazines: Full-Color Comics (S); Time Out (Thur).
President & Publisher ....Sherman Bodner
General Manager & Managing Editor Lois Wilson
Market Information: ADS; Split run; TMC; Zoned editions.
Mechanical Specifications: Type page 12 1/2 x 21 1/2; E - 6 cols, 2, 1/8 between; A - 6 cols, 2, 1/8 between; C - 9 cols, 1 7/16, 1/16 between.
Commodity Consumption: Avg. Page Number Per Issue - Daily 26; Avg. Page Number Per Issue - Plates Used 55000; Avg. Page Number Per Issue - Sunday 60; widths 54; Newsprint Used - Short Tons 2700; Printing Ink Used - Black 67000; Printing Ink Used - Color 11000; Printing Ink Use
Equipment; Editorial Hardware – APP/Mac, SII/Tandem; Editorial Equipment – Software ÃÐÂ SII. CLASSIFIED: Front-end Software – Mactive; Classified Hardware – Mac DISPLAY: Ad make-up applications – Multi-Ad/Creator, XIT/Clipper; Layout Software – MEI/ALS.; Display Printers – Clipper/3850 PRODUCTION: Pagination Software – Newsway; Production Equipment – 3 -Kodak Thermal plate processors PRESSROOM: Line 1 – KBA Colora 8 towers with 6 (44) & 2 (42), Two folders, online quarter folder & stitch ; Press Drives – KBA; Folders – 2-KBA; Pasters – 10 KBA; Press control system – EAE; Press registration system – KBAEAE MAILROOM: Counter stackers – 6 Quipp, 2 Gamblers; Inserters and stuffers – 2 NP630; Bundle tying machines – 6 Dynaric; Wrapping singles – 2 Samual shrink Wrap; Mailroom control system – Goss; Addressing machine – 2 Kodak; Business Hardware – 1-IBM/AS-400

GENEVA

FINGER LAKES TIMES

218 Genesee St., Geneva, N.Y., 14456-0393; gen tel (315) 789-3333; adv tel (315) 789-3333; ed tel (315) 789-3333; gen fax (315) 789-4077; adv fax (315) 789-3376; ed fax (315) 789-4077; gen e-mail adtimes@fltimes.com; adv e-mail dlahr@fltimes.com; ed e-mail fltimes@fltimes.com; web site www.fltimes.com
Group: Community Media Group
Published: Mon, Tues, Wed, Thur, Fri, Sun
Weekday Frequency: e
Circulation: 14,000; 17,000(sun)
Last Audit: Sworn September 30, 2009
Price: 2.25/wk, $1.00/wk (S only); 10.00/mo; 146.65/yr.
Advertising: Open inch rate $30.00
Insert rate: 75.00/m
News services: SHNS, AP, LAT-WP.
Politics: Independent. **Established:** 1895
Not Published: Saturdays
Special Editions: Quarterly Happenings Magazine; Business Directory (Jan) ; Tax Guide & Money Management (Feb); Bridal Magazine (Feb); Vacation Guide (May), Graduation (Jun); Car Care/Home Improvement (Oct); High School Football (Aug); Empire Farm Days (Aug); Indulge (Sept); Bridal Magazine (Oct); Christmas Gift Guide (Nov); Last Minute Gift Guide (Dec); Year in Review (Dec)
Special Weekly Sections: Homes (Thur).
Magazines: TV Times (S)
Happenings Magazine (Quarterly)
Publisher ....Paul M Barrett
Advertising Director ....Diane Lahr-Smith
Circulation Director ....Maurice Barcomb
Managing Editor ....Chuck Schading
Production Manager ....Jesse P. Bond
Executive Editor ....Michael J. Cutillo
Market Information: TMC.
Mechanical available: Offset; Black and 3 colors; inserts accepted; page cutoffs - 22 3/4.
Mechanical Specifications: Type page 12 x 21; E - 6 cols, 1 8/9, 1/8 between; A - 6 cols, 1 2/9, 1/8 between; C - 9 cols, 1 2/9, 1/16 between.
Commodity Consumption: Avg. Page Number Per Issue - Daily 24; Avg. Page Number Per Issue - Plates Used 4000; Avg. Page Number Per Issue - Sunday 46; widths 25; Newsprint Used - Short Tons 1200; Printing Ink Used - Black 20000; Printing Ink Used - Color 1000; Printing Ink Used
Equipment EDITORIAL: Front-end Software – MediaSpan, QPS/QuarkXPress 4.04. CLASSIFIED: Front-end Software – Media Span DISPLAY: Ad make-up applications – Managing Editor. PRODUCTION: Pagination Software – QPS/QuarkXPress 4.04.; Production Equipment – 2-Ultra Imagesetter; Cameras – 1-AG/RPS204 Vertical; Scanners – Epson/836 XL PRESSROOM: Line 1 – 5-G/Urbanite; Folders – 1 MAILROOM: Counter stackers – 1/KAN; Inserters and stuffers – 1-KAN/480; Bundle tying machines – 2-/MLN; Addressing machine – 1-/El.
Delivery method: Newsstand, Private Carrier, Racks

GLENS FALLS

GLENS FALLS NEWSPAPERS, INC.

Lawrence & Cooper Sts., Glens Falls, N.Y., 12801; gen tel (518) 792-3131; gen fax (518) 743-1684

THE POST-STAR

76 Lawrence and Cooper St., Glens Falls, N.Y., 12801; gen tel (518) 792-3131; gen fax (518) 761-1255; adv fax (518) 798-5679; ed e-mail letters@poststar.com; web site www.poststar.com
Published: Mon, Tues, Wed, Thur, Fri, Sat, Sun
Weekday Frequency: m
Saturday Frequency: m
Circulation: 26,133; 26,575(sat); 29,719(sun)
Last Audit: ABC September 30, 2011
Price: 3.25/wk (carrier); 23.50/mo (mail); 250.00/yr (mail).
Advertising: Open inch rate $47.40
News services: AP, MCT, LAT-WP, TMS.
Politics: Independent. **Established:** 1903
Not Published: Christmas.
Special Editions: Saratoga Horse Racing (Jul); Hockey (Oct); Football (Sept).
Magazines: Relish (Monthly); USA WEEKEND Magazine (S).
Pub. ....Rick Emanuel
Circ. Dir. ....Thomas Pottorff
Mng. Ed. ....Ken Tingley
City Ed. ....Bob Condon
Asst. City Ed. ....Scott Donnelly
Editorial Page Ed. ....Mark Mahoney
Photography Dir. ....Derek Pruitt
Sports Ed. ....Greg Brownell
Market Information: Split run; Zoned editions.
Mechanical available: Offset; Black and 3 ROP colors; insert accepted; page cutoffs - 22 3/4.
Mechanical Specifications: Type page 11 5/8 x 21 1/2; E - 6 cols, 1 5/6, 1/8 between; A - 6 cols, 1 5/6, 1/8 between; C - 9 cols, 1 9/50, 1/8 between.
Commodity Consumption: Avg. Page Number Per Issue - Daily 45; Avg. Page Number Per Issue - Plates Used 60000; Avg. Page Number Per Issue - Sunday 70; widths 12 1/2; Newsprint Used - Metric Tons 3200; Printing Ink Used - Black 108000; Printing Ink Used - Color 20000; Printing I
Equipment EDITORIAL: Front-end Software – QPS/QuarkXPress 4.04, NewsEngin.; Editorial Hardware – 2-Micron/5200, 3-IBM/327, 2-Sun/Sparc 20, 28-Dell/Optiplex G1, 15-APP/Mac G4, 2-APP/MAC G5; Editorial Printers – HP/8000 CLASSIFIED: Front-end Software – Vision Data/Island Write.; Classified Hardware – 3-APP/Mac G4, 1-Sun/Ultra, 10-Dell/Optiplex; Classified Printers – HP/5000 DISPLAY: Ad make-up applications – QPS/QuarkXPress 4.04, Adobe/Illustrator; Layout Software – SCS/Layout 8000.; Display Hardware – 17-APP/Mac G4, 2-Sun/Sparc 20; Display Printers – 1-HP/5000 PRODUCTION: Pagination Soft-

ware – QPS/QuarkXPress 4.04.; Production Equipment – 1-Nu/Flip Top FT40V6UPNS, Nu/Flip Top FT32V3UP-KR, 1-AU/3850; Scanners – Nikon/Coolscan IV, 2-Epson/164XL PRESSROOM: Line 1 – 10-G/Urbanite single width; Folders – 1; Reels and Stands – 8 MAILROOM: Counter stackers – 1-MM/338, 1-Id/Marathon, 1-Compass/180; Inserters and stuffers – 1-SLS/1000R; Bundle tying machines – 1-MLN/MLN2HS, 1/OVL, 1-/Dynaric; Wrapping singles – 1-HL/Monarch; Other equipment –MM/321. BUSINESS COMPUTERS: Business Software – Vision Data; Business Hardware – 10-Compaq/486, 1-Sun/Ultra

GLOVERSVILLE

THE LEADER-HERALD

8 E. Fulton St., Gloversville, N.Y., 12078; gen tel (518) 725-8616; adv tel (518) 725-8616; ed tel (518) 725-8616; adv fax (518) 773-3384; ed fax (518) 725-7407; adv e-mail advertising@leaderherald.com; ed e-mail news@leaderherald.com; web site www.leaderherald.com

Published: Mon, Tues, Wed, Thur, Fri, Sat, Sun
Weekday Frequency: e
Saturday Frequency: e
Circulation: 8,750; 9,295(sat); 10,845(sun)
Last Audit: ABC September 30, 2011
Price: 2.45/wk; 135.00/yr (carrier), $140.00/yr (motor route), $152.00/yr (mail).
News services: AP.
Politics: Independent.
Note: The Gloversville Leader-Herald (eS) has a combination rate of $43.00 with the Saranac Lake Adirondack Enterprise (e). Individual newspaper rates not made available.
Not Published: Christmas.
Special Editions: Spring Home Improvement & Garden Time (Apr); Lake Country (Aug); Portraits (Feb); Lake Country (Jul); Lake Country (Jun); Spring Car Care (Mar); Spring & Summer Vacation Guide (May); Real Estate (Monthly); Christmas Gift Guide (Nov); Fall Car Care (Oct);
Special Weekly Sections: Business-Stocks (S); Church News (Sat); Best Food (Wed).
Magazines: Parade (S).
Pub. ....Patricia Beck
Dir., Mktg./Promo. ....Doug Hill
Circ. Dir./Promo. Mgr. ....Toni Mosconi
Editorial Page Ed. ....Tim Fonda
Photo Ed ....Bill Trojan
Mgmt. Info Servs. Mgr. ....Chad Fleck
Prodn. Mgr., Mailroom ....Tim VanAernam
Market Information: TMC.
Mechanical available: Offset; Black and 3 ROP colors; insert accepted - cards and booklets; page cutoffs - 22 3/4.
Mechanical Specifications: Type page 13 x 21 1/4; E - 6 cols, 2 1/16, 1/8 between; A - 6 cols, 2 1/16, 1/8 between; C - 8 cols, 1 1/2, 1/8 between.
Commodity Consumption: Avg. Page Number Per Issue - Daily 20; Avg. Page Number Per Issue - Plates Used 7832; Avg. Page Number Per Issue - Sunday 53; widths 27; Newsprint Used - Short Tons 759; Printing Ink Used - Pages Printed 7286.
Equipment EDITORIAL: Front-end Software – QPS/QuarkXPress, Aldus/FreeHand, Adobe/Photoshop.; Editorial Hardware – COM/One 140, 5-APP/Mac; Editorial Equipment – 18-COM; Editorial Printers – APP/Mac LaserWriter, MON/ExpressMaster 1270, ECR/URL 36; Classified Hardware – 3-COM/One Sys 140. DISPLAY: Ad make-up applications – Multi-Ad/Creator, Adobe/Photoshop.; Display Hardware – 4-APP/Mac; Display Printers – NewGen/660B, ECR/VRL 36, MON/ExpressMaster 1270 PRODUCTION: Pagination Software – QPS/QuarkXPress 3.11.; Production Equipment – 1-WL/30C, 1-Imperial/Top Coater; Cameras – 1-R/5000H, 1-Acti; Scanners – 2-HP/ScanJet IIcx, 1-Kk/RS-2035 PRESSROOM: Line 1 – 6-G/Urbanite; Line 2 – 6-HI/V-15A; Folders – 1-G/2, 1-HI/Combination; Pasters – 4 MAILROOM: Counter stackers – 2-BG/Count-O-Veyor; Bundle tying machines – 2/MLN, 1-/Sa; Addressing machine – Ch.; Business Hardware – NCR/386, Unix/486 System

HERKIMER

THE EVENING TELEGRAM

111-113 Green St., Herkimer, N.Y., 13350; gen tel (315) 866-2220; adv tel (315) 866-2220; ed tel (315) 866-2220; gen fax (315) 866-5913; adv fax (315) 866-5913; ed fax (315) 866-5913; ed e-mail news@eveningtelegram.com; web site www.herkimertelegram.com

Published: Mon, Tues, Wed, Thur, Fri, Sat, Sun
Weekday Frequency: e
Saturday Frequency: m
Circulation: 6,657; 6,657(sat)
Last Audit: March 31, 2006
Price: 2.25/wk (carrier); 11.92/mo (mail); 104.00/yr; 29.25/3mo.
Advertising: Open inch rate $16.79
News services: AP.
Politics: Independent. **Established:** 1898
Not Published: New Year; Christmas.
Special Editions: Our Children (Apr); NASCAR (Feb); Who, What, Where (Jul); Spring Preview (May); Winter Sports Preview (Nov); Senior Life (Sept).
Special Weekly Sections: Bride (Sat); Entertainment (Thur); Senior Lifestyle (Tues); Senior Lifestyle (Wed).
Magazines: TV Guide Weekly (Sat); American Profile (Weekly).
Broadcast Affiliations: WKTV.
Pub. ....Beth A. Brewer
Controller ....Kim Knapp
Adv. Mgr. ....Pam Grande
Circ. Mgr. ....Ronald Sterling
Mng. Ed. ....Richard Petrillo
Trends Ed ....Donna Thompson
Market Information: TMC; Zoned editions.
Mechanical available: Offset; Black and 3 ROP colors; insert accepted; page cutoffs - 22 1/4.
Mechanical Specifications: Type page 13 1/4 x 21 1/2; E - 6 cols, 2 1/16, 1/8 between; A - 6 cols, 2 1/16, 1/8 between; C - 8 cols, 1 3/4, 1/8 between.
Commodity Consumption: Avg. Page Number Per Issue - Daily 16; Avg. Page Number Per Issue - Plates Used 16800; Avg. Page Number Per Issue - Saturday 20; widths 25; Newsprint Used - Short Tons 550; Printing Ink Used - Black 9400; Printing Ink Used - Color 350; Printing Ink Used
Equipment EDITORIAL: Front-end Software – Baseview/News Edit.; Editorial Hardware – APP/Mac; Editorial Printers – APP/Mac Ad-Writer CLASSIFIED: Front-end Software – Baseview/AdManager Pro.; Classified Hardware – APP/Mac; Classified Printers – TI PRODUCTION: Pagination Software – Adobe/Pagemaker, QPS/QuarkXPress.; Production Equipment – 1-COM/4961, SCREEN; Cameras – 1-B, Olympus/Digital PRESSROOM: Line 1 – 6-G/Community.; Bundle tying machines – 1/Sa; Addressing machine – 1-/El. BUSINESS COMPUTERS: Business Software – Microsoft/Excel; Business Hardware – Packard Bell

THE EVENING TIMES

1011 Green St., Herkimer, N.Y., 13350; gen tel (315) 823-3690; ed tel (315) 823-3682; gen fax (315) 866-5913; gen e-mail bethtimes@twcny.rr.com; web site www.littlefallstimes.com

Published: Mon, Tues, Wed, Thur, Fri, Sat
Weekday Frequency: e
Circulation: 4,015; 4,015(sat)
Last Audit: September 30, 2004
Price: 140.00/yr.
Advertising: Open inch rate $10.05
News services: NEA, AP.
Politics: 1886
Not Published: New Year; Memorial Day; Independence Day; Labor Day; Thanksgiving; Christmas.
Special Editions: Business Card (Monthly).
Special Weekly Sections: Seniors (Sat); Bridal (Tues); Doctors (Wed).
Magazines: American Profile (Weekly).
Pub. ....Beth Brewer
Adv. Mgr. ....Peggy Vespi
Adv. Mgr., Nat'l ....Kathy Kelly
Adv. Mgr., Classified ....Sue Randazzo
Circ. Mgr. ....Steve Sterusky
Ed. ....Todd Dewan
Sports Ed. ....Jon Rathbun
Prodn. Mgr. ....Hegg Ryan
Mechanical available: Offset; Black and 2 ROP colors; insert accepted; page cutoffs - 21 1/2.
Mechanical Specifications: Type page 11 7/8 x 21 1/2; E - 6 cols, 1 7/8, 1/8 between; A - 6 cols, 1 7/8, 1/8 between; C - 8 cols, 1 3/8, 1/8 between.
Commodity Consumption: Avg. Page Number Per Issue - Daily 14; Printing Ink Used - Pages Printed 3978.
Equipment EDITORIAL: Front-end Software – Microsoft/Word, Microsoft/Windows.; Editorial Hardware – DTK/486-66; Editorial Printers – HP/Laser CLASSIFIED: Front-end Software – Merrimac/Publishing Manager, Microsoft/Word.; Classified Hardware – DTK/486-25; Production Equipment – HP/LaserPrinter.; Addressing machine – 1/Wm.

HORNELL

THE EVENING TRIBUNE

85 Canisteo St., Hornell, N.Y., 14843; gen tel (607) 324-1425; adv tel (607) 324-1425; ed tel (607) 324-1425; gen fax (607) 324-2317; adv fax (607) 324-1753; ed fax (607) 324-2317; gen e-mail news@eveningtribune.com; adv e-mail advertising@eveningtribune.com; web site www.eveningtribune.com

Published: Sun
Circulation: 6,472; 10,069(sun)
Last Audit: September 30, 2003
Price: 10.20/mo (carrier/motor route); 135.00/yr (carrier/motor route), $146.40/yr (motor route).
Advertising: Open inch rate $10.95
News services: AP.
Politics: Independent.
Note: The Hornell Evening Tribune (e) and the Wellsville Daily Reporter (e) share a Sunday edition.
Not Published: New Year; Memorial Day; Independence Day; Labor Day; Thanksgiving; Christmas.
Special Editions: Chistmas (Dec); Interstate 86 Travel Guide (Fall); Interstate 86 Travel Guide (Spring).
Special Weekly Sections: TV Times (S).
Magazines: Parade (S).
Pub. ....Tom Connors
Mktg. Dir. ....John Frungillo
Mng. Ed. ....Andy Thompson
Sports Ed ....Derrick Balinsky
Prodn. Mgr. ....Gary Shaver
Press Foreman ....Mike Giglio
Mailroom Foreman ....Cindy Giglio
Market Information: ADS; TMC.
Mechanical available: Offset; Black and 3 ROP colors; insert accepted; page cutoffs - 22 3/4.
Mechanical Specifications: Type page 13 x 21 1/2; E - 6 cols, 2 1/16, 1/8 between; A - 6 cols, 2 1/16, 1/8 between; C - 6 cols, 2 1/16, 1/8 between.
Commodity Consumption: Avg. Page Number Per Issue - Daily 21; Avg. Page Number Per Issue - Sunday 32; widths 27 1/2; Newsprint Used - Short Tons 700.
Equipment EDITORIAL: Front-end Software – Baseview.; Editorial Hardware – APP/Macs; Editorial Printers – APP/Mac 630 Pro, HP/LaserJet 4MV, Xante/8300 CLASSIFIED: Front-end Software – Baseview.; Classified Hardware – APP/Macs; Classified Printers – APP/Mac Pro 630, HP/LaserJet 4MV; Display Hardware – 2-APP/Mac; Display Printers – HP/LaserJet 4MV. PRODUCTION: Pagination Software – Baseview.; Production Equipment – APP/Mac Pro 630, HP/LaserJet 4MV, Xante/8300; Cameras – 1-C/Spartan III; Scanners – HP/ScanJet PRESSROOM: Line 1 – 8-G/Community (with upper former).; Inserters and stuffers – 1-MM/EM 10, 1-KAN/7 unit; Bundle tying machines – 4-Bu/18, 1-Sa/1100, 1/Gd; Addressing machine – 1-Am/2605, 1-Am/2600, 1-S/5-E collator, 1-/Ch.; Business Hardware – 3-IBM/Nomad

HUDSON

HUDSON VALLEY NEWSPAPERS

364 Warren St., Hudson, N.Y., 12534; gen tel (518) 828-1616; gen fax (518) 828-9437; gen e-mail publisher@registerstar.com; web site www.registerstar.com

REGISTER-STAR

364 Warren St., Hudson, N.Y., 12534; gen tel (518) 828-1616; gen fax (518) 828-9437; gen e-mail editorial@registerstar.com; adv e-mail adsales@registerstar.com; web site www.registerstar.com

Published: Tues, Wed, Thur, Fri
Weekday Frequency: m
Saturday Frequency: m
Circulation: 4,406; 4,538(sat); 5,015(sun)
Last Audit: ABC September 30, 2011
Price: 2.97/wk; 228.00/yr (mail); 14.85/5wk.
Advertising: Open inch rate $21.12
News services: AP.
Politics: Independent.
Not Published: New Year; Memorial Day; Independence Day; Labor Day; Columbus Day; Christmas.
Special Editions: Car Care (Apr); Holiday (Dec); Progress (Feb); Bridal (Jan); Bridal (Jun); Holiday (Nov); Car Care (Oct); Home Improvement (Sept).
Special Weekly Sections: Best Food Days (S); Best Food Days (Wed).
Magazines: USA WEEKEND Magazine (S).
Pub. ....Roger F. Coleman
Bus. Mgr. ....Peter Rost
Adv. Dir. ....Pamela Geskie
Ed. ....Theresa E. Hyland
City Ed. ....Joseph A. Brill
Editorial Page Ed. ....Theresa Hyland
Prodn. Mgr., Mailroom ....Brenda Nickles
Prodn. Mgr., Pressroom ....Bruce Meiswinkle
Market Information: ADS; TMC.
Mechanical available: Offset; Black and 3 ROP colors; insert accepted; page cutoffs - 22 3/4.
Mechanical Specifications: Type page 13 x 21 1/2; E - 6 cols, 2 3/100, 1/6 between; A - 6 cols, 2 3/100, 1/6 between; C - 10 cols, 1 11/50, 1/12 between.
Commodity Consumption: Avg. Page Number Per Issue - Daily 22; Avg. Page Number Per Issue - Sunday 36; widths 27 1/2; Newsprint Used - Metric Tons 600; Printing Ink Used - Black 9900; Printing Ink Used - Color 180; Printing Ink Used - Pages Printed 6200.
Equipment EDITORIAL: Front-end Software – Baseview/NewsEdit Pro, QPS/QuarkXPress.; Editorial Hardware – APP/Power Mac, APP/Mac G3; Editorial Equipment – APP/Power Mac, APP/Mac G3, AG/1500; Editorial Printers – HP/4MV CLASSIFIED: Front-end Software – QPS/QuarkXPress.; Classified Hardware – APP/Mac G3; Classified Equipment – APP/Power Mac, APP/Mac G3, AG/1500; Classified Printers – HP/4MV DISPLAY: Ad make-up applications – Multi-Ad; Layout Software – APP/Mac.; Display Hardware – APP/Mac 7100, APP/Power Mac, APP/Mac G3; Display Printers – HP/4MV PRODUCTION: Pagination Software – QPS/QuarkXPress.; Production Equipment – Caere/OmniPro, AG/1500 Imagesetter; Cameras – Ret PRESSROOM: Line 1 – 13-G/Community; Folders – G/SC.; Inserters and stuffers – KAN/5-pocket; Bundle tying machines – Bu/Strapper.

ITHACA

THE ITHACA JOURNAL

123 W. State St., Ithaca, N.Y., 14850; gen tel (607) 272-2321; adv tel (607) 272-9300; ed tel (607) 272-2321; web site www.ithacajournal.com

Group: Gannett Co., Inc.
New York Newspaper Advertising Service, Inc.
Published: Mon, Tues, Wed, Thur, Fri, Sat
Weekday Frequency: m
Saturday Frequency: m
Circulation: 10,281; 15,306(sat)
Last Audit: ABC September 30, 2011
Price: 3.01/wk; 156.60/yr.
News services: AP, GNS,
Not Published: Sunday
Own facility?: Y
Magazines: The Real Estate Journal (Wed.) Ticket (Thurs.)
Pub. ....Sherman Bodner
Adv. Dir. ....Carol Becker
Circ. Dir. ....Steve Miller
Mng. Ed./General Manager ....Bruce Estes
Asst. Mng. Ed. ....Dave Bohrer
Photo Ed. ....Simon Wheeler
Mktg. Devel. Dir. ....Tony Valenta
Features Ed. ....Bob Jamieson
Sports Ed. ....Delaney Brian
Equipment PRESSROOM: Line 1 – KBA Colora; Press Drives – KBA; Folders – 2; Pasters – 10 MAILROOM: Counter stackers – 7; Inserters and stuffers – 2; Bundle tying machines – 7; Mailroom control system – Omnizone; Addressing machine – 2 Kodak; Other equipment –Offline stitch & Trim; online stitch

JAMESTOWN

THE POST-JOURNAL

15 W. Second St., Jamestown, N.Y., 14701; gen tel (716) 487-1111; adv tel (716) 487-1111; ed tel (716) 487-1111; gen fax (716) 664-3119; adv fax (716) 664-3119; ed fax (716) 664-5305; gen e-mail post-journal@oweb.com; adv e-mail advertising@post-journal.com; ed e-mail editorial@post-journal.com; web site www.post-journal.com

Published: Mon, Tues, Wed, Thur, Fri, Sat, Sun
Weekday Frequency: m
Saturday Frequency: m
Circulation: 14,916; 17,331(sat); 16,650(sun)
Last Audit: ABC September 30, 2011
Price: 2.40/wk; 10.40/mo; 124.80/yr.
News services: AP.
Politics: Independent-Republican.
Note: The Jamestown Post-Journal (mS) has a combination rate of $92.08 with the Dunkirk Observer (mS). Individual newspaper rates not made available.
Special Editions: Coupon Book (Apr); Coupon Book (Aug); Calendar (Dec); 9 (Feb); Spring Bridal Book (Jan); Forestry Tab (Jul); Chautauqua Institution Book (Jun); Hometown Magazine (Mar); Vacation Guide Book (May); Hunting Tab (Nov); Home Furnishings Tab (Oct); Football Tab
Special Weekly Sections: Best Food Day (Tues).
Magazines: Television Guide (S); Saturday Magazine (Sat).
Pub ....Micheal Bird
Adv. Mgr. ....Debbie Bruner
Adv. Clerk, Nat'l ....Beverly Laurin
Mktg./Promo ....Kirsten Johnson
Circ. Dir. ....Andy Gee
Bus./Finance Ed. ....Dennis Phillips
City Ed. ....John Whittaker
Editorial Page Ed. ....Cristie L. Herbst
Features Ed. ....Aimee Frederick
Librarian ....Linda Carlson
Magazine Ed. ....Brigetta Overcash
News Ed. ....Matt Spielman
Regl. Ed. ....Chris Kinsler
Sports Ed. ....James H. Riggs
Asst. Sports Ed. ....Scott Kindberg
Prodn. Mgr., Pre Press ....Peter C. Elofson
Market Information: ADS; Split run; TMC.
Mechanical available: Offset; Black and 3 ROP colors; insert accepted; page cutoffs - 22 3/4.
Mechanical Specifications: Type page 11 3/4 x 21 3/4; E - 6 cols, 1 7/8, 1/8 between; A - 6 cols, 1 7/8, 1/8 between; C - 8 cols, 1 3/8, 1/16 between.
Commodity Consumption: Avg. Page Number Per Issue - Daily 30; Avg. Page Number Per Issue - Plates Used 65800; Avg. Page Number Per Issue - Sunday 48; widths 34.
Equipment; Editorial Hardware – 2-Pentium/III Server, 22-CEL/366; Editorial Equipment – 3-RSK/TRS 100, 2-RSK/TRS 102, 2-RSK/TRS 200, 1-Lf/AP Leaf Picture Desk, Lf/Leafscan 35, HP/ScanJet 4C, 4-APP/Mac G3, 1-APP/Mac C500, 1-Nikon/Coolscan; Editorial Printers – 2-APP/Mac LaserWriter II, 1-MON/EM 1 CLASSIFIED: Front-end Software – Microsoft/Windows NT, Microsoft/Windows 98.; Classified Hardware – Pentium/III Server, 5-CEL/366; Classified Equipment – AG/Arcus II, 5-APP/Mac C500; Classified Printers – 2-APP/Mac LaserWriter II, 1-MON/EM 1270, 2-HP/4MV, 2-HP/LJ 2100 TN DISPLAY: Ad make-up applications – Multi-Ad/Creator 4.05; Layout Software – 5-APP/Mac C500.; Display Printers – 2-APP/Mac LaserWriter II, 1-MON/EM 1270, 2-HP/4MV; Production Equipment – Nu/Flip Top FT40UPNS, 1-Trek/25, 1-MON/EM 1270, 1-APP/Mac C500, 1-APP/Mac AWS-60 Server, 2-HP/4MV, 1-APP/Mac AWS-7250 Server, 2-HP/LT 2100 TN; Cameras – 1-C/Spartan II, 1-C/Pager; Scanners – 1-Lf/Leafscan 35, 1-Nikon/Coolscan, 1-HP/ScanJet 4C, PRESSROOM: Line 1 – 10-G/Urbanite single width; Press Drives – 2-Fin/150 h.p.; Folders – 1-G/Urbanite, 1-G/Suburban; Pasters – 6-Martin/Splicer. MAILROOM: Counter stackers – 1-RS/25, 3-HL/Monitor, 1/FDAB; Inserters and stuffers – HI/NP 1372; Bundle tying machines – 2-Mosca/P2, 1-/Power Strap/5; Addressing machine – 4-Typac/Label Dispenser; Other equipment –1-MM/Stitcher-Trimmer.; Business Hardware – NCR/Unix

KINGSTON

DAILY FREEMAN

79 Hurley Ave., Kingston, N.Y., 12401-2832; gen tel (845) 331-5000; gen fax (845) 338-0672; adv fax (845) 338-0672; ed fax (845) 331-3557; gen e-mail publisher@freemanonline.com; web site www.dailyfreeman.com; www.midhudsoncentral.com

Published: Mon, Tues, Wed, Thur, Fri, Sat, Sun
Weekday Frequency: m
Saturday Frequency: m
Circulation: 14,321; 13,653(sat); 18,078(sun)
Last Audit: ABC September 30, 2011
Price: 19.50/month(carrier/motor route); 19.50/mo (carrier/motor route); 225.00/yr (carrier/motor route).
Advertising: 29.50daily/35.96 Sunday
News services: AP, TMS.
Politics: Independent. **Established:** 1871
Own facility?: Y
Special Editions: Kingston Classic (Apr); Spotlight on the Arts (Aug); Last Minute Gift Guide (Dec); Internet Directory (Feb); Brides (Jan); Parenting (Jul); Graduation (Jun); Housing Solutions (Mar); Summer Car Care (May); Winter Lifestyles (Nov); Women's View
Special Weekly Sections: Entertainment (Fri); Financial (S); Best Food Edition (Wed).
Magazines: Preview Tab (Fri); People & Events Magazine (S).
Pub. ....Ira Fusfeld
Adv. Dir. ....Barbara Norton
Asst. Mng. Ed. ....Tony Adamis
City Ed. ....Jeremy Schiffres
Preview ....Ivan Lajara
Sports Ed. ....Ron Rosner
Controller ....Tony Sakellariou
Sales Manager ....Tim Tergeoglou
Gen. Mgr. ....Tom Cincotta
Controller ....Robert McClintock
Adv. Mgr., Classified ....Penny Ducker
Prodn. Dir. ....Bill Studt
Commodity Consumption: Avg. Page Number Per Issue - Daily 28; Avg. Page Number Per Issue - Plates Used 36000; Avg. Page Number Per Issue - Saturday 28; Avg. Page Number Per Issue - Sunday 72; widths 34; Newsprint Used - Short Tons 3000; Printing Ink Used - Black 65000; Printin
Equipment EDITORIAL: Front-end Software – Atex/Prestige Via Citrix (Cloud), Photoshop, 1 NDesign, 1N Copy; Editorial Hardware – HP 6000 (14); Editorial Equipment – 6 HP 6710; Editorial Printers – HP/5000 GN CLASSIFIED: Front-end Software – Enterprise/17.; Classified Hardware – Atex, 2-RS6000 Pagination Terminal; Classified Printers – HP/5000 GN DISPLAY: Ad make-up applications – Multi-Ad/Creator 3.6; Layout Software – APP/Mac.; Display Hardware – 4 G5 Mac 2 Lenova A4U; Display Printers – HP/5000 GN PRODUCTION: Pagination Software – QPS/QuarkXPress 3.32.; Scanners – 3-HP/4c; Business Hardware – 4 HP DC5800
Delivery method: Mail, Newsstand, Private Carrier, Racks

LITTLE FALLS

LIBERTY GROUP PUBLISHING CO.

347 S. Second St., Little Falls, N.Y., 13365; gen tel (315) 823-3680; gen fax (315) 823-4086; web site www.littlefallstimes.com

Published: Mon, Tues, Wed, Thur, Fri, Sat, Sun
Price: 140.00/yr.
Advertising: Open inch rate $10.05
Politics: 1886

LOCKPORT

UNION-SUN & JOURNAL

170 East Ave., Lockport, N.Y., 14094; gen tel (716) 439-9222; ed tel (716) 439-9222; adv fax (716) 439-9249; ed fax (716) 439-9249; gen e-mail postmaster@gnnewspaper.com; web site www.lockportjournal.com

Published: Mon, Tues, Wed, Thur, Fri, Sat, Sun
Weekday Frequency: e
Saturday Frequency: e
Circulation: 8,289; 9,502(sat); 7,514(sun)
Last Audit: ABC September 30, 2011
Price: 2.35/wk; 10.20/mo; 122.20/yr (home delivery).
Advertising: Open inch rate $23.00
News services: AP.
Politics: Independent.
Note: This publication shares a joint Sunday edition with the Niagara Falls (NY) Niagara Gazette and the North Tonawanda (NY) Tonawanda News.
Not Published: Christmas.
Special Editions: Spring Fashion (Apr); Farm Home (Aug); Car Care (Jun); Impact (Mar); Gift Guide (Nov); Better Homes (Oct); Women's World (Sept).
Pub ....Diane Crowe
Adv. Mgr. ....Chuck Sanderson
Mng. Ed. ....Tim Marren
Features Ed. ....Anne Calos
Sports Ed ....John D'Onofrio
Market Information: TMC.
Mechanical available: Offset; Black and 3 ROP colors; insert accepted - free-standing inserts; page cutoffs - 21 1/2.
Mechanical Specifications: Type page 12 1/2 x 21 1/2; E - 6 cols, 1 3/4, 1/10 between; A - 6 cols, 1 3/4, 1/10 between; C - 10 cols, 1 1/5, 1/15 between.
Commodity Consumption: Avg. Page Number Per Issue - Daily 18; Avg. Page Number Per Issue - Plates Used 7500; widths 27 1/2; Newsprint Used - Short Tons 700; Printing Ink Used - Pages Printed 7000.
Equipment EDITORIAL: Front-end Software – QPS/QuarkXPress, Baseview/NewsEdit, DTI.; Editorial Hardware – APP/Mac, APP/Mac; Editorial Equipment – 2-HP; Editorial Printers – APP/Mac Laser CLASSIFIED: Front-end Software – QPS/QuarkXPress, DTI.; Classified Hardware – APP/Mac, APP/Mac; Classified Printers – APP/Mac LaserWriter DISPLAY: Ad make-up applications – QPS/QuarkXPress, DTI; Layout Software – APP/Mac.; Display Hardware – APP/Mac, APP/Mac; Display Printers – APP/Mac LaserWriter PRODUCTION: Pagination Software – DTI 4.3.; Production Equipment – Panther Pro, APP/Mac PRESSROOM: Line 1 – 10-G/Community; Line 2 – 10-Unit/Community; Press Drives – 2-HP/60; Folders – 1; Press registration system – Duarte/Pin Registration.; Inserters and stuffers – 2-GMA/SLS 1000; Bundle tying machines – 2/Bu, 2-/Power Strappers; Wrapping singles – 2-/Bottom Wrappers.; Audio Hardware – CT BUSINESS COMPUTERS: Business Software – PBS; Business Hardware – Unix/E450, PBS

MALONE

MALONE NEWSPAPERS, INC.

469 E. Main St., Malone, N.Y., 12953; gen tel (518) 483-4700; gen fax (518) 483-8579

THE MALONE TELEGRAM

469 E. Main St., Malone, N.Y., 12953-0069; gen tel (518) 483-4700; adv tel (518) 483-4720; ed tel (518) 483-2000; gen fax (518) 483-8579; adv fax (518) 483-8579; ed fax (518) 483-8579; gen e-mail news@mtelegram.com; adv e-mail ads@mtelegram.com; ed e-mail news@mtelegram.com; web site mtelegram.com

Group: New York Newspaper Advertising Service, Inc.
Published: Mon, Tues, Wed, Thur, Fri, Sat
Weekday Frequency: m
Circulation: 4,721; 4,721(sat)
Last Audit: September 29, 2003
Price: 2.25/wk (carrier); 12.00/mo (out of county); 140.00/yr, $156.00/yr (out of county); 11.00/5wk (carrier/motor route in county).
Advertising: Open inch rate $9.54
News services: AP.
Not Published: New Year; Memorial Day; Independence Day; Labor Day; Thanksgiving; Christmas.
Special Editions: Fair Tab (Aug); Bridal Tab (Feb); Winter Carnival (Jan); Meet the Merchants (Jun); Spring Tab (Mar); Summer Visitor (May); Christmas Gift Guide (Nov).
Special Weekly Sections: TV Tab (Fri); Business Page (Sat).
Pub. ....Charles W. Kelly
Bus. Mgr., St. Lawrence Newspapers Brenda LaBrake
Bus. Mgr. ....Betsy McGivney
Adv. Mgr. ....Karen Carre
Circ. Mgr. ....Gert Jock
Ed. ....Connie Jenkins
News Ed. ....Darcy Fargo
Market Information: TMC.
Mechanical available: Offset; Black and 2 ROP colors; insert accepted; page cutoffs - 22 5/8.
Mechanical Specifications: Type page 13 x 21 1/2; E - 6 cols, 2 1/16, 1/8 between; A - 6 cols, 2 1/16, 1/8 between; C - 8 cols, 1 1/2, 1/8 between.
Commodity Consumption: Avg. Page Number Per Issue - Daily 14; Avg. Page Number Per Issue - Plates Used 9080; Avg. Page Number Per Issue - Saturday 10; widths 27 1/2; Newsprint Used - Metric Tons 250; Printing Ink Used - Black 7000; Printing Ink Used - Color 200; Printing Ink U
Equipment EDITORIAL: Front-end Software – Baseview/NewsEdit 4.1.; Editorial Printers – HP/LaserJet CLASSIFIED: Front-end Software – Baseview/Class Manager Plus 33.1.; Classified Printers – HP/LaserJet; Layout Software – Multi-Ad/Creator. PRODUCTION: Pagination Software – QPS/QuarkXPress 3.31.; Production Equipment – 2-APP/Mac Lasersetter; Cameras – SCREEN/Auto Companica 690D PRESSROOM: Line 1 – 4-G/Community; Folders – 1-G/2:1.; Bundle tying machines – Bu.; Business Hardware – 1-IBM/VDT Mid M

MEDINA

THE JOURNAL-REGISTER

541-543 Main St., Medina, N.Y., 14103; gen tel (585) 798-1400; gen fax (585 798-0290; gen e-mail thejournalregister@mail.com; adv e-mail praweld@gnnewspaper.com; web site www.journal-register.com
Published: Mon, Wed, Thur, Fri
Weekday Frequency: e
Circulation: 1,832
Last Audit: ABC September 30, 2011
Price: 110.24/yr (home delivery), $182.00/yr (mail).
Advertising: Open inch rate $10.64
News services: NEA, AP.
Politics: Independent-Republican. **Established:** 1903
Not Published: Christmas.
Special Editions: Bike Safety (Apr); Back-to-School (Aug); Don't Drink & Drive (Dec); Car Care (Feb); Bridal (Jan); July 4th (Jul); Graduation Tab (Jun); Home Improvement (Mar); Memorial Day (May); Senior Focus (Monthly); Gift Guide (Nov); Car Care (Oct); Home Improvement
Special Weekly Sections: Real Estate Review (Fri); Farm (Thur).
Magazines: USA WEEKEND Magazine (Fri).
Pub....Diane Crowe
Adv. Dir.....Cindy McPherson
Circ. Mgr.....Pat Langendorfer
City Ed.....Jessica R. Wasmund
Sports Ed.....Michael Wertman
Mechanical available: Offset; Black and 3 ROP colors; insert accepted; page cutoffs - 21.
Mechanical Specifications: Type page 13 x 21; E - 6 cols, 2 1/16, 1/8 between; A - 6 cols, 2 1/16, 1/8 between; C - 10 cols, 1/8 between.
Commodity Consumption: Avg. Page Number Per Issue - Daily 12; Avg. Page Number Per Issue - Plates Used 4460; widths 28; Newsprint Used - Short Tons 200; Printing Ink Used - Black 4380; Printing Ink Used - Color 62.
Equipment EDITORIAL: Front-end Software – Mk/Quark Express 5.0.; Editorial Hardware – Mk; Editorial Printers – APP/Mac LaserWriter Plus CLASSIFIED: Front-end Software – Mk.; Classified Hardware – Mk; Classified Printers – APP/Mac LaserWriter Plus DISPLAY: Ad make-up applications – Mk; Display Hardware – Mk; Display Printers – APP/Mac LaserWriter Plus PRODUCTION: Pagination Software – Baseview/Ad Layout Systems.; Production Equipment – Panther/Pro 46; Cameras – B/Horizontal PRESSROOM: Line 1 – 4-G/Community 1971; Line 2 – G/Community; Folders – 2; Inserters and stuffers – Quipp/SLS 1000; Bundle tying machines – Bu. BUSINESS COMPUTERS: Business Software – PBS; Business Hardware – IBM

MELVILLE

NEWSDAY

235 Pinelawn Rd., Melville, N.Y., 11747-4226; gen tel (631) 843-2020; adv tel (631) 843-3000; ed tel (631) 843-2700; ed fax (631) 843-2953; adv e-mail advertising@newsday.com; ed e-mail lidesk@newsday.com; web site www.newsday.com
Group: Cablevision
Tribune 365
Published: Mon, Tues, Wed, Thur, Fri, Sat, Sun
Weekday Frequency: m
Saturday Frequency: m
Circulation: 404,542; 389,812(sat); 476,723(sun)
Last Audit: ABC September 30, 2011
Advertising: Open inch rate $920.00
News services: AP, CSM, DJ, LAT-WP, NNS, RN, SHNS.
Politics: 1940
Note: Circulation is combined for Nasssau, Suffolk & Long Island editions.
Not Published: Christmas.
Own facility?: Y
Special Editions: Caribbean American Chamber (Apr); Back-to-School (Aug); Holiday Gift Guide (Dec); President's Forum (Feb); Bridal (Jan); Auto Leasing (Jul); Dads & Grads (Jun); Tax Advice-Your Financial Checklist (Mar); Home, Lawn & Garden II (May); Holiday Almanac (Nov)
Special Weekly Sections: Auto (Fri); Business & Technology (Mon); Fanfare (S); Health & Discovery (Tues).
Magazines: USA WEEKEND Magazine (Sat).
Broadcast Affiliations: News12
President....Terry A. Jimenez
Adv. Dir., Classified....Andrea Rothchild
Vice Pres., Mktg....Paul Fleishman
Dir., Mktg.....Debra Lund
Ed. in Chief....Debby Krenek
Mng. Ed.....Deborah Henley
Asst. Mng. Ed., Admin.....Mary Ann Skinner
Publisher....Fred Groser
Senior Vice President, Sales....Larry Dunn
Editor, Opinion....Rita Ciolli
Exec. Vice Pres./Gen. Mgr.....John McKeon
Exec. Vice Pres.....John Mancini
Dir., Multimedia Sales....David Wilkes
Adv. Sr. Mgr., Planning/Analysis Steven McKenna
Adv. Administrator, Newsday.com Bus. Chris Gennario
Mktg. Mgr., Newsday.com....Katie Sala
Circ. Dir., Bus. Admin.....Phil Ramacca
Vice Pres./Mng. Ed....Robert Keane
Vice Pres./Editorial Page Ed.....James Klurfeld
Mng. Ed., News....Richard Galant
Asst. Mng. Ed., Content Devel.....Phyllis Singer
Asst. Mng. Ed., Features....Alex Martin
Dir., Publishing Devel.....Peter Bengelsdorf
Market Information: ADS; Split run; TMC; Zoned editions.
Mechanical available: Offset; Black and 3 ROP colors; insert accepted - subscription blanks; page cutoffs - 21 1/2.
Mechanical Specifications: Type page 9 25/64 x 13; E - 6 cols, 1 1/2, 1/16 between; A - 6 cols, 1 1/2, 5/64 between; C - 8 cols, 1 3/16, 1/16 between.
Commodity Consumption: Avg. Page Number Per Issue - Daily 150; Avg. Page Number Per Issue - Plates Used 1775077; Avg. Page Number Per Issue - Sunday 320; widths 27 1/2; Newsprint Used - Metric Tons 115790; Printing Ink Used - Black 2281857; Printing Ink Used - Color 949404; Pr
Equipment EDITORIAL: Front-end Software – Unisys/Hermes 4.x.; Editorial Equipment – Dell/PC; Editorial Printers – HP/LaserJets CLASSIFIED: Front-end Software – AT/Sysdeco 4.37.; Classified Hardware – AT/IAS System 10 Series 6 DISPLAY: Ad make-up applications – QPS/QuarkXPress, Adobe/Photoshop; Layout Software – 4-Cascade/Image Flow-Data Flow, Sun/20-70.; Display Hardware – 67-APP/Power Mac; Display Printers – HP/LaserJet PRODUCTION: Pagination Software – Cascade.; Production Equipment – WL, 2-Dolev/800, 2-III/3850 Sierra, 2-MON/RIP Server, NEC, Scitex; Scanners – 1-AG/XY, 2-Eskofot, 1-Scitex/EverSmart Pro PRESSROOM: Line 1 – 2-G/Metro 144 pg., 4-G/Metro BB with half decks 1979, 4-G/Metro BB, 2-TKS/M-72; Line 2 – 1-G/Metro 144 pg., 4-G/Metro BB with half decks 1979, 4-G/Metro, 2-TKS/M-72; Line 3 – 1-G/Metro 144 pg., 4-G/Metro BB with half decks 1979, 4-G/Metro, 2-TKS/ MAILROOM: Counter stackers – 15-QWI/350, 23-QWI/400; Inserters and stuffers – 8/AM Graphics/NP 630, 2-HI/1472, 4-HI/2299; Bundle tying machines – 6-Dynaric/NP1, 54-Dynaric/NP2; Wrapping singles – 6-Overhead/Spiral Wrapper; Mailroom control system – Burt/NT. BUSINESS COMPUTERS: Business Software – ATEX/Enterprise, IBM/Lotus Notes, Unisys/Hermes; Business Hardware – Dell/Laptop, Dell/PC, 1-IBM/S-390 Parallel Enterprise Server 9672-R52, IBM/Netfinity Server, IBM/Laptop, IBM/PC, Sun/Enterprise Server

MIDDLETOWN

THE TIMES HERALD-RECORD

40 Mulberry St., Middletown, N.Y., 10940; gen tel (845) 341-1100; gen fax (845) 343-2050; adv fax (845) 343-6414; ed fax (845) 343-2170; gen e-mail letters@th-record.com; adv e-mail khammer@th-record.com; ed e-mail dosenenko@th-record.com; web site www.recordonline.com
Group: Dow Jones & Company, Inc.
Published: Mon, Tues, Wed, Thur, Fri, Sat, Sun
Weekday Frequency: m
Saturday Frequency: m
Circulation: 53,486; 54,286(sat); 67,037(sun)
Last Audit: ABC September 30, 2011
Price: $5.90/wk; $23.60/mo; $283.20/yr
Advertising: Rates based on modular sizes
News services: AP, NewsCore
Politics: 1960
Own facility?: Y
Special Editions: NY Auto Show (Apr); Back-to-School (Aug); Wish Book (Dec); Bridal (Feb); Progress (Jan); Star Spangled (Jul); Family Focus (Mar); Summer Guide (May); Inside Health (Monthly); Gift Guide (Nov); New Car (Oct); Family Focus (Sept).
Special Weekly Sections: Entertainment (Fri); Technology (Mon); Go Home (S); Health (Tues); Best Food Day (Wed).
Magazines: Go Plus (Fri); Relish (Monthly); Sunday Magazine (S); Auto Plus (Tues).
President and Publisher....Joe Vanderhoof
Advertising Director....Kathi Hammer
Human Resources Director....Gretchen Breedy
Circulation Director....Phil Hudson
Executive Editor....Derek Osenenko
Production Director....Stanton Frederick
Market Information: Split run; TMC; Zoned editions.
Mechanical available: Offset; Black and 3 ROP colors; insert accepted - print & deliver single sheets & tab inserts; page cutoffs - 12.
Mechanical Specifications: Type page 10 1/4 x 11; E - 4 cols, 3 1/6, 1/6 between; A - 6 cols, 1 1/2, 1/6 between; C - 8 cols, 1 1/4, 1/16 between.
Commodity Consumption: Avg. Page Number Per Issue - Daily 88; Avg. Page Number Per Issue - Plates Used 110772; Avg. Page Number Per Issue - Sunday 210; widths 64; Newsprint Used - Metric Tons 11400; Printing Ink Used - Black 214240; Printing Ink Used - Color 65832; Printing In
Equipment EDITORIAL: Front-end Software – Jazbox; Editorial Hardware – Dell Optiplex; Editorial Equipment – 21-Dell/Alpha; Editorial Printers – 1-DEC/LA 120, 1-DEC/LA 75, HP/LaserJet 4V, HP/LaserJet 4MV, HP/LaserJet 5si, HP/LaserJet 5si ; Classified Hardware – AT/Enterpriise, Dewar/View; Classified Printers – 1-AU/APS 3850. DISPLAY: Ad make-up applications – Adobe InDesign; Layout Software – ALS Pagination.; Display Hardware – PC's, APP/Power Mac 7100; Display Printers – HP/4MV LaserJet, HP/5MV LaserJet PRODUCTION: Pagination Software – InDesign; Production Equipment – Arkitex; Scanners – Agfa PRESSROOM: Line 1 – 7-Goss. MAILROOM: Counter stackers – 5-QWI/N200, 7-QWI; Inserters and stuffers – 3-GMA/SLS 1000 8:1, 4-Newstec; Bundle tying machines – 5/OVL, 7-Dynaric; Mailroom control system – Newscom; Addressing machine – 4-Mirajet.; Audio Hardware – Microvoice Systems BUSINESS COMPUTERS: Business Software – Microsoft/Office, Lawson; Business Hardware – IBM/AS-400
Delivery method: Mail, Newsstand, Private Carrier, Racks

NEW YORK

AMNEW YORK

330 W. 34th St., 17th Fl., New York, N.Y., 10001; gen tel (212) 239-5555; gen fax (212) 239-2828; gen e-mail am-info@amny.com; adv e-mail rachel.miller@amny.com; web site www.amny.com
Published: Mon, Tues, Wed, Thur, Fri
Weekday Frequency: All day
Circulation: 266,852
Last Audit: Sworn December 31, 2004
Politics: 2003
Publisher....Paul Turcotte
Bus. Mgr.....Donna Chibaro
Mng. Ed.....Rolando Pujol
City Ed.....Pete Catapano
Features Ed.....Perrie Samotin
National and Image Advertising Director Rachel Miller
Marketing Director....Stephen McCarthy
Retail Advertising Director....Robert Gordon
Equipment PRESSROOM: Line 1 – 212-239-5555

DIARIO DE MEXICO EDICION USA

167 Madison Ave, Ste 401, New York, N.Y., 10016; gen tel 646-285-3033; web site www.diariodemexicousa.com
Published: Mon, Tues, Wed, Thur, Fri
Weekday Frequency: m
Circulation: 12,181
Last Audit: ABC September 30, 2011

DOW JONES & CO., INC.

200 Liberty St., New York, N.Y., 10281; gen tel (212) 416-2000; gen e-mail kay.smith@dowjones.com; web site www.dowjones.com; www.wsj.com

HOY

330 W. 34th St., 17th Fl., New York, N.Y., 10001-2406; gen tel (212) 244-2327; ed e-mail editor@hoynyc.com; web site www.hoynyc.com
Group: Brydson Global Media Sales
Published: Mon, Tues, Wed, Thur, Fri, Sun
Weekday Frequency: m
Circulation: ; 22,053(sun)
Last Audit: March 31, 2005
Advertising: Open inch rate $45.00
News services: AFP, MCT, NYT, TMS, AP, LAT-WP, AccuWeather, Atlantic Syndication, EFE News, Firmas Press, TV Data/TMS, Universal Press Syndicate (UPS).
Politics: 1998
Note: Hoy is printed at the Newsday plant.
Advertising not accepted: Psychics; adult ads; abortion listings.
Not Published: Christmas.
Special Editions: Colombian Festival (Jul); Puerto Rican Parade (Jun); Hispanic Heritage (Sept).
Special Weekly Sections: Automotive & Entertainment (Fri); Education (Mon); Real Estate & Style (Thur); Travel (Tues); Health (Wed).
CEO/Pub.....Jorge L. Ayala
Adv. Mgr., General Sales....Giovanni Perla
Dir., Commun./Mktg....Selma Betancourt
Circ. Dir.....Carlos Reyes
Ed. in Chief....Javier Castano
Mng. Ed.....Ramon Frisneda
Prodn. Mgr.....Ivette Chestaro

N.Y.P. HOLDINGS, INC.

1211 6th Ave., New York, N.Y., 10036; gen tel (212) 930-8201

NEW YORK POST

1211 Ave. of the Americas, New York, N.Y., 10036-8790; gen tel (212) 930-8000; adv tel (212) 930-8222; ed tel (212) 930-8000; gen fax (212) 930-8540; gen e-mail editor@nypost.com; customerservice@nypost.com; ed e-mail letters@nypost.com; web site www.nypost.com
Group: Metro Newspaper Advertising Services, Inc.
Published: Mon, Tues, Wed, Thur, Fri, Sat, Sun
Weekday Frequency: m
Saturday Frequency: m
Circulation: 512,067; 393,829(sat); 379,673(sun)
Last Audit: ABC September 30, 2011
Advertising: Open inch rate $641.88
News services: AP, LAT-WP.
Politics: Independent.
Special Editions: Mexico (Apr); Ski Vacations (Dec); Alaska (Jan); Summer Get-Aways (Jun); Spring & Summer Cruises (Mar); Catskills (May); Mexico (Nov); Follow the Sun (Oct); Autumn Travel (Sept).
Special Weekly Sections: Travel (Tues).
Magazines: Page Six (Quarterly); Parade (S).
Chrmn.....K. Rupert Murdoch

Pub. ....Paul V. Carlucci
Comptroller ....David Del Grasio
Vice Pres., Adv. Sales ....Patrick Judge
Adv. Dir., Opns. ....James Rilley
Adv. Dir., Classified ....Ralf D'Onofrio
Adv. Mgr., Entertainment/Partnerships Amy Scialdone
Adv. Mgr., Internet ....Jill Carvajal
Adv. Mgr., Nat'l ....Ken Kiczales
Adv. Mgr., Research ....Mike DiPreta
Adv. Mgr., Retail ....Chris Golden
Vice Pres., Promo./Mktg. ....Vincent Montuori
Dir., Promo. ....Lisa Barnett
Dir., Mktg. ....Aimee Rametta
Circ. Vice Pres., Opns. ....Joe Gilkey
Circ. Dir., Opns. ....Gary Fescine
Circ. Mgr., City ....Ernie Roda
Circ. Mgr., Home Delivery ....Larry Strickland
Circ. Mgr., Opns. ....Mary Fennessey
Ed. in Chief ....Col Alan
Market Information: Split run.
Mechanical available: Letterpress (direct); Black and 1 ROP colors; insert accepted.
Mechanical Specifications: Type page 9 3/4 x 12 1/2; E - 6 cols, 1 1/2, 1/8 between; A - 6 cols, 1 1/2, 1/8 between; C - 7 cols, 1 5/16, 1/8 between.
Commodity Consumption: Avg. Page Number Per Issue - Daily 76; Avg. Page Number Per Issue - Plates Used 275000; Newsprint Used - Metric Tons 44863; Printing Ink Used - Black 2000000; Printing Ink Used - Color 60000.
Equipment; Editorial Hardware – 4-HI, 36-HI/1720, 29-HI/1740, 36-HI/1780, 55-AST.; Layout Software – 6-HI/2200 (on-line).; Production Equipment – 2-AU/APS 5, 1-Kk; Cameras – 2-C, 3-SCREEN/240; Scanners – 1-ECR/Autokon. PRESSROOM: Line 1 – 8-G/Headliner Mark II; Line 2 – 8-G/Headliner Mark II; Line 3 – 8-G/Headliner Mark II; Line 4 – 8-G/Headliner Mark II; Folders – 4-G/3:2, 4-G/2:1. MAILROOM: Counter stackers – 9/St, 1-/HL; Bundle tying machines – 9-/MLN; Addressing machine – 1-/Am.; Business Hardware – 2-Dec-10

THE NEW YORK SUN

105 Chambers St., Second Fl., New York, N.Y., 10007; gen tel (212) 406-2000; adv tel (212) 901-2700; gen fax (212) 571-9836; adv fax (212) 571-9836; ed fax (212) 571-9836; gen e-mail inquiries@nysun.com; adv e-mail advertising@nysun.com; classified@nysun.com; ed e-mail editor@nysun.com; web site www.nysun.com
Published: Mon, Tues, Wed, Thur, Fri
Weekday Frequency: m
Circulation: 45,763
Last Audit: September 30, 2004
Price: 2.50/wk; 130.00/yr.
Advertising: Open inch rate $31.50
News services: AP, Bloomberg, Jerusalem Post, Chicago Sun-Times, Daily Telegraph.
Politics: Independent.
Dir., Classified ....John Garrett
Circ. Dir. ....Linda Seto
Ed. ....Seth Lipsky
Mng. Ed. ....Ira Stoll
Art Ed. ....Dave Propson
Bus. Ed. ....Richard Thomson
Features Ed. ....Emily Gitter
Sports Ed. ....Michael Woodsworth

THE NEW YORK TIMES

620 8th Ave., New York, N.Y., 10018-1618; gen tel (212) 556-1234; ed tel (212) 556-1876; gen e-mail mainwall@nytimes.com; ed e-mail editorial@nytimes.com; letters@nytimes.com; web site www.nytimes.com
Published: Mon, Tues, Wed, Thur, Fri, Sat, Sun
Weekday Frequency: m
Saturday Frequency: m
Circulation: 1,150,589; 1,202,854(sat); 1,645,152(sun)
Last Audit: ABC September 30, 2011
Price: 7.20/wk.
Advertising: Open inch rate $1,340.00
News services: AP, RN, PR Newswire, DJ, Tass.
Politics: Independent.
Note: The New York Times prints a national satellite edition at eight locations around the U.S.: Chicago; Warren, OH; Austin, TX; Torrance, CA; Walnut Creek, CA; Tacoma, WA; Atlanta; Ft. Lauderdale, FL. The national edition serves the entire country, including
Special Editions: Business Travel (Apr); PGA Tour (Aug); Circuits (Dec); Business of Green (Feb); Deal Book (Mar); Wealth/Personal Finance (May); Giving (Nov); Retirement (Oct); Well (Children's Health) (Sept).
Special Weekly Sections: Weekend Arts (Fri); Arts & Leisure (S); ThursdayStyles (Thur); Science Times (Tues); Dining In/Dining Out (Wed).
Magazines: T (Other); The New York Times Magazine (S); Real Estate (S); Key (Semi-yearly).
Broadcast Affiliations: WHNT-TV Huntsville, AL; KFSM-TV Fort Smith, AR; WHO-TV Des Moines, IA; WQAD-TV Quad Cities, IA; WQAD-TV Quad Cities, IL; WQEW-AM/WQXR-FM New York; KFOR-TV Oklahoma City, OK; WNEP-TV Scranton, PA; WNEP-TV Wilkes-Barre, PA; WREG-TV Memphis, TN; WTKR-TV Norf
Chrmn./Pub. ....Arthur Ochs Sulzberger
Pres./Gen. Mgr. ....Scott H. Heekin-Canedy
Pres., News Servs. ....Cristian L. Edwards
CIO ....Joseph Seibert
Sr. Vice Pres./Deputy Gen. Mgr. .Dennis L. Stern
Sr. Vice Pres., Planning ....Thomas K. Carley
Sr. Vice Pres./Chief Adv. Officer Denise F. Warren
Sr. Vice Pres./CFO ....Roland A. Caputo
Vice Pres., HR ....Michael Valentine
Vice Pres., Labor Rel. ....Terry L. Hayes
Grp. Vice Pres. ....Virginia French
Adv. Sr. Vice Pres. ....Alexis Buryk
Adv. Vice Pres. ....Thomas Helling
Adv. Vice Pres. ....Mark W. Herlyn
Adv. Vice Pres. ....Paul Smurl
Adv. Vice Pres., Sales ....Guy D. Holliday
Adv. Vice Pres., Sales ....Seth Rogin
Adv. Vice Pres., Sales ....Andy Wright
Sr. Vice Pres., Mktg./Circ. ....Yasmin Namini
Dir., Community Affairs ....Diane McNulty
Market Information: Split run; Zoned editions.
Mechanical available: Offset; Black and 3 ROP colors; insert accepted; page cutoffs - 22 1/4.
Mechanical Specifications: Type page 13 x 21 3/8; E - 6 cols, 2, 1/8 between; A - 6 cols, 2, 1/8 between; C - 10 cols, 1 3/16, 1/16 between.
Commodity Consumption: Avg. Page Number Per Issue - Daily 75; Avg. Page Number Per Issue - Plates Used 600000; Avg. Page Number Per Issue - Sunday 400; widths 54; Newsprint Used - Metric Tons 278000; Newsprint Used - Short Tons 307000; Printing Ink Used - Black 4200000; Printi
Equipment EDITORIAL: Front-end Software – AT 4.7.; Editorial Hardware – 42-AT/J-11, Pentium/PC 850, APP/Mac 300; Editorial Equipment – 150-Think Pad, 100-RSK/Tandy 1500, 40-Panasonic; Editorial Printers – HP/LaserJet 60, HP/4M Plus CLASSIFIED: Front-end Software – IBM/CICS Custom Application.; Classified Hardware – 300-IBM/327, PC Custom Front End; Classified Equipment – AU/APS Imagesetter; Classified Printers – 1-HP/LaserJet, 3-C.Itoh DISPLAY: Ad make-up applications – NWI/Admarc 7.0, AII/Ad Manager; Layout Software – AT/Architect RS-6000, Computerease Page Finishing.; Display Hardware – IBM/9121-732, SUN/Enterprise 3000-128GB; Display Printers – MON/Output Manager, AT/Edpage News, AT/Ad Pagination; Production Equipment – 2-LE/2600 online, 3-LE/24-18-25A, 3-APP/Mac, 2-Fuji/603, 4-AU/PSPIP2, 3-AU/APS-6, 1-MON/Express Master; Cameras – Kk/Model 5068 vertical camera; Scanners – 3-ECR/Autokon 1000, 4-ECR/Autokon 2000, Scitex/Smart Scanner, AU/Information INtt3, Mon PRESSROOM: Line 1 – 72-PEC/Converted offset (NY) 1978; Line 2 – 60-G/Colorliner (Edison NJ) 1989; Press Drives – 7, 7, 1; Folders – 9, 6-G/Sovereign; Pasters – 1; Reels and Stands – 168 MAILROOM: Counter stackers – 20-QWI/1000, 20-Id/2000, 6-Id/3000; Inserters and stuffers – 8-HI/1472; Bundle tying machines – MLN/News 90, 12-Dynaric/Strap, 29-Metaveppa/Tyer; Addressing machine – KR, St.; Business Hardware – 2-IBM/9121-621

NY DAILY NEWS

4 New York Plaza, New York, N.Y., 10004; gen tel (212) 210-2100; adv tel (212) 949-2000; ed e-mail news@nydailynews.com; web site www.nydailynews.com
Published: Mon, Tues, Wed, Thur, Fri, Sat, Sun
Weekday Frequency: m
Saturday Frequency: m
Circulation: 605,677; 514,920(sat); 667,638(sun)
Last Audit: ABC September 30, 2011
Price: 3.95/wk (carrier); 35.50/mo (mail).
Advertising: Open inch rate $1,041.07
News services: AP, MCT, TMS.
Politics: Independent. **Established:** 1919
Special Weekly Sections: Friday (Weekend Entertainment Guide) (Fri); City Lights (S); Style (Thur); Food (Wed).
Magazines: Relish (Monthly); Sunday Gravure (S).
Chrmn./Pub. ....Mortimer B. Zuckerman
CFO ....Thomas H. Peck
Sr. Vice Pres., Circ./Distr. ....James Brill
Vice Pres./Dir., Editorial Admin. ......Edward Fay
Adv. Vice Pres., Opns ....Gary Sozzi
Vice Pres./Dir., Promo./Community Affairs John G. Campi
Vice Pres., Mktg ....Christine Curtin
Vice Pres., Commun. ....Jennifer Mauer
Sr. Vice Pres., Daily News Digital Stephen Lynas
Circ. Dir., City Sales ....Howard Wolcott
Circ. Dir., Nat'l Sales ....William Ward
CEO ....Marc Z. Kramer
Exec. Vice Pres./Chief Legal Offficer ..Martin Krall
Vice Pres./Dir., Commun. ....Ken Frydman
Vice Pres./Gen. Counsel ....Larry Marcus
Adv. Sr. Vice Pres., Opns. ....Guy D. Holliday
Sr. Vice Pres., Strategic Mktg./Sales Marie DeParis
Circ. Sr. Vice Pres. ....Rhonda Novick
Circ. Vice Pres. ....Rich Harknett
Circ. Promos. Vice Pres. ....Hugo Masslich
Market Information: Split run; Zoned editions.
Mechanical available: Offset; Black and 3 ROP colors; insert accepted; page cutoffs - 22.
Mechanical Specifications: Type page 9 3/8 x 14; E - 5 cols, 1 3/4, 3/8 between; A - 6 cols, 1 1/2, 1/8 between; C - 7 cols, 1 1/4, 1/8 between.
Commodity Consumption: Avg. Page Number Per Issue - Daily 110; Avg. Page Number Per Issue - Plates Used 600000; Avg. Page Number Per Issue - Sunday 216; widths 58 1/2; Newsprint Used - Metric Tons 153841; Printing Ink Used - Black 2100000; Printing Ink Used - Color 260000; Pri
Equipment EDITORIAL: Front-end Software – AT/J-11, AT/Ed.; Editorial Hardware – AT/Series 6, IBM/RS 6000; Editorial Equipment – 4-APP/Mac, 2-APP/Mac Plus; Editorial Printers – HP, Canon, AG; Classified Hardware – 5-AT/9000; Classified Equipment – 25-IBM/Selectric II, 25-TM/2277, APP/Mac. DISPLAY: Ad make-up applications – Adobe/Photoshop, QPS/QuarkXPress; Layout Software – 4-Cx/135, 8-Cx/2351.; Display Printers – HP, Canon; Production Equipment – 4-M/606, 3-Cx/Supersetter. PRESSROOM: Line 1 – 17-G/Newsliner Units double width (3-4 over 4 units) 1996; Line 2 – 17-G/Newsliner Units double width (3-4 over 4 units) 1996; Line 3 – 17-G/Newsliner Units double width (3-4 over 4 units) 1996; Folders – 9-G/Metro 3:2 Imperial Folder MAILROOM: Counter stackers – 30-Id/550, 12-HL/Monitor, 9-Fg/SCC, 18-S/Olympian, 9-Fg/SCC Conveyor; Bundle tying machines – 40-MVP/Ultra 5000 Strappers; Mailroom control system – Fg/Integrated Bundle Management System, 2-AT/Ferag PKT Plate Conveyor; Other equipment –Other equipment BUSINESS COMPUTERS: Business Software – DB/Millenium; Business Hardware – 1-IBM/MVS

THE WALL STREET JOURNAL

1211 Avenue of the Americas, New York, N.Y., 10036; gen tel (212) 416-2000; adv tel (212) 597-5600; ed tel (212) 416-2500; gen fax (212) 416-2755; web site wsj.com; www.dj.com; www.dowjones.com
Published: Mon, Tues, Wed, Thur, Fri, Sat, Sun
Weekday Frequency: m
Saturday Frequency: m
Circulation: 2,096,169; 2,026,740(sat); 2,026,740(sun)
Last Audit: ABC September 30, 2011
Price: 215.00/yr.
News services: AP, DJ.
Politics: Independent.
Note: The Wall Street Journal is published in three regional editions: Eastern, Central, and Western. News content is the same in all editions, but advertising can be purchased in one or all editions or a combination thereof. Eastern Edition printed in White Oa
Not Published: Presidents' Day; Memorial Day; Independence Day; Labor Day; Thanksgiving; Christmas.
Special Editions: Golf (Apr); Business Insight (Aug); Business Insight (Dec); Encore/Retirement Guide (Feb); Trend Report (Jan); Your Money Matters-Guide to Personal Finance (Jul); 401K (Jun); NCAA Men's Basketball (Mar); Best On The Street Analysts (May); Monthly Mutual F
Special Weekly Sections: Weekend Journal (Fri); Personal Journal (Thur); Personal Journal (Tues); Personal Journal (Wed).
Chrmn. ....Rupert Murdoch
Pub./CEO, Dow Jones ....Les Hinton
Sr. Vice Pres./COO ....Todd H. Larsen
Chief Revenue Officer ....Michael F. Rooney
Vice Pres., News Projects .....F. James Pensiero
Gen. Mgr., WSJ.com ....Daniel J. Bernard
Adv. Sr. Vice Pres. ....Judy Barry
Adv. Vice Pres., Bus. Grp. ....David Forgione
District Sales Mgr. ....Walter Hodge
Vice Pres., Mktg. Strategy ....Imtiaz Patel
Vice Pres., Circ. Mktg. ....Lynne K. Brennen
Mng. Ed./Ed. in Chief, Dow Jones Robert Thomson
Deputy Ed. in Chief ....Gerard Baker
Deputy Mng. Ed. ....Rebecca Blumenstein
Deputy Mng. Ed. ....Deborah Brewster
Deputy Mng. Ed. ....Alix M. Freedman
Deputy Mng. Ed. ....Michael W. Miller
Asst. Mng. Ed./Exec. Washington Ed. Gerald F. Seib
Bureau Chief, Atlanta ....Robert Rose
Bureau Chief, Chicago ....Kevin Helliker
Market Information: ADS; Split run; TMC; Zoned editions.
Mechanical available: Offset; Black and 3 ROP colors; insert accepted; page cutoffs - 22 3/4.
Mechanical Specifications: Type page 10 3/4 x 21 1/2.
Commodity Consumption: Avg. Page Number Per Issue - Daily 50.

THE WALL STREET JOURNAL-EASTERN EDITION

200 Liberty St., New York, N.Y., 10281; gen tel (212) 416-2000; adv tel (212) 597-5603; adv fax (212) 597-5888; adv e-mail deborah.howard@dowjones.com; web site www.wsj.com
Not Published: Presidents' Day; Memorial Day; Independence Day; Labor Day; Thanksgiving; Christmas.
Gen Mgr. ....Daniel Bernard
Vice Pres. Adv. Sales ....Brian Quinn
Market Information: Split run; Zoned editions.
Mechanical available: Offset; Black and 3 ROP colors; insert accepted; page cutoffs - 22 3/4.
Commodity Consumption: Avg. Page Number Per Issue - Daily 54.
Equipment; Editorial Hardware – 2-CSI/1170, 2-DEC/PDP 11-84, 2-DEC/VAX 8250, 18-CSI/VT.; Classified Hardware – 2-CSI/1170, 4-Sun/360, 18-CSI/VT 112.; Layout Software – 2-CSI/1170, Cx/Sun 360.; Production Equipment – 4-C, 3-C/R650, 3, 21-Dow/Recorder; Cameras – 2-C/Newspager II, C/Spartan III; Scanners – 2-ECR. PRESSROOM: Line 1 – 12-G/Metro Double Width, 12-G/Metro Double Width; Line 2 – 12-G/Metro Double Width, 12-G/Metro Double Width; Line 3 – 12; Line 4 – 12; Line 5 – 12; Line 6 – 12-G/Metro Double Width; Press Drives – 8; Folders – 5, 3; Pasters – 50, 30; Reels and Stands – Reels and Sta MAILROOM: Counter stackers – 16/QWI; Bundle tying machines – 6-/Dynamic, 16-/OVL, 16-/Power Strap, 12-/Ster-

ling; Addressing machine – 16-/CCL. BUSINESS COMPUTERS: Business Software – Word Processing; Business Hardware – 9-IBM/3090, 1-HP/1000, 1-HP/9845

NIAGARA FALLS

NIAGARA GAZETTE

310 Niagara St., Niagara Falls, N.Y., 14302-0549; gen tel (716) 282-2311; adv tel (716) 282-2311; ed tel (716) 282-2311; gen fax (716) 286-3895; adv fax (716) 286-3811; ed fax (716) 286-3895; adv e-mail classads@gnnewspapers.com; web site www.niagara-gazette.com

Group: New York Newspaper Advertising Service, Inc.
Published: Mon, Tues, Wed, Thur, Fri, Sat, Sun
Weekday Frequency: m
Saturday Frequency: m
Circulation: 14,135; 15,159(sat); 13,632(sun)
Last Audit: ABC September 30, 2011
Price: 3.50/wk (carrier); 180.96/yr.
Advertising: Open inch rate $52.67
News services: AP, GNS.
Politics: Independent. **Established:** 1854
Note: This publication shares a joint Sunday edition with the Lockport (NY) Union-Sun & Journal and the North Tonawanda (NY) Tonawanda News.
Special Editions: Senior Guide (Apr); Back-to-School (Aug); Holiday Greetings (Dec); Progress (Feb); Health & Wellness (Jan); Added Value Certificates (Jul); Dining Guide (Jun); Home Improvement (Mar); Summer Events (May); Holiday Gift Guide (Nov); Fall Dining Guide (Oct);
Special Weekly Sections: Home & Garden (Fri); Food (Mon); Comics (S); Religion (Sat).
Magazines: USA WEEKEND Magazine (S).
Pub. ....Peter Mio
Circ. Mgr. ....Paul Glaeser
Mng. Ed. ....Dick Lucinski
Copy Desk Chief ....Linda Noworyta
Graphics Ed. ....David Marra
Web Ed. ....James Neiss
Sports Ed., Sabres ....Tim Schmitt
Mechanical available: Letterpress Offset; Black and 3 ROP colors; insert accepted - single sheet; page cutoffs - 22 3/4.
Mechanical Specifications: Type page 11 5/8 x 21 1/2; E - 6 cols, 1 13/16, 1/6 between; A - 6 cols, 1 13/16, 1/6 between; C - 8 cols, 1 7/16, 1/16 between.
Commodity Consumption: Avg. Page Number Per Issue - Daily 24; Avg. Page Number Per Issue - Plates Used 28000; Avg. Page Number Per Issue - Sunday 48; widths 12 1/2; Newsprint Used - Metric Tons 1900; Printing Ink Used - Black 60000; Printing Ink Used - Color 9000; Printing Ink
Equipment EDITORIAL: Front-end Software – DTI 4.2.; Editorial Hardware – Sun/Enterprise 450; Editorial Equipment – 12-APP/Mac Centris 610, 10-APP/Mac G4, 7-APP/Mac G4 Graphics Server, 2-APP/iMac, 8-APP/Mac G4 CLASSIFIED: Front-end Software – DTI 4.2.; Classified Hardware – 6-APP/iMac; Classified Printers – APP/Mac LaserWriter Pro DISPLAY: Ad make-up applications – DTI/AdSpeed 4.2; Display Hardware – 1-APP/iMac, 7-APP/Mac G3; Display Printers – 1-NewGen/Turbo P.S., 1-APP/Mac LaserWriter Pro 630 PRODUCTION: Pagination Software – DTI/Speedwriter 4.2, DTI/SpeedDriver, DTI/AdSpeed; Production Equipment – 2-Nu/Flip Top, ECR/Scriptsetter VRL36, 1-3.5gig hard drive; Cameras – Acti/125 24x36; Scanners – 2-Umax/Astra 1200, UMAX/Powerlook 2100XL, Umax/Astra 24005, Epson/Perfection 1240u; Folders – 2 MAILROOM: Counter stackers – 2-QWI/350, 2/Rockbuilt, 1-/Count-o-Veyor; Inserters and stuffers – 2-GMA/SLS 1000 ID:1; Bundle tying machines – 2-/Power Strap; Wrapping singles – 2-QWI/Bottom Wrap.; Business Hardware – IBM/AS-400

NORTH TONAWANDA

TONAWANDA NEWS

435 River Rd., North Tonawanda, N.Y., 14120-0668; gen tel (716) 693-1000; adv tel (716) 693-1000; ed tel (716) 693-1007; gen fax (716) 693-8573; adv fax (716) 693-8573; ed fax (716) 693-0124; adv e-mail newsroom@tonawanda-news.com; web site www.tonawanda-news.com

Group: U.S. Suburban Press, Inc.
Published: Tues, Wed, Thur, Fri, Sat, Sun
Weekday Frequency: e
Saturday Frequency: m
Circulation: 5,059; 6,148(sat); 4,532(sun)
Last Audit: ABC September 30, 2011
Price: 3.65/wk.
Advertising: Open inch rate $52.67
News services: AP, U.S. Suburban Press Inc..
Politics: Independent. **Established:** 1880
Note: This publication shares a joint Sunday edition with the Lockport (NY) Union-Sun & Journal and the Niagara Falls (NY) Niagara Gazette.
Not Published: All legal holidays.
Own facility?: Y
Special Weekly Sections: USA Weekend (S); TV Times (Thur).
Pub. ....Peter Mio
Adv. Dir. ....John Brundo
Circ. Mgr. ....Ken Skryp
Mng. Ed. ....Eric Duvall
Graphics Ed. ....Cherryl Phillips
Night/Day Ed. ....Paul Lane
Chief Photographer ....James Neiss
Prodn. Mgr., Mailroom ....Barb Spears
Market Information: Split run; TMC; Zoned editions.
Mechanical available: Offset; Letter Press; Black and 3 ROP colors; insert accepted - single sheet; page cutoffs - 22 3/4.
Mechanical Specifications: Type page 11 5/8 x 21 1/2; E - 6 cols, 1 13/16, 1/6 between; A - 6 cols, 1 13/16, 1/6 between; C - 8 cols, 1 9/16, 1/16 between.
Commodity Consumption: Avg. Page Number Per Issue - Daily 12; Avg. Page Number Per Issue - Plates Used 4811; widths 12 1/2; Newsprint Used - Short Tons 459; Printing Ink Used - Black 15463; Printing Ink Used - Color 340; Printing Ink Used - Pages Printed 4921.
Equipment EDITORIAL: Front-end Software – DTI/SpeedWriter, DTI/Page Speed 4.2, DTI/SpeedPlanner 4.2.; Editorial Hardware – APP/Mac; Editorial Printers – APP/Mac LaserWriter 630 Pro, HP/500N CLASSIFIED: Front-end Software – System Facilities, DTI.; Classified Hardware – APP/iMac; Classified Printers – APP/Mac Pro 630 DISPLAY: Ad make-up applications – DTI/AdSpeed 4.2; Layout Software – APP/Mac.; Display Hardware – APP/Mac, 7-APP/Mac G3; Display Printers – 1-New Gen/Turbo PS, 1-APP/Mac Laserwriter Pro 630 PRODUCTION: Pagination Software – DTI/Speedwriter 4.2, DTI/PageSpeed 4.2, DTI/Spe; Production Equipment – 1-Nu/FT40V, 1-Nu/CN42, 3.5 GIG Hard Drive; Cameras – Acti/125-24x36; Scanners – AG/Studioscan IIsi, 2-Umax/Astra 1200, Umax/Powerlook 2100XL, Epson/Perfection 1240u, Umax/Astra 24005; Folders – 2 MAILROOM: Counter stackers – 2-QWI/350, 2/Rockbuilt, 1-/Count-O-Veyor; Inserters and stuffers – 2-GMA/SLS 1000 10:1; Bundle tying machines – 2-/Powerstrap; Wrapping singles – 2-QWI/BottomWrap; Addressing machine – 1-Am/1955P.; Business Hardware – PC System
Zip Codes served: 14120,14150,14217,14223
Delivery method: Newsstand, Private Carrier

NORWICH

THE EVENING SUN

29 Lackawanna Ave., Norwich, N.Y., 13815-0151; gen tel (607) 334-3276; adv tel (607) 334-3276; ed tel (607) 334-3276; gen fax (607) 334-8273; adv fax (607) 334-8273; ed fax (607) 334-8273; gen e-mail evesun@norwich.net; web site www.evesun.com

Published: Mon, Tues, Wed, Thur, Fri
Weekday Frequency: e
Circulation: 5,100
Last Audit: March 31, 2007
Price: 2.50/wk; 9.20/mo; 124.80/yr.
Advertising: Open inch rate $12.05
News services: AP.
Politics: Independent. **Established:** 1994
Not Published: Christmas.
Special Weekly Sections: The Weekend Sun (Fri); Sports (Mon); Lifestyle (Thur); Health (Tues); Farm (Wed).
Pub. ....Richard Snyder
Adv. Mgr. ....Russ Foote
Circ. Mgr. ....Brad Dick
Mng. Ed. ....Jeffrey Genung
Sports Ed. ....Pat Newell
Prodn. Mgr., Pressroom ....Tim Ryan
Market Information: Split run; TMC; Zoned editions.
Mechanical available: Offset; Black and 4 ROP colors; insert accepted; page cutoffs - 22 3/4.
Mechanical Specifications: Type page 13 x 21 1/2; E - 7 cols, 1 2/3, 1/8 between; A - 7 cols, 1 2/3, 1/8 between; C - 7 cols, 1 2/3, 1/16 between.
Commodity Consumption: Avg. Page Number Per Issue - Daily 14; Avg. Page Number Per Issue - Plates Used 2550; widths 27; Newsprint Used - Short Tons 110; Printing Ink Used - Black 4400; Printing Ink Used - Color 170; Printing Ink Used - Pages Printed 4403.
Equipment EDITORIAL: Front-end Software – Baseview/NewsEdit Pro.; Editorial Hardware – Mk, APP/Mac CLASSIFIED: Front-end Software – Baseview/Class Pro.; Classified Hardware – Mk, APP/Mac DISPLAY: Ad make-up applications – Multi-Ad/Creator; Layout Software – APP/Mac.; Display Hardware – APP/Mac PRODUCTION: Pagination Software – QPS/QuarkXPress 3.31.; Production Equipment – Caere/OmniPage Direct; Cameras – 1-AG PRESSROOM: Line 1 – Dec-88; Line 2 – G/Community single width 1970; Line 3 – G/Community single width 1970; Line 4 – G/Community single width 1974; Press Drives – Fin/100 HP; Folders – 1-G/SC, 1-G/Community SC. MAILROOM: Counter stackers – Baldwin/Count-O-Veyor 109; Bundle tying machines – MA, Bu.; Business Hardware – PC, Unix

OGDENSBURG

THE COURIER-OBSERVER, THE JOURNAL & THE ADVANCE-NEWS

308-310 Isabella St., Ogdensburg, N.Y., 13669; gen tel (315) 769-2451; adv tel (315) 393-1000; ed tel (315) 393-1000; gen fax (315) 393-5108; gen e-mail courier@ogd.com; adv e-mail class@ogd.com

Published: Sun
Circulation: 5,831; 5,831(sat); 10,720(sun)
Last Audit: September 30, 2003
Advertising: Open inch rate $11.50
News services: AP.
Politics: 1830
Advertising not accepted: Adoption.
Not Published: New Year; Memorial Day; Independence Day; Labor Day; Thanksgiving; Christmas.
Special Editions: Automotive (Aug); Progress (Jan); Dairy Month (Jun); Christmas Card (Nov); Sports Profiles (Sept).
Special Weekly Sections: TV (S).
Magazines: Parade (S).
Bus. Mgr. ....Brenda Labrake
Credit Mgr. ....Lisa Decker
Ed. ....Charles W. Kelly
Mng. Ed., Courier-Observer ....Ryne R. Martin
Mng. Ed., Journal/Advance News James E. Reagen
Sports Ed., Courier-Observer ....Allain St. Pierre
Sports Ed., Journal/Advance News ....David Shea
Prodn. Supt. ....Barbara Burnett
Prodn. Foreman, Pressroom ....Elmore Johnson
Market Information: TMC.
Mechanical available: Offset; Black and 1 ROP colors; insert accepted - min. 4-page tab; page cutoffs - 20.
Mechanical Specifications: Type page 13 x 21 1/2; E - 6 cols, 2 1/16, 1/8 between; A - 6 cols, 2 1/6, 1/8 between; C - 9 cols, 1 3/8, 1/16 between.
Commodity Consumption: Avg. Page Number Per Issue - Daily 13; Avg. Page Number Per Issue - Plates Used 4784; Avg. Page Number Per Issue - Sunday 33; widths 28; Newsprint Used - Short Tons 205; Printing Ink Used - Black 8700; Printing Ink Used - Color 1025; Printing Ink Used -
Equipment; Editorial Hardware – Mk.; Classified Hardware – 1-Mk/Mycro-Comp.; Production Equipment – 3-COM; Cameras – 1-C. PRESSROOM: Line 1 – 5-G/Urbanite (40 broadsheet pages).; Bundle tying machines – 1/Bu, 2-/Gd; Addressing machine – 4-/Am.; Business Hardware – Vision Data

OLEAN

OLEAN TIMES HERALD

639 Norton Dr., Olean, N.Y., 14760; gen tel (716) 372-3121; gen fax (716) 372-0740; gen e-mail news@oleantimesherald.com; adv e-mail jkeim@oleantimesherald.com; web site www.oleantimesherald.com

Group: New York Newspaper Advertising Service, Inc.
Published: Mon, Tues, Wed, Thur, Fri, Sat, Sun
Weekday Frequency: e
Saturday Frequency: e
Circulation: 11,360; 12,407(sat); 12,564(sun)
Last Audit: ABC September 30, 2011
Price: 16.15/mo (carrier); 183.00/yr (carrier).
Advertising: Open inch rate $27.00
News services: AP, NEA, SHNS, CNS.
Politics: Independent. **Established:** 2000
Note: This newspaper is published in tabloid format on Saturday.
Special Editions: Golf Tab (Apr); Christmas Stories (Dec); Tax Tab (Feb); Bridal (Jan); Frozen Food (Mar); Christmas (Nov); Hunting (Oct); Consumer Electronics (Sept); Spring Buyer Tab (Spring).
Special Weekly Sections: Directory (Fri); Best Food Day (Mon); TV Digest (S); Church Pages (Sat); House and Garden (Thur).
Magazines: Olean Review (Other); USA WEEKEND Magazine (S).
Pub. ....Jim Bonn
Adv. Mgr., Nat'l ....Julie Keim
Circ. Mgr. ....Thomas Foley
Features Ed. ....Jim Eckstrom
Online Ed. ....Chuck Massaro
School Ed. ....Rick Miller
Sports Ed. ....Chuck Pollock
Prodn. Foreman, Composing ....John Pfeiffer
Market Information: ADS; TMC.
Mechanical available: Offset; Black and 3 ROP colors; insert accepted - self-adhesive notes; page cutoffs - 21 1/2.
Mechanical Specifications: Type page 13 x 21 1/2; E - 6 cols, 2 1/16, 1/8 between; A - 6 cols, 2 1/16, 1/8 between; C - 9 cols, 1 3/8, 1/16 between.
Commodity Consumption: Avg. Page Number Per Issue - Daily 23; Avg. Page Number Per Issue - Plates Used 5900; Avg. Page Number Per Issue - Sunday 32; widths 26 1/2; Newsprint Used - Metric Tons 1360; Printing Ink Used - Black 27468; Printing Ink Used - Pages Printed 8916.
Equipment EDITORIAL: Front-end Software – QPS/QuarkXPress.; Editorial Hardware – APP/Power Mac; Editorial Printers – HP/LaserJet 5000N, Pre Press/Panther Plus 36, Pre Press/Panther Plus CLASSIFIED: Front-end Software – Baseview.; Classified Hardware – 3-APP/Power Mac; Classified Printers – Okidata/193 Line Printer, HP/LaserJet 5000N DISPLAY: Ad make-up applications – Multi-Ad/Creator; Layout Software – Multi-Ad/Creator, Adobe/Photoshop.; Display Hardware – APP/Power Mac; Display Printers – HP/LaserJet 5000N PRODUCTION: Pagination Software – Baseview.; Production Equipment – 1-

COM/7200, 2-COM/ACM9000, 2-COM/8600, 2-Unified/Composer; Cameras – 1-B/Commodore, 1-K/187; Scanners – 3-Dewar/Disc Net 55 Terminal, 3-Dewar/Discovery Display Ad Terminal PRESSROOM: Line 1 – 7-G/U 791 (1 balloon former).; Bundle tying machines – 2-MLN/ML2-EE.; Business Hardware – Vision Data

ONEIDA

THE ONEIDA DAILY DISPATCH

130 Broad St., Oneida, N.Y., 13421; gen tel (315) 363-5100; adv tel (315) 363-5100; ed tel (315) 363-5100; gen fax (315) 363-9832; adv fax (315) 363-0416; ed fax (315) 363-9832; adv e-mail kalvord@journalregister.com; ed e-mail newsroom@oneidadispatch.com; web site www.oneidadispatch.com

Group: Journal Register Company
Published: Mon, Tues, Wed, Thur, Fri, Sat
Weekday Frequency: m
Saturday Frequency: m
Circulation: 5,967; 6,800(sat)
Last Audit: ABC September 30, 2011
Price: $42.25/13 wks; $169/52 wks
Advertising: Open inch rate $14.99
Insert rate: $58/m
News services: AP.
Politics: Independent. **Established:** 1851
Not Published: Sunday
Own facility?: Y
Special Editions: Homestyle Magazine;Holiday Entertainment (Feb); Everything Spring(April); Let it Snow (Jan); Summer Fun (Jun); Progress (Mar); Christmas Planner (Nov); Brides(Jan.); Fall Sports (Sept).
Special Weekly Sections: Life &Times (Sat.).
Magazines: Parade Magazine (Sat).
Mng. Ed. ....Kurt Wanfried
Prodn. Dir. ....Robert Bennett
General Manager & Advertising Director Karen Alvord
Circulation Supervisor ....Sabrina Sharkey
Mechanical Specifications: 1 col. 1.557, 2 co9l. 3.223, 3 col. 4.89, 4 col. 6.557, 5 col. 8.223, 6 col. 9.89
Equipment EDITORIAL: Front-end Software – Cx, Baseview/News IQUE.; Editorial Hardware – APP/Mac G3 CLASSIFIED: Front-end Software – Cx.; Classified Hardware – IBM/XT DISPLAY: Ad make-up applications – Multi-Ad/Creator, Ofoto, QPS/QuarkXPress 3.32.; Display Hardware – APP/Power Mac 9300-200, APP/Mac G3; Display Printers – NewGen/Turbo PS, NewGen/DesignXpress 12; Cameras – B/Caravel, SCREEN/C-6500 D; Scanners – HP/ScanJet 4C.; Other equipment –None BUSINESS COMPUTERS: Business Software – Novell/MSSI; Business Hardware – IBM/60 fileserver, 1-IBM/30-286, 5-IBM/25
Zip Codes served: 13421, 13032, 13035, 13037, 13054, 13157, 13163,13310, 133354, 13346,13402, 13408, 13409,13461,13476, 13478
Delivery method: Mail, Newsstand, Private Carrier, Racks

ONEONTA

THE DAILY STAR

102 Chestnut St., Oneonta, N.Y., 13820-0250; gen tel (607) 432-1000; adv tel (607) 432-1000; ed tel (607) 432-1000; gen fax (607) 432-5847; adv fax (607) 432-5847; ed fax (607) 432-5707; gen e-mail publisher@thedailystar.com; adv e-mail advertise@thedailystar.com; ed e-mail editor@thedailystar.com; web site www.thedailystar.com

Published: Mon, Tues, Wed, Thur, Fri, Sat
Weekday Frequency: m
Saturday Frequency: m
Circulation: 14,131; 14,131(sat)
Last Audit: September 30, 2009
Price: 3.00/wk (carrier), $2.95/wk (motor); 171.80/yr.
Advertising: Open inch rate $34.31
News services: AP, DJ, ONS, LAT-WP, TMS.
Politics: Independent. **Established:** 1890
Not Published: New Year; Memorial Day; Independence Day; Labor Day; Thanksgiving; Christmas.
Special Editions: Chamber of Commerce (Apr); Real Estate Today (Aug); Last Minute Gift Guide (Dec); NASCAR (Feb); Job Fair (Jan); Home Improvement (Jul); Summer in the Heartland of NY (Jun); Spring in the Heartland of NY (Mar); Home & Garden (May); Holiday Recipes (Nov); C
Special Weekly Sections: Neighbors (Fri); Best Food Day (Sat); College Issues (Thur); Health Page (Tues); College Issues (Wed).
Magazines: Relish (Monthly); Parade (Weekly).
Pub. ....Armand Nardi
Controller ....Karen Chichester
Adv. Mgr., Sales ....Robert Evens
Circ. Mgr. ....Thomas G. Falk
Ed. ....Sam Pollak
Community Ed. ....Emily Farmer
Features Ed. ....Denielle Ziemba
Librarian ....Deb McCaffery
News Ed. ....Denise Richardson
Photo Dept. Mgr. ....Julie Lewis
Sports Ed. ....Dean Russin
Online Mgr. ....Jason Whitney
Prodn. Mgr., Mailroom ....William Cooper
Prodn. Mgr., Pre Press ....Olin Benedict
Prodn. Mgr., Pressroom ....John McCoy
Market Information: TMC; Zoned editions.
Mechanical available: Offset; Black and 3 ROP colors; insert accepted; page cutoffs - 22 3/4.
Mechanical Specifications: Type page 11 13/16 x 21 1/2; E - 6 cols, 1 13/16, 1/8 between; A - 6 cols, 1 13/16, 1/8 between; C - 9 cols, 1 1/4, 1/16 between.
Commodity Consumption: Avg. Page Number Per Issue - Daily 22; Avg. Page Number Per Issue - Plates Used 14479; Avg. Page Number Per Issue - Saturday 50; widths 12 1/2; Newsprint Used - Metric Tons 1001; Printing Ink Used - Black 22497; Printing Ink Used - Color 4800; Printing I
Equipment EDITORIAL: Front-end Software – AT/Dewarview.; Editorial Hardware – 17-Dell; Editorial Printers – 2-HP CLASSIFIED: Front-end Software – Atex/Enterprise.; Classified Hardware – 8-Dell; Classified Printers – 1-HP DISPLAY: Ad make-up applications – QPS/QuarkXPress 5.0, 7-Archetype/Corel Draw; Layout Software – MEI/ALS.; Display Hardware – 5-Dell; Display Printers – HP PRODUCTION: Pagination Software – QPS/QuarkXPress 3.0.; Production Equipment – 2-Konica/E-V Jetsetter, Konica/K-550; Cameras – 1-C/Spartan III PRESSROOM: Line 1 – 5-G/Urbanite single width 1974, 1-G/Urbanite 3-color single width 1999; Folders – 1-G/(with balloon); Reels and Stands – 5; Press control system – 2 MAILROOM: Counter stackers – QWI; Inserters and stuffers – MM/227E; Bundle tying machines – 2-Sa/SR1A, 3-Si/LB 2000; Addressing machine – Ch/Quarter folder Labeler. BUSINESS COMPUTERS: Business Software – 7-Microsoft/Office XP; Business Hardware – IBM/AS-400
Delivery method: Mail, Newsstand, Private Carrier, Racks

OSWEGO

THE PALLADIUM-TIMES

140 W. First St., Oswego, N.Y., 13126; gen tel (315) 343-3800; adv tel (315) 343-3800; gen fax (315) 343-0273; adv fax (315) 343-0273; adv e-mail classifieds@palltimes.com; web site www.palltimes.com

Published: Mon, Tues, Wed, Thur, Fri, Sat
Weekday Frequency: e
Circulation: 8,507; 8,507(sat)
Last Audit: September 30, 2006
Price: 2.25/wk (carrier); 9.75/mo (mail); 110.00/yr.
Advertising: Open inch rate $15.00
News services: AP, SHNS.
Politics: Independent.
Advertising not accepted: Mail order; Oil stock; Bed & board.
Not Published: New Year; Independence Day; Thanksgiving; Christmas.
Special Editions: Newcomer's Guide (Aug); Christmas Shopping (Dec); Welcome Back SUNY Tab (Feb); Weather (Jan); Auto Racing (Jul); Father's Day (Jun); Progress (Mar); Mother's Day (May); Historic (Monthly); Fall Sports (Oct); Bridal (Sept).
Special Weekly Sections: Health (Fri); Food (Mon); Entertainment (Thur); Business Pages (Tues).
Magazines: USA WEEKEND Magazine (Sat).
Pub. ....Jon Spaulding
Accountant ....Virginia DeCare
Adv. Mgr. ....Dusti Foley
Circ. Mgr. ....Toby Clawson
Mng. Ed. ....Debra Robillard
Sports Ed. ....Michael LeBoeuf
Prodn. Mgr., Composing ....Andrea Peeters
Market Information: TMC.
Mechanical available: Offset; Black and 3 ROP colors; insert accepted - free-standing cards; page cutoffs - 22 1/2.
Mechanical Specifications: Type page 13 x 21 1/2; E - 6 cols, 2 1/16, 1/8 between; A - 6 cols, 2 1/16, 1/8 between; C - 8 cols, 1 9/16, 1/16 between.
Commodity Consumption: Avg. Page Number Per Issue - Daily 18; Avg. Page Number Per Issue - Plates Used 3000; widths 27 1/2; Newsprint Used - Short Tons 341; Printing Ink Used - Black 8305; Printing Ink Used - Color 275; Printing Ink Used - Pages Printed 5400.
Equipment; Editorial Hardware – Mk; Editorial Equipment – APP/Mac Classic II; Editorial Printers – APP/Mac LaserPrinters.; Classified Hardware – Mk; Classified Printers – APP/Mac LaserPrinter.; Production Equipment – APP/Mac LaserPrinter; Cameras – LE/Horizontal. PRESSROOM: Line 1 – 8-G/Community (2 Forms) 1971.; Bundle tying machines – Aldebo/Bundler. BUSINESS COMPUTERS: Business Software – Multi-Ad/Creator, Microsoft/Works, Lotus 2.4, Claris/MacDraw; Business Hardware – APP/Mac, NEC/386

PLATTSBURGH

PLATTSBURGH PUBLISHING CO.

170 Margaret St., Plattsburgh, N.Y., 12901; gen tel (518) 561-2300; gen fax (518) 561-3362; gen e-mail news@pressrepublican.com; web site www.pressrepublican.com

PRESS-REPUBLICAN

170 Margaret St., Plattsburgh, N.Y., 12901; gen tel (518) 561-2300; adv tel (518) 561-2300; ed tel (518) 561-2300; gen fax (518) 561-3362; adv fax (518) 562-3361; ed fax (518) 561-3362; gen e-mail news@pressrepublican.com; adv e-mail grock@pressrepublican.com; web site www.pressrepublican.com

Published: Mon, Tues, Wed, Thur, Fri, Sat, Sun
Weekday Frequency: m
Saturday Frequency: m
Circulation: 17,865; 18,972(sat); 19,166(sun)
Last Audit: ABC September 30, 2011
Price: 3.00/wk (carrier), $3.50/wk (auto), $3.95/wk (mail); 166.14/yr (carrier), $204.00/yr(mail).
Advertising: Open inch rate $35.26
News services: AP, SHNS.
Politics: Independent.
Not Published: Christmas.
Special Editions: Bassmasters Fishing Guide (Aug); Holiday Bears (Dec); Health Mind and Body (Every other month); YMCA (Jan); FLW Fishing Guide (Jul); Lake Placid Horse Show (Jun); How To Guide (May); Senior Sentinel (Monthly); Celebrations (Nov); How To Guide (Oct); Battl
Special Weekly Sections: Best Food Day (S).
Magazines: North Country Scene (Every other month); Relish (Monthly); Parade (S); American Profile (Weekly).
Pub. ....Robert W. Parks
Controller ....Josie Tripp
Adv. Sales Mgr. ....Mike Morrison
Mktg. Dir. ....George Rock
Circ. Dir. ....James G. Frenya
Ed. ....Robert Grady
Circ. Mgr. ....Scott Bresett
Design/Systems Ed. ....John Downs
News Ed. ....Lois Clermont
Asst. News Ed. ....Rachael Osborne
Night Ed. ....Nathan Ovalle
Special Sections Ed. ....Jennifer Meschinelli
Sports Ed. ....Bob Goetz
Mgr., Mgmt. Info Servs. ....Kevin Richard
Webmaster ....Roger Black
Prodn. Dir. ....Daniel L. Thayer
Press, Night Supvr. ....Kevin Hidook
Market Information: TMC.
Mechanical available: Offset; Black and 3 ROP colors; insert accepted; page cutoffs - 22 3/4.
Mechanical Specifications: Type page 11 5/8 x 21 1/2; E - 6 cols, 1 5/6, 1/16 between; A - 6 cols, 1 5/6, 1/16 between; C - 9 cols, 1 1/4, 1/16 between.
Commodity Consumption: Avg. Page Number Per Issue - Daily 30; Avg. Page Number Per Issue - Plates Used 24000; Avg. Page Number Per Issue - Sunday 40; widths 12 1/2; Newsprint Used - Metric Tons 1419; Printing Ink Used - Black 34000; Printing Ink Used - Color 4800; Printing Ink
Equipment EDITORIAL: Front-end Software – Sysdeco, Dewar, QPS/QuarkXPress, QPS/QuarkXPress 3.32.; Editorial Hardware – COM/ONE, IBM/300PL; Editorial Equipment – AP/Photo Server, IBM/RS6000; Editorial Printers – 1-HP/4MV, 1-HP/5Si/MX CLASSIFIED: Front-end Software – AT/Enterprise.; Classified Hardware – IBM/PC; Classified Equipment – IBM/RS6000 Server; Classified Printers – HP/4MV DISPLAY: Ad make-up applications – Adobe/InDesign, QPS/QuarkXPress 3.32; Layout Software – MEI, APP/Mac Power PC.; Display Hardware – IBM/300 PL PIII 733 Mhz; Display Printers – HP/4MV PRODUCTION: Pagination Software – QPS/QuarkXPress 3.32, Dewar.; Production Equipment – 2-Nat/FT40, ECR/M6100; Cameras – Scanners □ Canon PRESSROOM: Line 1 – 8-G/Urbanite; Folders – 1 MAILROOM: Counter stackers – 2/Compass; Inserters and stuffers – GMA/SLS 1000; Bundle tying machines – 2-MLN/2EE, 1-/Power Strap; Mailroom control system – Newscom; Other equipment –MM/Minuteman.

POUGHKEEPSIE

POUGHKEEPSIE JOURNAL

85 Civic Center Plz., Poughkeepsie, N.Y., 12601-2410; gen tel (845) 454-2000; adv fax (845) 437-4903; ed fax (845) 437-4921; adv e-mail advert@poughkee.gannett.com; ed e-mail newsroom@poughkee.gannett.com; web site www.poughkeepsiejournal.com

Published: Mon, Tues, Wed, Thur, Fri, Sat, Sun
Weekday Frequency: m
Saturday Frequency: m
Circulation: 26,247; 29,308(sat); 38,366(sun)
Last Audit: ABC September 30, 2011
Price: 16.00/mo (carrier), $16.50/mo (motor route); 192.60/yr.
Advertising: Open inch rate $88.95
News services: AP, GNS, LAT-WP, CNS.
Politics: Independent. **Established:** 1785
Special Editions: Spring Home & Gardens (Apr); Luxury Auto (Aug); Songbook (Dec); Menus (Feb); Bridal (Jan); Decisions (Jun); Luxury Auto (Mar); Luxury Auto (May); Communities (Monthly); Luxury Auto (Nov); Celebrating Women (Oct); Verge Guide to Choosing a College (Sept).
Special Weekly Sections: Real Estate (Other).
Magazines: TV Log (S).
Profile: We are a newspaper and online publisher
Pub. ....Barry Rothfeld
Controller ....Randy S. Sutherland
HR Mgr. ....Nora Pietrafesa
Asst. to Pub. ....Roseann Simpson

Adv. Dir. ....Jan Dewey
Adv. Mgr., Classified ....Jeff Reiss
Adv. Mgr., Retail ....Bob O'Leary
Mktg. Mgr. ....Jean Harris
Circ. Mgr. ....Bill Farrell
Exec. Ed. ....Stuart Shinske
City Ed. ....Kevin Lenihan
Editorial Page Ed. ....John Penney
Asst. Features Ed. ....Barbara Gallo Farrell
Local Ed. ....John Nelson
Photo/Graphics Ed. ....Spencer Ainsley
Sports Ed. ....Dan Pietrafesa
Multimedia Web Developer ....Jared Hamburger
Systems Mgr. ....Betsy Hoxter
Market Information: ADS; Split run; TMC; Zoned editions.
Mechanical available: Offset; Black and 3 ROP colors; insert accepted; page cutoffs - 22.
Mechanical Specifications: Type page 11 5/8 x 21; E - 6 cols, 1 5/6, 1/8 between; A - 6 cols, 1 5/6, 1/8 between; C - 10 cols, 1, 1/16 between.
Commodity Consumption: Avg. Page Number Per Issue - Daily 42; Avg. Page Number Per Issue - Plates Used 65000; Avg. Page Number Per Issue - Sunday 80; widths 50; Newsprint Used - Metric Tons 5500; Newsprint Used - Short Tons 5036; Printing Ink Used - Pages Printed 18046.
Equipment EDITORIAL: Front-end Software – SII/Sys 55.; Editorial Hardware – 3-Tandem/CLX-1004; Editorial Equipment – Centronics, SII/XW soft typesetter, APP/Mac LAN, IPT/OPI, Hyphen/RIP, AG/Recorders, Taipan/RIPs; Editorial Printers – APP/Mac LaserPrinter CLASSIFIED: Front-end Software – SII/Sys 55A.; Classified Hardware – Tandem/CLX-K1004; Classified Equipment – 2-SII, Compaq/DeskPro; Classified Printers – Centronics, APP/Mac LaserPrinter, HP/LaserJet DISPLAY: Ad make-up applications – SII/SYS SS; Layout Software – Mac LAN, MEI/ALS 3.0.; Display Hardware – APP/Mac, PC; Display Printers – APP/Mac LaserJet III, NEC/Silent Writer 90, 3-Hyphen/Sun RIP, 1-AG/Accuset 1000, 2-AG/Proset 9800 PRODUCTION: Pagination Software – QPS/QuarkXPr; Production Equipment – 1-Hyphen/Sun RIP with AG Proset 9800, 1-AG/Accuset 1000, 3-AG/Accuset 1500, 1-Hp/LaserPrinter MV, 1-Epson/Stylus 3000; Scanners – APP/Mac, AG/3300S, AG/DuoScanner, UMax/Powerlook 2, 2-Epson/Expression, 2-Tecsa/Scanner PRESSROOM: Line 1 – MAN/Mediaman (32 couples, offset) 1991; Press Drives – Fin/650 np; Folders – 2-MAN/Double 3:2; Pasters – 9-HUR/50; Press control system – Rockwell/HMI. MAILROOM: Counter stackers – 4/QWI; Inserters and stuffers – S/630E; Bundle tying machines – 4-Dynaric/NP-2, 1-/Bu, 1-Dynaric/AM-500; Wrapping singles – Ideal, 1-St/3211, Arpac Plastic Wrap; Mailroom control system – OWI, 1-Nes/Totalizer; Addressing machine – 2-; Audio Hardware – Advance Technology Systems, Octel/Voice Mail, Mitel/Voice Mail BUSINESS COMPUTERS: Business Software – Microsoft/Office, Microsoft/Outlook, AdSpeed 3.0, Adobe/Photoshop, Adobe/Illustrator, Aldus/FreeHand 4.0; Business Hardware – IBM/AS-400

POUGHKEEPSIE NEWSPAPERS, INC.

85 Civic Center Plz., Poughkeepsie, N.Y., 12601; gen tel (845) 454-2000; gen fax (845) 437-4908

ROCHESTER

DEMOCRAT AND CHRONICLE.COM

55 Exchange Blvd., Rochester, N.Y., 14614-2001; gen tel (585) 232-7100; adv tel (585) 258-2552; ed tel (585) 258-2214; gen fax (585) 258-2265; adv fax (585) 258-2733; ed fax (585) 258-2237; gen e-mail feedback@democratandchronicle.com; ed e-mail metronews@democratandchronicle.com; web site www.democratandchronicle.com
Published: Mon, Tues, Wed, Thur, Fri, Sat, Sun
Weekday Frequency: m
Saturday Frequency: m
Circulation: 116,891; 132,801(sat); 173,429(sun)
Last Audit: ABC September 30, 2011
Price: 3.60/wk; 15.60/mo; 187.20/yr; 46.80/13wk, $93.60/26wk.
Advertising: Open inch rate $500.50
News services: AP, GNS, MCT, Bloomberg, National Weather Service, TMS.
Politics: Independent.
Special Editions: Living Here (Apr); HOME: Design for Rochester (Every other month); Auto Show (Feb); College Guide (Jan); Rochester Music Fest (Jul); Jazz Fest (Jun); March Madness (Mar); NACAC College Fair (May); Day In The Life (Monthly); Rochester's Choice Winners (Nov
Special Weekly Sections: Insider (Fri); E-Tech (Mon); World/Nation (S); Home & Real Estate (Sat); Our Towns (Wed).
Magazines: Comics (S); Weekend Magazine (Thur).
Pres./Pub. ....Ali Zoibi
Vice Pres., Finance ....Martha Deshong
Vice Pres., HR ....Linda B. Baird
Adv. Dir., Display ....Robêrt Teitgen
Adv. Mgr., Retail Territories ....Tibas Ahlberg
Vice Pres., Mktg./Commun. ....James J. Fogler
Circ. Vice Pres. ....Bryn Amber
Circ. Div. Mgr. ....John Demagistris
Vice Pres., News/Ed. ....Karen M. Magnuson
Gen. Mgr., Specialty Publications ...Dennis Floss
Asst. Mng. Ed., Admin. ....Matthew Dudek
Asst. Mng. Ed., Multimedia ....Traci Bauer
Bus. Ed. ....Steve Sink
Editorial Page Ed. ....James Lawrence
Deputy Editorial Page Ed. ....Tom Tobin
Features Ed. ....Cathy Robert
Asst. Features Ed. ....Lydia Fernandez
Asst. Metro Ed. ....Mindy Mozer
News Ed. ....Dick Moss
Pop Music/Nite Scene Reporter ....Jeff Spevak
Market Information: Split run; TMC; Zoned editions.
Mechanical available: Offset; Black and 3 ROP colors; insert accepted; page cutoffs - 22 1/32.
Mechanical Specifications: Type page 11 5/8 x 21; E - 6 cols, 1 5/6, 1/8 between; A - 6 cols, 1 5/6, 1/8 between; C - 10 cols, 1 5/6, 1/16 between.
Commodity Consumption: Avg. Page Number Per Issue - Daily 60; Avg. Page Number Per Issue - Plates Used 286000; Avg. Page Number Per Issue - Saturday 60; Avg. Page Number Per Issue - Sunday 92; widths 25; Newsprint Used - Short Tons 22250; Printing Ink Used - Black 354400; Prin
Equipment EDITORIAL: Front-end Software – Softwa; Editorial Hardware – AT/114; Editorial Equipment – 60-APP/Mac, ESE, Kk/2035 Plus Negative Scanner, HP/Server, 19-APP/Mac PowerBook, 6-Wintel, 22-NC/2000, AP/Digital Cameras, MS/NT Server; Editorial Printers – 1-Okidata, Pagescan, 7-HP, 3-HP, TI/Monoprint, HP/11x17, MON/Express CLASSIFIED: Front-end Software – Mactive.; Classified Hardware – SII/45 XA, SII/71 Coyote 3, 4-Tandem/K-1000 CPUS; Classified Equipment – IBM/Netfinity 5500; Classified Printers – Lexmark/Optra LXI DISPLAY: Ad make-up applications – QPS/QuarkXPress, Macromedia/Freehand, Adobe/PageMaker, Roudhouse/Ad Tracking 2.5.7, Adobe/Creative Suite 2, Adobe/Illustrator, Adobe/Photoshop, Adobe/A; Display Hardware – Dell/2100 fileserver, 20-APP/Mac, 5-Dell/5133, MS/NT Server LH3; Display Printers – 8-HP PRODUCTION: Pagination Software – QPS/QuarkXPress 4.1, CCI 6.7.0.2AT, Adobe/Creative Suite 2, SCS/Linx 4.13, SCS/Layout 8000 9.1, SCS/Inlay-In Design, Mactive.; Production Equipment – AG/Advantage 3350 DL; Scanners – 2-Scitex/320, AG/Duoscan 1200T, Umax/Powerlook 2100 XL PRESSROOM: Line 1 – MAN/Geoman 80 couples in 16 Footprints (2/3 presses) 1997; Press Drives – 35; Folders – 3-MAN/3.2, 3-MAN/2:3:3; Pasters – 16 MAILROOM: Counter stackers – 5-QWI/300, 5-QWI/350; Inserters and stuffers – 2-HI/630 Inserters (28:1 or 13:2); Bundle tying machines – 9/Power Strap/PSN-6, 9-Dynaric/1500, 1-Samuel/NT30; Mailroom control system – Prima, GSN, QWI/Cart Loading System; Addressing machine – Addressing m AUDIO: Audio Software – Octel/0100 3.1, OS/2 WARP3, 2-ISD/Chatterbox IYR, 2-Microsoft/Windows NT; Audio Hardware – IBM/Hulk Tower BUSINESS COMPUTERS: Business Software – Microsoft/Office 97, Microsoft/Office 2000, Microsoft/Windows 95, Microsoft/Windows 98, Microsoft/Windows 2000, Microsoft/Windows NT; Business Hardware – IBM/AS-400

ROME

DAILY SENTINEL

333 W. Dominick St., Rome, N.Y., 13440-0471; gen tel (315) 337-4000; gen fax (315) 339-6282; adv fax (315) 337-4704; ed fax (315) 339-6281; gen e-mail sentinel@rny.com; adv e-mail classad@rny.com; ed e-mail release@rny.com; web site www.romesentinel.com
Published: Mon, Tues, Wed, Thur, Fri, Sat, Sun
Weekday Frequency: e
Saturday Frequency: e
Circulation: 11,753; 12,506(sat); 25,000(sun)
Last Audit: ABC September 30, 2011
Price: 3.00/wk (carrier), $3.40/wk (motor route); 195.00/yr (in-county), $260.00/yr (out of county).
Advertising: Open inch rate $21.00
News services: AP, TMS.
Politics: Independent-Democrat. **Established:** 1821, predecessor Rome Republican first published; 1845-Named Rome Sentinel, 1864 became owned by current family, 1881 went daily; 1893 incorporated as Rome Sentinel Company
Advertising not accepted: N
Not Published: New Year; Memorial Day; Independence Day; Labor Day; Thanksgiving; Christmas.
Special Editions: Spring Fashion (Easter) (Apr); Back-to-School (Aug); Christmas Coupon (Dec); Know Your Retailer (Jan); Graduation (Jun); Bridal Planner (May); Senior Citizens Tab (Primetime) (Monthly); Santa's Tour (Nov); Fall Fashion (Oct); Recipe (Sept).
Special Weekly Sections: Bridal Page (Mon).
Magazines: TV Guide (S).
Publisher ....Stephen B. Waters
Advertising Manager ....Linda Carlson
Managing Editor ....David C. Swanson
Sports Editor ....Joseph Silkowski
Information Technology ....Daniel P. Bronson
Production Manager ....Linda Karsten
General Manager ....Bradley Waters
Market Information: ADS; TMC.
Mechanical available: Offset; Black and 3 ROP colors; insert accepted; page cutoffs - 21 1/2.
Mechanical Specifications: Type page 13 x 21 1/2; E - 6 cols, 2 1/16, 1/8 between; A - 6 cols, 2 1/16, 1/8 between; C - 9 cols, 1 3/8, 1/8 between.
Commodity Consumption: Avg. Page Number Per Issue - Daily 20; Avg. Page Number Per Issue - Plates Used 6255; widths 14; Newsprint Used - Short Tons 647; Printing Ink Used - Black 26200; Printing Ink Used - Color 300; Printing Ink Used - Pages Printed 6169.
Equipment EDITORIAL: Front-end Software – Saxotech; Editorial Hardware – APP/Mac G3, 1999-APP/iMac; Editorial Printers – Lexmark, Epson CLASSIFIED: Front-end Software – SCATS 1.0, Claris/Filemaker Pro 3.0.; Classified Hardware – APP/Mac ; Classified Printers – Lexmark DISPLAY: Ad make-up applications – Adobe inDesign; Display Hardware – APP/Mac PRODUCTION: Pagination Software – Mk/Page Director, Saxotech, Adobe inDesign; Production Equipment – Adobe/Photoshop, APP/Power Mac G3; Scanners – Epson/Scanner PRESSROOM: Line 1 – 6-G/Urbanite, 1-G/Urbanite (3 color); Press Drives – 1-100 HP; 1-75 HP; Folders – 1-G/Urbanite.; Inserters and stuffers – Kansa; Bundle tying machines – 2/Sa, 2-MLN/ML2EE, MLN. BUSINESS COMPUTERS: Business Software – Newzware; Business Hardware – Cloud
Delivery method: Mail, Newsstand, Private Carrier, Racks

SALAMANCA

SALAMANCA PRESS

36 River St., Salamanca, N.Y., 14779; gen tel (716) 945-1644; gen fax (716) 945-4285; gen e-mail salpressnews@verizon.net; web site www.salamancapress.com
Group: New York Newspaper Advertising Service, Inc.
Published: Thur
Weekday Frequency: e
Last Audit: September 30, 2005
Price: 9.80/mo (carrier); 117.00/yr (carrier).
Advertising: Open inch rate $6.75
News services: AP.
Politics: Independent.
Not Published: New Year; Memorial Day; Independence Day; Labor Day; Thanksgiving; Christmas.
Pub. ....Kip Boyle
Adv. Mgr. ....Kasey Stockman
Circ. Dir. ....Heather Skeels
Ed. ....Chris Chapman
Features Ed. ....Amanda Grabowski
Sports Ed. ....Jeff Madigan
Market Information: TMC.
Mechanical available: Offset; Black and 3 ROP colors; insert accepted; page cutoffs - 22 3/4.
Mechanical Specifications: Type page 13 x 21 1/2; E - 6 cols, 2, 1/8 between; A - 6 cols, 2, 1/8 between; C - 6 cols, 2, 1/8 between.
Commodity Consumption: Avg. Page Number Per Issue - Daily 10.
Equipment; Production Equipment – 1-B, APP/Mac SE20; Cameras – 1-B/Caravel. PRESSROOM: Line 1 – 5-G/Community (1 folder).; Bundle tying machines – 1/Akebono; Addressing machine – 1-/Am.; Business Hardware – Epson/Equity II

SARANAC LAKE

ADIRONDACK DAILY ENTERPRISE

54 Broadway, Saranac Lake, N.Y., 12983; gen tel (518) 891-2600; gen fax (518) 891-2756; gen e-mail adenews@adirondackdailyenterprise.com; adv e-mail advertising@adirondackdailyenterprise.com; web site www.adirondackdailyenterprise.com
Published: Mon, Tues, Wed, Thur, Fri, Sat, Sun
Weekday Frequency: e
Saturday Frequency: m
Circulation: 4,118; 4,118(sat)
Last Audit: September 24, 2003
Price: 4.20/wk; 136.00/yr; 28.00/3mo, $54.00/6mo.
News services: AP.
Politics: conservative. **Established:** 1899
Note: The Saranac Lake Adirondack Daily Enterprise (e) has a combination rate of $43.00 with the Gloversville Leader-Herald (eS). Individual newspaper rates not made available.
Not Published: New Year; Thanksgiving; Christmas.
Special Editions: Back-to-School (Aug); Seasons Greetings (Dec); Bridal (Feb); July 4th Blast (Jul); Adirondack Summer Guide (Jun); Human Services (Mar); Adirondack Living Real Estate Guide (Monthly); Christmas Gift Guide (Nov); North Country Dining Guide (Other); Bridal (
Profile: We are a community daily in the Adirondack Park printed Mon-Sat covering the Tri-Lake Olympic Region since 1899.
Adv. Mgr. ....Catherine Moore
Circ. Dir. ....Ruby Vann
Mng. Ed. ....Peter Cowley
City Ed. ....Brittany Bombard
Copy Ed. ....Duane Gould
Sports Ed. ....Tim Follos

Prodn. Mgr. ....Steve Bradley
Pressroom Foreman ....Rick Burman
Market Information: TMC.
Mechanical available: Offset; Black and 3 ROP colors; insert accepted - all; page cutoffs - 21.
Mechanical Specifications: Type page 13 x 21; E - 6 cols, 2 1/16, 1/8 between; A - 6 cols, 2 1/16, 1/8 between; C - 8 cols, 1 1/2, 1/8 between.
Commodity Consumption: Avg. Page Number Per Issue - Daily 16; Avg. Page Number Per Issue - Saturday 24; widths 25.
Equipment: Editorial Hardware – COM, APP/Mac Classic; Editorial Printers – Software ÂD WriteNow, QPS/QuarkXPress. DISPLAY: Ad make-up applications – QPS, Multi-Ad/Creator; Layout Software – APP/Mac.; Display Hardware – APP/Mac SE PRODUCTION: Pagination Software – QPS/QuarkXPress.; Production Equipment – X; Scanners – 4-APP/Mac PRESSROOM: Line 1 – 6-G/Community.; Business Hardware – NCR

SARATOGA SPRINGS

THE SARATOGIAN

20 Lake Ave., Saratoga Springs, N.Y., 12866-2314; gen tel (518) 584-4242; gen fax (518) 587-7750; adv fax (518) 584-2645; ed fax (518) 584-7750; gen e-mail news@saratogian.com; adv e-mail classified@saratogian.com; web site www.saratogian.com
Published: Mon, Tues, Wed, Thur, Fri, Sat, Sun
Weekday Frequency: m
Saturday Frequency: m
Circulation: 7,084; 7,923(sat); 7,668(sun)
Last Audit: ABC September 30, 2011
Price: 3.90/wk; 202.80/yr.
Advertising: Open inch rate $48.34
News services: AP, MCT.
Politics: Independent.
Special Editions: Thoroughbred Racing-Daily (Aug); Business Review (Jan); Summer Magazines (Jul); Summer Magazines (Jun); New Car Preview (Oct).
Special Weekly Sections: What's Happening (Thur).
Magazines: USA WEEKEND Magazine (S).
Pub. ....Michael F. O'Sullivan
Controller ....Tom Cleary
Adv. Dir. ....Lauren Rose
Circ. Dir. ....Devlin Toth
Mng. Ed. ....Barbara Lombardo
Asst. Mng. Ed. ....Betsey Demars
Community News Ed. ....Donna Bell
Copy Ed. ....Jill Wing
Photography Suprv. ....Ericka Miller
Web Ed. ....Stephen Shoemaker
Market Information: TMC; Zoned editions.
Mechanical available: Offset; Black and 4 ROP colors; insert accepted; page cutoffs - 22.
Mechanical Specifications: Type page 12 3/8 x 21; E - 6 cols, 1 7/8, 5/16 between; A - 6 cols, 1 7/8, 5/16 between; C - 9 cols, 1 1/4, 5/16 between.
Commodity Consumption: Avg. Page Number Per Issue - Daily 24; Avg. Page Number Per Issue - Sunday 38; widths 27; Newsprint Used - Short Tons 955; Printing Ink Used - Black 18100; Printing Ink Used - Color 2245; Printing Ink Used - Pages Printed 12462.
Equipment EDITORIAL: Front-end Software – Solaris/Unix 2.5, LinoPress.; Editorial Hardware – Sun/Ultra Enterprise 2 CLASSIFIED: Front-end Software – Dewar.; Classified Hardware – Novell/Network DISPLAY: Ad make-up applications – Solaris/Unix 2.5; Layout Software – Lino-Press/Ad Manager.; Display Hardware – Sun/Ultra Enterprise 2 PRODUCTION: Pagination Software – LinoPress/Pagination 4.0.; Production Equipment – Nikon/Coolscan, APP/Mac 7200 BUSINESS COMPUTERS: Business Software – Lotus 5.0; Business Hardware – IBM/AS-400

SCHENECTADY

THE DAILY GAZETTE

2345 Maxon Rd. Ext., Schenectady, N.Y., 12308; gen tel (518) 374-4141; adv tel (518) 395-3020; ed tel (518) 395-3140; gen fax (518) 395-3084; adv fax (518) 372-5986; ed fax (518) 395-3089; gen e-mail gazette@dailygazette.net; news@dailygazette.net; adv e-mail bberezansky@dailygazette.net; ed e-mail gazette@dailygazette.net; web site www.dailygazette.com
Published: Mon, Tues, Wed, Thur, Fri, Sat, Sun
Weekday Frequency: m
Saturday Frequency: m
Circulation: 60,360; 60,922(sat); 61,371(sun)
Last Audit: ABC September 30, 2011
Price: 4.99wk; 16.00/mo; 182.00/yr.
Advertising: Open inch rate $45.65
Insert rate: $55 cpm 2-8 pages
News services: AP, LAT-WP, CSM.
Politics: Independent. **Established:** 1894
Own facility?: Y
Special Weekly Sections: Ski Page (Dec-Mar) (Fri); Science & Technology (S); Outdoors (Thur); Food (Wed).
Magazines: Relish (Monthly); USA WEEKEND Magazine (S).
Vice Pres. ....Elizabeth L. Lind
Sec. ....William S. Hume
Treasurer ....Ernest R. Grandy
Bus. Mgr. ....Paula Opel
Gen. Mgr. ....Daniel Beck
Credit Mgr. ....Andrea Goldy
Publisher/Editor/President ....John E.N. Hume
Mng. Ed. ....Judith Patrick
City Ed. ....Irving Dean
Editorial Page Ed. ....Arthur J. Clayman
Online Ed. ....Jeff Haff
Prodn. Mgr. ....James Grandy
Circulation Mgr/Mailroom ......Dennis Donoghue
Prodn. Foreman, Mailroom ..Gerald Shoemaker
Adv. Mgr., Classified ....Christine Palmer
Adv. Mgr., Retail ....Scott Osswald
City Ed. ....George Walsh
Market Information: Split run; Zoned editions.
Mechanical available: Flexo; Black and 3 ROP colors; insert accepted; page cutoffs - 22 1/2.
Mechanical Specifications: Type page 12 x 21 1/8; E - 6 cols, 1 7/8, 1/6 between; A - 6 cols, 1 7/8, 1/6 between; C - 9 cols, 1 1/4, 1/8 between.
Commodity Consumption: Avg. Page Number Per Issue - Daily 46; Avg. Page Number Per Issue - Plates Used 20000; Avg. Page Number Per Issue - Sunday 104; widths 50; Newsprint Used - Metric Tons 5500; Printing Ink Used - Black 251670; Printing Ink Used - Color 4882; Printing Ink U
Equipment EDITORIAL: Front-end Software – CD/2400, HI/XP-21, Multi-Edit/Lantastic.; Editorial Hardware – 100-PC CLASSIFIED: Front-end Software – HI/Adpower-Adpag.; Classified Hardware – 35-PC; Classified Equipment – LaCie/Scanner DISPLAY: Ad make-up applications – Adobe/Photoshop 5.5, Adobe/InDesign CS; Layout Software – Brainworks.; Display Hardware – APP/Mac G3, APP/Mac G4; Display Printers – 1-HP/5000, HP/Design Jet 1050C (Full page color proofer) PRODUCTION: Pagination Software – HI/NT 3.5.15.1.; Production Equipment – ISSI/Scanning System, 2-HP/Printer, 2-ECR/3850, Konica/Jetsetter; Scanners – 2-ECR PRESSROOM: Line 1 – 4-G/PEC (1-color hump; 2-color decks); Folders – 1-G/PEC; Pasters – G/PEC Auto; Reels and Stands – 8-G/PEC. MAILROOM: Counter stackers – 5/QWI; Inserters and stuffers – 2-S/NP630; Bundle tying machines – Power Strap, NTP 40; Wrapping singles – 1-/QWI; Addressing machine – 1-/Ch. BUSINESS COMPUTERS: Business Software – Brainworks; Business Hardware – 1-IBM/AS-400, PC
Zip Codes served: 12008,12009, 12010, 12019, 12020, 12025, 12027, 12032, 12035, 12043, 12047, 12053, 12056, 12065, 12066, 12068, 12070, 12072, 12074, 12078, 12084, 12086, 12092, 12095, 12110, 12117, 12118, 12122, 12134, 12137, 12148, 12149, 12150, 12151, 12157, 12158, 12159, 12160, 12166, 12170, 12177, 12180, 12186, 12187, 12188, 12203, 12205, 12208, 12301, 12302, 12303, 12304, 12305, 12306, 12307, 12308, 12309, 12803, 12822, 12831, 12833, 12835, 12850, 12859, 12863, 12866, 13317, 13339, 13428, 13452, 13459
Delivery method: Newsstand, Private Carrier, Racks

STATEN ISLAND

STATEN ISLAND ADVANCE

950 Fingerboard Rd., Staten Island, N.Y., 10305-1453; gen tel (718) 981-1234; adv tel (718) 816-2815; gen fax (718) 981-1456; adv fax (718) 981-1456; ed fax (718) 981-5679; adv e-mail advertising@siadvance.com; web site www.silive.com
Group: C.M. Savage Associates
Published: Mon, Tues, Wed, Thur, Fri, Sat, Sun
Weekday Frequency: e
Saturday Frequency: e
Circulation: 37,896; 36,618(sat); 47,993(sun)
Last Audit: ABC September 30, 2011
Price: 3.90/wk.
Advertising: Open inch rate $73.71
News services: AP, NNS, LAT-WP, INS-BS.
Politics: Independent.
Not Published: New Year; Memorial Day; Independence Day; Labor Day; Thanksgiving; Christmas.
Special Editions: Parent & Child (Apr); Parent & Child (Aug); Gift Ideas (Dec); Personal Finance (Feb); % Off Clearance Sale Tab (Jan); Adult Living (Jul); Parent & Child (Jun); Eye Care Tab (Mar); Your Home-Summer (May); Coupon Tab (Monthly); Eye Care Tab (Nov); New Car P
Special Weekly Sections: Style (Fri); Health (Mon); Our Town (S); Money (Sat); Home (Thur); Relationships (Tues); Food (Wed).
Magazines: Sunday TV (S); AWE (Thur).
Pub. ....Caroline Diamond Harrison
Controller ....Arthur Silverstein
Credit Mgr. ....William Tosonotti
Sec. ....Helen Carsten
Dir., Adv. ....Gary V. Cognetta
Adv. Mgr., Classified ....Tony Mulholland
Adv. Mgr., Online ....Frank Cianciotta
Adv. Mgr., Serv. ....Andrea Germano
Adv. Mgr., TMC ....Ricardo Paoli
Circ. Mgr. ....Richard Salerno
Ed. ....Brian Laline
Mng. Ed. ....William Huus
Arts Ed. ....Michael Fressola
Automotive Ed. ....Sandra Zummo
City Ed. ....Dean Balsamini
Design Ed. ....Claire Regan
Editorial Page Ed. ....Mark Hanley
Educ. Ed. ....Amy Padnani
Market Information: Split run; TMC; Zoned editions.
Mechanical available: Offset; Black and 3 ROP colors; insert accepted; page cutoffs - 21 1/4.
Mechanical Specifications: Type page 11 5/8 x 21 1/4; E - 6 cols, 1 5/6, 1/8 between; A - 6 cols, 1 5/6, 1/8 between; C - 10 cols, 1 1/12, 1/12 between.
Equipment EDITORIAL: Front-end Software – HI/NME 3.5.16, QPS/QuarkXPress 4.1, Merlin 4, Adobe/Photoshop 5.5, Ado; Editorial Hardware – 70-Dell/Pentium PC, 1-Multiplexer 4 x 4, 4-Compaq/laptop, 3-Micron/laptop, 3-Gateway/laptop, 1-Gateway/desktop; Editorial Equipment – 10-APP/Mac G-3; Editorial Printers – 5-HP, 1-DP CLASSIFIED: Front-end Software – AT, Hi/Adpag.; Classified Hardware – 4-DEC/PDP 11-34; Classified Equipment – 4-Gateway/E 3200; Classified Printers – 2-HP/Laser DISPLAY: Ad make-up applications – HI/Dash 3.5.16, Intellitune 3.2, Asura 6.0, Garda 3.0, Macromedia/FreeHand 9, Adobe/Illustrator 8, Adobe/Photoshop 5.5, QPS/QuarkXPress 4.1, Adobe/Acrobat; Display Hardware – 10-Dell/Optiplex; Display Printers – 1-APP/Mac Laserwriter 8500, 1-HP/5000, 1-HP/1050 PRODUCTION: Pagination Software – HI/NMP 3.5.16.; Production Equipment – 1-Nu/Flip Top FT2CV, Merlin, 2-MON/3850; Scanners – Haligin/Rips 5.5, 1-HDF PRESSROOM: Line 1 – MAN/Geoman 70 2002; Folders – 2-MAN; Pasters – 6-MAN/Auto; Reels and Stands – 6-MAN; Press control system – MAN/PECOM 2000 2002. MAILROOM: Counter stackers – 4/HL, 1-S/13728; Inserters and stuffers – 1-S/624, 1-S/1372; Bundle tying machines – 2-MLN/2A, 1-MLN/2A Retrofit. BUSINESS COMPUTERS: Business Software – CJ; Business Hardware – 1-HP/3000-68

SYRACUSE

THE POST-STANDARD

Clinton Sq., Syracuse, N.Y., 13221-4915; gen tel (315) 470-0011; adv tel (315) 470-2088; ed tel (315) 470-2241; adv fax (315) 470-3030; ed fax (315) 470-3019; gen e-mail letters@syracuse.com; ed e-mail letters@syracuse.com; web site www.post-standard.com; www.syracuse.com
Published: Mon, Tues, Wed, Thur, Fri, Sat, Sun
Weekday Frequency: m
Saturday Frequency: m
Circulation: 80,720; 82,741(sat); 139,130(sun)
Last Audit: ABC September 30, 2011
Advertising: Open inch rate $213.70
News services: NNS, NYT, LAT-WP, AP, MCT, CSM.
Politics: Independent.
Special Editions: Spotlight on Auto (Apr); Automotive (Aug); Holiday Shopper (Dec); Lacrosse (Feb); Blues Fest (Jul); Parade of Homes (Jun); NCAA Hoops (Mar); Golf Tab (May); MoneySaver (Monthly); Job Search (Nov); Fall/Winter Clearance % Off (Oct); Your Wedding Day (Sept)
Special Weekly Sections: Weekend (Fri); Money Wise (Mon); Employment (S); Driving (Sat); Neighbors (Thur); Food (Wed).
Magazines: Weekend (Fri); Money Wise (S).
Pub. ....Stephen A. Rogers
Controller ....Alice Miranda
Credit Mgr. ....Theresa Kelly
Adv. Dir. ....William Allison
Asst. Advertising Director/Sales ....Ken Brill
Class./onine sales mgr. ....Gerard Carroll
Auto sales mgr. ....Joe Howard
Bus. Devel. Mgr. ....Patrick Hurley
Mktg. Commun. Mgr. ....Stephen Hodgens
Circ. Dir. ....Paul Thomas
Cir. mgr./new concepts ....Gary Valik
Circ. Mgr. ....Nancy Breault
Ast. cir. dir./operations ....Tim DeBlois
Circ. Mgr. ....David Robertson
Ast. cir. dir./systems ....Thomas Brown
Exec. Ed. ....Michael J. Connor
Sr. Mng. Ed. ....Stan Linhorst
Magazine Editor ....Mark Libbon
Ast. Advertising Dir./Local media ..Cathy Fischer
Market Information: Split run; Zoned editions.
Mechanical available: Letterpress; Black and 3 ROP colors; insert accepted - some samples; page cutoffs - 21 1/2.
Mechanical Specifications: Type page 12 x 21 1/2; E - 6 cols, 1 7/8, 1/8 between; A - 6 cols, 1 7/8, 1/6 between; C - 10 cols, 1 5/16, 1/32 between.
Commodity Consumption: Avg. Page Number Per Issue - Daily 56; Avg. Page Number Per Issue - Plates Used 175000; Avg. Page Number Per Issue - Sunday 158; widths 25; Newsprint Used - Short Tons 20500; Printing Ink Used - Black 650000; Printing Ink Used - Color 200000; Printing In
Equipment EDITORIAL: Front-end Software – HI/Newsmaker Editorial.; Editorial Hardware – Sun/Ultra 2 CLASSIFIED: Front-end Software – SII.; Classified Hardware – 1-Tandem/55 DISPLAY: Ad make-up applications – Aldus/FreeHand, Multi-Ad/Creator, QPS/QuarkXPress, Adobe/Photoshop, HI/Display Ad; Layout Software – CJ/Ad Layout.; Display Hardware – APP/Mac; Display Printers – APP/Mac LaserWriters PRODUCTION: Pagination Software – HI/XP 21.; Production Equipment – Na, 2-AU/APS-6; Cameras – 2-C; Scanners – 2-ECR/Autokon, 1-Umax/1200 PRESSROOM: Line 1 – WIFAG; Folders – 2-WIFAG/2:5:5.

MAILROOM: Counter stackers – 7-Id; Inserters and stuffers – 2/Fg, 1-GMA/28:1; Bundle tying machines – 10-/Dynaric; Other equipment – MM/Stitcher, Gammerler.; Audio Hardware – 1-Brite Voice Systems BUSINESS COMPUTERS: Business Software – CJ/AIM; Business Hardware – 2-HP/3000, HP/9000

THE SYRACUSE NEWSPAPERS, INC.

Clinton Sq., Syracuse, N.Y., 13221-4915; gen tel (315) 470-0011; gen fax (315) 470-3030; web site www.syracuse.com
Published: Mon, Tues, Wed, Thur, Fri, Sat, Sun
Price: 182.00/yr.
Advertising: Open inch rate $107.52

TROY

THE RECORD

501 Broadway, Troy, N.Y., 12180-3324; gen tel (518) 270-1200; adv tel (518) 270-1259; ed tel (518) 270-1280; adv fax (518) 270-1204 (display); ed fax (518) 270-1202; gen e-mail newsroom@troyrecord.com; adv e-mail classmgr@troyrecord.com; lpaulo@troyrecord.com; ed e-mail newsroom@troyrecord.com; web site www.troyrecord.com
Published: Mon, Tues, Wed, Thur, Fri, Sat, Sun
Weekday Frequency: m
Saturday Frequency: m
Circulation: 9,870; 10,322(sat); 10,436(sun)
Last Audit: ABC September 30, 2011
Price: 3.15/wk; 13.65/mo; 166.80/yr.
Advertising: Open inch rate $42.77
News services: AP, MCT.
Politics: Independent. **Established:** 1896
Special Editions: Spring Car Care (Apr); Truck Tab (Aug); Last Minute Gift Ideas (Dec); Baby Album (Feb); New Car Preview (Jan); Saratoga Life (Jul); Father's Day (Jun); Medical Physicians Guide (Mar); Mature Living (May); Christmas Gift Guide (Nov); Apple Fest (Oct); Heal
Special Weekly Sections: Gameday-High School Football (Sept-Nov) (Fri); Computers & Science (Mon); Gameday-High School Football (Sept-Nov) (Sat).
Magazines: Home Front (Monthly); Health Notes (Quarterly); TV & Cable quarter-fold magazine (S); Steppin' Out (Thur).
Pub.....................Jim Murphy
Controller....................Tom Cleary
Ed.....................Lisa Robert Lewis
Chief Photographer....................Mike McMahon
Sports Ed.....................Kevin Moran
Prodn. Dir.....................Randy Pobran
Market Information: Split run; TMC; Zoned editions.
Mechanical available: Offset; Black and 3 ROP colors; insert accepted; page cutoffs - 22 1/12.
Mechanical Specifications: Type page 12 x 21; E - 6 cols, 1 7/8, 1/8 between; A - 6 cols, 1 7/8, 1/8 between; C - 9 cols, 1 5/16, 3/16 between.
Commodity Consumption: Avg. Page Number Per Issue - Daily 28; Avg. Page Number Per Issue - Plates Used 34800; Avg. Page Number Per Issue - Saturday 28; Avg. Page Number Per Issue - Sunday 40; widths 25; Newsprint Used - Short Tons 4000; Printing Ink Used - Black 110000; Printi
Equipment EDITORIAL: Front-end Software – Dewar/View 2.1.; Editorial Hardware – Dewar/System CLASSIFIED: Front-end Software – Dewar/Sys IV.; Classified Hardware – Dewar/Information System DISPLAY: Ad make-up applications – Multi-Ad/Creator; Layout Software – Dewar/Sys.; Display Hardware – APP/Mac Network PRODUCTION: Pagination Software – QPS/QuarkXPress 3.32.; Production Equipment – 2-MON/Imagesetter 1000, 1-Kk/66S; Cameras – 2-C/Spartan III; Scanners – Lf/Leafscan 35, Kk/Negative Scanner PRESSROOM: Line 1 – 6-G/Headliner Offset w/gluer 1984; Folders – 1-G/quarter 2:1; Pasters – 6-G/Digital; Reels and Stands – 6 MAILROOM: Counter stackers – 1/QWI, 1-HT/Monitor; Inserters and stuffers – 3-MM/227 EM; Bundle tying machines – 4-/MLN, MLN/2HS, 3-MLN/2HS; Other equipment –MM/890 Trimmer.

TROY PUBLISHING CO., INC.

501 Broadway, Troy, N.Y., 12181; gen tel (518) 270-1200; gen fax (518) 270-1204

UTICA

OBSERVER-DISPATCH

221 Oriskany Plz., Utica, N.Y., 13501-1201; gen tel (315) 792-5000; adv tel (315) 792-5100; ed tel (315) 792-5005; adv fax (315) 792-5085; ed fax (315) 792-5033; gen e-mail news@uticaod.com; web site www.uticaod.com
Group: GateHouseMedia
Published: Mon, Tues, Wed, Thur, Fri, Sat, Sun
Weekday Frequency: m
Saturday Frequency: m
Circulation: 32,919; 32,919(sat); 40,887(sun)
Last Audit: ABC September 30, 2011
Price: 4.95/wk (carrier),
Advertising: Open inch rate $106.91
News services: AP, McClatchy
Politics: Independent.
Own facility?: Y
Special Editions: Back-to-School (Aug); Gift Guide (Dec); Business Review (Feb); Bridal (Jan); Boilermaker Sections (Jul); Living Here (May); Coupons (Monthly); Thanksgiving Day (Nov); @RecordBody:**Special Weekly Sections:** TV Book (Sat);315 (entertainment) (Thur)
Magazines: USA WEEKEND Magazine (S); TV Observer (Sat).
Pres./Pub.....................Donna M. Donovan
Controller....................Peter Mytych
Adv. Dir.....................Emilia Borelli
Adv. Mgr., Classified....................Pam Koenig
Circ. Dir.....................Richard Procida
Opinion Page Ed.....................Dave Dudajek
Photo Ed.....................Bill Cannon
Sports Ed.....................Fran Perritano
Market Information: Split run; TMC; Zoned editions.
Mechanical available: Offset; Black and 3 ROP colors; insert accepted; spadeas; front page tab-ons
Mechanical Specifications: Type page 11 x 20.9
Commodity Consumption: Avg. Page Number Per Issue - Daily 32; Avg. Page Number Per Issue - Plates Used 45538; Avg. Page Number Per Issue - Sunday 68; widths 55; Newsprint Used - Short Tons 4626; Printing Ink Used - Black 133199; Printing Ink Used - Color 23093; Printing Ink Us
Equipment EDITORIAL: Front-end Software – SII/Laser, APP/Mac 55, QPS, Mk/Page Director, QPS/QuarkXPress.; Editorial Hardware – SII/Sys 55 XR, Tandem/CLX-RISC, 50-PCs, 30-APP/Mac; Editorial Equipment – 37-SII/Coyote, APP/Macs for Pagination; Editorial Printers – QMS/860, Okidata, 18-HT; Classified Hardware – SII/Sys 55, 11-SII/Coyote, APP/Macs; Classified Equipment – 11-SII/Coyote; Classified Printers – Software □ SII/Ad Director, Pongrass/Classified Pagemaker. DISPLAY: Ad make-up applications – Pongrass, Mk/Ad Director, Multi-Ad/Creator, QPS; Layout Software – SCS/Layout 8000, SII/Ad Director.; Display Hardware – IBM/PC; Display Printers – QMS/860 PRODUCTION: Pagination Software – QPS/QuarkXPress.; Production Equipment – Caere/OmniPage 2.1, Lf/AP Leaf Picture Desk, LS/2800R; Cameras – C/Marathon; Scanners – APP/Mac Pac Interface, 3-Umax; Addressing machine – Ch.
Delivery method: Mail, Newsstand, Private Carrier, Racks

WATERTOWN

JOHNSON NEWSPAPER CORP.

260 Washington St., Watertown, N.Y., 13601; gen tel (315) 782-1000; gen fax (315) 661-2520; gen e-mail news@wdt.net; web site www.watertowndailytimes.com
Politics: 1861
Chrmn. of the Bd./CEO....................John B. Johnson
Pres./COO....................Harold B. Johnson
CFO....................Rich Babbit

WATERTOWN DAILY TIMES

260 Washington St., Watertown, N.Y., 13601; gen tel (315) 782-1000; adv tel (315) 661-2422; ed tel (315) 661-2359; oth tel 800-642-6222; gen fax (315) 661-2520; adv fax (315) 661-2522; ed fax (315) 661-2523; gen e-mail news@wdt.net; adv e-mail kromeo@wdt.net; ed e-mail news@wdt.net; web site www.watertowndailytimes.com
Published: Mon, Tues, Wed, Thur, Fri, Sat, Sun
Weekday Frequency: m
Saturday Frequency: m
Circulation: 32,919; 24,789(sat); 25,265(sun)
Last Audit: ABC September 30, 2011
Price: 3.55/wk; 184.60/yr.
Advertising: Open inch rate $40.81
News services: AP, NYT, LAT-WP, MCT.
Politics: Independent-Republican. **Established:** 1861
Not Published: New Year; Memorial Day; Independence Day; Labor Day; Thanksgiving; Christmas.
Own facility?: Y
Special Weekly Sections: Best Food Day (Tues).
Magazines: Relish (Monthly); USA WEEKEND Magazine (S); Farm & Garden Tab (newsprint) (Sat); American Profile (Weekly).
General Manager....................John Johnson
Exec. Ed.....................Albert E. Gault
Mng. Ed.....................Robert D. Gorman
Currents/Society Ed.....................Judy Jacobs
Editorial Page Ed.....................John McFadden
Photo Ed.....................Norman Johnston
Sports Ed.....................Gregory Gay
Sunday Ed.....................Mary Kaskan
CIO....................Jill VanHoesen
Prodn. Mgr.....................Dale Cronk
Market Information: ADS; Split run; Zoned editions.
Mechanical available: Offset; Black and 3 ROP colors; insert accepted; page cutoffs - 20 1/2.
Mechanical Specifications: Type page 13 x 21; E - 6 cols, 2 1/16, 1/8 between; A - 6 cols, 2 1/16, 1/8 between; C - 9 cols, 1 3/8, 1/16 between.
Commodity Consumption: Avg. Page Number Per Issue - Daily 30; Avg. Page Number Per Issue - Plates Used 65000; Avg. Page Number Per Issue - Sunday 68; widths 27 1/2; Newsprint Used - Metric Tons 3844; Printing Ink Used - Black 87500; Printing Ink Used - Color 27000; Printing In
Equipment EDITORIAL: Front-end Software – Saxotech Cloud; Editorial Hardware – HP/DELL/MAC CLASSIFIED: Front-end Software – AD PLUS DISPLAY: Ad make-up applications – Multi-Ad; Layout Software – ALS; Display Hardware – MAC PRESSROOM: Line 1 – 7-MAN/Uniman 4 x 2; Folders – 2; Pasters – 7-MEG; Reels and Stands – 7-MEG. MAILROOM: Counter stackers – 3/HL, 1-/KAN; Inserters and stuffers – 2-GMA/SLS 1000; Bundle tying machines – 1-MLN/ML2EE, 2-/Dynaric; Addressing machine – 1-Ch/582N.
Delivery method: Mail, Newsstand, Private Carrier, Racks

WELLSVILLE

WELLSVILLE DAILY REPORTER

901 Mission St., Wellsville, N.Y., 14895; gen tel (585) 593-5300; gen fax (585) 593-5303; adv e-mail wellsvillereader@aol.com; web site www.wellsvilledaily.com
Group: New York Newspaper Advertising Service, Inc.
Published: Sun
Circulation: 4,500; 10,390(sun)
Last Audit: March 31, 2006
Price: 7.50/mo (motor route).
Advertising: Open inch rate $8.50
News services: AP.
Politics: 1880
Note: The Wellsville Daily Reporter (e) and the Hornell Evening Tribune (e) share a Sunday edition.
Not Published: New Year; Memorial Day; Independence Day; Labor Day; Thanksgiving; Christmas.
Special Editions: Medical-Health Guide (Aug); Bride's Guide (Jan); Balloon Rally Guide (Jul); Graduation (Jun); Spring Outdoor (Mar); Christmas (Nov); Annual Fall Outdoor Guide (Sept).
Adv. Dir.....................Oak Duke
Circ. Mgr.....................Robert Polley
News Ed.....................John Anderson
Sports Ed.....................Paul Jannace
Market Information: TMC.
Mechanical available: Offset; Black and 3 ROP colors; insert accepted; page cutoffs - 22 3/4.
Mechanical Specifications: Type page 13 x 21 1/2; E - 6 cols, 2 1/16, 1/8 between; A - 6 cols, 2 1/16, 1/8 between; C - 6 cols, 2 1/16, 1/8 between.
Commodity Consumption: Avg. Page Number Per Issue - Daily 16; Avg. Page Number Per Issue - Sunday 56; widths 27 1/2.
Equipment; Editorial Hardware – Mk/1100; Editorial Equipment – 2-IBM/Selectric II.; Classified Hardware – Mk/1100.; Business Hardware – 1-DEC/Rainbow 100

WHITE PLAINS

THE JOURNAL NEWS

159 N. Main St., White Plains, N.Y., 10604; gen tel (914) 694-9300; adv tel (914) 694-5158; ed tel (914) 694-5003; adv fax (914) 696-8173; ed fax (914) 694-5018; web site www.lohud.com
Published: Mon, Tues, Wed, Thur, Fri, Sat, Sun
Weekday Frequency: m
Saturday Frequency: m
Circulation: 74,325; 86,686(sat); 98,374(sun)
Last Audit: ABC September 30, 2011
Price: 4.50/wk.
Advertising: Open inch rate $438.00
News services: AP, GNS, LAT-WP.
Politics: Independent. **Established:** 1850
Special Editions: Suburban Golf (Apr); Back-to-School (Aug); Holiday Food (Dec); Spring Bridal (Feb); Suburban Golf (Jul); Summer Dine Out Guide (Jun); Spring Home Design (Mar); Suburban Golf (May); Holiday Gift Guide (Nov); Fall Home Design (Oct); In the City (Quarterly);
Special Weekly Sections: Wheels (Fri); Tech E (Mon); Real Estate (S); The Line (Thur).
Magazines: USA WEEKEND Magazine (S).
Pres./Pub.....................Mike Fisch
Vice Pres., Circ.....................Anthony Simmons
Circ. Mgr., Single Copy....................Mauro Ferrotta
Vice Pres./Exec. News Ed.....................Henry Freeman
Sr. Mng. Ed.....................Cynthia Royle Lambert
Design Dir.....................Robert Rodriguez
Editorial Page Ed.....................Herb Pinder
Lifestyles Ed.....................Mary Dolan
Photo Ed.....................Hai Do
Sports Ed., Days....................Mark Faller
Asst. Sports Ed.....................Mary Susan Arth
Travel Ed.....................Kathy McClusky
Prodn. Dir.....................Nat Hogan
Market Information: ADS; Split run; TMC; Zoned editions.
Mechanical available: Offset; Black and 4 ROP colors; insert accepted; page cutoffs - 22 3/4.
Mechanical Specifications: Type page 13 x 21 1/2; E - 6 cols, 1 5/6, 1/8 between; A - 6 cols, 1 5/6, 1/8 between; C - 10 cols, 1 1/10, 3/50 between.
Commodity Consumption: Avg. Page Number Per Issue - Daily 48; Avg. Page Number Per Issue - Plates Used 329816; Avg. Page Number Per Issue - Sunday 116; widths 54; Newsprint Used - Short Tons 23644; Printing Ink Used - Black 427946; Printing Ink Used - Color 88435; Printing Ink
Equipment; Editorial Equipment – DEC/VAX Output Graphic Database; Editorial Printers – Okidata.; Production Equipment – LE, AII/3850; Cameras – C/Spartan; Scanners – Imagi-

Tex/940.; Inserters and stuffers – 1-HI/1472P; Bundle tying machines – 2-MLN/MLM 2EE; Addressing machine – 4-Barstrom/Labeler. BUSINESS COMPUTERS: Business Software – Admarc; Business Hardware – 1-IBM/AS-400 320

NORTH CAROLINA

ASHEBORO

THE COURIER-TRIBUNE

500 Sunset Ave., Asheboro, N.C., 27203; gen tel (336) 625-2101; adv tel (336) 626-6114; ed tel (336) 626-6123; gen fax (336) 626-7074; adv e-mail rfreemyer@courier-tribune.com; ed e-mail ajordan@courier-tribune.com; web site www.courier-tribune.com

Published: Mon, Tues, Wed, Thur, Fri, Sat, Sun
Weekday Frequency: m
Saturday Frequency: m
Circulation: 12,751; 12,751(sat); 14,279(sun)
Last Audit: September 30, 2008
Price: 9.25/mo (carrier); 140.00/yr (mail).
Advertising: Open inch rate $16.65
News services: AP, MCT, SHNS.
Politics: Independent.
Special Editions: Back-to-School (Aug); Progress (Jan); Lawn & Garden (Mar); Graduation (May); Textile (Oct).
Special Weekly Sections: Church (Fri); Children's Page (S); Business (Wed).
Magazines: USA WEEKEND Magazine (S); Food (Wed).
Office Mgr. ....Maria Shaw
Circ. Dir. ....Gary Lockhart
Ed. ....Ray Criscoe
News Ed. ....Annette Jordan
Sports Ed. ....Dennis Garcia
Prodn. Mgr. ....Hazel Saunders
Prodn. Mgr., Pressroom ....Ben Kane
Market Information: TMC.
Mechanical available: Offset; Black and 3 ROP colors; insert accepted; page cutoffs - 22 5/8.
Mechanical Specifications: Type page 13 x 21 1/2; E - 6 cols, 2 1/16, 1/8 between; A - 6 cols, 2 1/16, 1/8 between; C - 9 cols, 1 3/8, 1/16 between.
Commodity Consumption: Avg. Page Number Per Issue - Daily 20; Avg. Page Number Per Issue - Plates Used 9000; Avg. Page Number Per Issue - Sunday 52; widths 13 3/4; Newsprint Used - Metric Tons 910; Printing Ink Used - Black 16880; Printing Ink Used - Color 4320; Printing Ink U
Equipment EDITORIAL: Front-end Software – Baseview.; Editorial Hardware – 16-APP/Mac; Editorial Equipment – 2-APP/Mac, Lf/Leafscan 35, Lf/AP Leaf Picture Desk; Editorial Printers – 2-Pre Press/Panther Pro CLASSIFIED: Front-end Software – Baseview.; Classified Hardware – 5-APP/Mac DISPLAY: Ad make-up applications – Multi-Ad/Creator.; Display Hardware – 4-APP/Mac; Display Printers – APP/Mac LaserWriter; Production Equipment – Pre Press/Panther Pro; Cameras – C/Spartan III. PRESSROOM: Line 1 – 9-G/Urbanite 1990; Folders – 1 MAILROOM: Counter stackers – HL; Inserters and stuffers – MM/4:1, MM/6:1; Bundle tying machines – 1/MLN. BUSINESS COMPUTERS: Business Software – CJ; Business Hardware – 1-CJ, 1-HP/3000

ASHEVILLE

THE ASHEVILLE CITIZEN-TIMES

14 O. Henry Ave., Asheville, N.C., 28801; gen tel (828) 252-5611; adv tel (828) 252-5611; ed tel (828) 252-5611; gen fax (828) 252-5887; adv fax (828) 251-2659; ed fax (828) 251-0585; gen e-mail webmaster@citizen-times.com; ed e-mail editor@citizen-times.com; web site www.citizen-times.com

Published: Mon, Tues, Wed, Thur, Fri, Sat, Sun
Weekday Frequency: m
Saturday Frequency: m
Circulation: 32,201; 33,152(sat); 51,930(sun)
Last Audit: ABC September 30, 2011
Price: 3.50/wk; 15.17/mo; 182.00/yr.
Advertising: Open inch rate $127.37
News services: AP, GNS, NNS.
Politics: Independent.
Not Published: If holiday falls on a weekday, one combined issue is published.
Special Editions: Mountain Travel Guide (Apr); Football (Aug); Agenda (Feb); Best of (Jun); Campus Connection (Oct); West Asheville (Quarterly); Mountain Travel Guide (Sept).
Special Weekly Sections: Take Five (Fri); Health & Fitness (Mon); Travel (S); Family (Thur); Computers & Technology (Tues); Food (Wed).
Magazines: USA WEEKEND Magazine (S).
Broadcast Affiliations: AP; GNS; NNS.
Pres./Pub. ....Randy Hammer
Adv. Dir. ....Gayle Smith
Mgr., Mktg. Commun. ....Christina Corey
Circ. Mgr., Single Copy Sales ....Kim Mahle
Mng. Ed. ....Phil Fernandez
Deputy Mng. Ed. ....Jason Sandford
Assoc. Ed. ....Jim Buchanan
Editorial Page Ed. ....Joy Franklin
Entertainment Ed. ....Tony Kiss
Features Ed. ....Polly McDaniel
Metro Ed. ....Brian Ponder
Sports Ed. ....Bob Berghaus
Online Ed. ....Jammy Mckee
Info Tech. Dir. ....Stacey Wasielewski
New Media Dir. ....John Yenne
Prodn. Mgr. ....Vicki Harrison
Market Information: Split run.
Mechanical available: Offset; Black and 3 ROP colors; insert accepted; page cutoffs - 22.
Mechanical Specifications: Type page 11 5/8 x 21; E - 6 cols, 1/6 between; A - 6 cols, 1/6 between; C - 10 cols, 1/12 between.
Commodity Consumption: Avg. Page Number Per Issue - Daily 46; Avg. Page Number Per Issue - Plates Used 90700; Avg. Page Number Per Issue - Saturday 60; Avg. Page Number Per Issue - Sunday 116; widths 37 1/2; Newsprint Used - Short Tons 6896; Printing Ink Used - Black 139500; P
Equipment EDITORIAL: Front-end Software – ACT.; Editorial Hardware – ACI; Editorial Equipment – APP/Mac Quadra 950, Lf/AP Leaf Picture Desk, Photoview/News View Archives, APP/Mac G3, APP/Mac G4; Editorial Printers – Hyphen/108 Imagers CLASSIFIED: Front-end Software – Microsoft, PPI.; Classified Hardware – PPI; Classified Equipment – MEI/ALS, MEI/CLS; Classified Printers – Epson, QMS/Laser, Hyphen/108 Imager DISPLAY: Ad make-up applications – Baseview/Managing, Roundhouse, Ad Manager; Layout Software – MEI/ALS, ALS.; Display Hardware – APP/Mac G3, APP/Mac G4, APP/Mac 9500 PRODUCTION: Pagination Software – Baseview/Managing Editor, ALS, MEI/CLS.; Production Equipment – 2-ECR/108 Pelbox, 2-Powermatic/66RA, 1-QMS/860 Laser Printer; Scanners – 3-HP/ScanJet IIcx, Linotype-Hell/Desktop, Graphic Enterprises/TESCA Scanners PRESSROOM: Line 1 – Aug-86; Line 2 – 8-MAN/Colorman 75 double width (4 half decks) 1985; Folders – MAN/double 3:2; Pasters – 8-Wd-H/RTP. MAILROOM: Counter stackers – 1-QWI/301, 1-QWI/351, 1-QWI/401, 1/Gammerler; Inserters and stuffers – NP/630; Bundle tying machines – 2-EAM-Mosca, 2-/Sterling, 3-/Dynamic; Wrapping singles – Mailroom control system Â□ K&M; Mailroom control system – K&M; Addressing machine – 2-/Ch, 3-/Wm; Other equipment –MM/4head BUSINESS COMPUTERS: Business Software – Gannett Standard Applications, Microsoft/Office; Business Hardware – IBM/AS-400

BURLINGTON

TIMES-NEWS

707 S. Main St., Burlington, N.C., 27215; gen tel (336) 227-0131; adv tel (336) 227-0131; ed tel (336) 227-0131; gen fax (336) 229-2466; adv fax (336) 229-2462; ed fax (336) 229-2463; gen e-mail info@thetimesnews.com; web site www.thetimesnews.com

Group: Freedom Communications, Inc.
Published: Mon, Tues, Wed, Thur, Fri, Sat, Sun
Weekday Frequency: m
Saturday Frequency: m
Circulation: 22,000; 22,000(sat); 25,000(sun)
Last Audit: Sworn September 30, 2008
Price: 12.36.00/mo; 179.40/yr.
Advertising: Open inch rate $24.37
News services: U.S. Suburban Press Inc., MCT.
Politics: Independent. **Established:** 1887
Own facility?: Y
Special Editions: Lawn & Garden/Home Improvement (Apr); Football Preview (Aug); Gift Guide I (Dec); Racing Tab (Feb); Golf (Mar); Alamance Academics (May); Holiday Lifestyles (Nov); National Textile Week (Oct); Medical Reference Guide (Quarterly); Financial/Legal Reference
Special Weekly Sections: Accent on Entertainment (Fri); Youth Page (Mon); Automotive (S); Real Estate (Sat); Accent on Family (Thur); Health-Tech (Tues); Mini Page (Wed).
Magazines: USA WEEKEND Magazine (S); American Profile (Tues).
Publisher ....Paul Mauney
Sales Manager ....Serena Bowman
Mgr., Mktg./Promo. ....Michele Terry
Circ. Dir. ....Todd Benz
Ed. ....Madison Taylor
Mng. Ed. ....Jay Ashley
Asst. Mng. Ed. ....Frances Woody
Features Ed. ....Charity Apple
News Ed. ....Brent Lancaster
Sports Ed. ....Bob Sutton
New Media Director ....Roger Creasy
Prodn. Mgr., Mailroom ....Kelley Rorie
Prodn. Director ....Darryl Ayers
HR Manager ....Joyce Thompson
Controller ....Susan Richardson
GM/Adv. Director ....Mike Little
Pressroom Manager ....Sherwood Bland
Market Information: ADS; TMC.
Mechanical available: Offset; Black and 3 ROP colors; insert accepted; page cutoffs - 22 3/4.
Mechanical Specifications: Type page 11 5/8 x 21 1/2; E - 6 cols, 1 5/6, 1/8 between; A - 6 cols, 1 5/6, 1/8 between; C - 9 cols, 1 3/16, 1/8 between.
Commodity Consumption: Avg. Page Number Per Issue - Daily 30; Avg. Page Number Per Issue - Plates Used 25000; Avg. Page Number Per Issue - Saturday 44; Avg. Page Number Per Issue - Sunday 60; widths 12 1/2; Newsprint Used - Short Tons 2200; Printing Ink Used - Black 22000; Pri
Equipment EDITORIAL: Front-end Software – APT.; Editorial Hardware – PC; Editorial Equipment – Desk/Scanner, ; Editorial Printers – Sharp & Camera Probe 9000 CLASSIFIED: Front-end Software – APT.; Classified Hardware – PC; Classified Printers – HP DISPLAY: Ad make-up applications – InDesign; Layout Software – APT.; Display Hardware – PC, ; Display Printers – Okidata/2410, HP/LaserJet III; Scanners – Microtek PRESSROOM: Line 1 – 6-MAN/double width (2-half color deck) 1980; Press Drives – GE/Varitrol; Folders – 1-H/double 2:1; Pasters – 5; Reels and Stands – 5 MAILROOM: Counter stackers – QWI/351 QWI/501; Inserters and stuffers – 1-GMA/SLS 2000 9:2; Bundle tying machines – 2/MLN, 1-/Dynaric; Addressing machine – 1-/Ch; Other equipment –MM/Minuteman Stitcher-Trimmer.; Business Hardware – Microsoft/Office, Great Plains, AR/Works, PC Netware
Zip Codes served: 27215, 27217, 27244, 27249, 27253, 27258, 27302
Delivery method: Mail, Newsstand, Private Carrier, Racks

TIMES NEWS PUBLISHING CO.

707 S. Main St., Burlington, N.C., 27215; gen tel (336) 227-0131; gen fax (336) 229-2462

CHARLOTTE

THE CHARLOTTE OBSERVER

600 S. Tryon St., Charlotte, N.C., 28202; gen tel (704) 358-5000; adv tel (704) 358-5400; ed tel (704) 358-5040; gen fax (704) 358-5840; adv fax (704) 358-5542; ed fax (704) 358-5036; web site www.charlotteobserver.com

Group: North Carolina Press Service, Inc.
Published: Mon, Tues, Wed, Thur, Fri, Sat, Sun
Weekday Frequency: m
Saturday Frequency: m
Circulation: 145,595; 168,406(sat); 213,803(sun)
Last Audit: ABC September 30, 2011
Price: 3.06/wk; 13.25/mo; 159.12/yr.
Advertising: Open inch rate $366.00
News services: AP, MCT, LAT-WP, NYT.
Politics: Independent.
Special Editions: Boy Scouts (Apr); Back-to-School (Aug); Holiday Travel (Dec); Weddings (Feb); Business Review/Stocks (Jan); Back-to-School (Jul); Father's Day (Jun); Spring Fashion (Mar); Golf (May); Hornets Opener (Nov); Octoberfest (Oct); Home Improvement (Sept).
Special Weekly Sections: E&T (Fri); Business Monday (Mon); Travel (S); Faith & Values (Sat); Family (Tues); Food (Wed).
Magazines: Parade (S).
Pres./Pub. ....Ann Caulkins
CFO ....A. Victor Fields
Vice Pres. Opns. ....Chuck Griffiths
Bus. Devel. Mgr. ....Jenny Schafer
Customer Serv. Mgr. ....Jenny Funderburk
Adv. Vice Pres. ....Liz Irwin
Adv. Dir., Classified ....Ron Stokes
Adv. Dir., Display ....Darren Frank
Adv. Dir., Retail ....Donna Gordon
Head IT. ....Jim Lamm
Circ. Dir. ....Debbie Abels
Circ. Sales/Receptionist ....Nicole Deyton
Mng. Ed. ....Cheryl Carpenter
Ed. ....Tom Tozer
Sr. Ed., Recruiting/Training ....Jim Walser
Dir., Newsroom Systems ....Neil Mara
Mgr., Newsroom Budget ....Elaine Jacobs
Art Dir. ....Joanne Miller
Books Ed. ....Ann Allen
Bus. Ed. ....Patrick Scott
Market Information: ADS; Split run; TMC; Zoned editions.
Mechanical available: Flexo; Black and 3 ROP colors; insert accepted; page cutoffs - 23 9/16.
Mechanical Specifications: Type page 12 x 22 1/2; E - 6 cols, 1 13/16, 1/5 between; A - 6 cols, 1 13/16, 1/5 between; C - 10 cols, 1 1/16, 1/16 between.
Commodity Consumption: Avg. Page Number Per Issue - Daily 62; Avg. Page Number Per Issue - Plates Used 400000; Avg. Page Number Per Issue - Saturday 124; Avg. Page Number Per Issue - Sunday 132; widths 25; Newsprint Used - Metric Tons 40000; Printing Ink Used - Black 1200000;
Equipment EDITORIAL: Front-end Software – CCI.; Editorial Hardware – IBM/S-70; Editorial Printers – Okidata, HP/Laser CLASSIFIED: Front-end Software – SII/Server Net.; Classified Hardware – SII/Server Net; Classified Equipment – SII/ICP Pagination; Classified Printers – Okidata, HP/Laser DISPLAY: Ad make-up applications – Multi-Ad/Creator, AII/Ad Assistant, QPS/QuarkXPress 5.0, Adobe/Photoshop 5.0, Adobe/Illustrator 9.0; Display Hardware – APP/Mac 266, HP/LNZ, Sun/Enterprise 3500, APP/Mac G3; Display Printers – 3-III/3850, Plain Paper Clipper/11 x 17 1200 dpi, HP/1050; Production Equipment – HP/ScanJet 3P, 3-Na/Fx IV, Adobe/Photoshop, 4-APP/Mac with stations for Art, 5-APP/Mac G3, 2-HP/1050; Cameras – C/Spartan, 2-Clemco pagers; Scanners – Kk/RFS 3570 Scanner, Umax/Power-

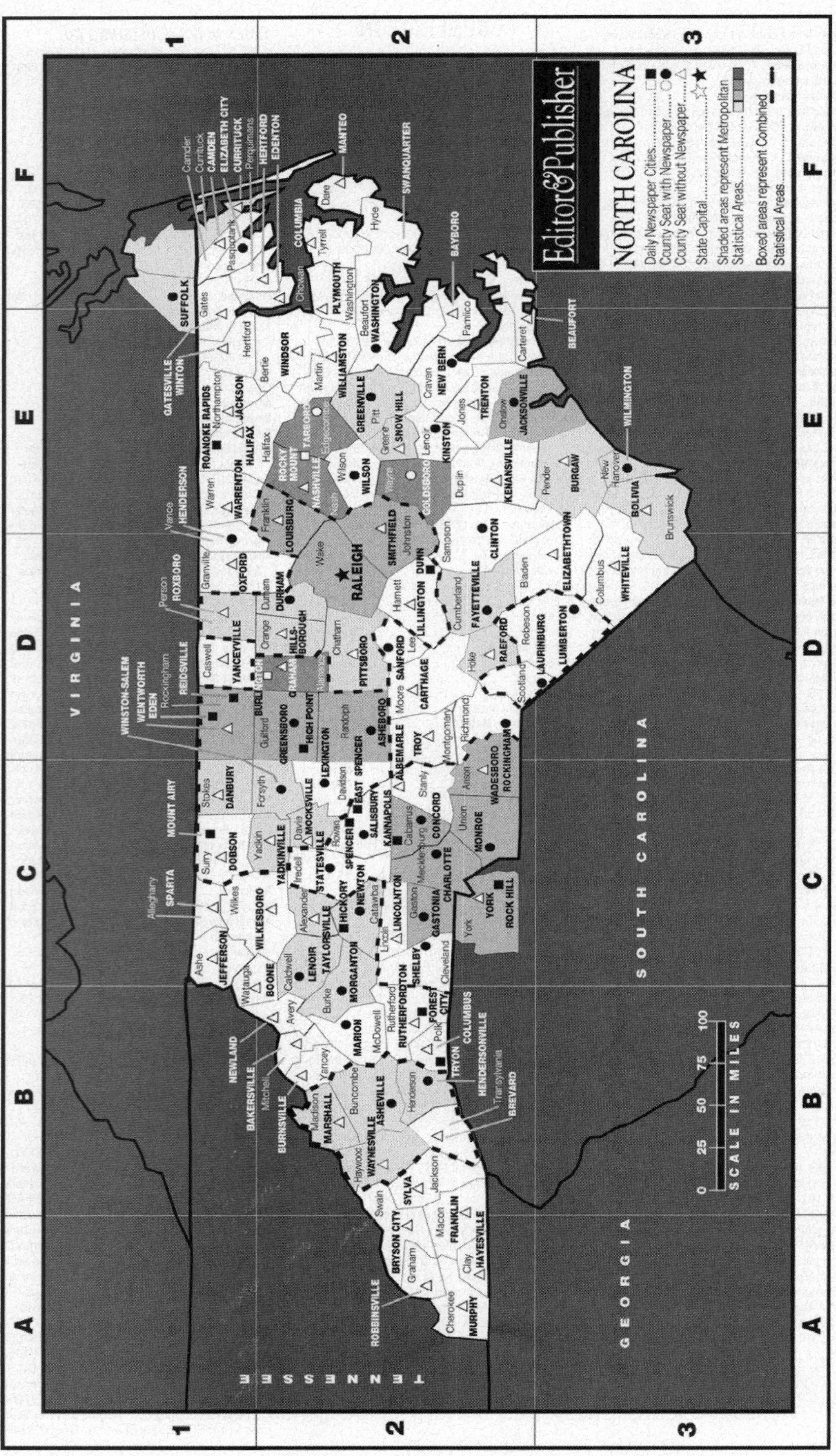

Look flatbed scanner, 8-LaCie/Silver Scan, 3-Topaz, Eskofot/1 PRESSROOM: Line 1 – 8-MAN/Flexoman 1995; Line 2 – 8-MAN/Flexoman 1996; Line 3 – 8-MAN/Flexoman 1996; Line 4 – 8-MAN/Flexoman 1996; Folders – 7; Reels and Stands – MAN/Roland. MAILROOM: Counter stackers – 4-HL/Monitor, 5-HL/Monitor HT, 4-HL/Monitor HT II, 3-QWI/350; Inserters and stuffers – 2-MM/375, 1/SLS 1000; Bundle tying machines – 13-/Power Strap, 6-MLN/MLN 2A, 6-Dynaric/NP2; Wrapping singles – Mailroom control system ☐ A&E Engineering/Totalizer BUSINESS COMPUTERS: Business Software – In-house; Business Hardware – 2-Sun/3800

KNIGHT PUBLISHING CO.

600 S. Tryon St., Charlotte, N.C., 28232; gen tel (704) 358-5000; gen fax (704) 358-5840

CLINTON

THE SAMPSON INDEPENDENT

303 Elizabeth St., Clinton, N.C., 28328; gen tel (910) 592-8137; adv tel (910) 592-8137; ed tel (910) 592-8137; gen fax (910) 592-8756; adv fax (910) 592-1419; ed fax (910) 592-8756; ed e-mail smatthews@myclintonnc.com; web site www.clintonnc.com

Published: Tues, Wed, Thur, Fri, Sat, Sun
Weekday Frequency: e
Saturday Frequency: m
Circulation: 7,962; 7,962(sat); 8,100(sun)
Last Audit: September 30, 2005
Price: 7.00/mo; 84.00/yr.
Advertising: Open inch rate $15.75
News services: AP.
Politics: 1946
Special Editions: Spring Fashion (Apr); Back-to-School (Aug); Xmas Gift Guide (Dec); Insight (Feb); Tobacco (Jul); Bridal (May); Cookbook (Nov); Fall Car Care (Oct); Fall Fashion (Sept).
Magazines: Parade (S).
Pub. .... Sandy Hurley
Adv. Dir., Classified .... Brenda McCullen
Adv. Dir., Retail .... Aothey Sampson
Circ. Dir. .... Alissa Bradford
Ed. .... Sherry Matthews
Asst. Ed. .... Doug Clark
Market Information: TMC.
Mechanical available: Offset; Black and 4 ROP colors; insert accepted - products, bags; page cutoffs - 22 3/4.
Commodity Consumption: Avg. Page Number Per Issue - Daily 22; Avg. Page Number Per Issue - Plates Used 3800; Avg. Page Number Per Issue - Sunday 34; widths 25; Newsprint Used - Short Tons 335; Printing Ink Used - Black 11352; Printing Ink Used - Color 649; Printing Ink Used -
Equipment EDITORIAL: Front-end Software – Baseview.; Editorial Hardware – 1-Mk/1100, 12-Mk/4100, APP/Mac; Editorial Printers – APP/Mac CLASSIFIED: Front-end Software – Baseview.; Classified Hardware – APP/Mac; Classified Printers – APP/Mac DISPLAY: Ad make-up applications – Multi-Ad, QPS/QuarkXPress; Layout Software – Multi-Ad, QPS/QuarkXPress.; Display Hardware – APP/Mac; Display Printers – APP/Mac PRODUCTION: Pagination Software – Pre Press/Panther Pro, QPS/QuarkXPress.; Production Equipment – Pre Press/Panther Pro, 1-COM/7200, 2-COM/Videosetter; Cameras – 1-CL/J-76CC; Scanners – 5-Astra, Umax, Nikon/Scanner PRESSROOM: Line 1 – 4-G/Community (1 folder), 8-G; Line 2 – 5; Bundle tying machines – 1/Malow, 2-/Malow.; Business Hardware – Software ☐ Baseview, Baseview, Navision

CONCORD

INDEPENDENT TRIBUNE

924 Cloverleaf Plz., Concord, N.C., 28083; gen tel (704) 782-3155; adv tel (704) 789-

9197; ed tel (704) 789-9150; gen fax (704) 786-0645; adv fax (704) 789-9159; ed fax (704) 786-0645; ed e-mail news@independenttribune.com; web site www.independenttribune.com
Published: Wed, Fri, Sun
Last Audit: September 30, 2008
Price: 9.00/mo; 110.93/yr.
Advertising: Open inch rate $22.00
News services: AP.
Politics: Independent.
Special Editions: Car Care (Apr); Football (Aug); Christmas Greetings (Dec); Progress (Feb); Chamber of Commerce Update (Jan); June Bride (Jun); Spring Fashion (Mar); World 600 Racing (May); Family Business Focus (Nov); National 500 Racing (Oct).
Special Weekly Sections: Religious Page (Fri); Health News (Mon); Weekly TV (S); School News (Thur); Racing Specials (Tues); Best Food Day (Wed).
Magazines: TV/Entertainment Magazine (Fri); USA WEEKEND Magazine (S); American Profile (Weekly).
Pub. ....Terry Coomes
Mng. Ed. ....Jonathan Coleman
Asst. Sports Ed. ....Steve Winzenread
Market Information: Split run; TMC.
Mechanical available: Offset; Black and 3 ROP colors; insert accepted - all types & sizes; page cutoffs - 21 1/2.
Mechanical Specifications: Type page 13 x 21 1/2; E - 6 cols, 2 1/16, 1/8 between; A - 6 cols, 2 1/16, 1/8 between; C - 9 cols, 1 3/8, 1/16 between.
Commodity Consumption: Avg. Page Number Per Issue - Daily 24; Avg. Page Number Per Issue - Plates Used 6000; Avg. Page Number Per Issue - Sunday 36; widths 27 1/2; Newsprint Used - Short Tons 850; Printing Ink Used - Black 34000; Printing Ink Used - Color 1400; Printing Ink Us
Equipment EDITORIAL: Front-end Software – QPS/QuarkXPress, Baseview.; Editorial Hardware – APP/Mac, Ethernet; Editorial Printers – APP/Mac LaserPrinter CLASSIFIED: Front-end Software – Fox.; Classified Hardware – APP/Mac; Classified Printers – APP/Mac LaserPrinter DISPLAY: Ad make-up applications – QPS/Ad Builder.; Display Hardware – APP/Mac; Display Printers – APP/Mac LaserWriter; Production Equipment – 2-COM/8400S; Cameras – C/Spartan III, AG/Repromaster 2100. PRESSROOM: Line 1 – 4-G/Urbanite. MAILROOM: Counter stackers – 1/BG; Inserters and stuffers – MM; Bundle tying machines – 1-/Bu; Addressing machine – Vista Data. BUSINESS COMPUTERS: Business Software – Vision Data; Business Hardware – Convergent

DUNN

THE DAILY RECORD

99 W. Broad St., Dunn, N.C., 28335; gen tel (910) 891-1234; adv tel (910) 891-1234; ed tel (910) 891-1234; gen fax (910) 891-4445; adv fax (910) 891-5253; ed fax (910) 891-4445; gen e-mail info@mydailyrecord.com; adv e-mail classifieds@mydailyrecord.com; web site www.mydailyrecord.com
Published: Mon, Tues, Wed, Thur, Fri
Weekday Frequency: e
Circulation: 8,419
Last Audit: September 30, 2008
Price: 5.55/mo; 64.00/yr; 16.50/3mo.
Advertising: Open inch rate $13.95
News services: AP.
Politics: Independent. **Established:** 1950
Advertising not accepted: Liquor.
Special Editions: Spring Car Care (Apr); Back-to-School (Aug); Christmas Greetings (Dec); Update (Feb); January Clearance (Jan); Best of Harnett County (Jul); Bridal (Mar); Graduation Tab (May); Holiday Gift Guide (Nov); Consumer How-to-Guide (Oct); Crepe Myrtle (Sept).
Special Weekly Sections: Weekend (Fri); Best Food Day (Wed).
Magazines: American Profile (Weekly).
Vice Pres. ....Brent Adams
Vice Pres./Sec./Treasurer ....Mellicent Adams
Adv. Dir. ....Kathy Pope
Ed. ....Bart S. Adams
Online Ed. ....Lisa Farmer
Travel Ed. ....Hoover Adams
Prodn. Mgr. ....Glenn Howard
Prodn. Mgr., Post Press ....Wendy Gregory
Prodn. Mgr., Pre Press ....Tracey Sinclair
Market Information: Zoned editions.
Mechanical available: Offset; Black and 264 ROP colors; insert accepted - any; page cutoffs - 22 3/4.
Mechanical Specifications: Type page 11 1/2 x 21 1/2; E - 6 cols, 1 5/6, 1/8 between; A - 6 cols, 1 5/6, 1/8 between; C - 6 cols, 1 5/6, 1/8 between.
Commodity Consumption: Avg. Page Number Per Issue - Daily 24; Avg. Page Number Per Issue - Plates Used 9600; widths 25; Newsprint Used - Short Tons 768; Printing Ink Used - Black 11000; Printing Ink Used - Color 5500; Printing Ink Used - Pages Printed 6240.
Equipment EDITORIAL: Front-end Software – Baseview/NewsEdit, QPS/QuarkXPress.; Editorial Hardware – APP/Mac; Editorial Printers – HP/LaserJet 5M CLASSIFIED: Front-end Software – Vision Data, QuarkXPress 4.04.; Classified Hardware – Unix/Server; Classified Printers – APP/HP 2300 N DISPLAY: Ad make-up applications – Vision Data; Layout Software – APP/Mac, Multi-Ad/Creator, Adobe/Photoshop, QPS/QuarkXPress, Adobe/Illustrator.; Display Hardware – Unix/Server; Display Printers – APP/Mac LaserWriter NTX PRODUCTION: Pagination Software – QPS/QuarkXPress with Vision Data Interface.; Production Equipment – Caere/OmniPage Pro 8.0, ECR/EV Jetsetter 2100, APP/Mac G3; Cameras – C/Spartan III; Scanners – Polaroid/Sprint Scan 4000, Polaroid/Sprint Scan 35, Umax/PowerLook III, HP/Scan Jet III PRESSROOM: Line 1 – 6-G/Community single width 1983, 1-stacked G/community 1999; Folders – 1-G/SE. MAILROOM: Counter stackers – BG/Count-O-Veyor; Inserters and stuffers – KAN/480; Bundle tying machines – 2/Bu; Addressing machine – X.; Audio Hardware – EduCom Services Inc. BUSINESS COMPUTERS: Business Software – Windows; Business Hardware – Vision Data

DURHAM

THE HERALD-SUN

2828 Pickett Rd., Durham, N.C., 27705; gen tel (919) 419-6500; adv tel (919) 419-6700; ed tel (919) 419-6675; adv fax (919) 419-6773; ed fax (919) 419-6837; ed e-mail news@heraldsun.com; web site www.heraldsun.com
Published: Mon, Tues, Wed, Thur, Fri, Sat, Sun
Weekday Frequency: m
Saturday Frequency: m
Circulation: 21,055; 25,111(sat); 22,832(sun)
Last Audit: ABC September 30, 2011
Price: 4.00/wk; 15.99/mo; 180.45/yr.
Advertising: Open inch rate $36.160
News services: AP
Politics: Independent. **Established:** 1889
Own facility?: Y
Special Editions: Physicians Guide (Annually); Senior Times (Quarterly).
Magazines: WE ARE DURHAM Magazine (Other); USA WEEKEND Magazine (S).
Pub. ....Rick Bean
Adv. Dir. ....Thomas Tuttle
Mrktg. Mgr. ....Thomas Massey
Circ. Dir. ....Brent Agurs
Exec. Ed. ....Nancy Wykle
Sports Ed. ....Jimmy Dupree
Dir., Info Technology ....Tim Anderson
Prodn. Dir. ....Chuck Friend
Market Information: TMC; Zoned editions.
Mechanical available: Offset; Black and 3 ROP colors; insert accepted - product samples, plastic delivery bags; page cutoffs - 22.
Mechanical Specifications: Type page 10 x 21; E - 6 cols, 1 9/16, 1/8 between; A - 6 cols, 1 9/16, 1/8 between; C - 8 cols, 1.046, 1/8 between.
Commodity Consumption: Avg. Page Number Per Issue - Daily 36; Avg. Page Number Per Issue - 36
Equipment EDITORIAL: Front-end Software – ACI/Open Pages.; Editorial Hardware – 45-Dell/Dimension P166, 30-Dell/Dimension P450; Editorial Equipment – 1998-Epson/ES-1200C Scanner; Editorial Printers – HP/LaserJet 5000 GN, 2-Au/APS RIP3, Au/Sierra Imagers, Au/APS Netproof CLASSIFIED: Front-end Software – HI/AdPower.; Classified Hardware – 12-Dell/Dimension P450; Classified Equipment – Visioneer/Strobe Pro 2000; Classified Printers – Au/APS RIP3, HP/LaserJet 4050N DISPLAY: Ad make-up applications – HI/AdPower; Layout Software – MEI/ALS 2.7.; Display Hardware – Dell/Dimension P450; Display Printers – HP/LaserJet 4000 PRODUCTION: Pagination Software – QPS/QuarkXPress 3.31.; Production Equipment – 2-AU/3850, 2-AU/3850, 2-LE/MX-2629, 1-LT-26, 1-LE/Maxium, LS/2600; Scanners – Omax PRESSROOM: Line 1 – 6-G/Headliner Offset double width (3 half decks) 1990; Line 2 – 1-G/Metro (Color Tower) double width 2000; Press Drives – 7; Folders – 1-G/3:2; Reels and Stands – 7; Press control system – G; Press registration system – G/Pin System, BG/Bender, Ca MAILROOM: Counter stackers – 4-QWI/300, 1-QWI/400; Inserters and stuffers – 1-MM/375-16, 1-H/1372; Bundle tying machines – 5/Power Straps; Wrapping singles – 2-QWI/Viper 3/4 Wraps; Addressing machine – 1-KR/211; Other equipment –1-MM/1375. BUSINESS COMPUTERS: Business Software – Great Plains, AMP5; Business Hardware – HP/3000-928
Delivery method: Mail, Newsstand, Private Carrier, Racks

EDEN

THE DAILY NEWS

PO Box 308, Eden, N.C., 27289-0308; gen tel (336) 623-2155; web site www.edendailynews.com

ELIZABETH CITY

THE DAILY ADVANCE

215 S. Water St., Elizabeth City, N.C., 27909; gen tel (252) 335-0841; adv tel (252) 335-8082; ed tel (252) 335-8110; gen fax (252) 335-4415; oth fax (252) 335-2953; gen e-mail elizabethcity@dailyadvance.com; ed e-mail elizabethcity@dailyadvance.com; web site www.dailyadvance.com
Group: Cooke Communications North Carolina, LLC
Published: Mon, Tues, Wed, Thur, Fri, Sat, Sun
Weekday Frequency: m
Saturday Frequency: m
Circulation: 9,555; 9,498(sat); 9,498(sun)
Last Audit: ABC September 30, 2011
Price: 10.50/mo; 126.00/yr.
Advertising: Open inch rate $16.50 (Oct. 2011).65
News services: AP.
Politics: Independent. **Established:** 1911
Own facility?: Y
Special Editions: Medical Directory (Jan.), Albemarle Magazine (quarterly), Dream Homes Real Estate Guide (monthly), Coast Guard Anniversary Tab (Aug.), Senior Living (Oct.), Holiday Recipe/Songbook (Dec.) Bridal Tab (Jan.)
Special Weekly Sections: Albemarle Life (Wed.-Sun.), Shelter pets (Mon.), School Page (Tues); Business Page (Sun.).
Magazines: Parade (S).
Albemarle Magazine (quarterly)
Pub. ....Ann Hoffman
Circ. Mgr. ....Chuck Edwards
Albemarle Life Ed. ....Robert Kelly-Goss
Editor/Editorial Page Editor ....Mike Goodman
News Ed. ....Julian Eure
Asst. News Ed. ....Chris Day
Creative Services Manager ....Brian Gray
Advertising Director ....Ruby Moore
Customer Service/Classified Managr Susan Harris
Financial/Accounting Manager. Maureen Brinson
IS Manager ....Lynne Watkins
Market Information: TMC; Zoned editions.
Mechanical available: Offset; Black and 3 ROP colors; insert accepted; page cutoffs - 22"
Mechanical Specifications: Type page 13 1/4 x 21 1/2; E - 6 cols, 2 1/16, 1/8 between; A - 6 cols, 2 1/16, 1/8 between; C - 9 cols, 1 5/16, 1/8 between.
Commodity Consumption: Avg. Page Number Per Issue - Daily 16; Avg. Page Number Per Issue - Plates Used 8500; Avg. Page Number Per Issue - Sunday 40; widths 32; Newsprint Used - Short Tons 1500; Printing Ink Used - Black 42000; Printing Ink Used - Color 4000; Printing Ink Used
Equipment EDITORIAL: Front-end Software – DTI.; Editorial Hardware – APP/Mac; Editorial Equipment – 1-APP/Power Mac 8600 Image Desk, Lf/AP Leaf Picture Desk; Editorial Printers – 2-ECR/VRL 36 CLASSIFIED: Front-end Software – SII.; Classified Hardware – 3-APP/Mac Quadra 605; Classified Printers – 2-ECR/VRL 36 DISPLAY: Ad make-up applications – Multi-Ad/Creator 3.70; Layout Software – 3-APP/Power Mac 7300, 1-APP/Power Mac 7600.; Display Hardware – APP/Mac Quadra 650 fileserver; Display Printers – 2-ECR/VRL 36 PRODUCTION: Pagination Software – QPS/QuarkXPress 3.3.; Production Equipment – Caere/OmniPage Pro 5.0, Mk, Jobo/Processor; Cameras – 1-R/500; Scanners – AG/Plus PRESSROOM: Line 1 – 1-G/Urbanite; Line 2 – 4-G/Urbanite; Folders – 1-G/2:1, 1-G/Half, 1-G/Quarter; Press registration system – Duarte/Pin Registration. MAILROOM: Counter stackers – 1/BG; Inserters and stuffers – 1-/MM; Bundle tying machines – 2-/Bu; Addressing machine – Digital Label, KAN/Label; Other equipment –MM/3-Blade Trimmer. BUSINESS COMPUTERS: Business Software – WordPerfect 6.0, Lotus 1-2-3 5.0, Microsoft/Windows 95, Microsoft/Office 97, Microsoft/Excel; Business Hardware – HP
Zip Codes served: 5 counties
Delivery method: Mail, Newsstand, Private Carrier, Racks

FAYETTEVILLE

THE FAYETTEVILLE OBSERVER

458 Whitfield St., Fayetteville, N.C., 28306; gen tel (910) 323-4848; adv tel (910) 323-4848; ed tel (910) 323-4848; gen fax (910) 486-3544; adv fax (910) 486-3531; ed fax (910) 486-3545; gen e-mail foto@fayobserver.com; web site www.fayobserver.com
Published: Mon, Tues, Wed, Thur, Fri, Sat, Sun
Weekday Frequency: m
Saturday Frequency: m
Circulation: 49,477; 51,149(sat); 58,773(sun)
Last Audit: ABC September 30, 2011
Price: 12.35/mo; 146.00/yr.
Advertising: Open inch rate $83.90
News services: AP, LAT-WP.
Politics: Independent. **Established:** 1816
Special Editions: Wildcats (Apr); Discover Fayetteville (Aug); Holiday Gift Guide (Dec); Honor Roll (Feb); Cumberland Parent (Jan); Back-to-School (Jul); Storm Watch (Jun); Military Appreciation (May); Cumberland Parent (Nov); Motor Sports (Oct); Reader's Choice (Sept).
Special Weekly Sections: Faith (Fri); Health (Mon); Business (S); Real Estate Marketplace (Sat); Business (Thur); Business (Tues); Business (Wed).
Magazines: Relish (Monthly); Parade (S); TV Week (Sat).
Pres./Pub ....Charles W. Broadwell
Sec./Treasurer ....Ashton L. Fox
Chrmn. ....Ramon L. Yarborough
Controller ....Ronda Graham
Dir., Finance ....Ken Kraft
Credit Mgr. ....Jill Koonce
Adv. Dir. ....Fred Benson
Adv. Mgr., Classified ....Mona Bass
Adv. Regl. Sales Mgr. ....Jim Sills
Circ.Dir ....David Ruffel

Exec. Ed. .....Mike Arnholt
Mng. Ed. .....Michael Arnholt
Asst. Mng. Ed. .....Mike Adams
Copy Desk Ed. .....David Coulton
Sports Ed .....Todd Adams
Columnist .....Rodger Mullen
Editorial Page Ed. .....Timothy White
Educ. Ed. .....Jessica Banov
Graphics Dir. .....Suzanne Schubert
Market Information: Split run; TMC; Zoned editions.
Mechanical available: Offset; Black and 3 ROP colors; insert accepted - all; page cutoffs - 22.
Mechanical Specifications: Type page 12 1/2 x 21; E - 6 cols, 1 17/20, 1/8 between; A - 6 cols, 1 17/20, 1/8 between; C - 10 cols, 1 3/16, 1/16 between.
Commodity Consumption: Avg. Page Number Per Issue - Daily 48.1; Avg. Page Number Per Issue - Plates Used 96000; Avg. Page Number Per Issue - Saturday 84.2; Avg. Page Number Per Issue - Sunday 87.6; widths 12 1/2; Newsprint Used - Short Tons 9800; Printing Ink Used - Black 1190
Equipment EDITORIAL: Front-end Software – Tera, 3-Good News.; Editorial Hardware – DEC, Intel, 2-Dell/4300; Editorial Equipment – APP/Mac G4, HP/ScanJet IIcx, Kk/RFS 2035 Scanner, Nikon/Coolscan, 102-Dell/PC; Editorial Printers – 12-HP/5000GN CLASSIFIED: Front-end Software – Mactive/Adbooker 2.8.18.; Classified Hardware – 2-Dell/6300; Classified Equipment – 30-Dell/PC; Classified Printers – HP/5000 GN DISPLAY: Ad make-up applications – Multi-Ad/Creator, SCS Track, Admarc; Layout Software – SCS/Layout 8000.; Display Hardware – APP/Mac, IBM/AS-400; Display Printers – HP/LaserPrinter PRODUCTION: Pagination Software – Good News III.; Production Equipment – WL/7AW-DW-OPB, 3-AU/Soft Pips (Window NT), 1-Au/3850 Doublewide; Scanners – 1-PixelCraft, 1-Nikon, Data/Oy-Plate Scanner PRESSROOM: Line 1 – 10-KB/Colora double width 1999; Press Drives – 1999; Folders – 1999; Pasters – 7-1999, 2-1999. MAILROOM: Counter stackers – 5-QWI/400W, 1-QWI/350, 1-Gammerler/Pathfinder 7.0; Inserters and stuffers – HI/1372, HI/630; Bundle tying machines – 2-Dynaric/NP2, 3-Dynaric/1500; Wrapping singles – 3-Id/Bottom Wrapper, 2-QWI/Cobra 3/4 Wrap w/inkjet, 2-QWI/Viper; Audio Hardware – VNN, Brite BUSINESS COMPUTERS: Business Software – PBS, Microsoft/Excel, AdMarc; Business Hardware – IBM/AS-400 F35

FOREST CITY

THE DAILY COURIER

601 Oak St., Forest City, N.C., 28043; gen tel (828) 245-6431; adv tel (828) 245-6431; ed tel (828) 245-6431; gen fax (828) 248-2790; gen e-mail dailycourier@blueridge.net; adv e-mail lfaulkner@digitalcourier.com; ed e-mail editor@thedigitalcourier.com; web site www.thedigitalcourier.com
Group: Paxton Media Group
Published: Tues, Wed, Thur, Fri, Sat, Sun
Weekday Frequency: m
Saturday Frequency: m
Circulation: 9,332; 9,332(sat); 9,332(sun)
Last Audit: October 1, 2003
Price: 12.25/mo
News services: AP.
Politics: 1969
Not Published: Monday
Own facility?: Y
Special Editions: Home Improvement (Apr); Christmas Gift Guide (Dec); Income Tax (Jan); Back-to-School (Aug); Fall Sports (Aug); Health-Fitness (Jun); Everything Rutherford (Apr); Graduation (May); Outdoors (Sept).
Special Weekly Sections: Television (S).
Magazines: USA WEEKEND Magazine (S).
Adv. Dir. .....Lori Faulkner
Circ. Dir. .....Antony Rollins
Photo Dept. Mgr. .....Garrett Byer
Travel Ed. .....Jean Gordon
Bus. Mgr. .....Joyce Ferguson
Adv. Mgr., Classified .....Beth Scultz
Nat'l Political Ed. .....Steven E. Parham
Society/Women's Ed. .....Abbe Byers
Market Information: TMC.
Mechanical available: Offset; Black and 3 ROP colors; insert accepted; page cutoffs - 21.
Mechanical Specifications: Type page 11 5/8 x 21; E - 6 cols, 1 5/6, 1/8 between; A - 6 cols, 1 5/6, 1/8 between; C - 9 cols, 1 3/8, 1/8 between.
Commodity Consumption: Avg. Page Number Per Issue - Daily 18; Avg. Page Number Per Issue - Plates Used 4797; Avg. Page Number Per Issue - Saturday 14; Avg. Page Number Per Issue - Sunday 28; widths 25; Newsprint Used - Short Tons 448; Printing Ink Used - Black 9948; Printing I
Equipment EDITORIAL: Front-end Software – APP/Mac, Baseview/NewsEdit Pro, QPS/QuarkXPress 4.04.; Editorial Hardware – APP/Mac; Editorial Printers – QMS/2060, QMS/860t CLASSIFIED: Front-end Software – APP/Mac, Baseview/Ad Mgr. Pro 2.4.; Classified Hardware – APP/Mac; Classified Printers – QMS/2060, QMS/860t DISPLAY: Ad make-up applications – APP/Mac, QPS/QuarkXPress 4.04, Adobe/Photoshop 5.05; Layout Software – Mk, 3-APP/Mac.; Display Hardware – Mk; Display Printers – QMS 2060, QMS 860 PRODUCTION: Pagination Software – APP/Mac, QPS/QuarkXPress 4.04.; Production Equipment – Amerigraph, AG/Imagesetter 1500 plus, Konica/EV JetSetter 3100S; Cameras – Acti; Folders – 1992 BUSINESS COMPUTERS: Business Software – Citrix/ICA Client (version 3.0); Business Hardware – 3-APP/Mac, Great Plains
Delivery method: Mail, Newsstand, Private Carrier, Racks

FOREST CITY PUBLISHING CO., INC.

601 Oak St., Forest City, N.C., 28043; gen tel (828) 245-6431; gen fax (828) 248-2790

GASTONIA

THE GASTON GAZETTE

1893 Remount Rd., Gastonia, N.C., 28054; gen tel (704) 869-1700; adv tel (704) 869-1735; ed tel (704) 869-1812; gen fax (704) 867-6988; adv fax (704) 867-6988; ed fax (704) 867-5751; gen e-mail gastongazette@link.freedom.com; web site www.gastongazette.com
Group: North Carolina Press Service, Inc.
Published: Mon, Tues, Wed, Thur, Fri, Sat, Sun
Weekday Frequency: m
Saturday Frequency: m
Circulation: 22,204; 21,356(sat); 25,200(sun)
Last Audit: ABC September 30, 2011
Price: 9.50/mo; 135.00/yr.
Advertising: Open inch rate $52.60
News services: AP, SHNS, NYT, NEA.
Politics: 1880
Special Editions: Stress (Apr); Senior Living (Aug); Church Directory (Dec); Senior Living (Feb); Bridal Tab (Jan); Christmas in July (Jul); Legal Guide (Jun); Home & Garden (Mar); Senior Living (May); Senior Living (Nov); New Car Show (Oct); Travel (Sept).
Special Weekly Sections: Business Spotlight (Tues).
Magazines: Home Magazine (Fri); Gaston Seasons (Quarterly); USA WEEKEND Magazine (S); Lake Novman Gazette (Weekly).
Pub .....Jennie Lambert
Adv. Dir. .....Titus Workman
Adv. Mgr., Classified .....Donna Ritter
Adv. Mgr., Retail .....Heather Holt
Dir., Mktg. .....Michael Sewell
Dir., Promo./NIE .....Sherry Collins
Bus. Ed. .....Thomas Monigan
Editorial Page Ed. .....Barry Bridges
Educ. Ed. .....Nancy Moore
Graphics Ed. .....Randy Erwin
Health/Medical Ed. .....Will MacDonald
Librarian .....Marian Clemmer
Music Ed. .....Alicia Mayes
News Ed. .....Lou Corsaro
Online Ed. .....Ray Martin
Market Information: ADS; TMC.
Mechanical available: Offset; Black and 3 ROP colors; insert accepted - product samples (prior approval required); page cutoffs - 22.
Mechanical Specifications: Type page 11 5/8 x 21 1/2; E - 6 cols, 1 5/6, 1/8 between; A - 6 cols, 1 5/6, 1/8 between; C - 9 cols, 1 3/16, 1/16 between.
Commodity Consumption: Avg. Page Number Per Issue - Daily 40; Avg. Page Number Per Issue - Plates Used 31000; Avg. Page Number Per Issue - Sunday 64; widths 27; Newsprint Used - Metric Tons 4123; Newsprint Used - Short Tons 4544; Printing Ink Used - Black 77000; Printing Ink U
Equipment EDITORIAL: Front-end Software – APT.; Editorial Hardware – APT/Paginaters (700 mhz), APT/Reporter (500 mhz); Editorial Printers – HP/Plotter, Pre Press/Panther 36, Autologic CLASSIFIED: Front-end Software – APT.; Classified Hardware – Compaq/Servers 300 mhz; Classified Printers – Autologic DISPLAY: Ad make-up applications – APT; Display Hardware – PC; Display Printers – Autologic PRODUCTION: Pagination Software – APT.; Production Equipment – Scanview Drum Scanner, Nikon/Super Coolscan, Zip Disk Readers PRESSROOM: Line 1 – 42-G/Magnum single width units 2001; Folders – 1-G/Universal w/ 4 formers, 1-G/Universal w/ 2 formers; Reels and Stands – 18; Press control system – G/GMI. MAILROOM: Counter stackers – 2-QWI/401; Inserters and stuffers – GMA/SLS 2000 12:2; Bundle tying machines – 2/Samuels, 2-/Dynaric; Wrapping singles – 1-/NJP; Addressing machine – 1-X/542-090. BUSINESS COMPUTERS: Business Software – Vision Data, Great Plains, APT, Brainworks, Ceridian; Business Hardware – MS/NT Network

GOLDSBORO

GOLDSBORO NEWS-ARGUS

310 N. Berkeley Blvd., Goldsboro, N.C., 27534; gen tel (919) 778-2211; adv tel (919) 778-2000; ed tel (919) 739-7791; gen fax (919) 778-9891; adv fax (919) 778-9891; ed fax (919) 778-5408; adv e-mail displayads@newsargus.com; ed e-mail news@newsargus.com; web site www.newsargus.com
Published: Mon, Tues, Wed, Thur, Fri, Sun
Weekday Frequency: e
Circulation: 16,109; 18,140(sun)
Last Audit: ABC September 30, 2011
Price: 11.50/mo; 138.00/yr.
Advertising: Open inch rate $25.75
News services: AP.
Politics: 1885
Not Published: Independence Day; Christmas.
Own facility?: Y
Special Editions: Jan - Bridal
Feb - Progress
Mar - Home Improvement
Apr - American Home Week
May - Destination Summer
Jun -Healthy Living
Aug - Back to School
Sep - Readers Choice
Oct - Health Care Directory
Nov - Holiday Planner
Dec - Last Minute Gift Guide, Spirit of the Season
Special Weekly Sections: TV Showtime (Fri); Military Page (S); Health Pages (Thur); Food (Wed).
Magazines: Parade (S).
Publisher .....Hal H. Tanner
Bus. Mgr. .....Jeff Hansen
Mgr., HR .....Debbie M. Pennell
Adv. Mgr., Nat'l .....Georgia Gurley
Mng. Ed. .....Dennis Hill
Amusements Ed./Books Ed. .....Matt Whittle
Editor .....Renee Carey
Educ./Health Ed. .....Phyllis Moore
Online Ed. .....Keith Taylor
Society/Women's Ed. .....Becky Barclay
Sports Ed. .....Rudy Coggins
Mgmt. Info Servs. Mgr. .....David Rouse
Mechanical available: Offset; Black and 3 ROP colors; insert accepted; page cutoffs - 22 3/4.
Mechanical Specifications: Type page 10 5/8 x 21 1/2; E - 6 cols, 1 4/5, 1/8 between; A - 6 cols, 1 4/5, 1/8 between; C - 8 cols, 1 1/5, 11/100 between.
Commodity Consumption: Avg. Page Number Per Issue - Daily 24;- Plates Used 18700; Avg. Page Number Per Issue - Sunday 42; widths 22; Newsprint Used - Short Tons 1082; Printing Ink Used - Black 21632; Printing Ink Used - Color 11520;
Equipment EDITORIAL: Front-end Software – MediaSpan 3.54; Editorial Hardware – 8-Apple iMacs, 7-Apple G5, 1-Apple MacPro; Editorial Printers – HP Laserjet 5200, HP Laserjet 2200 CLASSIFIED: Front-end Software – MediaSpan AMP4; Classified Hardware – 7-APP/iMac; Classified Printers – HP 4250 DISPLAY: Ad make-up applications – MediaSpan AMP4, Quark Express 6, ; Display Hardware – 7-Apple eMacs, 1-Apple iMac; Display Printers – HP 8150 PRODUCTION: Pagination Software – Baseview 3.5.4.; Production Equipment – 1-Nu, 7-APP/Mac, 1-PC, ECRM/Bluefin 62, 1-Xerox Phaser 7400, ECR/Scriptsetter VRL 36HS, Xante 3G laser printer; Scanners – 6-Umax PRESSROOM: Line 1 – 9-G/Urbanite (color deck) single width 1970; Press Drives – 2; Folders – 1; Reels and Stands – 5 MAILROOM: Counter stackers – Quipp 500 (3); Gammerler KL-5000; Inserters and stuffers – 1 MM SLS2000 12:1; Bundle tying machines – 2 - Dynaric NP3000 - Quipp Viper bottomwrap; Wrapping singles – Mailroom control system ☐ 1-MM/1509 Minuteman Saddle Stitcher; Addressing machine – 1-Cheshire/569; 1-Barstrom Labeler (inline) BUSINESS COMPUTERS: Business Software – DTI, BSI, Microsoft/Office ; Business Hardware – Dell PowerEdge R410, Sun Sunfire v240
Delivery method: Mail, Newsstand, Private Carrier, Racks

GREENSBORO

NEWS & RECORD

200 E. Market St., Greensboro, N.C., 27401; gen tel (336) 373-7000; adv tel (336) 373-7364; ed tel (336) 373-7010; gen fax (336) 373-7183; adv fax (336) 412-5911; ed fax (336) 412-5920; ed e-mail edpage@news-record.com; web site www.news-record.com
Group: Landmark Media Enterprises, LLC
Published: Mon, Tues, Wed, Thur, Fri, Sat, Sun
Weekday Frequency: m
Saturday Frequency: m
Circulation: 57,489; 58,971(sat); 86,932(sun)
Last Audit: ABC September 30, 2011
Politics: 1890
Special Editions: Discover the Triad (Aug); NASCAR Preview (Feb); ACC Men's Basketball Tournament (Mar); Holiday Countdown-Wrapping-Up (Nov); Sports Extra-Greater Greensboro Chrysler Classic (Oct); Southern Ideal Home Show (Sept).
Special Weekly Sections: Careers (S); Food (Wed).
Pres./Pub. .....Robin Saul
Bus. Mgr. .....Carol Lobisser
Adv. Mgr., Classified .....Catherine Kernels
Adv. Mgr., Retail .....Jill Ford
Circ. Mgr., Distr./Home Delivery/TMC .....David Berrier
Ed. .....John Robinson
Bus. Ed. .....John Nagy
Editorial Page Ed. .....Allen Johnson
Features Ed. .....Susan Ladd
Librarian .....Diane Lamb
New Ed. .....Teresa Prout
Sports Ed. .....Joe Sirera
Prodn. Dir. .....Dawn Swanson
Circulation director .....Regina Howard-Glaspie
New media director .....Chris Brewer
Commodity Consumption: Avg. Page Number Per Issue - Daily 33; Avg. Page Number Per Issue - Saturday 34; Avg. Page Number Per Issue - Sunday 56; widths 22

Equipment PRESSROOM: Line 1 – 13-G/Metro double width 1974
Delivery method: Newsstand, Private Carrier, Racks

GREENVILLE

THE DAILY REFLECTOR

1150 Sugg Pkwy., Greenville, N.C., 27835; gen tel (252) 329-9500; adv tel (252) 329-9503; ed tel (252) 329-9564; gen fax (252) 752-8181; adv fax (252) 752-9583; ed fax (252) 754-8140; adv e-mail bwilliams@reflector.com; ed e-mail aclark@reflector.com; web site www.reflector.com
Published: Mon, Tues, Wed, Thur, Fri, Sat, Sun
Weekday Frequency: m
Saturday Frequency: m
Circulation: 20,752; 17,601(sat); 20,104(sun)
Last Audit: ABC September 30, 2011
Price: 10.95/mo; 131.40/yr.
Advertising: Open inch rate $26.94
News services: AP, NYT, LAT-WP.
Politics: Independent.
Special Editions: Parade of Homes (Apr); Back to School (Aug); College Football Bowl Preview (Dec); Home Expo (Feb); Bridal Planner (Jan); Design an Ad (Mar); Graduation (May); Holiday Show (Nov); Medical Directory (Oct); Community Business (Sept).
Special Weekly Sections: NASCAR (Fri); Workweek (Mon); Auto (S); Real Estate (Sat); Best Food Day (Wed).
Magazines: SportsWeek (S); Pirate Gameday (during football season) (Sat); TV Week (Thur).
Pub. ....John Cook
Gen. Mgr. ....J. Tim Holt
CFO ....Mariann McQueen
HR Dir. ....Donna Allen
Display Adv. Dir. ....Betty Williams
Circ. Dir. ....Keven Zepezauer
Dir., Mktg./Bus. Devel./Customer Care Elizabeth Semple
Exec. Ed. ....Al Clark
Asst. Mng. Ed. ....Cherie Speller
Bus. Ed. ....Mike Grizzard
Features Ed. ....Steve Cagle
News Ed. ....Bobby Burns
Photography/Graphics Ed. ....Greg Eans
Sports Ed. ....Jim Gentry
Info Systems Mgr. ....Bill Wallberg
Dir., Opns. ....Dan Mastin
Commercial Print Sales Mgr. ....Leah Evans
Creative Servs. Mgr. ....Dawn Newton
Facilities Mgr. ....James Webb
Pre Press Mgr. ....Regina Lytle
Market Information: TMC.
Mechanical available: Offset; Black and 3 ROP colors; insert accepted; page cutoffs - 22.
Mechanical Specifications: Type page 11 5/8 x 21; E - 6 cols, 2 1/2, 1/6 between; A - 6 cols, 2 1/2, 1/6 between; C - 9 cols, 1 1/3, 1/8 between.
Commodity Consumption: Avg. Page Number Per Issue - Daily 34; Avg. Page Number Per Issue - Sunday 70; widths 25; Newsprint Used - Short Tons 4000; Printing Ink Used - Black 69705; Printing Ink Used - Color 32242; Printing Ink Used - Pages Printed 13948.
Equipment EDITORIAL: Front-end Software – DTI.; Editorial Hardware – APP/Macs, Unix/Server; Editorial Printers – HP, Xante CLASSIFIED: Front-end Software – DTI/ClassSpeed.; Classified Hardware – APP/Macs, Unix/Server; Classified Printers – HP, Xante DISPLAY: Ad make-up applications – DTI; Layout Software – DTI/Speed Planner, APP/Macs, Unix/Server.; Display Hardware – APP/Mac; Display Printers – 2-APP/Mac LaserWriter, HP, Xante PRODUCTION: Pagination Software – DTI/PageSpeed.; Production Equipment – 2-Konica/9200, 1-Olec/Ov 45Hd; Cameras – 1-C/Spartan III; Scanners – 4-Umax Flatbed, 2-Polaroid/SprintScan 35, 1-PixelCraft PRESSROOM: Line 1 – 16-DGM/850 single width 16; Line 2 – 18-DGM/430 single width 18; Line 3 – 8-DG/860 single width 1999; Line 4 – HI/Milo Single Wide 2001; Folders – 1, 4-4; Pasters – 8; Reels and Stands – 9-Jardis/Splicers. MAILROOM: Counter stackers – 3/Rhima, 4-/QWI; Inserters and stuffers – 2-GMA/SLS 1000; Bundle tying machines – 4-/Sterling, 2-Si; Addressing machine – 1-/KR; Other equipment –MM/Minuteman quarter folder Sticher-Trimmer, MM/251 Stitcher-Trimmer. BUSINESS COMPUTERS: Business Software – CJ, Geac/World Class; Business Hardware – HP/9000

HENDERSON

DAILY DISPATCH

304 S. Chestnut St., Henderson, N.C., 27536; gen tel (252) 436-2700; adv tel (252) 436-2821; ed tel (252) 436-2831; gen fax (252) 430-0125; adv fax (252) 430-0125; ed fax (252) 430-0125; gen e-mail news@hendersondispatch.com; adv e-mail advertising@hendersondispatch.com; ed e-mail lhorton@hendersondispatch.com; web site www.hendersondispatch.com
Published: Tues, Wed, Thur, Fri, Sat, Sun
Weekday Frequency: m
Saturday Frequency: m
Circulation: 7,015; 7,015(sat); 7,088(sun)
Last Audit: September 30, 2009
Price: 3.06/wk; 13.25/mo; 144.00/yr.
Advertising: Open inch rate $12.95
News services: AP.
Not Published: Christmas.
Own facility?: Y
Special Editions: Spring Home & Garden (Apr); Fall Sports (Aug); Christmas Greetings (Dec); Best of Vance County (Feb); Bridal (Jan); Funeral & Estate Planning (Jul); Graduation (Jun); Spring Fashion (Mar); Trade Show (May); Christmas Gift Guide (Nov); Football Contest (Se
Special Weekly Sections: Best Food Day (Wed).
Magazines: USA WEEKEND Magazine (S).
Pub ....James Edwards
Adv. Dir. ....Deborah Tuck
Circ. Mgr. ....................................A.J. Woodell
Photo Dept. Mgr. ....Ashley Steven Ayscue
Features Editor ....Dylan Wilson
Sports Ed. ....Kellen Holtzman
Editor ....Luke Horton
Market Information: TMC.
Mechanical available: Offset; Black and 3 ROP colors; insert accepted - any; page cutoffs - 22 3/4.
Mechanical Specifications: Type page 11 3/5 x 21 1/2; E - 6 cols, 1 5/6, 1/6 between; A - 6 cols, 1 5/6, 1/6 between; C - 8 cols, 1 1/3, 1/6 between.
Commodity Consumption: Avg. Page Number Per Issue - Daily 24; Avg. Page Number Per Issue - Plates Used 9000; Avg. Page Number Per Issue - Sunday 50; widths 12 1/2; Newsprint Used - Short Tons 940; Printing Ink Used - Black 39000; Printing Ink Used - Color 4000; Printing Ink Us
Equipment EDITORIAL: Front-end Software – Baseview. CLASSIFIED: Front-end Software – Baseview.; Classified Hardware – APP/Power Mac; Layout Software – Baseview.; Display Printers – APP/Mac, ECR/Konica 2100-EV Jetsetter, ECR/Konica 5100S EV Jetsetter; Cameras – 1-DAI/C-24-D-LA PRESSROOM: Line 1 – 7-G/Community 1973; Folders – 1 MAILROOM: Counter stackers – 1/PPK; Inserters and stuffers – 1-MM/227E; Bundle tying machines – 1-/MLN. BUSINESS COMPUTERS: Business Software – Baseview

HENDERSONVILLE

HENDERSONVILLE NEWSPAPER CO.

106 Henderson Crossing Plaza, Hendersonville, N.C., 28792; gen tel (828) 692-0505; gen fax (828) 692-2319; gen e-mail hillary.tweed@hendersonvillenews.comi; web site www.hendersonvillenews.com
Published: Mon, Tues, Wed, Thur, Fri, Sat, Sun
Weekday Frequency: m
Saturday Frequency: m
Circulation: 13,992; 13,992(sat); 14,643(sun)
News services: Associated Press
Politics: 1881

THE TIMES-NEWS

106 Henderson Crossing Plaza, Hendersonville, N.C., 28792; gen tel (828) 692-0505; gen fax 828-692-2319; ed fax 828-693-5581; web site www.blueridgenow.com
Published: Mon, Tues, Wed, Thur, Fri, Sat, Sun
Weekday Frequency: m
Saturday Frequency: m
Circulation: 12,459; 12,459(sat); 13,439(sun)
Last Audit: ABC September 30, 2011
Delivery method: Mail, Newsstand, Private Carrier, Racks

TIMES-NEWS

1717 Four Seasons Blvd., Hendersonville, N.C., 28792; gen tel (828) 692-0505; gen fax (828) 692-2319; ed fax (828) 693-5581; gen e-mail tnnews@blueridgenow.com; adv e-mail tnads@blueridgenow.com; ed e-mail tnletters@blueridgenow.com; web site www.blueridgenow.com
Published: Mon, Tues, Wed, Thur, Fri, Sat, Sun
Weekday Frequency: m
Saturday Frequency: m
Circulation: 14,207; 14,276(sat); 14,802(sun)
Last Audit: September 30, 2009
Price: 12.60/mo; 143.00/yr.
Advertising: Open inch rate $24.98
News services: AP, NYT.
Politics: Independent-Democrat. **Established:** 1881
Special Editions: Football (Aug); Last Minute Gift Guide (Dec); Almanac (Feb); Medical Directory (Mar); Holiday Gift Guide (Nov); Motorama (Oct).
Special Weekly Sections: Weekend (Fri); Blue Ridge Living (S); Church Directory (Sat); Best Food Day (Wed).
Magazines: Mountain Traditions (Quarterly); Parade (S).
Adv. Mgr. ....Heather Staton
Exec. Ed. ....William Moss
Chief Photographer ....Michael Dirks
Sports Ed. ....Dean Hensley
TN Weekly/Assoc. Magazine Ed. .Elizabeth Moss
Market Information: ADS; TMC.
Mechanical available: Offset; Black and 3 ROP colors; insert accepted - tabs,broadsheets,singlesheets; page cutoffs - 22 3/4.
Mechanical Specifications: Type page 11 5/8 x 21 1/2; E - 6 cols, 1 13/16, 1/8 between; A - 6 cols, 1 13/16, 1/8 between; C - 9 cols, 1 3/16, 1/16 between.
Commodity Consumption: Avg. Page Number Per Issue - Daily 36; Avg. Page Number Per Issue - Plates Used 29500; Avg. Page Number Per Issue - Sunday 60; widths 13 1/2; Newsprint Used - Short Tons 2029; Printing Ink Used - Black 60000; Printing Ink Used - Color 2000; Printing Ink
Equipment; Editorial Hardware – 23-Mac/G4; Editorial Printers – Dataproducts/8500. CLASSIFIED: Front-end Software – Baseview, Quark, Photoshop.; Classified Hardware – 5-Mac/G3; Classified Printers – HP/1600 DISPLAY: Ad make-up applications – Quark; Layout Software – Baseview.; Display Hardware – G3; Production Equipment – 2-Nu. PRESSROOM: Line 1 – 7-G/Urbanite (color deck). MAILROOM: Counter stackers – Id/440; Inserters and stuffers – MM/EM 102; Bundle tying machines – MLN; Wrapping singles – Id/Bottom wrap; Addressing machine – Am.; Business Hardware – IBM/Sys 3600

HICKORY

THE HICKORY DAILY RECORD

1100 Park Pl., Hickory, N.C., 28601; gen tel (828) 322-4510; adv tel (828) 322-4510; ed tel (828) 322-4510; gen fax (828) 322-8439; adv fax (828) 267-0294; ed fax (828) 324-8179; adv e-mail advertising@hickoryrecord.com; web site www.hickoryrecord.com
Group: North Carolina Press Service, Inc.
Published: Mon, Tues, Wed, Thur, Fri, Sat, Sun
Weekday Frequency: m
Saturday Frequency: m
Circulation: 20,096; 20,096(sat); 23,262(sun)
Last Audit: September 30, 2008
Price: 2.50/wk; 130.00/yr.
Advertising: Open inch rate $28.00
News services: AP.
Politics: Independent.
Special Editions: Hickory Hops (Apr); Hickory Heritage (Aug); Christmas (Dec); Health & Fitness (Feb); Visitor Guide (Jun); Taste of Hickory (Mar); Hickory Smoke (May); Christmas (Nov); Cultural Arts (Oct); Active Seniors (Quarterly); Best of Catawba (Sept).
Special Weekly Sections: Buzz (Thur).
Magazines: USA WEEKEND Magazine (S).
Regl. Pub. ....Tim Dearman
Adv. Dir. ....Cathy Fagan
Circ. Dir. ....David Eggers
Ed. ....Eric Millsaps
Mng. Ed. ....Todd A. Callaway
Bus. Ed. ....John Dayberry
City Ed. ....Patrick Jean
Lifestyle Ed ....Josh Yoder
News Ed. ....Michelle L. Bloomfield
Opinion Page Ed. ....Larry Clark
Sports Ed. ....Chris Hobbs
Prodn. Mgr. ....Jim Lillagore
Market Information: ADS; TMC.
Mechanical available: Offset; Black and 3 ROP colors; insert accepted; page cutoffs - 22.
Mechanical Specifications: Type page 13 x 21; E - 6 cols, 2 1/16, 1/8 between; A - 6 cols, 2 1/16, 1/8 between; C - 8 cols, 1 3/4, 1/16 between.
Commodity Consumption: Avg. Page Number Per Issue - Daily 36; Avg. Page Number Per Issue - Sunday 54; widths 27 1/2; Newsprint Used - Short Tons 2315; Printing Ink Used - Black 40070; Printing Ink Used - Color 6330.
Equipment EDITORIAL: Front-end Software – SII/Sys 77XR 5702A Coyote XE.; Editorial Hardware – Tandem/Server, 22-HP; Editorial Printers – Konica CLASSIFIED: Front-end Software – SII/Coyote XA.; Classified Hardware – 5-HP; Layout Software – ALS (version 2.5).; Display Hardware – HP PRODUCTION: Pagination Software – Coyote/Layout.; Production Equipment – 1-Nu, 1-AU/APS-6 PRESSROOM: Line 1 – 7-MAN/Uniman; Pasters – MEG; Reels and Stands – MEG. MAILROOM: Counter stackers – 2/MM; Inserters and stuffers – 2-/MM; Bundle tying machines – 2-/OVL.; Business Hardware – IBM/Sys 36

HIGH POINT

HIGH POINT ENTERPRISE

210 Church Ave., High Point, N.C., 27262; gen tel (336) 888-3500; adv tel (336) 885-3555 (class); ed tel (336) 888-3527; gen fax (336) 888-3642; adv fax (336) 885-7753; ed fax (336) 888-3644; adv e-mail retailadv@hpe.com; ed e-mail news@hpe.com; web site www.hpe.com
Group: North Carolina Press Service, Inc.
Published: Mon, Tues, Wed, Thur, Fri, Sat, Sun
Weekday Frequency: m
Saturday Frequency: m
Circulation: 15,907; 15,907(sat); 19,743(sun)
Last Audit: ABC September 30, 2011
Price: 11.25/4 wks; 131/yr
Advertising: Open inch rate $31.52
News services: AP, MCT, CNS, SHNS, TMS.
Politics: Independent. **Established:** 1883
Special Editions: Health & Healing (Other); Lawn & Garden (Semi-yearly).
Special Weekly Sections: TV (Fri); Business (S); Entertainment (Thur); Food (Wed).
Magazines: USA WEEKEND Magazine (S). American Profile (weekly); Athlon, Spry (1 a month)
Pub ....Jodi Brookshire
Controller ....Nancy Baker
Adv. Dir. ....John McClure
Adv. Mgr., Major Accts. ....Sandy Southards
Circ. Dir. ....Daniel Pittman
City Ed. ....Joe Feeney

Columnist............................Thomas L. Blount
Columnist..................................Jimmy Tomlin
Editorial Page Ed. ....Vince Wheeler
Davidson/Randolph counties ....Chanel Davis
Home Furnishings Ed...................Jimmy Carroll
News Ed...............................Sherrie Dockery
Radio/Television Ed.....................Vicki Knopfler
Business writer.........................Jordan Howse
High Point/Public Safety.......Patrick Kimbrough
Politics/business/general ....Paul Johnson
David Nivens
Market Information: ADS; Split run; TMC.
Mechanical available: Offset G/Metro; Black and 3 ROP colors; insert accepted; page cutoffs - 22.
Mechanical Specifications: Type page 13 x 21; E - 6 cols, 2 1/16, 1/8 between; A - 6 cols, 2 1/16, 1/8 between; C - 9 cols, 1 3/8, 1/16 between.
Commodity Consumption: Avg. Page Number Per Issue - Daily 32; Avg. Page Number Per Issue - Plates Used 30500; Avg. Page Number Per Issue - Sunday 74; widths 50; Newsprint Used - Short Tons 2500; Printing Ink Used - Black 68000; Printing Ink Used - Color 3600; Printing Ink Used
Equipment EDITORIAL: Front-end Software – TERA, TERA, Adobe/Photoshop, QPS/QuarkXPress, Microsoft/Word.; Editorial Hardware – 34-Dell, APP/Mac; Editorial Printers – Xante/8200, MON CLASSIFIED: Front-end Software – SCS.; Classified Hardware – 8-Dell; Classified Printers – CI/1000, CI/5000; Layout Software – SCS/Layout 8000, 6-APP/Mac G3, Multi-Ad/Creator.; Display Hardware – APP/Mac PRODUCTION: Pagination Software – QPS/QuarkXPress, Multi-Ad/Creator.; Production Equipment – 2-MON/NewsExpress, MSI/Spool Express, Adobe/Level 2 RIPs, LaserPlex/4x4; Cameras – 1-C/Marathon; Scanners – 1-Lf/Leafscan 35, 1-Umax/6000, 1-C/Autokon, 1-Polaroid/SprintScan PRESSROOM: Line 1 – 5-G/Metroliner double width; Press Drives – 5; Folders – 1-G/2:1; Pasters – 5 MAILROOM: Counter stackers – 2/TMSI; Inserters and stuffers – 2-MM/227, 2-/10-1, 1-/10:1, 2-/10:1, Electronic Repair Head; Bundle tying machines – 1-MLN/ML2EE, 2-/CCS.

JACKSONVILLE

THE DAILY NEWS

724 Bell Fork Rd., Jacksonville, N.C., 28546-0196; gen tel (910) 353-1171; gen fax (910) 353-7316; gen e-mail cepotter@jdnews.com; ed e-mail editor@jdnews.com; web site www.jdnews.com
Published: Mon, Tues, Wed, Thur, Fri, Sat, Sun
Weekday Frequency: m
Saturday Frequency: m
Circulation: 19,155; 19,155(sat); 19,962(sun)
Last Audit: September 30, 2008
Price: 9.50/mo; 84.00/yr (m, sat), $127.00/yr.
Advertising: Open inch rate $30.45
News services: AP.
Politics: Independent.
Special Editions: Spring Car Care (Apr); Answer Book (Aug); Christmas Color Book (Dec); NASCAR Preview (Feb); Super Bowl (Jan); Celebrate the Fourth (Jul); June Bride (Jun); Spring Gardening (Mar); Graduation (May); Coupon Book (Monthly); Cookbook (Nov); Swansboros Mullet
Special Weekly Sections: Business Page (Mon); Visions (S); Business Spotlights (Tues); Food (Wed).
Magazines: American Profile (Every other week); USA WEEKEND Magazine (S); Max Magazine (Thur).
Adv. Dir.....................................John Hettlzer
Circ. Mgr.....................................Don Wilson
Graphics Ed./Art Dir..................Paul Woodward
News Ed..................................Robert Holland
Photo Ed.......................................Don Bryan
Political/Gov't Ed. ....Elliott Potter
Travel Ed....J.T. Oliver
Prodn. Mgr., Pre Press........................Jeff Ashe
Prodn. Mgr., Pressroom ....George Farrior
Market Information: ADS; Split run; TMC; Zoned editions.
Mechanical available: Offset; Black and 3 ROP colors; insert accepted; page cutoffs - 22 3/4.
Mechanical Specifications: Type page 13 x 21 1/2; E - 6 cols, 2 1/16, 1/8 between; A - 6 cols, 2 1/16, 1/8 between; C - 8 cols, 1 1/2, 1/8 between.
Commodity Consumption: Avg. Page Number Per Issue - Daily 40; Avg. Page Number Per Issue - Plates Used 20000; Avg. Page Number Per Issue - Saturday 40; Avg. Page Number Per Issue - Sunday 64; widths 27 1/2; Newsprint Used - Metric Tons 22009; Printing Ink Used - Black 50000; P
Equipment EDITORIAL: Front-end Software – APT.; Editorial Hardware – PC Network; Editorial Equipment – APP/Mac; Editorial Printers – HP/5000 CLASSIFIED: Front-end Software – APT.; Classified Hardware – PC Network; Classified Printers – HP/5000 DISPLAY: Ad make-up applications – APT; Layout Software – APT.; Display Hardware – PC Network; Display Printers – HP/8000 PRODUCTION: Pagination Software – APT.; Production Equipment – 2-Nu, PrePress/Panther 46; Cameras – Spartan III; Scanners – Polaroid/Sprintscan, APP/ScanJet PRESSROOM: Line 1 – 8-HI/1660 1986; Line 2 – 6-G/Community; Folders – 2 MAILROOM: Counter stackers – HL; Bundle tying machines – 2/MLN. BUSINESS COMPUTERS: Business Software – Great Plains/AR2000; Business Hardware – PC Network

KINSTON

THE FREE PRESS

2103 N. Queen St., Kinston, N.C., 28501; gen tel (252) 527-3191; gen fax (252) 527-1813; ed fax (252) 527-9407; gen e-mail freepressnews@freedomenc.com; web site www.kinston.com
Published: Mon, Tues, Wed, Thur, Fri, Sat, Sun
Weekday Frequency: m
Saturday Frequency: m
Circulation: 11,143; 11,143(sat); 11,874(sun)
Last Audit: September 30, 2008
Price: 8.00/mo; 115.00/yr (carrier).
Advertising: Open inch rate $19.59
News services: AP.
Politics: 1882
Special Weekly Sections: Automotive (Fri); Entertainment (Thur); Home & Garden (Tues); Education (Wed).
Magazines: Homes Magazine (Every other month); USA WEEKEND Magazine (S); American Profile (Weekly).
Adv. Dir...Billy Moore
Circ. Dir......................................Jim Register
Circ. Coord., Newspapers in Educ.....Molly Taylor
Exec. Ed...................................Patrick Holmes
Prodn. Mgr...............................Donna Wallace
Prodn. Mgr., Pressroom ....Doug Shervey
Market Information: ADS; TMC.
Mechanical available: Offset; Black and 3 ROP colors; insert accepted; page cutoffs - 22 4/5.
Mechanical Specifications: Type page 13 x 21 1/2; E - 6 cols, 2 1/16, 1/8 between; A - 6 cols, 2 1/16, 1/8 between; C - 8 cols, 1 15/32, 5/32 between.
Commodity Consumption: Avg. Page Number Per Issue - Daily 26; Avg. Page Number Per Issue - Plates Used 9935; Avg. Page Number Per Issue - Sunday 64; widths 27 1/2; Newsprint Used - Metric Tons 718; Printing Ink Used - Black 14440; Printing Ink Used - Pages Printed 10162.
Equipment EDITORIAL: Front-end Software – QPS/QuarkXPress, Baseview.; Editorial Hardware – APP/Mac; Editorial Equipment – APP/Mac Scanner; Editorial Printers – APP/Mac Accel-a-Writer 8200 CLASSIFIED: Front-end Software – Baseview.; Classified Hardware – APP/Mac; Classified Printers – 2-Okidata/320 DISPLAY: Ad make-up applications – Managing Editor/ALS Page Director, Baseview/Managing Editor; Display Hardware – APP/Mac; Display Printers – APP/Mac LaserWriter II g PRODUCTION: Pagination Software – Baseview, QPS/QuarkXPress/with FSI Extensions.; Production Equipment – 2-Nu, 2-Xante/8200, Pre Press/Panther Pro 36, Pre Press/Panther Plus 46; Cameras – C/Spartan III; Scanners – AG, Kk/2035 plus, Linotype-Hell PRESSROOM: Line 1 – 3-G/Urbanite, 1-G/Urbanite (3 color).; Bundle tying machines – 2/MLN.; Business Hardware – 2-Compaq/Pro Linea 486, Great Plains, Ceridian, Microsoft/Office 97, Intel/Pentium II Fileserver, 4-Generic/Pentium PC, 1-Epson/DFX 8000 Printer, 1-Epson/DFX 5000 Printer, 2-Compaq/386 PC, 1-Compaq/486 DX PC, 1-Generic/486 PC, 1-Genicom Printer

LAURINBURG

THE LAURINBURG EXCHANGE

211 W. Cronly St., Laurinburg, N.C., 28352; gen tel (910) 276-2311; adv tel (910) 276-2311; ed tel (910) 276-2311; gen fax (910) 276-3815; adv fax (910) 276-3815; ed fax (910) 276-3815; web site www.laurinburgexchange.com
Group: North Carolina Press Service, Inc.
Published: Tues, Wed, Thur, Fri, Sat
Weekday Frequency: m
Circulation: 8,200; 8,200(sat)
Last Audit: May 2, 2003
Price: 63.00/yr (mail, town), $65.00/yr (out of town); 15.75/3mo, $30.00/6mo.
Advertising: Open inch rate $9.89
News services: AP.
Politics: 1882
Magazines: American Profile (Weekly).
Pub.....................................Denny Koenders
Circ. Mgr. ....Chris Carberry
Ed....Scott Witten
Sports Ed....................................Zach Colburn
Mechanical Specifications: Type page 13 x 21 1/2; E - 6 cols, 2 1/16, between; A - 6 cols, 2 1/16, between.

LENOIR

NEWS-TOPIC

123 Pennton Ave., Lenoir, N.C., 28645; gen tel (828) 758-7381; adv tel (828) 758-7381; ed tel (828) 758-7381; gen fax (828) 754-0110; adv fax (828) 754-0110; ed fax (828) 754-0110; gen e-mail ntnews@newstopic.net; adv e-mail cb@newstopic.net; ed e-mail ntnews@newstopic.net; web site www.newstopic.net
Published: Tues, Wed, Thur, Fri, Sat, Sun
Weekday Frequency: m
Saturday Frequency: m
Circulation: 7,616; 7,541(sat); 7,789(sun)
Last Audit: Sworn September 30, 2009
Price: 177.00/yr.
Advertising: Open inch rate $23.05
Insert rate: 60/m
News services: AP, SHNS.
Politics: Independent. **Established:** 1875
Own facility?: Y
Special Editions: Sports Tab (Aug); Progress (Feb); Sports Tab (Nov).
Special Weekly Sections: Church News (Sat).
Magazines: TV/Sun
Pub......................................Terese Almquist
Adv. Dir................................Chris Bumgarner
Ed. ....Nathan Key
Prodn. Mgr., Distr.......................Mike Lambert
Market Information: ADS; Split run; TMC; Zoned editions.
Mechanical available: Offset; Black and 3 ROP colors; insert accepted; page cutoffs - 21 1/2.
Mechanical Specifications: Type page 11 5/8 x 21 1/2; E - 6 cols, 1 5/6, 1/8 between; A - 6 cols, 1 5/6, 1/8 between; C - 9 cols, 1 19/100, 13/100 between.
Commodity Consumption: Avg. Page Number Per Issue - Daily 23.3; Avg. Page Number Per Issue - Plates Used 4200; widths 27 1/2; Newsprint Used - Short Tons 947; Printing Ink Used - Black 24000; Printing Ink Used - Color 950; Printing Ink Used - Pages Printed 7265.
Equipment EDITORIAL: Front-end Software – Baseview.; Editorial Hardware – 12-APP/Mac G3; Editorial Equipment – 1-Microtek/Scanner; Editorial Printers – Laser Master/Unity 1200, Xante CLASSIFIED: Front-end Software – Baseview.; Classified Hardware – 4-APP/Mac G3; Classified Equipment – APP/Laser Printer; Classified Printers – Okidata/3410 DISPLAY: Ad make-up applications – Baseview; Display Hardware – APP/Mac PRODUCTION: Pagination Software – QPS/QuarkXPress 4.0.; Production Equipment – PRO, Konica; Cameras – 1-C; Scanners – Microtek, Kk, Microtek PRESSROOM: Line 1 – 9-G/SSC Community 1997; Folders – 1 MAILROOM: Counter stackers – Mid America/Exact Stack; Inserters and stuffers – KAN/480 5:1; Bundle tying machines – 1/MLN; Other equipment –Si, Dynaric/Strapping Machine.; Audio Hardware – Brite Voice Systems BUSINESS COMPUTERS: Business Software – Great Plains, Citrix; Business Hardware – DPT/1800, APP/Mac

LEXINGTON

THE DISPATCH

30 E. First Ave., Lexington, N.C., 27292; gen tel (336) 249-3981; adv tel (336) 249-1637; ed tel (336) 249-3981; gen fax (336) 249-0712; adv fax (336) 249-2944; ed fax (336) 249-0712; gen e-mail news@the-dispatch.com; adv e-mail advertising@the-dispatch.com; ed e-mail news@the-dispatch.com; web site www.the-dispatch.com
Published: Tues, Wed, Thur, Fri, Sat
Weekday Frequency: m
Saturday Frequency: m
Circulation: 7,531; 7,531(sat)
Last Audit: ABC September 30, 2011
Price: 8.00/mo; 120.00/yr.
Advertising: Open inch rate $23.00
News services: AP, NYT.
Politics: Independent. **Established:** 1882
Own facility?: Y
Magazines: USA WEEKEND Magazine (Sat).
Assistant Controller of Western Carolinas
Stephanie Sprayberry
Adv. Mgr..................................Tammie Wright
Exec. Ed....................................Chad Killebrew
Bus. Ed...Vikki Hodges
Page Designer..........................Michelle Moore
Chief Photographer..................Donnie Roberts
Sports Ed. ....Mike Duprez
IT Mgr. ....Lindsay Hedrick
Publisher ....Steve Skaggs
Market Information: Split run; TMC; Zoned editions.
Mechanical available: Offset; Black and 3 ROP colors; insert accepted - coupon book, packages soap, etc..
Mechanical Specifications: Type page 13 x 21 1/2; E - 6 cols, 1 7/8, 1/8 between; A - 6 cols, 1 7/8, 1/8 between; C - 9 cols, 1 3/16, 1/16 between.
Commodity Consumption: Avg. Page Number Per Issue - Daily 26; Avg. Page Number Per Issue - Plates Used 19497; widths 25; Newsprint Used - Metric Tons 827; Printing Ink Used - Black 11921; Printing Ink Used - Color 3594; Printing Ink Used - Pages Printed 8026.
Equipment; Editorial Hardware – AT.; Classified Hardware – AT.; Production Equipment – V. PRESSROOM: Line 1 – G/Urbanite 1995; Folders – 1-HI.; Inserters and stuffers – KAN; Bundle tying machines – .
Delivery method: Mail, Newsstand, Private Carrier, Racks

LUMBERTON

THE ROBESONIAN

2175 Roberts Ave., Lumberton, N.C., 28359; gen tel (910) 739-4322; gen fax (910) 739-6553; gen e-mail robesonian@carolina.net; web site www.robesonian.com
Published: Mon, Tues, Wed, Thur, Fri, Sat, Sun
Saturday Frequency: m

Circulation: 12,562; 12,562(sat); 15,108(sun)
Last Audit: September 30, 2006
Price: 9.50/mo; 114.00/yr.
Advertising: Open inch rate $22.94
News services: AP, CN, CNS, NYT, SHNS, LAT-WP.
Politics: Independent.
Special Editions: Tobacco Market (Other).
Special Weekly Sections: Religious Page (Fri); Mini Page (S); Entertainment (Thur); Food Page (Wed).
Magazines: Parade (S).
Pub. ....M. Joseph Craig
Bus. Mgr. ....Adam Saunders
Adv. Dir....Trip Hatley
Circ. Dir...Ed Knight
Bus. Ed....Scott Witten
Editorial Page Ed.....................Donnie Douglas
Educ. Ed...........................Knight Chamberlain
Lifestyle Ed...........................Michael Jaenicke
Online Ed.....................................T.C. Hunter
Photo Dept. Mgr........................Steve Humbert
Mgmt. Info Servs. Mgr...............Cristal Graham
Prodn. Mgr., Pressroom................Mike Skipper
Prodn. Mgr., Mailroom.................Julian Tatum
Market Information: Split run; TMC.
Mechanical available: Offset; Black and 3 ROP colors; insert accepted; page cutoffs - 21 1/2.
Mechanical Specifications: Type page 11 9/16 x 21 1/2; E - 6 cols, 1 7/8, 1/8 between; A - 6 cols, 1 7/8, 1/8 between; C - 9 cols, 1 3/16, 1/16 between.
Commodity Consumption: Avg. Page Number Per Issue - Daily 20; Avg. Page Number Per Issue - Plates Used 3800; Avg. Page Number Per Issue - Sunday 30; widths 12 1/2; Newsprint Used - Short Tons 845; Printing Ink Used - Black 19100; Printing Ink Used - Color 3100; Printing Ink Us
Equipment EDITORIAL: Front-end Software – QPS/QuarkXPress, Baseview/Qtools, Baseview/NewsEdit.; Editorial Hardware – 4-APP/Mac Centris 650, APP/Mac LC III; Editorial Printers – 1-APP/Mac LaserPrinter IIg CLASSIFIED: Front-end Software – Baseview/Class Manager Plus.; Classified Hardware – APP/Mac, APP/Mac II, 3-APP/Mac LC III; Classified Printers – 1-Okidata/320 Billing Printer DISPLAY: Ad make-up applications – QPS/QuarkXPress, Caere/OmniPage, Baseview/NewsEdit; Layout Software – 3-Mk/Ad Setter.; Display Hardware – 3-APP/Mac Centris 650; Display Printers – 2-APP/Mac LaserWriter 11 x 17; Production Equipment – APP/Mac; Cameras – AG; Scanners – CD-Rom/Scanner, APP/Mac. PRESSROOM: Line 1 – 9-HI/V-15; Folders – 2-HI/2:1.; Bundle tying machines – 1-Sa/1 Strapping Machine.; Business Hardware – Software ☐ Vision Data

MARION

THE MCDOWELL NEWS

136 Logan St., Marion, N.C., 28752; gen tel (828) 652-3313; gen fax (828) 652-4769; gen e-mail news@mcdowellnews.com; adv e-mail ads@mcdowellnews.com; web site www.mcdowellnews.com
Published: Mon, Tues, Wed, Thur, Fri
Weekday Frequency: m
Circulation: 5,094
Last Audit: September 30, 2008
Price: 81.90/yr (delivery), $117.00 (mail).
Advertising: Open inch rate $10.87
News services: AP.
Special Weekly Sections: Entertainment-Weekend (Fri); Business Page (Tues); Foothills Life (Wed).
Magazines: American Profile (Weekly); USA WEEKEND Magazine (Weekly).
Pub..................................Lamar Smitherman
Adv. Dir...Keith Austin
Circ. Dir. ....Joey Smith
Ed...Scott Hollifield
Market Information: TMC.
Mechanical available: Offset; Black and 4 ROP colors; insert accepted; page cutoffs - 23.
Commodity Consumption: Avg. Page Number Per Issue - Daily 22; widths 27 1/2; Printing Ink Used - Pages Printed 7250.
Equipment; Editorial Hardware – COM.; Classified Hardware – COM.

MONROE

THE ENQUIRER-JOURNAL

500 W. Jefferson St., Monroe, N.C., 28111-5040; gen tel (704) 289-1541; adv tel (704) 261-2251; ed tel (704) 261-2252; gen fax (704) 289-2929; adv fax (704) 289-2929; ed fax (704) 289-2929; gen e-mail news@theej.com; web site www.enquirerjournal.com
Published: Tues, Wed, Thur, Fri, Sat, Sun
Weekday Frequency: m
Circulation: 6,668; 6,668(sat); 7,239(sun)
Last Audit: September 30, 2009
Price: 3.10/wk; 12.92/mo; 138.00/yr.
Advertising: Open inch rate $31.15
News services: AP.
Politics: Independent.
Special Editions: American Home Week (Apr); Home Improvement (Fall); Bridal (Feb); Year in Review (Jan); FYI (Jul); Salute to Fathers (Jun); Progress (Mar); Graduation Day (May); Gift Guide (Nov); Medical Directory (Oct); Home Improvement (Spring).
Special Weekly Sections: Business (S); Auto Showcase (Sat); Entertainment (Thur); Food (Wed).
Magazines: USA WEEKEND Magazine (S).
Pub........................................Marvin Enderle
Adv. Dir.......................................Janet Littler
Nat'l Adv. Sales..........................Elaine Bolick
Circ. Dir..................................Gray Grunwald
Mng. Ed...................................Stan Hojnacki
City Ed..................................Betsy O'Donovan
Sports Ed.....................................Jerry Snow
Composing Supvr........................Kenn Bowers
Prodn. Mgr., Pressroom..............David Benton
Market Information: ADS; Split run; TMC.
Mechanical available: Offset; Black and 3 ROP colors; insert accepted; page cutoffs - 22 3/4.
Mechanical Specifications: Type page 10 1/8 x 21; E - 6 cols, 1 29/50, 1/6 between; A - 6 cols, 1 29/50, 1/6 between; C - 8 cols, 23/50, 1/6 between.
Commodity Consumption: Avg. Page Number Per Issue - Daily 19.5; Avg. Page Number Per Issue - Plates Used 14400; Avg. Page Number Per Issue - Sunday 39; widths 25; Newsprint Used - Short Tons 1080; Printing Ink Used - Black 36000; Printing Ink Used - Color 10000; Printing Ink U
Equipment EDITORIAL: Front-end Software – Baseview/NewsEdit Pro 2.2.2, QPS/QuarkXPress 3.32.; Editorial Hardware – APP/Mac; Editorial Printers – ECR CLASSIFIED: Front-end Software – Baseview/Ad Manager Pro 1.0.4c.; Classified Hardware – APP/Mac; Classified Printers – ECR DISPLAY: Ad make-up applications – Multi-Ad/Creator 4.0, Adobe/Photoshop 4.0, Adobe/Acrobat 3.0.; Display Hardware – APP/Mac; Display Printers – ECR PRODUCTION: Pagination Software – QPS/QuarkXPress 3.32.; Production Equipment – ECR, LE/LD-220-QT; Cameras – DAI/Page Camera, DAI/Vertical Camera PRESSROOM: Line 1 – 9-G/Community 1977. MAILROOM: Counter stackers – AM Graphics; Inserters and stuffers – KAN; Bundle tying machines – MLN.; Business Hardware – APP/Mac

MORGANTON

THE NEWS HERALD

301 Collett St., Morganton, N.C., 28680-0280; gen tel (828) 437-2161; adv tel (828) 437-2161; ed tel (828) 437-2161; gen fax (828) 437-5372; adv fax (828) 437-5372; ed fax (828) 437-5372; gen e-mail news@morganton.com; web site www.morganton.com
Published: Mon, Tues, Wed, Thur, Fri, Sun
Weekday Frequency: e
Circulation: 9,528; 10,401(sun)
Last Audit: September 30, 2008
Price: 1.90/wk; 7.80/mo; 124.80/yr.
Advertising: Open inch rate $19.00
News services: AP.
Politics: Independent.
Special Editions: Home & Garden (Apr); Football (Aug); Last Minute Gift Ideas (Dec); Valentine's Gift Ideas (Feb); % Off Sale (Jan); % Off Sale (Jul); Father's Day Gift Guide (Jun); Review & Forecast (Mar); Mother's Day Gift Guide (May); Christmas Around Burke (Nov); Hallo
Special Weekly Sections: Church News (Fri); Business News (S); Food Day (Wed).
Magazines: TV Herald (Fri); USA WEEKEND Magazine (S); American Profile (Weekly).
Pub..................................Lamar Smitherman
Bus. Mgr...........................Rhonda Hirgenrider
Adv. Mgr. ....Keeley Duckworth
Mng. Ed....................................Steve Welker
Mgr., Pre Press..........................Ashley Martin
Market Information: ADS; TMC.
Mechanical available: Offset; Black and 3 ROP colors; insert accepted - all; page cutoffs - 22 3/4.
Mechanical Specifications: Type page 13 1/4 x 21 1/2; E - 6 cols, 2, 1/8 between; A - 6 cols, 2, 1/8 between; C - 10 cols, 1 3/16, 1/16 between.
Commodity Consumption: Avg. Page Number Per Issue - Daily 19; Avg. Page Number Per Issue - Plates Used 4200; Avg. Page Number Per Issue - Sunday 36; widths 27 1/2; Newsprint Used - Short Tons 650; Printing Ink Used - Black 15800; Printing Ink Used - Color 1000; Printing Ink Us
Equipment EDITORIAL: Front-end Software – Baseview.; Editorial Hardware – APP/Mac; Editorial Printers – ECR CLASSIFIED: Front-end Software – Baseview.; Classified Hardware – 3-APP/Mac DISPLAY: Ad make-up applications – QPS/QuarkXPress; Layout Software – APP/Mac G3.; Display Hardware – APP/Mac; Display Printers – 2-APP/Mac LaserPrinter; Production Equipment – 1-3M, Adobe/Photoshop; Cameras – 1-Nu; Scanners – APP/Mac. PRESSROOM: Line 1 – 9-G 1994; Folders – 1; Bundle tying machines – 1/Dynaric; Addressing machine – 1-X/730.; Business Hardware – 3-HP/Vision Data

MOUNT AIRY

MOUNT AIRY NEWS

319 N. Renfro St., Mount Airy, N.C., 27030; gen tel (336) 786-4141; adv tel (336) 786-4141; ed tel (336) 786-4141; gen fax (336) 789-2816; gen e-mail mtairynews@advi.net; web site www.mtairynews.com
Group: North Carolina Press Service, Inc.
Published: Mon, Tues, Wed, Thur, Fri, Sun
Weekday Frequency: m
Circulation: 11,017; 11,221(sun)
Last Audit: September 30, 2006
Price: 9.50/mo; 112.50/yr.
Advertising: Open inch rate $12.00
News services: AP.
Politics: Independent. **Established:** 1880
Not Published: Christmas (unless it falls on a Sunday).
Special Editions: Simple Pleasures (Apr); Simple Pleasures (Aug); Simple Pleasures (Jul); Simple Pleasures (Jun); Progress (Mar); Simple Pleasures (May); Foothill Farmer (Monthly); Simple Pleasures (Oct); Simple Pleasures (Sept).
Special Weekly Sections: Entertainment (Fri); Best Food Day (Wed).
Magazines: USA WEEKEND Magazine (S); American Profile (Weekly).
Pub.......................................Gary Lawrence
Adv. Mgr.......................................Nikki Hawks
Circ. Mgr. ....Martha Eaton
Circ. Mgr...................................Donna Krause
Bus. Mgr. ....Ferris Simpson
Ed....John Peters
Sports Ed. ....Thomas Smith
Prodn. Mgr................................Daryl Mumford
Market Information: ADS; TMC; Zoned editions.
Mechanical available: Offset; Black and 3 ROP colors; insert accepted; page cutoffs - 21 1/2.
Mechanical Specifications: Type page 11 1/2 x 21 1/2; E - 6 cols, 1 3/4, 3/16 between; A - 6 cols, 1 3/4, 3/16 between; C - 10 cols, 1 1/8, 1/16 between.
Commodity Consumption: Avg. Page Number Per Issue - Daily 24; Avg. Page Number Per Issue - Plates Used 6000; Avg. Page Number Per Issue - Sunday 38; widths 25; Newsprint Used - Short Tons 510; Printing Ink Used - Pages Printed 6000.
Equipment; Editorial Hardware – 7-APP/Mac 7200-120, 6-APP/Mac 7200-90, 4-APP/iMac, 3-APP/Mac G3, 3-APP/Mac 7200-120, APP/Mac 8500-120, 1-APP/Mac G4; Editorial Equipment – APP/Mac LC, Lf/AP Leaf Picture Desk, APP/Mac 8500-120, Polaroid/SprintScan, AG/Scanner, San/Disk, LF/AP Leaf Pictur CLASSIFIED: Front-end Software – Baseview.; Classified Hardware – 2-APP/Mac, 2-APP/Mac G3; Classified Printers – Okidata DISPLAY: Ad make-up applications – Multi-Ad/Creator, Mk/Touchwriter Plus, Mk/Ad Touch, Baseview; Layout Software – APP/Mac, Multi-Ad/Creator, QPS/QuarkXPress, APP/Mac; Display Hardware – APP/Mac, 5-APP/Mac 7200-120; Display Printers – APP/Mac LaserWriter IIg, HP/LaserJet 4mv PRODUCTION: Pagination Software – QPS/QuarkXPress, Multi-Ad/Creator.; Production Equipment – APP/Mac LaserWriter Plus, APP/Mac LaserWriter IIg, 2-APP/Mac G3, 2-APP/Mac 7200-120, 1-APP/Mac G4; Cameras – SCREEN/C-260-D; Scanners – Polaroid/SprintScan, AG/Argus II PRESSROOM: Line 1 – 6-G/Community 1975.; Inserters and stuffers – MM/267 9722; Bundle tying machines – 2-MLN/Spirit; Wrapping singles – KR/Quarterfolder 324; Addressing machine – KR.; Audio Hardware – EduCom Services Inc BUSINESS COMPUTERS: Business Software – Business/Software; Business Hardware – PC (IBM compatible)

NEW BERN

THE SUN JOURNAL

3200 Wellons Blvd., New Bern, N.C., 28562; gen tel (252) 638-8101; adv tel (252) 638-8101; ed tel (252) 638-8101; gen fax (252) 638-4664; adv fax (252) 638-4664; ed fax (252) 638-4580; gen e-mail sjwebmail@freedomenc.com; adv e-mail nbsjads@freedomenc.com; ed e-mail rfoster@freedomenc.com; web site www.newbernsj.com
Group: Freedom Communications Inc.
Published: Mon, Tues, Wed, Thur, Fri, Sat, Sun
Weekday Frequency: m
Saturday Frequency: m
Circulation: 14,202; 14,202(sat); 15,419(sun)
Last Audit: September 30, 2008
Price: 131.00/yr; 29.25/3mo, $58.50/6mo.
Advertising: Open inch rate $22.60
News services: AP, NEA.
Politics: Independent.
Special Editions: Back-to-School (Aug); Brides (Feb); Shriners (Jan); Hurricane Awareness (Jul); Home and Garden (Mar); Christmas Catalog (Nov); Fall Home Improvement (Sept).
Special Weekly Sections: TV View (S); Church News (Sat); Farm Page (Thur); Food (Wed).
Magazines: Real Estate (Monthly); Healthy Living (Quarterly); USA WEEKEND Magazine (S); American Profile (Weekly).
Pub........................................Vernon DeBolt
Vice Pres., Mktg...........................Judy Avery
Circ. Dir................................Sheila Meadows
Mng. Ed.....................................Randy Foster
Sports Ed. ....Jess Huffman
Ad director...............................Scott Embry
Market Information: Split run; TMC; Zoned editions.
Mechanical available: Offset; Black and 3 ROP colors; insert accepted - single sheet; page cutoffs - .
Mechanical Specifications: Type page 13 x 21 1/2; E - 6 cols, 2 1/16, 1/8 between; A - 6 cols, 2 1/16, 1/8 between; C - 8 cols, 1 1/2, 1/8 between.

Commodity Consumption: Avg. Page Number Per Issue - Daily 24; Avg. Page Number Per Issue - Plates Used 12500; Avg. Page Number Per Issue - Sunday 46; widths 27 1/2; Newsprint Used - Metric Tons 1350; Newsprint Used - Short Tons 1498; Printing Ink Used - Black 31000; Printing I
Equipment; Folders – 1; Inserters and stuffers – GMA; Bundle tying machines – Dynaric. BUSINESS COMPUTERS: Business Software – Vision Data, Southware; Business Hardware – PC
Delivery method: Mail, Newsstand, Private Carrier, Racks

NEWTON

THE OBSERVER-NEWS-ENTERPRISE

309 N. College Ave., Newton, N.C., 28658; gen tel (828) 464-0221; gen fax (828) 464-1267; gen e-mail onepublisher@charter.net; adv e-mail oneads@charter.net; ed e-mail onenews@charter.net; web site www.observernewsonline.com
Published: Tues, Wed, Thur, Fri, Sat
Weekday Frequency: m
Circulation: 2,303; 2,303(sat)
Price: 48.00/yr.
Advertising: Open inch rate $9.80
News services: AP.
Politics: Independent. **Established:** 1829
Not Published: Christmas.
Special Editions: Friday Magazine (Monthly).
Special Weekly Sections: Religion (Fri); Business (Thur); Mini Pages (Tues); Food (Wed).
Magazines: American Profile (Fri).
Pub. ....Michael Willard
Bus. Mgr. ....Cindy Williams
Mng. Ed. ....Chris Gilfellan
Circ. Dir. ....Cindy Tamez
Outlook Ed. ....LaDonna Beeker
Sports Ed. ....Adams Houston
Prodn. Mgr. ....Philip Rogers
Prodn. Foreman, Pressroom ....Richard Patton
Market Information: TMC.
Mechanical available: Offset; Black and 3 ROP colors; insert accepted; page cutoffs - 21 1/4.
Mechanical Specifications: Type page 13 x 21; E - 6 cols, 2 1/16, 1/8 between; A - 6 cols, 2 1/16, 1/8 between; C - 10 cols, 1 3/16, 3/32 between.
Commodity Consumption: Avg. Page Number Per Issue - Daily 14; Avg. Page Number Per Issue - Plates Used 5704; widths 28; Newsprint Used - Short Tons 406.29; Printing Ink Used - Black 7685; Printing Ink Used - Color 1458; Printing Ink Used - Pages Printed 6258.
Equipment; Editorial Hardware – COM; Editorial Printers – COM.; Classified Hardware – COM.; Layout Software – COM.; Display Printers – APP/Mac LaserPrinter; Production Equipment – COM; Cameras – LE. PRESSROOM: Line 1 – 7-KP/Offset web 1976; Line 2 – 1-Stubbs/Stacker; Press control system – TF&E/Press Room Devices.; Addressing machine – Am.; Business Hardware – L/9000

RALEIGH

THE NEWS & OBSERVER

215 S. McDowell St., Raleigh, N.C., 27601-1331; gen tel (919) 829-4500; adv tel (919) 829-4600; ed tel (919) 829-4517; gen fax (919) 829-4872; adv fax (919) 829-4824; ed fax (919) 829-4529; gen e-mail breakingnews@newsobserver.com; adv e-mail displayadv@nando.com; placeads@newsobserver.com; ed e-mail forum@newsobserver.com; web site www.newsobserver.com
Published: Mon, Tues, Wed, Thur, Fri, Sat, Sun
Weekday Frequency: m
Saturday Frequency: m
Circulation: 127,138; 134,402(sat); 191,923(sun)
Last Audit: ABC September 30, 2011
Price: 2.77/wk (carrier); 12.00/mo (carrier); 165.00/yr (carrier).
Advertising: Open inch rate $248.96
News services: AP, Bloomberg, CT, MCT, LAT-WP, NYT.
Politics: Independent-Democrat. **Established:** 1894
Special Editions: Business Expo (Apr); Fall Style (Aug); What's Up/1st Night (Dec); Taxes Work & Money (Feb); Economic Outlook (Jan); The N&O 100 (State's Public Companies) (Jun); Spring Style (Mar); Nurses Association (May); Expanded What's Up for the Holidays (Nov); Scho
Special Weekly Sections: What's Up (Fri); Mini Page (Mon); Channels (S); Real Estate (Sat); Auto (Thur); Food (Wed).
Magazines: Parade (S).
Pres./Pub. ....Orage Quarles
Vice Pres., HR ....Jackie Stark
Controller ....Keith Raffone
Employee Rel. Mgr. ....Sharon Vignali
Vice Pres., Classified Adv. .....Durwood Canaday
Vice Pres., Display Adv. ....Jim McClure
Adv. Mgr., Direct Mktg. ....Doug Rogers
Local Adv. Mgr. ....Sandy Fain
Adv. Prodn. Mgr. ....Matt Long
Adv. Mgr., Grp. Adv. ....Cathy Wallace
Adv. Mgr., Regl. ....Mack McCormick
Dir., Mktg./Research ....Bob Oney
Vice Pres., Circ. ....James Puryear
Circ. Mgr., Distr. ....Joedie Spence
Circ. Mgr., Sales/Mktg. ....Wendy Reeves
Circ. Mgr., State ....Worth Narron
Sr. Vice Pres./Exec. Ed. ....Melanie Sill
Mng. Ed. ....John Drescher
Deputy Mng. Ed. ....Dan Barkin
Deputy Mng. Ed. ....Steve Riley
Market Information: ADS; Split run; TMC; Zoned editions.
Mechanical available: Flexo (direct); Black and 3 ROP colors; insert accepted; page cutoffs - 22.
Mechanical Specifications: Type page 11 1/2 x 21; E - 6 cols, 1 13/16, 1/8 between; A - 6 cols, 1 13/16, 1/8 between; C - 10 cols, 1 1/12, 1/8 between.
Commodity Consumption: Avg. Page Number Per Issue - Daily 83; Avg. Page Number Per Issue - Plates Used 314895; Avg. Page Number Per Issue - Saturday 159; Avg. Page Number Per Issue - Sunday 140; widths 24; Newsprint Used - Metric Tons 31712; Printing Ink Used - Black 599106; P
Equipment EDITORIAL: Front-end Software – Quark/Copy Desk, QPS, QuickWire.; Editorial Hardware – 1-Sun/Enterprise 5000, 1-APP/Mac GPSserver G3, 240-APP/Power Mac, 2-Quickwire/Servers; Editorial Printers – Laser, HP/DesignJet 1050C CLASSIFIED: Front-end Software – SII, 110-SII/Coyote 3, Morcor/Xpance.; Classified Hardware – Tandem/Sys 77-ServerNet, 30-APP/Power Mac, 110-Intel/PCs; Classified Equipment – 1-Sun/Enterprise 5000; Classified Printers – HP/DesignJet 1050C, 3-HP/Dot Matrix DISPLAY: Ad make-up applications – Geac/AIM 7.0; Display Hardware – 1-HP/3000/979; Display Printers – 1-HP/LaserWriter Pro RB 121 30-N, 1-HP/LaserJet, 4-HP/LaserJet 4, 3-HP/LaserJet 4L, 1-HP/Resolution Enhance, 2-LaserWriter 1600, 2-HP/2000C, X/Phaser 1235, HP/DesignJet 1050C, 2-Docuprint N2025 PRODUCTION: Pagination Software – QPS, QPS/QuarkXPress.; Production Equipment – 3-Na/Flex, 2-HP, 2-Sun/5000S OPI, MON/RIPs, 7-Sun/Ultra 167 RIP, Alphaquest/Print Express PRESSROOM: Line 1 – 9-KBA/MOT double width (CIC Fullcolor) 1995; Line 2 – 9-KBA/MOT double width (CIC Fullcolor) 1995; Press Drives – 18; Folders – 3-KBA/MOT 3:2 160 page capacity; Pasters – 18-G/with AGS upgrader 1994; Press registration system – 4 MAILROOM: Counter stackers – 5-HL/Monitor, 4-HL/Dual Carriers, 2-QWI/400, 4-QWI/401; Inserters and stuffers – 3-HI/1472 online; Bundle tying machines – 1-GMA/SLS-3000, 3-Newstyer/2000, 1/Power Strap/PSN 4, 6-Dynaric/NP3, 3-GMA/Combistacks; Addressing machine – 1-C; Audio Hardware – Computalk BUSINESS COMPUTERS: Business Software – Microsoft/Office, GEAC/Financial & Circulation; Business Hardware – 1-HP/3000-979

REIDSVILLE

THE EDEN DAILY NEWS

PO Box 2157, Reidsville, N.C., 27323-2157; gen tel (336) 623-2155; ed tel (336) 349-4331; gen fax (336) 342-2513; gen e-mail news@reidsvillereview.com; web site www.godanriver.com
Group: North Carolina Press Service, Inc.
Published: Tues, Wed, Thur, Fri, Sun
Weekday Frequency: m
Circulation: 3,961; 3,961(sun)
Last Audit: March 31, 2007
Price: 75.00/yr.
Advertising: Open inch rate $9.88
News services: AP, Universal Press Syndicate, NEA.
Politics: Independent.
Advertising not accepted: 900 numbers.
Magazines: USA WEEKEND Magazine (S).
Pub. ....Steve Kaylor
Office Mgr. ....Dreama Armstrong
Retail Adv. Dir. ....Pam Durham
Circ. Mgr. ....T.J. Martin
Grp. Ed. ....Paul Long
Ed. ....Angela Evans
Market Information: TMC.
Mechanical available: Offset; Black and 3 ROP colors; insert accepted; page cutoffs - 22 3/4.
Mechanical Specifications: Type page 13 x 21 1/2; E - 6 cols, 2 1/16, 1/8 between; A - 6 cols, 2 1/16, 1/8 between; C - 9 cols, 1 1/3, 1/8 between.
Commodity Consumption: widths 27 1/2.
Equipment; Editorial Hardware – APP/Mac, 10-Mk; Editorial Equipment – Printers ☐ APP/Mac, HP/5000, APP/Mac LaserPrinter NT; Editorial Printers – Software ☐ QPS 3.3, Baseview/NewsEdit. CLASSIFIED: Front-end Software – Baseview.; Classified Hardware – 10-Mk, APP/Mac; Classified Printers – HP/5000 PRODUCTION: Pagination Software – QPS 3.3.; Production Equipment – P BUSINESS COMPUTERS: Business Software – Vision Data; Business Hardware – IBM

THE REIDSVILLE REVIEW

1921 Vance St., Reidsville, N.C., 27320-3254; gen tel (336) 349-4331; adv tel (336) 349-4331; ed tel (336) 349-4331; gen fax (336) 342-2513; adv fax (336) 342-2513; ed fax (336) 342-2513; gen e-mail news@reidsvillereview.com; web site www2.godanriver.com
Group: North Carolina Press Service, Inc.
Published: Tues, Wed, Thur, Fri, Sun
Weekday Frequency: m
Circulation: 5,195; 5,195(sun)
Last Audit: October 1, 2003
Price: 6.67/mo; 75.00/yr.
Advertising: Open inch rate $9.60
News services: AP.
Politics: Independent.
Not Published: Christmas.
Special Editions: Home Improvement (Apr); High School Football Tab (Aug); NASCAR Tab (Feb); Black History Tab (Jan); Progress (Mar); Summer Travel Guide (May); Hometown Christmas (Nov); Antique Valley Festival (Oct); Home Improvement (Sept).
Magazines: USA WEEKEND Magazine (S).
Pub. ....Steven K. Kaylor
Office Mgr. ....Dreama Armstrong
Sports Ed. ....Steve Cannuli
Market Information: TMC.
Mechanical available: Offset; Black and 3 ROP colors; insert accepted - up to 24 pages 8 1/2 x 11; page cutoffs - 21 1/2.
Mechanical Specifications: Type page 13 x 21 1/2; E - 6 cols, 2 1/16, 1/8 between; A - 6 cols, 2 1/16, 1/8 between; C - 9 cols, 1 5/16, 1/8 between.
Commodity Consumption: Avg. Page Number Per Issue - Daily 16; Avg. Page Number Per Issue - Plates Used 2017; Avg. Page Number Per Issue - Sunday 16; widths 27 1/2; Newsprint Used - Short Tons 280; Printing Ink Used - Black 9800; Printing Ink Used - Color 500; Printing Ink Used
Equipment EDITORIAL: Front-end Software – QPS/QuarkXPress, Baseview/NewsEdit.; Editorial Hardware – APP/Mac SE, APP/Mac IIcx; Editorial Equipment – APP/Mac Scanner; Editorial Printers – APP/Mac LaserWriter II CLASSIFIED: Front-end Software – Baseview/Class Manager.; Classified Hardware – APP/Mac SE; Classified Printers – APP/Mac LaserWriter II DISPLAY: Ad make-up applications – Multi-Ad/Creator; Layout Software – APP/Mac IIcx.; Display Hardware – APP/Mac IIcx; Display Printers – APP/Mac LaserWriter II; Production Equipment – APP/Mac IIcx; Cameras – C/Marathon; Scanners – APP/Mac. PRESSROOM: Line 1 – G/Community 1971; Line 2 – G/Community 1971; Line 3 – G/Community 1971; Line 4 – G/Community 1971; Line 5 – G/Community 1986; Line 6 – G/Community 1986. BUSINESS COMPUTERS: Business Software – IBM/Newzware; Business Hardware – IBM/Newzware, Smith Corona/PC 386SX HD

ROANOKE RAPIDS

DAILY HERALD

916 Roanoke Ave., Roanoke Rapids, N.C., 27870; gen tel (252) 537-2505; adv tel (252) 537-2505; ed tel (252) 537-2505; gen fax (252) 537-2314; adv fax (252) 537-2314; ed fax (252) 537-2384; gen e-mail lindasmith@rrdailyherald.com; web site www.rrdailyherald.com
Group: U.S. Suburban Press, Inc.
Published: Tues, Wed, Thur, Fri, Sun
Weekday Frequency: e
Circulation: 8,426; 9,095(sun)
Last Audit: Sworn December 31, 2010
Price: 2.10/wk; 9.10/mo; 119.60/yr; 8.40/4wk.
Advertising: Open inch rate $16.78
News services: AP.
Politics: Independent.
Not Published: New Year; Memorial Day; Independence Day; Labor Day; Thanksgiving; Christmas.
Special Editions: Football Kick-off Tab (Aug); Christmas Greetings (Dec); Bride & Groom (Feb); Honor Roll of Business (Jan); July 4th Sales (Jul); Home & Garden (Mar); Progress Tab (May); Christmas Gift Guide (Nov); Businesswomen's Week (Oct); Fall Opening (Sept).
Magazines: USA WEEKEND Magazine (S).
Office Mgr. ....Linda Smith
Adv. Mgr., Classified ....Linda Foster
Lifestyles Ed. ....Tia Bedwell
News Ed. ....John Moeur
Reporter ....Lance Martin
Prodn. Mgr., Distr. ....Carol Moseley
Prodn. Mgr., Mailroom ....Louise Harvey
Prodn. Mgr., Pre Press ....David Hager
Market Information: Split run; TMC.
Mechanical available: Offset; Black and 3 ROP colors; insert accepted - single sheets; page cutoffs - 22 3/4.
Mechanical Specifications: Type page 13 x 21 1/2; E - 6 cols, 2 1/16, 1/8 between; A - 6 cols, 2 1/16, 1/8 between; C - 9 cols, 1 5/16, 1/8 between.
Commodity Consumption: Avg. Page Number Per Issue - Daily 16; Avg. Page Number Per Issue - Plates Used 7000; Avg. Page Number Per Issue - Sunday 38; widths 13 3/4; Newsprint Used - Metric Tons 549; Printing Ink Used - Black 11500; Printing Ink Used - Color 700; Printing Ink Us
Equipment; Editorial Hardware – Mk/3000; Editorial Equipment – Nikon/Coolscan; Editorial Printers – 1-Xante/8200, 1-APP/Mac G3. CLASSIFIED: Front-end Software – Baseview 3.16.; Classified Hardware – APP/Mac G3 DISPLAY: Ad make-up applications – Multi-Ad/Creator 3.8; Layout Software – APP/Mac.; Display Hardware – 4-APP/Mac G3; Display Printers – 1-Xante/8200, 1-APP/Mac G3 PRODUCTION: Pagination Software – Baseview 3.16.; Production Equipment – Nat; Cameras – 1-B, Acti/Prod Camera; Scanners – Konica/Scanner PRESSROOM: Line 1 – 7-WPC/Web Atlas-Leader single width 1993; Pasters – Reels and Stands ☐ 6.; Bundle tying machines – 1/Bu; Addressing machine – Vision Data.; Business Hardware – Software ☐ Vision Data

ROCKINGHAM

RICHMOND COUNTY DAILY JOURNAL

105 E. Washington St., Rockingham, N.C., 28379; gen tel (910) 997-3111; gen fax (910) 997-4321; gen e-mail Rdjnews@heartlandpublications.com; adv e-mail Rbacon@heartlandpublications.com; ed e-mail Jrobbins@heartlandpublications.com; web site www.yourdailyjournal.com
Published: Tues, Wed, Thur, Fri, Sat
Weekday Frequency: m
Saturday Frequency: m
Circulation: 6,575; 7,000(sat)
Last Audit: Sworn September 30, 2006
Price: 81.00/yr; 21.00/3mo, $42.00/6mo.
Advertising: Open inch rate $17.40
Insert rate: 48/m
News services: AP.
Politics: Independent.
Not Published: Christmas.
Special Editions: Raider Football Review (Aug); Prime Time for Seniors (Dec); NASCAR Race Week (Feb); Wedding Planner (Jan); At Home in Richmond County (Jul); Prime Time for Seniors (Jun); Home Improvement (Mar); Graduation (May); Holiday Recipes (Nov); NASCAR Race Week (O
Special Weekly Sections: Local Life (S); Real Estate (Wed).
Magazines: Relish (Monthly); American Profile (S).
Pub. ....Rick Bacon
Adv. Dir. ....Gail Rainwater
Circ. Mgr. ....Julian Tatum
Lifestyles Ed. ....Catherine Monk
Sports/Copy Ed. ....Dennis Burton
Prodn. Supvr. ....Amanda Vaness
Market Information: TMC.
Mechanical available: Offset; Black and 3 ROP colors; insert accepted; page cutoffs - 21.
Mechanical Specifications: Type page 11x 21; E - 6 cols, 1 5/6, 1/8 between; A - 6 cols, 1 5/6, 1/8 between; C - 10 cols, 1 5/6, 1/8 between.
Commodity Consumption: Avg. Page Number Per Issue - Daily 20; Avg. Page Number Per Issue - Sunday 38; widths 25; Newsprint Used - Short Tons 400.
Equipment EDITORIAL: Front-end Software – Newsengine; Editorial Hardware – APP/Mac; Editorial Equipment – Rip Mac; Editorial Printers – APP/Mac LaserWriter Pro; Classified Hardware – Baseview. DISPLAY: Ad make-up applications – Multi-Ad/Creator 4.0; Layout Software – APP/Mac.; Display Hardware – APP/Mac; Display Printers – Rip Mac; Addressing machine – 2-/El.; Business Hardware – Vision Data
Delivery method: Private Carrier

ROCKY MOUNT

ROCKY MOUNT TELEGRAM

1000 Hunter Hill Rd., Rocky Mount, N.C., 27802; gen tel (252) 446-5161; adv tel (252) 446-5161; ed tel (252) 446-5161; gen fax (252) 446-8036; adv fax (252) 446-1484; ed fax (252) 446-4057; adv e-mail mwilson@rmtelegram.com; ed e-mail jherrin@rmtelegram.com; web site www.rockymounttelegram.com
Group: Cooke Communications North Carolina, LLC
Published: Mon, Tues, Wed, Thur, Fri, Sat, Sun
Weekday Frequency: m
Saturday Frequency: m
Circulation: 12,116; 11,965(sat); 13,673(sun)
Last Audit: ABC September 30, 2011
Price: 11.50/mo; 126.00/yr.
Advertising: Open inch rate $22.36
News services: AP.
Politics: Independent. **Established:** 1910
Own facility?: N
Special Editions: Home & Garden (Apr); Jolly Holly Xmas (Dec); Fall Fashion (Fall); To Your Good Health (Feb); Parade of Homes (Realtors) (Jan); Perspective (Mar); Mobile Home (May); New Car Preview (Nov); Downeast Fest. (Oct); Literacy (Sept); Car Care (Spring).
Special Weekly Sections: Religion (Fri); School (Mon); Technology (S); TV Magazine (Sat); Entertainment (Thur); Church News (Tues); Best Food Day (Wed).
Magazines: Relish (Monthly); Carolina Charm (Quarterly); Local Color Comics (S).
Pub. ....Rip Woodin
Controller ....Julie Howard
Mgr., HR ....Gwen Davis
Adv. Dir. ....Mark Wilson
Classified Adv. Mgr. ....Quasha McNeal
Content Ed. ....Gene Metrick
Editor ....Jeff Herrin
Features Ed. ....Ross Chandler
Online Ed. ....Jenny White
Opns. Mgr. ....Heidi Martin
Retail Sales & Marketing Mgr. ....Jon Noel
Circulation Sales & Marketing Mgr. David Killgallon
Mktg. Mgr. ....Paula DeLong
Market Information: TMC.
Mechanical available: Offset; Black and 3 ROP colors; insert accepted - single sheets, cards, coupons; page cutoffs - 21.
Mechanical Specifications: Type page 13 x 21; E - 6 cols, 2, 1/8 between; A - 6 cols, 2, 1/8 between; C - 9 cols, 1 1/8, 1/16 between.
Commodity Consumption: Avg. Page Number Per Issue - Daily 24; Avg. Page Number Per Issue - Plates Used 1025; Avg. Page Number Per Issue - Saturday 24; Avg. Page Number Per Issue - Sunday 48; widths 13 1/2; Newsprint Used - Short Tons 1050; Printing Ink Used - Black 16775; Prin
Equipment EDITORIAL: Front-end Software – DTI 4.2.; Editorial Hardware – APP/Power Mac; Editorial Equipment – APP/Mac; Editorial Printers – HP/5MP, Xante/8300 CLASSIFIED: Front-end Software – DTI 4.2.; Classified Hardware – APP/Power Mac DISPLAY: Ad make-up applications – DTI 4.2.; Display Hardware – APP/Power Mac; Production Equipment – DTI.; Bundle tying machines – 2/OVL. BUSINESS COMPUTERS: Business Software – GEAC; Business Hardware – PC
Delivery method: Newsstand, Private Carrier, Racks

SALISBURY

EVENING POST PUBLISHING CO., INC.

131 W. Innes St., Salisbury, N.C., 28144; gen tel (704) 633-8950; gen fax (704) 633-7373; gen e-mail klanter@salisburypost.com; web site www.salisburyport.com
Published: Mon, Tues, Wed, Thur, Fri, Sat, Sun
Circulation: 17,862; 17,862(sat); 18,937(sun)
Last Audit: ABC September 30, 2011
Price: 123.00/yr.
Advertising: Open inch rate $20.46
Politics: 1905

SALISBURY POST

131 W. Innes St., Salisbury, N.C., 28144; gen tel (704) 633-8950; adv tel (704) 633-8950; ed tel (800) 633-8957; gen fax (704) 639-0003; adv fax (704) 633-7373; ed fax (704) 639-0003; gen e-mail news@salisburypost.com; newsroom@salisburypost.com; ed e-mail editor@salisburypost.com; web site www.salisburypost.com
Group: North Carolina Press Service, Inc.
Published: Mon, Tues, Wed, Thur, Fri, Sat, Sun
Weekday Frequency: m
Saturday Frequency: m
Circulation: 17,862; 17,862(sat); 18,937(sun)
Last Audit: ABC September 30, 2011
Price: 2.30/wk; 10.00/mo (carrier); 162.70/yr.
Advertising: Open inch rate $32.94
News services: Papert (Landon), AP, NEA, SHNS, LAT-WP.
Politics: Independent. **Established:** 1905
Special Editions: Nat'l Sportscasters & Sportswriters Association (Apr); Explorer (Aug); Christmas Carol Book (Dec); Bridal (Feb); Tax (Jan); A Day in the Life (Jul); Graduation (Jun); Explorer (Mar); Summer Fun (May); Hometown Heroes (Nov); October Tour (Oct); Fall Home I
Special Weekly Sections: Youth Page (Fri); Book Page (S); TV (Sat); Weekend (Thur); Best Food Day (Wed); Time Out (Weekly).
Magazines: Relish (Monthly); USA WEEKEND Magazine (S); American Profile (Weekly).
Dir., Sales/Mktg. ....Chris Ratliff
Circ. Dir. ....Ron Brooks
Ed. ....Elizabeth G. Cook
Books Ed. ....Deirdre Parker Smith
Editorial Page Ed. ....Chris Verner
Educ. Ed. ....Holly Lee
Photo Dept. Mgr. ....Wayne Hinshaw
Political Ed. ....Mark Wineka
Religion Ed. ....Katie Olson
Sports Ed. ....Ronnie Gallagher
Teen-Age/Youth Ed. ....Katie Scarvey
Prodn. Vice Pres., Opns. ....Michael J. Bella
Prodn. Mgr., Post Press ....Sharon Jackson
Market Information: TMC.
Mechanical available: Offset; Black and 3 ROP colors; insert accepted - all; page cutoffs - 22.
Mechanical Specifications: Type page 11 1/2 x 21; E - 6 cols, 2 1/16, 1/8 between; A - 6 cols, 2 1/16, 1/8 between; C - 9 cols, 1 3/8, 1/16 between.
Commodity Consumption: Avg. Page Number Per Issue - Daily 30; Avg. Page Number Per Issue - Plates Used 30300; Avg. Page Number Per Issue - Sunday 67; widths 50; Newsprint Used - Short Tons 2266; Printing Ink Used - Black 37272; Printing Ink Used - Color 3000; Printing Ink Used
Equipment EDITORIAL: Front-end Software – ECS 4, QPS/; Editorial Hardware – Ik, QPS/QuarkXPress, APP/Mac Server, APP/iMac, APP/Mac G3, APP/Mac G4; Editorial Equipment – 1-APP/Mac, DTI/PageSpeed, Kk/2035 Scanner; Editorial Printers – 2-Epson, 2-C.Itoh, 1-Centronics, AU/APS 6600, APP/Mac LaserWriter, Phases/440 Color CLASSIFIED: Front-end Software – ECS 4, Ad Manager Pro, Classflow, QPS/QuarkXPress, Ad Force II.; Classified Hardware – Ik, Baseview, APP/Power Mac, 5-APP/Mac G3; Classified Printers – 1-Centronics DISPLAY: Ad make-up applications – QPS/QuarkXPress 3.25, Adobe/Photoshop, Adobe/Illustrator, Adobe/Acrobat, Macromedia/Freehand; Layout Software – 3-APP/Mac G3, 3-APP/Mac G4.; Display Hardware – 10-APP/Mac; Production Equipment – Caere/OmniPage 6.0, 1-APP/Super Mac, Adobe/Photoshop, Kk/Scanner, Adobe/Acrobat, Macromedia/Freehand, 36-Laser Imagers, 1-Xante/Color Proofer; Cameras – 1-C/Spartan II, 1-C/Spartan III; Scanners – 1-ECR/Autokon 1000, 2-Umax/1200 dpi color scan PRESSROOM: Line 1 – 7-G/Metroliner 3 decks double width 1982; Folders – 4-G/2:1, Regent/2:1. MAILROOM: Counter stackers – 1/HL, 1-/MM, 2-QWI/SJ300, 1-QWI/J400, 2-/HL; Inserters and stuffers – 1-/MM, 1-/1372P; Bundle tying machines – 1-/Dynaric, 1-/Dynaric, 1-/QWI; Addressing machine – 2-/Dispensa-Matic/U-45. AUDIO: Audio Software – Microsoft/Windows 95, Compute/Ease; Audio Hardware – Pentium/100 MH2 BUSINESS COMPUTERS: Business Software – Vision Data; Business Hardware – 2-Convergent/Mighty Frame, 8-Wyse

SANFORD

PAXTON MEDIA GROUP

PO Box 100, Sanford, N.C., 27331-0100; gen tel (919) 708-9000; adv tel (919) 718-1259; gen fax (919) 774-4269; adv fax (919) 708-9001; ed fax (919) 708-9001; gen e-mail classified@sanfordherald.com; ed e-mail news@sanfordherald.com; web site www.sanfordherald.com
Published: Tues, Wed, Thur, Fri, Sat, Sun
Weekday Frequency: m
Saturday Frequency: m
Politics: 1930

THE SANFORD HERALD

208 St. Clair Ct., Sanford, N.C., 27331-0100; gen tel (919) 708-9000; adv tel (919) 718-1552; ed tel (919) 718-1226; gen fax (919) 774-4269; adv fax (919) 708-9001; ed fax (919) 708-9001; adv e-mail adsales@sanfordherald.com; classified@sanfordherald.com; ed e-mail news@sanfordherald.com; web site www.sanfordherald.com
Published: Tues, Wed, Thur, Fri, Sat, Sun
Weekday Frequency: m
Saturday Frequency: m
Circulation: 7,978; 7,978(sat); 7,901(sun)
Last Audit: September 30, 2009
Price: 13.65/month
Advertising: Open inch rate $17.77
Insert rate: $45/<
News services: AP.
Politics: 1930
Not Published: Christmas.
Special Editions: Car Care (Apr); Football (Aug); Christmas Gift Guide (Dec); IRS (Feb); Summer Lifestyle (Jun); Small Business Expo (May); Fair (Sept).
Special Weekly Sections: Church (Fri); Business (Thur); Food (Wed).
Magazines: TV Preview (Fri); USA WEEKEND Magazine (S).
Mgr., Mktg./Promo. ....Bill Horner
Circ. Dir. ....Jeff Ayers
City Ed. ....R.V. Hight
News Ed. ....Jonathan Owens
Market Information: Split run; TMC; Zoned editions.
Mechanical available: Offset; Black and 3 ROP colors; insert accepted - up to 10 3/4 x 13; page cutoffs - 21 1/2.
Mechanical Specifications: Type page 13 x 21 1/2; E - 6 cols, 2, 1/6 between; A - 6 cols, 2 1/6, 1/8 between; C - 8 cols, 1 1/3, 1/8 between.
Commodity Consumption: Avg. Page Number Per Issue - Daily 24; Avg. Page Number Per Issue - Plates Used 4400; widths 27 1/2; Newsprint Used - Short Tons 750; Printing Ink Used - Black 10000; Printing Ink Used - Color 1000; Printing Ink Used - Pages Printed 8000.
Equipment EDITORIAL: Front-end Software – Baseview; Editorial Hardware – Apple; Classified Hardware – Apple; Classified Equipment – Baseview DISPLAY: Ad make-up applications – Baseview; Display Hardware – Apple; Folders – 1-G/2:1.; Inserters and stuffers – KAN/480 5:1; Bundle tying machines – 1/Bu, 1-/MLN. BUSINESS COMPUTERS: Business Software – Baseview; Business Hardware – Apple

SHELBY

THE STAR

315 E. Graham St., Shelby, N.C., 28150; gen tel (704) 484-7000; adv tel (704) 484-7000; ed tel (704) 484-7000; gen fax (704) 482-2631; adv fax (704) 482-2631; ed fax (704) 482-2631; gen e-mail shelbystar@freedom.com; adv e-mail aron_goss@link.freedom.com; web site www.shelbystar.com
Published: Mon, Tues, Wed, Thur, Fri, Sat, Sun
Weekday Frequency: m
Saturday Frequency: m
Circulation: 14,164; 14,164(sat); 14,389(sun)
Last Audit: September 30, 2005
Price: 11.00/mo; 123.48/yr.
Advertising: Open inch rate $23.40
News services: AP, SHNS.
Politics: Libertarian. **Established:** 1894
Special Editions: Your Health (Apr); Senior Living (Aug); Christmas Gift Guide (Dec); Senior Living (Feb); Your Health (Jan); Your Health (Jul); Cleveland Now (Mar); Senior Living (May); Real Estate (Lincoln & Cleveland counties) (Monthly); Senior LIving (Nov); Your Health
Special Weekly Sections: Outdoors (Fri); Business (S); NASCAR (Thur); Food (Wed).
Magazines: USA WEEKEND Magazine (S).
Pub. ....Skip Foster
Bus. Mgr. ....Chris Workman
Adv. Dir. ....Aron Goss
Adv. Mgr., Nat'l ....Earl Brackett
Ed. ....Jon Jimison
Mng. Ed. ....Alan Jenkins

Online Ed. ....Emily Killian
Chief Photographer ....Jeff Melton
Sports Ed. ....Alan Ford
Women's Ed. ....Jackie Bridges
Mgmt. Info Servs. Mgr. ....Mark Van Buren
Prodn. Dir., Mailroom ....Frankie Rice
Prodn. Mgr., Pressroom ....Barry Croucher
Market Information: TMC.
Mechanical available: Offset; Black and 3 ROP colors; insert accepted - product samples; page cutoffs - 27 1/2.
Mechanical Specifications: Type page 11 1/3 x 21 1/2; E - 6 cols, 1 4/5, 1/8 between; A - 6 cols, 1 4/5, 1/8 between; C - 9 cols, 1 1/5, 1/8 between.
Commodity Consumption: Avg. Page Number Per Issue - Daily 20; Avg. Page Number Per Issue - Saturday 20; Avg. Page Number Per Issue - Sunday 28; widths 13; Newsprint Used - Short Tons 1000.
Equipment; Editorial Hardware – 3-Compaq/Proliant Server 600; Editorial Equipment – 19-PC, 1-APP/Mac, 1-MS/NT Workstation, 1-SII/Workstation, 3-Compaq/Servers, 1-IBM Server, 1-Compaq/UniX Server; Editorial Printers – 1-HP/4000, 1-HP/4MV, 1-Epson/Stylus, 1-Pre Press/Panther 46, 2-HP/8150, 1-HP/5 CLASSIFIED: Front-end Software – APT/ACT 2.06.03.; Classified Hardware – 3-PC, 2-PC P166, 1-PC P100; Classified Printers – HP/4MV DISPLAY: Ad make-up applications – APT/ACT 2.06.03; Layout Software – APT, QPS/QuarkXPress 4.04.; Display Printers – HP/8150 PRODUCTION: Pagination Software – APT/ACT 2.06.03, Microsoft/NT 4.0.; Production Equipment – 2-Pre Press/Panther Pro 46, AG/Duoscan, Pentium/PC II, Microtek; Cameras – 1-B, 1-SCREEN; Scanners – 1-AG/Duoscan, 1-Acer/Microtech PRESSROOM: Line 1 – 6-G/Urbanite; Folders – G/2:1; Reels and Stands – 6 MAILROOM: Counter stackers – 1/QWI; Bundle tying machines – 2-/Strapex; Wrapping singles – 1-/QWI; Addressing machine – 1-/KR; Other equipment –1-Mueller/Stitcher-trimmer. BUSINESS COMPUTERS: Business Software – Great Plains Dynamics, Newzware, APT, Ceridian; Business Hardware – 1-IBM/Newzware

STATESVILLE

STATESVILLE RECORD & LANDMARK

222 E. Broad St., Statesville, N.C., 28677; gen tel (704) 873-1451; gen fax (704) 872-3150; adv e-mail advertising@statesville.com; ed e-mail news@statesville.com; web site www.statesville.com
Published: Mon, Tues, Wed, Thur, Fri, Sat, Sun
Weekday Frequency: m
Saturday Frequency: m
Circulation: 13,269; 13,269(sat); 16,545(sun)
Last Audit: September 30, 2008
News services: AP.
Politics: 1874
Own facility?: Y
Pub. ....Tim Dearman
Circ. Mgr. ....Bud Welch
Commodity Consumption: Avg. Page Number Per Issue - Daily 28; Avg. Page Number Per Issue - Saturday 24; Avg. Page Number Per Issue - Sunday 60; Printing Ink Used - Pages Printed 9500.
Equipment DISPLAY: Ad make-up applications – .; Bundle tying machines – Alles.
Delivery method: Private Carrier, Racks

TARBORO

THE DAILY SOUTHERNER

504 W. Wilson St., Tarboro, N.C., 27886; gen tel (252) 823-3106; adv tel (252) 823-3106; ed tel (252) 823-3106; gen fax (252) 823-4599; adv fax (252) 823-4599; ed fax (252) 823-4599; gen e-mail legalads@dailysoutherner.com; adv e-mail majoraccounts@dailysoutherner.com; ed e-mail cwigginton@dailysoutherner.com; web site www.dailysoutherner.com
Group: Community Newspaper Holdings, Inc.
Published: Mon, Tues, Wed, Thur, Fri
Weekday Frequency: All day
Circulation: 2,550
Last Audit: Sworn September 30, 2003
Price: 8.50/mo; 97.00/yr.
Advertising: Open inch rate $9.25
Insert rate: 56/M
News services: AP.
Politics: Democrat. **Established:** 1826
Not Published: Independence Day; Thanksgiving; Christmas.
Special Editions: Profile (Annually).
Special Weekly Sections: TGIF (Fri); Lifestyles (Mon); Business News (Thur); Farm News (Tues); Best Food Day (Wed).
Magazines: American Profile (Fri); Relish (Monthly); USA WEEKEND Magazine (Weekly).
Profile: Daily newspaper published Monday thru Friday afternoons serving the town of Tarboro and eastern section of Edgecombe County, NC.
Editor and Publisher ....Mosby L. Wigginton
Advertising Sales Manager ....Gene Hudson
Sports Editor ....Calvin Adkins
Market Information: TMC.
Mechanical available: Offset; Black and 3 ROP colors; insert accepted; page cutoffs - 22 3/4.
Mechanical Specifications: Type page 11 5/8 x 21 1/2; E - 6 cols, 1 3/16, 1/8 between; A - 6 cols, 1 3/16, 1/8 between; C - 9 cols, 1 1/8, 1/8 between.
Commodity Consumption: Avg. Page Number Per Issue - Daily 16; widths 24 1/2; Newsprint Used - Short Tons 760.
Equipment EDITORIAL: Front-end Software – Quark.; Editorial Hardware – 6-APP/Mac G4/G3 CLASSIFIED: Front-end Software – Baseview.; Classified Hardware – MAC G/3; Layout Software – 4-APP/Mac G/4.; Business Hardware – Vision Data

TRYON

THE TRYON DAILY BULLETIN

16 N. Trade St., Tryon, N.C., 28782; gen tel (828) 859-9151; adv tel (828) 859-9151; ed tel (828) 859-9151; gen fax (828) 859-5575; adv fax (828) 859-5575; ed fax (828) 859-5575; gen e-mail news@tryondailybulletin.com; adv e-mail classifieds@tryondailybulletin.com; ed e-mail news@tryondailybulletin.com; web site www.tryondailybulletin.com
Group: North Carolina Press Service, Inc.
Published: Mon, Tues, Wed, Thur, Fri
Weekday Frequency: m
Circulation: 4,993
Last Audit: September 30, 2006
Price: 60.00/yr.
Advertising: Open inch rate $8.36
Politics: Independent. **Established:** 1928
Not Published: New Year; Independence Day; Labor Day; Thanksgiving; Christmas; Postal holidays.
Special Editions: Come See Us Almanac (Newcomer's Guide) (Mar); Holiday Gift Guide (Nov).
Publsiher ....Betty Ramsey
Editor ....Samantha Hurst
Managing Editor ....Barbara Tilly
Mechanical available: Offset; Black; insert accepted; page cutoffs - 11.
Commodity Consumption: Avg. Page Number Per Issue - Daily 24; Newsprint Used - Metric Tons 50.
Equipment; Editorial Hardware – MAC; Editorial Equipment – Printers □ APP/Mac LaserPrinter, Canon/LBP4; Editorial Printers – Software □ Aldus/PageMaker. CLASSIFIED: Front-end Software – Aldus/PageMaker, Alpha 4.; Classified Hardware – PC; Layout Software – PC.; Display Hardware – Aldus/PageMaker PRODUCTION: Pagination Software – Aldus/PageMaker.; Production Equipment – Nu/Plate Maker PRESSROOM: Line 1 – 2-KP/News King.; Addressing machine – 1-Automecha/Accufast PL. BUSINESS COMPUTERS: Business Software – Merriman Publishing Management; Business Hardware – Varsity/ATC

WASHINGTON

WASHINGTON DAILY NEWS

217 N. Market St., Washington, N.C., 27889; gen tel (252) 946-2144; adv tel (252) 946-2144; ed tel (252) 946-2144; gen fax (252) 946-9797; adv fax (252) 946-9797; gen e-mail news@wdnweb.com; adv e-mail classified@wdnweb.com; web site www.wdnweb.com
Group: North Carolina Press Service, Inc.
Published: Mon, Tues, Wed, Thur, Fri, Sat, Sun
Weekday Frequency: m
Saturday Frequency: m
Circulation: 8,644; 8,644(sat); 8,829(sun)
Last Audit: March 31, 2008
Price: 7.00/mo; 108.00/yr.
Advertising: Open inch rate $20.00
News services: AP.
Politics: Independent-Democrat. **Established:** 1909
Not Published: Christmas.
Special Editions: Visitor's Tourist Guide Tab (Apr); Football Tab (Aug); Basketball Tab (Dec); Tax Tab (Jan); Summer Festival (Jul); Lawn and Garden Tab (Mar); Graduation Tab (May).
Special Weekly Sections: This Week (Fri); Channel Marker (S); Farm (Thur); Food (Wed).
Magazines: Parade (S).
Pres./Pub. ....Ashley B. Futrell
Vice Pres. ....Susan B. Futrell
Treasurer ....Rachel F. Futrell
Controller ....Addie B. Laney
Adv. Dir. ....Ray McKeithen
Adv. Mgr., Classified ....Brenda Foster
Ed. ....Mike Voss
Society Ed. ....Brenda Watters
Sports Ed. ....Kevin Travis
Prodn. Foreman, Mailroom ....Jerry Cox
Prodn. Foreman, Pressroom ....Vance Bell
Market Information: TMC; Zoned editions.
Mechanical available: Offset; Black and 3 ROP colors; insert accepted; page cutoffs - 22 3/4.
Mechanical Specifications: Type page 13 x 21 1/2; E - 6 cols, 2 1/16, 1/8 between; A - 6 cols, 2 1/16, 1/8 between; C - 6 cols, 2 1/16, 1/8 between.
Commodity Consumption: Avg. Page Number Per Issue - Daily 20; Avg. Page Number Per Issue - Plates Used 4200; Avg. Page Number Per Issue - Sunday 42; widths 27; Newsprint Used - Short Tons 513; Printing Ink Used - Black 21748; Printing Ink Used - Color 2500; Printing Ink Used -
Equipment; Editorial Hardware – 9-Mk.; Classified Hardware – Mk.; Layout Software – 1-Mk.; Production Equipment – 1-Nu, 1-M; Cameras – 1-Nu, C. PRESSROOM: Line 1 – 1-Zenith/Jobber 22, G/Community SC; Line 2 – 5-G/SC 210; Folders – 1, 1.; Inserters and stuffers – MM/2(3 Stations); Bundle tying machines – 1/Strap Tyer; Addressing machine – 4-/Wm. BUSINESS COMPUTERS: Business Software – Business/Software; Business Hardware – 1-Bs, 1-TI/300A, DSI/Papertrak

WASHINGTON NEWS PUBLISHING CO.

217 N. Market St., Washington, N.C., 27889; gen tel (252) 946-2144; gen fax (252) 946-9797; gen e-mail news@washingtondailynews.com
Published: Mon, Tues, Wed, Thur, Fri, Sat, Sun
Price: 108.00/yr.
Advertising: Open inch rate $11.00

WILMINGTON

STAR-NEWS

1003 S. 17th St., Wilmington, N.C., 28401; gen tel (910) 343-2000; adv tel (910) 343-2323 (Class); ed tel (910) 343-2312; adv fax (910) 343-2229 (Class); ed fax (910) 343-2004; adv e-mail wilmington.classified@starnewsonline.com (Class); ed e-mail letters@starnewsonline.com; web site www.starnewsonline.com
Published: Sun
Circulation: 41,299; 41,406(sat); 47,395(sun)
Last Audit: September 30, 2009
Price: 10.95/mo; 131.40/yr.
Advertising: Open inch rate $75.79
News services: AP, NYT, MCT, LAT-WP, TMS.
Politics: 1867
Special Editions: Parade of Homes (Apr); Commercial Real Estate (Aug); Real Estate Showcase (Dec); NASCAR (Feb); Real Estate Showcase (Jan); Back-to-School (Jul); Reader's Choice (Jun); Dining Guide (May); Fact Book (Nov); Dining Guide (Oct); Fashion (Sept).
Special Weekly Sections: Channels (S); Real Estate (Sat); Currents (Thur); Best Food Day (Wed).
Magazines: Wilmington Magazine (Monthly); Parade (S).
Profile: The Star-News is North Carolina's oldest paper in continuous publication. It was founded in 1867 by William H. Bernard, a Civil War veteran. It passed through a succession of owners before being bought by the Page family in 1927. The paper was bought by t
Pub. ....Robert Gruber
Controller ....Keith Raffone
Dir., HR ....Sherry Rich
Adv. Dir. ....Diane Keenan
Adv. Mgr., Classified ....Tamara Weil
Circ. Opns. Dir. ....Donnell Giles
Exec. Ed. ....Robyn Tomlin
Mng. Ed. ....Julie Martin
Book Critic ....Ben Steelman
City Ed. ....Vaughn Hagerty
Editorial Page Ed. ....Charles Riesz
Deputy Editorial Page Ed. ....Tricia Vance
Asst. Features Ed. ....Jeff Hidek
News Ed. ....Greene Gary
Deputy News Ed. ....Rosemary Tiller
Photo Ed. ....Mark Courtney
Deputy Photo Ed. ....Ken Blevins
Sports Ed. ....Neil Amato
Sports Ed. ....Dan Spears
Dir., Info Systems ....Edward Willis
Market Information: Split run; TMC; Zoned editions.
Mechanical available: Offset; Black and 3 ROP colors; insert accepted; page cutoffs - 22 3/4.
Mechanical Specifications: Type page 11 1/2 x 21 1/2; E - 6 cols, 1 5/6, 7/50 between; A - 6 cols, 1 5/6, 7/50 between; C - 9 cols, 1 9/50, 1/8 between.
Commodity Consumption: Avg. Page Number Per Issue - Daily 46; Avg. Page Number Per Issue - Plates Used 130000; Avg. Page Number Per Issue - Sunday 88; widths 12 1/2; Newsprint Used - Metric Tons 7539; Printing Ink Used - Black 145000; Printing Ink Used - Color 75000; Printing
Equipment EDITORIAL: Front-end Software – ATS/Newsdesk, ATS/Quik Layout.; Editorial Hardware – 50-Pentium/PC, MS/NT Server, NT/Enterprise; Editorial Equipment – 3-AU/3850, 2-AU/Oman, Online Transport, 3-Window/RIP, Compaq/Intranet Server; Editorial Printers – 5-HP/LaserJet CLASSIFIED: Front-end Software – ATS/Classified.; Classified Hardware – 28-Compaq/PC, MS/NT Server, Enterprise; Classified Printers – HP/LaserJet DISPLAY: Ad make-up applications – SCS/Ad-Tracking, SCS/Classified Page; Layout Software – 41-APP/Power Mac G4 & G5, Multi-Ad/Creator, SCS/Layout 8000.; Display Hardware – Compaq; Display Printers – HP/1050, 5-HP/LaserJet PRODUCTION: Pagination Software – ATS/Informatel.; Production Equipment – 3-AU/3850, 1-Nu, 1-Nat; Cameras – KI; Scanners – Umax PRESSROOM: Line 1 – 8-G 1970, 3-G/half decks 1970; Folders – 2-G/2:1, 2-G/3:2; Pasters – 8; Reels and Stands – 8 MAILROOM: Counter stackers – 4/QWI; Inserters and stuffers – 2-HI/1372; Bundle tying machines – 3-/Dynaric; Addressing machine – 1-/Inkjet; Other equipment –ST.; Audio Hardware – Brite BUSINESS COMPUTERS: Business Software

– DSI, PeopleSoft, Circ:PBS; Business Hardware – 1-Remote Network Servers, IBM/AS-400

STARNEWS MEDIA

1003 South 17th Street, Wilmington, N.C., 28401; gen tel 910-343-2000; web site www.starnewsonline.com
Published: Mon, Tues, Wed, Thur, Fri, Sat, Sun
Weekday Frequency: m
Saturday Frequency: m
Circulation: 36,999; 36,931(sat); 44,736(sun)
Last Audit: ABC September 30, 2011

WILSON

THE WILSON DAILY TIMES

2001 Downing St., Wilson, N.C., 27893; gen tel (252) 243-5151; adv tel (252) 265-7858; ed tel (252) 265-7812; gen fax (252) 243-2999; adv fax (252) 243-2999; ed fax (252) 243-7501; gen e-mail mpd@wilsontimes.com; adv e-mail ads@wilsontimes.com; ed e-mail editor@wilsontimes.com; web site www.wilsontimes.com
Group: North Carolina Press Service, Inc.
Published: Mon, Tues, Wed, Thur, Fri, Sat, Sun
Weekday Frequency: e
Saturday Frequency: m
Circulation: 15,718; 15,718(sat)
Last Audit: September 30, 2008
Price: 9.25/mo; 99.90/yr.
Advertising: Open inch rate $19.95
News services: AP, CNS, NEA, United Media Service, UPI.
Politics: Independent. **Established:** 1896
Advertising not accepted: Liquor.
Not Published: Christmas.
Special Editions: Back to School (Aug); Christmas Gift Guide I & II (Dec); Car Car (Fall); Bridal (Jan); Race Tab (Mar); Graduation (May); Spring Fashion (Spring).
Special Weekly Sections: Home (Fri); Farm Page (Mon); TV (Sat); Arts (Thur); Seniors (Tues); Family (Wed).
Magazines: Relish (Monthly); USA WEEKEND Magazine (Sat); Front Porch (Thur); American Profile (Weekly).
Pres./Pub. ....Morgan Paul Dickerman
Vice Pres./Sec./Treasurer ..Margaret Dickerman
Adv. Dir. ....Shana Bogue
Adv. Mgr., Creative Servs................Billie Taylor
Circ. Mgr. ....Frank Heacox
Lifestyle Ed.......................................Lisa Batts
Sports Ed. ....Paul Durham
Prodn. Mgr., Opns........................Tim Haywood
Market Information: TMC.
Mechanical available: Offset; Black and 3 ROP colors; insert accepted; page cutoffs - 22.
Mechanical Specifications: Type page 12 1/2 x 21; E - 6 cols, 1 13/16, 1/8 between; A - 6 cols, 1 13/16, 1/8 between; C - 9 cols, 1 13/16, 1/16 between.
Commodity Consumption: Avg. Page Number Per Issue - Daily 32; Avg. Page Number Per Issue - Plates Used 10000; widths 25; Newsprint Used - Short Tons 1100; Printing Ink Used - Black 18010; Printing Ink Used - Color 1120; Printing Ink Used - Pages Printed 10263.
Equipment EDITORIAL: Front-end Software – Baseview.; Editorial Hardware – APP/Mac; Editorial Equipment – 2-NewGen; Editorial Printers – 2-AU CLASSIFIED: Front-end Software – QPS/QuarkXPress.; Classified Hardware – PC; Classified Printers – 2-AU DISPLAY: Ad make-up applications – Multi-Ad 4.0, QPS/QuarkXPress 4.0; Layout Software – 6-APP/Mac, Baseview.; Display Printers – APP/Mac LaserWriter II, 1-HP PRODUCTION: Pagination Software – QPS/QuarkXPress 3.32.; Production Equipment – 1-Nu, AG/Arcus, LS/2000; Cameras – C PRESSROOM: Line 1 – 5-Dauphin; Line 2 – 4-Dauphin.; Bundle tying machines – MLN.; Business Hardware – IBM/Advance 36

WINSTON-SALEM

PIEDMONT PUBLISHING CO., INC.

418 N. Marshall, Winston-Salem, N.C., 27101; gen tel (336) 727-7211; gen fax (336) 727-7485; gen e-mail tcoones@wsjournal.com; web site www.journalnow.com
Published: Mon, Tues, Wed, Thur, Fri, Sat, Sun
Price: 137.80/yr.
Advertising: Open inch rate $60.44

WINSTON-SALEM JOURNAL

418 N. Marshall, Winston-Salem, N.C., 27101-3159; gen tel (336) 727-7211; adv tel (336) 727-7400; ed tel (336) 727-7360; gen fax (336) 727-4096; adv fax (336) 727-7485; ed fax (336) 727-7402; gen e-mail rnoftle@wsjournal.com; adv e-mail wdowney@wsjournal.com; ed e-mail news@wsjournal.com; web site www.journalnow.com
Group: North Carolina Press Service, Inc.
Published: Mon, Tues, Wed, Thur, Fri, Sat, Sun
Weekday Frequency: m
Saturday Frequency: m
Circulation: 56,946; 59,032(sat); 76,838(sun)
Last Audit: ABC September 30, 2011
Price: 2.96/wk; 137.80/yr.
Advertising: Open inch rate $119.00
News services: AP, NYT, LAT-WP.
Politics: 1897
Special Editions: Senior Scene (Monthly).
Special Weekly Sections: Automotive Friday (Classified) (Fri); Kid's SAM (Mon); Travel (S); People (Sat); Relish (Thur); Health & Fitness (Tues); Best Food Day (Wed).
Magazines: Parade (S).
Profile: Daily newspaper serving northwest North Carolina.
Pres./Pub. ....Michael J. Miller
Controller................................David Stanfield
Dir., HR.....................................Randy Noftle
Credit Mgr. ....Scott Blackburn
Adv. Dir. ....Jeff Green
Adv. Mgr., Classified......................Pat Ranson
Circ. Dir....Keith Petty
Mng. Ed.................................Ken Otterbourg
Exec. Ed. ....Carl Crothers
Continuing News. Ed..........................Les Gura
Features Ed. ....Alan Cronk
News Ed.................................Charles Elkins
Food Ed. ....Michael Hastings
Garden Ed. ....David Bare
Librarian ....Julie Harris
Multimedia Team Leader.........Michele Johnson
Dir., Electronic Publishing...............Bob Geiger
Market Information: ADS; Split run; TMC; Zoned editions.
Mechanical available: Offset; Black and 3 ROP colors; insert accepted; page cutoffs - 22.
Mechanical Specifications: Type page 12 x 21; E - 6 cols, 1 7/8, 1/8 between; A - 6 cols, 1 7/8, 1/8 between; C - 9 cols, 1 3/16, 1/16 between.
Commodity Consumption: Avg. Page Number Per Issue - Daily 52; Avg. Page Number Per Issue - Plates Used 125000; Avg. Page Number Per Issue - Saturday 80; Avg. Page Number Per Issue - Sunday 118; widths 50; Newsprint Used - Short Tons 15000; Printing Ink Used - Black 300000; Pri
Equipment EDITORIAL: Front-end Software – AT/Editorial 4.7.7.; Editorial Hardware – 6-AT/9000; Editorial Equipment – AT/Ed Page, 9-IBM/RS6000 CLASSIFIED: Front-end Software – AT/Enterprise.; Classified Hardware – 2-IBM/RS 6000-F40; Classified Equipment – IBM/RS6000, IBM/43P, HI/Classified Pagination; Classified Printers – HP/LaserJet 4000; Layout Software – SCS/Layout 8000.; Display Hardware – HP/Vectra-2; Display Printers – 2-HP/LaserJet 6P PRODUCTION: Pagination Software – AT.; Production Equipment – 3-III/3810, 1-III/3850, 1-ECR; Scanners – 1-III/3750, 1-III/3725 PRESSROOM: Line 1 – Jan-94; Folders – 2; Pasters – 10; Reels and Stands – 10 MAILROOM: Counter stackers – 3-HL/Monitor, 6-QWI/300; Inserters and stuffers – 2-GMA/SLS 1000 20:2; Bundle tying machines – 3/OVL, 6-/Dynaric; Addressing machine – 2-/Ch, 1-/KR.; Business Hardware – HP/3000 918LX

NORTH DAKOTA

BISMARCK

THE BISMARCK TRIBUNE

707 E. Front Ave., Bismarck, N.D., 58504; gen tel (701) 223-2500; adv tel (701) 250-8285; ed tel (701) 250-8251; gen fax (701) 223-4240; adv fax (701) 224-1412; ed fax (701) 223-2063; ed e-mail news@bismarcktribune.com; web site www.bismarcktribune.com
Group: Metro Suburbia, Inc./Newhouse Newspapers
Published: Mon, Tues, Wed, Thur, Fri, Sat, Sun
Weekday Frequency: m
Saturday Frequency: m
Circulation: 25,393; 24,665(sat); 28,643(sun)
Last Audit: ABC September 30, 2011
Price: 4.00/wk; 17.34/mo; 210.40/yr.
Advertising: Open inch rate $49.53
News services: AP, LAT-WP, NEA.
Politics: Independent.
Special Editions: Solutions (Quarterly).
Special Weekly Sections: Voices (Mon); Business Page (S); Religion Page (Thur); Business Page (Tues); Best Food Day (Wed).
Magazines: Parade Magazine (S).
Publisher..................................Brian Kroshus
Controller ....Libby Simes
HR Mgr................................Chad Kourajian
Adv. Sales Mgr. ....Kristin Wilson
Circ. Dir...Ken Bohl
Mng. Ed. ....Ken Rogers
Librarian......................................Vicky Weiss
News Ed. ....Steve Wallick
Photographer ....Mike McCleary
Religion Reporter.......................Karen Herzog
Market Information: ADS; Split run; TMC; Zoned editions.
Mechanical available: Offset; Black and 4 ROP colors; insert accepted; page cutoffs - 22 3/4.
Mechanical Specifications: Type page 13 x 21 1/2; E - 6 cols, 2 1/16, 1/8 between; A - 6 cols, 2 1/16, 1/8 between; C - 9 cols, 1 3/8, 1/16 between.
Commodity Consumption: Avg. Page Number Per Issue - Daily 24; Avg. Page Number Per Issue - Plates Used 36000; Avg. Page Number Per Issue - Saturday 24; Avg. Page Number Per Issue - Sunday 48; widths 27 1/2; Newsprint Used - Short Tons 2500; Printing Ink Used - Black 56000; Pri
Equipment EDITORIAL: Front-end Software – HI/PLS-PEN.; Editorial Hardware – 1-HI/8306, 4-HI/8903; Editorial Equipment – ISYS/Library System CLASSIFIED: Front-end Software – HI/CASH.; Classified Hardware – HI, Unix DISPLAY: Ad make-up applications – Multi-Ad/Creator, QPS/QuarkXPress; Layout Software – APP/Mac. PRODUCTION: Pagination Software – HI/PLS 6.5.; Production Equipment – 2-COM/8600, 1-Pre Press/Panther Pro 36, 1-Pre Press/Panther Pro 46; Cameras – 1-C/Spartan III, 2-Ik/530; Scanners – 2-Nikon/Coolscan, 2-Polaroid/SprintScan 35, 10-Microtek/Flatbed Scanmakers PRESSROOM: Line 1 – 10-G/Urbanite single width; Folders – 1-G/2:1, 1-G/1200 Quarter Folder.; Inserters and stuffers – 2-MM/227E; Bundle tying machines – 1-MLN/MLN2A, 2-MLN/Spirit; Addressing machine – 1-Ch/528-010, 1-Ch/542-093, 1-Ch/542-090; Other equipment –Ch/552-01 Quarter Folder.; Audio Hardware – VRI, Lee Enterprises, VRI; Business Hardware – IBM/AS-400

DEVILS LAKE

DEVILS LAKE JOURNAL

516 Fourth St. NE, Devils Lake, N.D., 58301; gen tel (701) 662-2127; adv tel (701) 662-2127; ed tel (701) 662-2127; gen fax (701) 662-3115; adv fax (701) 662-3115; ed fax (701) 662-3115; adv e-mail advertising@devilslakejournal.com; ed e-mail news@devilslakejournal.com; web site www.devilslakejournal.com
Group: North Carolina Press Service, Inc.
Published: Mon, Tues, Wed, Thur, Fri
Weekday Frequency: e
Circulation: 3,652
Last Audit: March 31, 2007
Price: 1.35/wk; 6.50/mo; 105.00/yr (carrier).
Advertising: Open inch rate $13.25
News services: AP.
Politics: Independent.
Not Published: Thanksgiving; Christmas.
Magazines: TV Preview (Fri); Golden Opportunities (Monthly); American Profile (Weekly).
Gen. Mgr. ....Kathy Svidal
Adv. Mgr., Retail......................Paula Ramsey
Circ. Mgr. ....Mary Joe Kilmer
Mng. Ed. ....Louise Oleson
Lifestyles Ed...................................Sue Kraft
Prodn. Mgr ....Jenny Leonard
Market Information: TMC.
Mechanical available: Offset; Black and 4 ROP colors; insert accepted; page cutoffs - 21.
Mechanical Specifications: Type page 13 x 21; E - 6 cols, 2, 1/6 between; A - 6 cols, 2, 1/6 between; C - 10 cols, 1 1/4, 1/12 between.
Commodity Consumption: Avg. Page Number Per Issue - Daily 12; Avg. Page Number Per Issue - Plates Used 6900; widths 14; Newsprint Used - Short Tons 225; Printing Ink Used - Pages Printed 4848.
Equipment EDITORIAL: Front-end Software – Mk/NewsTouch.; Editorial Hardware – Mk/1100 Plus; Editorial Printers – 2-APP/Mac LaserPrinter II; Classified Hardware – 2-Mk, AT; Classified Printers – 2-APP/Mac LaserPrinter II.; Layout Software – APP/Mac IIci.; Display Printers – APP/Mac LaserWriter II NTX; Production Equipment – Mk, 1-Amerigraph/457 SEDS; Cameras – 1-B/Caravel. PRESSROOM: Line 1 – 4-HI/Cotrell V-15A; Folders – 1; Bundle tying machines – 1-Felins/16; Addressing machine – 1-Am/2600.; Business Hardware – IBM/Sys 34

DICKINSON

DICKINSON PRESS

1815 First St. W., Dickinson, N.D., 58602; gen tel (701) 225-8111; ed tel (701) 225-8141; gen fax (701) 225-4205; ed fax (701) 225-6653; gen e-mail newsroom@thedickinsonpress.com; adv e-mail ropadvertising@thedickinsonpress.com; ed e-mail newsroom@thedickinsonpress.com; web site www.thedickinsonpress.com
Group: Forum Communications
North Carolina Press Service, Inc.
Published: Tues, Wed, Thur, Fri, Sat, Sun
Weekday Frequency: m
Saturday Frequency: m
Circulation: 6,504; 6,504(sat); 6,504(sun)
Last Audit: Sworn March 31, 2011
Price: 14.50/mo; 150.00/yr (in-state).
Advertising: Open inch rate $12.00
Insert rate: .55
News services: AP.
Politics: Independent. **Established:** 1883
Own facility?: Y
Special Editions: Weddings (Other).
Special Weekly Sections: Food (S); Farm (Sat); Business (Thur); Food (Wed).
Magazines: Relish (Monthly); TV Guide (Other); Parade (S).
Pub./Purchasing Agent ....Harvey Brock
Adv. Mgr............................Jerry Obriqewitsch
Sales Rep. ....Jenn Binnstock
Sports Ed. ....Dustin Monke
Prodn. Foreman, Pressroom ....Clayton Goyne
Managing Editor.....................Jennifer McBride
Business Manager ....Joy Schoch
Market Information: ADS; Split run; TMC; Zoned

editions.
Mechanical available: Offset; Black and 3 ROP colors; insert accepted; page cutoffs - 22 3/4.
Mechanical Specifications: Type page 13 x 21 1/2; E - 6 cols, 2 1/16, 1/8 between; A - 6 cols, 2 1/16, 1/8 between; C - 9 cols, 1 3/8, 1/8 between.
Commodity Consumption: Avg. Page Number Per Issue - Daily 16; Avg. Page Number Per Issue - Plates Used 3000; Avg. Page Number Per Issue - Sunday 30; widths 25; Newsprint Used - Short Tons 350; Printing Ink Used - Black 9000; Printing Ink Used - Color 329.
Equipment: Editorial Hardware – Mk.; Classified Hardware – Mk.; Production Equipment – 2-APP/Mac LaserPrinter, 4-APP/Mac; Cameras – 1-R/500. PRESSROOM: Line 1 – 7-G/Community; Folders – 1-G/SC.; Inserters and stuffers – Mueller 6 into 1; Bundle tying machines – 1/Bu; Addressing machine – Ink Jet; Business Hardware – IBM/PL, Lotus, CPPS, CJ

DICKINSON PRESS, INC.

1815 1st St. W., Dickinson, N.D., 58601; gen tel (701) 225-8111; gen fax (701) 225-4205; gen e-mail areed@dickinsonpress.com; web site www.dickinsonpress.com
Price: 145.00/yr.
Advertising: Open inch rate $8.40
Politics: 1883

FARGO

INFORUM

101 Fifth St. N., Fargo, N.D., 58102; gen tel (701) 235-7311; adv tel (701) 235-7311; ed tel (701) 235-7311; gen fax (701) 241-5406; adv fax (701) 241-5540; ed fax (701) 241-5487; gen e-mail in-forum@forumcomm.com; adv e-mail in-forum@forumcomm.com; ed e-mail in-forum@forumcomm.com; web site www.in-forum.com
Published: Mon, Tues, Wed, Thur, Fri, Sat, Sun
Weekday Frequency: m
Saturday Frequency: m
Circulation: 50,131; 51,374(sat); 55,414(sun)
Last Audit: September 30, 2009
Price: 3.70/wk (carrier, dS); 16.00/mo (carrier, dS); 182.40/yr (carrier, dS).
Advertising: Open inch rate $68.00
News services: AP, LAT-WP.
Politics: Independent-Republican.
Special Editions: Auto Care (Apr); Generations (+55) (Aug); Celebrate Christmas (Dec); Generations (+55) (Jan); Father's Day (Jun); Generations (+55) (May); Generations (+55) (Nov); Auto Care (Oct).
Special Weekly Sections: Farmers Forum (Fri); Sports (Mon); Travel (S); TV Forum (Sat); Financial (Tues); Food (Wed).
Magazines: Relish (Monthly); Parade (S).
Broadcast Affiliations: KBMY Bismarck, ND; WDAZ Devils Lake, ND; WDAY-AM Fargo, ND; WDAYTV Fargo, ND; WDAZ Grand Forks, ND; KMCY Minot, ND.
Pub./Chrmn./CEO .... William C. Marcil
Pres./COO .... Lloyd Case
CFO .... John Hajostek
HR Dir. .... Kate Freimanis
Gen. Mgr. .... James Boberg
Bus. Mgr. .... Glen Wolf
Adv. Dir. .... Marshall Johnson
Adv. Mgr., Inside Sales .... Sandy Olsen
Adv. Mgr., Outside Sales .... Dan Schmidt
Circ. Mgr., Distr. .... Barb Olson
Circ. Coord., Newspapers in Educ .... Kerri Kava
Ed. .... Matt Von Pinnon
Bus. Ed. .... Craig McEwen
Editorial Page Ed. .... Jack Zaleski
Features Ed. .... John Lamb
Librarian .... Carol Bradley-Bursack
Minnesota Ed. .... Mark Merck
Photo Ed. .... Mike Vosburg
News Ed., Night .... Jay Ulku
Presentation Ed. .... Rob Beer
Mechanical available: Offset; Black and 3 ROP colors; insert accepted - Poly bags and samples; page cutoffs - 22.
Mechanical Specifications: Type page 11 5/8 x 20 3/4; E - 6 cols, 1 7/8, 1/6 between; A - 6 cols, 1 7/8, 1/6 between; C - 9 cols, 1 3/16, 1/8 between.
Commodity Consumption: Avg. Page Number Per Issue - Daily 40; Avg. Page Number Per Issue - Plates Used 48500; Avg. Page Number Per Issue - Saturday 40; Avg. Page Number Per Issue - Sunday 82; widths 55; Newsprint Used - Metric Tons 5000; Printing Ink Used - Black 194500; Print
Equipment EDITORIAL: Front-end Software – Advanced Pub. Technology/Automated Complete Typesetting 2.06.4.; Editorial Hardware – MS/NT Server; Editorial Equipment – APP/Mac Quadra 800, Pentium/PC 233MMX; Editorial Printers – Okidata/Microline 320, HP/LaserJet CLASSIFIED: Front-end Software – PBS/Media Plus 8.3.; Classified Hardware – MS/NT Server; Classified Printers – HP/4000 DISPLAY: Ad make-up applications – PBS, Multi-Ad/Creator 2; Layout Software – Multi-Ad/ALS.; Display Hardware – APP/Power Mac 7600 PRODUCTION: Pagination Software – APT, QPS/QuarkXPress 3.3; Production Equipment – 2-AU/APS 6-108C, Caere/OmniPage 5.0, 2-Digital/1000 Alpha; Scanners – Kk, Nikon, Polaroid/SprintScan Plus, Epson/4996, Epson/10000XL, Polaroid/Sprintscan 4000 PRESSROOM: Line 1 – 8-MAN/Roland Media-Man (Offset, 4 wide) 1993; Line 2 – Press Drive □ Siemens; Folders – MAN/Roland; Pasters – MEG 1993; Reels and Stands – MEG/45 inch 1993; Press control system – 1993 MAILROOM: Counter stackers – 4-QWI/400; Inserters and stuffers – SLS/2000; Bundle tying machines – 3-Samual/NT30; Mailroom control system – Winlines; Addressing machine – 2-Scitex/5120. BUSINESS COMPUTERS: Business Software – GEAC/CIS 7.03, AIM 8.02; Business Hardware – 1-DEC/Alpha 2100

GRAND FORKS

GRAND FORKS HERALD

375 2nd Ave. N., Grand Forks, N.D., 58203-3707; gen tel (701) 780-1100; adv tel 701-780-1160; ed tel (701) 780-1100; adv fax (701) 780-1185; ed fax (701) 780-1123; ed e-mail gfhcity@gfherald.com; web site www.grandforks.com; www.grandforksherald.com
Group: Forum Communications Company
Published: Mon, Tues, Wed, Thur, Fri, Sat, Sun
Weekday Frequency: m
Saturday Frequency: m
Circulation: 26,663; 26,663(sat); 29,916(sun)
Last Audit: Sworn September 30, 2011
Price: 4.32/week;215.00/yr (mon-S), $148.00/yr (fri-S).
Advertising: Open inch rate $47.95
Insert rate: 77.77 cpm 2pp Sun
News services: AP.
Politics: Independent. **Established:** 1874
Advertising not accepted: Y
Own facility?: Y
Special Editions: Spring Car Care (Apr); Back-to-School (Aug); Bride & Groom (Dec); Outlook (Jan); East Grand Forks Pride (Jul); Senior Lifestyles (Jun); Coupon Book (Mar); Chamber of Commerce (May); Senior Lifestyles (Nov); Fall Home Improvement (Oct); College (Sept).
Special Weekly Sections: Entertainment (Fri); Expanded Sports (Mon); Agriculture (Other); Outdoors (S); Business (Sat); Food (Wed).
Magazines: Relish (Monthly); Parade (S).
Pub .... Michael Jacobs
Director of Finance .... Anita Geffre
Adv. Mgr., Classified .... Paula Walden
Circ. Dir. .... Dawn Zimney
Circ. Sales/Mktg .... Marsha Gunderson
Executive Editor .... Mike Jacobs
Mng. Ed. .... Kevin Grinde
News Editor .... Matt Cory
Assigning Ed. .... Kirsten Stromsodt
Editorial Page Ed .... Tom Dennis
Entertainment Writer .... Paulette Tobin
Food Columnist .... Jeff Tiedeman
Photo Ed. .... John Stennes
Religion Reporter .... Steve Lee
Sports Ed. .... Wayne Nelson
IT Dir. .... Mark Young
Prodn. Mgr., Pre Press .... Tina Chisholm
Prodn. Mgr., Pressroom .... Keith Haus
Market Information: ADS; Split run.
Mechanical available: Offset; Black and 3 ROP colors; insert accepted; page cutoffs - 22.
Mechanical Specifications: Type page 10 9/16 x 20 3/4; E - 6 cols, 1 5/8, 1/8 between; A - 6 cols, 1 5/8, 1/8 between; C - 9 cols, 1, 1/16 between.
Commodity Consumption: Avg. Page Number Per Issue - Daily 42; Avg. Page Number Per Issue - Plates Used 40000; Avg. Page Number Per Issue - Sunday 60; widths 27; Newsprint Used - Metric Tons 3200; Printing Ink Used - Black 43000; Printing Ink Used - Color 15000; Printing Ink Us
Equipment EDITORIAL: Front-end Software – AT, HI.; Editorial Hardware – 4-AT/9000, 3-HI/8900; Editorial Printers – 2-Dataproducts/ CLASSIFIED: Front-end Software – DTI; Classified Hardware – DTI; Classified Printers – 1-Dataproducts; Layout Software – 2-HI/8300, APP/Mac. DTI; Display Hardware – HI, APP/Mac 8500; Display Printers – Software □ HI, QPS/QuarkXPress 3.3 PRODUCTION: Pagination Software – HI/8900, HI/2100 CPAG 2.0.; Production Equipment – 2-AU/APS Micro 5, 2-MON/Express, 1-III/3850 Imagesetter; Cameras – C/Spartan III; Scanners – 2-ECR/Autokon 1000 DE PRESSROOM: Line 1 – 8-G/Urbanite 1973; Folders – G/2:1; Reels and Stands – 6-Kohler/Reels, 2-Roll/Stands. MAILROOM: Counter stackers – 1-Id/2000, 1-Id/660, 1-Id/440, 1-BG/108; Inserters and stuffers – 2-MM/227E; Bundle tying machines – 2-MLN/MLN2A; Wrapping singles – 1-Bu/BT16, 1-Bu/BT18; Addressing machine – 2/AVY. BUSINESS COMPUTERS: Business Software – Cyborg; Business Hardware – 1-HP/Spectrum 922RX
Zip Codes served: 582 and 567 inclusive
Delivery method: Mail, Newsstand, Private Carrier, Racks

JAMESTOWN

THE JAMESTOWN SUN

121 Third St. NW, Jamestown, N.D., 58401; gen tel (701) 252-3120; adv tel (701) 252-3120; ed tel (701) 252-3120; gen fax (701) 251-2873; adv fax (701) 952-0025; ed fax (701) 952-8477; gen e-mail js@jamestownsun.com; adv e-mail jsadvertising@daktel.com; ed e-mail kathys@jamestownsun.com; web site www.jamestownsun.com
Group: North Carolina Press Service, Inc.
Published: Mon, Tues, Wed, Thur, Fri, Sat
Weekday Frequency: m
Saturday Frequency: m
Circulation: 6,234; 6,742(sat)
Last Audit: March 31, 2006
Price: 13.00/mo; 135.00/yr.
Advertising: Open inch rate $13.60
News services: AP.
Politics: Independent.
Not Published: New Year; Independence Day; Thanksgiving; Christmas.
Special Editions: Auto Show (Apr); Sport and Home (Feb); Progress (Mar); Fire Prevention (Oct).
Special Weekly Sections: Outdoors (Fri); Food (Sat); TV & Entertainment (Thur); Bridal (Wed).
Magazines: Relish (Monthly); Parade (S).
Pub .... Bruce Henke
Bus. Mgr. .... Kathy Hilgeman
Adv. Dir. .... Gene Keller
Circ. Mgr. .... Jeremy Feldman
Asst. Ed. .... Logan Adams
Picture Ed. .... John M. Steiner
Sports Ed. .... Scott Throlson
Teen-Age/Youth Ed. .... Kathy Steiner
Press Foreman .... Boyd Anderson
Composing Mgr. .... Tina Olson
Market Information: Split run; TMC; Zoned editions.
Mechanical available: Offset; Black and 3 ROP colors; insert accepted; page cutoffs - 22 3/4.
Mechanical Specifications: Type page 12 3/4 x 21 1/2; E - 6 cols, 2, 1/6 between; A - 6 cols, 2, 1/6 between; C - 7 cols, 1 5/8, 1/6 between.
Commodity Consumption: Avg. Page Number Per Issue - Daily 24; Avg. Page Number Per Issue - Plates Used 6000; widths 32; Newsprint Used - Metric Tons 480; Printing Ink Used - Black 10050; Printing Ink Used - Color 1408.
Equipment: Editorial Hardware – 11-M/2800; Editorial Equipment – 1-RSK/TRS 80, 1-RSK/TRS 100; Editorial Printers – 2-APP/Mac LaserWriter. CLASSIFIED: Front-end Software – SunType.; Classified Hardware – IBM; Classified Printers – APP/Mac LaserWriter II DISPLAY: Ad make-up applications – Multi-Ad 4.0, Adobe/Photoshop 4.0, QPS/QuarkXPress 3.32.; Display Hardware – 2-APP/Power Mac 7200, 1-APP/Power Mac 7600; Display Printers – 2-APP/Mac LaserWriter Pro 810, 1-APP/Mac LaserWriter Pro 630; Production Equipment – Multi-Ad, Aldus/FreeHand, QuarkXPress, Adobe/Photoshop; Cameras – DAI/Screen G-24-D-LA; Scanners – Microtek/Scanmaster E6. PRESSROOM: Line 1 – 2-G/Community 1974, 2-G/Community 1991; Line 2 – 4-G/Community 1970; Press Drives – 75-1991; Folders – 1-G/Upper Former 1993.; Bundle tying machines – OVL/415, Bu; Addressing machine – 2/Dispensa-Matic/16. BUSINESS COMPUTERS: Business Software – Nomads/Listmaster; Business Hardware – IBM/Mega 4000, IBM/LEAT

MINOT

MINOT DAILY NEWS

301 Fourth St. SE, Minot, N.D., 58701; gen tel (701) 857-1900; adv tel (701) 857-1900; ed tel (701) 857-1950; gen fax (701) 857-1907; adv fax (701) 857-1907; ed fax (701) 857-1961; gen e-mail mdnews@minotdailynews.com; adv e-mail classads@minotdailynews.com; ed e-mail editor@minotdailynews.com; web site www.minotdailynews.com
Group: Ogden Newspapers
Published: Mon, Tues, Wed, Thur, Fri, Sat, Sun
Weekday Frequency: m
Saturday Frequency: m
Circulation: 16,024; 18,057(sat); 17,648(sun)
Last Audit: ABC September 30, 2011
Price: 14.25/mo (carrier); 162.00/yr.
Advertising: Open inch rate $50.75
Insert rate: varied
News services: AP.
Politics: Independent.
Own facility?: Y
Special Editions: Progress (Apr); Football (Aug); Year in Review (Dec); Bridal (Feb); Health & Fitness (Jan); Back to School (Jul); State Fair (Jun); Design an Ad (Mar); Graduation (May); Pulse (Nov); Norsk Fest (Oct); Hometown (Sept).
Special Weekly Sections: Agriculture (Mon); Outdoor (S); Agriculture (Sat); Best Automotive Day (Thur); Best Food Day (Wed).
Magazines: Parade (S).
Pub. .... Steve Herron
Ad. Dir. .... Doug Corbett
Circ. Dir. .... Steve Ewig
Ed. .... Bryan L. Obenchain
Asst. Ed .... Kent Olson
Copy Desk Chief .... Shelley Bryantt
Features Ed. .... Terry Aman
News Ed. .... David Caldwell
Online Ed. .... Pete Ladendorf
Sports Ed. .... Chris Bierl
MIS/Online Mgr. .... Peter Ladendorf
Circ. Mgr. .... Brian Boesl
Sports Ed. .... Mike Linnell
Market Information: ADS; Split run; TMC; Zoned editions.
Mechanical available: Offset; Black and 3 ROP colors; insert accepted - sample packs and pouches; page cutoffs - 22 3/4.
Mechanical Specifications: Type page 12 x 21

1/2; E - 6 cols, 2 1/16, 1/6 between; A - 6 cols, 1 13/16, 1/6 between; C - 9 cols, 1 9/32, 1/12 between.
Commodity Consumption: Avg. Page Number Per Issue - Daily 28; Avg. Page Number Per Issue - Plates Used 16000; Avg. Page Number Per Issue - Sunday 54; widths 24; Newsprint Used - Short Tons 2000; Printing Ink Used - Black 42000; Printing Ink Used - Color 4000.
Equipment EDITORIAL: Front-end Software – MS/NT.; Editorial Hardware – MS/NT; Editorial Equipment – APP/Mac; Editorial Printers – APP/Mac LaserWriter II, MON/Imagemaster 1270, HP/2100 CLASSIFIED: Front-end Software – MS/NT.; Classified Hardware – MS/NT; Classified Printers – APP/Mac LaserWriter II, MON/Imagemaster 1270, HP/2100 DISPLAY: Ad make-up applications – NTI; Layout Software – APP/Mac.; Display Hardware – APP/Mac; Display Printers – APP/Mac LaserWriter II, MON/Imagemaster 1270, HP/2100, EPSON/1520 PRODUCTION: Pagination Software – QPS/QuarkXPress 4.01.; Production Equipment – Magnum; Cameras – SCREEN; Scanners – VG, Epson PRESSROOM: Line 1 – G/Urbanite 1990. MAILROOM: Counter stackers – Id/440, Id/660, QWI/400; Inserters and stuffers – HI; Bundle tying machines – Bu, MLN; Addressing machine – Ch; Other equipment – MM/1509 W/2-1528 cover feeders.; Business Hardware – NCR

VALLEY CITY

VALLEY CITY TIMES-RECORD

146 Third St. NE, Valley City, N.D., 58072-0697; gen tel (701) 845-0463; adv tel (701) 845-0463; ed tel (701) 845-0463; gen fax (701) 845-0175; adv fax (701) 845-0175; ed fax (701) 845-0175; gen e-mail vctr@daktel.com; adv e-mail trads@daktel.com; ed e-mail treditor@daktel.com
Group: North Carolina Press Service, Inc.
Published: Mon, Tues, Wed, Thur, Fri
Weekday Frequency: e
Circulation: 2,610
Last Audit: October 1, 2003
Price: 10.00/mo; 95.00/yr; 54.00/6mo.
Advertising: Open inch rate $10.88
News services: AP, NEA.
Politics: Independent.
Not Published: New Year; Memorial Day; Independence Day; Labor Day; Thanksgiving; Christmas.
Special Editions: Car Care Tab (Apr); Back-to-School (Aug); Last Minute Gift Guide (Dec); Valentines (Feb); First Baby of the Year Tab (Jan); Progress (Jul); Senior Scene Tab (Jun); Girl Scouts (Mar); Graduation Tab (May); Holiday Preview (Nov); Fire Prevention Tab (Oct);
Special Weekly Sections: Church Directory (Fri); Business Page (Mon-fri); TV (Thur); Ag Page (Wed); Super Service Directory (Weekly).
Magazines: T-R Shopper (Other); American Profile (Weekly).
Pub. .... Nikki Zinke
Adv. Mgr. .... Mae Oss
Circ. Mgr. .... Brenda Tompt
Arts/Entertainment Ed. .... Brenda Gaarder
News Ed. .... Lee Morris
Composing Mgr. .... Pam Stark
Market Information: TMC; Zoned editions.
Mechanical available: Offset; Black and 1 ROP colors; insert accepted - self-adhesive notes, single sheet fliers; page cutoffs - 22 3/4.
Mechanical Specifications: Type page 11 3/4 x 21; E - 6 cols, 2, 1/8 between; A - 6 cols, 2, 1/8 between; C - 6 cols, 2, 1/8 between.
Commodity Consumption: Avg. Page Number Per Issue - Daily 10; Avg. Page Number Per Issue - Plates Used 2000; widths 25; Newsprint Used - Short Tons 140.
Equipment; Editorial Hardware – APP/Mac; Editorial Printers – GCC/Elite XL 20/600.; Classified Hardware – APP/Mac; Classified Printers – APP/Mac LaserWriter. DISPLAY: Ad make-up applications – Multi-Ad, Adobe/PageMaker; Layout Software – PC.; Display Hardware – APP/Mac; Display Printers – GCC/Elite XL 20/600; Production Equipment – APP/Mac; Cameras – 1-B/Commander; Scanners – Microtek/E-3.; Bundle tying machines – 1/Bu; Addressing machine – 1-/Am.; Business Hardware – APP/Mac

WAHPETON

THE DAILY NEWS

601 Dakota Ave., Wahpeton, N.D., 58074-0760; gen tel (701) 642-8585; adv tel (701) 642-8585; ed tel (701) 642-8585; gen fax (701) 642-1501; adv fax (701) 642-6068; ed fax (701) 642-1501; adv e-mail pamm@wahpetondailynews.com; web site www.wahpetondailynews.com

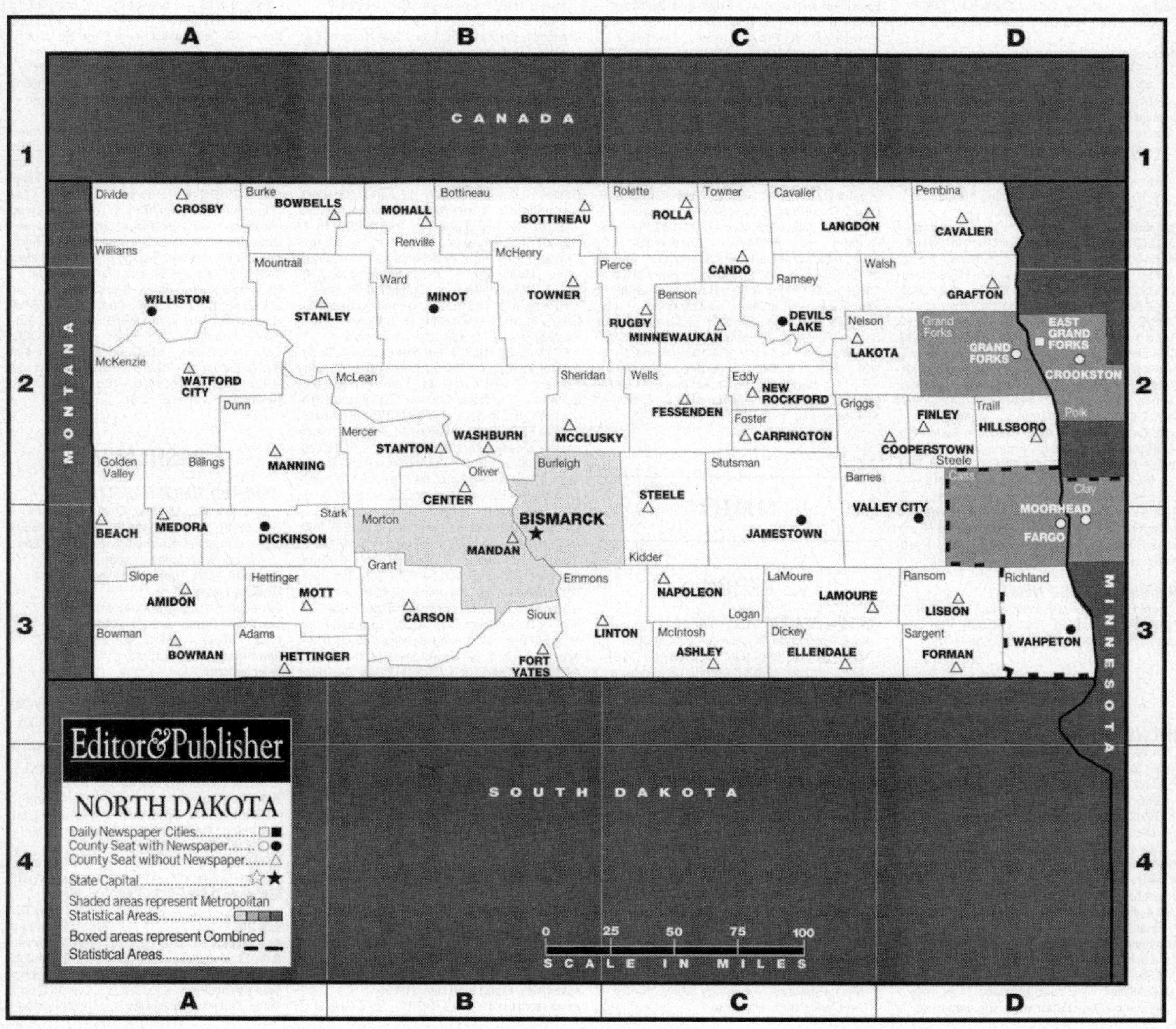

Published: Tues, Wed, Thur, Fri, Sun
Weekday Frequency: e
Circulation: 2,667; 2,883(sun)
Last Audit: March 31, 2007
Price: 10.50/mo; 102.00/yr, $130.00/yr (out of zone); 30.00/3mo, $55.00/6mo, $85.00/6mo (out of zone).
Advertising: Open inch rate $11.85
News services: AP.
Politics: Independent.
Not Published: New Year; Memorial Day; Independence Day; Labor Day; Thanksgiving; Christmas.
Special Editions: Progress Issue (Annually); School Activities Issue (Fall); News in Review (Jan); Voter's Guide (election years) (Nov); Bridal Issue (Other).
Magazines: Channeling (TV Section) (Fri); American Profile (Weekly).
Pub. ....Ken Harty
Adv. Mgr. ....Pam Marquart
News Ed. ....Anna Jauloa
Sports Ed. ....Scott Sorum
Prodn. Foreman, Composing ....Sharla Nordick
Prodn. Mgr ....Sandy Kraft
Prodn. Mgr., Pre Press/Prodn. Mgr., Pressroom Mark Lahaise
Market Information: TMC.
Mechanical available: Offset; Black and 3 ROP colors; insert accepted; page cutoffs - 21 3/4.
Mechanical Specifications: Type page 11 7/8 x 21; E - 6 cols, 1 7/8, 1/8 between; A - 6 cols, 1 7/8, 1/8 between; C - 8 cols, 1 3/8, 1/16 between.
Commodity Consumption: Avg. Page Number Per Issue - Daily 14; Avg. Page Number Per Issue - Plates Used 6000; Avg. Page Number Per Issue - Sunday 24; widths 12 1/2; Newsprint Used - Short Tons 242; Printing Ink Used - Black 8680; Printing Ink Used - Color 250; Printing Ink Used
Equipment EDITORIAL: Front-end Software – QPS/QuarkXPress 4.04.; Editorial Hardware – Mk/1100 Plus, APP/Mac G3; Editorial Equipment – Xante/Accel-a-Writer 36, HP/ScanJet 5300C; Editorial Printers – HP/LaserJet 5000N CLASSIFIED: Front-end Software – QPS/QuarkXPress 4.0, Baseview/News Edit Pro 3.1.; Classified Hardware – APP/Mac G3; Classified Printers – HP/LaserJet 5000N DISPLAY: Ad make-up applications – QPS/QuarkXPress 4.04.; Display Hardware – APP/Mac G3; Display Printers – HP/Laser Jet 5000N PRODUCTION: Pagination Software – QPS/QuarkXPress 4.04.; Production Equipment – HP/LaserJet 5000N; Cameras – 1-B; Scanners – Umax/Astra 1200S PRESSROOM: Line 1 – 6-G/Community single width; Folders – 1-G/Community.; Bundle tying machines – 2-Felin/Pak-Tyer; Addressing machine – 1-Am/R500. BUSINESS COMPUTERS: Business Software – Vision Data; Business Hardware – DEC

WAHPETON DAILY NEWS

Post Office Box 760, Wahpeton, N.D., 58074
Published: Tues, Wed, Thur, Fri, Sun
Last Audit: September 30, 2011Ken Harty

WILLISTON

WILLISTON DAILY HERALD

14 W. Fourth St., Williston, N.D., 58801; gen tel (701) 572-2165; adv tel (701) 572-2165; ed tel (701) 572-2165; gen fax (701) 572-1965; adv fax (701) 572-9563; ed fax (701) 572-9563; ed e-mail news@willistonherald.com; web site www.willistonherald.com
Published: Mon, Tues, Wed, Thur, Fri, Sun
Weekday Frequency: e
Circulation: 4,566; 4,566(sun)
Last Audit: March 31, 2007
Price: 8.50/mo; 99.00/yr.
Advertising: Open inch rate $12.60
News services: AP, TMS.
Politics: 1904
Not Published: New Year; Memorial Day; Independence Day; Labor Day; Thanksgiving; Christmas.
Special Editions: Spring Home & Garden (Apr); Back-to-School (Aug); Christmas Greetings (Dec); Valentine's Day (Feb); Crazee Days (Jul); County Fair (Jun); National Agriculture Day (Mar); National Hospital Week (May); Christmas Kick-Off (Nov); Basketball Tournament (Oct);
Special Weekly Sections: TV Guide (S).
Pub. ....Mitsy Moe
Bus. Mgr. ....Beverly Forthun
Adv. Mgr. ....Wanda Olaf
Market Information: Split run; TMC; Zoned editions.
Mechanical available: Offset; Black and 3 ROP colors; insert accepted; page cutoffs - 21 1/2.
Mechanical Specifications: Type page 13 x 21; E - 6 cols, 2 1/14, 1/8 between; A - 6 cols, 2 1/14, 1/8 between; C - 9 cols, 1 3/8, 1/12 between.
Commodity Consumption: Avg. Page Number Per Issue - Daily 12; Avg. Page Number Per Issue - Plates Used 6000; Avg. Page Number Per Issue - Sunday 18; widths 28; Newsprint Used - Short Tons 410; Printing Ink Used - Black 12000; Printing Ink Used - Color 600; Printing Ink Used -
Equipment EDITORIAL: Front-end Software – QPS/QuarkXPress, Adobe/Photoshop, Baseview/Newsedit Pro.; Editorial Hardware – APP/Mac 7200-120, APP/Mac 7300-180, APP/Mac 7600-120; Editorial Printers – HP/LaserWriter 5000N, Unity/1800XL Plus CLASSIFIED: Front-end Software – QPS/QuarkXPress, Adobe/Photoshop, Baseview/NewsEdit, Baseview/Class Pro.; Classified Hardware – APP/Mac 7200-120; Classified Printers – HP/Laser Writer 5000N, Unity/1800XL Plus DISPLAY: Ad make-up applications – Multi-Ad/Creator, Caere/OmniPage, Caere/OmniPhoto; Display Hardware – APP/Mac IIci, APP/Mac 7200-120; Display Printers – APP/Mac LaserWriter II, Unity/1800XL Plus, HP/LaserWriter 5000N PRODUCTION: Pagination Software – QPS/QuarkXPress 3.32c, Baseview/NewsEdit Pro 2.2.2.; Production Equipment – 1-Nu, Unity/1800 XL Plus, HP/5000 N; Cameras – B; Scanners – Epson, Nikon/LS 1000 PRESSROOM: Line 1 – 5-HI/V-15A 1985; Folders – 2-HI/F-7 (with 1 balloon).; Inserters and stuffers – KR/512; Bundle tying machines – EAM-Mosca/RO-M.; Business Hardware – Ethernet, APP/Mac

OHIO

AKRON

AKRON BEACON JOURNAL

44 E. Exchange St., Akron, Ohio, 44309-0640; gen tel (330) 996-3000; adv tel (330) 996-3333; ed tel (330) 996-3512; gen fax (330) 376-9235; adv fax (330) 996-3074; ed fax (330) 996-3033; ed e-mail vop@thebeaconjournal.com; web site www.ohio.com
Group: Ohio Newspaper Services, Inc.
Published: Mon, Tues, Wed, Thur, Fri, Sat
Weekday Frequency: m
Saturday Frequency: m
Circulation: 87,780; 107,834(sat); 125,227(sun)
Last Audit: ABC September 30, 2011
Price: 8.52/wk (mail); 34.08/mo (mail); 443.04/yr (mail).
Advertising: Open inch rate $123.87
News services: AP, MCT, LAT-WP, NYT, RN.
Politics: Independent.
Special Editions: Spring Golf (Apr); Parade of Homes (Aug); Online Holiday Shopping (Dec); Personal Technology (Feb); Personal Finance (Jan); Ohio College (Jul); Looking Good, Feeling Good (Jun); Best Homes (Mar); Personal Technology (May); Winter Car Care (Nov); Bridal Ga
Special Weekly Sections: Design (Fri); Business Extra (Mon); Real Estate (Sat); Enjoy! (Thur); Essentials (Tues); Food (Wed).
Magazines: Channels (S).
Pub. ....Andrea Mathews
Vice Pres., Admin./Finance ....John Kovatch
Vice Pres., HR ....Aaron Berg
Adv. Dir., Retail/Direct Mktg. ....Alton Brown
Adv. Mgr., Classified ....Christine Sabel
Adv. Mgr., CTS ....Jim Bye
Circ. Dir. ....Jim DeLuca
Asst. Mng. Ed., Features ....Kathy Fraze
Asst. Mng. Ed., Photos/Graphics .Susan Kirkman
Night Mng. Ed. ....Bruce Winges
Exec. News Ed. ....Mark Turner
Bus. Ed. ....Steve Berta
Columnist, Bus. ....Diane Evans
Columnist, Local ....Jewell Cardwell
Columnist, Local ....David Giffels
Copy Desk Chief ....James Kavanaugh
Editorial Cartoonist ....L. Chip Bok
Editorial Page Ed. ....Michael Douglas
Market Information: Split run; Zoned editions.
Mechanical available: Flexography; Black and 3 ROP colors; insert accepted; page cutoffs - 23 9/16.
Mechanical Specifications: Type page 12 7/8 x 22; E - 6 cols, 2 1/16, 1/8 between; A - 6 cols, 2 1/16, 1/8 between; C - 10 cols, 1 3/16, 1/8 between.
Commodity Consumption: Avg. Page Number Per Issue - Daily 62; Avg. Page Number Per Issue - Plates Used 165860; Avg. Page Number Per Issue - Sunday 125; widths 27; Newsprint Used - Metric Tons 23168; Newsprint Used - Short Tons 25538; Printing Ink Used - Black 642976; Printing
Equipment; Editorial Hardware – 6-Tandem/K1000, 150-SII/MTX layout workstations; Editorial Equipment – 3-Lf/AP Leaf Picture Desk, 2-Lf/Leafscan 35, Lf/Leafax 35, III/D, Sharp/Flatbed, 4-APP/Mac fx; Editorial Printers – 1-TI/810, 2-HP/LaserJet, 2-IBM/PPS II, 1-HP/755CM, 4-Lexmark/11x17, 1-Lexmark CLASSIFIED: Front-end Software – SII.; Classified Hardware – 6-Tandem/K1000, 70-SII/AMTX workstations; Classified Printers – 6-HP/LaserJet DISPLAY: Ad make-up applications – III, Multi-Ad/Creator, QPS/QuarkXPress, Pitstop/Pro 4.5; Display Hardware – 7-APP/Mac, 2-Umax, 1-Eskofot/Scanner, Scanmaster/7500, 1-Eskoscan/1318; Display Printers – 1-HP/LaserJet, 1-III/VP 600, Tektronix/300 I, Tektronix/580, GEI/Colorproof; Production Equipment – 2-Na/FP II (flexo), 1-AU/APS, 1-III/3850 Turbo, 3-LE/Online; Cameras – C/NewsPager; Scanners – ECR/720, ECR/8400.; Line 3 – MAN/Flexoman-double width (7 units; 2-5 color MLP, 1-1997, 3-1997; Line 4 – MAN/Flexoman-double width (7 units; 2-5 color MLP, 1-1997, 3-1997; Line 5 – MAN/Flexoman-double width (7 units; 2-5 color MLP, 1-1998, 3-1998; Folders – 3-MAN/3:2; Pasters – Pasters ☐ MAILROOM: Counter stackers – 5-QWI/350, 4-QWI/300; Inserters and stuffers – AM Graphics/NP 630 29:1; Bundle tying machines – 5/Power Strap/PSN-6, 7-/Power Strap/News Tyler 2000, 1-Samuel/P940 Manual Tyer; Wrapping singles – 5-QWI 3/4 wrap w/ Cobra ink jet; Addressing machine – Addres BUSINESS COMPUTERS: Business Software – Microsoft/Office; Business Hardware – 1-HP/3000 Series 969/120

ALLIANCE

THE REVIEW

40 S. Linden Ave., Alliance, Ohio, 44601-0180; gen tel (330) 821-1200; ed tel (330) 821-1300; gen fax (330) 821-8258; gen e-mail reviewedit@alliancelink.com; adv e-mail reviewads@alliancelink.com; web site www.the-review.com; www.alliancelink.com
Published: Mon, Tues, Wed, Thur, Fri, Sat
Weekday Frequency: m
Circulation: 10,826; 10,826(sat)
Last Audit: September 30, 2008
Price: 9.50/mo; 95.00/yr; 50.75/6mo.
Advertising: Open inch rate $16.95
News services: AP, CNS, DF, DJ, NYT, SHNS, TMS.
Politics: Republican. **Established:** 1888
Not Published: New Year; Memorial Day; Independence Day; Labor Day; Thanksgiving; Christmas.
Special Editions: Year in Review (Jan).
Special Weekly Sections: Real Estate (Fri); Church Page (Sat); Entertainment-Let's Go (Thur); Business Page (Wed).
Magazines: TV Magazine (Fri); American Profile (Weekly).
Pub. ....G. Charles Dix
Gen. Mgr. ....Robert C. Shaffer
Adv. Dir. ....Jeff Kaplan
Circ. Dir. ....Ken Pagani
Exec. Ed. ....Sarah Reed Gold
Mng. Ed. ....................K.C. Held
Accent Ed. ....Shannon Harsh
Copy Ed. ....John Whitacre
Sports Ed. ....Mike Brown
Web Ed. ....Joni Bowen
Market Information: ADS; Split run; TMC; Zoned editions.
Mechanical available: Offset; Black and 3 ROP colors; insert accepted; page cutoffs - 21 1/2.
Mechanical Specifications: Type page 13 x 21 1/2; E - 6 cols, 2 1/16, 1/8 between; A - 6 cols, 2 1/16, 1/8 between; C - 6 cols, 2 1/16, 1/8 between.
Commodity Consumption: Avg. Page Number Per Issue - Daily 20; Avg. Page Number Per Issue - Saturday 20; widths 12 1/2; Newsprint Used - Short Tons 1000; Printing Ink Used - Black 4000; Printing Ink Used - Color 350.
Equipment EDITORIAL: Front-end Software – Baseview.; Editorial Hardware – APP/Mac; Editorial Printers – 6-New Gen/DesignXpress CLASSIFIED: Front-end Software – Vision Data.; Classified Hardware – APP/Mac; Classified Printers – HP DISPLAY: Ad make-up applications – Data Sciences; Layout Software – Baseview.; Display Hardware – Wyse/Terminal, Dec/Processor; Display Printers – Okidata, Tally PRODUCTION: Pagination Software – Baseview.; Production Equipment – 1-Nu, Ultre/94E, Konica/K-550; Cameras – Kk/PMT; Scanners – Umax, AG PRESSROOM: Line 1 – 6-G/Urbanite 1967; Folders – 1 MAILROOM: Counter stackers – BG/Count-O-Veyor; Inserters and stuffers – MM; Bundle tying machines – Bu.; Audio Hardware – Educom of Ohio; Business Hardware – DSI

ASHLAND

ASHLAND TIMES-GAZETTE

40 E. 2nd St., Ashland, Ohio, 44805; gen tel (419) 281-0581; gen fax (419) 281-5591; gen e-mail newsroom@times-gazette.com; web site www.times-gazette.com
Published: Mon, Tues, Wed, Thur, Fri, Sat
Weekday Frequency: m
Circulation: 11,009; 11,009(sat)
Last Audit: September 30, 2009
Price: 1.95/wk; 8.45/mo; 99.75/yr.
Advertising: Open inch rate $14.00
News services: AP.
Politics: Independent. **Established:** 1885
Not Published: New Year; Memorial Day; Independence Day; Labor Day; Thanksgiving; Christmas.
Special Editions: Auto Tab (Apr); Football Preview (Aug); Christmas Songbook (Dec); Senior Citizens (Feb); Bridal Tab (Jan); Senior Citizens (Jul); Balloon Fest (Jun); Spring Home Improvement (Mar); Hospital Nursing (May); Holiday Cookbook (Nov); Health Focus (Oct); Fair (
Special Weekly Sections: Church (Fri); Farm (Sat); Health (Thur); Best Food Day (Wed).
Magazines: TV Weekly (Sat).
Pub. ....Troy Dix
Adv. Dir. ....Jason Gwennup
Circ. Mgr. ....Deb Boreman
Mng. Ed. ....Ted Daniels
Chief Photographer ....Tom Puskar
Teen-Age/Youth Ed. ....Jarred Opatz
Prodn. Foreman, Composing ....Debby Iceman

Market Information: TMC.
Mechanical available: Offset; Black and 3 ROP colors; insert accepted - single sheet; page cutoffs - 22 3/4.
Mechanical Specifications: Type page 12 1/2 x 21 1/2; E - 6 cols, 1 5/6, 1/8 between; A - 6 cols, 1 1/4, 1/8 between; C - 9 cols, 1 1/4, 1/8 between.
Commodity Consumption: Avg. Page Number Per Issue - Daily 24; Avg. Page Number Per Issue - Plates Used 12000; widths 25; Newsprint Used - Metric Tons 750; Newsprint Used - Short Tons 826; Printing Ink Used - Black 13438; Printing Ink Used - Color 723; Printing Ink Used - Pages
Equipment EDITORIAL: Front-end Software – Baseview.; Editorial Hardware – 2-Data General/Unix Server, 1-Data General/AV Disk Array, APP/Power Mac G3, APP/Power Mac G4; Editorial Printers – HP/Rip, Konica/Rip CLASSIFIED: Front-end Software – Baseview.; Classified Hardware – APP/iMac; Classified Printers – Okidata DISPLAY: Ad make-up applications – DSI.; Display Hardware – APP/Mac; Display Printers – APP/Mac LaserWriter NTX, 2-ECR/VR 36 Imagesetter PRODUCTION: Pagination Software – Baseview.; Production Equipment – 1-Nu, Adobe/Photoshop, QuarkXPress; Scanners – Epson PRESSROOM: Line 1 – 8-G/Community 1972, 1-G/Community 1992. MAILROOM: Counter stackers – BG/Count-O-Veyor; Bundle tying machines – Tri-Star/210, Mosca.; Business Hardware – DSI

ASHTABULA

STAR BEACON

4626 Park Ave., Ashtabula, Ohio, 44004; gen tel (440) 998-2323; adv tel (440) 994-3241; ed tel (440) 994-3243; gen fax (440) 998-5870 (admin); ed fax (440) 998-7938; adv e-mail classifieds@starbeacon.com; ed e-mail nfeditor@suite224.net; web site www.starbeacon.com

Published: Mon, Tues, Wed, Thur, Fri, Sat, Sun
Weekday Frequency: m
Saturday Frequency: m
Circulation: 15,247; 15,247(sat); 16,406(sun)
Last Audit: September 30, 2009
Price: 2.50/wk; 139.00/yr.
Advertising: Open inch rate $32.59
News services: AP.
Politics: Independent. **Established:** 1885
Special Editions: Football Features (Aug); Christmas (Dec); Bridal (Jan); Dog Days (Jul); Ashtabula County Almanac (Jun); Washington's Birthday (Mar); Health Care (May); Family Life (Monthly); Women in Business (Nov); Covered Bridge (Oct); Progress (Sept).
Special Weekly Sections: Entertainment (Fri); Best Food Day (Mon); Best Food Day (S); Church News (Sat).
Magazines: Relish (Monthly); TV Scene Magazine (S); American Profile (Weekly).
Pub. ....Jim Frustere
Adv. Dir. ....Jamie Beacom
Circ. Mgr. ....T. Mark Shorts
Ed. ....Neil Freider
Communities Ed. ....Nicki Wilpula
Lifestyle Ed. ....Carl Feather
Photographer ....Warren Dillaway
Special Sections Ed. ....Bob Lebzelter
Sports Ed. ....Don McCormack
Prodn. Dir. ....Jim Hanson
Market Information: ADS; Split run; TMC; Zoned editions.
Mechanical available: Offset; Black and 3 ROP colors; insert accepted - any; page cutoffs - 21 1/4.
Mechanical Specifications: Type page 13 x 21 1/2; E - 6 cols, 2 1/16, 1/8 between; A - 6 cols, 2 1/16, 1/8 between; C - 9 cols, 1 1/2, 1/16 between.
Commodity Consumption: Avg. Page Number Per Issue - Daily 24; Avg. Page Number Per Issue - Sunday 40; widths 27 1/2; Newsprint Used - Short Tons 2169; Printing Ink Used - Pages Printed 9812.
Equipment EDITORIAL: Front-end Software –

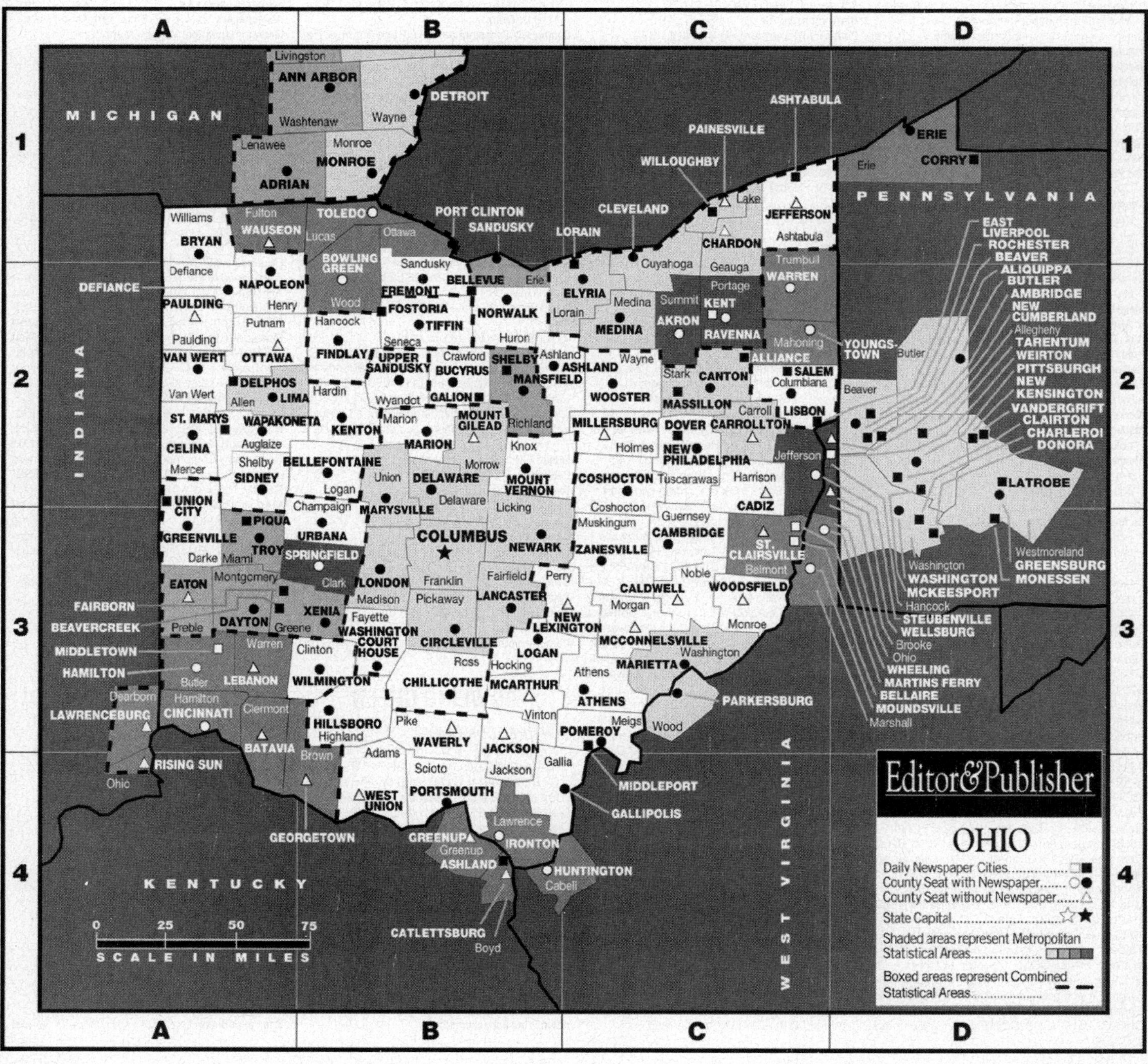

Mk.; Editorial Hardware – Mk, APP/Mac, IBM; Editorial Equipment – 1-Lf, 1-Lf; Editorial Printers – 1-II CLASSIFIED: Front-end Software – Mk.; Classified Hardware – 1-Mk; Classified Equipment – IBM; Classified Printers – 1-TI DISPLAY: Ad make-up applications – ATT; Layout Software – ATT.; Display Hardware – ATT; Production Equipment – Tegra/Varityper 5300, 17-AG/660; Cameras – 1-Nu. PRESSROOM: Line 1 – 6-G/Urbanite (1 color deck); Folders – 1 MAILROOM: Counter stackers – BG/108; Inserters and stuffers – MM/227; Bundle tying machines – Sa/S1100.; Business Hardware – 6-ATT/3B2-500, 1-DEC/1173, 1-DEC

ATHENS

THE ATHENS MESSENGER

9300 Johnson Rd., Athens, Ohio, 45701; gen tel (740) 592-6612; gen fax (740) 592-4647; gen e-mail info@athensmessenger.com; adv e-mail rwallace@athensmessenger.com; web site www.athensmessenger.com

Group: American Consolidated Media
Published: Mon, Tues, Wed, Thur, Fri, Sat, Sun
Weekday Frequency: m
Saturday Frequency: m
Circulation: 11,272; 11,272(sat); 11,375(sun)
Last Audit: March 31, 2006
Price: 2.20/wk (carrier); 9.53/mo; 109.25/yr.
Advertising: Open inch rate $23.94
News services: AP, SHNS.
Not Published: Memorial Day; Independence Day; Christmas.
Special Editions: New Babies (Apr); Football Tab (Aug); Wedding Guide (Feb); County Fair (Jul); Fashion (Mar); Spring/Summer Car Care (May); Basketball Tab (Nov); Fall Car Care (Oct).
Special Weekly Sections: Church Page (Fri); Home & Garden (S).
Magazines: Color Comics (S); American Profile (Weekly).
Circ. Mgr. ....Joseph Essman
Prodn. Supvr. ....Danny Turner
Regional VP and Publisher ....Monica Nieporte
Editor ....Angela Mitro
Advertising Manager ....Rhonda Wallace
Market Information: ADS; TMC.
Mechanical available: Offset; Black and 3 ROP colors; page cutoffs - 22 3/4.
Mechanical Specifications: Type page 11 5/8 x 21 1/4; E - 5 cols, 2 3/8, 3/16 between; A - 6 cols, 1 13/16, 3/16 between; C - 8 cols, 1 7/16, 3/16 between.
Commodity Consumption: Avg. Page Number Per Issue - Daily 16; Avg. Page Number Per Issue - Plates Used 20000; Avg. Page Number Per Issue - Sunday 38; widths 34; Newsprint Used - Metric Tons 1256; Printing Ink Used - Black 30000; Printing Ink Used - Color 6000; Printing Ink Use
Equipment EDITORIAL: Front-end Software – Baseview/News Edit Pro I QUE 3.1.8.; Editorial Hardware – 18-APP/Mac G3; Editorial Printers – Okidata/Pacemark 3410, Okidata/MicroLine 320 CLASSIFIED: Front-end Software – Baseview/Ad Manager Pro 2.0.5.; Classified Hardware – 3-APP/Mac G3 DISPLAY: Ad make-up applications – QPS/QuarkXPress, Aldus/PageMaker, Multi-Ad/Creator; Display Hardware – 2-APP/Mac Quadra 800, 2-APP/Mac Quadra 650, 1-APP/Mac IIci, 1-Global/Dos-486 PRODUCTION: Pagination Software – QPS; Production Equipment – 2-NewGen/Turbo PS-660B, 2-NewGen/Design Express 1200 dpi, ECR/VRL 45HS Imagesetter, Xante/Accel-a-Writer 8200; Cameras – 1-C/Spartan III, 1-C/Vertical; Scanners – 1-ECR/Autokon 1030N, Umax/UC-1260, Agfa/Accas II, Nikon/LS 2000 PRESSROOM: Line 1 – 5-G/Urbanite 1972, 1-G/Urbanite 1980, 1-G/Urbanite 1992; Line 2 – 4-G/Community 1983, 2-G/Community 1986; Press Drives – 3; Folders – 2; Press registration system – G/pin system. MAILROOM: Counter stackers – 1-HI/2510; Inserters and stuffers – 1/MM; Bundle tying machines – 1-Bu/Akebone, 2-Dynaric/RLM-1; Addressing machine – 1-Ch/596. BUSINESS COMPUTERS: Business Software – Vision Data; Business Hardware – 8 terminals, 3 PC's-Sun Ultra 10
Delivery method: Newsstand, Private Carrier, Racks

BELLEFONTAINE

BELLEFONTAINE EXAMINER

127 E. Chillicothe Ave., Bellefontaine, Ohio, 43311; gen tel (937) 592-3060; gen fax (937) 592-4463; gen e-mail news@examiner.org; adv e-mail ads@examiner.org; web site www.examiner.org

Group: Ohio Newspaper Services, Inc.
Published: Mon, Tues, Wed, Thur, Fri, Sat
Weekday Frequency: e
Saturday Frequency: m
Circulation: 9,130; 9,130(sat)
Last Audit: September 30, 2006
Price: 1.50/wk (carrier), $1.60/wk (motor route); 5.80/mo (carrier), $6.40/mo (motor route); 109.20/yr.
Advertising: Open inch rate $11.75
News services: AP.
Politics: Independent. **Established:** 1892
Not Published: New Year; Memorial Day; Independence Day; Labor Day; Thanksgiving; Christmas.
Own facility?: Y
Special Editions: Real Estate Tab (Apr); Sale Days (Aug); Christmas Greetings (Dec); Home Maintenance (Fall); Sale Days (Feb); Real Estate Tab (Jul); Bridal (Jun); Indian Lake Resort Tab (May); Real Estate Tab (Sept); Home Maintenance (Spring).
Pub. ....Janet K. Hubbard
Vice Pres. ....Jon B. Hubbard
Adv. Mgr. ....Bob Chapman
Circ. Mgr. ....Jill Thomas
Ed. ....Miriam Baier
Society/Educ. Ed. ....Sue Pitts
Sports Ed. ....Matt Hammond
Market Information: TMC.
Mechanical available: Offset; Black and 3 ROP colors; insert accepted; page cutoffs - 22 3/4.
Mechanical Specifications: Type page 13 x 21 1/2; E - 6 cols, 2 1/16, 1/8 between; A - 6 cols, 2 1/16, 1/8 between; C - 8 cols, 1 3/8, 1/16 between.
Commodity Consumption: Avg. Page Number Per Issue - Daily 22; Avg. Page Number Per Issue - Plates Used 8850; widths 27 1/2; Newsprint Used - Short Tons 562; Printing Ink Used - Black 16800; Printing Ink Used - Color 6200; Printing Ink Used - Pages Printed 5720.
Equipment EDITORIAL: Front-end Software – Dewar/Disc Net IV.; Editorial Hardware – Dewar/Disc Net IV, 16-AST/286, 5-SIA/386; Editorial Equipment – dBase/IV, XYQUEST/XyWrite III, Novell/Netware; Editorial Printers – Okidata/320 CLASSIFIED: Front-end Software – Dewar/Disc Net IV.; Classified Hardware – Dewar/Disc Net IV, 1-AST/286; Classified Printers – Okidata/393 DISPLAY: Ad make-up applications – Dewar/Discovery; Layout Software – Dewar, 2-SIA/386.; Display Hardware – Dewar/Discovery; Production Equipment – 1-Nu/Flip Top FT40APRNS; Cameras – 1-R/500.; Folders – 1 MAILROOM: Counter stackers – 1-BG/106; Inserters and stuffers – 5/KAN; Bundle tying machines – 1-/Bu, 1-EAM-Mosca; Addressing machine – 1-Ch/515. AUDIO: Audio Software – New Horizons/Info-Connect; Audio Hardware – Info-Connect, Northgate/486 BUSINESS COMPUTERS: Business Software – MSSI, Synaptic; Business Hardware – 2-Laser/486

BELLEVUE

BELLEVUE GAZETTE

250 Castalia St., Suite E, Bellevue, Ohio, 44811-0269; gen tel (419) 483-4190; adv tel (419) 483-4190; ed tel (419) 483-4190; gen fax (419) 483-3737; adv fax (419) 483-3737; ed fax (419) 483-3737; adv e-mail ads@gazettepublishingco.com; ed e-mail news@gazettepublishingco.com; web site www.ourtownsnews.com/Bel

Published: Tues, Wed, Thur, Fri, Sat
Weekday Frequency: m
Saturday Frequency: m
Circulation: 2,580; 2,580(sat)
Last Audit: September 30, 2006
Price: 2.40/wk; 10.50/mo; 185.00/yr.
Advertising: Open inch rate $11.60
News services: AP.
Politics: Independent. **Established:** 1867
Not Published: New Year; Memorial Day; Independence Day; Labor Day; Thanksgiving; Christmas.
Own facility?: N
Publisher ....Rick Miller
Editor ....Becky Brooks
Market Information: TMC.
Mechanical available: Offset; Black and 3 ROP colors; insert accepted - any; page cutoffs - 22 3/4.
Mechanical Specifications: Type page 13 3/4 x 21 1/2; E - 6 cols, 2 1/16, 1/8 between; A - 6 cols, 2 1/16, 1/8 between; C - 9 cols, 1 3/8, 1/16 between.
Commodity Consumption: Avg. Page Number Per Issue - Daily 10; Avg. Page Number Per Issue - Plates Used 3780; widths 13 3/4; Newsprint Used - Short Tons 500; Printing Ink Used - Black 15660; Printing Ink Used - Color 1172; Printing Ink Used - Pages Printed 3518.
Equipment: Editorial Hardware – Mk/3000; Editorial Equipment – 10-AP/Photostream.; Layout Software – 2-APP/Mac, Mk/Mycro-Comp Ad-Writer.; Production Equipment – 2-APP/Mac Plus Laser, 1-APP/Mac LaserWriter NTX; Cameras – R. PRESSROOM: Line 1 – 5-G/Community. MAILROOM: Counter stackers – 1-BG/Count-O-Veyor; Inserters and stuffers – 1-KAN/401; Bundle tying machines – 2-Bu/Quarter Poly Strapper, 2-Bu/String; Addressing machine – KR.
Delivery method: Mail, Racks

THE BELLEVUE GAZETTE

250 Castalia St. Suite E, Bellevue, Ohio, 44811-1425; gen tel (419) 483-4190; adv tel 419-483-4190; gen fax (419) 483-3737; adv fax 419-483-3737; adv e-mail sales@gazettepublishingco.com; ed e-mail news@gazettepublishingco.com; web site www.gazettepublishingco.com

Group: Ohio Community Media
Published: Tues, Wed, Thur, Fri, Sat
Weekday Frequency: All day
Saturday Frequency: All day
Circulation: 1,675; 1,675(sat)
News services: AP
Politics: 1867
Not Published: Sunday & Monday
Own facility?: N
Publisher ....Gaylord (Rick) Miller
Pres./Pub. ....Thomas R. Smith
Zip Codes served: 44811
Delivery method: Mail

BOWLING GREEN

SENTINEL COMPANY

300 E. Poe Rd., Bowling Green, Ohio, 43402-0088; gen tel (419) 352-4611; adv tel (419) 352-4611; ed tel (419) 352-4611; gen fax (419) 354-0314; adv fax (419) 354-0314; ed fax (419) 354-0314; oth fax (419) 352-6499; adv e-mail ads@sentinel-tribune.com; ed e-mail dmiller@sentinel-tribune.com; web site www.sent-trib.com

Published: Mon, Tues, Wed, Thur, Fri, Sat
Weekday Frequency: e
Saturday Frequency: e
Circulation: 10,062; 10,062(sat)
Last Audit: Sworn September 30, 2008
Price: 2.40/wk (carrier); 110.00/yr (carrier); 9.60/4wk (carrier).
Advertising: Open inch rate $13.45
News services: AP.
Politics: Independent. **Established:** 1901
Advertising not accepted: Y
Not Published: New Year; Memorial Day; Independence Day; Labor Day; Thanksgiving; Christmas.
Own facility?: Y
Special Editions: Art Walk (Apr); Back-to-College (Aug); Bride & Groom (Sep); Baby (Jan); Fair (Jun); Travel & Recreation (May); Christmas Gifts (Nov); Health & Fitness (Semi-yearly).
Special Weekly Sections: Church Page (Fri); Best Food Day (Thur).
Magazines: USA WEEKEND Magazine (Fri).
Pres./Pub. ....T.M. Haswell
Vice Pres./Gen. Mgr. ....Richard Morris
Sec./Treasurer ....Kathryn A. Haswell
Circ. Dir. ....Randy Machan
City Ed. ....Harold Brown
County Ed. ....Jan Larson
Educ. Ed. ....Marie Thomas
Features Ed. ....David C. Miller
Photo Ed. ....J.D. Pooley
Radio/Television Ed. ....David Dupont
Real Estate Ed. ....Deb Rogers
Religion Ed. ....Bill Ryan
Society/Women's Ed. ....Karen Cota
Ad Manager ....Elizabeth Kahlenberg
Market Information: Wood County
Mechanical available: Offset; Black and 3 ROP colors; insert accepted; page cutoffs - 22 3/4.
Mechanical Specifications: Type page 10 29/32 x 21; E - 6 cols, 1 9/16, 1/8 between; A - 6 cols, 1 9/16, 1/8 between; C - 7 cols, 1 11/32, 1/8 between.
Commodity Consumption: Avg. Page Number Per Issue - Daily 28; Avg. Page Number Per Issue - Plates Used 10982; widths 27 1/2; Newsprint Used - Short Tons 787; Printing Ink Used - Black 13125; Printing Ink Used - Color 2790; Printing Ink Used - Pages Printed 10732.
Equipment EDITORIAL: Front-end Software – Baseview/NewsEdit Pro.; Editorial Hardware – APP/Mac; Editorial Equipment – APP/Server NT; Editorial Printers – Various HP CLASSIFIED: Front-end Software – VisionData/Ad Manager Pro.; Classified Hardware – APP/Mac DISPLAY: Ad make-up applications – Multi-Ad/Creator 4.0, QPS/QuarkXPress 4.0; Layout Software – Baseview/Advertising Layout System.; Display Hardware – APP/Power Mac G3; Display Printers – APP/Mac LaserWriter Pro, HP/LaserJet 4V, HP/5000N PRODUCTION: Pagination Software – QPS/QuarkXPress 4.0.; Production Equipment – Kodak CTP; Scanners – Nikon/Coolscan III, HP/ScanJet 4C PRESSROOM: Line 1 – 5-G/Urbanite; Folders – 1 MAILROOM: Counter stackers – HL/Monitor; Inserters and stuffers – 1-KAN/760; Bundle tying machines – 1-Sa/SR2A; Addressing machine – 2-Wm/No 2. BUSINESS COMPUTERS: Business Software – Great Plains/VisionData
Delivery method: Mail, Newsstand, Private Carrier, Racks

BRYAN

THE BRYAN TIMES

127 S. Walnut St., Bryan, Ohio, 43506; gen tel (419) 636-1111; adv tel (419) 636-1111; ed tel (419) 636-1111; gen fax (419) 636-8937; adv fax (419) 636-8937; gen e-mail news@bryantimes.com; adv e-mail ads@bryantimes.com; ed e-mail news@bryantimes.com; web site www.bryantimes.com

Group: Ohio Newspaper Services, Inc.
Published: Mon, Tues, Wed, Thur, Fri, Sat
Weekday Frequency: e
Saturday Frequency: e
Circulation: 8,858; 9,569(sat)
Last Audit: ABC September 30, 2011
Price: 8.50/mo (county), $11.00/mo (OH), $12.00/mo (othr); 92.00/yr (county), $129.00/yr (OH), $142.00/yr (othr).
Advertising: Open inch rate $11.80
News services: AP, CT, CNS, CSM, TMS.
Politics: Independent.
Not Published: Legal holidays.
Special Editions: Car Care (Apr); Back to School

(Aug); Gift Guide Tab (Dec); Personal Tax & Finance Guide (Feb); News Review (Jan); Fair Tab (Jul); Eye Care/Vision (Mar); Summer Guide (May); Christmas Opening (Nov); Your Health Tab (Oct); Fall Home Improvement Tab (Sept).

Special Weekly Sections: Church (Fri); Business (Tues); Farm (Wed).

Magazines: Relish (Monthly); USA WEEKEND Magazine (Sat); American Profile (Weekly).

Chrmn./Pres./Pub. ....Christopher Cullis
Adv. Mgr., Nat'l ....Mary Nickels
Adv. Mgr., Classified ....Amy Thompson
Mgr., Mktg./Promo. ....Thomas Voigt
Circ. Mgr. ....Mark J. Keller
Ed. ....Teresa Melcher
Bus. Ed. ....Marci Hummel
Sports Ed. ....John Fryman
Sports Ed. ....Tami Brigle
Sports Ed. ....Nathan Parsons
Women's Ed. ....Sharon Patten
Online Mgr. ....Dawn Bohlein
Prodn. Mgr. ....Debby Dalton

Market Information: ADS; TMC.

Mechanical available: Offset; Black and 4 ROP colors; insert accepted; page cutoffs - 22 3/4.

Mechanical Specifications: Type page 11 5/8 x 21; E - 6 cols, 1 5/6, 1/8 between; A - 6 cols, 1 5/6, 1/8 between; C - 9 cols, 1 5/16, 1/8 between.

Commodity Consumption: Avg. Page Number Per Issue - Daily 24; Avg. Page Number Per Issue - Saturday 28; widths 27 1/2; Newsprint Used - Metric Tons 1000.

Equipment EDITORIAL: Front-end Software – Baseview/News Edit Pro 3.4, APP/Power Mac G4.; Editorial Hardware – APP/Power Mac 7300-20, Pre Press/Panther Pro; Editorial Printers – APP/Mac LaserWriter Plus CLASSIFIED: Front-end Software – Baseview/Ad Manager Pro 2.2.; Classified Hardware – APP/Power Mac G4, APP/Power Mac 7300/200; Classified Printers – Pre Press/Panther Pro 36 DISPLAY: Ad make-up applications – Multi-Ad/Creator, QPS/QuarkXPress; Layout Software – APP/Mac.; Display Hardware – 3-APP/Mac IIsi, APP/Mac G3, APP/Mac G4; Display Printers – 1-APP/Mac LaserWriter II NTX, Pre Press/Panther Pro 36 PRODUCTION: Pagination Software – QPS/QuarkXPress 4.1.; Production Equipment – Pre Press/Panther Pro 36, Adobe/Photoshop; Cameras – 1-B/Caravel, 1-DSA/Vertical Camera; Scanners – APP/Mac PRESSROOM: Line 1 – 5-G/Community 1968, 1-G/3-Color Unit; Line 2 – 4-G/Community 1992; Folders – 1-G/Community, 1-G/SC.; Inserters and stuffers – 1-KAN; Bundle tying machines – 3-EAM-Mosca, 1/Ty-Tech, 1-EAM-Mosca/Strapper; Addressing machine – Epson/DF-5000, Epson/Equity 2. BUSINESS COMPUTERS: Business Software – MSSI, Microsoft/Windows 95, Execubanc, ACH; Business Hardware – MSSI

BUCYRUS

BUCYRUS TELEGRAPHFORUM.COM

119 W. Rensselaer St., Bucyrus, Ohio, 44820-0471; gen tel (419) 562-3333; adv tel (419) 562-3333; ed tel (419) 562-3333; gen fax (419) 562-9162; adv fax (419) 562-9162; ed fax (419) 562-9162; gen e-mail tfnews@nncogannett.com; web site www.bucyrustelegraphforum.com

Published: Mon, Tues, Wed, Thur, Fri, Sat
Weekday Frequency: m
Saturday Frequency: m
Circulation: 4,484; 5,199(sat)
Last Audit: September 30, 2009
Price: 2.25/wk; 9.75/mo; 117.00/yr.
Advertising: Open inch rate $15.50
News services: AP, GNS, UPI.
Advertising not accepted: Fortune tellers; Clairvoyants.
Not Published: New Year; Memorial Day; Independence Day; Labor Day; Thanksgiving; Christmas.
Magazines: USA WEEKEND Magazine (Sat).

Pub. ....Tom Brennan
Gen. Mgr. ....David Kennard
Adv. Mgr. ....Diane Glassmyer
Circ. Mgr. ....Mike Fleming
Mng. Ed. ....Anthony Conchel
Sports Ed. ....Dan Clutter
Online Dir. ....Carl Lovern
Prodn. Asst., Creative Serv. ....Rita Pritchard

Market Information: TMC.

Mechanical available: Offset; Black and 4 ROP colors; insert accepted - anything mailable, some bag samples; page cutoffs - 21 1/4.

Mechanical Specifications: Type page 11 5/8 x 21; E - 6 cols, 1 5/6, 1/8 between; A - 6 cols, 1 5/6, 1/8 between; C - 6 cols, 1 5/6, 1/8 between.

Equipment EDITORIAL: Front-end Software – Baseview/News Edit.; Editorial Hardware – APP/Mac CLASSIFIED: Front-end Software – Ctext/Advision. DISPLAY: Ad make-up applications – QPS/QuarkXPress, Multi-Ad/Creator; Layout Software – APP/Mac.; Display Printers – HP; Business Hardware – PBS, Oracle, Unix

CAMBRIDGE

THE DAILY JEFFERSONIAN

831 Wheeling Ave., Cambridge, Ohio, 43725; gen tel (740) 439-3531; adv tel (740) 439-3531; ed tel (740) 439-3531; gen fax (740) 439-3533; adv fax (740) 439-3533; ed fax (740) 432-6219; gen e-mail office@daily-jeff.com; adv e-mail ads@daily-jeff.com; ed e-mail newsroom@daily-jeff.com; web site www.daily-jeff.com

Published: Sun
Circulation: 11,765; 12,090(sun)
Last Audit: September 30, 2008
Price: 2.50/wk; 10.85/mo; 130.00/yr.
Advertising: Open inch rate $16.00
News services: AP, Dixewire.
Politics: Independent.
Advertising not accepted: 900 numbers; Objectionable content.
Not Published: New Year; Memorial Day; Independence Day; Labor Day; Thanksgiving; Christmas (except if a Sunday).
Special Editions: Babies (Apr); Back-to-School (Aug); Elected Officials Greetings (Dec); Health & Fitness (Feb); Tax Guide (Jan); Ohio Hills Folk Fest (Jul); Father's Day (Jun); Lawn & Garden (Mar); In Memoriam (May); Yuletide Gift Guide & Cash Giveaway (Nov); Auto Care (
Special Weekly Sections: Church Page (Fri); TV Magazine (S); Farm Page (Thur); Engagement Announcements (Wed).
Magazines: Parade (S).

Pub ....Andrew S. Dix
Controller ....Joyce Yontz
Adv. Dir. ....Edward Archibald
Circ. Dir. ....Chris Cryder
Exec. Ed. ....Ray H. Booth
Lifestyle Ed. ....Pam Harmon
Sports Ed. ....Jeff Harrison
Reporter ....Judie Perkowski
Sunday Coord. ....Greg Parks
Prodn. Mgr. ....Ray Booth

Market Information: ADS; TMC; Zoned editions.

Mechanical available: Offset; Black and 3 ROP colors; insert accepted - min 6 x 9, max 11 1/2 x 15; page cutoffs - 21 1/2.

Mechanical Specifications: Type page 13 x 21 1/2; E - 6 cols, 2 1/16, 1/8 between; A - 6 cols, 2 1/16, 1/8 between; C - 9 cols, 1 3/8, 1/16 between.

Commodity Consumption: Avg. Page Number Per Issue - Daily 22; Avg. Page Number Per Issue - Plates Used 10800; Avg. Page Number Per Issue - Sunday 42; widths 12 1/2; Newsprint Used - Metric Tons 760; Printing Ink Used - Black 24000; Printing Ink Used - Color 3500; Printing Ink

Equipment EDITORIAL: Front-end Software – Baseview/NewsEdit Pro IQUE 3.1.3.; Editorial Hardware – APP/Mac G3, APP/G4, Imacs, APP/G5; Editorial Equipment – 2-Konica K-550; Editorial Printers – 1-HP/4MV LaserJet CLASSIFIED: Front-end Software – Baseview/Ad Manager Pro 2.0.; Classified Hardware – Baseview, APP/Mac; Classified Printers – 1-HP/LaserJet 6MP DISPLAY: Ad make-up applications – Mk, QPS/QuarkXPress 4.0, Multi-Ad/Creator 4.0; Layout Software – MEI/ALS 2.5.; Display Hardware – APP/Mac G3; Display Printers – HP/LaserJet 4MV PRODUCTION: Pagination Software – QPS/QuarkXPress 4.11.; Production Equipment – Adobe/Photoshop 3.0.4, 2-Konica/6100 EV Jetsetter, 2-Konica/6100 EV Jetsetter; Cameras – DAI/Screen-6500C; Scanners – 1-Umax/Mirage 11x17, 2-Umax/8 1/2 x 14 Scanner, 1-Polaroid/SprintScan PRESSROOM: Line 1 – 9-G/Community 1976; Line 2 – Jan-95; Press Drives – 2-HP/75; Folders – SC/folder.; Inserters and stuffers – KAN; Bundle tying machines – 1-EAM-Mosca/13992, EAM-MOSCA/ROM-P 60/50; Wrapping singles – 1-Sa/Table Top Spring Tyer; Addressing machine – Ch/995150-06. AUDIO: Audio Software – Newstalk/24 6.2; Audio Hardware – Edu Comm, Propriety PC BUSINESS COMPUTERS: Business Software – Papertrak 2000; Business Hardware – DSI

CANTON

THE REPOSITORY

500 Market Ave. S., Canton, Ohio, 44702; gen tel (330) 580-8300; adv tel (330) 580-8402; ed tel (330) 580-8300; gen fax (330) 454-5610; adv fax (330) 580-2117; ed fax (330) 454-5745; web site www.cantonrep.com

Published: Mon, Tues, Wed, Thur, Fri, Sat, Sun
Weekday Frequency: m
Saturday Frequency: m
Circulation: 55,327; 53,657(sat); 68,751(sun)
Last Audit: ABC September 30, 2011
Price: 3.30/wk (home delivery); 14.30/mo (home delivery), $31.00/mo (mail); 171.60/yr (home delivery), $243.00/yr (mail).
Advertising: Open inch rate $83.66
News services: AP, CNS, LAT-WP.
Politics: Independent.
Special Editions: Home and Garden (Apr); HS Football (Aug); Christmas Gift Guide (Dec); Weddings by Design (Jan); Professional Football Hall of Fame Tab (Jul); Senior Living (Jun); Spring Truck & Van (Mar); Summer Fun (May); Pizzazz (Monthly); Christmas Gift Guide (Nov); W
Special Weekly Sections: Garden (Fri); Monday Business (Mon); Television (S); Real Estate (Sat); Best Food Day (Wed).
Magazines: Comics (S).

Pub. ....Kevin Kampman
Finance Dir. ....Steve Hall
Adv. Mgr., Classified ....Gail Valli
Mktg. Dir. ....Maureen Heer
Circ. Dir. ....Jim Porter
Circ. Mgr., District Sales ....Anita Dunn
Circ. Sales/Mktg. Mgr. ....Cam Denbrock
Exec. Ed. ....Jeff Gauger
City Ed. ....Dave Sereno
Editorial Page Ed. ....Gayle Beck
Living Section Ed. ....Gary Brown
Photo Ed. ....Stan Myers
Sports Ed. ....Joe Frollo
Suburban Ed. ....Bob Russ
Online Mgr. ....James Hillibish
Mgr., Info. Technology ....Scott Whitman
Prodn. Mgr., Distr. ....Jim Eheezan
Prodn. Mgr., Pre Press ....Dawna DiAngelis

Market Information: TMC.

Mechanical available: Offset; Black and 3 ROP colors; insert accepted - envelopes, cards; page cutoffs - 22 3/4.

Mechanical Specifications: Type page 13 x 21 1/2; E - 6 cols, 2, 1/6 between; A - 6 cols, 2 1/16, 1/16 between; C - 10 cols, 1 1/4, 1/16 between.

Commodity Consumption: Avg. Page Number Per Issue - Daily 60; Avg. Page Number Per Issue - Plates Used 228000; Avg. Page Number Per Issue - Sunday 88; widths 27; Newsprint Used - Short Tons 9120; Printing Ink Used - Black 276000; Printing Ink Used - Color 40000; Printing Ink U

Equipment EDITORIAL: Front-end Software – QPS/QuarkXPress 3.31R, Baseview/NewsEdit Pro IQUE.; Editorial Hardware – 68-APP/Mac; Editorial Equipment – 1-Lf, 2-APP/Power Mac PC 8100, 1-APP/Mac Quadra 950; Editorial Printers – 1-Okidata/393, Graphic Enterprises/PageScan 18 x 24, 2-HP/4000N CLASSIFIED: Front-end Software – Baseview/Class Ad Manager Pro.; Classified Hardware – 16-APP/Mac; Classified Equipment – IBM/Selectric II; Classified Printers – 2-HP/4000N DISPLAY: Ad make-up applications – CD, QPS/QuarkXPress 3.31R; Layout Software – MEI/ALS.; Display Hardware – 1-APP/Mac; Display Printers – DEC/VT-800 Plain Paper, Pagescan, HP PRODUCTION: Pagination Software – Baseview/NewsEdit Pro IQue, QPS/QuarkXPress 4.1, 10-G4, 2-Imac.; Production Equipment – DAI, LE, 1-Konica/4550, Black Magic Newsprint Proofer/V24 Therman Printer; Cameras – DAI/Screen 475; Scanners – Tecsa/3050-double track PRESSROOM: Line 1 – G/Colorliner (10 stands; 40 couples) 2001, G/ColorLiner (10 stands; 40 couples) 2001; Folders – G/3:2 Sovereign; Pasters – G/RTP-50; Reels and Stands – G/RTP-50; Press control system – G/APCS 2001, G/APCS 2001. MAILROOM: Counter stackers – 2-Id, 1/Compass, 3-/QWI; Inserters and stuffers – 2-GMA/SLS 1000 16:1, GMA/20:1; Bundle tying machines – 6-Dynaric/MP-3; Wrapping singles – 3-QWI/Viper Bottom Wrap; Mailroom control system – Newstec-NewsCom; Addressing machine – Ch; Audio Hardware – TelePublishing, Inc; Business Hardware – NewzWare 6.0, Dell/Poweredge 6400, Linux

CELINA

THE DAILY STANDARD

123 E. Market St., Celina, Ohio, 45822; gen tel (419) 586-2371; adv tel (419) 584-1961; gen fax (419) 586-6271; gen e-mail newsroom@dailystandard.com; adv e-mail production@dailystandard.com; web site www.dailystandard.com

Published: Mon, Tues, Wed, Thur, Fri, Sat
Weekday Frequency: e
Circulation: 10,963; 10,963(sat)
Last Audit: October 1, 2006
Price: 2.40/wk; 124.80/yr; 31.20/13wk.
Advertising: Open inch rate $11.00
News services: AP, NYT, TMS.
Politics: Independent.
Advertising not accepted: Tobacco; Work from home.
Not Published: New Year; Memorial Day; Independence Day; Labor Day; Thanksgiving; Christmas.
Special Editions: Fall Sports (Aug); Christmas Greetings (Dec); Christmas Opening (Nov); Fall Opening (Sept).
Special Weekly Sections: Weekender (Fri); State Line Farmer (Tues).

Pub. ....Frank M. Snyder
Bus. Mgr. ....Dave Hoying
Adv. Mgr. ....John Lake
Circ. Mgr. ....Diane Buening
Mng. Ed. ....Pat Royse
Editorial Page Ed. ....Frank Snyder
Society/Women's Ed. ....Betty Lawrence
Sports Ed. ....Ryan Hines
Wire Ed. ....Kelly Braun
Prodn. Supt. ....Larry Smelser

Market Information: Split run; TMC.

Mechanical available: Web Offset; Black and 3 ROP colors; insert accepted - free standing; page cutoffs - 22 3/4.

Mechanical Specifications: Type page 15 x 21; E - 6 cols, 2, 1/8 between; A - 6 cols, 2, 1/8 between; C - 6 cols, 2, 1/8 between.

Commodity Consumption: Avg. Page Number Per Issue - Daily 20; Avg. Page Number Per Issue - Plates Used 4892; widths 27; Newsprint Used - Metric Tons 380; Printing Ink Used - Black 13100; Printing Ink Used - Pages Printed 6100.

Equipment: Editorial Hardware – APP/Mac.; Classified Hardware – APP/Mac, APP/Mac G4. DISPLAY: Ad make-up applications – APP/Mac.; Display Hardware – APP/Mac PRODUCTION: Pagination Software – QPS, Baseview.; Production Equipment – 1-Nu; Scanners – HP, AP

PRESSROOM: Line 1 – G/Suburban 1990.; Bundle tying machines – Bu.; Business Hardware – PC

THE STANDARD PRINTING CO.

123 E. Market St., Celina, Ohio, 45822; gen tel (419) 586-2371; gen fax (419) 586-6271

CHILLICOTHE

CHILLICOTHE GAZETTE

50 W. Main St., Chillicothe, Ohio, 45601; gen tel (740) 773-2111; adv tel (740) 775-7355; ed tel (740) 772-9360; gen fax (740) 772-9502; adv fax (740) 772-9501; ed fax (740) 772-9505; gen e-mail gaznews@nncogannett.com; web site www.chillicothegazette.com

Group: Ohio Newspaper Services, Inc.
Published: Mon, Tues, Wed, Thur, Fri, Sat
Weekday Frequency: e
Saturday Frequency: m
Circulation: 9,060; 10,173(sat); 11,841(sun)
Last Audit: ABC September 30, 2011
Price: 2.88/wk (carrier); 12.50/mo (carrier); 138.00/yr.
Advertising: Open inch rate $30.60
News services: AP, LAT-WP.
Politics: Independent. **Established:** 1800
Special Editions: Spring Home & Garden (Apr); Ross County Fair (Aug); Progress Magazine (Feb); Super Bowl (Jan); Weddings (Jul); Baby (Jun); Graduation (May); Check-up (Monthly); Holiday Gift Guide (Nov); Voter's Guide (Oct); Football Preview (Sept).
Special Weekly Sections: Snapshots (Fri); Religion (Sat); Transportation (Thur).
Magazines: TV Times (Sat).
Gen Mgr....Mike Throne
Adv. Dir.....Mark Rager
Circ. Mgr.....Monica Rogers
Circ. Mgr., Sales....Deborah Roush
Mng. Ed.....Michael W. Throne
Photo Ed....Frank Robertson
Weekend Ed.....Chris Balusic
Prodn. Mgr., Packaging....Brian Graves
Prodn. Mgr., Pressroom....Bill Bennett
Market Information: TMC.
Mechanical available: Offset; Black and 3 ROP colors; insert accepted - data books, other inserts require approval; page cutoffs - 22 3/4.
Mechanical Specifications: Type page 13 x 21 1/2; E - 6 cols, 2 1/16, 1/8 between; A - 6 cols, 2 1/16, 1/8 between; C - 9 cols, 2 1/16, 1/8 between.
Commodity Consumption: Avg. Page Number Per Issue - Daily 20; Avg. Page Number Per Issue - Plates Used 1300; widths 27 1/2; Newsprint Used - Short Tons 630; Printing Ink Used - Black 17700; Printing Ink Used - Color 500; Printing Ink Used - Pages Printed 6194.
Equipment EDITORIAL: Front-end Software – Baseview.; Editorial Hardware – APP/Mac CLASSIFIED: Front-end Software – Ad Vision.; Classified Hardware – APP/Mac DISPLAY: Ad make-up applications – QPS/QuarkXPress; Layout Software – APP/Mac.; Display Hardware – APP/Mac PRODUCTION: Pagination Software – QPS/QuarkXPress 4.0.; Production Equipment – 2-MON/1000; Cameras – 1-C/Spartan II, 1-AG/3500; Scanners – Lf/Leafscan 35, Nikon/1000 PRESSROOM: Line 1 – 10-G/Community SSC. MAILROOM: Counter stackers – 1/PPK, 1-/HI; Inserters and stuffers – 1-/MM; Bundle tying machines – 1-/MLN, 1-/Bu; Addressing machine – 1-/Am, 1-/Wm. BUSINESS COMPUTERS: Business Software – PBS; Business Hardware – PC

CINCINNATI

THE CINCINNATI ENQUIRER

312 Elm St., Cincinnati, Ohio, 45202; gen tel (513) 721-2700; adv tel (513) 768-8220; ed tel (513) 768-8600; gen fax (513) 768-8210; adv fax (513) 768-8250; ed fax (513) 768-8340; web site www.cincinnati.com; www.enquirer.com

Group: Ohio Newspaper Services, Inc.
Published: Mon, Tues, Wed, Thur, Fri, Sat, Sun
Weekday Frequency: m
Saturday Frequency: m
Circulation: 140,877; 154,323(sat); 285,345(sun)
Last Audit: ABC September 30, 2011
Price: 3.99/wk; 207.48/yr (mS).
Advertising: Open inch rate $365.63
News services: AP, NYT, MCT, GNS.
Politics: Independent. **Established:** 1986
Special Editions: Summer Vacations-Travel (Apr); Tennis Championships (Aug); Holiday Home Gift Guides (Dec); National Cruise Month Celebration (Feb); Warm Weather Travel Destinations (Jan); Regional Adventures (Jul); Homearama (Jun); Family Vacations (May); Holiday Gift Gu
Special Weekly Sections: Let's Go/Weekend (Fri); Travel (S); At Home (Sat); Food (Wed).
Magazines: USA WEEKEND Magazine (S).
Pres./Pub.....Margaret E. Buchanan
Dir., Finance....David Wuertenberger
Vice Pres., Market Devel.....Mark Woodruff
Circ. Dir., Home Delivery Stephanie Zimmerman
Circ. Dir., Single Copy....Valecia Quinn
Circ. Mgr., Transportation....Mark Guethlein
Ed....Tom Callinan
Asst. Mng. Ed., Features/Online....Sara Pearce
Asst. Mng. Ed., Local/Bus.....Richard Green
Bus. Ed....Carolyn Pione
Features Ed....Dave Caudill
Kentucky Ed....Mark Ivancic
Local News Ed.....Julie Engebrecht
News Ed.....Ken Amos
Online Ed....Brian Butts
Photography Dir.....Michael Mccarter
Sports Ed.....Josh Pichler
Systems Ed.....Maureen M. Kelley
Vice Pres., Info Technology....Terri J. Hovey
Dir., New Media....James C. Jackson
Market Information: Split run; Zoned editions.
Mechanical available: Offset; Black and 3 ROP colors; insert accepted - based on sample submitted; page cutoffs - 22 3/4.
Mechanical Specifications: Type page 11 5/8 x 21 1/2; E - 7 cols, 1 1/2, 1/8 between; A - 6 cols, 1 13/16, 1/8 between; C - 10 cols, 1 3/32, 1/8 between.
Commodity Consumption: Avg. Page Number Per Issue - Daily 66; Avg. Page Number Per Issue - Plates Used 467000; Avg. Page Number Per Issue - Sunday 162; widths 50; Newsprint Used - Short Tons 49344; Printing Ink Used - Black 927360; Printing Ink Used - Color 437695; Printing In
Equipment EDITORIAL: Front-end Software – SII/Sys 55, SII/Sys 7; Editorial Hardware – Tandem/CLX; Editorial Equipment – SII/Coyote QB, SII/Dakota, APP/Mac, SII/CAT-ST, SII/Coyote 22, SII/Coyote 3; Editorial Printers – Centronics/351, Dataproducts/LZR 2600, APP/Mac LaserWriter NTX, Xante/8200, Textronix/Phaser 300 I CLASSIFIED: Front-end Software – SII/Sys 55, C Text/ALPS Classified Pagination.; Classified Hardware – SII/Server Net; Classified Equipment – SII/Coyote QB, SII/Coyote 22, SII/Coyote 3; Classified Printers – Centronics/351, Dataproducts/LZR-2600, Tetromix/Phaser 780, HP/8500, HP/4050 DISPLAY: Ad make-up applications – APP/Mac Appleshare 4.0, First class/BBS software; Layout Software – Multi-Ad/Creator II.; Display Hardware – 16-APP/Mac 7500, 1-APP/Mac WGS 80, 1763-350; Display Printers – APP/Mac LaserWriter NTX, Textronix/Phaser 780 I, GEI Color Proofer; Production Equipment – Nova Publishing/Faxaction, 2-AU/APS 6108, 2-AU/APS 3850, 1-HQ-110PM; Cameras – 2-C/Newspager; Scanners – 1-ECR/Autokon 1000, Tecsa/3050. PRESSROOM: Line 1 – 10-G/Metro (6 half decks) 1978; Line 2 – 10-G/Metro (6 half decks) 1978; Line 3 – 10-G/Metro (6 half decks) 1980; Line 4 – 10-G/Metro (6 half decks) 1988; Folders – 4-G/double. MAILROOM: Counter stackers – 4-QWI/200, 5-QWI/400; Inserters and stuffers – 1-HI/1472, 1-HI/1372, AM Graphics/NP 630, 1/Magnapack; Bundle tying machines – 8-/Dynaric; Addressing machine – 1-/Ch, X; Other equipment –5-QWI/Automatic Cart Loader (ACL). AUDIO: Audio Software – AdLink, Microsoft/Windows NT; Audio Hardware – Pentium PC BUSINESS COMPUTERS: Business Software – Genesys; Business Hardware – IBM/AS-400 520, PC Micro, HP/9000

THE KENTUCKY POST

125 E. Court St., Cincinnati, Ohio, 45202; gen tel (859) 292-2600; ed tel (859) 292-2600; gen fax (859) 291-2525; ed fax (859) 291-2525; gen e-mail kypost@cincypost.com; ed e-mail kyedits@cincypost.com; web site www.kypost.com

Published: Mon, Tues, Wed, Thur, Fri, Sat, Sun
Weekday Frequency: e
Saturday Frequency: m
Circulation: 28,167; 28,167(sat)
Last Audit: October 1, 1998
Price: 7.50/mo; 282.00/yr.
Advertising: Open inch rate $61.61
News services: AP.
Politics: Independent.
Note: For detailed information on production, printing, advertising, circulation and general management personnel see Cincinnati (OH) Enquirer & Post listing. The Kentucky Post is an edition of the Cincinnati Post.
Ed.....Mike Philipps
Asst. Mng. Ed., News....Mike Kaiser
Educ. Ed.....Tom O'Neill
Features Ed.....Wayne Perry
Photo Ed.....Tim Stein
Sports Ed.....Keith Herrell
Market Information: TMC.
Mechanical available: Offset; Black and 1 ROP colors; insert accepted; page cutoffs - 21 1/2.
Mechanical Specifications: Type page 13 x 21 1/2; E - 6 cols, 2 1/16, 1/8 between; A - 6 cols, 2 1/16, 1/8 between; C - 10 cols, 1 3/16, 1/8 between.
Commodity Consumption: Avg. Page Number Per Issue - Daily 28.

CIRCLEVILLE

HERALD

120 Watt St., Circleville, Ohio, 43113; gen tel (740) 474-3131; ed tel (740) 474-3133; gen fax (740) 474-9525; gen e-mail info@circlevilleherald.com; web site www.circlevilleherald.com

Published: Mon, Tues, Wed, Thur, Fri, Sat, Sun
Weekday Frequency: e
Saturday Frequency: m
Circulation: 6,690; 6,690(sat)
Last Audit: March 31, 2006
Price: 9.40/mo (mail); 85.80/yr (carrier).
Advertising: Open inch rate $11.60
News services: AP, U.S. Suburban Press Inc..
Politics: Independent.
Not Published: New Year; Memorial Day; Independence Day; Labor Day; Christmas.
Special Editions: Real Estate (Apr); Football Review (Aug); Christmas Greetings (Dec); Progress (Feb); Graduation (Jun); 4-H (Mar); Basketball Preview (Nov); Pumpkin Show (Oct).
Special Weekly Sections: Best Food Days (Mon); Farm Pages (Sat); Best Food Days (Wed).
Magazines: USA WEEKEND Magazine (Sat); American Profile (Weekly).
Pub.....Steve Davies
Bus. Mgr.....Janet Rhoten
Adv. Mgr.....Jerry Shasteen
Circ. Mgr.....Darlene Rollins
Ed.....David Amey
Asst. Ed.....Brent Neal
Sports Ed.....Gregg Rettig
Market Information: TMC.
Mechanical available: Offset; Black and 3 ROP colors; insert accepted; page cutoffs - 22 3/4.
Mechanical Specifications: Type page 11 5/8 x 21 1/2; E - 6 cols, 1 13/16, 1/8 between; A - 6 cols, 1 13/16, 1/8 between; C - 8 cols, 1 5/16, 1/8 between.
Commodity Consumption: Avg. Page Number Per Issue - Daily 18; Avg. Page Number Per Issue - Plates Used 3875; widths 27 1/2; Newsprint Used - Metric Tons 611; Printing Ink Used - Black 22000; Printing Ink Used - Color 2100; Printing Ink Used - Pages Printed 5600.
Equipment EDITORIAL: Front-end Software – QPS/QuarkXPress 4.1, Baseview/NewsEdit.; Editorial Hardware – APP/Mac CLASSIFIED: Front-end Software – QPS/QuarkXPress 3.3, Baseview/Class Manager.; Classified Hardware – APP/Mac; Classified Printers – APP/Mac PRODUCTION: Pagination Software – QPS/QuarkXPress 4.1.; Production Equipment – APP/Mac; Cameras – 1-B/Caravel; Scanners – HP PRESSROOM: Line 1 – 12-G/Community; Folders – 2-G/(with upper former).; Bundle tying machines – 1/Bu, 1-/Akebono; Addressing machine – 1-/KR. BUSINESS COMPUTERS: Business Software – MSSI, Manifest; Business Hardware – IBM

CLEVELAND

THE PLAIN DEALER

Plain Dealer Plaza, 1801 Superior Ave., Cleveland, Ohio, 44114; gen tel (216) 999-5000; adv tel (216) 999-5555; ed tel (216) 999-4800; adv fax (216) 999-6206; ed fax (216) 999-6354; web site www.plaindealer.com

Group: Advance Publications, Inc.
Published: Mon, Tues, Wed, Thur, Fri, Sat, Sun
Weekday Frequency: m
Saturday Frequency: m
Circulation: 243,299; 238,261(sat); 403,945(sun)
Last Audit: ABC September 30, 2011
Price: $5.08/wk; $264.16/yr
Advertising: Open inch rate Daily $520; Sunday/Holiday $797.00
News services: AP, NYT.
Politics: Independent.
Own facility?: Y
Special Editions: Last Minute Gift Guide (Dec); Travel Feature: Wash DC, Maryland, Virginia (Jul); Travel Feature: Ohio Travel #1 (Mar); Travel Feature: Mi
Special Weekly Sections: Friday Magazine (Entertainment) (Fri); PDQ (Mon); Inside & Out (Thur); Health (Tues); Style & Taste (Wed).
Pres./Pub....Terrance C.Z. Egger
Vice Pres./Dir., Finance/Acct.....Virginia Wang
Vice Pres./Dir., Labor Rel./HR William Calaiacovo
Mgr. of Facilities and Fleet Opns. Terry Stineman
Credit Mgr.....Kimberly Archibald-Russell
Adv. Vice Pres., Classified Robert D. Ritterbusch
Adv. Vice Pres., Display and Mktg. Andrea Hogben
Adv. Dir., Mktg./Community Affairs Shirley Stineman
Circ. Vice Pres./Dir.....Robert Perona
Asst. Circ. Dir.....Bill Calaiacovo
Asst. Circ. Dir., Customer Rel./Systems Larry Vanderhoff
Asst. Circ. Dir., Home Delivery.Bryan Schneider
Asst. Circ. Dir., Sales Devel...Josie Passafiume
Asst. Circ. Dir., Retail Sales/Mktg. Michael Ferry
Circ. Mgr., Educational Servs.....Lori Marks
Circ. Mgr., Transportation....Mike Moloney
Editor....Debra Adams Simmons
Vice President and Director of Operations Joseph Bowman
Asst. Director of Operations....Keye Daus
Prepress Director....John Grigoli
Prodn. Mgr., Machinists/Engineers Damon Borom
Prodn. Mgr., Packaging....Pablo Vidlak
Prodn. Mgr., Printing/Night Operations Wally Schoenberger
Prepress Mgr., Commercial & Quality Assurance Bob Dagostino
Prodn. Tech. Service Mgr.....Nick Vangelos
Vice Pres. and Dir., Information Technology William Mickey
IT Mgr., Systems and Development Chris Chimes
IT Mgr., Infrastructure and Opns.....Bob Mazur
IT Mgr., Product Development....Brian Ritchie
Managing Editor....Thomas Fladung
Deputy Managing Editor....Daryl Kannberg
Asst. Managing Editor/Metro .Christopher Quinn
Asst. Managing Editor/Medical Ellen Stein-Bur-

bach
Asst. Managing Editor/Features Debbie Van Tassel
Online Editor....John Kroll
Asst. Managing Editor/Visuals...David Kordalski
Dir. Design & Graphics....Michael Tribble
Book Editor....Karen Long
Bus. Editor....Randy Roguski
Consumer Reporter....Sheryl Harris
Editorial Cartoonist....Jeff Darcy
Columbus Bureau Chief....Reginald Fields
Washington Bureau Chief....Steve Koff
Editorial Page Editor....Elizabeth Sullivan
Chief Editorial Writer....Joe Frolik
Chief Editorial Writer....Kevin O'Brien
Editorial Writer....Sharon Broussard
Editorial Writer....Christopher Evans
Deputy Features Editor....John Kappes
Deputy Features Editor....Emily Hamlin Smith
Online Entertainment Editor....Michael Norman
Food Editor....Joe Crea
Travel Editor....Susan Glaser
Home Editor....Julie Washington
Chief Librarian....David Kordalski
Metro Columnist....Phillip Morris
Metro Columnist....Connie Schultz
Metro Columnist....Regina Brett
Metro Editor....Karl Turner
Deputy Metro Editor....Barbara Galbincea
Deputy Metro Editor State....Jane Kahoun
Politifact Editor....Robert Higgs
Deputy Metro Editor....Kathy Siemon
Deputy Metro Editor....Mark Vosburgh
Movie Critic....Clint O'Connor
Classical Music Critic....Zachary Lewis
Pop Music Critic....John Soeder
Dir. Photography....William Gugliotta
Deputy Dir. Photography....Dale Omori
Night Photo Editor....Jon Fobes
Political Writer....Mark Naymik
Reader Rep....Ted Diadiun
Sports Editor....Roy Hewitt
Deputy Sports Editor....Mike Starkey
Asst. Sports Editor....Dave Campbell
Asst. Sports Editor....Kristen Davis
Market Information: Split run; TMC; Zoned editions.
Mechanical available: Offset; Black and 4 ROP colors; insert accepted; page cutoffs - 22.
Mechanical Specifications: Type page 11 5/8 x 21; E - 6 cols, 1 3/4, 1/8 between; A - 6 cols, 1 13/16, 1/8 between; C - 10 cols, 1 1/8, 1/16 between.
Commodity Consumption: Avg. Page Number Per Issue - Daily 47.65 (M-F); Avg. Page Number Per Issue - Plates Used 861,404; Avg. Page Number Per Issue - Saturday 69.83; Avg. Page Number Per Issue - Sunday 115.92; width 22.082 inches; Newsprint Used - Metric Tons 26,842; Newsprint Used - Short
Equipment EDITORIAL: Front-end Software – HI/NewsMaker Editorial 4.x.; Classified Hardware – Software Â Mactive.; Layout Software – Mactive. PRODUCTION: Pagination Software – HI/Data Center.; Production Equipment – 3-Kk/Trendsetter 150; 1 Trendsetter 200; PRESSROOM: Line 1 – 6-G/Colorliner double width 1993; Line 2 – 6-G/Colorliner; Line 3 – 6-G/Colorliner; Line 4 – 6-G/Colorliner; Press Drives – AB/AC Drives; Folders – 4-G/Double; Pasters – 32-G/CT 50; Press control system – Rockwell; Press registration system – Quad MAILROOM: Counter stackers – 20-HL/Monitor, 8-QWI, 2-QWI/Packman; Inserters and stuffers – 6-GMA/SLS 1000, 1-GMA/SLS 2000; Bundle tying machines – 22-Dynaric.
4-Quipp; Mailroom control system – SAM Plans; Addressing machine – 1-KAN.
2-Accraply labelers.
3-Miracom.; Other equipment –11-Cannon/Cart Loader.

COLUMBUS

THE COLUMBUS DISPATCH

34 S. Third St., Columbus, Ohio, 43215-4201; gen tel (614) 461-5000; adv tel (614) 461-5500; ed tel (614) 461-5271; adv fax (614) 469-6087; ed fax (614) 461-8793; gen e-mail newsinfo@dispatch.com; ed e-mail letters@dispatch.com; web site www.dispatch.com
Group: Ohio Newspaper Services, Inc.
Published: Mon, Tues, Wed, Thur, Fri, Sat, Sun
Weekday Frequency: m
Saturday Frequency: m
Circulation: 135,330; 177,786(sat); 265,892(sun)
Last Audit: ABC September 30, 2011
Price: 3.20/wk; 166.40/yr.
Advertising: Open inch rate $429.51
News services: AP, MCT, LAT-WP, NYT, RN.
Politics: Independent.
Special Editions: Showcase of Remodelers (Apr); High School Sports (Aug); Last-Minute Gift Guide (Dec); Valentine's Greetings (Feb); From House to Home (Jan); Employment (Jul); Parade of Homes Program (Jun); Delicious Deals (Mar); Memorial Daily 2 (May); Bonus Package (Nov
Special Weekly Sections: Faith & Values (Fri); Connect (Mon); Wheels (Sat); Weekender (Thur); Now (Wed).
Magazines: USA WEEKEND Magazine (Sat).
Chrmn./CEO/Pub.....John F. Wolfe
Vice Chrmn./COO/Assoc. Pub./Pres. Michael Fiorile
Asst. to Pres.....Katie Wolfe
Vice Pres./New Media....Phil Pikelny
Vice Pres., Prodn. Opns.....Del Varney
Vice Pres./CIO....Angelo D. Mazzocco
Vice Pres./Cor. Dir., HR....Diana J. Riggsby
Cor. Dir., Security....Clifford E. Davis
Gen. Mgr., Cor. New Media Div.....Gerry Barker
Adv. Mgr., Nat'l....Beth Damron
Adv. Mgr., Retail....Ann Daugherty
Adv. Mgr., Retail....Stacey Thomas
Mktg./Promos. Mgr.....Eric Wygle
Circ. Vice Pres.....Robert Bolone
Circ. Dir., Field Opns.....William A. Stille
Circ. Asst. Dir., Admin.....Gerald Wisemiller
Circ. Asst. Dir., Opns.....Rick Aniol
Circ. Mgr., City....Joe Boggioni
Circ. Mgr., Single Copy....John Marcano
Circ. Mgr., State....John Henry
Market Information: ADS; Split run; TMC; Zoned editions.
Mechanical available: Offset; Black and 3 ROP colors; insert accepted; page cutoffs - 22.
Mechanical Specifications: Type page 13 x 21; E - 6 cols, 2 1/16, 1/8 between; A - 6 cols, 2 1/16, 1/8 between; C - 10 cols, 1 5/16, 1/16 between.
Commodity Consumption: Avg. Page Number Per Issue - Daily 64; Avg. Page Number Per Issue - Sunday 161; widths 27 3/8; Newsprint Used - Metric Tons 50000; Printing Ink Used - Black 900000; Printing Ink Used - Color 400000.
Equipment EDITORIAL: Front-end Software – QPS/QuarkXPress, AT, Cx, Sun/Unix, 14-AT/Press; Editorial Hardware – AT, 220-IBM/PS2, 40-APP/Mac, 60-APP/Mac G4, 40-APP/Mac G3, 2-IBM/RS6000-25T; Editorial Equipment – Kk, AG/Scanners, Purup-Eskofot/; Editorial Printers – APP/Mac LaserWriter, NEC, DEC, HP, MON/Proof Express CLASSIFIED: Front-end Software – AT, Unix, AT/Enterprise Advertising, AT/Classified Pagination R5.; Classified Hardware – AT, 2-Sun, 3-IBM/RS6000-J40, 4-IBM/RS6000-25T; Classified Equipment – 114-Pentium/PC; Classified Printers – HP/5si, HP/4MV DISPLAY: Ad make-up applications – QPS/QuarkXPress, Macromedia/Freehand, Adobe/Illustrator; Layout Software – SCS/La; Display Hardware – 20-APP/Mac G3, APP/Mac G4, APP/Mac 9500; Display Printers – APP/Mac LaserWriters, QMS/Color, MON/Proof Express; Production Equipment – WL/347 Diamondsetter CTP, 1-WL/610 Diamondsetter CTP, 1-Scitex/Brisque, 3-MON/RIP Express, 2-Scitex/Dolev 4 News, 4-Mon/News Express; Scanners – 2-Purup-Eskofot 2047. PRESSROOM: Line 1 – 10-TKS/M-72 double width 1990, 1-TKS/6000 Press Tower 1999; Line 2 – 10-TKS/M-72 double width 1989, 1-TKS/6000 Press Tower 1999; Line 3 – 10-TKS/M-72 double width 1989, 1-TKS/6000 Press Tower 1999; Line 4 – 10-TKS/M-72 1989, 1-TKS/6000 Press Towe MAILROOM: Counter stackers – 9-Id/2000, 4/HI, 2-/Remor, 4-/QWI; Inserters and stuffers – 4-Fg/Drums (2/5:1); Bundle tying machines – 13-/Power Strap; Mailroom control system – Id/Newssort. BUSINESS COMPUTERS: Business Software – Microsoft/NT 4.X, Microsoft/SQL 7.0; Business Hardware – DEC/PDP 1183, Dell/PC Server

COSHOCTON

THE COSHOCTON TRIBUNE

550 Main St., Coshocton, Ohio, 43812-0010; gen tel (740) 622-1122; adv tel (740) 622-1122; ed tel (740) 622-1122; gen fax (740) 295-3460; adv fax (740) 295-3459; ed fax (740) 295-3460; gen e-mail coshocton@nncogannett.com; web site www.coshoctontribune.com
Group: Ohio Newspaper Services, Inc.
Published: Mon, Tues, Wed, Thur, Fri, Sat, Sun
Weekday Frequency: e
Saturday Frequency: m
Circulation: 4,112; 4,134(sat); 5,167(sun)
Last Audit: ABC September 30, 2011
Price: 12.40/mo (motor route); 148.80/yr.
Advertising: Open inch rate $17.50
News services: AP, GNS.
Politics: Independent.
Not Published: New Year; Memorial Day; Independence Day; Labor Day; Thanksgiving; Christmas.
Special Editions: Showcase of Homes (Other).
Special Weekly Sections: Best Food Days (Mon); TV Today (Other); Best Food Days (S); Farm News (Sat); Health & Science (Thur).
Magazines: USA WEEKEND Magazine (S).
Gen. Mgr.....Rick Szabrak
Adv. Mgr.....Brandie Davisson
Circ. Dir.....John Merriweather
Mng. Ed.....Pam James
Local Data Ed., Day....Valerie Boateng
Local Data Ed., Night....Dave Weidig
Local News Ed., Day....Tonya Shipley
Multimedia Ed.....Trevor Jones
Presentation Ed.....Beth Bailey
Online Dir.....Carl Lovern
Market Information: ADS; TMC.
Mechanical available: Offset; Black and 3 ROP colors; insert accepted - any; page cutoffs - 22 3/4.
Mechanical Specifications: Type page 12 1/2 x 21 1/4; E - 6 cols, 2 1/16, 1/8 between; A - 6 cols, 2 1/16, 1/8 between; C - 9 cols, 1 3/8, 1/16 between.
Commodity Consumption: Avg. Page Number Per Issue - Daily 16; Avg. Page Number Per Issue - Plates Used 2370; Avg. Page Number Per Issue - Sunday 32; widths 25; Newsprint Used - Short Tons 210; Printing Ink Used - Black 5108; Printing Ink Used - Color 201.
Equipment EDITORIAL: Front-end Software – Baseview/NewsEdit.; Editorial Hardware – APP/Mac, APP/iMac; Editorial Printers – Xante/8200, Pre Press/Panther Pro 46 CLASSIFIED: Front-end Software – ALPS.; Classified Hardware – IBM/PC; Classified Printers – Xante/8200 DISPLAY: Ad make-up applications – QPS/QuarkXPress 4.04; Layout Software – MEI/ALS.; Display Hardware – APP/Mac; Display Printers – Xante/8200 PRODUCTION: Pagination Software – QPS/QuarkXPress 3.31, Baseview/Q-Tools.; Production Equipment – Caere/OmniPage, Adobe/Photoshop 5.5, APP/Mac LaserWriter, QuarkXPress 4.04; Cameras – NON; Scanners – Umax/UL 1200 SE, Umax/Power Look II BUSINESS COMPUTERS: Business Software – Microsoft/Office Professional; Business Hardware – IBM/PC Clones, HP, Dell, Gateway, Toshiba, HP

DAYTON

DAILY NEWSPAPERS

1611 S. Main St., Dayton, Ohio, 45409; gen tel 888-397-6397
Published: Mon, Tues, Wed, Thur, Fri, Sat, Sun
Weekday Frequency: m
Saturday Frequency: m
Circulation: 140,968; 143,150(sat); 212,311(sun)
Last Audit: ABC September 30, 2011

DAYTON DAILY NEWS

1611 S. Main St., Dayton, Ohio, 45409; gen tel (937) 225-2000; adv tel (937) 225-2050; ed tel (937) 225-2212; gen fax (937) 225-2054; adv fax (937) 225-2088; ed fax (937) 225-2489; ed e-mail localnews@coxohio.com; web site www.daytondailynews.com
Group: Cox Enterprises, Inc.
Ohio Newspaper Services, Inc.
Published: Mon, Tues, Wed, Thur, Fri, Sat, Sun
Weekday Frequency: m
Saturday Frequency: m
Circulation: 93,259; 92,750(sat); 149,268(sun)
Last Audit: ABC September 30, 2011
Price: Daily Sunday $4.50(per week Carrier)$221.00 (year) $14.00 (EZPAY); Thursday, Friday, Saturday, Sunday - $3.25 a week, $156 a year; $10.00 EZ pay; Sunday/Thurday -$2.50 a week, $114.40 a year, $8.00 (EZpay); Sunday Only- $2.50 a week , $114.00 a year , $11.33 a month
Advertising: National Open Inch Rate $196
News services: Cox News Service, SHNS, AP, NYT, MCT, TV Data.
Politics: 1898
Not Published: N/A
Own facility?: Y
Special Editions: Pink Paper; Insight Section; Real Estate Plus; Wheels; Active Dayton; TV Week; Neighbors
Special Weekly Sections: Active Dayton (Friday)
Magazines: Parade (S).
Regional Vice President, Human Resourcs Emily Chambers
Vice President, Circulation....Phonda Gamble
Market Vice President....Julia Wallace
Senior Vice President, Sales....Rob Rohr
Senior Vice President, Operations..Brian Cooper
Senior Vice President, Marketing & Client Solutions Donna Hall
Editor in Chief....Jana Collier
Associate Editor....Ron Rollins
Assistant Managing Editor, Production & Online Mike Goheen
Assistant Managing Editor, Assignment Desk Mary Irby-Jones
Assistant Managing Editor, Content John Erickson
Vice President, Publishing Sales...Andy Blizzard
Senior Director, Local Sales Suzanne Klopfenstein
Sales Manager - National/Major...Bruce Karlson
Circ. Dir., Sales....Shawn DeWeese
Deputy Mng. Ed.....Ray Marcano
Circ. Dir., Retention....Mark Tormeno
Ed.....Jeff Bruce
Sales Manager - National/ Major..Bruce Karlson
Cartoonist....Mike Peters
Editorial Page Ed.....Ellen Belcher
Administrative Ed.....John Thomson
Senior Director, Local Accounts Suzanne Klopfenstein
Vice Pres., Circ.....Austin L. Smith
Circ. Dir., Retail Sales....Dick Fuller
Bus. Ed.....Jim Dillon
Mng. Ed.....Steve Sidlo
Fashion/Style Ed.....Connie Post
Environmental Ed.....John Erickson
Asst. Mng. Ed., Features/Entertainment Ron Rollins
Fashion/Style Ed.....Connie Post
Market Information: ADS; Split run; TMC; Zoned editions.
Mechanical available: Offset; Black and 3 ROP colors; insert accepted - samples and other by arrangement; page cutoffs - 22.
Mechanical Specifications: Type page 11 5/8 x 21; E - 6 cols, 1 5/6, 1/8 between; A - 6 cols, 1 5/6, 1/8 between; C - 10 cols, 1 1/4, 1/16 between.
Commodity Consumption: Avg. Page Number Per Issue - Daily 59; Avg. Page Number Per Issue - Plates Used 261121; Avg. Page Number Per Issue - Saturday 76; Avg. Page Number Per Issue - Sunday 147; widths 50; Newsprint Used - Short Tons 26711; Printing Ink Used - Black 758905; Pri
Equipment EDITORIAL: Front-end Software – DTI 5.5; Editorial Hardware – PCs/Macs; Editorial Printers – Konica Minolta;
HP Laserjets;

HP1050 proofers CLASSIFIED: Front-end Software – DTI 5.5; Classified Hardware – Sun Dell; Classified Equipment – PCs; Classified Printers – Konica-Minolta; HP laserjets HP1050 proofers DISPLAY: Ad make-up applications – DTI 5.5; Display Hardware – PCs; Display Printers – Konica Minolta; HP Laserjet; HP1050 Proofers PRODUCTION: Pagination Software – DTI 4.3.; Production Equipment – Caere/OmniPro, Harlequin/RIP, 2-AU/3850 Wide, Kk/RFS 2035 plus film scanner, Pixel-Craft/Pro Imager 8000, Nikon/Coolscan; Scanners – Scitex, Graphic Enterprises/PageScan, Tecsa PRESSROOM: Line 1 – 33-KBA/Colora couples double width 1999; Line 2 – 27-KBA/Colora couples double width 1999; Line 3 – 27-KBA/Colora couples double width 1999; Press Drives – EAE/KBA Drive Tronic Shaftless System; Folders – 3-KFM/96 Jaw; Reels and Stands – 18-KBA/Pa MAILROOM: Counter stackers – 5-HL/Monitor, 6-HL/DC, 1-HL/Monitor HT, 12/Olympian; Inserters and stuffers – 4-HI/632 26:2; Bundle tying machines – 10-MLN/MLN 2A, 3-Dynaric/NP 2, 12-/Dynaric; Wrapping singles – 12-HI/Eclipse Bottomwrap; Mailroom control system – Omnizone AUDIO: Audio Software – Call Mgr I3 ; Audio Hardware – Cisco BUSINESS COMPUTERS: Business Software – Peoplesoft Great Plains Hyperion ; Business Hardware – Dell PC's

Zip Codes served: 43072, 43078, 43128, 43160, 43215, 43228, 43311, 43318, 43324, 43331, 43343, 43348, 43357, 45004, 45032, 45036, 45044, 45050, 45054, 45056, 55066, 45067, 45068, 45113, 45169, 45177, 45302, 45303, 45304, 45305, 45306, 45308, 45309, 45310, 45311, 45312, 45314, 45315, 45317, 45318, 45320, 45321, 45322, 45323, 45324, 45325, 45326, 45327, 45328, 45330, 45331, 45333, 45334, 45335, 45337, 45338, 45339, 45341, 45342, 45344, 45345, 45346, 45347, 45358, 45350, 45351, 45354, 45356, 45358, 45359, 45361, 45362, 45363, 45365, 45370, 45371, 45373, 45377, 45378, 45380, 45381, 45382, 45383, 45384, 45385, 45387, 45388, 45389, 45390, 45401, 45402, 45403, 45404, 45405, 45406, 45408, 45409, 45410, 45414, 45415, 45416, 45417, 45418, 45420, 45422, 45424, 45426, 45427, 45428, 45429, 45430, 45431, 45432, 45433. 45434. 45435. 45439, 45440, 45449, 45458, 45459, 45469. 45502, 45503, 45504, 45505, 45822, 45826, 45828, 45845, 45846, 45860, 45865, 45869, 45871, 45883, 45885, 45895

Delivery method: Mail, Newsstand, Private Carrier, Racks

DEFIANCE

THE CRESCENT-NEWS

624 W. Second St., Defiance, Ohio, 43512; gen tel (419) 784-5441; adv tel (419) 784-5441; ed tel (419) 784-5441; gen fax (419) 784-1492; adv fax (419) 784-1492; ed fax (419) 782-2944; gen e-mail crescent@crescent-news.com; adv e-mail cnads@crescent-news.com; ed e-mail crescent@crescent-news.com; web site www.crescent-news.com

Published: Mon, Tues, Wed, Thur, Fri, Sun

Weekday Frequency: e

Circulation: 15,931; 17,454(sun)

Last Audit: ABC September 30, 2011

Price: 8.50/mo; 102.00/yr.

Advertising: Open inch rate $19.55

News services: AP, SHNS.

Politics: Independent. **Established:** 1888

Not Published: New Year; Memorial Day; Independence Day; Labor Day; Thanksgiving; Christmas.

Special Editions: Garage Sale (Apr); Football Tab (Aug); Holiday Gift Guide (Dec); Farm Review Forecast Tab (Feb); Brag Books (Jan); Sidewalk Days (Jul); Dairy Month (Jun); Lawn & Garden Tab (Mar); Graduation (May); Christmas Greetings (Nov); Focus Issue (Oct); Johnny Appl

Special Weekly Sections: Church Page (Fri); Food (Mon); Business Advice (S); Bulletin Board (Thur).

Magazines: USA WEEKEND Magazine (S); American Profile (Weekly).

Gen. Mgr. ....Steve VanDemark
Adv. Mgr. ....Mark Ryan
Circ. Mgr. ....Betty Lentz
Ed ....Dennis Van Scoder
Area Ed ....Teri Hageman
Educ. Ed. ....Jenny Derringer
Farm/Agribus. Ed. ....Mike Prigge
Features Ed. ....Mark Froelich
Health/Medical Ed. ....Darlene Prince
Lifestyle Ed ....Jack Palmer
Outdoor Ed. ....Al Smith
Political/Gov't Ed. ....Todd Helberg
Religion Ed ....Angela Westrick
Sports Ed ....Bruce Hefflinger

Market Information: Split run; TMC; Zoned editions.

Mechanical available: Offset; Black and 3 ROP colors; insert accepted - 11 x 14 max., 6 x 9 min.; page cutoffs - 22 5/8.

Mechanical Specifications: Type page 13 1/4 x 21; E - 6 cols, 2 1/16, 1/8 between; A - 6 cols, 2 1/16, 1/8 between; C - 8 cols, 1 5/8, 1/8 between.

Commodity Consumption: Avg. Page Number Per Issue - Daily 26; Avg. Page Number Per Issue - Plates Used 15526; Avg. Page Number Per Issue - Sunday 36; widths 25; Newsprint Used - Short Tons 1150; Printing Ink Used - Black 23000; Printing Ink Used - Color 7000; Printing Ink Used

Equipment EDITORIAL: Front-end Software – Baseview.; Editorial Hardware – APP/Mac; Editorial Printers – Xante/Accel-a-Writer 8200 CLASSIFIED: Front-end Software – Vision Data.; Classified Hardware – Digital; Classified Printers – Xante/Accel-a-Writer 8200 DISPLAY: Ad make-up applications – APP/Mac; Layout Software – Baseview, MEI.; Display Hardware – APP/Power Mac; Display Printers – Xante/Accel-a-Writer 8200 PRODUCTION: Pagination Software – QPS/QuarkXPress.; Production Equipment – 2-APP/Power Mac, Adobe/Photoshop; Cameras – 2-B; Scanners – 35-MM, Nikon, Howtek/Flatbed Scanner, Nikon/Coolscan PRESSROOM: Line 1 – 6-G/Urbanite 1968; Press Drives – 2-HP/100, 2; Folders – 1-G/Urbanite. MAILROOM: Counter stackers – HL/Monitor; Inserters and stuffers – MM; Bundle tying machines – 2/MLN; Addressing machine – Ch.; Audio Hardware – Educom BUSINESS COMPUTERS: Business Software – DataTrac; Business Hardware – DSI

DELAWARE

THE DELAWARE GAZETTE

18 E. William St., Delaware, Ohio, 43015-0100; gen tel (740) 363-1161; adv tel (740) 363-1161; ed tel (740) 363-1161; gen fax (740) 363-6262; adv fax (740) 363-6262; ed fax (740) 363-6262; gen e-mail newsroom@delgazette.com; adv e-mail addept@delgazette.com; ed e-mail newsroom@delgazette.com; web site www.delgazette.com

Group: Ohio Community Media

Published: Mon, Tues, Wed, Thur, Fri, Sat

Weekday Frequency: All day

Saturday Frequency: m

Circulation: 8,000; 8,500(sat)

Last Audit: Sworn September 30, 2006

Price: 2.28/wk; 114.00/yr.

Advertising: Open inch rate $12 .25

News services: AP, U.S. Suburban Press Inc..

Politics: Independent. **Established:** 1818

Not Published: New Year; Memoial Day; Independence Day; Thanksgiving; Christmas.

Own facility?: N

Special Editions: Fall Sports Tab (Aug); Bargain Days (Feb); Baby Bulletin (Jan); Father's Day (Jun); Spring Sports Tab (Mar); Graduation (May); Holiday Tab (Nov); Delaware Youth Create (Oct); Fair (Sept).

Special Weekly Sections: Entertainment Page (Fri); Lifestyle Page (Mon); Extended Sports Coverage (Sat); Lifestyle Page (Thur); Lifestyle Page (Tues); Business Page (Wed).

Pub ....Gary Merrell
Circulation Manager ....Austin Kempton
Sports Ed. ....Ben Stroup
Internet Serv. Mgr. ....Bret Dennis
Advertising Manager ....Ryan Oswald
Editor ....Devon Immelt

Market Information: TMC; Zoned editions.

Mechanical available: Offset; Black and 3 ROP colors; insert accepted; page cutoffs - 22 3/4.

Mechanical Specifications: Type page 13 x 21 1/2; E - 6 cols, 2 1/16, 1/8 between; A - 6 cols, 2 1/16, 1/8 between; C - 8 cols, 1 1/2, 1/8 between.

Commodity Consumption: Avg. Page Number Per Issue - Daily 16; Avg. Page Number Per Issue - Plates Used 4600; widths 27 1/2; Newsprint Used - Metric Tons 800; Printing Ink Used - Black 21000; Printing Ink Used - Color 7100; Printing Ink Used - Pages Printed 4992.

Equipment EDITORIAL: Front-end Software – QPS/QuarkXPress, 33-Claris/Macdraw Pro, Aldus/FreeHand, Baseview/NewsEdit 3.2.; Editorial Hardware – 8-PC 6100, 2-APP/Mac 610, 1-APP/Mac 7200-20, 3-APP/Power Mac 7300, 7-APP/iMac; Editorial Printers – APP/Mac 12/640 NT, APP/Mac LaserWriter NTX CLASSIFIED: Front-end Software – Baseview.; Classified Hardware – WG/Server 8150, 3-APP/Mac G3; Classified Printers – APP/Mac NTX, 2-APP/Mac ImageWriter II, 1-APP/Mac LaserWriter 12-640 DISPLAY: Ad make-up applications – Synaptic, Multi-Ad/Creator 4.0, Aldus/FreeHand 3.1; Layout Software – MEI/ALS.; Display Hardware – APP/Mac 7300, APP/Mac 7300, APP/Mac NTX, APP/Mac 7300 (with CD); Display Printers – HP/LaserJet 4MV/600dpi PRODUCTION: Pagination Software – Baseview/ALS 3.1.; Production Equipment – Caere/OmniPage Pro 4.1.0, Caere/OmniPage Direct, APP/NT Server, 1-HP 4MV/600, 5-APP/Mac G3, 1-Accel-a-Writer 3N/1200; Cameras – 4-Canon/EOS, 3-Nikon/Cool Pix 950; Scanners – 1-HP, 1-AP, 1-AG; Audio Hardware – New Horizons/Info-Connect

DELPHOS

DELPHOS DAILY HERALD

405 N. Main St., Delphos, Ohio, 45833; gen tel (419) 695-0015; gen fax (419) 692-7704; adv fax (419) 692-7704; ed fax (419) 692-7704; gen e-mail nspencer@delphosherald.com; adv e-mail dhemple@delphosherald.com; web site www.delphosherald.com

Group: Delphos Herald, Inc.

Published: Mon, Tues, Wed, Thur, Fri, Sat

Weekday Frequency: e

Saturday Frequency: m

Circulation: 2,883

Last Audit: Sworn September 30, 2006

Price: 79.00/yr; 22.00/3mo, $40.00/6mo.

Advertising: Open inch rate $12.10(e-mon)

News services: AP.

Politics: Independent. **Established:** 1869

Not Published: New Year; Memorial Day; Independence Day; Labor Day; Thanksgiving; Christmas.

Own facility?: Y

Special Editions: National Secretaries Week (Apr); Football Tab (Aug); New Year Baby (Dec); Cooking School (Feb); 2 Dollar Days (Jan); 2 Dollar Days (Jul); 4-H Tab (Mar); Bride Tab (May); Senior Scenes (Monthly); Christmas Opening (Nov); Get Ready for Winter Tab (Oct); Old

Magazines: American Profile (Weekly).

Pub ....Murray Cohen
Bus. Mgr. ....Ray Geary
Mktg. Dir. ....Don Hemple
Circ. Mgr. ....Tiffany Brancly
Ed. ....Nancy Spencer
Sports Ed. ....Jim Metcalfe
Prodn. Mgr. ....Dennis Klausing
Prodn. Mgr., Graphic Arts ....Sandra Bohn

Market Information: Split run; TMC.

Mechanical available: Offset; Black and 3 ROP colors; insert accepted - cards, envelopes; page cutoffs - 22 3/4.

Mechanical Specifications: Type page 13 1/8 x 21 1/2; E - 6 cols, 2 1/16, 1/8 between; A - 6 cols, 2 1/16, 1/8 between; C - 8 cols, 1 5/8, 1/8 between.

Commodity Consumption: Avg. Page Number Per Issue - Daily 16; Avg. Page Number Per Issue - Plates Used 25854; widths 34; Newsprint Used - Metric Tons 2677; Printing Ink Used - Black 76536; Printing Ink Used - Color 45325; Printing Ink Used - Pages Printed 4912.

Equipment; Editorial Hardware – MediaSpan CLASSIFIED: Front-end Software – Baseview.; Classified Equipment – 2-APP/Mac Plus Laser DISPLAY: Ad make-up applications – Baseview.; Production Equipment – 2-Nu, 1-Nat; Cameras – 1-R, 1-Ik. PRESSROOM: Line 1 – 8; Line 2 – 4; Folders – 2-HI/2:1, 1-HI/1:1; Pasters – 2 MAILROOM: Counter stackers – 3/BG; Bundle tying machines – 3-/Bu, 4-MLN/Strapper; Addressing machine – 1-/KR.; Business Hardware – 1-RSK/TRS 80 III, 1-IBM/PC

EAST LIVERPOOL

THE REVIEW

210 E. Fourth St., East Liverpool, Ohio, 43920-3144; gen tel (330) 385-4545; gen fax (330) 385-7114; adv fax (330) 385-7114; ed fax (330) 385-8142; web site www.reviewonline.com

Published: Mon, Tues, Wed, Thur, Fri, Sat, Sun

Weekday Frequency: m

Saturday Frequency: m

Circulation: 7,233; 8,137(sat); 7,103(sun)

Last Audit: ABC September 30, 2011

Price: 2.00/wk (carrier); 17.90/mo (mail); 122.20/yr.

Advertising: Open inch rate $22.57

News services: AP.

Politics: Independent.

Not Published: Christmas.

Special Editions: Car Care (Apr); Football (Aug); Basketball (Dec); Bridal (Jan); Bridal (Jul); Progress (Mar); Thanksgiving Day (Nov); Home Improvement (Oct); Car Care (Sept).

Special Weekly Sections: Church (Sat).

Magazines: Parade (S); TV Review (Entertainment TV) (Thur).

Pub. ....Tammie McIntosh
Adv. Dir. ....Lisa Ludovici
Circ. Mgr. ....Kevin Fenton
Mng. Ed. ....Jim Mackey
Prodn. Supvr., Graphics ....Barbara Mick

Market Information: TMC.

Mechanical available: Offset; Black and 3 ROP colors; insert accepted; page cutoffs - 22 1/2.

Mechanical Specifications: Type page 13 x 21 1/2; E - 6 cols, 2 1/16, 1/8 between; A - 6 cols, 2 1/16, 1/8 between; C - 9 cols, 1 1/3, 1/8 between.

Commodity Consumption: Avg. Page Number Per Issue - Daily 18; Avg. Page Number Per Issue - Saturday 18; widths 27.

Equipment EDITORIAL: Front-end Software – APP/Mac.; Editorial Hardware – APP/Mac; Editorial Equipment – Lf/Leafscan 35, APP/Mac, V/5300; Editorial Printers – V/8500 CLASSIFIED: Front-end Software – APP/Mac.; Classified Hardware – APP/Mac; Classified Printers – V/8500 DISPLAY: Ad make-up applications – QPS/QuarkXPress; Layout Software – QPS/QuarkXPress 4.0, PC.; Display Hardware – APP/Mac G3; Display Printers – V/8500 PRODUCTION: Pagination Software – APP/Mac.; Production Equipment – V; Cameras – SCREEN/Companica 680E PRESSROOM: Line 1 – 10-G/Community 1985; Folders – G/1/2, G/1/4.; Bundle tying machines – Interlake/TS 250; Addressing machine – 1/ATT.; Business Hardware – NCR

ELYRIA

CHRONICLE-TELEGRAM

225 East Ave., Elyria, Ohio, 44035; gen tel (440) 329-7000; adv fax (440) 329-7272; ed fax (440) 329-7282; gen e-mail ctnews@chronicletelegram.com; metro@chroniclet.com; ed e-mail ct-sports@chroniclet.com; letters@chroniclet.com; web site www.chroniclet.com

Published: Mon, Tues, Wed, Thur, Fri, Sat, Sun
Weekday Frequency: m
Saturday Frequency: m
Circulation: 24,152; 24,457(sat); 23,989(sun)
Last Audit: ABC September 30, 2011
Price: 2.75/wk (carrier), $3.30/wk (mail); 144.40/yr (carrier), $145.60/yr (motor route), $171.60/yr (mail).
Advertising: Open inch rate $33.65
News services: Papert (Landon), MCT, SHNS.
Politics: Independent-Republican.
Not Published: Christmas.
Special Editions: Earth Day (Apr); Melon Festival (Aug); Letters to Santa (Dec); Health & Fitness (Feb); Midway Mall Auto Show (Jan); Medical Society (Jul); International Festival Guide (Jun); Car Care (Mar); Ohio Edison Parade of Homes (May); Holiday Planning Guide (Nov);
Special Weekly Sections: Business (S); Mini Pages (Tues); Best Food Day (Wed).
Magazines: TV Weekly Booklet (Fri); Parade (S); American Profile (Weekly).
Broadcast Affiliations: WEDL-AM/WMWV-FM Elyria, OH.
Pub. ....Cooper Hudnutt
Mgr., Educ. Serv. ....Barbara Stephens
Adv. Mgr., Display ....Jeff Pfeiffer
Circ. Mgr. ....Gary Cozart
Editorial Page Ed. ....Dave Perozek
Film/Theater Ed. ....Steve Fogarty
Web Ed. ....Rona Proudfoot
Market Information: ADS; TMC; Zoned editions.
Mechanical available: Offset; Black and 3 ROP colors; insert accepted; page cutoffs - 23 9/16.
Mechanical Specifications: Type page 13 x 22 1/2; E - 6 cols, 2, 1/6 between; A - 6 cols, 2, 1/6 between; C - 9 cols, 1 5/12, 1/12 between.
Commodity Consumption: Avg. Page Number Per Issue - Daily 40; Avg. Page Number Per Issue - Plates Used 27500; Avg. Page Number Per Issue - Sunday 67; widths 27 1/2; Newsprint Used - Metric Tons 3500; Newsprint Used - Short Tons 3600; Printing Ink Used - Black 76000; Printing I
Equipment EDITORIAL: Front-end Software – CText.; Editorial Hardware – CText; Editorial Printers – Panasonic CLASSIFIED: Front-end Software – CText.; Classified Hardware – CText DISPLAY: Ad make-up applications – CJ; Layout Software – CJ/Layout.; Display Hardware – HP; Display Printers – HP/2564B; Production Equipment – XIT/Clipper, Douthitt; Cameras – 1-C, 1-B. PRESSROOM: Line 1 – 5-G/Metro 1969; Folders – 1 MAILROOM: Counter stackers – 2/HL; Inserters and stuffers – HI; Bundle tying machines – MLN. BUSINESS COMPUTERS: Business Software – CJ; Business Hardware – HP

THE LORAIN COUNTY PRINTING & PUB. CO.

PO Box 4010, Elyria, Ohio, 44036; gen tel (440) 329-7000; gen fax (440) 329-7272; gen e-mail letters@chroniclet.com; web site www.chroniclet.com

Published: Mon, Tues, Wed, Thur, Fri, Sat, Sun
Weekday Frequency: m
Saturday Frequency: m
Price: 145.60/yr.
Advertising: Open inch rate $2.15

FINDLAY

THE COURIER

701 W. Sandusky St., Findlay, Ohio, 45840; gen tel (419) 422-5151; adv tel (419) 422-5151; ed tel (419) 422-5151; gen fax (419) 422-2937; adv fax (419) 422-2937; ed fax (419) 427-8480; adv e-mail karifaulkner@thecourier.com; ed e-mail letterstotheeditor@thecourier.com; newsdepartment@thecourier.com; web site www.thecourier.com

Published: Mon, Tues, Wed, Thur, Fri, Sat
Weekday Frequency: m
Circulation: 20,655; 20,655(sat)
Last Audit: September 30, 2008
Price: 113.00/yr; 4.35/2wk, $28.75/3mo.
Advertising: Open inch rate $16.45
News services: AP, LAT-WP, TMS, CSM.
Politics: Independent. **Established:** 1836
Advertising not accepted: Mail order.
Not Published: New Year; Memorial Day; Independence Day; Labor Day; Thanksgiving; Christmas.
Special Editions: Home Improvement (Apr); Balloon Fest (Aug); Basketball (Dec); Progress (Feb); Wedding Showcase (Jul); Pet Parade (Jun); Agricultural Showcase (Mar); Seniors (May); Fall Coupon (Nov); This Is Findlay (Semi-yearly); College/Pro Football (Sept).
Special Weekly Sections: Saturday Plus (Sat); Entertainment Plus (Tues).
Magazines: USA WEEKEND Magazine (Fri).
Broadcast Affiliations: WFIN/WKXA Findlay, OH.
Bd. Chrmn. ....Edwin L. Heminger
Vice Chrmn. ....Kurt P. Kah
Pres./Pub./Treasurer ....Karl L. Heminger
Vice Pres., Broadcast Commun ....David P. Glass
Vice Pres. ....Kurt F. Heminger
Sec. ....Margaret H. Heminger
Adv. Mgr. ....Kari Faulkner
Adv. Mgr., Cor. Acct. Sales ....Gary Stevens
Adv. Supvr., Classified ....Chris Collins
Mktg. Mgr. ....James Zellner
Circ. Mgr. ....Kim Foos
Circ. Mgr., Sales ....Rob Jenney
Ed. ....Peter Mattiace
Bus./Finance Reporter ....Mike Sobczyk
City Ed. ....Kurt Leonard
Family Ed. ....Margaret Dwiggins
News Ed. ....James Harrold
Photo Ed. ....Randy Roberts
Sports Ed. ....Larry Alter
Market Information: TMC.
Mechanical available: Offset; Black and 3 ROP colors; insert accepted; page cutoffs - 22 3/4.
Mechanical Specifications: Type page 11 5/8 x 21; E - 6 cols, 1 13/16, 1/8 between; A - 6 cols, 1 13/16, 1/8 between; C - 8 cols, 1 3/8, 1/8 between.
Commodity Consumption: Avg. Page Number Per Issue - Daily 24; Avg. Page Number Per Issue - Plates Used 18000; Avg. Page Number Per Issue - Saturday 36; widths 25; Newsprint Used - Metric Tons 1250; Printing Ink Used - Black 20000; Printing Ink Used - Color 2500; Printing Ink U
Equipment EDITORIAL: Front-end Software – HI/Jazbox 3.31.006.; Editorial Hardware – 3-Gateway/755; Editorial Equipment – 27-Gateway/E4100C; Editorial Printers – 1-HP/5, 1-HP/4MV CLASSIFIED: Front-end Software – Vision Data.; Classified Hardware – 1-Gateway/P5-200, 7-Sun/Terminals, 2-Sparc/Station 20; Classified Printers – 1-HP/4MV LaserJet, 1-Dataproducts/LGO2 DISPLAY: Ad make-up applications – Adobe/InDesign; Layout Software – Layout/8000.; Display Hardware – Sun/Ultra Sparc 60, 2-Gateway/450, 2-Gateway/550, 1-E/3400; Display Printers – 2-Mon, Sun/Ultra Sparc Station 10 PRODUCTION: Pagination Software – HI/Jazbox.; Production Equipment – 2-MON/Papermaster, 2-MON/Expressmaster 6000; Cameras – SCREEN/Companica 680C PRESSROOM: Line 1 – 7-HI/845; Folders – 1; Pasters – 6-MEG. MAILROOM: Counter stackers – 1-HL/Compass, 1-HL/Dual Carrier; Inserters and stuffers – 1/AM Graphics/630; Bundle tying machines – Dynaric, 1-Sterling/MR40CH; Addressing machine – 1-Prism/Jetmail. AUDIO: Audio Software – Microsoft/Windows NT; Audio Hardware – New Horizons Group, 880-HP/Printer, 1-TI/Micro BUSINESS COMPUTERS: Business Software – Microsoft/Office Vision Data; Business Hardware – 1-Sun/Sparc 20

FOSTORIA

THE REVIEW TIMES

113 E. Center St., Fostoria, Ohio, 44830; gen tel (419) 435-6641; adv tel (419) 435-6641; ed tel (419) 435-6641; gen fax (419) 435-9073; adv fax (419) 435-9073; ed fax (419) 435-9073; adv e-mail composing@thecourier.com; advertising@reviewtimes.com; ed e-mail rtnews@reviewtimes.com; web site www.reviewtimes.com

Published: Mon, Tues, Wed, Thur, Fri, Sat, Sun
Weekday Frequency: e
Saturday Frequency: m
Circulation: 3,790; 3,790(sat)
Last Audit: March 31, 2006
Price: 1.85/wk; 90.00/yr; 23.50/3mo.
Advertising: Open inch rate $10.40
News services: AP, LAT-WP.
Politics: Independent.
Advertising not accepted: Mail order.
Not Published: New Year; Memorial Day; Independence Day; Labor Day; Thanksgiving; Christmas.
Special Editions: Home Improvement (Apr); Football (Aug); Progress (Feb); Bridal (Jan); Health (Mar); Design An Ad (May); Basketball (Nov).
Special Weekly Sections: Church Page (Fri); Saturday Plus (Sat); Entertainment Plus (Tues).
Magazines: USA WEEKEND Magazine (Fri).
Pres. ....Karl L. Heminger
Sec. ....Margaret H. Gordon
Asst. Sec. ....Kurt F. Heminger
Adv. Mgr. ....Mary Perkins
Mktg. Mgr. ....James Zellner
Circ. Mgr. ....Kim Foos
Ed. ....Robert Hesse
Features Ed. ....Mariah Mercer
News Ed. ....Linda Woodland
Sports Ed. ....Scott Cottos
Market Information: TMC.
Mechanical available: Offset; Black and 3 ROP colors; insert accepted; page cutoffs - 22 3/4.
Mechanical Specifications: Type page 11 5/8 x 21; E - 6 cols, 1 13/16, 1/8 between; A - 6 cols, 1 13/16, 1/8 between; C - 8 cols, 1 3/8, 1/8 between.
Commodity Consumption: Avg. Page Number Per Issue - Daily 12; Avg. Page Number Per Issue - Plates Used 5000; Avg. Page Number Per Issue - Saturday 14; widths 12 1/2; Newsprint Used - Metric Tons 150; Printing Ink Used - Black 2500; Printing Ink Used - Color 1000; Printing Ink
Equipment; Editorial Hardware – 3-Gateway/955; Editorial Equipment – Software ☐ HI/Jazbox. CLASSIFIED: Front-end Software – Vision Data. DISPLAY: Ad make-up applications – HI/Dash; Layout Software – Layout/8000.; Display Printers – 2-Mon, 2-Sun/Ultra Sparc 10 PRODUCTION: Pagination Software – HI/Jazbox.; Production Equipment – 2-MON/Papermaster, 2-Konica 166 RA; Cameras – SCREEN/Companica 680C PRESSROOM: Line 1 – 7-HI/845; Folders – 1; Pasters – 6-MEG. MAILROOM: Counter stackers – 1-HL/Dual Carrier, 1-HL/Compass; Inserters and stuffers – 1/AM Graphics/630; Bundle tying machines – Dynaric, Sterling/MR4OCH; Wrapping singles – Addressing machine ☐ 1-Prism/Jetmail. BUSINESS COMPUTERS: Business Software – Microsoft/Office Vision Data; Business Hardware – Sun/Sparc 20

FREMONT

GANNETT SATELLITE INFORMATION NETWORK, INC.

1700 Cedar St., Fremont, Ohio, 43420; gen tel (419) 332-5511; gen fax 419-332-9750; web site www.fremontnewsmessenger.com

THE NEWS-MESSENGER

1700 Cedar St., Fremont, Ohio, 43420-8230; gen tel (419) 332-5511; gen fax (419) 332-9750; ed fax (419) 334-1037; gen e-mail newsdesk@thenews-messenger.com; web site www.thenews-messenger.com

Published: Mon, Tues, Wed, Thur, Fri, Sat
Weekday Frequency: e
Saturday Frequency: e
Circulation: 6,283; 8,519(sat)
Last Audit: ABC September 30, 2011
Price: 2.50/wk (carrier); 130.00/yr (carrier).
Advertising: Open inch rate $29.20
News services: AP, GNS.
Politics: Independent.
Special Editions: Home Week (Apr); Fair (Aug); Gift Guide (Dec); Progress (Feb); Bridal (Jan); Wellness (Jun); Accent on Agriculture (Mar); Graduation (May); Winter Sports (Nov); Fall Home Improvement (Oct); Business Showcase (Sept).
Special Weekly Sections: NASCAR (Fri); Food (Mon); Marketplace (Sat); Go Weekly (Thur); Kids Sports (Tues); Real Estate Weekly (Wed).
Magazines: TV Week (Fri); USA WEEKEND Magazine (Sat).
Adv. Dir. ....Cindy George Bealer
Exec. Ed. ....Jill Nevels-Haun
Circ. Dir. ....Bred Bollinger
Multimedia Ed. ....Vince Guerrieri
Market Information: TMC.
Mechanical available: Offset; Black and 3 ROP colors; insert accepted; page cutoffs - 22 3/4.
Mechanical Specifications: Type page 11 5/8 x 21 1/2; E - 6 cols, 1 13/16, 1/8 between; A - 6 cols, 1 13/16, 1/8 between; C - 9 cols, 1 3/16, 1/16 between.
Commodity Consumption: Avg. Page Number Per Issue - Daily 20; Avg. Page Number Per Issue - Plates Used 13000; widths 27 1/4; Newsprint Used - Metric Tons 512; Newsprint Used - Short Tons 564; Printing Ink Used - Black 10338; Printing Ink Used - Color 2610; Printing Ink Used -
Equipment EDITORIAL: Front-end Software – Baseview/IQ Pro, QPS/QuarkXPress 4.11.; Editorial Hardware – APP/Mac; Editorial Equipment – APP/Server; Editorial Printers – AU/APS 6-82 ACS, AII/3850, QMS/2060 CLASSIFIED: Front-end Software – QPS/QuarkXPress, Advision.; Classified Hardware – APP/Mac; Classified Printers – HP/LaserJet 4000 N DISPLAY: Ad make-up applications – QPS/QuarkXPress 4.11; Layout Software – IBM/AS-400, SCS/Layout 8000.; Display Hardware – APP/Mac; Display Printers – AU/APS 6-82 ACS, QMS 2060 PRODUCTION: Pagination Software – QPS/QuarkXPress, Advision/ALPS 4.11.; Production Equipment – AU/APS 6-82 ACS, AII/3850, Umax; Scanners – Umax/Powerlook III, Epson/Perfection 1670, AG/Arcus II, Duoscan/TI200, AG/Duoscan PRESSROOM: Line 1 – 6-G/Urbanite; Folders – 1-G/Quarter, 1-G/2:1 Half; Pasters – 3; Reels and Stands – 3 MAILROOM: Counter stackers – 1-BG/107, 1-BG/109; Inserters and stuffers – K&M/Titan 1372; Bundle tying machines – 3-MLN/ML2-EE, 1-Dynaric/NPZ; Addressing machine – Ch/539.; Business Hardware – IBM/AS-400

GALION

THE GALION INQUIRER

129 Harding Way E, Galion, Ohio, 44833; gen tel (419) 468-1117; gen fax (419) 468-7255; gen e-mail inquire@galioninquirer.com; web site www.galioninquirer.com

Group: Ohio Newspaper Services, Inc.
Published: Tues, Wed, Thur, Fri, Sat
Weekday Frequency: m
Saturday Frequency: m
Circulation: 2,200; 2,250(sat)
Price: 10.50/mo; 117.00/yr.
Advertising: Open inch rate $10.00
Insert rate: $50M
News services: AP.
Politics: Independent.
Advertising not accepted: Y
Not Published: New Year; Memorial Day; Independence Day; Labor Day; Thanksgiving; Christmas.
Special Editions: Progress Edition (Mar);Spring Home Improvement (Apr); Ohio Day Trips

(May);Football Preview Tab, OSU Football Preview Tab (Aug); Fall Home & Garden Tab (Sept.) Ohio Day Trips (Oct); Gift Guide (Nov.); Season's Greetings (Dec)
Magazines: American Profile (Weekly).
Pub. ....Vicki Taylor
Circ. Dir. ....Amy Huckaba
Editor ....Rachel Mendell
Sports Ed. ....John Kleinknecht
Market Information: ADS; TMC.
Mechanical available: Offset; Black and 3 ROP colors; insert accepted; page cutoffs - 22 3/4.
Mechanical Specifications: Type page 13 x 21 1/2; E - 6 cols, 2, 1/6 between; A - 6 cols, 2, 1/6 between; C - 8 cols, 1 1/2, 7/50 between.
Commodity Consumption: er: Daily, 10; Avg. Page Number Per Issue - Plates Used 5600; widths 27 1/2; Newsprint Used - Short Tons 400; Printing Ink Used - Black 7600; Printing Ink Used - Color 1800; Printing Ink Used - Pages Printed 4014.
Equipment EDITORIAL: Front-end Software – Mk.; Editorial Hardware – Mk CLASSIFIED: Front-end Software – Mk.; Classified Hardware – Mk DISPLAY: Ad make-up applications – Mk/Mycro-Comp AdWriter.; Display Hardware – APP/Mac IIci, APP/Mac II; Production Equipment – 2-APP/Mac LaserWriter II NTX; Cameras – R/400. PRESSROOM: Line 1 – 6-G/Community (in-line) 1968.; Bundle tying machines – Tri-Star/210.; Business Hardware – 4-Pony/386

GALLIPOLIS

GALLIPOLIS DAILY TRIBUNE

825 Third Ave., Gallipolis, Ohio, 45631; gen tel (740) 446-2342; gen fax (740) 446-3008; gen e-mail news@mydailytribune.com; web site www.mydailytribune.com
Group: Ohio Newspaper Services, Inc.
Published: Sun
Circulation: 4,466; 9,068(sun)
Last Audit: September 30, 2006
Price: 9.95/mo; 119.40/yr.
Advertising: Open inch rate $10.15
News services: AP.
Politics: Independent.
Note: The Gallipolis Daily Tribune and the Pomeroy Daily Sentinel share their Sunday edition, the Sunday Times-Sentinel. The combination rate is $14.20.
Not Published: New Year; Memorial Day; Independence Day; Labor Day; Thanksgiving; Christmas.
Special Weekly Sections: TV Times (Fri); Best Food Day (S); Best Food Day (Wed).
Magazines: USA WEEKEND Magazine (S).
Pub. ....Diane Goodrich
Controller ....Diane Hill
Adv. Mgr. ....Pam Caldwell
Circ. Mgr. ....Rachel Patterson
Mng. Ed. ....Andrew Carter
Sports Ed. ....Brad Sherman
Prodn. Mgr. ....Fred Hoffman
Prodn. Foreman, Press/Camera ....Don Coleman
Market Information: TMC.
Mechanical available: Offset; Black and 3 ROP colors; insert accepted; page cutoffs - 21 1/4.
Mechanical Specifications: Type page 11 5/8 x 21 1/4; E - 6 cols, 1 7/8, 1/8 between; A - 6 cols, 1 7/8, 1/8 between; C - 9 cols, 1 3/16, 1/16 between.
Commodity Consumption: Avg. Page Number Per Issue - Daily 16; Avg. Page Number Per Issue - Sunday 64; Newsprint Used - Short Tons 222.
Equipment EDITORIAL: Front-end Software – Baseview 3.4.; Editorial Hardware – APP/Mac; Editorial Equipment – HP/ScanJet Plus; Editorial Printers – APP/Mac LaserWriter CLASSIFIED: Front-end Software – Baseview 3.4.; Classified Hardware – APP/Mac; Classified Printers – APP/Mac LaserWriter DISPLAY: Ad make-up applications – Baseview 3.4; Layout Software – Baseview.; Display Hardware – APP/Mac PRODUCTION: Pagination Software – Baseview 3.4.; Production Equipment – APP/Mac LaserWriter IIg, Panther Plus 46; Cameras – B/Caravel, ECR/Autokon 8400; Scanners – HP/ScanJet Plus PRESSROOM: Line 1 – 3-G/Urbanite 1967; Line 2 – 1-G/Urbanite 1970; Line 3 – 1-G/Urbanite 1973; Line 4 – G/Upper Former 1976; Folders – 1-G/Suburban, 1-G/Urbanite; Press control system – 1-Fin/Console. MAILROOM: Counter stackers – 1/BG; Inserters and stuffers – 6-MM/Main Feeder; Bundle tying machines – 3-/Bu, 1-MLN/Strapper; Addressing machine – 3-/Wm; Other equipment –Kirk-Rudy/Labeler, MM/Stitcher Trimmer. BUSINESS COMPUTERS: Business Software – PBS; Business Hardware – 1-IBM/AS-400

GREENVILLE

DAILY ADVOCATE

428 S. Broadway, Greenville, Ohio, 45331-0220; gen tel (937) 548-3151; adv tel (937) 548-3151; ed tel (937) 548-3151; gen fax (937) 548-3913; adv fax (937) 548-3913; ed fax (937) 548-3913; gen e-mail info@dailyadvocate.com; web site www.dailyadvocate.com
Published: Mon, Tues, Wed, Thur, Fri, Sat
Weekday Frequency: m
Circulation: 6,468; 6,468(sat)
Last Audit: September 30, 2002
Price: 2.25/wk; 9.75/mo; 117.00/yr.
Advertising: Open inch rate $22.00
News services: AP, NEA.
Politics: Independent. **Established:** 1883
Not Published: Memorial Day; Independence Day; Labor Day; Christmas.
Special Weekly Sections: Next Generation (Mon); Religion Page (Sat); Prime Time (Wed).
Magazines: Cooks Corner (Mon); USA WEEKEND Magazine (Sat); Darke County Farmer Page (Tues); American Profile (Weekly).
Grp. Pub. ....David W. Compton
Adv. Mgr. ....Christie Randall
Circ. Mgr. ....Barbara Wilson
Ed. ....Bob Robinson
Asst. Ed. ....Linda Moody
News Ed. ....Mike Buckmaster
Sports Ed. ....Ron Greeson
Market Information: TMC; Zoned editions.
Mechanical available: Offset; Black and 3 ROP colors; insert accepted - catabook and mini-tab size; page cutoffs - 22 3/4.
Mechanical Specifications: Type page 13 3/4 x 21 1/2; E - 6 cols, 1 3/4, 1/8 between; A - 6 cols, 1 3/4, 1/8 between; C - 8 cols, 1 5/16, 1/8 between.
Commodity Consumption: Avg. Page Number Per Issue - Daily 12; Avg. Page Number Per Issue - Saturday 16; Avg. Page Number Per Issue - Sunday 24; widths 25.
Equipment; Editorial Hardware – APP/Power Mac; Editorial Equipment – Software □ Baseview/NewsEdit Pro IQUE. CLASSIFIED: Front-end Software – Baseview.; Classified Hardware – APP/Power Mac; Layout Software – MEI/ALS. PRODUCTION: Pagination Software – QPS/QuarkXPress 3.32.; Production Equipment – 1-Nu, V/ImageSetter Plus; Cameras – R

HAMILTON

JOURNALNEWS

228 Court St., Hamilton, Ohio, 45011-2820; gen tel (513) 863-8200; ed tel (513) 705-2506; gen fax (937) 225-0588; adv fax (513) 863-0011; ed fax (513) 896-9489; web site www.journal-news.com
Published: Mon, Tues, Wed, Thur, Fri, Sat, Sun
Weekday Frequency: m
Saturday Frequency: m
Circulation: 15,247; 16,888(sat); 19,842(sun)
Last Audit: ABC September 30, 2011
Price: 2.95/wk; 11.80/mo; 153.40/yr, $247.00/yr (mail).
News services: AP.
Politics: Independent. **Established:** 1818
Note: Advertising is sold in combination with the Middletown Journal (mS) for $52.00(d) and $52.00(S). Individual newspaper rates not made available.
Special Editions: Perfect Wedding (Apr); Back to School (Aug); Progress (Feb); Perfect Wedding (Jan); Butler County Fair (Jul); NCAA (Mar); Explore Summer (May); Basketball Tip-Off (Nov); Fall Home Improvement (Sept).
Special Weekly Sections: Journal News (Mon); Test Drive (Sat).
Magazines: TV Update (S).
Controller ....Karen Lehman
Sr. Vice President Slaes ....Rob Rohr
Circ. Mgr. ....Mike Stephens
Ed. ....Kira Lisa Warren
Deputy Mng. Ed. ....Mike Wallace
City Ed. ....Rich Gillette
Editorial Page Ed. ....Mike Williams
Lifestyle Ed. ....Mandy Gambrell
Photo Ed. ....Greg Lynch
Religion Ed. ....Peggy McCracken
Sports Ed. ....John Boyle
Mgmt. Info Servs. Mgr. ....Carl Borsani
Market Information: TMC.
Mechanical available: Offset; Black and 3 ROP colors; insert accepted - all; page cutoffs - 22 1/2.
Mechanical Specifications: Type page 13 x 21 1/2; E - 6 cols, 2 1/16, 1/8 between; A - 6 cols, 2 1/16, 1/8 between; C - 10 cols, 1 5/16, 1/16 between.
Commodity Consumption: Avg. Page Number Per Issue - Daily 30; Avg. Page Number Per Issue - Sunday 36; widths 13 1/2.
Equipment EDITORIAL: Front-end Software – CText/AFM V6X, Expressline Pagination.; Editorial Hardware – CText/486-66; Editorial Equipment – Lf/AP Leaf Picture Desk, APP/Mac Laserphoto, SMS/Stauffer Library; Editorial Printers – Pre Press/Panther Plus CLASSIFIED: Front-end Software – CText/Classified, CText/ALPS Pagination.; Classified Hardware – CText, PC 486 66Mhz; Classified Equipment – APP/Mac LaserWriter II NTX, HP/ScanJet Plus; Classified Printers – Pre Press/Panther Plus DISPLAY: Ad make-up applications – CText/Adept 3.2, QPS/QuarkXPress 3.31; Layout Software – 3-APP/Mac, 3-; Display Hardware – 3-CText/486-66, APP/WGS 8100-110; Display Printers – 2-NewGen/Imager Plus 12, Pre Press/Panther Plus PRODUCTION: Pagination Software – QPS/QuarkXPress 3.31.; Production Equipment – Pre Press/Panther Plus, 2-NewGen/Imager Plus, SCREEN/LD-281-Q; Cameras – 1-C/Spartan III, 1-ECR/Autokon 8400; Scanners – Polaroid/SprintScan; Business Hardware – 1-HP/9000 K class server

JOURNAL NEWS

PO Box 298, Hamilton, Ohio, 45012-0298; gen tel (678) 645-0000; web site http://www.journal-news.com/
Group: Cox Media Group
Published: Mon, Tues, Wed, Thur, Fri, Sat, Sun
Weekday Frequency: m
Saturday Frequency: m
Circulation: 28,517; 31,748(sat); 36,316(sun)
Last Audit: ABC September 30, 2011

HILLSBORO

TIMES-GAZETTE

209 S. High St., Hillsboro, Ohio, 45133; gen tel (937) 393-3456; gen fax (937) 393-2059; adv e-mail classifieds@timesgazette.com; web site www.timesgazette.com
Published: Tues, Wed, Thur, Fri, Sat
Weekday Frequency: m
Circulation: 4,500; 4,500(sat)
Last Audit: March 31, 2007
Price: 95.00/yr.
Advertising: Open inch rate $14.70
News services: AP.
Politics: Independent.
Not Published: New Year; Memorial Day; Independence Day; Labor Day; Thanksgiving; Christmas.
Special Editions: Christmas Tab (Dec); Fall Festival of Leaves Tab (Fall); Basketball Tab (Other); Spring Tab (Spring); Summer Tab (Summer).
Special Weekly Sections: Church Page (Fri); Farm Page (Mon).
Magazines: USA WEEKEND Magazine (Sat); American Profile (Weekly).
Pub. ....Pamela Sticker
Adv. Mgr. ....Mickey Parrott
Circ. Mgr. ....Brenda Earley
Ed. ....Steve Roush
Web Ed. ....Lora Abernathy
Composing Mgr. ....Angie Matticks
Mechanical available: Offset; Black and 2 ROP colors; insert accepted; page cutoffs - 21 1/2.
Mechanical Specifications: Type page 13 x 21; E - 6 cols, 2 1/16, 1/8 between; A - 6 cols, 2 1/16, 1/8 between; C - 6 cols, 2 1/16, 1/8 between.
Commodity Consumption: Avg. Page Number Per Issue - Daily 16; widths 29 1/2; Newsprint Used - Short Tons 230; Printing Ink Used - Black 5000; Printing Ink Used - Color 500.
Equipment; Editorial Hardware – COM.; Production Equipment – 3-COM; Cameras – 1-B, 1-Nu. PRESSROOM: Line 1 – G.; Bundle tying machines – Bu; Addressing machine – 1/Am, 1-/El.

IRONTON

IRONTON PUBLICATIONS, INC.

2903 S. 5th St., Ironton, Ohio, 45638; gen tel (740) 532-1441; gen fax (740) 532-1506

THE IRONTON TRIBUNE

2903 S. Fifth St., Ironton, Ohio, 45638-0647; gen tel (740) 532-1441; adv tel (740) 532-1445; ed tel (740) 532-1445; gen fax (740) 532-1506; adv e-mail advertising@irontontribune.com; ed e-mail news@irontontribune.com; web site www.irontontribune.com
Group: Ohio Newspaper Services, Inc.
Published: Mon, Tues, Wed, Thur, Fri, Sun
Weekday Frequency: e
Circulation: 5,228; 5,228(sun)
Last Audit: October 1, 2003
Price: 10.95/m; 131.40/yr.
Advertising: Open inch rate $18.50
News services: AP, MCT.
Politics: Independent.
Not Published: Christmas.
Special Editions: Football Tab (Aug); Christmas (Dec); Profile (Feb); Bridal (Jan); Newcomer's Guide (Jul); Thanksgiving Day (Nov); Senior Citizen Guide (Sept).
Special Weekly Sections: Religion (Fri); Neighbors (S); Best Food Day (Wed).
Magazines: Parade (S).
Pres./Pub. ....Michael Caldwell
Adv. Mgr. ....Shawn Randolph
Circ. Dir. ....Josh Morrison
Sports Ed. ....James Walker
Photo Ed. ....Jessica St. James
Pressroom Foreman ....Bo Elliott
Market Information: ADS; TMC; Zoned editions.
Mechanical available: Offset; Black and 3 ROP colors; insert accepted; page cutoffs - 22 1/4.
Mechanical Specifications: Type page 11 5/8 x 21 1/4; E - 6 cols, 1/8 between; A - 6 cols, 1/8 between; C - 10 cols, between.
Commodity Consumption: Avg. Page Number Per Issue - Daily 18; Avg. Page Number Per Issue - Plates Used 5000; Avg. Page Number Per Issue - Sunday 64; widths 27 1/4; Newsprint Used - Short Tons 480; Printing Ink Used - Pages Printed 5000.
Equipment; Editorial Hardware – APP/Mac; Editorial Equipment – Software □ Baseview/NewsEdit, Baseview/Classified. CLASSIFIED: Front-end Software – Baseview/NewsEdit, Baseview/Classified.; Classified Hardware – APP/Mac DISPLAY: Ad make-up applications – QPS/QuarkXPress 4.0; Layout Software – APP/Mac.; Display Printers – Xante/Accel-A-Writer; Production Equipment – Milart, Adobe/Photoshop; Cameras – C. PRESSROOM: Line 1 – 6-G/Suburban 1974.; Inserters and stuffers – 4-KAN/320; Bundle tying machines – It. BUSINESS COMPUTERS:

Business Software – PBS, Excel, Quicken; Business Hardware – Gateway

KENTON

HARDIN COUNTY PUBLISHING CO.

201 E. Columbus St., Kenton, Ohio, 43326; gen tel (419) 674-4066; gen fax (419) 673-1125; gen e-mail kteditor@kentontimes.com; web site www.kentontimes.com

THE KENTON TIMES

201 E. Columbus St., Kenton, Ohio, 43326; gen tel (419) 674-4066; gen fax (419) 673-1125; ed e-mail kteditor@kentontimes.com; web site www.kentontimes.com

Group: Ohio Newspaper Services, Inc.
Published: Mon, Tues, Wed, Thur, Fri, Sat, Sun
Weekday Frequency: e
Saturday Frequency: m
Circulation: 7,200; 7,200(sat)
Last Audit: March 31, 2007
Price: 134.15/yr.
Advertising: Open inch rate $8.50
News services: AP.
Politics: Independent.
Special Editions: Car Care (Apr); Pre-Fair (Aug); First Baby Sections (Dec); Presidents' Day Promotion (Feb); Baby Times (Jan); Fair Premium (Jul); Moonlight Madness Promotion (Jun); 4-H (Mar); Graduation (May); Christmas Shopping Kick-off (Nov); Moonlight Madness Promotio
Magazines: American Profile (Weekly).
Pub./Gen. Mgr./Purchasing Agent......Jeff Barnes
Adv. Mgr...................................Lesa Heacock
Sports Ed.....................Kendrick Jesionowski
Wire Ed................................Timothy Thomas
Prodn. Supt./Prodn. Foreman, Composing Curt Mullholland
Market Information: TMC.
Mechanical available: Offset; Black and 3 ROP colors; insert accepted; page cutoffs - 21 1/2.
Mechanical Specifications: Type page 13 x 21 1/2; E - 6 cols, 2 1/16, 1/8 between; A - 6 cols, 2 1/16, 1/8 between; C - 6 cols, 2 1/16, 1/8 between.
Commodity Consumption: Avg. Page Number Per Issue - Daily 16; widths 27 1/2; Newsprint Used - Short Tons 422; Printing Ink Used - Black 9000; Printing Ink Used - Color 300.
Equipment; Editorial Hardware – Mk.; Layout Software – 2-APP/Mac SE.; Production Equipment – 2-APP/Mac LaserWriter Plus, 1-APP/Mac LaserWriter NTX; Cameras – 1-B. PRESSROOM: Line 1 – 1-G/Community; Folders – 1-G/2:1.; Bundle tying machines – 1/Bu; Addressing machine – 1-/Kr, 1-/St.; Business Hardware – 3-B/25

LANCASTER

EAGLE-GAZETTE MEDIA

138 W. Chestnut St., Lancaster, Ohio, 43130-0848; gen tel (740) 681-4500; adv tel (740) 681-4333; ed tel (740) 681-4348; gen fax (740) 681-4505; adv fax (740) 681-4505; ed fax (740) 681-4456; adv e-mail dnase@mncogannett.com; ed e-mail laneg@nncogannett.com; web site www.lancastereaglegazette.com

Published: Mon, Tues, Wed, Thur, Fri, Sat, Sun
Weekday Frequency: e
Saturday Frequency: e
Circulation: 8,052; 8,217(sat); 10,113(sun)
Last Audit: ABC September 30, 2011
Price: $14.35 mo; $172.20 yr
Advertising: Open inch rate $27.38
Insert rate: 39/M
News services: AP, GNS.
Politics: 1807
Special Editions: Spring Car Care (Apr); Fall Sports Preview (Aug); Chamber Tab (Jan); Lancaster Festival (Jul); Pictorial Review (Jun); Home & Garden (Mar); @Record-Body:**Special Weekly Sections:** Color Comics (Sun); Entertainment (Thur); Best Food Day (Wed); Life Styles (Sun)
Magazines: USA WEEKEND Magazine (S).
Pub./Gen. Mgr...........................Rick Szabrak
Adv. Dir....Dan Nase
Editorial Page Ed.............................Jim Sabin
News Ed......................................Carl Burnett
Market Information: ADS; TMC.
Mechanical available: Offset; Black and 3 ROP colors; insert accepted - free-standing card; page cutoffs - 22 3/4.
Mechanical Specifications: Type page 11 3/4 x 21; E - 6 cols, 1 5/6, 1/8 between; A - 6 cols, 1 5/6, 1/8 between; C - 9 cols, 1 1/4, 1/8 between.
Commodity Consumption: Avg. Page Number Per Issue - Daily 16; Avg. Page Number Per Issue - Plates Used 12000; Avg. Page Number Per Issue - Saturday 16; Avg. Page Number Per Issue - Sunday 32; widths 25; Newsprint Used - Short Tons 1000; Printing Ink Used - Black 25000; Printin
Equipment EDITORIAL: Front-end Software – Baseview/NewsEdit Pro.; Editorial Hardware – APP/Mac; Editorial Printers – Xante CLASSIFIED: Front-end Software – Advision.; Classified Hardware – IBM; Classified Printers – Xante DISPLAY: Ad make-up applications – QPS/QuarkXPress; Layout Software – MEI/ALS.; Display Hardware – APP/Mac; Display Printers – Xante PRODUCTION: Pagination Software – Mk, QPS/QuarkXPress.; Production Equipment – Wordlinx 20; Scanners – Umax/PowerLook; Bundle tying machines – 1-MLN/Strapper, 1/Akibono. BUSINESS COMPUTERS: Business Software – PBS, Oracle; Business Hardware – IBM

LIMA

THE LIMA NEWS

3515 Elida Rd., Lima, Ohio, 45807; gen tel (419) 223-1010; adv tel (419) 993-2040; ed tel (419) 993-2058; gen fax (419) 229-0426; adv fax (419) 221-2884; ed fax (419) 229-2926; gen e-mail limanews@limanews.com; web site www.limanews.com

Group: Ohio Newspaper Services, Inc.
Published: Mon, Tues, Wed, Thur, Fri, Sat, Sun
Weekday Frequency: m
Saturday Frequency: m
Circulation: 28,586; 28,575(sat); 37,185(sun)
Last Audit: ABC September 30, 2011
Price: 13.25/mo; 154.50/yr; 38.50/3mo.
Advertising: Open inch rate $70.05
News services: AP, CT, Freedom Wire, MCT, TMS.
Politics: Independent.
Special Editions: Spring Car Care (Apr); Regional Football Preview (Aug); Christmas Gift Sections (Dec); Regional Prep Basketball Tournament Preview (Feb); Health & Fitness (Jan); Best of the Lima Region (Jul); Regional Salute to Graduates (Jun); Celebrating Our Spirit (Ma
Special Weekly Sections: 360 Entertainment Tab & Drivers Seat (Fri); Best Food Day (Mon); Agri-Business, Family, Consumer (S); Lifestyle Feature , Religion & High School Sports (Sat); Home & Fashion (Thur); Health (Tues); Lifestyle Feature, Reminisce & Antiques (Wed).
Magazines: 360 Entertainment Tab TV listings (Fri); Color Comics (S).
Broadcast Affiliations: NBC; FOX.
Pub./Gen. Mgr...........................James Shine
Dir., HR.......................................Leila Osting
Administrative Asst.....................Mary Hanjore
Adv. Mgr., Local.....................Natalie Buzzard
Adv. Mgr., Regl...........................Steve Beck
Adv. Mgr., Servs.................Susie Rosengarten
Dir., Mktg.....................................Bill Clinger
Circ. Dir.................................Todd C. Russell
Circ. Mgr.............................John Quaintance
Ed...Jim Krumel
Mng. Ed.....................................Diane Pacetti
Editorial Page Ed.....................Ron Lederman
Lifestyle Ed...........................Adrienne Mcgee
News Ed......................................David Trinko
Photo Ed......................................Craig Orosz
Systems Integrated Mgr...............Eric Germann
Prodn. Mgr., Opns...........................Bob Rodi
Prodn. Supt., Bldg.........................Chip Moreo
Prodn. Supvr., Press........................Jack Hunt
Market Information: TMC; Zoned editions.
Mechanical available: Offset; Black and 3 ROP colors; insert accepted; page cutoffs - 22 3/4.
Mechanical Specifications: Type page 13 x 21 1/2; E - 6 cols, 1/8 between; A - 6 cols, 1/8 between; C - 9 cols, 1/16 between.
Commodity Consumption: Avg. Page Number Per Issue - Daily 32; Avg. Page Number Per Issue - Plates Used 48000; Avg. Page Number Per Issue - Saturday 54; Avg. Page Number Per Issue - Sunday 160; widths 37 1/2; Newsprint Used - Metric Tons 3500; Newsprint Used - Short Tons 3725;
Equipment EDITORIAL: Front-end Software – APT/ACT Editorial System.; Editorial Hardware – 2-Compaq/Proliant 3000; Editorial Equipment – 35-Gateway/Pentium PC; Editorial Printers – 2-Pre-Press/Panther Pro 36 Imagesetters, HP/8000, HP/750C Color Proofer, 2-HP/5000 CLASSIFIED: Front-end Software – Baseview.; Classified Hardware – 2-Compaq/Proliant 3000; Classified Equipment – 8-APP/Mac; Classified Printers – HP/DeskJet 870CSE, HP/LaserJet 4 DISPLAY: Ad make-up applications – MK/Managing Editor Layout; Layout Software – 9-Multi-Ad/Creator.; Display Hardware – Compaq/Prosignia; Display Printers – HP/LaserJet 6Lxi, HP/LaserJet 4, Epson/Stylus Color 3000, HP/DesignJet 1050 C PRODUCTION: Pagination Software – APT/ACT Pagination 3.0, Baseview/Classified, Managing Edit; Production Equipment – Nat/A-340, 2-Pre Press/Panther Pro 36 Imagesetters, APP/Mac Quadra 900, Polaroid/SprintScan 35; Cameras – Capanica #6500C; Scanners – 2-HP/Scan Jet II, 5-Umax/Powerlook II PRESSROOM: Line 1 – 6-MAN/Lithoflex double width; Folders – 2; Pasters – 6 MAILROOM: Counter stackers – 3-Hall/Monitor, TMSI/Dual Carrier; Inserters and stuffers – GMA/SLS 1000; Bundle tying machines – 2-Dynaric; Wrapping singles – 2-St/720.; Addressing machine – 1-Am/1906, 1-Gr/6331. BUSINESS COMPUTERS: Business Software – IBM/PS2, Vision Data, Southware, Great Plains; Business Hardware – PC Pentium II 350 Mhz, Gateway

LISBON

MORNING JOURNAL

308 W. Maple St., Lisbon, Ohio, 44432; gen tel (330) 424-9541; adv tel (330) 424-9541; ed tel (330) 424-9541; gen fax (330) 424-0048; ed fax (330) 424-0048; gen e-mail news@mojonews.com; web site www.morningjournalnews.com

Published: Mon, Tues, Wed, Thur, Fri, Sat, Sun
Weekday Frequency: m
Saturday Frequency: m
Circulation: 10,060; 14,491(sat); 9,781(sun)
Last Audit: ABC September 30, 2011
Price: 2.77/wk; 11.05/mo; 122.20/yr.
Advertising: Open inch rate $22.65
News services: AP.
Politics: Independent.
Not Published: New Year; Christmas.
Special Editions: Lawn & Garden (Apr); Fall Home Improvement (Aug); Songbook (Dec); Fact Book (Feb); Christmas in July (Jul); Car Care (Mar); Fun in the Sun (May); Christmas Gift Catalog (Nov); Car Care (Oct).
Special Weekly Sections: Dining Guide (Fri); TV Journal (S); Football (Sat); Entertainment (Thur); Roasts & Toasts (Tues); Farm (Wed).
Magazines: USA WEEKEND Magazine (S).
Pub.......................................Larry Dorschner
Circ. Dir......................................Heidi Grimm
Ed...Dorma Tolson
Asst. Ed.................................Dennis Spalvieri
Mgmt. Info Servs. Mgr.................Ron Flaviano
Prodn. Mgr., Press....................Mike Sweeney
Market Information: ADS; Split run; TMC.
Mechanical available: Offset; Black and 3 ROP colors; insert accepted - samples; page cutoffs - 21.
Mechanical Specifications: Type page 13 x 20; E - 6 cols, 2 1/16, 1/8 between; A - 6 cols, 2 1/16, 1/8 between; C - 9 cols, 1 15/16, 1/8 between.
Commodity Consumption: Avg. Page Number Per Issue - Daily 18; Avg. Page Number Per Issue - Plates Used 11500; Avg. Page Number Per Issue - Saturday 18; Avg. Page Number Per Issue - Sunday 32; widths 13 1/2; Newsprint Used - Short Tons 1000; Printing Ink Used - Black 125000; Pr
Equipment EDITORIAL: Front-end Software – Baseview.; Editorial Hardware – APP/Power Mac; Editorial Equipment – 5-APP/Power Mac G3; Editorial Printers – XIT/Imagesetter, ECR/Imagesetter CLASSIFIED: Front-end Software – Baseview.; Classified Hardware – APP/Power Mac; Classified Printers – XIT/Imagesetter, ECR/Imagesetter, HP/LaserJet 5000N DISPLAY: Ad make-up applications – Multi-Ad/Creator, QPS; Layout Software – 4-APP/Mac.; Display Hardware – APP/Mac; Display Printers – XIT/Imagesetter, ECR/Imagesetter, APP/Mac LaswerWriter 300, HP/LaserJet 5000N, Epson/Color Stylist 3000; Production Equipment – OmniPro 8.0, ECR/Imagesetter; Cameras – Scanners □ Epson, Microtek, HP; Scanners – Equipment □ QPS. PRESSROOM: Line 1 – 8-HI/NC 400; Folders – 2 MAILROOM: Counter stackers – 2/PPK; Bundle tying machines – 1-/Bu, 1-/Gs, 1-/Sa; Addressing machine – 2-/Am, 1-/Ch; Other equipment –Custom Built On-line Trimmer. BUSINESS COMPUTERS: Business Software – Brainworks; Business Hardware – Compaq

LOGAN

LOGAN DAILY NEWS

72 E. Main St., Logan, Ohio, 43138; gen tel (740) 385-2107; adv tel (740) 385-2107; ed tel (740) 385-2109; gen fax (740) 385-4514; adv fax (740) 385-4514; ed fax (740) 385-4514; gen e-mail info@logandaily.com; web site www.logandaily.com

Group: Ohio Newspaper Services, Inc.
Published: Mon, Tues, Wed, Thur, Fri, Sat, Sun
Weekday Frequency: e
Saturday Frequency: m
Circulation: 4,183; 4,183(sat)
Last Audit: September 30, 2005
Price: 120.00/yr.
Advertising: Open inch rate $14.65
News services: AP.
Politics: Independent. **Established:** 1838
Not Published: Christmas and holidays that fall on Mondays..
Magazines: American Profile (Weekly).
Bus. Mgr.................................Shelly Mouser
Adv. Mgr..............................Rhonda Wallace
Circ. Dir....................................Rich Burcham
Ed....Monica Nieporte
Mng. Ed..................................Rochelle Hawk
Prodn. Mgr..............................Lucy Burcham
Market Information: ADS; Split run; Zoned editions.
Mechanical available: Offset; Black and 3 ROP colors; insert accepted; page cutoffs - 22 3/4.
Mechanical Specifications: Type page 13 3/4 x 21 1/2; E - 6 cols, 2 3/16, 3/16 between; A - 6 cols, 2 3/16, 3/16 between; C - 8 cols, 1 1/16, 1/8 between.
Commodity Consumption: Avg. Page Number Per Issue - Daily 12; widths 27 1/2.
Equipment EDITORIAL: Front-end Software – Baseview/NewsEdit, QPS/QuarkXPress.; Editorial Hardware – APP/Mac 7100 CLASSIFIED: Front-end Software – Baseview, QPS/QuarkXPress.; Classified Hardware – APP/Mac IIsi; Classified Printers – Okidata/Microline 320 PRODUCTION: Pagination Software – APP/Mac 7100 7.5.; Production Equipment – HP/LaserJet 4MV, HP/LaserJet 4MV Plus; Cameras – 1-R; Scanners – HP/ScanJet IIcx; Bundle tying machines – 1/Bu; Addressing machine – 2-/Wm. BUSINESS COMPUTERS: Business Software – MSSI; Business Hardware – AST/Bravo LC 4-660

LONDON

THE MADISON PRESS

30 S. Oak St., London, Ohio, 43140-0390; gen tel (740) 852-1616; adv tel (740) 852-1616; ed tel (740) 852-1616; gen fax (740) 852-1620; adv fax (740) 852-1620; ed fax (740) 852-1620; adv e-mail dhamilton@madison-press.com; ed e-mail editor@madison-press.com; web site www.madison-press.com

Group: Ohio Community Media, LLC
Published: Tues, Wed, Thur, Fri, Sat
Weekday Frequency: m
Saturday Frequency: m
Circulation: 4,359; 4,359(sat)
Last Audit: Sworn March 31, 2006
Price: 117.00/yr.
Advertising: Open inch rate $9.10
Insert rate: $46 cpm single sheet
News services: AP.
Politics: Independent. **Established:** 1842
Not Published: Independence Day; Christmas.
Special Editions: Antique (Apr); Summer Tab (Jun); Farm & Garden Tab (Mar); Home Improvement Tab (May); Car Tab (Oct); Variety (Sept).
Special Weekly Sections: Farm Page (Fri); Food Page (Mon); Outdoor Page (Thur); Kids Page (Wed).
Magazines: American Profile (Weekly).
Publisher ....Devin Hamilton
Adv. Mgr., Classified ....Linda Marx
Mng. Ed. ....Fran Odyniec
Sports Ed. ....Gregg Rettig
Circ. Mgr. ....Tim Yost
Market Information: TMC.
Mechanical available: Offset; Black and 3 ROP colors; insert accepted; page cutoffs - 22 3/4.
Mechanical Specifications: Type page 13 x 21 1/2; E - 6 cols, 2 1/16, 1/8 between; A - 6 cols, 2 1/16, 1/8 between; C - 8 cols, 1 1/2, 1/8 between.
Commodity Consumption: Avg. Page Number Per Issue - Daily 14; widths 13 3/4; Newsprint Used - Short Tons 250.
Equipment EDITORIAL: Front-end Software – Mk. CLASSIFIED: Front-end Software – Mk. DISPLAY: Ad make-up applications – Multi-Ad/Creator with CD-Rom; Layout Software – APP/Mac.; Production Equipment – APP/Mac; Cameras – Acti/204; Scanners – APP/Mac. PRESSROOM: Line 1 – 6-G/S1075. MAILROOM: Counter stackers – BG/104; Inserters and stuffers – Bundle tying machines ☐ Bu; Addressing machine – KR.

LORAIN

THE MORNING JOURNAL

1657 Broadway Ave., Lorain, Ohio, 44052-3439; gen tel (440) 245-6901; adv tel (440) 245-6901; ed tel (440) 245-6901; gen fax (440) 245-6922; adv fax (440) 245-5637; ed fax (440) 245-6912; gen e-mail news@morningjournal.com; adv e-mail advertising@morningjournal.com; ed e-mail news@morningjournal.com; web site www.morningjournal.com

Published: Mon, Tues, Wed, Thur, Fri, Sat, Sun
Weekday Frequency: m
Saturday Frequency: m
Circulation: 21,435; 22,430(sat); 22,263(sun)
Last Audit: ABC September 30, 2011
Price: 3.35/wk; 13.40/mo; 174.20/yr.
Advertising: Open inch rate $69.60
News services: AP, NYT, MCT.
Politics: Independent.
Special Editions: Golf I (Apr); Tour of Homes (Aug); Truck I & II Tab (Dec); Finance/Tax (Feb); Town Crier (Jan); Truck I Tab (Jul); International Festival (Jun); BIA Home Craft Show (Mar); Lorain Pride (May); Early Holiday Gift Guide (Nov); BIA Home Tab (Oct); Country Liv
Special Weekly Sections: Arcade/Entertaiment (Fri); Real Estate (S); Real Estate (Sat).
Magazines: The Edge (sports edition) (Fri); Today's Woman (Mon); Job Digest (Other); TV Journal (S); Color Comics (6 pages) (Sat).
Pub. ....Jeff Sudbrook
CFO ....Ron Adams
Adv. Dir. / Gen. Mgr. ....Ron Beal
Circ. Dir. ....Micah Young
Ed ....Tom Skoch
Mng. Ed. ....April Elliott
Bus. Ed ....Alex Parker
Entertainment/Amusements Ed ....Howard Gollop
News Ed ....Jeff Arnett
Chief Photographer ....Tom Whittington
Sports Ed. ....Eric Stoessel
Television Ed. ....Daniel Smith
Mgmt. Info Servs. Mgr. ....Jerry Morog
Prodn. Mgr., Post Press ....Nelson Munoz
Prodn. Mgr., Pre Press ....Candy Berger
Prodn. Mgr., Pressroom ....Rick Mack
Market Information: ADS; TMC; Zoned editions.
Mechanical available: Offset; Black and 3 ROP colors; insert accepted; page cutoffs - 22 3/4.
Mechanical Specifications: Type page 12 x 21 1/2; E - 6 cols, 1 7/8, 1/8 between; A - 6 cols, 1 7/8, 1/8 between; C - 9 cols, 1 3/16, 1/16 between.
Commodity Consumption: Avg. Page Number Per Issue - Daily 38; Avg. Page Number Per Issue - Plates Used 30000; Avg. Page Number Per Issue - Sunday 70; widths 12 1/2; Newsprint Used - Short Tons 3500; Printing Ink Used - Black 125000; Printing Ink Used - Color 26500; Printing In
Equipment EDITORIAL: Front-end Software – Baseview.; Editorial Hardware – APP/Mac; Editorial Printers – 2-Linotype-Hell/Linotronic 500, Bidco/Imager, APP/Mac Laserwriter 8500, APP/Mac LaserWriter 630, APP/Mac Laser-Writer 16-600, GCC/Elite 12085 CLASSIFIED: Front-end Software – Baseview.; Classified Hardware – APP/Mac; Classified Printers – 1-Printronix/300, 1-Star/10, CG/8600 DISPLAY: Ad make-up applications – QPS/QuarkXPress 4.03; Layout Software – Baseview.; Display Hardware – APP/Mac; Display Printers – APP/Mac LaserWriter 630, APP/Mac Laser-Writer 16-600, GCC/Elite 12085, 2-Linotype-Hell/Linotronic 500, 1-Bidco/Imager PRODUCTION: Pagination Software – Baseview/Ad Manager Pro.; Production Equipment – CG/8600, 2-Linotype-Hell/L-500 Imagesetter, 1-Bidco/Imager, 1-P/24ML, 1-Konica/K720; Cameras – ECR/Spartan II, C/Newspager; Scanners – Lf/Leafscan 35, 2-Nikon/LS1000, 1-Kk, Umax/FlatBed Scanners PRESSROOM: Line 1 – 12-G/Urbanite single width 1990; Press Drives – 2; Folders – 2-G/2:1; Pasters – 9 MAILROOM: Counter stackers – 3-HL/Monitor, 1-HL/Monitor HT; Inserters and stuffers – 3-MM/227 7:1; Bundle tying machines – 3/Power Strap, 1-/MLN, 2-MLN/2E; Addressing machine – 1-/BH.; Business Hardware – 1-IBM/AS-400

MANSFIELD

NEWS JOURNAL

70 W. Fourth St., Mansfield, Ohio, 44902; gen tel (419) 522-3311; adv tel (419) 522-3311; ed tel (419) 522-3311; gen fax (419) 521-7414; adv fax (419) 521-7413; ed fax (419) 521-7415; web site www.mansfield-newsjournal.com

Published: Mon, Tues, Wed, Thur, Fri, Sat, Sun
Weekday Frequency: m
Saturday Frequency: m
Circulation: 18,236; 19,690(sat); 27,764(sun)
Last Audit: ABC September 30, 2011
Price: 14.15/mo; 169.80/yr.
Advertising: Open inch rate $44.90
News services: AP, GNS.
Politics: Independent. **Established:** 1930
Special Editions: He Is Risen (Apr); OSU Football (Aug); Share the Faith (Dec); Premier Living (Every other month); Progress (Feb); Bridal Guide (Jan); Living Here (Jul); Mid-Ohio Races (Jun); Golf Guide (Mar); Ohio Weekend (May); Real Estate Today (Monthly); Home for the
Special Weekly Sections: TV Book (Fri); Mind & Body (Mon); Living (S); Religion (Sat); Weekend Entertainment (Thur); Home & Garden (Tues); Food (Wed).
Magazines: USA WEEKEND Magazine (Sat).
Adv. Dir. ....Hearn Michael
Classified Sales Ctr. Mgr. ....Karie Sargent
Grp. Consumer Mktg. Mgr. ....Erik Gets
Circ. Dir. ....Pete Barend
Circ. Opns. Mgr. ....Mike Fleming
Exec. Ed. ....Tom Brennan
Mng. Ed. ....David Kennard
Bus. Writer ....Lisa Miller
Educ. Reporter ....Linda Martz
Librarian ....Ellen Smith
Online Ed. ....Fackler Holly
Multimedia Ed. ....Polcyn Dave
Photo Ed. ....Dave Polcyn
Religion Writer ....Karen Palmer
Sports Ed. ....Larry Phillips
Dir., Online Servs. ....Jayna McDaniel
Prodn. Dir. ....Jim Ferguson
Prodn. Mgr., Distr. Ctr. ....Brian Wilson
Prodn. Mgr., Plate ....Dora Britton
Market Information: Split run; TMC.
Mechanical available: Offset; Black and 3 ROP colors; insert accepted - free-standing cards; page cutoffs - 22.
Mechanical Specifications: Type page 12 x 20 1/2; E - 6 cols, 1 5/6, 1/8 between; A - 6 cols, 1 5/6, 1/8 between; C - 9 cols, 1 3/16, 1/8 between.
Commodity Consumption: Avg. Page Number Per Issue - Daily 32; Avg. Page Number Per Issue - Plates Used 25660; Avg. Page Number Per Issue - Sunday 62; widths 25; Newsprint Used - Short Tons 4146; Printing Ink Used - Black 164289; Printing Ink Used - Color 98669; Printing Ink Us
Equipment EDITORIAL: Front-end Software – Baseview/IQUE 322.; Editorial Hardware – APP/Mac G4 450; Editorial Printers – HP/8000N CLASSIFIED: Front-end Software – Net-linx/Advision 5.2.7.; Classified Hardware – IBM/RS 6000; Classified Equipment – Net-linx/ALPS Classified Pagination; Classified Printers – HP/4200N, HP/5M; Layout Software – Adobe/InDesign CS.; Display Hardware – APP/Mac G4 450, APP/Mac G4933; Display Printers – HP/2500CP, 2-HP/8150N PRODUCTION: Pagination Software – Baseview/IQUE.; Production Equipment – 1-AG/3850 Advantage DL, Veri-Color/2000; Scanners – 1-Umax/Mirage II SE, 4-Vmax/Powerlock III, 3-Epson, 2-StudioScan II PRESSROOM: Line 1 – 7-G/Metroliner (4 decks); Press Drives – 7-Fin; Folders – 1-G/double; Pasters – 6-Static Belt/CT50; Reels and Stands – 6; Press control system – Fin/Goss Digital Ink; Press registration system – Microtrack. MAILROOM: Counter stackers – 3-Idab, 1-Quipp/400; Inserters and stuffers – 1-GMA/SLS 1000A, 1-GMA/SLS1000; Bundle tying machines – 2-Dynaric/NP2, 1-Sterling/MR50; Mailroom control system – GMA/Lincs, GMA/Winlincs; Addressing machine – 1-Matthews/Inkjet; Other equipment – Other equip BUSINESS COMPUTERS: Business Software – PBS; Business Hardware – HP/9000

MARIETTA

THE MARIETTA TIMES

700 Channel Ln., Marietta, Ohio, 45750; gen tel (740) 373-2121; gen fax (740) 373-6251; adv fax (740) 373-6251; ed fax (740) 376-5475; gen e-mail postmaster@marietta-times.com; adv e-mail advertising@mariettatimes.com; ed e-mail news@mariettatimes.com; web site www.mariettatimes.com

Group: Ohio Newspaper Services, Inc.
Published: Mon, Tues, Wed, Thur, Fri, Sat
Weekday Frequency: e
Saturday Frequency: e
Circulation: 9,122; 11,159(sat)
Last Audit: ABC September 30, 2011
Price: 2.50/wk; 130.00/yr; 30.00/17wk.
Advertising: Open inch rate $24.58
News services: AP, GNS, GNS.
Politics: Independent. **Established:** 1864
Special Weekly Sections: Religion Page (Fri); Best Food Day (Mon); Times Weekend Edition (Sat); Entertainment (Thur); Education (Tues); Health & Fitness (Wed).
Magazines: USA WEEKEND Magazine (Sat).
Office Mgr. ....Patti Patton
Adv. Dir. ....Steve Herron
Classified Inside Sales Mgr. ....Lisa Kehl
Circ. Dir. ....Joseph Tranquill
Ed. ....Jennifer Houtman
Sr. Copy Ed. ....Jim Bartholow
Copy Ed. ....Claire Hogue-Heiby
News Ed. ....Evan Bevins
Photo Ed. ....Mitch Casey
Sports Ed. ....Joe Davis
Online Mgr. ....Art Smith
Info. Systems Mgr. ....Russ Ryan
Market Information: ADS; TMC; Zoned editions.
Mechanical available: Offset; Black and 3 ROP colors; insert accepted; page cutoffs - 22 3/4.
Mechanical Specifications: Type page 13 x 21 1/2; E - 6 cols, 2 1/16, 1/6 between; A - 6 cols, 2 1/16, 1/6 between; C - 9 cols, 1 3/8, 1/16 between.
Commodity Consumption: Avg. Page Number Per Issue - Daily 24; Avg. Page Number Per Issue - Plates Used 10967; widths 33; Newsprint Used - Short Tons 637; Printing Ink Used - Pages Printed 7121.
Equipment EDITORIAL: Front-end Software – Baseview.; Editorial Hardware – Dewar/Disc Net, APP/Mac CLASSIFIED: Front-end Software – ONI/Class.; Display Hardware – APP/Mac.; Production Equipment – 1-LE/LD 1800; Cameras – 1-B/Commodore. MAILROOM: Counter stackers – HI/Rima RS-2517; Bundle tying machines – 1/Ty-Tech; Mailroom control system – MM/Saddle Stitcher.; Business Hardware – IBM/PC

MARION

THE MARION STAR

150 Court St., Marion, Ohio, 43302-3026; gen tel (740) 387-0400; adv tel (740) 387-0400; ed tel (740) 387-0400; gen fax (740) 375-5199; adv fax (740) 375-5199; ed fax (740) 375-5199; web site www.marionstar.com

Group: Ohio Newspaper Services, Inc.
Published: Mon, Tues, Wed, Thur, Fri, Sat, Sun
Weekday Frequency: m
Saturday Frequency: m
Circulation: 7,359; 7,971(sat); 9,519(sun)
Last Audit: ABC September 30, 2011
Price: 2.25/wk; 9.75/mo; 143.52/yr.
Advertising: Open inch rate $26.80
News services: AP.
Politics: Independent.
Special Editions: Drum Corps Championships (Aug); Christmas Greetings (Dec); Bride (Jan); Progress (Mar); Christmas Gifts (Nov); Popcorn Festival (Sept).
Special Weekly Sections: Church (Fri); Feminine Trends (Mon); Business (S); Real Estate (Sat); Community Focus (Thur); Young Minds (Tues); Closer Look (Wed).
Magazines: Golden Opportunities (Senior Citizen) (Monthly); USA WEEKEND Magazine (S); Reflections (Wed).
Pub. ....Tom Brennan
Adv. Dir. ....Jeff Coppler
Circ. Mgr. ....Mike Fleming
Mng. Ed. ....Tom Graser
Local Content Ed. ....Jamie Steven
Conversation Ed. ....Kelle Gabriel
Presentation Ed. ....Don Tudor
Market Information: ADS; Split run; TMC; Zoned editions.
Mechanical available: Offset; Black and 3 ROP colors; insert accepted; page cutoffs - 22 3/4.
Mechanical Specifications: Type page 13 x 21 1/2; E - 6 cols, 2 1/16, 1/8 between; A - 6 cols, 2 1/16, 1/8 between; C - 9 cols, 1 3/8, 1/16 between.
Commodity Consumption: Avg. Page Number Per Issue - Daily 24; Avg. Page Number Per Issue - Plates Used 7765; Avg. Page Number Per Issue - Sunday 44; widths 13 3/4;

Newsprint Used - Short Tons 910; Printing Ink Used - Black 37000; Printing Ink Used - Color 10000; Printing Ink U

Equipment; Editorial Hardware – CText, 20-RSK/Tandy, CText.; Classified Hardware – 4-RSK/Tandy, CText.; Layout Software – CText/Adept.; Production Equipment – Nat/A-250, 2-Tegra/Varityper/5100A, 3-APP/Mac Laser 486 SX; Cameras – 1-R/500-LB, SCREEN/C-680; Scanners – Nu. PRESSROOM: Line 1 – 8-G/Community (2 half decks); Folders – 1-G/SSC.; Bundle tying machines – 1-Bu/Straping; Addressing machine – 2-Am/2000.; Business Hardware – ATT

MARTINS FERRY

EASTERN OHIO NEWSPAPER, INC.

200 S. Fourth St., Martins Ferry, Ohio, 43935; gen tel (740) 633-1131; gen fax (740) 633-1122; gen e-mail timesleaderonline.com; adv e-mail hclark@timesleaderonline.com; ed e-mail bkapral@timesleaderonline.com; web site timesleaderonline.com

Published: Mon, Tues, Wed, Thur, Fri, Sat, Sun
Weekday Frequency: e
Saturday Frequency: m
Own facility?: Y

THE TIMES LEADER

200 S. Fourth St., Martins Ferry, Ohio, 43935; gen tel (740) 633-1131; adv tel (740) 633-1131; ed tel (740) 633-1131; gen fax (740) 633-1122; adv fax (740) 633-1122; ed fax (740) 633-1122; gen e-mail timesleader@timesleaderonline.com; web site www.timesleaderonline.com

Published: Mon, Tues, Wed, Thur, Fri, Sat, Sun
Weekday Frequency: e
Saturday Frequency: m
Circulation: 12,469; 12,632(sat); 15,798(sun)
Last Audit: ABC September 30, 2011
Price: 8.50/mo; 149.00/yr (mail).
Advertising: Open inch rate $30.22
News services: AP.
Politics: Independent.
Not Published: New Year; Memorial Day; Independence Day; Labor Day; Christmas (except on a Sunday).
Special Editions: Home Improvement (Apr); Auto Racing Quarterly (Aug); Drunk Driving Page (Dec); National Children's Health Month (Feb); Tax & Investment Guide (Jan); Jamboree in the Hills (Jul); Vacation Guide (Jun); National Poison Prevention (Mar); Auto Racing Quarterly
Special Weekly Sections: Drive (Auto Section) (Thur).
Magazines: TV Times/TV Magazine (S); USA WEEKEND Magazine (Sat).
Adv. Dir. ....Kevin Kolanski
Circ. Dir. ....E.J. Miller
Mng. Ed. ....Robert Kapral
Lifestyles Ed. ....Trish Graham
News Ed ....Betty Pokas
Sports Ed ....Seth R. Staskey
Wire News Ed ....Stan Pawloski
Data Processing Mgr. ....Bruce Harkness
Online Mgr. ....Emily Dominici
Market Information: ADS; TMC; Zoned editions.
Mechanical available: Offset; Black and 3 ROP colors; insert accepted; page cutoffs - 23 9/16.
Mechanical Specifications: Type page 13 x 22; E - 6 cols, 2 1/16, 1/8 between; A - 6 cols, 2 1/16, 1/8 between; C - 8 cols, 1 9/16, 1/16 between.
Commodity Consumption: Avg. Page Number Per Issue - Daily 20; Avg. Page Number Per Issue - Sunday 40.
Equipment EDITORIAL: Front-end Software – QPS/QuarkXPress, Writenow, Teachtext.; Editorial Hardware – APP/Mac Fileserver; Classified Hardware – APP/Mac Fileserver; Classified Equipment – 3-COM. DISPLAY: Ad make-up applications – QPS/QuarkXPress, Adobe/Photoshop, Aldus/FreeHand, Multi-Ad/Creator; Layout Software – APP/Mac.; Display Hardware – APP/Mac Quadra 700, 2-APP/Mac Centris, APP/Mac G4; Display Printers – Dataproducts/LZR 1560, NewGen/Turbo 360; Production Equipment – Nat/A-250, MON/1270 Imagesetter; Cameras – 1-AG/2024; Scanners – RZ/Scanner, HP/IIC Nikon/35, 2-Microtek. PRESSROOM: Line 1 – 4-G/Mark (Offset) 1984; Line 2 – 2-PEC/Eagle (3 Color Ink) 1984; Press Drives – PEC/Bond; Pasters – PEC/Bond. MAILROOM: Counter stackers – 2-HL/Monitor, 1-HL/HI II; Inserters and stuffers – 5-HI/1372; Bundle tying machines – MLN/2EE, MLN/2, MLN/2A.; Business Hardware – NCR

MARYSVILLE

MARYSVILLE JOURNAL-TRIBUNE

207 N. Main St., Marysville, Ohio, 43040; gen tel (937) 644-9111; adv tel (937) 642-5656; ed tel (937) 642-6397; gen fax (937) 644-9211; adv fax (937) 644-9211; ed fax (937) 644-9211; adv e-mail jtads@marysvillejt.com; ed e-mail jtnews@marysvillejt.com; web site www.marysvillejt.com

Group: U.S. Suburban Press, Inc.
Published: Mon, Tues, Wed, Thur, Fri, Sat, Sun
Weekday Frequency: e
Saturday Frequency: m
Circulation: 5,982; 5,982(sat)
Last Audit: September 25, 2001
Price: 104.00/yr.
Advertising: Open inch rate $11.50
News services: AP, U.S. Suburban Press Inc..
Politics: Independent. **Established:** 1849
Special Editions: Football Opener (Aug); Christmas Greetings (Dec); 4-H Clubs (Mar); Christmas Shopping Guide (Nov); Automotive (Oct); Home Improvement (Spring); Honda Homecoming (Summer).
Magazines: TV (Sat); American Profile (Tues).
Bus. Mgr. ....Kevin Behrens
Accounting Exec ....Cheryl Welty
Adv. Dir. ....Marie Woodford
Adv. Mgr., Classified ....Brenda Maxwell
Mng. Ed. ....Chad Williamson
Editorial Page Ed ....Daniel E. Behrens
Society Ed ....Karlyn Byers
Sports Ed. ....Tim Miller
Online/Mgmt. Info Servs. Mgr. ..David Ohnsman
Prodn. Foreman, Composing ....Nancy Clark
Mechanical available: Offset; Black and 3 ROP colors; insert accepted; page cutoffs - 22.
Mechanical Specifications: Type page 13 x 21; E - 6 cols, 2 1/16, 1/8 between; A - 6 cols, 2 1/16, 1/8 between; C - 8 cols, 1 1/2, 1/8 between.
Commodity Consumption: Avg. Page Number Per Issue - Daily 18; widths 13 3/4; Newsprint Used - Short Tons 280; Printing Ink Used - Black 6300; Printing Ink Used - Color 60.
Equipment EDITORIAL: Front-end Software – Baseview/News Edit Pro, Adobe/PhotoShop 5, QPS/QuarkXPress 4.04.; Editorial Hardware – APP/Power Mac 4400-200, APP/Mac 7600, APP/Mac G4; Editorial Equipment – Printers ☐ APP/Mac LaserWriter, Epson/Stylus 3000, X/N2025 CLASSIFIED: Front-end Software – Baseview/AdManager Pro.; Classified Hardware – APP/Power Mac 4400-200; Classified Equipment – Zip Drive/100 Storage; Classified Printers – APP/Mac LaserWriter DISPLAY: Ad make-up applications – Adobe/Freehand 7, Multi-Ad/Creator 4, Adobe/PhotoShop 5; Display Hardware – APP/Mac Radius, APP/Power Mac 7300-180, APP/Mac G4; Display Printers – Epson/Stylus 3000, X/N2025 PRODUCTION: Pagination Software – QPS/QuarkXPress, Baseview/NewsEdit Pro.; Production Equipment – 1-LE; Cameras – 1-B; Scanners – Umax/Mirage II, Umax/Astra; Addressing machine – Add-Tac. BUSINESS COMPUTERS: Business Software – Quickbooks Pro; Business Hardware – APP/Mac G3 2000

MARYSVILLE NEWSPAPERS, INC.

207 N. Main St., Marysville, Ohio, 43040; gen tel (937) 644-9111; gen fax (937) 644-9211; gen e-mail dan@marysvillejt.com; web site www.marysvillejt.com

MASSILLON

THE INDEPENDENT

50 North Ave. NW, Massillon, Ohio, 44647; gen tel (330) 833-2631; adv tel (330) 833-2631; ed tel (330) 830-2631; gen fax (330) 833-2635; adv fax (330) 833-2635; ed fax (330) 834-3373; ed e-mail indenews@indeonline.com; web site www.indeonline.com

Published: Mon, Tues, Wed, Thur, Fri, Sat
Weekday Frequency: m
Saturday Frequency: m
Circulation: 9,775; 9,775(sat)
Last Audit: ABC September 30, 2011
Price: 3.30/wk (carrier); 171.60/yr (carrier).
Advertising: Open inch rate $25.90
News services: AP, CNS, DF, SHNS, TMS.
Politics: Independent. **Established:** 1863
Special Editions: Home & Garden (Apr); Football Contest (Aug); Gift Ideas (Dec); Valentine (Feb); Hall of Fame (Jul); Fun In The sun (Jun); Holy Week & Easter Church Guide (Mar); College Guide (May); Christmas Countdown (Nov); How To (Oct); Community Guide (Sept).
Special Weekly Sections: Best Food Days (Other); Church News (Sat); Business & Industry (Tues); Dining Guide (Wed).
Magazines: TV Times (entertainment tab) (S).
Pub. ....Ron Frailly
Circ. Dir. ....Sheila Casler
Ed. ....Robert McCune
Mng. Ed. ....Joe Shaheen
Lifestyles Ed. ....Amy Knapp
Sports Ed. ....Chris Easterling
Prodn./IT Dir. ....Michael Messer
Prodn. Mgr. ....Michelle McKelley
Mechanical available: Offset; Black and 3 ROP colors; insert accepted - broadsheet, less than 13 x 22; page cutoffs - 23 1/2.
Mechanical Specifications: Type page 12 x 22; E - 6 cols, 1 7/8, 1/8 between; A - 6 cols, 1 7/8, 1/8 between; C - 10 cols, 1 1/8, 1/8 between.
Commodity Consumption: Avg. Page Number Per Issue - Daily 27; Avg. Page Number Per Issue - Saturday 57; widths 12 1/2; Newsprint Used - Short Tons 865; Printing Ink Used - Pages Printed 10420.
Equipment EDITORIAL: Front-end Software – Baseview 3.5.7, QPS/QuarkXPress 6.5.; Editorial Hardware – Mac/G-4, Compaq/6000; Editorial Equipment – APP/Mac G3, APP/Mac 8500; Editorial Printers – HP/9000, Xante/3n, Xante/3g CLASSIFIED: Front-end Software – AdManager Pro, Admanager.; Classified Hardware – Imac; Classified Printers – HP/2200 PRODUCTION: Pagination Software – QPS/QuarkXPress 6.5, Baseview 3.5.7.; Scanners – Umax/2100, 1-Epson/4870, 1-Microtek/i700, 1-Microtek/4800; Bundle tying machines – 1/Bu, 1-Polychem/PC500, 2-MLN/MLN24; Addressing machine – Cheshire. BUSINESS COMPUTERS: Business Software – PBS/Media Plus, INSI; Business Hardware – 2-Dell/Dimension V350, 4-Gateway GP6-4000

MEDINA

THE MEDINA COUNTY GAZETTE

885 W. Liberty St., Medina, Ohio, 44256; gen tel (330) 725-4166; gen fax (330) 725-4299; gen e-mail ghudnutt@ohio.net; web site www.medina-gazette.com

Published: Mon, Tues, Wed, Thur, Fri, Sat
Weekday Frequency: m
Circulation: 12,737; 12,737(sat)
Last Audit: September 30, 2009
Price: 78.00/yr.
Advertising: Open inch rate $23.40
News services: AP.
Politics: Independent.
Not Published: Christmas.
Special Editions: Spring Time Showcase (Apr); Back-to-School (Aug); Last Minute Holiday Shopping Guide (Dec); Your Heart's Desire (Feb); Health & Fitness (Jan); Wheels II (Jul); Academic Excellence (Jun); Spring Home & Flower Tab (Mar); Wheels (May); Golden Guide (Monthly)
Special Weekly Sections: Accents/Entertainment (Fri); Best Food Day (Mon); Accents/Church (Sat); Accents/Community (Tues); Pastimes (Wed).
Magazines: Miscellaneous (Sat); American Profile (Weekly).
Pub. ....George D. Hudnutt
Adv. Dir., Sales ....Kristina High
Circ. Mgr. ....Wayne Workman
Mng. Ed. ....Liz Sheaffer
Data Processing Mgr. ....Russel Kunkler
Sports Ed. ....Betty Szudlo
Prodn. Supt. ....Rob Briggs
Market Information: ADS; Split run; TMC; Zoned editions.
Mechanical available: Offset; Black and 3 ROP colors; insert accepted - any; page cutoffs - 22 3/4.
Mechanical Specifications: Type page 13 x 21 1/2; E - 6 cols, 2 1/16, 1/8 between; A - 6 cols, 2 1/16, 1/8 between; C - 9 cols, 1 3/8, 1/16 between.
Commodity Consumption: Avg. Page Number Per Issue - Daily 30; widths 12 1/2; Newsprint Used - Metric Tons 998; Newsprint Used - Short Tons 1075; Printing Ink Used - Black 12350; Printing Ink Used - Color 6175; Printing Ink Used - Pages Printed 9180.
Equipment EDITORIAL: Front-end Software – CText.; Editorial Hardware – PCs; Editorial Equipment – PCs; Classified Hardware – PCs.; Layout Software – 2-CText/Adept.; Production Equipment – XIT/Clipper, XIT/Page Scan; Cameras – 1-LE/R500; Scanners – 1-Microtek/MS-300A Image Scanner. PRESSROOM: Line 1 – 8-G/Community; Folders – 1 MAILROOM: Counter stackers – HL/Stackpack, HL/Monitor; Inserters and stuffers – HI/NP 848; Bundle tying machines – 1/Bu, 1-/Sa, MLN; Addressing machine – 1-Am/6341, 1-/Ch; Other equipment – Rockbuilt/In-line Trimmer.; Business Hardware – 1-HP

MEDINA COUNTY PUBLICATIONS, INC.

885 W. Liberty, Medina, Ohio, 44256; gen tel (330) 725-4166; gen fax (330) 725-4299; gen e-mail newsed@ohio.net; web site www.medina-gazette.com

Published: Mon, Tues, Wed, Thur, Fri, Sat, Sun
Price: 78.00/yr.
Advertising: Open inch rate $16.56
Politics: 1832

MIDDLETOWN

MIDDLETOWN JOURNAL

1 N. Main St., Middletown, Ohio, 45042; gen tel (513) 422-3611; adv tel (513) 705-2860; ed tel (513) 705-2525; gen fax (513) 422-2734; adv fax (513) 422-2794; ed fax (513) 423-6940; ed e-mail news@coxohio.com; web site www.middletownjournal.com

Group: Ohio Newspaper Services, Inc.
Published: Mon, Tues, Wed, Thur, Fri, Sat, Sun
Weekday Frequency: m
Saturday Frequency: m
Circulation: 13,270; 14,860(sat); 16,474(sun)
Last Audit: ABC September 30, 2011
Price: 161.20/yr.
News services: AP.
Politics: Independent. **Established:** 1857
Note: Advertising is sold in combination with the Hamilton JournalNews (mS) for $50.00(m) and $52.00(S). Individual newspaper rates not made available.
Not Published: Independence Day.
Special Editions: Home Improvement (Apr); Football (Aug); Progress (Feb); Bridal (Jan); Health & Fitness (Jan); Tax Guide (Mar); Outdoor Living (May); Christmas Gift Guide (Nov); Fall Car Care (Oct); Home Improvement (Sept).
Special Weekly Sections: Garden Page (Fri); Food Day (Mon); Religion Page (Sat); Entertainment Pages (Thur); Seniors Page (Tues); Youth Page (Wed).
Magazines: TV Journal (S).
Adv. Mgr. ....Joan Hyland
Classified Dir. ....Terry Bouquot
Circ. Dir. ....J. Michael Stevens
City Ed. ....Kevin Aldridge

Editorial Page Ed. ....Michael Williams
Entertainment Ed. ....Eric Robinette
Features Ed...................................Rick McCrabb
Prodn. Mgr., Pre Press........Jenny McClanahan
Market Information: TMC.
Mechanical available: Offset; Black and 3 ROP colors; insert accepted; page cutoffs - 22 3/4.
Mechanical Specifications: Type page 13 x 21 1/2; E - 6 cols, 2 1/16, 1/8 between; A - 6 cols, 2 1/16, 1/8 between; C - 10 cols, 1 3/16, 1/8 between.
Commodity Consumption: Avg. Page Number Per Issue - Daily 28; Avg. Page Number Per Issue - Plates Used 65505; Avg. Page Number Per Issue - Saturday 20; Avg. Page Number Per Issue - Sunday 40; widths 17; Newsprint Used - Short Tons 12469; Printing Ink Used - Black 93155; Printi
Equipment EDITORIAL: Front-end Software – Baseview, QPS/QuarkXPress.; Editorial Hardware – APP/Mac, Baseview; Editorial Printers – Pre Press/Panther Imagesetter CLASSIFIED: Front-end Software – Baseview.; Classified Hardware – APP/Mac; Classified Printers – Pre Press/Imagesetter; Layout Software – QPS/QuarkXPress.; Display Hardware – APP/Mac PRODUCTION: Pagination Software – QPS/QuarkXPress.; Production Equipment – Caere/OmniPage; Cameras – 1-B/500LB; Scanners – AG/Arcus Plus BUSINESS COMPUTERS: Business Software – Oracle, PBS; Business Hardware – HP/9000 Model G30

MOUNT GILEAD

THE MORROW COUNTY SENTINEL

255 Neal Ave., Mount Gilead, Ohio, 43338; gen tel (419) 946-3010; gen fax (419) 947-7241; ed e-mail editor@newscolorpress.com; web site www.morrowcountysentinel.com
Published: Tues, Wed, Thur, Fri, Sat
Weekday Frequency: m
Saturday Frequency: m
Last Audit: N/A
Price: 37.00/yr.
Advertising: Open inch rate $10.30
Own facility?: N
Pub. ....Vicky Taylor
Delivery method: Mail, Newsstand, Racks

MOUNT VERNON

MOUNT VERNON NEWS

18 E. Vine St., Mount Vernon, Ohio, 43050-0791; gen tel (740) 397-5333; adv tel (740) 397-5333; ed tel (740) 397-5333; gen fax (740) 397-1321; adv fax (740) 397-1321; ed fax (740) 397-1321; adv e-mail advertising@mountvernonnews.com; obits@mountvernonnews.com; ed e-mail sports@mountvernonnews.com; web site www.mountvernonnews.com
Group: Ohio Newspaper Services, Inc.
Published: Mon, Tues, Wed, Thur, Fri, Sat, Sun
Weekday Frequency: e
Saturday Frequency: m
Circulation: 9,099; 9,099(sat)
Last Audit: September 30, 2008
Price: 5.65/mo; 73.00/yr.
Advertising: Open inch rate $14.54
News services: AP.
Politics: Independent.
Advertising not accepted: Vending machine; Mail order; Fortune teller.
Not Published: Christmas.
Pres./Pub...........................Kay H. Culbertson
Vice Pres. ....Michelle L. Hartman
Vice Pres...........................Andrew G. Weber
Sec./Treasurer/Asst. Pub........Elizabeth Lutwick
Adv. Mgr......................................Corby Wise
Adv. Mgr., Classified ....Cathy Conkling
Adv. Design Mgr. ....Marsha Wagner
NIE Coord............................Michelle Hartman
Circ./MIDS Mgr. ....Michael McNichols
Ed...Cheryl Splain
City Ed...Fred Main
Sports Ed. ....Joe Huddleston
Web Ed................................Joshua Morrison
Pressroom Mgr. ....Dean Hammons
Market Information: ADS; TMC.
Mechanical available: Offset; Black and 3 ROP colors; insert accepted; page cutoffs - 22 3/4.
Mechanical Specifications: Type page 13 x 21 1/2; E - 6 cols, 2 1/16, 1/8 between; A - 6 cols, 2 1/16, 1/8 between; C - 8 cols, 1 9/16, 1/16 between.
Commodity Consumption: Avg. Page Number Per Issue - Daily 18; Avg. Page Number Per Issue - Plates Used 6220; widths 27 1/2; Newsprint Used - Short Tons 490; Printing Ink Used - Black 19925; Printing Ink Used - Color 2300; Printing Ink Used - Pages Printed 5598.
Equipment EDITORIAL: Front-end Software – QPS/QuarkXPress 3.3.; Editorial Hardware – 11-APP/Mac Quadra 605; Editorial Printers – 1-XIT/Clipper; Classified Hardware – 4-APP/Mac Quadra 605; Classified Printers – 1-APP/Mac LaserWriter.; Layout Software – 7-APP/Mac.; Display Printers – 3-APP/Mac LaserWriter; Production Equipment – Caere/OmniPage Direct, 1-Nu/Flip Top FT4OLNS; Cameras – 1-B, 1-R; Scanners – Umax/UC 1200 SE, Nikon/Coolscan. PRESSROOM: Line 1 – 5-G/Urbanite; Folders – 1 MAILROOM: Counter stackers – 1-HI/RS-25; Inserters and stuffers – 4-KAN/480; Bundle tying machines – 2/Bu, 1-/Ca; Addressing machine – 1-/Ch, 2-/Am.; Audio Hardware – Sprint/United; Business Hardware – Basic IV/MHI

NAPOLEON

NORTHWEST SIGNAL

595 E. Riverview Ave., Napoleon, Ohio, 43545; gen tel (419) 592-5055; gen fax (419) 592-9778; gen e-mail nwsignal@bright.net; web site www.northwestsignal.net
Published: Mon, Tues, Wed, Thur, Fri, Sat
Weekday Frequency: e
Circulation: 4,454; 4,454(sat)
Last Audit: September 30, 2007
Price: 6.50/mo; 88.00/yr.
Advertising: Open inch rate $11.00
News services: AP.
Politics: Independent.
Not Published: New Year; Memorial Day; Independence Day; Labor Day; Thanksgiving; Christmas.
Special Editions: Pigskin Preview (Aug); Greetings (Dec); Bride/Groom (Feb); First Baby (Jan); Community Salute (Jul); Automotive (Mar); Christmas (Nov).
Special Weekly Sections: Church Weekender (Fri); Education (Thur); Health & Medicine (Tues); Business (Wed).
Magazines: Relish (Monthly); American Profile (Weekly).
Pres./Pub...........................Christopher Cullis
Sec./Treasurer........................Elizabeth Cullis
Vice Pres./Gen. Mgr. ....Thomas Voigt
Adv./Mktg. Dir...........................Sally Heaston
Adv. Mgr., Legal ....Peggy Woods
Circ. Mgr. ....Celeste Breece
Bus./Farm Ed. ....Brenna Griteman
Education/Health Ed. ....Courtney Foust
Family/Evening Ed......................Vicki Johnson
News Ed. ....Brian Koeller
Public Record/Church Ed. ....Misty Lawrence
Sr. Ed.......................................Moe Brubaker
Sports Ed.....................................Jeff Ratliff
Market Information: TMC.
Mechanical available: Offset; Black and 3 ROP colors; insert accepted - card; page cutoffs - 21 1/2.
Mechanical Specifications: Type page 13 x 21; E - 6 cols, 2 1/16, 1/8 between; A - 6 cols, 2 1/16, 1/8 between; C - 6 cols, 2 1/16, 1/8 between.
Commodity Consumption: Avg. Page Number Per Issue - Daily 12; Avg. Page Number Per Issue - Plates Used 3500; widths 28; Newsprint Used - Metric Tons 150; Printing Ink Used - Pages Printed 3500.
Equipment EDITORIAL: Front-end Software – Microsoft/Word, Baseview/NewsEdit.; Editorial Hardware – APP/Mac; Editorial Equipment – 1-APP/Mac LaserWriter; Editorial Printers – APP/Mac IIg CLASSIFIED: Front-end Software – Baseview/Class Manager, QPS/QuarkXPress.; Classified Hardware – APP/Mac; Layout Software – Mk. PRODUCTION: Pagination Software – Aldus/PageMaker 5.0.; Production Equipment – Caere/OmniPage; Cameras – 1-Nu; Scanners – Epson/800; Bundle tying machines – 1/MLN, 1-/Brainard; Addressing machine – 1-/Am.; Business Hardware – 1-CDS/PC-XT

NEW PHILADELPHIA

THE TIMES-REPORTER

629 Wabash Ave. NW, New Philadelpia, Ohio, 44663-0667; gen tel (330) 364-5577; adv tel (330) 364-8330; ed tel (330) 364-8417; gen fax (330) 364-8449; adv fax (330) 364-8449; ed fax (330) 364-8416; gen e-mail timesreporter@tasco.net; adv e-mail advertising@timesreporter.com; ed e-mail news@timesreporter.com; web site www.timesreporter.com
Published: Mon, Tues, Wed, Thur, Fri, Sat, Sun
Weekday Frequency: m
Saturday Frequency: m
Circulation: 19,222; 19,222(sat); 19,687(sun)
Last Audit: September 30, 2009
Price: 3.60/wk; 195.00/yr.
Advertising: Open inch rate $35.08
News services: AP, MCT, SHNS.
Politics: Independent.
Special Editions: Medical Booklet (Apr); Italian Festival (Aug); Gift Guide (Dec); Bridal (Feb); Progress (Jan); Christmas in July (Jul); Father's Day (Jun); Home & Garden (Mar); Lawn & Garden (May); Home Digest (Nov); Interior Design (Oct); Swiss Festival (Sept).
Special Weekly Sections: Entertainment (Fri); Best Food Day (Mon); Automotive Showcase (S); Religion (Sat); Senior Citizen (Tues); Family/Lifestyle (Wed).
Magazines: Parade (S).
Pub. ....Tom Jeckel
Circ. Dir...............................Michael J. Gorsich
Editorial Page Ed. ....Jon Baker
Features Ed. ....Stephanie Harris
Photo Ed...Pat Burk
Radio/Television Ed. ....Rex Huffman
Religion Ed..............................Lee Morrison
Sports Ed.................................Dave Whitmer
Wire Ed.......................................Joe Wright
Mgmt. Info Systems Mgr...................Mark Judy
Prodn. Foreman, Distr. ....Dan Mile
Prodn. Foreman, Pressroom ....Tim Larkin
Sunday Weekend Ed. ....Linda Davis Smith
Market Information: TMC.
Mechanical available: Offset; Black and 3 ROP colors; insert accepted - any; page cutoffs - 23 9/16.
Mechanical Specifications: Type page 12 x 22 1/4; E - 6 cols, 1 7/8, 3/16 between; A - 6 cols, 1 7/8, 3/16 between; C - 9 cols, 1 3/8, 1/16 between.
Commodity Consumption: Avg. Page Number Per Issue - Daily 24; Avg. Page Number Per Issue - Plates Used 42800; Avg. Page Number Per Issue - Sunday 40; widths 50; Newsprint Used - Short Tons 1650; Printing Ink Used - Black 30300; Printing Ink Used - Color 12600; Printing Ink Use
Equipment EDITORIAL: Front-end Software – HI/Composition.; Editorial Hardware – HI/Composition Sys 8300, ATS/Network CLASSIFIED: Front-end Software – HI/Composition.; Classified Hardware – HI/Composition System 8300, ATS/Network DISPLAY: Ad make-up applications – HI.; Display Hardware – APP/Mac, HI, ALS/Managing Editor PRODUCTION: Pagination Software – ALS/Managing Editor.; Production Equipment – 2-MON/Express, 2-Konica/EV Jetsetter; Cameras – SCREEN/458; Scanners – ECR PRESSROOM: Line 1 – 4-G/Metro (3 color decks) 1970; Line 2 – 11-G/Community 1999; Line 3 – 8-Ha/Mark 10 1986; Press Drives – Fin/Metro; Folders – 2, 2; Pasters – 2-Cary/Auto, 2-Enkel/Auto (Heat Set; Commercial). MAILROOM: Counter stackers – HL/Monitor, BG/107, 4/HI; Inserters and stuffers – 2-Mc/4-Packet; Bundle tying machines – 1-/Bu, 1-EAM-Mosca, 3-/MLN, 1-EAM-Mosca/Wrapper. BUSINESS COMPUTERS: Business Software – Commercial printing bidding analysts, INSI; Business Hardware – IBM/AS-400

NEWARK

THE ADVOCATE

22 N. First St., Newark, Ohio, 43055; gen tel (740) 345-4053; adv tel (740) 345-4053; ed tel (740) 328-8821; gen fax (740) 349-7466; adv fax (740) 328-8582; ed fax (740) 345-1634; ed e-mail advocate@newarkadvocate.com; web site www.newarkadvocate.com
Published: Mon, Tues, Wed, Thur, Fri, Sat, Sun
Weekday Frequency: e
Saturday Frequency: m
Circulation: 15,616; 12,584(sat); 15,616(sun)
Last Audit: ABC September 30, 2011
Price: 2.85/wk, $1.50/wk (wknd only); 12.35/mo; 148.20/yr.
Advertising: Open inch rate $35.50
News services: AP.
Politics: Independent.
Special Editions: Lawn & Garden (Apr); Football (Aug); Various Christmas Sections (Dec); Bridal Guide (Jan); Mature Years (Jul); Annual Progress (Mar); Summer Recipe Contest (May); Crossroads (Monthly); Basketball (Nov); Fall Car Care (Oct); Fall Home Improvement (Sept).
Special Weekly Sections: Stocks (S); Church News (Sat); Entertainment (Thur); Best Food Days (Wed).
Magazines: Color Comics (S); Real Estate Magazine (Sat).
Pres./Pub....................................Linda Greiwe
Adv. Dir.......................................Stacia King
Adv. Classified Telecenter Dir. ......Karie Sargent
Adv. Mgr., Nat'l ....Diane Glasseier
Adv. Mgr., Retail Sales................Randy Green
Circ. Dir....................................Jeff Simmons
Editorial Page Ed. ....Michael Shearer
Entertainment/Amusements Ed...........Brian Miller
Photo Ed........................................Jeff Groves
Sports Ed...................................Scott Hennen
Prodn. Plant Mgr. ....Dennise Cochran
Market Information: TMC.
Mechanical available: Offset; Black and 3 ROP colors; insert accepted; page cutoffs - 22 3/4.
Mechanical Specifications: Type page 13 x 21; E - 6 cols, 2 1/16, 1/8 between; A - 6 cols, 2 1/16, 1/8 between; C - 6 cols, 2 1/16, 1/8 between.
Commodity Consumption: Avg. Page Number Per Issue - Daily 24; Avg. Page Number Per Issue - Plates Used 84300; Avg. Page Number Per Issue - Sunday 36; widths 13 5/8; Newsprint Used - Short Tons 4510; Printing Ink Used - Black 165000; Printing Ink Used - Color 44800; Printing In
Equipment EDITORIAL: Front-end Software – Baseview.; Editorial Hardware – 1-APP/Mac; Classified Hardware – 4-Cx. DISPLAY: Ad make-up applications – PBS.; Display Hardware – HP PRODUCTION: Pagination Software – Baseview, QPS/QuarkXPress 3.0.; Production Equipment – 2-Pre Press/Panther Pro 46, SCREEN/281Q; Cameras – SCREEN/260 Horizontal; Scanners – Lf/Leafscan 35, Nikon/Coolscan, AG/Duoscan PRESSROOM: Line 1 – 8-G/Urbanite, 8-G/Urbanite (stacked); Line 2 – 8-G/Urbanite, 8-G/Urbanite (stacked); Folders – G/2:1; Reels and Stands – 8-G/Urbanite. MAILROOM: Counter stackers – 3-Id/2000; Inserters and stuffers – 2-GMA/SLS 1000; Bundle tying machines – 2/Dynaric, 2-/Bu; Mailroom control system – 1-Id, 2-GMA/PMS1; Addressing machine – 2-Ch/596; Other equipment –MM. BUSINESS COMPUTERS: Business Software – Oracle, PBS; Business Hardware – PBS, Oracle

NORWALK

NORWALK REFLECTOR

61 E. Monroe St., Norwalk, Ohio, 44857-0071; gen tel (419) 668-3771; gen fax (419) 668-2424; gen e-mail news@norwalkreflector.com; web site www.norwalkreflector.com
Group: Ohio Newspaper Services, Inc.
Published: Mon, Tues, Wed, Thur, Fri, Sat
Weekday Frequency: e
Saturday Frequency: e
Circulation: 9,280; 9,280(sat)
Last Audit: ABC September 30, 2011
Price: 2.10/wk; 117.00/yr.
Advertising: Open inch rate $15.59
News services: AP.
Politics: Independent.
Not Published: New Year; Memorial Day; Independence Day; Labor Day; Thanksgiving; Christmas.
Special Editions: Home and Garden (Apr); Firelands Factbook (Mar); Christmas Gift Guide (Nov); Car Care (Oct).
Magazines: USA WEEKEND Magazine (Fri); American Profile (Weekly).
Pub. .... Andy Prutsok
Adv. Dir. .... John Ringenberg
Mng. Ed. .... Joe Centers
News Ed. .... Matt Roche
Sports Ed. .... Mike Greco
Photo Ed. .... Lou Reda
Bus. Mgr. .... Richard Russell
Data Processing Mgr. .... Carol McLaughlin
Market Information: TMC.
Mechanical available: Offset; Black and 2 ROP colors; insert accepted; page cutoffs - 21 3/4.
Mechanical Specifications: Type page 13 x 21 1/2; E - 6 cols, 2 1/16, 1/8 between; A - 6 cols, 2 1/16, 1/8 between; C - 9 cols, 1 3/8, 1/16 between.
Commodity Consumption: Avg. Page Number Per Issue - Daily 18.6; Avg. Page Number Per Issue - Plates Used 3000; widths 27 1/2; Newsprint Used - Short Tons 406; Printing Ink Used - Black 9000; Printing Ink Used - Pages Printed 5712.
Equipment EDITORIAL: Front-end Software – Baseview/NewsEdit, QPS/QuarkXPress 3.3.; Editorial Hardware – APP/Mac; Editorial Equipment – Lf/AP Leaf Picture Desk, Lf/Leafscan 35, Kk/2035 Negative Scanner; Editorial Printers – APP/Mac LaserWriter II NTX, Xante/8200 CLASSIFIED: Front-end Software – Baseview/Class Manager.; Classified Hardware – APP/Mac SE30; Classified Printers – APP/Mac LaserWriter II NTX, Xante/8200 DISPLAY: Ad make-up applications – Multi-Ad/Creator; Display Hardware – APP/Power Mac PC 8100, CD, APP/Mac IIfx; Display Printers – APP/Mac LaserWriter II NTX, Xante/8200 PRODUCTION: Pagination Software – QPS/QuarkXPress 3.3.; Production Equipment – Caere/OmniPage Pro, 2-Xante/8200, 1-APP/Mac LaserWriter IINTX; Cameras – 1-DAI PRESSROOM: Line 1 – 4-G/Community single width 1964; Line 2 – 1-G/Community single width 1967; Press Drives – Emerson/DC; Folders – 1-G/941 Community.; Inserters and stuffers – 8/MM; Bundle tying machines – Bu/TS-21, Akebono/TS 250 APP. BUSINESS COMPUTERS: Business Software – Vision Data; Business Hardware – Unisys/S280

REFLECTOR-HERALD, INC.

61 E. Monroe St., Norwalk, Ohio, 44857; gen tel (419) 668-3771; gen fax (419) 668-2424; gen e-mail news@norwalkreflector.com; web site www.norwalkreflector.com
Published: Mon, Tues, Wed, Thur, Fri, Sat, Sun
Price: 160.00/yr.
Advertising: Open inch rate $11.72

PIQUA

PIQUA DAILY CALL

310 Spring St., Piqua, Ohio, 45356; gen tel (937) 773-2721; adv tel (937) 440-5252; ed tel (937) 773-2721 Ext. 14; gen fax (937) 773-2782; adv fax (937) 335-9321; ed fax (937) 773-2782; gen e-mail shartley@dailycall.com; adv e-mail lstewart@dailycall.com; ed e-mail editorial@dailycall.com; web site www.dailycall.com
Group: Ohio Community Media
Ohio Community Media
Published: Mon, Wed, Thur, Fri, Sat
Weekday Frequency: m
Saturday Frequency: m
Circulation: 6,789; 7,100(sat)
Last Audit: Sworn September 30, 2002
Price: 2.34/wk; 10.25/mo; 148.80/yr (mail), $118.50(in county).
Advertising: Open inch rate $17.00
News services: AP.
Politics: Independent. **Established:** 1883
Advertising not accepted: N
Not Published: Tuesdays, Sundays, and Christmas.
Own facility?: Y
Special Weekly Sections: Best Food Day (Mon.); iN75 Entertainment (Wed.); Remote Possibilities (TV Mag.-Sat.); @RecordBody:**Magazines:** USA WEEKEND Magazine (Sat); American Profile (Weekly);
Relish (Monthly);
Spry (Monthly);
Athlon Sports (Monthly);
SCORE (Quarterly).
Grp. Pub. .... Frank Beeson
Grp. Bus. Mgr. .... Betty Brownlee
Adv. Dir. .... Leiann Stewart
Circ. Mgr. .... Cheryl Hall
Exec. Ed. .... Susan Hartley
News Ed. .... Tom Millhouse
Sports Ed. .... Rob Kiser
Grp. Graphics Mgr. .... Greta Swarts
Prod. Mgr. .... Dan Chaffin
Prodn. Mgr., Mailroom .... Jane Smith
Market Information: TMC.
Mechanical available: Web Offset; Black and 3 ROP colors; insert accepted; page cutoffs - 22 3/4.
Mechanical Specifications: Type page 12 1/2 x 21 1/4; E - 6 cols, 1 5/6, 1/8 between; A - 6 cols, 1 5/6, 1/16 between; C - 8 cols, 1 3/8, 1/8 between.
Commodity Consumption: Avg. Page Number Per Issue - Daily 16; Avg. Page Number Per Issue - Saturday 20; widths 34.
Equipment EDITORIAL: Front-end Software – Baseview/News Edit.; Editorial Hardware – 10-APP/Mac G4; Editorial Equipment – APP/Mac, APP/Super Mac, Lf/Color Photo; Editorial Printers – HP/LaserJet 5000 CLASSIFIED: Front-end Software – PBS, Baseveiw.; Classified Hardware – 2-APP/Mac G4; Classified Printers – 1-HP/LaserJet 5 DISPLAY: Ad make-up applications – QPS/QuarkXPress, Adobe/Photoshop, Aldus/FreeHand, PBS; Layout Software – APP/Mac G3, APP/Mac G4.; Display Hardware – 4-APP/Mac G4, 4-APP/PowerMac; Display Printers – HP/LaserJet 5000; Production Equipment – Pre Press/Panther Pro 46, 1-LE/LD 220, Jobo/ATL 1500; Cameras – 1-DAI/Screen C/680-C. PRESSROOM: Line 1 – 5-G/Urbanite single width 1969; Folders – 1 MAILROOM: Counter stackers – Heidelberg; Inserters and stuffers – KAN/5:1 480; Bundle tying machines – OVL/415A; Addressing machine – SC/100. BUSINESS COMPUTERS: Business Software – PBS 3.0; Business Hardware – PC
Zip Codes served: 45356, 45365, 45333, 45380, 45318, 45308, 45326, 45317, 43072, 45373, 45359.
Delivery method: Mail, Newsstand, Private Carrier, Racks

POMEROY

THE DAILY SENTINEL/SUNDAY TIMES-SENTINEL

111 Court St., Pomeroy, Ohio, 45769; gen tel (740) 992-2155; gen fax (740) 992-2157; gen e-mail mdsnews@mydailysentinel.com; web site www.mydailysentinel.com
Published: Sun
Circulation: 3,471; 9,068(sun)
Last Audit: September 30, 2006
Price: 2.00/wk; 8.70/mo; 115.84/yr.
Advertising: Open inch rate $9.40
News services: AP.
Politics: Independent.
Note: The Pomeroy Daily Sentinel and Gallipolis Daily Tribune share their Sunday edition, the Sunday Times-Sentinel. The combination rate is $14.20.
Not Published: Christmas.
Special Editions: Senior Quarterly (Quarterly).
Special Weekly Sections: TV Times (Fri); Farm Page (S); Best Food Day (Wed).
Pub. .... Daniel Goodrich
Purchasing Agent .... Diane Hill
Adv. Mgr. .... Mat Rogers
Adv. Mgr., Classified .... Judy Clark
News Ed. .... Charlene Hoeflich
Prodn. Foreman, Pressroom .... Don Coleman
Market Information: TMC.
Mechanical available: Offset; Black and 3 ROP colors; insert accepted; page cutoffs - 21 1/4.
Mechanical Specifications: Type page 13 x 21 1/4; E - 6 cols, 2 1/16, 1/8 between; A - 6 cols, 2 1/16, 1/8 between; C - 8 cols, 1 1/2, 1/8 between.
Commodity Consumption: Avg. Page Number Per Issue - Daily 14; Avg. Page Number Per Issue - Sunday 36; Newsprint Used - Short Tons 183.
Equipment EDITORIAL: Front-end Software – Baseview.; Editorial Hardware – APP/Mac; Editorial Printers – APP/Mac LaserWriter CLASSIFIED: Front-end Software – Baseview.; Classified Hardware – APP/Mac; Production Equipment – Mk/Ad Typesetting.

PORT CLINTON

NEWS-HERALD

115 W. Second St., Port Clinton, Ohio, 43452; gen tel (419) 734-3141; adv tel (419) 734-7505; gen fax (800) 636-6906; web site www.portclintonnewsherald.com
Group: Gannett Co., Inc
Published: Mon, Tues, Wed, Thur, Fri, Sat
Weekday Frequency: All day
Saturday Frequency: m
Circulation: 3,285; 4,218(sat)
Last Audit: Sworn September 30, 2009
Price: 2.25/wk; 151.75/yr; 58.50/26wk, $29.25/13wk.
Advertising: Open inch rate $18.51
News services: AP.
Note: Printed under contract by the Fremont News-Messenger. For production information, see Fremont listing.
Not Published: Sun
Special Editions: Football (Aug); County Fair (Jul); Basketball (Nov).
Special Weekly Sections: Real Estate, Wed
Magazines: TV Weekly (Fri); USA WEEKEND Magazine (Sat).
Pub. .... Cindy George
ACcount Executive .... Jan Hackett
Market Information: TMC.
Mechanical available: Offset; Black and 3 ROP colors; insert accepted; page cutoffs - 22 3/4.
Mechanical Specifications: Type page 11 5/8 x 21 1/2; E - 6 cols, 1 13/16, 1/8 between; A - 6 cols, 1 13/16, 1/8 between; C - 9 cols, 1 3/8, 1/16 between.
Commodity Consumption: Avg. Page Number Per Issue - Daily 12.
Equipment EDITORIAL: Front-end Software – Baseview, QPS/QuarkXPress.; Editorial Hardware – APP/Mac CLASSIFIED: Front-end Software – Baseview/Class Manager.; Classified Hardware – APP/Mac; Business Hardware – IBM/PC II
Zip Codes served: Ottawa Co.
Delivery method: Newsstand, Private Carrier, Racks

PORTSMOUTH

THE PORTSMOUTH DAILY TIMES

637 Sixth St., Portsmouth, Ohio, 45662; gen tel (740) 353-3101; adv tel (740) 353-3101; ed tel (740) 353-3101; gen fax (740) 353-7280; adv fax (740) 353-7280; ed fax (740) 353-4676; gen e-mail pdtnews@portsmouth-dailytimes.com; web site www.portsmouth-dailytimes.com
Published: Mon, Tues, Wed, Thur, Fri, Sat, Sun
Weekday Frequency: m
Saturday Frequency: m
Circulation: 12,447; 12,447(sat); 11,631(sun)
Last Audit: March 31, 2006
Price: 2.65/wk (motor route); 11.48/mo (motor route); 170.04/yr (motor route).
Advertising: Open inch rate $22.68
News services: AP.
Politics: Independent. **Established:** 1852
Not Published: Christmas.
Special Editions: Back-to-School (Aug); Bridal (Jan); Home & Garden (Jun); Car Care (Mar); Christmas Preview (Nov); Car Care (Oct).
Special Weekly Sections: Education (Mon); Viewer's Digest (S); Religion (Sat); Entertainment (Thur).
Magazines: Parade (S).
Pub. .... John Clark
Circ. Mgr. .... LouAnn Blair
Prodn. Mgr., Mailroom .... Janice Deaton
Prodn. Foreman, Press/Stereo .... Jim Jenkins
Market Information: ADS; TMC.
Mechanical available: Offset; Black and 3 ROP colors; insert accepted - single sheet; page cutoffs - 23 9/16.
Mechanical Specifications: Type page 11 5/8 x 21 1/2; E - 6 cols, 2 1/16, 1/8 between; A - 6 cols, 2 1/16, 1/8 between; C - 9 cols, 1 3/8, 1/16 between.
Commodity Consumption: Avg. Page Number Per Issue - Daily 18; Avg. Page Number Per Issue - Saturday 18; Avg. Page Number Per Issue - Sunday 26; widths 25; Newsprint Used - Metric Tons 816; Newsprint Used - Short Tons 783; Printing Ink Used - Black 33485; Printing Ink Used - Co
Equipment EDITORIAL: Front-end Software – Baseview.; Editorial Hardware – APP/Mac CLASSIFIED: Front-end Software – Baseview.; Classified Hardware – APP/Mac; Layout Software – APP/Mac, 2-PE/10.; Display Printers – APP/Mac LaserPrinter PRODUCTION: Pagination Software – QPS/QuarkXPress.; Production Equipment – Laser; Cameras – 1-R/500 PRESSROOM: Line 1 – 10-G/Community; Pasters – Web/Cement.; Bundle tying machines – 1-MLN/ML2EE; Addressing machine – 1-Am/1900, FBM/90 Labeler.; Business Hardware – 1-NCR

RAVENNA

RECORD-COURIER

126 N. Chestnut St., Ravenna, Ohio, 44266; gen tel (330) 296-9657; adv tel (330) 296-9657; ed tel (330) 296-9657; gen fax (330) 296-2698; gen e-mail recordpub@recordpub.net; adv e-mail ads@recordpub.net; ed e-mail editor@recordpub.com; web site www.recordpub.com
Published: Mon, Tues, Wed, Thur, Fri, Sat, Sun
Weekday Frequency: m
Saturday Frequency: m
Circulation: 16,854; 16,854(sat); 17,187(sun)
Last Audit: September 30, 2008
Price: 9.50/mo; 112.00/yr.
Advertising: Open inch rate $20.50
News services: AP, SHNS.
Politics: Independent.
Not Published: New Year; Memorial Day; Independence Day; Labor Day; Christmas.
Special Editions: Home Improvement (Apr); Football & Fall Sports (Aug); Gift Guide (Dec); Progress (Feb); Bridal Tab (Jan); Bridal Tab (Jun); Car Care (Mar); Summer Lifestyles (May); Gift Guide (Nov); Car Care (Sept).
Special Weekly Sections: Entertainment (Thur);

Best Food Day (Tues).
Magazines: USA WEEKEND Magazine (S).
Broadcast Affiliations: WOGK-FM, Ocala, FL; WNDD-FM, Ocala, FL; WTBO/WKGO, Cumberland, MD; TV-8, Billings, MT; WFRB AM/FM, Frostby, MD; WKVX/WQKT, Wooster, OH; WRAD/WRIQ, Radford, VA.
Pub. ....David E. Dix
Gen. Mgr. ....Richard M. Sekella
Adv. Dir. ....Harry E. Newman
Dir., Web ....Andrew R. Dix
Mng. Ed. ....Heather Rainnoni
Books Ed. ....Mary Louiseruerh
Editorial Page Ed. ....Roger DiPaolo
Entertainment Ed. ....Cad Murphy
Photo Dept. Mgr. ....Richard Sweet
Religion Ed. ....Diane Smith
Society Ed. ....Laura Nethken
Sports Ed. ....Tom Nader
Wire Ed. ....Chris Burkey
Prodn. Foreman, Pressroom ....Gary Hurst
Market Information: Split run; TMC; Zoned editions.
Mechanical available: Offset; Black and 3 ROP colors; insert accepted; page cutoffs - 22 3/4.
Mechanical Specifications: Type page 12 7/8 x 21 1/2; E - 6 cols, 2 1/16, 1/8 between; A - 6 cols, 2 1/16, 1/8 between; C - 6 cols, 2 1/16, 1/8 between.
Commodity Consumption: Avg. Page Number Per Issue - Daily 24; Avg. Page Number Per Issue - Saturday 28; Avg. Page Number Per Issue - Sunday 39; widths 27; Newsprint Used - Short Tons 2000.
Equipment EDITORIAL: Front-end Software – Baseview.; Editorial Hardware – 25-APP/Mac; Editorial Printers – 3-HP/LaserJet 4MV CLASSIFIED: Front-end Software – Baseview.; Classified Hardware – 11-APP/Mac; Classified Printers – 2-APP/Mac LaserWriter NT XII, Okidata/5460 DISPLAY: Ad make-up applications – Multi-Ad/Creator II 1.5; Layout Software – 8-APP/Mac.; Display Hardware – APP/Mac; Display Printers – 2-HP/LaserJet 4MV PRODUCTION: Pagination Software – QPS, Baseview.; Production Equipment – 1-APP/Mac, 1-AG/Imagesetter, 1-Konica; Cameras – SCREEN; Scanners – Nikon/1000 PRESSROOM: Line 1 – 9-G/Urbanite; Line 2 – 13-G/Community; Folders – 1-G/1:1, 1-G/2:1. MAILROOM: Counter stackers – 1/BG; Inserters and stuffers – 6-/MM; Bundle tying machines – 1-/MLN, 2-/Sa; Wrapping singles – 1-/Sa; Addressing machine – 1-/Ch.; Audio Hardware – Software □ Educom; Business Hardware – 1-DSI

SAINT MARYS

THE EVENING LEADER

102 E. Spring St., Saint Marys, Ohio, 45885; gen tel (419) 394-7414; adv tel (419) 394-7414; ed tel (419) 394-7414; gen fax (419) 394-7202; adv e-mail ads@theeveningleader.com; classifieds@theeveningleader.com; ed e-mail editor@theeveningleader.com; web site www.theeveningleader.com
Published: Mon, Tues, Wed, Thur, Fri, Sat
Weekday Frequency: e
Saturday Frequency: m
Circulation: 4,470; 4,470(sat)
Price: 2.70/wk; 11.70/mo; 135.20/yr.
Advertising: Open inch rate $13.42
News services: AP.
Politics: Independent. **Established:** 1982
Not Published: New Year; Memorial Day; Independence Day; Labor Day; Thanksgiving; Christmas.
Own facility?: Y
Special Weekly Sections: NASCAR (Fri); Best Food Day (Mon); Business Page (Sat); Entertainment (Thur); Second Food Day (Wed).
Magazines: TV Listing (Thur); American Profile (Tues).
Pub. ....Deb Zwez
Bus. Office Mgr. ....Liva Vandenheuvel
Mktg. Mgr. ....Karen Brown
Mng. Ed. ....Mike Burkholder
Circ. Mgr. ....Bev Fink
Market Information: TMC.
Mechanical available: Offset; Black and 4 ROP colors; insert accepted - all; page cutoffs - 21.
Mechanical Specifications: Type page 13 x 21 1/2; E - 6 cols, 2 1/16, 1/8 between; A - 9 cols, 1 3/8, 3/16 between; C - 9 cols, 1 3/8, 3/16 between.
Commodity Consumption: Avg. Page Number Per Issue - Daily 16; Avg. Page Number Per Issue - Saturday 20; widths 32; Newsprint Used - Short Tons 1100.
Equipment EDITORIAL: Front-end Software – Baseview, QPS, Adobe/Photoshop.; Editorial Hardware – APP/Mac; Editorial Printers – 3-APP/Mac Laser; Layout Software – APP/Mac.; Display Hardware – 7-APP/Mac; Display Printers – 3-APP/Mac LaserPrinter; Production Equipment – 2-IBM; Cameras – Nikon; Scanners – 1-Nu, DEC.; Addressing machine – 1/MLN. BUSINESS COMPUTERS: Business Software – Great Plains; Business Hardware – 2-IBM
Delivery method: Mail, Newsstand, Private Carrier, Racks

SALEM

SALEM NEWS

161 N. Lincoln Ave., Salem, Ohio, 44460; gen tel (330) 332-4601; gen fax (330) 332-1441; adv fax (330) 332-3084; ed fax (330) 332-1441; gen e-mail salemnews@salemnews.net; web site www.salemnews.net
Group: Ogden Newspaper Inc.
Ohio Newspaper Services, Inc.
Published: Mon, Tues, Wed, Thur, Fri, Sat, Sun
Weekday Frequency: m
Saturday Frequency: m
Circulation: 4,656; 5,250(sat); 4,660(sun)
Last Audit: ABC September 30, 2011
Price: 1.95/wk; 122.20/yr.
Advertising: Open inch rate $19.80
Insert rate: $44/M Open Rate
News services: AP.
Politics: Independent. **Established:** 1889
Own facility?: Y
Special Editions: Spring Home Improvement (Apr); Fair (Aug); Christmas Gift Savings (Dec); Progress (Feb); Bridal (Jan); Jubilee (Jul); Family Business (Jun); Car Care (Mar); Health (Monthly); Thanksgiving (Nov); Cookbook (Oct); Football (Sept).
Special Weekly Sections: 50 Plus (Fri); Church (Sat); TV Edition (Thur); Yesteryears (Tues); Food Page (Wed).
Magazines: Parade (S);
Pub. ....Beth Volosin
Clerk ....Becky Panzott
Ed. ....J.D. Creer
Sports Ed. ....B.J. Lisko
Market Information: TMC.
Mechanical available: Offset; Black and 3 ROP colors; insert accepted
Mechanical Specifications: Type page 10 x 20; A - 6 cols, 1.583, 1/8 between; A - 6 cols, C - 9 cols, 1.022, 1/16 between.
Commodity Consumption: Avg. Page Number Per Issue - Daily 16; Avg. Page Number Per Issue - Saturday 18; widths 27 1/2; Newsprint Used - Metric Tons 419; Printing Ink Used - Black 9396; Printing Ink Used - Color 1000; Printing Ink Used - Pages Printed 6200.
Equipment; Editorial Hardware – Mk.; Classified Hardware – Mk.; Production Equipment – APP/Mac LaserWriters; Cameras – 1-R/500, 1-LE.; Business Hardware – 1-ATT/3B2 500
Delivery method: Mail, Newsstand, Private Carrier, Racks

SANDUSKY

SANDUSKY NEWSPAPER, INC.

314 W. Market St., Sandusky, Ohio, 44870; gen tel (419) 625-5500; oth tel Business Office; gen fax 419-625-8658; adv fax (419) 625-1137; ed fax (419) 625-3007; oth fax (419) 625-7211; web site sanduskyregister.com
Published: Mon, Tues, Wed, Thur, Fri, Sat, Sun
Weekday Frequency: e
Saturday Frequency: m
Circulation: 20,500; 20,500(sat); 24,500(sun)
Politics: 1822
Own facility?: Y

SANDUSKY REGISTER

314 W. Market St., Sandusky, Ohio, 44870-5071; gen tel (419) 625-5500; adv tel (419) 625-5500; ed tel (419) 625-5500; gen fax (419) 625-7211 (bus. office); adv fax (419) 625-1137; ed fax (419) 625-3007; adv e-mail advertising@sanduskyregister.com; ed e-mail newsroom@sanduskyregister.com; web site www.sanduskyregister.com
Group: Ohio Newspaper Services, Inc.
Published: Mon, Tues, Wed, Thur, Fri, Sat, Sun
Weekday Frequency: e
Saturday Frequency: e
Circulation: 20,994; 20,225(sat); 24,366(sun)
Last Audit: ABC September 30, 2011
Price: 2.45/wk (carrier), $2.55/wk (motor route); 127.40/yr (carrier), $132.60/yr (motor route).
Advertising: Open inch rate $34.15
News services: AP, SHNS, Capitol Wire.
Politics: Independent.
Special Editions: Progress (Apr); Football (Aug); Home Improvement (Mar); Thanksgiving Day Gift Guide (Nov); Fall Car Care (Oct).
Special Weekly Sections: Click TV (Thur).
Magazines: USA WEEKEND Magazine (Sat); American Profile (Weekly).
Vice Pres./Pub. ....Douglas D. Phares
Mgr., Bus. Office ....Jane Righi
Adv. Dir. ....Mark A. Yocum
Adv. Mgr., Retail ....Jep Bloor
Circ. Dir. ....Bill Ney
Circ. Asst. Dir. ....Don Stanley
Circ. Coord., Newspapers in Educ. Diana Pusateri
Editorial Page Ed. ....Don Lee
City Ed ....Cheryl Weoch
Features Ed ....Kathy Lilje
Outdoors/Sports Ed. ....Anthony Moujaes
Online Ed ....Karen Mork
Chief Photographer ....Jason Werling
Radio/Television Ed. ....Matt Westerhold
Sports Ed. ....Dan Angelo
Prodn. Foreman, Mailroom ....Mike Lippus
Prodn. Foreman, Pressroom ....Ric Miller
Market Information: TMC.
Mechanical available: Offset; Black and 3 ROP colors; insert accepted; page cutoffs - 22 3/4.
Mechanical Specifications: Type page 13 x 21 1/2; E - 6 cols, 2, 1/6 between; A - 6 cols, 2, 1/6 between; C - 9 cols, 1 5/16, 1/6 between.
Commodity Consumption: Avg. Page Number Per Issue - Daily 24; Avg. Page Number Per Issue - Plates Used 36740; Avg. Page Number Per Issue - Sunday 42; widths 25; Newsprint Used - Short Tons 1514; Printing Ink Used - Black 46257; Printing Ink Used - Color 10240; Printing Ink Use
Equipment EDITORIAL: Front-end Software – CD, Baseview/NewsEdit Pro, Baseview/IQUE, QPS/QuarkXPress.; Editorial Hardware – APP/Mac; Editorial Equipment – APP/Mac Apple Share, Remote Access, APP/Mac Stocks, E-mail; Editorial Printers – ECR/4550, Ultre/94E Imagesetter CLASSIFIED: Front-end Software – CD, Baseview/Ad Manager Pro, Baseview/ClassFlow.; Classified Equipment – 1-Panasonic/Plain Paper Fax, Okidata, MM; Classified Printers – 1-APP/Mac LaserWriter DISPLAY: Ad make-up applications – Multi-Ad/Creator 2, QPS/QuarkXPress.; Display Hardware – 1-APP/Mac 8100, 4-APP/Mac G3, APP/Mac G4; Display Printers – 2-XIT/Clipper, 1-HP/8100N PRODUCTION: Pagination Software – QPS/QuarkXPress.; Production Equipment – 1-Graham, Xante, ECR, Ultre; Cameras – SCREEN/Liberator; Scanners – Microtek/600ZS, Microtek/Scanmaker II HR, Umax/PowerLook, AG/11 x 18, Polaroid/35mm PRESSROOM: Line 1 – 8-G/Urbanite 1968; Folders – 1-G/Urbanite; Reels and Stands – 1968; Press control system – 1998 MAILROOM: Counter stackers – 1/QWI, 1-TMSI/Monitor, HT/16 Monitor; Inserters and stuffers – HI/Sheridan 13/72 12/1; Bundle tying machines – 1-/MR-45CH Sterling, SSN/40 Sterling; Addressing machine – MM/Pressure Sensitive. BUSINESS COMPUTERS: Business Software – Lotus, DSI; Business Hardware – Dell/Poweredge Server

SHELBY

DAILY GLOBE

37 W. Main St., Shelby, Ohio, 44875; gen tel (419) 342-4276; ed tel (419) 342-3261; gen fax (419) 342-4246; gen e-mail globe@sdgnewsgroup.com; web site www.sdgnewsgroup.com
Published: Mon, Tues, Wed, Thur, Fri, Sat
Weekday Frequency: e
Circulation: 4,025; 4,025(sat)
Last Audit: September 27, 2006
Price: 1.40/wk; 6.10/mo; 71.00/yr.
Advertising: Open inch rate $11.35
News services: AP.
Politics: Independent.
Not Published: New Year; Memorial Day; Independence Day; Labor Day; Thanksgiving; Christmas.
Special Editions: Home Improvement (Apr); Progress (Feb); Health & Fitness (Mar); Christmas Gift Guide (Nov); Car Care (Oct); City Directory (Sept).
Special Weekly Sections: Best Food Day (Mon); Farm Page (Thur).
Pres./Pub. ....Scott M. Gove
Adv. Dir. ....Patty Schab
Circ. Dir. ....Sally Howerton
News Ed. ....Sheryl DeLong
Sports Ed. ....Chuck Ridenour
Prodn. Mgr. ....Trent Gove
Market Information: ADS; TMC.
Mechanical available: Offset; Black and 3 ROP colors; insert accepted; page cutoffs - 22 3/4.
Mechanical Specifications: Type page 13 x 21 1/2; E - 6 cols, 2 1/16, 1/8 between; A - 6 cols, 2 1/16, 1/8 between; C - 6 cols, 2 1/16, 1/8 between.
Commodity Consumption: Avg. Page Number Per Issue - Daily 10; widths 27 1/2.
Equipment EDITORIAL: Front-end Software – Baseview.; Editorial Hardware – APP/Mac CLASSIFIED: Front-end Software – Baseview.; Classified Hardware – APP/Mac DISPLAY: Ad make-up applications – QPS/QuarkXPress; Layout Software – APP/Mac.; Production Equipment – 1-B, Xante/LaserWriter; Cameras – 1-SCREEN/Companica; Scanners – Ag/Arcus II. PRESSROOM: Line 1 – 4-G/Community.; Bundle tying machines – 1/Kogyo, 1-/Ty-Tech; Addressing machine – 1-/SC.; Business Hardware – 1-RSK/Tandy 3100, 1-Club

SIDNEY

THE SIDNEY DAILY NEWS

1451 N. Vandemark Rd., Sidney, Ohio, 45365-4099; gen tel (937) 498-8088; adv tel (937) 498-5915 (class); ed tel (937) 498-5979; gen fax (937) 498-5990; adv fax (937) 498-5990; ed fax (937) 498-5991; adv e-mail bsmith@sdnccg.com; ed e-mail jbilliel@sdnccg.com; web site www.sidneydailynews.com
Group: AdOhio, Ohio Newspaper Association ????
Ohio Newspaper Services, Inc.
Published: Mon, Wed, Thur, Fri, Sat
Weekday Frequency: m
Saturday Frequency: m
Circulation: 11,300; 11,500(sat)
Last Audit: Sworn September 30, 2003
Price: 2.60/wk; 138.06/yr.
Advertising: Open inch rate $19.95
Insert rate: $57 per M
News services: AP.
Politics: Independent. **Established:** 1891
Advertising not accepted: N
Not Published: Tuesday, New Year; Memorial

Day; Independence Day; Labor Day; Thanksgiving; Christmas.
Own facility?: Y
Special Editions: Home Improvement (Apr); Fall Sports (Aug); Gifts & Greeting (Dec); Bride (Feb); Progress (Jan); Fair (Jul); Spring Sports (Mar); Graduation (May); Cookbook (Nov); Home Improvement (Sept).
Special Weekly Sections: TV Book (Sat); Best Food Day (Mon); Real Estate (Other); Second Food Day (Sat)., Entertainment Magazine, iN75 (Wed.)
Magazines: USA WEEKEND Magazine (Sat); American Profile (Weekly).
Relish (Monthly),
Athlon Sports (monthly);
Spry (monthly);
SCORE (quarterly)
Grp. Pub. ....Frank Beeson
Exec. Editor ....Jeff Billiel
Bus. Mgr. ....Betty Brownlee
Adv. Dir. ....Becky Smith
Classified Dir. ....Mandy Yagle
News Ed. ....Melanie Speicher
Real Estate Ed. ....Mike Seffrin
Regl. Adv. Mgr. ....Chris Reynolds
Circ. Mgr. ....Ella Strunk
Editorial Page Ed. ....Jeffrey Billiel
Fashion/Style Ed. ....Roberta Rohrbach
Local Life Ed. ....Elize Heart
Online Ed. ....April Elliot
Market Information: ADS.
Mechanical available: Offset; Black and 3 ROP colors; insert accepted; page cutoffs - 22 1/4.
Mechanical Specifications: Type page 11 5/8 x 21 1/4; E - 6 cols, 1 5/6, 1/8 between; A - 6 cols, 1 5/6, 1/8 between; C - 9 cols, 1 1/3, 1/16 between.
Commodity Consumption: Avg. Page Number Per Issue - Plates Used 4200.
Equipment; Editorial Hardware – APP/Mac, PC; Editorial Equipment – 40-IBM/Selectric.; Classified Hardware – PPI, 5-PC; Classified Equipment – APP/Mac G4.; Layout Software – PPI.; Display Hardware – APP/Mac, 5-PC; Production Equipment – 2-AU/Micro 5, 2-Hyphen/Dash 600; Cameras – 1-C/Spartan III; Scanners – ECR/Autokon, Lf/Leafscan, 1-Cp/Super-Alpha.
Zip Codes served: 45365, 45356, 45333, 45383, 45768, 45845, 45388, 45351, 45865, 45869, 45885, 45871, 45337, 45306, 45334, 45360, 45302, 45340, 45353, 43318, 43343, 43070.
Delivery method: Mail, Newsstand, Private Carrier, Racks

SPRINGFIELD

SPRINGFIELD NEWS-SUN

202 N. Limestone St., Springfield, Ohio, 45503; gen tel (937) 328-0300; adv tel (937) 328-0241; ed tel (937) 328-0342; gen fax (937) 328-0227; adv fax (937) 328-0321; ed fax (937) 328-0328; gen e-mail newssuneditor@coxohio.com; ed e-mail newssuneditor@coxohio.com; web site www.springfieldnewssun.com
Group: Ohio Newspaper Services, Inc.
Published: Mon, Tues, Wed, Thur, Fri, Sat, Sun
Weekday Frequency: m
Saturday Frequency: m
Circulation: 112,451; 111,402(sat); 175,995(sun)
Last Audit: ABC September 30, 2011
Price: 195.52/yr.
Advertising: Open inch rate $52.08
News services: AP, MCT, LAT-WP, NYT, Cox News Service.
Politics: 1817
Special Weekly Sections: Sports (Fri); Financial (S); Entertainment (Sat); Entertainment (Thur); Finances (Tues); Best Food Day (Wed).
Magazines: Channels-TV Book (S).
Pub. ....Steve Sidlo
Dir., HR ....Emily Chambers
Adv. Dir. ....Robert Mercer
Circ. Dir. ....Don Jordan
Ed. ....Jim Bebbington
Bus. Ed. ....Tim Bucey
Editorial Page Ed. ....Keith Streitenberger
Film/Theater Ed. ....Steve Cooper
Graphics Ed./Art Dir. ....Tom Hawkins
Photo Ed. ....Marshall Gorby
Sports Ed. ....Kermit Rowe
Women's Ed. ....Tom Stafford
Prodn. Supvr., Bldg. ....Jerry Maurer
Market Information: ADS; Split run; TMC.
Mechanical available: Offset; Black and 3 ROP colors; insert accepted; page cutoffs - 22 3/4.
Mechanical Specifications: Type page 11 5/8 x 21; E - 6 cols, 2 1/16, 1/8 between; A - 6 cols, 2 1/16, 1/8 between; C - 9 cols, 1 3/8, 1/16 between.
Commodity Consumption: Avg. Page Number Per Issue - Daily 28; Avg. Page Number Per Issue - Plates Used 56000; Avg. Page Number Per Issue - Sunday 66; widths 40 1/2; Newsprint Used - Short Tons 6000; Printing Ink Used - Black 80000; Printing Ink Used - Color 17000; Printing Ink
Equipment EDITORIAL: Front-end Software – DTI 4.3.; Editorial Hardware – APP/Mac, Sun; Editorial Equipment – Printers □ APP/Mac LaserWriter Plus, 1-TI/800, HP/LaserPrinter CLASSIFIED: Front-end Software – DTI 5.4.1.; Classified Printers – 1-HP/LaserPrinter DISPLAY: Ad make-up applications – DTI 4.3; Layout Software – APP/Power Mac G3/G4.; Display Hardware – APP/Mac; Display Printers – HP/LaserPrinter PRODUCTION: Pagination Software – DTI 4.3.; Production Equipment – 2-AU/APS 6-82ACS, 1-AU/APS08FC, Pixel-Craft/Pro Imager 8000; Cameras – 1-C/Marathon, 1-C/Spartan PRESSROOM: Line 1 – 5-G/Metro double width 1975; Pasters – 5-G/RTP; Reels and Stands – 5-G/Reel. MAILROOM: Counter stackers – 4/QWI; Inserters and stuffers – 1-GMA/SLS 1000; Bundle tying machines – 1-MLN/News 90, Ty-Tech, 3-/Sterling; Addressing machine – 2-/KR; Other equipment –1-Mc/Quarter Folder Stitcher-Trimmer, 1-KAN/Quarter Folder. BUSINESS COMPUTERS: Business Software – HP/UX 8.02, CJ; Business Hardware – 1-HP/9000-817S

SPRINGFIELD NEWSPAPERS, INC.

202 N. Limestone St., Springfield, Ohio, 45503; gen tel (937) 328-0300; gen fax (937) 328-0227; web site www.springfield-newssun.com
Published: Mon, Tues, Wed, Thur, Fri, Sat, Sun
Price: 174.72/yr.
Advertising: Open inch rate $67.64

STEUBENVILLE

HERALD-STAR

401 Herald Sq., Steubenville, Ohio, 43952; gen tel (740) 283-4711; adv tel (740) 283-4711; ed tel (740) 283-4711; gen fax (740) 282-4261; ed fax (740) 284-7355; ed e-mail newsroom@heraldstaronline.com; web site www.heraldstaronline.com
Published: Mon, Tues, Wed, Thur, Fri, Sat, Sun
Weekday Frequency: e
Saturday Frequency: e
Circulation: 11,178; 11,178(sat); 13,576(sun)
Last Audit: ABC September 30, 2011
Price: 2.20/wk (carrier); 20.00/mo (mail).
Advertising: Open inch rate $48.82
News services: AP.
Politics: Independent.
Note: The Weirton (WV) Daily Times (e) is a zoned edition of the Steubenville Herald-Star.
Special Editions: Bridal (Apr); Football (Aug); Basketball (Dec); Progress (Feb); Fort Festival (Jun); Home & Garden (Mar); Car Care (May); Christmas Opening and Gift Guide (Nov); Car Care (Oct); Home Improvement (Sept).
Special Weekly Sections: Senior Page (Fri); Business (S); Food (Sat); Entertainment (Thur); Food (Wed).
Magazines: USA WEEKEND Magazine (S).
Pub. ....Alex Marshall
Bus. Mgr. ....Norma Eltringham
Adv. Dir. ....Jason Mayberry
Mng. Ed. ....Ross Gallabrese
Community Ed. ....Marian Houser
Metro Ed. ....Jody Powers
News Ed. ....Fred Rossano
Sports. Ed. ....Mike Mathison
Press. Mgr. ....Pete Vitale
Market Information: ADS; TMC; Zoned editions.
Mechanical available: Offset; Black and 3 ROP colors; insert accepted - catabook, card, envelope; page cutoffs - 22.
Mechanical Specifications: Type page 13 x 21 1/2; E - 6 cols, 1/8 between; A - 6 cols, 1/8 between; C - 9 cols, 1/16 between.
Commodity Consumption: Avg. Page Number Per Issue - Daily 24; Avg. Page Number Per Issue - Sunday 42; widths 27 1/2; Newsprint Used - Short Tons 1851; Printing Ink Used - Pages Printed 9859.
Equipment EDITORIAL: Front-end Software – Mk/ACE II, QPS/QuarkXPress 3.3.; Editorial Hardware – Mk/6000, APP/Mac; Editorial Printers – Tegra/Varityper 5000, 2-Tegra/Varityper 5300, Tegra/Varityper 5300 E CLASSIFIED: Front-end Software – Mk/ACE II.; Classified Hardware – Mk; Classified Printers – Tegra/Varityper 5000, Tegra/Varityper 5300 DISPLAY: Ad make-up applications – Multi-Ad/Creator 3.54; Layout Software – APP/Mac.; Display Hardware – APP/Mac; Display Printers – Tegra/Varityper 5000, Tegra/Varityper 5300 PRODUCTION: Pagination Software – Scanners □ Mirror/1200, Imax.; Production Equipment – 2-V, 3-Mk/VDT, Nikon/Color Access; Cameras – 2-DSA/680C, LE/121 PRESSROOM: Line 1 – 7-G/Urbanite 1990; Folders – G/Urbanite. MAILROOM: Counter stackers – 1-Id; Bundle tying machines – 1-MLN/Strapper, 1/Dynaric; Addressing machine – Packard Bell. BUSINESS COMPUTERS: Business Software – Lotus 4.0; Business Hardware – NCR, Packard Bell, HP

TIFFIN

THE ADVERTISER-TRIBUNE

320 N. Nelson St., Tiffin, Ohio, 44883; gen tel (419) 448-3200; adv tel (419) 448-3230; ed tel (419) 448-3240; gen fax (419) 447-3274; adv fax (419) 447-3274; ed fax (419) 447-3274; gen e-mail newsroom@advertiser-tribune.com; adv e-mail advertising@advertiser-tribune.com; web site www.advertiser-tribune.com
Published: Mon, Tues, Wed, Thur, Fri, Sat, Sun
Weekday Frequency: m
Saturday Frequency: m
Circulation: 8,281; 8,281(sat); 9,002(sun)
Last Audit: ABC September 30, 2011
Price: 11.50/mo (carrier), $12.50/mo (auto), 15.25/mo (mail); 142.80/yr (carrier), $154.80.00/yr (auto), $195.00/yr (mail).
Advertising: Open inch rate $20.53
News services: AP.
Politics: Independent.
Not Published: New Year; Memorial Day; Independence Day; Labor Day; Christmas.
Special Editions: Fall Sports Tab (Aug); Winter Sports Tab (Dec); Fair Tab (Jul); Home Improvement (Mar); Spring Car Care Tab (May); Cooking Contest (Nov); Home Improvement (Oct); Heritage Festival Tab (Sept).
Special Weekly Sections: Best Food Day (Mon); Best Real Estate Day (S); Best Auto Days (Sat); Best Auto Days (Thur); Home Front Page (Wed).
Magazines: USA WEEKEND Magazine (S).
Bus. Mgr. ....Mary Huss
Adv. Mgr. ....Chris Dixon
Circ. Mgr. ....Ron Clark
Entertainment/Amusements Ed. ....Mary Kramer
News Ed. ....Rob Weaver
Photo Ed. ....James Shobe
Prodn. Mgr. ....Janet Vallery
Market Information: ADS; TMC.
Mechanical available: Offset; Black and 3 ROP colors; insert accepted - all; page cutoffs - 22 3/4.
Mechanical Specifications: Type page 13 x 21 1/2; E - 6 cols, 1 7/8, 1/8 between; A - 6 cols, 1 7/8, 1/8 between; C - 8 cols, 1 7/16, 1/8 between.
Commodity Consumption: Avg. Page Number Per Issue - Daily 20; Avg. Page Number Per Issue - Plates Used 14000; Avg. Page Number Per Issue - Sunday 48; widths 25; Newsprint Used - Short Tons 980; Printing Ink Used - Black 12000; Printing Ink Used - Color 1500; Printing Ink Used
Equipment EDITORIAL: Front-end Software – In-House Customized.; Editorial Hardware – APP/Macs; Editorial Printers – 2-APP/Mac LaserWriter II NTX, 3-HP/LaserJet 4MV, 1-ECR/Scriptsetter VRL 36; Classified Hardware – 1-APP/Mac. PRODUCTION: Pagination Software – QPS/QuarkXPress.; Production Equipment – 3-HP/LaserJet 4MV, 1-ECR/Scriptsetter VRL 36; Scanners – Lf/AP Leaf Picture Desk 35, Polaroid/SprintScan 35, Umax/Vista-S6 PRESSROOM: Line 1 – 8-G/Community 1974; Folders – 1; Reels and Stands – 8 MAILROOM: Counter stackers – 1-BG/Count-O-Veyor; Bundle tying machines – 2-MLN/Strapper. BUSINESS COMPUTERS: Business Software – Custom software; Business Hardware – NCR

TOLEDO

THE BLADE

541 N. Superior St., Toledo, Ohio, 43660; gen tel (419) 724-6000; adv tel (419) 724-6350; ed tel (419) 724-6050; gen fax (419) 724-6471; adv fax (419) 724-6391; ed fax (419) 724-6439; gen e-mail info@toledoblade.com; adv e-mail natadv@toledoblade.com; ed e-mail webeditor@toledoblade.com; web site www.toledoblade.com
Published: Mon, Tues, Wed, Thur, Fri, Sat, Sun
Weekday Frequency: m
Saturday Frequency: m
Circulation: 113,786; 115,326(sat); 150,119(sun)
Last Audit: ABC September 30, 2011
Price: 2.60/wk (carrier); 135.20/yr (carrier).
Advertising: Open inch rate $179.14
News services: AP, RN, LAT-WP, MCT, CSM, NYT, SHNS, Bloomberg, TMS.
Politics: Independent. **Established:** 1835
Special Editions: MWP Hens Opening Day (Apr); Pro & College Football (Aug); Girls High School Hoops (Dec); Winter Olympics (Feb); Super Bowl (Jan); Toledo (Jul); Employment Connection Summer Issue (Jun); Baseball (Mar); OSU/UM (Nov); Toledo (Oct); Season of the Arts (Sept)
Special Weekly Sections: Real Estate (S).
Magazines: Comics (S).
Pres./Gen. Mgr. ....Joseph H. Zerbey
Co-Pub. ....Diana Block
Vice Pres., Admin. ....Gary Blair
Director of HR and Labor Relations William Nolan
Controller ....Steve Dolley
Dir., Info Technology ....Malcolm Edge
Adv. Director, Majors/Nat'l Sales ....Michael Mori
Adv. Mgr., Retail ....Jeff Pezzano
Adv. Mgr., Sales Devel. ....Sheldon Kowalski
Circ. Dir. ....Richard Fuller
Circ. Mgr., Direct Sales ....Clara Intagliata
Circ. Mgr., Distr. ....Brad Schwanbeck
Circ. Mgr., City Home Delivery ....Jeff Cole
Circ. Mgr., Single Copy ....Betsy Kenniston
Circ. Coord., Newspapers in Educ. .Debby Geyer
Ed. in Chief ....John Robinson Block
Director of Advertising and New Media John Crisp
Market Information: ADS; Split run; TMC; Zoned editions.
Mechanical available: Flexography; Black and 3 ROP colors; insert accepted; page cutoffs - 22.
Mechanical Specifications: Type page 13 1/2 x 22; E - 6 cols, 2 1/16, 1/8 between; A - 6 cols, 2 1/16, 1/8 between; C - 10 cols, 1 3/16, 1/8 between.
Commodity Consumption: Avg. Page Number Per Issue - Daily 52; Avg. Page Number Per Issue - Plates Used 135231; Avg. Page Number Per Issue - Sunday 128; widths 25; Newsprint Used - Metric Tons 18905; Printing Ink Used - Black 623720; Printing Ink Used - Color 240485; Printing I

Equipment EDITORIAL: Front-end Software – ATS/Mediadesk; Editorial Hardware – HP Win7; Editorial Equipment – Konia printers, XenServers CLASSIFIED: Front-end Software – ATS Advisor, SCS Class Pag; Classified Hardware – Windows 2005 servers; Classified Printers – Kionica 9030 DISPLAY: Ad make-up applications – Adobe Indesign; Layout Software – SCS/Layout 8000, Adobe/InDesign.; Display Hardware – Macs; Display Printers – APP/Mac Laser, AU/APS Broadsheet PRODUCTION: Pagination Software – CText/ALPS 5.1, AG, CNI/Ad Tracking.; Production Equipment – Na/Nappflex, 3-AU/3850, 1-LE/PC 18, 3-Konica/3850 OL; Cameras – 1-C/NewsPager, 1-SCREEN/690D; Scanners – 2-ECR/Autokon 1000DE, 1-HP/ScanJet 4C, 1-Screen/1030 AI PRESSROOM: Line 1 – 9-G/Flexoliner double width 1989; Line 2 – 9-G/Flexoliner double width 1990; Line 3 – 9-G/Flexoliner double width 1991; Folders – 3-G/3:2; Pasters – 18, 9; Reels and Stands – 18, 9. MAILROOM: Counter stackers – 2-HL/Monitor Programmable Laser, 7-HL/Monitor HT II, 5-TMSI/Compass; Inserters and stuffers – 1-S/1472P, 1/Heidelberger/632; Bundle tying machines – 7-/Power Strap, 8-Dynaric/NP-3; Wrapping singles – 4-Dynaric/SM 65. BUSINESS COMPUTERS: Business Software – CJ; Business Hardware – 2-HP/3000 Series 968
Windows 2005 servers

TROY

TROY DAILY NEWS

224 S. Market St., Troy, Ohio, 45373; gen tel (937) 335-5634; adv tel (937) 440-5252; ed tel (937) 335-5634; gen fax (937) 335-3552; adv fax (937) 335-9321; ed fax (937) 335-3552; gen e-mail editorial@tdnpublishing.com; adv e-mail lstewart@dailycall.com; ed e-mail editorial@tdnpublishing.com; web site www.troydailynews.com

Group: Ohio Community Media
Ohio Newspaper Services, Inc.
Published: Mon, Wed, Thur, Fri, Sat, Sun
Weekday Frequency: m
Saturday Frequency: m
Circulation: 7,918; 7,918(sat); 9,827(sun)
Last Audit: Sworn September 30, 2002
Price: 2.88/wk; 9.30/mo; 182.50/yr (mail), $150.00/yr (carrier).
Advertising: Open inch rate $19.90 (daily); $23.10 (Sun.)
Insert rate: $57 per M (net)
News services: AP,
Politics: Independent. **Established:** 1909
Advertising not accepted: N
Not Published: Tuesdays and Christmas (unless falls on Sun).
Own facility?: Y
Special Editions: Car Care (Fall); Bridal (Jan); Miami County Community Guide (May); Thanksgiving (Nov); Car Care (Spring).
Special Weekly Sections: Best Food Day (Mon.); iN75 Entertainment (Wed.); TV Magazine (Sun.); Color Comics (Sun.); Travel (Sun.); Business (Sat.).
Magazines: Color Comics (Other); USA WEEKEND Magazine (S); American Profile (Weekly)
Spry (Monthly); Relish (Monthly); Athlon Sports (Monthly); SCORE Magazine (quarterly).
Grp. Pub. ....Frank Beeson
Bus. Mgr. ....Betty Brownlee
Adv. Mgr. ....Leiann Stewart
Circ. Mgr. ....Cheryl Hall
Exec. Ed. ....David Fong
City Ed. ....Melody Vallieu
Copy Ed. ....Jim Davis
Chief Photographer ....Anthony Weber
Sports Ed. ....Henry Conte
Prodn. Dir. ....Jason Thurmond
Sports Editor ....Josh Brown
Market Information: ADS; TMC.
Mechanical available: Offset; Black and 3 ROP colors; insert accepted - all; page cutoffs - 22 3/4.
Mechanical Specifications: Type page 13 x 21 1/2; E - 6 cols, 1 5/6, 1/8 between; A - 6 cols, 1 5/6, 1/8 between; C - 8 cols, 1 1/3, 1/16 between.
Commodity Consumption: Avg. Page Number Per Issue - Daily 16; Avg. Page Number Per Issue - Plates Used 27000; Avg. Page Number Per Issue - Sunday 44; widths 34; Newsprint Used - Metric Tons 1985; Printing Ink Used - Black 55000; Printing Ink Used - Color 13000; Printing Ink Us
Equipment; Editorial Hardware – APP/Mac; Editorial Equipment – 1-APP/Mac IIci, 1-Lf/AP Leaf Picture Desk, 5-APP/Power Mac G3, 5-CD-Rom, Kk/2035 Plus Scanner, 1-APP/Mac II, 2-Iomega/Jazz IGB, 2-Iomega/Zip Drive 100MB, Power Computing/Power Center Pro 240 Web Server, Quantum/5 Cort DLT A CLASSIFIED: Front-end Software – Sun/Suntype.; Classified Hardware – Dell/NT Server, 5-Compaq; Classified Printers – 1-Xante/Accel-a-Writer 8200 DISPLAY: Ad make-up applications – Multi-Ad/Creator, QPS/QuarkXPress, Mk/Managing Editor; Display Hardware – 7-APP/Power Mac G3, 2-APP/Power Mac 7500; Display Printers – 1-QMS/2060, Dell/Power Edge 1300 RIP; Production Equipment – Xante/Accel-a-Writer 8200 Laserprinter, Pre-Press/System, Pre Press/Panther Pro 36 with Ap Power Mac RIP, 1-APP/Power Mac 8100, 2-Power Computing/Power Center Pro 210, 1-APP/Power Mac 7500 180 mhz Apple Share IP server, 2-AU/3850 Imagers, Comp PRESSROOM: Line 1 – 10-G/Urbanite single sheet 1990; Press Drives – 2; Folders – 2; Pasters – 2-Butler/Splicer. MAILROOM: Counter stackers – 2-H/RS 2512; Inserters and stuffers – 1-KAN/760; Bundle tying machines – 2-EAM-Mosca/4044; Addressing machine – 1/KR, PBS. BUSINESS COMPUTERS: Business Software – Microsoft/Excel, Microsoft/Office; Business Hardware – Solomon, PBS, APP/Mac, APP/Power Mac 7500, 2-APP/Power Mac 7200, Lotus, Microsoft/Word, Microsoft/Excel, ADP, Sun/Suntype
Zip Codes served: 45373, 45371, 45383, 45337, 45339, 45359, 45312, 45389, 45356, 45318, 45326, 45317, 43072, 45326.
Delivery method: Mail, Newsstand, Private Carrier, Racks

UPPER SANDUSKY

THE DAILY CHIEF-UNION

111 W. Wyandot Ave., Upper Sandusky, Ohio, 43351; gen tel (419) 294-2332; adv tel (419) 294-2332; ed tel (419) 294-2331; gen fax (419) 294-5608; adv fax (419) 294-5608; ed fax (419) 294-5608; adv e-mail dcuads@dailychiefunion.com; ed e-mail dcueditor@dailychiefunion.com; web site www.dailychiefunion.com

Published: Mon, Tues, Wed, Thur, Fri, Sat
Weekday Frequency: e
Circulation: 3,822; 3,822(sat)
Last Audit: September 30, 2003
Price: 110.80/yr.
Advertising: Open inch rate $6.00
News services: AP.
Politics: Independent.
Note: Printed by Kenton (OH) Times.
Advertising not accepted: Clairvoyants.
Not Published: New Year; Memorial Day; Independence Day; Labor Day; Thanksgiving; Christmas.
Special Editions: Christmas Greeting (Dec); Football (Fall); Presidents' Sale (Feb); January Sale (Jan); June Dairy (Jun); Memorial Day (May); Christmas Kick-Off (Nov); Boy and Girl Scouts (Other).
Special Weekly Sections: Entertainment (Thur).
Magazines: Business Cards (Other); American Profile (Weekly).
Bus./Finance Ed. ....Brandon Drake
Political/Gov't Ed. ....Aaron Corte
Science/Technology Ed. ....Brandon Trake
Sports Ed. ....Lonnie McMillan
Mgmt. Info Servs. Mgr. ....Jeff Barnes
Prodn. Mgr. ....Ronald Pool
Prodn. Mgr., Mailroom ....David Barnes
Market Information: ADS.
Mechanical available: Offset; Black and 3 ROP colors; insert accepted; page cutoffs - 21.
Mechanical Specifications: Type page 12 15/16 x 21 1/2; E - 6 cols, 2, 1/8 between; A - 6 cols, 2, 1/8 between; C - 6 cols, 2, 1/8 between.
Commodity Consumption: Avg. Page Number Per Issue - Daily 14; Avg. Page Number Per Issue - Saturday 14; widths 28.
Equipment; Editorial Hardware – APP/Mac; Editorial Printers – TI.; Classified Hardware – APP/Mac; Classified Printers – TI. DISPLAY: Ad make-up applications – Multi-Ad/Creator.; Display Hardware – APP/Mac IIsi; Display Printers – APP/Mac LaserWriter Plus PRODUCTION: Pagination Software – APP/Mac, Baseview.; Production Equipment – 2-APP/Mac LaserWriter Plus; Cameras – Nu/UV-1418; Bundle tying machines – Ty-Tech; Addressing machine – Am.

URBANA

BROWN PUBLISHING COMPANY

220 E. Court St., Urbana, Ohio, 43078; gen tel (937) 652-1331; gen fax (937) 652-1336; gen e-mail lmoon@brownpublishing.com; web site www.brownpublishing.com; www.urbanacitizen.com

Published: Mon, Tues, Wed, Thur, Fri, Sat, Sun
Price: 114.85/yr.
Advertising: Open inch rate $9.70

URBANA DAILY CITIZEN

1637 E. US Hwy 36, Suite 10, Urbana, Ohio, 43078; gen tel (937) 652-1331; adv tel (937) 652-1331; ed tel (937) 652-1331; gen fax (937) 652-1336; adv fax (937) 652-1336; ed fax (937) 652-1336; ed e-mail bburns@urbanacitizen.com; web site www.urbanacitizen.com

Group: Ohio Community Newspapers, LLC.
Published: Mon, Tues, Wed, Thur, Fri, Sat
Weekday Frequency: m
Saturday Frequency: m
Circulation: 5,300; 5,300(sat)
Last Audit: Sworn March 31, 2006
Price: 119.85/yr.
Advertising: Open inch rate $10.50
Insert rate: 57
News services: AP.
Politics: Independent. **Established:** 1838
Not Published: New Year; Memorial Day; Independence Day; Labor Day; Thanksgiving; Christmas.
Special Editions: Football Preview (Aug); Christmas Greetings (Dec); Bride (Feb); County Fair (Jul); Health & Fitness (Jun); House and Home (Mar); Progress (May); Winter Sports (Nov); Crafts (Oct).
Special Weekly Sections: Farm/Agriculture (S); Education (Tues); Business (Wed).
Magazines: USA WEEKEND Magazine (Sat).
Bus. Mgr. ....Brenda Amlin
Publisher/Adv Dir ....Lane Moon
Circ. Dir. ....Gina Riefftahl
Ed. ....Brenda Burns
Asst. Ed ....Kathy Fox
Sports Ed. ....Steve Stout
Market Information: ADS; TMC.
Mechanical available: Offset; Black and 3 ROP colors; insert accepted - poly bags; page cutoffs - 22 3/4.
Mechanical Specifications: 9.889 x 21
Commodity Consumption: Avg. Page Number Per Issue - Daily 16; Avg. Page Number Per Issue - Saturday 16; Avg. Page Number Per Issue - Sunday 8; widths 25; Newsprint Used - Short Tons 500.
Delivery method: Mail, Newsstand, Private Carrier

VAN WERT

DELPHOS HERALD INC., THE TIMES-BULLETIN

700 Fox Rd., Van Wert, Ohio, 45891; gen tel (419) 238-2285; gen fax (419) 238-0447; web site www.timesbulletin.com

Published: Mon, Wed, Thur, Fri, Sat, Sun
Weekday Frequency: m
Saturday Frequency: m
Not Published: Tuesday
Own facility?: Y
Delivery method: Mail, Newsstand, Private Carrier, Racks

THE TIMES BULLETIN

700 Fox Rd., Van Wert, Ohio, 45891-0271; gen tel (419) 238-2285; adv tel (419) 238-2285; ed tel (419) 238-2285; gen fax (419) 238-0447; adv fax (419) 238-0447; ed fax (419) 238-0447; gen e-mail sjohnson@timesbulletin.com; adv e-mail tbyrd@timesbulletin.com; ed e-mail kdougal@timesbulletin.com; web site www.timesbulletin.com

Published: Mon, Wed, Thur, Fri, Sat
Weekday Frequency: m
Saturday Frequency: m
Circulation: 5,500; 5,500(sat)
Last Audit: Sworn March 31, 2007
Price: 12.00/mo (carrier); 120.00/yr (carrier), $190.55/yr (mail).
Advertising: Open inch rate $13.50
News services: AP.
Politics: Independent. **Established:** 1846
Not Published: Christmas.
Own facility?: Y
Special Editions: Spring Sports Magazine (Apr); Fall Sports Magazine (Aug); Christmas Greetings (Dec); Progress (Jan); Weddings II (Jun); Agriculture Almanac (Mar); Graduation (May); Holiday Traditions (Nov); Weddings III (Oct); PrimeTime (Quarterly); Home Improvement (Sep
Special Weekly Sections: TV & Leisure (Fri); Farm & Agribusiness (Mon); Church & Religion (Sat); Youth of Today (Thur); Arts & Culture (Wed).
Magazines: USA WEEKEND Magazine (Sat); American Profile (Weekly).
Bus. Mgr. ....Kevin Wannemacher
Market Devel. Dir. ....Tina Byrd
Circ. Mgr. ....Mike Marchek
Ed. ....Kirk Dougal
Sports Ed. ....Drew Bittner
Ed. ....Sherry Missler
group publisher ....stephen johnson
Pub. ....Robert Krecklow
Market Information: ADS; TMC.
Mechanical available: Offset; Black and 4 ROP colors; insert accepted; page cutoffs - 22 3/4.
Mechanical Specifications: Type page 11 1/8 x 21 1/2; E - 6 cols, 1 3/4, 1/8 between; A - 6 cols, 1 3/4, 1/8 between; C - 8 cols, 1 5/16, 1/8 between.
Commodity Consumption: Avg. Page Number Per Issue - Daily 16; Avg. Page Number Per Issue - Plates Used 5200; widths 22 1/4; Newsprint Used - Metric Tons 280; Printing Ink Used - Black 9400; Printing Ink Used - Color 1200; Printing Ink Used - Pages Printed 4784.
Equipment EDITORIAL: Front-end Software – QPS/QuarkXPress.; Editorial Hardware – APP/Mac CLASSIFIED: Front-end Software – Baseview.; Classified Hardware – APP/Mac DISPLAY: Ad make-up applications – PBS. PRODUCTION: Pagination Software – Baseview, QPS/QuarkXPress 4.0.; Production Equipment – 1-Reconex; Cameras – 1-R/500; Scanners – AG/Arcus; Folders – 1-G/2:1.; Bundle tying machines – 1/Bu; Addressing machine – Kirk Rudy.; Business Hardware – PC, Applications: MSSI
Delivery method: Mail, Newsstand, Private Carrier, Racks

WAPAKONETA

WAPAKONETA DAILY NEWS

520 Industrial Dr., Wapakoneta, Ohio, 45895; gen tel (419) 738-2128; gen fax (419) 738-5352; adv e-mail retailadv@wapakwdn.com; ed e-mail blaney@wapakwdn.com; web site

www.wapakdailynews.com
Group: Ohio Newspaper Services, Inc.
Published: Mon, Tues, Wed, Thur, Fri, Sat, Sun
Weekday Frequency: e
Saturday Frequency: m
Circulation: 5,300; 5,300(sat)
Last Audit: March 31, 2007
Price: 11.00/mo (carrier); 156.75/yr.
Advertising: Open inch rate $14.52
News services: AP.
Politics: Independent.
Not Published: New Year; Memorial Day; Independence Day; Labor Day; Thanksgiving; Christmas.
Special Editions: Home Improvement (Apr); Personal Image (Aug); Gift Guide (Dec); Progress (Feb); Bridal (Jan); Fair (Jul); Newspapers in Education (Mar); Graduation (May); Christmas Kick-Off (Nov); Car Care (Oct); Indian Summerfest (Sept).
Special Weekly Sections: Best Food Day (Mon); Farm News (Sat); Entertainment (Thur); Business (Tues).
Magazines: Homes/Real Estate (Monthly); American Profile (Weekly).
Pub. .... Dianna Epperly
Mktg. Dir. .... Karen Brown
Circ. Mgr. .... Beverly Fink
Exec. Ed. .... William Laney
Prodn. Mgr., Composing/Printing .... Nina Laney
Market Information: TMC.
Mechanical available: Offset; Black and 3 ROP colors; insert accepted; page cutoffs - 22 3/4.
Mechanical Specifications: Type page 13 x 21 1/2; E - 6 cols, 2 1/16, 1/8 between; A - 6 cols, 2 1/16, 1/8 between; C - 9 cols, 1 5/16, 1/8 between.
Commodity Consumption: Avg. Page Number Per Issue - Daily 18; Avg. Page Number Per Issue - Plates Used 12000; widths 28.
Equipment EDITORIAL: Front-end Software – QPS/QuarkXPress 4.0.; Editorial Hardware – APP/Mac G4; Editorial Printers – APP/Mac LaserWriter 16-600 PS, APP/Mac CLASSIFIED: Front-end Software – QPS/QuarkXPress, Claris/FileMaker Pro, QPS.; Classified Hardware – APP/Power Mac; Classified Printers – APP/Mac LaserWriter 16-600 PS DISPLAY: Ad make-up applications – Adobe/PageMaker 5.0, Multi-Ad/Creator 3.63, QPS/QuarkXPress 4.0.; Display Hardware – APP/G4; Display Printers – APP/Mac LaserWriter 16-600 PS PRODUCTION: Pagination Software – QPS/QuarkXPress 4.0.; Production Equipment – APP/Mac 7200-90, APP/Mac 7200-75, Adobe/Photoshop, APP/Mac LaserWriter 16-600 PS; Cameras – 1-Nu, 1-LE, Nu/SST 923; Scanners – LE/Sprint Scan 35, AG/SnapScan 600; Bundle tying machines – 1/Sa; Addressing machine – 3-/Wm.; Business Hardware – 1-Samsung/S550

WARREN

THE TRIBUNE CHRONICLE

240 Franklin St. SE, Warren, Ohio, 44482-1431; gen tel (330) 841-1600; adv tel (330) 841-1621; gen fax (330) 841-1721; adv fax (330) 841-1639; ed fax (330) 841-1717; gen e-mail tribune@tribtoday.com; web site www.tribtoday.com
Published: Mon, Tues, Wed, Thur, Fri, Sat, Sun
Weekday Frequency: m
Saturday Frequency: m
Circulation: 25,681; 28,080(sat); 27,974(sun)
Last Audit: ABC September 30, 2011
Price: 137.80/yr (home delivery), $208.00/yr (mail).
Advertising: Open inch rate $63.55
News services: AP.
Politics: Independent.
Note: This newspaper is published in tabloid format on Saturday.
Special Editions: Bridal (Jan); Bridal (May).
Special Weekly Sections: Entertainment (Thur); Health (Tues); Food (Wed).
Magazines: USA WEEKEND Magazine (S).
Pub .... Charles Jarvis
Gen. Mgr. .... F. Len Blose
Adv. Mgr., Classified .... Pat Charity
Dir., Sales/Mktg. .... Chris D'Angelo
Circ. Dir. .... Ted Snyder
Ed. .... Frank Robinson
Sports Ed. .... Ed Puskas
Bus. Ed .... Larry Ringler
Editorial Page Ed. .... Guy Coviello
Entertainment/Amusements Reporter .. Andy Gray
Prodn. Mgr., Mailroom .... Scott Gee
Prodn. Foreman, Composing .... Nancy Warren
Market Information: TMC; Zoned editions.
Mechanical available: Offset; Black and 3 ROP colors; insert accepted; page cutoffs - 22 3/4.
Mechanical Specifications: Type page 12 x 21 1/2; E - 6 cols, 2 1/16, 1/8 between; A - 6 cols, 2 1/16, 1/8 between; C - 9 cols, 1 3/8, 1/16 between.
Commodity Consumption: Avg. Page Number Per Issue - Daily 32; Avg. Page Number Per Issue - Plates Used 96000; Avg. Page Number Per Issue - Saturday 44; Avg. Page Number Per Issue - Sunday 76; widths 27; Newsprint Used - Short Tons 4320; Printing Ink Used - Black 57484; Printin
Equipment; Classified Printers – TI/Postscript.; Layout Software – Adept.; Production Equipment – 1-V/5000, 1-V, 1-Pre Press/Panther Pro 45, 1-Xante; Cameras – 2-C. PRESSROOM: Line 1 – 8-H/mono double width (6 half decks) 1992; Folders – 2; Pasters – 8; Reels and Stands – 8 MAILROOM: Counter stackers – 3-HL/Monitor, 1-Id; Inserters and stuffers – HI/848, HI/1148; Bundle tying machines – 2/MLN, 2-/Dynaric; Addressing machine – 1-/Ohio mailing machine.

WASHINGTON COURT HOUSE

BROWN PUBLISHING CO., RECORD HERALD

138 S. Fayette St., Washington Court House, Ohio, 43160; gen tel (740) 335-3611; gen fax (740) 335-5728; gen e-mail gbrock@recordherald.com; web site www.recordherald.com

RECORD HERALD

138 S. Fayette St., Washington Court House, Ohio, 43160; gen tel (740) 335-3611; adv tel (740) 335-3611; ed tel (740) 335-3614; gen fax (740) 335-5728; adv fax (740) 335-5728; ed fax (740) 335-5728; gen e-mail info@recordherald.com; adv e-mail admanager@recordherald.com; web site www.recordherald.com
Published: Mon, Tues, Wed, Thur, Fri, Sat, Sun
Weekday Frequency: e
Saturday Frequency: m
Circulation: 5,235; 5,235(sat)
Last Audit: September 30, 2002
Price: 7.60/mo; 114.23/yr.
Advertising: Open inch rate $11.95
News services: AP.
Politics: Independent.
Advertising not accepted: 900 numbers.
Not Published: New Year; Memorial Day; Independence Day; Labor Day; Thanksgiving; Christmas.
Pub. .... Gary Brock
Adv. Dir. .... Sherri Sattler
Circ. Mgr. .... Tony Tompkins
Ed. .... Holly Cottrill
Prodn. Mgr., Composing .... Lyn Rogers
Market Information: ADS; TMC.
Mechanical available: Offset; Black and 3 ROP colors; insert accepted; page cutoffs - 22 3/4.
Mechanical Specifications: Type page 13 x 21 1/2; E - 6 cols, 2 1/16, 1/8 between; A - 6 cols, 2 1/16, 1/8 between; C - 8 cols, 1 3/4, 1/16 between.
Commodity Consumption: Avg. Page Number Per Issue - Daily 14; Avg. Page Number Per Issue - Plates Used 1893; Avg. Page Number Per Issue - Saturday 12; widths 14; Newsprint Used - Metric Tons 221; Printing Ink Used - Pages Printed 3786.
Equipment EDITORIAL: Front-end Software – QPS/QuarkXPress 7.11.; Editorial Hardware – 6-APP/Mac; Editorial Equipment – 2-APP/Mac Scanner; Editorial Printers – 1-APP/Mac; Classified Hardware – 1-APP/Mac. DISPLAY: Ad make-up applications – QPS/QuarkXPress, Multi-Ad/Creator, Mk/Ad Builder; Display Hardware – Printers ☐ 1-APP/Mac; Production Equipment – Cameras ☐ 1-B/Caravel.; Bundle tying machines – 1/Bu. BUSINESS COMPUTERS: Business Software – MSSI/Ad Manager; Business Hardware – 1-IBM/AT, 4-AST/Bravo LC 4-33

WILLOUGHBY

THE NEWS-HERALD

7085 Mentor Ave., Willoughby, Ohio, 44094; gen tel (440) 951-0000; adv tel (440) 951-0000; ed tel (440) 951-0000; gen fax (440) 951-0080; adv fax (440) 951-0917; ed fax (440) 975-2293; adv e-mail advertising@news-herald.com; ed e-mail editor@news-herald.com; web site www.news-herald.com
Published: Mon, Tues, Wed, Thur, Fri, Sat, Sun
Weekday Frequency: m
Saturday Frequency: m
Circulation: 33,340; 34,905(sat); 38,415(sun)
Last Audit: ABC September 30, 2011
Price: 4.75/wk; 247.00/yr.
Advertising: Open inch rate $57.05
Insert rate: $61cpm
News services: AP, MCT, CNS, SHNS.
Politics: 1879
Own facility?: Y
Special Editions: Golf (Apr); Most Beautiful Babies (Aug); Last Minute Gifts (Dec); Income Tax Guide (Feb); Chronology (Jan); Careers and Education (Jul); Graduation (Jun); Spring Lawn & Garden (Mar); Home Improvement (May); Elections (Nov); Fall Car Care (Oct); Fall Fashi
Special Weekly Sections: TGIF (Entertainment Tab) (Fri); Real Estate Today (S).
Magazines: Coupon Book (Monthly); USA WEEKEND Magazine (Sat); Homes Alamanac (Semi-monthly).
Pub. .... Jeff Sudbrook
Controller .... Ron Adams
Adv. Dir. .... Jeff Schell
Circ. Mgr. .... Tom Pottorff
Editor .... Tricia Ambrose
Mng. Ed. .... Laura Kessel
Entertainment Ed. .... Mark Meszoros
Environmental Writer .... Jeff Frischkorn
Photo Dept. Mgr. .... Duncan Scott
Radio/Television Writer .... David S. Glasier
GM .... Brian McCloskey
Prodn. Mgr., Pre Press .... Lee Ann Moran
Market Information: ADS; Split run; TMC; Zoned editions.
Mechanical available: Offset; Black and 3 ROP colors; insert accepted - poly bag, samples; page cutoffs - 22 1/12.
Mechanical Specifications: Type page 13 x 21; E - 6 cols, 2 1/16, 1/8 between; A - 6 cols, 2 1/16, 1/8 between; C - 8 cols, 1 5/8, 1/16 between.
Commodity Consumption: Avg. Page Number Per Issue - Daily 46; Avg. Page Number Per Issue - Plates Used 71825; Avg. Page Number Per Issue - Sunday 104; widths 37 1/2; Newsprint Used - Short Tons 6139; Printing Ink Used - Black 150490; Printing Ink Used - Color 62223; Printing I
Equipment EDITORIAL: Front-end Software – Baseview, Baseview/IQUE 313.; Editorial Hardware – HP/Compaq; Editorial Printers – APP/Mac LaserWriter 8500 CLASSIFIED: Front-end Software – Baseview/Ad Manager Pro.; Classified Hardware – HP/Compaq; Classified Printers – APP/Mac Laser Writer 8500; Layout Software – DTI/Make-up Sys.; Display Hardware – APP/Mac Network; Display Printers – Canon PRODUCTION: Pagination Software – QPS/QuarkXPress 4.0.4.
Indesign; Production Equipment – 2-ECRM Newsmatic HS PRESSROOM: Line 1 – 7-G/Metroliner (3 decks); Folders – 2-G/3:2; Pasters – 7 MAILROOM: Counter stackers – 5/Quipp-501; Inserters and stuffers – GMA/SLS 1000 (20:1)
2-GMA SLS 3000; Bundle tying machines – 1-Sterling/MR50
3-Dynaric NP-4000; Addressing machine – 1-/KR, Ch/596-552 Quarter folder
1- Cheshire 595; Other equipment –2-Quipp Viper Bottom Wrap BUSINESS COMPUTERS: Business Software – INSI; Business Hardware – 2-IBM/AS-400
Delivery method: Mail, Newsstand, Private Carrier, Racks

WILMINGTON

BROWN PUBLISHING CO., WILMINGTON NEWS JOURNAL

PO Box 25125, Wilmington, Ohio, 45177; gen tel (937) 382-2574; gen fax (937) 382-4392; web site www.wnewsj.com

WILMINGTON NEWS JOURNAL

47 South St., Wilmington, Ohio, 45177; gen tel (937) 382-2574; adv tel (937) 382-2574; ed tel (937) 382-2574; gen fax (937) 382-4392; adv fax (937) 382-4392; ed fax (937) 382-4392; gen e-mail info@wnewsj.com; mhuber@wnewsj.com; adv e-mail skersey@wnewsj.com; ed e-mail info@wnewsj.com; web site www.wnewsj.com
Group: Ohio Community Media LLC
Published: Mon, Tues, Wed, Thur, Fri, Sat
Weekday Frequency: m
Saturday Frequency: m
Circulation: 6,000; 8,000(sat)
Last Audit: Sworn September 30, 2006
Price: 2.50/wk; 130.00/yr.
Advertising: Open inch rate $15.75
News services: AP.
Politics: Republican.
Not Published: New Year; Independence Day; Christmas.
Own facility?: Y
Special Editions: Salt Magazine (Quarterly), Prep Sports (Fall); In Your Prime (Quarterly); Trip Travel Ohio (Semi-yearly); Prep Sports (Spring); Prep Sports (Winter). Clinton County Proud (yearly)
Magazines: USA WEEKEND Magazine (Fri). American Profile, Spry, Relish
Profile: Publishes 5 days/wk (tue-sat) newspaper for Clinton County abd TMC on Monday.
Publisher .... Pamela Stricker
Adv. Dir. .... Sharon Kersey
Circ. Dir. .... Lori Holcomb
Editor .... Dan Liggett
County Ed. .... Rose Cooper
Online Ed. .... Mark Huber
Graphics Mgr. .... Tina Murdock
Business Office .... Jody Tolle
Assistant Editor .... Margaret Jones
Market Information: ADS; TMC.
Mechanical available: Offset; Black and 3 ROP colors; insert accepted - we-prints, samples; page cutoffs - 22 3/4.
Mechanical Specifications: Type page 13 x 21 1/2; E - 6 cols, 2 1/16, 1/8 between; A - 6 cols, 2 1/16, 1/8 between; C - 8 cols, 1 3/16, 1/16 between.
Commodity Consumption: Avg. Page Number Per Issue - Daily 16; Avg. Page Number Per Issue - Saturday 16; widths 52.
Equipment; Editorial Printers – Software ☐ Baseview/NewsEdit, QPS/QuarkXPress, Adobe/Photoshop. CLASSIFIED: Front-end Software – PBS, QPS/QuarkXPress, PRODUCTION: Pagination Software – QPS/QuarkXPress.; Production Equipment – Caere/OmniPage 610, Xante/Accel-a-Writer 8200; Cameras – 1-B; Scanners – 2-AG/Arcus II
Zip Codes served: 45177 WILMINGTON 45107 BLANCHESTER 45169 SABINA 45113 CLARKSVILLE 45114 CUBA 45135 LEESBURG 45138 LEES CREEK 45142 LYNCHBURG 45146 MARTINSVILLE 45148 MIDLAND 45159 NEW VIENNA 45164 PORT WILLIAM 45166 REESVILLE 45335 JAMESTOWN
Delivery method: Mail, Newsstand, Private Carrier, Racks

WOOSTER

THE DAILY RECORD

210-212 E. Liberty St., Wooster, Ohio, 44691; gen tel (330) 264-1125; gen fax (330) 264-3756; adv e-mail rgeer@dixcom.com; ed e-mail lwhite@the-daily-record.com; web site www.the-daily-record.com

Group: Wooster Republican Printing Company
Published: Mon, Tues, Wed, Thur, Fri, Sat, Sun
Weekday Frequency: m
Saturday Frequency: m
Circulation: 21,093; 20,182(sat); 22,608(sun)
Last Audit: ABC September 30, 2011
Price: 11.50/mo (carrier), $11.95/mo (motor route); 136.15/yr (carrier), $140.85/yr (motor route).
Advertising: Open inch rate $27.85
News services: AP.
Politics: Independent.
Not Published: New Year; Memorial Day; Independence Day; Labor Day; Thanksgiving; Christmas.
Own facility?: Y
Special Editions: Home & Garden (Apr); Wayne County Fair (Aug); Holiday Greetings (Dec); Bridal Showcase (Feb); Bridal Showcase (Jun); Builders (Mar); Senior Memories (May); Cost Cutter (Monthly); Christmas Kick-Off (Nov); At Home (Oct); Football Preview (Sept).
Special Weekly Sections: Business Page (Fri); Farm Page (Tues).
Magazines: TV News (printed in plant) (S); American Profile (Weekly).
Broadcast Affiliations: Radio WKVX-AM; WQKT-FM.
Gen. Mgr. ....William C. McKinney
Adv. Dir. ....Rhonda Geer
Nat'l Adv. Sales ....Randy Wilson
Mng. Ed. ....Lance White
Agriculture Ed. ....Charolette Muenzenberger
Copy Ed. ....Becky Baker
Copy Ed. ....Christina Herrick
Copy Ed. ....Rachel Jackson
Copy Ed. ....Rhonda Rosner
Educ. Ed. ....Linda Hall
Sports Ed. ....Aaron Dorksen
Wire Ed. ....Jeanine kendle
Women's Ed. ....Lydia Gehring
Mgmt. Info Servs. Mgr. ....Dennis Monbarren
Market Information: TMC.
Mechanical available: Offset; Black and 3 ROP colors; insert accepted - slip sheets, samples.
Mechanical Specifications: Type page 12 x 21 1/2; E - 6 cols, 1 5/6, 1/8 between; A - 6 cols, 1 5/6, 1/8 between; C - 9 cols, 1 3/16, 1/8 between.
Commodity Consumption: Avg. Page Number Per Issue - Daily 32; Avg. Page Number Per Issue - Plates Used 10000; Avg. Page Number Per Issue - Saturday 32; Avg. Page Number Per Issue - Sunday 40; widths 12 1/2; Newsprint Used - Short Tons 2200; Printing Ink Used - Black 31305; Pri
Equipment EDITORIAL: Front-end Software – Baseview.; Editorial Hardware – 35-Mac Mini and Mac Books; Editorial Printers – HP/Laser 9040 CLASSIFIED: Front-end Software – APT.; Classified Hardware – 5-APP/iMac; Classified Printers – HP/Laser 4MV DISPLAY: Ad make-up applications – In Design; Display Hardware – 6 - Dual G4s; Display Printers – HP/Laser 9000 PRODUCTION: Pagination Software – Baseview.; Production Equipment – 1-W, APP/Mac Electronic Darkroom-PowerBook; Scanners – 1-Nikon/Coolscan, 4-Microtek/Flatbed, 2-U-Max, 1-Epson, 1-Microtek PRESSROOM: Line 1 – KBA/Comet; Press Drives – EAE; Folders – 2-KBA/Half, 1-KBA/Quarter; Pasters – 5-Amal; Press control system – EAE; Press registration system – Digital. MAILROOM: Counter stackers – 3/QWI 3 Gammeler; Inserters and stuffers – 1-GMA/SLS 2000
1-GMA/SLS 3000; Bundle tying machines – 4 Dynaric; Mailroom control system – Quipp; Addressing machine – 1-/Ch; Other equipment – 1-MM/Stitch-Trim. BUSINESS COMPUTERS: Business Software – APT; Business Hardware – IBM
Delivery method: Private Carrier

XENIA

BEAVERCREEK NEWS-CURRENT

30 S. Detroit St., Xenia, Ohio, 45385; gen tel (937) 879-1840; ed tel (937) 372-4444; gen fax (937) 372-3385; adv fax (937) 372-3385; ed fax (937) 372-1951; web site www.xeniagazette.com

Group: U.S. Suburban Press, Inc.
Published: Mon, Tues, Wed, Thur, Fri, Sat, Sun
Weekday Frequency: e
Saturday Frequency: m
Circulation: 3,805; 3,805(sat)
Last Audit: March 31, 1998
Price: 1.65/wk; 6.60/mo; 85.80/yr.
Advertising: Open inch rate $18.00
News services: AP.
Politics: Independent.
Not Published: New Year; Independence Day; Thanksgiving; Christmas.
Special Editions: Senior Life (Apr); School Bus Schedules (Aug); Gift Guide (Dec); Progress (Feb); Spring Bridal (Jan); Summer Bridal (Jul); Spring/Summer Car Care (Mar); Outdoor Living (May); Greene Co. Winterfest (Nov); Senior Life (Oct); Home Improvement (Sept).
Special Weekly Sections: Church Page (Sat); Entertainment Page (Thur).
Adv. Mgr. ....Barbara Vindevender
Circ. Dir. ....Gina Riefstahl
Ed. ....John Noel
Sports Ed. ....John Rudy
Market Information: TMC.
Mechanical available: Offset; Black and 3 ROP colors; insert accepted; page cutoffs - 22 3/4.
Mechanical Specifications: Type page 13 x 21 1/2; E - 6 cols, 1/6 between; A - 6 cols, 1/6 between; C - 9 cols, 1/6 between.
Commodity Consumption: Avg. Page Number Per Issue - Daily 14.
Equipment EDITORIAL: Front-end Software – QPS/QuarkXPress, Microsoft/Word, Caere/OmniPage, Adobe/Illustrator.; Editorial Hardware – APP/Mac; Editorial Printers – APP/Mac LaserWriter II; Layout Software – APP/Mac.; Display Printers – APP/Mac LaserWriter II; Production Equipment – 1-Nu; Cameras – 1-K/240. PRESSROOM: Line 1 – 3-G/Community; Line 2 – 3-G/Community; Folders – 1-G/2:1, 1-G/3:2. MAILROOM: Counter stackers – 1/BG; Bundle tying machines – 2-/Sa.

FAIRBORN DAILY HERALD

30 S. Detroit St., Xenia, Ohio, 45385; gen tel (937) 879-1840; adv tel (937) 372-4444; ed tel (937) 372-4444; gen fax (937) 372-1951; adv fax (937) 372-3385; ed fax (937) 372-1951; ed e-mail editor@xeniagazette.com; web site www.fairborndailyherald.com

Group: Ohio Newspaper Services, Inc.
Published: Mon, Tues, Wed, Thur, Fri, Sat
Weekday Frequency: e
Circulation: 3,999; 3,999(sat)
Last Audit: March 31, 1999
Price: 85.80/yr.
Advertising: Open inch rate $8.00
News services: AP, U.S. Suburban Press Inc..
Politics: Independent.
Not Published: New Year; Memorial Day; Independence Day; Labor Day; Christmas.
Special Editions: Private Property (Apr); Sidewalk Days (Jul); Business Directory (Mar); Car Care (May); Christmas Kick-Off (Nov); Home Improvement (Oct).
Magazines: USA WEEKEND Magazine (Sat).
Pub. ....Jon M. Noel
Adv. Dir. ....Barb Vandeventer
Circ. Dir. ....Gina Riefstahl
Sports Ed. ....John Rudy
Market Information: Split run; TMC.
Mechanical available: Offset; Black and 3 ROP colors; insert accepted; page cutoffs - 21 3/4.
Mechanical Specifications: Type page 13 x 21 1/2; E - 6 cols, 2 1/16, 1/8 between; A - 6 cols, 2 1/16, 1/8 between; C - 9 cols, 2 1/16, 1/8 between.
Commodity Consumption: Avg. Page Number Per Issue - Daily 20; Newsprint Used - Short Tons 1600.
Equipment; Editorial Hardware – APP/Mac; Editorial Equipment – Software ÂŒ Microsoft/Word, QPS.; Classified Hardware – APP/Mac.; Layout Software – APP/Mac.; Production Equipment – COM/MCS 8400, Linotype-Hell/Linotronic 101; Cameras – 1-B, 1-K/Vertical. PRESSROOM: Line 1 – 9-G/Suburban; Line 2 – 9-G/Suburban; Folders – 4 MAILROOM: Counter stackers – 1-MM/5 Station; Bundle tying machines – 2/Bu.; Business Hardware – IBM/PC

GREENE COUNTY DAILIES

30 S. Detroit St., Xenia, Ohio, 45385; gen tel (937) 372-4444; gen fax (937) 372-3385; adv fax (937) 372-1951; ed fax (937) 372-1951; gen e-mail editor@xeniagazette.com; web site www.xeniagazette.com

Group: Ohio Community Media
Published: Mon, Tues, Wed, Thur, Fri, Sat, Sun
Weekday Frequency: m
Saturday Frequency: m
Circulation: 5,858; 6,000(sat)
Last Audit: March 31, 2003
News services: AP
Not Published: Christmas, New Years Day
Own facility?: N
Publisher ....Mike Savage
Delivery method: Mail, Newsstand, Private Carrier

YOUNGSTOWN

THE VINDICATOR

Vindicator Sq., Youngstown, Ohio, 44503; gen tel (330) 747-1471; adv tel (330) 747-1471 ; ed tel (330) 747-1471; gen fax (330) 747-03999; adv fax (330) 747-3536; ed fax (330) 747-6712; ed e-mail news@vindy.com; web site www.vindy.com

Published: Mon, Tues, Wed, Thur, Fri, Sat, Sun
Weekday Frequency: m
Saturday Frequency: m
Circulation: 44,952; 53,978(sat); 60,662(sun)
Last Audit: ABC September 30, 2011
Price: 3.05/wk; 158.60/yr.
Advertising: $36.57 daily $52.94 Sun
Insert rate: $43.50/1000
News services: AP, CT, LAT-WP, MCT,
Politics: 1869
Advertising not accepted: Y
Own facility?: Y
Special Editions: How-to Section (Apr); Blitz High School Football Preview (Aug); Winter Destinations (Dec); Business Outlook (Feb); Bridal Planner (Jan); YSU Festival of the Arts (Jul); Destinations (Jun); Youngstown Jewish Community Center (Mar); Destinations (May); Holiday Gift Guide
Special Weekly Sections: Vibe entertainment
Magazines: Parade (S); TV Week (Sat).
Broadcast Affiliations: WFMJ (NBC).
Pres./Pub./Treasurer ....Betty H. Brown Jagnow
Vice Pres./Gen. Mgr./Sec./Asst. Treasurer Mark A. Brown
Asst. Gen. Mgr. ....Ted E. Suffolk
Personnel Mgr./Labor Rel. ....Robert Wiseman
Adv. Dir. ....Daniel Kasten
Adv. Mgr., Classified ....Dale Gresko
Adv. Mgr., Retail ....Lisa Arter
Promo. Mgr. ....Nena Perkins
Circ. Dir. ....David Enoch
Mng. Ed. ....Mark Sweetwood
Editorial Page Ed. ....Dennis Mangan
Editorial Writer ....Bertram deSouza
Education Ed. ....Harold Gwin
Garden Ed. ....Shirley Sallmen
Graphics Ed./Art Dir. ....Robert McFerren
Health/Medical Ed. ....Bill Alcorn
Living/Lifestyle Ed. ....Barbara Shaffer
Market Information: Split run.
Mechanical available: Offset Press; Black and 3 ROP colors; insert accepted; page cutoffs - 22 3/4.
Mechanical Specifications: Type page 10 7/8 x 21 1/2; E - 6 cols, 1 23/32, 1/8 between; A - 6 cols, 1 23/32, 1/8 between; C - 9 cols, 1 3/32, 1/8 between.
Commodity Consumption: Avg. PageNumber Per Issue - Daily 32; Avg. Page Number Per Issue - Sunday 100.
Equipment EDITORIAL: Front-end Software – Baseview/NewsEdit Pro IQUE with Hot Back Up.; Editorial Hardware – 2-Mac/G4 800 MHZ, 2-Apple/Power; Editorial Equipment – 80-APP/Mac G3; Editorial Printers – Ricoh/3800c CLASSIFIED: Front-end Software – Baseview 2.05, ClassFlow XT2-1B10, AMP 2.6.; Classified Hardware – 17-APP/Mac G4-400, APP/Mac G3 450; Classified Equipment – X/7017 automatic fax, 14-IBM/Selectric, 1-HI/Composition; Classified Printers – Centronics/351, HP/Rugged Writer, HP/4000 DISPLAY: Ad make-up applications – Baseview/Managing Editor ALS, CJ, Multi-Ad/Creator 4.0; Layout Software – MEI/ALS.; Display Hardware – APP/Power Mac G3, APP/Power Mac 63, 3-APP/Mac G4, 3-imac; Display Printers – HP/LaserJet 4MV, HP/LaserJet 5, Ricoh 4500 PRODUCTION: Pagination Software – XP 21, QPS/QuarkXPress 4.04, Baseview/Drag X with News Edit Pro, Qtools 98.; Production Equipment – 2-MON/1016, 1-LE, 1-News Express 1200, 1-HP 1050C, 1-Prepress Patara 62; Scanners – 3-ECR PRESSROOM: Line 1 – 9-G/Mark II Double Width 1972; Line 2 – 9-G/Mark II Double Width 1972; Folders – G/Imperial 3:2; Pasters – 18-1972; Reels and Stands – 18-1972. MAILROOM: Counter stackers – 2/QWI Sport, 2-/QWI 400; Inserters and stuffers – 1-H/630; Bundle tying machines – 8-/Sterling; Mailroom control system – 1-/HI. BUSINESS COMPUTERS: Business Software – Cort, CJ/Geac; Business Hardware – 1-HP/3000 928LX
Delivery method: Mail, Newsstand, Private Carrier, Racks

THE VINDICATOR PRINTING CO.

Vindicator Sq., Youngstown, Ohio, 44501-0780; gen tel (330) 747-1471

ZANESVILLE

TIMES RECORDER

34 S. Fourth St., Zanesville, Ohio, 43701; gen tel (740) 452-4561; adv tel (740) 452-4561; ed tel (740) 452-4561; gen fax (740) 450-6780; adv fax (740) 450-6780; ed fax (740) 450-6759; web site www.zanesvilletimesrecorder.com

Published: Mon, Tues, Wed, Thur, Fri, Sat, Sun
Weekday Frequency: m
Saturday Frequency: m
Circulation: 12,996; 13,213(sat); 15,610(sun)
Last Audit: ABC September 30, 2011
Price: 3.10/wk; 12.80/mo (motor route); 141.60/yr (delivery), $175.20/yr (mail).
Advertising: Open inch rate $35.50
News services: Landon Media Group, Newspapers Now, Gannett, NEA, TMS, GNS.
Politics: Independent. **Established:** 1852
Special Editions: Car Care (Apr); County Fair (Aug); Progress (Feb); Bridal (Jan); Bridal (Jun); Spring Sports (Mar); Graduation (May); Reader's Choice (Nov); Fall Sports (Sept).
Special Weekly Sections: House & Home (S).
Magazines: USA WEEKEND Magazine (S).
Gen. Mgr. ....Rick Szabrak
Adv. Dir. ....Brandie Davisson
Adv. Mgr., Display Sales ....Terry Tokie
Mktg. Research Analyst ....Sharon Walker
Mng. Ed. ....Pam James
Reporter ....Brian Gadd
Educ. Ed. ....Tonya Shipley
Photo Ed. ....Trevor Jones
Presentation Ed. ....Rick Harrison
Market Information: ADS; TMC.
Mechanical available: Offset; Black and 3 ROP colors; insert accepted - catabooks, coupon envelopes; page cutoffs - 22 3/4.
Mechanical Specifications: Type page 11 1/16 x 21; E - 6 cols, 1 5/6, 1/8 between; A - 6 cols, 1 4/5, 1/8 between; C - 6 cols, 1 4/5, 1/8 between.
Commodity Consumption: Avg. Page Number Per

Issue - Daily 24; Avg. Page Number Per Issue - Plates Used 6770; Avg. Page Number Per Issue - Saturday 20; Avg. Page Number Per Issue - Sunday 32; widths 25; Newsprint Used - Short Tons 1530; Printing Ink Used - Black 45500; Printing
Equipment EDITORIAL: Front-end Software – Mk.; Editorial Hardware – Mk; Editorial Printers – Xante CLASSIFIED: Front-end Software – CText/Alps, Baseview/Alps.; Classified Hardware – PCs; Classified Printers – Xante DISPLAY: Ad make-up applications – QPS/QuarkXPress, Adobe/Photoshop 4.0; Layout Software – APP/Mac.; Display Hardware – APP/Mac; Display Printers – Xante PRODUCTION: Pagination Software – QPS/QuarkXPress, Adobe/Acrobat 3.1.; Production Equipment – V/5160; Scanners – Polaroid/SprintScan 35, AG BUSINESS COMPUTERS: Business Software – PBS; Business Hardware – Windows 95, Gateway/PC

OKLAHOMA

ADA

ADA EVENING NEWS

116 N. Broadway, Ada, Okla., 74820; gen tel (580) 332-4433; adv tel (580) 310-7502; ed tel (580) 310-7550; gen fax (580) 332-8734; adv fax (580) 332-8841; ed fax (580) 332-8841; gen e-mail adanews@swbell.net; adv e-mail adaadv@swbell.net; web site www.adaeveningnews.com
Published: Mon, Tues, Wed, Thur, Fri, Sun
Weekday Frequency: e
Circulation: 7,879; 7,879(sun)
Last Audit: September 30, 2005
Price: 7.80/mo (city), $7.95/mo (RTZ); 98.50/yr (city), $95.00/yr (RTZ).
Advertising: Open inch rate $17.10
News services: AP.
Politics: Independent.
Not Published: Memorial Day; Independence Day; Labor Day.
Special Editions: Christmas (Dec); Football (Fall); Newcomer's Guide (Other).
Special Weekly Sections: Religion (Fri); Business (Mon); Real Estate (S); Education (Tues); Best Food Day (Wed).
Magazines: Sunday Comics (S).
Pub. ....H. Lone Beasley
Accountant ....Susan Pinley
Adv. Dir. ....Angie Love
Circ. Dir. ....Dawn Keathley
Lifestyle Ed. ....Brenda Tollett
Photo Ed. ....Richard R. Baaron
Sports Ed. ....Jeff Cali
Travel/Women's Ed. ....Talina Turner
Prodn. Mgr., Pressroom ....James Mouser
Market Information: ADS; TMC.
Mechanical available: Offset; Black and 3 ROP colors; insert accepted; page cutoffs - 22 7/8.
Mechanical Specifications: Type page 13 x 21 1/2; E - 6 cols, 2 1/16, 1/8 between; A - 6 cols, 2 1/16, 1/8 between; C - 9 cols, 1 3/8, 1/16 between.
Commodity Consumption: Avg. Page Number Per Issue - Daily 16; Avg. Page Number Per Issue - Sunday 32; widths 25; Newsprint Used - Short Tons 300; Printing Ink Used - Black 1000; Printing Ink Used - Color 50.
Equipment EDITORIAL: Front-end Software – QPS/QuarkXPress 3.32, Aldus/PageMaker; Editorial Hardware – Ofoto, Ethernet, Nikon/Coolscan 35-mm, APP/Mac G3 266; Editorial Equipment – 3-APP/Power Mac 7200 Layout Station; Editorial Printers – APP/Mac LaserWriter 16-600, HP/LaserJet 4MV, Xante/3N, ECR/Scriptsetter VRL 36 CLASSIFIED: Front-end Software – Baseview/Class Manager Pro 3.0.; Classified Hardware – APP/Mac Quadra 660AV, APP/Power Mac 7200; Classified Printers – APP/Mac LaserWriter NTX, Okidata/Pro 300LP DISPLAY: Ad make-up applications – Multi-Ad/Creator, QPS/QuarkXPress 3.32, Adobe/Photoshop 5.0; Display Hardware – APP/Power Mac 7200, APP/Mac Centris 650, APP/Mac Quadra 650AV, APP/Mac Performa 6200; Display Printers – HP/LaserJet 4MV PRODUCTION: Pagination Software – QPS 3.3.; Production Equipment – 2-APP/Mac LaserWriter NTX, APP/Mac LaserWriter IIg, APP/Mac LaserWriter 600-16, HP/LaserJet 4MV, ECR/VRL 36; Cameras – Acti; Scanners – APP/Mac OneScan PRESSROOM: Line 1 – 6-KP/News King.; Bundle tying machines – Akebono. BUSINESS COMPUTERS: Business Software – Vision Data/6.0, Microsoft/Office 97; Business Hardware – Compaq, WYSE, Unix/SCO Server

ALTUS

ALTUS TIMES

218 W. Commerce St., Altus, Okla., 73521; gen tel (580) 482-1221; gen fax (580) 482-5709; adv e-mail advertising@altustimes.com; ed e-mail editor@altustimes.com; web site www.altustimes.com
Published: Tues, Wed, Thur, Fri, Sun
Weekday Frequency: e
Circulation: 4,591; 4,591(sun)
Last Audit: September 29, 2003
Price: 7.00/mo; 84.00/yr.
Advertising: Open inch rate $8.80
News services: AP.
Politics: Independent.
Not Published: Christmas.
Special Weekly Sections: TV Listings (S); Best Food Day (Wed).
Magazines: USA WEEKEND Magazine (Fri); American Profile (Weekly).
Adv. Dir. ....Bill Murphy
Circ. Dir. ....Sandy Graham
Editorial Page Ed. ....Mike Bush
Sports Ed. ....Mark Glenn
Prodn. Supt. ....Jonathan Wetz
Market Information: TMC; Zoned editions.
Mechanical available: Offset; Black and 3 ROP colors; insert accepted; page cutoffs - 22 3/4.
Mechanical Specifications: Type page 13 x 21 1/2; E - 6 cols, 2 1/14, 1/6 between; A - 6 cols, 2 1/14, 1/6 between; C - 8 cols, 1 2/3, 1/6 between.
Commodity Consumption: Avg. Page Number Per Issue - Daily 16; Avg. Page Number Per Issue - Sunday 78; widths 25.
Equipment EDITORIAL: Front-end Software – Aldus/PageMaker 4.2.; Editorial Hardware – APP/Mac; Editorial Printers – APP/Mac; Classified Hardware – APP/Mac; Classified Printers – APP/Mac. DISPLAY: Ad make-up applications – Aldus/PageMaker 4.2, Multi-Ad/Creator 3.8; Layout Software – APP/Mac, PC.; Display Printers – APP/Mac NTX 360 Pro, HP/Laser; Production Equipment – 1-Nu; Cameras – R. PRESSROOM: Line 1 – 5-G/Community 1969.; Bundle tying machines – MLN/MCD-700; Addressing machine – Label/4 Across.

ALVA

ALVA REVIEW-COURIER

620 Choctaw St., Alva, Okla., 73717; gen tel (580) 327-2200; gen fax (580) 327-2454; gen e-mail manager@alvareviewcourier.net; adv e-mail sales@alvareviewcourier.net; ed e-mail news@alvareviewcourier.net; web site www.alvareviewcourier.com
Published: Wed, Fri, Sun
Weekday Frequency: m
Circulation: 1,900
Last Audit: Sworn October 3, 2003
Price: 8.00/mo; 96.00/yr.
Advertising: Open inch rate $5.20
Insert rate: 62.50/M
News services: AP.
Politics: Independent.
Not Published: Mon,Tue,Thu,Sat
Own facility?: Y
Special Editions: Back-to-School (Aug); Christmas (Dec); Basketball (Jan); Graduation (May).
Special Weekly Sections: Church News (Fri).
Ed. ....Marione Martin
Editorial Page Ed. ....Lynn L. Martin
Sports Ed. ....Roger McKenzie
News Editor ....Jim Stout
Mechanical available: Offset; Black and 3 ROP colors; insert accepted; page cutoffs - 16.
Mechanical Specifications: Type page 11 x 17; E - 5 cols, 2 1/16, 1/8 between; A - 5 cols, 2 1/16, 1/8 between; C - 5 cols, 2 1/16, 1/8 between.
Commodity Consumption: Avg. Page Number Per Issue - Daily 12; Avg. Page Number Per Issue - Sunday 16; widths 27 1/2.
Equipment EDITORIAL: Front-end Software – Microsoft Word; Editorial Hardware – 3-PC; Classified Hardware – 1-PC. DISPLAY: Ad make-up applications – Adobe CS5.5, Corel Draw X5; Display Hardware – 3-PC; Display Printers – HP/LaserJet 4; Production Equipment – CTP PRESSROOM: Line 1 – 4-HI/V-15A.; Addressing machine – 1/Am.; Business Hardware – 3-PC
Delivery method: Mail, Newsstand, Private Carrier

ANADARKO

THE ANADARKO DAILY NEWS

115 NE First St., Anadarko, Okla., 73005-0548; gen tel (405) 247-3331; gen fax (405) 247-5571; gen e-mail news@anadarko-news.com
Published: Mon, Tues, Wed, Thur, Fri, Sat
Weekday Frequency: e
Saturday Frequency: m
Circulation: 4,000; 4,000(sat)
Last Audit: Sworn March 31, 2006
Price: 7.50/mo, $6.00/mo (snr citizen); 72.00/yr (carrier), $75.00/yr (mail).
Advertising: $7.50 PCI
Insert rate: $60 CPM Single
News services: AP, NEA.
Politics: Independent. **Established:** 1901
Not Published: New Year; Memorial Day; Independence Day; Labor Day; Christmas.
Own facility?: Y
Special Editions: American Indian Exposition (Aug); Farm Tab (Mar); Visitor's Guide (May).
Co-Pub./Co-Owner ....Joe W. McBride
Mktg./Promo. ....Carla McBride-Alexander
Circ. Mgr. ....Philip Gomez
Weekender Ed. ....Carolyn N. McBride
Mechanical available: Offset; Black and 3 ROP colors; insert accepted; page cutoffs - 22 3/4.
Mechanical Specifications: Type page 13 5/16 x 21; E - 6 cols, 2 1/6, 1/6 between; A - 6 cols, 2 1/6, 1/6 between; C - 8 cols, 1 2/3, 1/6 between.
Commodity Consumption: Avg. Page Number Per Issue - Daily 13; Avg. Page Number Per Issue - Plates Used 3000; Avg. Page Number Per Issue - Saturday 10; widths 30; Newsprint Used - Short Tons 160; Printing Ink Used - Black 3800; Printing Ink Used - Color 210; Printing Ink Used -
Equipment EDITORIAL: Front-end Software – Quark XPress; Editorial Hardware – Apple; Editorial Printers – HP5200 CLASSIFIED: Front-end Software – Quark XPress; Classified Hardware – Apple; Classified Printers – HP5200 DISPLAY: Ad make-up applications – Quark XPress; Display Hardware – Apple; Display Printers – HP5200 PRODUCTION: Pagination Software – PhotoShop; Production Equipment – Apple; Scanners – Cannon PRESSROOM: Line 1 – 3-G/Community 1965, 1-G/Community 1984; Folders – G/Community.; Bundle tying machines – Miller-Bevco/Bun Strapper; Addressing machine – KAN. BUSINESS COMPUTERS: Business Software – Quark XPress, Acclivity, PhotoShop; Business Hardware – Apple

ARDMORE

THE DAILY ARDMOREITE

117 W. Broadway, Ardmore, Okla., 73401; gen tel (580) 223-2200; adv tel (580) 221-6501; ed tel (580) 221-6593; gen fax (580) 226-2363; adv fax (580) 223-3604; ed fax (580) 226-0050; gen e-mail news@ardmoreite.com; adv e-mail lisa.wilkinson@ardmoreite.com; web site www.ardmoreite.com
Published: Mon, Tues, Wed, Thur, Fri, Sat, Sun
Weekday Frequency: e
Circulation: 7,845; 7,845(sat); 7,845(sun)
Last Audit: September 30, 2011
Price: 8.00/mo; 92.00/yr (mai), $102.00/yr (carrier).
Advertising: Open inch rate $11.25
News services: AP.
Politics: Independent. **Established:** 1898
Special Editions: Fashion (Fall); Fashion (Spring).
Special Weekly Sections: Restaurant (Fri); Weddings/Engagements (S); Kids Page (Thur); Senior Lifestyles (Tues); Business (Wed).
Magazines: Relish (Monthly); Carousel (local, newsprint) (S); American Profile (Weekly).
Pub. ....Kim Benedict
Adv. Dir. ....Lisa Wilkinson
Circ. Mgr. ....Joe JHornbeck
News Ed. ....Marsha Miller
Online Ed. ....Shane Porter
Photo Dept. Mgr. ....Don Alquist
Data Processing Mgr. ....Kathy Worley
Prodn. Mgr. ....Charle Amons
Prodn. Mgr., Pressroom ....Bill Scruggs
Market Information: ADS; TMC.
Mechanical available: Offset; Black and 3 ROP colors; insert accepted - post cards, placards, etc.; page cutoffs - 22 3/4.
Mechanical Specifications: Type page 11 5/8 x 21 1/2; E - 6 cols, 1 5/6, 1/8 between; A - 6 cols, 1 5/6, 1/8 between; C - 8 cols, 1 1/2, 1/8 between.
Commodity Consumption: Avg. Page Number Per Issue - Daily 24; Avg. Page Number Per Issue - Plates Used 20000; Avg. Page Number Per Issue - Sunday 48; widths 25; Newsprint Used - Short Tons 800; Printing Ink Used - Black 20000; Printing Ink Used - Color 400; Printing Ink Used -
Equipment EDITORIAL: Front-end Software – Baseview, NewsEdit/Pro, QPS/QuarkXPress 4.1, Adobe/Photoshop 5.0.; Editorial Hardware – APP/Mac; Editorial Equipment – 1-APP/Mac; Editorial Printers – APP/Mac LaserWriter, MON/ExpressMaster 1270 CLASSIFIED: Front-end Software – Baseview, Class Manager/Plus, Adobe/Creator 4.03, Quark/Xpress 4.1.; Classified Hardware – APP/Mac; Classified Printers – APP/Mac LaserWriter NTX, Mon/Express Master 1270 DISPLAY: Ad make-up applications – Multi-Ad/Creator 4.0.3, Adobe/Photoshop 5.0, QPS/QuarkXPress 4.1; Layout Software – ALS.; Display Hardware – APP/Mac, CD, APP/Power Mac, Mk/Scanmaker II, APP/Mac; Display Printers – MON/Express Master 1270 PRODUCTION: Pagination Software – QPS/QuarkXPress 3.32.; Production Equipment – APP/Power Mac G3, 1-Richmond, P/26ML, Devotech 28 RA; Cameras – 1-LE/500, R; Scanners – APP/Mac Scanner Flat Top, Nikon/Scantouch PRESSROOM: Line 1 – 9-G; Line 2 – G/Community; Folders – 1; Press registration system – Duarte/Pin.; Inserters and stuffers – 6/MM; Bundle tying machines – 1-/Sa, 1-/Strapack; Addressing machine – Ch. BUSINESS COMPUTERS: Business Software – GEAC; Business Hardware – Epson/Tower, SMS/Stauffer Gold

BARTLESVILLE

EXAMINER-ENTERPRISE

4125 Nowata Rd., Bartlesville, Okla., 74006; gen tel (918) 335-8200; adv tel (918) 335-8252; ed tel (918) 335-8244; gen fax (918) 335-3111; adv fax (918) 335-3111; ed fax (918) 335-0601; gen e-mail examiner@examiner-enterprise.com; adv e-mail classads@examiner-enterprise.com; ed e-mail

examiner@examiner-enterprise.com; web site www.examiner-enterprise.com
Published: Mon, Tues, Wed, Thur, Fri, Sun
Weekday Frequency: e
Circulation: 10,075; 11,599(sun)
Last Audit: September 30, 2008
Price: 8.35/mo; 109.80/yr.
Advertising: Open inch rate $23.59
News services: AP.
Politics: Independent.
Special Editions: Tourism Guide (Apr); Christmas (Dec); Customer Appreciation (Jan); OK Mozart (Jun); Progress (Mar); Christmas (Nov); Our Hometown (Oct).
Special Weekly Sections: Church (Fri); Real Estate Guide (Other); Travel Page (S); Arts & Entertainment (Thur); Business (Wed).
Magazines: USA WEEKEND Magazine (S); American Profile (Weekly).
Pub. .... Jerry Quinn
Adv. Dir. .... Tom Bradley
Adv. Mgr., Classified .... Peggy Sanders
Adv. Acct. Exec. .... Janet Robinson
Adv. Acct. Exec. .... Jeannie Strachan
Circ. Dir. .... Richard Yakle
Mng. Ed. .... Kelli Williams
Community Ed. .... Susan Albert
Features Ed. .... Deanna Evans
Sports Ed. .... Mike Tupa
Systems Mgr. .... J. Hughey
Prodn. Mgr. .... Fawn Pooacha
Market Information: Split run; TMC.
Mechanical available: Offset; Black and 3 ROP colors; insert accepted - single sheets; page cutoffs - 22 3/4.
Mechanical Specifications: Type page 13 x 21 1/2; E - 6 cols, 2 1/16, 1/8 between; A - 6 cols, 2 1/16, 1/8 between; C - 9 cols, 1 3/8, 1/8 between.
Commodity Consumption: Avg. Page Number Per Issue - Daily 24; Avg. Page Number Per Issue - Plates Used 10000; Avg. Page Number Per Issue - Sunday 40; widths 27 1/4; Newsprint Used - Metric Tons 720; Printing Ink Used - Black 36000; Printing Ink Used - Color 2500.
Equipment EDITORIAL: Front-end Software – Baseview.; Editorial Hardware – APP/Mac; Editorial Printers – HP/4 MV, HP/4V, Pre Press/Panther Plus Imagesetter CLASSIFIED: Front-end Software – Baseview.; Classified Hardware – APP/Mac; Classified Printers – 2-HP/4V 4MV, 2-Pre Press/Panther Plus Imagesetters DISPLAY: Ad make-up applications – Baseview.; Display Hardware – APP/Mac; Display Printers – 2-HP/4V 4MV PRODUCTION: Pagination Software – Baseview.; Production Equipment – Nu/Plate Maker, Lf/AP Leaf Picture Desk; Cameras – C/Spartan III; Scanners – AG/Studio Stars PRESSROOM: Line 1 – 8-G/Urbanite single width 1962; Press Drives – 2-Fin/75 h.p.; Folders – 1; Reels and Stands – 16, 2. MAILROOM: Counter stackers – HL/Monitor; Inserters and stuffers – KAN; Bundle tying machines – MLN; Mailroom control system – BG/Count-O-Veyor, 2-MLN/Strapping Machines. BUSINESS COMPUTERS: Business Software – Lotus 1-2-3, Orchestrator; Business Hardware – SCS

BLACKWELL

BLACKWELL JOURNAL-TRIBUNE

113 E. Blackwell Ave., Blackwell, Okla., 74631; gen tel (580) 363-3370; adv tel (580) 363-3370; ed tel (580) 363-3370; gen fax (580) 363-4415; adv fax (580) 363-4415; ed fax (580) 363-4415; gen e-mail news@grcnet.net; adv e-mail ads@grcnet.net; ed e-mail news@grcnet.net; blackwellnews@grc.com
Published: Wed, Fri, Sun
Last Audit: March 21, 2008
Price: 6.00/mo, $6.25/mo (auto); 72.00/yr.
Advertising: Open inch rate $6.70
News services: AP.
Politics: 1893
Not Published: Thanksgiving; Christmas.
Special Editions: Tulips-A-Bloom (Apr); Crazy Days (Aug); Veteran's Day (Dec); Valentines

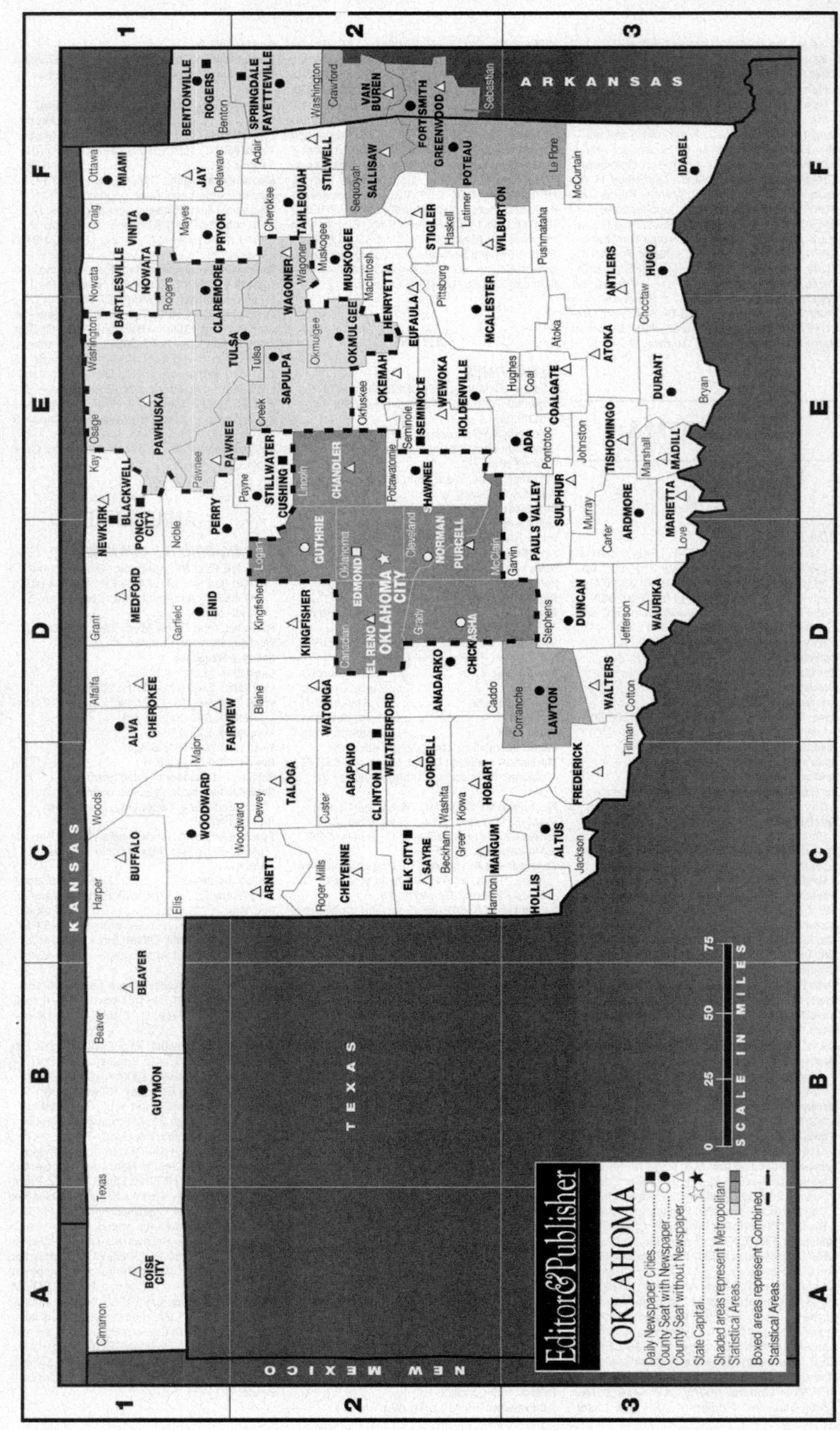

Day (Feb); Chamber of Commerce Ed. (Jan); July 4th (Jul); Rod Run (Jun); St. Patrick's Day (Mar); Graduation (May); Kay County Fair (Sept).
Special Weekly Sections: Church Pages (Fri); Food Pages (Wed).
Office Mgr. ....Monica Moore
Adv. Mgr. ....Julie Cassady
Circ. Mgr. ....Bill Johnson
Editorial Page Ed. ....Mark Evans
Home Furnishings Ed. ....Charles Abbott
Sports Ed. ....Gary Smith
Prodn. Supt., Pressroom ....John Franz
Mechanical available: Offset; Black and 1 ROP colors; insert accepted - standing cards; page cutoffs - 22 3/4.
Mechanical Specifications: Type page 13 x 21 1/2; E - 6 cols, 2 1/16, 1/8 between; A - 6 cols, 2 1/16, 1/8 between; C - 8 cols, 1 1/2, 1/16 between.
Commodity Consumption: Avg. Page Number Per Issue - Daily 8; Avg. Page Number Per Issue - Sunday 12; widths 13 1/2; Newsprint Used - Metric Tons 59; Printing Ink Used - Black 1125; Printing Ink Used - Color 50; Printing Ink Used - Pages Printed 2326.
Equipment EDITORIAL: Front-end Software – Baseview/NewsEdit Pro, QPS/QuarkXPress, Microsoft/Word, Adobe/Photoshop.; Editorial Hardware – Mk/Mycro-Comp 1100, APP/Mac 7500; Editorial Equipment – Polaroid/Photoscan, Epson/Scanner; Editorial Printers – 2-APP/Mac LaserWriter, Xante/Accel-a-Writer 8200 CLASSIFIED: Front-end Software – Baseview/Class Manager Pro 1.0.5A.; Classified Hardware – APP/Mac 7200; Classified Printers – Okidata/320 DISPLAY: Ad make-up applications – QPS/QuarkXPress, Adobe/Illustrator, Microsoft/Word, Adobe/Photoshop, Microtek/Scanmaker 600ZS; Layout Software – APP/Mac 7500.; Display Hardware – APP/Mac IIci, APP/Mac 7500; Display Printers – Xante/Accel-a-Writer 8200 PRODUCTION: Pagination Software – NEPro/Native, DragZ, QPS/Q-Tools, QPS/Quark-Native, Baseview/NewsEdit Pro.; Production Equipment – Xante/Accel-a-Writer 8200; Cameras – 1-R/Centurion PRESSROOM: Line 1 – 5-G/Community 1972.; Bundle tying machines – Miller-Bevco.

CHICKASHA

CHICKASHA EXPRESS STAR

PO Box E, Chickasha, Okla., 73023-0835; gen tel (405) 224-2600; web site chickashanews.com

THE EXPRESS-STAR

302 N. Third St., Chickasha, Okla., 73018; gen tel (405) 224-2600; gen fax (405) 224-7087; gen e-mail publisher@chickashanews.com; adv e-mail advertising@chickashanews.com; ed e-mail editor@chickashanews.com; web site www.chickashanews.com
Published: Mon, Tues, Wed, Thur, Fri, Sun
Weekday Frequency: m
Circulation: 6,100; 6,300(sun)
Last Audit: March 31, 2006
Price: 7.50/mo; 81.00/yr.
Advertising: Open inch rate $9.01
News services: AP.
Politics: 1892
Not Published: Christmas.
Special Editions: Fall Fashion (Aug); Progress (Feb); Christmas Gift Guides (Nov).
Special Weekly Sections: Farm Page (Wed).
Magazines: Relish (Monthly); TV Marquee (S).
Circ. Mgr. ....Vonnie Clark
Mailroom Supvr. ....Robin Rogers
Publisher ....Mark Millsap
Business Manager ....Kathy Black
Editor ....DeSilver-Terry Debi
Mechanical available: Offset; Black and 3 ROP colors; insert accepted; page cutoffs - 22 3/4.
Mechanical Specifications: Type page 13 x 21 1/2; E - 6 cols, 2 1/16, 1/8 between; A - 6 cols, 2 1/16, 1/8 between; C - 8 cols, 1 5/8, 1/8 between.
Commodity Consumption: Avg. Page Number Per Issue - Daily 10; Avg. Page Number Per Issue - Plates Used 3000; Avg. Page Number Per Issue - Sunday 30; widths 13 3/4; Newsprint Used - Metric Tons 220; Printing Ink Used - Black 8000; Printing Ink Used - Color 250; Printing Ink Use
Equipment; Folders – 1

CLAREMORE

THE CLAREMORE DAILY PROGRESS

315 W. Will Rogers Blvd., Claremore, Okla., 74017-7021; gen tel (918) 341-1101; adv tel (918) 341-1101; ed tel (918) 341-1101; gen fax (918) 341-1131; adv fax (918) 341-0838; gen e-mail publisher@claremoreprogress.com; adv e-mail addir@claremoreprogress.com; ed e-mail editor@claremoreprogress.com; web site www.claremoreprogress.com
Published: Mon, Tues, Wed, Thur, Fri, Sun
Weekday Frequency: e
Circulation: 5,500; 6,500(sun)
Last Audit: Sworn March 31, 2006
Price: 6.50/mo; 78.00/yr (carrier), $96.00/yr (mail); 39.00/6mo.
Advertising: Open inch rate $10.48
News services: AP, NEA, TMS.
Politics: Independent. **Established:** 1893
Own facility?: Y
Special Weekly Sections: Church (Fri); Health (S); Best Food Day (Wed).
Magazines: Relish (Monthly); American Profile (S).
Pub. ....Bailey Dabney
Adv. Dir. ....Cinda Vaughan
Exec. Ed ....Rebecca Hattaway
County Ed. ....Tom Fink
Ed. ....Randy Cowling
Bus. Mgr. ....Almetha Sizemore
HR Mgr. ....Sheila Knight
Market Information: TMC.
Mechanical available: Offset; Black and 3 ROP colors; insert accepted - hi-fi, spectacolor, speed 12; page cutoffs - 22 1/2.
Mechanical Specifications: Type page 13 x 21 1/2; E - 6 cols, 2 1/16, 1/8 between; A - 6 cols, 2 1/16, 1/8 between; C - 6 cols, 2 1/16, 1/8 between.
Commodity Consumption: Avg. Page Number Per Issue - Daily 22; Avg. Page Number Per Issue - Plates Used 5000; Avg. Page Number Per Issue - Sunday 36; widths 12 1/2; Newsprint Used - Short Tons 252; Printing Ink Used - Black 25000; Printing Ink Used - Color 1250; Printing Ink Us
Equipment EDITORIAL: Front-end Software – Mk.; Editorial Hardware – Mk; Classified Hardware – Mk; Classified Equipment – 1-DEC/LA 80.; Layout Software – APP/Mac II.; Display Hardware – Mk/Ad Builder; Production Equipment – 1-Mk/AdWriter; Cameras – 1-R; Scanners – 2-COM. PRESSROOM: Line 1 – 8-G/Community; Folders – 1; Inserters and stuffers – Kansa/420; Bundle tying machines – 2/Bu; Addressing machine – 1-/Am.; Business Hardware – 1-DPT/8200
Delivery method: Mail, Newsstand, Private Carrier, Racks

CLINTON

THE CLINTON DAILY NEWS

522 Avant Ave., Clinton, Okla., 73601-3436; gen tel (580) 323-5151; gen fax (580) 323-5154; gen e-mail cdnews@swbell.net; web site www.clintondailynews.com
Published: Mon, Tues, Wed, Thur, Fri, Sun
Weekday Frequency: e
Circulation: 4,463; 4,106(sun)
Last Audit: September 30, 2005
Price: 82.00/yr (carrier).
Advertising: Open inch rate $8.90
News services: AP.
Politics: Independent. **Established:** 1901
Not Published: New Year; Martin Luther King Jr. Day; Presidents' Day; Memorial Day; Independence Day; Labor Day; Columbus Day; Thanksgiving; Christmas (except when holidays other than Thanksgiving fall on Thur.).
Special Weekly Sections: Business (S); Legal (Thur).
Vice Pres. ....Carol Sander
Adv. Mgr., Classified ....Polly Powers
Adv. Mgr., Nat'l ....Christopher Crabtree
Circ. Mgr. ....Cindy Gagne
Ed. ....Rod Serfoss
News Ed. ....Steve Belcher
Photograher ....Robert Bryan
Sports Ed. ....Sean Stephens
Prodn. Supt. ....Eric Hunter
Market Information: TMC.
Mechanical available: Offset; Black and 2 ROP colors; insert accepted; page cutoffs - 22 3/4.
Mechanical Specifications: Type page 13 x 21 1/2; E - 6 cols, 2 1/16, 1/8 between; A - 6 cols, 2 1/16, 1/8 between; C - 8 cols, 1 1/2, 1/8 between.
Commodity Consumption: Avg. Page Number Per Issue - Daily 18; Avg. Page Number Per Issue - Plates Used 5000; Avg. Page Number Per Issue - Sunday 30; widths 30; Newsprint Used - Short Tons 324; Printing Ink Used - Black 7000; Printing Ink Used - Color 400; Printing Ink Used - P
Equipment EDITORIAL: Front-end Software – Mk.; Editorial Hardware – 4-COM/MDT, COM/Mk; Classified Hardware – COM/MDT.; Production Equipment – 1-LE, 1-COM/Trendsetter; Cameras – 1-Carey. PRESSROOM: Line 1 – 5-G/Community; Folders – 1; Inserters and stuffers – 1-KAN/3 station; Bundle tying machines – 1/Felins; Addressing machine – 1-/Am.; Business Hardware – 1-Wa/Professional

CUSHING

CUSHING DAILY CITIZEN

202 N Harrison Ave., Cushing, Okla., 74023; gen tel 918-285-5555; adv tel 918-223-6566; ed tel 918-285-5555; gen fax 918-285-5556; adv fax 918-285-5556; ed fax 918-285-5556; gen e-mail publisher@cushingcitizen.com; adv e-mail ads@cushingcitizen.com; ed e-mail news@cushingcitizen.com; web site www.cushingcitizen.com
Published: Wed, Sat
Weekday Frequency: m
Saturday Frequency: m
Circulation: 2,300; 2,300(sat)
Last Audit: Sworn March 31, 2006
Price: $27/yr local- $75 Out of state
Advertising: OR $9.29
Politics: conservative. **Established:** 1895
Own facility?: Y
Owner ....David Reid
Editor ....Jim Perry
Graphics ....Chris Reid
Accounting ....Myra Reid
Receptionist ....Crissy Kindley
Bus. Mgr. ....Shon Treat
Adv. Mgr. ....Gina Felix
Circ. Mgr. ....Lydia McCall
Mng. Ed. ....Molly Payne
Sports Ed. ....Jeff Holmes
Prodn. Mgr., Pressroom ....Chris Gomez
Market Information: Full run only
Mechanical available: Offset; full colors avail; insert accepted - all; page cutoffs - 21 1/2.
Mechanical Specifications: Type page 11.5 x 21 - 1.7778 col - 1 pica gutter
Equipment EDITORIAL: Front-end Software – Indesign; Editorial Hardware – mac; Editorial Printers – sharp; Classified Hardware – PC; Classified Printers – Sharp DISPLAY: Ad make-up applications – Adobe Creative Suite; Display Hardware – Mac; Display Printers – latest version mac. PRODUCTION: Pagination Software – indesign; Production Equipment – mac; Scanners – Umax; Folders – G/Community.; Inserters and stuffers – KAN/780; Bundle tying machines – Miner; Addressing machine – Miner. BUSINESS COMPUTERS: Business Software – Quik Books,; Business Hardware – IBM/Hard
Delivery method: Mail, Newsstand, Racks

DUNCAN

THE DUNCAN BANNER

1001 Elm St., Duncan, Okla., 73533; gen tel (580) 255-5354; gen fax (580) 255-8889; gen e-mail news@duncanbanner.com; web site www.duncanbanner.com
Published: Mon, Tues, Wed, Thur, Fri, Sun
Weekday Frequency: e
Circulation: 7,179; 8,212(sun)
Last Audit: December 31, 2006
Price: 9.00/mo; 99.00/yr.
Advertising: Open inch rate $14.45
News services: AP, NEA.
Politics: Independent.
Special Weekly Sections: TV Magazine (S).
Magazines: Relish (Monthly); American Profile (S).
Pub. ....Kevin Hook
Adv. Mgr. ....Dana Boyles
Adv. Mgr., Classified ....Paula Blair
Mng. Ed. ....Ron Booth
Prodn. Mgr., Mailroom ....Mike McCormack
Market Information: Split run; TMC; Zoned editions.
Mechanical available: Offset; Black and 3 ROP colors; insert accepted; page cutoffs - 22 3/4.
Mechanical Specifications: Type page 11 5/8 x 21 1/2; E - 6 cols, 1 5/6, 1/8 between; A - 6 cols, 1 5/6, 1/8 between; C - 8 cols, 1 1/3, 1/8 between.
Commodity Consumption: Avg. Page Number Per Issue - Daily 16; Avg. Page Number Per Issue - Plates Used 5227; Avg. Page Number Per Issue - Sunday 38; widths 27; Newsprint Used - Short Tons 429; Printing Ink Used - Black 12100; Printing Ink Used - Color 722; Printing Ink Used -
Equipment EDITORIAL: Front-end Software – Baseview/NewsEdit Pro.; Editorial Hardware – 15-APP/Power Mac; Editorial Equipment – 2-IBM/PC Notebook CLASSIFIED: Front-end Software – Baseview/Ad Manager Pro.; Classified Hardware – 2-APP/Power Mac; Classified Equipment – Iomega/Zip Drive; Classified Printers – APP/Mac LaserWriter Plus DISPLAY: Ad make-up applications – Aldus/Freehand, Adobe/InDesign, Adobe/Photoshop, Adobe/Illustrator; Display Hardware – APP/Power Mac 7600-120, APP/Power Mac 7300-200, APP/Power Mac 8500-120; Display Printers – APP/Mac LaserWriter 8500 PRODUCTION: Pagination Software – QPS/QuarkXPress 4.0.3, Baseview/Qtools 2.2.3, DragX (Inst. 1997) 2.2.2.; Production Equipment – Caere/OmniPage; Cameras – C/Spartan III; Scanners – Epson/Perf. 3170 PRESSROOM: Line 1 – 8-HI/Cotrell V-25; Folders – 1; Reels and Stands – HI/Cotrell; Press control system – HI/Cotrell.; Inserters and stuffers – 5-KAN/480; Bundle tying machines – 1-MLN/ML2-EE; Addressing machine – 2/Wm; Other equipment – Kohner/Quick Stitcher. BUSINESS COMPUTERS: Business Software – PBS; Business Hardware – 7-Sun/Ultra 5

DURANT

DURANT DAILY DEMOCRAT

200 W. Beech St., Durant, Okla., 74701; gen tel (580) 924-4388; adv tel (580) 924-4388; ed tel (580) 924-4388; gen fax (580) 924-6026; adv fax (580) 924-0962; ed fax (580) 924-6026; adv e-mail ads@durantdemocrat.com; ed e-mail news@durantdemocrat.com; web site www.durantdemocrat.com
Published: Mon, Tues, Wed, Thur, Fri, Sun
Weekday Frequency: e
Circulation: 6,784; 7,051(sun)
Last Audit: March 31, 2006
Price: 7.00/mo; 84.00/yr (carrier), $94.00/yr (mail).
Advertising: Open inch rate $12.58
News services: AP, NEA.
Politics: Democrat. **Established:** 1901
Not Published: New Year; Memorial Day; Independence Day; Labor Day; Thanksgiving; Christmas.

Special Editions: Christmas Greetings (Dec); Chamber of Commerce (Feb); Space Clearance (Jan); Graduation (May); Christmas Promotion (Nov); Basketball Opening (Oct); Football Opening (Sept).
Magazines: USA WEEKEND Magazine (Fri); Entertainment Showcase (local entertainment & TV listings) (S); American Profile (Weekly).
Pub. ....Chris Allen
Bus. Mgr......................Amanda Perschbacher
Circ. Mgr. ....Stacie Williams
Mng. Ed. ....Matt Swearengin
Sports Ed. ....Beau Simmons
Prodn. Mgr., Mailroom ....Robby Prshica
Prodn. Mgr., Composing/Pre Press .Karol Oakley
Prodn. Foreman, Press ....Dan Ballew
Market Information: TMC.
Mechanical available: Offset; Black and 3 ROP colors; insert accepted; page cutoffs - 22 3/4.
Mechanical Specifications: Type page 13 x 21 1/2; E - 6 cols, 2 1/16, 1/8 between; A - 6 cols, 2 1/16, 1/8 between; C - 8 cols, 1 1/2, 1/16 between.
Commodity Consumption: Avg. Page Number Per Issue - Daily 10; Avg. Page Number Per Issue - Plates Used 10000; Avg. Page Number Per Issue - Sunday 22; widths 27; Newsprint Used - Metric Tons 200; Printing Ink Used - Black 10000; Printing Ink Used - Color 1200; Printing Ink Used
Equipment EDITORIAL: Front-end Software – Microsoft/Word, QPS/QuarkXPress, SNews-Wire 3.15, Baseview.; Editorial Hardware – 7-APP/Mac G3; Editorial Equipment – MON/Imagesetter; Editorial Printers – 2-NewGen Design XP 12 CLASSIFIED: Front-end Software – Baseview.; Classified Hardware – 2-APP/Mac G3 DISPLAY: Ad make-up applications – ALS; Layout Software – Baseview/AdForce.; Display Hardware – APP/Mac G3 PRODUCTION: Pagination Software – QPS/QuarkXPress 4.0, Baseview.; Production Equipment – Caere/OmniPage 3.0; Cameras – 1-Walzberg/26-10; Scanners – 2-APP/Mac Scanner PRESSROOM: Line 1 – 5-KP/News King; Folders – 1; Bundle tying machines – 1/MLN; Wrapping singles – 4-/Sa. BUSINESS COMPUTERS: Business Software – Progress/4GC Base System, Smart/One modem, Brainworks, Window 3.1; Business Hardware – Starlit/386-DX-40, CTX/Monitor, 3-Acer/Open, 3-Acer/View 34T Monitor, Scout Classic 144C Modem

EDMOND

THE EDMOND SUN
123 S. Broadway, Edmond, Okla., 73034; gen tel (405) 341-2121; gen fax (405) 340-7363; gen e-mail news@edmondsun.com; web site www.edmondsun.com
Group: U.S. Suburban Press, Inc.
Published: Tues, Wed, Sat
Weekday Frequency: m
Saturday Frequency: m
Circulation: 1,561; 4,094(sat)
Last Audit: September 30, 2011
Price: 87.00/yr by carrier.
Advertising: Open inch rate $13.80
News services: U.S. Suburban Press Inc..
Politics: Independent. **Established:** 1889
Not Published: New Year; Independence Day; Thanksgiving; Christmas.
Special Editions: Here's to the Good Life (Apr); Cheers (Aug); Christmas Greetings (Dec); Lawn & Garden/Home Improvement (Feb); Chamber Plan of Action (Jan); IPRA Rodeo (Jul); Parade of Homes (Jun); Services & Celebrations (Mar); Salute to Seniors (May); Christmas Gift Gui
Special Weekly Sections: Religion (Fri); Sports (S); Business Pages (Thur); Health Page (Tues); Education Pages (Wed).
Magazines: Relish (Monthly); USA WEEKEND Magazine (S); American Profile (Weekly).
Pub......................................Steve Paterson
Bus. Mgr............................Stephanie Bracket
Adv. Dir......................................Karan Ediger
Circ. Dir. ....Chris Boarman
News Ed. ....Lisa Shearer
Features Ed..............................James Coburn
Educ. Reporter...............................Patty Miller
Sports Ed. ....Eric Spruill
Market Information: TMC.
Mechanical available: Offset; Black and 3 ROP colors; insert accepted; page cutoffs - 22 3/4.
Mechanical Specifications: Type page 13 x 21 1/2; E - 6 cols, 2, 1/8 between; A - 6 cols, 2, 1/8 between; C - 9 cols, 2, 1/8 between.
Commodity Consumption: Avg. Page Number Per Issue - Daily 24; Avg. Page Number Per Issue - Plates Used 4000; Avg. Page Number Per Issue - Sunday 40; widths 27 1/2; Newsprint Used - Short Tons 1000; Printing Ink Used - Black 10000; Printing Ink Used - Color 500; Printing Ink Us
Equipment; Editorial Hardware – APP/Mac. CLASSIFIED: Front-end Software – Baseview.; Classified Hardware – 4-APP/Mac; Layout Software – 2-APP/Mac AdWriter.; Display Hardware – Software ◻ Multi-Ad/Creator, QPS/QuarkXPress PRODUCTION: Pagination Software – SII.; Production Equipment – 3-APP/Mac LaserWriter, 2-ECR/Imagesetter; Cameras – 1-C/Spartan III PRESSROOM: Line 1 – 10-G/SSC, 1-G/SSC UOP. MAILROOM: Counter stackers – 1/BG; Inserters and stuffers – 1-/DG; Bundle tying machines – 2-/Bu.; Business Hardware – IBM/Personal Sys II

ENID

NEWS AND EAGLE
227 W. Broadway, Enid, Okla., 73701; gen tel 580 233-6600; web site www.enidnews.com
Published: Mon, Tues, Wed, Thur, Fri, Sat, Sun
Weekday Frequency: m
Saturday Frequency: m
Circulation: 14,530; 14,530(sat); 15,110(sun)
Last Audit: ABC September 30, 2011

ELK CITY

ELK CITY DAILY NEWS
200-206 W. Broadway, Elk City, Okla., 73644; gen tel (580) 225-3000; gen fax (580) 243-2414; gen e-mail ecdn@ecdailynews.com; adv e-mail ads@ecdailynews.com; ed e-mail news@ecdailynews.com; web site www.ecdailynews.com
Published: Tues, Wed, Thur, Fri, Sun
Weekday Frequency: e
Circulation: 5,740; 5,740(sun)
Last Audit: September 30, 2005
Price: 9.00/mo (in-city), $10.00/mo (mail); 93.00/yr (mail), $83.00/yr (carrier).
Advertising: Open inch rate $10.50
News services: AP.
Politics: Independent-Democrat. **Established:** 1901
Not Published: New Year; Easter Monday; Memorial Day; Independence Day; Labor Day; Thanksgiving; Christmas, Saturday
Special Weekly Sections: Entertainment Guide
Mng. Ed. ....Robert Fisher
Circ. Mgr. ....Kathy James
Sports Editor.................................Matt Mason
Religion Ed.......................................Bob Fisher
Society/Family Page Ed. ....Cheryl Overstreet
President............................Elizabeth Perkinson
Market Information: TMC; Zoned editions.
Mechanical available: Offset; Black and 2 ROP colors; insert accepted; page cutoffs - 21.
Mechanical Specifications: Type page 13 x 20 1/2; E - 6 cols, 2 1/16, 1/8 between; A - 6 cols, 2 1/16, 1/8 between; C - 6 cols, 2 1/16, 1/8 between.
Commodity Consumption: Avg. Page Number Per Issue - Daily 18; Avg. Page Number Per Issue - Plates Used 6596; Avg. Page Number Per Issue - Sunday 36; widths 30; Newsprint Used - Short Tons 320; Printing Ink Used - Black 7650; Printing Ink Used - Color 500; Printing Ink Used - P
Equipment PRODUCTION: Pagination Software – Adobe/Pagemaker.; Production Equipment – 1-WL, 1-Nat/A-250; Cameras – 1-B, 1-Acti/125 PRESSROOM: Line 1 – 4-G/Community; Folders – 1-G/2:1.; Inserters and stuffers – 1/Cr, KAN; Bundle tying machines – 1-/Cr; Addressing machine – Am/Farrington, Innovative Technology/PC. BUSINESS COMPUTERS: Business Software – Microsoft, Indesign
Delivery method: Mail, Newsstand, Private Carrier, Racks

GROVE

GROVE SUN DAILY
14 W. 3rd St., Grove, Okla., 74344-3223; gen tel (918) 786-9051; gen fax (918) 786-2156; gen e-mail editor@grovesun.com; web site www.grovesun.com
Published: Tues, Wed, Thur, Fri, Sun
Weekday Frequency: m
Advertising: Open inch rate $8.50
Pres. ....Peter M. Crow

GUTHRIE

GUTHRIE NEWS LEADER
107 W. Harrison, Guthrie, Okla., 73044; gen tel (405) 282-2222; gen fax (405) 282-7378; gen e-mail gnlnews@yahoo.com
Published: Tues, Wed, Thur, Fri, Sun
Weekday Frequency: e
Circulation: 5,649; 5,649(sun)
Last Audit: September 30, 2002
Price: 6.00/mo; 75.00/yr (carrier), $102.00/yr (mail).
Advertising: Open inch rate $7.00
News services: AP.
Politics: Independent. **Established:** 1898
Not Published: New Year; Labor Day; Day before Thanksgiving; Christmas.
Special Editions: Fall Sports Tab (Aug); Territorial Christmas Tab (Dec); Free Fair Information Tab (Jul); Father's Day (Jun); Christmas Gift Guide (Nov); 4-H/FAA Tab (Oct); Fall/Winter Visitors Guide (Sept).
Special Weekly Sections: Best Church News (Fri); Best Food Day (Wed).
Magazines: Entertainment Guide (television listings) (Fri).
Adv. Mgr.............................Vonnie Hollenback
Circ. Mgr. ....Paula Harvey
Sports Ed.....................................Brad Troust
Market Information: TMC.
Mechanical available: Offset; Black and 1 ROP colors; insert accepted; page cutoffs - 22 3/4.
Mechanical Specifications: Type page 13 x 21 1/2; E - 6 cols, 2 1/8, 1/6 between; A - 6 cols, 2 1/8, 1/6 between; C - 6 cols, 2 1/8, 1/6 between.
Commodity Consumption: Avg. Page Number Per Issue - Daily 10; Avg. Page Number Per Issue - Plates Used 1800; Avg. Page Number Per Issue - Sunday 16; widths 13 3/4; Newsprint Used - Short Tons 39; Printing Ink Used - Black 4900; Printing Ink Used - Color 150; Printing Ink Used
Equipment EDITORIAL: Front-end Software – Mk.; Editorial Hardware – Mk CLASSIFIED: Front-end Software – Mk.; Classified Hardware – Mk DISPLAY: Ad make-up applications – QPS/QuarkXPress; Display Hardware – APP/Mac IIsi; Display Printers – 1-APP/Mac LaserWriter; Production Equipment – APP/Mac LaserWriter; Cameras – Acti/204.; Bundle tying machines – Strapex.

GUYMON

GUYMON DAILY HERALD
515 N. Ellison St., Guymon, Okla., 73942-0019; gen tel (580) 338-3355; ed tel (580) 338-6397; gen fax (580) 338-5000; adv fax (580) 338-5000; ed fax (580) 338-5000; gen e-mail publisher@guymondailyherald.com; adv e-mail admanager@guymondailyherald.com; ed e-mail editor@guymondailyherald.com; web site www.guymondailyherald.com
Published: Mon, Tues, Wed, Thur, Fri, Sat, Sun
Weekday Frequency: e
Saturday Frequency: m
Circulation: 2,332; 2,332(sat)
Last Audit: March 31, 2006
Price: 6.00/mo; 86.00/yr.
Advertising: Open inch rate $8.07
News services: AP.
Politics: Independent.
Advertising not accepted: Adult in nature.
Not Published: New Year; Independence Day; Labor Day; Thanksgiving; Christmas.
Special Editions: Pioneer Days (Apr); Christmas Greetings (Dec); Progress (Feb); Graduation (May); Christmas Gift Guide (Nov); Texas County Fair (Sept).
Special Weekly Sections: Oklahoma Panhandle Weekly (Sat).
Magazines: TV Guide Tab (Fri); American Profile (Sat).
Office Mgr. ....Myrna Campbell
Adv. Dir. ....Alison Gipe
Adv. Mgr., Classified ....Carol Rayo
Circ. Mgr................................Peggy Martinez
Mng. Ed....Kitie Matire
Sports Ed................................Phill Samdavol
Market Information: TMC; Zoned editions.
Mechanical available: Offset; Black and 3 ROP colors; insert accepted - card; page cutoffs - 21 1/2.
Mechanical Specifications: Type page 13 x 21 1/2; E - 6 cols, 2 1/16, 1/8 between; A - 6 cols, 2 1/16, 1/8 between; C - 8 cols, 1 3/8, 1/16 between.
Commodity Consumption: Avg. Page Number Per Issue - Daily 12; Avg. Page Number Per Issue - Saturday 20; widths 27; Newsprint Used - Metric Tons 120; Printing Ink Used - Black 300; Printing Ink Used - Color 100; Printing Ink Used - Pages Printed 3696.
Equipment EDITORIAL: Front-end Software – Mk.; Editorial Hardware – Mk/4003; Editorial Printers – 2-APP/Mac LaserWriter; Classified Hardware – Mk/4003; Classified Printers – APP/Mac LaserWriter.; Layout Software – APP/Mac.; Display Printers – APP/Mac LaserWriter; Production Equipment – C/T-45; Cameras – Acti/214. PRESSROOM: Line 1 – 4-G/Community; Folders – 1-G/2:1.; Bundle tying machines – 1-Malow/Mc Heavy Duty.; Business Hardware – Vision Data

HENRYETTA

HENRYETTA FREE-LANCE
812 W. Main St., Henryetta, Okla., 74437; gen tel (918) 652-3311; gen fax (918) 652-7347; gen e-mail news@henryettanewspaper.com
Published: Wed, Sun
Circulation: 2,200
Last Audit: Estimate November 5, 2009
Advertising: Open inch rate $7.50
Adv. Dir. ....Stephanie Grist
Dir., Mktg./Promo. ....Robyn Brownfield
Circ. Mgr........................................Cari Stanton
Mng. Ed...Valerie Rice

HOLDENVILLE

HOLDENVILLE NEWS
112 S. Creek St., Holdenville, Okla., 74848; gen tel (405) 379-5411; adv tel (405) 379-5411; gen fax (405) 379-5413; adv fax (405) 379-5413; gen e-mail holdenville@itlnet.net
Published: Tues, Wed, Thur, Fri, Sun
Weekday Frequency: e
Circulation: 2,500; 2,500(sun)
Last Audit: October 1, 1996
Price: 6.00/mo; 52.00/yr.
Advertising: Open inch rate $4.25
News services: AP.
Politics: Democrat.

Special Editions: Fall Festival (Aug); Christmas Greetings (Dec); Sweetheart (Feb); Year in Review (Jan); Gift Guide (Nov); Homecoming (Oct); Football (Sept).
Magazines: TV Spotlight (S).
Pub. ....Robin Brown
Circ. Dir. ....Tammy White
Ed. ....Bill Crawford
Prodn. Mgr., Pre Press ....Tammi Giles
Market Information: ADS; Split run; TMC.
Mechanical available: Offset; Black and 1 ROP colors; insert accepted; page cutoffs - 21 1/2.
Mechanical Specifications: Type page 13 x 21 1/2; E - 6 cols, 2 1/16, 1/8 between; A - 6 cols, 2 1/16, 1/8 between; C - 6 cols, 2 1/16, 1/8 between.
Commodity Consumption: Avg. Page Number Per Issue - Daily 12; Avg. Page Number Per Issue - Sunday 18.
Equipment EDITORIAL: Front-end Software – QPS/QuarkXPress 3.32.; Editorial Hardware – APP/Mac 830; Editorial Equipment – 4-APP/Mac SE, 1-APP/Mac LaserWriter, 2-APP/Power Mac, 1-IBM/Laptop (with Appletalk Conversion); Editorial Printers – APP/Mac, Xante/Accel-a-Writer CLASSIFIED: Front-end Software – QPS/QuarkXPress 3.32.; Classified Hardware – APP/Power Mac, APP/Mac 840, APP/Mac 630; Classified Equipment – SCM/250; Classified Printers – Xante/Accel-a-Writer DISPLAY: Ad make-up applications – QPS/QuarkXPress 3.32; Layout Software – 2-APP/Mac 640, Archetype/Corel Draw, QPS/QuarkXPress.; Display Hardware – 2-APP/Mac 640, Archetype/Corel Draw; Display Printers – Xante PRODUCTION: Pagination Software – APP/Mac 630.; Production Equipment – Caere/OmniPage, APP/Mac 840, Xante/Accel-a-Writer; Scanners – Umax/Vista P630-12 PRESSROOM: Line 1 – 1-KP/3 unit; Folders – 1-KP/2:1.; Addressing machine – Wm.; Business Hardware – APP/Mac 640

HUGO

HUGO DAILY NEWS

128 E. Jackson St., Hugo, Okla., 74743; gen tel (580) 326-3311; adv tel 580 326-3311; ed tel 580 326-3311; oth tel 580 326-3311; gen fax (580) 326-6397; adv fax 580 326-6397; ed fax 580 326-6397; oth fax 580 326-6397; gen e-mail hugonews@sbcglobal.net; adv e-mail adsolutions@sbcglobal.net; ed e-mail editor@sbcglobal.net; web site www.hugonews.com
Group: Hugo Publishing Company
Published: Mon, Tues, Wed, Thur, Fri
Weekday Frequency: e
Circulation: 2,600
Last Audit: Sworn September 30, 2006
Price: 8.00/mo; 89.50/yr by mail, 72.50/yr by carrier.
Advertising: Open inch rate $6.00
Insert rate: $40-$60 / M
News services: AP.
Politics: . **Established:** 1907
Not Published: Major holidays.
Own facility?: Y
Special Editions: Bluegrass (Aug); Homecoming (Jun); Lake Edition (Mar); Health (Quarterly).
Special Weekly Sections: Real Estate (Fri); Best Food Day (Wed).
Vice Pres./Sec./Treasurer ....Judy Stamper
Adv. Dir. ....Linda Packard
News Ed. ....Stan Stamper
Prodn. Mgr. ....Homer Garrison
Sports Ed. ....Jerry Tims
Market Information:
Mechanical available: Offset; Black and 3 ROP colors; insert accepted; page cutoffs - 22 3/4.
Mechanical Specifications: Type page 13 x 21 1/2; E - 6 cols, 2 1/16, 1/8 between; A - 6 cols, 2 1/16, 1/8 between; C - 6 cols, 2 1/16, 1/8 between.
Commodity Consumption: Avg. Page Number Per Issue - Daily 10.
Equipment; Editorial Hardware – APP/Mac.; Classified Hardware – 1-APP/Mac. DISPLAY: Ad make-up applications – Multi-Ad/Creator.; Display Printers – APP/Mac LaserPrinter, New Gen Design XPress 12; Production Equipment – 2-APP/Mac LaserWriter, 1-Nu/Flip Top; Cameras – 1-B; Scanners – APP/Mac Scanner, HP/Scanner. PRESSROOM: Line 1 – 5-KP/Color King Offset; Folders – KP/KJ-6.; Bundle tying machines – 1/Bu.
Zip Codes served: 74743
Delivery method: Mail, Newsstand, Private Carrier, Racks

HUGO PUBLISHING CO.

128 E. Jackson St., Hugo, Okla., 74743; gen tel (580) 326-3311; gen fax (580) 326-6397; gen e-mail hugonews@sbcglobal.net; adv e-mail adsolutions@sbcglobal.net; ed e-mail editor@sbcglobal.net; web site www.hugonews.com
Published: Mon, Tues, Wed, Thur, Fri
Weekday Frequency: e
Circulation: 2,419
Price: .50
Politics: 1907
Not Published: Sat. / Sun.
Own facility?: Y
Delivery method: Mail, Newsstand, Private Carrier, Racks

IDABEL

MCCURTAIN DAILY GAZETTE

107 S. Central Ave., Idabel, Okla., 74745-0179; gen tel (580) 286-3321; ed tel (580) 286-3322; gen fax (580) 286-2208; gen e-mail paper@mccurtain.com; web site www.mccurtain.com
Published: Tues, Wed, Thur, Fri, Sun
Weekday Frequency: e
Circulation: 5,850; 7,800(sun)
Last Audit: March 31, 2006
Price: 3.60/mo (carrier); 62.50/yr.
Advertising: Open inch rate $8.65
News services: AP.
Politics: Independent. **Established:** 1905
Special Editions: Football (Aug); Christmas Kick-Off (Dec); Lawn & Garden (Feb); Owa-Chito Celebration (Jun); Hunters (Nov); Community Builders Annual (Oct).
Special Weekly Sections: Farm Page (S); Food (Wed).
Magazines: Sunday Showcase Entertainment Tab (S); American Profile (Weekly).
Vice Pres. ....Gwen Willingham
Adv. Dir. ....Shelly Davis
Ed. ....Bruce Willingham
Reporter ....Chris Willingham
Sports Ed. ....Brad Reesing
Prodn. Mgr., Pressroom ....Manuel Perez
Market Information: TMC.
Mechanical available: Offset; Black and 2 ROP colors; insert accepted; page cutoffs - 22 3/4.
Mechanical Specifications: Type page 13 x 21; E - 6 cols, 2 1/16, 1/8 between; A - 6 cols, 2 1/16, 1/8 between; C - 8 cols, 1 3/8, 1/16 between.
Commodity Consumption: Avg. Page Number Per Issue - Daily 12; Avg. Page Number Per Issue - Sunday 32; widths 28.
Equipment; Editorial Hardware – TC; Editorial Equipment – Software ☐ TC.; Classified Hardware – APP/Mac.; Layout Software – 3-APP/Mac.; Display Printers – APP/Mac LaserWriter; Production Equipment – TC/Laserwriter; Cameras – 1-B. PRESSROOM: Line 1 – 3-HI/V-15.; Bundle tying machines – 2/WT; Addressing machine – 1-RSK/TRS 80 Computer Printer.; Business Hardware – 2-RSK/TRS 80 II

LAWTON

THE LAWTON CONSTITUTION

102 S. Third St., Lawton, Okla., 73502; gen tel (580) 353-0620; adv tel (580) 585-5107; ed tel (580) 353-0620; gen fax (580) 585-5058; adv fax (580) 585-5103; ed fax (580) 585-5140; gen e-mail paper@sirinet.net; adv e-mail ads@lawton-constitution.com; ed e-mail paper@sirinet.net; web site www.lawton-constitution.com
Published: Sun
Circulation: 20,972; 20,972(sat); 23,146(sun)
Last Audit: September 30, 2009
Price: 11.75/mo; 90.00/yr.
Advertising: Open inch rate $19.45
News services: AP, CNS.
Politics: Democrat.
Special Weekly Sections: Markets/Financial (Fri); Neighbors (Sat); Home & Garden (Thur); Markets/Financial (Tues); Markets/Financial (Wed).
Magazines: USA WEEKEND Magazine (S).
Gen. Mgr. ....Mike Owensby
Bus. Mgr. ....James Cottingham
Credit Mgr. ....Jeannie Barnett
Adv. Dir. ....Jim Garrett
Circ. Dir. ....Larry Toth
Co-Ed. ....Don Bentley
Co-Ed. ....Stephen Bentley
City Ed. ....Steve Metzer
Editorial Page Ed. ....David Hale
Food Ed. ....Steve Robertson
Librarian ....Ronna Potts
News Ed. ....Dee Ann Patterson
Music Ed. ....Charles Clark
Market Information: TMC.
Mechanical available: Offset; Black and 3 ROP colors; insert accepted.
Mechanical Specifications: Type page 12 1/2 x 21 1/2; E - 6 cols, 2 1/16, 1/8 between; A - 6 cols, 2 1/16, 1/8 between; C - 9 cols, 1 5/16, 1/8 between.
Commodity Consumption: Avg. Page Number Per Issue - Daily 26.30; Avg. Page Number Per Issue - Plates Used 37802; Avg. Page Number Per Issue - Saturday 42.88; Avg. Page Number Per Issue - Sunday 62.65; widths 37 1/2; Newsprint Used - Short Tons 2016; Printing Ink Used - Black 3
Equipment EDITORIAL: Front-end Software – QPS/QuarkXPress, FSI.; Editorial Hardware – APP/Mac, Pentium/PC; Editorial Printers – TI/8920, HP/4MV CLASSIFIED: Front-end Software – FSI.; Classified Hardware – Pentium/PC; Classified Printers – TI/8920, HP/4MV DISPLAY: Ad make-up applications – Multi-Ad/Creator; Layout Software – Mk, FSI.; Display Hardware – APP/Mac PRODUCTION: Pagination Software – QPS/QuarkXPress 3.2.; Production Equipment – 2-ECR/3850, Lf/Leafscan-Umax; Cameras – 2-C; Scanners – Hel PRESSROOM: Line 1 – 6-HI/1650 offset double width 1978; Folders – HI/2:1 RBF; Pasters – 5-MEG. MAILROOM: Counter stackers – Id/440, Id/550, 2-MM/310; Inserters and stuffers – 2-MM/227S 0-6; Bundle tying machines – 2/Dynaric; Addressing machine – KR; Other equipment –MM/321, Fox Stitcher.; Audio Hardware – Brite Voice Systems BUSINESS COMPUTERS: Business Software – DSI; Business Hardware – Digital/6200

MCALESTER

MCALESTER NEWS-CAPITAL

500 S. Second St., McAlester, Okla., 74501; gen tel (918) 423-1700; adv tel (918) 421-2006; ed tel (918) 421-2022; gen fax (918) 426-3081; ed fax (918) 426-3082; adv e-mail advertising@mcalesternews.com; ed e-mail editor@mcalesternews.com; web site www.mcalesternews.com
Published: Mon, Tues, Wed, Thur, Fri, Sun
Weekday Frequency: e
Circulation: 9,577; 10,046(sun)
Last Audit: September 30, 2004
Price: 9.00/mo (carrier); 102.00/yr (carrier), 126.00/yr (mail within city).
Advertising: Open inch rate $16.75
News services: AP, NEA.
Politics: 1896
Not Published: Christmas.
Special Weekly Sections: Church (Fri); Business & Industry Page (Mon); TV Listings Book (S); Entertainment Page (Thur); Children's Mini Page (Tues).
Magazines: Relish (Monthly); USA WEEKEND Magazine (S).
Pub. ....Amy Johns
Circ. Mgr. ....Karen Johns
Sr. Ed. ....James Beaty
Living/Lifestyle Ed. ....Susan Brittingham
Online Ed. ....Carlton M. Lane
Prodn. Mgr. ....Debra Durbin
Market Information: Split run; TMC; Zoned editions.
Mechanical available: Offset; Black and 3 ROP colors; insert accepted - standing cards, samples, stick-ons; page cutoffs - 21 1/2.
Mechanical Specifications: Type page 12 x 21 1/2; E - 6 cols, 1 5/6, 1/8 between; A - 6 cols, 1 7/8, 1/8 between; C - 9 cols, 1 1/4, 1/12 between.
Commodity Consumption: Avg. Page Number Per Issue - Daily 22; Avg. Page Number Per Issue - Sunday 32; widths 12 1/2; Newsprint Used - Short Tons 550; Printing Ink Used - Black 8000; Printing Ink Used - Color 400; Printing Ink Used - Pages Printed 7198.
Equipment EDITORIAL: Front-end Software – Baseview.; Editorial Hardware – 9-APP/Mac G3, 3-APP/Mac G4; Editorial Equipment – APP/Mac One Scanner, Imagesetter; Editorial Printers – APP/Mac LaserWriter II CLASSIFIED: Front-end Software – Mk, Baseview.; Classified Hardware – 2-APP/Mac; Classified Printers – APP/Mac LaserWriter II DISPLAY: Ad make-up applications – Multi-Ad, Baseview; Layout Software – CD-Rom/Electronic Art.; Display Hardware – Mk, APP/Mac; Display Printers – APP/Mac LaserWriter II PRODUCTION: Pagination Software – Baseview, QPS/QuarkXPress 4.0.; Production Equipment – LF/AP Leaf Desk; Cameras – 1-C PRESSROOM: Line 1 – 9-G/Community; Folders – 1-G/SC.; Inserters and stuffers – KAN/420; Bundle tying machines – 1-Dynaric/SM-50, 1-Malow/Mc Heavy Duty Tyer.; Business Hardware – Software ☐ Vision Data

NEWS-CAPITAL & DEMOCRAT

PO Box 987, McAlester, Okla., 74502-0987; gen tel (918) 423-1700; web site www.mcalesternews.com

MIAMI

MIAMI NEWS-RECORD

14 First St. NW, Miami, Okla., 74354; gen tel (918) 542-5533; gen fax (918) 542-1903; adv e-mail mark.rogers@miaminewsrecord.com; web site www.miaminewsrecord.com
Published: Mon, Tues, Wed, Thur, Fri, Sun
Weekday Frequency: e
Circulation: 6,000; 6,100(sun)
Last Audit: March 31, 2006
Price: 8.50/mo; 111.00/yr.
Advertising: Open inch rate $10.46
News services: AP.
Politics: Independent. **Established:** 1902
Special Editions: Football (Aug); Christmas Greetings (Dec); Tax Tips (Feb); NEO Tournament (Jan); Sidewalk (Jul); Brides (Jun); Health (Mar); Graduation (May); Car Care (Nov); Community Visitor's Guide (Oct); Active Times (Quarterly); Hello Fall (Sept).
Magazines: TV Record (S).
Pub. ....James Abruzzo
Adv. Mgr., Display ....Mark Rogers
Sports Ed. ....Jim Ellis
Prodn. Mgr. ....Darrel Rector
Market Information: Split run; TMC; Zoned editions.
Mechanical available: Offset; Black and 3 ROP colors; insert accepted - standing cards; page cutoffs - 21 1/2.
Mechanical Specifications: Type page 13 x 21; E - 6 cols, 2 1/16, 1/8 between; A - 6 cols, 2 1/16, 1/8 between; C - 10 cols, 1 1/5, 1/16 between.
Commodity Consumption: Avg. Page Number Per Issue - Daily 14; Avg. Page Number Per Issue - Plates Used 4000; Avg. Page Number Per Issue - Sunday 40; widths 27; Newsprint Used - Short Tons 336; Printing Ink Used - Black 6000; Printing Ink Used - Color 200; Printing Ink Used - P

Equipment EDITORIAL: Front-end Software – QPS/QuarkXPress 3.3, Baseview/NewsEdit Pro.; Editorial Hardware – 7-APP/Mac; Classified Hardware – APP/Mac. DISPLAY: Ad makeup applications – QPS/QuarkXPress, Adobe/Photoshop; Layout Software – APP/Mac. PRODUCTION: Pagination Software – QPS/QuarkXPress 3.3.; Production Equipment – 2-APP/Mac II, 2-APP/Mac LaserWriter II; Cameras – 1-C/1244; Scanners – Lacie, Kk PRESSROOM: Line 1 – G/Offset.; Inserters and stuffers – KAN/320; Bundle tying machines – MLN; Wrapping singles – Sa/E; Addressing machine – 1-Am/1957E. BUSINESS COMPUTERS: Business Software – Microsoft/Windows 95, Microsoft/Office 98; Business Hardware – 1-Gateway/2000

MUSKOGEE

MUSKOGEE DAILY PHOENIX & TIMES DEMOCRAT

214 Wall St., Muskogee, Okla., 74401; gen tel (918) 684-2828; adv tel (918) 684-2810; ed tel (918) 684-2920; gen fax (918) 684-2878; adv fax (918) 687-6270; ed fax (918) 684-2865; web site www.muskogeephoenix.com

Published: Mon, Tues, Wed, Thur, Fri, Sat, Sun
Weekday Frequency: m
Saturday Frequency: m
Circulation: 13,044; 13,044(sat); 14,044(sun)
Last Audit: September 30, 2009
Price: 11.50/mo, $9.25/mo (d), $6.25/mo (S/holiday).
Advertising: Open inch rate $37.45
News services: AP, GNS.
Politics: Independent. **Established:** 1888
Advertising not accepted: Brokered.
Special Editions: Christmas Gift Guide (Annually); Visitors Guide (Semi-yearly).
Special Weekly Sections: Weekend (Entertainment) (Fri); Health and Fitness (Mon); Books (S); Recreation & Travel (Sat); Outdoor (Thur); E/Tech (Tues); Food (Wed).
Magazines: USA WEEKEND Magazine (S).
Pres./Pub. ....Lawrence Corvi
Controller ....Sandy Mcdanial
Dir., Market Devel. ....Becky Lucht
Exec. Ed. ....Ed Choate
City Ed. ....Liz McMahan
Asst. City Ed. ....Elizabeth Ridenour
Editorial Page Ed. ....David Jurkiewicz
Sports Ed. ....Mike Kays
Prodn. Mgr., Mailroom ....Kevin Kizzia
Prodn. Mgr., Pre Press ....Melissa Warren
Prodn. Mgr., Pressroom ....Stevan Bull
Market Information: TMC.
Mechanical available: Offset; Black and 3 ROP colors; insert accepted - Product Samples; page cutoffs - 22 3/4.
Mechanical Specifications: Type page 11 5/8 x 21 1/2; E - 6 cols, 2 1/16, 1/8 between; A - 6 cols, 2 1/16, 1/8 between; C - 9 cols, 1 3/8, 1/16 between.
Commodity Consumption: Avg. Page Number Per Issue - Daily 25; Avg. Page Number Per Issue - Plates Used 18000; Avg. Page Number Per Issue - Sunday 50; widths 12 1/2; Newsprint Used - Metric Tons 1357; Newsprint Used - Short Tons 1496; Printing Ink Used - Black 31000; Printing I
Equipment EDITORIAL: Front-end Software – Baseview/NewsEdit Pro, Baseview/IQUE 1.0.; Editorial Hardware – APP/Mac; Editorial Equipment – APP/Mac, AP/Photos; Editorial Printers – MON/1500 CLASSIFIED: Front-end Software – Baseview.; Classified Hardware – APP/Mac; Classified Printers – Okidata DISPLAY: Ad make-up applications – Multi-Ad/Creator, QPS/QuarkXPress; Display Hardware – APP/Mac IIci, APP/Mac fx; Display Printers – APP/Mac LaserWriter, Phaser/300i Color Proofer, MON/1500, HP/LaserJet 5000 11x17, HP/DesignJet 1055CM Proofer PRODUCTION: Pagination Software – QPS/QuarkXPress 4.0.; Production Equipment – Nat/A-250, Konica, ECR; Scanners – Lf/Leafscan 35, Nikon/Coolscan, Umax/Mirage II Scanner, Copy Dot Scanner PRESSROOM: Line 1 – 8-G/Urbanite 1972; Folders – 1; Pasters – 2 MAILROOM: Counter stackers – HI/RS 2510, MM/310; Inserters and stuffers – MM/227; Bundle tying machines – MLN/ML2EE, Si; Addressing machine – Ch; Other equipment –MM/Stitcher-Trimmer, Ch/Labeler. BUSINESS COMPUTERS: Business Software – Microsoft/Office 2000; Business Hardware – IBM/AS-400

OKLAHOMA PRESS PUBLISHING CO.

214 Wall Street, Muskogee, Okla., 74401; gen tel (918) 684-2828; gen fax (918) 684-2878

NORMAN

NORMAN TRANSCRIPT

215 E. Comanche St., Norman, Okla., 73069-6007; gen tel (405) 321-1800; adv tel (405) 366-3587; ed tel (405) 366-3543; gen fax (405) 366-3520; adv fax (405) 366-3516; ed fax (405) 366-3516; gen e-mail publisher@normantranscript.com; adv e-mail addir@normantranscript.com; ed e-mail news@normantranscript.com; web site www.normantranscript.com

Published: Mon, Tues, Wed, Thur, Fri, Sat, Sun
Weekday Frequency: m
Saturday Frequency: m
Circulation: 10,850; 11,526(sat); 11,366(sun)
Last Audit: ABC September 30, 2011
Price: 8.95/mo; 104.95/yr.
Advertising: Open inch rate $20.05
News services: AP, MCT, NEA.
Politics: Independent.
Special Editions: Garden Guide (Apr); Greetings (Dec); Salute to Business (Feb); Tax Guide (Jan); Gift Guide (Nov); Home Improvement (Oct); Football (Sept).
Special Weekly Sections: Pop (Fri); Channels (S); Norman Homes & More (Sat); Food (Wed).
Magazines: USA WEEKEND Magazine (S).
Pub. ....David R. Stringer
Adv. Dir. ....Saundra Morris
Circ. Dir. ....Ken McEwen
Exec. Ed. ....Andy Rieger
City Ed. ....Linda Henley
Sports Ed. ....Clay Horning
Prodn. Mgr. ....Rob Rasor
Market Information: TMC.
Mechanical available: Offset; Black and 3 ROP colors; insert accepted; page cutoffs - 22 3/4.
Mechanical Specifications: Type page 13 x 21 1/2; E - 6 cols, 2 3/8, 1/8 between; A - 6 cols, 2, 1/8 between; C - 6 cols, 2, 1/8 between.
Commodity Consumption: Avg. Page Number Per Issue - Daily 18; Avg. Page Number Per Issue - Plates Used 28800; Avg. Page Number Per Issue - Saturday 24; Avg. Page Number Per Issue - Sunday 60; widths 25; Newsprint Used - Metric Tons 1100; Printing Ink Used - Black 35000; Printi
Equipment EDITORIAL: Front-end Software – Baseview/NewsEdit Pro IQUE 3.0.3.; Editorial Hardware – APP/Mac; Editorial Printers – 2-Pre Press/Panther Imagesetter, 1-Pre Press/Panther Plus, 1-Pre Press/Panther Pro 36 CLASSIFIED: Front-end Software – Baseview/Ad Manager Pro 1.0.7.; Classified Hardware – APP/Mac DISPLAY: Ad make-up applications – Multi-Ad/Creator 4.0; Layout Software – MEI/ALS.; Display Hardware – APP/Mac; Display Printers – NEC/Imagerplus 12xf PRODUCTION: Pagination Software – Baseview 30, QPS/QuarkXPress 4.0.; Production Equipment – Caere/OmniPage 6, 1-Pre Press/Panther Pro 36; Cameras – 1-C/Spartan III; Scanners – Epson/Flatbed, Lf/Leafscan 35, Nikon/LS 1000 PRESSROOM: Line 1 – 8-G 1975, G/Urbanite single width; Folders – 1; Press registration system – 1; Inserters and stuffers – MM, 224; Bundle tying machines – Interlake/P 100, Interlake/P 940; Other equipment –MM/Minuteman Stitcher-Trimmer.

OKLAHOMA CITY

OKLAHOMA PUBLISHING CO.

9000 N. Broadway, Oklahoma City, Okla., 73125; gen tel (405) 475-3311

THE OKLAHOMAN

9000 N. Broadway, Oklahoma City, Okla., 73114-3708; gen tel (405) 475-3311; adv tel (405) 475-3493; ed tel (405) 475-3920; adv fax (405) 475-3444; ed fax (405) 475-3183; adv e-mail classified@oklahoman.com; display@oklahoman.com; ed e-mail newsroom@oklahoman.com; web site www.newsok.com

Published: Mon, Tues, Wed, Thur, Fri, Sat, Sun
Weekday Frequency: m
Saturday Frequency: m
Circulation: 132,294; 120,367(sat); 197,270(sun)
Last Audit: ABC September 30, 2011
Price: 14.00/mo; 151.20/yr.
Advertising: Open inch rate $373.74
News services: Newspapers First, CT, DJ, CNS, MCT, SHNS, TMS.
Politics: Independent. **Established:** 1903
Special Editions: Football (Aug); State Fair (Sept).
Special Weekly Sections: Business (Other); Real Estate (Sat).
Magazines: Parade (S).
Chrmn./CEO ....Christine Gaylord Everest
President & Publisher ....Christopher Reen
Vice Pres. Administration ....Scott Briggs
Vice Pres. Operations ....Pat Dennis
Financial Mgr. ....Kent Treadwell
Adv. Mgr., Classified ....Tom Hite
Chief Product Officer, Wimgo ....Robert Wescott
Adv. Mgr., Real Estate Sales ....Chris Carpenter
Database Mgr ....Joe Hight
Mng. Ed. ....Mike Shannon
Asst. Mng. Ed. ....Robby Trammell
Dir., Presentation ....Yvette Walker
Bus. Ed. ....Clytie Bunyan
Market Information: ADS; Split run; TMC; Zoned editions.
Mechanical available: Offset; Black and 3 ROP colors; insert accepted; page cutoffs - 22 3/4.
Mechanical Specifications: Type page 12 1/2 x 21 1/2; E - 5 cols, 2 3/16, 5/16 between; A - 6 cols, 1 3/4, 5/32 between; C - 10 cols, 1, 1/8 between.
Commodity Consumption: Avg. Page Number Per Issue - Daily 48; Avg. Page Number Per Issue - Plates Used 475000; Avg. Page Number Per Issue - Saturday 54; Avg. Page Number Per Issue - Sunday 130; widths 50; Newsprint Used - Short Tons 32500; Printing Ink Used - Black 620000; Pri
Equipment EDITORIAL: Front-end Software – HI/Newsmaker Editorial, Hi/NMP (pagination).; Editorial Hardware – 2-Sun/Enterprise 4000, 113-PC (editorial), 20-PC (pagination); Editorial Printers – HP/2500 CD, HP/5Si CLASSIFIED: Front-end Software – HI/AdPower, Hi/Pagination.; Classified Hardware – 2-Sun/Enterprise 4000 (ad entry), 80-PC (ad entry), 2-PC (pagination); Classified Printers – HP/LaserJet 5si DISPLAY: Ad make-up applications – AII/Ad Manager, Multi-Ad/Creator; Layout Software – 2-APP/Mac 9500; Display Hardware – Sun/Enterprise 3000, 25-APP/Mac; Display Printers – 3-HP/2500 CP, Canon/Fiery, HP/5si PRODUCTION: Pagination Software – PPI.; Production Equipment – 3-Glunz & Jensen, AG/Due Scan, ScanView/F8; Scanners – 3-Epson/1640 PRESSROOM: Line 1 – 10-G/Metroliner 1984; Line 2 – 10-G/Metroliner 1984; Line 3 – 10-G/Metroliner 1989; Line 4 – 2-G/Global Newslingers 2000; Folders – 3-G/3:2 Double Imperial, 1-G/2:3:3 Double Jaw 2000; Reels and Stands – 32; Press control system – EAE MAILROOM: Counter stackers – 11-QWI/351, 2-QWI/350, 3-HL/Monitor, 2-QWI/400, 2-Gammerler/STC 70; Inserters and stuffers – 1-HI/1372P, 3-HI/1472P, 1-HI/NP 630; Bundle tying machines – 11-Sterling/MR45CH, 2-Sterling/MR50CH; Mailroom control system – Burt; Addressing machine – Addressin BUSINESS COMPUTERS: Business Software – SAP; Business Hardware – Hitachi/Pilot Series/P4, Model 15

OKMULGEE

OKMULGEE DAILY TIMES

114 E. 7th St., Okmulgee, Okla., 74447-1218; gen tel (918) 756-3600; adv tel (918) 756-3691; ed tel (918) 756-3693; gen fax (918) 756-8197; adv fax (918) 756-8197; ed fax (918) 756-8197; gen e-mail drtimes@rapfire.net

Published: Tues, Wed, Thur, Fri, Sun
Weekday Frequency: m
Circulation: 4,483; 6,547(sun)
Last Audit: March 31, 2006
Price: 6.50/mo; 78.00/yr.
Advertising: Open inch rate $12.75
News services: AP.
Politics: Democrat.
Special Editions: Okmulgee Trade Show (Other).
Special Weekly Sections: Religion (Fri); Real Estate (S); Food Page (Wed).
Magazines: Entertainment Times (television section) (S); American Profile (Weekly).
Pub. ....Derek Sumner
Office Mgr. ....Robin Brownfield
Circ. Mgr. ....Phyllis Argyle
Ed. ....Herman L. Brown
Editorial Asst. ....Bettye Grant
Lifestyles Ed. ....Patrick Ford
Sports Ed. ....Larry Owen
Market Information: TMC; Zoned editions.
Mechanical available: Offset; Black and 3 ROP colors; insert accepted; page cutoffs - 23.
Mechanical Specifications: Type page 13 x 21 1/2; E - 6 cols, 2 1/16, 1/8 between; A - 6 cols, 2 1/16, 1/8 between; C - 8 cols, 1 1/2, 1/8 between.
Commodity Consumption: Avg. Page Number Per Issue - Daily 14; Avg. Page Number Per Issue - Plates Used 12000; Avg. Page Number Per Issue - Sunday 40; widths 13 1/2; Newsprint Used - Metric Tons 210; Newsprint Used - Short Tons 260; Printing Ink Used - Black 2000; Printing Ink
Equipment EDITORIAL: Front-end Software – Baseview/NewsEdit Pro, QPS/QuarkXPress 4.1.; Editorial Hardware – APP/Mac G4; Editorial Equipment – APP/Mac Classic; Editorial Printers – APP/Mac LaserWriter II NTX CLASSIFIED: Front-end Software – Baseview.; Classified Hardware – APP/Mac 630, APP/Mac G4; Classified Printers – APP/Mac LaserWriter NTX DISPLAY: Ad make-up applications – QPS/QuarkXPress 4.1, Baseview; Layout Software – APP/Mac G4, Baseview/Ad Force.; Display Hardware – APP/Mac; Display Printers – APP/Mac LaserWriter NTX PRODUCTION: Pagination Software – Baseview/NewsEdit Pro, QPS/QuarkXPress 4.1.; Production Equipment – NewGen/DesignXpress 12; Cameras – 1-Acti/225 PRESSROOM: Line 1 – 6-G/Community 1972.; Bundle tying machines – Ca/Bond Tyer; Addressing machine – Wm. BUSINESS COMPUTERS: Business Software – Ar/Works: Bus; Business Hardware – PC

PAULS VALLEY

PAULS VALLEY DEMOCRAT

108 S. Willow St., Pauls Valley, Okla., 73075; gen tel (405) 238-6464; gen fax (405) 238-3042; ed e-mail marie@pvdemocrat.com; web site www.pvdemocrat.com

Group: CNHI
Published: Tues, Thur, Sun
Weekday Frequency: m
Circulation: 2,950; 2,950(sun)
Last Audit: Sworn September 30, 2004
Price: 6.50 mth/ 78.00 annual
Advertising: Open inch rate $5.45
Insert rate: $50.00 perm
News services: AP.
Politics: 1904
Advertising not accepted: Y
Not Published: Thanksgiving; Christmas.
Own facility?: Y

Special Editions: Football (Aug); Christmas Greetings (Dec); After Christmas Clearance (Jan); Progress (Mar); Vacation (May); @RecordBody:**Magazines:** TV Outlook (S); American Profile (Weekly).
Office Manager........................Sheila Johnson
News Ed................................Barry Porterfield
Editor...Mike Arie
Advertising Account Executive........Katie Rankin
Publisher...............................Banks Dishmon
Advertising Account Executive..........Sara Fisher
Classified & Legal Account Rep.....Christy Harris
Reporter..Exra Mann
Market Information: TMC.
Mechanical available: Offset; Black and 3 ROP colors; insert accepted; page cutoffs - 21 1/2.
Mechanical Specifications: Type page 13 1/2 x 21 1/2; E - 6 cols, 2 1/16, 1/8 between; A - 6 cols, 2 1/16, 1/8 between; C - 8 cols, 1 1/2, 1/8 between.
Equipment EDITORIAL: Front-end Software – APP/Mac.; Editorial Hardware – 4-Mk/4003; Classified Hardware – APP/Mac.; Layout Software – APP/Mac.; Production Equipment – C/T-45; Cameras – 1-Acti. PRESSROOM: Line 1 – 4; Business Hardware – APP/Mac
Zip Codes served: 73075, 73074,73052,73057,73098,73433,74872
Delivery method: Mail, Newsstand, Racks

PERRY

THE PERRY DAILY JOURNAL

714 Delaware St., Perry, Okla., 73077-0311; gen tel (580) 336-2222; adv tel (580) 336-2222; ed tel (580) 336-2222; gen fax (580) 336-3222; adv fax (580) 336-3222; ed fax (580) 336-3222; gen e-mail news@perrydailyjournal.com; adv e-mail classified@perrydailyjournal.com; ed e-mail editorial@perrydailyjournal.com; web site www.perrydailyjournal.com; www.pdjnews.com
Published: Tues, Wed, Thur, Fri, Sat
Weekday Frequency: m
Saturday Frequency: m
Circulation: 3,250; 3,250(sat)
Last Audit: September 30, 2005
Price: 12.00/mo; 78.00/yr.
Advertising: Open inch rate $10.12
Politics: Independent.
Not Published: New Year; Memorial Day; Independence Day; Labor Day; Thanksgiving; Christmas.
Own facility?: Y
Special Editions: High School Graduation and Speical Edition in conjunction with Cherokee Strip Celebratioin
Owner/Pub. ....Phillip Reid
Adv. Dir., Accts. ....Lori Battles
Circ. Mgr.................................Bruce Atkinson
News Ed. ....Gloria G. Brown
Market Information: TMC.
Mechanical available: Offset; Black and 3 ROP colors; insert accepted - we-prints; page cutoffs - 21 1/2.
Mechanical Specifications: Type page 11 5/8 x 21 1/2; E - 6 cols, 1 5/6, 1/8 between; A - 6 cols, 1 5/6, 1/8 between; C - 6 cols, 1 5/6, 1/8 between.
Commodity Consumption: Avg. Page Number Per Issue - Daily 12; Avg. Page Number Per Issue - Plates Used 1900; widths 16; Newsprint Used - Short Tons 80; Printing Ink Used - Black 3250; Printing Ink Used - Pages Printed 3640.
Equipment EDITORIAL: Front-end Software – QPS/QuarkXPress.; Editorial Hardware – APP/Mac; Editorial Printers – NewGen CLASSIFIED: Front-end Software – SNews, QPS/QuarkXPress.; Classified Hardware – APP/Mac; Classified Printers – NewGen DISPLAY: Ad make-up applications – APP/Mac System 7.1; Layout Software – QPS/QuarkXPress, Adobe/PageMaker, Multi-Ad/Creator.; Display Hardware – 4-APP/Mac Centris 650; Display Printers – 2-NewGen/Turbo PS 660B PRODUCTION: Pagination Software – QPS/QuarkXPress 3.11.; Production Equipment – Caere/OmniPage Direct 2.0; Cameras – 1-Ik, SCREEN/DS; Scanners – Umax/VC840 PRESSROOM: Line 1 – 3-HI/Cotrell V-15A; Folders – 1, HI/JF-7.; Bundle tying machines – 1/Malow; Addressing machine – 1-/Am. BUSINESS COMPUTERS: Business Software – Micro, Casecom; Business Hardware – Max-Tech
Delivery method: Mail, Racks

PONCA CITY

THE PONCA CITY NEWS

300 N. Third St., Ponca City, Okla., 74601; gen tel (580) 765-3311; adv tel 580-765-3311; ed tel 580-765-3311; oth tel 580-765-3311; gen fax (580) 762-6397; adv fax 580-765-3311; ed fax (580) 765-7800; oth fax 580-765-3311; gen e-mail news@poncacitynews.com; adv e-mail ads@poncacitynews.com; ed e-mail news@poncacitynews.com; web site www.poncacitynews.com
Published: Mon, Tues, Wed, Thur, Fri, Sun
Weekday Frequency: e
Circulation: 7,706; 8,838(sun)
Last Audit: ABC September 30, 2011
Price: 7.50/mo; 86.00/yr, $87.00/yr (Armed Forces).
Advertising: Open inch rate $12.00
News services: AP.
Politics: Independent. **Established:** 1893
Not Published: Saturdays
Own facility?: Y
Special Editions: Spring Home Improvement (Mar); Oklahoma Football (Aug); Christmas Greetings (Dec); Brides (Feb); Income Tax Guide (Jan);Welcome Neighbors (May); Medical Guide (Jul); Spring Car Care (Mar); Back to School (Jul); Holiday Gift Guide (Nov); @RecordBody:**Magazines:** TV Week (S).
Broadcast Affiliations: Radio WBBZ.
Comptroller..................................Michael Ellis
Adv. Mgr....Pat Jordan
Editor/Publisher ....Tom Muchmore
Mng. Ed.....................................Kristie Hayes
Sports reporter............................David Miller
Sports Ed........................................Fred Hilton
Prodn. Mgr...................................Jerry Helems
Market Information: TMC.
Mechanical available: Offset; Black and 3 ROP colors; insert accepted - odd sizes upon approval; page cutoffs - 22 3/4.
Mechanical Specifications: Type page 13 x 21 1/2; E - 6 cols, 2 1/16, 1/8 between; A - 6 cols, 2 1/16, 1/8 between; C - 9 cols, 1 3/8, 1/16 between.
Commodity Consumption: Avg. Page Number Per Issue - Daily 14; Avg. Page Number Per Issue - Sun 34 Plates Used 7040; widths 28; Newsprint Used - Short Tons 650; Printing Ink Used - Black 15400; Printing Ink Used - Color 3500; Printing Ink Used -
Equipment EDITORIAL: Front-end Software – Baseview.; Editorial Hardware – APP/Mac; Editorial Equipment – Lf/AP Leaf Picture Desk, Lf/Leafscan 35, Umax/Flatbed Scanner; Editorial Printers – APP/Mac LaserWriter 630, NewGen/1200B, ECR/VR 36 CLASSIFIED: Front-end Software – Baseview.; Classified Hardware – APP/Mac DISPLAY: Ad make-up applications – InDesign 4, Aldus/FreeHand 4.0, Adobe/Illustrator 5.5, Microsoft/Word 5.1a,; Display Hardware – APP/Mac Quadra, APP/Mac Centris, DLI/CD-Roms, Sony, APP/Super Mac Monitors; Display Printers – APP/LW Pro 630, NewGen/1200B, ECR/VR 36 Imagesetter; Production Equipment – Caere/OmniScan Pro; Cameras – C. PRESSROOM: Line 1 – 8-G/Community 1975, 2-1992.; Inserters and stuffers – KAN; Bundle tying machines – .; Business Hardware – PCs
Zip Codes served: 74604
Delivery method: Mail, Newsstand, Private Carrier, Racks

PONCA CITY PUBLISHING CO., INC.

300 N. Third, Ponca City, Okla., 74601; gen tel (580) 765-3311; ed tel (580) 765-3311; gen fax (580) 762-6397; ed fax (580) 765-7800; gen e-mail news@poncacitynews.com; adv e-mail ads@poncacitynews.com; ed e-mail news@poncacitynews.com; web site www.poncacitynews.com
Published: Mon, Tues, Wed, Thur, Fri, Sun
Weekday Frequency: e
News services: AP
Politics: Independent. **Established:** 1897
Not Published: Saturday
Own facility?: Y
Special Weekly Sections: MidWeek
Broadcast Affiliations: WBBZ-AM
Delivery method: Mail, Newsstand, Private Carrier, Racks

POTEAU

POTEAU DAILY NEWS

804 N. Broadway, Poteau, Okla., 74953; gen tel (918) 647-3188; gen fax (918) 647-8198; gen e-mail publisher@poteaudailynews.com; adv e-mail addirector@poteaudailynews.com; ed e-mail editor@poteaudailynews.com; web site www.poteaudailynews.com
Published: Tues, Wed, Thur, Fri, Sat
Weekday Frequency: m
Circulation: 3,900; 4,518(sat)
Last Audit: March 31, 2006
Price: 65.00/yr (in county), $96.00/yr (outside county).
Advertising: Open inch rate $10.17
News services: AP.
Politics: 1886
Special Editions: Progress (Feb); Fact Book (Jul).
Special Weekly Sections: Church (S); Shopper's Guide (Wed).
Magazines: American Profile (Weekly).
Pub.......................................Samantha Hess
Circ. Dir. ....Melisa Adkins
Mng. Ed......................................Laura Young
Mechanical available: Offset; Black and 3 ROP colors.
Commodity Consumption: Avg. Page Number Per Issue - Daily 14; Avg. Page Number Per Issue - Sunday 24; widths 27 1/2; Newsprint Used - Short Tons 250.
Equipment: Editorial Hardware – APP/Mac.; Layout Software – APP/Mac, APP/Mac SE30.; Production Equipment – LE.

PRYOR

THE DAILY TIMES

105 S. Adair St., Pryor, Okla., 74361; gen tel (918) 825-3292; gen fax (918) 825-1965; gen e-mail publisher@pryordailytimes.com; web site www.pryordailytimes.com
Published: Tues, Wed, Thur, Fri, Sun
Weekday Frequency: e
Circulation: 3,787; 5,195(sun)
Last Audit: September 30, 2005
Price: 6.50/mo; 90.00/yr.
Advertising: Open inch rate $13.66
News services: AP, NEA.
Politics: Independent.
Not Published: New Year; Christmas.
Magazines: Relish (Monthly); American Profile (S).
Pub. ....Ken Jones
Classified Mgr...............................Ginny Free
Ed...Kathy Parker
Sports Ed. ....Kenny Howell
Web Ed. ....Summer Woodward
Market Information: TMC.
Mechanical available: Offset; Black and 2 ROP colors; insert accepted.
Mechanical Specifications: Type page 16 1/2 x 21; E - 6 cols, 2, 1/8 between; A - 6 cols, 2, 1/8 between; C - 8 cols, 2 1/16, 1/8 between.
Commodity Consumption: Avg. Page Number Per Issue - Daily 10; Avg. Page Number Per Issue - Sunday 30; widths 25; Newsprint Used - Metric Tons 40; Newsprint Used - Short Tons 14.
Equipment EDITORIAL: Front-end Software – QPS/QuarkXPress 4.x, Baseview/NewsEdit Pro, Adobe/Acrobat.; Editorial Hardware – APP/Mac; Editorial Equipment – Printers □ HP/LaserJet IT CLASSIFIED: Front-end Software – Baseview/Classman Pro.; Classified Hardware – APP/Mac DISPLAY: Ad make-up applications – QPS/QuarkXPress 4.x; Layout Software – AdForce.; Display Hardware – APP/Mac PRODUCTION: Pagination Software – QPS/QuarkXPress 4.x.; Production Equipment – 1-COM, 2-F; Cameras – 1-B, 1-K PRESSROOM: Line 1 – 4-G; Line 2 – 4-HI/Cotrell G; Line 3 – 4-HI/Cotrell G.; Addressing machine – 1/Am.

SAPULPA

SAPULPA DAILY HERALD

16 S. Park St., Sapulpa, Okla., 74066; gen tel (918) 224-5185; gen fax (918) 224-5196; ed e-mail editor@sapulpaheraldonline.com
Published: Mon, Tues, Wed, Thur, Fri, Sun
Weekday Frequency: e
Circulation: 4,501; 4,501(sun)
Last Audit: March 31, 2006
Price: 6.80/mo; 81.60/yr.
Advertising: Open inch rate $16.22
News services: AP.
Politics: Independent. **Established:** 1914
Advertising not accepted: NC-17 movies.
Not Published: Christmas.
Special Weekly Sections: Business (Mon); Expanded Society (S); Grocery Day (Wed).
Magazines: Relish (Monthly); TV Today (entertainment tab) (S); American Profile (Weekly).
Pub..................................Darren D. Sumber
Circ. Dir. ....Michael Valco
Mng. Ed...................................Brinda Shance
Prodn. Mgr...............................Teresa Cooper
Market Information: Split run; TMC.
Mechanical available: Offset; Black and 3 ROP colors; insert accepted; page cutoffs - 22 3/4.
Mechanical Specifications: Type page 13 x 21 1/2; E - 6 cols, 2 1/14, 1/8 between; A - 6 cols, 2 1/14, 1/8 between; C - 8 cols, 1 1/2, 1/8 between.
Commodity Consumption: Avg. Page Number Per Issue - Daily 12; Avg. Page Number Per Issue - Plates Used 10000; Avg. Page Number Per Issue - Sunday 18; widths 27 1/2; Newsprint Used - Short Tons 350; Printing Ink Used - Black 7825; Printing Ink Used - Color 840; Printing Ink Use
Equipment: Editorial Hardware – APP/Mac; Editorial Printers – APP/Mac Laser.; Classified Hardware – APP/Mac. PRODUCTION: Pagination Software – QPS/QuarkXPress.; Production Equipment – 2-APP/Mac LaserPrinter, Image Plus/12; Cameras – Uves/2024 MZ PRESSROOM: Line 1 – 5-G/Community double width 1967; Folders – 1-G/Suburban. MAILROOM: Counter stackers – BG/Count-O-Veyor; Bundle tying machines – Marlow.; Business Hardware – Software □ Vision Data

SEMINOLE

THE SEMINOLE PRODUCER

121 N. Main St., Seminole, Okla., 74868; gen tel (405) 382-1100; adv tel (405) 382-1100; ed tel (405) 382-1100; gen fax (405) 382-1104; adv fax (405) 382-1104; ed fax (405) 382-1104; gen e-mail news@seminoleproducer.com; web site www.seminoleproducer.com
Published: Tues, Wed, Thur, Fri, Sun
Weekday Frequency: e
Circulation: 5,600; 5,600(sun)
Last Audit: September 30, 2005
Price: 6.00/mo; 76.00/yr.
Advertising: Open inch rate $6.30
News services: CNS, NEA, Capitol Press Report.
Politics: Independent.
Not Published: Thanksgiving.
Adv. Mgr., Retail...........................Mike Gifford

Circ. Dir. ....John Lewis
Entertainment/Amusements Ed.....Cheryl Phillips
Religion Ed. ....Donny Cofer
Science/Technology Ed....................Stu Phillips
Teen-Age/Youth Ed......................Cody Phillips
Market Information: TMC.
Mechanical available: Offset; Black and 2 ROP colors; insert accepted; page cutoffs - 22 3/4.
Mechanical Specifications: Type page 13 x 21; E - 6 cols, 2 1/16, 1/8 between; A - 6 cols, 2 1/16, 1/8 between; C - 9 cols, 1 3/8, 1/16 between.
Commodity Consumption: Avg. Page Number Per Issue - Daily 10; Avg. Page Number Per Issue - Plates Used 2900; Avg. Page Number Per Issue - Sunday 18; widths 30; Newsprint Used - Short Tons 88; Printing Ink Used - Black 2180; Printing Ink Used - Pages Printed 2888.
Equipment EDITORIAL: Front-end Software – Microsoft/Windows.; Editorial Hardware – PC; Editorial Printers – HP/IV CLASSIFIED: Front-end Software – ListMaster.; Classified Hardware – PC; Classified Printers – HP/LaserWriter 4 DISPLAY: Ad make-up applications – Microsoft/Windows; Layout Software – PC 486-50.; Display Hardware – PC; Display Printers – HP/LaserWriter 4; Production Equipment – APP/Mac NT; Cameras – 1-CL/24. PRESSROOM: Line 1 – 3-G/Community; Folders – 1; Addressing machine – RSK/Model II-LP V, Wm. AUDIO: Audio Software – Community Information Systems 3.9; Audio Hardware – PC; Business Hardware – 2-RAM/486, 1-HP/386

SHAWNEE

SHAWNEE NEWS-STAR

215 N. Bell Ave., Shawnee, Okla., 74802-1688; gen tel (405) 273-4200; gen fax (405) 273-4207; gen e-mail newsroom@news-star.com; web site www.news-star.com
Published: Tues, Wed, Thur, Fri, Sat, Sun
Weekday Frequency: m
Circulation: 7,175; 7,175(sat); 8,334(sun)
Last Audit: September 30, 2009
Price: 9.25/mo; 96.00/yr.
Advertising: Open inch rate $10.00
News services: AP.
Politics: Independent.
Special Editions: School (Aug); Christmas (Dec); Bridal (Jan); Lawn and Garden (Mar); Gift Guide (Nov); Home Improvement (Sept).
Magazines: Relish (Monthly); Color Comics (Other); USA WEEKEND Magazine (S).
Bus. Mgr. ....Jeri McEntire
Adv. Mgr. ....Sherry J. Lankford
Adv. Mgr., Classified.....................Stacy Harris
Mng. Ed........................................Josh Burton
Editorial Page Ed...................Mike McCormick
Sports Ed...Fred Fehr
Prodn. Mgr.............................Robby Parsons
Mechanical available: Offset; Black and 3 ROP colors; insert accepted; page cutoffs - 21 1/2.
Mechanical Specifications: Type page 11 5/8 x 21 1/2; E - 6 cols, 1 5/6, 1/8 between; A - 6 cols, 1 5/6, 1/8 between; C - 9 cols, 1/6 between.
Commodity Consumption: Avg. Page Number Per Issue - Daily 28; Avg. Page Number Per Issue - Plates Used 17400; Avg. Page Number Per Issue - Sunday 66; widths 25; Newsprint Used - Short Tons 698; Printing Ink Used - Black 16711; Printing Ink Used - Color 6300; Printing Ink Used
Equipment EDITORIAL: Front-end Software – Baseview.; Editorial Hardware – APP/Mac, 6-APP/Mac G3, 6-APP/Mac 7300-180; Editorial Printers – APP/Mac LaserWriter 16-600, MON/1270 CLASSIFIED: Front-end Software – Baseview/Ad Manager Pro.; Classified Hardware – APP/Mac, 5-APP/Mac G4; Classified Printers – HP/5M; Layout Software – APP/Mac G3/G4, APP/Mac 8500-180, APP/Mac Quadra 800.; Display Hardware – Printers ☐ QMS/860 Plus, 2-Panther/RIP, HP/5000; Display Printers – Software ☐ Multi-Ad 6.5, Aldus/PageMaker 7.0, QPS/QuarkXPress 4.11 PRODUCTION: Pagination Software – Quark.; Production Equipment – APP/Mac LaserWriter, Caere/OmniPage Pro 2.1, Adobe/Photoshop, APP/Mac G4; Cameras – 1-R/500; Scanners – APP/Mac, Microtek/IIx, HP/9850A, HP/6100C PRESSROOM: Line 1 – 7-G/U 1083; Folders – 1 MAILROOM: Counter stackers – 1-BG/Count-O-Veyor; Inserters and stuffers – 1-MM/227; Bundle tying machines – 1-MLN/ML2EE; Addressing machine – KAN/550, KAN-Quarter Folder. BUSINESS COMPUTERS: Business Software – APP/Mac Share; Business Hardware – ATT/Unix PC

STILLWATER

THE NEWS PRESS

211 W. Ninth St., Stillwater, Okla., 74074; gen tel (405) 372-5000; adv tel (405) 372-5000; ed tel (405) 372-5000; gen fax (405) 372-3112; adv fax (405) 780-9993; ed fax (405) 372-3112; gen e-mail news@stwnewspress.com; adv e-mail advdept@stwnewspress.com; ed e-mail news@stwnewspress.com; web site www.stwnewspress.com
Published: Mon, Tues, Wed, Thur, Fri, Sat, Sun
Saturday Frequency: m
Circulation: 7,122; 7,122(sat); 7,956(sun)
Last Audit: September 30, 2009
Price: 8.75/mo; 97.00/yr.
Advertising: Open inch rate $14.85
News services: AP, SHNS.
Politics: Independent.
Advertising not accepted: Adult Industry.
Special Editions: Home Improvement (Apr); Back-to-School (Aug); Last Minute Gift Guide (Dec); Bridal (Jan); Payne County Fair (Jul); Progress (Jun); Home & Garden (Mar); Graduation (May); Christmas Gift Guide (Nov); Home Improvement (Oct); Fall Fashion (Sept).
Special Weekly Sections: Real Estate Weekly (Fri); Agriculture (S); Click (Thur); Food (Wed).
Magazines: Relish (Monthly); Comics (S).
Pub....Pam Nelson
Adv. Dir. ....Jill Hunt
Real Estate Ed. ....Laura Wilson
Prodn. Mgr., Pressroom..................Bart Clarke
Market Information: ADS; TMC.
Mechanical available: Offset; Black and 3 ROP colors; insert accepted; page cutoffs - 21 3/4.
Mechanical Specifications: Type page 11 1/8 x 21 1/2; E - 6 cols, 1 3/4, 1/8 between; A - 6 cols, 3 5/8, between; C - 8 cols, between.
Commodity Consumption: Avg. Page Number Per Issue - Daily 30; Avg. Page Number Per Issue - Plates Used 5460; Avg. Page Number Per Issue - Sunday 60; widths 12; Newsprint Used - Short Tons 836; Printing Ink Used - Black 24000; Printing Ink Used - Color 780; Printing Ink Used -
Equipment EDITORIAL: Front-end Software – FSI.; Editorial Hardware – 7-APP/Power Mac, 4-APP/Mac Quadra, APP/Mac G4, 7-APP/eMac, 4-APP/iMac; Editorial Printers – HP/Color Laser 5M, HP/8000 DN, HP/Laser Jet 6MP, Pre Press/Panther Plus 46 Imagesetter CLASSIFIED: Front-end Software – FSI.; Classified Hardware – APP/Mac G4, APP/eMac; Classified Printers – Okidata/Microline 320, APP/Mac LaserJet III DISPLAY: Ad make-up applications – Multi-Ad/Creator 4.02, Adobe/Photoshop 5.5, Adobe/Typesetter, QPS/QuarkXPres; Display Hardware – APP/iMac, 2-APP/Mac G4 400 mhz, 3-APP/Mac G4 466 mhz; Display Printers – HP/Color LaserJet 5M, APP/Mac LaserJet 8000DN, Pre Press/Panther Plus 46, ECR/Imagesetter PRODUCTION: Pagination Software – FSI.; Production Equipment – 1-Nu, ECR/Scriptsetter VRL-36, 1-HP/5M, 1-Pre Press/Panther Plus 46, APP/Mac LaserJet 8000 DN; Cameras – 1-L, 1-Companica/680c; Scanners – 3-HP/ScanJet 11cx, Scan Master/X6 PRESSROOM: Line 1 – 7-G/Community 1976; Folders – 1-G/Suburban. MAILROOM: Counter stackers – 1/BG; Inserters and stuffers – 1-KAN/480; Bundle tying machines – 3-/Bu; Addressing machine – St.; Business Hardware – 1-IBM/370-168

STILLWATER PUBLISHING CO.

211 W. 9th, Stillwater, Okla., 74076; gen tel (405) 372-5000; gen fax (405) 372-3112

TAHLEQUAH

TAHLEQUAH DAILY PRESS

106 W. Second St., Tahlequah, Okla., 74464; gen tel (918) 456-8833; gen fax (918) 456-2019; adv e-mail advertising@tahlequahdailypress.com; web site www.tahlequahdailypress.com
Published: Tues, Wed, Thur, Fri, Sun
Weekday Frequency: e
Circulation: 6,881; 6,881(sun)
Last Audit: September 30, 2005
Price: 84.00/yr.
Advertising: Open inch rate $11.25
News services: AP.
Politics: Independent. **Established:** 1844
Not Published: Christmas.
Special Editions: Progress (Apr); Football (Aug); Retirement (Jul); Vacation (May); Gift-A-Rama (Nov).
Special Weekly Sections: Church (Fri).
Magazines: Relish (Monthly); USA WEEKEND Magazine (S); American Profile (Weekly).
Pub.......................................Charlotte Klutts
Adv. Dir. ....Pam Hutson
Circ. Mgr. ....Jerry Harrington
Mng. Ed.................................Kim Poindexter
Market Information: TMC.
Mechanical available: Offset; Black and 3 ROP colors; insert accepted; page cutoffs - 21 1/2.
Mechanical Specifications: Type page 13 1/4 x 21 1/2; E - 6 cols, 2 1/16, 1/8 between; A - 6 cols, 2 1/16, 1/8 between; C - 9 cols, 1 1/2, 1/8 between.
Commodity Consumption: Avg. Page Number Per Issue - Daily 20; Avg. Page Number Per Issue - Sunday 50.
Equipment; Editorial Hardware – 9-APP/Mac; Editorial Equipment – 2-COM/II, 2-COM/7200.; Classified Equipment – 2-COM/Junior.; Production Equipment – 1-Nu; Cameras – 1-K/Vertical 240. PRESSROOM: Line 1 – 5; Bundle tying machines – 1/Bu; Addressing machine – 2-Am/1900.

TULSA

TULSA WORLD

315 S. Boulder Ave., Tulsa, Okla., 74103-3401; gen tel (918) 583-2161; adv tel (918) 581-8510; ed tel (918) 581-8330; adv fax (918) 583-3550; ed fax (918) 581-8353; gen e-mail webmaster@tulsaworld.com; ed e-mail news@tulsaworld.com; web site www.tulsaworld.com
Group: Metro Newspaper Advertising Services, Inc.
Published: Mon, Tues, Wed, Thur, Fri, Sat, Sun
Weekday Frequency: m
Saturday Frequency: m
Circulation: 97,580; 107,408(sat); 140,126(sun)
Last Audit: ABC September 30, 2011
Price: 18.00/mo; 216.00/yr.
Advertising: Open inch rate $145.00
News services: AP, LAT-WP, MCT, GNS.
Politics: Independent. **Established:** 1905
Special Editions: Football Preview (Aug); Christmas Gift Guide (Dec).
Special Weekly Sections: Entertainment (Fri); Entertainment (S); World of Homes (Sat); Fashion (Thur); Best Food Day (Wed).
Magazines: USA WEEKEND Magazine (S).
Chrmn. of the Bd.....................Robert E. Lorton
Pres....John R. Bair
Pub. ....Robert Lorton
Vice Pres./Treasurer ....Frank Hawkins
Sec. ....Harold Salisbury
Dir., HR................................Delbert L. Rice
Credit Mgr.....................................Sam Smith
Chief Accountant.......................Susan Cashon
Adv. Dir. ....Bernie Schutz
Exec. Ed........................................Joe Worley
Mng. Ed. ....Susan Ellerbach
Bus. Ed. ....John Stancavage
City Ed...................................Ziva Branstetter
Editorial Page Ed..........................David Averill
Editorial Writer ....Wayne Greene
Entertainment Ed. ....Mark Brown
Fashion/Style Ed...............Jason Ashley Wright
Graphics Ed. ....David Housh
Health/Medical Writer......................Kim Archer
Night Ed...................................Colleen Smith
Market Information: ADS; Split run; TMC.
Mechanical available: Offset; Black and 3 ROP colors; insert accepted; page cutoffs - 21.
Mechanical Specifications: Type page 12 1/4 x 21; E - 6 cols, 1 15/16, 1/8 between; A - 6 cols, 1 15/16, 1/8 between; C - 10 cols, 1 1/8, 1/16 between.
Commodity Consumption: Avg. Page Number Per Issue - Daily 60; Avg. Page Number Per Issue - Saturday 64; Avg. Page Number Per Issue - Sunday 120; widths 52; Newsprint Used - Short Tons 18000.
Equipment EDITORIAL: Front-end Software – SII.; Editorial Hardware – 2-Tandem/CLX RISC-File Server; Editorial Printers – DEC, Tandem CLASSIFIED: Front-end Software – SII.; Classified Hardware – 2-Tandem/CLX-RISC file-server; Classified Printers – Dataproducts, DEC, Tandem PRODUCTION: Pagination Software – SII/ICP (Classified).; Production Equipment – 3-AU/3850; Scanners – Data/Oy-Plate Scanner PRESSROOM: Line 1 – Wifag/OF 370 GTD double width 1998; Line 2 – Wifag/OF 370 GTD double width 2000; Folders – Wifag/Jaw Folder (one per line). MAILROOM: Counter stackers – 6-QWI/350, 2-HL/HT; Inserters and stuffers – 1-HI/NP 630; Bundle tying machines – 5-MLN/MLN2, 7/Power Strap; Wrapping singles – 4-/Power Strap 3/4; Mailroom control system – HI/Prima; Addressing machine – 1-/BH.

WORLD PUBLISHING CO.

315 S. Boulder Ave., Tulsa, Okla., 74103; gen tel (918) 583-2161; gen fax (918) 584-8966

VINITA

THE VINITA DAILY JOURNAL

138-140 S. Wilson St., Vinita, Okla., 74301-0328; gen tel (918) 256-6422; gen fax (918) 256-7100; gen e-mail vdjnews@cableone.net; vdj@cableone.net; ed e-mail vdjeditor@cableone.net
Published: Mon, Tues, Wed, Thur, Fri
Weekday Frequency: e
Circulation: 4,331
Last Audit: March 31, 2006
Price: 72.60/yr.
Advertising: Open inch rate $12.12
News services: AP, NEA.
Politics: Independent.
Not Published: New Year; Memorial Day; Independence Day; Labor Day; Thanksgiving; Christmas.
Special Editions: Home Improvement (Apr); Rodeo Pioneer (Aug); Christmas (Dec); Business Profiles (Jul); Christmas (Nov); Almanac (Oct); Calf Fry (Sept).
Magazines: Vinita Viewer (Fri).
Pres...Phillip R. Reid
Pub...John Link
Adv. Mgr. ....Jannett Link
Mng. Ed....................................David Burgess
Lifestyle Ed.............................Brenda Haskell
Prodn. Supt.....................................Joe Wallis
Market Information: Split run; TMC.
Mechanical available: Offset; Black and 2 ROP colors; insert accepted - cards; page cutoffs - 22 3/4.
Mechanical Specifications: Type page 13 x 21 1/2; E - 6 cols, 2 1/16, 1/8 between; A - 6 cols, 2 1/16, 1/8 between; C - 8 cols, 1 1/2, 1/16 between.
Commodity Consumption: Avg. Page Number Per Issue - Daily 8; Avg. Page Number Per Issue - Plates Used 3600; widths 27 1/2; Newsprint Used - Short Tons 66; Printing Ink

Used - Black 3600; Printing Ink Used - Color 150; Printing Ink Used - Pages Printed 2600.
Equipment; Editorial Hardware – APP/Mac. DISPLAY: Ad make-up applications – Aldus/PageMaker 3.0; Layout Software – APP/Mac.; Display Hardware – APP/Mac; Production Equipment – 1-Nu; Cameras – 1-R/HOR12. PRESSROOM: Line 1 – 3-KP/News King; Folders – 1; Inserters and stuffers – 1-DG/320, KAN; Addressing machine – 1/St.; Business Hardware – PC

WEATHERFORD

WEATHERFORD DAILY NEWS

118 S. Broadway, Weatherford, Okla., 73096-0191; gen tel (580) 772-3301; gen fax (580) 772-7329; gen e-mail wdn@wdnonline.com; adv e-mail wdn@wdnonline.com; web site www.wdnonline.com
Published: Tues, Wed, Thur, Fri, Sat
Weekday Frequency: m
Circulation: 4,464; 4,464(sat)
Last Audit: March 31, 2006
Price: 8.00/mo; 74.00/yr.
Advertising: Open inch rate $12.84
News services: AP, CNS, NYT, TMS.
Advertising not accepted: 900 numbers.
Special Editions: Parade of Homes (Apr); Koupon Kraze (Aug); Christmas Greetings (Dec); Valentine's Promo (Feb); Health Quarterly (Jan); Summer Clearance (Jul); Father's Day Gift Guide (Jun); Spring Home Improvement Tab (Mar); Sidewalk Sales (May); Gift Guide (Nov); 4-H We
Magazines: TV Entertainment Tab (S).
Sec./Treasurer....................Jeanne Ann Reid
Adv. Dir.....................Brenda Johnson
City Ed.....................Julie Harding
Sports Ed.....................Jeff Barron
Columnist....................Phillip R. Reid
Lifestyle Ed.....................Emily Sims
Prodn. Mgr.....................Bobby Vaughn
Market Information: ADS; TMC.
Mechanical available: Offset; Black and 3 ROP colors; insert accepted - any; page cutoffs - 18 1/2.
Mechanical Specifications: Type page 11 5/8 x 21 1/2; E - 6 cols, 1 7/8, 1/8 between; A - 6 cols, 1 7/8, 1/8 between; C - 6 cols, 1 7/8, 1/8 between.
Commodity Consumption: Avg. Page Number Per Issue - Daily 10; Avg. Page Number Per Issue - Plates Used 3500; Avg. Page Number Per Issue - Sunday 34; widths 25; Newsprint Used - Short Tons 11; Printing Ink Used - Black 46; Printing Ink Used - Color 12; Printing Ink Used - Pages
Equipment EDITORIAL: Front-end Software – IBM.; Editorial Hardware – IBM; Editorial Printers – HP/LaserWriter CLASSIFIED: Front-end Software – IBM, Microsoft/Word.; Classified Hardware – IBM; Classified Printers – HP/LaserPrinter DISPLAY: Ad make-up applications – Aldus/PageMaker, Adobe/Typestyler, APP/Mac Scan; Layout Software – IBM.; Production Equipment – P/24SQ, IBM/PC; Cameras – 1-Nu/SST 1822x2024; Scanners – HP/Scan. PRESSROOM: Line 1 – 4-G/0-1047; Folders – 1; Inserters and stuffers – KAN/320; Addressing machine – Bundle tying machines □ 1/Ca.; Business Hardware – 2-RSK, IBM

WOODWARD

WOODWARD NEWS

904 Oklahoma, Woodward, Okla., 73801; gen tel (580) 256-2200; adv tel (580) 256-2200; ed tel (580) 256-2200; gen fax (580) 254-2159; adv fax (580) 254-2159; ed fax (580) 254-2159; gen e-mail editor@woodwardnews.net; publisher@woodwardnews.net; adv e-mail publisher@woodwardnews.net; ed e-mail editor@woodwardnews.net; web site www.woodwardnews.net
Group: CNHI
Published: Tues, Wed, Thur, Fri, Sat, Sun
Weekday Frequency: e
Saturday Frequency: e
Circulation: 3,600; 3,600(sat); 3,700(sun)
Last Audit: Sworn September 30, 2005
Price: 9.30/mo; 109.00/yr.
Advertising: Open inch rate $7.48
News services: AP.
Politics: Independent.
Not Published: Thanksgiving; Christmas.
Own facility?: Y
Special Editions: Fall Sports (Aug); Spring Sports (Jan); Back-to-School (Jul); Progress (Mar).
Special Weekly Sections: Church (Fri); TV Magazine (S); Church (Sat)
Magazines: Relish (Monthly); American Profile (Weekly).
Adv. Dir.....................Sheila Gay
Sports Ed.....................Johnny McMahan
Pub.....................Rich Macke
Business Manager....................Lettie Chaisson
Market Information: TMC
Mechanical available: Offset; Black and 3 ROP colors; insert accepted; page cutoffs - 16 1/2.
Mechanical Specifications: Type page 10 3/4 x 16 1/2; E - 5 cols, 2 1/16, 1/8 between; A - 5 cols, 2 1/16, 1/8 between; C - 5 cols, 2 1/16, 1/8 between.
Commodity Consumption: Avg. Page Number Per Issue - Daily 20; Avg. Page Number Per Issue - Sunday 18; widths 35.
Equipment EDITORIAL: Front-end Software – Baseview/NewsEdit, QPS/QuarkXPress.; Editorial Hardware – APP/Mac; Editorial Printers – APP/Mac LaserWriter IIf CLASSIFIED: Front-end Software – Baseview.; Classified Hardware – APP/Mac; Classified Printers – APP/Mac LaserWriter IIg DISPLAY: Ad make-up applications – QPS/QuarkXPress, Claris/MacWrite, Microsoft/Excel.; Display Hardware – APP/Mac; Display Printers – APP/Mac LaserWriter IIg; Production Equipment – P, Adobe/Photoshops.
Delivery method: Mail, Racks

OREGON

ALBANY

ALBANY DEMOCRAT-HERALD

600 Lyon St. SW, Albany, Ore., 97321-0041; gen tel (541) 926-2211; gen fax (541) 926-4799; adv fax (541) 926-5298; ed fax (541) 926-5298; gen e-mail news@dhonline.com; ed e-mail news@dhonline.com; web site www.democratherald.com
Published: Mon, Tues, Wed, Thur, Fri, Sat, Sun
Weekday Frequency: m
Saturday Frequency: m
Circulation: 14,399; 16,068(sat); 15,084(sun)
Last Audit: ABC September 30, 2011
Price: 138.00/yr; 9.80/4wk.
Advertising: Open inch rate $66.25
News services: AP, LAT, WP.
Politics: Independent. **Established:** 1865
Special Editions: Home Improvement/Lawn & Garden (Apr); Back-to-School (Aug); Gift Guides (Dec); Half-off Extravaganza (Jan); Crazy Days (Jul); Timber Carnival (Jun); Progress (Mar); Summer Activities (May); Senior Page (Monthly); Christmas Opening (Nov); Holiday Bazaar (O
Special Weekly Sections: Home & Garden Advice (Fri); Business News (Mon); People (Sat); People (Thur); People (Tues); People (Wed).
Magazines: Relish (Monthly); USA WEEKEND Magazine (S).
Pub.....................Martha Wells
Controller....................Ed Bengtson
HR Mgr.....................Nancy Hawkins
Adv. Coord., Nat'l/Inserts....................Sherri Frost
Adv. Team Leader, Retail....................Judie Weissert
Circ. Mgr.....................Jeannetta Mickler
Online Ed.....................Graham Kislingbury
Bus. Ed.....................Bennett Hall
Editorial Page Ed.....................Hasso Hering
News Clerk....................Heather Crabtree
News Ed.....................Kim Jackson
People Ed.....................Steve Lundeberg
Photo Ed.....................Mark Ylen
Sports Ed.....................Rob Preiwe
Asst. Sports Ed., Mid Valley Sports....Aaron Yost
Sunday Ed.....................Mike Henneke
Dir., Mgmt. Info Servs.....................Bill Draper
Online Coord.....................Kim Frazier
Market Information: ADS; Split run; TMC.
Mechanical available: Offset; Black and 3 ROP colors; insert accepted - free-standing inserts; page cutoffs - 22 3/4.
Mechanical Specifications: Type page 11 5/8 x 21; E - 6 cols, 1 4/5, between; A - 6 cols, 1 4/5, between; C - 9 cols, 1 1/5, between.
Commodity Consumption: Avg. Page Number Per Issue - Daily 28; Avg. Page Number Per Issue - Plates Used 14402; widths 25; Newsprint Used - Metric Tons 1157; Newsprint Used - Short Tons 1275; Printing Ink Used - Black 28568; Printing Ink Used - Color 3485; Printing Ink Used - Pa
Equipment EDITORIAL: Front-end Software – QPS/QuarkXPress 4.1, Baseview/NewsEdit Pro 3.2, APP/TCP-IP Appleshare Network.; Editorial Hardware – 8-APP/iMac G3, 9-APP/Mac G4 Workstations, APP/Mac G4 Server; Editorial Equipment – APP/Mac G3 I Book; Editorial Printers – ECR/Scriptsetter IV, Xante/Accel-a-Writer 3G CLASSIFIED: Front-end Software – CText/Advisison, CText/Alps.; Classified Hardware – 5-Gateway/Pentium 200, APP/Mac G4 Server; Classified Printers – 1-HP/Laserjet 8000N DISPLAY: Ad make-up applications – Multi-Ad/Creator 4.02, Macromedia/Freehand 9.0, Adobe/Photoshop 6.0, Adobe/Acrobat 5.0; Layout Software – 6-APP/Mac G3 Worksation, APP/Powerma; Display Hardware – APP/Mac G4 Server; Display Printers – HP/Laserjet 8100N PRODUCTION: Pagination Software – QPS/QuarkXPress 4.1, ALS.; Production Equipment – 1-Panther/Pro, 1-ECR/Pelbox 1245 CS, ECR/Scriptsetter VRL-36/HS, APP/Powermac 8100/100, APP/Powermac 7500/100; Cameras – 1-C/Spartan II; Scanners – ECR/Autokon 1030C PRESSROOM: Line 1 – 6-G/Urbanite single width; Folders – 1; Press control system – 2; Press registration system – Duarte/Pin Registration System. MAILROOM: Counter stackers – 1/BG; Inserters and stuffers – 2-KAN/480 6:1; Bundle tying machines – 1-/Strapex, 2-EAM-Mosca; Addressing machine – 1-KAN/650, KR/label head. AUDIO: Audio Software – Phonemaster/2000 12-line #1590; Audio Hardware – U.S. Telecom; Business Hardware – NCR/10000-55

ASHLAND

THE ASHLAND DAILY TIDINGS

1661 Siskiyou Blvd., Ashland, Ore., 97520-0061; gen tel (541) 482-3456; adv tel (541) 488-1484; gen fax (541) 482-3688; gen e-mail class@dailytidings.com; web site www.dailytidings.com
Published: Mon, Tues, Wed, Thur, Fri, Sat
Weekday Frequency: e
Circulation: 5,010; 5,010(sat)
Last Audit: September 30, 2002
Price: 15.30/mo (in-state), $12.85/mo (out-of-state); 141.60/yr.
Advertising: Open inch rate $20.93
News services: AP.
Politics: Independent. **Established:** 1876
Not Published: New Year; Memorial Day; Independence Day; Labor Day; Thanksgiving; Christmas.
Special Editions: Scene (Apr); Back-to-School (Aug); Christmas Gift Guides (Dec); Fourth of July (Jun); Home and Garden (Mar); Shakespeare (May); Health and Fitness (Quarterly); Southern Oregon University (Sept).
Special Weekly Sections: Restaurant Page (Fri); Business (Mon); Revels (Thur); Best Food Day (Tues).
Magazines: Revels/On Television (Entertainment) (Thur).
Pub.....................James Grady Singletary
Circ. Dir.....................John Mihalyo
Adv. Dir.....................Dena DeRose
Ed.....................Bob Hunter
City Ed.....................Myles Murphy
Content Ed.....................Mike Green
Sports Ed.....................Joe Zavala
Market Information: ADS; TMC.
Mechanical available: Offset; Black and 3 ROP colors; insert accepted - any; page cutoffs - 22 3/4.
Mechanical Specifications: Type page 13 x 21 1/2; E - 6 cols, 1 7/8, 1/8 between; A - 6 cols, 1 7/8, 1/8 between; C - 9 cols, 1 3/4, 1/16 between.
Commodity Consumption: Avg. Page Number Per Issue - Daily 18; Avg. Page Number Per Issue - Plates Used 5100; widths 25 1/2; Newsprint Used - Metric Tons 330; Printing Ink Used - Black 6906; Printing Ink Used - Color 790; Printing Ink Used - Pages Printed 6400.
Equipment EDITORIAL: Front-end Software – Baseview/NewsEdit Pro IQ 3.1.; Editorial Hardware – 10-APP/Mac CLASSIFIED: Front-end Software – Baseview.; Classified Hardware – 3-APP/Mac; Production Equipment – 4-APP/Mac, 2-APP/Mac LaserPrinter, Konica/EV Jetsetter 5100S; Cameras – 1-SCREEN/650-D. PRESSROOM: Line 1 – 6-G/Community; Line 2 – 4; Folders – 1-G/2:1.; Bundle tying machines – MLN; Addressing machine – Pressure Sensitive/Labeling.; Business Hardware – NCR

ASTORIA

THE DAILY ASTORIAN

949 Exchange St., Astoria, Ore., 97103-0210; gen tel (503) 325-3211; adv tel (503) 325-3211; ed tel (503) 325-3211; gen fax (503) 325-6573; adv fax (503) 325-6573; ed fax (503) 325-6573; gen e-mail astoria@dailyastorian.com; adv e-mail sales@dailyastorian.com; ed e-mail astoria@dailyastorian.com; web site www.dailyastorian.com
Published: Mon, Tues, Wed, Thur, Fri
Weekday Frequency: e
Circulation: 7,500
Last Audit: Sworn September 30, 2008
Price: 9.00/mo (carrier), $13.00/mo (mail).
Advertising: Open inch rate $17.05
News services: AP, NYT.
Politics: Independent. **Established:** 1873
Not Published: Christmas.
Own facility?: Y
Special Editions: The Lives They Lived (Jan); Bridal Planner (Feb & October); Visitor's Guide (Jan); Good Health Directory (Mar); Spring Sports Tab (Mar); Crab, Seafood & Wine Festival (Apr.), Coastal Menu Guide (Jun); Scandinavian Festival (Jun); Car Care (Jun); Clatsop County Fair (July); At Home (July); Astoria Regatta (Aug); Who's Who in Clatsop Cty (Aug); Fall Sports Tab (Sept); Women In Business (Sept); Liberty Theater Presents (sept); Astor Street Opry (Oct); Home For the Holidays (Nov); Winter Sports Tab (Nov) & Property Lines (Jan, Mar, May, July, Sept., & Nov)
Special Weekly Sections: Community (Fri); Arts & Entertainment (Thur); TV (Wed).
Magazines: Coast Weekend (Thur).
Adv. Mgr.....................Betty Smith
Circ. Mgr.....................Samantha Mclaren
Editorial Page Ed.....................Stephen A. Forrester
Photo Dept. Mgr.....................Alex Pajunas
Sports Ed.....................Gary Henley
Wire Ed.....................Patrick Webb
Online Mgr.....................Cridalyn Lyster
Prodn. Mgr., Systems....................John Bruijin
Prodn. Mgr., Pressroom....................Jim Stanowich
Market Information: TMC.
Mechanical available: Web Offset; Black and 3 ROP colors; insert accepted; page cutoffs - 22 3/4.
Mechanical Specifications: Type page 12 3/4 x 21 1/2; E - 6 cols, 2, 1/6 between; A - 6 cols, 2, 1/6 between; C - 8 cols, 1 1/2, 1/8 between.

Commodity Consumption: Avg. Page Number Per Issue - Daily 20; Avg. Page Number Per Issue - Plates Used 2700; widths 27; Newsprint Used - Metric Tons 420; Printing Ink Used - Black 12000; Printing Ink Used - Color 1800; Printing Ink Used - Pages Printed 5120.
Equipment EDITORIAL: Front-end Software – QPS/QuarkXPress, Baseview, Multi-Ad.; Editorial Hardware – APP/Mac; Editorial Printers – APP/Mac LaserWriter NTX, APP/Mac LaserWriter IIg, APP/Mac LaserWriter Pro 630, Au/APS 6-84 Imagesetter CLASSIFIED: Front-end Software – QPS/QuarkXPress, Baseview, Multi-Ad.; Classified Hardware – APP/Mac DISPLAY: Ad make-up applications – Multi-Ad/Creator.; Display Hardware – APP/Mac; Display Printers – APP/Mac LaserWriter NTX, APP/Mac LaserWriter IIg, APP/Mac LaserWriter Pro 630 PRODUCTION: Pagination Software – QPS/QuarkXPress 3.3.; Production Equipment – Au/APS-6-84-ACS; Cameras – K/V-241; Scanners – LaCie/Silver Scan II, Nikon/LS52000 PRESSROOM: Line 1 – 7-G/Community 1970; Folders – 1-G/SC.; Inserters and stuffers – MM/227; Bundle tying machines – . BUSINESS COMPUTERS: Business Software – Excel 5; Business Hardware – Vision Data
Zip Codes served: 97102, 97103, 97110, 98614, 97016, 97138, 97121, 98624, 98631, 97130, 98637, 98638, 97131, 98640, 98641, 97138, 98644, 97145, 97146, 97016, 97147
Delivery method: Mail, Newsstand, Private Carrier, Racks

BAKER CITY

BAKER CITY HERALD

1915 1st St., Baker City, Ore., 97814-0807; gen tel (541) 523-3673; adv tel (541) 523-3673; ed tel (541) 523-3673; gen fax (541) 523-6426; adv fax (541) 523-6426; ed fax (541) 523-6426; gen e-mail info@bakercityherald.com; adv e-mail ads@bakercityherald.com; ed e-mail news@bakercityherald.com; web site www.bakercityherald.com
Group: Western Communications, Inc.
Published: Mon, Wed, Fri
Weekday Frequency: e
Circulation: 2,769
Last Audit: Sworn September 30, 2005
Price: 12.50/mo; 150.00/yr.
Advertising: Open inch rate$11.16
Insert rate: $58.75/m open rate
News services: AP, MCT.
Politics: Independent. **Established:** 1870
Not Published: Christmas.
Own facility?: Y
Special Editions: Health Directory (Jan); Miners' Jubilee (Jul); Agriculture Outlook(Mar)and Harvest (Oct.); Business Guide (Oct); Sports Previews (Mar., Aug., Nov); Baker County Visitors Guide (May); Winter Recreation Guide (Nov.)
Special Weekly Sections: Healthy Living (Fri); Food/Living (Wed.) A&E/TV (Wed.)
Magazines: GO! (TV, Arts & Leisure) (Thur); American Profile (Weekly).
Publisher .... Kari Borgen
Mgr., Promo. .... Lynette Perry
Health/Medical Ed. .... Christine Collins
News Ed. .... Jayson Jacoby
Photo Ed. .... S. John Collins
Sports Ed. .... Gerry Steele
Prodn. Mgr. .... Frank Everidge
Circ. Dir. .... Tom Hooton
Entertainment/Amusements Ed .... Lisa Britton
Farm/Agriculture Ed. .... Ed Merriman
Mgmt. Info Serv. Mgr. .... Mark Turner
Mechanical available: Offset; Black and 4 ROP colors; insert accepted - in-house printing, inserts must be 8 1/2 x 11; page cutoffs - 22.
Mechanical Specifications: Type page 11 3/4 x 21; E - 6 cols, 1 7/8, 1/8 between; A - 6 cols, 1 7/8, 1/8 between; C - 8 cols, 1 1/3, 1/8 between.
Commodity Consumption: widths 14; Newsprint Used - Short Tons 120; Printing Ink Used - Black 5400; Printing Ink Used - Color 600; Printing Ink Used - Pages Printed 3442.
Equipment EDITORIAL: Front-end Software – QPS/QuarkXPress ; Editorial Hardware – APP/Mac CLASSIFIED: Front-end Software – MediaSpan Ad Manager Pro 4, version 1.9; Classified Hardware – APP/Mac; Classified Printers – Okidata/591 DISPLAY: Ad make-up applications – QPS/QuarkXPress 3.32, Adobe/Illustrator; Layout Software – APP/Mac.; Display Printers – APP/Mac, HP/Laser 4MV; Cameras – Canon PRESSROOM: Line 1 – 6-G/Community; Folders – 1-G/SSC.; Inserters and stuffers – Mueller ; Bundle tying machines – MLN/Single strap; Addressing machine – Wm. BUSINESS COMPUTERS: Business Software – PBS, Advertising Management
Zip Codes served: 97814, 97833, 97834, 97877
Delivery method: Mail, Newsstand, Private Carrier, Racks

BEND

THE BULLETIN

1777 SW Chandler Ave., Bend, Ore., 97702-3200; gen tel (541) 382-1811; adv tel (541) 385-5809; ed tel (541) 383-0367; gen fax (541) 385-5802; adv fax (541) 385-5802; ed fax (541) 385-5804; gen e-mail bulletin@bendbulletin.com; adv e-mail jbrandt@bendbulletin.com; web site www.bendbulletin.com
Published: Mon, Tues, Wed, Thur, Fri, Sat, Sun
Weekday Frequency: m

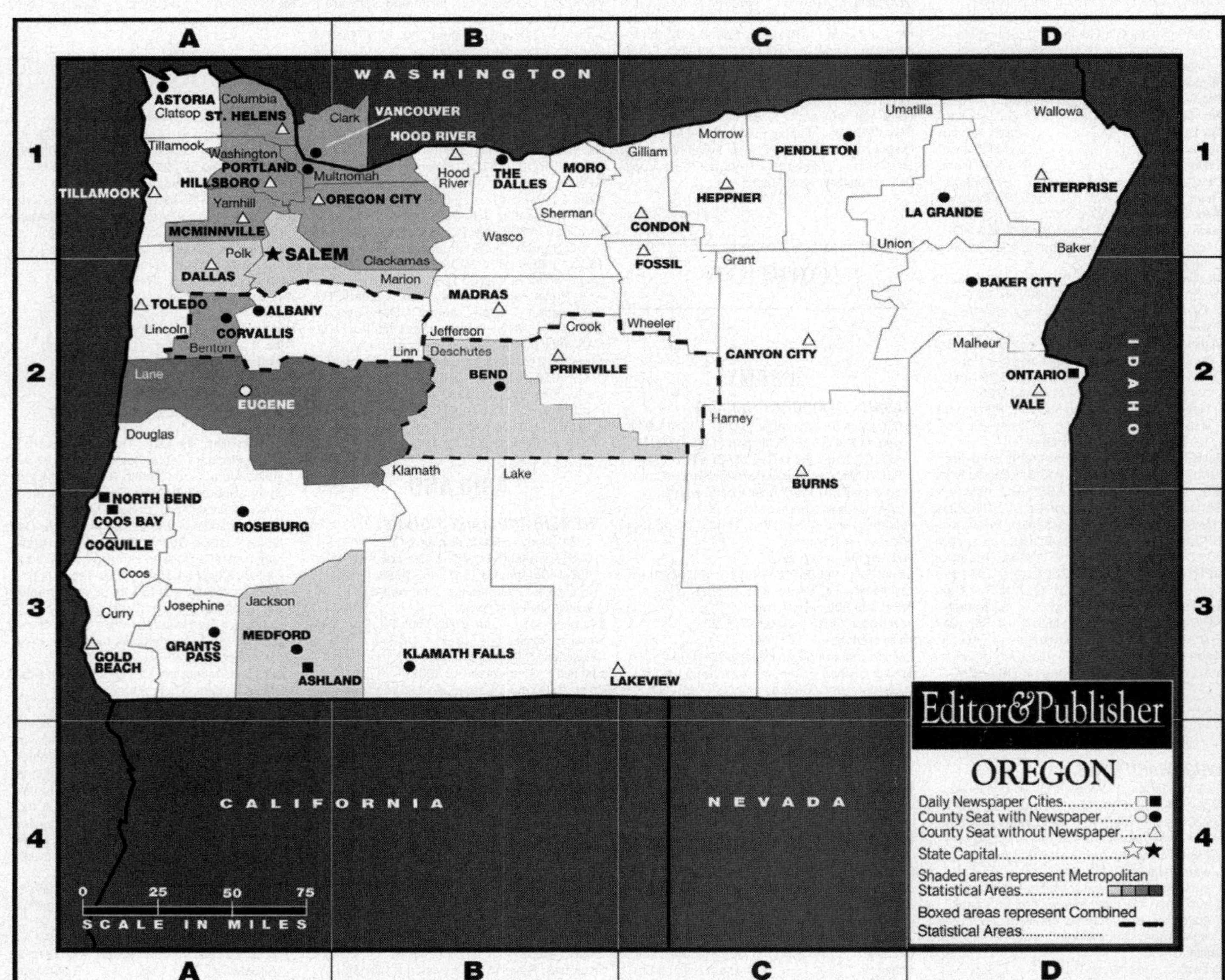

Saturday Frequency: m
Circulation: 31,893; 32,394(sat); 32,267(sun)
Last Audit: ABC September 30, 2011
Price: 11.00/mo (carrier), $18.00/mo (mail); 132.00/yr (carrier), $216.00/yr (mail); 8.00/mo, $96.00/yr (e-edition only).
Advertising: Open inch rate $65.50
Insert rate: $52 CPM
News services: AP, LAT-WP, MCT, NYT.
Politics: Independent. **Established:** 1903
Advertising not accepted: N
Own facility?: Y
Special Editions: PULSE Health Magazine (4x annually); Public School Directory (Aug); Sisters Magazine (Every other month); Sportsman's Show Guide (Feb); Baby Book (Jan); Deschutes County Fair (Jul); Graduation (Jun); Tee to Green: Golf Guide (May); Tour of Homes (July) PRCA Rodeo Guide (Nov); Fall Home Show Guide (Oct); Central Ore. U Magazine: Women's Mag. 4x annually). New Home Living (4x annually) Picture Your Home: Monthly Real Estate Magazine. Bid N Buy Advertiser Auctions 2x annually.
Special Weekly Sections: GO! Magazine (Fri); Green, Etc. (Mon); Color Comics (S); TV/Entertainment Book-Scene (Sat); Health & Fitness (Thur); At Home/Home/Food/Garden (Tues).
Magazines: U Magazine (Every other month); Picture Your Home (Monthly); Pulse (Quarterly); Parade (S).
Pub. .... Gordon R. Black
Dir., Finance .... Karen Anderson
Dir., HR .... Sharlene Crabtree
Adv. Dir. .... Jay Brandt
Adv. Mgr. .... Sean Tate
Classified Adv. Mgr. .... Kevin O'Connell
Special Projects Mgr. .... Martha Tiller
Circ. Mgr., Single Copy/Transportation Anthony Dezam
Ed. in Chief .... John Costa
Bus. Ed. .... John Stearns
Editorial Page Ed. .... Erik Lukens
Features Ed .... Denise Costa
Photo Ed. .... Dean Guernsey
Presentation Ed. .... Anders Ramberg
Sports Ed. .... Bill Bigelow
New Media Dir. .... Jan Even
Prodn. Dir., Opns., WESCOM .... Keith Foutz
Circ. Mktg. Mgr. .... Pam Denniston
IT Dir. .... Mark Turner
Market Information: TMC.
Mechanical available: Offset; Black and 3 ROP colors; insert accepted; page cutoffs - 20 1/2.
Mechanical Specifications: Type page 11 13/16 x 20 1/2; E - 6 cols, 2 1/16, 1/6 between; A - 6 cols, 2 1/16, 1/6 between; C - 9 cols, 1 2/5, 1/16 between.
Commodity Consumption: Avg. Page Number Per Issue - Daily 48.77; Avg. Page Number Per Issue - Plates Used 48500; Avg. Page Number Per Issue - Saturday 40; Avg. Page Number Per Issue - Sunday 52; widths 32; Newsprint Used - Short Tons 3744; Printing Ink Used - Black 49340; Prin
Equipment EDITORIAL: Front-end Software – SII/Synthesis 66 XR.; Editorial Hardware – SII/Synthesis 66 XR; Editorial Equipment – 32-SII; Editorial Printers – 1-Genicom/3410 CLASSIFIED: Front-end Software – DTI 5.5.; Classified Hardware – SII/Synthesis 66 XR; Classified Equipment – 10-SII; Classified Printers – 1-Genicom/3410 DISPLAY: Ad make-up applications – QPS/QuarkXPress, Adobe/Illustrator 3.2, Aldus/FreeHand, Adobe/InDesign; Layout Software – 15-APP/Mac.; Display Printers – HP/4VM, HP/5000 PRODUCTION: Pagination Software – QPS/QuarkXPress 4.0, QPS/QuarkXPress 5.0, Adobe/InDesign.; Production Equipment – Caere/OmniPage, 2-LE; Scanners – HP/ScanJet scanner, JKA Copydot PRESSROOM: Line 1 – 1-KBA 3 1/2 Tower Comit (14 printing couples); Press Drives – 2-KBA/Shaftless; Folders – KBA/64; Pasters – 5; Reels and Stands – 5-AMAL/AR60; Press control system – KBA/Ergotronic; Press registration system – KBA/Ergotronic. MAILROOM: Counter stackers – 1-MM/388, 1-BG/105, 1/MM, 2-QWI/400, 1-Gammerler/KL 50 7/1; Inserters and stuffers – 16-MM/375, 12-MM/375, 4-MM/227; Bundle tying machines – 1-/MLN, 1-Dynaric/NPI, 1-Dynaric/NPI; Other equipment – 1-/MM.
Zip Codes served: 20
Delivery method: Mail, Newsstand, Private Carrier, Racks

WESTERN COMMUNICATIONS, INC.

1777 SW Chandler Ave., Bend, Ore., 97702; gen tel (541) 382-1811; gen fax (541) 385-5802; gen e-mail bulletin@bendbulletin.com; web site www.bendbulletin.com
Published: Mon, Tues, Wed, Thur, Fri, Sat, Sun
Weekday Frequency: m
Saturday Frequency: m
Circulation: 31,893; 32,394(sat); 32,267(sun)
Politics: 1968
Note: Western Communications Inc. also publishes three weekly newspapers and one twice-weekly newspaper in Oregon.
Advertising not accepted: Y
Own facility?: Y
Profile: Western Communications Inc. specializes in newspaper publishing, special sections (tabs), real estate magazines, and commercial printing
Chrmn. of the Bd. .... Elizabeth C. McCool
Pres. .... Gordon R. Black
CFO .... Karen Anderson
Adv. Dir. .... Jay Brandt
New Media Dir. .... Jan Even
Prodn. Mgr. .... Keith Foutz

COOS BAY

SOUTHWESTERN OREGON PUB. CO.

350 Commercial Ave., Coos Bay, Ore., 97420; gen tel (541) 269-1222; gen fax (541) 267-0294

THE WORLD

350 Commercial Ave., Coos Bay, Ore., 97420; gen tel (541) 269-1222; adv tel (541) 269-1222 ext. 229; ed tel (541) 269-1222 ext. 242; gen fax (541) 267-0294; adv fax (541) 267-0294; ed fax (541) 269-5071; gen e-mail theworldnews@theworldlink.com; web site theworldlink.com
Published: Mon, Tues, Wed, Thur, Fri, Sat
Weekday Frequency: e
Saturday Frequency: m
Circulation: 9,697; 10,291(sat)
Last Audit: ABC September 30, 2011
Price: 11.25/mo (mail); 113.00/yr.
Advertising: Open inch rate $23.56
News services: AP, TMS.
Politics: Independent.
Not Published: Independence Day; Labor Day; Christmas.
Special Editions: Hunting & Outdoor (Aug); Year in Review (Dec); Bridal Tab (Feb); Medical Directory (Jan); Salute to Old Glory (Jul); Home Improvement I (May); Christmas Opening (Nov); Women In Business (Oct); Home Improvement II (Sept).
Special Weekly Sections: Auto (Fri); Outdoor (Sat); Best Food Day (Tues); Gardening (Wed).
Magazines: Relish (Monthly); Color Comics (Sat); American Profile (Weekly).
Broadcast Affiliations: KCBY (CBS).
Profile: Committed to stewardship of the mission of providing news, information and responsible, community service and market development for the citizens of Oregon's beautiful South Coast, which The World and its predecessor publications have served since 1878. W
Adv. Dir., Regl. .... Laurie Reynolds
Adv. Mgr., Classified .... Joanna McNeely
Circ. Dir. .... Albert Glick
Ed. .... Clark Walworth
City Ed. .... Elise Hamner
Cuisine Ed. .... Ron Jackimowicz
Entertainment Ed. .... Chip Dombrowski
Page Design Ed. .... Ginger Shepard
Systems Mgr. .... Duane Axelton
Prodn. Mgr., Pressroom .... Mike Travadiakis
Sports Ed .... John Gunther
Prodn. Foreman, Composing ... Andris Jaunzems
Online Mgr. .... Steve Mcdaniel
Prodn. Foreman, Mailroom .... Russell Hartley
Market Information: ADS; TMC.
Mechanical available: Offset; Black and 3 ROP colors; insert accepted - flyers, newspouch, samples; page cutoffs - 22 3/4.
Mechanical Specifications: Type page 12 1/2 x 21 1/2; E - 6 cols, 2 1/16, 1/8 between; A - 6 cols, 2 1/16, 1/8 between; C - 9 cols, 1 1/5, 11/100 between.
Commodity Consumption: Avg. Page Number Per Issue - Daily 24; Avg. Page Number Per Issue - Plates Used 11000; Avg. Page Number Per Issue - Saturday 26; widths 25; Newsprint Used - Short Tons 676.5; Printing Ink Used - Black 14125; Printing Ink Used - Color 6503; Printing Ink U
Equipment EDITORIAL: Front-end Software – Baseview.; Editorial Equipment – AU/3850; Editorial Printers – QMS/2060 CLASSIFIED: Front-end Software – Synaptic, Suntype.; Classified Hardware – Dell; Classified Printers – Okidata/393 DISPLAY: Ad make-up applications – Multi-Ad/Creator 6.; Display Printers – QMS/2060, AU/3850 PRODUCTION: Pagination Software – QPS/QuarkXPress.; Production Equipment – HP, Adobe/Photoshop 7, Mac/W/AP Server, Flatbed 35mm Film Scanner; Cameras – K; Scanners – Trecsa/TS-2470, Epson/Perfection 636 PRESSROOM: Line 1 – 8-G/Community 1974, 1-G/Community 1994, 2-G/Community 2001; Folders – 1 MAILROOM: Counter stackers – MM; Inserters and stuffers – 1/MM, 1-MM/EM 10, MM; Bundle tying machines – 2-/MLN; Wrapping singles – Monarch/Bottom Wrap; Addressing machine – 2-/Ch; Other equipment –Gestentner/Press. BUSINESS COMPUTERS: Business Software – Microsoft/Office XP; Business Hardware – Suntype/Classified System

CORVALLIS

CORVALLIS GAZETTE-TIMES

600 Jefferson Ave., Corvallis, Ore., 97333; gen tel (541) 753-2641; adv tel (541) 758-9556; gen fax (541) 758-9505; ed e-mail news@gtconnect.com; web site www.gtconnect.com
Group: Metro Suburbia, Inc./Newhouse Newspapers
Published: Mon, Tues, Wed, Thur, Fri, Sat, Sun
Weekday Frequency: m
Saturday Frequency: m
Circulation: 10,351; 12,081(sat); 10,517(sun)
Last Audit: ABC September 30, 2011
Price: 11.45/mo (city), $11.95/mo (motor route); 145.00/yr; 39.50/3mo.
Advertising: Open inch rate $51.01
News services: AP, MCT.
Politics: Independent.
Special Editions: Xmas Gift Guide (Dec); Fashion (Fall); Baby Book (Feb); Bridal (Jan); Da Vinci Days (Jul); Visitor's Guide (Mar); Community (May); Connection (Monthly); Xmas Gift Guide (Nov); Home Improvement (Oct); Our Town (Sept); Fashion (Spring).
Special Weekly Sections: Entertainment & Arts Tab (Fri); Senior Page (Mon); Travel (S); Church Page (Sat); Venture/Outdoor (Thur); Students Page (Tues); Best Food Day (Wed).
Magazines: Relish (Monthly); USA WEEKEND Magazine (S).
Broadcast Affiliations: KGUN, AZ; KREZ, CO; KGMB, HI; KSNC, KS; KSNG, KS; KSNK, KS; KSNT, KS; KSNW, KS; KMTV, NE; KBIM, NM; KRQE, NM; KOIN, OR; KZIA, TX; WSAZ, WV.
Pub. .... Mike McInally
Circ. Mgr. .... Cody Castellano
Sunday Ed. .... Mike Henneke
Prodn. Supvr., Distr. .... Bob Johnson
Market Information: TMC.
Mechanical available: Offset; Black and 3 ROP colors; insert accepted - standing card stock; page cutoffs - 22 3/4.
Mechanical Specifications: Type page 13 x 21; E - 6 cols, 2 1/16, 1/8 between; A - 6 cols, 2 1/16, 1/8 between; C - 9 cols, 1 5/16, 1/16 between.
Commodity Consumption: Avg. Page Number Per Issue - Daily 20; Avg. Page Number Per Issue - Plates Used 22000; Avg. Page Number Per Issue - Saturday 20; Avg. Page Number Per Issue - Sunday 40; widths 17 1/2; Newsprint Used - Metric Tons 943; Printing Ink Used - Black 25500; Pri
Equipment EDITORIAL: Front-end Software – CText.; Editorial Hardware – Gateway/P5-90; Editorial Printers – Pre Press/Panther Plus, Pre Press/Panther Pro 46, LaserMaster/Unity 1800, LaserMaster/Unity 1200, LaserMaster/Unity 1000 CLASSIFIED: Front-end Software – CText.; Classified Hardware – Gateway/P5-90; Classified Printers – HP/5P; Layout Software – 1-APP/Mac IIfx, 3-APP/Mac IIci, 10-APP/Mac 7200.; Display Printers – Pre Press/Panther Plus, Pre Press/Panther Pro 46, LaserMaster/Unity 1800, LaserMaster/Unity 1200, LaserMaster/Unity 1000; Production Equipment – 3-Laser, Pre Press/Panther Plus, Pre Press/Panther Pro, LaserMaster/Unity 1800, LaserMaster/Unity 1200, LaserMaster/Unity 1000; Cameras – 1-C/Spartan II, 1-Nu/2024. PRESSROOM: Line 1 – 5-G/Urbanite 1970; Folders – 2; Press control system – 2-Fin/Console.; Inserters and stuffers – 1/MM; Addressing machine – Bundle tying machines □ 2-/MLN. AUDIO: Audio Software – Talking Yellow Pages/proprietary; Audio Hardware – Auto Agent; Business Hardware – IBM/AS-400

EUGENE

GUARD PUBLISHING CO.

975 High St., Eugene, Ore., 97440; gen tel (541) 485-1234; gen fax (541) 984-4699

THE REGISTER-GUARD

3500 Chad Dr., Eugene, Ore., 97408-7348; gen tel (541) 485-1234; adv tel (541) 342-1212 (class.); ed tel (541) 485-1234; gen fax (541) 683-7631; adv fax (541) 687-6668 (class.); ed fax (541) 687-6674; gen e-mail bridget.baker@registerguard.com; adv e-mail gail.whiting@registerguard.com; ed e-mail jack.wilson@registerguard.com; web site www.registerguard.com
Published: Mon, Tues, Wed, Thur, Fri, Sat, Sun
Weekday Frequency: m
Saturday Frequency: m
Circulation: 54,325; 59,213(sat); 60,710(sun)
Last Audit: ABC September 30, 2011
Price: $16.50/mo
Advertising: Open inch rate $88.09
News services: AP, NYT, LAT-WP, TMS.
Politics: Independent. **Established:** 1867
Special Editions: College Football (Aug); Cycle Life (Jun); Fishing (Mar); Discovery Magazine (May); Home & Garden (Monthly); Holiday Gift Guide (Nov); Tastings (Quarterly); The Wedding Guide (Semi-yearly); Golf (Summer).
Special Weekly Sections: Complete Stock Listings (Fri); 20 Below (Mon); Resort, Travel (S); Homes (Sat); Complete Stock Listings (Thur); Complete Stock Listings (Tues); Entree (Wed).
Magazines: blue chip (business)
COO .... David Pero
Cor. Dir./Sec. .... Bridget D. Baker
Controller .... Bradley Phillips
CIO .... Richard A. Baker
Personnel/HR Mgr. .... Cynthia Walden
Adv. Dir. .... Gail Whiting
Adv. Mgr. .... Kelly Gant
Internet Sales/Devel. Mgr. .... Jeff Avgeris
Mktg. Mgr. .... Sally Wickes
Pub. Rels. Dir. .... Bridget Baker
Creative Servs. Mgr. .... Dan Villani
Circ. Dir. .... Charles Downing
Circ. Asst. Dir. .... Mark Ogle
Ed./Pub. .... Alton F. Baker
Mng. Ed. .... Dave Baker
Digital Media Director .... Tyler Mack
Chrmn. of the Bd. .... Edwin M. Baker
Classified Adv. Mgr. .... Kelly Gant
Targeted Media Mgr. .... Jim Hinton

NIE Coord. ....Susan McDonald
Market Information: ADS; Split run; TMC.
Mechanical available: Offset; Black and 3 ROP colors; insert accepted; page cutoffs - 22.
Mechanical Specifications: Type page 11 5/8 x 21; E - 6 cols, 1 5/6, 1/8 between; A - 6 cols, 2 1/16, 1/8 between; C - 9 cols, 1 1/4, 1/16 between.
Commodity Consumption: Avg. Page Number Per Issue - Daily 47; Avg. Page Number Per Issue - Plates Used 85200; Avg. Page Number Per Issue - Saturday 80; Avg. Page Number Per Issue - Sunday 76; widths 50; Newsprint Used - Metric Tons 7275; Printing Ink Used - Black 145000; Print
Equipment EDITORIAL: Front-end Software – DTI 4.23.; Editorial Hardware – 2-Sun/Sparc 3000, APP/Mac CLASSIFIED: Front-end Software – DTI 4.23.; Classified Hardware – Sun/Sparc 3000; Layout Software – DTI/Plan Builder (5.01).; Display Hardware – DEC/4000-300, Sun/Sparc 3000; Display Printers – X/Docuprint 75 PRODUCTION: Pagination Software – DTI 4.2.; Production Equipment – 2-III/3850, 1-WL/38G PRESSROOM: Line 1 – 10-Mitsubishi/Lithopia double width; Folders – 1-Mitsubishi/Double 3:2; Reels and Stands – 8 MAILROOM: Counter stackers – 5/QWI; Inserters and stuffers – 3-/AM Graphics/NP 630; Bundle tying machines – 5-/Dynaric; Mailroom control system – AM/Graphics/AMCS.; Business Hardware – 2-DEC/4000-300, 1-DEC/3100

GRANTS PASS

DAILY COURIER

409 SE 7th St., Grants Pass, Ore., 97526-3003; gen tel (541) 474-3700; adv tel (541) 474-3733; ed tel (541) 474-3823; gen fax (541) 474-3814; adv fax (541) 474-3814; ed fax (541) 474-3824; adv e-mail classified@thedailycourier.com; ed e-mail news@thedailycourier.com; web site www.thedailycourier.com
Published: Mon, Tues, Wed, Thur, Fri, Sat
Weekday Frequency: e
Saturday Frequency: e
Circulation: 14,561; 14,561(sat)
Last Audit: ABC September 30, 2011
Price: 12.00/mo; 138.00/yr.
Advertising: Open inch rate $12.88
News services: AP.
Politics: Independent. **Established:** 1885
Not Published: New Year; Thanksgiving; Christmas.
Own facility?: Y
Special Editions: Home & Garden (Apr); Josephine County Fair Program (Aug); Holiday Gift Guide (Dec); Spring Coupon Book (Feb); Tax Guide (Jan); Prime Time (Jul); Summer Coupon (Jun); Wheels (Mar); Horse Racing (May); Christmas Songbook (Nov); Community Christmas Catalog (
Special Weekly Sections: Churches (Fri); Local Business (Mon); Color Comics (Sat); Gardening (Thur); Best Food Day (Tues); Under 21 Youth Page (Wed).
Magazines: USA WEEKEND Magazine (Sat).
Pres./Owner ....John E. Voorhies
Pub....Dennis Mack
Purchasing Agent.............................Bill Parker
Circ. Mgr. ....Eileen Widdison
City Ed. ....Kevin Widdison
Editorial Page Ed..........................Dennis Roler
Educ. Ed. ....Amanda Haines
Librarian ....Mary Bradford
Music Ed. ....Dan Dillon
Real Estate Ed........................Susan Goracke
Sports Ed......................................Travis Moore
Teen-Age/Youth Ed.........................Edith Decker
Wire Ed...Jim Mitchell
Market Information: ADS; TMC; Zoned editions.
Mechanical available: Offset; Black and 3 ROP colors; insert accepted; page cutoffs - 22 3/4.
Mechanical Specifications: Type page 13 x 21 1/2; E - 6 cols, 2 1/16, 1/8 between; A - 6 cols, 2 1/16, 1/8 between; C - 6 cols, 2 1/16, 1/8 between.
Commodity Consumption: Avg. Page Number Per Issue - Daily 34; Avg. Page Number Per Issue - Plates Used 19200; widths 27 1/2; Newsprint Used - Metric Tons 1200; Printing Ink Used - Black 27020; Printing Ink Used - Color 1100; Printing Ink Used - Pages Printed 10481.
Equipment EDITORIAL: Front-end Software – AT.; Editorial Hardware – 27-AT/Series 4; Editorial Equipment – 6-APP/Mac, 1-Lf/AP Leaf Picture Desk CLASSIFIED: Front-end Software – DTI.; Classified Hardware – 6-APP/Mac, IBM/RS6000 DISPLAY: Ad make-up applications – Multi-Ad/Creator, Adobe/Illustrator, QPS/QuarkXPress; Display Hardware – 16-APP/Mac; Display Printers – APP/Mac LaserWriter II, Dataproducts/LZR-2600 PRODUCTION: Pagination Software – QPS.; Production Equipment – Nat/24, 2-AU/APS-6-108, 6-APP/Mac, 2-AU/APS-100; Cameras – R, AG/6100; Scanners – 2-Nikon/LS-3500 PRESSROOM: Line 1 – 5-G/Urbanite 1240; Line 2 – 6-G/Community; Folders – 2, 1-G/Quarter. MAILROOM: Counter stackers – 2-BG/Count-O-Veyor 108; Inserters and stuffers – 2-MM/227E; Bundle tying machines – 2-MLN/Strapper, 2-Bu/Tyer; Addressing machine – 3-Wm/Dick Gum labeler. BUSINESS COMPUTERS: Business Software – CJ; Business Hardware – IBM/RISC/6000
Delivery method: Mail, Newsstand, Private Carrier, Racks

KLAMATH FALLS

HERALD AND NEWS

2701 Foothills Blvd., Klamath Falls, Ore., 97603-3785; gen tel (541) 885-4410; adv tel (541) 885-4410; ed tel (541) 885-4410; gen fax (541) 883-4007; ed fax (541) 885-4456; gen e-mail heraldandnews@heraldandnews.com; web site www.heraldandnews.com
Published: Tues, Wed, Thur, Fri, Sat, Sun
Weekday Frequency: m
Circulation: 14,632; 14,632(sat); 15,005(sun)
Last Audit: September 30, 2008
Price: 9.00/mo; 106.00/yr.
Advertising: Open inch rate $20.76
News services: AP.
Politics: Independent.
Special Weekly Sections: Religious (Fri); Financial (S); Lifestyle (Sat); Home and Garden (Thur); Food (Tues); Farm (Wed).
Magazines: Relish (Monthly); Parade (S); American Profile (Weekly).
Pub....Heidi Wright
Bus. Mgr. ....Jeanine Day
Circ. Dir. ....Dusty Metsker
Ed....Steve Miller
Lifestyle Ed. ....Marcia McGonigle
Opinion Ed. ....Pat Bushey
Market Information: TMC.
Mechanical available: Offset; Black and 3 ROP colors; insert accepted - envelopes, cards, sacks, self-adhesive notes; page cutoffs - 22 3/4.
Mechanical Specifications: Type page 12 3/8 x 21 1/2; E - 6 cols, 1 5/6, 1/6 between; A - 6 cols, 1 5/6, 1/6 between; C - 9 cols, 1 1/6, 1/8 between.
Commodity Consumption: Avg. Page Number Per Issue - Daily 31; Avg. Page Number Per Issue - Sunday 42; widths 25; Newsprint Used - Metric Tons 1091; Printing Ink Used - Pages Printed 10386.
Equipment EDITORIAL: Front-end Software – QPS/QuarkXPress, Adobe/Photoshop, Baseview/NewsEdit.; Editorial Hardware – APP/Mac; Editorial Printers – 2-AG, COM/Accuset CLASSIFIED: Front-end Software – Baseview/Ad Manager Pro 2.0.6.; Classified Hardware – APP/Mac; Layout Software – QPS/QuarkXPress, MEI/ALS.; Display Hardware – APP/Mac; Production Equipment – 1-Nu/Flip Top; Cameras – 1-MG/Photomaster; Scanners – 4-HP/ScanJet Plus, 2-Nikon. PRESSROOM: Line 1 – 7-G/U 650; Folders – 1 MAILROOM: Counter stackers – 1-BG/Count-O-Veyor; Inserters and stuffers – 2-MM/Stitcher-Trimmer; Bundle tying machines – MLN; Wrapping singles – 1-Typak/#40.

KLAMATH PUBLISHING CO.

1301 Esplanade, Klamath Falls, Ore., 97601; gen tel (541) 885-4410; gen fax (541) 883-4456

LA GRANDE

THE OBSERVER

1406 Fifth St., La Grande, Ore., 97850; gen tel (541) 963-3161; gen fax (541) 963-7804; gen e-mail info@lagrandeobserver.com; adv e-mail ads@lagrandeobserver.com; ed e-mail news@lagrandeobserver.com; web site www.lagrandeobserver.com
Published: Mon, Tues, Wed, Thur, Fri
Weekday Frequency: e
Circulation: 6,030; 6,030(sat)
Last Audit: September 30, 2005
Price: 8.50/mo, 9.50 motor route;$15.00/mo (mail); 102.00/yr (home delivery).
Advertising: Open inch rate $13.81
Insert rate: open rate $52.88/m
News services: AP.
Politics: Independent. **Established:** 1896
Advertising not accepted: N
Not Published: Christmas.
Own facility?: Y
Special Editions: Health & Wellness (Jan); Northeast Oregon Living Directory (Sept.) Sports Calendars (Mar., Aug., Nov.); N.E. Oregon Visitors Guide (May); Women in Business (Oct); Home & Garden (April), Wedding Guide (Feb), Rodeo Guide (May).
Special Weekly Sections: Outdoors/Rec (Fri); Healthy Living (Tues.); Community Calendar (Thurs); Business (Wed); Food/Lifestyles (Tues); Wallowa Life (Thurs.)
Magazines: Go! (own, newsprint) (Fri); American Profile (Weekly).
Editor/Publisher.............................Ted Kramer
Operations. Dir. ....Frank Everidge
Office mgr......................................Tuck Mona
Adv. dir. ....Orcutt Glenas Gibson Carolyn
A&E editor.................................Jeff Petersen
Sports ed ....Mosher Brad
News assistant............................Eden Kruger
Adv. Dir. ....Mike Waltman
Circ. Dir..............................Thomas Hooton
Editorial Page Ed. ....Jess Peterson
Outdoors Ed. ....Dick Mason
Photo Ed. ....Phil Bullock
Sports Ed. ....Paul Harder
Theater/Music Ed. ....Jeff Petersen
Prodn. Mgr., Mailroom ....Terry Everidge
Market Information: ADS.
Mechanical available: Offset; Black and 3 ROP colors; insert accepted; page cutoffs - 21 1/2.
Mechanical Specifications: Type page 11.75 x 21 1/2; E - 6 cols, 2 1/16, 1/8 between; A - 6 cols, 2 1/16, 1/8 between; C - 6 cols, 1 9/16, 1/16 between.
Commodity Consumption: Avg. Page Number Per Issue - Daily 18; Avg. Page Number Per Issue - Plates Used 8000; widths 13 1/2; Newsprint Used - Metric Tons 580; Printing Ink Used - Black 15750; Printing Ink Used - Color 4200; Printing Ink Used - Pages Printed 4900.
Equipment EDITORIAL: Front-end Software – QPS/QuarkXPress 4.2, Baseview/Wire Manager, APP/Mac Sys 7.1.; Editorial Hardware – G4 1.25 MAC; Editorial Equipment – 1-IBM/Selectric CLASSIFIED: Front-end Software – Baseview/Class Manager, APP/Mac System 8.1, QPS/QuarkXPress 3.2.; Classified Hardware – IMAC; Classified Equipment – 1-IBM/Selectric; Classified Printers – B/W LASER PRINTER DISPLAY: Ad make-up applications – QPS/QuarkXPress 4.2, Adobe/Illustrator; Display Hardware – G4 1.25 MAC; Display Printers – 1-LaserMaster/Unity 1200 XL-T; Production Equipment – 1-KYOCERA B/W LASER PRINT AND 1 TRENDSETTER; Cameras – SCREEN/670 D Auto. PRESSROOM: Line 1 – 6-G/Community; Folders – 1-G/SSC.; Inserters and stuffers – Mueller; Bundle tying machines – MLN/MS-B; Addressing machine – 4/Wm, 1-/Dispensa-Matic/16 label picker. BUSINESS COMPUTERS: Business Software – PBS (MSDOS); Business Hardware – 2-Packard Bell/Microsphere
Zip Codes served: 97850; 97883; 97827; 97841; 97824; 97828;97846; 97885; 97867; 97857
Delivery method: Mail, Newsstand, Private Carrier, Racks

WESTERN COMMUNICATIONS, INC.

1406 5th St., La Grande, Ore., 97850; gen tel (541) 963-3161; gen fax (541) 963-7804

MEDFORD

MAIL TRIBUNE

111 N. First St., Medford, Ore., 97501; gen tel (541) 776-4411; adv tel (541) 776-4422; ed tel (541) 776-4477; adv fax (541) 776-4369; ed fax (541) 776-4376; gen e-mail letters@mailtribune.com; ed e-mail news@mailtribune.com; web site www.mailtribune.com
Published: Mon, Tues, Wed, Thur, Fri, Sat, Sun
Weekday Frequency: m
Saturday Frequency: m
Circulation: 23,393; 23,158(sat); 25,307(sun)
Last Audit: ABC September 30, 2011
Price: 12.95/mo; 156.00/yr.
Advertising: Open inch rate $20.93
News services: AP, DJ, LAT-WP.
Politics: Independent. **Established:** 1906
Special Editions: Real Estate Review (Apr); Football (Aug); Classroom Tribune (Dec); Tax & Financial Planning (Jan); Regional Recreation Guide (Jul); Our Valley (Mar); Pets (May); Ashland Festival of Lights (Nov); Fall Real Estate (Oct); Hunting (Sept).
Special Weekly Sections: Arts & Entertainment (Fri); Community Page (Mon); Business (S); Family Page (Sat); Teen Express (Thur); Health & Science (Tues); Best Food Day (Wed).
Magazines: Tempo (movies, radio, TV, entertainment) (Fri); Relish (Monthly); Parade (S); American Profile (Weekly).
Pub..........................James Grady Singletary
Adv. Mgr., Classified/Phone Sales.Angela Fraley
Circ. Dir....................................John Mahalyo
Ed....Robert Hunter
Bus. Ed. ....Greg Stiles
Columnist......................................Paul Fattig
Editorial Page Ed..........................Gary Nelson
Features Ed. ....Cathy Noah
Food/Garden Ed..........................Sarah Lemon
Librarian ....Pam Sieg
Music Ed.......................................Bill Varble
News Ed......................................Rob Galvin
Online Ed. ....Julie Worth
Outdoors Ed. ....Mark Freeman
Photo Ed....................................Bob Pennell
Radio/Television Ed. ....Richard Moeschel
Sports Ed....................................Tim Trower
Market Information: TMC.
Mechanical available: Offset; Black and 3 ROP colors; insert accepted - cards; page cutoffs - 22 3/4.
Mechanical Specifications: Type page 13 x 21 1/2; E - 6 cols, 2 1/16, 1/8 between; A - 6 cols, 2 1/16, 1/8 between; C - 9 cols, 1 3/8, 1/16 between.
Commodity Consumption: Avg. Page Number Per Issue - Daily 38; Avg. Page Number Per Issue - Plates Used 30000; Avg. Page Number Per Issue - Sunday 72; widths 27; Newsprint Used - Metric Tons 2430; Printing Ink Used - Black 38300; Printing Ink Used - Color 19150; Printing Ink Us
Equipment EDITORIAL: Front-end Software – Cybergraphics 7.5.; Editorial Hardware – DEC/VAX 4000-200, DEC/VAX 4000-300, 33-IBM/70, IBM/PS2; Editorial Equipment – 2-RSK/TRS 80-100, 4-RSK/TRS 80-200; Editorial Printers – DEC/LA 210, Compaq/LA-75, Printronix/LPM 600 Band Printer CLASSIFIED: Front-end Software – Cybergraphics 7.5.; Classified Hardware – IBM/PS2, DEC/VAX 4000-200, DEC/VAX 4000-300; Classified Equipment

– 12-IBM/Sys 70; Classified Printers – DEC/LA 210, DEC/LA 75 DISPLAY: Ad make-up applications – QPS/QuarkXPress 3.32, Adobe/Illustrator 7.0, Adobe/Photoshop 4.0; Layout Software – APP/Mac 6100, MEI/ALS 2.0.; Display Hardware – 6-IBM/PC, 3-APP/Power Mac; Display Printers – 2-HP/LaserJet 4MV, 1-HP/Color LaserJet; Production Equipment – 2-ECR/Autokon 12 max, 1-Anitec/D32; Cameras – 1-Spartan/III, 1-LE/17, 1-AP; Scanners – 2-Epson/ES-1200C. PRESSROOM: Line 1 – 6-G/Metroliner double width (two half decks) 1995; Folders – 2-G/3:2; Pasters – 6-G/Reel-Tension Paster; Reels and Stands – 6-G/Triple Reels. MAILROOM: Counter stackers – 2-HL/Monitor, 1-QWI/300, 1-QWI/351; Inserters and stuffers – GMA/SLS 1000 16 pocket; Bundle tying machines – 2/MLN, 1-/Power Strap/PSN-6, 1-/Power Strap/PSN-6E; Wrapping singles – 2-QWI/30; Addressing machine – KR; Other equipment –Other equipment ☐; Business Hardware – IBM/AS-400, DEC/VAX-4300

ONTARIO

ARGUS OBSERVER

1160 SW Fourth St., Ontario, Ore., 97914-0130; gen tel (541) 889-5387; adv tel (541) 823-4816; ed tel (541) 823-4818; gen fax (541) 889-3347; adv fax (541) 889-3347; gen e-mail JohnD@argusobserver.com; adv e-mail JohnD@argusobserver.com; ed e-mail larryh@argusobserver.com; web site www.argusobserver.com

Group: Wick Communications
Published: Tues, Wed, Thur, Fri, Sun
Weekday Frequency: e
Circulation: 6,734; 7,812(sun)
Last Audit: July 1, 2010
Price: 124.00/yr.
Advertising: Open inch rate $13.35
Insert rate: 57.00
News services: AP.
Politics: Independent. **Established:** 1891
Not Published: Monday and Saturday
Own facility?: Y
Special Weekly Sections: TV Guide (S); Church Page (Fri); Best Food Day (Tues); @RecordBody:**Magazines:** Parade (S).
Pub. .... John Dillon
Adv. Mgr., Retail .... Andy Shimojima
Editor .... Larry Hurrle
Prodn. Mgr. .... Wade Cordes
Bus Mgr. .... Dee Lee
News Editor .... Jessica Keller
Market Information: ADS; TMC.
Mechanical available: Offset; Black and 3 ROP colors; insert accepted - all sizes from 3 x 5 cards up; page cutoffs - 22 3/4.
Mechanical Specifications: Type page 13 x 21 1/2; E - 6 cols, 2 1/16, 1/8 between; A - 6 cols, 2 1/16, 1/8 between; C - 9 cols, 1 1/4, 1/8 between.
Commodity Consumption: Avg. Page Number Per Issue - Daily 24; Avg. Page Number Per Issue - Plates Used 5100; Avg. Page Number Per Issue - Sunday 72; widths 27; Newsprint Used - Metric Tons 490; Printing Ink Used - Black 13100; Printing Ink Used - Color 2000; Printing Ink Used
Equipment; Editorial Hardware – APP/Mac; Editorial Equipment – Pre Press/Panther Imagesetter; Editorial Printers – HP/LaserJet CLASSIFIED: Front-end Software – Baseview.; Classified Hardware – APP/Mac; Classified Equipment – Pre Press/Panther Imagesetter; Classified Printers – 2-HP/LaserJet DISPLAY: Ad make-up applications – Other ÃĐÂĐ APP/Mac with Baseview.; Layout Software – APP/Mac with Baseview.; Display Hardware – APP/Mac; Display Printers – 2-HP/LaserJet PRODUCTION: Pagination Software – Baseview.; Production Equipment – Nu/Ultra Plus; Cameras – SCREEN; Scanners – Umax, Polaroid/SprintScan PRESSROOM: Line 1 – 6-G; Folders – 1; Inserters and stuffers – KAN; Bundle tying machines – . BUSINESS COMPUTERS: Business Software – Vision Data; Business Hardware – DEC/Micro-VAX/3100
Zip Codes served: 97914, 97913, 97918, 97901, 97907, 83661, 83619, 83655, 83672, 83612, 83660
Delivery method: Mail, Newsstand, Private Carrier, Racks

PENDLETON

EAST OREGONIAN

211 S.E. Byers Ave., Pendleton, Ore., 97801-2346; gen tel (541) 276-2211; adv tel (541) 278-2678; ed tel (541) 966-0818; gen fax (541) 276-8314; adv fax (541) 278-2680; ed fax (541) 276-8314; gen e-mail eonews@eastoregonian.com; adv e-mail classifieds@eastoregonian.com; ed e-mail community@eastoregonian.com; web site www.eastoregonian.com

Published: Tues, Wed, Thur, Fri, Sat, Sun
Weekday Frequency: e
Saturday Frequency: m
Circulation: 7,868; 7,868(sat); 8,073(sun)
Last Audit: September 30, 2009
News services: AP
Politics: 1875
Not Published: Christmas
Own facility?: Y
Special Editions: Umatilla County Fair
Farm-City Pro Rodeo
Pendleton Round-Up
Health & Wellness
Agriculture
Discover Eastern Oregon
Hunting
Assoc. Publisher .... Kathryn B. Brown
Managing Editor .... Skip Nichols
Sports Editor .... Matt Entrup
Lead Pressman .... Dennis Duchek
Production Manager .... Kay Karlinsey
Circulation Manager .... Sue Cant
Publisher & Editor .... Tom Brown
City Editor .... Joe Ditzler
Business Office Manager .... Janna Heimgartner
Advertising Director .... Bill Marcum
Equipment EDITORIAL: Front-end Software – Quark, NewsEdit CLASSIFIED: Front-end Software – Baseview PRESSROOM: Line 1 – 9-G/Community SC1017; Folders – 1; Inserters and stuffers – KAN/320; Bundle tying machines – 1/Bu, 1-Gd/OVL; Addressing machine – Vision Data BUSINESS COMPUTERS: Business Software – Vision Data
Delivery method: Mail, Newsstand, Private Carrier, Racks

PORTLAND

DAILY JOURNAL OF COMMERCE

921 S.W. Washington St., Ste. 210, Portland, Ore., 97205; gen tel (503) 226-1311; gen fax (503) 226-1315; ed fax (503) 802-7329; adv e-mail advertising@djcoregon.com; ed e-mail newsroom@djcoregon.com; web site www.djcoregon.com

Published: Mon, Tues, Wed, Thur, Fri
Weekday Frequency: m
Circulation: 3,622
Last Audit: September 25, 2002
Price: 180.00/yr; 110.00/6mo.
Advertising: Open inch rate $19.00
News services: Business Wire, PR Newswire, RN, AP.
Politics: Independent. **Established:** 1872
Special Editions: Real Estate/Landscape (Apr); Design & Renovation (Aug); Architecture (Dec); Annual (Feb); Profiles of Excellence (Jan); Professional Services (Jul); Top Projects I (Jun); Engineering (Mar); Construction (May); Construction/Energy (Nov); Top Projects II (O
Special Weekly Sections: Law/Courts (Fri); Design & Construction (Mon); Finance (Thur); Finance (Tues); Contruction (Wed).
Pub .... Rynni Henderson
Bus. Mgr. .... Julie Aman
Adv. Dir. .... Cris Schulz
Circ. Mgr. .... Craig Bollen
Ed. .... Brian Hunt
Mechanical available: Offset; Black and 3 ROP colors; insert accepted; page cutoffs - 22 3/4.
Mechanical Specifications: Type page 10 3/16 x 13 3/4; E - 5 cols, 2 1/16, 1/8 between; A - 5 cols, 2 1/16, 1/8 between; C - 5 cols, 2 1/16, 1/8 between.
Commodity Consumption: Avg. Page Number Per Issue - Daily 36; widths 29; Newsprint Used - Short Tons 175.
Equipment EDITORIAL: Front-end Software – QPS/QuarkXPress 4.0, Adobe/Photoshop 5.5, Adobe/PageMaker 6.5, Adobe/Illustrator 8.0. CLASSIFIED: Front-end Software – Mk. DISPLAY: Ad make-up applications – Mk, QPS/QuarkXPress 3.32, Adobe/PageMaker 6.0, Adobe/Illustrator 5.5, Macromedia/Freehand 5.5; Display Hardware – Mk, APP/Mac PRODUCTION: Pagination Software – QPS/QuarkXPress 4.0, Adobe/Photoshop 5.5, Adobe/PageMaker 6.5, Adobe/Illustrator 8.0.; Production Equipment – V/5100, V/5000; Scanners – AG/Arcus II, AG/DuoScn T1200; Inserters and stuffers – S; Bundle tying machines – . BUSINESS COMPUTERS: Business Software – QuarkXPress 3.31, Mk, Multi-Ad/Creator 3.7; Business Hardware – Mk, Vs, APP/Mac cis, APP/Power Mac 9500

THE OREGONIAN

1320 SW Broadway, Portland, Ore., 97201-3411; gen tel (503) 221-8327; adv tel (503) 221-8334; ed tel (503) 221-8100; gen fax (503) 227-5306; adv fax (503) 294-4199; ed fax (503) 227-5306; adv e-mail mediakit@sales.oregonian.com; ed e-mail letterstotheeditor@news.oregonian.com; newsroom@news.oregonian.com; web site www.oregonlive.com

Published: Mon, Tues, Wed, Thur, Fri, Sat, Sun
Weekday Frequency: All day
Saturday Frequency: m
Circulation: 242,784; 240,354(sat); 300,922(sun)
Last Audit: ABC September 30, 2011
Price: 182.00/yr; 12.00/4wk.
Advertising: Open inch rate $273.61
News services: AP, LAT-WP, NYT, NNS, MCT.
Politics: Independent. **Established:** 1850
Special Weekly Sections: A & E (Fri); Accent on Health & Fitness (Mon); Arts Week (S); Accent on Religion & Ethics (Sat); Science (Thur); Accent on Pets (Tues).
Magazines: Parade (S).
Pres./Pub. .... N. Christian Anderson
Controller .... D.W. Palmer
Credit Mgr. .... Eric Flint
Mgr., HR .... Tom Whitehouse
Purchasing Agent .... Brian Maly
Transportation/Real Estate Mgr. .... Ed Merrick
Sales/Mktg. Dir .... Mario Van Dongen
Adv. Mgr., Gen. .... Debi Walery
Adv. Mgr., Retail .... Denice Williams
Dir., Mktg. Serv. .... Judy Rooks
Circ. Dir. .... Kevin Denny
Circ. Mgr., Opns. .... Jodie Krueger
Mng. Ed. .... Jolene Krazwczak
Circ. Mgr., Single Copy .... Neal Burke
Ed. .... Peter Bhatia
Mng. Ed., Enterprise .... Susan Gage
Mng. Ed., News .... Therese Bottomly
Arts/Culture Ed. .... Joany Carlin
Audiotex Ed. .... Jeff Wohler
Bus. Ed. .... Bruce Hammond
Market Information: Split run; TMC; Zoned editions.
Mechanical available: Offset; Black and 3 ROP colors; insert accepted; page cutoffs - 22 3/4.
Mechanical Specifications: Type page 11 7/8 x 21 1/2; E - 6 cols, 1 7/8, 1/8 between; A - 6 cols, 1 7/8, 1/8 between; C - 10 cols, 1 1/8, 1/16 between.
Commodity Consumption: Avg. Page Number Per Issue - Daily 84; Avg. Page Number Per Issue - Plates Used 505090; Avg. Page Number Per Issue - Sunday 164; widths 25 1/4; Newsprint Used - Short Tons 96500; Printing Ink Used - Black 1731828; Printing Ink Used - Color 517475.
Equipment; Editorial Hardware – HI/NewsMaker Editorial, HI/NMP; Editorial Equipment – 30-HI/NMP, 370-HI/NewsMaker Editorial. CLASSIFIED: Front-end Software – Mactive 2.21.; Classified Hardware – 3-Sun/V880; Classified Equipment – PC DISPLAY: Ad make-up applications – DPS; Layout Software – In-house.; Display Hardware – APP/Mac; Production Equipment – 2-WL/III, 7-III/3850, Nikon/3510, Polaroid/SprintScan, Nikon/4000 Ed; Cameras – 1-C/Marathon; Scanners – 2-ECR/Autokon, 2-Eskofots. PRESSROOM: Line 1 – 10-G/Metro double width 1974; Line 2 – 10-G/Metro 1974; Line 3 – 10-G/Metro double width 1974; Line 4 – 10-G/Metro double width 1974; Line 5 – 10-G/Metroliner 1992; Pasters – 50; Press control system – 1-G/PCS. MAILROOM: Counter stackers – 16/QWI; Inserters and stuffers – 3-S/72P, 1-GMA/SLS 2000 30:2; Bundle tying machines – 3-MLN/MEE, 2-MLN/MLNCC, 9-OVL/JP40, 10-Dynaric/NP2; Mailroom control system – Machine Design belt distribution; Addressing machine – 6-/Dm, 1-Am/23; Audio Hardware – Brite Voice Systems BUSINESS COMPUTERS: Business Software – Cyborg: Payroll, Platinum; Business Hardware – Unisys Clearpath

ROSEBURG

THE NEWS-REVIEW

345 NE Winchester St., Roseburg, Ore., 97470-0311; gen tel (541) 672-3321; adv tel (541) 957-4250; ed tel (541) 957-4201; gen fax (541) 673-5994; ed fax (541) 957-4270; gen e-mail nrsupport@nrtoday.com; adv e-mail classifieds@nrtoday.com; ed e-mail newsdesk@nrtoday.com; web site www.nrtoday.com

Published: Mon, Tues, Wed, Thur, Fri, Sun
Weekday Frequency: e
Circulation: 18,287; 19,290(sun)
Last Audit: September 30, 2008
Price: 9.25/mo; 102.95/yr.
Advertising: Open inch rate $35.54
News services: AP.
Politics: Independent. **Established:** 1867
Not Published: Christmas.
Special Editions: Recreational Vehicles (Apr); Blackberry Festival (Aug); Seasons Greetings (Dec); Readers Choice (Jan); Graffiti (Jul); All in the Family (Jun); How To Tab (Mar); Home & Garden (May); Senior Times (Monthly); Holiday Guide (Nov); DC Cou
Special Weekly Sections: Business (Sun); People Page (S); TV, Entertainment (Thur); @RecordBody:**Magazines:** Relish (Monthly); Parade (S); American Profile (Weekly).
Pub. .... Mark Raymond
Adv. Dir. .... Pat Bridges
Circ. Dir. .... Bob Franks
Editorial Writer .... Vicki Menard
Entertainment/N. County Reporter Heather Morse
Features Ed. .... Craig Reed
Sports Ed. .... Tom Eggers
Prodn. Mgr. .... Rod Carlson
Market Information: TMC.
Mechanical available: Offset; Black and 3 ROP colors; insert accepted; page cutoffs - 21 1/2.
Mechanical Specifications: Type page 13 x 21 1/2; E - 6 cols, 2 1/16, 1/8 between; A - 6 cols, 2 1/16, 1/8 between; C - 9 cols, 1 3/8, 1/16 between.
Commodity Consumption: Avg. Page Number Per Issue - Daily 32; Avg. Page Number Per Issue - Sunday 44; widths 27 1/2; Newsprint Used - Metric Tons 1175; Printing Ink Used - Pages Printed 9708.
Equipment; Editorial Hardware – APP/Mac, 26-APP/Mac SE 30, 2-TM, 1-APP/Mac Plus, 5-APP/Mac SE, 2-APP/Power Mac 7100; Editorial Equipment – 16-APP/Mac SE 30, 3-APP/Mac Plus; Editorial Printers – Software ☐ QPS/QuarkXPress.; Classified Hardware – 4-APP/Mac SE 30. DISPLAY: Ad make-up applications – QPS/QuarkXPress.; Display Hardware – 5-APP/Mac IIci, 4-APP/Mac Power PC 8100 PRODUCTION: Pagination Software – QPS/QuarkXPress.; Production Equipment – 1-APP/Mac II, SE, APP/Mac LaserWriter, 1-

COM/Universal, 2-QMS/800II, 2-Pre Press/Panther Imagesetter 11.0; Cameras – 1-SCREEN PRESSROOM: Line 1 – 6-G/Urbanite; Folders – 1-G/quarter folder. MAILROOM: Counter stackers – 1-Quipp/500; Inserters and stuffers – 1-MM/227E, 1-KAN/480; Bundle tying machines – 2-MLN/ML2EE.; Business Hardware – 1-PBS/Convergent

NEWS-REVIEW PUBLISHING CO.
345 NE Winchester St, Roseburg, Ore., 97470; gen tel (541) 672-3321; gen fax (541) 673-5994

SALEM

STATESMAN JOURNAL
280 Church St. NE, Salem, Ore., 97301-3734; gen tel (503) 399-6611; adv tel (503) 399-6602; adv fax (503) 399-6808; ed fax (503) 399-6706; adv e-mail ads@statesmanjournal.com; ed e-mail newsroom@statesmanjournal.com; web site www.statesmanjournal.com
Group: Gannett
Published: Mon, Tues, Wed, Thur, Fri, Sat, Sun
Weekday Frequency: m
Saturday Frequency: m
Circulation: 37,431; 35,802(sat); 46,704(sun)
Last Audit: ABC September 30, 2011
Price: 3.96/wk; 17.50/mo; 205.80/yr.
Advertising: Open inch rate $106.17
News services: AP, GNS.
Politics: Independent.
Special Editions: State Fair (Aug); Gift Guides (Nov); Home Show (Feb); Tour of Homes (Jun);
Special Weekly Sections: Real Living (Fri); Polk County Weekly (S); Auto Finder (Sat); Weekend Entertainment Guide (Thur); South Salem Weekly (Tues); Keizer Wednesday (Wed).
Magazines: Comics (S).
Pub. ....Steve Silberman
Controller/Opns. Dir. ....Jerry Scobie
Adv. Mgr., Classified ....Valerie Thorne
Exec. Ed. ....Bill Church
Bus./Finance Ed. ....Don Currie
Digital Ed. ....Amy Read
Editorial Page Ed. ....Dick Hughes
Metro Ed. ....Dan Bender
Photo Ed. ....Diane Stevenson
Senior Ed. ....Michelle Maxwell
Senior Ed. ....Victor Panichkul
Sports Ed. ....James Day
Theater/Music Ed. ....Kelly Williams Brown
IT Mgr. ....Kristina Salaz
Prodn. Mgr., Distr. ....John Witherspoon
Market Information: ADS; Split run; TMC.
Mechanical available: Offset; Black and 4 ROP colors; insert accepted; page cutoffs - 22 3/4.
Mechanical Specifications: Type page 10 x 21 1/2; E - 6 cols, 1 1/2, 1/6 between; A - 6 cols, 2, 1/6 between; C - 10 cols, 1, 1/12 between.
Commodity Consumption: Avg. Page Number Per Issue - Daily 32; Avg. Page Number Per Issue - Plates Used 52000; Avg. Page Number Per Issue - Sunday 52; widths 50; Newsprint Used - Metric Tons 6897; Printing Ink Used - Black 141000; Printing Ink Used - Color 18000; Printing Ink U
Equipment EDITORIAL: Front-end Software – QPS.; Editorial Hardware – IBM, APP/Mac G3 Workstation, Ethernet/100MP; Editorial Printers – V/5500, V/5300 B, HP/5si, HP/8100, HP/8500, HP/2500, HP/715 CLASSIFIED: Front-end Software – APT, MEI/CLS.; Classified Hardware – IBM/Servers, Ethernet/100MB-Dell/Workstation; Classified Equipment – 2-Harlequin/Software RIP (for V/5500), 1-V/5300 Pixelburst Software RIP; Classified Printers – V/5300 B, V/5500, HP/4000, HP/5SI, HP/8100, HP/8500 DISPLAY: Ad make-up applications – Multi-Ad/Creator, QPS, Archetype/Corel Draw, Managing Editor/ALS, Roundhouse/Ad Tracking; Display Hardware – IBM, APP/Mac G3; Display Printers – V/5300 B, HP/8100, HP/8500, HP/2500, HP/715 PRODUCTION: Pagination Software – MEI/CLS, QPS.; Production Equipment – V/5100, V/5500, V/5300 B, QMS; Cameras – Spartan/II Page; Scanners – CD, Lf/Leafscan 35, Sharp/Flatbed, Lf/Leafscan 45, 2-Tecsa/18 x 24, 2-Tecsa/14x24 PRESSROOM: Line 1 – 7-G/Metro double width 1975; Pasters – G/Digital Pilot & surface sensing; Reels and Stands – Spyder/arms. MAILROOM: Counter stackers – 4/Olympian; Inserters and stuffers – HI/NP 632; Bundle tying machines – 4-/Dynaric; Mailroom control system – HI w/Icon System; Addressing machine – Domino/InkJet.
Delivery method: Mail, Newsstand, Private Carrier, Racks

THE DALLES

THE DALLES DAILY CHRONICLE
315 Federal St., The Dalles, Ore., 97058; gen tel (541) 296-2141; gen fax (541) 298-1365; gen e-mail tdchron@eaglenewspapers.com; adv e-mail tdchron@eaglenewspapers.com; web site www.gorgenews.com
Published: Mon, Tues, Wed, Thur, Fri, Sun
Weekday Frequency: e
Circulation: 5,067; 5,468(sun)
Last Audit: September 30, 2006
Price: 6.57/mo (carrier), $7.75/mo (mail); 77.00/yr (carrier), $88.00/yr (mail).
Advertising: Open inch rate $11.06
News services: AP.
Politics: Independent.
Not Published: New Year; Memorial Day; Independence Day; Labor Day; Thanksgiving; Christmas.
Special Editions: Progress (Feb); Visit the Gorge (May).
Magazines: American Profile (Weekly).
Pub. ....Marilyn Roth
Circ. Dir. ....Jose Alamazon
Exec. Ed. ....Kathy Gray
News Ed. ....Rodger Nichols
Market Information: TMC; Zoned editions.
Mechanical available: Offset; Black and 3 ROP colors; insert accepted - zoning available; page cutoffs - 21.
Mechanical Specifications: Type page 13 x 21; E - 6 cols, 2, 1/8 between; A - 6 cols, 2, 1/8 between; C - 6 cols, 2, 1/8 between.
Commodity Consumption: Avg. Page Number Per Issue - Daily 14; Avg. Page Number Per Issue - Plates Used 5000; Avg. Page Number Per Issue - Sunday 14; widths 11 5/8; Newsprint Used - Metric Tons 133; Printing Ink Used - Black 7530; Printing Ink Used - Color 1000; Printing Ink Us
Equipment EDITORIAL: Front-end Software – Sun.; Editorial Hardware – Sun; Editorial Printers – QMS/810 T, 2-PS, Elite, IBM CLASSIFIED: Front-end Software – Synaptic.; Classified Hardware – 2-ScrippSat; Classified Printers – QMS/810 Turbo, Okidata/Microline 393 P14S; Layout Software – QPS/QuarkXPress, Archetype/Corel Draw, Adobe/Illustrator.; Display Printers – QMS/810 Turbo, 2-PS, Elite, IBM; Production Equipment – 2-QMS/810 Turbo, PostScript/Printer; Cameras – Nikon, Kk/Digital.; Folders – 1 BUSINESS COMPUTERS: Business Software – QuarkXPress, Synaptic, Microsoft/Office, Adobe/Photoshop, Adobe/Illustratoe, Archetype/Corel Draw (PC Software/Bus. Applications); Business Hardware – 19-Magitonic

PENNSYLVANIA

ALLENTOWN

THE MORNING CALL
101 N. 6th St., Allentown, Pa., 18105-1260; gen tel (610) 820-6500; adv tel (610) 820-6633; adv fax (610) 820-6617; ed fax (610) 820-6693; adv e-mail circweb@mcall.com; ed e-mail news@mcall.com; letters@mcall.com; web site www.mcall.com
Published: Mon, Tues, Wed, Thur, Fri, Sat, Sun
Weekday Frequency: m
Saturday Frequency: m
Circulation: 93,175; 77,141(sat); 123,409(sun)
Last Audit: ABC September 30, 2011
Note: I'm only updating and verifying the Publisher's contact information.
Publisher, President and CEO ....Timothy Ryan
Equipment CLASSIFIED: Front-end Software – SII.; Display Printers – HP

ALTOONA

ALTOONA MIRROR
301 Cayuga Ave., Altoona, Pa., 16602; gen tel (814) 946-7411; adv tel (814) 946-7411; ed tel (814) 946-7441; gen fax (814) 946-7547; adv fax (814) 946-7547; ed fax (814) 946-7540; gen e-mail information@altoonamirror.com; adv e-mail displayads@altoonamirror.com; ed e-mail news@altoonamirror.com; web site www.altoonamirror.com
Group: Pennsylvania Newspapers Association
Published: Mon, Tues, Wed, Thur, Fri, Sat, Sun
Weekday Frequency: m
Saturday Frequency: m
Circulation: 27,216; 29,443(sat); 36,143(sun)
Last Audit: ABC September 30, 2011
Price: 16/mo; 182/yr.
Advertising: Open inch rate $60.56
News services: AP.
Politics: Independent. **Established:** 1874
Special Editions: Home Improvement (Apr); Back-to-School (Aug); Winter Sports (Dec); Jaffa Sports Show (Feb); Eye Care Month (Jan); Tour de 'Toona (Jul); Relay For Life (Cancer Society) (Jun); March Madness (Mar); Children's Miracle Network (May); Senior Mirror (Monthly);
Special Weekly Sections: Penn State Gameday (Football Season) (Fri).
Magazines: The NASCAR Report (Monthly); Central Pennsylvania Woman (Other); USA WEEKEND Magazine (S); TV Week (Sat).
Pub. ....Ed Kruger
Gen. Mgr. ....Ray Eckenrode
Circ. Dir. ....Dan Slep
Circ. Mgr., Office ....Beth Claar
Editorial Page Ed. ....Steve Carpenter
Librarian ....Tim Doyle
Photo Ed. ....................J.D. Cavrich
Picture Desk Ed. ....Paul Singer
Sports Ed. ....Buck Frank
Women's Ed. ....Barbara Cowan
Prodn. Mgr. ....Rick Bacza
Market Information: TMC.
Mechanical available: Offset; Black and 3 ROP colors; insert accepted - others upon request-with publisher's approval; page cutoffs - 22 3/4.
Mechanical Specifications: Type page 13 x 21; E - 6 cols, 2 1/16, 1/8 between; A - 6 cols, 2 1/16, 1/8 between; C - 6 cols, 2 1/16, 1/8 between.
Commodity Consumption: Avg. Page Number Per Issue - Daily 40; Avg. Page Number Per Issue - Plates Used 19582; Avg. Page Number Per Issue - Sunday 56; widths 54; Newsprint Used - Short Tons 3300; Printing Ink Used - Black 12405; Printing Ink Used - Color 1500; Printing Ink Used
Equipment EDITORIAL: Front-end Software – QPS/QuarkXPress. CLASSIFIED: Front-end Software – Unix, CText.; Classified Printers – IBM, Konica/Marlins DISPLAY: Ad make-up applications – APP/Mac NLM 3.12, Novell/Netware 386 3.12, Microsoft/Windows, PBS, ReCas/4; Layout Software – SCS/Layout 8000, APP/Mac G3, APP/Mac G4, A; Display Hardware – HP, APP/Mac; Display Printers – Konica/Marlin 2500 PRODUCTION: Pagination Software – APP/Mac NLM 3.12, Novell/Netware 386 3.12, Microsoft/Windows, Cheyenne/Arcserve.; Production Equipment – KFM; Cameras – SCREEN, LD/281-Q; Scanners – ECR/Autokon, Sharp/35mm PRESSROOM: Line 1 – 6-G/Headliner Offset double width, 4-G/half decks double width; Folders – 2; Reels and Stands – 5-G/Stands, 5-G/3-Arm Reels. MAILROOM: Counter stackers – 2/PPK, 2-Id/2200; Inserters and stuffers – 6-/KAN, MC/660-20, GMA/SLS 1000; Bundle tying machines – 5-/Sa, 2-/MLN, Id; Mailroom control system – GMA; Addressing machine – PBS/CIS; Other equipment –MM.; Business Hardware – Software ÂD Excel, MS Word, Microsoft/Excel, Microsoft/Word

BEAVER

BEAVER COUNTY TIMES
400 Fair Ave., Beaver, Pa., 15009-1907; gen tel (724) 775-3200; gen fax (724) 775-4180; adv fax (724) 775-7212; gen e-mail timesnews@timesonline.com; adv e-mail timesclassifieds@timesonline.com; web site www.timesonline.com
Group: Pennsylvania Newspapers Association
Published: Mon, Tues, Wed, Thur, Fri, Sat, Sun
Weekday Frequency: m
Saturday Frequency: m
Circulation: 30,434; 33,012(sat); 37,113(sun)
Last Audit: ABC September 30, 2011
Price: 3.50/wk; 182.00/yr; 45.50/13wk; $86.45/26wk.
Advertising: Open inch rate $57.20
News services: AP, MCT, PR Newswire.
Politics: Independent.
Not Published: New Year; Memorial Day; Independence Day; Labor Day; Christmas.
Special Editions: NIE (Apr); Hookstown Fair (Aug); Basketball (Dec); Tax Guide (Feb); Economy (Jan); Big Knob Fair (Jul); Farm & Garden (Mar); Best of the Valley (May); Gift Guide (Nov); Car Care (Sept).
Magazines: USA WEEKEND Magazine (Fri); Sunday Times Magazine (S); TV Times (Sat).
Pub. ....Alan H. Buncher
Vice Pres. ....Stanley M. Ellis
Vice Pres. ....Sandra C. Hardy
Vice Pres. ....Charles Smith
Vice Pres./Sec. ....Shirley C. Ellis
Controller ....Lisa Reese
Credit Mgr. ....Debbie Hays
Mgr., Educ. Serv. ....Lorraine Shea
Exec. Sec. ....Susan Miller
Adv. Dir. ....Bob Woelfel
Adv. Mgr., Sales ....Dan Carr
Adv. Opns. Mgr. ....Rich Riffle
Circ. Dir. ....Larry Boggs
Circ. Mgr., Distr. ....Kurt Verrico
Circ. Mgr., Home Delivery ....William Budris
Circ. Mgr., Home Delivery ....Mark Zuchelli
Circ. Mgr., Mktg. ....Vaughn Vacar
Circ. Mgr., Opns. ....Mary Cotters
Exec. Ed. ....Keith W. Briscoe
Mng. Ed., Content ....Tom Bickert
Market Information: ADS; TMC; Zoned editions.
Mechanical available: Other; Black and 3 ROP colors; insert accepted - most sizes accepted; page cutoffs - 22 3/4.
Mechanical Specifications: Type page 13 x 21 1/2; E - 6 cols, 2 1/16, 1/8 between; A - 6 cols, 2 1/16, 1/8 between; C - 9 cols, 1 3/8, 1/16 between.
Commodity Consumption: Avg. Page Number Per Issue - Daily 43; Avg. Page Number Per Issue - Plates Used 34000; Avg. Page Number Per Issue - Sunday 74; widths 54; Newsprint Used - Metric Tons 4116; Printing Ink Used - Black 120552; Printing Ink Used - Color 16402; Printing Ink U
Equipment EDITORIAL: Front-end Software – ACI/Open Pages.; Editorial Hardware – 31-Dell/PC, 14-Compaq, 5-APP/Mac, 2-Compaq/Servers; Editorial Equipment – MON/SUN OPS System; Editorial Printers – MON/Proof Express, 2-MON/Expressmaster 1016, 3-HP/LaserJet Printer CLASSIFIED: Front-end Software – Mactive.; Classified Hardware – 7-Dell/PC, 2-Dell/Server; Classified Equipment – HP/LaserJet Printer; Classified Printers – MON/Expressmaster 1016 DISPLAY: Ad make-up applications – QPS/QuarkXPress 4.1, Adobe/Photoshop, Adobe/Illustrator, AdTracker; Display Hardware – 7-Dell/PC, 2-APP/Mac, 2-IBM/PC, 2-Compaq/Server;

Display Printers – MON/PaperMaster II, 2-MON/Expressmaster 1016 PRODUCTION: Pagination Software – QPS/QuarkXPress 3.2.; Production Equipment – OCR, Caere/Omni-Page, 2-Sun; Cameras – 1-C/Spartan III; Scanners – 4-HP/Scanner PRESSROOM: Line 1 – 6-G/Mark I Headliner 2362 double width 1964; Folders – 1-G/2:1; Pasters – G/RTP; Press control system – Ch/SCR. MAILROOM: Counter stackers – 1-HL/Stacker, 1-TMSI/Compass 360, 1-TMSI/Compass 180; Inserters and stuffers – GMA/2000; Bundle tying machines – 2/Dynaric; Addressing machine – 1-IBM/3031. BUSINESS COMPUTERS: Business Software – Microsoft/Office 97, Mactive, Open Pages; Business Hardware – IBM

BEDFORD

BEDFORD GAZETTE

424 W. Penn St., Bedford, Pa., 15522; gen tel (814) 623-1151; gen fax (814) 623-5055; gen e-mail bedfordgazette@embarqmail.com; adv e-mail advertise@bedfordgazette.com; web site www.bedfordgazette.com

Group: Pennsylvania Newspapers Association
Published: Mon, Tues, Wed, Thur, Fri, Sat
Weekday Frequency: m
Circulation: 9,837; 9,837(sat)
Last Audit: March 31, 2007
Price: 11.00/mo; 121.50/yr.
Advertising: Open inch rate $21.33
News services: AP.
Politics: Independent. **Established:** 1805
Not Published: New Year; Memorial Day; Independence Day; Labor Day; Christmas.
Special Editions: Home & Garden (Apr); Back-to-School (Aug); Christmas 3 (Dec); Boy Scout Week Pages (Feb); Jaycee Week Pages (Jan); Bedford County Fair (Jul); Dairy Farm (Jun); Bridal & Spring Fashion (Mar); Graduation & Careers (May); Golden Years (Monthly); Christmas Ed
Special Weekly Sections: Village Crier (Fri); Lifestyles (Mon); Church Page (Sat); Lifestyles (Thur); Lifestyles (Tues); Food Page (Wed).
Magazines: American Profile (Weekly).
Pres. ....George Sample
Adv. Dir. ....Joseph Beegle
Circ. Mgr. ....Barbara Diehl
Ed. ....Sharyn Maust
Features Ed. ....Vicki Henry
Prodn. Foreman, Pressroom ....Phil Lewis
Prodn. Mgr.,Post Press ....Eileen Davis
Market Information: TMC.
Mechanical available: Offset; Black and 4 ROP colors; insert accepted; page cutoffs - 22 3/4.
Mechanical Specifications: Type page 13 x 21 1/2; E - 6 cols, 2 1/16, 1/8 between; A - 6 cols, 2 1/16, 1/8 between; C - 6 cols, 2 1/16, 1/8 between.
Commodity Consumption: Avg. Page Number Per Issue - Daily 18; widths 28; Newsprint Used - Metric Tons 680; Printing Ink Used - Pages Printed 5525.
Equipment EDITORIAL: Front-end Software – Baseview/NewsEdit.; Editorial Hardware – APP/Mac; Editorial Printers – APP/Mac Laser CLASSIFIED: Front-end Software – Baseview.; Classified Hardware – APP/Mac; Classified Printers – APP/Mac Laser; Display Hardware – APP/Mac; Display Printers – Software ☐ Baseview.; Production Equipment – APP/Mac Laser; Cameras – K. PRESSROOM: Line 1 – 5-G/Community 1983; Folders – 1-G/S-C.; Bundle tying machines – Nichiro Kogyo; Addressing machine – Ch/515.; Audio Hardware – Gateway/2000; Business Hardware – Real World, PC

GAZETTE PUBLISHING CO., INC.

424 W. Penn St., Bedford, Pa., 15522; gen tel (814) 623-1151; gen fax (814) 623-5055; adv e-mail advertise@bedfordgazette.com; web site www.bedfordgazette.com

Price: 121.50/yr.
Advertising: Open inch rate $11.13
Politics: 1805

BLOOMSBURG

PRESS ENTERPRISE

3185 Lackawanna Ave., Bloomsburg, Pa., 17815; gen tel (570) 784-2121; adv tel (570) 387-1234 ext 1210; ed tel (570) 784-2121; gen fax (570) 784-9226; adv fax (570) 416-0220; ed fax (570) 784-9226; adv e-mail adv@pressenterprise.net; ed e-mail news@pressenterprise.net; web site www.pressenterpriseonline.com

Published: Mon, Tues, Wed, Thur, Fri, Sat, Sun
Weekday Frequency: m
Saturday Frequency: m
Circulation: 19,134; 19,134(sat); 20,160(sun)
Last Audit: Sworn September 30, 2008
Price: 3.75/wk; 139.95/yr; 13.00/4wk.
Advertising: Open inch rate $24.92
News services: AP.
Politics: Independent. **Established:** 1901
Special Editions: Your Home (Apr); Back-to-School (Aug); Gift Guide (Dec); Progress (Feb); Bridal (Jan); FYI (Jul); Recreation (Jun); MenuTabs (Mar); Senior Citizen (May); Gift Guide (Nov); New Autos (Oct); Fair (Sept).
Special Weekly Sections: Business & Service Directory (Thur); Best Food Day (Wed).
Magazines: Color Comics (S); TV Preview (Sat); American Profile (Weekly).
Pres. ....Paul R. Eyerly
Treasurer ....James T. Micklow
Pub. ....Brandon R. Eyerly
Bus. Office Mgr. ....Dennis Ashenfelder
Adv. Mgr. ....Sandra Sterner
Circ. Mgr. ....Donald Whitmire
Mng. Ed., News ....Dean Kashner
Editorial Page Ed. ....James Sachetti
Graphics Ed./Art Dir. ....Lori Getty
Photo Ed. ....Bill Hughes
Mgmt. Info Servs. Mgr. ....Jeff Cragle
Prodn. Mgr., Bindery/Post Press ....Julie Neitz
Prodn. Mgr., Opns. ....Bill Bason
Prodn. Mgr., PM ....Robert Temple
Prodn. Mgr., Press ....Brad Conklin
Market Information: ADS; TMC.
Mechanical available: Offset; Black and 4 ROP colors; insert accepted; page cutoffs - 22 3/4.
Mechanical Specifications: Type page 12 x 21 1/2; E - 6 cols, 1 11/16', 1/10 between; A - 6 cols, 1 11/16, 1/10 between; C - 9 cols, 1 1/16, 1/10 between.
Commodity Consumption: Avg. Page Number Per Issue - Daily 32; widths 27; Newsprint Used - Short Tons 2000; Printing Ink Used - Black 44000; Printing Ink Used - Color 14000; Printing Ink Used - Pages Printed 11648.
Equipment EDITORIAL: Front-end Software – Woodwing/InDesign; Editorial Hardware – Mac mini iMac, Xserve; Editorial Printers – Laser jet 8150 CLASSIFIED: Front-end Software – Brainworks; Classified Hardware – Dell 2850; Classified Printers – HP/Laserjet 4000 DISPLAY: Ad make-up applications – Multi-Ad/Creator 3.7; Layout Software – APP/Mac.; Display Printers – HP LaserJet 5si/MX PRODUCTION: Pagination Software – Baseview.; Production Equipment – Nexus, Creo transetter news; Scanners – Epson PRESSROOM: Line 1 – 8-G/Urbanite (3 color) single width 1972; Line 2 – 8-HI/NC 400 single width 1985; Line 3 – Tensor/1400 single width 1995; Line 4 – Tensor/1400 single width 1999; Folders – 2; Reels and Stands – Roll/Stands. MAILROOM: Counter stackers – 1-BG/108, 1-BG/107, 1/PPK, 2-HI/RS25; Inserters and stuffers – 1-/MM, GMA/SLS 1000; Bundle tying machines – 2-MLN/ML2EE, 1-/Sa, 3-/BU; Addressing machine – 1-KR/Communications, 1-/KAN; Other equipment –MM/Bravo 360. BUSINESS COMPUTERS: Business Software – DSI Software, Logic, Abra Suite, Great Plains; Business Hardware – Dell 2950

BRADFORD

THE BRADFORD ERA

43 Main St., Bradford, Pa., 16701; gen tel (814) 368-3173; ed tel (814) 362-6531; gen fax (814) 362-6510; adv fax (814) 362-6510; ed fax (814) 362-6510; gen e-mail info@bradfordera.com; adv e-mail display@bradfordera.com; classified@bradfordera.com; ed e-mail news@bradfordera.com; web site www.bradfordera.com

Group: Pennsylvania Newspapers Association
Published: Mon, Tues, Wed, Thur, Fri, Sat
Weekday Frequency: m
Circulation: 9,329; 9,329(sat)
Last Audit: Sworn September 30, 2010
Price: 3.05/wk; 13.00/mo (carrier), $14.00/mo (auto); 159.60/yr.
Advertising: Open inch rate $15.25
News services: AP.
Politics: Republican. **Established:** 1824
Not Published: July 5; Dec. 26.
Special Editions: Univ. of Pittsburgh at Bradford (Aug); Progress (Jan); Zippo Days (Jul); Sun 'n Fun (Jun); Brides (Mar); Design-an-Ad (May); Christmas Guide (Nov); Hunting Guide (Oct).
Magazines: USA WEEKEND Magazine (Sat).
Purchasing Agent ....Gretchen Gallagher
Adv. Mgr. ....Jill Henry
Ed. ....John H. Satterwhite
Mng. Ed. ....Marty Robacker Wilder
Prodn. Mgr., Mailroom/Post Press ....Rick Kautz
Prodn. Mgr. ....Linda Cardamone
Market Information: TMC.
Mechanical available: Offset; Black and 3 ROP colors; insert accepted - all; page cutoffs - 22 3/4.
Mechanical Specifications: Type page 12 x 21 1/2; E - 6 cols, 1 13/16, 1/6 between; A - 6 cols, 1 13/16, 1/6 between; C - 9 cols, 1 3/16, 1/12 between.
Commodity Consumption: Avg. Page Number Per Issue - Daily 21; Avg. Page Number Per Issue - Plates Used 7650; Avg. Page Number Per Issue - Saturday 26; widths 27 1/2; Newsprint Used - Short Tons 1200; Printing Ink Used - Black 33000; Printing Ink Used - Color 24000; Printing In
Equipment EDITORIAL: Front-end Software – Baseview.; Editorial Hardware – APP/Power Mac; Editorial Equipment – 1-APP/Mac IIsi, APP/GraphicsNet, 1-Lf/AP Leaf Picture Desk (with Laser Photo); Editorial Printers – LaserWriter/Pro, Pre Press/Panther Pro Imagesetter, Pre Press/Panther Plus Imagesetter CLASSIFIED: Front-end Software – Baseview.; Classified Hardware – APP/Mac; Classified Printers – Okidata/Microline 321 Turbo, Pre Press/Panther Pro Imagesetter DISPLAY: Ad make-up applications – Multi-Ad/Creator 4.0, Multi-Ad/Creator 2.0; Display Hardware – 2-APP/Mac G3, 1-APP/Mac Quadra; Display Printers – 1-APP/Mac LaserWriter, 2-Pre Press/Panther Plus 46 Imagesetter, PrePress/Panther Pro PRODUCTION: Pagination Software – QPS/QuarkXPress 4.0.; Production Equipment – Visioneer 2.0, 1-Pre Press/Panther Pro 46 (18 wide Imagesetter), 1-Pre Press/Panther Plus (13 1/3 wide Imagesetter); Cameras – R/500 Overhead; Scanners – 1-Lf/Leafscan 45, 3-Umax/Astra 12005 PRESSROOM: Line 1 – 8-HI/V-15D; Press Drives – 2; Folders – 2; Reels and Stands – 8; Press control system – 2-CH/Responder 210. MAILROOM: Counter stackers – 1/BG; Bundle tying machines – 2-/MLN; Addressing machine – 1-/St, 1-/KR. BUSINESS COMPUTERS: Business Software – Vision Data; Business Hardware – 1-Compaq/Unix Box, 5-PC

BUTLER

BUTLER EAGLE

114 W. Diamond St., Butler, Pa., 16001-5747; gen tel (724) 282-8000; adv tel (724) 282-8000; ed tel (724) 282-8000; gen fax (724) 282-1280; adv fax (724) 282-1280; ed fax (724) 282-4180; gen e-mail linemgr@butlereagle.com; adv e-mail classified@butlereagle.com; ed e-mail news@butlereagle.com; web site www.butlereagle.com

Group: Pennsylvania Newspapers Association
Published: Mon, Tues, Wed, Thur, Fri, Sun
Weekday Frequency: e
Circulation: 25,901; 28,156(sun)
Last Audit: ABC September 30, 2011
Price: 2.50/wk; 10.00/mo; 120.00/yr.
Advertising: Open inch rate $25.50
News services: AP.
Politics: Independent-Republican. **Established:** 1869
Not Published: Memorial Day; Labor Day; Thanksgiving; Christmas.
Special Editions: Summer Car Care (Apr); Football (Aug); Christmas Photos of Children (Dec); Funeral Directors (Feb); Family Health Guide (Jan); Farm Show (Jul); Father's Day (Jun); Progress (Mar); Christmas (Nov); Diner's Guide (Oct); Ethnic Festival (Sept).
Special Weekly Sections: Church (Fri).
Magazines: USA WEEKEND Magazine (S).
Profile: Family owned newspaper publisher with a daily and a Sunday and 4 weekly newspapers. We also are a heat-set commercial web printer.
Pres. ....Vernon L. Wise
Pub. ....Vernon Wiase
Adv. Dir. ....Keith Graham
Adv. Mgr., Classified ....Nedra Sutch
Dir., Mktg./Promo. ....Ronald A. Vodenichar
Circ. Dir. ....Alice Lunn
Ed. ....John Laing Wise
Mng. Ed. ....Mark Mann
Editorial Writer. ....Joseph Kaspryzk
Features Ed. ....Sandra Marwick
News Ed. ....David Heastings
Photo Ed. ....Justin Guido
Sports Ed. ....John Enrietto
Mgr., Mgmt. Info Servs. ....Tammy Schuey
Prodn. Mgr., Pressroom ....Ronald Huselton
Market Information: ADS; Split run; TMC.
Mechanical available: Offset; Black and 4 ROP colors; insert accepted - any; page cutoffs - 21.
Mechanical Specifications: Type page 11 5/8 x 20; E - 6 cols, 1 5/6, 1/8 between; A - 6 cols, 1 5/6, 1/8 between; C - 9 cols, 1 1/6, 1/12 between.
Commodity Consumption: Avg. Page Number Per Issue - Daily 28; Avg. Page Number Per Issue - Plates Used 8000; Avg. Page Number Per Issue - Sunday 56; widths 37 1/2; Newsprint Used - Short Tons 2000; Printing Ink Used - Black 47000; Printing Ink Used - Color 5000; Printing Ink U
Equipment EDITORIAL: Front-end Software – Microsoft/Word, CNI Open.; Editorial Hardware – PC; Editorial Printers – CTP CLASSIFIED: Front-end Software – Brainworks.; Classified Hardware – 7-APP/Mac IIci, PC; Classified Equipment – 1-Microtek/Scanner; Classified Printers – CTP DISPLAY: Ad make-up applications – Multi-Ad, Adobe/Photoshop, QPS/QuarkXPress; Layout Software – MEI/ALS.; Display Hardware – Mac/G-4 PRODUCTION: Pagination Software – QPS/QuarkXPress.; Production Equipment – Douthitt, GMTI; Cameras – 1-C, 1-B; Scanners – Graphic Enterprises/PageScan 800, AG/Arcus, CD/Scanner 645 IM, CD/Scanview 600, 1-Howtek/7500 PRESSROOM: Line 1 – 7-G/Cosmo double width; Folders – 1 MAILROOM: Counter stackers – Galnmeler; Inserters and stuffers – MM 3270; Bundle tying machines – Dynaric, Si, MLN.

EAGLE PRINTING CO.

114 W. Diamond St., Butler, Pa., 16001; gen tel (724) 282-8000; gen fax (724) 282-1280; adv e-mail advertising@butlereagle.com; ed e-mail news@butlereagle.com; web site www.butlereagle.com

Published: Mon, Tues, Wed, Thur, Fri, Sun
Weekday Frequency: e
Circulation: 28,000; 29,000(sun)
News services: AP
Politics: 1869
Not Published: christmas,4th of July,Memorial day,labor day and Thanksgiving Day

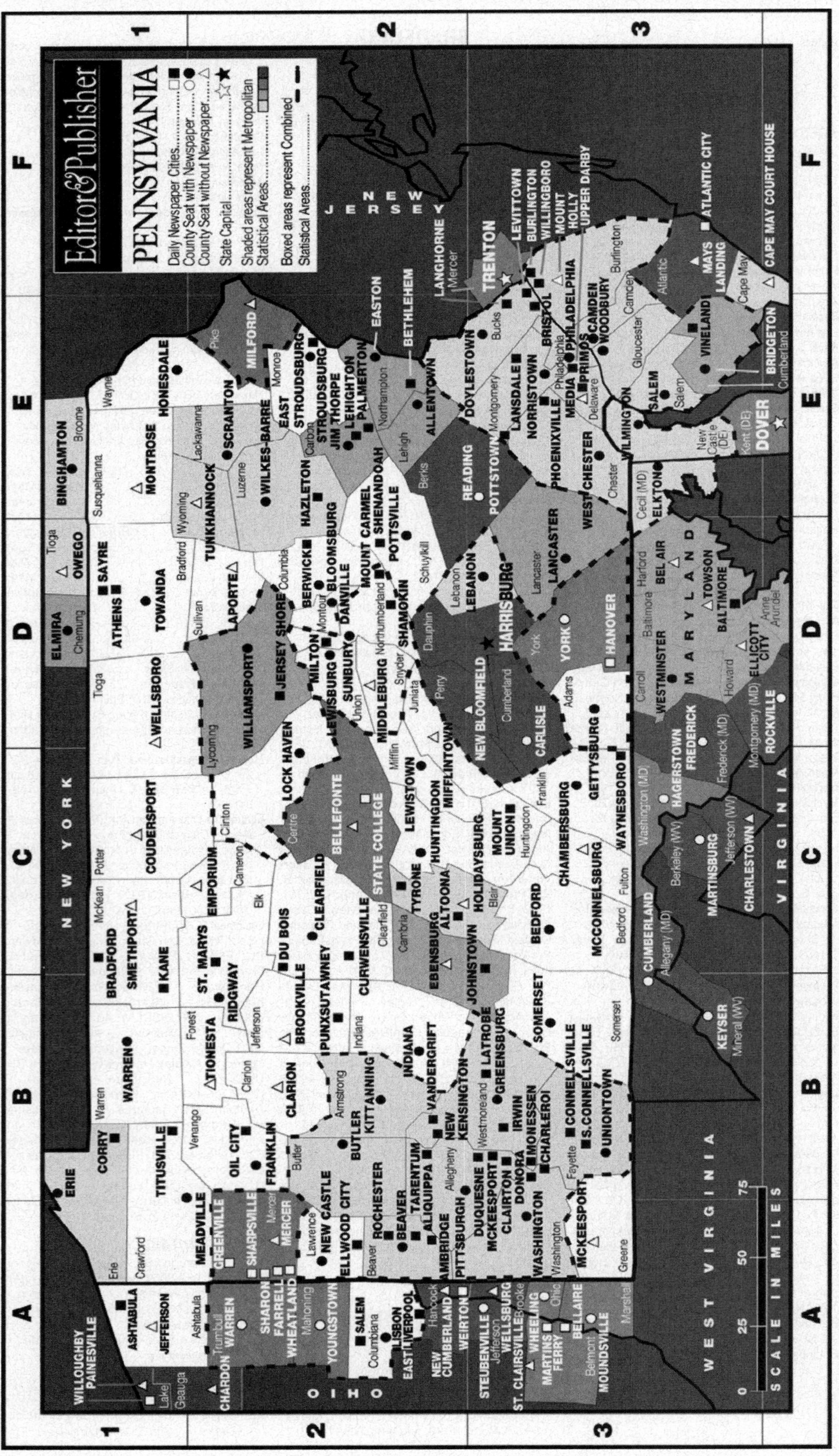

Own facility?: Y
Special Editions: progress
bridal
best of
fathers day
graduation
jeep festival
fall festival
Publisher and general manager Ronald Vodenichar
Director of Technology...............Tammy Schuey
Director of advertising.................Keith Graham
Circulation Director..........................Alice Lunn
Managing Editor............................Mark Mann
Equipment EDITORIAL: Front-end Software – Saxotech CLASSIFIED: Front-end Software – Brainworks DISPLAY: Ad make-up applications – Brainworks PRESSROOM: Line 1 – 4 towers Goss Uniliner BUSINESS COMPUTERS: Business Software – Dell Great Plains
Delivery method: Newsstand, Private Carrier, Racks

CARLISLE

THE SENTINEL

457 E. North St., Carlisle, Pa., 17013-0130; gen tel (717) 243-2611; adv tel (717) 243-2611; ed tel (717) 240-7125; gen fax (717) 243-3754; adv fax (717) 243-3754; ed fax (717) 243-3121; gen e-mail frontdoor@cumberlink.com; web site www.cumberlink.com
Published: Mon, Tues, Wed, Thur, Fri, Sat, Sun
Weekday Frequency: m
Saturday Frequency: m
Circulation: 12,118; 12,939(sat); 13,556(sun)
Last Audit: ABC September 30, 2011
Price: 3.23/wk; 14.00/mo; 84.00/yr.
Advertising: Open inch rate $31.15
News services: AP.
Politics: Independent.
Special Editions: Racing This Week (Apr); Welcome (Aug); Football This Week (Dec); Annual (Feb); Brides (Jan); Racing This Week (Jul); Graduation (Jun); Home Improvement (Mar); Car Care (May); Holiday Gift Guide (Nov); Car Care (Oct); Football This Week (Sept).
Special Weekly Sections: Church/Religion (Fri); Home (S); Food (Thur); Travel (Tues).
Magazines: USA WEEKEND Magazine (S); American Profile (Weekly).
Pub....Mark Blum
Controller...........................Stephen Peterson
Adv. Dir..................................Jim KleinKlaus
Adv. Sales Mgr...............................Jackie Cox
Exec. Ed....................................Hope Stephan
Assoc. Ed.......................Barbara Phillips-Long
Chief Photographer.....................Michael Bupp
Mng. Ed....Jeff Pratt
Prodn. Mgr., Opns......................Patrick Doane
Prodn. Mgr., Pressroom...................Lee Brown
Prodn. Foreman, Mailroom......Ryan McKeenan
Market Information: Split run; TMC.
Mechanical available: Offset; Black and 3 ROP colors; insert accepted; page cutoffs - 22 3/4.
Mechanical Specifications: Type page 11 5/8 x 21 1/2; E - 6 cols, 2 1/16, 1/8 between; A - 6 cols, 2 1/16, 1/8 between; C - 9 cols, 1 1/4, 1/4 between.
Commodity Consumption: Avg. Page Number Per Issue - Daily 30; Avg. Page Number Per Issue - Plates Used 16000; Avg. Page Number Per Issue - Saturday 24; Avg. Page Number Per Issue - Sunday 50; widths 27 1/2; Newsprint Used - Metric Tons 1800; Printing Ink Used - Black 37000; Pr
Equipment EDITORIAL: Front-end Software – Lotus/Domino Notes.; Editorial Hardware – 4-PC-NT Servers, 18-MS/NT Notes Clients; Editorial Equipment – 8-APP/Mac G3; Editorial Printers – 1-PT/RIP, 1-ECR/108S Pelbox CLASSIFIED: Front-end Software – Vision Data/Classified.; Classified Hardware – 7-Sun/Sparc II DISPLAY: Ad make-up applications – QPS/QuarkXPress 4.0, Adobe/Illustrator, Streamline.; Display Hardware – 9-APP/Mac G3; Display Printers – Software ☐ QPS/QuarkXPress 4.0, Adobe/Illustrator, Streamline.; Pro-

duction Equipment – Nat, 1-LE; Cameras – 1-SCREEN; Scanners – APP/Mac SE. PRESSROOM: Line 1 – 10-G/Community single width 1978; Folders – 1-G/SSC. MAILROOM: Counter stackers – 2-Id/Marathoner; Inserters and stuffers – 4/MM; Bundle tying machines – 1-/MLN; Addressing machine – 1-/Ch; Other equipment –Stitcher-Trimmer, Quarterfolder.; Audio Hardware – New Horizons/Info-Connect BUSINESS COMPUTERS: Business Software – Vision Data; Business Hardware – Sun/Ultra 2

CHAMBERSBURG

PUBLIC OPINION

77 N. 3rd St., Chambersburg, Pa., 17201-1812; gen tel (717) 264-6161; adv tel (717) 262-4720; ed tel (717) 262-4764; adv fax (717) 264-2009; ed fax (717) 264-0377; adv e-mail gharriger@mediaonepa; web site www.publicopiniononline.com

Group: Texas-New Mexico Newspaper Partners/Media News Group
Published: Mon, Tues, Wed, Thur, Fri, Sat, Sun
Weekday Frequency: m
Saturday Frequency: m
Circulation: 15,101; 15,080(sat); 18,083(sun)
Last Audit: ABC September 30, 2011
Price: $.50 Daily, $1.25 Sun
Advertising: Open inch rate $37.00
Insert rate: $50 daily card, $57 Sun card
News services: AP
Politics: 1869
Advertising not accepted: Y
Own facility?: Y
Special Editions: Baby Book (Feb), Builders Show (Mar), Golf Preview (Apr), Living in the Valley (Jul), Football Preview (Aug), Holiday Songbook (Dec)
Special Weekly Sections: Weekender (Thu) Real Estate (Fri),TV Book (Sun)
Magazines: USA WEEKEND Magazine (Sun).
Publisher....Ron Clausen
Controller....Caron Decker
Advertising Director....Ginny Harriger
Editor....Becky Bennett
Circulation Director....George Fuller
Production Director....Dave Myers
City Ed.....Andrea Wretch
Sports Editor....Ed Gotwals
Prodn. Mgr., Composing/Camera.Patty Clugston
Market Information: via MediaOne PA
Mechanical available: Offset - Black and 3 ROP colors; @RecordBody:**Mechanical Specifications:** Typed page 11 x 21 1/4
Commodity Consumption: Avg. Page Number Per Issue - Daily 28; Avg. Page Number Per Issue - Plates Used 16300; Avg. Page Number Per Issue - Saturday 40; widths 13 1/2; Newsprint Used - Metric Tons 1055.1; Newsprint Used - Short Tons 985; Printing Ink Used - Black 32000; Printin
Equipment EDITORIAL: Front-end Software – Baseview/NewsEdit Pro 3.2.3.; Editorial Hardware – APP/Mac; Editorial Equipment – Dell and Mac CLASSIFIED: Front-end Software – Mactive; Classified Hardware – PC; Classified Equipment – Dell DISPLAY: Ad make-up applications – Multi-Ad, Mactive/QuarkXPress; Display Hardware – Mac G4 PRODUCTION: Pagination Software – Baseview/NewsEdit Pro 3.2.3. PRESSROOM: Line 1 – 6 units-Goss Urbanite installed 2007. MAILROOM: Counter stackers – 2/QWI, 1-/SH; Inserters and stuffers – SH/1472; Bundle tying machines – MLN BUSINESS COMPUTERS: Business Software – MS Office 2003, JDE for business, Mactive for Adv, PBS for Circ; Business Hardware – PC
Zip Codes served: 17201 and surrounding in Franklin county, PA
Delivery method: Mail, Newsstand, Private Carrier, Racks

CLEARFIELD

THE PROGRESS

206 E. Locust St., Clearfield, Pa., 16830-0291; gen tel (814) 765-5581; adv tel (814) 765-9495; ed tel (814) 765-7813; gen fax (814) 765-5165; adv fax (814) 765-5165; ed fax (814) 765-5165; adv e-mail display@theprogressnews.com; ed e-mail news@theprogressnews.com; web site www.theprogressnews.com

Published: Mon, Tues, Wed, Thur, Fri, Sat
Weekday Frequency: e
Saturday Frequency: m
Circulation: 11,100; 11,100(sat)
Last Audit: Sworn September 30, 2008
Price: 2.50/wk (carrier); 10.00/mo (carrier), $15.00/mo (out-of-state); 112.00/yr (carrier), $170.00/yr (out-of-state).
Advertising: Open inch rate $18.73
Insert rate: $80 CPM
News services: AP, Mid Atlantic Newspaper Services, Inc..
Politics: Independent. **Established:** 1913
Not Published: New Year; Memorial Day; Independence Day; Labor Day; Thanksgiving; Christmas.
Own facility?: Y
Special Editions: Home & Garden (Apr); Football Tab (Aug); Bridal (Feb); Health & Fitness (Jan); County Fair (Jul); Summer Activities (May); Senior Lifestyles (Monthly); Hunting (Nov); Business (Oct).
Special Weekly Sections: Postscript TV (Fri); Food (Mon).
Magazines: USA WEEKEND Magazine (Fri).
Pub....Margaret Krebs
Treasurer/Controller....Linda Schultz
Credit Mgr./Purchasing Agent....Ann K. Law
Asst. Pub./Bus. Mgr.....Rebecca Johnson
Adv. Mgr., Classified....Barbara Garman
Adv. Mgr., Display....Jeannine Barger
Circ. Mgr.....Cindy Aughenbaugh
Ed....Jill Golden
Sports Ed....Jaclyn Yingling
Prodn. Supt., Plant....Steve Heichel
Assistant Editor....Liza Matia
Asst. Ed.....Linda Read
Mechanical available: Offset; Black and 3 ROP colors; insert accepted; page cutoffs - 22 3/4.
Mechanical Specifications: Type page 13 x 21 1/2; E - 6 cols, 2 1/16, 1/8 between; A - 6 cols, 2 1/16, 1/8 between; C - 8 cols, 1 5/8, 1/16 between.
Commodity Consumption: Avg. Page Number Per Issue - Daily 23; Avg. Page Number Per Issue - Plates Used 10000; widths 14; Newsprint Used - Short Tons 877; Printing Ink Used - Black 10600; Printing Ink Used - Color 300; Printing Ink Used - Pages Printed 7010.
Equipment EDITORIAL: Front-end Software – QPS/QuarkXpress 4.1.; Editorial Hardware – COM/One System; Editorial Printers – 4-NewGen CLASSIFIED: Front-end Software – QPS/Q-Sales.; Classified Hardware – OS; Classified Printers – MON PRODUCTION: Pagination Software – Quark 4.1.; Production Equipment – NewGen, Ultra 4000, Ultra/Plus; Cameras – Nipon/Screen; Scanners – HP/Scan Jet 6300C PRESSROOM: Line 1 – 9-G/Community; Folders – 1 MAILROOM: Counter stackers – 1-BG/Count-O-Veyor; Inserters and stuffers – KAN/320; Bundle tying machines – Sa.; Business Hardware – IBM
Delivery method: Mail, Newsstand, Private Carrier, Racks

PROGRESSIVE PUBLISHING CO.

206 E. Locust St., Clearfield, Pa., 16830-0291; gen tel (814) 765-5581; gen fax (814) 765-5165

CONNELLSVILLE

DAILY COURIER

127 W. Apple St., Connellsville, Pa., 15425; gen tel (724) 628-2000; adv tel (724) 628-2000; ed tel (724) 628-2000; adv fax (724) 626-3568; ed fax (724) 626-3567; gen e-mail dailycourier@tribweb.com; web site www.dailycourier.com

Published: Mon, Tues, Wed, Thur, Fri, Sat, Sun
Weekday Frequency: e
Saturday Frequency: m
Circulation: 7,544; 7,544(sat)
Last Audit: September 30, 2006
Price: 1.80/wk (carrier), $2.00/wk (motor route); 9.40/mo (mail); 92.10/yr (carrier), $104.00/yr (motor route); 40.50/3mo (mail).
Advertising: Open inch rate $15.00
News services: AP.
Politics: Independent. **Established:** 1879
Not Published: New Year; Memorial Day; Independence Day; Labor Day; Thanksgiving; Christmas.
Special Editions: Football Preview (Aug); Year in Review (Dec); Bridal (Jan); Fayette County Fair (Jul); Bridal (Jun); Progress (Mar).
Special Weekly Sections: Family (Mon); Health (Tues); Food (Wed).
Pub.....Richard M. Scaife
Adv. Dept. Mgr.....Karen Strickland
Circ. Mgr.....Mark Malone
Mng. Ed.....Roxanne Abramowitz
City Ed.....Rose Synder
Sports Ed.....Jason Black
Prodn. Supvr., Pre Press....Bonnie Killar
Market Information: TMC.
Mechanical available: Offset; Black and 2 ROP colors; insert accepted; page cutoffs - 22 3/4.
Mechanical Specifications: Type page 13 x 21 1/2; E - 6 cols, 2 1/16, 1/8 between; A - 6 cols, 2 1/16, 1/8 between; C - 9 cols, 1 3/8, 1/16 between.
Commodity Consumption: Avg. Page Number Per Issue - Daily 16; Avg. Page Number Per Issue - Plates Used 5500; widths 27 1/2; Newsprint Used - Short Tons 372; Printing Ink Used - Black 8736; Printing Ink Used - Color 1148; Printing Ink Used - Pages Printed 4932.
Equipment EDITORIAL: Front-end Software – QPS/QuarkXPress, Baseview, Adobe/Photoshop.; Editorial Hardware – APP/Mac; Classified Hardware – 3-Mk. DISPLAY: Ad make-up applications – QPS/QuarkXPress, Multi-Ad/Creator; Layout Software – 3-APP/Mac fileserver.; Display Hardware – Printers ☐ 1-APP/Mac LaserPrinter, 2-LaserPrinter/11x17; Production Equipment – 2-XIT/Clipper; Cameras – 1-B, 2-Nu, 1-SCREEN. PRESSROOM: Line 1 – 6; Folders – 1; Bundle tying machines – OVL.; Business Hardware – Software ☐ NCR/Software

CORRY

THE JOURNAL

28 W. South St., Corry, Pa., 16407-1810; gen tel (814) 665-8291; gen fax (814) 664-2288; gen e-mail corryjournal@tbscc.com; web site www.thecorryjournal.com

Published: Mon, Tues, Wed, Thur, Fri, Sat
Weekday Frequency: e
Circulation: 3,512; 3,512(sat)
Last Audit: September 30, 2003
Price: 132.00/yr.
Advertising: Open inch rate $8.50
News services: AP.
Politics: Independent.
Not Published: New Year; Memorial Day; Independence Day; Labor Day; Thanskgiving; Christmas.
Magazines: American Profile (Weekly).
Pub....George R. Sample
Gen. Mgr.....Bob Williams
Mng. Ed.....Doug Kates
Prodn. Foreman....Daniel Donohue
Market Information: TMC.
Mechanical available: Offset; Black and 3 ROP colors; insert accepted; page cutoffs - 22 1/4.
Mechanical Specifications: Type page 13 3/4 x 21 1/2; E - 6 cols, 2 1/16, 1/8 between; A - 6 cols, 2 1/16, 1/8 between; C - 6 cols, 2 1/16, 1/8 between.
Commodity Consumption: Avg. Page Number Per Issue - Daily 14; widths 34; Newsprint Used - Short Tons 300.
Equipment EDITORIAL: Front-end Software – Baseview/NewsEdit Pro 3.3.; Editorial Hardware – APP/iMac; Editorial Printers – Xante/Accel-a-Writer 3G, HP/8150N CLASSIFIED: Front-end Software – Class Act 1.0.; Classified Hardware – APP/Mac G3; Classified Printers – HP/8150N PRODUCTION: Pagination Software – QPS/QuarkXPress 4.0.; Production Equipment – APP/Mac Laser; Cameras – SCREEN; Scanners – 1-L/32 PRESSROOM: Line 1 – G/Community. MAILROOM: Counter stackers – Count-o-Veyor; Bundle tying machines – 1/Sa; Addressing machine – 1-/Am; Other equipment –Challenge/3 Knife Trimmer.; Business Hardware – Software ☐ ListMaster 10.26

DANVILLE

THE DANVILLE NEWS

345 Mill St., Danville, Pa., 17821-0020; gen tel (570) 275-3235; gen fax (570) 275-7624; gen e-mail kblackledge@dailyitem.com; web site www.dailyitem.com

Group: Pennsylvania Newspapers Association
Published: Mon, Tues, Wed, Thur, Fri
Weekday Frequency: e
Circulation: 2,623
Last Audit: October 1, 2001
Price: 2.50/wk; 130.00/yr.
Advertising: Open inch rate $10.00
News services: AP.
Politics: Independent. **Established:** 1897
Special Editions: Back-to-School (Aug); Progress (Mar); Newcomers (Sept).
Magazines: USA WEEKEND Magazine (Weekly).
Pub.....Gary Grossman
Controller....Len Machesic
Circ. Dir.....Fred Scheller
Ed.....Len Ingrassia
Reporter....Karen Blackledge
Market Information: ADS; TMC.
Mechanical available: Offset; Black and 3 ROP colors; insert accepted; page cutoffs - 22 3/4.
Mechanical Specifications: Type page 13 x 21 1/2; E - 6 cols, 2 1/16, 1/8 between; A - 6 cols, 2 1/16, 1/8 between; C - 9 cols, 1 5/16, 1/8 between.
Commodity Consumption: Avg. Page Number Per Issue - Daily 16; Avg. Page Number Per Issue - Plates Used 2750; widths 28; Newsprint Used - Metric Tons 654; Printing Ink Used - Black 3000; Printing Ink Used - Color 300; Printing Ink Used - Pages Printed 4500.
Equipment EDITORIAL: Front-end Software – Dewarview/Word.; Editorial Hardware – RS 6000 CLASSIFIED: Front-end Software – Enterprise.; Classified Hardware – Dell DISPLAY: Ad make-up applications – QPS/Quark 6; Display Hardware – Dell; Display Printers – Software ☐ QPS/Quark 6 PRODUCTION: Pagination Software – Dewarview, QPS.; Production Equipment – 1-Nu; Cameras – DAI/Screen PRESSROOM: Line 1 – 7-G/Community; Folders – 1-G/SC, 1-G/Community. MAILROOM: Counter stackers – BG/Count-O-Veyor; Bundle tying machines – OVL/Constellation. BUSINESS COMPUTERS: Business Software – Lawson; Business Hardware – AS 400

DOYLESTOWN

THE INTELLIGENCER

333 N. Broad St., Doylestown, Pa., 18901-3407; gen tel (215) 345-3000; adv tel (215) 345-3080; ed tel (215) 345-3050; gen fax (215) 345-3150; ed e-mail lmorgnanesi@phillyburbs.com; intell_news@phillyburbs.com; web site www.phillyburbs.com

Published: Mon, Tues, Wed, Thur, Fri, Sun
Weekday Frequency: m
Circulation: 31,810; 40,080(sun)
Last Audit: ABC September 30, 2011
Price: 3.75/wk; 175.50/yr.
News services: AP.
Politics: Independent. **Established:** 1804

Note: There is a Greater Philadelphia Newspaper group combination of $239.00 (d) & $251.00 (S) among Levittown Bucks County Courier (mS), Doylestown Intelligencer (mS) & Willingboro (NJ) Burlington County Times (mS). Individual newspaper rates not made availabl
Special Editions: Newspapers in Education (Apr); Savings (Jan); Auto (Oct).
Special Weekly Sections: At Home (Sat).
Magazines: Parade (S).
Pub.....Mike Scobey
Controller....Timothy J. Weaver
Adv. Dir.....Kim Noble
Adv. Mgr., Classified/Retail....Dale Machesic
Circ. Dir.....William B. Lobecker
Mktg. Dir.....Eric P. Eberhardt
Exec. Ed.....Lanny Morgnanesi
Editorial Page Ed.....Alan Kerr
Features Ed.....Stacy Briggs
Sports Ed.....Jeff Beideman
Systems Mgr.....Paul Rohrman
Prodn. Dir.....Bob Braun
Prodn. Foreman, Pressroom....Tom Newman
Market Information: Split run; TMC.
Mechanical available: Offset; Black and 3 ROP colors; insert accepted - odd sizes accepted; page cutoffs - 22 1/2.
Mechanical Specifications: Type page 13 x 21 1/2; E - 6 cols, 2 1/16, 1/8 between; A - 6 cols, 2 1/16, 1/8 between; C - 9 cols, 1 3/8, 1/16 between.
Commodity Consumption: Avg. Page Number Per Issue - Daily 38; Avg. Page Number Per Issue - Sunday 64; widths 13 1/2; Newsprint Used - Metric Tons 4500; Newsprint Used - Short Tons 4960; Printing Ink Used - Pages Printed 15000.
Equipment EDITORIAL: Front-end Software – ACI/Open Pages.; Editorial Hardware – 20-Dell; Editorial Equipment – Novell/File Server, 60-PC; Editorial Printers – 1-IBM/3287, 2-EM/Imagesetter 3850 CLASSIFIED: Front-end Software – Cras.; Classified Hardware – Mac/True DISPLAY: Ad make-up applications – Adobe/PageMaker; Layout Software – IBM, SCS/Layout 8000.; Display Hardware – 8-APP/Mac, 3-PC 486; Display Printers – HP/Laser PRODUCTION: Pagination Software – QPS/QuarkXPress.; Production Equipment – 1-NewGen/Laser, EM/Imagesetter 3850; Cameras – 1-C/Spartan II, 1-AG/6000; Scanners – 2-HP/Scanner PRESSROOM: Line 1 – 10-G/Urbanite 1973; Pasters – Enkel/Splicer; Reels and Stands – Press registration system □ Duarte/Pin. MAILROOM: Counter stackers – 1/QWI, QWI/350B; Inserters and stuffers – GMA/SLS 1000 8:1; Bundle tying machines – 1-/Power Strap, 1-/MLN; Wrapping singles – 1-/Sa; Addressing machine – 1-/KR.; Business Hardware – IBM/9672

DU BOIS

COURIER EXPRESS

500 Jeffers St., Dubois, Pa., 15801; gen tel 800-442-4217; web site www.thecourierexpress.com
Published: Mon, Tues, Wed, Thur, Fri
Weekday Frequency: e
Circulation: 8,983
Last Audit: ABC September 30, 2011

THE COURIER-EXPRESS/TRI-COUNTY SUNDAY

500 Jeffers St., Du Bois, Pa., 15801-0407; gen tel (814) 371-4200; gen fax (814) 371-3241; gen e-mail news@thecourierexpress.com; adv e-mail ads@thecourierexpress.com; ed e-mail newsroom@thecourierexpress.com; web site www.thecourierexpress.com
Group: Independent Publications Inc.
Published: Mon, Tues, Wed, Thur, Fri, Sun
Weekday Frequency: e
Circulation: 8,983; 14,551(sun)
Last Audit: ABC September 30, 2011
Price: 120/year
Advertising: Open inch rate $22.18
Insert rate: variable
News services: AP, SHNS.
Politics: Independent. **Established:** 1882
Advertising not accepted: Y
Not Published: New Year; Memorial Day; Independence Day; Labor Day; Thanksgiving; Buck Season opener;Christmas.
Own facility?: Y
Special Editions: Homes and Gardens (Apr); Fall Sports (Aug); Christmas Greetings (Dec); Cooking (Feb); Bridal (Jan); Little League All-Star (Jul); Vacation Close to Home (Jun); Easter Dining (Mar); Graduation and Careers (May); Christmas Kick-Off (Nov); Hunting (Oct); Fal
Special Weekly Sections: Snapshots Photo Page (Fri); Business Pages (S); Business Pages (Thur); Outdoors (Wed).
Magazines: Comics (S). TV (S)
Pub.....Dennis Bonavita
Controller....S.W. Kronenwetter
Adv. Dir., Nat'l....Linda L. Smith
Adv. Mgr., Classified....Dory Ferra
Circ. Mgr.....Jim Nestlerode
Mng. Ed.....Nick Hoffman
Copy Ed.....Dena Bosak
Living/Lifestyle Ed.....Jamie Hynes
News Ed.....Alice Bish Sylvis
Sports Ed.....Scott Shindledecker
Sunday Ed.....Joy Norwood
City Ed.....Chuck Ferra
Market Information: TMC; Zoned editions.
Mechanical available: Offset; Black and 3 ROP colors; insert accepted; page cutoffs - 22 3/4.
Mechanical Specifications: Type page 13 x 21 1/2; E - 6 cols, 2 1/16, 1/6 between; A - 6 cols, 2 1/16, 1/6 between; C - 8 cols, 1 1/2, 1/6 between.
Commodity Consumption: Avg. Page Number Per Issue - Daily 21; Avg. Page Number Per Issue - Plates Used 7400; Avg. Page Number Per Issue - Sunday 44; widths 25; Newsprint Used - Short Tons 623; Printing Ink Used - Black 12500; Printing Ink Used - Color 938; Printing Ink Used -
Equipment EDITORIAL: Front-end Software – MediaSpan; Editorial Hardware – Mac OSX 10.7; Editorial Printers – HP/4MV, QMS/2060 CLASSIFIED: Front-end Software – MediaSpan; Classified Hardware – Mac DISPLAY: Ad make-up applications – MediaSpan; Layout Software – InDesign, Illustrator; Display Hardware – Mac; Production Equipment – Kodak Trendsetter; Cameras – SCREEN/20 x 24 Horizontal Low Bed; Scanners – Umax PRESSROOM: Line 1 – 8-WPC/Atlas (with 2-Quadra-Color Unit); Line 2 – 8-KP/News King. MAILROOM: Counter stackers – 2-BG/Count-O-Veyor; Inserters and stuffers – 1-MM/227E; Bundle tying machines – 2/Sa, Power Strap/250. BUSINESS COMPUTERS: Business Software – Solomon; Business Hardware – IBM/RISC 6000
Zip Codes served: 15801, 15825
Delivery method: Mail, Newsstand, Private Carrier, Racks

EASTON

THE EXPRESS-TIMES

30 N. Fourth St., Easton, Pa., 18042; gen tel (610) 258-7171; adv tel (610) 258-7171; ed tel (610) 258-7171; gen fax (610) 258-6794 (Pub); adv fax (610) 258-0988; ed fax (610) 258-7130; ed e-mail news@express-times.com; web site www.express-times.com
Published: Mon, Tues, Wed, Thur, Fri, Sat, Sun
Weekday Frequency: m
Saturday Frequency: m
Circulation: 40,024; 36,960(sat); 51,092(sun)
Last Audit: ABC September 30, 2011
Price: 150.91/yr (carrier); 40.95/3mo (carrier).
Advertising: Open inch rate $66.00
News services: AP, Metro Suburbia Inc., LAT-WP, NNS.
Politics: Independent.
Special Editions: Home Re-Source (Apr); College/Pro Football (Aug); Holiday Spirit (Dec); Home, Health & Lifestyle (Feb); Health Tab (Jan); Makeover (Jul); Community Guide/Penn-Jersey Life (Jun); Baseball/Spring Sports (Mar); Fast Track (Oct); Fall Bridal Guide (Sept).
Special Weekly Sections: Enjoy, Entertainment Guide (Fri); Sports Plus (Mon); TV Book (S); Home Source, Building & Real Estate Guide (Sat); Best Food Day (Wed).
Magazines: Relish (Monthly); TV Update (quarterfold) (S).
Pub./CEO/Pres.....Martin K. Till
Controller....Kenneth R. Vance
Credit Mgr.....Rebecca Weaver
Dir., HR....Angela Connell
Major Accts. Sales Mgr.....Anthony Spina
Retail Sales Mgr., Bethlehem....Hasanna Birdsong
Adv. Coord., Special Sections....K.J. Galati
Circ. Vice Pres., Opns.....Robert F. Rothacker
Ed.....Joseph P. Owens
Mng. Ed.....Jim Deegan
Asst. Mng. Ed.....Tony Rhodin
Bus. Ed.....Tom Zanki
Easton Ed.....Rudy Miller
Copy Desk News Ed.....Scott Toole
Features Ed.....Marcia White
Editorial Page Ed.....James Flagg
Sports Ed.....Edward Laubach
Prodn. Mgr., Pre Press....Sue Tyson
Market Information: Split run; TMC; Zoned editions.
Mechanical available: Offset; Black and 3 ROP colors; insert accepted; page cutoffs - 22.
Mechanical Specifications: Type page 13 x 21; E - 6 cols, 2 1/16, 1/8 between; A - 6 cols, 1 5/6, 1/8 between; C - 10 cols, 1 3/16, 1/16 between.
Commodity Consumption: Avg. Page Number Per Issue - Daily 38; Avg. Page Number Per Issue - Plates Used 26279; Avg. Page Number Per Issue - Saturday 40; Avg. Page Number Per Issue - Sunday 56; widths 37 1/2; Newsprint Used - Metric Tons 4150; Newsprint Used - Short Tons 4575; P
Equipment EDITORIAL: Front-end Software – CNI/Database, Microsoft/Word, QPS/QuarkXPress 3.32.; Editorial Hardware – Compaq/3000, Compaq/PC WS; Editorial Equipment – Novell/Netware 4.11; Editorial Printers – AST/8200 CLASSIFIED: Front-end Software – PPI/Advertising Management System Classified, Class/Act Pagination.; Classified Hardware – 20-PPI/Advertising Management System Classified; Classified Equipment – Novell/Netware 4.11; Classified Printers – HP/3, APP/Mac 8500 DISPLAY: Ad make-up applications – QPS/QuarkXPress, CNI/Btrieve; Layout Software – MEI/ALS, Novell, Compaq/3000.; Display Hardware – Compaq/3000, Compaq/WS, APP/Mac; Display Printers – APP/Mac 8500 PRODUCTION: Pagination Software – QPS/QuarkXPress 3.32, CNI/Btrieve Data, MEI/CLS, ALS.; Production Equipment – Nu/Flip Top, RIP NT, 1-ECR/4500 RIP NT, G/OPI; Cameras – 1-C/Spartan II; Scanners – ECR/Autokon 1000, Umax/Mirage PRESSROOM: Line 1 – 10-G/Urbanite V-5064 single width; Pasters – 8-Enkel/Autoweb; Reels and Stands – Press registration system □ KFM/Lock-ups. MAILROOM: Counter stackers – 3-HL/Monitor, 1/MM; Inserters and stuffers – HI/1372; Bundle tying machines – 2-/OVL, 1-/Mg; Addressing machine – 1-/BH, 1-/MG.; Audio Hardware – Brite Voice Systems, Comstock, Brite Voice Systems/Bus-2000 BUSINESS COMPUTERS: Business Software – Geac CJ/AIM, CIS, Lotus 1-2-3, WordPerfect 5.0, CJ; Business Hardware – Dec/VAX 4000, Dec/Alpha, Addrox/50 VT 420, 20-PC WS

ELLWOOD CITY

ELLWOOD CITY LEDGER

835 Lawrence Ave., Ellwood City, Pa., 16117; gen tel (724) 758-5573; ed tel (724) 758-7529; gen fax (724) 758-2410; gen e-mail ecledger@ellwoodcityledger.com; adv e-mail ads@ellwoodcityledger.com; ed e-mail eclnews@ellwoodcityledger.com; web site www.ellwoodcityledger.com
Group: Pennsylvania Newspapers Association
Published: Mon, Tues, Wed, Thur, Fri, Sat
Weekday Frequency: m
Circulation: 3,425; 3,425(sat)
Last Audit: March 31, 2008
Price: 1.70/wk (carrier); 7.35/mo; 117.00/yr.
Advertising: Open inch rate $11.25
News services: AP, U.S. Suburban Press Inc..
Politics: 1920
Not Published: New Year; Memorial Day; Independence Day; Labor Day; Christmas.
Special Editions: Annual Progress (Apr); Fall Bridal (Aug); Arts, Crafts & Food Festival (Jul); Visitor's Guide (Jun); Lawn & Garden (Mar); Car Care (May); Homefinders (Monthly); Health Care (Oct); Home Improvement (Sept).
Special Weekly Sections: Food Day (Mon); Food Day (Sat); Food Day (Wed).
Pub.....Alan Buncher
Sports Ed.....Randy Senior
Mgr., Mgmt. Info Servs.....Scott R. Kegel
Prodn. Mgr., Pressroom....Tony Carroza
Market Information: ADS; TMC; Zoned editions.
Mechanical available: Offset; Black and 3 ROP colors; insert accepted - single sheet; page cutoffs - 22 3/4.
Mechanical Specifications: Type page 13 x 21 1/2; E - 6 cols, 2 1/14, 1/6 between; A - 6 cols, 2 1/14, 1/6 between; C - 6 cols, 2 1/14, 1/6 between.
Commodity Consumption: Avg. Page Number Per Issue - Daily 16; Avg. Page Number Per Issue - Plates Used 10040; widths 27 1/2; Newsprint Used - Short Tons 924; Printing Ink Used - Black 18400; Printing Ink Used - Color 1400; Printing Ink Used - Pages Printed 9509.
Equipment EDITORIAL: Front-end Software – Microsoft/Word, QPS/QuarkXPress 4.0.; Editorial Hardware – 7-PC; Editorial Equipment – Lf/AP Leaf Picture Desk; Editorial Printers – HP/8000, AG/Accuset CLASSIFIED: Front-end Software – Baseview, QPS/QuarkXPress 4.0.; Classified Hardware – 4-APP/iMac; Classified Printers – HP/8000, AG/Accuset DISPLAY: Ad make-up applications – Aldus/PageMaker, QPS/QuarkXPress, Multi-Ad/Creator 2.6; Layout Software – 3-APP/Power Mac, 2-APP/Mac G3.; Display Hardware – APP/iMac; Display Printers – HP/8000, AG/Accuset PRODUCTION: Pagination Software – QPS/QuarkXPress 4.0, Microsoft/Windows, APP/Mac.; Production Equipment – 1-K, HP/8000 Plain Paper; Cameras – 1-B PRESSROOM: Line 1 – 5-G/Community; Folders – 1-G/SSC.; Inserters and stuffers – 1-KAN/(with 5 stations); Bundle tying machines – 2-EAM-Mosca; Addressing machine – 2/Ch. BUSINESS COMPUTERS: Business Software – Baseview; Business Hardware – 3-APP/iMac

ERIE

ERIE TIMES-NEWS

205 W. 12th St., Erie, Pa., 16534; gen tel (814) 870-1600; adv tel (814) 878-1642; ed tel (814) 870-1715; gen fax (814) 870-1615; adv fax (814) 870-1632; ed fax (814) 870-1808; gen e-mail admin1@timesnews.com; adv e-mail retail@timesnews.com; ed e-mail newsdesk@timesnews.com; web site www.goerie.com
Group: Pennsylvania Newspapers Association
Published: Mon, Tues, Wed, Thur, Fri, Sat, Sun
Weekday Frequency: m
Saturday Frequency: m
Circulation: 49,351; 47,993(sat); 71,988(sun)
Last Audit: ABC September 30, 2011
Advertising: Open inch rate $103.97 (Natl-Sun); open rate for local Sunday $73.83; local open daily rate $52.73; Daily rate national $76.22
News services: AP, LAT-WP, MCT.
Politics: Independent. **Established:** 1888
Own facility?: Y
Special Editions: Spring Car Care (Apr); New Year's Dining Guide (Dec); Home Remodeling (Feb); Bridal (Jan); Senior Lifestyle (Jul); Graduation (Jun); Easter Dining (Mar); Golf (May); Thanksgiving Dining Guide (Nov); Fall Car Care (Oct); Progress (Quarterly);

Bridal (Sept)
Special Weekly Sections: Pulse (Fri); Sports Week (Mon); Business (S); House to Home (Sat); Showcase (Thur); Your Money (Tues); Best Food Day (Wed).
Magazines: TV Schedule (S).
Her Times
Lake Erie Lifestyle
CEO/Pub.......................Rosanne Cheeseman
HR Dir...Herb Gilroy
Adv. Dir...Terry Cascioli
Adv. Mgr., Classified...........Robert Hennessey
Adv. Mgr., Display...........Jeanne Moore-Yount
Adv. Supvr., Inside Sales........Susan Schreiner
Adv. Coord., Co-op..............MaryBeth Swoger
Mktg. Mgr........................................Lisa Shade
Circ. Dir..................................Glenn Caruso
Exec. Ed......................................Rick Sayers
Mng. Ed........................................Pat Howard
Mng. Ed., New Media..................Jeff Hileman
Mng. Ed., News.......................Doug Oathout
Lifestyle Ed.................................Kevin Cuneo
Sports Ed.......................................Matt Martin
Dir., Technology.......................Rich Forsgren
Tech. Serv. Mgr......................Patrick Kilgallon
Opns. Dir......................................David Stolar
Director of Finance.......................Tony Yonko
CFO.......................................Henry Bujalski
Vice Pres., Interactive Media..........Laurel Lane
Market Information: ADS; Split run; TMC; Zoned editions.
Mechanical available: Offset; Black and 3 ROP colors; insert accepted; page cutoffs - 22 3/4.
Mechanical Specifications: Type page 11 1/16 x 21 1/2; E - 6 cols, 1 13/16, 1/64 between; A - 6 cols, 1 5/6, 1/8 between; C - 10 cols, 1 1/8, 7/16 between.
Commodity Consumption: Avg. Page Number Per Issue - Daily 46; Avg. Page Number Per Issue - Plates Used 82000; Avg. Page Number Per Issue - Sunday 84; widths 54; Newsprint Used - Short Tons 7200; Printing Ink Used - Black 139750; Printing Ink Used - Color 39230; Printing Ink Us
Equipment EDITORIAL: Front-end Software – DEC/TMS, Agile/Teambase.; Editorial Hardware – DEC/PDP 11-84; Editorial Equipment – 30-NSSE/400, 4-APP/Mac Quadra CLASSIFIED: Front-end Software – Atex.; Classified Hardware – DEC/PDP 11-84; Classified Equipment – 12-NSSE/400, 2-Sun/Sparc II DISPLAY: Ad make-up applications – Multi-Ad/Creator 3.6.1; Layout Software – SCS/Layout 8000, Xpance/Multi-Ad, 2-Sun/Sparc II.; Display Hardware – 2-Cx, APP/Mac Quadras, 5-Cx, Sun/Sparc 5 Breeze, APP/Power Mac 8100-80, 2-Sun/Sparc 20 Server, 2-Sun/Sparc II Gateway; Production Equipment – Futura, AlfaQuest, Pantera/32; Scanners – 2-AG/T-5000 Plus. PRESSROOM: Line 1 – 7-G/Metro (3 half decks) 1969; Folders – 1-G/double 2:1. MAILROOM: Counter stackers – 1-Id/NS550, 2-Id/NS2000, 1-Id/2100; Inserters and stuffers – 1-GMA/SLS 1000 (17 head), 1-GMA/SLS 1000 (9 head); Bundle tying machines – 3-MLN/2A, 2/Sa, 3-/Power Strap.; Audio Hardware – New Horizons Group, VNN, AP Stockline, New Horizons/Info-Connect BUSINESS COMPUTERS: Business Software – Compushare, In-house; Business Hardware – 2-DEC/VAX 6510
Delivery method: Mail, Newsstand, Private Carrier, Racks

GETTYSBURG

GETTYSBURG TIMES

1570 Fairfield Rd., Gettysburg, Pa., 17325; gen tel (717) 334-1131; gen fax (717) 334-4243; ed fax (717) 334-7408; gen e-mail info@gburgtimes.com; adv e-mail ads@gburgtimes.com; ed e-mail news@gburgtimes.com; sports@gburgtimes.com; web site www.gettysburgtimes.com
Group: Times & News Publishing
Published: Mon, Tues, Wed, Thur, Fri, Sat
Weekday Frequency: m
Saturday Frequency: m
Circulation: 8,565; 8,819(sat)
Last Audit: September 30, 2009
Price: 15.00/mo; 89.00/yr.
Advertising: Open inch rate $14.24
News services: AP, DF, MCT, SHNS, TMS, Washington Post News Group.
Politics: Independent. **Established:** 1902
Not Published: New Year; Christmas.
Own facility?: Y
Special Editions: Spring Lawn & Garden (Apr); Football Preview (Fall); Bridal Faire (Feb); Medical/Wellness Guide (Jul); Community Fact Book (Jun); Spring Automotive (Mar); Holiday Songbook (Nov); Bridal Tab (Quarterly); Spring Home Improvement (Spring); Winter Sports Prev
Magazines: Parade (Sat).
Broadcast Affiliations: WGET-AM/WGTY-FM Gettysburg, PA.
Pres./Pub..............................Cynthia A. Ford
Ed...B.J. Small
Sports Ed....................................Josh Martin
Systems Analyst/Online Mgr..........Thomas Ford
Pre Press Opns. Mgr...................Kristi Cramer
Market Information: Zoned editions.
Mechanical available: Offset; Black and 3 ROP colors; insert accepted; page cutoffs - 21.
Mechanical Specifications: Type page 12 1/8 x 21; E - 6 cols, 1 5/6, 1/8 between; A - 6 cols, 1 5/6, 1/16 between; C - 9 cols, 1 5/24, 1/8 between.
Commodity Consumption: Avg. Page Number Per Issue - Daily 30; Avg. Page Number Per Issue - Plates Used 7267; widths 12 1/2; Newsprint Used - Short Tons 594; Printing Ink Used - Black 12597; Printing Ink Used - Color 900; Printing Ink Used - Pages Printed 9300.
Equipment EDITORIAL: Front-end Software – Newzware; Editorial Hardware – Dell PC; Editorial Equipment – Various Scanners; Editorial Printers – BizHub CLASSIFIED: Front-end Software – Newzware; Classified Hardware – Dell PC; Classified Printers – Various DISPLAY: Ad make-up applications – Adobe/Illustrator, Adobe InAdobe InDesign CS5 Adobe/Photoshop; Display Hardware – Dell PC; Display Printers – HP/Color Laserjet
BizHub PRODUCTION: Pagination Software – FSI.; Production Equipment – Panther Pro 62 Imagesetter, ; Cameras – Nikon still
Canon video; Scanners – Umax/600s, Umax/1200s, Coolscan III, Nikon PRESSROOM: Line 1 – 8-G/Community Offset 1982; Line 2 – 4-G 1982; Folders – 1, 2-G/2:1.; Inserters and stuffers – Kk/6 Pocket, KR; Bundle tying machines – 2/Sa; Audio Hardware – none BUSINESS COMPUTERS: Business Software – Microsoft Office; Business Hardware – Dell PC
Delivery method: Mail, Newsstand, Private Carrier, Racks

TIMES AND NEWS PUBLISHING CO.

1570 Fairfield Rd., Gettysburg, Pa., 17325; gen tel (717) 334-1131; gen fax (717) 334-4243

GREENVILLE

THE RECORD-ARGUS

10 Penn Ave., Greenville, Pa., 16125; gen tel (724) 588-5000; gen fax (724) 588-4691; gen e-mail nkennedy@recordargus.com
Published: Mon, Tues, Wed, Thur, Fri, Sat
Weekday Frequency: m
Circulation: 5,295; 5,295(sat)
Last Audit: September 24, 2003
Price: 1.70/wk; 7.95/mo; 95.40/yr.
Advertising: Open inch rate $11.00
News services: AP.
Politics: Independent. **Established:** 1848
Not Published: New Year; Memorial Day; Independence Day; Labor Day; Thanksgiving; Christmas.
Special Editions: Fishing (Apr); Fall Sports (Aug); Christmas (Dec); Business & Industry (Feb); Bridal (Jan); Camping (Jun); Easter (Mar); Camping (May); Thiel College (Oct).
Special Weekly Sections: Best Food Day (Mon); Best Food Day (Wed).
Magazines: TV & Entertainment (Thur); American Profile (Weekly).
Pres./Pub...............................Steve Gargasz
Vice Pres., Mktg................................Jim Rust
Ed........................................Natalie Kennedy
Sports Ed....................................Ed. Topelski
Market Information: ADS.
Mechanical available: Offset; Black and 3 ROP colors; insert accepted - standing card; page cutoffs - 21 1/2.
Mechanical Specifications: Type page 13 x 21 1/2; E - 6 cols, 2 1/16, 1/8 between; A - 6 cols, 2 1/16, 1/8 between; C - 9 cols, 1 3/8, 1/8 between.
Commodity Consumption: Avg. Page Number Per Issue - Daily 14; Avg. Page Number Per Issue - Saturday 18; widths 13 3/4; Printing Ink Used - Pages Printed 5250.
Equipment EDITORIAL: Front-end Software – Baseview.; Classified Hardware – Software ☐ Baseview.; Layout Software – Baseview.; Production Equipment – 1-Nu; Cameras – 1-Nu.; Bundle tying machines – 1/MLN, 1-S/Plastic Strap; Addressing machine – 1-/Am.

HANOVER

THE EVENING SUN

135 Baltimore St., Hanover, Pa., 17331; gen tel (717) 637-3736; gen fax (717) 637-7730; gen e-mail news@eveningsun.com; adv e-mail advertising@eveningsun.com; web site www.eveningsun.com
Published: Mon, Tues, Wed, Thur, Fri, Sat, Sun
Weekday Frequency: e
Saturday Frequency: e
Circulation: 18,476; 18,546(sat); 21,235(sun)
Last Audit: ABC September 30, 2011
Price: 2.50/wk; 10.00/mo; 125.00/yr.
Advertising: Open inch rate $46.35
News services: AP.
Politics: Independent.
Not Published: New Year; Christmas.
Special Editions: Spring Home (Apr); 4-H Fair (Aug); Holly (Dec); Bridal (Feb); Outdoor (May); Christmas Gifts (Nov); Auto Review (Oct); Football (Sept).
Special Weekly Sections: TV Views (S); Out & About-Entertainment & Travel (Wed).
Magazines: USA WEEKEND Magazine (S).
Controller...............................Robert Swisher
Adv. Mgr...........................Janelle Coolbaugh
Adv. Nat'l Sales..........................Nancy Myers
Ed. in Chief.............................Marc Charisse
Circ. Mgr...........................Robert Trazkovich
Bus. Ed................................Marc Charrisse
City Ed....Travis Lau
Features Ed.................................Kim Sterner
Graphics Ed.............................Wanda Murren
News Ed..................................Carl Whitehill
Sports Ed...............................Charles Curley
Style Ed.....................................Ann Diviney
Online Mgr.................................Bryan Byers
Mgr., Mgmt. Info Serv...............Stephen Arthur
Prodn. Foreman, Press.................David Myers
Market Information: ADS; Split run; TMC; Zoned editions.
Mechanical available: Offset; Black and 3 ROP colors; insert accepted; page cutoffs - 22 3/4.
Mechanical Specifications: Type page 13 x 21 1/2; E - 6 cols, 2 1/16, 1/8 between; A - 6 cols, 2 1/16, 1/8 between; C - 6 cols, 2 1/16, 1/8 between.
Commodity Consumption: Avg. Page Number Per Issue - Daily 26; Avg. Page Number Per Issue - Sunday 40; widths 13 1/2; Newsprint Used - Short Tons 1400; Printing Ink Used - Pages Printed 10034.
Equipment; Editorial Hardware – Software ☐ Baseview/NewsEdit. DISPLAY: Ad make-up applications – Adobe/PageMaker 5.0, QPS/QuarkXPress 3.2; Layout Software – APP/Mac. PRODUCTION: Pagination Software – QPS/QuarkXPress.; Production Equipment – Offset, V/5100, Pre Press/Panther Pro, V/5300E PRESSROOM: Line 1 – 8-G/Unitubular; Folders – 1-G/2:1; Press registration system – Duarte/Pin Register.; Bundle tying machines – 1/MLN; Addressing machine – 2-/Am; Other equipment –Stitcher-Trimmer.

HAZLETON

STANDARD-SPEAKER

21 N. Wyoming St., Hazleton, Pa., 18201-6068; gen tel (570) 455-3636; ed tel (570) 455-4408; gen fax (570) 455-4244; gen e-mail editorial@standardspeaker.com; web site www.standardspeaker.com
Published: Sun
Circulation: 20,008; 20,008(sat); 20,115(sun)
Last Audit: September 30, 2007
Price: 2.85/wk (home delivery), $3.00/wk (mail); 12.00/mo (mail); 39.00/yr.
Advertising: Open inch rate $32.00
News services: AP.
Politics: Independent.
Not Published: Christmas.
Special Editions: Home Improvement (Apr); Football Preview (Aug); Christmas Greetings (Dec); Bridal (Feb); Bridal II (Jul); Progress (Jun); Create An Ad (Mar); Senior Citizen (May); Holiday Gift Guide (Nov); Dining Guides (Oct); FunFest (Sept).
Special Weekly Sections: Arts (Fri); Outdoors (Mon); Food (S); Business (Thur); Health (Tues).
Magazines: TV Showtime (S); Best Food Days (Sat); Best Food Days (Wed); American Profile (Weekly).
Pres./Pub...................................Scott Lynett
Pub.......................................Paul N. Walser
Pub.................................Stephen H. Walser
Adv. Dir...Paul Ross
Circ. Mgr., Credit.........................John Patton
Circ. Mgr., Distr..........................Gary Klinger
Mng. Ed........................................Bob Wolfe
Lifestyle Ed..........................Mildred Rubinote
News Ed................................Carl Christopher
Sports Ed....................................Babe Conroy
Asst. Sunday Ed........................Edward Socha
Prodn. Mgr.............................James R. Seybert
Prodn. Supt., Composing.............David Steiner
Mechanical available: Offset; Black and 3 ROP colors; insert accepted; page cutoffs - 21 1/2.
Mechanical Specifications: Type page 13 x 21 1/2; E - 6 cols, 2 1/16, 1/8 between; A - 6 cols, 2 1/16, 1/8 between; C - 9 cols, 1 3/8, 5/64 between.
Commodity Consumption: Avg. Page Number Per Issue - Daily 37.5; Avg. Page Number Per Issue - Plates Used 26180; widths 27 1/2; Newsprint Used - Metric Tons 1579.5; Newsprint Used - Short Tons 1741.1; Printing Ink Used - Black 43000; Printing Ink Used - Color 7000; Printing Ink
Equipment EDITORIAL: Front-end Software – APT/Editorial.; Editorial Hardware – 18-HP/Vectra VL6/450, 3-HP/Net Server 3; Editorial Equipment – 2-ECR/Imagesetter; Editorial Printers – 2-HP/8000 N CLASSIFIED: Front-end Software – APT/Classified.; Classified Hardware – 8-HP/Vectra VE 8; Classified Equipment – APP/Mac Quadra 605, APP/Super Mac; Classified Printers – ECR/Scriptsetter, 2-HP/LaserJet DISPLAY: Ad make-up applications – QPS/QuarkXPress 4.04; Layout Software – APT/Ad Master.; Display Hardware – 8-HP/Vectra VL6/450, 2-APP/Mac G3; Display Printers – HP/8000 N PRODUCTION: Pagination Software – QPS/QuarkXPress 4.04.; Production Equipment – LE/Maxim 26, 2-RIP with ECRM Pelbox; Cameras – C/Spartan III; Scanners – HP/Scan Jet IIC, AG/T2000XL PRESSROOM: Line 1 – 5-G/Cosmo double width 1975; Press Drives – Fin w/2 GE 150 h.p. DC Motor; Press control system – Fin/Cabinet 2.; Bundle tying machines – 1-MLN/ML2EE, 1-EAM-Mosca. BUSINESS COMPUTERS: Business Software – Vision Data 7.0, APT; Business Hardware – IBM/C320 Power Station

HONESDALE

THE WAYNE INDEPENDENT

220 Eighth St., Honesdale, Pa., 18431; gen

tel (570) 253-3055; adv tel (570) 253-6666; gen fax (570) 253-5387; gen e-mail mhessling@wayneindependent.com; adv e-mail btucker@wayneindependent.com; ed e-mail editor@wayneindependent.com; web site www.wayneindependent.com
Group: GateHouse Media, Inc.
Published: Tues, Wed, Thur, Fri, Sat, Sun
Weekday Frequency: m
Saturday Frequency: m
Circulation: 4,020; 4,020(sat)
Last Audit: Sworn March 31, 2007
Price: 102/yr; 37.00/3mo.
Advertising: Open inch rate $15.74
Insert rate: Starting at $62/M NET
News services: AP.
Politics: Bi-Partisan. **Established:** 1878
Advertising not accepted: N
Not Published: Thanksgiving; Christmas, New Years, Independence Day.
Own facility?: Y
Special Editions: Bridal Guide
Progress Edition
Home Improvement
Wayne County Fair/Jr Livestock Edition
Health
Family Magazine
Real Estate Guide
Restaurant/Dining
Special Weekly Sections: Church (Fri); Business (Daily); Food (Wed), Home (Sat)
Magazines: American Profile (Weekly), Spry, Relish and Athlon (Monthly)
Editor ....Dino Ciliberti
Sports Editor ....Kevin Edwards
Production Mgr. ....Matt Skelton
Advertising Manager ....Ben Tucker
Graphics Manager ....Amy O'Hare
Circulation Manager ....Skip Mendler
Adv./Mktg. Mgr. ....Michelle Hessling
Market Information: TMC.
Mechanical available: Offset; Black and Full & Spot colors; inserts accepted - all; page cutoffs - 22 1/2.
Mechanical Specifications: Type page 13 x 21; E - 6 cols, 2 1/6, 1/4 between; A - 6 cols, 2 1/16, 1/4 between; C - 10 cols, 1 5/16, 13/100 between.
Commodity Consumption: Avg. Page Number Per Issue - Daily 12; Avg. Page Number Per Issue - Plates Used 4420; widths 22 inch; Newsprint Used - Short Tons 421; Printing Ink Used - Pages Printed 4250.
Equipment EDITORIAL: Front-end Software – News Edit Pro/Pagemaker/Quark; Editorial Hardware – Mac; Editorial Printers – APP/Mac LaserWriter II CLASSIFIED: Front-end Software – Baseview; Classified Hardware – Mac; Classified Printers – APP/Mac LaserWriter II; Display Hardware – Mac; Display Printers – APP/Mac LaserWriter; Production Equipment – Imagesetter PRESSROOM: Line 1 – 4-G/Suburban 1986; Folders – 1-G/SC.
Zip Codes served: 18431, 18473, 18428, 18464, 18426, 18445, 18427, 18444, 18436, 18438, 18459, 18472, 18407, 18456, 18421, 18462, 18405, 18469, 18445, 18415, 18847, 18455, 18461, 18439, 18453, 18437, 18417, 13783, 12723, 12764, 18460, 18451, 18462, 18458, 18407, 18465
Delivery method: Mail

HUNTINGDON

THE DAILY NEWS

325 Penn St., Huntingdon, Pa., 16652; gen tel (814) 643-4040; gen fax (814) 643-0376; adv fax (814) 641-9628; ed fax (814) 643-0376; gen e-mail dnews@getwireless.net
Published: Mon, Tues, Wed, Thur, Fri, Sat, Sun
Weekday Frequency: e
Saturday Frequency: m
Circulation: 9,258; 9,258(sat)
Last Audit: March 31, 2007
Price: 132.00/yr.
Advertising: Open inch rate $13.95
News services: AP.
Politics: Independent. **Established:** 1922
Not Published: New Year; Memorial Day; Independence Day; Labor Day; Thanksgiving; Christmas.
Special Editions: Business Directory (Annually); Bridal (Feb); Summer Travel (Jul); Summer Travel (May); TV (Monthly); Real Estate Guide (Other); Football (Sept).
Magazines: American Profile (Weekly).
Purchasing Agent ....Kenneth J. Smith
Adv. Dir. ....Carol A. Cutshall
Circ. Mgr. ....Heather Lohr
Ed. ....George R. Sample
Editorial Page Ed. ....George Germann
News Ed. ....Polly McMullen
Sports Ed. ....Terry Bowser
Prodn. Mgr. ....Robert Dietz
Market Information: Split run; TMC.
Mechanical available: Offset; Black and 3 ROP colors; insert accepted; page cutoffs - 22 1/2.
Mechanical Specifications: Type page 13 x 21 1/2; E - 6 cols, 2 1/16, 1/8 between; A - 6 cols, 2 1/16, 1/8 between; C - 9 cols, 1 3/8, 1/16 between.
Commodity Consumption: Avg. Page Number Per Issue - Daily 18; Avg. Page Number Per Issue - Plates Used 5600; Avg. Page Number Per Issue - Saturday 18.
Equipment EDITORIAL: Front-end Software – Baseview/NewsEdit.; Editorial Hardware – APP; Editorial Printers – APP, HP CLASSIFIED: Front-end Software – Baseview/Ad Manager Pro.; Classified Hardware – APP/Mac; Classified Printers – HP DISPLAY: Ad make-up applications – QPS/QuarkXPress, Adobe/Illustrator, Adobe/Photoshop; Layout Software – Baseview/Ad Manager, Baseview/Ad Force.; Display Hardware – APP/Mac; Display Printers – HP/LaserJet 5si/MX PRODUCTION: Pagination Software – QPS/QuarkXPress 4.0.; Production Equipment – Caere/OmniPage; Cameras – C; Scanners – HP; Bundle tying machines – Sa, WeldLoc; Addressing machine – Wm, KR. BUSINESS COMPUTERS: Business Software – Vision Data, AR 6.2, APGL 5.0; Business Hardware – DEC/486, 6-DEC

INDIANA

THE INDIANA GAZETTE

899 Water St., Indiana, Pa., 15701; gen tel (724) 465-5555; adv tel (724) 465-5555; ed tel (724) 465-5555; gen fax (724) 349-8267; adv fax (724) 349-4550; ed fax (724) 465-8267; gen e-mail gazedit@indianagazette.net; ed e-mail gazedit@indianagazette.net; web site www.indianagazette.com
Group: Pennsylvania Newspapers Association
Published: Mon, Tues, Wed, Thur, Fri, Sat, Sun
Weekday Frequency: e
Saturday Frequency: e
Circulation: 14,215; 14,676(sat); 14,489(sun)
Last Audit: ABC September 30, 2011
Price: 12.00/mo; 234.67/yr (mail).
Advertising: Open inch rate $16.98
News services: AP, NEA, NYT.
Politics: Independent-Republican. **Established:** 1890
Not Published: New Year; Memorial Day; Labor Day; Thanksgiving; Christmas.
Special Editions: Lawn & Garden (Apr); Football (Aug); Winter Sports (Dec); Financial Fitness (Feb); Bridal (Jan); Arts Festival (Jul); Car Care (Jun); Homebuilders Real Estate (Mar); Summer Recreation (May); Holiday Gift Guide (Nov); Car Care (Oct); Energy (Sept).
Special Weekly Sections: Business (S); Best Food Day (Wed).
Magazines: USA WEEKEND Magazine (S).
Pres./Pub. ....Michael J. Donnelly
Sec. ....Hastie D. Kinter
Treasurer ....Stacie D. Gottfredson
Gen. Mgr. ....Joseph L. Geary
Controller ....Robert W. Kanick
Adv. Dir., Mktg ....Cathy Reed
Circ. Mgr. ....Ron Seckar
Exec. Ed. ....Eric Ebeling
Mng. Ed. ....Michael Peterson
Photo Dept. Mgr. ....Thomas Peel
Sports Ed. ....Tony Coccagna
Prodn. Mgr., Post Press ....Samuel L. Parisse
Prodn. Mgr., Pre Press ....Donna Rethi
Prodn. Supt., Mechanical ....Ed Yasick
Prodn. Foreman, Pressroom ....Joseph Naman
Market Information: TMC.
Mechanical available: Offset; Black and 3 ROP colors; insert accepted - odd sizes accepted, zoned; page cutoffs - 22 3/4.
Mechanical Specifications: Type page 13 x 21 1/2; E - 6 cols, 2 1/16, 1/8 between; A - 6 cols, 2 1/16, 1/8 between; C - 8 cols, 1 1/2, 1/8 between.
Commodity Consumption: Avg. Page Number Per Issue - Daily 26; Avg. Page Number Per Issue - Saturday 24; Avg. Page Number Per Issue - Sunday 52; widths 27 1/2; Newsprint Used - Short Tons 3800; Printing Ink Used - Black 47960; Printing Ink Used - Color 1870; Printing Ink Used -
Equipment EDITORIAL: Front-end Software – APT.; Editorial Hardware – Compaq/Proliant 3000; Editorial Printers – HP/4000, HP/4000C CLASSIFIED: Front-end Software – APT.; Classified Hardware – Compaq/Proliant 3000; Classified Printers – HP/4000, AU/1000 DISPLAY: Ad make-up applications – APT, QPS/QuarkXPress.; Display Hardware – Compaq/Proliant 3000; Display Printers – HP/4000, AU/1000 PRODUCTION: Pagination Software – APT, QPS/QuarkXPress 4.0.; Production Equipment – AU/APS-6-82 ACS, AU/1000; Cameras – 1-C/Marathon; Scanners – AG/Horizon Scanner PRESSROOM: Line 1 – 6-G/Urbanite (1 color unit), 1-G/Urbanite 788; Line 2 – 10-HI/V-15D 1990; Folders – G/2:1; Reels and Stands – 2-G/Rollstands, 4-Martin/Splicer. MAILROOM: Counter stackers – MM/338, Gammerler/KL 503/1; Inserters and stuffers – MM/310; Bundle tying machines – MM; Addressing machine – 2/Ch; Other equipment –UniTrim (Rock Built), Gammerler/RS 111/530-4. AUDIO: Audio Software – Zimmers Interactive; Audio Hardware – VNN, PC BUSINESS COMPUTERS: Business Software – Platinum; Business Hardware – Compaq/Proliant 3000

INDIANA PRINTING & PUBLISHING CO.

899 Water St., Indiana, Pa., 15701; gen tel (724) 465-5555; gen fax (724) 465-0402

JOHNSTOWN

THE TRIBUNE-DEMOCRAT

425 Locust St., Johnstown, Pa., 15907-0340; gen tel (814) 532-5199; adv tel (814) 532-5150; ed tel (814) 532-5050; gen fax (814) 539-1409; adv fax (814) 539-2292; ed fax (814) 539-1409; gen e-mail tribdem@tribdem.com; adv e-mail tribads@tribdem.com; web site www.tribune-democrat.com
Published: Mon, Tues, Wed, Thur, Fri, Sat, Sun
Weekday Frequency: m
Saturday Frequency: m
Circulation: 32,722; 32,905(sat); 36,298(sun)
Last Audit: ABC September 30, 2011
Price: 12.50/mo; 141.00/yr (carrier).
Advertising: Open inch rate $53.09
News services: AP, NNS, GNS.
Politics: Independent. **Established:** 1853
Not Published: New Year; Memorial Day; Independence Day; Labor Day; Christmas.
Special Editions: Spring Outdoor Guide (Apr); Simply the Best (Aug); Holiday Gift Guides (Dec); Progress (Feb); Bridal Guide (Jan); Bridal Guide (Jul); Real Estate (Mar); Summer Lifestyle (May); Holiday Gift Guides (Nov); Kitchen & Bath (Oct); Simply the Best (Sept).
Special Weekly Sections: Weekend (Entertainment/Leisure) (Fri); Outdoors (Mon); Travel (S); Religion (Sat).
Magazines: Relish (Monthly); Parade (S).
Pub. ....Robin Quillon
Controller ....Louis Gjurich
Personnel Mgr. ....Joan Hunter
Classified Sales Mgr. ....Christine Pringle
Circ. Dir. ....Julie Fox-Arnott
Ed. ....Chip Minemyer
Mng. Ed. ....Sean Roane
City Ed. ....Arlene Johns
Editorial Page Ed. ....Bruce Wissinger
Sports Ed. ....Eric Knopsnyder
Style Ed. ....Renee Carthew
Prodn. Dir. ....Steve Sindleri
Prodn. Mgr., Mailroom ....David Baker
Market Information: Split run; TMC; Zoned editions.
Mechanical available: Offset; Black and 3 ROP colors; insert accepted; page cutoffs - 22 3/4.
Mechanical Specifications: Type page 13 x 21 1/2; E - 6 cols, 2 1/16, 1/8 between; A - 6 cols, 2 1/16, 1/8 between; C - 9 cols, 1 5/16, 1/8 between.
Commodity Consumption: Avg. Page Number Per Issue - Daily 34; Avg. Page Number Per Issue - Plates Used 34800; Avg. Page Number Per Issue - Saturday 330; Avg. Page Number Per Issue - Sunday 74; widths 27 1/2; Newsprint Used - Metric Tons 3518; Newsprint Used - Short Tons 3878;
Equipment EDITORIAL: Front-end Software – Baseview.; Editorial Hardware – APP/Mac; Editorial Equipment – APP/Mac 4400, APP/Mac 7300, APP/Mac 7200, APP/Mac G4; Editorial Printers – HP/Laser, APP/Mac CLASSIFIED: Front-end Software – Baseview/Ad Manager Pro.; Classified Hardware – APP/Mac; Classified Equipment – 10-APP/Mac 4400; Classified Printers – HP/6MP DISPLAY: Ad make-up applications – Vision Data; Layout Software – MEI/ALS.; Display Hardware – Sun/Sparc; Display Printers – 6-DEC/LG04 Plus; Production Equipment – 2-APP/Power Mac 7300 with Adobe Photoshop 4.0, Pre Press/Panther Pro 46, Konica/9449-163, Microtek/2SPX, Microtek/E6, Microtek/35T; Cameras – 1-K/Vertical 18, C/Marathon; Scanners – Microtek/2SPX, Mictrotek/E6, 1-Microtek/35T, Polaroid/SprintS PRESSROOM: Line 1 – 5-G/Metro (2 decks) 1969; Reels and Stands – 5-G/RTP. MAILROOM: Counter stackers – 2-QWI/SJ100A, CH/Mk II; Inserters and stuffers – S/848; Bundle tying machines – 2-MVP/P-53, Sterling/MR45CH, Sterling/MR40CH; Addressing machine – 1-MG/50. BUSINESS COMPUTERS: Business Software – Vision Data; Business Hardware – Sun/Sparc

KANE

THE KANE REPUBLICAN

200 N. Fraley St., Kane, Pa., 16735; gen tel (814) 837-6000; gen fax (814) 837-2227; adv e-mail kradvertising@verizon.net; kr-classifieds@verizon.net; ed e-mail krnews1@verizon.net; web site www.kanerepublican.com
Group: Pennsylvania Newspapers Association
Published: Mon, Tues, Wed, Thur, Fri, Sat, Sun
Weekday Frequency: e
Saturday Frequency: m
Circulation: 1,996; 1,996(sat)
Last Audit: September 30, 2003
Price: 135.00/yr.
Advertising: Open inch rate $7.50
News services: AP.
Politics: Independent. **Established:** 1984
Special Editions: Football Preview (Aug); Christmas (Dec); Design-An-Ad (Jun); Timber/Progress (Oct).
Special Weekly Sections: TV (Sat).
Magazines: American Profile (Weekly).
Ed. ....Brent Addlenan
Mgmt. Info Servs. Mgr. ....Peg Kepler
Mechanical available: Offset; Black and 1 ROP colors; insert accepted; page cutoffs - 22 3/4.
Mechanical Specifications: Type page 13 x 21 1/2; E - 6 cols, 2 1/16, 1/8 between; A - 6 cols, 2 1/16, 1/8 between; C - 8 cols, 1 1/2, 1/8 between.
Commodity Consumption: Avg. Page Number Per Issue - Daily 10.
Equipment EDITORIAL: Front-end Software – Mk/Newswriter.; Editorial Hardware – Mk/550 Sys; Bundle tying machines – 1/Sa; Addressing machine – 1-/Am.; Business Hardware – Mk/550, APP/Mac

KITTANNING

LEADER TIMES

11931 State Rd., 85, Ste. E, Kittanning, Pa., 16201; gen tel (724) 543-1303; gen fax (724) 545-6768; gen e-mail leadertimes@tribweb.com; web site www.leadertimes.com

Published: Mon, Tues, Wed, Thur, Fri, Sat
Weekday Frequency: e
Circulation: 8,104; 8,104(sat)
Last Audit: September 30, 2006
Price: 10.00/mo; 138.00/yr (mail).
Advertising: Open inch rate $8.10
News services: AP.
Politics: Independent.
Special Weekly Sections: Religion (Sat); Youth (Tues); Food (Wed).
Div. Mgr., North .... Nick Monico
Bus. Mgr. .... Tammy Bish
Adv. Coord .... Gus Naccarato
Circ. Mgr. .... Larry Shuster
Mng. Ed. .... Michael O'Hare
News Ed. .... Jim Heasley
Mechanical available: Offset; Black and 3 ROP colors; insert accepted; page cutoffs - 21 1/4.
Mechanical Specifications: Type page 13 x 21 1/4; E - 6 cols, 2 1/16, 1/8 between; A - 6 cols, 2 1/16, 1/8 between; C - 10 cols, 1 3/8, 1/8 between.
Commodity Consumption: Avg. Page Number Per Issue - Daily 16.
Equipment; Editorial Hardware – APP/Mac, SII.; Classified Hardware – PPI. PRODUCTION: Pagination Software – Multi-Ad/Creator.; Production Equipment – 2-COM/Trendsetter, 2-Mk, APP/Mac, 3-Laser; Folders – 1; Bundle tying machines – 1/Sterling.

LANCASTER

LANCASTER NEWSPAPERS, INC.

8 W. King St., Lancaster, Pa., 17603-3824; gen tel (717) 291-8811; adv tel (717)291-8711; ed tel (717)291-8622; gen fax (717) 399-6506; adv fax (717)399-6523; ed fax (717)399-6507; gen e-mail lnp@lnpnews.com; adv e-mail advertising@lnpnews.com; ed e-mail intell-news@lnpnews.com; sunnews@lnpnews.com; neweranews@lnpnews.com; web site www.lancasteronline.com

Published: Mon, Tues, Wed, Thur, Fri, Sat, Sun
Weekday Frequency: m
Saturday Frequency: All day
Circulation: 39,192; 83,427(sat); 97,158(sun)
Last Audit: September 30, 2008
Price: 143.20/yr(m)or(e), $82.20/yr (S).
Advertising: Open inch rate $102.00
News services: AP, NYT, MCT, LAT-WP, States News Service, NEA.
Politics: Independent. **Established:** 1764
Own facility?: Y
Special Editions: New Car Guide (Apr); High School Football (Aug); Countdown to Christmas (Dec); Careers and Education (Feb); Home-Your Guide to Home Design (Jan); Active Lifestyles July/Aug-Travel (Jul); Home-Guide to Home Design and Gardening (Jun); Active Lifestyles Mar
Special Weekly Sections: Entertainment (Fri); Business Monday (Mon); Entertainment (S); Church (Sat); Entertainment (Thur); Food (Wed).
Magazines: Relish (Monthly); Parade (S).
Pres./CEO .... Harold E. Miller
Exec. Vice Pres./CFO/Sec./Treasurer Dennis A. Getz
Controller .... Nancy D. Fisher
Tax Mgr. .... Wesley Lewis
Dir., HR/Admin. .... M. Steven Weaver
Mgr., HR .... Tonya J. Nevling
Credit Mgr. .... George M. Crognale
Adv. Dir., Classified .... Russell C. Gillespie
Adv. Dir., Retail .... John Derr
Mgr., Creative Servs .... Genine Antonelli
Mgr., Mktg .... Robert Magel
Mgr., Community Servs./NIE Dr. Ann Marie Steele
Circ. Dir. .... Keith S. Kirchner
Circ. Asst. Dir. .... William R. McMahon
Ed., Intelligencer Journal Charles Raymond Shaw
Ed., Sunday News .... Marvin I. Adams
Mng. Ed., Sunday News ... Barbara Hough Roda
Librarian .... Kim Gomoll
Bd. Chrmn. .... John M. Buckwalter
Ed., Lancaster New Era .... Ernie J. Schreiber
Market Information: Split run; TMC; Zoned editions.
Mechanical available: Flexographic; Black and 3 ROP colors; insert accepted; page cutoffs - 22.
Mechanical Specifications: Type page 12 x 21; E - 6 cols, 2 1/16, 1/8 between; A - 6 cols, 2 1/16, 1/8 between; C - 10 cols, 1 3/8, 1/16 between.
Commodity Consumption: Avg. Page Number Per Issue - Daily 43; Avg. Page Number Per Issue - Plates Used 133629; Avg. Page Number Per Issue - Sunday 121; widths 50; Newsprint Used - Short Tons 10806; Printing Ink Used - Black 255364; Printing Ink Used - Color 134741; Printing In
Equipment EDITORIAL: Front-end Software – SCS/Scoop.; Editorial Hardware – 2-Dell/6450, 2-Dell/6600; Editorial Equipment – 5-Lf/AP Server Desk, Photo Station Pro; Editorial Printers – 2-HP/4000, 2-HP/8100D,8150 CLASSIFIED: Front-end Software – Brainworks.; Classified Hardware – Brainworks; Classified Printers – HP/8150 DISPLAY: Ad make-up applications – XPance, Multi-Ad/Creator 4.02, QPS/QuarkXPress 4.04, Brainworks; Layout Software – SCS/Layout 8000, SCS/Lynx.; Display Hardware – APP/Mac G4; Display Printers – HP/8150,8100 PRODUCTION: Pagination Software – QPS/QuarkXPress 4.1, Adobe/Indesign 2.0.2.; Production Equipment – 2-K&F/4SPTB-V/PTB, 1-AU/3850T, 1-Au/3850 Sierra, 1-LE/MAX 26, 1-GS, III/3850, HS; Cameras – 1-C/Newspager, 1-C/Marathon; Scanners – Epson/a640XL, Epson/836XL, 1-X/7650C PRESSROOM: Line 1 – 7-MAN/Flexoman double width 1988; Line 2 – 7-MAN/Flexoman double width 1988; Folders – 3-MAN/3:2; Pasters – 14-MAN/Automatic; Reels and Stands – 14; Press registration system – CCI. MAILROOM: Counter stackers – 3/QWI; Inserters and stuffers – 1-HI/72, 1-HI/72; Bundle tying machines – 2-/MLN, 2-MLN/2A, 5-/Power Strap; Mailroom control system – Bert/K&M; Addressing machine – 1-/Ch, 1-/Buskro, KR; Other equipment –4-PMI/Bagger. AUDIO: Audio Software – Brite Voice Systems 3.21; Audio Hardware – Brite Voice Systems, VRU BUSINESS COMPUTERS: Business Software – CJ, Best Programs, Lawson, Lawson; Business Hardware – 2-DEC/VAX 7610, 1-Intell, Sun/3500
Delivery method: Mail, Newsstand, Private Carrier, Racks

LANCASTER NEWSPAPERS, INC.

8 W. King St., Lancaster, Pa., 17608-1328; gen tel (717) 291-8811; adv tel (717) 291-8711; gen fax (717) 291-8653; adv fax (717) 291-8728; gen e-mail lnp@lnpnews.com; web site www.lancasteronline.com

Published: Sun
Own facility?: Y
President & CEO .... Harold E. Miller

LANSDALE

THE REPORTER

307 Derstine Ave., Lansdale, Pa., 19446; gen tel (215) 855-8440; adv tel (215) 361-8849; ed tel (215) 361-8814; gen fax (215) 855-6147; ed fax (215) 855-3432; adv e-mail imaging@thereporteronline.com; ed e-mail letters@thereporteronline.com; web site www.thereporteronline.com

Published: Mon, Tues, Wed, Thur, Fri, Sat
Weekday Frequency: m
Saturday Frequency: m
Circulation: 9,516; 9,042(sat)
Last Audit: ABC September 30, 2011
Price: 3.00/wk (carrier); 156.00/yr (carrier), $196.00/yr (mail).
Advertising: Open inch rate $43.15
News services: AP, U.S. Suburban Press Inc., Robert Hitchings & Co..
Politics: Independent. **Established:** 1870
Special Editions: Garden (Apr); Fall Sports (Aug); Gift Guide (Dec); Business Outlook (Feb); Community Guide Book (Jul); Health & Fitness (Mar); Gift Guide (Nov); New Cars (Oct); Bridal (Quarterly).
Special Weekly Sections: Teen Page (Fri); Family (Mon); Weddings & Engagements (S); Real Estate Open House Directory (Sat); Garden (Thur); Health (Tues); Food (Wed).
Magazines: USA WEEKEND Magazine (S).
Pub. .... Dena Fritz
Controller/Purchasing Agent . Bernard DeAngelis
Adv. Dir. .... Shannon Cressman
Exec. Ed. .... Nona Breaux
Lifestyles Ed. .... Aixa Torregrosa
Night Ed. .... Evelyn Short
Chief Photographer .... Geoff Patton
Market Information: TMC.
Mechanical available: Offset; Black and 3 ROP colors; insert accepted; page cutoffs - 20 1/2.
Mechanical Specifications: Type page 11 5/8 x 20 1/2; E - 6 (& 7 columns front page) cols, 1 4/5, 1/8 between; A - 6 cols, 1 4/5, 1/8 between; C - 10 cols, 1 2/25, 1/16 between.
Commodity Consumption: Avg. Page Number Per Issue - Daily 34; Avg. Page Number Per Issue - Plates Used 18300; widths 12 1/2; Newsprint Used - Short Tons 1200; Printing Ink Used - Black 15120; Printing Ink Used - Color 9500; Printing Ink Used - Pages Printed 11193.
Equipment EDITORIAL: Front-end Software – Lino Press.; Editorial Hardware – Sun/Ultra 2, APP/Power Mac; Editorial Equipment – APP/Mac Quadra, AP/AdSend; Editorial Printers – HP/LaserJet 4MV CLASSIFIED: Front-end Software – Atex.; Classified Hardware – Sun/Ultra 2, APP/Power Mac; Classified Printers – LaserJet/5000 DISPLAY: Ad make-up applications – QPS/QuarkXPress, Adobe/Illustrator, Adobe/Photoshop; Layout Software – Lino Press.; Display Hardware – Sun/Ultra 2, APP/Power Mac; Display Printers – HP/LaserJet 4MV PRODUCTION: Pagination Software – Lino Press 4.2.02.39, Lino Press 4.1.14.17A.; Production Equipment – 2-Ultre/5400, D, Anitec/SN32; Cameras – C/Spartan II; Scanners – Hel/Sapphire, Tecsa/Copy Dot Scanner PRESSROOM: Line 1 – Man Roland Offset; Folders – 2; Pasters – 8-Cary/Automatic; Press control system – G/PA. MAILROOM: Counter stackers – HL/HT, 1/PRK, HI/RS 25, Gammerler, QWI/Sports Stacker; Inserters and stuffers – AlphaLine; Bundle tying machines – 2-/MLN, 2-/Dynaric; Wrapping singles – 1-/Power Strap, 1-/Dynaric; Mailroom control system – Linc; Addressing machine – Addressing machine BUSINESS COMPUTERS: Business Software – Microsoft/Excel, Microsoft/Word 6.1; Business Hardware – IBM/AS-400, IBM/RISC Model 170

LATROBE

THE LATROBE BULLETIN

1211 Ligonier St., Latrobe, Pa., 15650; gen tel (724) 537-3351; gen fax (724) 537-0489; adv e-mail bulletinads@verizon.net; ed e-mail lb.news@verizon.net

Group: Pennsylvania Newspapers Association
Published: Mon, Tues, Wed, Thur, Fri, Sat, Sun
Weekday Frequency: e
Saturday Frequency: m
Circulation: 7,767; 7,767(sat)
Last Audit: September 30, 2003
Price: 9.50/mo.
Advertising: Open inch rate $13.50
News services: AP, SHNS, TMS.
Politics: Independent.
Not Published: New Year; Memorial Day; Independence Day; Labor Day; Thanksgiving; Christmas.
Special Editions: Spring Car Care (Apr); Fall Bridal (Aug); Ligonier Greetings (Dec); Spring Bridal (Feb); Ligonier's Art About Town-Sidewalk Days (Jul); Spring Home Improvement (Mar); Mother's Day (May); Senior Citizen (Nov); Fort Ligonier Days (Oct); Fall Home Improvemen
Magazines: American Profile (Weekly).
Office Mgr. .... Jamie Knechtel
Adv. Dir. .... Gary Siegel
Editorial Dir. .... Steve Kittey
Sports Ed. .... Randy Skubek
Women's Ed. .... Louise F. Fritz
Prodn. Mgr., Pressroom .... Mike Feltes
Mechanical available: Offset; Black and 3 ROP colors; insert accepted; page cutoffs - 22 3/4.
Mechanical Specifications: Type page 12 x 21 1/2; E - 6 cols, 2 1/16, 1/8 between; A - 6 cols, 2 1/16, 1/8 between; C - 8 cols, 1 1/4, 3/16 between.
Commodity Consumption: Avg. Page Number Per Issue - Daily 20; widths 12 1/2; Newsprint Used - Metric Tons 500; Printing Ink Used - Black 2500.
Equipment; Editorial Hardware – Baseview. CLASSIFIED: Front-end Software – Baseview.; Classified Hardware – APP/Mac DISPLAY: Ad make-up applications – QPS/QuarkXPress.; Display Hardware – APP/Mac; Display Printers – HP/8000; Production Equipment – LE/LD-24-AQ, ECRM Stingray 63; Cameras – 24-B/Commodore, B. PRESSROOM: Line 1 – 7-G/Community; Folders – 1-G/SC; Press control system – FIN/3120. MAILROOM: Counter stackers – BG/108; Bundle tying machines – 1-Sa/SRIA 2460, 1-Sa/S1000 4991. BUSINESS COMPUTERS: Business Software – Baseview; Business Hardware – APP/Mac

LEBANON

THE LEBANON DAILY NEWS

718 Poplar St., Lebanon, Pa., 17042; gen tel (717) 272-5611; adv tel (717) 272-5611; ed tel (717) 272-5611; gen fax (717) 274-1608; adv fax (717) 274-1608; ed fax (717) 274-1608; gen e-mail sdowns@ldnews.com; adv e-mail sjmccoach@mediaonepa.com; ed e-mail editor@ldnews.com; web site www.ldnews.com

Group: MediaNews Group, Inc.
Published: Mon, Tues, Wed, Thur, Fri, Sat, Sun
Weekday Frequency: e
Saturday Frequency: e
Circulation: 17,642; 18,168(sat); 20,096(sun)
Last Audit: ABC September 30, 2011
Price: 176.39/year
Advertising: Open inch rate $38.75
News services: AP, NYT, TMS.
Politics: Independent. **Established:** 1872
Own facility?: Y
Special Editions: Valley Profiles (Progress)
Magazines: USA WEEKEND Magazine (S).
Circ. Mgr. .... Jarrod Lash
Features Editor .... Bill Warner
Managing Editor .... Paul Baker
City Editor .... Karol Gress
Photo Ed. .... Earl Brightbill
Sports Ed. .... Mike Givler
Editorial Page Editor .... Rahn Forney
Weekend Editor .... Jeff Clouser
Publisher .... Scott Downs
Controller .... Kevin Madden
Advertising Director .... ShaunJude McCoach
HR
Jean Taylor
Market Information: TMC
Mechanical available: Offset; Black and 3 ROP colors; insert accepted; page cutoffs - 22 3/4.
Mechanical Specifications: Type page 12 x 21 1/2; E - 6 cols, 2 1/16, 1/8 between; A - 6 cols, 2 1/16, 1/8 between; C - 9 cols, 1 3/8, 1/16 between.
Commodity Consumption: Avg. Page Number Per Issue - Daily 24; Avg. Page Number Per Issue - Sunday 140; widths 50; Newsprint Used - Metric Tons 1400.
Equipment EDITORIAL: Front-end Software – Baseview.; Editorial Hardware – APP/Mac; Editorial Printers – 1-TI; Classified Hardware – PC,

Microsoft/Windows NT, APP/iMac DISPLAY: Ad make-up applications – Multi-Ad/Creator; Layout Software – APP/Mac.; Display Hardware – APP/Mac G3; Display Printers – Xante PRODUCTION: Pagination Software – QPS/QuarkXPress.; Scanners – Polaroid; Folders – 2; Reels and Stands – 6; Wrapping singles – 1-/MLN.; Business Hardware – Oracle, PBS

LEVITTOWN

BUCKS COUNTY COURIER TIMES

8400 Rt. 13, Levittown, Pa., 19057; gen tel (215) 949-4000; adv tel (215) 949-4125; ed tel (215) 949-4162; gen fax (215) 949-4114; adv fax (215) 269-6030; ed fax (215) 949-4177; gen e-mail news@phillyburbs.com; web site www.phillyburbs.com

Group: Pennsylvania Newspapers Association
Published: Mon, Tues, Wed, Thur, Fri, Sun
Weekday Frequency: m
Saturday Frequency: m
Circulation: 42,655; 47,905(sat); 52,394(sun)
Last Audit: ABC September 30, 2011
Price: 3.75/wk; 25.00/mo (mail); 210.00/yr (carrier) $225.00/yr (mail).
Advertising: Open inch rate $40.05(3 lines for 3 days)no column inch rate
News services: AP, NEA, SHNS, TMS.
Politics: Independent. **Established:** 1910
Note: There is a Greater Philadelphia Newspaper group combination of $239.00 (d) & $251.00 (S) among Levittown Bucks County Courier (mS), Doylestown Intelligencer (mS) & Willingboro (NJ) Burlington County Times (mS). Individual newspaper rates not made availabl
Not Published: Christmas.
Special Editions: Investment Fair (Apr); Back-to-School (Aug); Bucks County Holiday (Dec); Job Fair (Feb); Mature Lifestyles (Jan); Mature Lifestyles (Jul); Internet Fair (Jun); Spring Home & Garden (Mar); Voter's Guide (May); Coupon Booklets (Monthly); Holiday Gift Guide
Special Weekly Sections: Focus On Newtown (Thur).
Magazines: Enjoy (entertainment magazine) (Fri); Parade (S).
Pub. .... Mike Scobey
Gen. Mgr. .... Thomas J. Spurgeon
Controller .... Robert M. White
Adv. Dir. .... Timothy J. Birch
Mgr., Promo. .... Carol Shapcott
Circ. Dir. .... Steve Todd
Exec. Ed. .... Patricia S. Meagher Walker
Mng. Ed., Content .... Rose McIver
Mng. Ed., Presentation .... James Pitrone
Asst. Mng. Ed., Content .... Carl LaVo
Content Ed. .... Jackie Massott
Editorial Page Ed. .... Guy Petroziello
Food Writer .... Betty Cichy
Librarian .... Carol Cavallo
Life Ed. .... Tom Haines
Life/Reality Writer .... Andy Vineberg
Online Ed. .... David Ralis
Religion Ed. .... Milt Krugman
Reporter .... Jo Ciavaglia
Sports Ed. .... Gary Silvers
Market Information: ADS; Split run; TMC; Zoned editions.
Mechanical available: Letterpress; Black and 3 ROP colors; insert accepted - all; page cutoffs - 22 3/4.
Mechanical Specifications: Type page 13 x 21 1/2; E - 6 cols, 2, 1/6 between; A - 6 cols, 2, 1/6 between; C - 9 cols, 1 1/3, 1/12 between.
Commodity Consumption: Avg. Page Number Per Issue - Daily 44; Avg. Page Number Per Issue - Plates Used 40945; Avg. Page Number Per Issue - Sunday 91; widths 40 1/2; Newsprint Used - Metric Tons 6771; Printing Ink Used - Black 236300; Printing Ink Used - Color 38503; Printing I
Equipment EDITORIAL: Front-end Software – ACI/Open Pages.; Editorial Hardware – PCs; Editorial Equipment – Printers □�□�□�□�□�□�□�□�□�□�□�□�□�□�□�□�□�; 4-HP/4MV CLASSIFIED: Front-end Software – Calkins/Adv & Acct System.; Classified Hardware – IBM/9672; Classified Equipment – 17-IBM/3179; Classified Printers – 1-IBM/3287 DISPLAY: Ad make-up applications – SCS/Layout 8000, QPS/QuarkXPress 3.32, CNI/Display Ad Tracking; Display Hardware – 15-PC; Display Printers – 1-QMS/2060 PRODUCTION: Pagination Software – Northwood Publishing/Class Page, QPS/QuarkXPress 3.32.; Production Equipment – 2-Na/Starlite, 1-MON/ExpressMaster 3850 PRESSROOM: Line 1 – 6-G 1960, 2-G 1972; Pasters – 8 MAILROOM: Counter stackers – QWI; Bundle tying machines – 2/Power Strap. AUDIO: Audio Software – New Horizons/Info-Connect; Audio Hardware – Pentium/PC BUSINESS COMPUTERS: Business Software – Calkins; Business Hardware – IBM/9672

LEWISTOWN

THE SENTINEL

352 Sixth St., Lewistown, Pa., 17044; gen tel (717) 248-6741; gen fax (717) 248-3481; gen e-mail sentinel@lewistownsentinel.com; adv e-mail ads@lewistownsentinel.com; classified@lewistownsentinel.com; web site www.lewistownsentinel.com

Published: Mon, Tues, Wed, Thur, Fri, Sat
Weekday Frequency: m
Saturday Frequency: m
Circulation: 10,268; 12,269(sat)
Last Audit: ABC September 30, 2011
Price: 10.25/mo; 113.40/yr.
Advertising: Open inch rate $17.72
News services: AP.
Politics: Independent. **Established:** 1903
Not Published: New Year; Thanksgiving; Christmas.
Special Editions: Home & Garden (Apr); Hall of Fame (Aug); Happy Holidays (Dec); Juniata Valley (Feb); Brides (Jan); Get to Know Us (Jul); Brides (Jun); Agriculture (Mar); Low-Fat Cookbook (May); Holiday Gift Guide (Nov); Winter Car Care (Oct); Goose Day (Sept).
Special Weekly Sections: Health (Fri); Auto Racing (Mon); People (Sat); Outdoors (Thur); Snapshots (Tues); Food (Wed).
Magazines: USA WEEKEND Magazine (Sat).
Pub. .... Ruth Eddy
Adv. Dir. .... Matt Bolich
Circ. Mgr. .... Ed Williams
Food Ed. .... Jean Mort
Mng. Ed. .... Frank Jost
Photo Dept. Ed. .... Buffy Boyer
Online Mgr. .... Brad Siddons
Prodn. Foreman, Pressroom .... Jay McCaulley
Market Information: TMC.
Mechanical available: Offset; Black and 3 ROP colors; insert accepted.
Mechanical Specifications: Type page 13 x 21 1/2; E - 6 cols, 2 1/16, 1/8 between; A - 6 cols, 2 1/16, 1/8 between; C - 6 cols, 2 1/16, 1/8 between.
Commodity Consumption: Avg. Page Number Per Issue - Daily 24; Avg. Page Number Per Issue - Plates Used 14000; widths 13 3/4; Newsprint Used - Short Tons 1516; Printing Ink Used - Black 35000; Printing Ink Used - Color 2000; Printing Ink Used - Pages Printed 7441.
Equipment EDITORIAL: Front-end Software – In-house.; Editorial Hardware – APP/Mac CLASSIFIED: Front-end Software – Baseview.; Classified Hardware – APP/Mac; Classified Printers – Okidata/210; Display Hardware – NCR; Display Printers – Talley; Production Equipment – APP/Mac Laser; Cameras – K/Vertical; Scanners – Polaroid. PRESSROOM: Line 1 – 9-G/Community 1973.; Inserters and stuffers – 4/MM; Bundle tying machines – Bu/Strapper; Addressing machine – KAN.; Audio Hardware – Brite Voice Systems, PEP BUSINESS COMPUTERS: Business Software – In-house, Microsoft/Windows 3.1; Business Hardware – NCR

LOCK HAVEN

THE EXPRESS

9-11 W. Main St., Lock Haven, Pa., 17745-0208; gen tel (570) 748-6791; adv tel (570) 748-6791; ed tel (570) 748-6791; gen fax (570) 748-1544; adv fax (570) 748-1544; ed fax (570) 748-1544; gen e-mail news@lockhaven.com; adv e-mail ad@lockhaven.com; ed e-mail news@lockhaven.com; web site www.lockhaven.com

Published: Mon, Tues, Wed, Thur, Fri, Sat
Weekday Frequency: e
Saturday Frequency: m
Circulation: 8,276; 9,192(sat)
Last Audit: ABC September 30, 2011
Price: 2.60/wk; 10.40/mo; 109.20/yr, $116.50/yr (outside PA).
News services: AP
Politics: Independent. **Established:** 1882
Note: Advertising is sold in combination with the Williamsport Sun-Gazette (mS) for $76.12 (d) and $82.11 (S). Individual newspapers rates not made available.
Not Published: July 4, New Year; Christmas unless on Saturdays
Own facility?: Y
Special Editions: Real Estate (monthly); New Year, New You (Jan.); Progress (March); Spring Home Improvement (Apr); Fishing (Apr); Visitors Guide (May); Salute to Graduates (June); Shop Local (July) Back-to-College (Aug); Back to School (Aug); Fall Sports (Aug); Fall Home Improvement (Sept); Cooking Show & Cookbook (Sept); Body, Mind & Spirit (Sept); Fall Bridal (Oct); Fall Car Care (Oct); Buck Fever (Nov); Gift Ideas (Nov); Holiday Shopping Ideas (Dec); Song Book (Dec).
Special Weekly Sections: Susquehanna Sunrise (Sat); Jersey Shore Weekly (Tues).
Magazines: USA WEEKEND Magazine (Sat).
Pub. .... Bob Rolley
Mktg. Mgr. .... Lisa Schropp
Circ. Mgr. .... Walter Corter
Community Ed. .... Wendy Stiver
News Ed. .... Lana Muthler
Sports Ed. .... Tom Fox
Online Mgr. .... Scott Johnson
Classified Line salesperson .... Linda Hinton
Advertising Sales Manager ..... Christine Gorham
Office Manager .... Tina Geyer
Mechanical available: Offset; Black and 4 ROP colors; insert accepted; page cutoffs - 21 1/2.
Mechanical Specifications: Type page 13 x 21 1/2; E - 6 cols, 2, 1/8 between; A - 6 cols, 2, 1/8 between; C - 9 cols, 1 1/3, 1/12 between.
Commodity Consumption: Avg. Page Number Per Issue - Daily 16; Avg. Page Number Per Issue - Plates Used 2968; Avg. Page Number Per Issue - Saturday 24; widths 27; Newsprint Used - Short Tons 330; Printing Ink Used - Black 10810; Printing Ink Used - Color 822; Printing Ink Used
Equipment EDITORIAL: Front-end Software – QPS/QuarkXPress.; Editorial Hardware – APP/Mac; Editorial Printers – HP/4MV CLASSIFIED: Front-end Software – QPS/QuarkXPress.; Classified Hardware – APP/Mac; Classified Printers – HP/6MP DISPLAY: Ad make-up applications – APP/Mac, QPS/QuarkXPress; Display Hardware – APP/Mac; Display Printers – HP/4MV PRODUCTION: Pagination Software – QPS/QuarkXPress 3.32.; Production Equipment – 1-Nu; Cameras – R; Scanners – 2-Umax/Vista 56 PRESSROOM: Line 1 – 8-G/Community 1975.; Bundle tying machines – 1/OVL; Addressing machine – Wm.
Delivery method: Mail, Newsstand, Private Carrier, Racks

MCKEESPORT

THE DAILY NEWS

409 Walnut St., McKeesport, Pa., 15132; gen tel (412) 664-9161; adv tel (412) 664-9161; ed tel (412) 664-3981; gen fax (412) 664-3972; adv fax (412) 664-3972; ed fax (412) 664-3972; gen e-mail mcknews@dailynewsemail.com; adv e-mail mckads@dailynewsemail.com; ed e-mail mcknews@dailynewsemail.com; web site www.dailynewsmckeesport.com

Group: Trib Total Media
Published: Mon, Tues, Wed, Thur, Fri, Sat
Weekday Frequency: m
Saturday Frequency: m
Circulation: 12,338; 12,338(sat)
Last Audit: September 30, 2008
Price: 3.10/wk; 10.90/mo; 156.00/yr.
Advertising: Open inch rate $32.50
News services: AP.
Politics: Independent. **Established:** 1884
Special Editions: Spring Car Care (Apr); Back-to-School (Aug); Christmas (3 times) (Dec); Bridal (Feb); Progress (Jan); Independence Day (Jul); Bridal (Jun); Easter (Mar); Health & Fitness (May); Christmas Gift Guide (Nov); Fall Coupon Book (Oct); Women in Business (Sept).
Magazines: USA WEEKEND Magazine (Sat).
Pub. .... Richard M. Scaife
City Ed. .... Bonniejean Adams
Editorial Page Ed. .... Jeffrey Sisk
Sports Ed. .... Mark Kaboly
Prodn. Foreman, Composing .... Mark Russell
Prodn. Foreman, Mailroom .... Terry Keeley
Prodn. Foreman, Pressroom ..... James Bumgard
News Editor .... David Fennerssy
Mechanical available: Offset; Black and 3 ROP colors; insert accepted - cards, booklets; page cutoffs - 22 3/4.
Mechanical Specifications: Type page 13 x 21 1/2; E - 6 cols, 2 1/16, 1/8 between; A - 6 cols, 2 1/16, 1/8 between; C - 9 cols, 1 3/8, 1/16 between.
Commodity Consumption: Avg. Page Number Per Issue - Daily 24; Avg. Page Number Per Issue - Plates Used 7650; widths 27 1/2; Newsprint Used - Short Tons 1200; Printing Ink Used - Black 65600; Printing Ink Used - Color 820; Printing Ink Used - Pages Printed 7500.
Equipment EDITORIAL: Front-end Software – Microsoft/Windows 95, Microsoft/Word 6.0.; Editorial Equipment – MS/Windows NT Servers, 30-Pentium/Workstation ACI Open Pages; Editorial Printers – 3-HP/4MV CLASSIFIED: Front-end Software – Vision Data.; Classified Hardware – Vision Data, Sun/Sparc 4 Server, 4-Tektronic/Terminal; Classified Equipment – Printers 3-HP/4MV, 2-Panasonic/KX-P3626 DISPLAY: Ad make-up applications – QPS/QuarkXPress 3.1, Microsoft/Windows 95, Microsoft/Word 6.0, Adobe/Illustrator, ACI/Open Pages, Adobe/Acrobat; Layout Software – 4-Pentium/ACI 133MHz Work Station.; Display Hardware – Printers 3-HP/4MV; Production Equipment – 1-Teaneck, 1-Nu; Cameras – 1-Bo. PRESSROOM: Line 1 – 6-G/Urbanite; Folders – 1-G/3:2. MAILROOM: Counter stackers – 1/QWI; Bundle tying machines – 1-/MLN.; Business Hardware – 2-PC 386-25 MHE Model Keen-2530, Vision Data/3 DEC 510
Delivery method: Mail, Newsstand, Private Carrier

MEADVILLE

THE MEADVILLE TRIBUNE

947 Federal Ct., Meadville, Pa., 16335; gen tel (814) 724-6370; gen fax (814) 724-8755; adv e-mail advertising@meadvilletribune.com; ed e-mail tribune@meadvilletribune.com; web site www.meadvilletribune.com

Group: Community Newspapers Holding Inc.
Published: Mon, Tues, Wed, Thur, Fri, Sat, Sun
Weekday Frequency: m
Saturday Frequency: m
Circulation: 11,749; 12,508(sat); 11,582(sun)
Last Audit: ABC September 30, 2011
Price: $13 1 month carrier/$135 12 months carrier
Advertising: Open inch rate $23.45
News services: AP.
Not Published: Christmas.
Special Editions: Home Improvement (Apr);

Back-to-School (Aug); Winter Sports (Dec); Report to People (Feb); Bridal (Jan); Heritage Days (Jul); Hot Air Balloons (Jun); AG Day (Mar); Country Living (Monthly); Christmas Opening (Nov); Cookbook (Oct); Outdoor (Sept).
Special Weekly Sections: Bravo! (entertainment) (Fri); Keystone Korner classifieds (Sat).
Magazines: Relish (Monthly); USA WEEKEND Magazine (S).
Pub. ....Sharon Sorg
Controller ....Michelle Brown
Circulation Director ....Devon Stout
Exec. Ed. ....Pat Bywater
Bus. Ed. ....Keith Gushard
Editorial Page Ed ....Ed Maillard
IT Mgr. ....Matt Digiacomo
Prodn. Mgr., Mailroom ....Allen Lyon
Director of Advertising Sales ....Heidi Gebhardt
Market Information: ADS; TMC; Zoned editions.
Mechanical available: Offset; Black and 3 ROP colors; insert accepted; page cutoffs - 22 3/4.
Mechanical Specifications: Type page 13 x 21 1/2; E - 6 cols, 2 1/16, 1/8 between; A - 6 cols, 2 1/16, 1/8 between; C - 9 cols, 1 5/16, 1/8 between.
Commodity Consumption: Avg. Page Number Per Issue - Daily 23; Avg. Page Number Per Issue - Plates Used 15442; Avg. Page Number Per Issue - Sunday 36; widths 25; Newsprint Used - Short Tons 1034; Printing Ink Used - Black 35000; Printing Ink Used - Color 1000; Printing Ink Used
Equipment EDITORIAL: Front-end Software – Baseview/NewsEdit Pro IQUE 1.0.; Editorial Hardware – APP/Mac; Editorial Equipment – APP/Mac LD; Editorial Printers – 2-HP/4MV, Pre Press/Panther Pro 36 CLASSIFIED: Front-end Software – Baseview/Class Manager Pro 1.7.; Classified Hardware – 3-APP/Mac; Classified Printers – 1-HP/4MV DISPLAY: Ad make-up applications – Multi-Ad/Creator 4.1, Adobe/Illustrator 6.0, QPS/QuarkXPress 3.32; Layout Software – MEI/ALS, MEI/ALS 2.1.; Display Hardware – 2-APP/Mac 7600, 1-APP/Mac 7300; Display Printers – 1-HP/4MV PRODUCTION: Pagination Software – QPS/QuarkXPress 3.32.; Production Equipment – 1-SCREEN/220, 1-SCREEN/LD281Q; Cameras – 1-C/Spartan, 1-SCREEN/680C; Scanners – 2-Polaroid/SprintScan, 1-AG/Duo scan, 1-Pixelcraft PRESSROOM: Line 1 – 10-G/Community (color deck) 1989; Folders – 1; Press registration system – Duarte/Pin System. MAILROOM: Counter stackers – 1/Hall Monitor; Inserters and stuffers – GMA/Alphaliner Gintol; Bundle tying machines – EAM-Mosca, ROM; Other equipment – 1-/Custom-Built/3 Knife Trimmer.
Delivery method: Mail, Newsstand, Private Carrier, Racks

MECHANICSBURG

THE PATRIOT-NEWS

2020 Technology Parkway, Suite 300, Mechanicsburg, Pa., 17050; gen tel (717) 255-8100; adv tel (717) 255-8141 (classified); adv fax (717) 255-8450 (retail); ed fax (717) 255-8456; ed e-mail citydesk@pnco.com; web site www.pennlive.com
Published: Mon, Tues, Wed, Thur, Fri, Sat, Sun
Weekday Frequency: m
Saturday Frequency: m
Circulation: 66,778; 62,442(sat); 116,609(sun)
Last Audit: ABC September 30, 2011
Price: $2.00/wk (S); $4.50/wk (D); $104/yr (S); $234/yr (D)
Advertising: Full pg. $2540
Insert rate: (S) $42.06 full run, 4pg; (D) $41.03 full run, 4pg
News services: AP, MCT, LAT-WP, NNS, NYT, Cox, SHNS.
Politics: Independent.
Own facility?: Y
Special Editions: Central PA Magazine (bi-mo.); Wedding Style (Feb); Body&Mind (6x yr.); Natl Engrs(Feb); Home Bldrs (Feb); Midstate Fam (March); Now (May/Nov); Best&Brightest (May); Livingin Midstate(June); Pride Mag (July); Back to School (Aug); Football Preview (Aug); Dental Guide (Oct)
Special Weekly Sections: (S) Parade; (W) Food; (TH) Go Entertainment; (F) Faith & Values
Magazines: Central PA magazine (bi-mo. edition)
Pres./Pub. ....John A. Kirkpatrick
Controller ....Michael J. Morrow
Adv. Mgr., Classified ....Janet Pietropaolo
Adv. Sales Asst., Nat'l ....Shannon Garman
Circ. Dir. ....Kurt Hower
Social Media Dir. ....Dan Christ
Editor ....David Newhouse
Exec. Ed. ....Cate Barron
Asst. Managing Ed. ....Michael Feeley
Systems Ed. ....Craig Hunt
Dir., Operations ....Christopher Spivey
Dir. Technology ....James Brighton
General Manager ....D. Lee Carlson
Market Information: Split run; Zoned editions.
Mechanical available: Letterpress; Black and 3 ROP colors; insert accepted - spadea-samples with prior approval; page cutoffs - 22 3/4.
Mechanical Specifications: Type page 11 5/8 x 21; E - 6 cols, 1 13/16, 1/6 between; A - 6 cols, 1 13/16, 1/6 between; C - 10 cols, 1 1/32, 1/8 between.
Commodity Consumption: Avg. Page Number Per Issue - Daily 62; Avg. Page Number Per Issue - Plates Used 240000; Avg. Page Number Per Issue - Sunday 150; widths 50; Newsprint Used - Metric Tons 15950; Newsprint Used - Short Tons 17581; Printing Ink Used - Black 237520; Printing
Equipment EDITORIAL: Front-end Software – HI/XP21 Newsmaker.; Editorial Hardware – Sun; Editorial Equipment – 26-HI/NMP, 101-HI/NME, 150-Dell/Optiplex, 20-Dell/Latitude, APP/Mac G3, APP/Mac G4; Editorial Printers – 3-HP/LaserJet 5M, 6-HP/LaserJet 6 CLASSIFIED: Front-end Software – Mactive AdBase.; Classified Hardware – SII/Tandem, 3-Sun/V880; Classified Equipment – 40-Dell/Optiplex DISPLAY: Ad make-up applications – 2-Multi-Ad/Creator, Morcor/DTP Xpance, Adobe/PhotoShop 7, Adobe/Illustrator 10, Adobe/Acrobat 6, 6-Quark; Layout Software – Mactive.; Display Hardware – 35-APP/Mac, 2-Dell/Server-NT, 2-Purup/Eskofot EskoScan 26365; Display Printers – GEI, HP, Xerox, All PRODUCTION: Pagination Software – 2-AU/3850 Wide.; Production Equipment – 2-Newslink Pro 28/G&J, 3-Kk/2035, 1-Kk/Dye Sublimation XLS 8600, 1-Kk/3570; Scanners – 2-Eskofat PRESSROOM: Line 1 – 7-G/Colorline double width; Line 2 – 56 couples; Folders – 1-G/Double 3:2, Allen-Bradley/1336; Pasters – Enkel/Auto 2001; Reels and Stands – 2001; Press registration system – 2001, Printe. MAILROOM: Counter stackers – 6-QWI/350; Inserters and stuffers – 2-GMA/SLS 2000 28:2; Bundle tying machines – 9-Dynaric/NP2, 5-AP/2, 4-NP/3; Wrapping singles – 1/Dynaric; Mailroom control system – Motion Systems; Addressing machine – 1-/Ch; Other equipment – 2-Ca AUDIO: Audio Software – New Horizons/Info-Connect, U.S. Telecom Voice Application Language 4.30; Audio Hardware – ITN, PC 486 BUSINESS COMPUTERS: Business Software – CJ, Mactive- Adv., AR, Epicor - AP GL- PO 7.2; Business Hardware – 2-DEC/Alpha 2100, Dell/4100, 3-Sun/V880
Delivery method: Mail, Newsstand, Private Carrier, Racks

MILTON

THE STANDARD-JOURNAL

21 N. Arch St., Milton, Pa., 17847-1211; gen tel (570) 742-9671; gen fax (570) 742-9876; gen e-mail newsroom@standard-journal.com; ed e-mail mike@standard-journal.com; web site www.standard-journal.com
Published: Mon, Tues, Wed, Thur, Fri, Sat, Sun
Weekday Frequency: e
Saturday Frequency: m
Circulation: 1,418; 1,418(sat)
Last Audit: September 30, 1997
Price: 1.95/wk; 108.11/yr (carrier), $112.32/yr (mail).
Advertising: Open inch rate $10.50
News services: AP.
Politics: Independent.
Not Published: New Year; Memorial Day; Independence Day; Labor Day; Christmas.
Special Editions: Progress (Feb).
Special Weekly Sections: Bridal (Sat); Entertainment (Thur).
Magazines: Relocation (Oct) (Annually).
Bus. Mgr. ....Karen Hendricks
Adv. Mgr. ....Amy Moyer
Circ. Dir. ....Kevin Mertz
Prodn. Mgr. ....Kevin Koch
Market Information: TMC.
Mechanical available: Offset; Black and 3 ROP colors; insert accepted - post card up to SAU size; page cutoffs - 22 3/4.
Mechanical Specifications: Type page 13 x 21 1/2; E - 6 cols, 2 1/14, 1/6 between; A - 6 cols, 2 1/14, 1/6 between; C - 9 cols, 1 1/5, 1/12 between.
Commodity Consumption: Avg. Page Number Per Issue - Daily 16; Avg. Page Number Per Issue - Plates Used 2400; Avg. Page Number Per Issue - Saturday 24; widths 34; Newsprint Used - Short Tons 52; Printing Ink Used - Black 1800; Printing Ink Used - Color 60; Printing Ink Used - P
Equipment EDITORIAL: Front-end Software – Mk.; Editorial Hardware – Mk/550, 3-Mk/NewsTouch; Editorial Printers – APP/Mac LaserWriter Plus CLASSIFIED: Front-end Software – Mk.; Classified Hardware – Mk/3000, 1-Mk/NewsTouch II; Classified Printers – APP/Mac LaserWriter Plus, Okidata/Microline 293 line printer DISPLAY: Ad make-up applications – Mk/NewsTouch II, Mk/Ad Touch.; Display Hardware – Mk; Display Printers – APP/Mac LaserWriter Plus; Production Equipment – 2-APP/Mac LaserWriter Plus; Cameras – LE/Horizontal. PRESSROOM: Line 1 – 6-G/Community 1973; Folders – 1-G/SC. MAILROOM: Counter stackers – 1-BG/Count-O-Veyor; Inserters and stuffers – DG/320 2:1; Bundle tying machines – 1-Bu/SP 505, 1-MLN/MS-T; Addressing machine – Dispensa-Matic/U 45. BUSINESS COMPUTERS: Business Software – Vision Data; Business Hardware – 4-ATT/Unix PC 7300-3B1

MONESSEN

THE VALLEY INDEPENDENT

19 Eastgate, Monessen, Pa., 15062; gen tel (724) 684-5200; adv tel (724) 684-5200; ed tel (724) 684-2631; gen fax (724) 684-2601; adv fax (724) 684-2602; ed fax (724) 684-2603; gen e-mail valley@tribweb.com; ed e-mail bburke@tribweb.com; web site www.valleyindependent.com
Published: Mon, Tues, Wed, Thur, Fri, Sat, Sun
Weekday Frequency: e
Saturday Frequency: m
Circulation: 13,211; 13,211(sat)
Last Audit: September 30, 2006
Price: 180.00/yr.
Advertising: Open inch rate $22.54
News services: AP.
Politics: Independent.
Note: Subscribers to The Valley Independent receive the Sunday edition of the Greensburg Tribune-Review. See the Greensburg listing for circulation and advertising rate.
Not Published: Memorial Day; Independence Day; Labor Day; Christmas.
Special Editions: Progress (Apr); Christmas Wrap-Up (Dec); Bridal (Jan); Christmas Preview (Nov); Car Care (Oct).
Special Weekly Sections: Best Food Day (Mon); Best Food Day (Wed).
Magazines: TV Section (Fri).
Administrative Asst. ....Regina Stefan
Adv. Dept. Mgr. ....Karen Strickland
Circ. Dir. ....Linda Hutchinson
Circ. Asst. Mgr. ....Lori Byron
Mng. Ed. ....Bob Burke
City Ed. ....Joe Abramowitz
Copy Ed ....Karen Peters
News Ed. ....Carl Hill
Chief Photographer ....Jim Ference
Sports Ed. ....Brian Herman
Prodn. Dir. ....William Lieb
Prodn. Mgr., Pre Press ....Shawn Yauger
Prodn. Mgr., Mailroom ....Ed Marcus
Market Information: TMC.
Mechanical available: Offset; Black and 3 ROP colors; insert accepted - front page self-adhesive notes, coupon books; page cutoffs - 22 3/4.
Mechanical Specifications: Type page 13 x 21 1/2; E - 6 cols, 2 1/16, 1/8 between; A - 6 cols, 2 1/16, 1/8 between; C - 10 cols, 1 3/10, 1/16 between.
Commodity Consumption: Avg. Page Number Per Issue - Daily 18; widths 13 3/4; Newsprint Used - Short Tons 1000; Printing Ink Used - Black 20860; Printing Ink Used - Color 672.
Equipment EDITORIAL: Front-end Software – Microsoft/Word, QPS/QuarkXPress.; Editorial Hardware – PC, APP/MAc; Editorial Printers – NewGen/Laser-Printer CLASSIFIED: Front-end Software – PPI/System.; Classified Hardware – PC, IBM; Classified Printers – NewGen/Laser-Printer DISPLAY: Ad make-up applications – Multi-Ad/Creator.; Display Hardware – 4-APP/Mac G3, 1-APP/Power Mac, Intel/P233; Display Printers – NewGen/LaserPrinter, HP/LaserJet 5000N PRODUCTION: Pagination Software – QPS/QuarkXPress 4.0.; Production Equipment – NewGen/LaserPrinters, Lf/Leafscan 35, Lf/AP Leaf Picture Desk; Cameras – 2-SCREEN/Companica 680C; Scanners – Umax/UC-1200-SE, AVR/8000 GSX, HP/6100C, 3-Umax/AG 1200 PRESSROOM: Line 1 – 8-G/Community & color stack unit 1988; Folders – G/SSC (with balloon), G/SC Quarterfolder.; Bundle tying machines – Mosca; Addressing machine – Wm. BUSINESS COMPUTERS: Business Software – Lotus 1-2-3, Oracle, PRS; Business Hardware – 2-PC, 2-HP/9000, HP/200 terminals, HP/60 terminals, HP/2300 Line Printer, HP/840 L Line Printer, HP/LaserJet 4si

NEW CASTLE

NEW CASTLE NEWS

27 N. Mercer St., New Castle, Pa., 16101-3806; gen tel (724) 654-6651; gen fax (724) 654-5616; adv fax (724) 654-9593; gen e-mail ncnews@ncnewsonline.com; adv e-mail classify@ncnewsonline.com; display@ncnewsonline.com; ed e-mail nceditor@ncnewsonline.com; web site www.ncnewsonline.com
Group: Pennsylvania Newspapers Association
Published: Mon, Tues, Wed, Thur, Fri, Sat
Weekday Frequency: e
Saturday Frequency: e
Circulation: 14,283; 14,283(sat)
Last Audit: ABC September 30, 2011
Price: 2.30/wk; 9.53/mo; 108.40/yr.
Advertising: Open inch rate $33.86
News services: AP, SHNS.
Politics: Independent.
Special Editions: Car Care (Apr); Football (Aug); First Baby (Dec); Business-Industrial Review (Feb); Brides (Jan); Senior Citizens (Jul); Summer Fun (Jun); Home Improvement (Mar); Mother's Day (May); Car Care (Oct); Home Improvement (Sept).
Magazines: Children's Mini Page (Fri); Relish (Monthly); USA WEEKEND Magazine (Sat).
Pub. ....Max Thomson
Mgr., Computer Serv. ....Tom Covert
Mgr., Educ. Serv. ....Matt Kingman
Adv. Mgr., Retail ....Rick Work
Circ. Mgr. ....DuWayne Nelson
Mng. Ed. ....Mitch Olszak
Educ. Rep. ....Lugene Hudson
News Ed. ....Patrick Litowitz
Political Ed. ....John K. Manna
Religion Ed. ....Dan Irwin
Reporter ....Debbie Wachter Morris
Sports Ed. ....Kayleen Cubbal
Television/Film Ed. ....Tim Kolodziej
Market Information: Split run; TMC.
Mechanical available: Offset; Black and 3 ROP

colors; insert accepted; page cutoffs - 22 3/4.
Mechanical Specifications: Type page 13 x 21 1/2; E - 6 cols, 2 1/16, 1/8 between; A - 6 cols, 2 1/16, 1/8 between; C - 9 cols, 1 3/8, 1/8 between.
Commodity Consumption: Avg. Page Number Per Issue - Daily 28; Avg. Page Number Per Issue - Plates Used 13604; widths 41 1/4; Newsprint Used - Short Tons 1200; Printing Ink Used - Black 21400; Printing Ink Used - Color 500; Printing Ink Used - Pages Printed 9010.
Equipment EDITORIAL: Front-end Software – Baseview.; Editorial Hardware – APP/Mac G3, APP/Macs CLASSIFIED: Front-end Software – III/Tecs 2.; Classified Hardware – 4-PC; Classified Printers – PAN/KXP-180 DISPLAY: Ad make-up applications – Multi-Ad/Creator; Layout Software – Baseview/ALS.; Display Hardware – 7-APP/Mac PRODUCTION: Pagination Software – QPS/QuarkXPress.; Production Equipment – 1-LE/24AQ, 1-LE/PC13; Cameras – 1-C/Marathon, 1-B/2000, 1-K/240 Vertical PRESSROOM: Line 1 – 4-G/Metro (color deck); Folders – 1; Pasters – G/Metro Automatic; Reels and Stands – G/Reels.; Bundle tying machines – 1-Sa/59SR1A, 1-MLN/ML2EE. BUSINESS COMPUTERS: Business Software – Microsoft/Excel; Business Hardware – PBS

NORRISTOWN

THE TIMES HERALD

410 Markley St., Norristown, Pa., 19401; gen tel (610) 272-2500; adv tel (610) 272-3830; ed tel (610) 272-2501; gen fax (610) 272-4003; adv fax (610) 272-9515; ed fax (610) 272-0660; gen e-mail editor@timesherald.com; adv e-mail advertising@timesherald.com; web site www.timesherald.com
Group: Journal Register Co.
Published: Mon, Tues, Wed, Thur, Fri, Sat, Sun
Weekday Frequency: m
Saturday Frequency: m
Circulation: 9,682; 11,437(sat); 19,593(sun)
Last Audit: ABC September 30, 2011
Price: 3.20/wk; 195.00/yr.
Advertising: Open inch rate $76.48
News services: AP, SHNS.
Politics: 1799
Advertising not accepted: Y
Own facility?: Y
Special Editions: Senior Lifestyles (Apr); Football (Aug); Song Book (Dec); Parenting (Feb); Super Sale (Jan); Fall Education (Jul); Children's Guide (Jun); Coupon Book (Mar); Coupon Book (May); Holiday Season Preview (Nov); Car Care (Oct); Fall Bridal (Sept).
Special Weekly Sections: Weekend Entertainment (Fri); TV Time (S); Business Directory (Sat); Church News (Thur); Best Food Day (Wed).
Magazines: USA WEEKEND Magazine (S).
Pub. ....Shelley Meenan
Asst. to Pub. ....Amy Bernstiel
Adv. Dir. ....Madeline Wood
Circ. Dir. ....Laurence Butts
Ed. ....Stan Huskey
Mng. Ed. ....Gordon Glantz
City Ed. ....Cheryl Kehoe Rodgers
Lifestyle Ed. ....Philomena Johns
Mgr., Systems ....John Brown
Prodn. Foreman, Composing ....Gary Mengle
Market Information: Split run; TMC.
Mechanical available: Offset; Black and ROP colors; insert accepted; page cutoffs - 21 1/2.
Mechanical Specifications: Type page 12 x 21 1/2; E - 6 cols, 1 7/8, 1/8 between; A - 6 cols, 1 7/8, 1/8 between; C - 10 cols, 1 3/16, 1/12 between.
Commodity Consumption: Avg. Page Number Per Issue - Daily 32; Avg. Page Number Per Issue - Plates Used 17549; Avg. Page Number Per Issue - Sunday 40; widths 25; Newsprint Used - Short Tons 1893; Printing Ink Used - Black 40699; Printing Ink Used - Color 8109; Printing Ink Used
Equipment EDITORIAL: Front-end Software – Dewar.; Editorial Hardware – ATS; Editorial Printers – HP/5000 CLASSIFIED: Front-end Software – Dewar/Sys IV.; Classified Hardware – Dewar; Classified Printers – Dataproducts/LB 325 DISPLAY: Ad make-up applications – Dewar; Layout Software – MEI.; Display Hardware – Dewar/Discovery; Display Printers – HP/882 PRODUCTION: Pagination Software – ATS/managing editor, Windows 2.7.; Production Equipment – LE, APP/Mac, 1-Ultra 4000, 1-Bibco; Cameras – C/Spartan III, R/Vertical; Scanners – ECR/Autokon, Ultra/4000 Full Page Imagesetter, Umax PRESSROOM: Line 1 – 5-HI/1650 1993; Press Drives – GE/200 h.p. Twin; Folders – 1-HI/double 2:1; Pasters – Reels and Stands ÃĐÂĐ 5-G/Manual Reel. MAILROOM: Counter stackers – KAN, QWI/SJ101; Inserters and stuffers – 1-KAN/480, 1-KAN/480; Bundle tying machines – MLN/ML2CC, 1-MLN/ML2EE; Wrapping singles – 1-HL/Monarch, 2/Si. BUSINESS COMPUTERS: Business Software – INSI; Business Hardware – IBM/AS-400
Delivery method: Mail, Newsstand, Private Carrier, Racks

OIL CITY

THE DERRICK

1510 W. First St., Oil City, Pa., 16301; gen tel (814) 676-7444; gen fax (814) 677-8347; adv fax (814) 677-8351; adv e-mail advertising@usachoice.com; ed e-mail newsroom@usachoice.net; web site www.thederrick.com
Published: Mon, Tues, Wed, Thur, Fri, Sat
Weekday Frequency: m
Circulation: 18,314; 18,314(sat)
Last Audit: October 1, 1999
Price: 129.48/yr; 9.95/4wk.
News services: AP.
Politics: Independent.
Note: Advertising is sold in combination with The Franklin News-Herald (m) for $62.23(d). Individual newspaper rates not made available. All business and production are handled by Venango Newspapers Inc.
Not Published: New Year; Memorial Day; Independence Day; Labor Day; Thanksgiving; Christmas.
Special Editions: Spring Car Care (Apr); Football (Aug); Safety Page (Dec); Insurance (Feb); Business Review (Jan); Senior Living (Jul); Today's Bride (Mar); Outdoor Living (May); Basketball (Nov); Cookbook I (Oct); Fall Car Care (Sept).
Special Weekly Sections: Good Times (Fri); Entertainment (Thur); Entertainment (Wed).
Sec. ....Peter T. Boyle
Treasurer ....E. Michael Boyle
Controller ....W.R. Lutz
Pub. ....Edward B. Cowart
Ed. ....Patrick C. Boyle
Editorial Page Ed. ....Glen Mohnkern
Sports Ed. ....Edward Brannon
Prodn. Mgr., Pressroom ....Melvin J. Basham
Market Information: ADS; TMC.
Mechanical available: Offset; Black and 3 ROP colors; insert accepted; page cutoffs - 22 3/4.
Mechanical Specifications: Type page 13 x 21 1/4; E - 6 cols, 2 1/16, 1/8 between; A - 6 cols, 2 1/16, 1/8 between; C - 9 cols, 1 3/8, 1/16 between.
Commodity Consumption: Avg. Page Number Per Issue - Daily 24; widths 13 1/2; Newsprint Used - Metric Tons 900.
Equipment; Editorial Hardware – CText; Editorial Printers – Graphic Enterprises/Pro Setter 1000.; Classified Hardware – CText; Classified Printers – Graphic Enterprises/Pro Setter 1000. DISPLAY: Ad make-up applications – CText/Adept, Multi-Ad/Creator; Layout Software – 1-SCS/Layout 8000.; Display Hardware – APP/Mac, PCs; Display Printers – Graphic Enterprise/Pro Setter 1000; Production Equipment – 2-COM/8600. PRESSROOM: Line 1 – 5-G/Community Offset.; Inserters and stuffers – 14-MM/227-2; Bundle tying machines – 2-MLN/SP 330; Addressing machine – 2-KR/211. AUDIO: Audio Software – New Horizons/Info-Connect; Audio Hardware – Info-Connect/Pottsville Republican, Gateway

THE NEWS-HERALD

1510 W. First St., Oil City, Pa., 16301; gen tel (814) 676-7444; gen fax (814) 677-8347; adv e-mail advertising@usachoice.net; ed e-mail newsroom@usachoice.net; web site www.thederrick.com
Published: Mon, Tues, Wed, Thur, Fri, Sat
Weekday Frequency: m
Circulation: 7,373; 7,373(sat)
Last Audit: October 1, 1999
Price: 9.95/mo; 129.48/yr.
News services: AP.
Politics: Independent.
Note: Advertising is sold in combination with the Oil City Derrick (m) for $62.23(d). Individual newspaper rates not made available. All business and production are handled by Venango Newspapers Inc.
Not Published: New Year; Memorial Day; Independence Day; Labor Day; Christmas.
Special Editions: Spring Car Care (Apr); Football (Aug); First Baby (Dec); Insurance (Feb); Senior Living (Jul); Today's Bride (Mar); Outdoor Living (May); Basketball (Nov); Cookbook I (Oct); Fall Car Care (Sept).
Special Weekly Sections: Good Times (Fri); Entertainment (Thur); Entertainment (Wed).
Magazines: American Profile (Weekly).
Pres. ....Patrick C. Boyle
Exec. Vice Pres./Treasurer ....E. Michael Boyle
Vice Pres./Controller ....W.R. Lutz
Sec. ....Peter T. Boyle
Pub. ....Edward B. Cowart
Ed. ....Glen Mohnkern
City Ed. ....Mark Oliver
Sports Ed. ....Edward Brannon
Prodn. Mgr., Pre Press ....Melvin J. Basham
Market Information: TMC.
Mechanical available: Black and 3 ROP colors; insert accepted - offset; page cutoffs - 22 3/4.
Commodity Consumption: Avg. Page Number Per Issue - Daily 24; widths 27; Newsprint Used - Metric Tons 900.
Equipment; Editorial Hardware – CText; Editorial Printers – Graphic Enterprises/Pro Setter 1000. CLASSIFIED: Front-end Software – CText/Adept.; Classified Hardware – CText; Classified Printers – Graphic Enterprises/Pro Setter 1000 DISPLAY: Ad make-up applications – CText/Adept, Multi-Ad/Creator; Layout Software – 1-SCS/Layout 8000.; Display Hardware – APP/Mac, PCs; Display Printers – Graphic Enterprise/Pro Setter 1000; Production Equipment – Glensen. PRESSROOM: Line 1 – G/Community.; Inserters and stuffers – 14-MM/227-2; Bundle tying machines – 2-MLN/SP 330; Addressing machine – 2-KR/211. AUDIO: Audio Software – New Horizons/Info-Connect; Audio Hardware – Info-Connect/Pottsville Republican, Gateway

PHILADELPHIA

THE PHILADELPHIA DAILY NEWS

400 N. Broad St., Philadelphia, Pa.; gen tel (215) 854-2000; adv tel (215) 854-5450; ed tel (215) 854-5907; adv fax (215) 854-4788; ed fax (215) 854-5910; web site www.philly.com/dailynews
Group: Philadelphia Media Network Inc.
Published: Mon, Tues, Wed, Thur, Fri, Sat
Weekday Frequency: m
Saturday Frequency: m
Circulation: 97,694; 68,098(sat)
Price: 3.60/wk.
Advertising: Open inch rate $44.00
News services: AP, MCT, SHNS, RN.
Politics: Independent. **Established:** 1925
Not Published: New Year; Memorial Day; Independence Day; Labor Day; Thanksgiving; Christmas.
Special Editions: Major League Baseball Opening Day Guide (Apr); Inside the Lives of Philadelphia Professional Athletes (Aug); Eagles Playbook (Dec); Rethinking Philadelphia (Feb); Mega Employment (Jan); African American Cultural Expo (Jun); NCAA Tournament (Mar); Shore Gu
Special Weekly Sections: Yo! Friday (Fri); Sportsweek (Thur); Food (Wed).
Magazines: USA WEEKEND Magazine (Weekly).
Ed., Philly.com/Vice Pres. ....Wendy Warren
Mng. Ed. ....Pat McLoone
Asst. Mng. Ed., Opns ....Michelle Bjork
Features Ed. ....Debi Licklider
Cartoonist ....Signe Wilkinson
Columnist, News ....Stuart D. Bykofsky
Columnist, News ....Ronnie Polaneczky
Columnist, News ....John Baer
Editor ....Larry Platt
Pres./CEO ....Brian Tierney
Pub. ....Mark Frisby
Sr. Vice Pres., Opns ....Sandra Long
Adv. Sr. Vice Pres., Mktg./Sales Todd Brownrout
Dir., Promo. ....Gari Brindle
Dir., Sales Devel. ....Mark Barry
Circ. Vice Pres. ....Michael Proebstle
Ed. ....Michael Days
City Ed. ....Kurt Heine
Deputy City Ed. ....Yvonne Dennis
Asst. City Ed. ....Julie Knipe-Brown
Columnist, News ....Dan Geringer
Mechanical available: Offset; Black and 3 ROP colors; insert accepted - all; page cutoffs - 22.
Mechanical Specifications: Type page 10 1/8 x 13; E - 5 cols, 1 29/32, 1/8 between; A - 5 cols, 1 29/32, 1/8 between; C - 8 cols, 1 13/64, 1/16 between.
Commodity Consumption: Avg. Page Number Per Issue - Daily 54; Avg. Page Number Per Issue - Plates Used 771981; widths 27; Newsprint Used - Metric Tons 134000; Printing Ink Used - Black 2304000; Printing Ink Used - Color 364800; Printing Ink Used - Pages Printed 47115.
Equipment EDITORIAL: Front-end Software – Hermes.; Editorial Hardware – Unisys/Hermes CLASSIFIED: Front-end Software – AT 4.7.4.; Classified Hardware – AT/IAS, 12-AT/CPU, 150-AT, 8-IBM/RS 6000; Classified Equipment – Fax Machines, 2-Konica, 2-Bs/DEX DISPLAY: Ad make-up applications – QPS/QuarkXPress 4.02, Comet; Layout Software – A; Display Hardware – 13-IBM/RS 6000, 10-APP/Mac; Display Printers – Graphic Enterprise/Express, 3-AU/108LS, 3-Au/3850, 3-Au/3810 PRODUCTION: Pagination Software – Unisys/Hermes, AT/Ia.; Production Equipment – 5-WL/Lith 10, 3-AU/3850, 1-KFM/Vision Bender; Cameras – 1-C/PagerII, 3-Eskofot, 2-Kk/RS2035, 2-Nikon/CoolScan; Scanners – 3-Au/Page Scanner, 3-ECR-Autokon PRESSROOM: Line 1 – 10-G/Colorliner double width (9 lines); Press Drives – 99; Folders – 9-Sovereign/160 Page 3:2; Pasters – 90-G/CT-50; Reels and Stands – 90-G/CT-50; Press control system – G/APCS. MAILROOM: Counter stackers – 24-HL/HT 2, 9-QWI/400; Inserters and stuffers – 1-GMA/SLS 1000 (11:1), 3-GMA/SLS 1000A (23:1), 6-GMA/SLS 1000 (9:1); Bundle tying machines – 40-Dynaric/SSB79; Mailroom control system – GMA/PCs, Mapcon, Carnegie Mellon/Machine Design T BUSINESS COMPUTERS: Business Software – Microsoft/Suite; Business Hardware – 1-IBM/390, 1-GRPIZ, 2-HP/937 Processor, 2-HP/957 Processor

THE PHILADELPHIA INQUIRER

400 N. Broad St., Philadelphia, Pa., 19130-4015; gen tel (215) 854-2000; adv tel (215) 854-5450; ed tel (215) 854-4500; adv fax (215) 854-4788; ed fax (215) 854-5099; gen e-mail info@phillynews.com; web site www.philly.com/inquirer
Published: Mon, Tues, Wed, Thur, Fri, Sat, Sun
Weekday Frequency: m
Saturday Frequency: m
Circulation: 331,134; 290,309(sat); 482,457(sun)
Last Audit: ABC September 30, 2011
Price: 4.30/wk.
Advertising: Open inch rate $365.00
News services: AP, DJ, MCT, LAT-WP, RN.
Politics: Independent.

Special Editions: PA Voters Guide (Apr); NFL Preview (Aug); High School Basketball Preview (Dec); Welcome Home Real Estate Guide (Feb); Philadelphia Home Show (Jan); Outdoors (Jul); New Jersey Voters Guide (Jun); Spring Employment Extra (Mar); Retirement Guide (May); Holid
Special Weekly Sections: Health & Science (Mon); Dining In & Out (S); Tech. Life (Thur).
Magazines: Philadelphia's Century (Monthly); Local TV (S).
Pub. .... Brian Tierney
Exec. Vice Pres., Prodn./Labor/Purchasing Mark J. Frisby
Vice Pres./Gen. Counsel .... Katherine Hatton
Vice Pres., HR .... Charles Cammack
Vice Pres., Systems/Technology Russell Nicolosi
Adv. Dir., Nat'l .... Doug Burke
Adv. Sales Devel./Mktg. Dir. (Philadelphia Newspapers Inc.) .... Randy Notter
Dir., Promo. .... Gari Brindle
Dir., Sales Devel. .... Mark Barry
Vice Pres., Circ. .... Michael Proebstle
Ed./Exec. Vice Pres. .... William K. Marimow
Ed., Philly.com/Vice Pres. .... Wendy Warren
Mng. Ed./Vice Pres. .... Anne Gordon
Mng. Ed. .... Sandra D. Long
Deputy Mng. Ed., Multimedia .... Chris Mills
Deputy Mng. Ed., News .... Carl Lavin
Deputy Mng. Ed., Nights .... Lou Ureneck
Deputy Mng. Ed., Sunday .... Tom McNamara
Deputy Mng. Ed., Visuals .... Rob King
Asst. Mng. Ed. .... Dawn Robinson
Market Information: Split run; Zoned editions.
Mechanical available: Offset; Black and 3 ROP colors; insert accepted - all; page cutoffs - 22.
Mechanical Specifications: Type page 13 x 21; E - 6 cols, 2 1/16, 1/8 between; A - 6 cols, 2 1/16, 1/8 between; C - 10 cols, 1 3/16, 1/16 between.
Commodity Consumption: Avg. Page Number Per Issue - Daily 68; Avg. Page Number Per Issue - Plates Used 950000; Avg. Page Number Per Issue - Sunday 200; widths 40 15/16; Newsprint Used - Metric Tons 123000; Printing Ink Used - Black 2400000; Printing Ink Used - Color 1185000; P
Equipment EDITORIAL: Front-end Software – AT 4.7.4, Hermes.; Editorial Hardware – AT/30, 14-AT/J-11, Unisys/Hermes; Editorial Equipment – AT, 27-APP/Mac CLASSIFIED: Front-end Software – AT 4.7.2, AT/ClassPage.; Classified Hardware – AT/IAS, 150-AT, RSK/6000; Classified Equipment – 2-Konica, 2-Bs/DEX DISPLAY: Ad make-up applications – QPS/QuarkXPress 4.02, Camex; Layout Software – AT/Ar; Display Hardware – 13-IBM/RS 6000, 10-APP/Mac; Display Printers – 2-Graphic Enterprises, 3-AU/108CS, 3-ACL/3850, 3-Au/3810 PRODUCTION: Pagination Software – Unisys/Hermes, AT/IAS.; Production Equipment – 3-AU/APS-6, 6-WL/Bender, 3-AU/3810; Cameras – 1-C/Pager II; Scanners – 3-AU/Page Scanners, 3-ECR/Autokon, Eskofot, 5-Kk/RS 2035, 5-Nikon/LS 2000 PRESSROOM: Line 1 – 10-G/Colorliner double width (9 lines); Press Drives – 99; Folders – 9-Sovereign/160 Page 3:2; Pasters – 90-G/CT-50; Reels and Stands – 90-G/CT-50; Press control system – G/APCS. MAILROOM: Counter stackers – 22-HL/HTZ, 10-QWI/400; Inserters and stuffers – 3-GMA/SLS 1000A (23:1), 7-GMA/SLS 100 (12:1); Bundle tying machines – 12-Dynaric/NPI, 28-Dynaric/NP2, 4/NP3; Mailroom control system – GMA/IPCs, Map Con, Carnegie Mellon/Machine Design BUSINESS COMPUTERS: Business Software – Microsoft/Suite; Business Hardware – 1-IBM/390, 2-HP/937, 2-HP/957 Processor

PHILADELPHIA MEDIA NETWORK

400 N. Broad St., Philadelphia, Pa., 19101; gen tel (215) 854-2000
Published: Mon, Tues, Wed, Thur, Fri, Sat, Sun
Weekday Frequency: m
Saturday Frequency: m
Circulation: 343,798; 297,094(sat); 488,286(sun)

PHOENIXVILLE

THE PHOENIX

225 Bridge St., Phoenixville, Pa., 19460-3449; gen tel (610) 933-8926; ed tel (610) 933-8926; gen fax (610) 933-1187; ed e-mail editor@phoenixvillenews.com; web site www.phoenixvillenews.com
Published: Mon, Tues, Wed, Thur, Fri, Sat
Weekday Frequency: m
Circulation: 2,566; 2,566(sat)
Last Audit: March 31, 2008
Price: 3.15/wk (carrier, motor route); 163.80/yr.
Advertising: Open inch rate $19.55
News services: AP, Robert Hitchings & Co..
Politics: Independent.
Note: The Phoenix is printed by Journal Register Offset in Exton, PA.
Special Editions: Christmas Mini Guide (Dec); Bridal (Feb); Progress Report (Jan); House & Garden (Mar); Senior Citizens (May); Holiday Gift Guide (Nov); Home & Garden (Oct); Football (Sept).
Special Weekly Sections: TV (Sat); Dining (Thur); Business (Tues); Food (Wed).
Magazines: USA WEEKEND Magazine (Sat).
Pub. .... Patricia Paul
Mng. Ed .... Sue Hlhnal
Ed. .... Leann Pettit
Market Information: TMC.
Mechanical available: Offset; Black and 3 ROP colors; insert accepted - up to 1/8 thickness.
Mechanical Specifications: Type page 11 5/8 x 21 1/2; E - 6 cols, 1 5/6, between; A - 6 cols, 1 5/6, between; C - 10 cols, 1 1/2, 1/8 between.
Commodity Consumption: Avg. Page Number Per Issue - Daily 24; Avg. Page Number Per Issue - Saturday 28; Newsprint Used - Short Tons 300; Printing Ink Used - Black 6000; Printing Ink Used - Color 800; Printing Ink Used - Pages Printed 7800.
Equipment EDITORIAL: Front-end Software – Baseview.; Editorial Hardware – Baseview, APP/iMacs; Classified Equipment – 1-Fax Telecopier. DISPLAY: Ad make-up applications – Multi-Ad/Creator Network, QPS/QuarkXPress, Adobe/Photoshop, Multi-Ad/Creator 2; Layout Software – 3-APP/Power Mac 8600-200.; Display Hardware – APP/Mac Network; Display Printers – DEC/VT-800, Xante/Accel-a-Writer 8300 PRODUCTION: Pagination Software – QPS/QuarkXPress 4.0.; Production Equipment – Intertext, V/600, Linotron/202; Cameras – 1-LE/5000H, 1-Spartan/III, C/1270, Autokon; Scanners – Nikon/Coolscan BUSINESS COMPUTERS: Business Software – MSSI, ADP; Business Hardware – PC Network

PITTSBURGH

PITTSBURGH POST-GAZETTE

34 Blvd. of the Allies, Pittsburgh, Pa., 15222; gen tel (412) 263-1100; adv tel (412) 263-1201 (class); ed tel (412) 263-1601; adv fax (412) 263-1263 (class); ed fax (412) 263-2014; web site www.post-gazette.com
Group: Newspapers First, Inc.
Published: Mon, Tues, Wed, Thur, Fri, Sat, Sun
Weekday Frequency: m
Saturday Frequency: m
Circulation: 173,160; 161,699(sat); 317,439(sun)
Last Audit: ABC September 30, 2011
Price: 3.00/wk; 156.00/yr.
Advertising: Open inch rate $499.55
News services: AP, NYT, DJ, MCT, NEA, SHNS, TMS, LAT-WP.
Politics: Independent.
Special Editions: Travel Pennsylvania (Apr); High School Football (Aug); Travel Las Vegas (Dec); Travel Skiing (Feb); Best of Seen (Jan); Diversity Job Fair (Jul); Travel W. Virginia (Jun); Top 50 Business (Mar); Explore Pittsburgh (May); Travel Mexico (Nov); Travel Florid
Special Weekly Sections: Magazine/Movies (Fri); Sports (Mon); Classified Employment (S); Home & Garden (Sat); Local News (Thur); Sports (Tues); Local News (Wed).
Magazines: Parade (S).
Chrmn. .... Allan Block
Vice Chrmn./Co-Pub./Ed. in Chief John Robinson Block
Co-Pub. .... Diana Block
Vice Pres./Treasurer .... Gary Blair
Dir., HR .... Stephen Spolar
Dir., Finance .... Robert J. Stamm
Dir., Mktg. .... Tracey DeAngelo
Circ. Mgr., Opns. .... Jeffrey Malone
Circ. Mgr., Transportation .... James M. Gorman
Exec. Ed. .... David Shribman
Mng. Ed. .... Susan L. Smith
Deputy Mng. Ed. .... Mary Leonard
Asst. Mng. Ed., Arts/Entertainment .... Allan Walton
Asst. Mng. Ed., Content .... Matt Kennedy
Asst. Mng. Ed., Special Coverage .... Mark Roth
Asst. Mng. Ed., Sports .... Jerry Micco
Arts Critic .... Mary Thomas
Bus. Ed .... Steve Massey
Books Ed. .... Robert Hoover
Staff Writer, Bus. .... Don Hammonds
Market Information: ADS; Split run; TMC; Zoned editions.
Mechanical available: Letterpress, Flexo; Black and 3 ROP colors; insert accepted; page cutoffs - 23 9/16.
Mechanical Specifications: Type page 11 1/2 x 22; E - 6 cols, 1 13/16, 1/8 between; A - 6 cols, 1 13/16, 1/8 between; C - 10 cols, 1 2/25, 2/25 between.
Commodity Consumption: Avg. Page Number Per Issue - Daily 62; Avg. Page Number Per Issue - Plates Used 278640; Avg. Page Number Per Issue - Saturday 58; Avg. Page Number Per Issue - Sunday 130; widths 50; Newsprint Used - Metric Tons 44183; Printing Ink Used - Black 1236677; P
Equipment EDITORIAL: Front-end Software – DTI/Indesign/InCopy.; Editorial Hardware – 2-Sun/Enterprise 2000, 2-Sun/V880's; Editorial Equipment – 265-PC; Editorial Printers – Toshiba, HP/LaserJet CLASSIFIED: Front-end Software – AdVision.; Classified Hardware – 2-CText/ALR, 4-CText/Proc; Classified Equipment – 62-PC Intel; Classified Printers – HP/Laser DISPLAY: Ad make-up applications – Sun/Solaris; Layout Software – MEI/ALS.; Display Hardware – Engage/DataFlow, 2-Sun/Ultra, 30-APP/Mac; Display Printers – X/Docuprint 390 PRODUCTION: Pagination Software – DTI/Edit.; Production Equipment – Na, 1-Na/Starlite, 2-NA/C220 PRESSROOM: Line 1 – 64-H/Colormatic 1975, 2-KB/Flexo 1995/2004; Line 2 – 6-H/Color Convertible 1952, 2-KP/Flexo 1995; Line 3 – 6-H/Colormatic 1952, 2-KB/Flexo 1995; Line 4 – 6-H/Colormatic 1968, 2-KP/Flexo 1995/2004; Line 5 – 6-H/Colomatic 1968, 2-KP/Flexo 1995/2004 MAILROOM: Counter stackers – 10-HL/Finishing System Olympian, 5-QUIPP; Inserters and stuffers – 27-GMA/SLS 1000, Heidelberg/Magnapak; Bundle tying machines – 10/Power Strap/PS5, 8-Dynaric/NP1500; Wrapping singles – 2-/Bu. BUSINESS COMPUTERS: Business Software – Microsoft/Office; Business Hardware – 2-DEC/VAX 7610

TRIBUNE-REVIEW

D.L. Clark Bldg., 503 Martindale St., 3rd Fl., Pittsburgh, Pa., 15212; gen tel (412) 321-6460; adv tel (412) 320-7895; ed tel (412) 321-6460; gen fax (412) 320-7860; adv fax (724) 729-7152; ed fax (412) 320-7965; web site www.pghtrib.com; www.pittsburghlive.com
Published: Mon, Tues, Wed, Thur, Fri, Sat, Sun
Weekday Frequency: m
Saturday Frequency: m
Circulation: 187,875; 169,612(sat); 202,181(sun)
Last Audit: ABC September 30, 2011
Price: 2.75/wk (carrier).
Advertising: Open inch rate $243.03
News services: AP, CNS, MCT, LAT-WP.
Politics: Independent-Republican.
Special Editions: College Football (Aug); RV Show (Dec); Enterprise (Feb); Bridal (Jan); Steeler Training Camp (Jul); Medical Directory (Mar); Summer Fun (May); Gift Guide (Nov); Quest for the Best (Oct); Pro Football (Sept).
Special Weekly Sections: Healthcare (Mon); Travel (S); Business Review Pages (Sat).
Magazines: Ticket (Fri); Relish (Monthly); USA WEEKEND Magazine (S); American Profile (Weekly).
Chrmn./Pub. .... Richard M. Scaife
Pres. .... Ralph Martin
COO .... Trish Hooper
Gen. Mgr., Westmoreland .... Arthur McMullen
Exec. Asst. to Pres. .... Martha Smith
Adv. Mgr., Major Accts. .... Nick Monico
Adv. Mgr., Nat'l .... Michele Vergenes
Vice Pres., Mktg. .... Kraig Cawley
Ed., Pittsburgh .... Frank L. Craig
Mng. Ed., Pittsburgh .... Bob Fryer
Mng. Ed., Westmoreland .... Sue McFarland
Deputy Mng. Ed., Features .... Sally Quinn
Bus. Ed. .... John Oravecz
Night City Ed. .... Joe Filip
City Ed., Westmoreland .... Frank Myers
Editorial Page Ed. .... Colin McNickle
Food Ed. .... Lynn Kuhn
Graphics Dir. .... Robert Newell
News Ed., Pittsburgh .... Sue Jones
News Ed., Westmoreland .... Gloria Ruane
Market Information: Split run; Zoned editions.
Mechanical available: Offset; Black and 3 ROP colors; insert accepted; page cutoffs - 22 3/4.
Mechanical Specifications: Type page 13 x 21 1/2; E - 6 cols, 2 1/16, 1/8 between; A - 6 cols, 2 1/16, 1/8 between; C - 10 cols, 1 1/4, 1/16 between.
Commodity Consumption: Avg. Page Number Per Issue - Daily 40; Avg. Page Number Per Issue - Plates Used 72000; Avg. Page Number Per Issue - Sunday 84; widths 41 3/4; Newsprint Used - Short Tons 10016; Printing Ink Used - Black 138000; Printing Ink Used - Color 27000; Printing I
Equipment EDITORIAL: Front-end Software – Newsengin.; Editorial Hardware – IBM; Editorial Equipment – APP/Mac Pagination CLASSIFIED: Front-end Software – PPI/Informatel.; Classified Hardware – Intel DISPLAY: Ad make-up applications – Multi-Ad/Creator; Layout Software – APP/Mac.; Display Hardware – APP/Mac; Display Printers – MON, HP PRODUCTION: Pagination Software – QPS/QuarkXPress.; Production Equipment – 3-MON/Express Master, 3-MON/Paper Express, 3-AG/Advantra 25, NewsWorks; Cameras – C, Spartan/II, Spartan/III PRESSROOM: Line 1 – 5-G/Metro (2 color) 1978; Line 2 – 1-G/Metro (Color Tower) 1994; Line 3 – 5-G/Newsliner (31 couples) 1997; Line 4 – 8-G/Universal 70 1999; Folders – G/double 2:1, G/double 3:2; Pasters – 2; Reels and Stands – 7, 6, 8. MAILROOM: Counter stackers – 2/HL, 2-/QWI, 6-/QWI; Inserters and stuffers – HI, GMA, 72-P/Double Out, 2-GMA/SLS 2000, 1-GMA/SLS 1000; Bundle tying machines – 2-/MLN, 5-/QWI; Mailroom control system – GMA/SAM; Addressing machine – KR. BUSINESS COMPUTERS: Business Software – Brainworks, PBS; Business Hardware – IBM

POTTSTOWN

THE MERCURY

24 N. Hanover St., Pottstown, Pa., 19464; gen tel (610) 323-3000; gen fax (610) 327-3308; adv fax (610) 970-4492; ed fax (610) 323-0682; gen e-mail mercury@pottsmerc.com; ed e-mail nmarch@pottsmerc.com; web site www.pottsmerc.com
Published: Mon, Tues, Wed, Thur, Fri, Sat, Sun
Weekday Frequency: m
Saturday Frequency: m
Circulation: 24,517; 23,606(sat); 26,985(sun)
Last Audit: ABC September 30, 2011
Price: 260.00/yr.
Advertising: Open inch rate $34.77
News services: AP, Robert Hitchings & Co..
Politics: Independent. **Established:** 1931
Special Editions: Lawn & Garden (Apr); Back-to-School (Aug); Last Minute Gift Guide (Dec); Washington's Birthday Auto (Feb); Education Outlook (Jan); Financial (Jul); Senior

Lifestyles (Jun); Home Improvement (Mar); Racer's Edge (May); Automotive Today (Monthly); Pre-Holid
Special Weekly Sections: Health (Mon); Schools (Thur); Generations (Tues); Food (Wed).
Magazines: USA WEEKEND Magazine (S); US Express (Sat); Market Place (Wed).
Pub. ....Thomas Abbot
Controller ....Patricia McKelvey
Adv. Dir. ....Steve Batten
Adv. Mgr., Classified.......Mary Ann Matalavage
Mgr., Penny Pincher.............Cindy Eisenhauer
Ed. ....Nancy March
City Ed.......................................Tony Phyrillas
Features Ed. ....Pat Sommers
Sports Ed.....................................Don Seeley
Online Ed.....................................Eileen Faust
Market Information: ADS; TMC; Zoned editions.
Mechanical available: Offset; Black and 3 ROP colors; insert accepted; page cutoffs - 21.
Mechanical Specifications: Type page 11 5/8 x 20 1/2; E - 6 cols, 1 5/6, 1/8 between; A - 6 cols, 1 5/6, 1/8 between; C - 10 cols, between.
Commodity Consumption: Avg. Page Number Per Issue - Daily 34; Avg. Page Number Per Issue - Plates Used 23689; Avg. Page Number Per Issue - Saturday 32; Avg. Page Number Per Issue - Sunday 64; widths 27 3/4; Newsprint Used - Short Tons 2310; Printing Ink Used - Black 67961; Pri
Equipment EDITORIAL: Front-end Software – CNI.; Editorial Hardware – 4-Compaq/ProLiant, Microsoft/Windows NT 4.0; Editorial Printers – 1-Xante/3G CLASSIFIED: Front-end Software – Intertext/REV 12G, AT/5.7.; Classified Hardware – AST/Bravo LC 5133, Dell/Gx150; Classified Equipment – MEI/CLS 2.6.6; Classified Printers – NewGen/660B DISPLAY: Ad makeup applications – QPS/QuarkXPress 4.0, Multi-Ad Creator 2 Adobe/Acrobat, 3.02; Layout Software – APP/Mac, 3-APP/Mac G3.; Display Hardware – 10-APP/Mac 8500, 3-APP/Mac G3, 1-APP/IMac, 2-APP/Mac G4; Display Printers – 2-NewGen 660B PRODUCTION: Pagination Software – MEI/ALS 2.5.1, MEI/CLS 2.6.6.; Production Equipment – Omnipage Pro 7.0, Na, 1-R/Vertical; Cameras – 1-C/Spartan III, 1-R/Vertical; Scanners – ECR/Autokon 1030, Nikon/Scanner, HP/Scanjet 6100C PRESSROOM: Line 1 – 3-MAN/double width; Line 2 – 3-MAN/double width; Pasters – Reels and Stands ÃÂ 8-MAN/CD 13; Press control system – PECOM. MAILROOM: Counter stackers – 2/HL; Inserters and stuffers – 1-HI/Injector 1372 w/ARS; Bundle tying machines – 2-Sa/Auto, 1-Sa/Man; Wrapping singles – 1-Sa/810; Addressing machine – 2-Am/1900, 1-Am/5000.; Business Hardware – AS 400

POTTSVILLE

SCHUYLKILL-NORTHUMBERLAND MEDIA GROUP

111 Mahantongo Street, Pottsville, Pa., 17901; gen tel 570-628-6059; gen e-mail ctrapani@republicanherald.com
Published: Mon, Tues, Wed, Thur, Fri, Sat, Sun
Weekday Frequency: m
Saturday Frequency: m
Circulation: 31,149
Last Audit: ABC September 30, 2011

REPUBLICAN HERALD

111 Mahantongo St., Pottsville, Pa., 17901-3008; gen tel (570) 622-3456; adv tel (570) 628-6060; ed tel (570) 622-3456; gen fax (570) 628-6092; adv fax (570) 628-6077; ed fax (570) 628-6092; gen e-mail news@republicanherald.com; adv e-mail mjoyce@republicanherald.com; ed e-mail news@republicanherald.com; web site www.republicanherald.com
Group: Times-Shamrock Communications
Published: Mon, Tues, Wed, Thur, Fri, Sat, Sun
Weekday Frequency: m
Saturday Frequency: m
Circulation: 22,555; 23,650(sat); 24,877(sun)
Last Audit: ABC September 30, 2011
Advertising: Open inch rate $45.82
News services: AP.
Politics: 1884
Not Published: Christmas.
Special Editions: Home & Garden (Apr); Back-to-College (Aug); Christmas Greetings (Dec); Annual Business Review (Feb); Health & Fitness (Jan); Summer Home Improvement (Jul); Summer (Jun); Home & Garden (Mar); Parenting (May); Holiday Gift Guide (Nov); Senior Citizens (Oct)
Magazines: Relish (Monthly); USA WEEKEND Magazine (S); American Profile (Sat); Mini-Page (Tues).
Pub. ....Henry H. Nyce
Bus. Office Mgr. ....Lori Everly
Dir., Circ. ....David Sickle
Adv. Dir.............................Michael A. Joyce
Adv. Mgr., Classified ....James Riotto
Sales Mgr. ....Charlie Trapani
Dir., Mktg./Community Serv. ....Janet Joyce
Home Delivery Mgr. ....Neal O'Brien
Ed...Pete Banko
Asst. Mng. Ed............................Ed Schreppel
Editorial Page Ed...................Florence Bautsch
Features Ed.....................................Tina Tym
News Ed...............Kathryn Campomizzi-Clews
Photo Ed. ....Johnathon Paroby
Special Sections Ed. ....Cindy D'Alio
Sports Ed....................................Leroy Boyer
Market Information: ADS; Split run; TMC; Zoned editions.
Mechanical available: Offset; Black and 3 ROP colors; insert accepted - product samples.
Mechanical Specifications: Type page 11 5/8 x 21; E - 6 cols, 1 5/6, 1/8 between; A - 6 cols, 1 5/6, 1/8 between; C - 10 cols, 1 1/16, 1/8 between.
Commodity Consumption: Avg. Page Number Per Issue - Daily 32; Avg. Page Number Per Issue - Plates Used 21912; Avg. Page Number Per Issue - Saturday 42; widths 50.
Equipment EDITORIAL: Front-end Software – HI/XP-21, HI/NewsMaker Pagination 3.5.15.1.; Editorial Hardware – Sun/Ultra 2, Dell/PII 350; Editorial Printers – AU/APS Broadsheeter, 2-AU/APS 6-84ACS 14 Imager, HP/LaserJet 5500 CLASSIFIED: Front-end Software – Unisys.; Classified Hardware – Dell/PIII 700; Classified Printers – 2-Panasonic/Dot Matrix DISPLAY: Ad make-up applications – QPS/QuarkXPress 5.0, Multi-Ad/Creator 4.06; Display Hardware – PC, APP/Mac Quadras, APP/Power Mac, APP/G3; Display Printers – AU/APS Broadsheeter, APP/Mac LaserWriters, HP/5000 6N PRODUCTION: Pagination Software – HI/NewsMaker Pagination 3.5.15.; Production Equipment – Calera/WordScan Plus, Graham/5327; Scanners – HP/Text Scanner, 1-ECR/Autokon 2045, 2-Umax/2400 PRESSROOM: Line 1 – 6-G/Urbanite 1970, 2-G/Urbanite 1997; Line 2 – 1-G/Urbanite 1980; Reels and Stands – 7; Press control system – 2; Inserters and stuffers – 3-MM/227E; Bundle tying machines – 1-MLN/ML2-EE, 1-Bu/TP-452, Sterling/MR40CH, Sterling/MR45CH; Addressing machine – Miller/Revco LS-385.

PRIMOS

DELAWARE COUNTY DAILY TIMES

500 Mildred Ave., Primos, Pa., 19018; gen tel (610) 622-8800; adv tel (610) 622-8860; ed tel (610) 622-8810; gen fax (610) 622-8829; adv fax (610) 622-8889; ed fax (610) 622-8887; adv e-mail classifieds@delcotimes.com; ed e-mail newsroom@delcotimes.com; web site www.delcotimes.com
Published: Mon, Tues, Wed, Thur, Fri, Sat, Sun
Weekday Frequency: m
Saturday Frequency: m
Circulation: 32,731; 28,288(sat); 30,555(sun)
Last Audit: ABC September 30, 2011
Price: 4.30/wk; 18.63/mo; 223.60/yr.
Advertising: Open inch rate $72.40
News services: AP, Robert Hitchings & Co., U.S. Suburban Press Inc..
Politics: Independent. **Established:** 1876
Special Editions: Easter Dine Out (Apr); Back-to-School (Aug); Great Gifting (Dec); Swimsuit Guide (Feb); Super Bowl Auto (Jan); 55 & Up (Jul); Father's Day Gift Pages (Jun); Prom Guide (Mar); Mother's Day Gift Guide (May); Where to Dine Thanksgiving (Nov); Energy & Home I
Special Weekly Sections: Best Food Day (S); Weddings & Engagements (Thur); Best Food Day (Wed).
Magazines: USA WEEKEND Magazine (S).
Pub...Frank Gothie
Controller....................................Debbie Birks
Adv. Mgr., Classified ....Leisha Shaffer
Circ. Dir. ....Joe Potts
Ed...Phil Heron
Mng. Ed. ....Linda DeMeglio
Asst. City Ed., Day.............R. Jonathan Tuleya
Asst. City Ed., Night........................Mike Crist
Asst. City Ed., Night.......................Bob Weiser
Features Ed.....................................Jim Atkins
Online Ed.....................................Vince Carey
Political/Gov't Ed. ....Jeff Miller
Science/Technology Ed. ....Solomon Leach
Sports Ed. ....Rob Parent
Wire Ed...Joe Hart
Youth Ed. ....Tom McNichol
Market Information: Split run; TMC.
Mechanical available: Offset; Black and 3 ROP colors; insert accepted - flexi, product samples (flat), cardstock; page cutoffs - 22 3/4.
Mechanical Specifications: Type page 10 1/4 x 13; E - 5 cols, 2, between; A - 6 cols, 1 9/16, 1/33 between; C - 8 cols, 1 3/16, 1/33 between.
Commodity Consumption: Avg. Page Number Per Issue - Daily 72; Avg. Page Number Per Issue - Plates Used 19800; Avg. Page Number Per Issue - Saturday 48; Avg. Page Number Per Issue - Sunday 96; widths 27 1/2; Newsprint Used - Short Tons 4900; Printing Ink Used - Black 98000; Pri
Equipment EDITORIAL: Front-end Software – ATS with Microsoft Windows, QPS/QuarkXPress, Adobe/Photoshop, ELS.; Editorial Hardware – PC; Editorial Equipment – Lf/AP Leaf Picture Desk, Polaroid/SprintScan CLASSIFIED: Front-end Software – Cx, Intertext.; Classified Hardware – PC, APP/Mac, AST/Bravo LC 5133; Classified Equipment – Minolta/3700, X/7017; Classified Printers – Okidata/2410 DISPLAY: Ad make-up applications – Multi-Ad 4.0; Layout Software – MEI/ALS & CLS.; Display Hardware – APP/Mac Quadra 840 AU, APP/Mac 8500-150; Display Printers – HP, ECR/VRL 36HS, NewGen/Imager 12 PRODUCTION: Pagination Software – MEI/ALS 1.7, MEI/CLS 1.6, MEI/ELS 1.6.; Production Equipment – Bidco/Imager, ECR/4550, Konica/Autokon, Sharp; Cameras – C/Spartan Vertical, BIDCO - Konica; Scanners – 1-ECR/Autokon PRESSROOM: Line 1 – 5-HI/1650 double width 1976; Line 2 – 1-HI/1650 double width 1992; Press Drives – SCR/DC 460-Volt, 3 phase, 300 h.p.; Folders – HI/1650; Pasters – 4-MEG; Reels and Stands – 1-Rewinder/Reel Stand. MAILROOM: Counter stackers – 2-HL/Monitor, 2-HL/HT; Inserters and stuffers – 2-GMA/SLS 1000 6:1, 1-KAN/480 6:1; Bundle tying machines – 2/Dynaric, 1-/MLN, 2-/Spirit; Wrapping singles – 1-/Na; Mailroom control system – GMA; Addressing machine – 1-/Na. BUSINESS COMPUTERS: Business Software – insi; Business Hardware – IBM/AS-400

PUNXSUTAWNEY

THE PUNXSUTAWNEY SPIRIT

510 Pine St., Punxsutawney, Pa., 15767; gen tel (814) 938-8740; adv tel (814) 938-8740; ed tel (814) 938-8740; gen fax (814) 938-3794; adv fax (814) 938-3794; ed fax (814) 938-3794; gen e-mail publisher@punxsutawneyspirit.com; ed e-mail editor@punxsutawneyspirit.com; web site www.punxsutawneyspirit.com
Published: Mon, Tues, Wed, Thur, Fri, Sat
Weekday Frequency: m
Circulation: 5,545; 5,545(sat)
Last Audit: September 22, 2003
Price: 12.00/mo; 132.00/yr.
Advertising: Open inch rate $18.00
News services: AP.
Politics: Independent.
Advertising not accepted: Pornography; adult entertainment; hate groups.
Not Published: New Year; Memorial Day; Independence Day; Labor Day; Thanksgiving; Christmas.
Special Editions: Home & Garden (Apr); Fall Sports (Aug); Senior Citizen (Feb); Spring Home Improvement (Mar); Home & Garden (May); Outdoors (Nov); Senior Citizen (Sept).
Magazines: American Profile (Tues).
Adv. Dir.............................Mary Jude Troupe
Adv. Mgr., Classified ....Candice Shirley
Circ. Mgr. ....Helen Long
Ed. ....Tom Chapin
Sports Ed........................................Dan Walk
Prodn. Supvr., Composing............Karen Petroff
Market Information: TMC; Zoned editions.
Mechanical available: Offset; Black and 3 ROP colors; page cutoffs - 22 3/4.
Mechanical Specifications: Type page 11 1/16 x 21 1/2; E - 6 cols, 1 11/16, 3/8 between; A - 6 cols, 1 11/16, 3/8 between; C - 9 cols, 1 1/8, 1/8 between.
Commodity Consumption: Avg. Page Number Per Issue - Daily 16; widths 25; Printing Ink Used - Pages Printed 6500.
Equipment EDITORIAL: Front-end Software – Baseview.; Editorial Hardware – 6-APP/Mac CLASSIFIED: Front-end Software – Baseview.; Classified Hardware – 9-APP/Mac; Layout Software – APP/Mac SE.; Production Equipment – Graham/5-1-27. PRESSROOM: Line 1 – 5-G/Community single width; Folders – 1, 1.; Bundle tying machines – Semi Ace Sk 707, Strapmatic 202A; Addressing machine – Ch.

THE PUNXSUTAWNEY SPIRIT

510 Pine St., Punxsutawney, Pa., 15767; gen tel (814) 938-8740; gen fax (814) 938-3446
Group: Hertiage
Published: Mon, Tues, Wed, Thur, Fri, Sat
Weekday Frequency: m
Saturday Frequency: m
Circulation: 5,105; 5,105(sat)
Politics: 1873
Advertising not accepted: Y
Not Published: Sunday
Own facility?: Y
Profile: Daily Newspaper and printing company
Delivery method: Mail, Newsstand, Private Carrier, Racks

READING

READING EAGLE

345 Penn St., Reading, Pa., 19601; gen tel (610) 371-5000; adv tel (610) 376-1527; ed tel (610) 371-5010; adv fax (610) 371-5193; ed fax (610) 371-5098; gen e-mail internet-services@readingeagle.com; adv e-mail advertising@readingeagle.com; ed e-mail news@readingeagle.com; web site www.readingeagle.com
Published: Mon, Tues, Wed, Thur, Fri, Sat, Sun
Weekday Frequency: m
Saturday Frequency: m
Circulation: 49,375; 51,219(sat); 70,832(sun)
Last Audit: ABC September 30, 2011
Price: 4.15/wk; 215.80/yr; 20.75/5wk.
Advertising: Open inch rate $54.45
News services: AP, LAT-WP, SHNS.
Politics: Independent. **Established:** 1904
Special Editions: Spring/Summer Dining Guide (Apr); Holiday Gift Guide (Dec); Spring/Summer Bridal Showcase (Jan); Bridal Showcase (Jul); Spring Home Improvement (Mar); Golf Pages (May); Clip-It Coupons (Monthly); Voter's Guide (Oct); Mature Living (Quarterly); Fall Home &
Special Weekly Sections: Garden Pages (Apr-Sept) (Mon); Home & Building/Real Estate (S); Church (Sat); Restaurant & Entertainment (Thur); Voices (Tues); Best Food Day (Wed).
Magazines: TV Times (local, newsprint) (S); Voices (Teen Section) (Tues).
Broadcast Affiliations: Radio WEEU.
Pres./Pub. ....William S. Flippin

CFO/Treasurer/Assoc. Pub........Michael J. Mizak
Chief Sales/Mktg. Officer..................Dave Kline
Building Supvr.....................Robert C. Drexel
Adv. Sr. Dir., Key Acct. Mgmt. Walter W. Woolwine
Adv. Dir...Keith Fritz
Adv. Mgr., Prodn.....................Terry L. Beilhart
Adv. Mgr., Sales........................Lori E. Gerhart
Manager, Internet Services Operations Eric Schaeffer
Adv. Mgr., Training/Sales Support Anne T. Chubb
Dir., Mktg./Promo....................John M. Ernesto
Newspapers in Educ................Connie Andrews
Circ. Dir...........................Richard D. Auman
Circ. Mgr., Sales........................Dave Kreibel
Circ. Mgr., Home Delivery.........Joseph Pelchar
Circ. Mgr., Single Copy.............William J. Lobb
Packaging/Distr. Dir..............Albert A. Stallone
Ed...Harry J. Deitz
Mng. Ed..................................David Mowery
Vice Pres./Sec......................James C. Flippin
Mechanical available: Flexography; Black and 3 ROP colors; insert accepted - plastic bags; page cutoffs - 22 3/4.
Mechanical Specifications: Type page 10 1/2 x 17; E - 6 cols, 2 1/16, 1/8 between; A - 6 cols, 1 1/16, 1/8 between; C - 8 cols, 1 1/4, 1/12 between.
Commodity Consumption: Avg. Page Number Per Issue - Daily 48; Avg. Page Number Per Issue - Plates Used 54792; Avg. Page Number Per Issue - Sunday 126; widths 24 7/8; Newsprint Used - Metric Tons 8211.80; Newsprint Used - Short Tons 9051; Printing Ink Used - Black 229732; Print
Equipment EDITORIAL: Front-end Software – Anygraaf/Doris Pagination System.; Editorial Hardware – PC Client Server; Editorial Equipment – 12-APP/Mac, Nikon/3510 scanners; Editorial Printers – 2-Panasonic, HP/LaserJet, APP/Mac LaserWriter CLASSIFIED: Front-end Software – Atex AdBase 3.0; Classified Hardware – Dell/Poweredge 4400-NT Cluster; Classified Printers – HP/4000 DISPLAY: Ad make-up applications – Multi-Ad/Creator; Layout Software – Doris/Planner.; Display Hardware – APP/Mac; Display Printers – HP/4000, Richo/e650, Tektronics/300I PRODUCTION: Pagination Software – QPS/QuarkXPress 4.0.; Production Equipment – Caere/OmniPage 1.0, Acfaline/30 OLP, AG/Duoscan T2000 XL; Cameras – 1-C/Marathon; Scanners – Epson/4990 Photo, AG/Duoscan T2000 XL, Epson/Expression 830XL PRESSROOM: Line 1 – 10-1996, 4-KBA/MOT; Folders – 2-G/3:2; Pasters – 11-1971, 2-1991; Reels and Stands – 11-1971, 2-1991; Press control system – 1994; Press registration system – 2 MAILROOM: Counter stackers – 3-QWI/SJ10X, 4-HI/Olympian NP502, 2-HI/Olympian NP502; Inserters and stuffers – 1-HI/NP632, 1-HI/NP632; Bundle tying machines – 2-OVL/JP80, 12-OVL/Strapmaster; Wrapping singles – 2-OVL/EX311, 2-OVL/415; Mailroom control system – Icon; Audio Hardware – Brite Voice Systems, Audio Lab BUSINESS COMPUTERS: Business Software – PBS; Business Hardware – 2-DEC/Alpha

READING EAGLE COMPANY

345 Penn St., Reading, Pa., 19603-0582; gen tel (610) 371-5000; gen fax (610) 371-5194

RIDGWAY

THE RIDGWAY RECORD

325 Main St., Ste. A, Ridgway, Pa., 15853; gen tel (814) 773-3161; ed tel (814) 773-3151; gen fax (814) 776-1086; ed e-mail ridgwayrecord@shop-right.com; web site www.ridgwayrecord.com
Group: Pennsylvania Newspapers Association
Published: Mon, Tues, Wed, Thur, Fri, Sat
Weekday Frequency: m
Saturday Frequency: m
Circulation: 2,656; 2,656(sat)
Price: 11.00/mo; 128.00/yr.
Advertising: Open inch rate $7.75
News services: AP.
Politics: Independent.
Not Published: New Year; Memorial Day; Independence Day; Labor Day; Thanksgiving; Christmas.
Own facility?: Y
Magazines: TV Section (Sat); American Profile (Weekly).
Pub........................................Darlene Coder
Bus. Mgr...............................Karen Kilhoffer
Circ.Mgr.............................Brandon Laiphner
Prodn....Mike Tucker
Editor...Joseph Bell
Adv. Dir...............................Krista Zameroski
Ed....Brent Addleman
Market Information: TMC.
Mechanical available: Offset; Black and 3 ROP colors; insert accepted - any; page cutoffs - 22 3/4.
Mechanical Specifications: Type page 11 31/50 x 21 1/2; E - 6 cols, 1 3/4, 1/8 between; A - 6 cols, 1 3/4, 1/8 between; C - 8 cols, 1 9/25, 1/8 between.
Commodity Consumption: Avg. Page Number Per Issue - Daily 14; widths 12 1/2; Newsprint Used - Short Tons 650.
Equipment EDITORIAL: Front-end Software – Baseview.; Editorial Hardware – APP/Mac; Editorial Printers – APP/Mac LaserWriter, HP/LaserPrinter CLASSIFIED: Front-end Software – Baseview.; Classified Hardware – APP/Power Mac; Classified Printers – APP/Mac LaserWriter; Display Hardware – APP/Mac. PRODUCTION: Pagination Software – Baseview.; Production Equipment – Kk/65A; Cameras – Kk PRESSROOM: Line 1 – 8-G/Community; Folders – 1-G/SE.; Bundle tying machines – 2/Sa, 2-Gd/808.
Delivery method: Mail, Newsstand, Private Carrier, Racks

SAINT MARYS

THE DAILY PRESS

245 Brussels St., Saint Marys, Pa., 15857; gen tel (814) 781-1539; adv tel (814) 781-1596; ed tel (814) 781-1539; gen fax (814) 834-7473; adv fax (814) 834-7473; ed fax (814) 834-7473; adv e-mail dailypressadv@alltel.net; web site www.smdailypress.com
Published: Mon, Tues, Wed, Thur, Fri, Sat, Sun
Weekday Frequency: e
Saturday Frequency: m
Circulation: 4,891; 4,891(sat)
Last Audit: September 29, 2001
Price: 11.00/mo; 134.00/yr.
Advertising: Open inch rate $8.60
News services: AP.
Politics: Non-Partisan.
Not Published: New Year; Memorial Day; Independence Day; Labor Day; Thanksgiving; Christmas.
Special Editions: Progress (Apr); Football (Aug); Elk Haven Greetings (Dec); Boy Scouts (Feb); Pet Parade (Jul); Spring Home Improvement (May); Holiday Gift Guide (Nov); Octoberfest (Oct); Hometown Festival (Sept).
Special Weekly Sections: Senior (Other); Weekender TV (Sat).
Magazines: American Profile (Weekly).
Pub........................................Darlene Coder
Bus. Mgr...............................James R. Bauer
Adv. Mgr., Classified......................Billie Kunes
Group Ed...............................Grace Kriegisch
Sports Ed..............................James Mulcahy
Market Information: Split run; TMC.
Mechanical available: Offset; Black and 3 ROP colors; insert accepted; page cutoffs - 21 1/2.
Mechanical Specifications: Type page 13 x 21 1/2; E - 6 cols, 1 13/16, 1/6 between; A - 6 cols, 1 13/16, 1/6 between; C - 8 cols, 1 3/8, 1/8 between.
Commodity Consumption: Avg. Page Number Per Issue - Daily 20; Avg. Page Number Per Issue - Plates Used 2204; widths 13 3/4; Newsprint Used - Short Tons 180; Printing Ink Used - Black 5200; Printing Ink Used - Color 56; Printing Ink Used - Pages Printed 5650.
Equipment EDITORIAL: Front-end Software – Baseview.; Editorial Hardware – APP/Mac; Editorial Printers – APP/Mac LaserJet, HP/Laser Jet 4MV CLASSIFIED: Front-end Software – Mk, Baseview.; Classified Hardware – APP/Mac; Classified Printers – Okidata/320 DISPLAY: Ad make-up applications – Aldus/PageMaker; Layout Software – APP/Mac.; Display Hardware – APP/Mac; Display Printers – APP/Mac LaserJet, HP/LaserJet 4MV PRODUCTION: Pagination Software – QPS/QuarkXPress.; Production Equipment – Kk/Kodamatic 65A; Cameras – Kk/Image Maker; Bundle tying machines – 1-JIA-IN/Industries Brand. BUSINESS COMPUTERS: Business Software – Tallgrass; Business Hardware – Dell

SAYRE

MORNING TIMES

201 N. Lehigh Ave., Sayre, Pa., 18840; gen tel (570) 888-9643; gen fax (570) 888-6463; gen e-mail news@morning-times.com; adv e-mail ads@morning-times.com; web site www.morning-times.com
Published: Mon, Tues, Wed, Thur, Fri, Sat
Weekday Frequency: m
Saturday Frequency: m
Circulation: 6,187; 6,187(sat)
Last Audit: October 1, 2001
Price: 168.00/yr.
Advertising: Open inch rate $11.87
News services: AP.
Politics: Independent. **Established:** 1890
Not Published: New Year; Memorial Day; Independence Day; Labor Day; Thanksgiving; Christmas.
Own facility?: Y
Special Weekly Sections: Times Extra TMC
Magazines: Parade (S); American Profile (Weekly).
Pub., Purchasing Agent................Kelly Luvison
Accounting Mgr...........................Sarah Ackley
Mng. Ed................................Warren Howeler
Sports Ed........................................Dave Post
Adv. Dir....................................Ashley Moore
Circ. Mgr......................................Fraley Matt
Market Information: TMC.
Mechanical available: Offset; Black and ROP colors; insert accepted; page cutoffs - 22 3/4.
Mechanical Specifications: Type page 11 3/4 x 21 1/2; E - 6 cols, 1 3/4, 1/6 between; A - 9 cols, 1 3/16, 1/6 between; C - 9 cols, 1 3/16, 1/6 between.
Commodity Consumption: Avg. Page Number Per Issue - Daily 20; Avg. Page Number Per Issue - Plates Used 3500; widths 25; Newsprint Used - Short Tons 335; Printing Ink Used - Black 6300; Printing Ink Used - Color 500; Printing Ink Used - Pages Printed 6140.
Equipment EDITORIAL: Front-end Software – Baseview.; Editorial Hardware – APP/Mac; Editorial Printers – Xante DISPLAY: Ad make-up applications – Aldus/PageMaker.; Display Hardware – APP/Mac; Display Printers – Xante; Production Equipment – Grahm; Cameras – B. PRESSROOM: Line 1 – 8-G/Community. MAILROOM: Counter stackers – BG/Count-O-Veyor; Bundle tying machines – Bu. BUSINESS COMPUTERS: Business Software – MSSI; Business Hardware – Dell
Delivery method: Mail, Newsstand, Private Carrier, Racks

SCRANTON

SCRANTON TIMES CO.

149 Penn Ave., Scranton, Pa., 18505; gen tel (570) 348-9150; gen fax (570) 348-9145

THE TIMES-TRIBUNE

149 Penn Ave., Scranton, Pa., 18503-2055; gen tel (570) 348-9100; adv tel (570) 348-9150; ed tel (570) 348-9100; gen fax (570) 348-9145; adv fax (570) 348-9178; ed fax (570) 348-9135; adv e-mail advertising@timesshamrock.com; ed e-mail newsroom@timesshamrock.com; web site www.thetimes-tribune.com
Published: Mon, Tues, Wed, Thur, Fri, Sat, Sun
Weekday Frequency: m
Saturday Frequency: m
Circulation: 48,216; 51,788(sat); 64,520(sun)
Last Audit: ABC September 30, 2011
Price: 3.60/wk; 117.00/yr.
News services: AP, NYT, MCT.
Politics: Independent. **Established:** 1895
Note: The Scranton Times-Tribune (mS) has a combination rate of $132.39 (m) and $133.68 (S) with the Wilkes-Barre Citizens' Voice (mS). Individual newspaper rates not made available.
Special Editions: Easter Dining Guide (Apr); Football Tab (Aug); Christmas Songbook (Dec); Home Builders Expo (Feb); Good Times (Jan); Good Times (Jul); Bridal Tab (Jun); Good Times (Mar); Good Times (May); Good Times (Nov); United Way Tab (Oct); Fall Home Improvement Tab
Special Weekly Sections: Entertainment (S); Real Estate Buy of Week (Thur); Business (Tues); Best Food Day (ROP) (Wed).
Magazines: Relish (Monthly); USA WEEKEND Magazine (Sat); Electric City (Thur); American Profile (Weekly).
Broadcast Affiliations: Radio WEJL/WBAX; WEZX/WQFM.
Pub................................Mathew E. Haggerty
Pub........................................Robert J. Lynett
Pub...................................William R. Lynett
Credit Mgr................................Carolyn Timlin
Controller/Purchasing Agent..............Alan Buntz
Dir., HR...................................William P. Nish
Adv. Mgr..................................Amy Lutheran
Adv. Mgr., Nat'l.....................Renee Puchalski
Dir., Mktg./Promo........................Cathy Labori
Circ. Dir........................................Jim Phillips
Mng. Ed....................................Larry Beaupre
Mng. Ed......................................Larry Holeva
Asst. Mng. Ed............................John Murphy
Automotive Ed................................Ted Geltner
Bus./Finance Ed....................Jessica Mathews
Cartoonist.......................................John Cole
Editorial Page Ed...............Patrick J. McKenna
Features Ed...............................Terry Bonifanti
Market Information: ADS; Split run; TMC; Zoned editions.
Mechanical available: Offset; Black and 3 ROP colors; insert accepted - cards, envelopes; page cutoffs - 21 1/2.
Mechanical Specifications: Type page 13 x 21 1/2; E - 6 cols, 2 1/16, 1/8 between; A - 6 cols, 2 1/16, 1/8 between; C - 9 cols, 1 3/8, 1/8 between.
Commodity Consumption: Avg. Page Number Per Issue - Daily 38; Avg. Page Number Per Issue - Plates Used 50900; Avg. Page Number Per Issue - Saturday 39; Avg. Page Number Per Issue - Sunday 113; widths 52; Newsprint Used - Metric Tons 6778; Printing Ink Used - Black 303655; Prin
Equipment EDITORIAL: Front-end Software – HI/NewsMaker.; Editorial Hardware – 48-PC, 2-Sun/Server; Editorial Printers – HP CLASSIFIED: Front-end Software – PPI.; Classified Hardware – PPI, 14-PC; Classified Printers – HP DISPLAY: Ad make-up applications – Multi-Ad/Creator 3.7; Layout Software – SCS/Layout 8000.; Display Hardware – 20-APP/Mac; Display Printers – NewGen/600 dpi PRODUCTION: Pagination Software – HI/NewsMaker Pagination.; Production Equipment – 1-AU/APS-108C, MON/3850, Adobe/RIPs, 1-ECR/4550; Cameras – 1-C/Spartan III; Scanners – Scitex/340, VMAX PRESSROOM: Line 1 – 1; Line 2 – 2; Line 3 – 6-G/ho double width; Folders – 1-G/3:2, 1-G/Page Jaw Folder; Pasters – 6; Press control system – 1-G/MPCS. MAILROOM: Counter stackers – 3-Id/2000, 2-QWI/350; Inserters and stuffers – 1-GMA/SLS 1000, 10/Pocket, 2-/Main Feeders; Bundle tying machines – 3-/Dynaric; Addressing machine – 3-/WM, 1-/Ch, 1-/KR; Other equipment – Mc/1800, 2-/Signature Feeder, 2-/Cover Feeder, 2; Business Hardware – IBM/AS-400

SHAMOKIN

THE NEWS-ITEM

707 N. Rock St., Shamokin, Pa., 17872; gen tel (570) 644-6397; gen fax (570) 644-0892; adv fax (570) 644-0892; ed fax (570) 648-7581; gen e-mail publisher@newsitem.com; ed e-mail andy_h@newsitem.com; web site www.newsitem.com

Group: Times-Shamrock Communications
Published: Mon, Tues, Wed, Thur, Fri, Sat, Sun
Weekday Frequency: m
Saturday Frequency: m
Circulation: 8,594; 8,762(sat); 8,638(sun)
Last Audit: ABC September 30, 2011
Advertising: Open inch rate $15.15
News services: AP.
Politics: 1893
Special Editions: Car Care (Apr); Back-to-School (Aug); Xmas Gift Guide (Dec); Progress/Economic Review (Feb); Bridal (Jan); Christmas Gift Guide (Nov); Christmas Lay-Away (Oct); Fall Football Preview (Sept).
Special Weekly Sections: Area Schools Page (Fri); Church Pages (Sat); Outdoors Sports Page (Thur); Wedding and Engagement Pages (Tues); Business World Page (Wed).
Magazines: American Profile (Weekly).
Broadcast Affiliations: WBRE; WNEP; WYOU.
Pub .... Greg Zyla
Adv. Dir. .... Mike Joyce
Dir., Circ. .... David Sickle
Exec. Ed .... Andrew Heintzelman
Sports Ed .... Charlie Rotch
Systems Mgr. .... Glenn Knarr
Prodn. Foreman, Composing .... Glenn A. Knarr
Mechanical available: Offset; Black and 3 ROP colors; insert accepted; page cutoffs - 22 3/4.
Mechanical Specifications: Type page 13 x 21 1/2; E - 6 cols, 2 1/16, 1/8 between; A - 6 cols, 2 1/16, 1/8 between; C - 10 cols, 1 3/8, 1/16 between.
Commodity Consumption: Avg. Page Number Per Issue - Daily 20; Avg. Page Number Per Issue - Plates Used 5105; Avg. Page Number Per Issue - Saturday 44; widths 13 3/4; Newsprint Used - Short Tons 501; Printing Ink Used - Black 10346; Printing Ink Used - Color 310; Printing Ink U
Equipment EDITORIAL: Front-end Software – APP/Mac System 8.6, Baseview/NewsEdit 3.32, QPS/QuarkXPress 4.04.; Editorial Hardware – APP/Mac G3, APP/iMac; Editorial Printers – Xante CLASSIFIED: Front-end Software – Baseview/Ad Manager Pro.; Classified Hardware – APP/Mac G3/233; Classified Printers – HP, Xante DISPLAY: Ad make-up applications – Multi-Ad/Creator, Aldus/FreeHand, Adobe/Photoshop 5.5, QPS/QuarkXPress 4.04; Display Hardware – APP/Mac G3; Display Printers – Xante/Accel-a-Writer 3G 1200 dpi, 2-ECR/Imagesetter PRODUCTION: Pagination Software – Baseview/News Edit 3.2.2, QPS/QuarkXPress 4.04.; Production Equipment – 2-ECR/Imagesetter, HP/4MV, Xante/Accel-A-Writer 3G; Cameras – 1-C; Scanners – Epson/Expression 836 XL, Nikon LS, Nikon Coolscan III PRESSROOM: Line 1 – Jun-72; Folders – 1; Inserters and stuffers – 3/MM; Bundle tying machines – 1-/Sa; Addressing machine – 1-RSK/Printer.; Business Hardware – IBM/AS-400

SHARON

THE HERALD

52 S. Dock St., Sharon, Pa., 16146; gen tel (724) 981-6100; gen fax (724) 981-5116; adv fax (724) 981-7844; gen e-mail edletters@sharonherald.com; adv e-mail heraldcreative@gmail.com; web site www.sharonherald.com

Published: Mon, Tues, Wed, Thur, Fri, Sat, Sun
Weekday Frequency: m
Saturday Frequency: m
Circulation: 16,855; 17,944(sat); 17,803(sun)
Last Audit: ABC September 30, 2011
Price: 2.95/wk; 150.64/yr.
Advertising: Open inch rate $37.45
News services: AP, ONS.
Politics: Independent.
Note: The Herald is printed at West Penn Facility, New Castle.
Not Published: Christmas.
Special Editions: Lawn & Garden (Apr); Football Magazine (Aug); Outlook (Feb); Summer Fun (Jun); Car Care (Mar); Golf Guide (May); Holiday Gift Guide (Nov); Women's World (Oct); National Fuel (Sept).
Magazines: Parade (S).
Pub .... John Lima
Controller .... Kelly Cummings
Adv. Mgr., Retail .... Jim Galantis
Coord., Educ. Serv. .... Mary Beth LoScalzo
Circ. Dir. .... Michael Linden
Ed .... Jim Raykie
Bus. Ed. .... Michael Roknick
Educ. Ed .... Kim Curry
Living/Lifestyle Ed .... Nancy Ash
News Ed. .... Sarah Adams
Online Ed. .... John Zavinski
Religion Ed. .... Jeff Turk
Sports Ed. .... Lynn Saternow
Travel Ed. .... Richard Young
Prodn. Mgr., Systems/Pre Press .... Barry Winger
Market Information: TMC.
Mechanical available: Offset; Black and 3 ROP colors; insert accepted; page cutoffs - 22 3/4.
Mechanical Specifications: Type page 13 x 21 1/2; E - 6 cols, 1 31/36, 1/6 between; A - 6 cols, 1 31/36, 1/6 between; C - 9 cols, 1 13/36, 1/12 between.
Commodity Consumption: Avg. Page Number Per Issue - Daily 30; Avg. Page Number Per Issue - Plates Used 36811; Avg. Page Number Per Issue - Sunday 48; widths 60; Newsprint Used - Metric Tons 1725; Printing Ink Used - Black 34512; Printing Ink Used - Color 5760; Printing Ink Use
Equipment; Editorial Hardware – AT/Pagination, 6-AT, 8-Dewar, AT/Remote Series 3.; Classified Hardware – 4-AT. DISPLAY: Ad make-up applications – Archetype/Corel Draw; Layout Software – 3-IBM/Aptiva, 6-IBM/300 PL, Managing Editor/ALS.; Display Printers – GCC/Elite Laser, HP/5500 PRODUCTION: Pagination Software – QPS/QuarkXPress.; Production Equipment – Caere/OmniPage; Cameras – 1-C/Spartan I, 1-C/Spartan III, 1-RZ; Scanners – 6-Umax PRESSROOM: Line 1 – 10-TKS/Offset; Folders – 2-TKS/3:2; Reels and Stands – TKS/30 Reels on 10 Stands. MAILROOM: Counter stackers – 2/SH; Inserters and stuffers – 1-Mc/4 Jacket; Bundle tying machines – 4-OVL/J80; Wrapping singles – 2-AR/DAC; Addressing machine – 2-/AVY.; Business Hardware – 2-IBM/Sys 38, IBM/AS-400

SOMERSET

DAILY AMERICAN

334 W. Main St., Somerset, Pa., 15501-0638; gen tel (814) 444-5900; adv tel (814) 444-5923; ed tel (814) 444-5928; gen fax (814) 445-2935; ed fax (814) 444-5966; gen e-mail news@dailyamerican.com; ed e-mail news@dailyamerican.com; web site www.dailyamerican.com

Published: Mon, Tues, Wed, Thur, Fri, Sat
Weekday Frequency: m
Saturday Frequency: m
Circulation: 12,456; 12,456(sat)
Last Audit: ABC September 30, 2011
Price: 112.00/yr.
Advertising: Open inch rate $20.95
News services: AP.
Politics: Republican. **Established:** 1929
Note: The Daily American publishes a Sunday edition in partnership with the Greensburg (PA) Tribune-Review, with original content wrapped around the Tribune-Review's Sunday edition. See the Tribune-Review for more information.
Not Published: New Year; Memorial Day; Independence Day; Labor Day; Thanksgiving; Christmas.
Special Editions: Outdoor ().
Special Weekly Sections: TV Week (Other); Best Food Day (Sat); Best Food Day (Wed).
Magazines: USA WEEKEND Magazine (Sat).
Pub. .... Andy Bruns
Office Mgr. .... Karen Thomas
Adv. Mgr. .... Tom Koppenhofer
Adv. Mgr., Classified .... Pat Foley
Circ. Mgr. .... Sam W. Foglesong
Editorial Page Ed. .... Brian Whipkey
Lifestyles Ed. .... Madolin Edwards
Sports Ed. .... Ronald Pritts
Data Processing Mgr. .... Rebecca Flyte
Market Information: ADS; Split run; TMC.
Mechanical available: Offset; Black and 3 ROP colors; insert accepted; page cutoffs - 22 3/4.
Mechanical Specifications: Type page 12 x 21 1/2; E - 6 cols, 1 3/4, 3/16 between; A - 6 cols, 1 3/4, 3/16 between; C - 9 cols, 1 3/16, 1/8 between.
Commodity Consumption: Avg. Page Number Per Issue - Daily 18; widths 25; Newsprint Used - Short Tons 715; Printing Ink Used - Black 5800; Printing Ink Used - Pages Printed 5400.
Equipment EDITORIAL: Front-end Software – Baseview.; Editorial Hardware – APP/Power Mac G3; Editorial Printers – HP/LaserJet 4V, Xante/Accel-a-Writer 3G CLASSIFIED: Front-end Software – Baseview/Ad Manager Pro.; Classified Hardware – APP/Power Mac G3; Classified Printers – HP/LaserJet 4V DISPLAY: Ad make-up applications – QPS/QuarkXPress, Multi-Ad/Creator 4.2, Adobe/Photoshop, Adobe/Illustrator, AP AdSend; Display Hardware – APP/Mac G3; Display Printers – APP/Mac LaserWriter II, HP/DeskJet 1600, HP/LaserWriter 4MV, NP/LaserWriter 8500, APP/LaserWriter Pro PRODUCTION: Pagination Software – QPS/QuarkXPress 4.0.; Production Equipment – PrePress/Panther Pro 46, 1-Nu/Flip Top FT40L; Cameras – 1-Ik/430, 1-Nu/Horizontal SST2024; Scanners – Microtek/Scanmaker IIXC, AG/Arcus 2 PRESSROOM: Line 1 – 6-G/Community 1980, 2-G/Community single width 1995; Folders – 1 MAILROOM: Counter stackers – 1-BG/105; Bundle tying machines – 2-Mosca/Rom 50-55; Addressing machine – 1-KR w/Accufast. BUSINESS COMPUTERS: Business Software – Brainworks, Visual Accountmate, Lotus, Microsoft/Office; Business Hardware – Compaq/Proliant, 13-Dell/PC

STATE COLLEGE

CENTRE DAILY TIMES

3400 E. College Ave., State College, Pa., 16801; gen tel (814) 238-5000; adv tel (814) 231-4651; ed tel (814) 238-5000; gen fax (814) 237-5966; adv fax (814) 238-1814; ed fax (814) 238-1811; adv e-mail dbrown@centredaily.com; ed e-mail cdtnewstips@centredaily.com; web site www.centredaily.com

Published: Mon, Tues, Wed, Thur, Fri, Sat, Sun
Weekday Frequency: m
Saturday Frequency: m
Circulation: 18,757; 19,583(sat); 26,379(sun)
Last Audit: ABC September 30, 2011
Price: 3.07/wk (carrier); 13.30/mo; 154.44/yr.
Advertising: Open inch rate $66.38
News services: AP, MCT.
Politics: Independent.
Special Editions: Active Life (Apr); This is Penn State (Aug); Gift Guide Two (Dec); The Wedding Album (Feb); Business Outlook (Jan); Art Festival Magazine (Jul); Newspapers in Education (Mar); Home Improvement (May); Real Estate Buyers Guide (Monthly); Gift Guide One (Nov
Special Weekly Sections: Weekender & More (Fri); Health (Mon); TV (quarterfold) (S); Worship/Values (Sat); Trends (Thur); Neighbors (Tues); Food (Wed).
Magazines: Parade (S).
Pres./Pub. .... Susan D. Leath
Finance Dir. .... Paul Mundil
Adv. Mgr., Nat'l/Major Accts .... Diane Brown
Mgr., Mktg. .... Ed Stoddard
Circ. Dir. .... Jim Wall
City Ed. .... Rich Kerstetter
Sports Ed .... Ron Bracken
Mgmt. Info Servs. Mgr. .... Harvey Wall
Prodn. Mgr., Prodn./Pre Press .... Greg Kimmich
Adv. Mgr., Retail .... Jeff Cordill
Market Information: ADS; TMC.
Mechanical available: Offset; Black and 3 ROP colors; insert accepted; page cutoffs - 22 3/4.
Mechanical Specifications: Type page 12 3/4 x 21 1/2; E - 6 cols, 2 1/16, 1/8 between; A - 6 cols, 2 1/16, 1/8 between; C - 10 cols, 1 1/4, 1/16 between.
Commodity Consumption: Avg. Page Number Per Issue - Daily 42; Avg. Page Number Per Issue - Saturday 46; Avg. Page Number Per Issue - Sunday 77; widths 27; Printing Ink Used - Black 65000; Printing Ink Used - Color 19000; Printing Ink Used - Pages Printed 18000.
Equipment EDITORIAL: Front-end Software – Baseview, QPS, Baseview/NewsEdit, Adobe/Photoshop.; Editorial Hardware – APP/Power Mac 7100-66S, APP/Mac G3; Editorial Equipment – Lf/AP Leaf Picture Desk; Editorial Printers – LaserMaster/Unity 1800 XLO, MON/1000; Classified Hardware – APP/Power Mac, APP/Mac G3. DISPLAY: Ad make-up applications – QPS 4.04, Adobe/Illustrator 8.0, Adobe/Photoshop 5.0, Adobe/Pagemaker 5.0; Display Hardware – APP/Mac G3, APP/Mac 7100-66S; Display Printers – Lazerpronters & typesetters PRODUCTION: Pagination Software – QPS/QuarkXPress.; Production Equipment – Caere/Omnipage Pro, AG/1500, MON/ImageMaster 1200; Cameras – 1-SCREEN/260D, 1-R/432 Mk II; Scanners – Kk/RFS-2035+, Sharp/JX-610, AG/Arcus+, RZ/4050 PRESSROOM: Line 1 – G/Urbanite single width 1973; Folders – 7-G/2:1. MAILROOM: Counter stackers – 1-Rima/RS 2517S N Compensating Stacker; Inserters and stuffers – 2-HI/Sheridan 1372; Bundle tying machines – M1255, Dynaric/NP2; Mailroom control system – Prism; Addressing machine – 1/Ch; Other equipment –in-line trimmer, custom BUSINESS COMPUTERS: Business Software – Microsoft/Office 97, Reflections, Netscape; Business Hardware – 1-HP/3000, 8-ATT/6300, 10-PCs, 5-HP/Vectra 386

STROUDSBURG

POCONO RECORD

511 Lenox St., Stroudsburg, Pa., 18360; gen tel (570) 421-3000; adv tel (570) 421-3000 (Display); ed tel (570) 421-3000; gen fax (570) 421-5936; adv fax (570) 424-2056 (Display); ed fax (570) 421-6284; adv e-mail advertising@poconorecord.com; ed e-mail newsroom@poconorecord.com; letters@poconorecord.com; web site www.poconorecord.com

Published: Mon, Tues, Wed, Thur, Fri, Sat, Sun
Weekday Frequency: m
Saturday Frequency: m
Circulation: 13,448; 14,267(sat); 19,462(sun)
Last Audit: ABC September 30, 2011
Price: 3.85/wk (carrier); 195.10/yr (carrier), $205.00/yr (motor route).
Advertising: Open inch rate $29.70
News services: AP.
Politics: Independent. **Established:** 1894
Special Editions: Spring Home & Garden (Apr); Medical Directory (Aug); Gift Guide (Dec); Medical Directory (Feb); Pocono Summer (Jul); Pocono Raceway (Jun); Newspapers in Education (Mar); Pocono Summer (May); Gift Guide (Nov); Fall Planting (Oct); Pocono Summer (Sept).
Special Weekly Sections: Weekend (Entertainment) (Fri).
Magazines: Pocono Property Showcase (Monthly); Pocono Summer (May, July, Aug) (Other); TV Week (S); American Profile (Weekly).
Pres. .... Joe Vanderhoof
Mgr., HR .... Sharon McGinnis
Adv. Dir. .... Peter L. Berry
Adv. Mgr., Sales .... Barbara S. Schoebel
Circ. Mgr. .... Lori Racki

Exec. Ed. ....William J. Watson
Bus. Ed. ....Susan Koomar
Editorial Page Ed...............Paula C. Heeschen
Lifestyle Ed. ....Marta Gouger
Chief Photographer.................David S. Kidwell
Prodn. Ed. ....Thomas J. DeSchriver
Sports Ed. ....Michael D. Kuhns
Mgmt. Info Servs. Mgr. ....David Kelso
Online Dir. ....Patrick Mullen
Prodn. Dir............................Vaughn M. Gravel
Prodn. Mgr., Creative Servs. Wendy S. Kraemer
Prodn. Mgr., Distr....................Bernard Kozen
Prodn. Mgr., Mailroom................Joseph Gilroy
Prodn. Foreman, Pressroom ....Bob LeBar
Market Information: TMC.
Mechanical available: Offset; Black and 4 ROP colors; insert accepted; page cutoffs - 22 3/4.
Mechanical Specifications: Type page 13 x 21 1/4; E - 6 cols, 2 1/16, 1/8 between; A - 6 cols, 2 1/16, 1/8 between; C - 8 cols, 1 7/16, 3/16 between.
Commodity Consumption: Avg. Page Number Per Issue - Daily 36; Avg. Page Number Per Issue - Plates Used 23700; Avg. Page Number Per Issue - Sunday 70; widths 30; Newsprint Used - Metric Tons 2270; Printing Ink Used - Black 30603; Printing Ink Used - Color 2500; Printing Ink Use
Equipment EDITORIAL: Front-end Software – Dewar/View 1.4, Microsoft/Word 6.0, QPS/QuarkXPress 3.31.; Editorial Hardware – PC, IBM/PC 350; Editorial Printers – HP/LaserJet 5si CLASSIFIED: Front-end Software – Dewar/Sys IV.; Classified Hardware – PC, Novell/Network, APP/Mac Quadra 800, APP/Mac II; Classified Printers – Okidata/393 Plus DISPLAY: Ad make-up applications – Dewar/Ad Dummy; Layout Software – MEI/ALS.; Display Hardware – PC PRODUCTION: Pagination Software – PC, QPS/QuarkXPress.; Production Equipment – 2-Nu/Flip Top FT40, Precision/Subtractive; Cameras – C/Spartan III; Scanners – HP/Scanner, Tecsa PRESSROOM: Line 1 – 6-G/Urbanite single width 1993; Line 2 – 8-G/Urbanite single width 1993. MAILROOM: Counter stackers – QWI; Inserters and stuffers – AM Graphics/NP 630; Bundle tying machines – Power Strap; Addressing machine – KR; Other equipment –Prism/Inkjet. BUSINESS COMPUTERS: Business Software – Lawson; Business Hardware – IBM/AS-400

SUNBURY

THE DAILY ITEM

200 Market St., Sunbury, Pa., 17801; gen tel (570) 286-5671; gen fax (570) 286-2570; adv fax (570) 988-5438; ed fax (570) 286-7695; gen e-mail news@dailyitem.com; web site www.dailyitem.com
Published: Mon, Tues, Wed, Thur, Fri, Sat, Sun
Weekday Frequency: m
Saturday Frequency: m
Circulation: 21,719; 20,538(sat); 22,973(sun)
Last Audit: ABC September 30, 2011
Price: 3.40/wk; 13.60/mo; 154.00/yr.
Advertising: Open inch rate $60.50
News services: AP, ONS, MCT, TMS.
Politics: Independent. **Established:** 1937
Special Editions: Real Estate Guide (Monthly); Today's Woman (Quarterly).
Special Weekly Sections: Business (S); TV Update (Sat); Entertainment (Thur); Health (Tues).
Magazines: Relish (Monthly); Parade (S); American Profile (Weekly).
Pub. ....Gary Grossman
Adv. Dir. ....Brad Bailey
Sr. Adv. Mgr. ....Patty Bennett
Circ. Dir.......................................Fred Scheller
Ed. ....Leonard M. Ingrassia
Mng. Ed., News......................David R. Hilliard
Mng. Ed., Features.................Joanne Arbogast
Community Ed................................Paul Boyer
Sports Ed...............................Tom Housenick
Prodn. Mgr., Distr...........................Brett Neidig
Prodn. Mgr., Pressroom............Thomas Hosey
Market Information: ADS; TMC.
Mechanical available: Offset; Black and 4 ROP colors; insert accepted; page cutoffs - 22 3/4.
Mechanical Specifications: Type page 13 1/4 x 21; E - 6 cols, 2 1/16, 1/8 between; A - 6 cols, 2 1/16, 1/8 between; C - 9 cols, 1 5/16, 1/8 between.
Commodity Consumption: Avg. Page Number Per Issue - Daily 40; Avg. Page Number Per Issue - Plates Used 16000; Avg. Page Number Per Issue - Sunday 84; widths 42; Newsprint Used - Metric Tons 2200; Printing Ink Used - Black 38000; Printing Ink Used - Color 5250; Printing Ink Use
Equipment EDITORIAL: Front-end Software – HI/Jazbox, Adobe/Photoshop, Adobe/Illustrator.; Editorial Hardware – 2-IBM/RS-6000; Editorial Equipment – Kk, Polaroid/35mm Scanner; Editorial Printers – HP/LaserJet CLASSIFIED: Front-end Software – Enterprise.; Classified Hardware – IBM/PC DISPLAY: Ad make-up applications – Microsoft/Office Suite, QPS/QuarkXPress, Adobe/Photoshop; Layout Software – Mk/Managing Editor.; Display Hardware – IBM/RS 6000 with Raid Drive; Display Printers – HP/LaserJet PRODUCTION: Pagination Software – HI/Jazbox.; Production Equipment – Caere/OmniPage Pro; Cameras – 2-Konica/Spartan; Scanners – Kk, Polaroid PRESSROOM: Line 1 – TKS/double width offset (1 half deck) 1979; Line 2 – TKS/double width (2:1 folder; 1 non-reversing 10); Folders – 2-TKS/2:1; Pasters – 3-TKS/Core Tension 1979, 5-TKS/3-arm Core Tension 1979; Reels and Stands – Press control system □ 1979. MAILROOM: Counter stackers – 2-Id, 2/PPC; Inserters and stuffers – AM/Sheridan 630; Bundle tying machines – Power Strap/PSN5; Wrapping singles – Power Strap/SP-555; Addressing machine – Machtronic, Wm; Other equipment – Mc/Stitcher-Trimmer, Q-Folder, Mac-troni AUDIO: Audio Software – New Horizons/Info-Connect; Audio Hardware – TMS, Voice News Network, PC 486; Business Hardware – IBM/AS-400

TARENTUM

VALLEY NEWS DISPATCH

210 4th Ave., Tarentum, Pa., 15084; gen tel (724) 224-4321; adv tel (724) 226-7701; ed tel (724) 226-4687; gen fax (724) 226-7787; adv fax (724) 226-7748; ed fax (724) 226-4677; ed e-mail jdomenick@tribweb.com; web site www.valleynewsdispatch.com
Group: U.S. Suburban Press, Inc.
Published: Mon, Tues, Wed, Thur, Fri, Sat, Sun
Saturday Frequency: m
Circulation: 28,135; 27,658(sat); 28,755(sun)
Last Audit: September 30, 2006
Price: 3.00/wk (carrier), $3.25/wk (motor route); 156.00/yr (carrier), $169.00/yr (motor route).
Advertising: Open inch rate $49.49
News services: AP, GNS.
Politics: Independent.
Special Editions: Progress (Feb).
Special Weekly Sections: Home (Fri); Just Kids (S); Food (Sat); Wrestling (Tues).
Magazines: USA WEEKEND Magazine (S); Go Entertainment Guide (Thur).
Adv. Dir. ....Jennifer Bertetto
Mng. Ed. ....Jeff Domenick
City Ed.....................................Matt Provenzo
Lifestyle Ed...........................Rebecca Killian
Chief Photographer.........................Eric Felack
Mgmt. Info Servs. Analyst.............Barbara Ruk
Prodn. Mgr., Mailroom......................Jim Dolny
Market Information: Split run.
Mechanical available: Offset; Black and 3 ROP colors; insert accepted - samples; page cutoffs - 22 3/4.
Mechanical Specifications: Type page 12 7/8 x 21 1/2; E - 6 cols, 2, 1/8 between; A - 6 cols, 2, 1/8 between; C - 10 cols, 1 1/4, 1/8 between.
Commodity Consumption: Avg. Page Number Per Issue - Daily 33; Avg. Page Number Per Issue - Plates Used 72552; Avg. Page Number Per Issue - Sunday 65; widths 27; Newsprint Used - Metric Tons 2479; Newsprint Used - Short Tons 2733; Printing Ink Used - Black 51528; Printing Ink U
Equipment EDITORIAL: Front-end Software – SII, QPS/QuarkXPress.; Editorial Hardware – SII; Editorial Printers – HP, Facit CLASSIFIED: Front-end Software – PPI.; Classified Hardware – PPI; Classified Printers – HP DISPLAY: Ad make-up applications – Multi-Ad, QPS/QuarkXPress; Layout Software – MEI/ALS.; Display Hardware – APP/Mac; Display Printers – HP, Epson color printer PRODUCTION: Pagination Software – QPS/QuarkXPress 3.3.; Production Equipment – G/OPI, G/RIPS, Konica/6200; Cameras – C/Spartan III; Scanners – Epson/Flatbed Scanner, Umax/Flatbed Scanner PRESSROOM: Line 1 – 6; Line 2 – 6-G/RTP; Folders – G/2:1; Reels and Stands – 6-G/RTP. MAILROOM: Counter stackers – 2-QWI/350B, QWI/1000, QWI/5J20X, BG; Inserters and stuffers – HI/1372P; Bundle tying machines – 2-MLN/M62NA, 2/Power Strap/PSN 25, 2-/Power Strap/PSN-6E; Mailroom control system – Id/On-line; Addressing machine – KR/InkJet, Barstrom/L

TITUSVILLE

THE TITUSVILLE HERALD

209 W. Spring St., Titusville, Pa., 16354-1687; gen tel (814) 827-3634; gen fax (814) 827-2512; gen e-mail news@titusvilleherald.com; adv e-mail advertising@titusvilleherald.com; web site www.titusvilleherald.com
Group: Pennsylvania Newspapers Association
Published: Mon, Tues, Wed, Thur, Fri, Sat
Weekday Frequency: m
Saturday Frequency: m
Circulation: 4,000; 4,000(sat)
Last Audit: Sworn October 4, 2005
Price: 2.44/wk; 126.88/yr; 10.30/4wk.
Advertising: Open inch rate $9.60
Insert rate: 62.50/M
News services: AP.
Politics: Independent-Republican. **Established:** 1865
Note: Printing contracted with Corry (PA) Journal.
Not Published: New Year; Memorial Day; Independence Day; Labor Day; Thanksgiving; Christmas.
Own facility?: Y
Special Editions: The Golden Years (Apr); Football (Aug); Recipe Book (Dec); Growth & Progress (Feb); Coupons (Jan); Oil Heritage Week (Jul); Graduation (Jun); Spring Preview & Bridal (Mar); Discover (May); Thanksgiving (Nov); Auto Promo (Oct); Spartansburg Fair (Sept).
Office Mgr.....................................Karol Carlin
Adv. Dir. ....Michael Sample
Graphic Coord. ....Dave Ohmer
Mng. Ed................................Stella Ruggiero
Reporter..Tom Boyle
Reporter...Mary Hill
Prodn. Mgr., Mailroom..........Paula Vandervort
Market Information: ADS; TMC.
Mechanical available: Offset; Black and 3 ROP colors; insert accepted.
Mechanical Specifications: Type page 11 5/8 x 21 1/4; E - 6 cols, 1 5/6, 1/8 between; A - 6 cols, 1 5/6, 1/8 between; C - 9 cols, 1 5/6, 1/16 between.
Commodity Consumption: Avg. Page Number Per Issue - Daily 14; widths 25; Printing Ink Used - Pages Printed 4112.
Equipment EDITORIAL: Front-end Software – Baseview/News Edit Pro, QPS/QuarkXPress 4.04.; Editorial Hardware – 5-APP/iMac, ; Editorial Printers – APP/Mac LaserWriter Pro 630, HP/4MV CLASSIFIED: Front-end Software – Baseview.; Classified Hardware – APP/iMac, APP/Mac G4; Classified Printers – HP 8150 DISPLAY: Ad make-up applications – Adobe CS 5; Display Hardware – Apple/Imac
; Display Printers – 1-APP/Mac LaserWriter Pro 630, HP/4MV PRODUCTION: Pagination Software – Indesign
; Production Equipment – Caere/OmniPage Professional; Cameras – 1-Acti/204; Business Hardware – Bs/20
Delivery method: Mail, Newsstand, Private Carrier, Racks

TOWANDA

THE DAILY REVIEW/THE SUNDAY REVIEW

116 Main St., Towanda, Pa., 18848-0503; gen tel (570) 265-2151; adv tel (570) 265-1603; ed tel (570) 265-1635; adv fax (570) 265-6130; ed fax (570) 265-1647; adv e-mail review-advertising@cqservices.com; ed e-mail reviewnews@epix.net; web site www.thedailyreview.com
Published: Mon, Tues, Wed, Thur, Fri, Sat, Sun
Weekday Frequency: m
Saturday Frequency: m
Circulation: 7,950; 7,723(sat); 9,296(sun)
Last Audit: Sworn September 30, 2008
Price: 3.90./wk; 202.80/yr; 19.50/5wk.
Advertising: Open inch rate $19.75
News services: AP.
Politics: 1879
Not Published: N/A
Special Editions: Spring Home Improvement II (Apr); Medical Directory (Aug); Winter Sports Profile (Dec); Women In Business (Feb); Bridal (Jan); Troy Fair (Jul); Graduation (Jun); Spring Tour Guide (Mar); Human Services (May); Our Schools (Monthly); Senior Style II (Nov);
Special Weekly Sections: Nascar (Fri); Senior's Column (S).
Magazines: Relish (Monthly); USA WEEKEND Magazine (Sat); American Profile (Weekly).
Vice Pres. ....James J. Haggerty
Vice Pres..............................Edward J. Lynett
Vice Pres...............................George V. Lynett
Vice Pres..............................William R. Lynett
Pub...Greg Zyla
Adv. Dir. ....Aimee O'Connor
Circ. Dir...Debbie Bump
Prodn. Mgr., Mailroom (Day) ....Rich Spencer
Prodn. Foreman, Pressroom (Day) Brian Schlosser
Kelly Andrus
Market Information: TMC.
Mechanical available: Offset; Black and ROP colors; insert accepted; page cutoffs - 22.
Mechanical Specifications: Type page 13 x 20 3/4; E - 6 cols, 1 13/16, 1/6 between; A - 6 cols, 1 13/16, 1/6 between; C - 10 cols, 1 1/16, 1/8 between.
Commodity Consumption: Avg. Page Number Per Issue - Daily 18; Avg. Page Number Per Issue - Plates Used 24000; Avg. Page Number Per Issue - Saturday 16; Avg. Page Number Per Issue - Sunday 40; widths 13 1/2; Newsprint Used - Metric Tons 1900; Printing Ink Used - Black 48600; Pr
Equipment EDITORIAL: Front-end Software – XYQUEST/XyWrite III.; Editorial Hardware – CText; Editorial Printers – HP/DeskJet 400 CLASSIFIED: Front-end Software – CText.; Classified Hardware – CText; Classified Printers – HP/LaserJet 4 DISPLAY: Ad make-up applications – QPS/QuarkXPress 3.32, Multi-Ad/Creator 4.0, Aldus/FreeH; Display Hardware – 3-APP/Power Mac 6100-66, 1-APP/Power Mac 7200-75, 1-APP/Power Mac 7200-120; Display Printers – APP/Mac LaserWriter Plus MODIA, NewGen/Turbo PS 880, HP/LaserJet 4, NewGen/DesignXpress 6 PRODUCTION: Pagination Software – QPS/Qua; Production Equipment – 2-ECR/VRL 36 Scriptsetter (PC level2 ECR/RIP), 1-Nu/Flip Top 40UP, Adobe/Photoshop 4.0, ECR/VRL 34 Scriptsetters; Cameras – 1-R/24-580; Scanners – Microtek/MS-II, 2-Polaroid/SprintScan 35, 2-Umax/Vista S-8, Umax/Vista S-12 PRESSROOM: Line 1 – DgM/430. MAILROOM: Counter stackers – 1-BG/Count-O-Veyor; Inserters and stuffers – 9-MM/227; Bundle tying machines – 4-Dynaric/Strapping Machines; Addressing machine – 1-Ch/538-525. BUSINESS COMPUTERS: Business Software – Windows 98, Microsoft/Excel, Microsoft/Word; Business Hardware – IBM
Zip Codes served:
13812,13827,14892,16901,16910,16914,16925,12626,1632,16933,16936,16945,16947,17101,17701,17724,17735,17765,18614,18

616,18623,18626,18628,18629,18630,18632,18657,18801,18810,18814,18815,18817,18818,18828,18829,18830,18831,18832,18833,18837,18839,18840,18845,18846,18848,18850,18851,18853,18854
Delivery method: Mail, Newsstand, Private Carrier, Racks

TOWANDA PRINTING CO.

116 Main St., Towanda, Pa., 18848-0503; gen tel (570) 265-1600; gen fax (570) 265-4200; gen e-mail editor@thedailyreview.com; web site www.thedailyreview.com
Published: Sun
Circulation: ; 8,889(sun)
Price: 175.00/yr.
Advertising: Open inch rate $11.29
Politics: 1884
Own facility?: Y
Delivery method: Mail, Newsstand, Private Carrier, Racks

TYRONE

THE DAILY HERALD

1067 Pennsylvania Ave., Tyrone, Pa., 16686; gen tel (814) 684-4000; adv tel (814) 684-4000; ed tel (814) 684-4000; gen fax (814) 684-4238; adv fax (814) 684-4238; ed fax (814) 684-4238; gen e-mail dherald@verizon.net
Published: Mon, Tues, Wed, Thur, Fri, Sat, Sun
Weekday Frequency: e
Saturday Frequency: m
Circulation: 1,737; 1,737(sat)
Last Audit: September 30, 2001
Price: 92.80/yr.
Advertising: Open inch rate $8.65
News services: Landon Media Group.
Politics: Independent. **Established:** 1867
Advertising not accepted: Work at home.
Not Published: New Year; Memorial Day; Independence Day; Labor Day; Thanksgiving; Christmas.
Special Editions: Home & Garden (Aug); Christmas Opening (Dec); Wedding (Feb); Business Direct (May); Home & Gardening (Sept).
Special Weekly Sections: TV Week (Fri).
Pres./Pub. ....George R. Sample
Adv. Sales Mgr. ....Linda Daniels
Circ. Mgr. ....Joyce Alley
Ed ....Christina Pryor
Market Information: ADS; TMC.
Mechanical available: Offset; Black and 3 ROP colors; insert accepted; page cutoffs - 21 1/2.
Mechanical Specifications: Type page 13 x 21 1/2; E - 6 cols, 2 1/16, 1/8 between; A - 6 cols, 2 1/16, 1/8 between; C - 9 cols, 1 3/8, 1/16 between.
Commodity Consumption: Avg. Page Number Per Issue - Daily 10; Avg. Page Number Per Issue - Plates Used 3700; Avg. Page Number Per Issue - Saturday 14; widths 27 1/2; Newsprint Used - Short Tons 190; Printing Ink Used - Black 6000; Printing Ink Used - Color 750.
Equipment EDITORIAL: Front-end Software – Mk/550.; Editorial Hardware – Mk/550 CLASSIFIED: Front-end Software – Mk/1100 Plus.; Classified Hardware – Mk/1100 Plus DISPLAY: Ad make-up applications – Mk/Mycro-Comp AdWriter.; Display Hardware – Mk, APP/Mac; Display Printers – APP/Mac LaserWriter; Production Equipment – APP/Mac LaserWriter; Scanners – APP/Mac Scanner, AG/Scanner.

UNIONTOWN

HERALD-STANDARD

8-18 E. Church St., Uniontown, Pa., 15401; gen tel (724) 439-7500; adv tel (724) 439-7520; ed tel (724) 439-7555; gen fax (724) 439-7528; adv fax (724) 439-7528; ed fax (724) 439-7559; gen e-mail hsnews@heraldstandard.com; web site www.heraldstandard.com
Published: Mon, Tues, Wed, Thur, Fri, Sun
Weekday Frequency: m
Saturday Frequency: m
Circulation: 20,556; 22,817(sat); 22,674(sun)
Last Audit: ABC September 30, 2011
Price: 3.15/wk (carrier), $3.35/wk (motor route & mail); 163.80/yr.
Advertising: Open inch rate $48.55
News services: AP, SHNS.
Politics: Independent.
Not Published: New Year; Memorial Day; Labor Day; Christmas.
Special Editions: Mature Years (Quarterly).
Special Weekly Sections: Religion (Fri); Health (Mon); Business (S).
Magazines: Enjoy (Fri); Parade (S).
Pub ....Val J. Laub
Vice Pres. ....Shirley C. Ellis
Vice Pres. ....Stanley M. Ellis
Vice Pres. ....Carolyn C. Smith
Sandra C. Hardy
Maureen M.
Adv. Servs. Supvr. ....Gloria Ryland
Eugene
Adv. Mgr., Retail ....Ann Renne
Maureen M.
Circ. Dir. ....Linda Toth
Mng. Ed., Day ....Mark O'Keefe
Mng. Ed., Night/Copy Desk Chief ....Phillip Brown
Assoc. Ed., Zone ....Pete Skirchak
James Pletcher
Editorial Page Ed. ....LouAnn Traud
Michael
Market Information: Split run; TMC; Zoned editions.
Mechanical available: Offset; Black and 3 ROP colors; insert accepted; page cutoffs - 22 3/4.
Mechanical Specifications: Type page 13 x 21 1/2; E - 6 cols, 2 1/16, 1/8 between; A - 6 cols, 2 1/16, 1/8 between; C - 9 cols, 1 5/16, 1/8 between.
Commodity Consumption: Avg. Page Number Per Issue - Daily 24; Avg. Page Number Per Issue - Plates Used 12000; Avg. Page Number Per Issue - Sunday 52; widths 27 1/2; Newsprint Used - Short Tons 1904; Printing Ink Used - Black 36720; Printing Ink Used - Color 10000; Printing Ink
Equipment EDITORIAL: Front-end Software – TMS/CMS 5.3.; Editorial Hardware – 2-DEC/PDP 11-70, 8-APP/Mac IIcx; Editorial Equipment – AP/GraphicsNet; Editorial Printers – 1-Compaq/LA-180; Classified Hardware – 1-DEC/PDP 11-70.; Layout Software – SCS/Layout 8000, Unix/SCO, SCS/Lynx.; Display Hardware – APP/Mac II; Display Printers – HP/LaserJet PRODUCTION: Pagination Software – QPS/QuarkXPress 3.2.; Production Equipment – 2-COM/8600, 2-MON/1016 HS, 1-LE; Cameras – 1-Bo, 1-K/V241; Scanners – 1-HP, 1-Sharp, 1-Microtek PRESSROOM: Line 1 – 8-HI/845; Folders – 2 MAILROOM: Counter stackers – 1-HPS/Dual Carrier; Inserters and stuffers – KAN/320 6 station; Bundle tying machines – 1-MLN/Sure Tyer.; Business Hardware – 2-DEC/PDP 11-70, SCS/Layout 8000

UNIONTOWN NEWSPAPERS

PO Box 848, Uniontown, Pa., 15401; gen tel (724) 439-7519; gen fax (724) 439-7528; gen e-mail vlaub@heraldstandard.com; web site www.heraldstandard.com
Price: 195.00/yr.
Advertising: Open inch rate $32.88

WARREN

TIMES-OBSERVER

205 Pennsylvania Ave. W., Warren, Pa., 16365; gen tel (814) 723-8200; adv tel (814) 723-1400; ed tel (814) 723-8200; gen fax (814) 723-6922; adv fax (814) 723-6922; ed fax (814) 723-6922; adv e-mail advertising@timesobserver.com; ed e-mail editorial@timesobserver.com; web site www.timesobserver.com
Published: Mon, Tues, Wed, Thur, Fri, Sat
Weekday Frequency: m
Saturday Frequency: m
Circulation: 8,577; 8,787(sat)
Last Audit: ABC September 30, 2011
Price: 10.40/mo (carrier), $10.80/mo (motor route), $12.00/mo (mail); 106.60/yr (carrier), $111.80/yr (motor route), $115.50/yr (mail).
Advertising: Open inch rate $20.99
News services: AP.
Politics: Independent.
Not Published: Christmas.
Special Editions: Coupon Books (Quarterly).
Special Weekly Sections: TV Times (Fri); Best Food Day (Sat); Spotlite (Thur).
Magazines: USA WEEKEND Magazine (Sat).
Pub. ....John Elchert
Bus. Mgr./Purchasing Agent..Brenda Musacchio
Adv. Mgr., Classified ....Jack Albaugh
Circ. Mgr. ....Bob Patchen
City Ed. ....Eric Paddock
Food Ed. ....Diana Paddock
Night Ed. ....Tom Schultz
Sports Ed. ....Jon Sitler
Market Information: TMC; Zoned editions.
Mechanical available: Offset; Black and 3 ROP colors; insert accepted; page cutoffs - 21 1/2.
Mechanical Specifications: Type page 11 37/50 x 21 1/2; E - 6 cols, 1 17/20, between; A - 6 cols, 1 17/20, between; C - 9 cols, 1 1/5, between.
Commodity Consumption: Avg. Page Number Per Issue - Daily 18; Avg. Page Number Per Issue - Plates Used 5000; Printing Ink Used - Black 5000; Printing Ink Used - Color 500; Printing Ink Used - Pages Printed 4800.
Equipment EDITORIAL: Front-end Software – DTI/PageSpeed, DTI/Speedwriter, Adobe/Photoshop 3.0, Caere/OmniPage 2.1.; Editorial Hardware – APP/Mac Quadra; Editorial Printers – APP/Mac LaserWriter, ECR/Imagesetter CLASSIFIED: Front-end Software – DTI/ClassSpeed, DTI/AdSpeed, DTI, Adobe/Photoshop 2.5.; Classified Hardware – APP/Mac Quadra; Classified Printers – ECR/Imagesetter DISPLAY: Ad make-up applications – DTI/AdSpeed, DTI, Adobe/Photoshop; Layout Software – DTI/SpeedPlanner, DTI.; Display Hardware – APP/Mac Quadra 650; Display Printers – APP/Mac LaserWriter PRODUCTION: Pagination Software – DTI/SpeedPlanner, DTI.; Production Equipment – Caere/OmniPage 2.1; Cameras – 1-B/Commodore 24, 1-R/432MK II; Scanners – 1-EC PRESSROOM: Line 1 – 5-G/Urbanite; Press Drives – Fin/100 h.p.; Folders – G/1/2. MAILROOM: Counter stackers – 1-BG/Count-O-Veyor; Bundle tying machines – 2/Sa, Gd, 1-/Nichiro Kogyo/Strapper; Wrapping singles – Olson/Bostitcher; Addressing machine – St.

WASHINGTON

OBSERVER-REPORTER

122 S. Main St., Washington, Pa., 15301-4904; gen tel (724) 222-2200; adv tel (724) 222-2200; ed tel (724) 222-2200; gen fax (724) 229-2754; adv fax (724) 222-3982; ed fax (724) 225-2077; web site www.observer-reporter.com
Published: Mon, Tues, Wed, Thur, Fri, Sat, Sun
Weekday Frequency: m
Saturday Frequency: m
Circulation: 28,927; 31,035(sat); 33,903(sun)
Last Audit: ABC September 30, 2011
Price: 2.70/wk; 142.50/yr; 36.00/3mo.
Advertising: Open inch rate $45.50
News services: AP, NYT.
Politics: Independent-Republican. **Established:** 1808
Not Published: Christmas.
Own facility?: Y
Special Editions: Health & Fitness (Apr); College & Pro Football (Aug); Monthly Planner (Dec); Economic Update (Feb); County Fair (Jul); Spring Home Improvement (Mar); Christmas Gift Guide (Nov); Fall Home Improvements (Sept).
Special Weekly Sections: Weekend Pass (Fri); Sports Plus (Mon); Seniors (S); Religion (Sat); Newspapers in Education (Tues).
Magazines: USA WEEKEND Magazine (S); American Profile (Weekly).
Pres./Pub. ....Thomas P. Northrop
CFO ....David F. Lyle
Director of News...................Lucy S. Northrop
Adv. Dir. ....Matt Miller
Retail Sales Mgr. ....Matt Talerico
Circ. Dir. ....Bridget Vilencia
Mng. Ed. ....Park Burroughs
Bus. Ed. ....Mike Bradwell
City/Metro Ed. ....Elizabeth Rogers
Entertainment/Amusements Ed. Denise Bachman
Asst. News Ed. ....Brant Newman
Sports Ed. ....Chris Dugan
Systems Mgr. ....Dan Fennell
Prodn. Mgr., Mailroom............Gerald Hickman
Prodn. Mgr./Foreman, Pressroom James Helicke
National Accounts.........................Rob Anders
Prodn. Foreman, Plate Prep ....John Johnson
Market Information: TMC; Zoned editions.
Mechanical available: MAN/Roland Offset, Mediaman; Black and 3 ROP colors; insert accepted; page cutoffs - 22.
Mechanical Specifications: Type page 13 x 21; E - 6 cols, 2, 3/16 between; A - 6 cols, 2, 3/16 between; C - 9 cols, 1 5/16, 1/8 between.
Commodity Consumption: Avg. Page Number Per Issue - Daily 32; Avg. Page Number Per Issue - Plates Used 62000; Avg. Page Number Per Issue - Sunday 56; widths 27; Newsprint Used - Short Tons 3800; Printing Ink Used - Black 120000; Printing Ink Used - Color 8600; Printing Ink Use
Equipment EDITORIAL: Front-end Software – Baseview IQ.; Editorial Hardware – APP/Mac 9500; Editorial Equipment – APP/Macs, APP/Mac PowerBooks CLASSIFIED: Front-end Software – Vision Data.; Classified Hardware – Axil/Unix Sun Clone; Classified Printers – C.Itoh/1000, Dataproducts, Dataproducts/Typhoon DISPLAY: Ad make-up applications – Multi-Ad/Creator, QPS/QuarkXPress 7.1; Layout Software – MEI/ALS.; Display Hardware – 3-APP/Mac Quadra 650, 1-APP/Mac Centris 610, 2-APP/Power Mac PC PRODUCTION: Pagination Software – QPS/QuarkXPress.; Production Equipment – 2-MON/Lasercomp, Mk/21, 1-X/P26 LaserPrinter, XIT/Schooner-Imagesetter, ECR/Pelbox 1045, 2-ECR/4550; Cameras – 1-C/Spartan III; Scanners – 1-ECR/Autokon News Graphics PRESSROOM: Line 1 – MAN/Roland Mediaman (3 half decks) 1993; Folders – 2-MAN/2:1; Pasters – MEG/2-45; Reels and Stands – 5-G/Reel. MAILROOM: Counter stackers – 2/Compass, 1-/QWI; Inserters and stuffers – 1-GMA/SLS 2000 16:2; Bundle tying machines – 2-EAM-Mosca, 3-/Dynaric; Addressing machine – 1-/KR, 5-/Wm. AUDIO: Audio Software – New Horizons/Info-Connect; Audio Hardware – Tribune News Services, AP, TI BUSINESS COMPUTERS: Business Software – Database, Word Processing, Microsoft/Word 6.0, Microsoft/Excel 5.0; Business Hardware – Axil/Unix Sun Clone, Vision Data
Delivery method: Mail, Newsstand, Private Carrier, Racks

WAYNESBORO

THE RECORD HERALD

30 Walnut St., Waynesboro, Pa., 17268; gen tel (717) 762-2151; gen fax (717) 762-3824; adv e-mail advertising@therecordherald.com; classified@therecordherald.com; ed e-mail news@therecordherald.com; web site www.therecordherald.com
Published: Mon, Tues, Wed, Thur, Fri, Sat
Weekday Frequency: e
Circulation: 8,005; 8,005(sat)
Last Audit: September 27, 2002
Price: 11.48/mo; 132.52/yr.
Advertising: Open inch rate $14.20
News services: AP.
Politics: Independent. **Established:** 1824
Not Published: New Year; Memorial Day; Independence Day; Labor Day; Thanksgiving; Christmas.
Special Editions: Home Improvement No. 1 (Apr); Back-to-School (Aug); Gift Guides (3

times) (Dec); Progress No. 1 (Feb); Bridal No. 1 (Jan); Spotlight Newcomers (Jul); Golden Years (Mar); Bridal No. 2 (May); Gift Guides (3 times) (Nov); Financial (Oct); Home Improvement No

Special Weekly Sections: Accent (TV Guide) (Sat).

Magazines: Relish (Monthly); American Profile (Weekly).

Pub. Pat Patterson
Adv. Mgr. Dennis Shockey
Adv. Mgr., Classified Shirley Gossert
Circ. Mgr. Barbara Paterno
Ed. Shawn Hardy
Educ. Ed. Nancy Mace
Sports Ed. Scott Weaver
Data Processing Mgr. Nicole Kype
Prodn. Supt. Jay Wetzel
Prodn. Foreman, Pressroom Darious Walter

Mechanical available: Offset; Black and 3 ROP colors; insert accepted; page cutoffs - 22 3/4.

Mechanical Specifications: Type page 13 x 21 1/2; E - 6 cols, 2 1/14, 1/6 between; A - 6 cols, 2 1/14, 1/6 between; C - 8 cols, 1 1/2, 1/6 between.

Commodity Consumption: Avg. Page Number Per Issue - Daily 21; Avg. Page Number Per Issue - Plates Used 15000; widths 34; Newsprint Used - Short Tons 600; Printing Ink Used - Pages Printed 6800.

Equipment EDITORIAL: Front-end Software – Mk/1100 Plus.; Editorial Hardware – Mk/1100 Plus; Editorial Equipment – Lf/AP Leaf Picture Desk; Editorial Printers – APP/Mac Laser-Writer CLASSIFIED: Front-end Software – Mk/1100 Plus.; Classified Hardware – Mk/1100 Plus; Classified Printers – APP/Mac Laser-Writer DISPLAY: Ad make-up applications – Aldus/PageMaker; Layout Software – APP/Mac.; Display Hardware – APP/Mac IIsi, APP/Mac IIci; Display Printers – APP/Mac LaserWriter IIf; Production Equipment – Nu/Flip Top FT40V3UPNS, APP/Mac Laser-Writer Pro 630; Cameras – C, VG/Graphline 760, K/Vertical 24; Scanners – HP/LaserJet Plus. PRESSROOM: Line 1 – 4-G/Urbanite 1964; Folders – 1-G/500.; Bundle tying machines – 2/OVL; Addressing machine – 1-/Ch.; Business Hardware – IBM/Sys 36

WEST CHESTER

DAILY LOCAL NEWS

250 N. Bradford Ave., West Chester, Pa., 19382; gen tel (610) 696-1775; adv tel (610) 430-1134; ed tel (610) 430-1130; gen fax (610) 430-1180; adv fax (610) 430-1190; ed fax (610) 430-1194; gen e-mail news@dailylocal.com; adv e-mail advertising@dailylocal.com; ed e-mail editor@dailylocal.com; web site www.dailylocal.com

Published: Mon, Tues, Wed, Thur, Fri, Sat, Sun
Weekday Frequency: m
Saturday Frequency: m
Circulation: 25,678; 23,184(sat); 26,319(sun)
Last Audit: ABC September 30, 2011
Price: 4.40/wk; 234.65/yr; 57.20/13wk.
Advertising: Open inch rate $52.87
News services: AP.
Politics: Independent.

Note: The Daily Local News also prints the Phoenixville (PA) Phoenix (m), a Journal Register Newspaper.

Special Editions: Fitness/Summer Fun (Apr); Back-to-School (Aug); Last Minute Gift Guide (Dec); Cutest Baby (Feb); Education Guide (Jan); Chester County Guide (Jul); Father's Day (Jun); Design-an-Ad (Mar); MADD Poster Contest (May); Employment Monthly (Monthly); Mature Lif

Special Weekly Sections: Church News (Fri); Chester County Living Tab (S); Food (Wed).

Magazines: USA WEEKEND Magazine (Sat).

Pub. Randy Notter
Controller Aimee M. Gallagher
Buss. Mgr. Arlene McGranaghan
Circ. Dir Jim Lindsey
Ed. in Chief Andy Hachadorian
City Ed. Michael Rellahan
Copy Desk Chief Patricia Matson
News Ed. William March
Photo Ed. Larry McDevitt
Special Sections Ed. Dorothy Van Gerbig
Sports Ed. Vic Monaco
Theater/Music Ed. John Chambless
Prodn. Mgr., Composing Karl Sikafus
Prodn. Mgr., Mailroom Duane Paskings

Market Information: TMC.

Mechanical available: Offset; Black and 3 ROP colors; insert accepted - single sheet; page cutoffs - 22 3/4.

Mechanical Specifications: Type page 12 x 21 1/2; E - 6 cols, 1 7/8, 1/8 between; A - 6 cols, 1 7/8, 1/8 between; C - 10 cols, 1 3/16, 3/32 between.

Commodity Consumption: Avg. Page Number Per Issue - Daily 48; Avg. Page Number Per Issue - Plates Used 35818; Avg. Page Number Per Issue - Sunday 95; widths 12; Newsprint Used - Short Tons 3743; Printing Ink Used - Black 89832; Printing Ink Used - Color 15346; Printing Ink Use

Equipment EDITORIAL: Front-end Software – CNI/Open, Lf/AP Leaf Picture Desk.; Editorial Hardware – CNI/Open, APP/Mac Network; Editorial Equipment – Kodak/Scanner; Editorial Printers – Bidco/Imagesetter CLASSIFIED: Front-end Software – PPI.; Classified Hardware – PPI; Classified Printers – Bidco DISPLAY: Ad make-up applications – QPS/QuarkXPress 3.3, APP/Mac Appleshare 4.0; Layout Software – APP/Mac Netw; Display Hardware – APP/Power Mac 8100; Display Printers – Bidco/486 PC-RTI RIP, Ultre/486 PC-Spreadsheet RIP PRODUCTION: Pagination Software – QPS/QuarkXPress 3.3, Adobe/Photoshop 4.0.; Production Equipment – Caere/OmniPage Pro 2.0, 1-Nu/Flip Top FT40APNS; Cameras – C/Spartan II; Scanners – Digi-Colour/Sys 3000, Lf/Leafscan 35, Kk/2035, Microtek/8003, Umax/Vista PRESSROOM: Line 1 – 10-G/Urbanite; Press Drives – 2-Fin/125H Drives; Folders – G/Urbanite 700; Pasters – 7-Enkel/Autoweb 1991. MAILROOM: Counter stackers – 2-HL/Monitor; Inserters and stuffers – 1-GMA/SLS 1000 10:1; Bundle tying machines – 2/Power Strap/PSN-6; Addressing machine – Ch. BUSINESS COMPUTERS: Business Software – INSI; Business Hardware – 2-IBM/Sys 400

WILKES-BARRE

THE CITIZENS' VOICE

75 N. Washington St., Wilkes-Barre, Pa., 18711-0502; gen tel (570) 821-2000; adv tel (570) 821-2030; ed tel (570) 821-2056; gen fax (570) 821-2249; adv fax (570) 825-2882; ed fax (570) 821-2247; gen e-mail yourvoice@citizensvoice.com; adv e-mail addept@citizensvoice.com; ed e-mail citydesk@citizensvoice.com; web site www.citizensvoice.com

Published: Mon, Tues, Wed, Thur, Fri, Sat, Sun
Weekday Frequency: m
Saturday Frequency: m
Circulation: 43,305; 30,822(sat); 44,270(sun)
Last Audit: ABC September 30, 2011
Price: 2.85/wk; 11.40/mo; 134.00/yr (carrier).
News services: AP, Papert (Landon).
Politics: Independent.

Note: The Wilkes-Barre Citizens' Voice (mS) has a combination rate of $132.39 (m) and $133.68 (S) with the Scranton Times-Tribune (mS). Individual newspaper rates not made available.

Special Editions: Home & Improvement (Apr); Pigskin Preview (Aug); Christmas Shopping Guide (Dec); Bridal (Feb); Super Bowl Preview (Jan); Estate Planning (Jul); Graduation (Jun); Today's Woman (Mar); Who's Who in Wyoming Valley (May); Thanksgiving Holiday Shopping Guide (

Special Weekly Sections: Weekend (Fri); Regional (S); Best Food Day (Sat).

Magazines: Relish (Monthly); USA WEEKEND Magazine (S); American Profile (Weekly).

Broadcast Affiliations: Shamrock Communications.

Pub. W. Scott Lynett
Pub. Danial Haggerty
Bus. Office Mgr. Irene Williams
Adv. Dir. Mark Altavilla
Coord. Judi Shaver
Asst. Circ. Dir. Joe Neaoon
Mng. Ed. Larry Holeva
Asst. Mng. Ed. Claire Schechter
Bus. Ed. Tim Gulla
Editorial Page Ed. Jim Gittens
Web Ed. Shanon Rushton
News Ed. Leonarda Bilbow
Sports Ed. Neil Corbett
Wire Ed. Michael McGlynn
Photo Ed. Mark Moran
Mgmt. Info Servs. Mgr. Dennis Briggs
Prodn. Mgr., Mailroom John McGurk

Mechanical available: Offset; Black and 3 ROP colors; insert accepted; page cutoffs - 22 3/4.

Mechanical Specifications: Type page 10 1/2 x 13; E - 5 cols, 2, 1/8 between; A - 5 cols, 2, 1/8 between; C - 10 cols, 1 1/16, 1/8 between.

Commodity Consumption: Avg. Page Number Per Issue - Daily 68; Avg. Page Number Per Issue - Plates Used 13000; Avg. Page Number Per Issue - Saturday 72; Avg. Page Number Per Issue - Sunday 120; widths 27 1/2; Newsprint Used - Short Tons 3200; Printing Ink Used - Black 49000; Pr

Equipment EDITORIAL: Front-end Software – Microsoft/Windows NT Server 4.0, Microsoft/SQL Server 6.5, Micros; Editorial Hardware – 2-HP/Netserver LD, 20-HP/Vectra VLS Pentium 233 mhz; Editorial Equipment – 1-Everex/Notebook, 2-APP/Power Mac 8100, 3-APP/Mac Power Book 190, APP/Power Book G3; Editorial Printers – 1-HP CLASSIFIED: Front-end Software – Unisys.; Classified Hardware – 1-Sun/Ultra 10, 4-GB/Tape Drives (Backup); Classified Printers – 1-HP/5M DISPLAY: Ad make-up applications – Multi-Ad/Creator 2 1.5, Adobe/Acrobat 4.0, Adobe/Illustrator 8.0, Caere/OmniPage 3.0, Microsoft/Word 9.8, Adobe/Photoshop 6.0, Adobe/; Display Hardware – 1-APP/Mac 9600, 1-APP/Mac 9500, 1-APP/iMac, 2-APP/Mac 8500, APP/Mac 8100, 5-APP/Mac G3, APP/Mac G4 PRODUCTION: Pagination Software – QPS/QuarkXPress 4.04, Adobe/In Design.; Production Equipment – Caere/OmniPage 3.0, Douthitt/Gemini; Scanners – 1-Epson/836L, 3-HP/ScanJet 6100C, 1-HP/ScanJet 4c, 2-HP/ScanJet G300 PRESSROOM: Line 1 – 8-G/Urbanite; Folders – G/1000. MAILROOM: Counter stackers – 3-QWI/300, 1/HL; Inserters and stuffers – 1-Biliner/8:1; Bundle tying machines – 4-MLN/Spirits, 2-/Sterling; Other equipment – 2-/Hall Bottom Wrap. BUSINESS COMPUTERS: Business Software – Vision Data, Accts receivable 6.2, Accts payable 5.0, Gen ledger 5.0, Circ 3.9; Business Hardware – 1-IBM/RISC 6000

TIMES LEADER

15 N. Main St., Wilkes-Barre, Pa., 18711; gen tel (570) 829-7100; adv tel (570) 829-7101; ed tel (570) 829-7242; gen fax (570) 829-2002; adv fax (570) 829-2002; ed fax (570) 829-5537; web site www.timesleader.com

Published: Mon, Tues, Wed, Thur, Fri, Sat, Sun
Weekday Frequency: m
Saturday Frequency: m
Circulation: 40,334; 32,404(sat); 70,696(sun)
Last Audit: ABC September 30, 2011
Price: 3.50/wk; 14.00/mo; 182.00/yr.
Advertising: Open inch rate $92.00
News services: AP, MCT, DF, DJ, NYT.
Politics: Independent.

Special Editions: Profile (Apr); Football (Aug); Gift Guide (Dec); Bride & Groom (Feb); How to Guide (Jul); Best of Times (Jun); Spring Home Improvement (Mar); Best & Brightest (May); Focus on Women (Nov); Fall Home Improvement (Oct).

Special Weekly Sections: The Guide (Fri); Consumer (Mon); Travel (S); Health (Tues); Food (Wed).

Magazines: Parade (S).

Broadcast Affiliations: WNEP (ABC); WYOU (CBS); WBRE (NBC).

Ed./Pub. Richard L. Connor
Sr. Vice Pres., Opns. Prashant B. Shitut
Vice Pres./CFO Allison Uhrin
Adv./Mktg. Vice Pres. Kim Dudick
Adv. Mgr., Retail Kathy Pelleschi
Circ. Vice Pres. Dick Dehavan
Exec. Ed/Vice Pres. Joe Butkiewicz
Ed. Rich Connor
Features Ed. Sandra Snyder
Night Ed. Joe Healey
News Ed. Anne Woelfel
Mgmt. Info Servs. Mgr. Brian Dudiek
Prodn. Mgr., Pre Press Shelly Mccann

Market Information: TMC; Zoned editions.

Mechanical available: Offset; Black and 3 ROP colors; insert accepted - min 7 3/4 x 5 1/2; page cutoffs - 22.

Mechanical Specifications: Type page 12 1/2 x 21; E - 6 cols, 2 1/16, 1/8 between; A - 6 cols, 2 1/16, 1/8 between; C - 10 cols, 1 3/8, 1/16 between.

Commodity Consumption: Avg. Page Number Per Issue - Daily 40; Avg. Page Number Per Issue - Plates Used 40980; Avg. Page Number Per Issue - Sunday 100; widths 50; Newsprint Used - Short Tons 6930; Printing Ink Used - Black 230400; Printing Ink Used - Color 38250; Printing Ink U

Equipment EDITORIAL: Front-end Software – CCI 6.7.0.2AQ, Solaris/9.; Editorial Hardware – 22-PC 486-66MHz fileserver, 2-PC 286, 5-PC 386, 30-Pentium/PC 133MHZ; Editorial Printers – 2-Pre Press/Panther 46, 1-HP/III, 1-Panasonic, ECR/Pelbox 1045CS, 2-Dataproducts/Typhoon CLASSIFIED: Front-end Software – PPI/Microsoft Windows NT, SQL 3.11.; Classified Hardware – 2-Pentium/Dual Processing Servers/266; Classified Printers – 1-HP/III, 1-C.Itoh, 2-Dataproducts/Typhoon DISPLAY: Ad make-up applications – Multi-Ad/Creator, QPS/QuarkXPress, Adobe/Illustrator, Adobe/Photoshop, Aldus/FreeHand, 2-Dataproducts; Display Hardware – 1-APP/Mac NZM 486 DX66 with Novell fileserver; Display Printers – ECR/1045 CS, 2-Pre-Press/Panther Pro Imagesetter, 2-Dataproducts/Typhoon PRODUCTION: Pagination Software – CCI/Editorial Sys. 6.7.0.2AQ, MEI/CLS, QPS/QuarkXPress 4.1, MEI/ALS 4.1.7.; Production Equipment – Caere/OmniPage, Na/NP40; Scanners – 2-AG/1200 dpi, 6-HP/ScanJet PRESSROOM: Line 1 – MAN/Roland double width (20 couples, offset; 3 tower, 1996; Folders – MAN/Roland; Pasters – MEG; Reels and Stands – MEG; Press control system – MAN/Rolland. MAILROOM: Counter stackers – 2-QWI/300, 3-QWI/350; Inserters and stuffers – 2-GMA/SLS 1000; Bundle tying machines – 2/Dynaric; Wrapping singles – 2-/QWI; Addressing machine – 1-/Wm, 1-/Ch, 1-Mc/2000 PB Folder. BUSINESS COMPUTERS: Business Software – Microsoft/Office 5.0, Boreland/Parabox 4.0; Business Hardware – HP/3000-928, HP/3000-918, HP/MPE-IY

WILLIAMSPORT

WILLIAMSPORT SUN-GAZETTE

252 West Fourth Street., Williamsport, Pa., 17701; gen tel (570) 326-1551; gen fax (570) 322-2532; adv fax (570) 323-0948; ed fax (570) 326-0314; gen e-mail info@sungazette.com; adv e-mail advertising@sungazette.com; ed e-mail news@sungazette.com; web site www.sungazette.com

Group: Odgen Newspapers
Published: Mon, Tues, Wed, Thur, Fri, Sat, Sun
Weekday Frequency: m
Saturday Frequency: m
Circulation: 22,839; 24,541(sat); 29,850(sun)
Last Audit: ABC September 30, 2011

Price: $3.11/weekly carrier or $143.21 yearly.
News services: AP.
Politics: Independent. **Established:** 1801
Note: Advertising is sold in combination with The Lock Haven Express (e) for $76.12 (d) and $82.11 (S). Individual newspaper rates not made available.
Own facility?: Y
Special Editions: Insurance (Apr); Back-to-School (Aug); Year in Review (Dec); Winter Bridal (Feb); Winter Furniture (Jan); Summer Furniture (Jul); Graduation (Jun); Women in Business (Mar); Outdoor Lifestyle (May); Christmas Opener (Nov); Fall Car Care (Oct); Fall Home Im
Special Weekly Sections: TV Magazine (S); Religion (Sat); Entertainment (Thur); Best Food Day (Wed).
Magazines: TV Week (S).
Publisher....Bernard Oravec
Adv. Dir.....John Leeser
Exec. News Ed.....David Troisi
City Ed.....L. Lee Janssen
Environmental Ed.....Mike Reuther
Lifestyle Ed.....Dena Borick
News Ed.....Laura Janssen
Regl. Ed.....James Carpenter
Sports Ed.....Ben Brigandi
Prodn. Supt., Composing....Charles Smith
Prodn. Supt., Pressroom....Richard Smith
Market Information: TMC.
Mechanical available: Offset; Black and 3 ROP colors; insert accepted - sample packs; page cutoffs - 22 3/4.
Mechanical Specifications: Type page 13 x 21 1/4; E - 6 cols, 2 1/16, 1/8 between; A - 6 cols, 2 1/16, 1/8 between; C - 8 cols, 1 9/16, 1/8 between.
Commodity Consumption: Avg. Page Number Per Issue - Daily 35; Avg. Page Number Per Issue - Plates Used 32110; Avg. Page Number Per Issue - Sunday 74; widths 54; Newsprint Used - Short Tons 3500; Printing Ink Used - Black 8050; Printing Ink Used - Color 2250; Printing Ink Used
Equipment; Editorial Hardware – Microsoft/Windows NT.; Classified Hardware – Microsoft/Winmdows NT.; Production Equipment – Nu/Flip Top FT40UP; Cameras – C/Spartan III; Scanners – Equipment Ã□Â□ QPS/QuarkXPress. PRESSROOM: Line 1 – 6-G/Metro 3007; Folders – 2 MAILROOM: Counter stackers – HL/Monitor; Inserters and stuffers – HI/72P; Bundle tying machines – .; Business Hardware – Motorola
Delivery method: Mail, Newsstand, Private Carrier, Racks

YORK

WEEKLY RECORD

1891 Loucks Rd., York, Pa., 17408; gen tel (717) 771-2000; gen fax (717) 771-2009; gen e-mail weekly@ydr.com; web site www.inyork.com/community
Group: Media News Group
Published: Tues, Wed, Thur, Fri
Weekday Frequency: All day
Circulation: 11,622
Last Audit: Sworn N/A
Advertising: Open inch rate $15.00
Own facility?: Y
Pub.....Fred Uffelman
Exec. Asst. to Pub.....Donna Mandl
Mng. Ed.....Randy Parker
Photo Ed.....Brad Jennings
Sports Ed.....Chris Otto
Editor....Jim McClure
Weekly Record Editor....Joan Concilio
Mechanical Specifications: Type page 9 2/3 x 12; A - 5 cols, 1 5/6, between.
Delivery method: Mail, Newsstand, Racks

YORK DAILY RECORD/YORK SUNDAY NEWS

1891 Loucks Rd., York, Pa., 17408-9708; gen tel (717) 771-2000; adv tel (717) 767-3554; ed tel (717) 771-2000; gen fax (717) 771-2009; adv fax (717) 764-6130; ed fax (717) 771-2009; gen e-mail news@ydr.com; ed e-mail news@ydr.com; web site www.ydr.com
Group: Media News Group
Metro Suburbia, Inc./Newhouse Newspapers
Published: Mon, Tues, Wed, Thur, Fri, Sat, Sun
Weekday Frequency: m
Saturday Frequency: m
Circulation: 55,128; 62,776(sat); 87,221(sun)
Last Audit: ABC September 30, 2011
Price: $4.22/wk; $18.28/mo.; $219.40/yr.
Advertising: Open inch rate $87.52
News services: AP, McClatchy.
Politics: Independent. **Established:** 1796
Note: For detailed advertising, circulation, printing and production information, see York Newspaper Company listing. Advertising in the York Daily Record automatically includes advertising in the York Dispatch (e).
Advertising not accepted: N
Own facility?: Y
Special Weekly Sections: Home Source (S); Flip-side (Thur).
Magazines: USA WEEKEND Magazine (S).
Publisher....Fred Uffelman
Exec. Asst. to Pub.....Donna Mandl
Ed.....James McClure
Mng. Ed.....Randy Parker
Asst. Mng. Ed., Features/Niche Buffy Andrews-Gross
Asst. Mng. Ed., Metro....Susan Martin
Asst. Mng. Ed., Sports....Chris Otto
Bus. Ed.....Cathy Hirko
Editorial Ed.....Scott Fisher
Visual Ed.....Brad Jennings
Weekly/Web Ed.....Joan Concilio
News Editor....Tom Barstow
News Ed.....Janeen Jones
Market Information: TMC; Zoned editions.
Mechanical Specifications: SAU
Equipment EDITORIAL: Front-end Software – HI.; Editorial Hardware – Dell/Sun; Editorial Equipment – HI/Pagination; Editorial Printers – HP/4000 CLASSIFIED: Front-end Software – AdBase
ATEX; Classified Hardware – Dell; Classified Printers – HP DISPLAY: Ad make-up applications – C2; Display Hardware – MAC; Display Printers – Misc.; Production Equipment – MAC; Scanners – Misc. PRESSROOM: Line 1 – 8 units
Goss Metro; Press Drives – Finiur; Folders – 2-2:1; Pasters – Goss; Press control system – Finiur MAILROOM: Counter stackers – 3-Idab; Inserters and stuffers – 1 Magnapack
2 - 14/72; Bundle tying machines – 3 Dynaric BUSINESS COMPUTERS: Business Software – Windows; Business Hardware – Dell
Delivery method: Mail, Newsstand, Private Carrier, Racks

THE YORK DISPATCH

205 N. George St., York, Pa., 17401; gen tel (717) 854-1575; adv tel (717) 767-6397; gen fax (717) 843-2958; adv fax (717) 764-6130; ed fax (717) 843-2814; ed e-mail news@yorkdispatch.com; web site www.yorkdispatch.com
Published: Mon, Tues, Wed, Thur, Fri
Weekday Frequency: e
Circulation: 21,761
Last Audit: September 30, 2009
Price: 10.00/mo (carrier); 156.00/yr.
Advertising: Open inch rate $83.35
News services: NYT, LAT-WP, AP, MNS, NEA, SHNS.
Politics: Independent.
Note: For detailed advertising, circulation, printing and production information, see York Newspaper Company listing. Advertising in the York Dispatch automatically includes advertising in the York Daily Record (m).
Broadcast Affiliations: ABC 27.
Owner....Phil Buckner
Pub.....David Martenz
Bus. Mgr.....Teresa Hoover
Ed.....Lori Goodlin
Mng. Ed.....Mark Franklin
Asst. Mng. Ed., Visuals....Randy Flaum
City Ed.....Gayle Eubank
Editorial Page Ed.....Patrick Delany
Entertainment/Weekend Ed.....Mel Barber
Food Ed.....Donna Hudelson
News/Design Ed.....John Sincoe
Sports Ed.....Steve Heiser
Style Ed.....Melissa Barber
Data Processing Mgr.....Charles Burkhardt
Mgmt. Info Servs./Online Mgr.....Scott Miller
Market Information: Split run; TMC; Zoned editions.
Mechanical available: Offset; Black and 3 ROP colors; insert accepted - all; page cutoffs - 22 3/4.
Equipment EDITORIAL: Front-end Software – AT, HI.; Editorial Hardware – AT, Dell; Editorial Equipment – HI/Pagination; Editorial Printers – Textronix/600 CLASSIFIED: Front-end Software – HI, HI/Pagination.; Classified Hardware – HI; Classified Printers – C.Itoh/CI 400 DISPLAY: Ad make-up applications – QPS/QuarkXPress 3.3, Adobe/Photoshop; Display Hardware – 1-APP/Power Mac 7100, DEC/Alpha NT Server, 1-APP/Mac 650 Quadra, 2-APP/Power Mac 8600, 3-APP/Power Mac G3; Display Printers – 2-HP/LaserJet 4MV, HP/LaserJet 4MV; Production Equipment – 2-MON/3850, 2-C/R660; Cameras – 1-C/Spartan III; Scanners – ECR/1000, ECR/2045. PRESSROOM: Line 1 – 8-G/Metro 1991, 2-G/Metro CIC 1991; Pasters – 8-G/RTP. MAILROOM: Counter stackers – 4-HL/Monitor HT II; Inserters and stuffers – 2-HI/1472; Bundle tying machines – 4/MLN. BUSINESS COMPUTERS: Business Software – CJ, DB, Vesoft; Business Hardware – 11-HP/928 RL

RHODE ISLAND

NEWPORT

THE EDWARD A. SHERMAN PUBLISHING CO.

101 Malbone Rd., Newport, R.I., 02840; gen tel (401) 849-3300; gen fax (401) 849-3306; gen e-mail circDept@newportRI.com; web site www.newportdailynews.com
Published: Mon, Tues, Wed, Thur, Fri, Sat, Sun
Price: 132.00/yr.
Advertising: Open inch rate $19.20
Politics: 1846

THE NEWPORT DAILY NEWS

101 Malbone Rd., Newport, R.I., 02840; gen tel (401) 849-3300; gen fax (401) 849-3335; ed fax (401) 849-3306; ed e-mail editor@newportri.com; web site www.newportdailynews.com
Published: Mon, Tues, Wed, Thur, Fri, Sat
Weekday Frequency: e
Saturday Frequency: m
Circulation: 11,040; 11,040(sat)
Last Audit: September 30, 2008
Price: 12.00/wk; 165.00/yr; 22.00/4wks.
Advertising: Open inch rate $22.00
News services: AP, McClatchy.
Politics: Independent. **Established:** 1846
Not Published: New Year; Memorial Day; Independence Day; Labor Day; Thanksgiving; Christmas.
Own facility?: Y
Special Editions: Spring Home & Garden (Apr); Back-to-School (Aug); Last Minute Gift Guide (Dec); Winter Festival (Feb); Health Fitness Sports (Jan); Flower Show (Jun); 50+ (Mar); Summer Activity Guide (May); Christmas Gift Guide (Nov); Fall Home & Garden (Oct); Fall Sport
Special Weekly Sections: Channels (Fri).
Magazines: USA WEEKEND Magazine (Sat).
Pres.....Albert K. Sherman
Pub.....William F. Lucey
Sec.....Bruce H. Sherman
Adv. Mgr.....Annemarie Brisson
Adv. Sales Mgr.....Robert L. Rufener
Circ. Mgr.....Robert M. Bidlack
Exec. Ed.....Sheila L. Mullowney
City Ed.....M. Catherine Callahan
News Ed.....Harvey B. Peters
Sports Ed.....Scott P. Barrett
Prodn. Mgr.....Kevin F. Schoen
Prodn. Mgr., Mail....Michael J. Morgan
Prodn. Mgr., Pre Press....Douglas W. Swass
Prodn. Foreman, Pressroom....John F. Dunn
Market Information: ADS; Split run; TMC; Zoned editions.
Mechanical available: Offset; Black and 3 ROP colors; insert accepted; page cutoffs - 22 3/4.
Mechanical Specifications: Type page 12 1/2 x 21 1/2; E - 6 cols, 2 1/16, 1/8 between; A - 6 cols, 2 1/16, 1/8 between; C - 8 cols, 1 9/16, 1/16 between.
Commodity Consumption: Avg. Page Number Per Issue - Daily 28; Avg. Page Number Per Issue - Plates Used 10000; Avg. Page Number Per Issue - Saturday 36; widths 27 1/2; Newsprint Used - Metric Tons 900; Newsprint Used - Short Tons 1000; Printing Ink Used - Black 22000; Printing
Equipment EDITORIAL: Front-end Software – ACI/Open Pages. CLASSIFIED: Front-end Software – Vision Data. DISPLAY: Ad make-up applications – Vision Data; Layout Software – Layout/8000 PRODUCTION: Pagination Software – QPS/QuarkXPress 4.0.; Production Equipment – 2-ECR/URL 36, Adobe/Photoshop 3.2 PRESSROOM: Line 1 – 10-G/Urbanite; Folders – 1; Press registration system – Burgess/Carlson. MAILROOM: Counter stackers – 1-HL/Monitor HT; Inserters and stuffers – 1-S/624P; Bundle tying machines – 1-MLN/ML2, 1-MLN/Suretyer; Addressing machine – 1/KR. BUSINESS COMPUTERS: Business Software – Vision Data

PAWTUCKET

THE TIMES

23 Exchange St., Pawtucket, R.I., 2860; gen tel (401) 722-4000; adv tel (401) 722-4000; ed tel (401) 722-4000; adv fax (401) 727-9252 (display); ed fax (401) 727-9280; adv e-mail advertising@pawtuckettimes.com; ed e-mail editor@pawtuckettimes.com; web site www.pawtuckettimes.com
Published: Mon, Tues, Wed, Thur, Fri, Sat
Weekday Frequency: m
Saturday Frequency: m
Circulation: 4,766; 6,469(sat)
Last Audit: ABC September 30, 2011
Price: 2.75/wk; 16.25/mo (carrier); 176.80/yr (carrier), $221.00 (mail); 88.40/6mo (carrier), $110.50/6mo (mail).
Advertising: Open inch rate $33.42
News services: AP.
Politics: Independent. **Established:** 1885
Special Editions: Spring Car Care (Apr); Bus Schedule (Aug); Holiday Gift Guide I & II (Dec); Business Profile (Feb); Bridal Showcase (Jan); Who's the Best-Ballot (Jul); Business Review (Jun); Profile-Massachusetts (Mar); Momentum (May); Monthly Kid's Tab (Monthly); Holida
Special Weekly Sections: Religion (Sat); Health (Tues); Food (Wed).
Magazines: USA WEEKEND Magazine (Sat).
Pub.....Barry Mechanic
Gen. Mgr.....Richard J. Blockson
Controller....Kathy Cardona
Adv. Mgr., Classified....Diane Ames
Sports Ed.....Terry Nau
Mgmt. Info Servs. Mgr.....Alvin Lefeiste
Prodn. Mgr.....Robert T. Hughes
Market Information: TMC.
Mechanical available: Offset; Black and 4 ROP colors; insert accepted; page cutoffs - 21 1/4.
Mechanical Specifications: Type page 12 x 21 1/2; E - 6 cols, 1 7/8, 3/16 between; A - 6 cols, 1 7/8, 3/16 between; C - 9 cols, 1 3/8, 1/8 between.
Commodity Consumption: Avg. Page Number Per Issue - Daily 25; Avg. Page Number Per Issue - Saturday 24; widths 24 3/4; Newsprint Used - Short Tons 906.6; Printing Ink Used - Pages Printed 9020.
Equipment EDITORIAL: Front-end Software – Mi-

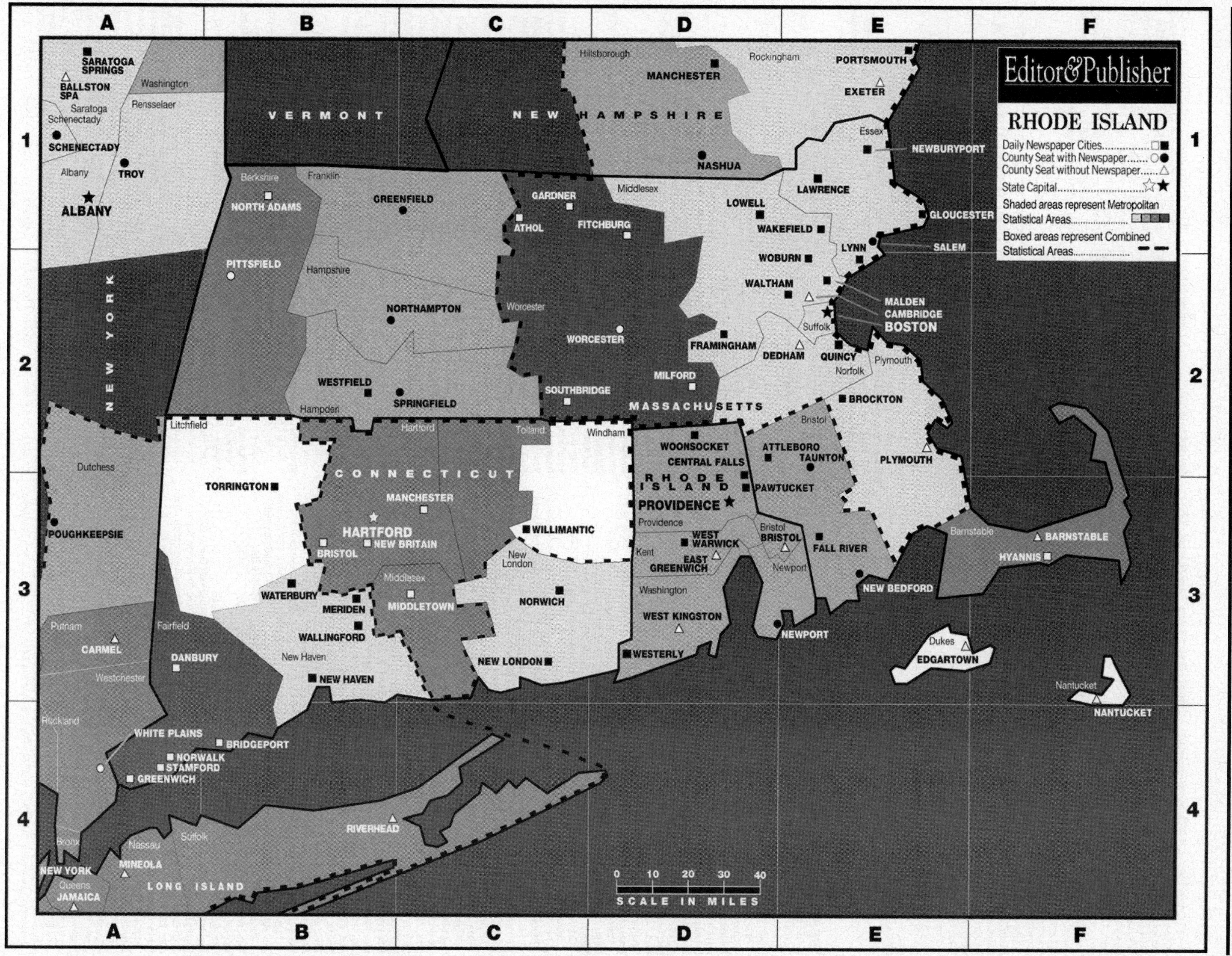
Editor&Publisher
RHODE ISLAND
Daily Newspaper Cities
County Seat with Newspaper
County Seat without Newspaper
State Capital
Shaded areas represent Metropolitan Statistical Areas
Boxed areas represent Combined Statistical Areas
0 10 20 30 40
SCALE IN MILES
VERMONT
NEW HAMPSHIRE
MASSACHUSETTS
CONNECTICUT
RHODE ISLAND
NEW YORK
LONG ISLAND
SARATOGA SPRINGS
BALLSTON SPA
SCHENECTADY
TROY
ALBANY
MANCHESTER
NASHUA
PORTSMOUTH
EXETER
NEWBURYPORT
LAWRENCE
LOWELL
GLOUCESTER
WAKEFIELD
LYNN
SALEM
WOBURN
WALTHAM
MALDEN
CAMBRIDGE
BOSTON
FRAMINGHAM
DEDHAM
QUINCY
BROCKTON
NORTH ADAMS
GREENFIELD
GARDNER
ATHOL
FITCHBURG
PITTSFIELD
NORTHAMPTON
WORCESTER
WESTFIELD
SPRINGFIELD
SOUTHBRIDGE
MILFORD
POUGHKEEPSIE
TORRINGTON
MANCHESTER
HARTFORD
NEW BRITAIN
BRISTOL
WILLIMANTIC
WOONSOCKET
CENTRAL FALLS
PAWTUCKET
PROVIDENCE
ATTLEBORO
TAUNTON
PLYMOUTH
WEST WARWICK
EAST GREENWICH
BRISTOL
FALL RIVER
BARNSTABLE
HYANNIS
NEW BEDFORD
WATERBURY
MERIDEN
MIDDLETOWN
NORWICH
WALLINGFORD
WEST KINGSTON
NEWPORT
CARMEL
DANBURY
NEW LONDON
WESTERLY
EDGARTOWN
NEW HAVEN
NANTUCKET
WHITE PLAINS
BRIDGEPORT
NORWALK
STAMFORD
GREENWICH
RIVERHEAD
NEW YORK
MINEOLA
JAMAICA

crosoft/Office 97, QPS/QuarkXPress 4.0, Adobe/Photoshop 4.0.; Editorial Hardware – Compaq/Desk Pro PC; Editorial Equipment – OCR Scanner, X/RFS 2035; Editorial Printers – APP/Mac LaserWriter II, Xante/Accel-A-Writer CLASSIFIED: Front-end Software – PPI/Classifield.; Classified Hardware – Compaq/PC Desk Pro CLS; Classified Printers – HP/Laserjet, Xante/Accel-O-Writer DISPLAY: Ad make-up applications – QPS/QuarkXPress, Adobe/Illustrator, Multi-Ad/Creator, FreeHand, Adobe/Photoshop; Display Hardware – APP/Mac IIcx, APP/Mac SE, APP/Mac Plus, 2-APP/Mac G3, 2-APP/Power Mac 6100; Display Printers – LaserWriter, Xante/Ultra 4000 PRODUCTION: Pagination Software – MEI/CLS 2.5.2, ALS 2.7.; Production Equipment – 2-Linotype-Hell/Linotron 202-N, Hyphen/Dash 72E, Ultra/4000; Cameras – 1-C/Spartan III, 1-R/Mark II, R/432; Scanners – HP/Flatbed B&W Scanner; Bundle tying machines – 1-MLN/ML2-EE. BUSINESS COMPUTERS: Business Software – INSI; Business Hardware – IBM/Sys 36, IBM/AS 400

PROVIDENCE

THE PROVIDENCE JOURNAL

75 Fountain St., Providence, R.I., 02902-0050; gen tel (401) 277-7000; ed tel (401) 277-7303; adv fax (401) 277-7802; ed fax (401) 277-7439; gen e-mail letters@projo.com; ed e-mail pjnews@projo.com; web site www.projo.com

Published: Mon, Tues, Wed, Thur, Fri, Sat, Sun
Weekday Frequency: m
Saturday Frequency: m
Circulation: 122,558; 115,892(sat); 129,024(sun)
Last Audit: ABC September 30, 2011
Price: 4.25/wk; 17.00/4wk; 221.60/yr.
Advertising: Open inch rate $286.00
News services: AP, NYT, LAT-WP, MCT, SHNS, TMS, CQ, DJ.
Politics: Independent. **Established:** 1829
Special Editions: Healthcare Career Fair (Apr); Continuing Education (Aug); Ski-Travel (Dec); Sales/Financial/Insurance Career Fair (Feb); Nursing/Allied Health Career (Jan); Student/Athlete Honor Roll (Jul); CVS Charity Classic (Jun); Camp Guide (Mar); Impact 50 (May); Co
Special Weekly Sections: Lifebeat Movies (Fri); More For Your Money (Mon); TV Book (S); Real Estate (Sat); Home (Thur); Spanish Page (Tues); Food (Wed).
Magazines: Parade (S).
Chrmn./Pres./Pub./CEO ....Howard G. Sutton
Exec. Vice Pres./Gen. Mgr. ....Thomas Heslin
Sr. Vice Pres., Finance ....Sandra J. Radcliffe
Vice Pres./Exec Ed. ....Thomas E. Heslin
Vice Pres./Editorial Page Ed. ..Robert Whitcomb
Dir., Community Servs. ....Mary Ellen Panzini
Dir., Inclusiveness ....Marcia Russell-Cintron
Asst. Dir., Employee Devel. ....Keith Mathews
Adv. Sr. Sales Dir., Display ....Scott Connolly
Adv. Sales Dir., Classified ....Sue Walsh
Adv. Sales Dir., Nat'l Chain/Food/Drug Al Strumolo
Adv. Sales Dir., Prof. Servs./Travel/Entertainment Ed Cabral
Adv. Sales Dir., Real Estate/Educ./Employment Ron Moreau
Mgr., Promo.....................Maureen M. Devine
Vice Pres., Circ. ....Barbara Nauman
Circ. Dir., Sales/Serv.........................Jeff Peffer
Deputy Exec. Ed........................Carol J. Young
Deputy Editorial Page Ed.......Edward C. Achorn
Mng. Ed., Features....................Philip Kukielski
Mng. Ed., Metro ....Susan Areson
Market Information: ADS; Split run; TMC; Zoned editions.
Mechanical available: Flexographic; Black and 3 ROP colors; insert accepted - some customer inserts are printed in-house; page cutoffs - 22.
Mechanical Specifications: Type page 12 x 21; E - 6 cols, 1 43/50, 1/6 between; A - 6 cols, 1 43/50, 1/6 between; C - 9 cols, 1 23/100, 1/8 between.
Commodity Consumption: Avg. Page Number Per Issue - Daily 60; Avg. Page Number Per Issue - Plates Used 231300; Avg. Page Number Per Issue - Saturday 65; Avg. Page Number Per Issue - Sunday 163; widths 50; Newsprint Used - Metric Tons 19475; Printing Ink Used - Black 461251; Pr
Equipment EDITORIAL: Front-end Software – AT, XYQUEST/XyWrite, QPS/QuarkXPress.; Editorial Hardware – 112-At, 204-PC, 45-APP/Mac; Editorial Printers – HP CLASSIFIED: Front-end Software – AT.; Classified Hardware – AT/IAS, 2-AT/CLSPAG; Classified Printers – HP, Data Printers; Layout Software – MEI/ALS, HI.; Display Hardware – 40-APP/Mac, In-house system, 110-PC; Display Printers – HP/LaserJet Printers PRODUCTION: Pagination Software – QPS/QuarkXPress, Alfaquest/Print Express CPM.; Production Equipment – 3-Pre Press/Panterras, Konica/Black Magic; Scanners – Nikon/35mm, 8-Microtek/III, 3-X, 1-Scitex/EverSmart, 2-Tecsa PRESSROOM: Line 1 – 6-W&H/Flexo 1987, 2-MOT/Flexo Tower 1992; Line 2 – 6-W&H/Flexo 1987, 2-MOT/Flexo Tower 1992; Line 3 – 6-W&H/Flexo 1987, 2-MOT/Flexo Tower 1992; Pasters – 18, 6; Reels and Stands – 18, 6. MAILROOM: Counter stackers – QWI/501; Inserters and stuffers – GMA/SLS-2000; Bundle tying machines – Dynaric/NP-3000; Wrapping singles – 1/St. BUSINESS COMPUTERS: Business Software – Oracle; Business Hardware – 450-Dell/XP PC

WEST WARWICK

THE KENT COUNTY TIMES

1353 Main St., West Warwick, R.I., 02893-3865; gen tel (401) 821-7400; gen fax (401) 828-0810; ed e-mail kceditor@ricentral.com

Published: Mon, Tues, Wed, Thur, Fri, Sat
Weekday Frequency: All day
Saturday Frequency: All day
Circulation: 2,850; 2,850(sat)
Last Audit: Sworn September 30, 2007
Advertising: Open inch rate $14.03
Insert rate: $52 CPM Single Sheet
Politics: Independent. **Established:** 1892
Own facility?: N
Adv. Mgr., Display.......................Jody Boucher
Circ. Dir. ....Phil Rowell
Nanci Batson
Pub...Terry Leifeste
Mechanical Specifications: Call for Info
Equipment CLASSIFIED: Front-end Software – .; Folders – 2; Bundle tying machines – 2/Bu.

WESTERLY

THE WESTERLY SUN

56 Main St., Westerly, R.I., 02891; gen tel (401) 348-1000; gen fax (401) 348-5080; web site www.thewesterlysun.com

Published: Mon, Tues, Wed, Thur, Fri, Sat, Sun
Saturday Frequency: m
Circulation: 8,365; 8,365(sat); 8,772(sun)
Last Audit: September 30, 2008
Price: 3.25/wk (carrier); 169.00/yr (carrier), $226.20/yr (mail); 424.25/3mo, $84.50/6mo (carrier); $56.55/3mo, $113.10/6mo (mail).
Advertising: Open inch rate $19.00
News services: AP.
Politics: Independent.
Not Published: Christmas.
Special Editions: Christmas Gift Guide (Dec); Automobile (Feb); Year-in-Review (Jan); Schoolboy Football (Nov); Automobile (Oct); Home Improvement (Sept).
Special Weekly Sections: Places in the Sun (Fri); Business (S); Business (Sat); The Guide (Thur); Food (Wed).
Magazines: Relish (Monthly); USA WEEKEND Magazine (S); American Profile (Weekly).
Pres./Pub..Tim Ryan
Controller...............................Kathleen Murray
Vice Pres./Adv. Dir...................Robert Cardosa
Adv. Mgr., Classified.....................Karen Davis
Circ. Dir................................Michael J. Smith
Local News Ed............................Angela Algier
Asst. Sports Ed..........................Robert L. Marr
Market Information: Split run; TMC.
Mechanical available: Offset; Black and 3 ROP colors; insert accepted - all; page cutoffs - 22 3/4.
Mechanical Specifications: Type page 11 5/8 x 21 1/2; E - 6 cols, 1 13/16, 1/8 between; A - 6 cols, 1 13/16, 1/8 between; C - 8 cols, 1 3/8, 1/8 between.
Commodity Consumption: Avg. Page Number Per Issue - Daily 28; Avg. Page Number Per Issue - Saturday 24; Avg. Page Number Per Issue - Sunday 40; widths 25; Newsprint Used - Metric Tons 500.
Equipment; Editorial Hardware – PC. CLASSIFIED: Front-end Software – Brainworks.; Classified Hardware – PC DISPLAY: Ad make-up applications – Aldus/FreeHand 3.1, Adobe/Photoshop 2.5, Microsoft/Word 5.1a, Multi-Ad/Creator 3.5; Layout Software – 3-APP/Mac Quadra 800.; Display Printers – 2-HP/LaserJet IV; Production Equipment – 2-COM/Unisetter; Cameras – 1-Nu/18 x 24; Scanners – Lf/AP Scanner, AG/Flatbed. PRESSROOM: Line 1 – 6-HI/V-15A single width. MAILROOM: Counter stackers – 1/QWI; Inserters and stuffers – 1-/S; Bundle tying machines – 1-/Strapex, 1-/Power Strap.; Business Hardware – 1-DEC/BL 2

WOONSOCKET

THE CALL

75 Main St., Woonsocket, R.I., 02895; gen tel (401) 762-3000; adv tel (401) 767-8500; ed tel (401) 767-8550; gen fax (401) 765-7059; adv fax (401) 767-8509; ed fax (401) 765-2834; gen e-mail notices@woonsocketcall.com; adv e-mail rblockson@woonsocketcall.com; ed e-mail editor@woonsocketcall.com; web site www.woonsocketcall.com

Published: Mon, Tues, Wed, Thur, Fri, Sat, Sun
Weekday Frequency: m
Saturday Frequency: m
Circulation: 6,352; 7,391(sat); 8,853(sun)
Last Audit: ABC September 30, 2011
Price: 3.25/wk; 13.00/mo; 187.20/yr.
Advertising: Open inch rate $29.75
Insert rate: $42 per 1000
News services: AP.
Politics: Independent. **Established:** 1892
Advertising not accepted: N
Own facility?: Y
Special Editions: Chamber of Commerce Annual Report (Jan).
Special Weekly Sections: Arcade (Fri); Focus Health (Mon); Travel (S); Business (Sat); Business (Thur); Business (Tues); Best Food Day (Wed).
Magazines: USA WEEKEND Magazine (S).
Publisher ....Barry Mechanic
Controller...........................Kathie Needham
Mng. Ed. ....Daniel H. Trafford
Market Information: Split run; TMC; Zoned editions.
Mechanical available: Offset; Black and 3 ROP colors; insert accepted; page cutoffs - 22 3/4.
Mechanical Specifications: Type page 12 x 21 1/2; E - 6 cols, 1 7/8, 1/8 between; A - 6 cols, 1 7/8, 1/8 between; C - 9 cols, 1 5/16, 1/16 between.
Commodity Consumption: Avg. Page Number Per Issue - Daily 28; Avg. Page Number Per Issue - Plates Used 19580; Avg. Page Number Per Issue - Saturday 28; Avg. Page Number Per Issue - Sunday 40; widths 25; Newsprint Used - Short Tons 1173; Printing Ink Used - Black 30000; Printin
Equipment EDITORIAL: Front-end Software – Agile/Teambase 1.0.2.8.; Editorial Hardware – 12-Compaq/Desk Pro; Editorial Printers – HP 5200 CLASSIFIED: Front-end Software – Vision Data; Classified Hardware – Compaq/Desk Pro; Classified Printers – 1-HP/Laserjets; Display Hardware – Mac G4 PRODUCTION: Pagination Software – Quark 6.5
Multi Ad Creator; Production Equipment – ECRM CTP PRESSROOM: Line 1 – 7-G/Urbanite U-615 single width (mono; 1-3 color unit) 1994; Press Drives – C.E.S./200 h.p.-PLC; Folders – 1; Pasters – 5-Enkel/Autoweb; Reels and Stands – 5; Press registration system – Stoesser/center pin. MAILROOM: Counter stackers – QWI/351; Inserters and stuffers – 2-MM/227E; Bundle tying machines – 1/MLN, 1-Dynaric/NP 1500; Wrapping singles – HL/Monitor; Addressing machine – X/Chesire 525 BUSINESS COMPUTERS: Business Software – INSI; Business Hardware – Dell

SOUTH CAROLINA

AIKEN

AIKEN STANDARD

326 Rutland Dr. NW, Aiken, S.C., 29801-4010; gen tel (803) 648-2311; adv tel (803) 648-2311; gen fax (803) 648-6052; adv fax (803) 648-6052; gen e-mail editorial@aikenstandard.com; ed e-mail editorial@aikenstandard.com; web site www.aikenstandard.com

Published: Mon, Tues, Wed, Thur, Fri, Sat, Sun
Weekday Frequency: m
Saturday Frequency: m
Circulation: 14,600; 15,496(sat); 15,918(sun)
Last Audit: ABC September 30, 2011
Price: 9.50/mo (carrier); 114.00/yr (carrier).
Advertising: Open inch rate $34.38
News services: AP, MCT.
Politics: Independent.
Special Editions: Masters Golf Tournament (Apr); Football (Aug); Brides Book (Jan); Horse Industry (Mar); Christmas Gift Guide (Nov); Car Care (Oct); Discover Aiken (Sept).
Special Weekly Sections: Religious Page (Fri); Home Hunter (S); Auto (Sat); Entertainment (Thur); Health (Wed).
Magazines: USA WEEKEND Magazine (S).
Pres./Pub................................Scott B. Hunter
Bus. Mgr. ....Ellen C. Priest
Customer Serv. Mgr.................Letitia Jefferson
Adv. Dir......................................Arthur Zappa
Adv. Mgr. ....Dee Taylor
Adv. Mgr., Composition..................Jean Yount
Adv. Mgr., Major Accts./Nat'l/Co-op ..Debra Price
Circ. Dir. ....Scot Newcom
Mng. Ed. ....Tim O'Briant
Ed. ....Jeffrey B. Wallace
Sports Ed......................................Larry Taylor
News Ed....................................Mike Gibbons
Photo Ed...........................Ginny Southworth
System Mgr....................................David Boyd
Prodn. Dir. ....Phillip Yates
Mgr., Mailroom...........................Kathy Lybrand
Market Information: TMC.
Mechanical available: Offset; Black and 3 ROP colors; insert accepted - poly bags, sample bags; page cutoffs - 22.
Mechanical Specifications: Type page 13 1/8 x 21; E - 6 cols, 1 5/6, 1/6 between; A - 6 cols, 1 5/6, 1/6 between; C - 8 cols, 1 1/3, 1/6 between.
Commodity Consumption: Avg. Page Number Per Issue - Daily 28; Avg. Page Number Per Issue - Plates Used 15600; Avg. Page Number Per Issue - Sunday 44; widths 14; Newsprint Used - Short Tons 950; Printing Ink Used - Black 21800; Printing Ink Used - Color 9270; Printing Ink Used
Equipment EDITORIAL: Front-end Software – Dragx 3.6, Baseview/NewsEdit Pro 3.3, QTools 2.5.1.; Editorial Hardware – APP/Macs; Editorial Printers – AU/APS-6-84, Konica/EV Jetsetter 5100 CLASSIFIED: Front-end Software – Vision Data 5.4.; Classified Hardware – Sun/Ultra 450 Server 256MB; Classified Printers – Genicom/4492XT DISPLAY: Ad make-up applications – QPS/QuarkXPress 4.1, Adobe/Photoshop 6.0, Adobe/Illustrator 9.0; Layout Software – APP/Power Mac G3.; Display Printers – HP/LaserJet 4MV, AU/APS 2000, AU/APS-6-84 ACS Imagesetter PRODUCTION:

Pagination Software – Baseview/IQ Server 3.1.8.; Production Equipment – Universal/26, Color Central; Cameras – Scanners ÂŒ Epson/2580 Photo PRESSROOM: Line 1 – 13-G/Community; Press Drives – 2; Folders – 1-G/SSC.; Inserters and stuffers – KAN/760; Bundle tying machines – It, Mosca/Strapper; Mailroom control system – Buskco Inkjet Labeler; Other equipment –KAN/Label Applicator. BUSINESS COMPUTERS: Business Software – Vision Data 6.0, Vision Data 6.3; Business Hardware – Sun/Ultra 450-256MB, Sun/Ultra 5, 10-XT, 2-APP/Mac G-3

ANDERSON

ANDERSON INDEPENDENT-MAIL

1000 Williamston Rd., Anderson, S.C., 29621-6508; gen tel (864) 224-4321; adv tel (864) 260-1204; ed tel (864) 260-1244; gen fax (864) 260-1276; adv fax (864) 260-1350; ed fax (864) 260-1276; ed e-mail newsroom@independentmail.com; web site www.independentmail.com

Published: Mon, Tues, Wed, Thur, Fri, Sat, Sun
Weekday Frequency: m
Saturday Frequency: m
Circulation: 23,121; 23,039(sat); 29,733(sun)
Last Audit: ABC September 30, 2011
Price: 14.45/mo; 173.40/yr.
Advertising: Open inch rate $67.03
News services: AP, The Newspaper Network, NYT, SHNS, NEA.
Politics: Independent. **Established:** 1899
Special Editions: Home Decorating (Apr); College Football Preview (Aug); HGTV Winter (Dec); NASCAR Preview (Feb); Homebuilders Tab (Jan); YMCA (Jul); South Carolina Factbook (Jun); HGTV Spring (Mar); High School Graduation Tab (May); Food Network Holiday Guide (Nov); YMCA
Special Weekly Sections: Automotive (Fri); Business (S); Automotive (Sat); Be (Thur); Food (Wed).
Magazines: Parade (S).
Pres./Pub. ....Butch Hughes
Pub., Orange & White....Phil Batson
Vice Pres., Finance ....Sharon Rochester
Major/Nat'l Adv. Mgr. ....Thomas E. Privett
Adv. Mgr., Retail Sales ....Karen Rommelmeyer
Dir., Mktg. Servs. ....Georgiana Wise
Ed. ....Donald H. Kausler
City Ed. ....David Williams
Asst. City Ed. ....Alison Newton
Editorial Page Ed. ....Bonnie Williams
Ed., HomeTowner....Willie Mattress
Lifestyle Ed.....Jeanne Malmgren
Sports Ed. ....John Brasier
IT Mgr. ....Bill Bussey
Vice Pres., Opns. ....James Lasley
Market Information: ADS; TMC; Zoned editions.
Mechanical available: Offset; Black and 3 ROP colors; insert accepted - all; page cutoffs - 22 3/4.
Mechanical Specifications: Type page 10 1/2 x 21 1/2; E - 6 cols, 1 13/20, 1/8 between; A - 6 cols, 1 13/20, 1/8 between; C - 9 cols, 1 1/10, 7/100 between.
Commodity Consumption: Avg. Page Number Per Issue - Daily 41; Avg. Page Number Per Issue - Plates Used 83290; Avg. Page Number Per Issue - Saturday 40; Avg. Page Number Per Issue - Sunday 66; widths 24 7/8; Newsprint Used - Short Tons 2791; Printing Ink Used - Black 66613; Pri
Equipment EDITORIAL: Front-end Software – DBEdit, QPS/QuarkXPress 4.11.; Editorial Hardware – HP; Editorial Equipment – APP/Server, Kk/35 Scanner, Nikon/LS2000 Coolscan, Nikon/Digital Imaging System, AG/Flatbed Sacnner Duoscan 11 x 17; Editorial Printers – HP/Postscript Laser Printer CLASSIFIED: Front-end Software – III/Tecs 2.; Classified Hardware – HP; Classified Equipment – HP/Office Jet Fax; Classified Printers – Epson/LQ-1170 DISPLAY: Ad make-up applications – Multi-Ad, QPS/QuarkXPress, Adobe/Photoshop; Layout Software – Media Command.; Display Hardware – APP/Mac G4; Display Printers – Canon/Color Laser Copier PRODUCTION: Pagination Software – QPS/QuarkXPress 4.03, AG/Duoscan 11 x 17, 7-AG/Scanner 8 1/2 x 11, HP/Scanjet.; Production Equipment – 1-Kk/Trendsetter News SA1423, 1-Kk/Trendsetter News SA1512 PRESSROOM: Line 1 – 10-G/Urbanite 1972; Line 2 – 6-Didde/Minicom-17 1995; Line 3 – 2-Ryobi/3302 1997; Press Drives – 2-HP/100 Motors 1972; Folders – 2-G/2:1; Pasters – 8-Cary 1980; Press control system – 1992 MAILROOM: Counter stackers – 1-QWI/350, 1-QWI/450; Inserters and stuffers – 1-GMA/SLS 1000; Bundle tying machines – 1-MLN/280, 1/OVL, 2-MLN/2CC, 2-Dynaric/NP 1500, Dynaric/DZ400; Wrapping singles – 2-QWI/00300; Mailroom control system – TMSI Drive/Navigator Convey; Audio Hardware – AP StockQuote BUSINESS COMPUTERS: Business Software – Peoplesoft 7.59, Accounting, HMRS; Business Hardware – HP/3000, 16-IBM/PC, DEC/200 NT Server, 3-DEC/PC

INDEPENDENT PUBLISHING CO.

1000 Williamston Rd., Anderson, S.C., 29622; gen tel (864) 224-4321; gen fax (864) 260-1276

BEAUFORT

THE BEAUFORT GAZETTE

1556 Salem Rd., Beaufort, S.C., 29902-5236; gen tel (843) 524-3183; ed tel (843) 524-3183; gen fax (843) 524-8728; gen e-mail gazette@beaufortgazette.com; adv e-mail advertise@beaufortgazette.com; ed e-mail letters@beaufortgazette.com; web site www.beaufortgazette.com

Published: Mon, Tues, Wed, Thur, Fri, Sat, Sun
Weekday Frequency: m
Saturday Frequency: m
Circulation: 9,431; 9,687(sat); 9,886(sun)
Last Audit: ABC September 30, 2011

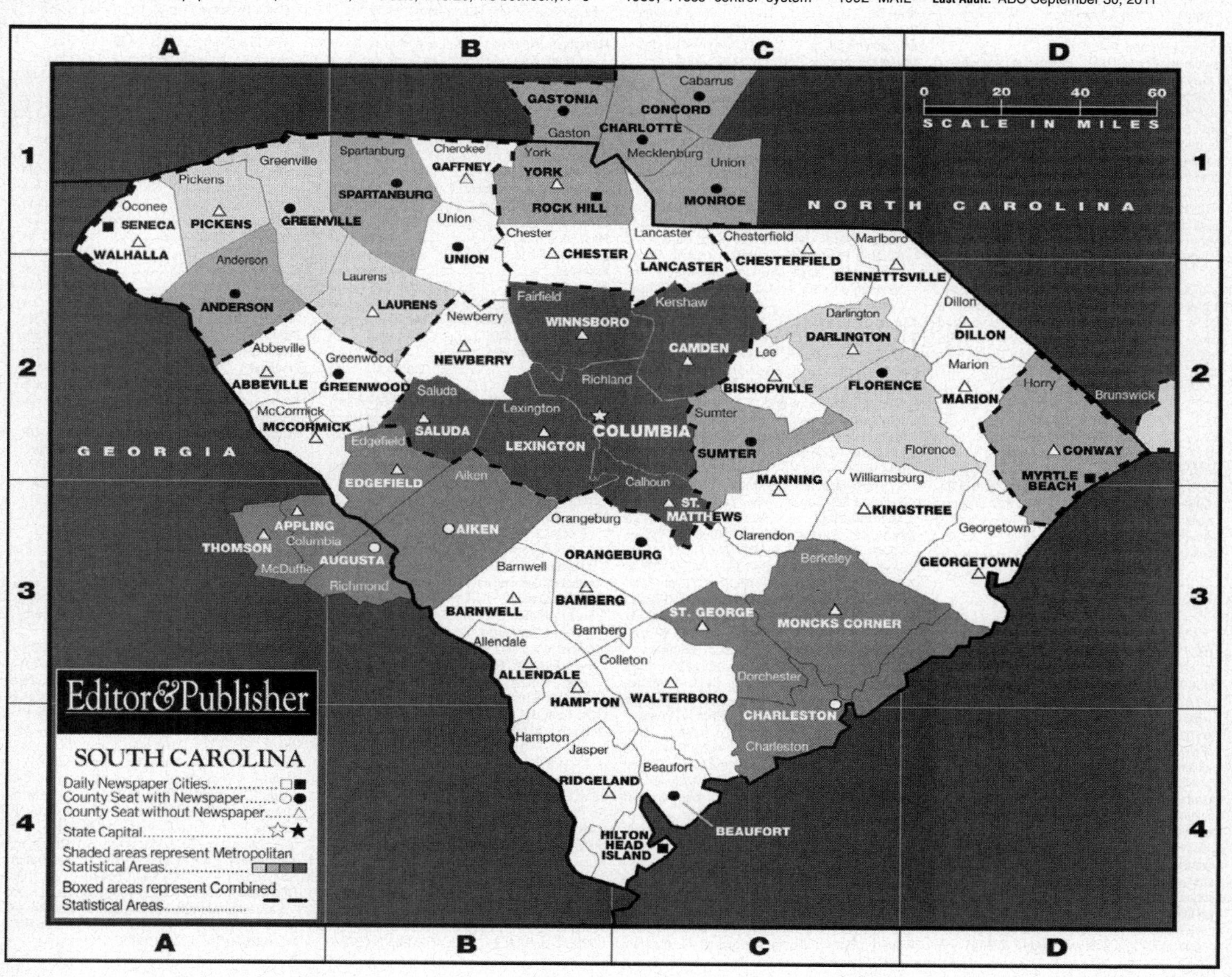

Price: 94.00/yr.
Advertising: Open inch rate $35.30
News services: AP.
Politics: Independent.
Special Editions: Garden & Home Improvement (Apr); Football (Aug); Coupon Pages (Dec); Income Tax (Feb); Bridal (Jan); Water Festival (Jul); Hurricane (Jun); Spring Tour of Homes (Mar); Gullah Festival (May); Cookbook/Gift Guide (Nov); Fall Tour of Homes (Oct); Coupon Page
Special Weekly Sections: Travel (S); TV (Sat); Best Food Days (Tues); Best Food Days (Wed).
Magazines: Parade (S).
Pres./Pub. ....Sara Johnson Borton
Adv. Dir. ....Sandy Gilles
Exec. Ed. ....Fitz McAden
Ed. ....Jeff Kidd
Features Ed. ....Tom Robinette
Photographer ....Bob Sofaly
Sports Ed. ....Lance Hanlin
Prodn. Dir. ....William King
Market Information: TMC.
Mechanical available: Offset; Black and 3 ROP colors; insert accepted; page cutoffs - 22 3/4.
Mechanical Specifications: Type page 13 x 21; E - 6 cols, 2 1/16, 1/8 between; A - 6 cols, 2 1/16, 1/8 between; C - 9 cols, 1 3/8, 1/8 between.
Commodity Consumption: Avg. Page Number Per Issue - Daily 30; Avg. Page Number Per Issue - Saturday 30; Avg. Page Number Per Issue - Sunday 38; widths 27; Newsprint Used - Metric Tons 2300; Printing Ink Used - Pages Printed 11400.
Equipment EDITORIAL: Front-end Software – Baseview.; Editorial Hardware – 22-APP/Mac; Editorial Equipment – APP/Mac Scanner; Editorial Printers – 2-APP/Mac CLASSIFIED: Front-end Software – Cx, Baseview.; Classified Hardware – Cx, 4-APP/Mac DISPLAY: Ad make-up applications – Baseview; Layout Software – 4-APP/Mac.; Display Hardware – 4-APP/Mac; Display Printers – 2-APP/Mac PRODUCTION: Pagination Software – Baseview, QPS/QuarkXPress.; Production Equipment – APP/Mac, 2-AG/Accuset; Cameras – SCREEN PRESSROOM: Line 1 – 6-G/Urbanite; Folders – 1-G/Urbanite. MAILROOM: Counter stackers – KAN, QWI; Inserters and stuffers – 2/GMA; Bundle tying machines – 2-/MLN, 1-/Power Strap, 1-/Dynaric.; Audio Hardware – PEP BUSINESS COMPUTERS: Business Software – CJ; Business Hardware – HP

BLUFFTON

BLUFFTON TODAY

6 Promenade St., Suite 1005, Bluffton, S.C., 29910; gen tel (843) 815-0800; web site www.blufftontoday.com
Published: Wed, Sun
Weekday Frequency: m

CHARLESTON

THE POST AND COURIER

134 Columbus St., Charleston, S.C., 29403-4800; gen tel (843) 577-7111; adv tel (843) 937-5468; ed tel (843) 937-5527; adv fax (843) 937-5463; ed fax (843) 937-5545; ed e-mail editor@postandcourier.com; web site www.charleston.net
Published: Mon, Tues, Wed, Thur, Fri, Sat, Sun
Weekday Frequency: m
Saturday Frequency: m
Circulation: 82,261; 75,812(sat); 91,862(sun)
Last Audit: ABC September 30, 2011
Price: 11.95/mo; 143.40/yr.
Advertising: Open inch rate $191.71
News services: AP, MCT, NYT.
Politics: Independent. **Established:** 1803
Own facility?: Y
Special Editions: Flowertown Festival (Apr); Football (Aug); Holiday Planner & Gifts (Dec); S.E. Wildlife (Feb); Brides (Jan); Brides (Jul); Hurricane (Jun); Spring Fashion (Mar); Summer Guide (May); Holiday Entertaining (Nov); Fall Fashion (Sept).
Special Weekly Sections: Fashion (Fri); Science/Health (Mon); Automotive (S); Automotive (Sat); Family Life (Thur); Schools Plus (Tues); Food Day (Wed).
Magazines: Television (TV Book) (Fri); Parade (S); Entertainment/Preview (Thur).
Broadcast Affiliations: KVOA Communnications Inc, KVOA-TV Tucson, AZ; Sangre de Cristo Communications Inc, KOAA-TV PuebloColorado Springs, CO; Sawtooth Communications Inc, KIVI-TV Nampa/Bosise, ID; KATC Communications Inc, KATC-TV Lafayette, LAKBZK Communications Inc, KBZK-TV Bo
Mgr., Bus./Accounting ....Pam Wier Gill
Credit Mgr. ....Cal Purvis
Cor. Prodn. Dir. ....Mickey Bella
Adv. Mgr., Retail ....Jamie Drolet
Adv. Mgr., Charleston.Net ....Zach Payer
Audience Devel. Dir. ....Steve Wagenlander
Exec. Ed. ....Bill Hawkins
Asst. Ed. ....Charles Rowe
Asst. Ed. ....Frank Wooten
Deputy Mng. Ed. ....Allen Greenberg
Automotive Ed. ....Jim Parker
Books Ed. ....Bill Thompson
Ad Director ....Gail Smith
Dir., HR ....Gwendolyn McCullough
Adv. Mgr., Classified ....Joel Cardwell
Dir., Mktg ....Craig Rogers
Promo. Coord. ....Chris Norden
Mng. Ed. ....Steve Mullins
Deputy Mng. Ed. ....Marsha Guerard
Amusements Ed. ....Christine Randall
Market Information: Split run; TMC; Zoned editions.
Mechanical available: Offset; Black and 3 ROP colors; insert accepted - card stock, outserts, poly bags; page cutoffs - 22.
Mechanical Specifications: Type page 11 5/8 x 21; E - 6 cols, 1 5/6, 1/8 between; A - 6 cols, 1 5/6, 1/8 between; C - 9 cols, 1 3/16, between.
Commodity Consumption: Avg. Page Number Per Issue - Daily 70; Avg. Page Number Per Issue - Plates Used 236790; Avg. Page Number Per Issue - Saturday 90; Avg. Page Number Per Issue - Sunday 140; widths 50; Newsprint Used - Metric Tons 17271; Printing Ink Used - Black 402156; Pr
Equipment EDITORIAL: Front-end Software – ATS/Media Desk, QPS/QuarkXPress 4.11, Microsoft/Word, Merlin.; Editorial Hardware – 2-Dell/Power-Edge 6450 Server, Power Vault/600 F San; Editorial Printers – 2-ACU/APS-Proofer CLASSIFIED: Front-end Software – ATS/Advisor, Microsoft/Word, Pongrass/Classified.
Brainwork's; Classified Hardware – 2-Dell/Power-Edge 6450, Power Vault/600 F San; Classified Printers – 5-X/DocuPrint N2125; Display Hardware – 3-APP/Mac 9150 Server, 3-APP/Mac G3 Server, APP/Mac 9650 Server, 3-Micronet/Raid 5 Storage Arrays, 2-Dell/Power-Edge 6450, Power Vault/660 F San; Display Printers – 3-APP/Mac LaserWriter 16/600 PS, 12-AU/Typhoon/16, HP/2500 CP, 2-AU/APS Accu-Proofer, 2 PRODUCTION: Pagination Software – QPS/QuarkXPress.; Production Equipment – 3-AU/APS6-108C, 1-WL/38-D, 1-Pre Press/Panther Pro 62, 2-Pixel-Craft/8200, 2-Nikon/Colorscan; Scanners – 1-ECR/Autokon 2045-C, 2-DD/1270 Page Scanners PRESSROOM: Line 1 – 10-G/Metroliner (7 half decks) 1979; Line 2 – 10-G/Metroliner (7 Half Decks) 1988; Press Drives – 10-Fin/5126 75 h.p., 10-Fin/5135 100 h.p.; Folders – 2-G/3:2 Double; Pasters – 20; Reels and Stands – 20; Press control system – Goss; Press registration system – CCI MAILROOM: Counter stackers – 9-QWI/SJ200; Inserters and stuffers – 1-HI/2299, 1-HI/1472
1-Titam G60; Bundle tying machines – 5/Power Strap/PSN2, 11-SAM/Mosca ROM 2, 5-/OVL; Wrapping singles – QWI 1/2 Bottom Wrap, QWI 3/4 Bottom Wrap; Mailroom control system – 1-QWI/CrossBelt; Addressing machine – 4 Video Jet Lablers; Other equipment –Muller Martini 335 stitch and trim machine AUDIO: Audio Software – Fluent; Audio Hardware – Spanlink BUSINESS COMPUTERS: Business Software – Microsoft/Windows, Microsoft/Office 97, DEC/Pathworks, GEAC/Vision Shift, GEAC/World Class 7.x
Brainwork's; Business Hardware – 3-DEC/Alpha 4100

COLUMBIA

THE STATE

1401 Shop Rd., Columbia, S.C., 29201; gen tel (803) 771-6161; adv tel (803) 771-8437; ed tel (803) 771-8465; gen fax (803) 771-8430; adv fax (803) 771-8363; ed fax (803) 771-8639; gen e-mail state@thestate.com; adv e-mail adv@thestate.com; ed e-mail steeditor@thestate.com; web site www.thestate.com
Published: Mon, Tues, Wed, Thur, Fri, Sat, Sun
Weekday Frequency: m
Saturday Frequency: m
Circulation: 71,181; 70,949(sat); 129,715(sun)
Last Audit: ABC September 30, 2011
Price: 3.85/wk; 16.69/mo; 189.80/yr; 30.80/8wk, $50.05/13wk, $96.72/26wk.
News services: AP, LAT-WP, NYT, MCT.
Politics: Independent.
Special Editions: Summer Fun (Apr); Welcome Back USC (Aug); A New Year, A New You (Dec); Body, Health & More (Feb); 20 Under 40 (Jan); CBJ Book of Lists (Jul); Readers Choice (Jun); Rooms & Blooms (Mar); Living Here (May); Faith Guide (Nov); Midlands Health (Oct); CareerBu
Magazines: Weekend (Fri); Lake Murray Columbia Magazine (Monthly); Go Gamecocks (Other); Sunday Comics (S); Wedding Book (Semi-yearly).
Pres./Pub. ....Henry Haitz
Vice Pres., Finance ....Kelly Edwards
Vice Pres., HR ....Diane Frea
Credit Mgr. ....Dru Wright
Circ. Vice Pres., Opns. ....Phillip Haggerty
Circ. Mgr., Home Delivery ....Rich Robb
Circ. Mgr., Single Copy ....Richard Curtis
Exec. Ed. ....Mark Lett
Mng. Ed ....Steve Brook
Asst. Mng. Ed. ....Eileen Waddell
Assoc. Ed. ....Warren Bolton
Assoc. Ed. ....Cindi Scoppe
Neighbors Ed ....Dawn Kujawa
Vice Pres., Interactive Media ....Matthew Ipsan
Info Systems Site Mgr. ....Derek Lawson
Newsroom Online Mgr. ....Gary Ward
Vice Pres. ....Caryn Manning
Sales Mgr. ....Bett Williams
Deputy Bus. Ed. ....Sara Svedberg
Features Ed. ....Carol Ward
Market Information: Split run; TMC; Zoned editions.
Mechanical available: Offset; Black and 3 ROP colors; insert accepted; page cutoffs - 22 1/2.
Mechanical Specifications: Type page 13 x 21; E - 6 cols, 2 1/16, 1/8 between; A - 6 cols, 2 1/16, 1/8 between; C - 10 cols, 1 3/16, 1/16 between.
Commodity Consumption: Avg. Page Number Per Issue - Daily 55; Avg. Page Number Per Issue - Plates Used 186000; Avg. Page Number Per Issue - Sunday 114; widths 27; Newsprint Used - Metric Tons 21982; Printing Ink Used - Black 358440; Printing Ink Used - Color 134880; Printing I
Equipment EDITORIAL: Front-end Software – CCI; Editorial Hardware – Dell/SAN; Editorial Printers – AU/APS 5, 3-AII/3850
Kodak CTP CLASSIFIED: Front-end Software – AT 4.5.2, Sysdeco Enterprise.; Classified Hardware – 2-IBM/RS 6000, AT/Enterprise 50-seat; Classified Printers – 3-AII/3850 DISPLAY: Ad make-up applications – QPS/QuarkXPress, Cascade/Adobe InDesign; Layout Software – MEI/ALS 8000.; Display Hardware – APP/Mac, Sun
; Display Printers – V/5000, V/5300E, AII/3850 PRODUCTION: Pagination Software – QPS/QuarkXPress.; Production Equipment – WL/Anocoil Processor, 1-AU/5u, AU/APS-6, III/3850, 1-P/ML26, 1-LE/TEK26, 3-LS/2600; Cameras – 1-C/Marathon, 1-C/Spartan III; Scanners – CD/645IE PRESSROOM: Line 1 – 14-G/HO (8-decks); Line 2 – 9-G/HO (5 decks); Folders – 3; Pasters – 23; Reels and Stands – 23-G/CT-50; Press control system – DEC/11-84, G/MPCS. MAILROOM: Counter stackers – 4-HL/Systems, 6-HL/HT Stacker; Inserters and stuffers – 1-HI, SLS 2000; Bundle tying machines – 8-/MLN, 2-/Power Strap, 2-/Dynaric; Addressing machine – 1-Ch/N-3000, 2-Ch/539.

FLORENCE

MORNING NEWS

310 S. Dargan St., Florence, S.C., 29506-2537; gen tel (843) 317-6397; adv tel (843) 317-7257; ed tel (843) 317-6397; gen fax (843) 317-7291; adv fax (843) 317-7290; ed fax (843) 317-7292; adv e-mail trafficdesk@florencenews.com; ed e-mail cnews@florencenews.com; web site www2.scnow.com
Published: Mon, Tues, Wed, Thur, Fri, Sat, Sun
Weekday Frequency: m
Saturday Frequency: m
Circulation: 29,721; 29,334(sat); 32,220(sun)
Last Audit: September 30, 2008
Price: 3.23/wk; 14.00/mo; 168.00/yr.
Advertising: Open inch rate $46.81
News services: AP, SHNS.
Politics: Independent.
Special Editions: Car Care Directory (Apr); Back-To-School (Aug); Christmas Guide (Dec); Furniture Selection (Feb); Super Bowl Preview (Jan); Grilling Made Easy (Jul); Summer Daze (Jun); Speed-Darlington Race (Mar); Mother's Day Gift Guide (May); Chamberlink (Monthly); Bas
Special Weekly Sections: TV Week (S); Pee Dee Homes (Sat).
Magazines: USA WEEKEND Magazine (S).
Broadcast Affiliations: WBTW-CBS.
Pub. ....Mark Laskowski
Controller ....John McElwee
Adv. Dir. ....Jason Dillon
Adv. Mgr., Interactive Sales ....Michelle Marlowe
Adv. Mgr., Nat'l Classified ....Faye Morris
Circ. Dir. ....David Johnson
Metro Ed. ....Jackie Torok
News Ed. ....Kimberly Ginfrida
Sports Ed. ....Sam Bundy
Asst. Sports Ed. ....Mark Haselden
Mgmt. Info Servs. Mgr. ....Jennifer Wolfe
Prodn. Dir. ....John Barlow
Prodn. Mgr., Pre Press ....Wanda Christmas
Prodn. Foreman, Mailroom ....Ray Reynolds
Prodn. Foreman, Pressroom ....Mark Attaway
Market Information: TMC.
Mechanical available: Offset; Black and 3 ROP colors; insert accepted - card stock; page cutoffs - 20 3/4.
Mechanical Specifications: Type page 12 x 20 1/2; E - 6 cols, 2 1/16, 1/8 between; A - 6 cols, 2 1/16, 1/8 between; C - 9 cols, 1 5/16, 1/8 between.
Commodity Consumption: Avg. Page Number Per Issue - Daily 55; Avg. Page Number Per Issue - Sunday 112; widths 13 3/4; Newsprint Used - Short Tons 3480; Printing Ink Used - Black 73080; Printing Ink Used - Color 26100.
Equipment; Editorial Hardware – PC; Editorial Equipment – Umax/Scanner, APP/Mac Workstation, Photo Scanner, APP/Server; Editorial Printers – LaserWriter/II NTX, Xante/Accel-a-Writer. CLASSIFIED: Front-end Software – HI/AdPower.; Classified Hardware – PC; Classified Printers – APP/Mac LaserWriter DISPLAY: Ad make-up applications – Multi-Ad/Creator2 1.5, Adobe/Illustrator 6.0, Aldus/FreeHand 7.0, Search, Macromedia/FreeHand 7.0, Search; Layout Software – 1-Page Director, 1-MEI/ALS.; Display Hardware – APP/Mac; Display Printers – 1-Xante/8300 PRODUCTION: Pagination Software – Multi-Ad/Creator 2 1.5, QPS/QuarkXPress 3.32.; Production Equipment – Caere/OmniPage, Pre Press/Panther Pro 46 (with Punch); Cameras – COM/C618C, COM/C660C, COM/C680C; Scanners –

COM/C680C PRESSROOM: Line 1 – 12-DGM/850 single width 1998; Line 2 – 12-DGM/850 single width; Press Drives – 2-GE/150 h.p., 4; Folders – 1-DGM/1050, 1-DGM/1030. MAILROOM: Counter stackers – MSI/220, Id, C/Marathon, Compass; Inserters and stuffers – MM/308 Biliner, GMA/SLS 1000; Bundle tying machines – MLN/Spirit, Samuel/NT 1000; Wrapping singles – Id/Bottom wrap; Other equipment –MM/Saddle Stitcher. BUSINESS COMPUTERS: Business Software – Unix/Informix, Newzware, Microsoft/Word, Microsoft/Excel, Microsoft/Power Point; Business Hardware – HP/K900 Server

GREENVILLE

THE GREENVILLE NEWS

305 S. Main St., Greenville, S.C., 29601-2605; gen tel (864) 298-4100; adv tel (864) 298-4216; ed tel (864) 298-4321; gen fax (864) 298-4805; adv fax (864) 298-4023; ed fax (864) 298-4395; adv e-mail localnews@greenvillenews.com; web site www.greenvilleonline.com

Group: Metro Newspaper Advertising Services, Inc.
Published: Mon, Tues, Wed, Thur, Fri, Sat, Sun
Weekday Frequency: m
Saturday Frequency: m
Circulation: 55,467; 57,309(sat); 118,686(sun)
Last Audit: ABC September 30, 2011
Price: 3.92/week; 9.42/mo (d); 203.84/yr.
Advertising: Open inch rate $176.25
News services: AP, LAT-WP, MCT, SHNS, TMS, GNS.
Politics: Independent. **Established:** 1874
Special Editions: Guide to Greenville (Apr); High School Football (Aug); Late Christmas Gift Guide (Dec); Southern Home & Garden (Feb); Spring Bride (Jan); Best of the Upstate (Jul); Early Christmas Gift Guide (Nov); Progress (Oct).
Special Weekly Sections: Upstate Weekend (Fri); Outdoors (S); Automotive (Sat); Health & Medicine (Thur); Children (Tues); City People (Wed).
Magazines: USA WEEKEND Magazine (S).
Pub. ....Steven R. Brandt
Controller ....James Gardner
Office Mgr. ....Gwen Shipman
Adv. Vice Pres./Dir. ....Coreen Fisher
Vice Pres., Market Devel. ...Susan Schwartzkopf
Sr. Vice Pres./Exec. Ed. ....John S. Pittman
Mng. Ed. ....Chris Weston
Books Ed. ....Jan Phillips
Bus. Ed. ....Woody White
City Ed. ....Lyn Riddle
Editorial Page Ed. ....Beth Padgett
Farm/Agriculture Ed. ....David Dykes
Film Writer ....Donna Walker
Food Ed. ....Wanda Owings
Market Information: ADS; Split run; TMC; Zoned editions.
Mechanical available: Offset; Black and 3 ROP colors; insert accepted - as requested; page cutoffs - 22.
Mechanical Specifications: Type page 11 5/8 x 21; E - 6 cols, 1 5/6, 1/8 between; A - 6 cols, 1 5/6, 1/8 between; C - 10 cols, 1 1/9, 1/20 between.
Commodity Consumption: Avg. Page Number Per Issue - Daily 64; Avg. Page Number Per Issue - Plates Used 156000; Avg. Page Number Per Issue - Saturday 84; Avg. Page Number Per Issue - Sunday 158; widths 12 1/2; Newsprint Used - Short Tons 17500; Printing Ink Used - Black 261900;
Equipment EDITORIAL: Front-end Software – HI/8900, HI/XP-21 Newsmaker.; Editorial Hardware – HI/XP-21; Editorial Equipment – Lf/AP Server, 110-HI/Newsmaker Editorial terminal, AU/108S, AU/3850, 70-Ethernet Network; Editorial Printers – Typhoon/Graphics pagescan 3 CLASSIFIED: Front-end Software – HI/windows cash.; Classified Hardware – Dell/Pentium 133; Classified Equipment – HI/CPAG; Classified Printers – Epson/DFX 5000 DISPLAY: Ad make-up applications – SCS/Layout 8000 7.03; Layout Software – SCS/Layout 8000.; Display Hardware – 2-Dell/Pentium; Display Printers – 2-HP/LaserJet 5 PRODUCTION: Pagination Software – HI/Newsmaker Pagination 8.4.; Production Equipment – Konica, LE, X/7650, Scitex, Eskoscan/20245; Cameras – C/Spartan III; Scanners – 2-X/7650, Eskoscan/20245 PRESSROOM: Line 1 – 8-G/Metroliner double width 1983; Line 2 – 4-G/Headliner double width 1992, 4-G/Headliner double width 1984; Folders – 4; Pasters – G/Hall Effect; Reels and Stands – 16; Press control system – G/PCS II; Press registration system – Hand Wheel/Side MAILROOM: Counter stackers – 4-QWI/350, 4-QWI/400; Inserters and stuffers – 14-GMA/SLS, 26-GMA/SLS; Bundle tying machines – 8/Dynaric, 3-EAM-Mosca; Mailroom control system – GMA/SAM; Addressing machine – 3-Wm/hand labelers, 1-/KR; Other equipment – MM/335. BUSINESS COMPUTERS: Business Software – Gannett, Genesys/VO1 M08: Advertising, Gannett, Genesys/V01 M08: Circulation, Microsoft/Exchange Server 2000 E-mail System, Microsoft/Office 2000: Desktop Suite, Lawson/R6 (GL and AP): Finance, Cyb; Business Hardware – IBM/Netinity PC Server, IBM/AS-400

GREENWOOD

THE INDEX-JOURNAL

610 Phoenix St., Greenwood, S.C., 29646; gen tel (864) 223-1411; adv tel (864) 943-2509; ed tel (864) 223-1811; gen fax (864) 223-7331; ed fax (864) 223-7331; gen e-mail newsrelease@indexjournal.com; web site www.indexjournal.com

Published: Mon, Tues, Wed, Thur, Fri, Sat, Sun
Weekday Frequency: m
Saturday Frequency: m
Circulation: 12,205; 13,601(sat); 13,008(sun)
Last Audit: ABC September 30, 2011
Price: 2.25/wk; 9.75/mo; 105.30/yr.
Advertising: Open inch rate $21.50
News services: AP, NEA.
Politics: Independent. **Established:** 1919
Magazines: Parade (S).
CEO/Pub ....Judith M. Burns
Exec. Controller ....Richard Jackson
Adv. Dir. ....Pam Still
Exec. Mktg. Dir. ....Harry L. Garrett
Circ. Mgr. ....Albert Ashley
Exec. Editorial Ed. ....William A. Collins
Exec. News Ed. ....Richard Whiting
Living/Lifestyle Ed. ....Joe Sitarz
Web Page Ed. ....Bob Simmonds
MIS Sys. Operator ....Jill Carlisle
Prodn. Sys. Mgr. ....Roger Burton
Prodn. Supvr. ....Cheryl Gurney
Prodn. Foreman, Pressroom ....Eddie Lithan
Prodn. Foreman, Mailroom ....Kevin Coleman
Market Information: Split run; TMC.
Mechanical available: Offset; Black and 3 ROP colors; insert accepted; page cutoffs - 22 3/4.
Mechanical Specifications: Type page 13 x 21 1/2; E - 6 cols, 1 5/6, 1/8 between; A - 6 cols, 1 5/6, 1/8 between; C - 6 cols, 1 5/6, 1/8 between.
Commodity Consumption: Avg. Page Number Per Issue - Daily 108; Avg. Page Number Per Issue - Plates Used 6200; Avg. Page Number Per Issue - Sunday 136; widths 27 1/2; Newsprint Used - Short Tons 800; Printing Ink Used - Black 2500; Printing Ink Used - Color 1000; Printing Ink U
Equipment EDITORIAL: Front-end Software – Oracle/8, FSI/METS, QPS/QuarkXPress, Mk.; Editorial Hardware – Mk, Microsoft/Windows NT Server CLASSIFIED: Front-end Software – Mk, Oaracle/8, FSI/Advance Sales, QPS/QuarkXPress.; Classified Hardware – FSI, Microsoft/Windows NT Server DISPLAY: Ad make-up applications – Other Equipment ☐ APP/Mac CD-Rom, APP/Mac Scanner.; Display Hardware – APP/Mac; Display Printers – LaserMaster/1200, APP/Mac LaserWriter NTX; Production Equipment – 1-Nat; Cameras – 1-VG/Daylighter, 1-C/Spartan III. PRESSROOM: Line 1 – HI/Cotrell 845 1971; Line 2 – 5-HI/Cotrell 845 1971; Line 3 – 1-HI/Cotrell 845 1987; Folders – 1; Reels and Stands – May-71; Press control system – 1-1971. MAILROOM: Counter stackers – BG/109; Inserters and stuffers – 2/MM; Bundle tying machines – MLN.

HILTON HEAD

THE ISLAND PACKET

10 Buck Island Rd., Bluffton, S.C., 29910; gen tel (843) 706-8100; adv tel (843) 706-8100; ed tel (843) 706-8111; gen fax (843) 706-5050; adv fax (843) 706-5050; ed fax (843) 706-3070; gen e-mail info@islandpacket.com; adv e-mail ads@islandpacket.com; ed e-mail newsroom@islandpacket.com; web site www.islandpacket.com

Published: Mon, Tues, Wed, Thur, Fri, Sat, Sun
Weekday Frequency: m
Saturday Frequency: m
Circulation: 17,785; 20,372(sat); 20,766(sun)
Last Audit: ABC September 30, 2011
Price: 12.00/mo; 108.00/yr.
Advertising: Open inch rate $43.00
News services: AP, MCT, NYT, Pony Wire, SHNS.
Politics: Independent. **Established:** 1970
Special Editions: Heritage Week Golf Special (Apr); Football (Aug); Last Minute Santa (Dec); Tax Pages (Feb); Business Expo (Jan); Summer Golf (Jul); Father's Day (Jun); Home & Garden (Mar); Mother's Day (May); Holiday Gift Guide (Nov); Lowcountry Living Home Decorating (O
Special Weekly Sections: Business (Fri); Homes & Real Estate (S); Family (Sat); People (Thur); Health (Tues); Food (Wed).
Magazines: Parade (S).
Pub ....Sara Johnson Borton
Finance Dir. ....Cindy Paulbee
HR Dir. ....Jolie Bagonzi
Adv. Dir. ....Sandy Gills
Adv. Mgr., Classified ....Susan Green
Mktg./Promo. Dir. ....Beth Patton
Exec. Ed. ....Fitz McAden
Mng. Ed. ....Sally Mahan
City Ed. ....Don McClaude
Editorial Page Ed. ....Janet Smith
Features Ed. ....Tom Robinette
Sports Ed. ....Lincee Hanlin
New Media Dir. ....David Feld
Audiotex Mgr. ....Matt Engles
Mgmt. Info Servs. Mgr. ....Bryan Webb
Prodn. Dir. ....William King
Mechanical available: Offset; Black and 3 ROP colors; insert accepted; page cutoffs - 21.
Mechanical Specifications: Type page 11 5/8 x 21; E - 6 cols, 1 4/5, 1/8 between; A - 6 cols, 1 4/5, 1/8 between; C - 9 cols, 1 1/5, 1/8 between.
Commodity Consumption: Avg. Page Number Per Issue - Daily 26; Avg. Page Number Per Issue - Sunday 75.
Equipment EDITORIAL: Front-end Software – Baseview/IQue.; Editorial Hardware – CD, APP/Mac; Editorial Printers – HP/LaserJet 4MV CLASSIFIED: Front-end Software – Baseview/Classified.; Classified Hardware – CD, APP/Mac; Classified Printers – HP/LaserJet 4Plus DISPLAY: Ad make-up applications – Multi-Ad/Creator 4.01, QPS/QuarkXPress 4.04, Aldus/FreeHand 8.0, Adobe/Photoshop 5.5, Adobe/Illustrator 5.0; Layout Software – APP/Mac.; Display Hardware – 9-APP/Power Mac; Display Printers – Graphic Enterprises/Pagescan 3, HP/Laser 4V PRODUCTION: Pagination Software – QPS/QuarkXPress 3.31.; Production Equipment – Caere/OmniPage 3.0, AG/Accuset 1500; Cameras – 1-Nu; Scanners – Polaroid/SprintScan 35, Microtek/Scanmaker III, Microtek/Scanmaker 6002S, Microtek/Scanmaker IV; Audio Hardware – PEP, Brite Voice Systems, Brite Voice Systems; Business Hardware – 1-HP/3000 Series 58

MYRTLE BEACH

THE SUN NEWS

914 Frontage Rd. E., Myrtle Beach, S.C., 29577; gen tel (843) 626-8555; adv tel (843) 626-0240; ed tel (843) 626-0300; gen fax (843) 626-0208 (Customer Serv.); adv fax (843) 626-0328; ed fax (843) 626-0356; gen e-mail service@thesunnews.com; ed e-mail opinions@thesunnews.com; web site www.myrtlebeachonline.com

Published: Mon, Tues, Wed, Thur, Fri, Sat, Sun
Weekday Frequency: m
Saturday Frequency: m
Circulation: 35,230; 39,559(sat); 50,607(sun)
Last Audit: ABC September 30, 2011
Price: 171.00/yr; 49.00/13wk, $94.00/6mo.
Advertising: Open inch rate $62.05
News services: AP, NYT, MCT.
Politics: Independent.
Special Editions: Home Improvement (Apr); Community Resource Guide (Aug); NASCAR (Feb); Volunteer of the Year (Jan); Health-Themed 2 (Jun); Myrtle Beach Hospitality Job Fair (Mar); Graduation (May); Design An Ad (Nov); Health-Themed 3 (Oct); Finance (Sept).
Special Weekly Sections: Kicks (Entertainment Section) (Fri); TV (S); Neighbors (Thur); Food (Wed).
Magazines: Parade (S).
Profile: An award-winning daily newspaper serving the coastal Carolinas.
Pub ....P. J. Browning
Vice Pres., Finance ....Manny Berdayes
Adv. Dir. ....Natalie Pruitt
Strategic Ventures Mgr. ....Jody Hazzard
Ed. ....Trisha O'Connor
Mng. Ed. ....Carolyn Murray
Sports Ed. ....Shane Vowen
Prodn. Dir., Opns. ....Mark Webster
Prodn. Mgr. ....Lynette Dudley
Prodn. Mgr., Packaging ....Walt Shrewsbury
Market Information: ADS; Split run; TMC; Zoned editions.
Mechanical available: Offset; Black and 3 ROP colors; insert accepted - spadea; page cutoffs - 21.
Mechanical Specifications: Type page 11 1/2 x 21; E - 6 cols, 1 11/16, 1/6 between; A - 6 cols, 1 11/16, 1/6 between; C - 10 cols, 1 1/20, 1/6 between.
Commodity Consumption: Avg. Page Number Per Issue - Daily 66; Avg. Page Number Per Issue - Plates Used 108000; Avg. Page Number Per Issue - Sunday 222; widths 50; Newsprint Used - Metric Tons 8048; Printing Ink Used - Black 141500; Printing Ink Used - Color 77981; Printing Ink
Equipment EDITORIAL: Front-end Software – AT 4.5.3, GEAC/Cybergraphics, GEAC/Cybernews, GEAC/Cyberpage 1.4.3.; Editorial Hardware – 5-AT, DEC/Alpha; Editorial Equipment – 8-APP/Mac; Editorial Printers – 2-QMS/2060, 1-HP/5000, 2-HP/1050C CLASSIFIED: Front-end Software – MS/NT 4.0, Cyber$ell.; Classified Hardware – 1-Cybergraphics, 1-Cybergraphics DISPLAY: Ad make-up applications – QPS/QuarkXPress 4.0, GEAC, All/Ad Manager; Layout Software – GEAC/World Class Series.; Display Hardware – 16-APP/Mac, Sun/Sparc 10; Display Printers – QMS/2060 PRODUCTION: Pagination Software – Cybergraphics, AU/Oman NT.; Production Equipment – Caere/OmniPage 3.0, 1-Nu/Flip Top FT40APRNS63, Adobe/Photoshop 5.5, C/66F; Cameras – 1-R/500, 1-C/Spartan II 1244 PRESSROOM: Line 1 – 6-G/Headliner offset double width (4 half decks); Folders – 1-G/3:2, 1-KAN/Quarterfolder Labeler; Pasters – 6-G/CT50; Press control system – 1-G/MPCS. MAILROOM: Counter stackers – HL/Monitors, HL/HT, HL/HT II, S/Olympian, QWI/400; Inserters and stuffers – 1-MM/275, S/472-NP100 Gripper System; Bundle tying machines – 1/MLN, 1-/Power Strap, 3-/Dynaric; Addressing machine – 1-/Quarterfolder Labeler, KAN/600.; Audio Hardware – Micro Voice BUSINESS COMPUTERS: Business Software – CJ; Business Hardware – HP/3000 model 947, HP/9000 model E55

ORANGEBURG

SUNBELT NEWSPAPERS, INC.

1010 Broughton St. SW, Orangeburg, S.C., 29115; gen tel (803) 533-5500; gen fax (803) 533-5526

THE TIMES AND DEMOCRAT

1010 Broughton St. SW, Orangeburg, S.C., 29115; gen tel (803) 533-5500; adv tel (803) 534-3352; ed tel (803) 534-1060; gen fax (803) 533-5557; adv fax (803) 533-5526; ed fax (803) 533-5595; gen e-mail info@timesanddemocrat.com; adv e-mail ads@timesanddemocrat.com; ed e-mail news@timesanddemocrat.com; web site www.tandd.com

Published: Mon, Tues, Wed, Thur, Fri, Sat, Sun
Weekday Frequency: m
Saturday Frequency: m
Circulation: 11,863; 14,899(sat); 12,351(sun)
Last Audit: ABC September 30, 2011
Price: 12.95/mo; 145.59/yr.
Advertising: Open inch rate $23.70
News services: AP.
Politics: Independent. **Established:** 1881
Not Published: Dec. 26.
Special Editions: Home Improvement (Apr); Football (Aug); Greetings (Dec); Progress (Feb); Bridal (Jan); Car Care (Jun); Spring Fashion (Mar); Health & Fitness (May); Gift Guide (Nov); Car Care (Oct).
Special Weekly Sections: Religion (Fri); Farm/Garden (Mon); Lifestyles/Home Decor (S); Kids (Sat); Arts/Leisure/Travel (Thur); Health/Fitness (Tues); Food (Wed).
Magazines: Relish (Monthly); USA WEEKEND Magazine (S); American Profile (Weekly).
Pub. ....Cathy C. Hughes
Controller ....Barbara Beach
Adv. Dir. ....Kayla Wiser
Mktg./Promo. ....Carla Hall
City Ed. ....Jeanne Crader
Editorial Page Ed. ....Lee Harter
Features Ed. ....Wendy Crader
Photographer ....Larry Hardy
Regl. Ed. ....Carol Barker
Sports Ed. ....Brian Linder
Data Processing Mgr. ....Georgianne Walton
Mgmt. Info Servs. Mgr. ....Jerry Harvill
Prodn. Mgr. ....Jim Spears
Prodn. Mgr., Distr. ....Barbara West-Ravenell
Prodn. Foreman, Pressroom ....Russell Cain
Market Information: TMC; Zoned editions.
Mechanical available: Offset; Black and 3 ROP colors; insert accepted; page cutoffs - 21.
Mechanical Specifications: Type page 13 x 21; E - 6 cols, 2 1/16, 1/8 between; A - 6 cols, 2 1/16, 1/8 between; C - 9 cols, 1 1/4, 1/8 between.
Commodity Consumption: Avg. Page Number Per Issue - Daily 28; Avg. Page Number Per Issue - Plates Used 10000; Avg. Page Number Per Issue - Saturday 20; Avg. Page Number Per Issue - Sunday 50; widths 27 1/2; Newsprint Used - Metric Tons 1250; Printing Ink Used - Black 20000; Pr
Equipment EDITORIAL: Front-end Software – Lotu; Editorial Hardware – PC, APP/Mac, APP/Mac G3; Editorial Equipment – 1-APP/Mac Scanner, 1-Artec/Viewstation ATIZ scanner, 1-AGFA/Horizon flatbed scanner, 1-Epson/836 XL Color Scanner, 1-HP/Scanjet 5p Scanner; Editorial Printers – 1-Lexmark/Optra Lxi, 1-HP/Laserjet IIIp CLASSIFIED: Front-end Software – IslandWrite 4.1, HP/LaserJet IIIp.; Classified Hardware – 4-Sun/Microsys 4-110, 3-Sun/Sparc Station DISPLAY: Ad make-up applications – QPS/QuarkXPress 4.04, Adobe/Illustrator 8.0, Adobe/Acrobat 4.0, Adobe/Photoshop 5.5; Display Hardware – APP/Mac, APP/Mac G3; Display Printers – 1-HP/Laserjet 4050N, 1-HP/Laserjet 5000GN, 1-HP Laserjet 4V PRODUCTION: Pagination Software – QPS/QuarkXPress 4.04.; Production Equipment – Caere/OmniPage 8.0, 1-LE; Cameras – 1-C PRESSROOM: Line 1 – 7-G/Urbanite; Folders – 1-G/Urbanite w/balloon former; Press registration system – Stoesser/Register Systems. MAILROOM: Counter stackers – 2-Id/Marathon, TMSI/HT2 Stacker; Inserters and stuffers – 1/MM; Bundle tying machines – 2-Si, 1-/OVL.; Business Hardware – Sun/Microsys 410

ROCK HILL

THE HERALD

132 W. Main St., Rock Hill, S.C., 29730; gen tel (803) 329-4000; gen fax (803) 909-4202; adv fax (803) 329-4028; ed fax (803) 329-4021; gen e-mail webmaster@heraldonline.com; ed e-mail posmundson@heraldonline.com; web site www.heraldonline.com

Published: Mon, Tues, Wed, Thur, Fri, Sat, Sun
Weekday Frequency: m
Saturday Frequency: m
Circulation: 20,892; 22,258(sat); 25,553(sun)
Last Audit: ABC September 30, 2011
Price: 8.50/mo; 97.00/yr.
Advertising: Open inch rate $43.35
News services: AP, LAT-WP, McClatchy, DF, SHNS, NYT.
Politics: Independent. **Established:** 1872
Special Editions: Come See Me (Apr); Back-to-School (Aug); Last Minute Gift Guide (Dec); York County Magazine (Feb); Health Horizons (Jan); Health Horizons (Jun); Newspapers in Education Student Stories (Mar); Emergency Medical Services (May); Wrap-up Christmas Early (Nov)
Special Weekly Sections: Automotive (Fri); TV Herald (S); Home & Real Estate (Sat); Star Watch (Wed).
Magazines: Parade (Fri).
Pub. ....Debbie Abels
Dir., Finance ....Elizabeth Williams
Dir., HR ....Beth Taylerson
Admin. Asst. ....Bette Christensen
Adv. Dir., Sales ....Kim Woods
Outside Sales Mgr. ....Sonya Van Sickle
Adv. Mgr., Nat'l/Preprint ....Eva Jenkins
Ed ....Paul Osmundson
Editorial Page Ed. ....James Werrell
Lifestyle Ed. ....Jennifer Becknell
News Ed. ....Chris Sherk
Photo Ed. ....Andy Burriss
Sports Ed. ....Gary McCann
Dir., New Media ....Mike Martoccia
New Media Mgr. ....Justin McGuire
Prodn. Dir. ....Patricia Simons
Market Information: ADS; TMC.
Mechanical available: Offset; Black and 3 ROP colors; insert accepted - books, envelopes; page cutoffs - 22 3/4.
Mechanical Specifications: Type page 11 1/2 x 21 1/2; E - 6 cols, 1 13/16, 1/8 between; A - 6 cols, 1 13/16, 1/8 between; C - 9 cols, 1 1/6, 1/16 between.
Commodity Consumption: Avg. Page Number Per Issue - Daily 38; Avg. Page Number Per Issue - Plates Used 30000; Avg. Page Number Per Issue - Sunday 50; widths 25; Newsprint Used - Metric Tons 2879; Printing Ink Used - Black 58000; Printing Ink Used - Color 31000; Printing Ink Us
Equipment EDITORIAL: Front-end Software – News Edit/Pro I QUE 3.4.3.; Editorial Hardware – APP/iMac, 15-APP/Mac G4, 3-APP/Mac G3, 23-APP/iMac; Editorial Equipment – Nikon/LS-3510AF, Kk/RFS 2035 Plus; Editorial Printers – HP/Laser Jet 8100 CLASSIFIED: Front-end Software – Baseview/Ad Manager/Pro 2.0.6.; Classified Hardware – 1-APP/Power Mac 7300/266, 6-APP/Power Mac G3/300; Classified Printers – HP/Laser Jet 4300 dtns DISPLAY: Ad make-up applications – Adobe/Photoshop 7.0, QPS/QuarkXPress 4.1, Macromedia/Freehand 10; Layout Software – Managing Editor/ALS, ALS/Page Di; Display Hardware – 5-APP/Mac G4, 11-APP/Mac G3; Display Printers – HP/Laserjet 8000N PRODUCTION: Pagination Software – QPS/QuarkXPress 4.0.; Production Equipment – Caere/OmniPage Pro 8, Accuset/1500 Plus, HP/Laserjet 8000N PRESSROOM: Line 1 – 10-G/Urbanite, 1-DEV; Press Drives – 2-GE/150 h.p. DC; Folders – G/Urbanite 1000 Series 2:1; Reels and Stands – 2 MAILROOM: Counter stackers – Id, HL, QWI; Inserters and stuffers – HI/848, HI/1372; Bundle tying machines – NT 40 Samuel; Addressing machine – Wink Jet; Other equipment –Muller/Minuteman. AUDIO: Audio Software – NT 24; Audio Hardware – Phoenix Marketing BUSINESS COMPUTERS: Business Software – CJ; Business Hardware – HP/3000-918 RX

SENECA

DAILY JOURNAL/MESSENGER

210 W. N. First St., Seneca, S.C., 29678; gen tel (864) 882-2375; gen fax (864) 882-2381; web site www.upstatetoday.com

Published: Tues, Wed, Thur, Fri, Sat
Weekday Frequency: m
Circulation: 9,676; 9,676(sat)
Last Audit: September 30, 2006
Price: 72.00/yr.
Advertising: Open inch rate $17.56
News services: AP, DF, DJ.
Magazines: American Profile (Weekly).
Owner ....Jerry Edwards
Pub. ....Michael Leonard
Office Mgr. ....Linda Garren
Adv. Dir. ....Diana Augustine
Circ. Dir. ....Scott Nickels
Mng. Ed. ....Brett McLaughlin
Graphics Coord. ....Vicki Tymon
Sports Ed. ....Steven Bradley
Pressroom Mgr. ....Michael Watts
Mechanical available: Offset; Black and 3 ROP colors; insert accepted; page cutoffs - 22.
Mechanical Specifications: Type page 11 1/2 x 21; E - 6 cols, 1 13/16, between; A - 6 cols, 1 13/16, between; C - 6 cols, 1 13/16, between.
Commodity Consumption: widths 25.

SPARTANBURG

HERALD-JOURNAL

189 W. Main St., Spartanburg, S.C., 29306; gen tel (864) 582-4511; adv tel (864) 582-4511; ed tel (864) 582-4511 ext. 7210; adv fax (864) 594-6349; ed fax (864) 594-6350; web site www.goupstate.com

Published: Mon, Tues, Wed, Thur, Fri, Sat, Sun
Weekday Frequency: m
Saturday Frequency: m
Circulation: 32,247; 32,347(sat); 42,405(sun)
Last Audit: ABC September 30, 2011
Price: 11.10/mo; 127.20/yr (carrier), $252.00/yr (mail).
Advertising: Open inch rate $104.78
News services: AP, NYT, MCT.
Politics: Independent.
Special Editions: Earth Day (Apr); Football (Aug); Gift Guide (Dec); Auto Racing (Feb); Brides (Jan); Cookbook (Jul); Prime Time (Jun); Lawn & Garden/Home Improvement (Mar); Showcase of Homes (May); Automotive Showcase (Nov); Duke Power-Energy (Oct); Arts Council (Sept).
Special Weekly Sections: Entertainment (Fri); Real Estate (S); Church News (Sat); Best Food Day (Wed).
Magazines: TV Magazine (S).
Pub. ....Roger Quinn
Controller ....Michele May
Dir., Finance Serv. ....Fred Klapper
Dir., HR ....Tracie Foster
Adv. Dir. ....Kathy Powell
Adv. Mgr., Classified ....Tom Doucet
Circ. Dir. ....Ken Smith
Exec. Ed. ....Carl E. Beck
Mng. Ed. ....Greg Retsinas
Bus. Ed. ....Bob Dalton
Columnist ....Lou Parris
Copy Ed. ....Ann Patterson
Editorial Page Ed. ....Mike Smith
Entertainment Writer ....Jose Franco
Graphics/Design Ed. ....Jeff Zehr
News. Ed. ....Dianne Norman
Photo Ed. ....Tom Pritty
Sports. Ed. ....Burke Noel
Audiotex Mgr. ....Babette Cubitt
Regl. IT Dir. ....Cathy Miller
Market Information: TMC.
Mechanical available: Offset; Black and 3 ROP colors; insert accepted; page cutoffs - 22.
Mechanical Specifications: Type page 13 x 21 1/4; E - 6 cols, 2 1/16, 1/8 between; A - 6 cols, 2 1/16, 1/8 between; C - 9 cols, 1 3/8, 1/16 between.
Commodity Consumption: Avg. Page Number Per Issue - Daily 48; Avg. Page Number Per Issue - Plates Used 81649; Avg. Page Number Per Issue - Sunday 90; widths 27; Newsprint Used - Metric Tons 8012; Printing Ink Used - Black 135845; Printing Ink Used - Color 61725; Printing Ink U
Equipment EDITORIAL: Front-end Software – AT.; Editorial Hardware – AT/Series 4; Editorial Equipment – APP/Mac II fx, APP/Mac IIci, AG/Arcus Scanners, 2-APP/Power Mac 8100-80; Editorial Printers – APP/Mac LaserWriter NTX, HP/4MV CLASSIFIED: Front-end Software – AT/IAS.; Classified Hardware – AT/Series 4; Classified Printers – Dataproducts/8500 DISPLAY: Ad make-up applications – QPS/QuarkXPress 3.3.1, Multi-Ad, Adobe/Photoshop 3.0.4; Display Hardware – 9-APP/Mac Quadra Graphics Workstation; Display Printers – APP/Mac LaserWriter II NTX, APP/Mac Select 360F; Production Equipment – Typereader 1.1, 2-Pre Press/Panther Pro, 1-APP/Mac Scanner; Cameras – 1-C/Spartan; Scanners – ECR/Autokon 1000DE, 3-AG/Arcus, 2-Umax/2400x. PRESSROOM: Line 1 – 8-G/Headliner (4 color decks); Folders – 1-G/3:2; Pasters – G/CT 45. MAILROOM: Counter stackers – 3-Id/2000; Inserters and stuffers – 1-HI/1472; Bundle tying machines – 3/Power Strap/PSN5; Addressing machine – 1-/KR. AUDIO: Audio Software – Brite Voice Systems; Audio Hardware – Brite Voice Systems/Bus-2000 BUSINESS COMPUTERS: Business Software – INSI, Microsoft/Excel; Business Hardware – IBM/AS-400 36

SUMTER

THE ITEM

20 N. Magnolia St., Sumter, S.C., 29150-4940; gen tel (803) 774-1200; adv tel (803) 774-1236; ed tel (803) 774-1226; gen fax (803) 775-1024; adv fax (803) 774-1288; ed fax (803) 774-1210; ed e-mail news@theitem.com; web site www.theitem.com

Published: Tues, Wed, Thur, Fri, Sat
Weekday Frequency: m
Saturday Frequency: m
Circulation: 14,325; 14,325(sat)
Last Audit: Sworn December 30, 2010
Price: 10.00/mo; 99.18/yr.
Advertising: Open inch rate $17
Insert rate: $55.00
News services: AP, NEA.
Politics: Independent. **Established:** 1894
Not Published: Thanksgiving; Christmas, New Years
Own facility?: Y
Special Editions: Gift Guide (Dec); Bride & Groom (Jan); Weddings (Jun); Home & Gardens (Mar); Readers Choice (June);Summertime (May); Parade of Shops (Nov); Extraordinary Women (Oct);
Special Weekly Sections: Local Events & Activities (Fri); The Mini Page (Mon); History/Community (S); Religion (Sat); Kids Scoop (Thur); Career Connection (Tues); Recipes & Ideas (Wed).
Magazines: Parade (S); Relish, Spree, Athlon Sports
Co-Pres. ....Graham Osteen
Co-Pres. ....Kyle Osteen
Vice Pres./Publisher ....Jack Osteen
SearchSumter.com Manager .....Mary Don Boyle
Classified ....Bobby Touchberry
Circ. Dir. ....Earle Woodward
Editor and Chairman ....Hubert D. Osteen
Features Ed. ....Ivy Moore
Living/Lifestyle Ed. ....Rhonda Barrick
Managing Editor ....Tonyia McGirt
General Manager ....Larry Miller
Market Information: TMC; Zoned editions.
Mechanical available: Offset; Black and 3 ROP

colors; insert accepted - min. 4 x 6; page cutoffs - 21 1/2.
Mechanical Specifications: Type page 12 1/2 x 21 1/2; E - 6 cols, 2 1/16, 1/6 between; A - 6 cols, 2 1/16, 1/6 between; C - 8 cols, 1 1/2, 1/12 between.
Commodity Consumption: Avg. Page Number Per Issue - Daily 36; Avg. Page Number Per Issue - Sunday 48; widths 12 1/2; Newsprint Used - Short Tons 1600; Printing Ink Used - Black 18000; Printing Ink Used - Color 1200.
Equipment; Editorial Hardware – Newsware; Editorial Printers – Various; Classified Hardware – Newsware; Classified Printers – Various DISPLAY: Ad make-up applications – QPS/QuarkXPress, Multi-Ad/Creator, Aldus/FreeHand, Adobe/Illustrator, In-Design, Microsoft/Word, Microsoft/Excel 4.0, Claris/MacDraw II; Display Hardware – APP/Mac; Display Printers – HP/LaserJet IV, HP/DeskWriter C, APP/Mac Personal LaserWriter; Production Equipment – 2-ECR/Pelbox 3850, Adobe/Photoshop, 1-Konica/4000, 1-Digi-Colour; Cameras – 1-Nu; Scanners – 1-AU, 5-Flatbed/Scanner.; Press Drives – 3 MAILROOM: Counter stackers – 1-BG/Count-O-Veyor, 2/QWI; Inserters and stuffers – 1-MM/6:1; Bundle tying machines – 2-/Dynaric; Wrapping singles – 1-/QWI; Addressing machine – 1-/KAN; Other equipment –1-/Trimmer, 4-/Stitcher.
Delivery method: Mail, Newsstand, Private Carrier, Racks

UNION

UNION DAILY TIMES

100 Times Blvd., Union, S.C., 29379; gen tel (864) 427-1234; adv tel (864) 427-1234; ed tel (864) 427-1234; gen fax (864) 427-1237; adv fax (864) 427-1237; ed fax (864) 427-1237; gen e-mail editor@uniondailytimes.com; adv e-mail asummerlin@uniondailytimes.com; ed e-mail gwilliams@uniondailytimes.com; web site www.uniondailytimes.com
Published: Mon, Tues, Wed, Thur, Fri, Sat
Weekday Frequency: e
Circulation: 6,409; 6,409(sat)
Last Audit: March 31, 2007
Price: 8.00/mo; 96.00/yr.
Advertising: Open inch rate $11.95
News services: NEA, AP.
Politics: Independent.
Not Published: Christmas.
Special Editions: Gardening (Apr); Football (Aug); Christmas (Dec); FYI-For Your Information (Jan); Graduation (May); Uniquely Union Festival (Oct); NASCAR Prime Time (Seniors) (Quarterly).
Magazines: American Profile (Sat).
Pub....Ty Ransdell
Adv. Mgr.....Donna McMurray
Features Ed....Julia Garmon
Sports Ed....Brian Whitmore
Women's Ed.....Graham Williams
Prodn. Mgr., Mailroom....Don Cody
Market Information: Split run; TMC.
Mechanical available: Offset; Black and 3 ROP colors; insert accepted; page cutoffs - 21 1/2.
Mechanical Specifications: Type page 12 1/2 x 21 1/2; E - 6 cols, 2, 1/8 between; A - 6 cols, 2, 1/8 between; C - 9 cols, 1 1/3, 1/8 between.
Commodity Consumption: Avg. Page Number Per Issue - Daily 14; Avg. Page Number Per Issue - Plates Used 12000; Avg. Page Number Per Issue - Saturday 12; widths 25; Newsprint Used - Short Tons 680; Printing Ink Used - Black 21000; Printing Ink Used - Color 3000; Printing Ink Used
Equipment EDITORIAL: Front-end Software – Baseview.; Editorial Hardware – APP/Mac; Editorial Equipment – Accuset/1200, Konica/Jetsetter 3100; Editorial Printers – APP/Mac LaserWriter II NTX CLASSIFIED: Front-end Software – Baseview.; Classified Hardware – APP/Mac; Classified Equipment – Accuset/1200; Classified Printers – APP/Mac LaserWriter II NTX, HP/LaserJet DISPLAY: Ad make-up applications – QPS/QuarkXPress, Aldus/PageMaker, Aldus/FreeHand, Adobe/Photoshop, Baseview; Layout Software – APP/Mac Quadra.; Display Hardware – APP/Mac; Display Printers – APP/Mac LaserWriter II NTX, Accuset/1200, HP/LaserJet PRODUCTION: Pagination Software – QPS/QuarkXPress 3.32.; Production Equipment – Accuset, Konica/Jetsetter 3100; Cameras – SCREEN; Scanners – AG/Arcus, Abaton, Nikon PRESSROOM: Line 1 – 9-KP/News King (KJ-8 balloon former); Press Drives – GE/100 h.p.; Press control system – 8-ATR/Tensioning System 1981. MAILROOM: Counter stackers – 1-BG/Count-O-Veyor; Inserters and stuffers – KANSA; Bundle tying machines – 2-Miller/Bevco Strapmatic. BUSINESS COMPUTERS: Business Software – BSI; Business Hardware – PC

SOUTH DAKOTA

ABERDEEN

ABERDEEN AMERICAN NEWS

PO Box 4430, Aberdeen, S.D., 57402-4430; gen tel (605) 225-4100; web site www.aberdeennews.com
Group: Schurz Communications Inc

AMERICAN NEWS

124 S. Second St., Aberdeen, S.D., 57401-4010; gen tel (605) 225-4100; adv tel (605) 225-4100; ed tel (605) 622-2318; gen fax (605) 229-7532; adv fax (605) 229-3954; ed fax (605) 225-0421; adv e-mail classified@aberdeennews.com; ed e-mail americannews@aberdeennews.com; web site www.aberdeennews.com
Published: Mon, Tues, Wed, Thur, Fri, Sat, Sun
Weekday Frequency: m
Saturday Frequency: m
Circulation: 14,958; 15,258(sat); 16,416(sun)
Last Audit: September 30, 2008
Price: 13.54/mo; 167.44/yr.
Advertising: Open inch rate $40.43
News services: AP, MCT.
Politics: Independent. **Established:** 1885
Special Editions: Back-to-School (Aug); Christmas Gift Guide (Dec); Dakota Decades (Other); Spring Car Care (Spring).
Special Weekly Sections: Cars Plus (Fri); Saver (Mon); Comics (S); Church Page (Sat); Out & About (Entertainment) (Thur); Best Food Day (Wed).
Magazines: Relish (Monthly); Parade (S); American Profile (Weekly).
Dir., Finance....Lori Salfrank
Dir., HR....Amy Jones
Adv. Dir.....Christy Orwig
Circ. Dir.....David Nelson
Sports Ed.....John Papendick
Women's Ed.....Jeff Bahr
Mgmt. Info Servs. Mgr.....Marcia Sebert
Prodn. Mgr.....Terry Salfrank
Market Information: TMC.
Mechanical available: Offset; Black and 3 ROP colors; insert accepted; page cutoffs - 22 3/4.
Mechanical Specifications: Type page 12 1/2 x 21 1/2; E - 6 cols, 2, 1/8 between; A - 6 cols, 2, 1/8 between; C - 9 cols, 1 1/4, 1/8 between.
Commodity Consumption: Avg. Page Number Per Issue - Daily 26; Avg. Page Number Per Issue - Plates Used 25500; Avg. Page Number Per Issue - Sunday 56; widths 12 1/2; Newsprint Used - Metric Tons 1644; Newsprint Used - Short Tons 1664; Printing Ink Used - Black 60200; Printing I
Equipment EDITORIAL: Front-end Software – DTI.; Editorial Hardware – DTI; Editorial Printers – HP/Laserjet 5000 CLASSIFIED: Front-end Software – DTI/ClassSpeed.; Classified Hardware – DTI; Classified Printers – HP/Laserjet 5000 DISPLAY: Ad make-up applications – Multi-Ad/Creator 4.01, QPS/QuarkXPress 4.1; Layout Software – DTI/Speed Planner.; Display Hardware – APP/Mac G3 PRODUCTION: Pagination Software – QPS/QuarkXPress 3.3.; Production Equipment – 2-AU/APS-6600, 1-AU/APS-6-82-ACS, AU/APS6-84ACS, Pre Press/Panther Plus 46, Pre Press/Panther Pro 62; Cameras – 1-B/4000, 1-C/Spartan II; Scanners – Lf/Leafscan 35 PRESSROOM: Line 1 – 7-G/Urbanite single width 1973; Folders – 1 MAILROOM: Counter stackers – 1-Id/NS440, 1-QWI/350, QWI/400; Inserters and stuffers – 1-MM/227S (10 station); Bundle tying machines – 1/Power Strap/PSN6E; Addressing machine – 1-Ch/528-010; Other equipment –MM/321 Fox.; Audio Hardware – Micro Voice BUSINESS COMPUTERS: Business Software – CJ, GEAC/AIM 8.02, GEAC/CIS 4.0.1.H, GEAC/2.09.M; Business Hardware – 1-HP/3000-5Y 937 RX

BROOKINGS

BROOKINGS PUBLISHING CO.

312 5th St., Brookings, S.D., 57006; gen tel (605) 692-6271; gen fax (605) 692-2979

BROOKINGS REGISTER

312 5th St., Brookings, S.D., 57006-1924; gen tel (605) 692-6271; gen fax (605) 692-2979; gen e-mail registernews@brookingsregister.com; web site www.brookingsregister.com
Published: Mon, Tues, Wed, Thur, Fri, Sat, Sun
Weekday Frequency: e
Saturday Frequency: m
Circulation: 4,263; 4,263(sat)
Last Audit: September 30, 2009
Price: 1.57/wk; 132.00/yr (carrier).
Advertising: Open inch rate $12.95
News services: AP.
Politics: Independent. **Established:** 1882
Not Published: New Year; Memorial Day; Independence Day; Labor Day; Christmas.
Special Editions: Our Town (Aug); Business People (Jun); Progress (Mar).
Special Weekly Sections: Club & Community News (Fri); Best Food Day (Mon); Arts (Thur); Business (Tues); Youth Features (Wed).
Magazines: American Profile (Weekly).
Mgr.....Kendra Deibert
Adv. Dir.....William McMacken
News Ed.....Doug Kott
Market Information: TMC.
Mechanical available: Offset; Black and 3 ROP colors; insert accepted; page cutoffs - 22 3/4.
Mechanical Specifications: Type page 13 x 21 1/2; E - 6 cols, 2, 3/16 between; A - 6 cols, 2, 3/16 between; C - 6 cols, 2, 3/16 between.
Commodity Consumption: Avg. Page Number Per Issue - Daily 16; Avg. Page Number Per Issue - Plates Used 6000; Avg. Page Number Per Issue - Saturday 16; widths 27; Newsprint Used - Short Tons 248; Printing Ink Used - Black 9500; Printing Ink Used - Color 1400.
Equipment EDITORIAL: Front-end Software – QPS/QuarkXPress, WriteNow.; Editorial Hardware – APP/Mac; Editorial Equipment – Dest/PC Scan 2000, Polaroid/SprintScan, APP/Power Mac with Adobe/Photoshop; Editorial Printers – APP/Mac Laserwriter II, APP/Mac LaserWriter Plus, Xante/1200 CLASSIFIED: Front-end Software – SMS, Baseview/Class Ad.; Classified Hardware – APP/Power Mac 6100; Classified Equipment – Dest/PC Scan 2000; Classified Printers – APP/Mac LaserWriter Plus, Xante/1200 DISPLAY: Ad make-up applications – Claris/MacDraw, Aldus/FreeHand, Multi-Ad/Creator; Layout Software – QPS/QuarkXPress.; Display Hardware – APP/Mac SE, APP/Mac with Radius monitors, APP/Power Mac 7100; Display Printers – APP/Mac LaserWriter Plus, Xante/1200 PRODUCTION: Pagination Software – QPS/QuarkXPress.; Production Equipment – APP/Mac LaserWriter Plus NTX, Xante/1200; Cameras – B/Horizontal PRESSROOM: Line 1 – 5-G/Community 1971; Folders – 1-G/SC (with upper former).; Inserters and stuffers – KAN/480 5:1; Bundle tying machines – 3/Bu; Addressing machine – Ch. BUSINESS COMPUTERS: Business Software – DSI/Paper Trak 2000; Business Hardware – 4-Dec

HURON

HURON PLAINSMAN

49 Third St. SE, Huron, S.D., 57350-1278; gen tel (605) 352-6401; adv tel (605) 353-7421; ed tel (605) 353-7425; gen fax (605) 353-7457; adv fax (605) 353-7422; ed fax (605) 352-7754; gen e-mail plainsman@midco.net; adv e-mail medemail@aol.com; ed e-mail editor.plainsman@midconetwork.com; web site www.plainsman.com
Group: Metro Newspaper Advertising Services, Inc.
Published: Tues, Wed, Thur, Fri, Sat, Sun
Weekday Frequency: m
Circulation: 5,377; 5,377(sat); 5,740(sun)
Last Audit: September 30, 2009
Price: 8.00/mo; 138.30/yr.
Advertising: Open inch rate $16.80
News services: AP.
Politics: Independent.
Advertising not accepted: Mail order.
Not Published: Christmas.
Special Weekly Sections: Extension (Fri); Heartland Happening (S); Extension (Thur); Around Town (Tues); Best Food Day (Wed).
Magazines: Parade (S).
Mgr., Mktg./Promo.....Mark Davis
Ed.....Darian Dudrick
Political Ed.....Roger Larsen
Regl. Ed.....Crystal Pugsley
Sports Ed.....Mike Carroll
Market Information: Split run; TMC; Zoned editions.
Mechanical available: Offset; Black and 3 ROP colors; insert accepted - card, envelope, single sheet; page cutoffs - 13.
Mechanical Specifications: Type page 13 x 21 1/2; E - 6 cols, 2 1/16, 1/8 between; A - 6 cols, 2 1/16, 1/8 between; C - 8 cols, 1 9/16, 1/16 between.
Commodity Consumption: Avg. Page Number Per Issue - Daily 16; Avg. Page Number Per Issue - Plates Used 9550; Avg. Page Number Per Issue - Saturday 16; Avg. Page Number Per Issue - Sunday 40; widths 13 3/4; Newsprint Used - Short Tons 403; Printing Ink Used - Black 10146; Print
Equipment EDITORIAL: Front-end Software – APT, QPS/QuarkXPress 4.0, Adobe/Photoshop 3.0.; Editorial Hardware – 10-PC, 3-APP/Power Mac, 3-PC Pagination Stations; Editorial Equipment – Polaroid/SprintScan 35; Editorial Printers – 1-APP/Mac Laser, 1-LaserMaster/XLO CLASSIFIED: Front-end Software – APT.; Classified Hardware – 4-PC; Classified Printers – 1-APP/Mac Laser DISPLAY: Ad make-up applications – Multi-Ad/Creator, QPS/QuarkXPress 4.0, Adobe/Illustrator; Display Hardware – 4-PC; Display Printers – 1-Xante/1200 dpi 11 x 17 Laser; Production Equipment – 1-Nu; Cameras – 1-Nikon, 1-SCREEN/Horizontal. PRESSROOM: Line 1 – 7-G/Community; Press Drives – 1; Folders – 1-G/SC.; Inserters and stuffers – 5/DG; Bundle tying machines – 1-/Bu; Addressing machine – 1-/Ch. BUSINESS COMPUTERS: Business Software – DSI; Business Hardware – 5-IBM

MADISON

HUNTER PUBLISHING, INC.

214 S. Egan Ave., Madison, S.D., 57042; gen tel (605) 256-4555; gen fax (605) 256-6190

THE MADISON DAILY LEADER

214 S. Egan Ave., Madison, S.D., 57042-0348; gen tel (605) 256-4555; gen fax (605) 256-6190; gen e-mail news@madisondailyleader.com; adv e-mail ads@madisondai-

lyleader.com; ed e-mail news@madisondailyleader.com; web site www.madisondailyleader.com
Published: Mon, Tues, Wed, Thur, Fri
Weekday Frequency: e
Circulation: 3,000
Last Audit: Sworn October 1, 2003
Price: 98.40/yr.
Advertising: Open inch rate $9.00
Insert rate: $55/M
News services: AP, South Dakota Newspaper Association.
Politics: 1880
Advertising not accepted: N
Not Published: New Year; Independence Day; Labor Day; Thanksgiving; Christmas; Memorial Day.
Own facility?: Y
Special Editions: Prairie Village Jamboree (Aug); Business Review & Forecast (Feb); Bridal Guide (Jan); Homeland Garden (May); Senior Scene (Oct).
Special Weekly Sections: TV Guide (Thu); Business (Mon); Grocery (Tues); Agri-News (Wed).
Adv. Mgr.....................................Melissa Hegg
City Ed.....................................Chuck Clement
Editorial Writer..........................Jon M. Hunter
Sports Ed.................................Ariy-El Boynton
Managing Editor...................Marcia Schoeberl
Technology Mgr...............................Jeff Boldt
Market Information: Split run; TMC.
Mechanical available: Offset; Black and 3 ROP colors; insert accepted; page cutoffs - 22 3/4.
Mechanical Specifications: Type page 13 1/10 x 21; E - 6 cols, 2 1/14, 1/8 between; A - 6 cols, 2 1/14, 1/8 between; C - 6 cols, 2 1/14, 1/8 between.
Commodity Consumption: Avg. Page Number Per Issue - Daily 12; Avg. Page Number Per Issue - Plates Used 3000; widths 28; Newsprint Used - Short Tons 120; Printing Ink Used - Pages Printed 3000.
Equipment EDITORIAL: Front-end Software – Suntype/Editorial, Adobe/Photoshop 5.0, QPS/QuarkXPress 4.0.; Editorial Hardware – PC CLASSIFIED: Front-end Software – QPS/QuarkXPress.
InDesign
; Classified Hardware – PC DISPLAY: Ad make-up applications – QPS/QuarkXPress, Adobe/Photoshop, Adobe/Illustrator PRODUCTION: Pagination Software – Evo/Preps; Production Equipment – Kodak Trendsetter CTP PRESSROOM: Line 1 – 10 units combo Quad-Stack/Goss single width; Folders – Atlas MAILROOM: Counter stackers – 1/BG; Inserters and stuffers – 1-Mueller-Martini; Bundle tying machines – 2-/Bu; Wrapping singles – 1-/Bu; Addressing machine – 1-W'Ink Jet; Other equipment –MM/Stitcher-Trimmer. BUSINESS COMPUTERS: Business Software – Synaptic/Advanced, CYMA/AP, CYMA/Payroll, CYMA/GL
Delivery method: Mail, Newsstand, Private Carrier, Racks

MITCHELL

THE DAILY REPUBLIC

120 S. Lawler St., Mitchell, S.D., 57301; gen tel (605) 996-5514; adv tel (605) 996-5515; ed tel (605) 996-5516; gen fax (605) 996-7793; ed fax (605) 996-5020; adv e-mail dailyads@mitchellrepublic.com; ed e-mail dailynews@mitchellrepublic.com; web site www.mitchellrepublic.com
Published: Mon, Tues, Wed, Thur, Fri, Sat
Weekday Frequency: m
Saturday Frequency: m
Circulation: 12,480; 12,742(sat)
Last Audit: March 31, 2007
Price: 2.05/wk (carrier); 11.20/mo; 99.00/yr.
Advertising: Open inch rate $19.65
News services: AP.
Politics: Independent.
Advertising not accepted: Morally offensive.
Not Published: New Year; Memorial Day; Independence Day; Labor Day; Thanksgiving; Christmas.
Special Editions: Car Care Series (Apr); Progress (Aug); Farm & Ranch (Feb); Bridal (Jan); Rodeo (Jul); Bridal (Jun); Home Improvement Series (Mar); Lawn & Garden (May); Christmas Preview (Nov); Hunting Guide (Oct); Fall Home Improvement Series (Sept).
Special Weekly Sections: Best Food Day (Tues).
Magazines: Relish (Monthly); Parade (S).
Pub...Ross Ulrich
Bus. Mgr................................Annette Kroger
Adv. Mgr................................Kevin Flemmer
Circ. Mgr......................................Jon Louder
Ed....Korrie Wenzel
Asst. Ed.....................................Seth Tupper
Sports Ed......................................Leah Rado
Internet/Systems Mgr...................Jessy Stroud
Prodn. Foreman, Pressroom.....Richard Popejoy
Market Information: TMC.
Mechanical available: Offset; Black and 3 ROP colors; insert accepted; page cutoffs - 22 3/4.
Mechanical Specifications: Type page 13 x 21 1/2; E - 6 cols, 2 1/16, 1/8 between; A - 6 cols, 2 1/16, 1/8 between; C - 9 cols, 1 1/2, 1/16 between.
Commodity Consumption: Avg. Page Number Per Issue - Daily 18; Avg. Page Number Per Issue - Plates Used 6448; widths 27 1/2; Newsprint Used - Short Tons 388; Printing Ink Used - Black 10800; Printing Ink Used - Color 900; Printing Ink Used - Pages Printed 5526.
Equipment EDITORIAL: Front-end Software – Windows 95, APT/ACT.; Editorial Hardware – Micron/6200 Prioris PC; Editorial Equipment – APP/Mac; Editorial Printers – AU/108-2, Dataproducts/Typhoon 16 CLASSIFIED: Front-end Software – MS/Windows 95, APT/ACT.; Classified Hardware – Micron/6200 Prioris PC; Classified Printers – AU/108-2, Dataproducts/Typhoon 16 DISPLAY: Ad make-up applications – Multi-Ad, QPS/QuarkXPress, Adobe/Illustrator, Aldus/FreeHand; Layout Software – 2-HAS, APP/Mac.; Display Hardware – APP/Mac; Display Printers – AU/108-2, Dataproducts/Typhoon 16 PRODUCTION: Pagina-

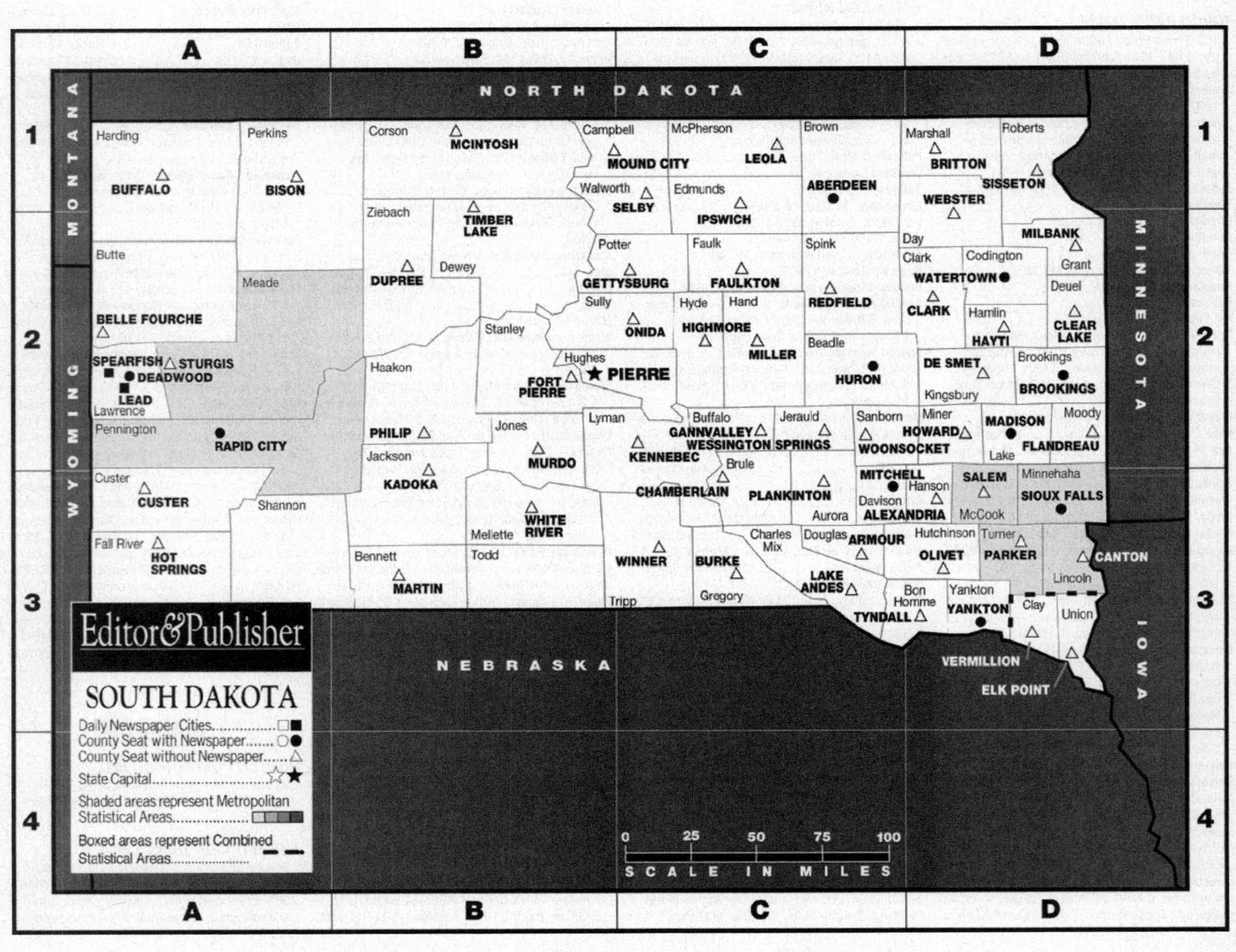

tion Software – CD, QPS/QuarkXPress 3.32.; Production Equipment – Nu/Ultra-Plus Flip Top, Dataproducts/Typhoon 16, DTI/Devotec 20; Cameras – 1-R/Press 500, 1-DSA/C-680-C; Scanners – Lf PRESSROOM: Line 1 – 7-G/Community; Press registration system – Duarte/Pin System.; Bundle tying machines – 2/Carlson; Addressing machine – 1-/KR. BUSINESS COMPUTERS: Business Software – Collier-Jackson Inc, Cort; Business Hardware – ATT, Digital

PIERRE

CAPITAL JOURNAL

333 W. Dakota Ave., Pierre, S.D., 57501; gen tel (605) 224-7301; gen fax (605) 224-9210; gen e-mail office@capjournal.com; toni.rhodes@capjournal.com; adv e-mail april.pullman@capjournal.com; ed e-mail news@capjournal.com; web site www.capjournal.com

Group: Wick Communications
Published: Mon, Tues, Wed, Thur, Fri
Weekday Frequency: m
Circulation: 4,100
Last Audit: Sworn November 23, 2011
Price: 2.00/wk; 7.50/mo; 95.00/yr.
Advertising: Open inch rate $10.62
Insert rate: 62.00
News services: AP.
Politics: Independent. **Established:** 1889
Not Published: New Year; Memorial Day; Independence Day; Labor Day; Thanksgiving; Christmas.
Special Editions: 4-H Finals Rodeo Booklet (Aug); Bridal Tab (Feb); Legislative (Jan); Crazy Days Downtown (Jul); Fourth of July Rodeo (Jun); Home & Garden/Real Estate Tab (Mar); Graduation Brochure (May); Chamber Brochure (Nov); Fire Prevention Tab (Oct); Hunting Guide Bo
Special Weekly Sections: TV Preview (Fri).
Magazines: Reminder Plus (Wed).
Pub. .... Steve Baker
Adv. Mgr. .... April Pullman
Business Manager .... Ona Arnold
Managing Editor .... Lance Nixon
Sports Editor .... Chris Mangen
Operations Manager .... Melanie Handl
Market Information: ADS; TMC.
Mechanical available: Offset; Black and 3 ROP colors; insert accepted; page cutoffs - 22 3/4.
Mechanical Specifications: Type page 13 x 21 1/2; E - 6 cols, 2 1/16, 1/8 between; A - 6 cols, 2 1/16, 1/8 between; C - 8 cols, 1 9/16, 1/8 between.
Commodity Consumption: Avg. Page Number Per Issue - Daily 14; Avg. Page Number Per Issue - Plates Used 8500; widths 28; Newsprint Used - Short Tons 380; Printing Ink Used - Black 6000; Printing Ink Used - Color 120; Printing Ink Used - Pages Printed 4550.
Equipment EDITORIAL: Front-end Software – In-Design; Editorial Hardware – PC; Editorial Printers – APP/Mac LaserWriter, Xante/8200. CLASSIFIED: Front-end Software – MediaSpan; Classified Hardware – Imac; Classified Printers – APP/Mac LaserWriter; Layout Software – APP/Mac.; Display Printers – APP/Mac LaserWriter, Xante; Production Equipment – TextBridge; Cameras – Nikon; Scanners – Polaroid/SprintScan, AG/Arcus II, Epson/800. PRESSROOM: Line 1 – 7-G/Community.; Inserters and stuffers – 5/MM; Bundle tying machines – 2-Bu/String Tyer, OVL; Addressing machine – 1-Ch/Model E base, 1-/Wm. AUDIO: Audio Software – Computer Group/Ads-on-call, Info Line; Audio Hardware – IBM; Business Hardware – 6-IBM/AT

RAPID CITY

RAPID CITY JOURNAL

507 Main St., Rapid City, S.D., 57701; gen tel (605) 394-8300; adv tel (605) 394-8331; ed tel (605) 394-8314; gen fax (605) 394-8446; adv fax (605) 394-8462; ed fax (605) 394-8463; gen e-mail news@rapidcityjournal.com; web site www.rapidcityjournal.com

Group: Lee Enterprises
Metro Suburbia, Inc./Newhouse Newspapers
Published: Mon, Tues, Wed, Thur, Fri, Sat, Sun
Weekday Frequency: m
Saturday Frequency: m
Circulation: 24,842; 26,872(sat); 29,829(sun)
Last Audit: ABC September 30, 2011
Price: 14.49/mo; 195.00/yr.
Advertising: Open inch rate $78.20 daily
News services: AP, LAT-WP, SHNS.
Special Weekly Sections: Black Hills Weekend (Fri); Health & Fitness (Mon); Living (S); Religion (Sat); Home & Garden (Thur); Sports (Tues); Food (Wed).
Magazines: Relish (Monthly); Parade (S); Athlon Sports (Monthly).
Director of Audience Development
Interim Publisher .... Kim Fowler
Adv. Dir. .... Troy Kilpatrick
Adv. Mgr., Retail .... Tim Christofferson
Ed .... Michael LeFort
Prodn. Dir. .... Mark Gibbens
Controller .... Vickie Jorgenson
Pub. .... Brad Slater
Adv. Mgr., Online .... Debbie Renner
IT Systems Support Mgr. .... Chad Ehret
Market Information: Split run; TMC; Zoned editions.
Mechanical available: Offset; Black and 3 ROP colors; insert accepted; page cutoffs - 22.
Mechanical Specifications: Type page 11 5/8 x 21; E - 6 cols, 2 1/16, 1/8 between; A - 6 cols, 2 1/16, 1/8 between; C - 9 cols, 1 3/8, 1/8 between.
Commodity Consumption: Avg. Page Number Per Issue - Daily 36; Avg. Page Number Per Issue - Plates Used 24000; Avg. Page Number Per Issue - Saturday 40; Avg. Page Number Per Issue - Sunday 56; widths 27 1/2; Newsprint Used - Metric Tons 2637; Printing Ink Used - Black 55000; Pr
Equipment EDITORIAL: Front-end Software – Quick Wire, QPS/QuarkXPress, Microsoft/Word, Microsoft/Windows NT.; Editorial Hardware – PC CLASSIFIED: Front-end Software – CText, Microsoft/Windows NT.; Classified Hardware – PC DISPLAY: Ad make-up applications – Multi-Ad/Creator, Adobe/Photoshop, QPS/QuarkXPress; Display Hardware – APP/Power Mac PRODUCTION: Pagination Software – QPS/QuarkXPress 4.1.; Production Equipment – Nu/FlipTop, Na/FX VIII; Cameras – C/Spartan III; Scanners – Umax, AG PRESSROOM: Line 1 – 5-G/Headliner double width (4-color decks); Line 2 – 8-G/Community single width; Folders – 4; Reels and Stands – 5 MAILROOM: Counter stackers – 4-HL/monitor; Inserters and stuffers – 1-MM/227E, 1-HI/1372; Bundle tying machines – 5/MLN; Addressing machine – 1-/Ch.
Delivery method: Mail, Newsstand, Private Carrier, Racks

SIOUX FALLS

ARGUS LEADER

200 S. Minnesota Ave., Sioux Falls, S.D., 57104-6314; gen tel (605) 331-2200; adv tel (605) 331-2355; ed tel (605) 331-2332; gen fax (605) 331-2260; adv fax (605) 331-2371; ed fax (605) 331-2294; ed e-mail editor@argusleader.com; web site www.argusleader.com

Group: Gannett Company, Inc.
Published: Mon, Tues, Wed, Thur, Fri, Sat, Sun
Weekday Frequency: m
Saturday Frequency: m
Circulation: 34,240; 37,797(sat); 53,065(sun)
Last Audit: ABC September 30, 2011
Price: $4.35/wk; $213.95/yr (carrier).
Insert rate: $50 CPM
News services: AP, GNS, MCT.
Politics: 1881
Pres./Pub. .... Randell Beck
Dir., Admin./Controller .... Greg Robinson
Principal HR Business Partner .... Jean Healy
Advertising Director .... Kelly Redfearn
Executive Editor .... Maricarrol Kueter
Managing Editor .... Patrick Lalley
Digital Media Manager .... Cory Myers
Sports Editor .... Stu Whitney
Circulation Director .... Owen Hotvet
Pressroom Mgr. .... Steve Huls
Marketing Director .... Sherry Szadziewicz
Production Manager .... Allen Jungels
IT Manager .... Mike Golden
Adv. Mgr., Retail .... Kristi Grooms
Editorial Page Ed. .... Iyvonne Hawkins
Online Content Ed. .... Cory Meyers
Mechanical available: Offset; Black and 3 ROP colors; insert accepted - inquire; page cutoffs - 22 3/4.
Mechanical Specifications: Type page 12 1/2 x 21 1/2; E - 6 cols, 2 1/16, 1/8 between; A - 6 cols, 2 1/16, 1/8 between; C - 10 cols, 1 7/32, 1/16 between.
Equipment EDITORIAL: Front-end Software – QPS/QuarkXPress 4.11, Copy Desk 2.11, QPS 2.11.; Editorial Hardware – Mac & PC CLASSIFIED: Front-end Software – Mactive/AdBase; Classified Hardware – Mac & PC; Classified Printers – HP/Laserjet 4 DISPLAY: Ad make-up applications – Indesign, Photoshop; Layout Software – 1-MEI/ALS, 13-MEI/ALS Page Director; Display Hardware – Mac & PC PRODUCTION: Pagination Software – Indesign; Production Equipment – AP/Server PRESSROOM: Line 1 – 10-HI/1650; Folders – 2; Pasters – 7-HI/Auto. MAILROOM: Counter stackers – 5-QWI/400; Inserters and stuffers – 1-HI/632; Bundle tying machines – 4-Dynaric/NP-1500; Mailroom control system – ICN; Addressing machine – 1/Ch; Other equipment –Mc/Stitcher-Trimmer PB2000.; Business Hardware – Mac & PC
Delivery method: Mail, Newsstand, Private Carrier, Racks

SPEARFISH

BLACK HILLS PIONEER

315 Seaton Cir., Spearfish, S.D., 57783-3212; gen tel (605) 642-2761; gen fax (605) 642-9060; gen e-mail news@bhpioneer.com; web site www.bhpioneer.com

Published: Mon, Tues, Wed, Thur, Fri, Sat, Sun
Weekday Frequency: e
Saturday Frequency: m
Circulation: 3,951; 3,951(sat)
Last Audit: September 30, 2006
Price: 7.50/mo; 96.00/yr.
Advertising: Open inch rate $9.50
News services: AP.
Politics: Independent. **Established:** 1876
Not Published: New Year; Memorial Day; Independence Day; Labor Day; Thanksgiving; Christmas.
Special Editions: Home Improvement (Apr); Deadwood Rodeo (Aug); Valentine's Day (Feb); New Year's Eve (Jan); 4th of July (Jul); Belle Fourche All Car Rally (Jun); St. Patrick's Day (Mar); Mother's Day (May); Christmas Greetings (Nov); Halloween (Oct); Football Contest (Sep
Special Weekly Sections: Sports (Other).
Magazines: American Profile (Weekly).
Circ. Mgr. .... Scott Lister
Exec. Ed. .... Letitia Lister
Ed. .... Mark Watson
Market Information: TMC.
Mechanical available: Offset; Black and 3 ROP colors; insert accepted - all sizes; page cutoffs - 22 3/4.
Mechanical Specifications: Type page 10 1/4 x 13 1/2; E - 5 cols, 1, 1/12 between; A - 5 cols, 1, 1/12 between; C - 5 cols, 1, 1/12 between.
Commodity Consumption: Avg. Page Number Per Issue - Daily 36; Avg. Page Number Per Issue - Plates Used 4000; Avg. Page Number Per Issue - Saturday 32; widths 28; Newsprint Used - Metric Tons 300; Printing Ink Used - Black 12000; Printing Ink Used - Color 2000; Printing Ink Use
Equipment; Editorial Hardware – 7-APP/Mac, 7-HI/Compuedit format, 1-APP/Mac; Editorial Equipment – APP/Mac Scanners; Editorial Printers – 3-APP/Mac LaserWriter, 1-NewGen/LaserWriter 1200 dpi, 2-HP.; Classified Hardware – 1-APP/Mac.; Layout Software – 2-APP/Mac.; Production Equipment – B, APP/Mac LaserWriter Plus, APP/Mac NT, APP/Mac NTX; Cameras – 1-B/4000; Scanners – 2-APP/Mac Scanner. PRESSROOM: Line 1 – 4-G; Folders – 1; Inserters and stuffers – 1-KAN/4 station; Bundle tying machines – 3/Bu; Wrapping singles – 1-/Bu; Addressing machine – 1-/Wm.; Business Hardware – APP/Mac II, IBM/XT, APP/Mac, RSK/Tandy 100

SEATON PUBLISHING CO.

315 Seaton Cir., Spearfish, S.D., 57783; gen tel (605) 642-2761; gen fax (605) 642-9060

Published: Mon, Tues, Wed, Thur, Fri, Sat
Weekday Frequency: e
Saturday Frequency: m
Circulation: 4,200; 4,200(sat)

WATERTOWN

WATERTOWN PUBLIC OPINION

120 3rd Ave. NW, Watertown, S.D., 57201-2311; gen tel (605) 886-6901; adv tel (605) 886-6901; ed tel (605) 886-6901; gen fax (605) 886-4280; adv fax (605) 886-4280; ed fax (605) 886-4280; adv e-mail advertise@thepublicopinion.com; ed e-mail news@thepublicopinion.com; web site www.thepublicopinion.com; ee.thepublicopinion.com

Group: UCC
Metro Newspaper Advertising Services, Inc.
Published: Mon, Tues, Wed, Thur, Fri, Sat
Weekday Frequency: e
Saturday Frequency: m
Circulation: 10,760; 11,803(sat)
Last Audit: ABC September 30, 2011
Price: 10.28/mo (carrier); 123.34/yr, $124.27/yr (mail).
Advertising: Open inch rate $26.50
News services: AP.
Politics: Independent. **Established:** 1887
Not Published: New Year; Independence Day; Thanksgiving; Christmas.
Own facility?: Y
Special Editions: Home & Garden (Apr); Family Resource (Aug); Sports (Dec); Farm Show (Feb); Bridal Showcase (Jan); Senior Focus (Jul); Health Tab (Jun); Health Tab (Mar); How To (May); Winter Car Care (Oct); Fall Sportsman (Sept).
Special Weekly Sections: Farm Review (Fri); Home (Sat); Business Tuesday (Tues); Real Estate Guide - Glacial Lakes Region (Wed).
Magazines: Parade (Sat).
Pub. .... Mark S. Roby
Dir., Admin. .... Chris Carter
Adv. Mgr. .... Tim Oviatt
Circ. Mgr. .... Paul C. Reinschmidt
Managing Ed. .... Rick Hoover
News Ed. .... Wayne Hammond
Sports Ed. .... Roger Merriam
Online Mgr. .... J.T. Fey
Prodn. Mgr., Press .... Dan Sumner
City Ed. .... Bob Mooney
Farm Ed. .... Terry O'Keefe
Market Information: ADS; Split run; TMC.
Mechanical available: Offset; Black and 3 ROP colors; insert accepted; page cutoffs - 21 1/2.
Mechanical Specifications: Type page 10 7/8 x 21 1/2; E - 6 cols, 10 7/8, 3/16 between; A - 6 cols, 10 7/8, 3/16 between; C - 8 cols, 10 7/8, 1/8 between.
Commodity Consumption: Avg. Page Number Per Issue - Daily 22; Avg. Page Number Per Issue - Plates Used 15000; Avg. Page Number Per Issue - Saturday 36; widths 34; Newsprint Used - Metric Tons 700; Printing Ink Used - Black 12000; Printing Ink Used - Color 3700; Printing Ink Us
Equipment EDITORIAL: Front-end Software – QPS/QuarkXPress 7, Baseview/NewsEdit Pro 5.3.; Editorial Hardware – APP/Mac; Editorial Printers – HPs CLASSIFIED: Front-end Software – Baseview/Class Manager Plus 3.5.1,

QPS/QuarkXPress 7, Baseview/NewsEdit Pro 1.0.4.; Classified Hardware – APP/Mac; Classified Printers – APP/Mac LaserPrinter DISPLAY: Ad make-up applications – QPS/QuarkXPress 7, Adobe/Photoshop 9, Adobe/Illustrator 9.0; Display Hardware – APP/Mac; Display Printers – HPs PRODUCTION: Pagination Software – QPS/QuarkXPress 7.; Production Equipment – Kodak CtP; Cameras – 1-B/1822 PRESSROOM: Line 1 – 5-HI/Cotrell 845 single width; Folders – 1-G.; Inserters and stuffers – 1-KAN/480 with Multi-Feeder; Bundle tying machines – 1-Bu/18, 1-Malow/40-M; Addressing machine – 1-KAN/650.

Delivery method: Mail, Newsstand, Private Carrier, Racks

YANKTON

YANKTON DAILY PRESS & DAKOTAN

319 Walnut St., Yankton, S.D., 57078; gen tel (605) 665-7811; adv tel (605) 665-7811; ed tel (605) 665-7811; gen fax (605) 665-1721; adv fax (605) 665-1721; ed fax (605) 665-1721; ed e-mail newsroom@yankton.net; web site www.yankton.net

Group: Yankton Media Inc.
Published: Mon, Tues, Wed, Thur, Fri, Sat
Weekday Frequency: m
Saturday Frequency: m
Circulation: 8,600; 8,600(sat)
Last Audit: Sworn September 30, 2006
Price: 7.95/mo; 107.84/yr.
Advertising: Open inch rate $18.36
News services: AP.
Politics: Independent. **Established:** 1861
Not Published: New Year; Memorial Day; Independence Day; Labor Day; Thanksgiving; Christmas.
Own facility?: Y
Special Editions: Spring Fashion Tab (Apr); Back-to-School Tab (Aug); Christmas Gift Ideas (Dec); Yankton Health (Feb); Progress (Jun); Weeder's Digest (Mar); Graduation Tab (May); Turkey Give-Away (Nov); Fall Fashion Tab (Oct); Fall Football (Sept). Her Voice Womens Magazine (6x year)
Special Weekly Sections: Church Listings (Fri); FYI (Sat); Dining & Entertainment (Thur); Dining & Entertainment (Tues).
Magazines: Relish (Monthly); USA WEEKEND Magazine (Sat); American Profile (Weekly).
Owner....Gary Wood
Bus. Mgr.....Tonya Schild
Adv. Dir.....Micki Schievelbein
Circ. Dir.....David Jeffcoat
Mng. Ed.....Kelly Hertz
City Ed.....Randy Dockendorf
Sports Ed.....James Cimburek
New Media Dir.....Beth Rye
Mechanical available: Offset; Black and 3 ROP colors; insert accepted - packaged material, samples 1/4 thick & under; page cutoffs - 22 3/4.
Mechanical Specifications: Type page 13 x 21 1/2; E - 6 cols, 2 1/16, 1/8 between; A - 6 cols, 2 1/16, 1/8 between; C - 6 cols, 2 1/16, 1/8 between.
Commodity Consumption: Avg. Page Number Per Issue - Daily 16; Avg. Page Number Per Issue - Plates Used 3750; Avg. Page Number Per Issue - Saturday 20; widths 33; Newsprint Used - Short Tons 565; Printing Ink Used - Black 22000; Printing Ink Used - Color 7000; Printing Ink Used
Equipment EDITORIAL: Front-end Software – QPS/QuarkXPress, Baseview/NewsEdit.; Editorial Hardware – APP/Mac; Editorial Equipment – NewGen/Imager Plus; Editorial Printers – APP/Mac LaserWriter, MON/ExpressMaster 1270 CLASSIFIED: Front-end Software – Baseview.; Classified Hardware – APP/Mac; Classified Printers – APP/Mac ImageWriter, APP/Mac LaserWriter DISPLAY: Ad make-up applications – Multi-Ad/Creator; Display Hardware – APP/Mac, APP/Mac IIcx, APP/Mac IIsi, APP/Mac SE, APP/Mac with Radius Monitor, 2-APP/Mac Quadra 800, 3-APP/Power Mac 6100, 1-APP/Power Mac 9500-132; Display Printers – APP/Mac LaserWriter IIq, MON/Express Master 1270 PRODUCTION: Pagination Software – QPS/QuarkXPress 3.3.; Production Equipment – Caere/OmniPage 2.0, APP/Mac; Cameras – B/Caravel; Scanners – APP/Mac, Nikon, APP/Mac Scanner; Inserters and stuffers – 4-KAN/DG-320; Bundle tying machines – 2-Bu/1900, 1-Malow/40; Addressing machine – 1/X, Ch/515. BUSINESS COMPUTERS: Business Software – PBS; Business Hardware – Unix/80486
Delivery method: Mail, Newsstand, Private Carrier, Racks

TENNESSEE

ATHENS

THE DAILY POST-ATHENIAN

320 S. Jackson St., Athens, Tenn., 37371-0340; gen tel (423) 745-5664; gen fax (423) 745-8295; gen e-mail dailypostathenian@xtn.net; web site www.dpa.xtn.net

Published: Mon, Tues, Wed, Thur, Fri
Weekday Frequency: e
Circulation: 10,330
Last Audit: September 30, 2008
Price: 7.50/mo; 90.00/yr.
Advertising: Open inch rate $18.90(e-fri)
News services: AP.
Politics: Independent. **Established:** 1848
Not Published: Christmas.
Own facility?: Y
Special Editions: Health & Fitness (Apr); Football Contest Pages (Aug); Friendly Fellow Greetings (Dec); Boy Scout Salute (Feb); Income Tax Guide (Jan); Crime Prevention (Jul); Dairy Salute (Jun); Farming Salute (Mar); Keepsake (May); Holiday Cookbook (Nov); Car Care Guide
Special Weekly Sections: Business (Thur); Education (Wed).
Magazines: Entertainment (Fri).
Pub.....Tommy Wilson
Bus. Mgr.....Rhonda Whaley
Adv. Mgr.....Ronda Elkins
Circ. Mgr.....Tom Cogdell
Mng. Ed.....Richard Edwards
Editorial Writer....Doug Headrick
Lifestyles Ed.....Autumn Hughes
Sports Ed.....Jack Slayton
Data Processing Mgr.....Scott Wall
Prodn. Supt., Pressroom....James King
Market Information: TMC.
Mechanical available: Offset; Black and 3 ROP colors; insert accepted - in-house printing; page cutoffs - 22.
Mechanical Specifications: Type page 10 x 21; E - 6 cols, 1.5625, 1/8 between; A - 6 cols, 1.5625, 1/8 between; C - 6cols, 1 5/32, 1/8 between.
Commodity Consumption: Avg. Page Number Per Issue - Daily 24; Avg. Page Number Per Issue - Plates Used 6000; widths 27; Newsprint Used - Short Tons 900; Printing Ink Used - Black 24000; Printing Ink Used - Color 2300; Printing Ink Used - Pages Printed 6240.
Equipment EDITORIAL: Front-end Software – FSI 1.3.0.; Editorial Hardware – 1-Mk, APP/Mac-PC Server NT, 16-APP/Mac G3 & G4, Pentium 11/400 mhz; Editorial Equipment – MON/Imagesetter, ECR/Imagesetter, News Express/Scriptsetter VRL36; Editorial Printers – 2-Dataproduct/Typhoon 8 CLASSIFIED: Front-end Software – SUN/Suntype 4.2.; Classified Hardware – Intel/Suntype; Classified Printers – APP/Mac Laser Writer Pro 630, Okidata/Microline 591 DISPLAY: Ad make-up applications – Indesign; Layout Software – APP/Mac G3.; Display Hardware – APP/Mac G3; Display Printers – Dataproduct/Typhoon 8 PRODUCTION: Pagination Software – FSI 5.0.0.0.; Production Equipment – 1-Nu, 1-Power/PC 8100; Cameras – 1-C/Spartan II PRESSROOM: Line 1 – 8-G; Folders – 1; Inserters and stuffers – 6/MM; Bundle tying machines – 2-/MLN, 1-/Mosca; Addressing machine – 1-KR/Single Head. AUDIO: Audio Software – Telecom 4.31, Update 3.1; Audio Hardware – AP, 2-PC, DEC BUSINESS COMPUTERS: Business Software – Visiondata 6.3; Business Hardware – 1-Flex Cache/20386 DT
Delivery method: Newsstand, Private Carrier, Racks

CHATTANOOGA

CHATTANOOGA TIMES FREE PRESS

400 E. 11th St., Chattanooga, Tenn., 37403; gen tel (423) 756-6900; adv tel (423) 757-6200 (class); ed tel (423) 757-6357; gen fax (423) 757-6337; adv fax (423) 757-6461; ed fax (423) 757-6383; web site www.timesfreepress.com

Group: Metro Suburbia, Inc./Newhouse Newspapers
Published: Mon, Tues, Wed, Thur, Fri, Sat, Sun
Weekday Frequency: m
Saturday Frequency: m
Circulation: 72,072; 79,071(sat); 103,419(sun)
Last Audit: ABC September 30, 2011
Price: 2.80/wk (mS); 12.14/mo.
Advertising: Open inch rate $115.62
News services: AP, CNS, DF, NYT, SHNS.
Politics: Independent. **Established:** 1869
Own facility?: Y
Special Editions: Home Improvements (Apr); Football (Aug); Progress (Feb); Products & Services (Jul); Gift Guide (Nov); Health Trends (Oct); Home Improvements (Sept).
Special Weekly Sections: Chatanooga Weekend (Fri); Lifestyle (Mon); Arts & Travel (S); Lifestyle (Sat); Health & Fitness (Thur); Lifestyle (Wed).
Magazines: Relish (Monthly); Parade (S).
Bd. Chrmn.....Walter E. Hussman
Pres.....Jason Taylor
Controller....Russell Lively
Credit Mgr.....Peggy Pate
Executive Assistant....Tonya Williamson
Circ. Dir.....Carroll Duckworth
Circ. Mgr.....Barry Pearcy
Bus. Ed.....Dave Flessner
Web Ed.....John Vass
Asst. City Desk Ed.....Alex Chambliss
Editorial Page Ed.....Harry Austin
Faith Ed.....Clint Cooper
Features Ed.....Mark Kennedy
Advertising Director....Leslie Kahana
Director of Targeted & Digital Initiatives Ed Bourn
HR Director....Matt Salada
Market Information: ADS; Split run; TMC; Zoned editions.
Mechanical available: Flexo; Black and 3 ROP colors; insert accepted; page cutoffs - 22 3/4.
Mechanical Specifications: Type page 12 1/2 x 21 1/2; E - 6 cols, 2 1/16, 1/8 between; A - 6 cols, 2 1/16, 1/8 between; C - 9 cols, 1 1/3, 1/12 between.
Commodity Consumption: Avg. Page Number Per Issue - Daily 52; Avg. Page Number Per Issue - Plates Used 100000; Avg. Page Number Per Issue - Sunday 172; widths 25; Newsprint Used - Short Tons 15000; Printing Ink Used - Black 534000; Printing Ink Used - Color 159600; Printing In
Equipment EDITORIAL: Front-end Software – Baseview/IQue, Baseview/NewsEdit IQue.; Editorial Hardware – 25-APP/Mac G4, 85-APP/iMac; Editorial Printers – HP, APP/Mac, NewGen, LaserMaster/Unity 1800 XL CLASSIFIED: Front-end Software – DTI.; Classified Hardware – Pentium/III PC, APP/Mac G4; Classified Printers – HP/5000; Layout Software – Mk/Managing Editor, Mk/Ad Director.; Display Hardware – APP/Mac G3 PRODUCTION: Pagination Software – QPS/QuarkXPress 4.01.; Production Equipment – 2-OVAC, Na/FP II, 1-Konica/Jetsetter; Cameras – 2-C; Scanners – 1-Sharp/JX-610, Kk, 2-ECR/Autokon, 2-Kk, 1-Duoscan, 1-Arcus PRESSROOM: Line 1 – 10-MAN/Flexoman 1999; Folders – 2; Pasters – 9-G/Automatic 1972, 10-HOE/Auto 1999; Reels and Stands – 9-1972, 10; Press control system – 1999 MAILROOM: Counter stackers – 4-Id/2100, 1/QWI, 3-Id/2220; Inserters and stuffers – 2-MM/375; Bundle tying machines – 8-/Power Strap; Wrapping singles – Addressing machine ÂD 2-/Ch. AUDIO: Audio Software – New Horizons/Info-Connect; Audio Hardware – TMS, AP, Pentium/PC BUSINESS COMPUTERS: Business Software – PBS, Lawson; Business Hardware – IBM/RS-6000, IBM/RS 6000
Delivery method: Mail, Newsstand, Private Carrier, Racks

CLARKSVILLE

THE LEAF-CHRONICLE

200 Commerce St., Clarksville, Tenn., 37040-0018; gen tel (931) 552-1808; adv tel (931) 245-0275; ed tel (931) 245-0282; gen fax (931) 648-8001; adv fax (931) 648-8001; ed fax (931) 552-5859; adv e-mail amymonson@theleafchronicle.com; ed e-mail news@theleafchronicle.com; letters@theleafchronicle.com; web site www.theleafchronicle.com

Published: Mon, Tues, Wed, Thur, Fri, Sat, Sun
Weekday Frequency: m
Saturday Frequency: m
Circulation: 14,291; 16,445(sat); 19,996(sun)
Last Audit: ABC September 30, 2011
Price: 2.85/wk; 12.65/mo; 148.20/yr.
Advertising: Open inch rate $51.69
News services: AP.
Politics: Independent. **Established:** 1808
Own facility?: Y
Special Editions: 50+ Lifestyles (Apr); Football (Aug); Holiday Greetings (Dec); 50+ Lifestyles (Jan); 50+ Lifestyles (Jul); Salute to Ft. Campbell (Jun); The Great Outdoors (Mar); Vacation (May); Christmas Gift Guide (Nov); Fall Car Care (Oct); Fall Home Improvement (Sept
Special Weekly Sections: Go-Weekly Entertainment (Fri); Food Days (Mon); TV Week (S); Living Well (Wed).
Magazines: USA WEEKEND Magazine (S).
Profile: Daily newspaper and website
Advertising Manager....Shirelle Fine
Exec. Ed.....Richard Stevens
Bus. Ed.....Jimmy Settle
Features Editor....Stacy Leiser
Editorial Page Ed.....Alane Megna
Educ. Ed.....Luke Thompson
News Ed.....Chris Smith
Sports Ed.....Jim Trodglen
Prodn. Supt., Graphic Arts....Ronald Kendrick
Market Information: Split run; TMC; Zoned editions.
Mechanical available: Offset; Black and 3 ROP colors; insert accepted - all; page cutoffs - 21 1/2.
Mechanical Specifications: Type page 12 x 21 1/2; E - 6 cols, 2, 1/6 between; A - 6 cols, 2, 1/6 between; C - 10 cols, 1 1/4, 1/12 between.
Commodity Consumption: Avg. Page Number Per Issue - Daily 34; Avg. Page Number Per Issue - Plates Used 8000; Avg. Page Number Per Issue - Sunday 100; widths 25; Newsprint Used - Short Tons 2048; Printing Ink Used - Black 49000; Printing Ink Used - Color 4900; Printing Ink Used
Equipment; Editorial Hardware – Mk.; Classified Hardware – Mk; Classified Equipment – 3-IBM/Selectric II.; Layout Software – Mk.; Production Equipment – 3M/Pyrofax, 1-LE/PC13; Cameras – 1-B/24, 1-ECR/Autokon; Scanners – 1-Graphic Enterprises/PageScan III. PRESSROOM: Line 1 – 10-G/Urbanite; Folders – 1, 1. MAILROOM: Counter stackers – 1-Id/2000; Inserters and stuffers – 1-HI/624, 1-MM/227; Bundle tying machines – 2-MLN/ML2EE; Addressing machine – 1-MG/602, 1-Am/8000, 1-AVY/5209.; Business Hardware – 1-IBM/AS-400
Zip Codes served: 37040, 37043, 37042, 37171, 37010, 37191, 37079, 37061, 42223
Delivery method: Mail, Newsstand, Private Carrier, Racks

CLEVELAND

CLEVELAND DAILY BANNER

1505 25th St. NW, Cleveland, Tenn., 37311; gen tel (423) 472-5041; gen fax (423) 476-1046; adv fax (423) 476-1046; ed fax (423) 614-6529; gen e-mail news@clevelandbanner.com; adv e-mail advertising@clevelandbanner.com; classifieds@clevelandbanner.com; ed e-mail news@clevelandbanner.com; sports@clevelandbanner.com; lifestyles@clevelandbanner.com; web site www.clevelandbanner.com

Published: Mon, Tues, Wed, Thur, Fri, Sun
Weekday Frequency: e
Circulation: 11,942; 13,973(sun)
Last Audit: ABC September 30, 2011
Price: 6.25/mo (carrier); 75.00/yr; 38.00/6mo.
Advertising: Open inch rate $11.00
News services: AP.
Politics: Independent. **Established:** 1854
Not Published: Christmas.
Special Editions: Baby (Apr); Christmas Greeting (Dec); Progress (Feb); Auto Winterize (Jan); Bride (Jun); Girl Scouts Page (Mar); Spring Car Care (May); Thanksgiving (Nov); Fall Home Improvement (Oct); Football (Sept).
Special Weekly Sections: Lifestyles (S); Lifestyles (Wed).
Magazines: American Profile (Fri); USA WEEKEND Magazine (S).
Credit Mgr. .... Joyce Taylor
Dir., Adv./Promo .... Jack Bennett
Circ. Dir. .... Herb Lacey
Ed. .... Stephen Crass
Mng. Ed. .... David Davis
Assoc. Ed. .... Gwen Swiger
Librarian .... Mary Matthews
Sports Ed. .... Richard Melvin
Women's Ed. .... Bettie Marlowe
Online Mgr. .... Jim Bryant
Prodn. Mgr., Pre Press .... Carrie Pettit
Prodn. Foreman, Pressroom .... Richard Yarber
Market Information: TMC.
Mechanical available: Offset; Black and 3 ROP colors; insert accepted - polybags; page cutoffs - 21 1/2.
Mechanical Specifications: Type page 11 5/8 x 21 1/2; E - 6 cols, 1 5/6, 1/8 between; A - 6 cols, 1 5/6, 1/8 between; C - 6 cols, 1 5/6, 1/8 between.
Commodity Consumption: Avg. Page Number Per Issue - Daily 24; Avg. Page Number Per Issue - Plates Used 12000; Avg. Page Number Per Issue - Sunday 56; widths 12 1/2; Newsprint Used - Metric Tons 919; Newsprint Used - Short Tons 801; Printing Ink Used - Black 25200; Printing Ink
Equipment EDITORIAL: Front-end Software – Baseview/NewsEdit Pro 3.23.; Editorial Hardware – 12-APP/Mac 15 color terminal; Editorial Printers – 1-Xante/Accel-a-Writer 8200, 1-QMS/810, GCC/Elite XL616 CLASSIFIED: Front-end Software – Baseview/Classflow.; Classified Hardware – 4-APP/Mac; Classified Equipment – IPC/HSPTR DISPLAY: Ad make-up applications – QPS/QuarkXPress 5.01, Multi-Ad/Creator 4; Display Printers – 2-Pre Press/Panther Plus Imagesetter, 1-Xante/Accel-a-Writer 8200, 1-QMS/810, GCC/Elite XL616 PRODUCTION: Pagination Software – QPS/QuarkXPress 5.01.; Production Equipment – APP/Mac 8100 with Adobe Photoshop 3.0.4; Scanners – Epson/2450, Polaroid/SprintScan 4000+ PRESSROOM: Line 1 – 1-WPC/Quadra-Color single width, 4-WPC/Perfector single width; Line 2 – 5-WPC/Perfector single width; Press Drives – 2-Marathon/200 AMP Drives; Folders – 2-Web Leader/Marc-25; Reels and Stands – 9-Web Leader/Marc-25 roll stand.; Inserters and stuffers – 6-MM/227; Bundle tying machines – Strapex.; Business Hardware – 1-Sun/Ultra 5
Delivery method: Mail, Newsstand, Private Carrier, Racks

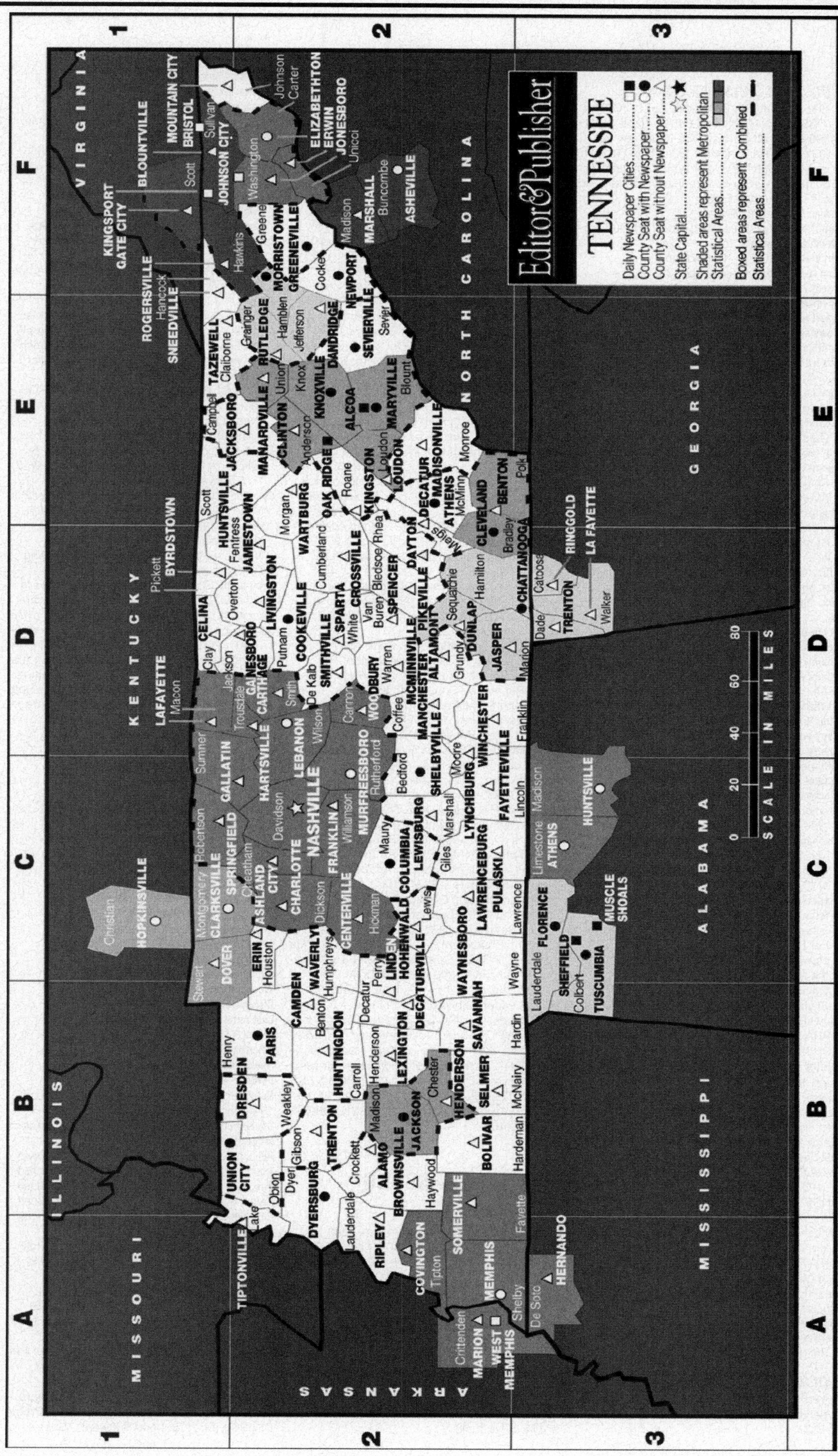

COLUMBIA

COLUMBIA DAILY HERALD

1115 S. Main St., Columbia, Tenn., 38401-3733; gen tel (931) 388-6464; adv tel (931) 388-6464; ed tel (931) 388-6464; gen fax (931) 388-1003; adv fax (931) 388-4101; ed fax (931) 388-1003; adv e-mail cduncan@c-dh.net; ed e-mail newsroomc@c-dh.net; web site www.c-dh.net

Group: Stephen's Media, LLC
Published: Mon, Tues, Wed, Thur, Fri, Sun
Weekday Frequency: m
Circulation: 10,470; 12,007(sun)
Last Audit: Sworn September 30, 2008
Price: 9.25/mo (carrier); 111.00/yr (mail).
Advertising: Open inch rate $13.85
Insert rate: 33.50 Single Sheet
News services: AP, NEA.
Politics: 1848
Advertising not accepted: N
Own facility?: Y
Special Editions: Spring Fashion (Apr); Football (Aug); Christmas Greetings (Dec); Bridal (Jun); Graduation (May); Christmas Gift Guide (Nov); Fall Fashion (Sept); Healthy Living (monthly).
Special Weekly Sections: Church Page (Fri); Showtime TV Guide (S); Best Food Day (Wed).
Magazines: USA WEEKEND Magazine (S).
Profile: Newspaper publishing, member Stephens Media Group.
Pub. ....Mark Palmer
Office Mgr. ....Betty Stewart
Adv. Mgr. ....Craig Duncan
Circ. Mgr. ....Dean Cole
Ed. ....Chris Fletcher
Photo Dept. Mgr. ....Susan Thurman
Reporter ....Samantha Ballard
Society Ed. ....Marvine Sugg
Sports Ed. ....Marion Wilhoite
IT Dir. ....Fay Hunt
Reporter ....Skyler Swisher
Reporter ....Richard Conn
Copy editor ....Alex Miller
Sports writer ....Justin Lamb
Editorial assistant ....Carla Hailey
Market Information: ADS; TMC; Zoned editions.
Mechanical available: Offset; Black and 3 ROP colors; insert accepted; page cutoffs - 21 1/2.
Mechanical Specifications: Type page 13 x 21 1/2; E - 6 cols, 2 1/16, 1/8 between; A - 6 cols, 2 1/16, 1/8 between; C - 8 cols, 1 3/8, 1/16 between.
Commodity Consumption: Avg. Page Number Per Issue - Daily 26; Avg. Page Number Per Issue - Plates Used 5600; Avg. Page Number Per Issue - Sunday 44; widths 25; Newsprint Used - Short Tons 640; Printing Ink Used - Black 18500; Printing Ink Used - Color 5400; Printing Ink Used -
Equipment EDITORIAL: Front-end Software – NewsEdit Pro, Indesign; Editorial Hardware – APP/Mac, Baseview; Editorial Printers – 4-APP/Mac LaserWriter II, 3-APP/Mac LaserWriter Plus. CLASSIFIED: Front-end Software – Ad Manager Pro 4; Classified Hardware – Apple; Classified Equipment – iMacG5; Classified Printers – HP LaserJet DISPLAY: Ad make-up applications – Adobe Suite; Display Hardware – Apple G5; Display Printers – HP/LaserJet 5100; Production Equipment – 2-Mk/Ad Touch, 2-Mk/TouchWriter Plus; Cameras – 1-C/Spartan II; Scanners – 1-APP/Mac. PRESSROOM: Line 1 – 8-G/Community; Folders – 6 MAILROOM: Counter stackers – Quipp 500; Inserters and stuffers – Muller 227; Bundle tying machines – 1 Signode LBX 2000 2 Ty-Tech; Addressing machine – Dispensamatic 6 in BUSINESS COMPUTERS: Business Software – MPA; Business Hardware – Unisys, HP
Zip Codes served: 38401; 38402
Delivery method: Mail, Newsstand, Private Carrier, Racks

COLUMBIA PUBLISHING CO., INC.

1115 S. Main St., Columbia, Tenn., 38401; gen tel (931) 388-6464; gen fax (931) 388-1003

COOKEVILLE

HERALD-CITIZEN

1300 Neal St., Cookeville, Tenn., 38501; gen tel (931) 526-9715; gen fax (931) 526-1209; adv e-mail advertising@herald-citizen.com; ed e-mail editor@herald-citizen.com; web site www.herald-citizen.com

Published: Mon, Tues, Wed, Thur, Fri, Sun
Weekday Frequency: e
Circulation: 9,352; 11,173(sun)
Last Audit: ABC September 30, 2011
Price: 5.50/mo (carrier); 120.00/yr (carrier); 65.00/6mo (mail).
Advertising: Open inch rate $12.73
News services: AP.
Politics: Independent.
Not Published: New Year; Independence Day; Labor Day; Thanksgiving; Christmas.
Special Editions: Cookeville Cookoff Community Festival (Aug); Home Show (Feb); Progress (Jan); Venture Tourist Magazine (May); Holidays in Upper Cumberland (Nov).
Special Weekly Sections: Auto Dealers (Fri); Best Food Day (Mon); Auto Dealers (S); School News (Thur); Business (Wed).
Magazines: Relish (Monthly); Focus TV Tab (S).
Adv. Mgr. ....David Shelton
Circ. Mgr. ....Keith McCormick
Wire Ed. ....Bob McMillan
Prodn. Mgr. ....Mike DeLapp
Market Information: ADS; TMC; Zoned editions.
Mechanical available: Offset; Black and 3 ROP colors; insert accepted; page cutoffs - 22 3/4.
Mechanical Specifications: Type page 13 x 21 1/2; E - 6 cols, 2 1/16, 1/8 between; A - 6 cols, 2 1/16, 1/8 between; C - 6 cols, 2 1/16, 1/8 between.
Commodity Consumption: Avg. Page Number Per Issue - Daily 16; Avg. Page Number Per Issue - Plates Used 6715; Avg. Page Number Per Issue - Sunday 40; widths 28; Newsprint Used - Short Tons 638; Printing Ink Used - Black 11635; Printing Ink Used - Color 1424; Printing Ink Used -
Equipment EDITORIAL: Front-end Software – Mk.; Editorial Hardware – Mk; Editorial Printers – APP/Mac LaserPrinter, Epson/Epl 7500 CLASSIFIED: Front-end Software – CText.; Classified Hardware – IBM, RSK/Tandy; Classified Equipment – PB/phone modem; Classified Printers – Panasonic/KX-P1624, APP/Mac LaserWriter Plus DISPLAY: Ad make-up applications – Multi-Ad/Creator, Adobe/Illustrator.; Display Hardware – 2-APP/Mac Quadra 700, APP/Mac Quadra; Display Printers – APP/Mac LaserPrinter, HP/LaserJet PRODUCTION: Pagination Software – QPS/QuarkXPress 3.3.; Production Equipment – HP, AG/Arcus Plus Scanner, V/3990; Cameras – SCREEN; Scanners – Umax/UC 840 PRESSROOM: Line 1 – WPC/Leader (4 b/w units;; Line 2 – WPC/Leader (3 b/w units); Folders – 2; Reels and Stands – 7-WPC/Leader; Press control system – WPC/Leader.; Inserters and stuffers – MM/227 5:1; Bundle tying machines – MLN/Spirit, Strapex, Minimatic/351; Addressing machine – 3/Dispensa-Matic/16. BUSINESS COMPUTERS: Business Software – PBS/MediaPlus; Business Hardware – RSK/4000LX, DEC/XL-466

DYERSBURG

STATE GAZETTE

294 Hwy. 51 Bypass, Dyersburg, Tenn., 38025; gen tel (731) 285-4091; adv tel (731) 285-4091; ed tel (731) 285-4091; gen fax (731) 285-9747; adv fax (731) 285-9747; ed fax (731) 285-9747; gen e-mail srose@stategazette.com; adv e-mail cdawson@stategazette.com; web site www.stategazette.com

Published: Mon, Tues, Wed, Thur, Fri, Sun
Weekday Frequency: e
Circulation: 7,900; 7,900(sun)
Last Audit: September 30, 2006
Price: 8.50/mo (carrier), $11.10/mo (mail); 133.20/yr (mail).
Advertising: Open inch rate $11.50
News services: AP.
Politics: Independent.
Advertising not accepted: Massage parlor.
Not Published: Independence Day; Christmas.
Special Editions: Home Improvement (Apr); Family Business (Aug); Home for the Holidays (Dec); Progress (Feb); NASCAR (Jan); Kitchen & Bath (Jul); Seniors Tab (Jun); Lawn & Garden (Mar); Spring Fashion (May); Holiday Shopping Guide (Nov); Newspaper Week Tab (Oct); Newcomers
Special Weekly Sections: Food (Fri); TV Entertainer (S); Food (Wed).
Magazines: Relish (Monthly); Parade (S); American Profile (Weekly).
Pub. ....Sheila Rouse Kelly
Bus. Mgr. ....Jina Jeffries
Circ. Dir. ....Terry Brock
Sports Ed. ....Mike Smith
Pressroom Mgr. ....Robert Pollard
Market Information: TMC.
Mechanical available: Offset; Black and 3 ROP colors; insert accepted - single cards or sheets; page cutoffs - 22 3/4.
Mechanical Specifications: Type page 13 x 21 1/2; E - 6 cols, 2 1/16, 1/8 between; A - 6 cols, 2 1/16, 1/8 between; C - 8 cols, 1 9/16, 1/16 between.
Commodity Consumption: Avg. Page Number Per Issue - Daily 18; Avg. Page Number Per Issue - Plates Used 3358; Avg. Page Number Per Issue - Sunday 28; widths 13; Newsprint Used - Short Tons 440; Printing Ink Used - Pages Printed 6242.
Equipment EDITORIAL: Front-end Software – Baseview. CLASSIFIED: Front-end Software – Baseview.; Layout Software – APP/Mac.; Production Equipment – 2-COM/8400; Cameras – 1-R/401. PRESSROOM: Line 1 – 8-G.; Inserters and stuffers – KAN/480; Bundle tying machines – 1-Yamada/Tom; Addressing machine – 1/El. BUSINESS COMPUTERS: Business Software – Baseview; Business Hardware – APP/Mac

ELIZABETHTON

ELIZABETHTON NEWSPAPERS, INC.

300 Sycamore St., Elizabethton, Tenn., 37643; gen tel (423) 542-4151; gen fax (423) 542-2004

ELIZABETHTON STAR

300 Sycamore St., Elizabethton, Tenn., 37643; gen tel (423) 542-4151; gen fax (423) 542-2004; gen e-mail webmaster@starhq.com; web site www.starhq.com

Published: Mon, Tues, Wed, Thur, Fri, Sun
Weekday Frequency: e
Circulation: 9,366; 9,366(sun)
Last Audit: September 27, 2002
Price: 80.00/yr.
Advertising: Open inch rate $15.00
News services: AP, Papert (Landon).
Politics: Independent.
Not Published: New Year; Memorial Day; Independence Day; Labor Day; Christmas.
Special Editions: Christmas Gift Guide (Other).
Magazines: American Profile (S).
Pub. ....Nathan Goodwin
Assoc. Pub. ....Harvey A. Pritchard
Bus. Mgr. ....Nathan O'Dell
Prodn. Supt. ....Delaney Scalf
Circ. Mgr. ....Kathy Scalf
Market Information: Zoned editions.
Mechanical available: Offset; Black and 3 ROP colors; insert accepted; page cutoffs - 22 5/8.
Mechanical Specifications: Type page 13 x 21 1/2; E - 6 cols, 2 1/16, 1/8 between; A - 6 cols, 2 1/16, 1/8 between; C - 9 cols, 1 1/2, 1/8 between.
Commodity Consumption: Avg. Page Number Per Issue - Daily 18; Avg. Page Number Per Issue - Sunday 38.
Equipment EDITORIAL: Front-end Software – Baseview.; Editorial Hardware – APP/Mac CLASSIFIED: Front-end Software – Baseview.; Classified Hardware – APP/Mac; Classified Printers – APP/Mac LaserWriter, HP DISPLAY: Ad make-up applications – QPS/QuarkXPress.; Display Hardware – APP/Mac; Display Printers – HP, NewGen; Production Equipment – 1-COM/8400, 3-APP/Mac Plus, 2-APP/Mac LaserWriter, ECR; Cameras – III/Spartan; Scanners – Equipment ◻ Baseview. PRESSROOM: Line 1 – 8-HI/V-15A.; Inserters and stuffers – KR; Addressing machine – KR/Inserter.; Business Hardware – 1-IBM/3600

GREENEVILLE

GREENEVILLE PUBLISHING CO.

121 W. Summer, Greeneville, Tenn., 37743; gen tel (423) 638-4181; gen fax (423) 638-3645

THE GREENEVILLE SUN

121 W. Summer St., Greeneville, Tenn., 37743-4923; gen tel (423) 638-4181; gen fax (423) 638-3645; adv fax (423) 638-7348; web site www.greenevillesun.com

Published: Mon, Tues, Wed, Thur, Fri, Sat, Sun
Weekday Frequency: e
Saturday Frequency: m
Circulation: 13,851; 15,060(sat)
Last Audit: September 30, 2008
Price: 9.30/mo; 109.00/yr.
Advertising: Open inch rate $24.50
News services: AP.
Politics: Independent. **Established:** 1879
Advertising not accepted: Liquor.
Not Published: Christmas.
Special Editions: Secretaries Week (Apr); Greene Co. Guidebook (Aug); Christmas Greetings (Dec); Basketball Tournament (Feb); Calendar Girls (Jan); June Bride (Jun); Benchmarks (Mar); TN Greene (May); Basketball (Nov); Car Care (Oct); Cheerleaders & Bands (Sept).
Special Weekly Sections: Health (Mon); TV Week (Sat); Business (Thur); Maturity (Seniors) (Tues); Agriculture (Wed).
Magazines: Parade (Sat); American Profile (Weekly).
Co-Pub. ....Gregg K. Jones
CFO, Jones Media, Inc. ....Jason Edmisten
Gen. Mgr. ....Steven K. Harbison
Gen. Mgr., GreenevilleSun.com ....Brian Cutshall
Adv. Dir. ....Arthur D. Wehenkel
Adv. Mgr., Major Accts. ....Richard Southerland
Ed. ....John M. Jones
Mng. Ed. ....Douglas Watson
Asst. Mng. Ed. ....Rich Jones
Editorial Page Ed. ....John M. Jones
Features Ed. ....Kathy Knight
Lifestyle Ed. ....Velma Southerland
Sports Ed. ....Wayne Phillips
Prodn. Mgr. ....Dale Long
Prodn. Foreman, Pressroom ....Jerry Ottinger
Market Information: TMC.
Mechanical available: Offset; Black and 3 ROP colors; insert accepted; page cutoffs - 22 3/4.
Mechanical Specifications: Type page 11 1/2 x 21 1/2; E - 6 cols, between; A - 6 cols, between; C - 9 cols, between.
Commodity Consumption: Avg. Page Number Per Issue - Daily 24; widths 25; Newsprint Used - Short Tons 900.
Equipment EDITORIAL: Front-end Software – FSI/Edit 1.10.; Editorial Hardware – 1-Mk/4001, Mk/Mycro-Comp 1100 Plus, APP/Mac; Editorial Printers – 1-APP/Mac LaserWriter Plus; Classified Hardware – 4-Sun/Publishing. DISPLAY: Ad make-up applications – QPS/QuarkXPress 3.3.2; Layout Software – APP/Mac.; Display Hardware – APP/Mac; Display Printers – 3-APP/Mac LaserWriter PRODUCTION: Pagination Software – FSI/Edit 1.1.0.; Production Equipment – Caere/Omni Page Pro 7.0, 2-Ultre, Hyphen/RIP; Cameras – 1-C/Spartan II; Scanners – Lf/Leafscan 45, Lf/Leafscan 35, Sharp/J600 Flatbed PRESSROOM: Line 1 – 8-G/Urbanite; Folders – 1 MAILROOM: Counter stackers – 1-HI/Graphics, RS/25; Inserters and stuffers – 1-MM/227E; Bundle tying machines – 1/Nichiro Kogyo/Semi-Ace; Addressing machine

– 1-DEC/LA 180, Ch/525E Stamping machine. BUSINESS COMPUTERS: Business Software – Vision Data; Business Hardware – ALR

JACKSON

THE JACKSON SUN

245 W. Lafayette, Jackson, Tenn., 38301; gen tel (731) 427-3333; adv tel (731) 425-9610; ed tel (731) 425-9686; gen fax (731) 425-9604; adv fax (731) 425-9604; ed fax (731) 425-9639; gen e-mail contactus@jacksonsun.com; web site www.jacksonsun.com

Group: Metro Newspaper Advertising Services, Inc.
Published: Mon, Tues, Wed, Thur, Fri, Sat, Sun
Weekday Frequency: m
Saturday Frequency: m
Circulation: 21,307; 20,052(sat); 31,713(sun)
Last Audit: ABC September 30, 2011
Price: 3.15/wk; 13.65/mo (carrier); 198.80/yr (mail).
Advertising: Open inch rate $61.75
News services: AP, GNS.
Politics: Independent.
Special Editions: Football (Aug); Fact Book (Feb); How To (Jan); Back-to-School (Jul); NAIA (Mar); Apple (Monthly); Home Builders (Nov); Design An Ad (Oct).
Special Weekly Sections: Color Comics (S); Auto (Sat); Best Food Day (Wed).
Magazines: TV Week (own, newsprint) (S); Weekend Plus (Thur).
Pub./Pres. ....Roy Heatherly
Finance Mgr. ....Tammy Gilliam
Credit Mgr. ....Betty Allen
Adv. Dir. ....Ron Prince
Adv. Mgr., Display ....Sarah Scott
Dir., Market Devel. ....Cathy Garrett
Circ. Mgr. ....Alice Sellers
Exec. Ed. ....Steve Coffman
Editorial Page Ed. ....Tom Bohs
Chief Content Ed. ....Kelly South
Sports Ed. ....Brandon Shields
Online Mgr. ....Martin Jelinek
Prodn. Servs. Mgr. ....Brad Isaacs
Prodn. Mgr., Commercial Print Shop Beth Walker
Prodn. Mgr., Bldg. ....Andy Curtis
Market Information: Split run; TMC.
Mechanical available: Offset (KBA Comet 70); Black and 3 ROP colors; insert accepted - all; page cutoffs - 21 1/2.
Mechanical Specifications: Type page 11 5/8 x 20 1/4; E - 6 cols, 1 4/5, 7/24 between; A - 6 cols, 1 4/5, 7/24 between; C - 9 cols, 1 1/5, 1/12 between.
Commodity Consumption: Avg. Page Number Per Issue - Daily 28; Avg. Page Number Per Issue - Plates Used 42864; Avg. Page Number Per Issue - Saturday 40; Avg. Page Number Per Issue - Sunday 64; widths 27; Newsprint Used - Metric Tons 2810; Newsprint Used - Short Tons 3097; Print
Equipment EDITORIAL: Front-end Software – DTI 4.3.; Editorial Hardware – DTI/Unix; Editorial Equipment – 6-Toshiba/1100 portable; Editorial Printers – HP/5si CLASSIFIED: Front-end Software – DTI 4.2.3.; Classified Hardware – DTI/Unix; Classified Equipment – 6-Toshiba/1100 portable; Classified Printers – HP/5si DISPLAY: Ad make-up applications – Multi-Ad/Creator 2; Layout Software – DTI/PlanBuilder.; Display Hardware – APP/Mac G3, APP/Mac G4; Display Printers – HP/5si PRODUCTION: Pagination Software – DTI/PlanBuilder V7.; Production Equipment – Caere/OmniPage Pro, Konica/3650, Konica/6500; Scanners – Kk/Professional PRESSROOM: Line 1 – KBA/Comet 70 single width (4 color) 5 towers 2001; Folders – 2 MAILROOM: Counter stackers – 2-QWI/400, 1-QWI/SJ200, 1-QWI/SJ350; Inserters and stuffers – S/NP630; Bundle tying machines – 1-MLN/MAG-330, 1-Dynaric/NP2, 2-Dynaric/NP3; Wrapping singles – Addressing machine ☐ 1/Cheshire; Other equipment –MM/Presto, MM/Stitcher-Trimmer.; Business Hardware – IBM/AS-400 RISC

JOHNSON CITY

JOHNSON CITY PRESS

204 W. Main St., Johnson City, Tenn., 37604; gen tel (423) 929-3111; gen fax (423) 929-1674; adv fax (423) 929-9097 (class); ed fax (423) 929-7484; adv e-mail adsales@johnsoncitypress.com; ed e-mail newsroom@johnsoncitypress.com; web site www.johnsoncitypress.com

Group: Metro Newspaper Advertising Services, Inc.
Published: Mon, Tues, Wed, Thur, Fri, Sat, Sun
Weekday Frequency: m
Saturday Frequency: m
Circulation: 28,140; 27,446(sat); 30,598(sun)
Last Audit: ABC September 30, 2011
Price: 2.32/wk; 6.75/mo (mon-fri), $7.50/mo (fri-S); 110.00/yr.
Advertising: Open inch rate $32.00
News services: AP, NYT.
Politics: Independent-Democrat.
Special Editions: Bristol Motor Speedway Tab-Ford City 500 (Apr); Bristol Motor Speedway Tab-Sharpie 500 (Aug); Christmas Gifts (Dec); Children's Valentines (Feb); Wedding Guide (Jan); Progress (Mar); Outdoor Recreation (May); Thanksgiving (Nov); Car Care (Oct); School (Se
Special Weekly Sections: TV Press (Fri); Teen Pages (Mon); Senior Lifestyles (Other); Southeastern Color Comics (S); Church Page (Sat); Best Food Day (Wed).
Magazines: Parade (S).
Broadcast Affiliations: WJHL (CBS); WCYB (NBC); WKPT (ABC); WEMT (FOX).
Pub. ....Arthur S. Powers
Opns. Mgr. ....John Castle
Dir., Sales/Mktg. ....Tom Harris
Adv. Sales Mgr. ....Bill Cummings
Circ. Dir. ....Phil Hensley
Mng. Ed. ....John Molley
Editorial Page Ed. ....Robert Houk
Educ./School Ed. ....Sam Watson
Photo Dept. Mgr. ....Lee Talbert
Religion Ed. ....Robert Pierce
Ski Ed. ....Brad Jolly
Sports Ed. ....Kelly Hodge
Travel Ed. ....Jan Hearn
Mechanical available: Offset; Black and 3 ROP colors; insert accepted - samples up to 13 x 11 x 1/8; page cutoffs - 22 3/4.
Mechanical Specifications: Type page 13 x 21 1/2; E - 6 cols, 2 1/16, 1/8 between; A - 6 cols, 2 1/16, 1/8 between; C - 9 cols, 1 3/8, 1/16 between.
Commodity Consumption: Avg. Page Number Per Issue - Daily 31; Avg. Page Number Per Issue - Plates Used 21000; Avg. Page Number Per Issue - Sunday 64; widths 27 1/2; Newsprint Used - Metric Tons 2937; Newsprint Used - Short Tons 2670; Printing Ink Used - Black 75000; Printing I
Equipment EDITORIAL: Front-end Software – ECR, Baseview.; Editorial Hardware – 30-ECR, 30-APP/iMac, 14-APP/Mac G4; Editorial Printers – 1-Centronics, 3-Qms/Laser Printers CLASSIFIED: Front-end Software – Vision Data/Total Advertising.; Classified Hardware – Sun/Ultra 250-300 mhz; Classified Equipment – APP/Mac G3, QMS/2060 Laserprinter; Classified Printers – 1-Centronics, HP/Laser Printer DISPLAY: Ad make-up applications – Multi-Ad/Creator 3.8.; Display Hardware – 4-APP/Mac G4, APP/Mac G3, 3-APP/Mac G3; Display Printers – 3-QMS/2060 PRODUCTION: Pagination Software – Baseview, QPS/QuarkXPress 4.1.; Production Equipment – Caere/OmniPage Pro 8.0, 1-AG/II, Nikon/Cool Scan; Cameras – 1-Robinson/480, 1-C/Sparton; Scanners – 1-AG/II PRESSROOM: Line 1 – Jun-73; Press Drives – GE/DC-300; Reels and Stands – 6; Press control system – 1986 MAILROOM: Counter stackers – 1/QWI; Inserters and stuffers – 1-HI/48P (8-Intol), 1-/MM 5:1; Bundle tying machines – 2-/MLN; Addressing machine – 1-/KAN. BUSINESS COMPUTERS: Business Software – Vision Data; Business Hardware – IBM/RISC-6000

KINGSPORT

DAILY NEWS

310 E. Sullivan St., Kingsport, Tenn., 37660-4404; gen tel (423) 246-4800; adv tel (423) 246-4800 ext. 5; ed tel (423) 246-4800 ext. 1; gen fax (423) 247-2502; adv fax (423) 247-2502; ed fax (423_ 247-2502; adv e-mail sd@kingsportdailynews.com; ed e-mail robin@kingsportdailynews.com; web site www.kingsportdailynews.com

Published: Mon, Tues, Wed, Thur, Fri, Sat, Sun
Weekday Frequency: m
Saturday Frequency: m
Circulation: 2,308
Last Audit: September 30, 1998
Price: 90.00/yr.
Advertising: $18.50 national rate
Insert rate: .045 per copy
News services: Reuters
Politics: . **Established:** 1971
Not Published: Postal holidays; Christmas.
Own facility?: Y
Special Editions: JANUARY
What's New in the New Year Section - businesses list new hours, products, services, etc.
FEBRUARY
Boy Scout Section - saluting Boy Scout Month
Home Show Section - published in conjunction with the Kingsport Homebuilders Association annual Home Show
MARCH
Annual Progress Edition
Spring Car Care Section
APRIL
Volunteer Section - saluting area volunteers during Volunteer Week.
Spring Clean-Up, Fix-Up, Paint-Up Section
MAY
Memorial Day Weekend Section
Graduation Section
JUNE
NICKELSVILLE DAYS SECTION - special section for annual festival held in Nickelsville VA
JULY
Fun Fest Section - special section for Kingsport's annual week-long Summer Festival.
Highlands Festival Section - special section for Abingdon VA's annual two-week summer festial
Just for Women Section - a special section just for women for Summer.
AUGUST
Appalachian Fair Special Section - all about the annual Appalachian Fair held at Gray TN
Race Section - our special section for the NASCAR race at Bristol, VA.
Duffield Daze Section - special section for the 3-day annual late Summer festival in Duffield VA
SEPTEMBER
Fall Home Improvement Section
Jonesborough Storytelling Festival Section - about the annual festival in Jonesborough TN
OCTOBER
Fall Car Care Section
Holiday Cookbook Section
NOVEMBER
Holiday Gift Guide Section
Christmas Carol Section
DECEMBER
Christmas Greeting Section
Magazines: SENIORITYA - monthly magainze for senior readers.
Adv. Mgr. ....Steven J. Dykes
Circ. Mgr. ......................................D.R. Dykes
Ed. ....Pete Dykes
Prodn. Foreman ....Jean Fletcher
Market Information: Split run; TMC; Zoned editions.
Mechanical available: Offset; Black and white
Mechanical Specifications: Page size 5 column by 16 inches. Columns are 2 inches wide. Full page - 10 3/4 inches wide by 16 inches tall.
Equipment; Production Equipment – 1-COM; Cameras – 1-K.
Zip Codes served: 37660, 37662, 37663, 37664, 37665, 37645, 37642, 24251, 37601,37604,37659,37615
Delivery method: Mail, Newsstand, Private Carrier, Racks

KINGSPORT TIMES-NEWS

701 Lynn Garden Dr., Kingsport, Tenn., 37660; gen tel (423) 246-8121; adv tel (423) 392-1315 (Retail); ed tel (423) 392-1322; gen fax (423) 246-8059; adv fax (423) 392-1392; ed fax (423) 392-1385; web site www.timesnews.net

Group: Metro Newspaper Advertising Services, Inc.
Published: Mon, Tues, Wed, Thur, Fri, Sat, Sun
Weekday Frequency: All day
Saturday Frequency: m
Circulation: 34,865; 33,165(sat); 43,035(sun)
Last Audit: ABC September 30, 2011
Price: 7.15/mo (d), $10.95/mo (d&S); 228.00/yr (d&S).
Advertising: Open inch rate $17.00
News services: AP, MCT, CQ.
Politics: Independent. **Established:** 1916
Special Editions: American Home & Garden (Apr); Football Preview (Aug); Christmas Gallery of Gifts (3 times) (Dec); Chamber Annual Report (Feb); Celebrating Diversity (Jan); Readers Choice V (Jun); Progress (Mar); Spring Tune-Up (May); Christmas Gallery of Gifts (2 times)
Special Weekly Sections: TV Week (Fri); Food Day (S); Food Day (Wed).
Magazines: USA WEEKEND Magazine (S).
Pub./Vice Pres./Treasurer ....Keith D. Wilson
Bus. Mgr. ....Debbie Salyers
Adv. Dir. ....George Coleman
Adv. Mgr., Classified ....Lee Bellamy
Adv. Mgr., Retail ....Pat Donaldson
Circ. Dir. ....Glen Tabor
Mng. Ed. ....Ted Como
Asst. Mng. Ed., News ....Stanley W. Whitlock
Amusements/Arts Ed. ....Brad Lifford
Books/Films Ed. ....Edward Como
City Ed. ....Stephanie McLellan
Editorial Page Ed. ....Don Fenley
Fashion/Features Ed. ....Leigh Ann Laube
News Ed. ....Stephanie McClellan
Photo Dept. Mgr. ....David Grace
Radio/Television Ed. ....Becky Whitlock
Real Estate Ed. ....Sharon Hayes
Market Information: Split run; TMC; Zoned editions.
Mechanical available: Offset; Black and 3 ROP colors; insert accepted; page cutoffs - 23 9/16.
Mechanical Specifications: Type page 13 x 22 1/2; E - 6 cols, 2, 1/6 between; A - 6 cols, 2, 1/6 between; C - 9 cols, 1 3/8, 1/4 between.
Commodity Consumption: Avg. Page Number Per Issue - Daily 33; Avg. Page Number Per Issue - Plates Used 42512; Avg. Page Number Per Issue - Saturday 34; Avg. Page Number Per Issue - Sunday 70; widths 55; Newsprint Used - Short Tons 3968; Printing Ink Used - Black 65500; Printin
Equipment EDITORIAL: Front-end Software – Tera/GNS.; Editorial Hardware – 32-Dell/OptiFlex, 20-Dell/Latitude, 27-Dell/PE4400; Editorial Equipment – APP/NT Server, Sun/Workstation, Sharp/JX-610 Scanner; Editorial Printers – 2-X/Laser Printer, 1-HP/4000N Laser Printer CLASSIFIED: Front-end Software – HI/Metro CASH.; Classified Hardware – Dell; Classified Equipment – Lind/500, Imagitex/scanner, Ethernet linked to HI/XP21 for graphic calls; Classified Printers – Epson/DFX 5000, Epson/LQ850, HP/LaserJet 4; Layout Software – SCS/Layout 8000.; Display Printers – HP/4000N PRODUCTION: Pagination Software – Tera/GN3.; Production Equipment – Solaris 2.1, Images 2.0; Cameras – C/Marathon; Scanners – Umax/Astra 1200A, Sharp/JX-610, Nikon/3510 AF, Umaz/PowerLook 2100XL, Epson/Perfection 1200 Photo, Epson/ES 1200C PRESSROOM: Line 1 – 4-G/Metro 3077 (2 half decks) 1970; Folders – 1-G/2:1. MAILROOM: Counter stackers – 2/MM, 2-QWI/300; Inserters and stuffers – AM Graphics/NP 630; Bundle tying machines – 2-/Power Strap, 2-/MLN; Mailroom control system – lc; Addressing machine – Wm; Other equipment –MM. BUSINESS COMPUT-

ERS: Business Software – CJ, Best, FAS, Willowbend, RouteExpert; Business Hardware – DEC

KNOXVILLE

KNOXVILLE NEWS SENTINEL

2332 News Sentinel Dr., Knoxville, Tenn., 37921-5766; gen tel (865) 523-3131; ed tel (865) 342-6300; adv fax (865) 342-6509; ed fax (865) 342-6400; gen e-mail kns@knews.com; adv e-mail ads@knews.com; ed e-mail letters@knews.com; news@knews.com; web site www.knoxnews.com

Group: Publishers Representatives of Florida, Inc.
Published: Mon, Tues, Wed, Thur, Fri, Sat, Sun
Weekday Frequency: m
Saturday Frequency: m
Circulation: 91,867; 92,721(sat); 120,881(sun)
Last Audit: ABC September 30, 2011
Price: 17.95/mo (dS, carrier), $22.10/mo (mail).
Advertising: Open inch rate $188.75(m-fri)
News services: AP, SHNS, NEA, LAT-WP, INS Bizwire, PR Newswire.
Politics: Independent.
Special Editions: Employer Spotlight (Apr); Prep Football (Aug); Fox 43 Winter Adventures (Dec); Childrens' Miracle Network Radiothon (Feb); Employer Spotlight (Jan); Employer Spotlight (Jul); Lenoir City Arts & Crafts Festival (Jun); Home Show (Mar); A Day in the Life (Ma
Special Weekly Sections: Preview (Fri); Science (Mon); Real Estate (S); Faith & Family (Sat); Style (Thur); Schools (Tues); Food (Wed).
Magazines: Parade (S).
Pres./Pub. ....Bruce Hartmann
Dir., Finance ....Paul Abraham
Dir., HR ....Debi Welch
Adv. Mgr., Retail ....Nancy Nabors
Classified Adv. Mgr. ....Brenda Crisp
Mktg. Dir. ....Lisa Duncan
Circ. Dir. ....Jim Boyd
Ed. ....Jack McElroy
Ed., Special Publications ....Wade Saye
Deputy Mng. Ed. ....Tom Chester
Asst. Mng. Ed., Graphics ....Michael Apuan
Bus. Ed. ....David Keim
Columnist ....Sam Venable
Editorial Page Ed. ....Hoyt Canady
Asst. Editorial Page Ed. ....Jan Avent
Entertainment Ed. ....Chuck Campbell
Film Ed. ....Betsy Pickle
Home Furnishings Ed. ....Susan Alexander
Librarian ....James Gill
Market Information: ADS; Split run; TMC; Zoned editions.
Mechanical available: Offset; Black and 3 ROP colors; insert accepted - Post-it notes; page cutoffs - 23 9/16.
Mechanical Specifications: Type page 13 x 22 1/2; E - 6 cols, 1 5/6, 1/8 between; A - 6 cols, 1 5/6, 1/8 between; C - 10 cols, between.
Commodity Consumption: Avg. Page Number Per Issue - Daily 58; Avg. Page Number Per Issue - Plates Used 186900; Avg. Page Number Per Issue - Saturday 82; Avg. Page Number Per Issue - Sunday 160; widths 37 5/16; Newsprint Used - Metric Tons 18828; Printing Ink Used - Black 32572
Equipment EDITORIAL: Front-end Software – ATS/Newsdesk.; Editorial Hardware – Compaq/Proliant server 7000, 4-PPRO/400 Client, Compaq/EN 400; Editorial Printers – HP/5si, HP/5si mx, HP/6L, HP/755 CLASSIFIED: Front-end Software – Unisys/AD2000.; Classified Hardware – Compaq/Proliant 8500, 4-PPRO/550 Client, Compaq/4000 DeskPro; Classified Printers – HP/5si mx, HP/8100, HP/8150 DISPLAY: Ad make-up applications – Baseview/Ad Manager, Multi-Ad/Creator.; Display Hardware – Compaq/Proliant 8500 Server 4-550 Client, Compaq 4000 Deskpro; Display Printers – HP/8100, HP/8150, HP/5si mx PRODUCTION: Pagination Software – ATS, Media Desk.; Production Equipment – 1-Burgess/Consolux, 1-Scitex/Eversmart Pro, AP/Picture Desk; Scanners – Scitex/Eversmart Jazz PRESSROOM: Line 1 – 12-MAN/Regioman (4 pages wide); Folders – 2-MAN/3:2; Press control system – MAN. MAILROOM: Counter stackers – 6-GMA/Combi Stacks, 4-Compass; Inserters and stuffers – 2-GMA; Bundle tying machines – 3-Dynaric/1500; Wrapping singles – 2-GMA, 1-Dynaric/Strapper.; Audio Hardware – Pony/120Mb, Pony/700Mb; Business Hardware – Software □ Cobol, Unisys, Unisys

LEBANON

THE LEBANON DEMOCRAT

402 N. Cumberland St., Lebanon, Tenn., 37087; gen tel (615) 444-3952; gen fax (615) 444-1358; ed fax (615) 444-0899; gen e-mail production@lebanondemocrat.com; adv e-mail classified@lebanondemocrat.com; rop@lebanondemocrat.com; ed e-mail editphoto@lebanondemocrat.com; web site www.lebanondemocrat.com

Published: Mon, Tues, Wed, Thur, Fri, Sat
Weekday Frequency: m
Circulation: 7,236; 7,236(sat)
Last Audit: September 30, 2006
Price: 77.00/yr.
Advertising: Open inch rate $11.70
News services: NEA, AP.
Not Published: New Year; Independence Day; Labor Day; Thanksgiving; Christmas.
Special Weekly Sections: TV/Entertainment (Thur).
Magazines: USA WEEKEND Magazine (Fri).
Pub./Vice Pres. ....Joe Adams
Mgr., Accounting ....Shelagh Mason
Adv. Dir. ....Roger Wells
Adv. Mgr., Classified ....Melanie Ray
Ed. ....Amelia Hipps
Sports Ed. ....Andy Reed
Prodn. Mgr. ....Mark Rodgers
Prodn. Foreman, Pressroom ....Richard Knowles
Market Information: TMC; Zoned editions.
Mechanical available: Offset; Black and 3 ROP colors; insert accepted; page cutoffs - 22 1/2.
Mechanical Specifications: Type page 13 x 21 1/2; E - 6 cols, 2 1/16, 1/8 between; A - 6 cols, 2 1/16, 1/8 between; C - 6 cols, 2 1/16, 1/8 between.
Commodity Consumption: Avg. Page Number Per Issue - Daily 24; widths 27 3/4; Newsprint Used - Short Tons 405; Printing Ink Used - Black 7200; Printing Ink Used - Color 1890; Printing Ink Used - Pages Printed 5380.
Equipment EDITORIAL: Front-end Software – Mk.; Editorial Hardware – Mk CLASSIFIED: Front-end Software – Baseview.; Classified Hardware – APP/Mac; Layout Software – APP/Mac, APP/Mac IIcx, APP/Power Mac.; Production Equipment – 1-Nu/Flip Top FT40L, Pre-Press/Panther Plus Imagesetter, APP/Mac NTX, P; Cameras – 1-R/400, SCREEN/Companica. PRESSROOM: Line 1 – 8-G/Community (color stock); Folders – 1 MAILROOM: Counter stackers – 1/Newstack; Bundle tying machines – Bu; Addressing machine – 1-/Ch.; Business Hardware – Vision Data

MARYVILLE

THE DAILY TIMES

307 E. Harper Ave., Maryville, Tenn., 37804-5724; gen tel (865) 981-1100; adv tel (865) 981-1152; ed tel (865) 981-1143; gen fax (865) 981-1175; ed e-mail editor@thedailytimes.com; web site www.thedailytimes.com

Group: Blount County Publishers, LLC
Published: Mon, Tues, Wed, Thur, Fri, Sat, Sun
Weekday Frequency: m
Saturday Frequency: m
Circulation: 18,902; 19,018(sat); 19,409(sun)
Last Audit: ABC September 30, 2011
Price: 3.10/wk; 13.50/mo; 136.00/yr (carrier)
Advertising: Open inch rate $24.00
Insert rate: Variable
News services: AP.
Politics: Independent. **Established:** 1883
Own facility?: Y
Special Editions: Townsend Traveler (Apr); Football Round-up (Aug); Progress (Feb); Father's Day (Jun); Home Improvement (Mar); Brides (May); Car Care (Oct); Fall Home Improvement (Sept).
Special Weekly Sections: Real Estate (Wed); TV Times (Mon); Religious News (Sat); Food (Wed).Weekend Entertainment (Thu)
Magazines: USA WEEKEND Magazine (S), Relish, Athlon Sports
Adv. Dir. ....Evelyn Sandlin
Circulation Director ....Bryan Sandmeier
Exec. Ed. ....Larry Aldridge
Mng. Ed. ....Frank Trexler
City/Metro Ed. ....Bob Norris
Editorial Page Ed. ....Dean Stone
Entertainment/Amusements Ed. Steven Wildsmith
Features Ed. ....Melanie Tucker
News Ed. ....Richard Dodson
Sports Ed. ....Leonard Butts
Telecom Mgr. ....Tim Malone
Prodn. Mgr., Pre Press ....David Ledford
Publisher ....Carl Esposito
Market Information: TMC - Times Too!
Mechanical available: Offset; Black and 3 ROP colors.
Mechanical Specifications: Type page 11 x 21.
Commodity Consumption: Avg. Page Number Per Issue - Daily 32; Avg. Page Number Per Issue - Plates Used 21275; widths 27; Newsprint Used - Metric Tons 1961; Printing Ink Used - Black 46613; Printing Ink Used - Color 11066; Printing Ink Used - Pages Printed 10464.
Equipment EDITORIAL: Front-end Software – MediaSpan; Editorial Hardware – Macintosh; Editorial Printers – Kyocera CLASSIFIED: Front-end Software – Vision Data; Classified Hardware – Macintosh; Classified Printers – HP/4MV, AG/Accuset DISPLAY: Ad make-up applications – Vision Data; Layout Software – Adobe/Photoshop, InDesign; Display Hardware – Macintosh; Display Printers – Genicom, Okidata PRODUCTION: Pagination Software – Adobe InDesign; Scanners – Kk/RFS 2035 Plus, Microtek/ScanMaker 3 PRESSROOM: Line 1 – 11-G/Urbanite (10 black; 1 tri-color) 1982; Folders – 1; Pasters – 6-1991. BUSINESS COMPUTERS: Business Software – Vision Data; Business Hardware – Macintosh
Delivery method: Mail, Newsstand, Private Carrier, Racks

MEMPHIS

THE COMMERCIAL APPEAL

495 Union Ave., Memphis, Tenn., 38103-3217; gen tel (901) 529-2211; adv tel (901) 529-2251; ed tel (901) 529-2322; gen fax (901) 529-6467; adv fax (901) 529-2245; ed fax (901) 529-6476; gen e-mail metro@commercialappeal.com; web site www.commercialappeal.com

Published: Mon, Tues, Wed, Thur, Fri, Sat, Sun
Weekday Frequency: m
Saturday Frequency: m
Circulation: 111,618; 92,828(sat); 146,594(sun)
Last Audit: ABC September 30, 2011
Price: 224.12/yr; 17.25/4wk.
Advertising: Open inch rate $284.85
News services: AP, NYT, SHNS, LAT-WP, Bloomberg, MCT.
Politics: Independent. **Established:** 1841
Special Editions: Playoff (Apr); How-to Guide (Aug); HGTV (Dec); Job Fair (Feb); NASCAR (Jul); Living Here (Jun); Vesta Home Expo (Mar); Grilling (May); Community Coupon (Monthly); Grizzlies (Nov); Ms. Home Fest (Oct); Weekend of Wheels (Sept).
Special Weekly Sections: Playbook (Fri); Health & Fitness (Mon); Autos (S); Real Estate (Sat); Neighbors (Thur); Food (Wed).
Magazines: Parade (S).
Pres./Pub. ....Joseph Pepe
Vice Pres., Finance ....Daniel Moehle
Vice Pres./Gen. Mgr. ....John F. Dennan
Credit Mgr. ....Debbie Wright
HR Dir./Gen. Counsel ....Warren C. Funk
Mgr., Purchasing ....Robbie Jones
Budget/Gen. Acctg. Mgr. ....Anne Deeds
Adv. Mgr., Classified ....Mark Busby
Nat'l/Major Acct. Mgr. ....Fred Ellison
Retail Adv. Mgr. ....Ronald Prince
Classified Transportation Mgr. ....Doug Barnett
Adv. Sales Mgr., DeSoto Appeal ....Amy Mills
Dir., Mktg./Community Rel. ....Elena Cainas
Mgr., Mktg. ....Paul Jewell
Circ. Dir. ....Darrell Jones
Circ. Mgr., Administrative ....Jeff N. Kimbro
Circ. Mgr., Metro ....David Eddins
Ed. ....Chris Peck
Mng. Ed. ....Scott Sines
Asst. Mng. Ed., Features ....Peggy McKenzie
Market Information: Split run; TMC; Zoned editions.
Mechanical available: Offset; Black and 3 ROP colors; insert accepted; page cutoffs - 23 9/16.
Mechanical Specifications: Type page 11 1/2 x 22 1/2; E - 6 cols, between; A - 6 cols, between; C - 10 cols, between.
Commodity Consumption: Avg. Page Number Per Issue - Daily 60; Avg. Page Number Per Issue - Plates Used 235000; Avg. Page Number Per Issue - Sunday 134; widths 25; Newsprint Used - Metric Tons 33452; Printing Ink Used - Black 605000; Printing Ink Used - Color 186000; Printing I
Equipment EDITORIAL: Front-end Software – GN3/Tera System.; Editorial Hardware – 160-ATS/News Desk; Editorial Equipment – 30-APP/Mac on Ethernet; Editorial Printers – 5-HP/5si CLASSIFIED: Front-end Software – AT/Enterprise 4.1.; Classified Hardware – 65-AT/Enterprise; Classified Printers – 7-Lexmark/Optra S DISPLAY: Ad make-up applications – AII; Layout Software – III/Display Ad composition, SCS/Layout 8000.; Display Hardware – 20-AII/Ad Manager PRODUCTION: Pagination Software – ATS.; Production Equipment – 3-C, 1-WL/75; Cameras – 1-C/Newspager; Scanners – 3-ECR/Autokon, FUJIC/550 PRESSROOM: Line 1 – 16-G/Metro 1975; Line 2 – 16-G/Metro 1975; Folders – 4-G/Double; Pasters – 32; Reels and Stands – 32 MAILROOM: Counter stackers – 12-HL/Monitor; Inserters and stuffers – GMA/SLS 1000, 3/28:2 machines, 3-/20:2 machines; Bundle tying machines – 15-/Dynaric; Addressing machine – 1-MG/851, 1-Ch/NR. BUSINESS COMPUTERS: Business Software – Admarc; Business Hardware – IBM/9121M311

MEMPHIS PUBLISHING CO.

495 Union Ave., Memphis, Tenn., 38103; gen tel (901) 529-2211; gen fax (901) 529-5833

MORRISTOWN

CITIZEN TRIBUNE

1609 W. 1st N. St., Morristown, Tenn., 37815; gen tel (423) 581-5630; gen fax (423) 581-3061; ed fax (423) 581-8863; adv e-mail ctadsend@lcs.net; web site www.citizentribune.com

Published: Mon, Tues, Wed, Thur, Fri, Sun
Weekday Frequency: e
Circulation: 18,988; 25,045(sun)
Last Audit: ABC September 30, 2011
Price: 9.30/mo (carrier); 111.00/yr (mail).
Advertising: Open inch rate $23.41
News services: AP, U.S. Suburban Press Inc..
Politics: Independent. **Established:** 1966
Not Published: Labor Day; Christmas.
Special Weekly Sections: Church Page (Fri); Lakeway Living (S); Best Food Day (Wed).
Magazines: Relish (Monthly); Parade (S).
Ed. ....R. Jack Fishman
Mng. Ed. ....John Gullion
Bus. Ed. ....Bobbie Young
Features Ed. ....Stan Johnson
Health/Medical Ed. ....Bob Moore
Photo Ed. ....Gary Smith
Sports Ed. ....Brian Trent
Theater/Music Ed. ....Jamia Blazer
Travel Ed. ....Denise Williams
Women's Ed. ....Diane Barnes

Prodn. Mgr. ....Rick Ball
Market Information: TMC.
Mechanical available: Offset; Black and 3 ROP colors; insert accepted; page cutoffs - 22 3/4.
Mechanical Specifications: Type page 11 5/8 x 21 1/2; E - 6 cols, 1 5/6, 1/8 between; A - 6 cols, 1 5/6, 1/8 between; C - 8 cols, 1 19/50, 1/8 between.
Commodity Consumption: Avg. Page Number Per Issue - Daily 26; Avg. Page Number Per Issue - Sunday 64.
Equipment; Editorial Hardware – 1-Ik/Minitek II (CPS 1020).; Production Equipment – 1-Nu; Cameras – 1-C, 1-Cl. PRESSROOM: Line 1 – 5-G/U; Folders – 1 MAILROOM: Counter stackers – 1/BG; Inserters and stuffers – 4-/MM; Bundle tying machines – 1-/MLN.; Business Hardware – 1-DEC/11-70

MURFREESBORO

THE DAILY NEWS JOURNAL

224 N. Walnut St., Murfreesboro, Tenn., 37130; gen tel (615) 893-5860; adv tel (615) 893-5860; ed tel (615) 893-5860; gen fax (615) 896-8702; adv fax (615) 896-8702 (Classified); adv e-mail adcopy@dnj.com; ed e-mail pirtle@dnj.com; web site www.dnj.com
Published: Mon, Tues, Wed, Thur, Fri, Sat, Sun
Weekday Frequency: m
Saturday Frequency: m
Circulation: 11,251; 12,604(sat); 16,425(sun)
Last Audit: ABC September 30, 2011
Price: 12.00/mo; 144.00/yr.
Advertising: Open inch rate $21.06
News services: AP, U.S. Suburban Press Inc..
Politics: Independent. **Established:** 1849
Special Editions: Letters to Santa (Other).
Special Weekly Sections: Movie Review (Fri); Job Solutions (Mon); Sports (S); Public Record (Sat); Health & Fitness (Thur); Seniors (Tues); Best Food Day (Wed).
Magazines: USA WEEKEND Magazine (S).
Pres./Pub. ....Andrew Oppmann
Exec. Asst. ....Tara Wann
Adv. Mgr. ....Heather Kent
Adv. Mgr., Classified.........................Al Werner
Educ. Ed. ....Mike West
Lifestyles Ed. ....Sande Suitt
News Ed. ....Sam Stockard
Online Servs. Dir. ....Kevin Halpern
Chief Photographer ....Jim Davis
Exec. Sports Ed. ....Greg Pogue
Market Information: ADS; Zoned editions.
Mechanical available: Offset; Black and 3 ROP colors; insert accepted; page cutoffs - 22 3/4.
Mechanical Specifications: Type page 12 x 21 1/2; E - 6 cols, 2, 1/8 between; A - 6 cols, 2, 1/8 between; C - 9 cols, 1, 1/8 between.
Commodity Consumption: Avg. Page Number Per Issue - Daily 24; Avg. Page Number Per Issue - Plates Used 28100; Avg. Page Number Per Issue - Sunday 62; widths 30; Newsprint Used - Short Tons 1801; Printing Ink Used - Black 39450; Printing Ink Used - Color 8493; Printing Ink Used
Equipment EDITORIAL: Front-end Software – QPS/QuarkXPress 3.31.; Editorial Hardware – APP/Mac; Editorial Equipment – 1-APP/Mac Quadra 650, 1-APP/Mac SE 30, AP/Wire, 1-Scanmaker/II Scanner; Editorial Printers – 1-APP/Mac LaserWriter 810 CLASSIFIED: Front-end Software – APP/Mac Appleshare 4.0, Baseview/Class Manager.; Classified Hardware – 1-APP/Mac fileserver, 5-APP/Mac LC III; Classified Printers – 1-APP/Mac 630 Pro Printer DISPLAY: Ad make-up applications – QPS/QuarkXPress 3.3, Multi-Ad/Creator, Typeset; Display Hardware – 2-APP/Mac Quadra 800, 1-APP/Mac 51, 4-APP/Mac Quadra 650; Display Printers – 2-APP/Mac LaserWriter NTX, 2-APP/Mac LaserWriter IIf, APP/Mac LaserWriter 630 Pro PRODUCTION: Pagination Software – QPS/QuarkXPress 3.31.; Production Equipment – Caere/OmniPage, APP/Mac LaserWriter NTX; Cameras – C/Spartan II; Scanners – APP/Mac One Scanner PRESSROOM: Line 1 – 5-G/Urbanite 1974, 4-DEV/Horizon 1985; Pasters – 3 MAILROOM: Counter stackers – 1-HI/RS-2517; Inserters and stuffers – 6/MM; Bundle tying machines – 6-/MLN; Addressing machine – 2-/KR. AUDIO: Audio Software – Baseview; Audio Hardware – 8-PC 486-8x, 33-CPU/16-250 BUSINESS COMPUTERS: Business Software – Foxbase, Acctmate; Business Hardware – 6-IBM/PC XT

MID SOUTH PUB. CO.

224 N. Walnut St., Murfreesboro, Tenn., 37130; gen tel (615) 893-5860; gen fax (615) 896-8702

NASHVILLE

THE TENNESSEAN

1100 Broadway, Nashville, Tenn., 37203-3116; gen tel (615) 259-8000; adv tel (615) 259-8338; gen fax (615) 259-8875; adv fax (615) 259-8820; ed fax (615) 259-8093; gen e-mail publisher@tennessean.com; adv e-mail adv@tennessean.com; ed e-mail living@tennessean.com; newstip@tennessean.com; web site www.tennessean.com
Published: Mon, Tues, Wed, Thur, Fri, Sat, Sun
Weekday Frequency: m
Saturday Frequency: m
Circulation: 120,805; 125,924(sat); 224,440(sun)
Last Audit: ABC September 30, 2011
Price: 17.25/mo (carrier); 207.00/yr (carrier).
Advertising: Open inch rate $345.39
News services: NYT, LAT-WP, MCT, SHNS, GNS.
Politics: 1812
Note: The Tennessean is owned by Gannett Co., Inc. which owns more than 90 daily newspapers.
Own facility?: Y
Special Editions: College Football (Aug); Auto Show (Jan); How To Guide (Jun); Spring Fashion (Mar); Gift Guides (Nov); Pro Football (Sept).
Special Weekly Sections: Weekend (Fri); School News & Classroom (Mon); Travel (S); Home Improvement (Sat); Health & Fitness (Tues).
Magazines: USA WEEKEND Magazine (S).
Profile: The Tennessean is a major daily newspaper serving Middle Tennessee. We also publish weekly newspapers in surrounding area and various niche publications throughout the year.
Vice Pres., Adv. ....Dave Gould
Adv. Mgr., Nat'l......................Wendell Pedigo
Market Devel. Dir. ....Bob Faricy
Research Mgr. ....Reginald Northern
NIE Mgr. ....Ann Zangri
Vice Pres., Circ. ....Jay Winkler
Asst. Mng. Ed., Business...........Deborah Fisher
Asst. Mng. Ed., Davidson A.M. ....Cindy Smith
Dir/Design Studio ....Jeff Glick
Asst. Bus. Ed..........................Randy McClain
Entertainment Ed.........................Linda Zettler
Music Writer ....Peter Cooper
News Ed. ....Ted Rayburn
Night/Weekend Ed........................Dwight Lewis
Vice Pres., Finance ....Andy Royer
Vice Pres., HR ....Kathy Cheatham
VP/Finance ....Kevin Huff
President & Publisher...................Carol Hudler
Editor & VP/Content & Audience Dev. Mark Silverman
Production Director ....Thom Gregory
Pres./Pub. ....Ellen Leifeld
Vice Pres., Audience Mgmt. ..Andrew Oppmann
Asst. Mng. Ed., Nights ....Kevin Paulk
Editorial Writer...........................Mike Morrow
Asst. Features Ed., Presentation ....Bill Greer
Pres. ....Carol Hudler
President & Publisher....................Carol Hudler
Market Information: ADS; Split run; TMC; Zoned editions.
Mechanical available: Offset; Black and 3 ROP colors; insert accepted; page cutoffs - 22, 21.5
Mechanical Specifications: Type page 10 x 21 3/16; 10 x 20 1/2
Commodity Consumption: Avg. Page Number Per Issue - Daily 56; Avg. Page Number Per Issue - Plates Used 330000; Avg. Page Number Per Issue - Sunday 133; widths 24 15/16; Newsprint Used - Short Tons 38000; Printing Ink Used - Black 958530; Printing Ink Used - Color 128393; Print
Equipment EDITORIAL: Front-end Software – CCI Newsgate; Editorial Hardware – Dell/Server; Editorial Equipment – 205-Intel/PC CLASSIFIED: Front-end Software – ATEX Mactive; Classified Hardware – DELL PRODUCTION: Pagination Software – CCI Newsgate, Newsway; Production Equipment – 3-AGFA CL, DL Platesetters PRESSROOM: Line 1 – 10-G/Colorliner; Line 2 – 10-G/Colorliner; Line 3 – 48-MAN/Uniset 70; Press Drives – G/Fincor, MAN/Baumuller; Folders – 4-G/3:2, 2-MAN/2:3:3; Pasters – 20-G/CT50, 9-MAN; Press control system – G/APCS MAN/PECOM MAILROOM: Counter stackers – 10-QWI/400, 2-QWI/500; Inserters and stuffers – 2-KM/2299, 1-KM/1472; Bundle tying machines – 14-OVL/Strap; Mailroom control system – Quipp Newscom, BURT Mountain; Addressing machine – 1-Ch/596, 2-VIP/9100; Other equipment –1-Osako/Trimmer, BUSINESS COMPUTERS: Business Software – Microsoft Office; Business Hardware – 2-IBM/AS-400
Delivery method: Mail, Newsstand, Private Carrier, Racks

NEWPORT

NEWPORT PLAIN TALK

145 E. Broadway, Newport, Tenn., 37821-2324; gen tel (423) 623-6171; gen fax (423) 625-1995; web site www.newportplaintalk.com
Published: Tues, Wed, Thur, Fri, Sun
Weekday Frequency: e
Circulation: ; 6,480(sun)
Last Audit: October 1, 2004
Advertising: Open inch rate $21.90
News services: AP.
Politics: 1900
Not Published: Christmas.
Own facility?: Y
Magazines: Parade (S).
Co-Pub. ....John M. Jones
Adv. Mgr. ....Betty McMillan
Circ. Mgr...................................Patrick Helms
Ed. ....David Popiel
Mng. Ed. ....Rick Hooper
Market Information: TMC.
Commodity Consumption: Avg. Page Number Per Issue - Daily 16; Avg. Page Number Per Issue - Sunday 40; widths 25; Newsprint Used - Short Tons 300; Printing Ink Used - Black 10000.
Equipment PRODUCTION: Pagination Software – QPS/QuarkXPress 4.0, Adobe/InDesign CS. PRESSROOM: Line 1 – G.

OAK RIDGE

THE OAK RIDGER

785 Oak Ridge Tpk., Oak Ridge, Tenn., 37830-7076; gen tel (865) 482-1021; adv tel (865) 482-7355; ed tel (865) 220-5502; gen fax (865) 220-5460; adv fax (865) 220-5539; ed fax (865) 482-7834; gen e-mail oakridge@oakridger.com; adv e-mail advertising@oakridger.com; web site www.oakridger.com
Published: Mon, Tues, Wed, Thur, Fri
Weekday Frequency: e
Circulation: 7,554
Last Audit: October 1, 2003
Price: 11.00/mo (carrier), $14.00/mo (mail).
Advertising: Open inch rate $14.60
News services: AP.
Politics: Independent.
Special Editions: Women in Business (Apr); Football (Aug); Greetings (Dec); Progress (Feb); Bride (Jan); Bride (Jun); Gardening (Mar); Outdoor (May); Cooking (Oct); Silver Salute (Sept).
Special Weekly Sections: TV (Fri); Weekend Sports (Mon); Focus on Community Issues (Thur); Lifestyle (Tues); Health News (Wed).
Magazines: USA WEEKEND Magazine (Fri); Relish (Monthly); American Profile (Weekly).
Bus. Mgr. ....Carol Skyberg
Adv. Dir........................................Janet Wood
Circ. Dir......................................Steve Traud
Ed...............................Darrell G. Richardson
News Ed.....................................Tank Johnston
Photographer ....Scott Fraker
Market Information: TMC.
Mechanical available: Offset; Black and 3 ROP colors; insert accepted - any; page cutoffs - 22 3/4.
Mechanical Specifications: Type page 11 5/8 x 21 1/2; E - 6 cols, 1 13/16, 1/8 between; A - 6 cols, 1 13/16, 1/8 between; C - 9 cols, 1 3/16, 1/8 between.
Commodity Consumption: Avg. Page Number Per Issue - Daily 22; widths 13 1/2; Newsprint Used - Short Tons 800; Printing Ink Used - Pages Printed 7614.
Equipment EDITORIAL: Front-end Software – Baseview/NewsEdit Pro.; Editorial Hardware – APP/Mac; Editorial Printers – MON/1270 Imager, 2-APP/Mac LaserWriter, 1999-Pre Press/Panther 46 CLASSIFIED: Front-end Software – Baseview.; Classified Hardware – APP/Mac, 2-PEC; Classified Printers – APP/Mac LaserWriter; Layout Software – Multi-Ad/Creator.; Display Hardware – APP/Power Macs; Display Printers – 1-APP/Mac LaserWriter 630 Pro; Production Equipment – 1-Nat/A-250; Cameras – 1-C. PRESSROOM: Line 1 – 8; Pasters – Reels and Stands □ 2-DEV/4-high, 1-DEV/3-high. MAILROOM: Counter stackers – BG/Count-O-Veyor; Inserters and stuffers – KAN/480; Bundle tying machines – 1-MLN/Spirit, 1-Si. BUSINESS COMPUTERS: Business Software – NCR/SMS Business Applications; Business Hardware – NCR/Unix

PARIS

THE PARIS POST-INTELLIGENCER

208 E. Wood St., Paris, Tenn., 38242; gen tel (731) 642-1162; gen fax (731) 642-1165; gen e-mail parispi@parispi.net; adv e-mail advertising@parispi.net; web site www.parispi.net
Published: Mon, Tues, Wed, Thur, Fri
Weekday Frequency: e
Circulation: 7,793
Last Audit: September 30, 2003
Price: 40.00/yr (in county).
Advertising: Open inch rate $8.47
News services: AP, NEA, KFS, Universal Press.
Politics: Independent.
Advertising not accepted: Liquor; wine; tobacco; beer.
Not Published: New Year; Memorial Day; Independence Day; Labor Day; Thanksgiving; Christmas.
Special Editions: Miss Spring (Apr); Reader's Choice Awards (Aug); Holiday Greeting (Dec); Future Farmers (Feb); Brides (Jan); Business Anniversary (Mar); Graduation (May); Veterans Salute (Nov); How To Guide (Oct); Fall-Winter Home & Auto (Sept).
Bus. Mgr..............................Evonne Williams
Office Mgr.......................................Kim Foster
Systems Mgr................................Jacquta Burke
Circ. Mgr......................................Tim Forrest
Ed........................................Michael Williams
News Ed. ....Ken Walker
Outdoors Ed. ....Steve McCadams
Sports Ed..................................Tommy Priddy
Prodn. Supt. ....Jimmy Williams
Market Information: Split run; TMC.
Mechanical available: Offset; Black and 3 ROP colors; insert accepted - do not accept mini catalogs; page cutoffs - 22 3/4.
Mechanical Specifications: Type page 11 5/8 x 21 1/2; E - 6 cols, 1 5/6, 1/8 between; A - 6 cols, 1 5/6, 1/8 between; C - 9 cols, 1 3/16, 3/32 between.
Commodity Consumption: Avg. Page Number Per

Issue - Daily 18; Avg. Page Number Per Issue - Plates Used 3500; widths 12 1/2; Newsprint Used - Short Tons 250; Printing Ink Used - Black 12000; Printing Ink Used - Color 1000; Printing Ink Used - Pages Printed 4588.

Equipment EDITORIAL: Front-end Software – Baseview 3.5.2.; Editorial Hardware – 4-APP/Mac G4, InDesign 12.02, 11-APP/iMac, Baseview/NewsEdit Pro; Editorial Equipment – 2-RSK/M100 lap top, 3-Olympus/Digital Camera, 2-Canon/EOS Rebel; Editorial Printers – 1-Epson/Stylus Photo CLASSIFIED: Front-end Software – Baseview/AdManager Pro 2.1.4.; Classified Hardware – 1-APP/Mac Quadra 630, APP/iMac, APP/eMac, Baseview/Ad Manager Pro; Classified Printers – 1-Panasonic/XP3200 DISPLAY: Ad make-up applications – Multi-Ad/Creator 6.5.8.; Display Hardware – Printers ☐ 1-Xante/Accel-a-Writer 8200 PRODUCTION: Pagination Software – QPS/QuarkXPress 4.1, Adobe/InDesign 2.0.1.; Production Equipment – ECR, Harlequin/Rip 6.02; Cameras – 1-DAI/2400; Scanners – Epson/Flattop PRESSROOM: Line 1 – 7-G/Community; Folders – 1-G/SC.; Inserters and stuffers – 6-KAN/320; Bundle tying machines – 2-Bu/18; Addressing machine – Dispensa-Matic 16.; Business Hardware – 2-IBM/AS-400, 1-Mega

PARIS PUBLISHING CO., INC.

208 E. Wood, Paris, Tenn., 38242; gen tel (731) 642-1162; gen fax (731) 642-1165; web site http://parispi.net/

SEVIERVILLE

THE MOUNTAIN PRESS

119 Riverbend Dr., Sevierville, Tenn., 37876; gen tel (865) 428-0746; adv tel (865) 428-0748; ed tel (865) 428-0748; gen fax (865) 453-4913; adv e-mail jwhaley@themountainpress.com; ed e-mail editor@themountainpress.com; web site www.themountainpress.com

Published: Mon, Tues, Wed, Thur, Fri, Sat, Sun
Weekday Frequency: m
Saturday Frequency: m
Circulation: 7,824; 7,824(sat); 7,824(sun)
Last Audit: September 24, 2003
Price: 11.00/mo; 128.00/yr.
Advertising: Open inch rate $21.11
News services: AP.
Politics: Independent.
Advertising not accepted: Brokered.
Not Published: Christmas.
Special Editions: Football (Aug); Christmas Greetings (Dec); Progress (Feb); Health & Fitness (Jan); Newcomer's Guide (Jul); Graduation (Jun); Christmas Carol Book (Nov); Reader's Choice (Sept).
Special Weekly Sections: Spotlight (S).
Magazines: Experienced Living (Monthly); USA WEEKEND Magazine (S).

Pub. ....Jana M. Thomasson
Adv. Dir. ....Joi Whaley
Ed. ....Stan Voit
Mng. Ed. ....Jamia Blazer
Community News Ed. ....Lin Brownoo
Sports Ed. ....Jason Davis
Prodn. Dir. ....R. Thomas McCarter

Market Information: TMC.
Mechanical available: Offset; Black and 3 ROP colors; insert accepted; page cutoffs - 22 3/4.
Mechanical Specifications: Type page 13 x 21; E - 6 cols, 2 1/16, 1/8 between; A - 6 cols, 2 1/16, 1/8 between; C - 9 cols, 1 5/16, 1/8 between.
Commodity Consumption: Avg. Page Number Per Issue - Daily 16; Avg. Page Number Per Issue - Plates Used 8000; Avg. Page Number Per Issue - Sunday 30; widths 27; Newsprint Used - Short Tons 600; Printing Ink Used - Black 15000; Printing Ink Used - Color 7200; Printing Ink Used -

Equipment EDITORIAL: Front-end Software – Baseview, QPS/QuarkXPress 4.1.; Editorial Hardware – Editorial System, APP/Power Mac; Editorial Printers – NewGen/Imager Plus 12, ECR/VRL 36 HS-Mako, QMS/1660 CLASSIFIED: Front-end Software – Baseview/Class.; Classified Hardware – Printers ☐ QMS/1660E DISPLAY: Ad make-up applications – Multi-Ad/Creator 4.0; Layout Software – APP/Mac 4400, APP/Mac 200.; Display Printers – HP/5000; Production Equipment – 2-APP/Mac LaserWriter, Nu/Flip Top FT40UPNS, 1-NewGen/Imager Plus 12, Polaroid/SprintScan; Cameras – Spartan/III Chemco. PRESSROOM: Line 1 – 9-G/Community single width; Press Drives – 2-HP/50; Folders – G/SSC; Press registration system – Duarte/Pin System.; Inserters and stuffers – KR/512; Bundle tying machines – 2-Malow/50; Addressing machine – KR/211. BUSINESS COMPUTERS: Business Software – Baseview; Business Hardware – APP/Mac

SHELBYVILLE

SHELBYVILLE TIMES-GAZETTE

323 E. Depot St., Shelbyville, Tenn., 37160; gen tel (931) 684-1200; gen fax (931) 684-3228; adv e-mail display@t-g.com; ed e-mail news@t-g.com; web site www.t-g.com

Published: Mon, Tues, Wed, Thur, Fri, Sun
Weekday Frequency: e
Circulation: 7,385; 7,385(sun)
Last Audit: September 30, 2006
Price: 38.00/yr (mail), $52.00/yr (carrier).
Advertising: Open inch rate $10.75
News services: AP, DF.
Politics: Independent.
Advertising not accepted: Fortune tellers; Speculative non-local corp.
Not Published: New Year; Memorial Day; Independence Day; Labor Day; Thanksgiving; Christmas.
Special Editions: Private Property (Apr); Back-to-School (Aug); Fashion (Fall); Jaycees (Jan); Dairy (Jun); Farm (Mar); Bride (May); Sports (Monthly); Gift Guide (Nov).
Special Weekly Sections: Church (Fri); Senior Citizen (Mon); Farm (Thur); Farm (Tues); Best Food Day (Wed).
Magazines: Relish (Monthly); Parade (S); American Profile (Weekly).

Pub. ....Hugh Jones
Gen. Mgr. ....William Mitchell
Bus. Mgr. ....Becky McBee
Display Adv. Mgr. ....Sandra (Sissy) Smith
City Ed. ....John I. Carney
Sports Ed. ....Danny Parker
Prodn. Dir., Commercial Printing Wayne Osbourne

Market Information: TMC.
Mechanical available: Offset; Black and 3 ROP colors; insert accepted.
Mechanical Specifications: Type page 13 x 21 1/2; E - 7 cols, 2 1/16, 1/8 between; A - 7 cols, 2 1/6, 1/8 between; C - 9 cols, 1 9/16, 1/8 between.
Commodity Consumption: Avg. Page Number Per Issue - Daily 16; Avg. Page Number Per Issue - Plates Used 2000; widths 25; Newsprint Used - Short Tons 245; Printing Ink Used - Black 7200; Printing Ink Used - Pages Printed 4274.

Equipment EDITORIAL: Front-end Software – CText.; Editorial Hardware – PC; Editorial Printers – APP/Mac LaserWriter CLASSIFIED: Front-end Software – Baseview/Class Pro.; Classified Hardware – Mac; Layout Software – QuarkXpress.; Display Hardware – APP/Mac; Production Equipment – Fuji. PRESSROOM: Line 1 – 6-KP/Color King Web (Non heat O.S.) 1963.; Inserters and stuffers – KAN; Bundle tying machines – 2/Bu.; Business Hardware – Centurion/7000

UNION CITY

THE MESSENGER

613 Jackson St., Union City, Tenn., 38261-5239; gen tel (731) 885-0744; gen fax (731) 885-0782; gen e-mail dgc@ucmessenger.com; ed e-mail dryder@ucmessenger.com; web site www.ucmessenger.com

Published: Mon, Tues, Wed, Thur, Fri
Weekday Frequency: e
Circulation: 8,335
Last Audit: October 1, 2003
Price: 8.00/mo; 88.00/yr.
Advertising: Open inch rate $8.50
News services: AP.
Politics: Independent-Democrat.
Not Published: Independence Day; Thanksgiving; Christmas.
Special Weekly Sections: Business (Mon); Church (Thur); Farm (Tues); Food (Wed).

Pres./Pub. ....David Critchlow
Vice Pres./Office Mgr. ....F. Scott Critchlow
Bus. Mgr. ....Penella Davis
Adv. Mgr., Classified ....Glenda Langford
Adv. Mgr., Retail ....Gloria Chesteen
Farm Ed. ....Donna Ryder
Online Ed. ....David Critchlow
Photo Mgr. ....David Critchlow
Sports Ed. ....Mike Hutchens
Women's Ed. ....Darlene Hayes
Online Mgr. ....Jeremy Leckey
Prodn. Mgr., Pressroom ....Rob Smith
Prodn. Mgr., Mailroom/Post Press John Travatham
Prodn. Mgr., Pre Press ....David Fuzzell

Market Information: TMC.
Mechanical available: Offset; Black and 3 ROP colors; insert accepted; page cutoffs - 22.
Mechanical Specifications: Type page 11 5/8 x 21; E - 6 cols, 1 13/16, 1/8 between; A - 6 cols, 1 13/16, 1/8 between; C - 9 cols, 1 3/16, 1/8 between.
Commodity Consumption: Avg. Page Number Per Issue - Daily 14; Avg. Page Number Per Issue - Plates Used 9; widths 27 1/2; Newsprint Used - Short Tons 700.

Equipment EDITORIAL: Front-end Software – Baseview/NewsEdit Pro.; Editorial Hardware – 2-APP/Mac 6200, 8-APP/Mac G3, 2-APP/Mac 7200, 1-APP/Mac G4; Editorial Printers – HP/LaserJet 5simx, Konica/Jetsetter CLASSIFIED: Front-end Software – Baseview.; Classified Hardware – 2-APP/Mac 4400; Classified Printers – APP/Mac LaserWriter, ECR/Imagesetter DISPLAY: Ad make-up applications – Multi-Ad/Creator.; Display Hardware – 2-APP/Mac G3; Display Printers – APP/Mac LaserWriter, GCC/Elite XL, ECR/Imagesetter, HP/5simx-Konica/Jetsetter PRODUCTION: Pagination Software – QPS/QuarkXPress 3.32.; Production Equipment – ECR/VR 36 Imagesetter, Nu/631; Cameras – 1-C/Spartan; Scanners – Umax/Vista 56, Umax/Vista 56E, Lf/Leafscan 35 PRESSROOM: Line 1 – DGM/6 mono; Folders – 2-SLN/2:1, 2-DGM/430. MAILROOM: Counter stackers – BG/108, 2-BG/Count-D-Veyor; Bundle tying machines – 2/Bu, 2-/Signode; Addressing machine – 1-/Dispensa-Matic.; Business Hardware – APP/Mac, Baseview

MESSENGER PUBLISHING CO.

613 Jackson St., Union City, Tenn., 38261; gen tel (731) 885-0744; gen fax (731) 885-0782

TEXAS

ABILENE

ABILENE REPORTER-NEWS

101 Cypress St., Abilene, Texas, 79601-5816; gen tel (325) 673-4271; gen fax (325) 670-6797; ed fax (325) 670-5242; gen e-mail citydesk@reporternews.com; web site www.reporternews.com

Group: Metro Newspaper Advertising Services, Inc.
Published: Mon, Tues, Wed, Thur, Fri, Sat, Sun
Weekday Frequency: m
Saturday Frequency: m
Circulation: 23,164; 26,023(sat); 31,174(sun)
Last Audit: ABC September 30, 2011
Price: 185.45/yr; 15.00/4wk.
Advertising: Open inch rate $50.00
News services: AP, NYT, SHNS.
Politics: Independent. **Established:** 1881
Special Editions: ALPS Gazette (Apr); Kickoff (Aug); Letter to Santa (Dec); Big Country Farm and Ranch Show (Feb); Outlook (Jan); Reader's Choice Awards (Jul); Ft. Griffin Fandangle (Jun); Rattlesnake Round-up (Mar); Western Heritage Classic (May); City Sidewalks (Nov); He
Special Weekly Sections: Business Pages (Fri); Oil (S); Business Pages (Sat); Business Pages (Thur); Oil (Tues); Best Food Day (Wed).
Magazines: Abilene Magazine (Other); Parade (S).
Broadcast Affiliations: KTX5 (ABC); KRBC (NBC); KTAB (CBS).

Pres./Pub. ....Kim Nussbaum
CFO ....Carla Draper
Circ. Dir. ....David Rowe
Ed. ....Barton Cromeens
Editorial Page Ed. ....Sidney Levesque
Online Dir. ....Dann Reagan
Prodn. Dir., Opns. ....Mike Hall
Prodn. Mgr. ....Christian Wells
Prodn. Mgr., Mailroom (Nights) .Scott Pentecost
Prodn. Mgr., Pressroom ....David Nunez

Market Information: ADS; Split run; TMC; Zoned editions.
Mechanical available: Black and 3 ROP colors; insert accepted; page cutoffs - 21.
Mechanical Specifications: Type page 11 5/8 x 21; E - 6 cols, 1 5/6, 1/8 between; A - 6 cols, 1 5/6, 1/8 between; C - 10 cols, 1 5/64, 1/6 between.
Commodity Consumption: Avg. Page Number Per Issue - Daily 40; Avg. Page Number Per Issue - Plates Used 48326; Avg. Page Number Per Issue - Sunday 72; widths 50; Newsprint Used - Metric Tons 4021; Newsprint Used - Short Tons 4432; Printing Ink Used - Black 97019; Printing Ink U

Equipment EDITORIAL: Front-end Software – DPS/DBEdit.; Editorial Hardware – Compaq/Proliant 3000; Editorial Printers – HP/Laser Jet 4000 CLASSIFIED: Front-end Software – SII/Sys 25, AT/Enterprise 1.411.; Classified Hardware – Compaq/Proliant 2500; Classified Printers – 1-HP/4000N, HP/2567, 2-HP/5 si DISPLAY: Ad make-up applications – CJ/Aim; Layout Software – MEI/ALS.; Display Hardware – HP/3000; Display Printers – HP/LaserJet II, HP/2567 PRODUCTION: Pagination Software – DPS DB Edit.; Production Equipment – 2-Nu/Flip Top, 3-Nat, 1-W, 1-Pre Press/Panther Pro 46 Imagesetter, 1-Pre Press/Panther Pro Imagesetter 5300W, 1-Pre Press/Panther Pro 46115; Cameras – 2-C; Scanners – APP/Mac, PixelCraft/Pro Imager 8000 PRESSROOM: Line 1 – 3-G/Community single width 1984; Line 2 – 7-G/Headliner double width (offset, open fountain, 4 1/2 deck) 1984; Line 3 – 8-Didde/Web single width 1997; Press Drives – 4-GE/150LP motor; Folders – 2-Regent/2:1, 1-G/506, 1-G/Jaws; Pasters – G/Auto. MAILROOM: Counter stackers – 1-Id, 2-QWI/350; Inserters and stuffers – KAN/760 Inserters, 1-KAN/4-head Multifeeder; Bundle tying machines – 1-OVL/JP-80, 2/Dynaric; Addressing machine – 1-/Scitex Ink Jet; Other equipment –1-MM/Sticher-trimmer.; Audio Hardware – Brite Voice Systems, Brite Voice Systems; Business Hardware – HP/3000 937LX

REPORTER PUBLISHING CO.

101 Block Cypress St., Abilene, Texas, 79601; gen tel (325) 673-4271; gen fax (325) 670-5250; web site http://www.reporternews.com/

ALICE

ALICE ECHO-NEWS JOURNAL

405 E. Main St., Alice, Texas, 78332-4968; gen tel (361) 664-6588; adv tel (361) 664-6588; ed tel (361) 664-6588; gen fax (361) 668-1030; adv fax (361) 668-1030; ed fax (361) 668-1030; adv e-mail ads.aenj@aliceechonews.com; web site www.aliceechonews.com

Published: Mon, Tues, Wed, Thur, Fri, Sun
Weekday Frequency: e
Circulation: 3,845; 3,845(sun)
Last Audit: September 24, 2002
Price: 108.00/yr (carrier), $124.00/yr (mail).
Advertising: Open inch rate $13.00
News services: AP.
Special Editions: Senior Life (Apr); Football Preview (Aug); Senior Life (Dec); Senior Life (Feb); Visitor's Guide (Jul); Senior Life (Jun); Winter Texans (Nov); Senior Life (Oct).
Special Weekly Sections: TV Listings (S).
Magazines: American Profile (Weekly).
Adv. Dir. ....Tony Morris
Adv. Sales ....Javier Ramos
Classified Sales Mgr. ....Russel Gruber
Circ. Dir. ....Jamie Gonzalez
Mng. Ed. ....Christopher Maher
Sports Ed. ....Pete Garcia
Webmaster ....Lois Stephens
Prodn. Foreman, Press ....Paul Poe
Market Information: ADS; TMC.
Mechanical available: Offset; Black and 3 ROP colors; insert accepted; page cutoffs - 22 1/2.
Mechanical Specifications: Type page 13 x 21 1/2; E - 6 cols, 2 1/16, 1/8 between; A - 6 cols, 2 1/16, 1/8 between; C - 8 cols, 1 1/2, 1/8 between.
Commodity Consumption: Avg. Page Number Per Issue - Daily 10; Avg. Page Number Per Issue - Sunday 36; Printing Ink Used - Black 10000; Printing Ink Used - Color 2000.
Equipment EDITORIAL: Front-end Software – Claris/MacWrite Pro, QPS/QuarkXPress.; Editorial Hardware – APP/Mac; Editorial Equipment – Microtek/Scanner; Editorial Printers – APP/Mac LaserWriters CLASSIFIED: Front-end Software – Baseview.; Classified Hardware – APP/Mac DISPLAY: Ad make-up applications – QPS/QuarkXPress; Layout Software – APP/Mac.; Production Equipment – APP/Mac; Cameras – R.; Inserters and stuffers – 4/KAN; Bundle tying machines – Ca; Addressing machine – Am.; Business Hardware – Onyx

AMARILLO

AMARILLO GLOBE-NEWS

900 S. Harrison St., Amarillo, Texas, 79101-3424; gen tel (806) 376-4488; adv tel (806) 345-3231; ed tel (806) 345-3358; gen fax (806) 376-9217; adv fax (806) 372-3717; ed fax (806) 373-0810; adv e-mail mike.distelhorst@amarillo.com; web site www.amarillo.com
Published: Mon, Tues, Wed, Thur, Fri, Sat, Sun
Weekday Frequency: m
Saturday Frequency: m
Circulation: 36,142; 39,276(sat); 45,287(sun)
Last Audit: ABC September 30, 2011
Price: 10.85/mo (mS), $10.25/mo (eS).
Advertising: Open inch rate $65.29
News services: AP, MCT, LAT-WP, DF.
Politics: Independent. **Established:** 1909
Special Editions: Goodlife (over 50's) (Monthly).
Special Weekly Sections: Get Out-Entertainment (Fri); Business & Financial (S); Faith (Sat); Food (Wed).
Magazines: Relish (Monthly); USA WEEKEND Magazine (S).
Pub ....Les Simpson
Personnel Dir. ....Valerie Bintliff
Adv. Dir. ....Mike Distelhorst
Exec. Ed. ....Dawn Dressler
Bus. Ed. ....Jim McBride
Editorial Page Ed. ....John Kanelis
Photo Dept. Mgr. ....Michael Schumacher
Real Estate Ed. ....Cheryl Berzanskis
Prodn. Dir., Opns. ....Mike O'Connor
Market Information: Split run; TMC; Zoned editions.
Mechanical available: Offset; Black and 3 ROP colors; insert accepted; page cutoffs - 22 3/4.
Mechanical Specifications: Type page 13 x 21 1/2; E - 6 cols, 2 1/16, 1/8 between; A - 6 cols, 2 1/16, 1/8 between; C - 10 cols, 1 3/16, 1/8 between.
Commodity Consumption: Avg. Page Number Per Issue - Daily 35; Avg. Page Number Per Issue - Plates Used 76610; Avg. Page Number Per Issue - Sunday 74; widths 54; Newsprint Used - Short Tons 7952; Printing Ink Used - Black 119310; Printing Ink Used - Color 41122; Printing Ink Us
Equipment EDITORIAL: Front-end Software – MPS.; Editorial Hardware – 32-Gateway/2000, 13-APP/Mac; Editorial Printers – Okidata/Microline 320 CLASSIFIED: Front-end Software – DTI.; Classified Hardware – APP/Mac DISPLAY: Ad make-up applications – Multi-Ad/Creator, Adobe/Illustrator; Display Hardware – 16-APP/Power Mac; Display Printers – APP/Mac LaserWriter II, Xante/Accel-a-Writer PRODUCTION: Pagination Software – DTI/Adobe Indesign 3.1.; Production Equipment – AG/Accuset 1000, 1-Nu/Flip Top, AG/Accuset 1500, Xante; Cameras – 2-C/Spartan III; Scanners – AG/Horizon, 4-Microtek/Scanmaker E6 PRESSROOM: Line 1 – 6-G/Metro (3 half decks) 1979; Folders – G/3:1; Pasters – 6; Reels and Stands – 6 MAILROOM: Counter stackers – 4-QWI/300; Inserters and stuffers – 2-GMA/SLS 1000 18:1; Bundle tying machines – 4-Dynaric/NP-2, 2-Dynaric/Turntable; Wrapping singles – 2-QWI/Cobra wraps; Mailroom control system – PMS; Addressing machine – Wm.; Audio Hardware – Wyse/WY2214 BUSINESS COMPUTERS: Business Software – Lotus 1-2-3, WordPerfect; Business Hardware – 4-IBM/Sys II, 10-Memorex/Telex 11918

ATHENS

ATHENS DAILY REVIEW

201 S. Prairieville St., Athens, Texas, 75751-2541; gen tel (903) 675-5626; adv tel (903) 675-5626; ed tel (903) 675-5626; gen fax (903) 675-9450; adv fax (903) 675-6870; ed fax (903) 675-9450; gen e-mail news2@athensreview.com; adv e-mail adverts@athensreview.com; ed e-mail news2@athensreview.com; web site www.athensreview.com
Published: Mon, Tues, Wed, Thur, Fri, Sun
Weekday Frequency: e
Circulation: 4,905; 4,905(sun)
Last Audit: October 1, 2003
Price: 7.00/mo; 94.25/yr.
Advertising: Open inch rate $12.46
News services: AP.
Politics: Independent. **Established:** 1901
Not Published: Christmas.
Special Editions: Football (Aug); Religion (Mar); Local calendar (Monthly); Industrial (Oct).
Special Weekly Sections: Best Food Days (S); Best Food Days (Tues).
Magazines: Relish (Monthly); USA WEEKEND Magazine (S); American Profile (Weekly).
Pub ....Lange Svehlak
Adv. Dir. ....Andi Green
Circ. Mgr. ....Ginger McDaniel
Ed. ....Jayson Larson
Sports Ed ....Benny Rogers
Market Information: TMC.
Mechanical available: Offset; Black and 3 ROP colors; insert accepted; page cutoffs - 22 3/4.
Mechanical Specifications: Type page 13 x 21 1/2; E - 6 cols, 2 1/16, 1/8 between; A - 6 cols, 2 1/16, 1/8 between; C - 8 cols, 1 1/2, 1/16 between.
Commodity Consumption: Avg. Page Number Per Issue - Daily 15; Avg. Page Number Per Issue - Plates Used 2470; Avg. Page Number Per Issue - Sunday 18; widths 25; Newsprint Used - Metric Tons 340; Printing Ink Used - Black 9340; Printing Ink Used - Pages Printed 4910.
Equipment EDITORIAL: Front-end Software – Baseview.; Editorial Hardware – APP/Mac; Editorial Printers – 2-Pre Press/Panther Imagesetter CLASSIFIED: Front-end Software – Baseview.; Classified Hardware – APP/Mac; Classified Printers – 2-Pre Press/Panther Imagesetter; Layout Software – APP/Mac.; Display Printers – 2-Pre Press/Panther Imagesetter PRODUCTION: Pagination Software – QPS/QuarkXPress 3.1.; Production Equipment – 1-Kamerak/8% Shrink; Cameras – 1-Acti/183; Scanners – 2-APP/Mac Scanner PRESSROOM: Line 1 – 6-HI/V-15A (upper former); Folders – 1; Inserters and stuffers – 4-KAN/320; Bundle tying machines – 2/Bu; Addressing machine – 1-KR/215 (with 211).; Business Hardware – Software ÃÂÃÂ Brainworks

AUSTIN

AUSTIN AMERICAN-STATESMAN

305 S. Congress, Austin, Texas, 78704-1200; gen tel (512) 445-4000; adv tel (512) 445-3742; ed tel (512) 445-3851; gen fax (512) 445-3503; adv fax (512) 443-4047; ed fax (512) 445-3679; gen e-mail news@statesman.com; web site www.statesman.com
Published: Mon, Tues, Wed, Thur, Fri, Sat, Sun
Weekday Frequency: m
Saturday Frequency: m
Circulation: 119,885; 120,919(sat); 186,803(sun)
Last Audit: ABC September 30, 2011
Advertising: Open inch rate $233.40
News services: AP, Cox News Service, MCT, LAT-WP, NNS, NYT, TMS.
Politics: Independent.
Special Editions: Kinko's Classic (Apr); High School & College Football (Aug); Gift Guide (Dec); Camp Guide (Feb); Healthcare (Jan); This is Austin (Jul); SXSW (Mar); Diversity (Nov); Pro Football Preview (Oct); Austin City Limits Music Festival (Sept).
Special Weekly Sections: Movies (Fri); Tech Monday (Mon); Insight (S); Sports Extra (Sat); XL (Thur); Food (Wed).
Magazines: Parade (S); Vista (Sat).
Vice Pres./CFO ....Eddie Burns
Gen. Mgr., statesman.com ....Tim Lott
Exec. Asst. to Pub. ....Peg Ball
Vice Pres., Mktg. ....Lisa Sullivan
Vice Pres., Circ. ....Harry Davis
Circ. Dir. ....Jana Dobson
Ed. ....Fred Zipp
Mng. Ed. ....Debbie Hiott
Editorial Page Ed ....Arnold Garcia
Photo Dir. ....Zach Ryall
Prodn. Dir. ....Kit Yearty
Publisher ....Jane Williams
Controller ....Craig Wohlfort
Manager, Human Resources ....Libby McGhee
Pub. ....Michael Vivio
Controller ....Robert Stewart
Adv. Vice Pres. ....Michael Wilson
Dir., InfoVentures/Commun. ....Retta Kelley
Dir., Info/Technology Servs. ....Paul Mowry
Prodn. Vice Pres., Opns. ....Bob Tucker
Market Information: Split run; TMC; Zoned editions.
Mechanical available: Offset; Black and 3 ROP colors; insert accepted; page cutoffs - 22.
Mechanical Specifications: Type page 12 1/2 x 21; E - 6 cols, 2, 1/6 between; A - 6 cols, 2, 1/6 between; C - 10 cols, 1 1/5, 1/9 between.
Commodity Consumption: Avg. Page Number Per Issue - Daily 85; Avg. Page Number Per Issue - Plates Used 443000; Avg. Page Number Per Issue - Saturday 100; Avg. Page Number Per Issue - Sunday 140; widths 49 3/4; Newsprint Used - Short Tons 44600; Printing Ink Used - Black 710000
Equipment EDITORIAL: Front-end Software – DTI/PageSpeed, DTI/SpeedPlanner.; Editorial Hardware – APP/Mac, Sun/Enterprise 4000; Editorial Printers – HP CLASSIFIED: Front-end Software – AT.; Classified Hardware – AT; Classified Equipment – Ad Fast/Ad Fax (Future Tense), Ad On Time; Classified Printers – HP DISPLAY: Ad make-up applications – DTI/AdSpeed 4.3; Layout Software – DTI/Plan Builder.; Display Hardware – APP/Mac; Display Printers – HP PRODUCTION: Pagination Software – DTI/AdSpeed 5.5, DTI/ImageSpeed 4.3, DTI/PageSpeed, DTI/Speed Planner 4.3.; Production Equipment – 2-BKY, 2-WL/Lith-X-Pozer III, 1-GJ/550; Cameras – 1-C/Newspager I; Scanners – 1-Nikon/Pro Imager 8000, 1-Epson/1640 PRESSROOM: Line 1 – 9-G/Metroliner double width (5 half decks) 1981; Line 2 – 9-G/Metroliner double width (5 half decks) 1981; Line 3 – 9-G/Metroliner double width (5 half decks) 1984, KBA/(2 Towers); Line 4 – 7-KBA/Towers (43 Couples); Folders – 4-G/3:2, 1-G/2:5:5 MAILROOM: Counter stackers – 9-QWI/351, 3-HL/Monitor; Inserters and stuffers – 1-S/1472, 1-S/1372, 1-GMA/SLS 2000 30:2, 1-GMA/SLS 1000 14:1; Bundle tying machines – 9-QWI/NS45 Strap, 2/Oval Strap; Addressing machine – 2-Scitex.; Audio Hardware – Brite Voice Systems BUSINESS COMPUTERS: Business Software – Microsoft/Windows XP, Microsoft/NT, Lawson; Business Hardware – 1-IBM/7060-H30, Sun/3500

BAYTOWN

THE BAYTOWN SUN

1301 Memorial Dr., Baytown, Texas, 77520-2401; gen tel (281) 422-8302; adv tel (281) 425-8036; ed tel (281) 425-8016; gen fax (281) 427-6283; adv fax (281) 427-6283; ed fax (281) 427-1880; gen e-mail baytownsun@aol.com; adv e-mail sunadvertising@baytownsun.com; ed e-mail sunnews@baytownsun.com; web site baytownsun.com
Published: Tues, Wed, Thur, Fri, Sun
Weekday Frequency: m
Saturday Frequency: m
Circulation: 6,631; 6,631(sun)
Last Audit: Sworn September 30, 2006
Price: $10.75/$129.00
Advertising: Open inch rate $14.50
Insert rate: 53.00
News services: AP, NEA, CNS, TMS.
Not Published: Saturday/Monday
Own facility?: Y
Special Editions: Forecast (Feb); Back-to-School (Jul); Coastal Views (Jun); Forecast (Mar); Outdoors (Sept).
Special Weekly Sections: Arts & Entertainment (Fri); TV Guide (S); Religious (Sat); Business (Tues); Best Food Days (Wed).
Magazines: USA WEEKEND Magazine (S); American Profile (Weekly).
Circ. Mgr. ....Joshua Hart
Business Manager/HR ....Sandy Denson
Pub. ....Cliff Clements
Publisher ....Janie Gray
Adv. Mgr. ....Gordon Gallatin
Mng. Ed. ....David Bloom
Sports Ed. ....Dave Rogers
Market Information: ADS; TMC; Zoned editions.
Mechanical available: Offset; Black and 3 ROP colors; insert accepted; page cutoffs - 21.
Mechanical Specifications: Type page 12 1/2 x 21; E - 6 cols, 2 1/16, 1/8 between; A - 6 cols, 2 1/16, 1/8 between; C - 9 cols, 1 5/16, 1/8 between.
Commodity Consumption: Avg. Page Number Per Issue - Daily 20; Avg. Page Number Per Issue - Sunday 36; widths 25; Newsprint Used - Short Tons 800.
Equipment EDITORIAL: Front-end Software – Mk/Proprietary.; Editorial Hardware – Mk/4000, 13-Mk/AT; Editorial Equipment – APP/Mac Quadra 700; Editorial Printers – APP/Mac LaserWriter II NTX CLASSIFIED: Front-end Software – Mk/Proprietary.; Classified Printers – APP/Mac LaserWriter II NTX DISPLAY: Ad make-up applications – Mk/Proprietary; Layout Software – Mk/4000.; Display Hardware – 2-APP/Mac IIcx, 2-APP/Mac IIsi; Display Printers – APP/Mac LaserWriter II NTX; Production Equipment – APP/Mac LaserWriter II NTX; Cameras – 1-C/Spartan III.; Folders – 1
Delivery method: Mail, Newsstand, Private Carrier, Racks

SOUTHERN NEWSPAPERS, INC.

1301 Memorial Dr., Baytown, Texas, 77520; gen tel (281) 422-8302; gen fax (281) 427-6283

BEAUMONT

THE BEAUMONT ENTERPRISE

380 Main St., Beaumont, Texas, 77701-2331; gen tel (409) 833-3311; adv tel (409) 838-2819; ed tel (409) 838-2802; gen fax (409) 838-2865; adv fax (409) 838-2865; ed fax (409) 880-0757; gen e-mail local-news@beaumontenterprise.com; web site www.beaumontenterprise.com; www.south-easttexaslive.com

Group: Metro Newspaper Advertising Services, Inc.

Published: Mon, Tues, Wed, Thur, Fri, Sat, Sun

Weekday Frequency: m

Saturday Frequency: m

Circulation: 23,388; 30,899(sat); 33,957(sun)

Last Audit: ABC September 30, 2011

Price: 12.00/mo (carrier), $17.00/mo (mail).

Advertising: Open inch rate $61.22

News services: HN, NYT, AP.

Politics: Independent. **Established:** 1880

Special Editions: Home Improvement (Apr); Football (Aug); Christmas Essay Contest (Dec); Health Care (Feb); Outlook (Jan); Summer Sale (Jul); Pre-Fourth Sale (Jun); Today's Woman (Mar); Reader's Choice (May); Homes of Southeast Texas (Monthly); Auto Preview (Nov); Shop S.E

Special Weekly Sections: TV Week (S); Church (Sat); Beaumont Journal (Thur); Orange County News (Wed).

Magazines: Parade (S).

Pub.....................John Newhouse
Circ. Dir., Opns.....................Jeffrey Reedy
Ed.....................Timothy M. Kelly
Asst. Mng. Ed.....................David Lauricella
Assoc. Mng. Ed.....................Sheila Friedeck
Editorial Page Ed.....................Tom Taschinger
Features Ed.....................Ashley Sanders
Librarian....................Terrye Maillet-Jones
Photo Ed.....................Pete Churton
Mgmt. Info Servs. Mgr...........Freddie Campbell
Online Mgr.....................Dave Constantine

Market Information: Split run; TMC; Zoned editions.

Mechanical available: Offset; Black and 3 ROP colors; insert accepted - card, tab, standard; page cutoffs - 22 3/4.

Mechanical Specifications: Type page 11 1/2 x 21 1/2; E - 6 cols, 1 3/4, 1/8 between; A - 6 cols, 1 3/4, 1/8 between; C - 9 cols, 1 1/6, 1/8 between.

Commodity Consumption: Avg. Page Number Per Issue - Daily 36; Avg. Page Number Per Issue - Plates Used 49200; Avg. Page Number Per Issue - Saturday 40; Avg. Page Number Per Issue - Sunday 60; widths 50; Newsprint Used - Short Tons 5747; Printing Ink Used - Black 96000; Printin

Equipment EDITORIAL: Front-end Software – APT.; Editorial Hardware – APT, Gateway, ALR/8200; Editorial Equipment – Gateway/PC 3200, Gateway/PC 4200; Editorial Printers – HP/5000 CLASSIFIED: Front-end Software – APT.; Classified Hardware – APT, Gateway, ALR/8200; Classified Equipment – Gateway/PC E1000; Classified Printers – IBM/Network 17 printer DISPLAY: Ad make-up applications – QPS/QuarkXPress 4.0, Multi-Ad/Creator G2, Adobe/Photoshop 5.5; Layout Software – OS 8.5, APP/Mac G3, Multi-Ad/Creator.; Display Printers – Xante/Accel-A-Writer 3G PRODUCTION: Pagination Software – QPS/QuarkXPress 4.0.; Production Equipment – 2-ECR/Knockout (Harlequin RIP), 1-Nu/Flip Top FT40UPNS, 2-C/OL Conveyor System PRESSROOM: Line 1 – 9-G/Cosmo 3502 (double balloon); Folders – 2; Pasters – 7-G/Automatic. MAILROOM: Counter stackers – 2-QWI/300; Inserters and stuffers – 1-S/72P, HI/12 Hopper; Bundle tying machines – 2-Dynaric/NPI; Wrapping singles – 2-Id.; Business Hardware – Software Â□ ADMARC, Discus

BIG SPRING

BIG SPRING HERALD

710 Scurry St., Big Spring, Texas, 79720-2723; gen tel (432) 263-7331; gen fax (432)

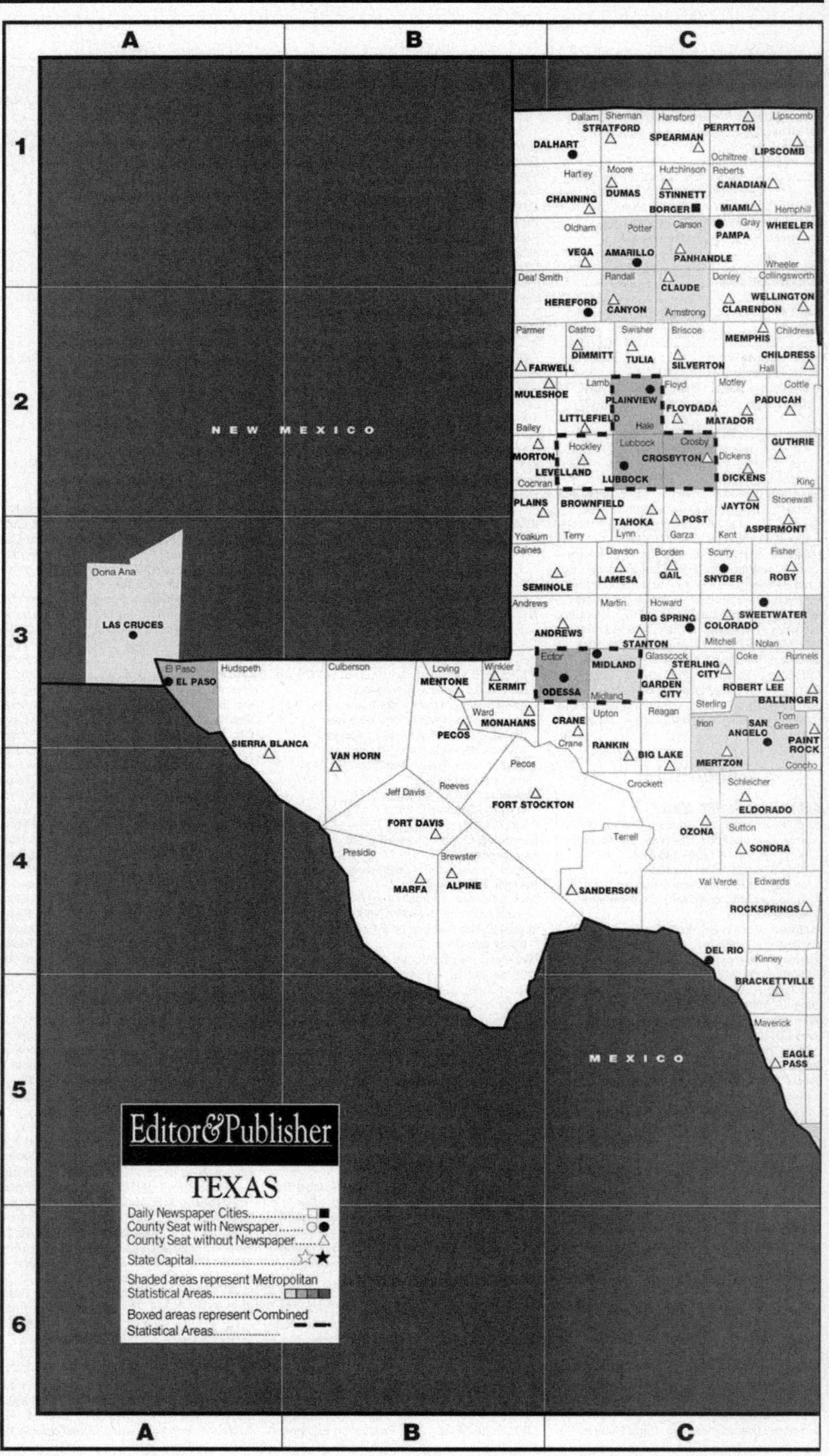

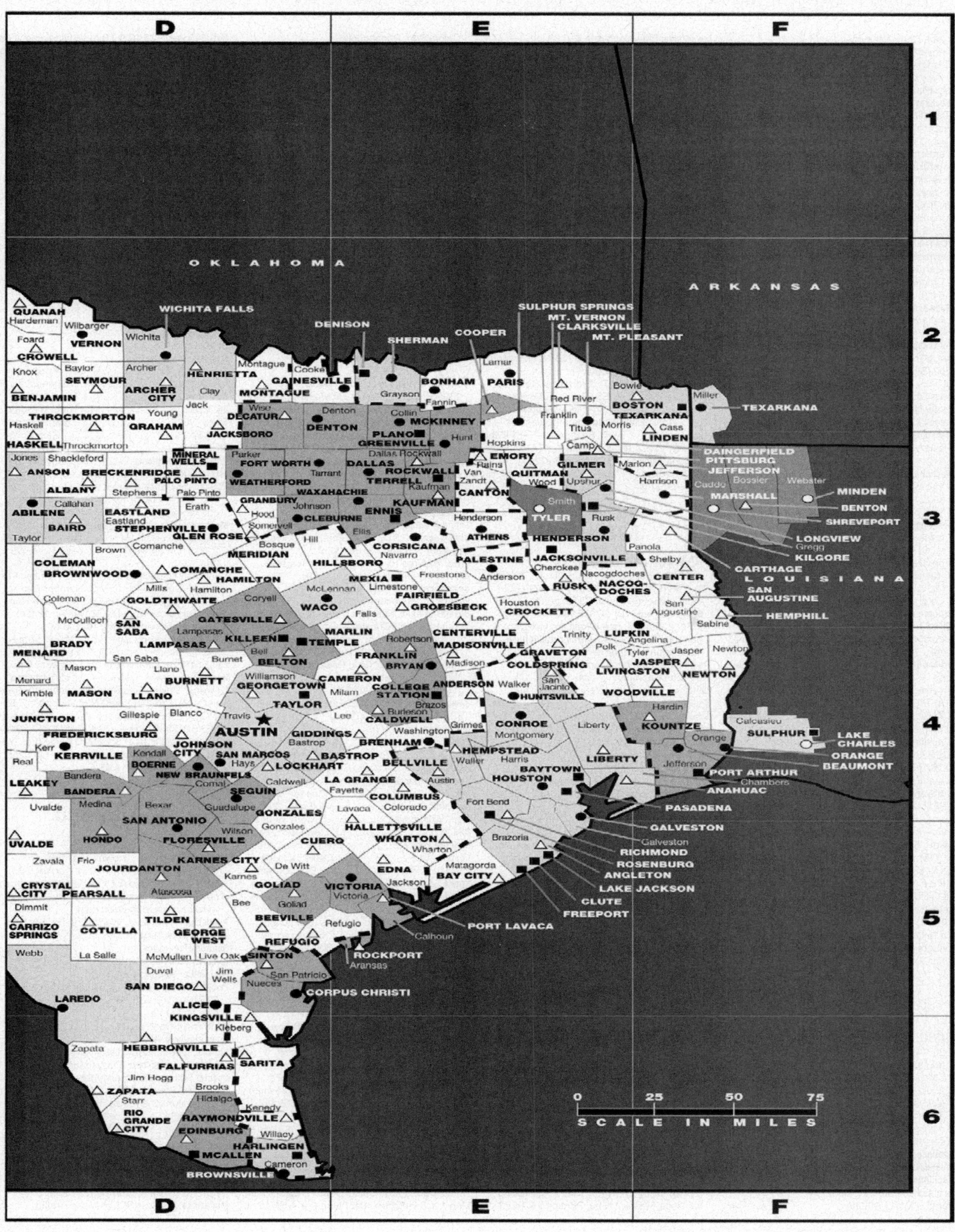
D
E
F
1
2
3
4
5
6
O K L A H O M A
A R K A N S A S
L O U I S I A N A
QUANAH
VERNON
CROWELL
SEYMOUR
BENJAMIN
WICHITA FALLS
HENRIETTA
ARCHER CITY
GAINESVILLE
MONTAGUE
DENISON
SHERMAN
BONHAM
COOPER
PARIS
SULPHUR SPRINGS
MT. VERNON
CLARKSVILLE
MT. PLEASANT
BOSTON
TEXARKANA
LINDEN
THROCKMORTON
GRAHAM
HASKELL
DECATUR
JACKSBORO
DENTON
MCKINNEY
PLANO
GREENVILLE
EMORY
QUITMAN
GILMER
DAINGERFIELD
PITTSBURG
JEFFERSON
MARSHALL
MINDEN
BENTON
SHREVEPORT
LONGVIEW
KILGORE
CARTHAGE
TYLER
HENDERSON
JACKSONVILLE
RUSK
NACOGDOCHES
CENTER
SAN AUGUSTINE
HEMPHILL
ANSON
BRECKENRIDGE
MINERAL WELLS
PALO PINTO
FORT WORTH
WEATHERFORD
DALLAS
ROCKWALL
TERRELL
CANTON
KAUFMAN
WAXAHACHIE
ENNIS
ALBANY
ABILENE
BAIRD
EASTLAND
GRANBURY
CLEBURNE
STEPHENVILLE
GLEN ROSE
ATHENS
CORSICANA
PALESTINE
MERIDIAN
HILLSBORO
COLEMAN
BROWNWOOD
COMANCHE
HAMILTON
MEXIA
FAIRFIELD
GROESBECK
GOLDTHWAITE
WACO
CROCKETT
LUFKIN
GATESVILLE
SAN SABA
KILLEEN
TEMPLE
MARLIN
CENTERVILLE
MADISONVILLE
BRADY
LAMPASAS
MENARD
BELTON
FRANKLIN
BRYAN
GRAVETON
COLDSPRING
LIVINGSTON
JASPER
NEWTON
WOODVILLE
MASON
LLANO
BURNETT
CAMERON
GEORGETOWN
COLLEGE STATION
ANDERSON
HUNTSVILLE
TAYLOR
CALDWELL
CONROE
KOUNTZE
SULPHUR
LAKE CHARLES
ORANGE
BEAUMONT
JUNCTION
FREDERICKSBURG
AUSTIN
GIDDINGS
BRENHAM
HEMPSTEAD
KERRVILLE
JOHNSON CITY
SAN MARCOS
BASTROP
LOCKHART
BELLVILLE
BAYTOWN
LIBERTY
PORT ARTHUR
ANAHUAC
BOERNE
NEW BRAUNFELS
LA GRANGE
HOUSTON
LEAKEY
BANDERA
SEGUIN
COLUMBUS
PASADENA
GALVESTON
SAN ANTONIO
GONZALES
HALLETTSVILLE
WHARTON
UVALDE
HONDO
FLORESVILLE
CUERO
RICHMOND
ROSENBURG
ANGLETON
LAKE JACKSON
CLUTE
FREEPORT
KARNES CITY
JOURDANTON
EDNA
BAY CITY
CRYSTAL CITY
PEARSALL
GOLIAD
VICTORIA
BEEVILLE
PORT LAVACA
CARRIZO SPRINGS
COTULLA
TILDEN
GEORGE WEST
REFUGIO
SINTON
ROCKPORT
SAN DIEGO
CORPUS CHRISTI
LAREDO
ALICE
KINGSVILLE
HEBBRONVILLE
FALFURRIAS
SARITA
ZAPATA
RIO GRANDE CITY
RAYMONDVILLE
EDINBURG
HARLINGEN
MCALLEN
BROWNSVILLE
0 25 50 75
S C A L E I N M I L E S

264-7205; adv e-mail advertising@bigspringherald.com; ed e-mail editor@bigspringherald.com; web site www.bigspringherald.com
Published: Mon, Tues, Wed, Thur, Fri, Sun
Weekday Frequency: e
Circulation: 4,337; 5,364(sun)
Last Audit: September 30, 2002
Price: 8.65/mo (carrier), $12.50/mo (out-of-state); 93.42/yr (home delivery).
Advertising: Open inch rate $14.44
News services: AP.
Politics: Independent. **Established:** 1904
Not Published: Christmas, july 4, labor day, memorial day, new years day. Unless any fall on Sunday and we publish
Own facility?: Y
Special Editions: Football (Aug); Year In Review (Jan); Community Guide (Jul); Rodeo (Jun); Progress (Mar); Christmas Shopping Guide (Nov).
Magazines: TV-Leisure (newsprint) (Other); American Profile (S).
Pub. ....Ron Midkiff
Bookkeeper ....Rachael Martinez
Adv. Mgr., Retail ....Rick Nunez
Circ. Mgr. ....Robert Smith
Ed. ....John A. Moseley
News Ed. ....Bill McClellan
Prodn. Mgr. ....Tony Hernandez
Market Information: TMC.
Mechanical available: Offset; Black and 3 ROP colors; insert accepted; page cutoffs - 22 3/4.
Mechanical Specifications: Type page 12 1/2 x 21 1/2; E - 6 cols, 1 3/4, 1/16 between; A - 6 cols, 1 3/4, 1/16 between; C - 9 cols, 1 1/8, 1/16 between.
Commodity Consumption: Avg. Page Number Per Issue - Daily 10; Avg. Page Number Per Issue - Plates Used 4564; Avg. Page Number Per Issue - Sunday 28; widths 25; Newsprint Used - Short Tons 275; Printing Ink Used - Black 6600; Printing Ink Used - Color 800; Printing Ink Used - P
Equipment EDITORIAL: Front-end Software – QPS/QuarkXPress, Adobe/Illustrator, Aldus/FreeHand, Baseview/Ne; Editorial Hardware – APP/Mac, 10-APP/Mac Performa 6200; Editorial Equipment – 1-PowerBook/190 Laptop, Umax/1200 Scanner, 1-Polaroid/SprintScan 35-LE; Editorial Printers – 1-APP/Mac 16/1600 PS, 1-Laserwriter/II CLASSIFIED: Front-end Software – Baseview.; Classified Hardware – 2-APP/Power Mac 180-35; Classified Printers – APP/Mac LaserWriter 16-600PS DISPLAY: Ad make-up applications – QPS/QuarkXPress, Adobe/Illustrator, Aldus/FreeHand, Baseview/NewsEdit; Layout Software – APP/Mac Performa 6200, APP/iMac.; Display Hardware – APP/Mac Performa 6200, APP/iMac; Display Printers – Xante/Accel-a-Writer 8300; Production Equipment – Roconex; Cameras – 1-R/500. PRESSROOM: Line 1 – 8-G/Community 1974; Folders – 1; Inserters and stuffers – 4; Bundle tying machines – Delta/Strapping AQ7. BUSINESS COMPUTERS: Business Software – PBS; Business Hardware – 1-IBM/PC-XT, IBM/PC-AT, 1-IBM/PC
Zip Codes served: 79720 plus
Delivery method: Mail, Newsstand, Private Carrier, Racks

BORGER

BORGER NEWS-HERALD

207 N. Main St., Borger, Texas, 79007-4715; gen tel (806) 273-5611; adv tel (806) 273-5611; ed tel (806) 273-5611; gen fax (806) 273-2552; adv fax (806) 273-2552; ed fax (806) 273-2552; adv e-mail advertising@borgernewsherald.com; ed e-mail editor@borgernewsherald.com; web site www.borgernewsherald.com
Published: Mon, Tues, Wed, Thur, Fri, Sun
Weekday Frequency: e
Circulation: 4,255; 5,200(sun)
Last Audit: March 31, 2007
Price: 7.50/mo; 90.00/yr.
Advertising: Open inch rate $10.33
News services: AP.
Politics: Independent. **Established:** 1927
Not Published: Christmas.
Special Editions: Christmas Card (Dec); Business & Industrial Review (Mar).
Special Weekly Sections: Church News (Fri); Food (S); Food (Thur); Food (Wed).
Magazines: Relish (Monthly); TV tab (S); American Profile (Weekly).
Pub. ....Kim Duso
Circ. Dir. ....Wanda Mathews
Ed. ....Michele Berry
Picture Ed. ....Don Rice
Sports Ed. ....Rusty Berry
Market Information: TMC.
Mechanical available: Offset; Black and 3 ROP colors; insert accepted - cards, catalogs; page cutoffs - 22 3/4.
Mechanical Specifications: Type page 13 x 21 1/2; E - 6 cols, 2 1/16, 1/8 between; A - 6 cols, 2 1/16, 1/8 between; C - 8 cols, 1 1/2, 1/8 between.
Commodity Consumption: Avg. Page Number Per Issue - Daily 12; Avg. Page Number Per Issue - Sunday 26; widths 13 3/4; Newsprint Used - Metric Tons 300.
Equipment EDITORIAL: Front-end Software – Baseview. CLASSIFIED: Front-end Software – Baseview. DISPLAY: Ad make-up applications – Multi-Ad/Creator; Production Equipment – 1-Nu; Cameras – Acti; Scanners – APP/Mac Scanner. PRESSROOM: Line 1 – 6-G; Folders – 1; Bundle tying machines – 1-Bu/77011.; Business Hardware – 1-IBM/PS2 MODEL 30, 1-Unisys/5000-50

BRENHAM

BRENHAM BANNER-PRESS

2430 Stringer St., Brenham, Texas, 77834; gen tel (979) 836-7956; adv tel (979) 836-7956; ed tel (979) 836-7956; gen fax (979) 830-8577; adv fax (979) 836-0727; ed fax (979) 830-8577; gen e-mail cmoser@brenhambanner.com; adv e-mail retail@brenhambanner.com; ed e-mail edit@brenhambanner.com; web site www.brenhambanner.com
Published: Mon, Tues, Wed, Thur, Fri, Sun
Weekday Frequency: e
Circulation: 5,729; 5,860(sun)
Last Audit: Sworn December 31, 2006
Price: 8.50/mo; 90.00/yr.
Advertising: Open inch rate $9.24
News services: AP, NEA.
Politics: Independent. **Established:** 1866
Not Published: New Year; Thanksgiving; Christmas.
Special Editions: Visitor's Guide (Apr); Back-to-School (Aug); Gift Guide (Dec); Progress (Jan); Real Estate Guide (Mar); Graduation (May); Cookbook (Nov); Businesswomen (Oct); Visitor's Guide (Sept).
Special Weekly Sections: Church (Fri); Food (Tues).
Magazines: Relish (Monthly); TV Guide/Scene (S).
Office Mgr. ....Annell Meyer
Gen. Mgr. ....Danny Hukel
Adv. Mgr., Retail ....Helen Nowicki
Editorial Writer, Political ....Charles Moser
Features Ed. ....Bud Chambers
News Ed. ....Arthur Hahn
Teen-Age/Youth Ed. ....Melissa Mccaghren
Women's Ed. ....Melissa Mcaghren
Prodn. Foreman, Pressroom ....Clem Krolczyk
Market Information: TMC.
Mechanical available: Offset; Black and 3 ROP colors; insert accepted; page cutoffs - 22 3/4.
Mechanical Specifications: Type page 13 x 21; E - 6 cols, 2, 1/3 between; A - 6 cols, 2, 1/3 between; C - 9 cols, 1 3/8, 1/6 between.
Commodity Consumption: Avg. Page Number Per Issue - Daily 10; Avg. Page Number Per Issue - Plates Used 12500; Avg. Page Number Per Issue - Sunday 14; widths 27 1/2; Newsprint Used - Short Tons 700; Printing Ink Used - Black 11500; Printing Ink Used - Color 3700; Printing Ink U
Equipment EDITORIAL: Front-end Software – Baseview, QPS.; Editorial Hardware – APP/Mac; Editorial Equipment – Imagesetter; Editorial Printers – APP/Mac LaserWriter II NTX CLASSIFIED: Front-end Software – Baseview, QPS.; Classified Hardware – APP/Mac; Classified Equipment – Imagesetter; Classified Printers – APP/Mac LaserWriter II NTX, Okidata/Microline 320 DISPLAY: Ad make-up applications – QPS/QuarkXPress; Layout Software – QPS/QuarkXPress.; Display Hardware – Baseview; Display Printers – APP/Mac LaserWriter II NTX PRODUCTION: Pagination Software – QPS/QuarkXPress.; Production Equipment – B; Cameras – C/Spartan II PRESSROOM: Line 1 – 5-WPC/Leader. MAILROOM: Counter stackers – BG; Inserters and stuffers – 3/KAN; Bundle tying machines – 2-/MLN. BUSINESS COMPUTERS: Business Software – Baseview; Business Hardware – APP/Mac

BROWNSVILLE

THE BROWNSVILLE HERALD

1135 E. Van Buren St., Brownsville, Texas, 78520-7055; gen tel (956) 542-4301; adv tel (956) 982-6636; ed tel (956) 982-6625; gen fax (956) 504-1119; adv fax (956) 982-4201; ed fax (956) 542-0840; gen e-mail tbh-press@brownsvilleherald.com; web site www.brownsvilleherald.com
Group: U.S. Suburban Press, Inc.
Published: Mon, Tues, Wed, Thur, Fri, Sat, Sun
Weekday Frequency: m
Saturday Frequency: m
Circulation: 12,918; 11,783(sat); 14,024(sun)
Last Audit: September 30, 2009
Price: 7.25/mo (carrier); 105.00/yr (carrier).
Advertising: Open inch rate $23.79
News services: AP, MCT.
Politics: Independent.
Special Editions: Mother's Day (Apr); Back-to-School (Aug); Christmas Gift Guide (Dec); Golden Years (Feb); Health & Fitness (Jan); Today's Women (Jul); Home & Garden (Mar); Spring Car Care (May); Welcome Winter Texans (Nov); National Car Care (Oct); Fall Fashion (Sept).
Special Weekly Sections: El Extra (Fri); Business (S); Education Extra (Wed).
Magazines: Parade (S).
Pub. ....Daniel R. Cavazos
Bus. Mgr. ....Olga Saldivar
Adv. Dir. ....Karen Shanholtzer
Adv. Mgr., Classified ....Letty Rios
Adv. Mgr., Retail ....Speedy Aldape
Nat'l Adv. ....Ira Sema Garcia
Mgr., Mktg./Promo. ....Cody Sparks
Circ. Mgr. ....Abe Gonzalez
Editorial Page Ed. ....Rachel Benavides
Features Ed. ....Marcie Lasseigne
Photo Dept. Mgr. ....Brad Doherty
Sports Ed. ....M.E. Benavides
Prodn. Mgr., Mailroom ....Bobbie Saldivar
Prodn. Mgr., Pressroom ....Luis Cisneros
Prodn. Mgr., Systems ....Odie Cardon
Asst. Pre Press Mgr. ....Pinky Moreno
Market Information: Split run; TMC; Zoned editions.
Mechanical available: Offset; Black and 3 ROP colors; insert accepted; page cutoffs - 22 3/4.
Mechanical Specifications: Type page 13 x 21; E - 6 cols, 2 1/16, 1/8 between; A - 6 cols, 2 1/16, 1/8 between; C - 10 cols, 1 1/4, 1/16 between.
Commodity Consumption: Avg. Page Number Per Issue - Daily 20; Avg. Page Number Per Issue - Plates Used 12729; Avg. Page Number Per Issue - Sunday 48; widths 13 3/4; Newsprint Used - Metric Tons 1166; Printing Ink Used - Black 36800; Printing Ink Used - Color 3622; Printing Ink
Equipment; Editorial Hardware – APT.; Classified Hardware – APT.; Layout Software – APT.; Production Equipment – 2-Tegra/Varityper, Nu/Lithoplate; Cameras – 1-C. PRESSROOM: Line 1 – 6-HI/Cotrell 845; Line 2 – 4-HI/Cotrell 845; Folders – 2-HI/2:1.; Bundle tying machines – 2-Si; Addressing machine – 1/Ch.; Business Hardware – 1-IBM

FREEDOM COMMUNICATIONS, INC.

1135 E. Van Buren, Brownsville, Texas, 78520; gen tel (956) 542-4301; gen fax (956) 504-1119

EL NUEVO HERALDO

1135 E. Van Buren St., Brownsville, Texas, 78520; gen tel (956) 542-4301; adv tel (956) 982-6636; ed tel (956) 982-6625; gen fax (956) 504-1119; adv fax (956) 982-4201; ed fax (956) 430-6233; gen e-mail tbhpress@brownsvilleherald.com; web site www.brownsvilleherald.com
Published: Mon, Tues, Wed, Thur, Fri, Sat, Sun
Weekday Frequency: m
Saturday Frequency: m
Circulation: 5,450; 5,450(sat); 5,221(sun)
Last Audit: September 30, 2009
Price: 4.00/mo; 51.00/yr.
Advertising: Open inch rate $8.95
News services: AP, Notimex.
Magazines: Vista (Fri).
Pub. ....R. Daniel Cavazos
Adv. Dir. ....Karen Ashanholtzer
Circ. Dir. ....Abe Gonzalez
Ed. ....Rachel Benavides
Ed. ....Marci Ponce
News Ed. ....Gary Long
Photo Ed. ....Brad Doherty
Prodn. Mgr., Systems ....Speedy Aldape
Market Information: TMC; Zoned editions.
Mechanical available: Front end system; Black and 3 ROP colors; insert accepted; page cutoffs - 21 1/4.
Mechanical Specifications: Type page 13 x 21 1/4; E - 6 cols, 2 1/4, 1/8 between; A - 6 cols, 2 1/16, 1/8 between; C - 10 cols, 1 1/4, 3/8 between.
Commodity Consumption: Avg. Page Number Per Issue - Daily 16; Avg. Page Number Per Issue - Plates Used 10000; Avg. Page Number Per Issue - Sunday 56; widths 13 3/4; Newsprint Used - Metric Tons 1000; Newsprint Used - Short Tons 109.71; Printing Ink Used - Black 20339; Printing
Equipment; Editorial Hardware – Dewar.; Classified Hardware – Dewar.; Layout Software – Dewar, 2-Dewar/Discovery.; Production Equipment – 2-Tegra/Varityper, Nu/Lithoplate; Cameras – C; Scanners – CD/Scanner. PRESSROOM: Line 1 – 6-HI/Cotrell 845.; Bundle tying machines – Ca/TM36 Bank Tyer, Yamada/Tom 45; Addressing machine – Ch/525E.; Business Hardware – IBM

BROWNWOOD

BROWNWOOD BULLETIN

700 Carnegie St., Brownwood, Texas, 76804; gen tel (325) 646-2541; ed tel (325) 641-3100; gen fax (325) 646-6835; ed e-mail news@brownwoodbulletin.com; web site www.brownwoodbulletin.com
Published: Mon, Tues, Wed, Thur, Fri, Sat, Sun
Weekday Frequency: m
Saturday Frequency: m
Circulation: 7,120; 7,120(sat); 8,100(sun)
Last Audit: September 30, 2005
Price: 11.95/mo (in RTZ), $13.50/mo (outside RTZ); 132.00/yr (in RTZ), $162.00/yr (outside RTZ).
Advertising: Open inch rate $14.78
News services: AP.
Politics: Independent. **Established:** 1900
Advertising not accepted: In bad taste.
Special Editions: Emergency Directory (Apr); Football Preview (Aug); Christmas Greetings (Dec); Horizons (Feb); Parade of Progress (Jan); Little League Yearbook (Jul); Visitor's Guide (Jun); Spring Fix-Up (Mar); Graduation (May); Central Texas Outdoors (Nov); Central Texas
Special Weekly Sections: Church (Fri); Real Estate Guide (Monthly); TV Week (S); Business (Sat); Best Food Days (Tues).
Magazines: Parade (S); American Profile

(Weekly).
Pub. ....Robert Brincefield
Adv. Mgr. ....Juliet LeMond
Circ. Mgr. ....John Kliebenstein
Mng. Ed. ....Gene Deason
Sports Ed. ....Derrick Stuckly
Market Information: TMC.
Mechanical available: Offset; Black and 3 ROP colors; insert accepted - all considered; page cutoffs - 22 3/4.
Mechanical Specifications: Type page 12 x 21 1/2; E - 6 cols, 1 5/6, 1/8 between; A - 6 cols, 1 5/6, 1/8 between; C - 10 cols, 1 1/25, 1/8 between.
Commodity Consumption: Avg. Page Number Per Issue - Daily 14; Avg. Page Number Per Issue - Plates Used 15200; Avg. Page Number Per Issue - Sunday 40; widths 12 1/2; Newsprint Used - Short Tons 800; Printing Ink Used - Black 22000; Printing Ink Used - Color 3600; Printing Ink U
Equipment EDITORIAL: Front-end Software – Baseview.; Editorial Hardware – 1-APP/Power Mac, 1-APP/Mac G3 CLASSIFIED: Front-end Software – Baseview.; Classified Hardware – APP/Power Mac; Layout Software – QPS/QuarkXPress.; Display Hardware – DTI/Adbuilders; Production Equipment – 1-APP/Mac LaserWriter II, 2-HP/LaserJet 4MV, Pre Press/Panther Pro Imagesetter; Cameras – 1-C/Spartan II Automatic; Scanners – LaCie/Silverscanner II. PRESSROOM: Line 1 – 7-G/Community; Folders – 1-G/SC 240.; Inserters and stuffers – 6-KAN/402; Bundle tying machines – 1-MLN/7CD 700; Addressing machine – 1/El.; Business Hardware – Compaq/486, Dell/486, 2-ALR/386

BRYAN

THE EAGLE

1729 Briarcrest Dr., Bryan, Texas, 77802; gen tel (979) 776-4444; adv tel (979) 776-4444 ext 300; ed tel (979) 776-4444 ext 401; gen fax (979) 774-0496; adv fax (979) 774-0053; ed fax (979) 776-8923; adv e-mail advertising@theeagle.com; ed e-mail news@theeagle.com; web site www.theeagle.com
Published: Mon, Tues, Wed, Thur, Fri, Sat, Sun
Weekday Frequency: m
Saturday Frequency: m
Circulation: 22,191; 21,654(sat); 25,524(sun)
Last Audit: ABC September 30, 2011
Price: 10.50/mo; 116.64/yr.
Advertising: Open inch rate $41.55
News services: AP.
Politics: Independent.
Special Editions: Day Care (Apr); Back-to-School (Aug); Bridal Showcase (Jan); Senior Adults (Jun); Lawn & Garden (Mar); Holiday on the Brazos (Nov); Home Builders (Oct).
Special Weekly Sections: Garden (Fri); Business (S); Religion Pages (Sat); Entertainment (Thur); Best Food Days (Wed).
Magazines: Golden Eagle (Monthly); USA WEEKEND Magazine (S); American Profile (Weekly).
Pub. ....Jim Wilson
Finance Dir. ....Rod Armstrong
Asst. Adv. Dir. ....Chris Zoeller
Classified Adv. Mgr. ....Luecke Meyer
Circ. Dir. ....Nee Ley
Direct Mail Mgr. ....Wayne Nedbalek
Exec. Ed. ....Donnis Bagget
Mng. Ed. ....Kelly Brown
Editorial Page Ed. ....Robert C. Borden
Entertainment Ed. ....Jim Butler
News Ed. ....Jeremy Pafford
Photo Dept. Mgr. ....David McDermand
Sports Ed. ....Robert Cessna
Mgmt. Info Servs. Mgr. ....Ben Tedrick
Dir., Internet/New Media ....Matthew Crawley
Prodn. Dir. ....Mark Manning
Mailroom Mgr. ....Donald Crawford
Pre Press Mgr. ....Tammy Zimmerman
Pressroom Mgr. ....Robert Chapman
Market Information: TMC.
Mechanical available: Offset; Black and 3 ROP colors; insert accepted - any; page cutoffs - 22 3/4.
Mechanical Specifications: Type page 11 5/8 x 21 1/2; E - 6 cols, 2 1/16, 1/8 between; A - 6 cols, 2 1/16, 1/8 between; C - 9 cols, 1 3/8, 1/16 between.
Commodity Consumption: Avg. Page Number Per Issue - Daily 24; Avg. Page Number Per Issue - Plates Used 32000; Avg. Page Number Per Issue - Saturday 32; Avg. Page Number Per Issue - Sunday 80; widths 25; Newsprint Used - Short Tons 2400; Printing Ink Used - Black 71064; Printin
Equipment EDITORIAL: Front-end Software – QPS/QuarkXPress 4.11, Adobe/Photoshop 5.5, Baseview/NewsEdit Pro 3.2, Baseview/Ique Server 3.3.; Editorial Hardware – Ethernet, APP/Mac 7200-120, APP/Mac G3, APP/Mac G4; Editorial Equipment – 1-APP/Mac Server; Editorial Printers – HP/LaserJet 4MV, HP/LJ 5000 CLASSIFIED: Front-end Software – Baseview/Ad Manager Pro 2.2.; Classified Hardware – APP/Mac, APP/Mac G3, APP/iMac 400SE; Classified Equipment – 1-APP/Mac Server; Classified Printers – HP/LaserJet 4MV DISPLAY: Ad make-up applications – QPS/QuarkXPress 4.12, Adobe/Photoshop 5.5; Layout Software – Baseview/Page Director, MEI/ALS 2.1.; Display Hardware – APP/Mac 7300-200, APP/Mac G3, APP/Mac G4; Display Printers – HP/LJ 4MV, HP/LJ5000 PRODUCTION: Pagination Software – QPS/QuarkXPress 4.11, Adobe/PageM; Production Equipment – 1-Nu/FT40 APNS, 1-Douthitt/Gemini 29X40, 1-Nu/FT40 APNS; Cameras – 1-C/Spartan II; Scanners – HP/ScanJet 4c, Nikon/1000-35, Lf/Leafscan 35, All/APS Scan 3750, Microtek/ScanMaker 9600XL, AU/Copydot PRESSROOM: Line 1 – 9-G/Urbanite single width 1979; Press Drives – Fin/125 h.p. motor. MAILROOM: Counter stackers – 2-Id/NS660 Counter Stacker, 1-QWI/400; Inserters and stuffers – 1-NP/1372; Bundle tying machines – 1-MLN/ML2EE, MLN/SP 330, Sterling/GP30C; Addressing machine – 1-KR/12. BUSINESS COMPUTERS: Business Software – PeopleSoft, Reflections, Microsoft/Office; Business Hardware – HP/3000, PC Network

CLEBURNE

CLEBURNE TIMES-REVIEW

108 S. Anglin St., Cleburne, Texas, 76031-5602; gen tel (817) 558-2855; gen fax (817) 645-4020; adv fax (817) 645-4020; ed fax (817) 357-8031; ed e-mail editor@trcle.com; web site www.cleburnetimesreview.com
Published: Mon, Tues, Wed, Thur, Fri, Sun
Weekday Frequency: e
Circulation: 6,708; 6,708(sun)
Last Audit: September 24, 2003
Price: 8.00/mo; 96.00/yr (in county).
Advertising: Open inch rate $13.15
News services: AP.
Politics: Independent.
Not Published: New Year; Memorial Day; Independence Day; Labor Day; Thanksgiving; Christmas.
Special Editions: Active Times & Springfest (Apr); Football (Aug); Wrap it Up & Greetings (Dec); Active Times (Feb); Chamber of Commerce (Jan); Active Times (Jul); Graduation (May); Month Before Xmas (Nov); Just Say No to Drugs Coloring Book (Oct).
Special Weekly Sections: Best Food Days (S); Best Food Day (Tues).
Magazines: Relish (Monthly); USA WEEKEND Magazine (S); American Profile (Weekly).
Adv. Dir. ....Kay Helms
Adv. Mgr., Classified.......................Lynn Coplin
Circ. Dir. ....Gloria Chavez
Asst. Ed. ....Michael O'Connor
Graphics Ed./Art Dir. ....Ashley Garey
Radio/Television Ed. ....Dale Gosser
Market Information: TMC.
Mechanical available: Offset; Black and 3 ROP colors; insert accepted; page cutoffs - 22 3/4.
Mechanical Specifications: Type page 10 1/4 x 21 1/4; E - 6 cols, 1 9/16, 1/8 between; A - 6 cols, 1 9/16, 1/8 between; C - 6 cols, 1 9/16, 1/8 between.
Commodity Consumption: Avg. Page Number Per Issue - Daily 20; Avg. Page Number Per Issue - Plates Used 6000; Avg. Page Number Per Issue - Sunday 40; widths 11 1/2; Newsprint Used - Metric Tons 420; Printing Ink Used - Black 12860; Printing Ink Used - Color 100; Printing Ink Us
Equipment EDITORIAL: Front-end Software – Baseview/NewsEdit Pro.; Editorial Hardware – APP/Power Mac; Editorial Printers – Pre Press/Panthers, HP/11x17 LaserPrinter CLASSIFIED: Front-end Software – Baseview/Ad Manager Pro.; Classified Hardware – APP/Power Mac DISPLAY: Ad make-up applications – QPS/QuarkXPress; Layout Software – APP/Power Mac.; Display Hardware – APP/Power Mac; Display Printers – 1-APP/Mac LaserWriter, Pre Press/Panther, HP/11x17 LaserPrinter PRODUCTION: Pagination Software – QPS/QuarkXPress.; Production Equipment – Pre Press/VT1200, Adobe/Photoshop 4.0.1, Pre Press/Panther Pro; Cameras – AG, Epson/Digital, Kk/Digital; Scanners – Umax/Vista 12 PRESSROOM: Line 1 – 6-G/Community 1976; Folders – 1; Bundle tying machines – 1/MLN; Addressing machine – Wm. BUSINESS COMPUTERS: Business Software – Brainworks; Business Hardware – PC, DOS

CLUTE

THE FACTS

720 S. Main St., Clute, Texas, 77531; gen tel (979) 265-7411; gen fax (979) 265-9052; adv fax (979) 265-9052; ed fax (979) 265-9052; gen e-mail news@thefacts.com; adv e-mail deana.lesco@thefacts.com; retail@thefacts.com; ed e-mail news@thefacts.com; web site www.thefacts.com
Published: Mon, Tues, Wed, Thur, Fri, Sat, Sun
Weekday Frequency: m
Saturday Frequency: m
Circulation: 14,969; 14,969(sat); 16,020(sun)
Last Audit: September 30, 2008
Price: 10.75/mo (d), $8.75/mo (S); 129.00/yr.
Advertising: Open inch rate $13.10
News services: AP, NEA.
Politics: Independent.
Special Editions: Fishing (Apr); Fashion (Aug); Chamber of Commerce (Feb); Bridal (Jan); Profile/Progress (Jul); Fishing Fiesta (Jun); Spring Fashion (Mar); Brazoria County Fair (Oct); Football (Sept).
Special Weekly Sections: Gardening (Fri); Focus & Forecast (Mon); TV & Entertainment (S); Church (Sat); Business (Thur); Lifestyle (Wed).
Magazines: USA WEEKEND Magazine (S).
Pub. ....Bill Cornwell
Gen. Mgr. ....Judy Starnes
Adv. Mgr., Retail ....Deana Lesco
Adv. Mgr., Classified ....Dena Matthews
Mng. Ed. ....Yvonne Mintz
Info Servs./Online Mgr. ....Waylon Smart
Prodn. Mgr. ....Frankie Ramirez
Prodn. Mgr., Mailroom ....Glenn Blount
Market Information: TMC; Zoned editions.
Mechanical available: Offset; Black and 3 ROP colors; insert accepted; page cutoffs - 22 3/4.
Mechanical Specifications: Type page 13 x 21; E - 6 cols, 2 1/16, 1/8 between; A - 6 cols, 2 1/16, 1/8 between; C - 9 cols, 1 3/8, 1/16 between.
Commodity Consumption: Avg. Page Number Per Issue - Daily 30; Avg. Page Number Per Issue - Plates Used 12154; Avg. Page Number Per Issue - Sunday 52; widths 13 3/4; Newsprint Used - Short Tons 1150; Printing Ink Used - Black 38140; Printing Ink Used - Color 1730; Printing Ink
Equipment; Editorial Hardware – 7-PC, 5-APP/Mac Centris 650, 2-APP/Mac IIc, 1-APP/Power Mac 8500, APP/Mac Quadra, 2-APP/Power Mac 7100, 1-APP/Power Mac 8600; Editorial Equipment – Lf/AP Leaf Picture Desk, 2-Umax/Scanner, 1-Nikon/Coolscan 1000, 1-APP/Mac 1400 Laptop; Editorial Printers – APP/Mac CLASSIFIED: Front-end Software – Baseview, Adobe/Photoshop, Adobe/Illustrator.; Classified Hardware – 7-APP/Power Mac 7300, 1-APP/Power Mac 7100, 1-APP/Mac Quadra 650; Classified Printers – APP/Mac LaserWriter IIg, TI/Omni 800, LaserMaster/Unity, APP/Mac LaserWriter 16/600 DISPLAY: Ad make-up applications – Aldus/PageMaker, QPS/QuarkXPress, Multi-Ad/Creator, Adobe/Illustrator, Adobe/Photoshop; Display Hardware – 3-APP/Mac IIci, 2-APP/Power Mac 7100, 2-APP/Power Mac 8600; Display Printers – APP/Mac LaserWriter IIg, APP/Mac LaserWriter 16/600 PRODUCTION: Pagination Software – QPS/QuarkXPress 3.32.; Production Equipment – APP/Mac LaserWriter IIg, APP/Mac LaserWriter Pro 630, ECR/3850, 2-APP/Mac LaserWriter 16/600PS; Cameras – C/Spartan III with Transport; Scanners – ECR/Autokon 1000 PRESSROOM: Line 1 – G/Urbanite 35 1993; Press Drives – A/C Drive Motors w/Belt to Drive Shaft; Folders – G/500; Reels and Stands – Roll/Stands. MAILROOM: Counter stackers – HL/Monitor; Inserters and stuffers – HI; Bundle tying machines – MLN; Addressing machine – Miller, Bevgo.; Business Hardware – Software ☐ Quattro/Pro, FileMaker Pro

SOUTHERN NEWSPAPERS, INC.

720 S. Main St., Clute, Texas, 77531; gen tel (979) 265-7411; gen fax (979) 265-2213

CONROE

COURIER

100 Ave. A, Conroe, Texas, 77301; gen tel (936) 756-6671; gen fax (936) 521-3301; ed fax (936) 756-6729; gen e-mail courier@hcnonline.com; ed e-mail couriernews@hcnonline.com; web site www.thecourier-online.com
Published: Mon, Tues, Wed, Thur, Fri, Sat, Sun
Weekday Frequency: m
Saturday Frequency: m
Circulation: 10,621; 10,668(sat); 9,256(sun)
Last Audit: ABC September 30, 2011
Price: 9.75/mo; 120.00/yr.
Advertising: Open inch rate $32.00
News services: U.S. Suburban Press Inc., AP.
Politics: Independent.
Special Editions: Back-to-School (Aug); Last Minute Gifts (Dec); Progress (Feb); Bridal (Jan); Montgomery County Magazine (Jul); Montgomery County Fair (Mar); Mother's Day (May); Holiday Cookbook (Nov); Answer Book (Oct); High School Football (Sept).
Special Weekly Sections: TV Week (S); Medical (Thur).
Magazines: USA WEEKEND Magazine (S).
Grp. Pub. ....Jim Fredricks
Adv. Mgr. ....Karen Maurmann
Circ. Dir. ....Rod Mcfarland
City Ed. ....Nancy Flake
Features Ed. ....Sandra Bosse
Sports Ed. ....Mike Jones
Mgmt. Info Servs. Mgr. ....Ann Toppel
Asst. Opns. Mgr. ....Kelly Lawson
Market Information: ADS; Split run; Zoned editions.
Mechanical available: Offset; Black and 3 ROP colors; insert accepted - all; page cutoffs - 22 3/4.
Mechanical Specifications: Type page 13 x 21 1/2; E - 6 cols, 2 1/16, 1/8 between; A - 6 cols, 2 1/16, 1/8 between; C - 9 cols, 1 11/32, 1/16 between.
Commodity Consumption: Avg. Page Number Per Issue - Daily 18; Avg. Page Number Per Issue - Plates Used 18000; Avg. Page Number Per Issue - Saturday 22; Avg. Page Number Per Issue - Sunday 42; widths 27; Newsprint Used - Short Tons 1600; Printing Ink Used - Black 44800; Printin
Equipment EDITORIAL: Front-end Software – Microsoft/Word, QPS/QuarkXPress 3.32, Adobe/Photoshop.; Editorial Hardware – IBM/MS-DOS, APP/Mac G3; Editorial Printers – APP CLASSIFIED: Front-end Software –

Dewar.; Classified Hardware – IBM/MS-DOS; Classified Printers – HP DISPLAY: Ad make-up applications – QPS/QuarkXPress 4.0, Adobe/Photoshop 4.0; Layout Software – Dewar.; Display Hardware – APP/Mac; Display Printers – AG/Accuset, Lexmark PRODUCTION: Pagination Software – Dewar.; Production Equipment – 1-Nu, 1-BKY; Cameras – 1-C/Spartan III; Scanners – SCREEN/1350 PRESSROOM: Line 1 – 10-G/C; Folders – 1 MAILROOM: Counter stackers – 1/BG; Inserters and stuffers – MM/227-Z; Bundle tying machines – 2-/Malow.; Business Hardware – IBM/MS-DOS

CORPUS CHRISTI

CALLER-TIMES PUBLISHING CO.

820 Lower N. Broadway, Corpus Christi, Texas, 78401; gen tel (361) 884-2011; gen fax (361) 886-3670

CORPUS CHRISTI CALLER-TIMES

820 N. Lower Broadway, Corpus Christi, Texas, 78401-2025; gen tel (361) 884-2011; adv tel (361) 886-4301; ed tel (361) 886-3787; gen fax (361) 884-3664; adv fax (361) 886-3670; ed fax (361) 886-3732; adv e-mail classifieds@caller.com; web site www.caller.com

Published: Mon, Tues, Wed, Thur, Fri, Sat, Sun
Weekday Frequency: m
Saturday Frequency: m
Circulation: 43,214; 44,521(sat); 57,936(sun)
Last Audit: ABC September 30, 2011
Price: 16.25/mo; 187.50/yr.
Advertising: Open inch rate $96.60
News services: AP, NYT, MCT, SHNS.
Politics: Independent. **Established:** 1883
Special Editions: South Texas Football (Aug); Best of Best (Dec); Horizons (Jan); Mi Vida (Monthly); Best of Best (Sept).
Special Weekly Sections: Foc'sle (Fri); Health & Fitness (Mon); Oil & Gas (S); Church Page (Sat); Arts & Entertainment (Thur); Best Food Day (Wed).
Magazines: Parade (S).
Pres./Pub. .... Patrick J. Birmingham
Vice Pres., HR .... Arthur Acuna
Gen. Mgr. Online .... Libby Averyt
CFO .... Michelle Koesema
Exec. Sec. .... Sylvia Perez
Credit Mgr. .... Debra Villarreal
Mktg. Dir. .... Steve Arnold
Circ. Vice Pres. .... Jeff Deloach
Circ. Opns. Mgr. .... Bob Gage
Ed. .... Shane Fitzgerald
Editorial Page Ed. .... Sandy Moorhead
Features Ed. .... Cynthia Wilson
Librarian .... Allison Ehrlich
Bus. Ed. .... Tom Whitehurst
Asst. Metro Ed .... Allison Pollan
News Ed .... Jen Deselms
Sports Ed .... John Allen
Television Ed .... Tina Vasquez
Market Information: Split run; TMC; Zoned editions.
Mechanical available: Offset; Black and 3 ROP colors; insert accepted - small product samples with prior approval; page cutoffs - 22.
Mechanical Specifications: Type page 11 1/2 x 20 5/8; E - 6 cols, 1 5/6, 1/8 between; A - 6 cols, 1 5/6, 1/8 between; C - 10 cols, 1 1/16, 1/16 between.
Commodity Consumption: Avg. Page Number Per Issue - Daily 48; Avg. Page Number Per Issue - Plates Used 55800; Avg. Page Number Per Issue - Saturday 68; Avg. Page Number Per Issue - Sunday 120; widths 25; Newsprint Used - Metric Tons 9200; Printing Ink Used - Black 392000; Prin
Equipment EDITORIAL: Front-end Software – Microsoft/NT, SQL/DPS Editorial.; Editorial Hardware – PC P350; Editorial Printers – HP/5si CLASSIFIED: Front-end Software – CText.; Classified Hardware – HP/Net Server LH4; Classified Equipment – Konica/K550 Processor; Classified Printers – HP/LaserJet 5si DISPLAY: Ad make-up applications – Multi-Ad/Creator, Adobe/Illustrator, Adobe/Photoshop, Managing Editor/ALS; Display Printers – HP/8000 N PRODUCTION: Pagination Software – DPS/Ad Tracker.; Production Equipment – 2-Konica/Powermatic 66f, Pre Press/Panther Pro, 1-W/Auto Unit; Cameras – 1-ECR/8400, 1-B/2000, 2-C/Spartan III; Scanners – Scan-View/ScanMate 5000, Kk/RFS 2035, Umax/Mirage 16L, Umax/Super Vista S-12 PRESSROOM: Line 1 – 9-G/Metroliner double width (offset; 5 half decks) 1994; Line 2 – 8-Tandemer/Narrow Web 1992; Line 3 – 10-HI/V15; Press Drives – Fin/Incom; Folders – 1-G/3:2; Pasters – G/Auto; Reels and Stands – 9; Press control system – G/PCS. MAILROOM: Counter stackers – 3-HL/Monitor, 2-HL/Monitor; Inserters and stuffers – 1-GMA/SLS 1000 10:2, 1-KAN/7:1; Bundle tying machines – 2/MLN, 2-/Dynaric; Addressing machine – 3-Wm/III, 2-/BH, 1-/Ink Jet Printer. AUDIO: Audio Software – Unix, Brite Voice Systems; Audio Hardware – Brite Voice Systems, PC 486 BUSINESS COMPUTERS: Business Software – GEAC 7016, MCBA 2.0, GEAC/CIS 6.06, GEAC/Aim; Business Hardware – HP/3000-947

CORSICANA

CORSICANA DAILY SUN

405 E. Collin St., Corsicana, Texas, 75110; gen tel (903) 872-3931; adv tel (903) 872-3931; ed tel (903) 872-3931; gen fax (903) 872-6878; adv fax (903) 872-6878; ed fax (903) 872-6878; gen e-mail dailysun@corsicanadailysun.com; web site www.corsicanadailysun.com

Published: Mon, Tues, Wed, Thur, Fri, Sat, Sun
Saturday Frequency: m
Circulation: 5,690; 5,690(sat); 6,544(sun)
Last Audit: March 31, 2006
Price: 9.75/mo; 117.00/yr.
Advertising: Open inch rate $13.50
News services: AP.
Politics: Independent.
Not Published: Christmas.
Special Editions: Football (Aug); Progress (Jun); Newcomers (Sept).
Special Weekly Sections: Entertainment (S); Mini Page (Sat); Best Food Day (Tues).
Magazines: Relish (Monthly); USA WEEKEND Magazine (S).
Pub. .... Raymond Linex
Bus. Mgr. .... Jodi Brown
Circ. Mgr. .... David Smith
Mng. Ed. .... Raymond Linex
Asst. Ed. .... Bob Belcher
Photo Ed. .... Chris Smith
Data Processing Mgr. .... Deana Pawlowski
Market Information: Split run; TMC; Zoned editions.
Mechanical available: Offset; Black and 3 ROP colors; insert accepted; page cutoffs - 22 3/4.
Mechanical Specifications: Type page 13 3/4 x 21 1/2; E - 6 cols, 2 1/16, 1/8 between; A - 6 cols, 2 1/16, 1/8 between; C - 9 cols, 1 3/8, 1/16 between.
Commodity Consumption: Avg. Page Number Per Issue - Daily 16; Avg. Page Number Per Issue - Plates Used 3000; Avg. Page Number Per Issue - Sunday 36; widths 27 1/2; Newsprint Used - Short Tons 650; Printing Ink Used - Black 51000; Printing Ink Used - Color 3000; Printing Ink Us
Equipment EDITORIAL: Front-end Software – Baseview/NewsEdit, QPS/QuarkXPress.; Editorial Hardware – 7-APP/Mac; Editorial Printers – 1-APP/Mac LaserWriter IIg, 1-APP/Mac LaserWriter IIf; Classified Hardware – APP/Mac.; Production Equipment – 1-Nat/225; Cameras – SCREEN, 1-C. PRESSROOM: Line 1 – 5-G/Urbanite. MAILROOM: Counter stackers – 1/BG; Bundle tying machines – 2-/MLN; Addressing machine – 1-/KR.; Business Hardware – 1-MDS, 1-HP, 3-IBM/AT

DALHART

DALHART TEXAN

410 Denrock St., Dalhart, Texas, 79022-2628; gen tel (806) 244-4511; gen fax (806) 244-2395; gen e-mail daltexan@xit.net; web site www.thedalharttexan.com

Published: Mon, Wed, Fri
Circulation: 2,300
Last Audit: Estimate November 6, 2009
Advertising: Open inch rate $7.30
Insert rate: $262.00/M.
Politics: Independent. **Established:** 1901
Gen. Mgr. .... Tammy Cruz
Adv. Mgr. .... Gina Milton
Circ. Mgr. .... Dino Cruz
Ed. .... Susan Clay
Mechanical Specifications: Type page 15 x 21; E - 6 cols, 2 1/16, 1/8 between; A - 6 cols, 2 1/16, 1/8 between; C - 6 cols, 2 1/16, 1/8 between.

DALLAS

THE DALLAS MORNING NEWS

508 Young St., Dallas, Texas, 75202-4808; gen tel (214) 977-8222; adv tel (214) 977-8222; ed tel (214) 977-8205; gen fax (214) 977-8319; adv fax (214) 977-7644; ed fax (972) 263-0456; gen e-mail letterstoeditor@dallasnews.com; adv e-mail classified@dallasnews.com; ed e-mail letterstoeditor@dallasnews.com; web site www.dallasnews.com

Group: Metro Newspaper Advertising Services, Inc.
Published: Mon, Tues, Wed, Thur, Fri, Sat, Sun
Weekday Frequency: m
Saturday Frequency: m
Circulation: 409,642; 578,902(sat); 374,653(sun)
Last Audit: ABC September 30, 2011
Price: 13.00/mo; 156.00/yr (carrier).
Advertising: Open inch rate $822.25
News services: AP, NYT, RN, MCT.
Special Weekly Sections: The Movies (Fri); Discoveries (Mon); Sunday Reader (S); Homes (Sat); Texas Living (Thur); Education Extra (Tues); Texas Taste (Wed).
Magazines: Parade (S).
Broadcast Affiliations: KOTV (CBS) Tulsa, OK; WFAA-TV (ABC) Dallas; KHOU-TV (CBS) Houston; WVEC-TV (ABC) Hampton, VA; WVEC-TV (ABC) Norfolk, VA; KING-TV (NBC) Seattle/Tacoma, WA; KTVK (IND) Phoenix, AZ; KENS-TV (CBS) San Antonio, TX; KMOV-TV (CBS) St. Louis, MO; KGW-TV (NBC) Por
Pub./CEO .... James M. Moroney
Pres./Gen. Mgr. .... John McKeon
Vice Pres. .... Keven Ann Willey
Adv. Sr. Vice Pres., Sales .... Cynthia Carr
Sr. Vice Pres., Interactive/Mktg. .... Fran Wills
Sr. Vice Pres., Circ. .... John G. Walsh
Circ. Dir., Acquisition/Retention .... Mark Medici
Circ. Asst. Dir., Alternate Publication Distr. Gene Chavez
Ed. .... Robert Mong
Sr. Deputy Mng. Ed., News Mgmt. Walt Stallings
Deputy Mng. Ed., Lifestyles .... Lisa Kresl
Deputy Mng. Ed., Local News .... Leona Allen
Deputy Mng. Ed., Local News .... Mark Edgar
Deputy Mng. Ed., Projects .... Maud S. Beelman
Deputy Mng. Ed., Sports .... Bob Yates
Asst. Mng. Ed./Sunday Ed. .... Tom Huang
Asst. Mng. Ed., Local News .... Mike Drago
Asst. Arts/Entertainment Ed. Jerry W. Bokamper
Asst. Arts/Entertainment Ed. .... Anne Bothwell
Arts/Entertainment Critic .... Scott Cantrell
Market Information: Split run; TMC; Zoned editions.
Mechanical available: Offset; Black and 3 ROP colors; insert accepted; page cutoffs - 22.
Mechanical Specifications: Type page 11 5/8 x 21; E - 6 cols, 1 5/6, 1/8 between; A - 6 cols, 1 5/6, 1/8 between; C - 10 cols, 1 3/32, 1/16 between.
Commodity Consumption: Avg. Page Number Per Issue - Daily 133; Avg. Page Number Per Issue - Plates Used 1482646; Avg. Page Number Per Issue - Saturday 198; Avg. Page Number Per Issue - Sunday 374; widths 43 3/4; Newsprint Used - Metric Tons 165210; Printing Ink Used - Black 30
Equipment EDITORIAL: Front-end Software – SII/Tandem, AT/IAS, SUN.; Editorial Hardware – CCI; Editorial Equipment – APP/Mac, Sun/Ethernet network, Dell/PC; Editorial Printers – Dataproducts/; Classified Hardware – AT, IBM/RS 6000, CText/AdVision. DISPLAY: Ad make-up applications – Managing Editor/ALS; Layout Software – MEI/ALS.; Display Hardware – Sun PRODUCTION: Pagination Software – CCI.; Production Equipment – 4-ALL/3850, 2-ALL/3750 color, 3-Esko fot/2636s, 3-Scitex/Smortsan, 3-Kodiak/RFS 2035 film; Scanners – 1-ECR/Autokon 2045, 2-ECR/Autokon 2045C, 1-Scitex/Smart Scanner, 12-Desktop/Scanner, 2-Scitex/Smart Scanner 342L PRESSROOM: Line 1 – 1-TKS/Offset double width 1985; Line 2 – 1-TKS/Offset double width 1985; Line 3 – 1-TKS/Offset double width 1987; Line 4 – 1-TKS/Offset double width 1988; Line 5 – 1-TKS/Offset double width 1989; Line 6 – 1-TKS/Offset double width 1990 MAILROOM: Counter stackers – 32-QWI/350B; Inserters and stuffers – 5-HI/1472, 4-GMA/SLS 1000A 28:2, 1-GMA/SLS 1000A 8:2; Bundle tying machines – 34-Dynaric/NP-2, 2-Sterling/SSM 40; Mailroom control system – 2-Id/Tray, 1/Mach Design Serv. Inc. w/ Carnegie Mellon Co BUSINESS COMPUTERS: Business Software – CCI, Advision, Merlin, Datatime, Ad Manager, Finger Rest, TriActive; Business Hardware – Multiprise, Admarc, Marketinfo, Management Sales System

AL DIA

508 Young St., 2nd Fl., Dallas, Texas, 75202; gen tel (469) 977-3600; gen fax (469) 977-3601; gen e-mail preguntas@aldiatx.com; circulation@aldiatx.com; web site www.aldiatx.com

Published: Mon, Tues, Wed, Thur, Fri, Sat
Weekday Frequency: m
Circulation: 31,784; 31,784(sat)
Last Audit: March 31, 2005
Advertising: Open inch rate $78.00
Magazines: Vista (Sat).
Gen. Mgr. .... Alex Sanchez
Exec. Asst. .... Yeradi Lara
Adv. Mgr., Nat'l Sales .... Becci Reyes
Mktg. Exec. .... Iris Diaz
Circ. Dir. .... Rosario Heredia
Cliente Serv. Coord. .... Yadira Gonzalez
Ed. in Chief .... Alfredo Carbajal
Online Ed. .... Anthony Trejo
Sports Ed. .... Mauro Diaz

DESOTO

BEST SOUTHWEST FOCUS

1337 Marilyn Ave., DeSoto, Texas, 75123-1714; gen tel (972) 223-9175; adv tel 9722239175; ed tel 9722232998; gen fax (972) 223-9202; adv fax 9722239202; ed fax 9722239202; gen e-mail focusnews@wans.net; adv e-mail focusnews@wans.net; ed e-mail focuseditor@sbcglobal.net; web site www.focusdailynews.com

Published: Tues, Wed, Thur, Fri, Sun
Weekday Frequency: m
Circulation: 34,932; 46,419(sun)
Last Audit: Sworn N/A
Advertising: Open inch rate $40.00
Insert rate: $55.00/M.
Politics: 1987
Own facility?: Y
Pub. .... Marlon Hanson
Adv. Mgr. .... Carmela Hanson
Prodn. Mgr. .... Alex Hanson
Editor .... Joshua Johnson
Circ. Mgr. .... Ginger Bolton
Ed. .... Elizabeth Taylor
Mechanical Specifications: Type page 11 1/2 x 21; E - 6 cols, 1 3/4, between; A - 6 cols, 1 3/4, between; C - 6 cols, 1 3/4, between.
Zip Codes served: 75115, 75104, 75116, 75137, 75165, 75146, 75104, 75051, 75050, 75154,

75237, 75234
Delivery method: Mail, Newsstand, Private Carrier, Racks

DEL RIO

DEL RIO NEWS-HERALD

2205 Bedell Ave., Del Rio, Texas, 78840; gen tel (830) 775-1551; adv tel (830) 775-1551; ed tel (830) 775-1551; gen fax (830) 774-2610; adv fax (830) 774-2610; ed fax (830) 774-2610; gen e-mail drnews@delrionewsherald.com; graphics@delrionewsherald.com; ed e-mail newsroom@delrionewsherald.com; web site www.delrionewsherald.com
Group: Metro Newspaper Advertising Services, Inc.
Published: Mon, Tues, Wed, Thur, Fri, Sat, Sun
Saturday Frequency: m
Circulation: 4,858; 4,858(sat); 4,858(sun)
Last Audit: September 30, 2008
Price: 9.00/mo; 108.00/yr.
Advertising: Open inch rate $14.10
News services: AP, NEA.
Politics: Independent.
Special Weekly Sections: View (S).
Magazines: Parade (S).
Bus. Mgr.....Mary Rodriguez
Adv. Mgr.....Guy Aguirre
Circ. Mgr.....Joe San Miguel
Mng. Ed.....Rosa Delgado
Spanish Ed.....Norma Moreno
Sports Ed....Brian Argabright
Press Foreman....Joel Salazar
Market Information: ADS; TMC.
Mechanical available: Offset; Black and 3 ROP colors; insert accepted; page cutoffs - 22 3/4.
Mechanical Specifications: Type page 13 x 21 1/2; E - 6 cols, 2 1/16, 1/8 between; A - 6 cols, 2 1/16, 1/8 between; C - 9 cols, 1 3/8, 1/16 between.
Commodity Consumption: Avg. Page Number Per Issue - Daily 20; Avg. Page Number Per Issue - Sunday 56; widths 27 1/2; Newsprint Used - Short Tons 407; Printing Ink Used - Pages Printed 3242.
Equipment; Editorial Hardware – Mk/1100 System.; Classified Hardware – Mk.; Layout Software – Mk/Ad Touch.; Production Equipment – 1-COM/Computype II, 1-COM/4961, 2-COM/8400; Cameras – 1-C/Spartan III. PRESSROOM: Line 1 – 7-G/Community; Folders – 1-G/Community.; Bundle tying machines – MLN; Addressing machine – 1/KR.; Business Hardware – IBM, AT, XT, PC

DENTON

DENTON PUBLISHING CO.

314 E. Hickory, Denton, Texas, 76201; gen tel (940) 387-3811; gen fax (940) 381-9666

DENTON RECORD-CHRONICLE

314 E. Hickory St., Denton, Texas, 76201-4272; gen tel (940) 387-3811; adv tel (940) 566-6858; ed tel (940) 566-6860; gen fax (940) 566-6846; ed fax (945) 566-6888; gen e-mail drc@dentonrc.com; web site www.dentonrc.com
Published: Mon, Tues, Wed, Thur, Fri, Sat, Sun
Weekday Frequency: m
Saturday Frequency: m
Circulation: 11,645; 11,645(sat); 14,993(sun)
Last Audit: September 30, 2008
Price: 9.50/mo; 216.00/yr.
Advertising: Open inch rate $43.00(m-wed)
News services: AP.
Politics: Independent.
Special Editions: Back-to-School (Aug); Christmas (Dec); Progress (Jan).
Special Weekly Sections: Entertainment Chronicle (Thur).
Magazines: USA WEEKEND Magazine (Sat).
Pub.....Bill Patterson
Dir., Mktg./Promo.....Sandra Kelly
Circ. Dir.....Dan Hammond
Ed....Dawn Cobb
Arts/Entertainment Ed.....Lucinda Breeding
City Ed.....Matt Zabel
Graphics Ed./Art Dir.....Carolyn Martin
Librarian....Barry Vermillion
Photo Ed./Chief Photographer....Barron Ludlum
Political Ed.....Mike Trimble
Real Estate Ed.....Kaycee Key
Market Information: TMC.
Mechanical available: Flexography/Letterpress; Black and 3 ROP colors; insert accepted - card, single sheet; page cutoffs - 22 3/4.
Mechanical Specifications: Type page 13 x 21 1/2; E - 6 cols, 2 1/16, 1/6 between; A - 6 cols, 2 1/16, 1/6 between; C - 9 cols, 1 3/8, 1/8 between.
Commodity Consumption: Avg. Page Number Per Issue - Daily 32; Avg. Page Number Per Issue - Plates Used 24740; Avg. Page Number Per Issue - Sunday 60; widths 27 1/2; Newsprint Used - Short Tons 1818; Printing Ink Used - Black 106500; Printing Ink Used - Color 35000; Printing In
Equipment EDITORIAL: Front-end Software – SII/Sys 55XR.; Editorial Hardware – Compudyne/386; Editorial Printers – Okidata CLASSIFIED: Front-end Software – SII/Sys 55XR.; Classified Hardware – Compudyne/386; Classified Printers – Okidata DISPLAY: Ad make-up applications – SCS/Layout 8000; Layout Software – SCS/Layout 8000.; Display Hardware – IBM/AT; Display Printers – CI/300 Plus; Production Equipment – AG/3400, 2-Na/NP20, ECR/Scriptsetter VRL 36; Cameras – 2-C/Spartan III; Scanners – ECR/Autokon 1000. PRESSROOM: Line 1 – 2-FOL/4-LP 1986; Line 2 – 2-KBA/Conversion 1986; Pasters – 6; Press control system – 1986 MAILROOM: Counter stackers – 3/SH; Inserters and stuffers – 2-/MM; Bundle tying machines – 1-EAM-Mosca; Addressing machine – 1-/KR.; Business Hardware – ATT

EDINBURG

EDINBURG REVIEW

215 E. University Dr., Edinburg, Texas, 78539; gen tel (956) 383-2705; gen fax (956) 383-3172; gen e-mail edinrev@aol.com; web site www.edinburgreview.com
Published: Wed
Circulation: 69,350
Last Audit: November 29, 2005
Advertising: Open inch rate $13.00
News services: AP.
Not Published: Independence Day; Labor Day; Christmas.
Special Weekly Sections: Church Page (Fri); Business & Industrial Page (Tues); Best Food Day (Wed).
Pres./Pub....Pearl A. Mathis
Adv. Mgr.....Debbie Moczygemba
Adv. Mgr., Classified....Sujey Ramirez
Exec. Ed.....Gilbert Tagle
Mng. Ed.....Brad Nibert
Photo Ed.....Beng Lim
Prodn. Supvr.....Pearl Mathis
Prodn. Supt., Pressroom....Rick Abrego
Mechanical available: Offset; Black and 3 ROP colors; insert accepted.
Mechanical Specifications: Type page 13 x 21 1/2; E - 6 cols, 2 1/16, 1/8 between; A - 6 cols, 2 1/16, 1/8 between; C - 9 cols, 1 3/8, 1/16 between.
Commodity Consumption: Avg. Page Number Per Issue - Daily 24; Avg. Page Number Per Issue - Sunday 56; widths 13.
Equipment; Editorial Hardware – APP/Mac.; Classified Hardware – APP/Mac.; Production Equipment – Nu; Cameras – R. PRESSROOM: Line 1 – 4-G/Suburban.; Addressing machine – 1/Am.; Business Hardware – Tandy/3000, IBM

EL PASO

EL PASO TIMES

300 N. Campbell St., El Paso, Texas, 79901-1402; gen tel (915) 546-6100; adv tel (915) 546-6250; ed tel (915) 546-6118; gen fax (915) 546-6415; adv fax (915) 546-6404; ed fax (915) 546-6415; gen e-mail business@elpasotimes.com; adv e-mail advertising@elpasotimes.com; ed e-mail news@elpasotimes.com; web site www.elpasotimes.com
Group: MediaNews Group
Published: Mon, Tues, Wed, Thur, Fri, Sat, Sun
Weekday Frequency: m
Saturday Frequency: m
Circulation: 62,280; 47,280(sat); 71,395(sun)
Last Audit: ABC September 30, 2011
Price: 12.75/mo (dS), $9.75/mo (wknd); 153.00/yr.
Advertising: Open inch rate $135.44
News services: AP, GNS, LAT-WP, MCT.
Politics: Independent. **Established:** 1881
Special Editions: Healthcare Directory (Apr); Football (Aug); Last Minute Gift Guide (Dec); Legal Directory (Feb); Women in Business (Jan); Career Tab + Expo (Jul); Family-Owned Business (Jun); Sport Utility Vehicles (Mar); Career Tab + Expo (May); Early Christmas Gift Gui
Special Weekly Sections: Cars & Trucks (Fri); Jobs (Mon); Homes of El Paso (S); Auto Showcase (Sat).
Magazines: Eastside Reporter (Fri); USA WEEKEND Magazine (S).
CEO/President & Publisher....Sergio Salinas
Dir., HR....Malena Field
Senior VP of Advertising and Marketing....Cecilia Uebel
VP of Online/Digital....Jim Weddell
Mktg. Dir.....Kent Hummel
Circ. Dir.....Jim Dove
Circ. Mgr., City Home Delivery....Craig Pogorzelski
Circ. Mgr., Transportation....Randy Waldrop
Bus. Ed.....Ramon Bracamontes
City/Metro Ed....Armando V. Durazo
Design Ed.....Carlita Costello
Editorial Page Ed....Charlie Edgren
Editorial Writer....Joe Muench
Features Ed.....Melissa Martinez
Online Sales Mgr.....Mario Ontiveros
Information Technolgy Dir.....Paz Garcia
VP of Production....Patsy Hernandez
Sports Editor....Margaret Gallardo
Market Information: ADS; Split run; TMC; Zoned editions.
Mechanical available: Black and 3 ROP colors; insert accepted; page cutoffs - 22.
Mechanical Specifications: Type page 12 x 21; E - 6 cols, 1 1/3, 1/6 between; A - 6 cols, 1 1/3, 1/6 between; C - 10 cols, 1 1/6, 1/2 between.
Commodity Consumption: Avg. Page Number Per Issue - Daily 38; Avg. Page Number Per Issue - Plates Used 65320; Avg. Page Number Per Issue - Sunday 86; widths 37 1/2; Newsprint Used - Short Tons 10100; Printing Ink Used - Black 384000; Printing Ink Used - Color 96300; Printing I
Equipment EDITORIAL: Front-end Software – Decade.; Editorial Hardware – SII, 40-SII/Coyote 15, 26-SII/Coyote 22, 15-SII/Cat 30, QPS; Editorial Equipment – 5-APP/Mac, GMTI/DiGiCol; Editorial Printers – 1-Tandem/5512, 3-HP/8000; Classified Hardware – SII, 22-SII/Coyote 15, 2-SII/Coyote 22, 2-SII/Cat 30, 3-GE/Engineering; Classified Equipment – 2-SII, ICP; Classified Printers – 1-Tandem/5512, DEC/LA 75. DISPLAY: Ad make-up applications – Other Equipment ÂО Microtek/ScanMaker IIsp; Display Hardware – 8-X/Scanner, 2-APP/Mac Power PC, AP AdSend, AdLink, 16-APP/Mac G3; Display Printers – 2-APP/Mac LaserWriter, 2-APP/Mac, 1-HP/DesignJet 755CM PRODUCTION: Pagination Software – QPS.; Production Equipment – KFM, AG/Intellitune; Scanners – HP/Flatbed Color, Kk/RFS 2035, AG/II PRESSROOM: Line 1 – G/Metrocolor (23 couples) double width 1997; Line 2 – G/Metrocolor (23 couples) double width 1997; Pasters – G/Digital; Reels and Stands – CT/50; Press control system – G/MPCS. MAILROOM: Counter stackers – 6-QWI/351; Inserters and stuffers – GMA/5652000 24:2, GMA/562000 20:2; Bundle tying machines – 5-Dynaric/NP 500; Mailroom control system – GMA/SAM; Addressing machine – 1-Cheshire/Labeler; Other equipment –1-MM/321 Fox Saddle Stitcher.

ENNIS

ELLIS COUNTY NEWSPAPER, INC.

213 N. Dallas St., Ennis, Texas, 75119; gen tel (972) 875-3801; gen fax (972) 875-9747

ENNIS DAILY NEWS

213 N. Dallas St., Ennis, Texas, 75119-0100; gen tel (972) 875-3801; gen fax (972) 875-9747; gen e-mail publisher@ennisdailynews.com; adv e-mail admanager@ennisdailynews.com; ed e-mail editor@ennisdailynews.com; web site www.ennisdailynews.com
Published: Tues, Wed, Thur, Fri, Sun
Weekday Frequency: e
Circulation: 3,214; 3,214(sun)
Last Audit: September 25, 2003
Price: 6.50/mo; 84.00/yr.
Advertising: Open inch rate $9.70
News services: AP.
Not Published: New Year; Memorial Day; Independence Day; Labor Day.
Special Editions: Football Preview (Aug); Christmas (Dec); History (Jun); Progress-Directions (Mar); Real Estate (Monthly); Christmas (Nov); Cookbook (Oct); Seniors (Quarterly).
Special Weekly Sections: Making Tracks (Weekly).
Pres....Tre Bischos
Circ. Mgr.....Dick O'Brien
Sports Ed.....Tye Chandler
Prodn. Mgr., Pressroom....Brian Trailer
Market Information: TMC.
Mechanical available: Offset; Black and 3 ROP colors; insert accepted; page cutoffs - 21 1/2.
Mechanical Specifications: Type page 13 x 21 1/2; E - 6 cols, 2 1/16, 1/8 between; A - 6 cols, 2 1/16, 1/8 between; C - 6 cols, 2 1/16, 1/8 between.
Commodity Consumption: Avg. Page Number Per Issue - Daily 12; Avg. Page Number Per Issue - Sunday 16; widths 27; Newsprint Used - Short Tons 200; Printing Ink Used - Black 2500; Printing Ink Used - Color 200; Printing Ink Used - Pages Printed 16.
Equipment EDITORIAL: Front-end Software – QPS.; Editorial Hardware – APP/Mac; Editorial Printers – GCC/XL20/600 CLASSIFIED: Front-end Software – BMF.; Classified Hardware – PC; Classified Printers – TI/Micro Laser DISPLAY: Ad make-up applications – QPS.; Display Hardware – APP/Mac; Display Printers – GCC; Production Equipment – Reconex, 1-COM/7200; Cameras – 1-B; Scanners – AG/Snap Scan, Minolta/Quick Scan. PRESSROOM: Line 1 – 6-G/Community single width; Folders – 1-G/2:1.; Bundle tying machines – 1/Strap Tyer.

FORT WORTH

FORT WORTH STAR-TELEGRAM

400 W. 7th St., Fort Worth, Texas, 76102-4701; gen tel (817) 390-7400; adv tel (817) 390-7765; ed tel (817) 390-7150; gen fax (817) 336-2790; adv fax (817) 390-7869; ed fax (817) 390-7321; ed e-mail jwitt@star-telegram.com; web site www.star-telegram.com
Group: Newspapers First, Inc.
Published: Mon, Tues, Wed, Thur, Fri, Sat, Sun
Weekday Frequency: m
Saturday Frequency: m
Circulation: 189,795; 266,170(sat); 230,809(sun)
Last Audit: ABC September 30, 2011
Price: 159.00/yr.
Advertising: Open inch rate $381.90
News services: Newspapers First, MCT, LAT-WP, SHNS, DJ (Dow Jones).
Politics: Independent. **Established:** 1906
Special Editions: Summer Vacation (Apr); Football (Aug); Gift Guide III (Dec); Texas Golf &

Resort (Feb); Stock Show I (Jan); Education (Jul); Primetime (Jun); Primetime (Mar); Top 25 (May); Healthcare (Monthly); Primetime (Nov); The Answer Book (Oct); Fall Home & Garden S
Special Weekly Sections: Travel (S); Home (Sat); Food (Wed).
Magazines: StarTime (Fri); Tarrant Business (Mon); Relish (Monthly); TV Star (weekly TV Guide) (S).
Pres./Pub. ....Gary Wortel
Pub., Arlington Star-Telegram ....Gary Hardee
Pub., Northeast Tarrant Star-Telegram Steve Jacob
Vice Pres./CFO..........................Roger Provost
Sr. Vice Pres., Adv. ....Michael J. Winter
Vice Pres., Mktg. ....Jerry Scott
Circ. Vice Pres. ....Dolan Stidom
Circ. Dir., Arlington............................Terry Foley
Circ. Dir., Sales/Training ....Lonna Hoffman
Sr. Vice Pres./Exec. Ed.........................Jim Witt
Vice Pres./Editorial Dir. ....Paul K. Harral
Vice Pres./Assoc. Ed. ....Bob Ray Sanders
Mng. Ed., Enterprise ....Kathy Vetter
Mng. Ed., Investigations..................Lois Norder
Mng. Ed., News ....Rex Seline
Mng. Ed., Sports ....Ellen Alfano
Asst. Mng. Ed., Bus. ....Steve Kaskovich
Asst. Mng. Ed., Features.......Catherine Mallette
Asst. Mng. Ed., Gov't Affairs.........John Gravois
Asst. Mng. Ed., Sports.............Celeste Williams
Market Information: Split run; TMC; Zoned editions.
Mechanical available: Offset; Black and 3 ROP colors; insert accepted; page cutoffs - 22.
Mechanical Specifications: Type page 11 5/8 x 21 1/4; E - 6 cols, 2 1/14, 1/6 between; A - 6 cols, 2 1/14, 1/6 between; C - 6 cols, 1 1/5, 1/6 between.
Commodity Consumption: Avg. Page Number Per Issue - Daily 100; Avg. Page Number Per Issue - Plates Used 714074; Avg. Page Number Per Issue - Saturday 145; Avg. Page Number Per Issue - Sunday 231; widths 41; Newsprint Used - Metric Tons 66433; Printing Ink Used - Black 1026598;
Equipment EDITORIAL: Front-end Software – Dewar.; Editorial Hardware – Compaq/Pentium, Dell/Pentium; Editorial Printers – Epson, HP, Lexmark CLASSIFIED: Front-end Software – CText.; Classified Hardware – IBM/RS 6000; Classified Printers – Lexmark DISPLAY: Ad make-up applications – Mk/Page Director, Mk/Ad Director, QPS/QuarkXPress, Adobe/Photoshop, Adobe/Illustrator; Layout Software – MEI.; Display Hardware – APP/Mac; Display Printers – APP/Mac LaserWriter III, HP, QMS, Lexmark PRODUCTION: Pagination Software – QPS/QuarkXPress, Adobe/Photoshop, Adobe/Illustrator, Macromedia/Freehand.; Production Equipment – 4-AU/3850, 2-AU/F108, 1-AU/30 double truck, 6-Gluntz & Jensen; Cameras – 1-Acti, 1-C/New, 1-C/Marathon; Scanners – 4-Scanmate/Scanview PRESSROOM: Line 1 – 11-G/Headliner (with 8 half decks) 1986, 2-G/Metro Color Tower 1999; Line 2 – 11-G/Headliner (with 8 half decks) 1986, 2-G/Metro Color Tower 1999; Line 3 – 11-G/Headliner(w/8 half decks) 1986, 2-G/Metro Color Tower 1999; Line 4 – 11-G/Headliner (MAILROOM: Counter stackers – 17-HL/Monitor, 2-QWI/351, 6-QWI/351; Inserters and stuffers – 3-HI/72P, 2-HI/630; Bundle tying machines – 18-Dynaric/NP2, 3-Dynaric/Am-9000, 3/Bu; Wrapping singles – 3-Signode/HLS; Addressing machine – 2-/Ch, 1-/MM, 2-/Video jet; Other equipment –Other; Business Hardware – DEC, DEC/4100

STAR-TELEGRAM OPERATING LTD.

685 Sias Pkwy., Fort Worth, Texas, 76134; gen tel (817) 390-7400; gen fax (817) 336-2790

GAINESVILLE

GAINESVILLE DAILY REGISTER

306 E. California St., Gainesville, Texas, 76240; gen tel (940) 665-5511; adv fax (940) 665-0920; ed fax (940) 665-1499; adv e-mail registeradv@ntin.net; web site www.gainesvilleregister.com
Published: Mon, Tues, Wed, Thur, Fri, Sun
Weekday Frequency: e
Circulation: 5,902; 5,902(sun)
Last Audit: September 30, 2006
Price: 7.00/mo; 84.00/yr.
Advertising: Open inch rate $12.92
News services: AP.
Politics: Independent. **Established:** 1890
Advertising not accepted: 900 numbers; Dating services.
Not Published: New Year; Independence Day; Labor Day; Christmas.
Special Weekly Sections: Church News (Fri); Best Food Day (S); Best Food Day (Wed).
Magazines: Relish (Monthly); USA WEEKEND Magazine (S); American Profile (Weekly).
Bus. Mgr. ....Bernice Trimble
Adv. Mgr. ....Armand Nardi
Circ. Mgr. ....Jack Bills
Mng. Ed...J. Osborne
Sports Ed. ....Darin Allred
Women's Ed. ....Jodelle Greiner
Prodn. Supt., Composing..................Joe Grotte
Prodn. Supt., Pressroom..................Tom Baker
Mechanical available: Offset; Black and 3 ROP colors; insert accepted; page cutoffs - 19.
Mechanical Specifications: Type page 13 x 21 1/2; E - 6 cols, 2 1/16, 1/8 between; A - 6 cols, 2 1/16, 1/8 between; C - 9 cols, 1 3/8, 1/8 between.
Commodity Consumption: Avg. Page Number Per Issue - Daily 10; Avg. Page Number Per Issue - Sunday 16; widths 27; Newsprint Used - Metric Tons 200.
Equipment EDITORIAL: Front-end Software – Baseview.; Editorial Hardware – APP/Mac 7300; Editorial Printers – APP/Mac LaserWriter II, NewGen CLASSIFIED: Front-end Software – Baseview.; Classified Hardware – APP/Mac 7300; Classified Printers – APP/Mac LaserWriter II DISPLAY: Ad make-up applications – Multi-Ad/Creator, Baseview; Layout Software – APP/Mac 7300.; Display Hardware – APP/Mac IIci; Display Printers – APP/Mac LaserWriter II NTX, NewGen/Printer PRODUCTION: Pagination Software – QPS/QuarkXPress.; Production Equipment – Mk; Cameras – 1-Nu PRESSROOM: Line 1 – 24-G/Community.; Bundle tying machines – MLN. BUSINESS COMPUTERS: Business Software – AR Works; Business Hardware – Brainworks

GALVESTON

THE GALVESTON COUNTY DAILY NEWS

8522 Teichman Rd., Galveston, Texas, 77554; gen tel (409) 683-5200; adv tel (409) 683-5224; ed tel (409) 683-5239; gen fax (409) 744-6268; adv fax (409) 744-7679; ed fax (409) 740-3421; oth fax 409-683-5344; adv e-mail scott.moon@galvnews.com; ed e-mail newsroom@galvnews.com; web site www.galvnews.com
Group: Southern Newspapers
????
Published: Mon, Tues, Wed, Thur, Fri, Sat, Sun
Weekday Frequency: m
Saturday Frequency: m
Circulation: 21,697; 21,697(sat); 22,061(sun)
Last Audit: September 30, 2008
Price: 12.00/mo; 144.00/yr.
Advertising: Open inch rate $31.00
News services: AP.
Politics: Independent. **Established:** 1842
Own facility?: Y
Special Editions: Seniors Over 55 (Annually); Calendar of Events (Monthly); Dining Guide (Semi-yearly).
Special Weekly Sections: Entertainment (Fri); Books (S); Lifestyle (Wed).
Magazines: Relish (Monthly); USA WEEKEND Magazine (S).
Pres./Pub. ....Dolph Tillotson
Bus. Mgr................................D'Lorah Collier
Adv. Mgr., Retail ....Debbie Keith
Circ. Mgr.............................Yvonne Mascorro
Ed...Heber Taylor
Assoc. Ed. ....Michael A. Smith
Community News Editor...............Angela Taylor
Online Ed. ....Greg Mefford
Prodn. Foreman, Pressroom ....Brett Baker
Sports Editor ....Jordan Gordwin
Advertising Director........................Scott Moon
News Editor.................................Melissa Rivera
Photo Editor
Jennifer Reynolds
Lifestyle Ed...............................Michael Smith
Sports Ed. ....Joshua Buckley
Market Information: TMC.
Mechanical available: Offset; Black and 3 ROP colors; insert accepted - all; page cutoffs - 22 3/4.
Mechanical Specifications: Type page 13 x 21 1/2; E - 6 cols, 2 1/16, 1/8 between; A - 6 cols, 2 1/16, 1/8 between; C - 9 cols, 1 3/8, 1/16 between.
Commodity Consumption: Avg. Page Number Per Issue - Daily 24; Avg. Page Number Per Issue - Plates Used 18000; Avg. Page Number Per Issue - Sunday 48; widths 27 1/2; Newsprint Used - Short Tons 2420; Printing Ink Used - Black 3500; Printing Ink Used - Pages Printed 12702.
Equipment EDITORIAL: Front-end Software – Microsoft/Word, QPS/QuarkXPress, Custom-Developed.; Editorial Hardware – APP/Mac; Editorial Printers – APP/Mac LaserWriter IIg, AG/Imagesetters CLASSIFIED: Front-end Software – DEC.; Classified Hardware – APP/Mac, DEC; Classified Printers – Unified/Laser DISPLAY: Ad make-up applications – Multi-Ad/Director; Layout Software – Mk/Ad Director, Mk/Managing Editor.; Display Hardware – APP/Mac, 2-APP/Mac IIg; Display Printers – LaserMaster; Production Equipment – 1-Nu, AG/Star 400, 2-AG/1000 Imagesetter; Cameras – C/Spartan III; Scanners – ECR, RZ/Diadem. PRESSROOM: Line 1 – 8-HI/Cotrell 845 1980; Folders – 1-HI/2:1, G/Urbanite. MAILROOM: Counter stackers – 1/S; Inserters and stuffers – 1-/S; Bundle tying machines – 1-/MLN; Addressing machine – 1-/KAN.; Business Hardware – Data General
Zip Codes served: 77550, 77551, 77554, 77568, 77590, 77591, 77563
Delivery method: Mail, Newsstand, Private Carrier, Racks

GALVESTON NEWSPAPERS, INC.

8522 Teichman Rd., Galveston, Texas, 77554; gen tel (409) 683-5200; adv tel 409 683 5224; ed tel 409-683-5239; gen fax (409) 744-6268; adv fax (409) 744-7679; ed fax 409-740-3421; oth fax 409-683-5344; adv e-mail scott.moon@galvnews.com; ed e-mail newsroom@galvnews.com; web site galvnews.com
Published: Mon, Tues, Wed, Thur, Fri, Sat, Sun
Weekday Frequency: m
Saturday Frequency: m
Price: 12.00/mo; 144.00/yr.
Advertising: Open inch rate $31.00
News services: AP.
Politics: Independent. **Established:** 1842
Own facility?: Y
Special Weekly Sections: Entertainment (Fri); Books (S); Lifestyle (Wed).
Market Information: TMC.
Commodity Consumption: Avg. Page Number Per Issue - Daily 24; Avg. Page Number Per Issue - Plates Used 18000; Avg. Page Number Per Issue - Sunday 48; widths 27 1/2; Newsprint Used - Short Tons 2420; Printing Ink Used - Black 3500; Printing Ink Used - Pages Printed 12702.
Equipment EDITORIAL: Front-end Software – Microsoft/Word, QPS/QuarkXPress, Custom-Developed. DISPLAY: Ad make-up applications – Multi-Ad/Director
Zip Codes served: 77550, 77551, 77554, 77568, 77590, 77591, 77563
Delivery method: Mail, Newsstand, Private Carrier, Racks

GREENVILLE

HERALD-BANNER PUBLICATIONS

2305 King St., Greenville, Texas, 75401; gen tel (903) 455-4220; gen fax (903) 455-6281; adv fax (903) 455-3100; gen e-mail publisher@heraldbanner.com; adv e-mail advertising@heraldbanner.com; web site www.heraldbanner.com
Published: Mon, Tues, Wed, Thur, Fri, Sat, Sun
Weekday Frequency: m
Saturday Frequency: m
Circulation: 7,945; 7,945(sat); 8,621(sun)
Last Audit: September 30, 2005
Price: 9.25/mo; 111.00/yr (carrier).
Advertising: Open inch rate $19.56
News services: AP.
Politics: Independent. **Established:** 1869
Advertising not accepted: Fortune tellers; Adoption; 900 numbers.
Not Published: Christmas.
Special Weekly Sections: TV Tabloid (S).
Magazines: Relish (Monthly); USA WEEKEND Magazine (S).
Pub...Lisa Chappell
Bus. Mgr. ....Mary Standfield
Adv. Dir. ....Leslie McMannis
Circ. Dir...................................Robert Spillers
Ed...Daniel Walker
Mng. Ed. ....Warren Morrison
Features Ed. ....Carol Ferguson
Sports Ed...............................David Claybourn
Prodn. Mgr..................................David Benini
Market Information: TMC.
Mechanical available: Offset; Black and 3 ROP colors; insert accepted; page cutoffs - 22 3/4.
Mechanical Specifications: Type page 13 x 21 1/2; E - 6 cols, 1 5/6, 1/8 between; A - 6 cols, 1 4/5, 1/8 between; C - 9 cols, 1 4/5, 1/16 between.
Commodity Consumption: Avg. Page Number Per Issue - Daily 16; Avg. Page Number Per Issue - Plates Used 16326; Avg. Page Number Per Issue - Sunday 28; widths 25; Newsprint Used - Short Tons 794; Printing Ink Used - Black 19298; Printing Ink Used - Color 5120; Printing Ink Used
Equipment EDITORIAL: Front-end Software – QPS/QuarkXPress 3.32, Baseview/N; Editorial Hardware – APP/Mac Classic, APP/Mac LC, APP/Mac IIsi, APP/Power Mac G3; Editorial Equipment – Hayes/Smart modem 9600, Express/28.8; Editorial Printers – APP/Mac LaserWriter IIg, APP/Mac LaserWriter 16-600, APP/Mac LaserWriter 8500 CLASSIFIED: Front-end Software – QPS/QuarkXPress 3.1.; Classified Hardware – 3-APP/Mac LC; Classified Printers – Okidata/Microline 320 DISPLAY: Ad make-up applications – QPS/QuarkXPress 3.32, Adobe/Illustrator 3.0; Layout Software – APP; Display Hardware – APP/Mac Quadra 700, APP/Power Mac G3; Display Printers – APP/Mac LaserWriter IIg, APP/Mac LaserWriter 16-600; Production Equipment – Nat/A-250, APP/Mac Quadra 700, APP/Power Mac G-3; Cameras – SCREEN/Rollmatic C-475-D, SCREEN/Companica 680C; Scanners – APP/Mac One Scanner, Mita/DC-1656 Copier, Polaroid/SprintScan 35, Umax/Vista S-12. PRESSROOM: Line 1 – 8-G/Community 1974; Folders – 1-G/SC; Press control system – VEE ARC/PWM 7000 1974. MAILROOM: Counter stackers – BG/108; Inserters and stuffers – KAN; Bundle tying machines – 1-MLN/ML2EE, Dynaric/5580.; Business Hardware – IBM, EKI/Televideo

HARLINGEN

VALLEY MORNING STAR

1310 S. Commerce St., Harlingen, Texas, 78550; gen tel (956) 430-6200; adv fax (956) 430-6231; ed fax (956) 430-6233; gen e-mail starnewsroom@valleystar.com; web site www.valleystar.com
Group: U.S. Suburban Press, Inc.
Published: Mon, Tues, Wed, Thur, Fri, Sat, Sun
Weekday Frequency: m
Saturday Frequency: m
Circulation: 17,332; 17,332(sat); 18,215(sun)
Last Audit: September 30, 2009
Price: 9.00/mo; 114.00/yr (mS carrier).
Advertising: Open inch rate $30.68
News services: AP, Freedom Wire, MCT, TMS.

Politics: Independent. **Established:** 1912
Advertising not accepted: 900 numbers; International numbers.
Special Editions: Winter Visitor's Tourist Guide (Nov).
Magazines: Vista (Fri); Parade (S).
Pub. ....Douglas Hardie
Gen. Mgr./Pub. ....Tyler Patton
Bus. Mgr. ....Jill Stout
Accounting Mgr. ....Melva Juarez
Adv. Dir. ....Richard Guerrero
Adv. Opns. Mgr. ....Peggy Elder
Mktg./Sales Promo. Mgr. ....Marcia Kitten
Circ. Mgr. ....Rusty Hall
Ed. ....Paul Binz
Mng. Ed. ....Lucio Castillo
City Ed. ....Charlene Vandini
Sports Ed. ....Dave Favila
Society/Women's Ed. ....Ramon Rodriguez
Market Information: TMC.
Mechanical available: Offset; Black and 3 ROP colors; insert accepted - all; page cutoffs - 22 3/4.
Mechanical Specifications: Type page 13 x 21; E - 6 cols, 2 1/16, 1/8 between; A - 6 cols, 2 1/16, 1/8 between; C - 10 cols, 1 1/4, 1/16 between.
Commodity Consumption: Avg. Page Number Per Issue - Daily 36; Avg. Page Number Per Issue - Plates Used 16000; Avg. Page Number Per Issue - Sunday 70; widths 27 1/2; Newsprint Used - Metric Tons 2425; Printing Ink Used - Black 83600; Printing Ink Used - Color 32150; Printing In
Equipment; Editorial Hardware – APT; Editorial Equipment – AP/Photo Server; Editorial Printers – HP/5000.; Classified Hardware – APT; Classified Printers – HP/4000. DISPLAY: Ad make-up applications – APT; Layout Software – 1-Compaq, APT.; Display Hardware – 1-Compaq; Display Printers – HP/5si PRODUCTION: Pagination Software – APT.; Production Equipment – ECR/3850, ECR/4550; Cameras – 1-C/Spartan III; Scanners – 3-HP/Scanner PRESSROOM: Line 1 – 6-HI/Cotrell 845; Line 2 – 6-HI/Cotrell 845; Folders – 2-H/2:1; Pasters – 8-Jardis/FP 4540. MAILROOM: Counter stackers – Id, QWI; Bundle tying machines – 2-MLN/MLN2, Dynaric. BUSINESS COMPUTERS: Business Software – Brainworks, Southware; Business Hardware – Prosig, 4-PC 4DX2-66, SCSI, 7-Compaq/486

HENDERSON

HENDERSON DAILY NEWS

1711 S. Hwy. 79, Henderson, Texas, 75654; gen tel (903) 657-2501; adv tel (903) 657-2501; ed tel (903) 657-2501; gen fax (903) 657-2452; adv fax (903) 657-2452; ed fax (903) 657-0056; adv e-mail classifieds@hendersondailynews.com; ed e-mail joyslaymaker@hendersondailynews.com; web site www.hendersondailynews.com
Published: Mon, Tues, Wed, Thur, Fri, Sun
Weekday Frequency: e
Circulation: 6,039; 7,206(sun)
Last Audit: March 31, 2006
Price: 7.00/mo; 86.00/yr.
Advertising: Open inch rate $8.30
News services: AP, NEA.
Politics: 1930
Not Published: Independence Day; Labor Day; Christmas.
Own facility?: Y
Magazines: Relish (Monthly); TV Magazine (S).
Pub. ....Les Linebarger
Accountant ....Nancy Harris
Circ. Mgr. ....John Garrison
News Ed. ....Tony Floyd
Sports Ed. ....Hughes Ellis
Prodn. Supt./Foreman, Composing Joy Slaymaker
Market Information: TMC.
Mechanical available: Offset; Black and 3 ROP colors; insert accepted; page cutoffs - 21 1/2.
Mechanical Specifications: Type page 13 x 21 1/2; E - 6 cols, 2 1/16, 1/8 between; A - 6 cols, 2 1/16, 1/8 between; C - 8 cols, 1 3/8, 1/16 between.
Commodity Consumption: Avg. Page Number Per Issue - Daily 10; Avg. Page Number Per Issue - Plates Used 2200; Avg. Page Number Per Issue - Sunday 34; widths 27 1/2; Newsprint Used - Short Tons 210; Printing Ink Used - Black 5400; Printing Ink Used - Color 560; Printing Ink Used
Equipment; Editorial Hardware – APP/Mac; Editorial Equipment – 4-APP/Mac. CLASSIFIED: Front-end Software – Baseview/Class Manager.; Display Hardware – APP/Mac.; Production Equipment – 3-APP/Mac LaserWriter Plus; Cameras – R/500; Scanners – 2-COM/MDR. PRESSROOM: Line 1 – 6-HI/V-15A (upper former).; Bundle tying machines – 1-Bu/64808.
Delivery method: Mail, Newsstand, Private Carrier, Racks

HENDERSON NEWSPAPERS, INC.

1711 Hwy. 79 S., Henderson, Texas, 75653; gen tel (903) 657-2501; gen fax (903) 657-2452

HEREFORD

THE HEREFORD BRAND

313 N. Lee St., Hereford, Texas, 79045; gen tel (806) 364-2030; adv tel (806) 364-2030; ed tel (806) 364-2030; gen fax (806) 364-8364; adv fax (806) 364-8364; ed fax (806) 364-8364; gen e-mail pub@herefordbrand.com; adv e-mail retail@herefordbrand.com; ed e-mail editor@herefordbrand.com; web site www.herefordbrand.com
Published: Tues, Wed, Thur, Fri, Sun
Weekday Frequency: e
Saturday Frequency: e
Circulation: 2,100; 2,500(sun)
Last Audit: Sworn September 30, 2007
Price: 8.45/mo; 77.40/yr.
Advertising: Open inch rate $9.00
News services: AP.
Politics: Independent.
Not Published: New Year; Thanksgiving; Christmas.
Special Weekly Sections: Television (S).
Magazines: American Profile (Weekly).
Lifestyle Ed. ....Tyler Jameson
Sports Ed. ....Skip Leon
General Manager ....Dana Jameson
Advertising Director ....Ray Leverett
Staff Writer ....Eric Hanna
Market Information: Split run; TMC.
Mechanical available: Offset; Black and 3 ROP colors; insert accepted; page cutoffs - 21.
Mechanical Specifications: Type page 13 x 21; E - 6 cols, 2 1/16, 1/8 between; A - 6 cols, 2 1/16, 1/8 between; C - 6 cols, 2 1/16, 1/8 between.
Commodity Consumption: Avg. Page Number Per Issue - Daily 12; Avg. Page Number Per Issue - Sunday 36; widths 28; Newsprint Used - Short Tons 300.
Equipment EDITORIAL: Front-end Software – WordPerfect.; Editorial Hardware – 1-Wyse/3225, 6-VGA Monitor; Editorial Printers – QMS/PS-810 CLASSIFIED: Front-end Software – WordPerfect.; Classified Hardware – 1-Wyse/3225, VGA Monitor; Classified Printers – QMS/PS-810 DISPLAY: Ad make-up applications – Microsoft/Windows; Layout Software – Aldus/PageMaker, Archetype/Corel Draw.; Display Hardware – 1-Archetype/386 SX, 1-Wyse/3225, 2-VGA Monitor; Display Printers – 1-QMS/PS-810; Production Equipment – 1-Nat/A-340; Cameras – 1-R, 1-Argyle/18-Process G18; Scanners – CK Optical/SQU-7. PRESSROOM: Line 1 – 4-HI/V-15 1981. MAILROOM: Counter stackers – 1-BG/Count-O-Veyor; Bundle tying machines – 1/Bu, 1-/Bu; Addressing machine – 1-/Elliot Dynamic/3101. BUSINESS COMPUTERS: Business Software – SBT; Business Hardware – 1-Wyse/386

HOUSTON

HOUSTON CHRONICLE

801 Texas St., Houston, Texas, 77002-2904; gen tel (713) 362-7171; adv tel (713) 224-6868; ed tel (713) 362-7491; gen fax (713) 362-3575; adv fax (713) 362-7835; ed fax (713) 362-6806; adv e-mail classifieds@chron.com; ed e-mail news@chron.com; viewpoints@chron.com; web site www.chron.com
Group: Hearst Corporation Newspapers First, Inc.
Published: Mon, Tues, Wed, Thur, Fri, Sat, Sun
Weekday Frequency: m
Saturday Frequency: m
Circulation: 369,710; 346,979(sat); 911,564(sun)
Last Audit: ABC September 30, 2011
Price: 22.00/mo; 264.00/yr.
Advertising: Open inch rate $736.00
News services: AP, MCT, HN, NYT, CQ, Bloomberg, EFE, Getty Images, Sports Network, Financial Content.
Politics: Independent.
Special Editions: Baseball (Apr); Football (Aug); Super Bowl (Feb); How-To Guide (Jul); Houston Open (Mar); Chronicle Top 100 (May); Health (Monthly); Holiday Guide (Nov); NBA Preview (Oct).
Special Weekly Sections: Houston Belief (Fri); In-Motion (Other); Color Comics (S); New Homes (Sat); Preview/Dining Guide (Thur); Flavor (Wed).
Magazines: Zest (ROP) (S).
Market Information: ADS; Split run; TMC; Zoned editions.
Mechanical available: Offset; Black and 3 ROP colors; insert accepted - cards, bags; page cutoffs - 22 3/4, 22, 21.
Mechanical Specifications: Type page 12 3/4 x 21 1/4; E - 6 cols, 1/6 between; A - 6 cols, 1/6 between; C - 6 cols, between.
Commodity Consumption: Avg. Page Number Per Issue - Daily 240; Avg. Page Number Per Issue - Plates Used 1008040; Avg. Page Number Per Issue - Saturday 178; Avg. Page Number Per Issue - Sunday 342; widths 38 13/16; Newsprint Used - Short Tons 179371; Printing Ink Used - Black 4
Equipment EDITORIAL: Front-end Software – DTI/Newspaper Systems Millenium Editoria; Editorial Hardware – SII, Sun/Microsys; Editorial Equipment – AU/APS 5, Lf/AP Leaf Picture Desk, APP/Mac, Sun/Phoenix T-1, Merlin/Photo Archive, Fox/Prodatabase, BH/Proquest Publisher; Editorial Printers – QMS/2060, HP/Laserjet CLASSIFIED: Front-end Software – SII, CKP.; Classified Hardware – SII, PC, Sun/Enterprise 3000, Sun/Enterprise 4000, Sun/450; Classified Equipment – DP/CD Merge System; Classified Printers – HP/LaserJet DISPLAY: Ad make-up applications – Sun/Breeze; Layout Software – Cx, AdControl.; Display Hardware – Sun PRODUCTION: Pagination Software – ProImage; Production Equipment – 4 AGFA Polaris CTp, 4 NELA VPB benders & sorter WL/Offset, 2-WL/Lith 7, 2-WL/Lith-X-Pozer, Scitex/342, AG/Horizon Flatbed, APP/Mac All Platform, Avanta/25 Imagers, Avanta/30 Imagers PRESSROOM: Line 1 – 12-G/Metro 1978; Line 2 – 12-G/Metro
1979; Line 3 – 12-G/Metroliner 1984; Line 4 – 12-G/Metro 1978; Line 5 – 12-G/Metroliner 1984; Line 6 – 12-G/Metroliner 1982; Press Drives – Fincor; Folders – 6G/3:2; Pasters – Simplified Tension; Reels and Stands – 60 reel stands; Press control system – Denex; Press registration system – Web/Tech. MAILROOM: Counter stackers – Quipp 350 to 550; Inserters and stuffers – 5-HI/1372P, 3-HI/Model 630 30 head, 1-G 22-99; Bundle tying machines – Dynaric; Mailroom control system – Burt/Enternet; Addressing machine – 6-Sitma/Plastic Wrap w/18 head, 1/KR; Other equipment –2-HI AUDIO: Audio Software – UNIX, Voicetek; Audio Hardware – Voicenet Technologies, Celebration Computer Systems, Compaq/Prosigna, IBUS/486, VRUs BUSINESS COMPUTERS: Business Software – Microsoft; Business Hardware – IBM

HOUSTON CHRONICLE PUBLISHING CO.

801 Texas St., Houston, Texas, 77002; gen tel (713) 220-3391; gen fax (713) 220-6288

HOUSTON COMMUNITY NEWSPAPERS

523 N. Sam Houston Pkwy. E., Ste. 600, Houston, Texas, 77060; gen tel (281) 668-1100; gen fax (281) 668-1103; web site www.hcnonline.com
CEO Jim Hopson
CFO Chuck Baldwin
Delivery method: Private Carrier

HUNTSVILLE

THE HUNTSVILLE ITEM

1409 10th St., Huntsville, Texas, 77320; gen tel (936) 295-5407; adv tel (936) 295-5407; ed tel (936) 295-5407; gen fax (936) 435-0135; adv fax (936) 435-0135; ed fax (936) 435-0135; adv e-mail jnavasard@itemonline.com; ed e-mail newsroom@itemonline.com; web site www.itemonline.com
Group: Community Newspapers Holding Inc.
Published: Mon, Tues, Wed, Thur, Fri, Sat, Sun
Weekday Frequency: m
Saturday Frequency: m
Circulation: 6,940; 6,940(sat); 7,650(sun)
Last Audit: September 30, 2006
Price: 10.95/mo (home delivery), $13.00/mo (mail); 129.00/yr.
Advertising: Open inch rate $19.50
News services: AP.
Politics: Independent. **Established:** 1850
Own facility?: Y
Special Editions: Health (Apr); Welcome Back SHSU Bearkats (Aug); Christmas Greetings (Dec); Restaurant Guide (Feb); Brides (Jan); Health Guide (Jul); Newcomers (Jun); Walker County Fair (Mar); Graduation (May); Holiday Cookbook (Nov); Women in Business (Oct); New Car Guid
Special Weekly Sections: Teleview (S).
Magazines: Texas Dept. Corrections News Roundup (Monthly); USA WEEKEND Magazine (S); American Profile (Weekly).
Managing Editor ....Lisa Trow
Adv. Dir. ....Jason Navasard
Circ. Mgr. ....Polly Johnson
Sports Ed. ....Tom Waddill
Mgr., Opns. ....Rex Harding
Publisher ....Amy Lee
Mailroom Manager ....Christina Blount
Market Information: TMC.
Mechanical available: Offset; Black and 3 ROP colors; insert accepted - all; page cutoffs - 22 3/4.
Mechanical Specifications: Type page 13 x 21 1/2; E - 6 cols, 2 1/16, 1/8 between; A - 6 cols, 2 1/16, 1/8 between; C - 9 cols, 1 3/8, 1/16 between.
Commodity Consumption: Avg. Page Number Per Issue - Daily 16; Avg. Page Number Per Issue - Plates Used 21600; Avg. Page Number Per Issue - Sunday 40; widths 13 3/4; Newsprint Used - Short Tons 1262; Printing Ink Used - Black 24364; Printing Ink Used - Color 10432; Printing Ink
Equipment EDITORIAL: Front-end Software – Baseview/NewsEdit, QPS/QuarkXPress 4.0.; Editorial Hardware – Mk, APP/Mac CLASSIFIED: Front-end Software – Baseview/Ad Manager Pro.; Classified Hardware – Mk, APP/Mac; Layout Software – APP/Mac.; Display Hardware – Software ÂŒ QPS/QuarkXPress 4.1, Adobe/Photoshop 5.5, Multi-Ad, Adobe/Illustrator PRODUCTION: Pagination Software – QPS/QuarkXPress 4.0.; Production Equipment – V, Pre Press/Panther Pro 46; Cameras – 1-SCREEN/C-260; Scanners – Unimax PRESSROOM: Line 1 – 10-G/Community single width 1991; Folders – G/SSC (with upper and lower former) 1991. MAILROOM: Counter stackers – 1-BG/Count-O-Veyor 108; Inserters and stuffers – MM/7 Station; Bundle tying machines – 1-MLN/MLI-EE-ML-MS; Other equipment – MM/Stitcher-Trimmer.; Business Hardware – Software ÂŒ PBS

Delivery method: Mail, Newsstand, Private Carrier, Racks

JACKSONVILLE

JACKSONVILLE DAILY PROGRESS

525 E. Commerce St., Jacksonville, Texas, 75766-0711; gen tel (903) 586-2236; adv tel (903) 586-2236; ed tel (903) 586-2236; gen fax (903) 586-0987; adv fax (903) 586-0987; ed fax (903) 586-0987; adv e-mail addirector@jacksonvilleprogress.com; ed e-mail editor@jacksonvilleprogress.com; web site www.jacksonvilleprogress.com

Group: Community Newspaper Holdings, Inc. (CNHI)
Published: Tues, Wed, Thur, Fri, Sun
Weekday Frequency: m
Circulation: 3,600; 3,900(sun)
Last Audit: March 31, 2007
Price: 7.00/mo; 87.00/yr.
Advertising: Open inch rate $10.50
News services: AP.
Politics: Independent. **Established:** 1910
Not Published: New Year; Christmas.
Own facility?: Y
Special Editions: Industrial Progress (Apr); Christmas Gift Guide (Dec); Chamber of Commerce (Jan); Tops in Texas Rodeo (Jul); Graduation (May); Christmas Gift Guide (Nov); Fire Prevention (Oct); Football Preview (Sept).
Special Weekly Sections: Church (Fri); Lifestyle (S); Best Food Day (Tues); Business (Wed).
Magazines: Television (Fri); American Profile (S).
Profile: daily newspaper
Office Mgr. ....Tammy Minton
Sports Ed. ....Jay Neal
Composing Mgr. ....Clara Thompson
Publisher / Editor ....Janet Gregg
Mechanical available: Offset; Black and 3 ROP colors; insert accepted - any; page cutoffs - 23.
Mechanical Specifications: Type page 12 1/2 x 21 1/2; E - 6 cols, 1 5/6, 1/8 between; A - 6 cols, 1 5/6, 1/8 between; C - 9 cols, 1 3/16, 1/8 between.
Commodity Consumption: Avg. Page Number Per Issue - Daily 12; Avg. Page Number Per Issue - Plates Used 2100; Avg. Page Number Per Issue - Sunday 24; widths 27; Newsprint Used - Metric Tons 135; Printing Ink Used - Black 2500; Printing Ink Used - Color 300; Printing Ink Used -
Equipment EDITORIAL: Front-end Software – Baseview, QPS/QuarkXPress, Adobe/Photoshop.; Editorial Hardware – APP/Power Mac; Editorial Equipment – Epson/Scanner, Nikon/Coolscan; Editorial Printers – NewGen/Design Express 1200 CLASSIFIED: Front-end Software – Baseview.; Classified Hardware – APP/Power Mac; Classified Equipment – Zip Drive; Classified Printers – NewGen/Design Express DISPLAY: Ad make-up applications – Baseview, QPS/QuarkXPress; Layout Software – QPS/QuarkXPress.; Display Hardware – APP/Power Mac; Production Equipment – 1-Nu/Flip Top FT400P; Cameras – 1-Acti/CL240. PRESSROOM: Line 1 – 6-HI/V-15A 1986.; Bundle tying machines – 1/MLN. BUSINESS COMPUTERS: Business Software – Brainworks; Business Hardware – PC
Delivery method: Mail, Private Carrier

KERRVILLE

KERRVILLE DAILY TIMES

429 Jefferson St., Kerrville, Texas, 78028-4412; gen tel (830) 896-7000; gen fax (830) 896-1150; adv fax (830) 896-1150; ed fax (830) 896-1150; gen e-mail kdtnews@dailytimes.com; web site www.dailytimes.com

Published: Mon, Tues, Wed, Thur, Fri, Sun
Weekday Frequency: m
Circulation: 8,327; 10,205(sun)
Last Audit: September 30, 2008
Price: 10.95/mo (carrier), $12.10/mo (mail).
Advertising: Open inch rate $16.30
News services: AP.
Politics: Independent. **Established:** 1910
Not Published: Memorial Day; Labor Day.
Special Editions: Football (Aug); Christmas (Dec); Brides (Mar); Graduation (May); Hunting & Wild Game Guide (Nov); New Car (Oct).
Special Weekly Sections: Religion (Fri); Business (S); Entertainment (Thur); Food (Wed).
Magazines: Real Estate (Monthly); Parade (S); American Profile (Weekly).
Adv. Dir. ....Marie Schwartzkopf
Circ. Dir. ....Jack Parker
Ed. ....Mike Graxiola
Mng. Ed. ....Carlina Villalpando
Photographer ....Tom Holden
Prodn. Mgr., Press ....Jimmie Rios
Market Information: ADS; TMC.
Mechanical available: Offset; Black and 3 ROP colors; insert accepted - 8 x 10 min.; page cutoffs - 22 3/4.
Mechanical Specifications: Type page 11 5/8 x 21 1/2; E - 6 cols, 1 13/16, 1/8 between; A - 6 cols, 1 13/16, 1/8 between; C - 9 cols, 1 1/8, 1/8 between.
Commodity Consumption: Avg. Page Number Per Issue - Daily 20; Avg. Page Number Per Issue - Plates Used 9100; Avg. Page Number Per Issue - Sunday 40; widths 25; Newsprint Used - Metric Tons 770; Printing Ink Used - Black 15000; Printing Ink Used - Color 300; Printing Ink Used -
Equipment EDITORIAL: Front-end Software – Baseview/NewsEdit Pro.; Editorial Hardware – APP/Mac G4; Editorial Equipment – 4-APP/Mac G4, Nikon/Coolscan; Editorial Printers – HP/4M CLASSIFIED: Front-end Software – Baseview/Class Pro.; Classified Hardware – APP/iMac; Layout Software – QPS/QuarkXPress.; Display Hardware – APP/Mac G3, APP/Mac G4; Display Printers – HP/4M; Production Equipment – Anitec/Imagesetter; Cameras – 1-SCREEN/Companica 680C; Scanners – Equipment □ Baseview, QPS/QuarkXPress. PRESSROOM: Line 1 – 6-G/Community single width; Folders – 1-G/SC. MAILROOM: Counter stackers – KAN; Inserters and stuffers – KAN/380; Bundle tying machines – 1-Us/Q, 1-Us/TE, 1/Md.; Business Hardware – Software □ PBC

KILGORE

KILGORE NEWS HERALD

610 E. Main St., Kilgore, Texas, 75662-2612; gen tel (903) 984-2593; adv tel (903) 984-2593; ed tel (903) 984-2593; gen fax (903) 984-7462; adv fax (903) 984-7462; ed fax (903) 984-7462; gen e-mail news@kilgorenews1.com; adv e-mail addirector@kilgorenewsherald.com; ed e-mail knhedit@kilgorenewsherald.com; web site www.kilgorenewsherald.com

Published: Tues, Wed, Thur, Fri, Sun
Weekday Frequency: e
Circulation: 2,954; 3,584(sun)
Last Audit: March 31, 2007
Price: 6.00/mo; 78.00/yr.
Advertising: Open inch rate $9.70
News services: AP.
Politics: Independent.
Not Published: New Year; Memorial Day; Independence Day; Labor Day; Thanksgiving; Christmas.
Special Editions: Spring Savings Spree (Apr); Back-to-School (Aug); Christmas Greetings (Dec); Chamber of Commerce (Feb); Oil & Progress (Jul); Graduation (May); Christmas Gift Guide (Nov).
Special Weekly Sections: Oil Page (S); Best Food Day (Tues).
Magazines: TV Week (S).
Mktg. Mgr. ....Valerie Melton
Adv. Mgr. ....Linda Ballard
Mng. Ed. ....Bill Woodall
Sports Ed. ....Mitch Lucas
Prodn. Foreman, Composing/Press Royce Baxley
Mechanical available: Offset; Black and 3 ROP colors; insert accepted; page cutoffs - 22 3/4.
Mechanical Specifications: Type page 11 1/2 x 21 1/2; E - 6 cols, 2 1/16, 1/8 between; A - 6 cols, 2 1/16, 1/8 between; C - 8 cols, 1 1/2, 1/8 between.
Commodity Consumption: Avg. Page Number Per Issue - Daily 10; Avg. Page Number Per Issue - Plates Used 2910; Avg. Page Number Per Issue - Sunday 34; widths 25; Newsprint Used - Metric Tons 140; Newsprint Used - Short Tons 100; Printing Ink Used - Pages Printed 4410.
Equipment EDITORIAL: Front-end Software – Baseview/NewsEdit Pro, QPS/QuarkXPress.; Editorial Hardware – APP/Mac SE, APP/Power Mac 9600, APP/Mac G3, APP/Mac G4; Editorial Printers – HP/LaserJet 5M, APP/Mac LaserWriter II CLASSIFIED: Front-end Software – Baseview.; Classified Hardware – APP/Mac SE DISPLAY: Ad make-up applications – QPS/QuarkXPress; Layout Software – APP/Mac IIcx.; Display Hardware – APP/Mac PRODUCTION: Pagination Software – QPS/QuarkXPress.; Production Equipment – 1-B/UL 1500, V/ImageSetter 1000; Cameras – Kk/Model 5060 vertical camera; Scanners – Epson/836 PRESSROOM: Line 1 – 5-G/Community; Folders – 1 BUSINESS COMPUTERS: Business Software – Lotus 1-2-3, Microsoft/Windows 3.1, Brainworks; Business Hardware – PC, Brainworks

KILLEEN

KILLEEN DAILY HERALD

1809 Florence Rd., Killeen, Texas, 76541; gen tel (254) 634-2125; adv tel (254) 501-7530; ed tel (254) 501-7540; ed fax (254) 200-7640; gen e-mail kdh@kdhnews.com; web site www.kdhnews.com

Published: Mon, Tues, Wed, Thur, Fri, Sat, Sun
Weekday Frequency: m
Saturday Frequency: m
Circulation: 14,199; 15,920(sat); 19,937(sun)
Last Audit: ABC September 30, 2011
Price: 9.00/mo (home delivery); 116.00/yr (home delivery).
Advertising: Open inch rate $24.93
News services: AP, Landon Media Group.
Politics: Independent-Democrat.
Special Editions: Car Care (Apr); UMHB Sports (Aug); Wrap it Up 2 (Dec); Progressive (Feb); Boat Show (Jan); Mile Maker (Jul); 100 Best (Jun); Design An Ad (Mar); Festival of Flags (May); UCT Birthday (Nov); AUSA (Oct); Medical Directory (Sept).
Special Weekly Sections: Weekender (Fri); TV Book (S); Dollar Saver (Wed).
Magazines: USA WEEKEND Magazine (S).
Pub. ....Sue Mayborn
Gen. Mgr. ....Terry E. Gandy
Bus. Mgr. ....Rodney Sparks
Adv. Mgr. ....Tiffany Muller
Mng. Ed. Olga PeÃ£££Ã££Ã£Â¤a
Asst. Mng. Ed. ....David Miller
Sports Ed. ....Mark Miller
Coord., Telecommun. ....Jason Browne
Market Information: ADS; TMC.
Mechanical available: Offset; Black and 3 ROP colors; insert accepted - subject to publisher's approval; page cutoffs - 22 3/4.
Mechanical Specifications: Type page 13 x 21 1/2; E - 6 cols, 2 1/16, 1/8 between; A - 6 cols, 2 1/16, 1/8 between; C - 9 cols, 1 3/8, 1/16 between.
Commodity Consumption: Avg. Page Number Per Issue - Daily 24; Avg. Page Number Per Issue - Plates Used 42600; Avg. Page Number Per Issue - Saturday 24; Avg. Page Number Per Issue - Sunday 67; widths 27 1/2; Newsprint Used - Short Tons 1395; Printing Ink Used - Black 32160; Pri
Equipment EDITORIAL: Front-end Software – APT.; Editorial Hardware – ALR; Editorial Equipment – Lf/AP Leaf Picture Desk, Lf/Leafscan 35, Linotype-Hell/L 190, Mark/40 EX, SCREEN/Katana 5055; Editorial Printers – GCC/Elite 808 CLASSIFIED: Front-end Software – APT.; Classified Hardware – ALR; Classified Printers – GCC/Elite 808 DISPLAY: Ad make-up applications – APT; Layout Software – APT.; Display Hardware – ALR; Display Printers – GCC/Elite 808 PRODUCTION: Pagination Software – QPS/QuarkXPress, APT.; Production Equipment – Textbridge/Pro, Linotronic/Mark 40EX Postscript, SCREEN/Katana 5055, SCREEN/LD-M1060; Cameras – 1-C/Spartan III; Scanners – 1-Lf, Umax, SCREEN/Cezanne, Nikon/2000 PRESSROOM: Line 1 – 7-G/Urbanite 1978, 3-G/Urbanite 1985. MAILROOM: Counter stackers – 1/HL; Inserters and stuffers – 1-/S; Bundle tying machines – 1-/MLN, 1-/EC; Addressing machine – 2-/St. BUSINESS COMPUTERS: Business Software – MAS 90, AR-2000; Business Hardware – Dell

LAREDO

LAREDO MORNING TIMES

111 Esperanza Dr., Laredo, Texas, 78041-2607; gen tel (956) 728-2500; adv tel (956) 728-2512; ed tel (956) 728-2563; gen fax (956) 723-1227; adv fax (956) 728-2593; ed fax (956) 724-3036; gen e-mail frankesc@lmtonline.com; adv e-mail ads@lmtonline.com; ed e-mail odie@lmtonline.com; web site www.lmtonline.com

Group: Metro Newspaper Advertising Services, Inc.
Published: Mon, Tues, Wed, Thur, Fri, Sat, Sun
Weekday Frequency: m
Saturday Frequency: m
Circulation: 12,303; 13,977(sat); 15,365(sun)
Last Audit: ABC September 30, 2011
Price: 6.00/mo; 91.00/yr.
Advertising: Open inch rate $51.35
News services: AP, LAT-WP, NYT, MCT, HN, CNS.
Politics: Independent.
Special Editions: Fall Fashion (Aug); Washington's Birthday (Feb); Border Olympics (Spring); Border Olympics (Summer).
Special Weekly Sections: Business (S); Food Day (Wed).
Magazines: USA WEEKEND Magazine (S); American Profile (Weekly).
Pub. ....William B. Green
Controller ....Joe Vied
Adv. Mgr. ....Adriana Devally
Photo Dept. Mgr. ....Cuate Santos
Sunday Ed. ....Odie Arambula
Market Information: Split run; TMC; Zoned editions.
Mechanical available: Offset; Black and 3 ROP colors; insert accepted - pocket book size (5 x 7).
Mechanical Specifications: Type page 13 7/8 x 21; E - 6 cols, 2 1/16, 1/8 between; A - 6 cols, 2 1/16, 1/8 between; C - 6 cols, 2 1/16, 1/8 between.
Equipment; Editorial Hardware – AT, 14-IBM/71.; Classified Hardware – M, 3-CRT terminal; Classified Equipment – 4-IBM/71, 1-NCR/memory unit, Dewar; Classified Printers – 1-NCR/Lineprinter.; Production Equipment – 1-Am/450, 2-Am/430, 1-Comp/Set 4510; Cameras – 1-C/Spartan II, 1-VG/320; Scanners – ECR/Autokon 5200. PRESSROOM: Line 1 – 10; Line 2 – 1-Multi-Lith/1250; Folders – 1, 1.; Inserters and stuffers – 1-KAN/501, 1-DG/320; Bundle tying machines – 2-Bu/PAT 27,744; Addressing machine – 1-Am/Class 640, 1-Am/4000.; Business Hardware – 1-NCR/8200

LONGVIEW

LONGVIEW NEWS-JOURNAL

320 E. Methvin St., Longview, Texas, 75601; gen tel (903) 757-3311; adv tel (903) 237-7736; ed tel (903) 237-7744; gen fax (903) 236-3874; adv fax (903) 236-3874; ed fax (903) 757-3742; gen e-mail news-journal@coxnews.com; web site www.news-journal.com

Group: Metro Newspaper Advertising Services,

Inc.
Published: Mon, Tues, Wed, Thur, Fri, Sat, Sun
Weekday Frequency: m
Saturday Frequency: m
Circulation: 24,983; 25,503(sat); 29,799(sun)
Last Audit: September 30, 2009
Price: 11.95/mo (delivery), $18.00/mo (mail); 150.00/yr (delivery, dS), $216.00/yr (mail, dS).
Advertising: Open inch rate $56.97
News services: AP, Cox News Service, NYT, LAT-WP.
Politics: Independent.
Special Weekly Sections: Entertainment (Fri); Your Money (Mon); Business (S); Sports (Sat); Health (Thur); Cyberspace (Tues); Best Food Day (Wed).
Magazines: Parade (S); American Profile (Weekly).
Pub. .... Gary Borders
Adv. Dir. .... Alan Todd
Adv. Mgr., Classified .... Zoie Perry
Circ. Dir. .... Erik Buck
Ed. .... Ana Pecina Walker
Mng. Ed. .... Juan Elizondo
Action Line Ed. .... Jo Lee Ferguson
City Ed. .... Jack Stallard
Editorial Page Ed. .... Pete Litterski
Home Furnishings Ed. .... Charlotte Stewart
Chief Photographer .... Kevin Green
Prodn. Dir. .... Robert Billings
Prodn. Mgr., Mailroom .... Ester Jones
Prodn. Mgr., Post Press .... Terresa Garrison
Prodn. Asst. Mgr. .... Thomas Holder
Prodn. Asst. Mgr. .... Danny Moore
Market Information: TMC.
Mechanical available: Offset; Black and 3 ROP colors; insert accepted - single cards; page cutoffs - 22.
Mechanical Specifications: Type page 11 5/8 x 21; E - 6 cols, 1 5/6, 1/8 between; A - 6 cols, 1 5/6, 1/8 between; C - 9 cols, 1 1/5, 1/16 between.
Commodity Consumption: Avg. Page Number Per Issue - Daily 32; Avg. Page Number Per Issue - Plates Used 28322; Avg. Page Number Per Issue - Sunday 76; widths 12 1/2; Newsprint Used - Short Tons 2586; Printing Ink Used - Black 56118; Printing Ink Used - Color 10404; Printing Ink
Equipment EDITORIAL: Front-end Software – DTI 4.2.; Editorial Hardware – APP/Mac CLASSIFIED: Front-end Software – DTI/ClassSpeed 4.2.; Classified Hardware – DTI; Layout Software – DTI/AdSpeed. PRODUCTION: Pagination Software – DTI 4.2.; Production Equipment – 2-Nat/A-250, 1-Nu/Flip Top FT40, 1-DAI/LD-24AQ; Cameras – 2-C/Spartan III, 1-R/MK 432V; Scanners – 1-Nikon/Slide Scanner, 1-Howtek/Print Scanner, 1-PixelCraft 11 x 17 Scanner, 2-Esko Scan/20245-LWCT Copy Dot Scanner PRESSROOM: Line 1 – 16-DGM/850 single width; Press Drives – 3-Fin/150 h.p.; Folders – 1-DGM/1030, 1-DGM/1050; Pasters – Inkel/2. MAILROOM: Counter stackers – 2-HL/Monitor; Inserters and stuffers – 2-HI/1472; Bundle tying machines – 3-MLN/ML2EE; Addressing machine – 1/Wm, 1-/KR; Other equipment –1-Mc/Stitcher 6 into 1 plus cover.; Business Hardware – HP/9000

LONGVIEW NEWSPAPERS, INC.

320 E. Methvin, Longview, Texas, 75601; gen tel (903) 757-3311; gen fax (903) 236-3874

LUBBOCK

LUBBOCK AVALANCHE-JOURNAL

710 Ave. J, Lubbock, Texas, 79401-1808; gen tel (806) 762-8844; adv tel (806) 766-8616; ed tel (806) 766-8701; gen fax (806) 765-8770; adv fax (806) 765-5826; ed fax (806) 744-9603; web site www.lubbockonline.com
Published: Mon, Tues, Wed, Thur, Fri, Sat, Sun
Weekday Frequency: m
Saturday Frequency: m
Circulation: 34,836; 36,048(sat); 44,425(sun)
Last Audit: ABC September 30, 2011
Price: 13.95/mo; 167.40/yr.
Advertising: Open inch rate $69.95
News services: AP, MCT, LAT-WP.
Politics: Independent.
Special Editions: Medical Directory (Aug); 50 Plus (Fall); Best of Lubbock (Jul); Life in Lubbock (Jun); 50 Plus (Spring); Sharing The Season (Winter).
Special Weekly Sections: Special Entertainment Tab (Fri); Business & Industrial (Mon); TV Magazine (S); Creative Living (Sat); Food (Wed).
Magazines: Relish (Monthly); USA WEEKEND Magazine (S).
Pub. .... Stephen A. Beasley
Div. Controller .... Charlene Harris
Dir., HR .... Shelby Caballero
Adv. Dir., Sales .... Jeff Brown
Adv. Mgr., Classified Sales .... Sarah Kelley
Retail Sales Mgr. .... Kevin Dyer
Dir., Consumer Mktg. .... Julia Childs
Circ. Mgr. .... Brandon Hughes
Circ. Mgr., State .... James Grimmett
Ed. .... Terry Greenberg
Mng. Ed. .... Mel Tittle
Asst. Mng. Ed., News/Features .... Karen Brehm
Asst. Mng. Ed., Sports/Design Courtney Linehan
Bus./Finance Ed. .... Chris Van Wagenen
Editorial Page Ed. .... Joe Hughes
Entertainment Ed. .... Bill Kerns
Editorial Writer/Columnist .... Joe Gulick
Features Ed. .... Shelly Gonzales
News Ed. .... David (Crash) Daniel
Photo Dept. Mgr. .... Zack Long
Market Information: TMC.
Mechanical available: Offset; Black and 3 ROP colors; insert accepted; page cutoffs - 22 7/8.
Mechanical Specifications: Type page 11 5/8 x 21 1/2; E - 4 cols, 1/8 between; A - 6 cols, 1 5/6, 1/8 between; C - 9 cols, between.
Commodity Consumption: Avg. Page Number Per Issue - Daily 44; Avg. Page Number Per Issue - Saturday 74; Avg. Page Number Per Issue - Sunday 88; widths 25; Newsprint Used - Short Tons 7806; Printing Ink Used - Black 301780; Printing Ink Used - Color 54000; Printing Ink Used - P
Equipment; Editorial Hardware – Gateway/2000, Gateway/P5-200, Gateway/G6-233, Gateway/2000, PS-60, 1-APP/Mac SE, 5-APP/Power Mac 8100-80, 1-APP/Mac IIfx, 5-APP/Mac 9100; Editorial Equipment – APP/Mac IIfx, Proteon/LAN, Asanti/Eathernet; Editorial Printers – Toshiba/P351, APP/Mac LaserWriter II, CLASSIFIED: Front-end Software – MPS, DTI.; Classified Hardware – Gateway/2000 G6-233, DTI; Classified Equipment – Proteon/LAN; Classified Printers – Toshiba/P351, 2-Xante, Konica/EV9200 DISPLAY: Ad make-up applications – APP/Mac, Adobe/Photoshop, Multi-Ad/Creator 3.0.1, Adobe/Acrobat, QuarkXpress, Adobe/Illustrator, Adobe/InDesign, Adobe/Distiller; Display Hardware – 4-APP/Power PC 9100; Display Printers – AG/Imager 1000/1500, 2-Xante, Konica/EV9200; Production Equipment – Accuset/1000, Accuset/1500, 2-Xante, Konica/EV9200; Cameras – Epson/1640 XL; Scanners – 1-AG/T2000XL, UMAX, HP/Scanjet. PRESSROOM: Line 1 – 12-G/Metro; Folders – 2; Pasters – G/Automatic. MAILROOM: Counter stackers – 4/T.M.S.I, 2-/H.T.; Inserters and stuffers – 2-GMA/1000 18:2; Bundle tying machines – 4-/Dynamic; Wrapping singles – 2-/Dynaric; Addressing machine – 1-/Ch. BUSINESS COMPUTERS: Business Software – MPS, DTI; Business Hardware – 56-IBM/PC-AT, 1-APP/Mac SE, 1-APP/Mac IIfx, Dell/Optiplex GX270

LUFKIN

THE LUFKIN DAILY NEWS

300 Ellis Ave., Lufkin, Texas, 75904-3817; gen tel (936) 632-6631; adv tel (936) 631-2630; ed tel (936) 631-2623; gen fax (936) 632-6655; adv fax (936) 632-6655; ed fax (936) 632-6655; adv e-mail jcook@lufkindailynews.com; ed e-mail news@lufkindailynews.com; web site www.lufkindailynews.com
Group: Southern Newspapers, Inc.
Published: Mon, Tues, Wed, Thur, Fri, Sat, Sun
Weekday Frequency: m
Saturday Frequency: m
Circulation: 10,804; 10,560(sat); 12,656(sun)
Last Audit: Sworn June 30, 2007
Price: 14.00/mo; 168.00/yr.
Advertising: Open inch rate $27.36
News services: AP.
Politics: Independent.
Advertising not accepted: Y
Own facility?: Y
Special Editions: Parade of Homes (Annually); Back-to-School (Aug); Christmas Shopping Guide (Dec); Progress (Feb); Graduation (May).
Special Weekly Sections: Travel (Fri); Technology (Mon); Lifestyle (S); NASCAR (Sat); Food (Wed).
Magazines: USA Weekend (S); American Profile (Weekly); Athon Sports (Weekly); Relish (Monthly); Spry (Monthly)
Profile: 1907
Pub. .... Greg Shrader
Controller .... Elizabeth Adams
Adv. Dir. .... Jeannie Cook
Adv. Mgr. .... Tammy Kedrowicz
Circ. Dir. .... Jennifer Ricks
Ed. .... Andy Adams
Lifestyles Ed. .... Beverly Johnson
News Ed. .... Jeff Pownall
Photo Ed. .... Joel Andrews
Sports Ed. .... Josh Havard
Data Processing Mgr. .... Renee Guajardo
Opns. Dir. .... Ferris H. Fain
Prodn. Mgr., Mailroom .... Billy Ricks
Prodn. Mgr., Pre Press .... Robin Nevills
Prodn. Foreman, Pressroom .... Steve Reed
Market Information: ADS; TMC.
Mechanical available: Offset; Black and 3 ROP colors; insert accepted; page cutoffs - 22 3/4.
Mechanical Specifications: Type page 11 5/8 x 21; E - 6 cols, 1 5/6, 1/8 between; A - 6 cols, 1 5/6, 1/8 between; C - 9 cols, 1 3/16, 1/8 between.
Commodity Consumption: Avg. Page Number Per Issue - Daily 18; Avg. Page Number Per Issue - Plates Used 25000; Avg. Page Number Per Issue - Sunday 45; widths 25; Newsprint Used - Short Tons 300; Printing Ink Used - Black 47500; Printing Ink Used - Color 7200; Printing Ink Use
Equipment EDITORIAL: Front-end Software – DTI/PageSpeed 4.3.; Editorial Hardware – APP/Mac G3, APP/Mac G4 700; Editorial Equipment – 1-Nikon/RS 3500, Howtek/ScanMaster II, Nikon/Digital Camera; Editorial Printers – HP/8150 CLASSIFIED: Front-end Software – DTI/ClassSpeed 4.2.3.; Classified Hardware – 2-APP/Power Mac 7100-66, APP/Mac G4; Classified Equipment – Kk/DC 120 Digital Camera, APP/Mac One Scanner, HP/ScanJet 4C; Classified Printers – HP/2100 DN DISPLAY: Ad make-up applications – DTI/AdSpeed 4.2; Layout Software – D; Display Hardware – Power Computing/Pro 2001 (Mac Clone), APP/Mac G4; Display Printers – APP/Mac LaserWriter, Epson/Stylus Color 3000, HP/2100N PRODUCTION: Pagination Software – DTI/AdSpeed, DTI/AdPlanner, DTI/ClassSpeed 4.3.; Production Equipment – Konica/JetSetter 6100, Adobe/Photoshop; Cameras – Spartan III; Scanners – Microtek/60025, 1-Nikon/L5-3510 PRESSROOM: Line 1 – 7-G/Urbanite 1979, 1-G/Urbanite (3 color) 1979; Press Drives – 2-Fin/Digital 100 h.p. DC motor; Folders – 1 MAILROOM: Counter stackers – QWI/200; Inserters and stuffers – 2-MM/227S 6:1; Bundle tying machines – 2-MLN/MLI-EE. BUSINESS COMPUTERS: Business Software – DTI, Geac/Vision Shift; Business Hardware – 1-HP/9000, HP/8175S
Zip Codes served: 75901,75904,75941,75949,75969,75980,75925,75976,75944,75937,75939,75929,75926,75845.
Delivery method: Mail, Newsstand, Private Carrier, Racks

MARBLE FALLS

THE RIVER CITIES SUNDAY TRIBUNE

1007 Ave. K, Marble Falls, Texas, 78654; gen tel (830) 693-7152; gen fax (830) 693-3085; ed e-mail editor@thepicayune.com; web site www.dailytrib.com
Published: Tues, Wed, Thur, Fri, Sat
Weekday Frequency: m
Circulation: 3,381; 3,381(sat)
Last Audit: March 31, 2006
Advertising: Open inch rate $6.53
Politics: 1991
Co-Pub. .... Dan Alvey
Co-Pub. .... Lee Alvey
Circ. Mgr. .... Mandy Wyatt
Ed. .... Thomas Edwards
Prodn. Mgr. .... Florence Edwards
Mechanical Specifications: Type page 11 7/8 x 21; E - 6 cols, 1/6 between; A - 6 cols, 1/6 between; C - 6 cols, 1/6 between.
Equipment; Editorial Hardware – APP/Mac.; Layout Software – QPS/QuarkXPress, Multi-Ad/Creator, Adobe/Freehand, Adobe/Illustrator. PRESSROOM: Line 1 – G/Community.

MARSHALL

MARSHALL NEWS MESSENGER

309 E. Austin St., Marshall, Texas, 75670-3475; gen tel (903) 935-7914; adv tel (903) 935-7914; ed tel (903) 935-7914; gen fax (903) 935-6242; adv fax (903) 935-6242; ed fax (903) 935-6242; gen e-mail newsmessenger@coxnews.com; adv e-mail nfriend@coxnews.com; web site www.marshallnewsmessenger.com
Published: Mon, Tues, Wed, Thur, Fri, Sat, Sun
Weekday Frequency: m
Saturday Frequency: m
Circulation: 6,258; 6,258(sat); 6,392(sun)
Last Audit: September 30, 2009
Price: 10.05/mo; 120.60/yr (carrier), $135.00/yr (mail).
Advertising: Open inch rate $22.87
News services: AP.
Politics: Independent.
Advertising not accepted: 900 numbers; Dating services.
Magazines: Parade (S); American Profile (Weekly).
Bus. Mgr. .... Dana Morton
Adv. Mgr. .... Nan Friend
Circ. Dir. .... Rick Bryant
District Mgr. .... Chris Kundtson
Ed. .... Phil Latham
Asst. News Ed. .... D.D. Turner
Features Ed. .... Robin Richardson
Market Information: Split run; TMC.
Mechanical available: Offset; Black and 4 ROP colors; insert accepted - single sheet; page cutoffs - 22 3/4.
Mechanical Specifications: Type page 13 3/4 x 21 1/4; E - 6 cols, 1 5/6, 1/8 between; A - 6 cols, 1 5/6, 1/8 between; C - 9 cols, 1 9/50, 1/8 between.
Equipment EDITORIAL: Front-end Software – Mk/Ace 1.3.2, Mk/NewsTouch AT, QPS/; Editorial Hardware – Mk/4000, APP/Mac IIcx, APP/Mac Quadra 610; Editorial Equipment – APP/Mac Scanner, Lf/LeafScan 35, Lf/AP Leaf Picture Desk; Editorial Printers – TI/Omni 800 line printer, 2-Xante/8200, APP/Mac LaserWriter Plus, V/4990 CLASSIFIED: Front-end Software – DTI/ClassSpeed 1.3.2.; Classified Hardware – APP/iMac; Classified Printers – TI/Omni 800 line printer DISPLAY: Ad make-up applications – Aldus/PageMaker 5.0, Adobe/Illustrator 5.5.; Display Hardware – APP/Mac G4; Display Printers – APP/Mac LaserJet; Production Equipment – 2-APP/Mac Radius, 2-APP/Mac IIcx.; Business Hardware – IBM/PC-AT

MCALLEN

THE MONITOR

1400 E. Nolana Ave., McAllen, Texas, 78504-6111; gen tel (956) 683-4000; adv tel

(956) 971-1875; ed tel (956) 683-4400; gen fax (956) 683-4201; adv fax (956) 683-4101; gen e-mail ads@themonitor.com; web site www.themonitor.com
Published: Mon, Tues, Wed, Thur, Fri, Sat, Sun
Weekday Frequency: m
Saturday Frequency: m
Circulation: 35,595; 32,013(sat); 39,476(sun)
Last Audit: September 30, 2009
Price: 9.50/mo; 126.00/yr (carrier), $180.00/yr (mail).
Advertising: Open inch rate $53.55
News services: AP.
Politics: Independent.
Special Editions: B-T-S (Aug); Gift Guide (Dec); Golden Texan (Feb); Golden Texan (Jan); Bride's Guide (Jun); Golden Texan (Mar); Cinco de Mayo (May); Golden Texan (Nov); Golden Texan (Oct); Football (Sept).
Special Weekly Sections: Religious Directory (Fri); Let's Talk Business (Mon); Automotive Showcase (S); Lifestyle (Wed).
Magazines: Vista (Fri); USA WEEKEND Magazine (S).
Pub. ....Olaf Randsen
Bus. Mgr. ....Jenise Diaz
Adv. Dir. ....Benita Mendell
Adv. Mgr., Classified ....Linda Gonzalez
Adv. Mgr., Retail ....Linda Madrano
Circ. Dir. ....Robert Levrier
Ed. ....Steve Fagan
Asst. Mng. Ed. ....Marcia Caltabiano
Arts/Entertainment Ed ....Nora Garza
Editorial Page Ed. ....Mack Harrison
Features Ed. ....Henry Miller
Asst. Metro Ed. ....David Gragg
Photo Ed. ....Larry Clubb
Sports Ed ....Oscar Gonzales
Data Processing Mgr. ....Jason Arms
Online Mgr. ....Matt Crocker
Prodn. Mgr., Composing/Ad Serv. ....Ernie Cortez
Prodn. Mgr., Mailroom ....Craig Bricker
Prodn. Mgr., Press ....Baldemar Romero
Market Information: ADS.
Mechanical available: Offset; Black and 3 ROP colors; insert accepted - all; page cutoffs - 22 3/4.
Mechanical Specifications: Type page 13 x 21 1/2; E - 6 cols, 2 1/8, 1/6 between; A - 6 cols, 2 1/8, 1/6 between; C - 10 cols, 1 1/6, 1/6 between.
Commodity Consumption: Avg. Page Number Per Issue - Daily 40; Avg. Page Number Per Issue - Plates Used 18000; Avg. Page Number Per Issue - Saturday 40; Avg. Page Number Per Issue - Sunday 100; widths 27 1/2; Newsprint Used - Metric Tons 4440.7; Printing Ink Used - Black 91000;
Equipment EDITORIAL: Front-end Software – APT.; Editorial Hardware – Compaq; Editorial Printers – HP/5000 CLASSIFIED: Front-end Software – APT.; Classified Hardware – Compaq; Classified Printers – HP/4MV DISPLAY: Ad make-up applications – APT.; Display Hardware – Compaq; Display Printers – HP/5000 PRODUCTION: Pagination Software – APT.; Production Equipment – Pre Press/Panther 36, Pre Press/Panther 46; Cameras – C/Spartan III PRESSROOM: Line 1 – 7-HI/845 single width; Line 2 – 7-HI/845 single width; Folders – 2-HI/2:1; Pasters – 8-1993. MAILROOM: Counter stackers – 3/HL; Inserters and stuffers – 1-GMA/SLS 2000 10:2; Bundle tying machines – 2-/MLN, Dynaric; Addressing machine – Other equipment □ 1-MM/Minuteman.; Other equipment –Addressing machine □ Am, El/3101. BUSINESS COMPUTERS: Business Software – Vision Data; Business Hardware – Brainworks/AR Package

MCKINNEY

MCKINNEY COURIER-GAZETTE

1650 W. Virginia St., Ste. 202, McKinney, Texas, 75069-7703; gen tel (972) 542-2631; adv tel (972) 542-2631; ed tel (972) 542-2631; gen fax (972) 529-1684; adv e-mail scarr@acnpapers.com; ed e-mail dsorter@acnpapers.com; web site www.courier-gazette.com
Published: Mon, Tues, Wed, Thur, Fri, Sun
Weekday Frequency: e
Circulation: 4,938; 4,938(sun)
Last Audit: March 31, 2007
Price: 15.00/mo; 75.00/yr.
Advertising: Open inch rate $11.35
News services: AP, NEA.
Politics: Independent.
Not Published: Christmas.
Special Editions: Football (Aug); Christmas (Dec); Progress (Feb); Drug Awareness (Jan); Newcomers (Jul); Spring Fashion (Mar); Thanksgiving (Nov); Health/Fitness (Oct); Fall Fashion (Sept).
Grp. Pub. ....Bill Weaver
Adv. Dir. ....Scott Carr
Circ. Dir. ....Ken McKenen
Mng. Ed. ....Dave Sorter
Sports Ed. ....Jim Donovan
Prodn. Supt. ....David Thornhill
Market Information: TMC.
Mechanical available: Offset; Black and 3 ROP colors; insert accepted; page cutoffs - 22 3/4.
Mechanical Specifications: Type page 13 x 21 1/2; E - 6 cols, 2 1/16, 1/8 between; A - 6 cols, 2 1/16, 1/8 between; C - 8 cols, 1 1/2, 1/8 between.
Commodity Consumption: Avg. Page Number Per Issue - Daily 18; Avg. Page Number Per Issue - Plates Used 8500; Avg. Page Number Per Issue - Sunday 32; widths 27 1/2; Newsprint Used - Short Tons 360; Printing Ink Used - Black 34000; Printing Ink Used - Color 6000; Printing Ink Us
Equipment EDITORIAL: Front-end Software – Baseview/NewsEdit Pro, QPS/QuarkXPress 4.0.; Editorial Hardware – 5-APP/Mac; Editorial Printers – APP/Mac CLASSIFIED: Front-end Software – Baseview/Class Manager.; Classified Hardware – 5-APP/Mac; Classified Printers – APP/Mac DISPLAY: Ad make-up applications – Baseview/Ad Manager Pro; Layout Software – 3-APP/Mac.; Display Hardware – AP/Mac; Display Printers – AP/Mac LaserPrinter PRODUCTION: Pagination Software – QPS/QuarkXPress 4.0.; Production Equipment – 1-LE/24 Q; Cameras – 1-Acti; Scanners – B PRESSROOM: Line 1 – 6-HI/V-15A; Folders – 1-HI. MAILROOM: Counter stackers – 1/BG; Bundle tying machines – 1-/Bu.; Business Hardware – IBM

MEXIA

THE MEXIA DAILY NEWS

214 N. Railroad St., Mexia, Texas, 76667; gen tel (254) 562-2868; gen fax (254) 562-3121; adv e-mail advertising@themexianews.com; ed e-mail mdillin@themexianews.com; web site themexianews.com
Group: Moser Community Media, LP
Published: Tues, Thur, Sat
Weekday Frequency: m
Saturday Frequency: m
Circulation: 2,325; 2,300(sat)
Last Audit: Sworn September 30, 2003
Price: 5.75/mo.
Advertising: Open inch rate $6.75
Insert rate: $58/M
News services: .
Politics: 1899
Not Published: New Year; Memorial Day; Independence Day; Labor Day; Thanksgiving; Christmas.
Own facility?: Y
Special Editions: Letters to Santa (Dec); Wedding (Jan); Western (Jul); Progress (Mar); Graduation (May); Cookbook (Nov); Women (Oct); Football (Sept).
Special Weekly Sections: Best Food Day (Tues).
Magazines: Relish (Monthly); American Profile (Sat).
Publisher ....Mark Henry
Business Manager ....Kim Walpole
Managing Editor ....Michael Dillin
Market Information: TMC.
Mechanical available: Offset; Black and 3 ROP colors; insert accepted; page cutoffs - 21 1/2.
Mechanical Specifications: Type page 11 5/8 x 21 1/2; E - 6 cols, 2 1/16, 1/8 between; A - 6 cols, 2 1/16, 1/8 between; C - 8 cols, 1 1/2, 1/8 between.
Commodity Consumption: Avg. Page Number Per Issue - Daily 12; widths 25.
Equipment; Editorial Hardware – APP/Mac; Editorial Equipment – HP/Scanner IIp; Editorial Printers – APP/Mac LaserWriter CLASSIFIED: Front-end Software – AdPro; Classified Hardware – APP/Mac; Classified Printers – APP/Mac LaserWriter DISPLAY: Ad make-up applications – QPS/QuarkXPress.; Display Hardware – APP/Mac; Display Printers – APP/Mac LaserWriter; Production Equipment – APP/Mac LaserWriter; Cameras – SCREEN/Companica Screen. PRESSROOM: Line 1 – 8 units Goss Community; Inserters and stuffers – 5; Bundle tying machines – Bu; Addressing machine – Wm.
Delivery method: Mail, Newsstand, Private Carrier, Racks

MIDLAND

MIDLAND REPORTER-TELEGRAM

201 E. Illinois St., Midland, Texas, 79701; gen tel (432) 682-5311; adv tel (432) 687-8894; ed tel (432) 687-8855; gen fax (432) 682-6173; adv fax (432) 682-3793; ed fax (432) 570-7650; ed e-mail gott@hearstnp.com; web site www.mywesttexas.com
Published: Mon, Tues, Wed, Thur, Fri, Sat, Sun
Weekday Frequency: m
Saturday Frequency: m
Circulation: 14,464; 16,764(sat); 18,946(sun)
Last Audit: ABC September 30, 2011
Price: 12.00/mo (home delivery); 132.00/yr (home delivery).
Advertising: Open inch rate $27.65
News services: AP, HN, NYT.
Politics: Independent.
Special Editions: Youth Services (Apr); Back-to-School (Aug); Christmas Gift Guide (Dec); Primetime (Every other month); Outlook (Feb); Best of Midland (Jul); Senior Directory (Jun); Spring Home & Garden (Mar); Family Health (Nov); Oil (Oct); Fall Home & Garden (Sept).
Special Weekly Sections: Prime Time (Seniors) (Fri); Money Matters (Mon); Brides/Engagements (S); Church/Religion (Sat); Business & Industry (Tues); Food (Wed).
Magazines: Relish (Monthly); TV Times (S); American Profile (Weekly).
Broadcast Affiliations: KMID-TV (ABC); KOSA-TV (CBS); KPEJ-TV (FOX); KTPX-TV (NBC); KWES-TV (NBC).
Pub. ....Dave Wedel
Adv. Dir. ....Brandy Price
Circ. Mgr. ....Reg Foretaugh
Ed. ....Gary Ott
Mng. Ed. ....Stewart Doreen
City/Metro Ed. ....Shanna Sissom
Entertainment/Amusements Ed. ....Georgia Temple
Lifestyle Ed. ....Mary Dearen
News Ed. ....Missy Hallmark
Oil/Gas Writer ....Mella McEwen
Photo Ed. ....Tim Fischer
Sports Ed. ....Len Heyward
Mgmt. Info Servs. Mgr. ....David T. Wedel
Mgr., Info Systems ....Lynn Kmiec
Online Mgr. ....Nancy Adamson
Prodn. Dir. ....John Maddox
Prodn. Mgr., Mailroom ....Earl Titsworth
Prodn. Mgr., Pressroom ....Jeff Longabaugh
Market Information: TMC.
Mechanical available: Offset; Black and 3 ROP colors; insert accepted - free-standing stock cards, envelope inserts; page cutoffs - 22 3/4.
Mechanical Specifications: Type page 11 1/2 x 21 1/2; E - 6 cols, 1 3/4, 1/6 between; A - 6 cols, 1 3/4, 1/6 between; C - 10 cols, 1 1/10, 1/18 between.
Commodity Consumption: Avg. Page Number Per Issue - Daily 34.8; Avg. Page Number Per Issue - Plates Used 41600; Avg. Page Number Per Issue - Sunday 80.8; widths 50; Newsprint Used - Short Tons 2175; Printing Ink Used - Black 76000; Printing Ink Used - Color 10000; Printing Ink
Equipment EDITORIAL: Front-end Software – Baseview/NewsEdit.; Editorial Hardware – APP/Mac G4; Editorial Printers – APP/Mac LaserWriter NT, Konica, ECR/1045, Lexmark/Optra, Konica/EV Jetsetter 6200 CLASSIFIED: Front-end Software – Baseview/Ad Manager Pro.; Classified Printers – Lexmark/Optra M DISPLAY: Ad make-up applications – QPS/QuarkXPress, Multi-Ad/Creator, Adobe/Photoshop, Macromedia/Freehand; Layout Software – 6-APP; Display Hardware – APP/Mac; Display Printers – APP/Mac LaserPrinter, Tektronix/Phaser 380, V, ECR/1045, Konica/EV Jetsetter 6200, Lexmark/Optra PRODUCTION: Pagination Software – QPS/QuarkXPress 3.32.; Production Equipment – Tektronix/Optra 380, Konica/EV Jetsetter 6200, ECR/1045, Lf/Leafscan 45; Cameras – 1-C/Spartan III; Scanners – Lf/Leafscan 35, Lf/Leafscan 45, HP/ScanJet 6100-C PRESSROOM: Line 1 – 6-HI/1650 double width 1974; Line 2 – 6-G/Community, 2-G/Community Universal Color single width; Line 3 – 2-G/SSC; Folders – 2-HI/2:1, 1; Pasters – Reels and Stands □ 6; Press control system – CH/Drive. MAILROOM: Counter stackers – 3-Id/NS440, 1-QWI/350; Inserters and stuffers – S/48P (9 head); Bundle tying machines – Power Strap/PSM-4, 2-MLN/ML2EE, 1-MLN/2A; Addressing machine – 1-KR/Model 211; Other equipment –1-Gammerter/RS 111/530.; Audio Hardware – APP/Mac G4 BUSINESS COMPUTERS: Business Software – Neasl Weber; Business Hardware – 5-IBM, IBM/AS-400

MINERAL WELLS

MINERAL WELLS INDEX

300 SE First St., Mineral Wells, Texas, 76067; gen tel (940) 325-4465; gen fax (940) 325-2020; ed e-mail editor@mineralwellsindex.com; web site www.mineralwellsindex.com
Published: Tues, Wed, Thur, Fri, Sun
Weekday Frequency: m
Circulation: 3,500; 3,500(sun)
Last Audit: March 31, 2007
Price: 7.50/mo; 84.00/yr.
Advertising: Open inch rate $12.50
News services: AP.
Politics: Independent.
Advertising not accepted: Adoption; 900 numbers.
Not Published: New Year; Memorial Day; Independence Day; Labor Day; Thanksgiving; Christmas.
Special Editions: Back-to-School (Aug); Christmas Gift Guide (Dec); Rodeo (May); Economic Development (Oct); Best of Mineral Wells (Sept).
Magazines: Relish (Monthly); TV Book (S); American Profile (Weekly).
Pub. ....Mel Rhodes
Ed. ....David May
Market Information: ADS; TMC.
Mechanical available: Offset; Black and 3 ROP colors; insert accepted - all; page cutoffs - 22 3/4.
Mechanical Specifications: Type page 13 3/4 x 21 1/2; E - 6 cols, 2, 1/8 between; A - 6 cols, 2, 1/8 between; C - 8 cols, 1 1/2, 1/8 between.
Commodity Consumption: Avg. Page Number Per Issue - Daily 8; Avg. Page Number Per Issue - Plates Used 1500; Avg. Page Number Per Issue - Sunday 16; widths 25; Newsprint Used - Short Tons 110; Printing Ink Used - Black 2400; Printing Ink Used - Color 210; Printing Ink Used - Pa
Equipment EDITORIAL: Front-end Software – Multi-Ad/Creator, QPS/QuarkXPress.; Editorial Hardware – 5-APP/Mac G3; Editorial Printers – GCC/20-800 CLASSIFIED: Front-end Software – QPS/QuarkXPress, Multi-Ad/CAMS.; Classified Hardware – APP/Mac G3; Classified Printers – GCC/20-800 PRESSROOM: Line 1 – 6-G/Community.; Bundle tying machines –

MC/Poly Strapper

MOUNT PLEASANT

MOUNT PLEASANT DAILY TRIBUNE

1705 Industrial Rd., Mount Pleasant, Texas, 75455; gen tel (903) 572-1705; gen fax (903) 572-6026; adv e-mail advertise@dailytribune.net; advertisemp@gmail.com; ed e-mail news@dailytribune.net; web site www.dailytribune.net

Published: Mon, Tues, Wed, Thur, Fri, Sun
Weekday Frequency: e
Circulation: 4,988; 4,988(sun)
Price: 7.50/mo; 90.00/yr.
Advertising: Open inch rate $16.00
News services: AP, NEA.
Politics: Independent.
Advertising not accepted: Fortune tellers; work from home.
Not Published: Christmas.
Special Editions: Progress (Jan); Rodeo (Jun); Graduation (May); Women in Business (Oct); Modern Living (Quarterly); Football (Sept).
Special Weekly Sections: Mid Week (Wed).
Magazines: TV Viewing (Fri); Color Comics (S); American Profile (Weekly).
Office Mgr. ....Sharon Palmer
Adv. Mgr. ....Amy Hinton
Circ. Mgr. ....Larry Belcher
Ed. ..........R.L. Palmer
Mng. Ed. ....Lou Antonelli
Sports Ed. ....Nick Counts
Prodn. Dir. ....Racheal Moss
Market Information: ADS; TMC.
Mechanical available: Offset; Black and 3 ROP colors; insert accepted; page cutoffs - 22 3/4.
Mechanical Specifications: Type page 13 x 21; E - 6 cols, 2 1/16, 1/8 between; A - 6 cols, 2 1/16, 1/8 between; C - 8 cols, 1 9/16, 1/16 between.
Commodity Consumption: Avg. Page Number Per Issue - Daily 20; Avg. Page Number Per Issue - Plates Used 4000; Avg. Page Number Per Issue - Sunday 40; widths 13 1/2; Newsprint Used - Short Tons 400; Printing Ink Used - Pages Printed 6560.
Equipment EDITORIAL: Front-end Software – WordPerfect.; Editorial Hardware – PC; Editorial Printers – APP/Mac LaserWriter CLASSIFIED: Front-end Software – BMF.; Classified Hardware – PC; Classified Printers – APP/Mac LaserWriter DISPLAY: Ad make-up applications – Aldus/PageMaker; Layout Software – APP/Mac.; Display Printers – APP/Mac LaserWriter; Production Equipment – APP/Mac LaserWriter. PRESSROOM: Line 1 – 5-HI/V-15A 1984; Line 2 – 2-HI/V-15A 1993.; Inserters and stuffers – 14-KAN/840; Bundle tying machines – 2/Bu; Addressing machine – 1-/KAN. AUDIO: Audio Software – SMS; Audio Hardware – SMS BUSINESS COMPUTERS: Business Software – BMF; Business Hardware – PC

NACOGDOCHES

THE DAILY SENTINEL

4920 Colonial Dr., Nacogdoches, Texas, 75961; gen tel (936) 564-8361; gen fax (936) 560-4267; ed e-mail kdeluca@coxnews.com; web site www.dailysentinel.com

Published: Mon, Tues, Wed, Thur, Fri, Sat, Sun
Weekday Frequency: m
Saturday Frequency: m
Circulation: 7,621; 7,555(sat); 8,914(sun)
Last Audit: June 30, 2007
Price: 9.25/mo; 120.00/yr (mail), $132.00/yr (home delivery).
Advertising: Open inch rate $18.03
News services: AP.
Politics: Independent.
Special Weekly Sections: Business & Financial Pages (S); Best Food Day (Tues).
Magazines: Parade (S); American Profile (Weekly).
Pres./Gen. Mgr. ....Ferris H. Fain
Bus. Office Mgr. ....Kristi McGuire
Mng. Ed. ....Robbie Goodrich
News Ed. ....Debi Ryan
Asst. News Ed. ....Kendal Rogers
Sports Ed. ....Kevin Gore
Data Processing Mgr. ....Karen Standridge
Market Information: TMC.
Mechanical available: Offset; Black and 3 ROP colors; insert accepted; page cutoffs - 22 3/4.
Mechanical Specifications: Type page 13 x 21 1/4; E - 6 cols, 2 1/16, 1/8 between; A - 6 cols, 2 1/16, 1/8 between; C - 9 cols, 1 5/16, 1/8 between.
Commodity Consumption: Avg. Page Number Per Issue - Daily 17; Avg. Page Number Per Issue - Sunday 51; widths 27; Newsprint Used - Short Tons 459; Printing Ink Used - Pages Printed 8400.
Equipment EDITORIAL: Front-end Software – DTI/PageSpeed.; Editorial Hardware – APP/Mac; Editorial Printers – APP/Mac LaserWriter NTX, HP/4MV LaserJet CLASSIFIED: Front-end Software – DTI/ClassSpeed.; Classified Hardware – Wyse/150ES; Classified Printers – TI/880 DISPLAY: Ad make-up applications – DTI/AdSpeed; Layout Software – DTI/AdSpeed.; Display Hardware – APP/Mac, APP/Mac NTX; Production Equipment – APP/Mac NTX; Cameras – Scanners ÂD Lf/Leafscan.

NEW BRAUNFELS

NEW BRAUNFELS HERALD-ZEITUNG

707 Landa St., New Braunfels, Texas, 78130; gen tel (830) 625-9144; gen fax (830) 625-1224; ed fax (830) 606-3413; gen e-mail news@herald-zeitung.com; ed e-mail news@herald-zeitung.com; web site www.herald-zeitung.com

Published: Tues, Wed, Thur, Fri, Sat, Sun
Weekday Frequency: m
Circulation: 8,057; 8,057(sat); 9,340(sun)
Last Audit: September 30, 2008
Price: 99.00/yr.
Advertising: Open inch rate $13.45
News services: AP.
Politics: Independent.
Special Editions: Medical Tab (Apr); Visitors' Guide (Aug); Babies on Parade (Feb); Chamber Tab (Jan); Visitors' Guide (Jul); Visitors' Guide (Jun); Visitors' Guide (Mar); Small Business (May); Wurstfest Guide (Oct).
Special Weekly Sections: Church Page (Fri); Sunday Comics (S); Best Food Day (Wed).
Magazines: American Profile (Weekly).
Adv. Mgr. ....Andy Tayslon
Circ. Mgr. ....Jeff Fowler
Circ. Asst. Mgr. ....Lee Stahle
Ed. ....Douglas Toney
Mng. Ed. ....Gerard MacCrossan
News Ed. ....Autumn Phillips
Sports Ed. ....Chris Hossman
Prodn. Mgr. ....Henry Coello
Pressroom Supvr. ....Gus Elbel
Market Information: TMC.
Mechanical available: Offset; Black and 3 ROP colors; insert accepted; page cutoffs - 21.
Commodity Consumption: Avg. Page Number Per Issue - Daily 20; Avg. Page Number Per Issue - Plates Used 3502; Avg. Page Number Per Issue - Sunday 42; widths 25; Newsprint Used - Short Tons 550; Printing Ink Used - Pages Printed 7004.
Equipment EDITORIAL: Front-end Software – Microsoft/Word, QPS/QuarkXPress.; Editorial Hardware – APP/Mac G3 CLASSIFIED: Front-end Software – Mk.; Classified Hardware – Mk; Classified Printers – TI DISPLAY: Ad make-up applications – Microsoft/Word, QPS/QuarkXPress 4.1.; Display Printers – 1-APP/Mac LaserPrinter PRODUCTION: Pagination Software – QPS/QuarkXPress.; Production Equipment – 1-Nu; Cameras – R PRESSROOM: Line 1 – G/Community.; Bundle tying machines – Dynaric.; Business Hardware – Software □ Quattro, Microsoft/Word

ODESSA

ODESSA AMERICAN

222 E. 4th St., Odessa, Texas, 79761; gen tel (432) 337-6262; adv tel (432) 333-7602; ed tel (432) 333-7764; gen fax (432) 334-8671; adv fax (432) 334-8641; ed fax (432) 333-7742; gen e-mail oa@link.freedom.com; adv e-mail oa_adv@link.freedom.com; ed e-mail oa@link.freedom.com; web site www.oaoa.com

Group: Metro Newspaper Advertising Services, Inc.
Published: Mon, Tues, Wed, Thur, Fri, Sat, Sun
Weekday Frequency: m
Saturday Frequency: m
Circulation: 16,595; 14,074(sat); 17,207(sun)
Last Audit: ABC September 30, 2011
Price: 11.50/mo; 132.00/yr.
Advertising: Open inch rate $28.89
News services: AP, MCT.
Politics: Independent.
Special Editions: Football (Aug); Auto Preview (Dec); Father's Day (Jun); Mother's Day (May); Oil Show (Oct); Seniors (Quarterly).
Special Weekly Sections: Ticket (Fri); Business Weekly (Mon); Lifestyle (S); Real Estate & Home Showcase (Sat); Auto Market (Thur); Best Food Day (Wed).
Magazines: Parade (S).
Broadcast Affiliations: KWES; KPEJ; KMID; KOSA.
Pub. ....Patrick Canty
Bus. Mgr. ....Frances Irvine
Adv./Mktg. Dir. ....Stacey Ream
Adv. Mgr., Classified ....Angie Fuentes
Circ. Dir. ....Linda Barron-Fury
Editorial Page Ed. ....Ken Brodnax
News Ed. ....Ben Adams
Photo Dept. Mgr. ....Mark Sterkel
Sports Ed. ....Chris Gove
Travel Ed. ....Laura Dennis
Prodn. Dir. ....Bob Braswell
Prodn. Foreman, Mailroom ....Gary Hesson
Market Information: ADS; Split run; TMC.
Mechanical available: Offset; Black and 3 ROP colors; insert accepted; page cutoffs - 22 3/4.
Mechanical Specifications: Type page 11 1/2 x 21 1/2; E - 6 cols, 1 25/32, 1/12 between; A - 6 cols, 1 25/32, 1/12 between; C - 9 cols, 1 3/16, 1/12 between.
Commodity Consumption: Avg. Page Number Per Issue - Daily 32; Avg. Page Number Per Issue - Plates Used 43669; Avg. Page Number Per Issue - Saturday 42; Avg. Page Number Per Issue - Sunday 80; widths 12 1/2; Newsprint Used - Metric Tons 2412; Printing Ink Used - Black 56269; Pr
Equipment EDITORIAL: Front-end Software – Microsoft/Word 7.0, QPS/QuarkXPress 4.0, APT/ACT.; Editorial Hardware – Compaq/Pentium 350mhz; Editorial Printers – HP/8100 CLASSIFIED: Front-end Software – Microsoft/Word 7.0, QPS/QuarkXPress 4.0, APT/ACT.; Classified Hardware – Compaq/Pentium 350mhz; Classified Printers – QMS/2060 DISPLAY: Ad make-up applications – QPS/QuarkXPress, Adobe/Illustrator, Adobe/Photoshop; Layout Software – Microsoft/Windows NT, QPS/QuarkXPress, Adobe/Indesign.; Display Hardware – Dell/Pentium 800 mhz; Display Printers – QMS/2060, ECR/VR 36, Konica/VRL4550 PRODUCTION: Pagination Software – APT/ACT.; Production Equipment – ECR/VR 36, ECR/VR 36, Konica/VRL 4550; Cameras – C/Spartan II; Scanners – Umax/Powerlook PRESSROOM: Line 1 – 6-HI/1650 double width 1976; Press Drives – 2-CH/150 HP; Folders – 2-HI/2:1; Pasters – MEG/Flying. MAILROOM: Counter stackers – QWI; Inserters and stuffers – 1-GMA/SLS 1000A 8:1; Bundle tying machines – 2-Dynaric/NP 1500; Other equipment –MM/Minuteman 1509 Saddle Stitcher. BUSINESS COMPUTERS: Business Software – Great Plains, AR2000, Vision Data; Business Hardware – 1-Compaq/Proliant

ORANGE

THE ORANGE LEADER

841B DalSasso Dr., Orange, Texas, 77630; gen tel (409) 883-3571; gen fax (409) 883-6342; adv e-mail advertising@orangeleader.com; ed e-mail editorial@orangeleader.com; web site www.orangeleader.com

Published: Mon, Tues, Wed, Thur, Fri, Sat, Sun
Weekday Frequency: m
Saturday Frequency: m
Circulation: 3,695; 3,695(sat); 4,084(sun)
Last Audit: September 30, 2009
Price: 9.75/mo; 117.00/yr.
Advertising: Open inch rate $17.38
News services: AP.
Politics: Independent. **Established:** 1875
Special Editions: Home Improvement (Apr); Football (Aug); Last Minute Gifts (Dec); Chamber of Commerce Report (Jan); Meet your Neighbor (Jul); Health Care (Jun); Tax Tab (Mar); Gumbo Cook-off (May); Homes (Monthly); Holiday Cookbook (Nov); Rodeo (Oct); Hunting & Fishing Gu
Special Weekly Sections: Outdoors Page (Thur).
Magazines: Relish (Monthly); American Profile (Other); USA WEEKEND Magazine (S).
Pub. ....Eric Bauer
Circ. Dir. ....Glenda Bland
Ed. ....Gabe Prewertt
Data Processing Mgr. ....Ron Harris
Market Information: TMC.
Mechanical available: Offset; Black and 3 ROP colors; insert accepted - all; page cutoffs - 22 3/4.
Mechanical Specifications: Type page 11 5/8 x 21 1/2; E - 6 cols, 1 13/16, 1/8 between; A - 6 cols, 1 13/16, 1/8 between; C - 9 cols, 1 13/16, 1/8 between.
Commodity Consumption: Avg. Page Number Per Issue - Daily 16; Avg. Page Number Per Issue - Sunday 36; widths 25; Newsprint Used - Short Tons 440; Printing Ink Used - Black 13716; Printing Ink Used - Color 3904; Printing Ink Used - Pages Printed 6900.
Equipment EDITORIAL: Front-end Software – Baseview, QPS/QuarkXPress.; Editorial Hardware – APP/Mac; Editorial Printers – APP/Mac Laser CLASSIFIED: Front-end Software – Baseview.; Classified Hardware – APP/Mac DISPLAY: Ad make-up applications – Multi-Ad, QPS/QuarkXPress, Ofoto, Caere/OmniPage; Layout Software – APP/Mac.; Display Hardware – APP/Mac, APP/Mac II NTX; Production Equipment – Caere/OmniPage 8, Lf/AP Leaf Picture Desk, APP/Mac; Cameras – C/500. PRESSROOM: Line 1 – G/Urbanite 64 (single width); Folders – 1; Reels and Stands – 2 MAILROOM: Counter stackers – BG/105; Inserters and stuffers – 4-MM/227E; Bundle tying machines – MLN/L-2; Other equipment –MM/Stitcher-Trimmer. BUSINESS COMPUTERS: Business Software – SMS/Stauffer; Business Hardware – ATT

PALESTINE

PALESTINE HERALD-PRESS

519 Elm St., Palestine, Texas, 75801; gen tel (903) 729-0281; gen fax (903) 729-0284; adv fax (903) 729-1057; gen e-mail community@palestineherald.com; ed e-mail editor@palestineherald.com; web site www.palestineherald.com

Published: Tues, Wed, Thur, Fri, Sun
Weekday Frequency: m
Saturday Frequency: m
Circulation: 5,013; 6,200(sun)
Price: $8.75/mth; $105/yr
Advertising: Open inch rate $10.30
News services: AP.
Not Published: Monday and Saturday
Own facility?: Y
Special Editions: Graduation - May
Holiday Gift Guide - November
OctoberFest -October
Special Weekly Sections: Entertainment (Fri); Community (S); Weekend (Sat); Best Food Day (Tues); Community (Wed).
Magazines: American Profile (Weekly).

Parade
Pub.....................Gary Connor
Bus. Mgr.....................Liz Falesch
Circ. Mgr.....................Candy Facklaeo
Mng. Ed.....................Angie Alvardo
Features Ed.....................Cheril Vermon
Sports Ed.....................Scott Tyler
Prodn. Mgr.....................Jim Buckley
Market Information: TMC.
Mechanical available: Offset; Black and 3 ROP colors; insert accepted; page cutoffs - 22 1/2.
Mechanical Specifications: Type page 13 x 21 1/2; E - 6 cols, 2 1/16, 1/8 between; A - 6 cols, 2 1/16, 1/8 between; C - 9 cols, 1 3/8, 1/8 between.
Commodity Consumption: Avg. Page Number Per Issue - Daily 16; Avg. Page Number Per Issue - Plates Used 9100; Avg. Page Number Per Issue - Sunday 40; widths 11; Newsprint Used - Short Tons 550; Printing Ink Used - Black 15104; Printing Ink Used - Color 563; Printing Ink Used -
Equipment EDITORIAL: Front-end Software – Baseview, QPS/QuarkX; Editorial Hardware – 2-Ethernet/10T Hub, 6-APP/Mac Yosemite G3, 4-APP/Mac Quadra 800, APP/Mac Apple share IP Manager; Editorial Equipment – LE/2100 Rapid Access Processor, Glunz & Jensen/720 Processor; Editorial Printers – 2-APP/Mac LaserWriter Pro 630 CLASSIFIED: Front-end Software – Baseview.; Classified Hardware – 2-APP/iMac; Classified Printers – Okidata/Microline 320 DISPLAY: Ad make-up applications – QPS/QuarkXPress 4.0, Multi-Ad/Creator, Adobe/Photoshop; Layout Software – Baseview/Ad Force, APP/Power Mac 8100/100.; Display Hardware – 2-APP/Mac Yosemite G3, APP/Power Mac 7350/180 PRODUCTION: Pagination Software – Baseview/NewsEdit Pro IQue 3.2.1, QPS/QuarkXPress 4.02.; Production Equipment – 1-Nu, Pre Press/Panther Plus VR Imagesetter; Cameras – B; Scanners – 2-Microtek/II XE, 2-Pre Press/Panther Plus RIP (1-VR & 1-IR), Microtek/Scanmaker 6400 XL PRESSROOM: Line 1 – 7-HI/V-15A 1973; Line 2 – 8-HI/V-15A 1999; Press Drives – 75hp and 60 hp; Bundle tying machines – Bu. BUSINESS COMPUTERS: Business Software – CJ; Business Hardware – 1-HP/3700
Delivery method: Mail

PAMPA

THE PAMPA NEWS

403 W. Atchison St., Pampa, Texas, 79065-6303; gen tel (806) 669-2525; adv tel (806) 669-2525; ed tel (806) 669-2525; gen fax (806) 669-2520; adv fax (806) 669-2520; ed fax (806) 669-2520; gen e-mail rpribble@thepampanews.com; adv e-mail rwoods@thepampanews.com & spribble@thepampanews.com; ed e-mail editor@thepampanews.com; web site www.thepampanews.com
Published: Mon, Tues, Wed, Thur, Fri, Sat
Weekday Frequency: m
Saturday Frequency: m
Circulation: 4,100; 4,100(sat)
Last Audit: Sworn March 31, 2007
Price: $114 per year
Advertising: Open inch rate $12.35
Insert rate: $75M
News services: AP.
Politics: Independent. **Established:** circa 1921
Advertising not accepted: Y
Not Published: New Years Day; Independence Day; Christmas Day, Memorial Day, Presidents Day, Columbus Day, Thanksgiving Day,
Own facility?: Y
Special Editions: Christmas Greetings/Letters to Santa
Gray County Visitor's Guide
Pride and Progress
Football Guide
Area Dining Guide
Gray County Church Directory
Magazines: Gray County Visitor's Guide (Annually).
Publisher....................Randall Pribble
Advertising Representative....................Sue Pribble
Advertising Manager....................ReDonn Woods
Classified Sale Representative....................Beverly Taylor
Managing Editor....................Arnie Aurellano
Mechanical available: Offset; Black and 3 ROP colors; insert accepted; page cutoffs - 21 1/2.
Mechanical Specifications: Type page 10 3/8 x 21; E - 6 cols, 1 5/8, 1/8 between; A - 6 cols, 1 5/8, 1/8 between; C - 9 cols, 1 1/16, 1/16 between.
Commodity Consumption: Avg. Page Number Per Issue - 12Plates Used 7200; widths 27 1/2; Newsprint Used - Metric Tons 214; Printing Ink Used - Black 5400; Printing Ink Used - Color 174; Printing Ink Used - Pages Printed 5500.
Equipment; Production Equipment – APP/Mac, Pre Press/Panther PRESSROOM: Line 1 – 6-G/Suburban.; Bundle tying machines – 1/Bu; Addressing machine – 1-/Dispensa-Matic (computer labels).
Zip Codes served: 79065
Delivery method: Mail, Newsstand, Racks

PARIS

THE PARIS NEWS

5050 SE Loop 286, Paris, Texas, 75460; gen tel (903) 785-8744; adv tel (903) 785-8744; ed tel (903) 785-8744; gen fax (903) 785-1263; adv fax (903) 785-1263; ed fax (903) 785-1263; gen e-mail editor@theparisnews.com; adv e-mail ads@theparisnews.com; ed e-mail editor@theparisnews.com; web site www.theparisnews.com
Published: Mon, Tues, Wed, Thur, Fri, Sun
Weekday Frequency: e
Circulation: 8,607; 9,968(sun)
Last Audit: September 30, 2008
Price: 9.75/mo; 129.00/yr (carrier & mail).
Advertising: Open inch rate $18.00
News services: AP.
Politics: Independent.
Special Editions: Brides (Apr); Newcomer's Guide (Aug); Greetings (Dec); Home Furnishings (Feb); Quarterly Farm & Ranch Review (Jun); Quarterly Farm & Ranch Review (Mar); Progress (May); Car Care (Nov); New Car (Oct); Football (Sept).
Special Weekly Sections: Religion Pages (Fri); Lifestyle (S); Outdoor Page (Thur); Farm Page (Wed).
Magazines: TV & Entertainment Guide (Fri); Parade (S).
Bus. Mgr.....................Relan Walker
Adv. Dir.....................Mel Parker
Circ. Mgr.....................Scott Baendy
Ed.....................Patrick Graham
Online Ed.....................Mary Madewell
Sports Ed.....................Van Hilburn
Prodn. Mgr., Mailroom....................Tammy Barnes
Prodn. Mgr., Pressroom....................Fred Downs
Market Information: ADS; TMC.
Mechanical available: Offset; Black and 3 ROP colors; insert accepted - standard; page cutoffs - 21 1/2.
Mechanical Specifications: Type page 11 5/8 x 21 1/2; E - 6 cols, 2 5/8, 1/8 between; A - 6 cols, 2 5/8, 1/8 between; C - 9 cols, 1 3/8, 1/8 between.
Commodity Consumption: Avg. Page Number Per Issue - Daily 18; Avg. Page Number Per Issue - Plates Used 9120; Avg. Page Number Per Issue - Sunday 40; widths 25; Newsprint Used - Short Tons 800; Printing Ink Used - Black 15000; Printing Ink Used - Color 4000; Printing Ink Used -
Equipment EDITORIAL: Front-end Software – QPS/QuarkXPress, Baseview/NewsEdit.; Editorial Hardware – APP/Mac; Editorial Equipment – AG/Accuset 1000, Microtek/ScanMaker III, Polaroid/SprintScan; Editorial Printers – APP/Mac LaserWriter CLASSIFIED: Front-end Software – Baseview.; Classified Hardware – APP/Mac; Classified Printers – APP/Mac LaserWriter II NTX DISPLAY: Ad make-up applications – Multi-Ad/Creator; Layout Software – APP/Mac.; Display Hardware – APP/Mac; Display Printers – APP/Mac LaserWriter Pro 630, APP/Mac LaserWriter 1600-600 PRODUCTION: Pagination Software – QPS/QuarkXPress 3.32.; Production Equipment – Caere/OmniPage Pro, AG/Accuset 1000, APP/Mac LaserWriter 1600-600; Cameras – LE, R/500; Scanners – Microtek/ScanMaker III, Microtek/ScanMaker II, Polaroid/SprintScan PRESSROOM: Line 1 – 8-G/Community 1974.; Inserters and stuffers – 5-KAN/320; Bundle tying machines – MLN/ML2 Et; Addressing machine – Uarco/4930. BUSINESS COMPUTERS: Business Software – Netware, Circ; Business Hardware – 1-Compaq/Proliant 1600, 5-HP/Vectra VL2

PASADENA

PASADENA CITIZEN

102 S. Shaver St., Pasadena, Texas, 77506; gen tel (713) 477-0221; adv tel (713) 477-0221; ed tel (713) 477-0221; gen fax (713) 477-9090; adv fax (713) 477-9090; ed fax (713) 477-4172; gen e-mail pasadenacitizen@hcnonline.com; web site www.thepasadenacitizen.com
Group: U.S. Suburban Press, Inc.
Published: Tues, Wed, Thur, Fri, Sun
Weekday Frequency: m
Circulation: 4,472; 4,363(sun)
Last Audit: September 30, 2006
Price: 5.95/mo; 72.00/yr.
Advertising: Open inch rate $24.52
News services: NEA, AP.
Politics: Independent.
Special Editions: Christmas (Dec); Progress (Feb); Baseball (Jul); Drug Awareness (Oct); Rodeo (Sept).
Magazines: American Profile (Weekly).
Controller....................Glenda Hicks
Adv. Dir.....................Dan Tomlison
Circ. Dir.....................Rick Flores
Mng. Ed.....................David Taylor
Sports Ed.....................Robert Avery
Data Processing Mgr.....................David Moran
Prodn. Mgr., Pre Press....................Steve Holder
Market Information: Split run; TMC; Zoned editions.
Mechanical available: Offset; Black and 3 ROP colors; insert accepted; page cutoffs - 22 3/4.
Mechanical Specifications: Type page 11 1/2 x 21 1/2; E - 6 cols, 2, 1/6 between; A - 6 cols, 2, 1/6 between; C - 10 cols, 1 1/8, 1/6 between.
Commodity Consumption: Avg. Page Number Per Issue - Daily 14; Avg. Page Number Per Issue - Plates Used 32000; Avg. Page Number Per Issue - Sunday 24; widths 30; Newsprint Used - Short Tons 3400; Printing Ink Used - Black 48000; Printing Ink Used - Color 20000; Printing Ink Use
Equipment EDITORIAL: Front-end Software – Microsoft/Word, QPS/QuarkXPress.; Editorial Hardware – APP/Mac; Editorial Printers – APP/Mac, HP/LaserJet; Classified Printers – HP/LaserJet. DISPLAY: Ad make-up applications – QPS/QuarkXPress; Layout Software – APP/Mac.; Display Hardware – APP/Mac; Display Printers – HP/LaserJet; Production Equipment – TI/Laser; Cameras – 1-Argyle/24, 1-Opti/30; Scanners – Microtek/MS II. PRESSROOM: Line 1 – 18-G/Urbanite; Line 2 – 14-G/Community; Folders – 1 MAILROOM: Counter stackers – 1-BG/105, 1-Id; Bundle tying machines – 2/MLN, 1-/Strapack; Addressing machine – 1-/C. BUSINESS COMPUTERS: Business Software – BMF; Business Hardware – PC

PLAINVIEW

THE HEARST CORP. PLAINVIEW DAILY HERALD DIVISION

820 Broadway, Plainview, Texas, 79072; gen tel (806) 296-1300; gen fax (806) 296-1315

PLAINVIEW HERALD

820 Broadway, Plainview, Texas, 79072-7316; gen tel (806) 296-1340; adv tel (806) 296-1320; ed tel (806) 296-1350; gen fax (806) 296-1315; adv fax (806) 296-1315; gen e-mail saven@hearstnp.com; adv e-mail vramsower@plainviewdailyherald.com; ed e-mail Klewis@hearstnp.com; web site www.myplainview.com
Group: Hearst
Published: Tues, Wed, Thur, Fri, Sun
Weekday Frequency: e
Circulation: 5,000; 6,000(sun)
Last Audit: Sworn September 28, 2003
Price: 11.75/mo
Advertising: Open inch rate $17.85
News services: AP, HN, NYT.
Politics: Independent. **Established:** 1889
Advertising not accepted: Y
Not Published: Christmas, Monday, Saturday
Own facility?: Y
Special Editions: Back-to-School (Aug); Honor Roll (Mar).
Special Weekly Sections: Church (Fri); Business & Industrial Review (Mon); Business (S); Best Food Day (Tues); Agriculture (Wed).
Magazines: Relish (Monthly); Parade (S); American Profile (Weekly).
Pub.....................Sandra Aven
Adv. Mgr., Retail....................Vernah Ramsower
Editorial Page Ed.....................Kevin Lewis
Lifestyle Ed.....................Nicki Logan
News/Wire Ed.....................Doug McDonough
Online Mgr.....................Jason Johnson
Prodn. Mgr., Mailroom....................Charles Lawson
Prodn. Foreman, Pressroom....................Bill Rushing
Prodn. Supvr., Pre Press....................Carol McGill
Market Information: SMC.
Mechanical available: Offset; Black and 3 ROP colors; insert accepted; page cutoffs - 21 1 you/2.
Commodity Consumption: Avg. Page Number Per Issue - Daily 11; Avg. Page Number Per Issue - Sunday 34; widths 25; Newsprint Used - Short Tons 599; Printing Ink Used - Pages Printed 4516.
Equipment CLASSIFIED: Front-end Software – FSI. PRESSROOM: Line 1 – 7-HI/V-15A 1975; Folders – 1, HI/JF-25.; Inserters and stuffers – 1-KAN/480; Bundle tying machines – Md/1862.
Delivery method: Mail, Newsstand, Private Carrier, Racks

PLANO

PLANO STAR COURIER

624 Krona Dr., Ste. 170, Plano, Texas, 75074; gen tel (972) 424-6565; gen fax (972) 398-4470; web site www.scntx.com
Group: U.S. Suburban Press, Inc.
Published: Thur, Sun
Weekday Frequency: m
Circulation: 1,415; 1,497(sun)
Last Audit: Sworn March 31, 2007
Price: 8.00/mo; 85.00/yr.
Advertising: Open inch rate $19.23
News services: AP.
Politics: Independent.
Special Weekly Sections: Health (Fri); Real Estate (S); Working (Sat); Arts (Thur); Working (Wed).
Magazines: USA WEEKEND Magazine (S).
Pres./Pub.....................Bill Weavers
CFO....................Dave Kosossky
Adv. Dir., Retail....................Scott Carr
Adv. Mgr., Classified....................Gina Burkhart
Circ. Mgr.....................Lorenzo Vigliante
Mng. Ed.....................Rick Mann
Prodn. Dir.....................Randy Loyd
Prodn. Dir., Pre Press....................Dennis Easily
Market Information: TMC.
Mechanical available: Offset; Black and 3 ROP colors; insert accepted - pre-packed; page cutoffs - 22 1/2.
Mechanical Specifications: Type page 12 1/2 x 21; E - 6 cols, 2 1/16, 1/8 between; A - 6 cols, 2 1/16, 1/8 between; C - 6 cols, 2 1/16, 1/8 between.
Commodity Consumption: Avg. Page Number Per Issue - Daily 28; Avg. Page Number Per

Issue - Plates Used 80000; Avg. Page Number Per Issue - Sunday 56; widths 13 1/2; Newsprint Used - Short Tons 2253; Printing Ink Used - Black 45000; Printing Ink Used - Color 9000; Printing Ink

Equipment EDITORIAL: Front-end Software – Mk.; Editorial Hardware – Mk/4000; Editorial Equipment – Pre Press/Panther Imagesetter; Editorial Printers – Pre Press/Panther RIP Station CLASSIFIED: Front-end Software – CText.; Classified Hardware – CText; Classified Equipment – APP/Macs; Classified Printers – Pre Press/Panther Pro Imagesetter DISPLAY: Ad make-up applications – CJ; Layout Software – CJ.; Display Hardware – HP/3000 series 58; Display Printers – HP/2566, 3-HP/2563, 1-HP/2564, 1-Dataproducts/B1000 PRODUCTION: Pagination Software – QPS/QuarkXPress, Adobe/Photoshop.; Production Equipment – Pre Press/Panther Pro Imagesetter PRESSROOM: Line 1 – 5-G/Urbanite (1 3-color unit) 1987. MAILROOM: Counter stackers – HL; Inserters and stuffers – KAN; Bundle tying machines – Miller-Bevco. BUSINESS COMPUTERS: Business Software – CJ/AIM, IDEAS; Business Hardware – 2-HP/Vectra

PORT ARTHUR

PORT ARTHUR NEWS

3501 Turtle Creek Dr., Port Arthur, Texas, 77642; gen tel (409) 721-2400; ed fax (409) 724-6849; gen e-mail panews@panews.com; adv e-mail classads@panews.com; ed e-mail panews@panews.com; web site www.panews.com

Published: Mon, Tues, Wed, Thur, Fri, Sat, Sun
Weekday Frequency: m
Saturday Frequency: m
Circulation: 10,223; 10,343(sat); 11,063(sun)
Last Audit: ABC September 30, 2011
Price: 9.00/mo (carrier); 108.00/yr (delivery), $168.00/yr (mail).
Advertising: Open inch rate $31.25
News services: AP.
Politics: Independent. **Established:** 1897
Special Editions: Family-Owned Business (Jan); Visitor's Guide (May); Cav-oil-cade (Oct).
Magazines: American Profile (Fri); Relish (Monthly); USA WEEKEND Magazine (S).
Pub. ....Roger Underwood
Bus. Mgr. ....Jeree Powell
Adv. Dir. ....Merle Hebert
Editorial Page Ed. ....Roger Cowles
Life/Entertainment Ed. ..Darragh Doiron Castillo
Sports Ed. ....Bob West
Mechanical available: Offset; Black and 3 ROP colors; insert accepted - news color; page cutoffs - 22 3/4.
Mechanical Specifications: Type page 11 5/8 x 21 1/2; E - 6 cols, 1 5/6, 1/8 between; A - 6 cols, 1 5/6, 1/8 between; C - 9 cols, 1 3/16, 1/16 between.
Commodity Consumption: Avg. Page Number Per Issue - Daily 22; Avg. Page Number Per Issue - Plates Used 27160; Avg. Page Number Per Issue - Sunday 48; widths 13 1/2; Newsprint Used - Short Tons 3100; Printing Ink Used - Black 60200; Printing Ink Used - Color 45570; Printing Ink
Equipment EDITORIAL: Front-end Software – Baseview.; Editorial Hardware – APP/Mac, 1-APP/Mac; Editorial Printers – 1-APP/Mac Laser-Printer, Imagesetters/1270 Resolution CLASSIFIED: Front-end Software – Baseview.; Classified Hardware – APP/Mac; Classified Printers – APP/Mac LaserWriter DISPLAY: Ad make-up applications – Multi-Ad, QPS/QuarkXPress; Layout Software – 8-APP/Mac G3.; Display Hardware – APP/Mac; Display Printers – Imagesetters PRODUCTION: Pagination Software – QPS/QuarkXPress.; Production Equipment – Laser Red/460 HS Imagesetters, 1-Nu/Flip Top FT40V4UPNS, 2-Douthitt; Cameras – 1-C/Spartan II, 1-C/Spartan III; Scanners – Microteks PRESSROOM: Line 1 – 6-G/Urbanite (3 color); Line 2 – 4-G/Urbanite (balloon former); Press Drives – 2-HP/100; Folders – 2-G/2:1; Reels and Stands – G. MAILROOM: Counter stackers – 2/BG, 1-/HL; Inserters and stuffers – 2-MM/227; Bundle tying machines – 2-MLN/ML2EE, 1-MLN/2AHS; Addressing machine – 1-/CH; Other equipment –1-MM/Stitcher.; Business Hardware – PBS

ROSENBERG

FORT BEND HERALD

1902 4th St., Rosenberg, Texas, 77471-5140; gen tel (281) 342-4474; gen fax (281) 342-3219; gen e-mail newsroom@fbherald.com; web site www.fbherald.com

Group: Hartman Newspapers, L.P.
Published: Mon, Tues, Wed, Thur, Fri, Sun
Weekday Frequency: e
Circulation: 7,003; 7,450(sun)
Last Audit: Sworn December 31, 2006
Price: 8.00/mo; 86.40/yr (home delivery).
Advertising: Open inch rate $13.70
News services: AP.
Politics: Independent.
Not Published: Christmas.
Magazines: Relish (Monthly); American Profile (Weekly).
Pub. ....Stanley Woody
Pres. ....Clyde C. King
General Manager ....Lee Hartman
Circ. Mgr. ....Jim Ellis
News Ed. ....Jeff Osborne
Online Ed. ....Chris Sansone
Sports Ed. ....Gary Martin
Advertising Director ....Dennis Garrison
Living/Lifestyle Ed. ....B.J. Pollock
Prodn. Mgr. ....Stephanie Welch
Prodn. Mgr., Pre Press ....Estevan Nevarez
Prodn. Mgr., Pressroom ....Louis Moody
Market Information: TMC.
Mechanical available: Offset; Black and 3 ROP colors; insert accepted; page cutoffs - 22 3/4.
Mechanical Specifications: Type page 13 x 21; E - 6 cols, 2, 1/6 between; A - 6 cols, 2, 1/6 between; C - 9 cols, 1 1/5, 1/12 between.
Commodity Consumption: Avg. Page Number Per Issue - Daily 12; Avg. Page Number Per Issue - Sunday 22; widths 27 1/2; Newsprint Used - Short Tons 1100.
Equipment EDITORIAL: Front-end Software – Baseview.; Editorial Hardware – APP/Mac; Editorial Equipment – HP/Flatbed Scanner; Editorial Printers – ECR/Scriptsetter CLASSIFIED: Front-end Software – Baseview.; Classified Hardware – Macintosh; Classified Printers – ECR/Scriptsetter, HP/LaserJet 4V DISPLAY: Ad make-up applications – Adobe Creative Suite; Display Hardware – Macintosh; Display Printers – Xerox PRESSROOM: Line 1 – WPC/Atlas-Leader single width 1992; Line 2 – WPC/Atlas-Leader single width 1992.; Bundle tying machines – Wilton/Strap Pack SS-80. BUSINESS COMPUTERS: Business Software – Ad Manager Pro; Business Hardware – Macintosh

HARTMAN NEWSPAPERS LP

1914 Fourth St., Rosenberg, Texas, 77471-1390; gen tel (281) 342-8691; gen fax (281) 342-6968

Politics: 1974
Chrmn. ....J. William Hartman
Pres. ....Clyde C. King
Vice Chairman ....Fred B. Hartman

SAN ANGELO

SAN ANGELO STANDARD-TIMES

34 W. Harris St., San Angelo, Texas, 76903; gen tel (325) 653-1221; gen fax (325) 659-8171; adv fax (325) 659-8172; ed fax (325) 659-8173; web site www.gofiniancial.com

Group: Metro Newspaper Advertising Services, Inc.
Published: Mon, Tues, Wed, Thur, Fri, Sat, Sun
Weekday Frequency: m
Saturday Frequency: m
Circulation: 18,129; 20,926(sat); 21,657(sun)
Last Audit: ABC September 30, 2011
Price: 14.95/mo; 179.40/yr.
Advertising: Open inch rate $44.79
News services: AP, SHNS.
Politics: Independent.
Special Editions: San Angelo Living (Other).
Special Weekly Sections: Entertainment (Fri); TV Book (S); Best Food Day (Wed).
Magazines: Scene (local news weekly, broadsheet) (Other); Parade (S).
Pub. ....Becky Brackin
Controller ....Duane Pruitt
HR Dir. ....Monty Stanley
Circ. Mgr. ....Joseph Solley
Ed. ....Tim Archuleta
Columnist ....Rick Smith
Market Information: Split run; TMC; Zoned editions.
Mechanical available: Offset; Black and 3 ROP colors; insert accepted; page cutoffs - 22 3/4.
Mechanical Specifications: Type page 11 5/8 x 21 1/2; E - 6 cols, 2 1/16, 1/8 between; A - 6 cols, 2 1/16, 1/8 between; C - 10 cols, 1 3/16, 4/5 between.
Commodity Consumption: Avg. Page Number Per Issue - Daily 28; Avg. Page Number Per Issue - Plates Used 42900; Avg. Page Number Per Issue - Sunday 52; widths 13 1/2; Newsprint Used - Metric Tons 2556; Printing Ink Used - Black 57000; Printing Ink Used - Color 15000; Printing In
Equipment EDITORIAL: Front-end Software – III 2.39.; Editorial Hardware – Austin; Editorial Equipment – APP/Power Mac G3; Editorial Printers – 1-Panasonic/KX P2411I, X/DC 220 CLASSIFIED: Front-end Software – Baseview/AMP 2.1.; Classified Hardware – APP/iMac, APP/Mac G3; Classified Equipment – APP/Mac G4 Server; Classified Printers – 1-APP/Mac LaserWriter, 1-Lexmark/Optma LX Plw DISPLAY: Ad make-up applications – Multi-Ad/Creator II, Adobe/Photoshop 6.0, Adobe/Illustrator 5.5; Display Hardware – 7-APP/Mac G4, 10-APP/Power G3, Dell/Power Edge 4300; Display Printers – HP/5si MX, HP/750C Plotter, 2-HP/DeskJet 1200 c-ps, HP/DeskJet 1600C, HP/755C Plotter PRODUCTION: Pagination Software – QPS/QuarkXPress 3.3, MEI/CLS 2.6, QPS/QuarkXPress 4.1.; Production Equipment – APP/Mac NT Server, 2-Pre Press/Panther Pro 46; Cameras – C/Spartan II; Scanners – Kk/2035, AG/Arcus Flatbed, Nikon/Coolscan PRESSROOM: Line 1 – 7-G/Cosmo double width 1980; Folders – 2; Pasters – 6, 2. MAILROOM: Counter stackers – 3/KAN; Inserters and stuffers – 2-KAN/480; Bundle tying machines – 5-/MLN; Addressing machine – KR, Scitex/Ink Jet; Other equipment –MM/Minuteman Saddle Stitcher. BUSINESS COMPUTERS: Business Software – PeopleSoft; Business Hardware – HP/3000-937 RX

SAN ANTONIO

THE EXPRESS-NEWS CORP.

Ave. E & 3rd St., San Antonio, Texas, 78205-2082; gen tel (210) 250-3000

SAN ANTONIO EXPRESS-NEWS

PO Box 2171, San Antonio, Texas, 78297-2171; gen tel (210) 250-3711; adv tel (210) 250-2500; ed tel (210) 250-3195; gen fax (210) 250-3715; adv fax (210) 250-2565; ed fax (210) 250-3105; gen e-mail community-support@express-news.net; ed e-mail editors@express-news.net; web site www.express-news.com; www.mysanantonio.net

Published: Mon, Tues, Wed, Thur, Fri, Sat, Sun
Weekday Frequency: m
Saturday Frequency: m
Circulation: 137,514; 144,790(sat); 344,120(sun)
Last Audit: ABC September 30, 2011
Price: 3.65/wk; 189.80/yr (carrier), $286.00/yr (mail).
Advertising: Open inch rate $346.77
News services: AP, NYT, LAT-WP, Bloomberg, MCT, GNS.
Politics: Independent. **Established:** 1865
Special Editions: Homestyle (Apr); Guide To S.A. (Aug); Homestyle (Dec); Rodeo (Feb); Jobs (Jan); Homestyle (Jun); Texas Living (Mar); Top Performing Co. (May); Party Planner Holiday Guide (Nov); Physician Guide (Oct); Mature Matters (Sept).
Special Weekly Sections: Weekender (Fri); Travel/Leisure (S); Drive (Sat); Stock Listings (Thur); Stock Listings (Tues); Adsmart Jobs Express (Wed).
Magazines: Best Homes (Monthly); Health Careers Job Fairs (Quarterly); TV Now (S).
Pres./Pub. ....Thomas A. Stephenson
Vice Pres., Finance ....Fred Mergele
Vice Pres., HR ....Susan Ehrman
Vice Pres., Classified Adv. ....Charlotte Aaron
Sales Dir. ....Rebecca Named Chavez-Becker
Adv. Mgr., Automotive ....Doug Bennight
Adv. Mgr., Telemktg./Classified Roxanne Beavers
Adv. Mgr., Telemktg./Retail ....Pat Harvey
Vice Pres., Mktg. ....Dean Aitken
Vice Pres., Mktg. ....Patrick Magallanes
Target Mktg. Mgr. ....Liz English
Circ. Sr. Vice Pres. ....Scott Frantzen
Circ. Dir., Admin. ....Paul Borrego
Dir., Metro Home Delivery ....Sammy Aburumuh
Ed. ....Robert Rivard
Mng. Ed. ....Brett Thacker
Asst. Mng. Ed., Features ....Terry Scott-Bertling
Asst. Mng. Ed., Graphics/Design/Photo Hallie Paul
Asst. Mng. Ed., News ....Craig Thomason
Market Information: Split run; TMC; Zoned editions.
Mechanical available: Offset; Black and 3 ROP colors; insert accepted; page cutoffs - 22.
Mechanical Specifications: Type page 11 5/8 x 21; E - 6 cols, 2 1/16, 1/8 between; A - 6 cols, 2 1/16, 1/8 between; C - 10 cols, 1 5/16, 1/16 between.
Commodity Consumption: Avg. Page Number Per Issue - Daily 76; Avg. Page Number Per Issue - Plates Used 450000; Avg. Page Number Per Issue - Saturday 118; Avg. Page Number Per Issue - Sunday 160; widths 25; Newsprint Used - Metric Tons 55000; Printing Ink Used - Black 857243; P
Equipment EDITORIAL: Front-end Software – CCI, Newsdesk, CCI/Layout Champ 4.20.; Editorial Hardware – Unix/Enterprise 6000 Servers NT desktops; Editorial Equipment – Graphic Enterprise/Page Scan; Editorial Printers – HP/LaserJet, Canon/350, HP/3500 Color, HP/4000, HP/8000, HP/5000 CLASSIFIED: Front-end Software – Czar, Coyote/3.; Classified Hardware – SII; Classified Equipment – 100-PC Terminals, 100-NT/NT Client DISPLAY: Ad make-up applications – QPS/QuarkXPress 4.4; Layout Software – SCS/Layout 8000.; Display Hardware – APP/Macs, APP/Power Mac, APP/Mac G3; Display Printers – MON/Proofers, Canon/Fieny, Iris PRODUCTION: Pagination Software – QPS/QuarkXPress, CCI/Layout Champ, Newsdesk.; Production Equipment – 2-MON/ExpressMaster 3850, 2-MON/Lasercomp Express, Futuro; Cameras – 2-Newspagers, 1-C/Spartan III; Scanners – CD/636 Drum, CD/240 Drum, EskoFot/26365 Copydot PRESSROOM: Line 1 – 3-G/Colorliner double width (8 units) 1994; Line 2 – 3-G/Colorliner doble width (8 units); Line 3 – 3-G/Colorliner double width (8 units); Folders – 4, 2-G/Sovereign 3:2 Single, 1-G/Sovereign 3:2 Double; Pasters – 30-G/CT50; Reels and Stands – 30 MAILROOM: Counter stackers – 9-QWI/300, 4-QWI/SJ201A; Inserters and stuffers – 3-HI/72P, 1-GMA/SLS 1000; Bundle tying machines – 8/Power Strap, 6-Sterling/Tying Machine. BUSINESS COMPUTERS: Business Software – Admarc (7.0): Adv (input & ordering); Business Hardware – 1-B/4955, 1-V/340, Bs, IBM/ES9000-150

SAN MARCOS

SAN MARCOS DAILY RECORD

1910 I.H. 35 S., San Marcos, Texas, 78666-5901; gen tel (512) 392-2458; gen fax (512) 392-1514; adv fax (512) 392-4655; gen e-mail rray@sanmarcosrecord.com; web site www.sanmarcosrecord.com

Published: Tues, Wed, Thur, Fri, Sun
Weekday Frequency: e
Circulation: 6,464; 6,464(sun)
Last Audit: September 30, 2006
Price: 5.00/mo; 72.00/yr (in town), $108.00/yr (outside town).
Advertising: Open inch rate $15.79
News services: AP.
Politics: Independent.
Special Editions: Back-to-School (Aug); Progress (Feb).
Special Weekly Sections: TV Magazine (S); Entertainment Page (Thur); Food Page (Wed).
Magazines: USA WEEKEND Magazine (S); American Profile (Weekly).
Bus. Mgr. ....Dean Leach
Adv. Dir. ....James Jones
Circ. Dir. ....Elise Wines
Editorial Page Ed. ....Rowe H. Ray
Neighbors Ed. ....Jeff Walker
News Ed. ....Anita Miller
Sports Ed. ....Randy Stevens
Prodn. Supvr. ....Karen Ray
Prodn. Foreman, Pressroom ....Frank Gonzales
Market Information: TMC.
Mechanical available: Offset; Black and 3 ROP colors; insert accepted; page cutoffs - 22 3/4.
Mechanical Specifications: Type page 13 x 21 1/2; E - 6 cols, 2 1/16, 1/8 between; A - 6 cols, 2 1/16, 1/8 between; C - 9 cols, 1 3/8, 1/16 between.
Commodity Consumption: Avg. Page Number Per Issue - Daily 24; Avg. Page Number Per Issue - Sunday 56.
Equipment; Editorial Hardware – EKI/Televideo.; Production Equipment – 1-COM/4961, 1-COM/2961; 1-COM/Unisetter; Cameras – 1-C/J75CC; Scanners – EKI/Televideo. PRESSROOM: Line 1 – 7-G/Community; Folders – 1; Bundle tying machines – 1/Bu; Addressing machine – 1-/El.; Business Hardware – DPT/1100, IBM

SEGUIN

THE SEGUIN GAZETTE-ENTERPRISE

1012 Schriewer Rd., Seguin, Texas, 78155; gen tel (830) 379-5402; gen fax (830) 379-8328; gen e-mail news@seguingazette.com; adv e-mail advertising@seguingazette.com; ed e-mail editor@seguingazette.com; web site www.seguingazette.com
Published: Tues, Wed, Thur, Fri, Sun
Weekday Frequency: m
Circulation: 4,076; 5,205(sun)
Last Audit: September 30, 2008
Price: 72.00/yr.
Advertising: Open inch rate $12.43
News services: AP.
Politics: Independent. **Established:** 1888
Special Weekly Sections: Church Page (Fri); Business (S); Entertainment (Thur); Best Food Day (Tues).
Magazines: Weekly TV Guide/Comics (S); American Profile (Weekly).
Pub. ....Neice Bell
Bus. Mgr. ....Maggie Clarkson
Adv. Dir. ....Gay Lynn Oslovsky
City Ed. ....Michael Cary
News Ed. ....Misty Sweet
Sports Ed. ....Jason Chlapek
Mgmt. Info Servs. Mgr. ....Chris Lykins
Prodn. Mgr., Pressroom ....Rigo Vargas
Market Information: TMC.
Mechanical available: Offset; Black and 3 ROP colors; insert accepted; page cutoffs - 21.
Mechanical Specifications: Type page 13 x 21; E - 6 cols, 2 1/16, 1/8 between; A - 6 cols, 2 1/16, 1/8 between; C - 9 cols, 1 3/8, 1/16 between.
Commodity Consumption: Avg. Page Number Per Issue - Daily 14; Avg. Page Number Per Issue - Plates Used 3600; Avg. Page Number Per Issue - Sunday 24; widths 27 1/2; Newsprint Used - Short Tons 250; Printing Ink Used - Black 8500; Printing Ink Used - Color 1500; Printing Ink Use
Equipment EDITORIAL: Front-end Software – APP/Mac Sys 7.55-9.10, QPS/QuarkXPress 4.0, Baseview/NewsEdit 3.3.; Editorial Hardware – 6-APP/Mac Quadra 610, 650; Editorial Printers – 1-APP/Mac II NTX, HP/Laserjet 5M GN CLASSIFIED: Front-end Software – QPS/QuarkXPress 4.0, Baseview 3.2.; Classified Hardware – APP/Mac G3; Classified Printers – H/P Laserjet 5M GN, 1-APP/Mac II NTX DISPLAY: Ad make-up applications – APP/Mac System 8-8.6, QPS/QuarkXPress 4.0, Aldus/PageMaker 6.5, Baseview/NewsEdit; Layout Software – APP/Power Mac 6100, APP/Mac Quadra G3.; Display Hardware – APP/Power Mac 6100, APP/Mac G3; Display Printers – HP/Laserjet 5m GN PRODUCTION: Pagination Software – QPS/QuarkXPress 4.0.; Production Equipment – Caere/OmniPage; Cameras – Acti/125 PRESSROOM: Line 1 – 7-G/Suburban. MAILROOM: Counter stackers – 1-BG/Count-O-Veyor; Inserters and stuffers – 1-KAN/320; Addressing machine – 1/AM.; Business Hardware – 3-IBM

SOUTHERN NEWSPAPERS, INC.

1012 Schriewer Rd., Seguin, Texas, 78155; gen tel (830) 379-5402; adv tel (830) 379-5441 x210; ed tel (830) 379-5441 x221; gen fax (830) 379-8328; adv fax (830) 379-8328; ed fax (830) 379-8328; adv e-mail advertising@seguingazette.com; ed e-mail editor@seguingazette.com; web site www.seguingazette.com
Published: Tues, Wed, Thur, Fri, Sun
Weekday Frequency: m
Circulation: 5,800; 7,646(sun)
Advertising: 11.70
Insert rate: 60.00
Politics: 1888
Advertising not accepted: Y
Not Published: sat, mon
Own facility?: Y
Mechanical available: yes
Mechanical Specifications: 1 col - 1.55
Equipment; Inserters and stuffers – hand; Bundle tying machines – strap
Zip Codes served: 78155
Delivery method: Mail, Newsstand, Private Carrier, Racks

SHERMAN

HERALD DEMOCRAT

603 S. Sam Rayburn Fwy., Sherman, Texas, 75090; gen tel (903) 893-8181; gen fax (903) 868-1930; ed fax (903) 868-2106; gen e-mail mail@herald-democrat.com; adv e-mail advertising@herald-democrat.com; ed e-mail news@herald-democrat.com; web site www.heralddemocrat.com
Published: Mon, Tues, Wed, Thur, Fri, Sun
Weekday Frequency: m
Circulation: 20,744; 22,069(sun)
Last Audit: September 30, 2008
Price: 10.50/mo; 126.00/yr.
Advertising: Open inch rate $38.85
News services: AP, SHNS.
Politics: Independent. **Established:** 1879
Not Published: Christmas.
Special Editions: Home Improvement (Apr); Home Improvement (Aug); Christmas Greetings (Dec); Home Improvement (Jul); Car Care (Jun); Chamber of Commerce Industrial Review (Mar); Brides (May); Christmas Gift Guide (Nov); Car Care (Oct); Football (Sept).
Special Weekly Sections: Church (Fri); TV Week (Other); Color Comics (S); Best Food Day (Wed).
Magazines: Relish (Monthly); USA WEEKEND Magazine (S).
Pub. ....John P. Wright
Credit Mgr. ....Dianne Harp
Adv. Mgr., Classified ....Jennifer Parker
Mgr., Mktg./Promo. ....Wes King
Circ. Dir. ....Mike Brezina
City Ed. ....Gary Carter
Editorial Page Ed. ....Don Eldredge
Features Ed. ....Kathy Williams
News/Wire Ed. ....Darrell McCorstin
Sports Ed. ....Bill Spinks
Mgmt. Info Servs. Mgr. ....Doug Simpson
Mailroom Supvr. ....Raymond Hodge
Prodn. Mgr., Composing ....Teresa Redd
Prodn. Mgr., Pressroom ....Mike Harkey
Market Information: TMC; Zoned editions.
Mechanical available: Offset; Black and 3 ROP colors; insert accepted; page cutoffs - 22 3/4.
Mechanical Specifications: Type page 11 5/8 x 21 1/2; E - 6 cols, 1 3/4, 3/16 between; A - 6 cols, 1 3/4, 3/16 between; C - 9 cols, 1 1/4, 1/8 between.
Commodity Consumption: Avg. Page Number Per Issue - Daily 30; Avg. Page Number Per Issue - Plates Used 6760; Avg. Page Number Per Issue - Sunday 64; widths 25; Newsprint Used - Metric Tons 1800; Printing Ink Used - Black 50000; Printing Ink Used - Color 6000; Printing Ink Used
Equipment EDITORIAL: Front-end Software – Baseview.; Editorial Hardware – APP/Mac; Editorial Printers – 2-Pre Press/Panther Pro CLASSIFIED: Front-end Software – Baseview.; Classified Hardware – APP/Mac; Classified Printers – 1-APP/Mac LaserPrinter DISPLAY: Ad make-up applications – Baseview; Layout Software – MEI/ALS.; Display Hardware – APP/Mac; Production Equipment – 2-Pre Press/Panther Pro Imagesetter; Cameras – C/Spartan III; Scanners – Equipment ☐ Baseview, QPS/QuarkXPress 3.31. PRESSROOM: Line 1 – 7-G/Urbanite 1973, 1-G/Urbanite 1989; Folders – 1 MAILROOM: Counter stackers – 1-MRS/1220, 1/QWI; Inserters and stuffers – 1-/1372PS; Bundle tying machines – 2-MLN/ML2EE. BUSINESS COMPUTERS: Business Software – CJ; Business Hardware – 1-Unisys/5000, 1-HP/3000 927LX

SINTON

SAN PATRICIO COUNTY NEWS

117 So. Rachal Ave, Sinton, Texas, 78387; gen tel (361) 364-1270; gen fax (361) 364-3833; gen e-mail editor@sanpatpublishing.com; adv e-mail advertising@sanpatpublishing.com; web site www.sanpatriciopublishing.com
Published: Mon, Tues, Wed, Thur, Fri, Sat, Sun
Weekday Frequency: All day
Saturday Frequency: All day
Circulation: 2,500
Last Audit: Sworn N/A
Advertising: Open inch rate $7.55
Insert rate: $191.25/M; Rate for 4-pgs.
Politics: 1901
Advertising not accepted: Y
Own facility?: Y
Profile: Newspaper Publishing
Ed. ....James F. Tracy
Edtior ....Belinda Tracy
Mechanical Specifications: Type page 107/8 x 211/2.. See Specs on Web Page..www.sanpatpublishing.com
Equipment; Cameras – canon; Inserters and stuffers – BY HAND; Wrapping singles – BY HAND
Delivery method: Mail, Newsstand, Racks

SNYDER

SNYDER DAILY NEWS

3600 College Ave., Snyder, Texas, 79549; gen tel (325) 573-5486; gen fax (325) 573-0044; adv e-mail advertising@snyderdailynews.com; ed e-mail editor1@snyderdailynews.com; web site www.snyderdailynews.com
Published: Mon, Tues, Wed, Thur, Fri, Sat
Weekday Frequency: e
Saturday Frequency: e
Circulation: 4,688; 4,688(sun)
Last Audit: March 31, 2007
Price: 11.75/mo; 92.20/yr.
Advertising: Open inch rate $9.25
News services: AP.
Politics: Independent.
Not Published: Independence Day; Christmas.
Special Editions: Christmas Greetings (Dec); Progress (Jan); Progress (Sept).
Magazines: American Profile (Weekly).
Asst. Pub. ....Wade Warren
Adv. Dir. ....Wayne Burney
Adv. Mgr., Classified ....Donna Browning
Sports Ed. ....Larry McCarthy
Wire Ed. ....Shirley A. Gorman
Publisher ....Bill Crist
Business Manager ....Christie Adams
Pres./Pub. ....Roy McQueen
Circ. Mgr. ....Jacalyn Lowrance
Market Information: TMC.
Mechanical available: Offset; Black and 3 ROP colors; insert accepted; page cutoffs - 21.
Mechanical Specifications: Type page 14 1/2 x 21; E - 6 cols, 2 1/16, 1/8 between; A - 6 cols, 2 1/16, 1/8 between; C - 6 cols, 2 1/16, 1/8 between.
Commodity Consumption: Avg. Page Number Per Issue - Daily 12; Avg. Page Number Per Issue - Sunday 48; widths 27 1/2; Newsprint Used - Short Tons 276.
Equipment; Editorial Hardware – FSI.; Classified Hardware – FSI. PRESSROOM: Line 1 – 6-G/Community; Folders – 1-G/SC.; Business Hardware – TI

SNYDER PUBLISHING CO., INC.

3600 College Ave., Snyder, Texas, 79549; gen tel (325) 573-5486; gen fax (325) 573-0044
Published: Mon, Tues, Wed, Thur, Fri, Sun
Weekday Frequency: e
Advertising not accepted: Y

STEPHENVILLE

STEPHENVILLE EMPIRE-TRIBUNE

590 E. South Loop, Stephenville, Texas, 76401; gen tel (254) 965-3124; adv tel (254) 965-3124; ed tel (254) 965-3124; gen fax (254) 965-4269; adv fax (254) 965-4269; ed fax (254) 965-4269; gen e-mail news@empiretribune.com; adv e-mail rochelle.stidham@empiretribune.com; ed e-mail sara.vandenberge@empiretribune.com; web site www.empiretribune.com
Published: Tues, Wed, Thur, Fri, Sun
Weekday Frequency: m
Circulation: 4,752; 4,500(sun)
Last Audit: September 30, 2006
Advertising: Open inch rate $15.80
Insert rate: 67.50 cpm
News services: AP, General Media.
Politics: 1900
Advertising not accepted: Y
Not Published: Monday, Saturday
Own facility?: N
Special Editions: Progress (Feb); Mature Time (Monthly).
Special Weekly Sections: Restaurant Dining (Fri); Agriculture (S); School Page/NIE (Tues).
Magazines: American Profile (S).
SPRY
Atholon Sports
Pub. ....Rochelle Stidham
Circ. Mgr. ....Daryl Robinson
Mng. Ed. ....Sara Vanden Berge
Market Information: TMC.
Mechanical available: Offset; Black and 3 ROP colors; insert accepted - product samples; page cutoffs - 23.
Mechanical Specifications: Type page 11 x 21 1/2; E - 6 cols, 1/8 between; A - 6 cols, 1/8 between; C - 10 cols, 1/8 between.
Commodity Consumption: Avg. Page Number Per Issue - Daily 14; Avg. Page Number Per Issue - Sunday 40; widths 25.
Equipment EDITORIAL: Front-end Software – QPS/QuarkXPress 4.0.; Editorial Hardware – APP/Mac; Editorial Printers – APP/Mac Laser CLASSIFIED: Front-end Software – Baseview/AdManager Pro.; Classified Hardware – APP/Mac; Classified Printers – APP/Mac DISPLAY: Ad make-up applications – PBS; Layout Software – APP/Mac, QPS/QuarkXPress.; Display Hardware – APP/Mac; Display Printers – APP/Mac Laser, 3-HP/4MV; Production Equipment – APP/Mac Laser, Imagesetter; Cameras – C/Spartan II Roll Camera; Scanners – Equip-

ment □ QPS/QuarkXPress 4.0. PRESSROOM: Line 1 – 7-G/Community Offset 1972; Folders – 1-G/SC (with upper former).; Inserters and stuffers – KAN/320 7 station; Bundle tying machines – MLN/Strapper (plastic). BUSINESS COMPUTERS: Business Software – Microsoft/Word, Microsoft/Excel, Microsoft/Outlook, Microsoft/Windows 98; Business Hardware – IBM
Zip Codes served: 76401
Delivery method: Mail, Newsstand, Private Carrier, Racks

SULPHUR SPRINGS

SULPHUR SPRINGS NEWS-TELEGRAM

401 Church St., Sulphur Springs, Texas, 75482; gen tel (903) 885-8663; gen fax (903) 885-8768; gen e-mail news@ssecho.com; adv e-mail ads@ssecho.com; ed e-mail editor@ssecho.com; web site www.ssnewstelegram.com; www.ssecho.com
Published: Mon, Tues, Wed, Thur, Fri, Sun
Weekday Frequency: e
Circulation: 5,860; 6,118(sun)
Last Audit: March 31, 2007
Price: 6.50/mo (carrier); 97.00/yr (in town), $103.00/yr (out of town).
Advertising: Open inch rate $11.48
News services: AP.
Politics: Independent.
Not Published: New Year; Independence Day; Labor Day; Thanksgiving; Christmas.
Special Weekly Sections: T-Viewing (Fri); Best Food Days (S); Business Pages (Thur); Best Food Days (Tues).
Pres./Pub. ....Scott Keys
Vice Pres./Controller ....Jim Butler
Sec./Treasurer ....Carolyn Keys
Gen. Mgr. ....Butch Burney
Adv. Dir. ....Angie Dunn
Adv. Mgr. ....Johnie Hardgrave
Circ. Mgr. ....Kristi Hayes
News Ed. ....Faith Huffman
Sports Ed. ....Bobby Burney
MIS Mgr./Websmaster ....Davy Moseley
Market Information: TMC.
Mechanical available: Offset; Black and 3 ROP colors; insert accepted; page cutoffs - 22 1/2.
Mechanical Specifications: Type page 13 x 21; E - 6 cols, 2 1/16, 1/8 between; A - 6 cols, 2 1/16, 1/8 between; C - 6 cols, 2 1/16, 1/8 between.
Commodity Consumption: Avg. Page Number Per Issue - Daily 14; Avg. Page Number Per Issue - Plates Used 3065; Avg. Page Number Per Issue - Sunday 38; widths 27 1/2; Newsprint Used - Short Tons 301; Printing Ink Used - Black 7895; Printing Ink Used - Color 500; Printing Ink Used
Equipment; Editorial Hardware – APP/Mac SE, APP/Mac SE30, APP/Mac Classic, APP/Mac fx, APP/Mac si, 2-APP/Power Mac 8100.; Classified Hardware – 2-APP/Mac SE. PRODUCTION: Pagination Software – QPS/QuarkXPress.; Production Equipment – 3-APP/Mac LaserWriter Plus, 1-LaserMaster/1200 Laser Printer, ECR; Cameras – 1-Acti; Scanners – 4-APP/Mac SE PRESSROOM: Line 1 – 7-HI/Cotrell V-15A; Line 2 – 8-KP/Color King; Folders – 1 MAILROOM: Counter stackers – 1/BG; Inserters and stuffers – 1-/KR; Bundle tying machines – 1-/Bu, 1-/Cn; Addressing machine – 1-/KR.; Business Hardware – 2-Northstar/Horizon, 2-IBM

SWEETWATER

SWEETWATER REPORTER

112 W. Third St., Sweetwater, Texas, 79556; gen tel (325) 236-6677; gen fax (325) 235-4967; gen e-mail publisher@sweetwaterreporter.com; adv e-mail advertising@sweetwaterreporter.com; ed e-mail editor@sweetwaterreporter.com; web site www.sweetwaterreporter.com
Published: Mon, Tues, Wed, Thur, Fri, Sun
Weekday Frequency: e
Circulation: 4,176; 4,176(sun)
Last Audit: March 31, 2007
Price: 7.50/mo; 87.00/yr.
Advertising: Open inch rate $10.65
News services: AP.
Politics: 1881
Not Published: New Year; Memorial Day; Independence Day; Labor Day; Thanksgiving; Christmas.
Special Editions: AJRA National Finals Tab (Jul); Rattlesnake Tab (Mar).
Special Weekly Sections: Church News (Fri); Business (S); Grocery Inserts (Tues).
Magazines: American Profile (Weekly).
Pub ....Sharon Friedlander
Bus. Mgr. ....Danica Hickson
Adv. Sales Mgr. ....Brenda Morales
Adv. Sales Mgr. ....Justin Ramirez
Composing Mgr. ....Pablo Rodriguez
Prodn. Mgr., Pressroom ....Bleu Reyes
Market Information: ADS; TMC.
Mechanical available: Offset; Black and 3 ROP colors; insert accepted - all; page cutoffs - 22.
Mechanical Specifications: Type page 12 x 21 1/2; E - 6 cols, 2 1/16, 1/8 between; A - 6 cols, 2 1/16, 1/8 between; C - 8 cols, 1 1/2, 1/8 between.
Commodity Consumption: Avg. Page Number Per Issue - Daily 12; Avg. Page Number Per Issue - Plates Used 6; Avg. Page Number Per Issue - Sunday 20; widths 25; Newsprint Used - Short Tons 110; Printing Ink Used - Black 135; Printing Ink Used - Color 50.
Equipment EDITORIAL: Front-end Software – QPS/QuarkXPress.; Editorial Hardware – APP/Mac; Editorial Printers – NewGen/LaserWriters CLASSIFIED: Front-end Software – Baseview.; Classified Hardware – APP/Mac; Classified Printers – Okidata/320; Layout Software – Baseview.; Display Printers – 2-APP/Mac LaserWriter II NTX; Production Equipment – 2-NewGen/Laserwriter; Cameras – 1-R/500. PRESSROOM: Line 1 – 5-G 1963, 1-G 1977.; Bundle tying machines – 1/Bu; Addressing machine – 1-/Wm. BUSINESS COMPUTERS: Business Software – ARWorks; Business Hardware – Acer/PCs

TAYLOR

TAYLOR DAILY PRESS

211 W. Third St., Taylor, Texas, 76574; gen tel (512) 352-8535; gen fax (512) 352-2227; gen e-mail news@taylordailypress.net; web site www.taylordailypress.net
Published: Tues, Wed, Thur, Fri, Sun
Weekday Frequency: m
Circulation: 4,658; 4,658(sun)
Last Audit: September 30, 2003
Price: 9.00/mo (carrier); 84.00/yr.
Advertising: Open inch rate $10.25
News services: AP.
Politics: Independent. **Established:** 1911
Special Editions: Health & Fitness Tab (Apr); Back-to-School Tab (Aug); Christmas Greetings (Dec); Tax Facts Tab (Feb); Chamber Tab (Jan); Business in Taylor (Jul); Taylor F.Y.I (Jun); Lawn & Garden/Home Improvement Tab (Mar); Graduation Tab (May); Christmas Gift Guide (No
Special Weekly Sections: Church Page (Fri); TV Listings (Mon); Best Food Day (Wed).
Bus. Mgr. ....Laura Harms
Adv. Dir. ....Loretta Shirley
Adv. Mgr., Classified ....Suzannah Curik
Circ. Mgr. ....Mark Groves
Mng. Ed. ....Emily Boswell
Sports Ed. ....Mike Craven
Prodn. Mgr., Pre Press ....Grace Rangel
Prodn. Foreman, Press ....Severino Torres
Mechanical available: Offset; Black and 3 ROP colors; insert accepted; page cutoffs - 22 3/4.
Mechanical Specifications: Type page 13 x 21; E - 6 cols, 2 1/16, 1/8 between; A - 6 cols, 2 1/16, 1/8 between; C - 9 cols, 1 3/8, 1/16 between.
Commodity Consumption: Avg. Page Number Per Issue - Daily 10.2; Avg. Page Number Per Issue - Plates Used 1816; widths 28; Newsprint Used - Short Tons 585; Printing Ink Used - Black 13500; Printing Ink Used - Pages Printed 2652.
Equipment EDITORIAL: Front-end Software – QPS/QuarkXPress 4.0.; Editorial Hardware – 5-APP/Mac; Editorial Printers – Konica/Imagesetter, ECR/Imagesetter CLASSIFIED: Front-end Software – Baseview, QPS/QuarkXPress 3.3.; Classified Hardware – 2-APP/Mac, 1-IBM DISPLAY: Ad make-up applications – QPS/QuarkXPress 3.3.; Display Hardware – 2-APP/Mac; Display Printers – APP/Mac LaserWriter 16/1600 PS PRODUCTION: Pagination Software – QPS/QuarkXPress 4.0.; Production Equipment – 1-Nu/Flip Top, Konica/Imagesetter, ECR/Imagesetter; Cameras – 1-C/Spartan III; Scanners – 1-GAM PRESSROOM: Line 1 – 7-G/Community; Folders – 1 MAILROOM: Counter stackers – 1-BG/Count-O-Veyor; Inserters and stuffers – 1-KAN/320 with quarter-fold; Bundle tying machines – 1/Malow; Addressing machine – 1-/KR.; Business Hardware – 1-IBM/System 34

TEMPLE

TEMPLE DAILY TELEGRAM

10 S. Third St., Temple, Texas, 76501-7619; gen tel (254) 778-4444; gen fax (254) 778-2117; adv fax (254) 771-3516; ed fax (254) 778-4444; gen e-mail tdt@temple-telegram.com; adv e-mail tdtads@temple-telegram.com; advertiz@temple-telegram.com; ed e-mail tdt@temple-telegram.com; web site www.temple-telegram.com
Published: Mon, Tues, Wed, Thur, Fri, Sat, Sun
Weekday Frequency: m
Saturday Frequency: m
Circulation: 16,627; 17,728(sat); 19,760(sun)
Last Audit: ABC September 30, 2011
Price: 9.00/mo; 104.50/yr.
Advertising: Open inch rate $23.80
News services: AP.
Politics: Independent-Democrat. **Established:** 1907
Special Editions: Senior Living (Apr); Area Football Tab (Aug); Last Minute Gift Guide (Dec); Income Tax Tab (Feb); Readers Choice (Jan); Senior Living (Jul); Belton Rodeo (Jun); Readers Choice (Mar); Memorial Day (May); Chamber Business Focus (Monthly); Gift Guide (Nov);
Special Weekly Sections: Farm Page (Mon); Best Food Day (S); Auto Page (Thur); Best Food Day (Wed).
Magazines: Chamber of Commerce Update Tab (Monthly); Parade (S).
Adv. Dir. ....Gary Garner
Circ. Mgr. ....Mack Wolf
Ed. ....Sue Mayborn
City Desk Mgr. ....Tammy Latham
Editorial Page Ed. ....Cara Wilson
Medical Writer ....Janice Gibbs
Sports Ed. ....Greg Willie
Prodn. Dir., Technical/Pre Press ..William Horton
Prodn. Mgr., Mailroom ....Ken Woodward
Mechanical available: Offset; Black and 3 ROP colors; insert accepted - hi-fi rolls; page cutoffs - 22 3/4.
Mechanical Specifications: Type page 11 5/8 x 21 1/2; E - 6 cols, 1 13/16, 1/8 between; A - 6 cols, 1 13/16, 1/8 between; C - 9 cols, 1 3/16, 1/16 between.
Commodity Consumption: Avg. Page Number Per Issue - Daily 22; Avg. Page Number Per Issue - Plates Used 18125; Avg. Page Number Per Issue - Sunday 54; widths 12 1/2; Newsprint Used - Short Tons 1541; Printing Ink Used - Black 33117; Printing Ink Used - Color 6487; Printing Ink
Equipment EDITORIAL: Front-end Software – APT.; Editorial Hardware – ALR/Pentium II, 1-Nikon/Coolscan; Editorial Printers – Okidata/320, 1-Okidata/591, 1-Okidata/321, 1-Epson/Stylus Pro, HP/LaserJet IID CLASSIFIED: Front-end Software – APT.; Classified Hardware – ALR/Pentium II, ALR/Fileserver; Classified Equipment – 1-Microtek/b&w Scanner with OCR, 1-Kk/40 Digital Camera, 1-QuickTake/150 Digital Camera, 1-ABS/486; Classified Printers – Okidata/320; Display Hardware – 1-APP/Mac 7100 Image Workstation, APP/Mac SE, 1-APP/Mac 7200-120 Image Workstation; Display Printers – 1-LaserMaster/XLO Postscript Typesetter PRODUCTION: Pagination Software – APT, QPS/QuarkXPress 4.0.; Production Equipment – 1-L/190 Postscript Imagesetter Full Page, BKY/30A, 1-Konica/EV Jetsetter, 2-Elite XL Postscript; Cameras – 1-C/Spartan II PRESSROOM: Line 1 – 10-G/Urbanite; Folders – 1-G/2:1; Pasters – 6 MAILROOM: Counter stackers – 3-HL/Monitor; Inserters and stuffers – 1-GMA/SLS 1000 8:2; Bundle tying machines – 1-MLN/Plastic, 1-MLN/2E. BUSINESS COMPUTERS: Business Software – Mas 90, IBM/AR 2000; Business Hardware – 7-Dell/Pentium III

TERRELL

THE TERRELL TRIBUNE

150 Ninth St., Terrell, Texas, 75160; gen tel (972) 563-6476; gen fax (972) 563-0340; gen e-mail ttrib@swbell.net; web site www.terrelltribune.com
Published: Mon, Tues, Wed, Thur, Fri, Sun
Weekday Frequency: e
Circulation: 2,450; 2,950(sun)
Last Audit: Sworn December 31, 2007
Price: 6.50/mo; 120.00/yr.
Advertising: Open inch rate $11.78
News services: AP, NEA.
Politics: Independent.
Magazines: Relish (Monthly); American Profile (Weekly).
Interim Pub. ....Michael Gresham
Adv. Dir. ....Jeff Jordan
Circ. Dir. ....Pat Williams
Lifestyle Ed. ....Alison Walker
Sports Ed. ....Cliff Gibson
Prodn. Mgr., Composing ....Debbie Hall
Prodn. Foreman, Pressroom ....Marvin Love
Market Information: TMC.
Mechanical available: Offset; Black and 2 ROP colors; insert accepted - card; page cutoffs - 22 1/2.
Mechanical Specifications: Type page 13 x 21 1/2; E - 6 cols, 2 1/16, 1/8 between; A - 6 cols, 2 1/16, 1/8 between; C - 8 cols, 1 1/2, 1/8 between.
Commodity Consumption: Avg. Page Number Per Issue - Daily 8; Avg. Page Number Per Issue - Plates Used 1400; Avg. Page Number Per Issue - Sunday 16; widths 27 1/2; Newsprint Used - Short Tons 264; Printing Ink Used - Black 3000; Printing Ink Used - Color 600; Printing Ink Used
Equipment EDITORIAL: Front-end Software – Baseview/NewsEdit, Baseview/QXEdit.; Editorial Hardware – APP/Mac CLASSIFIED: Front-end Software – Baseview/Class Manager.; Classified Hardware – APP/Mac; Production Equipment – 2-COM/LaserPrinter; Cameras – 1-C. PRESSROOM: Line 1 – 5-HI/Cotrell V-15A; Folders – 1 MAILROOM: Counter stackers – 1-BG/Count-O-Veyor; Bundle tying machines – 1-Akebono/Semi-Ace, 1/Bu; Addressing machine – 2-/Am.

TEXARKANA

TEXARKANA GAZETTE

315 Pine St., Texarkana, Texas, 75501; gen tel (903) 794-3311; gen fax (903) 792-7183; adv fax (903) 792-7183; ed fax (903) 794-3315; ed e-mail opinion@texarkanagazette.com; web site www.texarkanagazette.com
Group: Arkansas Press Services
Published: Mon, Tues, Wed, Thur, Fri, Sat, Sun
Weekday Frequency: m
Saturday Frequency: m
Circulation: 26,589; 29,282(sun)
Last Audit: ABC September 30, 2011

Price: 11.50/mo; 138.00/yr.
Advertising: Open inch rate $45.28
News services: AP, TMS, SHNS, CNS, Roll Call Report Syndicate.
Politics: Independent. **Established:** 1875
Special Editions: Football (Aug); Kids' Letters to Santa (Dec); Tax (Feb); Bride (Jan); Newcomers (Jun); Spring Fashion (Mar); Progress (May); Active Age (Monthly); Thanksgiving (Nov); Quality Control (Oct); Fall Fashion (Sept).
Special Weekly Sections: TV Times (Sat); Best Food Day (Wed).
Magazines: Relish (Monthly); USA WEEKEND Magazine (S); American Profile (Weekly).
Pub. ....Buddy King
Office Mgr. ....Janet Barnes
Adv. Sales Mgr. ....Rick Meredith
Mktg. Dir. ....Kirk Blair
Circ. Mgr. ....Bobby Perry
Ed. ....Les Minor
Mng. Ed. ....Ethel Channon
City Ed. ....Christy Busby
Editorial Page Ed. ....Russell McDermott
Farm Reporter ....Greg Bischof
Features Ed. ....Judy Morgan
News Ed. ....Andrea Miller
Photo Ed. ....Evan Lewis
Religion Ed. ....Rhonda Morrow
Sports Ed. ....Louie Avery
Technical Serv. Administrator ....Guy Wheatley
Prodn. Mgr., Mailroom ....Thomas Leonti
Prodn. Mgr., Press ....Sammy Lee
Pres. ....Walter E. Hussman
Jr. ....Walter E. Hussman
Market Information: ADS; TMC.
Mechanical available: Headliner Offset; Black and 3 ROP colors; insert accepted; page cutoffs - 22 3/4.
Mechanical Specifications: Type page 11 5/8 x 21 1/2; E - 6 cols, 1 13/16, 1/8 between; A - 6 cols, 1 13/16, 1/8 between; C - 9 cols, 1 1/4, 1/8 between.
Commodity Consumption: Avg. Page Number Per Issue - Daily 24; Avg. Page Number Per Issue - Plates Used 25200; Avg. Page Number Per Issue - Sunday 40; widths 25; Newsprint Used - Short Tons 2105; Printing Ink Used - Black 39947; Printing Ink Used - Color 17066; Printing Ink Use
Equipment EDITORIAL: Front-end Software – QPS/QuarkXPress, Adobe/Photoshop, Baseview 3.2.1, Red Hat Linux 8.; Editorial Hardware – 24-APP/iMac, 2-APP/Mac G3, 1-APP/Mac Power PC 8100, 1-APP/Mac Power PC 8600, Quantum/4000 NAS; Editorial Printers – 2-AG/Accuset 1500 with Xitron software RIP CLASSIFIED: Front-end Software – Baseview/ClassFlow.; Classified Hardware – 1-Ad/iMac, 1-APP/G4 Mini Tower, 6-APP/iMac DISPLAY: Ad make-up applications – Multi-Ad/Creator, QPS/QuarkXPress, Multi-Ad/Cr; Display Hardware – 4-APP/Power Mac G3, 3-APP/Power Mac G4, 2-E-Mac; Display Printers – APP/Mac LaserWriter 360, Epson/Stylus 18x24 Color Printer, Tektronic/Phaser 560, Canon/Image Runner 5000, HP/Desinejet 1050C PRODUCTION: Pagination Software – QPS/; Production Equipment – 1-Nu/404, 2-AG/Accuset 1500 with Xytron RIP, 1-Glunz & Jensen/550; Cameras – 1-C/Spartan III; Scanners – Microtek/ScanMaker IIXE flatbed color, APP/Mac IIfx, Microtek/FB scanner, Calera/Wordscan, HP/ScanJet (plus flatbed b&w) PRESSROOM: Line 1 – 5-G/Headliner Offset 5044-Double Width; Folders – 2-G/2:1. MAILROOM: Counter stackers – 2/QWI; Inserters and stuffers – 1372; Bundle tying machines – 1-MLN/2EE, 2-MLN/2A, Dynaric; Mailroom control system – Fincor; Addressing machine – 1-Ch/515 (with quarter folder), 1-/WM; Other equipment –Quipp/Bottom Wrap 5114. BUSINESS COMPUTERS: Business Software – Lawson, PBS; Business Hardware – Wyse, Dell, APP/Mac, IBM/RS6000

TEXARKANA NEWSPAPERS, INC.

315 Pine St., Texarkana, Texas, 75501; gen tel (903) 794-3311; adv tel 903-794-3311; gen fax (903) 792-7183; adv fax 903-792-7183; adv e-mail ads2@texarkanagazette.com; web site www.texarkanagazette.com
Published: Mon, Tues, Wed, Thur, Fri, Sat, Sun
Weekday Frequency: m
Saturday Frequency: m
Circulation: 27,114; 27,114(sat); 29,186(sun)
Insert rate: 64 per M
Politics: 1873
Advertising not accepted: N
Own facility?: Y
Delivery method: Mail, Newsstand, Private Carrier, Racks

TYLER

T.B. BUTLER PUBLISHING CO., INC.

410 W. Erwin St., Tyler, Texas, 75702; gen tel (903) 597-8111; gen fax (903) 595-0335

TYLER MORNING TELEGRAPH

410 W. Erwin St., Tyler, Texas, 75702-7133; gen tel (903) 597-8111; adv tel (903) 597-8111; ed tel (903) 597-8111; gen fax (903) 596-6368; adv fax (903) 597-4987; ed fax (903) 595-0335; gen e-mail opinion@tylerpaper.com; circulation@tylerpaper.com; adv e-mail r19@tylerpaper.com; web site www.tylerpaper.com
Published: Mon, Tues, Wed, Thur, Fri, Sat, Sun
Weekday Frequency: m
Saturday Frequency: m
Circulation: 26,357; 31,784(sat); 30,826(sun)
Last Audit: ABC September 30, 2011
Price: 8.95/mo (carrier), $12.25/mo (mail); 107.40/yr.
Advertising: Open inch rate $28.33
News services: AP, SHNS.
Politics: Independent. **Established:** 1929
Not Published: Christmas.
Special Editions: Business & Industry (Apr); Football (Aug); Christmas Greetings (Dec); Engineer's Week (Feb); Pillars of Progress (Jan); Parade of Homes (Jul); Senior Citizens (Jun); TALC (Mar); Discover Summer (May); Rose Festival (Oct); Clubs & Organizations (Sept).
Special Weekly Sections: Entertainment Showcase (Fri); Color Comics (S); Food (Wed).
Magazines: Parade (S).
Pres./Pub ....Nelson Clyde
CFO ....Thomas Clyde
Vice Pres., Sales/Mktg. ....Art McClelland
Adv. Mgr., Nat'l ....Robin Land
Adv. Mgr., Opns. ....Jasper Curtis
Adv. Mgr., Classified ....Shannon Hildreth
Circ. Dir. ....Jerry Rives
Asst. Circ. Mgr. ....Bill Campbell
Exec. Ed. ....Jim Giametta
Mng. Ed. ....Dave Berry
Asst. Mng. Ed. ....Richard Loomis
Asst. Mng. Ed. ....Danny Mogle
Bus. Ed. ....Greg Junek
Community Ed. ....Joyce Turner
Educ. Ed. ....Betty Waters
Librarian ....Diane May
Religion Ed. ....Patrick Butler
Sports Ed. ....Phil Hicks
Travel Ed. ....Terry Cannon
Mgmt. Info Servs. Mgr. ....John Albright
Mechanical available: Offset; Black and 3 ROP colors; insert accepted - hi fi, spadea; page cutoffs - 22 3/4.
Mechanical Specifications: Type page 11 5/8 x 21 1/2; E - 6 cols, 1 5/6, 1/8 between; A - 6 cols, 1 5/6, 1/8 between; C - 9 cols, 1 3/16, 1/8 between.
Commodity Consumption: Avg. Page Number Per Issue - Daily 44; Avg. Page Number Per Issue - Plates Used 84000; Avg. Page Number Per Issue - Saturday 36; Avg. Page Number Per Issue - Sunday 96; widths 24 3/4; Newsprint Used - Short Tons 5000; Printing Ink Used - Black 84000; Pri
Equipment EDITORIAL: Front-end Software – Advanced Pub. Technology/Automated Complete Typesetting.; Editorial Hardware – Novell/Network (PC Based) Client Server 4.1; Editorial Printers – ECR/VRL 36, Tektronix/Phaser 600 CLASSIFIED: Front-end Software – Brainworks.; Classified Hardware – Novell/Network (PC Based) Client Server 4.1; Classified Printers – Tektronix/Phaser 600 DISPLAY: Ad make-up applications – QPS/QuarkXPress, Adobe/Illustrator, Adobe/Photoshop; Layout Software – Advanced Pub. T; Display Hardware – 6-PC; Display Printers – Tektronix/Phaser 600 PRODUCTION: Pagination Software – APT, MEI/ALS, QPS/QuarkXPress.; Production Equipment – Text Bridge/Pro, Macro/JetSetter; Cameras – 3-Kk/DC50, Digital Cameras; Scanners – Lf/Leafscan, Umax/Flatbed, Epson/Flatbed, Visioneer/Single Sheet Scanner, Kk/Film Scanner, Konica/Scanner PRESSROOM: Line 1 – 12-HI/845N single width 1974; Press Drives – SECO/Warner Baldor; Folders – 2-HI/RBC-2; Pasters – 6; Press control system – Entertron/PLC. MAILROOM: Counter stackers – 3/HL, 2-QWI/401; Inserters and stuffers – 1-K & M/1372; Bundle tying machines – 3-OVL/415, 1-OVL/515; Mailroom control system – K & M/Image PC, QWI/Program 32; Addressing machine – 1-KR/215; Other equipment –3-QWI/Viper w/Mathews ink AUDIO: Audio Software – Info-Connect (Pottsville Republican); Audio Hardware – AP SelectStox, New Horizons/Info-Connect (Pottsville Republican) BUSINESS COMPUTERS: Business Software – Advanced Publishing Technology; Business Hardware – Advanced Publishing Technology

VERNON

THE VERNON DAILY RECORD

3214 Wilbarger St., Vernon, Texas, 76384; gen tel (940) 552-5454; adv tel (940) 552-5454; ed tel (940) 552-5454; gen fax (940) 553-4823; adv fax (940) 553-4823; ed fax (940) 553-4823; gen e-mail vdr@vernonrecord.com; adv e-mail vdr@vernonrecord.com; ed e-mail vdr@vernonrecord.com; web site www.vernonrecord.com
Published: Mon, Tues, Wed, Thur, Fri, Sun
Weekday Frequency: e
Circulation: 3,600; 4,000(sun)
Last Audit: Sworn March 31, 2007
Price: 12.00/mo; 114.00/yr.
Advertising: Open inch rate $9.90
Insert rate: 100 cpm
News services: AP.
Politics: Independent.
Not Published: Independence Day; Christmas.
Own facility?: Y
Magazines: American Profile (Weekly).
Sec ....Walter Buckel
Treasurer ....Keith McCormick
Adv. Dir. ....Jim Surber
Circ. Coord. ....Beverly Kenedy
News Ed. ....Kathy McClellan
Society Ed. ....Joyce Ashley
Sports Ed. ....Demetrius Thompson
Prodn. Mgr. ....Charles Ashley
President / Publisher ....Bret McCormick
Classified & New Media Director Teri McCormick
Pres./Pub. ....Larry L. Crabtree
Market Information: Split run; TMC.
Mechanical available: Offset; Black and 3 ROP colors; insert accepted; page cutoffs - 22 3/4.
Mechanical Specifications: Type page 13 x 21; E - 6 cols, 2 1/16, 1/8 between; A - 6 cols, 2 1/16, 1/8 between; C - 6 cols, 2 1/16, 1/8 between.
Commodity Consumption: Avg. Page Number Per Issue - Daily 12; Avg. Page Number Per Issue - Sunday 24; widths 27 1/2; Newsprint Used - Short Tons 90.
Equipment EDITORIAL: Front-end Software – FSI.; Editorial Hardware – FSI CLASSIFIED: Front-end Software – FSI.; Classified Hardware – FSI; Classified Printers – Xante/Accel-a-Writer DISPLAY: Ad make-up applications – FSI; Layout Software – FSI.; Display Hardware – FSI; Display Printers – Xante/Accel-a-Writer; Production Equipment – 1-Nu; Cameras – C. PRESSROOM: Line 1 – 6-G/Community 1986.; Inserters and stuffers – KAN/340; Bundle tying machines – Bu.; Addressing machine – Yes; Business Hardware – PC

VERNON RECORD, INC.

3214 Wilbarger, Vernon, Texas, 76384; gen tel (940) 552-5454; gen fax (940) 553-4823

VICTORIA

VICTORIA ADVOCATE

311 E. Constitution St., Victoria, Texas, 77901-8140; gen tel (361) 575-1451; adv tel (361) 574-1241; ed tel (361) 574-1222; gen fax (361) 574-1220; adv fax (361) 574-1225; ed fax (361) 574-1220; adv e-mail advertising@vicad.com; ed e-mail newsroom@vicad.com; web site www.victoriaadvocate.com
Published: Mon, Tues, Wed, Thur, Fri, Sat, Sun
Weekday Frequency: m
Saturday Frequency: m
Circulation: 30,143; 30,143(sat); 31,991(sun)
Last Audit: September 30, 2009
Price: 11.50/mo, $13.00/mo (county); 144.00/yr.
Advertising: Open inch rate $54.83
News services: AP, NYT.
Politics: Independent. **Established:** 1846
Special Editions: Looking Good, Feeling Food (Aug); Holiday Inspirations (Dec); Livestock (Feb); Home Product Show (Mar); Meet Your Local Merchants (May); All In Good Taste (Nov); Farm & Ranch (Oct).
Special Weekly Sections: Crossroads Events & Entertainment (Fri); TV Week (S).
Magazines: Parade (S).
Pres./Pub ....John M. Roberts
Sec./Treasurer ....Catherine McHaney
Vice Pres./Controller ....Stephen McHaney
Adv. Mgr., Nat'l ....Mark Mulholland
Circ. Mgr. ....Al H. Johnston
Ed. ....Chris Cobler
Online Ed. ....Tim Delaney
Local editor ....Becky Cooper
Mgr., Bus. Office ....Pat Strauss
Adv. Mgr., Classified ....Lucille Janecka
Exec. Ed. ....James Bishop
Mng. Ed. ....Scot Walker
Editorial Page Ed. ....Joe Bean
Lifestyle Ed. ....Janet Jones
Metro Ed. ....Leah Leach
News Ed. ....Sara Hendricks
Photo Ed. ....Frank Tilley
Sports Ed. ....Coy Slavik
Market Information: Split run; TMC; Zoned editions.
Mechanical available: Offset; Black and 3 ROP colors; insert accepted; page cutoffs - 22 3/4.
Mechanical Specifications: Type page 11 5/8 x 21 1/2; E - 6 cols, 1 5/6, 1/8 between; A - 6 cols, 1 5/6, 1/8 between; C - 9 cols, 1 3/8, 1/16 between.
Commodity Consumption: Avg. Page Number Per Issue - Daily 34; Avg. Page Number Per Issue - Plates Used 56940; Avg. Page Number Per Issue - Saturday 52; Avg. Page Number Per Issue - Sunday 76; widths 37 1/2; Newsprint Used - Short Tons 3700; Printing Ink Used - Black 80000; Pri
Equipment EDITORIAL: Front-end Software – CNI/Agile Teambase Special Edition.; Editorial Hardware – IBM; Editorial Printers – 3-HP/Laser SL, 1-Epson/Color CLASSIFIED: Front-end Software – PPI.; Classified Hardware – Compaq; Classified Printers – HP/5si; Display Hardware – IBM.; Production Equipment – Kk/XL-7700 Printer, QPS, Lf/AP Leaf Picture Desk; Scanners – Nikon/35AF, Kk/2055 Plus, 2-AG/Arcus. PRESSROOM: Line 1 – 6-HI/N1650 (5 Registron reels) 1978; Press Drives – Haley/Controls/Emerson; Folders – 2-HI/2:1; Reels and Stands – 5-HI/Registron; Press control system – Haley/Emerson. MAILROOM: Counter stackers – 1-Id/550, 1-Id/2100, 2-Id/2000; Inserters and stuffers – 2/AM Graphics/848; Bundle tying machines – 1-MLN/ML2-EE, 1-OVL/JP80, 1-OVL/JP40, 1-OVL/415-A. BUSINESS COMPUTERS: Business Software – SBS Business Software, PPI Advertising Software; Business Hardware – Compaq/Prosignia 300

WACO

WACO TRIBUNE-HERALD

900 Franklin Ave., Waco, Texas, 76701-1906; gen tel (254) 757-5757; adv tel (254) 757-5830; ed tel (254) 757-5701; gen fax (254) 757-0302; adv fax (254) 756-6906; ed fax (254) 757-0302; gen e-mail letters@wacotrib.com; ed e-mail letters@wacotrib.com; web site www.wacotrib.com

Group: Robinson Media Company, LLC
Metro Newspaper Advertising Services, Inc.
Published: Mon, Tues, Wed, Thur, Fri, Sat, Sun
Weekday Frequency: m
Saturday Frequency: m
Circulation: 32,815; 32,193(sat); 38,586(sun)
Last Audit: ABC September 30, 2011
Price: 12.95/mo; 138.00/yr.
Advertising: Open inch rate $98.20
News services: AP, NYT, Cox News Service, LAT-WP.
Politics: Independent. **Established:** 1927
Own facility?: Y
Special Editions: Garden & Landscape (Apr); Back-to-School (Aug); Christmas Gift Guide (Dec); Spring Fashion (Feb); Bridal (Jan); This is Central Texas (Jul); Business & Industry (May); Seniors (Monthly); Health Directory (Nov); New Cars (Oct); Home Furnishings (Sept).
Special Weekly Sections: Business (Fri); Senior Citizens (Mon); Business (S); Religion (Sat); Neighbor (Thur); Hot Classifieds (Tues); Food (Wed).
Magazines: Waco Today (Monthly); Startime (local TV supplement) (S).
Human Resource Manager ....Lynn Chaney
Controller ....Donna Tadlock
Circ. Dir. ....Rick Deaver
Mng. Ed. ....Becky Gregory
Asst. Mng. Ed. ....Bruce Kabat
Bus./Finance Ed. ....Mike Copeland
City Ed. ....Bill Whitaker
Asst. City Ed. ....Jeff Osborne
Chief Photographer ....Rod Aydelotte
Radio/Television Ed. ....Chris Oliver
Systems Ed. ....Freida Jackson
Prodn. Mgr., Systems ....Phil Gutkowski
Interim Pub. ....Dan Savage
Dir., HR ....Lura Hancock
Mktg. Dir. ....Ann Roznovsky
Ed. ....Carlos Sanchez
Lifestyles Ed. ....Catherine Atkinson
Market Information: Split run; TMC; Zoned editions.
Mechanical Specifications: Type page 13 x 21 1/4; E - 6 cols, 2, 1/6 between; A - 6 cols, 2, 1/6 between; C - 9 cols, 1 3/8, 1/12 between.
Commodity Consumption: Avg. Page Number Per Issue - Daily 30; Avg. Page Number Per Issue - Plates Used 41252; Avg. Page Number Per Issue - Sunday 85; widths 54; Newsprint Used - Short Tons 4725; Printing Ink Used - Black 17751; Printing Ink Used - Color 30359; Printing Ink Use
Equipment EDITORIAL: Front-end Software – DTI/PageSpeed 4.2, DTI/SpeedWriter 4.2.; Editorial Hardware – Sun/E3000, APP/Mac G3, APP/Mac 7300; Editorial Printers – APP/Mac LaserWriter 8500 CLASSIFIED: Front-end Software – AT, DTI/ClassSpeed 4.2.3.; Classified Hardware – Sun/E3000, APP/Mac G3; Classified Printers – HP/LaserJet, APP/Mac LaserWriter 8500 DISPLAY: Ad make-up applications – Solaris 2.6.1, Sybase 11.0.3.3, DTI/AdSpeed 4.2; Layout Software – DTI/Planbuilder (7.8.4).; Display Hardware – Sun/E3000, APP/Mac G3; Display Printers – HP/LaserJet, APP/Mac LaserWriter 8500, Epson/Stylus PRODUCTION: Pagination Software – DTI 4.2.3.; Production Equipment – AU/APS-6, Adobe/Photoshop, APP/Power Mac G3, 8-AG/Studio Star 11x17; Cameras – C; Scanners – 2-AG/Horizon Plus, 1-HP/ScanJet 4S, 8-AG/Studio Star 11x17
Delivery method: Mail, Newsstand, Private Carrier, Racks

WAXAHACHIE

WAXAHACHIE DAILY LIGHT

200 W. Marvin Ave., Waxahachie, Texas, 75165; gen tel (972) 937-3310; gen fax (972) 937-1139; web site www.waxahachiedailylight.com

Published: Mon, Tues, Wed, Thur, Fri, Sun
Weekday Frequency: e
Circulation: 5,250; 5,662(sun)
Last Audit: September 30, 2006
Price: 9.50/mo; 114.00/yr.
Advertising: Open inch rate $11.60
News services: AP.
Politics: Independent. **Established:** 1867
Special Editions: Profile (Feb); Newcomers (Jul); Gingerbread Trail (Jun); Football (Sept).
Special Weekly Sections: Health (Fri); Business (S); Food (Wed).
Magazines: American Profile (Weekly).
Pub. ....Ray Pike
Bus. Mgr. ....Rachael Loftis
Adv. Mgr. ....Donna McFarland
Circ. Mgr. ....Brian Jones
Ed. ....Neal White
Mng. Ed. ....JoAnn Livingston
Prodn. Mgr. ....Joe Constancio
Market Information: TMC.
Mechanical available: Offset; Black and 4 ROP colors; insert accepted; page cutoffs - 22 3/4.
Mechanical Specifications: Type page 13 x 21 1/2; E - 6 cols, 1 5/6, 1/8 between; A - 6 cols, 1 5/6, 1/8 between; C - 10 cols, 1 5/6, 1/8 between.
Commodity Consumption: Avg. Page Number Per Issue - Daily 16; Avg. Page Number Per Issue - Plates Used 5000; Avg. Page Number Per Issue - Sunday 42; widths 12 1/2; Newsprint Used - Short Tons 409; Printing Ink Used - Black 12000; Printing Ink Used - Color 300; Printing Ink Use
Equipment EDITORIAL: Front-end Software – QPS/QuarkXPress, Adobe/Photoshop.; Editorial Hardware – APP/Mac SE30, APP/Mac G3, APP/Mac G4; Editorial Printers – HP/4MV CLASSIFIED: Front-end Software – Baseview.; Classified Hardware – APP/Mac SE30 DISPLAY: Ad make-up applications – QPS/QuarkXPress, Adobe/Photoshop; Layout Software – APP/Mac, APP/Mac II, APP/Mac G3, APP/Mac G4.; Display Printers – HP/4MV; Production Equipment – PrePress/Panther Pro; Cameras – 1-C/Spartan III. PRESSROOM: Line 1 – 6-G/Community (upper former); Folders – 1-G/Community SC.; Inserters and stuffers – 4/KAN; Bundle tying machines – 4-/Sa, 1-/MLN; Addressing machine – 1-Am/1900. BUSINESS COMPUTERS: Business Software – PBS, Accounting; Business Hardware – Gateway

WAXAHACHIE NEWSPAPER, INC.

200 W. Marvin, Waxahachie, Texas, 75165; gen tel (972) 937-3310; gen fax (972) 937-1139

WEATHERFORD

THE WEATHERFORD DEMOCRAT

512 Palo Pinto St., Weatherford, Texas, 76086; gen tel (817) 594-7447; gen fax (817) 594-9734; adv e-mail advertising@weatherforddemocrat.com; ed e-mail editor@weatherforddemocrat.com; web site www.weatherforddemocrat.com

Published: Tues, Wed, Thur, Fri, Sun
Weekday Frequency: m
Circulation: 3,740; 4,122(sun)
Last Audit: Sworn September 30, 2006
Price: 7.00/mo; 84.00/yr.
Advertising: Open inch rate $10
News services: AP.
Politics: Independent. **Established:** 1895
Not Published: New Year; Memorial Day; Independence Day; Labor Day; Christmas.
Special Editions: Christmas Gift Guides (Dec); Chamber of Commerce (Feb); Frontier Days (Jul); Christmas Gift Guides (Nov); Football (Sept).
Magazines: Relish (Monthly); USA WEEKEND Magazine (S); American Profile (Weekly).
Bus. Mgr. ....Sharon George
Circ. Mgr. ....Janette Fant
Sports Ed. ....Gregg Webb
Mechanical available: Offset; Black and 3 ROP colors; insert accepted - card; page cutoffs - 23.
Mechanical Specifications: Type page 13 x 21 1/2; E - 6 cols, 2 1/16, 1/8 between; A - 6 cols, 2 1/16, 1/8 between; C - 8 cols, 1 1/2, 1/8 between.
Commodity Consumption: Avg. Page Number Per Issue - Daily 21; Avg. Page Number Per Issue - Plates Used 9984; Avg. Page Number Per Issue - Sunday 39; widths 27 1/2; Newsprint Used - Metric Tons 320; Printing Ink Used - Black 20250; Printing Ink Used - Color 1590; Printing Ink U
Equipment EDITORIAL: Front-end Software – Baseview/NewsEdit Pro.; Editorial Hardware – 8-APP/Power Mac; Editorial Printers – GCC CLASSIFIED: Front-end Software – Baseview/Class Manager Pro, Baseview/Class Flow.; Classified Hardware – 2-APP/Mac G3; Classified Printers – APP/Mac LaserPrinter NT; Layout Software – Adforce.; Display Hardware – 2-APP/Power Mac; Display Printers – APP/Mac LaserPrinter NT; Production Equipment – GCC, 6-APP/Mac G4; Cameras – Acti; Scanners – APP/Mac, 4-Umax. PRESSROOM: Line 1 – 8-G/Community; Folders – 6-G/2:1.; Bundle tying machines – 1-Mk/ACE 420, 1/MLN.; Business Hardware – Unisys/3105-00
Delivery method: Mail, Private Carrier

WICHITA FALLS

WICHITA FALLS TIMES RECORD NEWS

1301 Lamar St., Wichita Falls, Texas, 76301-7032; gen tel (940) 767-8341; adv tel (940) 720-3418; ed tel (940) 767-8341; gen fax (940) 720-3414; adv fax (940) 720-3453; ed fax (940) 767-1741; gen e-mail circulation@timesrecordnews.com; web site www.timesrecordnews.com

Group: E.W. Scripps
Metro Newspaper Advertising Services, Inc.
Published: Mon, Tues, Wed, Thur, Fri, Sat, Sun
Weekday Frequency: m
Saturday Frequency: m
Circulation: 21,483; 21,700(sat); 24,961(sun)
Last Audit: ABC September 30, 2011
Price: 15.35/mo; 184.20/yr.
Advertising: Open inch rate $38.91
News services: AP.
Politics: Independent-Democrat. **Established:** 1907
Special Weekly Sections: Next (Fri); Book Reviews (S); Garden Page (Sat); Financial Markets (Thur); Financial Markets (Tues); Best Food Day (Wed).
Magazines: Parade (S).
Relish
Athalon
Adv. Dir. ....Christy Ridinger
Adv. Mgr., Internet ....Tony Kouri
Adv. Coord., Nat'l ....Penny Webb
Mktg./Promo. Dir. ....Jackie Riley
Circ. Dir. ....Don Boyd
Ed. ....Carroll Wilson
Books Ed. ....Frances Tate
Bus./Oil Ed. ....Angel Riggs
Food Ed. ....Judith McGinnis
Librarian ....Jill Sexton
Photo Dept. Mgr. ....Gary Lawson
Radio/Television Ed. ....Lana Sweeten Shults
Regl. Ed. ....Suzanne Moore
Society/Women's Ed. ....Bridget Knight
Sports Ed. ....Nick Gholson
Dir., Information Systems ....Bill Lindemann
Publisher ....Dwayne Bivona
Pub. ....Darrell Coleman
Market Information: Split run; TMC; Zoned editions.
Mechanical available: Offset; Black and 3 ROP colors; insert accepted - all; page cutoffs - 22 3/4.
Mechanical Specifications: Type page 13 x 21 1/2; E - 6 cols, 2 1/16, 1/8 between; A - 6 cols, 2 1/16, 1/8 between; C - 10 cols, 1 1/10, 1/16 between.
Commodity Consumption: Avg. Page Number Per Issue - Daily 32; Avg. Page Number Per Issue - Plates Used 50000; Avg. Page Number Per Issue - Sunday 48; widths 54; Newsprint Used - Short Tons 4300; Printing Ink Used - Black 70000; Printing Ink Used - Color 16000; Printing Ink Use
Equipment; Editorial Hardware – Ik; Editorial Equipment – APP/Mac; Editorial Printers – NewGen. CLASSIFIED: Front-end Software – Ik.; Classified Hardware – Ik; Classified Printers – NewGen DISPLAY: Ad make-up applications – Multi-Ad/Creator 3.6.3; Layout Software – CJ/Layout 80.; Display Hardware – APP/Mac; Display Printers – NewGen, Tegra PRODUCTION: Pagination Software – QPS/QuarkXPress 3.3.1.; Production Equipment – Nat, Tegra; Cameras – C; Scanners – ECR, Umax PRESSROOM: Line 1 – 7-G/Cosmo 1984. MAILROOM: Counter stackers – 3-Id, HL; Inserters and stuffers – 3/MM; Bundle tying machines – 4-/MLN; Addressing machine – 1-/KR.; Business Hardware – HP/3000

UTAH

LOGAN

CACHE VALLEY PUBLISHING CO.

75 W. 3rd North St., Logan, Utah, 84321; gen tel (435) 752-2121; gen fax (435) 753-6642

THE HERALD JOURNAL

75 W. 300 North St., Logan, Utah, 84321; gen tel (435) 752-2121; adv tel (435) 752-2121; gen fax (435) 753-6642; adv fax (435) 753-6642; adv e-mail sbrady@hjnews.com; ed e-mail cmcollum@hjnews.com; web site www.hjnews.com

Published: Mon, Tues, Wed, Thur, Fri, Sat, Sun
Weekday Frequency: m
Saturday Frequency: m
Circulation: 16,052; 16,052(sat); 17,279(sun)
Last Audit: September 30, 2008
Price: 9.50/mo.
Advertising: Open inch rate $14.47
News services: AP, CSM.
Politics: Independent.
Advertising not accepted: Liquor; Cigarettes.
Special Editions: Home & Garden (Apr); Football (Aug); Sidewalk Days (Jul); Customer Appreciation Days (Jun); Progress (Mar); Tourist (May); Basketball (Nov); Hunter's Guide (Sept).
Special Weekly Sections: Outdoor (Fri); Homefront (Mon); Focus (S); Discover (Thur); Health & Fitness (Tues); Food (Wed).
Magazines: Parade (S).
Pres./Pub. ....Bruce K. Smith
Adv. Dir. ....Shawn Brady
Circ. Mgr. ....Russ Davis
City Ed. ....Tyler Ricks
Editorial Page Ed. ....Charles McCollum
News Ed. ....Jamie Baer
Sports Ed. ....Shawn Harrison
Prodn. Mgr., Systems ....Paul Davis
Market Information: ADS; TMC; Zoned editions.
Mechanical available: Offset; Black and 3 ROP colors; insert accepted; page cutoffs - 21 1/2.
Mechanical Specifications: Type page 12 x 20 1/2; E - 6 cols, 2, 1/8 between; A - 6 cols, 2, 1/8 between; C - 9 cols, 1 3/8, 1/16 between.
Commodity Consumption: Avg. Page Number Per Issue - Daily 28; Avg. Page Number Per Issue - Plates Used 9000; Avg. Page Number Per Issue - Saturday 22; Avg. Page Number Per Issue - Sunday 44; widths 12; Newsprint Used - Metric Tons 750; Printing Ink Used - Pages Printed 11000.
Equipment; Editorial Hardware – APP/Mac Centris 660AU, APP/Mac G4 400mhz, APP/Mac G3 350mhz, APP/Mac G4 350mhz, APP/Mac G3

300mhz, APP/Power Mac 7500, APP/Power Mac 8500, APP/Power Mac, APP/Mac Centris 650; Editorial Equipment – HP/1050c, Tektronix/740; Editorial Printers – HP/5000, HP/1050C, HP CLASSIFIED: Front-end Software – Baseview/AdManager Pro 2.1.1.; Classified Hardware – APP/iMac; Classified Printers – Tektronix/Phaser 740, HP/LaserJet 6MP, Epson/Ink Jets DISPLAY: Ad make-up applications – QPS/QuarkXPress 4.0, Adobe/Photoshop 5.5, Adobe/Illustrator 9.0, APP/Mac Appleshare; Layout Software – 1-APP/Mac G3, 3-APP/Power Mac G4, 1-Power Compu; Display Hardware – 1-HP/Net Server; Display Printers – HP/LaserJet 6MP, HP/LJ 5000 PRODUCTION: Pagination Software – QPS/QuarkXPress 4.11.; Production Equipment – Offset, 2-APP/Power Mac G4 400mhz; Cameras – Nikon/DI-DIX; Scanners – COM, 1-Nikon/Scantouch 210, 2-Nikon/Super Coolscan LS1000, Epson/536XL PRESSROOM: Line 1 – 20-Dauphin/440 2001; Press Drives – 2001; Folders – 1-Dauphin/1035 with Quarterfold 2001; Pasters – 3-Tandem/Jardis 50 2001. MAILROOM: Counter stackers – BG/108, 2-QWI/SJ400, 3-QWI/SJ300, BG/Count-O-Veyor, Rima/RS25; Inserters and stuffers – SUR; Bundle tying machines – 2-Samuel/NP30. BUSINESS COMPUTERS: Business Software – Microsoft/Word, Microsoft/Works 5.0; Business Hardware – Sun/Sparc workstation

OGDEN

OGDEN PUBLISHING CORP. (STANDARD-EXAMINER)

332 South Ward Ave., Ogden, Utah, 84412; gen tel (801) 625-4200; gen fax (801) 625-4508; web site www.standard.net

Published: Mon, Tues, Wed, Thur, Fri, Sat, Sun
Weekday Frequency: m
Saturday Frequency: m
Price: 136.50/yr.
Advertising: Open inch rate $39.02
Own facility?: Y

STANDARD-EXAMINER

332 Standard Way, Ogden, Utah, 84412; gen tel (801) 625-4200; adv tel (801) 625-4300; ed tel (801) 625-4506; gen fax (801) 625-4508; adv fax (801) 625-4508; ed fax (801) 625-4299; gen e-mail news@standard.net; inquires@standard.net; adv e-mail advertise@standard.net; ed e-mail news@standard.net; web site www.standard.net

Published: Mon, Tues, Wed, Thur, Fri, Sat, Sun
Weekday Frequency: m
Saturday Frequency: m
Circulation: 62,603; 62,784(sat); 73,770(sun)
Last Audit: ABC September 30, 2011
Price: 9.85/mo; 136.50/yr.
Advertising: Open inch rate $55.16(m-fri)
News services: AP, MCT, SHNS, DJ, LAT-WP.

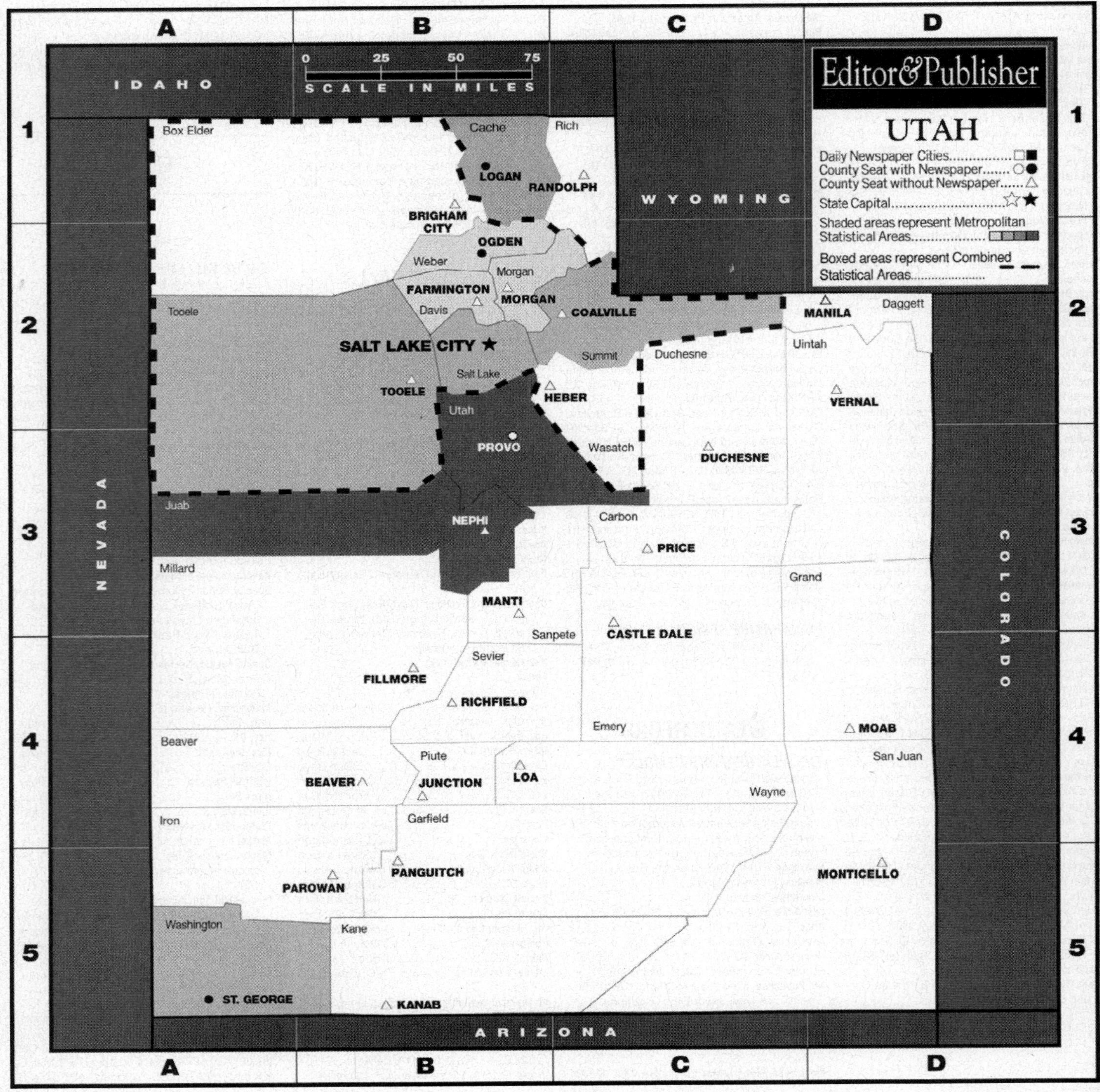

Politics: Independent. **Established:** 1888
Own facility?: Y
Special Editions: Parade of Homes (Aug); Neighborhoods (Dec); Bride & Groom (Jan); Pioneer Days (Jul); Home & Garden (Mar); Coupon Power (Monthly); Auto Guide (Nov); Car Care (Oct); Health & Fitness (Quarterly); Homemaker's School (Sept).
Special Weekly Sections: Classified Auto (Fri); Real Estate (S); TV Preview (Sat); Outdoors (Thur); Best Food Day (Tues).
Magazines: Relish (Monthly); USA WEEKEND Magazine (S); American Profile (Weekly).
Pub. VP..........Lee Carter
Exec. Asst. to the Pub...........Anne Paul
Dir., Sales..........Bradley N. Roghaar
Adv. Mgr., Classified..........David Newman
Adv. Mgr., Display..........Jared Bird
Adv. Mgr., Major/Nat'l..........Julie Hartman
Adv. Supvr., Classified Telephone Sales Karie Gardner
Mgr., Creative..........Brad Roghaar
Circ. Dir...........Ron Thornburg
Davis Co. Ed./Bureau Chief..........Shauna Lund
Editorial Page Ed...........Don Porter
Educ. Ed...........Amy Stewart
Features Ed...........Vanessa Zimmer
Graphics Ed...........Andy Howell
Metro Ed...........David Greiling
Sports Ed...........Chris Miller
Market Information: TMC; Zoned editions.
Mechanical available: Offset; Black and 3 ROP colors; insert accepted - product samples; page cutoffs - 21 1/2.
Mechanical Specifications: Type page 11 1/2 x 20 1/2; E - 6 cols, 1 5/6, 1/8 between; A - 6 cols, 1 5/6, 1/8 between; C - 9 cols, 1 1/3, 1/8 between.
Commodity Consumption: Avg. Page Number Per Issue - Daily 45; Avg. Page Number Per Issue - Plates Used 38000; Avg. Page Number Per Issue - Saturday 49; Avg. Page Number Per Issue - Sunday 65; widths 17; Newsprint Used - Short Tons 8100; Printing Ink Used - Black 108000; Printi
Equipment: Editorial Hardware – Tandem/CLX, Sun, 7-APP/Servers, 70-Baseview/NewsEditPro, 12-Baseview/NewsEditPro IQ; Editorial Equipment – APP/Mac IIfx, AP/GraphicsNet, APP/Mac One Scanner, HP/ScanJet IIc; Editorial Printers – 1-HP/5si, 1-HP/3si, 2-HP/4, HP/II, 4-HP/8100. CLASSIFIED: Front-end Software – SII/Classified, SII/ICP Sys.; Classified Hardware – SII/Sys 66, 23-SII/Coyote 3, 3-SII, 3-SII/Echo, iQue, Tandem/CLX, Sun; Classified Printers – 1-HP/5si, 1-HP/4L DISPLAY: Ad make-up applications – SII/Classified, CZAR II; Layout Software – SII/IAL, SCS Layout 8000.; Display Hardware – SII/Sys 66, 5-SII/Coyote III, 1-Umax/C600; Display Printers – 1-HP/5si PRODUCTION: Pagination Software – SII/System 66, SCS.; Production Equipment – Caere/OmniPage, Na/20, WL, HP/Laser Jet Series IV, 3-AJ/Graphic Ripps PRESSROOM: Line 1 – 6-KBA/Comet (6 towers, 48 couples) single width; Press Drives – Indramet/Shaftless; Reels and Stands – Amal/AR-80; Press registration system – Quad Tech/RGS 5. MAILROOM: Counter stackers – 2-Id/2100, 2-QWI/2100; Inserters and stuffers – GMA/SLS 2000; Bundle tying machines – 2/Dynaric; Mailroom control system – Ferag/Single Gripper; Addressing machine – Marconi; Other equipment – MM/Stitcher-Trimmer. BUSINESS COMPUTERS: Business Software – WordPerfect, Microsoft/Office, ADP, Great Plains; Business Hardware – 42-PC

PROVO

THE DAILY HERALD

1555 N. Freedom Blvd., Provo, Utah, 84604; gen tel (801) 373-5050; adv tel 801-344-2957; ed tel (801) 344-2540; adv fax (801) 356-3012; ed fax (801) 344-2985; adv e-mail sehrmantraut@heraldextra.com; ed e-mail rwright@heraldextra.com; web site www.heraldextra.com
Published: Mon, Tues, Wed, Thur, Fri, Sat, Sun
Weekday Frequency: m
Saturday Frequency: m
Circulation: 27,948; 26,993(sat); 43,586(sun)
Last Audit: ABC September 30, 2011
Price: 2.55/wk; 124.80/yr.
Advertising: Open inch rate $60.00
News services: AP, CNS, MCT, TMS.
Politics: Independent.
Own facility?: Y
Special Editions: Summer Recreation & Travel (Apr); Football (Aug); Gift Guide (Dec); Valentine's Day (Feb); Father's Day (Jun); Progress (Mar); Provo Open (May); Home Interiors (Oct); Best of Utah Valley (Sept).
Special Weekly Sections: Wheels (Fri); TV Magazine (Sat); UV-Utah Valley's Weekly Entertainment Guide (Thur); Best Food Day (Tues).
Magazines: Relish (Monthly)
Parade
Pres./Pub...........Rona Rahlf
Adv. Dir...........Sarah Ehrmantraut
Circ. Dir...........Stephen Kelsey
Exec. Ed...........Randy Wright
Metro Ed...........Amie Rose
Editorial Page Ed...........James E. Tynen
Lifestyle Ed...........Elyssa Andrus
News Ed...........Jessica Eyre
Religion Ed...........Cody Clark
Michele Bates
Sports Editor..........Jared Lloyd
Market Information: TMC.
Mechanical available: Offset; Black and 3 ROP colors; insert accepted; page cutoffs - 21 3/8.
Mechanical Specifications: Type page 11 5/8 x 21 1/2; E - 6 cols, 1 3/4, 1/8 between; A - 6 cols, 1 3/4, 1/8 between; C - 10 cols, 1, 1/8 between.
Commodity Consumption: Avg. Page Number Per Issue - Daily 46; Avg. Page Number Per Issue - Plates Used 18000; Avg. Page Number Per Issue - Saturday 46; Avg. Page Number Per Issue - Sunday 76; widths 25; Newsprint Used - Metric Tons 4200; Printing Ink Used - Black 110000; Print
Equipment EDITORIAL: Front-end Software – Baseview/NewsEdit IQUE 3.2.3.; Editorial Hardware – 30-APP/Mac, 40-APP/Mac; Editorial Equipment – 2-AU/3850, 2-AG/Accuset 1000-1500; Editorial Printers – 2-HP/8150 CLASSIFIED: Front-end Software – Baseview/Ad Manager Pro, Baseview/Ad Manager pro 2.0.6.; Classified Hardware – APP/Mac, 15-APP/Mac; Layout Software – MEI/ALS, MEI/ALS 4.0.; Display Hardware – Dell/PC, APP/Mac 7200, APP/Mac G4; Display Printers – 1-HP/5000, HP/5si PRODUCTION: Pagination Software – QPS/QuarkXPre; Cameras – COM/680C, AG/Repromaster 2200; Scanners – AG/Focus Colorscanner, Nikon/3500 Slide Scanner, 3-Nikon/Coolscan, Nikon/Scantouch 1200 PRESSROOM: Line 1 – ; Folders – 1; Inserters and stuffers – Inserter BUSINESS COMPUTERS: Business Software – Microsoft/Excel, Microsoft/Word, Lotus, PBS/MediaPlus; Business Hardware – IBM/PC, PBS, APP/Mac

SAINT GEORGE

THE SPECTRUM

275 E. St. George Blvd., Saint George, Utah, 84770; gen tel (435) 674-6200; adv tel (435) 674-6261; ed tel (435) 674-6286; gen fax (435) 674-6265; adv fax (435) 674-6264; ed fax (435) 674-6265; adv e-mail jbrowning@thespectrum.com; ed e-mail tseifert@thespectrum.com; web site www.thespectrum.com
Published: Mon, Tues, Wed, Thur, Fri, Sat, Sun
Weekday Frequency: m
Saturday Frequency: m
Circulation: 16,372; 19,542(sat); 20,548(sun)
Last Audit: ABC September 30, 2011
Price: 8.50/wk; 13.00/mo (mail); 91.80/yr.
Advertising: Open inch rate $24.65
News services: AP, GNS, LAT-WP.
Politics: 1963
Special Editions: Spring Home & Garden (Apr); Iron County Parade of Homes (Aug); Last Minute Gifts (Dec); St. George Parade of Homes (Feb); Bridal Fair (Jan); Washington County Fair (Jul); Tuacahn Tabloid (Jun); Getting in the Spirit (Nov); Complete Health (Oct); Kids Toda
Special Weekly Sections: Horsin' Around (Fri); Youth & Kidscoop (Mon); Lifestyles (S); Southern Homes (Sat); Automotive (Thur); e-technology/Biz (Tues); Home & Food (Wed).
Magazines: Where It's @ (Fri); USA WEEKEND Magazine (S).
Pres./Pub...........Donnie Welch
Adv. Dir...........James English
Online Ed...........Todd Seifert
Online Mgr...........Jackie Hermans
Market Information: ADS; Split run; TMC; Zoned editions.
Mechanical available: Offset; Black and 3 ROP colors; insert accepted - print, insert, deliver; page cutoffs - 22 3/4.
Mechanical Specifications: Type page 12 x 21 1/2; E - 6 cols, 1 1/9, 1/6 between; A - 6 cols, 1 1/9, 1/8 between; C - 6 cols, 1 1/9, 1/8 between.
Commodity Consumption: Avg. Page Number Per Issue - Daily 34; Avg. Page Number Per Issue - Plates Used 35205; Avg. Page Number Per Issue - Sunday 64; widths 25; Newsprint Used - Metric Tons 1633; Printing Ink Used - Black 26218; Printing Ink Used - Color 11626; Printing Ink Us
Equipment EDITORIAL: Front-end Software – QPS/QuarkXPress 4.1, Baseview/NewsEdit Pro 3.4.; Editorial Hardware – Microsoft/NT, APP/Mac, Mac; Editorial Equipment – Nikon/Super Coolscan, Canon/Digital; Editorial Printers – Canon/LBP860, Pre Press/Panther, Pre Press/Pro 46, HP/5000 GN CLASSIFIED: Front-end Software – Baseview.; Classified Hardware – APP/Mac; Classified Equipment – Kk/Digital Imaging; Classified Printers – HP/4MV, Pre Press/Panther Pro 46 DISPLAY: Ad make-up applications – Multi-Ad, QPS/QuarkXPress, Adobe/Photoshop, Adobe/Acrobat, Adobe/PageMaker, Archetype/Corel Draw, Adobe/Illustrator; Display Hardware – APP/Mac, PC; Display Printers – HP/4MV, Pre Press/Panther Pro PRODUCTION: Pagination Software – QPS/QuarkXPress 3.3, QPS/QuarkXPress 4.1.; Production Equipment – Caere/OmniPage, Pre Press/Panther Plus, Adobe/Photoshop, Caere/OmniPage; Scanners – Umax/680 Color Flatbed, Lf/Leafscan 35, ECR/Autokon 3850, AG/SnapScan PRESSROOM: Line 1 – 9-G/Community; Folders – 1-G/2:1. MAILROOM: Counter stackers – QWI/301W, BG/Count-O-Veyor; Inserters and stuffers – 5-MM/227; Bundle tying machines – 1-OVL/415; Addressing machine – Cheshire/534.; Business Hardware – Software ☐ Newzware

SALT LAKE CITY

DESERET NEWS

30 E. 100 S., Salt Lake City, Utah, 84111; gen tel (801) 236-6000; adv tel (801) 204-6300; ed tel (801) 237-2100; gen fax (801) 237-2121; ed e-mail citydesk@desnews.com; web site www.deseretnews.com
Group: Metro Newspaper Advertising Services, Inc.
Published: Mon, Tues, Wed, Thur, Fri, Sat, Sun
Weekday Frequency: m
Saturday Frequency: m
Circulation: 68,745; 70,871(sat); 78,742(sun)
Last Audit: September 30, 2009
Price: 172.64/yr; 5.76/4wk (d), $9.24/4wk (d&S), $7.00/4wk (S).
Advertising: Open inch rate $202.77
News services: AP, CSM, CT, LAT-WP, NNS, NYT.
Politics: Independent. **Established:** 1850
Note: For advertising, circulation, production personnel and information on production and printing, see Salt Lake City Newspaper Agency Corp. The Deseret News (mS) and The Salt Lake Tribune (mS) have a combination rate of $253.50(d) and $298.90(S).
Special Weekly Sections: Leisure (Fri); Education (Mon); Arts (S); Ethics-Religion (Sat); Family (Thur); Best Food Day (Tues); Science-Technology (Wed).
Magazines: Parade (S).
Chrmn...........Mark H. Willes
Pres./Pub...........Jim Wall
CFO..........Michael Todd
Ed...........Joseph A. Cannon
Mng. Ed...........Richard Hall
Asst. Mng. Ed...........Wendy Ogata
Editorial Page Ed...........Jay Evensen
Features Ed...........Angelyn Nelson-Hutchinson
Film Critic..........Jeff Vice
Food Ed...........Valerie Phillips
Graphics Dir...........Heather Tuttle
Health/Medical Writer..........Lois Collins
Music Ed...........Scott Iwasaki
NIE Ed...........Brenda Smith
Photo Ed...........Ravell Call
Political Ed...........Bob Bernick
Religion Ed...........Carrie Moore
Sports Ed...........Kent Condon
Television Ed...........Scott Pierce
Dir., Interactive Media..........Charlie Craine
Market Information: ADS; Split run; TMC; Zoned editions.
Commodity Consumption: Avg. Page Number Per Issue - Daily 64; Avg. Page Number Per Issue - Sunday 120.
Equipment EDITORIAL: Front-end Software – DTI.

DESERET NEWS PUBLISHING CO.

30 East 100 South, Salt Lake City, Utah, 84110; gen tel (801) 237-2120; gen fax (801) 237-2154

THE SALT LAKE TRIBUNE

90 S. 400 W., Ste. 700, Salt Lake City, Utah, 84101; gen tel (801) 257-8500; adv tel (801) 237-2815; ed tel (801) 257-8742; gen fax (801) 257-8525; adv fax (801) 237-2519; ed fax (801) 257-8525; gen e-mail newsroom@sltrib.com; web site www.sltrib.com
Group: Metro Newspaper Advertising Services, Inc.
Published: Mon, Tues, Wed, Thur, Fri, Sat, Sun
Weekday Frequency: m
Saturday Frequency: m
Circulation: 105,746; 103,748(sat); 122,782(sun)
Last Audit: ABC September 30, 2011
Price: 4.00/wk (home delivery); Daily $.75, Sunday $2.00
Advertising: Open inch rate $239.12
News services: AP, GNS, MCT, LAT-WP, CQ, Scripps McClatchy, West Wire, Religious News Service.
Politics: Independent. **Established:** 1871
Note: For advertising, circulation, production personnel and information on production and printing, see Salt Lake City Newspaper Agency Corp. The Salt Lake Tribune (mS) and The Deseret News (mS) have a combination rate of $253.50(d) and $298.90(S).
Special Editions: Yard & Home (Apr); Football (Aug); Christmas Gift (Dec); Wedding (Feb); Health & Fitness (Jan); Franklin Quest Golf (Jul); Father's Day (Jun); Progress (Mar); Seniors I (May); Early Bird Gift (Nov); Home & Garden (Oct); Focus on Business (Sept).
Special Weekly Sections: Business Pages (Fri); TV Book (S); Business Pages (Sat); Business Pages (Thur); Recreation Pages (Tues); Business Pages (Wed).
Magazines: Parade (S).
Pub...........Dean Singleton
Admin. Asst..........Shirley Jones
Ed...........Nancy Conway
Mng. Ed...........Tim Fitzpatrick
Mng. Ed., News/Bus...........Terry Orme
Art Ed...........Todd Adams
Cartoonist..........Pat Bagley
Editorial Page Ed...........Vern Anderson
Editorial Writer..........Paul Wetzel
Food Ed...........Kathy Stephenson
News Ed...........Lisa Carraburu
Political Ed...........Tom Harvey
Religion Ed...........Brooke Adams
School Ed...........Jon Keahey
Online Mgr...........Tony Semerad

Market Information: ADS; Split run; TMC; Zoned editions.
Mechanical available: Offset; Black and 3 ROP colors; insert accepted - various, call for information; page cutoffs - 22 3/4.
Mechanical Specifications: Type page 13 3/4 x 21 1/2; E - 6 cols, 2 1/4, 1/6 between; A - 6 cols, 2 1/4, 1/6 between; C - 10 cols, 1 1/4, 1/6 between.
Commodity Consumption: Avg. Page Number Per Issue - Daily 66; Avg. Page Number Per Issue - Plates Used 145200; Avg. Page Number Per Issue - Saturday 66; Avg. Page Number Per Issue - Sunday 126; widths 50; Newsprint Used - Metric Tons 32500; Printing Ink Used - Black 225000; Pr
Equipment EDITORIAL: Front-end Software – XYQUEST/XyWrite, DTI.; Editorial Hardware – APP/mac; Classified Hardware – PC. DISPLAY: Ad make-up applications – AT, QPS/QuarkXPress, All; Layout Software – MEI/ALS 8000, All.; Display Hardware – APP/Mac PRODUCTION: Pagination Software – DT4.; Production Equipment – WL, Nu/Flip Tops; Cameras – DSA; Scanners – Scitex/340 EZ Scanner PRESSROOM: Line 1 – 10-G/Metro double width (5 color decks) 1978; Line 2 – 10-G/HO double width (5 color decks) 1989; Line 3 – 10-G/HO double width (W/5 color decks); Line 4 – 20-G/Urbanite single width 1987; Folders – 3-Imperial/Folder 3.2, 1. MAILROOM: Counter stackers – 8/QWL, 2-/HL, 2-Id; Inserters and stuffers – S/1372, HI/1372, AM Graphics/2299; Bundle tying machines – 2-/Dynaric, 2-/Power Strap, 8-/Power Strap; Wrapping singles – 2-/Power Strap; Mailroom control system – ARS/1372, Icom/2299; Business Hardware – CJ

VERMONT

BARRE

THE TIMES ARGUS

540 N. Main St., Barre, Vt., 05641-0707; gen tel (802) 479-0191; adv tel (802) 479-0191; ed tel (802) 479-0191; gen fax (802) 479-4032; adv fax (802) 479-4097; ed fax (802) 479-4096; gen e-mail news@timesargus.com; web site www.timesargus.com
Published: Mon, Tues, Wed, Thur, Fri, Sat, Sun
Weekday Frequency: m
Saturday Frequency: m
Circulation: 7,251; 7,215(sat); 7,937(sun)
Last Audit: ABC September 30, 2011
Price: 3.45/wk; 13.44/mo (carrier), $15.52/mo (auto), $33.75/mo (mail); 172.50/yr.
Advertising: Open inch rate $20.50
News services: AP, NYT, McLatchy.
Politics: Independent. **Established:** 1806
Not Published: Christmas.
Special Editions: Christmas Gift Guide ().
Special Weekly Sections: TV Weekly (S).
Magazines: Relish (Monthly); Vermont Sunday Magazine (S).
Pres./Pub. ....R. John Mitchell
Gen. Mgr. ....Catherine Nelson
Bus. Office Mgr. ....Elizabeth Wechsler
Sales Supvr. ....Peter Borden
Circ. Mgr. ....Melodie Hudson
Ed. ....Sue Allen
Deputy Ed. ....Steve Pappas
Arts Ed. ....James Lowe
News Ed. ....Tom Sivret
Sports Ed. ....Jamie Biggam
Digital Media Dir. ....Russell Glitman
Prodn. Dir. ....Shawn Stabell
Prodn. Supvr., Mailroom ....Mark Wheaton
Prodn. Coord. ....Alice Laperle
Market Information: TMC.
Mechanical available: Offset; Black and 3 ROP colors; insert accepted; page cutoffs - 22 3/4.
Mechanical Specifications: Type page 11 5/8 x 21 1/4; E - 6 cols, 2, 3/8 between; A - 6 cols, 1 13/16, 3/16 between; C - 9 cols, 1 1/8, 1/8 between.
Commodity Consumption: Avg. Page Number Per Issue - Daily 24; Avg. Page Number Per Issue - Plates Used 21800; Avg. Page Number Per Issue - Saturday 24; Avg. Page Number Per Issue - Sunday 60; widths 12 1/2; Newsprint Used - Metric Tons 1088; Newsprint Used - Short Tons 1200; P
Equipment EDITORIAL: Front-end Software – Open Pages.; Editorial Hardware – ACI; Editorial Printers – HP, Xante; Classified Hardware – Vision Data; Classified Equipment – 5-APP/Mac G3. DISPLAY: Ad make-up applications – Multi-Ad/Creator, QPS/QuarkXPress 4.0, Adobe/Photoshop 5.0; Layout Software – MEI/ALS.; Display Hardware – 1-APP/Mac SE, 8-APP/Mac G3, 4-CD-Rom; Display Printers – HP/8500 PRODUCTION: Pagination Software – American Computer Innovators, QPS/QuarkXPress.; Production Equipment – 2-Nu/Flip Top FT40UPNS; Cameras – 1-C/Spartan III; Scanners – Nikon/Coolscan, 2-Umax PRESSROOM: Line 1 – 4-G/Urbanite; Folders – 1 MAILROOM: Counter stackers – BG/Count-O-Veyor 108, 1-S/Olympian, 1-MM/310-14; Inserters and stuffers – 1-S/1472, Heidleberg; Bundle tying machines – MLN/2A, Signode/Tyer, Alaebond Tyer; Wrapping singles – 2-S/Eclipse; Mailroom control system – Icon; Addressing machine – Addressing m BUSINESS COMPUTERS: Business Software – Vision Data; Business Hardware – Sun

TIMES ARGUS ASSOCIATION, INC.

540 N. Main St., Barre, Vt., 05641; gen tel (802) 479-0191; gen fax (802) 479-4032

BENNINGTON

BENNINGTON BANNER

425 Main St., Bennington, Vt., 05201-5027; gen tel (802) 447-2025; adv tel (802) 447-7567; gen fax (802) 442-3413; adv e-mail advertise@benningtonbanner.com; ed e-mail news@benningtonbanner.com; web site www.benningtonbanner.com
Group: Metro Suburbia, Inc./Newhouse Newspapers
Published: Mon, Tues, Wed, Thur, Fri, Sat
Weekday Frequency: m
Saturday Frequency: m
Circulation: 5,998; 6,642(sat)
Last Audit: ABC September 30, 2011
Price: 11.00/mo (in county), $15.00/mo (out of county); 105.00/yr.
Advertising: Open inch rate $20.90
News services: AP.
Politics: Independent. **Established:** 1905
Special Editions: Spring Home & Garden (Apr); Business & Industry (Feb); Christmas Gift Guide (Nov); Fall Home Improvement (Oct); Bennington Antique Car Show (Sept).
Special Weekly Sections: Entertainment (Fri); Sports (Mon); Entertainment (Sat); Entertainment (Thur); Food Day (Wed).
Magazines: USA WEEKEND Magazine (Sat); American Profile (Weekly).
Pub. ....Edward Woods
Adv. Sales Mgr. ....Doug Woodard
Circ. Dir. ....Christopher Oldham
Ed. ....James Therrien
Mng. Ed. ....Adam Samrov
Arts/Entertainment Ed. ....Stefanie Ryan
Local News Ed. ....Mark Rondeau
Sports Ed. ....Adam White
Interactive Media Dir. ....Bernard Re
Market Information: ADS; TMC.
Mechanical available: Offset; Black and 3 ROP colors; insert accepted - any; page cutoffs - 22 3/4.
Mechanical Specifications: Type page 13 x 21 1/4; E - 6 cols, 2 1/16, 1/8 between; A - 6 cols, 2 1/16, 1/8 between; C - 9 cols, 1 3/8, 1/16 between.
Commodity Consumption: Avg. Page Number Per Issue - Daily 18; Avg. Page Number Per Issue - Plates Used 6486; Avg. Page Number Per Issue - Saturday 28; widths 25; Newsprint Used - Short Tons 298; Printing Ink Used - Pages Printed 6486.
Equipment EDITORIAL: Front-end Software – QPS/QuarkXPress.; Editorial Hardware – APP/Power Mac; Editorial Equipment – 2-AST/PC 286 Premium, 1-Leading Edge/286, 2-PC 386SX CLASSIFIED: Front-end Software – PPI.; Classified Printers – 1-TI/810 Printer DISPLAY: Ad make-up applications – QPS/QuarkXPress, Adobe/Photoshop, Multi-Ad/Creator; Layout Software – APP/Power Mac.; Production Equipment – 2-APP/Power Mac, Konica/Imagesetter. BUSINESS COMPUTERS: Business Software – GEAR; Business Hardware – DEC/PDP 11-73

BRATTLEBORO

BRATTLEBORO REFORMER

62 Black Mountain Rd., Brattleboro, Vt., 5301; gen tel (802) 254-2311; adv tel (802) 254-2311; ed tel (802) 254-2311; gen fax (802) 257-1305; adv fax (802) 257-1305; ed fax (802) 257-1305; ed e-mail news@reformer.com; web site www.reformer.com
Group: Metro Suburbia, Inc./Newhouse Newspapers
Published: Mon, Tues, Wed, Thur, Fri
Weekday Frequency: m
Saturday Frequency: m
Circulation: 7,565; 8,901(sat); 8,901(sun)
Last Audit: ABC September 30, 2011
Price: 16.10/mo (carrier); 115.00/yr (carrier).
Advertising: Open inch rate $22.60
News services: AP.
Politics: Independent.
Not Published: Christmas.
Special Weekly Sections: Best Food Days (Mon); TV Tab (Sat); Entertainment (Thur); Education Page (Tues); Living (Wed).
Magazines: USA WEEKEND Magazine (Sat); American Profile (Weekly).
Pub. ....Edward L. Woods
Adv. Dir. ....Pat Finnell
Arts/Entertainment Ed. ....Jon Potter
Night News Ed. ....Randy Holhut
Wire Ed. ....Josephine Howard
Mailroom Mgr. ....Michael Colberg
Market Information: TMC.
Mechanical available: Offset; Black and 3 ROP colors; insert accepted; page cutoffs - 22 3/4.
Mechanical Specifications: Type page 13 x 21 1/4; E - 6 cols, 2 1/16, 1/8 between; A - 6 cols, 2 1/16, 1/8 between; C - 9 cols, 1 3/8, 1/16 between.
Commodity Consumption: Avg. Page Number Per Issue - Daily 22; Avg. Page Number Per Issue - Plates Used 7500; widths 27; Newsprint Used - Short Tons 483; Printing Ink Used - Black 13500; Printing Ink Used - Color 800; Printing Ink Used - Pages Printed 7500.
Equipment EDITORIAL: Front-end Software – Dewar.; Editorial Hardware – 2-Dewar/Sys II CLASSIFIED: Front-end Software – Dewar.; Classified Hardware – 2-Dewar/Sys II DISPLAY: Ad make-up applications – Dewar, Aldus/PageMaker, Archetype/Corel Draw; Layout Software – Dewar/Discovery.; Display Hardware – 3-Dewar/Discovery, PC 386; Production Equipment – C; Cameras – C/Marathon; Scanners – Panasonic/505. PRESSROOM: Line 1 – 8-G/Community; Folders – 2-G/SSC. MAILROOM: Counter stackers – 1/Fg; Bundle tying machines – 1-/MLN, 1-/OVL; Addressing machine – Wm. BUSINESS COMPUTERS: Business Software – Vision Data; Business Hardware – DEC/PDP 11-73

NEW ENGLAND NEWSPAPERS, INC.

Black Mountain Rd., Brattleboro, Vt., 05302; gen tel (802) 254-2311; gen fax (802) 257-1305; gen e-mail news@reformer.com; web site www.reformer.com
Published: Mon, Tues, Wed, Thur, Fri, Sat, Sun
Price: 108.00/yr.
Advertising: Open inch rate $14.40
Politics: 1904

BURLINGTON

THE BURLINGTON FREE PRESS

191 College St., Burlington, Vt., 5401; gen tel (802) 863-3441; ed tel (802) 865-0940; gen fax (802) 862-5622; adv fax (802) 863-4702; ed fax (802) 660-1802; adv e-mail nationalads@bfp.burlingtonfreepress.com; ed e-mail metro@bfp.burlingtonfreepress.com; web site www.burlingtonfreepress.com
Published: Mon, Tues, Wed, Thur, Fri, Sat, Sun
Weekday Frequency: m
Saturday Frequency: m
Circulation: 31,095; 33,489(sat); 40,708(sun)
Last Audit: ABC September 30, 2011
Price: 3.85/wk (carrier); 16.68/mo (carrier); 220.00/yr.
Advertising: Open inch rate $81.10
News services: AP, GNS, LAT-WP, NYT.
Politics: Independent. **Established:** 1827
Special Editions: Golf Expo (Apr); College (Aug); Gift Guide (Dec); Bridal (Jan); 4-Wheel Jamboree (Jul); Food Festival (Jun); Reader's Choice (Mar); Marathon (May); Vermont House & Home (Monthly); Giving Season (Nov); Vermont Skier (Oct); Menu Guide (Semi-monthly); Explor
Special Weekly Sections: Wheels (Fri); Business Monday (Mon); Outdoor (S); Home (Sat); Weekend (Thur); Food (Tues).
Magazines: USA WEEKEND Magazine (S).
Profile: The Burlington Free Press is a subsidary of Gannett Co., Inc. Gannett Co. is a large diversified news and information company.
Pres./Pub. ....Bradley I. Robertson
Adv. Dir. ....Tammy Shannon
Exec. Ed. ....Mike Townsend
Editorial Page Ed. ....Aki Soga
Features/Living Ed. ....Becky Holt
Asst. Metro Ed. ....Terri Hallenbeck
Asst. News Ed. ....Patrick Garrity
Dir., IT ....Trevor Chase
Prodn. Dir. ....Larry Stasulis
Prodn. Asst. Dir. ....Dennis Latulippe
Market Information: TMC.
Mechanical available: Offset; Black and 3 ROP colors; insert accepted - free standing; page cutoffs - 22 3/4.
Mechanical Specifications: Type page 13 x 21 1/2; E - 6 cols, 2 1/16, 1/8 between; A - 6 cols, 2 1/16, 1/8 between; C - 10 cols, 1 1/4, 1/16 between.
Commodity Consumption: Avg. Page Number Per Issue - Daily 48; Avg. Page Number Per Issue - Plates Used 32550; Avg. Page Number Per Issue - Sunday 88; widths 50; Newsprint Used - Metric Tons 5215; Newsprint Used - Short Tons 5748; Printing Ink Used - Black 100008; Printing Ink
Equipment EDITORIAL: Front-end Software – HI/NMP Newsmaker HI/NME Newsmaker Edit.; Editorial Hardware – 13-PC P300, 37-PC P100 CLASSIFIED: Front-end Software – HI/Ad Power.; Classified Hardware – 17-PC P111; Classified Printers – HP/LaserJet DISPLAY: Ad make-up applications – QPS/QuarkXPress 4.11; Layout Software – 3-APP/G3, 20-APP/Mac G4, 15-APP/G4.; Display Printers – 1-HP/800, 1-QMS/Magicolor 330 PRODUCTION: Pagination Software – HI/NMP Newsmaker, HI/CPAG Classified Pagination.; Production Equipment – 2-MON/Express Master 6000, 1-OCE/Thermal Proofer 9000G, 1-Alfa Quest/Proof Xpress II PRESSROOM: Line 1 – 5-G/Metro (2 color decks) double width 1967; Press Drives – 6-Fin/3260 1989; Folders – 2; Pasters – G/Automatic. MAILROOM: Counter stackers – 2-QWI/SJ20X, 1-HI/Rima RS-30, 2-QW/501; Inserters and stuffers – 1-HI/1472A, 2-Dynaric/NP-3; Bundle tying machines – 1-MLN/2A, 1-MLN/2EE, 2/Power Strap; Addressing machine – KR; Other equipment – MM/Stitcher, Trimmer. BUSINESS COMPUTERS: Business Software – Microsoft/Windows 95, Microsoft/Windows NT, Microsoft/Office 97, Microsoft/Windows 2000; Business Hardware – 1-IBM/AS-400

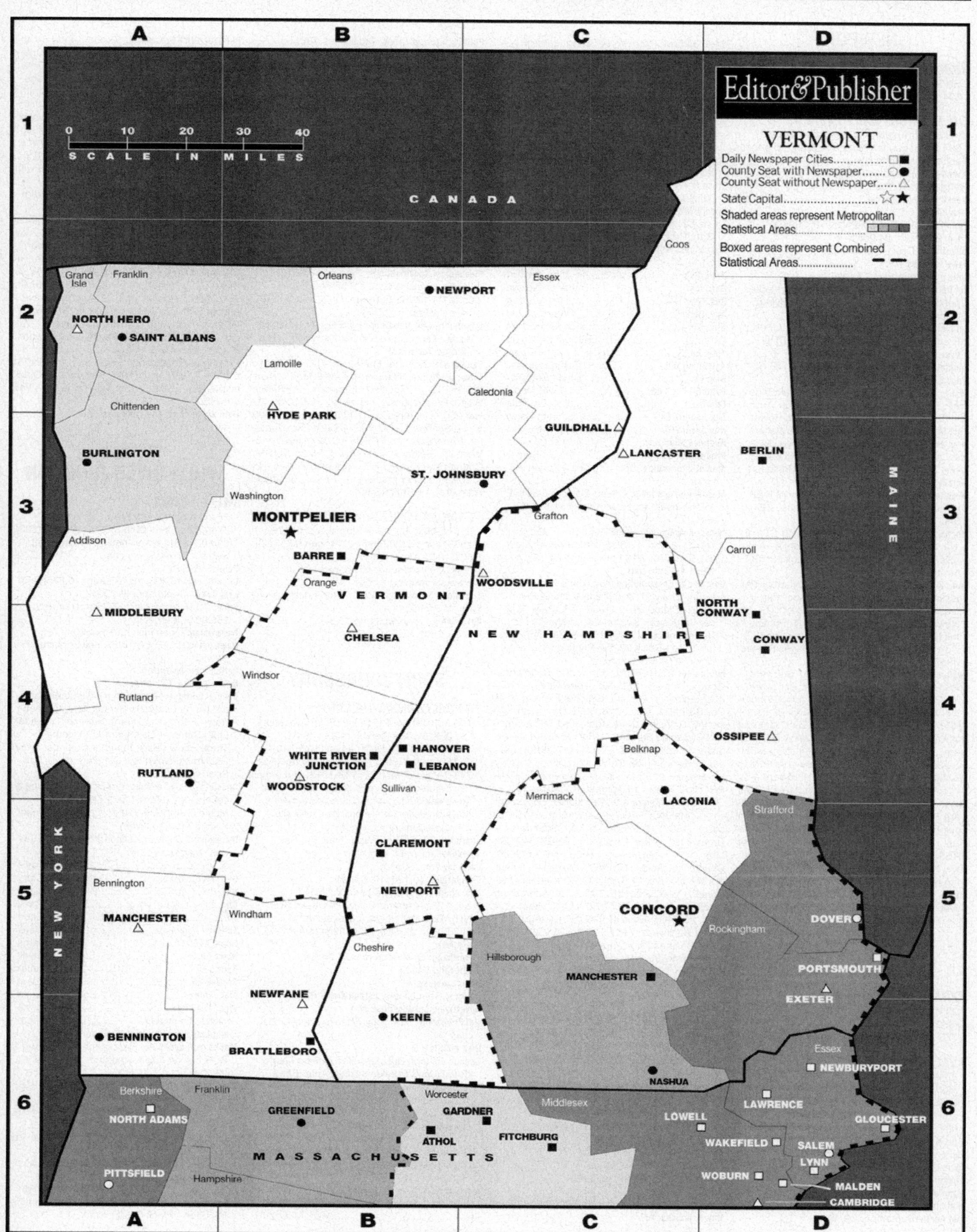
Editor&Publisher
VERMONT
Daily Newspaper Cities
County Seat with Newspaper
County Seat without Newspaper
State Capital
Shaded areas represent Metropolitan Statistical Areas
Boxed areas represent Combined Statistical Areas
SCALE IN MILES
CANADA
VERMONT
NEW HAMPSHIRE
NEW YORK
MAINE
MASSACHUSETTS
NORTH HERO
SAINT ALBANS
NEWPORT
HYDE PARK
BURLINGTON
GUILDHALL
LANCASTER
BERLIN
ST. JOHNSBURY
MONTPELIER
BARRE
WOODSVILLE
MIDDLEBURY
CHELSEA
NORTH CONWAY
CONWAY
OSSIPEE
HANOVER
WHITE RIVER JUNCTION
LEBANON
WOODSTOCK
RUTLAND
LACONIA
CLAREMONT
NEWPORT
CONCORD
MANCHESTER
DOVER
PORTSMOUTH
EXETER
MANCHESTER
NEWFANE
KEENE
BENNINGTON
BRATTLEBORO
NASHUA
NEWBURYPORT
NORTH ADAMS
GREENFIELD
GARDNER
ATHOL
FITCHBURG
LOWELL
LAWRENCE
GLOUCESTER
WAKEFIELD
SALEM
LYNN
PITTSFIELD
WOBURN
MALDEN
CAMBRIDGE

NEWPORT

HORIZON PUBLICATIONS INC

Hill St., Newport, Vt., 05855; gen tel (802) 334-6568; gen fax (802) 334-6891

THE NEWPORT DAILY EXPRESS

Hill St., Newport, Vt., 05855; gen tel (802) 334-6568; gen fax (802) 334-6891; ed e-mail editor@newportdailynews.com; web site www.newportdailynews.com

Published: Mon, Tues, Wed, Thur, Fri
Weekday Frequency: m
Circulation: 5,000
Last Audit: Sworn September 30, 2006
Price: 2.00/wk; 104.00/yr.
Advertising: Open inch rate $9.85
News services: AP.
Politics: Independent. **Established:** 1936
Not Published: New Year; Memorial Day; Independence Day; Labor Day; Thanksgiving; Christmas.
Special Editions: Gardening (Apr); Bridal (Feb); Progress (Jun); National Kitchen & Bath Week (Oct).
Special Weekly Sections: TV Weekender (Fri).
Magazines: American Profile (Weekly).
CFO .... Roland L. McBride
Pub. .... Ken Wells
Adv. Dir. .... Ellen Howell
Circ. Mgr. .... Sadie Watters
Mng. Ed. .... Steve Blake
Pres., Opns. .... David Radler
Prodn. Mgr. .... Karen Bartleson
Market Information: TMC.
Mechanical available: Offset; Black and 3 ROP colors; insert accepted; page cutoffs - 22 3/4.
Mechanical Specifications: Type page 13 1/8 x 21 1/2; E - 6 cols, 2 1/5, 1/12 between; A - 6 cols, 2 1/8, 1/12 between; C - 6 cols, 2 1/8, 1/12 between.
Commodity Consumption: Avg. Page Number Per Issue - Daily 14; Avg. Page Number Per Issue - Plates Used 4400; widths 27; Newsprint Used - Metric Tons 160; Printing Ink Used - Black 4600; Printing Ink Used - Color 500; Printing Ink Used - Pages Printed 3847.
Equipment EDITORIAL: Front-end Software – QPS/QuarkXPress 4.0.; Editorial Hardware – APP/Mac; Editorial Equipment – Adobe/Photoshop, Sprint/ScanMaker E6; Editorial Printers – APP/Mac Laser 8500 CLASSIFIED: Front-end Software – QPS/Class Flo 4.0.; Classified Hardware – APP/Mac; Classified Printers – Okidata/320 Turbo; Layout Software – APP/Mac G3, Multi-Ad/Creator.; Display Hardware – 2-ScrippSat/PC; Display Printers – APP/Mac Laser 12-640 PRODUCTION: Pagination Software – QPS/QuarkXPress 4.0.; Production Equipment – Paper Port/Strobe Scanner; Cameras – 1-K/241; Scanners – HP/ScanJet PRESSROOM: Line 1 – 4-G/Community; Folders – 1 MAILROOM: Counter stackers – Bundle tying machines □ 1/Saxmyer; Addressing machine – Wm.; Business Hardware – Synaptic/Micro Solutions, Acct/100, Okidata/393 Plus, Sun/Suntype

RUTLAND

HERALD ASSOCIATION, INC.

27 Wales St., Rutland, Vt., 05701; gen tel (802) 747-6121 ext. 2201; gen fax (802) 775-2423

RUTLAND HERALD

27 Wales St., Rutland, Vt., 05701; gen tel (800) 498-4296; adv tel (802) 747-6126; ed tel (802) 747-6133; gen fax (802) 775-2423; adv fax (802) 775-2423; ed fax (802) 773-0311; adv e-mail ads@rutlandherald.com; ed e-mail letters@rutlandherald.com; web site www.rutlandherald.com

Published: Mon, Tues, Wed, Thur, Fri, Sat
Weekday Frequency: m
Saturday Frequency: m
Circulation: 12,516; 13,680(sat); 14,778(sun)
Last Audit: September 30, 2009
Price: 3.25/wk (carrier); 14.08/mo (carrier); 16.25/5wk; 162.50/yr (carrier).
Advertising: Open inch rate $28.95
News services: AP, NYT, MCT.
Politics: Independent. **Established:** 1794
Not Published: Christmas.
Special Editions: Spring Car Care (Apr); Vermont State Fair (Aug); Photo Calendar (Dec); Valentine's Day (Feb); Healthy Lifestyles (Jan); Side Walk Sales (Jul); Graduation (Jun); Business Outlook (Mar); Mother's Day (May); Show & Sell (Monthly); Gift Guide (Nov); Fall Verm
Special Weekly Sections: Weekend (Fri); Best Food Day (Mon); Living (S); TV Magazine (Sat); People & Places (Thur).
Magazines: Relish (Monthly); Sun Magazine (S).
Pres./Pub. .... R. John Mitchell
Gen. Mgr. .... Catherine Nelson
Bus. Mgr. .... Doug Stuart
Adv. Dir. .... Peter Columd
Circ. Dir. .... Rob Arrowsmith
Ed. .... Randal Smathers
Mng. Ed. .... John Dolan
Asst. Mng. Ed. .... Sabina Haskell
Bus. Ed. .... Bruce Edwards
Editorial Page Ed. .... David Moats
Sports Ed. .... Bob Fredette
Asst. Sports Ed. .... Tom Haley
New Media Dir. .... Ernesto Burden
Audiotex Mgr. .... Robert G. Miller
Prodn. Dir. .... Shawn Stabell
Market Information: Split run; TMC; Zoned editions.
Mechanical available: Offset; Black and 3 ROP colors; insert accepted; page cutoffs - 22 3/4.
Mechanical Specifications: Type page 12 1/2 x 21 1/4; E - 6 cols, 1 13/16, 1/8 between; A - 6 cols, 1 13/16, 1/16 between; C - 9 cols, 1 1/8, 1/16 between.
Commodity Consumption: Avg. Page Number Per Issue - Daily 27; Avg. Page Number Per Issue - Plates Used 11950; Avg. Page Number Per Issue - Sunday 72; widths 12 1/2; Newsprint Used - Metric Tons 1200; Printing Ink Used - Black 22290; Printing Ink Used - Color 4270; Printing Ink
Equipment EDITORIAL: Front-end Software – Open Pages.; Editorial Hardware – PC, ACI/Pagination System; Editorial Printers – HP CLASSIFIED: Front-end Software – New Vision/4GL, Vision Data.; Classified Hardware – HP; Classified Printers – HP/2100 DISPLAY: Ad make-up applications – Multi-Ad/Creator; Layout Software – Mk/Managing Editor.; Display Hardware – APP/Mac G3; Display Printers – HP PRODUCTION: Pagination Software – QPS/QuarkXPress 4.0.; Production Equipment – 1-Xante/3N, 1-AG/Accuset 1000, 2-AG/Accuset 1500; Cameras – C; Scanners – Umax/840, Nikon/CoolScan PRESSROOM: Line 1 – 6-G/Urbanite 1965. MAILROOM: Counter stackers – 1-NP/500, Olympian; Inserters and stuffers – 1-KAN/480; Bundle tying machines – 1-MLN/ML1EE, 1-MLN/2A; Addressing machine – 1-KAN/600-650 Label Head (1/4 fold). AUDIO: Audio Software – Integra 5.3; Audio Hardware – PC BUSINESS COMPUTERS: Business Software – Vision Data; Business Hardware – Vision Data, Sun/Enterprise 450

SAINT ALBANS

ST. ALBANS MESSENGER

281 N. Main St., Saint Albans, Vt., 05478; gen tel (802) 524-9771; gen fax (802) 527-1948; gen e-mail news@samessenger.com; adv e-mail ads@samessenger.com; web site www.samessenger.com

Published: Mon, Tues, Wed, Thur, Fri, Sat, Sun
Weekday Frequency: e
Saturday Frequency: m
Circulation: 5,695; 5,930(sat)
Last Audit: September 30, 2006
Price: 113.60/yr.
Advertising: Open inch rate $16.00
News services: AP.
Politics: Independent. **Established:** 1861
Not Published: New Year; Independence Day; Labor Day; Thanksgiving; Christmas.
Special Editions: Energy (Fall); Dairy (Jun); Meet Your Business and Professional Communities (May); Christmas (Nov); Home Improvements (Spring); Sports (Winter).
Bus. Mgr./Controller .... Suzanne Lynn
Adv. Dir. .... Jeremy Read
Bus. Ed. .... Gary Rutkowski
Editorial Page Ed. .... Emerson Lynn
Sports Ed. .... Josh Kaufmann
Prodn. Mgr. .... Lynne Fletcher
Press Mgr. .... Alex Domina
Market Information: TMC; Zoned editions.
Mechanical available: Offset; Black and 3 ROP colors; insert accepted - any; page cutoffs - 22 3/4.
Mechanical Specifications: Type page 13 1/2 x 21; E - 6 cols, 2 1/16, 1/8 between; A - 6 cols, 2 1/16, 1/8 between; C - 6 cols, 2 1/16, 1/8 between.
Commodity Consumption: Avg. Page Number Per Issue - Daily 20; widths 32; Newsprint Used - Metric Tons 550.
Equipment; Editorial Hardware – 17-APP/Mac Plus; Editorial Printers – 4-APP/Mac LaserWriter Plus.; Classified Hardware – APP/Mac Plus.; Production Equipment – 1-B/3200, 1-Nat/250; Cameras – 1-Nu/20-24, 1-K/18-20 V241; Scanners – AG/FJF74/2200, Densitometer, Entre/Scanner. PRESSROOM: Line 1 – 6-Wd/240; Folders – 1-Wd/2:1. MAILROOM: Counter stackers – 1/BG; Wrapping singles – 2-/Us; Addressing machine – 1-/Am.; Business Hardware – RSK/TRS 80

VERMONT PUBLISHING CORP.

281 N. Main St., Saint Albans, Vt., 05478-2503; gen tel (802) 524-9771; gen fax (802) 527-1948; gen e-mail news@samessenger.com; web site www.samessenger.com

Published: Mon, Tues, Wed, Thur, Fri, Sat, Sun
Price: 113.60/yr.
Advertising: Open inch rate $9.50
Politics: 1861

SAINT JOHNSBURY

THE CALEDONIAN-RECORD

190 Federal St., PO Box 8, Saint Johnsbury, Vt., 05819-0008; gen tel (802) 748-8121; adv tel (802) 748-8121; ed tel (802) 748-8121; gen fax (802) 748-1613; adv fax (802) 748-1613; ed fax (802) 748-1613; gen e-mail news@caledonian-record.com; adv e-mail adv@caledonian-record.com; ed e-mail news@caledonian-record.com; web site www.caledonianrecord.com

Published: Mon, Tues, Wed, Thur, Fri, Sat
Weekday Frequency: m
Saturday Frequency: m
Circulation: 10,129; 10,129(sat)
Last Audit: ABC September 30, 2011
Price: 4.75/wk (carrier); 19.00/4 weeks (VT, NH), $22.00/4 weeks (other states); 212.00/yr (VT, NH), $235.00/yr (other states).
Advertising: Open inch rate $8.25 net
Insert rate: $45/M
News services: AP.
Politics: Republican. **Established:** 1837
Advertising not accepted: N
Not Published: New Year; Thanksgiving; Christmas.
Own facility?: Y
Special Editions: Business Recognition (Jan); Bridal (Jan); Presidents' Day Auto (Feb); Real Estate/Home Improvement (Apr); Travel Guide (Jun); Sports Year in Review (Jun); Car Care (Sept); Winter Guide (Oct); Christmas Gift Guide (Nov); @Record-Body:**Special Weekly Sections:** School (Mon); Business (Sat); Health Beat (Thur); Weddings (Wed)., Entertainment (Fri), Home and Garden (Tue)
Magazines: American Profile (Weekly); Relish (Monthly); Spry (Monthly).
Pres. .... Mark M. Smith
Publisher/Vice President .... Todd Smith
Bookkeeper .... Judy Burke
Exec. Ed. .... Dana Gray
City/Metro Ed. .... Andrew McGregor
Editorial Page Ed. .... Todd M. Smith
Educ. Services Director .... Rosie Smith
Picture Ed. .... Peter Lynch
Sports Ed. .... Michael Beniash
Advertising Director/Online Mgr. Michael Gonyaw
Mechanical Specifications: Type page 10 7/8 x 21; E - 6 cols per page, each col. 1.708 with 1/8 between columns
Equipment EDITORIAL: Front-end Software – GPS; Editorial Hardware – Various HP'S Mac G3; Editorial Equipment – Nikon/CoolScan III, AG/Arcus II Scanner; Editorial Printers – Various HP CLASSIFIED: Front-end Software – Falcon; Classified Hardware – Various HP; Classified Printers – Various HP DISPLAY: Ad make-up applications – QPS/QuarkXPress 8.02, Adobe/Photoshop CS2, Adobe/Acrobat 7; Layout Software – Falcon; Display Hardware – Various HP, 1 Mac G3; Display Printers – Various HP PRODUCTION: Pagination Software – FAlcon; Scanners – AG/Arcus II, Epson/636 Pro, Nikon/CoolScan III; Folders – 1 BUSINESS COMPUTERS: Business Software – Quickbooks, DSI, Falcon; Business Hardware – Various HP
Delivery method: Mail, Newsstand, Private Carrier

WHITE RIVER JUNCTION

VALLEY NEWS

24 Interchange Dr., West Lebanon, Vt., 3784; gen tel (603) 298-8711; gen fax (603) 298-0212; ed e-mail news@vnews.com; web site www.vnews.com

Published: Sun
Circulation: 16,435; 16,435(sat); 16,875(sun)
Last Audit: September 30, 2009
Price: 3.15/wk (carrier); 15.75/mo (carrier); 158.90/yr (carrier).
Advertising: Open inch rate $24.30
News services: AP, LAT-WP, New England Wire Service.
Politics: Independent.
Not Published: Christmas.
Special Editions: Homes (Apr); Summer Calendar (Aug); Letters to Santa (Dec); Coupon Book (Feb); Bridal (Jan); Summer Calendar (Jul); Summer Calendar (Jun); Home & Trade Show (Mar); Summer Calendar (May); Christmas (Nov); Fall Car Care (Oct); Fall Sports (Sept).
Special Weekly Sections: Books (Fri); Science & Technology (Mon); Life & Leisure (S); Movies (Sat); Arts (Thur); Education (Tues); Food & Garden (Wed).
Magazines: Valley Television (S); USA WEEKEND Magazine (Sat).
Pub. .... Mark Travis
Gen. Mgr. .... Daniel D. McClory
Adv. Dir. .... Richard Wallace
Circ. Dir. .... James Caey
Ed. .... Jeffrey Good
Editorial Page Ed. .... Martin Frank
Home/Food Ed. .... Anne Adams
News Ed. .... Susan Bowtwell
Sports Ed. .... Donald Mahler
Sunday Ed. .... Ernie Kohlsaat
Mgr., Opns. .... Bob Mathewson
Mgr., Pre Press .... Glenn Grote
Foreman, Pressroom .... Larry Leonard
Market Information: ADS; Split run; TMC.
Mechanical available: Flexography; Black and 3 ROP colors; insert accepted; page cutoffs - 22.
Mechanical Specifications: Type page 13 x 21; E - 6 cols, 2 1/16, 1/8 between; A - 6 cols, 2 1/16, 1/8 between; C - 9 cols, 1 5/16, 1/8 between.
Commodity Consumption: Avg. Page Number Per Issue - Daily 30; Avg. Page Number Per Issue - Plates Used 41731; Avg. Page Number Per Issue - Saturday 42; Avg. Page Number Per Issue - Sunday 64; widths 55; Newsprint Used - Metric Tons 1273; Printing Ink Used - Black 53515; Printi

Equipment EDITORIAL: Front-end Software – Novell/Network 3.12, QPS/QuarkXPress 3.31, Microsoft/Word 6.0, Azimuth Wire Capture.; Editorial Hardware – 40-PC, Compaq/fileserver; Editorial Printers – QMS/860, HP/LaserJet 4 CLASSIFIED: Front-end Software – Graph-X.; Classified Hardware – PC Clones; Classified Printers – QMS/860 DISPLAY: Ad make-up applications – Multi-Ad/Creator 4.X; Layout Software – 1-Mk/Managing Editor.; Display Hardware – 3-APP/Mac Quadra 650, 1-PC; Display Printers – QMS/860; Production Equipment – Na, AG/Imagesetter 1500, PixelCraft/Quickscan 8000, Kk/RSS-2035 Plus; Cameras – R; Scanners – Lf/Leafscan 35, Howtech/4500, PixelCraft/Quickscan 8000, Kk/RSS-2035 Plus. PRESSROOM: Line 1 – 5-H/PEC (Colormatic Flexo Conversion) 1988; Line 2 – 5-H/PEC (Colormatic Flexo Conversion) 1988; Folders – 2-H/3:2; Press registration system – 4 MAILROOM: Counter stackers – 3-HL/Monitor HT; Inserters and stuffers – HI/848 W/Icon System; Bundle tying machines – 1-EAM-Mosca, 2/MVP; Mailroom control system – Ic; Other equipment –MM/A492 quarter folder. BUSINESS COMPUTERS: Business Software – DSI, Circ, Solomon, ABRA, DSI; Business Hardware – 2-Windows NT

VIRGINIA

ALEXANDRIA

THE EXAMINER

6408 Edsall Rd., Alexandria, Va., 22312; gen tel (703) 846-8375; adv tel (703) 846-8375; ed tel (703) 846-8324

Vice Pres., Adv. Scott H. Brooks
Exec. Ed. Stephen G. Smith
Mng. Ed. Nicholas Horrock
Maryland Ed. Timothy W. Maier
Sports Ed. Dan Rubin
Virginia Ed. Mary Ann Kuhn

BRISTOL

BRISTOL HERALD COURIER

320 Morrison Blvd., Bristol, Va., 24201-3812; gen tel (276) 669-2181; adv tel (276) 645-2525; ed tel (276) 645-2534; gen fax (276) 669-3696; adv fax (276) 645-2527; ed fax (276) 669-3696; gen e-mail bnews@bristolnews.com; adv e-mail heraldcourier@mgads.com; ed e-mail letters@bristolnews.com; web site www.tricities.com

Group: Metro Newspaper Advertising Services, Inc.
Published: Mon, Tues, Wed, Thur, Fri, Sat, Sun
Weekday Frequency: m
Saturday Frequency: m
Circulation: 24,900; 29,127(sat); 30,694(sun)
Last Audit: ABC September 30, 2011
Price: 3.04/wk; 14.69/mo; 151.32/yr.
Advertising: Open inch rate $54.25
News services: AP, SHNS.
Politics: Independent.
Special Editions: Football (Aug); Progress (Feb); Basketball (Nov).
Magazines: On Air (Fri); Relish (Monthly); USA WEEKEND Magazine (S).
Broadcast Affiliations: WJHL.
Regl. Pub. ....Carl Esposito
Regl. Adv. Dir. ....John Kimbel
Grp. Adv. Mgr. ....David M. Millsap
Regl. Creative Servs. Mgr. ....Harry Fox
Circ. Dir., Audience Growth ....Chris Dorton
Mng. Ed. ....J. Todd Foster
City Ed. ....Susan Cameron
Features Ed. ....Jan Patrick
Opinion Ed. ....Suzanne Tate
Chief Photographer ....David Crigger
Prodn. Mgr. ....Danny Hall
Prodn. Mgr., Mailroom ....Cathy Leonard
Market Information: TMC; Zoned editions.
Mechanical available: Offset; Black and 3 ROP colors; insert accepted; page cutoffs - 21.
Mechanical Specifications: Type page 9 7/8 x 19 3/4; E - 6 cols, 1 9/16, 1/8 between; A - 6 cols, 1 9/16, 1/8 between; C - 10 cols, 15/16, 1/16 between.
Commodity Consumption: Avg. Page Number Per Issue - Daily 32; Avg. Page Number Per Issue - Plates Used 14000; Avg. Page Number Per Issue - Sunday 58; widths 12 1/2; Newsprint Used - Short Tons 3340; Printing Ink Used - Black 95000; Printing Ink Used - Color 6000; Printing Ink
Equipment EDITORIAL: Front-end Software – Dewar/Disc IV.; Editorial Hardware – SIA; Editorial Equipment – Okidata/393, HP/ScanJet IIP, APP/Mac Quadra 650, 5-IBM/Laptop, Kk/DC 40 Digital Camera, 2-Polaroid/SprintScan 35, APP/Power Mac 9500, 2-APP/Power Mac 9500; Editorial Printers – 2-LaserMaster/1200, 2-ECR/4550 CLASSIFIED: Front-end Software – Dewar/Disc IV.; Classified Hardware – SIA; Classified Equipment – Polaroid/SprintScan 35, Kk/DC 40 Digital Camera; Classified Printers – 2-LaserMaster/1200, 2-ECR/4550 DISPLAY: Ad make-up applications – QPS/QuarkXPress; Layout Software – APP/Power M; Display Hardware – APP/Mac, 1-APP/Mac IIci, APP/Mac Quadra 650, 4-APP/Power Mac 9500; Display Printers – LaserMaster/1200, LaserMaster/Unity 1800, PMR, 2-ECR/4550; Production Equipment – LaserMaster/Unity 1800XL-0, 2-ECR/4550; Cameras – 1-C/1270; Scanners – Equipment ☐ Dewar/Disk IV. PRESSROOM: Line 1 – 6-G/Urbanite single width 1969, 4-G/Urbanite single width 1980; Press Drives – 1-Fin/2193A-100, 1-Fin/2193E-150; Folders – 1; Pasters – 8-Cary/Flying Pasters. MAILROOM: Counter stackers – 2-MM/CV70; Inserters and stuffers – 1-GMA/SLS 1000 8 head, HI/1372; Bundle tying machines – 1-MLN/2, 1-MLN/2A; Addressing machine – 6/Wm.

CHARLOTTESVILLE

THE DAILY PROGRESS

685 W. Rio Rd., Charlottesville, Va., 22901; gen tel (434) 978-7200; adv tel (434) 978-7209; ed tel (434) 978-7240; gen fax (434) 978-7214; adv fax (434) 978-7204; ed fax (434) 978-7252; adv e-mail ccullen@dailyprogress.com; web site www.dailyprogress.com

Published: Mon, Tues, Wed, Thur, Fri, Sat, Sun
Weekday Frequency: m
Saturday Frequency: m
Circulation: 21,510; 23,232(sat); 24,970(sun)
Last Audit: ABC September 30, 2011
Price: 2.99/wk.
Advertising: Open inch rate $57.88
News services: AP, LAT-WP.
Politics: Independent. **Established:** 1892
Special Weekly Sections: Best Food Day (S); Best Food Day (Wed).
Magazines: USA WEEKEND Magazine (S).
Pub. ....Lawrence McConnell
Bus. Mgr. ....Pamela J. Davis
Adv. Mgr., Retail Sales ....Carolyn Cullen
Circ. Dir. ....Fred Greer
Mng. Ed. ....McGregor McCance
Editorial Page Ed. ....Anita Shelburne
Entertainment Ed. ....Jane Dunlap Norris
Features Ed. ....Mary Alice Blackwell
News Ed. ....Jenny Rector
Chief Photographer ....Andrew Shurtleff
Sports Ed. ....Jerry Ratcliffe
Market Information: TMC; Zoned editions.
Mechanical available: Offset; Black and 3 ROP colors; insert accepted; page cutoffs - 22.
Mechanical Specifications: Type page 12 1/2 x 21; E - 6 cols, 2, 1/8 between; A - 6 cols, 2, 1/8 between; C - 9 cols, 1 1/8, 1/16 between.
Commodity Consumption: Avg. Page Number Per Issue - Daily 36; Avg. Page Number Per Issue - Plates Used 21250; Avg. Page Number Per Issue - Sunday 72; widths 50; Newsprint Used - Short Tons 3100; Printing Ink Used - Black 75697; Printing Ink Used - Color 13000; Printing Ink Use
Equipment EDITORIAL: Front-end Software – ACT.; Editorial Hardware – HP; Editorial Equipment – 2-NewGen, Lf/Leafscan for Color Seperation; Editorial Printers – 4-APP/Mac Laser II NTX CLASSIFIED: Front-end Software – ACT.; Classified Hardware – 5-Compaq; Classified Equipment – NewGen, Imager Plus/12; Classified Printers – HP/LaserPrinter; Layout Software – DTI/AD Makeup II, Adobe/Photoshop.; Production Equipment – WL/Plater, 1-NewGen, Image Plus 12; Cameras – 1-C/Spartan III L270, SCREEN; Scanners – RZ. PRESSROOM: Line 1 – 5-MAN/Uniman 4 x 12 double width; Pasters – 5-MEG; Reels and Stands – Press control system ☐ 3-GE/100 h.p. motor drive. MAILROOM: Counter stackers – 3-Id; Inserters and stuffers – HI/NP 1372 S, Id; Bundle tying machines – 2-MLN/ML2EE; Addressing machine – 5/Wm.; Business Hardware – HP

COVINGTON

COVINGTON VIRGINIAN, INC.

128 N. Maple Ave., Covington, Va., 24426; gen tel (540) 962-2121; gen fax (540) 962-5072

VIRGINIAN REVIEW

128 N. Maple Ave., Covington, Va., 24426; gen tel (540) 962-2121; gen fax (540) 962-5072; gen e-mail virginianreview@aol.com; web site www.alleghanyhighlands.com

Published: Mon, Tues, Wed, Thur, Fri, Sat
Weekday Frequency: e
Circulation: 7,119; 7,119(sat)
Last Audit: September 30, 2007
Price: 7.70/mo (carrier); 92.40/yr (carrier).
Advertising: Open inch rate $9.50
News services: AP.
Politics: Independent. **Established:** 1914
Advertising not accepted: Erroneous medical cures.
Not Published: New Year; Independence Day; Labor Day; Thanksgiving; Christmas.
Special Editions: Christmas Greetings (Dec); Christmas Shopping (Nov).
Vice Pres. ....Ewell S. Beirne
Adv. Dir. ....Mary A. Beirne
News Ed. ....Horton P. Beirne
Sports Ed. ....Adam Crawford
Online Mgr. ....David Crosier
Prodn. Mgr., Pressroom ....Coite Charles Beirne
Market Information: ADS; TMC.
Mechanical available: Offset; Black and 3 ROP colors; insert accepted; page cutoffs - 22 3/4.
Mechanical Specifications: Type page 11 5/8 x 21; E - 6 cols, 1 13/16, 3 1/14 between; A - 6 cols, 1 13/16, 3/16 between; C - 8 cols, 1 3/8, 1/8 between.
Commodity Consumption: Avg. Page Number Per Issue - Daily 14; Avg. Page Number Per Issue - Plates Used 3000; widths 12 1/2; Newsprint Used - Short Tons 425; Printing Ink Used - Black 12000; Printing Ink Used - Color 400; Printing Ink Used - Pages Printed 4000.
Equipment EDITORIAL: Front-end Software – NewsCraft/Editorial System.; Editorial Hardware – IBM; Editorial Printers – Konica/Imagesetter, HP/LaserJet CLASSIFIED: Front-end Software – NewsCraft/Classified.; Classified Hardware – IBM; Classified Printers – Konica/Imagesetter, HP/LaserJet DISPLAY: Ad make-up applications – NewsCraft, QPS/QuarkXPress, Multi-Ad, APP/Mac.; Display Hardware – IBM, APP/Mac; Display Printers – Konica, HP; Production Equipment – Nu/Flip Top Ultra Plus; Cameras – B. PRESSROOM: Line 1 – 5-G/Community single width 1973; Line 2 – 1998; Inserters and stuffers – KAN/550; Addressing machine – Ch/515. BUSINESS COMPUTERS: Business Software – Novell, dBase; Business Hardware – IBM

CULPEPER

CULPEPER STAR-EXPONENT

122 W. Spencer St., Culpeper, Va., 22701; gen tel (540) 825-0771; adv tel (540) 825-0771; ed tel (540) 825-0771; gen fax (540) 825-0778; adv fax (540) 825-0778; ed fax (540) 825-5211; ed e-mail rhumphreys@starexponent.com; web site www.starexponent.com

Published: Mon, Tues, Wed, Thur, Fri, Sat, Sun
Weekday Frequency: m
Saturday Frequency: m
Circulation: 5,738; 6,384(sat); 6,034(sun)
Last Audit: ABC September 30, 2011
Price: 1.95/wk (carrier), $2.62/wk (mail); 101.40/yr (carrier), $135.80/yr (mail).
Advertising: Open inch rate $24.15
News services: AP.
Politics: Independent.
Special Editions: American Women (Sept).
Special Weekly Sections: Best Food Days (S); Church Pages (Sat); Health Directory (Tues); Best Food Days (Wed).
Magazines: Bridal (Monthly); USA WEEKEND Magazine (S).
Pub. ....Mitch Sneed
Adv. Mgr. ....Gloria Williams
Circ. Dir. ....Patricia Graham
Mng. Ed. ....Robert Humphreys
Entertainment Ed. ....Jeff Say
Night News Ed. ....Kevin Olmstead
Sports Ed. ....Shane Mettlen
Prodn. Foreman, Composing ....Jeff Vogel
Prodn. Foreman, Pressroom ....Jack Griffin
Market Information: Split run; TMC.
Mechanical available: Offset; Black and 3 ROP colors; insert accepted; page cutoffs - 22 3/4.
Mechanical Specifications: Type page 13 x 21 1/2; E - 6 cols, 2 1/16, 1/8 between; A - 6 cols, 2 1/16, 1/8 between; C - 9 cols, 1 3/8, 1/16 between.
Commodity Consumption: Avg. Page Number Per Issue - Daily 14; Avg. Page Number Per Issue - Plates Used 14400; widths 14; Newsprint Used - Short Tons 400; Printing Ink Used - Black 7000; Printing Ink Used - Color 1500; Printing Ink Used - Pages Printed 4276.
Equipment EDITORIAL: Front-end Software – Microsoft/Windows.; Editorial Hardware – 4-HP/VE; Editorial Printers – HP/LaserJet 4MV; Classified Hardware – HP/VE. DISPLAY: Ad make-up applications – Aldus/PageMaker; Layout Software – 1-APP/Power Mac.; Display Hardware – Printers ☐ HP/LaserJet 4MV; Display Printers – HP/LaserJet 4MV; Production Equipment – 1-ECR/VL36, 1-Konica; Cameras – 1-C/Spartan III, 1-LE/MD-480. PRESSROOM: Line 1 – 6-G/Urbanite; Folders – 1 MAILROOM: Counter stackers – 1-BG/Count-O-Veyor; Inserters and stuffers – 1-MM/4:1; Bundle tying machines – 1/Bu, 1-/MLN; Other equipment – Mc/Saddlematic.; Business Hardware – HP/VE

DANVILLE

DANVILLE REGISTER & BEE

700 Monument St., Danville, Va., 24541; gen tel (434) 793-2311; gen fax (434) 797-2299; adv fax (434) 799-0595; web site www.godanriver.com

Published: Mon, Tues, Wed, Thur, Fri, Sat, Sun
Weekday Frequency: m
Saturday Frequency: m
Circulation: 14,692; 15,954(sat); 17,834(sun)
Last Audit: ABC September 30, 2011
Price: 10.00/mo; 115.00/yr.
Advertising: Open inch rate $28.85
News services: AP.
Politics: Independent.
Special Editions: Chamber of Commerce Tab (Monthly); Postive Parenting (Quarterly).
Special Weekly Sections: TV Weekly (Fri); The Scene (S); Church Page (Weekly).
Magazines: USA WEEKEND Magazine (S).
Broadcast Affiliations: WILS; NBC.
Pub. ....Steve Kaylor
Adv. Dir. ....Rob Eilts

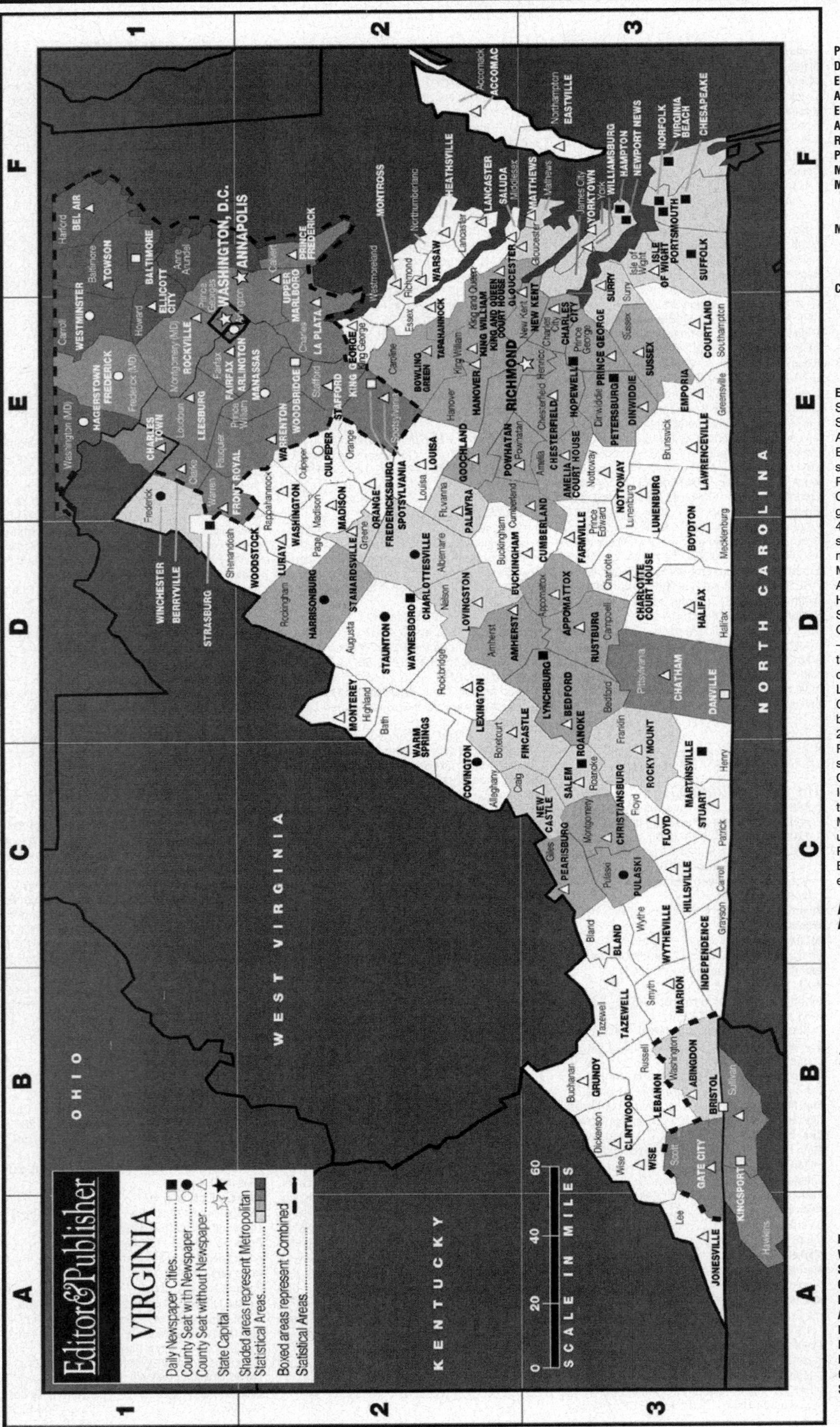

Promos. Mgr./NIE Dir. ....Janet Miller
Distr. Mgr. ....Fia Tanksley
Ed. ....Arnold Hendrix
Asst. City Ed.............................Bernard Baker
Editorial Page Ed. ....Robert Benson
Audiotex Mgr. ....Don Webb
Regl. Dir., Info Servs....................Tony Canody
Prodn. Mgr. ....Gloria Clark
Market Information: ADS; TMC.
Mechanical available: Offset; Black and 3 ROP colors; insert accepted - all; page cutoffs - 22 3/4.
Mechanical Specifications: Type page 13 x 21 1/2; E - 6 cols, 2 1/16, 1/8 between; A - 6 cols, 2 1/16, 1/8 between; C - 9 cols, 1 3/8, 1/16 between.
Commodity Consumption: Avg. Page Number Per Issue - Daily 26; Avg. Page Number Per Issue - Plates Used 27400; Avg. Page Number Per Issue - Sunday 60; widths 14 1/4; Newsprint Used - Short Tons 1675; Printing Ink Used - Black 36860; Printing Ink Used - Color 5888; Printing Ink
Equipment EDITORIAL: Front-end Software – SII/Synthesis 66 XR.; Editorial Hardware – 1-SII/Synthesis 66XR, 20-Roadrunner/PC 486, 4-APP/Mac, 1-APP/Mac fileserver; Editorial Equipment – 1-APP/Power Mac 8500-120 fileserver; Editorial Printers – 3-APP/Mac LaserPrinter, 2-APP/Mac LaserWriter Pro CLASSIFIED: Front-end Software – Pongrass/Page Integrator.; Classified Hardware – 4-SII/Synthesis 66, Roadrunner/PC 486; Classified Printers – 1-APP/Mac IIG DISPLAY: Ad make-up applications – Adobe/Photoshop, Multi-Ad/Creator; Layout Software – 1-APP/Power Mac 8500-120 fileserver.; Display Hardware – 7-APP/Mac 7200-90, 6-Mk/Flatbed Scanner PRODUCTION: Pagination Software – QPS/QuarkXPress 3.1.; Production Equipment – 2-Accuset/Laser Imager, 1-AU/APS 6600 (Hitachi Engine), APP/Mac Quadra 840 AV, Microtek/Flatbed Scanner, Lf/Leafscan 35, Lf/Leafscan 45; Cameras – 1-C/Pager, 1-C/Spartan III PRESSROOM: Line 1 – 11-G/Urbanite 1215-1244 single width 1978, 2-G/Urbanite 1214-1244 single width 1993; Press Drives – 2; Folders – 2; Press registration system – Duarte/Pin Registration. MAILROOM: Counter stackers – 1-HL/Monitor, 1-Id/2000, 1-Id/2100; Inserters and stuffers – HI/48P; Bundle tying machines – 1-MLN/ML, 1-MLN/Spirit, 1-MLN/SP330; Addressing machine – 1-MM/Minuteman quarter folder.; Audio Hardware – PEP/Voice Print System, BDR/Audio Package; Business Hardware – DEC/XL-590, Data Sciences

REGISTER PUBLISHING COMPANY, INC.

700 Monument St., Danville, Va., 24541; gen tel (434) 793-2311; gen fax (804) 739-0951

FREDERICKSBURG

THE FREE LANCE-STAR

616 Amelia St., Fredericksburg, Va., 22401-3887; gen tel (540) 374-5000; adv tel (540) 374-5460; ed tel (540) 374-5400; oth tel (540) 645-5555; gen fax (540) 373-8450; adv fax (540) 373-8450; ed fax (540) 373-8455; gen e-mail information@freelancestar.com; adv e-mail advertising@freelancestar.com; ed e-mail newsroom@freelancestar.com; web site www.freelancestar.com; www.fredericksburg.com
Published: Mon, Tues, Wed, Thur, Fri, Sat, Sun
Weekday Frequency: m
Saturday Frequency: m
Circulation: 40,195; 42,934(sat); 46,560(sun)
Last Audit: ABC September 30, 2011
Advertising: Open inch rate $31.50
News services: AP, MCT.
Politics: Independent. **Established:** 1885
Not Published: N/A
Own facility?: Y
Special Editions: Bride & Groom (Jan); Parenting(Feb;

Horse Scene(Mar); Garden Week (Apr); Pets (May);
Spring Home Guide (May);
One Tank - Travel (May);
Wedding Guide (Jun); Guide To Living (July) ; Back To School (Aug);
High School Football (Aug);
Active Living: Guide for Senior 55 & Over (Oct); Holiday Gift Guide (Nov); Holiday Trimming (Dec);.
Special Weekly Sections: House & Home (Fri); Viewpoints (S); Town & Country (Sat); Weekender (Thur); My Line (Tues); Food & Life (Wed).
Magazines: USA WEEKEND Magazine (S).
Broadcast Affiliations: 93.3 WFLS, 96.9 WWUZ, 99.3 WVBX., 1350 AM ESPN
Profile: The Free Lance-Star is an independently owned and locally operated multi-media company. The newspaper was established in 1885 and now publishes 7 days a week and includes a TMC product. The company has expanded to include 4 local radio stations, WFLS, WYS
Vice President/Assoc. Pub. ..Florence C. Barnick
President/Publisher ..Nicholas J. Cadwallender
Exec. Asst. ....Samantha Ashley
HR Dir. ....Teresa R. Trott
Bus. Mgr. ....Karen Harris
Adv. Dir. ....William P. Smith
Adv. Team Leader ....Beth Loveless
Classified Call Ctr. Sales Mgr. ....Opal Curtis
Print Advertising Manager ....Brad Cooper
Editor ....Edward W. Jones
Mng. Ed. ....Phil Jenkins
Bus. Ed. ....Howard Owen
Assistant Managing Editor ....Betty Snider
Editorial Page Ed. ....Paul E. Akers
Graphics/Design Dir. ....Catherine Davis
Life Ed. ....Katherine Shapleigh
Local News Ed. ....Richard J. Hammerstrom
Operations Director ....John Jenkins
Mktg. Dir. ....Deneal Helms
Circ. Dir. ....Tom Bibs
Local News Ed. ....Laura Hutchison
Market Information: TMC; Zoned editions.
Mechanical available: Offset; Black and 3 ROP colors; insert accepted - Post-it ads; page cutoffs - 21.
Mechanical Specifications: Type page 11 5/16 x 20 1/2; E - 6 cols, 1 4/5, 1/8 between; A - 6 cols, 1 4/5, 1/8 between; C - 9 cols, 1 1/5, between.
Commodity Consumption: Avg. page Number Per Issue - Daily 44; Avg. Page Number Per Issue - Plates Used 32000; Avg. Page Number Per Issue - Saturday 64; Avg. Page Number Per Issue - Sunday 99; widths 28; Newsprint Used - Metric Tons 5980; Printing Ink Used - Black 128000; Print
Equipment EDITORIAL: Front-end Software – Tera/GN3 B85, Binuscan.; Editorial Hardware – 2-Dell/PowerEdge 6300, 1-Dell/Poweredge 4300; Editorial Printers – 1-HP/4000, 1-HP/8100 CLASSIFIED: Front-end Software – Vision Data 6.0.; Classified Hardware – 15-Xterms, 1-Sun/Enterprise 250; Classified Printers – HP/4000 DISPLAY: Ad make-up applications – Multi-Ad/Creator 4.04, AG/AdTracking 6.x, Binuscan; Layout Software – SCS/Layout 8000.; Display Hardware – 2-APP/Mac G3, 16-APP/PowerMac G4/450; Display Printers – 1-HP/5Simx, 1-Tektronix/Phaser 780, 1-HP/8100; Production Equipment – Kodak News Generation 300
Thermac Imager, 1 Creo TS
100 Thermal Imager PRESSROOM: Line 1 – 2 Unit 72 Triplewide Goss FPS Press-2010; Line 2 – 2 Unit 72 Triplewide Goss FPS Press-2010; Line 3 – 1 11 Meter Goss Conti Webb Dryer; Folders – 2 Goss 5:5:2 Folders and 1 Goss Quarterfold; Pasters – 4 Goss Contiweb Pasters; Press control system – Goss Omnicon; Press registration system – QIPC Registration and Cut-Off MAILROOM: Counter stackers – 4 Ferag Smart Stacks; Inserters and stuffers – 1 32 Pocket Goss Magnapack with 2 DTP; Bundle tying machines – 6 Samuel Tiers; Wrapping singles – 1 CMC JWR30; Mailroom control system – Goss Omnicon; Addressing machine – Inline Domino Inkjet; Other equipment –1 Marianni Robotic Palletizer, 1 5 Pocket Muller Saddle Binder
Delivery method: Mail, Newsstand, Private Carrier, Racks

HARRISONBURG

DAILY NEWS-RECORD

231 S. Liberty St., Harrisonburg, Va., 22801; gen tel (540) 433-9112; adv tel (540) 574-6220; ed tel (540) 574-6230; gen fax (540) 433-9112; adv fax (540) 433-5503; ed fax (540) 433-9112; adv e-mail ads@dnronline.com; ed e-mail rlongley@dnronline.com; web site www.dnronline.com
Published: Mon, Tues, Wed, Thur, Fri, Sat
Weekday Frequency: m
Saturday Frequency: m
Circulation: 26,887; 28,623(sat)
Last Audit: ABC September 30, 2011
Price: 10.00/mo; 88.00/yr.
Advertising: Open inch rate $32.00
News services: AP.
Politics: Independent.
Not Published: New Year; Memorial Day; Independence Day; Labor Day; Thanksgiving; Christmas.
Special Editions: Spring Car and Motorcycle Care (Apr); Community Guide (Aug); First Night (Dec); Valentines Day (Feb); Honor Roll of Business (Jan); Flag Insert (Jul); Graduation (Jun); Home & Garden (Mar); Our Valley (May); Real Estate Showcase (Monthly); Yuletide Gift G
Special Weekly Sections: TV Week (Fri); Escape (Thur); Valley Weekender (Weekly).
Pub. ....Thomas T. Byrd
Asst. to Gen. Mgr. ....Kendrick D. McNulty
Adv. Dir. ....Steven Turner
Circ. Dir. ....Tommy Bridges
Ed. ....Peter S. Yates
Mng. Ed. ....R. Cort Kirkwood
Bus. Ed. ....Kate Prahlad
Educ. Ed. ....Jeff Mellott
Features Ed. ....Katheryn Huff
Graphics Ed./Art Dir. ....John Rose
Day News Ed. ....Rob Longley
Night News Ed. ....Jerry Blair
Photo/Graphics Dept. Mgr. ....Pete Marovich
Religion Ed. ....Tom Mitchell
Sports Ed. ....Chris Simmons
Wire Ed. ....Lewis Sword
Mgmt. Info Servs. Mgr. ....Penny Anderson
Prodn. Dir. ....David H. Shiplett
Market Information: TMC.
Mechanical available: Offset; Black and 3 ROP colors; insert accepted; page cutoffs - 21 1/2.
Mechanical Specifications: Type page 11 1/8 x 21 1/2; E - 6 cols, 1 3/4, 1/8 between; A - 6 cols, 1 3/4, 1/8 between; C - 9 cols, 1 1/8, 1/8 between.
Commodity Consumption: Avg. Page Number Per Issue - Daily 32; Avg. Page Number Per Issue - Plates Used 10200; Avg. Page Number Per Issue - Saturday 32; widths 12 1/2; Newsprint Used - Short Tons 2688; Printing Ink Used - Black 70000; Printing Ink Used - Color 5300; Printing In
Equipment EDITORIAL: Front-end Software – Apt/Act 2001.; Editorial Hardware – Compaq; Editorial Printers – HP/5000 CLASSIFIED: Front-end Software – Vision Data/Total Advertising.; Classified Hardware – Sun/Enterprise 250; Classified Printers – HP/5000 DISPLAY: Ad make-up applications – Multi-Ad; Layout Software – APT.; Display Hardware – Compaq; Display Printers – HP/5000 PRODUCTION: Pagination Software – APT/ACT.; Production Equipment – LE; Scanners – Tecsa PRESSROOM: Line 1 – 8-G/Urbanite; Press control system – Fin. MAILROOM: Counter stackers – 3-QWI/501; Inserters and stuffers – 1-MM/227S, 1-MM/227S; Bundle tying machines – 1-Sterling/MR45CHDR, 1-Sterling/MR50CH, 1-Sterling/GP30, 1-Sterling/GP30; Addressing machine – 1/Ch, 1-/BH; Other equipment – TMSI/Conveyor System.; Business Hardware – 10-Vision Data, 2-IBM/PC, 1-Inteva/PC

HOPEWELL

THE HOPEWELL NEWS

516 E. Randolph Rd., Hopewell, Va., 23860; gen tel (804) 458-8511; gen fax (804) 458-7556; adv e-mail advertising@hopewellnews.com; ed e-mail newsroom@hopewellnews.com; web site www.hopewellnews.com
Published: Tues, Fri
Last Audit: March 20, 2007
Advertising: Open inch rate $9.00
Not Published: Labor Day; Christmas.
Special Editions: Football (Aug); Santa Greeting (Dec); Auto Care (Fall); Richmond Racing (Feb); Bridal (Jan); Home Improvement (Mar); Reflections (Progress) (May); Auto Care (Spring).
Special Weekly Sections: Church Page (Fri); Best Food Day (Wed).
Magazines: TV Channels (Fri); The Homebook Real Estate Magazine (Monthly).
Pub. ....Rod Collins
Office Mgr. ....Cynthia Collins
Acctg. Mgr. ....Kristie Moore
Adv. Mgr. ....Paul Damron
Circ. Mgr. ....William Hendricks
Graphic Designer ....Lisa Wells
Sports Ed. ....Hank Bilyeu
Webmaster ....Kenny Holley
Prodn. Mgr. ....Winston Thomas
Prodn. Mgr., Pre Press ....Patricia Cook
Pressroom Foreman ....Ed Lane
Market Information: TMC.
Mechanical Specifications: Type page 13 x 21 1/2; E - 6 cols, 2 1/16, 1/8 between; A - 6 cols, 2 1/16, 1/8 between; C - 9 cols, 1 3/8, 1/8 between.
Equipment PRESSROOM: Line 1 – 9-G/Community; Folders – G/Community. MAILROOM: Counter stackers – 2/Bu, PPK; Inserters and stuffers – 4-/DG; Bundle tying machines – 2-/Bu; Addressing machine – KR; Other equipment –Mc/Speed Binder.

LYNCHBURG

THE NEWS & ADVANCE

101 Wyndale Dr., Lynchburg, Va., 24501; gen tel (434) 385-5400; adv tel (434) 385-5450; ed tel (434) 385-5555; gen fax (434) 385-5472; ed fax (434) 385-5538; ed e-mail landerson@newsadvance.com; web site www.newsadvance.com
Published: Mon, Tues, Wed, Thur, Fri, Sat, Sun
Weekday Frequency: m
Saturday Frequency: m
Circulation: 26,300; 28,615(sat); 33,620(sun)
Last Audit: ABC September 30, 2011
Advertising: Open inch rate $59.00
News services: AP, NYT.
Politics: Independent. **Established:** 1866
Special Editions: Greater Lynchburg Chamber of Commerce Report (); Garden Week (Apr); Kaleidoscope (Aug); Last Minute Gifts (Dec); Best of Health (Every other month); Progress (Feb); Bride & Groom (Jan); How-To-Guide (Jul); Summer Living (Jun); Who's Who in Construction (M
Special Weekly Sections: Automotive (Fri); Real Estate (S); Entertainment (Sat); Community (Thur); Community (Tues); Food (Wed).
Magazines: USA WEEKEND Magazine (S).
Profile: Daily newspaper serving the city of Lynchburg and the counties of Amherst, Bedford, Appomattox and Campbell.
Pub. ....Terry Jamerson
Adv. Dir. ....Barbara Staples
Classified Adv. Mgr. ....Dina Bennett
City Ed. ....Caroline Glickman
Editorial Page/Opinion. Ed. ......Logan Anderson
Sports Ed. ....Chris Morris
Market Information: Split run; TMC.
Mechanical available: Offset; Black and 3 ROP colors; insert accepted; page cutoffs - 22 3/4.
Mechanical Specifications: Type page 13 x 21 1/2; E - 5 cols, 2 1/2, 13/100 between; A - 6 cols, 2 1/25, 1/6 between; C - 9 cols, 1 3/8, 1/20 between.
Commodity Consumption: Avg. Page Number Per Issue - Daily 32; Avg. Page Number Per Issue - Plates Used 18672; Avg. Page Number Per Issue - Sunday 54; widths 28; Newsprint Used - Short Tons 3076; Printing Ink Used - Black 52186; Printing Ink Used - Color 15123; Printing Ink Use
Equipment EDITORIAL: Front-end Software – APT/Editorial System, QPS/QuarkXPress, Microsoft/Word.; Editorial Hardware – HP/PC; Editorial Equipment – 1-Lf/AP Leaf Picture Desk, 1-Lf/Leafscan 35; Editorial Printers – 1-NewGen/1200T, HP/4MV, QMS/2060 CLASSIFIED: Front-end Software – EKI.; Classified Hardware – 10-EKI/Televideo; Classified Printers – 1-NewGen/480 DISPLAY: Ad make-up applications – DTI, QPS/QuarkXPress, Adobe/Photoshop, Adobe/Illustrator; Display Hardware – 1-PC 386 fileserver; Display Printers – 1-NewGen/1200T, 1-NewGen/480, 1-NewGen/Turbo Plus 1200B; Production Equipment – 1-Graham/GNS 28, 1-BKY/5000, NewGen/1200T; Cameras – 1-C/Spartan III. PRESSROOM: Line 1 – 5-HI/1650 1974; Press Drives – 2-Fin/250 h.p.; Folders – HI/2:1. MAILROOM: Counter stackers – 2/QWI; Inserters and stuffers – 1-HI/1372; Bundle tying machines – 1-/Dyanric, 1-Si; Addressing machine – 1-/KR.; Audio Hardware – Software □ New Horizons/Info-Connect, TMS; Business Hardware – APT

MANASSAS

MANASSAS JOURNAL MESSENGER

9009 Church St., Manassas, Va., 20110-5410; gen tel (703) 368-3101; adv tel (703) 368-3101; ed tel (703) 368-3101; gen fax (703) 368-9017; adv fax (703) 368-9017; ed fax (703) 368-9017; gen e-mail bpotter@insidenova.com; adv e-mail mstalter@insidenova.com; ed e-mail ssvihlik@insidenova.com; web site www.insidenova.com
Group: U.S. Suburban Press, Inc.
Published: Mon, Tues, Wed, Thur, Fri
Weekday Frequency: m
Circulation: 7,449; 17,205(sat); 17,092(sun)
Last Audit: September 30, 2008
Price: 8.50/mo; 93.50/yr; 48.50/6mo.
Advertising: Open inch rate $36.96
News services: AP.
Politics: Independent. **Established:** 1869
Note: This publication shares its Saturday and Sunday editions with the Woodbridge (VA) Potomac News.
Advertising not accepted: Brokered preprints.
Special Editions: Back-to-School (Aug); Santa Welcome (Dec); Brides (Feb); Newcomer's Guide (Jul); Automotive (Mar); Graduation (May); Santa Welcome (Nov); Restaurant Guide (Oct).
Special Weekly Sections: Home Focus (Fri); Leisure (Thur); Family (Tues); Body Slam (Wed).
Pub. ....Bruce Potter
Bus. Mgr. ....Yelena Gureyeva
Adv. Dir. ....Gary Graff
Adv. Sales Mgr. ....Mike Stalter
Circ. Dir. ....Pat Graham
Exec. Ed. ....Susan Svihlik
Health Ed. ....Stacey Shelton
Sports Ed. ....Dave Fawcett
Copy Ed., Features ....Kari Pugh
Manassas Ed. ....Keith Walker
Photo Ed. ....Scott Lamar
Religion Ed. ....Courtney Scites
Market Information: Split run; TMC.
Mechanical available: Offset; Black and 3 ROP colors; insert accepted - flyers up to 64 pgs; page cutoffs - 22 3/4.
Mechanical Specifications: Type page 13 x 21 1/4; E - 6 cols, 2 1/16, 1/8 between; A - 6 cols, 2 1/16, 1/8 between; C - 9 cols, 1 3/8, 1/8 between.
Commodity Consumption: Avg. Page Number Per Issue - Daily 24; Avg. Page Number Per Issue - Plates Used 8500; Avg. Page Number Per Issue - Saturday 20; Avg. Page Number Per Issue - Sunday 40; widths 29; Newsprint Used - Metric Tons 673;

Newsprint Used - Short Tons 547; Printing
Equipment EDITORIAL: Front-end Software – Baseview.; Editorial Hardware – APP/Mac; Editorial Equipment – Lf/AP Leaf Picture Desk; Editorial Printers – NewGen/Laser, HP/LaserJet CLASSIFIED: Front-end Software – Baseview.; Classified Hardware – APP/Mac; Classified Printers – HP/LaserJet DISPLAY: Ad make-up applications – QPS/QuarkXPress, Adobe/Photoshop; Layout Software – APP/Mac.; Display Hardware – APP/Mac; Display Printers – HP/LaserPrinter PRODUCTION: Pagination Software – QPS/QuarkXPress, Baseview/NewsEdit.; Production Equipment – ECR, APP/Mac; Bundle tying machines – MLN.; Business Hardware – HP

MARTINSVILLE

MARTINSVILLE BULLETIN

204 Broad St., Martinsville, Va., 24112; gen tel (276) 638-8801; gen fax (276) 638-4153; ed fax (276) 638-7409; gen e-mail info@martinsvillebulletin.com; adv e-mail advertising@martinsvillebulletin.com; ed e-mail info@martinsvillebulletin.com; web site www.martinsvillebulletin.com

Published: Mon, Tues, Wed, Thur, Fri, Sun
Weekday Frequency: m
Circulation: 13,981; 16,507(sun)
Last Audit: ABC September 30, 2011
Price: 8.25/mo; 95.00/yr.
Advertising: Open inch rate $18.54
News services: NEA, AP.
Politics: Independent. **Established:** 1889
Special Editions: Race (Apr); Football (Aug); Christmas Greetings (Dec); Brides (Feb); Health & Fitness (Jan); Graduation (Jun); Spring (Mar); Real Estate (May); Christmas Shopping (Nov).
Magazines: Parade (S).
Chrmn. of the Bd. ....Antoinette M. Haskell
Pres./Pub. ....Robert H. Haskell
Vice Pres./Gen. Mgr. ....George H. Harris
Vice Pres. ....Elizabeth H. Haskell
Bus. Mgr. ....Tammy Foster
Adv. Mgr. ....Tammy Jones
Circ. Mgr. ....Matthew Dishman
Circ. Mgr. ....Matthew Smith
Mng. Ed. ....Amanda Buck
Editorial Writer ....Ginny Wray
Food/Women's Ed. ....Holly Kozelski
Librarian ....Sue Carter
Photo Ed. ....Mike Wray
Prodn. Mgr. ....George Harris
Market Information: TMC.
Mechanical available: Offset; Black and 3 ROP colors; insert accepted; page cutoffs - 22 3/4.
Mechanical Specifications: Type page 11 2/3 x 21 1/2; E - 6 cols, 1 4/5, 1/8 between; A - 6 cols, 1 4/5, 1/8 between; C - 9 cols, 1 1/4, 1/8 between.
Commodity Consumption: Avg. Page Number Per Issue - Daily 22; Avg. Page Number Per Issue - Plates Used 5200; Avg. Page Number Per Issue - Sunday 42; widths 12 1/2; Newsprint Used - Short Tons 10400; Printing Ink Used - Pages Printed 7930.
Equipment EDITORIAL: Front-end Software – Baseview.; Editorial Hardware – APP/Mac; Editorial Equipment – Lf/Leafscan 35, AG/Flatbed Scanner; Editorial Printers – 2-AU/Laser Film Imager, 3-Okidata CLASSIFIED: Front-end Software – Baseview.; Classified Hardware – APP/Mac; Classified Printers – 2-AU/Laser Film Imager, 3-Okidata PRODUCTION: Pagination Software – Baseview.; Production Equipment – AU, W; Scanners – Lf/Leafscan 35, Leica/Flatbed, AU/Drum Scanner PRESSROOM: Line 1 – 5-G/Urbanite U-920; Line 2 – 5-DEV/2400. MAILROOM: Counter stackers – HI/Rima RS255; Inserters and stuffers – KAN/480; Bundle tying machines – MLN, Dynaric, Interlake. BUSINESS COMPUTERS: Business Software – MSSI; Business Hardware – IBM/PCs

MCLEAN

USA TODAY

7950 Jones Branch Dr., McLean, Va., 22108-0605; gen tel (703) 854-3400; adv tel (703) 854-6503; ed tel (703) 854-7121; gen fax (703) 854-2139; adv fax (703) 854-2049; ed fax (703) 854-2053; ed e-mail editor@usatoday.com; web site www.usatoday.com

Published: Mon, Tues, Wed, Thur, Fri
Weekday Frequency: m
Circulation: 1,784,242
Last Audit: ABC September 30, 2011
Price: 169.00/yr.
News services: Crain Communications, AP, GNS, RN, AFP, DJ, UPI.
Politics: Independent. **Established:** 1982
Note: USA Today does not sell advertising on an inch rate basis: advertisers can purchase the specific sizes offered by the newspaper. Classified advertising is sold at a line rate. USA Today is published in Rosslyn, VA, and pages are transmitted via satellite
Not Published: New Year; Memorial Day; Independence Day; Labor Day; Thanksgiving; Christmas.
Special Editions: Business Travel (Apr); Markets (Dec); Super Bowl (Jan); Technology (Jun); NCAA Playoffs (Mar); Motor Racing (May); Technology (Nov); Business Travel (Sept).
Special Weekly Sections: Destinations & Diversions (Fri).
Pres./Pub. ....David Hunke
Sr. Vice Pres./Pub., usatoday.com/Adv. Sr. Vice Pres. ....Jeff Webber
Vice Pres., Finance ....Myron Maslowsky
Vice Pres., HR ....Janet Richardson
Adv. Vice Pres., Bus. Devel. ....Tony Hill
Adv. Vice Pres., Sales ....Johanna DeBonte
Adv. Vice Pres., Sales ....Lori Erdos
Adv. Vice Pres., Sales ....Ben Laurence
Adv. Vice Pres., Sales ....Jodi Vevoda
Sr. Vice Pres., Mktg. ....Susan Lavington
Vice Pres., Mktg., Bus. ....Cindy Freed
Vice Pres., Mktg., Commun./Event Mktg. Ed Cassiday
Vice Pres., Mktg., Strategy ....Chris McGill
Circ. Sr. Vice Pres. ....Larry G. Lindquist
Circ. Vice Pres. ....Russell Ford
Circ. Vice Pres. ....Brad Jones
Circ. Vice Pres. ....Doris Kasold
Circ. Vice Pres. ....Tom Kelly
Circ. Vice Pres. ....John McGee
Circ. Gen. Mgr., Atlanta ....Chris Hansen
Mechanical available: Offset; Black and 3 ROP colors; insert accepted; page cutoffs - 22 3/4.
Mechanical Specifications: Type page 13 x 21; E - 6 cols, 2 1/16, 1/8 between; A - 6 cols, 2 1/16, 1/8 between; C - 9 cols, 1 3/8, 1/16 between.
Commodity Consumption: Avg. Page Number Per Issue - Daily 42; Avg. Page Number Per Issue - Plates Used 828356; widths 55; Newsprint Used - Metric Tons 150000; Printing Ink Used - Black 3590000; Printing Ink Used - Color 2058000; Printing Ink Used - Pages Printed 10947.
Equipment; Editorial Hardware – AT/9000, 1-AT/9080, 40-AT/A500, 60-TM, IBM.; Classified Hardware – 2-AT/5000.; Production Equipment – 2-Nu/Flip Top, 1-CD/645IE, 1-DP/24L; Cameras – 2-C/Spartan III; Scanners – 6-Laps/Transport & Processor.; Business Hardware – 3-IBM/4381, 1-IBM/4361, S/38, S/36

NEWPORT NEWS

DAILY PRESS

7505 Warwick Blvd., Newport News, Va., 23607-0746; gen tel (757) 247-4600; adv tel (757) 247-4678; ed tel (757) 247-4730; gen fax (757) 247-7899; adv fax (757) 247-4651 (retail); ed fax (757) 245-4675; gen e-mail dailypress@dailypress.com; ed e-mail news@dailypress.com; web site www.dailypress.com

Published: Mon, Tues, Wed, Thur, Fri, Sat, Sun
Weekday Frequency: m
Saturday Frequency: m
Circulation: 59,200; 67,119(sat); 90,924(sun)
Last Audit: ABC September 30, 2011
Price: 3.81/wk; 187.72/yr (carrier), $414.44/yr (mail).
Advertising: Open inch rate $71.94
News services: AP, MCT, TMS.
Politics: Independent. **Established:** 1896
Special Editions: H.S. All Stars (Apr); H.S. Football (Aug); H.S. All Stars (Dec); Home Expo (Feb); H.S. All Stars (Jul); Prime Time (Jun); New Cars-Trucks-Vans (Mar); Guide to Pre-Owned Vehicles (May); College Basketball (Nov); New Cars (Oct); Arts Calendar (Quarterly); P
Special Weekly Sections: Deals On Wheels (Fri); This Week (Mon); Good Life (S); Health & Fitness (Sat); Home & Garden (Thur); Savvy Shopper (Tues); Food & Drink (Wed).
Magazines: Hampton Roads Mom & Me (Monthly); MyTime for Hampton Roads Women (Other); TV Hampton Roads Magazine (S).
Pres./Pub./CEO ....Digby Solomon
CFO/Vice Pres., Finance ....Ann B. Wilson
HR Dir. ....Keith Potts
Dir., Commun./Community Rel. Melissa Hespenhide
Financial Planning Mgr. ....Charlie E. Giles
Interim Adv. Dir. ....Deborah Nadell
Adv. Dir., Key Accts. Sales ....Donna Jebson
Adv. Dir., Key Accts. Sales Lourdes Malave-Baber
Adv. Gen. Mgr., Automotive/Recruitment Adam Shelnut
Adv. Gen. Mgr., Real Estate ...Deborah A. Nadell
Dir., Consumer Mktg. ....David Messick
Target Mktg. Mgr. ....Ursla Gallagher
Creative Servs. Mgr. ....David Thomas
Circ. Mgr. ....Todd Hubbard
Vice Pres./Ed. ....Ernie Gates
Mng. Ed., Digital ....Marisa Porto
Mng. Ed., Print ....Robin McCormick
Assoc. Ed., Editorial Page ....Carol Capo
Admin./Planning Mgr. ....Cindy Laraway
Features Ed. ....Karen Morgan
Market Information: ADS; Split run; TMC; Zoned editions.
Mechanical available: Offset; Black and full color ROP colors; insert accepted - product samples; page cutoffs - 22.
Mechanical Specifications: Type page 10 1/2 x 21; E - 6 cols, 1 19/32, 1/10 between; A - 6 cols, 1 19/32, 1/10 between; C - 10 cols, 1 3/32, 3/32 between.
Commodity Consumption: Avg. Page Number Per Issue - Daily 56; Avg. Page Number Per Issue - Plates Used 200000; Avg. Page Number Per Issue - Saturday 73; Avg. Page Number Per Issue - Sunday 102; widths 50; Newsprint Used - Metric Tons 14183; Printing Ink Used - Black 273345; Pr
Equipment EDITORIAL: Front-end Software – Open Pages.; Editorial Hardware – 130-Pentium/PC, 15-APP/Power Mac CLASSIFIED: Front-end Software – CText/ADV 5.1.; Classified Hardware – Dell/Pentium, Advision/GX110, ALPS/GX110; Classified Printers – HP/8000 DISPLAY: Ad make-up applications – QPS/QuarkXPress 4.1; Layout Software – SCS/Layout 8000.; Display Hardware – Sun, Ultra II; Display Printers – HP/4000, HP/551, Canon/Fiery PRODUCTION: Pagination Software – Open Pages, ALPS 5.1.; Production Equipment – 3-AII/3850 Typesetter, AP/Server; Scanners – 1-GEI/Tecsa Scanners, 2-Umax/2100 XL PRESSROOM: Line 1 – 16-G/3346-3347 (8 color half decks); Folders – 2 MAILROOM: Counter stackers – 6-GMA/CombiStacks, 4-QWI/401 Stackers, 2-Gammerler/Stackers; Inserters and stuffers – 1-GMA/SLS3000 14:2, 1-GMA/SLS3000 30:2 (dual delivery); Bundle tying machines – 3-Dynaric/Tyer NP2, 1-Dynaric/NP3000; Mailroom control system – GMA/SA AUDIO: Audio Software – Micro Voice/Audiotext 2000; Audio Hardware – VNN, PC, DELL/GS BUSINESS COMPUTERS: Business Software – Microsoft/Office; Business Hardware – Admarc, IBM/CICS, CJ, Open Pages, CCI, Advision

NORFOLK

THE VIRGINIAN-PILOT

150 W. Brambleton Ave., Norfolk, Va., 23510-2018; gen tel (757) 446-2000; adv tel (757) 446-2100; ed tel (757) 446-2321; gen fax (757) 446-2983; adv fax (757) 662-2534; ed fax (757) 446-2051; adv e-mail adnsite@pilotonline.com; ed e-mail letters@pilotonline.com; web site www.thevirginianpilot.com; www.pilotonline.com

Published: Mon, Tues, Wed, Thur, Fri, Sat, Sun
Weekday Frequency: m
Saturday Frequency: m
Circulation: 145,785; 136,897(sat); 176,054(sun)
Last Audit: ABC September 30, 2011
Price: 166/yr; 14/mo
Advertising: Open inch rate $258.00
News services: AP, MCT, LAT-WP, NYT, Landmark News Service.
Politics: Independent. **Established:** 1865
Not Published: N/A
Own facility?: Y
Special Editions: Career Day (Apr); Hurricane Alert (Aug); Technical Career Banners (Feb); Forecast (Jan); Discover Hampton Roads (Jul); Scholastic Achievement (Jun); Discover the Albemarle (Mar); Spring Outer Banks Vacation Guide (May); Auto Show (Nov); Career Day (Oct);
Special Weekly Sections: Auto Weekly (Fri); Gracious Living (S); Hampton Roads Real Estate (Sat); Daily Break/Weekend (Thur); Flavor (Wed).
Magazines: Parade (S).
President and Publisher ....Maurice Jones
Press Operations Manager ....Allen Byrd
Director of Systems/Technology ....Barbara Elliott
Adv. Mgr., Co-op ....Randolph U. Hargrave
Adv. Mgr., Mktg. Servs. ....Robert Morgan
Editor ....Denis Finley
Managing Editor ....Maria Carrillo
Senior Editor, Local Teams ....Joe Coccaro
Senior Editor, Enterprise/Sports/State & Military William Henry
Senior Editor, Features/Photo/Business Michele Vernon-Chesley
Director of Newsroom Operations Denise Bridges
Pres. ....Bruce R. Bradley
CIO ....Steven J. Peters
Credit Mgr. ....Carol Lewis
Mgr., Performance Devel. ....Kathleen Anderson
Mktg. Dir. ....Pam Smith-Rodden
Circ. Mgr., Mktg. ....Nancy Lewis
Circ. Mgr., Single Copy ....Jack Frost
Circ. Mgr., State ....Joseph Brown
Deputy Mng. Ed., Presentation ..Deborah Withey
Dir., Commun. News ....Marian Anderfuren
Market Information: ADS; Split run; TMC; Zoned editions.
Mechanical available: Offset; Black and 3 ROP colors; insert accepted; page cutoffs - 22 3/4.
Mechanical Specifications: Type page 11 1/2 x 21 1/2; E - 6 cols, 1 4/5, 1/8 between; A - 6 cols, 1 4/5, 1/8 between; C - 10 cols, 1 9/16, 1/16 between.
Commodity Consumption: Avg. Page Number Per Issue - Daily 83; Avg. Page Number Per Issue - Plates Used 320209; Avg. Page Number Per Issue - Saturday 134; Avg. Page Number Per Issue - Sunday 120; widths 37 1/2; Newsprint Used - Short Tons 46582; Printing Ink Used - Black 445024
Equipment EDITORIAL: Front-end Software – Adobe InDesign; Editorial Hardware – 200-AT, 10-APP/Mac Portable, 20-IBM/Portable, 40-IBM/Compatable, 12-AT/News Layout, 36-APP/Mac Page Design, 10-Tandem/Portable; Classified Hardware – 35-AT.; Layout Software – 3-Sun, AT/R2, 28-AT. PRODUCTION: Pagination Software – AII/Oman.; Production Equipment – 1-AG/Avantra 30E, 1-K&F/PlatXpress with Vision Bender PRESSROOM: Line 1 – 30-G/Metro offset double width; Press Drives – FINCOR DRIVE SHAFT; Folders – 5-G/Metro 3:2 Imperial Folder (with double delivery); Pasters – 30-G/Tension System; Reels and Stands – 30 MAILROOM: Counter stackers – 14 SMS Ferag; Inserters and stuffers – 3 Goss

Magna-Pak Inserters; Bundle tying machines – 15 Mosca Z-5 Tyers; Mailroom control system – Omni-zone; Addressing machine – 4 Kodak Printers; Other equipment -2 CMC Polywrappers; Business Hardware – 13-IBM/4381, 1-IBM/AS-400 B60 (midrange)
Delivery method: Mail, Newsstand, Private Carrier, Racks

PETERSBURG

THE PROGRESS-INDEX

15 Franklin St., Petersburg, Va., 23803; gen tel (804) 732-3456; gen fax (804) 861-9452; ed fax (804) 732-8417; ed e-mail newsroom@progress-index.com; web site www.progress-index.com
Group: Times-Shamrock Communications
Published: Mon, Tues, Sun
Weekday Frequency: e
Circulation: 10,152; 11,429(sat); 12,206(sun)
Last Audit: ABC September 30, 2011
Price: 9.95/mo (carrier); 145.00/yr (mail).
Advertising: Open inch rate $25.50
News services: Associated Press, McClathy, NYT
Special Editions: Spring Fix-up (Apr); Cruisin' (Aug); Dear Santa (Dec); Life Underwriters (Feb); First Aid (Jan); Customer Appreciation (Jul); School's Out-Summer Fun Guide (Jun); Progress (Mar); Dining Guide (May); Holiday Happenings (Nov); Fall Fix-up (Oct); Literacy Ta
Special Weekly Sections: Best Auto Day (Fri); Agriculture (S); Church Schedules (Sat); Health (Thur); Entertainment (Tues); Best Auto Day (Wed).
Magazines: Relish (Monthly); USA WEEKEND Magazine (S); American Profile (Weekly).
Mgr., Accounting....Peggy Simon
Circ. Dir.....Bob Seals
Photo Dept. Mgr.,....Patrick Kane
Sports Ed.....Tom Dozier
Wire Ed.....Cathy Ballou
Prodn. Mgr., Pressroom....Ron Shifflet
Managing Editor....Brian Couturier
Advertising Director....Michael Gochenour
Publisher....Cindy Morgan
Adv. Dir.....Catherine Oakley
Sunday Ed.....Brian Courtier
Market Information: TMC.
Mechanical available: Offset; Black and 3 ROP colors; insert accepted; page cutoffs - 23 1/4.
Mechanical Specifications: Type page 13 x 21 1/2; E - 6 cols, 2 1/16, 1/8 between; A - 6 cols, 2 1/16, 1/8 between; C - 9 cols, 1 5/16, 1/8 between.
Commodity Consumption: Avg. Page Number Per Issue - Daily 18.3; Avg. Page Number Per Issue - Plates Used 5320; Avg. Page Number Per Issue - Sunday 36; widths 27 1/2; Newsprint Used - Short Tons 1195; Printing Ink Used - Black 19400; Printing Ink Used - Color 4550; Printing Ink
Equipment EDITORIAL: Front-end Software – QPS/QuarkXPress 3.11.; Editorial Hardware – APP/Mac; Editorial Printers – TI CLASSIFIED: Front-end Software – Mk/4000, Multi-Ad/Creator, QPS/QuarkXPress.; Classified Hardware – Mk, APP/Mac; Classified Printers – TI DISPLAY: Ad make-up applications – Multi-Ad/Creator, QPS/QuarkXPress, Aldus/FreeHand; Layout Software – APP/Mac.; Display Hardware – 2-APP/Mac; Display Printers – V/5100; Production Equipment – 2-V/5100, 1-V/5300, 1-V/Panther Plus; Cameras – SCREEN/C-690-C; Scanners – Equipment ☐ QPS/QuarkXPress 3.1.1. PRESSROOM: Line 1 – 8-G/Community; Folders – 1-G/SSC.; Bundle tying machines – 1/MLN, 1-/MLN.; Business Hardware – ATT

PULASKI

THE SOUTHWEST TIMES

34 Fifth St. NE, Pulaski, Va., 24301-0391; gen tel (540) 980-5220; gen fax (540) 980-3618; gen e-mail editor@southwesttimes.com; adv e-mail advertising@southwesttimes.com; web site www.southwesttimes.com
Published: Tues, Wed, Thur, Fri, Sun
Weekday Frequency: e
Circulation: 4,700; 5,200(sun)
Last Audit: Sworn October 7, 2002
Advertising: Open inch rate $12.00
Insert rate: call for quote
News services: AP.
Not Published: New Year; Memorial Day; Independence Day; Labor Day; Christmas.
Own facility?: Y
Special Editions: Home Improvement (Apr); Football Tab (Aug); Progress (Feb); Senior Years (Jan); Fair Tab (Jul); Guide to Pulaski County (Jun); Graduation (May); Christmas Guide (Nov).
Special Weekly Sections: Religion (Fri); Best Food Day (S); Best Food Day (Wed).
Pub.....Kay Kline
Sports Ed.....Jeremy Norman
Prodn. Mgr.....Jim Presley
Composing Mgr.....Angela Repass
Online Ed.....Roger Ballas
Market Information: TMC.
Mechanical available: Offset; Black and 3 ROP colors; insert accepted - single sheets 8 1/2 x 11; page cutoffs - 22 3/4.
Mechanical Specifications: Type page 13 1/16 x 21 1/2; E - 6 cols, 2 3/64, 1/6 between; A - 6 cols, 2 3/64, 1/6 between; C - 9 cols, 1 5/16, 1/8 between.
Commodity Consumption: Avg. Page Number Per Issue - Daily 10; Avg. Page Number Per Issue - Plates Used 6800; Avg. Page Number Per Issue - Sunday 18; widths 28; Newsprint Used - Short Tons 400; Printing Ink Used - Black 7500; Printing Ink Used - Color 400; Printing Ink Used - P
Equipment EDITORIAL: Front-end Software – Microsoft/DOS TSS.; Editorial Hardware – Samtron; Editorial Equipment – Lf/AP Leaf Picture Desk; Editorial Printers – NewGen/Turbo 400s CLASSIFIED: Front-end Software – System Facilities/Newscraft.; Classified Hardware – Amdek/AM432N; Classified Printers – Epson/DFX-8000; Layout Software – ATT, APP/Mac.; Production Equipment – Lf/AP Leaf Picture Desk, Roconex; Cameras – DAI/Screen. PRESSROOM: Line 1 – 6-HI/V-15A (upper former) 1982.; Bundle tying machines – 2-MLN/Strapper. BUSINESS COMPUTERS: Business Software – Cougar Mountain; Business Hardware – EKI/Televideo
Zip Codes served: 24301,24084,,24141 24312,24382,24347
Delivery method: Mail, Private Carrier, Racks

RICHMOND

RICHMOND TIMES-DISPATCH

300 E. Franklin St., Richmond, Va., 23219; gen tel (804) 649-6000; adv tel (804) 649-6251; ed tel (804) 649-6305; adv fax (804) 775-8019; ed fax (804) 819-5520; gen e-mail circulation@timesdispatch.com; ed e-mail letters@timesdispatch.com; web site www.timesdispatch.com
Published: Mon, Tues, Wed, Thur, Fri, Sat, Sun
Weekday Frequency: m
Saturday Frequency: m
Circulation: 110,732; 124,966(sat); 164,137(sun)
Last Audit: ABC September 30, 2011
Price: 6.45/wk; 27.97/mo (mail); 335.58/yr.
Advertising: Open inch rate $218.00
News services: AP, Business Wire, LAT-WP, Media General News, NYT, SHNS, Bloomberg, MCT.
Politics: Independent. **Established:** 1850
Special Editions: Monument Avenue 10K (Apr); Discover Richmond (Aug); Holiday Books (Dec); Super Bowl (Feb); Year-End Stock Report (Jan); New Homes (Mar); Race Week (Sun) (May); UVA-Tech Game (Nov); Medical Jobs (Oct); Race Week (Sun) (Sept).
Special Weekly Sections: Prime Living (Mon); Travel (S); T-D Channels (Sat); Health & Science (Thur); Balance (Wed).
Magazines: Parade (S).
Broadcast Affiliations: WTVR Channel 6 (CBS); WRIC Channel 8 (ABC); WWBT Channel 12 (NBC); WRLH Channel 35 (FOX); WCVE Channel 23 (PBS).
Pres./Pub.....Thomas A. Silvestri
Sr. Vice Pres./Bus. Mgr.....O. Scott Leath
Vice Pres., Opns....Sam Hightower
Controller....Raymond McDowell
Credit Mgr.....Cynthia Smith
Sales Devel. Mgr.....Judy Cheadle
Recruitment Adv. Sales Mgr.....Chris Barker
Mgr., Pre Press Design Servs.....Karen Dillon
Classified Adv. Mgr.....Scott Christino
Real Estate Mgr.....Amy Magee
Telephone Sales Mgr.....Terry Hall
South Zone Mgr.....Julie Ketcham
Mktg. Mgr.....T. Floyd Spencer
Promo. Mgr.....Frazier Millner
Market Devel. Mgr.....Tanya Henderson
Research Mgr.....Ed Martin
Vice Pres., Circ.....David B. Kirkman
Circ. Mgr., Metro....Thomas C. Smith
Circ. Mgr., Sales/Serv.....Richard A. Neely
Circ. Mgr., Single Copy....Teresa Blackwell
Market Information: ADS; Split run; TMC; Zoned editions.
Mechanical available: Offset; Black and 3 ROP colors; insert accepted; page cutoffs - 22.
Mechanical Specifications: Type page 11 5/8 x 21; E - 6 cols, 2 1/16, 1/8 between; A - 6 cols, 2 1/16, 1/8 between; C - 10 cols, 1 1/4, 1/18 between.
Commodity Consumption: Avg. Page Number Per Issue - Daily 72; Avg. Page Number Per Issue - Plates Used 310080; Avg. Page Number Per Issue - Saturday 83; Avg. Page Number Per Issue - Sunday 141; widths 37 1/2; Newsprint Used - Short Tons 34471; Printing Ink Used - Black 683353;
Equipment EDITORIAL: Front-end Software – HI/NME 4.0, Microsoft/Windows XP.; Editorial Hardware – 6-Sun/Ultra II servers, Client/200-PC 3.40; Editorial Equipment – 2-Dell/NAS Servers; Editorial Printers – HP/MV4, 4-HP/LaserJet 2200, X CLASSIFIED: Front-end Software – APP/Order Entry 1.4.172, Oracle/Database 7.3.4.; Classified Hardware – AT/Enterprise RS 6000, 1-Clarion Raid; Classified Equipment – 2-IBM/RS 6000 Workstations; Classified Printers – 2-HP/5000TN DISPLAY: Ad make-up applications – SCS/Layout 8000 8.0; Display Hardware – 2-HP/Vectras, 2-Cascade/450E SunServers, 2-RAID/D1000; Display Printers – HP/LaserJet 4200, Xerox/Fiery color printer PRODUCTION: Pagination Software – HI/Newsmaker Pagination 2.05.12, AT/Classified Pagination 5.76.; Production Equipment – 2-WL/3, AII/3850, 4-AG/Alpha Harlequin RIP; Scanners – 4-Epson PRESSROOM: Line 1 – 36-MHI/Print couples (4 reversible half decks; 2 mono units); Line 2 – 36-MHI/Print couples (4 reversible half decks; 2 mono units); Line 3 – 36-MHI/Print couples (4 reversible half decks; 2 mono units); Folders – 2-MHI/180-page; Reels and Stands – Reels and Stands MAILROOM: Counter stackers – 11-Id/2100, 4/QWI, 3-HL/SH, 2-Rima/RS3100, 13-QWI/500; Inserters and stuffers – 1-S/b-72P, 4-S/22-99, AM Graphics; Bundle tying machines – 13-/Dynaric; Mailroom control system – Id/Newssort, Id/Newslink; Addressing machine – Ch/539, C; Audio Hardware – Computalk BUSINESS COMPUTERS: Business Software – CJ, Visimage, Omnidex; Business Hardware – HP/917, HP/935, HP/950, HP/949, HP/947

ROANOKE

THE ROANOKE TIMES

201 W. Campbell Ave., Roanoke, Va., 24011-2491; gen tel (540) 981-3100; adv tel (540) 981-3261; ed tel (540) 981-3257; gen fax (540) 981-3346; adv fax (540) 981-3171; ed fax (540) 981-3458; web site www.roanoke.com
Group: Landmark Media Enterprises, LLC
Published: Mon, Tues, Wed, Thur, Fri, Sat, Sun
Weekday Frequency: m
Saturday Frequency: m
Circulation: 78,797; 74,317(sat); 90,177(sun)
Last Audit: ABC September 30, 2011
Price: 3.23/wk (carrier).
Advertising: Open inch rate $57.29.67
News services: AP, LAT-WP, NYT.
Politics: 1886
Own facility?: Y
Special Editions: Baseball Preview (Apr); Football (Aug); Ski Pages (Dec); Your Wedding Tab (Feb); Economy (Jan); Salem Fair (Jul); Senior Style Tab (Jun); Trout Pages (Mar); American Home Week (May); NBA Previews (Nov); Hunting Pages (Oct); Fall Fashion (Sept).
Special Weekly Sections: Dine & Dance (Entertainment) (Thur); Food (Wed).
Magazines: Parade (S).
Chief Financial Officer....Tonya Hart
Circulation Director....Angela Campbell
President and Publisher....Debra Meade
Adv. Dir.....Stefan Babich
Adv. Mgr., Retail Sales....Mary Whelchel
Marketing Manager....Molly Bell
Sr. Ed., New Channels....Dwayne Yancey
Editor....Carole Tarrant
Books Ed.....Nona Nelson
Human Resources Director....Jean Sokolofski
Editor....Liz Hock
Features Ed.....Kathy Lu
Market Information: Split run; TMC; Zoned editions.
Commodity Consumption: Avg. Page Number Per Issue - Daily 48; Avg. Page Number Per Issue - Plates Used 120000; Avg. Page Number Per Issue - Sunday 79; widths 27; Newsprint Used - Short Tons 13685; Printing Ink Used - Black 236860; Printing Ink Used - Color 85960; Printing Ink
Equipment EDITORIAL: Front-end Software – DTI; Editorial Hardware – DTI CLASSIFIED: Front-end Software – DTI.; Classified Hardware – DTI; Layout Software – DTI; Display Hardware – DTI
Delivery method: Mail, Newsstand, Private Carrier, Racks

TIMES-WORLD CORP.

201-209 W. Campbell Ave., Roanoke, Va., 24010-2491; gen tel (540) 981-3278; gen fax (504) 981-3194

SPRINGFIELD

THE WASHINGTON EXAMINER

6850 Versar Ctr., Springfield, Va., 22151; gen tel (703) 560-4000; ed tel (202) 903-2000; adv fax (703) 738-0610; gen e-mail mphelps@washingtonexaminer.com; web site www.washingtonexaminer.com
Published: Mon, Tues, Wed, Thur, Fri, Sat, Sun
Weekday Frequency: m
Circulation: 259,906
Last Audit: September 30, 2007
Advertising: Open inch rate $79.69(wknd)
News services: AP, SHNS.
Advertising not accepted: NC-17 movies.
Not Published: Postal holidays.
Special Weekly Sections: Healthy Living (Other); Green Scene (S); Real Estate (Thur).
Magazines: USA WEEKEND Magazine (Sat); Relish (Thur).
CEO/Pub.....Michael Phelps
Sr. Vice Pres., Sales/Mktg.....Annie Hager
Circ. Vice Pres., Distribution....Stephen Sparks
Ed.....Stephen Smith
Mng. Ed.....Mike Hedges
Mng. Ed., Web....Matthew Sheffield
Editorial Page Ed.....Mark Tapscott
Market Information: ADS; Split run; TMC.
Mechanical available: Offset; Black and 4 ROP colors; insert accepted.
Commodity Consumption: Avg. Page Number Per Issue - Daily 40; Avg. Page Number Per Issue - Plates Used 140000; widths 55; Newsprint Used - Short Tons 11000; Printing Ink Used - Black 198000; Printing Ink Used - Color 70000.
Equipment EDITORIAL: Front-end Software – AT, Euromax.; Editorial Hardware – AT, Euromax

CLASSIFIED: Front-end Software – AT.; Classified Hardware – AT; Classified Printers – Teletype DISPLAY: Ad make-up applications – Multi-Ad/Creator, QPS/QuarkXPress; Layout Software – Euromax.; Display Hardware – APP/Mac; Display Printers – HP/LaserJet II; Production Equipment – 2-Cx, 1-Linotype-Hell/Linotronic 100, 1-Kk/30, 1-3M; Cameras – 1-C/Spartan III, 1-C/Spartan II; Scanners – 2-ECR/Autokon 1000. PRESSROOM: Line 1 – 8-G/Metro (4 half decks); Line 2 – 8-G/Metro (4 half decks); Line 3 – 8-G/Metro (4 half decks); Line 4 – G/Colorliner (4 stacks/1 mono); Folders – 2-G/double 3:2, 1-G/3:2, 1-G/Jaw, 2-G/double 2:1. MAILROOM: Counter stackers – 2-Fg/H500, 1-MM/259, 3-MM/288, 2-MM/1231, 5-HL/Monitor; Inserters and stuffers – 1-S/48P Double Delivery, 2-S/72P Double, 1-MM/308; Bundle tying machines – 2-MLN/2A, 1-MLN/2, 1-MLN/2EE, 1-MLN/MA, 5-J/80; Wrapping singles – 5-Ideal/505-3; Business Hardware – Software ☐ AT, Vision Data, Lotus, WordPerfect

STAUNTON

LEADER PUBLISHING CO.

PO Box 59, Staunton, Va., 24402; gen tel (540) 885-7281; gen fax (540) 885-1904

THE NEWS LEADER

11 N. Central Ave., Staunton, Va., 24401; gen tel (540) 885-7281; adv tel (540) 213-9199; ed tel (540) 213-9128; gen fax (540) 885-1904; adv fax (540) 885-8779; ed fax (540) 885-1904; adv e-mail ads@newsleader.com; ed e-mail news@newsleader.com; web site www.newsleader.com

Published: Mon, Tues, Wed, Thur, Fri, Sat, Sun
Weekday Frequency: m
Saturday Frequency: m
Circulation: ; 16,873(sun)
Last Audit: Sworn September 30, 2009
Price: 2.30/wk (carrier); 9.20/mo; 150.80/yr (mail).
Advertising: Open inch rate $45.43
News services: GNS, AP, LAT-WP.
Politics: Independent. **Established:** 1901
Special Editions: Home & Garden (Apr); Football (Aug); Bride's World (Feb); America's Birthday (Jun); Fact Book (Mar); Graduation (May).
Special Weekly Sections: Real Estate (Every other week); Color Comics (S); GO! (Thur); Health (Tues).
Magazines: USA WEEKEND Magazine (S).
Pub....Roger Watson
Controller....Wilma Raybin
Admin., HR....Susan Armstong
Adv. Mgr., Calssified....Tricia Bryant
Adv. Mgr., Retail....Mark Chamberlin
Adv. Servs. Mgr.....Amy Smith
Circ. Dir.....Kathy Myers
Exec. Ed....David Fritz
City Ed.....Cindy Corell
Editorial Page Ed.....Dennis Neal
Sports Ed.....Hubert Grim
Online Content Developer....Chris Beard
Prodn. Dir.....Bryce Connelly
Market Information: TMC; Zoned editions.
Mechanical available: Offset; Black and 3 ROP colors; insert accepted; page cutoffs - 21 1/2.
Mechanical Specifications: Type page 13 x 21 1/4; E - 6 cols, 2 1/16, 1/8 between; A - 6 cols, 2 1/16, 1/8 between; C - 9 cols, 1 3/8, 1/16 between.
Commodity Consumption: Avg. Page Number Per Issue - Daily 20; Avg. Page Number Per Issue - Plates Used 10000; Avg. Page Number Per Issue - Sunday 44; widths 27 1/2; Newsprint Used - Short Tons 1180; Printing Ink Used - Black 21500; Printing Ink Used - Color 1380; Printing Ink
Equipment EDITORIAL: Front-end Software – QPS/QuarkXPress.; Editorial Hardware – APP/Mac Server, APP/Mac workstation CLASSIFIED: Front-end Software – Baseview. DISPLAY: Ad make-up applications – Baseview; Layout Software – APP/Mac, QPS/QuarkXPress.; Display Hardware – APP/Mac; Display Printers – Linotronic, ECR/Imagesetter, HP, APP/Mac LaserPrinter PRODUCTION: Pagination Software – QPS/QuarkXPress 3.32.; Production Equipment – 1-LE/LD-2600A, Harlequin, Linotronic/Ultre, ECR; Cameras – 1-C/Spartan II, 1-R/432, ECR; Scanners – 1-ECR/Autokon 1000, AG/Horizon Plus, Umax, Microtek, Nikon, Flatbed/Scanner PRESSROOM: Line 1 – 6-G/Urbanite; Line 2 – 1-AM/1650 MC Offset; Press Drives – 2-HP/100; Folders – 1-G/Urbanite. MAILROOM: Counter stackers – 1-Id/2000, 1-QWI/350; Inserters and stuffers – GMA/Alphaliner; Bundle tying machines – 1/Bu, 1-MLN/MA, 1-/Akebono, 1-/Power Strap; Mailroom control system – GMA; Addressing machine – 1-KR/Mailer, 1-KR/Quarter Folder; Other equipment –Other equipment ☐ BUSINESS COMPUTERS: Business Software – Lotus 3.1, Microsoft/Office; Business Hardware – IBM/AS-400

STRASBURG

NORTHERN VIRGINIA DAILY

152 N. Holliday St., Strasburg, Va., 22657-2143; gen tel (540) 465-5137; gen fax (540) 465-9388; adv fax (540) 465-6166; ed fax (540) 465-6164; gen e-mail generalmanager@nvdaily.com; info@nvdaily.com; adv e-mail salemanager@nvdaily.com; ed e-mail letterstoeditor@nvdaily.com; web site www.nvdaily.com

Published: Mon, Tues, Wed, Thur, Fri, Sat
Weekday Frequency: m
Saturday Frequency: m
Circulation: 12,568; 12,568(sat)
Last Audit: ABC September 30, 2011
Price: 80.00/yr.
Advertising: Open inch rate $16.05
News services: AP, SHNS.
Politics: Independent. **Established:** 1932
Not Published: New Year; Memorial Day; Independence Day; Labor Day; Christmas.
Special Editions: Discover the Valley/Tourism (Apr); Football (Aug); Bridal (Jan); Winchester County Guide (Jul); Farm & Home (Mar); Warren County Guide (May); Restaurants & Recipes (Nov); Winterize Home & Auto (Oct); Outdoors (Sept).
Special Weekly Sections: Wedding & Engagements (Mon); Real Estate/Home (Sat); Weekend + More (Thur); NASCAR (Wed).
Magazines: American Profile (Mon); Relish (Monthly); USA WEEKEND Magazine (Sat).
Vice Pres.....John D. Keister
Sec.....Hilda L. Keister
Gen. Mgr.....Elizabeth Smoot
Adv. Dir.....Jim Gainey
Editorial Page Ed.....John F. Horan
News Ed.....Bob Wooten
Special Sections Ed.....Jessica Wiant
Sports Ed.....Jeff Nations
Mgmt. Info Servs. Mgr.....Bob Storey
Opns. Mgr.....Harry F. Long
Prodn. Mgr., Mailroom....Beverly George
Market Information: TMC.
Mechanical available: Offset; Black and 3 ROP colors; insert accepted; page cutoffs - 22 3/4.
Mechanical Specifications: Type page 11 5/8 x 21 1/4; E - 6 cols, 2 1/16, 1/8 between; A - 6 cols, 1 5/8, 1/8 between; C - 9 cols, 1 3/8, 1/16 between.
Commodity Consumption: Avg. Page Number Per Issue - Daily 29; Avg. Page Number Per Issue - Plates Used 10000; Avg. Page Number Per Issue - Saturday 40; widths 12 1/2; Newsprint Used - Short Tons 932; Printing Ink Used - Black 28518; Printing Ink Used - Color 3630; Printing Ink
Equipment EDITORIAL: Front-end Software – Baseview/Newsedit Pro IQUE, QPS/QuarkXPress 4.11, Adobe/Photoshop.; Editorial Hardware – APP/Mac G4 400 MHZ Towers, APP/Mac G4 933 Mhz, APP/Mac 800Mhz; Editorial Equipment – LiMax/Scanner, Nikon/Scanner; Editorial Printers – HP/4000 CLASSIFIED: Front-end Software – Vison Data/Classified Pagination System.; Classified Hardware – SUN/Server, APP/eMac Workstation, ON X11; Classified Printers – HP/4 Plus DISPLAY: Ad make-up applications – Corel Draw, QPS/QuarkXPress 4.11, Adobe/Photoshop, Baseview/Production Manager Pro, Adobe/Typesetter 3, Adobe/Acrobat 5.0; Display Hardware – APP/Mac G4 500 MHZ Dual Processors; Display Printers – HP/4100, HP 1700d, HP/4300 PRODUCTION: Pagination Software – Baseview/Managing Editor, ALS/Page Director 40.4, Adobe/Quark 4.11; Production Equipment – Nu/Flip Top FT40V6 UPNS, ECR, HP/1700D, ECRM/EVJet 6200, ECRM/EVJet 3100; Cameras – 1-B/18 x 24; Scanners – Nikon/CoolScan, Umax/UTA 11 8 1/2 x 14 Page Scanner PRESSROOM: Line 1 – 6-G/Urbanite 1978; Line 2 – 2-DEV/Horizon 1985; Reels and Stands – 6 MAILROOM: Counter stackers – BG/Count-O-Veyor; Inserters and stuffers – KAN; Bundle tying machines – Dynaric/Strapper; Addressing machine – 2/St.

SHENANDOAH PUBLISHING HOUSE, INC.

152 N. Holliday St., Strasburg, Va., 22657; gen tel (540) 465-5137; gen fax (540) 465-9388

SUFFOLK

SUFFOLK NEWS-HERALD

130 S. Saratoga St., Suffolk, Va., 23434-5323; gen tel (757) 539-3437; gen fax (757) 539-8804; adv fax (757) 539-3000; ed e-mail news@suffolknewsherald.com; web site www.suffolknewsherald.com

Published: Tues, Wed, Thur, Fri, Sat, Sun
Weekday Frequency: m
Circulation: 3,930; 3,930(sat); 3,868(sun)
Last Audit: March 31, 2007
Price: 6.05/mo; 72.60/yr.
Advertising: Open inch rate $19.18
News services: AP.
Politics: Independent.
Not Published: Christmas.
Special Editions: The Great Outdoors (Apr); Football (Aug); Christmas Greetings (Dec); Progress (Feb); Year in Review (Jan); Summer Lifestyles (Jul); June Bride (Jun); Home Improvement (Mar); Senior Citizens (May); Buckle Up for Safety Coloring Book (Nov); Peanut Festival
Special Weekly Sections: Church News (Fri); Best Food Days (S); Schools (Thur); Farm Page (Tues); Best Food Days (Wed).
Bus. Mgr.....Cathy Leonard
Adv. Dir.....Earl Jones
Ed....Res Spears
Sports Ed.....Andrew Giermak
Market Information: Split run; TMC.
Mechanical available: Offset; Black and 3 ROP colors; insert accepted; page cutoffs - 22 3/4.
Mechanical Specifications: Type page 13 x 21 1/2; E - 5 cols, 2 3/8, 1/8 between; A - 6 cols, 2 1/16, 1/8 between; C - 9 cols, 1 3/8, 1/16 between.
Commodity Consumption: Avg. Page Number Per Issue - Daily 10; Avg. Page Number Per Issue - Plates Used 5000; Avg. Page Number Per Issue - Sunday 20; widths 32; Printing Ink Used - Black 30000; Printing Ink Used - Color 2500; Printing Ink Used - Pages Printed 5036.
Equipment EDITORIAL: Front-end Software – QPS/QuarkXPress.; Editorial Hardware – HP; Editorial Printers – HP/5000 CLASSIFIED: Front-end Software – Baseview.; Classified Hardware – APP/iMac; Classified Printers – HP/5000 DISPLAY: Ad make-up applications – QPS/QuarkXPress; Layout Software – APP/Mac G4.; Display Hardware – APP/Mac G4; Display Printers – HP/5000 PRODUCTION: Pagination Software – QPS/QuarkXPress.; Production Equipment – APP/Mac LaserPrinter PRESSROOM: Line 1 – 6-G/Community (24 pg b/w capacity).; Bundle tying machines – 1/Us.; Business Hardware – 2-EKI/Televideo 950

WAYNESBORO

THE NEWS VIRGINIAN

1300 W. Main St., Waynesboro, Va., 22980-0747; gen tel (540) 949-8213; adv tel (540) 949-8213; ed tel (540) 949-8216; gen fax (540) 949-6173; adv fax (540) 941-8859; ed fax (540) 942-4542; gen e-mail newsvirginian@mgads.com; adv e-mail newsvirginian@mgads.com; ed e-mail nvnews@mgads.com; web site www.newsvirginian.com

Published: Mon, Tues, Wed, Thur, Fri, Sat, Sun
Weekday Frequency: m
Saturday Frequency: m
Circulation: 6,015; 6,112(sat); 6,003(sun)
Last Audit: ABC September 30, 2011
Price: 9.75/mo (carrier), $11.67/mo (mail); 99.00/yr (carrier), $140.00/yr (mail); 8.75/mo (EZ-Pay).
Advertising: Open inch rate $22.93
News services: AP, NEA, TMS, Media General News Service.
Politics: Independent.
Special Editions: Tourist Guide (Fall); Bridal Guide (Jan); Senior Lifestyles (Jun); Home & Garden (Mar); Hunting (Oct); Tourist Guide (Spring); Tourist Guide (Summer).
Special Weekly Sections: Wellness (Fri); Business (Mon); Buzz (S); Golden (Sat); TwoFifty (Wed).
Magazines: USA WEEKEND Magazine (S); TV Time (Sat).
Interim Pub.....Lawrence McConnell
Bus. Mgr.....Denise Carter
Adv. Dir.....Sherry Suggs
Circ. Dir.....Paul Wash
Mng. Ed.....Lee Wolverton
Features Ed.....Sage Merritt
Sports Ed.....Jim Sacco
Market Information: TMC.
Mechanical available: Offset; Black and 3 ROP colors; insert accepted - Post-its, polybags, samples; page cutoffs - 22.
Mechanical Specifications: Type page 10 7/8 x 20 3/4; E - 6 cols, 1 73/100, 1/10 between; A - 6 cols, 1 73/100, 1/10 between; C - 10 cols, 1 2/25, 1/8 between.
Commodity Consumption: Avg. Page Number Per Issue - Daily 20; Avg. Page Number Per Issue - Plates Used 80; Avg. Page Number Per Issue - Saturday 24; Avg. Page Number Per Issue - Sunday 26; widths 27 1/2; Newsprint Used - Short Tons 427; Printing Ink Used - Black 10824; Printin
Equipment EDITORIAL: Front-end Software – Microsoft/Word 6.0, QPS/QuarkXPress 4.1, ACT.; Editorial Hardware – Mk/3000, 10-PC Microsystem; Editorial Printers – HP/4MV Postscript, HP/4 Plus CLASSIFIED: Front-end Software – HI/AdPower, Microsoft/Word 6.0, QPS/QuarkXPress 4.1.; Classified Hardware – Mk/3000, 7-PC Microsystem DISPLAY: Ad make-up applications – QPS/QuarkXPress, Adobe/Photoshop, Caere/OmniPage, Ofoto; Display Printers – 2-APP/Mac LaserWriter PRODUCTION: Pagination Software – QPS/QuarkXPress, Adobe/Photoshop, Caere/OmniPage.; Production Equipment – Visioneer/Paper Port, Caere/OmniPage; Cameras – 1-B/24 x 24, COM/M, 1-LE/R 20 x 24 PRESSROOM: Line 1 – 4-G/Urbanite; Folders – 1; Bundle tying machines – 1-Bu/42409, 1/MLN.; Business Hardware – Software ☐ Vision Data

WINCHESTER

THE WINCHESTER STAR

2 N. Kent St., Winchester, Va., 22601; gen tel (540) 667-3200; adv tel (540) 665-4950; ed tel (540) 665-4941; gen fax (540) 667-0012; ed fax (540) 667-1649; gen e-mail info@winchesterstar.com; ed e-mail news@winchesterstar.com; web site www.winchesterstar.com

Published: Mon, Tues, Wed, Thur, Fri, Sat
Weekday Frequency: m
Saturday Frequency: m
Circulation: 18,968; 23,784(sat)
Last Audit: ABC September 30, 2011

Advertising: Open inch rate $24.00
News services: AP, LAT-WP, Media General News Service.
Politics: Independent. **Established:** 1896
Not Published: New Year; Memorial Day; Independence Day; Labor Day; Christmas.
Special Editions: Christmas Gifts (Dec); Bridal (Feb); Our Community (Gov't) (Jan); Planting (Mar); Graduation (May); Real Estate Guide (Monthly); College & Pro Football (Sept).
Special Weekly Sections: TV Showtime (Sat).
Magazines: USA WEEKEND Magazine (Sat).
Pub. ....Thomas T. Byrd
Adv. Mgr., Classified ....Ann Whitacre
Circ. Mgr. ....Bill Green
Mng. Ed. ....Mario Hileman
Online Editor ....Bobby Ford
City Ed. ....Brian Brehm
Editorial Page Ed. ....Adrian O'Connor
Life Ed. ....Frances C. Lowe
Sports Ed. ....Ben Brooks
Prodn. Mgr. ....Brenda Poole
Prodn. Foreman, Pressroom ....Glen Stickel
Systems Mgr. ....Joyce Williams
Market Information: Split run; Zoned editions.
Mechanical available: Offset; Black and 3 ROP colors; insert accepted; page cutoffs - 21 1/2.
Mechanical Specifications: Type page 13 x 21 1/2; E - 6 cols, 2, 1/5 between; A - 6 cols, 2, 1/5 between; C - 9 cols, 1 5/16, 1/5 between.
Commodity Consumption: Avg. Page Number Per Issue - Daily 33; widths 25; Newsprint Used - Short Tons 2000; Printing Ink Used - Black 32582; Printing Ink Used - Color 4273.
Equipment EDITORIAL: Front-end Software – Good News, Adobe/Photoshop 5.01.; Editorial Hardware – COM, Dell/Optiplex-GS, Dell/2100, Dell/200, 2-Dell/PowerEdge 4200 Server; Editorial Equipment – 1-APP/Mac Quadra 700, 1-APP/Mac SE; Editorial Printers – HP/LaserJet 4000N, NewGen/Design Express 6 CLASSIFIED: Front-end Software – SCS/Admax, SCS/Classpag.; Classified Hardware – Dell/2300; Classified Printers – CText/ALPS ALQ324E, NewGen/Turbo PS-400, HP/Laserjet 5000 DISPLAY: Ad make-up applications – SCS/Admax; Layout Software – Layout/8000.; Display Hardware – 2-Dell/4300 Server; Display Printers – HP/LaserJet 4000N, C.Itoh/CI-1000SQE PRODUCTION: Pagination Software – Good News.; Production Equipment – 4-Xante/8200, Konica, 2-ECR; Cameras – C/Spartan III, SCREEN; Scanners – Microtek/ScanMaker III, HP ScanJet II cx PRESSROOM: Line 1 – 8-G/Urbanite U-1327 single width 1981; Folders – 1-G/Double former; Press control system – 1-Ebway/SU 300. MAILROOM: Counter stackers – 1-HL/Dual Carrier, 2-QWI/501; Inserters and stuffers – GMA/Alphaliner; Bundle tying machines – 2-EAM-Mosca, 1-Samuel/Automatic; Addressing machine – 2-Am/1900; Other equipment –MM.; Business Hardware – IBM/Sys 3600

WOODBRIDGE

NEWS & MESSENGER

14010 Smoketown Rd., Woodbridge, Va., 22192; gen tel (703) 878-8000; adv tel (703) 878-3843; ed tel (703) 878-8057; gen fax (703) 878-3993; ed fax (703) 878-8099; adv e-mail ggraff@insidenova.com; ed e-mail news@insidenova.com; kpugh@insidenova.com; opinion@insidenova.com; web site www.insidenova.com
Published: Mon, Tues, Wed, Thur, Fri, Sat, Sun
Weekday Frequency: m
Saturday Frequency: m
Circulation: 18,242; 17,205(sat); 17,092(sun)
Last Audit: September 30, 2008
Price: 2.65/wk; 10.60/mo; 124.00/yr.
Advertising: Open inch rate $36.96
News services: AP, Landon Media Group, Papert (Landon).
Politics: Independent.
Special Editions: Bug (Apr); Welcome Guide (Aug); Manassas Holiday (Dec); Spring Home & Garden (Feb); Bridal (Jan); Discover Quantico (Jun); Hoops (Mar); Golf (May); Coupon Book 1 (Oct); Parade of Homes South (Sept).
Special Weekly Sections: Real Estate (Fri); Business (Mon); Transportation (S); Entertainment (Thur); Health (Tues); Young Life (Wed).
Magazines: USA WEEKEND Magazine (S); American Profile (Weekly).
Pub. ....Bruce Potter
Controller ....Josh Rineholts
Mgr., Natl. Sls. ....Rick Bockes
Circ. Mgr. ....Tom Snellings
Circ. Mgr., Home Delivery ....John Finley
Circ. Mgr., Office ....Lisa Abrahams
Circ. Mgr., Sales/Mktg. ....Kevin Sullivan
Exec. Ed. ....Susan Svihlik
Copydesk Chief ....Scott Lamar
Features Ed. ....Susan Bruchett
Editorial Page Ed. ....Alex Granados
News Ed. ....Kari Pugh
Dir., Photography ....Aleks Dolzenko
Sports Ed. ....Dave Fawcett
Info Servs. Mgr. ....Amargaret Ramsay
Mgmt. Info Servs. Technician ....James Trofit
Market Information: TMC; Zoned editions.
Mechanical available: Offset; Black and 3 ROP colors; insert accepted; page cutoffs - 22.
Mechanical Specifications: Type page 12 x 21; E - 6 cols, 2 1/16, 1/8 between; A - 6 cols, 2 1/16, 1/8 between; C - 9 cols, 1 3/8, 1/16 between.
Commodity Consumption: Avg. Page Number Per Issue - Daily 33; Avg. Page Number Per Issue - Plates Used 36000; Avg. Page Number Per Issue - Saturday 32; Avg. Page Number Per Issue - Sunday 59; widths 37 1/2; Newsprint Used - Short Tons 2250; Printing Ink Used - Black 35535; Pri
Equipment EDITORIAL: Front-end Software – Baseview 2.2.; Editorial Hardware – APP/Mac; Editorial Printers – HP/LaserJet 5000N CLASSIFIED: Front-end Software – Baseview.; Classified Hardware – APP/Mac; Classified Printers – 1-APP/Mac LaserPrinter, 1-Dataproducts/DS-400 DISPLAY: Ad make-up applications – DTI, QPS/QuarkXPress 4.0, Adobe/Photoshop, Adobe/Illustrator; Display Hardware – APP/Power Mac; Display Printers – 1-HP/LaserJet 4 5000GN PRODUCTION: Pagination Software – Baseview.; Production Equipment – 2-Nu; Cameras – 1-C; Scanners – 1-ECR PRESSROOM: Line 1 – 4-MAN/Uniman 4x2 1983; Folders – MAN/Jaw 2-3-2; Pasters – 2-MEG 1983; Reels and Stands – 2 MAILROOM: Counter stackers – 4-Id/440; Inserters and stuffers – 48-HI/8; Bundle tying machines – 3-MLN/MLEE. BUSINESS COMPUTERS: Business Software – CJ, Microsoft/Office, Baseview; Business Hardware – HP/3000, 3-EKI/Televideo, 2-EKI/Earthstation, 1-IBM/PS2

WASHINGTON

ABERDEEN

THE DAILY WORLD

315 S. Michigan St., Aberdeen, Wash., 98520-0071; gen tel (360) 532-4000; adv tel (360) 532-4000; ed tel (360) 532-4000; gen fax (360) 533-1328; adv fax (360) 533-1328; ed fax (360) 533-6039; gen e-mail pub@thedailyworld.com; letters@thedailyworld.com; adv e-mail advert@thedailyworld.com; ed e-mail press_releases@thedailyworld.com; editor@thedailyworld.com; web site www.thedailyworld.com
Published: Mon, Tues, Wed, Thur, Fri, Sat, Sun
Saturday Frequency: m
Circulation: 11,731; 11,731(sat); 12,066(sun)
Last Audit: September 30, 2008
Price: 9.60/mo.
Advertising: Open inch rate $27.85
News services: AP.
Politics: Independent.
Special Editions: Real Estate Showcase (Monthly).
Special Weekly Sections: Entertainment (Fri); Church Page (Sat); Best Food Day (Wed).
Magazines: Preview (Fri); USA WEEKEND Magazine (S).
Bus. Mgr. ....Claudia Bearden
Adv. Mgr. ....Bridget Dannell
Circ. Dir. ....Gerald Atkinson
Ed. ....John C. Hughes
City Ed. ....Bill Lindstrom
Asst. City Ed. ....Dan Jackson
Entertainment Ed., Preview Magazine Jeff Burlingame
Photo Dept. Mgr. ....Kathy Quigg
Religion Ed. ....Tommi Gatlin
Sports Ed. ....Rick Anderson
Mgr., Distr. ....Ryan Parson
Prodn. Mgr., Pre Press Systems ....David Dutton
Prodn. Foreman, Pressroom ....Larry Schoening
Market Information: TMC.
Mechanical available: Offset; Black and 3 ROP colors; insert accepted - any; page cutoffs - 22 3/4.
Mechanical Specifications: Type page 13 x 21 1/2; E - 6 cols, 2 1/16, 1/8 between; A - 6 cols, 2 1/16, 1/8 between; C - 9 cols, 1 3/8, 1/16 between.
Commodity Consumption: Avg. Page Number Per Issue - Daily 22; Avg. Page Number Per Issue - Plates Used 10000; Avg. Page Number Per Issue - Saturday 20; Avg. Page Number Per Issue - Sunday 24; widths 13 1/2; Newsprint Used - Metric Tons 830; Printing Ink Used - Black 36000; Pri
Equipment EDITORIAL: Front-end Software – Baseview, SII.; Editorial Hardware – 17-APP/Mac; Editorial Printers – HP/4MV CLASSIFIED: Front-end Software – Baseview.; Classified Hardware – 4-APP/Mac; Classified Printers – Okidata/Pacemark 3410 DISPLAY: Ad make-up applications – GEAC 8.2; Layout Software – 4-APP/Mac.; Display Hardware – HP; Display Printers – HP/8000N PRODUCTION: Pagination Software – QPS/QuarkXPress 4.1.1.; Production Equipment – 1-Nu/Flip Top FT40APNS, 1-Pre-Press/7145DB; Cameras – 1-C/Spartan III; Scanners – TECSA/2470 PRESSROOM: Line 1 – 6-G/Urbanite 1973; Press Drives – 2 MAILROOM: Counter stackers – 1-MM/CS20; Inserters and stuffers – MM/5 Station; Bundle tying machines – 1/MLN, 1-OVL/415. BUSINESS COMPUTERS: Business Software – Word Processing; Business Hardware – GEAC-Advertising, Baseview-Classified

BELLINGHAM

THE BELLINGHAM HERALD

1155 N. State St., Bellingham, Wash., 98225-5037; gen tel (360) 676-2600; adv tel (360) 676-2660; ed tel (360) 676-2660; adv fax (360) 756-2819; ed e-mail newsroom@bellinghamherald.com; web site www.bellinghamherald.com
Group: McClatchy
Published: Mon, Tues, Wed, Thur, Fri, Sat, Sun
Weekday Frequency: m
Saturday Frequency: m
Circulation: 16,759; 19,277(sat); 21,304(sun)
Last Audit: ABC September 30, 2011
Price: $15 a month
News services: AP, GNS, MCT
Politics: 1890
Own facility?: N
Magazines: Northwest Auto (Every other week); Parade (Fri); Relish (Monthly); Color Comics (4 pages) (S); Take Five (leisure guide) (Thur).
Publisher ....Mark Owings
Advertising Director ....Amber Aldrich
Executive Editor ....Julie Shirley
Managing Editor ....Debbie Townsend
Business Editor ....Dave Gallagher
Whatcom Magazine Editor ....Dean Kahn
Picture Editor ....Russ Kendall
Presentation Editor ....Andy Norstadt
Sports Editor ....David Rasbach
Human Resources Manager Kristen Reams
Market Information: ADS; Split run; TMC.
Mechanical available: Offset; Black and 3 ROP colors; insert accepted - single sheet card stock; page cutoffs - 22 3/4.
Commodity Consumption: Avg. Page Number Per Issue - Daily 38; Avg. Page Number Per Issue - Plates Used 26492; Avg. Page Number Per Issue - Sunday 74; widths 25; Newsprint Used - Short Tons 2228; Printing Ink Used - Black 35988; Printing Ink Used - Color 8765; Printing Ink Used
Equipment; Editorial Hardware – APT
Delivery method: Private Carrier

BREMERTON

KITSAP SUN

545 Fifth St., Bremerton, Wash., 98337-0053; gen tel (360) 377-3711; adv tel (360) 377-3711; ed tel (360) 377-3711; gen fax (360) 377-9237; adv fax (360) 377-9237; ed fax (360) 415-2681; gen e-mail jzuehl-miller@kitsapsun.com; adv e-mail ad-support@kitsapsun.com; ed e-mail sunnews@kitsapsun.com; web site www.kitsapsun.com
Published: Mon, Tues, Wed, Thur, Fri, Sat, Sun
Weekday Frequency: m
Saturday Frequency: m
Circulation: 31,728; 20,717(sat); 22,688(sun)
Last Audit: ABC September 30, 2011
Price: 2.87/wk; 11.50/mo; 130.00/yr (carrier), $264.00/yr (mail).
Advertising: Open inch rate $49.87(m-fri)
News services: AP, SHNS.
Politics: Independent. **Established:** 1935
Special Editions: Visitor's Guide (Apr); 5 Days til Christmas (Dec); Home & Garden (May); Festival of Trees (Nov); Football (Oct).
Special Weekly Sections: A & E (Fri); TV Tab (S); Drive (Sat).
Magazines: USA WEEKEND Magazine (S).
Profile: The Sun's mission is to serve West Sound with timely delivery of authoritative news and effective advertising, creating a profitable relationship with employees, readers and advertisers.
Credit Mgr. ....Robin Alexander
Dir., Adv./Mktg. ....Mike Stevens
Nat'l Adv. Mgr., Co-op ....Don Dosa
President & Publisher ....Charles Horton
Ed. ....David Nelson
Entertainment Writer ....Michael Moore
Environmental/Tech. Writer Christopher Dunagan
Sports Ed. ....Chuck Stark
Submitted Content Ed. ....Jim Campbell
Opns. Dir. ....Ron Muhleman
Pre Press Mgr. ....Randi Watson
Market Information: ADS; TMC; Zoned editions.
Mechanical available: Web Offset; Black and 4 ROP colors; insert accepted - we-prints, product sample bags; page cutoffs - 22 3/4.
Mechanical Specifications: Type page 10 1/2 x 21 1/2; E - 6 cols, 1 14/25, 1/8 between; A - 6 cols, 1 14/25, 1/8 between; C - 9 cols, 1 7/100, 1/8 between.
Commodity Consumption: Avg. Page Number Per Issue - Daily 40; Avg. Page Number Per Issue - Plates Used 2400; Avg. Page Number Per Issue - Sunday 64; Newsprint Used - Metric Tons 3000; Printing Ink Used - Black 75000; Printing Ink Used - Color 7000; Printing Ink Used - Pages Pri
Equipment EDITORIAL: Front-end Software – QPS/QuarkXPress, Adobe/Photoshop 3.0, Adobe/Illustrator 6.0, P.INK.; Editorial Hardware – APP/Mac; Editorial Equipment – Microtek/Scanner, Nikon/FilmScanner, Kk/Film-Scanner, Lf/AP Leaf Picture Desk; Editorial Printers – Hyphen/Typesetters, TI CLASSIFIED: Front-end Software – Dewar/Information Sys, XYQUEST/XyWrite.; Classified Hardware – PC Network; Classified Printers – Epson DISPLAY: Ad make-up applications – Multi-Ad/Creator 3.8, Mk/Ad Director, QPS/QuarkXPress 3.32, Adobe/Photoshop 3.0, Adobe/PageMaker 6.0, Adobe/Illustrator 6; Display Hardware – APP/Mac; Display Printers – APP/Mac Laser-Writer, Hyphen/Pelbox Typesetter, AG/Select

Set 5000, Hyphen/Ultra Typesetter PRODUCTION: Pagination Software – QPS/QuarkXPress.; Production Equipment – 1-BKY/Ascor, 1-Burgess, SpectraSet/3100; Cameras – 1-Acti/24V, 1-R/432 Mark II; Scanners – Microtek PRESSROOM: Line 1 – 5-HI/N1650 double width 1993; Press Drives – GE/200h.p.; Folders – 2-G/2:1; Reels and Stands – 4-G/double. MAILROOM: Counter stackers – 2-HL/Monitor, 1-HL/HT II; Inserters and stuffers – GMA/SLS 1000 8:1; Bundle tying machines – 1-MLN/ML2, 1-MLN/MLEE, 1/Power Strap/PSNG; Addressing machine – 1-KR/Quarter Folder, Ch.; Business Hardware – IBM/AS-400

CENTRALIA

THE CHRONICLE

321 N. Pearl St., Centralia, Wash., 98531; gen tel (360) 736-3311; adv tel (360) 736-3311; ed tel (360) 736-3311; gen fax (360) 736-4796; adv fax (360) 736-1568; ed fax (360) 736-4796; gen e-mail chronline@chronline.com; adv e-mail classifieds@chronline.com; ed e-mail letters@chronline.com; web site www.chronline.com

Group: Lafromboise Communication Inc
Published: Mon, Tues, Wed, Thur, Fri, Sat
Weekday Frequency: e
Saturday Frequency: m
Circulation: 13,200; 13,800(sat)
Last Audit: Sworn March 31, 2006
Price: $12.90/mo; $35.15/3 mo; $65.15/6 mo. 122.00/yr
Advertising: Open $16.75 pci
Insert rate: sliding scale
Politics: Independent. **Established:** 1966
Not Published: New Year; Presidents Day; Memorial Day; Independence Day; Labor Day; Veterans Day; Thanksgiving; Christmas.
Special Editions: Quarterly senior and health; April tourism; July Best of; August Fair; Sept/Oct Football; Nov/Dec Gift guide & holiday
Special Weekly Sections: M-business, T-outdoors, W-food, Th-Arts & entertainment, F-Home, S-Religion
Magazines: USA Weekend Sat; Relish 1st Wed; Athlon Sports, Last Fri.

CFO....Steve Walker
HR Dir. ....Rosie O'Connor
Publisher ....Christine Fossett
Exec. Ed. ....Michael Wagar
Prodn. Dir. ....Jeff Andersen
IT Director ....Jon Bennett
CEO ....Dennis R. Waller
Ad. Mgr. ....J. Alexander
Pub. ....Dennis R. Waller
Print Pro Sales Exec. ....Jeff Martin
Pressroom Foreman ....Dennis Beebe
Prodn. Mgr., Distr. ....Becky Criscola

Market Information: TMC.
Mechanical available: Offset; Black and 3 ROP colors; insert accepted - single sheets, min. 70 lb. stock; page cutoffs - 22.
Mechanical Specifications: Type page 9.98x20.43 5 column, classifieds 7 column
Commodity Consumption: Avg. Page Number Per Issue - Daily 32; Avg. Page Number Per Issue - Plates Used 8400; Avg. Page Number Per Issue - Saturday 36; widths 34; Newsprint Used - Metric Tons 1200; Printing Ink Used - Black 30000; Printing Ink Used - Color 10000; Printing Ink U
Equipment EDITORIAL: Front-end Software – InDesign 3; Editorial Hardware – 2-APP/Mac G3 fileserver, 13-APP/Mac imac 350 mhz, 5-APP/Mac G3 pagination station; Editorial Printers – APP/Mac LaserWriter IIg, Dataproducts/LZR 1560, APP/Mac ImageWriter CLASSIFIED: Front-end Software – Newzware classified; Classified Hardware – 6-APP/Mac, APP/Mac fileserver, 1-APP/Mac Classic II; Classified Printers – APP/Mac LaserWriter II NT, Okidata/320 Turbo DISPLAY: Ad make-up applications – InDesign 3; Display Hardware – 6-APP/Mac G3 ad layout, Sony/200ES Monitor, 2-APP/Mac G3 fileserver; Display Printers – 2-HP/8100 N, Dataproducts/LZR 1560, HP/1055C Plotter PRODUCTION: Pagination Software – InDesign 3; Production Equipment – 2-ECR/4550 knockout, 1-Konica/k720 PRESSROOM: Line 1 – 11-Dauphin/single width 1998; Press Drives – Baldor/Series 28 twin 100 hp digital control; Pasters – 3-Jardis/HS 35000. MAILROOM: Counter stackers – 1-MM/Counter Stacker 288; Inserters and stuffers – 1-MM/275;

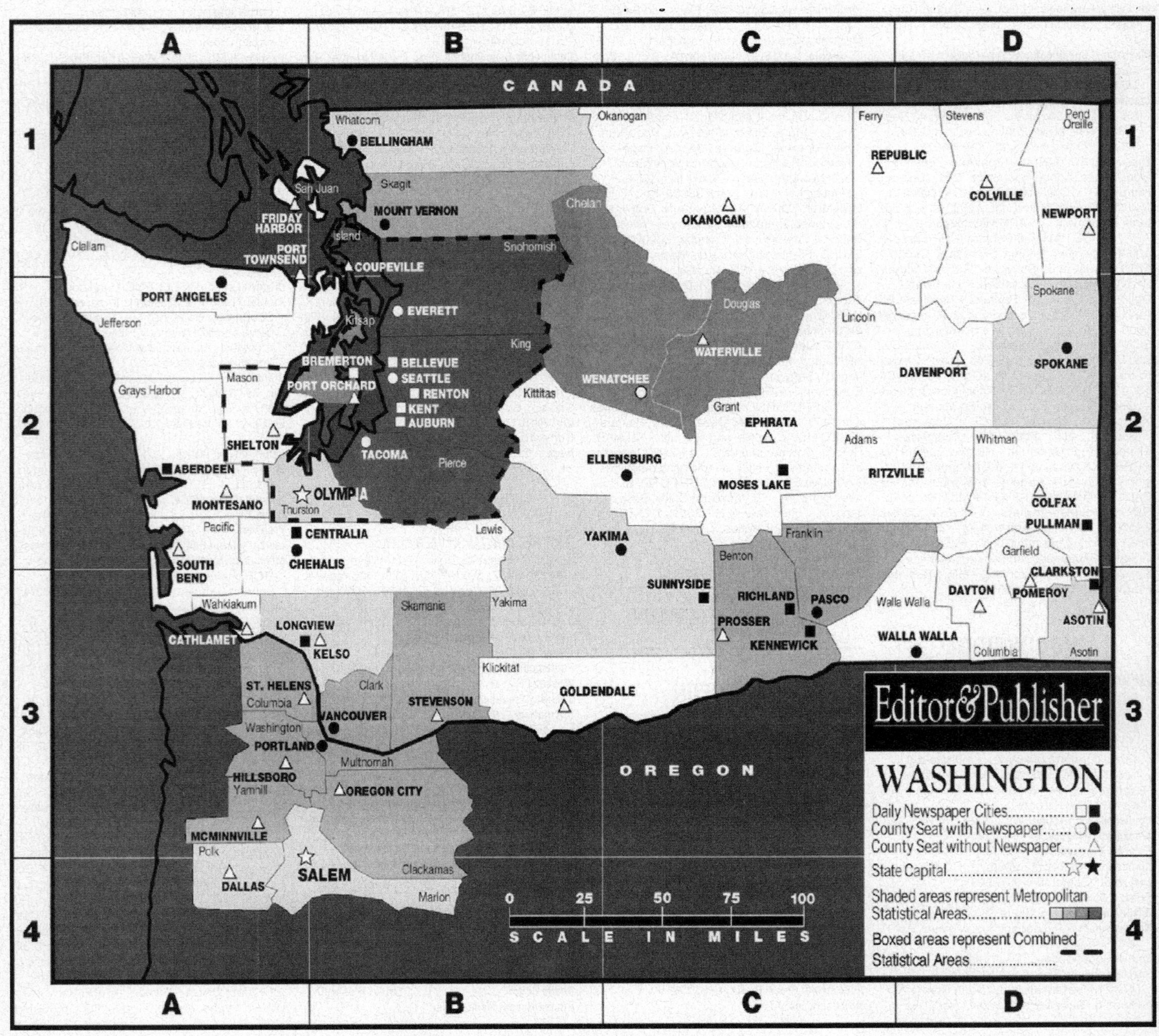

Bundle tying machines – LB/3000, 2-LB/2000; Mailroom control system – 1/Consolidated, 4-/Station Jetstream/230 Auto Saddle Stitcher, Trimmer System, 1-New Jersey/Stitcher BUSINESS COMPUTERS: Business Software – Baseview:, MS/Excel, MS/Word; Business Hardware – APP/Mac-Network, PCs

Delivery method: Newsstand, Private Carrier, Racks

LAFROMBOISE COMMUNICATIONS, INC.

PO Box 580, Centralia, Wash., 98531; gen tel (360) 736-3311; gen fax (360) 807-8253

ELLENSBURG

DAILY RECORD

401 N. Main St., Ellensburg, Wash., 98926; gen tel (509) 925-1414; adv tel (509) 925-1414; ed tel (509) 925-1414; gen fax (509) 925-5696; adv fax (509) 925-5696; ed fax (509) 925-5696; gen e-mail dailyrecord@kvnews.com; adv e-mail classifieds@kvnews.com; ed e-mail jrobinson@kvnews.com; web site www.kvnews.com

Published: Mon, Tues, Wed, Thur, Fri, Sat, Sun
Weekday Frequency: e
Saturday Frequency: m
Circulation: 5,523; 5,523(sat)
Last Audit: March 31, 2007
Price: 8.50/mo; 96.00/yr.
Advertising: Open inch rate $14.20
News services: AP.
Politics: Independent. **Established:** 1909
Not Published: New Year; Independence Day; Thanksgiving; Christmas.
Special Editions: Conservation/Agriculture (Apr); Fair Guide (Aug); Vintage View (Seniors) (Feb); Vintage View (Seniors) (Jul); Spring Visitor's Guide (May); Holiday Gift Guide (Nov); Vintage View (Oct); Rodeo (Sept).
Special Weekly Sections: Mini Page (Fri); Religion (Sat); Ag Page (Tues).
Magazines: American Profile (Fri); Relish (Monthly); Parade (S).
Pub. .... Matt Davison
Office Mgr. .... Diane Ewing
Adv. Dir. .... Tyler Millar
Circ. Mgr. .... Justice Metsker
Educ./Features Ed. .... Jeff Robinson
Online Ed. .... Jill Whiteside
Women's Ed. .... Marie Swift
Telecom Mgr. .... Richard Dalton
Market Information: TMC.
Mechanical available: Offset; Black and 3 ROP colors; insert accepted; page cutoffs - 22 3/4.
Mechanical Specifications: Type page 12 15/16 x 21; E - 6 cols, 2, 1/6 between; A - 6 cols, 2, 1/6 between; C - 9 cols, 1 1/2, 1/12 between.
Commodity Consumption: Avg. Page Number Per Issue - Daily 16; Avg. Page Number Per Issue - Plates Used 3600; widths 14; Newsprint Used - Metric Tons 225; Printing Ink Used - Black 4500; Printing Ink Used - Color 150; Printing Ink Used - Pages Printed 5100.
Equipment EDITORIAL: Front-end Software – Baseview, QPS/QuarkXPress, Adobe/Photoshop, Caere/OmniPage.; Editorial Hardware – APP/Mac; Editorial Equipment – APP/Mac; Editorial Printers – Xante/Accel-a-Writer 8200 CLASSIFIED: Front-end Software – Baseview.; Classified Hardware – APP/Mac; Classified Printers – Okidata/Microline 320 Turbo DISPLAY: Ad make-up applications – QPS/QuarkXPress 3.3.2, Adobe/Photoshop 5.0, Aldus Freehand 8.0, Adobe/PageMaker 6.5, Multi Ad Creator, ALS/Managing Editor; Display Hardware – APP/Mac; Display Printers – Xante/Accel-a-writer 8200 PRODUCTION: Pagination Software – QPS/QuarkXPress 3.32.; Production Equipment – Caere/OmniPage Pro 8.0, Konica/EV-Jetsetter; Cameras – APP/Mac QuickTake 150, Olympus/620-L; Scanners – Sprint/Scan 35, Epson/ES-1200, Umax/Astra 12205 PRESSROOM: Line 1 – 2-G/Community 1968, 2-G/Community 1969, 2-G/Community 1980.; Inserters and stuffers – KAN/3-gate; Bundle tying machines – . BUSINESS COMPUTERS: Business Software – PBS; Business Hardware – Sun/Sparc Station 10

EVERETT

THE HERALD

1213 California St., Everett, Wash., 98201-3445; gen tel (425) 339-3000; adv tel (425) 339-3030; ed tel (425) 339-3400; gen fax (425) 339-3049; adv fax (425) 339-3049; ed fax (425) 339-3435; gen e-mail editor@heraldnet.com; letters@heraldnet.com; adv e-mail advertising@heraldnet.com; ed e-mail newstips@heraldnet.com; web site www.heraldnet.com

Published: Mon, Tues, Wed, Thur, Fri, Sat, Sun
Weekday Frequency: m
Saturday Frequency: m
Circulation: 46,346; 43,990(sat); 51,494(sun)
Last Audit: ABC September 30, 2011
Price: 11.70/mo; 119.40/yr.
Advertising: Open inch rate $73.29
News services: AP, LAT-WP, Scripps McClatchy News Service.
Politics: Independent. **Established:** 1901
Own facility?: Y
Special Editions: Health & Fitness (Other).
Special Weekly Sections: Arts & Entertainment (Fri); Business Update (Mon); Real Estate (S); Outdoors (Sat); Home & Garden (Thur); Living (Tues); Food (Wed).
Magazines: Relish (Monthly); Access (S).
Controller/Dir., Labor Rel. .... Dan Amundsen
HR Mgr. .... Jessica Willard
Mktg. Dir. .... Kelly Hulin
Circ. Opns. Mgr. .... Jere Grubb
Exec. Ed. .... Neal Pattison
Bus. Ed. .... Mike Benbow
City Ed. .... Robert Frank
Editorial Page Ed. .... Bob Bolerjack
Features/Food Ed. .... Melanie Munk
Librarian/TV Ed. .... Bill Pedigo
News Ed. .... Mark Carlson
Photo Ed. .... Justin Best
Sports Ed. .... Kevin Brown
Advertising Director .... Ron Lee
Classified Manager .... Trina Alger
Retail Advertising Manager .... Ken Clements
Director of Circulation and Operations Jorge Rivera
Production Director .... Susan Strong
Pressroom Manager .... Mat Orbeck
Market Information: Split run; TMC; Zoned editions.
Mechanical available: Offset; Black and 3 ROP colors; insert accepted; page cutoffs - 22.
Mechanical Specifications: Type page 13 x 21; E - 6 cols, 2 1/16, 1/8 between; A - 6 cols, 2 1/16, 1/8 between; C - 10 cols, 1 3/16, 1/8 between.
Commodity Consumption: Avg. Page Number Per Issue - Daily 40; Avg. Page Number Per Issue - Plates Used 48500; Avg. Page Number Per Issue - Sunday 76; widths 27 1/2; Newsprint Used - Metric Tons 7118; Printing Ink Used - Black 292429; Printing Ink Used - Color 62600; Printing I
Equipment EDITORIAL: Front-end Software – QPS/QuarkXPress 4.0, Microsoft/Word 6.0, APT/ACT.; Editorial Hardware – 70-HP/Pentium II, 4-APP/Power Mac, 2-HP/NT fileserver CLASSIFIED: Front-end Software – Cybergraphics/Genesis 7.7.; Classified Hardware – 1-DEC/Micro VAX 4000-200, 25-HP/Pentium II; Layout Software – MEI/ALS.; Display Hardware – 22-APP/Power Mac; Display Printers – Software ÂD Multi-Ad/Creator 3.5, Multi-Ad/Creator II PRODUCTION: Pagination Software – QPS/QuarkXPress 4.0.; Production Equipment – 1-AG/Selectset 5000, 1-III/3850, 1-ECR/Scriptwriter; Cameras – 1-C/Marathon, 1-R/400, 1-R/475; Scanners – X/7650, 1-SCREEN/1030 PRESSROOM: Line 1 – 9-G/Metrocolor double width 1993; Folders – 2, G/3:2; Reels and Stands – 3-G/Ct-50 RIP; Press control system – Rockwell/Automation Print View. MAILROOM: Counter stackers – 3/QWI, 2-Gammerler/KL 503/1; Inserters and stuffers – 1-MM/227E, 1-/AM Graphics/NP 630, 1-G/Heidelberg 1280; Bundle tying machines – 5-/Dynaric; Addressing machine – 3-KR/Paper Labeler, Scitex/Ink Jet; Other equipment – S/SP705 Stitche

LONGVIEW

THE DAILY NEWS

770 11th Ave., Longview, Wash., 98632; gen tel (360) 577-2500; adv fax (360) 577-2536; ed fax (360) 577-2538; gen e-mail letters@tdn.com; adv e-mail ads@tdn.com; ed e-mail news@tdn.com; web site www.tdn.com

Published: Mon, Tues, Wed, Thur, Fri, Sat, Sun
Weekday Frequency: m
Saturday Frequency: m
Circulation: 19,709; 19,709(sat); 19,754(sun)
Last Audit: September 30, 2009
Price: 11.75/mo (carrier); 141.00/yr (carrier).
Advertising: Open inch rate $30.09
News services: AP, LAT-WP.
Politics: Independent. **Established:** 1923
Special Editions: Thanksgiving (Other).
Special Weekly Sections: TV Times-Flexi (Fri); Entertainment (Thur); Food (Wed).
Magazines: Real Estate (Monthly); Parade (S).
Profile: The Daily News is the daily newspaper of record for Cowlitz County in Washington. Serving southwestern Washington and northwest Oregon since 1923
Adv. Mgr., Retail .... Steve Quaife
Adv. Mgr., Classified .... Sherrie Meyers
Cir. Dir., Audience .... Wyatt Gardiner
Mng. Ed. .... Cal FitzSimmons
City Ed. .... Andre Stepankowsky
Community Ed. .... Brenda McCorkle
Editorial Page Ed. .... James Bross
Copy Ed. .... Julie Cozby
Features Ed. .... Cathy Zimmerman
Librarian .... Donna Yardley
Online Ed. .... Scott Heisel
Outdoors Ed. .... Tom Paulu
Regl. Ed. .... Nancy Edwards
Sports Ed. .... Rick Alvord
Mgr., Systems .... Jim Wallingford
Prodn. Mgr., Mailroom .... Deborah D. Hannah
Prodn. Mgr., Pressroom .... Bruce Myers
Market Information: ADS; TMC; Zoned editions.
Mechanical available: Offset; Black and 3 ROP colors; insert accepted - Product Sample Bags; page cutoffs - 22 3/4.
Mechanical Specifications: Type page 11 1/8 x 21 1/2; E - 6 cols, 1 11/16, 1/8 between; A - 6 cols, 1 11/16, 1/8 between; C - 9 cols, 1 1/8, 1/16 between.
Commodity Consumption: Avg. Page Number Per Issue - Daily 36; Avg. Page Number Per Issue - Plates Used 24500; widths 25; Newsprint Used - Metric Tons 1800; Printing Ink Used - Black 52959; Printing Ink Used - Color 15000; Printing Ink Used - Pages Printed 13444.
Equipment EDITORIAL: Front-end Software – Lotus/Notes News Engin 4.6.; Editorial Hardware – 2-Micron, 25-Dell/PC, APP/Mac Workstations; Editorial Equipment – Umax/Astra 1200; Editorial Printers – HP/5000, HP/4050 CLASSIFIED: Front-end Software – Vision Data/Classified.; Classified Hardware – Sun/Sparc workstations; Classified Printers – HP/4050, Printronix/Line Printer DISPLAY: Ad make-up applications – Other Equipment Sharp/JX-600 Scanner, HP/ScanJet, HP/ScanJet CX, 2-Umax/S-12 Scanner, 1-HP/5000, 1-HP/2500 Color Proofer; Layout Software – SCS/Layou; Display Hardware – 8-APP/Mac G3, G4 Power Computing 8.01, 2-Sun/Servers; Display Printers – Software Aldus/FreeHand, QPS/QuarkXPress 4.04 PRODUCTION: Pagination Software – QPS/QuarkXPress 4.04.; Production Equipment – 1-Wd, 2-ECR/Scriptsetter RIP, 1-1PT Turbo Rip; Cameras – 1-C/Spartan II; Scanners – Nikon/LS-3510AF, Epson, Nikon/Coolscan PRESSROOM: Line 1 – 4-G/Urbanite single width 1970; Line 2 – 3-G/Urbanite single width 1970; Press Drives – 2; Folders – 2-G/Urbanite. MAILROOM: Counter stackers – 1-Id/Marathoner, 2-TMSI/Compass; Inserters and stuffers – 2-MM/227 5:1; Bundle tying machines – 1-MLN/2EE, 2-MLN/2A, 3-MLN/2; Wrapping singles – 2-Windab/UP720 Bottom Wrap; Addressing machine – KR/215 Mailing System; Other equipment –M BUSINESS COMPUTERS: Business Software – Vision Data; Business Hardware – Sun/Sparc

MOSES LAKE

COLUMBIA BASIN HERALD

813 W. 3rd Ave., Moses Lake, Wash., 98837-0136; gen tel (509) 765-4561; adv tel (509) 765-4561; ed tel (509) 765-4561; gen fax (509) 765-8659; adv fax (509) 765-8659; ed fax (509) 765-8659; adv e-mail advertising@colmbiabasinherald.com; ed e-mail editor@columbiabasinherald.com; web site www.columbiabasinherald.com

Published: Mon, Tues, Wed, Thur, Fri
Weekday Frequency: e
Circulation: 7,780
Last Audit: October 1, 2003
Advertising: Open inch rate $16.81
News services: AP.
Politics: Independent.
Advertising not accepted: Enhancement drug.
Not Published: New Year; Memorial Day; Independence Day; Labor Day; Thanksgiving; Christmas.
Special Editions: Create Your Own Adventure (Apr); Fair Tab (Aug); Lighted Ag Parade (Dec); Night on the Town (Feb); Spokane Boat Show (Jan); Home Buyers Guide (Jun); Spring Fair (Mar); All City Real Estate Guide (May); Horse & Rider (Monthly); Holiday Directory (Nov); His
Special Weekly Sections: Biggest Loser (Weekly).
Magazines: USA WEEKEND Magazine (Fri).
Pub. .... Harlan Beagley
Bus. Mgr. .... Denise Lembeke
Adv. Dir. .... Jim McKiernan
Circ. Dir. .... Tom Hinde
Mng. Ed. .... Bill Stevenson
Sports Ed. .... Brad Redford
Prodn. Mgr., Pressroom .... Rick Horton
Prodn. Mgr., Distr. .... Joyce McLanahan
Prodn. Supt. .... Curt Weaver
Market Information: ADS; TMC.
Mechanical available: Offset; Black and 3 ROP colors; insert accepted - others accepted; page cutoffs - 22 3/4.
Mechanical Specifications: Type page 13 x 21 1/2; E - 6 cols, 1 5/6, 1/8 between; A - 6 cols, 1 5/6, 1/8 between; C - 8 cols, 1 1/3, 1/8 between.
Commodity Consumption: Avg. Page Number Per Issue - Daily 20; Avg. Page Number Per Issue - Plates Used 11090; widths 25; Printing Ink Used - Pages Printed 6500.
Equipment EDITORIAL: Front-end Software – Quark 4.0.; Editorial Hardware – Mac/G4; Editorial Printers – HP/4200 CLASSIFIED: Front-end Software – Baseview 2.1.4.; Classified Hardware – Mac/G4; Classified Printers – HP/4200 DISPLAY: Ad make-up applications – Baseview 2.1.4; Layout Software – Adforce.; Display Hardware – Mac/G4; Display Printers – HP/4200; Production Equipment – 2-Fr, 1-P, 1-Ma, 1-Fi; Cameras – 1-K.; Inserters and stuffers – MM/4 head; Bundle tying machines – 1/Bu, 1-/El; Addressing machine – Ch/730S.

MOUNT VERNON

SKAGIT VALLEY HERALD

1215 Anderson Rd., Mount Vernon, Wash., 98274; gen tel (360) 424-3251; ed tel (360) 416-2160; gen fax (360) 424-5300; ed fax (360) 428-0400; adv e-mail adservices@skagitpublishing.com; ed e-mail news@skagitpublishing.com; web site www.goskagit.com; www.skagitpublishing.com

Published: Mon, Tues, Wed, Thur, Fri, Sat, Sun
Saturday Frequency: m
Circulation: 16,187; 16,187(sat); 17,567(sun)
Last Audit: September 30, 2008
Price: 11.85/mo (carrier); 127.20/yr (carrier).

Advertising: Open inch rate $22.20
News services: AP, MCT, LAT-WP.
Politics: Independent. **Established:** 1884
Special Editions: Builders Assoc. Home Show (Apr); Anacortes Arts & Crafts (Aug); Bridal (Feb); Highland Games (Jul); Loggerodeo (Jun); Spring Home & Garden (Mar); Holiday Gift Guide (Nov); Swan (Woman of the Year) (Oct); Good Living (Quarterly); Healthy Living (Semi-yearl
Special Weekly Sections: Books (Fri); People (Mon); Skagit Living (S); Real Estate Open House (Sat); A&E 360 (Thur); Healthy Living (Wed).
Magazines: Business Pulse (Monthly); USA WEEKEND Magazine (S); TV Week Magazine (Weekly).
Pres. ....Leighton P. Wood
Pub. ....Stedem Wood
Finance Dir. ....Kelly Bachman
Adv. Dir. ....Vallerie Feltus
Adv. Mgr., Classified/Inside Sales Jeanette Kales
Adv. Mgr., Co-op ....Katie Sundermeyer
Adv. Mgr., Display ....Deb Bundy
Adv. Mgr., Majors/Natl. Accts. Stephanie Harper
NIE Mgr. ....Eileen Woods
Circ. Dir. ....Manny Nevarez
Mng. Ed., Administration ....Colette Weeks
Mng. Ed., News ....Dick Clever
Features Ed. ....Beverly Crichfield
Photo Ed. ....Scott Terrell
Sports Ed. ....Dan Ruthemeyer
Info Systems Mgr. ....Dan MacDonald
Interactive Media Mgr. ....Patrick Dougherty
Prodn. Dir. ....Tom Larsen
Market Information: ADS; TMC.
Mechanical available: Offset; Black and 3 ROP colors; insert accepted - cards; page cutoffs - 22 3/4.
Mechanical Specifications: Type page 10 x 20 1/2; E - 6 cols, 1 19/32, 3/32 between; A - 6 cols, 1 19/32, 3/32 between; C - 6 cols, 1 19/32, 3/32 between.
Commodity Consumption: Avg. Page Number Per Issue - Daily 28; Avg. Page Number Per Issue - Plates Used 19681; Avg. Page Number Per Issue - Saturday 32; widths 27; Newsprint Used - Metric Tons 1201; Printing Ink Used - Black 17200; Printing Ink Used - Pages Printed 10411.
Equipment EDITORIAL: Front-end Software – Baseview/NewsEdit 3.3.2, QPS/QuarkXPress 4.1.; Editorial Hardware – APP/Mac G4; Editorial Equipment – Nikon/LS-3510 Negative Scanner, HP/ScanJet IIcx; Editorial Printers – APP/Mac LaserWriter IIg CLASSIFIED: Front-end Software – Baseview/Class Manager Plus 3.21.; Classified Hardware – APP/Power Mac 7200; Classified Equipment – APP/Mac Scanner for OCR; Classified Printers – APP/Mac, Epson/LQ870, APP/Mac LaserWriter NTX DISPLAY: Ad make-up applications – QPS/QuarkXPress 4.1, Adobe/Photoshop 5.5; Display Hardware – APP/Mac 8-Quadra 700, APP/Power Mac 7100, APP/Mac Quadra 605, APP/Mac G4; Display Printers – APP/Mac LaserWriter 8500, APP/Mac LaserWriter 16-600, Harlequin/GSI Rip, AG/9800 PRODUCTION: Pagination Software – QPS/QuarkXPress 4.1.; Production Equipment – Caere/OmniPage, APP/Power Mac 8100, APP/Mac G4; Cameras – SCREEN/Auto Companica 690D, Canon/Xapshot; Scanners – Nikon/3510 scanner, HP/ScanJet IIcx PRESSROOM: Line 1 – 16-G/Community; Folders – 2, G/Community; Press registration system – Stoesser/Register System. MAILROOM: Counter stackers – 2-MM/310-20; Inserters and stuffers – 2-MM/5-pocket; Bundle tying machines – 2/Gd, 1-MLN/ML2EE, 2-MLN/2A; Addressing machine – Ch/525; Other equipment –MM/235. AUDIO: Audio Software – Microsoft/Windows NT 1998; Audio Hardware – ITN, PC BUSINESS COMPUTERS: Business Software – MSSI, PBS; Business Hardware – IBM, Unix

OLYMPIA

FEDERATED PUBLICATIONS, INC.

PO Box 407, Olympia, Wash., 98507; gen tel (360) 754-5400; gen fax (360) 754-5408

THE OLYMPIAN

111 Bethel St. NE, Olympia, Wash., 98506-4365; gen tel (360) 754-5400; adv tel (360) 754-5428; ed tel (360) 754-5420; gen fax (360) 357-0207; adv fax (360) 357-0740; ed fax (360) 357-0202; gen e-mail homedelivery@theolympian.com; news@theolympian.com; ed e-mail sports@theolympian.com; web site www.theolympian.com
Published: Mon, Tues, Wed, Thur, Fri, Sat, Sun
Weekday Frequency: m
Saturday Frequency: m
Circulation: 23,665; 24,008(sat); 28,887(sun)
Last Audit: ABC September 30, 2011
Price: 186.00/yr; 16.50/month
Advertising: Open inch rate $77.60
News services: AP, MCT, LAT-WP.
Politics: Independent. **Established:** 1889
Special Editions: After Christmas Sale (Dec); Legislative Session (Jan); Tour of Homes (Jul); Source Book (Jun); Holiday Gift Guide (Nov); Best of South Sound (Oct)
Special Weekly Sections: TV Week (S); Weekend (Fri); Food (Wed).
Magazines: Parade (S).
Dir., HR ....Carol Achatz
Major Accounts Rep ....Bernie Fernandez
VP Circulation ....Christian Lee
Mng. Ed. ....Jerry Wakefield
Team Leader ....Dusti Demarest
Day City Editor ....Jerre Redecker
Editorial Page Ed. ....Mike Oakland
Librarian ....Tammy McGee
Political Ed. ....Brad Shannon
VP Finance ....Jennifer Matts-Sprague
CFO ....Dionne Tarter
Adv. Dir. ....Frank Bauer
Adv. Mgr., Classified ....Cindy Broome
Online Sales Mgr. ....Paddy Seid
Adv. Mgr., Retail Territory .....Lacy Waltermeyer
Exec. Ed. ....Vickie Kilgore
Bus. Ed. ....Jim Szymanski
City Ed. ....Barry Ginter
City Ed., Night ....Cindy Yingst
Online News Ed. ....Paul Bucalo
Photo Ed. ....Steven Herppich
Market Information: TMC; Zoned editions.
Mechanical available: Offset; Black and 3 ROP colors; insert accepted - with prior approval; page cutoffs - 22 3/4.
Mechanical Specifications: Type page 11 5/8 x 21 1/2; E - 6 cols, 1 3/4, 1/6 between; A - 6 cols, 1 3/4, 1/6 between; C - 9 cols, 1 3/4, 1/8 between.
Commodity Consumption: Avg. Page Number Per Issue - Daily 41; Avg. Page Number Per Issue - Plates Used 32651; Avg. Page Number Per Issue - Sunday 79; widths 24; Newsprint Used - Metric Tons 3145; Newsprint Used - Short Tons 3466; Printing Ink Used - Black 68485; Printing Ink U
Equipment EDITORIAL: Front-end Software – APT/32-bit.; Editorial Hardware – IBM, Netfinity/5500; Editorial Equipment – HP/8000; Editorial Printers – Tegra/5300B, Pre Press/Panther Pro 62 CLASSIFIED: Front-end Software – AdBase DISPLAY: Ad make-up applications – AdBase; Layout Software – MEI/ALS PRODUCTION: Pagination Software – APT, Adobe/QuarkXPress 4.1, MEI/CLS 3.0.; Production Equipment – Caere/OmniPage 3.0, Pre Press/Panther Pro 62, Intellitune; Scanners – Polaroid/SprintScan, Kk/RSF 2350, Umax/PowerLook II, 1-TECSA/Fullpage 2570, 1-TECSA/Fullpage 2570
Delivery method: Mail, Newsstand, Private Carrier, Racks

PORT ANGELES

PENINSULA DAILY NEWS

305 W. First St., Port Angeles, Wash., 98362; gen tel (360) 452-2345; adv tel 360-417-3540; ed tel 360-417-3531; gen fax (360) 417-3521; adv fax (360) 417-3554; ed fax (360) 417-3521; gen e-mail letters@peninsuladailynews.com; adv e-mail adsinfo@peninsuladailynews.com; ed e-mail news@peninsuladailynews.com; web site www.peninsuladailynews.com
Group: Northwest Media (Washington) L.P./Horvitz Newspapers
Published: Mon, Tues, Wed, Thur, Fri, Sun
Weekday Frequency: m
Circulation: 14,096; 15,858(sun)
Last Audit: ABC September 30, 2011
Price: $135.20/yr M&S (carrier)
Advertising: Open inch rate $27.55 M/ $29.60/S
Insert rate: $43-$79/CPM
News services: AP. New York Times News Service.
Politics: Independent. **Established:** 1916
Not Published: Saturday
Own facility?: Y
Special Editions: Spring/Summer Viz Guide (May); Fairs (Aug); Christmas Gift Guide (Dec); Health and Welness (quarterly); Spring Home (Mar); Travel (May); New Cars (Nov); Fall-Winter Visitors Guide (Oct).
Special Weekly Sections: Sequim This Week (Wed); Arts and Entertainment (Fri); Weekend (Fri); Peninsula Woman (S); Real Estate (S); Seniors (Thur); Food (Wed); Outdoors (Thurs and Fri).
Magazines: USA WEEKEND Magazine (S). Relish (monthly) and Spry (monthly)
Broadcast Affiliations: None
Bus./Finance Dir. ....Bonnie Meehan
Adv Ops Manager ....Susan Stoneman
Circulation Marketing Assistant Jasmine Birkland
Director of Circulation ....Michelle Lynn
Publisher and Editor ....John C. Brewer
Executive Editor ....Rex Wilson
Letters to Editors/Commentary ....Paul Gottlieb
Photo Chief ....Keith Thorpe
Sports Ed. ....Brad LaBrie
Director of Production ....Dean Mangiantini
Advertising Director ....Suzanne Delaney
Managing Editor ....Leah Leach
Adv. Dir. ....Suzanne Williams
Features Ed. ....Marcie Miller
IT/Tech. Servs. Dir. ....Dave Weikel
Prodn. Supvr., Pressroom ....Kevin Boe
Market Information: ADS; Split run; TMC; Zoned editions.
Mechanical available: Offset; Black and 3 ROP colors; insert accepted - cards, 70 lb. stock; page cutoffs - 22.
Mechanical Specifications: 22-inch web; 6-col ROP
Commodity Consumption: Avg. Page Number Per Issue - Daily 24; Avg. Page Number Per Issue - Plates Used 12500; Avg. Page Number Per Issue - Sunday 90; widths 10/6; Newsprint Used - Metric Tons 850; Printing Ink Used - Black 22000; Printing Ink Used - Color 5000.
Equipment EDITORIAL: Front-end Software – Adobe CS4 Suite; Editorial Hardware – MediaSpan; Editorial Equipment – Macs; Classified Hardware – Brainworks ; Classified Equipment – PC DISPLAY: Ad make-up applications – Multi-Ad/Creator; Quark; Adobe Suite; Display Hardware – Macs; Production Equipment – 3-AG/Accuset 1000; Cameras – None PRESSROOM: Line 1 – 6-G/Community 1969; Press Drives – 1-Fin/40 h.p. motor; Folders – G/Suburban (with upper former); Press registration system – Stoesser/Pin Registration. MAILROOM: Counter stackers – 2-BG/Count-O-Veyor 105; Inserters and stuffers – 1-MM/5-station 4:1, 1-MM/4-station 3:1; Bundle tying machines – 2-MLN/Powerstrapper; Addressing machine – 1/KR. BUSINESS COMPUTERS: Business Software – Brainworks; Business Hardware – PC/Macs
Zip Codes served: 98362, 98363, 98368, 98382, 98331, 98305, 98320, 98324,98325, 98326, 98334, 98339, 98343, 98350, 98357, 98365, 98376, 98381

SEATTLE

SEATTLE DAILY JOURNAL OF COMMERCE

83 Columbia St., Seattle, Wash., 98104; gen tel (206) 622-8272; adv tel (206) 622-8272; ed tel (206) 622-8272; gen fax (206) 622-8416; adv fax (206) 622-8416; ed fax (206) 622-8416; web site www.djc.com
Published: Mon, Tues, Wed, Thur, Fri, Sat
Weekday Frequency: m
Circulation: 4,500; 4,500(sat)
Last Audit: March 31, 2007
Price: 210.00/yr.
Advertising: Open inch rate $24.00
News services: AP, Business Wire.
Politics: Independent.
Special Weekly Sections: Travel (Fri); Heavy Equipment (Mon); Plan Bulletin (Sat); Real Estate (Thur); Environment (Tues); Architecture & Engineering (Wed).
Pub. ....Phil Brown
Adv. Mgr. ....Matt Brown
Circ. Mgr. ....Val Valdez
Ed. ....Laura Heberlein
Asst. Ed. ....Trista Allen
Mng. Ed. ....Maude Scott
Construction Ed. ....Ben Minnick
Real Estate Ed. ....Lynn Porter
Travel Ed. ....John Silver
Web Ed. ....Lisa Lannigan
IT Dir. ....John Elliott
Prodn. Mgr. ....Nancy Slaney
Prodn. Foreman, Pressroom ....David Elleby
Market Information: TMC.
Mechanical available: Offset; Black and 3 ROP colors; insert accepted; page cutoffs - 22 3/4.
Mechanical Specifications: Type page 15 x 21 1/2; E - 7 cols, 2, 1/6 between; A - 7 cols, 2, 1/6 between; C - 8 cols, 1 2/3, 1/4 between.
Commodity Consumption: Avg. Page Number Per Issue - Daily 18; Avg. Page Number Per Issue - Plates Used 10; Avg. Page Number Per Issue - Saturday 64; widths 32; Newsprint Used - Metric Tons 220; Printing Ink Used - Black 2500; Printing Ink Used - Pages Printed 5400.
Equipment EDITORIAL: Front-end Software – News Engine.; Editorial Hardware – PCs; Editorial Printers – 1-HP/LaserWriter CLASSIFIED: Front-end Software – PBS.; Classified Hardware – AST; Classified Printers – Panasonic/KX-P1624, HP/LaserJet 4M; Layout Software – QPS/QuarkXPress.; Display Hardware – PC, APP/Mac; Display Printers – HP PRODUCTION: Pagination Software – QPS/QuarkXPress.; Production Equipment – Nu/Flip Top FT4OV3UPNS, LE/Line 17; Cameras – 2-SCREEN/Auto Companica LE, R; Scanners – Umax/840 MaxVision (color) PRESSROOM: Line 1 – 5-Econ/Web 1979. MAILROOM: Counter stackers – KR/3-Station Inserter; Bundle tying machines – Bu, EAM-Mosca; Wrapping singles – Manual; Addressing machine – KR/Label Head. BUSINESS COMPUTERS: Business Software – PBS; Business Hardware – Microsoft/Windows

SEATTLE POST-INTELLIGENCER/SEATTLE TIMES

1000 Denny Way, Seattle, Wash., 98109; gen tel (206) 464-2900; adv tel (206) 464-2400; ed tel (206) 464-2496; gen fax (206) 515-5577; adv fax (206) 493-0993 ; ed fax (206) 382-6760; adv e-mail advertising@seattletimes.com; ed e-mail opinion@seattletimes.com; web site www.seattletimes.com
Group: Metro Newspaper Advertising Services, Inc.
Published: Mon, Tues, Wed, Thur, Fri, Sat, Sun
Weekday Frequency: m
Saturday Frequency: m
Circulation: 242,814; 222,810(sat); 333,937(sun)
Last Audit: ABC September 30, 2011
Price: 5.60/wk in our primary home delivery area (King, Pierce and Snohomish Counties)
Advertising: Open inch rate $539.60
News services: AP, WP, Bloomberg, MCT-LAT
Politics: 1886

Special Editions: Outdoor living (Feb); Opening Day Boating (Apr); Seattle Home Show (Feb); Careers (Jan); High Tech Employment (Jul); Health & Fitness (Jun); High Tech Employment (Mar); Spring Home and Garden (May); Restaurant Guide (Nov);Summer Guide (May); Spring Home Design (May); Architecture (Sep); Fall Arts Guide (Sep); Travel (Oct); Fall Home Design (Oct); Wine (Nov); Holiday Cuisine (Nov); Arts (Dec)
Special Weekly Sections: Classified/Autos (Sat); WeedendPlus(Fri); Pacific magazine; Northwest Arts and Life
Magazines: Parade (S);Pacific Magazine
Bd. Chrmn./Pub./CEO ....................F.A. Blethen
Associate Publisher & Editorial page Editor Ryan Blethen
Senior Vice President, Sales & marketing Alan Fisco
Executive Editor & Senior Vice President David Boardman
Managing Editor, Digital News and Innovation Kathy Best
Managing Editor, News Coverage and Enterprise Suki Dardarian
Executive Producer Stanley Farrar
Assistant Managing Editor, Features Carole Carmichael
Deputy Managing Editor, Strategy and Product Dev. Heidi de Laubenfels
Books Ed...............................Mary Ann Gwinn
Arts and Entertainment Editor Lynn Jacobson
Director of Visuals and News Projects Denise Clifton
Executive News Editor Leon Espinoza
Assistant Managing Editor, Local News Jim Simon
Senior Vice President, Business Operations Michael Shepard
Senior Vice President, Finance......Buster Brown
Vice President, Public Affairs............Jill Mackie
Pres./COO ....Carolyn Kelly
Vice Pres./CFO........................Eileen Takeuchi
Dir., Labor Rel./Safety..............Chris Biencourt
Vice Pres., Adv...........................Mei-Mei Chan
Adv. Dir., Major Accts. ....Charlie Gardner
Adv. Mgr., Mktg............................Ann Zeman
Mktg. Dir., New Media...............Anna Bertrand
Circ. Dir., Opns.........................Mike Sheehan
Aerospace/Boeing Reporter.........Dominic Gates
Arts Critic/Visual Arts Reporter..........Sheila Farr
Market Information: TMC; Zoned editions.
Mechanical available: Offset; Black and 3 ROP colors; page cutoffs - 23 9/16.
Commodity Consumption: Avg. Page Number Per Issue - Daily 66; Avg. Page Number Per Issue - Plates Used 640000; Avg. Page Number Per Issue - Saturday 80; Avg. Page Number Per Issue - Sunday 160; widths 25; Newsprint Used - Metric Tons 60000; Printing Ink Used - Black 870000; Pr
Equipment EDITORIAL: Front-end Software – CCI, Thunderstone, APS, SCC CLASSIFIED: Front-end Software – AT/IAS 4.7. DISPLAY: Ad make-up applications – AT/Architect, Cascade/Dataflow; Layout Software – AT/Architect. PRODUCTION: Pagination Software – Morcor, ProImage, OneVision, News Color; Production Equipment – TextBridge, 5-GJ/720, 1-AN/XPH 36, 2-WL/7, 1-AII/3850, 5-AII/3850 PRESSROOM: Line 1 – 8-G/Colorliner double width 1996; Line 2 – 8-G/Colorliner double width 1992; Line 3 – 8-G/Colorliner double width 1992; Line 4 – 8-G/Colorliner double width 1992; Press Drives – 1-Fin, 3-RKW/B 1395 1992, 1-RKW MAILROOM: Counter stackers – 27-QWI; Inserters and stuffers – Goss NP2299; Bundle tying machines – 30-Dynaric; Wrapping singles – 25-QWI; Mailroom control system – Mirasert
Delivery method: Mail, Newsstand, Private Carrier, Racks

SPOKANE

THE SPOKESMAN-REVIEW

999 W. Riverside Ave., Spokane, Wash., 99210; gen tel (509) 459-5000; adv tel (509) 459-5005; ed tel (509) 459-5430; gen fax (509) 459-5234; adv fax (509) 459-5083; ed fax (509) 459-5482; gen e-mail circulation@spokesman.com; adv e-mail advertising@spokesman.com; ed e-mail editor@spokesman.com; web site www.spokesman.com
Published: Mon, Tues, Wed, Thur, Fri, Sat, Sun
Weekday Frequency: m
Saturday Frequency: m
Circulation: 69,748; 80,525(sat); 89,995(sun)
Last Audit: ABC September 30, 2011
Price: $16.00/mo (mS); $12.00/mo (m); $11.00/mo (wknd only, Sat Sun only or Sunday Only).
Advertising: Sun. main news $86.79
News services: Metro Suburbia, McClatchy, LAT-WP, MCT.
Politics: Independent-Republican. **Established:** 1883
Own facility?: Y
Special Editions: Fishing (Apr); Golf Tab (Apr, June, Aug); Activities Guide (May/Sept); Hunting Guide (Sept). Holiday Shopping (Nov/Dec)
Special Weekly Sections: TV Week (S); Automotive (Sat); Food in Today Section (Wed).
Magazines: Parade (S); American Profile (Sat); Athlon Sports (Thur -1x per month); Dash (Wed - 1x per month)
Pres./Pub...................William Stacey Cowles
Sec./Treasurer ....Steven Rector
Bus. Mgr. ....Robert Davis
Mgr., HR.....................................Connie Bantz
Display Adv. Mgr. ....Mike Dixon
Retail Adv. Mgr................................Dan Fritts
Real Estate/Contract Classified Mgr. Diane Bobiak
Dir., Distr./Audience Devel. ....Dan Johnson
Home Delivery Mgr. ....Tina Sanborn
Customer Relationship Mgr./NIE Coord. Karen Payne
Logistics Mgr. ....Bill Fuzak
Ed..Gary Graham
Asst. Mng. Ed., Digital Media............Ryan Pitts
City Ed. ....Addy Hatch
City Ed., Night...........................Ken Paulman
Asst. City Ed............................Scott Maben
Asst. City Ed............................Dave Wasson
Editorial Page Ed. ....Doug Floyd
Entertainment Ed. ....Richard Bonino
Market Information: ADS; Split run; TMC; Zoned editions.
Mechanical available: Offset; Black and 3 ROP colors; insert accepted - some product samples; page cutoffs - 22 3/4.
Mechanical Specifications: Type page 12 1/2 x 21 1/2; E - 6 cols, 1 7/8, 1/8 between; A - 6 cols, 1 13/16, 1/8 between; C - 10 cols, 1 1/8, 1/25 between.
Commodity Consumption: Avg. Page Number Per Issue - Daily 40; Avg. Page Number Per Issue - Plates Used 179500; Avg. Page Number Per Issue - Saturday 56; Avg. Page Number Per Issue - Sunday 112; widths 50; Newsprint Used - Metric Tons 12025; Printing Ink Used - Black 160882; Pr
Equipment EDITORIAL: Front-end Software – CCI NewsDesk; Editorial Hardware – 2 SUN V880; Editorial Printers – Lexmark/Laser printer CLASSIFIED: Front-end Software – DTI Classified; Classified Hardware – 2 Dell Power R710 DISPLAY: Ad make-up applications – Ad Manager6; Layout Software – SCS/Layout 8000.; Display Hardware – 2 Sun V240 PRODUCTION: Pagination Software – CCI. Ad Suite, ; Production Equipment – 2-Krause Ls Jets 170 with Krause Bluefin processors; Scanners – Epson 10000 XL PRESSROOM: Line 1 – 6-G/Metro (4 decks) double width 1981; Line 2 – 6-G/Metro (4 decks) double width 1981; Line 4 – 2-TKS/(3 towers) double width 1996; Press Drives – 1980; Folders – 2-G/Metro 1980; Pasters – 12-G/Metro 1980, 2-TKS 1996; Press control system – TKS/T- MAILROOM: Counter stackers – 2-QWI/300, 4-QWI/300, 2-QWI/350; Inserters and stuffers – 1-G/630 (26 head), 1-G/632 (14 head), 1-G/632 (14 head); Bundle tying machines – 6-Dynaric/NP1500; Mailroom control system – G/OMNI Zone; Addressing machine – 2-Ch; Other equipment –Other equipme BUSINESS COMPUTERS: Business Software – DTI; Business Hardware – 2-Sun Servers
Delivery method: Newsstand, Private Carrier, Racks

SUNNYSIDE

DAILY SUN NEWS

600 S. Sixth St., Sunnyside, Wash., 98944; gen tel (509) 837-4500; gen fax (509) 837-6397; gen e-mail bstory@sunnewspapers.com; web site www.dailysunnews.com
Published: Mon, Tues, Wed, Thur, Fri
Weekday Frequency: e
Circulation: 3,818
Last Audit: October 1, 2003
Price: 4.25/mo; 51.00/yr (in county).
Advertising: Open inch rate $9.00
Politics: 1901
Not Published: New Year; Memorial Day; Independence Day; Labor Day; Thanksgiving; Christmas.
Special Editions: Auto Car Care (Apr); Sports Review (Aug); Letters to Santa (Dec); Presidents' Day (Feb); Reflections Year-in-Review (Jan); Vacation Getaway (Jul); Vacation Getaway (Jun); Easter (Mar); Graduation (May); Holiday Gift Guide (Nov); Women in Business (Oct); F
Special Weekly Sections: Sunshine Days (Weekly).
Magazines: American Profile (Fri).
Broadcast Affiliations: NBC; ABC; CBS; PBS; FOX.
Pub....Tim J. Graff
Circ. Mgr. ....Debbie Guerreo
News Ed....Bob Story
Prodn. Mgr. ....Kim Taylor Morris
Market Information: TMC.
Mechanical available: Offset; Black and 1 ROP colors; insert accepted; page cutoffs - 22 3/4.
Mechanical Specifications: Type page 10 1/3 x 16 1/2; E - 5 cols, 1 93/100, 1/6 between; A - 5 cols, 1 93/100, 1/6 between; C - 5 cols, 1 93/100, 1/6 between.
Commodity Consumption: Avg. Page Number Per Issue - Daily 18; widths 35; Newsprint Used - Metric Tons 58; Printing Ink Used - Black 1800; Printing Ink Used - Color 300; Printing Ink Used - Pages Printed 4500.
Equipment EDITORIAL: Front-end Software – Microsoft/Word 5.1.; Editorial Hardware – 3-APP/Mac Quadra, 3-APP/Power Mac; Editorial Equipment – Pre Press/Panther Pro Imagesetter; Editorial Printers – APP/Mac LaserPrinter NTX, NewGen/1200 x 1200 dpi, X, Design/XL Laspr Printer CLASSIFIED: Front-end Software – Synaptic.; Classified Hardware – 2-Pentium; Classified Equipment – Micron/Dot Matrix; Classified Printers – NewGen/1200 dpi DISPLAY: Ad make-up applications – Aldus/PageMaker 6.5, Broderbund/Typestyler, Adobe/Illustrator 8, Adobe/Photoshop 6, Macromedia/Freehand 8.; Display Hardware – APP/Power Mac 640-132, 1-APP/Power Mac Pro 240, 2-APP/Power Mac G3; Display Printers – X PRODUCTION: Pagination Software – Adobe/PageMaker 6.5.; Production Equipment – APP/Mac LaserWriter, Pre Press/Panther Pro; Cameras – Nu/SST 20 x 24; Scanners – Microtek/Scanner PRESSROOM: Line 1 – 5-G/Community (with sc folder), 1-G/OUP; Folders – 1; Press registration system – Stoesser/PinSystem.; Inserters and stuffers – MM/6:1; Bundle tying machines – Bu, Cypack, Mosca/Strapper; Addressing machine – Wm. BUSINESS COMPUTERS: Business Software – Synaptic, Cyma IV, Microsoft/Windows 98, Microsoft/Office 97, MS/Outlook e-mail; Business Hardware – Mitac

TACOMA

THE NEWS TRIBUNE

1950 S. State St., Tacoma, Wash., 98405; gen tel (253) 597-8742; adv tel (253) 572-9511; ed tel (253) 597-8686; gen fax (253) 597-8263; adv fax (253) 597-8263; ed fax (253) 597-8274; gen e-mail david.zeeck@thenewstribune.com; web site www.thenewstribune.com
Published: Mon, Tues, Wed, Thur, Fri, Sat, Sun
Weekday Frequency: m
Saturday Frequency: m
Circulation: 78,838; 77,378(sat); 102,645(sun)
Last Audit: ABC September 30, 2011
Price: $10.25/mo (S), $13.50/mo (fri-mon), $16.50/mo; 186.00/yr.
Advertising: Open inch rate $194.93
News services: AP, LAT-WP, MCT, McClatchy, DJ.,Bloomberg
Politics: Independent. **Established:** 1880
Special Weekly Sections: Go (Fri); 50+ (Monthly); SouthSound TV (S); Religion (Sat); Adventure (S); Food (Wed).
Magazines: Parade (S).
Pres./Pub................................David A. Zeeck
Mgr., Research ....Gary Pederson
Exec. Ed.................................Karen Peterson
Mng. Ed.......................................Dale Phelps
Crime/Breaking News Team Leader Randy McCarthy
Editorial Page Editor ....Patrick O'Callahan
Photography Dir. ....Jeremy Harrison
Info. Systems Dir. ....Rodney Robinson
Prodn. Dir., Opns. ....Robin Semegen
Packaging & Dist. Manager..............Wes Corey
VP/Advertising...............................Steven Gall
AME online.............................John Henrikson
Prod. & OP maint. manager..........Doug Sanford
VP of Circulation..........................Chrstian Lee
Adv. Vice Pres.............................Frank Bauer
Asst. Mng. Ed., Online ....Doug Conarroe
Trade/Ports/Jobs Reporter ....Kelly Kearsley
Market Information: ADS; Split run; TMC.
Mechanical available: Offset; Black and 3 ROP colors; insert accepted; page cutoffs - 22 3/4.
Mechanical Specifications: Type page 10 x 21.5; E - 6 cols, 1.562, .125between; A - 6 cols, 1.562, .125between; C - 6 cols, 1.562, .125between.
Commodity Consumption: Avg. Page Number Per Issue - Daily 28; Avg. Page Number Per Issue - Sunday 76 - Plates Used 62,000; widths 44inch; Newsprint Used - Metric Tons 5700; Printing Ink Used - Black 115,202lbs; Printing Ink Used - Color 86,754lbs
Equipment EDITORIAL: Front-end Software – Unisys 10.2.; Editorial Hardware – Sun V880 Sun Solaris 9; Editorial Equipment – Mac's and PC's; Editorial Printers – Okidata/393, HP/LaserJet IV, APP/Mac LaserWriters CLASSIFIED: Front-end Software – Mactive 2.26; Classified Hardware – Dell Servers; Classified Equipment – Mixture of Dell/HP laptops and workstations; Classified Printers – HP and Brother DISPLAY: Ad make-up applications – MEI Adtrack; Display Hardware – Dell Servers PRODUCTION: Pagination Software – Unisys 10.2.; Production Equipment – 2-Nu/Flip Top FTUP, AG, Nikon, 1-Lf/AP Leaf Picture Desk PRESSROOM: Line 1 – 9-G/Metro double width (5 half decks, 1 stack unit); Line 2 – 9-G/Metro double width (5 half decks, 1 stack unit); Press Drives – AAB-DC drives; Folders – 4-G/Metro 3:2; Pasters – 18; Reels and Stands – 18 MAILROOM: Counter stackers – 3/HL, 6-QWI/301, 2Harris RIMA; Inserters and stuffers – 1-GMA/15-72, 2-GMA/SLS 1000A 24:2; Bundle tying machines – 6-Signode, 4 Dynaric, 4 Ovalstrap; Mailroom control system – Prism. BURT BUSINESS COMPUTERS: Business Software – ATEX Mactive 2.26; Business Hardware – Dell Servers
Delivery method: Mail, Newsstand, Private Carrier, Racks

TACOMA NEWS, INC.

1950 S. State St., Tacoma, Wash., 98405; gen tel (253) 447-0541; gen fax (253) 597-8499

TRI-CITIES

TRI-CITY HERALD

333 W. Canal Dr., Kennewick, Wash., 99336; gen tel (509) 582-1500; adv tel (509) 582-1464; ed tel (509) 582-1515; adv fax (509) 582-1453; ed fax (509) 582-1510; gen e-mail letters@tricityherald.com; adv e-mail dgilchrist@tricityherald.com; ed e-mail news@tricityherald.com; web site www.tri-cityherald.com

Published: Mon, Tues, Wed, Thur, Fri, Sat, Sun
Weekday Frequency: m
Saturday Frequency: m
Circulation: 31,820; 31,326(sat); 37,598(sun)
Last Audit: ABC September 30, 2011
Price: 12.00/mo; 144.00/yr.
Advertising: Open inch rate $60.64
News services: Metro Suburbia Inc./Newhouse Newspapers, LAT-WP, MCT, NYT, McClatchy.
Politics: Independent. **Established:** 1947
Special Weekly Sections: Life, Arts & Entertainment (Fri); Real Estate (S); Autolog (Sat); KidZone (Tues).
Magazines: Parade (S).

Pub. ....Rufus M. Friday
Exec. Ast ....Kati Toms
Dir., Finance ....Gerald Hug
Dir., HR ....Kelly Nite
Adv. Dir. ....David Gilchrist
Adv. Mgr., Sales ....Shelley Ransier
Online Mktg./Sales ....Angel Westover
Exec. Ed. ....Ken Robertson
Asst. Mng. Ed. ....Laurie Williams
Online Mng. Ed. ....Eric Degerman
Agriculture ....Anna King
Arts/Entertainment Ed. ....Dori O'Neal
Asst. City Ed. ....Kristina Lord
Librarian ....Deborah Carver
Chief Photographer ....Bob Brawdy
Coord., Promo./Mktg. ....Melissa O'Neil
Circ. Mgr. ....Tim Zilar
Mng. Ed. ....Rick Larson
Graphics Ed. ....Sherry Emery
Political Ed. ....Chris Mulick

Market Information: ADS; TMC.
Mechanical available: Offset; Black and 3 ROP colors; insert accepted - all; page cutoffs - 21.
Mechanical Specifications: Type page 11 1/2 x 21; E - 6 cols, 1 3/4, 3/16 between; A - 6 cols, 1 3/4, 3/16 between; C - 9 cols, 1 3/16, 1/8 between.
Commodity Consumption: Avg. Page Number Per Issue - Daily 32; Avg. Page Number Per Issue - Plates Used 17508; Avg. Page Number Per Issue - Sunday 44; widths 12 1/2; Newsprint Used - Metric Tons 2806; Newsprint Used - Short Tons 3093; Printing Ink Used - Black 50580; Printing I
Equipment EDITORIAL: Front-end Software – QPS/QuarkXPress 3.32, Baseview/News Edit Pro.; Editorial Hardware – 4-APP/Mac G3-400 CLASSIFIED: Front-end Software – SCS/AdMax 8.0.3, SCS/ClassPag 3.96.; Classified Hardware – SCS, Dell/4200 DISPLAY: Ad make-up applications – Multi-Ad/Creator 4.0.3, Aldus/FreeHand 10, Adobe/Photoshop 6.x; Layout Software – SCS/Layout 8000.; Display Hardware – Dell/Poweredge 4400; Production Equipment – Nat/A-340, Kk/2035+ 35mm Scanner; Cameras – 1-C/1211, DAI/C-690-AX. PRESSROOM: Line 1 – 6-MAN/MediaMan 1992; Line 2 – 7-G/Community 1982; Reels and Stands – 4-MEG. MAILROOM: Counter stackers – 4-Id/2000; Inserters and stuffers – GMA/SLS 1000, HI/1372; Bundle tying machines – 1/Power Strap, 1-/Power Strap, 2-/Power Strap; Addressing machine – 1-Ch/520-E. BUSINESS COMPUTERS: Business Software – SCS, CJ: Circ (TMC), People Soft Financials; Business Hardware – DEC/Micro VAX 4000 Model 50, SCS, Dell/4200

VANCOUVER

THE COLUMBIAN

701 W. 8th St., Vancouver, Wash., 98660-3008; gen tel (360) 694-3391; gen fax (360) 735-4503; adv fax (360) 735-4494; ed fax (360) 735-4598; oth fax (360) 735-4598 (news); gen e-mail metrodesk@columbian.com; adv e-mail advertising@columbian.com; classified@columbian.com; ed e-mail letters@columbian.com; web site www.columbian.com

Published: Mon, Tues, Wed, Thur, Fri, Sat, Sun
Weekday Frequency: m
Saturday Frequency: m
Circulation: 47,601; 31,099(sat); 47,393(sun)
Last Audit: ABC September 30, 2011
Price: 20.00/mo; 240.00/yr.
Advertising: Open inch rate $62.38
Insert rate: Open 81/2x11$50 cpm
News services: AP, CNS, MCT - LAT, WP - Bloomberg.
Politics: Independent. **Established:** 1890
Own facility?: Y
Special Editions: At Home (Apr); Clark County Fair (Aug); Home for Holidays II (Dec); Focus 50+ (Fall); Portrait and Birthday Review (Feb); Live Well (Jan); Parade of Homes (Jul); At Home (Jun); Best of Clark County (Mar); Live Well (May); Home for Holidays I (Nov); At Home
Special Weekly Sections: Weekend (Fri); TV Times (own) (S); Cruise Control (Sat); Life (Thur); Life (Tues); Life (Wed).
Magazines: Relish (Monthly); Parade (S); American Profile (Weekly).

Pub. ....Scott Campbell
Controller ....Brandon Zarzana
CFO ....Douglas Ness
HR Mgr. ....Denise Sandvig
Adv. Dir. ....Teresa Keplinger
Circ. Dir. ....Marc Dailey
Circ. Mgr., Promo./Sales ....Rachel Rose
Circ. Mgr., Sales/Home Delivery ....Jim Cox
Circ. Mgr., Single Copy ....Peter Geloff
Ed. ....Louis Brancaccio
Editorial Page Ed. ....John Laird
Metro Ed. ....Craig Brown
Asst. Metro Ed. ....Mark Bowder
News Ed. ....Micah Rice
Advertising Sales Mgr ....Laura Wenrick
Business/Features Editor ....Courtney Sherwood
Production Director ....Jeff Stalcup
IT Manager ....Olaf Rove
Circulation Systems Administrator Greg Hartgrave
Sports Ed ....Greg Jayne
Adv. Sales Mgr. ....Carol Doane
Adv. Mgr., Classified ....Mike Ripley
Circ. Mgr., Transportation ....Duane Buell
Bus. Ed. ....Julia Anderson
Features Ed. ....Elisa Williams

Market Information: TMC.
Mechanical available: Offset G/Metro; Black and 4 ROP colors; insert accepted; page cutoffs - 22 3/4.
Commodity Consumption: Avg. Page Number Per Issue - Daily 42; Avg. Page Number Per Issue - Plates Used 213; Avg. Page Number Per Issue - Saturday 36; Avg. Page Number Per Issue - Sunday 60; widths 50, 37 1/2 & 25; Newsprint Used - Metric Tons 2458; Newsprint Used - Short Tons 2709; P
Equipment EDITORIAL: Front-end Software – Adobe/InDesign, Saxotech; Editorial Hardware – Acer/HP/Mac; Editorial Printers – AU/APS 3850 Imager, HP/Laser/Ricoh CLASSIFIED: Front-end Software – DTI Mediaplus; Classified Hardware – Acer/HP/Mac; Classified Printers – HP/Laserjet, Xerox DocCentre DISPLAY: Ad make-up applications – Adobe/InDesign; Layout Software – SCS/Layout 8000 11.0; Display Hardware – Acer/HP; Display Printers – HP/Laserjet, Xerox DocCentre, APS Broadsheeter PRODUCTION: Pagination Software – Adobe/InDesign, Mediaplus/Classifier, Saxotech; Production Equipment – Glunz & Jensen, WL/AQL32, DS/Drum Scanner; Scanners – ECR/Autokon 2030, DAI/DTS 1030 AI, Nikon/LS-3510 AF PRESSROOM: Line 1 – 6-G/Metro Double Width; Line 2 – 11-G/SSC Community; Press Drives – 7-Control Technique Mentor II; Folders – 2-G/Metro Uniflow 2:1, 1-G/SSC Community; Pasters – 2-MEG, 6-G; Reels and Stands – 4-G/SSC Community. MAILROOM: Counter stackers – 5-Quipp 501N, 1-Gammerler/KL 5000; Inserters and stuffers – 2-Muller SLS3000 12:1 and 10:1; Bundle tying machines – 5-Dynamic NP5000's; Wrapping singles – 5 Quipp Viper bottom wraps; Addressing machine – 2-Kodak 5120 Inkjet Printers BUSINESS COMPUTERS: Business Software – DTI Circ. Mgmt 3.5, DTI Adv Mgmt 3.5, ADP, Solomon IV; Business Hardware – Acer/HP
Delivery method: Private Carrier

WALLA WALLA

WALLA WALLA UNION-BULLETIN

112 S. First Ave., Walla Walla, Wash., 99362; gen tel (509) 525-3300; gen fax (509) 525-1232; gen e-mail newsdept@wwub.com; adv e-mail classified@wwub.com (Classified); advertising@wwub.com (Display); ed e-mail letters@wwub.com; web site www.union-bulletin.com

Group: Metro Suburbia, Inc./Newhouse Newspapers
Published: Mon, Tues, Wed, Thur, Fri, Sun
Weekday Frequency: e
Circulation: 13,664; 13,158(sun)
Last Audit: ABC September 30, 2011
Price: 8.50/mo, $4.50/mo (S); 102.00/yr (carrier), $162.00/yr (mail).
Advertising: Open inch rate $22.75
News services: AP.
Politics: Independent. **Established:** 1869
Not Published: Christmas.
Special Editions: On the Grow (Sept).
Special Weekly Sections: Channels (Mon); Panorama (S); Food & Family (Tues).
Magazines: Parade (S).

Pub ....Rob Blethen
Controller ....Bill Thyken
Mgr., HR ....Lacey Town
Adv. Mgr., Classified ....Jay Brodt
Circ. Mgr. ....Michael Cibart
Ed. ....Rick Doyle
Editorial Page Ed. ....Rick Eskil
Asst. News Ed. ....Alasdair Stewart
Political Ed. ....Andy Porter
Sports Ed. ....Jim Buchan
Wire Ed. ....Catherine Hicks
Systems Specialist ....Josh Gesler
Prodn. Mgr. ....John Partlow

Market Information: ADS; TMC.
Mechanical available: Offset; Black and 3 ROP colors; insert accepted; page cutoffs - 22 3/4.
Mechanical Specifications: Type page 11 1/2 x 21 1/2; E - 6 cols, 1 5/6, 1/8 between; A - 6 cols, 1 5/6, 1/16 between; C - 9 cols, 1 9/50, 1/8 between.
Commodity Consumption: Avg. Page Number Per Issue - Daily 26; Avg. Page Number Per Issue - Plates Used 13092; Avg. Page Number Per Issue - Sunday 44; widths 25; Newsprint Used - Short Tons 830; Printing Ink Used - Black 14900; Printing Ink Used - Color 4150; Printing Ink Used
Equipment EDITORIAL: Front-end Software – Cybergraphic.; Editorial Hardware – 20-PC CLASSIFIED: Front-end Software – Cybergraphics.; Classified Hardware – 4-PC DISPLAY: Ad make-up applications – QPS/QuarkXPress; Layout Software – MEI/AdForce.; Display Hardware – 4-PC PRODUCTION: Pagination Software – Cybergraphic.; Production Equipment – 2-Nu; Cameras – 1-C/Marathon, SCREEN; Scanners – 2-Nikon/Cool Scan PRESSROOM: Line 1 – 5-G/Urbanite 1969; Folders – 1 MAILROOM: Counter stackers – 1/MM; Inserters and stuffers – 2-MM/5 heads; Bundle tying machines – Dynaric; Other equipment –MM Stitcher/Trimmer.; Audio Hardware – PC BUSINESS COMPUTERS: Business Software – Adv, Circ, Accts payable, Gen ledger; Business Hardware – 1-HP/3000

WENATCHEE

THE WENATCHEE WORLD

14 N. Mission St., Wenatchee, Wash., 98801; gen tel (509) 663-5161; adv tel (509) 664-7130; adv fax (509) 663-9110; ed fax (509) 663-1183; gen e-mail newsroom@wenatcheeworld.com; adv e-mail advertising@wenatcheeworld.com; web site www.wenatcheeworld.com

Group: Metro Suburbia, Inc./Newhouse Newspapers
Published: Mon, Tues, Wed, Thur, Fri, Sun
Weekday Frequency: e
Circulation: 23,750; 24,477(sun)
Price: 11.25/mo (carrier), $11.25/mo (motor route); 114.00/yr (carrier), $123.00/yr (motor route).
Advertising: Open inch rate $35.80
News services: AP.
Politics: Independent.
Advertising not accepted: Alcoholic beverages.
Not Published: Christmas.
Special Editions: Fishing (Apr); Gift Guide (Dec); Home Improvement (Feb); Brides (Jan); Summer Recipe Guide (Jul); Annual Report (Jun); Spring Fashions (Mar); Ag World (Monthly); Winter Sports (Nov); Home Furnishings (Oct); Seasons For Senior Citizens (Quarterly); Fairtim
Special Weekly Sections: Religion (Fri); TV World (S); Go! Entertainment Tab (Thur); Food (Tues).
Magazines: Relish (Monthly); USA WEEKEND Magazine (S).

Chrmn. of the Bd. ....Wilfred R. Woods
COO ....Steve Robinson
Vice Pres./Sec. ....Nancy McMahon
Purchasing Agent/Credit Mgr. ....Ken Hunnycut
Adv. Mgr. ....Matt Kearny
Ed. ....Rufus Woods
Mng. Ed. ....Gary Jasinek
City Ed. ....Christine Pratt
Copy Ed. ....Dave Riggs
Editorial Page Ed. ....Tracy Warner
Features Ed. ....Marco Martinez
News Ed. ....Jarod Johnson
Photo Ed. ....Don Seabrook
Sports Ed. ....Steve Maher

Market Information: ADS.
Mechanical available: Offset; Black and 3 ROP colors; insert accepted; page cutoffs - 21 1/2.
Mechanical Specifications: Type page 11 5/6 x 20 7/20; E - 6 cols, 1 5/6, 1/6 between; A - 6 cols, 1 5/6, 1/6 between; C - 8 cols, 1 19/50, 1/9 between.
Commodity Consumption: Avg. Page Number Per Issue - Daily 30; Avg. Page Number Per Issue - Plates Used 32000; Avg. Page Number Per Issue - Sunday 40; widths 33; Newsprint Used - Metric Tons 1600; Printing Ink Used - Black 52500; Printing Ink Used - Color 8200; Printing Ink Use
Equipment EDITORIAL: Front-end Software – Baseview/NewsEdit Pro 2.22.; Editorial Hardware – 43-APP/Mac; Editorial Equipment – Telecopier; Editorial Printers – 2-HP/LaserJet, 2-Laserwriter/12-640 CLASSIFIED: Front-end Software – Baseview/Ad Manager Pro 2.0.; Classified Hardware – APP/Mac G3; Classified Printers – 2-HP/4050 DISPLAY: Ad make-up applications – QPS/QuarkXPress 3.32; Layout Software – MEI/ALS.; Display Hardware – APP/Mac; Display Printers – 1-Okidata/Printer, HP/4050 PRODUCTION: Pagination Software – QPS/QuarkXPress.; Production Equipment – WL/Plater 30D, 2-Pre Press/Panther Pro 36 Imagesetter with online processor; Scanners – Microtek/300Z Scanner, 2-APP/Mac, 1-Nikon/Slide Scanner, Epson/836XL PRESSROOM: Line 1 – KBA/Comet 4 over 4 32 couples 1999; Folders – 1; Pasters – Amal/AR 60 C; Press control system – KBA/DriveTronic. MAILROOM: Counter stackers – 1-BG/Count-O-Veyor 108, Rima/RS30, Rima RS/3117 SL; Inserters and stuffers – 1-MM/227S, 2-MM/227E; Bundle tying machines – 2-MLN/2EE, 1-Dynaric/1500, 2-Dynaric/NP1; Wrapping singles – 1-MM/1509; Other equipment –1-MM/1509 Stitcher-Trim; Audio Hardware – Software □ New Horizons/Info-Connect, New Horizons/Info-

Connect, V.I.S; Business Hardware – 1-PBS/SBS

YAKIMA

YAKIMA HERALD-REPUBLIC

114 N. Fourth St., Yakima, Wash., 98901-2707; gen tel (509) 248-1251; adv tel (509) 577-7719; ed tel (509) 577-7672; gen fax (509) 577-7766; adv fax (509) 577-7765; ed fax (509) 577-7767; gen e-mail circulation@yakimaherald.com; hr@yakimaherald.com; adv e-mail LKime@yakimaherald.com; ed e-mail news@yakimaherald.com; web site www.yakimaherald.com

Published: Mon, Tues, Wed, Thur, Fri, Sat, Sun
Weekday Frequency: m
Saturday Frequency: m
Circulation: 28,432; 32,635(sat); 32,767(sun)
Last Audit: ABC September 30, 2011
Price: 10.50/mo; 126.00/yr (carrier), $168.00/yr (mail).
Advertising: Open inch rate $39.30
News services: AP, MCT, LAT-WP, NEA, TMS.
Politics: 1903
Own facility?: Y
Special Editions: Annual Local Focus Section (Apr); Prep Basketball Preview (Dec); Spring Home/Garden (Feb); Baby Brag Book (Jan); Cooking School (Mar); Indulge (May); Holiday Gift Guide (Nov); Prep Footbal tab (Sept)Fall Home (Oct); Women in Business (Oct)
Special Weekly Sections: Families (Mon); Home and Garden (Other); Travel (S); Wheels (Sat); Shop and Serve (Tues); Taste (Wed).
Magazines: Yakima Magazine (Every other month); PlayDate (Every other month); Wheels (Bi-Weekly); On Magazine (Fri); Home Buyers Guide (Monthly); Parade (S);Yakima Valley Bride (Semi-yearly); American Profile (Weekly).
Finance Dir. .... Wendie Hansen
HR Mgr. .... Leticia Gonzales
Adv. Dir. .... James E. Stickel
Editor .... Robert Crider
Operations Director .... Rick Oram
Publisher .... Sharon Prill
Market Information: ADS; TMC.
Mechanical available: Offset; Black and 3 ROP colors; insert accepted - single sheet inserts produced inhouse; page cutoffs - 21 1/2.
Mechanical Specifications: Type page 12 1/2 x 21 1/2; E - 6 cols, 2 1/16, 1/8 between; A - 6 cols, 2 1/16, 1/8 between; C - 9 cols, 1 3/8, 3/32 between.
Commodity Consumption: Avg. Page Number Per Issue - Daily 36; Avg. Page Number Per Issue - Plates Used 21200; Avg. Page Number Per Issue - Sunday 48; widths 25; Newsprint Used - Metric Tons 3200; Newsprint Used - Short Tons 3637; Printing Ink Used - Black 102000; Printing Ink
Equipment EDITORIAL: Front-end Software – Baseview/IQ Pro, QPS/QuarkXPress-Translator.; Editorial Hardware – APP/Mac; Editorial Equipment – APP/Mac; Editorial Printers – 3-Pre Press/Panther CLASSIFIED: Front-end Software – Baseview; Brainworks; Classified Hardware – APP/Mac; Classified Printers – 3-Pre Press/Panther DISPLAY: Ad make-up applications – Multi-Ad/Creator; Layout Software – Multi-Ad/Creator.; Display Hardware – 12-APP/Mac; Display Printers – 3-Pre Press/Panther Plus PRODUCTION: Pagination Software – Multi-Ad/Creator.; Production Equipment – 1-Pre Press/Panther Plus Imagesetter, 1-Nu/Flip-Top; Cameras – 1-C/Marathon, 1-ATF/Horizontal; Scanners – Umax, 6-X PRESSROOM: Line 1 – 4.5-KBA/Comet Towers; Folders – KF3; Reels and Stands – 7-Amal. MAILROOM: Counter stackers – QWI/350; Inserters and stuffers – 2-GMA/1000; Bundle tying machines – 2-Dynaric/Strapper; Wrapping singles – QWI; Mailroom control system – Lincs; Addressing machine – 1-KR/215; Other equipment –MM/227 Stitcher.
Delivery method: Mail, Newsstand, Private Carrier, Racks

WEST VIRGINIA

BECKLEY

THE REGISTER HERALD

801 N. Kanawha St., Beckley, W.Va., 25801; gen tel (304) 255-4400; adv tel (304) 255-4424; ed tel (304) 255-4462; gen fax (304) 255-4427; adv fax (304) 255-4427; ed fax (304) 256-5625; gen e-mail rhnews@register-herald.com; adv e-mail bnads@register-herald.com; ed e-mail editor@inetone.net; web site www.register-herald.com

Published: Mon, Tues, Wed, Thur, Fri, Sat, Sun
Weekday Frequency: m
Saturday Frequency: m
Circulation: 23,717; 23,717(sat); 25,165(sun)
Price: 12.50/mo; 167.40/yr.
Advertising: Open inch rate $40.26
News services: AP.
Politics: Independent.
Special Weekly Sections: Teen (Fri); School (Mon); Lifestyles (S); Church Page (Sat); Best Food Day (Wed).
Magazines: Relish (Monthly); Parade (S).
Pub .... Frank Wood
Bus. Dir. .... Drema Radford
Adv. Mgr., Classified .... Diana Slone
Adv. Mgr., Retail .... Charles Jessup
Circ. Dir. .... Randy Taylor
Circ. Dir., Single Copy Sales .... Mark Bowling
Ed. .... Butch Antolini
Mng. Ed. .... Dawn Keyes
Online Ed. .... Mary Spillwell
Chief Photographer .... Rick Barbero
Regl. Ed. .... Pat Hanna
Sports Ed. .... David Morrison
Vice Special Editions Ed. .... Judy Karbonit
Women's Ed. .... Bev Davis
Systems Mgr. .... John Hart
Market Information: ADS; Split run; TMC; Zoned editions.
Mechanical available: Offset; Black and 3 ROP colors; insert accepted - special inserts upon request; page cutoffs - 22 3/4.
Mechanical Specifications: Type page 13 x 21 3/4; E - 6 cols, 2 1/16, 1/8 between; A - 6 cols, 2 1/16, 1/8 between; C - 9 cols, 1 11/32, 1/16 between.
Commodity Consumption: Avg. Page Number Per Issue - Daily 24; Avg. Page Number Per Issue - Plates Used 264; Avg. Page Number Per Issue - Sunday 44; widths 27; Printing Ink Used - Black 4125; Printing Ink Used - Color 510; Printing Ink Used - Pages Printed 220.
Equipment EDITORIAL: Front-end Software – CText, QPS/QuarkXPress 3.31r5.; Editorial Hardware – CText, DEC, APP/Power Mac 8100-00; Editorial Equipment – 1-Tegra/Varityper 6990, 2-Pre Press/Panther Pro 36; Editorial Printers – 2-Tegra/Varityper 5100e CLASSIFIED: Front-end Software – CText, CText/ALPS Pagination.; Classified Hardware – CText, DEC/486; Classified Printers – 2-Tegra/Varityper 5100e, 1-Tegra/Varityper 6990, 2-Pre Press/Panther Pro 36 DISPLAY: Ad make-up applications – Microsoft/Word, Multi-Ad/Creator, QPS/QuarkXPress, Adobe/Photoshop, Aldus/Freehand; Layout Software – 5-APP/Mac Centris 650.; Display Hardware – 1-APP/Mac LC III; Display Printers – Tegra/Varityper 5100e, 1-Tegra/Varityper 6990, 2-Pre Press/Panther Pro 36 PRODUCTION: Pagination Software – CText, QPS/QuarkXPress 7.0.; Production Equipment – 2-Tegra/Varityper 5100e Laser-printer, 1-Tegra/Varityper 6990 Laser, APP/Power Mac 8100-100; Cameras – C/Spartan III, C/Newspager; Scanners – 2-Lf/Leafscan 35, 2-Flatbed, Microtek/Scanmaker III PRESSROOM: Line 1 – 10-G/Urbanite 1981; Press Drives – 2-Fin/150 h.p.; Folders – 1 MAILROOM: Counter stackers – 1-Id, 1/Olympian; Inserters and stuffers – GMA/9 pockets, MM/7 pockets; Bundle tying machines – 2-Dynaric/NP 30; Wrapping singles – St; Addressing machine – Chegier. BUSINESS COMPUTERS: Business Software – Oracle, NewzWare; Business Hardware – IBM/AS-400

BLUEFIELD

BLUEFIELD DAILY TELEGRAPH

928 Bluefield Ave., Bluefield, W.Va., 24701; gen tel (304) 327-2800; adv tel (304) 327-2816; ed tel (304) 327-2811; gen fax (304) 325-6176; adv fax (304) 327-6179; ed fax (304) 327-6179; gen e-mail editor@bdtonline.com; adv e-mail advertising@bdtonline.com; ed e-mail editor@bdtonline.com; web site www.bdtonline.com

Published: Mon, Tues, Wed, Thur, Fri, Sat, Sun
Weekday Frequency: m
Saturday Frequency: m
Circulation: ; 15,953(sun)
Last Audit: ABC September 30, 2011
Price: 12.25/mo; 162.00/yr.
Advertising: Open inch rate $37.75
News services: AP, Scripps Howard News Digest.
Politics: Independent. **Established:** 1896
Special Editions: Bluefield Chamber (Apr); Football (Aug); Holiday Cookbook (Dec); Senior Citizens (Feb); Super Bowl (Jan); Business Profiles (Jul); Bridal (Jun); Lawn & Garden (Mar); Mt. Festival (May); Holiday Lifestyles (Nov); Women in the Area (Oct); Home Improvement (
Special Weekly Sections: Medley (Fri).
Magazines: Parade (S).
Pub .... Randy Deason
Adv. Dir. .... Terri Hale
Circ. Dir. .... Chris Dorton
Exec. Ed. .... Tom Colley
Mng. Ed. .... Samantha Perry
Ed., WV .... Barbara Hawkins
Bus. Ed. .... Rhonda Watson
City Ed .... Jim Terry
News Ed. .... Tammy Toter
Prodn. Mgr., Opns. .... Leigh McVey
Prodn. Foreman, Camera .... Danny Akers
Prodn. Foreman, Mailroom .... Henry Meade
Market Information: ADS; TMC.
Mechanical available: Offset; Black and 3 ROP colors; insert accepted - spadea wrap; page cutoffs - 22 3/4.
Mechanical Specifications: Type page 13 x 21 1/2; E - 6 cols, 2 1/16, 1/8 between; A - 6 cols, 2 1/16, 1/8 between; C - 9 cols, 1 3/8, 1/11 between.
Commodity Consumption: Avg. Page Number Per Issue - Daily 24; Avg. Page Number Per Issue - Plates Used 72000; Avg. Page Number Per Issue - Sunday 44; widths 41 1/4; Newsprint Used - Short Tons 1650; Printing Ink Used - Black 74700; Printing Ink Used - Color 18000; Printing Ink
Equipment EDITORIAL: Front-end Software – Baseview/NewsEdit Pro.; Editorial Hardware – 25-EKI/Televideo, Baseview; Editorial Printers – Pre Press/Panthers CLASSIFIED: Front-end Software – CText.; Classified Hardware – 3-EKI/Televideo DISPLAY: Ad make-up applications – Multi-Ad/Creator; Layout Software – APP/Mac.; Display Hardware – 3-APP/Mac IIci, 2-APP/Mac Quadra 950; Display Printers – 2-V/5100, 1-V/5300E PRODUCTION: Pagination Software – QPS/QuarkXPress 4.0.; Production Equipment – Nu, Graham/Sub., Xante/Accel-A-Writer; Cameras – C/Spartan III, SCREEN/C-680C; Scanners – Nikon, MK, Umax PRESSROOM: Line 1 – 6-G/Cosmo double width; Folders – 2; Pasters – 4; Reels and Stands – 5 MAILROOM: Counter stackers – HL/2; Inserters and stuffers – MM/2; Bundle tying machines – 1/Power Strap, 1-/Power Strap. BUSINESS COMPUTERS: Business Software – Microsoft/Office 97, Microsoft/Office 98, Microsoft/Office 2000, Oracle/Version 1.0, Newsware 5.1; Business Hardware – 7-ATT/3B25100, Newsware 5.1

CHARLESTON

CHARLESTON DAILY MAIL

1001 Virginia St. E., Charleston, W.Va., 25301; gen tel (304) 348-5140; adv tel (304) 348-4860; ed tel (304) 348-4830; gen fax (304) 348-5133; adv fax (304) 348-5133; ed fax (304) 348-4847; ed e-mail dmnews@dailymail.com; web site www.dailymail.com

Group: Metro Suburbia, Inc./Newhouse Newspapers
Published: Mon, Tues, Wed, Thur, Fri
Weekday Frequency: m
Circulation: 18,156; 55,691(sat); 68,940(sun)
Price: 11.20/mo; 88.50/yr.
Advertising: Open inch rate $95.95
News services: AP.
Politics: Independent-Conservative.
Note: For detailed general management, business personnel & production information, see Charleston Newspapers listing. The Saturday Gazette-Mail and the Sunday Gazette-Mail are published jointly by the Daily Mail Publishing Co. and the Daily Gazette Co.
Special Editions: Home & Garden (Apr); Regatta (Aug); Health File (Dec); In Step with Women (Every other month); Forecast II (Feb); Bridal (Jan); Health & Fitness (Jul); Health File (Jun); Parenting (Mar); Newspapers in Education-Great Adventure (May); Flipside (Monthly);
Special Weekly Sections: Business (Mon); Travel (S); Entertainment/Weekend (Thur); Best Food Day (Wed).
Magazines: USA WEEKEND Magazine (S).
Ed. .... Nanya Friend
Mng. Ed. .... Bob Kelly
City Ed. .... Brad McElhinny
Editorial Page Ed. .... Johanna Maurice
Web Ed. .... Jessica Karmasek
Sports Ed. .... Jack Bogaczyk
Graphics Ed. .... Phillip Maramba
Music Ed. .... Monica Orosz
News Ed. .... Becky Calwell
Photo Dept. Mgr. .... Craig Cunningham
Features Reporter .... Charlotte Smith
Educ. Reporter .... Zack Herald
Market Information: Split run; TMC; Zoned editions.
Mechanical available: Offset; Black and 3 ROP colors; insert accepted - all; page cutoffs - 22 3/4.
Mechanical Specifications: Type page 13 x 21 3/4; E - 6 cols, 2, 1/9 between; A - 6 cols, 2, 1/9 between; C - 9 cols, between.
Commodity Consumption: Avg. Page Number Per Issue - Daily 30; Avg. Page Number Per Issue - Sunday 84.
Equipment EDITORIAL: Front-end Software – T base.; Editorial Hardware – PC Network; Editorial Printers – PC Network printers CLASSIFIED: Front-end Software – Tecs.; Classified Hardware – PC Network; Classified Printers – PC Network printers DISPLAY: Ad make-up applications – Admarc; Layout Software – Layout/8000.; Display Hardware – IBM/AS-400; Display Printers – IBM/AS-400 BUSINESS COMPUTERS: Business Software – Elite/400, Elite/5250, JD Edwards; Business Hardware – IBM/AS-400, Advance Series/300

THE CHARLESTON GAZETTE, SUNDAY GAZETTE-MAIL

1001 Virginia St. E., Charleston, W.Va., 25301; gen tel (304) 348-5140; adv tel (304) 348-4860; gen fax (304) 348-1233; adv fax (304) 348-5118; gen e-mail gazette@wvgazette.com; web site www.wvgazette.com

Published: Sat, Sun
Circulation: 40,671; 49,895(sat); 65,429(sun)
Price: 3.00/wk; 13.00/mo; 156.00/yr.
Advertising: Open inch rate $95.95(m-thur to fri)
News services: AP, MCT.
Politics: Independent-Democrat.
Note: For detailed general management, business personnel & production information, see Charleston Newspapers listing. The Saturday Gazette-Mail and the Sunday Gazette-Mail are published jointly by the Daily Mail Publishing Co. and the Daily Gazette Co.
Special Editions: Home & Garden (Apr); Dance

(Aug); Outlook (Feb); Bridal (Jan); WV Home Show (Mar); Fall Home Improvement (Oct); Hunting (Sept).
Special Weekly Sections: Building Page (S); Restaurants & Theaters (Thur); Food Day (Wed).
Magazines: USA WEEKEND Magazine (S).
Broadcast Affiliations: WSAZ (NBC); WVAH (FOX); WOWK (CBS); WCHS (ABC).
Pres./Pub. .... Elizabeth E. Chilton
Ed. .... James A. Haught
City Ed. .... Robert Byers
Columnist .... Phil Kabler
Columnist .... Rick Steelhammer
Editorial Page Ed. .... Dawn Miller
Educ. Ed. .... Eric Eyre
Lifestyles Ed. .... Rosalie Earle
News Ed. .... Victor Burkhammer
Photographer .... Kenny Kemp
Sports Ed. .... Mitch Vingle
Market Information: Split run; TMC; Zoned editions.
Mechanical available: Offset; Black and 3 ROP colors; insert accepted - all; page cutoffs - 22 3/4.
Mechanical Specifications: Type page 12 1/4 x 21 3/4; E - 6 cols, 1 7/8, 1/9 between; A - 6 cols, 1 7/8, 1/9 between; C - 9 cols, between.
Equipment EDITORIAL: Front-end Software – Microsoft/Word.; Editorial Hardware – IBM/Netfinity, 2-IBM/Netfinity; Editorial Equipment – Dell/PC; Editorial Printers – HP/8100 CLASSIFIED: Front-end Software – TECS-2.; Classified Hardware – Dell/PC, 14-Dell/PC DISPLAY: Ad make-up applications – SCC/Layout 8000; Layout Software – SCS/Layout 8000, 2-Dell/PC.; Display Hardware – Dell/PC PRODUCTION: Pagination Software – QPS/QuarkXPress 4.0, 50-IBM PC.; Production Equipment – AP Leafdesk, 3-Prepress Panther 4600 Imagesetters, 2-Ap Leafdesk; Scanners – 1-Graphic Enterprise TESCA PRESSROOM: Line 1 – 11-G/Metro offset (double width) 1973; Folders – 3 MAILROOM: Counter stackers – 7/QWI; Inserters and stuffers – HI; Bundle tying machines – 4-/Dynaric; Wrapping singles – PM; Mailroom control system – Icon; Addressing machine – 2-/KR, AVY. BUSINESS COMPUTERS: Business Software – JD Edwards GL, APP/Neasi-Weber Admarc 6.4; Business Hardware – IBM/AS 400

DAILY GAZETTE CO.

1001 Virginia St. E., Charleston, W.Va., 25301; gen tel (304) 348-5140; gen fax (304) 348-1233; gen e-mail news@wvgazette.com; web site www.dailymail.com; www.wvgazette.com
Published: Mon, Tues, Wed, Thur, Fri, Sat, Sun
Price: 147.00/yr.
Advertising: Open inch rate $27.00
Politics: 1873

DAILY MAIL PUBLISHING CO.

1001 Virginia St. E., Charleston, W.Va., 25330; gen tel (304) 348-5124; gen fax (304) 348-4847; gen e-mail news@dailymail.com; web site www.dailymail.com
Published: Mon, Tues, Wed, Thur, Fri, Sat, Sun
Price: 147.00/yr.
Advertising: Open inch rate $28.00
Politics: 1873

CLARKSBURG

CLARKSBURG PUBLISHING CO.

324-326 Hewes Ave., Clarksburg, W.Va., 26301; gen tel (304) 626-1413; gen fax (304) 624-9441

THE EXPONENT TELEGRAM

324-326 Hewes Ave., Clarksburg, W.Va., 26302; gen tel (304) 626-1400; adv tel (304) 626-1430; adv fax (304) 622-3629; ed fax (304) 624-4188; gen e-mail webmast@cpubco.com; adv e-mail advertising@exponent-telegram.com; web site

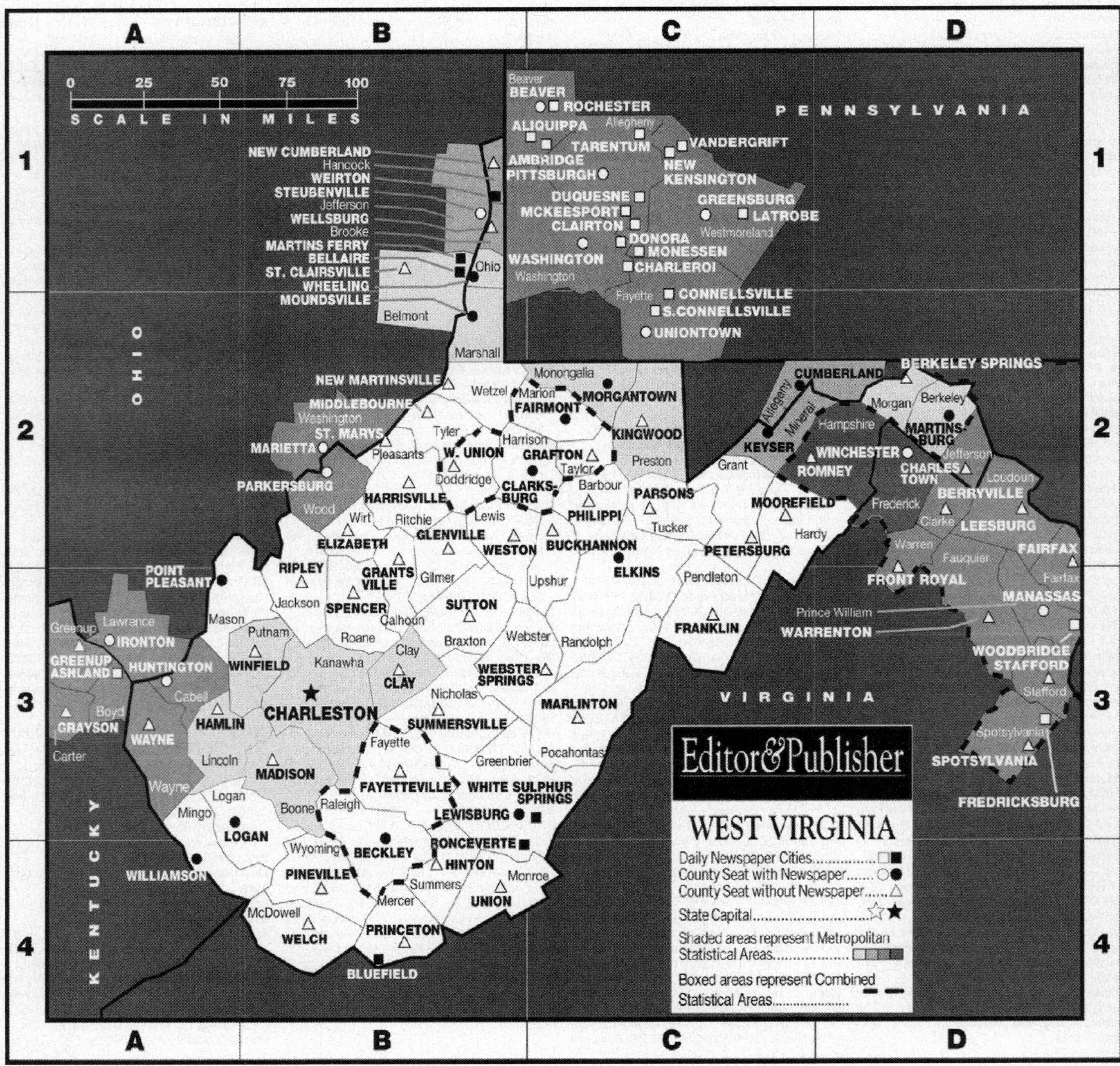

cpubco.com
Published: Mon, Tues, Wed, Thur, Fri, Sat, Sun
Weekday Frequency: m
Saturday Frequency: m
Circulation: 13,942; 14,570(sat); 18,491(sun)
Last Audit: ABC September 30, 2011
Price: 15.35/mo; 161.20/yr.
Advertising: Open inch rate $23.21
News services: AP.
Not Published: New Year; Memorial Day; Independence Day; Labor Day; Thanksgiving; Christmas.
Magazines: Parade (S).
Pres./Pub. ....William Highland
Asst. Treasurer ....Steve Morris
Adv. Mgr., Retail......................Mickey Carlock
Circ. Mgr. ....Robert Gaston
Mng. Ed...John Miller
Lifestyle Ed...................................Julie Perine
Market Information: TMC.
Mechanical available: Letterpress; Black and 2 ROP colors; insert accepted; page cutoffs - 21 3/4.
Mechanical Specifications: Type page 13 5/8 x 20; E - 6 cols, 2 1/8, 1/6 between; A - 6 cols, 2 1/8, 1/6 between; C - 10 cols, 1 1/4, 1/12 between.
Commodity Consumption: Avg. Page Number Per Issue - Daily 34; Avg. Page Number Per Issue - Plates Used 16000; Avg. Page Number Per Issue - Sunday 45; widths 29; Newsprint Used - Metric Tons 1000; Printing Ink Used - Black 40000; Printing Ink Used - Color 3000; Printing Ink Use
Equipment EDITORIAL: Front-end Software – CD/TOPS.; Editorial Hardware – CD/2330; Editorial Equipment – 5-Leading Edge/D-2 CLASSIFIED: Front-end Software – CD/TOPS.; Classified Hardware – CD/2330; Classified Printers – Okidata DISPLAY: Ad make-up applications – SCS/Layout 8000; Layout Software – SCS/Layout 8000.; Display Hardware – Dell/PC; Display Printers – C.Itoh/5000, HP/Laser PRODUCTION: Pagination Software – CD, Magician Plus, APP/Mac Quadra 950, APP/Mac Quadra 800, APP/Mac Sys 7.5.; Production Equipment – 1-LE/Verter, APP/Mac Sys 7.5, Multi-Ad/Creator, Adobe/Photoshop; Cameras – 1-C/Spartan III; Scanners – Microtek/Flatbed, Microtek/35mm, Adobe/Photoshop PRESSROOM: Line 1 – 1-G/High Speed Straight Line; Line 2 – H/Right Angle; Folders – 1, 1. MAILROOM: Counter stackers – KAN/MSI; Inserters and stuffers – MM; Bundle tying machines – 1/Bu, 1-/Power Strap. BUSINESS COMPUTERS: Business Software – IBM/Sys 36; Business Hardware – IBM/Sys 36

ELKINS

THE INTER-MOUNTAIN

520 Railroad Ave., Elkins, W.Va., 26241; gen tel (304) 636-2121; adv tel (304) 636-2127; ed tel (304) 636-2124; gen fax (304) 636-8252; adv e-mail addirector@theintermountain.com; ed e-mail editor@theintermountain.com; newsroom@theintermountain.com; web site www.theintermountain.com
Published: Mon, Tues, Wed, Thur, Fri, Sat
Weekday Frequency: e
Saturday Frequency: m
Circulation: 8,891; 9,905(sat)
Last Audit: ABC September 30, 2011
Price: 10.20/mo; 99.95/yr; 30.60/3mo, $61.20/6mo.
Advertising: Open inch rate $21.23
News services: AP.
Politics: Independent-Republican.
Not Published: New Year; Memorial Day; Independence Day; Labor Day; Thanksgiving; Christmas.
Magazines: USA WEEKEND Magazine (Sat).
Pub..Donald Smith
Circ. Mgr.................................Jerry Ferguson
Ed. ....Linda Skidmore
Local Ed........................................Heath Quint
Region Ed. ....Juliann Cooper
Sports Ed. ....Edgar Kelley
Prodn. Press Mgr............................Dave Ickes
Market Information: Zoned editions.
Mechanical available: Offset; Black and 3 ROP colors; insert accepted; page cutoffs - 22 3/4.
Mechanical Specifications: Type page 13 x 22; E - 6 cols, 2 1/16, 1/8 between; A - 6 cols, 2 1/16, 1/8 between; C - 6 cols, 2 1/16, 1/8 between.
Commodity Consumption: Avg. Page Number Per Issue - Daily 24; Avg. Page Number Per Issue - Plates Used 5650; widths 27; Newsprint Used - Short Tons 420; Printing Ink Used - Black 11239; Printing Ink Used - Pages Printed 6240.
Equipment; Editorial Hardware – 8-COM/350.; Classified Hardware – 1-COM/350.; Display Hardware – 1-COM/Display IV.; Production Equipment – 1-COM/2961, 1-COM/Trendsetter; Cameras – 1-Nu. PRESSROOM: Line 1 – 8-HI/Cotrell V-15A; Folders – 1 MAILROOM: Counter stackers – 1-BG/108; Bundle tying machines – .; Business Hardware – 1-NCR

FAIRMONT

TIMES WEST VIRGINIAN

300 Quincy St., Fairmont, W.Va., 26554; gen tel (304) 367-2500; adv tel (304) 367-2500; ed tel (304) 367-2540; gen fax (304) 367-2569; adv fax (304) 367-2569; ed fax (304) 367-2565; gen e-mail timeswv@timeswv.com; adv e-mail twvadvertising@timeswv.com; ed e-mail timeswv@timeswv.com; web site www.timeswv.com
Published: Mon, Tues, Wed, Thur, Fri, Sat, Sun
Weekday Frequency: m
Saturday Frequency: m
Circulation: 10,764; 10,604(sat); 11,812(sun)
Last Audit: ABC September 30, 2011
Price: 5.26/wk; 17.90/mo; 165.00/yr.
Advertising: Open inch rate $22.05
News services: AP.
Politics: Independent.
Special Editions: Spring Home Improvements (Apr); Football Tab (Aug); Christmas Greetings (Dec); Spring Sports (Feb); Senior Times (Jan); Senior Times (Jul); 4 T Arena Rodeo (Jun); Annual Report (Mar); Three Rivers Festival (May); Christmas Gift Guide 1 (Nov); Small Busine
Special Weekly Sections: Wheels (S); Faith Journeys (Sat); Ticket (Thur); Food (Wed).
Magazines: Parade (S).
Pub...............................Andrew B. Kniceley
Controller ....Jo Ellen Howell
Adv. Dir. ....Craig Richards
Classified Mgr...........................Baverly Miller
Mktg. Dir. ....Mark Long
Circ. Dir....................................Betsy Haught
Community Ed.............................John Veasey
Prodn. Mgr. ....James Short
Prodn. Foreman, Pressroom...........Gerald Price
Market Information: TMC; Zoned editions.
Mechanical available: Offset; Black and 3 ROP colors; insert accepted; page cutoffs - 22 3/4.
Mechanical Specifications: Type page 11 63/100 x 21 1/2; E - 6 cols, 1 5/6, 1/8 between; A - 6 cols, 1 5/6, 1/8 between; C - 9 cols, 1 5/6, 1/16 between.
Commodity Consumption: Avg. Page Number Per Issue - Daily 20; Avg. Page Number Per Issue - Sunday 56; widths 25; Newsprint Used - Short Tons 840.
Equipment EDITORIAL: Front-end Software – Baseview/News Edit Pro, QPS/QuarkXPress, Baseview, Adobe/Photoshop; Editorial Hardware – APP/Mac Pagination System, APP/MAC G3; Editorial Equipment – APP/Mac Quadra 950, Lf/Leafscan 35, APP/Mac G3, APP/Server NT, Nikon/Cool Scan; Editorial Printers – TI/Lineprinter, HP/4050 CLASSIFIED: Front-end Software – QPS/QuarkXPress, Baseview/Ad Manager Pro.; Classified Hardware – APP/Mac G3, APP/Mac Pagination System; Classified Printers – TI/Lineprinter, HP/405N PRODUCTION: Pagination Software – Equipment □�; Production Equipment – 1-COM/IV, Lf/AP Leaf Picture Desk, ApServer NT, APP/Mac G3, Pre Press/Panther Pro 36, 3-HP/4050N, PrePress/Panther Plus 46; Cameras – 1-R/500, C, SCREEN/Companica 680; Scanners – Lf/Leafscan 35, Nikon/Cool Scan, UMAX/PowerLook III PRESSROOM: Line 1 – 7-G/Urbanite; Folders – 1 MAILROOM: Counter stackers – 1-BG/Count-O-Veyor 109; Inserters and stuffers – 1-KAN/480; Bundle tying machines – 1-SP/330, 1/Gd. BUSINESS COMPUTERS: Business Software – Lotus, WordPerfect; Business Hardware – Pentium/PC

HUNTINGTON

THE HERALD-DISPATCH

946 5th Ave., Huntington, W.Va., 25701; gen tel (304) 526-4000; adv tel (304) 526-2836; ed tel (304) 526-2763; gen fax (304) 526-2858; adv fax (304) 526-2863; ed fax (304) 526-2857; gen e-mail news@herald-dispatch.com; web site www.herald-dispatch.com
Group: Champion Industries
Published: Mon, Tues, Wed, Thur, Fri, Sat, Sun
Weekday Frequency: m
Saturday Frequency: m
Circulation: 26,909; 24,192(sat); 29,771(sun)
Last Audit: ABC September 30, 2011
Price: 3.58/wk; 15.05/mo; 186.00/yr (carrier).
Advertising: Open inch rate $82.73
News services: AP
Politics: Independent. **Established:** 1909
Own facility?: Y
Special Editions: Progress (Mar); @Record-Body:**Magazines:** USA WEEKEND Magazine (S).
Pub....Ed Dawson
Adv./Mktg. Dir...............................Amy Howat
Circ. Dir. ....Mark Campbell
Mng. Ed. ....Les Smith
Features Ed................................Robyn Rison
News Ed....Don Willis
Sports Ed. ....Rick McCann
Prodn. Mgr., Distr. Ctr. ....Danny Watson
Prodn. Mgr., Pressroom ....Vernon Lovejoy
Production Director ....David Hamilton
Operations manager ....Jeff Hutchinson
Market Information: Split run; TMC; Zoned editions.
Mechanical available: Letterpress; Black and 3 ROP colors; insert accepted - any through a HI/1472 hopper; page cutoffs - 21 1/2.
Mechanical Specifications: Type page 13 x 21 1/2; E - 6 cols, 2, 1/6 between; A - 6 cols, 2, 1/6 between; C - 10 cols, 1 1/5, 1/10 between.
Commodity Consumption: Avg. Page Number Per Issue - Daily 32; Avg. Page Number Per Issue - Plates Used 50000; Avg. Page Number Per Issue - Sunday 72; widths 40 1/2; Newsprint Used - Metric Tons 2854; Newsprint Used - Short Tons 3146; Printing Ink Used - Black 118811; Printing
Equipment EDITORIAL: Front-end Software – Newsedit pro; Editorial Hardware – Apple Server X version 10.5; Editorial Printers – HP/4000 CLASSIFIED: Front-end Software – AdPower; Classified Hardware – Subsystem, Dell/Workstations; Classified Printers – HP/4000 DISPLAY: Ad make-up applications – APP/Mac, QPS/QuarkXPress, Adobe/Photoshop, Adobe/Illustrator; Layout Software – Dewar/Layout 8000.; Display Hardware – APP/Macs; Display Printers – HP/4000; Production Equipment – 1-EV-jetsetter 7100
1-EV-jetsetter 6200
2 Harlequin Rips, version 7.2; Scanners – 1-11X17 flatbed scanner
1- 8.5X11 flatbed scanner PRESSROOM: Line 1 – 6-Wd/Metropolitan double width (3 half decks) 1957; Press Drives – 5-GE/Motors 1994; Folders – 1-SC/3:2, 1-SC/Folder 2:1. MAILROOM: Counter stackers – HL/HT, HL/Monitor; Inserters and stuffers – HI/1472 (13 Heads); Bundle tying machines – 2/Power Strap/PSD 5; Other equipment –MM/321 Stitcher-Trimmer. BUSINESS COMPUTERS: Business Software – Newzware; Business Hardware – Dell, Linux Red Hat server
Zip Codes served: 25502 25503 25504 25506 25507 25510 25514 25515 25520 25526 25530 25535 25537 25541 25545 25550 25555 25557 25559 25560 25570 25571 25701 25702 25703 25704 25705 41101 41102 41129 41230 45619 45623 45638 45669 45678 45680
Delivery method: Mail, Newsstand, Private Carrier, Racks

KEYSER

MINERAL DAILY NEWS-TRIBUNE

24 Armstrong St., Keyser, W.Va., 26726; gen tel (304) 788-3333; ed tel (301) 786-4488; gen fax (304) 788-3398; ed e-mail newsroom@newstribune.info; web site www.newstribune.info
Published: Mon, Tues, Wed, Thur, Fri
Weekday Frequency: m
Circulation: 3,935; 4,064(sat)
Last Audit: October 22, 2003
Price: 127.00/yr.
Advertising: Open inch rate $7.67
News services: AP.
Politics: Independent. **Established:** 1885
Not Published: New Year; Memorial Day; Independence Day; Labor Day; Thanksgiving; Christmas.
Special Weekly Sections: Entertainment (Fri); Senior Citizen (Mon); Food (Sat); Gardening (Thur); Food & Recipes (Wed).
Magazines: American Profile (Weekly).
Pub..Dave Boden
Accounting Mgr..........................Kathy Murphy
Adv. Mgr. ....Randy Lewis
Circ. Mgr........................................Paul Curry
News Ed..................................Andrew Arthur
Prodn. Mgr., Composing ....Brenda Mullen
Market Information: Split run; TMC; Zoned editions.
Mechanical available: Offset; Black and 2 ROP colors; insert accepted; page cutoffs - 21 1/2.
Mechanical Specifications: Type page 13 x 21 1/2; E - 6 cols, 2 1/16, 1/8 between; A - 6 cols, 2 1/16, 1/8 between; C - 6 cols, 2 1/16, 1/8 between.
Commodity Consumption: Avg. Page Number Per Issue - Daily 18; Avg. Page Number Per Issue - Plates Used 12000; widths 27 1/2; Newsprint Used - Short Tons 379; Printing Ink Used - Black 11000; Printing Ink Used - Color 1000; Printing Ink Used - Pages Printed 5900.
Equipment; Editorial Hardware – 7-IBM.; Classified Hardware – 1-ATT.; Layout Software – 1-APP/Mac.; Production Equipment – 1-Nu, 3-COM/MDT; Cameras – 1-K/241, 1-LE/480. PRESSROOM: Line 1 – 8-G/Community; Folders – 1 MAILROOM: Counter stackers – 1/St; Inserters and stuffers – 1-/KAN; Bundle tying machines – 2-/Bu; Addressing machine – 1-/KR.

LEWISBURG

WEST VIRGINIA DAILY NEWS

200 S. Court St., Lewisburg, W.Va., 24901-0471; gen tel (304) 645-1206; gen fax (304) 645-7104; gen e-mail wvdailynews@suddenlinkmail.com
Published: Mon, Tues, Wed, Thur, Fri
Weekday Frequency: e
Circulation: 4,100
Last Audit: September 30, 1998
Price: 4.95/mo; 108.00/yr (mail); 34.00/3mo, $58.50/6mo.
Advertising: Open inch rate $6.85
News services: NEA, TMS.
Politics: Republican. **Established:** 1969
Not Published: New Year; Memorial Day; Independence Day; Labor Day; Thanksgiving; Christmas.
Special Editions: Home Improvement (Apr); State Fair (Aug); Bridal (Jan); Christmas Gift Guide (Nov); Home Improvement (Sept).
Pub..Judy Steele
Adv. Dir..................................Barbara Cordial
Ed. ....Bill Frye

Prodn. Mgr., Camera ....Peggey Weikle
Prodn. Mgr., Mailroom ....Susan Wade
Prodn. Mgr., Pressroom...................Lea Ballard
Market Information: ADS; TMC.
Mechanical available: Offset; Black and 1 ROP colors; insert accepted; page cutoffs - 21 1/2.
Mechanical Specifications: Type page 13 x 21 1/2; E - 6 cols, 2 1/16, 1/8 between; A - 6 cols, 2 1/16, 1/8 between; C - 6 cols, 2 1/16, 1/8 between.
Commodity Consumption: Avg. Page Number Per Issue - Daily 8; Avg. Page Number Per Issue - Plates Used 1196; widths 27; Newsprint Used - Short Tons 250; Printing Ink Used - Black 5400; Printing Ink Used - Color 700; Printing Ink Used - Pages Printed 2392.
Equipment EDITORIAL: Front-end Software – Aldus/PageMaker 5.0.; Editorial Hardware – 3-APP/Mac; Editorial Printers – X/N 2025 DISPLAY: Ad make-up applications – Multi-Ad/Creator 3.6, Aldus/PageMaker 6.0, QPS/QuarkXPress 5.0; Layout Software – 3-APP/Mac.; Display Hardware – 3-APP/Mac; Display Printers – 1-Xante/3N, 1-Xante/8300; Production Equipment – 1-P; Cameras – 1-R. PRESSROOM: Line 1 – 5-G/Community.; Inserters and stuffers – 1/St; Bundle tying machines – 1-/CE, 1-/Signode.; Business Hardware – 2-Leading Edge/MOD 2

LOGAN

THE LOGAN BANNER

435 Stratton St., Logan, W.Va., 25601; gen tel (304) 752-6950; gen fax (304) 752-1239; gen e-mail news@loganbanner.com; web site www.loganbanner.com
Published: Mon, Tues, Wed, Thur, Fri, Sun
Weekday Frequency: e
Circulation: 9,579; 9,751(sun)
Last Audit: September 30, 2000
Price: 7.00/mo; 143.00/yr.
Advertising: Open inch rate $12.36
News services: AP.
Politics: Independent-Democrat. **Established:** 1888
Not Published: Thanksgiving; Christmas.
Special Editions: Home Improvement (Apr); Football Signature Pages (Aug); Christmas Songbook (Dec); Basketball Pages (Feb); A-Z (Jul); Father's Day Photos (Jun); Girl Scout Page (Mar); Mother's Day Photos (May); Veteran's Day Page (Nov); Hunting (Oct); Football Pages (Sept
Special Weekly Sections: Church Page (Fri); Business Page (Tues); TV Times (Weekly).
Magazines: Parade (S).
Pub..James Jenkins
Adv. Mgr....................................Kathy Chafin
Mng. Ed.............................Michael Browning
Sports Ed.......................................Paul Adkins
Webmaster ....Martha Sparks
Prodn. Foreman, Composing.....Gaynell Hughes
Market Information: TMC.
Mechanical available: Offset; Black and 3 ROP colors; insert accepted - all; page cutoffs - 22 3/4.
Mechanical Specifications: Type page 13 3/4 x 21 1/2; E - 6 cols, 2 1/16, 1/8 between; A - 6 cols, 2 1/16, 1/8 between; C - 9 cols, 1 3/8, 1/16 between.
Commodity Consumption: Avg. Page Number Per Issue - Daily 16; Avg. Page Number Per Issue - Sunday 24.
Equipment EDITORIAL: Front-end Software – QPS/QuarkXPress.; Editorial Hardware – 5-APP/Mac Quadra 610; Editorial Printers – APP/Mac LaserWriter Pro 600 CLASSIFIED: Front-end Software – QPS/QuarkXPress.; Classified Printers – APP/Mac LaserWriter Pro 600; Production Equipment – 2-APP/Mac LaserWriter Pro 600, AG/Arcus Plus Scanner; Cameras – R/500. PRESSROOM: Line 1 – 8; Folders – 2 MAILROOM: Counter stackers – 1/Fg; Inserters and stuffers – 3-/DG; Bundle tying machines – 1-Ty-Tech/Tyer; Addressing machine – 2-/Am.

MARTINSBURG

THE JOURNAL

207 W. King St., Martinsburg, W.Va., 25401; gen tel (304) 263-8931; ed tel (304) 263-3381; gen fax (304) 263-8058; adv fax (304) 267-2829; ed fax (304) 267-2903; ed e-mail news@journal-news.net; web site www.journal-news.net
Published: Mon, Tues, Wed, Thur, Fri, Sat, Sun
Weekday Frequency: m
Saturday Frequency: m
Circulation: 15,259; 16,274(sat); 17,446(sun)
Last Audit: ABC September 30, 2011
Price: 1.85/wk; 109.00/yr; 27.30/3mo (carrier), $14.30/3mo (S, carrier).
Advertising: Open inch rate $32.50
News services: AP.
Politics: Independent. **Established:** 1907
Special Editions: Home Show (Apr); Fall Sports Tab (Aug); Christmas Songbook (Dec); Welcome Home (Feb); Bridal (Jan); Welcome Home (Jul); Welcome Home (Jun); Spring Sports Tab (Mar); Mother's Day Tab (May); Welcome Home (Nov); Halloween Safety (Oct); Welcome Home (Sept).
Special Weekly Sections: Weekender (Entertainment) (Fri); Welcome Home (Mon); Business/Stocks (S); Auto Pages (Sat); Food (Wed).
Magazines: Parade (S).
Pub....................................Craig Bartoldson
Editorial Page Ed..........................John McVey
Chief Photographer..........................Ron Agnir
Sports Ed. ....Jeff Nations
Online Mgr...........................Nicholas Werder
Prodn. Mgr., Opns.............................Art Taylor
Market Information: Split run; TMC; Zoned editions.
Mechanical available: Offset; Black and 3 ROP colors; insert accepted - all; page cutoffs - 22 3/4.
Mechanical Specifications: Type page 11 4/5 x 21 1/2; E - 6 cols, 1 7/8, 1/8 between; A - 6 cols, 1 7/8, 1/8 between; C - 8 cols, 1 5/16, 1/16 between.
Commodity Consumption: Avg. Page Number Per Issue - Daily 24; Avg. Page Number Per Issue - Plates Used 57177; Avg. Page Number Per Issue - Sunday 61; widths 25; Newsprint Used - Short Tons 3610; Printing Ink Used - Black 55352; Printing Ink Used - Color 37927; Printing Ink Use
Equipment EDITORIAL: Front-end Software – ONI/Class 0.5.4.; Editorial Hardware – APP/Mac G4, 6-Umax/C500; Editorial Equipment – APP/Mac Centris 610, APP/Mac Centris 650, APP/Mac PC 6100-66, APP/Mac G-3 Workgroup Server; Editorial Printers – HP/8000 N CLASSIFIED: Front-end Software – ONI/Class 0.5.4.; Classified Hardware – Umax/C500-240; Classified Equipment – NCR/UNIX, 2-Sun; Classified Printers – HP/8150 DN; Display Hardware – Umax/C500-200, APP/Power Mac G3, 6-APP/Mac G4, Sun/Ultra Sparc Server 690 MP; Display Printers – APP/Mac LaserWriter NTX, 2-HP/8150 DN, 2-HP/8000 N, MON/ExpressMaster 2000, Konica/EV Jetsetter 4500 Imagesetter PRODUCTION: Pagination Software – QPS/QuarkXPress 4., Adobe/Photoshop 6.0, Mult; Production Equipment – TextBridge/Pro, MON/XPRESS Master 2000, Konica/EV Jetsetter 4500; Cameras – P, C/Spartan II; Scanners – Microtek/ScanMaker, HP/ScanJet IIcx, Nikon/35mm LS-3510 AF, Linotype-Hell/Jade 2 PRESSROOM: Line 1 – 10-G/Urbanite single width; Line 2 – 6-HI/Cotrell 845 single width; Press Drives – 3; Folders – 1-G/2:1 (with balloon), 2-HI/2:1 (with balloon) Plus K25/AW; Press control system – 6; Press registration system – Carlson/Center Pin Lock Up/adjustabl MAILROOM: Counter stackers – Id, HL/Monitors, HPS/Dual Carrier, MM/288, MM/310-20, HT; Inserters and stuffers – HI/NP 1372, DoBoy; Bundle tying machines – MLN, Arpac 55-GI-20; Addressing machine – KR, Domino/InkJet; Other equipment –MM/Stitcher-Trimmer.; Business Hardware – NCR, Unix

MORGANTOWN

THE DOMINION POST

1251 Earl L. Core Rd., Morgantown, W.Va., 26505-5881; gen tel (304) 292-6301; adv tel (304) 291-9449; ed tel (304) 291-9425; gen fax (304) 291-2326; adv fax (304) 292-3704; ed fax (304) 291-2326; gen e-mail info@dominionpost.com; adv e-mail advertising@dominionpost.com; ed e-mail newsroom@dominionpost.com; web site www.dominionpost.com
Published: Mon, Tues, Wed, Thur, Fri, Sat, Sun
Weekday Frequency: m
Saturday Frequency: m
Circulation: 20,097; 21,255(sat); 23,922(sun)
Last Audit: ABC September 30, 2011
Price: 4.20/wk; 18.20/mo; 212.94/yr.
Advertising: Open inch rate $35.61
Insert rate: 4 pg tab/$76 per 1,000
News services: AP, MCT, NEA.
Politics: Independent. **Established:** 1923
Advertising not accepted: Y
Own facility?: Y
Special Editions: Auto Care (Tab) (Apr); College Football (Aug); Xmas Gift Guide (3 times) (Dec); Health Fair (Tab) (Feb); Chamber of Commerce (Tab) (Jan); West Virginia's Birthday Party (Tab) (Jun); Progress (Mar); Summer Fun (May); Basketball (Nov); Goal Post (Oct); Buck
Special Weekly Sections: TV Week (S); Marquee (Thur).
Magazines: Parade (S).
Broadcast Affiliations: Radio WAJR/WVAQ./WKKW
Vice Pres./Sec./Treasurer ....James M. Troy
Controller....................................Brian D. Cole
Pub..David A. Raese
Assoc. Pub. ....Kathleen A. Raese
Adv. Dir. ....Eric Willson
Mktg./Promo. Coord................Jessica Roberts
Circ. Mgr., Sales ....Mike Campbell
Asst. Circ. Coord., NIE ....Stephanie Farber
Circ. Mgr., Opns.........................Joseph Duley
Senior Reporter............................David Beard
Editor..Geri Ferrara
Editorial Page Ed. ....Randy Vealey
Online Coord. ....David Whisler
Prodn. Mgr., Distr.......................Mike Bonnette
Prodn. Mgr., Pre Press/Systems Chris Halterman
Market Information: TMC.
Mechanical available: Offset; Black and 3 ROP colors; insert accepted; page cutoffs - 22 3/4.
Mechanical Specifications: Type page 13 1/4 x 21 1/2; E - 6 cols, 2 1/16, 1/8 between; A - 6 cols, 2 1/16, 1/8 between; C - 9 cols, 1 3/8, 1/16 between.
Commodity Consumption: Avg. Page Number Per Issue - Daily 27; Avg. Page Number Per Issue - Plates Used 19635; Avg. Page Number Per Issue - Sunday 80; widths 28; Newsprint Used - Short Tons 2076; Printing Ink Used - Black 30957; Printing Ink Used - Color 9000; Printing Ink Used
Equipment EDITORIAL: Front-end Software – SII.; Editorial Hardware – SII/Tandem 31 PC, 10-APP/Mac; Editorial Printers – QMS/860 Laser CLASSIFIED: Front-end Software – SII.; Classified Hardware – SII; Classified Printers – QMS/860 Laser; Layout Software – SII.; Display Hardware – APP/Mac PRODUCTION: Pagination Software – QPS/QuarkXPress.; Production Equipment – 2-AG/Accusets 1500 Plus; Cameras – 1-Bo; Scanners – AG/Arcus Plus, AG/Horizon Plus PRESSROOM: Line 1 – 7-G/Urbanite; Folders – 1 MAILROOM: Counter stackers – 1/QWI, 1-QWI/400; Inserters and stuffers – MM/8:1; Bundle tying machines – 1-/MLN; Addressing machine – KAN. AUDIO: Audio Software – New Horizons/Info-Connect; Audio Hardware – AP, TMS, Texas Micro/PC BUSINESS COMPUTERS: Business Software – Vision Data, DSI; Business Hardware – 5-Dec
Delivery method: Mail, Newsstand, Private Carrier, Racks

WEST VIRGINIA NEWSPAPER PUB. CO.

1251 Earl L Core Rd., Morgantown, W.Va., 26505; gen tel (304) 292-6301; gen fax (304) 291-2326; gen e-mail newsroom@dominionpost.com; web site www.dominionpost.com
Published: Mon, Tues, Wed, Thur, Fri, Sat, Sun
Price: 174.64/yr.
Advertising: Open inch rate $23.84
Politics: 1930

MOUNDSVILLE

MOUNDSVILLE DAILY ECHO

713 Lafayette Ave., Moundsville, W.Va., 26041; gen tel (304) 845-2660; adv tel (304) 845-2660; ed tel (304) 845-2660; gen fax (304) 845-2661; adv fax (304) 845-2661; ed fax (304) 845-2661
Published: Mon, Tues, Wed, Thur, Fri, Sat
Weekday Frequency: e
Circulation: 3,902; 3,902(sat)
Last Audit: October 1, 2002
Price: 47.70/yr.
Advertising: Open inch rate $4.17
News services: AP.
Politics: Independent-Democrat. **Established:** 1891
Advertising not accepted: Alcoholic beverages.
Adv. Mgr., Retail/Nat'l ....Marian Walton
Circ. Mgr...................................Linda Massie
City Ed. ....Hugh Anderson
Sports Ed. ....Charlie Walton
Mechanical available: Offset; Black and ROP colors; insert accepted; page cutoffs - 22 3/4.
Mechanical Specifications: Type page 15 1/8 x 21 5/8; E - 7 cols, 2, 1/8 between; A - 7 cols, 2, 1/8 between; C - 7 cols, 2, 1/8 between.
Commodity Consumption: Avg. Page Number Per Issue - Daily 4; Avg. Page Number Per Issue - Plates Used 600; Avg. Page Number Per Issue - Saturday 4; widths 32; Newsprint Used - Short Tons 42; Printing Ink Used - Black 1389.
Equipment EDITORIAL: Front-end Software – Aldus/PageMaker 3.01, Microsoft/Windows 3.1.; Editorial Hardware – PC; Editorial Printers – APP/Mac LaserWriter DISPLAY: Ad make-up applications – Aldus/PageMaker 3.01, Microsoft/Windows 3.1, Archetype/Corel Draw 3.0.; Display Hardware – PC; Display Printers – APP/Mac LaserWriter; Production Equipment – APP/Mac Laser Plus; Cameras – R. PRESSROOM: Line 1 – Feb-92; Press control system – GE/SCR.; Addressing machine – 2-Am/Dispensa-Matic.; Business Hardware – 1-PC 586

PARKERSBURG

OGDEN NEWSPAPERS, INC.

519 Juliana St., Parkersburg, W.Va., 26101; gen tel (304) 485-1891; gen fax (304) 485-2061; gen e-mail asmith@oweb.com; web site www.newsandsentinel.com
Published: Mon, Tues, Wed, Thur, Fri, Sat, Sun
Price: 140.40/yr.
Advertising: Open inch rate $21.70
Politics: 1906

PARKERSBURG NEWS & SENTINEL

519 Juliana St., Parkersburg, W.Va., 26102-1787; gen tel (304) 485-1891; adv tel (304) 485-1891; ed tel (304) 485-1891; gen fax (304) 485-2061; adv fax (304) 485-2061; ed fax (304) 485-5122; ed e-mail editorial@newsandsentinel.com; web site www.newsandsentinel.com
Published: Mon, Tues, Wed, Thur, Fri
Weekday Frequency: e
Circulation: 2,812; 21,653(sat); 28,990(sun)
Last Audit: September 30, 2008
Price: 25.78/mo; 140.40/yr.
Advertising: Open inch rate $75.00
News services: AP.
Special Editions: Video News (Monthly).
Special Weekly Sections: Best Food Day (S); Best Food Day (Thur); Best Food Day (Wed).
Magazines: Free Time (Entertainment) (Fri); Parade (S); Religion Tab (Sat).
Pub. ....James T. Spanner

Circ. Dir. ....Joe Tranquill
Exec. Ed. ....James Smith
Mng. Ed. ....Paul LaPann
City Ed. ....Jess Mancini
Editorial Page Ed. ....Larry Cox
Film/Theater Ed. ....Brett Dunlap
Sports Ed. ....Dave Poe
Opns. Mgr. ....Mike Warren
Market Information: TMC.
Mechanical available: Offset; Black and 3 ROP colors; insert accepted; page cutoffs - 21 3/4.
Mechanical Specifications: Type page 12 1/2 x 21 3/4; E - 6 cols, 2 1/16, 1/8 between; A - 6 cols, 2 1/16, 1/8 between; C - 8 cols, 1 9/16, 1/16 between.
Commodity Consumption: Avg. Page Number Per Issue - Daily 28; Avg. Page Number Per Issue - Sunday 54.
Equipment EDITORIAL: Front-end Software – Microsoft/Windows NT 4.0.; Editorial Hardware – PC; Editorial Printers – HP/6M CLASSIFIED: Front-end Software – Microsoft/Windows NT 4.0.; Classified Hardware – PC DISPLAY: Ad make-up applications – QPS/QuarkXPress, Multi-Ad/Creator.; Display Hardware – 2-APP/Mac G3; Display Printers – APP/Mac 8500, ECR/VRL 36; Production Equipment – 1-WL/30B, ECR/VRL 36; Cameras – 1-K/N243, 1-C/Newspager. PRESSROOM: Line 1 – 12-Urbinite; Folders – 2-Urbinite. MAILROOM: Counter stackers – 2-Quipp/401; Inserters and stuffers – 1-HI/NP 1372; Bundle tying machines – MLN/ML2EE, 1/Power Strap/TS2504.

POINT PLEASANT

POINT PLEASANT REGISTER

200 Main St., Point Pleasant, W.Va., 25550; gen tel (304) 675-1333; gen fax (304) 675-5234; ed e-mail news@mydailyregister.com; web site www.mydailyregister.com
Published: Mon, Tues, Wed, Thur, Fri, Sat
Weekday Frequency: e
Circulation: 3,918; 3,918(sat)
Last Audit: September 30, 2006
Price: 1.60/wk; 6.50/mo; 103.90/yr.
Advertising: Open inch rate $9.95
News services: AP.
Politics: Independent.
Note: Printed at the Gallipolis (OH) Daily Tribune. For pressroom information, see the Gallipolis Daily Tribune listing.
Not Published: New Year; Memorial Day; Labor Day; Thanksgiving; Christmas.
Special Weekly Sections: Church Page (Fri); Farm Page (S).
Pub. ....Dan Goodrich
Gen. Mgr. ....Pam Caldwell
Circ. Mgr. ....David Lucas
Ed. ....Andrew Carter
Sports Ed. ....Larry Crum
Market Information: TMC.
Mechanical available: Offset; Black and 3 ROP colors; insert accepted; page cutoffs - 21 1/4.
Mechanical Specifications: Type page 13 x 21 1/4; E - 6 cols, 2 1/16, 1/8 between; A - 6 cols, 2 1/16, 1/8 between; C - 8 cols, 1 1/2, 1/8 between.
Commodity Consumption: Avg. Page Number Per Issue - Daily 14; widths 13 3/4; Newsprint Used - Short Tons 202.
Equipment EDITORIAL: Front-end Software – Baseview.; Editorial Hardware – APP/Mac Quadra 650, APP/Mac Quadra 610; Editorial Printers – APP/Mac LaserWriter Pro CLASSIFIED: Front-end Software – Baseview.; Classified Hardware – APP/Mac; Production Equipment – Caere/OmniPage; Scanners – HP/ScanJet Plus.; Business Hardware – IBM, IBM/AS-400

WEIRTON

WEIRTON DAILY TIMES

114 Lee Ave, Weirton, W.Va., 26062-4619; gen tel (304) 748-0610; web site www.weirtondailytimes.com/
Group: Nutting Newspapers
Published: Mon, Tues, Wed, Thur, Fri, Sat, Sun
Weekday Frequency: e
Saturday Frequency: e
Circulation: 4,483; 4,753(sun)
Last Audit: ABC September 30, 2011

WHEELING

THE INTELLIGENCER/WHEELING NEWS-REGISTER

1500 Main St., Wheeling, W.Va., 26003; gen tel (304) 233-0100; adv tel (304) 233-0100; ed tel (304) 233-0100; gen fax (304) 233-0327; adv fax (304) 233-0327; ed fax (304) 232-1399; gen e-mail pnardo@theintelligencer.net; web site www.news-register.net; www.theintelligencer.net
Published: Mon, Tues, Wed, Thur, Fri, Sun
Weekday Frequency: e
Circulation: 10,547; 27,155(sat); 31,964(sun)
Last Audit: ABC September 30, 2011
Price: 2.25/wk; 9.00/mo; 127.40/yr.
Advertising: Open inch rate $30.91
News services: AP.
Not Published: New Year; Memorial Day; Independence Day; Labor Day; Thanksgiving; Christmas (News-Register).
Special Editions: Home Improvement (Apr); Football (Aug); Bride (Feb); Car Care (Mar); NASCAR (Monthly); Recipe Cookbook (Nov); Car Care (Sept).
Special Weekly Sections: Entertainment (TGIF) (Fri); NFL Report (Football Season) (Mon).
Magazines: TV Book (own, local, newsprint) (S).
Pub. ....G. Ogden Nutting
Gen. Mgr. ....Perry A. Nardo
Controller ....Charles Deremer
Adv. Mgr., Classified ....Shelly Higgins
Adv. Mgr., Retail ....Pam Bennett
Adv. Telemarketing ....Crystal Coffield
Circ. Dir. ....Gregg Pohl
Bus./Finance Ed. ....John McCabe
City Ed., News-Register ....Chip Warren
Editorial Page Ed., News-Register J. Michael Myer
Entertainment Ed. ....Betsy Bethel
Features Ed. ....Linda Comins
Food/Women's Ed. ....Phyllis Sigal
News Ed., Intelligencer ....Christina Myer
News Ed., News-Register ....Jacque Bland
Online Ed. ....Mike Goddard
Market Information: ADS; Split run; TMC; Zoned editions.
Mechanical available: Offset; Black and 3 ROP colors; insert accepted; page cutoffs - 23 9/16.
Mechanical Specifications: Type page 13 x 22; E - 6 cols, 2 1/16, 1/8 between; A - 6 cols, 2 1/16, 1/8 between; C - 8 cols, 1 9/16, 1/16 between.
Commodity Consumption: Avg. Page Number Per Issue - Daily 24; Avg. Page Number Per Issue - Plates Used 67500; Avg. Page Number Per Issue - Sunday 54; widths 27; Newsprint Used - Short Tons 6000; Printing Ink Used - Black 130500; Printing Ink Used - Color 27000.
Equipment EDITORIAL: Front-end Software – Microsoft/Windows NT.; Editorial Hardware – PC CLASSIFIED: Front-end Software – Microsoft/Windows NT.; Classified Hardware – PC DISPLAY: Ad make-up applications – QPS/QuarkXPress 3.31, Adobe/Photoshop 3.05, Multi-Ad/Creator 3.7, AP AdSend; Layout Software – APP/Mac, Multi-Ad/Creator; Display Hardware – 4-APP/Mac G3, 2-Konica/Knock Out Imagesetter; Display Printers – 2-Konica/Knock Out Imagesetter PRODUCTION: Pagination Software – QPS/QuarkXPress 3.31.; Production Equipment – 2-APP/Mac LaserWriter NTX, 2-MON/1270 Imagesetter, 2-Konica/4550 Imagesetters; Cameras – 1-C/Pager, 1-AG/2024; Scanners – HP IIci, Kk/RFS-2035, Nikon/Coolscan, Umax PRESSROOM: Line 1 – 4-G/Mark I (offset) 1984; Line 2 – 2-PEC/Eagle (3 color ink) 1984; Press Drives – PEC/Bond. MAILROOM: Counter stackers – 2-HL/Monitor, 1-HL/HI II; Inserters and stuffers – S/1372; Bundle tying machines – 2-MLN/2EE, 1-MLN/2, 1-MLN/2A; Wrapping singles – Sa; Addressing machine – Ch. BUSINESS COMPUTERS: Business Software – In house; Business Hardware – NCR S20

THE OGDEN NEWSPAPERS, INC.

1500 Main St., Wheeling, W.Va., 26003; gen tel (304) 233-0100; gen fax (304) 233-9397; gen e-mail myer@news-register.net; web site www.oweb.com
Published: Mon, Tues, Wed, Thur, Fri, Sat, Sun
Price: 127.40/yr.
Advertising: Open inch rate $165.96
Politics: 1800
Chrmn ....G. Ogden Nutting
Pres./CEO ....Robert M. Nutting
Vice Pres./Bus. Mgr. ....William O. Nutting
Vice Pres. ....William C. Nutting
Treasurer/CFO ....Duane D. Wittman

WILLIAMSON

WILLIAMSON DAILY NEWS

100 E. 3rd Ave., Williamson, W.Va., 25661; gen tel (304) 235-4242; gen fax (304) 235-0730; gen e-mail rvarney@msmgmt.com; adv e-mail rkessler@msmgmt.com; web site www.williamsondailynews.com
Published: Mon, Tues, Wed, Thur, Fri, Sat, Sun
Weekday Frequency: m
Saturday Frequency: m
Circulation: 8,028; 8,028(sat); 8,028(sun)
Last Audit: October 6, 2004
Price: 160.28/yr; 37.44/3mo, $68.64/6mo.
Advertising: Open inch rate $10.25
News services: AP.
Politics: Independent. **Established:** 1912
Not Published: New Year; Memorial Day; Independence Day; Labor Day; Thanksgiving; Christmas.
Special Editions: Visitor's Guide (Jun); Golden News (Monthly); Red Ribbon Salute (Oct); Bride's Guide (Semi-yearly).
Special Weekly Sections: Sports Preview (6/8 pgs broad, Sept-Nov) (Weekly).
Magazines: Golden News (Monthly); Parade (S).
Broadcast Affiliations: WXCC 96.5 FM.
Pres./Pub. ....D. Gaither Perry
Bus. Mgr. ....Raitchell Lipps
Mgr., Mktg./Promo ....Drew Martin
Circ. Mgr. ....Chad Whitt
Science Ed. ....Loretta Tackett
Prodn. Foreman, Composing ....Clifford Marcum
Market Information: ADS; TMC.
Mechanical available: Offset; Black and 3 ROP colors; insert accepted - single sheets, envelopes, samples; page cutoffs - 21 1/2.
Mechanical Specifications: Type page 13 x 21 3/4; E - 6 cols, 1 5/6, 1/8 between; A - 6 cols, 1 5/6, 1/8 between; C - 9 cols, between.
Commodity Consumption: Avg. Page Number Per Issue - Daily 24; widths 25; Newsprint Used - Short Tons 4.5.
Equipment EDITORIAL: Front-end Software – Baseview.; Editorial Hardware – Server; Editorial Printers – 3-APP/Mac LaserWriter 16-600 PS CLASSIFIED: Front-end Software – APP/Mac Pro, APP/Mac Class Pro.; Classified Hardware – Server; Classified Printers – APP/Mac LaserWriter 16-600PS DISPLAY: Ad make-up applications – QPS/QuarkXPress 3.32, Adobe/Freehand 5.0, Adobe/Photoshop 4.0; Layout Software – APP/Power Mac 9500.; Display Printers – AG/Accuset, Star/400 RIP, APP/Mac LaserWriter 16-600 PS PRODUCTION: Pagination Software – QPS/QuarkXPress 3.32.; Production Equipment – 2-COM/Unisetters, AG/Accuset, Star/400 RIP; Cameras – 1-B/24x24, 1-DAI/24x24; Scanners – Nikon/Coolscan, AG/Arcus Flatbed PRESSROOM: Line 1 – 6-KP/Daily King. MAILROOM: Counter stackers – 1/BG; Inserters and stuffers – 4-DG/320; Bundle tying machines – 1-Bu/42409; Addressing machine – 1-/Am, 1-/KR.; Business Hardware – Solomon/PC

WISCONSIN

ANTIGO

ANTIGO DAILY JOURNAL

612 Superior St., Antigo, Wis., 54409 -2049; gen tel (715) 623-4191; adv tel (715) 623-4191; ed tel (715) 623-4191; gen fax (715) 623-4193; adv fax (715) 623-4193; ed fax (715) 623-4193; gen e-mail adj@dwave.net; adv e-mail adj@dwave.net; ed e-mail adj@dwave.net; web site www.antigodailyjournal.com
Published: Mon, Tues, Wed, Thur, Fri, Sat
Weekday Frequency: e
Saturday Frequency: m
Circulation: 5,660; 5,760(sat)
Last Audit: Sworn March 24, 2010
Price: 89.75/yr.
Advertising: Open inch rate $6.45
Insert rate: Varies by weight and quantity; contact us.
News services: AP
Politics: 1905
Not Published: Sundays and Legal Holidays
Own facility?: Y
Special Editions: Impressions (Jan.); Bridal Guide (Feb.); Fitness & Health (march); Spring Home & Garden (April); Graduation (May); Market Street Fest (June); 4-H Youth Fair Days (July); Back to Back-to-School (Aug.); Northwoods Recreation (Sept.); Holiday Recipes (Nov.); Christmas Magazine (Nov.)
Special Weekly Sections: School (Tues.); Around Town (Thurs.); Farm (Fri.); Church (Fri.); TV Listings (Sat.)
Pub. ....Marie Berner
Ed. ....Fred A. Berner
Reporter ....Debbie Igl
Teen-Age/Youth Ed. ....Lisa Haefs
Pressman ....Allan Gelhausen
Market Information: TMC.
Mechanical available: Offset; Black and 3 ROP colors; insert accepted; page cutoffs - 22 3/4.
Mechanical Specifications: Type page 11.625 x 21; E - 6 cols, 1 13/16, 1/8 between; A - 6 cols, 1 13/16, 1/8 between; C - 6 cols, 1 3/8, 1/16 between.
Commodity Consumption: 18
Equipment EDITORIAL: Front-end Software – Baseview.; Editorial Hardware – Mac; Editorial Printers – HP CLASSIFIED: Front-end Software – Baseview.; Classified Hardware – Mac; Classified Printers – HP; Display Hardware – MAC; Display Printers – HP PRODUCTION: Pagination Software – QuarkXpress, Adobe Photoshop; Production Equipment – Mac; Scanners – HP, Epson PRESSROOM: Line 1 – 5-G/Community.; Inserters and stuffers – KAN; Bundle tying machines – 1/Bu; Addressing machine – Stepper; Business Hardware – PC/Business Mac/Production
Delivery method: Mail, Newsstand, Private Carrier, Racks

APPLETON

POST CRESCENT

306 W. Washington St., Appleton, Wis., 54911; gen tel 920-733-4411; web site www.postcrescent.com
Published: Mon, Tues, Wed, Thur, Fri, Sat, Sun
Weekday Frequency: m
Circulation: 38,421; 45,799(sat); 56,095(sun)
Last Audit: ABC September 30, 2011

THE POST-CRESCENT

306 W. Washington St., Appleton, Wis., 54911-5452; gen tel (920) 993-1000; adv tel (920) 993-1000; ed tel (920) 993-1000; gen fax (920) 954-1945; adv fax (920) 954-1945; ed fax (920) 733-1945; gen e-mail pc-

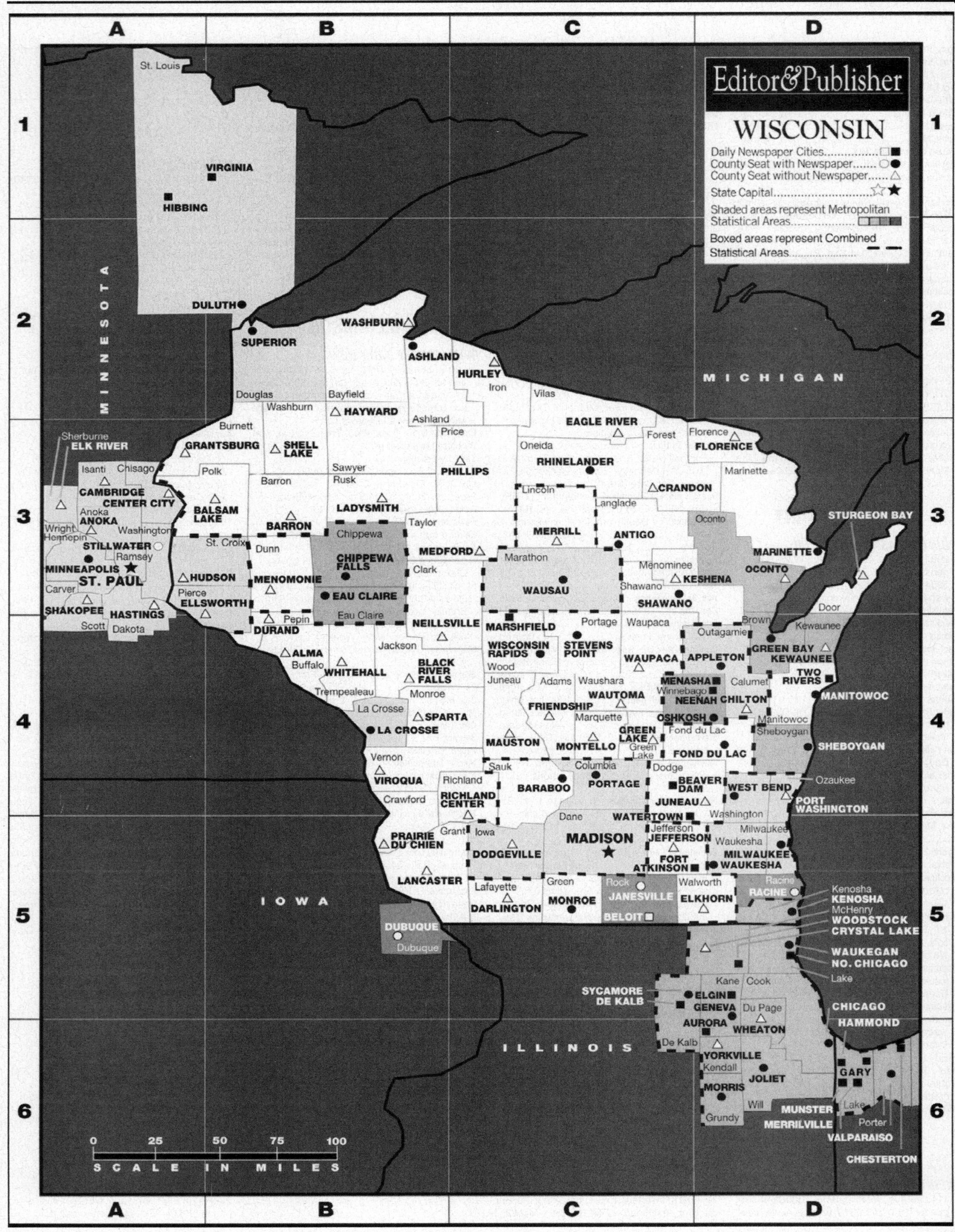

Editor&Publisher
WISCONSIN
Daily Newspaper Cities
County Seat with Newspaper
County Seat without Newspaper
State Capital
Shaded areas represent Metropolitan Statistical Areas
Boxed areas represent Combined Statistical Areas
MINNESOTA
MICHIGAN
IOWA
ILLINOIS
VIRGINIA
HIBBING
DULUTH
SUPERIOR
WASHBURN
ASHLAND
HURLEY
HAYWARD
EAGLE RIVER
GRANTSBURG
SHELL LAKE
PHILLIPS
RHINELANDER
FLORENCE
CRANDON
ELK RIVER
CAMBRIDGE
CENTER CITY
ANOKA
BALSAM LAKE
LADYSMITH
BARRON
MERRILL
ANTIGO
STURGEON BAY
STILLWATER
MINNEAPOLIS
ST. PAUL
HUDSON
MENOMONIE
CHIPPEWA FALLS
EAU CLAIRE
MEDFORD
WAUSAU
MARINETTE
OCONTO
KESHENA
SHAWANO
SHAKOPEE
HASTINGS
ELLSWORTH
DURAND
NEILLSVILLE
MARSHFIELD
ALMA
WHITEHALL
BLACK RIVER FALLS
WISCONSIN RAPIDS
STEVENS POINT
WAUPACA
APPLETON
GREEN BAY
KEWAUNEE
MENASHA
NEENAH
TWO RIVERS
CHILTON
MANITOWOC
WAUTOMA
FRIENDSHIP
OSHKOSH
SPARTA
LA CROSSE
MAUSTON
MONTELLO
GREEN LAKE
FOND DU LAC
SHEBOYGAN
VIROQUA
BARABOO
PORTAGE
BEAVER DAM
WEST BEND
RICHLAND CENTER
JUNEAU
PORT WASHINGTON
WATERTOWN
PRAIRIE DU CHIEN
DODGEVILLE
MADISON
JEFFERSON
FORT ATKINSON
MILWAUKEE
WAUKESHA
LANCASTER
DARLINGTON
MONROE
JANESVILLE
BELOIT
ELKHORN
RACINE
KENOSHA
WOODSTOCK
CRYSTAL LAKE
WAUKEGAN
NO. CHICAGO
DUBUQUE
SYCAMORE
DE KALB
ELGIN
GENEVA
AURORA
WHEATON
CHICAGO
HAMMOND
YORKVILLE
JOLIET
GARY
MORRIS
MUNSTER
MERRILLVILLE
VALPARAISO
CHESTERTON
0 25 50 75 100
SCALE IN MILES

news@postcrescent.com; adv e-mail pcads@appleton.gannett.com; ed e-mail pc-news@postcrescent.com; web site www.postcrescent.com
Published: Mon, Tues, Wed, Thur, Fri, Sat, Sun
Saturday Frequency: m
Circulation: 42,085; 47,582(sat); 57,469(sun)
Price: 3.85/wk; 200.20/yr (carrier), $378.29/yr (mail).
Advertising: Open inch rate $79.10
News services: MCT, Landon Media Group, AP, SHNS, Gannett.
Politics: Independent. **Established:** 1853
Special Editions: Vacation & Travel (Apr); Fall Home Improvement (Aug); Winter Wonderland of Homes (Jan); EAA (Jul); Fall Brides (Jun); American Dream Home Show (Mar); Wisconsin Recreation (May); Gift Guide I (Nov); Fall Home Improvement (Oct); Parade of Homes (Sept).
Special Weekly Sections: Packers Preview (Fri); Business (Mon); Color Comics (S); Home (Sat); Encore Entertainment (Thur); Food (Wed).
Magazines: USA WEEKEND Magazine (S).
Pres./Pub. ....Genia Lovett
Vice Pres., Finance ....Mike Seeber
Mktg. Dir. ....Melinda Vonderahe
Circ. Dir. ....Joe Braunschweig
Exec. Ed. ....Dan Flannery
Mng. Ed. ....Jamie Mara
Bus. Ed. ....Larry Avila
Community Conversation Sr. Ed. ....Larry Gallup
Custom Publishing Sr. Ed. ....Ed Berthiaume
Custom Publishing Asst. Ed. ....Julie Gilkay
Digital Opns. Ed. ....Terry Lipshetz
Librarian ....Denise Wagner
Multimedia Sr. Ed. ....Dwight Nale
Print Opns. Ed. ....Dan Roherty
School Ed. ....Kathy Nufer
Asst. Sports Ed. ....Dan VanderPas
Vice President Gannett Wisconsin Media Steve Broas
Adv. Dir. ....Paul Gaier
Adv. Dir., Grp. Majors ....John Rowe
Religion Ed. ....Cheryl Sherry
Market Information: ADS; TMC; Zoned editions.
Mechanical available: Offset; Black and 3 ROP colors; insert accepted; page cutoffs - 21 1/2.
Mechanical Specifications: Type page 11 1/8 x 20 5/8; E - 6 cols, 1 3/4, 1/8 between; A - 6 cols, 1 3/4, 1/8 between; C - 10 cols, 1 1/20, 1/8 between.
Commodity Consumption: Avg. Page Number Per Issue - Daily 44; Avg. Page Number Per Issue - Plates Used 143520; Avg. Page Number Per Issue - Saturday 56; Avg. Page Number Per Issue - Sunday 96; widths 12 1/2; Newsprint Used - Short Tons 5000; Printing Ink Used - Black 100000; P
Equipment EDITORIAL: Front-end Software – Atex Prestige 4.2.1.0.; Editorial Hardware – Microsoft/Windows NT-95-2000; Editorial Equipment – 4-Pre Press/Panther Pro 46 Imagesetter, 2-AG; Editorial Printers – HP/4MV, HP/5000, HP/8000 CLASSIFIED: Front-end Software – Harris Ad Power 2.1.337.36.; Classified Hardware – Microsoft/Windows NT-95-2000; Classified Equipment – 4-Pre Press/Panther Pro 46 Imagesetter, AG/Polaris; Classified Printers – HP/4MV DISPLAY: Ad make-up applications – QPS/QuarkXPress 4.0; Layout Software – MEI/ALS.; Display Hardware – APP/Power Mac, APP/Mac G3; Display Printers – HP/4MV, HP/5000 PRODUCTION: Pagination Software – QPS/QuarkXPress, Classified Pagination Software, Harris-Ad Pagination 3.5.16.10.; Production Equipment – AG/Polaris; Line 2 – 8 (32 Couples)-2000; Line 3 – 8 (32 Couples)-2000; Folders – 3; Press registration system – Prazision/Comet EP. MAILROOM: Counter stackers – 8-Compass/180; Inserters and stuffers – 3-Printroll/GMA; Bundle tying machines – 7/Strapmaster; Wrapping singles – 3-Dynaric/D2100; Mailroom control system – GMA; Other equipment –MM Stitches/Trimmer. BUSINESS COMPUTERS: Business Software – Microsoft/Windows 95,98,00, Compaq/proline 6000 NT, Dell; Business Hardware – PBS, 2-HP-Unix, Genesys, IBM AS400

ASHLAND

THE DAILY PRESS

122 W. Third St., Ashland, Wis., 54806; gen tel (715) 682-2313; gen fax (715) 682-4699; gen e-mail pressnews@ashlanddailypress.net; web site www.ashlandwi.com
Published: Mon, Tues, Wed, Thur, Fri, Sat
Weekday Frequency: m
Circulation: 6,153; 6,153(sat)
Last Audit: September 30, 2006
Price: 15.00/mo (carrier); 120.00/yr.
Advertising: Open inch rate $12.00
News services: AP.
Politics: Independent.
Not Published: New Year; Memorial Day; Independence Day; Labor Day; Thanksgiving; Christmas.
Special Editions: Spring Car Care & Home Improvement (Apr); Bayfield County Fair Tab (Aug); Songs of Christmas/Gift Guide & Holiday Greetings (Dec); Valentine's Day Gift Tab (Feb); Super Bowl Tab (Jan); Father's Day Gifts (Jun); Progress (Mar); Graduation Gift Guides (May)
Magazines: Relish (Monthly); American Profile (Weekly).
Pub. ....Gary Pennington
Adv. Dir ....Garyx Pennington
Adv. ....Jeff Swiston
Circ. Mgr. ....Linda Olson
Mng. Ed. ....Clair S. Duquette
Mgmt. Info Servs. Dir. ....Robert Bischoff
Prodn. Supt. ....Todd Juoni
Market Information: Split run.
Mechanical available: Offset; Black and 3 ROP colors; insert accepted; page cutoffs - 22 3/4.
Mechanical Specifications: Type page 11 5/8 x 21 1/2; E - 6 cols, 1 5/6, 1/8 between; A - 6 cols, 1 5/6, 1/8 between; C - 6 cols, 1 5/6, 1/8 between.
Commodity Consumption: Avg. Page Number Per Issue - Daily 16; widths 25; Newsprint Used - Metric Tons 291; Newsprint Used - Short Tons 495; Printing Ink Used - Black 17000; Printing Ink Used - Color 2400; Printing Ink Used - Pages Printed 5420.
Equipment; Editorial Hardware – APP/Mac.; Classified Hardware – APP/Mac.; Layout Software – APP/Mac. PRODUCTION: Pagination Software – Baseview.; Production Equipment – 1-NuArc/Flip Top; Cameras – AG/2200II, 1-B; Scanners – Microtek/E6 PRESSROOM: Line 1 – 8 (single width)-G/Community; Press Drives – HP/60 Motor; Folders – SC/Folder.; Bundle tying machines – 3/Bu. BUSINESS COMPUTERS: Business Software – Quickbooks 5.0; Business Hardware – 2-RSK/12, 2-RSK/3000 HD, APP/Power Mac

BARABOO

BARABOO NEWS-REPUBLIC

714 Matts Ferry Rd., Baraboo, Wis., 53913-0009; gen tel (608) 356-4808; adv tel (608) 745-3800; ed tel (608) 356-4808; gen fax (608) 356-0344; gen e-mail bnr-news@capitalnewspapers.com; ed e-mail bnr-editorial@capitalnewspapers.com; web site www.wiscnews.com/bnr
Group: Metro Suburbia, Inc./Newhouse Newspapers
Lee Enterprises
Published: Mon, Tues, Wed, Thur, Fri, Sat
Weekday Frequency: m
Saturday Frequency: m
Circulation: 3,780; 3,780(sat)
Price: 113.60/yr.
Advertising: Open inch rate $29.20
News services: AP.
Not Published: New Year; Memorial Day; Independence Day; Labor Day; Christmas.
Own facility?: Y
Magazines: Relish (Monthly); Parade (Sat); American Profile (Weekly).
Pub. ....George Althoff
Adv. Dir. ....Julie Brown
Circ. Dir. ....Teresa Klinger
Asst. Ed. ....Andrew Analore
Feature Ed. ....Ben Bromley
Sports Ed. ....Pete Watson
Prodn. Mgr., Mailroom ....Nancy Preston
General Manager ....Matt Meyers
Market Information: TMC.
Mechanical available: Offset; Black and 3 ROP colors; insert accepted; page cutoffs - 21 3/4.
Mechanical Specifications: Type page 13 x 21 1/2; E - 6 cols, 1 7/8, 1/8 between; A - 6 cols, 1 7/8, 1/8 between; C - 9 cols, 1 3/16, 1/8 between.
Commodity Consumption: Avg. Page Number Per Issue - Daily 14; Avg. Page Number Per Issue - Plates Used 14; widths 34; Newsprint Used - Short Tons 200; Printing Ink Used - Black 800.
Equipment EDITORIAL: Front-end Software – Baseview. CLASSIFIED: Front-end Software – Baseview.; Display Printers – APP/Mac LaserPrinter. PRODUCTION: Pagination Software – QPS/QuarkXPress 4.0.; Production Equipment – 2-Nu; Cameras – B/Vertical; Scanners – 3-COM/2961HS, 1-COM/7200, 1-COM/4 PRESSROOM: Line 1 – 12-G/Community 1998. MAILROOM: Counter stackers – 1/MM; Inserters and stuffers – 2-KAN/8; Bundle tying machines – 1-/Bu; Addressing machine – VideoJet.; Business Hardware – SMS

BEAVER DAM

DAILY CITIZEN

805 Park Ave., Beaver Dam, Wis., 53916-0558; gen tel (920) 887-0321; adv tel (920) 887-0321; ed tel (920) 887-0321; gen fax (920) 887-8790; adv fax (920) 887-8790; ed fax (920) 887-8790; adv e-mail dc-ads@capitalnewspapers.com; ed e-mail dc-news@capitalnewspapers.com; web site www.wiscnews.com
Group: U.S. Suburban Press, Inc.
Published: Mon, Tues, Wed, Thur, Fri, Sat
Weekday Frequency: All day
Saturday Frequency: All day
Circulation: 8,365; 9,978(sat)
Last Audit: ABC September 30, 2011
Price: 143.00/yr.
Advertising: Open inch rate $14.82
News services: AP, NYT.
Politics: Independent.
Not Published: New Year; Memorial Day; Independence Day; Labor Day; Thanksgiving; Christmas.
Magazines: Relish (Monthly); USA WEEKEND Magazine (Sat); American Profile (Weekly).
General Manager ....Scott Zeinemann
Circ. Dir. ....Teresa Klinger
Ed. ....Aaron Holbrook
Pub. ....James Kelsh
Editorial Page Ed. ....Jim Kelsh
Market Information: TMC; Zoned editions.
Mechanical available: Offset; Black and 3 ROP colors; insert accepted; page cutoffs - 22 3/4.
Mechanical Specifications: Type page 15 1/4 x 21 3/8; E - 6 cols, 2 1/16, 1/8 between; A - 8 cols, 1 9/16, 1/8 between; C - 8 cols, 1 3/8, 1/16 between.
Commodity Consumption: Avg. Page Number Per Issue - Daily 16; Avg. Page Number Per Issue - Plates Used 2626; Avg. Page Number Per Issue - Saturday 24; widths 29; Newsprint Used - Short Tons 379; Printing Ink Used - Black 5116; Printing Ink Used - Color 1010; Printing Ink Used
Equipment EDITORIAL: Front-end Software – Concept.; Editorial Hardware – 2-APP/Mac Plus, 8-APP/Mac II; Classified Hardware – 3-APP/Mac II.; Layout Software – 5-APP/Mac II. PRODUCTION: Pagination Software – Concept.; Production Equipment – 1-Nu/Flip Top FT40LNS, 1-Nu/Flip Top FT40UPNS; Cameras – 1-B/Commodore PRESSROOM: Line 1 – 12-G/Community; Line 2 – 20-G/Community; Folders – 5-G/Community; Pasters – 7-MEG. MAILROOM: Counter stackers – 5-BG/Count-O-Veyor 104-108; Inserters and stuffers – 4-MM/227E, 6-MM/227; Bundle tying machines – 4/Bu, 1-/CYP; Addressing machine – 2-/Am, 1-/Kk.; Business Hardware – 10-IBM/PS2, 6-APP/Mac II

BELOIT

BELOIT DAILY NEWS

149 State St., Beloit, Wis., 53511-6251; gen tel (608) 365-8811; gen fax (608) 365-1420; gen e-mail dbehling@beloitdailynews.com; adv e-mail abackus@beloitdailynews.com; ed e-mail bbarth@beloitdailynews.com; web site www.beloitdailynews.com
Group: The Hagadone Corporation
Published: Mon, Tues, Wed, Thur, Fri, Sat
Weekday Frequency: e
Saturday Frequency: m
Circulation: 11,489
Last Audit: Sworn October 5, 2001
Price: 149.50/yr (carrier), $169.00/yr (mail/motor route).
Advertising: Open inch rate $29.92
Insert rate: Single sheet - $52 cpm (net)
News services: AP, United Media Service.
Politics: Independent. **Established:** 1848
Not Published: New Year; Memorial Day; Independence Day; Labor Day; Thanksgiving; Christmas.
Own facility?: Y
Special Editions: Progress (Mar); Map/Guide (May).
Special Weekly Sections: Your Home (Fri); Step n Out (Thur).
Magazines: USA WEEKEND Magazine (Sat).
Pub. ....Kent D. Eymann
City Ed. ....Clint Wolf
Editorial Page Ed. ....Bill Barth
Features Ed. ....Debra Jensen Dehart
Sports Ed. ....James Franz
Prodn. Mgr., Post Press ....Dave Shaw
Prodn. Mgr., Pre Press ....Don Behling
Prodn. Mgr., Pressroom ....Tim Sager
Business Manager ....Sherry Roach
Market Information: Split run; TMC.
Mechanical available: Offset; Black and 3 ROP colors; insert accepted; page cutoffs - 21 1/2.
Mechanical Specifications: Type page 11 5/8 x 21 1/2; E - 6 cols, 1 5/6, 1/8 between; A - 6 cols, 1 5/6, 1/8 between; C - 8 cols, 1 9/25, 1/8 between.
Commodity Consumption: Avg. Page Number Per Issue - Daily 24; Avg. Page Number Per Issue - Plates Used 12000; widths 25; Newsprint Used - Short Tons 650; Printing Ink Used - Black 9800; Printing Ink Used - Color 3000; Printing Ink Used - Pages Printed 7444.
Equipment EDITORIAL: Front-end Software – News Edit and DTI; Editorial Hardware – Mac; Editorial Equipment – Mac; Editorial Printers – HP CLASSIFIED: Front-end Software – DTI; Classified Hardware – Mac; Classified Equipment – Mac; Classified Printers – OTC/850X2 DISPLAY: Ad make-up applications – Multi-Ad/Creator, Indesign; Display Hardware – Mac; Display Printers – HP, Toshiba PRODUCTION: Pagination Software – DTI; Production Equipment – Mac computers, ECRM CTP plate setter.; Cameras – None; Scanners – Dest top PRESSROOM: Line 1 – 6-G/Urbanite; Folders – 1-G/2:1.; Inserters and stuffers – MM/227 5:1; Bundle tying machines – 1-MLN/Plastic Strap. BUSINESS COMPUTERS: Business Software – Micro/VMS 5.1; Business Hardware – 1-DEC/TC 3800
Zip Codes served: 53511,53525,61080,61072,61073
Delivery method: Mail, Newsstand, Private Carrier, Racks

GREATER BELOIT PUBLISHING CO., INC.

149 State St., Beloit, Wis., 53511; gen tel (608) 365-8811; gen fax (608) 365-1420
Price: 143.00/yr.
Advertising: Open inch rate $27.00
Politics: 1848

CHIPPEWA FALLS

THE CHIPPEWA HERALD

321 Frenette Dr., Chippewa Falls, Wis., 54729-0069; gen tel (715) 723-5515; adv tel (715) 723-5515; ed tel (715) 723-5515; gen fax (715) 723-9644; adv fax (715) 723-9644; ed fax (715) 723-9644; gen e-mail publisher@chippewa.com; adv e-mail advertising@chippewa.com; ed e-mail news@chippewa.com; web site www.chippewa.com; www.chippewavalleynewspapers.com

Group: Lee Enterprises
Published: Mon, Tues, Wed, Thur, Sat, Sun
Weekday Frequency: m
Saturday Frequency: m
Circulation: 5,388; 5,936(sat); 5,462(sun)
Last Audit: ABC September 30, 2011
Price: 12.50/mo; 132.00/yr.
Advertising: Open inch rate $14.91
News services: AP, DJ, TMS.
Politics: Independent. **Established:** 1870
Not Published: New Year; Memorial Day; Independence Day; Labor Day; Christmas.
Special Editions: Home Improvement (Apr); Chippewa Valley Business Report (Quarterly).
Special Weekly Sections: Wall Street Journal Sunday (S).
Magazines: Parade (S).
Circ. District Mgr. ....Adam Polden
Community Ed. ....Candice White
Editor....................Ross Evavold
Prodn. Mgr. ....Joe Webb
Business editor ....Mark Gunderman
advertising director ....Brian Maki
sports editor ....Brandon Berg
Market Information: ADS; TMC.
Mechanical available: Offset; Black and 3 ROP colors; insert accepted - any; page cutoffs - 21 1/2.
Mechanical Specifications: Type page 12 1/2 x 21 1/2; E - 6 cols, 2 1/16, 1/8 between; A - 6 cols, 2 1/16, 1/8 between; C - 6 cols, 2 1/16, 1/8 between.
Commodity Consumption: Avg. Page Number Per Issue - Daily 16; Avg. Page Number Per Issue - Sunday 24; widths 25; Newsprint Used - Metric Tons 1200.
Equipment EDITORIAL: Front-end Software – Baseview.; Editorial Hardware – APP/Power Macs; Editorial Equipment – Nikon/Coolscan; Editorial Printers – APP/Mac LaserPrinter CLASSIFIED: Front-end Software – APT.; Classified Hardware – Gateway DISPLAY: Ad makeup applications – Multi-Ad/Creator, QPS/QuarkXPress; Layout Software – 2-APP/Mac, APP/Power Mac. PRODUCTION: Pagination Software – QPS/QuarkXPress.; Production Equipment – 2-COM/Laserwriter, Pre Press/Panther Pro; Cameras – SCREEN; Scanners – HP/ScanJet Plus, 2-Nikon/Coolscan PRESSROOM: Line 1 – G/4-hi, 2-DEV/Flexicolor; Folders – 4-G/2:1. MAILROOM: Counter stackers – 2/BG; Inserters and stuffers – USA/Leader; Bundle tying machines – 2-/Bu, 1-/It; Addressing machine – KR.

CHIPPEWA PUBLISHING CO., INC.

321 Frenette Dr., Chippewa Falls, Wis., 54729; gen tel (715) 723-5515; gen fax (715) 723-9644

Price: 132.00/yr.
Advertising: Open inch rate $14.61
Politics: 1870

EAU CLAIRE

LEADER-TELEGRAM

701 S. Farwell St., Eau Claire, Wis., 54701-3831; gen tel (715) 833-9200; adv tel (715) 833-7420; ed tel (715) 833-9203; gen fax (715) 833-9244; adv fax (715) 833-9244; ed fax (715) 858-7308; gen e-mail leadertelegram@cvol.net; web site www.leadertelegram.com

Published: Mon, Tues, Wed, Thur, Fri, Sat, Sun
Weekday Frequency: m
Saturday Frequency: m
Circulation: 23,370; 25,453(sat); 30,109(sun)
Last Audit: ABC September 30, 2011
Price: 3.30/wk; 13.20/mo (carrier); 169.00/yr.
Advertising: Open inch rate $34.70
News services: AP, SHNS, MCT.
Politics: Independent. **Established:** 1912
Not Published: Christmas; New Year.
Special Editions: Impressions (Quarterly).
Special Weekly Sections: Outdoors (Fri); Senior (Mon); Arts/Entertainment (S); Home & Garden (Sat); Expanded Entertainment (Thur); Best Food Day (Tues).
Magazines: USA WEEKEND Magazine (Sat).
Broadcast Affiliations: WEAU (NBC); WQOW (ABC); WKBT (CBS); WEUX (Fox).
Pres./CEO....................Pieter Graaskamp
Adv. Dir.....................Daniel Graaskamp
Mgr., Retail Sales ....Cathy Hayden
Mktg. Mgr.....................Mike Carlson
Circ. Dir. ....Steve Svihovec
Circ./Promo. Mgr. ....Mark Haas
Ed. ....Don Huebscher
Editorial Page Ed. ....Tom Giffey
Food Ed. ....Blythe Wachter
Local Ed. ....Gary Johnson
Religion Ed.....................Alyssa Waters
Market Information: Split run; TMC.
Mechanical available: Offset; Black and ROP colors; insert accepted - all; page cutoffs - 22.
Mechanical Specifications: Type page 12 1/2 x 21; E - 6 cols, 1 13/16, 1/8 between; A - 6 cols, 1 13/16, 1/8 between; C - 9 cols, 1 3/16, 1/8 between.
Commodity Consumption: Avg. Page Number Per Issue - Daily 28; Avg. Page Number Per Issue - Plates Used 27000; Avg. Page Number Per Issue - Saturday 48; Avg. Page Number Per Issue - Sunday 56; widths 12 1/2; Newsprint Used - Short Tons 3000; Printing Ink Used - Black 33525; Pri
Equipment EDITORIAL: Front-end Software – Microsoft/Word, QPS/QuarkXPress 4.11rl, ATS/Mediadesk.; Editorial Hardware – 35-PC; Editorial Printers – Canon/BXII, HP/LS9700 CLASSIFIED: Front-end Software – Mactive.; Classified Hardware – 10-PC, Microsoft/Windows NT 4.0; Classified Printers – Canon/BX-II, HP/LJ 4ML DISPLAY: Ad make-up applications – Adobe/Illustrator, QPS/QuarkXPress, Adobe/Photoshop; Layout Software – Mactive.; Display Hardware – MS/NT PC 4.0 wka, 2-APP/Mac G3; Display Printers – 1-Canon/BX-II, Epson/Stylus Color 3000, 1-AGFA PRODUCTION: Pagination Software – QPS/QuarkXPress 4.11rl, Adobe/Illustrator 5.5,6.5.; Production Equipment – 1-AG/5000 Recorder, 1-AG/Phoenix 2250, 1-AG/Avatru 44; Cameras – 1-Liberator; Scanners – 2-Nikon, 2-Epson/Expressions 800XL PRESSROOM: Line 1 – 14-DGM/850 single width 1998; Folders – 1-G/Half, 1-G/Quarter. MAILROOM: Counter stackers – 2-QWI/350; Inserters and stuffers – 1-GMA/10:1; Bundle tying machines – 2/MLN; Wrapping singles – Mailroom control system □ GMA; Addressing machine – 2-/KR; Other equipment –MM. BUSINESS COMPUTERS: Business Software – Mactive; Business Hardware – 1-HP, 2-Dell Poweredge 6300, 1-Dell Poweredge 6400

FOND DU LAC

THE REPORTER

N 6637 Rolling Meadows Drive, Fond du Lac, Wis., 54937; gen tel (920) 922-4600; gen fax (920) 922-5388; adv fax (920) 922-3552; ed fax (920) 922-3552; gen e-mail treporter@fdlreporter.com; web site www.fdlreporter.com

Published: Mon, Tues, Wed, Thur, Fri, Sun
Weekday Frequency: e
Circulation: 10,355; 13,853(sun)
Last Audit: ABC September 30, 2011
Price: 3.25/wk (carrier); 13.00/mo, $6.60/mo (S); 182.00/yr (mail), $91.00/yr (S, mail); 14.00/4wk (mail).
Advertising: Open inch rate $55.40
News services: AP, GNS.
Politics: Independent. **Established:** 1870
Special Editions: Answer Book (Oct).
Special Weekly Sections: Go!/Entertainment (S); Automotive (Thur); Food (Wed).
Magazines: USA WEEKEND Magazine (S).
Mng. Ed.....................Michael Mentzer
Photo Dept. Mgr.....................Pat Flood
Sports Ed.....................Paul Keup
Market Information: ADS; TMC.
Mechanical available: Offset; Black and 3 ROP colors; insert accepted - Newspac; page cutoffs - 21 1/2.
Mechanical Specifications: Type page 11 5/8 x 21 1/2; E - 6 cols, 1 5/6, 1/8 between; A - 6 cols, 1 5/6, 1/8 between; C - 9 cols, 1 1/4, 1/16 between.
Equipment; Editorial Hardware – Atex/Pagination System; Editorial Printers – HP/P1180. CLASSIFIED: Front-end Software – Ad Power.; Classified Hardware – 1-HI DISPLAY: Ad make-up applications – Multi-Ad/Creator, Adobe/Illustrator, Aldus/Freehand, QPS/QuarkXPress; Layout Software – Ethernet, Appletalk/Network.; Display Hardware – APP/Mac II, APP/Mac IIcx, APP/Mac IIci, 5-APP/Power Mac; Display Printers – APP/Mac LaserWriter II, V/5060W, Tegra/Varityper Rm.3 PRODUCTION: Pagination Software – CText.; Production Equipment – LaserJet 4mv, Digital Darkroom, Adobe/Photoshop, V/Film Recorder; Cameras – Auto/Companica 690D; Scanners – AG/StudioScan PRESSROOM: Line 1 – 7-G/Urbanite single width 1977; Line 2 – 1-Ik/Sheet Fed Press 1992; Line 3 – 12-G/Urbanite; Line 4 – Feb-98; Line 5 – Aug-98; Line 6 – 7-G/Urbanite; Folders – 1-G/Half, 1-G/Quarter, 2-G/Folders-Half Width, 2-1998; Pasters – 8-Enkel/Auto Splicers MAILROOM: Counter stackers – HL/Monitor HT, 2/HL, 2-/MRS; Inserters and stuffers – 2-GMA/SLS 1000 2:12; Bundle tying machines – OVL, 2-/Samuel, 1-/Dynaric, 2-OVL/415; Wrapping singles – 2-/Samuel, 2-Id; Addressing machine – Video Jet/Ink Jet, Ch. BUSINESS COMPUTERS: Business Software – IBM; Business Hardware – ATT, Oracle

FORT ATKINSON

DAILY JEFFERSON COUNTY UNION

28 W. Milwaukee Ave., Fort Atkinson, Wis., 53538-2018; gen tel (920) 563-5553; adv tel (920) 563-5553; ed tel (920) 563-5553; gen fax (920) 563-2329; adv fax (920) 563-2329; ed fax (920) 563-2329; gen e-mail dailyunion@dailyunion.com; web site www.dailyunion.com

Published: Mon, Tues, Wed, Thur, Fri
Weekday Frequency: e
Circulation: 8,000
Last Audit: Sworn September 28, 2001
Price: 95.00/yr.
Advertising: Open inch rate $12.65
Insert rate: 55/m
News services: AP.
Politics: Independent-Republican. **Established:** 1870
Advertising not accepted: Y
Not Published: New Year; Memorial Day; Independence Day; Labor Day; Thanksgiving; Christmas.
Own facility?: Y
Special Editions: Home Improvement (Apr); Health (Aug); Christmas (Dec); Health (Feb); Money Matters (Jan); Outdoor Recreation (Jun); Bridal (Mar); Health (May); Health (Nov); Car Care (Oct); Home Improvement (Sept).
Magazines: American Profile (Weekly).
Pres./Pub. ....Brian V. Knox
Mktg. Dir. ....Diane Niemeyer
Circ. Dir. ....Jim Furle
Farm Ed.....................Randall Dullum
Features Ed.....................Christine Spangler
News Ed. ....Randall Dullam
Sports Ed.....................Jeff Seisser
Mgmt. Info Servs. Mgr. ....Gregory Mode
Prodn. Mgr., Mailroom ....Judy Schnell
Prodn. Mgr., Pre Press ....Gary Romens
Prodn. Mgr., Pressroom....................Rick Peters
Circulation Manager....................Furley Jim
Market Information: TMC.
Mechanical available: Offset; Black and 3 ROP colors; insert accepted; page cutoffs - 22 3/4.
Mechanical Specifications: Type page 11.625 X 21 1/2; E - 6 cols, 2 1/16, 1/8 between; A - 6 cols, 2 1/16, 1/8 between; C - 8 cols, 1 9/16, 1/16 between.
Commodity Consumption: Avg. Page Number Per Issue - Daily 20.
Equipment EDITORIAL: Front-end Software – Baseview.; Editorial Hardware – APP/Mac; Editorial Printers – HP CLASSIFIED: Front-end Software – Baseview.; Classified Hardware – APP/Mac; Classified Printers – HP; Display Hardware – APP/Mac; Display Printers – HP. PRODUCTION: Pagination Software – QPS/QuarkXPress 4.1.; Production Equipment – 2-P/MK 1, 1-COM/7200; Cameras – 1-R/Cl PRESSROOM: Line 1 – 4-G/Community; Folders – 1-G/Community. MAILROOM: Counter stackers – 1-BG/Count-O-Veyor; Bundle tying machines – 1/Bu, 3-Malow/Strap-tyer; Addressing machine – 1-MG/602.; Business Hardware – APP/Mac
Delivery method: Mail, Newsstand, Private Carrier, Racks

W. D. HOARD & SONS

28 W. Milwaukee Ave., Fort Atkinson, Wis., 53538-2018; gen tel (920) 563-5553; gen fax (920) 563-7298

Price: 104.00/yr.
Advertising: Open inch rate $10.00
Politics: 1870

GREEN BAY

THE GREEN BAY NEWS-CHRONICLE

133 S. Monroe St., Green Bay, Wis., 54301; gen tel (920) 432-2941; adv tel (920) 432-2941; ed tel (920) 432-2941; gen fax (920) 432-8581; adv fax (920) 432-8581; ed fax (920) 432-8581; gen e-mail chronicle@gogreenbay.com; ed e-mail editorial@gogreenbay.com; web site www.greenbaynewschronicle.com

Published: Mon, Tues, Wed, Thur, Fri, Sun
Weekday Frequency: m
Circulation: 6,617; 6,617(sun)
Last Audit: September 19, 2003
Price: 108.00/yr.
Advertising: Open inch rate $21.95
News services: Landon Media Group, NYT, AP.
Politics: Independent. **Established:** 1972
Note: The Green Bay News-Chronicle ceased publication June 3, 2005.
Not Published: New Year; Memorial Day; Independence Day; Labor Day; Thanksgiving; Christmas.
Special Editions: Car Care (Apr); Monday Morning Football (Dec); Home Improvement & Garden (Feb); Our Town (Jan); Bridal Showcase (Jun); Home Improvement & Garden (Mar); Home Improvement & Garden (May); Monday Morning Football (Nov); Bridal Showcase (Sept).
Magazines: Rave! (local, newsprint) (Thur).
Gen. Mgr.....................Al Rasmussen
Bus. Mgr. ....Jane Stedl
Sales Mgr.....................Kathy Schmidt
Adv. Supvr., Classified ....Kelly Sweet
Circ. Dir. ....Keith Davis
Ed.....................Thomas Brooker
Copy Ed. ....Bill Huber
Copy Ed. ....Amanda Luebke
Features Ed.....................Brenda Erickson
News Ed.....................Ray Barrington
Sports Ed.....................Todd McMahon
Web Page Ed. ....Jeremy Shaw
Market Information: TMC.
Mechanical available: Offset; Black and 3 ROP colors; insert accepted - self-adhesive notes APS, single sheets; page cutoffs - 13.
Mechanical Specifications: Type page 10 1/2 x 11 1/2; E - 5 cols, 1 13/16, 1/8 between; A - 5 cols, 1 13/16, 1/8 between; C - 7 cols, 1 5/8, 1/8 between.
Commodity Consumption: Avg. Page Number Per Issue - Daily 48; Avg. Page Number Per Issue - Sunday 42; widths 25; Newsprint

Used - Short Tons 1500; Printing Ink Used - Black 42000; Printing Ink Used - Color 10000; Printing Ink Used - Pages Printed 19105.

Equipment EDITORIAL: Front-end Software – Baseview.; Editorial Hardware – 12-APP/Mac G3; Editorial Equipment – Lf/AP Leaf Picture Desk; Editorial Printers – APP/Mac LaserWriter, QMS, Xante/Accel-a-Writer 8300 CLASSIFIED: Front-end Software – Baseview.; Classified Hardware – 4-APP/Mac G3; Classified Printers – HP/4ML DISPLAY: Ad make-up applications – QPS/QuarkXPress, Multi-Ad/Creator, Aldus/PageMaker, Adobe/Illustrator; Layout Software – APP/Mac 7200.; Display Printers – HP/LaserJet 4M PRODUCTION: Pagination Software – Baseview.; Production Equipment – 2-COM/9000, 2-M/Linotron; Cameras – 2-B; Scanners – APP/Mac Scanner, Nikon/35mm Film Scanner PRESSROOM: Line 1 – 5-G/Community; Line 2 – 6-G/Community; Line 3 – 4-G/SSC; Folders – 3-G/2:1. MAILROOM: Counter stackers – 5/BG; Bundle tying machines – 4-/Bu; Addressing machine – 2-/Am, 1-/Ch, 1-/Mg.; Business Hardware – Vision Data

GREEN BAY PRESS-GAZETTE

435 E. Walnut St., Green Bay, Wis., 54301-5001; gen tel (920) 435-4411; adv tel (920) 431-8293; ed tel (920) 431-8400; gen fax (920) 431-8665; adv fax (920) 431-8308; ed fax (920) 431-8379; gen e-mail online@greenbaypressgazette.com; adv e-mail prepress@greenbaypressgazette.com; ed e-mail localnews@greenbaypressgazette.com; web site www.greenbaypressgazette.com

Published: Mon, Tues, Wed, Thur, Fri, Sat, Sun
Weekday Frequency: m
Saturday Frequency: m
Circulation: 41,904; 54,314(sat); 67,619(sun)
Last Audit: ABC September 30, 2011
Price: 3.75/wk; 16.25/mo; 195.00/yr (carrier).
Advertising: Open inch rate $79.10
News services: MCT, AP, GNS.
Politics: Independent.
Special Editions: Design an Ad (Apr); Menu Guide (Aug); Last Minute Gifts (Dec); Bridal (Feb); Home & Garden (Jan); Home & Garden (Jul); Bridal (Jun); Home & Garden (Mar); Health First (Monthly); Home & Garden (Nov); Coupon Book (Oct); Coupon Book (Semi-monthly); Home & Ga
Special Weekly Sections: Finally Friday (Fri); Careers (S); On the Road and Off (Sat); Weekend (Thur); Careers (Wed).
Magazines: USA WEEKEND Magazine (S).

Pub. ....Kevin Corrado
HR Mgr. ....Wendy Nelson
Exec. Ed. ....John Dye
Film/Theater Ed. ....Warren Gerds
News Ed. ....Peter Frank
Sports Ed ....Mike Vandermause
Travel Ed. ....Steve Kirchman
Online Mgr. ....Julie Riebe
Chrmn. ....William T. Nusbaum
Controller ....Tom Ricci
Adv. Mgr., Nat'l ....Jim Lobas
Circ. Dir. ....Scott Daily
Mng. Ed. ....Barbara Janesh
Features Ed. ....Kim McAuliffe
Librarian ....Diane Robb
IT Dir. ....Phil Legler
Prodn. Mgr., Pre Press ....Denise Markowski

Market Information: Split run; Zoned editions.
Mechanical available: DiLitho; Black and 3 ROP colors; insert accepted - bags; page cutoffs - 23 9/16.
Mechanical Specifications: Type page 11 5/8 x 20 3/4; E - 6 cols, 1 5/6, 1/8 between; A - 6 cols, 1 5/6, 1/8 between; C - 9 cols, 1 6/25, 1/16 between.
Commodity Consumption: Avg. Page Number Per Issue - Daily 37; Avg. Page Number Per Issue - Plates Used 44000; Avg. Page Number Per Issue - Sunday 93; widths 40 7/8; Newsprint Used - Metric Tons 6000; Printing Ink Used - Black 210000; Printing Ink Used - Color 44000; Printing I
Equipment EDITORIAL: Front-end Software – AT, Aldus/Freehand, QPS/QuarkXPress, Adobe/Photoshop.; Editorial Hardware – 28-AT/7000, 60-AT/Prestige 4.2.1; Editorial Equipment – 4-APP/Mac CLASSIFIED: Front-end Software – HI/AdPower 1.2.; Classified Hardware – Sun; Classified Printers – AU/APS DISPLAY: Ad make-up applications – Multi-Ad/Creator, Adobe/Photoshop, QPS/QuarkXPress; Layout Software – 10-APP/Mac.; Display Hardware – APP/Mac; Display Printers – 3-AU/APS Software RIP & Imagesetter, AU/Sierra 3850 PRODUCTION: Pagination Software – QPS/QuarkXPress 3.5, AT.; Production Equipment – 3-AU/Software RIP & Imagesetter, 5-LE; Cameras – 1-C/Marathon, 1-B/Admiral; Scanners – 1-Hel/Sapphire, 1-ECR/Autokon 1000, 1-X/1200 dpi, 3-Umax/Color 1200 DPI, 2-Epson, 2-Nikon/Slide Scanner PRESSROOM: Line 1 – 6-G/Mark II double width, 2-G/Mark I double width 1969; Press Drives – CH/60 h.p.; Folders – 2-G/2:1; Reels and Stands – G/3-Arm. MAILROOM: Counter stackers – 4/HL, QWI/Hall; Inserters and stuffers – HI/1472, S/NP630; Bundle tying machines – 2-MLN/2A, 2-/Dynaric, 1-/Power Strap; Wrapping singles – QWI/Hall; Mailroom control system – Ic, HL/Spec 09; Addressing machine – Dispensa-Matic-V4. BUSINESS COMPUTERS: Business Software – Microsoft/Office 97; Business Hardware – IBM/AS-400

JANESVILLE

THE JANESVILLE GAZETTE

1 S. Parker Dr., Janesville, Wis., 53547-5001; gen tel (608) 754-3311; gen fax (608) 754-8038; adv fax (608) 754-8179; ed fax (608) 755-8349; gen e-mail gazextra@gazetteextra.com; adv e-mail retailad@gazetteextra.com; ed e-mail newsroom@gazetteextra.com; web site www.gazetteextra.com

Published: Mon, Tues, Wed, Thur, Fri, Sat, Sun
Weekday Frequency: m
Saturday Frequency: m
Circulation: 17,738; 19,010(sat); 22,826(sun)
Last Audit: ABC September 30, 2011
Price: 3.80/wk (motor route), $3.65/wk (carrier); 197.60/yr (motor route), $189.80/yr (carrier).
Advertising: Open inch rate $45.26
News services: AP, MCT.
Politics: 1845
Not Published: New Year; Memorial Day; Independence Day; Labor Day; Thanksgiving; Christmas.
Own facility?: Y
Special Editions: Home & Garden (Apr); Football (Aug); Bride's (Feb); Progress Week (Jan); 4-H Fair (Jul); Spring Car Care (Mar); Summer Fun Vacation Tab (May); Building & Remodeling (Monthly); Xmas Opener (Nov); Auto Show (Oct); Parade of Homes (Sept).
Special Weekly Sections: AMP Youth pages (Fri); Business (Mon); Marketplace (S); On TV (Sat); Kicks (Thur); Food & Fitness (Tues); Faith & Ethics (Wed).
Magazines: USA WEEKEND Magazine (S).
Broadcast Affiliations: WCLO-AM/WJVL-FM Janesville, WI; WBKV-AM/WBWI-FM West Bend, WI; WFHR-AM/WGLX-FM Wisconsin Rapids, WI; WRJN-AM/WEZY-FM Racine, WI.

CEO/Pub. ....Sidney H. Bliss
Benefits Mgr. ....Jennifer Revels
Sec. ....Pam Milheiser
Adv. Mgr., Retail ....Tom Bradley
Circ. Opns. Mgr. ....Lon Haneal
Ed. ....Scott W. Angus
Mng. Ed. ....Sid Schwartz
Bus. Ed. ....James Leute
Community Living Ed. ....Shelly Birkelo
Design Ed. ....Andrew Beaumont
Editorial Page Ed ....Greg Peck
Educ. Reporter ....Frank Schultz
Asst. Features Ed. ....Ann Fiore
Graphics Ed./Art Dir. ....Tony DiNicola
Sports Ed. ....David Wedeward
Photo Ed. ....Bill Olmsted
Women's Ed. ....Rochelle Birkelo
Mgmt. Info Servs. Mgr. ....Charles A. Flynn
Dir., Online Services ....Jonathan Lindquist

Market Information: ADS; TMC.
Mechanical available: Offset; Black and 3 ROP colors; insert accepted; page cutoffs - 22 3/4.
Mechanical Specifications: Type page 13 x 21 1/2; E - 6 cols, 2 1/16, 1/8 between; A - 6 cols, 2 1/16, 1/8 between; C - 9 cols, 1 3/8, 1/16 between.
Commodity Consumption: Avg. Page Number Per Issue - Daily 30; Avg. Page Number Per Issue - Plates Used 39000; Avg. Page Number Per Issue - Saturday 32; Avg. Page Number Per Issue - Sunday 97; widths 13 3/4; Newsprint Used - Metric Tons 1950; Printing Ink Used - Black 55200; Pr
Equipment EDITORIAL: Front-end Software – SII.; Editorial Hardware – Tandem/CLX; Editorial Equipment – 1-APP/Mac IIci, APP/Power Mac 8100 Color Darkroom, Epson/Color Dye Subprinter CLASSIFIED: Front-end Software – SII.; Classified Hardware – Tandem/CLX DISPLAY: Ad make-up applications – Adobe/Photoshop, Multi-Ad/Creator, QPS/QuarkXPress.; Display Hardware – 2-APP/Mac 840AV, 2-APP/Mac 6100, 2-APP/Mac 8100; Display Printers – GCC/1200p Laser Printer; Production Equipment – 2-Pre Press/Panther Pm 36 with Mac RIP, APP/Mac Quadra 950; Cameras – 1-B/Commodore; Scanners – 4-Epson/Flatbed, 1-HP/Flatbed, Kk/Neg Scanner. PRESSROOM: Line 1 – 4-G/Metro; Folders – 1-G/2:1. MAILROOM: Counter stackers – 1-Id/2000, 1-Id/2200; Inserters and stuffers – GMA/SLS 1000 8 x 1; Bundle tying machines – MLN/Spirit; Addressing machine – BH/1530; Other equipment –MM/Saddle Stitcher. BUSINESS COMPUTERS: Business Software – CJ; Business Hardware – 1-HP/3000
Delivery method: Newsstand, Private Carrier, Racks

KENOSHA

KENOSHA NEWS

5800 7th Ave., Kenosha, Wis., 53140-4131; gen tel (262) 657-1000; adv tel (262) 657-1000; ed tel (262) 657-1000; gen fax (262) 656-1820; adv fax (262) 657-5101; ed fax (262) 657-8455; adv e-mail classad@kenoshanews.com; ed e-mail kfrederick@kenoshanews.com; web site www.kenoshanews.com

Group: Metro Suburbia, Inc./Newhouse Newspapers
Published: Mon, Tues, Wed, Thur, Fri, Sat, Sun
Weekday Frequency: m
Saturday Frequency: m
Circulation: 22,959; 26,540(sun)
Price: 4.60/wk (delivery), $5.25/wk (mail); 195.00/yr (delivery), $273.00/yr (mail); 52.00/13wk (delivery), $68.25/13wk (mail).
Advertising: Open inch rate $29.25
News services: AP, LAT-WP, SHNS.
Politics: Independent. **Established:** 1894
Not Published: Christmas.
Own facility?: Y
Special Editions: Lawn & Garden (Apr); Bridal (Aug); Tax (Feb); Bridal (Jan); Home Improvement (Mar); New Car (Nov); Fall Car Care (Oct); Home Improvement (Sept).
Special Weekly Sections: Get Out (Fri); Color Comics (S).
Magazines: Homes Guide (Monthly); Parade (S).

Publisher ....Kenneth L. Dowdell
Gen. Mgr. ....Ronald J. Montemurro
Bus. Mgr ....Fred E. Ricker
Adv. Dir. ....Lani Renneau
Asst. Adv. Dir. ....Dennis Serpe
Adv. Customer Serv. Mgr. ....Sharon Groenke
Mgr., Sales/Mktg. ....Jared Thorson
Circ. Asst. Mgr., Delivery/Collections Mark Kretschmer
Ed. ....Jon Losness
Mng. Ed. ....Karl Frederick
Asst. Mng. Ed., Nights ....John Sloca
Bus. Writer ....Deneen Smith
Editorial Page Ed. ....Steve Lund
Get Out Ed. ....Brian Sharkey
Chief Photographer ....Kevin Poirier
Sports Ed. ....David Marran
Web Servs. Supvr. ....Terry Maraccini
Mgr., Computer Servs. ....Michael Bain
Prodn. Mgr., Distr. ....Jim De Marco
Prodn. Mgr., Opns. ....Delia Chiappetta

Market Information: TMC.
Mechanical available: Black and 3 ROP colors; insert accepted - any; page cutoffs - 22 3/4.
Mechanical Specifications: Type page 10.743 inches x 20 inches
Commodity Consumption: Avg. Page Number Per Issue - Daily 32; Avg. Page Number Per Issue - Plates Used 75000; Avg. Page Number Per Issue - Sunday 58; widths 37 1/2; Newsprint Used - Metric Tons 2855; Printing Ink Used - Black 39800; Printing Ink Used - Color 29600; Printing In
Equipment EDITORIAL: Front-end Software – CTEXT/Dateline Expressline, HP/5Si.; Editorial Hardware – SIA; Editorial Printers – Kyocera/Royal, 4P5si CLASSIFIED: Front-end Software – Unysis/Ad Management Systems 3.; Classified Hardware – SIA/NT 4.0; Classified Printers – HP/6MP DISPLAY: Ad make-up applications – Multi-Ad/Creator 6.0; Layout Software – SCS/Layout 8000.; Display Hardware – APP/Mac G4; Display Printers – HP/5Si PRODUCTION: Pagination Software – In-Design Suite; Production Equipment – production off site PRESSROOM: Line 1 – production off-site. MAILROOM: Counter stackers – production off-site
Delivery method: Newsstand, Private Carrier, Racks

LA CROSSE

LA CROSSE TRIBUNE

401 Third St. N., La Crosse, Wis., 54601; gen tel (608) 782-9710; adv tel (608) 791-8213; ed tel (608) 782-9710; adv fax (608) 782-9721; ed fax (608) 782-9723; adv e-mail graphics@lacrossetribune.com; web site www.lacrossetribune.com

Group: Metro Suburbia, Inc./Newhouse Newspapers
Published: Mon, Tues, Wed, Thur, Fri, Sat, Sun
Weekday Frequency: m
Saturday Frequency: m
Circulation: 25,720; 32,627(sat); 45,332(sun)
Last Audit: ABC September 30, 2011
Price: 17.60/mo; 234.00/yr.
Advertising: Open inch rate $109.40
News services: AP, MCT, Metro Suburbia, Inc./Newhouse Newspapers.
Special Editions: Football (Aug); Gift Guide (Dec); Winter Getaway (Feb); Winter Getaway (Jan); Graduation (May); Coupon Book (Monthly); Christmas Opening (Nov); Credit Unions (Oct); Ourtime (Quarterly); Super Saver Coupons (Semi-monthly); Kids Fest (Sept).
Special Weekly Sections: Sports Monday (Mon); Real Estate (S); Primetime (Sat); Outdoors (Thur); Food & Families (Tues); Health & Science (Wed).
Magazines: Relish (Monthly); Parade (S).

Pub. ....Rusty Cunningham
Adv. Supvr., Classified ....Tess Thruman
Circ. Dir. ....Nicholas Nicks
Ed. ....Chris Hardie
Bus. Ed. ....Steve Cahalan
City Ed. ....Scott Rada
Editorial Page Ed. ....Mark Wehrs
Health Reporter ....Terry Rindfleisch
News Ed. ....Keith O'Donnell
Online Ed. ....Marc Wehrs
Sports Ed. ....Jeff Brown
Data Processing Mgr. ....Bill Lenardson

Market Information: TMC.
Mechanical available: Offset; Black and 3 ROP colors; insert accepted - sample bags, self-adhesive notes; page cutoffs - 21 3/4.
Mechanical Specifications: Type page 11 5/8 x 21 1/2; E - 6 cols, 1 13/16, 1/8 between; A - 6 cols, 1 13/16, 1/8 between; C - 6 cols, 1 13/16, 1/8 between.
Commodity Consumption: Avg. Page Number Per Issue - Daily 30; Avg. Page Number Per Issue - Plates Used 50000; Avg. Page Number Per Issue - Sunday 56; widths 12 1/2; Newsprint Used - Metric Tons 3358; Printing

Ink Used - Black 73600; Printing Ink Used - Color 20800; Printing In

Equipment EDITORIAL: Front-end Software – APT, Microsoft/Word XP 4.1, QPS/QuarkXPress CopyDesk 2.09.; Editorial Hardware – 6-Compaq/Server, 1-Netwave, 4-Microsoft/2000 XP; Editorial Printers – HP/8000N CLASSIFIED: Front-end Software – CText.; Classified Hardware – 3-Compaq/Server, 1-Netwave, 22-Microsoft/Windows NT; Classified Printers – HP/8000N DISPLAY: Ad make-up applications – Multi-Ad/Creator 6.5, QPS/QuarkXPress 4.1, Adobe/Illustrator 8.0, Adobe/Photoshop 7.0, Layout 8000 8; Layout Software – 10-Compaq/Server, 1-Netwave, 5-Microsoft/Windows NT/2000, 25-APP/Mac G3/G4.; Display Printers – HP/5Si MX PRODUCTION: Pagination Software – QPS/QuarkXPress 4.1, HI/CPAG.; Production Equipment – Offset, 1-Pre Press/Panther Pro 62, Wing-Lynch, LE/LD 2600A; Cameras – 3-Canon/EOS 1D; Scanners – 1-Microtek/ScanMaker 8700 PRESSROOM: Line 1 – 9-DGM/850, 5-G/Urbanite single width 1999; Line 2 – 4-Lincoln/ink pumps; Folders – 1-G/2:1, 1-Web/Specialties Quadra Folder 1996, 1-DGM/1030 1999. MAILROOM: Counter stackers – 2-HL/Dual Carrier, 2-HL/Monitor, 1-Gammler/STC 70; Inserters and stuffers – MM/227, 1-S/1372; Bundle tying machines – 2-MLN/ML2EE, 2/Dynaric, 1-Mosca/Portable Strapper; Wrapping singles – 1-/QWI; Mailroom control system – Addressing machine □ Ch/525E, BH/1530.; Business Hardware – 1-IBM/AS-400

MADISON

THE CAPITAL TIMES

1901 Fish Hatchery Rd., Madison, Wis., 53713-1248; gen tel (608) 252-6400; adv tel (608) 252-6200; gen fax (608) 252-6445; adv fax (608) 252-6333; ed fax (608) 252-6445; gen e-mail citydesk@madison.com; ed e-mail citydesk@madison.com; web site www.madison.com/tct/

Group: Metro Newspaper Advertising Services, Inc.
Published: Mon, Tues, Wed, Thur, Fri, Sat
Weekday Frequency: e
Saturday Frequency: e
Circulation: 16,335; 17,479(sat)
Last Audit: March 31, 2008
Price: 3.75/wk; 185.25/yr; 48.75/13wk.
Advertising: Open inch rate $80.35
News services: Metro Suburbia Inc./Newhouse Newspapers, LAT-WP, SHNS.
Politics: Independent. **Established:** 1917
Advertising not accepted: Based on Publisher's approval.
Special Weekly Sections: Books (Fri); Travel (Sat); Rhythm (Entertainment) (Thur).
Broadcast Affiliations: NBC-15; WISC-TV-3 (CBS); WKOW-TV27 (ABC).

Pub. .... Clayton Frink
Ed .... Dave Zweifel
Mng. Ed. .... Judy Ettenhofer
Mng. Ed. .... Phil Haslanger
Books Ed. .... Lynn Danielson
Exec. Ed .... Paul Fanlund
City Ed .... Ron McCrea
Consumer Interest Ed. .... Dennis Punzel
Copy Desk Chief .... Judie Kleinmaier
Educ. Ed .... Matt Pommer
Higher Educ. Writer .... Aaron Nathans
Environmental/Ecology Writer .... Mike Ivey
Features Ed .... Linda Brazill
Film/Theater Ed. .... Jake Stockinger
Food Writer .... Debra Carr-Elsing
Graphics Ed. .... Gary Neuenschwander
Librarian .... Ron Larson

Market Information: Split run; TMC.
Mechanical available: Offset; Black and 3 ROP colors; insert accepted - samples, coupons, catalogs; page cutoffs - 22 3/4.
Mechanical Specifications: Type page 11 5/8 x 21 1/2; E - 6 cols, 1 5/6, 1/8 between; A - 6 cols, 1 5/6, 1/8 between; C - 9 cols, 1 1/6, between.
Commodity Consumption: Avg. Page Number Per Issue - Daily 40; Avg. Page Number Per Issue - Saturday 40; widths 12 1/2.

Equipment EDITORIAL: Front-end Software – HI/Newsmaker 4.3.0.0.; Editorial Hardware – Sun/fileservers, Dell/Clients PC; Editorial Equipment – Dell/Latitude Laptops-remote access, Compaq/Presario Laptop; Editorial Printers – HP/LaserJet CLASSIFIED: Front-end Software – Insiight 1.4.18.; Classified Hardware – Pentium/PCs; Classified Printers – HP/LaserJets DISPLAY: Ad make-up applications – HI/PLL 4.3.0.0; Display Hardware – Sun/Fileservers, Dell/PCs PRODUCTION: Pagination Software – HI 4.3.0.0.; Production Equipment – Adobe/Photoshop on Ap/Mac; Scanners – 2-AG/Horizon Plus, AG/Scanner PRESSROOM: Line 1 – 17-G/Metro double width 1975; Line 2 – G/Community (2-Four H16A; 4-mono units, single width) 1994; Folders – 3-G/Metro 3:2, 2-G/Community SSE; Pasters – 17; Reels and Stands – 15-G/Metro; Press registration system – Web Tech/Auto Registration. MAILROOM: Counter stackers – 7-Id/N5550, BG/Count-o-Veyor; Inserters and stuffers – 2-HI/1372, GMA/SLS 2000; Bundle tying machines – 5-Dynaric/NP2; Wrapping singles – 4-Bu/Strapper; Mailroom control system – GMA; Addressing machine – 2-Ch/545, 5/CH, 1-/GMA inline BUSINESS COMPUTERS: Business Software – Microsoft/Office; Business Hardware – IBM/AS-400

WISCONSIN STATE JOURNAL

1901 Fish Hatchery Rd., Madison, Wis., 53713-1248; gen tel (608) 252-6100; adv tel (608) 252-6000; ed tel (608) 252-6200; gen fax (608) 252-6119; adv fax (608) 256-6333; ed fax (608) 252-4155; gen e-mail wsj@madison.com; adv e-mail tsears@madison.com; ed e-mail jsmalley@madison.com; web site www.madison.com

Published: Mon, Tues, Wed, Thur, Fri, Sat, Sun
Weekday Frequency: m
Saturday Frequency: m
Circulation: 84,191; 86,823(sat); 119,192(sun)
Last Audit: ABC September 30, 2011
Price: $247.00 per year
Advertising: Open inch rate $152.45
News services: Metro Suburbia Inc./Newhouse Newspapers, NYT, MCT.
Politics: Independent.
Special Weekly Sections: Seniors (Mon); Homes/Real Estate (S); Rhythm (Entertainment) (Thur); Kids & Family (Tues); Art (Wed).
Magazines: Comics (S).

Pub. .... Bill Johnston
Dir., HR .... Debbie Reed
Ed .... John Smalley
On-Line Director .... Tim Kelley
Managing Editor .... Teryl Franklin
City Ed. .... Phil Glende
Advertising Director .... Todd Sears
Circulation Director .... Phil Stoddard
Operations Director .... Rob Strabala

Market Information: ADS; Split run; TMC; Zoned editions.
Mechanical available: Black and 3 ROP colors; insert accepted - samples, coupons, catalogs; page cutoffs - 23 3/4.
Mechanical Specifications: Type page 11 5/8 x 21 1/2; E - 6 cols, 1 5/6, 1/8 between; A - 6 cols, 2 1/16, 1/8 between; C - 10 cols, 1 1/6, between.
Commodity Consumption: Avg. Page Number Per Issue - Daily 40; Avg. Page Number Per Issue - Plates Used 140000; Avg. Page Number Per Issue - Saturday 46; Avg. Page Number Per Issue - Sunday 160; widths 37 1/2; Newsprint Used - Metric Tons 14749; Printing Ink Used - Black 336000

Equipment EDITORIAL: Front-end Software – HI/Newsmaker 2.6.; Editorial Hardware – Sun/fileservers, Dell/Workstations; Editorial Equipment – Dell/Latitude Laptops, Nikon/Digital Camera; Editorial Printers – HP/LaserJet CLASSIFIED: Front-end Software – Insiight 5.0.; Classified Hardware – 56-Pentium/PC; Classified Printers – HP/LaserJet DISPLAY: Ad make-up applications – HI/PLS 2.0; Layout Software – DEC/Layout 80, HI/PLS Ad Display System.; Display Hardware – Sun/fileservers, Dell/450L PRODUCTION: Pagination Software – HI 2.0.; Production Equipment – AU/APS-108-S, 3-AU/3850; Cameras – 1-C/Newspaper, 2-DSA; Scanners – 3-AG/Horizon Plus, AG/XL 2000, AG/Scanner, Tecsa/Scanner PRESSROOM: Line 1 – 17-G/Metro double width 1975; Line 2 – 5-G/Community (2-Four H16A; 4-single width) 1994; Folders – 3-G/Imperial 3:2, 2-G/Community SSE; Pasters – 17; Reels and Stands – 15-G/Metro; Press registration system – Web Tech/Auto Registration. MAILROOM: Counter stackers – 7-Id/N5550, BG/Count-O-Veyor; Inserters and stuffers – 2-HI/1372, GMA/SLS 2000; Bundle tying machines – 5-Dynaric/NP2; Wrapping singles – 4-Bu/Strapper; Mailroom control system – GMA; Addressing machine – 2-Ch/545, 5/CH, 4-/Ideal BUSINESS COMPUTERS: Business Software – Microsoft/Office; Business Hardware – IBM/AS-400

MANITOWOC

HERALD TIMES REPORTER

902 Franklin St., Manitowoc, Wis., 54220; gen tel (920) 684-4433; gen fax (920) 684-4416; adv fax (920) 686-2961; ed fax (920) 686-2103; gen e-mail htrnews@htrnews.com; web site www.htrnews.com

Group: Gannett
Published: Mon, Tues, Wed, Thur, Fri, Sat, Sun
Weekday Frequency: e
Saturday Frequency: e
Circulation: 10,285; 11,660(sat); 12,604(sun)
Last Audit: ABC September 30, 2011
Price: 3.15/wk; 13.65/mo; 156.95/yr.
Advertising: Open inch rate $33.90
News services: AP, NEA, SHNS, GNS.
Politics: Independent. **Established:** 1898
Special Editions: Annual Business Issue (March) 50+ (monthly)
Special Weekly Sections: Entertainment (Fri); Kids (Mon); TV (S); Tech (Tues); Food (Wed).
Magazines: USA WEEKEND Magazine (S).
General Manager / Advertising Director Lowell Johnson
Business, City of Manitowoc .. Charles Matthews
Editor
Mike Knuth
Market Information: TMC.
Mechanical available: Offset; Black and 3 ROP colors; insert accepted - card stuffs; page cutoffs - 21 1/2.
Mechanical Specifications: Type page 11 5/8 x 20 1/4; E - 6 cols, 1 13/16, 1/8 between; A - 6 cols, 1 13/16, 1/8 between; C - 9 cols, 1 3/16, 1/16 between.
Commodity Consumption: Avg. Page Number Per Issue - Daily 22; Avg. Page Number Per Issue - Sunday 40; widths 25.

Equipment EDITORIAL: Front-end Software – QPS/QuarkXPress 3.32, Dewar/Dewarview.; Editorial Hardware – AT, DEC; Editorial Equipment – Nikon/Scanners; Editorial Printers – Pre Press/Panther, AGFA/CTP AG; Classified Hardware – AT. DISPLAY: Ad make-up applications – PBS; Layout Software – ALS. PRODUCTION: Pagination Software – Lf/AP Leaf Picture Desk, Adobe/Photoshop.; Bundle tying machines – 1/Bu, 1-/MLN.; Business Hardware – Oracle, PBS

Zip Codes served: 54220, 54221
Delivery method: Private Carrier

MARINETTE

EAGLEHERALD

1809 Dunlap Ave., Marinette, Wis., 54143; gen tel (715) 735-6611; gen fax (715) 735-7580; adv fax (715) 735-6562; ed fax (715) 735-0229; gen e-mail news@eagleherald.com; web site www.ehextra.com

Published: Mon, Tues, Wed, Thur, Fri, Sat
Weekday Frequency: m
Circulation: 10,153; 10,153(sat)
Last Audit: September 29, 2003
Price: 154.80yr
Advertising: Open inch rate $33.20
News services: AP.
Politics: Independent. **Established:** 1867
Not Published: New Year; Memorial Day; Independence Day; Labor Day; Thanksgiving; Christmas.
Special Editions: Football Preview (Aug); Christmas Gift Guide (Dec); Community in Review (Feb); Menominee County Fair (Jul); Home Improvement (Mar); Graduation '05 (May); Insights (Oct); Home Improvement (Sept).
Special Weekly Sections: TV Week (Fri).
Magazines: American Profile (Weekly). USA Weekend

Bus. Mgr. .... Janice Schleihs
Ed. .... Terri Lescelius
Presentation Ed. .... Rob Becker
Regl. Ed. .... Dan Kitkowski
Sports Ed. .... Jody Korch
Prodn. Mgr., Press .... Roger Zink
Distribution Mgr. .... Donald Young
Adv Mgr. .... Kelly Boucher
Adv. Mgr. .... James Hofer
Prodn. Mgr., Mailroom .... Donna Stanke

Market Information: ADS; TMC.
Mechanical available: Offset; Black and 3 ROP colors; insert accepted - any; page cutoffs - 22 3/4.
Mechanical Specifications: Type page 10 x 21 1/2; E - 6 cols, 1 5/6, 1/8 between; A - 6 cols, 1 5/6, 1/8 between; C - 6 cols, 1 5/6, 1/8 between.
Commodity Consumption: Avg. Page Number Per Issue - Daily 24; Avg. Page Number Per Issue - Plates Used 3000; Avg. Page Number Per Issue - Saturday 24; Avg. Page Number Per Issue - Sunday 20; widths 25; Newsprint Used - Metric Tons 710; Printing Ink Used - Pages Printed 6776.

Equipment EDITORIAL: Front-end Software – Baseview.; Editorial Equipment – 1-APP/Mac CLASSIFIED: Front-end Software – Baseview.; Layout Software – 3-APP/Mac.; Production Equipment – 1-3M/Deadliner, 3M/Pyrofax. PRESSROOM: Line 1 – 6-G/Urbanite Single Width; Line 2 – 4-G/Community Single Width; Folders – 1-G/2:1, 1-G/4:1.; Inserters and stuffers – KAN/480; Bundle tying machines – 2/Bu, 1-Sa/SR1A. BUSINESS COMPUTERS: Business Software – Vision Data; Business Hardware – IBM

MARSHFIELD

MARSHFIELD NEWS-HERALD

111 W. Third St., Marshfield, Wis., 54449; gen tel (715) 384-3131; adv tel (715) 384-3131; ed tel (715) 384-3131; gen fax (715) 387-4175; adv fax (715) 387-4175; ed fax (715) 387-4175; gen e-mail areanews@marshfieldnewsherald.com; web site www.marshfieldnewsherald.com

Group: Gannett
Published: Mon, Tues, Wed, Thur, Fri, Sat
Weekday Frequency: e
Saturday Frequency: e
Circulation: 8,365; 8,365(sat)
Last Audit: ABC September 30, 2011
Price: 156.00/yr.
Advertising: Open inch rate $28.20
News services: AP.
Politics: Independent. **Established:** 1927
Special Editions: Fairs (Aug); Basketball (Dec); Valentine's (Feb); Taxes (Jan); Mad Market Days (Jul); Spring Builders & Auto (Mar); Dairyfest (May); Deer Hunting (Nov); Fall Auto (Oct); Fall Home Improvements (Sept).
Special Weekly Sections: TV Listings (Fri); Best Food Days (Sat); Entertainment Page (Thur).

General manager/editor .... Jonathan Gneiser
Gen. Mgr. .... Jonathan Gneiser
Adv. Mgr. .... Tara Marcoux
Mng. Ed. .... Johnathan Gneiser
Photo Dir. .... Dan Young
Opns. Mgr. .... Terri Hansen

Market Information: Split run; TMC.
Mechanical available: Offset; Black and 3 ROP

colors; insert accepted - anything 11 1/4 wide, 14 deep or less; page cutoffs - 21 1/2.
Mechanical Specifications: Type page 13 1/2 x 22 1/2; E - 6 cols, 2 1/16, 1/8 between; A - 6 cols, 2 1/16, 1/8 between; C - 8 cols, 1 1/2, 1/8 between.
Commodity Consumption: Avg. Page Number Per Issue - Daily 20; Avg. Page Number Per Issue - Plates Used 8000; widths 27; Newsprint Used - Short Tons 650; Printing Ink Used - Black 20000; Printing Ink Used - Color 5000; Printing Ink Used - Pages Printed 6500.
Equipment; Editorial Hardware – 1-COM.; Classified Hardware – 4-COM.; Layout Software – 2-APP/Mac Radius Two Page Display, 1-APP/Mac Radius Full Page Display.; Production Equipment – 2-APP/Mac LaserWriter II; Cameras – 1-B. PRESSROOM: Line 1 – 6-G/Urbanite; Folders – 1 MAILROOM: Counter stackers – 1-BG/108; Bundle tying machines – 2/Bu; Addressing machine – 2-Am/4000, St/labeler.; Business Hardware – NCR/Tower

MILWAUKEE

MILWAUKEE JOURNAL SENTINEL

333 W. State St., Milwaukee, Wis., 53203-1305; gen tel (414) 224-2000; adv tel (414) 224-2498; ed tel (414) 224-2047; gen fax (414) 224-2287; adv fax (414) 224-2485; ed fax (414) 224-2047; ed e-mail jsedit@journalsentinel.com; web site www.jsonline.com
Group: Metro Newspaper Advertising Services, Inc.
Published: Mon, Tues, Wed, Thur, Fri, Sat, Sun
Weekday Frequency: m
Saturday Frequency: m
Circulation: 188,819; 158,542(sat); 326,262(sun)
Last Audit: ABC September 30, 2011
Price: 3.85/wk.
Advertising: Open inch rate $484.00
News services: LA Times Sportswire, AP, MCT, LAT-WP, NYT, Entertainment News Service, Bloomberg.
Politics: Independent. **Established:** 1882
Special Editions: Auto (Apr); Parade of Homes (Aug); Gift Guide (Dec); Auto (Feb); Big Employment (Jan); Circus Parade (Jul); First Time Homebuyers (Jun); Auto (Mar); Baseball (May); Auto Mil Bucks (Nov); Weddings (Oct); First Time Homebuyers (Sept).
Special Weekly Sections: Weekend Cue (Fri); Health (Mon); Food (S); Auto (Sat); mjs.tech Jump (Tues); Entree (Wed).
Magazines: Holiday (Nov) (Other); USA WEEKEND Magazine (S).
Broadcast Affiliations: WTMJ-TV Milwaukee.
Asst. to Ed.....Ellen Delaney
Chrmn. of the Bd....Steven Smith
Pres./Pub.....Elizabeth Brenner
Sr. Vice Pres./CFO....Ken McNamee
Vice Pres., Info Technologies/CIO James Herzfeld
Vice Pres., Legal....Paul E. Kritzer
Vice Pres., Commun....Robert Dye
Vice Pres./Controller....Claudia Booth
Vice Pres., HR....James Spangler
Adv. Sr. Vice Pres.....Richard Dobson
Adv. Vice Pres.....Jandell Herum
Adv. Vice Pres., Pre Press....Kristin Baker
Adv. Dir., Classified....Marilyn Tanious
Adv. Dir., Display....Andy Narrai
Vice Pres., Mktg.....Tom Pierce
Gen. Mgr., Direct Mktg.....Scott Pompe
Circ. Sr. Vice Pres.....Mark Thomas
Circ. Asst. Dir., Distr.....Darnell Rupnow
Sr. Vice Pres./Ed.....Martin Kaiser
Mng. Ed.....George Stanley
Market Information: Split run; TMC; Zoned editions.
Mechanical available: DiLitho; Black and 3 ROP colors; insert accepted - product samples when pre-approved; page cutoffs - 22 3/4.
Mechanical Specifications: Type page 13 x 21 7/16; A - 6 cols, 2 1/16, 1/8 between; C - 10 cols, 1 1/4, 1/16 between.
Commodity Consumption: Avg. Page Number Per Issue - Daily 46; Avg. Page Number Per Issue - Plates Used 500000; Avg. Page Number Per Issue - Sunday 220; widths 54 1/2; Newsprint Used - Metric Tons 70000; Printing Ink Used - Black 2400950; Printing Ink Used - Color 850000; Print
Equipment EDITORIAL: Front-end Software – SII/Coyote, Coyote/3.; Editorial Hardware – SII/Tandem, 6-Tandem/K1000 Himalaya; Editorial Printers – HP/Laser Jet 4000, HP/Laser Jet 5000, HP/Laser Jet 6000 CLASSIFIED: Front-end Software – Mactive/Ad Base 2.10.17.; Classified Hardware – 2-Sun/Enterprisr 4500, 3-Dell/1300; Classified Printers – HP/Laser Jet 4000, HP/Laser Jet 5000, HP/Laser Jet 6000 DISPLAY: Ad make-up applications – ALS; Layout Software – ALS.; Display Hardware – 3-APP/Mac; Display Printers – HP/LaserJet 4000, HP/Laser Het 5000 PRODUCTION: Pagination Software – HI/CPAG; Production Equipment – 5-MON/Express, MAS/1000, 5-Konica/Processor, 1-MON/Futuro, 1-Carnfelot/Processor; Cameras – 1-C/Marathon, 1-C/Olympia, 2-C/Newspager; Scanners – 2-Pro/Imager 8000, Linotype-Hell/Linocolor Opal, 1-Scitex/Eversmart Supreme PRESSROOM: Line 1 – 9-H/Colormatic double width 1962; Line 2 – 9-H/Colormatic double width 1962; Line 3 – 9-H/Colormatic double width 1967; Line 4 – 9-H/Colormatic double width 1967; Folders – 8-H/2:1; Reels and Stands – 36-H; Press control system – H/Reflex drive (MAILROOM: Counter stackers – 12-HL/Dual Carrier, 2-HL/Monitor, 5-TMSI/Compass 180; Inserters and stuffers – 1-HI/1372P, 1-HI/1472P, 1-GMA/SLS 1000, 1-HI/1472, 1-GMA/SLS 2000; Bundle tying machines – 28/Dynamic; Wrapping singles – 5-HL/3/4 wrap, 5-Id/3-4 wrap, 2-5/ BUSINESS COMPUTERS: Business Software – Ross, CJ, Discus; Business Hardware – 2-Dec-50

MONROE

MONROE PUBLISHING CO.

1065 4th Ave. W., Monroe, Wis., 53566-0230; gen tel (608) 328-4202; gen fax (608) 328-4217
Price: 140.00/yr.
Advertising: Open inch rate $20.00
Politics: 1898

THE MONROE TIMES

1065 Fourth Ave. W., Monroe, Wis., 53566-1318; gen tel (608) 328-4202; adv tel (608) 328-4202; ed tel (608) 328-4202; gen fax (608) 328-4217; adv fax (608) 328-4217; ed fax (608) 328-4217; gen e-mail editor@themonroetimes.com; adv e-mail advprod@themonroetimes.com; ed e-mail editor@themonroetimes.com; web site www.themonroetimes.com
Published: Mon, Tues, Wed, Thur, Fri, Sat
Weekday Frequency: All day
Saturday Frequency: All day
Circulation: 3,559; 3,559(sat)
Last Audit: Sworn October 14, 2008
Price: 3.60/wk; 158.00/yr (carrier).
Advertising: Open inch rate $21.56
News services: AP.
Politics: 1898
Not Published: New Year; Memorial Day; Independence Day; Labor Day; Thanksgiving; Christmas.
Special Editions: Spring Sports (Apr); Fall Sports (Aug); Letters to Santa (Dec); Chamber Home Show (Feb); Spring Bridal (Jan); Dairy Queen Pages (Jul); Ag (Mar); Dairy Breakfast (May); Christmas (Nov).
Special Weekly Sections: Health (Fri); Food (Mon); Religion (Sat); Connections (Thur); Business (Tues).
Magazines: Spry (Monthly); American Profile (Sat).
Vice Pres./Gen. Mgr.....Carl C. Hearing
Office Mgr.....Connie Flint
Adv. Mgr., Retail....Laura Hughes
Editorial Page Ed.....Mary Jane Grenzow
Sports Ed.....Adam Krebs
Market Information: ADS; TMC.
Mechanical available: Offset; Black and full color ROP colors; insert accepted.
Mechanical Specifications: Type page 11 x 20; E - 6 cols, 1 3/4, 1/8 between; A - 6 cols, 1 3/4, 1/8 between; C - 9 cols, 1 1/8, 1/16 between.
Commodity Consumption: Avg. Page Number Per Issue - Daily 14.3; Avg. Page Number Per Issue - Plates Used 5356; widths 27 1/2; Newsprint Used - Short Tons 221; Printing Ink Used - Black 18000; Printing Ink Used - Color 4000; Printing Ink Used - Pages Printed 5148.
Equipment EDITORIAL: Front-end Software – Adobe/Photoshop, QPS/QuarkXPress 4.0, Claris 4.0, Baseview.; Editorial Hardware – 10-APP/Mac G4, Baseview/Editorial System, OCR Scanner; Editorial Printers – Xante/Accel-A-Writer G3; Classified Hardware – 2-APP/Mac G4; Classified Equipment – Baseview; Classified Printers – 1-Xante, Adobe/Postscript 3.0 DISPLAY: Ad make-up applications – Multi-Ad/Creator 4.0, QPS/QuarkXPress 3.3, Baseview.; Display Hardware – 4-APP/Power Mac; Display Printers – Xante, Adobe Postscript 3.0 PRODUCTION: Pagination Software – QPS/QuarkXPress 4.03.; Production Equipment – 1-B, Xante, Adobe/Postscript 3.0; Cameras – 1-Screen; Scanners – AG/Studio Star, Umax/Powerlook II; Folders – 1; Reels and Stands – 7; Bundle tying machines – 2-/MLN BUSINESS COMPUTERS: Business Software – Vision Data; Business Hardware – 6-ATT, Digital VT 510

OSHKOSH

OSHKOSH NORTHWESTERN

224 State St., Oshkosh, Wis., 54903; gen tel (920) 235-7700; adv tel (920) 426-6639; ed tel (920) 426-6687; gen fax (920) 235-1316; adv fax (920) 235-1316 (Class); ed fax (920) 235-1316; gen e-mail oshkoshletters@thenorthwestern.com; adv e-mail oshkoshad@smgpo.gannett.com; ed e-mail oshkoshnews@thenorthwestern.com; web site www.thenorthwestern.com
Published: Mon, Tues, Wed, Thur, Fri, Sat, Sun
Weekday Frequency: m
Saturday Frequency: m
Circulation: 14,538; 16,381(sat); 20,315(sun)
Last Audit: ABC September 30, 2011
Price: 3.25/wk (carrier); 169.00/yr (carrier), $182.00/yr (motor route).
Advertising: Open inch rate $45.20
News services: AP, GNS, MCT.
Special Editions: Lawn-Garden-Home (Apr); Football (Aug); Holiday Greetings (Dec); Bridal (Jan); Experimental Aircraft (Jul); Parade of Homes (Jun); Mid-WI Fun Guide (May); Basketball (Nov); Home Interiors (Oct); Answer Book (Sept).
Special Weekly Sections: Business (S); Church (Sat); Best Food Day (Tues).
Magazines: USA WEEKEND Magazine (S).
Gen Mgr.....Stewart Rieckman
Adv. Dir.....Lisa O'Halloran
Circ. Dir.....Ryan Lenz
Mng. Ed.....Jim Fitzhenry
City Ed.....Carl Ebert
Chief Photographer....Joe Sienkiewicz
Market Information: ADS; Split run; TMC.
Mechanical available: Offset; Black and 3 ROP colors; insert accepted; page cutoffs - 22 3/4.
Mechanical Specifications: Type page 13 x 22; E - 6 cols, 1 5/6, 1/8 between; A - 6 cols, 1 5/6, 1/8 between; C - 9 cols, 1 3/16, 1/8 between.
Commodity Consumption: Avg. Page Number Per Issue - Daily 26.3; Avg. Page Number Per Issue - Plates Used 32204; Avg. Page Number Per Issue - Saturday 26.3; Avg. Page Number Per Issue - Sunday 65; widths 55; Newsprint Used - Metric Tons 1588; Printing Ink Used - Black 32899; Pr
Equipment EDITORIAL: Front-end Software – ATEX/D; Editorial Hardware – 1-APP/Power Mac 6100, 10-Pentium/200, 4-Pentium/100, 13-Pentium/166, 6-Compaq/fileserver Pentium 200 dual processors; Editorial Equipment – Lf/Leafscan 35, APP/Mac 8100-100, APP/Mac IIfx, APP/Mac 8500-180; Editorial Printers – 1-HP/5000, AU/6600 CLASSIFIED: Front-end Software – Harris/Classified, Informatel/Classified Pagination, Novell/Network 4.1, Novell/SFT III.; Classified Hardware – 6-Pentium/PC, 2-Compaq/fileserver Pentium 150; Classified Printers – 1-HP/4MP DISPLAY: Ad make-up applications – QPS/QuarkXPress, Aldus/Freehand, Adobe/Photoshop; Layout Software – Other; Display Hardware – 1-APP/Mac G3, 1-APP/Mac G4, 1-APP/Mac Quadra 700, 1-APP/Mac IIci, 1-APP/Mac IIfx; Display Printers – HP/5000N, HP/8500 PRODUCTION: Pagination Software – ATEX/Dewarview.; Production Equipment – Caere/OmniPage; Scanners – Umax/PowerLook PRESSROOM: Line 1 – 5-HI/1660 1979; Folders – 2; Pasters – 5-MEG/D500.; Bundle tying machines – 1/Dynaric. BUSINESS COMPUTERS: Business Software – PBS, Media Plus, SBS; Business Hardware – 1-Sun/Sparcstation 20

PORTAGE

DAILY REGISTER

1640 LaDawn Dr., Portage, Wis., 53901; gen tel (608) 745-3500; adv tel (608) 745-3500; ed tel (608) 745-3511; gen fax (608) 742-8346; adv fax (608) 745-4718; ed fax (608) 742-8346; gen e-mail pdr-news@capitalnewspapers.com; web site www.portagedailyregister.com
Published: Mon, Tues, Wed, Thur, Fri, Sat
Weekday Frequency: m
Saturday Frequency: m
Circulation: 4,207; 4,115(sat)
Last Audit: ABC September 30, 2011
Price: 8.00/mo; 84.00/yr.
Advertising: Open inch rate $29.20
News services: AP.
Politics: 1886
Not Published: New Year; Memorial Day; Independence Day; Labor Day; Christmas.
Magazines: Best Time (Monthly); Parade (Sat); American Profile (Weekly).
Adv. Dir.....Julie Brown
Circ. Dir....Teresa Klinger
Ed.....Jason Maddux
Lifestyle Ed.....Craig Spychalla
Sports Ed.....Travis Houslet
Prodn. Mgr.....Tim Meyer
General Manager....Matt Meyers
Market Information: TMC.
Mechanical available: Offset; Black and 3 ROP colors; insert accepted; page cutoffs - 22 3/4.
Mechanical Specifications: Type page 12 1/8 x 21 1/2; E - 6 cols, 1 7/8, 1/8 between; A - 6 cols, 1 7/8, 1/8 between; C - 9 cols, 1 3/16, 1/16 between.
Commodity Consumption: Avg. Page Number Per Issue - Daily 16; Avg. Page Number Per Issue - Plates Used 6000; widths 25; Newsprint Used - Short Tons 200; Printing Ink Used - Black 6500; Printing Ink Used - Color 1000; Printing Ink Used - Pages Printed 5032.
Delivery method: Mail, Newsstand, Private Carrier, Racks

RACINE

THE JOURNAL TIMES

212 Fourth St., Racine, Wis., 53403-1005; gen tel (262) 634-3322; adv tel (262) 634-3322; ed tel (262) 634-3322; gen fax (262) 631-1702; adv fax (262) 631-1705; ed fax (262) 634-9194; gen e-mail sitemaster@journaltimes.com; web site www.journaltimes.com
Published: Mon, Tues, Wed, Thur, Fri, Sat, Sun
Weekday Frequency: m
Saturday Frequency: m
Circulation: 25,532; 27,134(sat); 28,330(sun)
Last Audit: ABC September 30, 2011
Price: 4.00/wk; 16.92/mo; 187.20/yr.
Advertising: Open inch rate $46.75
News services: AP, MCT.
Special Weekly Sections: TV Times (Fri); Celebrate Racine (Mon); Religion (Sat); Out and About (Thur); Food (Tues); Health (Wed).
Magazines: Relish (Monthly); Parade (S); Amer-

ican Profile (Weekly).

Pub. ....Mark Lewis
Adv. Mgr., Retail ....Heidi Ward
Adv. Mgr., Classified ....Donna Mueller
Circ. Mgr. ....Mathew Johnsrud
Circ. Mgr., Pennysaver ....Arne Arnold
Ed. ....Steve Lovejoy
News Ed. ....Tom Farley
Asst. News Ed. ....Heather Gascoigne
Photo Dir. ....Mark Hertzberg
Reporter ....Jeffrey Wilford
Sports Ed. ....Susan Shemanske
Prodn. Supvr., Pressroom ....Carl Simon

Market Information: TMC; Zoned editions.
Mechanical available: Flexo (direct); Black and 3 ROP colors; insert accepted - product samples; page cutoffs - 22 3/4.
Mechanical Specifications: Type page 13 x 21 1/2; E - 6 cols, 2 1/16, 1/8 between; A - 6 cols, 2 1/16, 1/8 between; C - 10 cols, 1 1/4, 1/16 between.
Commodity Consumption: Avg. Page Number Per Issue - Daily 33; Avg. Page Number Per Issue - Plates Used 26000; Avg. Page Number Per Issue - Sunday 55; widths 12 1/2; Newsprint Used - Metric Tons 2860; Printing Ink Used - Black 98747; Printing Ink Used - Color 22974; Printing In
Equipment EDITORIAL: Front-end Software – HI 8.0, Baseview/IQue.; Editorial Hardware – APP/Mac G3; Editorial Equipment – 2-AG/Avantra Select set 25, 2-APP/OSX Servers, Harlequin/NT RIPs; Editorial Printers – OCC/9400, HP/2000C, HP/8500C CLASSIFIED: Front-end Software – HI 3.6, CText/advision, Sybase.; Classified Hardware – Compaq/Proliant; Classified Printers – HP/2000C, OCE/9400 DISPLAY: Ad make-up applications – Quark/4.11, Adobe/Photoshop, Adobe/Illustrator; Layout Software – Managing Editor/ALS.; Display Hardware – 2-APP/OSX Server; Display Printers – HP/2000C, OCE/9400 PRODUCTION: Pagination Software – QPS/QuarkXPress 4.0.; Production Equipment – 2-AG/Avantra 25, 1-Na/FX VIII; Cameras – C/Spartan III; Scanners – Epson/836XL, Lf/Leafscan 35, Polaroid/SprintScan PRESSROOM: Line 1 – 1-MOT/Colormax double width (Flexo 1-5 Impression Unit) 1994; Line 2 – 1-MOT/Colormax double width (Flexo 1-5 Impression Unit) 1995; Line 3 – 1-MOT/Colormax double width (Flexo 1-3 Impression Unit) 1995; Folders – 2-G/2:1; Reels and Stands – G/Re MAILROOM: Counter stackers – 3-Compass/180, HL/Monitor HT; Inserters and stuffers – 1372 HI/Inserter; Bundle tying machines – 1/Power Strap/PNS6, 1-/Power Strap/PNS5, 2-Dynaric/NP2; Wrapping singles – 2-QWI/Viper, Powerstrap w/siderollers, Bottom wrapppers BUSINESS COMPUTERS: Business Software – WordPerfect, Microsoft/Excel, Microsoft/Word, XYQUEST/XyWrite, Paradox; Business Hardware – IBM/AS-400

RHINELANDER

THE DAILY NEWS

314 S. Courtney St., Rhinelander, Wis., 54501; gen tel (715) 365-6397; gen fax (715) 365-6367; gen e-mail news@rhinelanderdailynews.com; web site www.rhinelanderdailynews.com

Published: Mon, Tues, Wed, Thur, Fri, Sun
Weekday Frequency: e
Circulation: 5,302; 5,302(sun)
Last Audit: September 30, 2003
Price: 10.00/mo (county), $12.80/mo (mail); 114.00/yr (county), $120.00(mail).
Advertising: Open inch rate $16.20
News services: AP.
Politics: Independent. **Established:** 1882
Not Published: New Year; Memorial Day; Independence Day; Labor Day; Christmas.
Special Editions: Spring Home Improvement Guide (Apr); Fall Home Improvement Guide (Aug); Christmas Church Service (Dec); Valentine's Day (Feb); Financial Planning & Tax Time Feature (Jan); Customer Appreciation Sale (Jul); Father's Day Gift Guide (Jun); Progress (Mar); Mo
Special Weekly Sections: UP NORTH (Fri).
Magazines: Best Years (Monthly); Parade (S).

COO/Pub., The Daily News ......Gregory A. Mellis
Ed. ....Luke Laggis
Community Ed. ....Heather Schaefer

Market Information: TMC.
Mechanical available: Offset; Black and 3 ROP colors; insert accepted - any; page cutoffs - 21 1/2.
Mechanical Specifications: Type page 11 5/8 x 21 1/2; E - 6 cols, 1 5/6, 1/8 between; A - 6 cols, 1 5/6, 1/8 between; C - 6 cols, 1 5/6, 1/8 between.
Commodity Consumption: Avg. Page Number Per Issue - Daily 14; Avg. Page Number Per Issue - Sunday 48; widths 27; Newsprint Used - Short Tons 209; Printing Ink Used - Pages Printed 5014.
Equipment EDITORIAL: Front-end Software – Baseview.; Editorial Hardware – APP/Mac; Editorial Equipment – Printers Ã□Â□Ã□Â□Ã□Â□Ã□Â□Ã□Â□Ã□Â□Ã□Â□Ã□Â□ Ã□Â□Ã□Â□Ã□Â□Ã□Â□Ã□Â□Ã□Â□Ã□Â□Ã□Â□ 2-QMS/810 CLASSIFIED: Front-end Software – Suntype.; Classified Hardware – PC; Classified Printers – QMS/810 DISPLAY: Ad make-up applications – QPS/QuarkXPress; Layout Software – Multi-Ad.; Display Hardware – APP/Mac; Display Printers – 2-QMS/810, 1-Unity/1800x60; Production Equipment – 2-QMS/Laserprinter; Cameras – 1-K/241, 1-K/V2 41; Scanners – HP/ScanJet 3C. PRESSROOM: Line 1 – 4-G/Community; Folders – 1; Bundle tying machines – 1-Bu/69175.; Business Hardware – 4-Mk/Acer

SHAWANO

SHAWANO LEADER

1464 E. Green Bay St., Shawano, Wis., 54166-2258; gen tel (715) 526-2121; adv tel (715) 526-7012; ed tel (715) 526-7019; gen fax (715) 524-3941; adv e-mail advertising@shawanoleader.com; ed e-mail editor@shawanoleader.com; web site www.shawanoleader.com

Group: Wolf River Media/division of BlueLine Media Holdings
Metro Suburbia, Inc./Newhouse Newspapers
Published: Wed, Thur, Fri, Sat
Weekday Frequency: m
Saturday Frequency: m
Circulation: 6,525; 6,906(sun)
Last Audit: March 31, 2008
Price: 9.95/mo (carrier); 119.40/yr (carrier).
Advertising: Open inch rate $19.15
News services: AP.
Politics: Independent. **Established:** 1881
Advertising not accepted: N
Not Published: New Year; Memorial Day; Independence Day; Labor Day; Christmas.
Own facility?: Y
Special Editions: Sports (Aug); Packer Pre-Game (Fall); Finance (Jan); Dairy (Jun); Home Improvement (Mar); Vacation (May); Seniors (Monthly); Christmas Opener (Nov).
Special Weekly Sections: TV Guide (Fri); Business (Mon); Business (S); Entertainment (Thur); Agriculture (Tues); Education (Wed).
Magazines: Parade
(Weekly).

CEO/President BlueLine Media Holdings Paul Seveska
Community News Editor ....Cory Dellenbach
COO/Publisher ....Greg Mellis
Group Controller ....Berni Hollinger
Editorial Director ....Roger Bartel
Regional Advertising Director ......Chris Kennedy
vice president production ....Bob Perini

Market Information: TMC.
Mechanical available: Offset; Black and 3 ROP colors; insert accepted; page cutoffs - 22 3/4.
Mechanical Specifications: Type page 12 x 21 1/2; E - 6 cols, 1 13/16, 1/6 between; A - 6 cols, 1 13/16, 1/6 between; C - 9 cols, 1 1/8, 1/8 between.
Commodity Consumption: Avg. Page Number Per Issue - Daily 14; Avg. Page Number Per Issue - Plates Used 8832; Avg. Page Number Per Issue - Sunday 28; widths 25; Newsprint Used - Metric Tons 358; Newsprint Used - Short Tons 395; Printing Ink Used - Black 8478; Printing Ink Used
Equipment EDITORIAL: Front-end Software – Baseview/NewsEditPro.; Editorial Hardware – APP/Mc G3, APP/iMac; Editorial Printers – HP/LaserJet CLASSIFIED: Front-end Software – APP/Mac.; Classified Hardware – Baseview; Classified Equipment – 2-APP/Mac; Classified Printers – APP/Mac LaserWriter Plus, HP/4 Laser DISPLAY: Ad make-up applications – Multi-Ad/Creator 3.7, QPS/QuarkXPress 3.31; Layout Software – Mult; Display Hardware – APP/Mac 8100-80, APP/Mac 7100-80, APP/Mac IIci, APP/Mac 9600, APP/Mac 96 4GB-HD; Display Printers – Pre Press/Panther Pro 46, Pre Press/Panther CTP, HP/DesignJet 755CM, HP/LaserJet IV PRODUCTION: Pagination Software – Adobe/Photoshop, QPS/QuarkXPress, After Dark, Color Expert, Multi-Ad/Creator, Baseview.; Production Equipment – 1-Nu/Flip Top, Pre Press/Panther Pro 46, Pre Press/Panther CTP; Cameras – B, AG PRESSROOM: Line 1 – May-79; Line 2 – 11-G/SSC Community 1989; Line 3 – 8-G/SCC Community single width 2001; Folders – 1, 2-G/SSC; Pasters – 9; Press control system – Phnuematic/RGS IV. MAILROOM: Counter stackers – Amerigraph/RS-12; Bundle tying machines – 5-Bu/Tyer; Wrapping singles – Bu, Sitma/5-into-1; Addressing machine – Ch/Video jet 4000 JsII, 3/Ch. BUSINESS COMPUTERS: Business Software – Vision Data; Business Hardware – Sun/Server
Delivery method: Mail, Newsstand, Private Carrier, Racks

SHEBOYGAN

PRESS PUBLISHING CO.

632 Center Ave., Sheboygan, Wis., 53082-0358; gen tel (920) 457-7711; gen fax (920) 457-0178

Price: 155.00/yr.
Advertising: Open inch rate $22.00
Politics: 1907

THE SHEBOYGAN PRESS

632 Center Ave., Sheboygan, Wis., 53082-0358; gen tel (920) 457-7711; adv tel (920) 457-7711; ed tel (920) 457-7711; gen fax (920) 457-0178; adv fax (920) 457-7043; ed fax (920) 457-3573; gen e-mail news@sheboyganpress.com; web site www.sheboyganpress.com

Published: Mon, Tues, Wed, Thur, Fri, Sat, Sun
Weekday Frequency: m
Saturday Frequency: m
Circulation: 14,425; 14,425(sat); 19,050(sun)
Last Audit: ABC September 30, 2011
Price: 3.50/wk; 155.00/yr (carrier), $208.00/yr (mail).
Advertising: Open inch rate $45.20
News services: AP, GNS.
Politics: Independent. **Established:** 1907
Special Editions: Newspapers in Education (Apr); Football (Aug); Packers (Dec); Bridal Showcase (Jan); Graduation (Jun); Basketball (Nov); Fall Building (Oct); You (Mag.) (Quarterly); Packers (Sept).
Special Weekly Sections: Food (Mon); Pulse (Thur); At Home (Tues).
Magazines: USA WEEKEND Magazine (S).

Adv. Dir. ....Scott Harlan
Retail Adv. Mgr. ....David Liebelt
Home Delivery Mgr. ....Steve S. Ewig
Ed. ....Michael Knuth
Mng. Ed. ....Mike McQuade
City Gov't ....Bob Petrie
Community Ed ....Jennifer Kuszynski
Editorial Page Ed. ....Joe Gulig
Online Ed ....Jamie Piontkowski
Photo Lab ....Bruce Halmo
Presentation Ed ....Robert Farina
Sports Ed. ....Pete Barth
State Ed. ....Berk Williams
Mgmt. Info Servs. Mgr. ....Paul Schicker
Transportation Supvr. ....Allen Burgard

Market Information: ADS; TMC.
Mechanical available: Offset; Black and 3 ROP colors; insert accepted - sample packs; page cutoffs - 22 3/4.
Mechanical Specifications: Type page 12 x 22 3/4; E - 6 cols, 1 5/6, 1/6 between; A - 6 cols, 1 5/6, 1/6 between; C - 9 cols, 1 1/20, 1/8 between.
Commodity Consumption: Avg. Page Number Per Issue - Daily 35; Avg. Page Number Per Issue - Plates Used 21722; Avg. Page Number Per Issue - Sunday 60; widths 55; Newsprint Used - Short Tons 2080; Printing Ink Used - Black 64200; Printing Ink Used - Color 6525; Printing Ink Used
Equipment EDITORIAL: Front-end Software – Prestige.; Editorial Hardware – AText; Editorial Equipment – APP/Mac IIci, APP/Mac SE 30; Editorial Printers – Pre Press/Panther CLASSIFIED: Front-end Software – AText.; Classified Hardware – AText; Classified Printers – Pre Press/Panther; Layout Software – ALS.; Display Hardware – 4-Dewar/386 PC, 2-Dewar/PC 286, AText; Display Printers – APP/Mac Printer IIXL PRODUCTION: Pagination Software – QPS/QuarkXPress 4.0.; Production Equipment – AG PRESSROOM: Line 1 – 5-G/Headliner Anti-Friction double width Letterpress 1954; Folders – 2-G/2:1.; Bundle tying machines – 1/Bu, 2-Wilton Pro/Standard 80; Addressing machine – KAN/550 2.; Business Hardware – CTS, IBM/36

STEVENS POINT

STEVENS POINT JOURNAL

1200 Third Ct., Stevens Point, Wis., 54481-2855; gen tel (715) 344-6100; gen fax (715) 344-7229; gen e-mail news@stevenspointjournal.com; web site www.wisinfo.com/journal; www.stevenspointjournal.com

Published: Mon, Tues, Wed, Thur, Fri, Sat
Weekday Frequency: e
Saturday Frequency: e
Circulation: 8,073; 8,073(sat)
Last Audit: ABC September 30, 2011
Price: 9.00/mo (carrier), $14.00/mo (mail); 89.75/yr (carrier), $143.00(mail).
Advertising: Open inch rate $26.90
News services: AP, GNS.
Politics: Independent.
Special Editions: Packer Final (Fall).
Special Weekly Sections: Track & Speed (NASCAR) (Fri); Home (Sat).
Broadcast Affiliations: WFRV; WADW.

Gen. Mgr. ....Mark Baldwin
Adv. Mgr., Classified ....Barb Soik
Editorial Page Ed. ....Lisa Nellessen-Lara
Lifestyles Ed. ....Jamie Jung
News Ed. ....Harold Goodridge
Picture Ed. ....Doug Wojcik
Sports Ed. ....Scott Williams
Prodn. Mgr. ....Kevin Kusava
Prodn. Mgr., Pre Press ....Robin Spindler
Prodn. Supt., Pressroom ....Gary Moyer

Market Information: TMC.
Mechanical available: Offset; Black and 4 ROP colors; insert accepted; page cutoffs - 22.
Mechanical Specifications: Type page 12 1/2 x 21; E - 6 cols, 2 1/16, 1/8 between; A - 6 cols, 2 1/16, 1/8 between; C - 9 cols, 1 2/3, 1/8 between.
Commodity Consumption: Avg. Page Number Per Issue - Daily 28; Avg. Page Number Per Issue - Saturday 28; Avg. Page Number Per Issue - Sunday 42; widths 25; Newsprint Used - Short Tons 850.
Equipment EDITORIAL: Front-end Software – Baseview/Ad Manager Pro 2.06.; Editorial Hardware – Baseview; Editorial Printers – 2-HP/5M CLASSIFIED: Front-end Software – I-Que Server 3.16.; Classified Hardware – Baseview; Classified Printers – 2-HP/5M; Layout Software – MEI/ALS. PRODUCTION: Pagination Software – QPS/QuarkXPress 4.1.; Production Equipment – Caere/Omni Page Pro 6.0, 2-Caere/Panther Pro 46; Cameras – 2-R PRESSROOM: Line 1 – 12-G/Community; Folders – 2; Pasters – 4 MAILROOM: Counter stackers – 1/BG; Inserters and stuffers – 1-/KAN; Bundle

tying machines – 4-/Bu; Addressing machine – 2-/Ch; Other equipment –1-/MM. BUSINESS COMPUTERS: Business Software – Synaptic, Gyma; Business Hardware – PC LAN

SUPERIOR

THE DAILY TELEGRAM

1226 Ogden Ave., Superior, Wis., 54880; gen tel (715) 395-5000; gen fax (715) 395-5002; gen e-mail telegram@superiortelegram.com; web site www.superiortelegram.com

Published: Mon, Tues, Wed, Thur, Fri, Sat, Sun
Weekday Frequency: e
Saturday Frequency: m
Circulation: 8,180; 8,180(sat)
Price: 2.16/wk; 9.36/mo; 112.32/yr.
Advertising: Open inch rate $18.50
News services: AP, SHNS.
Politics: Independent.
Not Published: New Year; Memorial Day; Independence Day; Labor Day; Christmas.
Special Weekly Sections: Church Page (Fri); Automotive (Sat); Best Food Day (Wed).
Broadcast Affiliations: WISC-TV Madison, WI.
Pub. ....Ken Browall
Bus. Mgr. ....Deb Williams
Adv. Dir. ....Randy Johnson
Circ. Dir. ....Naomi Stein
Exec. Ed. ....Ron Brochu
Asst. Ed. ....Shelley Nelson
Prodn. Mgr. ....Lynn Tarnowski
Market Information: TMC.
Mechanical available: Offset; Black and 4 ROP colors; insert accepted; page cutoffs - 22 3/4.
Mechanical Specifications: Type page 12 1/2 x 21 1/2; E - 6 cols, 2 1/16, 1/8 between; A - 6 cols, 2 1/16, 1/8 between; C - 9 cols, 1 3/8, 1/16 between.
Commodity Consumption: Avg. Page Number Per Issue - Daily 24; Avg. Page Number Per Issue - Plates Used 9189; Avg. Page Number Per Issue - Saturday 24; widths 13 3/4; Newsprint Used - Short Tons 985; Printing Ink Used - Black 14100; Printing Ink Used - Color 1510; Printing Ink
Equipment EDITORIAL: Front-end Software – DP, Cx, APP/Mac OS 5.0.; Editorial Hardware – DP, Cx, APP/Mac OS; Editorial Printers – Okidata, QMS/8000S LaserJet CLASSIFIED: Front-end Software – DP, Cx, Baseview.; Classified Hardware – DP, Cx, APP/Mac OS; Classified Printers – TI/820, QMS/LaserWriter DISPLAY: Ad make-up applications – SCS/Layout 8000, Managing Editor/ALS; Layout Software – SCS/Layout 8000, MEI/ALS.; Display Hardware – PC, APP/Mac; Display Printers – C.Itoh PRODUCTION: Pagination Software – Baseview.; Production Equipment – 1-Nu, Nat/250-A, MON/ImageMaster 1000; Cameras – R, R/with Carlson Exposure; Scanners – ECR/Autokon, Umax/Astra 1200S, Umax/Vista 563, Autokon/1000 DE PRESSROOM: Line 1 – 5-G/Urbanite 1972. MAILROOM: Counter stackers – Id; Inserters and stuffers – AM Graphics/848; Bundle tying machines – EAM-Mosca, Dynaric; Mailroom control system – HI/148NC; Addressing machine – Dispensa-Matic. BUSINESS COMPUTERS: Business Software – Vision Data; Business Hardware – Vision Data, 10-PC

SUPERIOR TELEGRAM

1226 Ogden Ave Suite 1, Superior, Wis., 54880-1516; gen tel (715)395-5000; adv tel (715) 395-5000; ed tel (715) 395-5000; gen fax (715) 395-5002; ed e-mail editorial@superiortelegram.com; web site www.superiortelegram.com

Group: Forum Communications Co.
Published: Wed, Fri
Weekday Frequency: m
Politics: 1890
Advertising not accepted: Y

WATERTOWN

TIMES PUBLISHING CO.

113-115 W. Main St., Watertown, Wis., 53094-0140; gen tel (920) 261-4949; adv tel 920-261-4902; ed tel 920-261-5161; gen fax (920) 261-5102; adv fax 920-261-5102; ed fax 920-261-5102; gen e-mail news1@wdtimes.com; adv e-mail judyk@wdtimes.com; ed e-mail news1@wdtimes.com; web site WDTIMES.COM

Published: Mon, Tues, Wed, Thur, Fri, Sat
Weekday Frequency: e
Saturday Frequency: m
Circulation: 7,750; 7,750(sat)
Insert rate: $42 per M
Politics: 1895
Not Published: Sunday
Own facility?: Y
Delivery method: Mail, Newsstand, Private Carrier, Racks

WATERTOWN DAILY TIMES

113-115 W. Main St., Watertown, Wis., 53094-0140; gen tel (920) 261-4949; ed tel (920) 261-5161; gen fax (920) 261-5102; ed e-mail news1@wdtimes.com; web site www.wdtimes.com

Group: New York Newspaper Advertising Service, Inc.
Published: Mon, Tues, Wed, Thur, Fri, Sat, Sun
Weekday Frequency: e
Saturday Frequency: m
Circulation: 9,287; 9,287(sat)
Last Audit: September 27, 2001
Price: 110.40/yr (city & out of town carrier).
Advertising: Open inch rate $12.72
News services: AP.
Politics: Independent.
Not Published: New Year; Memorial Day; Independence Day; Labor Day; Thanksgiving; Christmas.
Special Editions: Earth Day (Apr); Child Care/Back to School (Aug); Christmas Greetings (Dec); Financial (Feb); Bridal Section (Jan); Senior Style (Jul); Wedding Bells (Jun); Spring Home Improvement (Mar); Summer Life Styles (May); Christmas Open (Nov); Fall Tune Up (Oct);
Special Weekly Sections: Real Estate (Fri); Best Food Day (Mon); Dining & Entertainment (Thur); Commerce Page (Tues); Agri-Business (Wed).
Magazines: USA WEEKEND Magazine (Sat); American Profile (Weekly).
Vice Pres. ....Patricia L. Clifford
Sec. ....Margaret A. Krueger
Treasurer/Bus. Mgr. ....Ralph H. Krueger
Gen. Mgr. ....Kevin Clifford
Adv. Dir., Retail/Nat'l ....Judy A. Kluetzmann
Adv. Mgr., Classified ....Mark Shingler
Circ. Dir. ....Mark D. Kuehl
Ed. ....James M. Clifford
Editorial Page Ed. ....Thomas L. Schultz
Photo Ed. ....John Hart
Sports Ed. ....Kevin Wilson
Prodn. Mgr. ....Gregory J. Thrams
Market Information: Split run; TMC.
Mechanical available: Offset; Black and 3 ROP colors; insert accepted; page cutoffs - 22 3/4.
Mechanical Specifications: Type page 11 5/8 x 21 1/2; E - 6 cols, 1 5/6, 1/8 between; A - 6 cols, 1 5/6, 1/8 between; C - 8 cols, 1 1/3, 1/8 between.
Commodity Consumption: Avg. Page Number Per Issue - Daily 28; Avg. Page Number Per Issue - Plates Used 12000; Avg. Page Number Per Issue - Saturday 24; widths 25; Newsprint Used - Short Tons 600; Printing Ink Used - Black 16000; Printing Ink Used - Color 3500; Printing Ink Use
Equipment EDITORIAL: Front-end Software – Baseview 2.0.6.; Editorial Hardware – APP/Mac; Editorial Printers – Okidata, 3-APP/Mac LaserWriter, Xante/3G CLASSIFIED: Front-end Software – Baseview.; Classified Hardware – APP/Mac; Classified Printers – Okidata DISPLAY: Ad make-up applications – QPS/QuarkXPress, Adobe/Illustrator.; Display Hardware – APP/Mac, Baseview/Ad Manager Pro; Display Printers – APP/Mac LaserWriter PRODUCTION: Pagination Software – QPS/QuarkXPress 6.1, Adobe/Photoshop.; Production Equipment – 30-Nu/Flip Top FT40APRNS, APP/Power Mac G3, Nikon/Coolscan, APP/Power Mac 7200, APP/Power Mac 200; Cameras – B/Horizontal; Scanners – APP/Mac One Scanner, Microtek/ScanMaker, Nikon/Coolscan PRESSROOM: Line 1 – 5-G/Community 1971; Line 2 – 1-G/Community 1984; Line 3 – 1-G/Community 1989; Folders – 1-G/Community.; Inserters and stuffers – 6-KAN/480; Bundle tying machines – 2-Ty-Tech/TM45; Addressing machine – St/1600-2344.; Business Hardware – ATT/382-500

WAUKESHA

THE FREEMAN

801 N. Barstow St., P.O. Box 7, Waukesha, Wis., 53186-4801; gen tel (262) 542-2500; adv tel (262) 513-2621; ed tel (262) 513-2671; oth tel (262) 542-2501; gen fax (262) 542-6082; adv fax (262) 542-6082; ed fax (262) 542-8259; oth fax (262) 542-2015; gen e-mail webmaster@conleynet.com; adv e-mail jbaumgart@conleynet.com; ed e-mail byorth@conleynet.com; web site www.gmtoday.com

Published: Tues, Wed, Thur, Fri, Sat
Weekday Frequency: e
Circulation: 11,621; 11,621(sat)
Last Audit: September 30, 2009
Price: 112.32/yr (carrier), $121.68/yr (motor); 31.20/3mo (carrier), $33.80/3mo (motor), $59.28/6mo (carrier).
Advertising: Open inch rate $29.76
News services: AP.
Politics: Independent-Conservative. **Established:** 1859
Not Published: New Year; Memorial Day; Independence Day; Labor Day; Thanksgiving; Christmas.
Own facility?: Y
Special Editions: Tax Directory (Apr); Health/Medical Directory (Aug); Holiday Fun (Dec); Tax Directory (Feb); License Plate Contest (Jan); Antique Directory (Jul); Sidewalk Sale (Jun); National Women's History Month (Mar); National Home Decorating Month (May); Coupon Book
Special Weekly Sections: Time Out (Thur).
Magazines: Relish (Monthly); USA WEEKEND Magazine (Sat); American Profile (Weekly).
Grp. Pub. ....Phil Paige
Adv. Mgr. ....Jim Baumgart
Adv. Supvr., Classified ....Kristy Wolf
Circ. Mgr., Mktg./Promo. ....Tom Badger
Ed. ....Bill Yorth
Automotive Ed. ....Mary Carlson
Online/Mgmt. Info Servs. Mgr. ....Hays Goodman
Prodn. Coord., Mailroom ....Joe Rocha
Adm. Asst. ....Patrice Shanks
Dist. Circ. Director ....Tim Haffemann
Composing ....Patricia Scheel
VP Operations ....Matt Marlett
Production Manager ....Bob Myers
Editorial Page Ed. ....Shana Duffy
Photo Ed. ....Kevin Harnack
Prodn. Mgr., Facility ....John K. Otto
Market Information: ADS; TMC; Zoned editions.
Mechanical available: Web Offset; Black and 3 ROP colors; insert accepted - single sheets, product samples; page cutoffs - 22 3/4.
Mechanical Specifications: Type page 13 x 21 1/2; E - 6 cols, 2, 3/16 between; A - 6 cols, 2, 3/16 between; C - 9 cols, 1 3/8, 1/16 between.
Commodity Consumption: Avg. Page Number Per Issue - Daily 30; Avg. Page Number Per Issue - Plates Used 16000; widths 27 1/2; Newsprint Used - Short Tons 1800; Printing Ink Used - Black 52000; Printing Ink Used - Color 2800.
Equipment EDITORIAL: Front-end Software – Adobe/Illustrator, Adobe/Photoshop, Concept/Adworks, Concept/Copy Works.; Editorial Hardware – APP/Mac G3; Editorial Printers – GCC/Elite 1208, HP/Laserjet 5M CLASSIFIED: Front-end Software – Concept/Classworks.; Classified Hardware – APP/iMac; Classified Printers – HP/Laserjet 4000N DISPLAY: Ad make-up applications – Concept/AdNet.; Display Hardware – APP/Mac; Display Printers – HP/Laserjet 4000N; Production Equipment – NU/FT 40V6UPNS, 2-Violet Laser/VSP85-S. PRESSROOM: Line 1 – 8-G/Urbanite. MAILROOM: Counter stackers – 2/MM, Id; Inserters and stuffers – 2-/MM; Bundle tying machines – 2-/Dynaric; Addressing machine – KR. BUSINESS COMPUTERS: Business Software – Microsoft/Office 97, Microsoft/Office 2000, Oracle, PBS; Business Hardware – APP/iMac
Delivery method: Mail, Newsstand, Private Carrier, Racks

WAUSAU

THE WAUSAU DAILY HERALD

800 Scott St., Wausau, Wis., 54403; gen tel (715) 842-2101; adv tel (715) 845-0754; ed tel (715) 845-0661; gen fax (715) 848-9360; adv fax (715) 848-9360; ed fax (715) 848-9361; gen e-mail opinions@wausaudailyherald.com; adv e-mail shehir@gannett.com; ed e-mail mbaldwin@wausau.gannett.com; web site www.wausaudailyherald.com

Group: Metro Newspaper Advertising Services, Inc.
Published: Mon, Tues, Wed, Thur, Fri, Sat, Sun
Weekday Frequency: e
Saturday Frequency: e
Circulation: 15,826; 17,834(sat); 41,914(sun)
Last Audit: ABC September 30, 2011
Price: 3.40/wk; 13.60/mo; 176.80/yr.
Advertising: Open inch rate $55.40
News services: AP, GNS.
Politics: Independent. **Established:** 1907
Special Editions: Career Choices (Apr); Prep Football (Aug); Winter Coupon Book (Jan); Sidewalk Sale (Jul); Bridal (Jun); Environment (Mar); Summer Events (May); Real Estate Guide (Monthly); Thanksgiving (Nov); Forest Forever (Oct); Wheels (Semi-monthly); Escape (Semi-year
Special Weekly Sections: Church Page (Fri); Life/medical (Mon); Color Comics (S); Homestyle (Sat); Outdoor Pages (Thur); Food (Wed).
Magazines: HomeStyle (Every other month); CW Business (Monthly); USA WEEKEND Magazine (S).
Pres./Pub. ....Michael Beck
Adv. Mgr., Retail/Classified/Nat'l ....Scott Hehir
Exec. Ed. ....Mark F. Baldwin
Mng. Ed. ....Mark Treinen
Home Ed. ....Jamie Orcutt
Librarian ....Debra Siburt
Lifestyle Ed. ....Amy Kimmes
Opinion Page Ed. ....Pete Wasson
Photo Dept. Ed. ....Rob Orcutt
Presentation Ed. ....Kerry Lechner
Sports Ed. ....Chris Schulte
Television Ed. ....Cathy Emerson
Prodn. Mgr., Distr. Ctr. ....Glenn Palder
Market Information: ADS; TMC.
Mechanical available: Offset; Black and 3 ROP colors; insert accepted; page cutoffs - 22 3/4.
Mechanical Specifications: Type page 11 13/100 x 21 1/2; E - 6 cols, 1 3/4, 1/8 between; A - 6 cols, 1 3/4, 1/8 between; C - 10 cols, 1 1/20, 7/100 between.
Commodity Consumption: Avg. Page Number Per Issue - Daily 26; Avg. Page Number Per Issue - Plates Used 42000; Avg. Page Number Per Issue - Sunday 60; widths 50; Printing Ink Used - Black 65000; Printing Ink Used - Color 21000; Printing Ink Used - Pages Printed 25300.
Equipment EDITORIAL: Front-end Software – Mk/ACE II, Caere/OmniPage.; Editorial Hardware – Mk/6000; Editorial Equipment – Mk; Editorial Printers – APP/Mac LaserPrinter CLASSIFIED: Front-end Software – Baseview.; Classified Hardware – APP/Mac G3; Classified Printers – TI/810, HP/LaserJet 5M, HP/LaserJet 400N DISPLAY: Ad make-up applications – Quark 4.1, Adobe/Illustrator; Layout Software – APP/Mac.; Display Hardware – APP/Mac; Display Printers – HP/8000 Laser, HP/2500C Color,

HP/1050C DesignJet PRODUCTION: Pagination Software – QPS/QuarkXPress, Baseview/Newsedit Pro.; Production Equipment – Nu, Ultra/Plus; Cameras – 2-Tesca Copydot; Scanners – 1-AG/Duoscan, 1-AG/Duoscan T1200 PRESSROOM: Line 1 – 4-G/Metro double width (Hump on 3-10 side) 1968; Line 2 – 2-G/Metro double width 5-10; Folders – 1-G/2:1; Pasters – G/Flying Paster. MAILROOM: Counter stackers – 3-QWI/401 Narrow; Inserters and stuffers – HI/1372, HI/Alphaliner; Bundle tying machines – 2/Power Strap; Addressing machine – Ch.; Business Hardware – 1-IBM/AS-400

WEST BEND

THE DAILY NEWS

100 S. 6th Ave., West Bend, Wis., 53095; gen tel (262) 306-5000; gen fax (262) 338-1984; adv fax (262) 338-5271; ed fax (262) 338-1984; gen e-mail dailynews@conleynet.com; web site www.gmtoday.com

Published: Tues, Wed, Thur, Fri, Sat
Weekday Frequency: All day
Saturday Frequency: m
Circulation: 8,876; 9,409(sat)
Last Audit: ABC September 30, 2011
Price: 2.15/wk; 9.10/mo (carrier), $10.30/mo (mail); 102.95/yr (carrier), $114.40(mail).
Advertising: Open inch rate $13.24
News services: AP, NYT.
Politics: Independent.
Not Published: New Year; Memorial Day; Independence Day; Labor Day; Thanksgiving; Christmas.
Special Editions: Senior Citizens (Aug); Christmas Gift Guide (Dec); County Fair (Jul); Home Improvement (Mar); Christmas Opening (Nov); Fall Home Improvement (Sept).
Special Weekly Sections: Business (Sat); Food (Wed).
Magazines: Relish (Monthly); USA WEEKEND Magazine (Sat); American Profile (Weekly).
Pub. ....Steve Ciccantelli
Adv. Mgr. ....Lois Evans
Adv. Mgr., Classified ....Kristi Wolf
Circ. Mgr. ....Kim Dietrich
Mng. Ed. ....Jill Badzinski
Features Ed. ....Dave Rank
News Ed ....Dan Muckelbauer
Sports Ed. ....Larry Hanson
Prodn. Mgr. ....Andy Crass
Prodn. Mgr., Pre Press ....Kelly Marquardt
Market Information: TMC.
Mechanical available: Offset; Black and ROP colors; insert accepted - smaller units than full-page, tabs, booklets; page cutoffs - 23 9/16.
Mechanical Specifications: Type page 13 x 21 1/2; E - 6 cols, 2 1/6, 1/8 between; A - 6 cols, 2 1/6, 1/8 between; C - 9 cols, 1 3/8, 1/16 between.
Commodity Consumption: Avg. Page Number Per Issue - Daily 19.4; Avg. Page Number Per Issue - Plates Used 7000; widths 13 3/4; Newsprint Used - Short Tons 3000; Printing Ink Used - Black 200000; Printing Ink Used - Color 5000; Printing Ink Used - Pages Printed 4960.
Equipment EDITORIAL: Front-end Software – Mk/Ace II.; Editorial Hardware – Mk/6000; Editorial Equipment – Mk/Magitronic II; Editorial Printers – 2-V/5100 CLASSIFIED: Front-end Software – Mk/ACE II.; Classified Hardware – 4-Mk/6000; Classified Printers – V/5100 DISPLAY: Ad make-up applications – QPS, Aldus, Multi-Ad, QPS/QuarkXPress; Layout Software – APP/Mac IIci.; Display Hardware – APP/Mac IIci; Production Equipment – Lf/AP Leaf Picture Desk, V; Cameras – SCREEN/Companica 680; Scanners – 1-SCREEN/680C. PRESSROOM: Line 1 – 8-G/Community; Line 2 – 10-G/Community; Folders – G/SC.; Inserters and stuffers – Mueller-Martini; Bundle tying machines – 1-Bu/St, 1/Power Strap; Addressing machine – 1-SAC/JR.; Business Hardware – 1-IBM/PC-XT, ATT

WISCONSIN RAPIDS

DAILY TRIBUNE

220 First Ave. S., Wisconsin Rapids, Wis., 54495; gen tel (715) 423-7200; adv tel (715) 422-6716; ed tel (715) 422-6723; gen fax (715) 421-1545; adv fax (715) 422-6758; ed fax (715) 421-1545; gen e-mail publisher@wisconsinrapidstribune.com; ed e-mail editor@wisconsinrapidstribune.com; web site www.wisinfo.com; www.wisconsinrapidstribune.com

Published: Mon, Tues, Wed, Thur, Fri, Sat
Weekday Frequency: e
Saturday Frequency: e
Circulation: 8,180; 8,180(sat)
Last Audit: ABC September 30, 2011
Price: 13.00/mo; 139.00/yr.
Advertising: Open inch rate $28.20
News services: AP.
Politics: Independent.
Special Editions: Boating Guide (Apr); Rivercities Fun Fest (Aug); Sports (Dec); Health Pages (Every other month); Badger State Games (Feb); Bridal Tab (Jan); Water Ski Tourney (Jul); Father's Day Honor Roll (Jun); Boating Guide (Mar); Graduation Tab (May); Sports (Nov); R
Special Weekly Sections: Fast Tracks (Fri); Weekend Sports (Mon); Seniors Page (Sat); Dining & Entertainment (Thur); Food (Tues); Farm Page (Wed).
Broadcast Affiliations: WAOW - Wausau; WSAW Wausau.
Adv. Mgr. ....Gara Marcoux
Exec. Ed. ....Allen Hicks
Photo Chief ....Tom Loucks
Religion Ed. ....Jamie Jung
Sports Ed. ....Jery Rhoden
Market Information: TMC.
Mechanical available: Offset; Black and 3 ROP colors; insert accepted; page cutoffs - 21.
Mechanical Specifications: Type page 11 5/8 x 21 1/2; E - 6 cols, 1 5/6, 1/6 between; A - 6 cols, 1 5/16, 1/6 between; C - 9 cols, 1 1/5, 2/25 between.
Commodity Consumption: Avg. Page Number Per Issue - Daily 22; Avg. Page Number Per Issue - Saturday 24.
Equipment EDITORIAL: Front-end Software – QPS/QuarkXPress, Baseview/IQUE.; Editorial Hardware – APP/Mac G3, APP/iMac; Editorial Equipment – Printers ☐ HP/5000 CLASSIFIED: Front-end Software – Baseview.; Classified Hardware – APP/Mac G3; Classified Printers – HP/5000 DISPLAY: Ad make-up applications – QPS/QuarkXPress; Layout Software – APP/Mac.; Display Hardware – APP/Mac; Display Printers – HP/5000 PRODUCTION: Pagination Software – QPS/QuarkXPress.; Production Equipment – Caere/OmniPage Pro, AP; Scanners – Epson PRESSROOM: Line 1 – 10-G/Community 1989.; Bundle tying machines – 1/MLN.

WYOMING

CASPER

CASPER STAR-TRIBUNE

170 Star Ln., Casper, Wyo., 82604; gen tel (307) 266-0500; adv tel (307) 266-0504; ed tel (307) 266-0575; gen fax (307) 266-0501; adv fax (307) 266-0501; ed fax (307) 266-0568; gen e-mail news@trib.com; web site www.trib.com

Group: Metro Newspaper Advertising Services, Inc.
Published: Mon, Tues, Wed, Thur, Fri, Sat, Sun
Weekday Frequency: m
Saturday Frequency: m
Circulation: 24,516; 21,825(sat); 24,172(sun)
Last Audit: ABC September 30, 2011
Advertising: Open inch rate $41.96
News services: AP, NYT.
Politics: Independent.
Special Editions: Football (Aug); Bridal Guide (Jan); College National Finals Rodeo (Jun); Growing Tomorrows (Mar); Discover Casper (May); Holiday Guide (Nov).
Special Weekly Sections: Open Spaces (Fri); Wyoming Business (S); Going Places (Thur); Science & Technology (Tues); Enjoy (Wed).
Magazines: Relish (Monthly); Sunday Comics (S); American Profile (Weekly).
Pub. ....Nathan Bekke
Controller ....Ron Kay
Adv. Dir. ....Marvin Rone
Circ. Dir ....Tom Biermann
Ed. ....Chad Baldwin
Sports/City Ed. ....David Mayberry
Online Dir. ....Ron Gullberg
Opns. Dir. ....Randy Ware
Market Information: TMC.
Mechanical available: Offset; Black and 3 ROP colors; insert accepted; page cutoffs - 22 3/4.
Mechanical Specifications: Type page 12 x 21 1/2; E - 6 cols, 1 13/16, 1/8 between; A - 6 cols, 1 13/16, 1/8 between; C - 9 cols, 1 7/32, 1/16 between.
Commodity Consumption: widths 37 1/4; Newsprint Used - Metric Tons 2600; Printing Ink Used - Pages Printed 11750.
Equipment; Editorial Hardware – 1-Sun/Sparc.; Classified Hardware – 1-Sun/Sparc.; Layout Software – SCS, ECR/Pelbox.; Production Equipment – 1-Nu, 2-COM/8600, LaCie; Cameras – 2-SCREEN/Companica; Scanners – 2-Data Copy/730GS. PRESSROOM: Line 1 – 9-G/Cosmo offset double width; Pasters – 5; Reels and Stands – 5 MAILROOM: Counter stackers – 3/HL; Inserters and stuffers – 2-/MM; Bundle tying machines – 2-/MLN.; Business Hardware – 2-Sun, 1-Unix/PC

CHEYENNE

WYOMING TRIBUNE-EAGLE

702 W. Lincolnway, Cheyenne, Wyo., 82001; gen tel (307) 634-3361; adv tel (307) 633-3151; ed tel (307) 634-3361; gen fax (307) 633-3191; adv fax (307) 633-3191; ed fax (307) 633-3189; gen e-mail class@wyomingnews.com; adv e-mail advsec@wyomingnews.com; web site www.wyomingnews.com

Published: Mon, Tues, Wed, Thur, Fri, Sat, Sun
Weekday Frequency: m
Saturday Frequency: m
Circulation: 13,867; 15,549(sat); 15,292(sun)
Last Audit: ABC September 30, 2011
Price: 12.50/mo (carrier); 137.50/yr.
Advertising: Open inch rate $22.00
News services: NEA, AP, MCT.
Special Editions: Football (Aug); Estate Planning (Feb); Cheyenne Frontier Days (Jul); Investing (Jun); Entrepreneurs (May); Reader's Choice (Oct); Home Improvement (Sept).
Special Weekly Sections: TV Week (Fri); Health (Sat); Outdoors (Thur); Foods (Wed).
Magazines: USA WEEKEND Magazine (Sat).
Pres./Pub. ....L. Michael McCraken
Vice Pres./Sec. ....Ronald M. Brown
Treasurer/Controller ....Larry D. Catalano
Adv. Dir. ....Scott P. Walker
Adv. Mgr., Classified ....Lashay Hernandez
Adv. Mgr., Nat'l ....Cynthia M. Marek
Circ. Dir. ....Gina Larsen
Mng. Ed. ....D. Reed Eckhardt
Editorial Page Ed. ....Scott W. Smith
Features Ed. ....C.J. Putnam
Sports Ed. ....Robert Gagliardi
Prodn. Dir. ....James K. Thompson
Prodn. Mgr., Mailroom ....Joyce Girardin
Prodn. Foreman, Pressroom Larry E. Bechtholdt
Market Information: TMC.
Mechanical available: Offset; Black and 3 ROP colors; insert accepted - printing available, also bags and samples; page cutoffs - 22 3/4.
Mechanical Specifications: Type page 11 5/8 x 21 1/2; E - 6 cols, 2 1/16, 1/8 between; A - 6 cols, 1 13/16, 1/8 between; C - 9 cols, 1 1/4, 1/16 between.
Commodity Consumption: Avg. Page Number Per Issue - Daily 24; Avg. Page Number Per Issue - Plates Used 15600; Avg. Page Number Per Issue - Saturday 27; widths 25; Newsprint Used - Metric Tons 1275; Printing Ink Used - Black 36800; Printing Ink Used - Color 6000; Printing Ink U
Equipment EDITORIAL: Front-end Software – Automated Complete Typesetting System.; Editorial Hardware – 25-Dell CLASSIFIED: Front-end Software – Automated Complete Typesetting System.; Classified Hardware – 6-Dell DISPLAY: Ad make-up applications – QPS/QuarkXPress 4.01, Adobe/Illustrator 8.0, Adobe/Photoshop 5.0; Layout Software – Automated Complete Typesetting System.; Display Hardware – 18-Dell/NT Workstation, 1-Dell/Laptop; Display Printers – Tegra/Varityper 5300 H, Pre Press/Panther Pro, Konica/9100 PRODUCTION: Pagination Software – QPS/QuarkXPress 4.01, Automated Complete Typesetting System, Konica/9100.; Production Equipment – P, 1-Nu, QPS, Photoshop; Cameras – C/Spartan III; Scanners – Microtek/Flatbed, HP/ScanJet II, Nikon/4000 PRESSROOM: Line 1 – 8-G/Urbanite 1010 (1 color unit) 1972; Folders – 1-G/Urbanite SU. MAILROOM: Counter stackers – S; Inserters and stuffers – GMA/SLS 1000; Bundle tying machines – MLN; Addressing machine – Mg; Other equipment –S/8 pocket & cover feeder. BUSINESS COMPUTERS: Business Software – PBS, SBS; Business Hardware – Sun/Ultra 10

GILLETTE

THE NEWS-RECORD

1201 W. Second St., Gillette, Wyo., 82716; gen tel (307) 682-9306; gen fax (307) 686-9306; gen e-mail publisher@gillettenewsrecord.com; adv e-mail newsad@vcn.com; ed e-mail news@gillettenewsrecord.com; web site www.gillettenewsrecord.com

Published: Mon, Tues, Wed, Thur, Fri, Sun
Weekday Frequency: e
Circulation: 6,479; 6,479(sun)
Last Audit: March 31, 2005
Price: 12.50/mo (mail); 99.00/yr (carrier), $150.00/yr (mail).
Advertising: Open inch rate $14.30
News services: AP.
Politics: Independent.
Not Published: New Year; Memorial Day; Independence Day; Labor Day; Thanksgiving; Christmas.
Magazines: Health & Fitness Tab (Monthly); What's On (local entertainment and TV) (S); American Profile (Weekly).
Pres. ....Betty Kennedy
Bus. Mgr. ....Valerie Kettrey
Adv. Dir. ....Cher Rhoades
Circ. Dir. ....Joni Siebenaler
Mng. Ed ....Deb Holbert Sutton
Editorial Page Ed. ....Ann Franscell
Sports Ed. ....Kathy Brown
Prodn. Mgr. ....Mike Urlaub
Market Information: TMC.
Mechanical available: Offset; Black and 3 ROP colors; insert accepted; page cutoffs - 22 3/4.
Mechanical Specifications: Type page 13 x 21; E - 6 cols, 2 1/16, 1/8 between; A - 6 cols, 2 1/16, 1/8 between; C - 8 cols, 1 1/2, 1/8 between.
Commodity Consumption: Avg. Page Number Per Issue - Daily 14; Avg. Page Number Per Issue - Plates Used 11600; Avg. Page Number Per Issue - Sunday 24; widths 27 1/2; Newsprint Used - Metric Tons 235; Printing Ink Used - Black 11750; Printing Ink Used - Color 720; Printing Ink U
Equipment; Editorial Hardware – 1-Mk, 9-APP/Power Mac G3, 1-APP/Mac Blue G3, 1-APP/Mac Server Blue G3, 1-APP/Power Mac 7100/80; Editorial Equipment – 1-Polaroid/SprintScan 35 Plus, 1-HP/ScanJet 3c, 1-Iomega/Jaz Drive; Editorial Printers – 1-HP/LaserJet 4MV, 1-ECR/Scriptsetter VRL 36 CLASSIFIED: Front-end Software – Baseview/AdManagerPro 2.0.5, QPS/QuarkXPress

4.0, Caere/OmniPage Pro 8.0.; Classified Hardware – 3-APP/Power Mac G3, 1-APP/iMac; Classified Equipment – 1-Nikon/ScanTouch 210; Classified Printers – 1-Epson/Stylus Color 850 Ne DISPLAY: Ad make-up applications – QPS/QuarkXPress 3.32, Adobe Illustrator 8.0, Adobe/Photoshop 5.0, APP/AdSend 1.4.5, Adobe/Acrobat 4.0; Display Hardware – 1-APP/Power Mac G3, 1-APP/Mac Server G3; Display Printers – HP/LaserJet 4MV PRODUCTION: Pagination Software – QPS/QuarkXPress 3.31.; Production Equipment – 1-LE; Cameras – 1-SCREEN/Companica PRESSROOM: Line 1 – 6-G; Folders – 1-G/2:1.; Bundle tying machines – 1/Bu, Felins/F16, Allpack/351.610.001; Addressing machine – 1-/El.

LARAMIE

LARAMIE DAILY BOOMERANG

320 Grand Ave., Laramie, Wyo., 82070-3712; gen tel (307) 742-2176; gen fax (307) 742-2046; gen e-mail newsone@laramieboomerang.com; adv e-mail ads@laramieboomerang.com; web site www.laramieboomerang.com

Published: Tues, Wed, Thur, Fri, Sat, Sun
Weekday Frequency: m
Circulation: 5,233; 5,233(sat); 5,233(sun)
Last Audit: September 30, 2008
Price: 1.32/wk (carrier); 6.50/mo (carrier), $7.50/mo (motor route); 72.00/yr (carrier), $135.00/yr (mail).
Advertising: Open inch rate $12.75
News services: AP.
Politics: Independent.
Not Published: Christmas.
Special Editions: Business Showcase (Apr); University (Aug); Christmas Greeter (Dec); Brides (Feb); Back-to-School (Jan); Crazy Days (Jul); Senior Scene (Jun); Spring Home Improvement (Mar); High School Graduation (May); Winter Recreation (Nov); Car Care (Oct); Brides (Sep
Special Weekly Sections: Food (S); Religion (Sat); Food (Wed).
Magazines: USA WEEKEND Magazine (S); Encore-TV and Entertainment (Sat).
Pub. .... Don Black
Adv. Dir. .... Matt Petrie
Circ. Mgr. .... Steve Wagner
Sports Ed. .... Robert Hammond
Women's Ed. .... Debra Thomsen
Market Information: TMC.
Mechanical available: Offset; Black and 3 ROP colors; insert accepted; page cutoffs - 22 3/4.
Mechanical Specifications: Type page 12 3/4 x 21 1/4; E - 6 cols, 2 1/16, 1/8 between; A - 6 cols, 2 1/16, 1/8 between; C - 6 cols, 2 1/16, 1/8 between.
Commodity Consumption: Avg. Page Number Per Issue - Daily 22; Avg. Page Number Per Issue - Plates Used 4680; Avg. Page Number Per Issue - Sunday 30; widths 27 1/2; Newsprint Used - Short Tons 320; Printing Ink Used - Black 5900; Printing Ink Used - Pages Printed 7500.
Equipment EDITORIAL: Front-end Software – QPS/QuarkXPress.; Editorial Hardware – PC CLASSIFIED: Front-end Software – QPS/QuarkXPress.; Classified Hardware – PC; Classified Printers – Okidata/320 DISPLAY: Ad make-up applications – QPS/QuarkXPress, Adobe/Photoshop, Fifth Generation Systems/Suitcase, CTA/Textpert; Display Hardware – 2-APP/Mac Centris 650; Display Printers – HP/5 PRODUCTION: Pagination Software – QPS/QuarkXPress.; Production Equipment – 2-ECR/VRL36 PRESSROOM: Line 1 – 6-G/Community.; Inserters and stuffers – 4/MM; Bundle tying machines – . BUSINESS COMPUTERS: Business Software – Cyma; Business Hardware – PC

RAWLINS

RAWLINS DAILY TIMES

522 W. Buffalo St., Rawlins, Wyo., 82301; gen tel (307) 324-3411; gen fax (307) 324-2797; gen e-mail news@rawlinstimes.com; adv e-mail ads@rawlinstimes.com; web site www.rawlinstimes.com

Published: Tues, Wed, Thur, Fri, Sat
Weekday Frequency: m
Circulation: 4,000; 4,000(sat)
Last Audit: October 1, 2003
Price: 98.00/yr.
Advertising: Open inch rate $7.75
News services: AP.
Politics: Independent.
Not Published: Days after holidays.
Special Editions: Fair (Aug); Christmas Shopping Guide (Nov); Hunter's (Sept).

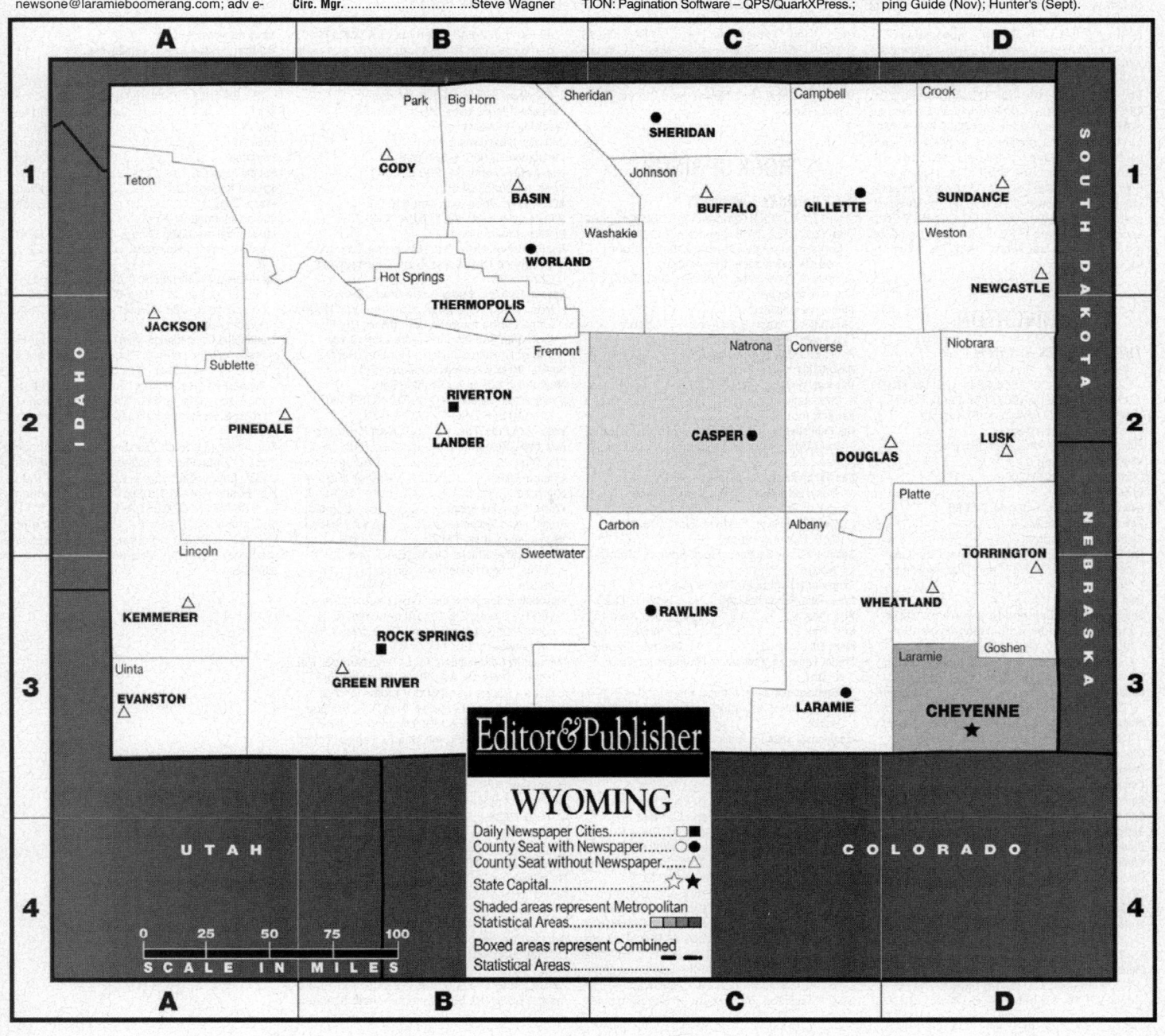

Editor&Publisher
WYOMING
Daily Newspaper Cities
County Seat with Newspaper
County Seat without Newspaper
State Capital
Shaded areas represent Metropolitan Statistical Areas
Boxed areas represent Combined Statistical Areas
0 25 50 75 100 SCALE IN MILES

Magazines: American Profile (Weekly).
Sec. ....Larry D. Catalano
Mng. Ed. ....Jessy Mullen
Bus./Finance Ed................................Missey Turney
Entertainment/Amusements Ed. ....Jerry Raehal
Prodn. Mgr., Distr./Mailroom.........L.B. Brantner
Prodn. Mgr., Pressroom........Jefferson Haworth
Mechanical available: Offset; Black and 3 ROP colors; insert accepted - special arrangements; page cutoffs - 22 5/8.
Mechanical Specifications: Type page 10 1/2 x 14; E - 5 cols, 2 1/16, 1/8 between; A - 5 cols, 2 1/16, 1/8 between; C - 5 cols, 2 1/16, 1/8 between.
Commodity Consumption: Avg. Page Number Per Issue - Daily 20; Avg. Page Number Per Issue - Saturday 24; widths 15; Newsprint Used - Metric Tons 43; Printing Ink Used - Black 1840; Printing Ink Used - Color 50; Printing Ink Used - Pages Printed 4700.
Equipment EDITORIAL: Front-end Software – Synaptic/Micro Solutions, SunType.; Editorial Hardware – Synaptic/Micro Solution; Editorial Printers – 2-APP/Mac LaserWriter II NTX, APP/Mac LaserWriter Pro 2-640, APP/Mac LaserWriter Pro 600 CLASSIFIED: Front-end Software – Synaptic/Micro Solutions, SunType.; Classified Hardware – Synaptic/Micro Solutions DISPLAY: Ad make-up applications – QPS/QuarkXPress, Adobe; Layout Software – APP/Mac 75-100, APP/Mac 6100-66, Power Computing/Power Tower 225. PRODUCTION: Pagination Software – QPS/QuarkXPress 3.31, QPS/QuarkXPress 4.0.; Production Equipment – APP/Mac LaserWriter Pro 600, 2-APP/Mac LaserWriter II; Cameras – 1-Argyle/23; Scanners – APP/Mac, 2-Nikon/ScanTouch, 2-Nikon/Coolscan PRESSROOM: Line 1 – 6-HI/Cotrell V-15A; Folders – 1; Addressing machine – 1-Data/Star 486-335X, Microsoft/Wordperfect Labels 6.0. BUSINESS COMPUTERS: Business Software – Synaptic/Micro Solutions 4.06; Business Hardware – MaxTech, Synaptic/Micro Solutions

RIVERTON

THE RIVERTON RANGER

421 E. Main St., Riverton, Wyo., 82501-0993; gen tel (307) 856-2244; gen fax (307) 856-0189; adv fax (307) 856-2560; gen e-mail ranger@wyoming.com; web site www.dailyranger.com
Published: Tues, Wed, Thur, Fri, Sun
Weekday Frequency: e
Circulation: 7,200; 7,200(sun)
Price: 60.00/yr.
Advertising: Open inch rate $15.50
News services: AP, MCT.
Politics: Independent.
Not Published: New Year; Memorial Day; Independence Day; Labor Day; Thanksgiving; Christmas.
Own facility?: Y
Special Editions: Fair and Rodeo (Aug); Christmas (Dec); Bridal (Jan); Rendezvous-Balloon Rally (Jul); State Mining (Jun); Community Roots (Mar); Agriculture (Nov); Fire Prevents (Oct); Hunt-Fish (Sept).
Special Weekly Sections: Home (Mon); Business (Thur); Health (Tues); Food (Wed).
Magazines: American Profile (S); Entertainment, TV Area-wide Schedule (Tues).
Office Mgr. ....Marcia McBeath
Columnist/Editorial Page Ed........Steven R. Peck
Columnist ....Carolyn B. Tyler
Photo Dept. Mgr. ....Wayne Nichols
Sports Ed. ....Bruce Tippetts
Systems Mgr. ....Carl Manning
Prodn. Mgr., Commercial Printing.Robert Stover
Prodn. Supt., Mailroom ....Mary Treber
Dir., Mktg./Promos. ....Heidi Coulson
Ed...Keith Domke
Market Information: TMC.
Mechanical available: Offset; Black and 3 ROP colors; insert accepted - all; page cutoffs - 22 3/4.
Mechanical Specifications: Type page 13 x 21 1/2; E - 6 cols, 2 1/16, 1/8 between; A - 6 cols, 2 1/16, 1/8 between; C - 6 cols, 2 1/16, 1/8 between.
Commodity Consumption: Avg. Page Number Per Issue - Daily 14; Avg. Page Number Per Issue - Plates Used 3987; Avg. Page Number Per Issue - Sunday 30; widths 27 1/2; Newsprint Used - Metric Tons 330; Printing Ink Used - Black 6500; Printing Ink Used - Color 1000; Printing Ink Us
Equipment EDITORIAL: Front-end Software – Scoop/Editorial.; Editorial Hardware – 6-Scoop Editorial; Editorial Equipment – 3-APP/Mac G4; Editorial Printers – 2-APP/Mac 8500, LaserMaster/1800, APP/Mac LaserPro CLASSIFIED: Front-end Software – CAMS, CAMS.; Classified Hardware – CAMs; Classified Equipment – Polaroid/SprintScan, Polaroid/SprintScan, Microtek/Scanmaker, Microtek/Scanmaker DISPLAY: Ad make-up applications – QPS/QuarkXPress 3.3, Adobe/Photoshop.; Display Hardware – APP/Mac iMac Intel; Display Printers – 2-APP/Mac 8500 PRODUCTION: Pagination Software – QPS/QuarkXPress 8.5.; Production Equipment – Caere/OmniPage, Magic/Separator; Cameras – 1-Nu PRESSROOM: Line 1 – 6-G/Community offset 1973; Line 2 – 2-G/Community offset 1983; Line 3 – 2-G/Community offset 1999; Folders – 1-G/Suburban.; Inserters and stuffers – KAN/480; Bundle tying machines – . BUSINESS COMPUTERS: Business Software – Quick Books; Business Hardware – 3-IBM/PC, Pentium
Delivery method: Mail, Newsstand, Private Carrier, Racks

ROCK SPRINGS

DAILY ROCKET-MINER

215 D St., Rock Springs, Wyo., 82901; gen tel (307) 362-3736; gen fax (307) 382-2763; gen e-mail rocket@sweetwaterhsa.com; web site www.rocketminer.com
Published: Tues, Wed, Thur, Fri, Sat, Sun
Weekday Frequency: m
Saturday Frequency: m
Circulation: 7,081; 8,367(sat); 7,342(sun)
Last Audit: ABC September 30, 2011
Price: 68.00/yr (carrier/mail).
Advertising: Open inch rate $11.06
News services: AP, NEA, TMS, Wyoming Press Association.
Politics: Independent-Democrat.
Not Published: Jan. 2; Memorial Day; Independence Day; Labor Day; Thanksgiving; Christmas.
Special Editions: Election (Aug); Christmas (Dec); Bridal (Feb); Western Wyoming Review of Progress (Mar); Western Wyoming Vacation (May); Festival (Nov); Cooking (Oct); Hunting (Sept).
Special Weekly Sections: Rock Springs Marquee (Wed).
Magazines: American Profile (S).
Pres./Pub./Personnel Mgr. ....Holly P. Dabb
Vice Pres. ....Anne McCracken
Circ. Mgr. ....Pam Haynes
Mng. Ed. ....Michele Depue
Prodn. Foreman, Pressroom/Mailroom Jonathon Smith
Mechanical available: Offset; Black and 3 ROP colors; insert accepted - most; page cutoffs - 21 1/2.
Mechanical Specifications: Type page 13 1/2 x 21 1/2; E - 6 cols, 2 1/16, 1/8 between; A - 6 cols, 2 1/16, 1/8 between; C - 8 cols, 1 3/4, 1/12 between.
Commodity Consumption: Avg. Page Number Per Issue - Daily 16; Avg. Page Number Per Issue - Plates Used 4000; Avg. Page Number Per Issue - Saturday 16; widths 27; Newsprint Used - Short Tons 200541; Printing Ink Used - Pages Printed 4240.
Equipment EDITORIAL: Front-end Software – QPS 4.0, Synaptic 3.1.; Editorial Hardware – HP, IBM; Editorial Equipment – 6-COM/MDT 350, 3-M/Correcterm, 1-COM/MCS 10; Editorial Printers – HP CLASSIFIED: Front-end Software – Microsoft/Windows 95, Archetype/Corel Draw, QPS, APP/Mac.; Classified Hardware – HP, IBM; Classified Equipment – Cp; Classified Printers – HP DISPLAY: Ad make-up applications – Microsoft/Windows 95, Archetype/Corel Draw, QPS; Layout Software – IBM.; Display Hardware – IBM; Display Printers – HP PRODUCTION: Pagination Software – QPS 4.0.; Production Equipment – 1-B, HP; Cameras – 1-K/241; Scanners – HP PRESSROOM: Line 1 – 5-G/Community 1974; Folders – 1; Inserters and stuffers – 3/DG; Bundle tying machines – 1-It/MS-AF, 1-Us/TE; Addressing machine – 2-Am/4000. BUSINESS COMPUTERS: Business Software – Synaptic; Business Hardware – 1-IBM

ROCK SPRINGS NEWSPAPERS, INC.

215 D St., Rock Springs, Wyo., 82901; gen tel (307) 362-3736; gen fax (307) 382-2763

SHERIDAN

SHERIDAN NEWSPAPERS, INC.

144 Grinnell, Sheridan, Wyo., 82801; gen tel (307) 672-2431; gen fax (307) 672-7950

THE SHERIDAN PRESS

144 Grinnell St., Sheridan, Wyo., 82801; gen tel (307) 672-2431; gen fax (307) 672-7950; gen e-mail carl@thesheridanpress.com; adv e-mail classified@thesheridanpress.com; ed e-mail editor@thesheridanpress.com; web site www.thesheridanpress.com
Published: Mon, Tues, Wed, Thur, Fri
Weekday Frequency: e
Saturday Frequency: m
Circulation: 6,565; 6,565(sat)
Last Audit: March 31, 2003
Price: 9.00/mo; 84.00/yr.
Advertising: Open inch rate $13.00
News services: AP, MCT, NEA, TMS.
Politics: Independent.
Not Published: New Year; Memorial Day; Independence Day; Labor Day; Thanksgiving; Christmas.
Special Editions: Bridal Issue (Feb); Senior Health & Leisure (Jan); Sheridan-WY Rodeo (Jun); Home Improvement (Mar); Big Horn Mountain Tourist and Recreation Guide (May); Christmas (Nov); Hunting (Sept).
Special Weekly Sections: Options (Fri).
Magazines: American Profile (Sat).
Broadcast Affiliations: KOTA-TV; KULR-TV; KTVQ-TV; KTWO-TV; KCWY-TV.
Exec. Vice Pres./Pub. ....Carl P. Sanders
Adv. Mgr., Retail/Nat'l.....................Beth Smith
Circ. Mgr. ....Annette Bryl
Editorial Writer ....Patrick Murphy
Sports Ed....................................Ken Hamerik
Prodn. Mgr., Pre Press.................Rick Schmidt
Prodn. Mgr., Systems ....Alvin Nielsen
Market Information: TMC.
Mechanical available: Offset; Black and 3 ROP colors; insert accepted - all; page cutoffs - 22 3/4.
Mechanical Specifications: Type page 12 3/4 x 21 1/2; E - 6 cols, 2 1/16, 1/8 between; A - 6 cols, 2 1/16, 1/8 between; C - 7 cols, 1 3/4, 1/8 between.
Commodity Consumption: Avg. Page Number Per Issue - Daily 18; Avg. Page Number Per Issue - Plates Used 6000; widths 27 1/2; Newsprint Used - Metric Tons 377; Printing Ink Used - Black 6000; Printing Ink Used - Color 450; Printing Ink Used - Pages Printed 6100.
Equipment EDITORIAL: Front-end Software – Baseview 1.1, QPS/QuarkXPress 3.32r5, APP/Mac Appleshare 5.0.2.; Editorial Hardware – 3-APP/G4, 5-APP/Power Mac; Editorial Equipment – 2-APP/Mac 30SE, APP/Power Mac fileserver; Editorial Printers – Xante/Accel-a-Writer 39 CLASSIFIED: Front-end Software – Baseview 4.0.; Classified Hardware – 4-APP/Power Mac, 4-APP/G4; Classified Printers – Xante/Accel-a-Writer 39 DISPLAY: Ad make-up applications – Multi-Ad/Creator II, Adobe/Photoshop 7.0, Adobe/Illustrator 10.; Display Hardware – 2-APP/Power Mac PRODUCTION: Pagination Software – QPS/QuarkXPress 3.32r5.; Production Equipment – ECR/VRL 36; Cameras – Acti; Scanners – 1-Epson/836XL, Epson/1680, Nikon/4000 PRESSROOM: Line 1 – 9-G/Community 1975, 2; Folders – 1-G/SC.; Inserters and stuffers – 6/MM; Bundle tying machines – 1-Samuel/SA 625 Strapping, MLN, Signode. BUSINESS COMPUTERS: Business Software – Baseview; Business Hardware – Pentium

WORLAND

BIG HORN BASIN NEWSPAPERS, INC.

201 N. Eighth St., Worland, Wyo., 82401-2614; gen tel (307) 347-3241; gen fax (307) 347-4267

NORTHERN WYOMING DAILY NEWS

201 N. 8th St., Worland, Wyo., 82401; gen tel (307) 347-3241; gen fax (307) 347-4267; gen e-mail leel@wyodaily.com; web site wyodaily.com
Published: Tues, Wed, Thur, Fri, Sat
Weekday Frequency: m
Circulation: 3,468; 3,468(sat)
Last Audit: September 30, 2002
Price: 6.50/mo (carrier); 73.00/yr.
Advertising: Open inch rate $9.50
News services: AP.
Politics: Independent. **Established:** 1905
Not Published: Dec. 26.
Magazines: Country Review (own, newsprint) (S); American Profile (Weekly).
Sec. ....Ronald M. Brown
Adv. Mgr. ....Dustin Fuller
Educ. Ed.....................................Lee Lockhart
Librarian.....................................Dennis Koch
People Page Ed. ....Christine Weber
Special Projects Ed..................Susan Lockhart
Prodn. Supt....................................John Elliott
Market Information: TMC.
Mechanical available: Offset; Black and 3 ROP colors; insert accepted; page cutoffs - 22 3/4.
Mechanical Specifications: Type page 13 x 21 1/2; E - 6 cols, 2 1/16, 1/8 between; A - 6 cols, 2 1/16, 1/8 between; C - 6 cols, 2 1/16, 1/8 between.
Commodity Consumption: Avg. Page Number Per Issue - Daily 14; Avg. Page Number Per Issue - Plates Used 1200; widths 28; Newsprint Used - Short Tons 100; Printing Ink Used - Black 4500; Printing Ink Used - Color 200; Printing Ink Used - Pages Printed 4548.
Equipment; Editorial Hardware – DP/Imaging 2355.; Classified Hardware – DP/Imaging 2355.; Layout Software – 1-COM/350.; Production Equipment – 1-Nu/Flip Top FT40; Cameras – 1-SCREEN. PRESSROOM: Line 1 – 4-G/Community; Folders – 1; Bundle tying machines – 1-Bu/BT 16 String Tyer; Addressing machine – 2/Wm.; Business Hardware – 2-IBM/OS 2

DAILY NEWSPAPERS PUBLISHED IN CANADA

ALBERTA

CALGARY

CALGARY HERALD

PO Box 2400, Calgary, AB, T2E 7P5, Canada; gen tel (403) 235-7100; adv tel (403) 235-7168; ed tel (403) 235-7400; adv fax (403) 235-8787; ed fax (403) 235-7379; adv e-mail online@theherald.canwest.com; ed e-mail letters@theherald.canwest.com; web site www.calgaryherald.com

Published: Mon, Tues, Wed, Thur, Fri, Sat, Sun
Weekday Frequency: m
Saturday Frequency: m
Circulation 124,559; 119,402(sat); 114,642(sun)
Last Audit: ABC September 30, 2011
Group: CanWest Media Sales
Price: 3.75/wk; 16.25/mo; 195.00/yr.
Advertising: Open inch rate $6.68
News services: AP, Southam Newspapers, Aditus, RN, LAT-WP, DJ, CSM.
Politics: Independent
Not Published: Christmas.
Special weekly sections: Spring Fashion (Neighbours) (Apr); Back To School (Neighbours) (Aug); BOMA (Dec); Calgary Foundation (Feb); Neighbours' Weddings (Jan); Discover the Columbia Valley (Jul); Energy (Jun); CRHBA Home Renovation Tour (Mar); Environment Week (May); Neighbours-
Magazines: TV Times (Fri); e-Business (Mon); Color Comics (Sat).
Broadcast Affiliations: Global TV.
Pub. ....Malcolm Kirk
Vice Pres., Finance/Opns. ....Ross Butler
Adv. Vice Pres. ....Rob Maleschuk
Adv. Mgr., Classified ....Kellie Bowden
Adv. Mgr., Key Accts. ....Sherry Burgess
Circ. Vice Pres., Reader Servs./Sales Travis Engebretson
Ed. in Chief ....Lorne Motley
Mng. Ed. ....Monica Zurowski
Acting Bus. Ed. ....Gord Smiley
Cartoonist ....Vance Rodewalt
Columnist ....Don Braid
Editorial Page Ed. ....Licia Corbella
Editorial Writer ....Paula Arab
Educ. Reporter ....Colette Derworiz
Entertainment Ed. ....Tom Babin
Features Ed. ....Lisa Monforton
Librarian ....Karen Crosby
Music Critic ....Heath McCoy
News Ed. ....Paul Harvey
Market information: ADS; Split run; Zoned editions.
Mechanical available: Offset; Black and 3 ROP colors; insert accepted - Poly Bags; page cutoffs - 22.
Mechanical Specifications: Type page 11 1/2 x 22 1/8; E - 5 cols, 2 3/16, 1/6 between; A - 10 cols, 1, 1/6 between; C - 10 cols, 1, 1/6 between.
Commodity Consumption: Avg. Page Number Per Issue - Daily 80; Avg. Page Number Per Issue - Plates Used 211575; Avg. Page Number Per Issue - Saturday 148; Avg. Page Number Per Issue - Sunday 64; widths 37 2/5; Newsprint Used - Metric Tons 24082; Printing Ink Used - Black 409447
Equipment EDITORIAL: Front-end Software – QPS, Quark/Copy Desk, Quickwire.; Editorial Hardware – APP/Mac G3, APP/iMac, APP/Mac Power Book; Editorial Equipment – Printers Ã□Â□ QMS/11 x 17 x 2, QMS/11 13 x 24 CLASSIFIED: Front-end Software – Cybergraphics.; Classified Hardware – Cybergraphics; Classified Printers – HP/4S1 DISPLAY: Ad make-up applications – Multi-Ad/Creator, QPS/QuarkXPress; Layout software – ALS/30.; Display Hardware – APP/Macs; Production Equipment – 2-AU/APS-108 C-6, 2-AU/APS-3850 SST, 1-WL, 2-LE/On-line Processor; Cameras – Scanners Ã□Â□ Topaz, 1-HI/Opal Ultras, Linotype-Hell, Eskofot/2024; Scanners – Equipment Ã□Â□ QPS 1.12, QPS/QuarkXPress, Multi-Ad/Creator. PRESSROOM: Line 1 – 9-G/Metro double width 1981, 2-G/Metro double width 1998; Line 2 – 9-G/Metro double width 1981, 2-G/Metro double width 1998; Line 3 – Pasters Ã□Â□ G/Metro; Reels and Stands – G/Metro.; MAILROOM-Counter stackers – 4-QWI/300, 2-QWI/350, 2-QWI/350; Inserters and stuffers – Heidelberg/2299; Bundle tying machines –6/Dynaric, 1-/Constellation, 1-/Dynamic; Wrapping singles – 1-St/PM 720; Mailroom control system – ICON/NT, QWI/Bundle Distribution ContBUSINESS COMPUTERS: Audio Software – In-house; Audio Hardware – 3-DEC/VAX 4000-100

THE CALGARY SUN

2615 12th St. NE, Calgary, AB, T2E 7W9, Canada; gen tel (403) 250-4200; adv tel (403) 250-4240; ed tel (403) 250-4122; gen fax (403) 250-4180; ed e-mail calnews@calgarysun.com; web site www.calgarysun.com

Published: Mon, Tues, Wed, Thur, Fri, Sat, Sun
Weekday Frequency: m
Saturday Frequency: m
Circulation 37,248; 40,886(sat); 52,589(sun)
Last Audit: BPA December 30, 2010
Price: 3.25/wk.
Advertising: Open inch rate $4.21(m-fri)
News services: CP, UPI, RN, GNS, CNW.
Politics: Independent
Note: Corporate rates are offered on a collective basis between the Edmonton, Calgary and Toronto markets.
Not Published: Christmas.
Special weekly sections: The Edge (Dec-April) (Monthly).
Magazines: TV Magazine (S); F.A.S.T. (Sat).
Pub ....Gord Norrie
Controller ....Murray Matieshen
Adv. Dir. ....Ed Huculak
Mktg. Mgr. ....Diane Wensel
Circ. Dir. ....Bruce MacPherson
Ed. in Chief ....Jose Rodriguez
Mng. Ed. ....Martin Hutson
City Ed. ....Dave Naylor
Info Servs. Mgr. ....Chris Gibson
Prodn. Mgr., Pre Press ....Sheldon Ball
Market information: TMC.
Mechanical available: Offset; Black and 3 ROP colors; insert accepted; page cutoffs - 22 3/4.
Mechanical Specifications: Type page 10 1/4 x 14 1/4; E - 6 cols, 1 1/2, 1/6 between; A - 8 cols, 1 3/16, 1/6 between; C - 8 cols, 1 3/16, 1/6 between.
Commodity Consumption: Avg. Page Number Per Issue - Daily 88; Avg. Page Number Per Issue - Plates Used 52000; Avg. Page Number Per Issue - Saturday 80; Avg. Page Number Per Issue - Sunday 170; widths 13 1/2; Newsprint Used - Metric Tons 8300; Printing Ink Used - Pages Printed
Equipment; Editorial Hardware – 2-Sun/Sparc 10-151, 1-Sun/Sparc 10-51, 1-Sun/Sparc 10-41; Editorial Equipment – 14-APP/Mac PowerBook 150, 14-APP/Mac Quadra 610, 18-APP/Mac Quadra 650, 4-APP/Mac Quadra 700, 8-APP/Mac Quadra 800, 2-APP/Mac Quadra 840 AV, 2-APP/Power Mac 7100, 4-APP/Mac D CLASSIFIED: Front-end Software – Composition Systems.; Classified Hardware – 2-DEC/PDP 11-70; Classified Equipment – 9-CT/90; Classified Printers – 1-Chelgraph/PPT-600 DISPLAY: Ad make-up applications – Multi-Ad/Creator, QPS/QuarkXPress 3.3, Scitex, Adobe/Photoshop; Layout software – 7-APP/Mac; Display Hardware – 2-APP/Power Mac 7500, 2-APP/Power Mac 8100, 2-APP/Mac Quadra 840AV; Display Printers – ECR/VR30, 1-Canon/Color Copier; Production Equipment – 2-Polychrome, Harlequin, 4-DEC/Alpha with AU RIPs; Cameras – C/Spartan III, 1-AG; Scanners – Scitex/Smart Plus, 2-Scitex/340L, Howtek/D4000. PRESSROOM: Line 1 – 3-G/HO (mono), 4-G/decks 1992; Folders – G/Imperial; Pasters – 6-G/CT50 RTP; Reels and Stands – 6-G/CT-50.; MAILROOM-Counter stackers – 3/HL, 3-/QWI; Inserters and stuffers – 1-/HI, 1-/S; Bundle tying machines –2-/Dynaric, 2-/MLN; Wrapping singles – 1-/QWI, 1-/NJP, 1-/SH; Address machine – Dm; Other equipment – KAN/Quarter Folder, 1-MM/321 Stitcher-Trimmer, Polar/

EDMONTON

EDMONTON JOURNAL

PO Box 2421, Edmonton, AB, T5J 2S6, Canada; gen tel (780) 429-5100; adv tel (780) 429-5400; ed tel (780) 429-5200; gen fax (780) 498-5659; adv fax (780) 429-5308; ed fax (780) 498-5677; adv e-mail adv_reception@thejournal.canwest.com; web site www.edmontonjournal.com

Published: Mon, Tues, Wed, Thur, Fri, Sat, Sun
Weekday Frequency: m
Saturday Frequency: m
Circulation 100,438; 102,329(sat); 100,026(sun)
Last Audit: ABC September 30, 2011
Group: Postmedia Network Inc.
CanWest Media Sales
Price: 24.26/mo; 291.12/yr.
Advertising: Open inch rate $9.64
News services: CanWest Media Sales.
Politics: Independent **Established:** 1903
Not Published: New Year; Christmas.
Special editions: Destination West (Annually); Recreation Property (Other).
Special weekly sections: Golf-Masters (Apr); RV Showcase (Aug); Babies of the Year (Dec); Edmonton Motorshow (Feb); Banff Winter Festival (Jan); Golf-The Open Championship (Jul); Golf-U.S. Open (Jun); Alberta Health & Wellness Report (Mar); BC Report - Wine, Golf, Spa (May); Cana
Magazines: What's On (Fri); Body & Health (Mon); Sunday Reader (S); Real Estate Marketplace (Sat); At Home (Thur); Look (Tues); Working (Wed).
Broadcast Affiliations: Global Edmonton (Can-West).
Publisher ....John Connolly
Adv. Mgr., Classified ....Joseph Wuest
Adv. Mgr., Local Territory ....John Kopeck
Adv. Mgr., Sales Planning/Nat'l Sales Gordon Deeks
Adv. Mgr., Servs. ....Lyn Propp
Adv. Local Online Sales Specialist Dene Lingelbach
Adv. Local Online Sales Specialist ..Robert Valpy
Deputy Ed., Readership/Features Barb Wilkinson
City Ed. ....Peter Maser
Culture Ed. ....Keri Sweetman
Vice Pres., Finance ....David Becker
Vice Pres., HR ....Ken Wickenberg
Credit Mgr. ....David Marshall
Adv. Mgr., Retail Multi-Market Sales Ian Newman
Vice Pres., Mktg. ....Patricia Hutchison
Mktg. Research Mgr. ....Cindy Mah
Circ. Vice Pres., Reader Servs. ....Douglas Wass
Ed. in Chief ....Allan Mayer
Deputy Ed., News ....Roy Wood
At Home/Look Ed. ....Chris Standring
Market information: ADS; TMC.
Mechanical available: Cold Web Offset; Black and 3 ROP colors; insert accepted - Post-it notes, Tag-a-longs, Poly bags, Belly bands; page cutoffs - 23 9/16.
Mechanical Specifications: Type page 11 9/16 x 22 1/8; E - 5 cols, 2 1/20, 1/8 between; A - 10 cols, 1 1/16, 1/8 between; C - 10 cols, 1 1/16, 1/8 between.
Commodity Consumption: Avg. Page Number Per Issue - Daily 78.12; Avg. Page Number Per Issue - Plates Used 248381; Avg. Page Number Per Issue - Saturday 128.3; Avg. Page Number Per Issue - Sunday 66.2; widths 37 2/5; Newsprint Used - Metric Tons 19746; Printing Ink Used - Black
Equipment EDITORIAL: Front-end Software – QPS/QuarkXPress 3.32, QPS/Copydesk 1.12, Quickwire 4.09, Adobe/Photoshop 5.5, Adobe/Illustrator 6, Adobe/CS.; Editorial Hardware – APP/Mac G3, APP/Mac G4, APP/iMac, APP/iBook; Editorial Printers – HP/5simmx, Graphic Enterprises, Page San III/Broadsheet Printer CLASSIFIED: Front-end Software – Cybergraphics/Genesis 22.; Classified Hardware – PC, DEC/VAX 4000, APP/Mac DISPLAY: Ad make-up applications – Adobe/Illustrator CS, Adobe/Photoshop CS, Adobe/InDesign CS, Adobe/Acrobat PDF 6.0; Layout software – APP/Mac, SCS/Layout 8000.; Display Hardware – APP/Mac G4; Display Printers – APP/Mac LaserWriter; Production Equipment – 2-Southern/Litho; Cameras – Scanners Ã□Â□Ã□Â□ PixelCraft 8200, 2-Linotype-Hell/Saphires, 2-Kk 2035, 2-HI/Opal Scanner, 2-ECR/2045C; Scanners – Equipment Ã□Â□Ã□Â□ Southam/Ad Trak, AU/Softpip, SCS/Linx, Asura 6.0. PRESSROOM: Line 1 – 11-G/Metroliner (6 half decks); Line 2 – 11-G/Metroliner (6 half decks); Press Drives – Press control system Ã□Â□Ã□Â□ G/PCS.; MAILROOMCounter stackers – 8-HL/Monitor, 8/QWI 401; Inserters and stuffers – 4-Fg/Drum; Bundle tying machines –16-Dynaric/NP 1500; Wrapping singles – Manual.BUSINESS COMPUTERS: Audio Software – MS Office/Exchange/Outlook 97-2000, Keaterm; Audio Hardware – 2-DEC/VAX 4000

THE EDMONTON SUN

4990 92nd Ave., Ste. 250, Edmonton, AB, T6B 3A1, Canada; gen tel (780) 468-0100; adv tel (780) 468-0181; ed tel (780) 468-0281; adv fax (780) 468-0128; ed fax (780) 468-0242; gen e-mail edsun@edmsun.com; ed e-mail edmbiz@edmsunpub.com; web site www.edmontonsun.com

Published: Mon, Tues, Wed, Thur, Fri, Sat, Sun
Weekday Frequency: m
Saturday Frequency: m
Circulation 44,865; 43,227(sat); 55,858(sun)
Last Audit: BPA December 30, 2010
Price: 3.30/wk.
Advertising: Open inch rate $4.11
News services: RN, CP, AP, SHNS, LAT-WP, TMS.
Politics: 1978
Note: Corporate rates are available on a collective basis between Sun Media Market newspapers across Canada.
Not Published: Christmas.
Special weekly sections: Saturday Home Improvement (Monthly).
Magazines: Car Market (Fri); Comics (S); Travel (Sat); Fashion (Tues); Food (Wed).
Pub. ....David Black
Controller ....Gunther Motsch
Dir., Adv. ....Gord Schwinghamer
Adv. Mgr., Classified ....Bob Paterson
Mgr., Promo. ....Shauna Heryford
Circ. Dir. ....Nigel Wainwright
Ed. in Chief ....Graham Dalziel
City Ed. ....Nicole Bergot
Columnist ....Kerry Diotte
Columnist ....Neil Waugh
Columnist ....Mindelle Jacobs
Editorial Page Ed. ....Mike Jenkinson
News Ed. ....Tony Saloway
Photo Dept. Mgr. ....Tom Baraid
Sports Ed. ....Keith Brantford

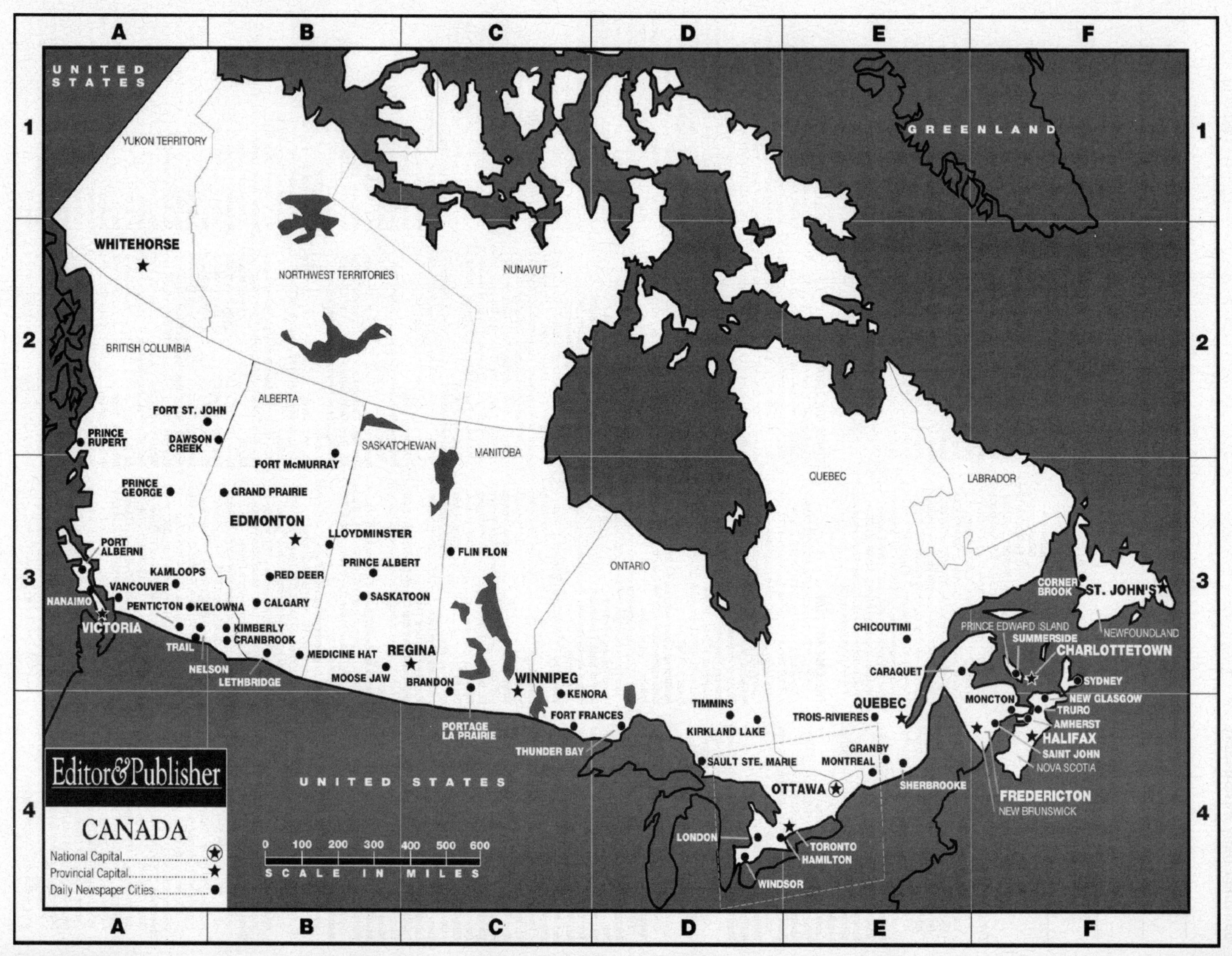
Editor&Publisher
CANADA
National Capital
Provincial Capital
Daily Newspaper Cities
SCALE IN MILES
0 100 200 300 400 500 600
UNITED STATES
GREENLAND
YUKON TERRITORY
NORTHWEST TERRITORIES
NUNAVUT
BRITISH COLUMBIA
ALBERTA
SASKATCHEWAN
MANITOBA
ONTARIO
QUEBEC
LABRADOR
NEWFOUNDLAND
PRINCE EDWARD ISLAND
NOVA SCOTIA
NEW BRUNSWICK
WHITEHORSE
PRINCE RUPERT
FORT ST. JOHN
DAWSON CREEK
PRINCE GEORGE
FORT McMURRAY
GRAND PRAIRIE
EDMONTON
LLOYDMINSTER
PORT ALBERNI
KAMLOOPS
VANCOUVER
NANAIMO
VICTORIA
PENTICTON
KELOWNA
TRAIL
NELSON
KIMBERLY
CRANBROOK
LETHBRIDGE
RED DEER
CALGARY
MEDICINE HAT
PRINCE ALBERT
SASKATOON
MOOSE JAW
REGINA
BRANDON
PORTAGE LA PRAIRIE
FLIN FLON
WINNIPEG
KENORA
FORT FRANCES
THUNDER BAY
TIMMINS
KIRKLAND LAKE
SAULT STE. MARIE
LONDON
WINDSOR
TORONTO
HAMILTON
OTTAWA
MONTREAL
GRANBY
SHERBROOKE
TROIS-RIVIERES
QUEBEC
CHICOUTIMI
CARAQUET
MONCTON
FREDERICTON
SAINT JOHN
HALIFAX
AMHERST
TRURO
NEW GLASGOW
SYDNEY
SUMMERSIDE
CHARLOTTETOWN
CORNER BROOK
ST. JOHN'S
A B C D E F
1 2 3 4

Television Ed.............................Jenny Feniak
Wire Ed...................................Gary Poignant
Info. Serv. Mgr...........................Glenn Kaiser
Prodn. Dir.................................Will Stephani
Market information: Split run.
Mechanical available: Offset; Black and 3 ROP colors; insert accepted; page cutoffs - 22 3/4.
Mechanical Specifications: Type page 11 1/4 x 13 1/2; E - 8 cols, 1 1/6, 7/50 between; A - 8 cols, 1 1/6, 7/50 between; C - 8 cols, 1 1/6, 7/50 between.
Commodity Consumption: Avg. Page Number Per Issue - Daily 92; Avg. Page Number Per Issue - Plates Used 66000; Avg. Page Number Per Issue - Saturday 98; Avg. Page Number Per Issue - Sunday 215; widths 27; Newsprint Used - Metric Tons 10600; Printing Ink Used - Black 204000; Pri
Equipment EDITORIAL: Front-end Software – QPS/QuarkXPress 3.3, P.INK/Database 2030, P.INK/Software 2.3.2.; Editorial Hardware – 57-APP/Mac; Editorial Equipment – 2-Ricoh/fax; Editorial Printers – 1-NewGen, 2-QMS, 2-HP/LaserJet, 1-Tektronix/Phaser III pix CLASSIFIED: Front-end Software – CSI, CJ.; Classified Hardware – Sun/Enterprise 3000, 3-Sun/Enterprise 450; Classified Equipment – Ricoh/fax DISPLAY: Ad make-up applications – Mk/Managing Editor; Layout software – CJ.; Display Hardware – 2-APP/Mac 7100 PPC; Display Printers – 2-HP/LaserJet III, APP/Mac LaserWriter Pro 63; Production Equipment – 2-Howson, 3-III/3850, CCC 700i, Canon; Cameras – 2-C/Spartan Horizontal; Scanners – 1-Epson/Flatbed. PRESSROOM: Line 1 – G/Metro (7 units; 3 half decks) 1981; Folders –1-G/Double.; MAILROOMCounter stackers – 3-G/Stackmaster, 3-Id; Inserters and stuffers – 2-S/72P; Bundle tying machines – 2/MLN, MLN/News 90; Wrapping singles – 3-/Cyclops; Address machine – 3-MVP/BW50, 1-AVY/Labeler.; Audio Hardware – 3-IBM

FORT MCMURRAY

FORT MCMURRAY TODAY

Bag 4008, Fort McMurray, AB, T9H 3G1, Canada; gen tel (780) 743-8186; gen fax (780) 715-3820; gen e-mail today@fortmcmurraytoday.com; adv e-mail today.advertising@fortmcmurraytoday.com; ed e-mail today.editorial@fortmcmurraytoday.com; web site www.fortmcmurraytoday.com
Published: Mon, Tues, Wed, Thur, Fri, Sat
Weekday Frequency: e
Circulation 3,049
Last Audit: ABC September 30, 2008
Price: 2.50/wk; 10.00/mo; 175.00/yr.
Advertising: Open inch rate $.99(e-fri)
News services: CP.
Politics: Independent **Established:** 1974
Not Published: New Year; Feb. 17; Good Friday; Victoria Day; Canada Day; Aug. 4; Labor Day; Thanksgiving; Christmas; Boxing Day.
Own facility?: Y
Special weekly sections: Mystery Face (Apr); Back to School (Aug); Child's Christmas Eve (Dec); Your Money (Feb); Minor Hockey Week (Jan); Summer Sizzler (Jul); Environment (Jun); Slogan & Logo Contest (Mar); Forestry Week (May); Christmas Song Book (Nov); Fire Prevention Week (O
Pub........................................Darren Gawron
Adv. Mgr..................................Daren Gawron
Circ. Mgr.................................Sonya Lacroixe
Online Ed.................................Justin Holmes
Sports Ed.................................Corey Atkinson
Market information: Split run; TMC.
Mechanical available: Offset; Black and 3 ROP colors; insert accepted; page cutoffs - 22 3/4.
Mechanical Specifications: Type page 11 7/16 x 21 3/16; E - 6 cols, 1 3/4, 1/8 between; A - 6 cols, 1 3/4, 1/8 between; C - 9 cols, 1 1/4, 1/8 between.
Commodity Consumption: Avg. Page Number Per Issue - Daily 20; Avg. Page Number Per Issue - Plates Used 4400; widths 11 7/16; Newsprint Used - Metric Tons 160; Printing Ink Used - Black 8992; Printing Ink Used - Color 2240; Printing Ink Used - Pages Printed 5020.
Equipment EDITORIAL: Front-end Software – Microsoft, QPS.; Editorial Hardware – APP/Mac CLASSIFIED: Front-end Software – Baseview, QPS.; Classified Hardware – APP/Mac DISPLAY: Ad make-up applications – Mk/Ad Touch, APP/Mac SE IIs; Layout software – APP/Mac.; Display Hardware – APP/Mac, NEC/600; Production Equipment – 2-M/Linotron 202W, 1-Fuji; Cameras – 1-Acti. PRESSROOM: Line 1 – 7-G/Community; Folders –1-G/Suburban 2:1.; MAILROOMCounter stackers – 1-BG/Count-O-Veyor; Bundle tying machines –2-Weld Loc/SP-505; Address machine – Bostich, Polar, CAT.; Audio Hardware – 4-NCR/Tower

GRANDE PRAIRIE

DAILY HERALD-TRIBUNE

Bag 3000, Grande Prairie, AB, T8V 6V4, Canada; gen tel (780) 532-1110; gen fax (780) 532-2120; adv e-mail class@bowesnet.com; web site www.dailyheraldtribune.com
Published: Mon, Tues, Wed, Thur, Fri
Weekday Frequency: e
Circulation 6,600
Last Audit: ABC September 30, 2008
Price: 8.50/mo; 95.00/yr.
Advertising: Open inch rate $.91(e-fri)
News services: CP.
Politics: Independent
Not Published: Legal holidays.
Special weekly sections: Tourist Book (Apr); Business Review (Feb); On The Land (Mar); Homes (Monthly); Visitor's Guide (Other).
Magazines: Color Comics (Other).
Pub........................................Kent Keebaugh
Assoc. Pub................................Doug Hare
Office Mgr................................Margaret Steele
Adv. Mgr., Nat'l.........................Fern Hickson
Circ. Mgr.................................Wanda Lee Bowen
Mng. Ed...................................Jeff McCoshen
City Ed....................................Dianne Rinne
Sports Ed.................................Terry Farrell
Prodn. Mgr., Distr......................Joanne Blais
Prodn. Foreman, Press................Cody Hodges
Market information: Split run; TMC.
Mechanical available: Offset; Black and 3 ROP colors; insert accepted - door hangers, belly wraps, stickies; page cutoffs - 23.
Mechanical Specifications: Type page 11 1/2 x 21 1/4; E - 10 cols, 1 1/16, 1/8 between; A - 10 cols, 1 1/16, 1/8 between; C - 10 cols, 1

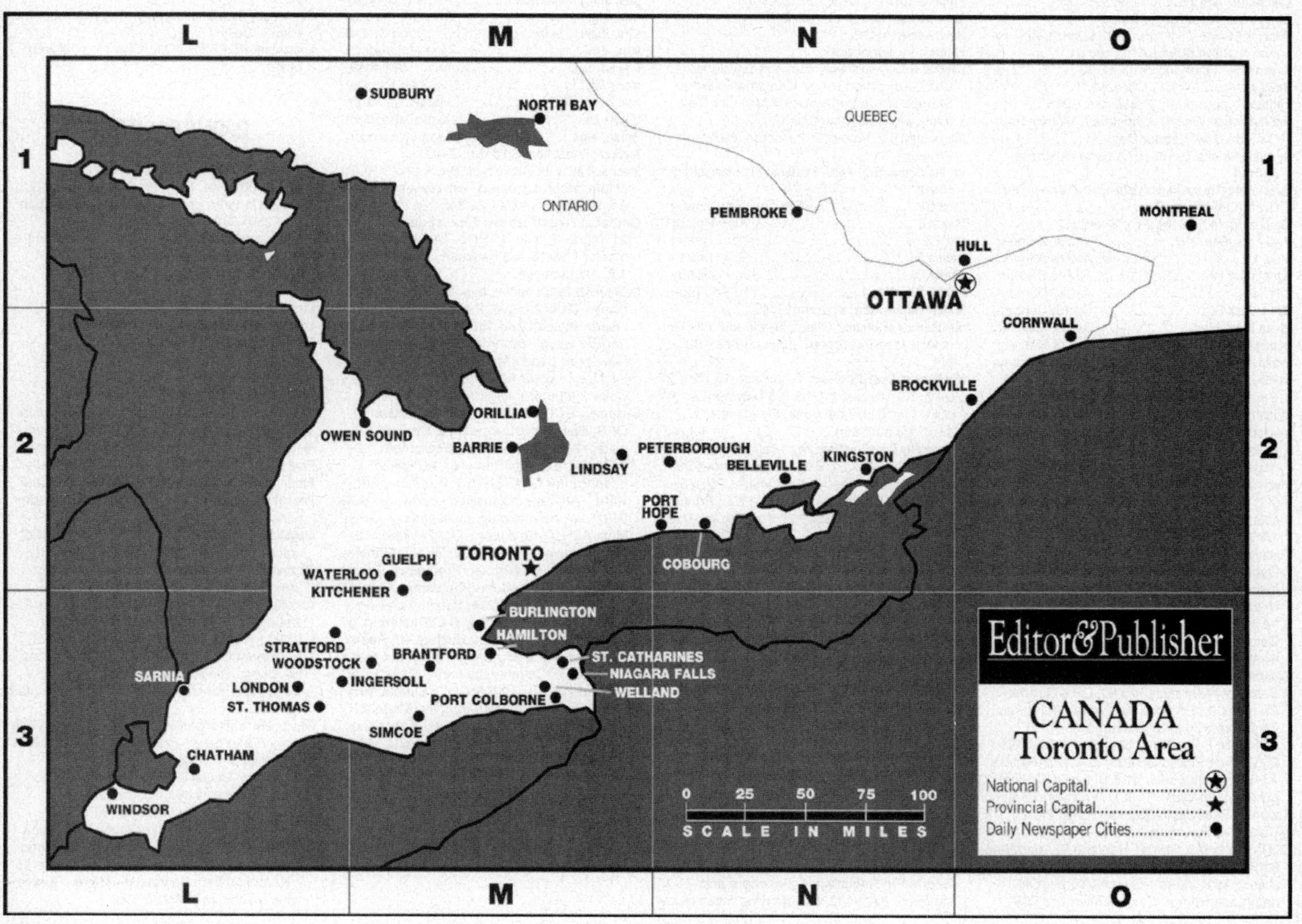

1/16, 1/8 between.
Commodity Consumption: Avg. Page Number Per Issue - Daily 24; Avg. Page Number Per Issue - Plates Used 7500; widths 25; Newsprint Used - Metric Tons 800; Printing Ink Used - Black 17418.5; Printing Ink Used - Color 770.93; Printing Ink Used - Pages Printed 8263.
Equipment; Editorial Hardware – Mk.; Classified Hardware – Mk. DISPLAY: Ad make-up applications – QPS, Aldus/PageMaker; Layout software – 5-APP/Mac.; Production Equipment – ECR/PelBox, 1-Nu/Flip Top; Cameras – 1-Acti; Scanners – Equipment Ã□Â□ QPS 3.2. PRESSROOM: Line 1 – 10-G/Community (8 down; 2 stack; Balloon former); Press Drives – G/Community.; MAILROOMCounter stackers – 1/BG, CH; Bundle tying machines –1-/Sa, 2-/Sivaron; Address machine - 1-/Am, 1-/IBM; Other equipment – Kansa/480.; Audio Hardware – 2-NCR

LETHBRIDGE

THE LETHBRIDGE HERALD

PO Box 670, Lethbridge, AB, T1J 3Z7, Canada; gen tel (403) 328-4411; adv tel (430) 328-4410; ed tel (403) 328-4418; gen fax (403) 328-4536; adv fax (430) 329-8089; ed fax (403) 329-9355; adv e-mail lethads@lethbridgeherald.com; web site www.lethbridgeherald.com
Published: Mon, Tues, Wed, Thur, Fri, Sat, Sun
Weekday Frequency: m
Saturday Frequency: m
Circulation 15,765; 15,463(sat); 13,814(sun)
Last Audit: ABC September 30, 2011
Group: CanWest Media Sales
Price: 3.50/wk; 15.17/mo; 182.00/yr (home delivery), $214.00/yr (motor route).
Advertising: Open inch rate $1.69
News services: AP, CP, CSM, MCT.
Politics: Independent **Established:** 1905
Not Published: Easter; Christmas; Victory Day; Canada Day; Labour Day.
Special editions: Southern Alberta Business (Other).
Special weekly sections: Year-End Review Car Care (Other).
Magazines: Wheelers (Fri); Event (Thur).
Vice Pres./Gen. Mgr. ....Bob Carey
Mng. Ed. ....Doyle MacKinnon
Agriculture Ed ....Ric Swihart
City Ed. ....Craig Albrecht
News Desk Ed. ....Randy Jensen
Photo Dept. Mgr. ....David Rossiter
Sports Ed. ....Trevor Kenney
Prodn. Mgr., Commercial Print ....Bill Hartley
Prodn. Systems Mgr./Foreman, Composing Room Brad Brand
Market information: ADS; TMC; Zoned editions.
Mechanical available: Offset; Black and 3 ROP colors; insert accepted - samples, catalogs; page cutoffs - 21 1/2.
Mechanical Specifications: Type page 12 5/8 x 21 1/2; E - 10 cols, 1 1/16, 1/16 between; A - 10 cols, 1 1/16, 1/16 between; C - 10 cols, 1 1/16, 1/16 between.
Commodity Consumption: Avg. Page Number Per Issue - Daily 39.40; Avg. Page Number Per Issue - Plates Used 24120; widths 31; Newsprint Used - Metric Tons 1723; Printing Ink Used - Black 45000; Printing Ink Used - Color 4500; Printing Ink Used - Pages Printed 152000.
Equipment EDITORIAL: Front-end Software – Baseview/NewsEdit Pro IQ, QPS/QuarkXPress 4.03.; Editorial Hardware – APP/Mac G3 Server; Editorial Equipment – 4-APP/Mac PowerBook G-3, 8-APP/Mac G3-266, 15-APP/Mac G3-233; Editorial Printers – 2-Genicom/Model 3810 SP, 1-GCC/Elite LaserPrinter CLASSIFIED: Front-end Software – Baseview/AdManager Pro 2.0.2.; Classified Hardware – Mircosoft/Windows NT Server 4.0, MS/NT Server 4.0, Acer/Altos 930; Classified Equipment – 11-APP/Mac; Classified Printers – Okidata/Turbo, Okidata/LaserPrinter, Okidata/Microline DISPLAY: Ad make-up applications – QPS 4.03, Adobe/Photoshop 5.0, Adobe/Illustrator 7.0, Archetype/Designer, Multi-Ad/Creator 3.5, Archetype/Designer 3.1, QPS/QuarkXPress; Display Hardware – APP/Mac, G-3/266; Display Printers – 2-APP/Mac LaserPrinter, 1-APP/Mac Color StyleWriter PRODUCTION: Pagination software – QPS/QuarkXPress, APP/Mac 4.03.; Production Equipment – 1-Pre Press/Panther Pro; Cameras – C/Spartan III, Companica/680C Vertical; Scanners – 2-Kk/RFS-2035, 2-AG/Arcus II flatbed PRESSROOM: Line 1 – 7-G/Urbanite (1-3 color unit) single width 1973; Folders – G/Cole Quarter, G/Suburban Half, G/Urbanite Quarter.; Bundle tying machines –3-MLN/2; Wrapping singles – 1-MLN/MS-7; Address machine – 1/Am; Other equipment – MM/Stitcher-Trimmer.BUSINESS COMPUTERS: Audio Software – IBM/Newzware, Microsoft/Office; Audio Hardware – HP/9000, Unix System

MEDICINE HAT

MEDICINE HAT NEWS

PO Box 10, Medicine Hat, AB, T1A 7E6, Canada; gen tel (403) 527-1101; adv tel (403) 527-1101; gen fax (403) 528-5696; adv fax (403) 527-0737; ed fax (403) 527-1244
Published: Mon, Tues, Wed, Thur, Fri, Sat
Weekday Frequency: m
Saturday Frequency: m
Circulation 11,221; 11,221(sat)
Last Audit: ABC September 30, 2011
Group: CanWest Media Sales
Price: 3.15/wk; 13.65/mo; 163.80/yr.
Advertising: Open inch rate $1.03
News services: CP.
Politics: Independent
Special weekly sections: Homes & Gardens (Apr); Education (Aug); Christmas (Dec); Stampede (Jul); Progress (Mar); Car Care (Oct); Fall Shopping (Sept).
Magazines: TV Times (Fri); Homes (Sat); Wheels (Thur).
Sr. Vice Pres./Grp. Pub., Southern Alberta Michael Hertz
Circ. Dir. ....Gordon Waterhouse
Mng. Ed ....Alan Poirier
City Ed. ....Kerri Hamel
Online Ed. ....Greg Marsh
Sports Ed ....Sean Rooney
Prodn. Dir., Mfg. ....Tom Peterson
Market information: Split run; TMC.
Mechanical available: Offset; Black and 3 ROP colors; insert accepted; page cutoffs - 22 3/4.
Mechanical Specifications: Type page 11 1/2 x 21 9/16; E - 10 cols, 1 1/16, 1/8 between; A - 10 cols, 1 1/16, 1/8 between; C - 10 cols, 1 1/16, 1/8 between.
Commodity Consumption: Avg. Page Number Per Issue - Daily 27.51; Avg. Page Number Per Issue - Plates Used 29000; widths 25; Newsprint Used - Metric Tons 1200; Printing Ink Used - Black 21145.37; Printing Ink Used - Pages Printed 8392.
Equipment EDITORIAL: Front-end Software – Quickwire, QPS/QuarkXPress.; Editorial Hardware – APP/Power Mac 7100-80; Editorial Printers – Select/360, QMS/1600, Fuji/Imagesetter, AU/Imagesetter CLASSIFIED: Front-end Software – Baseview, Quickwire.; Classified Hardware – 5-RSK/Tandy 3000, RSK/Tandy VGM 100 DISPLAY: Ad make-up applications – Adobe/Illustrator 6.0; Display Printers – 1-QMS/860 plus PRODUCTION: Pagination software – QPS/QuarkXPress 3.31.; Production Equipment – Caere/OmniPage Pro, AU/Imagesetter; Cameras – 1-B/Caravel; Scanners – PixelCraft, Umax PRESSROOM: Line 1 – 10-G/Community single width; Press Drives – 2; Folders –G/SC (upper former, 1/4 folder), BG/Count-O-Veyor 109; Press registration system – Duarte/Pin Registration.; Inserters and stuffers – KAN/480; Bundle tying machines – 2-Sa/S1120, 1/MLN, 1-/Ca; Other equipment – 1-Challenge/3K Trimmer, 1-Lawson/Seriebb 3K Trimmer.

RED DEER

RED DEER ADVOCATE

PO Bag 5200, Red Deer, AB, T4R 1M9, Canada; gen tel (403) 343-2400; adv tel (403) 314-4343; ed tel (403) 314-4328; gen fax (403) 341-4772; adv fax (403) 342-4051; ed fax (403) 341-6560; gen e-mail administration@reddeeradvocate.com; adv e-mail advertising@reddeeradvocate.com; ed e-mail editorial@reddeeradvocate.com; web site www.reddeeradvocate.com
Published: Mon, Tues, Wed, Thur, Fri, Sat
Weekday Frequency: e
Saturday Frequency: m
Circulation 14,132; 13,745(sat)
Last Audit: ABC September 30, 2011
Price: 23.97/mo (mail), $13.00/mo (carrier); 158.75/yr.
Advertising: Open inch rate $2.76(e-fri)
News services: CP, AP, SHNS.
Politics: Independent **Established:** 1894
Not Published: New Year; Good Friday; Victoria Day; Canada Day; Labor Day; Thanksgiving; Heritage Day; Christmas.
Magazines: TV Today (Fri); Local Sports (Mon); Outdoor (Other); Color Comics (Sat); Food (Thur); Community Focus (Tues); Wheels (Wed).
Pub. ....Fred Gorman
Bus. Mgr. ....Dan Relkow
Adv. Dir. ....Callum Scott
Adv. Mgr., Classified ....Patricia Stamm
Adv. Mgr., Major Accts ....Richard Smalley
Circ. Mgr. ....Allan Melbourne
Circ. Supvr., Sales ....Doug Sibbet
Mng. Ed. ....Joe McLaughlin
City Ed. ....Carolyn Martindale
News Ed. ....John Stewart
Red Deer Life Ed. ....Harley Richards
Sports Ed ....Greg Meachem
Prodn. Mgr ....Scott Williamson
Market information: Split run; TMC.
Mechanical available: Offset; Black and 3 ROP colors; insert accepted - envelopes & cards 8 x 11; page cutoffs - 22 3/4.
Mechanical Specifications: Type page 11 7/10 x 21 1/2; E - 6 cols, 1 13/16, 1/8 between; A - 6 cols, 1 13/16, 1/8 between; C - 9 cols, 1 1/8, 1/8 between.
Commodity Consumption: Avg. Page Number Per Issue - Daily 24; Avg. Page Number Per Issue - Plates Used 15000; Avg. Page Number Per Issue - Saturday 32; widths 30; Newsprint Used - Metric Tons 1500; Printing Ink Used - Black 50000; Printing Ink Used - Color 20000; Printing Ink
Equipment EDITORIAL: Front-end Software – QPS, Baseview/NewsEdit.; Editorial Hardware – APP/Mac; Editorial Equipment – 2-X/Copier; Editorial Printers – APP/Mac LaserPrinter CLASSIFIED: Front-end Software – AdTaker.; Classified Hardware – IBM DISPLAY: Ad make-up applications – QPS, Multi-Ad; Layout software – APP/Mac.; Display Hardware – APP/Mac; Display Printers – APP/Mac LaserPrinter; Production Equipment – WL/300, Adobe/Photoshop; Cameras – 1-Acti/24B, 1-Acti/204; Scanners – Nikon. PRESSROOM: Line 1 – 40-G/Suburban, 32-G/Urbanite single width; Folders –2; Reels and Stands – 2-G/Urbanite, 2-G/Suburban.; MAILROOMCounter stackers – KAN; Inserters and stuffers – 2-KAN/480; Bundle tying machines –2-Gd/Oval Strapping Model EX-415; Wrapping singles – 1/Poly-Bag; Other equipment – MM/Saddle Stitcher.BUSINESS COMPUTERS: Audio Software – Sun, PBS; Audio Hardware – Sun/Sparc 20

BRITISH COLUMBIA

CRANBROOK

CRANBROOK DAILY TOWNSMAN

822 Cranbrook St. N., Cranbrook, BC, V1C 3R9, Canada; gen tel (250) 426-5201; gen fax (250) 426-5003; gen e-mail accounting@dailytownsman.com; adv e-mail advertising@dailytownsman.com; ed e-mail townsman@cyberlink.bc.ca; web site www.dailytownsman.com
Published: Mon, Tues, Wed, Thur, Fri
Weekday Frequency: e
Circulation 3,310
Last Audit: Estimate January 15, 2002
Group: Post Media representation
Price: 8.75/mo; 93.96/yr.
Advertising: Open inch rate $1.18
Insert rate: $50/000
News services: SNS.
Politics: Independent **Established:** 1956
Not Published: Sat/Sun
Special weekly sections: Community Update (Mar).
Publisher ....Karen Johnston
Ed. ....Barry Coulter
Sports Ed. ....Matt Coxford
Prodn. Mgr. ....Tim Fix
Market information: paid and EMC
Mechanical available: Web Offset; Black and 3 ROP colors; insert accepted - all sizes; page cutoffs - 22 1/2.
Mechanical Specifications: Type page 10.25 x 13.50
Commodity Consumption: Avg. Page Number Per Issue - Daily 12.
Equipment PRESSROOM: Line 1 – cold web offset

DAWSON CREEK

DAWSON CREEK DAILY NEWS

901 100th Ave., Dawson Creek, BC, V1G 1W2, Canada; gen tel (250) 782-4888; gen fax (250) 782-6770; adv e-mail compose@prbn.ca; national@prbn.ca; ed e-mail news@prbn.ca
Published: Mon, Tues, Wed, Thur, Fri
Weekday Frequency: e
Circulation 2,004
Last Audit: Estimate July 31, 1996
Price: 132.57/yr (mail).
Advertising: Open inch rate $.94
News services: SNS.
Special weekly sections: Christmas (Other).
Pub. ....William Julian
Circ. Mgr. ....Margot Owens
Mng. Ed. ....Megan Gorecki
Prodn. Mgr., Pre Press ....Tracy Keller
Prodn. Mgr., Pressroom ....Martin Ferrante
Market information: Split run; TMC; Zoned editions.
Mechanical available: Offset; Black and 3 ROP colors; insert accepted; page cutoffs - 21.
Mechanical Specifications: Type page 13 x 21 3/8; E - 10 cols, 1 1/16, 1/16 between.
Commodity Consumption: Avg. Page Number Per Issue - Daily 12; Avg. Page Number Per Issue - Plates Used 11000; widths 27 1/2; Newsprint Used - Metric Tons 265; Printing Ink Used - Black 2200; Printing Ink Used - Color 725; Printing Ink Used - Pages Printed 4975.
Equipment; Editorial Hardware – APP/Mac; Editorial Equipment – Printers Ã□Â□ APP/Mac LaserWriter II.; Classified Hardware – 1-APP/Mac; Classified Printers – APP/Mac LaserWriter II.; Layout software – 4-APP/Mac.; Display Printers – APP/Mac LaserWriter IIg PRODUCTION: Pagination software – QPS/QuarkXPress 3.3.; Production Equipment – COM/Headliner; Cameras – K/Vertical 240; Scanners – Umax; Bundle tying machines –1/Weld Loc.

FORT SAINT JOHN

ALASKA HIGHWAY DAILY NEWS

9916 98th St., Fort Saint John, BC, V1J 3T8, Canada; gen tel (250) 785-5631; adv tel (250) 785-5631; ed tel (250) 785-5631; gen fax (250) 785-3522; adv fax (250) 785-3522; ed fax (250) 785-3522; gen e-mail news@ahnfsj.ca

Published: Mon, Tues, Wed, Thur, Fri
Weekday Frequency: e
Circulation 3,790
Last Audit: Estimate September 30, 2000
Price: 8.00/mo (carrier); 234.00/yr.
Advertising: Open inch rate $1.06
News services: SNS, CP, AP.
Politics: Independent
Not Published: Statutory holidays.
Adv. Mgr. ....William Julian
Adv. Consultant ....Barbara Newell
Circ. Rep. ....Debbie Kowalski
Market information: TMC.
Mechanical available: Offset; Black and 3 ROP colors; insert accepted; page cutoffs - 22 3/4.
Mechanical Specifications: Type page 13 x 21 1/2; E - 10 cols, 1 1/16, 1/8 between; A - 10 cols, 1 1/16, 1/8 between; C - 8 cols, 1 1/2, 1/8 between.
Commodity Consumption: Avg. Page Number Per Issue - Daily 16.
Equipment EDITORIAL: Front-end Software – QPS/QuarkXPress 4.1.; Editorial Hardware – APP/Mac; Classified Hardware – 1-Mk/1100. PRODUCTION: Pagination software – QPS/QuarkXPress 4.1.; Production Equipment – 1-Nu/Flip Top; Cameras – 1-B/Caravel; Scanners – COM; Bundle tying machines –1-Tom/Tying machine.

KAMLOOPS

KAMLOOPS DAILY NEWS

393 Seymour St., Kamloops, BC, V2C 6P6, Canada; gen tel (250) 372-2331; adv tel (250) 372-2331; ed tel (250) 372-2331; gen fax (250) 372-0823; adv fax (250) 372-0823; ed fax (250) 374-3884; gen e-mail kamloopsnews@telus.net; adv e-mail sales@kamloopsnews.ca; ed e-mail kamloopsnews@telus.net; web site www.kamloopsnews.ca

Published: Mon, Tues, Wed, Thur, Fri, Sat
Weekday Frequency: m
Saturday Frequency: m
Circulation 11,250
Last Audit: Estimate March 31, 2008
Group: Glacier Media Group
CanWest Media Sales
Price: 14.25/mo; 171.00/yr.
Advertising: Open inch rate $1.40
Insert rate: $45/M
News services: CP, SOU.
Politics: 1931
Advertising not accepted: N
Not Published: Sunday
Own facility?: Y
Special editions: Kamloops Business (6x/year)
Kamloops Currents (6x/year)
Vision (annual)

Special weekly sections: Mega Thursday EMC (Thu) Motoring (Thu) Real Estate Weekly (Thu) Spotlight (Sat).
Magazines: Real Estate Weekly (Thu); Spotlight (Sat); Motoring (Thur)
Circ. Mgr. ....Rick Major
Sports Ed. ....Greg Drinnan
Publisher ....Tim Shoults
Director of Advertising ....John Morash
National Advertising, Special Publications and Online Sales Manager ....Kevin Dergez
Editor ....Mel Rothenburger
City Editor ....Tracy Gilchrist
News Editor ....Mike Cornell
New Media Editor ....Mark Rogers
Business Manager ....Debbi Beauchamp
Pub. ....Peter Kvarnstrom
Adv. Mgr., Retail ....Al Guthro
City Ed. ....Susan Duncan
Prodn. Mgr., Pressroom ....Leland Harmon
Market information: ADS; TMC.
Mechanical available: Offset; Black and 3 ROP colors; insert accepted; page cutoffs - 22 3/4.
Mechanical Specifications: Type page 11 1/2 x 21 1/2; E - 5 cols, 2 1/4, 1/8 between; A - 10 cols, 1 1/16, 1/8 between; C - 5 cols, 1 3/8, 1/8 between.
Commodity Consumption: Avg. Page Number Per Issue - Daily 24; Avg. Page Number Per Issue - Plates Used 7000; widths 22; Newsprint Used - Metric Tons 1200; Printing Ink Used - Black 26400; Printing Ink Used - Color 3725; Printing Ink Used - Pages Printed 10000.
Equipment; Press Drives – 2
Zip Codes Served: V2C
Delivery Method: Newsstand, Private Carrier

KELOWNA

THE DAILY COURIER

550 Doyle Ave., Kelowna, BC, V1Y 7V1, Canada; gen tel (250) 762-4445; adv tel (250) 470-0761; ed tel (250) 470-0741; gen fax (250) 762-3866; adv fax (250) 762-0258; ed fax (250) 860-5058; gen e-mail webmaster@ok.bc.ca; ed e-mail letters@ok.bc.ca; web site www.kelownadailycourier.ca

Published: Mon, Tues, Wed, Thur, Fri, Sat, Sun
Weekday Frequency: m
Saturday Frequency: m
Circulation 13,209; 13,375(sat); 12,860(sun)
Last Audit: ABC September 30, 2011
Price: 169.00/yr.
Advertising: Open inch rate $2.12
News services: CP.
Politics: Independent **Established:** 1905
Not Published: Statutory holidays.
Magazines: Fashion Trends (Fri); Trends (S); Skiing (Sat); Golf (Wed).
Vice Pres./Grp. Pub. ....Terry Armstrong
Office/Financial Mgr. ....Michael Grundy
Advertising Dir. ....Krista Frasz
Mng. Ed. ....Jon Manchester
Bus. Ed. ....Steve MacNaull
Coming Events Ed. ....Andre Wetjen
Prodn. Vice Pres., Opns. ....Willy Kerntopf
Sports Ed. ....Dave Trifunov
Westside Ed. ....John McDonald
Market information: ADS; TMC; Zoned editions.
Mechanical available: Offset; Black and 3 ROP colors; insert accepted; page cutoffs - 22 3/4.
Mechanical Specifications: Type page 11 5/8 x 21 1/2; E - 5 cols, 2 1/16, 1/8 between; A - 10 cols, 1 1/16, 1/8 between.
Commodity Consumption: Avg. Page Number Per Issue - Daily 28; Avg. Page Number Per Issue - Plates Used 16800; Avg. Page Number Per Issue - Sunday 40; widths 25; Newsprint Used - Metric Tons 2520; Printing Ink Used - Black 39600; Printing Ink Used - Color 15840; Printing Ink Us
Equipment EDITORIAL: Front-end Software – QPS/QuarkXPress 3.3.; Editorial Hardware – APP/Mac; Editorial Printers – Pre Press/Panther Pro, DEC/VT 1200 CLASSIFIED: Front-end Software – QPS/QuarkXPress, CText.; Classified Hardware – APP/Mac, DEC; Layout software – MEI/ALS.; Display Hardware – PBS; Display Printers – ATT/477, DEC/VT 400; Production Equipment – Caere/OmniPage 3.0, Kodamatic/520 Processor; Cameras – Scanners ÃÂÃÂ Nikon/3510 AF, Polaroid/SprintScan, Microtek; Scanners – Equipment ÃÂÃÂ QPS/QuarkXPress 3.3. PRESSROOM: Line 1 – 10-G/Community (3 color, Balloon); Press Drives – Fin/50 h.p. & 60 h.p. motors; Folders –G/SC 518.; Bundle tying machines –Terminator; Other equipment – Fox/321 Stitcher-Trimmer.

KIMBERLEY

THE KIMBERLEY DAILY BULLETIN

335 Spokane St., Kimberley, BC, V1A 1Y9, Canada; gen tel (250) 427-5333; gen fax (250) 427-5336; gen e-mail bulletin@cyberlink.bc.ca; web site www.dailytownsman.com

Published: Mon, Tues, Wed, Thur, Fri
Weekday Frequency: e
Circulation 1,852
Last Audit: Estimate
Price: 88.56/yr.
Advertising: Open inch rate $1.04
News services: SNS.
Politics: Independent **Established:** 1936
Not Published: Statutory holidays.
Magazines: East Kootenay Weekly (Wed); Real Estate Guide (Weekly).
Interim Pub. ....Pierre Pelletier
Adv. Rep. ....Nicole Koran
Ed. ....Barry Coulter
Market information: Split run; TMC.
Mechanical available: Offset; Black and 3 ROP colors; insert accepted; page cutoffs - 23.
Mechanical Specifications: Type page 12 3/4 x 21 3/8; E - 6 cols, 2 1/16, 1/8 between; A - 6 cols, 2 1/16, 1/8 between; C - 6 cols, 2 1/16, 1/8 between.
Commodity Consumption: Avg. Page Number Per Issue - Daily 12.
Equipment; Editorial Hardware – APP/Mac II.

NANAIMO

NANAIMO DAILY NEWS

2575 McCullough Rd., Ste. B1, Nanaimo, BC, V9S 5W5, Canada; gen tel (250) 729-4200; ed tel (250) 729-4224; gen fax (250) 729-4256; adv fax (250) 729-4263; ed fax (250) 729-4288; gen e-mail dnews@nanaimodailynews.com; web site www.nanaimodailynews.com

Published: Mon, Tues, Wed, Thur, Fri, Sat
Weekday Frequency: m
Saturday Frequency: m
Circulation 5,866; 5,866(sat)
Last Audit: ABC September 30, 2011
Group: CanWest Media Sales
Price: 2.95/wk; 11.75/mo; 140.98/yr.
Advertising: Open inch rate $.90
News services: CP.
Special editions: Vitality (Monthly).
Magazines: TV Scene (Fri); Real Estate (Sat).
Pub. ....Curt Duddy
Bus. Mgr. ....Rachel Mason
Adv. Mgr. ....Andrea Rosato-Taylor
Mng. Ed. ....Cale Cowan
Circ. Mgr. ....Les Gould
Deputy Ed. ....Philip Wolf
Features Ed. ....Walter Cordery
Market information: ADS; Split run; TMC.
Mechanical available: Offset; Black and 3 ROP colors; insert accepted; page cutoffs - 21 1/2.
Mechanical Specifications: Type page 11 1/2 x 21 1/2; E - 6 cols, 1 7/8, 1/8 between; A - 10 cols, 1 1/16, 1/8 between; C - 10 cols, 1 1/10, 1/8 between.
Commodity Consumption: Avg. Page Number Per Issue - Daily 24; Newsprint Used - Metric Tons 1100.
Equipment EDITORIAL: Front-end Software – Baseview/NewsEdit 2.2, QPS/QuarkXPress 3.31, Adobe/Photoshop.; Editorial Hardware – APP/Mac; Editorial Equipment – Printers ÃÂÃÂÃÂ Dataproducts/LZR, Design Express, Accellerator CLASSIFIED: Front-end Software – Baseview/Class Pro.; Classified Hardware – APP/Mac; Classified Printers – Baseview/Class Pro DISPLAY: Ad make-up applications – PBS; Layout software – Ad Force.; Production Equipment – RIP, Pre Press/Panther Plus 36; Cameras – 1-B; Scanners – Equipment ÃÂÃÂÃÂ QPS/QuarkXPress. PRESSROOM: Line 1 – 12-G/Community 1997; Folders –G/Quarter, G/2:1.; MAILROOMCounter stackers – Id; Inserters and stuffers – MM; Bundle tying machines –Id; Other equipment – MM.; Audio Hardware – PBS

PENTICTON

PENTICTON HERALD

101-186 W. Nanaimo Ave., Penticton, BC, V2A 1N4, Canada; gen tel (250) 492-4002; gen fax (250) 492-2403; adv fax (250) 490-4829; adv e-mail sales@pentictonherald.ca; ed e-mail editor@pentictonherald.ca; web site www.pentictonherald.ca

Published: Mon, Tues, Wed, Thur, Fri, Sat, Sun
Weekday Frequency: m
Saturday Frequency: m
Circulation 6,960; 6,842(sat); 6,399(sun)
Last Audit: ABC September 30, 2011
Group: CanWest Media Sales
Price: 2.75/wk (incl. tax); 11.95/mo; 139.00/yr (delivery); 149.00/yr (motor route).
Advertising: Open inch rate $.1.04
News services: CP, SNS.
Politics: Independent **Established:** 1910
Not Published: New Year; Victoria Day; Civic Holiday; Labor Day; Thanksgiving.
Special weekly sections: Home Improvement (Apr); Home Improvement (Mar); Home Improvement (Sept).
Magazines: Real Estate (Fri); Business (Mon); TV Weekly (Thur); Business (Wed).
Gen. Mgr. ....Andre Martin
Circ. Mgr. ....Shannon Huggard
Mng. Ed. ....James Miller
Sports Ed. ....Dave Crompton
Market information: TMC.
Mechanical available: Offset; Black and 3 ROP colors; insert accepted - coupons, envelopes, small catalogs; page cutoffs - 21 1/2.
Mechanical Specifications: Type page 10.4 x 21 1/2; E - 6 cols, 2 1/16, 1/8 between; A - 10 cols, 1 1/16, 1/8 between; C - 8 cols, 1 1/3, 1/8 between.
Commodity Consumption: Avg. Page Number Per Issue - Daily 20; Avg. Page Number Per Issue - Plates Used 13000; widths 27 1/2; Newsprint Used - Metric Tons 330; Printing Ink Used - Black 2400; Printing Ink Used - Color 200; Printing Ink Used - Pages Printed 6400.
Equipment EDITORIAL: Front-end Software – QPS.; Editorial Hardware – APP/Mac; Classified Hardware – CText. DISPLAY: Ad make-up applications – QPS/QuarkXPress.; Display Hardware – APP/Mac; Production Equipment – Pre Press/Panther; Cameras – Acti; Scanners – Equipment ÃÂÃÂ QPS.; Bundle tying machines –1-Gd/OVL; Address machine – ATT.; Audio Hardware – PBS

PORT ALBERNI

ALBERNI VALLEY TIMES

4918 Napier St., Port Alberni, BC, V9Y 3H5, Canada; gen tel (250) 723-8171; gen fax (250) 723-0586; adv e-mail ads@avtimes.net; ed e-mail news@avtimes.net; web site www.avtimes.net

Published: Mon, Tues, Wed, Thur, Fri
Weekday Frequency: e
Circulation 3,748
Last Audit: ABC September 30, 2011
Price: 120.00/yr.
Advertising: Open inch rate $.90
News services: SNS, CP.
Politics: Conservative **Established:** 1967
Not Published: Statutory holidays; Easter Monday.
Special editions: Weekender Magazine (own, offset) (Fri).
Special weekly sections: Salmon Derby (Aug); Christmas (Dec); Car Care (Fall); Travel (Feb); Salmon Derby (Jul); New Auto Supplement (Mar); Vacation (May); Remembrance Day (Nov); New Auto Supplement (Oct); Car Care (Spring).
Pub. ....Linda Patterson
Gen. Mgr. ....Curt Duddy
Circ. Mgr. ....John Richardson
Mng. Ed. ....Cale Cowan
Mgmt. Info Servs. Mgr. ....Debbie Reid
Market information: ADS; TMC.
Mechanical available: Offset; Black and 3 ROP

colors; insert accepted - flyers for one customer as part of press run; page cutoffs - 21.
Mechanical Specifications: Type page 12 1/4 x 21; E - 10 cols, 1, 1/4 between; A - 10 cols, 1, 1/4 between; C - 10 cols, 1, 1/4 between.
Commodity Consumption: Avg. Page Number Per Issue - Daily 18; Avg. Page Number Per Issue - Plates Used 12000; widths 12 1/2; Newsprint Used - Short Tons 293; Printing Ink Used - Pages Printed 4028.
Equipment; Editorial Hardware – APP/Mac Plus System.; Classified Printers – APP/Mac LaserWriter.; Display Hardware – APP/Mac G3, APP/Mac 7200; Display Printers – APP/Mac LaserWriter, APP/Mac 8500.; Production Equipment – 3-APP/Mac, APP/Mac LaserWriter; Cameras – 2-K/V.; Audio Hardware – Nomads

PRINCE GEORGE

THE PRINCE GEORGE CITIZEN

PO Box 5700, Prince George, BC, V2L 5K9, Canada; gen tel (250) 562-2441; gen fax (250) 562-7453; adv fax (250) 562-9201; gen e-mail news@princegeorgecitizen.com; adv e-mail ads@princegeorgecitizen.com; ed e-mail letters@princegeorgecitizen.com; web site www.princegeorgecitizen.com
Published: Mon, Tues, Wed, Thur, Fri, Sat
Weekday Frequency: m
Saturday Frequency: m
Circulation 12,227; 12,972(sat); 12,972(sun)
Last Audit: ABC September 30, 2009
Price: 13.50/mo; 176.40/yr.
Advertising: Open inch rate $1.53
News services: CP.
Politics: Independent **Established:** 1916
Not Published: New Year; Mar. 29; May 20; July 1; Aug. 5; Labor Day; Thanksgiving; Nov. 11; Christmas; Boxing Day.
Special weekly sections: Home Improvement (Apr); Parkwood Place Back to School (Aug); Boxing Week Savings (Dec); Cougars Den (Feb); Cougars Den (Jan); Home and Garden (Jul); Father's Day (Jun); Making a Difference (Mar); Mother's Day (May); Central Interior Business (Nov); Cougar
Magazines: TV Times (Fri); Homes (Sat); Motoring Trends (Thur).
Pub. ....Hugh Nicholson
Adv. Dir. ....Lu Verticchio
Circ. Dir., Reader Sales/Serv. ..Colleen Sparrow
Sports Ed. ....Jim Swanson
Prodn. Mgr., Mailroom/Pressroom George Lesniewicz
Prodn. Foreman, Pressroom ....Kevin Eikum
Market information: Split run; TMC; Zoned editions.
Mechanical available: Offset; Black and 3 ROP colors; insert accepted; page cutoffs - 22 3/4.
Mechanical Specifications: Type page 11 1/2 x 21 1/2; E - 5 cols, 2 1/4, 3/8 between; A - 10 cols, 1 1/16, 1/8 between; C - 8 cols, 1 3/4, 1/8 between.
Commodity Consumption: Avg. Page Number Per Issue - Daily 34; Avg. Page Number Per Issue - Plates Used 10000; widths 25; Newsprint Used - Metric Tons 1600; Printing Ink Used - Black 48500; Printing Ink Used - Color 8000; Printing Ink Used - Pages Printed 9350.
Equipment EDITORIAL: Front-end Software – QPS/QuarkXPress.; Editorial Hardware – CText, 2-RSK/Tandy 4000, 27-RSK/Tandy 3000 (PC LAN), 7-RSK/Tandy 4000 (PC LAN); Classified Hardware – CText, 9-RSK/Tandy 3000 LAN; Classified Printers – 1-APP/LaserWriter II NTX. DISPLAY: Ad make-up applications – Multi-Ad/Creator 3.6, QPS/QuarkXPress 3.3; Layout software – SCS/Layout 8000.; Display Hardware – APP/Mac II, APP/Power Mac 7100-66; Display Printers – APP/Mac LaserWriter, 2-AU/APS-6-108; Production Equipment – Canon; Cameras – 1-C/Auto Companica 690C; Scanners – Equipment Ã□Â□ QPS/QuarkXPress 3.3. PRESSROOM: Line 1 – 6-G/11RB single width; Folders –1; MAILROOMCounter stackers – 1-BG/109, 1-MM/310; Inserters and stuffers – 1-MM/227; Bundle tying machines –2/MLN; Other equipment – 1-MM/1528.; Audio Hardware – DEC/PDP 11-44

PRINCE RUPERT

THE DAILY NEWS

801 2nd Ave. W., Prince Rupert, BC, V8J 1H6, Canada; gen tel (250) 624-6781; gen fax (250) 624-2851; ed e-mail publisher@princerupertdailynews.ca; web site www.canada.com/cityguides/princerupert
Published: Mon, Tues, Wed, Thur, Fri
Weekday Frequency: e
Circulation 3,020
Last Audit: ABC September 30, 1998
Price: 8.50/mo; 101.65/yr.
Advertising: Open inch rate $.93
News services: CP, SNS.
Politics: Independent
Special weekly sections: Community Updates (Apr); Northwest Host (May).
Magazines: Health (Fri); Finance (Mon); TV Magazine (Thur); Computers (Tues); People (Wed).
Pub. ....William Julian
Adv. Mgr. ....Ed Evans
Market information: TMC; Zoned editions.
Mechanical available: Offset; Black and 3 ROP colors; insert accepted; page cutoffs - 21 1/2.
Mechanical Specifications: Type page 11 1/2 x 21 1/2; E - 6 cols, 2 1/16, 1/8 between; A - 10 cols, 1 1/16, 1/8 between; C - 5 cols, 2 1/4, 1/8 between.
Commodity Consumption: Avg. Page Number Per Issue - Daily 16; Avg. Page Number Per Issue - Plates Used 4800; widths 27; Printing Ink Used - Pages Printed 4000.
Equipment EDITORIAL: Front-end Software – Microsoft/Word, QPS.; Editorial Hardware – APP/Mac CLASSIFIED: Front-end Software – Microsoft/Word, QPS, Claris/FileMaker Pro.; Classified Hardware – APP/Mac DISPLAY: Ad make-up applications – QPS, Multi-Ad; Layout software – APP/Mac.; Production Equipment – QMS/860; Cameras – Scanners COM. PRESSROOM: Line 1 – G/Community 1974.; Audio Hardware – APP/Mac

TRAIL

TRAIL DAILY TIMES

1163 Cedar Ave., Trail, BC, V1R 4B8, Canada; gen tel (250) 368-8551; adv tel (250) 364-1416; ed tel (250) 364-1242; gen fax (250) 368-8550; adv fax (250) 368-8550; adv e-mail sales@trailtimes.ca; ed e-mail editor@trailtimes.ca; web site www.trailtimes.ca
Published: Mon, Tues, Wed, Thur, Fri
Weekday Frequency: e
Circulation 5,002
Last Audit: Estimate February 1, 2002
Group: Black Press
Price: 8.90/mo; 100.68/yr.
Advertising: Open inch rate $1.31
News services: SNS, CP.
Politics: 1895
Not Published: Saturday/Sunday
Own facility?: N
Magazines: West Kootenay Weekender (Fri).
Publisher ....Barbara Blatchford
Circ. Mgr. ....Michelle Bedford
Editor ....Guy Bertrand
production manager ....Kevin Macintyre
accounting ....Tammy Crockett
classifieds ....Jeanine Margoreeth
sales ....Dave Dykstra
Market information: Split run; TMC.
Mechanical available: Offset; Black and 3 ROP colors; insert accepted; page cutoffs - 14.
Mechanical Specifications: Type page 10 1/4 x 14; E - 6 cols, 1 1/2, 1/8 between; A - 6 cols, 10 1/4, 1/8 between; C - 6 cols, 10 1/4, 1/8 between.
Commodity Consumption: Avg. Page Number Per Issue - Daily 16.
Equipment EDITORIAL: Front-end Software – In-Design, Adobe/Photoshop 4.0.; Editorial Hardware – APP/Power Mac G3; Editorial Printers – LexMark/Optra S 1650, Optra S 1650; Production Equipment – 1-COM/7200, 2-COM/4961, 1-COM/Unisetter; Cameras – 1-AG.
Zip Codes Served: V1R
Delivery Method: Mail, Newsstand, Private Carrier

VANCOUVER

THE PROVINCE

200 Granville St., Suite 1, Vancouver, BC, V6C 3N3, Canada; gen tel (604) 605-2000; adv tel (604) 605-2478; ed tel (604) 605-2030; gen fax (604) 605-2720; adv fax (604) 605-2704; ed fax (604) 605-2759; gen e-mail circservice@sunprovince.com; adv e-mail adinquiries@sunprovince.com; ed e-mail tabtips@theprovince.com; web site www.theprovince.com
Published: Mon, Tues, Wed, Thur, Fri, Sun
Weekday Frequency: m
Circulation 144,996; 158,146(sun)
Last Audit: ABC September 30, 2011
Group: Postmedia Network
Advertising: Open inch rate $15.25(m-fri)
Politics: Independent **Established:** 1898
Not Published: Saturdays and selected holidays.
Magazines: Color Comics (S).
Pres./Pub. ....Kevin D. Bent
Ed. in Chief ....Wayne Moriarty
Deputy Ed. ....Ros Guggi
News Ed. - Editorial Pages ....Gordon Clark
Sports Ed. ....Jonathan McDonald
Lifestyles Ed. ....Hardip Johal
Deputy Ed. ....Fabian Dawson
Senior News. Ed. ....Paul Chapman
News Ed. - Online ....Erik Rolfsen
Metro Ed. ....Shannon Miller
Entertainment Ed. ....Hans Ongsansoy
Mechanical available: Web Offset; Black and 3 ROP colors; insert accepted; page cutoffs - 22.
Mechanical Specifications: Type page 10 3/4 x 13; E - 5 cols, 2 1/16, 1/8 between; A - 5 cols, 2 1/16, 1/8 between; C - 8 cols, 1 1/4, 1/16 between.
Equipment; Editorial Hardware – DEC/Alpha, APP/Mac; Editorial Printers – Data Products/LZR1560, HP/4MV PRESSROOM: Line 1 – Pasters Ã□Â□ 2.
Delivery Method: Mail, Newsstand, Racks

THE VANCOUVER SUN

200 Granville St., Ste. 1, Vancouver, BC, V6C 3N3, Canada; gen tel (604) 605-2000; adv tel (604) 605-2478; ed tel (604) 605-2445; gen fax (604) 605-2720; adv fax (604) 605-2704; ed fax (604) 605-2323; gen e-mail info@vancouversun.com; adv e-mail tshipman@sunprovince.com; ed e-mail sunnewstips@vancouversun.com; sunletters@vancouversun.com; web site www.vancouversun.com
Published: Mon, Tues, Wed, Thur, Fri, Sat
Weekday Frequency: m
Saturday Frequency: m
Circulation 156,769; 185,174(sat)
Last Audit: ABC September 30, 2011
Group: Postmedia Inc.
Price: 13.28/mo; 215.07/yr.
Advertising: Open inch rate $15.25(m-fri)
News services: SOU, CP, AP, RN, TSS, NYT.
Politics: Independent **Established:** 1898
Note: The Vancouver Sun (m) and The Province (mS) have a combination rate of $17.22(m-mon-thur) & $21.99(m-fri, sat & S) per Agate line. For advertising, circulation, promotion, accounting, human resources, mechanical, personnel and production specifications, s
Not Published: New Year; B.C. Day; Christmas.
Own facility?: Y
Magazines: TV Times (Fri); Color Comics (Sat).
Ed. in Chief ....Patricia Graham
Exec. Ed. ....Valerie Casselton
Deputy Mng. Ed. ....Harold Munro
Bus. Ed ....Hugh Dawson
Editorial Page Ed. ....Fazil Mihlar
Sr. Ed. ....Nicholas Palmer
Projects Editor ....Bev Wake
Weekend Review Ed. ....Stephen Snelgrove
Deputy Managing Editor, Digital ....Paul Bucci
Mechanical available: Web Offset; Black and 3 ROP colors; insert accepted; page cutoffs - 22.
Mechanical Specifications: Type page 12 1/2 x 22; E - 6 cols, 2 1/16, 1/8 between; A - 6 cols, 2 1/16, 1/8 between; C - 10 cols, 1 1/4, 1/16 between.
Equipment EDITORIAL: Front-end Software – MS Windows XP Mac OS X MS Windows Server; Editorial Hardware – HP Wintel Clients
Apple Clients
HP Intel Servers; Editorial Printers – HP Printers CLASSIFIED: Front-end Software – HP DSS Software
Atex Genera Cyber$ell; Classified Hardware – HP Inetl Servers; Classified Printers – HP Printers PRODUCTION: Pagination software – PPI
Saxotech; Production Equipment – HP Wintel Clients
HP Intel Servers PRESSROOM: Line 1 – ManRoland Colorman XI
Nine Towers 62 printing couples; Line 2 – ManRoland Colorman XI
Nine Towers 62 printing couples; Press Drives – Seimens DC Drives
Shafted press line; Folders –2/1 Rotary Folders; Pasters – 26 Manroland CD15 Two arm Reelstand's; Reels and Stands – 26 Manroland CD15 Two arm Reelstand's; Press control system – E.A.E; Press registration system – None; MAILROOMCounter stackers – 14 Quipp stackers and Viper Bottomwrappers; Inserters and stuffers – Four 14 pocket Muller-Martini (GMA) SLS 2000 inserters ; Bundle tying machines –28 Dynaric strappers with 14 turntables; Wrapping singles – None
; Mailroom control system – Muller-Martini Sams SystemBUSINESS COMPUTERS: Audio Software – MS Windows XP
Mac OS X
MS Windows Server; Audio Hardware – HP Wintel Clients
Apple Clients
HP Intel Servers
Delivery Method: Mail, Newsstand, Private Carrier, Racks

VICTORIA

TIMES COLONIST

PO Box 300, Victoria, BC, V8W 2N4, Canada; gen tel (250) 380-5211; adv tel (250) 380-5249; ed tel (250) 380-5333; gen fax (250) 380-5353; adv fax (250) 380-5285 (classified); ed fax (250) 380-5353; ed e-mail edit@tc.canwest.com; web site www.timescolonist.com
Published: Mon, Tues, Wed, Thur, Fri, Sat, Sun
Weekday Frequency: m
Saturday Frequency: m
Circulation 58,840; 57,922(sat); 57,632(sun)
Last Audit: ABC September 30, 2011
Price: 16.98/mo (carrier), $17.25/mo (motor route); 216.00/yr (carrier), $200.79/yr (motor route).
Advertising: Open inch rate $3.76
News services: CanWest Media Sales, CP, CSM, LAT-WP, NYT.
Politics: Independent **Established:** 1981
Not Published: New Year; Victoria Day; Canada Day; Civic Holiday; Labor Day; Thanksgiving; Christmas.
Magazines: TV Times (Fri); Comics (S); Classifieds (Sat); Classifieds (Wed).
Broadcast Affiliations: CH TV Victoria.
Pub. ....Bob McKenzie
Dir., Finance ....Catherine McConnell

Accounting Mgr.......................Kulwant Atwal
Credit Mgr. ....Maureen Gans
Vice Pres., Adv./Sales & Mktg. ....Peter Baillie
Adv. Sales Mgr.......................Pablo Miranda
Promo. Mgr...............................Kathy Baun
Circ. Mgr., Distr./Mktg. ....Bruce Cousins
Ed. in Chief......................Luscinda Chodan
Arts/Entertainment Reporter Adrian Chamberlain
Arts/Entertainment Reporter......Michael D. Reid
Bus./Finance Reporter ....Stew Lang
Columnist....................................Jim Gibson
Columnist.....................................Jack Knox
Editorial Page Ed. ....Dave Obee
Garden Writer ....Helen Chesnut
Web Ed......................................Denise Helm
Features Ed........................Bruce Mackenzie
Bryan Drewry
Phillip Jang
Market information: ADS; Split run; TMC.
Mechanical available: Offset; Black and 3 ROP colors; insert accepted; page cutoffs - 22 3/4.
Mechanical Specifications: Type page 11 9/16 x 21 7/8; E - 5 cols, 2 5/16, 1/8 between; A - 10 cols, 1 1/16, 3/32 between; C - 10 cols, 1 1/16, 3/32 between.
Commodity Consumption: Avg. Page Number Per Issue - Daily 44; Avg. Page Number Per Issue - Plates Used 58000; Avg. Page Number Per Issue - Saturday 72; Avg. Page Number Per Issue - Sunday 40; widths 25; Newsprint Used - Metric Tons 7710; Printing Ink Used - Black 146000; Print
Equipment EDITORIAL: Front-end Software – Phrasea, Baseview/NewsEdit IQ.; Editorial Hardware – APP/Mac G3; Editorial Equipment – Printers ÃÐÂÐ HP/XV4 CLASSIFIED: Front-end Software – Baseview/Ad Manager Pro, Baseview/Classified Layout System.; Classified Hardware – APP/iMac DISPLAY: Ad make-up applications – SCS/Layout 8000, PBS; Layout software – Multi-Ad/Creator, QPS/QuarkX; Display Hardware – APP/Mac, APP/Mac server, HP/1150; Display Printers – Pre Press/Panther Pro 46L paper, Pre Press/Panther Pro 46L film, Pre Press/Panther Plus 36 paper, Pre Press/Panther Plus 36 film; Production Equipment – Caere/OmniPage, APP/Mac, Adobe/Photoshop, Pre Press/Panther Pro 46, Pre Press/Panther Plus 36, Phrasea/Archive; Cameras – Equipment ÃÐÂÐ QPS/QuarkXPress, Multi-Ad, Adobe/Photoshop, Adobe/Illustrator-Streamline. PRESSROOM: Line 1 – 9-G/Colorliner double width (35 couples) 1989; Folders –2-G/2:3; Reels and Stands – G/RTP50; Press control system – G/APCS.; MAILROOM-Counter stackers – 1-MM/288, 1-MM/388; Inserters and stuffers – 2-MM/308 Biliner; Bundle tying machines –2-OVL/JP-80; Wrapping singles – 2-K-Jack/Filmwraps; Mailroom control system – PC Interface with PBS System; Address machine – 1/LinePrinter.BUSINESS COMPUTERS: Audio Software – Microsoft/Excel, Microsoft/Word, Microsoft/Windows 95, Acc-Pac, PBS, SITG; Audio Hardware – HP/9000-D380

MANITOBA

BRANDON

BRANDON SUN

501 Rosser Ave., Brandon, MB, R7A 0K4, Canada; gen tel (204) 727-2451; gen fax (204) 725-0976; ed fax (204) 727-0385; gen e-mail opinion@brandonsun.com; web site www.brandonsun.com
Published: Mon, Tues, Wed, Thur, Fri, Sat, Sun
Weekday Frequency: e
Saturday Frequency: e
Circulation 13,697; 16,066(sat); 21,987(sun)
Last Audit: ABC September 30, 2009
Group: CanWest Media Sales
Price: 2.50/wk (carrier); 14.50/mo (carrier), $17.10/mo (motor route); 174.40/yr (carrier), $205.60/yr (motor route).
Advertising: Open inch rate $2.12
News services: CP.
Politics: Independent
Pub. ....Ewan Pow
Bus. Mgr.....................................Jeff Hood
Sales Mgr..................................Glen Parker
Circ. Mgr., Sales/Mktg. ....Shane Robins
Mng. Ed. ....James O'Connor
Copy Ed..................................Ken Coleman
News Ed. ....Jim Lewthwaite
Photographer ....Bruce Bumstead
Photographer ....Colin Corneau
Sports Ed............................James Shewaga
Sunday Ed.............................John Hughes
Prodn. Foreman, Mail Room (Day)....Mark Jones
Prodn. Foreman, Mail Room (Night) .Jim Gratten
Prodn. Foreman, Pressroom ....Randy Smith
Market information: ADS; TMC.
Mechanical available: Offset; Black and 3 ROP colors; insert accepted; page cutoffs - 22 3/4.
Mechanical Specifications: Type page 12 1/2 x 22; E - 6 cols, 2 1/16, 1/8 between; A - 6 cols, 2 1/16, 1/8 between; C - 9 cols, between.
Commodity Consumption: Avg. Page Number Per Issue - Daily 23; Avg. Page Number Per Issue - Plates Used 4500; widths 13 3/4; Newsprint Used - Metric Tons 909; Printing Ink Used - Black 25000; Printing Ink Used - Color 2600; Printing Ink Used - Pages Printed 6900.
Equipment: Editorial Hardware – 1-Ik/Minitek II; Editorial Equipment – 2-Te/Remote Terminal, 2-RSK/TRS 100, 1-RSK/TRS 200.; Classified Hardware – Ik/Minitek II.; Layout software – Ik/Minitek II.; Display Hardware – 8-ZC/Model 40, 1-Xenotron; Production Equipment – 2-M/Linotron 202, 1-Enco; Cameras – 2-Nu/2024. PRESSROOM: Line 1 – 16-G/Community.; MAILROOMCounter stackers – 2-BG/105; Inserters and stuffers – 1-KAN/320, 1-KAN/480; Bundle tying machines –2-Gd/Constellation; Other equipment – MM/Stitch & Trimmer.; Audio Hardware – IBM/Sys 36

FLIN FLON

THE REMINDER

10 North Ave., Flin Flon, MB, R8A 0T2, Canada; gen tel (204) 687-3454; gen fax (204) 687-4473; gen e-mail reminder@mb.sympatico.ca
Published: Mon, Tues, Wed, Thur, Fri
Weekday Frequency: e
Circulation 3,200
Price: 156.00/yr.
Advertising: Open inch rate $.65
News services: CP.
Politics: Independent **Established:** 1946
Circ. Mgr. ....Rose Daneliuk
News Ed....................................Ron Dobson
Prodn. Foreman, Pressroom......Randy Daneliuk

PORTAGE LA PRAIRIE

THE DAILY GRAPHIC

PO Box 130, Portage la Prairie, MB, R1N 3B4, Canada; gen tel (204) 857-3427; gen fax (204) 239-1270; adv e-mail dailyads@cpheraldleader.com; ed e-mail news.dailygraphic@shawcable.com; web site www.thedailygraphic.com
Published: Mon, Tues, Wed, Thur, Fri
Weekday Frequency: e
Circulation 2,382
Last Audit: ABC September 30, 2009
Price: 200.00/yr.
Advertising: Open inch rate $.86
News services: CP.
Politics: Independent
Not Published: New Year; Good Friday; Victoria Day; Canada Day; Civic Holiday; Labor Day; Thanksgiving; Remembrance Day; Christmas; Boxing Day.
Magazines: TV Guide (Sat).
Pub........................................Barry Clayton
Office Mgr...................................Mae Barter
Mng. Ed. ....Clarise Klassen
Market information: TMC.
Mechanical available: Offset; Black and 3 ROP colors; insert accepted; page cutoffs - 21.
Mechanical Specifications: Type page 14 1/2 x 21; E - 6 cols, 2 1/8, 1/8 between; A - 6 cols, 2 1/8, 1/8 between; C - 6 cols, 2 1/8, 1/8 between.
Commodity Consumption: Avg. Page Number Per Issue - Daily 14; Avg. Page Number Per Issue - Plates Used 7560; widths 34; Newsprint Used - Metric Tons 525.7; Printing Ink Used - Black 14784; Printing Ink Used - Color 916; Printing Ink Used - Pages Printed 5550.
Equipment EDITORIAL: Front-end Software – APP/Mac System 7.5 3.; Editorial Hardware – APP/Mac G4; Classified Hardware – APP/Mac. DISPLAY: Ad make-up applications – APP/Mac System 7.5 3; Layout software – APP/Mac Desktop.; Production Equipment – 1-WL, Fuji/PI 2800 Imagesetter; Cameras – 1-Kk; Scanners – LE, Nikon/LS 1000. PRESSROOM: Line 1 – 7-G/Community; Folders –G/SSC, G/SC.; MAILROOMCounter stackers – 2-BG/Count-O-Veyor; Bundle tying machines –MLN, Gd/Constellation; Address machine – St/Label Mailer, IBM/Label System 36.; Audio Hardware – IBM/Sys 36

WINNIPEG

WINNIPEG FREE PRESS

1355 Mountain Ave., Winnipeg, MB, R2X 3B6, Canada; gen tel (204) 697-7000; adv tel (204) 697-7123; ed tel (204) 697-7301; gen fax (204) 697-7344; adv fax (204) 697-7370; ed fax (204) 697-7412; gen e-mail citydesk@freepress.mb.ca; web site www.winnipegfreepress.com
Published: Mon, Tues, Wed, Thur, Fri, Sat
Weekday Frequency: m
Saturday Frequency: m
Circulation 107,616; 145,237(sat); 122,654(sun)
Last Audit: ABC September 30, 2011
Group: CanWest Media Sales
Price: 3.25/wk; 247.00/yr.
Advertising: Open inch rate $8.94
News services: CP, AP, MCT, NYT, LAT-WP, SHNS.
Politics: Independent **Established:** 1876
Not Published: New Year; Good Friday; Victoria Day; Canada Day; Civic Holiday; Labor Day; Thanksgiving; Remembrance Day; Christmas.
Special weekly sections: Golf Guide (Apr); Continuing Education (Aug); Christmas Supplement #2 (Dec); Youth Publication (Feb); Mutual Funds (Jan); Town & Country (MC Icelandic) (Jul); MCC Relief Sale (Jun); Parade of Homes (Mar); Cottage Reflections (May); Christmas Song Sheets &
Magazines: TV Plus (Sat); Neighbours (Wed).
Pub...Bob Cox
Credit Mgr. ....Harold Prysazniuk
Adv. Dir., Sales/Mktg. ....Laurie Finley
Circ. Dir. ....Dean Lytle
Ed. ....Margo Goodhand
Deputy Ed., Online ....John White
Art Dir...................................Gordon Preece
Bus. Ed.......................................Steve Pona
Cartoonist............................Dale Cummings
City Ed.....................................Paul Samyn
Asst. City Ed................................Jason Bell
Asst. City Ed. ....Carl DeGurse
Asst. City Ed. ....Helen Fallding
Columnist.......................................Dan Lett
Columnist..........................Catherine Mitchell
Columnist ....Dave O'Brien
Columnist.....................................Tom Oleson
Columnist.............................Lindor Reynolds
Columnist ....Gordon Sinclair
Market information: Split run; TMC; Zoned editions.
Mechanical available: Letterpress (direct); Black and 3 ROP colors; insert accepted; page cutoffs - 22 3/4.
Mechanical Specifications: Type page 13 x 22 1/8; E - 6 cols, 2 1/16, 1/8 between; A - 10 cols, 1 1/16, 1/8 between; C - 10 cols, 1 1/4, 1/8 between.
Commodity Consumption: Avg. Page Number Per Issue - Daily 63; Avg. Page Number Per Issue - Plates Used 140000; Avg. Page Number Per Issue - Sunday 32; widths 54; Newsprint Used - Metric Tons 21697; Printing Ink Used - Black 880320; Printing Ink Used - Color 103600; Printing In
Equipment EDITORIAL: Front-end Software – HAS/Magician Plus, MeD/CSI-103, MeD/CSI-105.; Editorial Hardware – 1-CSI/PDP 1170, 1-HAS/2330; Classified Hardware – Software ÃÐÂÐ MeD/CSI-107.; Production Equipment – 2-Na/Superstar, 3-COM, 1-Fuji; Cameras – 2-C/SP-3; Scanners – 2-ECR/Autokon. PRESSROOM: Line 1 – 7-G/Mark I; Line 2 – 7-G; Line 3 – 7-G/Mark I; Folders –4; Pasters – 7-G/Digital, 14; Reels and Stands – 7, 14.; MAILROOM-Counter stackers – 2-CH/MK-IV, 1-SH/257S; Inserters and stuffers – 1-S/24P; Bundle tying machines –7/MLN; Wrapping singles – 1-/St.; Audio Hardware – 1-IBM/Sys 34

THE WINNIPEG SUN

1700 Church Ave., Winnipeg, MB, R2X 3A2, Canada; gen tel (204) 694-2022; adv tel (204) 632-2721; ed tel (204) 632-2774; adv fax (204) 632-8709; ed fax (204) 697-0759; gen e-mail wpgsun.citydesk@sunmedia.ca; web site www.winnipegsun.com
Published: Mon, Tues, Wed, Thur, Fri, Sat, Sun
Weekday Frequency: m
Saturday Frequency: m
Circulation 25,338; 25,986(sat); 29,697(sun)
Last Audit: BPA December 30, 2010
Price: 3.50/wk; 15.17/mo; 241.80/yr.
Advertising: Open inch rate $3.77
News services: CP.
Politics: Independent **Established:** 1981
Not Published: Christmas.
Magazines: ENT (S).
Pub. ....Kevin Klein
Controller.................................John Speidel
Adv. Dir.......................................Kevin Kline
Adv. Mgr., Classified Sales .....Maureen Spence
Adv. Mgr., Retail....................Daria Zmiyiwsky
Circ. Dir. ....Bonny Brennan
Ed. in Chief...........................Stephen Ripley
Comment Ed. ....Paul Ruthetfoerd
Entertainment Ed........................Daryl Sterdan
Sports Ed. ....Ted Wyman
Mgmt. Info Servs. Mgr. ....Tim Happychuk
Prodn. Mgr., Mailroom ....Karen Toulman
Prodn. Mgr., Pre Press..............Ken Waterman
Mechanical available: Offset; Black and 3 ROP colors; insert accepted; page cutoffs - 22 3/4.
Mechanical Specifications: Type page 10 7/16 x 14 1/4; E - 8 cols, 1 5/32, 1/8 between; A - 8 cols, 1 5/32, 1/8 between; C - 8 cols, 1 5/32, 1/8 between.
Commodity Consumption: Avg. Page Number Per Issue - Daily 56; Avg. Page Number Per Issue - Plates Used 30000; Avg. Page Number Per Issue - Sunday 80; widths 34; Newsprint Used - Metric Tons 6000; Printing Ink Used - Black 58000; Printing Ink Used - Color 15000; Printing Ink Us
Equipment EDITORIAL: Front-end Software – QPS/QuarkXPress 4.11, Baseview/; Editorial Hardware – APP/Mac G3, APP/Mac G4, APP/iMac, APP/Mac PPC 7300, APP/Mac PPC 7600, APP/Mac PPC 8600, APP/Mac PPC 6100, APP/Mac PPC 7100, Quadra/840 AU; Editorial Equipment – Printers ÂÐ X/Docucolor 12, 332 ST, Xante, APP/Mac LaserWriter CLASSIFIED: Front-end Software – Baseview, Ad Manager Pro.; Classified Hardware – 7-APP/Mac; Classified Printers – X/Docucolor 12, 332 ST DISPLAY: Ad make-up applications – Baseview/Display Manager, Managing Editor/ALS, QPS/QuarkXPress 4.11; Layout software – APP/Mac, Baseview/ALS,

QPS/QuarkXPress 4.11.; Display Hardware – COM/MD7 350 MCS with preview, 2-APP/Mac PRODUCTION: Pagination software – QPS/QuarkXPress 4.1; Production Equipment – COM/MCS work stations, AM Graphics, APP/Mac G4, Compaq/DeskPro 8600, AG/25XT Imagesetters, AG/Apogee Typan NT; Cameras – DS/240, B/4000; Scanners – Hel/DB-300, COM/8400, AG/TS5000, Polaroid/SprintScan, AG/T2000 PRESSROOM: Line 1 – 10-G/Urbanite single width 1997; Folders –1-G/Half, 1-DGM/Quarter; Pasters – 6; MAILROOMCounter stackers – 2-HL/Monitor; Inserters and stuffers – 2-KAN/760; Bundle tying machines –3/MLN.BUSINESS COMPUTERS: Audio Software – Accpac 6.15, Microsoft/MSOffice 2000/97, Lotus/SS ME; Audio Hardware – DEC/486-66, DEC/P5, Pentium/OEM

NEW BRUNSWICK

CARAQUET

L'ACADIE NOUVELLE

CP 5536, 476 Blvd. St. Pierre Ouest, Caraquet, NB, E1W 1A3, Canada; gen tel (506) 727-4444; adv tel (506) 383-7433; ed tel (506) 727-0502; gen fax (506) 727-7620; adv fax (506) 383-7440; ed fax (506) 727-7620; gen e-mail infos@acadienouvelle.com; ed e-mail nouvelle@acadienouvelle.com; web site www.acadienouvelle.com

Published: Mon, Tues, Wed, Thur, Fri, Sat
Weekday Frequency: m
Saturday Frequency: m
Circulation 20,152; 20,152(sat)
Last Audit: Estimate March 27, 2006
Price: 248.16/yr.
Advertising: Open inch rate $1.27
News services: CP.
Magazines: Seniors (Mon); Seniors (S); Show (Sat); Seniors (Thur); Seniors (Tues); Food (Wed).
Promo./Mktg. Mgr. .... Gilles Hache
Circ. Mgr. .... Denis Jeam
Ed. .... Francis Sonier
Market information: ADS; Split run.
Mechanical available: Offset; Black and 3 ROP colors; insert accepted; page cutoffs - 14 3/16.
Mechanical Specifications: Type page 10 3/8 x 12 1/8; E - 10 cols, 1/6 between; A - 5 cols, 1 15/16, 1/6 between; C - 10 cols, 1/6 between.
Commodity Consumption: Avg. Page Number Per Issue - Daily 42; Avg. Page Number Per Issue - Plates Used 4400; widths 28 5/8; Newsprint Used - Metric Tons 850; Printing Ink Used - Pages Printed 9240.
Equipment EDITORIAL: Front-end Software – Mk.; Editorial Hardware – COM, APP/Mac CLASSIFIED: Front-end Software – Informatel.; Classified Hardware – PC DISPLAY: Ad make-up applications – QPS/QuarkXPress, Adobe/Illustrator.; Display Hardware – APP/Mac; Display Printers – AG/Selectset 5000; Production Equipment – Enco/Negative Plate Processor Model N-322. PRESSROOM: Line 1 – 6-HI/D-150.; Bundle tying machines –2/OVL, 1-/Nichiro Kogyo/Model EX311; Address machine – 4-/Wm.BUSINESS COMPUTERS: Audio Software – AccPac; Audio Hardware – IBM

FREDERICTON

THE DAILY GLEANER

PO Box 3370, Fredericton, NB, E3B 2T8, Canada; gen tel (506) 452-6671; adv tel (506) 452-6671; ed tel (506) 452-6671; gen fax (506) 452-7405; adv fax (506) 452-7405; ed fax (506) 452-7405; gen e-mail horncastle.michele@dailygleaner.com; web site www.canadaeast.com

Published: Mon, Tues, Wed, Thur, Fri, Sat
Weekday Frequency: m
Saturday Frequency: m
Circulation 18,889; 19,344(sat)
Last Audit: ABC September 30, 2011
Group: Brydson Global Media Sales
Price: 3.35/wk (carrier); 197.60/yr; 43.55/3mo.
Advertising: Open inch rate $1.72
News services: CP.
Politics: Independent **Established:** 1881
Not Published: Good Friday; Christmas.
Special weekly sections: Gardening (Apr); First Snow of Winter (Dec); Bridal (Jan); Woodstock Old Home Week (Jul); Creative Ad.Venture (Jun); Home Improvement (Mar); Downtown (Monthly); Fall Car Care (Oct); Northside (Other).
Magazines: TV/Radio Guide (Fri); Real Estate Guide (Mon); Cars Plus B/S (Wed).
Pub. .... Eric Lawson
Mng. Ed. .... Catherine Metcalfe
Asst. Mng. Ed. .... Anne Mooers
Book Page Ed. .... Forrest Orser
Features Ed. .... Brookee La Pointe
News Ed. .... Bill Witcomb
Sports Ed. .... Dave Ritchie
Prodn. Mgr. .... Diane Wall
Prodn. Foreman, Pressroom .... Kevin Scott
Market information: Split run; TMC.
Mechanical available: Offset; Black and 3 ROP colors; insert accepted; page cutoffs - 22 5/8.
Mechanical Specifications: Type page 11 1/2 x 21 1/2; E - 5 cols, 1, 1/6 between; A - 10 cols, 1, 1/6 between; C - 5 cols, 1, 1/6 between.
Commodity Consumption: Avg. Page Number Per Issue - Daily 36; Avg. Page Number Per Issue - Plates Used 30200; Avg. Page Number Per Issue - Saturday 48; widths 24 1/2; Newsprint Used - Metric Tons 1744; Printing Ink Used - Black 41831; Printing Ink Used - Color 8263; Printing I
Equipment EDITORIAL: Front-end Software – HI/NewsMaker 4.; Editorial Hardware – PCs; Editorial Equipment – 2-CD/Electronic Picture Desk CLASSIFIED: Front-end Software – HI/AdPower 3, HI/Cash System.; Classified Hardware – PCs DISPLAY: Ad make-up applications – QPS/QuarkXPress, Adobe/Photoshop, Adobe/Illustrator, Adobe/Acrobat; Layout software – SCS/Layout 8000.; Display Hardware – PCs, APP/Mac G4; Production Equipment – 2-MON/3850, 1-Nu. PRESSROOM: Line 1 – 8-G/Urbanite single width 1979, 4-G/Urbanite single width 1990; Folders –G/2:1; Reels and Stands – 2-G/4 High.; MAILROOM-Counter stackers – 3/HL; Inserters and stuffers – 1-HI/NP630; Bundle tying machines –2-/Gd, 3-/Gd; Address machine – 2-Panasonic/1925S PC.BUSINESS COMPUTERS: Audio Software – Great Plains Dynamics

MONCTON

TIMES & TRANSCRIPT

Box 1001, Moncton, NB, E1C 8P3, Canada; gen tel (506) 859-4900; adv tel (506) 859-4900; ed tel (506) 859-4901; gen fax (506) 383-2588; adv fax (506) 859-4899; ed fax (506) 859-4904; adv e-mail advertising@timestranscript.com; ed e-mail news@timestranscript.com; web site www.canadaeast.com

Published: Mon, Tues, Wed, Thur, Fri, Sat
Weekday Frequency: m
Saturday Frequency: m
Circulation 33,141; 35,575(sat)
Last Audit: ABC September 30, 2011
Price: 3.50/wk, $3.75/wk (outside city); 15.17/mo, $16.25/mo (outside city); 190.06/yr.
Advertising: Open inch rate $3.88
News services: CP, SHNS.
Politics: Independent **Established:** 1881
Not Published: New Year; Christmas.
Special weekly sections: Christmas Cookbook (Dec); Outlook (Mar).
Magazines: TV Showtime (Fri); Color Comic (Sat); Homes (Thur).
Pub. .... Eric Lawson
Controller .... Kevin Publicover
Reader Sales/Servs. ... Michelle Foster-Manning
Mng. Ed. .... Al Hogan
Bus. Ed. .... John Wishart
Editorial Page Ed. .... Norbert Cunningham
Life/Times Ed. .... Brent Mazerolle
Sports Ed. .... Dawyne Tingley
Mgmt. Info Servs. Mgr. .... Dan Mlokdecki
Market information: Split run; TMC; Zoned editions.
Mechanical available: Offset; Black and 3 ROP colors; insert accepted; page cutoffs - 22.
Mechanical Specifications: Type page 13 x 21 1/2; E - 5 cols, 2 1/4, 1/8 between; A - 10 cols, 1 1/16, 1/8 between; C - 5 cols, 2 1/4, 1/8 between.
Commodity Consumption: Avg. Page Number Per Issue - Daily 38; Avg. Page Number Per Issue - Saturday 68; widths 37 1/2; Newsprint Used - Metric Tons 2649; Printing Ink Used - Black 43500; Printing Ink Used - Color 15500.
Equipment EDITORIAL: Front-end Software – HI/NewsMaker Editorial 2.61.; Editorial Hardware – Compaq/2000-30 Deskpro; Editorial Equipment – 8-APP/Power Mac, 3-Canon/Digital Cameras; Editorial Printers – HP/LaserJet 4MT, MON/Page Master 600, MON/Proof Express CLASSIFIED: Front-end Software – HI/Cash 5.1.; Classified Hardware – 6-Compaq/Prolinea 575; Classified Printers – HP/LaserJet 4MV DISPLAY: Ad make-up applications – QPS/QuarkXPress 3.3, Multi-Ad/Creator 3.5.2, Adobe/Photoshop 4.0, Adobe/Illustrator 7.0; Layout software – PBS.; Display Hardware – APP/Mac; Display Printers – Tektronix/Phaser 300, 1-MON/Page Master II PRODUCTION: Pagination software – HI/NewsMaker Pagination 1.6.; Production Equipment – Kk, Solo/Listener; Cameras – 3-Kk/DC53, 10-Kk/DC50; Scanners – PixelCraft/7860C, 2-Umax/Powerlook, 8-Umax/Super Vistor S-12, 2-Polaroid/SprintScan 35 PRESSROOM: Line 1 – G/Headliner double width; Line 2 – G/Headliner double width; Line 3 – G/Headliner double width; Line 4 – G/Headliner double width; Line 5 – G/Headliner double width; Line 6 – G/Headliner double width; Reels and Stands – G/3:2, G/Jaw; Press control system – Pasters ÃÂÃÂ 6-G/RT-50.; MAILROOMCounter stackers – 1/HL, 1-Gammerler/KL 503/1, 3-/HI, Olympian; Inserters and stuffers – NP/630, HI, 26-/Hopper; Bundle tying machines –2-/MLN, 1-/Dynamic; Wrapping singles – 3-ARPAC/55 GI; Other equipment – 1-MM/Presto.; Audio Hardware – PBS

SAINT JOHN

NEW BRUNSWICK TELEGRAPH-JOURNAL

PO Box 2350, Saint John, NB, E2L 3V8, Canada; gen tel (506) 632-8888; adv tel (506) 633-6733; ed tel (506) 632-8888; gen fax (506) 633-6758; adv fax (506) 633-5784; ed fax (506) 633-6758; adv e-mail classads@telegraphjournal.com; ed e-mail newsroom@telegraphjournal.com; web site www.canadaeast.com

Published: Mon, Tues, Wed, Thur, Fri, Sat
Weekday Frequency: m
Saturday Frequency: m
Circulation 30,440; 32,253(sat)
Last Audit: ABC September 30, 2011
Price: 3.50/wk (carrier); 14.50/mo; 192.00/yr.
Advertising: Open inch rate $3.70(m-fri)
News services: Canadian Media Connection, DJ, LAT-WP, Presslink, SOU.
Politics: Independent **Established:** 1858
Not Published: Christmas.
Special weekly sections: Spring Fashions (Apr); Focus on Education (Aug); Christmas Greetings (Dec); Brides (Feb); January Discount (Jan); Travel Guide (Jul); NB Travel Guide (Jun); Time for Thought (Mar); Auto Dealer Profiles (May); Remembrance Day (Nov); Fire Prevention (Oct);
Magazines: Showtime TV Guide (Fri); Travel (Sat).
Broadcast Affiliations: Radio CHSJ.
Pub. .... James C. Irving
Adv. Mgr. .... Michael Horncastle
Mng. Ed. .... David Spragg
Bus. Ed. .... David Stonehouse
Editorial Page Ed. .... Eric Mark
Market information: ADS; TMC; Zoned editions.
Mechanical available: Letterpress (direct); Black and 3 ROP colors; insert accepted - product samples; page cutoffs - 21.
Mechanical Specifications: Type page 13 x 22; E - 6 cols, 1/8 between; A - 10 cols, 1 1/16, 1/8 between; C - 10 cols, 1 1/16, 1/8 between.
Commodity Consumption: Avg. Page Number Per Issue - Daily 36; Avg. Page Number Per Issue - Saturday 84; widths 50.
Equipment: Editorial Hardware – 18-APP/Mac G3, 2-APP/Mac G4, 19-Compaq/DeskPro PIII, 3-Toshiba/Laptop PII, 1-Compaq/Laptop PIII, 1-APP/Mac Powerbook; Editorial Equipment – APP/Mac Powermac 7200/180, APP/Mac Powermac 8100/80, 5-Sun/Sparc 5; Editorial Printers – HP/Laserjet 4MV, HP/Laserjet 4000, CLASSIFIED: Front-end Software – DTI/Class Speed 5.01, DTI/PlanBuilder 6.3, DTI/SpeedPlanner 4.3, Microsoft/Office 97.; Classified Hardware – 2-APP/Mac G3, 6-Compaq/Deskpro PIII; Classified Equipment – HP/Laserjet 4, HP/Laserjet 4000, Lexmark/3200; Classified Printers – Okidata/OL840 DISPLAY: Ad make-up applications – DTI/ClassSpeed 5.01, Microsoft/Office 97, Telemagic 3.5; Layout software – PBS.; Display Hardware – 22-Compaq/Deskpro PIII, 1-Toshiba/Laptop; Display Printers – HP/Laserjet 4, HP/LaserJet 5000 PRODUCTION: Pagination software – DTI/AdSpeed 4.3, DTI/PageSpeed 4.3, DTI/SpeedPlanner 4.3.; Production Equipment – 8-Caere/OmniPage, Digital camera card reader; Cameras – Kk/DCS520; Scanners – 2-Epson/Expression 836XLBUSINESS COMPUTERS: Audio Software – Microsoft/Office 97, Telemagic, PBS/Circulation, PBS/Media Plus; Audio Hardware – 4-Mk/Compaq Deskpro, Pentium/PC, 2-Sun/Enterprise 450, 4-Sun/Sparc 5

NEWFOUNDLAND

CORNER BROOK

THE WESTERN STAR

PO Box 460, Corner Brook, NL, A2H 6E7, Canada; gen tel (709) 634-4348; adv tel (709) 637-4652; ed tel (709) 634-4669; gen fax (709) 637-4675; adv fax (709) 637-4675; ed fax (709) 634-9824; adv e-mail advertising@thewesternstar.com; ed e-mail newsroom@thewesternstar.com; web site www.thewesternstar.com

Published: Mon, Tues, Wed, Thur, Fri, Sat
Weekday Frequency: m
Saturday Frequency: m
Circulation 5,884; 6,725(sat)
Last Audit: BPA December 30, 2010
Price: 3.80/wk; 16.46/mo (carrier); 197.60/yr (carrier).
Advertising: Open inch rate $.89
News services: Aditus.
Politics: Independent **Established:** 1900
Not Published: New Year; Good Friday; Empire Day; Dominion Day; Labor Day; Thanksgiving; Armistice Day; Christmas.
Magazines: Star Scene (Sat).
Broadcast Affiliations: Global Television Network.

Bus. Mgr./Accountant ....Gladys Leonard
Mng. Ed.......................................Troy Turner
Editorial Page Ed. ....Ray Sweetapple
Sports Ed. ....David Kearsey
Prodn. Foreman ....Ken Bennett
Market information: TMC.
Mechanical available: Offset; Black and 1 ROP colors; insert accepted.
Mechanical Specifications: Type page 12 1/2 x 22 3/4; E - 6 cols, 2 1/16, 1/8 between.
Commodity Consumption: Avg. Page Number Per Issue - Daily 25.
Equipment; Editorial Hardware – HI.; Classified Hardware – HI.; Production Equipment – 2-COM/Unisetter. PRESSROOM: Line 1 – 8-G/Community Single Width 1980.; Bundle tying machines –1/Whig, 1-/Gd; Address machine – 1-/Am.

SAINT JOHN'S

THE TELEGRAM

PO Box 5970, Saint John's, NL, A1C 5X7, Canada; gen tel (709) 364-6300; adv tel (709) 364-6300; ed tel (709) 364-2323; gen fax (709) 364-9333; adv fax (709) 364-9333; ed fax (709) 364-3939; gen e-mail telegram@thetelegram.com; adv e-mail adv@thetelegram.com; ed e-mail telegram@thetelegram.com; web site www.thetelegram.com
Published: Mon, Tues, Wed, Thur, Fri, Sat
Weekday Frequency: m
Saturday Frequency: m
Circulation 20,433; 36,715(sat)
Last Audit: BPA December 30, 2010
Price: 3.75/wk; 16.25/mo; 402.50/yr.
Advertising: Open inch rate $1.36
News services: CP, CSM.
Politics: 1879
Not Published: New Year; Good Friday; Victoria Day; Canada Day; Labor Day; Thanksgiving; Christmas; Boxing Day.
Comptroller..............................Paul Newhook
Adv. Mgr. ....Keith Connolly
Circ. Mgr., Home Delivery Sales ....Dean Jacobs
Ed...Charles Stacey
Assoc. Ed....................................Moira Baird
Features Ed. ....Peter Jackson
News Ed. ....Russell Wangersky
Sports Ed.....................................Robin Short
Prodn. Mgr., Mailroom..................Don Mackey
Market information: ADS; Split run; TMC.
Mechanical available: Offset; Black and 3 ROP colors; insert accepted; page cutoffs - 21 1/2.
Mechanical Specifications: Type page 11 1/2 x 21 1/2; E - 5 cols, 2 1/6, 1/6 between; A - 10 cols, 1, 1/12 between; C - 10 cols, 1, 1/12 between.
Commodity Consumption: Avg. Page Number Per Issue - Daily 48; Avg. Page Number Per Issue - Plates Used 16000; Avg. Page Number Per Issue - Saturday 64; Avg. Page Number Per Issue - Sunday 32; widths 25; Newsprint Used - Short Tons 3200; Printing Ink Used - Black 40800; Printin
Equipment EDITORIAL: Front-end Software – Baseview/NewsEdit Pro IQ 2.05.; Editorial Hardware – 17-APP/Mac Performa 580, 18-APP/Mac G3; Editorial Equipment – 1-Umax/1260 Scanner, 1-Polaroid/SprintScan; Editorial Printers – 1-APP/Mac LaserPrinter 360, 2-Pre Press/Panther Pro 36 Imagesetters CLASSIFIED: Front-end Software – Baseview/Class Manager Pro 1.05D2.; Classified Hardware – 9-APP/Mac 7300/200; Classified Printers – 2-APP/Mac Laser-Printer 360 DISPLAY: Ad make-up applications – QPS/QuarkXPress 4.1, Adobe/Illustrator 8.0, Adobe/Photoshop 5.5, Adobe/Streamline 3.07; Display Hardware – 6-APP/Mac G3; Display Printers – APP/Mac Personal Laser NT, 1-HP/LaserJet 4MV, Tektronix/Phaser 380, Epson 3000 PRODUCTION: Pagination software – QPS/QuarkXPress 4.0.3, Fifi/Quark Extension.; Production Equipment – 1-Nu, 2-APP/Mac G-3; Cameras – 1-Nu/SST 2024 C, ECR/Autokon 1000; Scanners – CD, 2-Nikon/3510 Slide, 1-Nikon/Coolscan, 3-Umax/1260 Flatbed PRESSROOM: Line 1 – 7-G/Cosmo (offset) double width.; MAILROOMCounter stackers – 1-Id; Bundle tying machines –2-Gd/Q; Address machine – 1-Am/6250; Other equipment – MM/Trimmer.BUSINESS COMPUTERS: Audio Software – Microsoft/Windows 95, Microsoft/Office, PBS; Audio Hardware – HP/9000

NOVA SCOTIA

AMHERST

AMHERST DAILY NEWS

PO Box 280, Amherst, NS, B4H 3Z2, Canada; gen tel (902) 667-5102; adv tel (902) 667-5102; ed tel (902) 661-5426; gen fax (902) 667-0419; adv fax (902) 667-0419; gen e-mail bworks@amherstdaily.com; web site www.cumberlandnewsnow.com
Published: Mon, Tues, Wed, Thur, Fri
Weekday Frequency: m
Saturday Frequency: m
Circulation 3,054; 3,262(sat)
Last Audit: ABC September 30, 2006
Group: Transcontinental Media
Price: 4.00/wk (carrier); 152.40/yr.
Advertising: Open inch rate $.76
News services: CP.
Politics: Independent
Special weekly sections: Christmas (Dec); Valentine (Feb).
Magazines: TV Guide (Other).
Pub. ....Richard Russell
Gen. Mgr. ....Gregg Landry
Adv. Mgr. ....Gladys Coish
Circ. Mgr. ....Chuck MacInnes
Night Ed..David French
Online Ed.......................................Brad Works
Sports Ed. ....Darrell Cole
Prodn. Mgr., Postpress..............Chuck McInnis
Prodn. Mgr., Pre Press...............Greg Landry
Market information: ADS; Split run; TMC; Zoned editions.
Mechanical available: Offset; Black and 3 ROP colors; insert accepted; page cutoffs - 22 3/4.
Mechanical Specifications: Type page 12 7/8 x 21 1/2; E - 6 cols, 2 1/16, 1/8 between; A - 6 cols, 2 1/16, 1/8 between; C - 6 cols, 2 1/16, 1/8 between.
Commodity Consumption: Avg. Page Number Per Issue - Daily 16; Avg. Page Number Per Issue - Plates Used 7000; widths 27 1/2; Newsprint Used - Metric Tons 750; Printing Ink Used - Black 10000; Printing Ink Used - Color 3000.
Equipment EDITORIAL: Front-end Software – APP/Mac System, QPS/QuarkXPress 4.0.; Editorial Hardware – APP/Mac G3; Editorial Printers – HP/LaserJet 5000 CLASSIFIED: Front-end Software – Claris/FileMaker 4.0.; Classified Hardware – APP/Mac Performa; Layout software – QPS/QuarkXPress 4.0.; Display Hardware – APP/Mac G3 PRODUCTION: Pagination software – QPS/QuarkXPress 4.0.; Production Equipment – COMTegra/Varityper 4000, AG/Accuset; Cameras – Nu; Scanners – Linotype-Hell PRESSROOM: Line 1 – 8-HI/Cotrell JF25B V-15A 1987; Folders –HI/1:1, HI/JF-25 b-2-1; Reels and Stands – 6-HI/Standard.; Bundle tying machines –2-AMP/Cyclop Rotant N; Address machine – 4-Wm/Chauncy; Other equipment – MM/Minutman Saddle Binder, Champion/305 Cutter.; Audio Hardware – APP/Mac

HALIFAX

THE CHRONICLE HERALD

PO Box 610, Halifax, NS, B3J 2T2, Canada; gen tel (902) 426-2811; adv tel (902) 426-2811; ed tel (902) 426-2811; gen fax (902) 426-1164; adv fax (902) 426-1190; ed fax (902) 426-1158; gen e-mail reception@herald.ca; adv e-mail advertising@herald.ca; ed e-mail newsroom@herald.ca; web site thechronicleherald.ca
Published: Mon, Tues, Wed, Thur, Fri, Sun
Weekday Frequency: m
Saturday Frequency: m
Circulation 108,639; 112,391(sat); 97,283(sun)
Last Audit: ABC September 30, 2011
Price: 1.27/wk; 5.48/mo; 65.80/yr.
Advertising: Open inch rate $4.98
Insert rate: $55 CPM
News services: CP, LAT-WP, NYT, Times of London, AP.
Politics: Independent **Established:** 1875
Not Published: New Year; Easter; Labor Day; Christmas.
Special editions: Homes Etc. (Other); Comics (Sat).
Special weekly sections: NSHBA New Homes Month (Apr); Fall Class Lineup (Aug); Last Minute Christmas Gifts (Dec); Educating Investors (Feb); Nova Scotia Business Review & Forecast (Jan); Environment Week (Jun); NSHBA Home Show (Mar); Summer Camps for Kids (May); Christmas Gift Gu
Magazines: Setions:
Sports (Mon); At Home (S); Travel (Sat); Wheels/Classified (Thur); Living (Tues); Living (Wed).
Pub. ....G.W. Dennis
Pub./CEO/Vice Pres. ....Sarah Dennis
Dir., Cor. Admin. ....Mary Lou Croft
HR Mgr...............................Theresa Williams
Purchasing ....Ken Jennex
Adv. Mgr., Retail Sales ....Paul Jacquart
Mktg. Mgr. ....Pam Nauss-Redden
Research Analyst/ROP Specialist .....Tracey King
Circ. Mgr., District........................Jim LaPierre
Dir., News Admin. ....Terry O'Neil
Dir., News Content..........................Dan Leger
Asst. Dir., Design ....John Howitt
Asst. Dir., Newsroom..............Frank De Palma
Assignment Ed., Day....................Brian Ward
Assignment Ed., Night ....Eva Hoare
Books Ed............................Christine Soucie
Editorial Page Ed......................Robert Howse
Entertainment Ed. ....Greg Guy
Lifestyle Ed. ....Margaret MacKay
Director of Sales ....Barry Saunders
Vice Pres., Bus. Devel. ....Bruce MacCormack
Market information: ADS; Split run; TMC; Zoned editions.
Mechanical available: Offset; Black and 3 ROP colors; insert accepted; page cutoffs - 20.
Mechanical Specifications: Type page 11 3/4 x 20; E - 6 cols, 1.5, 1/8 between; A - 10 cols, 1 1/16, 1/8 between; C - 10 cols, 1 1/16, 1/8 between.
Commodity Consumption: Avg. Page Number Per Issue - Daily 54; Avg. Page Number Per Issue - Plates Used 108000; Avg. Page Number Per Issue - Saturday 90; Avg. Page Number Per Issue - Sunday 48; widths 50; Newsprint Used - Metric Tons 12320; Printing Ink Used - Black 440000; Pri
Equipment EDITORIAL: Front-end Software – HI/Linopress 4.2, CCI/Newsdesk.; Editorial Hardware – Sun/Enterprise 3000, 2-Ultra/Sparc, APP/Mac 8500, APP/Mac 7600; Editorial Equipment – 2-CD/EPD, In-house News Photo Archive System; Editorial Printers – GCC/Elite, 2-AII/NT-Rip, 2-AII/3850 CLASSIFIED: Front-end Software – HI/Linopress 4.2.; Classified Hardware – Sun/Enterprise 3000, 2-Ultra/Sparc, APP/Mac 8500, APP/Mac 7600; Classified Printers – GCC/Elite DISPLAY: Ad make-up applications – Multi-Ad/Creator 4.0; Layout software – SCS/Layout 8000.; Display Hardware – Sun/Enterprise 3000, 2-Ultra/Sparc, APP/Mac 8500, APP/Mac 7600; Display Printers – Asente, HP/2500, 2-AII/3850, 2-AII/NT-Rip; Production Equipment – AG/3850 CTP Advantage, 2-AII/NT Rip; Cameras – Scanners ÃÂÃÂÃÂ Sharp XJ610, 1-ECR/Autokon 1000, Linotype-Hell/Opal, 2-Polaroid/Sprint Scan, Kk/2035; Scanners – Equipment ÃÂÃÂÃÂ HI/Linopress 4.2, CCI/Newsdesk. PRESSROOM: Line 1 – 4-Wifag/370 Tower (22 couples, 4 pgs. wide); Press Drives – Indramat; Folders –2-Wifag/KZA 2:5:5; Reels and Stands – 5-Wifag/Autopasters; Press control system – EAE; Press registration system – Wifag.; MAILROOMCounter stackers – 2-QWI/351, 4-Fg/Multistack, 1-QWI/Stacker 351 B; Inserters and stuffers – 2-Fg/MSD with Rollstream; Bundle tying machines –4-Mosca/Strappers; Wrapping singles – 1-K/Pac, 1-K/Pac; Mailroom control system – Fg/Linemaster; Address machine – Addressing mach
Zip Codes Served: Throughout NS
Delivery Method: Mail, Newsstand, Private Carrier, Racks

THE DAILY NEWS

Box 8330, Stn. A, Halifax, NS, B3K 5M1, Canada; gen tel (902) 444-4444; adv tel (902) 444-4444; ed tel (902) 421-5807; gen fax (902) 468-3609; adv fax (902) 422-5610; ed fax (902) 468-2645; gen e-mail citydesk@hfxnews.ca; adv e-mail advertise@hfxnews.ca; ed e-mail citydesk@hfxnews.ca; web site www.hfxnews.ca
Published: Mon, Tues, Wed, Thur, Fri, Sat, Sun
Weekday Frequency: m
Saturday Frequency: m
Circulation 20,246
Last Audit: September 30, 2007
Price: 3.80/wk (home delivery); 15.45/mo; 193.00/yr; 95.21/6mo.
Advertising: Open inch rate $1.84
News services: CP, SOU, SHNS.
Politics: Independent **Established:** 1974
Not Published: New Year; Christmas.
Special editions: Bedford Sackville Weekly News (Wed).
Broadcast Affiliations: Global TV.
Pub. ....March Ouellette
Adv. Dir. ....Gavin Beer
Circ. Mgr. ....Irma Moore
Mng. Ed................................Jack Romanelli
City Ed. ....Richard Dooley
Online Ed. ....Marie Salah
Sports Ed. ....Carl Fleming
Sunday Ed.............................Jane Davenport
Mgmt. Info Servs. Mgr. ....Frank Zinck
Prodn. Mgr. ....Rob Batten
Mechanical available: Offset; Black and 3 ROP colors; insert accepted; page cutoffs - 13 1/2.
Mechanical Specifications: Type page 10 1/4 x 11 1/2; E - 5 cols, 7/16 between; A - 8 cols, 1 1/8, 3/16 between; C - 8 cols, 1 1/8, 3/16 between.
Commodity Consumption: Avg. Page Number Per Issue - Daily 56; Avg. Page Number Per Issue - Plates Used 11000; Avg. Page Number Per Issue - Saturday 68; Avg. Page Number Per Issue - Sunday 100; widths 26; Newsprint Used - Metric Tons 3000; Printing Ink Used - Pages Printed 2500
Equipment; Editorial Hardware – 18-APP/Mac, 10-APP/Mac G4, 29-APP/iMac, 3-PC; Editorial Equipment – 9-PC; Editorial Printers – 1-HP/800N, 1-Xante/8200.; Classified Hardware – 4-IBM; Classified Equipment – 1-HP/4M. DISPLAY: Ad make-up applications – 1-QuakrXPress 3.30, 1-SCS/Linkx 4.1; Layout software – Layout/8000 6.; Display Hardware – 1-APP/Mac 7300/200, 1-PC; Display Printers – 1-HP/5M; Production Equipment – 2-Autologic/3850, LE/PC 13; Cameras – QPS/QuarkXPress 4.1. PRESSROOM: Line 1 – 17-G/Community; Folders – 1-G/Community 1979, 1-G/SSC 1986.; MAILROOMCounter stackers – HI/Graphics, Baldwin/Count-O-Veyor; Bundle tying machines –2/Samuel, 4-/Strapex; Other equipment – Mueller/Martini JGV.; Audio Hardware – IBM/System 38

THE HALIFAX HERALD LTD.

PO Box 610, Halifax, NS, B3J 2T2, Canada;

gen tel (902) 426-2811; gen fax (902) 426-1164; gen e-mail newsroom@herald.ca; web site www.chronicleherald.ca
Published: Mon, Tues, Wed, Thur, Fri, Sat, Sun
Circulation 108,639; 112,391(sat); 97,283(sun)
Last Audit: ABC September 30, 2011
Price: 193.20/yr.
Advertising: $4.98

NEW GLASGOW

THE NEWS

PO Box 159, New Glasgow, NS, B2H 5E2, Canada; gen tel (902) 752-3000; adv tel (902) 752-3000; ed tel (902) 752-3000; gen fax (902) 752-1945; adv fax (902) 928-1515; gen e-mail news@newglasgownews.ca; ed e-mail news@newglasgownews.ca; web site www.newglasgownews.com
Published: Mon, Tues, Wed, Thur, Fri, Sat
Weekday Frequency: m
Saturday Frequency: m
Circulation 7,826; 7,826(sat)
Last Audit: ABC September 30, 2006
Price: 2.95/wk; 12.82/mo; 176.76/yr.
Advertising: Open inch rate $1.40
News services: CP.
Not Published: New Year; Good Friday; Victoria Day; Labor Day; Thanksgiving; Christmas.
Special weekly sections: Fishing (Apr); Brides (May); Business (Monthly); Car Care (Oct); Cookbook (Sept).
Magazines: Real Esate (Every other week); TV Scene (Sat).
Pub. ....Richard Russell
Controller ....Bernadine Hyson
Adv. Mgr. ....Bruce Priske
Circ. Dir., Reader Sales/Serv. ....Paul MacDonald
Mng. Ed. ....Dave Glenen
Market information: ADS; TMC.
Mechanical available: Offset; Black and 3 ROP colors; insert accepted; page cutoffs - 22 3/4.
Mechanical Specifications: Type page 11 1/2 x 21 1/2; E - 5 cols, 2 1/8, 1/8 between; A - 10 cols, 1, 1/8 between; C - 8 cols, 1 1/3, 1/8 between.
Commodity Consumption: Avg. Page Number Per Issue - Daily 16; widths 27 1/2; Newsprint Used - Metric Tons 300; Printing Ink Used - Pages Printed 5000.
Equipment: Editorial Hardware – Software ÃÂ Mk. CLASSIFIED: Front-end Software – Mk. DISPLAY: Ad make-up applications – Mk.; Production Equipment – Mk; Cameras – B. PRESSROOM: Line 1 – 8-G/Community.; Bundle tying machines –Gd; Address machine – Mailrite/Computer.; Audio Hardware – IBM/Newzware

SYDNEY

THE CAPE BRETON POST

PO Box 1500, Sydney, NS, B1P 6K6, Canada; gen tel (902) 564-5451; adv tel (902) 564-5451; ed tel (902) 563-3838; gen fax (902) 562-7077; adv fax (902) 564-6280; ed fax (902) 562-7077; adv e-mail adman@cbpost.com; ed e-mail news@cbpost.com; web site www.capebretonpost.com
Published: Mon, Tues, Wed, Thur, Fri, Sat
Weekday Frequency: m
Saturday Frequency: m
Circulation 20,490; 21,473(sat)
Last Audit: BPA December 30, 2010
Group: CanWest Media Sales
Price: 3.55/wk; 15.38/mo; 198.80/yr.
Advertising: Open inch rate $1.68
News services: AP, CP, SOU.
Politics: Independent
Not Published: New Year; Good Friday; Canada Day; Labor Day; Thanksgiving; Christmas.
Special weekly sections: Fishing (Apr); Tourist (Aug); Brides (Feb); Tourist (Jul); Tourist (Jun); Automobile (May); Computers (Nov); Hunting (Oct); Home Improvement (Sept).
Magazines: Family (Fri); Health (Mon); Style (Sat); Entertainment/Arts (Thur); Food (Tues); Seniors (Wed).
Broadcast Affiliations: Global Television.
Bus. Mgr. ....Shaw Robinson
Adv. Dir., Serv. ....Robert Edshaw
Adv. Mgr., Classified ....Helen Mccoy
Adv. Mgr. ....Rob EdShaw
Circ. Mgr., Promotional ....Matt Dawson
Mng. Ed. ....Fred Jackson
Editorial Page Ed. ....Doug McGee
News Ed. ....Steve Macinnis
Sports Ed. ....Bob Duchemin
Online Mgr. ....Heather MacKenzie
Prodn. Mgr. ....Paul Bruce
Prodn. Mgr., Pressroom ....Paul King
Market information: ADS; TMC.
Mechanical available: Offset; Black and 3 ROP colors; insert accepted - product samples; page cutoffs - 21.
Mechanical Specifications: Type page 11 1/2 x 21 1/2; E - 6 cols, 2 1/4, 3/16 between; A - 10 cols, 1 1/16, 3/16 between; C - 10 cols, 1 1/16, 3/16 between.
Commodity Consumption: Avg. Page Number Per Issue - Daily 26; Avg. Page Number Per Issue - Plates Used 6166; Avg. Page Number Per Issue - Saturday 36; widths 12 1/4; Newsprint Used - Metric Tons 1342; Printing Ink Used - Black 3862; Printing Ink Used - Color 9525; Printing Ink
Equipment EDITORIAL: Front-end Software – Baseview/NewsEdit IQ, Baseview, QPS/QuarkXPress.; Editorial Hardware – APP/Mac; Editorial Equipment – Polaroid/Slide Scanners, 2-Umax/Scanner; Editorial Printers – Xante/1200 dpi CLASSIFIED: Front-end Software – Baseview/Class Manager Pro.; Classified Hardware – APP/Mac DISPLAY: Ad make-up applications – Metro/AdCreation Tool Kit, QPS/QuarkXPress, Adobe/Photoshop, Adobe/Illustrator; Layout software – ALS.; Display Hardware – 4-APP/Power Mac 8100; Production Equipment – Pre Press/Panther; Cameras – Nu/18x24; Scanners – Equipment ÃÂÃÂÃÂÃÂÃÂÃÂÃÂ QPS/QuarkXPress with MetroAd Creation Tool Kit. PRESSROOM: Line 1 – 8-G/Urbanite; Folders –1; MAILROOMCounter stackers – 1/MSI; Bundle tying machines –3-Gd/Constellation; Address machine – 1-/Am.BUSINESS COMPUTERS: Audio Software – Lotus, Microsoft/Windows 3.1, HP; Audio Hardware – PC, Newzware

TRURO

THE DAILY NEWS

PO Box 220, Truro, NS, B2N 5C3, Canada; gen tel (902) 893-9405; adv tel (902) 893-9405; ed tel (902) 893-9405; gen fax (902) 893-0518; adv fax (902) 895-6104; ed fax (902) 893-0518; gen e-mail news@trurodaily.com; adv e-mail bpearson@trurodaily.com; ed e-mail cfleming@trurodaily.com; web site www.trurodaily.com
Published: Mon, Tues, Wed, Thur, Fri, Sat
Weekday Frequency: e
Saturday Frequency: m
Circulation 6,540
Last Audit: Estimate September 30, 2006
Group: Transcontinental
Price: 6.35bi/wkly (carrier); 11.70/mo; 169.00/yr (carrier), $193.00/yr (home delivery).
Advertising: Open inch rate $1.40
News services: CP.
Politics: Independent **Established:** 1891
Advertising not accepted: N
Not Published: Statutory holidays; New Year; Good Friday; Victoria Day; Canada Day; Civic Holiday; Labor Day; Thanksgiving; Christmas.
Own facility?: N
Special weekly sections: Automotive (Fall); Stay & Play (Jul); Stay & Play (Jun); Industrial (Mar); Brides (May); Fashion (Spring); Outdoors (Summer); Energy (Winter).
Pub. ....Richard Russell
Bus. Mgr. ....Bernadine Hyson
Adv. Mgr. ....Bruce Pearson
Circ. Mgr. ....Paul MacDonald
Mng. Ed. ....Dave Glennen
Assignment Ed. ....Frank Cassidy
Prodn. Mgr. ....Dave Conrad
Market information: ADS; TMC; Zoned editions.
Mechanical available: Offset; Black and 3 ROP colors; insert accepted - packaging, booklets, samples; page cutoffs - 22 3/4.
Mechanical Specifications: Type page 11 1/2 x 21; E - 5 cols, 2 1/4, 1/16 between; A - 10 cols, 2 1/5, 1/16 between; C - 8 cols, 1 1/3, 1/16 between.
Commodity Consumption: Avg. 32
Equipment EDITORIAL: Front-end Software – Mk.; Editorial Hardware – Mac CLASSIFIED: Front-end Software – Mk.; Classified Hardware – Mac; Classified Printers – assorted; Production Equipment – Mac; Cameras – .; Bundle tying machines –1-Gd/Oval Strapper.BUSINESS COMPUTERS: Audio Software – PBS; Audio Hardware – Dell
Delivery Method: Private Carrier

ONTARIO

BARRIE

THE BARRIE EXAMINER

PO Box 370, Barrie, ON, L4M 4Z9, Canada; gen tel (705) 726-6537; gen fax (705) 726-7706; adv fax (705) 726-5414; ed fax (705) 725-7717; gen e-mail news@thebarrieexaminer.com; web site www.thebarrieexaminer.com
Published: Mon, Tues, Wed, Thur, Fri, Sat
Weekday Frequency: m
Saturday Frequency: m
Circulation 4,602; 4,700(sat)
Last Audit: BPA December 30, 2010
Group: CanWest Media Sales
Price: 14.25/mo (carrier); 165.00/yr (carrier).
Advertising: Open inch rate $1.44
News services: CP.
Politics: Independent
Not Published: New Year; Good Friday; July 1; August Civic Holiday; Labor Day; Thanksgiving; Christmas.
Pub. ....Mike Power
Ed. ....Brain Rodnick
Retail Sales Rep. ....Michelle Kennedy
Circ. Mgr. ....Scott Murphy
Mng. Ed. ....Mike Beaudin
Market information: Split run; TMC; Zoned editions.
Mechanical available: Offset; Black and 3 ROP colors; insert accepted; page cutoffs - 21 1/2.
Mechanical Specifications: Type page 13 x 21 1/2; E - 6 cols, 2 1/16, 1/8 between; A - 6 cols, 2 1/16, 1/8 between; C - 9 cols, 1 1/3, 1/8 between.
Commodity Consumption: Avg. Page Number Per Issue - Daily 19; Avg. Page Number Per Issue - Saturday 32.
Equipment: Editorial Hardware – Printers ÃÂÃÂÃÂ 3-TTS.; Production Equipment – 7-L.

BELLEVILLE

THE INTELLIGENCER

PO Box 5600, Belleville, ON, K8N 5C7, Canada; gen tel (613) 962-9171; gen fax (613) 962-9652; ed e-mail newsroom@intelligencer.ca; web site www.intelligencer.ca
Published: Mon, Tues, Wed, Thur, Fri, Sat
Weekday Frequency: e
Saturday Frequency: m
Circulation 9,659; 9,948(sat)
Last Audit: BPA December 30, 2010
Price: 3.50/wk (carrier); 183.67/yr.
Advertising: Open inch rate $1.87
News services: CP, AP.
Politics: Independent
Not Published: New Year; Good Friday; Easter; Victoria Day; Canada Day; Civic Holiday; Labor Day; Thanksgiving; Christmas.
Magazines: Prime Time-Seniors (Mon); Dressing Up (Thur); Pulse (Tues); Cookin' (Wed).
Pres. ....John Knowles
Adv. Dir. ....Amy Doyle
Circ. Mgr. ....Tim Devine
Mng. Ed. ....Roger Cazabon
City Ed. ....Christopher Malette
Lifestyles Ed. ....Linda O'Connor
Sports Ed. ....Ady Vos
Market information: ADS; TMC.
Mechanical available: Offset; Black and 3 ROP colors; insert accepted; page cutoffs - 21 1/2.
Mechanical Specifications: Type page 13 x 21 1/2; E - 6 cols, 2 1/16, 1/8 between; A - 6 cols, 2 1/16, 1/8 between; C - 9 cols, 1 1/4, between.
Commodity Consumption: Avg. Page Number Per Issue - Daily 22; Avg. Page Number Per Issue - Saturday 28; Avg. Page Number Per Issue - Sunday 22.
Equipment; Editorial Hardware – CText, CD/EPD, ECR/Autokon Graphic System; Editorial Equipment – Nikon/Color Scanners.; Classified Hardware – CText, 6-COM, Baseview.; Production Equipment – 2-COM. PRESSROOM: Line 1 – 7-G/Urbanite.; Bundle tying machines –2/Gd; Address machine – 2-/Am.; Audio Hardware – ATT

BRANTFORD

THE EXPOSITOR

PO Box 965, Brantford, ON, N3T 5S8, Canada; gen tel (519) 756-2020; adv tel (519) 756-2020; ed tel (519) 756-2020; gen fax (519) 756-3285; adv fax (519) 756-4911; ed fax (519) 756-9470; gen e-mail cwright@theexpositor.com; adv e-mail comp@theexpositor.com; ed e-mail exp-news@theexpositor.com; web site www.brantfordexpositor.ca
Published: Mon, Tues, Wed, Thur, Fri, Sat
Weekday Frequency: m
Saturday Frequency: m
Circulation 16,137; 16,939(sat)
Last Audit: BPA December 30, 2010
Price: 3.50/wk; 15.00/mo; 173.00/yr (carrier).
Advertising: Open inch rate $1.72
News services: CP, SOU.
Politics: Independent
Not Published: New Year; Good Friday; Victoria Day; Canada Day; Civic Holiday; Labor Day; Thanksgiving; Christmas.
Special editions: Weekender (Sat).
Special weekly sections: Community Guide (Other).
Magazines: TV Times (Fri); Sports (Mon); Comics (Sat); Showcase (Thur); Midweek (Tues); Crossroads (Wed).
Pub. ....Mike Walsh
Educ. Ed. ....Cheryl Bauslaugh
Music Ed. ....Richard Beales
News Ed., Night ....Sam Colaiacovo
Political Ed. ....Michael-Alan Marion
Sports Ed. ....Brian Smiley
Prodn. Mgr., Pre Press ....Alan Oakes
Market information: ADS; TMC.
Mechanical available: Offset; Black and 3 ROP colors; insert accepted - product samples, catalogues; page cutoffs - 23 3/8.
Mechanical Specifications: Type page 11 1/2 x 22 3/8; E - 5 cols, 2 3/16, 1/6 between; A - 10 cols, 1 1/16, 1/12 between; C - 8 cols, 1 3/8, 1/12 between.
Commodity Consumption: Avg. Page Number Per Issue - Daily 34; Avg. Page Number Per Issue - Plates Used 21120; widths 50; Newsprint Used - Metric Tons 1919; Printing Ink Used - Black 20000; Printing Ink Used - Color 12000; Printing Ink Used - Pages Printed 10000.
Equipment EDITORIAL: Front-end Software – QPS/QuarkXPress.; Editorial Hardware – APP/Mac G3, APP/Mac G4; Editorial Equip-

ment – Umax/600 DPI Scanner; Editorial Printers – ECR/PelBox Imagesetter CLASSIFIED: Front-end Software – Baseview.; Classified Hardware – APP/Mac G3; Classified Printers – APP/Mac LaserWriter II NTX DISPLAY: Ad make-up applications – QPS/QuarkXPress 3.31, Aldus/Freehand 5.0, Adobe/Photoshop 3.01; Display Hardware – APP/Mac G3, APP/Mac G4; Display Printers – 3-APP/Mac LaserWriter II NTX, QMS/860 600dpi laser; Production Equipment – Calera/Wordscan, APP/Mac G3; Cameras – Scanners ÃŪÂŪ APP/Mac G3, Nikon, Umax; Scanners – Equipment ÃŪÂŪ SCG/Ad Trac System, SCS/Linx, QPS/QuarkXPress 3.31. PRESSROOM: Line 1 – 8-G/Metro 3183 double width (3 half decks); Line 2 – 8-G/Metro 3184 double width (3 half decks); Line 3 – 8-G/Metro 3185 double width (3 half decks); Folders – 4-G/3:2.; Inserters and stuffers – Manual; Mailroom control system – HL/Dock console; Other equipment – Rolmaster/Conveyor System.; Audio Hardware – DEC/9200, PC

BROCKVILLE

THE BROCKVILLE RECORDER AND TIMES

PO Box 10, Brockville, ON, K6V 5T8, Canada; gen tel (613) 342-4441; gen fax (613) 342-4456; adv fax (613) 342-4542; ed fax (613) 342-4093; gen e-mail publisher@recorder.ca; ed e-mail editor@recorder.ca; web site www.recorder.ca

Published: Mon, Tues, Wed, Thur, Fri, Sat
Weekday Frequency: e
Saturday Frequency: m
Circulation 8,878; 9,252(sat)
Last Audit: BPA December 30, 2010
Price: 3.30/wk; 14.30/mo; 174.20/yr (carrier), $167.80/yr (motor route), $216.00/yr (mail).
Advertising: Open inch rate $1.35
News services: CP, AP, RN.
Politics: Independent
Special weekly sections: Spring Fashion (Apr); Agricultural tab (Aug); Year-End Review (Dec); Industrial Showcase (Feb); Prescott Fashion (Jan); Who's Who 1 (Jul); Riverfest (Jun); Spring Car Care (Mar); Boating (May); Ottawa Senators (Monthly); Christmas Gift Guide 1 (Nov); Cons
Magazines: Real Estate (Fri); Celebrations (Sat).
Pub. .... Liza Nelson
Adv. Dir. .... Jeff Lawson
Circ. Supvr. .... Lesley Longchamps
Ed .... Michael Jiggins
Sports Ed. .... Ron Smith
Wire Ed. .... Phil Kall
Reporter .... Deanna Clark
Market information: Split run; TMC; Zoned editions.
Mechanical available: Offset; Black and 3 ROP colors; insert accepted - up to 13 1/2 x 11 1/2; page cutoffs - 22 3/8.
Mechanical Specifications: Type page 11 1/2 x 21 3/8; E - 6 cols, 1 3/4, 1/8 between; A - 6 cols, 1 3/4, 1/8 between; C - 6 cols, 1 3/4, 1/8 between.
Commodity Consumption: Avg. Page Number Per Issue - Daily 30; Avg. Page Number Per Issue - Plates Used 21000; widths 12 1/2; Newsprint Used - Metric Tons 900; Printing Ink Used - Black 20000; Printing Ink Used - Color 300; Printing Ink Used - Pages Printed 9303.
Equipment EDITORIAL: Front-end Software – Dewar/System 4.; Editorial Hardware – 14-PC 386, 8-Pentium/160, 1-APP/Mac fx; Editorial Printers – Okidata/320 CLASSIFIED: Front-end Software – Baseview/ClassFlow, Baseview/Class Manager.; Classified Hardware – 5-APP/Power Mac 7200/75; Classified Printers – Okidata/393-320, Star/NX1001 DISPLAY: Ad make-up applications – Multi-Ad/Creator, QPS/QuarkXPress, Adobe/Photoshop, Archetype/Corel Draw.; Display Hardware – 1-APP/Mac ci, 4-Power Computing/225, 1-APP/Power Mac 8180, 2-PC, APP/Mac 6100; Display Printers – Canon/Bubble Jet BJC 800 PRODUCTION: Pagination software – Baseview/Extension, QPS/QuarkXPress.; Production Equipment – 1-XIT/Clipper, 2-XIT/Schooner, 1-QMS/1660E, 1-QMS/2060; Cameras – Eskofot/480; Scanners – LE/480 PRESSROOM: Line 1 – 8-G/Community, 1-G/Community (with Color Hump) 1972; Folders –G/SSC.; Bundle tying machines –1/GD, OVL/R101, Cyclops.; Audio Hardware – Pottsville Republican, PC 386; Audio Hardware – IBM/AS-400

CHATHAM

THE CHATHAM DAILY NEWS

PO Box 2007, Chatham, ON, N7M 5M6, Canada; gen tel (519) 354-2000; adv tel (519) 354-2000; ed tel (519) 354-2000; gen fax (519) 436-0949; adv fax (519) 354-3448; ed fax (519) 436-0949; gen e-mail news@chathamdailynews.ca; ed e-mail news@chathamdailynews.ca; web site www.chathamdailynews.ca

Published: Mon, Tues, Wed, Thur, Fri, Sat
Weekday Frequency: e
Saturday Frequency: m
Circulation 8,006; 8,281(sat)
Last Audit: BPA December 30, 2010
Group: Sun Media
Price: 2.95/wk; 12.80/mo; 165.00/yr (carrier), $184.24/yr (mail).
Advertising: Open inch rate $1.07
News services: QMI Reuters
Politics: Independent
Not Published: New Year; Good Friday; Victoria Day; Canada Day; Labor Day; Thanksgiving; Christmas, Senior day, Family day.
Special editions: Home Hunting Guide (Mon).
Pub. .... Dean Muharrem
Adv. Mgr. .... Jeanine Foulon
Circ. Mgr. .... Ron McClintock
Ed. .... Bruce Corcoran
Sports Reporter .... Mark Malone
Photo Dept. Mgr./Picture Ed. .... Diana Martin
Market information: ADS; TMC.
Mechanical available: Offset; Black and 3 ROP colors; insert accepted - single sheet, stitched or inserted; page cutoffs - 22 3/4.
Mechanical Specifications: Type page 13 x 21 1/2; E - 5 cols, 2 1/4, 1/8 between; A - 10 cols, 1 1/8, 1/8 between; C - 6 cols, 1 1/4, 1/8 between.
Commodity Consumption: Avg. Page Number Per Issue - Daily 20; Avg. Page Number Per Issue - Saturday 32; widths 27; Printing Ink Used - Pages Printed 6500.
Equipment EDITORIAL: Front-end Software – Hx.; Editorial Hardware – 2-Hx/HS43, 1-DEC/PDP 11-04, APP/Mac; Classified Hardware – 1-Hx/HS43, 3-Hx, Baseview.; Display Hardware – APP/Mac.; Production Equipment – 1-Nat, APP/Mac System, L2R/1800 HT; Cameras – 1-B; Scanners – 2-Hx. PRESSROOM: Line 1 – 7-G/Urbanite.; Bundle tying machines –1/Gd, 1-/WT; Address machine – 1-/El.

COBOURG

COBOURG DAILY STAR

PO Box 400, Cobourg, ON, K9A 4L1, Canada; gen tel (905) 372-0131; gen fax (905) 372-4966; adv e-mail cdsclassified@northumberlandtoday.com; ed e-mail letters@northumberlandtoday.com; web site www.northumberlandtoday.com

Published: Mon, Tues, Wed, Thur, Fri
Weekday Frequency: e
Circulation 4,402
Last Audit: Estimate March 31, 2004
Group: CanWest Media Sales
Price: 2.65/wk; 11.50/mo; 136.00/yr.
Advertising: Open inch rate $.71(fri)
News services: SOU.
Politics: Independent
Not Published: New Year; Good Friday; Victoria Day; Dominion Day; Civic Holiday; Labor Day; Thanksgiving; Christmas; Boxing Day.
Pub. .... Gordon Brewerton
Adv. Dir. .... Gerry Drage
Mng. Ed. .... Mandy Martin
Prodn. Supvr. .... Julie Hall
Market information: TMC.
Mechanical available: Offset; Black and 3 ROP colors; insert accepted.
Mechanical Specifications: Type page 13 1/2 x 21 1/2; E - 6 cols, 2 1/16, 1/8 between.
Commodity Consumption: Avg. Page Number Per Issue - Daily 26; widths 28; Newsprint Used - Metric Tons 500; Printing Ink Used - Black 7181; Printing Ink Used - Color 700.
Equipment EDITORIAL: Front-end Software – Mk.; Editorial Hardware – Mk CLASSIFIED: Front-end Software – Mk.; Production Equipment – LE/Processor, Ik.

CORNWALL

STANDARD-FREEHOLDER

1150 Montreal Rd., Cornwall, ON, K6H 1E2, Canada; gen tel (613) 933-3160; adv tel (613) 933-3160; ed tel (613) 933-3160; gen fax (613) 933 -7521; adv fax (613) 933-7521; ed fax (613) 933-7521; gen e-mail news@standard-freeholder.com; adv e-mail ads@standard-freeholder.com; ed e-mail news@standard-freeholder.com; web site www.standard-freeholder.com

Published: Mon, Tues, Wed, Thur, Fri, Sat
Weekday Frequency: m
Saturday Frequency: m
Circulation 14,545; 14,545(sat)
Group: Sun Media, A Quebecor Media Company
Price: 2.95/wk; 197.60/yr.
Advertising: Open inch rate $1.48
News services: CP, AP.
Politics: Independent **Established:** 1846
Advertising not accepted: N
Not Published: Sunday
Own facility?: N
Special weekly sections: Home & Garden (Apr); Brides (Feb); Progress (Mar); Car Care (Oct).
Magazines: Hometown (Sat); TV (Thur).
Adv. Dir. .... Peter Padbury
Circ. Dir. .... Anthony Joubert
Managing Editor .... Andrew Carroll
Office Mgr. .... Sylvia Leroux-Lanthier
Purchasing Agent .... Milton Ellis
Adv. Supvr., Classified .... Shelly Lafave
Market information: Split run; TMC; Zoned editions.
Mechanical available: Offset; Black and 3 ROP colors; insert accepted - 36 pages max.; page cutoffs - 22 3/4.
Mechanical Specifications: Type page 13 x 21 1/2; E - 6 cols, 2 1/16, 1/8 between; A - 6 cols, 2 1/16, 1/8 between; C - 9 cols, 1 1/3, 1/8 between.
Commodity Consumption: Avg. Page Number Per Issue - Daily 25; widths 27 1/2; Newsprint Used - Metric Tons 600; Printing Ink Used - Black 14400; Printing Ink Used - Color 1200; Printing Ink Used - Pages Printed 6200.
Equipment CLASSIFIED: Front-end Software – HI.
Delivery Method: Mail, Newsstand, Private Carrier, Racks

FORT FRANCES

FORT FRANCES DAILY BULLETIN

PO Box 339, Fort Frances, ON, P9A 3M7, Canada; gen tel (807) 274-5373; gen fax (807) 274-7286; adv e-mail ads@fortfrances.com; ed e-mail news@fortfrances.com; web site www.fortfrances.com

Published: Mon, Tues, Wed, Thur, Fri
Weekday Frequency: e
Circulation 2,500
Last Audit: Estimate January 28, 2002
Price: 55.00/yr; 3.25/2wk.
Advertising: Open inch rate $1.02
News services: CP.
Politics: 1938
Special weekly sections: Farm Agriculture (Apr); B.A.S.S. Tournament (Jul); Fun in the Sun (Jun); Outdoor Living (May); Christmas Shopping (Nov); Farm Agriculture (Oct).
Magazines: Food Recipe (Thur).
Pub. .... James R. Cumming
Adv. Mgr. .... Debbie Ballard
Circ. Mgr. .... Pam Munn
Ed. .... Michael Behan
Online Mgr. .... Corey Westover
Prodn. Mgr. .... Don Cumming
Market information: ADS; TMC.
Mechanical available: Offset; Black and 3 ROP colors; insert accepted; page cutoffs - 16.
Mechanical Specifications: Type page 10 13/16 x 15; E - 5 cols, 2 1/16, 1/8 between; A - 5 cols, 2 1/16, 1/8 between; C - 5 cols, 2 1/16, 1/8 between.
Commodity Consumption: Avg. Page Number Per Issue - Daily 10; Avg. Page Number Per Issue - Plates Used 550; widths 16; Newsprint Used - Metric Tons 21; Printing Ink Used - Pages Printed 2442.
Equipment; Editorial Hardware – APP/Mac; Editorial Printers – Xante, V, Screen/3050, Imagesetters. CLASSIFIED: Front-end Software – Baseview/Class Manager.; Classified Hardware – APP/Mac DISPLAY: Ad make-up applications – Baseview/Ad Manager Pro; Layout software – APP/Mac.; Display Hardware – APP/Mac PRODUCTION: Pagination software – QPS.; Production Equipment – XD/Copy GS Plus; Cameras – 1-DS/CD240, DAI; Scanners – XD/Copy GS Plus, 1-Datacopy/GS Plus, HEL/Sapphire Scanner with Line Color Software PRESSROOM: Line 1 – 4-HI/Cotrell V-15AB.; MAILROOMCounter stackers – 1-BG/Count-O-Veyor; Bundle tying machines –1/Bu; Address machine – 1-/Am, 1-/Gp.; Audio Hardware – 2-IBM, APP/Mac

GUELPH

THE GUELPH MERCURY

8-14 Macdonnell St., Guelph, ON, N1H 6P7, Canada; gen tel (519) 822-4310; adv tel (519) 823-6010; ed tel (519) 823-6060; gen fax (519) 767-1681; adv fax (519) 822-4272; ed fax (519) 767-1681; ed e-mail editor@guelphmercury.com; web site www.guelphmercury.com

Published: Mon, Tues, Wed, Thur, Fri, Sat
Weekday Frequency: e
Circulation 11,325; 12,274(sat)
Last Audit: BPA December 30, 2010
Price: 3.20/wk (carrier); 176.42/yr.
Advertising: Open inch rate $1.94
News services: CP.
Politics: Independent **Established:** 1853
Not Published: New Year; Family Day; Good Friday; Victoria Day; Canada Day; Labor Day; Thanksgiving; Christmas; Boxing Day.
Pub. .... J. Fred Kuntz
Adv. Mgr. .... Sally Bond
Circ. Mgr. .... Peter Hill
Mng. Ed. .... Phil Andrews
City Ed. .... Brian Williams
Prodn. Mgr., Opns. .... Jonathan Scott
Prodn. Mgr., Pre Press .... Chris Imrie
Prodn. Foreman, Mailroom .... Steven Cowley
Market information: Split run; TMC.
Mechanical available: Offset; Black and 3 ROP colors; insert accepted; page cutoffs - 22 3/4.
Mechanical Specifications: Type page 13 x 21 1/2; E - 6 cols, 2 1/16, 1/8 between; A - 6 cols, 2 1/16, 1/8 between; C - 9 cols, 1 1/3, 1/8 between.
Commodity Consumption: Avg. Page Number Per Issue - Daily 28; widths 54; Newsprint Used - Metric Tons 995.
Equipment; Editorial Hardware – HAS, HI.; Classified Hardware – 4-HAS.; Production Equipment – 1-Nu; Cameras – 1-B, 1-Nu.

PRESSROOM: Line 1 – 7-G; Folders –1; Bundle tying machines –1/Gd; Address machine – 1-/Am.; Audio Hardware – ATT

HAMILTON

THE HAMILTON SPECTATOR

PO Box 300, Hamilton, ON, L8N 3G3, Canada; gen tel (905) 526-3333; adv tel (905) 526-3330; ed tel (905) 526-3420; gen fax (905) 526-0147; adv fax (905) 522-1696; ed fax (905) 526-1395; adv e-mail classified@thespec.com; ed e-mail letters@thespec.com; web site ^www.thespec.com

Published: Mon, Tues, Wed, Thur, Fri, Sat
Weekday Frequency: m
Saturday Frequency: m
Circulation 90,156; 99,542(sat)
Last Audit: BPA December 30, 2010
Price: 3.86/wk (carrier); 16.10/mo; 196.47/yr (carrier).
Advertising: Open inch rate $7.81
News services: CP, UPI, LAT-WP, AP.
Politics: Independent
Not Published: Good Friday; Victoria Day; Dominion Day; Civic Holiday; Thanksgiving; Christmas.
Special weekly sections: Auction Advantage (Apr); Talent Show (Aug); Christmas Gift Guide 3 (Dec); Career Pathways (Feb); Personal Finance (Jan); Reader's Choice (Jul); Golf Shoot-Out (Jun); Travel Ontario (Mar); Minor Sports (May); Christmas Gift Guide 1 (Nov); Fall Car Care (Oc
Magazines: Fashion (Fri); Spectator TV (Sat); Home & Garden (Thur); Car & Trucks (Tues); Food (Wed).
Pres. .... Ian Oliver
Vice Pres., Bus. Admin. .... Derek Fleming
Dir., HR .... Jamie Poehlman
Adv. Vice Pres. .... Kelly Montague
Adv. Mgr., Nat'l/Multi-Market ... Susan Azzopard
Adv. Mgr., Retail Sales .... Donna Gardener
Adv. Mgr., Servs. .... Cathryn Easterbrook
Vice Pres., Circ./Mktg. .... Gary Myers
Mktg. Mgr. .... Jane Allison
Circ. Mgr., Home Delivery .... Chris Switalski
Ed. in Chief .... Dana Robbins
Mng. Ed., Days .... Casey Korstanje
Mng. Ed., Nights .... Roger Gillespie
Bus. Ed. .... Heather Angus
City Ed. .... Jim Poling
Editorial Page Ed. .... Howard Elliott
Entertainment Ed. .... Tom Hogue
Forum Ed. .... Robert Howard
Letters Ed. .... Ron Levett
Life Ed. .... Carla Ammerata
Market information: ADS; Split run; TMC.
Mechanical available: Offset; Black and 3 ROP colors; insert accepted - min. 50lbs. bookstack single sheet, max.3/8 thick; page cutoffs - 23 9/16.
Mechanical Specifications: Type page 11 1/2 x 22 1/4; E - 6 cols, 2 1/16, 1/8 between; A - 10 cols, 1 1/16, 1/12 between; C - 10 cols, 1 1/16, 1/12 between.
Commodity Consumption: Avg. Page Number Per Issue - Daily 56; Avg. Page Number Per Issue - Plates Used 300000; Avg. Page Number Per Issue - Saturday 102; widths 25; Newsprint Used - Metric Tons 14600; Printing Ink Used - Black 310000; Printing Ink Used - Color 460000; Printing
Equipment EDITORIAL: Front-end Software – QPS 1.12.; Editorial Hardware – APP/Mac; Editorial Equipment – APP/Mac Graphics System CLASSIFIED: Front-end Software – Cybergraphics, HI/PLS.; Classified Hardware – Cybergraphics, DEC/VAX 4000, PCs DISPLAY: Ad make-up applications – HI/Layout, QPS/QuarkXPress, Multi-Ad/Creator, Aldus/Freehand, Adobe/Photoshop, Ofoto, Broderbund/Type; Display Hardware – HI/8900, APP/Mac Quadra 700, APP/Mac Quadra 950, Microtek/Scanners, APP/Mac IIsi, Abaton/Scan 300-85; Display Printers – HP/Laserwriter II PRODUCTION: Pagination software – QPS/QuarkXPress 3.3, Adobe/Photoshop.; Production Equipment – 2-AU/3850, 1-Au/108-C, III/Automatic with KFM Vision Bender; Cameras – 1-C/1211, 1-C/1270; Scanners – 1-ECR, 1-PixelCraft, 1-Kk, 1-Epson PRESSROOM: Line 1 – 8-G/Metro 3183 double width (3 half decks) 1976; Line 2 – 8-G/Metro 3184 double width (3 half decks) 1976; Line 3 – 8-G/Metro 3185 double width (3 half decks) 1976; Press Drives – Fin; Folders –4-G/3:2.; MAILROOMCounter stackers – 2-HL/HT2, 4-QWI/Hall, 3-QWI/Sport, 2-QWI/Sport 2; Inserters and stuffers – 4-GMA/SLS 1000 8:1, Fg/Gripper, HI (on-line); Bundle tying machines –2/Power Strap/PSN5, 4-/Power Strap/PSN6, 2-Newstyer/2000, 4-Dynaric/NP3; Wrapping singles – Wrapping singles; Audio Hardware – Brite Voice Systems, QNX/24 line; Audio Hardware – 2-DEC/VAX 6220

KAWARTHA LAKES

LINDSAY POST

17 William St. S., Kawartha Lakes, ON, K9V 3A3, Canada; gen tel (705) 324-2113; adv tel (705) 324-2113; ed tel (705) 324-2113; gen fax 705 324-0174; adv fax (705) 324-0174; ed fax (705) 324-0174; adv e-mail management@thepost.ca; ed e-mail lineditorial@thepost.ca; web site www.thepost.ca

Published: Tues, Fri
Weekday Frequency: m
Circulation 4,274
Last Audit: December 30, 2008
Price: 80.00 /yr.
Advertising: Open inch rate $1.18
Politics: Independent
Pub. .... Darren Murphy
Circ. Mgr. .... Kelly Westerby
Mng. Ed. .... Jason Bain
Mechanical Specifications: Type page 11 1/2 x 21 1/2; E - 6 cols, 1 1/8, 1/8 between; A - 10 cols, 1 1/8, 1/8 between; C - 8 cols, 1 1/8, 1/8 between.

KENORA

DAILY MINER & NEWS

PO Box 1620, Kenora, ON, P9N 3X7, Canada; gen tel (807) 468-5555; gen fax (807) 468-4318; gen e-mail minerandnews@bowes.com; web site www.kenoradailyminerandnews.com

Published: Mon, Tues, Wed, Thur, Fri
Weekday Frequency: e
Circulation 3,036
Last Audit: ABC September 30, 2007
Price: 120.00/yr (carrier); 130.00/yr (mail).
Advertising: Open inch rate $.79
News services: CP.
Politics: Independent
Not Published: Statutory holidays.
Special weekly sections: Our Community (Feb); Our Community (Oct).
Pub. .... Mitch Wolfe
News Ed. .... Bob Stewart
Online Ed. .... Lloyd Mack
Circ. Dir. .... Jan Persian
Market information: ADS; Split run; TMC; Zoned editions.
Mechanical available: Offset; Black and 3 ROP colors; insert accepted; page cutoffs - 22 3/4.
Mechanical Specifications: Type page 13 x 21 1/4; E - 6 cols, 2 1/16, 1/8 between; A - 6 cols, 2 1/16, 1/8 between; C - 9 cols, 1 1/3, 1/8 between.
Commodity Consumption: Avg. Page Number Per Issue - Daily 16; Avg. Page Number Per Issue - Saturday 16; widths 28.
Equipment; Editorial Hardware – APP/Mac, 7-Mk.; Classified Hardware – APP/Mac.; Production Equipment – Fuji; Cameras – 1-Acti; Scanners – APP/Mac. PRESSROOM: Line 1 – 5-G/Community; Folders –1; Bundle tying machines –1/Samuel, 1-/Gd; Address machine – 1-/Am.

KINGSTON

THE KINGSTON WHIG-STANDARD

PO Box 2300, Kingston, ON, K7L 4Z7, Canada; gen tel (613) 544-5000; ed tel (613) 544-5000; gen fax (613) 530-4118; adv fax (613) 530-4121 (Class); gen e-mail kinwhig@thewhig.com; adv e-mail ads@thewhig.com; ed e-mail whiged@thewhig.com; whiglocal@thewhig.com; web site www.thewhig.com

Published: Mon, Tues, Wed, Thur, Fri, Sat
Weekday Frequency: m
Saturday Frequency: m
Circulation 20,292; 23,888(sat)
Last Audit: BPA December 30, 2010
Price: 3.65/wk (carrier); 15.82/mo (carrier), $17.33/mo (motor route); 208.01/yr (carrier), $241.52/yr (motor route).
Advertising: Open inch rate $2.04
News services: CP, AP, SOU.
Politics: Conservative
Not Published: New Year; Good Friday; Victoria Day; Dominion Day; Civic Holiday; Labor Day; Thanksgiving; Christmas.
Special weekly sections: Home & Garden (Apr); Back to School (Aug); Baby of the Year (Dec); Brides (Feb); Managing Your Money (Jan); Dining Guide (Jul); Vacation Guide (May); Mutual Funds (Monthly); Christmas (Nov); Women in Business (Oct); Fall Activity Guide (Sept).
Magazines: Entertainment (Fri); Fashion (Mon); Companion/Travel (Sat); Entertainment (Thur); Health (Tues); Food (Wed).
Pub. .... Ron Laurin
Bus. Mgr. .... Cherie Stewart
Adv. Dir. .... Doug Kane
Adv. Supvr., Special Sections .... Debbie Tindal
Promo./Community Serv./Mktg. ..... Joan Willison
Circ. Mgr., Reader Sales .... Jeff Lundy
Ed. .... Steve Serviss
Features Ed. .... Sarah Crossbie
Sports Ed. .... Mike Koreen
Prod. Mgr. .... Sean Daly
Market information: TMC.
Mechanical available: Offset; Black and 3 ROP colors; insert accepted; page cutoffs - 22 3/4.
Mechanical Specifications: Type page 11 3/4 x 21 1/2; E - 5 cols, 2 3/16, 3/16 between; A - 10 cols, 1, 1/16 between; C - 8 cols, 1 1/3, 1/8 between.
Commodity Consumption: Avg. Page Number Per Issue - Daily 36; Avg. Page Number Per Issue - Plates Used 24500; widths 12 1/2; Newsprint Used - Metric Tons 5087; Printing Ink Used - Black 85500; Printing Ink Used - Color 25544; Printing Ink Used - Pages Printed 10898.
Equipment EDITORIAL: Front-end Software – QPS.; Editorial Hardware – APP/Mac; Editorial Printers – QMS/860 CLASSIFIED: Front-end Software – Cybergraphics.; Classified Hardware – 1-Cybergraphics; Classified Printers – QMS/860 DISPLAY: Ad make-up applications – QPS/QuarkXPress, Aldus/Freehand, Adobe/Illustrator; Layout software – SCS/Layout 80; Display Hardware – APP/Mac; Display Printers – APP/LaserWriter II NTX, 2-AU/APS-6-108, Lexmark/Optra N; Production Equipment – Caere/OmniPage, Aqualith/32; Cameras – Scanners Ã□Â□ 1-ECR/Autokon 1000; Scanners – Equipment Ã□Â□ QPS/QuarkXPress. PRESSROOM: Line 1 – 10-G/Urbanite single width 1992; Folders –1, 1-SU/Jaw Folder w/ 1/4 Folder; Pasters – 7; MAILROOMCounter stackers – 2-HL/HT II; Inserters and stuffers – GMA/SLS 1000; Bundle tying machines –1/OVL, 2-OVL/JP-40; Mailroom control system – PMS-6; Address machine – 2-/Wm; Other equipment – 2-MM/Saddle Stitcher H325.; Audio Hardware – 5-IBM, Service Bureau

KIRKLAND LAKE

NORTHERN NEWS

PO Box 1030, Kirkland Lake, ON, P2N 3L4, Canada; gen tel (705) 567-5321; gen fax (705) 567-6162; adv fax (705) 567-5377; ed fax (705) 567-6162; gen e-mail news@northernnews.ca; adv e-mail display@northernnews.ca; web site www.northernnews.ca

Published: Mon, Tues, Wed, Thur, Fri, Sat
Weekday Frequency: e
Saturday Frequency: e
Circulation 3,122
Last Audit: March 31, 2004
Price: 2.55/wk (carrier); 139.60/yr (carrier/mail).
Advertising: Open inch rate $.57
News services: CP.
Politics: Independent
Not Published: Statutory holidays.
Adv. Mgr. .... Tim Creswell
Circ. Mgr. .... Tony Howell
Mng. Ed. .... Tom Perry
Farm Ed. .... Joe O'Grady
Photo Ed. .... Rick Owen
Sports Ed. .... Jeff Wilkinson
Prodn. Foreman, Composing/Pressroom Bob Aube
Market information: Split run; TMC.
Mechanical available: Offset; Black and 3 ROP colors; insert accepted; page cutoffs - 21 1/2.
Mechanical Specifications: Type page 13 x 21 1/2; E - 6 cols, 2 1/16, 1/8 between; A - 6 cols, 2 1/16, 1/8 between; C - 9 cols, 1 1/2, 1/8 between.
Commodity Consumption: Avg. Page Number Per Issue - Daily 12.
Equipment; Editorial Hardware – Software Ã□Â□ Mk. CLASSIFIED: Front-end Software – Mk.; Production Equipment – Mk.; Bundle tying machines –1/BST.

KITCHENER

THE RECORD

160 King St. E., Kitchener, ON, N2G 4E5, Canada; gen tel (519) 894-2231; gen fax (519) 894-3912; adv fax (519) 894-1258; ed fax (519) 894-3829; ed e-mail newsroom@therecord.com; web site www.therecord.com

Published: Mon, Tues, Wed, Thur, Fri, Sat
Weekday Frequency: m
Saturday Frequency: m
Circulation 63,864; 71,410(sat)
Last Audit: September 30, 2007
Price: 15.68/mo (carrier); 186.99/yr (carrier).
Advertising: Open inch rate $7.34
News services: CP, LAT-WP, NYT.
Politics: Independent **Established:** 1878
Not Published: New Year; Good Friday; Victoria Day; Canada Day; Civic Holiday; Labor Day; Thanksgiving; Christmas.
Special weekly sections: Financial Forum (Monthly).
Magazines: Wheels (Fri); TV Week (Sat); Entertainment Tab (Thur); Small Business (Wed).
Pub. .... Paul McCuaig
Dir., Finance .... Claire Bentzen
HR .... Lisa Voll-Leggo
Adv. Mgr., Classified .... Margaret Thibaudeau
Adv. Mgr., Nat'l/Multi-Market .... John Thompson
Circ. Dir. .... Jonathan Scott
Circ. Mgr., Systems/Admin. .... Craig Campbell
Ed. in Chief .... Lynn Haddrall
Mng. Ed. .... Don McCurdy
Bus. Ed. .... Kevin Crowley
City Ed. .... Harvey Taylor
Deputy City Ed. .... Susan Chilton
Editorial Page Ed. .... John Roe
Entertainment Ed. .... Philip Bast
Librarian .... Christine Masterman
Lifestyle Ed. .... Carol Jankowski
News Ed. .... Neil Ballantyne
Online Ed. .... Dwight Storring
Market information: Split run; TMC.
Mechanical available: Offset; Black and 3 ROP colors; insert accepted - envelopes; page cutoffs - 22.
Mechanical Specifications: Type page 13 x 21; E - 10 cols, 1 1/16, 1/16 between; A - 10 cols, 1 1/16, 1/16 between; C - 10 cols, 1 1/16, 1/16 between.
Commodity Consumption: Avg. Page Number Per

Issue - Daily 62; Avg. Page Number Per Issue - Plates Used 50000; Avg. Page Number Per Issue - Saturday 92; widths 25; Newsprint Used - Metric Tons 7500; Printing Ink Used - Black 300000; Printing Ink Used - Color 46000; Printing Ink

Equipment EDITORIAL: Front-end Software – QPS/QuarkXPress 4, QPS.; Editorial Hardware – APP/Mac, PC; Editorial Printers – 1-NewGen/660B, 1-NewGen/Xcelerwriter CLASSIFIED: Front-end Software – Cybergraphics.; Classified Hardware – 2-DEC/VAX 4000-60; Classified Printers – HP/LaserJet IV DISPLAY: Ad make-up applications – SCS/Layout 8000; Layout software – SCS/Layout 8000.; Display Hardware – DEC/VAX 4105 Lluster; Display Printers – C.Itoh/300, 1-Mannesman/660, 1-Mannesman/690; Production Equipment – Calera/Wordscan.; MAILROOMCounter stackers – 4-QWI/401, HL; Inserters and stuffers – 2-GMA/SLS 2000 12:2; Bundle tying machines –4-Dynaric/NP-3, 1-MLN/ML0AE-16977, 2/Power Strap; Wrapping singles – 4-QWI/Viper Bottom Wrap.; Audio Hardware – Admarc, Cybergraphics 4096, Discus, Intel/Layout 8000, QPS, Quicktrac, Smartstream

LONDON

THE LONDON FREE PRESS

PO Box 2280, London, ON, N6A 4G1, Canada; gen tel (519) 679-1111; adv tel (519) 667-4598 (sales); ed tel (800) 265-4167; gen fax (519) 667-4620; adv fax (519) 667-4523; ed fax (519) 667-4528; gen e-mail feedback@lfpress.com; informationnie@lfpress.com; ed e-mail editor@lfpress.com; newsdesk@lfpress.com; web site www.lfpress.com

Published: Mon, Tues, Wed, Thur, Fri, Sat
Weekday Frequency: m
Saturday Frequency: m
Circulation 67,498; 79,407(sat)
Last Audit: BPA December 30, 2010
Price: 4.40/wk; 17.97/mo; 215.60/yr.
Advertising: Open inch rate $7.06
News services: GNS, CP, Canada News Wire.
Politics: Independent **Established:** 1849
Not Published: Christmas.
Special editions: M Magazine For Men (Every other month); Home Magazine (Quarterly); TV Magazine (Sat); Decor Magazine (Semi-yearly).
Special weekly sections: Garden Center Book (Apr); Continuing Education (Aug); Countdown to Christmas (Dec); Campbook (Feb); Health Guide (Jan); National Fishing Week (Jun); Fashion Statement (Mar); Escapes (May); Downtown Living (Monthly); Holiday Shopping (Nov); Hot Toys (Oct);
Magazines: Wheels (Fri); Business Monday (Mon); Homes (Sat); Ticket (Thur).
Pub./CEO....Susan Muszak
Credit Mgr.....Ben Thay
Dir., HR....Nancy Tyndall
Asst. to Pub.....Darlene Ropp
Adv. Dir.....Lisa Catania Chiaramida
Adv. Mgr., Auto/Real Estate....Chris Kubinski
Adv. Mgr., Bus. Devel.....Cathy Forster
Adv. Mgr., Classified....Kathy Smith
Adv. Mgr., Natl./Major Retail/Inserts Nelson Parreira
Circ. Dir., Reader Sales/Serv./Mktg. .Sherri Scott
Ed. in Chief....Paul Berton
Mng. Ed.....Joe Ruscitti
City Ed.....Greg VanMoorsel
News Ed.....Barbara Taylor
Chief Photographer....Susan Bradnam
Sports Ed.....David Langford
Today Ed.....Howard Burns
Mgmt. Info Servs. Mgr.....Glen Besley
Dir., Opns.....John Pacitto
Market information: TMC.
Mechanical available: Offset; Black and 3 ROP colors; insert accepted - poly bags, outsert packages, sampling; page cutoffs - 22 3/4.
Mechanical Specifications: Type page 11 1/2 x 21 1/2; E - 6 cols, 1 3/4, 3/16 between; A - 10 cols, 2 1/4, 1/8 between; C - 10 cols, 2 1/4, 1/8 between.
Commodity Consumption: Avg. Page Number Per Issue - Daily 44; Avg. Page Number Per Issue - Plates Used 69200; Avg. Page Number Per Issue - Saturday 112; Avg. Page Number Per Issue - Sunday 28; widths 49 1/2; Newsprint Used - Metric Tons 10000; Printing Ink Used - Black 452902;
Equipment EDITORIAL: Front-end Software – QPS/Quark Publishing System 2.08, QPS/Copydesk 2.08, QPS/QuarkXPress 4.11.; Editorial Hardware – APP/Mac, APP/Mac G3; Editorial Printers – Xante CLASSIFIED: Front-end Software – Adacus.; Classified Hardware – Compaq/PC P111-400 EN; Classified Printers – HP/4050 N DISPLAY: Ad make-up applications – Managing Editor/ALS, Managing Editor/CLS, QPS/QuarkXPress; Layout software – MEI/ALS 4.1.6, MEI/CLS 3.0.1, QPS/QuarkXPress 4.11.; Display Hardware – APP/Mac G3; Display Printers – HP/LaserJet, HP/4050 N; Production Equipment – 2-C, 4-Imagesetter, 4-RIP, P; Cameras – Scanners ÃÂ ECR/M2045, Epson, Scitex/Smart 340, PixelCraft/7650 C, PixelCraft/8000; Scanners – Equipment ÃÂ QPS. PRESSROOM: Line 1 – G/Headliner offset; Line 2 – 9-G/Urbanite single width 1979; Folders –G/Offset 2:1, G/Letterpress; Pasters – G/Digital Predrive, Butler/Splicers; Reels and Stands – G/Simplified Tension.; MAILROOMCounter stackers – 6-Id/2000; Inserters and stuffers – 5-GMA/SLS 1000; Bundle tying machines –5/Power Strap; Wrapping singles – Manual; Address machine – 1-/Ch; Other equipment – HI/Trimmer.BUSINESS COMPUTERS: Audio Software – Cobol; Audio Hardware – 2-Alpha/1000

NIAGARA FALLS

NIAGARA FALLS REVIEW

PO Box 270, Niagara Falls, ON, L2E 6T6, Canada; gen tel (905) 358-5711; ed tel (905) 358-5711; gen fax (905) 356-0785; ed fax (905) 374-0461; gen e-mail reporter@nfreview.com; adv e-mail adman@nfreview.com; ed e-mail citydesk@nfreview.com; web site www.niagarafallsreview.ca

Published: Mon, Tues, Wed, Thur, Fri, Sat
Weekday Frequency: m
Saturday Frequency: m
Circulation 10,657; 10,749(sat)
Last Audit: BPA December 30, 2010
Group: CanWest Media Sales
Price: 3.65/wk; 15.80/mo; 194.70/yr.
Advertising: Open inch rate $1.58(m-fri)
News services: CP.
Politics: Independent
Special weekly sections: Niagara-on-the-Lake Tourist Guide (Apr); Niagara Family Fun Tourist Guide (Aug); Niagara Family Fun Tourist Guide (Jul); Niagara Family Fun Tourist Guide (Jun); Niagara Family Fun Tourist Guide (May); Winter Festival of Lights (Oct).
Magazines: Home Buyer's Guide (Real Estate) (Sat).
Broadcast Affiliations: CanWest Global-ONTV.
Pub.....Dave Martineau
Adv. Mgr.....Mark Holmes
Mng. Ed.....Peter Coniadi
Night Ed.....Gord Howard
City Ed.....Joe Wallace
News Ed.....Brad Peters
Prodn. Mgr., Post Press....Martha Cochrane
Market information: ADS; TMC.
Mechanical available: Offset; Black and 3 ROP colors; insert accepted - product samples, non-newsprint publications; page cutoffs - 22 3/4.
Mechanical Specifications: Type page 11 1/2 x 21 1/2; E - 10 cols, 1 1/16, 1/16 between; A - 10 cols, 1 1/16, 1/16 between; C - 9 cols, between.
Commodity Consumption: Avg. Page Number Per Issue - Daily 28; Avg. Page Number Per Issue - Plates Used 1098; Avg. Page Number Per Issue - Saturday 36; widths 25; Newsprint Used - Metric Tons 118.9; Printing Ink Used - Black 1803.96; Printing Ink Used - Pages Printed 847.
Equipment EDITORIAL: Front-end Software – QPS/QuarkXPress 4.0.; Editorial Hardware – APP/Mac; Editorial Printers – HP CLASSIFIED: Front-end Software – QPS.; Classified Hardware – APP/Mac; Classified Printers – HP; Layout software – APP/Mac, MEI/ALS.; Display Hardware – APP/Mac; Display Printers – HP PRODUCTION: Pagination software – CD 3.1.; Production Equipment – 2-COM/9400 Laser, LE/1200; Cameras – 1-C/Spartan II 1244, ECR/Autokon 1000; Scanners – HP/Scantec PRESSROOM: Line 1 – 7-G/Urbanite; Press Drives – 2-G/Motor; Folders –1, 1.; MAILROOMCounter stackers – 1/KAN; Inserters and stuffers – 1-/KAN; Bundle tying machines –1-/OVL.BUSINESS COMPUTERS: Audio Software – HP, Epson, NEC; Audio Hardware – SITG

NORTH BAY

THE NORTH BAY NUGGET

PO Box 570, North Bay, ON, P1B 8J6, Canada; gen tel (705) 472-3200; gen fax (705) 472-1438; adv fax (705) 472-4899 (Classified); gen e-mail nugget@nugget.ca; adv e-mail ads@nugget.ca; ed e-mail letters@nugget.ca; news@nugget.ca; sports@nugget.ca; web site www.nugget.ca

Published: Mon, Tues, Wed, Thur, Fri, Sat
Weekday Frequency: e
Saturday Frequency: e
Circulation 11,550; 12,395(sat)
Last Audit: BPA December 30, 2010
Group: CanWest Media Sales
Price: 3.65/wk, $3.90/wk (motor route); 15.60/mo; 193.80/yr (carrier); 206.40/yr (mail).
Advertising: Open inch rate $1.44
News services: CP, SOU, Fin. Times, Can. Bus. Wire.
Politics: Independent
Not Published: New Year; Good Friday; Christmas.
Special editions: Weekly TV Times Mini Tab (Fri); Vintage Times (Monthly); Weekly Broadsheet (Sat); Parenting (Semi-monthly).
Special weekly sections: Car Care (Apr); Boys & Girls of Summer (Aug); Baby Review (Dec); Cookbook (Jun); Brides (Mar); Home & Garden (May); New Car (Nov); Fall Car Care (Oct); Community Guide (Sept).
Magazines: Real Estate (Fri); Weekender (Sat); Entertainment (Thur); Business (Tues); Food (Wed).
Pub.....Dan Johnson
Purchasing Agent....June Hamilton
Adv. Assoc. Mgr., Sales....Steve Page
Mng. Ed.....Steve Hardy
Columnist....Ken Pagen
Sports Ed.....Jim Hutchison
Prodn. Mgr., Post Press....Paul Chapman
Prodn. Foreman, Pressroom....Steve Hevenor
Market information: TMC; Zoned editions.
Mechanical available: Web Offset; Black and 3 ROP colors; insert accepted - product samples; page cutoffs - 22 3/4.
Mechanical Specifications: Type page 11 1/2 x 21 1/2; E - 5 cols, 2 1/16, 1/8 between; A - 10 cols, 1 1/16, 1/8 between; C - 9 cols, 1 3/16, 1/8 between.
Commodity Consumption: Avg. Page Number Per Issue - Daily 22; Avg. Page Number Per Issue - Plates Used 3000; Avg. Page Number Per Issue - Saturday 36; widths 24 1/2; Newsprint Used - Metric Tons 1500; Printing Ink Used - Pages Printed 9069.
Equipment EDITORIAL: Front-end Software – QPS/QuarkXPress 5, Microsoft/Office Suite, Adobe/Photoshop, QPS.; Editorial Hardware – APP/Mac; Editorial Equipment – Kk/Negscanner; Editorial Printers – Xante CLASSIFIED: Front-end Software – CText.; Classified Hardware – PC, APP/Mac; Classified Printers – XIT/Laser Printer 11x17 DISPLAY: Ad make-up applications – SCS/Layout 8000; Layout software – SCS/Layout 8000.; Display Hardware – DEC/VAX; Display Printers – DEC/LG02; Production Equipment – Caere/OmniPage, APP/Mac, Adobe/Photoshop, Adobe/Illustrator; Cameras – Scanners ÃÂ Epson/Negative Scanner. PRESSROOM: Line 1 – 13-G/Community; Folders –G/SSC, G/Community.; MAILROOMCounter stackers – BG/Count-O-Veyor 108, MM/285; Inserters and stuffers – 13-KAN/760; Bundle tying machines –2/Stappers; Other equipment – Trimmer (3 knife).BUSINESS COMPUTERS: Audio Software – Microsoft/Excel, Microsoft/Word; Audio Hardware – PCs

ORILLIA

THE PACKET & TIMES

PO Box 220, Orillia, ON, L3V 7R2, Canada; gen tel (705) 325-1355; adv tel (705) 325-1355 (Display); ed tel (705) 325-1357; gen fax (705) 325-4033; adv fax (705) 325-7691 (Classified); ed fax (705) 325-4033; adv e-mail ads@orilliapacket.com; ed e-mail newsroom@orilliapacket.com; web site www.orilliapacket.com

Published: Mon, Tues, Wed, Thur, Fri, Sat
Weekday Frequency: m
Saturday Frequency: m
Circulation 5,336; 5,407(sat)
Last Audit: BPA December 30, 2010
Price: 3.25/wk; 165.00/yr.
Advertising: Open inch rate $1.68
News services: Sun Media
Politics: Independent
Advertising not accepted: Y
Not Published: Sunday
Own facility?: N
Profile: Daily Paper Monday to Saturday
Publisher/General Manager....John Hammill
Circ. Mgr.....Shelley Gardy
Night Ed.....Julie Langpeter
News Ed.....Randy Lucenti
Market information: ADS; TMC.
Mechanical available: Offset; Black and 3 ROP colors; insert accepted; page cutoffs - 22 3/4.
Mechanical Specifications: Type page 12 15/16 x 21 1/2; E - 6 cols, 2 1/16, 1/8 between; A - 6 cols, 2 1/16, 1/8 between; C - 9 cols, 1 1/3, 1/8 between.
Commodity Consumption: Avg. Page Number Per Issue - Daily 20; widths 27 1/2; Newsprint Used - Metric Tons 410.
Equipment: Editorial Hardware – CD/Pagination; Editorial Equipment – APP/Mac Graphic.; Production Equipment – F/Plate Maker; Cameras – 1-B/3000.; Bundle tying machines –1/Gd; Address machine – 1-/El.

OTTAWA

LE DROIT

PO Box 8860, Sta. T, Ottawa, ON, K1G 3J9, Canada; gen tel (613) 562-0111; adv tel (613) 562-7747; ed tel (613) 562-0333; gen fax (613) 562-6280 (Admin); adv fax (613) 562-7572; ed fax (613) 562-7539; gen e-mail ledroit@ledroit.com; adv e-mail publicite@ledroit.com; ed e-mail nouvelles@ledroit.com; web site www.cyberpresse.ca

Published: Mon, Tues, Wed, Thur, Fri
Weekday Frequency: m
Saturday Frequency: m
Circulation 35,884; 35,862(sat); 35,862(sun)
Last Audit: ABC September 30, 2011
Group: CanWest Media Sales
Price: 3.40/wk; 14.73/mo; 197.52/yr (carrier), $840.00/yr (mail).
Advertising: Open inch rate $2.07
News services: CP, AFP.
Politics: Independent
Not Published: New Year; Christmas.
Magazines: Weekend (entertainment) (Fri); TV Guide (Sat); Societe (Living) (Thur); Internet

and Science (Tues).
Pub.....Jacques Pronovost
Comptroller....Patrice Dellehuneur
Dir., Sales/Promo.....Claude Tremblay
Ed. in Chief....Andre Lorocque
Arts Ed.....Valerie Lessard
Editorial Page Ed.....Pierre Jury
News Ed.....John Jajnon
Sports Ed.....Marc Brassard
Online Mgr.....Antonie Boulet
Prodn. Mgr., Computer Systems Louis Simoneau
Market information: TMC; Zoned editions.
Mechanical available: Offset; Black and 3 ROP colors; insert accepted; page cutoffs - 15.
Commodity Consumption: Avg. Page Number Per Issue - Daily 60; Avg. Page Number Per Issue - Plates Used 29500; Avg. Page Number Per Issue - Saturday 120; widths 60; Newsprint Used - Metric Tons 2400; Printing Ink Used - Black 90000; Printing Ink Used - Color 20000; Printing Ink
Equipment EDITORIAL: Front-end Software – Baseview/NewsEdit Pro DB, APP/Mac, OS.; Editorial Hardware – 4-APP/Power Mac, APP/Mac G3-333 Server, 24-APP/Mac, 9-APP/Power Mac G3-266; Editorial Equipment – 25-RSK/Tandy 1100 FD, 7-APP/Mac PowerBook; Editorial Printers – 1-HP/5MP, 1-APP/Mac LaserWriter Pro 630 CLASSIFIED: Front-end Software – SCS/AdMax, Unix/SCO.; Classified Hardware – 2-Dell/Power Edge 4100-200 Server, 16-Dell; Classified Printers – HP/LaserJet 4M Plus; Display Hardware – 2-Star Max, 2-APP/Power Mac 7200/120, 1-APP/Power Mac 7300-180, 1-APP/Mac G3-333 Server, 3-APP/Power Mac G3-233, 1-APP/Mac G3-266, 1-Dell/Optiplex Pentium II/400; Display Printers – APP/Mac LaserWriter 8500, HP/LaserJet II, Tex Tronix/Phaser 300i PRODUCTION: Pagination software – QPS/QuarkXPress 3.32, SCS/Linx 4.0.; Production Equipment – STF/Auto OCR, Adobe/Rips, APP/Mac 9500, Comulus/DataBase; Cameras – B; Scanners – 1-Nikon/Coolscan, 1-Kk/2035, AG/Horizon, AG/Duo Scan PRESSROOM: Line 1 – 10-RKW/Creusotloire (2 1/2 units; 3 Quad units) single width; Line 2 – 3-RKW/Creusotloire color single width 1998; Folders –2; MAILROOMCounter stackers – MM/Wamack, MM; Inserters and stuffers – MM/2 4:1; Bundle tying machines –OVL/JP-80.AUDIO: Audio Software – Microsoft/Works 7.0; Audio Hardware – VMX; Audio Hardware – Sun

THE OTTAWA CITIZEN

PO Box 5020, Ottawa, ON, K2C 3M4, Canada; gen tel (613) 829-9100; adv tel (613) 829-9321 (Classified); ed tel (613) 596-3664; gen fax (613) 726-5852; adv fax (613) 596-3619 (Classified); ed fax (613) 726-1198; gen e-mail rss@thecitizen.canwest.com; adv e-mail adinquiries@thecitizen.canwest.com; ed e-mail letters@thecitizen.canwest.com; web site www.ottawacitizen.com
Published: Mon, Tues, Wed, Thur, Fri, Sat, Sun
Weekday Frequency: m
Saturday Frequency: m
Circulation 114,846; 114,495(sat); 105,143(sun)
Last Audit: ABC September 30, 2011
Group: CanWest Media Sales
Price: 5.65/wk (includes GST); 22.58/mo; 270.94/yr (home delivery).
Advertising: Open inch rate $8.34
News services: CP, AP, SOU, LAT-WP, NYT, MCT, RN, SHNS, Bloomberg, HN, Independent, Telegraph.
Politics: Independent
Not Published: New Year; Christmas.
Special weekly sections: New Homes Interiors & Lifestyles (Apr); Local Business Profile (Aug); Winter Travel Directory (Dec); March Break Destination (Feb); National Ski Week (Jan); Taste Of Ottawa (Jul); Armed Forces (Jun); High Tech Report (Mar); Ottawa Business Show (May); Ski
Magazines: Wheels (Fri); High Tech (Mon); TV Times (Sat); Style (Thur); Food (Wed).
Pres./Pub.....Jim Orban
Vice Pres., HR/Finance....Deborah Bennett
Controller....Shirley Tam
Adv. Mgr., Classified/Career/Category Sales Eric Kalbfleisch
Circ. Mgr., Sales/Serv.....Gerry Lennon
Circ. Mgr., Customer Serv.....Joanne Campbell
Circ. Mgr., Single Copy....William Berry
Circ. Mgr., City Subscriptions....Andre Boileau
Circ. Mgr., Country Subscriptions....Rob Frame
Circ. Mgr., Systems Admin.....Robert Littlemore
Ed. in Chief....Scott Anderson
Books Ed.....Susan Allan
Bus. Ed.....Drew Gragg
Citizen Weekly Magazine Style Ed. Lynn McAuley
City Ed.....Rob Warner
Columnist....Charles Gordon
Columnist....Susan Riley
Fashion Ed.....Wendy Warburton
Food Ed.....Ron Eade
Market information: ADS; Split run; TMC.
Mechanical available: Offset; Black and 3 ROP colors; insert accepted; page cutoffs - 23 3/4.
Mechanical Specifications: Type page 11 1/2 x 22 1/8; E - 6 cols, 2 1/16, 1/8 between; A - 10 cols, 1 1/16, 1/8 between; C - 10 cols, 1 1/16, 1/8 between.
Commodity Consumption: Avg. Page Number Per Issue - Daily 68; Avg. Page Number Per Issue - Plates Used 130000; Avg. Page Number Per Issue - Saturday 108; Avg. Page Number Per Issue - Sunday 56; widths 25; Newsprint Used - Metric Tons 21800; Printing Ink Used - Black 200000; Pr
Equipment EDITORIAL: Front-end Software – DEC, QPS/QuarkXPress, QPS/Quark Dispatch, QPS/Quark Copy Desk, QuickWire.; Editorial Hardware – PC 386, PC 486, APP/Mac ci, APP/Power Mac 6100-66, APP/Mac Power Book 150; Editorial Printers – AU/APS 6, V/VT-600, APP/Mac LaserWriters, HP/LaserJet 4 PWS CLASSIFIED: Front-end Software – Cybergraphics.; Classified Hardware – PCs; Classified Equipment – Sharp/610 scanner DISPLAY: Ad make-up applications – QPS/QuarkXPress; Layout software – SCS/Layout 8000.; Display Hardware – APP/Mac; Production Equipment – 1-Nu/Flip Top FTUP, 1-All/Sierra, 1-All/3850, 1-DAI/LD-2600; Cameras – Scanners ÃÐÂÃÐÂÃÐ 1-Sharp/Flatbed, 4-Nikon/Negative Scanner, 1-ECR, 3-Epson, 1-PixelCraft; Scanners – Equipment ÃÐÂÃÐÂÃÐ QPS. PRESSROOM: Line 1 – 9-G/Metro Offset 1973; Line 2 – 9-G/Metro Offset 1973; Line 3 – 9-G/Metro Offset 1994; Folders –3-G/3:2; Reels and Stands – 24; MAILROOMCounter stackers – 6-QWI/300, 2-SH/257; Inserters and stuffers – 3/AM Graphics/NP 630; Bundle tying machines –5-/Power Strap/PSN-6, 2-/Dynaric.BUSINESS COMPUTERS: Audio Software – Microsoft/Office 6.0; Audio Hardware – Compaq/DeskPro 5120

THE OTTAWA SUN

PO Box 9729, Stn. T, Ottawa, ON, K1G 5H7, Canada; gen tel (613) 739-7000; adv tel (613) 739-7100; ed tel (613) 739-5113; gen fax (613) 739-0930; adv fax (613) 739-8044; ed fax (613) 739-0930; gen e-mail ottawa.city_desk@ott.sunpub.com; adv e-mail classads@ott.sunpub.com (Classified); ottawa.advertising@ott.sunpub.com (Display); ed e-mail ottsun.oped@sunmedia.ca; web site www.ottawasun.com
Published: Mon, Tues, Wed, Thur, Fri, Sat, Sun
Weekday Frequency: m
Saturday Frequency: m
Circulation 39,298; 30,593(sat); 34,745(sun)
Last Audit: BPA December 30, 2010
Price: 3.25/wk (carrier); 13.00/mo; 181.39/yr.
Advertising: Open inch rate $4.52
News services: AP, CP, GNS, RN.
Politics: 1988
Not Published: New Year; Christmas.
Special editions: Show Time (S).
Special weekly sections: Welcome Home (Renovation Guide) (Monthly).
Magazines: Car Market (Thur).
Pub./CEO....Rick Gibbons
Adv. Dir.....Bruce Holmes
Adv. Mgr., Classified....Marietta D'Alessio
Mktg. Dir., Commercial Sales/Promos. Susan Dagg Fulton
Circ. Dir.....Randy Hayley
Circ. Mgr.....George Norlock
Ed. in Chief....Mike Therien
City Ed.....Don Ermen
Entertainment Ed.....Drew McAnulty
News Ed.....Mitchell Axelrad
Photo Ed.....Errol McGihon
Sports Ed.....Tim Baines
Dir., Computer Servs.....Steve Walsh
Prodn. Dir.....Charles Stapley
Prodn. Dir., Mfg.....Claire-Anne Lalonde
Prodn. Mgr.....Tracey Legault
Market information: TMC.
Mechanical available: Offset; Black and 3 ROP colors; insert accepted - 11 x 13 1/2, single sheets must be folded; page cutoffs - 13 1/2.
Mechanical Specifications: Type page 10 1/4 x 12 1/2; E - 8 cols, 1 3/16, 1/8 between; A - 8 cols, 1 3/16, 1/8 between; C - 8 cols, 1 3/16, 1/8 between.
Commodity Consumption: Avg. Page Number Per Issue - Daily 64; Avg. Page Number Per Issue - Sunday 54; widths 23; Newsprint Used - Metric Tons 6700; Printing Ink Used - Black 56357; Printing Ink Used - Color 46875.
Equipment EDITORIAL: Front-end Software – QPS/QuarkXPress 3.3.1, Adobe/Illustrator 8.0, Phoenix/Client, Aldus/Freehand 9.0, Newsline/Solo (5X), Adobe/Photoshop 4.0, Adobe/Photoshop 5.0.; Editorial Hardware – APP/iMac, APP/Power Mac, APP/iBook, APP/Mac G4; Editorial Printers – X/2025, X/432 ST CLASSIFIED: Front-end Software – Multi-Ad 4.0, Aldus/Freehand 9.0, Adobe/Illustrator 8.0.; Classified Hardware – Compaq/Pentium; Classified Printers – X/2025, X/432 ST, QMS/1725 DISPLAY: Ad make-up applications – Multi-Ad/Creator 4.0, Adobe/Illustrator 8.0, Aldus/Freehand 7.0, QPS/QuarkXPress 3.32, Adobe/Photoshop 5.5; Layout software – MEI/ALS.; Display Hardware – APP/Power Mac 8600, APP/Mac G3, APP/Mac G4; Display Printers – X/2825, X/DC12 PRODUCTION: Pagination software – Mk/Ad Director 2.0.; Production Equipment – 2-Burgess/Plate Burners, III/3850, LE/1800; Cameras – ECR/Autokon, Marathon/Horizontal; Scanners – Kk/Neg Scanner PRESSROOM: Line 1 – 10-G/Urbanite single width 1989; Line 2 – 4-G/Urbanite single width 1995; Folders –2-G/Urbanite 2:1; Pasters – 8; MAILROOMCounter stackers – 1-Id, 1-Id, 1-Id; Inserters and stuffers – 2-MM/227, 1-HI/1372; Bundle tying machines –2/MLN, 1-/Dynamic.; Address machine – ATT/Computer Print Out.BUSINESS COMPUTERS: Audio Software – Lotus, WordPerfect 6.0, Microsoft/Office 98; Audio Hardware – Pentium/PCs

OWEN SOUND

THE SUN TIMES

PO Box 200, Owen Sound, ON, N4K 5P2, Canada; gen tel (519) 376-2250; adv tel (519) 372-4310; ed tel (519) 372-4328; gen fax (519) 376-7190; adv fax (519) 376-7190; ed fax (519) 372-1861; adv e-mail classifieds@thesuntimes.ca; ads@thesuntimes.ca; ed e-mail news@thesuntimes.ca; web site www.owensoundsuntimes.com
Published: Mon, Tues, Wed, Thur, Fri, Sat
Weekday Frequency: e
Saturday Frequency: e
Circulation 12,464; 12,737(sat)
Last Audit: BPA December 30, 2010
Price: 2.95/wk (carrier); 12.70/mo; 168.00/yr.
Advertising: Open inch rate $1.55(e-fri)
News services: CP, SOU.
Politics: Independent **Established:** 1922
Not Published: New Year; Good Friday; Victoria Day; Canada Day; Civic Holiday; Labor Day; Thanksgiving; Christmas.
Special weekly sections: Home Improvement 1 (Apr); Back to School (Aug); Xmas Greetings (Dec); Business Outlook (Feb); Brides (Jan); The Sale (Jul); Home Improvement 2 (May); Xmas Gift Guide (Nov); Almanac (Oct); Financial Planning 1 (Sept).
Magazines: Real Estate (Fri); Sports (Mon); Auto (Thur); Seniors (Tues); Lifestyles (Wed).
Pub.....Cheryl McMenemy
Adv. Dir.....Loise Kazarian-Hodder
Adv. Supvr., Classified....Barbara Floto
Circ. Mgr.....Brent Radbourne
Mng. Ed.....Michael Den-Tandt
News Ed.....Jim Merrian
Photo Dept. Mgr.....Willy Waterton
Sports Ed.....William Walker
Coord., Computer Servs.....Sandy Hayes
Market information: ADS; TMC.
Mechanical available: Offset; Black and 3 ROP colors; insert accepted - envelopes, samples; page cutoffs - 21 3/4.
Mechanical Specifications: Type page 11 1/2 x 21 3/4; E - 5 cols, 2 3/16, 1/8 between; A - 10 cols, 1, 1/8 between; C - 5 cols, 2 3/16, 1/8 between.
Commodity Consumption: Avg. Page Number Per Issue - Daily 26; Avg. Page Number Per Issue - Plates Used 20000; widths 17; Newsprint Used - Metric Tons 2500; Printing Ink Used - Pages Printed 7200.
Equipment EDITORIAL: Front-end Software – APP/Mac, QPS/QuarkXPress.; Editorial Hardware – 5-APP/Mac Quadra 950; Editorial Equipment – Smith Corona/XDS 20; Editorial Printers – 3-APP/Mac LaserWriter CLASSIFIED: Front-end Software – CText 6.0.; Classified Hardware – APP/Mac; Classified Equipment – 1-APP/Mac LaserScanner DISPLAY: Ad make-up applications – QPS/QuarkXPress, Adobe/Illustrator, Aldus/Freehand, Adobe/Photoshop; Layout software – 3; Display Hardware – 1-APP/Mac, 5-APP/Mac fx, 5-APP/Power PC 7600; Display Printers – 3-APP/Mac Laser-Printer; Production Equipment – ECR/Imagesetter, AU/APS108; Cameras – Scanners ÃÐÂÐ AG/Repromaster-3000; Scanners – Equipment ÃÐÂÐ Ad Trac 2.1. PRESSROOM: Line 1 – 5-G/Community single width (1 Community 4-high); Folders –1-G/SC.; MAILROOMCounter stackers – 2/BG; Inserters and stuffers – MM/8-into-1; Bundle tying machines –MLN.BUSINESS COMPUTERS: Audio Software – Lotus 2.2; Audio Hardware – 1-Compaq/LTE 286, 1-IBM/PS2 Model 60, 2-IBM/PS2 Model 30

PEMBROKE

OBSERVER

PO Box 190, Pembroke, ON, K8A 6X3, Canada; gen tel (613) 732-3691; adv fax (613) 732-2645; adv e-mail ads@thedailyobserver.ca; ed e-mail editor@thedailyobserver.ca; web site www.thedailyobserver.ca
Published: Mon, Tues, Wed, Thur, Fri, Sat
Weekday Frequency: m
Saturday Frequency: m
Circulation 4,179; 4,772(sat)
Last Audit: BPA December 30, 2010
Price: 3.10/wk (carrier); 176.80/yr.
Advertising: Open inch rate $1.09
News services: CP, SOU.
Politics: Independent **Established:** 1855
Magazines: Home Finder (Fri); Channels (Sat).
Pub.....Steve Gloster
Purchasing Agent....Pat Hahn
Circ. Mgr.....David Bell
Editorial Page Ed.....Peter Lapinskie
Asst. News Ed.....Debbie Robinson
Prodn. Mgr., Mailroom....Lisa Bell
Market information: ADS; TMC.
Mechanical available: Offset; Black and 3 ROP colors; insert accepted; page cutoffs - 21 1/2.
Mechanical Specifications: Type page 13 3/4 x 21 1/2; E - 5 cols, 2 1/4, 1/8 between; A - 10 cols, 1 1/16, 1/8 between; C - 8 cols, 1 5/16, 1/8 between.
Commodity Consumption: Avg. Page Number Per Issue - Daily 14; Avg. Page Number Per

Issue - Saturday 16.
Equipment EDITORIAL: Front-end Software – QPS/QuarkXPress, APP/Mac, Baseview.; Editorial Hardware – APP/Mac; Editorial Printers – 2-F; Layout software – APP/Mac, QPS/QuarkXPress.; Display Printers – Xante; Production Equipment – COM/II 316, COM/II 40348. PRESSROOM: Line 1 – G/Community.; Bundle tying machines – 1/Gd, TS/210; Address machine – Mail Rite.

PETERBOROUGH

THE PETERBOROUGH EXAMINER

PO Box 3890, Peterborough, ON, K9J 8L4, Canada; gen tel (705) 745-4641; gen fax (705) 741-3217; ed fax (705) 743-4581; gen e-mail newsroom@peterboroughexaminer.com; adv e-mail retail1@peterboroughexaminer.com; ed e-mail letters@peterboroughexaminer.com; web site www.thepeterboroughexaminer.com
Published: Mon, Tues, Wed, Thur, Fri, Sat
Weekday Frequency: e
Saturday Frequency: m
Circulation 13,414; 14,291(sat)
Last Audit: BPA December 30, 2010
Price: 3.36/wk (carrier); 14.56/mo (pre-authorized payment); 182.20/yr (carrier), $195.50/yr (mail).
Advertising: Open inch rate $3.31(e-fri)
News services: Hollinger Inc., AP, RN.
Politics: 1847
Not Published: Statutory holidays.
Special editions: TV Channels (Sat).
Special weekly sections: Cook Book (Dec); Brides (Jan); Progress (Mar); Home Improvement (May); Seniors Monthly (Monthly); Cook Book (Spring).
Pub. .... Darren Murphy
Mng. Ed. .... Ed N. Arnold
District Entertainment Ed. .... Werner Bergen
Editorial Page Ed. .... Jim Hendry
Sports Ed. .... Bob Feaver
Features Ed. .... Gary Ball
Prodn. Mgr., Press Room .... Jeff Wilson
Prodn. Foreman, Composing .... Terry Keating
Market information: ADS; TMC.
Mechanical available: Offset; Black and 3 ROP colors; insert accepted - samples, tags, etc.; page cutoffs - 22 3/4.
Mechanical Specifications: Type page 13 x 23 1/2; E - 5 cols, 2 1/4, 1/16 between; A - 10 cols, 1 1/16, 1/16 between; C - 8 cols, 1 1/3, 1/16 between.
Commodity Consumption: Avg. Page Number Per Issue - Daily 32; Avg. Page Number Per Issue - Saturday 64; Avg. Page Number Per Issue - Sunday 28; widths 25; Newsprint Used - Metric Tons 1600; Printing Ink Used - Pages Printed 11424.
Equipment EDITORIAL: Front-end Software – Softwar; Editorial Hardware – Intel/486, Intel/386; Editorial Equipment – 1-APP/Mac IIcx, 2-APP/Mac Quadra, 1-APP/Mac Quadra 950, 1-Sharp/JX-610 flatbed scanner, 2-CD/Newsline 2644 Picture Desk, 2-Nikon/3500 Scanner, 2-AG/Arcus Flatbed Scanner; Editorial Printers – APP/Mac LaserWriter CLASSIFIED: Front-end Software – CText/Classified Pagination (Alps-0S2), CText/Adept (Ad building).; Classified Hardware – Intel/386 DISPLAY: Ad make-up applications – SCS/Layout 8000; Layout software – SCS/Layout 8000.; Display Hardware – Intel/386 PRODUCTION: Pagination software – QPS/QuarkXPress 3.1.; Production Equipment – 2-V/Series 6000 Imagesetter, 1-QMS/860 Print System; Cameras – 1-DS/Horizontal Page Camera C-260-D; Scanners – 2-Nikon/3500 PRESSROOM: Line 1 – 1; Bundle tying machines –3/OVL.; Audio Hardware – ATT

PORT HOPE

PORT HOPE EVENING GUIDE

PO Box 296, Port Hope, ON, L1A 3W4, Canada; gen tel (905) 372-0131; gen fax (905) 885-7442; gen e-mail eargyris@northumberlandtoday.com; web site www.northumberlandtoday.com
Published: Mon, Tues, Wed, Thur, Fri
Weekday Frequency: e
Circulation 2,393
Last Audit: ABC September 30, 2006
Group: CanWest Media Sales
Price: 2.50/wk (carrier); 164.70/yr.
Advertising: Open inch rate $.71
News services: Bardal, Gosbee & Assoc..
Politics: Independent
Not Published: Statutory holidays.
Pub. .... Gordon Brewerton
Adv. Dir. .... Jerry Crage
Mng. Ed. .... Mandy Martin
Mechanical Specifications: Type page 13 3/4 x 21 1/2; E - 6 cols, 2 1/16, 1/8 between.
Commodity Consumption: Avg. Page Number Per Issue - Daily 30; widths 28; Newsprint Used - Metric Tons 500; Printing Ink Used - Black 16000; Printing Ink Used - Color 700.

SAINT CATHARINES

THE STANDARD

17 Queen St., Saint Catharines, ON, L2R 5G5, Canada; gen tel (905) 684-7251; adv tel (905) 684-7251 (Retail); ed tel (905) 684-7251; gen fax (905) 684-6670; adv fax (905) 684-9981 (Classified); ed fax (905) 684-6032; gen e-mail standard@stcatharinesstandard.ca; adv e-mail classad@stcatharinesstandard.ca (Classified); advertising@stcatharinesstandard.ca; ed e-mail Wmetcalfe@stcatharinesstandard.ca; web site www.stcatharinesstandard.ca
Published: Mon, Tues, Wed, Thur, Fri, Sat
Weekday Frequency: e
Saturday Frequency: e
Circulation 19,011; 21,269(sat)
Last Audit: BPA December 30, 2010
Advertising: Open inch rate $3.02(e-fri)
News services: QMI Agency
Politics: 1891
Not Published: Sunday
Own facility?: Y
Special weekly sections: Autonet, Homes
Sr. Group Publisher, Niagara
Publisher, St. Catharines Standard ..... Judy Bullis
Adv. Dir. .... Julia Coles
Mng. Ed. .... Audrea Kriluck
Bus. Ed. .... Don Fraser
Editorial Page Ed. .... Kelvin Reid
Health Ed. .... Peter Downs
Society Ed. .... Brian Collins
Sports Ed. .... Bernie Puchalski
Data Processing Mgr. .... Wayne Bourner
Prodn. Mgr., Mailroom .... Keith Matheson
Market information: TMC.
Mechanical available: Black and 3 ROP colors; insert accepted - self-adhesive notes; page cutoffs - 22 3/4.
Mechanical Specifications: Type page 11 1/2 x 21 1/2; E - 5 cols, 2 1/4, 1/8 between; A - 10 cols, 1 1/16, 1/8 between; C - 10 cols, 1 1/16, 1/8 between.
Equipment EDITORIAL: Front-end Software – Microsoft/Windows NT 4.0, Microsoft/Windows 2000.; Editorial Hardware – 4-Compaq/Proliant ML530; Editorial Equipment – APP/Power Mac 7300, APP/Mac 7200, APP/Mac 8500, AP/PictureDesk, 6-APP/Mac G4; Editorial Printers – 2-HP/LaserJet 4MV DISPLAY: Ad make-up applications – SCS/Layout 8000; Layout software – SCS/Layout 8000.; Inserters and stuffers – KAN; Bundle tying machines –.
Delivery Method: Newsstand, Private Carrier

SAINT THOMAS

ST. THOMAS TIMES-JOURNAL

16 Hincks St., Saint Thomas, ON, N5R 5Z2, Canada; gen tel (519) 631-2790; adv tel (519) 631-2790; ed tel (519) 631-2790; gen fax (519) 631-5653; adv fax (519) 631-5653; ed fax (519) 631-5653; adv e-mail bevponton@bowesnet.com; web site www.stthomastimesjournal.com
Published: Mon, Tues, Wed, Thur, Fri, Sat
Weekday Frequency: e
Circulation 4,165; 4,069(sat)
Last Audit: BPA December 30, 2010
Price: 2.60/wk; 11.27/mo; 170.40/yr (carrier).
Advertising: Open inch rate $1.45
News services: CP, AP, RN.
Politics: Independent
Not Published: New Year; Good Friday; Victoria Day; Canada Day; Civic Holiday; Labor Day; Thanksgiving; Christmas; Boxing Day.
Special weekly sections: Calendar (Annually); The Great Outdoors (Apr); Back to School (Aug); Christmas Wishbook II (Dec); Hearty Strokes (Feb); All Aboard (Jan); London Profile (Jul); Tourist Guide (Mar); She's My Mom (May); Christmas Crafts (Nov); City Directory (Oct); 911 Serv
Magazines: TV Tab (Fri).
Adv. Mgr. .... Bev Ponton
Circ. Mgr. .... Karen Van Herten
News Ed. .... Ross Porter
Market information: TMC.
Mechanical available: Offset; Black and 3 ROP colors; insert accepted; page cutoffs - 12 1/5.
Mechanical Specifications: Type page 10 1/4 x 16; E - 6 cols, 1 3/8, 1/8 between; A - 6 cols, 1 3/8, 1/8 between; C - 7 cols, 1 1/3, 1/8 between.
Commodity Consumption: Avg. Page Number Per Issue - Daily 28; Avg. Page Number Per Issue - Plates Used 3600; Avg. Page Number Per Issue - Saturday 24; widths 30; Newsprint Used - Short Tons 300.9; Printing Ink Used - Black 2400; Printing Ink Used - Pages Printed 4380.
Equipment EDITORIAL: Front-end Software – QPS/QuarkXPress, Baseview/NewsEdit.; Editorial Hardware – APP/Mac Quadra 610; Editorial Equipment – QMS/860 Print System; Editorial Printers – QMS/860 CLASSIFIED: Front-end Software – Baseview.; Classified Hardware – APP/Power Mac; Classified Equipment – QMS/86 Print System, QMS/Print System; Classified Printers – APP/Mac LaserWriter Pro 630 DISPLAY: Ad make-up applications – QPS/QuarkXPress, Adobe/Photoshop, Adobe/Illustrator/; Layout software – Other Equipment ÃÛÃÛ DTI/Imagesetter, P/Processor.; Display Hardware – APP/Power Mac; Display Printers – QMS/Laser Printers, HP/LaserJet 5si/MX; Production Equipment – QMS/860 Laser Printer, APP/Mac, Epson/Stylus Colour 3000, Fugi/PI 2800 Imagesetter; Cameras – Acti, Kk/Digital Science DC 50 Zoom; Scanners – Umax/UC840, Epson/Expression 636. PRESSROOM: Line 1 – 8-G/Community 1981; Press Drives – 1; Folders –1-G/Quarter 1993.; MAILROOM-Counter stackers – BG/Count-O-Veyor, BG/209; Bundle tying machines –2/Gd, 1-/Dynaric; Address machine – 1-/El.; Audio Hardware – ATT/3B2-500

SARNIA

OBSERVER

140 S. Front St., Sarnia, ON, N7T 7M8, Canada; gen tel (519) 344-3641; ed fax (519) 332-2951; adv e-mail classifieds@theobserver.ca (Classified); sales@theobserver.ca (Retail); ed e-mail editorial@theobserver.ca; web site www.theobserver.ca
Published: Mon, Tues, Wed, Thur, Fri, Sat
Weekday Frequency: e
Saturday Frequency: m
Circulation 12,749; 14,447(sat)
Last Audit: BPA December 30, 2010
Advertising: 1.09
Politics: Independent **Established:** 1853
Not Published: Statutory holidays.
Pub. .... Daryl C. Smith
Office Mgr. .... Barb Mcbride
Adv. Mgr. .... Paul Brown
Circ. Mgr. .... Marc Roberts
Managing Editor .... Rod Hilts
Market information: ADS; TMC.
Mechanical available: Letterpress (direct); Black and 3 ROP colors; insert accepted; page cutoffs - 21 1/2.
Mechanical Specifications: Type page 13 1/2 x 21 5/16; E - 6 cols, 2 1/16, 1/8 between.
Delivery Method: Newsstand, Private Carrier

SAULT STE MARIE

THE SAULT STAR

PO Box 460, Sault Ste Marie, ON, P6A 5M5, Canada; gen tel (705) 759-3030; adv tel (705) 759-5802 (Classified); gen fax (705) 759-5947; adv fax (705) 759-0678 (Classified); ed fax (705) 759-0102; gen e-mail ssmstar@saultstar.com; adv e-mail starads@saultstar.com; web site www.saultstar.com
Published: Mon, Tues, Wed, Thur, Fri, Sat
Weekday Frequency: e
Circulation 13,817; 14,153(sat)
Last Audit: BPA December 30, 2010
Group: Sun Media
Price: 4.35/wk; 18.10/mo; 181.20/yr (carrier).
Advertising: Open inch rate $1.88
Politics: Independent **Established:** 1912
Not Published: New Year; Good Friday; Victoria Day; Canada Day; Civic Holiday; Labor Day; Thanksgiving; Christmas; Boxing Day.
Own facility?: Y
Special weekly sections: Fall Fashion (Aug); Christmas Greetings (Dec); RRSP (Feb); Brides '07 (Jan); Station Mall Side Walk Sale (Jul); Side Walk Sale (Jun); Car Care (May); Home Front (Monthly); Queenstown Christmas (Nov); Station Mall (Oct); Brides (Sept).
Magazines: TV Times (Fri); Comics (Sat); Classified (Wed).
Publisher, General Manager .... Lou Maulucci
Mgr., Admin. .... Jackie DePasquale
Adv. Mgr. .... Mike Kennedy
Dir., Reader Sales/Serv. .... Bruno Vit
City Ed. .... Bill Montague
Editorial Page Ed. .... Frank Rupnik
Data Processing Mgr. .... Steve Shooks
Prodn. Mgr. .... Kevin Caron
Prodn. Foreman, Pressroom .... Gary Graham
Market information: ADS; TMC.
Mechanical available: Offset; Black and 3 ROP colors; insert accepted - Samples, Catalogues; page cutoffs - 22 3/4.
Mechanical Specifications: Type page 11 1/2 x 21 1/2; E - 5 cols, 2 9/50, 1/8 between; A - 10 cols, 1, 1/8 between; C - 10 cols, 1, 1/8 between.
Commodity Consumption: Avg. Page Number Per Issue - Daily 33; Avg. Page Number Per Issue - Plates Used 15600; Avg. Page Number Per Issue - Saturday 28; widths 24 1/2; Newsprint Used - Metric Tons 1650; Printing Ink Used - Black 33039.65; Printing Ink Used - Color 17621.15; Pri
Equipment EDITORIAL: Front-end Software – NT, Baseview, APP/Mac System 9.2 3, QPS, Microsoft/Window-NT.; Editorial Hardware – Compaq/fileservers, APP/Mac, Compaq; Editorial Printers – QMS/860, APP/Mac LaserWriter NTX, APP/Mac LaserWriter IIg, AU/APS-108-12C, HP/Laserjet 9000, HP/Laxerjet 4050 CLASSIFIED: Front-end Software – Baseview.; Classified Hardware – Compaq/File servers, Compaq; Classified Printers – APP/Mac LaserWriter NTX; Layout software – SCS/Layout 8000.; Display Hardware – ACER; Display Printers – HP/4050 PRODUCTION: Pagination software – QPS/QuarkXPress 3.1, Ad Tracking 3.0.; Production Equipment – 2-Nu/Flip Top FT4OUP, 4-APP/Mac LaserPrinter, 2-AU/APS 108-12C; Cameras – 1-C/Spartan

III; Scanners – APP/Mac, APP/Mac G3 PRESSROOM: Line 1 – 8-G/Urbanite; Folders –1; MAILROOMCounter stackers – BG/Count-O-Veyor; Inserters and stuffers – 1-KAN/320 8 station, 1-MM/Saddle Stitcher, MM/Quarter; Bundle tying machines –1-MLN/ML2EE, 6-Gd/Q; Address machine – 1/WM; Other equipment – MM/Minuteman.BUSINESS COMPUTERS: Audio Software – Smart Stream; Audio Hardware – PBS

Delivery Method: Newsstand, Private Carrier, Racks

SIMCOE

THE SIMCOE REFORMER

50 Gilbertson Dr., Simcoe, ON, N3Y 4L2, Canada; gen tel (519) 426-5710; gen fax (519) 426-9255; web site www.simcoereformer.ca

Published: Mon, Tues, Wed, Thur, Fri
Weekday Frequency: e
Circulation 8,950
Last Audit: Estimate November 12, 1997
Price: 2.00/wk; 8.67/mo (carrier); 116.00/yr (carrier), $188.70/yr (mail).
Advertising: Open inch rate $1.10
News services: CP.
Politics: Independent
Not Published: New Year; Good Friday; Victoria Day; Dominion Day; Civic Holiday; Labor Day; Thanksgiving; Christmas.
Gen. Mgr. ....David Hawkins
Adv. Dir., Nat'l Sales ....Michael Walsh
Adv. Mgr. ....Sue Downs
Sports Ed. ....Jeff Dertinger
Women's/Society Ed. ....Kim Novak
Prodn. Mgr., Distr./Mailroom ....Diane Kiss
Market information: TMC; Zoned editions.
Mechanical available: Offset; Black and 3 ROP colors; insert accepted; page cutoffs - 21 1/2.
Mechanical Specifications: Type page 13 x 21 1/2; E - 6 cols, 2 1/15, 1/8 between; A - 6 cols, 2 1/15, 1/8 between; C - 9 cols, 1 1/3, 1/8 between.
Commodity Consumption: Avg. Page Number Per Issue - Daily 16; Avg. Page Number Per Issue - Plates Used 5676; widths 27; Newsprint Used - Metric Tons 281; Printing Ink Used - Pages Printed 4524.
Equipment; Editorial Hardware – Mk.; Classified Hardware – Mk.; Layout software – APP/Mac.; Production Equipment – 1-Fuji/360F; Cameras – 2-R. PRESSROOM: Line 1 – 6-G; Folders –1-G/Quarter and Half fold.; Bundle tying machines –2/Bu, 2-/Strapper; Address machine – ATT.; Audio Hardware – ATT

STRATFORD

THE BEACON-HERALD

PO Box 430, Stratford, ON, N5A 6T6, Canada; gen tel (519) 271-2220; adv tel (519) 271-2220; ed tel (519) 271-2220; gen fax (519) 271-1026; adv fax (519) 271-1031; adv e-mail bhadvertising@bowesnet.com (Display); bhclassified@bowesnet.com (Classified); web site www.stratfordbeaconherald.com

Published: Mon, Tues, Wed, Thur, Fri, Sat
Weekday Frequency: e
Circulation 7,834; 8,158(sat)
Last Audit: BPA December 30, 2010
Price: 3.25/wk (includes GST); 174.07/yr; 42.96/3mo (includes GST).
Advertising: Open inch rate $1.00
News services: CP.
Politics: Independent
Not Published: New Year; Good Friday; Victoria Day; Dominion Day; Labor Day; Thanksgiving; Christmas; Boxing Day.
Special weekly sections: Festival (May).
Pub. ....Dave Carter
Credit Mgr. ....Janice Humphrey
Circ. Mgr. ....Barb Boyne
Mng. Ed. ....John Kastner
City Ed. ....Brian Shypula
Editorial Page Ed. ....Diana Loveless
Chief Photographer ....Scott Wisharg
Sports Ed. ....Steve Rice
Wire Ed. ....Mike Beitz
Prodn. Mgr. ....Leigh McCann
Market information: TMC.
Mechanical available: Offset; Black and 3 ROP colors; insert accepted; page cutoffs - 22 3/4.
Mechanical Specifications: Type page 11 1/2 x 21 1/4; E - 6 cols, 1 13/16, 1/8 between; A - 6 cols, 3 3/4, 1/8 between; C - 6 cols, between.
Commodity Consumption: Avg. Page Number Per Issue - Daily 25; Avg. Page Number Per Issue - Plates Used 5398; widths 25; Newsprint Used - Metric Tons 551; Printing Ink Used - Black 7074.89; Printing Ink Used - Color 2374.45; Printing Ink Used - Pages Printed 7544.
Equipment EDITORIAL: Front-end Software – QPS/QuarkXPress, Microsoft/Windows NT Server 4.0, HP/Netserver.; Editorial Hardware – APP/Mac NT Server; Editorial Printers – 2-Xante, 1-Lexmark/Optra, 2-XIT/Clipper, 1-Schooner CLASSIFIED: Front-end Software – CAMS 4.0.; Classified Hardware – APP/Mac G3; Classified Printers – 1-XIT/Schooner, 2-XIT/Clipper DISPLAY: Ad make-up applications – Multi-Ad 4.0, QPS/QuarkXPress 3.3, Adobe/Photoshop 4.0, Caere/OmniPage Pro 8.0.; Display Hardware – APP/Mac 4.0; Display Printers – 2-XIT/Clipper, 1-XIT/Schooner, 2-Xante, 1-Lexmark/Optra PRODUCTION: Pagination software – QPS/QuarkXPress 4.0.; Production Equipment – Caere/OmniPro 8.0, 2-XIT/Clippers LaserPrinter, 2-Xante/LaserPrinter, 1-Lexmark/LaserPrinter; Cameras – 1-Acti/204; Scanners – 5-Scanmaker Scanner PRESSROOM: Line 1 – 8-SLN/Offset 1988.; MAILROOMCounter stackers – BG/108; Bundle tying machines – 1/Nichiro Kogyo/TS-210; Wrapping singles – Beacon.; Audio Hardware – 1-DEC/1123

SUDBURY

THE SUDBURY STAR

33 Mackenzie St., Sudbury, ON, P3C 4Y1, Canada; gen tel (705) 674-5271; gen fax (705) 674-0624; ed fax (705) 674-6834; gen e-mail editorial@thesudburystar.com; adv e-mail advertising@thesudburystar.com; web site www.thesudburystar.com

Published: Mon, Tues, Wed, Thur, Fri, Sat
Weekday Frequency: e
Saturday Frequency: m
Circulation 13,326; 14,333(sat)
Last Audit: BPA December 30, 2010
Group: CanWest Media Sales
Price: 3.75/wk; 16.03/mo; 184.60/yr (carrier), $403.00/yr (mail); 47.45/3mo, $93.60/6mo.
Advertising: Open inch rate $2.09
News services: CP.
Politics: Independent
Not Published: Christmas.
Special editions: Weekend Alive (Fri).
Magazines: TV Listings (Fri); Travel (Sat); Real Estate Guide (Thur).
Pub. ....Bruce Cowan
Office Mgr. ....Mary Valade
Adv. Mgr. ....Ray Lavigne
Dir., Mktg./Promo. ....Marriette Valate
Circ. Mgr. ....Dave Pocket
City Ed. ....Don MacDonald
Editorial Page Ed. ....Brian MacLeod
Life Ed. ....Wayne Chamberlain
News Ed. ....Chris Krejlgaard
Sports Ed. ....Bruce Heidman
Mgmt. Info Servs. Mgr. ....Dan Johnson
Prodn. Mgr., Pre Press ....Merle Smith
Market information: ADS; Split run; TMC; Zoned editions.
Mechanical available: Letterpress; Black and 3 ROP colors; insert accepted - all; page cutoffs - 21 1/2.
Mechanical Specifications: Type page 11 1/2 x 21 1/2; E - 5 cols, 2 1/6, 1/8 between; A - 10 cols, 1 1/64, 1/8 between; C - 10 cols, 1 1/64, 1/8 between.
Commodity Consumption: Avg. Page Number Per Issue - Daily 28; Avg. Page Number Per Issue - Plates Used 23400; Avg. Page Number Per Issue - Saturday 32; widths 55; Newsprint Used - Metric Tons 1450; Printing Ink Used - Black 36200; Printing Ink Used - Color 3200; Printing Ink U
Equipment; Editorial Hardware – 1-Acer/Veriton S100, 1-APP/iMac Power Mac 8600-300, 10-APP/Power Mac 7300-200, Mitsubishi/Diamond Scan 15VX, Mitsubishi/Diamond Pro 91TXV; Editorial Equipment – Microtech/Card Reader, Poloroid/SprintScan 35 Plus, Umax/Astra 1200S flat-bed scanner; Editorial Printers – Printe CLASSIFIED: Front-end Software – Software Ã□Â□ Ad Manager Pro 1.05, APP/Mac 8.1.; Classified Hardware – 1-APP/iMac, 4-APP/Mac Power Mac G3; Classified Printers – APP/Mac LaserWriter Pro 60 DISPLAY: Ad make-up applications – Lotus 123, WordPerfect; Layout software – NewzWare.; Display Hardware – 2-Compaq/Desktop Pro 575, Touch; Display Printers – Samsung/ML-4600 PRODUCTION: Pagination software – Adobe/Acrobat 4.0, Adobe/Pagemake; Production Equipment – Graham, Laser Red 1800HT 2, Newsline Solo/Listener, Hoechst/Encomatic; Cameras – B/3-in-1, 4-Kk/DC26S Zoom; Scanners – ECR/Autokon, Microtec Photo Card Reader, Umax/Astra 1200S 2, Umax/Astra 2400S PRESSROOM: Line 1 – Multilith/1850; Line 2 – 10-G/Urbanite 1999.; Bundle tying machines –3-Acme/P5N250APB, Gd Oval Strapping; Wrapping singles – Manual; Address machine – 1/Am.; Audio Hardware – IBM/Sys 34

THUNDER BAY

THE CHRONICLE-JOURNAL

75 S. Cumberland St., Thunder Bay, ON, P7B 1A3, Canada; gen tel (807) 343-6200; ed tel (807) 343-6215; gen fax (807) 345-5991; adv fax (807) 345-3582; ed fax (807) 343-9409; gen e-mail editor@chroniclejournal.com; adv e-mail graphics@chroniclejournal.com; ed e-mail editor@chroniclejournal.com; web site www.chroniclejournal.com

Published: Mon, Tues, Wed, Thur, Fri, Sat, Sun
Weekday Frequency: m
Saturday Frequency: m
Circulation 24,544; 24,725(sat); 21,826(sun)
Last Audit: ABC September 30, 2011
Price: 4.41/wk (carrier); 19.10/mo (carrier); 217.79/yr.
Advertising: Open inch rate $2.08
News services: CP, AP.
Politics: Independent **Established:** 1899
Not Published: New Year; Good Friday; Victoria Day; Canada Day; Civic Holiday; Labour Day; Thanksgiving; Christmas; Boxing Day.
Special weekly sections: Building & Home Improvement (Apr); Dining Guide (Aug); Weddings By Design (Jul); Transportation Week (May); Shop Canada (Monthly); Under the Tree (Nov); Weddings By Design (Oct); Garden Time (Spring).
Magazines: TV Scene (Sat).
Pub. ....Colin J. Bruce
Dir., Finance ....Hilda Caverly
Dir., Mktg./Sales ....Clint Harris
Circ. Mgr. ....Harry Brown
Mng. Ed. ....Bryan Dryden
Assignment Ed. ....John Ayearst
Editorial Page Ed ....Ian Pattison
News Ed. ....Joanne Kushnier
Sports Ed. ....John Nagy
Prodn. Mgr. ....Dave Dafoe
Prodn. Foreman, Composing Room Dave Wadson
Prodn. Foreman, Pressroom ...Joe St. Lawrence
Market information: TMC; Zoned editions.
Mechanical available: Offset; Black and 3 ROP colors; insert accepted; page cutoffs - 22 3/4.
Mechanical Specifications: Type page 12 1/2 x 21 1/2; E - 6 cols, 1/8 between; A - 10 cols, 1 1/6, 1/8 between; C - 6 cols, 1 3/4, 1/8 between.
Commodity Consumption: Avg. Page Number Per Issue - Daily 32; Avg. Page Number Per Issue - Plates Used 1500; Avg. Page Number Per Issue - Saturday 40; Avg. Page Number Per Issue - Sunday 28; widths 34; Newsprint Used - Metric Tons 3150; Printing Ink Used - Black 54454; Printin
Equipment EDITORIAL: Front-end Software – QPS/QuarkXPress 3.32, Baseview/NewsEditPro IQ 2.2.; Editorial Hardware – APP/Mac Performa, APP/Power Mac 7200, APP/Power Mac 8500, G3; Editorial Printers – Pre Press/Panther Catara, Pre Press/Panther Pro 46, HP/5000 CLASSIFIED: Front-end Software – QPS/QuarkXPress 3.3.2, Baseview/Adman Pro 1.050.; Classified Hardware – HAS, APP/Power Mac 4400; Classified Printers – APP/Mac LaserWriter 8500 DISPLAY: Ad make-up applications – QPS/QuarkXPress 3.32, Adobe/Photoshop 5.5, Adobe/Illustrator 8.0, Aldus/Freehand 8.0.; Display Hardware – APP/Power Mac, Polaroid/SprintScan (35), APP/Mac G4; Display Printers – Pre Press/Panther Catara 46, Pre Press/Panther Pro 46, HP/5000, APP/Mac 8500 PRODUCTION: Pagination software – QPS/QuarkXPress 3.2, Baseview/News; Production Equipment – WL Plate Processor, Pre Press/Panther Catara 46, Pre Press/Panther Pro 46, HP/5000, APP/Mac 8500; Cameras – ACTI/125; Scanners – Linotype Hell Ultr 2, Polaroid/SprintScan (35), AGFA Snapscan E25 PRESSROOM: Line 1 – 8-G/Urbanite single width 1977; Press Drives – 2-DC Motors/100 h.p.; Folders –1; MAILROOM-Counter stackers – Id; Inserters and stuffers – 1-MM/Alphaliner; Bundle tying machines – 2/Akibono, 2-Gd/Constellation; Wrapping singles – 2-/IDAB Baggers; Other equipment – MM/Saddle Stitcher.BUSINESS COMPUTERS: Audio Software – Microsoft/Excel 98; Audio Hardware – HP, IBM/Newzware

TIMMINS

THE DAILY PRESS

187 Cedar St. S., Timmins, ON, P4N 7G1, Canada; gen tel (705) 268-5050; gen fax (705) 268-7373; adv e-mail advertising@thedailypress.ca; ed e-mail editorial@thedailypress.ca; web site www.timminspress.com

Published: Mon, Tues, Wed, Thur, Fri, Sat
Weekday Frequency: m
Saturday Frequency: m
Circulation 6,634; 6,714(sat)
Last Audit: BPA December 30, 2010
Price: 3.25/wk; 13.00/mo; 154.25/yr.
Advertising: Open inch rate $1.35
News services: CP.
Politics: Independent
Not Published: New Year; Christmas.
Special editions: Mining (Annually).
Special weekly sections: Business & Industry North (Monthly); Frontier Mining (Quarterly).
Magazines: TV Scene (Fri).
Pub. ....Bruce Cowan
Bus. Mgr. ....Lisa Cote
Adv. Mgr. ....Lisa Wilson
Circ. Mgr. ....Gio Crispo
Sports Ed. ....Tom Perry
Prodn. Foreman, Pressroom ....Joe Vodusek
Market information: TMC.
Mechanical available: Offset; Black and 3 ROP colors; insert accepted; page cutoffs - 22 3/4.
Mechanical Specifications: Type page 13 x 21 1/2; E - 6 cols, 2 1/16, 1/8 between; A - 6 cols, 2 1/16, 1/8 between; C - 9 cols, 1 1/3, 1/8 between.
Commodity Consumption: Avg. Page Number Per Issue - Daily 12; widths 27; Printing Ink Used - Pages Printed 5600.
Equipment; Editorial Hardware – CText.; Classified Hardware – CText.; Production Equip-

ment – CD; Cameras – 1-Nu. PRESSROOM: Line 1 – 8-G/Community; Folders – 1; Bundle tying machines –1/Gd; Other equipment – MM/Minuteman.

TORONTO

THE GLOBE AND MAIL

444 Front St. W., Toronto, ON, M5V 2S9, Canada; gen tel (416) 585-5000; gen fax (416) 585-5085; gen e-mail comments@globeandmail.com; adv e-mail sales@globeandmail.com; ed e-mail newsroom@globeandmail.com; web site www.theglobeandmail.com
Published: Mon, Tues, Wed, Thur, Fri, Sat
Weekday Frequency: m
Saturday Frequency: m
Circulation 309,154; 372,649(sat)
Last Audit: ABC September 30, 2011
Price: 5.53/wk; 23.96/mo; 287.56/yr.
Advertising: Open inch rate $47.99
News services: AFP, CP, DJ, Economist, NYT, RN, SHNS, TMS.
Politics: Independent
Not Published: Christmas.
Special weekly sections: Report on Mutual Funds (Monthly); Gusto (Other).
Magazines: Travel (Sat); Technology (Thur); Travel (Wed); Globe Television (Weekly).
Pub./CEO ....Phillip Crawley
Vice Pres., HR ....Brenda Scacht
CFO ....Sandra Bailey
Controller ....Steve Craig
Circ. Branch Mgr., Montreal ....Bob Laplante
Circ. Regl. Mgr., E. Canada ....Joann Perrott
Exec. Ed. ....Neil A. Campbell
Ed. in Chief ....John Stackhouse
Assoc. Ed. ....Sylvia Stead
Commentary Ed. ....Natasha Hassan
Editorial Art Dir. ....David Pratt
Globe Review Ed. ....Andrew Gorham
Photo Ed. ....Moe Doiron
Report on Bus. Ed. ....Michael Babad
Sports Ed. ....Steve McAllister
Customs Content Mgr. ....Simon Beck
Prodn. Mgr., Pre Press ....Brad Mollison
Market information: ADS; Split run.
Mechanical available: Offset; Black and 3 ROP colors; insert accepted - magazines, product samples; page cutoffs - 22 3/4.
Mechanical Specifications: Type page 11 1/2 x 21 1/2; E - 6 cols, 1 13/16, 3/16 between; A - 6 cols, 1 13/16, 3/16 between; C - 6 cols, 1 13/16, 3/16 between.
Commodity Consumption: Avg. Page Number Per Issue - Daily 80; Avg. Page Number Per Issue - Plates Used 109200; Avg. Page Number Per Issue - Saturday 120; widths 25; Newsprint Used - Metric Tons 34000; Printing Ink Used - Pages Printed 22082.
Equipment EDITORIAL: Front-end Software – AT.; Editorial Hardware – AT, HI/NMP Pagination System, CCI; Editorial Equipment – Ethernet; Classified Hardware – HI/Ad /Power; Classified Printers – HP/7970. DISPLAY: Ad make-up applications – HI; Layout software – HI/8300 Pagination System.; Production Equipment – HI/Images Graphic Subsystem, Prosetter; Cameras – Scanners ÃÂ ECR/Autokon 2045, Sharp/600, Nikon, Linotype-Hell, AG.; Audio Hardware – Software ÃÂ Oracle

NATIONAL POST

1450 Don Mills Rd., Toronto, ON, M3B 2X7, Canada; gen tel (416) 383-2300; adv tel (800) 668-5617; ed tel (416) 383-2300; gen fax (416) 442-2209; adv fax (416) 386-2696; ed fax (416) 383-2443; gen e-mail queries@nationalpost.com; adv e-mail advqueries@nationalpost.com; web site www.nationalpost.com
Published: Mon, Tues, Wed, Thur, Fri, Sat
Weekday Frequency: m
Saturday Frequency: m
Circulation 146,245; 154,177(sat)
Last Audit: ABC September 30, 2011
Price: 4.50/wkly; 18.00/mo; 276.06/yr.
Advertising: Open inch rate $18.92
News services: APP, AP, CP, DJ, NYT, RN.
Not Published: New Year; Christmas; Boxing Day.
Special weekly sections: Year in Review (Annually); FP Mutual Funds (Monthly); Annual Reports (2) (Other); Car Models (Quarterly); Business Schools (Semi-yearly).
Magazines: Driver's Edge (Fri); Saturday Post (Sat).
President ....Gordon Fisher
Publisher ....Doug Kelly
Vice President, Advertising ....Kirk Allen
Director of Sales ....Maria McDonald
VP, Reader Sales and Service .Trevor Fredericks
VP, Marketing ....Lori Morgan
Circ. Vice Pres., Reader Sales/Serv. Craig Barnard
Sports Ed. ....Jim Bray
Market information: Split run; TMC; Zoned editions.
Mechanical available: Offset; Black and 3 ROP colors; insert accepted - min. 6 x 8; page cutoffs - 21 3/4.
Mechanical Specifications: Type page 11 1/2 x 21 3/4; E - 5 cols, 1 1/16, between; A - 10 cols, 1 1/16, between; C - 10 cols, 1 1/16, between.
Commodity Consumption: Avg. Page Number Per Issue - Daily 70; Avg. Page Number Per Issue - Saturday 64; widths 50.
Equipment EDITORIAL: Front-end Software – QPS 1.12, QPS/QuarkXPress 3.32.; Editorial Hardware – APP/Mac G3; Editorial Equipment – Au/Apscom; Editorial Printers – HP, Xante, Graphic Enterprises/ DISPLAY: Ad make-up applications – QuickTrac 6.0, QPS/QuarkXPress 3.32; Layout software – SCS/Layout-8000, ALS.; Display Hardware – APP/Mac G3; Display Printers – HP; Production Equipment – Au/APS-3850, T/One Merlin; Cameras – Scanners ÃÂ Eskoscan/2024, Eskoscan/2636, Epson, Kk; Scanners – Equipment ÃÂ QPS/QuarkXPress 3.32, QuickTrac, SCS, Linx.BUSINESS COMPUTERS: Audio Software – Microsoft/Office, Microsoft/Exchange; Audio Hardware – In-house Southam System-Vax based

TORONTO STAR

1 Yonge St.reet, Toronto, ON, M5E 1E6, Canada; gen tel (416) 367-2000; adv tel (416) 777-7777; ed tel (416) 869-4300; adv fax 416-814-3270; ed fax (416) 869-4328; gen e-mail editorial@thestar.ca; ed e-mail city@thestar.ca; web site www.thestar.com
Published: Mon, Tues, Wed, Fri, Sat, Sun
Weekday Frequency: m
Saturday Frequency: m
Circulation 266,143; 417,809(sat); 295,589(sun)
Last Audit: BPA December 30, 2010
Price: 4.85/wk; 304.91/yr.
Advertising: Full Page, National Rate, A-Section: $98,235
Insert rate: CPM: From $43.50/1 pg, $81/48 pg.
News services: CP, TR, WP, TMS, NYT, Bloomberg, Getty Images
Politics: 1892
Not Published: Christmas
Own facility?: Y
Special editions: Starweek (Sat).
Special weekly sections: Travel, Wheels, New In Homes, Condos, Comics, NYT Weekly
Magazines: Golf, Do-It (Home Improvement), various special section opportunities.
Broadcast Affiliations: TMGTV
Publisher ....John Cruickshank
CIO, Metroland & Star Media Group, Group IT, Torstar Corporation ....Paula Sinclair
VP & CFO ....Peter Bishop
Adv. Sr. Grp. Dir., Homes/Condos/Food/Dept. Stores/Travel ....Sandy Muir
Adv. Grp. Dir., Home/Automotive/Sports/Entertainment ....Norm Laing
Adv. Grp. Dir., Nat'l/Technology ...Carolyn Sadler
Adv. Mgr., Customer Accts ....Susan Luttrell
Adv. Mgr., Mktg. Research/Info ....Jim Fahey
Adv. Mgr., Syndicate ....Robin Graham
Vice Pres., Mktg. ....Sandy MacLeod
Dir. Cir. ....Terry Willows
Circ. Mgr., Home Delivery ....Brenda Yarwood
Ed. in Chief ....Michael Cooke
Mng. Ed. ....Joe Hall
Books Ed. ....Dan Smith
Advertising Director ....Mark Spencer
EVP-Torstar Printing Group ....Dean Zavarise
Circ. Mgr., Opns./Customer Servs. Sarkis Harmandayan
Mng. Ed. ....Mary Deanne Shears
Ombudsman ....Don Sellar
Asst. Mng. Ed., Digital Media ....Phil Bingley
Asst. Mng. Ed., Entertainment/Life ....John Ferri
Market information: Split run; TMC.
Mechanical available: Offset; Black and 3 ROP colors; insert accepted; page cutoffs - 22.
Mechanical Specifications: Type page 11 1/2 x 21 1/8; E - 6 cols, 1 3/4, 1/6 between; A - 10 cols, 1 1/16, 1/12 between; C - 10 cols, 1 1/16, 1/12 between.
Commodity Consumption: Avg. Page Number Per Issue - Daily 92; Avg. Page Number Per Issue - Plates Used 900000; Avg. Page Number Per Issue - Saturday 280; Avg. Page Number Per Issue - Sunday 84; widths 50; Newsprint Used - Metric Tons 110000; Printing Ink Used - Black 1982378.9
Equipment EDITORIAL: Front-end Software – CCI Newsgate, SCC; Editorial Hardware – Dell PC,
MAC PC; Editorial Equipment – CCI/Pagination System; Editorial Printers – 16-HP/LaserJet CLASSIFIED: Front-end Software – CCI, ADS; Classified Hardware – Hitachi/Ex 80,
Dell PCs,
Dell Servers,
Sun Servers, ; Classified Printers – HP, Cannon, Xerox DISPLAY: Ad make-up applications – NW/Admarc , ADS; Layout software – TEDS, In-house.; Display Hardware – Sun, DELL, Apple, NEC's ; Display Printers – HP, Cannon, Xerox PRODUCTION: Pagination software – CCI/Layout Champ, CCI/AD Champ.; Production Equipment – Prima, Newsway ; Scanners – Epson PRESSROOM: Line 1 – 12-MAN/Colorman (60 printing couples) 1992; Line 2 – 12-MAN/Colorman (60 printing couples) 1992; Line 3 – 12-MAN/Colorman (60 printing couples) 1992; Line 4 – 12-MAN/Colorman (60 printing couples) 1992; Line 5 – 12-MAN/Colorman (60 printing coupl; Line 6 – 12-MAN/Colorman (60 printing coupl; MAILROOMCounter stackers – 9-HL/II; Inserters and stuffers – 6/AM Graphics/630; Bundle tying machines –6-/Power Strap, 14-Dynaric/NP3, 18-/Power Strap/inserting; Wrapping singles – 18-/Power Strap/Three Quarter Wrap, 9-/Power Strap/PSN 250; Mailroom control system – Mailroom control sysAUDIO: Audio Software – Brite Voice Systems; Audio Hardware – Brite Voice Systems/Starphone, US AudiotextBUSINESS COMPUTERS: Audio Software – Microsoft/PC Products, Discus, CCI
Adobe,
Quark; Audio Hardware – Hitachi/EX 80, HP/client server system, Sun/client server system

THE TORONTO SUN

333 King St. E., Toronto, ON, M5A 3X5, Canada; gen tel (416) 947-2222; adv tel (416) 947-2333; ed tel (416) 947-2222; gen fax (416) 368-0374; adv fax (416) 947-3139; ed fax (416) 947-1664; ed e-mail torsun.editor@sunmedia.ca; web site www.torontosun.ca; www.canoe.ca
Published: Mon, Tues, Wed, Thur, Fri, Sat, Sun
Weekday Frequency: m
Saturday Frequency: m
Circulation 141,144; 123,510(sat); 187,433(sun)
Last Audit: BPA December 30, 2010
Price: 50 cents M-Thurs, $1 on Fri & Sat, Sun $1.50
Advertising: Open line rate M-Sat $6.83. Su $9.89
Insert rate: Su - Up to 16 p. tab. $60, 17-28 p. tab. $63. Pre-printed; based on full distribution, cost per M
News services: QMi, AFP, RN, Wenn News, TSN
Politics: 1971
Advertising not accepted: Y
Not Published: Christmas
Own facility?: N
Special editions: Tribute (Every other month).
Special weekly sections: TV Book
Broadcast Affiliations: Sun News
Cor. Dir., HR ....Chris Krygiel
Editor ....Rob Granatstein
Sr. Assoc. Ed. ....Lorrie Goldstein
Cartoonist ....Andrew Donato
City Ed. ....Kevin Hann
Travel Ed. ....Robin Robinson
Sports Ed. ....Bill Pierce
Corporate Entertainment Editor ....John Kryk
Lifestyle/Food Ed. ....Rita DeMontis
News Research Dept. ....Julie Kirsh
VP, Info Serv. ....Richard Roy
Vice President, Advertising Sales Darren Murphy
Sales Director/Director of Promotion Lesley Annett
Vice President, Finance ....Piero Menicucci
Editor-in-Chief ....James Wallace
Executive Assistant to the Publisher Christina Fleming
Vice Pres., Fin. ....Piero Menicicci
Credit Mgr. ....Peter Kotzer
Adv. Vice Pres., Sales ....Sandy Muir
Dir., Promos ....Pat Surphils
Ed. in Chief ....Lou Clancy
Mng. Ed. ....Mike Burke-Gaffney
Deputy Mng. Ed. ....Alan Parker
Bus./Finance Ed. ....Linda Leatherdale
Cor. Sports Ed. ....George Gross
Mechanical available: Printing Process: Cold Web OffSET
Mechanical Specifications: Format Tabloid, Live Area 10.3330 x 11.4290 Column Width 0.8330 Column Depth 160 agate lines x 10 columns
Commodity Consumption: Avg. Page Number Per Issue - Daily 121; Avg. Page Number Per Issue - Plates Used 280000; Avg. Page Number Per Issue - Saturday 101; Avg. Page Number Per Issue - Sunday 262; widths 30; Newsprint Used - Metric Tons 49000; Printing Ink Used - Black 1300000;
Equipment EDITORIAL: Front-end Software – MediaSpan Jazzbox; Editorial Hardware – Dell Blades
HP EVA
EMC San; Editorial Equipment – APP/Mac/PCs; Editorial Printers – Sharp; Classified Hardware – Dell Blades
HP EVA
EMC San; Classified Equipment – DTI MediaPlus; Classified Printers – Sharp DISPLAY: Ad make-up applications – Indesign /QuarkXPress, Adobe/Illustrator; Layout software – MediaSpectrum; Display Hardware – Dell Blades
HP EVA
EMC San; Display Printers – Sharp BUSINESS COMPUTERS: Audio Software – DTI; Audio Hardware – IBM xseries
Dell Blades
HP EVA
EMC San
Zip Codes Served: Toronto and surrounding areas - including Kingston, Windsor, Sudbury
Delivery Method: Newsstand, Private Carrier

WELLAND

WELLAND TRIBUNE

228 E. Main St., Welland, ON, L3B 5P5, Canada; gen tel (905) 732-2411; adv tel (905) 732-2411; ed tel (905) 732-2411; gen fax (905) 732-4883; adv fax (905) 732-0965; ed fax (905) 732-3660; gen e-mail tribune@wellandtribune.ca; adv e-mail ltait@wellandtribune.ca; ed e-mail tribune@wellandtribune.ca; web site www.wellandtribune.ca
Published: Mon, Tues, Wed, Thur, Fri, Sat
Weekday Frequency: m
Saturday Frequency: m
Circulation 10,204; 10,296(sat)
Last Audit: BPA December 30, 2010
Group: CanWest Media Sales

Price: 3.45/wk (carrier); 191.00/yr.
Advertising: Open inch rate $1.66(m-fri)
News services: CP.
Politics: Independent
Not Published: New Year; Labor Day; Thanksgiving; Christmas.
Special weekly sections: Cookbook (Aug); Progress (Feb); Fashion (Monthly).
Magazines: Television Listings Guide (Fri); Homes (Sat).
Pub.....................................Ken Koyama
Office Mgr................................Anna Latham
Adv. Dir................................Daria Zmiyiwsky
Circ. Mgr. ....Karin Vanderzee
Mng. Ed......................................Angus Scott
City Ed....................................Joe Barkovich
Market information: TMC.
Mechanical available: Offset; Black and 3 ROP colors; insert accepted - Post It; page cutoffs - 22 3/4.
Mechanical Specifications: Type page 11 1/2 x 21 1/2; E - 10 cols, 1 1/16, between; A - 10 cols, 1 1/16, between; C - 9 cols, 1 5/16, between.
Commodity Consumption: Avg. Page Number Per Issue - Daily 26; Avg. Page Number Per Issue - Plates Used 48000; Avg. Page Number Per Issue - Saturday 30; widths 32; Newsprint Used - Metric Tons 4600; Printing Ink Used - Pages Printed 8845.
Equipment EDITORIAL: Front-end Software – QPS/QuarkXPress 3.3.; Editorial Hardware – APP/Mac; Editorial Equipment – Imagesetter; Editorial Printers – APP, HP CLASSIFIED: Front-end Software – QPS/QuarkXPress.; Classified Hardware – APP/Mac; Classified Printers – App, HP DISPLAY: Ad make-up applications – Managing Editor/ALS; Layout software – Baseview.; Display Hardware – PC; Display Printers – Ap, HP PRODUCTION: Pagination software – QPS 3.3.; Production Equipment – ECR/Knockout, ECR/Stingray; Cameras – 1-Liberator; Scanners – Microtek/ScanMaker PRESSROOM: Line 1 – 12-G/Urbanite single width; Folders –2, 1-G/with balloon upper former; Reels and Stands – 7; MAILROOM-Counter stackers – 2-Id; Inserters and stuffers – 1/KAN; Bundle tying machines – Gd, OVL.BUSINESS COMPUTERS: Audio Software – Microsoft/Office; Audio Hardware – PC

WINDSOR

THE WINDSOR STAR

167 Ferry St., Windsor, ON, N9A 4M5, Canada; gen tel (519) 255-5711; adv tel (519) 255-5720; ed tel (519) 255-5743; gen fax (519) 255-5762; adv fax (519) 255-5525; ed fax (519) 255-5515; gen e-mail news@thestarcanwest.com; web site www.windsorstar.com
Published: Mon, Tues, Wed, Thur, Fri, Sat
Weekday Frequency: m
Saturday Frequency: m
Circulation 54,680; 58,088(sat)
Last Audit: ABC September 30, 2011
Group: CanWest Media Sales
Price: 3.30/wk; 14.30/mo; 212.12/yr.
Advertising: Open inch rate $9.33
News services: Southam Newspapers, CP, SOU, LAT-WP, SHNS.
Politics: Independent
Not Published: New Year; Good Friday; Victoria Day; Canada Day; Civic Holiday; Labor Day; Thanksgiving; Christmas.
Special weekly sections: Car Care (Apr); Christmas Greetings (Dec); Bridal Feature (Feb); Financial Investment Review (Jan); Fun in the Sun (Jun); Automotive Report (Mar); Garden Feature (May); Forever Young (Monthly); Senior Citizens Days (Nov); Automotive Report (Oct); Symphony
Magazines: TV Times (Sat).
Pub....Jim Benny
Dir., Mfg................................Doug Shillington
Personnel Mgr.............................Louise Veres
Adv. Mgr.......................................Ray Woods
Adv. Mgr., Classified ....Ed Mosco
Adv. Mgr., Inside Classified ....Ken Stewart
Dir., Mktg./Reader Sales ....Bob Thwaites
Mgr., Mktg./Promo..................Beth-Ann Prince
Books Ed..................................Marty Gervais
Columnist, Auto ....Doug Williamson
Editorial Page Ed. ....John Coleman
Editorial Writer.................Chris Vanderdoelen
Educ. Ed. ....Dave Battagello
Entertainment Ed..........................Owen Jones
Labor Ed. ....Mary Agnes Welch
Metro Ed................................Marty Beneteau
Asst. Metro Ed. ....M. Frezell
Asst. Metro Ed..........................Tom McMahon
Sports Ed. ....Mark Falkner
Market information: Split run; TMC.
Mechanical available: Offset; Black and 3 ROP colors; insert accepted - hi-fi, partials, zones, catalogs; page cutoffs - 22.
Mechanical Specifications: Type page 12 1/2 x 21 1/2; E - 6 cols, 2 1/16, 1/8 between; A - 6 cols, 2 1/16, 1/8 between; C - 10 cols, 1 7/32, 1/12 between.
Commodity Consumption: Avg. Page Number Per Issue - Daily 56; Avg. Page Number Per Issue - Saturday 130; widths 41 3/16; Newsprint Used - Metric Tons 7800.
Equipment EDITORIAL: Front-end Software – QPS 1.1.; Editorial Hardware – APP/Mac; Editorial Printers – HP, APP/Mac CLASSIFIED: Front-end Software – SyD, Cyber-graphics.; Classified Hardware – HP, HP; Classified Printers – Graphic Enterprises DISPLAY: Ad make-up applications – QPS/QuarkXPress, Adobe/Photoshop; Layout software – SCS/Layout 8000, Southam/Ad Track.; Display Hardware – APP/Mac; Display Printers – Graphic Enterprises; Production Equipment – AU/3850 Sierra, Nu/Flip Top; Cameras – Scanners Ã□Â□Ã□Â□Ã□Â□Ã□Â□ ECR. PRESSROOM: Line 1 – 7-KB/Colora double width 1996; Folders –1-KB/MOT/3:2, 1; Pasters – KB/EAE; Reels and Stands – KB/EAE.; MAILROOMCounter stackers – 4-QWI/351; Inserters and stuffers – 1-Dynaric/NP630-2, 1-Dynaric/NP630-4; Bundle tying machines –4-Id/Pwa 5750 plastic wrap, 4-QWI/Cobra Underwrap; Mailroom control system – HI/Prima.AUDIO: Audio Software – Telepublishing Inc.; Audio Hardware – Telepublishing Inc., Telepublishing Inc.; Audio Hardware – DEC/Micro VAX 3800, DEC/Micro VAX

WOODSTOCK

THE SENTINEL-REVIEW

16 Brock St., Woodstock, ON, N4S 8A5, Canada; gen tel (519) 537-2341; gen fax (519) 537-8542; gen e-mail sentinelreview@bowesnet.com; adv e-mail rbruyns@bowesnet.com; ed e-mail burquahart@bowesnet.com; web site www.woodstocksentinelreview.com
Published: Mon, Tues, Wed, Thur, Fri
Weekday Frequency: m
Circulation 6,000
Last Audit: Estimate September 30, 1995
Price: 3.53/wk; 182.70/yr
Advertising: $0.74/line - Sentinel Review; $1.20/line - IMC
Insert rate: $55.00/m
News services: UPI.
Politics: 13
Not Published: New Year; Good Friday; Victoria Day; Canada Day; Civic Holiday; Labor Day; Thanksgiving; Christmas; Boxing Day.
Special weekly sections: Spring Home Improvement (Apr); Brides (Jan); Tourist Guide (Jun); Annual Business & Industrial Review (Mar); Home & Garden (May); Holiday Gift Guide (Nov); Fall Home Improvement (Oct); Agriculture (Quarterly).
Magazines: Sports (Thur).
Pub....Andrea Demeer
Adv. Mgr. ....Rosaline Bruyns
Mng. Ed..................................Bruce Urquhart
Sports Ed........................................Cory Smith
Prodn. Mgr...........................Debbie Campbell
Circ. Mgr...................................Mike Sissing
Market information: ADS; TMC.
Mechanical available: Offset; Black and full color ROP colors; insert accepted - samples; page cutoffs - 21 1/2.
Mechanical Specifications: Type page 11 1/2 x 21 1/2; E - 6 cols, 1 9/16, 1/8 between; A - 10 cols, 15/16, 2/16 between; C - 10 cols, 15/16, 2/16 between.
Commodity Consumption: Avg. Page Number Per Issue - Daily 14; Avg. Page Number Per Issue - Plates Used 4000; widths 26 1/2; Newsprint Used - Metric Tons 330; Printing Ink Used - Black 5000; Printing Ink Used - Color 1800; Printing Ink Used - Pages Printed 5700.
Equipment; Editorial Hardware – 1-HI, 12-HAS; Editorial Equipment – HAS/Pagination.; Classified Hardware – 1-HI, HAS.; Layout software – APP/Mac Graphics System.; Display Hardware – APP/Mac; Display Printers – APP/Mac; Production Equipment – 2-COM/MCS 8400, 2-COM/9400 Laser; Cameras – B/2000; Scanners – Microtek. PRESSROOM: Line 1 – 8-G/Community.; Bundle tying machines –Gd/Q 200A, Gd/RM 174 Strap; Audio Hardware – MAC; Audio Hardware – 5-ATT

PRINCE EDWARD ISLAND

CHARLOTTETOWN

THE GUARDIAN

PO Box 760, Charlottetown, PE, C1A 4R7, Canada; gen tel (902) 629-6000; adv tel (902) 629-6068; ed tel (902) 629-6039; gen fax (902) 566-3808; adv fax (902) 566-9830; ed fax (902) 566-3808; ed e-mail newsroom@theguardian.pe.ca; web site www.theguardian.pe.ca
Published: Mon, Tues, Wed, Thur, Fri, Sat
Weekday Frequency: m
Saturday Frequency: m
Circulation 17,298; 19,187(sat)
Last Audit: BPA December 30, 2010
Group: Transcontinental
Price: 3.50/wk; 15.25/mo; 195.00/yr.
Advertising: Open inch rate $1.32
News services: Hollinger Inc., CP.
Politics: Independent
Not Published: New Year; Good Friday; Victoria Day; Canada Day; Labor Day; Thanksgiving; Christmas.
Special weekly sections: Emergency Preparedness (Apr); Old Home Week (Aug); Last Minute Gift Guide (Dec); Winter Carnival (Feb); Road Builders (Jan); Grads 2008 (Jul); PEI Council of the Disabled (Jun); Christmas Cookbook (Mar); Leave A Legacy (May); Seniors (Monthly); Shop Kensi
Magazines: Real Estate Guide (Thur).
Pub...Don Brander
Controller...Ron Kelly
Adv. Dir. ....Heather Tedford
Circ. Mgr. ....Ed Kennedy
Mng. Ed...........................Gary J. MacDougall
Editorial Page Ed. ....Roseanne MacDonald
Features Ed. ....Carolyn Drake
News Ed. ....Bill McGuire
Online Ed. ....Gary MacDougall
Sports Ed. ....Garth Hurley
Prodn. Mgr., Pre Press.................Karen Peters
Market information: ADS.
Mechanical available: Offset; Black and 2 ROP colors; insert accepted - poly bags, samples; page cutoffs - 22 3/4.
Mechanical Specifications: Type page 11 1/2 x 21 1/2; E - 5 cols, 2 1/4, 1/8 between; A - 10 cols, 1 3/32, 1/8 between; C - 6 cols, 1 5/6, 1/8 between.
Commodity Consumption: Avg. Page Number Per Issue - Daily 32; Avg. Page Number Per Issue - Plates Used 10140; widths 24 1/2; Newsprint Used - Metric Tons 1142; Printing Ink Used - Black 26500; Printing Ink Used - Color 1300; Printing Ink Used - Pages Printed 10294.
Equipment EDITORIAL: Front-end Software – HAS 2.5.; Editorial Hardware – 28-HAS, 32-APP/Mac, 2-MS/NT Server; Editorial Equipment – Poloroid/SprintScan, Wing Lynch/Film Processor; Editorial Printers – 2-HP/4MV CLASSIFIED: Front-end Software – HP/4.; Classified Hardware – Baseview, 3-APP/Mac DISPLAY: Ad make-up applications – QPS/QuarkXPress 4.0; Layout software – Ad-Force.; Display Hardware – 2-APP/Mac; Display Printers – HP/LaserJet, 2-HP/4MV PRODUCTION: Pagination software – QPS/QuarkXPress 4.0.; Production Equipment – 1-B, Polaroid/SprintScan; Cameras – 1-B, 1-SCREEN; Scanners – AG, Sprint Scan PRESSROOM: Line 1 – G/Community (8 units; 1 stack unit) 1976; Folders –G/SC.; Bundle tying machines –2-Gd/Ex 311; Address machine – 2/Am.; Audio Hardware – Newzware
Delivery Method: Newsstand, Private Carrier, Racks

SUMMERSIDE

THE JOURNAL PIONEER

PO Box 2840, Summerside, PE, C1N 4K5, Canada; gen tel (902) 436-2121; adv tel (902) 432-8238; ed tel (902) 432-8216; gen fax (902) 436-3027; adv fax (902) 436-0784; ed fax (902) 436-0784; gen e-mail journal@journalpioneer.com; adv e-mail pramsay@journalpioneer.com; ed e-mail rleblanc@journalpioneer.com; web site www.journalpioneer.com
Published: Mon, Tues, Wed, Thur, Fri, Sat
Weekday Frequency: m
Saturday Frequency: m
Circulation 7,748; 8,014(sat)
Last Audit: BPA December 30, 2010
Group: Transcontinental
Price: 2.65/wk (carrier); 177.00/yr.
Advertising: Open inch rate $.86
News services: CP.
Politics: Independent **Established:** 1865
Not Published: New Year; Good Friday; Victoria Day; Dominion Day; Labor Day; Thanksgiving; Christmas.
Magazines: TV Guide (local, newsprint) (Thurs).
Pub...Sandy Rundle
Business Manager..............................Ron Kelly
Adv. Mgr. ....Paul Ramsay
Dir., Reader Sales/Serv. ....Edward Kennedy
Sports Ed.............................Jason Simmonds
Managing Editor ....Roger Leblanc
Market information: ADS; TMC.
Mechanical available: Offset; Black and 3 ROP colors; insert accepted; page cutoffs - 22 3/4.
Mechanical Specifications: Type page 11 1/2 x 21 1/2; E - 5 cols, 2 1/8, 1/8 between; A - 10 cols, 1 1/16, between; C - 5 cols, 2 1/8, between.
Commodity Consumption: Avg. Page Number Per Issue - Daily 16; widths 27 1/2; Newsprint Used - Metric Tons 331.
Equipment EDITORIAL: Front-end Software – QPS/QuarkXPress, Microsoft/Word.; Editorial Hardware – 8-APP/Mac, 2-APP/Mac IIci; Editorial Equipment – Ven-Tel/Modem(1200 baud); Editorial Printers – APP/Mac LaserWriter II CLASSIFIED: Front-end Software – Claris/FileMaker Pro, QPS, Microsoft/Word, QPS/QuarkXPress.; Classified Hardware – APP/Mac LC, APP/Mac; Classified Printers – APP/Mac Stylewriter DISPLAY: Ad make-up applications – Multi-Ad/Creator, QPS, Microsoft/Word, Adobe/Illustrator, Zedcor/Deskpaint, Adobe/Streamline; Layout software – APP/Mac.; Display Hardware – 2-APP/Mac IIci; Display Printers – 2-APP/Mac LaserWriter II; Production Equipment – 1-P/SQ24; Cameras – 1-B. PRESSROOM: Line 1 – 6-G/Community, 3-G/Community Color; Folders –1; Bundle tying machines – 1-Pak/F16; Wrapping singles – Weld-Loc/Strapping; Address machine –

1-EI/3301.
Delivery Method: Mail, Newsstand, Private Carrier, Racks

QUEBEC

CHICOUTIMI

LE QUOTIDIEN

1051 Talbot Blvd., Chicoutimi, QC, G7H 5C1, Canada; gen tel (418) 545-4474; ed tel (418) 690-8800; gen fax (418) 690-8805; adv fax (418) 690-8824; gen e-mail webmaster@lequotidien.com; adv e-mail annomces@lequotidien.com; ed e-mail redaction@lequotidien.com; web site www.lequotidien.com
Published: Mon, Tues, Wed, Thur, Fri, Sat, Sun
Circulation 26,451; 25,859(sat); 36,705(sun)
Last Audit: ABC September 30, 2011
Group: CanWest Media Sales
Price: 4.03/wk; 16.12/mo; 187.49/yr.
Advertising: Open inch rate $1.94
News services: CP.
Politics: Independent
Not Published: New Year; Jan. 2; Easter Monday; Fete de Dollard; Fete de la Saint-Jean-Baptiste; Confederation Day; Labor Day; Action de Graces; Christmas.
Special weekly sections: Le Cahier Economique (Oct).
Pres. ....Michel Simard
Adv. Mgr. ....Linda Cantin
Ed. in Chief ....Denis Bouchard
Editorial Page Ed. ....Francois Segelais
Sports Ed. ....Serge Emond
Prodn. Mgr., Distr. ....Bernard Bellei
Prodn. Mgr., Pre Press ....Silvain Tremblai
Market information: Split run; TMC; Zoned editions.
Mechanical available: Offset; Black and 3 ROP colors; insert accepted; page cutoffs - 21 1/2.
Mechanical Specifications: Type page 10 1/4 x 14 1/4; E - 5 cols, 1 15/16, 1/8 between; A - 10 cols, 15/16, 1/8 between; C - 5 cols, 1 15/16, 1/8 between.
Commodity Consumption: Avg. Page Number Per Issue - Daily 40; Avg. Page Number Per Issue - Plates Used 50000; Avg. Page Number Per Issue - Sunday 160; widths 30; Newsprint Used - Metric Tons 3000; Printing Ink Used - Black 170000; Printing Ink Used - Color 80000.
Equipment EDITORIAL: Front-end Software – C, Cenotext 1.1.2.; Editorial Hardware – APP/Mac LC475, Centris/650, APP/Mac PPC 6100, APP/Mac PPC 7300, APP/Mac Power Book; Editorial Equipment – Lf/AP Picture Desk, APP/Mac Quadra 800; Editorial Printers – HP/LaserJet 5M, HP/4050 CLASSIFIED: Front-end Software – Baseview/Class Manager.; Classified Hardware – 4-Mk, APP/Mac, Power PC 4400; Classified Printers – APP/Mac, HP/4050 DISPLAY: Ad make-up applications – Adobe/Illustrator 8.01, Adobe/Photoshop 5.0, QPS/QuarkXPress 4.1; Layout software – Minimac.; Display Hardware – APP/Mac G3, APP/Mac G3-333; Display Printers – QMS/860, Canon/ImageClass C2100 PRODUCTION: Pagination software – QPS/QuarkXPress 4.1, Informatel/Geometry.; Production Equipment – Olec/OV45HD, Kk/Polychrome Graphics SN32, Accuset/1000; Cameras – 1-B, 1-R; Scanners – Cp, Umax/Mirage II PRESSROOM: Line 1 – 12-G/Urbanite; Press Drives – Westinghouse/Litholine; Folders –G/SSC; Pasters – 7-Martin/Automatic; Press control system – 1-SC/200 Litho.; MAILROOMCounter stackers – MM; Bundle tying machines –1/MLN; Address machine – 1-/Am.BUSINESS COMPUTERS: Audio Software – Microsoft/Windows NT 4; Audio Hardware – IBM, Sun/Sparc, IBM/AS-400, HP

GRANBY

LA VOIX DE L'EST

76 Dufferin St., Granby, QC, J2G 9L4, Canada; gen tel (450) 375-4555; gen fax (450) 372-1308; ed fax (450) 777-4865; ed e-mail redaction@lavoixdelest.qc.ca; web site www.cyberpresse.ca
Published: Mon, Tues, Wed, Thur, Fri, Sat
Weekday Frequency: m
Saturday Frequency: m
Circulation 15,018; 16,406(sat)
Last Audit: ABC September 30, 2011
Group: CanWest Media Sales
Price: 3.15/wk; 187.21/yr.
Advertising: Open inch rate $1.23
News services: CP, AP, RN, AFP.
Politics: Independent
Not Published: New Year; Jan. 2; Easter Monday; Victoria Day; St. Jean Baptiste Day; Canada Day; Labor Day; Thanksgiving; Christmas; Boxing Day.
Special weekly sections: Lac Brome (Apr); Le troisieme age (Aug); Voeux des Presidents (Dec); Vivre a deux (Feb); Ass, placements et economie (Jan); Festival de musiciens de Rue de Cowansville (Jul); Demenagement et decoration (Jun); Salon Habitat (Mar); Golf (May); Cadeaux (Nov)
Magazines: La Voix de l'Est Plus (S).
Broadcast Affiliations: Radio CHEF (1450, MA Station).
Dir., Information ....Francois Beaudoin
Dir., Finance/Admin. ....Gilbert Arl
Adv. Mgr., Sales ....Daniel Touchet
Circ. Dir. ....Christian Malo
Ed ....Guy Granger
News Ed. ....Haswa Budway
Sports Ed. ....Andre Bilodeau
Prodn. Mgr., Pre Press ....Claudette Ospiguy
Mechanical available: Offset; Black and 3 ROP colors; insert accepted; page cutoffs - 13 3/4.
Mechanical Specifications: Type page 11 1/4 x 13 3/4; E - 5 cols, 2, 1/8 between; A - 5 cols, 2, 1/8 between; C - 5 cols, 2, 1/8 between.
Commodity Consumption: Avg. Page Number Per Issue - Daily 39; Avg. Page Number Per Issue - Saturday 77; widths 55.
Equipment EDITORIAL: Front-end Software – Signature.; Editorial Hardware – 1-HI/1730; Editorial Printers – APP/Mac LaserWriter 8500 CLASSIFIED: Front-end Software – HI/CASH.; Classified Hardware – IBM/300 GL; Classified Printers – Lexmark/2380 Plus DISPLAY: Ad make-up applications – Morris.; Display Hardware – IBM; Display Printers – HP/2500; Production Equipment – Au; Cameras – Equipment ÃÂ Layout 8000.; Bundle tying machines –GD, OVL; Address machine – IBM/400.; Audio Hardware – IBM/400, PC

MONTREAL

LE DEVOIR

2050 de Bleury, 9th Fl., Montreal, QC, H3A 3M9, Canada; gen tel (514) 985-3333; adv tel (514) 985-3399; gen fax (514) 985-3360; adv fax (514) 985-3390; ed fax (514) 985-3360; ed e-mail redaction@ledevoir.com; web site www.ledevoir.com
Published: Mon, Tues, Wed, Thur, Fri, Sat
Weekday Frequency: m
Saturday Frequency: m
Circulation 30,206; 48,616(sat)
Last Audit: ABC September 30, 2011
Price: 3.66/wk (carrier); 269.95/yr.
Advertising: Open inch rate $2.47
News services: CP, AP, LE Monde, RN, AFP, CNW, Telbec.
Politics: Independent **Established:** 1910
Note: All printing and distribution of Le Devoir Inc. is outsourced.
Not Published: New Year; Jan. 2; Easter Monday; Victoria Day; St. Jean Baptiste Day; Confederation Day; Labor Day; Thanksgiving; Christmas; Boxing Day.
Magazines: L'Agenda (Sat).
Pub. Bernard Descoteaux
Vice Pres., Bus./Finance Catherine Laberge
Dir., Promo. Jose Chriffaro
Circ. Dir. Carolyn Simarde
Ed. in Chief Josee Boileau
Economics Ed. Gerard Berube
Cultural Pages Michel Belair
Prodn. Dir. Christian Goulet
Market information: TMC.
Mechanical available: Offset; Black and 3 ROP colors; insert accepted; page cutoffs - 21 3/4.
Mechanical Specifications: Type page 13 3/4 x 21 3/4; E - 6 cols, 2 1/16, 1/8 between; A - 6 cols, 2 1/16, 1/8 between; C - 9 cols, 1 5/16, 1/6 between.
Commodity Consumption: Avg. Page Number Per Issue - Daily 20; Avg. Page Number Per Issue - Saturday 48.
Equipment EDITORIAL: Front-end Software – Baseview/NewsEdit, QPS/QuarkXPress, Adobe/Photoshop; Editorial Hardware – APP/Mac; Editorial Equipment – Sharp/11x17 scanner, AG/Arcus, Nikon/3510AF, Radius/Vision Video Capture; Editorial Printers – AG/Selectset 5000, AG/Selectset 7000, QMS/860, APP/Mac LaserWriter IIg, HP CLASSIFIED: Front-end Software – Informatel.; Classified Hardware – Novell/486 server DISPLAY: Ad make-up applications – QPS/QuarkXPress, Aldus/Freehand, Adobe/Illustrator, Adobe/Streamline, Adobe/Photoshop; Layout software – APP/Macs.; Display Hardware – APP/Macs; Display Printers – QMS/860; Production Equipment – AG/Selectset 5000, AG/Selectset 7000; Cameras – Scanners ÃÂ AG/Arcus, Sharp, 2-Nikon/LS 3510AF.BUSINESS COMPUTERS: Audio Software – AccPac, Informatel; Audio Hardware – PC System

THE GAZETTE

1010 Sainte-Catherine St. W., Ste. 200, Montreal, QC, H3B 5L1, Canada; gen tel (514) 987-2222; adv tel (514) 987-7653; gen fax (514) 987-2270; adv fax (514) 987-2380; adv e-mail gazadv@montrealgazette.com; web site www.montrealgazette.com
Published: Mon, Tues, Wed, Thur, Fri, Sat, Sun
Weekday Frequency: m
Saturday Frequency: m
Circulation 116,446; 133,438(sat); 84,307(sun)
Last Audit: ABC September 30, 2011
Group: Postmedia Network Inc.
Price: Monthly pre-authorized credit card or bank withdrawal: $25.99 + tax. Annual by cheque or credit card: $335.88+ tax.
Advertising: Open line rate $7.75.
Insert rate: Total distribution/M = $58.00; Over 100,000 pieces-less than total/M = $64.00; 50,000 ÃÂ 99,999 pieces/M = $67.00.
News services: MCT News and graphics, NYT, Bloomberg, Reuters, AFP, Postmedia News Service.
Politics: Independent **Established:** 1778
Advertising not accepted: Y
Not Published: New Year's Day; Easter Sunday; Victoria Day (Sunday before); St-Jean Baptiste Day; Canada Day; Labor Day (Sunday before); Thanksgiving (Sunday before); Christmas Day.
Own facility?: Y
Special weekly sections: The Gazette West Island community edition; TVtimes.
Magazines: Urban Expressions.
Exec. Asst. to Pub. & Ed. in Chief Helen Ciampini
Dir., Finance ....Mario Belluscio
Mgr., HR ....Lina Guerra
Admin. Mgr. ....Donna Dudka
Adv. Mgr., Sales ....Randy Gates
Adv. Mgr., Sales ....Benoit Parent
Adv. Mgr., Sales ....Giancarlo Lanzetta
Adv. Mgr., Research/Planning ....David Klimek
Mgr., Reader Sales/Serv. ....Pamela Stevenson
Pub./Ed. in Chief ....Alan Allnutt
Executive Ed. ....Raymond Brassard
Deputy Mng. Ed. ....Asmaa Malik
Assoc. Mng. Ed., Visuals ....Michael Shenker
Assoc. Mng. Ed., Prodn ....Ross Teague
Deputy Ed. ....Katherine Sedgwick
Managing Editor ....Catherine Wallace
Vice-President, Operations Wendy Desmarteaux
Vice-President, Sales and Marketing StÃ£Â©phane Le Gal
Manager, Digital Media Sales - QuÃ£Â©bec Charlene Assels
Sales Manager, New Business Development Gino Iannuzzi
Vice Pres., HR ....Jean-Pierre Tremblay
Adv. Mgr., Classified Admin ....Anita Boutara
Vice Pres., Mktg./Reader Sales/Serv. Bernard Asselin
Mgr., Mktg. ....Gisele Bernier-White
Market information: Split run; Zoned editions.
Mechanical available: Offset;
CMYK;
Insert accepted - product samples; Broadsheet dimensions: Minimum format: 4 pages folded to 11ÃÂ h X 11ÃÂ v. Maximum format: 48 pages folded to 11ÃÂ h X 11ÃÂ v.
Page cutoffs ÃÂ 22 inch.

Mechanical Specifications: Type page Broadsheet 10.5ÃÂ x 20.857ÃÂ; E - 6 cols= 6.25ÃÂ; A - 10 cols = 10.5ÃÂ.
Commodity Consumption: Avg. Page Number per Issue - Daily 68; Avg. Page Number Per Issue - Plates Used 763 average per issue; Avg. Page Number per Issue - Saturday 123; Widths 37 1/2; Newsprint Used - Metric Tons 11915; Printing Ink Used ÃÂ Black: 87,000 Kg per year, Color: 45,000Kg per year.
Equipment EDITORIAL: Front-end Software – SaxoPress 6.6, InDesign, Adobe/Photoshop; Editorial Hardware – HP Compaq 8000 Elite SFF; Editorial Printers – HP 5100

CLASSIFIED: Front-end Software – Cybergraphics.; Classified Hardware – Compaq DC 5100 SFF

DISPLAY: Ad make-up applications – Multi-Ad/Creator, Adobe/Photoshop, Adobe/Illustrator, InDesign; Layout software – PPI Publishing Solution PlanPag
; Display Hardware – Dell 17ÃÂ

; Display Printers – HP 5100

; Production Equipment – Creo Ver. 5.0.6.1; TransSetter Model N11155;
PPI Publishing Solution Pilot OM.

PRESSROOM: Line 1 – 6-Goss/Metroliner; 2 PPSI 4/4 Towers.; Line 2 – 6-Goss/Metroliner; 2 PPSI 4/4 Towers.; Folders –3-Line 1; 1-Line 2.; MAILROOMCounter stackers – 10-QWI/400; Inserters and stuffers – 4-Fg/7-into-1; Bundle tying machines –10/Dynaric; Wrapping singles – 9-QWI/Viper, 2-Id; Mailroom control system – Fg; Address machine – 6-/DM.
Delivery Method: Mail, Newsstand, Private Carrier, Racks

LE JOURNAL DE MONTREAL

4545 Frontenac St., Montreal, QC, H2H 2R7, Canada; gen tel (514) 521-4545; adv tel (514) 521-4545; ed tel (514) 521-4545; gen fax (514) 521-4416
Published: Mon, Tues, Wed, Thur, Fri, Sat, Sun
Weekday Frequency: m
Saturday Frequency: m
Circulation 206,490; 228,340(sat); 209,175(sun)
Last Audit: BPA December 30, 2010
Price: 4.50/wk (carrier); 221.00/yr.
Advertising: Open inch rate $10.89
News services: CP, Telbec, DJ, CNW, AFP.
Politics: Independent
Magazines: Cahier Week-End (Sat).
Pres./Pub. ....Lyne Robipaille
Adv. Mgr. ....Gilles Lamoureux
Mgr., Mktg. ....Denise Lareau
Circ. Mgr. ....Christianne Benjamin
Ed. in Chief ....Danny Doucet
News Ed. ....Serge LaBrosse
Sports Ed. ....Denis Poissant

Data Processing Mgr. ....Luc Trudel
Audiotex Mgr., Servs. ....Marie Andre Lessard
Prodn. Mgr. ....Denis Tetrault
Market information: TMC.
Mechanical available: Offset; Black and 3 ROP colors; insert accepted; page cutoffs - 22 3/4.
Mechanical Specifications: Type page 10 7/32 x 12 19/32; E - 8 cols, 1 3/16, 1/8 between; A - 8 cols, 1 3/16, 1/8 between; C - 8 cols, 1 3/16, 1/8 between.
Commodity Consumption: Avg. Page Number Per Issue - Daily 104; Avg. Page Number Per Issue - Plates Used 47245; Avg. Page Number Per Issue - Saturday 212; Avg. Page Number Per Issue - Sunday 88; widths 29 13/16; Newsprint Used - Metric Tons 35000; Printing Ink Used - Black 7378
Equipment EDITORIAL: Front-end Software – TMS, QPS 1.12.; Editorial Hardware – DEC/PDP 11-70, 50-DEC/VAX, APP/Mac Power PC 8550-/200; Editorial Printers – 4-HP/5000 CLASSIFIED: Front-end Software – Unix/OS-2 2.1, CText/Advision, CText/Alps.; Classified Hardware – 2-Sun/Sparc 10-51, 42-PC, CText/Advision, CText/Alps; Classified Printers – 2-QMS/860 DISPLAY: Ad make-up applications – QPS/QuarkXPress 3.32; Layout software – SCS/Layout 8000.; Display Hardware – DEC/VAX 4000-300, Open Voll 5.5-2; Display Printers – AU/APS 1560; Production Equipment – 3-AU/F/08-C, 3-AU/F108FC, Coatsworth Communications; Cameras – Scanners ÃÂ Eskofot/8200S, Chromograph/2000, 2-PixelCraft/7650, 2-PixelCraft 8000; Scanners – Equipment ÃÂ QPS/QuarkXPress 3.32. PRESSROOM: Line 1 – 12-G/Cosmo double width 1984; Line 2 – 18-G/Metro double width 1984; Folders –2-G/2:1, 3-G/3:2; Pasters – 10-G/Cosmo, 15-G/Metro.; MAILROOMCounter stackers – 6-RKW/40; Bundle tying machines –6-MLN/85495; Wrapping singles – 2-Ideal/7100.AUDIO: Audio Software – In-house; Audio Hardware – PCs; Audio Hardware – DEC/VAX/4000-300

LA PRESSE

7 Rue St. Jacques, Montreal, QC, H2Y 1K9, Canada; gen tel (514) 285-7272; ed tel (514) 285-7070; gen fax (514) 285-6808; gen e-mail commentaires@lapresse.ca; ed e-mail forum@lapresse.ca; web site www.cyberpresse.ca
Published: Mon, Tues, Wed, Thur, Fri, Sat
Weekday Frequency: m
Saturday Frequency: m
Circulation 205,411; 264,235(sat)
Last Audit: ABC September 30, 2011
Group: CanWest Media Sales
Price: 4.20/wk; 16.80/mo; 241.00/yr.
Advertising: Open inch rate $9.90
News services: AFP, CP, AP, UPI, DJ, RN.
Politics: Independent
Not Published: New Year; Jan. 2; Good Friday; Easter Monday; Victoria Day; Canada Day; Labor Day; Thanksgiving; Christmas; Boxing Day.
Special editions: Tele-Presse TV-Radio Tab Magazine (Sat).
Special weekly sections: Plus Weekend Review (Other).
Pub. ....Guy Crevier
Vice Pres., Personnel/Labor Rel. Jacques Tousignant
Vice Pres., Commun. ....Caroline Jamet
Asst. to Pres./Legal Counsel Philippe-Denis Richard
Controller ....Robert Julien
Adv. Dir., Retail ....Yves Lalonde
Vice Pres., Mktg. ....Jean Durocher
Dir., Promo. ....Christiane Dube
Circ. Dir. ....Jocelyn Godbout
Vice Pres./Ed. ....Philippe Cantin
Mng. Ed. ....Eric Trottier
Books Ed. ....Jocelyne Lepage
Editorial Dir. ....Andre Pratte
Educ. Ed ....Marie Allard
Finance Ed. ....Jon Sebastian Gagmom
Music Ed., Classical ....Claude Gingras
Music Ed., Pop ....Alain Brunet
Ottawa Bureau ....Gilles Toupin
Photo Ed. ....Benoit Giguere
Market information: Split run.
Mechanical available: Letterpress - Napp Plates; Black and 3 ROP colors; insert accepted; page cutoffs - 23 9/16.
Mechanical Specifications: Type page 11 1/2 x 22 1/8; E - 5 cols, 2 3/16, 3/16 between; A - 10 cols, 1 1/16, 3/16 between; C - 10 cols, 1 1/16, 3/32 between.
Commodity Consumption: Avg. Page Number Per Issue - Daily 60; Avg. Page Number Per Issue - Plates Used 150000; Avg. Page Number Per Issue - Saturday 160; Avg. Page Number Per Issue - Sunday 48; widths 48; Newsprint Used - Metric Tons 28000; Printing Ink Used - Black 900000; Pr
Equipment EDITORIAL: Front-end Software – AT 3.6, AT/40.; Editorial Hardware – IBM/PS2-LAN, 85-IBM/PS2-30-286, COM/Ethernet; Editorial Equipment – HI/Images Picture Desk 3, 2-Sun/Sparc, 3-HI/KM, 1-X/Scanner; Classified Hardware – 2-APP/Mac II.; Layout software – SCS/Layout 8000.; Display Hardware – 8-HI/8300, 4-Zenith, 4-AT, 8-IBM/PS2 30; Production Equipment – Na, 2-ECR/Autokon-1000; Cameras – Scanners ÃÂ 2-Eskofot; Scanners – Equipment ÃÂ HI. PRESSROOM: Line 1 – 36-G/Headliner double width; Folders –4; MAILROOMCounter stackers – 7/HL; Inserters and stuffers – 1-S/72P, 1-HI/632; Bundle tying machines –7-/Power Strap; Wrapping singles – 6-Mosca/(ACME).; Audio Hardware – 2-IBM/4381

QUEBEC

LE SOLEIL

PO Box 1547, Succ. Terminus, Quebec, QC, G1K 7J6, Canada; gen tel (418) 686-3233; adv tel (418) 686-3435; ed tel (418) 686-3209; gen fax (418) 686-3225; adv fax (418) 686-3260; ed fax (418) 686-3374; adv e-mail marketing@lesoleil.com; ed e-mail redaction@lesoleil.com; web site www.cyberpresse.ca
Published: Mon, Tues, Wed, Thur, Fri, Sat, Sun
Weekday Frequency: m
Saturday Frequency: m
Circulation 76,230; 103,965(sat); 82,741(sun)
Last Audit: ABC September 30, 2011
Group: CanWest Media Sales
Price: 4.00/wk (carrier); 15.53/mo; 236.00/yr.
Advertising: Open inch rate $4.84
News services: CP, AFP, NYT, TELBEC, CN Wire, RN, AP.
Politics: Independent **Established:** 1816
Not Published: New Year; Jan. 2; Easter Monday; St. Jean Baptiste Day; Canada Day; Dollar Day; Labour Day; Christmas.
Special editions: WEM (week-end magazine) (Fri); Tele-Magazine (Mon); Dimanche Magazine (S); Le Soleil Tele-Magazine (Sat); Actualite Magazine (Thur); Mode Magazine (Tues); Plein Air (openair) (Wed).
Magazines: Entertainment (Fri); Automobile (Mon); Entertainment (S); Entertainment (Sat).
Pres. ....Claude Daniel
Bus. Mgr. ....Gilles Ouellet
Supvr. ....Therese Cote
Adv. Dir ....Louis Gendron
Cartoonist ....Andre-Philippe Cote
Editorial Page Ed. ....Pierre-Paul Noreau
Librarian ....Yves Bellefleur
Music Ed. ....Daphne Bedard
Online Ed ....Michel Samson
Real Estate ....Gilles Angers
Sports Dir. ....Maurice Dumas
Travel Ed. ....Raymond Tardif
Prodn. Dir. ....Gilles Garneau
Prodn. Mgr., Graphic Arts ....Line Baillargeon
Market information: ADS.
Mechanical available: Letterpress (direct); Black and 3 ROP colors; insert accepted; page cutoffs - 23 3/4.
Mechanical Specifications: Type page 11 1/2 x 21; E - 5 cols, 2 1/16, 1/8 between; A - 10 cols, 3/16 between; C - 10 cols, 1/16 between.
Commodity Consumption: Avg. Page Number Per Issue - Daily 44; Avg. Page Number Per Issue - Plates Used 55682; Avg. Page Number Per Issue - Saturday 132; Avg. Page Number Per Issue - Sunday 42; widths 50; Newsprint Used - Metric Tons 10000; Printing Ink Used - Black 480000; Pri
Equipment; Editorial Hardware – 6-APP/Mac IIvx, 2-APP/Mac SE, 7-APP/Power Mac 8100, 18-APP/Power Mac 6100, 4-APP/Mac Quadra 700, 1-APP/Mac IIfx, 1-APP/Mac Quadra 800, 1-APP/Mac IIx, 1-APP/Mac SE30, 3-APP/Mac LC II, 10-APP/Mac Power Book, 13-LC/475; Editorial Equipment – 3-APP/Mac Laser CLASSIFIED: Front-end Software – Cenoad 1.33, QPS/QuarkXPress 4.1.; Classified Hardware – APP/Mac 6100, 11-HP/LC; Classified Equipment – Electronic Mail Box, TTS, Umax/300; Classified Printers – QMS DISPLAY: Ad make-up applications – Service Bureau; Layout software – Managing Editor/ALS 2.5.; Display Hardware – APP/Power Mac G4; Display Printers – 1-C.Itoh/5000, 2-Printronics, 5-Fuji/4500, APP/Mac Pro; Production Equipment – AU, Adobe/Photoshop 6.0; Cameras – Equipment ÃÂ QPS/QuarkXPress 3.3, Adobe/Illustrator 10.AUDIO: Audio Software – Adobe/Fetch 1.2; Audio Hardware – APP/Mac IIxx, Senior 450 LuxxonBUSINESS COMPUTERS: Audio Software – Solaris 2.6, UShare 5.0.1; Audio Hardware – Sun/Enterprise 3000, Microsoft/NT Server 2000

SHERBROOKE

THE RECORD

PO Box 1200, Sherbrooke, QC, J1H 5L6, Canada; gen tel (819) 569-9525; adv tel (819) 569-9511; ed tel (819) 569-6345; gen fax (819) 821-3179; adv fax (819) 821-3179; ed fax (819) 569-3945; ed e-mail newsroom@sherbrookerecord.com; web site www.sherbrookerecord.com
Published: Mon, Tues, Wed, Thur, Fri
Weekday Frequency: m
Circulation 4,271
Last Audit: ABC September 30, 2011
Price: 2.20/wk (carrier); 138.03/yr.
Advertising: Open inch rate $1.08
News services: CP, Telbec.
Politics: Independent
Not Published: New Year; Jan. 3; Dominion Day; Good Friday; Easter Monday; Victoria Day; St. Jean Baptiste Day; Thanksgiving; Christmas.
Special weekly sections: Annual Review (Apr); Fashions (Fall); Ski (Jan); Holiday (Jun); Fashions (Spring); County Fairs (Summer).
Circ. Mgr. ....Laurie Schoolcraft
Ed. ....Sharon Mccully
Prodn. Mgr. ....Richard Lessard
Prodn. Mgr., Composing ....Francine Thibault
Market information: TMC.
Mechanical available: Black and 3 ROP colors; insert accepted; page cutoffs - 13 15/16.
Mechanical Specifications: Type page 11 1/2 x 14 3/4; E - 5 cols, 1 7/8, 1/8 between; A - 5 cols, 1 7/8, 1/8 between; C - 5 cols, 1 7/8, 1/8 between.
Commodity Consumption: Avg. Page Number Per Issue - Daily 56.
Equipment; Editorial Hardware – Printers ÃÂ 3-COM/AKI.; Production Equipment – 1-COM/ACM9000, 2-COM/2961HS, 1-COM/7200, 1-COM/4961; Cameras – 1-Nu. PRESSROOM: Line 1 – 1; Bundle tying machines –3/Bu; Address machine – 1-Am/1955B.

LA TRIBUNE

1950 Roy St., Sherbrooke, QC, J1K 2X8, Canada; gen tel (819) 564-5450; adv tel (819) 564-5450; ed tel (819) 564-5454; gen fax (819) 564-5480; adv fax (819) 564-5482; ed fax (819) 564-8098; gen e-mail latribune@latribune.qc.ca; web site www.cyberpresse.ca
Published: Mon, Tues, Wed, Thur, Fri, Sat
Weekday Frequency: m
Saturday Frequency: m
Circulation 31,053; 34,192(sat)
Last Audit: ABC September 30, 2011
Group: CanWest Media Sales
Price: 4.05/wk; 28.76/mo (includes tax); 194.99/yr.
Advertising: Open inch rate $2.95
News services: CP.
Politics: Independent
Not Published: New Year; Jan. 2; St. Jean Baptiste Day; Labor Day; Christmas; Boxing Day.
Special editions: Weekend Magazine (Sat).
Pres./Ed. ....Louis Boisvert
Adv. Asst. Mgr. ....Alain LeClerc
Circ. Mgr. ....Andre Custeau
Newsroom Dir. ....Louis Eric Allard
Photo Dept. Mgr. ....Renee Marquis
Radio/Television Ed. ....Andre Laroche
Sports Ed. ....Sonia Bolduc
Prodn. Mgr. ....Andre Roberge
Prodn. Foreman, Composing ......Steve Rancourt
Market information: TMC.
Mechanical available: Offset; Black and 3 ROP colors; insert accepted; page cutoffs - 22 3/4.
Mechanical Specifications: Type page 12 x 21 9/16; E - 5 cols, 1 1/16, 1/16 between; A - 10 cols, 1 1/16, 1/16 between; C - 10 cols, 1 1/16, 1/16 between.
Commodity Consumption: Avg. Page Number Per Issue - Daily 40; Avg. Page Number Per Issue - Plates Used 49900; widths 48; Newsprint Used - Metric Tons 3500; Printing Ink Used - Black 103616; Printing Ink Used - Color 14550; Printing Ink Used - Pages Printed 18538.
Equipment; Editorial Hardware – HI/8900, Sun/Server XP21. CLASSIFIED: Front-end Software – Unix.; Classified Hardware – HI/Cash, PCs; Layout software – SCS/Layout 8000.; Display Hardware – HI/8900, Sun/Server XP21; Display Printers – X/Proofer, AU/Typesetter, HP/2500; Production Equipment – 2-AU/APS108C, Turbo 3850; Cameras – 1-C/Spartan II-2606, 1-C/Spartan III, 1-III/VGC-TC; Scanners – 1-ECR/Autokon, 3-X, 1-AG. PRESSROOM: Line 1 – 6-G/Cosmo 3526 (Web Press Offset).; MAILROOMCounter stackers – 1/HL; Bundle tying machines –1-MLN/ML2EE, 1-MLN/MLL2A; Wrapping singles – 2-Gd/Q7070; Address machine – 1-Am/6400, 1-Am/2605.; Audio Hardware – IBM/AS-400

TROIS-RIVIERES

LE NOUVELLISTE

PO Box 668, Trois-Rivieres, QC, G9A 3Y2, Canada; gen tel (819) 376-2501; gen fax (819) 376-0946; adv e-mail pub@lenouvelliste.qc.ca; ed e-mail information@lenouvelliste.qc.ca; web site www.cyberpresse.ca/lenouvelliste
Published: Mon, Tues, Wed, Thur, Fri, Sat
Weekday Frequency: m
Saturday Frequency: m
Circulation 43,508; 46,592(sat)
Last Audit: ABC September 30, 2011
Price: 3.95/wk; 241.80/yr.
Advertising: Open inch rate $2.80
News services: Target Media Inc., AP, AFP, RN, UPI, Telbec, Laserphoto.
Politics: 1920
Not Published: New Year; Jan. 2; Christmas; Boxing Day.
Special editions: Nouvelliste Plus (Sat).
Special weekly sections: Tourist (Other).
Mgr., Personnel ....Marc Auger
Adv. Dir. ....Yves Neault
Mktg./Promo. Dir. ....Ginette Panneton
Circ. Mgr. ....Patrick Giassom
Ed. ....Marc Rochette
News Ed. ....Stephen Frappier
Prodn. Mgr. ....Raymond Pitre
Prodn. Mgr., Printing ....Pierre Cote
Market information: Split run.

Mechanical available: Offset; Black and 3 ROP colors; insert accepted - roll-fed; page cutoffs - 22 3/4.
Mechanical Specifications: Type page 11 1/2 x 21 3/8; E - 10 cols, 1 1/16, 1/12 between; A - 10 cols, 1 1/16, 1/12 between; C - 10 cols, 1 1/16, 1/12 between.
Commodity Consumption: Avg. Page Number Per Issue - Daily 32; Avg. Page Number Per Issue - Saturday 64; widths 12; Newsprint Used - Metric Tons 2615; Printing Ink Used - Pages Printed 12500.
Equipment EDITORIAL: Front-end Software – HI/PEN, HI/XP-21, HI/2100.; Editorial Hardware – 2-HI/XP-21; Editorial Equipment – AU/Rip; Editorial Printers – AU/3850 CLASSIFIED: Front-end Software – HI/PEN, HI/XP-21, HI/2100.; Classified Hardware – HI/Cash, 2-HI/XP-21; Classified Equipment – AU/Rip; Classified Printers – AU/3850 DISPLAY: Ad make-up applications – HI/2100, HI/XP-21; Layout software – SCS/Layout 8000.; Display Hardware – HI/2100, HI/XP-21; Display Printers – AU/3850; Production Equipment – WL/Litho Plater, 2-X/Power PC 8100; Cameras – 2-X/Scanner 7650, 2-X/8000; Scanners – Equipment ÃÂ HI/2100 2.1. PRESSROOM: Line 1 – 6-HI/1600 1982; Line 2 – 8-HI/V-15 1989; Folders –KAN/1/4 folder 1994; Pasters – 4-MEG, 4.; MAILROOMCounter stackers – 2-MM/CS25, 1-MM/S70; Bundle tying machines –3-Si; Address machine – 1-Head/R-4800-X, CH/Base 522.BUSINESS COMPUTERS: Audio Software – Dun & Bradstreet 4.0; Audio Hardware – IBM/AS-400, IBMs

VANIER

LE JOURNAL DE QUEBEC

450 Bechard Ave., Vanier, QC, G1M 2E9, Canada; gen tel (418) 683-1573; gen fax (418) 683-8886; adv fax (418) 683-1027; ed fax (418) 688-8181; web site lejournaldequebec.canoe.ca
Published: Mon, Tues, Wed, Thur, Fri, Sat, Sun
Weekday Frequency: m
Saturday Frequency: m
Circulation 89,852; 99,106(sat); 87,741(sun)
Last Audit: BPA December 30, 2010
Price: 3.99/wk; 338.00/yr.
Advertising: Open inch rate $6.32
News services: PC, UPI, Canada News Wire, Telbec, AFP.
Not Published: New Year; Jan. 2; Easter Monday; St. Jean Baptiste Day; Confederation Day; Labor Day; Christmas; Boxing Day.
Special weekly sections: Mode (Apr); La rentree (Aug); Informatique/Electronique (Dec); Reer (Feb); La Mariee (Jan); 50% (Jul); Sante Mieux-etre (Jun); Formule 1 (Mar); Golf (May); Sports d'hiver (Nov); Automobile (Oct); Votre Argent et Vous (Sept).
Magazines: Automotive (Mon); Tele-Haire (TV listings) (Other); Entertainment (Sat); Fashion (Tues); Food and Health (Wed).
Vice Pres., Finance ....Andre Berube
Controller....................................Louis Ouellet
Adv. Vice Pres., Sales.................Daniel Houde
Mgr., Promo..........................Pierre Villeneuve
Circ. Mgr....................................Marc Couture
Entertainment Ed................Karen Vezilleneube
Gen. Ed..................................Donald Charette
Data Processing Mgr...............Louis Chretien
Prodn. Vice Pres., Logistics Jean Pierre Robitaille
Prodn. Mgr., Pre Press.............Maurice Vezina
Prodn. Mgr., Pressroom...................Ulric Kusik
Market information: Zoned editions.
Mechanical available: Offset; Black and 3 ROP colors; insert accepted - all; page cutoffs - 22.
Mechanical Specifications: Type page 10 1/4 x 12 1/2; E - 8 cols, 1 1/6, 1/8 between; A - 8 cols, 1 1/6, 1/8 between; C - 8 cols, 1 1/6, 1/8 between.
Commodity Consumption: Avg. Page Number Per Issue - Daily 84; Avg. Page Number Per Issue - Plates Used 36000; Avg. Page Number Per Issue - Saturday 133; Avg. Page Number Per Issue - Sunday 77; widths 27; Newsprint Used - Metric Tons 8642; Printing Ink Used - Black 242548; Prin
Equipment EDITORIAL: Front-end Software – TMS/V5-3.; Editorial Hardware – DEC/PDP 11-70, 37-DEC/VT-72, 16-APP/Mac LC, 15-APP/Mac PowerBook 100; Editorial Equipment – 10-APP/Mac Power PC 6500; Editorial Printers – 2-Printronix CLASSIFIED: Front-end Software – CMS 2.3.; Classified Hardware – 1-DEC/PDP 11-70, DEC/VT 173C; Classified Printers – 1-DEC/Letterwriter DISPLAY: Ad make-up applications – QPS/QuarkXPress 3.32, Adobe/Illustrator 6.0, Adobe/Photoshop 5.0.; Display Hardware – 20-APP/Mac Power PC; Display Printers – Xante/8200, Xante/8300, Accel-A-Writer, Au/Aps 2000 PRODUCTION: Pagination software – QPS/QuarkXPress 3.32.; Production Equipment – 2-AU/APS Micro 5, 2-AU/APS 7 AV25; Cameras – 1-Acti, 1-R; Scanners – 2-AG/Horizon Plus, 1-AG/Horizon Ultra, 1-Umax PRESSROOM: Line 1 – 11-G/Urbanite 5000 Series single width 1990; Line 2 – 11-G/Urbanite 5000 Series single width 1990; Press Drives – Feb-90; Folders –2-G/Urbanite 1990; Pasters – 16-MEG/Flying DME Pasters 1990.; MAILROOMCounter stackers – 2/FG; Bundle tying machines –3-/Cyclops, 2-/Power Strap; Wrapping singles – 2-/RKW; Mailroom control system – 1-/HL.; Audio Hardware – Micro Vax/3000/80

SASKATCHEWAN

MOOSE JAW

THE MOOSE JAW TIMES-HERALD

PO Box 3000, Moose Jaw, SK, S6H 6E4, Canada; gen tel (306) 692-6441; adv tel (306) 692-6441; ed tel (306) 692-6441; gen fax (306) 692-2101; adv fax (306) 694-1216; ed fax (306) 692-2101; ed e-mail editorial@mjtimes.sk.ca; web site www.mjtimes.sk.ca
Published: Mon, Tues, Wed, Thur, Fri, Sat
Weekday Frequency: e
Circulation 8,200; 8,200(sat)
Last Audit: Estimate September 1, 2006
Price: 2.50/wk (includes GST); 10.85/mo; 129.99/yr (Moose Jaw), $175.00/yr (SK), $210.00/yr (rest of Canada).
Advertising: Open inch rate $1.20
News services: CP, AP, RN, SNS, Toronto Star Syndicate.
Politics: Independent
Not Published: New Year; Good Friday; Victoria Day; Canada Day; Labor Day; Christmas; Civic Holiday; Thanksgiving; Remembrance Day; Family Day.
Special weekly sections: Year-End Review (Dec); Golden Years (Fall); Minor Hockey Special (Jan); Progress (Mar); Christmas Specials (Nov); Guide to Good Farming (Oct); Vacation Guide (Other); Golden Years (Spring).
Magazines: On Entertainment (Fri); Color Comics (Sat).
Pub. ....Rob Clark
Bus. Mgr...................................Polly Veroba
Adv. Mgr....................................Glenn Haug
Adv. Supvr., Classified.......................Judy Ellis
Mng. Ed...............................Lesley Sheppard
Prodn. Mgr., Pre Press................Wanda White
Prodn. Mgr., Pressroom..........Fraser Wareham
Market information: ADS; TMC.
Mechanical available: Offset; Black and 3 ROP colors; insert accepted; page cutoffs - 22 3/4.
Mechanical Specifications: Type page 11 1/2 x 21 1/2; E - 5 cols, 2 1/8, 1/8 between; A - 10 cols, 1 1/16, 1/8 between; C - 10 cols, 1 1/16, 1/8 between.
Commodity Consumption: Avg. Page Number Per Issue - Daily 40.
Equipment EDITORIAL: Front-end Software – APP/Mac System 8.6 3.0, QPS/QuarkXPress 3.32/4.01.; Editorial Hardware – APP/Mac; Editorial Printers – APP/Mac LaserWriter CLASSIFIED: Front-end Software – Baseview/Class Manager Pro.; Classified Hardware – APP/Macs DISPLAY: Ad make-up applications – QPS/QuarkXPress 4.0.1, Adobe/Photoshop 4.0; Layout software – QPS/QuarkXPress.; Display Hardware – APP/Mac, APP/Power Mac G3; Display Printers – Linotype-Hell, Pre Press/Panther Plus 46 PRODUCTION: Pagination software – QPS/QuarkXPress 4.01.; Production Equipment – PrePress/Panther Pro 46, Linotype-Hell, Pre Press/Panther; Cameras – ACI/125; Scanners – Polaroid/U-Max PRESSROOM: Line 1 – 12-G/Community 1994; Folders –2-G/SC 818 Quarter.; Bundle tying machines –1/Gd.BUSINESS COMPUTERS: Audio Software – Lotus 1-2-3, Microsoft/Word, Microsoft/Excel; Audio Hardware – SITG

PRINCE ALBERT

PRINCE ALBERT DAILY HERALD

30-10th St E, Prince Albert, SK, S6V 0Y5, Canada; gen tel (306) 764-4276; adv tel (306) 764-4276; ed tel (306) 764-4276; gen fax (306) 763-3331; adv fax (306) 763-6747; ed fax (306) 763-3331; adv e-mail production@paherald.sk.ca; ed e-mail editorial@paherald.sk.ca; web site www.paherald.sk.ca
Published: Mon, Tues, Wed, Thur, Fri, Sat
Weekday Frequency: e
Circulation 5,458; 5,842(sat)
Last Audit: BPA December 30, 2010
Group: CanWest Media Sales
Price: 6.65/wk (carrier); 159.60/mo; 1915.20/yr.
Advertising: Open inch rate $1.23(e-fri)
News services: CP, SNS, Leader-Star.
Politics: Independent
Not Published: New Year; Good Friday; Victoria Day; Dominion Day; Labor Day; Thanksgiving; Armistice Day; Christmas.
Special weekly sections: Car Care (Fall); Winter Festival (Feb); Brides (Jan); Progress (Mar); Cookbook (Nov); Chamber of Commerce (Quarterly).
Magazines: Entertainment Guide (local, newsprint) (Fri); Rural Roots (agriculture) (S).
Bus. Mgr................................Lonny Deobald
Adv. Mgr........................................Ian Jensen
Circ./Mktg. Mgr...................Darrell Rathgeber
Mng. Ed...................................Vern Faulkner
Market information: ADS; TMC.
Mechanical available: Offset; Black and 3 ROP colors; insert accepted; page cutoffs - 22 3/4.
Mechanical Specifications: Type page 11 1/2 x 21 1/2; E - 5 cols, 2 1/8, 1/8 between; A - 10 cols, 1 1/16, 1/8 between; C - 10 cols, 1 1/16, 1/8 between.
Commodity Consumption: Avg. Page Number Per Issue - Daily 18.1; Avg. Page Number Per Issue - Plates Used 5700; widths 25; Newsprint Used - Metric Tons 565; Printing Ink Used - Black 12000; Printing Ink Used - Color 3500; Printing Ink Used - Pages Printed 5500.
Equipment EDITORIAL: Front-end Software – QPS/QuarkXPress 4.1, Adobe/Photoshop 5.0, Macromedia/Freehand 5.0.; Editorial Hardware – APP/Mac; Editorial Printers – 3-COM, APP/Mac CLASSIFIED: Front-end Software – Baseview.; Classified Hardware – APP/Mac DISPLAY: Ad make-up applications – Multi-Ad/Creator.; Display Hardware – APP/Mac; Display Printers – APP/Mac PRODUCTION: Pagination software – QPS/QuarkXPress 4.1.; Production Equipment – Ultra/94E Imagesetter; Cameras – 1-B; Scanners – Polaroid/PrintScan, Umax/Vista PRESSROOM: Line 1 – 8-G/Community single width 1974; Folders –1; Inserters and stuffers – KAN/6 pocket; Bundle tying machines –1-Gd/Q; Mailroom control system – ATT; Address machine – 1/El; Other equipment – Cole/3 bladetrimmer.; Audio Hardware – ATT

REGINA

THE LEADER-POST

PO Box 2020, Regina, SK, S4P 3G4, Canada; gen tel (306) 781-5211; adv tel (306) 781-5211; ed tel (306) 781-5300; gen fax (306) 781-5350; adv fax (306) 781-5350; ed fax (306) 566-2588; ed e-mail newsroom@leaderpost.canwest.com; web site www.leaderpost.com
Published: Mon, Tues, Wed, Thur, Fri, Sat
Weekday Frequency: m
Saturday Frequency: m
Circulation 42,996; 45,049(sat)
Last Audit: ABC September 30, 2011
Price: 4.48/wk; 232.80/yr.
Advertising: Open inch rate $5.10(m-fri)
News services: CP, AP.
Politics: Independent **Established:** 1883
Not Published: Statutory holidays.
Special editions: Weekender (Sat).
Special weekly sections: International Dance Day (Apr); Around Town (Aug); Activity Planner (Dec); Golf Expo (Feb); World No Smoking Day (Jan); Get Away In Saskatchewan (Jul); Career Frontiers (Jun); A Place To Call Home (Mar); Southeast Vacation Guide (May); Real Estate Coloring
Magazines: Driver's Seat (Fri); Real Estate (Sat); Entertainment (Thur); Careers (Weekly).
Broadcast Affiliations: CanWest Global TV.
Pub. ....Marty Klyne
Mgr., HR................Twyla Clermont-Anderson
Adv. Dir.......................................Les Wagman
Ed. in Chief............................Janice Dockham
Deputy Ed., Online.......................Kevin Blevins
Assoc. Ed. ....Marlon Marshall
City Coord.............................Veronica Rhodes
Finance Ed. ....Bruce Johnstone
Librarian....................................Sue Marshall
News Coord...............................Chris Harbron
Photo Dept. Mgr.................................Roy Antal
Sports Ed....................................Rob Vanstone
Prodn. Mgr., Bldg. ....Brad Montague
Prodn. Foreman, Pre Press ....Cal Martin
Prodn. Mgr., Pressroom/Distr. ....Bill Ruddy
Market information: TMC; Zoned editions.
Mechanical available: Letterpress (offset); Black and 3 ROP colors; insert accepted - samples, sticky notes; page cutoffs - 21 3/4.
Mechanical Specifications: Type page 10 1/2 x 21 3/4; E - 5 cols, 2 3/16, 1/8 between; A - 10 cols, 1/8 between; C - 10 cols, 1/8 between.
Commodity Consumption: Avg. Page Number Per Issue - Daily 58; Avg. Page Number Per Issue - Plates Used 40000; widths 21; Newsprint Used - Metric Tons 7743; Printing Ink Used - Black 40000; Printing Ink Used - Color 14000; Printing Ink Used - Pages Printed 17400.
Equipment EDITORIAL: Front-end Software – Baseview/Newsedit 3.2.2.; Editorial Hardware – 5-APP/Mac G3; Editorial Equipment – 40-APP/Mac G3; Editorial Printers – HP/8150 CLASSIFIED: Front-end Software – Cybersell 2.9.; Classified Hardware – 6-PC; Classified Equipment – 21-PC; Classified Printers – HP DISPLAY: Ad make-up applications – MS Office, Sam, Mk/Ad Director; Layout software – SCS/Layout 8000.; Display Hardware – PC P4; Display Printers – HP/8150; Production Equipment – 1-Au/APS 3850, 1-Au/APS Sierra, Pre Press/Panther Pro 46, 1-V; Cameras – Scanners ÃÂ Umax, Kk/Negscanner, AG/Arcus, AG/Horizon Ultra, Pusup-Eskofot 2024; Scanners – Equipment ÃÂ QPS/QuarkXPress 4.11. PRESSROOM: Line 1 – 8-G/Metroliners double width (4-black; 4-color decked) 1985; Folders –2-G/3:2; Pasters – 8; Press registration system – G/pin system.; MAILROOMCounter stackers – 3/KAN, 1-MM/227, 1-Id; Inserters and stuffers – 1-MM/Gintol, 2-KAN/480 8 into 1; Bundle tying machines –1-Si/MLNZ, 1-

/Acme, 1-/Mini-mark, 3-Dynaric/NP 15000; Wrapping singles – 2-/RKW, 2-/QWI (bottom wrap); Address machine – 2-Am/2BUSINESS COMPUTERS: Audio Software – SCS/Layout 8000; Audio Hardware – PBS/MediaPlus, DEC/486 DX2 66

SASKATOON

THE STARPHOENIX

204 5th Ave. N., Saskatoon, SK, S7K 2P1, Canada; gen tel (306) 657-6397; adv tel (306) 657-6340; ed tel (306) 657-6231; gen fax (306) 657-6433; adv fax (306) 657-6208; ed fax (306) 657-6437; gen e-mail generaloffice@sp.canwest.com; adv e-mail advertising@sp.canwest.com; ed e-mail spnews@sp.canwest.com; web site www.thestarphoenix.com

Published: Mon, Tues, Wed, Thur, Fri, Sat
Weekday Frequency: m
Saturday Frequency: m
Circulation 51,078; 52,944(sat)
Last Audit: ABC September 30, 2011
Price: 11.46/mo (carrier); 415.80/yr (mail).
Advertising: Open inch rate $4.73
News services: CP, AP, NYT, CanWest News Service.
Politics: Independent **Established:** 1902
Not Published: Statutory holidays.
Magazines: TV Times (Fri); Saskatoon Sun (S); Saskatoon Shopper (Wed).
Broadcast Affiliations: Global Saskatoon.
Profile: The StarPhoenix is the daily newspaper in Saskatoon, SK, Canada. It is a morning publication which is distributed Monday through Saturday. We also publish and distribute the Saskatoon Sun (a free TMC product delivered on sundays), Home Showcase, tv times,

Pub. .... Dale Brin
Controller .... Eldon Amundson
Mgr., HR .... Sharon Wacker
Admin. Asst .... Helen Male
Adv. Dir. .... Callum Scott
Mgr., Promotions .... Craig Peterson
Circ. Dir. .... Shannon Simpson
Ed .... Steve Gibb
Mng. Ed .... Cam Hutchinson
Prodn. Mgr., Pre Press .... Murray Hill
Prodn. Mgr., Pressroom .... Keith Coulter

Market information: ADS; TMC.
Mechanical available: Black and full color ROP colors; insert accepted - catalogues,sample products.

YUKON

WHITEHORSE

WHITEHORSE STAR

2149 2nd Ave., Whitehorse, YT, Y1A 1C5, Canada; gen tel (867) 668-2002; adv tel (867) 668-2060; ed tel (867) 667-4481; gen fax (867) 668-7130; ed fax (867) 668-7130; gen e-mail star@whitehorsestar.com; ed e-mail editor@whitehorsestar.com; web site www.whitehorsestar.com

Published: Mon, Tues, Wed, Thur, Fri
Weekday Frequency: e
Circulation 1,820
Last Audit: ABC September 30, 2011
Price: 27.00/mo; 321.00/yr (mail-Canada); 500.00/yr (mail-US).
Advertising: Open inch rate $1.61
News services: AP, CP, UPI, MCT.
Politics: Independent
Advertising not accepted: Anything libelous or against the law.
Not Published: Canadian holidays.
Special weekly sections: Xmas Greetings (Dec); Yukon Quest (Feb).
Magazines: Friday TV Guide (Fri); Yukon Real Estate (Other).

Pres./Pub. .... Jackie Pierce
Adv. Mgr. .... Michele Pierce
Circ. Mgr. .... John Stuckey
Ed. .... Jim Butler
Photo Ed. .... Vince Fedoroff
Sports Ed. .... Annalee Grant
Wire Ed .... Eric Murphy
Head Pressman .... Don Campbell

Market information: Split run; TMC.
Mechanical available: Offset Web; Black and 3 ROP colors; insert accepted; page cutoffs - 14 1/2.
Mechanical Specifications: Type page 10 1/4 x 13 1/2; E - 5 cols, 1 17/20, 1/6 between; A - 5 cols, 1 17/20, 1/6 between; C - 6 cols, 1 1/2, 1/6 between.
Commodity Consumption: Avg. Page Number Per Issue - Daily 32; Avg. Page Number Per Issue - Plates Used 2565; widths 30; Newsprint Used - Short Tons 200; Printing Ink Used - Pages Printed 10272.
Equipment EDITORIAL: Front-end Software – APP/Mac, OS 9.1.; Editorial Hardware – APP/Mac on Ethernet, APP/Mac Server; Editorial Printers – XEROX CLASSIFIED: Front-end Software – QPS/QuarkXPress 4.1, Multi-Ad/Creator 6.0, Adobe/PhotoShop 6.0, Adobe/Acrobat 4.0.; Classified Hardware – APP/Mac; Classified Printers – XEROX; Layout software – QPS/QuarkXPress 4.1, 4-Adobe/Acrobat, 6-Adobe/Photoshop.; Display Hardware – APP/Mac PRODUCTION: Pagination software – QPS/QuarkXPress

Section II

U.S. and Canadian Daily Newspaper Groups and Special Services Dailies

U.S. NEWSPAPER GROUPS

A

A. H. Belo Corp.–400 S. Record St., Dallas, TX, 75202, USA; tel (214) 977-6606; fax (214) 977-6603; e-mail blc@belo.com; web site www.belo.com
Est.: 1842
Chrmn. of the Bd./CEO – Robert W. Decherd; Exec. Vice Pres., Law & Government/Sec. – Guy H. Kerr; Exec. Vice Pres. – Donald F. (Skip) Cass; Sr. Vice Pres./CFO – Alison K. Engel; Sr. Vice Pres./Chief Accounting Officer – Carey Hendrickson; Sr. Vice Pres., Bus. Devel. – Edward Olkkola; Vice Pres., Techn. – W. Craig Harper; Daily Newspapers: The Press-Enterprise, Riverside, CA; Al Dia, Dallas, TX; La Prensa, Riverside, CA; The Providence Journal, Providence, RI; The Dallas Morning News, Dallas, TX; Denton Record-Chronicle, Denton, TX;

ASP Westward LP–9800 Mounty Pyramid Court, Suite 100, Englewood, CO, 80112, USA; tel 303-566-4100; fax 303-797-1909; web site www.ourcoloradonews.com
Est.: 2000
President & CEO – Jim Diaz;Daily Newspapers: Courier, Conroe, TX; Pasadena Citizen, Pasadena, TX; The Englewood Herald, Littleton, CO; The Highlands Ranch Herald, Littleton, CO; The Littleton Independent, Littleton, CO; Douglas County News Press, Castle Rock, CO; Pikes Peak Courier View, Woodland Park, CO; Elbert County News, Castle Rock, CO; Tri-Lakes Tribune, Woodland Park, CO; Ute Pass Courier, Woodland Park, CO; The Atlanta Citizens Journal, Atlanta, TX; Big Sandy & Hawkins Journal and Tri-Area News, Big Sandy, TX; Bowie County Citizens Tribune, New Boston, TX; Panola Watchman, Carthage, TX; Cleveland Advocate, Cleveland, TX; The Bee, Daingerfield, TX; De Kalb News, New Boston, TX; Edgewood Enterprise, Edgewood, TX; Friendswood Journal, Pearland, TX; Gladewater Mirror, Gladewater, TX; The Grand Saline Sun, Grand Saline, TX; The Waller County News-Citizen, Hempstead, TX; The Lindale News & Times, Lindale, TX; Cass County Sun, Linden, TX; Mineola Monitor, Mineola, TX; Pearland Journal, Pearland, TX; The Pittsburg Gazette, Pittsburg, TX; Wood County Democrat, Quitman, TX; Pasadena Broadcaster, Pasadena, TX; The Exchange News, Houston, TX; Red River Review, New Boston, TX; Kingwood Observer, Humble, TX; Cass County Shopper, Linden, TX; Panola Shopper, Carthage, TX; Clear Lake Extra, Webster, TX; Courier Extra, Woodland Park, CO; The Citizen, Webster, TX;

Advance Publications, Inc.–950 Fingerboard Rd., Staten Island, NY, 10305, USA; tel (718) 981-1234; fax (718) 981-1456; web site www.advance.net
Chrmn. of the Bd. – S.I. Newhouse; Pres. – Donald E. Newhouse; Pub., Staten Island Advance – Caroline Diamond Harrison; Daily Newspapers: Bayonne Journal, Jersey City, NJ; Kearny Journal, Jersey City, NJ; Secaucus Journal, Jersey City, NJ; Waterfront Journal, Jersey City, NJ; The Birmingham News, Birmingham, AL; The Huntsville Times, Huntsville, AL; Press-Register, Mobile, AL; Times-Picayune, New Orleans, LA; The Republican, Springfield, MA; The Ann Arbor News, Ann Arbor, MI; The Bay City Times, Bay City, MI; The Flint Journal, Flint, MI; The Grand Rapids Press, Grand Rapids, MI; Jackson Citizen Patriot, Jackson, MI; Kalamazoo Gazette, Kalamazoo, MI; The Muskegon Chronicle, Muskegon, MI; The Saginaw News, Saginaw, MI; The Mississippi Press, Pascagoula, MS; The News of Cumberland County, Bridgeton, NJ; The Jersey Journal, Jersey City, NJ; The Star-Ledger, Newark, NJ; Today's Sunbeam, Salem, NJ; The Times, Trenton, NJ; The Gloucester County Times, Woodbury, NJ; Staten Island Advance, Staten Island, NY; The Post-Standard, Syracuse, NY; The Plain Dealer, Cleveland, OH; The Oregonian, Portland, OR; The Express-Times, Easton, PA; The Patriot-News, Harrisburg, PA; The Advance-Progess, Vidalia, GA; Ada-Cascade-Forest Hills Advance, Jenison, MI; North West Advance, Jenison, MI; The Burton News, Flint, MI; The Community Journal, Flint, MI; Davison Flagstaff, Flint, MI; East Grand Rapids Cadence, Jenison, MI; The Flushing Observer, Flint, MI; Grand Blanc News, Flint, MI; Kentwood Advance, Jenison, MI; Northeast Advance, Jenison, MI; Sparta-Kent City Advance, Jenison, MI; Penasee Globe, Jenison, MI; Wyoming Advance, Jenison, MI; The News, Belvidere, NJ; Cranford Chronicle, New Providence, NJ; Cranford Chronicle, Clark, NJ; The Star Gazette, Flemington, NJ; Hunterdon County Democrat, Flemington, NJ; Metuchen/Edison Review, Somerville, NJ; Piscataway Review, Somerville, NJ; The Reporter, Somerville, NJ; Somerset Messenger-Gazette, Somerville, NJ; South Plainfield Reporter, Somerville, NJ; Independent Press, New Providence, NJ; Herald & Dispatch, New Providence, NJ; Suburban News, Clark, NJ; Record Press, Clark, NJ; West Geauga Sun, Cleveland, OH; The Sun, Cleveland, OH; The Sun Press, Cleveland, OH; Bedford Sun Banner, Valley View, OH; The News Sun, Cleveland, OH; The Sun Courier, Cleveland, OH; Brooklyn Sun Journal, Cleveland, OH; Brunswick Sun Times, Berea, OH; Chagrin Herald Sun, Cleveland, OH; Sun Scoop Journal, Beachwood, OH; Euclid Sun Journal, Cleveland, OH; Garfield-Maple Sun, Cleveland, OH; Lakewood Sun Post, Olmsted, OH; The Sun Messenger, Cleveland, OH; The Medina Sun, Cleveland, OH; Sun Herald, Cleveland, OH; Nordonia Hills Sun, Cleveland, OH; Sun Banner Pride, Cleveland, OH; Parma Sun Post, Cleveland, OH; Solon Herald Sun, Cleveland, OH; The Sun Star, Cleveland, OH; The Twinsburg Sun, Cleveland, OH; Wadsworth Sun Banner, Medina, OH; West Side Sun News, Cleveland, OH; Hillsboro Argus, Hillsboro, OR; Duncannon Record, New Bloomfield, PA; Juniata Sentinel, Mifflintown, PA; Perry County Times, New Bloomfield, PA; The News-Sun, New Bloomfield, PA; Advantage, Vidalia, GA; Extra Home Shopper, Flint, MI; Chronicle Shopping Guide, Muskegon, MI; El Nuevo Hudson, Jersey City, NJ; West Akron Sun, Cleveland, OH; The Swartz Creek News, Flint, MI; Montrose Sun, Cleveland, OH; Grand Valley Advance, Jenison, MI; The Flint Township News, Flint, MI; The Fenton Press, Flint, MI; Warren Reporter, Hackettstown, NJ;

Aiken Communications, Inc.–326 Rutland Dr. NW, Aiken, SC, 29801-4010, USA; tel (803) 648-2311; fax (803) 648-6052; web site www.aikenstandard.com
Pub. – Scott B. Hunter;Daily Newspapers: Aiken Standard, Aiken, SC; The Star, North Augusta, SC;
Note: The Aiken Communications, Inc., Davie County Publishing, Inc., Georgetown Communications, Inc., Island Publications, Inc. and the Summerville Communications, Inc. are subsidiaries of the Evening Post Community Publications Group, Inc. and together own fou

American Community Newspapers LLC–10917 Valley View Rd., Eden Prairie, MN, 55344-3730, USA; tel (952) 392-6854; fax (952) 941-3588; web site www.americancommunitynewspapers.com
Est.: 1998
CEO – Gene Carr; CFO – David Kosofsky; Cor. Controller – Richard D. Hendrickson; Daily Newspapers: Delaware News, Columbus, OH; Ramsey County Sun Focus, Columbia Heights, MN; Mounds View/New Brighton/St. Anthony Sun Focus, Eden Prairie, MN; Stillwater Gazette, Stillwater, MN; McKinney Courier-Gazette, McKinney, TX; Plano Star Courier, Plano, TX; Apple Valley-Rosemount Sun-Current, Bloomington, MN; Brooklyn Center/Brooklyn Park Sun-Post, Eden Prairie, MN; Brooklyn Park Sun-Post, Robbinsdale, MN; Burnsville/Savage Sun-Current, Eden Prairie, MN; Lakeville Sun-Current, Eden Prairie, MN; Robbinsdale/Crystal/New Hope/Golden Valley Sun-Post, Eden Prairie, MN; Eagan/Apple Valley/Rosemount Sun Current, Eden Prairie, MN; Eden Prairie Sun-Current, Eden Prairie, MN; Edina Sun-Current, Eden Prairie, MN; Excelsior/Shorewood/Chanhasssen Sun Sailor, Eden Prairie, MN; Columbia Heights/Fridley Sun Focus, Eden Prairie, MN; Hopkins Sun-Sailor, Eden Prairie, MN; Minnetonka Sun-Sailor, Eden Prairie, MN; Monticello Times, Monticello, MN; New Hope-Golden Valley Sun-Post, Robbinsdale, MN; Norwood Young America Times, Eden Prairie, MN; Plymouth Sun-Sailor, Minnetonka, MN; Richfield Sun-Current, Eden Prairie, MN; St. Louis Park Sun-Sailor, Eden Prairie, MN; Wayzata/Orono/Long Lake Sun-Sailor, Eden Prairie, MN; West St. Paul-Mendota Heights Sun-Current, Eden Prairie, MN; The Booster, Columbus, OH; Bexley News, Columbus, OH; The Times, Columbus, OH; Dublin News, Columbus, OH; Gahanna News, Columbus, OH; German Village Gazette, Columbus, OH; Tri-Village News, Columbus, OH; Grove City News, Columbus, OH; Hilliard Northwest News, Columbus, OH; New Albany News, Columbus, OH; Northland News, Columbus, OH; Northwest Columbus News, Columbus, OH; The Pickerington Times-Sun, Columbus, OH; Olentangy Valley News, Columbus, OH; Reynoldsburg News, Columbus, OH; The Upper Arlington News, Columbus, OH; Westerville News & Public Opinion, Columbus, OH; Westland News, Columbus, OH; Whitehall News, Columbus, OH; Worthington News, Columbus, OH; The Allen American, Plano, TX; Celina Record, Mckinney, TX; The Frisco Enterprise, McKinney, TX; Little Elm Journal, Frisco, TX; Arlington Sun Gazette, Springfield, VA; Leesburg Today, Leesburg, VA; Sun Gazette, Springfield, VA; Monticello Shopper, Monticello, MN; Stillwater Gazette Valley Life, Stillwater, MN; The Big Walnut News, Columbus, OH; The Mesquite News, Mesquite, TX; Rowlett Lakeshore Times, Mesquite, TX; The Penny Saver, McKinney, TX;

American Consolidated Media–212 E. Liberty St., Dallas, TX, 75247-4932; tel (214) 691-4066; fax (214) 691-4086
Est.: 1998
Pres./COO – Randy Cope; Sr. Vice Pres./CFO – Denise Lytle; Vice Pres., Accounting – Bob Wallace; Dir., Payroll/HR – Diana Deluna;
Daily Newspapers: The People's Defender, West Union, OH; Enon Messenger, Enon, OH; Miami County Advocate, Troy, OH; Pikaway County Paper, Circleville, OH; The County Shopper, Hillsboro, OH; Community Shopper, Jackson, OH; Peninsula News, Marblehead, OH; The Star-Democrat, Easton, MD; Cecil Whig, Elkton, MD; The Daily Tribune, Hibbing, MN; Mesabi Daily News, Virginia, MN; The Athens Messenger, Athens, OH; Bellevue Gazette, Bellevue, OH; Herald, Circleville, OH; The Delaware Gazette, Delaware, OH; Fairborn Daily Herald, Xenia, OH; The Galion Inquirer, Galion, OH; Daily Advocate, Greenville, OH; Times-Gazette, Hillsboro, OH; Logan Daily News, Logan, OH; The Madison Press, London, OH; Piqua Daily Call, Piqua, OH; The Sidney Daily News, Sidney, OH; Troy Daily News, Troy, OH; Urbana Daily Citizen, Urbana, OH; The Times Bulletin, Van Wert, OH; Record Herald, Washington Court House, OH; Wilmington News Journal, Wilmington, OH; Gazette News-Current, Xenia, OH; Miami News-Record, Miami, OK; Alice Echo-News Journal, Alice, TX; Edinburg Review, Edinburg, TX; Stephenville Empire-Tribune, Stephenville, TX; Waxahachie Daily Light, Waxahachie, TX; The Daily Press, Ashland, WI; Newark Post, Newark, DE; The Times Record, Denton, MD; Kent County News, Chestertown, MD; The Dorchester Star, Cambridge, MD; Queen Anne's Record Observer, Centreville, MD; The Avenue News, Essex, MD; Gladwin County Record, Gladwin, MI; The Pilot-Independent, Walker, MN; The Chisholm Tribune Press, Chisholm, MN; Cook County News-Herald, Grand Marais, MN; Ada Herald, Ada, OH; Amherst News-Times, Amherst, OH; Vandalia Drummer News, Vandalia, OH; Centerville-Bellbrook Times, Kettering, OH; The Clyde Enterprise, Clyde, OH; Putnam County Vidette/Pandora Times, Columbus Grove, OH; Fulton County Expositor, Wauseon, OH; The News Democrat, Georgetown, OH; Huber Heights Courier, Vandalia, OH; The Jackson County Times-Journal, Jackson, OH; Kettering-Oakwood Times, Kettering, OH; The Mechanicsburg Telegram, Urbana, OH; The Morrow County Sentinel, Mount Gilead, OH; The Tribune, London, OH; New Carlisle Sun, New Carlisle, OH; Perry County Tribune, New Lexington, OH; Ottawa County Exponent, Oak Harbor, OH; Oberlin News-Tribune, Oberlin, OH; Plain City Advocate, London, OH; Community Common, Portsmouth, OH; The Register-Herald, Eaton, OH; Putnam County Sentinel, Ottawa, OH; Englewood Independent, Englewood, OH; Ripley Bee, Ripley, OH; The Sunbury News, Sunbury, OH; Swanton Enterprise, Swanton, OH; Sunday Record Herald, Tipp City, OH; Vinton County Courier, McArthur, OH; News Watchman, Waverly, OH; Wellington Enterprise, Wellington, OH; Sunday Record Herald, Tipp City, OH; The Ballinger Ledger, Ballinger, TX; Nueces County Record-Star, Robstown, TX; The Freer Press, Freer, TX; The Hearne Democrat, Hearne, TX; Valley Town Crier, McAllen, TX; The Midlothian Mirror, Midlothian, TX; Ellis County Chronicle, Waxahachie, TX; Rio Grande Herald, Rio Grande, TX; The Winters Enterprise, Winters, TX; Sawyer County Record, Hayward, WI; Park Falls Herald, Park Falls, WI; The Bee, Phillips, WI; Spooner Advocate, Spooner, WI; The Bayfield County Journal, Washburn, WI; The Bargaineer, Aberdeen, MD; Herald-Review/Manney's Shopper, Grand Rapids, MN; Manney's Shopper, Hibbing, MN; Co-Pilot, Walker, MN; Gazette Extra, Bellevue, OH; The Scoop, Kettering, OH; Weekly Ad-Visor, Galion, OH; Greene County Shopper, Xenia, OH; Tribune Shopping News, New Lexington, OH; Shopping News, Oberlin, OH; Miami News Record Plus, Miami, OK; The Fannin County Special, Bonham, TX; Bargain Book, Brownsville, TX; Extra Shopper, Phillips, WI; Evergreen Shopping Guide, Spooner, WI; The Bay Times, Stevensville, MD; Trading Post, Alice, TX; Cross Timbers Trading Post, Stephenville, TX; Daily Light Shopper, Waxahachie, TX; Grand Rapids Herald-Review, Grand Rapids, MN; Hayward Four Seasons Shopper, Hayward, WI; Ennis Journal, Waxahachie, TX; Springboro Sun, Kettering, OH; Alvarado Post, Waxahachie, TX; Premont Journal, Alice, TX; Franklin Advocate, Hear
Note: American Consolidated Media is owned by Macquarie Media Group (MMG).

American Hometown Publishing–110 3rd Ave. N., Franklin, TN, 37064-2506, USA; tel (615) 599-8751; fax (615) 599-8752; e-mail bsmith@americanhometownpublishing.com; web site www.americanhometownpublishing.com
Vice President HR – Stephanie L. Jameson; President & COO – Brian Smith; Daily Newspapers: Blackwell Journal-Tribune, Blackwell, OK; Guthrie News Leader, Guthrie, OK; Brownsville States-Graphic, Brownsville, TN; Tri-City Reporter, Dyer, TN; Chester County Independent, Henderson, TN; The Chronicle, Humboldt, TN; The Leader, Covington, TN; The Herald Gazette, Trenton, TN; The Wayne County News, Waynesboro, TN; The Post, Big Stone Gap, VA; Dickenson Star, Clintwood, VA; The Coalfield Progress, Norton, VA;

American-Republican Inc–PO Box 2090, Waterbury, CT, 06722-2090; tel –(203) 574-3636; web site www.rep-am.com

The Anschutz Co.–555 17th St., Ste. 2400, Denver, CO, 80202-3941, USA; tel (303) 298-1000; fax (303) 298-8881
Chrmn./CEO – Philip F. Anschutz; Pres./CEO – Cannon Y. Harvey; CEO, Clarity Media Grp. – Ryan McKibben; CFO – Wayne A. Barnes; Exec. Vice Pres./CFO, Clarity Media Grp. – Frederick Anderson; Daily Newspapers: Examiner, San Francisco, CA; The Washington Examiner, Springfield, VA;

Arkansas Democrat-Gazette–121 E. Capitol Ave., Little Rock, AR, 72201, USA; tel (501) 378-3400; fax (501) 378-3591; e-mail news@ardemgaz.com; web site www.arkansasonline.com
Pub. – Walter E. Hussman; Vice Pres., Opns. – Lynn Hamilton; Vice Pres./Gen. Mgr. – Paul R. Smith; Controller – Terrell Strickland; Mgr., Accounting – Adam Jordan; Bus. Mgr. – Judy Nethercutt; Mgr., Data Processing/Typeset – Clay Carson; Mgr., Personnel – Kay Brewer; Adv. Dir. – John Mobbs; Adv. Dir., Classified – Scott Stine; Adv. Mgr., Classified Inside Sales – Katie Nikpour; Adv. Mgr., Recruitment – Gary Troutman; Adv. Mgr., Retail Sales – David Brown; Adv. Mgr., Retail Sales – Carol Dawson; Adv. Supvr., Customer Sales – Phyllis White; Adv. Supvr., Opns. – Gail Newton; Dir., Promo. – Estel Jeffery; Circ. Dir. – Larry Graham; Exec. Ed. – Griffin Smith; Deputy Ed. – Frank Fellone; Daily Newspapers: Benton County Daily Record, Bentonville, AR; Northwest Arkansas Times, Fayetteville, AR; The Weekly Vista, Bella Vista, AR; Decatur Herald, Decatur, AR; White River Journal, Des Arc, AR; Gentry Courier-Journal, Gentry, AR; Gravette News Herald, Gravette, AR; The Times of Northeast Benton County, Pea Ridge, AR; Hometown News, Rogers, AR; The Herald-Leader, Siloam Springs, AR;
Note: Arkansas Democrat-Gazette owns two daily newspapers as well at eight weekly newspapers all located in Arkansas.

Ashland Publishing Co. LLC–40 E. 2nd St., Ashland, OH, 44805, U.S.; tel (419) 281-0581; fax (419) 281-5591; web site www.times-gazette.com
Group: Dix Communications
Est.: 1850
Publisher – Troy Dix; Editor and General Manager – Ted Daniels; Sports Editor – Doug Haidet; Special Projects Editor – Jarred Opatz; Advertising Director – Jason Gwinnup; Circulation Director – Deborah Boreman; Business Manager – Lynnette Cross; Composing Manager – Deborah Iceman; Daily Newspapers: The Review, Alliance, OH; Ashland Times-Gazette, Ashland, OH; The Loudonville Times, Loudonville, OH; Mohican Area Shopper, Ashland, OH; The Muskokan, Bracebridge, ON;
Note: Ashland Publishing Co. LLC is part of Dix Communications which is owned by the Wooster Republican Printing Co. Dix also owns two television stations in Montana and seven radio stations. Through it's subsidiaries, Alliance Publishing Co. LLC, Ashland Publ

ASP Westward LP–523 N Sam Houston Pkwy East, Houston, TX, 77060; tel (866)446-5979; web site www.hcnonline.com

Auburn Journal, Inc.–1030 High St., Auburn, CA, 95603-4707, USA; tel (530) 885-5656; fax (530) 885-7235; e-mail ajournal@goldcountrymedia.com; web site www.auburnjournal.com\
Group: U.S. Suburban Press, Inc.
Est.: 1872
Pub. – Tony Hazarian; Bus. Dir. – Staci Orlando; Bus. Opns. Mgr. – Sandy Stockton; Adv. Dir., Classified – Suzanne Stevenson; Adv. Mgr. – Beth O'Brien; Circulation Dir. – Kelly Leibold; Ed. – Deric Rothe; Bus./Finance Ed. – Gloria Young; News Ed. – Michelle Miller-Carl; Sports Ed. – Todd Mordhorst; Gen. Mgr., Print Div. – Jim Easterly; Prodn. Mgr., Post Press – Randy Jaworski; Prodn. Mgr., Pressroom – Keith Bowen; Prodn. Supvr., Imaging – Mary Hazelwood; Pub. – Tommy Hazarian; Daily Newspapers: Auburn Journal, Auburn, CA; Colfax Record, Colfax, CA;
Note: Auburn Journal, Inc. is owned by Brehm Communications Inc. Through it's subsidiaries, Democrat Co., Gull Communications, Hi-Desert Publishing Co., Inc., News West Publishing Company Inc., Penny Power Publications Inc., Placer Community Newspapers, Inc. a

B

Bangor Publishing Company–PO Box 1329, Bangor, ME, 04402-1329; tel (207) 990-8000; web site www.bangordailynews.com

Ray Barnes Newspapers, Inc.–201 E. Columbus St., Kenton, OH, 43326-1583; tel (419) 674-4066; fax (419) 673-1125; web site www.kentontimes.com
Chrmn. of the Bd. – Jack L. Barnes; Pres. – Charles Barnes; Daily Newspapers: Elwood Call-Leader, Elwood, IN; Tipton County Tribune, Tipton, IN; The Kenton Times, Kenton, OH; The Daily Chief-Union, Upper Sandusky, OH; Alexandria Times-Tribune, Alexandria, IN; Leader Tribune-Review West, Tipton, IN;

Beacon Communications–1944 Warwick Avenue, Warwick, RI, 02889; tel (401) 732-3100; web site www.warwickonline.com

Bliss Communications Inc–PO Box 5001, Janesville, WI, 53547-5001; tel (608) 754-3311; web site www.blissnet.net

Bliss Communications, Inc.–One S. Parker Dr., Janesville, WI, 53545-3928, USA; tel (608) 754-3311; fax (608) 754-8038; e-mail sbliss@gazetteextra.com; web site www.blissnet.net
Est.: 1845
Pres./Chrmn./CEO – Sidney H. Bliss; CFO – Robert Lisser; Vice Pres., HR – Mary Jo Villa; Controller – Pam Schmoldt; Vice Pres., Ad Sales – Daniel J. White; Vice Pres., News – Scott W. Angus; Vice Pres., Technical Servs. – Charles A. Flynn; Daily Newspapers: The Janesville Gazette, Janesville, WI; EagleHerald, Marinette, WI; The Monroe Times, Monroe, WI; Delavan Enterprise, Delavan, WI; Janesville Messenger, Janesville, WI; Stateline News, Beloit, WI; Freeport Shopping News, Freeport, IL; Range Shopper, Ironwood, MI; The Jotter, Janesville, WI; Eagle Herald Sunday, Marinette, WI; Stateline Buyer's Guide, Monroe, WI; Wednesday/Sunday Messenger, Janesville, WI; Walworth County Shopper-Advertiser/Sunday Shopper, Delavan, WI;
Note: Bliss Communications Inc. also owns six AM-FM radio stations.

Block Communications, Inc.–3101 N. US Hwy. 30, Toledo, OH, 43604; tel (419) 724-6212; fax (419) 724-6167; e-mail info@blockcommunications.com; web site www.blockcommunications.com
Est.: 1900
Chrmn. – Allan Block; Pres. – Gary Blair; Daily Newspapers: The Blade, Toledo, OH; Pittsburgh Post-Gazette, Pittsburgh, PA;
Note: Block Communications Inc. is a privately held media company which operates cable television in Toledo and Sandusky, Ohio, four television stations, a telecom business and a residential security business. Block Communications also owns The Blade located i

BlueLine Media Holdings–2419 Maple Grove Dr., Neenah, WI, 54956-6100; tel (715) 526-7016; fax (715) 524-2212; web site www.bluelinemediaholdings.com

Pres./CEO/Pub., The Shawano Leader – Paul Seveska; Group Controller – Bernadette Hollinger; Vice Pres., Prodn./Techn. – Robert Perini; Daily Newspapers: The Daily News, Rhinelander, WI; Shawano Leader, Shawano, WI; Shawano Shopper, Shawano, WI;

Boone Newspapers, Inc.–15222 Freeman's Bend Rd., Northport, AL, 35475-3800, USA; tel (205) 330-4100; fax (205) 330-4140; e-mail bni@boonenewspapers.com; web site www.boonenewspapers.com
Chrmn. of the Bd./CEO/Dir. – James B. Boone; Pres./COO – Todd H. Carpenter; Sr. Vice Pres. – William T. Beckner; Sr. Vice Pres. – David D. Churchill; Vice Pres. – Jason Cannon; Vice Pres. – Joseph C. Davis; Vice Pres. – Michele Cox Gerlach; Vice Pres. – Michael R. Kelley; Vice Pres. – Dennis M. Palmer; Vice Pres. – Joseph C. Davis; Daily Newspapers: Marengo County Shoppers Guide, Demopolis, AL; Greene/Hale County Shoppers Guide, Demopolis, AL; Wilcox County Shoppers Guide, Demopolis, AL; Clarke County Shoppers Guide, Demopolis, AL; Atmore Advance, Atmore, AL; Alexander City Outlook, Alexander City, AL; Andalusia Star-News, Andalusia, AL; The Selma Times-Journal, Selma, AL; The Messenger, Troy, AL; Dowagiac Daily News, Dowagiac, MI; Niles Daily Star, Niles, MI; Albert Lea Tribune, Albert Lea, MN; Austin Daily Herald, Austin, MN; Fergus Falls Daily Journal, Fergus Falls, MN; The Natchez Democrat, Natchez, MS; The Ironton Tribune, Ironton, OH; Suffolk News-Herald, Suffolk, VA; Atmore Advance, Atmore, AL; The Brewton Standard, Brewton, AL; The Clanton Advertiser, Clanton, AL; Shelby County Reporter, Columbiana, AL; Dadeville Record, Alexander City, AL; Demopolis Times, Demopolis, AL; Eclectic Observer, Wetumpka, AL; Lowndes Signal, Fort Deposit, AL; The Greenville Advocate, Greenville, AL; Hartselle Enquirer, Hartselle, AL; The Luverne Journal, Luverne, AL; Madison County Record, Madison, AL; Franklin County Times, Russellville, AL; Messenger Bonus, Troy, AL; The Post-Searchlight, Bainbridge, GA; Cassopolis Vigilant, Niles, MI; Edwardsburg Argus, Niles, MI; Gates County Index, Gatesville, NC; Roanoke-Chowan News Herald, Ahoskie, NC; The Ironton Tribune Extra, Ironton, OH; The Tidewater News, Franklin, VA; Talla-Coosa Advertiser, Alexander City, AL; Escambia Advertiser, Atmore, AL; The Extra, Clanton, AL; Shoppers Guide, Demopolis, AL; Butler Express, Greenville, AL; Hartselle Shopping Guide, Hartselle, AL; Franklin County Times Plus, Russellville, AL; Dollar Saver, Selma, AL; Shelby County Shopping News, Columbiana, AL; Post-Searchlight Extra, Bainbridge, GA; The Leader, Niles, MI; Weekender, Fergus Falls, MN; Tribune Shopping News, Albert Lea, MN; Freeborn County Shopper, Albert Lea, MN; Mower County Shopper, Austin, MN; Miss-Lou Buyers Guide, Natchez, MS; Andalusia Star News-Extra, Andalusia, AL; Herald Shopping News, Austin, MN; The Roanoke-Chowan's Shopper Weekly, Ahoskie, NC; Butler County News, Greenville, AL;

Booth Newspapers, Inc.–155 Michigan St. NW, Grand Rapids, MI, 49503-2302; tel (616) 222-5825; fax (616) 222-5225; web site www.boothnewspapers.com
Pres. – Donald E. Newhouse; Sales Mgr. – Kim Brown; Sales Mgr. – Steve Davis; Classified Mgr. – Michelle Covington; Daily Newspapers: The Ann Arbor News, Ann Arbor, MI; The Bay City Times, Bay City, MI; The Flint Journal, Flint, MI; Jackson Citizen Patriot, Jackson, MI; Kalamazoo Gazette, Kalamazoo, MI; The Muskegon Chronicle, Muskegon, MI; The Saginaw News, Saginaw, MI;

BOOTH-MICHIGAN NEWSPAPER GROUP–155 Michigan St. NW, Grand Rapids, MI, 49503; tel 616-222-5825

Bradford Publishing Co.–43 Main St., Bradford, PA, 16701; tel (814) 368-3173; fax (814) 362-6510; e-mail info@bradfordera.com; web site www.bradfordera.com

Pres. – John H. Satterwhite;Daily Newspapers: Olean Times Herald, Olean, NY; Salamanca Press, Salamanca, NY; The Bradford Era, Bradford, PA;

Brehm Communications, Inc.–16644 W. Bernardo Dr., Ste. 300, San Diego, CA, 92127, USA; tel (858) 451-6200; fax (858) 451-3814; e-mail debbiel@brehmmail.com; web site www.brehmcommunications.com
Est.: 1919
Chairman of the Board – W.J. Brehm; President – William Brehm; Controller – Jeff Johnson; Vice President / General Manager – Thomas Taylor; Executive Assistant – Debbie Lindsay; Daily Newspapers: Clippin' the River, Bullhead City, AZ; El Dorado Hills Telegraph, Folsom, CA; Mohave Valley Daily News, Bullhead City, AZ; Auburn Journal, Auburn, CA; Daily Republican Register, Mount Carmel, IL; Princeton Daily Clarion, Princeton, IN; The Daily Democrat, Fort Madison, IA; Daily Gate City, Keokuk, IA; The Wickenburg Sun, Wickenburg, AZ; Big Bear Grizzly, Big Bear Lake, CA; Colfax Record, Colfax, CA; Crestline Courier-News, Crestline, CA; Folsom Telegraph, Folsom, CA; Mountain News, Lake Arrowhead, CA; Lincoln News Messenger, Lincoln, CA; The Loomis News, Loomis, CA; Leader, Lucerne Valley, CA; Needles Desert Star, Needles, CA; The Placer Herald, Rocklin, CA; The Press-Tribune, Roseville, CA; Desert Trail, Twenty-Nine Palms, CA; Hi-Desert Star, Yucca Valley, CA; Donnellson Star, West Point, IA; West Point Bee, West Point, IA; Hancock County Journal-Pilot, Carthage, IL; Boonville Standard, Boonville, IN; Newburgh Chandler Register, Boonville, IN; Oakland City Journal, Princeton, IN; Laughlin Nevada Times, Laughlin, NV; Emery County Progress, Castle Dale, UT; Sun Advocate, Price, UT; The Richfield Reaper, Richfield, UT; Shopper News, Wickenburg, AZ; CoverStory, Auburn, CA; Market Place, Folsom, CA; Mountain Shopper, Lake Arrowhead, CA; Today, Princeton, IN; Warrick County Today, Boonville, IN; Des Moines County Shopper Spree, Burlington, IA; Bonny Buyer, West Point, IA; Observation Post, Yucca Valley, CA; Valley Views, Bullhead City, AZ; Grizzly Weekender, Big Bear Lake, CA; Bullhead City Booster, Bullhead City, AZ; Big Bear Shopper, Big Bear Lake, CA; Laughlin Entertainer, Bullhead City, AZ; The Gibson County Today Section, Princeton, IN;
Note: Subsidiaries: The Democrat Co.; Gull Communications, Inc.; Hi-Desert Publishing Co., Inc.; News West Publishing Company Inc.; Auburn Journal, Inc.; Penny Power Publications, Inc.; Placer Community Newspapers, Inc.; Princeton Publishing, Inc.; Mt. Carmel Register Co.; Warrick Publishing Co.,

Inc.;Wine Country Publications LLC

Bryan Publishing Co.–127 S. Walnut St., Bryan, OH, 43506-1718; tel (419) 636-1111; fax (419) 636-8937; e-mail news@bryantimes.com; web site www.bryantimes.com
Est.: 1949
Chrmn./Pres./Pub. – Christopher Cullis; Vice Pres./Gen. Mgr. – Thomas Voigt; Circ. Mgr. – Mark Keller; Daily Newspapers: The Bryan Times, Bryan, OH; Northwest Signal, Napoleon, OH; Montpelier Leader-Enterprise, Montpelier, OH; Countyline, Bryan, OH;
Note: Daily newspaper for Bryan and Williams County

Byrd Newspapers–231 S. Liberty St., Harrisonburg, VA, 22801, USA; tel (540) 574-6200; fax (540) 574-6299; web site www.dnronline.com or www.winchesterstar.com
Est.: 1896
Pub. – Thomas T. Byrd; Gen. Mgr. – Peter S. Yates; Daily Newspapers: Daily News-Record, Harrisonburg, VA; The Winchester Star, Winchester, VA; The Warren Sentinel, Front Royal, VA; Page News and Courier, Luray, VA; The Valley Banner, Elkton, VA; The Shenandoah Valley-Herald, Woodstock, VA; The Shenandoah Journal, Dayton, VA; The North Fork Journal, Broadway, VA;
Note: Byrd Newspapers owns Rockingham Publishing Co. , publisher of the Daily News-Record and The Winchester Evening Star. Inc, publisher of The Winchester (VA) Star. Several weekly newspapers are also included in the group.

C

California Newspapers Partnership–21860 Burbank Blvd., Ste. 200, Woodland Hills, CA, 91367, USA; tel (818) 713-3000; fax (818) 713-0057; web site www.dailynews.com
Pub./Pres. – Jack Klunder;Daily Newspapers: Chico Enterprise-Record, Chico, CA; Times-Standard, Eureka, CA; The Argus, Fremont, CA; The Daily Review, Hayward, CA; Lake County Record-Bee, Lakeport, CA; Marin Independent Journal, Novato, CA; The Oakland Tribune, Oakland, CA; Tri-Valley Herald/San Ramon Valley Herald, Pleasanton, CA; Daily News, Red Bluff, CA; San Mateo County Times, San Mateo, CA; Ukiah Daily Journal, Ukiah, CA; The Reporter, Vacaville, CA; Vallejo Times-Herald, Vallejo, CA; The Whittier Daily News, Whittier, CA; The Daily Democrat, Woodland, CA; Azusa Herald Highlander, West Covina, CA; Clear Lake Observer-American, Clear Lake, CA; Covina Press Courier Highlander, West Covina, CA; Diamond Bar Highlander, West Covina, CA; Fort Bragg Advocate-News, Fort Bragg, CA; Glendora Press Highlander, West Covina, CA; Hacienda Heights Highlander, West Covina, CA; La Puente Highlander, West Covina, CA; Milpitas Post, Milpitas, CA; Pacifica Tribune, Pacifica, CA; Paradise Post, Paradise, CA; Rowland Heights Highlander, West Covina, CA; San Dimas/La Verne Highlander, West Covina, CA; Walnut Highlander, West Covina, CA; West Covina Highlander, West Covina, CA; The Willits News, Willits, CA; Tri-City Weekly, Eureka, CA; Wave, Pacifica, CA; Hometown Shopper, Ukiah, CA; Weekly Star, Vacaville, CA; Fremont Bulletin, Milpitas, CA; Penny Slaver, Clearlake, CA; Times Standard Plus, Eureka, CA; Bee Smart Shopper, Lakeport, CA; On The Market, Eureka, CA;

Calkins Media–8400 Rte. 13, Levittown, PA, 19057-5198; tel (215) 949-4011; fax (215) 949-4021; web site www.phillyburbs.com
COO – Michael Scobey; Sr. Vice Pres. – Micheal White; Sec. to Pres. – Carolyn Crawford; Dir., Adv./Mktg. – Kim Noble; Dir., Information Servs. – Edward E. Emberger; Dir., Interactive Media – Robert R. Kellagher; Daily Newspapers: Burlington County Times, Willingboro, NJ; Beaver County Times, Beaver, PA; The Intelligencer, Doylestown, PA; Ellwood City Ledger, Ellwood City, PA; Bucks County Courier Times, Levittown, PA; Herald-Standard, Uniontown, PA; South Dade News Leader, Homestead, FL; Greene County Messenger, Waynesburg, PA; The Post, Willingboro, NJ;
Note: Calkins Media also owns and operates the ABC affiliate TV station in Sarasota, Florida.

Capital Newspapers–1901 Fish Hatchery Rd., Madison, WI, 53713-1248, USA; tel (608) 252-6200; fax (608) 252-6028; e-mail customerservice@madison.com; web site www.capitalnewspapers.com
Pres./Pub. – Clayton Frink; CFO – Pam Wells; Chrmn., Board – John H. Lussier; Treasurer – Philip Blake; Ed. – Paul Fanlund; Daily Newspapers: Wisconsin Reminder Extra, Mauston, WI; Shopper View, Beaver Dam, WI; Baraboo News-Republic, Baraboo, WI; Daily Citizen, Beaver Dam, WI; The Capital Times, Madison, WI; Wisconsin State Journal, Madison, WI; Daily Register, Portage, WI; Columbus Journal, Columbus, WI; Juneau County Star-Times, Mauston, WI; Reedsburg Times-Press, Reedsburg, WI; Neighbors, Waupun, WI; Wisconsin Dells Events, Portage, WI; Monday-Mini, Beaver Dam, WI; Tri-County, Beaver Dam, WI; Shopping Reminder, Columbus, WI; Wisconsin Reminder, Mauston, WI; Shopper Stopper, Portage, WI; Shopper Stopper Extra, Portage, WI; The Leader Advantage, Shawano, WI; Monday Marketeer, Waupun, WI; Sauk Prairie Eagle, Sauk City, WI;
Note: Capital Newspapers is partially owned by Lee Enterprises Inc. Capital Newspapers owns five daily newspapers and 16 non-daily publications.

Chesapeake Publishing Corp.–601 N. Bridge St., Elkton, MD, 21921-5307, USA; tel (410) 398-3311; fax (410) 398-4044; web site www.chespub.com
Pres./CEO – Thomas F. Bradlee; Treasurer – Stanley Wallace; Exec. Asst. – Nancy J. Crawford; @RecordBody:**Note:** Chesapeake Publishing Corp. owns 16 monthly publications, two specialty publications as well as four business ledgers. Chesapeake also owns Chesapeake Direct (mailing services), two web printing operations and one commerical printing plant.

Cleveland Newspapers, Inc.–525 Office Park Dr., Birmingham, AL, 35223-2413, USA; tel (205) 870-1684; fax (205) 870-9531
Est.: 1956
Chrmn. of Bd./Vice Pres. – C. Lee Walls; Pres./CEO – C. Lee Walls; Daily Newspapers: Daily Mountain Eagle, Jasper, AL; The Daily Tribune News, Cartersville, GA; Abilene Reflector-Chronicle, Abilene, KS; The Bolivar Commercial, Cleveland, MS; The Monett Times, Monett, MO; Cleveland Daily Banner, Cleveland, TN; Herald-Citizen, Cookeville, TN; The Herald-Tribune, Cartersville, GA; Chatsworth Times, Chatsworth, GA; St. John Valley Times, Madawaska, ME;

Community Media Group–805 S. Logan St., West Frankfort, IL, 62896, USA; tel (618) 937-6412; fax (618) 932-3848; web site www.communitymediagroup.com
Chrmn./Pres./CEO – Larry J. Perrotto; Vice Chrmn. – John H. Satterwhite; Exec. Vice Pres. – John D. Perrotto; Exec. Vice Pres. – Mark J. Perrotto; Exec. Vice Pres. – Joan R. Williams; Vice Pres. – Paul Barrett; VP Accounting – Kristen Ahlberg; Daily Newspapers: Dollar Saver, Atlantic, IA; Southwest Iowa Shopper, Atlantic, IA; JP Trader, Oelwein, IA; Dollar Saver, Wellsboro, PA; Times-Republic, Watseka, IL; News-Times, Hartford City, IN; Herald Journal, Monticello, IN; Republican, Rensselaer, IN; The News-Gazette, Winchester, IN; Atlantic News-Telegraph, Atlantic, IA; The Register, Oelwein, IA; Cedar Valley Daily Times, Vinton, IA; Finger Lakes Times, Geneva, NY; Audubon County Advocate Journal, Audubon, IA; Bremer County Independent, Waverly, IA; Independence Bulletin-Journal, Independence, IA; Waverly Democrat, Waverly, IA; The Chronicle, Hoopeston, IL; Brook Reporter, Rensselaer, IN; Kankakee Valley Post-News, Demotte, IN; Fountain County Neighbor, Attica, IN; The Jackson County Banner, Brownstown, IN; The Newton County Enterprise, Kentland, IN; Remington Press, Rensselaer, IN; Lafayette Leader, Lafayette, IN; The Review-Republican, Williamsport, IN; Iosco County News Herald, East Tawas, MI; Oscoda Press, Oscoda, MI; Potter Leader-Enterprises, Coudersport, PA; Port Allegany Reporter-Argus, Coudersport, PA; The Wellsboro Gazette, Wellsboro, PA; Free Press-Courier, Westfield, PA; The Extra, Hoopeston, IL; Times-Republic Spirit Shopping Guide, Watseka, IL; Messenger, Attica, IN; Indiana Spirit, Kentland, IN; Action Plus Shopper, Rensselaer, IN; Shoppers' News, Rensselaer, IN; The Reminder, Monticello, IN; Shopper's Reminder, Oelwein, IA; Vinton Livewire, Vinton, IA; Bremer-Butler Super Shopper, Waverly, IA; The Reporter, Casey, IL; The Marshall Independent Choice, Marshall, IL; The Marketplace, Marshall, IL;
Note: Community Media Group owns ten daily newspapers, 23 weekly and 18 shopper publications.

Community Newspaper Co.–33 New York Ave., Framingham, MA, 01701-8857, USA; tel (781) 433-6700; fax (508) 626-3885; web site ^www.wickedlocal.com
Pres./CEO/Pub. – Kirk Davis; Vice Pres. Promos./Mktg. – Robin Lorenzen; Daily Newspapers: Metrowest Daily News, Framingham, MA; Milford Daily News, Milford, MA;

Community Newspaper Holdings, Inc.–445 Dexter Avenue, Suite 7000, Montgomery, AL, 36104, USA; tel (334) 293-5800; fax (334) 293-5913; web site www.cnhi.com
Pres./CEO – Donna Barrett; Executive VP/CFO – Lynn Pearson; Executive VP of Corporate Operations – F. Steve McPaul; VP of Revenue – Jack Robb; VP of Circulation – Linwood Pride; Executive VP/COO – Keith Blevins; Chief Digital Officer – Matthew Ipsan; Daily Newspapers: The News-Courier, Athens, AL; The Cullman Times, Cullman, AL; Americus Times-Recorder, Americus, GA; Cordele Dispatch, Cordele, GA; The Daily Citizen, Dalton, GA; The Union-Recorder, Milledgeville, GA; The Moultrie Observer, Moultrie, GA; Thomasville Times-Enterprise, Thomasville, GA; The Tifton Gazette, Tifton, GA; Valdosta Daily Times, Valdosta, GA; Commercial News, Danville, IL; Effingham Daily News, Effingham, IL; Register-News, Mount Vernon, IL; Daily Union, Shelbyville, IL; The Herald Bulletin, Anderson, IN; The Goshen News, Goshen, IN; Greensburg Daily News, Greensburg, IN; The Evening News, Jeffersonville, IN; Kokomo Tribune, Kokomo, IN; The Reporter, Lebanon, IN; Pharos-Tribune, Logansport, IN; Tribune, New Albany, IN; Rushville Republican, Rushville, IN; The Tribune Star, Terre Haute, IN; The Washington Times-Herald, Washington, IN; Ad Express & Daily Iowegian, Centerville, IA; Clinton Herald, Clinton, IA; Oskaloosa Herald, Oskaloosa, IA; The Ottumwa Courier, Ottumwa, IA; The Daily Independent, Ashland, KY; Times-Tribune, Corbin, KY; Glasgow Daily Times, Glasgow, KY; The Richmond Register, Richmond, KY; The Commonwealth-Journal, Somerset, KY; The Cumberland Times-News, Cumberland, MD; Gloucester Daily Times, Gloucester, MA; The Eagle-Tribune, North Andover, MA; The Daily News, Newburyport, MA; The Salem News, Beverly, MA; Record-Eagle, Traverse City, MI; The Free Press, Mankato, MN; Laurel Leader-Call, Laurel, MS; The Meridian Star, Meridian, MS; Picayune Item, Picayune, MS; The Joplin Globe, Joplin, MO; Union-Sun & Journal, Lockport, NY; The Journal-Register, Medina, NY; Niagara Gazette, Niagara Falls, NY; Tonawanda News, North Tonawanda, NY; The Daily Star, Oneonta, NY; Press-Republican, Plattsburgh, NY; The Daily Southerner, Tarboro, NC; Star Beacon, Ashtabula, OH; Ada Evening News, Ada, OK; The Express-Star, Chickasha, OK; The Claremore Daily Progress, Claremore, OK; The Duncan Banner, Duncan, OK; The Edmond Sun, Edmond, OK; Enid News & Eagle, Enid, OK; McAlester News-Capital, McAlester, OK; Muskogee Daily Phoenix & Times Democrat, Muskogee, OK; Norman Transcript, Norman, OK; Pauls Valley Daily Democrat, Pauls Valley, OK; The Daily Times, Pryor, OK; Sapulpa Daily Herald, Sapulpa, OK; The News Press, Stillwater, OK; Tahlequah Daily Press, Tahlequah, OK; Woodward News, Woodward, OK; The Danville News, Danville, PA; The Tribune-Democrat, Johnstown, PA; The Meadville Tribune, Meadville, PA; New Castle News, New Castle, PA; The Herald, Sharon, PA; The Daily Item, Sunbury, PA; Athens Daily Review, Athens, TX; Cleburne Times-Review, Cleburne, TX; Corsicana Daily Sun, Corsicana, TX; Gainesville Daily Register, Gainesville, TX; The Huntsville Item, Huntsville, TX; Jacksonville Daily Progress, Jacksonville, TX; Mineral Wells Index, Mineral Wells, TX; The Orange Leader, Orange, TX; Palestine Herald-Press, Palestine, TX; Port Arthur News, Port Arthur, TX; San Marcos Daily Record, San Marcos, TX; The Weatherford Democrat, Weatherford, TX; The Register Herald, Beckley, WV; Bluefield Daily Telegraph, Bluefield, WV; Times West Virginian, Fairmont, WV; North Jefferson News, Gardendale, AL; The Leeds News, Leeds, AL; St. Clair News-Aegis, Pell City, AL; Branford News, Branford, FL; Jasper News, Jasper, FL; Suwannee Democrat, Live Oak, FL; Mayo Free Press, Live Oak, FL; Coffee County News, Douglas, GA; The Knoxville Journal-Express, Knoxville, IA; Pella Chronicle, Pella, IA; McLeansboro Times Leader, Mount Vernon, IL; The Herald Tribune, Batesville, IN; The Greensburg Times, Greensburg, IN; Image, Greenfield, IN; Hendricks County Flyer, Avon, IN; The Weekend Flyer, Avon, IN; Zionsville Times Sentinel, Zionsville, IN; Grayson Journal-Enquirer, Grayson, KY; Greenup County News-Times, Greenup, KY; The Sentinel-Echo, London, KY; The McCreary County Record, Whitley City, KY; The Wayne County Outlook, Monticello, KY; Olive Hill Times, Olive Hill, KY; The Morehead News, Morehead, KY; Andover Townsman, Andover, MA; The Star-Herald, Koscius

Community Newspaper Holdings Inc–3500 Colonnade Pkwy Ste 600, Birmingham, AL, 35243-8301; tel (205) 298-7100; web site www.cnhi.com

Community Newspapers, Inc.–2365A Prince Avenue, Athens, GA, 30606, USA; tel (706) 548-0010; fax (706) 548-0808; web site www.cninewspapers.com
Est.: 1967
Chrmn. – Tom Wood; Pres. – William H. Dink NeSmith; CFO – Mark Major; Corporate Marketing Director / Major Account Manager – Joel Jenkins; Daily Newspapers: Lake City Reporter, Lake City, FL; Palatka Daily News, Palatka, FL; News-Leader, Fernandina Beach, FL; Nassau County Record, Callahan, FL; The News Observer, Blue Ridge, GA; Camden County Tribune & Southeast Georgian, Saint Marys, GA; White County News, Cleveland, GA; The Northeast Georgian, Cornelia, GA; The Dahlonega Nugget, Dahlonega, GA; Dawson News & Advertiser, Dawsonville, GA; The Elberton Star, Elberton, GA; Franklin County Citizen, Lavonia, GA; The News Leader, Lavonia, GA; The Hartwell Sun, Hartwell, GA; The Press-Sentinel, Jesup, GA; The Telfair Enterprise,

McRae, GA; The Clayton Tribune, Clayton, GA; The Toccoa Record, Toccoa, GA; The Andrews Journal, Andrews, NC; Crossroads Chronicle, Cashiers, NC; Clay County Progress, Hayesville, NC; The Franklin Press, Franklin, NC; The Graham Star, Robbinsville, NC; The Highlander, Highlands, NC; Cherokee Scout, Murphy, NC; Mitchell News-Journal, Spruce Pine, NC; Tribune & Georgian, Saint Marys, GA; Smoky Mountain Times, Bryson City, NC;
Note: Community Newspapers Inc. maintains 28 subscriber newspapers and affliates in Georgia, Florida and North Carolina. Also, select non-duplicating TMC's are available.

Community Publishers Inc–PO Box 1049, Bentonville, AR, 72712-1049; tel (479) 271-3782; web site www.commpub.com

Community Publishers, Inc.–900 SE 5th ST, Ste 22, Bentonville, AR, 72712, USA; tel (479) 271-3772; fax (479) 271-3788; web site www.commpub.com
Est.: 1982
Pres. – Steve Trolinger; Exec. Vice Pres. – Michael Brown; Vice Pres. – Dave Berry; CFO – Tom Bruns; Prodn. Mgr. – Charles Heidelberg; Ronnie Bell; Roger Frye; Adv./Mktg. Mgr. – Ted Lawrence; Daily Newspapers: Harrison Daily Times, Harrison, AR; The Newton County Times, Jasper, AR; Bolivar Herald-Free Press, Bolivar, MO; Buffalo Reflex, Buffalo, MO; The Marshfield Mail, Marshfield, MO; Christian County Headliner News, Ozark, MO; The Republic Monitor, Republic, MO; Cedar County Republican/Stockton Journal, Stockton, MO; Bixby Bulletin, Broken Arrow, OK; Collinsville News, Collinsville, OK; Coweta American, Coweta, OK; Glenpool Post, Jenks, OK; Jenks Journal, Jenks, OK; Mannford Eagle, Mannford, OK; Owasso Reporter, Owasso, OK; Sand Springs Leader, Sand Springs, OK; Skiatook Journal, Skiatook, OK; Wagoner Tribune, Wagoner, OK; Tulsa Daily Commerce & Legal News, Broken Arrow, OK; Neighbor Classified, Broken Arrow, OK; South County Mail, Rogersville, MO;
Note: Community Publishers Inc. owns the Harrison Daily Times in Harrison, AR and one daily business newspaper plus 22 weekly and semi-weekly community newspapers as well as three commercial printing plants.

Conley Publishing Group–55 E Sumner St, Hartford, WI, 53027-1537; tel (262)760-1500; web site www.gmtoday.com

Conley Publishing Group Ltd.–115 Monroe Street, Beaver Dam, WI, 53916, USA; tel (920) 885-7800; fax (920) 887-7065; e-mail hrd@conleynet.com; web site www.gmtoday.com
Est.: 1970
Pres./CEO – James E. Conley; Vice Pres., Sales/Mktg. – Steve Ciccantelli; Grp. Pub. – Phil Page; Commun. Coord. – Sarah Diels; Employment Manager – Lydia Fritsche; CFO – Penny Kottke; VP of Media Operations – Matt Marlett; Daily Newspapers: The Freeman, Waukesha, WI; The Daily News, West Bend, WI; The Hartford Times Press, Hartford, WI; Oconomowoc Enterprise, Oconomowoc, WI; Ozaukee County News Graphic, Cedarburg, WI; The Ozaukee Sunday Post, Cedarburg, WI; Ozaukee County Guide, Cedarburg, WI; AdVantage, West Bend, WI; Lake Country Sunday Post, Oconomowoc, WI; Waukesha Area Post, Waukesha, WI; The Sunday Post, West Bend, WI;
Note: Conley Publishing Group Ltd. is a printing and publishing corporation with locations throughout Wisconsin, Colorado and Arizona. Conley Publishing publishes nine non-daily publications along with two daily newspapers in WI. Conley also publishes lifestyle magazines.

Consolidated Publishing Co.–PO Box 189, Anniston, AL, 36202-0189; tel (256) 235-9200; fax (256) 241-1980; web site www.annistonstar.com
Chrmn. – H. Brandt Ayers; Pres. – Phillip A. Sanguinetti; Vice Pres. – Chris Waddle; Vice Pres., Opns. – Ed Fowler; Controller/Treasurer – Scott Calhoun; Daily Newspapers: The Anniston Star, Anniston, AL; The Daily Home, Talladega, AL; The Cleburne News, Heflin, AL; The Jacksonville News, Anniston, AL; The Saint Clair Times, Pell City, AL;
Note: Consolidated Publishing Co. also owns three weekly publications: the Jacksonville (AL) News, Heflin (AL) The Cleburne News and Pell (AL) The Saint Clair Times.

Contra Costa Newspapers–2640 Shadelands Dr., Walnut Creek, CA, 94596-2578, USA; tel (925) 935-2525; fax (925) 977-8410; web site www.contracostatimes.com
Group: Newspapers First, Inc.
Grp. Pub. – John Armstrong;

Cooke Communications LLC–3420 Northside Drive, Key West, FL, 33040; tel (305) 292-7777; web site www.cookecommunications.com

Coopwood Newspapers, Inc–PO Box 117, Cleveland, MS, 38732; tel (662) 843-2700; web site www.coopwoodpublishinggroup.com

Cox Newspapers, Inc.–6205 Peachtree Dunwoody Rd., 9th Fl., Atlanta, GA, 30328-4524, USA; tel (678) 645-0000; fax (678) 645-5002; web site www.coxnewspapers.com
Est.: 1898
Chrmn./CEO, Cox Enterprises Inc. – James C. Kennedy; Pres./COO, Cox Enterprises Inc. – Jimmy Hayes; Pres. – Sandy Schwartz; Exec. Vice Pres./CFO, Cox Enterprises Inc. – John Dyer; Exec. Vice. Pres. – Douglas Franklin; Vice Pres./CFO – Melody Darch; Vice Pres./CIO – Christopher Caneles; Vice Pres./HR – Susan S. Davidson; Vice Pres., Adv. – Cathy B. Coffey; Vice Pres., Circ. – Al Smith; Vice Pres., Mktg./Grp. Vice Pres., Community Newspapers – Caroline C. John; Vice Pres., Newsprint Supply – Mark P. Mansfield; Vice Pres., Digital Media – Leon Levitt; Gen. Mgr., COXnet – John Reetz; Dir., Classified/Internet Adv. – Dean Welch; Dir., Newsprint Supply – Greg Tant; Nat'l Online Sales Mgr. – Bill Sullivan; Vice Pres., Opns. – Stanley P. Richmond; Daily Newspapers: La Palma, West Palm Beach, FL; ahora si!, Austin, TX; The Daily Sentinel, Grand Junction, CO; Palm Beach Daily News, Palm Beach, FL; The Palm Beach Post, West Palm Beach, FL; The Atlanta Journal-Constitution, Atlanta, GA; The Daily Advance, Elizabeth City, NC; Dayton Daily News, Dayton, OH; JournalNews, Hamilton, OH; Middletown Journal, Middletown, OH; Springfield News-Sun, Springfield, OH; Austin American-Statesman, Austin, TX; Longview News-Journal, Longview, TX; Marshall News Messenger, Marshall, TX; Fairfield Echo, Liberty Township, OH; The Western Star, Lebanon, OH; The Oxford Press, Oxford, OH; Pulse-Journal, Liberty Township, OH; The Pflugerville Pflag, Pflugerville, TX; The Bastrop Advertiser, Bastrop, TX; The Smithville Times, Smithville, TX; Westlake Picayune, Austin, TX; The Nickel, Grand Junction, CO; Florida Pennysaver, West Palm Beach, FL; North Lake Travis Log, Lago Vista, TX; Lake Travis View, Austin, TX; Mundo Hispanico, Atlanta, GA;
Note: Cox Newspapers Inc. also owns Valpak; Cox Custom Media, and PAGAS. Cox Newspapers also has 50% ownership of Trader Publishing Co. and 33% of SP Newsprint. Cox Newspapers is a subsidiary of Cox Enterprises, Inc. and owns Austin Community Newspapers Gro

Crescent Media Group, Inc.–172 E. Main St., Ste. 300, Spartanburg, SC, 29306, USA; tel (864) 583-2907; fax (864) 573-7640; e-mail ababb@msmgmt.com; web site www.midsouthmanagement.com

Pres. – Andrew M. Babb;

D

Defiance Publishing LLC–624 W. Second St., Defiance, OH, -2105; tel (419) 784-5441; fax (419) 782-2944; e-mail crescent@crescent-news.com; web site www.crescent-news.com
Gen. Mgr. – Steve Van DeMark; Adv. Mgr. – Mark Ryan; Circ. Mgr. – Betty Lentz; Ed. – Dennis Van Scoder; Sports Ed. – Bruce Hefflinger; Prepress Mgr. – Beverly Stahl; Pressroom/Mailroom Mgr. – Gary Richey; Daily Newspapers: The Crescent-News, Defiance, OH; Henry County Ad-Pak, Defiance, OH;
Note: Defiance Publishing LLC is part of Dix Communications which is owned by the Wooster Republican Printing Co. Dix also owns two television stations in Montana and seven radio stations. Through it's subsidiaries, Alliance Publishing Co. LLC, Ashland Publishi

Delphos Herald Inc–405 N Main St, Delphos, OH, 45833-1577; tel (419) 695-0015

Democrat Co.–1226 Ave. H, Fort Madison, IA, 52627, USA; tel (319) 372-6421; fax (319) 372-3867; e-mail msmidt@dailygate.com; web site www.dailydem.com
Publisher – Mark Smidt; Business Manager – Mary Older; Daily Newspapers: Daily Gate City, Keokuk, IA; Donnellson Star, West Point, IA; West Point Bee, West Point, IA; Hancock County Journal-Pilot, Carthage, IL; Des Moines County Shopper Spree, Burlington, IA; Bonny Buyer, West Point, IA;
Note: Democrat Co. is owned by Brehm Communications Inc. Through it's subsidiaries, Democrat Co., Gull Communications, Hi-Desert Publishing Co., Inc., News West Publishing Company Inc., Penny Power Publications Inc., Placer Community Newspapers, Inc. and Princ

Dix Communications–212 E. Liberty St., Wooster, OH, 44691, USA; tel (330) 264-3511; fax (330) 263-5013; web site www.dix-com.com
Pres. – G. Charles Dix; Vice Pres. – Ann Dix-Maenza; CFO – Dale E. Gerber; Sec. – David E. Dix; Daily Newspapers: The State Journal, Frankfort, KY; The Review, Alliance, OH; Ashland Times-Gazette, Ashland, OH; The Crescent-News, Defiance, OH; The Daily Jeffersonian, Cambridge, OH; Record-Courier, Ravenna, OH; The Daily Record, Wooster, OH; Aurora Advocate, Stow, OH; Barnesville Enterprise, Barnesville, OH; Cuyahoga Falls News-Press, Stow, OH; Hudson Hub-Times, Stow, OH; The Loudonville Times, Loudonville, OH; The News Leader, Minerva, OH; Maple Heights Press, Stow, OH; The Homes County Hub, Millersburg, OH; New Concord Area Leader, Cambridge, OH; Newcomerstown News, Newcomerstown, OH; The News Leader, Stow, OH; Stow Sentry, Stow, OH; Gateway News, Stow, OH; Tallmadge Express, Stow, OH; The Bulletin Twinsburg, Stow, OH; Buyer's Guide, Frankfort, KY; Mr. Thrifty, Alliance, OH; Jeffersonian Advantage, Cambridge, OH; Henry County Ad-Pak, Defiance, OH; Byesville Village Reporter, Cambridge, OH; Mohican Area Shopper, Ashland, OH;
Note: Dix Communications is owned by the Wooster Republican Printing Co. The company also owns two television stations in Montana and seven radio stations. Through it's subsidiaries, Dix owns seven daily newspapers and more than 20 weekly and shopper publicat

Dow Jones & Company Inc–PO Box 300, Princeton, NJ, 08543-0300; tel (609) 520-4000; web site www.dj.com

Dow Jones & Company–1 World Financial Ctr., 200 Liberty St., New York, NY, 10281-1003, USA; tel (212) 416-2000; web site www.dowjones.com
Est.: 1882
CEO – Leslie Hinton; Pres., Dow Jones Online – Gordon McLeod; Exec. Vice Pres./CFO – Stephen Daintith; Exec. Vice Pres., Enterprise Media Grp. – Clare Hart; Exec. Vice Pres./Gen. Counsel – Mark H. Jackson; Sr. Vice Pres., Local Media Grp. – John N. Wilcox; Sr. Vice Pres./Chief HR Officer – Greg Giangrande; Sr. Vice Pres., Special Projects – Ian Weston; Vice Pres., Commun. – Linda E. Dunbar; Vice Pres., Security – Joseph J. Cantamessa; Ed. in Chief – Robert Thomson; Daily Newspapers: The Record, Stockton, CA; Cape Cod Times, Hyannis, MA; The Standard-Times, New Bedford, MA; Portsmouth Herald, Portsmouth, NH; The Times Herald-Record, Middletown, NY; The Wall Street Journal, New York, NY; The Ashland Daily Tidings, Ashland, OR; Mail Tribune, Medford, OR; Pocono Record, Stroudsburg, PA; Barnstable Patriot, Hyannis, MA; The Inquirer and Mirror, Nantucket, MA; York County Coast Star, Kennebunk, ME; The York Weekly, Portsmouth, NH; The Hampton Union, Portsmouth, NH; Cooperstown Crier, Cooperstown, NY; Valley Market Place, Stockton, CA; Medford Nickel, Medford, OR;
Note: Dow Jones is the world's premier publisher of business news and information in every form of media

E

Eagle Newspapers, Inc.–4901 Indian School Rd. NE, Salem, OR, 97305, USA; tel (503) 393-1774; fax (503) 463-9898; e-mail dsmith@eaglenewspapers.com; web site www.eaglenewspapers.com
Est.: 1933
Chrmn. – Dennis A. Smith;Daily Newspapers: The Dalles Daily Chronicle, The Dalles, OR; Daily Sun News, Sunnyside, WA; Idaho County Free Press, Grangeville, ID; The Canby Herald, Canby, OR; The Polk County Itemizer-Observer, Dallas, OR; Hood River News, Hood River, OR; The Madras Pioneer, Madras, OR; Molalla Pioneer, Molalla, OR; The Newberg Graphic, Newberg, OR; Central Oregonian, Prineville, OR; Wilsonville Spokesman, Wilsonville, OR; Woodburn Independent, Woodburn, OR; The Chronicle, Omak, WA; The Enterprise, White Salmon, WA; Moneysaver-Lewis Clark Edition, Lewiston, ID;
Note: Eagle Newspapers Inc. owns two daily newspapers, 13 weekly newspapers, three specialty publications, four printing operations and two mailing companies located throughout Oregon, Washington and Idaho.

East Oregonian Publishing Co.–PO Box 2048, Salem, OR, 97308-2048; tel (503) 364-4431; fax (503) 385-4932; web site www.eastoregonian.org
Est.: 1875
COO – John Perry;Daily Newspapers: The Daily Astorian, Astoria, OR; East Oregonian, Pendleton, OR; Wallowa County Chieftain, Enterprise, OR; Blue Mountain Eagle, John Day, OR; Chinook Observer, Long Beach, WA;
Note: East Oregonian Publishing Co. also owns three weekly publications, the Enterprise (OR) Wallowa County Chieftain, John Day (OR) Blue Mountain Eagle and the Long Beach (WA) Chinook Observer. East Oregonian also publishes the Capital Press, a weekly agricultural newspaper for Oregon, Washington, Idaho and California.

East Oregonian Publishing Co–PO Box 1089, Pendleton, OR, 97801; tel (503) 694-2165; web site http://www.eopubco.org/

Eau Claire Press Company–701 S. Farwell St., Eau Claire, WI, 54701, United States; tel (715) 833-9200; fax 715-833-9244; web site www.leadertelegram.com
Group: Eau Claire Press Co.
Est.: 1881

Elwood Publishing Co., Inc.–317 S. Anderson St., Elwood, IN, 46036-2018, USA; tel (765) 552-

3355; fax (765) 552-3358; e-mail elpub@elwoodpublishing.com; web site www.elwoodpublishing.com
Pub. – Bob Nash;Daily Newspapers: Elwood Call-Leader, Elwood, IN; Tipton County Tribune, Tipton, IN; Alexandria Times-Tribune, Alexandria, IN; Leader Tribune-Review West, Tipton, IN;

Emmerich Newspapers Inc–PO Box 16709, Jackson, MS, 39236, USA; tel (601) 957-1122; fax (601) 957-1533; e-mail wyatt@northsidesun.com; web site www.northsidesun.com
Pres./CEO – J. Wyatt Emmerich;Daily Newspapers: The Clarksdale Press Register, Clarksdale, MS; Delta Democrat Times, Greenville, MS; The Greenwood Commonwealth, Greenwood, MS; Enterprise-Journal, McComb, MS; Dumas Clarion, Dumas, AR; The Era-Leader, Franklinton, LA; Madison Journal, Tallulah, LA; The Conservative, Winona, MS; Sun Sentinel, Charleston, MS; The Columbian-Progress, Columbia, MS; The Enterprise-Tocsin, Indianola, MS; Northside Sun, Jackson, MS; The Magee Courier, Magee, MS; Southwest Sun, McComb, MS; Simpson County News, Mendenhall, MS; The DeSoto County Tribune, Hernando, MS; Clarke County Tribune, Quitman, MS; Scott County Times, Forest, MS; The Winona Times, Winona, MS; The Yazoo Herald, Yazoo City, MS; Delta Advertiser, Greenwood, MS; Rankin Record, Brandon, MS;
Note: Emmerich Newspapers Inc. also owns seven printing operations and mailing services located throughout Oregon, Washington, and Idaho.

The Salem News–32 Dunham Road, Beverly, MA, 01915, USA; tel (978) 922-1234; fax (978) 927-4330; web site www.salemnews.com
Group: CNHI

Evening Post Community Publications Group, Inc.–134 Columbus St., Charleston, SC, 29403-4800, USA; tel (843) 577-7111; fax (843) 937-5788; e-mail dherres@postandcourier.com; web site www.charleston.net

Pres., Evening Post Community Publications Grp. – Dan Herres; Vice Pres., Evening Post Community Publications Grp. – Kathy Wilkinson; Daily Newspapers: Salisbury Post, Salisbury, NC; Aiken Standard, Aiken, SC; The Post and Courier, Charleston, SC; The Eagle, Bryan, TX; The Clemmons Courier, Clemmons, NC; Davie County Enterprise Record, Mocksville, NC; Berkeley Independent, Moncks Corner, SC; The Georgetown Times, Georgetown, SC; The News, Kingstree, SC; The Star, North Augusta, SC; Summerville Journal-Scene, Summerville, SC;
Note: Evening Post Community Publications Group, Inc. also owns the Buenos Aires (Argentina) Herald (mS) and operates 11 television stations as well as Solo Syndicate, LTD. in London. The company also owns and manages timberland in Soth Carolina through White

Evening Post Publishing Co–134 Columbus St, Charleston, SC, 29403-4800, USA; tel (843) 577-7111; fax (843) 937-5328; web site http://www.evepost.com/
Est.: 1894

F

Fackelman Newspapers, FL; tel (704) 852-9524; fax (704) 852-9523; e-mail afnixon@aol.com
Chrmn. of the Bd. – Ann F. Nixon; Pres. – Frank E. Nixon; Vice Pres., Opns. – Marc A. Richard; Treasurer – Broward E. Ratliff; Sec. – David H. Davis; Daily Newspapers: Jennings Daily News, Jennings, LA; Ruston Daily Leader, Ruston, LA; The Daily News, Richmond, MO; Ennis Daily News, Ennis, TX; The Southwest Times, Pulaski, VA; Town & Country Leader, Excelsior Springs, MO;
Note: Fackelman Newspapers shares ownership of the Crowley (LA) Post-Signal with B I Moody III (The Moody Company). In addition, this partnership owns three weekly newspapers in Louisiana. Fackelman Newspapers is also affiliated with two twice-weekly newspapers in Texas, a twice-weekly newspaper in Florida, two twice-weekly newspapers in Missouri, a weekly newspaper in Louisiana and several TMC publications.

The Findlay Publishing Co.–701 W. Sandusky St., Findlay, OH, 45840; tel (419) 422-5151; fax (419) 422-2937; web site www.findlaypublishing.com; www.thecourier.com
Chrmn. of the Bd. – Edwin L. Heminger; Pres./Treasurer – Karl L. Heminger; Vice Pres. – Kurt F. Heminger; Sec. – Margaret H. Heminger; Daily Newspapers: The Courier, Findlay, OH; The Review Times, Fostoria, OH; Courier Plus, Findlay, OH;
Note: The Findlay Publishing Co. owns two daily newspapers as well as the Findlay (OH) Courier Plus. Findlay also owns seven broadcast radio stations.

Forum Communications Co.–101 Fifth St. N., Fargo, ND, 58102, USA; tel (701) 235-7311; fax (701) 241-5406; e-mail wmarcil@forumcomm.com; web site www.forumcomm.com
Pres./CEO – Lloyd Case; CFO – John Hajostek; Pub. – William C. Marcil; Daily Newspapers: The Rosemount Town Pages, Farmington, MN; The Pioneer, Bemidji, MN; Duluth News Tribune, Duluth, MN; Republican Eagle, Red Wing, MN; West Central Tribune, Willmar, MN; The Daily Globe, Worthington, MN; Dickinson Press, Dickinson, ND; InForum, Fargo, ND; Grand Forks Herald, Grand Forks, ND; The Jamestown Sun, Jamestown, ND; The Daily Republic, Mitchell, SD; The Daily Telegram, Superior, WI; Echo-Press, Alexandria, MN; The American, Blackduck, MN; The Pine Journal, Cloquet, MN; South Washington County Bulletin, Cottage Grove, MN; The Becker County Record, Detroit Lakes, MN; The Detroit Lakes Tribune, Detroit Lakes, MN; Duluth Budgeteer News, Duluth, MN; The Farmington Independent, Farmington, MN; The Hancock Record, Hancock, MN; Hastings Star Gazette, Hastings, MN; Morris Sun Tribune, Morris, MN; New York Mills Herald, New York Mills, MN; Contact, New York Mills, MN; Osakis Review, Alexandria, MN; Park Rapids Enterprise, Park Rapids, MN; Enterprise Bulletin, Perham, MN; Lake County News-Chronicle, Two Harbors, MN; Wadena Pioneer Journal, Wadena, MN; Woodbury Bulletin, Woodbury, MN; West Fargo Pioneer, West Fargo, ND; The Hudson Star-Observer, Hudson, WI; New Richmond News, New Richmond, WI; Pierce County Herald, Ellsworth, WI; River Falls Journal, River Falls, WI; Lakeland Shopping Guide, Alexandria, MN; Valley Midweek Marketplace, West Fargo, ND; Courier News, Stillwater, MN; The Pine Journal, Cloquet, MN;
Note: Forum Communications Co. owns eleven daily newspapers and 28 non-daily publications. Forum Communications also owns several television and radio stations, a commerical printing division and a new media division.

Forum Communications Company–PO Box 6100, Fargo, ND, 58108-6100; tel (701) 235-7311; web site www.forumcomm.com

Fox Valley Publications–3101 N. US Hwy. 30, Plainfield, IL, 60544; tel (815) 439-5300; fax (815) 439-5357
Pres. – Fred Lebolt;
Note: Fox Valley Press Inc. also own 11 weekly newspapers and one shopper publication.

Frankfort Publishing Co.–1216 Wilkson Blvd., Frankfort, KY, 40601, USA; tel (502) 227-4556; fax (502) 227-2831; e-mail info@state-journal.com; web site www.state-journal.com
Publisher – Ann Dix Maenza;Daily Newspapers: The State Journal, Frankfort, KY; Buyer's Guide, Frankfort, KY;
Note: Frankfort Publishing Co. is part of Dix Communications which is owned by the Wooster Republican Printing Co. Dix also owns two television stations in Montana and seven radio stations. Through it's subsidiaries, Alliance Publishing Co. LLC, Ashland Publis

Freedom Communications, Inc.–17666 Fitch, Irvine, CA, 92614-6022, USA; tel (949) 253-2300; fax (949) 474-7675; e-mail info@freedom.com; web site www.freedom.com
Est.: 1955
CEO – Mitchell Stern; Pres., Freedom Newspapers, Inc. – Jonathan Segal; Daily Newspapers: East Valley Tribune, Mesa, AZ; Daily News-Sun, Sun City, AZ; Yuma Sun, Yuma, AZ; Desert Dispatch, Barstow, CA; Appeal-Democrat, Marysville, CA; The Orange County Register, Santa Ana, CA; The Porterville Recorder, Porterville, CA; Daily Press, Victorville, CA; The Gazette, Colorado Springs, CO; Northwest Florida Daily News, Fort Walton Beach, FL; The News Herald, Panama City, FL; The Telegraph, Alton, IL; Jacksonville Journal-Courier, Jacksonville, IL; The Tribune, Seymour, IN; The Sedalia Democrat, Sedalia, MO; Clovis News Journal, Clovis, NM; Portales News-Tribune, Portales, NM; Times-News, Burlington, NC; The Gaston Gazette, Gastonia, NC; The Daily News, Jacksonville, NC; The Free Press, Kinston, NC; The Sun Journal, New Bern, NC; The Star, Shelby, NC; The Lima News, Lima, OH; The Brownsville Herald, Brownsville, TX; Valley Morning Star, Harlingen, TX; The Monitor, McAllen, TX; Odessa American, Odessa, TX; The Glendale Today, Sun City, AZ; Ahwatukee Foothills News, Phoenix, AZ; Aliso Viejo News, Lake Forest, CA; Anaheim Bulletin, Anaheim, CA; Anaheim Hills News, Anaheim, CA; Star Progress, Anaheim, CA; Dana Point News, San Clemente, CA; Fullerton News-Tribune, Anaheim, CA; La Habra Star, Anaheim, CA; Laguna News Post, Lake Forest, CA; Laguna Niguel News, Lake Forest, CA; Laguna Woods Globe, Laguna Woods Globe, CA; Saddleback Valley News, Lake Forest, CA; Orange City News, Anaheim, CA; Placentia News-Times, Anaheim, CA; Rancho Santa Margarita News, Lake Forest, CA; Sun-Post News, San Clemente, CA; The Tustin News, Santa Ana, CA; Yorba Linda Star, Anaheim, CA; The Carrabelle Times, Apalachicola, FL; The Destin Log, Destin, FL; The Apalachicola Times, Apalachicola, FL; The Star, Port Saint Joe, FL; Scuppernong Reminder, Washington, NC; The Havelock News, Havelock, NC; The Hickory News, Hickory, NC; The Jones Post, Washington, NC; Quay County Sun, Tucumcari, NM; The Shopper, New Bern, NC; Bajo El Sol, Yuma, AZ; Desert Warrior, Yuma, AZ; Cannon Connection, Clovis, NM; Windsock, Havelock, NC; The Walton Sun, Santa Rosa Beach, FL; Hesperia Star, Hesperia, CA; The Mid-Valley Town Crier, Weslaco, TX; Surprise Today, Sun City, AZ;
Note: Freedom Communications, headquartered in Irvine, Calif., is a national privately owned information and entertainment company of print publications, broadcast television stations and interactive businesses. The company's print portfolio includes more than 100 publications, including 27 daily newspapers, weekly newspapers, magazines and other specialty publications. The broadcast stations Ã» five CBS, two ABC network affiliates and one CW affiliate Ã» reach more than 3 million households across the country. Freedom's news, information and entertainment websites and mobile applications complement its print and broadcast properties.

G

Gannett Co., Inc.–7950 Jones Branch Dr, McLean, VA, 22107; tel (703)854-6000; fax (703) 854-2001; e-mail gcishare@gannett.com; web site www.gannett.com
Est.: 1906
Chrmn./Pres./CEO – Craig Dubow; Chrmn./Chief Exec., Newsquest plc. – Paul Davidson; Pres., Gannett US Community Publishing – Robert J. Dickey; Pres., Gannett Digital – John A. (Jack) Williams; Sr. Vice Pres./CFO – Gracia C. Martore; Sr. Vice Pres., HR – Roxanne V. Horning; Sr. Vice Pres., News/Newspaper Div. – Philip R. Currie; Vice Pres./Controller – George R. Gavagan; Vice Pres./Assoc. Counsel/Sec. – Todd A. Mayman; Vice Pres./Treasurer – Michael A. Hart; Vice Pres./Sr. Labor Councel – Wendell J. Van Lare; Vice Pres., Cor. Commun. – Tara Connell; Vice Pres., Compensation/Benefits – Robert B. Oliver; Vice Pres., Taxes – Christopher W. Baldwin; Vice Pres., Planning/Devel. – Daniel S. Ehrman; Vice Pres., HR/Diversity – Virgil Smith; Vice Pres., News Media – Kate Marymont; Vice Pres., Sun Coast Grp - LA – Leslie J. Hurst; Vice Pres., Innovation/Design – Michael L. Maness; Sr. Grp. Pres., Gannett South Newspaper Grp. & Pres./Pub., Florida Today – Michael J. Coleman; Vice Pres., Planning/Devel. – Daniel S. Ehrman; Daily Newspapers: Montgomery Advertiser, Montgomery, AL; The Arizona Republic, Phoenix, AZ; Tucson Citizen, Tucson, AZ; The Baxter Bulletin, Mountain Home, AR; The Desert Sun, Palm Springs, CA; The Salinas Californian, Salinas, CA; Visalia Times-Delta & Tulare Advance-Register, Visalia, CA; Visalia Times-Delta, Visalia, CA; The Coloradoan, Fort Collins, CO; Greenwich Time, Greenwich, CT; The News Journal, Wilmington, DE; The News-Press, Fort Myers, FL; Florida Today, Melbourne, FL; Pensacola News Journal, Pensacola, FL; Tallahassee Democrat, Tallahassee, FL; The Honolulu Advertiser, Honolulu, HI; The Indianapolis Star, Indianapolis, IN; Journal and Courier, Lafayette, IN; The Star Press, Muncie, IN; The Noblesville Ledger, Fishers, IN; Palladium-Item, Richmond, IN; The Des Moines Register, Des Moines, IA; Iowa City Press-Citizen, Iowa City, IA; The Courier-Journal, Louisville, KY; The Town Talk, Alexandria, LA; The Daily Advertiser, Lafayette, LA; The News-Star, Monroe, LA; The Daily World, Opelousas, LA; The Shreveport Times, Shreveport, LA; The Daily Times, Salisbury, MD; Battle Creek Enquirer, Battle Creek, MI; Detroit Free Press, Detroit, MI; Lansing State Journal, Lansing, MI; Times Herald, Port Huron, MI; St. Cloud Times, Saint Cloud, MN; Hattiesburg American, Hattiesburg, MS; The Clarion-Ledger, Jackson, MS; Springfield News-Leader, Springfield, MO; Great Falls Tribune, Great Falls, MT; Reno Gazette-Journal, Reno, NV; Courier News, Somerville, NJ; Courier-Post, Cherry Hill, NJ; Home News Tribune, East Brunswick, NJ; Daily Record, Parsippany, NJ; Asbury Park Press, Neptune, NJ; The Daily Journal, Vineland, NJ; Press & Sun-Bulletin, Binghamton, NY; Star-Gazette, Elmira, NY; The Ithaca Journal, Ithaca, NY; Poughkeepsie Journal, Poughkeepsie, NY; Democrat and Chronicle.com, Rochester, NY; The Journal News, White Plains, NY; The Asheville Citizen-Times, Asheville, NC; Bucyrus TelegraphForum.com, Bucyrus, OH; Chillicothe Gazette, Chillicothe, OH; The Cincinnati Enquirer, Cincinnati, OH; The Coshocton Tribune, Coshocton, OH; The News-Messenger, Fremont, OH; Lancaster Eagle-Gazette, Lancaster, OH; News Journal, Mansfield, OH; The Marion Star, Marion, OH; The Advocate, Newark, OH; News-Herald, Port Clinton, OH; Times Recorder, Zanesville, OH; Statesman Journal, Salem,

OR; The Greenville News, Greenville, SC; Argus Leader, Sioux Falls, SD; The Leaf-Chronicle, Clarksville, TN; The Jackson Sun, Jackson, TN; The Daily News Journal, Murfreesboro, TN; The Tennessean, Nashville, TN; The Spectrum, Saint George, UT; The Burlington Free Press, Burlington, VT; USA TODAY, McLean, VA; The News Leader, Staunton, VA; The Post-Crescent, Appleton, WI; The Reporter, Fond du Lac, WI; The Green Bay News-Chronicle, Green Bay, WI; Green Bay Press-Gazette, Green Bay, WI; Herald Times Reporter, Manitowoc, WI; Marshfield News-Herald, Marshfield, WI; Oshkosh Northwestern, Oshkosh, WI; The Sheboygan Press, Sheboygan, WI; Stevens Point Journal, Stevens Point, WI; The Wausau Daily Herald, Wausau, WI; Daily Tribune, Wisconsin Rapids, WI; Prattville Progress, Prattville, AL; Windsor Beacon, Windsor, CO; Delaware Beachcomber, Bethany Beach, DE; Delaware Coast Press, Rehoboth Beach, DE; The Delaware Wave, Bethany Beach, DE; Lehigh Acres News-Star, Lehigh Acres, FL; Star Advocate, Titusville, FL; Herald Index, Altoona, IA; Ankeny Press Citizen, Ankeny, IA; Star Press Union, Belle Plaine, IA; Poweshiek County CR, Brooklyn, IA; Record-Herald and Indianola Tribune, Indianola, IA; Marengo Pioneer-Republican, Marengo, IA; Montezuma Republican, Montezuma, IA; North English Record, North English, IA; Williamsburg Journal Tribune, Williamsburg, IA; Boone Community Recorder, Fort Mitchell, KY; Campbell Community Recorder, Fort Mitchell, KY; Kenton Community Recorder, Fort Mitchell, KY; Worcester County Times, Ocean City, MD; Maryland Beachcomber, West Ocean City, MD; Somerset Herald, Princess Anne, MD; Birmingham Eccentric, Detroit, MI; Canton Observer, Plymouth, MI; Towne Courier, Mason

Note: Gannett Co. Inc. owns 95 daily newspapers, including USA Today. Gannett also owns more than 300 non-daily newspapers and shoppers and publishes the USA Weekend magazine. Gannett operates 22 television stations in the United States. In the United Kingdom

GateHouse Media Inc.–350 WillowBrook Office Park, Fairport, NY, 14450, USA; tel (585)598-0030; fax (585) 248-2631; web site www.gatehousemedia.com

Est.: 1997

CEO – Michael E. Reed; Pres./COO – Kirk Davis; Sr. Vice Pres./CFO – Melinda A. Janik; CIO – Paul Ameden; Vice Pres., Sales & Marketing – Brad Harmon; Vice Pres., Content/News Opns. – Brad Dennison; Regional VP - Midwest – Gloria Fletcher; Regional VP - Atlantic – James O'Rourke; Regional VP - Western – Nick Monico; Regional VP - New England – Rick Daniels; Regional VP - Great Lakes – Kevin Kampman; Daily Newspapers: Arkadelphia Siftings Herald, Arkadelphia, AR; The Daily World, Helena, AR; Hope Star, Hope, AR; Newport Independent, Newport, AR; Stuttgart Daily Leader, Stuttgart, AR; The Daily Independent, Ridgecrest, CA; Daily Midway Driller, Taft, CA; Siskiyou Daily News, Yreka, CA; La Junta Tribune-Democrat, La Junta, CO; Norwich Bulletin, Norwich, CT; Benton Evening News, Benton, IL; Daily Ledger, Canton, IL; Carmi Times, Carmi, IL; Du Quoin Evening Call, Du Quoin, IL; Eldorado Daily Journal, Harrisburg, IL; The Clay County Advocate-Press, Flora, IL; The Journal-Standard, Freeport, IL; The Register-Mail, Galesburg, IL; The Daily Register, Harrisburg, IL; Star-Courier, Kewanee, IL; The Courier, Lincoln, IL; Macomb Journal, Macomb, IL; The Marion Daily Republican, Marion, IL; Daily Review Atlas, Monmouth, IL; Olney Daily Mail, Olney, IL; Pekin Daily Times, Pekin, IL; Journal Star, Peoria, IL; The Daily Leader, Pontiac, IL; Rockford Register Star, Rockford, IL; The State Journal-Register, Springfield, IL; The Daily American, West Frankfort, IL; Charles City Press, Charles City, IA; Augusta Daily Gazette, Augusta, KS; The Derby Reporter, Derby, KS; Dodge City Daily Globe, Dodge City, KS; The El Dorado Times, El Dorado, KS; Kansas City Kansan, Kansas City, KS; The Leavenworth Times, Leavenworth, KS; McPherson Sentinel, McPherson, KS; The Newton Kansan, Newton, KS; The Morning Sun, Pittsburg, KS; The Pratt Tribune, Pratt, KS; Bastrop Daily Enterprise, Bastrop, LA; Beauregard Daily News, De Ridder, LA; The Leesville Daily Leader, Leesville, LA; Southwest Daily News, Sulphur, LA; The Enterprise, Randolph, MA; The Herald News, Fall River, MA; Metrowest Daily News, Framingham, MA; Milford Daily News, Milford, MA; The Patriot Ledger, Quincy, MA; Taunton Daily Gazette, Taunton, MA; The Daily Telegram, Adrian, MI; Cheboygan Daily Tribune, Cheboygan, MI; The Daily Reporter, Coldwater, MI; Hillsdale Daily News, Hillsdale, MI; The Holland Sentinel, Holland, MI; Sentinel-Standard, Ionia, MI; The Evening News, Sault Sainte Marie, MI; Sturgis Journal, Sturgis, MI; Crookston Daily Times, Crookston, MN; The Examiner, Independence, MO; Boonville Daily News, Boonville, MO; Linn County Leader, Brookfield, MO; Lake Sun Leader, Camdenton, MO; The Carthage Press, Carthage, MO; Constitution-Tribune, Chillicothe, MO; Hannibal Courier-Post, Hannibal, MO; The Examiner, Independence, MO; Kirksville Daily Express, Kirksville, MO; Macon Chronicle-Herald, Macon, MO; The Maryville Daily Forum, Maryville, MO; Mexico Ledger, Mexico, MO; Moberly Monitor-Index & Evening Democrat, Moberly, MO; Neosho Daily News, Neosho, MO; Rolla Daily News, Rolla, MO; Daily Guide, Waynesville, MO; Elko Daily Free Press, Elko, NV; Messenger Post Newspapers, Canandaigua, NY; The Leader, Corning, NY; The Evening Telegram, Herkimer, NY; The Evening Tribune, Hornell, NY; The Evening Times, Herkimer, NY; Observer-Dispatch, Utica, NY; Wellsville Daily Reporter, Wellsville, NY; Devils Lake Journal, Devils Lake, ND; The Repository, Canton, OH; The Times-Reporter, New Philadelphia, OH; Norwood Bulletin, Needham, MA; The Independent, Massillon, OH; The Daily Ardmoreite, Ardmore, OK; Shawnee News-Star, Shawnee, OK; The Wayne Independent, Honesdale, PA; Hopkinton Crier, Framingham, MA; Shrewsbury Chronicle, Marlborough, MA; The Record Herald, Waynesboro, PA; The Oak Ridger, Oak Ridge, TN; Mineral Daily News-Tribune, Keyser, WV; The Gurdon Times, Prescott, AR; The Sun-Times, Heber Springs, AR; Nevada County Picayune, Prescott, AR; White Hall Journal, White Hall, AR; The Gridley Herald, Gridley, CA; The Fowler Tribune, Fowler, CO; Bent County Democrat, Las Animas, CO; Dover Post, Dover, DE; The Sussex Countian, Georgetown, DE; The Middletown Transcript, Middletown, DE; Smyrna Sun-Times, Smyrna, DE; Times Plain Dealer, Cresco, IA; Eldora Herald-Ledger, Eldora, IA; Eldora Newspapers, Eldora, IA; Hamburg Reporter, Hamburg, IA; Addison Press, Downers Grove, IL; Ashley News, Du Quoin, IL; Augusta Eagle-Scribe, A

Note: GateHouse Media Inc. is owned by Fortress Investment Group LLC.

GREATER PHILADELPHIA NEWSPAPERS–8400 Bristol Pike, Levittown, PA, 19057; tel 215-949-4150

Gwinnette Daily Post–725 Old Norcross Rd., Lawrenceville, GA, 30045, USA; tel (770) 963-9205; fax (770) 277-5271; e-mail news@gwinnettdailypost.com; web site www.gwinnettdailypost.com

Pub. – J.K. Murphy; Financial Dir. – Susan Andrews; Adv. Dir., Retail – Brenda Bohn; Adv. Mgr., Classified – Kellie Moore; Adv. Mgr., Legal Notices – Cindy Carter; Adv. Mgr., Major Accts. – Janet McCray; Circ. Dir. – Thom Bell; Circ. Mgr., Sales/Customer Serv. – Sherry Brown; Ed. – Todd Cline; Copy Desk Chief – Nate McCullough; Graphics Ed. – Nicole Finley; Photo Ed. – Anthony Stalcup; Sports Ed. – Will Hammock; Tech. Dir./Online Mgr. – Howard F. Reed; Prodn. Mgr., Distribution – Ken Walker; Chrmn./CEO/Dir. – J. Mack Robinson; Vice Chrmn. – Hilton H. Howell; Sr. Vice Pres., Finance/CFO – James C. Ryan; Vice Pres., Law/Devel. – Robert A. Beizer; @RecordBody:**Note:** Gray Television, Inc. owns 28 television stations as well as the shopper, Albany (GA) Albany Area Advertiser.

H

Hagadone Corp.–111 S. First St., Coeur d'Alene, ID, 83814, USA; tel (208) 667-3431; fax (208) 664-7206; e-mail info@hagadone.com; web site www.hagadone.com

Est.: 1966

Chrmn. of the Bd. – Duane B. Hagadone; Vice Pres. – Bradley D. Hagadone; CFO – Doug Magnuson; Sec. – John R. Barlow; Mgr., MIS Dept. – William Tunison; Daily Newspapers: Coeur d'Alene Press, Coeur d'Alene, ID; Shoshone News-Press, Kellogg, ID; Bonner County Daily Bee, Sandpoint, ID; Daily Inter Lake, Kalispell, MT; Columbia Basin Herald, Moses Lake, WA; Beloit Daily News, Beloit, WI; Bonners Ferry Herald, Bonners Ferry, ID; Priest River Times, Priest River, ID; The Bigfork Eagle, Bigfork, MT; Hungry Horse News, Columbia Falls, MT; The Western News, Libby, MT; Lake County Leader, Polson, MT; Clark Fork Valley Press, Plains, MT; The Whitefish Pilot, Whitefish, MT; Advertiser, Polson, MT; Saturday Sampler, Beloit, WI; West Shore News, Bigfork, MT;

Note: Hagadone Corp., also owns a Printing, Hospitality and Real Estate Division.

Hagadone Newspapers–PO Box 6200, Coeur d'Alene, ID, 83816; tel (208) 667-3431; web site http://www.hagadone.com/

HarborPoint Media Group–125 Basin St., Ste. 210, Daytona Beach, FL, 32114; tel (386) 252-9921

CEO – Micheal Redding;Daily Newspapers: The Daily Commercial, Leesburg, FL; South Lake Press, Clermont, FL; The News-Sun, Sebring, FL; Washington Jewish Week, Rockville, MD;

Harris Enterprises, Inc.–1 N. Main St., Ste. 520, Hutchinson, KS, 67501, USA; tel (620) 694-5830; fax 620-259-8253

Pres./CEO – Bruce Buchanan; Bus. Mgr. – Sarah Liebl; Vice President – John Montgomery; Daily Newspapers: The Bee, Hutchinson, KS; The Hawk Eye, Burlington, IA; The Garden City Telegram, Garden City, KS; The Hays Daily News, Hays, KS; The Hutchinson News, Hutchinson, KS; The Ottawa Herald, Ottawa, KS; The Salina Journal, Salina, KS; Ottawa Times Shopper, Ottawa, KS; Hawk Eye Shopper, Burlington, IA; Shopmate, Garden City, KS; The Hays Daily News Extra, Hays, KS; Buyer's Guide, Salina, KS; Country Roads, Salina, KS; La Semana en el Suroeste de Kansas, Garden City, KS;

Hartman Newspapers LP–1914 Fourth St., Rosenberg, TX, 77471-1390, USA; tel (281) 342-8691; fax (281) 342-6968

Est.: 1974

Chrmn. – J. William Hartman; Pres. – Clyde C. King; Vice Chairman – Fred B. Hartman; Daily Newspapers: Brenham Banner-Press, Brenham, TX; Henderson Daily News, Henderson, TX; Fort Bend Herald, Rosenberg, TX; The Terrell Tribune, Terrell, TX; The Alvin Sun, Alvin, TX; Anahuac Progress, Anahuac, TX; The Katy Times, Katy, TX; The Kaufman Herald, Kaufman, TX; The Bayshore Sun, La Porte, TX; The Liberty Vindicator, Liberty, TX; Fort Bend Mirror, Sugarland, TX; The Port Lavaca Wave, Port Lavaca, TX; Rockport Pilot, Rockport, TX; Rusk County Community News, Henderson, TX; Bargain Hunter, Terrell, TX; Rockwall County News, Rockwall, TX;

Haynes Publishing Co.–170 S. Penn Ave., Oberlin, KS, 67749-2243, USA; tel (785) 475-2206; fax (785) 475-2800; e-mail obherald@nwkansas.com; web site www.nwkansas.com

Group: Haynes Publishing Co.

Est.: 1879

Pres. – Stephen C. Haynes; CFO – Cynthia A. Haynes; Daily Newspapers: Colby Free Press, Colby, KS; The Goodland Star-News, Goodland, KS; The Norton Telegram, Norton, KS; Bird City Times, Bird City, KS; The Oberlin Herald, Oberlin, KS; The Saint Francis Herald, Saint Francis, KS; Country Advocate, Goodland, KS;

Note: Company publishes six newspapers and two shoppers in Northwest Kansas.

Heartland Publications LLC–1 W. Main St., Clinton, CT, 06413, USA; tel (860) 664-1075; fax (860) 664 -1085; web site www.heartlandpublications.com

President /CEO – Michael Bush; COO – Gary Lawrence; CFO – John Adams; Controller – Bob Bertz; Director of Customer Relations – Paul Rector; Regional Publisher – Joseph Craig; Marketing & Promotional Manager – Lynn McLamb; COO – Dan Goodrich; CFO – Jim Kreps; Daily Newspapers: La Grange Daily News, LaGrange, GA; The Harlan Daily Enterprise, Harlan, KY; Middlesboro Daily News, Middlesboro, KY; The Sampson Independent, Clinton, NC; The Laurinburg Exchange, Laurinburg, NC; The Robesonian, Lumberton, NC; Mount Airy News, Mount Airy, NC; Richmond County Daily Journal, Rockingham, NC; Gallipolis Daily Tribune, Gallipolis, OH; The Daily Sentinel/Sunday Times-Sentinel, Pomeroy, OH; The Portsmouth Daily Times, Portsmouth, OH; Altus Times, Altus, OK; Durant Daily Democrat, Durant, OK; Union Daily Times, Union, SC; The Logan Banner, Logan, WV; Point Pleasant Register, Point Pleasant, WV; Williamson Daily News, Williamson, WV; The Thomaston Times, Thomaston, GA; The Hazard Herald, Hazard, KY; Grayson County News-Gazette, Leitchfield, KY; Floyd County Times, Prestonsburg, KY; The News Democrat & Leader, Russellville, KY; Apex Herald, Fuquay-Varina, NC; Jefferson Post, West Jefferson, NC; Bladen Journal, Elizabethtown, NC; The Tribune, Elkin, NC; The Weekly Independent, King, NC; Fuquay-Varina Independent, Fuquay-Varina, NC; Garner News, Fuquay Varina, NC; The Stokes News, Walnut Cove, NC; The Pilot, Pilot Mountain, NC; The St. Pauls Review, Saint Pauls, NC; Surry Scene, Mount Airy, NC; The Anson Record, Wadesboro, NC; The Yadkin Ripple, Yadkinville, NC; Frederick Leader, Frederick, OK; The Cheraw Chronicle, Cheraw, SC; The Newberry Observer, Newberry, SC; The Pickens Sentinel, Pickens, SC; The Easley Progress, Easley, SC; The Herald Independent, Winnsboro, SC; Macon County Times, Lafayette, TN; Claiborne County Progress, Tazewell, TN; Carroll News, Hillsville, VA; Coal Valley News, Madison, WV; The Independent Herald, Pineville, WV; Yadkin Valley Advertiser, Elkin, NC; Gilbert Times, Gilbert, WV; La Grange Shopper, LaGrange, GA; JP Shopper, West Jefferson, NC; Community News Advertiser, Laurinburg, NC; Times Advertiser, Union, SC;

Herald Media, Inc.–1 Herald Sq., Boston, MA, 02118; tel (617) 426-3000; fax (617) 451-3506; e-mail ppurcell@bostonherald.com; web site www.bostonherald.com

Est.: 1987

Pres./Pub. – Patrick J. Purcell;Daily Newspapers: Boston Herald, Boston, MA;

Herald Media, Inc.–1 Herald Sq., Boston, MA,

02118-2096; tel (617) 426-3000; fax (617) 451-3506; e-mail ppurcell@bostonherald.com; web site www.heraldmedia.com; www.bostonherald.com
Est.: 1987
Pres./Pub. – Patrick J. Purcell;

Home News Enterprises–333 Second St., Columbus, IN, 47202-3011, USA; tel (812) 379-5612; fax (812) 379-5706; web site www.homenewsenterprises.com
Est.: 1872
Pres. – Jeffrey N. Brown; CFO – Jeffery B. Rogers; Dir., HR – Jennifer L. Manning; Dir., Info. Servs. – Karen Fox Thompson; Exec. Asst. – Susan Rep; Daily Newspapers: The Republic, Columbus, IN; Daily Journal, Franklin, IN; Daily Reporter, Greenfield, IN; The Daily Journal Go, Franklin, IN; Brown County Democrat, Nashville, IN; Marketplace, Nashville, IN;

Horizon Publications–1120 N. Carbon Ste. 100, Marion, IL, 62959, USA; tel (618) 993-1711; fax (618) 997-4018; web site www.horizonpublicationsinc.com
Est.: 1999
Exec. Vice Pres./CFO – Roland McBride;Daily Newspapers: The Benton Courier, Benton, AR; Malvern Daily Record, Malvern, AR; The Observer, New Smyrna Beach, FL; The Morning News, Blackfoot, ID; The Post & Mail, Columbia City, IN; Decatur Daily Democrat, Decatur, IN; Pilot News, Plymouth, IN; Starkville Daily News, Starkville, MS; Daily Times Leader, West Point, MS; The Observer-News-Enterprise, Newton, NC; Valley City Times-Record, Valley City, ND; The Evening Leader, Saint Marys, OH; Wapakoneta Daily News, Wapakoneta, OH; Guymon Daily Herald, Guymon, OK; Poteau Daily News, Poteau, OK; The Kane Republican, Kane, PA; The Punxsutawney Spirit, Punxsutawney, PA; The Ridgway Record, Ridgway, PA; The Daily Press, Saint Marys, PA; Big Spring Herald, Big Spring, TX; Borger News-Herald, Borger, TX; Sweetwater Reporter, Sweetwater, TX; The Newport Daily Express, Newport, VT; Inyo Register, Bishop, CA; Mammoth Times, Mammoth Lakes, CA; Berne Shopping News, Berne, IN; Bourbon News-Mirror, Bourbon, IN; Bremen Enquirer, Bremen, IN; The Culver Citizen, Plymouth, IN; The Monroeville News, Monroeville, IN; Advance News, Nappanee, IN; Custer County Chief, Broken Bow, NE; The Community Post, Minster, OH; Antlers American, Antlers, OK; Jefferson County Neighbors, Punxsutawney, PA; The Daily Courier, Kelowna, BC; Penticton Herald, Penticton, BC; The Chronicle-Journal, Thunder Bay, ON; Statesman-Examiner, Colville, WA; Deer Park Tribune, Deer Park, WA; Shoppers Extra, Blackfoot, ID; Daily Press, Saint Marys, PA; Extra, Deer Park, WA; Chief X-tra, Broken Bow, NE;

Houston Community Newspapers–523 N. Sam Houston Pkwy. E., Ste. 600, Houston, TX, 77060, USA; tel (281) 668-1100; fax (281) 668-1103; web site www.hcnonline.com
CEO – Jim Hopson; CFO – Chuck Baldwin;

Huckle Media, LLC–125 Park St., Ste. 375, Traverse City, MI, 49684, USA; tel 507-645-1102; fax (231) 645-1142; e-mail rhmittelstaedt@charter.net
Pres./CEO – Renee Huckle Mittelstaedt; Sr. Vice Pres. – Ron Ensley; CFO – Rob Mittelstaedt; Vice Pres. of Develop. – Sam Gett; COO – Steve Pope; Daily Newspapers: Faribault Daily News, Faribault, MN; Owatonna People's Press, Owatonna, MN; Janesville Argus, Janesville, MN; Kenyon Leader, Kenyon, MN; The Le Center Leader, Le Center, MN; Le Sueur News-Herald, Le Sueur, MN; Northfield News, Northfield, MN; St. Peter Herald, Saint Peter, MN; Waseca County News, Waseca, MN; Northfield Area Shopper, Northfield, MN; Owatonna Area Shopper, Owatonna, MN; Faribault Area Shopper, Faribault, MN; Minnesota River Valley Shopper, Saint Peter, MN; Waseca Area Shopper, Waseca, MN;

I

impreMedia LLC–1 MetroTech Ctr., 18th Fl., Brooklyn, NY, 11201; tel (212) 807-4785; fax (212) 807-4746; e-mail john.paton@impremedia.com; web site www.impremedia.com
Chrmn./CEO – John Paton; Vice Chrmn. – Jose Lozano; CEO & Pub./CEO, La Opinion – Monica Lozano; CEO, ImpreMedia Digital – Arturo Duran; Sr. Vice Pres., Sales – Erich Linker; Sr. Vice Pres., Online Sales – Liz Saracheck; Daily Newspapers: Rumbo de Houston, Houston, TX; La Opinion, Los Angeles, CA; El Diario La Prensa, Brooklyn, NY; La Opinion, Los Angeles, CA; La Raza Newspaper, Chicago, IL; El Diario La Prensa, Brooklyn, NY; Hoy, New York, NY

Independent Newspapers, Inc. (DE)–110 Galaxy Dr., Dover, DE, 19901, USA; tel (302) 674-3600; fax (877) 377-2424; e-mail newsroom@newszap.com; web site www.newszap.com
Est.: 1953
Chrmn. of the Bd./CEO – Joe Smyth; Corp. Pres. – Tamra Brittingham; Pres., Opns. – Ed Dulin; Vice Pres., Adv. – Darel LaPrade; Dir., Research/Devel. – Chris Engel; Exec. Asst. – Sheila Clendaniel; Daily Newspapers: Delaware State News, Dover, DE; Okeechobee News, Okeechobee, FL; The Daily Banner, Cambridge, MD; Apache Junction Independent, Apache Junction, AZ; Chandler/Sun Lakes Independent, Chandler, AZ; East Mesa Independent, Apache Junction, AZ; Town of Paradise Valley Independent, Phoenix, AZ; Northeast Phoenix Independent, Scottsdale, AZ; Arrowhead Ranch Independent, Sun City, AZ; Sun Cities Independent, Sun City, AZ; Sussex Post, Milford, DE; The Harrington Journal, Harrington, DE; Milford Chronicle, Milford, DE; The Leader & State Register, Seaford, DE; The Sun, Clewiston, FL; Clewiston News, Clewiston, FL; Immokalee Bulletin, La Belle, FL; Caloosa Belle, La Belle, FL; Glades County Democrat, Clewiston, FL; The Crisfield Times, Crisfield, MD; North Scottsdale Independent, Phoenix, AZ; Peoria Independent, Sun City, AZ; Surprise Independent, Sun City, AZ; Delaware Capitol Review, Dover, DE; Gold Canyon Independent, Apache Junction, AZ;
Note: Independent Newspapers Inc. owns three daily newspapers and 25 weekly publications.

Independent Publications Inc–945 Haverford Rd, Bryn Mawr, PA, 19010-3814, USA; tel (610) 527-6330; fax (610) 527-9733; web site www.independent-publications.com

Pres./CEO – Andrew T. Bickford; Sr. Vice Pres./Treasurer – Charles E. Catherwood; Vice Pres./Sec. – William McLean; Daily Newspapers: The Telegraph, Hudson, NH; The Courier-Express/Tri-County Sunday, Du Bois, PA; News Leader, Clermont, FL; Eustis News, Mount Dora, FL; The Mount Dora Topic, Mount Dora, FL; Osceola News-Gazette, Kissimmee, FL; News Gazette, Kissimmee, FL; Hollis Brookline Journal, Milford, NH; The Cabinet, Milford, NH; Jeffersonian Democrat, Brookville, PA; The Leader-Vindicator, New Bethlehem, PA; Triangle News Leader, Mount Dora, FL; Pasco Shopper, Dade City, FL; Sumter Shopper, Dade City, FL; Bedford Journal, Milford, NH; Merrimack Journal, Milford, NH

Inland Industries, Inc.–14500 W. 105th St., Lenexa, KS, 66215; tel (913) 492-9050; fax (913) 492-6217; e-mail inmc1@inlandnews.com
Est.: 1910
Chrmn. of the Bd. – Brian D. Murray;Daily Newspapers: The Fairfield Ledger, Fairfield, IA; Mt. Pleasant News, Mount Pleasant, IA; The Washington Evening Journal, Washington, IA; Washington County Shoppers Guide, Washington, IA; Mt. Pleasant Shopper, Mount Pleasant, IA; Fairfield Town Crier, Fairfield, IA
Note: Inland Industries Inc. owns the Mt. Pleasant News (IA); Fairfield Ledger (IA); Washington Evening Journal (IA)

Iowa Newspapers, Inc.–317 Fifth St., Ames, IA, 50010, USA; tel (515) 232-2160; fax (515) 232-2364; e-mail news@amestrib.com; web site www.amestrib.com
Chrmn. – Verle Burgason; Pres. – John Goossen; Vice Pres./Controller – Pat Snyder; Circ. Dir. – Daniel Cronin; Daily Newspapers: The Tribune, Ames, IA; Dallas County News, Adel, IA; Nevada Journal, Nevada, IA; The Tri-County Times, Nevada, IA; Story Today, Ames, IA; Boone County Shopping News, Boone, IA; Dallas County Round-Up, Adel, IA; Story County Advertiser, Ames, IA; Northeast Dallas County Record, Adel, IA;

J

Jeffersonian Co. LLC–831 Wheeling Ave., Cambridge, OH, 43725, USA; tel (740) 439-3531; fax (740) 439-3533; e-mail newsroom@daily-jeff.com; web site www.daily-jeff.com

Publisher – Andrew S. Dix; Controller – Joyce Yontz; Daily Newspapers: The Daily Jeffersonian, Cambridge, OH; Barnesville Enterprise, Barnesville, OH; New Concord Area Leader, Cambridge, OH; Newcomerstown News, Newcomerstown, OH; Jeffersonian Advantage, Cambridge, OH; Byesville Village Reporter, Cambridge, OH;
Note: Jeffersonian Co. LLC owns The Daily Jeffersonian in Cambridge, OH. Jeffersonian Co. LLC is part of Dix Communications which is owned by the Wooster Republican Printing Co. Through it's subsidiaries, Alliance Publishing Co. LLC, Ashland Publishing Co. LL

Johnson Newspaper Corp.–260 Washington St., Watertown, NY, 13601, USA; tel (315) 782-1000; fax (315) 661-2520; e-mail news@wdt.net; web site www.watertowndailytimes.com
Est.: 1861
Chrmn. of the Bd./CEO – John B. Johnson; Pres./COO – Harold B. Johnson; CFO – Rich Babbit; Daily Newspapers: The Daily News, Batavia, NY; The Daily Mail, Catskill, NY; Register-Star, Hudson, NY; The Malone Telegram, Malone, NY; The Courier-Observer, The Journal & The Advance-News, Ogdensburg, NY; Watertown Daily Times, Watertown, NY; Watertown Daily Times, Watertown, WI; Carthage Republican Tribune, Carthage, NY; Greene County News, West Coxsackie, NY; Lowville Journal and Republican, Lowville, NY; Jefferson County Pennysaver, Watertown, NY; Chatham Courier, Chatham, NY; Windham Journal, Windham, NY; Mountain Eagle, Stamford, NY; St. Lawrence Plaindealer, Canton, NY;

Jones Media Inc–PO Box 1630, Greeneville, TN, 37744; tel (423) 638-4181; web site xtn.net

Jones Media, Inc.–103 W. Summer St., Greeneville, TN, 37743, USA; tel (423) 638-4181; fax (423) 639-9701; web site www.greenevillesun.com
Est.: 1879
President and CEO – Gregg K. Jones; Co-Pub. – John M. Jones; Dir., HR – Jo Ann Hobbson; CFO – Jason Edmiston; Vice Pres., Adv. – John E. Cash; Vice Pres., Circ. – Duane Uhls; Vice Pres., Special Projects – Steven K. Harbison; COO – Ralph Baldwin; Vice Pres., Western North Carolina Div. – Thomas G. Wilson; Vice Pres., Tourism – Michael J. Smith; Daily Newspapers: Village Connection, Lenoir City, TN; The Daily Post-Athenian, Athens, TN; The Greeneville Sun, Greeneville, TN; The Blowing Rocket, Blowing Rock, NC; The Mountain Times, Boone, NC; Watauga Democrat, Boone, NC; Avery Journal-Times, Newland, NC; Newport Plain Talk, Newport, TN; Rogersville Review, Rogersville, TN; The News-Herald, Lenoir City, TN; Monroe County Advocate & Democrat, Sweetwater, TN; The Herald-News, Dayton, TN;
Note: Jones Media Inc. publishes one monthly business publication, one monthly running publication, one monthly outdoor publication and a monthly tourism publication. Jones Media Inc. also operates three internet service provider companies as well as a telephon

Journal Communications Inc–333 W State St, Milwaukee, WI, 53203-1305; tel (414) 224-2000; web site www.jc.com

Journal Publishing Company–7777 Jefferson N.E., Albuquerque, NM, 87109, United States; tel (505) 823-3800; fax (505) 823-3994; web site www.abqjournal.com

Journal Register Co.–790 Township Line Rd., Yardley, PA, 19067, USA; tel (215) 504-4200; fax (215) 867-2174; e-mail rvenengas@journalregister.com; web site www.journalregister.com

CEO – John Strek; Sr. Vice Pres., Technology – Gary Terwilliger; Vice Pres., Adv – Adam M. Burnham; Vice Pres., Adv – Richard Mederios; Vice Pres., Circ. – Michael J. Murray; Vice Pres., Prodn. – William J. Higginson; Daily Newspapers: The Middletown Press, Middletown, CT; New Haven Register, New Haven, CT; The Register Citizen, Torrington, CT; The Macomb Daily, Mount Clemens, MI; Morning Sun, Mount Pleasant, MI; The Oakland Press, Pontiac, MI; The Daily Tribune, Mt. Clemens, MI; The Trentonian, Trenton, NJ; Daily Freeman, Kingston, NY; The Oneida Daily Dispatch, Oneida, NY; The Saratogian, Saratoga Springs, NY; The Record, Troy, NY; The News-Herald, Willoughby, OH; The Morning Journal, Lorain, OH; The Reporter, Lansdale, PA; The Times Herald, Norristown, PA; The Phoenix, Phoenixville, PA; The Mercury, Pottstown, PA; Delaware County Daily Times, Primos, PA; Daily Local News, West Chester, PA; Branford Review, New Haven, CT; Regional Standard, Middletown, CT; The East Hartford Gazette, East Hartford, CT; East Haven Advertiser, New Haven, CT; Fairfield Minuteman, Westport, CT; Shore Line Times, Guilford, CT; Hamden Chronicle, Milford, CT; The Litchfield County Times, New Milford, CT; Milford Weekly, Milford, CT; The Housatonic Times, New Milford, CT; The Post, Milford, CT; Pictorial Gazette, New Haven, CT; The Bulletin, Milford, CT; Thomaston Express, Torrington, CT; West Hartford News, Bristol, CT; Westport Minuteman, Westport, CT; Windsor Journal, Bristol, CT; Windsor Locks Journal, Bristol, CT; North Attleboro Free Press, North Attleboro, MA; Armada Times, New Baltimore, MI; Press & Guide Newspapers, Dearborn, MI; The Dexter Leader, Chelsea, MI; Ile Camera, Southgate, MI; The County Press, Lapeer, MI; The Advisor, Shelby Township, MI; Macomb Voice, New Baltimore, MI; The Manchester Enterprise, Saline, MI; Blue Water Voice, New Baltimore, MI; Downriver Voice, New Baltimore, MI; The Milan News-Leader, Saline, MI; The Voice, New Baltimore, MI; The North Macomb Voice, New Baltimore, MI; The Saline Reporter, Saline, MI; News-Herald, Southgate, MI; Record-Breeze, Blackwood, NJ; The Central Record, Medford, NJ; Pennington Post, Pennington, NJ; Ambler Gazette, Fort Washington, PA; Main Line Life, Wynnewood, PA; The Southern Berks News, Boyertown, PA; Boyertown Area Times, Boyertown, PA; Bristol Pilot, Bristol, PA; Township Voice, Phoenixville, PA; Tri-County

Record, Phoenixville, PA; Village News, West Chester, PA; Garnet Valley Press, Newtown Square, PA; The Recorder, Conshohocken, PA; News of Delaware County, Holmes, PA; Doylestown Patriot, Doylestown, PA; Upper Darby and Drexel Hill Press, Newtown Square, PA; The Globe, Fort Washington, PA; Elizabethtown Chronicle, Elizabethtown, PA; Glenside News, Fort Washington, PA; Hamburg Item, Hamburg, PA; Public Spirit, Fort Washington, PA; Haverford Press, Newtown Square, PA; Times Chronicle, Fort Washington, PA; King of Prussia Courier, Wayne, PA; The Kutztown Area Patriot, Hamburg, PA; Main Line Times, Ardmore, PA; Suburban Advertiser, Exton, PA; The Review, Philadelphia, PA; Montgomery Life, Fort Washington, PA; North Penn Life, Fort Washington, PA; The Oxford Tribune, Oxford, PA; News-Herald, Perkasie, PA; Mercury Sampler, Pottstown, PA; Solanco Sun-Ledger, Quarryville, PA; The Valley Item, Royersford, PA; Souderton Independent, Souderton, PA; The Kennett Paper, Kennett Square, PA; Southern Chester County Times Record, West Chester, PA; Springfield Press, Springfield, PA; Springfield Sun, Fort Washington, PA; The Suburban & Wayne Times, Wayne, PA; Willow Grove Guide, Fort Washington, PA; Yardley News, Newtown, PA; Connecticut's County Kids, Westport, CT; Lake County Kids, Willoughby, OH; Real Estate Guide, Fall River, MA; Homes for Sale, Pontiac, MI; Homes for Sale, Pontiac, MI; Homes for Sale, Pontiac, MI; Homes for Sale, Pontiac, MI; Homes for Sale, Pontiac, MI; Homes Magazine, West Chester, PA; Regional Express, Colchester, CT; Pennysaver, Old Saybrook, CT; Tradewinds, New Britain, CT; Alma Reminder, Alma, MI; Alpena Star, Alpena, MI; Straits Area Star, Cheboygan, MI; The Shoppers Guide, Alma, MI; Mt. Pleasant Buyers Guide, Mount Pleasant, MI; Presque Isle Star, Alpena, MI; Petoskey/Charlevoix Star Advertiser, Pet

Note: Journal Register Company is a newspaper company that owns 22daily newspapers, including the New Haven Register, and 346 non-daily publications. All of the company's operations in six geographic areas: Connecticut, Greater Philadelphia, Greater Cleveland,

K

KPC Media Group Inc.–102 N. Main St., Kendallville, IN, 46755-1714; tel (260) 347-0400; fax (260) 347-7281; e-mail kpc@kpcnews.net; web site www.kpcnews.com

Est.: 1911

Principal Owner – George O. Witwer; Pres./CEO/Pub. – Terry Housholder; CFO – Donna Scanlon; VP of Sales & Mkt/GM – Don Cooper; Daily Newspapers: The Evening Star, Auburn, IN; The News-Sun, Kendallville, IN; Herald-Republican, Angola, IN; The Garrett Clipper, Garrett, IN; Advance-Leader, Ligonier, IN; Smart Shopper, Angola, IN; Smart Shopper, Kendallville, IN;

Note: KPC Media Group publishes: 3 dailies - The News Sun, The Star and The Herald Republican. 3 weeklies - The Garrett Clipper, Butler Bulletin and Advance-Leader. Fort Wayne Business Weekly, Times Publications (4 shoppers direct mailed to 72,000 residence in Fort Wayne). Three phone books covering 4 north east Indiana counties. Commercial printing and mailing operation.

King County Publications–1705 132nd Ave., NE, Bellevue, WA, 98005-2251; tel (253) 872-6600; fax (425) 455-4989; web site www.kingcowww.reporternewspapers.com/;untyjournal.com

Gen. Mgr. – Don Kendall; Vice Pres., Adv. – Sandy Payson; Circ. Mgr. – Jeff Ross; Daily Newspapers: The Daily Times, Maryville, TN; Mercer Island Reporter, Mercer Island, WA; Snoqualmie Valley Record, Snoqualmie, WA;

Note: King County Publications also owns the Mercer Island Reporter and the Snoqualmie Valley Record, two weekly publications in Washington state.

L

Lakeway Publishers, Inc.–1609 W. First N. St., Morristown, TN, 37814; tel (423) 581-5630; fax (423) 581-3061; web site www.lakewaypublishersinc.com

Est.: 1966

Pub. – R. Michael Fishman; Vice Pres., Middle TN/Cor. Sec./Treasurer – Jeffrey Fishman; @RecordBody:**Note:** Lakeway Publishers Inc. also own the Morristown (TN) Citizen Tribune, a daily publication.

Lancaster Management, Inc.–645 Walnut St., Gadsden, AL, 35902, USA; tel (256) 543-3417; fax (256) 543-3548; e-mail mschuver@lminews.com; web site www.lminews.com

Pres. – Charles W. Lancaster; Vice Pres. – Michael F. Schuver; Vice Pres. – Jeff R. Selsor; John Lancaster; Ben Lancaster; Daily Newspapers: De Queen Daily Citizen, De Queen, AR; Southwest Daily Times, Liberal, KS; The Murray Ledger & Times, Murray, KY; Branson Tri-Lakes Daily News, Branson, MO; The Hopewell News, Hopewell, VA; Ashley News Observer, Crossett, AR; De Queen Bee, De Queen, AR; Mena Star, Mena, AR; The Citizen, Waldron, AR; The Waldron News, Waldron, AR; The McDuffie Progress, Thomson, GA; Albia Union-Republican, Albia, IA; Chariton Herald-Patriot, Chariton, IA; The Chariton Leader, Chariton, IA; Corydon Times Republican, Corydon, IA; Moravia Union, Moulton, IA; The Humeston News Era, Corydonn, IA; Georgetown News-Graphic, Georgetown, KY; The Paintsville Herald, Paintsville, KY; The Appalachian News-Express, Pikeville, KY; Sea Coast Echo, Bay Saint Louis, MS; Stone County Enterprise, Wiggins, MS; The Moore County News-Press, Dumas, TX; Ouachita Trading Post, Mena, AR; Scott County Advertiser, Waldron, AR; Dollar Saver, Thomson, GA; Ashley County Shopper Guide, Crossett, AR; The Advisor, Albia, IA; Chariton Shopper's Guide, Chariton, IA; Corydon Penny Saver, Corydon, IA; The Scott Shopper, Georgetown, KY; Eastern Kentucky Shopper, Pikeville, KY; The Mountain Bargain Hunter, Pikeville, KY; The Discover Deal Shopper, Branson, MO; Tri-Cities Advertiser, Hopewell, VA; Moulton Weekly Tribune, Albia, IA; Monroe County News, Albia, IA; Los Tiempos, Liberal, KS; Eastern Kentucky Shopper, Paintsville, KY;

Note: Lancaster Management Inc. owns one daily newspapers and more than 30 weekly and shopper publications.

Landmark Communications, Inc.–150 W. Brambleton Ave., Norfolk, VA, 23510-2018, USA; tel (757) 446-2010; fax (757) 446-2004; e-mail info@landmarkinteractive.com; web site http://www.landmarkinteractive.com; www.landmarkinteractive.com

Chrmn. of the Bd./CEO – Frank Batten; Vice Chrmn. – Richard F. Barry; Pres./COO – Decker Anstrom; Exec. Vice Pres./Sec./Gen. Counsel – Guy Friddell; Exec. Vice Pres./Pres., Landmark Publishing Grp. – R. Bruce Bradley; Exec. Vice Pres., HR – Charlie W. Hill; Vice Pres., Finance – Colleen Pittman; Daily Newspapers: Citrus County Chronicle, Crystal River, FL; The News Enterprise, Elizabethtown, KY; Carroll County Times, Westminster, MD; Las Vegas Optic, Las Vegas, NM; Los Alamos Monitor, Los Alamos, NM; News & Record, Greensboro, NC; The Virginian-Pilot, Norfolk, VA; The Roanoke Times, Roanoke, VA; Brighton Standard Blade, Brighton, CO; Commerce City Express, Brighton, CO; The Canyon Courier, Evergreen, CO; Fort Lupton Press, Brighton, CO; Clear Creek Courant, Idaho Springs, CO; Columbine Courier, Littleton, CO; La Salle Leader, Brighton, CO; Cedar Key Beacon, Cedar Key, FL; Chiefland Citizen, Chiefland, FL; Riverland News, Dunnellon, FL; Gadsden County Times, Quincy, FL; Sumter County Times, Bushnell, FL; Wakulla News, Crawfordville, FL; Williston Pioneer Sun News, Williston, FL; Opinion-Tribune, Glenwood, IA; Red Oak Express, Red Oak, IA; Mount Vernon Democrat, Mount Vernon, IN; Perry County News, Tell City, IN; Spencer County Journal-Democrat, Rockport, IN; Kentucky Standard, Bardstown, KY; Trimble Banner, Bedford, KY; Pioneer News, Shepherdsville, KY; Central Kentucky News-Journal, Campbellsville, KY; News-Democrat, Carrollton, KY; Cynthiana Democrat, Cynthiana, KY; Grant County Express, Williamstown, KY; Grant County News, Williamstown, KY; LaRue County Herald News, Hodgenville, KY; Oldham Era, La Grange, KY; The Anderson News, Lawrenceburg, KY; Lebanon Enterprise, Lebanon, KY; Casey County News, Liberty, KY; Henry County Local, New Castle, KY; News-Herald, Owenton, KY; The Sentinel-News, Shelbyville, KY; Springfield Sun, Springfield, KY; Spencer Magnet, Taylorsville, KY; New Albany Gazette, New Albany, MS; The Brunswick Beacon, Shallotte, NC; News & Reporter, Chester, SC; Lancaster News, Lancaster, SC; Pageland Progressive-Journal, Pageland, SC; Harriman Record, Kingston, TN; La Follette Press, La Follette, TN; Morgan County News, Wartburg, TN; Roane County News, Kingston, TN; Rockwood Times, Kingston, TN; Bedford Bulletin, Bedford, VA; Gazette, Galax, VA; The Declaration, Independence, VA; Tidewater-Peninsula Parent, Norfolk, VA; Central Kentucky Homes Real Estate, Elizabethtown, KY; Eastern Panhandle Real Estate Guide, Martinsburg, WV; Fayette County Shopper, Vandalia, IL; Posey County Advantage, Mount Vernon, IN; Lincoln's Country, Rockport, IN; LincolnLand Shopping Guide, Tell City, IN; Town & Country Shopper, Glenwood, IA; Express Extender, Red Oak, IA; Kentucky Standard Extra, Bardstown, KY; Central Kentucky News-Journal (CKNJ) Extra, Campbellsville, KY; River City Trading Post, Carrollton, KY; Harrison Shopper, Cynthiana, KY; The Anderson Advertiser, Lawrenceburg, KY; Marketplace, La Grange, KY; Sentinel News Plus, Shelbyville, KY; Pioneer News Extra, Shepherdsville, KY; Mason-Dixon Marketplace, Westminster, MD; Gazette Guide, New Albany, MS; The Shopper, Kingston, TN; Bedford Bullet, Bedford, VA; Gazette Plus, Galax, VA; Style Weekly, Richmond, VA; Port Folio Weekly, Norfolk, VA; Turret, Fort Knox, KY; Fort Hood Sentinel, Temple, TX; Brighton Advertiser, Brighton, CO; Adams County Advertiser, Brighton, CO; East Weld Advertiser, Brighton, CO; Fort Lupton Advertiser, Brighton, CO;

Note: Landmark Communications Inc. has a 49.9% interest in Capital-Gazette Communications Inc. in Annapolis, MD. Landmark owns and operates two CBS affiliated television stations and cable channel networks. Landmark is also 50% owner, with Cox Communications,

Landmark Community Newspapers, LLC–601 Taylorsville Rd., Shelbyville, KY, 40065, USA; tel (502) 633-4334; fax (502) 633-4447; web site www.lcni.com

Est.: 1973

President – Michael G. Abernathy; Adv. Dir. – Tony Martinette; Daily Newspapers: Citrus County Chronicle, Crystal River, FL; The News Enterprise, Elizabethtown, KY; Carroll County Times, Westminster, MD; Las Vegas Optic, Las Vegas, NM; Los Alamos Monitor, Los Alamos, NM; Brighton Standard Blade, Brighton, CO; Commerce City Express, Brighton, CO; The Canyon Courier, Evergreen, CO; Fort Lupton Press, Brighton, CO; Columbine Courier, Littleton, CO; Chiefland Citizen, Chiefland, FL; Riverland News, Dunnellon, FL; Gadsden County Times, Quincy, FL; Sumter County Times, Bushnell, FL; Wakulla News, Crawfordville, FL; Williston Pioneer Sun News, Williston, FL; Opinion-Tribune, Glenwood, IA; Red Oak Express, Red Oak, IA; Leader-Union, Vandalia, IL; Mount Vernon Democrat, Mount Vernon, IN; Perry County News, Tell City, IN; Spencer County Journal-Democrat, Rockport, IN; Kentucky Standard, Bardstown, KY; Trimble Banner, Bedford, KY; Pioneer News, Shepherdsville, KY; Central Kentucky News-Journal, Campbellsville, KY; News-Democrat, Carrollton, KY; Cynthiana Democrat, Cynthiana, KY; Grant County Express, Williamstown, KY; Grant County News, Williamstown, KY; LaRue County Herald News, Hodgenville, KY; Oldham Era, La Grange, KY; The Anderson News, Lawrenceburg, KY; Lebanon Enterprise, Lebanon, KY; Casey County News, Liberty, KY; Henry County Local, New Castle, KY; News-Herald, Owenton, KY; The Sentinel-News, Shelbyville, KY; Springfield Sun, Springfield, KY; Spencer Magnet, Taylorsville, KY; New Albany Gazette, New Albany, MS; News & Reporter, Chester, SC; Lancaster News, Lancaster, SC; Pageland Progressive-Journal, Pageland, SC; Harriman Record, Kingston, TN; La Follette Press, La Follette, TN; Morgan County News, Wartburg, TN; Roane County News, Kingston, TN; Rockwood Times, Kingston, TN; Bedford Bulletin, Bedford, VA; Gazette, Galax, VA; The Declaration, Independence, VA; Fayette County Shopper, Vandalia, IL; Posey County Advantage, Mount Vernon, IN; Lincoln's Country, Rockport, IN; LincolnLand Shopping Guide, Tell City, IN; Town & Country Shopper, Glenwood, IA; Express Extender, Red Oak, IA; Kentucky Standard Extra, Bardstown, KY; Central Kentucky News-Journal (CKNJ) Extra, Campbellsville, KY; River City Trading Post, Carrollton, KY; Harrison Shopper, Cynthiana, KY; The Anderson Advertiser, Lawrenceburg, KY; Marketplace, La Grange, KY; Sentinel News Plus, Shelbyville, KY; Pioneer News Extra, Shepherdsville, KY; Mason-Dixon Marketplace, Westminster, MD; Gazette Guide, New Albany, MS; The Shopper, Kingston, TN; Bedford Bullet, Bedford, VA; Gazette Plus, Galax, VA; Brighton Advertiser, Brighton, CO; Adams County Advertiser, Brighton, CO; East Weld Advertiser, Brighton, CO; Fort Lupton Advertiser, Brighton, CO;

Landmark Media Enterprises LLC–150 W Brambleton Ave, Norfolk, VA, 23510-2018; tel (757) 446-2010; web site www.landmarkcommunications.com

Landmark Metro West Newspapers–139 N. Main St., Brighton, CO, 80601; tel (303) 659-1141; fax (303) 659-2901; e-mail news@metrowestnewspaper.com; web site www.metrowestfyi.com

Pub. – Karen Lambert;

Lee Enterprises, Inc.–201 N. Harrison St., Davenport, IA, 52801-1939, USA; tel (563) 383-2100; fax (563) 328-4319; e-mail information@lee.net; web site www.lee.net

Est.: 1890

Chrmn./Pres./CEO – Mary E. Junck; Vice Pres./CFO/Treasurer – Carl G. Schmidt; Vice Pres. – Michael R. Gulledge; Vice Pres., Commun. – Daniel K. Hayes; Vice Pres., HR – Vytenis P. Kuraitis; Vice Pres., Sales/Mktg. – Paul M. Farrell; Vice Pres., Publishing – Kevin Mowbray; Vice Pres., Publishing – Greg R. Veon; Vice Pres., News – Joyce Dehli; Vice Pres., Interactive Media/Cor. Counsel – Greg P. Schermer; Vice Pres., Prodn./Chief Info. Officer – Brian Kardell; Dir., Classified Adv. – Chelle Davila; Daily Newspapers: Flagstaff Live!, Flagstaff, AZ; American Canyon Eagle, Napa, CA; Valley Free Press, Sandwich, IL; Arizona Daily

Sun, Flagstaff, AZ; Arizona Daily Star, Tucson, AZ; North County Times, Escondido, CA; The Sentinel, Hanford, CA; The Lompoc Record, Lompoc, CA; Napa Valley Register, Napa, CA; Santa Maria Times, Santa Maria, CA; The Garden Island, Lihue, HI; The Times-News, Twin Falls, ID; The Pantagraph, Bloomington, IL; The Southern Illinoisan, Carbondale, IL; Times-Courier, Mattoon, IL; Herald & Review, Decatur, IL; Journal-Gazette, Mattoon, IL; The Times, Munster, IN; Quad-City Times, Davenport, IA; Globe-Gazette, Mason City, IA; Muscatine Journal, Muscatine, IA; Sioux City Journal, Sioux City, IA; The Courier, Waterloo, IA; The Ledger Independent, Maysville, KY; Winona Daily News, Winona, MN; Daily Journal, Park Hills, MO; St. Louis Post-Dispatch, Saint Louis, MO; Billings Gazette, Billings, MT; The Montana Standard, Butte, MT; Ravalli Republic, Hamilton, MT; Independent Record, Helena, MT; Missoulian, Missoula, MT; Beatrice Daily Sun, Beatrice, NE; Columbus Telegram, Columbus, NE; Fremont Tribune, Fremont, NE; Lincoln Journal Star, Lincoln, NE; Citizen, Auburn, NY; The Post-Star, Glens Falls, NY; The Bismarck Tribune, Bismarck, ND; Albany Democrat-Herald, Albany, OR; The World, Coos Bay, OR; Corvallis Gazette-Times, Corvallis, OR; The Sentinel, Carlisle, PA; The Times and Democrat, Orangeburg, SC; Rapid City Journal, Rapid City, SD; The Daily Herald, Provo, UT; The Daily News, Longview, WA; The Chippewa Herald, Chippewa Falls, WI; La Crosse Tribune, La Crosse, WI; The Journal Times, Racine, WI; Casper Star-Tribune, Casper, WY; Times-Press-Recorder, Santa Maria, CA; The Weekly Calistogan, Calistogan, CA; Twin City Times, Riverdale, CA; The Coalinga Record, Coalinga, CA; The Kingsburg Recorder, Kingsburg, CA; Lemoore Advance, Lemoore, CA; St. Helena Star, Saint Helena, CA; The Selma Enterprise, Selma, CA; Santa Ynez Valley News/Extra, Solvang, CA; The Britt Tribune-News, Britt, IA; The Forest City Summit, Forest City, IA; Mitchell County Press-News, Osage, IA; Gooding County Leader, Gooding, ID; Wood River Journal, Hailey, ID; North Side News, Jerome, ID; Belleville Journal, Swansea, IL; Cahokia-Dupo Journal, Swansea, IL; Collinsville Journal, Collinsville, IL; Clarion Enterprise Journal, Columbia, IL; The MidWeek, Sycamore, IL; East St. Louis Journal, Swansea, IL; Edwardsville Journal, Collinsville, IL; Fairview Heights Journal, Swansea, IL; Farmer City Journal, Farmer City, IL; Granite City Press-Record Journal, Collinsville, IL; Heyworth Star, Heyworth, IL; Le Roy Journal, Le Roy, IL; Enterprise Journal, Columbia, IL; The Woodford County Journal, Eureka, IL; Houston County News, La Crescent, MN; Jefferson County Journal, Festus, MO; Florissant/Black Jack-North County Journal, Hazelwood, MO; Chesterfield Journal, Saint Louis, MO; Southwest County Journal, Town and Country, MO; West County Journal, Town and Country, MO; Bellefontaine Neighbors/Jennings-North County Journal, Hazelwood, MO; News Democrat Journal, Chesterfield, MO; Meramec Journal, Festus, MO; Democrat News, Fredericktown, MO; St. Charles County Journal, Saint Peters, MO; Hazelwood/Bridgeton Journal-North County Journal, Hazelwood, MO; Tri-County Journal, Town and Country, MO; Mid-County Journal, Town and Country, MO; South County Journal, Saint Louis, MO; South Side Journal, Saint Louis, MO; SouthWest City Journal, Saint Louis, MO; St. Charles Journal, Saint Peters, MO; North Side Journal, Hazelwood, MO; Overland/St. Ann Journal-North Couny Journal, Hazelwood, MO; St. Peters Journal, Saint Peters, MO; Citizen Journal, Town and Country, MO; Warrenton Journal, Warrenton, MO; Webster-Kirkwood Journal, Town and Country, MO; Wentzville Journal, Warrenton, MO; Mandan News, Mandan, ND; The Chadron Record, Chadron, NE; The Banner-Press, David City, NE; Neighborhood Extra, Lincoln, NE; The Plattsmouth Journal, Plattsmouth, NE; The Schuyler Sun, Schuyler, NE; Burt County P

Note: Lee Enterprises Inc. owns more than 40 daily newspapers and a joint interest in six others, along with associated online services. Lee Enterprises also publishes nearly 200 weekly newspapers, shoppers and specialty publications. Capital Newspapers of M

Lee Enterprises Incorporated–201 N Harrison St Ste 600, Davenport, IA, 52801-1918; tel (563)383-2100; e-mail information@lee.net; web site www.lee.net
Est.: 1890

Lewis Newspapers–302 S. Cross St., Robinson, IL, 62454, United States; tel (618) 544-2101; fax (618) 544-9533; e-mail news@robdailynews.com; web site www.robdailynews.com
Est.: 1919
Pub. – Kathleen Lewis;Daily Newspapers: Daily Record, Lawrenceville, IL; Daily News, Robinson, IL; Lawrence County News, Lawrenceville, IL; The Constitution, Robinson, IL;
Note: Lewis Newspapers also owns the Robinson (IL) Constitution and the Lawrence (IL) County News, two weekly newspapers, and the Lawrenceville (IL) Daily Record.

Lorain County Printing & Publishing Corp.–225 East Ave., Elyria, OH, 44035-5634, USA; tel (440) 329-7000; fax (440) 329-7272; e-mail ctnews@chroniclet.com; web site www.chroniclet.com
Group: Lorain County Printing & Publishing Co.
Est.: 1927
President and CEO – Paul Martin;Daily Newspapers: Chronicle-Telegram, Elyria, OH; The Medina County Gazette, Medina, OH;

Louisiana State Newspapers–600 Jefferson St., Lafayette, LA, 70502-6942, USA; tel (337) 266-2154; fax (337) 266-2127
Chrmn. – B.I. Moody; Pres. – Stephen Moody; COO – Darrell Guillory; Loan Officer – Willie Pitre; Daily Newspapers: Abbeville Meridional, Abbeville, LA; The Crowley Post-Signal, Crowley, LA; Amite Tangi-Digest, Amite, LA; Avoyelles Journal, Marksville, LA; Bunkie Record, Bunkie, LA; Church Point News, Church Point, LA; The Watchman, Clinton, LA; Caldwell Watchman Progress, Columbia, LA; The News Journal, Columbia, LA; The Delhi Dispatch, Rayville, LA; Eunice News, Eunice, LA; Gueydan Journal, Gueydan, LA; Hammond Vindicator, Amite, LA; The Kaplan Herald, Kaplan, LA; The Kentwood News-Ledger, Kentwood, LA; Kinder Courier News, Kinder, LA; The Mamou Acadian Press, Ville Platte, LA; The Marksville Weekly News, Marksville, LA; The Oakdale Journal, Oakdale, LA; The Rayne-Acadian Tribune, Rayne, LA; Richland Beacon-News, Rayville, LA; St. Helena Echo, Greensburg, LA; Breaux Bridge Marketplace, Saint Martinville, LA; Teche News, Saint Martinville, LA; Ville Platte Gazette, Ville Platte, LA; The Welsh Citizen, Welsh, LA; The West Carroll Gazette, Oak Grove, LA; St. Francisville Democrat, Saint Francisville, LA; The Plainsman-News, Zachary, LA;
Note: Louisiana State Newspapers owns two daily newspapers and 27 weekly publications.

M

Maine Today Media Inc.–One City Center, Fifth floor, Portland, ME, 04101; tel (207) 791-6650; web site www.mainetoday.com
Pres./Pub. – Richard L. Connor;Daily Newspapers: Kennebec Journal, Augusta, ME; Portland Press Herald/Maine Sunday Telegram, Portland, ME; Morning Sentinel, Waterville, ME; Coastal Journal, Bath, ME;

Mainstreet Media Group–6400 Monterey Rd., Gilroy, CA, 95021-2365, USA; tel (408) 842-6400; fax (408) 842-7105; e-mail aaallegretti@yahoo.com
Est.: 2003
Pres./CEO – Anthony Allegretti; Sr. Vice Pres./COO – Stephen Staloch; CFO – Chris Lake; Daily Newspapers: The Dispatch, Gilroy, CA; Free Lance, Hollister, CA; Del Mar Times, Lajolla, CA; Carmel Valley Leader, La Jolla, CA; Solano Beach, La Jolla, CA; Amador Ledger-Dispatch, Jackson, CA; La Jolla Light, La Jolla, CA; Morgan Hill Times, Morgan Hill, CA; The Pinnacle, Hollister, CA; Good Times, Santa Cruz, CA;
Note: Mainstreet Media Group owns 12 weekly newspapers, clustered in San Diego, south of San Jose

Mainstreet Media Group LLC–6400 Monterey Road, Gilroy, CA, 95020-6628; tel (408) 842-6400; web site www.mainstreetmg.com

Frank Mayborn Enterprises, Inc.–10 S. Third St., Temple, TX, 76501; tel (254) 778-4444; fax (254) 774-9391; e-mail tdt@temple-telegram.com; web site www.tdtnews.com
Est.: 1979
Pres. – Anyse Sue Mayborn;Daily Newspapers: Killeen Daily Herald, Killeen, TX; Temple Daily Telegram, Temple, TX;

The McClatchy Company–2100 Q St., Sacramento, CA, 95816-6899, USA; tel (916) 321-1855; fax (916) 321-1869; web site www.mcclatchy.com
Est.: 1857
Chairman, President & CEO – Gary Pruitt; Vice Pres./Sec./Gen. Counsel – Karole Morgan-Prager; Vice Pres., Finance/CFO – Patrick Talamantes; Vice Pres., HR – Heather Fagundes; Vice Pres., Adv. – Stephen Bernard; Vice President, Operations – Robert Weil; Vice Pres., Interactive Media – Christian Hendricks; Vice President, Operations – Mark Zieman; Vice President, News and Washington Editor – Anders Gyllenhaal; Vice Pres., Opns. – Frank Whittaker; Controller – Hai Nguyen; Daily Newspapers: Anchorage Daily News, Anchorage, AK; The Fresno Bee, Fresno, CA; Merced Sun-Star, Merced, CA; The Modesto Bee, Modesto, CA; Valley Times, Pleasanton, CA; West County Times, Richmond, CA; The Sacramento Bee, Sacramento, CA; The Tribune, San Luis Obispo, CA; The Bradenton Herald, Bradenton, FL; The Miami Herald, Miami, FL; Columbus Ledger-Enquirer, Columbus, GA; The Macon Telegraph, Macon, GA; The Idaho Statesman, Boise, ID; Belleville News-Democrat, Belleville, IL; The Olathe News, Olathe, KS; The Wichita Eagle, Wichita, KS; Lexington Herald-Leader, Lexington, KY; The Sun Herald, Biloxi, MS; The Kansas City Star, Kansas City, MO; The Charlotte Observer, Charlotte, NC; The News & Observer, Raleigh, NC; Nuevo Mundo, San Jose, CA; Centre Daily Times, State College, PA; The Beaufort Gazette, Beaufort, SC; The State, Columbia, SC; The Island Packet, Hilton Head, SC; The Sun News, Myrtle Beach, SC; The Herald, Rock Hill, SC; Fort Worth Star-Telegram, Fort Worth, TX; The Bellingham Herald, Bellingham, WA; The Olympian, Olympia, WA; Tri-City Herald, Tri-Cities, WA; The News Tribune, Tacoma, WA; El Nuevo Herald, Miami, FL; Alameda Journal, Alameda, CA; Atwater Signal, Merced, CA; The Cambrian, Cambria, CA; The Chowchilla News, Chowchilla, CA; The Clovis Independent, Clovis, CA; The Cupertino Courier, San Jose, CA; Brentwood News, Antioch, CA; El Cerrito Albany Journal, Walnut Creek, CA; Lamorinda Sun, Walnut Creek, CA; Los Banos Enterprise, Los Banos, CA; Campbell Reporter, San Jose, CA; Sun-Bulletin, Morro Bay, CA; Sierra Star, Oakhurst, CA; The Montclarion, Walnut Creek, CA; Pacifica Tribune, Pacifica, CA; Salinas Valley Weekly, Salinas, CA; Willow Glen Resident, San Jose, CA; Saratoga News, San Jose, CA; The Sunnyvale Sun, San Jose, CA; Florida Keys Keynoter, Marathon, FL; The Reporter, Tavernier, FL; Highland News Leader, Highland, IL; O'Fallon Progress, O'Fallon, IL; Pinckneyville Democrat, Pinckneyville, IL; Sparta News-Plaindealer, Belleville, IL; Star-Herald, Belton, MO; Cass County Democrat-Missourian, Harrisonville, MO; Lee's Summit Journal, Lee's Summit, MO; The Cary News, Raleigh, NC; Chapel Hill News, Chapel Hill, NC; The Herald, Smithfield, NC; Eastern Wake News, Zebulon, NC; York and Clover Enquirer-Herald, York, SC; Fort Mill Times, Fort Mill, SC; The Keller Citizen, Keller, TX; Mansfield News-Mirror, Mansfield, TX; The Peninsula Gateway, Gig Harbor, WA; Los Gatos Weekly-Times, Los Gatos, CA; Sierra Home Advertiser, Oakhurst, CA; El Nuevo Herald, Miami, FL; La Estrella, Fort Worth, TX; Berkeley Voice, Richmond, CA; Piedmonter, Alameda, CA; Vida en el Valle, Fresno, CA; The Puyallup Herald, Puyallup, WA; Almaden Resident, San Jose, CA; Rose Garden Resident, San Jose, CA;
Note: The McClatchy Company is a leading news and information provider, offering a wide array of print and digital products in each of the markets it serves. As the third largest newspaper company in the United States, McClatchy's operations include 30 daily newspapers, community newspapers, websites, mobile news and advertising, niche publications, direct marketing and direct mail services. McClatchy's largest newspapers include The Miami Herald, The Sacramento Bee, the Fort Worth Star-Telegram, The Kansas City Star, The Charlotte Observer and The News & Observer in Raleigh, N.C. McClatchy is listed on the New York Stock Exchange under the symbol MNI.

McNaughton Newspapers–1250 Texas St., Fairfield, CA, 94533, USA; tel (707) 425-4646; fax (707) 425-5924; web site www.dailyrepublic.com
Pres./CEO – Foy McNaughton; Vice Pres. – R. McNaughton; Adv. Dir. – Sharon Guy; Daily Newspapers: The Davis Enterprise, Davis, CA; Daily Republic, Fairfield, CA; Mountain Democrat, Placerville, CA; El Dorado Gazette, Georgetown Gazette & Town Crier, Georgetown, CA; Winters Express, Winters, CA; Village Life, Placerville, CA; Folsom Life, Folsom, CA;
Note: McNaughton also owns the El Dorado Gazette, Georgetown Gazette & Town Crier, Folsom Life Folsom, the Village Life and the Winters Express all weekly publications located in California.

Media General Inc–PO Box 85333, Richmond, VA, 23293-0001; tel (804) 649-6000; web site www.mediageneral.com

Media General, Inc.–333 E. Franklin St., Richmond, VA, 23219-0001, USA; tel (804) 649-6000; fax (804) 649-6865; web site www.mediageneral.com
Chrmn. of the Bd. – J. Stewart Bryan; Pres./CEO – Marshall N. Morton; COO – O. Reid Ashe; Vice Pres., Finance/CFO/Treasurer – John A. Schauss; Vice Pres., Media General/Pres., Interactive Media – Neal F. Fondren; Vice Pres., Media General/Pres., Broadcast Div. – James A. Zimmerman; Vice Pres., Cor. Commun. – Lou Anne Nabhan; Sec./Gen. Counsel – George L. Mahoney; Controller – Stephen Y. Dickinson; Mgr., Cor. Commun. – Ray Kozakewicz; Pres., Community Newspapers – Robert E. MacPherson; Pres., Florida Commun. Grp. – John Schueler; Daily Newspapers: The Dothan Eagle, Dothan, AL; The Enterprise Ledger, Enterprise, AL; Opelika-Auburn News, Opelika, AL; Hernando Today, Brooksville, FL; Highlands Today, Sebring, FL; Jackson County Floridan, Marianna, FL; The Tampa Tribune, Tampa, FL; Independent Tribune, Concord, NC; The Eden Daily News, Reidsville, NC; The Hickory Daily Record, Hickory, NC; The McDowell News, Marion, NC; The News Herald, Morganton, NC; The Reidsville Review, Reidsville, NC; Statesville

Record & Landmark, Statesville, NC; Winston-Salem Journal, Winston-Salem, NC; Morning News, Florence, SC; Bristol Herald Courier, Bristol, VA; The Daily Progress, Charlottesville, VA; Culpeper Star-Exponent, Culpeper, VA; Danville Register & Bee, Danville, VA; The News & Advance, Lynchburg, VA; Manassas Journal Messenger, Manassas, VA; Richmond Times-Dispatch, Richmond, VA; The News Virginian, Waynesboro, VA; News & Messenger, Woodbridge, VA; Dothan Progress, Dothan, AL; Eufaula Tribune, Eufaula, AL; The Suncoast News, New Port Richey, FL; The Messenger, Reivsville, NC; Mooresville Tribune, Mooresville, NC; The Messenger, Hartsville, SC; Washington County News, Abingdon, VA; Amherst New Era-Progress, Amherst, VA; The Goochland Gazette, Mechanicsville, VA; Nelson County Times, Amherst, VA; Mechanicsville Local, Mechanicsville, VA; Richlands News Press, Richlands, VA; Stafford County Sun, Stafford, VA;

MediaNews Group Inc–101 W Colfax Ave, Ste 1100, Denver, CO, 80202, USA; tel (303)Â 954-6360; fax (303) 954-6320; e-mail contact@medianewsgroup.com; web site www.medianewsgroup.com
Vice Chrmn./CEO – William Dean Singleton; Vice Pres./CFO – Ron Mayo; Vice Pres./Controller – Michael J. Koren; Vice Pres. of Sales – Michael Petrak; Vice Pres., HR – Charles Kamen; Vice Pres., Tax – Steve Barkmeir; Vice Pres., News – David J. Butler; Treasurer – James McDougald; Assistant to the CEO / Corp. Sec. – Pat Robinson; Vice President of Field Operations – Sara Glines; Sr. Vice President Circulation – Steve Hesse; Vice President, IT – Mel Gordon; Chrmn. of the Board – Richard B. Scudder; Pres. – Joseph J. Lodovic; Exec. Pres./COO – Steven B. Rossi; Sr. Vice Pres., Opns. – Anthony F. Tierno; Sr. Vice Pres., New Bus. Devel. – Liz Gaier; Vice Pres./CIO – David Bessen; Daily Newspapers: Morgan Times Review, Fort Morgan, CO; Fairbanks Daily News-Miner, Fairbanks, AK; Kodiak Daily Mirror, Kodiak, AK; Chico Enterprise-Record, Chico, CA; Times-Standard, Eureka, CA; The Argus, Fremont, CA; The Daily Review, Hayward, CA; Lake County Record-Bee, Lakeport, CA; Press-Telegram, Long Beach, CA; Daily News, Woodland Hills, CA; Marin Independent Journal, Novato, CA; The Monterey County Herald, Monterey, CA; The Oakland Tribune, Oakland, CA; Inland Valley Daily Bulletin, Ontario, CA; Palo Alto Daily News, Menlo Park, CA; Pasadena Star-News, Pasadena, CA; Tri-Valley Herald/San Ramon Valley Herald, Pleasanton, CA; Daily News, Red Bluff, CA; Redlands Daily Facts, Redlands, CA; San Bernardino County Sun, San Bernardino, CA; San Gabriel Valley Tribune, Covina, CA; San Jose Mercury News, San Jose, CA; San Mateo County Times, San Mateo, CA; Santa Cruz Sentinel, Scotts Valley, CA; Daily Breeze, Torrance, CA; Ukiah Daily Journal, Ukiah, CA; The Reporter, Vacaville, CA; Vallejo Times-Herald, Vallejo, CA; Contra Costa Times, Walnut Creek, CA; The Whittier Daily News, Whittier, CA; The Daily Democrat, Woodland, CA; The Denver Post, Denver, CO; Fort Morgan Times, Fort Morgan, CO; Lamar Ledger, Lamar, CO; Journal-Advocate, Sterling, CO; The News-Times, Danbury, CT; The Advocate, Stamford, CT; Sentinel & Enterprise, Fitchburg, MA; The Sun, Lowell, MA; North Adams Transcript, North Adams, MA; The Berkshire Eagle, Pittsfield, MA; The Detroit News, Detroit, MI; St. Paul Pioneer Press, Saint Paul, MN; The Humboldt Sun, Winnemucca, NV; Alamogordo Daily News, Alamogordo, NM; Current-Argus, Carlsbad, NM; Deming Headlight, Deming, NM; The Daily Times, Farmington, NM; Las Cruces Sun-News, Las Cruces, NM; Public Opinion, Chambersburg, PA; The Evening Sun, Hanover, PA; The Lebanon Daily News, Lebanon, PA; York Daily Record, York, PA; El Paso Times, El Paso, TX; The Salt Lake Tribune, Salt Lake City, UT; Bennington Banner, Bennington, VT; Brattleboro Reformer, Brattleboro, VT; Charleston Daily Mail, Charleston, WV; Azusa Herald Highlander, West Covina, CA; Clear Lake Observer-American, Clear Lake, CA; Covina Press Courier Highlander, West Covina, CA; Diamond Bar Highlander, West Covina, CA; Fort Bragg Advocate-News, Fort Bragg, CA; Glendora Press Highlander, West Covina, CA; Hacienda Heights Highlander, West Covina, CA; La Puente Highlander, West Covina, CA; Milpitas Post, Milpitas, CA; Palos Verdes Peninsula News, Rolling Hills Estates, CA; Paradise Post, Paradise, CA; Rowland Heights Highlander, West Covina, CA; San Dimas/La Verne Highlander, West Covina, CA; Walnut Highlander, West Covina, CA; West Covina Highlander, West Covina, CA; The Willits News, Willits, CA; Akron News-Reporter, Akron, CO; The Brush News-Tribune, Brush, CO; Burlington Record, Burlington, CO; Estes Park Trail-Gazette, Estes Park, CO; Julesburg Advocate, Julesburg, CO; The Public Spirit, Ayer, MA; Greenfield Town Crier, Greenfield, MA; Broadcaster, Lowell, MA; The Ruidoso News, Ruidoso, NM; The Battle Mountain Bugle, Battle Mountain, NV; Breckenridge American, Breckenridge, TX; Burleson Star, Burleson, TX; The Graham Leader, Graham, TX; The Jack County Herald, Jacksboro, TX; Jacksboro Gazette-News, Jacksboro, TX; Joshua Star, Burleson, TX; The Olney Enterprise, Olney, TX; Park Record, Park City, UT; Bellows Falls Town Crier, Brattleboro, VT; Brattleboro Town Crier, Brattleboro, VT; Manchester Journal, Manchester, VT; Tri-City Weekly, Eureka, CA; Wave, Pacifica, CA; Hometown Shopper, Ukiah, CA; Tri-State Trader, Lamar, CO; Weekly Star, Vacaville, CA; The Nazareth US, Easton, PA; Sun Marketplace, Hanover, PA; Weekly Record, York, PA; Burlington Plains Dealer, Burlington, CO; The Eagle Shopper, Pittsfield, MA; Lebanon Valley Review, Lebanon, PA; Lake Country Shopper, Graham, TX; Fremont Bulletin, Milpitas, CA; Penny Slaver, Clearlake, CA; Times Standard Plus, Eureka, CA; Bee Smart Shopper, Lakeport, CA; The Palm Advertiser, Lebanon, PA; The Shopping News, Sterling, CO; Alvarado

Mid-South Management Co., Inc.–172 E. Main St., Ste. 300, Spartanburg, SC, 29306, USA; tel (864) 583-2907; fax (864) 573-7640; e-mail ababb@msmgmt.com; web site www.mid-southmanagement.com
Est.: 1948
Chrmn. of the Bd. – Phyllis B. DeLapp; Pres. – Andrew M. Babb; Vice Pres./Sec./Treasurer – Loretta W. Conner; Technology Systems Dir. – Keith Young;

Moffitt Newspapers–PO Box 8565, Roanoke, VA, 24014; tel (304) 645-1206; fax (304) 645-7104; e-mail WVDN2@aol.com
Est.: 1969
Chrmn. of the Bd./CEO – John F. Moffitt; Vice Pres./Pub. – Frank L. Spicer; Vice Pres. – W.A. Johnson; Daily Newspapers: West Virginia Daily News, Lewisburg, WV; The Welch News, Welch, WV;

Morgan City Newspapers LLC.–1014 Front St., Morgan City, LA, 70381; tel (985) 384-8370; fax (985) 384-4255; web site www.daily-review.com
Est.: 1872
Pub. – Steve Shirley; Gen. Mgr. – Andy Shirley; Daily Newspapers: The Franklin Banner-Tribune, Franklin, LA; The Daily Review, Morgan City, LA; St. Mary Journal, Morgan City, LA;
Note: Morgan City Newspapers LLC also owns the St. Mary Journal, a twice a week publication located in Morgan City, LA.

Morris Communications Co. LLC–725 Broad St., Augusta, GA, 30901, USA; tel (706) 724-0851; fax (706) 722-7125; e-mail morris@morris.com; web site www.morris.com
Chrmn./CEO – William S. Morris; Pres. – William S. Morris; Pres., Morris Digital Works – Michael R. Romaner; Sr. Vice Pres., Finance/Sec./Treasurer – Craig S. Mitchell; Sr. Vice Pres./CFO, Newspapers/Shared Services – Steve K. Stone; Exec. Vice Pres., Newspapers – James C. Currow; Vice Pres., Cowboy Publishing Grp – J. Tyler Morris; Daily Newspapers: Juneau Empire, Juneau, AK; Peninsula Clarion, Kenai, AK; Log Cabin Democrat, Conway, AR; The Florida Times-Union, Jacksonville, FL; The St. Augustine Record, Saint Augustine, FL; Athens Banner-Herald, Athens, GA; The Augusta Chronicle, Augusta, GA; Savannah Morning News, Savannah, GA; The Topeka Capital-Journal, Topeka, KS; Brainerd Dispatch, Brainerd, MN; Amarillo Globe-News, Amarillo, TX; Alaska Star, Eagle River, AK; Homer News, Homer, AK; Capital City Weekly, Juneau, AK; The Columbia County News Times, Evans, GA; The News and Farmer, Louisville, GA; Sylvania Telephone, Sylvania, GA; Lake Country Echo, Pequot Lakes, MN; Pine River Journal, Pine River, MN; The People-Sentinel, Barnwell, SC; The Citizen News, Edgefield, SC; Hampton County Guardian, Hampton, SC; Hardeeville Today, Bluffton, SC; The Shopper's Weekly, Dodge City, KS; Tip-Off Shopping Guide, Jonesville, MI; Echoland Shopper, Pequot Lakes, MN; Piper Shopper, Pine River, MN; The Jasper Shopper Monthly, Ridgeland, SC; The McDuffie Mirror, Thomson, GA;
Note: Morris Communications Co. LLC is a privately held media company with diversified holdings that include 41 daily and non-daily newspapers, more than 20 magazines and specialized publications; 33 radio stations, two network television stations, an outdoor a

Morris Communications Co LLC–725 Broad St, Augusta, GA, 30901-1305; tel (706) 724-0851; web site www.morris.com

Morris Multimedia, Inc.–27 Abercorn St, Savannah, GA, 31401, USA; tel (912) 233-1281; fax (912) 238-4639; web site www.morris-multimedia.com
Est.: 1970
Chrmn./CEO – Charles H. Morris; Vice Pres./CFO – Jeffrey Samuels; Pres./Morris Network, Inc. – H. Dean Hinson; Regional Vice Pres. – Joe McGlamery; HR Coord. – Jackie Haynes; Asst. to President – Kathy Kurazawa; Daily Newspapers: Chandler-Evans Pennysaver, Statesboro, GA; Manteca Bulletin, Manteca, CA; The Signal, Santa Clarita, CA; Turlock Journal, Turlock, CA; The Gainesville Times, Gainesville, GA; Statesboro Herald, Statesboro, GA; Great Bend Tribune, Great Bend, KS; The Ceres Courier, Ceres, CA; Colusa County Sun-Herald, Colusa, CA; Corning Observer, Corning, CA; Escalon Times, Oakdale, CA; Oakdale Leader, Oakdale, CA; The Riverbank News, Riverbank, CA; Willows Journal, Willows, CA; Richmond Hill-Bryan County News, Richmond Hill, GA; The Covington News, Covington, GA; The Coastal Courier, Hinesville, GA; Independent Reporter, Ellsworth, KS; The Marquette Tribune, Marquette, KS; Lee County Observer, Bishopville, SC; Chronicle Independent, Camden, SC; The News Journal, Florence, SC; Southern Standard, McMinnville, TN; The Smithville Review, Smithville, TN; The Boscobel Dial, Boscobel, WI; Tri-County Press, Cuba City, WI; Republican-Journal, Darlington, WI; Fennimore Times, Fennimore, WI; Independent & The Kickapoo Scout, Gays Mills, WI; Herald Independent, Lancaster, WI; Platteville Journal, Platteville, WI; Mike's Shopper, Conyers, GA; The News and Advertiser, Covington, GA; Liberty County Pennysaver, Hinesville, GA; Wayne-Long Pennysaver, Hinesville, GA; Savannah Pennysaver, Savannah, GA; The Ad-Pak, Wilmington, NC; The Hartsville News Journal, Hartsville, SC; Round-Up Shopper, Cuba City, WI; Reminder, Lancaster, WI; The Frontline, Hinesville, GA; Fort Jackson Leader, Camden, SC; The Shaw News, Camden, SC; Effingham Herald, Rincon, GA; Bulletin Extra, Manteca, CA; Pennysaver, Statesboro, GA; Marion County Pennysaver, Marion, SC; SCV Express, Santa Clarita, CA; Bulloch Pennysaver, Statesboro, GA; Tri-County Ad-Pak, Wilmington, NC;
Note: Morris Multimedia, Inc. is the parent company of Morris Newspapers Corp. which owns and publishes more than 90 daily and non daily newspapers, shoppers and niche publications.

Morris Newspaper Corp.–27 Abercorn St., Savannah, GA, 31401, USA; tel (912) 233-1281; fax (912) 232-4639; web site www.morris-multimedia.com
Chrmn./CEO – Charles H. Morris; Vice Pres./CFO – Jeffrey Samuels; Daily Newspapers: Chandler-Evans Pennysaver, Statesboro, GA; Manteca Bulletin, Manteca, CA; The Signal, Santa Clarita, CA; Turlock Journal, Turlock, CA; The Gainesville Times, Gainesville, GA; Statesboro Herald, Statesboro, GA; Great Bend Tribune, Great Bend, KS; The Ceres Courier, Ceres, CA; Colusa County Sun-Herald, Colusa, CA; Corning Observer, Corning, CA; Escalon Times, Oakdale, CA; Oakdale Leader, Oakdale, CA; The Riverbank News, Riverbank, CA; Willows Journal, Willows, CA; Richmond Hill-Bryan County News, Richmond Hill, GA; The Covington News, Covington, GA; The Coastal Courier, Hinesville, GA; Independent Reporter, Ellsworth, KS; The Marquette Tribune, Marquette, KS; Lee County Observer, Bishopville, SC; Chronicle Independent, Camden, SC; The News Journal, Florence, SC; Southern Standard, McMinnville, TN; The Smithville Review, Smithville, TN; The Boscobel Dial, Boscobel, WI; Tri-County Press, Cuba City, WI; Republican-Journal, Darlington, WI; Fennimore Times, Fennimore, WI; Independent & The Kickapoo Scout, Gays Mills, WI; Herald Independent, Lancaster, WI; Sentry-Enterprise, Hillsboro, WI; Platteville Journal, Platteville, WI; Mike's Shopper, Conyers, GA; The News and Advertiser, Covington, GA; Liberty County Pennysaver, Hinesville, GA; Wayne-Long Pennysaver, Hinesville, GA; Savannah Pennysaver, Savannah, GA; The Ad-Pak, Wilmington, NC; The Hartsville News Journal, Hartsville, SC; Round-Up Shopper, Cuba City, WI; Reminder, Lancaster, WI; The Frontline, Hinesville, GA; Fort Jackson Leader, Camden, SC; The Shaw News, Camden, SC; Effingham Herald, Rincon, GA; Bulletin Extra, Manteca, CA; Pennysaver, Statesboro, GA; Marion County Pennysaver, Marion, SC; SCV Express, Santa Clarita, CA; Bulloch Pennysaver, Statesboro, GA; Tri-County Ad-Pak, Wilmington, NC;
Note: Morris Multimedia Inc. parent company of Morris Newspaper Corp. and Morris Network, is a privately-held media enterprise which owns and operates approximately 70 daily and non daily newspapers, shoppers and niche publications as well as six television stations.

N

NPG Newspapers, Inc.–825 Edmond St., Saint Joseph, MO, 64502-0029; tel (816) 271-8500; fax (816) 271-8695; e-mail steve.boohner@newspapersnow.com; web site www.newspressnow.com
Est.: 1845
Pres. – Brian Bradley; Exec. Vice President – Lee M. Sawyer;

New England Newspaper Group–620 8th Ave., New York, NY, 10018; tel (212) 556-1234; fax (646) 428-2197; web site www.nytimes.com

Arthur Ochs Sulzberger; Vice Chrmn. – Michael Golden; CEO – Janet Robinson; CFO – James Follo; Sr. Vice Pres. – R. Anthony Benten; Sr. Vice Pres. – James Lessersohn; Sr. Vice Pres. – Martin Nisenholtz; Sr. Vice Pres./Gen. Counsel & Sec. – Kenneth Richieri; Sr. Vice Pres. – Joseph Seibert; Laurena Emhoff; Exec. Ed. – Bill Keller; Daily Newspapers: The Boston Globe, Boston, MA; Telegram & Gazette, Worcester, MA; The Item, Clinton, MA;

Note: New England Newspaper Group also owns The Item, a non-daily publication located in Clinton, MA.

New England Newspapers, Inc.–75 S. Church St., Pittsfield, MA, 01201, USA; tel (413) 447-7311; fax (413) 442-7611; e-mail news@berkshireeagle.com; web site www.berkshireeagle.com
Pres./Pub. – Andy Mick;Daily Newspapers: Sentinel & Enterprise, Fitchburg, MA; North Adams Transcript, North Adams, MA; The Berkshire Eagle, Pittsfield, MA; Bennington Banner, Bennington, VT; Brattleboro Reformer, Brattleboro, VT; Greenfield Town Crier, Greenfield, MA; Bellows Falls Town Crier, Brattleboro, VT; Brattleboro Town Crier, Brattleboro, VT; Manchester Journal, Manchester, VT; The Eagle Shopper, Pittsfield, MA;

The New York Times Co.–620 8th Ave., New York, NY, 10018-1618; tel (212) 556-1234; fax (212) 556-4011; web site www.nytco.com
Est.: 1896
Pub. – Stephen Dunbar-Johnson; Chrmn., The New York Time Co./ Pub., The New York Times – Arthur O. Sulzberger; Vice Chrmn., The New York Times Co./Pub., International Herald Tribune – Michael Golden; Pres./CEO – Janet L. Robinson; CIO – Joseph Seibert; Sr. Vice Pres., Digital Opns. – Martin A. Nisenholtz; Sr. Vice Pres., Finance/Cor. Controller – R. Anthony Benten; Vice Pres./Deputy Gen. Counsel – Kenneth A. Richieri; Vice Pres./Treasurer – Laurena Emhoff; Vice Pres., Finance/Cor. Devel. – James C. Lessersohn; Vice Pres., Internal Audit – Philip A. Ciuffo; Vice Pres., Labor Rel. – Terry L. Hayes; Vice Pres., Compensation/Benefits – Ann S. Kraus; Vice Pres., Orgn./Devel. – Neal Roberts; Vice Pres., Forest Pdct. – Jennifer C. Dolan; Cor. Sec./Sr. Counsel – Rhonda L. Brauer; Pres., Broadcast Media Grp. – Robert H. Eoff; Pres., New York Times – Scott Heekin-Canedy; Pres., Boston Globe – Richard J. Daniel; Sr. Vice Pres. – James M. Follo; Daily Newspapers: The Gadsden Times, Gadsden, AL; The Tuscaloosa News, Tuscaloosa, AL; The Press Democrat, Santa Rosa, CA; The Gainesville Sun, Gainesville, FL; The Ledger, Lakeland, FL; Ocala Star-Banner, Ocala, FL; Sarasota Herald-Tribune, Sarasota, FL; News Chief, Winter Haven, FL; The Courier, Houma, LA; The Daily Comet, Thibodaux, LA; The Boston Globe, Boston, MA; Telegram & Gazette, Worcester, MA; The New York Times, New York, NY; Times-News, Hendersonville, NC; The Dispatch, Lexington, NC; Star-News, Wilmington, NC; Herald-Journal, Spartanburg, SC; Argus-Courier, Petaluma, CA; The Item, Clinton, MA; Polk Shopper, Winter Haven, FL;

Note: The New York Times Co. publishes The New York Times, the International Herald Tribune, The Boston Globe as well as 16 other newspapers. The New York Times Co. also owns more than 40 web sites and two New York City radio stations.

The New York Times Reg'l Newspaper Group–2202 NW Shore Blvd., Ste. 370, Tampa, FL, 33607; tel (813) 864-6000; fax (813) 281-2729; web site www.nytimes.com
Vice Pres./CMO – James Gold;Daily Newspapers: The Gadsden Times, Gadsden, AL; The Tuscaloosa News, Tuscaloosa, AL; The Press Democrat, Santa Rosa, CA; The Gainesville Sun, Gainesville, FL; The Ledger, Lakeland, FL; Ocala Star-Banner, Ocala, FL; Sarasota Herald-Tribune, Sarasota, FL; The Courier, Houma, LA; The Daily Comet, Thibodaux, LA; Times-News, Hendersonville, NC; The Dispatch, Lexington, NC; Star-News, Wilmington, NC; Herald-Journal, Spartanburg, SC; Argus-Courier, Petaluma, CA;

Note: The New York Times Reg'l Newspaper Group also owns the Argus-Courier, a weekly publications located in Petaluma, CA.

News-Gazette Inc.–15 Main St., Champaign, IL, 61820; tel (217) 351-5252; fax (217) 351-5291; e-mail ccc@news-gazette.com; web site www.news-gazette.com
Est.: 1852
Online Editor – Mike Howie; Columnist – Tom Kacich; Librarian – Carolyn Vance; Photo Editor – Darrell Hoemann; Sports Editor – Jim Rossow; Publisher – John Foreman; Circulation Director – Pete Jones; VP: Chief Financial Officer – John Reed; VP: Director of Human Resources – Tracy Nally; VP: General Manager Radio Center – Mike Haile; Advertising Director – Tom Zalabak; Advertising Sales Manager & National Sales – Jackie Martin; Customer Care Center Manager – Denny Santarelli; Editor in Chief – John Beck; Managing Editor – Dan Corkery; Opinions Page Editor – Jim Dey; Features Editor – Tony Mancuso; Director of Market Development – Amy George; Daily Newspapers: The News-Gazette, Champaign, IL; Mahomet Citizen, Mahomet, IL; Piatt County Journal-Republican, Monticello, IL; Rantoul Press, Rantoul, IL; Savoy Star, Champaign, IL; Independent News, Georgetown, IL; The Leader, St. Joseph, IL; The Regional, Tuscola, IL;

News Media Corp.–211 Hwy. 38 E., Rochelle, IL, 61068, USA; tel (815) 562-2061; fax (815) 562-2161; web site www.newsmediacorporation.com
Est.: 1975
Pres. – John C. Tompkins; Vice Pres. – Michael Tompkins; Gen. Mgr. – John Shank; Controller – Michael Rand; Daily Newspapers: Register-Pajaronian, Watsonville, CA; The Valley Courier, Alamosa, CO; Clinton Journal, Clinton, IL; Brookings Register, Brookings, SD; Huron Plainsman, Huron, SD; San Carlos Apache Moccasin, Globe, AZ; Arizona Silver Belt, Globe, AZ; Lake Powell Chronicle, Page, AZ; Atascadero News, Atascadero, CA; Gonzales Tribune, Gonzalez, CA; The Rustler, King City, CA; Paso Robles Press, Paso Robles, CA; Soledad Bee, Soledad, CA; Berthoud Recorder, Berthoud, CO; The Conejos County Citizen, Monte Vista, CO; The Mineral County Miner, Monte Vista, CO; The Del Norte Prospector, Monte Vista, CO; The Lyons Recorder, Lyons, CO; The Monte Vista Journal, Monte Vista, CO; The South Fork Times, Monte Vista, CO; The Amboy News, Amboy, IL; The Ashton Gazette, Ashton, IL; Mendota Reporter, Mendota, IL; The Ogle County Life, Oregon, IL; The Rochelle News-Leader, Rochelle, IL; The Business Farmer, Scottsbluff, NE; Siuslaw News, Florence, OR; News-Times, Newport, OR; Moody County Enterprise, Flandreau, SD; The Redfield Press, Redfield, SD; Record Delta, Buckhannon, WV; Mountain Statesman, Grafton, WV; Bridger Valley Pioneer, Lyman, WY; Uinta County Herald, Evanston, WY; The Kemmerer Gazette, Kemmerer, WY; The Lusk Herald, Lusk, WY; The Pinedale Roundup, Pinedale, WY; The Torrington Telegram, Torrington, WY; The Platte County Record-Times, Wheatland, WY; Taylor County Value Guide, Grafton, WV; Uinta County Herald Shoppers Guide, Evanston, WY; Gile County Advantage, Globe, AZ; Greenfield News, King City, CA; Guernsey Gazette, Guernsey, WY;

News-Press & Gazette Co.–825 Edmond St., Saint Joseph, MO, 64502-0029, USA; tel (816) 271-8500; fax (816) 271-8695; web site www.npgco.com
Pres. – David R. Bradley;Daily Newspapers: Atchison Globe, Atchison, KS; Hiawatha World, Hiawatha, KS; St. Joseph News-Press, Saint Joseph, MO; The Daily Star-Journal, Warrensburg, MO; The Sun Newspapers, Overland Park, KS; Louisburg Herald, Louisburg, KS; Osawatomie Graphic, Osawatomie, KS; The Miami County Republic, Paola, KS; Sun-Tribune, Gladstone, MO; The Kearney Courier, Kearney, MO; Liberty Tribune, Liberty, MO; The Smithville Herald, Smithville, MO; The Kansas City Jewish Chronicle, Overland Park, KS;

Note: News-Press & Gazette Co. also owns the Kansas City Sun Publications which owns eight weekly newspapers.

News Publishing Company–PO Box 1633, Rome, GA, 30162; tel (706) 290-5281; web site www.npco.com

News West Publishing Company Inc.–2435 Miracle Mile, Bullhead City, AZ, 86442, USA; tel (928) 763-2505; fax (928) 763-7820; web site www.mojavedailynews.com
Pub. – Chuck Rathbun; Bus. Mgr. – Sue Anderson; Daily Newspapers: Clippin' the River, Bullhead City, AZ; Mohave Valley Daily News, Bullhead City, AZ; The Wickenburg Sun, Wickenburg, AZ; Needles Desert Star, Needles, CA; Laughlin Nevada Times, Laughlin, NV; Shopper News, Wickenburg, AZ; Valley Views, Bullhead City, AZ; Bullhead City Booster, Bullhead City, AZ; Laughlin Entertainer, Bullhead City, AZ;

Note: News West Publishing Company Inc. is owned by Brehm Communications Inc. Through it's subsidiaries, Democrat Co., Gull Communications, Hi-Desert Publishing Co., Inc., News West Publishing Company Inc., Penny Power Publications Inc., Placer Community Newspa

Newspapers of New England–1 Monitor Dr., Concord, NH, 03302-1177; tel (603) 224-5301; fax (603) 224-6949; web site www.concordmonitor.com
Chrmn. – John Kuhns; Pres./CEO – Aaron Julian; CFO – Dan McClory; Pub. – Geordie Wilson; Daily Newspapers: The Recorder, Greenfield, MA; Concord Monitor, Concord, NH; Valley News, White River Junction, VT; Monadnock Ledger, Peterborough, NH;

Note: Newspapers of New England also owns the Peterborough (NH) Monadnock Ledger, a weekly publication.

Nutting Newspapers–1500 Main St, Wheeling, WV, 26003-2826; tel (304) 233-0100; fax (304) 233-9397; web site www.oweb.com
Pres./CEO – Robert M. Nutting; Vice Pres. – William O. Nutting; Treasurer – Duane D. Wittman; Daily Newspapers: Daily Press, Escanaba, MI; The Daily Mining Gazette, Houghton, MI; The Review, East Liverpool, OH; Salem News, Salem, OH; Herald-Star, Steubenville, OH;

Note: Nutting Newspapers also publishes the Capper's, Grit, Mother Earth News, Brave Hearts, The Herb Companion, Herbs for Health, Farm Collector, Gas Engine Magazine, and Steam Traction.

O

The Ogden Newspapers, Inc.–1500 Main St., Wheeling, WV, 26003, USA; tel (304) 233-0100; fax (304) 233-9397; e-mail myer@news-register.net; web site www.oweb.com
Est.: 1800
Chrmn. – G. Ogden Nutting; Pres./CEO – Robert M. Nutting; Vice Pres./Bus. Mgr. – William O. Nutting; Vice Pres. – William C. Nutting; Treasurer/CFO – Duane D. Wittman; Daily Newspapers: Cape Coral Daily Breeze, Cape Coral, FL; The Maui News, Wailuku, HI; The News-Sentinel, Fort Wayne, IN; Estherville Daily News, Estherville, IA; The Messenger, Fort Dodge, IA; Times-Republican, Marshalltown, IA; The Daily Freeman-Journal, Webster City, IA; The Alpena News, Alpena, MI; The Daily News, Iron Mountain, MI; Sentinel, Fairmont, MN; Independent, Marshall, MN; The Journal, New Ulm, MN; Observer, Dunkirk, NY; The Leader-Herald, Gloversville, NY; The Post-Journal, Jamestown, NY; Adirondack Daily Enterprise, Saranac Lake, NY; Minot Daily News, Minot, ND; Morning Journal, Lisbon, OH; The Marietta Times, Marietta, OH; The Times Leader, Martins Ferry, OH; The Advertiser-Tribune, Tiffin, OH; The Tribune Chronicle, Warren, OH; Altoona Mirror, Altoona, PA; The Sentinel, Lewistown, PA; The Express, Lock Haven, PA; Times-Observer, Warren, PA; Williamsport Sun-Gazette, Williamsport, PA; The Inter-Mountain, Elkins, WV; The Journal, Martinsburg, WV; Parkersburg News & Sentinel, Parkersburg, WV; The Intelligencer/Wheeling News-Register, Wheeling, WV; Gasparilla Gazette, Boca Grande, FL; Captiva Current, Sanibel, FL; Fort Myers Beach Observer, Fort Myers Beach, FL; Fort Myers Beach Bulletin, Fort Myers Beach, FL; Island Reporter, Sanibel, FL; The Sanibel-Captiva Islander, Sanibel Island, FL; The Dysart Reporter, Dysart, IA; The Democrat, Emmetsburg, IA; The Reporter, Emmetsburg, IA; Northern-Sun Print, Gladbrook, IA; Reinbeck Courier, Reinbeck, IA; The Tama News-Herald, Tama, IA; Toledo Chronicle, Tama, IA; The Traer Star-Clipper, Traer, IA; Faribault County Register, Blue Earth, MN; Pierce County Tribune, Rugby, ND; The Lake Placid News, Lake Placid, NY; Mayville Sentinel, Westfield, NY; Sentinel News, Westfield, NY; The Westfield Republican, Westfield, NY; Austintown Town Crier, Boardman, OH; The Town Crier, Youngstown, OH; Canfield Town Crier, Boardman, OH; Town Crier, Boardman, OH; County Observer, Reedsville, PA; The Luminary, Hughesville, PA; Wetzel Chronicle, New Martinsville, WV; Tyler Star News, Sistersville, WV; Mahoning Valley Parent Magazine, Youngstown, OH; Lee County Shopper, Cape Coral, FL; Consumer News, Fort Dodge, IA; Messenger Extra, Fort Dodge, IA; PennySaver, Marshalltown, IA; Tama County Shopper, Tama, IA; UP Action Shopper, Escanaba, MI; Advertiser, Iron Mountain, MI; New Ulm Shopper/Post Review, New Ulm, MN; Quality Guide, Westfield, NY; East Lycoming Shopper, Hughesville, PA; Green Tab, Moundsville, WV; Lehigh Acres Citizen, Lehigh Acres, FL; The Pine Island Eagle, Bokeelia, FL; Action Shopper, Marquette, MI; Town Crier Shopper, Blue Earth, MN;

Omaha World-Herald–1314 Douglas St., Ste. 1500, Omaha, NE, 68102-1848, USA; tel (402) 444-1000; fax (402) 444-1231; e-mail news@owh.com; web site www.omaha.com
Est.: 1865
Chrmn. – John Gottschalk; Pub./CEO – Terry J. Kroeger; CFO/Sr. Vice Pres. – Duane Polodna; Vice Pres./Gen. Counsel – Scott Searl; Vice Pres., Opns. – Doug Hiemstra; Finance Dir./Controller – Mike Kirk; Dir., Communications – Joel Long; Credit Dept. Mgr. – Steven Woods; Mgr., Training – Gary Domet; Adv. Dir. – Thom Kastrup; Adv. Dir., Online/Digital – Jeff Shabram; Adv. Mgr., Auto Sales – Brett Snead; Adv. Mgr., Classified – Larry Etienne; Retail Sales Mgr. – Lowell Miller; Adv. Mgr., Custom Publishing/Events – Tam Webb; Adv. Mgr., Employment – Terri Campbell; Adv. Mgr., Local Retail Sales – Vicki Denker; Adv. Mgr., Major Accts. – Bob Gerken; Adv. Mgr., Real Estate – Debbie Cavalier; Dir., HR – Roshelle Campbell; Dir., Marketing – Rich Warren; Dir., Circulation – Dennis Cronin; Managing Editor for Digital Development – Jeff Carney; Dir., IT – Phil Tomek; Treasurer & Controller – Brenda Draheim; Dir., Production – Kristy Gerry; VP, News & Content – Larry King; VP & General Counsel – Scott Searl; Cor. HR

Mgr. – Steve Hoff; Dir., Marketing – Rich Warren; Dir., IT – Phil Tomek; Managing Editor for Digital Development – Jeff Carney; Treasurer & Controller – Brenda Draheim; Dir., Production – Kristy Gerry; Dir., Circulation – Dennis Cronin; VP, News & Content – Larry King; Executive Editor – Mike Reilly; National Advg Acct Exec – Brandon Bell; Pres/CEO/Pub. – Terry Kroeger; Daily Newspapers: The Tribune, Ames, IA; Valley News Today, Shenandoah, IA; The Grand Island Independent, Grand Island, NE; Kearney Hub, Kearney, NE; The North Platte Telegraph, North Platte, NE; Omaha World-Herald, Omaha, NE; Star-Herald, Scottsbluff, NE; York News-Times, York, NE; Dallas County News, Adel, IA; The Algona Upper Des Moines, Algona, IA; The Clarinda Herald-Journal, Clarinda, IA; Denison Bulletin and Review , Denison, IA; The Logan Herald-Observer, Logan, IA; Nevada Journal, Nevada, IA; The Tri-County Times, Nevada, IA; Woodbine Twiner, Woodbine, IA; The Ashland Gazette, Ashland, NE; Bellevue Leader, Bellevue, NE; Lexington Clipper-Herald, Lexington, NE; Papillion Times, Papillion, NE; Ralston Recorder, Ralston, NE; Wahoo Newspaper, Wahoo, NE; The News, Waverly, NE; Reminder, Algona, IA; Weekend Express, Algona, IA; Story Today, Ames, IA; Boone County Shopping News, Boone, IA; Dallas County Round-Up, Adel, IA; Story County Advertiser, Ames, IA; People Plus, Lexington, NE; Market Weekly, Wahoo, NE; Twin City Weekly, Scottsbluff, NE; Air Pulse, Bellevue, NE; Northeast Dallas County Record, Adel, IA;

Dow Jones Local Media Group–40 Mulberry Street, Middletown, NY, 10940, USA; tel (845) 341-1100; web site www.dowjoneslmg.com
Group: Dow Jones
Est.: 1936
CFO – Jonathan Kahan; COO – William T. Kennedy; SVP, Printing & Distribution – Don Waterman; Vice Pres., HR – Patricia Gatto; Senior VP, Advertising Sales – Molly Evans; Senior VP, Digital Media & Product Mgmt. – Kurt Lozier; Treasurer – Chet D. Krinsky; Vice Pres., Information Servs. – John Treglia; Vice Pres., Opns./Adv. – Zeke Fleet; Ed. – Ken Hall; Daily Newspapers: The Record, Stockton, CA; Cape Cod Times, Hyannis, MA; The Standard-Times, New Bedford, MA; Portsmouth Herald, Portsmouth, NH; The Times Herald-Record, Middletown, NY; The Ashland Daily Tidings, Ashland, OR; Mail Tribune, Medford, OR; Pocono Record, Stroudsburg, PA; Barnstable Patriot, Hyannis, MA; The Chronicle, Dartmouth, MA; Middleboro Gazette, Middleboro, MA; The Inquirer and Mirror, Nantucket, MA; The Advocate, Fairhaven, MA; The Spectator, Somerset, MA; York County Coast Star, Kennebunk, ME; The York Weekly, Portsmouth, NH; The Hampton Union, Portsmouth, NH; Cooperstown Crier, Cooperstown, NY; Valley Market Place, Stockton, CA; Medford Nickel, Medford, OR;

P

Pacific Sierra Publishing, Inc.–3033 N. G St., Merced, CA, 95341; tel (209) 722-1812; fax (209) 726-1839
Vice Pres., Adv. – Kevin Davis; Vice Pres., Mktg. – Bob McLaughlin; Vice Pres., Circ. – Mike Belles; Controller – Kelli Pico;

Paddock Publications–PO Box 280, Arlington Heights, IL, 60006-0280; tel (847)427-4300; web site www.dailyherald.com

Paxton Media Group LLC–201 S. Fourth St., Paducah, KY, 42003-1524, USA; tel (270) 575-8630; fax (270) 442-8188
Est.: 1896
Pres./CEO – David M. Paxton; Pres. & COO, Newspaper Division – Jay Frizzo; Vice Pres./CFO – Richard E. Paxton; Asst. – Milinda Harnice; Daily Newspapers: NEA Shopper, Jonesboro, AR; Caldwell Weekly, Lenoir, NC; The Jonesboro Sun, Jonesboro, AR; Paragould Daily Press, Paragould, AR; The Courier, Russellville, AR; Daily Citizen, Searcy, AR; Times-Georgian, Carrollton, GA; Douglas County Sentinel, Douglasville, GA; Griffin Daily News, Griffin, GA; Connersville News-Examiner, Connersville, IN; The Times, Frankfort, IN; Huntington Herald-Press, Huntington, IN; Herald-Argus, La Porte, IN; Chronicle-Tribune, Marion, IN; News Dispatch, Michigan City, IN; The Courier-Times, New Castle, IN; The Peru Tribune, Peru, IN; The Shelbyville News, Shelbyville, IN; Vincennes Sun-Commercial, Vincennes, IN; Wabash Plain Dealer, Wabash, IN; The Messenger, Madisonville, KY; Messenger-Inquirer, Owensboro, KY; The Paducah Sun, Paducah, KY; The Daily Star, Hammond, LA; The Herald-Palladium, Saint Joseph, MI; The Daily Corinthian, Corinth, MS; The Herald-Sun, Durham, NC; The Daily Courier, Forest City, NC; Daily Dispatch, Henderson, NC; High Point Enterprise, High Point, NC; News-Topic, Lenoir, NC; The Enquirer-Journal, Monroe, NC; The Sanford Herald, Sanford, NC; The Mountain Press, Sevierville, TN; Dardanelle Post-Dispatch, Dardanelle, AR; Paulding County Sentinel, Douglasville, GA; The Haralson Gateway Beacon, Bremen, GA; The Villa Rican, Villa Rica, GA; The Metropolis Planet, Metropolis, IL; The Extra, Shelbyville, IN; Tribune-Courier, Benton, KY; The Cadiz Record, Cadiz, KY; Franklin Favorite, Franklin, KY; The Herald-Ledger, Eddyville, KY; McLean County News, Calhoun, KY; Harbor Country News, New Buffalo, MI; South Haven Tribune, South Haven, MI; Southcounty Gazette, Three Oaks, MI; The Banner-Independent, Booneville, MS; Archdale Trinity News, Archdale, NC; The Thomasville Times, High Point, NC; The Portland Leader, Portland, TN; Community Shopper, Searcy, AR; Carrollton Weekly News, Carrollton, GA; Town and Country Shopper, Griffin, GA; Times Review, Frankfort, IN; Town & Country Shopper, Griffin, GA;
Note: Paxton Media Group LLC owns 32 daily newspapers and more than 20 non-daily publications. Paxton Media also owns and operates an NBC-affiliated television station in Paducah, KY.

Philadelphia Media Holdings, LLC–400 N. Broad St., Philadelphia, PA, 19130-4015; tel (215) 854-2000; fax (215) 854-5954; web site www.pnionline.com
Est.: 2006
CEO – Brian Tierney; Exec. Vice Pres./Finance – Richard Thayer; Chrmn. – Richard Thayer; CIO – Jeffrey Berger; CMO – Edward Mahlman; Exec. Vice Pres., Prodn./Labor/Purchasing – Mark Frisby; Daily Newspapers: The Philadelphia Inquirer, Philadelphia, PA; The Philadelphia Daily News, Philadelphia, PA; The Trend Midweek, Trevose, PA; Northeast Times, Trevose, PA;
Note: Philadelphia Media Holdings, LLC also owns the Northeast Times in Trevose, PA and the Trend Midweek in Trevose, PA both weeky publications.

Philadelphia Media Network Inc–400 N Broad St, Philadelphia, PA, 19130-4099; tel (215) 854-2000; web site www.philly.com

Pioneer Newspapers Inc–221 1st Ave W Ste 405, Seattle, WA, 98119-4224, USA; tel (206) 284-4424; fax (206) 282-2143; e-mail mgugliotto@pioneernewspapers.com; web site www.pioneernewspapers.com
Est.: 1976
Pres. – Mike Gugliotto; CFO – Jeffrey Hood; Corp. Controller – Erica Hagel; Opns. Controller – Larry Wells; Dir., HR – Anita McGillie; Information Systems Mgr. – Julie Hughes; Daily Newspapers: Idaho Press-Tribune, Nampa, ID; Idaho State Journal, Pocatello, ID; Bozeman Daily Chronicle, Bozeman, MT; Herald and News, Klamath Falls, OR; The Herald Journal, Logan, UT; Daily Record, Ellensburg, WA; Skagit Valley Herald, Mount Vernon, WA; Teton Valley News, Driggs, ID; Messenger-Index, Emmett, ID; Preston Citizen, Preston, ID; The Standard-Journal, Rexburg, ID; Lone Peak Lookout, Big Sky, MT; The West Yellowstone News, West Yellowstone, MT; Lake County Examiner, Lakeview, OR; The Leader, Tremonton, UT; Anacortes American, Anacortes, WA; Courier-Times, Sedro-Woolley, WA; The Argus, Burlington, WA; The Nickel, Klamath Falls, OR;
Note: Pioneer Newspapers owns seven daily newspapers and 11 publications throughout the northwestern United States.

Prairie Mountain Publishing Co, LLP–1048 Pearl St, Boulder, CO, 80302; tel (303) 442-1202

Princeton Publishing Co., Inc.–100 N. Gibson St., Princeton, IN, 47670; tel (812) 385-2525; fax (812) 386-6199; web site www.pdclarion.com
Est.: 1846
Pres. – Gary Blackburn;Daily Newspapers: Princeton Daily Clarion, Princeton, IN; Oakland City Journal, Princeton, IN; Today, Princeton, IN; The Gibson County Today Section, Princeton, IN;
Note: Princeton Publishing Co., Inc. is owned by Brehm Communications Inc. Through it's subsidiaries, Democrat Co., Gull Communications, Hi-Desert Publishing Co., Inc., News West Publishing Company Inc., Penny Power Publications Inc., Placer Community Newspaper

Pulitzer, Inc.–900 N. Tucker Blvd., Saint Louis, MO, 63101, USA; tel (314) 340-8000; fax (314) 340-3145; web site www.pulitzerinc.com
Est.: 1878
Chrmn. of the Bd. – Michael E. Pulitzer; Pres./CEO – Robert C. Woodworth; Sr. Vice Pres., Finance/CFO – Alan G. Silverglat; Vice Pres. – Matthew G. Kraner; Cor. Sec./Dir., Investor Realtions – James V. Maloney; Cor. Controller – Jan P. Pallares; Treasurer/Asst. Sec. – Jon H. Holt; Asst. Sec. – Joyce I. Cousino; @RecordBody:**Note:** Pulitzer Inc., through its various subsidiaries and affliated entities, is engaged in newspaper publishing and related new media activities.

Pulitzer Newspapers, Inc.–900 N. Tucker Blvd., Saint Louis, MO, 63101, USA; tel (314) 340-8890; fax (314) 340-3145; web site www.pulitzernewspapers.com
Vice Pres./CFO – Robin A. Davis; Vice Pres. & Pres./Pub., The Arizona Daily Sun – Don Rowley; Vice Pres. & Pres./Pub., The Pantagraph – Henry Bird; Vice Pres., Mktg./Research & E-Media – Charles Kolsky; Vice Pres., News & Pub./Ed., Arizona Daily Star – Jane Amari; Vice Pres., Information Technology & Pres./Pub., Daily Journal – Jim York; @SectionHead:Q

Quincy Newspapers Inc–PO Box 909, Quincy, IL, 62306-0909; tel (217) 223-5100

Quincy Newspapers, Inc.–130 S. Fifth St., Quincy, IL, 62301; tel (217) 223-5100; fax (217) 223-5019; e-mail info@qni.biz; web site www.quincynewspapers.co
Pres./CEO – Ralph M. Oakley; Controller – David A. Graff; Director of Accounting – Brad Eaton; Asst. to Pres./CEO – Morey Taraska; Dir., HR – Jena Schulz; Dir., Facilities/Capital Project/Broadcast Engineering – Brady Dreasler; Dir., Opns. Support – Brenda Wiskirchen; VP, Newspapers & Interactive – Mary Winters; IT Mgr. – Michael Funk; Daily Newspapers: The Quincy Herald-Whig, Quincy, IL; New Jersey Herald, Newton, NJ; Shopper's Guide, Newton, NJ;
Note: Quincy Newspapers Inc. also owns the Newton (NJ) Shopper's Guide, a weekly shopper publication; eleven television stations and two radio stations.

R

North Jersey Media Group–1 Garret Mountain Plz., Woodland Park, NJ, 07424, USA; tel (973) 569-7000; fax (201) 457-2520; e-mail njmg@northjersey.com; web site www.northjersey.com
Group: North Jersey Media Group
Est.: 1895
President & Publisher – Stephen A. Borg; Vice Pres., HR – Susan Beard; National Avertising Sales Manager – Rod Rodrigues; Assistant Managing Editor/Administration – Douglas Clancy; Director of News Assignments – Deirdre Sykes; Editorial Page Editor – Alfred Doblin; News Graphics Director – Jerry Luciani; Director of News Production – Elizabeth Houlton; Projects Editor – Tim Nostrand; Director of Features – Stephanie Rivers; Director of Photography – Jon Naso; Director of Sports – John Balkun; Business Editor – Bill Donnellon; Food Editor – Susan Sherrill; Travel Editor – Jill Schensul; Director of Digital Assets – Amre Youssef; News Editor – Gary Miller; News Editor – Scott Muller; VP/Internet Technology – Yuri Demidov; VP/Manufacturing – Bob Konig; Director of Manufacturing – John King; VP/Corp Secy & Genl Counsel – Jennifer A. Borg; Director, Real Estate and Corporate Advertising – Tim Gerstmyer; Director, Advertising TeleCenter – Kerry Rubin; Automotive Sales Manager – Thomas DiChiara; Local Retail Sales Manager – Chris Allen; VP/Digital Sales – Brian Burns; Web Editor – Sean Oates; VP/Circulation – Mala Lawrence; VP/Marketing – Kirsten vonHassel;

The Record-Journal Publishing Co.–11 Crown St., Meriden, CT, 06450, USA; tel (203) 235-1661; fax (203) 235-6345; e-mail newsroom@record-journal.com; web site www.myrecordjournal.com
Pres./Pub. – Eliot C. White; Sr. Vice Pres. – Tim Ryan; Sr. Vice Pres., Sales/Mktg. – Michael F. Killian; vp new media – liz white; Daily Newspapers: Record-Journal, Meriden, CT; The Plainville Citizen, Plainville, CT; The Berlin Citizen, Kensington, CT; Town Times, Middlefield, CT; The Southington Citizen, Southington, CT; The Westerly Sun, Westerly, RI;
Note: The Record-Journal Publishing Co. also owns five weekly newspapers.

Record Publishing Co.–126 N. Chestnut St., Ravenna, OH, 44691, USA; tel (330) 296-9657; fax (330) 296-2698; e-mail hnewman@recordpub.com; web site www.recordpub.com
Marketing Director – Harry Newman; Gen. Mgr. – Richard M. Sekella; Daily Newspapers: Record-Courier, Ravenna, OH; Aurora Advocate, Stow, OH; Cuyahoga Falls News-Press, Stow, OH; Hudson Hub-Times, Stow, OH; Maple Heights Press, Stow, OH; The News Leader, Stow, OH; Stow Sentry, Stow, OH; Gateway News, Stow, OH; Tallmadge Express, Stow, OH; The Bulletin Twinsburg, Stow, OH;
Note: Record Publishing Co. is part of Dix Communications which is owned by the Wooster Republican Printing Co. Through it's subsidiaries, Alliance Publishing Co. LLC, Ashland Publishing Co. LLC, Defiance Publishing LLC, Frankfort Publishing Co., Jeffersonian C

Rockingham Publishing Co.–231 S. Liberty St., Harrisonburg, VA, 22801-3621, USA; tel (540) 574-6200; fax 540-574-6299; e-mail business@dnronline.com; web site www.dnronline.com
Est.: 1913
Pres. – Thomas T. Byrd; Gen. Mgr. – Peter S. Yates; Daily Newspapers: Daily News-Record, Harrisonburg, VA; The Valley Banner, Elkton, VA; The Shenandoah Journal,

Dayton, VA; The North Fork Journal, Broadway, VA;
Note: Rockingham Publishing Co. is owned by Byrd Newspapers which also owns one daily and three weekly newspapers.

Rust Communications–301 Broadway, Cape Girardeau, MO, 63702-0699, USA; tel (573) 335-6611; fax (573) 334-9258; e-mail advertising@semissourian.com; web site www.semissourian.com
Chrmn. – Gary W. Rust; Co-Pres./Pub. – Jon K. Rust; Co-Pres. – Rex D. Rust; Vice Pres./COO – Wally Lage; Vice Pres., Opns. – Jim Maxwell; Daily Newspapers: Blytheville Courier News, Blytheville, AR; The Brazil Times, Brazil, IN; Banner-Graphic, Greencastle, IN; Chronicle Times, Cherokee, IA; Le Mars Daily Sentinel, Le Mars, IA; Pilot Tribune, Storm Lake, IA; Southeast Missourian, Cape Girardeau, MO; The Daily Statesman, Dexter, MO; The Daily Dunklin Democrat, Kennett, MO; The Marshall Democrat-News, Marshall, MO; The Nevada Daily Mail/Herald, Nevada, MO; Daily American Republic, Poplar Bluff, MO; Standard Democrat, Sikeston, MO; McCook Daily Gazette, McCook, NE; State Gazette, Dyersburg, TN; Shelbyville Times-Gazette, Shelbyville, TN; Eureka Springs Times-Echo, Berryville, AR; The Town Crier, Manila, AR; Tri-City Tribune, Marked Tree, AR; The Piggott Times, Piggott, AR; Clay County Democrat, Rector, AR; Kingsley News-Times, Kingsley, IA; Dickinson County News, Spirit Lake, IA; Mountain Home News, Mountain Home, ID; Marshall County Tribune, Lewisburg, TN; Mountain Home News, Mountain Home, ID; Shoppers Guide, Le Mars, IA; Southeast Missourian Plus, Cape Girardeau, MO; Daily Dunklin Democrat Extra, Kennett, MO; Marble Hill Banner Press, Marble Hill, MO; Sioux Valley News, Le Mars, IA;

S

Sample News Group LLC–28 W South St., Corry, PA, 16407-1810; tel (814) 665-8291
CEO – George Sample;Daily Newspapers: Journal Tribune, Biddeford, ME; The Times Record, Brunswick, ME; The Palladium-Times, Oswego, NY; Bedford Gazette, Bedford, PA; The Journal, Corry, PA; The Daily News, Huntingdon, PA; The Standard-Journal, Milton, PA; Morning Times, Sayre, PA; The Daily Herald, Tyrone, PA; The Patroller, Brunswick, ME;

Sandusky Newspapers Inc–17 Pope Ave Exec Park Ste 3A, Hilton Head Island, SC, 29928; tel (843) 842-9162

Sandusky Newspapers, Inc.–17 Executive Park, Ste. 3A, Hilton Head Island, SC, 29928-4738, USA; tel (843) 842-9162; fax (843) 842-9617
Chrmn./Pres./CEO – David Rau; Vice Pres./Gen. Counsel/CFO – Peter Vogt; Sec. – Susan White; Daily Newspapers: Grand Haven Tribune, Grand Haven, MI; Norwalk Reflector, Norwalk, OH; Sandusky Register, Sandusky, OH; Johnson City Press, Johnson City, TN; Kingsport Times-News, Kingsport, TN; The Lebanon Democrat, Lebanon, TN; Standard-Examiner, Ogden, UT; News Review, Grand Haven, MI; The Erwin Record, Erwin, TN; The Tomahawk, Mountain City, TN; Mt. Juliet News, Mount Juliet, TN; The Hartsville Vidette, Hartsville, TN; Herald and Tribune, Jonesborough, TN;

Schurz Communications Inc–1301 E Douglas Road, Mishawaka, IN, 46545, USA; tel (574)Â 247-7237; fax (574) 247-7238; web site www.schurz.com
Chrmn. – Franklin D. Schurz; Pres./CEO/COO – Todd F. Schurz; Sr. Vice Pres./CFO – Gary N. Hoipkemier; Sr. Vice Pres., Newspaper Opns. – Charles V. Pittman; Vice Pres., Finance/Admin. – Martin D. Switalski; Cor. Controller – Gesumino A. Agostino; Daily Newspapers: Imperial Valley Press, El Centro, CA; The Times-Mail, Bedford, IN; The Herald-Times, Bloomington, IN; The Reporter-Times, Martinsville, IN; South Bend Tribune, South Bend, IN; The Advocate-Messenger, Danville, KY; The Winchester Sun, Winchester, KY; The Herald-Mail, Hagerstown, MD; Petoskey News-Review, Petoskey, MI; Daily American, Somerset, PA; American News, Aberdeen, SD; The Mooresville-Decatur Times, Mooresville, IN; The Noblesville Daily Times, Noblesville, IN; Southside Times, Beech Grove, IN; The Jessamine Journal, Nicholasville, KY; The Interior Journal, Stanford, KY; Charlevoix Courier, Charlevoix, MI; Gaylord Herald Times, Gaylord, MI; White Sheet, Lake Havasu City, AZ; White Sheet, Palm Desert, CA; Green Sheet, Redlands, CA; Herald-Mail Express, Hagerstown, MD; Marketplace UpNorth, Gaylord, MI;
Note: Schurz Communications Inc. also owns Associated Desert Shoppers Inc. in Palm Desert, CA.

E. W. Scripps Co.–312 Walnut St., Ste. 2800, Cincinnati, OH, 45202-4067, USA; tel (513) 977-3000; fax (513) 977-3019; web site www.scripps.com
Pres., Scripps Network Interactive – Kenneth W. Lowe; Pres., E.W. Scripps – Richard A. Boehne; Exec. Vice Pres., Scripps Network Interactive – Joseph G. NeCastro; Sr. Vice Pres./CFO – Timothy E. Stautberg; Vice Pres./Sec. – M. Denise Kuprionis; Vice Pres., Newspapers Opns. – Mark G. Contreras; Daily Newspapers: Birmingham Post-Herald, Birmingham, AL; Record Searchlight, Redding, CA; Ventura County Star, Camarillo, CA; Daily Camera, Boulder, CO; Rocky Mountain News, Denver, CO; Naples Daily News, Naples, FL; Treasure Coast News/Press-Tribune, Stuart, FL; Evansville Courier & Press, Evansville, IN; The Kentucky Post, Cincinnati, OH; The Gleaner, Henderson, KY; The Albuquerque Tribune, Albuquerque, NM; The Cincinnati Post, Cincinnati, OH; Anderson Independent-Mail, Anderson, SC; Knoxville News Sentinel, Knoxville, TN; The Commercial Appeal, Memphis, TN; Abilene Reporter-News, Abilene, TX; Corpus Christi Caller-Times, Corpus Christi, TX; San Angelo Standard-Times, San Angelo, TX; Wichita Falls Times Record News, Wichita Falls, TX; Kitsap Sun, Bremerton, WA; Valley Post, Anderson, CA; Bonita Banner, Bonita Springs, FL; Sebastian Sun, Vero Beach, FL; Jupiter Courier, Stuart, FL; Marco Island Eagle, Marco Island, FL; Colorado Daily, Boulder, CO;
Note: The E. W. Scripps Company is a diverse media concern with interests in newspaper publishing, broadcast television, cable television programming and interactive media.

Scripps Howard Newspapers–312 Walnut St., Ste. 2800, Cincinnati, OH, 45202-4067; tel (513) 977-3000; fax (513) 977-3019; e-mail porters@scripps.com; web site www.scripps.com
Vice Pres., Newspaper Opns. – Mark G. Contreras;Daily Newspapers: Birmingham Post-Herald, Birmingham, AL; Record Searchlight, Redding, CA; Ventura County Star, Camarillo, CA; Daily Camera, Boulder, CO; Rocky Mountain News, Denver, CO; Naples Daily News, Naples, FL; Treasure Coast News/Press-Tribune, Stuart, FL; Evansville Courier & Press, Evansville, IN; The Kentucky Post, Cincinnati, OH; The Gleaner, Henderson, KY; The Albuquerque Tribune, Albuquerque, NM; The Cincinnati Post, Cincinnati, OH; Anderson Independent-Mail, Anderson, SC; Knoxville News Sentinel, Knoxville, TN; The Commercial Appeal, Memphis, TN; Abilene Reporter-News, Abilene, TX; Corpus Christi Caller-Times, Corpus Christi, TX; San Angelo Standard-Times, San Angelo, TX; Wichita Falls Times Record News, Wichita Falls, TX; Kitsap Sun, Bremerton, WA; Bonita Banner, Bonita Springs, FL; Sebastian Sun, Vero Beach, FL; Jupiter Courier, Stuart, FL; Marco Island Eagle, Marco Island, FL;

Seattle Times Co.–1120 John St., Seattle, WA, 98109; tel (206) 464-2111; fax (206) 464-2261; e-mail customerservices@seattletimes.com; web site www.seattletimes.com; www.seattletimescompany.com
CEO – Frank A. Blethen; Pres./COO – Carolyn S. Kelly; Sr. Vice Pres. – Michael R. Fancher; Sr. Vice Pres., Affiliate Newspapers – Charles Cochrane; Vice Pres./CFO – S. Mae Numata-Fujita; Vice Pres., New Media – Nancy J. Bruner; Vice Pres., HR/Labor Relations – Alayne Fardella; Vice Pres., Cor. Mktg. – Robert C. Blethen; Vice Pres., Opns. – Frank M. Paiva; Vice Pres., Adv. – Mei-Mei Chan; Cor. Commun. Mgr. – Corey Digiacinto; Daily Newspapers: The Seattle Times, Seattle, WA; Walla Walla Union-Bulletin, Walla Walla, WA; Yakima Herald-Republic, Yakima, WA; The Issaquah Press, Issaquah, WA;

Shaw Media–444 Pine Hill Dr., Dixon, IL, 61021, USA; tel (815) 284-4000; fax (815) 284-9290; e-mail tshaw@shawmedia.com; web site www.shawmedia.com
Est.: 1851
Chrmn. – Ryan McKibben; Pres./CEO – Tom Shaw; CFO – Terri Swegle; Sr. VP Media Operations
Publisher Northwest Herald – John Rung; VP Shaw Media
Publisher Dixon Telegraph & Sterling Gazette – Trevis Mayfield; Secretary
Administrative Assistant – Peggy Campbell; Chief Digital Officer – Ben Shaw; Daily Newspapers: Northwest Herald, Crystal Lake, IL; Daily Chronicle, De Kalb, IL; Sauk Valley Newspapers, Dixon, IL; Kane County Chronicle, Saint Charles, IL; Morris Daily Herald, Morris, IL; Daily Gazette, Sterling, IL; Creston News Advertiser, Creston, IA; Newton Daily News, Newton, IA; Osceola Sentinel-Tribune, Osceola, IA; Forreston Journal, Oregon, IL; The Grayslake Journal, Grayslake, IL; Hampshire Register, Sycamore, IL; Lindenhurst News, Grayslake, IL; Mount Morris Times, Oregon, IL; Mundelein News, Grayslake, IL; Oregon Republican-Reporter, Oregon, IL; Tri-County Press, Polo, IL; Bureau County Republican, Princeton, IL; Round Lake Journal, Grayslake, IL; Sauk Valley Shopper, Sterling, IL; De Kalb County Weekly, De Kalb, IL; Northwest Citizen Shopper, Crystal Lake, IL; Southwest Iowa Advertiser, Creston, IA; El Conquistador, Aurora, IL; Great Lakes Bulletin, Grayslake, IL; Jasper County Advertiser, Newton, IA;
Note: Shaw Media's 60 print and online award winning publications represent communities throughout Illinois and Iowa.

Shearman Corporation–4900 Hwy. 90E, Lake Charles, LA, 70615-4037; tel (337) 494-4033; fax (337) 494-4008; e-mail atinsley@americanpress.com; web site www.americanpress.com
Pres. – Thomas B. Shearman; Bus. Mgr. – Anita Tinsley; Classified Mgr. – Connie Perkins; Daily Newspapers: The Chronicle-News, Trinidad, CO; American Press, Lake Charles, LA; Hobbs News-Sun, Hobbs, NM;

Small Newspaper Group, Inc.–8 Dearborn Sq., Kankakee, IL, 60901-3909; tel (815) 937-3300; fax (815) 937-3301; web site www.sngnews.com
Pres. – Len Robert Small; Executive Vice President – Thomas P. Small; Vice Pres. – Robert Hill; Vice Pres. – Cordell Overgaard; Treasurer – Joseph E. Lacaeyse; Administrative Asst. – Brenda Montgomery; Daily Newspapers: The Daily Journal, Kankakee, IL; The Dispatch, Moline, IL; The Times, Ottawa, IL; The Rock Island Argus, Rock Island, IL; The Times-Press, Streator, IL; Post-Bulletin, Rochester, MN; Palisadian-Post, Pacific Palisades, CA; Leader, Davenport, IA; Post Shopper, Pacific Palisades, CA;
Note: Small Newspaper Group Inc. publishes the Pacific Palisades (CA) Palisades Post, a weekly newspaper, and one shopper, Pacific Palisades (CA) Post Shopper. The company also owns Agri-News in IA and MN, and 3 magazines: The Gold Book, Rochester Magazine, and Exposed (Rochester, MN).

Small Newspaper Group Inc–8 Dearborn Square, Kankakee, IL, 60901, USA; tel (815) 937-3300; fax (815) 937-3301; web site www.sngnews.com
President – Len Small;Daily Newspapers: Kankakee (IL) The Daily Journal and Weekend Edition; Moline (IL) The Dispatch; Ottawa (IL) The Times; Rock Island (IL) The Argus; Rochester (MN) Post-Bulletin

SmarTTargeT Marketing–1501 Venera Ave., Ste. 210, Miami, FL, 33146, USA; tel (305) 667-6665; web site www.smarttarget.com

Southern Newspapers, Inc.–5701 Woodway Dr., Ste. 131, Houston, TX, 77057, USA; tel (713) 266-5481; fax (713) 266-1847; e-mail mwalls@sninews.com; web site www.sninews.com
Est.: 1967
Chrmn. of the Bd./Pres./CEO – Martha Ann Walls; Vice Pres./Sec./COO & Owner-Times Journal (AL) – Lissa Walls Vahldiek; Treasurer – Barbara Zavodny; Daily Newspapers: The Times-Journal, Fort Payne, AL; The Daily Sentinel, Scottsboro, AL; The Tribune, Bay City, TX; The Baytown Sun, Baytown, TX; The Facts, Clute, TX; Del Rio News-Herald, Del Rio, TX; Kerrville Daily Times, Kerrville, TX; The Lufkin Daily News, Lufkin, TX; The Daily Sentinel, Nacogdoches, TX; New Braunfels Herald-Zeitung, New Braunfels, TX; The Paris News, Paris, TX; The Seguin Gazette-Enterprise, Seguin, TX; The Sand Mountain Reporter, Albertville, AL; The Weekly Post, Rainsville, AL; The Walton Tribune, Monroe, GA; Times Journal Extra, Fort Payne, AL; Buyer's Express, Clute, TX; News In Review, Paris, TX; The Seguin/Guadalupe County PennySaver, Seguin, TX; The Shopper, Albertville, AL; Sand Mountain Shopper's Guide, Rainsville, AL;
Note: The Fort Payne (AL) Times Journal is managed by Southern Newspapers Inc. The Fort Payne (AL) Times Journal is owned by Lissa Walls Vahldiek.

Southern Rhode Island Newspapers–187 Main St., Wakefield, RI, 02880, USA; tel (401) 789-9744; fax (401) 789-1550; web site www.ri-central.com
Publisher – Nanci Batson;Daily Newspapers: The Times, Pawtucket, RI; The Kent County Times, West Warwick, RI; The Call, Woonsocket, RI; Chariho Times, Wakefield, RI; Coventry Courier, Wakefield, RI; East Greenwich Pendulum, East Greenwich, RI; Standard-Times, North Kingstown, RI; Narragansett Times, Wakefield, RI; Kent County Daily Times, West Warwick, RI;
Note: Southern Rhode Island Newspapers is owned by RISN (Rhode Island Suburban Newspapers) Operations.

Star Community Newspapers–624 Krona Dr., Ste. 170, Plano, TX, 75074, USA; tel (972) 424-6565; fax (972) 398-4470; web site www.planostar.com
Pres. – Gene Carr; Adv. Dir. – Scott Carr; Daily Newspapers: Plano Star Courier, Plano, TX; The Allen American, Plano, TX; Celina Record, Mckinney, TX; The Frisco Enterprise, McKinney, TX; Little Elm Journal, Frisco, TX; The Mesquite News, Mesquite, TX; Rowlett Lakeshore Times, Mesquite, TX;
Note: Star Community Newspapers is owned by Community Newspapers LLC. which owns various daily and weekly newspapers.
Stephens Media LLC–1111 W. Bonanza Rd., Las Vegas, NV, 89106, USA; tel (702) 383-0211; fax (702) 383-0402; web site www.stephens-media.com

Est.: 1993
Chief Executive Officer – Mike Ferguson; Vice Pres./Gen. Counsel, Director-Human Resources – Mark A. Hinueber; Daily Newspapers: The Farmington Post, Lincoln, AR; Nye County Nifty Nickel, Pahrump, NV; Goldfield News, Tonopah, NV; The Goodman News-Dispatch, Pineville, MO; The Anderson Graphic, Pineville, MO; The Southwest City Republic, Pineville, MO; Northwest Arkansas Newspapers, LLC., Fayetteville, AR; Times Record, Fort Smith, AR; Jacksonville Patriot, Jacksonville, AR; Pine Bluff Commercial, Pine Bluff, AR; The Morning News of Northwest Arkansas, Springdale, AR; Hawaii Tribune-Herald, Hilo, HI; West Hawaii Today, Kailua-Kona, HI; Ely Times, Ely, NV; Las Vegas Review-Journal, Las Vegas, NV; The Courier-Tribune, Asheboro, NC; Examiner-Enterprise, Bartlesville, OK; River Valley Advertisier, Fort Smith, AR; Fayetteville Free Weekly, Fayetteville, AR; Columbia Daily Herald, Columbia, TN; Herald Democrat, Sherman, TX; The Daily World, Aberdeen, WA; Booneville Democrat, Booneville, AR; Cabot Star-Herald, Cabot, AR; Carlisle Independent, Carlisle, AR; Charleston Express, Charleston, AR; Van Buren County Democrat, Clinton, AR; Greenwood Democrat, Greenwood, AR; Hot Springs Village Voice, Hot Springs Village, AR; The Lincoln Leader, Lincoln, AR; Lonoke Democrat, Lonoke, AR; The Times, North Little Rock, AR; Paris Express, Paris, AR; Sherwood Voice, Sherwood, AR; Press Argus-Courier, Van Buren, AR; McDonald County News-Gazette, Pineville, MO; McDonald County Press, Pineville, MO; The Eureka Sentinel, Ely, NV; Pahrump Valley Times, Pahrump, NV; Tonapah Times Bonanza, Tonopah, NV; Pawhuska Journal-Capital, Pawhuska, OK; Van Alstyne Leader, Van Alstyne, TX; The Vidette, Montesano, WA; The North Coast News, Ocean Shores, WA; South Beach Bulletin, Aberdeen, WA; City Life, Las Vegas, NV; Maumelle Monitor, Maumelle, AR; North Hawaii News, Kamuela, HI; Alma Journal, Van Buren, AR; La Prensa Libres, Springdale, AR; Nifty Nickel, Las Vegas, NV;

Suburban Journals of Greater St. Louis, LLC–14522 S. Outer Forty, 3ed Floor, Town & Country, MO, 63017, USA; tel (314) 821-1110; fax (314) 821-0745; web site www.yourjournal.com

Sun Coast Media Group Inc–23170 Harbor View Rd, Pt Charlotte, FL, 33980; tel (941) 206-1000

Sun-Times Media Group Inc.–350 N. Orleans St., Chicago, IL, 60654-1975, USA; tel (312) 321-3000; fax (312) 321-6426; web site www.thesuntimesgroup.com; www.suntimes.com
Chrmn./CEO – Jeremy L. Halbreich; Treasurer – Dennis M. Byrd; Daily Newspapers: The Beacon News, Aurora, IL; Southtown-Star, Tinley Park, IL; Chicago Sun-Times, Chicago, IL; The Courier News, Elgin, IL; The Herald News, Joliet, IL; The Lake County News-Sun, Waukegan, IL; Post-Tribune, Merrillville, IN; Barrington Courier-Review, Glenview, IL; The Bolingbrook Sun, Plainfield, IL; Buffalo Grove Countryside, Arlington Heights, IL; Cary-Grove Countryside, Glenview, IL; Lakeview Booster, Oak Park, IL; Harlem-Foster Times, Lincolnwood, IL; Harlem-Irving Times, Park Ridge, IL; Jefferson Park/Portage Park/Bel-Cragin Times, Glenview, IL; News Star, Lincolnwood, IL; Lincoln Park/Lake View/Near North/Downtown Skyline, Oak Park, IL; Morton Grove/Niles Life, Glenview, IL; Edgebrook-Sauganash Times Review, Glenview, IL; Deerfield Review, Waukegan, IL; Elm Leaves, Glenview, IL; Elmwood Park/River Grove Times, Lincolnwood, IL; Evanston Review, Glenview, IL; Fox Valley Villages Sun, Naperville, IL; Franklin Park Herald-Journal, Oak Park, IL; Glencoe News, Glenview, IL; Glenview Announcements, Glenview, IL; Grayslake Review, Waukegan, IL; Gurnee Review, Glenview, IL; Highland Park News, Glenview, IL; West Proviso Herald, Glenview, IL; The Doings, Hinsdale, IL; Hoffman Estates Review, Glenview, IL; Lake Forester, Glenview, IL; Lake Villa Review, Glenview, IL; Lake Zurich Courier, Glenview, IL; Libertyville Review, Glenview, IL; Lincolnwood Life, Lincolnwood, IL; Lincolnwood Review, Glenview, IL; The Lisle Sun, Naperville, IL; Maywood Herald, Glenview, IL; The Melrose Park Herald, Glenview, IL; Morton Grove Champion, Glenview, IL; Mount Prospect Times, Park Ridge, IL; Mundelein Review, Glenview, IL; The Naperville Sun, Naperville, IL; Niles Herald-Spectator, Glenview, IL; Pioneer Press News Star, Oak Park, IL; Northbrook Star, Glenview, IL; Northlake Herald-Journal, Glenview, IL; Edison-Norwood Times Review, Glenview, IL; Norridge/Harwood Heights/Norwood Park News, Glenview, IL; Oak Leaves, Oak Park, IL; Palatine Countryside, Glenview, IL; Park Ridge Herald Advocate, Glenview, IL; Forest Leaves, Glenview, IL; Rolling Meadows Review, Arlington Heights, IL; Schaumburg Review, Glenview, IL; The Skokie Review, Glenview, IL; Star Newspapers, Tinley Park, IL; Vernon Hills Review, Glenview, IL; Westchester Herald, Glenview, IL; The Wheaton Sun, Naperville, IL; Wheeling Countryside, Glenview, IL; Wilmette Life, Glenview, IL; Winnetka Talk, Glenview, IL; Crown Point Star, Crown Point, IN; Crown Point Register, Crown Point, IN; The Beacon News Extra, Aurora, IL; Homer Sun, Naperville, IL; Penny Saver, Tinley Park, IL; Fox Valley Shopping News, Yorkville, IL; Star/Shopper, Crown Point, IN; The Geneva Sun, Aurora, IL; The St. Charles Sun, Naperville, IL; The Batavia Sun, Aurora, IL; Glen-Ellyn Sun, Aurora, IL; Plainfield Sun, Plainfield, IL; Downers-Grove Sun, Aurora, IL; Lincoln-Way Sun, Plainfield, IL; Arlington Heights Post, Glenview, IL; Antioch Review, Glenview, IL; Naperville Extra!, Naperville, IL;

Superior Publishing Corp.–1105 Tower Ave., Superior, WI, 54880-1502, USA; tel (715) 395-5725; fax (715) 395-5729
Pres./CEO – Charles R. Johnson; CFO/Treasurer – Robert J. Wallace; HR Mgr. – Bonnie L. Ratajek; @RecordBody:**Note:** Superior Publishing Corp. owns three daily newspapers as well as 14 non-daily publications.

Swift Communications, Inc.–580 Mallory Way, Carson City, NV, 89701-5360, USA; tel (775) 850-7676; fax (775) 850-7677; e-mail info@swiftcom.com; web site www.swiftcom.com
Chrmn., Bd. – Richard K. Larson; Pres./CEO – Arne L. Hoel; COO – Robert L. Brown; Cor. Controller – Bill J. Waters; Cor. Dir. – Debbie Spieker-Martin; Daily Newspapers: The Union, Grass Valley, CA; Tahoe Daily Tribune, South Lake Tahoe, CA; The Aspen Times, Aspen, CO; Summit Daily News, Frisco, CO; Glenwood Springs Post Independent, Glenwood Springs, CO; Greeley Daily Tribune, Greeley, CO; Vail Daily, Vail, CO; Nevada Appeal, Carson City, NV; Lahontan Valley News/Fallon Eagle Standard, Fallon, NV; The News-Review, Roseburg, OR; Sierra Sun, Truckee, CA; Valley Journal, Carbondale, CO; The Eagle Valley Enterprise, Eagle, CO; Citizen Telegram, Rifle, CO; Snowmass Sun, Snowmass Village, CO; Summit County Journal, Frisco, CO; The Record-Courier, Gardnerville, NV; North Lake Tahoe Bonanza, Incline Village, NV;
Note: Swift Newspapers Inc. also publishes two farm and ranch magazines as well as Northern Nevada Business Weekly.

T

The Tennessean–1100 Broadway, Nashville, TN, 37203-3116, USA; tel (615) 259-8000; fax (615) 259-8875; e-mail publisher@tennessean.com; web site www.tennessean.com
Est.: 1812
Vice Pres., Adv. – Dave Gould; Adv. Mgr., Nat'l – Wendell Pedigo; Market Devel. Dir. – Bob Faricy; Research Mgr. – Reginald Northern; NIE Mgr. – Ann Zangri; Vice Pres., Circ. – Jay Winkler; Asst. Mng. Ed., Business – Deborah Fisher; Asst. Mng. Ed., Davidson A.M. – Cindy Smith; Dir/Design Studio – Jeff Glick; Asst. Bus. Ed. – Randy McClain; Entertainment Ed. – Linda Zettler; Music Writer – Peter Cooper; News Ed. – Ted Rayburn; Night/Weekend Ed. – Dwight Lewis; Vice Pres., Finance – Andy Royer; Vice Pres., HR – Kathy Cheatham; VP/Finance – Kevin Huff; President & Publisher – Carol Hudler; Editor & VP/Content & Audience Dev. – Mark Silverman; Production Director – Thom Gregory; Pres./Pub. – Ellen Leifeld; Vice Pres., Audience Mgmt. – Andrew Oppmann; Asst. Mng. Ed., Nights – Kevin Paulk; Editorial Writer – Mike Morrow; Asst. Features Ed., Presentation – Bill Greer; Pres. – Carol Hudler; President & Publisher – Carol Hudler; Daily Newspapers: The Daily News Journal, Murfreesboro, TN; Ashland City Times, Ashland City, TN; Dickson Herald, Dickson, TN; Stewart-Houston Times, Erin, TN; Fairview Observer, Fairview, TN; News-Examiner, Gallatin, TN; Hendersonville Star News, Gallatin, TN; Nashville Record, Nashville, TN; Robertson County Times, Springfield, TN; Dickson Shopper, Dickson, TN; The Sumner County Shopper, Gallatin, TN; Cheatham County Money Saver, Ashland City, TN;
Note: The Tennessean is owned by Gannett Co., Inc. which owns more than 90 daily newspapers.

Tennessee Valley Printing Co., Inc.–201 1st Ave. SE, Decatur, AL, 35601; tel (256) 353-4612; fax (256) 340-2366; web site www.decaturdaily.com
Pres./Pub. – Barrett C. Shelton Jr.; Gen. Mgr. – Clint Shelton; Daily Newspapers: The Decatur Daily, Decatur, AL; TimesDaily, Florence, AL; The Moulton Advertiser, Moulton, AL;

The Dispatch Printing Company–34 S Third Street, Columbus, OH, 43215; tel (614) 461-5150

The E W Scripps Company, USA; tel (513) 977-3000; web site www.scripps.com

The Hearst Corporation–300 W 57th Street, New York, NY, 10019, USA; tel (212) 649-2000; web site www.hearstcorp.com
Est.: 1887
Vice Chrmn./CEO – Frank Bennack; Pres., Hearst Newspapers – Steven R. Swartz; Sr. Vice Pres., Finance – John M. Condon; Vice Pres., Digital Media – Neeraj Khemlani; Sr. Vice Pres. – Mark E. Aldam; Daily Newspapers: San Francisco Chronicle, San Francisco, CA; Connecticut Post, Bridgeport, CT; Edwardsville Intelligencer, Edwardsville, IL; The Huron Daily Tribune, Bad Axe, MI; Midland Daily News, Midland, MI; Times Union, Albany, NY; The Beaumont Enterprise, Beaumont, TX; Houston Chronicle, Houston, TX; Laredo Morning Times, Laredo, TX; Midland Reporter-Telegram, Midland, TX; Plainview Daily Herald, Plainview, TX; San Antonio Express-News, San Antonio, TX; Seattle Post-Intelligencer, Seattle, WA; Darien News, New Canaan, CT; Fairfield Citizen-News, Fairfield, CT; Westport News, Fairfield, CT; The Marlette Leader, Marlette, MI; The Vassar Pioneer Times, Vassar, MI; The Canyon News, Canyon, TX; The Hardin County News, Lumberton, TX; The Jasper NewsBoy, Jasper, TX; Muleshoe Journal, Muleshoe, TX; Mid County Chronicle, Beaumont, TX; Connecticut Post, Bridgeport, CT; Ballston Journal, Ballston Spa, NY; Beaumont Journal, Beaumont, TX; Orange County News, Beaumont, TX; New Milford Spectrum, New Milford, CT; The Advertiser, Clifton Park, NY; The Pennysaver, Clifton Park, NY; Norwalk Citizen-News, Darien, CT; Greenwich Citizen, Old Greenwich, CT;
Note: The Hearst Corporation is a diversified communications company, with interests in magazine, newspaper and business publishing; television and radio stations; newspaper comics and features syndication; cable TV networks; television production and syndicati

The McClatchy Company/Knight Ridder–35 S Market Street, San Jose, CA, 95113; tel (408) 938-6000; web site www.knightridder.com

The New York Times Company–620 8th Ave, New York, NY, 10018-1405; tel (212) 556-1234; web site www.nytco.com

The Poynter Institute–801 Third St S/Media Studies lib, St Petersburg, FL, 33701-4920; tel (727) 821-9494; web site www.poynter.org

The Washington Post Company–1150 15th St NW, Washington, DC, 20071-0001; tel (202) 334-6000; web site www.washpostco.com

Times Citizen Communications–406 Stevens Street, Iowa Falls, IA, 50126; tel (641) 648-2521

Times Community News (TCN)–221 N. Brand Blvd., Fl. 2, Glendale, CA, 91203; tel (818) 637-3200; fax (818) 241-1975; e-mail gnp@latimes.com; web site www.glendalenewspress.com
CFO – Gordon Tomaske; Gen. Mgr. – Tom Johnson; Bus. Mgr. – Debbie Feyerabend; Opns. Mgr. – Neil McAnally; Daily Newspapers: News-Press, Glendale, CA; Daily Pilot, Costa Mesa, CA; Burbank Leader, Glendale, CA; Huntington Beach/Fountain Valley Independent, Coasta Mesa, CA; La Canada Valley Sun, La Canada Flintridge, CA; Laguna Beach Coastline Pilot, Laguna Beach , CA;
Note: Times Community News (TCN) is owned by the Los Angeles Times.

Times-Journal, Inc.–580 Fairground St., Marietta, GA, 30060, USA; tel (770) 428-9411; fax (770) 428-7945; web site www.mdjonline.com
Est.: 1866
Pres. – R. Terry Smith; Pub. – Otis Brumby; Adv. Dir. – David McGee; Circ. Mgr. – Rusty Powell; Daily Newspapers: Marietta Daily Journal, Marietta, GA; The North Fulton Neighbor, Roswell, GA; Bartow Neighbor, Cartersville, GA; De Kalb Neighbor, Atlanta, GA; Cherokee Tribune, Canton, GA; South Cobb Neighbor, Marietta, GA; The Douglas Neighbor, Douglasville, GA; East Cobb Neighbor, Marietta, GA; Fayette Neighbor, Forest Park, GA; South Fulton Neighbor, Forest Park, GA; Henry Neighbor, Forest Park, GA; The Clayton Neighbor, Forest Park, GA; Kennesaw-Acworth Neighbor, Marietta, GA; Paulding Neighbor, Dallas, GA; The Rockdale Neighbor, Conyers, GA; The Smyrna/Vinings Neighbor, Marietta, GA; North De Kalb Neighbor, Atlanta, GA; North-side-Sandy Springs Neighbor, Atlanta, GA; Cherokee Tribune Plus, Canton, GA;

Times Publishing Co–205 W 12th St, Erie, PA, 16534; tel (814) 870-1600; web site www.goerie.com

TIMES REPORTER– Po Box 667, New Philadelphia, OH, 44663; tel 880-686-5577; web site www.timesreporter.com

Times-Shamrock Communications–149 Penn Ave., Scranton, PA, 18503, USA; tel (570) 348-9100; fax (570) 348-9149; web site www.thetimes-tribune.com
Est.: 1895
Pub. – William R. Lynett; Gen. Mgr. – Jim Towner; Daily Newspapers: Standard-Speaker, Hazleton, PA; Republican Herald, Pottsville, PA; The Times-Tribune, Scranton, PA; The News-Item, Shamokin, PA; The Daily Review/The Sunday Review, Towanda, PA; The Citizens' Voice, Wilkes-Barre, PA;

The Susquehanna County Independent, Montrose, PA; Wyoming County Press Examiner, Tunkhannock, PA; The Citizen-Standard, Valley View, PA; Owego Pennysaver, Owego, NY; The Pocono Shopper, East Stroudsburg, PA; The Valley Advantage, Scranton, PA; Troy Pennysaver, Troy, PA; Orlando Weekly, Orlando, FL; City Paper, Baltimore, MD; Metro Times, Detroit, MI; San Antonio Current, San Antonio, TX;

Trib Total Media, USA ; tel (412) 856-7400; fax (412) 243-2843; web site triblive.com
Est.: 1889
Publisher – Richard M. Scaife; Pres./COO – Ralph J. Martin; Sales/Mktg. Dir. – William M. Cotter; Vice Pres. – Jennifer Bertetto ; CFO – Jennifer Walters;

Tribune Co.–435 N. Michigan Ave, Chicago, IL, 60611; tel (312) 222-9100; fax (312) 222-1573; web site www.tribune.com
Est.: 1847
Chrmn. – Sam Zell; CFO – Chandler Bigelow; COO/Chicago Tribune Company – Vincent Casanova; SVP/Corporate Relations – Gary Weitman; CEO, Tribune Company – Eddy Haretenstein; CEO, Tribune Publishing – Tony Hunter; CEO, Tribune Broadcasting – Nils Larsen; COO, Los Angeles Times Media Group – Kathy Thomson; Daily Newspapers: am New York, New York, NY; Los Angeles Times, Los Angeles, CA; The Hartford Courant, Hartford, CT; Sun-Sentinel.com, Fort Lauderdale, FL; Orlando Sentinel, Orlando, FL; Chicago Tribune, Chicago, IL; The Baltimore Sun, Baltimore, MD; The Morning Call, Allentown, PA; Daily Press, Newport News, VA; Arbutus Times, Catonsville, MD; Baltimore Messenger, Towson, MD; Jeffersonian, Towson, MD; Northeast Booster, Towson, MD; Northeast Reporter, Towson, MD; Catonsville Times, Columbia, MD; Columbia Flier, Columbia, MD; The Aegis, Bel Air, MD; The Weekender, Bel Air, MD; Howard County Times, Columbia, MD; Laurel Leader, Laurel, MD; Towson Times, Towson, MD; Fairfield County Weekly, New Haven, CT; Hartford Advocate, Hartford, CT; New Haven Advocate, New Haven, CT; Valley Advocate, Northampton, MA; Hoy Chicago, Chicago, IL; North County News, Towson, MD;
Note: TRIBUNE is one of the country's leading multimedia companies, operating businesses in broadcasting, publishing, and interactive. The company's broadcasting group owns and/or operates 23 television stations, WGN America on national cable and Chicago's WGN-AM. In publishing, Tribune's leading daily newspapers include the Los Angeles Times, Chicago Tribune, The Baltimore Sun, Sun Sentinel (South Florida), Orlando Sentinel, Hartford Courant, The Morning Call and Daily Press. Popular news and information websites complement Tribune's print and broadcast properties and extend the company's nationwide audience.

Tribune-Review Publishing Co.–622 Cabin Hill Dr., Greensburg, PA, 15601-1657, USA; tel (724) 834-1151; fax (724) 834-1151; e-mail release@tribweb.com; web site www.tribune-review.com
Chrmn./Pres. – Ralph Martin; Sr. Vice Pres./CFO – Raymond Hartung; COO – Nickolas F. Monico; COO – Trish Hooper; Daily Newspapers: Daily Courier, Connellsville, PA; Tribune-Review, Pittsburgh, PA; Leader Times, Kittanning, PA; The Daily News, McKeesport, PA; The Valley Independent, Monessen, PA; Valley News Dispatch, Tarentum, PA;

Triple Crown Media–725 Old Norcross Rd., Lawrenceville, GA, 30045; tel (770) 963-9205; fax (770) 338-7353; e-mail investor.relations@triplecrownmedia.com; web site www.triplecrownmedia.com
Est.: 2006
Chrmn. – Robert S. Parther; Pres./CEO/Dir. – Michael Gebhart; Exec. Vice Pres./CFO – Mark G. Meikle; Exec. Vice Pres. – Michael Steve Cornwell; Daily Newspapers: The Newton Citizen, Covington, GA; The Albany Herald, Albany, GA; The Rockdale Citizen, Conyers, GA; News/Daily, Jonesboro, GA; Gwinnett Daily Post, Lawrenceville, GA; Jackson Progress-Argus, Jackson, GA; Albany Area Advertiser, Albany, GA;

U

United Communications Corporation–5800 7th Ave., Kenosha, WI, 53140, United States; tel (262) 657-1000; fax (262) 657-6226; e-mail kdowdell@kenoshanews.com; web site www.kenoshanews.com
Est.: 1969
Vice President – Kenneth L. Dowdell; Vice President – Ronald J. Montemurro; Pres. – Howard J. Brown; Daily Newspapers: The Sun Chronicle, Attleboro, MA; Watertown Public Opinion, Watertown, SD; Kenosha News, Kenosha, WI; Bargaineer, Zion, IL; Coteau Shopper, Watertown, SD;
Note: United Commmunications Corp. operates the following dailies: The Kenosha News (WI), The Watertown Public Opinion (SD) and The Sun Chronicle (MA). Weeklies: the (WI) Bulletin, The Zion Benton News (IL), Lake Geneva Regional News (WI) and the Foxboro (MA) Reporter. Marketing and research company, Media Innovations LLC (WI). UCC also operates two television stations; KEYC-TV (MN), WWNY-TV, (NY)

W

Wehco Media, Inc.–115 E. Capitol Ave., Little Rock, AR, 72201, USA; tel (501) 378-3400; fax (501) 378-3591; e-mail news@arkansasonline.com; web site www.arkansasonline.co
Owner/Pub. – Walter E. Hussman; Pres. – Paul R. Smith; Sec. – Philip S. Anderson; Nat Lea; Daily Newspapers: Benton County Daily Record, Bentonville, AR; Camden News, Camden, AR; El Dorado News-Times, El Dorado, AR; Northwest Arkansas Times, Fayetteville, AR; The Sentinel-Record, Hot Springs, AR; Arkansas Democrat-Gazette, Little Rock, AR; Banner-News, Magnolia, AR; The Fulton Sun, Fulton, MO; News Tribune, Jefferson City, MO; Chattanooga Times Free Press, Chattanooga, TN; Texarkana Gazette, Texarkana, TX; The Weekly Vista, Bella Vista, AR; Decatur Herald, Decatur, AR; White River Journal, Des Arc, AR; Gentry Courier-Journal, Gentry, AR; Gravette News Herald, Gravette, AR; The Times of Northeast Benton County, Pea Ridge, AR; Hometown News, Rogers, AR; The Herald-Leader, Siloam Springs, AR; Smackover Journal, Smackover, AR; California Democrat, California, MO;
Note: Wehco Media Inc. also owns the California (MO) Democrat and The Lake Today, both weekly publications.

Western Communications, Inc.–1777 SW Chandler Ave., Bend, OR, 97702, USA; tel (541) 382-1811; fax (541) 385-5802; e-mail bulletin@bendbulletin.com; web site www.bendbulletin.com
Est.: 1968
Chrmn. of the Bd. – Elizabeth C. McCool; Pres. – Gordon R. Black; CFO – Karen Anderson; Adv. Dir. – Jay Brandt; New Media Dir. – Jan Even; Prodn. Mgr. – Keith Foutz; Daily Newspapers: The Daily Triplicate, Crescent City, CA; The Union Democrat, Sonora, CA; Baker City Herald, Baker City, OR; The Bulletin, Bend, OR; The Observer, La Grande, OR; Curry Coastal Pilot, Brookings, OR; The Hermiston Herald, Hermiston, OR; The Redmond Spokesman, Redmond, OR; Central Oregon Nickel Ads, Bend, OR;
Note: Western Communications Inc. also publishes three weekly newspapers and one twice-weekly newspaper in Oregon.

Western Newspapers, Inc.–1748 S. Arizona Ave., Yuma, AZ, 85364-5727, USA; tel (928) 783-3311; fax (928) 783-3313; e-mail urnumber1@westernnews.com; web site www.westernnews.com
Est.: 1958
Pres./CEO – Joseph E. Soldwedel; Sr. Vice Pres. – Blake DeWitt; Vice Pres./CFO – David Montgomery; Vice Pres./Dir., HR – D.J. Johnson; Vice Pres./CEO, Prescott Newspapers Inc. – Kit Atwell; Daily Newspapers: Kingman Daily Miner, Kingman, AZ; Today's News-Herald, Lake Havasu City, AZ; The Daily Courier, Prescott, AZ; Chino Valley Review, Chino Valley, AZ; River Extra, Lake Havasu City, AZ; Parker Pioneer, Parker, AZ; Prescott Valley Tribune, Prescott Valley, AZ; Williams-Grand Canyon News, Williams, AZ; Palo Verde Valley Times/Quartzsite Times, Blythe, CA; Navajo Hopi Observer, Flagstaff, AZ; Big Bug News, Prescott, AZ;
Note: Western Newspapers Inc. shares 50% ownership of the Lake Havasu City (AZ) Today's News Herald (mS), and the weekly Parker (AZ) Parker Pioneer (w) with Wick Communicatons.

Wick Communications Co Inc–333 W Wilcox Dr Ste 302, Sierra Vista, AZ, 85635, USA; tel (520) 458-0200; fax (520) 458-6166; web site www.wickcommunications.com
Est.: 1984
Pres./CEO – John Matthew; Vice Pres. – Walter M. Wick; CFO – Don Root; Sec./Treasurer – Robert J. Wick; Daily Newspapers: Bisbee Daily Review, Bisbee, AZ; The Daily Dispatch, Douglas, AZ; Sierra Vista Herald, Sierra Vista, AZ; The Montrose Daily Press, Montrose, CO; Daily News, Bogalusa, LA; The Daily Iberian, New Iberia, LA; Slidell Sentry-News, Slidell, LA; Daily Herald, Roanoke Rapids, NC; The Daily News, Wahpeton, ND; Williston Daily Herald, Williston, ND; Argus Observer, Ontario, OR; Capital Journal, Pierre, SD; Frontiersman, Wasilla, AK; San Pedro Valley News-Sun, Benson, AZ; Eastern Arizona Courier, Safford, AZ; Copper Era, Safford, AZ; Nogales International, Nogales, AZ; Bravo, Sierra Vista, AZ; Arizona Range News, Willcox, AZ; Half Moon Bay Review, Half Moon Bay, CA; Kern Valley Sun, Lake Isabella, CA; Independent Enterprise, Payette, ID; The Jeanerette Enterprise, Jeanerette, LA; L'Observateur, La Place, LA; St. Tammany News, Covington, LA; Sidney Herald, Sidney, MT; News-Monitor, Hankinson, ND; Cibola County Beacon, Grants, NM; The Rio Rancho Observer, Rio Rancho, NM; Anchorage Press, Anchorage, AK; Tucson Weekly, Tucson, AZ; The Bulletin, Nogales, AZ;
Note: Wick Communications shares 50% ownership of the Lake Havasu City (AZ) Today's News-Herald (mS), and the weekly Parker (AZ) Pioneer with Western Newspapers Inc.

Womack Publishing Co.–30 N. Main St., Chatham, VA, 24513-5436, USA; tel (434) 432-1654; fax (434) 432-1005; web site www.womackpublishing.com; www.womacknewspapers.com; www.wpcva.com
Chrmn. – Charles Zan Womack; Pres./COO – Diane C. White; Pres., Womack Newspapers Inc. – Charles Womack; Grp. Pub. – David Crawley; Grp. Pub – Chad Harrison; HR Mgr. – Ron Cox; Accounting Mgr. – Jim Glidewell; Circ. Mgr. – Shirley Adkins; Editorial Dir. – Tim Davis; Press Opns. Mgr. – Randy Velvin; Daily Newspapers: Caswell Messenger, Yanceyville, NC; The News of Orange County, Hillsborough, NC; Jamestown News, Jamestown, NC; The Mebane Enterprise, Mebane, NC; Montgomery Herald, Troy, NC; Warren Record, Warrenton, NC; Altavista Journal, Altavista, VA; Times-Virginian, Appomattox, VA; Smith Mountain Eagle, Wirtz, VA; Union Star, Brookneal, VA; Star-Tribune, Chatham, VA; Independent-Messenger, Emporia, VA; The South Hill Enterprise, South Hill, VA; Outer Banks Sentinel, Nags Head, NC;

Wooster Republican Printing Co.–212 E. Liberty St., Wooster, OH, 44691, USA; tel (330) 264-3511; fax (330) 263-5013; e-mail wrpc@dixcom.com; web site www.the-daily-record.com
Gen. Mgr. – William C. McKinney;Daily Newspapers: The Daily Record, Wooster, OH; The Homes County Hub, Millersburg, OH;
Note: Wooster Republican Printing LLC is part of Dix Communications which is owned by the Wooster Republican Printing Co. Dix also owns two television stations in Montana and seven radio stations. Through it's subsidiaries, Alliance Publishing Co. LLC, Ashland

World Company–PO Box 888, Lawrence, KS, 66044-0888; tel (785) 843-1000; web site www.ljworld.com

WorldWest LLC–609 New Hampshire St., Lawrence, KS, -2243; tel (785) 843-1000; fax (785) 832-7207
Est.: 1995
Owner – Dan Simons; Cor. Sec. – Ralph D. Gage; Co-Mgr. – Dolph C. Simons; General Manager - Steamboat Pilot & Today – Scott Stanford; Publisher - Craig Daily Press – Bryce Jacobson; Publisher - Payson Roundup – John Naughton; Daily Newspapers: Craig Daily Press, Craig, CO; Steamboat Today, Steamboat Springs, CO; The Payson Roundup, Payson, AZ; Hayden Valley Press, Steamboat Springs, CO; Steamboat Pilot, Steamboat Springs, CO;
Note: WorldWest LLC owns the Payson (AZ) Roundup, Hayden Valley (CO) Press and the Steamboat Springs (CO) Pilot, all weekly publications. The company also owns the Steamboat Springs (CO) Today, and the Craig (CO) Daily Press, both daily publications

Wyoming Newspaper Group–702 W. Lincolnway Ave., Cheyenne, WY, 82001; tel (307) 634-3361; fax (307) 633-3189; e-mail news@wyomingnews.com; web site www.wyomingnews.com
Pres. – L. Michael McCraken;Daily Newspapers: Wyoming Tribune-Eagle, Cheyenne, WY; Laramie Daily Boomerang, Laramie, WY; Rawlins Daily Times, Rawlins, WY; Northern Wyoming Daily News, Worland, WY;

Y

Yellowstone Newspapers–401 S. Main St., Livingston, MT, 59047, USA; tel (406) 222-2000; fax (406) 222-8580; e-mail enterprise@livent.net; web site www.livingstonenterprise.com
Pres. – John Sullivan; Comptroller – Scott Squillace; Mktg. Dir. – Jim Durfey; Daily Newspapers: Judith Basin Press, Stanford, MT; The Livingston Enterprise, Livingston, MT; Miles City Star, Miles City, MT; The Stillwater County News, Columbus, MT; Dillon Tribune Examiner, Dillon, MT; The Independent Press, Forsyth, MT; Glendive Ranger-Review, Glendive, MT; Big Horn County News, Hardin, MT; Lewistown News-Argus, Lewistown, MT; Carbon County News, Red Lodge, MT; The Terry Tribune, Terry, MT; Park County Super Shopper, Livingston, MT;
Note: Yellowstone Newspapers owns two daily newspapers, two twice weeklies and seven weekly newspapers. Yellowstone also owns KATL, an AM radio station in Miles City, Montana Best Times, a monthly senior publication and two commerical job and web printing plan

CANADIAN NEWSPAPER GROUPS

B

Black Press Ltd. – 3175 Beach Drive Victoria BC, V8R 6L7, Canada; tel (250) 480-3220; fax 250-480-3219; web site www.black-press.ca
CEO – David Black
COO – Richard O'ConnorDaily Newspapers: Rimbey Review, Rimbey, AB; Ponoka News, Ponoka, AB; Red Deer Life, Red Deer, AB; Central Alberta Life, Red Deer, AB; Stettler Independent, Stettler, AB; 100 Mile House Free Press, 100 Mile House, BC; The Abbotsford News, Abbotsford, BC; The Aldergrove Star, Aldergrove, BC; The Ashcroft Journal, Ashcroft, BC; Star/Journal, Barriere, BC; Times, Clearwater, BC; Burnaby/New Westminster News Leader, Burnaby, BC; Lakes District News, Burns Lake, BC; The Campbell River Mirror, Campbell River, BC; North Island Midweek, Campbell River, BC; The Chilliwack Progress, Chilliwack, BC; Comox Valley Record, Courtenay, BC; The Cowichan News Leader, Duncan, BC; Caledonia Courier, Fort Saint James, BC; Golden Star, Golden, BC; Victoria News, Victoria, BC; Hope Standard, Hope, BC; Valley Echo, Invermere, BC; Kelowna Capital News, Kelowna, BC; Northern Sentinel, Kitimat, BC; The Ladysmith-Chemainus Chronicle, Ladysmith, BC; Langley Times, Langley, BC; The Maple Ridge News, Maple Ridge, BC; Merritt Herald, Merritt, BC; Mission Record, Mission, BC; Arrow Lakes News, Nakusp, BC; Nanaimo News Bulletin, Nanaimo, BC; North Island Gazette, Port Hardy, BC; Oak Bay News, Victoria, BC; Parksville Qualicum Beach News, Parksville, BC; Penticton Western News, Penticton, BC; Prince George Free Press, Prince George, BC; Princeton Similkameen Spotlight, Princeton, BC; Quesnel Cariboo Observer, Quesnel, BC; Revelstoke Times-Review, Revelstoke, BC; Richmond Review, Richmond, BC; Salmon Arm Observer, Salmon Arm, BC; Shuswap Market News, Salmon Arm, BC; Eagle Valley News, Sicamous, BC; The Peninsula News Review, Sidney, BC; The Interior News, Smithers, BC; The Sooke News Mirror, Sooke, BC; Summerland Review, Summerland, BC; Surrey Leader, Surrey, BC; The Terrace Standard, Terrace, BC; WestEnder, Vancouver, BC; Omineca Express, Vanderhoof, BC; The Morning Star, Vernon, BC; Goldstream Gazette, Victoria, BC; The Peace Arch News, White Rock, BC; The Tribune, Williams Lake, BC; Red Deer Advocate, Red Deer, AB; The Merritt Herald Weekender, Merritt, BC; Saanich News, Victoria, BC; Kamloops This Week, Campbell, BC; Tri-City News, Port Coquitlam, BC;

Brunswick News, Inc. – 939 Main St. PO Box 1001 Moncton NB, E1C 8P3, Canada; tel (506) 859-4900; fax (506) 859-5648; web site www.canadaeast.com
Co-Pub. – Eric LawsonDaily Newspapers: Victoria Star, Grand Falls, NB; The Northern Light, Bathurst, NB; Le Madawaska, Edmundston, NB; La Cataracte, Grand Falls, NB; Miramichi Leader, Miramichi, NB; Miramichi Weekend, Miramichi, NB; The Oromocto Post-Gazette, Oromocto, NB; The Kings County Record, Sussex, NB; The Bugle-Observer, Woodstock, NB; The Daily Gleaner, Fredericton, NB; Times & Transcript, Moncton, NB; New Brunswick Telegraph-Journal, Saint John, NB; Northside This Week, Fredericton, NB;

C

CanWest Global Communications Corp. – 3100 CanWest Global Pl., 201 Portage Ave. Winnipeg MB, R3B 3L7, Canada; tel (204) 956-2025; fax (204) 947-9841; e-mail corporateinquiries@canwest.com; web site www.canwest.com
Est.: 1977
Chrmn. – Derek H. Burney
Pres./CEO – Leonard J. Asper
Exec. Vice Pres. – David A. Asper
Vice Pres./Gen. Counsel – Richard Leipsic
CFO – John Maguire
Corp. Sec. – Gail AsperDaily Newspapers: Harbour City Star, Nanaimo, BC; Burnaby Now, Burnaby, BC; Chilliwack Times, Chilliwack, BC; Comox Valley Echo, Courtenay, BC; Delta Optimist, Ladner, BC; Langley Advance, Langley, BC; Maple Ridge/Pitt Meadow Times, Maple Ridge, BC; The Record, Burnaby, BC; North Shore News, North Vancouver, BC; The Oceanside Star, Parksville, BC; Richmond News, Richmond, BC; The Now Newspaper, Surrey, BC; The Vancouver Courier, Vancouver, BC; The Lakeshore News, Tecumseh, ON; The Kingsville Reporter, Kingsville, ON; Shoreline Week, Tecumseh, ON; The Tilbury Times, Tilbury, ON; Calgary Herald, Canada, AB; Edmonton Journal, Edmonton, AB; Nanaimo Daily News, Nanaimo, BC; Alberni Valley Times, Port Alberni, BC; The Daily News, Prince Rupert, BC; The Province, Vancouver, BC; The Vancouver Sun, Vancouver, BC; Times Colonist, Victoria, BC; The Ottawa Citizen, Ottawa, ON; National Post, Don Mills, ON; The Windsor Star, Windsor, ON; The Gazette, Montreal, QC; The Leader-Post, Regina, SK; The StarPhoenix, Saskatoon, SK; Westerly News, Ucluelet, BC; Abbotsford-Mission Times, Abbotsford, BC;
Notes: CanWest Global Communications Corp. is an international media company. CanWest owns and operates newspapers, conventional television, out-of-home advertising, specialty cable channels, web sites and radio networks in Canada, New Zealand, Australia, Irela

CanWest MediaWorks Publications, Inc. – 1450 Don Mills Rd. Don Mills ON, M3B 2X7, Canada; tel (416) 383-2300; fax (416) 442-2077; e-mail sfernandez@canwest.com; web site www.canwestglobal.com; www.canwestmediaworks.com; www.canwest.com
Pres./CEO – Leonard AsperDaily Newspapers:
Harbour City Star, Nanaimo, BC; Burnaby Now, Burnaby, BC; Chilliwack Times, Chilliwack, BC; Comox Valley Echo, Courtenay, BC; Delta Optimist, Ladner, BC; Langley Advance, Langley, BC; Maple Ridge/Pitt Meadow Times, Maple Ridge, BC; The Record, Burnaby, BC; North Shore News, North Vancouver, BC; The Oceanside Star, Parksville, BC; Richmond News, Richmond, BC; The Now Newspaper, Surrey, BC; The Vancouver Courier, Vancouver, BC; The Lakeshore News, Tecumseh, ON; The Kingsville Reporter, Kingsville, ON; Shoreline Week, Tecumseh, ON; The Tilbury Times, Tilbury, ON; Calgary Herald, Canada, AB; Edmonton Journal, Edmonton, AB; Nanaimo Daily News, Nanaimo, BC; Alberni Valley Times, Port Alberni, BC; The Province, Vancouver, BC; The Vancouver Sun, Vancouver, BC; Times Colonist, Victoria, BC; The Ottawa Citizen, Ottawa, ON; National Post, Don Mills, ON; The Windsor Star, Windsor, ON; The Gazette, Montreal, QC; The Leader-Post, Regina, SK; The StarPhoenix, Saskatoon, SK; Westerly News, Ucluelet, BC; Abbotsford-Mission Times, Abbotsford, BC;

Citymedia Group – 44 Frid St. Hamilton ON, L8N 3G3, Canada; tel (905) 526-3333; fax (905) 526-1696
Vice Pres., Adv. – Gary Myers

G

Gesca Ltd. – 7 St. Jacques St. Montreal QC, H2Y 1K9, Canada; tel (514) 285-6859; fax (514) 285-8943; web site www.powercorporation.com
Chrmn. – Andre Desmarais
Pres. – Guy CrevierDaily Newspapers: La Voix de L'Est Plus, Granby, QC; Le Droit, Ottawa, ON; Le Quotidien, Chicoutimi, QC; La Voix de l'Est, Granby, QC; La Presse, Montreal, QC; Le Soleil, Quebec, QC; La Tribune, Sherbrooke, QC; Le Nouvelliste, Trois-Rivieres, QC;
Notes: Gesca Ltd. is a subsidiary of Power Corporation of Canada, a diversified management and holding company.

Glacier Media Inc. – 1970 Alberta St. Vancouver BC, V5Y 3X4, Canada; tel (604) 872-8565; fax (604) 879-1483; web site www.glacierventures.com
Dir. – Sam Grippo
Pres./CEO – Jonathan J.L. Kennedy
Grp. Pub. – Peter Ng
Sec – Bruce W. AungerDaily Newspapers: The Free Press, Fernie, BC; The Northerner, Fort Saint John, BC; The Grand Forks Gazette, Grand Forks, BC; Brome County News, Knowlton, QC; Assiniboia Times, Assiniboia, SK; Carlyle Observer, Carlyle, SK; Mercury, Estevan, SK; Hudson Bay Post-Review, Hudson Bay, SK; The Northerner, La Ronge, SK; The Tisdale Recorder, Tisdale, SK; Naicam News, Watson, SK; Weyburn Review, Weyburn, SK; Yorkton This Week, Yorkton, SK; Cranbrook Daily Townsman, Cranbrook, BC; Dawson Creek Daily News, Dawson Creek, BC; Alaska Highway Daily News, Fort Saint John, BC; Kamloops Daily News, Kamloops, BC; The Kimberley Daily Bulletin, Kimberley, BC; Nelson Daily News, Nelson, BC; The Prince George Citizen, Prince George, BC; Trail Daily Times, Trail, BC; The Record, Sherbrooke, QC; Trader Express, Estevan, SK; Parkland Review, Tisdale, SK; The Marketplace, Yorkton, SK;

H

The Halifax Herald Ltd. – 2717 Joseph Howe Dr Halifax NS, B3J 2T2, Canada; tel (902) 426-2811; fax (902) 426-1164; e-mail newsroom@herald.ca; web site www.chronicleherald.ca

Hollinger, Inc. – 10 Toronto St. Toronto ON, M5C 2B7, Canada; tel (416) 363-8721; fax (416) 364-2088; web site www.marketwire.com
Chrmn. – Stanley Beck
Chief Restructuring Officer – Randall C. Bensen
Treasurer – Tatiana Samila

M

Metroland Media Group – 3125 Wolfedale Rd. Mississauga ON, L5C 1W1, Canada; tel (905) 279-0440; fax (905) 279-5103; e-mail result@metroland.com; web site www.metroland.com
Pres. – Ian Oliver
Sr. Vice Pres. – Tim Whittaker
Sr. Vice Pres. – Ian McLeod
Vice Pres. – Ian Proudfoot
Vice Pres., HR – Brenda Biller
Vice Pres. – Joe Anderson
Vice Pres. – Bruce Danford
Vice Pres. – Ron Lenyk
Vice Pres. – Ken Nugent
Vice Pres. – Carol PeddieDaily Newspapers: Ajax-Pickering News Advertiser, Ajax, ON; The Herald, Alliston, ON; Ancaster News, Stoney Creek , ON; Arthur Enterprise News, Arthur, ON; Caledon Enterprise, Bolton, ON; Clarington This Week, Oshawa, ON; Bracebridge Examiner, Bracebridge, ON; The Muskokan, Bracebridge, ON; Brampton Guardian, Brampton, ON; The Burlington Post, Burlington, ON; Cambridge Times, Cambridge, ON; The Stayner Sun, Wasaga Beach, ON; Collingwood Connection, Collingwood, ON; The Dresden Leader, Dresden, ON; Dundas Star-News, Stoney Creek, ON; The East York Mirror, Willowdale, ON; The Elmira Independent, Elmira, ON; The Erin Advocate, Erin, ON; Etobicoke Guardian, Etobicoke, ON; Times Advocate, Exeter, ON; The Fergus-Elora News Express, Fergus, ON; The Flamborough Review, Waterdown, ON; Georgetown Independent, Georgetown, ON; The Georgina Advocate, Keswick, ON; The Gravenhurst Banner, Gravenhurst, ON; Guelph Tribune, Guelph, ON; Huntsville Forester, Huntsville, ON; Kawartha Lakes This Week, Lindsay, ON; The Listowel Banner, Listowel, ON; Markham Economist & Sun, Markham, ON; The Mirror, Midland, ON; The Milton Canadian Champion, Milton, ON; The Mount Forest Confederate, Mount Forest, ON; The Newmarket Era-Banner, Newmarket, ON; North York Mirror, Toronto, ON; Oakville Beaver, Oakville, ON; The Orangeville Banner, Orangeville, ON; Orillia Today, Orillia, ON; Peterborough This Week, Peterborough, ON; Northumberland News, Cobourg, ON; The Port Perry Star, Port Perry, ON; Port Perry Star, Port Perry, ON; The Richmond Hill Liberal, Richmond Hill, ON; Journal Argus, Saint Marys, ON; The Scarborough Mirror, Toronto, ON; Stoney Creek News, Stoney Creek, ON; Uxbridge Times-Journal, Uxbridge, ON; Herald-Times, Walkerton, ON; The Wasaga Sun, Wasaga Beach, ON; Waterloo Chronicle, Waterloo, ON; New Hamburg Independent, New Hamburg, ON; The Wingham Advance-Times, Wingham, ON; The York Guardian, Toronto, ON; The Guelph Mercury, Guelph, ON; The Hamilton Spectator, Hamilton, ON; The Record, Kitchener, ON; Oshawa-Whitby This Week, Oshawa, ON; The Independent, Brighton, ON; Shopping News, Oakville, ON; Niagara This Week, Thorold , ON; The Grimsby Lincoln News, Grimsby , ON; Bloor West Villager, Toronto, ON; Annex Guardian, Toronto, ON; The Barrie Advance, Barrie, ON; Beach-Riverdale Mirror, Toronto, ON; Brock Citizen, Cannington, ON; Minto Express, Palmerston, ON; Stouffville Sun-Tribune, Stouffville, ON;

O

Osprey Media Group – 100 Renfew Dr., Ste. 110 Markham ON, L3R 9R6, Canada; tel (905) 752-1132; fax (905) 752-1138; e-mail privacy@ospreymedialp.com; web site www.qmisales.ca; www.ospreymedialp.com
Est.: 2001
Pres./CEO – Pierre Karl Peladeau
Sr. Vice Pres., Opns. – Julia Kamula
CFO – John Leader
Vice Pres., Technology – Jack Mulchinock
Exec. Asst. – Dina Alker
Classified Dir. – Donna GlasspooleDaily Newspapers:
The Barrie Examiner; The Intelligencer; The Expositor; The Chatham Daily News; Cobourg Daily Star; Standard-Freeholder; The Kingston Whig-Standard; Northern News; Lindsay Post; Niagara Falls Review; The North Bay Nugget; The Packet & Times; The Sun Times; Observer; The Peterborough Examiner; Port Hope Evening Guide; The Standard; Observer; The Sault Star;

The Sudbury Star; The Daily Press; Welland Tribune;

Q

Quebecor Communications, Inc. – 999 De Maisonneuve Blvd. W, Ste. 1100 Montreal QC, H3A 3L4, Canada; tel (514) 877-5334; fax (514) 954-3624; web site www.quebecor.com
Vice Pres. – Tony RossDaily Newspapers: Airdrie Echo, Airdrie, AB; Banff Crag & Canyon, Banff, AB; Crowsnest Pass Promoter, Blairmore, AB; The Camrose Canadian, Camrose, AB; Canmore Leader, Banff, AB; Cochrane Times, Cochrane, AB; Drayton Valley Western Review, Drayton Valley, AB; Edmonton Examiner, Edmonton, AB; Edson Leader, Edson, AB; Fairview Post, Fairview, AB; The Fort Saskatchewan Record, Fort Saskatchewan, AB; The High River Times, High River, AB; The Hinton Parklander, Hinton, AB; The Jasper Booster, Jasper, AB; Lacombe Globe, Lacombe, AB; Leduc Representative, Leduc, AB; Lloydminster Meridian Booster, Lloydminster, AB; The Freelancer, Whitecourt, AB; The Nanton News, High River, AB; The Record-Gazette, Peace River, AB; Pincher Creek Echo, Pincher Creek, AB; Strathmore Standard, Strathmore, AB; Sherwood Park News, Sherwood Park, AB; The Grove Examiner, Spruce Grove, AB; The Stony Plain Reporter, Spruce Grove, AB; Vermilion Standard, Vermilion, AB; Advocate, Vulcan, AB; Times-Advertiser, Wetaskiwin, AB; The Whitecourt Star, Whitecourt, AB; The Red River Valley Echo, Altona, MB; The Beausejour Review, Beausejour, MB; The Valley Leader, Carman, MB; Lac du Bonnet Leader, Lac du Bonnet, MB; Morden Times, Morden, MB; Central Plains Herald Leader, Portage La Prairie, MB; Selkirk Journal, Selkirk, MB; The Stonewall Argus/Teulon Times, Stonewall, MB; Winkler Times, Winkler, MB; Amherstburg Echo, Winvsor, ON; The Spirit of Bothwell, Bothwell, ON; Clinton News-Record, Clinton, ON; Colborne Chronicle, Colborne, ON; The Enterprise-Bulletin, Collingwood, ON; Delhi News Record, Delhi, ON; Dunnville Chronicle, Dunnville, ON; The Standard, Elliot Lake, ON; The Mid-North Monitor, Espanola, ON; The Fort Erie Times, Fort Erie, ON; The Reporter, Gananoque, ON; Goderich Signal-Star, Goderich, ON; West Niagara News, Beamsville, ON; Haliburton County Echo, Haliburton, ON; The Minden Times, Minden, ON; Hanover Post, Hanover, ON; The Ingersoll Times, Ingersoll, ON; Northern Times, Kapuskasing, ON; The Kincardine News, Kincardine, ON; Kingston This Week, Kingston, ON; Leamington Post, Leamington, ON; The Lucknow Sentinel, Lucknow, ON; The Markdale Standard, Markdale, ON; The Free Press, Midland, ON; The Mitchell Advocate, Mitchell, ON; The Niagara Advance, Virgil, ON; The Norwich Gazette, Norwich, ON; Paris Star, Paris, ON; Petrolia Topic, Petrolia, ON; Shoreline Beacon, Port Elgin, ON; Sarnia This Week, Sarnia, ON; Sault Ste. Marie This Week, Sault Sainte Marie, ON; The Huron Expositor, Seaforth, ON; The Age Dispatch, Strathroy, ON; The Tillsonburg News, Tillsonburg, ON; Timmins Times, Timmins, ON; Trentonian, Trenton, ON; Chronicle, West Lorne, ON; The Wiarton Echo, Wiarton, ON; L'Avant-Poste Gaspesien, Amqui, QC; Les Actualites, Asbestos, QC; Objectif Plein Jour, Baie Comeau, QC; Plein Jour sur Manicouagan, Baie Comeau, QC; Brossard Eclair, Longueuil, QC; La Sentinelle de Chibougamau, Chibougamau, QC; Le Reveil, Jonquiere, QC; Le Point, Dolbeau-Mistassini, QC; Plein-Jour en Haute Cote Nord, Baie Comeau, QC; Le Pharillon, Gaspe, QC; Le Reveil de Jonquiere, Jonquiere, QC; Le Reveil, Jonquiere, QC; Plein Jour de Charlevoix, La Malbaie, QC; Journal Le Peuple, Levis, QC; Le Courrier du Sud/South Shore Courier, Longueuil, QC; Peuple de Lotbiniere, Laurier-Station, QC; La Voix Gaspesienne, Matane, QC; L'Information, Mont Joli, QC; Le Peuple Cote du Sud, Montmagny, QC; L'Echo de la Baie, New Richmond, QC; Le Port Cartois, Sept-Iles, QC; Le Progres-Echo, Rimouski, QC; Le Rimouskois, Rimouski, QC; Le Saint-Laurent Portage, Riviere-du-Loup, QC; Beauce Nouvelle/L'Eclaireur-Progres, Saint Georges, QC; L'Echo du Nord, Saint Jerome, QC; Le Mirabel, Saint-Jerome, QC; Le Journal de Saint-Hubert, Longueuil, QC; Le Journal des Pays D'en Haut Le vallee, Sainte-Adele, QC; Information Du Nord Sainte-Agathe, Mont Tremblant, QC; Beauce Media, Sainte Marie-de-Beauce, QC; Le Citoyen de la Vallee de l'Or, Val d'Or, QC; The Kinistino Birch Hills Post Gazette, Melfort, SK; Meadow Lake Progress, Meadow Lake, SK

S

Southern Alberta Newspaper Group – 504 Seventh St. S. Lethbridge AB, T1J 2H1, Canada; tel (403) 328-4411; fax (403) 328-4536
Vice Pres./Gen. Mgr. – Bob Carey
Circ. Dir. – Tony LeBlancDaily Newspapers: The 40-Mile County Commentator, Bow Island, AB; The Sunny South News, Coaldale, AB; The Taber Times, Taber, AB; Vauxhall Advance, Vauxhall, AB; The Lethbridge Herald, Lethbridge, AB; Medicine Hat News, Medicine Hat, AB; The Southern Sun Times, Lethbridge, AB; Medicine Hat Shopper, Medicine Hat, AB; The Shopper, Medicine Hat, AB;
Notes: Southern Alberta Newspaper Group owns two daily newspapers, four weekly newspapers and three shopper publication.

Sun Media Corp. – 1540 N. Routledge Park London ON, N6H 5L6, Canada; tel (519) 471-8520; fax (519) 471-1892; web site www.sunmedia.ca
Exec. Vice Pres./COO – Brad Taylor
Sr. Vice Pres./COO – Wayne Jobb

Sun Media Corp. – 333, Rue King Est. Toronto ON, M5A 3X5, Canada; tel (416) 947-2222; fax (416) 947-2209; web site www.canoe.ca/SunMedia/home.html
Exec. Advisor to Pres./CEO – William R. Dempsey
Pub. – Mike Power
Vice Pres., HR – Chris Krygiel
Vice Pres., Cor. Sales – Bill McDonald
Vice Pres., Cor. Editorial – Serge Gosselin
Vice Pres., Opns. (Central Canada) – David Swail
Vice Pres., Western Grp. – Craig MartinDaily Newspapers:
Airdrie Echo, Airdrie, AB; Banff Crag & Canyon, Banff, AB; Crowsnest Pass Promoter, Blairmore, AB; The Calgary Country, Cochrane, AB; The Camrose Canadian, Camrose, AB; Canmore Leader, Banff, AB; Cochrane Times, Cochrane, AB; Drayton Valley Western Review, Drayton Valley, AB; Edmonton Examiner, Edmonton, AB; Fairview Post, Fairview, AB; The Fort Saskatchewan Record, Fort Saskatchewan, AB; The High River Times, High River, AB; The Hinton Parklander, Hinton, AB; The Jasper Booster, Jasper, AB; Lacombe Globe, Lacombe, AB; Leduc Representative, Leduc, AB; Lloydminster Meridian Booster, Lloydminster, AB; The Freelancer, Whitecourt, AB; The Nanton News, High River, AB; The Record-Gazette, Peace River, AB; Pincher Creek Echo, Pincher Creek, AB; Strathmore Standard, Strathmore, AB; Sherwood Park News, Sherwood Park, AB; The Grove Examiner, Spruce Grove, AB; The Stony Plain Reporter, Spruce Grove, AB; Vermilion Standard, Vermilion, AB; Advocate, Vulcan, AB; Times-Advertiser, Wetaskiwin, AB; The Whitecourt Star, Whitecourt, AB; The Red River Valley Echo, Altona, MB; The Beausejour Review, Beausejour, MB; The Valley Leader, Carman, MB; Lac du Bonnet Leader, Lac du Bonnet, MB; Morden Times, Morden, MB; Central Plains Herald Leader, Portage La Prairie, MB; Selkirk Journal, Selkirk, MB; The Stonewall Argus/Teulon Times, Stonewall, MB; Winkler Times, Winkler, MB; Amherstburg Echo, Winvsor, ON; The Spirit of Bothwell, Bothwell, ON; Clinton News-Record, Clinton, ON; Delhi News Record, Delhi, ON; Goderich Signal-Star, Goderich, ON; The Ingersoll Times, Ingersoll, ON; Northern Times, Kapuskasing, ON; The Kincardine News, Kincardine, ON; Leamington Post, Leamington, ON; The Lucknow Sentinel, Lucknow, ON; The Mitchell Advocate, Mitchell, ON; The Norwich Gazette, Norwich, ON; Paris Star, Paris, ON; Sarnia This Week, Sarnia, ON; The Huron Expositor, Seaforth, ON; The Age Dispatch, Strathroy, ON; The Tillsonburg News, Tillsonburg, ON; Timmins Times, Timmins, ON; Chronicle, West Lorne, ON; The Wiarton Echo, Wiarton, ON; L'Avant-Poste Gaspesien, Amqui, QC; Les Actualites, Asbestos, QC; Objectif Plein Jour, Baie Comeau, QC; Plein Jour sur Manicouagan, Baie Comeau, QC; Brossard Eclair, Longueuil, QC; La Sentinelle de Chibougamau, Chibougamau, QC; Le Reveil, Jonquiere, QC; Le Point, Dolbeau-Mistassini, QC; Plein-Jour en Haute Cote Nord, Baie Comeau, QC; Le Pharillon, Gaspe, QC; Le Reveil de Jonquiere, Jonquiere, QC; Le Reveil, Jonquiere, QC; Plein Jour de Charlevoix, La Malbaie, QC; Journal Le Peuple, Levis, QC; Le Courrier du Sud/South Shore Courier, Longueuil, QC; Peuple de Lotbiniere, Laurier-Station, QC; La Voix Gaspesienne, Matane, QC; L'Information, Mont Joli, QC; L'Echo de la Baie, New Richmond, QC; Le Port Cartois, Sept-Iles, QC; Le Progres-Echo, Rimouski, QC; Le Rimouskois, Rimouski, QC; Le Saint-Laurent Portage, Riviere-du-Loup, QC; Beauce Nouvelle/L'Eclaireur-Progres, Saint Georges, QC; L'Echo du Nord, Saint Jerome, QC; Le Mirabel, Saint-Jerome, QC; Le Journal de Saint-Hubert, Longueuil, QC; Le Journal des Pays D'en Haut Le vallee, Sainte-Adele, QC; Information Du Nord Sainte-Agathe, Mont Tremblant, QC; Beauce Media, Sainte Marie-de-Beauce, QC; Le Citoyen de la Vallee de l'Or, Val d'Or, QC; The Kinistino Birch Hills Post Gazette, Melfort, SK; Meadow Lake Progress, Meadow Lake, SK; The Melfort Journal, Melfort, SK; Nipawin Journal, Nipawin, SK; The Calgary Sun, Calgary, AB; The Edmonton Sun, Edmonton, AB; Fort McMurray Today, Fort McMurray, AB; Daily Herald-Tribune, Grande Prairie, AB; The Daily Graphic, Portage la Prairie, MB; The Winnipeg Sun, Winnipeg, MB; The Brockville Recorder and Times, Brockville, ON; Daily Miner & News, Kenora, ON; The London Free Press, London, ON; The Ottawa Sun, Ottawa, ON; St. Thomas Times-Journal, Saint Thomas, ON; The Simcoe Reformer, Simcoe, ON; The Beacon-Herald, Stratford, ON; The Toronto Sun, Toronto, ON; The Sentinel-Review, Woodstock, ON; Le Journal de Montreal, Montreal, QC; Le Journal de Quebec, Vanier, QC;

T

Torstar – One Yonge St. Toronto ON, M5E 1P9, Canada; tel (416) 869-4010; fax (416) 869-4183; e-mail torstar@torstar.ca; web site www.torstar.ca
Chrmn. of the Bd. – Frank Ialobucci
Pres./CEO – Dr. Robert Prichard
Exec. Vice Pres./CFO – David P. Holland-Daily Newspapers:
Ajax-Pickering News Advertiser, Ajax, ON; The Herald, Alliston, ON; Ancaster News, Stoney Creek , ON; Arthur Enterprise News, Arthur, ON; Caledon Enterprise, Bolton, ON; Clarington This Week, Oshawa, ON; Bracebridge Examiner, Bracebridge, ON; The Muskokan, Bracebridge, ON; Brampton Guardian, Brampton, ON; The Burlington Post, Burlington, ON; Cambridge Times, Cambridge, ON; The Stayner Sun, Wasaga Beach, ON; Collingwood Connection, Collingwood, ON; The Dresden Leader, Dresden, ON; Dundas Star-News, Stoney Creek, ON; The East York Mirror, Willowdale, ON; The Elmira Independent, Elmira, ON; The Erin Advocate, Erin, ON; Etobicoke Guardian, Etobicoke, ON; Times Advocate, Exeter, ON; The Fergus-Elora News Express, Fergus, ON; The Flamborough Review, Waterdown, ON; Georgetown Independent, Georgetown, ON; The Georgina Advocate, Keswick, ON; The Gravenhurst Banner, Gravenhurst, ON; Guelph Tribune, Guelph, ON; Huntsville Forester, Huntsville, ON; Kawartha Lakes This Week, Lindsay, ON; The Listowel Banner, Listowel, ON; Markham Economist & Sun, Markham, ON; The Mirror, Midland, ON; The Milton Canadian Champion, Milton, ON; The Mount Forest Confederate, Mount Forest, ON; The Newmarket Era-Banner, Newmarket, ON; North York Mirror, Toronto, ON; Oakville Beaver, Oakville, ON; The Orangeville Banner, Orangeville, ON; Orillia Today, Orillia, ON; Peterborough This Week, Peterborough, ON; Northumberland News, Cobourg, ON; The Port Perry Star, Port Perry, ON; Port Perry Star, Port Perry, ON; The Richmond Hill Liberal, Richmond Hill, ON; Journal Argus, Saint Marys, ON; The Scarborough Mirror, Toronto, ON; Stoney Creek News, Stoney Creek, ON; Uxbridge Times-Journal, Uxbridge, ON; Herald-Times, Walkerton, ON; The Wasaga Sun, Wasaga Beach, ON; Waterloo Chronicle, Waterloo, ON; New Hamburg Independent, New Hamburg, ON; The Wingham Advance-Times, Wingham, ON; The York Guardian, Toronto, ON; The Guelph Mercury, Guelph, ON; The Hamilton Spectator, Hamilton, ON; The Record, Kitchener, ON; Oshawa-Whitby This Week, Oshawa, ON; The Toronto Star, Toronto, ON; Shopping News, Oakville, ON; Niagara This Week, Thorold , ON; The Grimsby Lincoln News, Grimsby , ON; Bloor West Villager, Toronto, ON; Annex Guardian, Toronto, ON; The Barrie Advance, Barrie, ON; Beach-Riverdale Mirror, Toronto, ON; Brock Citizen, Cannington, ON; Minto Express, Palmerston, ON; Stouffville Sun-Tribune, Stouffville, ON;
Notes: Torstar owns Metroland Media Group, which owns three daily newspapers.

Transcontinental, Inc. – 1 Place Ville Marie, Ste. 3315 Montreal QC, H3B 3N2, Canada; tel (514) 954-4000; fax (514) 954-4016; e-mail info@transcontinental.ca; web site www.transcontinental.com
Est.: 1976
Exec. Chrmn. of the Bd. – Remi Marcoux
Pres./CEO – Francois Olivier
CFO – Benoit Huard
Pres., Trancontinental Media Inc. – Natalie LariviÃ£££Ã£Â¯ Ã£Â¿Ã£Â½re
Vice Pres./Chief Legal Officer/Cor. Sec. – Christine Desaulniers
Vice Pres. Corp. Devel. – Isabelle Marcoux
Sr. Vice Pres., Transcontinental Media Inc./Newspapaper Grp. – Marc N. Ouellette
Media Relations Dir. – Nessa Brendergast-Daily Newspapers:
The Times, Winnipeg, MB; The Lance, Winnipeg, MB; The Metro, Winnipeg, MB; The Herald, Winnipeg, MB; The Sackville Tribune Post, Sackville, NB; The Compass, Carbonear, NF; The Packet, Clarenville, NF; The Gander Beacon, Gander, NF; The Advertiser, Grand Falls, NF; The Labradorian, Happy Valley, NF; Harbour Breton Coaster, Harbour Breton, NF; The Aurora, Labrador City, NF; The Pilot, Lewisporte, NF; The Southern Gazette, Marystown, NF; The Gulf News, Port aux Basques, NF; Northern Pen, Saint Anthony, NF; The Nor'Wester, Springdale, NF; The Georgian, Stephenville, NF; The Spectator, Middleton, NS; Register, Kentville, NS; The Citizen, Amherst, NS; Courier, Digby, NS; The Advertiser, Kentville, NS; Advance, Liverpool, NS; The Coast

Guard, Shelburne, NS; Springhill & Parrsboro Record, Springhill, NS; Hants Journal, Windsor, NS; The Vanguard, Yarmouth, NS; The Star, Ottawa, ON; Courrier-Ahuntsic, Saint-Laurent, QC; Le Lac St. Jean, Alma, QC; La Voix du Sud, Lac-Etchemin, QC; L'-Express, Drummondville, QC; La Revue de Gatineau, Gatineau, QC; L'Action, Joliette, QC; L'Action Wednesday, Joliette, QC; L'Echo de La Tuque, La Tuque, QC; Le Trait d'Union, Lachenaie, QC; Courrier Laval, Laval, QC; Courrier-Laval, Laval, QC; L'Echo de Maskinonge, Louiseville, QC; La Voix Populaire, Lasalle, QC; Le Courrier Bordeaux/Cartierville, St. Laurent, QC; Progres Saint-Leonard, St-Leonard, QC; Courrier-Sud, Nicolet, QC; L'Avenir de L'Erable, Plessisville, QC; Journal L'Actuel, Quebec, QC; Charlesbourg Express, Quebec, QC; L'Artisan, Repentigny, QC; Hebdo Rive Nord, Repentigny, QC; L'Etoile du Lac, Roberval, QC; Journal de Rosemont, Montreal, QC; La Petite Nation, Saint Andre-Avellin, QC; Saint-Laurent News, Saint-Laurent, QC; L'Hebdo Mekinac/des Chenaux, Shawinigan, QC; Journal L'Appel, Quebec, QC; Hebdo du St. Maurice, Shawinigan, QC; L'Hebdo Journal, Trois-Rivieres, QC; Journal L'Union, Victoriaville, QC; La Nouvelle, Victoriaville, QC; The Chronicle, Dollard-des-Ormeaux, QC; The Westmount Examiner, West Mount, QC; Deep South Star, Radville, SK; Broadview Express, Grenfell, SK; Grenfell Sun, Grenfell, SK; The Oxbow Herald, Oxbow, SK; Radville Star, Radville, SK; The Southwest Booster, Swift Current, SK; The Western Star, Corner Brook, NF; The Telegram, Saint John's, NF; Amherst Daily News, Amherst, NS; The Daily News, Halifax, NS; The News, New Glasgow, NS; Cape Breton Post, Sydney, NS; The Daily News, Truro, NS; The Guardian, Charlottetown, PEI; The Journal-Pioneer, Summerside, PEI; The Moose Jaw Times-Herald, Moose Jaw, SK; Prince Albert Daily Herald, Prince Albert, SK; Corriere Italiano, Montreal, QC;

PROFESSIONAL, BUSINESS AND SPECIAL SERVICES FOR DAILIES

AGRICULTURAL

URNER BARRY'S PRICE-CURRENT

(mon to fri) (Agricultural)
PO Box 389, Toms River, NJ, 08754-0389; gen tel (732) 240-5330; gen fax (732) 341-0891; gen e-mail mail@urnerbarry.com; web site www.urnerbarry.com
Circulation: N/A

Price:
120.00/mo (e-mail service); 415.00/yr (mail); 360.00/3mo (fax service).

Advertising:
Open inch rate $17.00
Pres. Paul B. Brown

APPAREL

WOMEN'S WEAR DAILY

(mon to fri) (Apparel)
750 3rd Ave., New York, NY, 10017; gen tel 800-289-0273; gen fax (212) 630-4606; adv fax (212) 630-4580; web site www.wwd.com
Circulation: 56,562(pd); ABC September 30, 2011

Price:
99.00/yr (retail); $135.00/yr (manufacturers).

Advertising:
Open inch rate $322.00Established: 1910
Chrmn./Editorial Dir. Patrick McCarthy
Pres./CEO, Fairchild Fashion Grp. Gina Sanders
Robert Sauerberg
Pub. Christine Guilfoyle
Dale Reich
Ed. in Chief Ed Nardoza
Mng. Ed. Richard Rosen
Mng. Ed., Special Reports Dianne Pogoda
Prodn. Mgr., Distr. Cristina Mojca

Method of Printing:
MECHANICAL PRODUCTION INFORMATION
Offset

ARCHITECTURE

DODGE CONSTRUCTION NEWS CHICAGO

(mon to fri) (Architecture)
130 E. Randolph St., 14th Fl., Chicago, IL, 60601; gen tel (800) 257-0993; gen fax (312) 233-7486
Circulation: N/A

Price:
1,424.00/yr.

Advertising:
Open inch rate $34.00Established: 1946
Ed. Craig Barner

Method of Printing:
MECHANICAL PRODUCTION INFORMATION
Offset

BANKING

BROOKLYN DAILY EAGLE & DAILY BULLETIN

(mon to fri) (Banking)
30 Henry St., Brooklyn, NY; gen tel (718) 858-2300; gen fax (718) 858-8281; gen e-mail publisher@brooklyneagle.net; web site www.brooklyneagle.net
Circulation: N/A

Price:
125.00/yr; 40.00/3mo.

Advertising:
Open inch rate $24.00
Pub. J.D. Hasty
Adv. Mgr. Patricia Higgins
Adv. Mgr., Legal Daniel Doctorow
Adv. Mgr., Special Projects Ted Cutler
Sam Howe
Mng. Ed. Ron Geberer

BUILDING

TACOMA DAILY INDEX

(mon to fri) (Building)
PO Box 1303, Tacoma, WA, 98401; gen tel (253) 627-4853; adv tel (253) 627-4853; gen fax (253) 627-2253; adv fax (253) 627-2253; ed fax (253) 627-2253; gen e-mail legals@tacomadailyindex.com; ed e-mail editor@tacomadailyindex.com; web site www.tacomadailyindex.com
Circulation: December 23, 1998

Price:
50.00/yr; 15.00/3mo; $30.00/6mo.

Advertising:
Open inch rate $9.65

News services:
American Court & Commercial Printing. Established: 1890
Pub. Ken Spurrell
legals@tacomadailyindex.com Todd

BUSINESS

DAILY COMMERCIAL RECORD

(mon to fri) (Business)
706 Main St., Dallas, TX, 75202; gen tel (214) 741-6366; gen fax (214) 741-6373; gen e-mail dcr@dailycommercialrecord.com; web site www.dailycommercialrecord.com
Circulation: December 23, 1998

Price:
168.00/yr; 53.00/3mo; $88.00/6mo.

Advertising:
Open inch rate $14.76
Pub. E. Nuel Cates
Ed. Emily Cates

Method of Printing:
MECHANICAL PRODUCTION INFORMATION
Offset

THE DAILY COMMERCIAL RECORDER

(mon to fri) (Business)
17400 Judson Rd., San Antonio, TX; gen tel (210) 250-2327; gen fax (210) 736-5506; gen e-mail dcr@primetimenewspapers.com; web site www.primetimenewspapers.com
Circulation: N/A

Price:
150.00/yr; 55.00/3mo.

Advertising:
Open inch rate $25.00

News services:
ACCN, Creator Syndicates, LAT-WP, National American Press Syndicate, NYT..
Ed. Charlotte Aaron
Prodn. Ed. Sylvia P. Sepulveda

Method of Printing:
MECHANICAL PRODUCTION INFORMATION
Web

DAILY COURT REVIEW

(mon to fri) (Business)
PO Box 1889, TX, 77251-1889; gen tel (713) 869-5434; ed tel (713) 869-5434; gen fax (713) 869-8887; ed e-mail editor@dailycourtreview.com; web site www.dailycourtreview.com
Circulation: December 23, 1998

Price:
25.00/mo; 145.00/yr; 70.00/3mo.

Advertising:
Open inch rate $16.80

News services:
RN, National Newspaper Association, Texas Press Association. Established: 1889
Pub. Tom Morin
Ed. Tom Morin

Method of Printing:
MECHANICAL PRODUCTION INFORMATION
Offset

THE DAILY DEAL

(mon to fri) (Business)
105 Madison Ave., New York, NY, 10016; gen tel (212) 313-9200; adv tel (212) 313-9264; gen fax (212) 545-8442; ed fax (212) 313-9293; gen e-mail advertising@thedeal.com; ed e-mail epaisley@thedeal.com; rteitelman@thedeal.com; web site www.thedeal.com
Circulation: N/A

Price:
498.00/yr.
Pres./Pub. Kevin Worth
COO Robert Clark
CFO Kurt Streams
Adv. Sr. Mgr. Mike Danforth
Tom Spanos
Dir., Cor. Commun. Martha Brown
Circ. Vice Pres. Jeff Hartford
Circ. Sr. Mgr. Carol Harms
Ed. in Chief Robert Teitelman
Exec. Ed. Yvette Kantrow
Asst. Mng. Ed. Josh Karlen
Asst. Mng. Ed. Frances A. McMorris
Asst. Mng. Ed. Richard Morgan
Asst. Mng. Ed. John E. Morris
Asst. Mng. Ed. Alain Sherter
Asst. Mng. Ed. Robert Walzer
Art/Design Dir. Lawrence R Gendron
Statistics Ed. Anthony Baldo
Dir., Info Techology Adam S. Feinberg
Thomas Groppe

Method of Printing:
MECHANICAL PRODUCTION INFORMATION
Cold Set Offset

THE DAILY JOURNAL

(mon to fri) (Business)
1114 W. 7th Ave., Ste. 100, Denver, CO, 80204; gen tel (303) 756-9995; adv tel (303) 584-6737; ed tel (303) 584-6724; gen fax (303) 584-6717; adv fax (303) 584-6717; ed fax (303) 756-4465; web site colorado.construction.com
Circulation: N/A

Price:
1,384.00/yr.

Advertising:
Open inch rate $25.20Established: 1897Open inch rate $25.20 John
Adv. Dir. John Rhoades
Adv. Mgr. Michael Branigan
Ed. Melissa Leslie
Mark Shaw

Method of Printing:
MECHANICAL PRODUCTION INFORMATION
Offset

DAILY JOURNAL OF COMMERCE

(mon to fri) (Business)
PO Box 10127, Portland, OR, 97296; gen tel (503) 226-1311; adv tel (503) 226-1311; gen fax (503) 226-1315; adv fax (503) 802-7219; ed fax (503) 802-7239; gen e-mail newsroom@djcoregon.com; web site

www.djcoregon.com
Circulation: N/A
Price:
180.00/yr; 65.00/3mo; $110.00/6mo; $350.00/2yr.
Advertising:
Open inch rate $25.00
News services:
AP, RN, TMS. Established: 1872
Pub. Brian Hunt
Adv. Dir. Cris Schulz
Ed. Stephanie Basalyga
Craig Bollen

THE DAILY LEGAL NEWS
(mon to fri) (Business)
501 Texas St., Rm. M-103, Shreveport, LA, 71101; gen tel (318) 222-0213; web site www.dailylegalnews.net
Circulation: December 22, 1998
Price:
22.00/mo; 264.00/yr.
Advertising:
Open inch rate $15.00/wk (3 1/2 x 1), $25.00/2wk, $35.00/3wk
Pub. Lee Ann Bryce
Ed. Lee Ann Bryce

THE DAILY LEGAL NEWS AND CLEVELAND RECORDER
(tues to sat) (Business)
2935 Prospect Ave., Cleveland, OH, 44115-2688; gen tel (216) 696-3322; gen fax (216) 696-6329; gen e-mail dln@dln.com; web site www.dln.com
Circulation: N/A
Price:
85.00/yr; 36.00/3mo; $55.00/6mo.
Advertising:
Open inch rate $16.00
News services:
AP, National Newspaper Association, Ohio Newspaper Association.
Chrmn./Pres./Pub. Lucien B. Karlovec
Exec. Vice Pres./Asst. Pub. Jeffrey B. Karlovec
Sec./Gen. Counsel John D. Karlovec
Treasurer Charles E. Bergstresser
Richard Karlovec
Ed. Lisa Cech
Mng. Ed. Jeffrey B. Karlovec
editor@dln.com Lisa Cech
Prodn. Mgr. Terry Machovina
Kurt Gutwein
Method of Printing:
MECHANICAL PRODUCTION INFORMATION
Offset

THE DAILY NEWS
(mon to fri) (Business)
193 Jefferson Ave., Memphis, TN, 38103; gen tel (901) 523-1561; gen fax (901) 526-5813; adv e-mail advertising@memphisdailynews.com; web site www.memphisdailynews.com
Circulation: N/A
Price:
80.00/yr.
Advertising:
Open inch rate $13.50 (legal)
News services:
CNS. Established: 1886
Adv. Mgr. Don Fancher
Marketing Director Donna Waggener
Publisher Eric Barnes
Associate Publisher James Overstreet
Method of Printing:
MECHANICAL PRODUCTION INFORMATION
Offset

THE DAILY RECORD
(mon to fri) (Business)
PO Box 1062, Louisville, KY, 40201; gen tel (502) 583-4471; gen fax (502) 585-5453; gen e-mail janicep@nacms-c.com
Circulation: October 31, 1997
Price:
275.00/yr; 86.25/3mo; $162.50/6mo.
Advertising:
Open inch rate $1.20 (legal line)
News services:
National Association of Credit Management. Established: 40201
Pub. Connie J. Cheak
Mng. Ed. Janice Prichard
Method of Printing:
MECHANICAL PRODUCTION INFORMATION
Offset

THE DAILY RECORD
(mon to fri) (Business)
PO Box 30006, Rochester, NY, 14603-3006; gen tel (585) 232-6920; gen fax (585) 232-2740; gen e-mail kevin.momot@nydailyrecord.com; web site www.nydailyrecord.com
Circulation: October 1, 2000
Price:
122.00/yr; 86.00/3mo; $96.00/6mo.
Advertising:
Open inch rate $.90 (agency line), $.75 (retail line)
News services:
American Court & Commercial Newspapers, National Newspaper Association. Established: 14603-3006
Chrmn./CEO James P. Dolan
Vice Pres./Pub. Kevin Momot
CFO Scott Pollei
Tara Buck
Method of Printing:
MECHANICAL PRODUCTION INFORMATION
Offset

THE DAILY RECORD
(mon to fri) (Business)
PO Box 3595, Little Rock, AR, 72203; gen tel (501) 374-5103; gen fax (501) 372-3048; gen e-mail bobby@dailydata.com; adv e-mail jedwards@dailydata.com; ed e-mail editor@dailydata.com; web site www.dailyrecord.us
Circulation: December 13, 2007
Price:
26/yr (mon&fri); $13.00/yr (tue or fri).
Advertising:
Column Inch Rate - $20.00
News services:
NNS, TMS, DRNW, INS. Established: 1925
Pres Don Bona
Pub. Bill F. Rector
Adv./Mktg. Dir. Jay Edwards
Prodn. Mgr. Amy Sherrill
Method of Printing:
MECHANICAL PRODUCTION INFORMATION
Web Press/Tab Size

THE DAILY RECORDER
(mon to fri) (Business)
PO Box 1048, Sacramento, CA, 95812; gen tel (916) 444-2355; adv tel (800) 652-1700; gen fax (916) 444-0636; gen e-mail daily_recorder@dailyjournal.com; ed e-mail jt_long@dailyjournal.com; web site www.dailyjournal.com
Circulation: N/A
Price:
246.00/yr, $137.00/yr (student rate).
Advertising:
Open inch rate $26.00
News services:
AP, dj. Established: 1901
Pres./Pub. Jerry Salzman
Cor. Office Dir. Raymond Chagolla
Personnel Dir. Dorothy Salzman
Ed. Michael Gottlieb
Raymond Chagolla
Tom Barragan
Prodn. Designer Houay Keobouth
Method of Printing:
MECHANICAL PRODUCTION INFORMATION
Offset

DAILY REPORT
(mon to fri) (Business)
190 Pryor St. SW, Atlanta, GA, 30303-3685; gen tel (404) 521-1227; gen fax (404) 523-5924; gen e-mail fcdr@amlaw.com; web site www.dailyreportonline.com
Circulation: March 31, 2000
Price:
290.00/yr.
Advertising:
Open inch rate $1,800.00 (page)Established: 1890
Pub. Blair Matthews
Assoc. Pub. Ed Bean
Office Mgr. Sarah Wagner
Adv. Dir. Mischelle Grant
Ed Bean
Mng. Ed. Jonathan Ringel
Art. Dir. Jason Bennitt
Method of Printing:
MECHANICAL PRODUCTION INFORMATION
Offset

THE DAILY TRANSCRIPT
(mon to fri) (Business)
PO Box 85469, San Diego, CA, 92186-5469; gen tel (619) 232-4381; adv fax (619) 239-4312; ed fax (619) 236-8126; gen e-mail editor@sddt.com; adv e-mail sales@sddt.com; ed e-mail editor@sddt.com; web site www.sddt.com
Circulation: N/A
Price:
200.00/yr; 70.00/3mo; $124.00/6mo.
Advertising:
Open inch rate $89.00
News services:
AP, NNS, NYT, TMS.
Pub. Robert Loomis
Dir., Mktg. Christine Tran
Circ. Mgr. Shelley Barry
Ed. in Chief Joe Guerin
Joseph Schmitt
Prodn. Mgr. Steve Lovelace
Method of Printing:
MECHANICAL PRODUCTION INFORMATION
Offset

FINANCE AND COMMERCE
(tues to sat) (Business)
730 2nd Ave S., Ste. 100, Minneapolis, MN, 55402; gen tel (612) 333-4244; gen fax (612) 333-3243; gen e-mail info@finance-commerce.com; web site www.finance-commerce.com
Circulation: October 20, 2003
Price:
175.00/yr; 99.00/6mo.
Advertising:
Open inch rate $12.00
News services:
AP. Established: 1887
Vice Pres./Pub. Steve Jahn
Bus. Mgr. Joann Barquest
Jeanne Reiland
Prodn. Mgr. Nancy Spangler
Method of Printing:
MECHANICAL PRODUCTION INFORMATION
Web Offset

THE INTER-CITY EXPRESS
(mon to fri)
171 12th St., Ste. 203, Oakland, CA, 94607-441; gen tel (510) 465-3121; gen fax (510) 465-1576
Circulation: N/A
Price:
140.00/yr.
Pub. Nell Fields
Adv. Dir. Dan Gougherty
Adv. Mgr., Legal Tonya Peacock
Ed. Tom Barkley
Ronald McNees

THE JOURNAL RECORD
(mon to fri) (Business)
PO Box 26370, Oklahoma City, OK, 73126-0370; gen tel (405) 235-3100; adv tel (405) 278-2830; ed tel (405) 278-2850; gen fax (405) 278-6907; ed fax (405) 278-2890; ed e-mail news@journalrecord.com; web site www.journalrecord.com
Group:
The Dolan Company
Circulation: N/A
Price:
189.00/yr (in Oklahoma), $190.00/yr (outside Oklahoma); 43.00/3mo; $80.00/6mo.
Advertising:
Open inch rate $18.62
News services:
AP, CSM, DMN. Established: 1903
Chrmn. of the Bd. James P. Dolan
Pub. Mary Melon
Gen. Mgr. Terri Vanhooser
Editor Ted Streuli
Prodn. Mgr. Gary Berger
Method of Printing:
MECHANICAL PRODUCTION INFORMATION
Offset

THE LOS ANGELES DAILY JOURNAL
(mon to fri) (Business)
915 E. First St., Los Angeles, CA, 90012; gen tel (213) 229-5300; gen fax (213) 229-5481; ed fax (213) 229-5462; web site www.dailyjournal.com
Circulation: December 31, 2000
Price:
70.00/mo; 575.00/yr; 340.00/6mo.
Advertising:
Open inch rate $69.16 (page)
News services:
AP, NYT, CNS, McClatchy.
Chrmn. of the Bd. Charles T. Munger
Vice Chrmn. of the Bd. J.P. Guerin
Pub. Gerald Salzman
Adv. Dir. Audrey Miller
Ramond Chagolla
Ed. Martin Berg
Method of Printing:
MECHANICAL PRODUCTION INFORMATION
Offset

MIAMI DAILY BUSINESS REVIEW
(mon to fri) (Business)
PO Box 010589, Miami, FL, 33101-9998; gen tel (305) 377-3721; adv tel (305) 347-6623; ed tel (305) 347-6694; gen fax (305) 374-8474; adv fax (305) 347-6644; ed fax (305) 347-6626; gen e-mail DailyBusinessReview@alm.com; adv e-mail shemmerich@alm.com; ed e-mail DBR_Editor@alm.com; web site www.dailybusinessreview.com
Circulation: March 1, 2007
Price:
$409.00/yr
Advertising:
Q4-2011/2012 Media Planner Interactive E-book
News services:
AP, Bloomberg, Florida News Service. Established: 1926
Group Publisher, FL/GA/TX Chris Mobley
Associate Publisher/Chief Financial Officer Jeff Fried
Director of Products Carlos Curbelo
Editor-in-Chief David Lyons
Business Editor Jay Rees
Law Editor Catherine Wilson
Director of Creative Services John Michael Rindo
Director of Operations & MIS Guillermo Garcia
Web Adminstrator John Hernandez
Director of Client Development Stephanie Hemmerich
Group Subscriptions Manager Annette Martinez
Audience Development Manager Adam Kaplan
Vice President/Miami-Dade Legal & Court Relations Sookie Williams
Method of Printing:
MECHANICAL PRODUCTION INFORMATION
Offset
Note:
See Daily Business Review editions in Broward and Palm Beach, FL.

PALM BEACH DAILY BUSINESS REVIEW
(mon to fri) (Business)
324 Datura St.,, Suite 140, West Palm Beach, FL, 33401; gen tel (561) 820-2066; adv tel (305) 347-6623; ed tel (305) 347-6694; gen fax (561) 820-2077; adv fax (305) 347-6644; ed fax (305) 347-6626; gen e-mail DailyBusinessReview@alm.com; adv e-mail shemmeerick@alm.com; ed e-mail DBR_Editor@alm.com; web site www.dailybusinessreview.com
Circulation: June 30, 2001

Price:
409/yr
Advertising:
Q4-2011/2012 Media Planner Interactive E-book
News services:
AP, Bloomberg, Florida News Service.
Group Publisher, FL/GA/TX Chris Mobley
Associate Publisher/Chief Financial Officer Jeff Fried
Editor-in-Chief David Lyons
Vice President/Broward & Palm Beach Legals Deborah Mullin
Director of Products Carlos Curbelo
Director of Client Development Stephanie Hemmerich
Audience Development Manager Adam Kaplan
Group Subscriptions Manager Annette Martinez
Web Administrator John Hernandez
Business Editor Jay Rees
Law Editor Cathy Wilson
Method of Printing:
MECHANICAL PRODUCTION INFORMATION
Offset
Note:
See Daily Business Reviews editions in Broward and Miami, FL.

THE ST. LOUIS COUNTIAN
(mon to sat; S) (Business)
319 N. Fourth St., Saint Louis, MO, 63102; gen tel (314) 421-1880; adv tel (314) 421-1880; ed tel (314) 421-1880; gen fax (314) 421-0436; adv fax (314) 421-0436; ed fax (314) 421-0436; adv e-mail carol.prycma@thedailyrecord.com; ed e-mail willc@thedailyrecord.com; web site www.thedailyrecord.com
Circulation: N/A
Price:
187.20/yr.
Advertising:
Open inch rate $6.56
News services:
RN.
Pub. Richard Gard
Bus. Mgr. Amanda Passmore
Adv. Dir. Amy Burdge
Circ. Mgr. Stacey Fish
William B. Connaghan
Prodn. Mgr. John M. Reno
Method of Printing:
MECHANICAL PRODUCTION INFORMATION
Web Offset

COMMERCE

AMERICAN METAL MARKET
(mon to fri)
1250 Broadway, 26th Fl., New York, NY, 10001; gen tel (212) 213-6202; adv tel (412) 281-4400; ed tel (212) 213-6202; gen fax (212) 213-1804; adv fax (412) 471-7203; ed fax (212) 213-6202; gen e-mail amm-news@amm.com; adv e-mail kross@amm.com; ed e-mail ammnews@amm.com; web site www.amm.com
Circulation: N/A
Price:
750.00/yr.
Advertising:
Open inch rate $36.48 (page)
News services:
RN, AP, PRN, Bridge News, Business Wire..
Established: 1882Roger Daswani
Pricing Dir.Derek Lundquist
Mng. Ed. Jo Isenberg-O'Loughlin
Americas Steel News Ed. Maria Guzzo
Assoc. Ed. Dianne McLarty
Art Dir. Adam Deher

COMMERCIAL RECORDER
(mon to fri) (Commerce)
PO Box 11038, Fort Worth, TX, 76110; gen tel (817) 926-5351; gen fax (817) 926-5377; gen e-mail recorder@flash.net; web site www.commercialrecorder.com
Circulation: N/A
Price:
150.00/yr.
Advertising:
Open inch rate $9.00
Pres./Pub. Genevieve Ratcliff
Adv. Mgr. Richard Herrera
Circ. Mgr. Janet R. Ratcliff
Genevieve Ratcliff
Method of Printing:
MECHANICAL PRODUCTION INFORMATION
Offset

THE DAILY RECORD
(mon to fri) (Commerce)
11 E. Saratoga St., Baltimore, MD, 21202-2199; gen tel (443) 524-8100; adv tel (443) 524-8100; gen fax (410) 752-2894; adv fax (410) 752-2894; ed fax (410) 752-2894; gen e-mail suzanne.huettner@thedailyrecord.com; adv e-mail advertising@thedailyrecord.com; ed e-mail tom.linthicum@thedailyrecord.com; web site www.thedailyrecord.com
Circulation: N/A
Price:
190.00/yr; 290.00/2yr.
Advertising:
Open inch rate $3,043.00 (full page display)Established: 1888
President Christopher A. Eddings
Publisher Suzanne Fischer-Huettner
Prodn. Dir., Opns. Rebecca Snyder
Method of Printing:
MECHANICAL PRODUCTION INFORMATION
Offset

THE DAILY REPORTER
(mon to fri) (Commerce)
580 S. High St., Ste. 316, Columbus, OH, 43215-5644; gen tel (614) 224-4835; gen fax (614) 224-8649; gen e-mail editor@sourcenews.com; web site www.sourcenews.com
Circulation: December 13, 2007
Price:
95.00/yr.
Advertising:
Open inch rate $2,990.00 (Page)
News services:
AP. Established: 1896
Pres. Ed Frederickson
Vice Pres./Pub. Dan Shillingburg
Adv. Mgr., Sales Jeff Zeigler
Editor Cindy Ludlow
Assoc. Ed. Chris Bailey

DAILY SHIPPING NEWS
(mon to fri)
PO Box 1029, Camas, WA, 98607; gen tel (360) 254-5504; gen fax (360) 254-7145; gen e-mail dsnews@europa.com; web site www.wwshipper.com
Circulation: December 23, 1998
Price:
170.00/yr.
Advertising:
Open inch rate $5.00Established: 98607
Pub. Jim Egger

DETROIT LEGAL NEWS
(mon to fri) (Commerce)
1409 Allen Rd., Ste. B, Troy, MI, 48083-4003; gen tel (248) 577-6100; adv tel (248) 577-6100; ed tel (248) 577-6100; gen fax (248) 577-6111; adv fax (248) 577-6111; ed fax (248) 967-5532; gen e-mail editor@legalnews.com; adv e-mail nborders@legalnews.com; ed e-mail editor@legalnews.com; web site www.legalnews.com
Circulation: N/A
Price:
140.00/yr; 80.00/6mo.
Advertising:
Open inch rate $23.00
News services:
AP.
Pub. Susanne Favale
Treasurer Richard J. Swiftney
Adv. Dir. Paul A. Arlon
Circ. Mgr. Christina Jacobs
Brian Cox
Prodn. Mgr., Pre Press Jessica Mosier
Method of Printing:
MECHANICAL PRODUCTION INFORMATION
Offset

CONSTRUCTION

DAILY COMMERCIAL NEWS AND CONSTRUCTION RECORD
(mon to fri) (Construction)
500 Hood Rd., 4th Fl., Markham, ON, L3R 9Z3; gen tel (905) 752-5540; gen fax (905) 752-5450; gen e-mail bev.akerfeldt@cmdg.com; adv e-mail cindy.littler@cmdg.com; ed e-mail john.leckie@cmdg.com; web site www.dc-nonl.com
Price:
834.00/yr (Canadian, tax included).
Advertising:
Open inch rate $63.00 (Canadian)
Vice Pres./Pub. Andrew Cook
Circ. Mgr. Rod Oyco
Ed. Tarin Elbert
Todd McGill
Adv. Sales Mgr.-Display Elena Langlois

THE DAILY JOURNAL
(mon to fri) (Construction)
1114 W. 7th Ave., Ste. 100, Denver, CO, 80204; gen tel (303) 756-9995; adv tel (303) 584-6737; ed tel (303) 584-6724; gen fax (303) 584-6717; adv fax (303) 584-6717; ed fax (303) 756-4465; web site colorado.construction.com
Circulation: N/A
Price:
1,384.00/yr.
Advertising:
Open inch rate $25.20Established: 1897Open inch rate $25.20 John
Adv. Dir. John Rhoades
Adv. Mgr. Michael Branigan
Ed. Melissa Leslie
Mark Shaw
Method of Printing:
MECHANICAL PRODUCTION INFORMATION
Offset

DAILY JOURNAL OF COMMERCE
(mon to fri) (Construction)
111 Veterans Blvd., Ste. 1440, Metairie, LA, 70005; gen tel (504) 293-9249; gen fax (504) 832-3534; gen e-mail mail@nopg.com; web site www.djcgulfcoast.com
Circulation: October 31, 1997
Price:
495.00/yr; 190/3mo; $345/6mo.
Advertising:
Open inch rate $10.00
Pub. Mark Singletary
Gen. Mgr. Anne Lovas
Ed. Autumn Giusti

THE DAILY REPORTER
(mon to fri) (Construction)
PO Box 514033, Milwaukee, WI, 53203-3433; gen tel (414) 276-0273; adv fax (414) 276-8057; ed fax (414) 276-4416; gen e-mail news@dailyreporter.com; web site www.dailyreporter.com
Circulation: December 13, 2007
Price:
159.00/yr.
Advertising:
Open inch rate $12.30 (R.O.P. & classified), $1.75 (legal line)
News services:
AP.
Pres./CEO James P. Dolan
Vice Pres./Pub. Ann Richmond
Adv. Dir. Denise Vandervest
Ed. Chris Thompson
Jayne Laste
Method of Printing:
MECHANICAL PRODUCTION INFORMATION
Offset by Subcontract

DODGE CONSTRUCTION NEWS CHICAGO
(mon to fri) (Construction)
130 E. Randolph St., 14th Fl., Chicago, IL, 60601; gen tel (800) 257-0993; gen fax (312) 233-7486
Circulation: N/A
Price:
1,424.00/yr.
Advertising:
Open inch rate $34.00Established: 1946
Ed. Craig Barner
Method of Printing:
MECHANICAL PRODUCTION INFORMATION
Offset

DODGE CONSTRUCTION NEWS GREENSHEET
(mon to fri) (Construction)
1333 S. Mayflower Ave., 3rd Fl., Monrovia, CA, 91016; gen tel (626) 932-6161; ed tel (626) 932-6175; gen fax (626) 932-6163; ed fax (626) 932-6163; web site www.construction.com
Circulation: December 22, 1998
Price:
1,685.00/yr; 587.00/3mo; $992.00/6mo.
Advertising:
Open inch rate $36.90 (display); $25.00 (classified)Established: 91016
Pub. James McGraw
Method of Printing:
MECHANICAL PRODUCTION INFORMATION
Offset

COURT

COMMERCIAL RECORDER
(mon to fri) (Court)
PO Box 11038, Fort Worth, TX, 76110; gen tel (817) 926-5351; gen fax (817) 926-5377; gen e-mail recorder@flash.net; web site www.commercialrecorder.com
Circulation: N/A
Price:
150.00/yr.
Advertising:
Open inch rate $9.00
Pres./Pub. Genevieve Ratcliff
Adv. Mgr. Richard Herrera
Circ. Mgr. Janet R. Ratcliff
Genevieve Ratcliff
Method of Printing:
MECHANICAL PRODUCTION INFORMATION
Offset

THE DAILY EVENTS
(mon to fri) (Court)
PO Box 1, Springfield, MO, 65801-0001; gen fax (417) 866-1401; adv fax (417) 866-1491; gen e-mail editor@dailyevents.com; web site www.thedailyevents.com
Circulation: N/A
Price:
88.00/yr.
News services:
American Court & Commercial Newspapers.
Established: 1881
Pub. Jeff Schrag
Adv. Dir. Jeff Schrag
Ed. Wendy Greyowl
Prodn. Mgr. Jeff Schrag
Method of Printing:
MECHANICAL PRODUCTION INFORMATION
Digital Press Sheet

THE DAILY LEGAL NEWS
(mon to fri) (Court)

501 Texas St., Rm. M-103, Shreveport, LA, 71101; gen tel (318) 222-0213; web site www.dailylegalnews.net
Circulation: December 22, 1998
Price:
22.00/mo; 264.00/yr.
Advertising:
Open inch rate $15.00/wk (3 1/2 x 1), $25.00/2wk, $35.00/3wk
Pub. Lee Ann Bryce
Ed. Lee Ann Bryce

THE DAILY RECORD
(mon to fri) (Court)
11 E. Saratoga St., Baltimore, MD, 21202-2199; gen tel (443) 524-8100; adv tel (443) 524-8100; gen fax (410) 752-2894; adv fax (410) 752-2894; ed fax (410) 752-2894; gen e-mail suzanne.huettner@thedailyrecord.com; adv e-mail advertising@thedailyrecord.com; ed e-mail tom.linthicum@thedailyrecord.com; web site www.thedailyrecord.com
Circulation: N/A
Price:
190.00/yr; 290.00/2yr.
Advertising:
Open inch rate $3,043.00 (full page display)Established: 1888
President Christopher A. Eddings
Publisher Suzanne Fischer-Huettner
Prodn. Dir., Opns. Rebecca Snyder
Method of Printing:
MECHANICAL PRODUCTION INFORMATION
Offset

THE DAILY RECORD
(mon to fri) (Court)
PO Box 1062, Louisville, KY, 40201; gen tel (502) 583-4471; gen fax (502) 585-5453; gen e-mail janicep@nacms-c.com
Circulation: October 31, 1997
Price:
275.00/yr; 86.25/3mo; $162.50/6mo.
Advertising:
Open inch rate $1.20 (legal line)
News services:
National Association of Credit Management. Established: 40201
Pub. Connie J. Cheak
Mng. Ed. Janice Prichard
Method of Printing:
MECHANICAL PRODUCTION INFORMATION
Offset

THE DAILY REPORTER
(mon to fri) (Court)
580 S. High St., Ste. 316, Columbus, OH, 43215-5644; gen tel (614) 224-4835; gen fax (614) 224-8649; gen e-mail editor@sourcenews.com; web site www.sourcenews.com
Circulation: December 13, 2007
Price:
95.00/yr.
Advertising:
Open inch rate $2,990.00 (Page)
News services:
AP. Established: 1896
Pres. Ed Frederickson
Vice Pres./Pub. Dan Shillingburg
Adv. Mgr., Sales Jeff Zeigler
Editor Cindy Ludlow
Assoc. Ed. Chris Bailey

DETROIT LEGAL NEWS
(mon to fri) (Court)
1409 Allen Rd., Ste. B, Troy, MI, 48083-4003; gen tel (248) 577-6100; adv tel (248) 577-6100; ed tel (248) 577-6100; gen fax (248) 577-6111; adv fax (248) 577-6111; ed fax (248) 967-5532; gen e-mail editor@legalnews.com; adv e-mail nborders@legalnews.com; ed e-mail editor@legalnews.com; web site www.legalnews.com
Circulation: N/A
Price:
140.00/yr; 80.00/6mo.
Advertising:
Open inch rate $23.00
News services:
AP.
Pub. Susanne Favale
Treasurer Richard J. Swiftney
Adv. Dir. Paul A. Arlon
Circ. Mgr. Christina Jacobs
Brian Cox
Prodn. Mgr., Pre Press Jessica Mosier
Method of Printing:
MECHANICAL PRODUCTION INFORMATION
Offset

THE LOS ANGELES DAILY JOURNAL
(mon to fri) (Court)
915 E. First St., Los Angeles, CA, 90012; gen tel (213) 229-5300; gen fax (213) 229-5481; ed fax (213) 229-5462; web site www.dailyjournal.com
Circulation: December 31, 2000
Price:
70.00/mo; 575.00/yr; 340.00/6mo.
Advertising:
Open inch rate $69.16 (page)
News services:
AP, NYT, CNS, McClatchy.
Chrmn. of the Bd. Charles T. Munger
Vice Chrmn. of the Bd. J.P. Guerin
Pub. Gerald Salzman
Adv. Dir. Audrey Miller
Ramond Chagolla
Ed. Martin Berg
Method of Printing:
MECHANICAL PRODUCTION INFORMATION
Offset

THE RECORDER
(mon to fri) (Court)
10 United Nations Plz., 3rd Fl., San Francisco, CA, 94102; gen tel (415) 749-5400; adv tel (415) 749-5444; gen fax (415) 749-5449; adv fax (415) 749-5566; ed fax (415) 749-5549; web site www.therecorder.com
Circulation: N/A
Price:
575.00/yr.
Advertising:
Open inch rate $3,200.00 (Full Page Display)
News services:
AP. Established: 1877
Pub. Chris Braun
Controller Janice Tang
Adv. Mgr., Classified Patrick Vigil
Adv. Mgr., Display Jim Tamietti
Robert Salapuddin
Adv. Coord., Display Heather Ragsdale
Mktg. Dir. John Cosmides
Circ. Mgr. Ed Vergara
Scott Graham
Mng. Ed. Greg Mitchell
Prodn. Mgr./Art Dir. Tess Herrmann
Method of Printing:
MECHANICAL PRODUCTION INFORMATION
Offset

THE ST. LOUIS COUNTIAN
(mon to sat; S) (Court)
319 N. Fourth St., Saint Louis, MO, 63102; gen tel (314) 421-1880; adv tel (314) 421-1880; ed tel (314) 421-1880; gen fax (314) 421-0436; adv fax (314) 421-0436; ed fax (314) 421-0436; adv e-mail carol.prycma@thedailyrecord.com; ed e-mail willc@thedailyrecord.com; web site www.thedailyrecord.com
Circulation: N/A
Price:
187.20/yr.
Advertising:
Open inch rate $6.56
News services:
RN.
Pub. Richard Gard
Bus. Mgr. Amanda Passmore
Adv. Dir. Amy Burdge
Circ. Mgr. Stacey Fish
William B. Connaghan
Prodn. Mgr. John M. Reno
Method of Printing:
MECHANICAL PRODUCTION INFORMATION
Web Offset

TACOMA DAILY INDEX
(mon to fri) (Court)
PO Box 1303, Tacoma, WA, 98401; gen tel (253) 627-4853; adv tel (253) 627-4853; gen fax (253) 627-2253; adv fax (253) 627-2253; ed fax (253) 627-2253; gen e-mail legals@tacomadailyindex.com; ed e-mail editor@tacomadailyindex.com; web site www.tacomadailyindex.com
Circulation: December 23, 1998
Price:
50.00/yr; 15.00/3mo; $30.00/6mo.
Advertising:
Open inch rate $9.65
News services:
American Court & Commercial Printing. Established: 1890
Pub. Ken Spurrell
legals@tacomadailyindex.com Todd

TOLEDO LEGAL NEWS
(mon to fri) (Court)
247 Gradolph St., Toledo, OH, 43612; gen tel (419) 470-8600; gen fax (419) 470-8602; gen e-mail tlnmain@buckeye-express.com; web site www.toledolegalnews.com
Circulation: December 13, 2007
Price:
85.00/yr; 40.00/3mo; $50.00/6mo.
Advertising:
Open inch rate $12.00Established: 1894
Pub. Virginia A. Seitz
Asst. Ed. Ann Pajak
Method of Printing:
MECHANICAL PRODUCTION INFORMATION
Web Press

CREDIT

CHICAGO DAILY LAW BULLETIN
(mon to fri) (Credit)
415 N. State St., Chicago, IL, 60610-4674; gen tel (312) 644-7800; gen fax (312) 644-4255; gen e-mail displayads@lbpc.com; web site www.lawbulletin.com
Circulation: N/A
Price:
185.00/yr; 120.00/6mo.
Advertising:
Open inch rate $26.40 (Classified), $2,588.00 (Full Page Display)
News services:
AP, NYT.
Chrmn. Lanning Macfarland
Pres./CEO Brewster Macfarland
Exec. Vice Pres. Neil Breen
James Banich
Consultant Bernie Judge
Adv. Sr. Dir., Sales/Mktg. Mark Menzies
Ed. Michael Kramer
Mng. Ed. Stephen Brown
Fred Faulkner
Method of Printing:
MECHANICAL PRODUCTION INFORMATION
Offset

ENTERTAINMENT

DAILY VARIETY
(mon to fri) (Entertainment)
5900 Wilshire Blvd., 31st Fl., Los Angeles, CA, 90036; gen tel (323) 857-6600; adv tel (323) 857-6600; ed tel (323) 965-4476; adv fax (323) 932-0393; web site www.variety.com
Circulation: N/A
Price:
219.00/yr.
Advertising:
Open inch rate $216.00
News services:
DJ, AP.
Grp. Vice Pres./Pub. Charles C. Koones
CMO, Variety Entertainment Grp. Madelyn Hammond
Peter Bart
Adv. Dir., West Coast Sales Craig Hitchcock
Dan Hart
Circ. Dir. Christopher Wessel
Circ. Mgr. Joseph Brescia
Grp. Ed. Timothy M. Gray
Ed. Leo Wolinsky
Mng. Ed. Ted Johnson
Assoc. Ed. Phil Gallo
Assoc. Ed., Special Reports Stuart Levine
Asst. Mng. Ed. Kirstin Wilder
Deputy News Ed. Cynthia Littleton
Sr. Ed. Lindsay Chaney
Sr. Ed. Patricia Saperstein
Sr. Ed., Special Reports Steve Chagollan
Sr. Ed., Special Reports Sharon Swart
Michael Schneider
Method of Printing:
MECHANICAL PRODUCTION INFORMATION
Offset

THE HOLLYWOOD REPORTER
(mon to fri) (Entertainment)
5055 Wilshire Blvd., Los Angeles, CA, 90036-4396; gen tel (323) 525-2000; adv fax (323) 525-2372; ed fax (323) 525-2377; web site www.hollywoodreporter.com
Circulation: N/A
Advertising:
Open inch rate $100.00(fri)(classified)
News services:
AP. Eric Mika
Vice Pres./Assoc. Pub., Sales/Mktg. Rose Einstein
Audience Mktg. Dir. Katie Fillingame
Ed. Elizabeth Guider
David Morgan
Mng. Ed. Mike Barnes
Vice Pres., Digital Content Scott McKenzie
Film Ed. Gregg Kilday
Steve Brennan
News Ed Erik Pedersen
.Nellie Andreeva

FINANCE

AMERICAN BANKER
(mon to fri) (Finance)
1 State Street Plz., New York, NY, 10004; gen tel (212) 803-8500; adv tel (212) 803-8686; ed tel (212) 803-8399; gen fax (212) 843-9618; web site www.americanbanker.com
Circulation: 9,111(pd); ABC September 30, 2011
Price:
995.00/yr.
News services:
AP, RN, UPI.
CEO James Malkin
Pub. John DelMauro
Barbara A. Rehm
Ed. Niamh Ring
Exec. Dir., Mfg. Stacy Ferrara
Method of Printing:
MECHANICAL PRODUCTION INFORMATION
Web Offset

THE DAILY LEGAL NEWS
(mon to fri) (Finance)
501 Texas St., Rm. M-103, Shreveport, LA, 71101; gen tel (318) 222-0213; web site www.dailylegalnews.net
Circulation: December 22, 1998
Price:
22.00/mo; 264.00/yr.
Advertising:
Open inch rate $15.00/wk (3 1/2 x 1), $25.00/2wk, $35.00/3wk

Pub. Lee Ann Bryce
Ed. Lee Ann Bryce

THE DAILY NEWS
(mon to fri) (Finance)
193 Jefferson Ave., Memphis, TN, 38103; gen tel (901) 523-1561; gen fax (901) 526-5813; adv e-mail advertising@memphisdailynews.com; web site www.memphisdailynews.com
Circulation: N/A
Price:
80.00/yr.
Advertising:
Open inch rate $13.50 (legal)
News services:
CNS. Established: 1886
Adv. Mgr. Don Fancher
Marketing Director Donna Waggener
Publisher Eric Barnes
Associate Publisher James Overstreet
Method of Printing:
MECHANICAL PRODUCTION INFORMATION
Offset

THE DAILY RECORD
(mon to fri) (Finance)
PO Box 1062, Louisville, KY, 40201; gen tel (502) 583-4471; gen fax (502) 585-5453; gen e-mail janicep@nacms-c.com
Circulation: October 31, 1997
Price:
275.00/yr; 86.25/3mo; $162.50/6mo.
Advertising:
Open inch rate $1.20 (legal line)
News services:
National Association of Credit Management. Established: 40201
Pub. Connie J. Cheak
Mng. Ed. Janice Prichard
Method of Printing:
MECHANICAL PRODUCTION INFORMATION
Offset

THE DAILY TRANSCRIPT
(mon to fri) (Finance)
PO Box 85469, San Diego, CA, 92186-5469; gen tel (619) 232-4381; adv fax (619) 239-4312; ed fax (619) 236-8126; gen e-mail editor@sddt.com; adv e-mail sales@sddt.com; ed e-mail editor@sddt.com; web site www.sddt.com
Circulation: N/A
Price:
200.00/yr; 70.00/3mo; $124.00/6mo.
Advertising:
Open inch rate $89.00
News services:
AP, NNS, NYT, TMS.
Pub. Robert Loomis
Dir., Mktg. Christine Tran
Circ. Mgr. Shelley Barry
Ed. in Chief Joe Guerin
Joseph Schmitt
Prodn. Mgr. Steve Lovelace
Method of Printing:
MECHANICAL PRODUCTION INFORMATION
Offset

THE LOS ANGELES DAILY JOURNAL
(mon to fri) (Finance)
915 E. First St., Los Angeles, CA, 90012; gen tel (213) 229-5300; gen fax (213) 229-5481; ed fax (213) 229-5462; web site www.dailyjournal.com
Circulation: December 31, 2000
Price:
70.00/mo; 575.00/yr; 340.00/6mo.
Advertising:
Open inch rate $69.16 (page)
News services:
AP, NYT, CNS, McClatchy.
Chrmn. of the Bd. Charles T. Munger
Vice Chrmn. of the Bd. J.P. Guerin
Pub. Gerald Salzman
Adv. Dir. Audrey Miller
Ramond Chagolla
Ed. Martin Berg
Method of Printing:
MECHANICAL PRODUCTION INFORMATION
Offset

THE ST. LOUIS COUNTIAN
(mon to sat; S) (Finance)
319 N. Fourth St., Saint Louis, MO, 63102; gen tel (314) 421-1880; adv tel (314) 421-1880; ed tel (314) 421-1880; gen fax (314) 421-0436; adv fax (314) 421-0436; ed fax (314) 421-0436; adv e-mail carol.prycma@thedailyrecord.com; ed e-mail willc@thedailyrecord.com; web site www.thedailyrecord.com
Circulation: N/A
Price:
187.20/yr.
Advertising:
Open inch rate $6.56
News services:
RN.
Pub. Richard Gard
Bus. Mgr. Amanda Passmore
Adv. Dir. Amy Burdge
Circ. Mgr. Stacey Fish
William B. Connaghan
Prodn. Mgr. John M. Reno
Method of Printing:
MECHANICAL PRODUCTION INFORMATION
Web Offset

STANDARD & POOR'S CORPORATION RECORDS
(mon to fri) (Finance)
55 Water St., New York, NY, 10041; gen tel (212) 438-1000; ed tel (212) 438-2000; web site www.advisorinsight.com
Circulation: N/A
Price:
1,465.00/yr.
Exec. Vice Pres./Gen. Counsel Kenneth M. Vittor
Exec. Vice Pres./CFO Robert Bahash
Method of Printing:
MECHANICAL PRODUCTION INFORMATION
Offset

GOVERNMENT

THE DAILY RECORDER
(mon to fri) (Government)
PO Box 1048, Sacramento, CA, 95812; gen tel (916) 444-2355; adv tel (800) 652-1700; gen fax (916) 444-0636; gen e-mail daily_recorder@dailyjournal.com; ed e-mail jt_long@dailyjournal.com; web site www.dailyjournal.com
Circulation: N/A
Price:
246.00/yr, $137.00/yr (student rate).
Advertising:
Open inch rate $26.00
News services:
AP, dj. Established: 1901
Pres./Pub. Jerry Salzman
Cor. Office Dir. Raymond Chagolla
Personnel Dir. Dorothy Salzman
Ed. Michael Gottlieb
Raymond Chagolla
Tom Barragan
Prodn. Designer Houay Keobouth
Method of Printing:
MECHANICAL PRODUCTION INFORMATION
Offset

SAN FRANCISCO DAILY JOURNAL
(mon to fri) (Government)
44 Montgomery St., Ste. 250, San Francisco, CA, 94104; gen tel (415) 296-2400; gen fax (415) 296-2440; web site www.dailyjournal.com
Circulation: N/A
Price:
68.00/mo; 557.00/yr.
Advertising:
Open inch rate $754.00 (quarter page)
News services:
AP.
Pub. Linda Hubbell
Adv. Dir. Linda Hubbell
Ed. Linda Hubbell

LAW

AKRON LEGAL NEWS
(mon to fri) (Law)
60 S. Summit St., Akron, OH, 44308-1775; gen tel (330) 376-0917; gen fax (330) 376-7001; gen e-mail aln97@apk.net; web site www.akronlegalnews.com
Circulation: September 27, 1999
Price:
70.00/yr; 30.00/3mo; $45.00/6mo.
Advertising:
Open inch rate $11.00
News services:
AP.
Pres./Pub. John L.
Vice Pres./Gen. Mgr. Robert Heffern
Ed. Rick Smith
Method of Printing:
MECHANICAL PRODUCTION INFORMATION
Offset

BROOKLYN DAILY EAGLE & DAILY BULLETIN
(mon to fri) (Law)
30 Henry St., Brooklyn, NY; gen tel (718) 858-2300; gen fax (718) 858-8281; gen e-mail publisher@brooklyneagle.net; web site www.brooklyneagle.net
Circulation: N/A
Price:
125.00/yr; 40.00/3mo.
Advertising:
Open inch rate $24.00
Pub. J.D. Hasty
Adv. Mgr. Patricia Higgins
Adv. Mgr., Legal Daniel Doctorow
Adv. Mgr., Special Projects Ted Cutler
Sam Howe
Mng. Ed. Ron Geberer

CHICAGO DAILY LAW BULLETIN
(mon to fri) (Law)
415 N. State St., Chicago, IL, 60610-4674; gen tel (312) 644-7800; gen fax (312) 644-4255; gen e-mail displayads@lbpc.com; web site www.lawbulletin.com
Circulation: N/A
Price:
185.00/yr; 120.00/6mo.
Advertising:
Open inch rate $26.40 (Classified), $2,588.00 (Full Page Display)
News services:
AP, NYT.
Chrmn. Lanning Macfarland
Pres./CEO Brewster Macfarland
Exec. Vice Pres. Neil Breen
James Banich
Consultant Bernie Judge
Adv. Sr. Dir., Sales/Mktg. Mark Menzies
Ed. Michael Kramer
Mng. Ed. Stephen Brown
Fred Faulkner
Method of Printing:
MECHANICAL PRODUCTION INFORMATION
Offset

CINCINNATI COURT INDEX
(mon to fri) (Law)
119 W. Central Pkwy., Cincinnati, OH, 45202; gen tel (513) 241-1450; gen fax (513) 684-7821; gen e-mail support@courtindex.com; web site www.courtindex.com
Circulation: December 23, 1998
Price:
85.00/yr; 30.00/3mo; $50.00/6mo.
Advertising:
Open inch rate $9.00
News services:
AP.
Gen. Mgr. Mark Veatty
Ed. Mark Veatty
Method of Printing:
MECHANICAL PRODUCTION INFORMATION
Offset

DAILY COMMERCIAL RECORD
(mon to fri) (Law)
706 Main St., Dallas, TX, 75202; gen tel (214) 741-6366; gen fax (214) 741-6373; gen e-mail dcr@dailycommercialrecord.com; web site www.dailycommercialrecord.com
Circulation: December 23, 1998
Price:
168.00/yr; 53.00/3mo; $88.00/6mo.
Advertising:
Open inch rate $14.76
Pub. E. Nuel Cates
Ed. Emily Cates
Method of Printing:
MECHANICAL PRODUCTION INFORMATION
Offset

THE DAILY COMMERCIAL RECORDER
(mon to fri) (Law)
17400 Judson Rd., San Antonio, TX; gen tel (210) 250-2327; gen fax (210) 736-5506; gen e-mail dcr@primetimenewspapers.com; web site www.primetimenewspapers.com
Circulation: N/A
Price:
150.00/yr; 55.00/3mo.
Advertising:
Open inch rate $25.00
News services:
ACCN, Creator Syndicates, LAT-WP, National American Press Syndicate, NYT..
Ed. Charlotte Aaron
Prodn. Ed. Sylvia P. Sepulveda
Method of Printing:
MECHANICAL PRODUCTION INFORMATION
Web

DAILY COURT REPORTER
(mon to fri) (Law)
120 W Second St Ste 418, Dayton, OH, 45402; gen tel (937) 222-6000; gen fax (937) 341-5020; gen e-mail info@thedailycourt.com; web site www.dailycourt.com
Circulation: N/A
Price:
85.00/yr; 40.00/3mo; $50.00/6mo.
Advertising:
Open inch rate $12.00
News services:
American Court & Commercial Newspapers.
Pres./Pub. Jeffrey Foster
Editorial Mgr. Virginia Steitz

DAILY COURT REVIEW
(mon to fri) (Law)
PO Box 1889, TX, 77251-1889; gen tel (713) 869-5434; ed tel (713) 869-5434; gen fax (713) 869-8887; ed e-mail editor@dailycourtreview.com; web site www.dailycourtreview.com
Circulation: December 23, 1998
Price:
25.00/mo; 145.00/yr; 70.00/3mo.
Advertising:
Open inch rate $16.80
News services:
RN, National Newspaper Association, Texas Press Association. Established: 1889
Pub. Tom Morin
Ed. Tom Morin
Method of Printing:
MECHANICAL PRODUCTION INFORMATION
Offset

THE DAILY EVENTS
(mon to fri) (Law)
PO Box 1, Springfield, MO, 65801-0001; gen fax (417) 866-1401; adv fax (417) 866-1491; gen e-mail editor@dailyevents.com; web site www.thedailyevents.com
Circulation: N/A
Price:
88.00/yr.
News services:
American Court & Commercial Newspapers. Established: 1881

Pub. Jeff Schrag
Adv. Dir. Jeff Schrag
Ed. Wendy Greyowl
Prodn. Mgr. Jeff Schrag
Method of Printing:
MECHANICAL PRODUCTION INFORMATION
Digital Press Sheet

THE DAILY JOURNAL
(mon to fri) (Law)
1114 W. 7th Ave., Ste. 100, Denver, CO, 80204; gen tel (303) 756-9995; adv tel (303) 584-6737; ed tel (303) 584-6724; gen fax (303) 584-6717; adv fax (303) 584-6717; ed fax (303) 756-4465; web site colorado.construction.com
Circulation: N/A
Price:
1,384.00/yr.
Advertising:
Open inch rate $25.20Established: 1897Open inch rate $25.20 John
Adv. Dir. John Rhoades
Adv. Mgr. Michael Branigan
Ed. Melissa Leslie
Mark Shaw
Method of Printing:
MECHANICAL PRODUCTION INFORMATION
Offset

THE DAILY LEGAL NEWS
(mon to fri) (Law)
501 Texas St., Rm. M-103, Shreveport, LA, 71101; gen tel (318) 222-0213; web site www.dailylegalnews.net
Circulation: December 22, 1998
Price:
22.00/mo; 264.00/yr.
Advertising:
Open inch rate $15.00/wk (3 1/2 x 1), $25.00/2wk, $35.00/3wk
Pub. Lee Ann Bryce
Ed. Lee Ann Bryce

DAILY LEGAL NEWS
(mon to fri) (Law)
100 Federal Plz. E., Ste. 126, Youngstown, OH, 44503; gen tel (330) 747-7777; gen fax (330) 747-3977; gen e-mail john@akronlegalnews.com; web site www.dlnnews.com
Circulation: N/A
Price:
72.00/yr.
Advertising:
Open inch rate $5.00
Pres. John Burleson
Office Mgr. Kim Pierson
Adv. Dir. Ellen Dellaserra
Method of Printing:
MECHANICAL PRODUCTION INFORMATION
Offset

THE DAILY LEGAL NEWS AND CLEVELAND RECORDER
(tues to sat) (Law)
2935 Prospect Ave., Cleveland, OH, 44115-2688; gen tel (216) 696-3322; gen fax (216) 696-6329; gen e-mail dln@dln.com; web site www.dln.com
Circulation: N/A
Price:
85.00/yr; 36.00/3mo; $55.00/6mo.
Advertising:
Open inch rate $16.00
News services:
AP, National Newspaper Association, Ohio Newspaper Association.
Chrmn./Pres./Pub. Lucien B. Karlovec
Exec. Vice Pres./Asst. Pub. Jeffrey B. Karlovec
Sec./Gen. Counsel John D. Karlovec
Treasurer Charles E. Bergstresser
Richard Karlovec
Ed. Lisa Cech
Mng. Ed. Jeffrey B. Karlovec
editor@dln.com Lisa Cech
Prodn. Mgr. Terry Machovina
Kurt Gutwein
Method of Printing:
MECHANICAL PRODUCTION INFORMATION
Offset

DAILY RECORD
(mon to fri) (Law)
3323 Leavenworth St., Omaha, NE, 68105-1915; gen tel (402) 345-1303; gen fax (402) 345-2351; web site www.omahadailyrecord.com
Circulation: N/A
Price:
84.00/yr; 30/3mo; $50.00/6mo; $150/24mo.
Advertising:
Open inch rate $7.25
News services:
NNA, United Media, WP Writers Group, LATS. Established: 68105-1915
Pres./Pub. Ronald A. Henningsen
Assoc. Pub. Lynda K. Henningsen
Ed. Lorraine Boyd
Brian Henningsen
Method of Printing:
MECHANICAL PRODUCTION INFORMATION
Offset

THE DAILY RECORD
(mon to sat; S) (Law)
405 E. 13th St., Ste. 101, Kansas City, MO, 64106; gen tel (816) 931-2002; adv tel (816) 931-2002; gen fax (816) 561-6675; adv fax (816) 561-6675; gen e-mail mail@kcdailyrecord.com; adv e-mail www.kcdailyrecord.com
Circulation: N/A
Price:
139.00/yr.
Advertising:
Open inch rate $9.80
Pub. Richard Gard
Bus. Mgr. Amanda Passmore
Kansas City Office Mgr. Peter Crawford
Prodn. Mgr. John Reno
Method of Printing:
MECHANICAL PRODUCTION INFORMATION
Offset

THE DAILY RECORD
(mon to fri) (Law)
PO Box 30006, Rochester, NY, 14603-3006; gen tel (585) 232-6920; gen fax (585) 232-2740; gen e-mail kevin.momot@nydailyrecord.com; web site www.nydailyrecord.com
Circulation: October 1, 2000
Price:
122.00/yr; 86.00/3mo; $96.00/6mo.
Advertising:
Open inch rate $.90 (agency line), $.75 (retail line)
News services:
American Court & Commercial Newspapers, National Newspaper Association. Established: 14603-3006
Chrmn./CEO James P. Dolan
Vice Pres./Pub. Kevin Momot
CFO Scott Pollei
Tara Buck
Method of Printing:
MECHANICAL PRODUCTION INFORMATION
Offset

THE DAILY RECORD
(mon to fri) (Law)
PO Box 1062, Louisville, KY, 40201; gen tel (502) 583-4471; gen fax (502) 585-5453; gen e-mail janicep@nacms-c.com
Circulation: October 31, 1997
Price:
275.00/yr; 86.25/3mo; $162.50/6mo.
Advertising:
Open inch rate $1.20 (legal line)
News services:
National Association of Credit Management. Established: 40201
Pub. Connie J. Cheak
Mng. Ed. Janice Prichard
Method of Printing:
MECHANICAL PRODUCTION INFORMATION
Offset

THE DAILY RECORD
(mon to fri) (Law)
PO Box 3595, Little Rock, AR, 72203; gen tel (501) 374-5103; gen fax (501) 372-3048; gen e-mail bobby@dailydata.com; adv e-mail jedwards@dailydata.com; ed e-mail editor@dailydata.com; web site www.dailyrecord.us
Circulation: December 13, 2007
Price:
26/yr (mon&fri); $13.00/yr (tue or fri).
Advertising:
Column Inch Rate - $20.00
News services:
NNS, TMS, DRNW, INS. Established: 1925
Pres Don Bona
Pub. Bill F. Rector
Adv./Mktg. Dir. Jay Edwards
Prodn. Mgr. Amy Sherrill
Method of Printing:
MECHANICAL PRODUCTION INFORMATION
Web Press/Tab Size

THE DAILY RECORDER
(mon to fri) (Law)
PO Box 1048, Sacramento, CA, 95812; gen tel (916) 444-2355; adv tel (800) 652-1700; gen fax (916) 444-0636; gen e-mail daily_recorder@dailyjournal.com; ed e-mail jt_long@dailyjournal.com; web site www.dailyjournal.com
Circulation: N/A
Price:
246.00/yr, $137.00/yr (student rate).
Advertising:
Open inch rate $26.00
News services:
AP, dj. Established: 1901
Pres./Pub. Jerry Salzman
Cor. Office Dir. Raymond Chagolla
Personnel Dir. Dorothy Salzman
Ed. Michael Gottlieb
Raymond Chagolla
Tom Barragan
Prodn. Designer Houay Keobouth
Method of Printing:
MECHANICAL PRODUCTION INFORMATION
Offset

DAILY REPORT
(mon to fri) (Law)
190 Pryor St. SW, Atlanta, GA, 30303-3685; gen tel (404) 521-1227; gen fax (404) 523-5924; gen e-mail fcdr@amlaw.com; web site www.dailyreportonline.com
Circulation: March 31, 2000
Price:
290.00/yr.
Advertising:
Open inch rate $1,800.00 (page)Established: 1890
Pub. Blair Matthews
Assoc. Pub. Ed Bean
Office Mgr. Sarah Wagner
Adv. Dir. Mischelle Grant
Ed Bean
Mng. Ed. Jonathan Ringel
Art. Dir. Jason Bennitt
Method of Printing:
MECHANICAL PRODUCTION INFORMATION
Offset

THE DAILY REPORTER
(mon to fri) (Law)
PO Box 514033, Milwaukee, WI, 53203-3433; gen tel (414) 276-0273; adv fax (414) 276-8057; ed fax (414) 276-4416; gen e-mail news@dailyreporter.com; web site www.dailyreporter.com
Circulation: December 13, 2007
Price:
159.00/yr.
Advertising:
Open inch rate $12.30 (R.O.P. & classified), $1.75 (legal line)
News services:
AP.
Pres./CEO James P. Dolan
Vice Pres./Pub. Ann Richmond
Adv. Dir. Denise Vandervest
Ed. Chris Thompson
Jayne Laste
Method of Printing:
MECHANICAL PRODUCTION INFORMATION
Offset by Subcontract

DAILY TRANSCRIPT
(mon to fri) (Law)
PO Box 1541, Colorado Springs, CO, 80901; gen tel (719) 634-1048; gen fax (719) 634-0596; ed e-mail editorial@csbj.com; web site www.dailytranscript.com
Circulation: December 22, 1998
Price:
115.00/yr.
Advertising:
Open inch rate $16.00
News services:
CNS, LAT-WP.
Pub. Lon Matejczyk
Bus. Mgr. Kim Barker
Adv. Mgr. Lon Matejczyk
Ed. Mike Boyd
Method of Printing:
MECHANICAL PRODUCTION INFORMATION
Offset

THE DAILY TRANSCRIPT
(mon to fri) (Law)
PO Box 85469, San Diego, CA, 92186-5469; gen tel (619) 232-4381; adv fax (619) 239-4312; ed fax (619) 236-8126; gen e-mail editor@sddt.com; adv e-mail sales@sddt.com; ed e-mail editor@sddt.com; web site www.sddt.com
Circulation: N/A
Price:
200.00/yr; 70.00/3mo; $124.00/6mo.
Advertising:
Open inch rate $89.00
News services:
AP, NNS, NYT, TMS.
Pub. Robert Loomis
Dir., Mktg. Christine Tran
Circ. Mgr. Shelley Barry
Ed. in Chief Joe Guerin
Joseph Schmitt
Prodn. Mgr. Steve Lovelace
Method of Printing:
MECHANICAL PRODUCTION INFORMATION
Offset

FINANCE AND COMMERCE
(tues to sat) (Law)
730 2nd Ave S., Ste. 100, Minneapolis, MN, 55402; gen tel (612) 333-4244; gen fax (612) 333-3243; gen e-mail info@finance-commerce.com; web site www.finance-commerce.com
Circulation: October 20, 2003
Price:
175.00/yr; 99.00/6mo.
Advertising:
Open inch rate $12.00
News services:
AP. Established: 1887
Vice Pres./Pub. Steve Jahn
Bus. Mgr. Joann Barquest
Jeanne Reiland
Prodn. Mgr. Nancy Spangler
Method of Printing:
MECHANICAL PRODUCTION INFORMATION
Web Offset

THE JOURNAL RECORD
(mon to fri) (Law)
PO Box 26370, Oklahoma City, OK, 73126-0370; gen tel (405) 235-3100; adv tel (405) 278-2830; ed tel (405) 278-2850; gen fax (405) 278-6907; ed fax (405) 278-2890; ed e-mail news@journalrecord.com; web site www.journalrecord.com
Group:
The Dolan Company
Circulation: N/A
Price:
189.00/yr (in Oklahoma), $190.00/yr (outside Oklahoma); 43.00/3mo; $80.00/6mo.
Advertising:
Open inch rate $18.62
News services:
AP, CSM, DMN. Established: 1903
Chrmn. of the Bd. James P. Dolan
Pub. Mary Melon
Gen. Mgr. Terri Vanhooser
Editor Ted Streuli
Prodn. Mgr. Gary Berger

Method of Printing:
MECHANICAL PRODUCTION INFORMATION
Offset

THE LEGAL INTELLIGENCER
(mon to fri) (Law)
1617 John F. Kennedy Blvd., Ste. 1750, Philadelphia, PA, 19103; gen tel (215) 557-2300; adv tel (215) 557-2359; ed tel (215) 557-2489; gen fax (215) 557-2301; adv fax (215) 557-2301; ed fax (215) 557-2301; gen e-mail hcohen@alm.com; adv e-mail dchalphin@alm.com; ed e-mail hgrezlak@alm.com; web site www.thelegal-intelligencer.com
Group:
ALM Media
Circulation: N/A
Price:
650/yr
News services:
AP. Established: 1843
Publisher Hal Cohen
CFO Thomas Fiegel
Method of Printing:
MECHANICAL PRODUCTION INFORMATION
Offset

THE LOS ANGELES DAILY JOURNAL
(mon to fri) (Law)
915 E. First St., Los Angeles, CA, 90012; gen tel (213) 229-5300; gen fax (213) 229-5481; ed fax (213) 229-5462; web site www.dailyjournal.com
Circulation: December 31, 2000
Price:
70.00/mo; 575.00/yr; 340.00/6mo.
Advertising:
Open inch rate $69.16 (page)
News services:
AP, NYT, CNS, McClatchy.
Chrmn. of the Bd. Charles T. Munger
Vice Chrmn. of the Bd. J.P. Guerin
Pub. Gerald Salzman
Adv. Dir. Audrey Miller
Ramond Chagolla
Ed. Martin Berg
Method of Printing:
MECHANICAL PRODUCTION INFORMATION
Offset

METROPOLITAN NEWS-ENTERPRISE
(mon to fri)
210 S. Spring St., Los Angeles, CA, 90012; gen tel (213) 628-4384; gen fax (213) 687-3886; gen e-mail news@metnews.com; web site www.metnews.com
Circulation: December 22, 1998
Price:
20.00/mo; 179.00/yr.
Advertising:
Open inch rate $6.00
News services:
AP. Established: 90012
Co-Pub. Jo-Ann W. Grace
Co-Pub. Rodger M. Grace
Gen. Mgr. S. John Babigan
Asst. Mgr. Vahn C. Babigan

MIAMI DAILY BUSINESS REVIEW
(mon to fri) (Law)
PO Box 010589, Miami, FL, 33101-9998; gen tel (305) 377-3721; adv tel (305) 347-6623; ed tel (305) 347-6694; gen fax (305) 374-8474; adv fax (305) 347-6644; ed fax (305) 347-6626; gen e-mail DailyBusiness-Review@alm.com; adv e-mail shemmerich@alm.com; ed e-mail DBR_Editor@alm.com; web site www.daily-businessreview.com
Circulation: March 1, 2007
Price:
$409.00/yr
Advertising:
Q4-2011/2012 Media Planner Interactive E-book
News services:
AP, Bloomberg, Florida News Service. Established: 1926
Group Publisher, FL/GA/TX Chris Mobley
Associate Publisher/Chief Financial Officer Jeff Fried
Director of Products Carlos Curbelo
Editor-in-Chief David Lyons
Business Editor Jay Rees
Law Editor Catherine Wilson
Director of Creative Services John Michael Rindo
Director of Operations & MIS Guillermo Garcia
Web Adminstrator John Hernandez
Director of Client Development Stephanie Hemmerich
Group Subscriptions Manager Annette Martinez
Audience Development Manager Adam Kaplan
Vice President/Miami-Dade Legal & Court Relations Sookie Williams
Method of Printing:
MECHANICAL PRODUCTION INFORMATION
Offset
Note:
See Daily Business Review editions in Broward and Palm Beach, FL.

NEW YORK LAW JOURNAL
(mon to fri) (Law)
120 Broadway, 5th Fl., New York, NY, 10271; gen tel (212) 457-9545; gen fax (212) 437-7361; gen e-mail cservice@nylj.com; web site www.nylj.com
Circulation: N/A
Price:
395.00/yr.
Advertising:
Open inch rate $99.40
News services:
AP. Established: 10271
Pres./CEO William L. Pollak
CFO Eric Lundberg
Pub. George Dillehay
Adv. Vice Pres., Nat'l Steve Lincoln
Martha Sturgeon
Circ. Mktg. Mgr. Michael Bennett
Ed. in Chief Rex Bossert
Method of Printing:
MECHANICAL PRODUCTION INFORMATION
Offset

PALM BEACH DAILY BUSINESS REVIEW
(mon to fri) (Law)
324 Datura St.,, Suite 140, West Palm Beach, FL, 33401; gen tel (561) 820-2066; adv tel (305) 347-6623; ed tel (305) 347-6694; gen fax (561) 820-2077; adv fax (305) 347-6644; ed fax (305) 347-6626; gen e-mail DailyBusinessReview@alm.com; adv e-mail shemmeerick@alm.com; ed e-mail DBR_Editor@alm.com; web site www.daily-businessreview.com
Circulation: June 30, 2001
Price:
409/yr
Advertising:
Q4-2011/2012 Media Planner Interactive E-book
News services:
AP, Bloomberg, Florida News Service.
Group Publisher, FL/GA/TX Chris Mobley
Associate Publisher/Chief Financial Officer Jeff Fried
Editor-in-Chief David Lyons
Vice President/Broward & Palm Beach Legals Deborah Mullin
Director of Products Carlos Curbelo
Director of Client Development Stephanie Hemmerich
Audience Development Manager Adam Kaplan
Group Subscriptions Manager Annette Martinez
Web Administrator John Hernandez
Business Editor Jay Rees
Law Editor Cathy Wilson
Method of Printing:
MECHANICAL PRODUCTION INFORMATION
Offset
Note:
See Daily Business Reviews editions in Broward and Miami, FL.

PITTSBURGH LEGAL JOURNAL
(mon to fri) (Law)
400 Koppers Bldg., 436 7th Ave., Pittsburgh, PA, 15219; gen tel (412) 261-6255; gen e-mail plj@acba.org; web site www.acba.org
Group:
Pennsylvania Newspaper Association
Circulation: October 23, 1997
Price:
175.00/yr.
Advertising:
Open inch rate $8.75Established: 1853
Exec. Dir. David Blaner

THE RECORDER
(mon to fri) (Law)
10 United Nations Plz., 3rd Fl., San Francisco, CA, 94102; gen tel (415) 749-5400; adv tel (415) 749-5444; gen fax (415) 749-5449; adv fax (415) 749-5566; ed fax (415) 749-5549; web site www.therecorder.com
Circulation: N/A
Price:
575.00/yr.
Advertising:
Open inch rate $3,200.00 (Full Page Display)
News services:
AP. Established: 1877
Pub. Chris Braun
Controller Janice Tang
Adv. Mgr., Classified Patrick Vigil
Adv. Mgr., Display Jim Tamietti
Robert Salapuddin
Adv. Coord., Display Heather Ragsdale
Mktg. Dir. John Cosmides
Circ. Mgr. Ed Vergara
Scott Graham
Mng. Ed. Greg Mitchell
Prodn. Mgr./Art Dir. Tess Herrmann
Method of Printing:
MECHANICAL PRODUCTION INFORMATION
Offset

ST. JOSEPH DAILY COURIER
(mon to fri) (Law)
1020 S. Tenth St., Saint Joseph, MO, 64503; gen tel (816) 279-3441; gen fax (816) 279-2091; gen e-mail sjdailycourier@sbcglobal.net
Circulation: N/A
Price:
9.67/mo; 53.74/yr.
Pres./Pub. Bill Cunningham
Ed. Bill Cunningham
Prodn. Mgr. Bill Cunningham
Method of Printing:
MECHANICAL PRODUCTION INFORMATION
Offset

THE ST. LOUIS COUNTIAN
(mon to sat; S) (Law)
319 N. Fourth St., Saint Louis, MO, 63102; gen tel (314) 421-1880; adv tel (314) 421-1880; ed tel (314) 421-1880; gen fax (314) 421-0436; adv fax (314) 421-0436; ed fax (314) 421-0436; adv e-mail carol.prycma@thedailyrecord.com; ed e-mail willc@thedailyrecord.com; web site www.thedailyrecord.com
Circulation: N/A
Price:
187.20/yr.
Advertising:
Open inch rate $6.56
News services:
RN.
Pub. Richard Gard
Bus. Mgr. Amanda Passmore
Adv. Dir. Amy Burdge
Circ. Mgr. Stacey Fish
William B. Connaghan
Prodn. Mgr. John M. Reno
Method of Printing:
MECHANICAL PRODUCTION INFORMATION
Web Offset

ST. LOUIS DAILY RECORD
(mon to sat; S) (Law)
PO Box 88910, Saint Louis, MO, 63188; gen tel (314) 421-1880; adv tel (314) 421-1880; ed tel (314) 421-1880; gen fax (314) 421-0436; adv fax (314) 421-7080; ed fax (314) 421-0436; gen e-mail editcopy@thedailyrecord.com; adv e-mail wildk@thedailyrecord.com; ed e-mail will.connaghan@molawyersmedia.com; web site www.thedailyrecord.com
Group:
Missouri Press Service, Inc.
Circulation: N/A
Price:
210.00/yr.
Advertising:
Open inch rate $6.56
News services:
RN.
Pub. Richard Gard
Bus. Mgr. Amanda Passmore
Adv. Dir. Amy Burdge
Circ. Mgr. Stacey Fish
Richard Jackoway
Assoc. Ed. William B. Connaghan
Information Servs. Mgr. Robert Doyle
Prodn. Mgr. John M. Reno
Method of Printing:
MECHANICAL PRODUCTION INFORMATION
Offset

SAINT PAUL LEGAL LEDGER
(mon to thur)
332 Minnesota St., Ste. E-1432, Saint Paul, MN, 55101-1163; gen tel (651) 222-0059; ed tel (651) 602-0575; gen fax (651) 222-2640; gen e-mail pboulay@legal-ledger.com; web site www.legal-ledger.com
Circulation: October 20, 2003
Price:
110.00/yr; 70.00/6mo.
Advertising:
Open inch rate $12.00 (legal)
News services:
AP. Established: 55101-1163
Pub. Patrick Boulay
Bus. Mgr. Barbara St. Martin
Adv. Mgr., Display Jay Kodytek
Ed. Patrick Boulay
Bill Wolfe
Prodn. Supvr., Pressroom Mike Wolfe

SAN FRANCISCO DAILY JOURNAL
(mon to fri) (Law)
44 Montgomery St., Ste. 250, San Francisco, CA, 94104; gen tel (415) 296-2400; gen fax (415) 296-2440; web site www.dailyjournal.com
Circulation: N/A
Price:
68.00/mo; 557.00/yr.
Advertising:
Open inch rate $754.00 (quarter page)
News services:
AP.
Pub. Linda Hubbell
Adv. Dir. Linda Hubbell
Ed. Linda Hubbell

SONOMA COUNTY HERALD-RECORDER
(mon to fri)
PO Box 877, Santa Rosa, CA, 95402; gen tel (707) 545-1166; adv tel (800) 652-1700; gen fax (707) 545-6310; gen e-mail herald_recorder@dailyjournal.com; web site www.dailyjournal.com
Circulation: N/A
Price:
188.00/yr.
Advertising:
Open inch rate $8.16Established: 95404
Pub. Christine K. Griego
Adv. Mgr., Display Susan Green
Circ. Dir. Christine K. Griego
Erik H. Cummins
Prodn. Mgr. Robin Davidson

MUNICIPAL BONDS

DAILY JOURNAL OF COMMERCE

(mon to fri) (Municipal Bonds)
111 Veterans Blvd., Ste. 1440, Metairie, LA, 70005; gen tel (504) 293-9249; gen fax (504) 832-3534; gen e-mail mail@nopg.com; web site www.djcgulfcoast.com
Circulation: October 31, 1997
Price:
495.00/yr; 190/3mo; $345/6mo.
Advertising:
Open inch rate $10.00
Pub. Mark Singletary
Gen. Mgr. Anne Lovas
Ed. Autumn Giusti

MUNICIPAL FINANCE

THE BOND BUYER

(mon to fri) (Municipal Finance)
1 State Street Plz., New York, NY; gen tel (212) 803-8200; adv tel (212) 843-9617; gen fax (212) 803-1592; adv fax (212) 843-9617; ed fax (212) 843-9614; gen e-mail michael.stanton@sourcemedia.com; web site www.bondbuyer.com
Circulation: December 14, 2007
Price:
1,997.00/yr.
Advertising:
Open inch rate $168.00
CEO Jim Malkin
Pub. Michael Stanton
Adv. Dir., Legal Bill Baneky
Ed. in Chief Amy Resnick

PUBLIC NOTICE

THE DAILY RECORD

(mon to sat; S) (Public Notice)
405 E. 13th St., Ste. 101, Kansas City, MO, 64106; gen tel (816) 931-2002; adv tel (816) 931-2002; gen fax (816) 561-6675; adv fax (816) 561-6675; gen e-mail mail@kcdailyrecord.com; adv e-mail www.kcdailyrecord.com
Circulation: N/A
Price:
139.00/yr.
Advertising:
Open inch rate $9.80
Pub. Richard Gard
Bus. Mgr. Amanda Passmore
Kansas City Office Mgr. Peter Crawford
Prodn. Mgr. John Reno
Method of Printing:
MECHANICAL PRODUCTION INFORMATION
Offset

REAL ESTATE

BROOKLYN DAILY EAGLE & DAILY BULLETIN

(mon to fri) (Real Estate)
30 Henry St., Brooklyn, NY; gen tel (718) 858-2300; gen fax (718) 858-8281; gen e-mail publisher@brooklyneagle.net; web site www.brooklyneagle.net
Circulation: N/A
Price:
125.00/yr; 40.00/3mo.
Advertising:
Open inch rate $24.00
Pub. J.D. Hasty
Adv. Mgr. Patricia Higgins
Adv. Mgr., Legal Daniel Doctorow
Adv. Mgr., Special Projects Ted Cutler
Sam Howe
Mng. Ed. Ron Geberer

MIAMI DAILY BUSINESS REVIEW

(mon to fri) (Real Estate)
PO Box 010589, Miami, FL, 33101-9998; gen tel (305) 377-3721; adv tel (305) 347-6623; ed tel (305) 347-6694; gen fax (305) 374-8474; adv fax (305) 347-6644; ed fax (305) 347-6626; gen e-mail DailyBusinessReview@alm.com; adv e-mail shemmerich@alm.com; ed e-mail DBR_Editor@alm.com; web site www.dailybusinessreview.com
Circulation: March 1, 2007
Price:
$409.00/yr
Advertising:
Q4-2011/2012 Media Planner Interactive E-book
News services:
AP, Bloomberg, Florida News Service. Established: 1926
Group Publisher, FL/GA/TX Chris Mobley
Associate Publisher/Chief Financial Officer Jeff Fried
Director of Products Carlos Curbelo
Editor-in-Chief David Lyons
Business Editor Jay Rees
Law Editor Catherine Wilson
Director of Creative Services John Michael Rindo
Director of Operations & MIS Guillermo Garcia
Web Adminstrator John Hernandez
Director of Client Development Stephanie Hemmerich
Group Subscriptions Manager Annette Martinez
Audience Development Manager Adam Kaplan
Vice President/Miami-Dade Legal & Court Relations Sookie Williams
Method of Printing:
MECHANICAL PRODUCTION INFORMATION
Offset
Note:
See Daily Business Review editions in Broward and Palm Beach, FL.

PALM BEACH DAILY BUSINESS REVIEW

(mon to fri) (Real Estate)
324 Datura St.,, Suite 140, West Palm Beach, FL, 33401; gen tel (561) 820-2066; adv tel (305) 347-6623; ed tel (305) 347-6694; gen fax (561) 820-2077; adv fax (305) 347-6644; ed fax (305) 347-6626; gen e-mail DailyBusinessReview@alm.com; adv e-mail shemmeerick@alm.com; ed e-mail DBR_Editor@alm.com; web site www.dailybusinessreview.com
Circulation: June 30, 2001
Price:
409/yr
Advertising:
Q4-2011/2012 Media Planner Interactive E-book
News services:
AP, Bloomberg, Florida News Service.
Group Publisher, FL/GA/TX Chris Mobley
Associate Publisher/Chief Financial Officer Jeff Fried
Editor-in-Chief David Lyons
Vice President/Broward & Palm Beach Legals Deborah Mullin
Director of Products Carlos Curbelo
Director of Client Development Stephanie Hemmerich
Audience Development Manager Adam Kaplan
Group Subscriptions Manager Annette Martinez
Web Administrator John Hernandez
Business Editor Jay Rees
Law Editor Cathy Wilson
Method of Printing:
MECHANICAL PRODUCTION INFORMATION
Offset
Note:
See Daily Business Reviews editions in Broward and Miami, FL.

SPORTS

DAILY RACING FORM

(mon to sat; S) (Sports)
100 Broadway, 7th Fl., New York, NY, 10005; gen tel (212) 366-7600; adv tel (212) 366-7607; ed fax (212) 366-7718; gen e-mail Daily Racing Form publishes several editions nationwide.; adv e-mail advert@drf.com; ed e-mail editor@drf.com; web site www.drf.com
Circulation: N/A
Price:
169.19/mo (1st class); $109.72/mo (2nd class); 2,030.28/yr (1st class); $1,317.24/yr (2nd class).
Advertising:
Open inch rate $21.75 (national)
News services:
RN, UPI.
Pres./Gen. Mgr. Jim Kostas
Pub. Steven Crist
Dir., HR Jim Hajney
Jeffery Burch
Circ. Mgr. Joel Brady
Ed. in Chief Rich Rosenbush
Irwin Cohen
Method of Printing:
MECHANICAL PRODUCTION INFORMATION
Offset
Note:
Daily Racing Form publishes several editions nationwide.

Section III

Newspapers Published in Foreign Countries

NEWSPAPERS OF THE BRITISH ISLES
(CHANNEL ISLANDS, ENGLAND, NORTHERN IRELAND, REPUBLIC OF IRELAND, SCOTLAND & WALES)

Newspapers, personnel, circulation, advertising rates, etc.

IRELAND

DUBLIN

SUNDAY WORLD (S)
5th Floor, Independent House, Dublin, 1, Ireland; tel (353) 11 8849000; fax 9001Circ.: 292,124
Advertising: Euro 69.00 cm; Euro 15,740.00 pg.
Adv. Dir. – Mairead Kearns
Ed. – Colm Macginty

IRISH INDEPENDENT (M)
Independent House, Dublin, 1, Ireland; tel (353) 11 7055403; fax 7055498; e-mail independent@team400.ie; web site www.independent.ieCirc.: 159,363
Advertising: Euro 75.15 cm; Euro 29,425.00 pg.
Adv. Mgr. – Eoin Healy
Ed. – Gerald O'Regan

EVENING HERALD (E)
Independent House, Dublin, 1, Ireland; tel (353) 11 7055416; fax 7055497Circ.: 82,084
Advertising: Euro 48.95 cm; Euro 10,430.00 pg.
Adv. Mgr. – Rachel Armstrong
Ed. – Stephen Rae

SUNDAY INDEPENDENT (S)
Independent House, Dublin, 1, Ireland; tel (353) 11 7055448; fax 7055497Circ.: 283,024
Advertising: Euro 83.10 cm; Euro 34,115.00 pg.
Adv. Mgr. – Aidan Hanley
Ed. – Aengus Fanning

IRISH DAILY STAR (M)
Level 5, Building 4, Dundrum Town Centre, Sandyford Road, Dundrum, Dublin 16., Dublin, Ireland; tel (353) 1 4901228; fax 4907425Circ.: 109,413
Advertising: Euro 85.25 cm; Euro 20,330 pg.
Adv. Mgr. – Neil Walsh
Ed. – Ger Colleran

IRISH MAIL ON SUNDAY (S)
Embassy House, Dublin, 4, Ireland; tel (353) 11 6375580; fax 6375940; web site www.irelandonsunday.comCirc.: 123,580
Advertising: Euro 40.95 cm; Euro 9,884.70 pg.
Adv. Mgr. – Alacoque Doyle
Ed. – Paul Field

THE IRISH TIMES (M)
The Irish Times Bldg., 24-28 Tara St., Dublin, 2, Ireland; tel (353) 11 6758585; fax 6758002; e-mail editorial@irish-times.com; lettersed@irish-times.com; web site www.irish-times.comCirc.: 118,259
Advertising: Euro 63.35 cm; Euro 24,670.00 pg.
Adv. Mgr. – Liam Holland
Ed. – Geraldine Kennedy

SUNDAY BUSINESS POST (S)
80 Harcourt St., Dublin, 2, Ireland; tel (353) 11 6056300; web site www.thepost.ieCirc.: 55,971
Advertising: Euro 34.50 cm; Euro 12,597.00 pg.
Adv. Mgr. – Cian O'Mongain
Ed. – Cliff Taylor

SUNDAY TRIBUNE (S)
15 Lower Baggot St., Dublin, 2, Ireland; tel (353) 11 6314300; fax 6614656Circ.: 65,717
Advertising: Euro 49.50 cm; Euro 19,600.00 pg.
Adv. Mgr. – Andrew Mernagh
Ed. – Noirin Hegarty

LAPPS QUAY, CORK

IRISH EXAMINER (M)
City Quarter, Lapps Quay, Cork, Ireland; tel (353) 121 272722; e-mail news.ed@examiner.ie; web site www.examiner.ieCirc.: 54,191
Advertising: Euro 42.00 cm; Euro 16,750.00 pg.
Adv. Mgr. – Aidan Forde
Ed. – Tim Vaughan

CORK EVENING ECHO (E)
City Quarter, Lapps Quay, Cork, Ireland; tel (353) 121 272722; fax 273846Circ.: 25,904
Advertising: Euro 22.65 cm; Euro 4,600.00 pg.
Adv. Mgr. – Valerie Dean
Ed. – Maurice Gubbins

UNITED KINGDOM

ABERDEEN, GRAMPIAN

THE PRESS & JOURNAL (M)
PO Box 43, Aberdeen, Grampian, AB9 8AF, United Kingdom; tel (44) 1224 690222; fax 694613; web site www.pressandjournal.co.ukCirc.: 80,136
Advertising: 26.25 cm; 11,550.00 pg.
Adv. Dir. – Janis Gallon Smith
Ed. – Derek Tucker

EVENING EXPRESS (E)
PO Box 43, Aberdeen, Grampian, AB9 8AF, United Kingdom; tel (44) 1224 690222; fax 694613Circ.: 53,130
Advertising: 17.85 cm; 3,948.00 pg.
Adv. Mgr. – Janis Gallon Smith
Ed. – Damian Bates

BARROW-IN-FURNESS, CUMBRIA

NORTH WEST EVENING MAIL (E)
Abbey Rd., Barrow-in-Furness, Cumbria, LA14 5QS, United Kingdom; tel (44) 1229 821835; fax 832141; web site www.nwemail.co.ukCirc.: 18,386
Advertising: 15.65 cm; 3,834.00 pg.
Chief Exec. – Robin Burgess
Mng. Dir. – Tony Raymond
Adv. Mgr. – Gregory Wallsworth
Ed. – Jonathan Lee

BASILDON, ESSEX

BASILDON AND SOUTHEND ECHO (E)
Chester Hall Lane, Basildon, Essex, SS14 3BL, United Kingdom; tel (44) 1268 522792; fax 532060Circ.: 34,692
Advertising: 7.57 cm; 2,279.00 pg.
Chief Exec. – Paul Davidson
Adv. Dir. – Ron Westrop
Ed. – Martin McNeil

BATH, AVON

BATH CHRONICLE (E)
Windsor Bridge, Bath, Avon, ENG, BA2 3AV, United Kingdom; tel (44) 1225 322322; fax 322290
Advertising: 5.65 cm; 1,627.00 pg.
Chief Exec. – Michael Pelosi
Adv. Mgr. – Sally Cook
Ed. – Sam Holliday

BELFAST, ANTRIM

DAILY IRELAND
2 Hannahstown Hill, Belfast, Antrim, BT1 7OLT, United Kingdom; tel (44) 1232 906 12345
Adv. Mgr. – Jacqueline O'Donnell
Ed. – Maria McCourt

SUNDAY LIFE (S)
124 Royal Ave., Belfast, Antrim, BT12 2QY, United Kingdom; tel (44) 1232 264000; fax 554507Circ.: 66,763
Advertising: 13.90 cm; 3,785.00 pg.
Adv. Dir. – Simon Mann
Ed. – Jim Flanagan

BELFAST TELEGRAPH (E)
124-144 Royal Ave., Belfast, Antrim, NI, BT1 1EB, United Kingdom; tel (44) 1232 264000; fax 554506; e-mail newseditor@belfasttelegraph.co.uk; web site www.belfasttelegraph.co.ukCirc.: 33,678
Advertising: 19.88 cm; 11,132.00 pg.
Adv. Mgr. – Richard McClean
Ed. – Martin Lindsay

IRISH NEWS (M)
113-117 Donegall St., Belfast, Antrim, BT1 2GE, United Kingdom; tel (44) 1232 322226; fax 239103; e-mail internet@irishnews.com; web site www.irishnews.comCirc.: 49,911
Advertising: 8.30 cm; 2,922.00 pg.
Adv. Mgr. – Sean Higgins
Ed. – Noel Doran

ULSTER NEWS LETTER (M)
45-56 Boucher Cres., Belfast, Antrim, BT12 6QY, United Kingdom; tel (44) 1232 680000; fax 664412Circ.: 26,199
Advertising: 13.80 cm; 2,773.00 pg.
Adv. Mgr. – Pamela Arnold
Ed. – Darwin Templeton

BIRMINGHAM, WEST MIDLANDS

BIRMINGHAM MAIL (E)
Floor 6, Fort Dunlop, Fort Pkwy., Birmingham, West Midlands, B24 9FF, United Kingdom; tel (44) 121 2363366; fax 2333958Circ.: 66,166
Advertising: 33.90 cm; 8,353.00 pg.
Chief Exec. – Sly Bailey
Adv. Dir. – Dawn Sweeney
Ed. – Steve Dyson

SUNDAY MERCURY (S)
Floor 6, Fort Dunlop, Fort Pkwy., Birmingham, West Midlands, B24 9FF, United Kingdom; tel (44) 121 2363366; fax 2332958Circ.: 57,470
Advertising: 16.71 cm; 4,238.00 pg.
Chief Exec. – Sly Bailey
Ed. – David Brookes

THE BIRMINGHAM POST (M)
Floor 6, Fort Dunlop, Fort Pkwy., Birmingham, West Midlands, B24 9FF, United Kingdom; tel (44) 121 2363366; fax 2333958Circ.: 12,795
Advertising: 11.59 cm; 5,913.00 pg.
Chief Exec. – Sly Bailey
Adv. Dir. – Dawn Sweeney
Ed. – Marc Reeves

BLACKBURN, LANCASHIRE

LANCASHIRE TELEGRAPH (E)
High Street, Blackburn, Lancashire, BB1 1HT, United Kingdom; tel (44) 1254 678678; fax 682034; e-mail webmaster@newsquest.co.uk; web site www.thisislancashire.co.uk/lancashire/blackburnCirc.: 29,753
Advertising: 6.25 cm; 1,969.00 pg.
Chief Exec. – Paul Davidson
Mng. Dir. – Brenda T. Rudge
Adv. Mgr. – Mark Robinson
Ed. – Kevin Young

BLACKPOOL, LANCASHIRE

THE GAZETTE (E)
Blackpool Business Park, Blackpool, Lancashire, FY4 2DP, United Kingdom; tel (44) 1258 400888; fax 400333Circ.: 28,340
Advertising: 15.17 cm; 4,642.00 pg.
Chief Exec. – John Fry
Adv. Mgr. – Paul Bentham
Ed. – David Helliwell

BOLTON, LANCASHIRE

BOLTON NEWS (E)
Churchgate, Bolton, Lancashire, BL1 1DE, United Kingdom; tel (44) 1204 522345; fax 385103; e-mail beneditorial@newsquest.co.uk; mrossiter@newsquest.co.uk; web site www.thisislancashire.co.uk/lancashire/bolton Circ.: 28,835
Advertising: 5.80 cm; 1,764.00 pg.
Chief Exec. – Paul Davidson
Mng. Dir. – John Waters
Adv. Mgr. – Helen Turnbull
Ed. – Ian Savage

BOURNEMOUTH, DORSET

DAILY ECHO (E)
Richmond Hill, Bournemouth, Dorset, BH2 6HH, United Kingdom; tel (44) 1202 554601; fax 293676Circ.: 32,085
Advertising: 5.75 cm; 1,811.00 pg.
Chief Exec. – Paul Davidson
Adv. Mgr. – Shelley Gorham
Ed. – Neal Butterworth

BRADFORD, WEST YORKSHIRE

TELEGRAPH & ARGUS (E)
Hall Ings, Bradford, West Yorkshire, BD1 1JR, United Kingdom; tel (44) 1274 729511; fax 724907Circ.: 35,592
Advertising: 7.50 cm; 2,295.00 pg.
Chief Exec. – Paul Davidson
Mng. Dir. – J.P. Banville
Adv. Mgr. – John Lee
Ed. – Perry Austin-Clarke

BRIGHTON, WEST SUSSEX

THE ARGUS (E)
Crowhurst Rd., Brighton, West Sussex, BN1 8AR, United Kingdom; tel (44) 1273 544544; fax 566114Circ.: 31,703
Advertising: 7.50 cm; 2,900.00 pg.
Ed. – Mike Beard

BRISTOL, AVON

EVENING POST (E)
Temple Way, Bristol, Avon, BS99 7HD, United Kingdom; tel (44) 117 9343000; fax 9343570; e-mail mail@epost.co.uk; web site www.epost.co.ukCirc.: 49,386
Advertising: 14.40 cm; 4,147.00 pg.
Chief Exec. – Michael Pelosi
Ed. – Mike Norton

WESTERN DAILY PRESS (M)
Temple Way, Bristol, Avon, BS99 7HD, United Kingdom; tel (44) 117 9343000; fax 9343570; e-mail mail@westpress.co.uk; letters@westpress.co.uk; web site www.westpress.co.ukCirc.: 40,432
Advertising: 9.65 cm; 2,779.00 pg.
Chief Exec. – Michael Pelosi
Ed. – Andy Wright

BURTON-ON-TRENT, STAFFORDSHIRE

BURTON MAIL (E)
65-68 High St., Burton-On-Trent, Staffordshire, DE14 1LE, United Kingdom; tel (44) 1283 512345; fax 510075Circ.: 14,509
Advertising: 5.70 cm; 1,796.00 pg.
Chief Exec. – Lord Iliffe
Adv. Mgr. – Tim Bishop
Ed. – Steve Lowe

CAMBRIDGE, CAMBRIDGESHIRE

CAMBRIDGE EVENING NEWS (E)
Winship Rd., Cambridge, Cambridgeshire, CB5 8EJ, United Kingdom; tel (44) 1223 434343; fax 361720; e-mail editorial@cambridge-news.co.uk; web site www.cambridge-news.co.ukCirc.: 26,462
Advertising: 9.35 cm; 2,945.00 pg.
Adv. Mgr. – Chris Brown
Ed. – Paul Brackley

CARDIFF, SOUTH GLAMORGAN

SOUTH WALES ECHO (E)
Havelock St., Thomson House, Cardiff, South Glamorgan, CF1 1WR, United Kingdom; tel (44) 1222 223333; fax 237539
Advertising: 19.82 cm; 5,391.00 pg.
Ed. – Mike Hill

WALES ON SUNDAY (S)
Thompson House, Havelock St., Cardiff, South Glamorgan, CF1 1WR, United Kingdom; tel (44) 1222 223333; fax 224668Circ.: 42,763
Advertising: 10.74 cm; 2,921.00 pg.
Adv. Mgr. – Gerald Griffiths
Ed. – Tim Gordon

WESTERN MAIL (M)
Thompson House, Havelock St., Cardiff, South Glamorgan, CF1 1WR, United Kingdom; tel (44) 1222 583583; fax 237539Circ.: 37,152
Advertising: 21.14 cm; 5,750.00 pg.
Adv. Mgr. – Lynn Cardwell
Ed. – Alan Edmunds

CARLISLE, CUMBRIA

NEWS & STAR (D-EX FRI.)
Dalston Rd., Carlisle, Cumbria, CA2 5UA, United Kingdom; tel (44) 1228 612600; fax 612601Circ.: 22,626
Advertising: 7.33 cm; 1,796.00 pg.
Ed. – Neil Hodgkinson

CHELTENHAM, GLOUCESTERSHIRE

GLOUCESTERSHIRE ECHO (E)
1 Clarence Parade, Cheltenham, Gloucestershire, GL50 3NZ, United Kingdom; tel (44) 1242 271900; fax 271792Circ.: 20,613
Advertising: 6.60 cm; 1,958.00 pg.
Adv. Mgr. – John Clements
Ed. – Kevan Blackadder

COLCHESTER, ESSEX

GAZETTE (D)
43-44 North Hill, Colchester, Essex, CO1 1TZ, United Kingdom; tel (44) 1206 506000; fax 508195; e-mail webadmin@thisisessex.co.uk; web site www.thisisessex.co.ukCirc.: 21,194
Advertising: 5.15 cm; 920.00 pg.
Adv. Mgr. – Samantha Bruce
Ed. – Irene Kettle

COVENTRY, WEST MIDLANDS

COVENTRY TELEGRAPH (E)
Corporation St., Coventry, West Midlands, CV1 1FP, United Kingdom; tel (44) 1203 633633; fax 631736Circ.: 46,297
Advertising: 16.35 cm; 3,764.00 pg.
Adv. Mgr. – Debbie Davies
Ed. – Alan Kirby

DARLINGTON, DURHAM

THE NORTHERN ECHO (M)
Priestgate, Darlington, Durham, DL1 1NF, United Kingdom; tel (44) 1325 381313; fax 380539; e-mail echo@nne.co.uk; web site www.thisisthenortheast.co.uk/neCirc.: 50,427
Advertising: 18.21 cm; 8,814.00 pg.
Adv. Mgr. – Ian Clarke
Ed. – Peter Barron

DERBY, DERBYSHIRE

DERBY EVENING TELEGRAPH (E)
Meadow Rd., Derby, Derbyshire, DE1 2DW, United Kingdom; tel (44) 1332 291111; fax 253022Circ.: 41,799
Advertising: 11.60 cm; 3,341.00 pg.
Adv. Mgr. – Fiona Shaw
Ed. – Steve Hall

DUNDEE, TAYSIDE

COURIER & ADVERTISER (M)
80 Kingsway East, Dundee, Tayside, SCO, DD4 8SL, United Kingdom; tel (44) 1382 23131; fax 454599; e-mail courier@dcthomson.co.ukCirc.: 72,527
Advertising: 17.72 cm; 8,030.00 pg.
Adv. Mgr. – Craig McGeoghie
Ed. – Bill Hutcheon

EVENING TELEGRAPH (E)
80 Kingsway East, Dundee, Tayside, SCO, DD4 8SL, United Kingdom; tel (44) 1382 23131; fax 22214; e-mail tele@dcthomson.co.uk; web site www.dcthomson.co.uk/mags/teleCirc.: 24,533
Advertising: 7.00 cm; 1,485.00 pg.
Adv. Mgr. – Craig McGeohie
Ed. – Gordon Wishart

SUNDAY POST (M)
Albert Sq., Dundee, Tayside, DD1 9QJ, United Kingdom; tel (44) 1382 23131; fax 22214; web site www.dcthomson.co.uk/mags/postCirc.: 386,162
Advertising: 48.50 cm; 10,885.00 pg.
Adv. Mgr. – Arthur McEwan
Ed. – David Pollington

EDINBURGH, LOTHIAN

EVENING NEWS (E)
20 North Bridge, Edinburgh, Lothian, EH1 1YT, United Kingdom; tel (44) 131 2252468; fax 2257302Circ.: 49,208
Advertising: 17.04 cm; 4,685.00 pg.
Ed. – John McLellan

SCOTLAND ON SUNDAY (M)
20 North Bridge, Edinburgh, Lothian, EH1 1YT, United Kingdom; tel (44) 131 6208620; fax 2202443Circ.: 69,251
Advertising: 26.52 cm; 11,881.00 pg.
Ed. – Les Snowdon

THE SCOTSMAN (M)
20 North Bridge, Edinburgh, Lothian, EH1 1YT, United Kingdom; tel (44) 131 6208620; fax 2267420; e-mail online@scotsman.com; web site www.scotsman.com
Advertising: 26.52 cm; 5,410.00 pg.
Ed. – John McLellan

EXETER, DEVON

EXPRESS & ECHO (E)
Heron Rd., Exeter, Devon, EX2 7NF, United Kingdom; tel (44) 1392 442211; fax 442297Circ.: 20,625
Advertising: 7.15 cm; 2,059.00 pg.
Adv. Mgr. – Ivor Bull
Ed. – Mark Astley

GLASGOW, STRATHCLYDE

DAILY RECORD (M)
One Central Quay, Glasgow, Strathclyde, G3 8DA, United Kingdom; tel (44) 141 309 3000; e-mail editors@dailyrecord.co.uk; web site www.record-mail.co.uk/rmCirc.: 372,837
Advertising: 41.18 cm; 9,600.00 pg.
Commercial Director – Denise West
Ed. in Chief – Bruce Waddell

EVENING TIMES (E)
200 Renfield St., Glasgow, Strathclyde, G2 3PR, United Kingdom; tel (44) 141 309 3300; fax 5521344; e-mail 10072.2732@compuserve.com; web site www.eveningtimes.co.ukCirc.: 72,535
Advertising: 29.50 cm; 6,500.00 pg.
Ed. in Chief – Donald Martin

SUNDAY HERALD (S)
200 Renfield St., Glasgow, Strathclyde, G2 3PR, United Kingdom; tel (44) 141 309 3300; e-mail herald@cins.co.uk; web site www.theherald.comCirc.: 42,369
Advertising: 15.00 cm; 6,563.00 pg.
Ed. – Richard Walker

SUNDAY MAIL (M)
One Central Quay, Glasgow, Strathclyde, G3 8DA, United Kingdom; tel (44) 141 309 3000; e-mail editor@features.sundaymail.co.uk; web site www.record-mail.co.uk/rmCirc.: 481,456
Advertising: 54.40 cm; 12,688.00 pg.
Adv. Mgr. – Denise West
Ed. in Chief – Bruce Waddell

THE HERALD (M)
200 Renfield St., Glasgow, Strathclyde, G2 3PR, United Kingdom; tel (44) 141 309 3300; e-mail herald@cins.co.uk; web site www.theherald.co.ukCirc.: 66,191
Advertising: 29.50 cm; 11,500.00 pg.
Ed. in Chief – Donald Martin

GLOUCESTER, GLOUCESTERSHIRE

THE CITIZEN (E)
St. John's Lane, Gloucester, Gloucestershire, GL1 2AY, United Kingdom; tel (44) 1452 424442; fax 505597Circ.: 25,681
Advertising: 6.80 cm; 1,958.00 pg.
Adv. Dir. – Phil Inman
Ed. – Ian Mean

GREENOCK, STRATHCLYDE

GREENOCK TELEGRAPH (E)
2 Crawford St., Greenock, Strathclyde, PA15 1LH, United Kingdom; tel (44) 1475 26511; fax 83734Circ.: 17,070
Advertising: 10.30 cm; 2,719.00 pg.
Adv. Mgr. – David Connell
Ed. – Wendy Metcalfe

GRIMSBY, LINCOLNSHIRE

GRIMSBY TELEGRAPH (E)
80 Cleethorpe Rd., Grimsby, Lincolnshire, DN31 3EH, United Kingdom; tel (44) 1472 360360; fax 372235
Advertising: 8.40 cm; 2,333.00 pg.
Adv. Mgr. – Julia Arthur
Ed. – Michelle Laylor

HALIFAX, WEST YORKSHIRE

EVENING COURIER (E)
PO Box 19, Halifax, West Yorkshire, HX1 2SF, United Kingdom; tel (44) 1422 260200; fax 330021Circ.: 19,681
Advertising: 11.67 cm; 3,722.00 pg.
Adv. Mgr. – Mandy Baker
Ed. – John Furbisher

HARTLEPOOL, TEESSIDE

THE MAIL (E)
Wesley Sq., Hartlepool, Teesside, TS24 88X, United Kingdom; tel (44) 1429 239333; fax 265818Circ.: 17,773
Advertising: 9.34 cm; 2,858.00 pg.
Adv. Mgr. – Sheila Argument
Ed. – Joy Yates

HUDDERSFIELD, WEST YORKSHIRE

HUDDERSFIELD DAILY EXAMINER (E)
PO Box A26, Huddersfield, West Yorkshire, HD1 2TD, United Kingdom; tel (44) 1484 430000; fax 423722; e-mail editor@examiner.co.uk; webmaster@examiner.co.uk; web site www.examiner.co.ukCirc.: 24,853
Advertising: 6.40 cm; 2,808.00 pg.
Adv. Dir. – Philip Walker
Ed. – Roy Wright

HULL, NORTH HUMBERSIDE

HULL DAILY MAIL (E)
Beverley Rd., Blundell's Corner, Hull, North Humberside, HU3 1XS, United Kingdom; tel (44) 1482 327111; fax 584353; web site www.thisishull.co.ukCirc.: 56,287
Advertising: 15.60 cm; 4,205.00 pg.
Adv. Mgr. – Mark Price
Ed. – John Meehan

IPSWICH, SUFFOLK

EAST ANGLIAN DAILY TIMES (M)
30 Lower Brook St., Ipswich, Suffolk, ENG, IP4 1AN, United Kingdom; tel (44) 1473 230023; fax 232529; e-mail webmaster@ecn.co.uk; web site www.ecn.co.ukCirc.: 34,055
Advertising: 8.76 cm; 2,523.00 pg.
Adv. Dir. – Adrian Rawlinson
Ed. – Terry Hunt

EVENING STAR (E)
30 Lower Brook St., Ipswich, Suffolk, ENG, IP4 1AN, United Kingdom; tel (44) 1473 230023; fax 232529; e-mail webmaster@ecn.co.uk; web site www.ecn.co.ukCirc.: 19,319
Advertising: 7.53 cm; 2,169.00 pg.
Adv. Mgr. – Adrian Rawlinson
Ed. – Nigel Pickover

JERSEY

JERSEY EVENING POST (E)
PO Box 582, Jersey, JEF 8XQ, United Kingdom; tel (44) 1534 611611; fax 611620Circ.: 21,098
Advertising: 11.97 cm; 3,352.00 pg.
Chrmn. – John Averty
Adv. Mgr. – Paul Carter
Ed. – Chris Bright

KETTERING, NORTHAMPTONSHIRE

NORTHAMPTONSHIRE EVENING TELEGRAPH (E)
Rothwell Rd., Kettering, Northamptonshire, NN16 8GA, United Kingdom; tel (44) 1536 506100; fax 410101Circ.: 22,231
Advertising: 9.06 cm; 2,772.00 pg.
Ed. – Jeremy Clifford

LEEDS, WEST YORKSHIRE

YORKSHIRE EVENING POST (E)
PO Box 168, Leeds, West Yorkshire, LS1 1RF, United Kingdom; tel (44) 113 2432701; fax 2388525; e-mail eped@ypn.co.uk; web site www.yorkshireeveningpost.co.ukCirc.: 53,262
Advertising: 21.05 cm; 6,441.00 pg.
Ed. – Paul Napier

YORKSHIRE POST (M)
Wellington St., Leeds, West Yorkshire, LS1 1RF, United Kingdom; tel (44) 113 2441234; e-mail ypinfo@pressconnect.com; web site www.ypn.co.ukCirc.: 51,081
Advertising: 16.55 cm; 10,195.00 pg.
Ed. – Peter Charlton

LEICESTER, LEICESTERSHIRE

LEICESTER MERCURY (E)
St. George St., Leicester, Leicestershire, LE1 9FQ, United Kingdom; tel (44) 116 25125; fax 25306; e-mail webmaster@thisisleicestershire.co.uk; web site www.thisisleicestershire.co.ukCirc.: 69,069
Advertising: 16.20 cm; 4,666.00 pg.
Adv. Dir. – Phil Young
Ed. – Keith Perch

SUNDAY SPORT
848 Melton Rd. Thurmaston, Leicester, Leicestershire, LE4 8BJ, United Kingdom; tel (44) 116 2694892; fax 2640948
Advertising: 45 cm; 4,000.00 pg.
Adv. Dir. – Denize Smith
Ed. – Mark Harris

LINCOLN, LINCOLNSHIRE

LINCOLNSHIRE ECHO (E)
Brayford Wharf East, Lincoln, Lincolnshire, LN5 7AT, United Kingdom; tel (44) 1522 820000; fax 804491Circ.: 21,565
Advertising: 7.00 cm; 2,016.00 pg.
Ed. – John Grubb

LISKEARD, CORNWALL

SUNDAY INDEPENDENT (M)
Webbs House, Tindle Ste., Liskeard, Cornwall, PL14 6AH, United Kingdom; tel (44) 1579 342174; fax 341852Circ.: 24,812
Advertising: 6.25 cm; 1,750.00 pg.
Adv. Mgr. – Hazel Bradley
Ed. – John Noble

LIVERPOOL

DAILY POST (M)
PO Box 48, Liverpool, L69 3EB, United Kingdom; tel (44) 151 2272000; fax 236468; e-mail webmaster@liverpool.com; web site www.liverpool.com
Advertising: 14.03 cm; 4,041.00 pg.
Adv. Dir. – Warren Butcher
Ed. – Mark Thomas

LIVERPOOL ECHO (E)
PO Box 48, Liverpool, L69 3EB, United Kingdom; tel (44) 151 2272000; fax 236468; e-mail davies@liverpool.com; web site www.trinity.plc.ukCirc.: 102,488
Advertising: 26.97 cm; 7,767.00 pg.
Adv. Dir. – Warren Butcher
Ed. – Alastair Machray

LONDON

DAILY MAIL (M)
Northcliffe House, 2 Derry St., London, W8 5TT, United Kingdom; tel (44) 171 9386000; fax 9373251; web site www.dailymail.co.ukCirc.: 2,214,117
Advertising: 129.00 cm; 32,508.00 pg.
Adv. Dir. – John Teal
Ed. – Paul Dacre

DAILY MIRROR (M)
1 Canada Sq., Canary Wharf, London, E14 5AP, United Kingdom; tel (44) 171 2933000; fax 2933110; e-mail online@mgn.co.uk; web site www.mirror.co.ukCirc.: 1,416,994
Advertising: 142.00 cm; 32,508.00 pg.
Adv. Dir. – David Emin
Ed. – Richard Wallace

DAILY TELEGRAPH (M)
111 Buckingham Palace Rd., London, SW1W ODT, United Kingdom; tel (44) 171 9312000; fax 5383810; e-mail letters@telegraph.co.uk; suggestions@telegraph.co.uk; web site www.telegraph.co.ukCirc.: 845,167
Advertising: 104.00 cm; 66,750.00 pg.
Adv. Mgr. – Matthew Watkins
Ed. – Will Lewis

EVENING STANDARD (E)
Northcliffe House, 2 Derry St., London, ENG, W8 5EE, United Kingdom; tel (44) 171 9386000; fax 9373193; e-mail editor@thisislondon.com; web site www.thisislondon.co.uk/dynamic/index.html-Circ.: 286,873
Advertising: 100.00 cm; 16,800.00 pg.
Adv. Dir. – Simon Davies
Ed. – Geordie Grieg

INDEPENDENT ON SUNDAY (S)
Northcliffe House, 2 Derry St., London, W8 5EE, United Kingdom; tel (44) 171 7005 2000; web site www.independent.co.ukCirc.: 179,315
Advertising: 37.00 cm; 22,900.00 pg.
Adv. Dir. – Simon Cooke
Ed. – John Mullin

THE INDEPENDENT (M)
Northcliffe House, 2 Derry St., London, ENG, W8 5EE, United Kingdom; tel (44) 171 7005 2000; web site www.independent.co.ukCirc.: 214,597
Advertising: 42.00 cm; 13,050.00 pg.
Adv. Dir. – Simon Cooke
Ed. – Roger Alton

LONDON LITE (A)
Northcliffe House, 2 Derry St., Kensington, London, W8 STT, United Kingdom; tel (44) 171 9386000; web site www.thelondonlite.co.ukCirc.: 390,353
Advertising: 70.00 cm; 17,640.00 pg.
Adv. Dir. – Rosemary Gorman
Ed – Ted Young

MAIL ON SUNDAY
2 Derry St., London, W8 5EE, United Kingdom; tel (44) 171 9386000; fax 9373745Circ.: 2,187,649
Advertising: 156.00 cm; 55,800.00 pg.
Adv. Mgr. – Simon Davies
Ed. – Peter Wright

METRO (M)
Northcliffe House, 2 Derry St., Kensington, London, W8 STT, United Kingdom; tel (44) 171 9386000; web site www.metro.co.ukCirc.: 1,349,121
Advertising: 95.20 cm; 22,657.00 pg.
Adv. Mgr. – James Hooper
Ed. – Kenny Campbell

SUNDAY TIMES (M)
1 Virginia St., London, ENG, E98 1XY, United Kingdom; tel (44) 171 7825000; fax 7825658; e-mail webmaster@thetimes.co.uk; web site www.the-times.co.ukCirc.: 1,192,939
Advertising: 137.00 cm; 93,000.00 pg.
Chrmn. – Rupert Murdoch
Adv. Dir. – Paul Hayes
Ed. – John Witherow

THE SUN (M)
Virginia St., London, E1 9XJ, United Kingdom; tel (44) 171 7824000; fax 7825605Circ.: 3,073,106
Advertising: 169.00 cm; 50,975.00 pg.
Commercial Dir. – Ian Clark
Media Dir. – Mark Chippendale
Ed. – Rebekah Wade

THE TIMES (DAILY)
1 Virginia St., London, ENG, E98 1XY, United Kingdom; tel (44) 171 7825000; fax 7825658; e-mail webmaster@thetimes.co.uk; web site www.the-times.co.ukCirc.: 619,456
Advertising: 117.00 cm; 25,900.00 pg.
Chrmn. – Rupert Murdoch
Adv. Dir. – Paul Hayes
Ed. – James Harding

DAILY STAR (M)
10 Lower Thames St., London, EC3R 6EN, United Kingdom; tel (44) 870 211 7760; fax 434 7577; web site www.megastar.co.ukCirc.: 726,527
Advertising: 63.00 cm; 15,295.00 pg.
Ed. – Dawn Neesom

SUNDAY EXPRESS (S)
10 Lower Thames St., London, EC3R 6EN, United Kingdom; tel (44) 870 211 7760; fax 211 7577Circ.: 656,514
Advertising: 166.00 cm; 27,500.00 pg.
Adv. Mgr. – Jane Putley
Ed. – Martin Townsend

DAILY STAR SUNDAY (S)
10 Lower Thames St., London, EC3R 6EN, United Kingdom; tel (44) 870 211 7760; fax 434 7577; web site www.megastar.co.ukCirc.: 369,096
Advertising: 86.00 cm; 19,000.00 pg.
Adv. Dir. – Jane Putley
Ed. – Gareth Morgan

DAILY EXPRESS (M)
10 Lower Thames St., London, ENG, EC3R 6EN, United Kingdom; tel (44) 870 211 7760; fax 211 7577Circ.: 740,647
Advertising: 85.00 cm; 31,500.00 pg.
CEO – Richard Desmond
Adv. Mgr. – Jane Putley
Ed. – Peter Hill

FINANCIAL TIMES (M)
1 Southwark Bridge, London, ENG, SE1 9HL, United Kingdom; tel (44) 171 8733000; fax 8733922; e-mail letters.editor@ft.com; site.feedback@ft.com; web site www.ft.comCirc.: 434,196
Advertising: 162.00 cm; 67,800.00 pg.
Adv. Dir. – Dominic Good
Ed. – Lionel Barber

SUNDAY MIRROR (S)
1 Canada Sq., Canary Wharf, London, E14 5AP, United Kingdom; tel (44) 171 2933000; fax 2933280Circ.: 1,282,037
Advertising: 150.00 cm; 51,600.00 pg.
Adv. Dir. – David Emin
Ed. – Tina Weaver

SUNDAY TELEGRAPH (S)
111 Buckingham Palace Rd., London, SW1W ODT, United Kingdom; tel (44) 171 9312000; fax 5381330Circ.: 618,322
Advertising: 78.00 cm; 45,250.00 pg.
Adv. Dir. – Matthew Watkins
Ed. – Ian MacGregor

THE BUSINESS
292 Vauxhall Bridge Rd., London, SW1V 1SS, United Kingdom; tel (44) 171 963 7000
Advertising: 28.00 cm; 16,000.00 pg.
Adv. Dir. – David Walsh

THE GUARDIAN (M)
Kings Pl., 90 York Way, London, N1 9GU, United Kingdom; tel (44) 171 2782332; fax 2781449; e-mail online@guardian.co.uk; web site www.guardianunlimited.co.ukCirc.: 345,884
Advertising: 58.00 cm; 18,000.00 pg.
Adv. Dir. – Mark Angell
Ed. – Alan Rusbridger

THE OBSERVER (S)
Kings Pl., 90 York Way, London, ENG, N1 9GU, United Kingdom; tel (44) 171 2782332; fax 2781449; e-mail bill@dial.pipex.comCirc.: 436,060
Advertising: 92.00 cm; 22,000.00 pg.
Mgr. – Joe Clark
Adv. Dir. – Mark Angell
Ed. – John Mulholland

THE PEOPLE (S)
1 Canada Sq., London, E14 5AP, United Kingdom; tel (44) 171 2933000; fax 2933280Circ.: 619,788
Advertising: 115.00 cm; 29,500.00 pg.
Adv. Dir. – David Emin
Ed. – Lloyd Embley

THELONDONPAPER (A)
1 Virginia St., London, E98 1XY, United Kingdom; tel (44) 171 7825000; web site www.thelondonpaper.com
Advertising: 88.00 cm; 18,850.00 pg.
Adv. Mgr. – Naim Halloum

Ed. – Stefano Hatfield

WALL STREET JOURNAL EUROPE (D)
10 Fleet Pl., London, ENG, EC4M 7QN, United Kingdom; tel (44) 20 7842 9900; web site europe.wsj.com
Ed. in Chief – Patience Wheatcroft

MANCHESTER, LANCASHIRE

MANCHESTER EVENING NEWS (E)
164 Deansgate, Manchester, Lancashire, M60 2RD, United Kingdom; tel (44) 161 8327200; fax 8317481Circ.: 180,236
Advertising: 38.65 cm; 11,827.00 pg.
Adv. Mgr. – Mark Dodson
Ed. – Paul Horrocks

MIDDLESBROUGH

EVENING GAZETTE (E)
Borough Road, Middlesbrough, United Kingdom; tel (44) 1642 245401; fax 210565; e-mail editor@eveninggazette.co.uk; web site www.eveninggazette.co.ukCirc.: 50,431
Last Audit: November 23, 2011
Group: Trinity Mirror
Advertising: 15.35 cm; 4,175.00 pg.

NEWCASTLE UPON TYNE

EVENING CHRONICLE (E)
Groat Market, Newcastle upon Tyne, NE1 1ED, United Kingdom; tel (44) 191 2327500; fax 2304144; e-mail comments@evening-chronicle.co.ukCirc.: 71,877
Advertising: 21.30 cm; 5,964.00 pg.
Adv. Dir. – Gary Ramsay
Ed. – Paul Robertson

SUNDAY SUN (S)
Groat Market, Newcastle upon Tyne, NE1 1ED, United Kingdom; tel (44) 191 2327500; fax 2304144Circ.: 63,953
Advertising: 16.60 cm; 4,648.00 pg.
Adv. Dir. – Gary Ramsay
Ed. – Colin Paterson

THE JOURNAL (M)
Groat Market, Newcastle upon Tyne, NE1 1ED, United Kingdom; tel (44) 191 2327500; fax 2304144; e-mail mail.list@northeast-on-line.co.uk; web site www.the-journal.co.uk-Circ.: 34,370
Advertising: 14.35 cm; 4,108.00 pg.
Adv. Dir. – Gary Ramsay
Ed. – Brian Aitken

NEWPORT, GWENT

SOUTH WALES ARGUS (E)
Cardiff Rd., Maesglas, Newport, Gwent, NP9 1QW, United Kingdom; tel (44) 1633 810000; fax 810100Circ.: 28,236
Advertising: 10.80 cm; 5,000.00 pg.
Adv. Mgr. – Shaun Walters
Ed. – Gerry Keighley

NORTHAMPTON, NORTHAMPTONSHIRE

CHRONICLE & ECHO (E)
Upper Mounts, Northampton, Northamptonshire, NN1 3HR, United Kingdom; tel (44) 1604 467000; fax 467240; e-mail 100556.2032@compuserve.com; web site ourworld.compuserve.com/homepages/oec-Circ.: 19,827
Advertising: 7.83 cm; 2,326.00 pg.
Ed. – David Summers

NORWICH, NORFOLK

EASTERN DAILY PRESS (M)
Rouen Rd., Norwich, Norfolk, NR1 1RE, United Kingdom; tel (44) 1603 772140; fax 772149; e-mail webmaster@ecn.co.uk; web site www.ecn.co.ukCirc.: 63,508
Advertising: 11.84 cm; 3,220.00 pg.
Adv. Mgr. – Chris Wood
Ed. – Peter Franzen

EVENING NEWS (E)
Rouen Rd., Norwich, Norfolk, NR1 1RE, United Kingdom; tel (44) 1603 628311; e-mail webmaster@ecn.co.uk; web site www.ecn.co.ukCirc.: 22,250
Advertising: 8.76 cm; 2,523.00 pg.
Adv. Mgr. – Chris Wood
Ed. – James Foster

NOTTINGHAM, NOTTINGHAMSHIRE

NOTTINGHAM EVENING POST (E)
Castle Wharf House, Nottingham, Nottinghamshire, NG1 7EU, United Kingdom; tel (44) 191 9482000; fax 2484753; web site www.thisisnottingham.co.ukCirc.: 55,507
Advertising: 16.90 cm; 4,867.00 pg.
Ed. – Malcolm Pheby

NUNEATON, WARWICKS

NUNEATON NEWS (D)
11-15 Newtown Rd., Nuneaton, Warwicks, CV11 4HR, United Kingdom; tel (44) 1203 353534; fax 353481Circ.: 4,480
Advertising: 4.65 cm; 1,465.00 pg.
Adv. Mgr. – L. Clark
Ed. – Tony Parratt

OLDHAM, LANCASHIRE

EVENING CHRONICLE (E)
172 Union St., Oldham, Lancashire, OL1 1EQ, United Kingdom; tel (44) 161 6332121; fax 6270905Circ.: 20,149
Advertising: 9.93 cm; 1,132.00 pg.
Adv. Mgr. – Jim Whittingham
Ed. – Jim Williams

OXFORD, OXFORDSHIRE

OXFORD MAIL (E)
Osney Mead, Oxford, Oxfordshire, OX2 OEJ, United Kingdom; tel (44) 1865 425262; fax 790423Circ.: 24,503
Advertising: 8.10 cm; 2,479.00 pg.
Advertising Manager – Shane Harding
Ed. – Simon O'Neill

PAISLEY, STRATHCLYDE

PAISLEY DAILY EXPRESS (M)
14 New St., Paisley, Strathclyde, PA1 1XY, United Kingdom; tel (44) 141 3312444; fax 3324912Circ.: 9,289
Advertising: 8.80 cm; 2,693.00 pg.
Adv. Mgr. – Janis Heaney
Ed. – Jonathan Russell

PETERBOROUGH, CAMBRIDGESHIRE

PETERBOROUGH EVENING TELEGRAPH (E)
Telegraph House, Priestgate, Peterborough, Cambridgeshire, PE1 1JW, United Kingdom; tel (44) 1733 555111; fax 555188Circ.: 18,933

Advertising: 8.51 cm; 2,604.00 pg.
Ed. – Rebecca Stephens

PLYMOUTH, DEVON

THE HERALD (E)
17 Brest Rd., Plymouth, Devon, PL6 5AA, United Kingdom; tel (44) 1752 765500; fax 765543Circ.: 36,236
Advertising: 9.06 cm; 2,609.00 pg.
Adv. Mgr. – Lesa Brown
Ed. – Bill Martin

WESTERN MORNING NEWS (M)
17 Brest Rd., Plymouth, Devon, PL6 5AA, United Kingdom; tel (44) 1752 765500; fax 765543Circ.: 39,561
Advertising: 9.06 cm; 2,609.00 pg.
Adv. Mgr. – Lesa Brown
Ed. in Chief – Alan Qualtrough

PORTSMOUTH, HAMPSHIRE

THE NEWS (E)
The News Centre, Hilsea, Portsmouth, Hampshire, PO2 9SX, United Kingdom; tel (44) 1705 664488; fax 692280; e-mail letters@thenews.co.uk; newsdesk@thenews.co.uk; web site www.thenews.co.ukCirc.: 53,159
Advertising: 14.22 cm; 4,351.00 pg.
Ed. – Mark Waldron

PRESTON, LANCASHIRE

LANCASHIRE EVENING POST (E)
Olivers Place, Fulwood, Preston, Lancashire, PR2 4ZA, United Kingdom; tel (44) (44-1772) 254841; fax (44-1772) 204941Circ.: 38,265
Advertising: 18.38 cm; 5,264.00 pg.
Adv. Dir. – Michael Harper
Ed. – Simon Reynolds

READING, BERKSHIRE

READING EVENING POST (E)
8 Tessa Rd., Reading, Berkshire, RG1 8NS, United Kingdom; tel (44) 1734 (44-1734) 588588; fax 503592Circ.: 13,549
Advertising: 9.29 cm; 2,926.00 pg.
Adv. Mgr. – Judith Toner
Ed. – Andy Murrill

SCARBOROUGH, NORTH YORKSHIRE

SCARBOROUGH EVENING NEWS (E)
17-23 Aberdeen Walk, Scarborough, North Yorkshire, YO11 1BB, United Kingdom; tel (44) 1723 363636; fax 354092Circ.: 13,382
Advertising: 15.45 cm; 4,728.00 pg.
Adv. Mgr. – Denise Tile
Ed. – Ed Asquith

SCUNTHORPE, N. LINCOLNSHIRE

SCUNTHORPE TELEGRAPH (E)
4-5 Park Sq., Laneham St., Scunthorpe, N. Lincolnshire, DN16 6JH, United Kingdom; tel (44) 1724 273273; fax 854395Circ.: 20,132
Advertising: 6.10 cm; 1,699.00 pg.
Ed. – Mel Cook

SHEFFIELD, SOUTH YORKSHIRE

THE STAR (E)
Johnston Press, Sheffield, South Yorkshire, S1 1PU, United Kingdom; tel (44) 114 2767676Circ.: 50,285
Advertising: 25.91 cm; 7,928.00 pg.
Ed. – Alan Powell

SOUTH SHIELDS, TYNE AND WEAR

THE GAZETTE (E)
Chapter Row, South Shields, Tyne And Wear, NE33 1BL, United Kingdom; tel (44) 191 4554661; fax 4568270Circ.: 18,152
Advertising: 10.29 cm; 3,057.00 pg.
Adv. Mgr. – Linda Potts
Ed. – John Symanski

SOUTHAMPTON, HAMPSHIRE

SOUTHERN DAILY ECHO (E)
Test Lane, Redbridge, Southampton, Hampshire, 5016 9JX, United Kingdom; tel (44) 1703 424777; fax 424969Circ.: 38,974
Advertising: 6.55 cm; 2,063.00 pg.
Adv. Mgr. – Sue Meheux
Ed. – Ian Murray

STOKE-ON-TRENT, STAFFORDSHIRE

EVENING SENTINEL (E)
Sentinel House, Stoke-On-Trent, Staffordshire, ST1 5SS, United Kingdom; tel (44) 1782 602525; fax 260516; e-mail admin@thisisstaffordshire.co.uk; web site www.thisisstaffordshire.co.ukCirc.: 60,776
Advertising: 11.80 cm; 3,398.00 pg.
Adv. Mgr. – Michelle Gesell
Ed. – Mike Sassi

SENTINEL SUNDAY (S)
Sentinel House, Stoke-On-Trent, Staffordshire, ENG, ST1 5SS, United Kingdom; tel (44) 1782 602525; fax 260516; e-mail admin@thisisstaffordshire.com; web site www.thisisstaffordshire.co.uk
Advertising: 7.00 cm; 4,158 pg.
Adv. Mgr. – Graham White
Ed. – Sean Dooley

SENTINEL SUNDAY (S)
Sentinel House, Stoke-On-Trent, Staffordshire, ST1 5SS, United Kingdom; tel (44) 1782 602525; fax 260516; e-mail admin@thisisstaffordshire.co.uk; web site www.thisisstaffordshire.co.uk
Advertising: 7.00 cm; 4,158.00 pg.
Adv. Mgr. – Michelle Gesell
Ed. – Mike Sassi

SENTINEL SUNDAY (S)
Sentinel House, Stoke-On-Trent, Staffordshire, ST1 5SS, United Kingdom; tel (44) 1782 602525; fax 260516; e-mail admin@thisisstaffordshire.co.uk; web site www.thisisstaffordshire.co.uk
Advertising: 7.00 cm; 4,158.00 pg.
Adv. Mgr. – Michelle Gesell
Ed. – Mike Sassi

SUNDERLAND, TYNE AND WEAR

SUNDERLAND ECHO (E)
Pennywell, Sunderland, Tyne And Wear, SR4 9ER, United Kingdom; tel (44) 191 5343011; fax 5345975; e-mail echo.news@northeast-press.co.uk; web site www.sunderland.com/echoCirc.: 41,153

Advertising: 16.22 cm; 4,963.00 pg.
Ed. – Rob Lawson

SWANSEA, WEST GLAMORGAN

SOUTH WALES EVENING POST (E)
Adelaide St., Swansea, West Glamorgan, SA1 1QT, United Kingdom; tel (44) 1792 650841; fax 644008Circ.: 51,269
Advertising: 10.80 cm; 3,072.00 pg.
Adv. Mgr. – Patrick McVeigh
Ed. – Spencer Feeney

SWINDON, WILTSHIRE

EVENING ADVERTISER (E)
100 Victoria Rd., Swindon, Wiltshire, SN1 3BE, United Kingdom; tel (44) 1793 528144; fax 523883Circ.: 21,828
Advertising: 7.25 cm; 2,096.00 pg.
Adv. Mgr. – John Pajak
Ed. – Dave King

TELFORD, SHROPSHIRE

SHROPSHIRE STAR (E)
Ketley, Telford, Shropshire, TF1 4HU, United Kingdom; tel (44) 1952 242424; fax 254605Circ.: 70,484
Advertising: 9.20 cm; 3,018.00 pg.
Adv. Mgr. – Colin Spicer
Ed. – Sarah Jane Smith

TORQUAY, DEVON

HERALD EXPRESS (E)
Barton Hill Rd., Torquay, Devon, TQ2 8JN, United Kingdom; tel (44) 1803 676000; fax 676799Circ.: 23,992
Advertising: 6.50 cm; 1,872.00 pg.
Ed. – Andy Phelan

VALE, GUERNSEY

GUERNSEY PRESS & STAR (D)
PO Box 57, Braye Rd., Vale, Guernsey, ENG, GY1 3BW, United Kingdom; tel (44) 1481 240240; fax 240275; e-mail shart@guernsey-press.com; web site www.guernsey-press.comCirc.: 16,023
Advertising: 10.07 cm; 2,600.00 pg.
Chief Exec. – John Averty
Adv. Dir. – Steve Mauger
Adv. Mgr. – Paul Carter
Ed. – Richard Digard

WEYMOUTH, DORSET

DORSET ECHO (E)
Fleet House, Hampshire Rd., Granby Ind. Estate, Weymouth, Dorset, DT4 9XD, United Kingdom; tel (44) 1305 830930; fax 830869Circ.: 18,702
Advertising: 6.15 cm; 1,937.00 pg.
Adv. Mgr. – Guy Neale
Ed. – Toby Granville

WOLVERHAMPTON, WEST MIDLANDS

EXPRESS & STAR (E)
51-53 Queen St., Wolverhampton, West Midlands, WV1 3BU, United Kingdom; tel (44) 1902 313131; fax 21467; e-mail editor@expressandstar.co.uk; agoldstraw@expressandstar.co.uk; web site www.westmidlands.comCirc.: 137,948
Advertising: 24.50 cm; 8,036.00 pg.
Ed. – Adrian Faber

WORCESTER

WORCESTER NEWS (E)
Hylton Rd., Worcester, WR2 5JX, United Kingdom; tel (44) 1905 748200; fax 429605Circ.: 17,573
Advertising: 5.20 cm; 2,237.00 pg.
Adv. Mgr. – Jenny Matthews
Ed. – Kevin Ward

WREXHAM, CLWYD

EVENING LEADER (E)
Wrexham Rd., Mold, Wrexham, Clwyd, CH7 1XY, United Kingdom; tel (44) 1352 707707; fax 700048Circ.: 21,159
Advertising: 8.15 cm; 2,567.00 pg.
Ed. – Barrie Jones

YORK, NORTH YORKSHIRE

THE PRESS (E)
PO Box 29, York, North Yorkshire, YO1 1YN, United Kingdom; tel (44) 1904 653051; fax 611488; web site www.digital-yorkshire.co.ukCirc.: 32,856
Advertising: 9.00 cm; 2,754.00 pg.
Ed. – Kevin Booth

NEWSPAPERS OF EUROPE

ALBANIA

TIRANA

BASHKIMI KOMBETAR (D-EX MON.)
Blvd. Zhan D'Ark, Tirana, Albania; tel (355) 42 28110
Circ.: 30,000
Ed. in Chief – Qemal Sakajera

ALBANIAN NEWSPAPER (M)
Rruga e Dibres, Tirana, Albania; tel (355) 42 32646
Circ.: 11,000
Ed. – Carlo Bollino

ALBANIAN DAILY NEWS (D)
Dervish Hima St., ADA Tower, No.1, Tirana, Albania; tel (355) 42 56112; fax 40888; e-mail adn@albnet.net; infoadn@albnet.net; web site www.albaniannews.com
Ed. – Arben Leskaj

KOHA JONE (D) EST. 1991
Rr. Aleksander Moisiu, Tirana, Albania; tel (355) 4 257 004; fax 239 584; e-mail redakskj@kohajone.com; web site www.kohajone.com
Circ.: 400,000
Ed. – Edison Kurani

REPUBLIKA (2X WK.)
Blvd. Zhan D'Ark, No. 66, Tirana, Albania; tel (355) 42 25988; fax 25988
Ed. in Chief – Ylli Rakipi

RILINDJA DEMOKRATIKE (M-6X WK.)
Prane Selise Se Pd, Tirana, Albania; tel (355) 4 232 355; fax 230 329; e-mail gazetard@albaniaonline.net; web site www.rilindjademokratike.com
Circ.: 50,000
Ed. in Chief – Astrit Patozi

ZERI I POPULLIT (D-EX MON.)
Blvd. Zhan D'Ark, Tirana, Albania; tel (355) 42 22 192; fax 27 813; web site www.zeripopullit.com
Circ.: 105,000

ANDORRA

ANDORRA LA VELLA

CORREU ANDORRA
Avda. Meritxell, No. 112, Andorra la Vella, Andorra; tel (376) 822500; fax 822938; web site correu.andorra.ad
Circ.: 2,000
Dir. – Cristina Cornella

DIARI D'ANDORRA (D)
Avda. Riberaygua, 39, 5th Fl., Andorra la Vella, AD500, Andorra; tel (376) 877 477; fax 863 802; e-mail diaridigital@diariandorra.ad; web site www.diariandorra.ad
Circ.: 3,000
Adv. Mgr – Joseph Maria Gomez
Ed. – Gabriel Fernandez

INDEPENDANT (D)
Avda. Meritxell, No.95, Andorra la Vella, Andorra; tel (376) 21056

INFORMACIONS
Calle de la Unio, No. 2, Andorra la Vella, Andorra; tel (376) 21134; fax 60839
Mng. Dir. – Dr. Anna Ruiz

INFORMACIONS DIARI (D)
Avda. Meritxell, No. 101 1r, Andorra la Vella, Andorra; tel (376) 62942; fax 63319
Mng. Dir. – Franesc Ruiz

POBLE ANDORRA (WEEKLY)
Carretera de la Comella, Andorra la Vella, Andorra; tel (376) 822506; fax 826696
Circ.: 3,000
Dir. – M. Carme Grau

ARMENIA

EREVAN

ARAVOT (D)
2 Arshakuniats, 15 Fl., Erevan, 375023, Armenia; tel (374) 10 568 968; fax 528 752; web site www.aravot.am
Ed. in Chief – Aram Abrahamian

MOLORAK (D)
Arshakunyats Ave. 5, Erevan, 375023, Armenia; tel (374) 2 526212; fax 562070
Ed. in Chief – Haykaz Ghaghrinian

RESPUBLICA ARMENIA (D)
Arshakunyats Ave. 2, 9th Flr., Erevan, 375023, Armenia; tel (374) 10 545 700
Ed. in Chief – Armen Khanbabian

YEREVAN

AZG (5X WK.)
Hanrapetutian St. 47, Yerevan, 375010, Armenia; tel (374) 10 521 635; fax 562 863; e-mail azg@azg.am; web site www.azg.am
Ed. in Chief – Hagob Avedikian

GOLOS ARMENII (3X WK.)
Arshakunyats Ave. 2, 7th Flr., Yerevan, 375023, Armenia; tel (37410) 2 529 226; e-mail gonline@arminco.com; gonline@press.arminco.com; web site www.golos.am
Circ.: 20,000
Last Audit: November 23, 2011
Ed. – Flora Nakhshkaryan

AUSTRIA

1040 VIENNA

WIENER ZEITUNG (D)
Wiedner Gurtel 10, 1040 Vienna, Austria; tel (43) 1 206 990; fax 2069 9433; e-mail leser@wienerzeitung.at; web site www.wienerzeitung.at
Circ.: 22,000
Pub. – Dr. Wolfgang Schussel
Mktg. Dir. – Lisa Rajchl
Ed. in Chief – Peter Bochskanl

8010 GRAZ

KLEINE ZEITUNG (D) EST. 1904
Schoenaugasse 64, 8010 Graz, Austria; tel (43) 316 875 3200; fax 875 3244; e-mail online@kleinezeitung.at; web site www.kleinezeitung.at
Circ.: 300,000
CEO – Horst Pirker
Adv. Dir. – Gerhard Valeskini
Reg'l Sales Dir. – Richard Brandstaetter
Circ. Mgr. – Martin Taxa
Ed. in Chief – Erwin Zankel

A-1014 VIENNA

DER STANDARD (6X WK.)
Herrengasse 19-21, A-1014 Vienna, Austria; tel (43) 1 5317 0; fax 5317 0131; e-mail chefredaktion@derstandard.at; web site www.derstandard.at
Pub. – Oscar Bronner

Adv. Mgr. – Robert Beck

A-1015 VIENNA

DIE PRESSE (D)
Parkring 12a, A-1015 Vienna, Austria; tel (43) 1 514 140; fax 5141 4400; web site www.diepresse.at
Circ.: 102,598
Advertising: 11,850 (Euro) - 1 pg b/w; 14,220 (Euro) 1 pg 4C.
Ed. in Chief – Michael Fleischhacker
Mktg. Mgr . – Georg Tfrerer

A-6021 INNSBRUCK

TIROLER TAGESZEITUNG
Ing.-Etzel-Strabe 30, A-6021 Innsbruck, Austria; tel (43) 512 5354 0; fax 5354 3899; e-mail anzeigen@tt.com; web site www.tt.com
Chrmn. – Josef Propst
Chief Exec. – Hermann Petz
Ed. in Chief – Claus Reitan
Deputy Ed. in Chief – Peter Nindler
Deputy Ed. in Chief – Walter Schrott
Deputy Ed. in Chief – Peter Plaikner

BREGENZ, VORARLBERG

NEUE VORARLBERGER TAGESZEITUNG (D-EX MON.)
Arlbergstr. 117, Bregenz, Vorarlberg, 6901, Austria; tel (43) 5574 4090; fax 409300
Circ.: 20,136
No Title – No Name

GRAZ

STEIRERKRONE: NEUE KRONEN ZEITUNG (D)
Muenzgrabens trasse No. 39, Graz, A-8010, Austria; tel (43) 316 78400; fax 713 385; e-mail steirer@kronezeitung.at; web site www.krone.at
Pub. – Hans Dichand
Ed. in Chief – Christoph Biro
Mng. Ed. – W. Baustadter

GRAZ, STYRIA

NEUE ZEIT (D)
Ankerstr. 4, Graz, Styria, 8054, Austria; tel (43) 316
Pub./Ed. in Chief – Josef Riedler
Adv. Dir. – Josef Wawrzyniak

KLAGENFURT

KARNTNER TAGESZEITUNG (M-6X WK.)
Viktringer Ring 28, Klagenfurt, 9020, Austria; tel (43) 463 58660; fax 54121; e-mail redaktions@ktz.at; web site www.kverlag.at
Ed. – Ralf Moser

KARNTNER KRONE: NEUE KRONEN ZEITUNG (D)
Kronetlatz 1, Klagenfurt, 9020, Austria; tel (43) 463 381 5000; web site www.krone.at
Pub. – Hans Dichand

KLEINE ZEITUNG (D)
Funderstr. 1a, Klagenfurt, 9020, Austria; tel (43) 463 58000; fax 580 0313; e-mail kaernten@kleinezeitung.at; web site www.kleinezeitung.at
Circ.: 300,000
Adv. Dir. – Gerhard Valeskini
Ed. in Chief – Reinhold Dottolo
Deputy Ed. in Chief – Adolf Winkler
Services Dir. – Michael Sabath

LINZ

OBEROSTERREICHISCHE RUNDSCHAU (5X WK.)
Hafenstr. 1, Linz, 4010, Austria; tel (43) 732 76160; fax 732 7616; e-mail office@rundschau.co.at; web site www.rundschau.co.at
Circ.: 259,000
Ed. in Chief – Rudolf Chmelir

LINZ, UPPER AUSTRIA

OBEROSTERREICHISCHE NACHRICHTEN (D-EX S)
Promenade 23, Linz, Upper Austria, 4020, Austria; tel (43) 732 780 5333; fax 780 5373; e-mail redaktion@nachrichten.at; web site www.oon.at; www.nachrichten.at
Pub. – R.A. Cuturi

OBEROSTERREICHISCHE NEUE KRONEN ZEITUNG (6X WK.)
Industriezeile 56 b, Linz, Upper Austria, 4020, Austria; tel (43) 732 7805; fax 782 5329; e-mail ooe@kronezeitung.at; web site www.nachrichten.at
Circ.: 238,500
Pub. – H. Dichand
Ed. in Chief – Klaus Herrmann
Mng. Ed. – R. Schmitt

NEUES VOLKSBLATT (6X WK.)
Hafenstr. 1-3, Linz, Upper Austria, 4010, Austria; tel (43) 732 76060; fax 760 6707; e-mail verlagsleitung@volksblatt.at; web site www.volksblatt.at
Circ.: 32,300
CEO – Walter Dipolt
Ed. in chief – Werner Rohrhoser

SALZBURG

SALZBURG KRONE: NEUE KRONEN ZEITUNG (D)
Karolingerstr. 36, Salzburg, 5020, Austria; tel (43) 662 83860; fax 832 490; e-mail salzburg@kronezeitung.de; web site www.krone.at
Circ.: 64,100
Pub. – Hans Dichand
Ed. in Chief – Hans-Peter Hasenorhl
Mng. Ed. – R. Ruess

SALZBURGER VOLKSZEITUNG (D)
Scrannengasse 6, Salzburg, 5020, Austria; tel (43) 662 879 491; fax 8794 9113; e-mail redaktion@svz.at ; aboservice@svz.at; web site www.svz.at
Circ.: 12,030
Ed. in Chief – Helmut Modlhammer

SALZBURG, SALZBURG

SALZBURGER NACHRICHTEN (6X WK.)
Karolingerstr. 40, Salzburg, Salzburg, 5021, Austria; tel (43) 662 837 3301; fax 837 3399; e-mail service@salzburg.com; web site www.salzburg.com
Circ.: 99,123
Pub./Bus. Mgr. – Max Dasch
Mng. Ed. – Gerhard Schwischei
Ed. in Chief – Manfred Perterer

SCHWARZACH

VORARLBERGER NACHRICHTEN (D-EX S)
Gutenberg 1, Schwarzach, 6858, Austria; tel (43) 5572 501 735; fax 501 227; e-mail info@medienhaus.at; web site www.vol.at; www.medienhaus.at
Pub. – Eugen A. Russ
Adv. Mgr. – Nordrag Fthecher

VIENNA

TAGLICH ALLES (D)
Ignaz-Kock-Str. 17, Vienna, 1210, Austria; tel (43) 1 291600; fax 29160622
Pub./Bus. Mgr. – K. Falk
Ed. in Chief – M. Kroll

NEUE KRONENZEITUNG (D)
Muthgasse 2, Vienna, 1190, Austria; tel (43) 1 5210 02401; fax 3601 13541; e-mail krone@krone.at; web site www.krone.at
Pub. – Hans Dichand

KURIER (DS)
Lindengasse 52, Vienna, A-1070, Austria; tel (43) 1 52100; fax 5210 02624; e-mail leser@kurier.at; web site www.kurier.at
Advertising: Publicitas.
Pub. – Thomas Kralinger
Ed. in Chief – Christopher Totanto

AZERBAIJAN

BAKU

ADALAT (D)
Matbuat prospekti, Mahalla 529, Baku, 370146, Azerbaijan; tel (994) 12 380550; fax 651064

AYDINLIG
Bulbul St. 20, Baku, 370014, Azerbaijan; tel (994) 12 (994-12) 937586

AZERBAIJAN (5X WK.)
Metbuat Ave., Block 529, Baku, 370140, Azerbaijan; tel (994) 12 439 4920; fax 438 2087; e-mail azerbaijan_newspaper@azeronline.com; az_reklam@azeronline.com; web site www.azerbaijan.news.az
Ed. in Chief – A. Mustafayev

AZERBAIJAN GANJLARI (3X WK.)
Matbuat prospekti, Mahalla 529, 8th Fl., Baku, 370146, Azerbaijan; tel (994) 12 321 265
Circ.: 161,000
Ed. – Yu A. Kerimov

BAKU
Matbuat prospekti, Mahalla 529, Baku, 370146, Azerbaijan; tel (994) 12 390074

ISTIKLAL (WEEKLY)
28 May St. 3-11, Baku, 370014, Azerbaijan; tel (994) 12 933 378; fax 987 555; e-mail istiklal@ngonet.baku.az
Circ.: 5,000
Ed. – Zardusht Alizadeh

MILLAT
Matbuat prospekti, Mahalla 529, Baku, Azerbaijan; tel (994) 12 323082

MUKHALIFAT (D)
24 Metbuat Ave., Baku, 1073, Azerbaijan; tel (994) 12 439 5952; fax 439 5952; e-mail muxalifet@rambler.ru

RESPUBLIKA (WEEKLY)
Metbuat Ave., Block 529, Baku, 370140, Azerbaijan; tel (994) 12 380114; fax 921905
Circ.: 4,634
Ed. in Chief – T. Ahmadov

SAHAR
Matbuat prospekti, Mahalla 529, Baku, 370146, Azerbaijan; tel (994) 12 385173

BELARUS

MINSK

BELARUSKI RYNOK (WEEKLY)
17 Rabkorovskaya, Minsk, 220007, Belarus; tel (375) 172 228029; fax 228000; e-mail root@belmarket.belpak.minsk.by
Circ.: 20,000
Ed. – V. Chodosovski

BELARUSKI TCHAS (WEEKLY)
21 Masherava Pr-t., Minsk, 220126, Belarus; tel (375) 172 239628; fax 238447
Circ.: 19,500
Ed. – M. Michaltchik

BELORUSSKAYA DELOVAYA GAZETA (2X WK.)
18 Pervomayskaya Vul., Minsk, 220088, Belarus; tel (375) 172 365 051; fax 365 362; e-mail edit@bdg.belpak.minsk.by
Circ.: 20,000
Ed. – P. Martsev

BELORUSSKAYA GAZETA (2X WK.)
17a Kalvariskaya Vul., Minsk, 220035, Belarus; tel (375) 172 232 640; fax 204 050; e-mail dima@gazetbel.belpak.minsk.by
Circ.: 15,000
Ed. – A. Valvatchov

BELORUSSKAYA NIVA (5X WK.)
vul. B Hmyalnitskaga 10A, Minsk, 220013, Belarus; tel (375) 172 232 3962; fax 268 2643
Circ.: 80,000
Ed. – E. Semashko

CHYRVONAYA ZMENA (4X WK.)
vul. B Hmyalnitskaga 10A, Minsk, 220013, Belarus; tel (375) 172 2322103; fax 2322103
Circ.: 43,900
Ed. – A. Karlukievich

NARODNAYA HAZETA (5X WK.)
vul. B Hmyalnitskaga 10A, Minsk, 220013, Belarus; tel (375) 17 287 1870; fax 287 1870; e-mail veche@ng-daily.by; web site www.ng.by
Circ.: 259,597
Ed. in Chief – Vladimir Vladimirovich

NARODNAYA VOLYA (5X WK.)
34a Engelsa Vul., Minsk, 220030, Belarus; tel (375) 17 206 6156; fax 206 6904; e-mail nv@promedia.by
Circ.: 60,000
Ed. – Iosif Syaredzitch

RESPUBLIKA (5X WK.)
vul. B Hmyalnitskaga 10A, Minsk, 220013, Belarus; tel (375) 172 2682612; fax 2682615; e-mail root@republ.belpak.minsk.by
Circ.: 130,000
Ed. – Sergey Dubovik

SELYSKAYA GAZETA (6X WK.)
77 Leninski Prosp., Minsk, 220041, Belarus; tel (375) 172
Ed. – L.K. Tolkatch

SOVETSKAYA BELORUSSIYA (5X WK.)
vul. B Hmyalnitskaga 10A, Minsk, 220013, Belarus; tel (375) 172 2321432; fax 2321451; e-mail sb@sovbel.belpak.minsk.by
Circ.: 330,000
Ed. – Pavel Yakubovich

SVABODA
56 Ivanovskaya Vul., Minsk, 220088, Belarus; tel (375) 172 362441; fax 362441
Circ.: 90,000
Ed. – I. Germenchuk

VECHERNII MINSK (5X WK.)
Nezavisimosti 44, Minsk, 220005, Belarus;

tel (375) 17 284 5044; fax 276 8005; e-mail vm@nsys.by; web site www.newsvm.com
Circ.: 111,000
Ed. – S. Sverkunou

ZNAMYA YUNOSTI (5X WK.)
ul. B Hmelnitskogo 10A, 9-y etazh, Minsk, 220013, Belarus; tel (375) 17 287 1684; fax 287 1547
Circ.: 30,000
Ed. in Chief – Igor Gukovski

ZVYAZDA (5X WK.)
vul. B Hmyalnitskaga 10A, Minsk, 220013, Belarus; tel (375) 172 232 3892; fax 268 2783; e-mail reklama@zvyazda.minsk.by; web site www.zvyazda.minsk.by
Circ.: 90,000
Ed. – Uladizimir B. Narkevich

BELGIUM

1000 BRUSSELS

LE SOIR (D-EX S)
rue Royale 100, 1000 Brussels, Belgium; tel (32) 2 225 5432; fax 225 5914; e-mail internet@lesoir.be; web site www.lesoir.be
Advertising: Publicitas.
Pres. – Patrick Hubrain

LA LIBRE BELGIQUE (D)
Blvd. Emile Jacqmain, 127, 1000 Brussels, Belgium; tel (32) 2 744 4444; fax 211 2783; e-mail llb.redaction@saipm.com; web site www.lalibre.be
Ed. in Chief – Jean-Paul Marthoz
Assoc. Ed. in Chief – Jean-Paul Duchateau

DE MORGEN (6X WK.)
Erguimtaai 29, 1000 Brussels, Belgium; tel (32) 2 556 6811; fax 520 3515; e-mail info@demorgen.be; web site www.demorgen.be
Circ.: 70,000
Ed. – Bart Van Doorne

1730 KOBBEGEM

HET LAATSTE NIEUWS (6X WK.)
Brusselsesteenweg 347, 1730 Kobbegem, Belgium; tel (32) 2 454 2831; fax 454 2831; e-mail redactie.hln@persgroep.be; web site www.hln.be
Adv. Contact – Patrick Van Waeyenberge
Mng. Ed. – Paul Daenen

2050 ANTWERP

GAZET VAN ANTWERPEN (D)
Katwilgweg 2, 2050 Antwerp, Belgium; tel (32) 3 210 0210; fax 210 3018; web site www.gva.be
Adv. Rep. – Ingrid De Vocht
Adv. Rep. – Heidi Saenen
Adv. Rep. – Chantal Jannsens
Ed. in Chief – Pascal Kerkhove
Ed. – Jan Mulleman

3500 HASSELT

HET BELANG VAN LIMBURG (6X WK.)
Herckenrodesingel 10, 3500 Hasselt, Belgium; tel (32) 1 187 8111; fax 187 8204; e-mail hbvlsecretariaat@concentra.be; web site www.hbvl.be
Circ.: 100,980
Project Mgr. – Marcel Grauls
Ed. – Izo Zindetertthoze Kerckhoze

ANTWERP

GAZET VAN ANTWERPEN (D)
Katwilgweg 2, Antwerp, 2050, Belgium; tel (32) 3 210 0210; fax 210 3018; e-mail gvainfocenter@concentra.be; web site www.gva.be
Adv.Mgr. – Vadeenna Debrdder
Ed. in Chief – Luc Rademakers

GAZET VAN ANTWERPEN (D)
Katwilgweg 2, Antwerp, 2050, Belgium; tel (32) 3210 0210; fax 3219 4041; web site www.gva.be
Circ.: 177,898
Ed. in Chief – Luc Rademakers

HET LAATSTE NIEUWS (D)
Regnknaai 26-27, Antwerp, 2000, Belgium; tel (32) 3 212 1330; web site www.hln.be
Gen. Mgr. – Leo De Nijn

LE LLOYD (D-EX MON.) EST. 1858
Jan van Gentstraat 1 box 102, Antwerp, 2000, Belgium; tel (32) 3 234 0550; fax 234 2593; e-mail info@lloyd.be; web site www.lloyd.be
Dir. – Michel Schuuring

ANTWERP, ANTWERP

DE ANTWERPSE MORGEN (D)
Leopoldstraat 10, Antwerp, Antwerp, 2000, Belgium; tel (32) 3233 1708; fax 3233 3574
Circ.: 52,000

HET VOLK/DE NIEUWE GIDS (D)
Aalmoezenierstraat 14-16, Antwerp, Antwerp, 2000, Belgium; tel (32) 3226 2590; fax 3226 4529
Ed. in Chief – Luc Martens

HET LAATSTE NIEUWS (D)
Rynkaai 2627, Antwerp, Antwerp, 2000, Belgium; tel (32) 3212 1348; fax 3212 1300; web site www.hln.be
Contact – Philippe Truyts

ANTWERPEN

GAZET VON ANTWERPEN (6X WK.)
Katwilgweg 2, Antwerpen, 2050, Belgium; tel (32) 2 210 02 10; e-mail gvaredactie@concentro.be; web site www.gva.be
Ed. in Chief – Pascal Kerkhov

ARLON, LUXEMBURG

L'AVENIR DU LUXEMBOURG (D)
38 rue des Deportes, Arlon, Luxemburg, 6700, Belgium; tel (32) 6322 0349; fax 6322 0516
Circ.: 139,960
Dir./Ed. in Chief – Jean-Luc Henquinet

LA MEUSE-LUXEMBOURG (D)
Pl. Leopold 5-6, Arlon, Luxemburg, 6700, Belgium; tel (32) 6320 375; fax 6317 754
Pub. – Michel Fromont
Ed. in Chief – Wally Meurens

LE SOIR (D)
Rue Saint-Donat 30, Arlon, Luxemburg, 6700, Belgium; tel (32) 6323 516; fax 6328 275
Pub. – Annie Gaspard

BAGAARDEN

HET VOLK (D)
Gossetlaan 30 Brootig, Bagaarden, 1702, Belgium; tel (32) 467 2749; fax 466 3093; e-mail nvcrebactie@nieuwsblad.be; web site www.nieuwsblad.be

Ed. – Dirk Remmerie

BERCHEM, ANTWERP

DE NIEUWE GAZET (D)
5 Posthhoflei, Berchem, Antwerp, 2600, Belgium; tel (32) 3286 8930; fax 3286 8940
Circ.: 306,240
Ed. in Chief – Marcel Wilmet

BOUGE

VERS L'AVENIR (6X WK.)
Houte de Hannut. 38, Bouge, 5004, Belgium; tel (32) 8124 8811; fax 8122 6024; web site www.actu24.be
Circ.: 139,960
Ed. – Pascal Belpaire

BRUGES, W. FLANDERS ST.

GAZET VAN ANTWERPEN (D)
Geerwijnstratt 22, Bruges, W. Flanders St., 8000, Belgium; tel (32) 5033 5253; fax 5033 5253

BRUGES, WEST FLANDERS

HET LAATSTE NIEUWS (D)
Vlamingstraat 62, Bruges, West Flanders, 8000, Belgium; tel (32) 5033 6883; fax 5033 1721

HET VOLK (D)
Nieuwstraat 7, Bruges, West Flanders, 8000, Belgium; tel (32) 50 337278; fax 342226

BRUSSEL

DE FINANCIEEL ECONOMISCHE TIJD (M-5X WK.)
Havenlaan 86C Bus 309, Brussel, 1000, Belgium; tel (32) 2 423 1611; fax 423 1610; e-mail info@detyjd.be; web site www.detyjd.be
Circ.: 50,000
CEO – Dirk Verghe
Pub. – De Persjroep

BRUSSELS

L'ECHO (6X WK.)
Avenue du port 86 C Boite 309, Brussels, 1000, Belgium; tel (32) 2 423 1611; fax 423 1610; e-mail info@lecho.be; web site www.lecho.be
Ed. in Chief – Fredrick Delaplace

LA DERNIERE HEURE (D)
79 Rue Des Francs, Brussels, 1040, Belgium; tel (32) 6922 1093; fax 6922 1094; e-mail dhnet@saipm.com; web site www.dhnet.be
Circ.: 100,000
Dir. – Francois Le Hodey
Ed. in Chief – Ralph Vankrinkelveldt

LE SOIR (6X WK.)
100 rue Royale, Brussels, 1000, Belgium; tel (32) 2225 5555; fax 2225 5914; web site www.lesoir.be
Pres. – Patrick Hurbain
Mktg. Mgr. – Oliver Simonis

LA DERNIERE HEURE-LES SPORTS (D)
Blvd. Emile Jacqmain, 127, Brussels, 1000, Belgium; tel (32) 2 744 4455; e-mail dhnet@saipm.com; web site www.dhnet.be
Circ.: 73,130
Dir. – Francois Le Hodey
Mng. Ed. – Eric Valentin

BRUSSELS, BRABANT

DE NIEUWE GIDS (D)
Koningsstraat 105, Brussels, Brabant, 1000, Belgium; tel (32) 2218 5605; fax 2218 5906
Circ.: 171,350
Dir. – E. Kornttheuer
Ed. in Chief – Konel Olnthierens

DE FINANCIEEL EKONOMISCHE TYJD (D)
Pl. St. Lazare 2, bte 6, Brussels, Brabant, 1210, Belgium; tel (32) 2217 2205; fax 2217 0976

HET BELANG VAN LIMBURG (D)
Kunstlaan 3, Brussels, Brabant, 1210, Belgium; tel (32) 2 227 9310; web site www.hbvl.be
Ed. – Ivo Van de Kerkhove

HET BELGISCH SLAATSBLAD (D)
Leiwenseweg 40-42, Brussels, Brabant, 1000, Belgium; tel (32) 2512 0026; fax 2511 0184

LA CAPITALE (D)
120 rue Royale, Brussels, Brabant, 1000, Belgium; tel (32) 2 225 5600; fax 225 5913; web site www.sudpresse.be; www.rossel.be
Circ.: 129,840
Dir. Gen. – Didier Hamann
Dir. – Dernarg Marchand

LA MEUSE/LA LANTERNE/LA NOUVELLE GAZETTE
Pl. de Louvain 21, Brussels, Brabant, 1000, Belgium; tel (32) 2218 2100; fax 2217 8149
Pub. – Michel Fromont
Ed. in Chief – Benoit Degardin

LE COURRIER DE LA BOURSE/ LA COTE LIBRE (D)
Rue de Birmingham 131, 3rd Fl., Brussels, Brabant, 1070, Belgium; tel (32) 2526 5666; fax 2526 5526
Circ.: 7,000
Dir./Ed. in Chief – O. De Beauffort

LE JOURNAL ET INDEPENDENCE (D)
Blvd. Emile Jacqmain 79, Brussels, Brabant, 1000, Belgium; tel (32) 2

LE MONITEUR BELGE (D)
Rue de Louvain 40-42, Brussels, Brabant, 1000, Belgium; tel (32) 2 552 2211; fax 511 0184; e-mail info@just.fgov.be; web site ^www.just.fgov.be
Dir. – B. Van Damme
Adv. Mgr. – Wilfried Verrezen

CHARLEROI

LE RAPPEL (D)
Boulevard Tirou, 203, Charleroi, 6000, Belgium; tel (32) 0715 32930; fax 0715 32938; e-mail infoal@actu24.be; web site www.actu24.be
Circ.: 10,000
Dir. – Jacques de Thysebaert
Ed. in Chief – Carl van Doorne

CHARLEROI, HAINAULT

LA NOUVELLE GAZETTE (D)
2 quai de Flandre, Charleroi, Hainault, 6000, Belgium; tel (32) 71 276 411; fax 276 567; e-mail gazette@charline.be; web site www.lanouvellegazette.be
Circ.: 94,600
MD – Patrick Hurbain
Ed. – M. Frohont

LE JOURNAL ET INDEPENDENCE/LE PEUPLE
Rue du College 18, Charleroi, Hainault, 6000, Belgium; tel (32) 7131 0190; fax 7133 1650

Circ.: 94,600
Dir./Ed. in Chief – Jean Guy
Gen. Mgr. – C. Renard

LE SOIR
Blvd. Tirou 203, bte 9, Charleroi, Hainault, 6000, Belgium; tel (32) 7132 7916; fax 7132 0593
Administrator – Olivier Collot

EUPEN, LIEGE

GRENZ-ECHO (6X WK.)
8 Marktplatz, Eupen, Liege, 4700, Belgium; tel (32) 8759 1300; fax 0877 43820; e-mail info@grenzecho.be; web site www.grenze-cho.be
Circ.: 12,040
Mng. Ed. – Alfred Kuchenberg

GENT, EAST FLANDERS

DE NIEUWE GIDS
Forelstraat 22, Gent, East Flanders, 9000, Belgium; tel (32) 9265 6111; fax 9225 2071

HET LAASTSTE NIEUWS
Kouter 19-25, Gent, East Flanders, 9000, Belgium; tel (32) 9225 6711; fax 9224 0935
No Title – No Name

GHENT, EAST FLANDERS

DE GENTENAAR (D)
102 Lousbergskaai, Ghent, East Flanders, 9000, Belgium; tel (32) 9265 6851; fax 9265 6850; e-mail gentenaar@vum.be; web site www.corelio.be
Circ.: 372,410
Gen. Dir. – Guido Verdeyen
Ed. in Chief – Pol Van den Driessche

GOSSELIES, HAINAULT

LE JOURNAL ET INDEPENDENCE (D)
Ave. des Etats Units 7, Gosselies, Hainault, 6200, Belgium; tel (32)

GROOT BIJGAARDEN

DE STANDAARD (6X WK.)
30 Gossetlaan, Groot Bijgaarden, 1702, Belgium; tel (32) 2 467 2211; fax 466 3299; e-mail standaard@corelio.be; web site www.standaard.be
Circ.: 100,000
Pub. – Vert Sturvvagen
Ed. in Chief – Peter Vandermeersch
Adv. Mgr. – Christine Van den Berghe

HET NIEUWSBLAD/DE GENTENAAR (D)
30 Gossetlaan, Groot Bijgaarden, 1702, Belgium; tel (32) 2 467 2211; fax 467 2696; e-mail nieuwsblad@vum.be; web site www.nieuwsblad.be
Finance Mgr. – Peter Boon
Adv. Mgr. – Christine Van de Berghe
Ed. in Chief – Peter Vandermeersch
Assoc. Ed. in Chief – Bart Sturtewagin
Mktg. Mgr . – Mia Venken

GROOT-BIJGAARDEN

HET VOLK (D)
Gossetlaan 28, Groot-Bijgaarden, 1702, Belgium; tel (32) 2 467 2247; fax 466 5946; e-mail nbantwerpen@nieuwsblad.be; web site www.hetvolk.be
Adv. Mgr. – Peter Vhndermeersth
Ed. in Chief – Dirk Remmerie

HASSELT, LIMBURG

HET LAATSTE NIEUWS (D)
Koningin Astridlaan 7, Hasselt, Limburg, 3500, Belgium; tel (32) 1122 1214
Pub. – Theo Claes

HUY, LIEGE

LA MEUSE (D)
Rue des Brasseurs 17, Huy, Liege, 4500, Belgium; tel (32) 8521 1536; fax 8523 5140
Pub. – Michel Fromont
Ed. in Chief – Wally Meurens

VERS L'AVENIR (6X WK.)
Quai de Namur,2, Huy, Liege, 4500, Belgium; tel (32) 8521 4911; web site www.actu24.be
Gen. Mgr. – Ch. Dodet

KORTRIJK, WEST FLANDERS

GAZET VAN ANTWERPEN (D)
Louis Verweestraat 4, Kortrijk, West Flanders, 8500, Belgium; tel (32) 5621 1751; fax 5620 1580

HET LAATSTE NIEUWS (D)
Vlasmarkt 18, Kortrijk, West Flanders, 8500, Belgium; tel (32) 2454 2484; web site www.hln.be

HET VOLK (D)
Budastraat 17, Kortrijk, West Flanders, 8500, Belgium; tel (32) 5622 4001; fax 5620 1664

LA LOUVIERE, HAINAULT

LA NOUVELLE GAZETTE (D)
Rue Hamoir 65, La Louviere, Hainault, 7100, Belgium; tel (32) 6422 3197
Pub. – Patrick Hurbain
Dir. – Philippe Dautez
Ed. in Chief – Andre Thioux

LIEGE

LA GAZETTE DE LIEGE (6X WK.)
26-28 Blvd. d`Avroy, Liege, 4000, Belgium; tel (32) 4223 1933; fax 4290 0481; e-mail llb.gazettedeliege@llb.be; web site www.lalibre.be
Circ.: 80,140
Ed. – Paul Vaute

LIEGE, LIEGE

LA MEUSE (D)
8-12 Blvd. de la Sauveniere, Liege, Liege, 4000, Belgium; tel (32) 4220 0840; fax 4220 0859; e-mail maredliege.lameuse@sudpresse.be; web site www.sudpresse.be
Circ.: 73,000
Gen. Mgr. – Ericsson Brodt
Ed. – Thirrw Delhawe

LA DERNIERE HEURE (D)
26 Blvd. d'Avroy, Liege, Liege, 4000, Belgium; tel (32) 4222 1830; fax 4223 1588; e-mail dh.redecteion@dh.be; web site www.dhnet.be
– Jean Michel Crestin
– Hubert LarcclartGen. Mgr.s

LA WALLONIE (D)
Rue de la Regence 55, Liege, Liege, 4000, Belgium; tel (32) 4 201811; fax 2233117
Circ.: 48,200
Pub. – Rene Piron
Ed. in Chief – Fabrice Jacquemart

LE SOIR
Rue de Bex 15, Liege, Liege, 4000, Belgium; tel (32) 4 224 697; fax 235 929
Gen. Mgr. – Guy Depas

VERS L'AVENIR
26 Blvd. d'Avroy, Liege, Liege, 4000, Belgium; tel (32) 4 233626; fax 233490
Ed. in Chief – Yvon Lambert

MAASMECHELEN, LIMBURG

HET BELANG VAN LIMBURG-DE WEEKKRANT-JET MAGAZINE (D)
Rijksweg 404, Maasmechelen, Limburg, 3630, Belgium; tel (32) 8976 4319; fax 8976 7032

MARCHE-EN-FAMENNE, LUXEMBURG

LA MEUSE LUXEMBOURG (D)
Rue de Luxembourg 54, Marche-en-Famenne, Luxemburg, 6900, Belgium; tel (32) 8432 1232; fax 8431 6559

L'AVENIR DU LUXEMBOURG (D)
Pl. Roi Albert 9, Marche-en-Famenne, Luxemburg, 6900, Belgium; tel (32) 8431 1913; fax 8431 5439; web site www.actu24.be
Gen. Mgr. – Daneal Laprelle

MONS, HAINAULT

L'ECHO DU CENTRE
Pl. du Marche aux Herbes 11-12, Mons, Hainault, 7000, Belgium; tel (32) 6534 8304; fax 6534 7368
Dir./Ed. in Chief – Andre Farine

LA PROVINCE (D)
29 rue des Capucins, Mons, Hainault, 7000, Belgium; tel (32) 6531 7151; fax 6533 8477
Dir. – Philippe Dautez
Ed. in Chief – Benoit Degardin

LE JOURNAL DE MONS (D)
Pl. du Marche aux Herbes 11-12, Mons, Hainault, 7000, Belgium; tel (32) 6534 8304; fax 6534 7368
Dir./Ed. in Chief – Andre Farine

NORD-ECLAIR BELGE (D)
Pl. du Marche aux Herbes 11-12, Mons, Hainault, 7000, Belgium; tel (32) 6534 8304; fax 6534 7368
Dir./Ed. in Chief – Andre Farine

MOUSCRON, HAINAULT

NORD-ECLAIR (D)
Grand Pl. 32, Mouscron, Hainault, 7700, Belgium; tel (32) 5634 1472; fax 5633 5476
Circ.: 43,880
Dir./Ed. in Chief – Andre Farine

NAMUR

LE SOIR
Rue Julie Billiart 21, bte 5, Namur, 5000, Belgium; tel (32) 81 (32-81) 231703; fax 231 768
Information Chief – Pierre Hermans

NAMUR, NAMUR

DE STANDAARD (D)
Rue LeliUvre 8, Namur, Namur, 5000, Belgium; tel (32) 8122 4418; fax 8122 1872

LA LANTERNE/LA PROVINCE
Quai de Meuse 25, Jambes, Namur, Namur, 5100, Belgium; tel (32) 8130 8989; fax 8130 8832
Pub. – Michel Fromont
Dir./Ed. in Chief – Jean-Pierre Vandermeuse

LA MEUSE
Quai de Meuse 25, Jambes, Namur, Namur, 5100, Belgium; tel (32) 8130 9494; fax 8130 9468
Pub. – Michel Fromont
Ed. in Chief – Wally Meurens

LA NOUVELLE GAZETTE (D)
Quai de Meuse 25, Jambes, Namur, Namur, 5100, Belgium; tel (32) 81 309292; fax 309468
Pub. – Edith Heye

NIVELLES, BRABANT

LA NOUVELLE GAZETTE (D)
Rue de l'Eveche 12, Nivelles, Brabant, 1400, Belgium; tel (32) 6722 0353; fax 6721 1070
Gen. Dir. – Patrick Hurbain
Dir. – Philippe Dautez
Ed. in Chief – Andre Thioux

OSTENDE, WEST FLANDERS

HET LAATSTE NIEUWS (D)
Ooststraat 42B, bte 7, Ostende, West Flanders, 8400, Belgium; tel (32) 5950 3747; fax 5933 1721
Pub. – A. Vollmacher

PHILIPPEVILLE, NAMUR

LA NOUVELLE GAZETTE (D)
Rue du Corbeau, bte 91, Philippeville, Namur, 5600, Belgium; tel (32) 7166 7747; fax 7166 7427
Pub. – Patrick Hurbain
Dir. – Philippe Dautez
Ed. in Chief – Andre Thioux
Ed. – Michel Fromont

VERS L'AVENIR E.S.M.
Pl. d'Armes 11, Philippeville, Namur, 5600, Belgium; tel (32) 7166 6949
Pub. – Bruno Malter

ROULERS, WEST FLANDERS

HET VOLK/DE NIEUWE GIDS (D)
Noordstraat 6, Roulers, West Flanders, 8800, Belgium; tel (32)

SAINT HUBERT, LIEGE

HET LAATSTE NIEUWS (D)
Mercatorstraat 7, Saint Hubert, Liege, Belgium; tel (32)

SAINT NICOLAS, EAST FLANDERS

GAZET VAN ANTWERPEN (D)
Mercatorstraat 75-77, Saint Nicolas, East Flanders, 9100, Belgium; tel (32) 3766 3636; fax 3777 8417
Gen. Mgr. – Rita Van Meir

SAINT VITH, LIEGE

GRENZ-ECHO (5X WK.)
Hauptstr. 91, Saint Vith, Liege, 4780, Bel-

gium; tel (32) 8022 8676; fax 8022 6591; e-mail info@grenzecho.be; web site www.grenzecho.be
MD – Alfred Kuchenberg

TOURNAI, HAINAULT

NORD-ECLAIR BELGE (D)
Rue des Puits-l'Eau 10, Tournai, Hainault, 7500, Belgium; tel (32) 6922 8171; fax 6923 3392; web site www.nordeclair.be; tournai.nordeclair.be
Pub. – Jean-Pierre De Rouck

LE COURRIER DE L'ESCAUT (6X WK.)
10 rue Paris, Tournai, Hainault, 7500, Belgium; tel (32) 6988 9620; fax 6988 9660
Circ.: 25,000
Ed. – John Derouck

VERVIERS, HEUSY

LE JOUR/LE COURRIER (D)
Avenue de Spa n 87, Verviers, Heusy, 4802, Belgium; tel (32) 8732 2090; fax 8732 2089; e-mail infolj@actu24.be; web site www.votrejournal.be
Circ.: 15,000
Ed. in Chief – Claude Gillet
Ed., Le Courrier – Jean-Pierre De Rouck

VERVIERS, LIEGE

LA MEUSE (D)
Boulevard de la Sauveni□re, 38, Verviers, Liege, 4000, Belgium; tel (32) 4220 0840; fax 4220 0859
Ed. in Chief – Michel Royer

WAVRE, BRABANT

LE SOIR (6X WK.)
Rue Barbier 12B, Wavre, Brabant, 1300, Belgium; tel (32) 1024 2775; fax 1024 2579; e-mail redaction.wavre @lesoir.be; web site ^www.lesoir.be
Mgr. – Jean-Philippe de Vogelaere
Ed. – Didier Hamann

VERS L'AVENIR (D)
Ch□e de Louvain 9, Wavre, Brabant, 1300, Belgium; tel (32) 1084 9800; fax 1084 9819; e-mail infobw@verslavenir.be; infobw@actu24.be; web site www.actu24.be
Ed. – Andre-Marie Douillet

BOSNIA

SARAJEVO

OSLOBODJENJE (D)
Dzemala Bijedica 185, Sarajevo, 71000, Bosnia; tel (387) 33 467 723; e-mail redaction@oslobodjenje.ba; web site www.oslobodjenje.ba
Circ.: 56,000
Ed. in Chief – Veldana Saoenvagovec
Adv. Mgr. – Meliha Hodzic

VECERNJE NOVINE (D)
Pruscakova St. 13, Sarajevo, 71000, Bosnia; tel (387) 33 664874; fax 664875
Circ.: 15,000
Exec. Ed. – Berin Ekmecic
Ed. in Chief – Feto Ramovic

BULGARIA

BLAGOEVGRAD

PIRINSKO DELO (D)
19 Assen Khristove St., Blagoevgrad, 2700, Bulgaria; tel (359) 23736; fax 23106
Circ.: 20,000
Ed. in Chief – Katya Z. Catkova

BURGAS

CHERNOMORSKY FAR (M-EX S)
9 Milin Kamak St., Burgas, 8000, Bulgaria; tel (359) 56 42396; fax 42396
Circ.: 37,000
Ed. in Chief – Galentin Vlahov

LOVECH

NOV GLAS (D)
24 G Dimitrov St., 3rd Flr., Lovech, 5500, Bulgaria; tel (359) 68 22242
Circ.: 50,000
Ed. in Chief – Venetsii Georgiev

PLOVDIV

MARITZA (D)
PO Box 27; PO Box 348, Plovdiv, 4000, Bulgaria; tel (359) 32 268434; fax 274760
Circ.: 40,000
Ed. in Chief – Spass Vassilev

OTECHESTVEN GLAS (D)
9 Krakra St., Plovdiv, 4000, Bulgaria; tel (359) 32 226740
Circ.: 100,000
Ed. in Chief – Mihail Milchev

RAZGRAD

VAZKHOD (D)
3 Dondukov St., Razgrad, Bulgaria; tel (359)
Circ.: 45,000

SOFIA

ZEMEDELSKO ZNAME (M)
23 Yanko Zabunov St., Sofia, 1000, Bulgaria; tel (359) 2 873851; fax 874535
Circ.: 178,000

BULGARSKA ARMIYA (D)
PO Box 629, Sofia, 1080, Bulgaria; tel (359) 2 874793; fax 9879126
Circ.: 30,000
Ed. in Chief – Vladi Vladkov

TRUD (M)
52 Kniyas Dondukov Blvd., Sofia, 1000, Bulgaria; tel (359) 2 942 2059; fax 943 3940; e-mail trud@zgb.bg; sofia@zgb.bg; web site www.trud.bg
Circ.: 200,000
Ed. in Chief – Tosho Toshev

DUMA (6X WK.)
Blvd. Tzarigradsko Shosse 47, Sofia, 1000, Bulgaria; tel (359) 2 970 5220; fax 975 2604; web site www.duma.bg
Circ.: 130,000
Ed. – Evgeny Stantchev
Ed. in Chief – Yuri Borisov

OTECHESTVEN VESTNIK (M)
47 Tzarigradsko Shosse Blvd., Sofia, 1000, Bulgaria; tel (359) 2 (359-2) 43431; fax (359-2) 463108
Circ.: 16,000
Ed. in Chief – Konstance Anschva

PODKREPA (D)
37 Ekzarkh Yosif St., Sofia, 1000, Bulgaria; tel (359) 2 831227; fax 467374
Circ.: 18,000

DEMOKRATSIYA (M)
134 Rakovski St., Sofia, 1000, Bulgaria; tel (359) 2 9812979; fax 9807342
Circ.: 45,000
Ed. in Chief – Neven Kopandanova

VECHERNI NOVINI (E-EX S)
47 Tzarigradsko Shosse Blvd., Sofia, 1000, Bulgaria; tel (359) 2 441469; fax 467365
Circ.: 35,000
Ed. in Chief – Lyubomir Kolarov
Dir. – Georgi Ganchev

ZEMYA (D)
18 11th August St., Sofia, 1000, Bulgaria; tel (359) 2 885033; fax 835227
Circ.: 53,000
Ed. in Chief – Kosta Andreev

VARNA

NARODNO DELO (D)
St. Br. Miladinovi 68, Varna, 9000, Bulgaria; tel (359) 52 663 603; fax 615 080; e-mail office@narodnodelo.bg; web site www.narodnodelo.bg
Circ.: 56,000
Ed. in Chief – Angel Petrichev

CROATIA

OSIJEK

GLAS SLAVONIJE (D)
Hrvatske Republike 20, Osijek, 31000, Croatia; tel (385) 31 223 200; fax 223 203; e-mail glas@glas-slavonije.tel.hr; web site www.glas-slavonije.hr
Circ.: 25,000
Ed. in Chief – Damir Regorvic

RIJEKA

NOVI LIST (D)
PO Box 130, Rijeka, 51000, Croatia; tel (385) 51 650 011; fax 672 114; e-mail redakcija@novilist.hr; web site www.novilist.hr
Circ.: 60,000
Dir. – Natasha Mijacika
Ed. in Chief – Ivica Dikic
Ed. – Goran Kukic

LA VOCE DEL POPOLO (D)
Zvonimirova 20a, Rijeka, 51000, Croatia; tel (385) 51 672 153; fax 672 151; e-mail lavoce@edit.hr; web site www.edit.hr
Circ.: 4,000
Ed. – Selveo Sorza

SPLIT

NEDJELJNA DALMACIJA (WEEKLY)
Gunduliceva 23, Split, 21000, Croatia; tel (385) 21 362 821; fax 362 526
Circ.: 45,000
Ed. – Drazen Gudic

ZAGREB

SPORTSKE NOVOSTI (M)
Slavonska Ave. 4, Zagreb, 10000, Croatia; tel (385) 1 341 920; fax 341 950
Circ.: 55,000
Ed. – Darko Tironi

VECERNJI LIST (M)
Slavonska Ave. 4, Zagreb, 10000, Croatia; tel (385) 1 630 0444; fax 630 0676; e-mail redakcija@vecernji.net; web site www.vecernji.hr
Circ.: 200,000
Ed. in Chief – Goran Ogurlic

CYPRUS

LATSIA

ALITHIA (M)
PO Box 12669, Latsia, 2252, Cyprus; tel (357) 2 276 3040; fax 276 3945; web site www.alithia.cy
Circ.: 11,000
Advisor – Alekos Konstantinidis

NICOSIA

AGON (D)
PO Box 1417, Nicosia, Cyprus; tel (357) 2 477182; fax 457887
Circ.: 5,000
Dir. – Leonidas Koshis
Pub. – Nicos Koshis

HARAVGHI (M)
Ezekias Papaioannou 4, Nicosia, 1075, Cyprus; tel (357) 22 766 666; fax 765 154; web site www.haravgi.com.cy
Circ.: 9,000
Ed. in Chief – Androulla Giiouros

CYPRUS MAIL (6X WK.)
PO Box 21144, Nicosia, 1502, Cyprus; tel (357) 2281 8585; fax 2267 6385; e-mail editor@cyprus-mail.com; web site www.cyprus-mail.com
Ed. – Jean Christou

CYPRUS WEEKLY
PO Box 4977, Nicosia, Cyprus; tel (357) 2 666047; fax 668665
Circ.: 15,000
Dir. – Georges der Parthogh
Dir. – Alex Efthyvoulos
Dir. – A. Hadjipapas
Ed. in Chief – Martyn Henry

YENI DEMOKRAT
1 Cengiz Han Cad., Koskluciftlik, Nicosia, Cyprus; tel (357) 2 281485; fax 272558
Circ.: 450
Ed. – Mustafa Okan

SIMERINI (6X WK.)
PO Box 1836, Nicosia, Cyprus; tel (357) 2258 0580; fax 2258 0570; web site www.simerini.com.cy
Circ.: 9,000
MD – Kostas Hadjikostis
Ed. in Chief – George Giorgios

APOGEVMATINI (D)
PO Box 5603, Nicosia, Cyprus; tel (357) 2 353603; fax 353223
Circ.: 8,000
Dir. – Efthymios Hadjiefthimiou
Dir. – Antonis Stavrides
Ed. in Chief – Alkis Andreou

TA NEA (WEEKLY)
PO Box 4349, Nicosia, Cyprus; tel (357) 2

476575; fax 476512
Circ.: 3,000
Ed. in Chief – Phytos Socratous

VIMA TIS KYPROU (M)
PO Box 3356, Nicosia, Cyprus; tel (357) 2 496411; fax 496790
Circ.: 3,000
Dir. – George Eliades
Ed. in Chief – Costakis Antoniou
Ed. in Chief – Babis Vatis

ERGATIKO VIMA (WEEKLY)
PO Box 21185, Nicosia, 1514, Cyprus; tel (357) 22 349400
Circ.: 15,000

OFFICIAL GAZETTE (WEEKLY)
Printing Office of the Republic of Cyprus, Nicosia, Cyprus; tel (357) 2 302 202; fax 303 175

HALKIN SESI (M)
172 Kyrenia Sok., Nicosia, Cyprus; tel (357) 2 273141
Circ.: 6,000
Ed. – Akay Cemal

THE CYPRUS FINANCIAL MIRROR (WEEKLY)
PO Box 4280, Nicosia, 2007, Cyprus; tel (357) 2 495790; fax 495907
Circ.: 3,500
– Masis der Parthogh
– Shavasb BohdjalianDir.s

KYPROS
PO Box 4349, Nicosia, 1096, Cyprus; tel (357) 2 451000; fax 448299
Circ.: 800
Pub./Dir. – George Aristidou
Ed. in Chief – George Constantinou

ERGATIKI PHONI (WEEKLY)
PO Box 5018, Nicosia, Cyprus; tel (357) 22 441142; fax 476360
Circ.: 10,000
Dir. – Michalakis Ioannou
Ed. in Chief – Xenis Xenofontos

PARASKINIO (WEEKLY)
39 Kennedy Ave., Nicosia, Cyprus; tel (357) 2 313334; fax 314193
Circ.: 3,000
Dir./Ed. in Chief – D. Michael

PHILELEFTHEROS (D)
PO Box 21094, Nicosia, 1501, Cyprus; tel (357) 2274 4000; fax 2259 0122; e-mail mailbox@phileleftheros.com; philenewslive@phileleftheros.com; web site www.phileleftheros.com
Circ.: 26,000
MD – Nicole Pattichis
Gen. Mgr. – Michael Karis
Dir., Sales/Mktg. – Renos Onoufriou
Ed. in Chief – Takis Kounnafis

ORTAM (M)
158A Girne Cad, Nicosia, Cyprus; tel (357) 2 274872
Circ.: 1,250
Ed. – Ozal Ziya

BIRLIK (M)
PK 841, Nicosia, Cyprus; tel (357) 2 272959; fax 283959
Circ.: 4,500
Ed. – Lutfi Ozter

YENI DUZEN (M)
Yeni Sanayi Sok., Nicosia, Cyprus; tel (357) 256658; fax 253240; e-mail yeniduze@northcyprus.net
Circ.: 1,000
Ed. – Ozkan Yorgancioglu

VATAN
unknown, Nicosia, Cyprus; tel (357)
Circ.: 500
Ed. – Erten Kasimoglu

YENI SANAYI B LGESI

KIBRIS
Dr. Fazil Kucuk Bulvari, Yeni Sanayi B□lgesi, Cyprus; tel (90) 392 225 2555; fax 225 2934; e-mail kibris@cypronet.net; web site www.kibrisgazetesi.com
Circ.: 13,000
Ed. – Mehmet Ali Akpinar

CZECH REPUBLIC

BRNO, MORAVIA

BRNENSKY VECERNIK (E)
Jakubske n m. 7, Brno, Moravia, 65844, Czech Republic; tel (420) 5 42321227; fax 45215150
Circ.: 16,000
Ed. in Chief – Petr Hoskovec

ROVNOST (M)
M. Horakove 9, Brno, Moravia, 65822, Czech Republic; tel (420) 5 45321121; fax 45212873
Circ.: 62,000
Advertising: Nielsen Communications.
Ed. in Chief – Lubomir Selinger

CESKE BUDEJOVIC, BOHEMIA

JIHOCESKE LISTY (M)
Vrbensk 23, Ceske Budejovic, Bohemia, 37045, Czech Republic; tel (420) 38 22081
Circ.: 53,000
Ed. in Chief – Vladimir Majer

HRADEC KRALOVE, BOHEMIA

HRADECKE NOVINY (D)
Skroupova 695, Hradec Kralove, Bohemia, 50172, Czech Republic; tel (420) 49 613511; fax 615681
Circ.: 30,000
Ed. in Chief – Jaromir Fridrich

OLOMOUC, MORAVIA

HANACKE NOVINY (D)
Michalsk 4, Olomouc, Moravia, 77186, Czech Republic; tel (420) 68 23663; fax 28723
Circ.: 10,000
Pub. – Marcelo Zurkova
Ed. in Chief – Ing Tom s Tichak

OSTRAVA, MORAVIA

GLOS LUDU (D-4X WK.)
Novin rsk 3, Ostrava, Moravia, 70907-1, Czech Republic; tel (420) 69 5844111
Ed. in Chief – Marian Siedlaczek

MORAVSKOSLEZSKY DEN (D)
Novinarska 7, Ostrava, Moravia, 70000-1, Czech Republic; tel (420) 69 55134; fax 57021
Circ.: 130,000
Ed. in Chief – Vladimir Vavrda

SVOBODA (M)
Mlynska 10, Ostrava, Moravia, 70111, Czech Republic; tel (420) 69 2472311; fax 2472312
Circ.: 100,000
Ed. in Chief – Josef Lys

PLZEN, MORAVIA

PLZENSKY DENIK (D)
Husova 15, Plzen, Moravia, 30483, Czech Republic; tel (420) 19 551111; fax 551234
Circ.: 50,000
Ed. in Chief – Jan Pertl

PRAGUE

BLESK (D)
U Pruhonu 13, Prague, 170 00, Czech Republic; tel (420) 2 2597 7779; fax 2597 7466; e-mail blesk@blesk.cz; web site www.blesk.cz
Circ.: 420,000
Ed. – Vladimir Muzik

BOHEMIA DAILY STANDARD (D)
Senov zne n m. 21, Prague, 11000-1, Czech Republic; tel (420) 24102300; fax 24102324
Circ.: 5,000
Pub. – Erik Best
Ed. – Francis Harris
Mng. Ed. – Joe Cook

CESKY DENIK (D)
Na Florenci 19, Prague, 11121-1, Czech Republic; tel (420) 2 2823246; fax 24811416
Pub. – Josef Kudlacek
Ed. – Jan Patocka

HOSPODARSKE NOVINY (M-5X WK.)
Dobrovskeho 25, Prague, 17055-7, Czech Republic; tel (420) 2 3307 1111; fax 3307 3002; e-mail data@hn.economia.cz; web site www.economia.cz
Circ.: 130,000
Mgr. – Martin Tenemark
Ed. in Chief – Petr Simunek

LIDOVA DEMOKRACIE (M-EX S)
Na Florenci 19, Prague, 11121-1, Czech Republic; tel (420) 2 282 3332; fax 2422 6061
Circ.: 230,000
Pub. – Fidelis Schlee
Ed. – Ivan Cervenka

LIDOVE NOVINY (M-EX S)
Zerotinova 32, Prague, 13000-3, Czech Republic; tel (420) 2 2506 3417; fax 2506 3416; e-mail pes@aci.cvut.cz; web site www.lidovenoviny.cz
Circ.: 68,230
Mgr. – Peter Pesek

METROPOLITINI TELEGRAF (D)
Na Florenci 19, Prague, 11121-1, Czech Republic; tel (420) 2 2367487; fax 267231

MLADA FRONTA DNES (M)
Karla Englise 519/11, Prague, 15000-5, Czech Republic; tel (420) 2 2506 1111; fax 2506 6203; e-mail mfdnes@mfdnes.cz; web site www.mfdnes.cz; www.idnes.cz
Circ.: 350,000
Ed. in Chief – Robert Casensky

OBANSKY DENIKOF (M-EX S)
Na Florenci 19, Prague, 11121-1, Czech Republic; tel (420) 2 2326051; fax 2320925
Circ.: 109,000
Ed. – Jan Vavra

PRACE (D-EX S)
V clavske n m. 17, Prague, 11258-1, Czech Republic; tel (420) 2 24224969; fax 24226475
Circ.: 220,600
Ed. in Chief – Vladimir Stehlik

RUDE PRAVO (D)
Florenci 19, Prague, 11121-1, Czech Republic; tel (420) 2 2822441; fax 24811607
Circ.: 350,000
Ed. in Chief – Zdenek Porybny

SVOBODNE SLOVO (D-EX S)
V clavske n m. 36, Prague, 11212-1, Czech Republic; tel (420) 2 260341; fax 266468; e-mail slovo@svobodne-slovo.anet.cz; web site www.slovo.cz
Circ.: 230,000
Ed. in Chief – Pavel Parma

TELEGRAF (D)
V clavske n m. 15, Prague, 11121-1, Czech Republic; tel (420) 2 24217581; fax 24219186

VECERNIK PRAHA (E)
Na Florenci 19, Prague, 11121-1, Czech Republic; tel (420) 2 24227625; fax 2327361
Circ.: 130,000
Ed. in Chief – Ivan Cervenka

USTI NAD LABEM, BOHEMIA

SEVEROCESKY DENIK (D)
Velka Hradebni 50, Usti nad Labem, Bohemia, 40001, Czech Republic; tel (420) (42-47) 5220525; fax (42-47) 5220587
Circ.: 95,000
Ed. in Chief – Marie Srpova

DENMARK

AABENRAA, JUTLAND

NORDSCHLESWIGER (M-6X WK.)
Skibbroen 4, Aabenraa, Jutland, 6200, Denmark; tel (45) 7462 3880; fax 7463 2656; e-mail redaktion@nordschleswiger.dk; web site www.nordschleswiger.dk
Circ.: 2,877
Ed. – Siegfried Matlok
Adv. Mgr. – Kurt Honnens

AARHUS, JUTLAND

ARHUUS STIFTSTIDENDE (DS)
Banegaar Pladsem 11, Aarhus, Jutland, 8000, Denmark; tel (45) 8740 1010; fax 8740 1321; e-mail redaktion@stiften.dk; web site www.stiften.dk
Circ.: 176,000
Ed. in Chief – Dorthe Carlsen
Adv. Mgr. – Necolai Jemsen

ALBORG, OST.

NORDJYSKE STIFTSTIDENDE (DS)
PO Box 8000, Alborg, Ost., 9220, Denmark; tel (45) 9935 3535; fax 9935 3375; e-mail direktionen@nordjyske.dk; web site www.nordjyske.dk
Last Audit: April 25, 2010
Ed. in Chief – Per Lyngby

COPENHAGEN, SJAELLAND

BERLINGSKE TIDENDE-DETAILHANDLERE/LANDSANNONCORE R (MS)
Pilestraede 34, Copenhagen, Sjaelland, 1147-K, Denmark; tel (45) 3375 7575; fax 3375 2020; e-mail redaktionen@business.dk; web site www.berlingske.dk
– Lisepeth Knutsen
– Lise GoettscheEd. In. Chiefs

BORSEN (M-5X WK.)
Montergade 19, Copenhagen, Sjaelland, 1140-K, Denmark; tel (45) 3332 0102; fax 3315 4001; e-mail redaktionen@borsen.dk; online@borsen.dk; web site www.borsen.dk
Circ.: 42,700
Ed. in Chief – Leif Beck Fallesen
Adv. Mgr. – Allan Hansen

B.T.-DETAILHANDLERE/LANDSANNONCORER (MS)
Pilestr□de 34, Copenhagen, Sjaelland, 1147-K, Denmark; tel (45) 3375 7533; fax 3375 2050; e-mail bwa@weekendavisen.dk; web site www.weekendavisen.dk
Ed. in Chief – Peter BrÅ£chmann

EKSTRA BLADET (DS)
Radhuspladsen 37, Copenhagen, Sjaelland, 1785-V, Denmark; tel (45) 3311 1313; fax 3314 1000; e-mail post@ekstrabladet.dk; web site www.eb.dk
Ed.-in-Cheif – Paul Madsen
Mktg. Mgr – Thomas Rydberg

EKSTRA BLADET-VESTUDGAVE (D)
Radhuspladsen 37, Copenhagen, Sjaelland, 1785-V, Denmark; tel (45) 3311 1313; fax 3314 1000; e-mail post@ep.dk; web site www.ep.dk
Ed. in Chief – Paul Madsen
Adv. Mgr. – Pia Parfod

INFORMATION (M-6X WK.)
St. Kongensgade 40C, Copenhagen, Sjaelland, 1264-K, Denmark; tel (45) 3369 6000; fax 3369 6079; e-mail i@information.dk; web site www.information.dk
Circ.: 21,500
Journalist – Palle Weis
Ed. in Chief – Pent Winther

KRISTELIGT DAGBLAD (M-6X WK.)
Rosengarden 14, Copenhagen, Sjaelland, 1174-K, Denmark; tel (45) 3348 0505; fax 3348 0501; e-mail net@kristeligt-dagblad.dk; web site www.kristeligt-dagblad.dk
Circ.: 58,000
Ed. – Erik Bjerager

POLITIKEN-DETAILHANDLERE/LANDSANNONCORER (MS)
Politikens Hus, Radhuspladsen 37, Copenhagen, Sjaelland, 1585-V, Denmark; tel (45) 3311 8511; fax 3315 4117; web site www.politiken.dk
Ed. in Chief – Toger Seidenfaden
Mktg. Mgr. – Paul Skott

DET FRI AKTUELT-DETAILPRISER/LANDSPRISER (M-6X WK.)
Radhuspladsen 45-47, Copenhagen, Sjaelland, 1595-V, Denmark; tel (45) 3332 4001; fax 3313 0048
Circ.: 42,262
Ed. in Chief – Lisbeth Knudsen

ESBJERG, JUTLAND

JYDSKE VESTKYSTEN (MS) EST. 1991
Banegardspladsen, Esbjerg, Jutland, 6700, Denmark; tel (45) 7912 4500; fax 7513 2207; e-mail jydskevestkysten@jv.dk; web site www.jv.dk
Circ.: 60
Dir./Ed. – Peter Orry Jensen

FJERRITSLEV, JUTLAND

FJERRITSLEV AVIS (E-6X WK.)
Ostergade 33-35, Fjerritslev, Jutland, 9690, Denmark; tel (45) 9821 2200; fax 9821 3234
Circ.: 3,878
Pub. – Einar Darnsgaard
Editorial Mgr. – Anne Marie Larsen
Ed. – Jens Darnsgaard

FLENSBURG

FLENSBORG AVIS (6X WK.)
PO Box 2662, Flensburg, 24916, Denmark; tel (49) 4615 0450; fax 4615 0451; e-mail redaktion@flensborg-avis.de; web site www.flensborg-avis.de
Ed.-in-Cheif – Bjarne Lonborg

FREDERICIA, JUTLAND

FREDERICIA DAGBLAD (6X WK.)
Danmarksgade 28, Fredericia, Jutland, 7000, Denmark; tel (45) 7592 2600; fax 7592 3355; web site www.fredericiadagblad.dk
Circ.: 7,500
Ed. in Chief – Hogens Sorensen
Adv. Mgr. – Elex Peterson

FREDERIKSHAVN, JUTLAND

FREDERIKSHAVNS AVIS (E-6X WK.)
Danmarksgade 3, Frederikshavn, Jutland, 9900, Denmark; tel (45) 9842 2277; fax 9842 2490
Circ.: 6,368
Ed. – Bent Eilertsen

HELSINGOR, SJAELLAND

HELSINGOR DAGBLAD (E-6X WK.)
Klostermosevej 101, Helsingor, Sjaelland, 3000, Denmark; tel (45) 4222 2110; fax 4222 0650
Circ.: 6,920
Ed. in Chief – John Bech

HERLEV

LICITATIONEN (M-5X WK.)
Marielundvej 46 E, Herlev, 2730, Denmark; tel (45) 7015 0222; fax 4485 8877; e-mail licitationen@licitationen.dk; web site www.licitationen.dk
Circ.: 5,892
Ed. – Claus Toettrup

HERNING, JUTLAND

HERNING FOLKEBLAD (E-6X WK.)
Ostergade 25, Herning, Jutland, 7400, Denmark; tel (45) 9626 3700; fax 9722 3600; e-mail hf@herningfolkeblad.dk; web site www.herningfolkeblad.dk
Circ.: 13,500
Ed. – Flemming Larsen
Adv. Mgr. – Gitte Soender Gaard

HILLEROD, SJAELLAND

FREDERIKSBORG AMTS AVIS (M-6X WK.)
Slotsgrtegade 1, Hillerod, Sjaelland, 3400, Denmark; tel (45) 4824 4100; fax 4824 4840; web site www.tagblade.dk
Circ.: 38,000
Ed. – Torben Dalley Larsen

HJORRING, JUTLAND

HJORRING (DS)
Frederikshavnsvej 79-81, Hjorring, Jutland, 9800, Denmark; tel (45) 9892 1700; fax 9892 1670
Circ.: 14,429

VENDSYSSEL TIDENDE (E-6X WK.)
Frederikshavnsvej 79-81, Hjorring, Jutland, 9800, Denmark; tel (45) 7585 7788; fax 9892 6601
Circ.: 114,000
Ed. – Claus Dindler

HOLBAEK, SJAELLAND

HOLBAEK AMTS VENSTREBLAD (E-6X WK.)
Ahlgade 1, Holbaek, Sjaelland, 4300, Denmark; tel (45) 8888 4300; fax 5944 2810; web site www.nordvestnyt.dk
Circ.: 18,000
Adv. Mgr. – Peter Matsen
Ed. in Chief – Mogens Flyvholm

HOLSTEBRO, JUTLAND

DAGBLADET HOLSTEBRO-STRUER (E-6X WK.)
Laegardvej 86, Holstebro, Jutland, 7500, Denmark; tel (45) 9912 8300; fax 9741 0320; web site www.bergske.dk
Circ.: 41,000
Ed. – Erik Moller

HORSENS, JUTLAND

HORSENS FOLKEBLAD (E-6X WK.)
Sondergade 47, Horsens, Jutland, 8700, Denmark; tel (45) 7627 2000; web site www.horsens-folkeblad.dk
Circ.: 23,277
Adv. Mgr. – Sven Grnuoneorg
Ed. – Jens Bebe

KALUNDBORG, SJAELLAND

KALUNDBORG FOLKEBLAD (6X WK.)
Skibbrogade 40-42, Kalundborg, Sjaelland, 4400, Denmark; tel (45) 8888 4400; fax 5951 0280; e-mail red.kf @ nordvest.dk; web site www.nordvestnyt.dk
Circ.: 9,648
Ed. – Claus Sorensen
Adv. Mgr. – Peter Madsen

KERTEMINDE, FYN

KJERTEMINDE AVIS (E-5X WK.)
Nordre Ringvej 54, Kerteminde, Fyn, 5300, Denmark; tel (45) 6532 1004; fax 6532 2704; e-mail info@kj-avis.dk; web site www.kj-avis.dk
Circ.: 1,651
Ed. in Chief – Jorgen Wind-Hansen
Adv. Mgr. – Jorgen Wind

KOBENHAVN

ERHVERVS-BLADET (E-5X WK.)
Pilestr□de 34, Kobenhavn, 1117, Denmark; tel (45) 3375 3801; fax 3375 3696; e-mail info@erhvervsbladet.dk; web site www.erhvervsbladet.dk
Circ.: 109,971
Ed. – Morten Asmussen

KOLDING, JUTLAND

FOLKEBLADET-SYDJYLLAND (E-6X WK.)
Jernbanegade 33-35, Kolding, Jutland, 6000, Denmark; tel (45) 7552 2000; fax 7552 2768
Circ.: 17,497
Ed. in Chief – Tage Rasnussen

LOGSTOR, JUTLAND

LOGSTOR AVIS (D)
Torvegade 2, Logstor, Jutland, 9670, Denmark; tel (45) 9867 1211; fax 9867 1150
Circ.: 2,776
Ed. in Chief – Ejnar Damsgaard

MIDDELFART, FYN

MIDDELFART VENSTREBLAD (D)
Algade 48, Middelfart, Fyn, 5500, Denmark; tel (45) 6441 1303; fax 6441 1307
Circ.: 6,200
Ed. in Chief – Lars Bech Nielsen

NAESTVED, SJAELLAND

SJAELLANDSKE (M-6X WK.)
Dania 38, Naestved, Sjaelland, 4700, Denmark; tel (45) 5572 4511; fax 7245 1219; e-mail red@sj-medier.dk; web site www.sn.dk
Circ.: 19,240
Ed. – Helt Wetel

NAKSKOV, LLOLAND

NY DAG (E-6X WK.)
Hojevej 15, Nakskov, Lloland, 4900, Denmark; tel (45) 5392 1400; fax 5392 1109
Circ.: 9,200
Ed. in Chief – Klaus Sivebaek

NYKOBING, LLOLLAND-FALSTER

FOLKETIDENDE (E-6X WK.)
Tvaergade 20, Nykobing, Llolland-Falster, 4800-F, Denmark; tel (45) 5488 0200; fax 5488 0296; e-mail redaktion@folketidende.dk; web site www.folketidende.dk
Circ.: 22,000
Ed. – SÅ£ren Knudsen

MORSO FOLKEBLAD (E-6X WK.)
Elsovej 105, Nykobing, Llolland-Falster, 7900-M, Denmark; tel (45) 9772 1000; fax 9772 1010; e-mail mf@mf.dk; web site www.mf.dk
Circ.: 5,000
Last Audit: March 25, 2010
Ed. – Claus Thomsen

ODENSE, FYN

FYENS STIFTSTIDENDE (D)
Banegaardspladsen 1, Odense, Fyn, 5000, Denmark; tel (45) 6611 1111; fax 6545 5296; e-mail redaktion@fyens.dk; web site www.fyens.dk
Mng. Dir. – Paul Eric Andersen
Adv. Mgr. – Lars Anderson

RANDERS, JUTLAND

AMTSAVISEN (E-6X WK.)
Narregade 7, Randers, Jutland, 8900, Denmark; tel (45) 8642 7511; fax 8641 9211
Circ.: 28,986
Ed. in Chief – Ole C. Jorgensen

RINGKOBING, JUTLAND

DAGBLAD RINGKOBING SKYERN (E-6X WK.)
Skt. Blichersvej 5, Ringkobing, Jutland, 6950, Denmark; tel (45) 9975 7300; fax 9975 7430; e-mail ringkoebing@bergske.dk; web site www.bergske.dk
Circ.: 17,061
Ed. – F. Haytslt

RINGSTED, SJAELLAND

DAGBLADET (E-6X WK.)
Sogade 4-12, Ringsted, Sjaelland, 4100, Denmark; tel (45) 5361 2500; fax 5767 3113
Circ.: 30,804
Ed. in Chief – Torben Dalby Larsen

RONNE, BORNHOLM

BORNHOLMEREN (E-6X WK.)
PO Box 140, Ronne, Bornholm, 3700, Denmark; tel (45) 5695 2526; fax 5695 2588
Circ.: 5,963
Ed. in Chief – Bo Schriver

BORNHOLMS TIDENDE (E-6X WK.)
Norregade 11-19, Ronne, Bornholm, 3700, Denmark; tel (45) 5690 3000; fax 5690 3091; e-mail redaktion@bornholmstidende.dk; web site www.bornholmstidende.dk
Circ.: 13,000
Mktg. Mgr. – Lisbeth Riemann
Ed. in Chief – Dan Qeitzau

ROSKILDE, SJAELLAND

DAGBLADET/ROSKILDE TIDENDE (E-6X WK.)
Hersegade 22, Roskilde, Sjaelland, 4000, Denmark; tel (45) 4235 8500; fax 4235 8040
Circ.: 30,824

SILKEBORG, JUTLAND

MIDTJYLLANDS AVIS (D-6X WK.)
Papirfabrikken 18, Silkeborg, Jutland, 8600, Denmark; tel (45) 8682 1300; fax 8681 3577; web site www.midtjyllandsavis.dk
Circ.: 30,000
Adv.Mgr. – Flemming Eidere
Ed. in Chief – Steffen Lange

SKAGEN, JUTLAND

SKAGENS AVIS (E-6X WK.)
Skolevej 8-12, Skagen, Jutland, 9990, Denmark; tel (45) 9844 1155; fax 9845 0570
Circ.: 4,392
Ed. in Chief – Johs Brunn-Bindslev

SKIVE, JUTLAND

SKIVE FOLKEBLAD (E-6X WK.)
Gemsevej 7-9, Skive, Jutland, 7800, Denmark; tel (45) 9751 3411; fax 9751 2835; e-mail abonnement@skivefolkeblad.dk; annonce@skivefolkeblad.dk; web site www.skivefolkeblad.dk
Circ.: 12,000
Ed. – Ole Dall

SLAGELSE, SJAELLAND

SJAELLANDS TIDENDE (6X WK.)
Korsgade 6, Slagelse, Sjaelland, 4200, Denmark; tel (45) 7245 1100; fax 7245 1459; e-mail red@sj-medier.dk; web site ^www.sn.dk
Circ.: 15,247
Ed. in Cheif – Helge Wedel

SVENDBORG, FYN

FYNS AMTS AVIS (MS)
Skt Nicolaigade 3, Svendborg, Fyn, 5700, Denmark; tel (45) 6221 4621; fax 6222 0610; e-mail post@fynsamtsavis.dk; web site www.fynsamtsavis.dk
Adv. Mgr. – Mogens Balle
Ed. in Chief – Joegen Krebs

THISTED, JUTLAND

THISTED DAGBLAD (MS)
Jernbanegade 15-17, Thisted, Jutland, 7700, Denmark; tel (45) 9919 9300; fax 9791 0720; web site www.nordjyske.dk
Ed. – Hans Peter Kragh

VEJLE, JUTLAND

VEJLE AMTS FOLKEBLAD/FREDERICIA DAGBLAD (D-5X WK.)
Bugattivej 8, Vejle, Jutland, 7100, Denmark; tel (45) 7585 7788; fax 7585 7476
Circ.: 32,626
Ed. – Arne Mariager

VIBORG, JUTLAND

VIBORG STIFTS FOLKEBLAD (E-6X WK.)
Vesterbrogade 8, Viborg, Jutland, 8800, Denmark; tel (45) 8927 6300; fax 8927 6370; web site www.bergske.dk
Circ.: 13,131
Sales Mgr. – Ean Soerensen
Ed. – Lars Norup

VIBY, JUTLAND

MORGENAVISEN JYLLANDS-POSTEN (MS) EST. 1871
Grondalsvej 3, Viby, Jutland, 8260-J, Denmark; tel (45) 8738 3838; fax 8611 2629; e-mail jp@jp.dk; web site www.jp.dk
Ed. in Chief – Jorn Mikkelson
Adv. Mgr. – Morten Kallmayer

ESTONIA

PARNU

PARNU POSTIMEES (5X WK.)
Ruutli 14, Parnu, 80010, Estonia; tel (372) 447 7090; fax 7088; e-mail postimees@parnupostimees.ee; web site www.parnupostimees.ee
Circ.: 18,600
Pub. – Margus Mets
Mng. Ed. – Iira Igasta

TALLINN

ARIPAEV (5X WK.)
Parnu mnt 105, Tallinn, 19094, Estonia; tel (372) 667 0111; fax 667 0165; e-mail aripaev@aripaev.ee; web site www.aripaev.ee
Circ.: 16,000
Ed. in Chief – Melis Mandel

MOLODEZH ESTONII (5X WK.)
Tartu Mnt. 53, Tallinn, 10115, Estonia; tel (372); e-mail info@moles.ee; web site www.moles.eeSergei Grigorjev

NOORTE HAAL (6X WK.)
67a, Pyarnusskoe Shosse, Tallinn, 200090, Estonia; tel (372)
Circ.: 150,000
Ed. – T. Tare

OHTULEHT (6X WK.)
Narva mnt. 13, Tallinn, 10502, Estonia; tel (372) 614 4000; fax 614 4001; e-mail leht@ohtuleht.ee; web site www.ohtuleht.ee
Circ.: 65,000
Chrmn. – Kristjan Mauer
Ed. in Chief – Vaino Koorberg

PAEVALEHT (6X WK.)
Narva mnt 13th Fl., Tallinn, 10151, Estonia; tel (372) 680 4400; fax 680 4401; e-mail mail@epl.ee; web site www.epl.ee
Circ.: 40,000
Ed. in Chief – Lea La Arin
Mng. Ed. – Merike Pinn

RAHVA HAAL (6X WK.)
67a, Parnu Maantee, Tallinn, 200090, Estonia; tel (372)
Circ.: 175,000
Ed. in Chief – Toomas Leito

SONUMILEHT (D)
Vana-Louna 37, Tallinn, 0001, Estonia; tel (372) 2 6408930; fax 6408911; e-mail sleht@ruuter.sl.ee; web site www.sl.ee
Circ.: 30,000
Ed. in Chief – Mark Luik

TARTU

POSTIMEES (D-EX S)
Gildi 1, Tartu, 50095, Estonia; tel (372) 666 2202; fax 739 0300; e-mail online@postimees.ee; web site www.postimees.ee
Circ.: 53,000
Adv. Mgr. – Marika Jahilo
Ed. in Chief – Merit Kopli

FAROE ISLANDS

TOESHAVN

OYGGJATIDINDI (2X WK.)
PO Box 3312, Toeshavn, 110, Faroe Islands; tel (298) 314 411; fax 316 410; e-mail oyggjat@post.olivant.fo; web site www.oyggjatidindi.com
Circ.: 4,500
Ed. – Dan Klein

TORSHAVN

SOSIALURIN (5X WK.)
PO Box 76, Torshavn, FO-100, Faroe Islands; tel (298) 341 800; fax 341 801; e-mail post@sosialurin.fo; web site www.sosialurin.fo
Circ.: 6,400
Pub. – Eirikur Lindenskov
Ed. – Jan Muller

T RSHAVN

DIMMALAETTING (5X WK.) EST. 1878
PO Box 3019, T□rshavn, 110, Faroe Islands; tel (+298) 79 02 00; fax 79 02 01; e-mail redaktion@dimma.fo; web site www.dimma.fo
Last Audit: November 23, 2011
Managing editor – Arni Gregersen

FINLAND

BORGA

BORGABLADET (D) EST. 1861
PB 20, Borga, Finland; tel (358) (0)207569656; fax (0)195348244; web site www.ostnyland.fi
Circ.: 7,900
Group: KSF Media
Vice Editor-In-Chief – Stefan Holmstrom
Ed. in Chief – Maj-Britt Hoglund

EKENAS, TURKU-PORI

VASTRA NYLAND (M-6X WK.)
PO Box 26, Ekenas, Turku-Pori, 10601, Finland; tel (358) 19 222 800; fax 222 812; web site www.vastranyland.fi
Circ.: 10,800
Ed. in Chief – Tommy Westerlund

FORSSA

FORSSAN LEHTI (D)
PL 38, Forssa, 30100, Finland; tel (358) 3 415 51; fax 415 5724; e-mail toimitus@forssanlehti.fi; web site www.forssanlehti.fi
Circ.: 14,388
Ed. in Chief – Kari Grahn

HAME

HAMEEN SANOMAT (D)
PO Box 530, Hame, 13111, Finland; tel (358) 3 61511; fax 615 1492; e-mail toimitus@hameensanomat.fi; web site www.hameensanomat.fi
Circ.: 30,097
Ed. in Chief – Pauli Uusi-Kilponen

HEINOLA

ITA-HAME (6X WK.)
PL 10, Heinola, 18101, Finland; tel (358) 3 757 505; fax 883 7565; e-mail internet@iha.ess.fi
Circ.: 11,600
Ed. in Chief – Jari Miami

HELSINGFORS, UUSIMA

HUFVUDSTADSBLADET (DS) EST. 1864
PO Box 217, Helsingfors, Uusima, 00101, Finland; tel (358) 9 12531; fax 642 930; e-mail nyheter@hbl.fi; web site www.hbl.fi
Circ.: 48,046
Group: KSF-Media
news editor – Katarina Koivisto

HELSINKI

KANSAN UUTISET (4X WK.)
Vilhovuorenkatu 11, C7, Helsinki, 00500, Finland; tel (358) 9 759 601; fax 7596 0319; e-mail ku@kansanuutiset.fi; web site www.kansanuutiset.fi
Circ.: 16,000
Adv. Mgr. – Makko Nurmela
Ed. in Chief – Jouko Joentausta

KAUPPALEHTI (5X WK.) EST. 1898
PO Box 830, Helsinki, 00101, Finland; tel (358) 10 665 8120; fax 665 2424; web site

www.kauppalehti.fi
Circ.: 80,139
Ed. in Chief – Hannu Leinonen

HELSINKI, UUSIMA

ILTALEHTI (6X WK.)
PO Box 372, Helsinki, Uusima, 00101, Finland; tel (358) 9 50781; fax 5078641; web site www.iltalehti.fi
Ed. in Chief – Pekka Karhuvaara

UUSI SUOMI (M)
PL 139, Helsinki, Uusima, 00101, Finland; tel (358) 90 50771; fax 5078683
Circ.: 73,284

HELSINKI, UUSIMAA

UUTISPAIVA DEMARI (E-5X WK.) EST. 1895
PO Box 338, Helsinki, Uusimaa, 00531, Finland; tel (358) 9 701 041; e-mail toimitus@demari.fi; web site www.demari.fi
Circ.: 15,000
Editor – Juha Peltonen
Adv. Mgr. – Aila Paakko

HYVINKAA, UUSIMA

HYVINKAAN SANOMAT (D-6X WK.)
PL 93, Hyvinkaa, Uusima, 05801, Finland; tel (358) 19 485100; fax 485117; web site www.hysa.fi
Circ.: 12,340
Ed. in Chief – Pentti Kiiski

IISALMI, KUOPIO

IISALMEN SANOMAT (M)
PL 11, Iisalmi, Kuopio, 74101, Finland; tel (358) 17 835 1301; fax 835 1401; web site www.iisalmensanomat.fi
Circ.: 13,205
Ed. in Chief – Mai Koivula

IMATRA, KYMI

YLA-VUOKSI (M-6X WK.)
PL 11, Imatra, Kymi, 55101, Finland; tel (358) 954 66066; fax 67789
Circ.: 15,504
Ed. in Chief – Markku Soikkeli

JAKOBSTAD, JAKOBSTAD

OSTERBOTTENS TIDNING (D)
PL 22, Jakobstad, Jakobstad, 68601, Finland; tel (358) 6 784 8800; fax 785 3298; web site www.ot.fi
Circ.: 12,500
CEO – Jens Sunde Lill
Asst. Ed. – Henrik Othman

JOENSUU, POHJOIS-KARJALA

KARJALAINEN (D)
PO Box 99, Joensuu, Pohjois-Karjala, 80141, Finland; tel (358) 13 2551; fax 255 2315; e-mail toimitus@karjalainen.fi; web site www.karjalainen.fi
Circ.: 47,363
Ed. – Pasi Koivuma

JYVASKYLA, KESKI-SUOMI

KESKISUOMALAINEN (D)
PO Box 159, Jyvaskyla, Keski-Suomi, 40101, Finland; tel (358) 14 622 000; fax 622 272; e-mail hartio@keski.suomalainen.fi; web site www.ksml.fi
Circ.: 74,840
Ed. – Pekka Mervola

J MS

KOILLIS-HAME (5X WK.)
Lindemaninkatu 3, J□ms□, 42100, Finland; tel (358) 10 665 5148; fax 665 5152; e-mail kh.toimitus@sps.fi; web site www.jamsanseutu.fi
Circ.: 9,613
Ed. in Chief – Pekka Hyytinen

KAJAANI, OULU

KAINUUN SANOMAT (D)
Kauppakatu 11, Kajaani, Oulu, 87100, Finland; tel (358) 8 61661; fax 623 013; e-mail toimitus@kainuunsanomat.fi; web site www.kainuunsanomat.fi
Circ.: 23,000
Ed. in Chief – Matti Piirainen
Mng. Ed. – Pekka Vasala

KEMI, VAIHDE

POHJOLAN SANOMAT (D)
Sairaalakatu 2, Kemi, Vaihde, 94100, Finland; tel (358) 10 665 011; web site www.pohjolansanomat.fi
Circ.: 29,221
Ed. in Chief – Heikki Laakkola

KOKKOLA, VAASA

KESKIPOHJANMAA (M)
PO Box 45, Kokkola, Vaasa, 67101, Finland; tel (358) 20 750 4680; fax 750 4686; e-mail toimitus@kpk.fi; web site www.keskipohjanmaa.net
Circ.: 31,241
Ed. in Chief – Jouko Pensaari

KOTKA

KYMEN SANOMAT (DS)
PO Box 27, Kotka, 48101, Finland; tel (358) 5 210 0111; fax 216 377; e-mail uutiset@kymensanomat.fi; web site www.kymensanomat.fi
Circ.: 25,000
Last Audit: March 22, 2010
Ed. in Chief – Juha Oksanen
Ed. – Marku Aspo

KUUSAMO

KOILLISSANOMAT (M-5X WK.)
Koillissanomat Oy, Kitkantie 31-33, Kuusamo, 93600, Finland; tel (358) 8 8600 600; fax 860 0611; e-mail toimitus@koillissanomat.fi; web site www.koillissanomat.fi
Circ.: 8,000
Ed. – Seppo Salminen

LAPPEENRANTA, VILLMANSTRAND

ETELA-SAIMAA (D)
PO Box 3, Lappeenranta, Villmanstrand, 53501, Finland; tel (358) 5 (358-5) 5591; fax (358-5) 559209
Circ.: 36,399
Mng. Dir. – Esa Lavander
Ed. – Kari Vaisanen

LOHJA

LANSI-UUSIMAA (M-6X WK.)
PL 60, Lohja, 08101, Finland; tel (358) 0800 90000; fax 2077 03045; e-mail lu.toimitus@lehtiyhtyma.fi; web site www.lansi-uusimaa.fi
Circ.: 13,712
Ed. in Chief – Jaakko Puomila

MARIEHAMN

ALAND (M-6X WK.)
PO Box 50, Mariehamn, 22101, Finland; tel (358) 18 26026; fax 15755; e-mail nyheter@alandstidningen.ax; web site www.alandstidningen.ax
Circ.: 10,351
Ed. in Chief – Niklas Lampi

MIKKELI

LANSI-SAVO (D)
PO Box 6, Mikkeli, 50101, Finland; tel (358) 15 3501; fax 350 3351; e-mail toimitus@lansi-savo.fi; web site www.lansi-savo.fi
Circ.: 25,000
– Tapio Honkanaa
– Anssi MehtalaEd.s

OULAINEN

PYHAJOKISEUTU (E-4X WK.)
PO Box 1, Oulainen, 86301, Finland; tel (358) 1066 55145; fax 8479 5125; web site www.pyhajokiseutu.fi
Circ.: 9,415
Ed. – Simo Husso

OULU

KALEVA (D)
PO Box 170, Oulu, 90401, Finland; tel (358) 8 537 7111; fax 537 7195; e-mail kaleva@kaleva.fi; web site www.kaleva.fi
Circ.: 74,741
– Heikki Nurmi
– Markku JurvelinCirc. Dir.s

KANSAN TAHTO (3X WK.)
PL 61, Oulu, 90101, Finland; tel (358) 8 537 1722; fax 371 314; e-mail toimitus@kansantahto.fi; web site www.kansantahto.fi
Circ.: 10,201
Mng. Dir. – Irpa Kovalainen

SUOMENMAA (5X WK.)
PL 52, Oulu, 90101, Finland; tel (358) 8 447 370312; fax 537 0229; e-mail ilmoitukset.suomenmaa@suomenmaa.fi; web site www.suomenmaa.fi
Circ.: 18,135
Ed. in Chief – Timo Laaninen

PIEKSAMAKI

PIEKSAMAEN LEHTI (5X WK.)
PL 45, Pieksamaki, 76100, Finland; tel (358) 15 348 1722; fax 341 421; e-mail toimitus@pieksamaenlehti.fi; web site www.pieksamaenlehti.fi
Circ.: 7,945
Ed. – Sinikka Hakkarainen

PORI

SATAKUNNAN KANSA (M) EST. 1873
PO Box 58, Pori, 28101, Finland; tel (358) 10 665 132; web site SK24.fi
Circ.: 5,237
Ed. in Chief – Petri Hakala

PORVOO

UUSIMAA (6X WK.)
PL 15, Porvoo, 06151, Finland; tel (358) 2061 00140; fax 20770 3021; e-mail etilaajapalvlu.uusimaa@lehtiyhtyma.fi; web site www.uusimaa.fi
Circ.: 12,314
MD – Jari Lammassaari

RAAHE

RAAHEN SEUTU (4X WK.)
PO Box 61, Raahe, 92101, Finland; tel (358) 8 10 665 108; fax 220 702; web site www.almamedia.fi; www.raahenseutu.fi
Circ.: 10,107
Ed. in Chief – Martti Nousiainen

RAUMA

LANSI-SUOMI (D)
Susivuorentie 2, Rauma, 26100, Finland; tel (358) 2 83361; fax 833 6299; web site www.lansi-suomi.fi
Circ.: 17,000
Ed. in Chief – Pasi Katajamaki

ROVANIEMI

LAPIN KANSA (D)
Veitikantie 2-8, Rovaniemi, 96100, Finland; tel (358) 16 066 5022; fax 665 7720; web site www.lapinkansa.fi
Circ.: 37,578
Ed.- in -Chief – Heikki Tuomi-Nikula

SALO

SALON SEUDUN SANOMAT (D) EST. 1919
PO Box 117, Salo, 24101, Finland; tel (358) 2 77021; fax 7702 222; web site www.sss.fi
Circ.: 21,828
Mktg. Mgr. – Mikko Ruosteenoja
Editor-in-Chief – Ville Pohjonen
Ed. – Jukka Holmberg

SANOMA

ILTA-SANOMAT (D-6X WK.)
PO Box 45, Sanoma, 00089, Finland; tel (358) 9 1221; fax 122 3419; e-mail ilta-sanomat@sanoma.fi; web site www.iltasanomat.fi; www.sanoma.com
Advertising: Publicitas.
Ed. in Chief – Tapio Sadeoja

HELSINGIN SANOMAT (D)
PO Box 77, Sanoma, 00089, Finland; tel (358) 9 1221; fax 605 709; e-mail janne.virkkunen@sanoma.fi; web site www.hs.fi
Advertising: Publicitas.
Pub. – Mikael Pentikainen
Mng. Ed. – Kimmo Pietinen
Mng. Ed. – Antero Mukka
Mng. Ed. – Kaius Niemi

SAVONLINNA

ITA-SAVO (MS)
PO Box 35, Savonlinna, 57231, Finland; tel (358) 15 29171
editor-in-chief – Tuomo Yli-Huttula

SEINAJOKI

ETELA-POHJANMAA (E-5X WK.)
Koulukatu 10, Seinajoki, 60100, Finland; tel (358) 6 4186711; fax 4144905
Circ.: 9,203
Ed. in Chief – Raimo Vaisto

ILKKA (D)
PO Box 60, Seinajoki, 60101, Finland; tel (358) 6 2477 830; fax 2477 855; web site www.ilkka.fi
Circ.: 56,340
Ed. – Matti Kalliokoski

TAMPERE

AAMULEHTI (DS)
PO Box 327, Tampere, 33101, Finland; tel (358) 10 665 111; fax 665 3140; web site www.aamulehti.fi

TURKU, ABO

ABO UNDERRATTELSER (M-5X WK.)
PB 211, Turku, Abo, 20101, Finland; tel (358) 2 274 9900; fax 231 1394; e-mail newsdesk@fabsy.fi; web site www.abounderrattelser.fi
Circ.: 7,928
Ed. in Chief – Torbjorn Kevin
Mng. Ed. – Harry Serlo

TURUN PAIVALEHTI (M-5X WK.)
PL 230, Turku, Abo, 20101, Finland; tel (358) 2 2502777; fax 2502110
Circ.: 7,646
Ed. in Chief – Antti Vuorenrinne

TURUN SANOMAT (MS)
PO Box 95, Turku, Abo, 20100, Finland; tel (358) 2 269 3311; fax 269 3274; e-mail ts.toimitus@ts-group.fi; uutiset@ts.fi; bookings@ts.fi; web site www.turunsanomat.fi
MD – Keijo Ketonen
Ed. in Chief – Kari Yainio

TUUSULA

KESKI-UUSIMAA (D)
Klaavolantie 5, Tuusula, 04301, Finland; tel (358) 9 100 100; web site www.keski-uusimaa.fi
Circ.: 22,000
Ed. – Pentti Hiishi

VAASA

POHJANMAAN DEMARI (5X WK.)
PL 18, Vaasa, 65101, Finland; tel (358) 6 174150
Circ.: 10,054
Ed. in Chief – Jaakko Elenius

VAASA, VASA

KANSAN AANI
Pitkanlandenk 55, Vaasa, Vasa, 65100, Finland; tel (358) 6 3122133; fax 3120107
Circ.: 10,988

VALKEAKOSKI

VALKEAKOSKEN SANOMAT (M-5X WK.)
Kirjask. 1, Valkeakoski, 37600, Finland; tel (358) 937 7171
Circ.: 8,627

VARKAUS

WARKAUDEN LEHTI (M-6X WK.)
PL 161, Varkaus, 78201, Finland; tel (358) 17 778 3632; fax 552 2374; e-mail paatoimittaja@warkaudenlehti.fi; web site www.warkaudenlehti.fi
Ed. in Chief. – Mai Koivula

VASA

VASABLADET (D)
PO Box 52, Vasa, 65101, Finland; tel (358) 6 326 0211; fax 784 8881; e-mail nyheter@vasabladet.fi; web site www.vasabladet.fi
Circ.: 26,700
Ed. – Margareta BjÂ£rklund
Adv. Mgr. – Nilsson Quist

YLIVIESKA

KALAJOKILAAKSO (M-5X WK.)
PL 7, Ylivieska, 84101, Finland; tel (358) 20 750 4600; fax 750 4618; web site www.kalajokilaakso.fi
Circ.: 9,777
Mgr. – Seppo Kangas

FRANCE

21000 DIJON

LE BIEN PUBLIC (D)
7 Blvd. Chanoine Kir, 21000 Dijon, France; tel (33) 3 8042 4242; fax 8042 4250; e-mail bienpublic@lebienpublic.fr; web site www.bienpublic.com
Gen. Dir. – Jean Viansson Ponte
Ed. in Chief – Jean-Louis Pierre

29205 MORIAX

LE TELEGRAMME (D)
BP 243, 29205 Moriax, France; tel (33) 2 9862 1133; fax 9863 4545; e-mail telegramme@letelegramme.com; web site www.letelegramme.com
Circ.: 199,710
Pres./MD – Edouard Coudurier
Adv. Dir. – Yves Gourvennec
Editorial Dir. – Hubert Coudurier
Ed. in Chief – Marcel Quiveger
Ed. in Chief – Olivier Clech

31095 TOULOUSE

LA DEPECHE DU MIDI (M)
Ave. Jean Baylet, 31095 Toulouse, France; tel (33) 5 6211 3300; fax 6144 7474; e-mail correspondants@ladepeche.com; web site www.ladepeche.com
Circ.: 218,214
Chrmn./MD – Jean Michel Baylet

33094 BORDEAUX

SUD-OUEST/SUD-OUEST DIMANCHE (M)
Place Jacques-Lemoine, 33094 Bordeaux, France; tel (33) 5 5600 3333; fax 5600 5031; web site www.sudouest.com
Dir. – Bruno Franeschi

35051 RENNES CEDEX 9

OUEST-FRANCE (D)
10, rue du Breil, 35051 Rennes Cedex 9, France; tel (33) 2 9932 6000; fax 9932 6025; e-mail actualite@france-ouest.com; web site www.ouest-france.fr
Circ.: 786,205
Chrmn. – Francois-Regis Hutin

57140 WOIPPY

LE REPUBLICAIN LORRAIN (D)
3rd Ave. Des Deux Fontaines, 57140 Woippy, France; tel (33) 3 8734 1789; fax 8734 1790; web site www.republicain-lorrain.fr
Mng. Dir. – Keirffr Wecrtar

AGEN

LE PETIT BLEU DU LOT-ET-GARONNE (D)
750 Ave. de Colmar, Agen, 4700, France; tel (33) 53 981 150; fax 965 451
Circ.: 12,548
Pub. – Jean-Marie Hellian
Dir. – Francis Milliard

AJACCIO

JOURNAL DE LA CORSE (D)
BP 255, Ajaccio, 20179, France; tel (33) 495 210 184; e-mail redaction@journaldelacorse.net
Circ.: 3,200
Pub. – Catherine Fieschi-Livrelli

AMIENS

LE COURRIER PICARD (D)
BP 1021, Amiens, 80010, France; tel (33) 3 2282 6000; fax 2282 6011; e-mail info@courrier-piccard.fr; web site www.courrier-picard.fr
Circ.: 82,739
Ed. – Daniel Hutiel

ANGERS

LE COURRIER DE L'OUEST (D) EST. 1905
BP 728, Angers, 49007, France; tel (33) 2 4168 8688; fax 4168 1327; web site www.quotidiens-associes.fr
Circ.: 108,802
Chrmn./MD – Christian Coustal
Chief Ed. – Patrice Juillier

ANGOULEME

LA CHARENTE LIBRE (D-EX S)
BP 1025, Angouleme, 16001, France; tel (33) 5 4594 1600; fax 4594 1719; e-mail charente@charentelibre.fr; web site www.charentelibre.fr
Circ.: 40,496
Dir. – Jacques Guyon
Adv. Mgr – Jeaan Phille Neyrolles

AUXERRE

L'YONNE REPUBLICAINE (D)
8-12 Ave. Jean Moulin, Auxerre, 89000, France; tel (33) 3 8649 5200; fax 8646 9990; e-mail redaction.sports@lyonne-republicaine.fr; web site www.lyonne-republicaine.fr
Circ.: 44,036
Pres. – Joel Loubert

AVIGNON

LA MARSEILLAISE VAUCLUSE (D)
4 rue Agricol-Perdiguier, Avignon, 84000, France; tel (33)
Ed. – Marc Berrus

VAUCLUSE MATIN (DS)
BP 134, Avignon, 84000, France; tel (33) 490 823 280
Ed. – Pierre Bail

BASTIA

LE PETIT BASTIAIS (D)
2 rue Saint-Angelo, Bastia, 20200, France; tel (33) 953 10499
Circ.: 1,200
– Catherine Fieschi-Livrelli
– Lois RioniPub.s

BEAUVAIS

OISE-MATIN (D)
7 rue Saint-Pierre, Beauvais, 60000, France; tel (33)
Ed. – Pascal Sellier

BOULOGNE

CENTRE-PRESSE RODEZ (D)
83 rue du Chateau, Boulogne, 92513, France; tel (33) 1460 50506
Circ.: 25,144

BOULOGNE BILLANCOURT

L'EQUIPE (D)
4 rue Rouget-de-L'Isle, Boulogne Billancourt, 92100, France; tel (33) 1 4093 2020; fax 4093 2003; web site www.lequipe.com
Circ.: 388,914
MD – Francois Moriniere

BOURGES

LE BERRY REPUBLICAIN (D)
BP 141, Bourges, 18000, France; tel (33) 2 4827 6378; fax 4827 6869; web site www.leberry.fr
Circ.: 40,000
Pub. – Guy Dugne

CALAIS

NORD-LITTORAL (D-EX MON.)
BP 108, Calais, 62100, France; tel (33) 3 2119 1212; web site www.nordlittoral.fr
Circ.: 7,498
Ed. in Chief – Henri Desvignes

CHALON-SUR-SAONE

LE JOURNAL DE SAONE-ET-LOIRE (D)
BP 134, Chalon-sur-Saone, 71104, France; tel (33) 3 8590 6800; fax 8593 0296; e-mail

archive@lejsl.fr; web site www.lejsl.com
Circ.: 46,021
Dir. – Jean Viansson Ponte

CHARLEVILLE-MEZIERES

L'ARDENNAIS (D)
BP 220, Charleville-Mezieres, 08102, France; tel (33) 243 39151; fax 30260
Circ.: 27,477
Pub. – Pierre Didry
Ed. in Chief – Pierre Delohen

CHARTRES

L'ECHO REPUBLICAIN (D)
BP 189, Chartres, 28000, France; tel (33)
Circ.: 35,000
Chrmn./Mng. Dir. – Alain Gascon

CHATEAUROUX

LA MARSEILLAISE DU BERRY (D)
BP 152, Chateauroux, 36000, France; tel (33) (33) 54340015
Circ.: 11,880

CHAUMONT

LA HAUTE MARNE LIBEREE (D)
14 rue du Patronage-Laique, Chaumont, 52003, France; tel (33) 253 21988
Circ.: 14,651
Ed. and Pub. – Jean Bletner

CHERBOURG

LA PRESSE DE LA MANCHE (D)
9 rue Gambetta, Cherbourg, 50104, France; tel (33) 2 3397 1616; fax 3397 1606; e-mail redaction.locale@lapressedelamanche.fr; web site www.lapressedelamanche.fr
Circ.: 27,397
Pub. – Marcel Clairet
Adv. Mgr. – Ilippe Restout

CLERMONT-FERRAND

LA MONTAGNE/LA MONTAGNE DIMANCHE (D)
45 rue du clos Four, Clermont-Ferrand, 63000, France; tel (33) 4 7317 1717; fax 7317 1819; e-mail lamontagne@centre-france.com; web site www.lamontagne.fr
MD – Jean-Pierre Caillard

COMPIEGNE

LE COURRIER DE L'OISE (D)
33 rue des Trois-Barbeaux, Compiegne, 60204, France; tel (33)
Circ.: 14,671
Mgr. – Serge Donneux

DEVILLE-LES-ROUEN

PARIS-NORMANDIE (D)
33 rue des Grosses-Pierres, Deville-les-Rouen, 76250, France; tel (33) 2 3514 5656; fax 0208 0983; web site www.paris-normandie.fr
Circ.: 104,327
Adv. Mgr – Jean Luc Sontag
Adv. Rep. – Sanny Lepovac

DIJON

LES DEPECHES DU CENTRE-EST (D)
BP 570, Dijon, 21015, France; tel (33) 3 8042 1616
Circ.: 42,000
Chrmn. – Xavier Ellie
Mng. Dir. – Pierre Villez

EPINAL

LIBERTE DE L'EST/LIBERTE DE L'EST DIMANCHE (D)
40 quai des Bons Enfants, Epinal, 88000, France; tel (33) 3 2982 9800; fax 2982 3057
Circ.: 31,319
Mgr. – Gerald Moel

GORCEIX

L'ECHO DORDOYNE (6X WK.)
17 rue Claude Henri, Gorceix, 24003, France; tel (33) 5 5353 1444; fax 5353 0230; e-mail dordojne@l-echo.fr
Circ.: 11,041
Mgr. – Ewen Cousin
Mktg. Mgr. – Michele Duban

GRENOBLE

LE DAUPHINE LIBERE/LE DAUPHINE LIBERE DIMANCHE (DS)
Les Iles Cordees, Grenoble, 38113, France; tel (33) 4 7688 7100; fax 7688 7180
MD – Denis Huertas
Ed. in Chief – Hubert Perrin

HEILLECOURT

L'EST REPUBLICAIN (D)
rue Theophraste-Renaudot, Houdemont, Heillecourt, 54180, France; tel (33) 835 68054; fax 98013
Circ.: 214,965

LE HAVRE

HAVRE LIBRE (D)
BP 1384, Le Havre, 76066, France; tel (33) 2 3519 1727; fax 3521 4852
Circ.: 26,466
Ed. in Chief – Mrsf Brulu Salmon

LE HAVRE PRESSE (D)
25 rue Jules Siegfried, Le Havre, 76066, France; tel (33) 2 3519 1727; fax 3542 0043
Circ.: 17,831
Ed. in Chief – Pascal Lachaux

LE MANS

LE MAINE LIBRE (D)
BP 299, Le Mans, 72007, France; tel (33) 2 4383 7250; fax 4328 2819
Circ.: 54,891
Pres. – Mongra Gorn

LE PUY

L'EVEIL DE LA HAUTE-LOIRE/L'EVEIL DU DIMANCHE (D)
BP 24, Le Puy, 43001, France; tel (33) 4 7109 3214; fax 7102 9408; web site www.leveil.fr
Circ.: 13,367
Pub. – Henri Merle

LENS

NARODOWIEC (D)
BP 79, Lens, 62302, France; tel (33) (33) 21281821
Pub. – Michel-Alexandre Kwiatowski

LILLE

LIBERTE (D-6X WK.)
BP 1269, Lille, 59014, France; tel (33) 3 2836 8850; fax 2030 1176; e-mail leberte-hebdo@nordnet.fr
Pub. – Albert Debosschere
Pub. – Jean-Raymond de Greve
Ed. in Chief – Jean-Louis Bouzin

NORD-MATIN (D-EX MON.)
22-24 Ave. Charles-Saint-Venant, Lille, 59023, France; tel (33) 3 2006 4520; fax 2082 8363
Circ.: 76,896
Chrmn./Mng. Dir. – Michel Noziere

LA VOIX DU NORD (M-6X WK.)
BP 549, Lille, 59023, France; tel (33) 3 2078 4040; fax 2078 4244; e-mail lille@lavoixdunord.fr; contact@lavoixdunord.fr; web site www.lavoixdunord.fr
Circ.: 356,903
Ed. – Jean Michel Beretownier

LIMOGES

L'ECHO DU CENTRE (6X WK.)
BP 1582, Limoges, 87022, France; tel (33) 5 5504 4999; fax 5504 4986
Circ.: 26,853
MD – Christian Audouin

LA MARSEILLAISE DU BERRY (D)
46 rue Turgot, Limoges, 87011, France; tel (33) 5 5534 3635
Circ.: 11,880

LE POPULAIRE DU CENTRE (D)
BP 541, Limoges, 87011, France; tel (33) 5 5558 5960; fax 5558 5979; web site www.lepopulaire.fr
Circ.: 53,622
Ed. – Gilahdi Slancoes

LORIENT

LA LIBERTE DU MORBIHAN (D)
8 place de Clairambault, Lorient, 56101, France; tel (33) 972 11018
Circ.: 7,011
Ed. and Pub. – Herve Le Gouallac

LYON

LE PROGRES/LE PROGRES DIMANCHE (D)
4 rue Montrochet, Lyon, 69002, France; tel (33) 4 7222 2323; fax 7214 7677; e-mail redactionenchef@leprogres.fr; web site www.leprogres.fr
Ed. in Chief – Xavier Antoye

LYON-FIGARO (D)
14 rue de la Charite, Lyon, 69215, France; tel (33)
Circ.: 13,644
Ed. and Pub. – Alain Buhler

LYON-LIBERATION (D)
24 rue Childebert, Lyon, 69002, France; tel (33) 4 7842 0809; fax 7842 2172
Circ.: 11,934
Ed. and Pub. – Michel Lepinay

LYON-MATIN/LYON-MATIN DIMANCHE (M-6X WK.)
52/54 rue Servient, Lyon, 69003, France; tel (33) 4 7222 2323; e-mail quartiers@leprogres.fr; web site www.leprogres.fr
Ed. in Chief – Angoy Entoye

MARSEILLE

LA PROVENCE (D)
248 Ave. Roger Salengro, Marseille, 13015, France; tel (33) 4 9184 4545; fax 9184 4995
Mgr. – Stephen Duhamel

LA MARSEILLAISE (D)
19 cours Honore d'Estienne d'Orves, Marseille, 13001, France; tel (33) 4 9157 7500; fax 9157 7525
Circ.: 78,900
MD – Paul Biaggini

LA PROVENCE (D)
248 Ave. Roger Salengro, Marseille, 13015, France; tel (33) 4 9184 4545; fax 9184 4995; e-mail redaction@laprovence-presse.fr; web site www.laprovence.com
MD – Jean-Pierre Milet
Ed. in Chief – Laurent Gilardino
Ed. – Didier Pillet

LE SOIR (E)
248 Ave. Roger Salengro, Marseille, 13015, France; tel (33) 4 9184 4545
Contact Sebastian

MARSEILLE, CEDEX 16

L'ANTENNE (5X WK.)
BP 36, Marseille, Cedex 16, 13221, France; tel (33) 4 9133 2581; web site www.lantenne.com
Dir. – Richard Reverchon
Ed. – Ricco Bono

MAZAMET

LA MONTAGNE NOIRE (D)
14 rue Mejanel, Mazamet, 81200, France; tel (33)
Circ.: 2,500
Ed. and Pub. – Jacques Thiebault

MONTBELIARD

LE PAYS DE FRANCHE-COMTE (D)
10, Rue M□gevand, Montbeliard, 25000, France; tel (33) 3 8131 2410; fax 8194 4387; web site www.lepays.fr
Ed. – Catherine Daudinhan

MONTPELLIER

MIDI LIBRE/MIDI LIBRE DIMANCHE (D)
Cedex 9, Montpellier, 34923, France; tel (33) 4 6707 6707; fax 6707 6694; e-mail redac.ig@midilibre.com; web site www.midilibre.com
MD – Alain Plombat

MULHOUSE

L'ALSACE (D)
18 rue de Thann, Mulhouse, 68053, France; tel (33) 3 8932 7000; fax 436 359
Circ.: 124,997
Ed. – Leffon Farmces

NANCY

L'EST REPUBLICAIN/L'EST REPUBLICAIN DIMANCHE (D)
rue Theophraste-Renaudot, Nancy Houdemont, Nancy, 54185, France; tel (33) 3 8359 8054; fax 8359 8013; e-mail secretariat.general @ estrepublicain.fr; web site www.estrepublicain.fr
Circ.: 230,922
Chrmn. – Gerard Lignac
Ed. in Chief – Pierre Taribo

NANTES

PRESSE OCEAN (D)
8 rue Santeuil, Nantes, 44024, France; tel (33) 2 4073 4445; fax 4044 2440; e-mail redac.locale.nantes@presse-ocean.com; web site www.presseocean.fr
Circ.: 18,137
Dir. – David Lacinoux

PRESSE-OCEAN (D)
BP 1142, Nantes, 44000, France; tel (33) 2 4044 2400; fax 4044 2440; e-mail redac.locale.nantes@presse-ocean.com; web site www.presseocean.fr
Circ.: 50,000
Mgr. – Domeinique Luneau
Sales Mgr. – Philippe Pele

NEVERS

LE JOURNAL DU CENTRE (D)
3 rue du Chemin de Fer, Nevers, 58002, France; tel (33) 3 8659 8989; fax 8671 4510; web site www.lejdc.fr
Circ.: 37,348
MD – Jean-Pierre Caillard
Ed. in Chief – Philippe Vazeille

NICE

NICE-MATIN (D-7X WK.)
BP 4, Nice, 06290, France; tel (33) 4 9318 2838; fax 9383 9397; e-mail infoslocales@nicematin.fr; web site www.nicematin.fr
Dir. – Eric Debry
Adv. Mgr. – Philippe Dunesme

ORLEANS

LA REPUBLIQUE DU CENTRE (6X WK.)
rue de la Halte, Orleans, 45770, France; tel (33) 2 3878 7960; fax 3878 7979; web site www.larep.com
Circ.: 61,044
Ed. in Chief – Jacques Camus
Mktg. Mgr. – Belmonte Melchchor

PARIS

L'AGEFI (5X WK.)
48 rue Notre-Dame des Victoires, Paris, 750023, France; tel (33) 1 4488 4646; fax 4233 1236
Circ.: 6,700
Advertising: AdMarket Int'l.
Pub. – Jean-Louis Servan-Schreiber
Ed. – Henri Paul Vanel
Mng. Ed. – Jean-Michel Quatrepoint

LA CROIX (E-EX S)
3-5 rue Bayard, Paris, 75393, France; tel (33) 8258 25832; web site www.la-croix.com
Circ.: 98,233
Ed. in Chief – Bruno Frappat

LA TRIBUNE (E)
26, Rue d'Oradour sur Glane, Paris, France; tel (33) 1 4482 1616; fax 4482 1792; e-mail directiondelaredaction@latribune.fr; web site www.latribune.fr
Ed. – Olivier Provost
Circ. Dir. – Claire Balthazard
Ed. in Chief – Erik Izraelewicz

EUROPE JOURNAL (D)
167 rue Lecourbe, Paris, 75015, France; tel (33) 5555 5555
Ed. and Pub. – Nicolas Druz

EVENEMENTS ET PERSPECTIVES (D)
4 rue du Faubourg-Poissonniere, Paris, 75010, France; tel (33) 1
Pub./Ed. in Chief – Gaston Gosselin

L'EXPANSION (MTHLY)
29 rue de Chateaudun, Paris, 75308, France; tel (33) 1 7555 1000; fax 7555 4105; web site www.lexpansion.com
Circ.: 200,000
Mgr. – Yves Adaken

LE FIGARO (D)
14 Haussmann Blvd., Paris, 75009, France; tel (33) 1 5708 5000; e-mail contact@lefigaro.fr; web site www.lefigaro.fr

FINANCIAL TIMES (6X WK.)
40 Rue de la Boetie, Paris, 75008, France; tel (33) 1 5376 8256; web site www.ft.com/home/europe
Ed. – Lionel Barber

FRANCE-SOIR (D)
37 rue du Louvre, Paris, 75081, France; tel (33) 1 4482 8700; fax 4482 8845
Circ.: 184,000
Ed. in Chief – Claude Lambert

LES ECHOS (D)
16 street of September 4, Paris, 75112, France; tel (33) 1 4953 6565; fax 4561 4892; e-mail service.client@lesechos.com; web site www.lesechos.com
Circ.: 135,000
Advertising: Regent Advertising Sales.
Chrmn. – Daniel Gunauel
Ed. in Chief – Michel Dabaji

HARATCH (D)
83 rue d'Hauteville, Paris, 75010, France; tel (33) 1 4770 8660; fax 4800 0670; e-mail jharatch@aol.com
Pub. – A. Missakian

INTERNATIONAL HERALD TRIBUNE (M-EX S)
6 Bis Rue Des Graviers, Paris, 92521, France; tel (33) 1 4143 9300; fax 4143 9393; e-mail iht@iht.com; web site www.iht.com; www.ihtinfo.com
Circ.: 210,000
Pub. – Stephen Dunbar-Johnson
Ed. – Alison Smale

LE JOURNAL OFFICIEL DE LA REPUBLIQUE FRANCAISE (6X WK.)
26 rue Desaix, Paris, 75727, France; tel (33) 1 4058 7500; fax 4579 1784; web site www.journal-officiel.gouv.fr
Dir. – Xavier Bertrand

LA COTE DESFOSSES (D)
5-7 rue St. Augustine, Paris, 75002, France; tel (33) 1 4233 2130; fax 4233 1236
Circ.: 25,618
Pub. – Jean Chamboulive
Mng. Ed. – Paul-Francois Trioux

LE PARISIEN (M-EX S)
25 Ave. Michelet, Paris, 93408, France; tel (33) 1 4010 3030; fax 4010 3517; e-mail info@leparisien.fr; web site www.leparisien.fr
Circ.: 457,244
MD – Jean Germain

MARCHES AGRICOLES-L'ECHO DES HALLES (D)
42 rue Olivier-Metra, Paris, 75020, France; tel (33) 5555 5555
Pub. – Rene-Charles Millet
Ed. in Chief – Robert Raure

LE MATIN DE PARIS/LE MATIN DE DIMANCHE (D)
57 Blvd. de la Villette, Paris, 75010, France; tel (33)
Circ.: 178,352
Pub. – Didier Tourancheau
Ed. in Chief – Pierre Feydel

PANORAMA DU MEDECIN (D)
15 bis rue de Marignan, Paris, 75008, France; tel (33) 1 5533 6800; fax 5533 6912
Pub. – Gerard Dongradi
Ed. in Chief – Alain Trebucq

PARIS-TURF/DIMANCHE TURF (D)
100 rue Reaumur, Paris, 75002, France; tel (33) 1 4001 8200; e-mail info@paris-turf.com; web site www.paris-turf.org
Circ.: 150,000
Pub. – Roger Alexandre
Ed. in Chief – M. Francois Hallope

LE QUOTIDIEN DU MAIRE (D)
122 Ave. Charles-de-Gaulle, Paris, 92200, France; tel (33)
Mng. Ed. – Robert Toubon

LE QUOTIDIEN DU MEDECIN (D)
140 rue Jules Guesde, Paris, 92300, France; tel (33) 1 4140 7500; fax 4140 7575; e-mail redaction@quotimed.com; web site www.quotimed.com
Circ.: 82,000
Dir. – Dr. Marie-Claude Tesson-Millet
Ed. – Renee Carton
Ed. – Bruno Keller
Ed. – Emmanuel De Viel
Ed. in Chief – Richard Liscia

LE QUOTIDIEN DE PARIS (M-EX S)
140 rue Jules Guesde, Paris, 92300, France; tel (33) 1 4730 7800; fax 4730 7878
Circ.: 75,000
Ed. and Pub. – Phillipe Tesson
Adv. Dir. – Patrice Gelobter

BULLETIN QUOTIDIEN (D)
13 Ave. de l'Opera, Paris, 75001, France; tel (33)
Pub. – Georges Berard-Quelin
Mng. Ed. – Etienne Lacour

CORRESPONDANCE DE LA PRESSE (D) EST. 1944
13 Ave. de l'Opera, Paris, 75001, France; tel (33) 1 4015 1789; fax 4015 1715; e-mail redaceco@sgpresse.fr; web site www.sgpresse.fr
Pub. Ed. – Marianne Berard-Quelin
Mng. Ed. – Etienne Lacour

CORRESPONDANCE DE LA PUBLICITE (D)
13 Ave. de l'Opera, Paris, 75001, France; tel (33) 1 4015 1789; web site www.sgpresse.fr
Circ.: 1,000
Pres. – Marianne Berard-Quelin
Mng. Ed. – Etienne Lacour
Dir – Laurent BERARD-QUELIN
Red Chief – Tanguy DEMANGE

CORRESPONDANCE ECONOMIQUE (D)
13 Ave. de l'Opera, Paris, 75039, France; tel (33) 4015 1789; fax 4015 1715; e-mail sgp@sgpresse.fr; web site www.sgpresse.fr
Pres./Pub. Dir. – Marianne Berard-Quelin

L'EQUIPE: LE QUOTIDIEN DU SPORT ET DE L'AUTOMOBILE (D)
4 rue Rouget de L'Isle, Paris, 92137, France; tel (33) 1 5555 5555
Pub. – Jean-Pierre Courcol
Mng. Ed. – Henri Garcia

LE SPORT (D)
9-13 rue du Colonel Pierre Avia, Paris, 75015, France; tel (33) 1 4662 2000
Pub. – Rene Teze
Ed. in Chief – Patrick Blain

PARIS CEDEX

LIAISONS SOCIALES (D)
1 rue Eugene et Armand Peugeot, Paris Cedex, 92856, France; tel (33) 1 7673 3000; e-mail contact@wk-rh.fr; web site www.wk-rh.fr
Ed. in Chief – Denis Boissard

PARIS CEDEX 03

LIBERATION (D)
11, Rue Beranger, Paris Cedex 03, 75154, France; tel (33) 1 4276 1789; fax 4276 1640; web site www.liberation.fr
Dir. – Laurent Joffrin
Adv. Mgr. – Marie Giraud

PARIS CEDEX 13

LE MONDE/LE MONDE DIMANCHE (D)
80 Auguste Blanqui Blvd., Paris Cedex 13, 75707, France; tel (33) 1 5728 3900; fax 5728 3926; e-mail mail@mondepub.fr; web site www.mondepub.fr
Circ.: 368,856
Mng. Dir. – Stephane Corre
Ed. in Chief – Jean-Marie Colombani
Adv. Dir. – Brune Le Gall

PAU

ECLAIR PYRENEES (D)
BP 629, Pau, 64006, France; tel (33) 5 5982 2929; web site www.pyrenees.com
Circ.: 9,801
Pub. – Henri Loustalan
Ed. – Paul Guilhot

LA REPUBLIQUE DES PYRENEES (D)
6-8 rue Despourrins, Pau, 64040, France; tel (33) 5 5982 2020; e-mail desk@pyrenees.com; redaction-pp@pyrenees.com; orthez-pp@pyrenees.com; web site www.larepubliquedespyrenees.fr
Circ.: 29,478
Ed. – Jean-Pierre Cassagne

PERIGUEUX

LA DORDOGNE LIBRE (6X WK.)
4, allee d'Aquitaine, Perigueux, 24003, France; tel (33) 5533 55900; fax 5530 94918; web site www.dordogne.com
Circ.: 3,860
Pub. – Stephan Vacchiani
Mktg. Mgr. – Thierrw Merlet

L'ECHO DORDOGNE (D)
BP 40, Perigueux, 24000, France; tel (33) (33) 531444
Circ.: 11,041

POITIERS

CENTRE-PRESSE (D-EX S)
5 rue Victor Hugo, Poitiers, 86000, France; tel (33) 49 411 780; fax 559 375
Circ.: 23,126
Advertising: Nielsen Communications Ltd.
Pub. – Cyrille Duval
Ed. in Chief – Roland Barrat

REIMS

L'UNION (D)
5, rue de Talleyrand, Reims, 51083, France; tel (33) 3 2650 5050; fax 2650 5169; e-mail dirgen@journal-lunion.fr; web site www.lunion.presse.fr

Circ.: 137,518
Chrmn. – Michel Noziere
Ed. in Chief – Michel Grenouilloux
Mng. Dir. – Daniel Hutier

RIVESALTES

L'INDEPENDANT (D)
Mas de la Garrigue, 2 Ave. Alfred Sauvy, Rivesaltes, 66605, France; tel (33) 4 6864 8888; fax 6864 8840; web site www.lindependant.com
Circ.: 82,110
Mgr. – Michelle Atrijnans
Adv. Mgr – Josh Lozino

RODEZ

CENTRE PRESSE (D)
BP 137, Rodez, 12001, France; tel (33)
Circ.: 10,000
Pub. – Alain Almeras
Ed. in Chief – Pierre Molier

ROUBAIX

NORD-ECLAIR (D)
42, rue du General Sarrail, Roubaix, 59100, France; tel (33) 3 2025 0250; fax 2025 6298; e-mail osrar.crssao@nordeclair.fr; region@nordeclair.fr; metropole@nordeclair.fr; web site www.nordeclair.fr
Circ.: 96,661
Dir. – Jacques Hardoin

SAINT-DENIS

L'HUMANITE/L'HUMANITE DIMANCHE (MS)
164 rue Ambroise Croizat, Saint-Denis, 93528, France; tel (33) 1 4922 7300; fax 4922 7400; e-mail humanite@humanite.presse.fr; web site www.humanite.fr
Pres./Pub. – Patrick Le Hyaric
Ed. in Chief – Pierre Laurent

SAINT-ETIENNE

L'ESPOIR (D)
110 rue Bergson, Saint-Etienne, 42000, France; tel (33)
Ed. – Hubert Perrin

LA TRIBUNE-LE PROGRES (D)
110 rue Bergson, Saint-Etienne, 42000, France; tel (33) 5555 5555
Ed. – Hubert Perrin

LOIRE-MATIN/LES DEPECHES (DS)
16 Pl. Drouet d'Erlon, Saint-Etienne, 51052, France; tel (33) (33) 77327997
Ed. – Hubert Perrin

STRASBOURG

LES DERNIERES NOUVELLES D'ALSACE (D)
17-21 rue de la Nuee-Bleue, Strasbourg, 67077, France; tel (33) 3 8821 5500; fax 8821 5641; e-mail dnasug@sdv.fr; web site www.dna.fr
Circ.: 215,460
Pub. – Gerard Lignac
Gen. Dir. – Jean-Claude Bonnaud

TARBES

LA NOUVELLE REPUBLIQUE DES PYRENEES (D)
48 Ave. Bertrand-Barere, Tarbes, 65001, France; tel (33) 6293 9090; fax (33) 62938143
Circ.: 16,473
Pub./Ed. in Chief – Claude Gaits

TOULON

VAR MATIN (D-6X WK.)
BP 116, Toulon, 83196, France; tel (33) 4 9406 9191; fax 9463 4998
Chrmn. – Jean-Pierre Milet
Ed. in Chief – Daniel Cuxac
Mng. Dir. – Rene Clau

LE VAROIS-LA MARSEILLAISE (D)
BP 946, Toulon, 83050, France; tel (33)
Ed. in Chief – Rene Fredon

TOURS

LA NOUVELLE REPUBLIQUE DU CENTRE-OUEST (M-EX S)
232 Ave. de Grammont, Tours, 37048, France; tel (33) 2 4731 7000; fax 4731 7070
Circ.: 259,606
Ed. in Chief – Herve Gueneron
Chrmn. – Jacques Saint Circq
Chrmn. – David Bohbot

TOURS CEDEX 1

LA FRANCE-LA NOUVELLE REPUBLIQUE (D)
232, avenue de Grammont, Tours cedex 1, 37048, France; tel (33) 2 47 31 70 00; fax 47 31 70 00; e-mail nr.redactionenchef@nrco.fr; web site www.lanouvellerepublique.fr
Circ.: 8,210
Pub. – Olivier Saint Cricq

TROYES

L'EST ECLAIR (D)
71 Ave. du Marechal Leclerc, Troyes, 10120, France; tel (33) 3 2571 7575; fax 2578 3943; e-mail redaction@lest-eclair.fr; web site www.lest-eclair.fr
Circ.: 33,000
Dir. – Francois Le Sache

LIBERATION CHAMPAGNE/LIBERATION CHAMPAGNE DU DIMANCHE (D)
BP 713, Troyes, 10003, France; tel (33)
Circ.: 11,918
Pub. – Francois le Saxhe
Ed. – Gilbert Boutsoque

GEORGIA

TBILISI

VESTNIK GRUZZI (5X WK.)
Tiflis, Tbilisi, Georgia; tel (995)
Ed. – V. Keshelava

GERMANY

AACHEN

AACHENER NACHRICHTEN (M-6X WK.)
PF 500110, Aachen, 52085, Germany; tel (49) 241 51010; fax 5101790; e-mail verlagsleitung@zeitungsverlag-aachen.de; chefredaktion@mail.an-online.de; web site www.an-online.de; www.zeitungsverlag-aachen.de
Circ.: 70,000
Ed. in Chief – Bernd Mathieu
Ed. – Achin Kaiser

AACHENER ZEITUNG (M-6X WK.)
PF 500110, Aachen, 52085, Germany; tel (49) 241 51010; fax 510 1120; e-mail verlagsleitung@zeitungsverlang-aachen.de; web site www.aachener-zeitung.de; www.zeitungsverlag-aachen.de
Circ.: 107,000
Ed. in Chief – Bernd Mathieu
Mng. Ed. – Erich Behrendt
News Ed. – Peter Pappert

AALEN

SCHWABISCHE POST (6X WK.)
Bahnhofstr. 65, Aalen, 73430, Germany; tel (49) 7361 5940; fax 594 207; e-mail info@sdz-medien.de; web site www.sdz-medien.de; www.schwaebische-post.de
Circ.: 27,611
MD – Bernhard Theiss
Distr. Mgr. – Friedrich Schied
Ed. – Frank Buhl
Ed. – Manfred Moll
Ed. – Ulrich Gessler

ACHIM

ACHIMER-KREISBLATT (6X WK.)
Obernstr. 54, Achim, 28832, Germany; tel (49) 42 42580; fax 58200; e-mail anzeigen@kreiszeitung.de; web site www.achimer-kreisblatt.de
Circ.: 29,300
Bus. Mgr. – Hans Sahl
Adv. Mgr. – Arnim Wollschlanger
Distr. Mgr. – Udo Nerz
Ed. – Manfred Brodt

AHLEN

AHLENER ZEITUNG (6X WK.)
An der Hansalinie 1, Ahlen, 59227, Germany; tel (49) 2382 80 880; fax 80 8848; e-mail redaktion@ahlener-zeitung.de; web site www.ahlener-zeitung.de
Circ.: 8,700
Ed. Chief – Norbert Tiemann
Ed. – Peter Harke

ALFELD

ALFELDER ZEITUNG (6X WK.)
PF 1164, Alfeld, 31041, Germany; tel (49) 5181 80020; fax 800 247; web site www.alfelder-zeitung.de
Circ.: 10,900
Pub./MD – Ewald Dobler
Ed. in Chief – Markus Kater

OBERHESSISCHE ZEITUNG (6X WK.)
PF 220, Alfeld, 36292, Germany; tel (49) 6631 96690; fax 966923; e-mail vertrieb@oz.ehrenklau.de; web site www.oz.ehrenklau.de
Circ.: 7,900
Proprietor – Martin Ehrenklau
Ed. in Chief – Roland Walter Heinrich

ALTENA

ALTENAER KREISBLATT (6X WK.)
PF 1661, Altena, 58746, Germany; tel (49) 2352 91870; fax 918 713; web site www.come-on.de
Circ.: 5,000
Ed. – Thomas Bender

ANSBACH

FRANKISHE LANDESZEITUNG (6X WK.)
PF 1362, Ansbach, 91504, Germany; tel (49) 981 95000; fax 950 0122; e-mail lisa.serivce@flz.de; web site www.flz.de
Circ.: 50,000
Pub. – Rainer Mehl
Pub. – Klaus W. Wiedfeld
Pub. – Bruno Schnell
Distr. Mgr. – W. Wilczek
Ed. in Chief – P.M. Szymanowski
Ed. – Karl Friedrich

ASCHAFFENBURG

MAIN-ECHO (D)
PF 548, Aschaffenburg, 63741, Germany; tel (49) 6021 3960; fax 396 499; e-mail info@main-netz.de; web site www.main-echo.de
Ed. in Chief – Claus Morhart
Ed. – Peter Freudenberger

AUGSBURG

AUGSBURGER ALLGEMEINE (M-6X WK.)
Curt-Frenzel-Str. 2, Augsburg, 86167, Germany; tel (49) 821 7770; fax 704 471; e-mail online-redaktion@augsburger-allgemeine.de; web site www.augsburger-allgemeine.de
Circ.: 350,000
Proprietor – Ellinor Holland
Bus. Mgr. – Stefan Hillscher
Distr. Mgr. – G. Nitsche
Ed. in Chief – Rainer Bonhorst
Mng. Ed. – Karl Rauch

LANDSBERGER TAGBLATT (6X WK.)
Curt-Frenzel Str. 2, Augsburg, 86167, Germany; tel (49) 821 7770; fax 777 2139; e-mail desk@augsburger-allgemeine.de; web site www.landsberger-tagblatt.de
Circ.: 344,000
Proprietor – Ellinor Holland
Bus. Mgr. – Stefan Hillscher
Distr. Mgr. – G. Nitsche

AURICH

OSTFRIESISCHE NACHRICHTEN (6X WK.)
PF 1540, Aurich, 26585, Germany; tel (49) 4941 170 894; fax 170 813; e-mail info@on-online.de; web site www.on-online.de
Circ.: 14,500
Bus. Mgr. – Robert Dunkmann
Distribution Mgr. – Sven Buenting
Ed. in Chief – Stefan Dunkmann
Ed. in Chief – Ralf Kloker

BACKNANG

BACKNANGER KREISZEITUNG (6X WK.)
PF 1169, Backnang, 71522, Germany; tel (49) 7191 8080; fax 808 111; e-mail

info@bkz-online.de; redaktion@bkz-online.de; web site www.bkz-online.de
Circ.: 18,000
Proprietor – W. Stroh
Ed. in Chief – Reinhard Fiedler

BAD GANDERSHEIM

GANDERSHEIMER KREISBLATT (6X WK.)

PF 1109, Bad Gandersheim, 37581, Germany; tel (49) 5382 98110; fax 6356; e-mail kreisblatt@t-online.de; web site www.gandersheimer-kreisblatt.de
Circ.: 5,900
Ed. – Thomas Fischer

BAD HERSFELD

HERSFELDER ZEITUNG (6X WK.)

Gutenbergstr. 1, Bad Hersfeld, 36225, Germany; tel (49) 6621 1610; fax 161148; e-mail anzeigen@hersfelder-zeitung.de; web site www.hersfelder-zeitung.de
Circ.: 18,800
Bus. Mgr. – Markus Pfromm

BAD LAUTERBERG

BAD LAUTERBERGER TAGEBLATT (6X WK.)

PF 1241, Bad Lauterberg, 37422, Germany; tel (49) 5524 85000; fax 850039
Circ.: 3,800
Pub. – Dr. K. Freund
Bus. Mgr. – J. Freund
Distr. – R. Kiesslinger
Ed. – H.A. Kuhne
Ed. – K.H. Bless

BAD MERGENTHEIM

TAUBER-ZEITUNG (6X WK.)

PF 1804, Bad Mergentheim, 97980, Germany; tel (49) 7931 5960; fax 59644; e-mail tauber-zeitung@t-online.de; web site www.tauber-zeitung.de
Circ.: 6,700
Ed. in Chief – Claus Peter Muhleck
Ed. – Thomas Weller

BAD NEUSTADT

RHON UND SAALEPOST (6X WK.)

PF 1560, Bad Neustadt, 97616, Germany; tel (49) 9771 91930; fax 919 355; web site www.rhon-undsaalepost.de
Circ.: 5,150
Bus. Mgr. – Wolfgang Markert
Ed. in Chief – Gerhard Rotter

BAD REICHENHALL

REICHENHALLER TAGBLATT (6X WK.)

PF 2153, Bad Reichenhall, 83435, Germany; tel (49) 8651 9810; fax 981 160; e-mail info@bgl-medien.de; web site www.reichenhaller-tagblatt.de
Circ.: 11,400
Bus. Mgr. – Petra Wiedemann

BAD SALZUNGEN

SUDTHURINGER ZEITUNG (6X WK.)

Andreasstr. 11, Bad Salzungen, 36433, Germany; tel (49) 3695 555 050; fax 555 051; e-mail redaktion@stz-online.de; web site www.stz-online.de

Circ.: 174,300
Mktg. Mgr. – Pierre Doring
Ed. in Chief – Berthod Ducker
Ed. – Silke Wolf

BAD WINDSHEIM

WINDSHEIMER ZEITUNG (6X WK.)

PF 140, Bad Windsheim, 91438, Germany; tel (49) 9841 90334; fax 90315; e-mail Windsheimer-Zeitung@odn.de
Circ.: 5,300
Proprietor – Bruno Schnell
Proprietor – Johann Delp
Ed. in Cheif – Orrnn Telt

BADEN-BADEN

BADISCHES TAGBLATT (D)

PF 100033, Baden-Baden, 76530, Germany; tel (49) 7221 2150; fax 215 1469; e-mail info@badisches-tagblatt.de; web site www.badisches-tagblatt.de
Distr. Mgr. – Ingo Sax
Ed. in Chief – Markus Langer
Ed. – Albert Noll
Ed. – Gerold Hammes

BALINGEN

ZOLLERN-ALB KURIER (6X WK.)

Grunewaldstr. 15, Balingen, 72336, Germany; tel (49) 7433 2660; fax 266 201; e-mail zak@zak.de; web site www.zak.de
Circ.: 28,000
Proprietor – Heiner Weidle
Proprietor – Klaus Jetter
Ed. – Karl-Otto Muller
Adv. Mgr – Katja Kiene

BAMBERG

FRANKISCHER TAG (6X WK.)

Gutenbergstr. 1, Bamberg, 96050, Germany; tel (49) 951 1880; fax 188 118; e-mail redaktion@fraenkischer-tag.de; redaktion.bamberg@infranken.de; web site www.fraenkischer-tag.de
Circ.: 70,000
Proprietor – Dr. Helmuth Jungbauer
Mng. Ed. – Wolfgang Bauer
News Ed. – Christian Reinisch

BARSINGHAUSEN

DEISTER-LEINE-ZEITUNG (6X WK.)

Bahnhofstr. 5, Barsinghausen, 30882, Germany; tel (49) 5105 77070; fax 770733; e-mail info@t-online.de; web site www.deister-leine-zeitung.de
Circ.: 7,200
Proprietor – Emke Hillrichs
Ed. – Juretz Helltrud

BATH SEGEBERG

SZ SEGEBERGER ZEITUNG (6X WK.)

Hamburger Str. 26, Bath Segeberg, 23795, Germany; tel (49) 4551 9040; fax 90464; e-mail info@segeberger-zeitung.de; web site www.segeberger-zeitung.de
Circ.: 14,800
Proprietor – Hans Christian Wulff
Ed. – Petra Stover
Mng. Ed. – S. Ures

BAUTZEN

SERBSKE NOWINY (5X WK.)

PF 1448, Bautzen, 02605, Germany; tel (49) 3591 5770; fax 577 243; e-mail domowinaverlag@t-online.de; web site www.domowinaverlag.de
Circ.: 1,400
Distr. Mgr. – Manja Bujnowska
Mng. Ed. – Axel Arlt
News Ed. – Marko Wjenka

BAYREUTH

NORDBAYERISCHER KURIER (6X WK.)

PF 100735, Bayreuth, 95448, Germany; tel (49) 921 5000; fax 294 107; e-mail verlag@kurier.tmt.de; regionalredaktion@kurier.tmt.de; web site www.bayreuth.de
Proprietor – Laurent Fischer
Proprietor – Woldgang Ellwanger
Circ. Mgr. – Herbert Angerer
Adv. Mgr. – Andreas Waess
Ed. – G.D. Meier

BENSHEIM

BA BERGSTRABER ANZEIGER (6X WK.)

Rodensteinstr. 6, Bensheim, 64625, Germany; tel (49) 6251 10080; fax 100841; web site www.bergstrasser-anzeiger.de
Circ.: 17,600
Bus. Mgr. – G. Haeberle
Adv. Mgr. – Werner Essinger
Ed. in Chief – Karl-Heinz Schlitt
Ed. – Karl-Heinz Schiltt
Ed. – M. Ranker
Ed. – Karl-Josef Banker

BERCHTESGADEN

BERCHTESGADENER ANZEIGER (5X WK.)

PF 1153, Berchtesgaden, 83471, Germany; tel (49) 8652 95840; fax 958 419; e-mail info@berchtesgadener-anzeiger.de; web site www.berchtesgadener-anzeiger.de
Circ.: 6,900
Ed. – Iris Melcher

BERLIN

B.Z. (MD)

Kurfurstendamm 21/22, Berlin, 10874, Germany; tel (49) 30 25910; fax 73131; e-mail redaktion@bz-berlin.de; web site www.bz-berlin.de
Circ.: 370,000
Ed. in Chief – Peter Huth

BERLINER MORGENPOST (M-6X WK.)

Axel-Springer-Str. 65, Berlin, 10969, Germany; tel (49) 30 25910; fax 73131; e-mail wirtschast@weld.de; web site www.morgenpost.de
Circ.: 178,605
Bus. Mgr. – Michael Meyer-Bohm
Ed. – Carsten Erdmann

BERLINER ZEITGUNG (M-6X WK.)

Karl-Liebknecht Str. 29, Berlin, 10178, Germany; tel (49) 30 23279; fax 2327 5357; e-mail info@berlinonline.de; web site www.berlinonline.de; www.berlinzeitung.de
Bus. Mgr. – Peter Skulimma
Ed. – Hartmut Augustin
Mng. Ed. – Bettina Urbanski

BILD (M-6X WK.)

Axel-Springer Str. 65, Berlin, 10867, Germany; tel (49) 40 34700; fax 3472 2134; e-mail info@bild.de; web site www.bild.de
Circ.: 5,674,400

Ed. in Chief – Kai Diekmann

DER TAGESSPIEGEL (M-7X WK.)

PO Box 10876, Berlin, 10963, Germany; tel (49) 30 260 090; fax 29021 1994090; e-mail redaktion@tagesspiegel.de; web site www.tagesspiegel.de
Circ.: 150,000
Advertising: Publicitas.
Adv. Mgr. – Jens Robotta
Ed. – Dasgorss Stephanandreas

DIE TAGESZEITUNG (M-6X WK.)

PF 610229, Berlin, 10923, Germany; tel (49) 30 259 020; e-mail redaktion@taz.de; web site www.taz.de
Circ.: 81,800
Bus. Mgr. – Karl-Heinez Ruch
Ed. in Chief – Bascha Mika
Mng. Ed. – Klaus Hillenbrand
News Ed. – Sabine Herre

DIE WELT (M-EX S)

Axel-Springer-Platz 65, Berlin, 10777, Germany; tel (49) 30 25910; fax 2591 72244; web site www.welt.de
Ed. in Chief – Jan-Eric Peters
Ed. – Eberhard von Elterlein
Mng. Ed. – Volker Stahlschmidt
News Ed. – Dietrich Menkens

BERLINER KURIER (MD)

PF 102001, Berlin, 10171, Germany; tel (49) 30 23279; fax 2327 5254; web site www.berlinonline.de
Circ.: 222,300
Ed. in Chief – Depen Brock
Adv. Mgr. – Sgefan Wiegandt

JUNGE WELT (M-6X WK.)

Torstraáe 6, Berlin, 10119, Germany; tel (49) 30 536 3550; fax 5363 550; e-mail redaktion@jungewelt.de; web site www.jungewelt.de
Circ.: 15,000
Bus. Mgr. – Dietmar Koschmieder
Ed. in Chief – Arnold Scholzel

NEUES DEUTSCHLAND (M-6X WK.) EST. 1946

Franz-Mehring-Platz 1, Berlin, 10243, Germany; tel (49) 30 2978 1111; fax 2978 1600; e-mail redaktion@nd-online.de; web site www.neues-deutschland.de
Circ.: 40,000
Last Audit: March 24, 2010
CEO - Chief Executive Manager – Olaf Koppe
Ed. in Chief – Jurgen Reents

DER NORD-BERLINER (6X WK.)

PF 280380, Berlin, 13469, Germany; tel (49) 30 419090; fax 4190 9156; e-mail nb@moellerdruck.de; web site www.moellerdruck.de
Circ.: 32,000
Proprietor – Adolf Moller
Proprietor – Wolfgang Moller
Ed. in Chief – Michael Fischer

TAGESSPIEGEL (6X WK.) EST. 1945

Askanischer Platz 3, Berlin, 10969, Germany; tel (49) 30 29021 0; web site www.tagesspiegel.de
Circ.: 29,102
Editors in Chief – Stephan-Andreas Casdorff Lorenz Maroldt

ULLSTEIN

Kurfurstendamm 21/22, Berlin, 10874, Germany; tel (49) 30 25910; fax 2591 73131; e-mail redaktion@bz-berlin.de; web site www.bz-berlin.de
Ed. in Chief – Peter Huth

BIELEFELD

NEUE WESTFALISCHE (M-6X WK.)

PF 100225, Bielefeld, 33602, Germany; tel (49) 521 555 300; fax 555 598; e-mail redak-

tion@nw.owl-online.de; web site www.nw-news.de
Circ.: 250,000
Last Audit: March 24, 2010
Bus. Mgr. – Axel Walker
Distr. Mgr. – Schaefer nolte
Ed. in Chief – Thomas Sein
Adv. Mgr – Michael Joachin Appelt
Mng. Ed. – Dietmar Koniczek
Mng. Ed. – Eckhard Sohn
News Ed. – Jorg Rinne

WEINHEIMER NACHRICHTEN (6X WK.)
PF 103171, Bielefeld, 33531, Germany; tel (49) 521 5850; fax 585 402; e-mail wb@westfalen-blatt.de; web site www.westfalen-blatt.de
Circ.: 104,000
Ed. in Chief – Rolf Dressler
Mng. Ed. – Matthias Boge

WESTFALEN-BLATT (M-6X WK.)
PF 103171, Bielefeld, 33611, Germany; tel (49) 521 5850; fax 585 230; e-mail wb@westfalen-blatt.de; web site www.westfalen-blatt.de
Circ.: 140,000
Bus. Mgr. – Michael Best

BIETIGHEIM-BISSINGEN

BIETIGHEIMER ZEITUNG (6X WK.)
Kronenbergstr. 10, Bietigheim-Bissingen, 74321, Germany; tel (49) 7142 4030; fax 403125; e-mail info@bietigheimerzeitung.de; web site www.bietigheimerzeitung.de
Proprietor – Stefan Glasar
Mng. Ed. – Armin Schulz

BOCHOLT

BOCHOLTER-BORKENER VOLKSBLATT (6X WK.)
PF 1254, Bocholt, 46399, Germany; tel (49) 2871 2840; fax 2840 220; e-mail verlag@bbv-net.de; redaktion@bbv-net.de; web site www.bbv-net.de
Circ.: 26,400
Proprietor – Jorg Terheyden
Adv. Mgr. – Juergen Angenent
Ed. in Chief – Volker Morgenbrod

BOEBLINGEN

KREISZEITUNG (6X WK.)
PF 1560, Boeblingen, 71034, Germany; tel (49) 7031 62000; fax 227 443; e-mail info@bb-live.de; web site www.bb-live.de
Circ.: 19,000
Ed. in Chief – M. Schlecht
News Ed. – Otto Kuhnle

BONN

BONNER RUNDSCHAU (6X WK.)
PF 1248, Bonn, 53111, Germany; tel (49) 228 98420; fax 9842230; e-mail bonner.rundschau@kr-redaktion.de; web site www.rundschau-online.de
Circ.: 66,800
Proprietor – Helmut Helnen

GENERAL ANZEIGER (6X WK.)
Justus-von-Liebig Str. 15, Bonn, 53121, Germany; tel (49) 228 66880; fax 668 8114; e-mail verlag@ga-bonn.de; web site ^www.ga-bonn.de; www.general-anzeiger-bonn.de
Circ.: 92,600
Proprietor – Hermann Neusser
Distr. Mgr. – Uwe Gilles
Bus. Mgr. – Friedrich Orths
Bus. Mgr. – Norbert Finken
Ed. in Chief – Andreas Tyrock

Ed. – Wolfgang Wentsch
Mng. Ed. – Andreas Boettcher

BORKEN

BORKENER ZEITUNG (6X WK.)
PF 1563, Borken, 46325, Germany; tel (49) 2861 9440; fax 944 109; e-mail verlag@borkenerzeitung.de; web site www.borkenerzeitung.de
Circ.: 18,000
Proprietor – Stephan Schmidt
Bus. Mgr. – Wolfgang Rickert
Distr. Mgr. – Hubert Kab

BORKUM

BORKUMER ZEITUNG UND BADEZEITUNG (4X WK.)
PF 2066, Borkum, 26746, Germany; tel (49) 4922 91240; fax 912416; e-mail verlag@borkumer-zeitung.de; web site www.borkumer-zeitung.de
Circ.: 1,900
Ed. in Chief – Wilke Specht

BRAUNSCHWEIG

BRAUNSCHWEIGER ZEITUNG (6X WK.)
PF 8052, Braunschweig, 38130, Germany; tel (49) 531 39000; fax 390 0304; e-mail chefredaktion@vzv.de; web site www.newsclick.de
Klaesener Stephen

BREMEN

BREMER NACHRICHTEN (D)
PF 107801, Bremen, 28078, Germany; tel (49) 421 36710; fax 328 327; e-mail vertrieb@bremer-nachrichten.de; web site www.bremer-nachrichten.de
Circ.: 220,000
Proprietor – Herbert C. Ordemann
Proprietor – Ulrich Hackmack
Distr. Mgr. – Hajo Nienaber
Ed. in Chief – Dietrich Ide

WESER-KURIER (D)
PF 107801, Bremen, 28078, Germany; tel (49) 421 36710; fax 3671 1000; e-mail vertrieb@weser-kurier.de; web site www.weser-kurier.de
Circ.: 77,500
Proprietor – Ulrech Haskmack
Distr. Mgr. – Helge Schweers
Ed. in Chief – Volker Weise
Ed. – Klaus Grunewald
Mng. Ed. – Kai A. Struthoff

BREMERHAVEN

NORDSEE-ZEITUNG (6X WK.)
PF 101228, Bremerhaven, 27512, Germany; tel (49) 471 5970; fax 597 551; e-mail nzbremerhaven@nordsee-zeitung.de; web site www.nordsee-zeitung.de
Circ.: 70,000
Proprietor – Roswitha Ditzen-Blanke
Bus. Mgr. – Hans Peter Schlicher
Distr. Mgr. – Sascha Hoffman

BREMERVOERDE

BREMERVOERDER ZEITUNG (6X WK.)
PF 1161, Bremervoerde, 27421, Germany; tel (49) 4761 9970; fax 99 759; e-mail bremervoerder.zeitung@t-online.de
Circ.: 9,000
Bus. Mgr. – Jurgen Borgardt

Distr. Mgr. – T. Bubbel
Ed. in Chief – Rolf Borgardt

BUCKEBURG

SCHAUMBURG-LIPPISCHE LANDES-ZEITUNG (6X WK.)
PF 1260, Buckeburg, 31675, Germany; tel (49) 5722 96870; fax 968 7566; e-mail schaumburger-zeitung@t-online.de; web site www.dewezet.de
Circ.: 4,000
Proprietor – Gunther Niemeyer
Proprietor – Hans Niemeyer
Bus. Mgr. – Stefan Reineking
Distr. Mgr. – Heiko Reckemeyer
Ed. – Raimund Cremers

BURG

FEHMARNSCHES TAGEBLATT (6X WK.)
PF 1169, Burg, 23763, Germany; tel (49) 4371 86750; fax 867 550; e-mail redaktion@fehmarnsches-tageblatt.de; web site www.fehmarnsches-tageblatt.de
Circ.: 2,500
Mng. Dir. – Dirck Eppen
Bus. Mgr. – Manfred Grell
Ed. in Chief – Heiko Witt

BURSTADT

BURSTADTER ZEITUNG (6X WK.)
Mainstr. 13-15, Burstadt, 68642, Germany; tel (49) 6206 98290; fax 9829 7935; web site www.buchdruckverlage.de
Circ.: 2,800
Ed. in Chief – Uwe Radon

BUTZBACH

BUTZBACHER ZEITUNG (6X WK.)
Langgasse 18, Butzbach, 35510, Germany; tel (49) 60 339 6060; fax 3396 0649; e-mail mail@butzbacher-zeitung.de; web site www.butzbacher-zeitung.de
Circ.: 8,100
Proprietor – Karola Wilhelmine Gratzfeld
Ed. in Chief – Christel Gratzfeld
Mng. Ed. – Wilfried Gratzfeld

CELLE

CELLESCHE ZEITUNG (6X WK.)
PF 1502, Celle, 29205, Germany; tel (49) 5141 9900; fax 990 290; e-mail verlag@cellesche-zeitung.de; web site www.cellesche-zeitung.de
Circ.: 35,000
Proprietor – Ernst Andreas Pfingsten
Ed. in Chief – Ralf Leineweber
Ed. – Volker Franke
Adv. Mgr – Carsten Wiessner

CHEMNITZ

FREIE PRESSE (6X WK.)
PF 261, Chemnitz, 09002, Germany; tel (49) 371 6560; fax 643 042; e-mail die.tageszeitung@freiepresse.de; web site www.freiepresse.de
Circ.: 502,600
Bus. Mgr. – Johannes Schulze
Ed. in Chief – Udo Landner
Mng. Ed. – Gunter Sonntag
News Ed. – Christoph Ulrich

CLOPPENBURG

MUNSTERLANDISCHE TAGESZEITUNG (6X WK.)
PF 1420, Cloppenburg, 49661, Germany; tel (49) 4471 1780; fax 17830; e-mail redacteon@mt-news.de; web site www.mt-clp.de
Circ.: 20,000
Ed. in Chief – Angelika Hauke

COBURG

COBURGER TAGEBLATT (6X WK.)
PF 1443, Coburg, 96404, Germany; tel (49) 9561 888 174; fax 888 199; e-mail feuilleton@coburger-tageblatt.de; web site www.coburger-tageblatt.de
Circ.: 18,100
Pub. – Helmuth Young Farmer
Editorial Dir. – Werner Baier
Ed. – Armin Mouse

NEUE PRESSE (6X WK.)
PF 2553, Coburg, 96414, Germany; tel (49) 9561 8500; fax 850 110; e-mail redaktion@np-coburg.de; verlag@np-coburg.de; web site www.np-coburg.de
Circ.: 35,000
Bus. Mgr. – Thomas Regge
Adv. Mgr – Antje Habermann
Ed. in Chief – Wolfgang Braunschmidt
News Ed. – Martin Fleischmann

COESFELD

ALLGEMEINE ZEITUNG (6X WK.)
PF 1343, Coesfeld, 48653, Germany; tel (49) 2541 9210; fax 921 155; e-mail redaktion@azonline.de; web site www.azonline.de
Circ.: 19,000
Pub. – Douglas Russ
Bus. Mgr. – R. Meyer
Distr. Mgr. – H. Messing
Ed. – Norbert Klein

COTTBUS

LAUSITZER RUNDSCHAU (6X WK.)
PF 100279, Cottbus, 03050, Germany; tel (49) 355 4810; fax 481246; e-mail lr@lr-online.de; web site www.lr-online.de
Ed. in Chief – Dieter Schultz
Ed. – Susann Michel

CRAILSHEIM

HOHENLOHER TAGBLATT (6X WK.)
Lugwigstr. 6, Crailsheim, 74552, Germany; tel (49) 7951 4090; fax 409 329; web site www.hohenlohertagblatt.de
Circ.: 15,500
Ed. – Mathias Bartels

CUXHAVEN

CUXHAVENER NACHRICHTEN (6X WK.)
Kaemmererplatz 2, Cuxhaven, 27472, Germany; tel (49) 4721 5850; fax 585 336; e-mail cn@cuxonline.de; redaktion@cuxonline.de; web site www.cn-online.de
Adv. Mgr. – Raos Droffner
Ed. in Chief – Hans-Christian Winters

DARMSTADT

DARMSTADTER ECHO (6X WK.)
PF 100155, Darmstadt, 64201, Germany; tel

(49) 6151 3871; fax 387 448; e-mail kontakt@echo-online.de; redaktion@darmstaedter-echo.de; web site www.echo-online.de
Circ.: 70,100
Proprietor – Hans-Peter Bach
Distr. Mgr. – Peter Kemper
Mng. Ed. – Jeff Riebartsch

ODENWALDER ECHO (6X WK.)
Holzhofallee 25-31, Darmstadt, 64295, Germany; tel (49) 6151 3871; fax 315 959; e-mail kontakt@echo-online.de; web site www.echo-online.de
Circ.: 15,400
Proprietor – Hans-Peter Bach
Proprietor – Horst Bach
Distr. Mgr. – Peter Kemper
Ed. – Gerhard Grunewald

RUSSELSHEIMER ECHO (6X WK.)
PF 100155, Darmstadt, 64295, Germany; tel (49) 6151 3871; fax 387 448; web site www.echo-online.de
Circ.: 100,000
Proprietor – Hans-Peter Bach

DELMENHORST

DELMENHORSTER KREISBLATT (6X WK.)
PF 1232, Delmenhorst, 27749, Germany; tel (49) 4221 156 666; fax 156 999; e-mail redaktion@dk-online.de; vertrieb@dk-online.de; web site www.dk-online.de
Circ.: 25,300
Proprietor – Dirk Schulte Strathaus
Proprietor – Frank Dallmann
Adv. Mgr. – Sven Dittelbach
Ed. in Chief – Ralf Freitag

DETMOLD

LIPPISCHE LANDES-ZEITUNG (6X WK.)
PF 2163, Detmold, 32758, Germany; tel (49) 5231 9110; fax 911 145; e-mail lz@lz-online.de; web site www.lz-online.de
Circ.: 47,100
Bus. Mgr. – Helmut Schmermund
Ed. – Michael Dahl

DILLENBURG

DILL-ZEITUNG (D)
PF 1262, Dillenburg, 35683, Germany; tel (49) 2771 8740; fax 874220; e-mail anzeigen@dz.dill.de; web site www.dill.de
Proprietor/Adv. Mgr. – Martin Simon
Distr. Mgr. – T. Scafer

DINGOLFING

DINGOLFINGER ANZEIGER (6X WK.)
PF 1360, Dingolfing, 84130, Germany; tel (49) 9421 7030; fax 70333; e-mail service@idowa.de; web site www.idowa.de
Circ.: 11,300
Ed. – Heinrich Walischmiller

DOBELN

DOBELNER ANZEIGER (6X WK.)
PF 169, Dobeln, 04713, Germany; tel (49) 3431 71940; fax 719499; e-mail daanzeigen@aol.com; web site www.doebelneranzeiger.de
Circ.: 19,000
Proprietor – Gunter Rubens
Bus. Mgr. – Wilfried Graul
Distr. Mgr. – Michael Kretzschmar
Ed. in Chief – K. Seifert

DORTMUND

RUHR NACHRICHTEN (M-EX S)
PF 105051, Dortmund, 44137, Germany; tel (49) 231 9059-7905; fax 9059 8601; e-mail rn@westline.de; web site www.westline.de/rn
Proprietor – Florian Lensing-Wolff
Proprietor – Lambert Lensing-Wolff
Bus. Mgr. – Christoph Sandmann
Ed. in Chief – Hermann Beckfeld
Ed. in Chief – Dr. Wolfram Kiwit
News Ed. – Michael Fritsch
News Ed. – P. Mering

WR WESTFALISCHE RUNDSCHAU (6X WK.)
PF 105067, Dortmund, 44135, Germany; tel (49) 231 9573 1292; fax 9573 1299; e-mail ztg.gruppewaz@cityweb.de; redaktion.dortmund@waz.de; sport.dortmund@waz.de; web site www.derwesten.de
Circ.: 166,100
Ed. in Chief – Frank Bunte
Mng. Ed. – Karl Heinz Evers
News Ed. – Hans Fullbrunn

DRESDEN

SACHSISCHE ZEITUNG (M-6X WK.)
Ostra-Allee 20, Dresden, 01067, Germany; tel (49) 351 48640; fax 4864 2800; e-mail sz.geschaeftsfuehrung@dd-v.de; web site www.sz-online.de
Circ.: 300,000
Bus. Mgr. – Thomas DÅ£ffert
Adv. Mgr. – Tobias Fpitzhorn
Ed. – Thomas Schultz-Homberg

DRESDNER MORGENPOST (6X WK.)
Ostra-Allee 18, Dresden, 01067, Germany; tel (49) 351 48640; fax 4864 2800; e-mail sz.geschaeftsfuehrung@dd-v.de; web site www.sz-online.de
Circ.: 100,000
Bus. Mgr. – Carsten Dietmann
Dist. Mgr. – Bernd Rademann
Ed. in Chief – Peter Rzepus
Ed. – Joachim Becker
Mng. Ed. – Frank Stein

DRESDNER NEUESTE NACHRICHTEN (6X WK.)
PF 100520, Dresden, 01075, Germany; tel (49) 351 80750; fax 8075212; e-mail info@dnn.de; web site www.dnn-online.de
Circ.: 40,000
Distr. Mgr. – Mario Knappe
Ed. in Chief – Dirk Birgel
Mng. Ed. – Barbara Stock
Deputy Ed. – Karla Tolksdorf

DULMEN

DULMENER ZEITUNG (6X WK.)
Markstr. 25, Dulmen, 48249, Germany; tel (49) 2594 9560; fax 95649; web site www.westline.de
Circ.: 10,200
Pub. – Mark Bednara
Ed. in Chief – Ralf Repoehler

DUSSELDORF

DUSSELDORF EXPRESS (6X WK.)
PF 101132, Dusseldorf, 40002, Germany; tel (49) 211 13930; e-mail duesseldorf@express.de; web site www.express.de
Circ.: 131,200
Proprietor – Alfred Neven DuMont
Bus. Mgr. – Konstantin Neven DuMont
Bus. Mgr. – Frank Reiners
Ed. in Chief – Michael Grixa

RHEINISCHE POST (M-6X WK.)
Zulpicher Str. 10, Dusseldorf, 40196, Germany; tel (49) 211 5050; fax 504 2555
Circ.: 443,100
Advertising: Publicitas.
Proprietor – Dr. Esther Betz
Proprietor – Dr. Gottfried Arnold
Ed. – Sven Gosmann

HANDELSBLATT (5X WK.)
PF 101102, Dusseldorf, 40213, Germany; tel (49) 211 8870; fax 887 1247; e-mail handelsblatt@vhb.de; web site www.handelsblatt.de
Circ.: 155,000
Ed. in Chief – Waldemar Schafer
Mng. Ed. – Peter Pfister

WZ WESTDEUTSCHE ZEITUNG (6X WK.)
PF 101132, Dusseldorf, 40002, Germany; tel (49) 211 83820; fax 8382 2272; e-mail wzn@wz-newsline.de; web site www.wz-newsline.de
Circ.: 219,720
Pub. – Michael Girardet
Bus. Mgr. – Hans-Georg Roth
Mktg. Mgr. – Brigitte Kurtscher

EBERBACH

EBERBACHER ZEITUNG (6X WK.)
PF 1343, Eberbach, 69412, Germany; tel (49) 6271 925525; fax 925 540; web site www.eberbacher-zeitung.de
Circ.: 4,100
Bus. Mgr. – Gerald Krauth
Ed. – Reinhard Goller

ECKERNFOERDE

ECKERNFORDER ZEITUNG (6X WK.)
PF 1169, Eckernfoerde, 24331, Germany; tel (49) 4351 90080; fax 900 891; web site www.shz.de
Circ.: 9,300
Proprietor – Uwe Boyens
Ed. – Michael Doring

EINBECK

EINBECKER MORGENPOST (M-EX S)
PF 1613, Einbeck, 37557, Germany; tel (49) 5561 4002; fax 73383; web site www.einbecker-morgenpost.de
Circ.: 10,800
Bus. Mgr. – Jurgen Ruttgerodt
Ed. in Chief – Edith Kondziella

ELMSHORN

ELMSHORNER NACHRICHTEN (6X WK.)
Schulstr. 62-66, Elmshorn, 25335, Germany; tel (49) 4121 212 970; fax 297 2818; e-mail redaktion@en-online.de; leserservice@shz.de; web site www.shz.de
Circ.: 13,800
Ed. – Markus Arndt

EMDEN

EMDER ZEITUNG (6X WK.)
PF 1453, Emden, 26721, Germany; tel (49) 4921 89000; fax 890 0489; web site www.emderzeitung.de
Circ.: 12,300
Bus. Mgr. – Peter Fischer
Distr. Mgr. – Armin Goring
Ed. – Klaus Fackert

EMSDETTEN

EMSDETTENER VOLKSZEITUNG (6X WK.)
Muhlenstr. 23, Emsdetten, 48282, Germany; tel (49) 2572 95600; fax 956 029; web site www.emsdettenervolkszeitung.de
Circ.: 7,200
Proprietor – Florian Lensing-Wolff
Bus. Mgr. – Christoph Sandmann
Distr. Mgr. – Goerg Euler
Ed. – Erich Ortmeier

ERFURT

THURINGER ALLGEMEINE (6X WK.)
Gottstedter Landstr. 6, Erfurt, 99092, Germany; tel (49) 361 2274; fax 227 5023; e-mail redaktion@thueringer-allgemeine.de; web site www.thueringer-allgemeine.de
Circ.: 589,700
Ed. in Chief – Sergej Lochthofen
Mng. Ed. – Dick Lohr
Mng. Ed. – Wolfgang Lindenlaub
News Ed. – Axer Fock

ESCHWEGE

WERRA-RUNDSCHAU (D)
Vor dem Berge 2, Eschwege, 37256, Germany; tel (49) 5651 60024; fax 335 944; e-mail redaktion@werra-rundschau.de; web site www.werra-rundschau.de
Circ.: 12,000
Bus. Mgr. – Dr. Peter Kluthe

ESSEN

NRZ (NEUE RHEIN-ZEITUNG-NEUE RUHR-ZEITUNG) (6X WK.)
Friedrichstr. 34, Essen, 45128, Germany; tel (49) 201 8040; fax 804 2621; web site www.derwesten.de
Circ.: 182,900
Bus. Mgr. – Bodo Hombach
Bus. Mgr. – Erich Schumann
News Ed. – Christian Peters

WESTDEUTSCHE ALLGEMEINE WAZ (6X WK.)
PF 104161, Essen, 45128, Germany; tel (49) 201 8040; fax 804 8862; e-mail kontakt@waz-mediengruppe.de; web site www.waz-mediengruppe.de
Circ.: 1,313,400
Bus. Mgr. – Bodo Hombach
Ed. in Chief – Ulrich Reitz

ESSLINGEN

ESSLINGER ZEITUNG (6X WK.)
Zeppelinstr. 116, Esslingen, 73730, Germany; tel (49) 711 93100; fax 316 9124; e-mail info@ez-online.de; web site www.ez-online.de
Circ.: 38,900
Proprietor – Otto Wolfgang Bechtle
Proprietor – Christine Bechtle-Kobarg
News Ed. – Markus Bleistein

EUTIN

OSTHOLSTEINER ANZEIGER (6X WK.)
PF 320, Eutin, 23701, Germany; tel (49) 4521 7790; fax 779 185; e-mail struve-technik@t-online.de; web site www.oha-online.de
Circ.: 10,000
Adv. Mgr. – George Aoddt
Ed. – Achim Krauskopf

FEUCHT

DER BOTE FUR NURNBERG-LAND (6X WK.)
Nurnberger Str. 5, Feucht, 90537, Germany; tel (49) 9128 70720; fax 707 225; e-mail anzeigen@der-bote.de; web site www.der-bote.de
Proprietor – Bruno Schnell
Proprietor – Ulrich Bollmann
Ed. – Lorenz Martl

FLENSBURG

FLENSBORG AVIS (6X WK.)
PF 2662, Flensburg, 24916, Germany; tel (49) 461 50450; fax 504 5140; e-mail redaktion@flensborg-avis.de; web site www.flensborg-avis.de
Circ.: 6,000
Bus. Mgr. – B. Loenborg
News Ed. – Jan Christensen

NORDDEUTSCHE RUNDSCHAU (6X WK.)
PF 1553, Flensburg, 24905, Germany; tel (49) 461 8080; fax 808 348; e-mail info@shz.de; web site www.shz.de
Circ.: 23,000
Bus. Mgr. – Asghar A. Azmayesh
Adv. Mgr. – Ingeborg Schwarz

FLENSBURGER TAGEBLATT (6X WK.)
PF 1553, Flensburg, 24905, Germany; tel (49) 461 8080; fax 808 348; e-mail info@shz.de; web site www.shz.de
Circ.: 37,000
Bus. Mgr. – Asghar A. Azmayesh

MARNER ZEITUNG (6X WK.)
PF 1553, Flensburg, 24937, Germany; tel (49) 0461 8080; e-mail info@shz.de; web site www.shz.de
Circ.: 3,400
– A. Dethleffsen
– G. Christiansen
– H. Anderson
– H.P. Rossen
– I. Macknow
– Prof. W. PetersenProprietors

STORMARNER TAGEBLATT (6X WK.)
PF 1553, Flensburg, 24937, Germany; tel (49) 461 8080; fax 808 348; e-mail info@shz.de; web site www.shz.de
Circ.: 6,243
Proprietor – A. Dethleffsen
Proprietor – G. Christiansen
Proprietor – H. Andresen
Proprietor – I. Macknow Lisboa
Proprietor – P. Peterson
Proprietor – W. Petersen
Bus. Mgr. – Thomas Kessler

WILSTERSCHE ZEITUNG (6X WK.)
PF 1553, Flensburg, 24937, Germany; tel (49) 461 8080; fax 808 1058; e-mail info@shz.de; web site www.shz.de
Circ.: 2,181
Ed. in Chief – S. Richter
Adv. Mgr. – Ingeborg Schwarz

FRANKFURT

BORSEN-ZEITUNG (4X WK.)
Dusseldorfer Str. 16, Frankfurt, 60044, Germany; tel (49) 69 27320; e-mail redakteon@boersen-zeitung.de; web site www.boersen-zeitung.de
Dir. – Ernst Padberg
Ed. in Chief – Claus Doring

FRANKFURT AM MAIN

FRANKFURTER ALLGEMEINE (D)
Hellerhofstr. 2, Frankfurt am Main, 60327, Germany; tel (49) 69 75910; fax 7591 1743; e-mail redaktion@faz.de; web site www.faz.de
Circ.: 471,000
Advertising: Publicitas.
Distr. Mgr. – Werner Fischer
Editorial Dir. – Werner D'Inka
Ed. in Chief – Frank Schirmacher
News Ed. – Jasper v. Altenbockum

FRANKFURTER NEUE PRESSE (M-6X WK.)
PF 100801, Frankfurt am Main, 60327, Germany; tel (49) 69 75010; fax 7501 4877; e-mail fsd@fsd.de; web site www.fnp.de
Ed. in Chief – Gerhard Mumme

FRANKFURTER RUNDSCHAU (6X WK.)
Karl-Gerold-Platz 1, Frankfurt am Main, 60594, Germany; tel (49) 69 21991; fax 2199 3666; e-mail datchefredaktyon@fr-online.de; web site www.fr-online.de
Circ.: 201,600
Bus. Mgr. – Karlheinz Kroke

FINANCIAL TIMES (6X WK.)
Nibelungenplatz 3, Frankfurt am Main, 60318, Germany; tel (49) 69 156 850; fax 596 4478; web site www.ft.com
Circ.: 24,204
Adv. Mgr. – Regina Gill
Ed. in Chief – Ralph Atkins

FRANKFURT AN DER ODER

MARKISCHE ODERZEITUNG (M-6X WK)
PF 1178, Frankfurt an der Oder, 15230, Germany; tel (49) 335 55300; fax 553 0211; e-mail verlagsleitung@moz.de; web site www.moz.de
Circ.: 100,000
MD – Dr.Boda Almert

FREIBURG

BADISCHE ZEITUNG (M-6X WK.) EST. 1946
Freiburg, 79115, Germany; tel (+49) 761 4960; fax 496 4709; e-mail redaktion@badische-zeitung.de; web site www.badische-zeitung.de
Circ.: 205,500
Proprietor/Publisher – Christian H. Hodeige
Ed. in Chief – Thomas Hauser
News Ed. – Thomas Fricker

FULDA

FULDAER ZEITUNG (6X WK.)
PF 1454, Fulda, 36043, Germany; tel (49) 661 2800; fax 280 209; e-mail verlag@parzeller.de; web site www.fuldaerzeitung.de
Circ.: 60,000
Bus. Mgr. – Michael Schmitt
Ed. in Chief – Michael Tillmann

GAILDORF

RUNDSCHAU FUR DEN SCHWABISCHEN WALD (D-6X WK.)
PF 130, Gaildorf, 74405, Germany; tel (49) 7971 95880; fax 958 822
Circ.: 5,200
Bus. Mgr. – Uaern Bauerl
Ed. – Klaus Michael Osswald

GEISLINGEN AN DER STEIGE

GEISLINGER ZEITUNG (6X WK.)
PF 1254, Geislingen an der Steige, 73312, Germany; tel (49) 7331 2020; fax 20250; web site www.geislinger-zeitung.de
Circ.: 16,500
Bus. Mgr. – Wolfgang Braig

GELNHAEUSEN

GELNHAUSER NEUE ZEITUNG (6X WK.)
PF 1564, Gelnhaeusen, 63571, Germany; tel (49) 6051 8330; fax 833 230; e-mail redaktion@gnz.de; web site www.gnz.de
Circ.: 9,000
Distr. Mgr. – Ronald Schmidt
Ed.- in -Chief – Ehrhard Naumann

GELNHAUSER TAGEBLATT (6X WK.)
Barbarossastr. 5, Gelnhaeusen, 63571, Germany; tel (49) 6051 8240; fax 824333; e-mail anzeigen@gelnhaeuser-tageblatt.de; web site www.gelnhaeuser-tageblatt.de
Circ.: 7,500
Bus. Mgr. – Wolfgang Maass

GELSENKIRCHEN

BUERSCHE ZEITUNG (6X WK.)
PF 200252, Gelsenkirchen, 45837, Germany; tel (49) 209 360010; fax 3600111; web site www.westline.de/bz
Circ.: 13,600
Proprietor – Heinz Klocknert
Bus. Mgr. – Norbert Steinig
Distr. Mgr. – Martin Heith
Ed. – Norbert Neubaum

GERA

OSTTHURINGER ZEITUNG (6X WK.)
PF 1365, Gera, 04626, Germany; tel (49) 3447 524; fax 525 914; web site www.otz.de
Circ.: 58,000
Ed. in Chief – Ullrich Erzigkeit

GIESSEN

GIEBENER ALLGEMEINE (6X WK.)
PF 100462, Giessen, 35390, Germany; tel (49) 641 30030; fax 37579; e-mail mailmaster@mdv-online.de; web site www.giessener-allgemeine.de
Circ.: 71,900
Pub. – Christian Rempel

GIEBENER ANZEIGER (6X WK.)
Am Urnenfeld 12, Giessen, 35396, Germany; tel (49) 641 95040; fax 9504 3411; e-mail redaktion@anzeigerlokal.de; web site www.anzeigerlokal.de
Circ.: 18,000
Circ. Mgr. – Michael Emmerich
Ed. – Dieter Lemmer

GIFHORN

ALLER-ZEITUNG (M-6X WK.)
PF 1120, Gifhorn, 38501, Germany; tel (49) 5371 8080; fax 808 117; e-mail az@madsack.de; web site www.aller-zeitung.de
Circ.: 38,000
Ed. in Chief – Carsten Baschin

GOPPINGEN

NWZ GOPPINGER KREISNACHRICHTEN (DS)
PF 1469, Goppingen, 73033, Germany; tel (49) 7161 2040; fax 204 152; e-mail nwz.anzeigen@swp.de; web site www.suedwest-aktiv.de
Circ.: 43,000
Distribution Mgr./Adv. Mgr. – J. Schniepp
Ed. – Rudiger Gramsch

GOSLAR

GOSLARSCHE ZEITUNG (6X WK.)
PF 1580, Goslar, 38640, Germany; tel (49) 5321 3330; fax 333 130; e-mail anzeigen@goslarsche-zeitung.de; web site www.goslarsche-zeitung.de
Circ.: 30,000
Ed. in Chief – Christian Otto

GOTTINGEN

GOTTINGER TAGEBLATT (6X WK.)
Dransfelder Str. 1, Gottingen, 37079, Germany; tel (49) 551 901 200; fax 901 278; e-mail info@goettinger-tageblatt.de; web site www.goettinger-tageblatt.de
Circ. Mgr. – Oliva Moll
Ed. – Angela Brunjes
News Ed. – Hermann Hillebrecht

GRONAU

LEINE DEISTER ZEITUNG (D-6X WK.)
PF 1254, Gronau, 31028, Germany; tel (49) 5182 92190; fax 921 925; e-mail ldz-anzeigen@leinetal-online.de; web site www.leinetal-online.de
Circ.: 6,000
Distr. Mgr. – Manfred Mackeler
Ed. – Hartmut Muller

GUNZENHAUSEN

ALTMUHL-BOTE (6X WK.)
PF 1464, Gunzenhausen, 91704, Germany; tel (49) 9831 50080; fax 500 841; e-mail verlag@altmuehl-bote.de; web site www.altmuehl-bote.de
Circ.: 9,300
Proprietor – Bruno Schnell
Bus. Mgr. – Dieter Vitzthum
Distr. Mgr. – Barbel Schnell
Ed. – Werner Falk

HAGEN

WP WESTFALENPOST (6X WK.)
PF 3929, Hagen, 58097, Germany; tel (49) 2331 9170; fax 917 4206; e-mail leserservice@waz.de; hagen@westfalenpost.de; web site www.westfalenpost.de; www.derwesten.de
Circ.: 57,900
Ed. in Chief – Ulrich Manastarni

HALLE

HALLER KREISBLATT (6X WK.)
PF 1452, Halle, 33790, Germany; tel (49) 5201 1501; fax 15166; e-mail redaktion@haller-kreisblatt.de; web site www.haller-kreisblatt.de
Circ.: 14,100
Bus. Mgr. – Hans Brachvogel
Distr. Mgr. – Alfred Kaschub
Ed. – Herbert Gontek

MITTELDEUTSCHE ZEITUNG (6X WK.)
Delitzscher Str. 65, Halle, 06112, Germany; tel (49) 345 5650; fax 565 4350; e-mail service@mz-web.de; kontakt@mz-web.de; web site www.mz-web.de
Circ.: 414,500
Proprietor – Alfred Neven DuMont
Distr. Mgr. – Uls Kiedelamp
Ed. in Chief – Monika Zimmermann

HAMBURG

BERGEDORFER ZEITUNG (6X WK.)
Curslacker Neuer Deich 50, Hamburg, 21029, Germany; tel (49) 40 725 660; fax 7256 6209; e-mail redaktion@bergedorfer-zeitung.de; web site www.bergedorfer-zeitung.de
Bus. Mgr. – Hans Pirch
Mng. Ed. – Bolsgang Radh

HAMBURGER ABENDBLATT (M-6X WK.)
Axel-Springer-Platz 1, Hamburg, 20350, Germany; tel (49) 40 34700; fax 3472 6110; e-mail briefe@abendblatt.de; web site www.abendblatt.de
Circ.: 329,000
Group: Axel Springer Verlag AG
Bus. Mgr. – M. Meyer-Bohm
Distr. Mgr. – H.J. Gut
Ed. in Chief – Claus Strunz
Mng. Ed. – Horst Gleich
Mng. Ed. – Peter Meyer

HAMBURGER MORGENPOST (D)
PF 501006, Hamburg, 22763, Germany; tel (49) 40 8090 57336; fax 8090 57275; e-mail verlag@mopo.de; web site www.mopo.de
Circ.: 300,000
Ed. – Frank Wieding
Adv. Mgr. – Hansjoaeaim Eggrm

HARBURGER ANZEIGEN UND NACHRICHTEN (6X WK.)
PF 902262, Hamburg, 21073, Germany; tel (49) 40 771 770; fax 7650 262; web site www.han-online.de
Circ.: 28,000
Ed. in Chief – Thomas Oldach
Ed. In Cheif – Jens Kalkowski

HAMELN

DEISTER-UND WESERZEITUNG (M-6X WK.)
Osterstr. 15, Hameln, 31785, Germany; tel (49) 5151 2000; fax 200 305; e-mail mail@dewezet.de; web site www.dewezet.de
Circ.: 78,400
Ed. in Chief – Julia Niemeyer
Adv. Mgr. – Gunther Seifert

HAMM

WESTAFALISCHER ANZEIGER (6X WK.)
Gutenbergstr. 1, Hamm, 59065, Germany; tel (49) 2381 1050; e-mail servicecenter@westfalischer-anzeiger.de; web site www.wa-online.de
Circ.: 56,200
Pub. – Daniel Schuonengh
Bus. Mgr. – Burckhardt Schmidt
Ed. – Robert Vornholt
Ed. in Chief – Martin Krigar
Adv. Mgr. – Stefen Schulle

HANAU

HANAUER ANZEIGER (6X WK.)
PF 1945, Hanau, 63409, Germany; tel (49) 6181 29030; fax 290 3500; web site www.hanauer-anzeiger.de
Circ.: 18,000
Bus. Mgr. – Thomas Bauer
Ed. in Chief – Dieter Schreier
Ed. – Reinhard Breyer
News Ed. – Robert Gobel

HANNOVER

HANNOVERSCHE ALLGEMEINE ZEITUNG (M-6X WK.)
August-Madsack Str. 1, Hannover, 30559, Germany; tel (49) 511 5180; fax 518 2886; e-mail haz@madsack.de; web site www.madsack.de
Circ.: 250,000
Mng. Ed. – Wilfred Heinemann

NEUE PRESSE (D-6X WK.)
August-Madsack-Str. 1, Hannover, 30559, Germany; tel (49) 511 5180; fax 5101 2275; e-mail np@madsack.de; mol@madsack.de; web site www.neuepresse.de
Ed. – Harad Jem
News Ed. – H. Schmuda
News Ed. – Ulla Behn-Mangold

HASSFURT

HASSFURTER-TAGBLATT (6X WK.)
PF 1313, Hassfurt, 97437, Germany; tel (49) 9521 6990; fax 69911; e-mail redaktion@hassfurter-tagblatt.de; web site www.hassfurter-tagblatt.de
Circ.: 6,400
Adv. Mgr. – Hubert Gerhart
Ed. – Barbara Gerhart
Ed. – Wolfgang Sandler

HECHINGEN

HOHENZOLLERISCHE ZEITUNG (6X WK.)
PF 1264, Hechingen, 72379, Germany; tel (49) 7471 931 517; fax 2045; web site www.hohenzollerische-zeitung.de
Circ.: 9,000
Ed. in Chief – Eberhard Wais

HEIDE

DITHMARSCHER LANDESZEITUNG (6X WK.)
PF 1880, Heide, 25738, Germany; tel (49) 481 68860; fax 688 6469; e-mail redaktion@boyens-medien.de; web site www.boyens-medien.de
Circ.: 29,000
Proprietor – Uwe Boyens
Bus. Mgr. – Klaus Bohlke
Distr. Mgr. – Ralf Haiduck
Ed. in Chief – Gerhard Wagner
Ed. – Frank Zabel
News Ed. – Stefan Schmid

HEIDELBERG

RHEIN-NECKAR-ZEITUNG (6X WK.)
PF 104560, Heidelberg, 69117, Germany; tel (49) 6221 5191; fax 519 217; e-mail rnz-kontaktrnz.de; web site www.rnz.de
Circ.: 114,000
Proprietor – Ludwig Knorr
Proprietor – Ruprecht Schulze
Proprietor – Winfried Knorr
Ed. in Chief – Manfred Fritz
Ed. in Chief – Joachim Knorr

HEIDENHEIM AN DER BRENZ

HEIDENHEIMER NEUE PRESSE (6X WK.)
PF 1423, Heidenheim an der Brenz, 89518, Germany; tel (49) 7321 347201; fax 347200
Circ.: 9,100
Proprietor – Hans-Jorg Wilhelm
Ed. – Dr. Manfred Allenhofer
Mng. Ed. – Margot Maier

HEIDENHEIMER ZEITUNG (6X WK.)
PF 1425, Heidenheim an der Brenz, 89518, Germany; tel (49) 7321 3470; fax 347100; e-mail pressehaus@hz-online.de; web site www.hz-online.de
Circ.: 36,200
Bus. Mgr. – Hans Jorg Wilhelm

HEILBRONN

HEILBRONNER STIMME (6X WK.)
Allee 2, Heilbronn, 74010, Germany; tel (49) 7131 6150; fax 615 318; e-mail servicecenter@stimme.de; web site www.stimme.de
Circ.: 105,100
Ed. in Chief – Kilman Cistelbarth

HERFORD

HERFORDER KREISBLATT (6X WK.)
Bruderstr. 30, Herford, 32052, Germany; tel (49) 5221 59080; fax 590816; e-mail herforder@westfalen-blatt.de; web site www.westfalen-blatt.de
Circ.: 20,900
Ed. – Ralf Meistes

HERRENBERG

GAUBOTE (6X WK.)
PF 1161, Herrenberg, 71070, Germany; tel (49) 7032 95250; fax 952 5109; e-mail info@gaeubote.de; web site www.gaeubote.de
Circ.: 12,600
Bus. Mgr. – Rainer Schollkopf
Adv. Mgr. – Tina Samel
Distr. Mgr. – Bertold Wark

HERSBRUCK

HERSBRUCKER ZEITUNG (6X WK.)
PF 440, Hersbruck, 91213, Germany; tel (49) 9151 73070; fax 2000; e-mail verlag@hersbrucker-zeitung.de; web site www.hersbrucker-zeitung.de
Proprietor – Bruno Schnell
Proprietor – Ursula Pfeiffer
Ed. – Walter Grzesiek

HILDESHEIM

HILDESHEIMER ALLGEMEINE ZEITUNG (6X WK.)
PF 100555, Hildesheim, 31134, Germany; tel (49) 5121 1060; fax 106241; e-mail online@gerstenberg.com; web site www.gerstenberg.com
Circ.: 52,700
Proprietor – Dr. Bruno Gerstenberg
Ed. in Chief – Dr. Hartmut Reichardt
Ed. – Mathias Bartels

HOF

FRANKENPOST (6X WK.)
PF 1320, Hof, 95028, Germany; tel (49) 9281 8160; fax 816 283; e-mail fp-redaktion@frankenpost.de; web site www.frankenpost.de
Circ.: 60,000
Mktg. Mgr. – Michael Toeppel
Ed. in Chief – Johann Pirthauer
Author. – Thomas Hanel

MUNCHBERG-HELMBRECHSTER ZEITUNG (6X WK.)
Poststr. 9/11, Hof, 95028, Germany; tel (49) 9251 995 420; fax 995 425; e-mail redaktion.mhz@frankenpost.de; web site www.frankenpost.de
Circ.: 70,000
Ed. in Chief – Thomas Reggae

SELBER TAGBLATT FRANKENPOST (6X WK.)
PF 1320, Hof, 95028, Germany; tel (49) 9281 8160; fax 816 423; e-mail verlag@frankenpost.de; web site www.frankenpost.de
Circ.: 6,000
Adv. Mgr. – Torsten Klose
Ed. in Chief – Johann Pirthauer

HOLZMINDEN

TAGLICHER ANZEIGER (D-6X WK.)
PF 1453, Holzminden, 37603, Germany; tel (49) 5531 93040; fax 930 441; e-mail info@tah.de; web site www.tah.de
Circ.: 13,300
Proprietor – Gerlinde Mahnkopf
Bus. Mgr. – Andreas Homburg
Bus. Mgr. – Constanze Mahnkopf
Distribution Mgr. – Tobias Neanstedt
Ed. in Chief – Kuno Mahnkopf
Ed. – Birgit Schneider
Ed. – Gudrun Reiking
Thomas Specht

IBBENBUREN

IBBENBURENER VOLKSZEITUNG (6X WK.)
Wilhelmstr. 240, Ibbenburen, 49477, Germany; tel (49) 5451 9330; fax 933192; e-mail redaktion@@ivz-online.de; info@ivz-online.de; web site www.ivz-online.de
Circ.: 17,800
Pub. – Claus Kossag

IMMENSTADT

ALLGAUER ANZEIGEBLATT (6X WK.)
PF 1164, Immenstadt, 87501, Germany; tel (49) 8323 8020; fax 802 112; e-mail info@allgauer-anzeigeblatt.de; web site www.eberl.de
Circ.: 21,300
Proprietor – G. Eberl
Proprietor – G. Furst von Waldberg zu Zeil
Proprietor – G. Holland
Ed. in Chief – Markus Raffler

INGOLSTADT

DONAUKURIER (6X WK.)
PF 100259, Ingolstadt, 85002, Germany; tel (49) 841 96660; fax 9666 255; e-mail redaktion@donaukurier.de; web site www.donaukurier.de
Circ.: 89,900
Adv. Mgr. – George Schaess
Ed. in Chief – Michael Schmatloch
Mng. Ed. – Wolfgang Lichtenegger

ISERLOHN

ISERLOHNER KREISANZE UND ZEITUNG (6X WK.)
Theodor-Heuss-Ring 426, Iserlohn, 58636, Germany; tel (49) 2371 8220; fax 822 102; e-mail red.iserlohn@ikz-online.de; web site www.ikz-online.de
Circ.: 34,100
Mng. Ed. – Ulrich Steden
News Ed. – Thomas Reunert

JEVER

JEVERSCHES WOCHENBLATT (6X WK.)
PF 1120, Jever, 26441, Germany; tel (49) 4461 9440; fax 944 119; e-mail redaktion@jeversches-wochenblatt.de; web site www.jewo-online.de; www.jeversches-

wochenblatt.de
Circ.: 9,800
Proprietor – Elisabeth Allmers
Proprietor – Manfred Adrain
Bus. Mgr. – Doortje Sabin
Ed. in Chief – Helmut Burlager
Adv. Mgr. – Tadd Eigs

KAISERSLAUTERN

THE STARS AND STRIPES (D)
PF 1980, Kaiserslautern, 67607, Germany; tel (49) 6155 601 202; fax 601 395; e-mail news@mail.estripes.osd.mil; web site www.stripes.com
Circ.: 93,000
Mng. Ed. – Doug Clawson

KARLSRUHE

BADISCHE NEUESTE NACHRICHTEN (6X WK.)
Linkenheimer Landstr. 133, Karlsruhe, 76149, Germany; tel (49) 721 7890; fax 789 156; web site www.bnn.de
Circ.: 1,050,000
Proprietor/Bus. Mgr. – Hans Wilhelm Baur
Bus. Mgr. – Brunhilde Baur

KASSEL

HNA HESSISCHE/NIEDERSACHSISCHE ALLGEMEINE (6X WK.)
Frankfurter Str. 168, Kassel, 34121, Germany; tel (49) 561 20300; fax 203 2334; e-mail info@hna.de; web site www.hna.de
Circ.: 278,000
Proprietor – Dirk Ippen
Ed. in Chief – Horst Seidenfaden
News Ed. – Wolfgang Blieffert

KEMPTEN

ALLGAUER ZEITUNG (M-6X WK.)
PF 3155, Kempten, 87440, Germany; tel (49) 831 2060; fax 206379; e-mail info@all-in.de; web site www.all-in.de
Circ.: 150,000
Proprietor – Georg Furst von Waldburg zu Zeil
Proprietor – Gunter Holland
Distribution Mgr. – K.-H. Erhard
Ed. in Chief – Hermann Konig
Ed. – Claudia Benz
Mng. Ed. – Rolf Nehrig
News Ed. – Jurgen Gerstenmaier

KIEL

KIELER NACHRICHTEN (6X WK.)
PF 1111, Kiel, 24103, Germany; tel (49) 431 9030; fax 903 2935; e-mail service@kieler-nachrichten.de; web site www.kn-online.de
Circ.: 100,000
Circ. Mgr. – Reinhold A. Bumke
Ed. in Chief – Juergen Heinemann
Ed. – Ralph Bottcher
Mng. Ed. – Dr. Ralph J. Schroeder

KIRCHHEIM UNTER TECK

DER TECKBOTE (6X WK.)
PF 1553, Kirchheim Unter Teck, 73230, Germany; tel (49) 7021 97500; fax 975 033; e-mail info@teckbote.de; web site www.teckbote.de
Circ.: 16,500
Bus. Mgr. – Dr. Claus Gottlieb
Distr. Mgr. – Gunter Tannenberger
Ed. in Chief – Frank Hoffmann

KITZINGEN

DIE KITZINGER (6X WK.)
PF 40, Kitzingen, 97302, Germany; tel (49) 9321 70090; fax 700 944; e-mail anzeigen@diekitzinger.de; web site www.diekitzinger.de
Circ.: 10,000
Ed. in Chief – Daniela Rollinger

KOBLENZ

RHEIN-ZEITUNG (M-6X WK.)
August-Horsch Str. 28, Koblenz, 56070, Germany; tel (49) 261 89200; fax 892 770; e-mail redaktion@rhein-zeitung.de; aboservice@rhein-zeitung.net; web site www.rhein-zeitung.de
Circ.: 259,800
Proprietor – Walterpeter Twer
Bus. Mgr. – Walter Thul
Ed. in Chief – Christian Lindner

RHEIN-HUNSRUCK ZEITUNG (6X WK.)
August-Horch Str. 28, Koblenz, 56070, Germany; tel (49) 261 89200; fax 892 770; e-mail redaktion@rhein-zeitung.net; aboservice@rhein-zeitung.net; web site www.rhein-zeitung.de
Circ.: 230,000
Proprietor – Walter Twer
Bus. Mgr. – Valter Thul

KOLN

EXPRESS (D)
Amsterdamer Str. 192, Koln, 50735, Germany; tel (49) 221 2240; fax 224 2142; e-mail redaktion@express.de; web site www.express.de
Circ.: 468,800
Proprietor – Alfred DuMont
Proprietor – Konstantin Neven DuMont
Proprietor – Christian DuMont Schutte
Ed. in Chief – Rudolf Krietz
Mng. Ed. – Christian Hautop

KOLNER STADT-ANZEIGER (M-6X WK.)
PF 100410, Koln, 50450, Germany; tel (49) 221 2240; fax 224 2079; e-mail ksta-herausgeber@mds.de; web site www.ksta.de
Circ.: 305,100
Proprietor – Alfred Neven DuMont
Adv. Mgr. – Schulz Ute
Ed. in Chief – Franz Sommerfeld

KOLNISCHE RUNDSCHAU (6X WK.)
PF 102145, Koln, 50461, Germany; tel (49) 221 163 2558; fax 163 2557; e-mail print@krredaktion.de; web site www.rundschau-online.de
Circ.: 120,000
Ed. in Chief – Engelbert Greis
News Ed. – Raimund Neuss

KONSTANZ

SUDKURIER (M-6X WK.)
PF 102001, Konstanz, 78420, Germany; tel (49) 7531 9990; fax 999 1485; e-mail online-redaktion@suedkurier.de; sk-online@suedkurier.de; web site www.skol.de
Circ.: 136,280
Bus. Mgr. – Rainer Wiesner
Distr. Mgr. – Andreas Gruczek
Ed. in Chief – Thomas Satinssky

KORBACH

WALDECKSICHE LANDESZEITUNG (6X WK.)
PF 1780, Korbach, 34487, Germany; tel (49) 5631 56000; fax 560 159; e-mail info@wlz-fz.de; web site www.wlz-fz.de

Circ.: 28,000
Bus. Mgr. – Stephen Schindler

KORNWESTHEIM

KORNWESTHEIMER ZEITUNG (6X WK.) EST. 1908
PF 1760, Kornwestheim, 70806, Germany; tel (49) 7154 13120; fax 131299; e-mail info@kornwestheimer-zeitung.zgs.de; web site www.kornwestheimer -zeitung.de
Circ.: 5,600
Bus. Mgr. – Uwe Reichert

LAHR

LAHRER ZEITUNG (6X WK.)
PF 2120, Lahr, 77911, Germany; tel (49) 7821 278 3132; fax 278 3150; e-mail info@lahrer-zeitung.de; redaktion@lahrer-zeitung.de
Circ.: 15,000
MD – Ulrike Lambarg

LAMPERTHEIM

LAMPERTHEIMER ZEITUNG (6X WK.)
Alte Viernheimer Str. 9, Lampertheim, 68623, Germany; tel (49) 6206 952 021; fax 952 020; e-mail impressum@vrm.de; web site www.lampertheimer-zeitung.de
Circ.: 3,000
Ed. – Hans-Karl Asel

LANDSHUT

LANDSHUTER ZEITUNG (6X WK.)
PF 1586, Landshut, 84028, Germany; tel (49) 871 8500; fax 850 132; web site www.idowa.de
Proprietor – Hermann Balle
Ed. – Focher-Jukec Immanuel
Ed. – George Soller

LEER

OSTFRIESEN ZEITUNG (6X WK.)
Maiburg Str. 8, Leer, 26789, Germany; tel (49) 491 979 0172; e-mail redaktion@ostfriesen-zeitung.de; info@oz-online.de; web site www.ostfriesen-zeitung.de
Circ.: 45,900
Ed. – Gunk Mann

LEIPZIG

LEIPZIGER VOLKSZEITUNG (M-6X WK.)
Peterssteinweg 19, Leipzig, 04107, Germany; tel (49) 341 21810; fax 2181 1640; web site www.lvz-online.de
Circ.: 375,700
Ed. in Chief – Hartwig Hochstein
Ed. – Thomas Seidler
Mng. Ed. – Micha Schneider
News Ed. – Andre Bohmer

LEONBERG

LEONBERGER KREISZEITUNG (6X WK.)
PF 1562, Leonberg, 71226, Germany; tel (49) 7152 9370; fax 937 2819; e-mail redaktion@leonberger-kreiszeitung.zgs.de; web site ^www.leonberger-kreiszeitung.de
Circ.: 18,000
Ed. in Chief – Michael Schmidt
Adv. Mgr. – Uwe Reichart

LEUTKIRCH

SCHWABISCHE ZEITUNG (6X WK.)
PF 1145, Leutkirch, 88299, Germany; tel (49) 7561 80102; fax 80378; e-mail redaktion@schwaebische-zeitung.de; web site www.schwaebische-zeitung.de; www.szon.de
Circ.: 200,000
Ed. in Chief – Ralf Teisenhanslueke

LICHTENFELS

OBERMAIN-TAGBLATT (6X WK.) EST. 1857
Hirtenstr. 5, Lichtenfels, 96215, Germany; tel (49) 9571 95050; fax 950 561; e-mail redaktion@obermain.de; web site www.obermain.de
Circ.: 14,300
Proprietor – Irmgard Wilkening
Ed. in Chief – Roger Martin

LIPPSTADT

DER PATRIOT (6X WK.)
PF 2350, Lippstadt, 59533, Germany; tel (49) 2941 20100; fax 201 285; e-mail zeitungsverlag@derpatriot.de; web site www.derpatriot.de
Circ.: 26,000
Proprietor – Michael Laumanns
Proprietor – Reinhard Laumanns
Adv. Mgr – Georg Boer

LORRACH

OBERBADISCHES VOLKSBLATT (6X WK.)
PF 2040, Lorrach, 79539, Germany; tel (49) 7621 40330; fax 403 380; e-mail anzeigen@verlagshaus-jaumann.de; web site www.oberbadischesvolksblatt.de
Circ.: 21,500
Bus. Mgr. – Martin Pfortner
Adv. Mgr. – Thomas Dunke

LUBECK

LUBECKER NACHRICHTEN/LUBECKER NACHRICHTEN AM SONNTAG (M-6X WK.)
Herrenholz 10, Lubeck, 23556, Germany; tel (49) 451 1440; web site www.ln-online.de
Proprietor – J. Wessel
Distr. Mgr. – Rainer Bremer
Adv. Mgr. – Rudiger Kruppa
Ed. in Chief – Uli Exner
Mng. Ed. – Andreas Hess

LUCHOW

ELBE-JEETZEL-ZEITUNG (6X WK.)
PF 1163, Luchow, 29439, Germany; tel (49) 5841 1270; fax 127 350; e-mail ejz@ejz.de; web site www.ejz.de
Circ.: 40,000
Bus. Mgr. – W. Kopper
Ed. – Hans-Hermann Muller

LUDENSCHEID

LUDENSCHEIDER NACHRICHTEN (6X WK.)
Schillerstr. 20, Ludenscheid, 58511, Germany; tel (49) 2351 1580; fax 158 223; e-mail ln@come-on.de; web site www.come-on.de
Circ.: 38,000
Bus. Mgr. – Burckhardt Schmidt

Ed. in Chief – Hans Willms

ALLGEMEINER ANZEIGER (6X WK.)
Schillerstr. 20, Ludenscheid, 58511, Germany; tel (49) 2351 1580; fax 158 223; e-mail ln@come-on.de; web site www.come-on.de
Circ.: 16,000
Bus. Mgr – Burckhardt Schmidt
Ed. in Chief – Hans Willms

SUDERLANDER VOLKSFREUND (6X WK.)
Schillerstr. 20, Ludenscheid, 58511, Germany; tel (49) 2351 1580; fax 158 223; e-mail ln@lnnz.de; web site www.come-on.de
Circ.: 3,400
Distr. Mgr. – Wolfgang Schabo

LUDENSCHELD

MEINERZHAGENER ZEITUNG (6X WK.)
Schillerstr. 20, Ludenscheid, 58511, Germany; tel (49) 2351 1580; fax 158 223; e-mail ln@come-on.de; web site www.come-on.de
Circ.: 7,800
Bus. Mgr. – Burckhardt Schmidt
Ed. in Chief – Martin Krigar

LUDWIGSBURG

LUDWIGSBURGER KREISZEITUNG (6X WK.)
Kornerstr. 14, Ludwigsburg, 71610, Germany; tel (49) 7141 130 222; fax 130 200; e-mail aza@u-u.de; web site www.lkz.de
Circ.: 44,800
Bus. Mgr. – Gerhard Ulmer
Adv. Mgr. – Juergen Merkle

LUDWIGSHAFEN AM RHEIN

DIE RHEINPFALZ (M-6X WK.)
PF 211147, Ludwigshafen am Rhein, 67059, Germany; tel (49) 621 590 201; e-mail rheinpfalz@rheinpfalz.de; web site www.ron.de
Circ.: 258,300
Distribution Mgr. – Hans A. Bruckner
Ed. in Chief – Michael Garthe
Ed. – Stefan Keller
Mng. Ed. – Peter Leister

LUNEBURG

LANDESZEITUNG FUR DIE LUNEBERGER HEIDE (6X WK.)
PF 2125, Luneburg, 21335, Germany; tel (49) 4131 7400; fax 740 225; e-mail redaktion@landeszeitung.de; web site www.landeszeitung.de
Proprietor – Jens Wiesemann
Proprietor – Thomas von Stern
Ed. in Chief – Christoph Steiner
Mng. Ed. – Joachim Ziessler
News Ed. – Dietlinde Terjung
Mktg. Mgr. – Christian Stern

NIEDERSACHSISCHES TAGEBLATT (D)
PF 2320, Luneburg, 21313, Germany; tel (49) 4131 44009; fax 702 285; e-mail service@nt-anzeigen.de; web site www.nt-anzeigen.de
Ed. – Thomas von Stern

MAGDEBURG

MAGDEBURG VOLKSSTIMME (D-EX S)
PF 3649, Magdeburg, 39104, Germany; tel (49) 391 59990; fax 599 9400; e-mail anzeigen@volksstimme.de; web site www.volksstimme.de
Bus. Mgr. – Klaus Lange
Distr. Mgr. – Lutz Lucke
Ed. in Chief – Franz Kadell
Mng. Ed. – Thomas Rauwald
Ed. – Jens Uwe Jahns
News Ed. – Michael Bock

MAINBURG

HALLERTAUER ZEITUNG (6X WK.)
PF 100340, Mainburg, 84028, Germany; tel (49) 871 8500; fax 850132; e-mail service@idowa.de; web site www.idowa.de; www.hallertauer-zeitung.de
Circ.: 6,000
Bus. Mgr. – Hermann Balle
Dist. Mgr. – Joachim Melzer

MAINTAL

MAINTAL TAGESANZEIGER (6X WK.)
PF 1269, Maintal, 63462, Germany; tel (49) 6181 40900; fax 409 030; e-mail aboservice@maintaltagesanzeiger.de; web site www.maintaltagesanzeiger.de
Circ.: 7,200
Bus. Mgr. – Richard Brandl
Dist. Mgr. – Norbert Albrecht

MAINZ

ALLGEMEINE ZEITUNG (6X WK.)
PF 3120, Mainz, 55021, Germany; tel (49) 6131 4830; fax 485 133; e-mail verlag@rhein-main-wochenblatt.de; web site www.allgemeine-zeitung.de
Circ.: 142,900
Last Audit: March 25, 2010
Pub. – Hans Georg Schade
Sec. – Rita Kasper

MAIN-SPITZE (6X WK.)
PF 3120, Mainz, 55127, Germany; tel (49) 6131 4830; fax 485 833; web site www.main-spitze.de
Circ.: 14,500
Ed. – Klaus Beck

MANNHEIM

MANNHEIMER MORGEN (M-6X WK.)
PF 102164, Mannheim, 68161, Germany; tel (49) 621 39201; fax 392 1379; e-mail verlag@mamo.de; info@mamo.de; web site www.morgenweb.de
Ed. in Chief – Horst Roth
News Ed. – Michael Schroder
Adv. Mgr. – Gerhard Haederle

MARBACH

MARBACHER ZEITUNG (6X WK.)
PF 1118, Marbach, 71672, Germany; tel (49) 7144 85000; fax 5001; e-mail redaktion@marbacher-zeitung.zgs.de; web site www.marbacher-zeitung.de
Circ.: 8,000
Last Audit: April 1, 2010
Proprietor – Kai Keller
Distribution Mgr. – Christel Fiechtner
Ed. in Chief – Carlyn Kaotz

MARBURG

OBERHESSISCHE PRESSE (6X WK.)
Franz-Tuczek-Weg 1, Marburg, 35039, Germany; tel (49) 6421 4090; fax 409 117; e-mail info@op-marburg.de; web site www.op-marburg.de
Circ.: 34,100
Proprietor – Dr. Wolfram Hitzeroth
Mktg. Mgr. – Michael Acker
Ed. – Christoph Linne

MARKTOBERDORF

ALLGAUER ZEITUNG (6X WK.)
PF 1352, Marktoberdorf, 87616, Germany; tel (49) 8342 96966; e-mail info@all-in.de; web site www.all-in.de
Circ.: 10,200
Proprietor – Georg Furst von Waldburg zu Zeil

ALLGAUER ZEITUNG (D-6X WK.)
PF 1352, Marktoberdorf, 87611, Germany; tel (49) 8342 969 690; fax 969 689; e-mail anzetgen.marktoberdorf@azy.de
Circ.: 11,900
Proprietor – Gunter Holland
Proprietor – Georg Furst von Waldburg zu Zeil
Bus. Mgr. – Ottmar Schnitzer
Distr. Mgr. – Elizabeth Weiss
Ed. – Reinhold Lochle

MARL

RECKLINGHAUSER ZEITUNG (6X WK.)
Kampstr. 84b, Marl, 45772, Germany; tel (49) 2365 1070; fax 1071 490; e-mail info@medianhaus-bauer.de; anzeigenservice@medianhaus-bauer.de; web site www.recklinghaeuser-zeitung.de
Circ.: 69,000
Adv. Mgr. – Carsten Dingerkus
Ed. in Chief – Kurt Bauer

MEININGEN

FREIES WORT (M-6X WK.)
PF 100362, Meiningen, 98617, Germany; tel (49) 3681 8510; fax 851 211
Circ.: 174,300
Ed. – Waltraud Griego

MEMMINGEN

MEMMINGER ZEITUNG (6X WK.)
PF 1651, Memmingen, 87700, Germany; tel (49) 8331 1090; fax 109 102; e-mail info@mm-zeitung.de; web site www.all-in.de
Circ.: 24,000
Mgr. – Raener Elsinger

MENDEN

MENDENER ZEITUNG (6X WK.)
PO Box 2554, Menden, 58706, Germany; tel (49) 2373 17300; fax 173 015; e-mail lokales@mendener-zeitung.de; web site www.mendener-zeitung.de
Circ.: 7,600
Ed. in Chief – Martin Krigar

METZINGEN

SUDWEST PRESSE (6X WK.)
PF 1163, Metzingen, 72555, Germany; tel (49) 7071 9340; fax 994109; e-mail verlagsleitung@tagblatt.de; web site www.tagblatt.de
Circ.: 14,100
Bus. Mgr. – Dr. Helmut Schomaker
Ed. – Hans-Peter Jans
Mng. Ed. – Wieland Lehmann

MINDEN

MINDENER TAGEBLATT (6X WK.)
PF 2140, Minden, 32423, Germany; tel (49) 571 8820; fax 882 249; e-mail mt@mt-online.de; web site www.mt-online.de
Circ.: 37,000
Proprietor – R. Thomas
Publishing Dir. – Carsten Lohmann
Ed. in Chief – Christopher Pepper

MORFELDEN-WAILDORF

TURKIYE (D)
Starkenburgstr. 7-9, Morfelden-Waildorf, 64546, Germany; tel (49) 6105 98130; fax 981 3170
Circ.: 55,000
Ed. in Chief – F. Ergum

MORFELDEN-WALDORF

HURRIYET (D)
Ander Brucke 20, Morfelden-Waldorf, 64546, Germany; tel (49) 6105 327 130; e-mail haber@hurriyet.de; web site www.hurriyet.de
Circ.: 98,000
Proprietor – Aydin Dogan
Gen. Mgr. – Sevda Boduroglu

MUHLACKER

MUHLACKER TAGBLATT (5X WK.)
PF 1351, Muhlacker, 75417, Germany; tel (49) 7041 8050; fax 80570; e-mail info@muehlacker-tagblatt.de; web site www.muehlacker-tagblatt.de
Circ.: 9,900
Proprietor – Brigitte Wetzel-Handle
Bus. Mgr. – H.U. Wetzel
Adv. Mgr. – Urich Wetzel

MUNCHEN

ABENDZEITUNG (E-6X WK.)
Rundfunkplatz 4, Munchen, 80335, Germany; tel (49) 89 23770; fax 237 7409; e-mail info@abendzeitung.de; web site www.abendzeitung.de
Circ.: 256,900
Proprietor – Anneliese Friedmann
Proprietor – Johannes Friedmann
Ed. in Chief – Arno Makowski

MUNICH

MUNCHNER MERKUR (6X WK.)
Paul-Heyse-Str. 2, Munich, 80282, Germany; tel (49) 89 53060; fax 5306 8656; e-mail info@merkur-online.de; web site www.merkur-online.de
Circ.: 218,300
Proprietor – A. Doser
Proprietor – D. Ippen
Ed. in Chief – Karl Schbrmann
Mng. Ed. – Andreas Liegsalz
Ed. – Peter Schmidt

SUDDEUTSCHE ZEITUNG (M-6X WK.)
Hultschiner Strasse 8, Munich, 81677, Germany; tel (49) 89 21830; fax 2183 9777; e-mail verlag@sueddeutsche.de; syndication@sueddeutsche.de; web site www.sueddeutsche.de
Circ.: 470,200
Ed. in Chief – Hans-Werner Kilz

TZ (6X WK.) EST. 1968
PO Box 80 282, Munich, 80336, Germany; tel (49) 89 53060; fax 530 6201; e-mail sekretariat@tz-online.de; web site www.tz-online.de

Circ.: 131,333
Group: Zeitungsverlag tz München GmbH & Co. KG
Proprietor/Pub. – Dirk Ippen
Alfons Döser

MUNSINGEN

ALB BOTE (6X WK.)
PF 1150, Munsingen, 72521, Germany; tel (49) 7381 1870; fax 3171; e-mail i.zoldos-muhr@swp.de; web site www.suedwest-presse.de
Circ.: 5,100
Bus. Mgr. – H. Schomaker
Distributing Mgr. – Irene Zoldos-Muhr
Ed. in Chief – Jurgen Kuhnemund

MUNSTER, WESTFALEN

MUNSTERSCHE ZEITUNG (6X WK.)
Neubruckenstr. 8, Munster, Westfalen, 48143, Germany; tel (49) 251 5920; fax 592 8651; e-mail redaktion@westline.de; web site www.westline.de/mz
Circ.: 29,217
Bus. Mgr. – Christoph Sandmann
Ed. in Chief – Stefan Bargmann

WESTFALISCHE NACHRICHTEN/ZENO ZEITUNGEN (6X WK.)
An der Hansalinie 1, Munster, Westfalen, 48163, Germany; tel (49) 251 6900; fax 690 143; e-mail buchverlag@aschendorff.de; web site www.westfaelische-nachrichten.de
Circ.: 244,800
Bus. Mgr. – J.B. Huffer
Bus. Mgr. – Paul Huffer
Bus. Mgr. – Dirk F. Passmann
Mktg. Mgr. – Marc Zahlmann

MURRHARDT

MURRHARDTER ZEITUNG (6X WK.)
PO Box 1262, Murrhardt, 71540, Germany; tel (49) 7192 92900; fax 929 019; e-mail info@murrhardter-zeitung.de; web site www.murrhardter-zeitung.de
Circ.: 3,900
Distr. Mgr. – Michael Mauser

NEU-ISENBURG

ARZTE ZEITUNG (M-5X WK.)
PF 200251, Neu-Isenburg, 63077, Germany; tel (49) 6102 5060; fax 58870; e-mail info@aerztezeitung.de; web site www.aerztezeitung.de
Circ.: 65,000
Bus. Mgr. – Harm Van Maanen
Bus. Mgr. – Lothar Kuntz
Mng. Ed. – Michael Schurmann

NEUBRANDENBURG

NORDKURIER (6X WK.)
PF 200121, Neubrandenburg, 17034, Germany; tel (49) 395 45750; fax 457 5255; e-mail kurier-verlag@nordkurier.de; mega@nordkurier.de; web site www.nordkurier.de
Circ.: 147,100
Ed. in Chief – Dr. Andre Uzulis
Ed. in Chief – Jorg Spreemann
Mng. Ed. – Norbert Glamann
News Ed. – Christian Stelzer

NEUENBURG

DER ENZTALER (6X WK.)
Bahnhofstr. 5, Neuenburg, 75305, Germany; tel (49) 7082 94390; fax 943 995; e-mail redaktion@schwarzwaelder-bote.de; anzeigen@schwarzwaelder-bote.de; web site www.schwarzwaelder-bote.de
Circ.: 6,000
– Heinz-Ludwig Giebel
– Carsten HuberMgr.s

NEUMUNSTER

HOLSTEINISCHER COURIER (6X WK.)
Gansemarkt 1, Neumunster, 24534, Germany; tel (49) 4321 9460; fax 946 104; web site www.shz.de
Circ.: 20,100
Ed. in Chief – Holger Loose

NEUSS

NEUSSER ZEITUNGSVIG (6X WK.)
PF 101152, Neuss, 41464, Germany; tel (49) 2131 404 233; fax 404 249; web site www.ngz-online.de
Circ.: 54,200
Ed. – Ludger Baten

NIENBURG

DIE HARKE (D)
PF 1360, Nienburg, 31563, Germany; tel (49) 5021 9660; fax 966 113; e-mail info@dieharke.de; web site www.dieharke.de
Proprietor – Christian Rumpeltin
Ed. in Chief – Martina Thielking-Rumpeltin
Mng. Ed. – Holger Lachnit

NORDEN

OSTFRIESISCHER KURIER (6X WK.)
PF 100450, Norden, 26506, Germany; tel (49) 4931 9250; fax 925 360; web site www.skn-druck-verlag.de
Circ.: 16,500
Bus. Mgr. – Christian Basse
Ed. in Chief – Thomas Aldick
Mng. Ed. – M. Menssen

NORDENHAM

KREISZEITUNG WESERMARSCH (6X WK.)
PF 1155, Nordenham, 26954, Germany; tel (49) 4731 9430; fax 943101; e-mail nordenham.redaktion@kreiszeitung-wesermarsch.de; web site www.kreiszeitung-wesermarsch.de
Circ.: 8,600
Proprietor – Joachim Ditzen-Blanke
Proprietor – Roswitha Ditzen-Blanke
Bus. Mgr. – Matthias Ditzen-Blanke

NORDERNEY

NORDERNEYER BADEZEITUNG (6X WK.)
PF 1465, Norderney, 26548, Germany; tel (49) 4932 643; fax 82185; e-mail info@norderneyer-badezeitung.de; web site www.norderneyer-badezeitung.de
Circ.: 2,000

NORDHORN

GRAFSCHAFTER NACHRICHTEN (6X WK.)
PF 1449, Nordhorn, 48527, Germany; tel (49) 5921 7070; fax 15166; e-mail gn@gn-online.de; web site www.gn-online.de
Pub. – Juergen Wegmann
Adv. Mgr. – Mattheas Lechter
Mng. Ed. – Freimuth Schulze

NURNBERG

ERLANGER NACHRICHTEN (D-6X WK.)
Marienstr. 9/11, Nurnberg, 90327, Germany; tel (49) 911 2160; fax 216 2670; e-mail nav@pressenetz.de; info@pressenetz.de; web site www.erlanger-nachrichten.de
Circ.: 42,100
Proprietor – Bruno Schnell
Mktg. Mgr. – Willfied Willner

NURNBERGER NACHRICHTEN (6X WK.)
Marienstrasse 9/11, Nurnberg, 90402, Germany; tel (49) 911 2160; fax 216 2326; e-mail nav@pressenetz.de; info@pressenetz.de; web site www.nn-online.de
Circ.: 350,200
Proprietor – Bruno Schnell
Ed. in Chief – Heinz-Joachim Hauck
Ed. in Chief – Wolfgang Schmieg
Ed. – Hans Peter Reitzner
Mng. Ed. – Peter Ehler

NZ NURNBERGER ZEITUNG (M-EX S)
PF 3347, Nurnberg, 90402, Germany; tel (49) 911 23510; fax 2351 2000; e-mail nz-redaktion@pressenetz.de; nz-lokales@pressenetz.de; web site www.nz-online.de
Circ.: 28,000
Last Audit: April 29, 2010
Bus. Mgr. – D. Puschmann
Distribution Mgr. – Barbel Schnell
Ed. in Chief – Diethard Prell
Ed. in Chief – Raimund Kirch
Ed. – Dr. Andre Fischer

PEGNITZ-ZEITUNG (6X WK.)
Marienstr. 9/11, Nurnberg, 90327, Germany; tel (49) 911 2160; fax 216 2432; e-mail nav@pressenetz.de; web site www.nn-online.de
Proprietor – Bruno Schnell
Ed. – Clemens Fischer

SCHWABACHER TAGBLATT (6X WK.)
Marienstr. 9, Nurnberg, 90402, Germany; tel (49) 911 2160; e-mail nav@pressenetz.de; web site www.nn-online.de
Proprietor – Bruno Schnell

NURTINGEN

NURTINGER ZEITUNG (6X WK.)
PF 1849, Nurtingen, 72622, Germany; tel (49) 7022 94640; fax 946 4111; e-mail forum@ntz.de; anzeigen@ntz.de; web site www.ntz.de
Circ.: 24,600
Proprietor – Monika Krichenbauer
Adv. Mgr – Victor Strroner
Ed. in Chief – Anneliese Lieb

OBERKIRCH

ACHER-RENCH-ZEITUNG (6X WK.)
Marktplatz 4, Oberkirch, 77704, Germany; tel (49) 7802 8040; fax 80431; web site www.baden-online.de
Circ.: 14,500
Proprietor – Peter Reiff
Ed. – Rudiger Keller

OBERNDORF

SCHWARZWALDER BOTE (6X WK.)
PF 1380, Oberndorf, 78727, Germany; tel (49) 7423 780; fax 78328; e-mail service@schwarzwaelder-bote.de; web site www.schwarzwaelder-bote.de
Circ.: 13,000
Last Audit: March 29, 2010
Bus. Mgr. – Heinz-Ludwig Giebel
Ed. in Chief – Klaus Siegmeier

OCHTRUP

TAGEBLATT FUR DEN KREIS STEINFURT (6X WK.)
PF 1245, Ochtrup, 48607, Germany; tel (49) 2553 93940; fax 3000; e-mail kirch@tageblattonline.de; web site www.tageblatt-online.de
Circ.: 4,600
Ed. – Peter-Georg Zaun

OELDE

DIE GLOCKE (6X WK.)
PF 3240, Oelde, 59281, Germany; tel (49) 2522 730; fax 73166; e-mail postmaster@die.glocke.de; web site www.die-glocke.de
Circ.: 65,000
Proprietor – Dirk Holterdorf
Ed. in Chief – Fried Gehring

OFFENBACH

OFFENBACH-POST (6X WK.)
PF 100263, Offenbach, 63071, Germany; tel (49) 69 850 080; fax 8500 8298; e-mail service@op-online.de; web site www.op-online.de
Circ.: 42,623
Ed. in Chief – Frank Proefe
News Ed. – Ulrich Kaiser

OFFENBURG

OFFENBURGER TAGEBLATT (6X WK.)
Marlener Str. 9, Offenburg, 77656, Germany; tel (49) 781 5040; fax 504 1119; e-mail info@reiff.de; web site www.reiff.de
Circ.: 76,000
Proprietor – Peter Reiff

OLDENBURG

NORDWEST ZEITUNG (6X WK.)
PF 2527, Oldenburg, 26121, Germany; tel (49) 441 998 801; fax 9988 2048; web site www.nwzonline.de
Circ.: 120,000
Ed. in Chief – Rolf Seelheim
Ed. – Gaby Schneider-Schelling

ORANIENBURG

ORANIENBURGER GENERALANZIEGER (6X WK.)
PF 100263, Oranienburg, 16515, Germany; tel (49) 3301 59630; fax 596 350; e-mail lokales@oranienburger-generalanzeiger.de; web site www.die-mark-online.de
Circ.: 38,800
Ed. – Michael Hielscher

OSNABRUCK

NEUE OZ OSNABRUCKER ZEITUNG (M-6X WK.)
PF 4260, Osnabruck, 49032, Germany; tel (49) 541 3100; fax 310 234; e-mail redaktion@neue-oz.de; web site www.neue-oz.de
Circ.: 332,600
Pub./Bus. Mgr. – Hermann Elstermann
Ed. in Chief – Jurgen Wermser
News Ed. – Heiko Schlottke
Sports Ed. – Harold Pistorius

OSTERODE

HARZ KURIER (6X WK.)
PF 1527, Osterode, 37505, Germany; tel (49) 5522 31700; fax 902 029; e-mail redaktion@harzkurier.de; web site www.harzkurier.de
Circ.: 25,000
Proprietor – Sigfried Jungfer
Ed. – Peter Bischof

OSTERODE AM HARZ

OSTERODER KREIS-ANZEIGER (6X WK.)
PF 1593, Osterode am Harz, 37505, Germany; tel (49) 5522 2018; fax 2755
Circ.: 8,100
Pub. – H.H. Giebel
Bus. Mgr. – P.J. Lesemann
Ed. – D. Kuhn
Distr. Mgr. – J. Nitsche

OTTERNDORF

NIEDERELBE-ZEITUNG (6X WK.)
PF 1153, Otterndorf, 21762, Germany; tel (49) 4751 9010; fax 901 149; e-mail anzeigen@nez.de; web site www.nez.de
Circ.: 11,800
Ed. – Alebert Schoeder

PADERBORN

WESTFALISCHES VOLKSBLATT (6X WK.)
Imadstr. 40, Paderborn, 33102, Germany; tel (49) 5251 8960; fax 896 169
Circ.: 49,500
Ed. – Rudiger Kache

PASSAU

PASSAUER NEUE PRESSE (M-EX S)
PF 2040, Passau, 94036, Germany; tel (49) 851 8020; fax 802 256; e-mail npv@vgp.de; web site www.pnp.de
Circ.: 172,400
Distribution Mgr. – Mario Seewald
Simone Tucci-Diekmann

PEINE

PEINER ALLGEMEINE ZEITUNG (6X WK.)
PF 1660, Peine, 31224, Germany; tel (49) 5171 4060; fax 406 138; e-mail paz@madsack.de; web site www.paz-online.de
Circ.: 22,500
Ed. in Chief – Jorg Schmidt

PFORZHEIM

PFORZHEIMER ZEITUNG (6X WK.)
PF 1360, Pforzheim, 75172, Germany; tel (49) 7231 9330; fax 933 250; e-mail redaction@pz-news.de; web site www.pz-news.de
Circ.: 45,000
Pub./Bus. Mgr. – Albert Esslinger-Kiefer
Distr. Mgr. – Rosemarie Schlumpp
Adv. Mgr. – Ralf Recklies
Ed. – Thomas Frei
Mng. Ed. – Ulrike Trampus
News Ed. – Michael Wohlers

PINNEBERG

PINNEBERGER TAGEBLATT (6X WK.)
PF 1251, Pinneberg, 25421, Germany; tel (49) 4101 5350; fax 535 481; web site www.a-beig.de
Circ.: 15,152
Group: Axel Springer Verlag AG
Mgr. Dir. – Manfred Klatt
Adv. Mgr. – Karsten Raasch
Ed. – Rolf Roehling

WEDEL-SCHULAUER TAGEBLATT (6X WK.)
PF 1251, Pinneberg, 25402, Germany; tel (49) 4101 535 353; fax 535 383; e-mail info@a-beig.de; leserservice@a-beig.de; web site www.a-beig.de
Circ.: 3,431
Bus. Mgr. – Manfred Klatt
Sales. Mgr. – Karsten Raasch
Mng. Ed. – Peter Schweinberger

PINNEPERG

BARMSTEDTER ZEITUNG (6X WK.)
PF 1251, Pinneperg, 25421, Germany; tel (49) 4101 5350; fax 535 281; e-mail leserservice@a-beig.de; web site www.barmstedter-zeitung.de
Circ.: 2,118
Bus. Mgr. – Mansred Klatt
Ed. – Peter Schwienberger
Distr. Mgr. – Karsten Raasch

PIRMASENS

PZ PIRMASENSER ZEITUNG (6X WK.)
PF 1553, Pirmasens, 66924, Germany; tel (49) 6331 80050; fax 800 529; e-mail verlag@pirmasenser-zeitung.de; web site www.pirmasenser-zeitung.de
Circ.: 16,500
Mktg. Mgr. – Alexander Hoffman

PLETTENBERG

SUDERLANDER TAGEBLATT (6X WK.)
PF 1609, Plettenberg, 58840, Germany; tel (49) 2391 90930; fax 10904; e-mail st@mzv.net
Circ.: 6,900
Distr. Mgr. – Camilla Hundt
Ed. – G. Dickopf
Ed. – Guido Gunther
Mng. Ed. – Stefan Aschauer-Hundt

POTSDAM

MARKISCHE ALLGEMEINE (6X WK.)
PF 601153, Potsdam, 14473, Germany; tel (49) 331 28400; fax 284 0310; e-mail maz.cvd@berlin.snafu.de; web site www.markischeallgemeine.de
Circ.: 240,600
Dir. – Peter At Mussen

POTSDAMER NEUESTE NACHRICHTEN (M-6X WK.)
PF 601261, Potsdam, 14411, Germany; tel (49) 331 23760; fax 237 6200; e-mail pnn@potsdam.de; web site www.potsdam.de; www.pnn.de
Circ.: 12,400
Ed. in Chief – Michael Erbach

REGENSBURG

MITTLEBAYERISCHE ZEITUNG (6X WK.)
Margaretenstr. 4, Regensburg, 93047, Germany; tel (49) 941 2070; fax 207 212; e-mail mittelbayerische@mittelbayerische.de; kontakt@post.mittelbayerische.de; web site www.mittelbayerische.de
Last Audit: March 25, 2010
Bus. Mgr. – Peter Esser
Adv. Mgr – Michael Kusch

REMSCHEID

REMSCHEIDER GENERAL-ANZEIGER (6X WK.)
PF 100761, Remscheid, 42853, Germany; tel (49) 2191 9090; fax 909 180; e-mail verlag@rga-online.de; redaction@rga-online.de; web site www.rga-online.de
Circ.: 27,200
Proprietor – W. Putz
News Ed. – Andrea Kargus

RENDSBURG

SCHLESWIG-HOLSTEINISCHE LANDESZEITUNG (6X WK.)
Stegen 1, Rendsburg, 24768, Germany; tel (49) 4331 4640; fax 464 2424; e-mail martina.laville@shz.de; web site www.schleswig.de
Circ.: 30,000
Adv. Mgr. – Fmoenke Geffen
Ed. in Chief – Kessler Azmayesh

REUTLINGEN

REUTLINGER GENERAL-ANZEIGER (6X WK.)
PO Box 1642, Reutlingen, 72706, Germany; tel (49) 7121 3020; fax 302 677; e-mail gea@gea.de; web site www.gea.de
Circ.: 49,400
Bus. Mgr. – V. Lehari
Distribution Mgr. – Stephen Koerting
Ed. in Chief – Harmut Troebs
Ed. in Chief – Christoph Irion

REUTLINGER NACHRICHTEN (D)
PF 2454, Reutlingen, 72764, Germany; tel (49) 7121 93020; fax 930 246; e-mail rn@redaktionswp.de; web site www.swp.de/reutlingen
Circ.: 15,800
Ed. in Chief – Helmut Schomaker

RHAUDERFEHN

GENERAL-ANZEIGER (6X WK.)
PF 1165, Rhauderfehn, 26811, Germany; tel (49) 4952 927 500; fax 927 555; e-mail ga@ga-online.de; info@ga-online.de; web site www.ga-online.de
Circ.: 11,900
Proprietor – Klara Engelberg
Bus. Mgr. – Helmut Schreiber
Ed. in Chief – Gerfried Engleberg

RINTELN

SCHAUMBURGER ZEITUNG (6X WK.)
PF 1240, Rinteln, 31737, Germany; tel (49) 5751 40000; fax 400 0544; e-mail schaumburger-zeitung@t-online.de; sz-redaktion@schaumburger-zeitung.de; web site www.schaumburger-zeitung.de
Circ.: 12,000
Bus. Mgr. – Stefan Reineking
Ed. – Ulrich Reineking

ROSENHEIM

OBERBAYERISCHES VOLKSBLATT (6X WK.)
Hafnerstr. 5, Rosenheim, 83022, Germany; tel (49) 8031 2130; fax 213 216; e-mail info@ovb.net; web site www.ovb-online.de
Circ.: 80,000
Proprietor – Alfons Doser

ROSTOCK

NORDDEUTSCHE NEUESTE NACHRICHTEN (M-6X WK.)
PF 102091, Rostock, 18057, Germany; tel (49) 381 491 1610; fax 491 1621; e-mail redaktion@svz.de; nnn@nnn.de; web site www.nnn.de
Circ.: 20,000
Branch Office Mgr. – Birgit Klockow
Ed. in Chief – Thomas Sung
Ed. – Katja Bulow
Mng. Ed. – Tilo Herzog

OSTSEE-ZEITUNG (M-6X WK.)
PF 101181, Rostock, 18055, Germany; tel (49) 381 3650; fax 381 368; e-mail redaktion@ostee-zeitung.de; web site www.osteezeitung.de
Circ.: 227,800
Group: Axel Springer Verlag AG
Ed. in Chief – Gan Emendoerfer

ROTENBURG, LOWER SAXONY

ROTENBURGER KREISZEITUNG (6X WK.)
PF 1580, Rotenburg, Lower Saxony, 27356, Germany; tel (49) 4261 720; fax 72200; web site www.rotenburger-kreiszeitung.de
Circ.: 12,600
Bus. Mgr. – Gerd Richter
Distribution Mgr. – Roland Stegmann
Ed. in Chief – Siegfried Franke

ROTH

ROTH-HILPOLTSTEINER VOLKSZEITUNG (6X WK.)
PF 1353, Roth, 91154, Germany; tel (49) 9171 970 311; fax 970 326; e-mail verlag@roth-hilpoltsteiner-volkszeitung.de; web site www.roth-hilpoltsteiner-volkszeitung.de
Circ.: 12,000
Proprietor – Bruno Schnell
Ed. – Detles Tsanter

ROTHENBURG

FRANKISCHER ANZEIGER (6X WK.)
Erlbacherstr. 102, Rothenburg, 91541, Germany; tel (49) 911 400 120; fax 40016; e-mail info@rotabene.de; web site www.fraenkischer-anzeiger.de; www.nn-online.de
Circ.: 6,000
Proprietor – Wolfgang Schneider

SAARBRUCKEN

SAARBRUCKER ZEITUNG (6X WK.)
Gutenbergstr. 11, Saarbrucken, 66117, Germany; tel (49) 681 5020; fax 502 2500; e-

mail verlag@sz-sb.de; web site www.sz-newsline.de
Circ.: 170,000
Bus. Mgr. – Thomas Rochel

SALZWEDEL

ALTMARK ZEITUNG (6X WK.)
PF 1154, Salzwedel, 29410, Germany; tel (49) 3901 8314 93110; fax 8314 93190; web site www.altmark-zeitung.de
Circ.: 42,900
Proprietor – Ulrike Meineke
Bus. Mgr. – Martin Schmelzer
Ed. in Chief – Marc Rath
Mng. Ed. – Beatrix Koberstein

SCHIFFERSTADT

SCHIFFERSTADTER TAGBLATT (6X WK.)
PF 1163, Schifferstadt, 67105, Germany; tel (49) 6235 926 90; e-mail info@schiffer-stadter-tagblatt.de; web site www.schiffer-stadter-tagblatt.de
Circ.: 3,200
Distr. Mgr. – Susanne Geier
Disr. Mgr. – G. Weber
Ed. – Emil Geier
Mng. Ed. – Kurt Claus

SCHLITZ

SCHLITZER BOTE (6X WK.)
PF 180, Schlitz, 36110, Germany; tel (49) 6642 96200; fax 6408; e-mail redaktion@schlitzer-bote.de; web site www.schlitzerbote.de
Circ.: 2,400
Proprietor – Klaus Scheele
Distr. Mgr. – G. Weber
Ed. in Chief – Jurgen Gruler
Ed. – Klaus Busse

SCHONGAU

SCHONGAUER NACHRICHTEN (6X WK.)
PF 1347, Schongau, 86956, Germany; tel (49) 8861 920; fax 92139; e-mail sog-nachrichten@merkur-online.de; web site www.merkur-online.de
Circ.: 9,900
Proprietor – Dirk Ippen
Bus. Mgr. – Gerd Waldenmaier
Ed. – Poris Forstner
Mktg. Mgr. – Siegsriet Angerer

SCHWABISCH-GMUND

GMUNDER TAGESPOST (D)
PF 100113, Schwabisch-Gmund, 73513, Germany; tel (49) 7171 60010; fax 600 1763; e-mail gt-anzeigen@tagespost.de; web site www.tagespost.de
Circ.: 12,800
Adv. Mgr – Hans Peter Menlrd
Ed. in Chief – Michael Lange

REMS-ZEITUNG (6X WK.)
Paradiesstr. 12, Schwabisch-Gmund, 73525, Germany; tel (49) 7171 60060; fax 600 659; e-mail info@rems-zeitung.de; web site www.rems-zeitung.de
Circ.: 18,400
Ed. in Chief – Meinrad Sigg
Mng. Ed. – Heinz Strohmaier

SCHWABISCH-HALL

HALLER TAGBLATT (6X WK.)
PF 100340, Schwabisch-Hall, 74523, Germany; tel (49) 791 4040; fax 404 411; e-mail info@hallertagblatt.de; web site www.hohen-lohelive.com
Circ.: 18,000
Pub. – Mattheis Koester
Circ. Mgr. – Alexander Wolf
Ed. – Rainer Hocher
Mng. Ed. – Kurt Neuffer

SCHWERIN

SCHWERINER VOLKSZEITUNG (M-6X WK.)
Gutenbergstr. 1, Schwerin, 19061, Germany; tel (49) 385 63780; fax 397 5140; e-mail info@svz.de; web site www.svz.de
Circ.: 166,500
Ed. in Chief – Thomas Schunck

SCHWETZINGEN

SCHWETZINGER ZEITUNG (6X WK.)
Carl-Theodor-Str. 1, Schwetzingen, 68723, Germany; tel (49) 6202 205 205; fax 205 206; e-mail sz-redaktion@schwetzinger-zeitung.de; web site www.schwetzinger-zeitung.de
Circ.: 19,700
Dir. – Juergen Truler

SEESEN

BEOBACHTER (6X WK.)
Lautenthaler Str. 3, Seesen, 38723, Germany; tel (49) 5381 93650; fax 936 526; web site www.seesener-beobachter.de
Circ.: 6,500
Chief Ed. – Hans Joachim Poerschke

SIEGEN

SIEGENER ZEITUNG (6X WK.)
Obergraben 39, Siegen, 57072, Germany; tel (49) 271 59400; fax 594 0298; e-mail sekre-tariat@siegener-zeitung.de; web site www.siegener-zeitung.de
Circ.: 65,100
Proprietor – W. Rothmaler
Ed. in Chief – Eberhard Winterhager
Mng. Ed. – Joachim Volkel
News Ed. – Klaus-J. Heun

SINDELFINGEN

SZ SINDELFINGER ZEITUNG (D)
Boblinger Str. 76, Sindelfingen, 71060, Germany; tel (49) 7031 8620; fax 862 201; e-mail redaktion@szbz.de; web site www.szbz.de
Circ.: 15,200
Proprietor – Wolfgang Rohm
Ed. in Chief – Hans-Jorg Zurn
Ed. in Chief – Jurgen Haar

SOEST

SOESTER ANZEIGER (6X WK.)
PF 1565, Soest, 59494, Germany; tel (49) 2921 6880; fax 688 121; e-mail sekre-tariat@wa-online.de; web site www.soester-anzeiger.de
Circ.: 150,000
Proprietor – Dr. Dirk Ippen
Bus. Mgr. – Burckhardt Schmidt
Ed. in Chief – Martin Krigar
Mktg. Mgr. – Stefan Barta

SOLINGEN

ST SOLINGER TAGEBLATT (6X WK.)
PF 101226, Solingen, 42612, Germany; tel (49) 212 2990; fax 299 118; e-mail b.boll@solingen-online.de; web site www.solingen-online.de
Circ.: 30,700
Proprietor – Bernhard Boll
Distr. Mgr. – Wolfgang Bauer
Ed. in Chief – Stefan M. Kob
News Ed. – Hans-Peter Meurer

SOLTAU

BOHME-ZEITUNG (6X WK.)
PF 1344, Soltau, 29603, Germany; tel (49) 5191 8080; fax 808 165; e-mail bohme-zeitung@mundschenk.de; web site www.boehme-zeitung.de
Circ.: 14,300
Bus. Mgr. – Wolff Martin Mundschenk

SPEYER

SPEYERER MORGENPOST (6X WK.)
Ludwigstr. 9, Speyer, 67346, Germany; tel (49) 6232 60110; fax 601 149; e-mail ver-lag@mopo-speyer.de; web site www.speyer.de
Circ.: 7,000
Ed. in Chief – Wolfgang Martin

SPRINGE

NEUE DEISTER ZEITUNG (6X WK.)
Bahnhofstr. 18, Springe, 31832, Germany; tel (49) 5041 78910; fax 78989; e-mail foto-satz@ndz.de; web site www.ndz.de
Circ.: 7,600
Proprietor – Ellen Schaper
Proprietor – Burkhard Schaper
Ed. – Marc Fugmann

STADE

BUXTEHUDER TAGEBLATT (6X WK.)
PF 2249, Stade, 21662, Germany; tel (49) 4141 9360; fax 936 294; e-mail redaktion-std@tageblatt.de; web site www.tageblatt.de
Circ.: 12,300
Bus. Mgr. – Rudiger Frund
Adv. Mgr. – Kai Braguna

STADER TAGEBLATT (6X WK.)
PF 2249, Stade, 21662, Germany; tel (49) 4141 9360; fax 936 290; e-mail redaktion.std@tageblatt.de; web site www.tageblatt.de
Circ.: 28,200
Bus. Mgr. – Georg Lempke
Ed. – Christopher Gillen

STADTHAGEN

GENERAL-ANZEIGER FUR DEN LANDKREIS SCHAUMBURG UND UMGEBUNG (5X WK.)
PF 1365, Stadthagen, 31655, Germany; tel (49) 5721 97100; fax 9710599; e-mail Schaumburger-Zeitung@t-online.de
Circ.: 3,600
Pub. – G. Niemeyer
Bus. Mgr.-Chief Ed. – Stefan Reineking
Pub. – H. Niemeyer
Distributing Mgr. – Heiko Reckemeyer

SN SCHAUMBURGER NACHRICHTEN (6X WK.)
PF 1653, Stadthagen, 31646, Germany; tel (49) 5721 809 215; fax 809 241; e-mail sn@madsack.de; web site www.sn-online.de
Circ.: 16,400
Bus. Mgr. – Uwe Graells

STETTENER

FELLBACHER ZEITUNG (6X WK.)
PF 104452, Stettener, 70039, Germany; tel (49) 711 72050; fax 7205 730; e-mail cvd@stn.zgs.de; land@stn.zgs.de; web site www.stuttgarter-nachrichten.de
Circ.: 6,800
Ed. in Chief – Christoph Grote

STRAUBING

STRAUBINGER TAGBLATT (6X WK.)
PF 354, Straubing, 94303, Germany; tel (49) 9421 9400; fax 940 1119; e-mail service@idowa.de; web site www.idowa.de
Circ.: 140,000
Bus. Mgr. – Hermann Balle
Bus. Mgr. – Martin Balle
Distr. Mgr. – Harald Zeindl
Ed. in Chief – Hans Gotzl
Ed. – Bernd Hielscher
Mng. Ed. – Ottmar Guggeis

STUTTGART

CANNSTATTER ZEITUNG (6X WK.)
PF 500249, Stuttgart, 70372, Germany; tel (49) 711 955 680; fax 955 6833; web site www.cannstatterzeitung.de
Circ.: 10,900
Ed. in Chief – Sigfried Baumann

STUTTGARTER NACHRICHTEN (6X WK.)
PO BOX 104452, Stuttgart, 70039, Germany; tel (49) 711 72050; fax 7205 11009; e-mail leserpost@stn.zgs.de; land@stn.zgs.de; web site www.stuttgarter-nachrichten.de
Circ.: 250,000
Bus. Mgr. – R.W. Harich
Ed. – Bruno Bienzle
Ed. – Wolfgang Molitor

NORD-STUTTGARTER RUNDSCHAU (6X WK.)
PO Box 104452, Stuttgart, 70039, Germany; tel (49) 711 72050; fax 720 5747; e-mail cvd@stn.zgs.de; web site www.stuttgarter-nachrichten.de
Circ.: 5,400
Ed. – S. Dingler

STUTTGARTER ZEITUNG (M-6X WK.)
PF 106032, Stuttgart, 70049, Germany; tel (49) 711 7205 8665; fax 7205 1234; e-mail vertrieb@zvs.zgs.de; web site www.stuttgarter-zeitung.de
Circ.: 150,000
Bus. Mgr. – Dr. Richard Rebamnn
Ed. in Chief – Joachim Dorfs

SYKE

KREISZEITUNG FUR DIE LANDKREISE DIEPHOLZ UND VERDEN (6X WK.)
PF 1265, Syke, 28857, Germany; tel (49) 4242 580; fax 58238; e-mail anzeigen@kreiszeitung.de; web site www.kreiszeitung.de
Circ.: 88,700
Proprietor – Burkard Plenge
Proprietor – Dirk Ippen
Proprietor – Lothar Krieghoff
Proprietor – Walter Schroder
Bus. Mgr. – Ernst-Jurgen Wenske
Distribution Mgr. – Wolfgang Nielsen
Ed. in Chief – Heinz-Jurgen Ziller
News Ed. – Gregor Diekmann

WILDESHAUSER ZEITUNG (6X WK.)
PF 1265, Syke, 28857, Germany; tel (49) 4242 580; fax 58238; e-mail anzeigen@kreiszeitung.de; web site www.kreiszeitung.de
Circ.: 80,000
Proprietor – J.A. Loschen
Bus. Mgr. – Ernst-Jurgen Wenske
Distr. Mgr. – Wolfgang Nielsen

TAUBERBISCHOFSHEIM

FRANKISCHE NACHRICHTEN (6X WK.)
PF 1260, Tauberbischofsheim, 97932, Germany; tel (49) 9341 830; fax 83146; web site www.fnweb.de
Circ.: 31,100
Bus. Mgr. – Michael Grethe
Distr. Mgr. – Jorgen Hein

TITTMONING

SUDOSTBAYERISCHE RUNDSCHAU (6X WK.)
Watzmannstr. 2a, Tittmoning, 84529, Germany; tel (49) 8683 955; fax 958; e-mail info@suedostbayerische-rundschau.de; web site www.suedostbayerische-rundschau.de
Circ.: 5,800
Bus. Mgr. – Wulf Pustet

TRAUNSTEIN

TRAUNSTEINER TAGBLATT (6X WK.)
PF 1560, Traunstein, 83278, Germany; tel (49) 861 98770; fax 987 7120; e-mail lokales@traunsteiner-tagblatt.de; web site www.traunsteiner-tagblatt.de
Circ.: 16,400
Bus. Mgr. – Thomas Miller
Circ. Mgr. – Patricia Millier
Ed. in Chief – Martin Miller

TRIER

TRIERISCHER VOLKSFREUND (6X WK.)
Hans Martin-Schleyer-Str. 8, Trier, 54294, Germany; tel (49) 651 71990; fax 719 9990; e-mail verlag@intrinet.de; web site ^www.volksfreund.de
Circ.: 100,000
Bus. Mgr. – Worsgang Sturges
Mng. Ed. – Bernd Wienties
Mng. Ed. – Damian Schwickerath
Ed. in Chie – Issabel Funk
News Ed. – Peter Reinhart
Mng. Ed. – Michael Schmetc

TROSTBERG

TROSTBERGER TAGBLATT (6X WK.)
Gabelsbergerstr. 4/6, Trostberg, 83308, Germany; tel (49) 8621 8080; fax 80810; e-mail info@chiemgau-online.de; web site www.trostberger-tagblatt.de
Circ.: 15,000
Distr. Mgr. – Zennit Aiter
Ed. in Chief – Karlheinz Kas
Ed. – Thomas Grabmuller

TUBINGEN

SUDWEST PRESSE (SCHWABISCHES TAGBLATT) (6X WK.)
PF 2420, Tubingen, 72014, Germany; tel (49) 7071 9340; fax 934 109; e-mail verlagsleitung@tagblatt.de; web site www.tagblatt.de
Circ.: 45,000
Proprietor – Elisabeth Frate
Mng. Ed. – Hans-Martin Mayer

UELZEN

ALLGEMEINE ZEITUNG DER LUNEBURGER HEIDE (D-6X WK.)
PF 1161, Uelzen, 29501, Germany; tel (49) 581 8080; fax 808 9191; e-mail info@cbeckers.de; web site www.az-online.de
Circ.: 18,000
Proprietor – Dirk Ippen

UETERSEN

UETERSENER NACHRICHTEN (6X WK.)
Grosser Sand 3, Uetersen, 25429, Germany; tel (49) 4122 92500; fax 1858; e-mail info@uena.de; redaktion@uena.de; web site www.uena.de
Circ.: 6,000
Proprietor – Lebrecht von Ziehlberg
Ed. – Roland Von Ziehlberg

ULM

SUDWEST PRESSE ULM (6X WK.)
PF 3333, Ulm, 89073, Germany; tel (49) 731 1560; fax 156 659; e-mail info@swp.de; web site www.swp.de
Proprietor – Votel Brack
Bus. Mgr. – Thomas Brackvogel
Distr. Mgr. – Karl Bacherle
Ed. in Chief – Hens Coert Wibdenhaus
Ed. – Hans-Uli Thierer
Mng. Ed. – Joachim Spiegler
News Ed. – Wilhelm Holkemeir

UNNA

HELLWEGER ANZEIGER (6X WK.)
PF 1842, Unna, 59423, Germany; tel (49) 2303 2020; fax 202 163; e-mail verlag@hellwegeranzeiger.de; web site www.hellwegeranzeiger.de
Circ.: 27,500
Proprietor – Gunter Rubens
Proprietor – Hans Christian Harrmann
Ed. in Chief – Klaus Seifert

USINGEN

USINGER ANZEIGER (6X WK.)
PF 1160, Usingen, 61250, Germany; tel (49) 6081 1050; fax 105 100; e-mail redaktion@usinger-anzeiger.de; web site www.usinger-anzeiger.de
Circ.: 7,400
Bus. Mgr. – Wolfgang Maass
Dist. Mgr. – H.P. Schmidt
Ed. – Frank Bugge

VAIHINGEN

VAIHINGER KREISZEITUNG (6X WK.)
PF 1140, Vaihingen, 71654, Germany; tel (49) 7042 9190; fax 91955; e-mail info@vkz.de; web site www.vkz.de
Circ.: 9,500
Mgr. – Helmut Schuermann
Ed. – Albert Arning

VECHTA

OLDENBURGISCHE VOLKSZEITUNG (D)
Neuer Markt 2, Vechta, 59377, Germany; tel (49) 4441 95600; fax 956 0310; e-mail info@ov-online.de; web site www.ov-online.de
Bus. Mgr. – Jorg Peter Knochen
Adv. Mgr. – Reinhard Brannekaemper
Dist. Mgr. – A. Sieve
Ed. in Chief – Uwe Haring
Ed. – Andreas Kathe
News Ed. – Wolfgang E. Kupczyk

VIERNHEIM

VIERNHEIMER TAGEBLATT (6X WK.)
Rathausstr. 53, Viernheim, 68519, Germany; tel (49) 6204 966 660; fax 966 666; e-mail redaktion@viernheimertageblatt.de; web site www.viernheimertageblatt.de
Circ.: 6,500
Last Audit: March 29, 2010
Proprietor – Hans Nikolaus Martin
Bus. Mgr. – Wolfgang Johannes Martin

VILLINGEN-SCHWENNINGEN

SUDWEST PRESSE (DIE NECKARQUELLE) (6X WK.)
Bert-Brecht Str. 15, Villingen-Schwenningen, 78054, Germany; tel (49) 7720 3940; fax 394 175; web site www.suedwest-aktiv.de
Circ.: 9,500
Proprietor – H.U. Ziegler
Ed. in Chief – Gunther Baumann

WAIBLINGEN

SCHORNDORFER NACHRICHTEN (6X WK.)
PF 1813, Waiblingen, 71332, Germany; tel (49) 7151 5660; fax 566 400; e-mail info@zvw.de; web site www.zvw.de
Circ.: 45,000
Proprietor – Ullrich Villinger
Adv. Mgr. – Reinhard Busda

WAIBLINGER KREISZEITUNG (6X WK.)
PF 1813, Waiblingen, 71332, Germany; tel (49) 7151 5660; fax 566 400; e-mail info@zvw.de; web site www.zvw.de
Circ.: 19,400
Bus. Mgr. – Bernd Schwer
Bus. Mgr. – Ullrich Villinger
Ed. in Chief – Werner Muller
Ed. in Chief – Frank Nipkau

WELZHEIMER ZEITUNG (6X WK.)
PF 1813, Waiblingen, 71332, Germany; tel (49) 7151 5660; fax 566; e-mail info@zvw.de; web site www.zvw.de
Circ.: 45,000
Bus. Mgr. – Bernd Schwer
Bus. Mgr. – Ullrich Villinger
Ed. – Frank Nepkau

WINNENDER ZEITUNG (6X WK.)
PF 1813, Waiblingen, 71328, Germany; tel (49) 7151 5660; fax 566 400; e-mail info@zvw.de; web site www.zvw.de
Circ.: 9,400
Bus. Mgr. – Ullrich Villinger
Adv. Mgr. – Michael Sessler

WALDSHUT-TIENGEN

ALB-BOTE (6X WK.)
Bismarchstr. 10, Waldshut-Tiengen, 79761, Germany; tel (49) 7751 83250; fax 8325 7491
Circ.: 8,400
Bus. Mgr. – R. Wiesner
Ed. – Werner Huff

WALLDORF

MILLIYET (D)
An Der Bruecke 20-22, Walldorf, 64546, Germany; tel (49) 6105 327 130; fax 327 177; e-mail milliyet.haber@milliyet.de; web site www.doganmedia.de
Circ.: 26,000
Mgr. – Sevda Boduroglu
Adv. Mgr. – Ilker Gok

WALSRODE

WALSRODER-ZEITUNG (6X WK.)
Lange Str. 14, Walsrode, 29664, Germany; tel (49) 5161 60050; fax 600 528; e-mail walsroderzeitung@wz-net.de; web site www.wz-net.de
Circ.: 13,900
Proprietor – Martin Rohrbein

WEENER

RHEIDERLAND ZEITUNG (6X WK.)
PF 260, Weener, 26826, Germany; tel (49) 4951 9300; fax 930 150; e-mail redaktion@rheiderland.de; web site www.rheiderland.de/rz/index.php
Circ.: 6,400
Ed. in Chief – Gunther Faupel

WEIDEN

DER NEUE TAG (6X WK.)
PF 1340, Weiden, 92603, Germany; tel (49) 961 850; fax 447 47; e-mail info@zeitung.org; web site www.oberpfalznetz.de
Circ.: 95,300
Ed. in Chief – Hans Klemm
Mng. Ed. – Michael Ascherl

WEILER-SIMMERBERG

DER WESTALLGAUER (6X WK.)
PF 1246, Weiler-Simmerberg, 88169, Germany; tel (49) 8387 3990; fax 39955; e-mail info@westallgaeuer-zeitung.de; web site www.westallgaeuer-zeitung.de
Circ.: 9,100
Proprietor – Elmar Holzer
Proprietor – Georg Furst von Waldburg zu Zeil
Proprietor – Gunter Holland
Ed. – Armin Dorner

WEIMAR

TLZ WEIMAR THURINGISCHE LANDESZEITUNG (M-6X WK.)
PF 2329, Weimar, 99423, Germany; tel (49) 3643 206 400; fax 206 422; web site www.tlz.de
Circ.: 33,800
Distribution Mgr. – E. Heinze
Ed. in Chief – Hans Hoffmeister
Exec. Ed. – Norbert Block
Mng. Ed. – Dieter Lucke

WEISSENBURG

WEISSENBURGER TAGBLATT (6X WK.)
Wildbadstr. 16, Weissenburg, 91781, Germany; tel (49) 9141 859 090; fax 859 030; e-mail redaktion@weissenburger-tagblatt.com; web site www.weissenburger-tagblatt.com
Circ.: 12,400
Proprietor – Waltraud Braun

WETZLAR

WETZLARER NEUE ZEITUNG (D)
PF 2940, Wetzlar, 35578, Germany; tel (49) 6441 9590; fax 959 292; e-mail redaktion.wnz@mail.mittelhessen.de; web site www.mittelhessen.de
Circ.: 80,000
Proprietor – Martin Grude
Ed. in Chief – Aloif Koesters

WIESBADEN

WIESBADENER KURIER (6X WK.)
PF 6029, Wiesbaden, 65183, Germany; tel (49) 611 3550; fax 355 3333; e-mail rhein-gau-kurier@vrm.de; web site www.wiesbadener-kurier.de
Circ.: 92,500
Bus. Mgr. – Hans Schnuecker
Ed. in Chief – Matthias Friedrich
News Ed. – Christian Stang

WIESBADENER TAGBLATT (D-6X WK.)
PO Box 6029, Wiesbaden, 65050, Germany; tel (49) 611 3490; fax 349 2233; web site www.wiesbadener-tagblatt.de
Circ.: 25,000
Bus. Mgr. – Hans Schnuecker
Ed. in Chief – Klaus Beck

WILHELMSHAVEN

WILHELMSHAVENER ZEITUNG (E-6X WK.)
PF 1265, Wilhelmshaven, 26382, Germany; tel (49) 4421 4880; fax 488259; e-mail whv@wz.online.de; web site www.wzonline.de
Circ.: 32,200
Proprietor – M. Adrian
Proprietor – W. Brune
Bus. Mgr. – Dr. Stephan Kolschen

WINSEN

WINSENER ANZEIGER (6X WK.)
PF 1354, Winsen, 21413, Germany; tel (49) 4171 6580; fax 658 140; e-mail info@winsener-anzeiger.de; web site www.winsener-anzeiger.de
Circ.: 11,300
Bus. Mgr. – Lebrecht Maack
Ed.-in -Chief – Jurgen Peter Ravens
Ed. – Burkhard Meyer

WITTINGEN

ISENHAGENER KREISBLATT (6X WK.)
PF 1220, Wittingen, 29378, Germany; tel (49) 5831 291 492 100; fax 291 492 190; e-mail redaktion.ik@cbeckers.de; web site www.isenhagener-kreisblatt.de
Circ.: 6,500
Proprietor – Dr. Dirk Ippen

WITTMUND

ANZEIGER FUR HARLINGERLAND (6X WK.)
PF 1352, Wittmund, 26400, Germany; tel (49) 4462 9890; fax 989190; e-mail anzeiger@ost-friesland.de; web site www.ost-friesland.de
Circ.: 16,300
Proprietor – Elisabeth Allmers
Proprietor – Manfred Adrian
Bus. Mgr. – Helmut Loerts-Sabin
Ed. in Chief – Klaus-Dieter Heimann

WURZBURG

MAIN POST (6X WK.)
PF 6160, Wurzburg, 97084, Germany; tel (49) 931 60010; fax 600 1285; e-mail redaktion@mainpost.de; web site www.mainpost.de
Circ.: 161,400
Ed. in Chief – Michael Reinhard
News Ed. – Peter Mack

BOTE VOM GRABFELD (D)
PF 6160, Wurzburg, 97084, Germany; tel (49) 931 60010; fax 600 1285; e-mail info@mainpostlogistik.de; web site www.mainpost.de
Circ.: 3,400
Proprietor – Christa Schunk
Distr. Mgr. – Joachim Liebler

ZEVEN

ZEVENER ZEITUNG (6X WK.)
PF 1555, Zeven, 27395, Germany; tel (49) 4281 9450; fax 945 222; e-mail technik@zevener-zeitung.de; web site www.zevener-zeitung.de
Circ.: 9,900
Ed. – Torsten Kratzmann

ZWEIBRUCKEN

PFAALZISCHER MERKUR (6X WK.)
PF 2064, Zweibrucken, 66482, Germany; tel (49) 6332 800 050; fax 800 059; e-mail merkur@pm-zw.de; web site www.pfaelzischer-merkur.de
Circ.: 13,000
Ed. in Chief – MIchael Klein
Ed. – W. Kipper
Ed. – Lutz Frohlich

GIBRALTAR

GIBRALTAR

THE DEMOCRAT
PO Box 156, Gibraltar, Gibraltar; tel (350) 78363; fax 78990

THE GIBRALTAR ECHO (M)
56 Devil's Tower Rd., Gibraltar, Gibraltar; tel (350)
Ed. – Eddie Campello
Pub. – Paul Campello

GIBRALTAR CHRONICLE (M)
2 Library Gardens, Gibraltar, Gibraltar; tel (350) 78589; fax 79927; web site www.chronicle.gi
Circ.: 6,000
Ed. – F. Cantos
Mng. Ed. – D. Searle

THE NEW PEOPLE (WEEKLY)
PO Box 593, Gibraltar, Gibraltar; tel (350) 72867
Ed. – C. Golt

PANORAMA (WEEKLY)
93-95 Irish Town, Gibraltar, Gibraltar; tel (350) 79797; fax 74664; web site www.gibraltarpanorama.com ; www.panorama.gi
Circ.: 4,000
Ed. – Joe Garcia

VOX (FRIDAY)
PO Box 306, Gibraltar, Gibraltar; tel (350) 77414; fax 72531; e-mail vox@gibnet.gi; web site vox.gi
Circ.: 1,800
Ed. – E. Campello

GREECE

AGIOS NICOLAOS, CRETE

ANATOLI
7 Polytechniou St., Agios Nicolaos, Crete, 72100, Greece; tel (30) 28410 22242; fax 23843
Pub. – E. Koziris

ALEXANDROUPOLIS, THRACE

ELEFTHERI THRAKI (D)
30 E. Venizelou St., Alexandroupolis, Thrace, 68100, Greece; tel (30) 25510 26445; fax 24445; e-mail elthraki@otenet.gr
Pub. – S. Kondylis
Adv. Mgr. – Diopa Nijolaidou

EPARCHIAKOS TYPOS (D)
10 Philippoupoleos St., Alexandroupolis, Thrace, 68100, Greece; tel (30) 551 28008; fax 24077
Pub. – Andrew Dagas

GNOMI (D)
4 Moshonision St., Alexandroupolis, Thrace, 68100, Greece; tel (30) 551 24222; fax 31445
Pub./Ed. – C. Hatjopoulos

ARTA, EPIRUS

DEMOCRATIS (D)
Alkaiou and Arionos, Arta, Epirus, 47100, Greece; tel (30) 22510 25524; fax 28741; web site www.dimokratis.gr
Pub. – Niko Sauofu

ICHO TIS ARTIS (D)
2 Spirou Lambrou St., Arta, Epirus, 47100, Greece; tel (30) 681 75100; fax 27940
Pub. – K. Tsaktsiras

MAHITIS (D)
7 S. Matsou St., Arta, Epirus, 47100, Greece; tel (30) 26810 22779; fax 22779
Pub. – D. Spyrou

PARATIRITIS TIS ARTIS (D)
51 Pl. 24 Iouniou, Arta, Epirus, 47100, Greece; tel (30) 26810 72690; fax 75074
Pub. – E. Drodaris

PROINI (6X WK.)
Gnbakola 47, Arta, Epirus, 47100, Greece; tel (30) 26810 71888; fax 72221
Pub. – K. Getsis

ATHENS

DAILY EXOUSIA (D)
116 Kifisias Ave., Athens, 15125, Greece; tel (30) 210 6496000; fax 6483707
Pub. – Michael Androulidakis

ATHENS, CENTRAL GREECE

APOYEVMATINI (ES)
12 Odos Phidiou, Athens, Central Greece, 10678, Greece; tel (30) 210 643 0011; fax 360 9876; e-mail info@apogevmatini.gr; web site www.apogevmatini.gr
Pub. – Saran Topoulos
Ed. in Chief – Athanasiabis Titos

ATHLITIKI FONI (D)
1 Aristoyos St., Athens, Central Greece, 10441, Greece; tel (30) 1 5248200; fax 5226994
Circ.: 24,117
Pub. – G. Georgalas

AVGI (6X WK.)
Odos Agiou Konstantinou 12, Athens, Central Greece, 10431, Greece; tel (30) 210 523 1831; fax 523 1822; e-mail epipors@avgi.gr; web site www.avgi.gr
Circ.: 5,400
Ed. – Kostas Karis

AVRIANI (ES)
Odos Dimitros 11, Athens, Central Greece, 17778, Greece; tel (30) 210 3424090; fax 3452190
Pub. – George Kouris

AZAT OR (D)
21 Raftoponlon St., Athens, Central Greece, 11745, Greece; tel (30) 210 9345237; fax 9346229
Circ.: 600
Ed. – H. Bazaziay

DIMOPRASSIAKA NEA O KOSMOS (D)
49 Didotou St., Athens, Central Greece, 10680, Greece; tel (30) 210 363 9485
Pub. – P. Konstandinis

NEA (5X WK.)
Michalakopoulou 80, Athens, Central Greece, 11528, Greece; tel (30) 210 776 6000; fax 211 3658301; e-mail info@tanea.gr; web site www.tanea.gr
Pub. – C. Lambrakis

ELEFTHERI ORA (E)
Odos Akademias 32, Athens, Central Greece, 10672, Greece; tel (30) 1 3621868; fax 3603258
Circ.: 1,026
Ed. – G. Mihalopoulos

ELEFTHEROS (D)
18 Amerikis St., Athens, Central Greece, 10671, Greece; tel (30) 210 363 0521; fax 361 9502
Pub. – John Mastoral

ELEFTHEROS TYPOS/TYPOS TIS KIPIAKIS (D)
Iroos Matsi 1, Athens, Central Greece, 17456, Greece; tel (30) 210 994 2431
Circ.: 167,186
Dir. – Ch. Pasalaris

ENIMEROSSI POLITIKI IKONOMIKI (D)
55-59 Deligiorgi St., Athens, Central Greece, 10437, Greece; tel (30) 1 5238526
Pub. – K. Roubinetis

EPHIMERIS DIAKIRIXEON (D)
18 Ypsilantou St., Athens, Central Greece, Greece; tel (30) 1 3214857
Pub. – T.H. Mallios

EPHIMERIS DIMOPRASION & PLEISTIRIASMON (6X WK.) EST. 1929
10 Emmanuel Benaki St. & Panepistimiou , Athens, Central Greece, 10564, Greece; tel (30) 210 321 5692; fax 321 5877; e-mail dimonews@dimoprasion.gr; web site www.dimoprasion.gr
Managing Dir. – John Lefkofrydis
Ed. – John Lefkofrydi

ESTIA (6X WK.)
Odos Anthimou Gazi 9, Athens, Central Greece, 10561, Greece; tel (30) 210 323 0650; fax 324 3071; e-mail estianews@otenet.gr
Circ.: 60,000
Pub. – Koinonia Astikou Dikaiou

ETHNOS (E)
Odos Benaki 152, Metamorfosi Chalandriou,

Athens, Central Greece, 15235, Greece; tel (30) 1 6580640; fax 6396515
Circ.: 84,735
Pub. – George Bobolas
Dir. – Th Kaloudis

EXORMISSI
13-15 Solomou St., Athens, Central Greece, 10682, Greece; tel (30) 210 3803311; fax 3842187
Pub. – D. Sapountzis

EXOUSIA
116 Kifisias Ave., Athens, Central Greece, Greece; tel (30) 210 6496000; fax 6483707
Pub. – Michael Androvlioakis

FILATHLOS (M)
Odos Dimitros 11, Athens, Central Greece, 17778, Greece; tel (30) 1 3424090
Circ.: 40,000
Dir. – Nick Karagiannidis
Pub./Ed. – G.A. Kouris

FOS TON SPOR (D)
122 Athinon Ave., Athens, Central Greece, 10442, Greece; tel (30) 1 5245516; fax 5147805
Ed. – T. Nickolaids

GENIKI DIMOPRASION (6X WK.)
Sonirou 20, Palaiogou 6, Athens, Central Greece, 10438, Greece; tel (30) 210 524 4858; fax 523 2584; e-mail geniki@otenet.gr; web site www.geniki-dimoprasion.gr
Pub. – N. Papanikolaou

ICHO TON DIMOPRASSION (D)
15 Amerikis St., Athens, Central Greece, 10672, Greece; tel (30) 1 3630279; fax 3626073
Pub. – C. Tzinis

IMERISIA (M)
Odos Geraniou 7a, Athens, Central Greece, 10552, Greece; tel (30) 210 523 1195; web site www.imerisia.gr
Circ.: 11,000
Dir. – N. Tsaganelis
Ed. – A. Mothonios

KERDOS (6X WK.)
Vassileos George & Kalvou St. 44, Athens, Central Greece, 15233, Greece; tel (30) 210 674 7881; fax 674 7893; e-mail kerdos@kerdos.gr; web site www.kerdos.gr
Circ.: 18,000
Pub. – Th. Liakounakos
Ed. in Chief – Evangelo Dimos
Mng. Ed. – Serafim Konstandinidis

KINONIKI (D)
21 Alkminis St., Athens, Central Greece, 11854, Greece; tel (30) 210 411 5225
Pub. – S.T. Karambezopolous

LOGOS (M)
40 Praxitelons St., Athens, Central Greece, 10561, Greece; tel (30) 1 3313161; fax 3313161
Pub. – K. Geronikolos

MACHITIKI FONI (D)
9 Ag. Georgiou St., Athens, Central Greece, 15234, Greece; tel (30) 210 6822555
Pub. – G. Nikolopoulos

ORA GIA SPOR (D)
8 John Mettxe St., Athens, Central Greece, 17343, Greece; tel (30) 210 976 1200; fax 976 1211; e-mail oraspor@otenet.gr
Dir. – Evangelos Sembos

PARON
24 Voulis St., Athens, Central Greece, 10563, Greece; tel (30) 1 3229688; fax 3233263
Pub. – Panagis Koutoufas

PONTIKI (WEEKLY)
Odos Massalias 10, Athens, Central Greece, 10681, Greece; tel (30) 210 360 9531
Dir./Ed. – K. Papaioannou

RIZOSPASTIS (M)
Lefkis 134, Athens, Central Greece, 14565, Greece; tel (30) 210 629 7000; fax 629 7999; web site www.rizospastis.gr
Circ.: 28,740
Dir. – T. Tsigas
Adv. Mgr. – Bagelis Gelakis

SPORT TIME (D)
116 Kifisias & Davaki St., Athens, Central Greece, 11526, Greece; tel (30) 210 622 9022
Pub. – Michalis Androulidakis

STAR (D)
31 Demetros St., Athens, Central Greece, 17778, Greece; tel (30) 210 3474700; fax 3474945
Group: Admarket International (Div. of Marcom International, Inc.)

TA NEA (E)
Odos Christou Lada 3, Athens, Central Greece, 10237, Greece; tel (30) 210 333 3555; fax 322 8797; e-mail tanea@dolnet.gr; web-tanea@dolnet.gr; web site www.dolnet.gr; www.tanea.gr
Circ.: 135,000
Dir. – Leon Karapanayiotis
Ed. – Christos Lambrakis

KYRIAKATIKI ELEFTHEROTYPIA (D)
10-16 Minoos St., Athens, Central Greece, 11743, Greece; tel (30) 210 929 6001; fax 902 8319; web site www.enet.gr
Ed. in Chief – Kanasis Pegoboulos

TO VIMA (D)
80 Michalakopoulou Str., Athens, Central Greece, 11528, Greece; tel (30) 211 365 7000; fax 365 8004; e-mail tovima@dolnet.gr; web site www.tovima.gr
Circ.: 250,000
Ed. – Stavros R. Psycharis

ELEFTHEROTYPIA (D)
Odos Minoou 10-16, Athens, Central Greece, 11743, Greece; tel (30) 210 929 6001; fax 902 8311; e-mail elef@enet.gr; web site www.enet.gr
Pub. – Chr Tegopoulos
Dir. – Bama Bopoulos

CHANIA, CRETE

HANIOTIKI ELEFTHEROTYPIA (D)
74 Mjlogiayyi St., Chania, Crete, 73100, Greece; tel (30) 821 97174; fax 90400
Pub. – A. Spanoudakis
Dir. – M. Spanoudakis

KIRYX (D)
22 K. Hiotaki St., Chania, Crete, 73100, Greece; tel (30) 821 98240; fax 94074
Pub. – S. Nikifrackis

CHIOS, AEGEAN ISLAND

ALITHIA (D)
1 Polihronopoulou St., Chios, Aegean Island, 82100, Greece; tel (30) 271 25838; fax 25838; e-mail news@alithia.gr; web site www.alithia.gr
Pub. – Yannis Tzoumas

CHIAKOS LAOS (D)
8 Rodokanaki St., Chios, Aegean Island, 82100, Greece; tel (30) 22710 24329; fax 28596
Pub. – G. Douvlis

DIMOKRATIKI (D)
11 Evaggelistrias Str., Chios, Aegean Island, 82100, Greece; tel (30) 271 22260; fax 23445
Pub. – E. Tsouri

PROODOS (6X WK.)
44 Rodokanaki St., Chios, Aegean Island, 82100, Greece; tel (30) 22710 23085; fax 26898
– N. Frangoulis
– K. FrangoulisPub.s

CORFU

ELEFTHERIA (6X WK.)
9 Delvinioti St., Corfu, 49100, Greece; tel (30) 26610 30001; fax 22022; e-mail el-news@otenet.gr
Pub./Dir. – I. Tzevelikas

IDISSEIS TIS KERKIRAS (D)
Agios Elias St., Corfu, 49100, Greece; tel (30) 26610 37986; fax 37986
Pub. – S.T.G. Karvounis

KERKYRAIKO VIMA (D)
13 Korinthion St., Corfu, 49100, Greece; tel (30) 26610 37990; fax 24970; e-mail kerkyraikovima@otennet.gr; web site www.kerkyraikovima.gr
Adv. Mgr – K. Balos

CORFU, IONIAN ISLANDS

SIMERINI
Palaiokastritsas National Rd., Corfu, Ionian Islands, 49100, Greece; tel (30) 661 361206; fax 39483
Dir. – E. Vergis

DRAMA, MACEDONIA

DRAMINI (6X WK.)
Adrianoueoleos 17, Drama, Macedonia, 66100, Greece; tel (30) 25210 21992; fax 21333
Pub. – John Melidis

ICHO (D)
Stoa Gatzouli, Drama, Macedonia, 66100, Greece; tel (30) 25210 23444; fax 23444
Pub. – Thanassis Papadimitriou

PROINOS TYPOS (D)
3 G. Zervou St., Drama, Macedonia, 66100, Greece; tel (30) 521 22364; fax 25611
Pub. – G. Stavridis

FLORINA

POLITIS (D)
27 Kallergi St., Florina, 53100, Greece; tel (30) 385 23732; fax 23920
Pub. – I. Nikoltsannis

GIANNITSA

GIANNITSA (D)
113 E. Venizelou St., Giannitsa, Greece; tel (30) 382 82333; fax 82333

GREVEMA

ENIMEROSSI (D)
3 Koystaytiyoupoleon, Grevema, 51100, Greece; tel (30) 462 24714; fax 28005
Pub. – Y. Papadopoulos

IMMERISSIOS LOGOS (D)
2 Evagelistrias St., Grevema, 51100, Greece; tel (30) 462 26427; fax 26427
Pub. – Anastasia Migdani

GREVENA

PROINI (5X WK.)
3 Mitropoleas St., Grevena, 51100, Greece; tel (30) 24620 28924; fax 80388
Pub. – Efth Tsaknakis

HALKIDA

EVOIKOS TYPOS (M-5X WK.)
Segote 15, Halkida, 34100, Greece; tel (30) 22210 76686; fax 87728
Pub. – N. Smirnis

HANIA, CRETE

AGONAS TIS KRITIS (D)
10 Peridou St., Hania, Crete, 73100, Greece; tel (30) 28210 94800; fax 95888
Pub. – D. Agelakis

DIMOKRATIS TON HANION (D)
25 Peridou St., Hania, Crete, 73100, Greece; tel (30) 821 23836; fax 58010
Pub. – I. Malamadakis

HANIOTIKA NEA (6X WK.)
49 Karaiskaki St., Hania, Crete, 73100, Greece; tel (30) 28210 70 563; fax 91 900; e-mail han-nea@otenet.gr; web site www.hani-otika-nea.gr
Circ.: 9,500
Last Audit: December 28, 2006
Ed. – John Garedakis

IGOUMENITSA, EPIRUS

ELEFTHERO VIMA (D)
19-23 Februaaiou St., Igoumenitsa, Epirus, 46100, Greece; tel (30) 665 23767; fax 25451
Pub./Dir. – D. Saloukas

THESPROTIKI (D)
Square Dimarcheiou, Igoumenitsa, Epirus, 46100, Greece; tel (30) 26650 24355; fax 24355
Dir. – Evangeles Athanasiou

IOANNINA, EPIRUS

PROINOS LOGOS (5X WK.)
F. Tzavela 11b, Ioannina, Epirus, 45333, Greece; tel (30) 26510 25677; fax 30350; e-mail info@proinoslogos.gr; web site www.proinoslogos.gr
Owner/Pub./Dir. – Vas Koutsoliontos
Gen. Mgr. – V. Skoulika
Adv. Mgr. – Maria Zaharopoulos

EPIROTIKOS AGON (5X WK.)
17 O. Poutetsi St., Ioannina, Epirus, 45333, Greece; tel (30) 2651 026300; fax 2651 034862; e-mail info@epirotikosagon.gr; web site www.epirotikosagon.gr
Pub. – Lucia Tzalla

ELEFTHERIA (D)
6 Michaelidi St., Ioannina, Epirus, 45444, Greece; tel (30) 651 35239; fax 31602
Pub. – K. Kaltsis

NEOI AGONES EPIROU (5X WK.)
7 Dagkli St., Ioannina, Epirus, 45444, Greece; tel (30) 26510 77466; fax 37880; e-mail nagones@ioa.forthnet.gr; web site www.neoiagones.gr
Circ.: 1,300
Pub. – Evagelos Athanasiou

PROINA NEA (D)
A. Marinas & Katsari St., Ioannina, Epirus, 45221, Greece; tel (30) 26510 26296; fax 20067

Pub./Dir. – P. Christopoulos

IRAKLIOU, CRETE

ALLAGHI (D)
4 Kozani St., Iraklìou, Crete, 71110, Greece; tel (30) 81 280 022; fax 243 370
Pub. – E. Karellis

DEMOCRATIS (D)
17 Kantanoleon St., Iraklìou, Crete, 71202, Greece; tel (30) 2810 224 225; web site www.dimokratis.gr
Pub. – Anthousa E. Papageorgiou

IRAKLIOTIKA NEA (D)
25 Komninon St., Iraklìou, Crete, 71307, Greece; tel (30) 81 225466; fax 228661
Pub. – D. Petrakis

MESOGHIOS (D)
20 Handakos St., Iraklìou, Crete, 71202, Greece; tel (30) 81 283138; fax 282138
Pub. – C. Grammatikakis

PATRIS (6X WK.)
7 Lappa St., Iraklìou, Crete, 71305, Greece; tel (30) 2810 282 625; fax 258 161; e-mail patris@patris.gr; info@patris.gr; patris@her.forthnet.gr; web site www.patris.gr
Pub. – A. Mykoniatis
Ed. in Chief – George Lagoufaldos

TOLMI (D)
51 Dikeossinis St., Iraklìou, Crete, 71202, Greece; tel (30) 81 229011; fax 221332
Pub. – N. Vidakis

KALAMATA

ELEFTHERIA (D)
Georgouli 26, Kalamata, 24100, Greece; tel (30) 27210 21421; fax 27747; e-mail elefkal@otenet.gr; web site www.eleftherianews.gr
Circ.: 4,800
Pub./Dir. – Konstandinos Clemmenos
Adv. Mgr. – Leonidia Dafiady

KALAMATA, PELOPONNESE

SIMAEA (D)
Nikitara 3, Kalamata, Peloponnese, 24100, Greece; tel (30) 27210 22214; fax 23214
Dir. – Panacos Dimopoulos

THARROS (EX-MON)
45 Stadiou St., Kalamata, Peloponnese, 24100, Greece; tel (30) 27210 22355; fax 89455; e-mail tharros@kal.forthnet.gr; web site www.tharrosnews.gr
Pub. – Alexandra Apostolakis
Ed. in Chief – Dimitris Giatrakos

KALITHEA, CENTRAL GREECE

ADESMEYTOS TYPOS (E)
Thaseos 218, Kalithea, Central Greece, 17675, Greece; tel (30) 210 940 5888; fax 940 7174; e-mail adesmeytostypos@aias.gr; web site www.adesmeytos.gr
Pub. – Dimitris Rizos
Ed. in Chief – Giorgos Brtsos
Ed. in Chief – Koitassarri Kosstas

KARDITSA, THESSALY

MAHI (D)
30 Valvi St., Karditsa, Thessaly, 43100, Greece; tel (30) 24410 40200; fax 42300
Dir. – A. Foukalas

NEOI KEROI (D)
Andre Bandrea 40, Karditsa, Thessaly, 43100, Greece; tel (30) 24410 71571; fax 20998
Ed. – Chris Tsavalos

NEOS AGON (D)
27 S. Lappa St., Karditsa, Thessaly, 43100, Greece; tel (30) 24410 21544; fax 24410 40344; e-mail info@neosagon.gr; web site www.neosagon.gr
Circ.: 8,000
Pub. – George Alexiou

THESSALIKI ICHO (D)
5 Kraterou St., Karditsa, Thessaly, 43100, Greece; tel (30) 44121541; fax 44125565
Pub./Dir. – E. Missas

KASTORIA

KATHIMERINI FONI (D)
4-B Kolototroni St., Kastoria, 52100, Greece; tel (30) 46727678; fax 46726177
Pub. – Sergios-Paraskevi Iatrou

OSIZONTESS (D)
6 Dalipi St., Kastoria, 52100, Greece; tel (30) 46724983; fax 46724783
Pub. – Agzata Zatta

KATERINI

PIERIKOI ANTILALOI (5X WK.)
1st Parodos Botsi 6, Katerini, 60100, Greece; tel (30) 23510 25753; fax 75331; e-mail pierantil@kat.forthnet.gr
Pub. – George Dermisis

PIEROFONIA (D)
126 7th Merarhias St., Katerini, 60100, Greece; tel (30) 23510 35927
Pub. – P. Tzikas

KAVALA

PROINI (D)
Kasandra 15, Kavala, Greece; tel (30) 2510 222 288; fax 223 329; web site www.proininews.gr
Pub. – Genni Kopoulos

KAVALA, MACEDONIA

EVDOMI (D)
3 Filota St., Kavala, Macedonia, 65403, Greece; tel (30) 51 836900; fax 834566

PROINI (6X WK.)
12 Damianoy St., Kavala, Macedonia, 65302, Greece; tel (30) 2510 222 288; fax 223 331
Pub. – M. Genikopoulos

TAHIDROMOS (D)
24 Pavlou Mela St., Kavala, Macedonia, 65302, Greece; tel (30) 51 223348; fax 839263

KEFALONIA, IONIAN ISALND

KATHE MERA (D)
4 Vourvahi St., Kefalonia, Ionian Isalnd, Greece; tel (30) 671 25278; fax 25278

KEFALONIA, IONIAN ISLAND

VRADINES ORES (D)
4 Vourvahi St., Kefalonia, Ionian Island, Greece; tel (30) 671 25278; fax 25278
Pub. – M. Georgatos

KILKIS, MACEDONIA

IMERISSIA (5X WK.)
2? klm. ?etaliko, Kilkis, Macedonia, 61100, Greece; tel (30) 23410 22900; fax 24100; web site www.maxitis.gr
Pub. – S. Orphanides

KOMOTINI, THRACE

AKRITIKI FONI (D)
7 Miltiadou St., Komotini, Thrace, 69100, Greece; tel (30) 531 29223
Pub. – D. Gogou

HRONOS (5X WK.)
22-24 N. Zoidou St., Komotini, Thrace, 69100, Greece; tel (30) 25310 22791; fax 31302; e-mail xronos@otenet.gr; xronos@xronos.gr; info@xronos.gr; web site www.xronos.gr
Circ.: 3,500
Last Audit: March 26, 2010
Dir. – Stazros Fanfanis

PARATIRITIS TIS THRAKIS (D)
Reverse Housing Hephaestus - Against University, Komotini, Thrace, 69100, Greece; tel (30) 531 33474; fax 26027; web site www.paratiritis-news.gr

PATRIDA (D)
57 N. Zoidou St., Komotini, Thrace, 69100, Greece; tel (30) 25310 31892; fax 27300
Pub. – Hipiros Demetries

KORINTHOS, PELOPONNESE

IMERISSIA KORINTHOU (D)
28 Adimadou St., Korinthos, Peloponnese, 20100, Greece; tel (30) 27410 22810
Pub. – Jennie Papasideris

KORINTHIAKA GEGONOTA (D)
28 A. Parlou St., Korinthos, Peloponnese, 20100, Greece; tel (30) 27410 29444; fax 72803

KOZANI, MACEDONIA

HRONOS (5X WK.)
2 Ol. Georgaki St., Kozani, Macedonia, 50100, Greece; tel (30) 24610 25246; fax 45500; e-mail xronos@hol.gr
Pub. – Nikos Kostarellas

PROINOS LOGOS (D)
2 I. Dragoumi St., Kozani, Macedonia, 50100, Greece; tel (30) 4614 0427; fax 4614 0427

TAHIDROMOS (D)
21 Dinrokratios St., Kozani, Macedonia, 50100, Greece; tel (30) 24610 22304; fax 40525
Pub. – G. Papadopoulos

THARROS (5X WK.)
2 Tsontza St., Kozani, Macedonia, 50100, Greece; tel (30) 24610 38611; fax 34611; e-mail tharos@otenet.gr
Circ.: 3,500
Dir. – Xenoson Baraliakos

LAMIA, CENTRAL GREECE

ENIMEROSI FTHIOTIKI (D)
23 Diakou St., Lamia, Central Greece, 35314, Greece; tel (30) 22310 43580; fax 43500
Pub. – P. Dakoglou

EPIKEROS (D)
6 Panourgia St., Lamia, Central Greece, 35100, Greece; tel (30) 22310 37583
Pub. – Chr Karayannis

FOS (D)
55 Ipsilantou St., Lamia, Central Greece, 35100, Greece; tel (30) 231 22397; fax 26970
Dir. – D. Papaefthimiou

LAMIAKOS TYPOS (5X WK.)
3 Iroon, Lamia, Central Greece, 35100, Greece; tel (30) 22310 51414; fax 22310 29331; e-mail info@lamiakos-typos.gr; lamiakos@lam.forthnet.gr; web site www.lamiakos-typos.gr
Pub./Dir. – D. Rizos

PROINA NEA (D)
31 Karaiskaki St., Lamia, Central Greece, 35100, Greece; tel (30) 22310 34666; fax 34244
Pub. – F.I. Papalexis

LARISSA, THESSALY

ELEFTHERIA (D)
6 Papastavrou St., Larissa, Thessaly, 41222, Greece; tel (30) 2410 531894; fax 2410 536449; e-mail info@eleftheria.gr; web site www.eleftheria.gr
Circ.: 22,000
Pub. – Danay Dimitrakopoulou
Adv. Mgr. – Grigoris Papaharalapus

IMERISSIOS KYRIKAS (D)
37 M. Alexandrou St., Larissa, Thessaly, 41222, Greece; tel (30) 41 252013; fax 250762
Pub. – A.T.H. Zisopoulos

LEVADIA, CENTRAL GREECE

NEA TIS VIOTIAS
22 Athinon St., Levadia, Central Greece, 32100, Greece; tel (30) 261 27180; fax 27423
Pub. – Chr Kalintassis

VIOTIKI ORA
Pl. Ethnikis Antistaseos, Levadia, Central Greece, Greece; tel (30) 261 23175; fax 28489
Pub. – P. Houtzoumis

MEGARA, CENTRAL GREECE

MEGARIKOS TYPOS (D)
52 28 Octobriou St., Megara, Central Greece, Greece; tel (30) 229 602 7410
Pub./Dir. – M. Papasideris

MESSOLONGHI, CENTRAL GREECE

ETHNIKI ICHO (D)
2-4 M. Makri St., Messolonghi, Central Greece, 30200, Greece; tel (30) 631 28040; fax 26154
Dir. – Irene K. Riga

MYTILENE, AEGEAN ISLANDS

EOLIKA NEA (6X WK.)
3B Irini St., Mytilene, Aegean Islands, 81100, Greece; tel (30) 22510 42750; fax 22510 40666; web site eolikanea.gr

Pub. – George Kondyloudis

LESBIAKOS KERIX (D)
Stoa Grigoriou, Mytilene, Aegean Islands, 81100, Greece; tel (30) 251 28159; fax 28159
Pub. – A. Karvela

NAFPLIO

ARGOLIKI ENIMEROSSI (D)
32 Asklipiou St., Nafplio, 21100, Greece; tel (30) 751 221014; fax 223037
Pub. – P. Dakoglou

EIDISSEIS
2 Koleth St., Nafplio, 21100, Greece; tel (30) 27510 25805; fax 2316
Pub. – K. Kalkanis

NEO FALIRO, ATHENS

KATHIMERINI (M-6X WK.)
E.Makariou & Falireos 2, Neo Faliro, Athens, 10431, Greece; tel (30) 210 480 8000; fax 480 8225; web site www.ekathimerini.com
Circ.: 34,085
Ed. – E. Karayiannis

PATRAS, PELOPENNESE

ALLAGHI (D)
31 Maizonos St., Patras, Pelopennese, Greece; tel (30) 61 31104; fax 311322
Pub./Dir. – G. Alexopoulos

PATRAS, PELOPONNESE

IMERA (M-6X WK.)
Koritau 296, Patras, Peloponnese, 26221, Greece; tel (30) 2610 315 010; fax 344 160; e-mail news@imeranews.gr; web site www.imeranews.gr
Ed. in Chief – Theodoros Kamperos

PELOPONNESOS (D)
Maizonos 206, Patras, Peloponnese, 26222, Greece; tel (30) 2610 312 530; fax 312 535
Circ.: 7,000
– S. Doukas
– Nana DoukasPub.s

PIRAEUS, CENTRAL GREECE

CHRONOGRAPHOS (D)
58 Karaiskov St., Piraeus, Central Greece, 18532, Greece; tel (30) 210 417 8079; fax 417 8079
Pub. – M. Karayiannis

I FONI TOU PIRAIA (D)
77 Notara St., Piraeus, Central Greece, 18535, Greece; tel (30) 1 4174233; fax 4119083
Pub. – P. Petsas

KINONIKI (D)
38 Kolokotroni St., Piraeus, Central Greece, 18531, Greece; tel (30) 210 411 5225; fax 411 5225
Pub. – S. Karamperopoulos

NAFTEMBORIKI (D)
3 Akti Miaouli, Piraeus, Central Greece, 18535, Greece; tel (30) 1 4178691; fax 4179030
Pub. – N. Athanassiades
Editorial Dir. – N. Saranthenas

NEOI DROMOI (D)
99-101 Ypsilandou St., Piraeus, Central Greece, 18532, Greece; tel (30) 210 412 0986; fax 412 0986
Pub. – I. Raissis

NEOS LOGOS (D)
5 A. Konstantinou St., Piraeus, Central Greece, 18531, Greece; tel (30) 210 417 5256
Pub. – P. Konstantinidis

O DIMOTIS (D)
99-101 Ypsiladou St., Piraeus, Central Greece, 18532, Greece; tel (30) 210 413 4804; fax 412 0986; e-mail imdemotis@gmail.com
Ed. – Fotis Raissis

PIRAIKO VIMA (D)
58 Karaiskou St., Piraeus, Central Greece, 18531, Greece; tel (30) 210 417 7359; fax 417 8079
Dir. – Nick Paraskevas

PREVEZA, EPIRUS

ADESMEFTOS (D)
97 P. Tsaldari St., Preveza, Epirus, 48100, Greece; tel (30) 26820 22814
Dir. – Dimitrius Loupas

NEO VIMA (D)
7 L. Virona St., Preveza, Epirus, 48100, Greece; tel (30) 682 22804
Pub. – P.E. Baizis

TOPIKI FONI (D)
28 E. Antistasseos St., Preveza, Epirus, 48100, Greece; tel (30) 682 27538; fax 28277
Pub./Dir. – K. Zervas

VIMA TIS PREVEZAS (D)
84 E. Antistasseos St., Preveza, Epirus, 48100, Greece; tel (30) 26820 29753; fax 29753; e-mail vima_pr@otenet.gr
Pub. – D. Katsipanelis

PYRGOS, PELOPONNESE

PATRIS (D)
13 Themistokleous St., Pyrgos, Peloponnese, 27100, Greece; tel (30) 26210 30087; fax 26683; web site www.patrisnews.gr
Circ.: 7,000
Last Audit: March 23, 2010
Pub. – E. Varouxis
Adv. Mgr. – Konstantions Varouxis
Chief Ed. – Mary Karabatsos

PATRIS TIS KYRIAKIS (D)
13 Themistokleous St., Pyrgos, Peloponnese, 27100, Greece; tel (30) 621 26683
Pub. – E. Varouxis

PROINI (D)
37-28 Oktovriou St., Pyrgos, Peloponnese, 27100, Greece; tel (30) 26210 26008; fax 31665; e-mail sales@eproini.gr; web site www.eproini.gr
Ed. in Chief – Thomas Rigas

RETHYMNON, CRETE

ELEFTHERI GNOMI (D)
E. Venizelou Prokymaia, Rethymnon, Crete, Greece; tel (30)
Pub. – L.G. Sbokos

KRITIKI EPITHEORISSIS (D)
138 L. Kountouriotou St., Rethymnon, Crete, 74100, Greece; tel (30) 28310 22867; fax 28258; e-mail info@kritet.gr; web site www.kalaitzakis.net
Pub. – John Kalaitzakis
Adv. Mgr. – Anni Stesanakis

RETHYMNIOTIKA NEA (5X WK.)
PO Box 111, Rethymnon, Crete, 74100, Greece; tel (30) 28310 29292; fax 50040; e-mail info@rethnea.gr; web site ^www.rethnea.gr
Dir. – I. Halkiadakis
Adv. Mgr. – Ioiuana Ganalmoudaki

VIMA (D)
20 P. Koroyarou St., Rethymnon, Crete, 74100, Greece; tel (30) 831 24177
Pub. – F. Kafatos

RHODOS, AEGEAN ISLANDS

DIMOKRATIKI TIS RODOU (6X WK.)
77 The W. Sofouli, Rhodos, Aegean Islands, 85100, Greece; tel (30) 22410 26728; fax 37333; e-mail info@dimokratiki.gr; contact@dimokratiki.gr; web site www.dimokratiki.gr
Pub./Dir. – V. Athanasiou

PROODOS (6X WK.)
3 M. Maliaraki St., Rhodos, Aegean Islands, 85100, Greece; tel (30) 22410 34101; fax 20643; e-mail info@proodos.net; web site www.proodos.net
Pub,/Dir. – Pierre Kalivouris

RODIAKI (6X WK.) EST. 1915
11 M. Maliaraki St., Rhodos, Aegean Islands, 85100, Greece; tel (30) 22410 75640; fax 75641; e-mail irodiaki@otenet.gr; web site www.rodiaki.gr
Circ.: 4,500
Insert rate: 7/month
Advertising: Yes
Pub. – Yioi S. Tsopanakis H. Kotidis
Editor, co-owner – Ivi-Alexandra Tsopanaki

SERRES, MACEDONIA

AKRITIKI FONI (D)
12 D. Solomou St., Serres, Macedonia, 62125, Greece; tel (30) 321 22380; fax 25621
Pub. – A. Arabadgis

KATHIMERINOS PARATIRITIS (D)
27 Spetson St., Serres, Macedonia, 62125, Greece; tel (30) 2321 62600; fax 62345
Pub./Dir. – I. Nomidis

NEA EPOHI (D)
7 P. Grigoriu St., Serres, Macedonia, 62125, Greece; tel (30) 23210 64600; fax 26191
Pub. – A. Giannakou

PROODOS (D)
3 Tsimiski St., Serres, Macedonia, 62122, Greece; tel (30) 23210 22212; fax 23680
– A. Kolokotronis
– K.B. KomitoudisPub.s

SERRAIKON THARROS (D)
177 E. Venizelou St., Serres, Macedonia, 62122, Greece; tel (30) 23210 24845; fax 25621

SPARTA, PELOPONNESE

SPARTIATIKA NEA
114 Likourgon St., Sparta, Peloponnese, 23100, Greece; tel (30) 27310 21103; fax 21103
Pub. – F. Giayyakou

SPARTI

LAKONIKA KATHIMERINA NEA (D)
114 Likourgon St., Sparti, 23100, Greece; tel (30) 731 (30-731) 21103; fax (30-731) 21103
Pub. – T.H. Xeniotis

THESSALONIKI, MACEDONIA

AVRIANI VORIOU HELLADOS (D)
23 Karolou Dil St., Thessaloniki, Macedonia, 54623, Greece; tel (30) 31 233550; fax 279282
Pub. – G. Gavrielatos

BONUS (D)
153 Monastiriou St., Thessaloniki, Macedonia, 54627, Greece; tel (30) 2310 252520; fax 254980
Pub. – S. Vlahopoulos

MACEDONIA (M-6X WK.)
85 Moyastirion St., Thessaloniki, Macedonia, 54627, Greece; tel (30) 2310 521 621; fax 281 033; e-mail gramm3@newspaper.gr; web site www.makthes.gr
Pub. – Z. Simitzi

PANELLINIA DIMOPRASION-DIAKIRIXEON (D)
2 Mitseon St., Thessaloniki, Macedonia, 54631, Greece; tel (30) 2310 232 536; fax 243 896
Pub. – I.K. Papadopoulos

SPOR TOU VORRA (D)
85 Monastiriou St., Thessaloniki, Macedonia, 54627, Greece; tel (30) 2310 560 200; fax 534 898
Pub. – Z. Simitzi

TRIKALA, THESSALY

ENIMEROSI (5X WK.)
2 Koukoulari St., Trikala, Thessaly, 42100, Greece; tel (30) 24310 23328; fax 28357; e-mail enimerosi@periferia.gr; web site www.e-enimerosi.gr
Pub. – K. Tolis

EREVNA (6X WK.)
8 Kapodistriou St., Trikala, Thessaly, 42100, Greece; tel (30) 24310 27127; fax 30008; e-mail erevna@otenet.gr; web site www.e-erevna.gr
– Elias L. Katsiabas
– Vasilas KogiasPub.s

PROINOS LOGOS (D)
Themistokleous 34, Trikala, Thessaly, 42100, Greece; tel (30) 24310 24230; fax 24953; e-mail plogos@otenet.gr; web site www.wiw.gr
Pub. – Michalis Tsarouchas

TRIKALINA NEA (D)
5 Paparigopoulou St., Trikala, Thessaly, 42100, Greece; tel (30) 24310 27519; fax 29772
Pub. – E. Sabanikou

TRIPOLI, PELOPONNESE

KATHIMERINA NEA
69-71 Kalavriton St., Tripoli, Peloponnese, 22100, Greece; tel (30) 23390; fax 31890
Pub. – E. Karidis

PROINA NEA TIS ARKADIAS
13 Malliaropoulou St., Tripoli, Peloponnese, 22100, Greece; tel (30) 712 27031; fax 39290
Pub. – A.E. Deltoj

VERIOA, MACEDONIA

IMERISIA (6X WK.)
195 Kentnikis St., Verioa, Macedonia, 59100, Greece; tel (30) 23310 66736; fax 66455; e-mail imerisia@odenet.gr; web site www.imerisia.gr
Pub. – D. Bouthas

LAOS (D)
10 Venizelou St., Verioa, Macedonia, 59100, Greece; tel (30) 23310 66913; fax 66979; e-mail laosver@laos.gr; web site www.laos.gr
Ed. – Michael Patsikas
Co Ed. – Anastasios Patsikas

VOLOS, THESSALY

NEOS DROMOS (D)
36 Koutarelia St., Volos, Thessaly, 38221, Greece; tel (30) 24210 29367; fax 29368
Pub. – T.H. Popotas

TACHYDROMOS (D)
133 Angelopoulou St., Volos, Thessaly, 38221, Greece; tel (30) 231 300 3733; web site www.tachydromos.com
Pub. – A. Popotas

THESSALIA (MD)
1 Kreoytos St., Volos, Thessaly, 38334, Greece; tel (30) 24210 23303; fax 23303; web site www.e-thessalia.gr
Pub. – T.H. Samaras

XANTHI, THRACE

ADESMEFTI (D)
8 Hatzistavrou St., Xanthi, Thrace, 67100, Greece; tel (30) 541 28725; fax 28725
Pub./Dir. – P. Papadopoulos

AGONAS (D)
4 Macedoyias St., Xanthi, Thrace, 67100, Greece; tel (30) 25410 21717; fax 21155; e-mail agonas@xan.forthnet.gr; web site www.agonas.gr
Circ.: 1,100
Pub. – N. Georgiadis

AKRITAS (D)
21-23 Venizelou St., Xanthi, Thrace, 67100, Greece; tel (30) 25410 71672; fax 72491
Pub. – E. Vasiliades

EMPROS (5X WK.)
Station 16, Xanthi, Thrace, 67100, Greece; tel (30) 25410 77828; fax 25608; e-mail empros@ixanthi.gr; web site www.empros.gr
Owner/Ed./Dir. – John Diafonidis
Pub. – Eleni Eiasonidou
Adv. Mgr. – Zourpodlou Eleni

FONI TIS XANTHIS (D)
9 Velissariou St., Xanthi, Thrace, 67100, Greece; tel (30) 541 23262; fax 22549
Pub. – S. Vlachopoulou

GREENLAND

NUUK

AG ATUAGAGDLIUTIT/GRONLANDSPOSTEN (2X WK.)
Postboks 39, Nuuk, 3900, Greenland; tel (299) 38 39 50; fax 32 24 99; e-mail adm@ag.gl; web site www.ag.gl
Ed. – Inga Dora Markussen

SERMITSIAQ (WEEKLY) EST. 1958
PO Box 150, Nuuk, 3900, Greenland; tel (299) 383940; fax 322 499; e-mail administration@sermitsiaq.ag; web site sermitsiaq.ag
Circ.: 3,000
Ed. – Poul Krarup

HUNGARY

BEKESCSABA, BEKES

BEKES MEGYEI HIRLAP (6X WK.)
Munkacsy u. 4, Bekescsaba, Bekes, 5601, Hungary; tel (36) 66 527 247; fax 527 231; e-mail webmaster@bekes.hungary.net; web site www.bekes.hungary.net
Circ.: 49,000
Ed. – Otto Darga

NAPI DELKELET
Szigligetu u. 6, Bekescsaba, Bekes, 5601, Hungary; tel (36) 66 324204; fax 322373
Pub. – Janos Kepenyes
Ed. in Chief – Ilona Szatmari
Ed. – Sandor Seres
Ed. – Mihaly Tomka

BUDAPEST, PEST

BLIKK (D)
Robert Karoly krt. 61-65, Budapest, Pest, 1134, Hungary; tel (36) 1 2698 588; fax 2698 589
Dir./Ed. in Chief – Peter Toke

ESTI HIRLAP (E-EX S)
Blaha Lujza ter 3, Budapest, Pest, 1962, Hungary; tel (36) 1 1382399; fax 1384550
Circ.: 70,000
Ed. in Chief – Denes Maros

EXPRESSZ
Jozsef krt. 9, Budapest, Pest, 1085, Hungary; tel (36) 1 1338398
Circ.: 75,000
Pub. – Jozsef Horti
Ed. – Janos Mendel
Ed. – Istvanne Odor
Ed. – Janosne Sofalvi

NEPSPORT (D-EX TUES.)
Somogyi Bela ut. 6, Budapest, Pest, 1085, Hungary; tel (36) 1 1384366; fax 1382463
Circ.: 250,000
Ed. in Chief – Dr. Ferenc Kiraly

KURIR
PF 614, Budapest, Pest, 1425, Hungary; tel (36) 1 1112659
Circ.: 80,000
Ed. in Chief – Gabor Szucs

MAGYAR HIRLAP (D-EX S)
Thokoly ut. 105-107, Budapest, Pest, 1145, Hungary; tel (36) 1 887 3230; fax 887 3253; e-mail levelezes@magyarhirlap.hu; web site www.magyarhirlap.hu
Circ.: 75,000
Dir. – Stefka Istvan

MAGYAR NEMZET (D-EX S)
PO Box 74, Budapest, Pest, 91450, Hungary; tel (36) 1 476 2131; fax 476 2105; web site www.mno.hu
Circ.: 70,000
Advertising: Nielsen Communications Ltd.
Ed. in Chief – Gabor Liszkay

MAI NAP (D-EX SAT.)
Konyves Kalman krt 76, Budapest, Pest, 1087, Hungary; tel (36) 1 210 1483; fax 333 9153; e-mail mainap@mail.datanet.hu
Circ.: 100,000
Ed. in Chief – Ferenc Koszegi

NAPI GAZDASAG (5X WK.)
Csata u. 32, Budapest, Pest, 1135, Hungary; tel (36) 1 450 9600; fax 450 9601; e-mail napi@napi.hu; web site www.napi.hu
Circ.: 16,000
Mng. Dir. – Balazs Ronai

NEMZETI SPORT (D)
PF 330, Budapest, Pest, 1591, Hungary; tel (36) 1 460 2600; fax 460 2601; e-mail szerkesztoseg@nemzetisport.hu; web site www.nemzetisport.hu
Circ.: 140,000
Ed. – Jozsef Buzdo

NEPSZABADSAG (D-EX S)
1034 Budapest, Becsi ut. 122-124, Budapest, Pest, 1960, Hungary; tel (36) 1 436 4407; fax 387 8695; e-mail online@nepszabadsag.hu; web site www.nol.hu
Circ.: 316,000
Group: Ringier
Int. Editor in Chief – Levente Toth

NEPSZAVA (M-6X WK.) EST. 1873
Konyves Kalman krt. 76., Budapest, Pest, 1087, Hungary; tel (36) 1 477 9000; fax 477 9020; e-mail nepszava@nepszava.hu; web site www.nepszava.hu
Circ.: 40,000
Ed. in Chief – Peter Nemeth

PEST MEGYEI HIRLAP (D-EX S)
Semogyi B. u. 6, Budapest, Pest, 1446, Hungary; tel (36) 1 1382399
Circ.: 43,000
Ed. in Chief – Dr. Andras Bard

PESTI HIRLAP
Oktober 6 u. 8, Budapest, Pest, 1051, Hungary; tel (36) 1 1176162; fax 1176029
Circ.: 50,000
Ed. in Chief – Andras Bencsik

PESTI RIPORT
Blaha Lujza ter 3, Budapest, Pest, 1085, Hungary; tel (36) 1 1382461; fax 1384773
Circ.: 50,000
Pub. – Szikra Lapnyomda
Pub. – Dr. Zoltan Csondes
Ed. in Chief – Tibor Hamori

UJ MAGYARORSZAG
PO Box 199, Budapest, Pest, 1410, Hungary; tel (36) 1 1185009; fax 1222288
Circ.: 60,000
Pub. – Zoltan E. Horvath
Ed. in Chief – Laszlo Fabian

UZLET
Bajcsy-Zsilinszky ut. 78, Budapest, Pest, 1055, Hungary; tel (36) 1 1118260
Ed. in Chief – Ivan Ersek

VILAGGAZDASAG (D-EX S)
PO Box 3, Budapest, Pest, 1426, Hungary; tel (36) 1 1756722; fax 1754191; e-mail vg@vilaggazdasag.hu; web site www.vilaggazdasag.hu
Circ.: 17,000
Pub./Ed. – Tamas Forro
Ed. in Chief – Ilona Kocsi

DEBRECEN, HAJDU-BIHAR

HAJDU-BIHARI NAPLO (D-EX S)
Dosa nador ter 10, Debrecen, Hajdu-Bihar, 4024, Hungary; tel (36) 52 413 395; fax 412 326; e-mail naplo@iscomp.hu
Circ.: 60,000
Ed. in Chief – Zsolt Porcsin

DUNAUJVAROS

DUNAUJVAROSI HIRLAP (6X WK.)
Vasmut ut. 39. II. emelet, Dunaujvaros, 2400, Hungary; tel (36) 25 412 626; fax 410 999; e-mail szerkesztoseg@dh.plt.hu; web site www.dh-online.hu
Circ.: 10,000
Ed. in Chief – Elekes Andras

EGER, HEVES

HEVES MEGYEI HIRLAP (6X WK.)
Barkoczy u. 7, Eger, Heves, 3301, Hungary; tel (36) 36 513 644; fax 513 605; e-mail webhirszerk@axelspringer.hu; web site www.hevesmegyeihirlap.hu
Circ.: 33,000
Ed. in Chief – Zoltan Szalay

GYOR, GYOR-SOPRON

KISALFOLD (D)
Ujlak u. 4/a, Gyor, Gyor-Sopron, 9021, Hungary; tel (36) 96 504 555; fax 504 414; e-mail kisalfold@kisafold.hu; web site www.kisalfold.hu
Circ.: 80,000
Mktg. Mgr. – Varonika Kozicz
Ed. in Chief – Nyerges Csaba

NYUGATI HIRLAP
Kazinczy u. 16, Gyor, Gyor-Sopron, 9021, Hungary; tel (36) 96 11451; fax 15374
Circ.: 24,000
Pub. – Nyugat Kiado
Pub. – Sandor Nagy
Ed. in Chief – Tibor N. Magyar

UJ HIREK
Monus ut. 47-49, Gyor, Gyor-Sopron, 9024, Hungary; tel (36) 96 10277
Circ.: 40,000
Pub. – Szo-Kep Kiadoi
Pub. – Denes Lukacsfly
Ed. in Chief – Sandor Illes

KAPOSVAR, SOMOGY

SOMOGYI HIRLAP (D)
PF 31, Kaposvar, Somogy, 7401, Hungary; tel (36) 82 528-100; fax 528-155; e-mail somogyihirlap@axels.hu; web site www.somogyihirlap.hu
Circ.: 59,000
Dir. – Arpasi Zoltan

KECSKEMET

PETOFI NEPE (D)
Szechenyi krut 29, Kecskemet, 6001, Hungary; tel (36) 76 518 200; fax 481 434; e-mail petofinepe@axels.hu; web site www.petofinepe.hu
Circ.: 60,000
Gen. Dir. – Toth Miklos

MISKOLC, BORSOD ABAUJ-ZEMPLEN

ESZAK-MAGYARORSZAG (M)
Bajcsy-Zsilinszky ut. 15, Miskolc, Borsod Abauj-Zemplen, 3527, Hungary; tel (36) 46 341888; fax 341630
Circ.: 45,000
Ed. in Chief – Laszlo Gorombolyi

NYIREGYHAZA, SZABOLCS-SZATMAR

KELET-MAGYARORSZAG (D-EX S)
Zrinyi u. 3-5, Nyiregyhaza, Szabolcs-Szatmar, 4401, Hungary; tel (36) 42 11277
Circ.: 80,000
Ed. in Chief – Dr. Sandor Angyal

UJ KELET (D)
Bercsenyi u. 8, Nyiregyhaza, Szabolcs-Szatmar, 4400, Hungary; tel (36) 42 312 903

PECS, BARANYA

UJ DUNANTULI NAPLO (E)
Hunyadi ut. 11, Pecs, Baranya, 7601, Hungary; tel (36) 72 15000
Circ.: 84,000
Ed. in Chief – Jeno Lombosi

SALGOTARJAN, NOGRAD

NOGRAD MEGYEI HIRLAP (6X WK.)
Erzsebet ter 6, Salgotarjan, Nograd, 3100, Hungary; tel (36) 32 416 455; fax 423 931; e-mail kopkam@szdsz.hu; web site www.nogradmegyeihirlap.hu; www.nmedia.hu; www.nport.hu
Circ.: 21,000
Ed.-in-Cheif – Kopka Miklos
Adv. Mgr. – Lafclo Namath

UJ NOGRAD (D-EX S)
Palocz Imre ter 4, Salgotarjan, Nograd, 3100, Hungary; tel (36) 32 10589
Circ.: 23,000
Ed. in Chief – Laszlo Sulyok

SZEGED, CSONGRAD

CSONGRAD MEGYEI HIRLAP (D-EX S)
Stefania ut. 10, Szeged, Csongrad, 6740, Hungary; tel (36) 62 481281; fax 481333
Circ.: 67,000
Ed. in Chief – Imre Dlusztus
Ed. – Istvan Sandi
Ed. – Istvan Szavay
Ed. – Lajos Tandi

DEL MAGYARORSZAG (D-EX S)
Stefania 10, Szeged, Csongrad, 6740, Hungary; tel (36) 62 481281
Circ.: 70,000
Ed. in Chief – Imre Dlusztus

DELVILAG (M-6X WK.)
Sabadkae 10, Szeged, Csongrad, 6740, Hungary; tel (36) 62 567 888; fax 567 881; web site www.delmagyar.hu
Circ.: 50,000
Ed. in Chief – Nyerges Csaba

REGGELI DELVILAG
Stefania u. 10, Szeged, Csongrad, 6740, Hungary; tel (36) 62 472 872; fax 472 244
Circ.: 26,000
Pub. – Dr. Zsolt Szigeti
Ed. in Chief – Dr. Istvan Nikolenyi

SZEKESFEHERVAR, FEJER

FEJER MEGYEI HIRLAP (D-EX S)
Ady Endre u. 15, Szekesfehervar, Fejer, 8000, Hungary; tel (36) 22 542 700; fax 542 719; e-mail szerkesztoseg@fmh.plt.hu; web site www.fmh.hu
Circ.: 52,000
Ed. in Chief – Andras Elekes

SZEKSZARD, TOLNA

TOLNA MEGYEI NEPUJSAG
Liszt Ferenc ter 3, Szekszard, Tolna, 7100, Hungary; tel (36) 74 16211
Circ.: 32,000
Ed. in Chief – Gyorgyne Kamaras

SZOLNOK, SZOLNOK

UJ NEPLAP (D-EX S)
PF 105, Szolnok, Szolnok, 5000, Hungary; tel (36) 56 516 700; fax 516 740; e-mail ujneplap@axels.hu; web site www.ujneplap.hu
Circ.: 46,000
Dir. – Ban Janos

SZOMBATHELY, VAS

VAS NEPE (D-EX S)
Szell Kalman u. 40, Szombathely, Vas, 9700, Hungary; tel (36) 94 522 560; fax 522 596; e-mail vasnepe@vn.plt.hu; web site www.vasnepe.hu
Circ.: 65,000
Pub. – Pannon Lapok Tarsasaga
Mgr. – HalmÅ gyi MiklÃ¢s

TATABANYA, KOMAROM

24 ORA (D)
So Ter 4, Tatabanya, Komarom, 2800, Hungary; tel (36) 34 514 010; fax 514 011; e-mail szerk.kom@axels.hu; web site www.24ora.hu
Circ.: 43,000
Ed. in Chief – Csaba Szerdahelyi

VESZPREM, VESZPREM

NAPLO (D-EX S)
Szabadsag ter 15, Veszprem, Veszprem, 8201, Hungary; tel (36) 80 27444
Circ.: 58,000
Ed. in Chief – Elemer Balogh

ZALAEGERSZEG, ZALA

ZALAI HIRLAP (D-EX S)
Ady Endre u. 62, Zalaegerszeg, Zala, 8901, Hungary; tel (36) 92 502 231; fax 502 240; e-mail zalaihirlap@zh.plt.hu; web site www.zalaihirlap.hu
Circ.: 71,000
Mgr. – Mihovics Jozsef

ICELAND

AKUREYRI

DAGUR-TIMINN
PO Box 58, Akureyri, 600, Iceland; tel (354) 6 (354-6) 4606100; fax (354-6) 4627639
Ed. – Stefan Jon Hafstein

REYKJAVIK

ALTHYDUBLADID (D)
Hverfisgata 8-10, Reykjavik, 101, Iceland; tel (354) 1 5625566; fax 5629244
Circ.: 4,000
Ed. – Hrafn Jokulsson

MORGUNBLADID (M-6X WK.)
Hadegismoar 1, Reykjavik, 110, Iceland; tel (354) 569 1100; fax 569 1110; e-mail ritstjorn@mbl.is; web site www.mbl.is
Circ.: 53,000
Ed. – Matthias Johannessen
Mng. Ed. – Oskar MacNusson

DAGBLADID/VISIR (M-6X WK.)
PO Box 5380, Reykjavik, 105, Iceland; tel (354) 1 5505000; fax 5505020; e-mail dvdreif@ff.is; web site www.skyrr.is/dv
Circ.: 44,000
Ed. – Jonas Kristjansson

TIMINN (M-5X WK.)
Brautarholt 1, Reykjavik, 105, Iceland; tel (354) 1 540 4300; fax 540 4301
Circ.: 14,000
Adv. Mgr. – Steingrimur Gislason
Ed. – Jon Kristjansson

ITALY

ANCONA

LA GAZZETTA DI ANCONA (D)
Via D Spadoni 19 (Baraccola Ovest), Ancona, 60100, Italy; tel (39) 071 28691
Ed. – Paolo Farneti

GAZZETTA ASTE E APPALTI PUBBLICI (D)
Via Valle Miano 13/h, Ancona, 60125, Italy; tel (39) 071 280 0983; fax 280 4267; web site www.sific.it
Dir. – Daniele Scuccato

CORRIERE ADRIATICO (M)
Via Berti 20, Ancona, 60126, Italy; tel (39) 071 4581; fax 42980; e-mail info@corriereadriatico.it; web site www.corriereadriatico.it
Circ.: 32,180
Mgr. – Paolo Traini

AREZZO

CORRIERE DI AREZZO (D)
Via Petrarca 4, Arezzo, 52100, Italy; tel (39) 575 28388; fax 302 063; web site www.corr.it
Circ.: 3,500
MD – Federico Fioravanti

LA GAZZETTA DI AREZZO (D)
Via Cavour 119, Arezzo, 52100, Italy; tel (39) 0575 350 881; fax 300 320
Dir. – Paolo Farneti

ASCOLI PICENO

LA GAZZETTA DI ASCOLI PICENO (D)
Via dei Guiderocchi 7, Ascoli Piceno, 63100, Italy; tel (39) 0736 255 530
Dir. – Paolo Farneti

BARI

LA GAZZETTA DEL MEZZOGIORNO (D) EST. 1922
Viale Scipione l'Africano 264, Bari, 70124, Italy; tel (39) 080 547 0200; fax 547 0488; web site www.lagazzettadelmezzogiorno.it
Circ.: 79,070
Mng. Dir. – Giuseppe De Tomaso

PUGLIA (6X WK.)
5/7 Via delle Petunie, Modugno, Bari, 70121, Italy; tel (39) 080 531 5716; fax 531 5718; e-mail pubblicita@sigma86.it; web site www.quotidianopuglia.it
Circ.: 15,000
MD – Mario Gismondi

IL QUOTIDIANO (6X WK.)
Piazza Aldo Moro 31, Bari, 70100, Italy; tel (39) 80 524 0473; fax 524 5486; web site www.quotidianodibari.it
Circ.: 28,000
Dir. – Luciano Ventura

BERGAMO

IL GIORNALE DI BERGAMO OGGI (M)
Via Palazzolo 29, Bergamo, 24100, Italy; tel (39) 035 244 154
Circ.: 10,000
Dir. – Andrea Barberi

L'ECO DI BERGAMO (6X WK.) EST. 1880
Viale Papa Giovanni XXIII 118, Bergamo, 24121, Italy; tel (39) 35 386 111; fax 386 217; e-mail sesaab@eco.bg.it; web site www.ecodibergamo.it
Circ.: 69,573
MD – Ettore Ongis

BOLOGNA

IL RESTO DEL CARLINO (M) EST. 1885
Via Monte Rosa 106, Bologna, 40128, Italy; tel (39) 051 600 6111; fax 538 181
Circ.: 251,173
Pres. – Maria Luisa Monti Riffeser
Vice Pres. – Andrea Riffeser Monti

BOLZANO

ALTO ADIGE (D) EST. 1945
Via Alessandro Volta 10, Bolzano, 39100, Italy; tel (39) 0471 904 111; fax 904 263; e-mail bolzano@altoadige.it; web site www.altoadige.it
Circ.: 47,595
Pres. – Giorgio Pasquali
Vice Pres. – Pietro Tosolini
Mng. Dir. – Serjio Daraldi
Adv. Mgr – Ileuro Caccieoli

DOLOMITEN (D-EX S)
Lauben 41, Bolzano, 39100, Italy; tel (39) 0471 925 544; fax 925 546; web site www.stol.it/Athesia
Circ.: 47,809
Pres. – Michl Ebner
Mgr. – Toni Ebner

IL MATTINO DI BOLZANO E PROVINCIA (D) EST. 1988
Via Dante 5, Bolzano, 39100, Italy; tel (39) 0471 980 766; fax 990 729
Circ.: 4,915
Dir. – Paolo Ghezzi
Ed. in Chief – Riccardo Dello Sbarba

BRESCIA

BRESCIA OGGI (M) EST. 1974
Via Eritrea 20, Brescia, 25100, Italy; tel (39) 030 22941; web site www.bresciaoggi.it
Circ.: 15,000
Dir. – Mino Allione

GIORNALE DI BRESCIA (D-EX MON.)
Via Solferino 22, Brescia, 25121, Italy; tel (39) 030 37901; fax 379 0289; e-mail info@giornaledibrescia.it; web site www.giornaledibrescia.it
Circ.: 69,814
Dir. – Giacomo Scanzi

BRINDISI

QUOTIDIANO DI BRINDISI (6X WK.)
Via Dalmazia 21/a, Brindisi, 72100, Italy; tel (39) 831 (39-831) 517124; fax (39-831) 517571
Circ.: 24,680
Dir. – Guilio Mastroianni
Vice Dir. – Alessandro Barbano

CAGLIARI

L'UNIONE SARDA (D) EST. 1889
Viale Regina Elena 12, Cagliari, 09124, Italy; tel (39) 070 60131; fax 601 3274; e-mail unione@unionesarda.it; web site www.unionesarda.it
Circ.: 82,091
Adv. Mgr. – Podda Piervin Cenzo
Ed. in Chief – Paolo Figus

CARPI

GAZZETTA DI CARPI (D)
Via Ciro Menotti 29, Carpi, MO, 41012, Italy 059
Circ.: 10,405
Mng. Ed. – Pier Vittorio Marvasi

CATANIA

ESPRESSO SERA-CORRIERE DI SICILIA (E-EX S)
Viale Odorico da Pordenone 50, Catania, 95126, Italy; tel (39) 095 333 070; fax 336 466
Dir. – Giuseppe Simili
Ed. in Chief – Salvatore Barbagallo

LA SICILIA (M)
Viale Odorico da Pordenone 50, Catania, 95126, Italy; tel (39) 095 330544; fax 337077; e-mail administrazione@lasicilia.it; web site www.lasicilia.it
Circ.: 73,382
Mgr. – Mario Ciancio Sanfilippo

CATANZARO

IL GIORNALE DI CALABRIA (6X WK.)
Via Filanda 11, Catanzaro, 88100, Italy; tel (39) 0961 792 793; fax 792 489; e-mail redazione@giornaledicalabria.net; web site www.giornaledicalabria.net
Circ.: 11,000
Dir. – Giuseppe Soluri

CESENA

CORRIERE DI CESENA (D)
Via Fantaguzzi 35, Cesena, 47023, Italy; tel (39) 0547 611 900; fax 610 350
Circ.: 4,000
Dir. – Patrizia Lanzetti

COMO

LA PROVINCIA DI COMO (D)
Via Pasquale Paoli 21, Como, 22100, Italy; tel (39) 031 582 311; fax 505 003; e-mail laprovincia@laprovincia.it; web site www.laprovinciadicomo.it
Circ.: 48,810
Dir. – Georgeo Gandola
News Ed. – Umberto Montin

CREMONA

LA PROVINCIA DI CREMONA (D)
Via delle Industrie 2, Cremona, 26100, Italy; tel (39) 0372 4981; fax 28 487; web site www.laprovinciadicremona.it
Circ.: 27,802
Pres. – Antonio Piva
Vice Pres. – Cesare Pasquali
Dir. – Vittoriano Zanolli

LA PROVINCIA (D)
Via delle Industrie 2, Cremona, 26100, Italy; tel (39) 0372 4981; fax 28487; e-mail laprovincia@cremononline.it; web site www.laprovinciadicremona.it
Ed. in Chief – Socieca Cremonese

FERRARA

LA GAZZETTA DI FERRARA (D)
Via Ravenna 163, Ferrara, 44100, Italy; tel (39) 0532 740 160; fax 740 478
Dir. – Paolo Farneti
Ed. in Chief – Angelo Frignani

LA NUOVA FERRARA (D) EST. 1989
Via Girolamo Baruffaldi, 22, Ferrara, 44100, Italy; tel (39) 0532 214 211; fax 247 689; web site www.lanuovaferrara.it
Circ.: 15,787
Mgr. – Valentino Pesci

FLORENCE

LA GAZZETTA DI FIRENZE (D-EX MON.)
Via Locchi 35/r, Florence, 50141, Italy; tel (39) 055 439 811; fax 416 004
Dir. – Paolo Farneti
Ed. in Chief – Ivo Brocchi

LA NAZIONE (M)
Via Ferdinando Paolieri 2, Florence, 50100, Italy; tel (39) 055 87951; fax 247 8207
Circ.: 213,901
Pres. – Maria Luisa Monti Riffeser
Vice Pres. – Andrea Riffeser Monti
Vice Pres. – Carlo Pesenti
Mgr. – Umberto Cecchi
Vice Mgr. – Guiseppe Mascambruno

FOGGIA

IL QUOTIDIANO DI FOGGIA (6X WK.)
Via Gramsci 73/A, Foggia, 71100, Italy; tel (39) 0881 686 967; fax 632 247; web site www.quotidianodifoggia.it
Circ.: 25,000
Dir. – Luciano Ventura

FORLI

CORRIERE DI FORLI (D)
Via Maroncelli 3, Forli, 47100, Italy; tel (39) 0543 35520; fax 5470
Circ.: 2,500
Ed. in Chief – Gaetano Foggetti

FROSINONE

CIOCIARIA OGGI (6X WK.)
Pizza De Matthaeies No.41, Frosinone, 03100, Italy; tel (39) 0775 8291; fax 829 348; e-mail direttore@ciociariaoggi.net; web site www.ciociariaoggi.info
Circ.: 11,000
Dir. – Alessandro Panigutti
Ed in Chief – Silvio Giuliani

GENOA

CORRIERE MERCANTILE (6X WK.)
Via Archimede 169/R, Genoa, Italy; tel (39) 010 53691; fax 504 148; e-mail directore@corrieremercantile.it; web site http://www.publikompass.it/pagine/pagina.aspx?ID=Contatti018&L=IT
Circ.: 15,000
Dir. – Gerolamo Angeli

IL LAVORO (M-6X WK.)
Via Donghi 38, Selpi, Genoa, 16132, Italy; tel (39) 010 35331; fax 353 3263
Circ.: 19,954
Dir. – Franco Manzitti
Ed. in Chief – Luigi Gia

GENOVA

L'AVVISATORE MARITTIMO (5X WK.)
Via Piccapietra 21, Genova, 16121, Italy; tel (39) 010 536 4243; fax 536 4241; web site www.avvisatoremarittimo.it
Circ.: 5,000
Dir. – Umberto Larocca
Adv. Mgr. – Stephano Milano

IL SECOLO XIX (D) EST. 1886
Piazza Piccapietra 21, Genova, 16121, Italy; tel (39) 010 53881; fax 538 8388; e-mail info@ilsecoloxix.it; web site www.ilsecoloxix.it
Circ.: 161,449
Advertising: Publicitas.
Pres. – Carlo Perrone
Mktg. Mgr. – Jessima Kimberlake

LATINA

LATINA OGGI (6X WK.)
Corso della Republica 200, Latina, 04100, Italy; tel (39) 0773 4191; fax 692 370; e-mail redazione@latinaoggi.net; web site www.latina-oggi.it
Circ.: 11,000
Dir. – Alessandro Panigutti

LECCE

QUOTIDIANO DI LECCE (D)
Via dei Mocenigo, 27-29, Lecce, 73100, Italy; tel (39) 0832 338 804; fax 338 244
Circ.: 14,643
Dir. – John Carlo Minicuci

LIVORNO

IL TIRRENO (M) EST. 1877
Viale Vittorio Alfieri 9, Livorno, 57100, Italy; tel (39) 0586 220 111; fax 220 713; e-mail iltirreno@finegilpal.inet.it; web site www.iltirreno.it
Circ.: 114,793
Pres. – Carlo Caracciolo
Mgr. – Nino Sofia

IL TELEGRAFO (D)
Via Marradi 30, Livorno, 57100, Italy; tel (39) 0586 813 211; fax 854 451
Dir. – Aurelio Seciba
Ed. in Chief – Giuseppe Isozio

LODI

IL CITTADINO (6X WK.)
Via Paolo Gorini 34, Lodi, 20075, Italy; tel (39) 0371 544 200; fax 544 201; web site www.ilcittadino.it
Circ.: 10,000
Dir. – Ferruccio Pallavera

MACERATA

LA GAZETTA DI MACERATA (D)
Via Garibaldi 85, Macerata, 62100, Italy; tel (39) 0733 231 333
Dir. – Paolo Farneti
Ed. in Chief – Giancarlo Padula

MANTUA

GAZETTA DI MANTOVA (D)
Viale Fratelli Bandiera, 32, Mantua, 46100, Italy; tel (39) 376 303 270; fax 303 263; web site www.gazzettadimantova.it
Circ.: 43,082
MD – Lorenzo Bertoli

MESSINA

GAZETTA DEL SUD (DS) EST. 1952
Via Uberto Bonino 15/C, Messina, 98100, Italy; tel (39) 090 2261; fax 293-6359
Circ.: 76,962
Pres. – Giovanni Morgante
Mgr. – Nino Calarco
Vice Mgr. – Alfredo Leto

MILAN

IL GIORNO (MS) EST. 1956
Piazza Cavour 2, Milan, 20121, Italy; tel (39) 02 77-681; fax 760-0665; web site ilgiorno.quotidiano.net
Circ.: 174,662
Pres. – Franco Capparelli
Gen. Mgr. – Giuseppe Ferrauto
Mgr. – Andrea Biavardi
Vice Mgr. – Tiziana Abate

ITALIA OGGI (D) EST. 1986
Via Marco Burigozzo 5, Milan, 20122, Italy; tel (39) 02 582 191; e-mail italiaoggi@class.it; web site www.italiaoggi.it
Circ.: 68,694
Pub. – Paulo Panerai

LA GAZZETTA DELLO SPORT (MS) EST. 1896
Via Solferino 28, Milan, 20121, Italy; tel (39) 02 6339; fax 6282 7916; web site www.gazzetta.it
Circ.: 525,784
Dir. – Andra Monti
Journalist – Gaetano De Stefano

CORRIERE DELLA SERA (MS)
Via Solferino 28, Milan, 20121, Italy; tel (39) 02 6339; fax 2900 9668; e-mail quotidiani@rcs.it; gio.der@tin.it; web site www.corriere.it
Circ.: 700,000
Advertising: Publicitas.
Mktg. Mgr. – Luisa Sacchi
Ed. – Ferruccio de Bortoli

IL GIORNALE (MS)
Via Gaetano Negri 4, Milan, 20123, Italy; tel (39) 02 85661; fax 7202 3859; web site www.ilgiornale.it
Circ.: 351,786
Advertising: Publicitas.
Ed. in Chief – Mario Giordano
Ed. – Mario Cervi

LA NOTTE (E)
Via Vitruvio 43, Milan, 20124, Italy; tel (39) 02 67171; fax 671 7210
Circ.: 51,695
Chrmn. – Angelo DeMartini
Dir. – Massimo Donelli
Vice Dir. – Luigi Santambrogio

IL SOLE-24 ORE (M-6X WK.)
Via Monte Rosa, 91, Milan, 20149, Italy; tel (39) 02 30221; fax 3022 2736; e-mail gruppo24ore@ilsole24ore.com; web site www.ilsole24ore.com
Circ.: 455,451
Advertising: Publicitas.
Chm. – Giancarlo Cerutti

MILANO

AVVENIRE (6X WK.) EST. 1968
Piazza Carbonari 3, Milano, 20125, Italy; tel (39) 02 67801; fax 678 0208; e-mail lettere@avvenire.it; web site www.avvenire.it
Circ.: 150,000
Ed. – Marco Tarquinio

L'INDIPENDENTE (D)
Via Valcava 6, Milano, 20155, Italy; tel (39) 02 330 251
Circ.: 110,000
Dir. – Daniele Vimercati

MODENA

NUOVA GAZZETTA DI MODENA (D) EST. 1981
Via Ricci, 56, Modena, 41100, Italy; tel (39) 059 247 311; fax 218 903
Circ.: 13,317
Pres. – Carlo Caracciolo
Vice Pres. – Giulio Anselmi
Mgr. – Antonio Mascolo

NAPLES

IL MATTINO (MS) EST. 1892
Via Chiatamone 65, Naples, 80121, Italy; tel (39) 081 794 7111; fax 794 7288; e-mail posta@ilmattino.it; web site www.ilmattino.it
Circ.: 139,578
Mgr. – Mario Orfeo

IL GIORNALE DI NAPOLI (E)
Via Chiatamone 7, Naples, 80125, Italy; tel (39) 081 245 8111; fax 245 8209
Circ.: 16,300
Dir. – Antonio Sasso

NAPOLI

LA GAZZETTA DEL MATTINO (D)
VC. S. Pietro Maiella 6, Napoli, 80138, Italy; tel (39) 081 298 307
Circ.: 11,300
Dir. – Ugo Ragozzino

PADOVA

IL MATTINO DI PADOVA (M) EST. 1978
Via N. Tommaseo, 65/B, Padova, 35131, Italy; tel (39) 049 808 3411; fax 807 0067; e-mail mattino@mattinopadova.it; web site www.mattinopadova.quotidianiespresso.it
Circ.: 36,871
Pres. – Carlo Caracciolo
Vice Pres. – Mario Lenzi
MD – Omar Monestier

PALERMO

GIORNALE DI SICILIA (M)
Via Lincoln 21, Palermo, 90133, Italy; tel (39) 091 662 7111; fax 662 7280; e-mail segreteria.direzione.gds@gestelnet.it; web site www.gds.it
Circ.: 85,764
Dir. – Antonio Ardizzone

L'ORA (E-EX S)
Piazza Napoli 5, Palermo, 90141, Italy; tel (39) 091 581 733; fax 333 439
Circ.: 42,000
Dir. – Anselmo Calaciuria
Ed. in Chief – Guido Valdini

PARMA

GAZZETTA DI PARMA (D) EST. 1735
Via Emilio Casa 5/a, Parma, 43100, Italy; tel (39) 0521 2251; fax 285 515; web site www.gazzettadiparma.it
Circ.: 45,539
Mgr. – Giuliano Molossi

PAVIA

LA PROVINCIA PAVESE (M) EST. 1870
Viale Canton Ticino 16, Pavia, 27100, Italy; tel (39) 0382 434 511; fax 473 875; e-mail direttore@laprovinciapavese.it; web site www.laprovinciapavese.quotidianiespresso.it
Circ.: 30,568
Pres. – Filippo Agusto Carbone
Vice Pres. – Mario Lenzi
Mgr. – Roberto Galli

PERUGIA

CORRIERE DELL'UMBRIA (D) EST. 1983
Via Pievaiola Km. 5,700, Perugia, 06132, Italy; tel (39) 075 52 731; fax 527 3279; web site www.corrieredellumbria.it
Circ.: 25,000
Pres. – Federico Fioravanti
Ed. – Riccardo Regi

PESARO

LA GAZZETTA DI FANO (D)
Piazza Matteotti 22A, Pesaro, 61100, Italy; tel (39) 0721 69545
Dir. – Paolo Farneti
Ed. in Chief – Michele Romano

LA GAZZETTA DI PESARO (D)
Piazza Matteotti 22A, Pesaro, 61100, Italy; tel (39) 0721 69545; fax 68065
Dir. – Paolo Farneti
Ed. in Chief – Michele Romano

PESCARA

IL CENTRO (D) EST. 1986
Via Michelangelo 18, Pescara, 65124, Italy; tel (39) 085 20521; fax 421 4568; e-mail lettere@ilcentro.it; web site www.ilcentro.it
Circ.: 31,880
Pres. – Carlo Caracciolo
Dir. – Luigi Vicinanza

PIACENZA

LIBERTA (M) EST. 1883
Via Benedettine 68, Piacenza, 29100, Italy; tel (39) 0523 393 939; fax 393 962; e-mail info@liberta.it; web site www.liberta.it
Circ.: 36,281
Mgr. – Rizzuto Gaetano

PORDENONE

CORRIERE DI PORDENONE (D)
Corso V. Emanuele 21/G, Pordenone, 33170, Italy; tel (39) 0434 521 911; fax 366 869
Dir. – Giorgio Zicari
Ed. in Chief – Pietro Angelillo

PRATO

LA GAZZETTA DI PRATO (D)
Via Piero della Francesca 2, Prato, 50047, Italy; tel (39) 0574 570 830; fax 570 547
Dir. – Paolo Franeti
Ed. in Chief – Cristiano Draghi

REGGIO EMILIA

GAZZETTA DI REGGIO (D) EST. 1860
Viale Isonzo, 72 A/B, Reggio Emilia, 42100, Italy; tel (39) 0522 501 511; fax 511 370; e-mail redazione.re@gazzettadireggio.it; web site gazzettadireggio.gelocal.it
Circ.: 20,123
Pres. – Carlo Caracciolo

RIMINI

CORRIERE DI RIMINI (D)
Piazza Tre Martiri 43/a, Rimini, 47037, Italy; tel (39) 0541 354 111; fax 354 199; e-mail rimini@corriereromagna.it; web site www.corriereromagna.it
Circ.: 6,000
Dir. – Maria Patrizia Lenvetti

ROME

L'AGENZIA DI VIAGGI (6X WK.)
Via Rasella 155, Rome, 00187, Italy; tel (39) 06 482 1539; fax 482 6721
Circ.: 12,000
Dir. – Alberto Garlanda

IL POPOLO (M-EX S)
Piazza Cinque Lune 113, Rome, 00186, Italy; tel (39) 06 68251; fax 689 6716
Circ.: 13,105
Dir. – Guido Bodrato
Ed. in Chief – Romano Bartoloni

CORRIERE DELLO SPORT/STADIO (D) EST. 1924
Piazza dell'Indipendenza 11/b, Rome, 00185, Italy; tel (39) 06 49921; fax 499 2690; e-mail redazione@corsport.it; web site www.corrieredellosport.it
Circ.: 399,931.
Pres. – Roberto Amodei
Mgr. – Guiseppe Pistilli
Mgr. – Luigi Ferrajolo
Mktg. Mgr. – Tudini Dominico

IL TEMPO (D)
Piazza Colonna 366, Rome, 00187, Italy; tel (39) 06 675 881; fax 675 8869; web site www.iltempo.it
Circ.: 125,474
Pres. – Domenico Bonifaci
Mgr. – Maria Julia Pozzi
Ed. – Giuseppe Sanzotta

IL FIORINO (5X WK.)
Via Parigi 11, Rome, 00185, Italy; tel (39) 06 474 901; fax 488 3435
Circ.: 4,945
Dir. – Luigi D'Amato

IL GIORNALE D'ITALIA (D)
Via Parigi 11, Rome, 00185, Italy; tel (39) 06 (39-6) 474901; fax (39-6) 463435
Circ.: 24,920
Dir. – Franco Simeoni
Ed. in Chief – Franco Rossi
Ed. in Chief – Romano Tripodi

LA REPUBBLICA (MD) EST. 1976
Via Christoper.Colombo 90, Rome, 00147, Italy; tel (39) 06 49821; fax 4982-2923; e-mail larepubblica@repubblica.it; web site www.repubblica.it
Circ.: 700,000
Advertising: Publicitas.
Pres. – Carlo De Benedetti
Ed. in Chief – Ezio Mauro

INFORMAZIONI PER IL COMMERCIO ESTERO (D)
Via Liszt 21, Rome, 00144, Italy; tel (39) 06 59921; fax 438 7030

INTERNATIONAL COURIER (D)
Via di Ripetta 22, Rome, Italy; tel (39) 06
Gen. Dir. – Christopher Winner
Ed. – Roberto Scio

INTERNATIONAL DAILY NEWS (D)
Via Barberini 3, Rome, 00186, Italy; tel (39) 06
Pub./Ed. – Robert H. Cunningha
Dir. – Giulio Carlo Riposio

IL MANIFESTO (D) EST. 1971
Via Tomacelli 146, Rome, 00186, Italy; tel (39) 06 687 191; fax 6871 9573; e-mail redazione@ilmanifesto.it; web site www.ilmanifesto.it
Circ.: 83,259
Pres. – Valentino Parlato
Adv. Mgr – Gabriele Polo
Journalist – Francesco Paterno

IL MESSAGGERO (M) EST. 1878
Via del Tritone 152, Rome, 00187, Italy; tel (39) 06 47201; fax 472 072; e-mail posta@ilmessagero.it; web site www.ilmessaggero.it
Circ.: 337,500
Advertising: Publicitas.
Mgr. – Roberto Napoletino
Mktg. Mgr. – Dicesare Angelo

DAILY AMERICAN (D)
Via S. Maria in Via 12, Rome, 00187, Italy; tel (39) 06
Dir. – Chantal Dubois

ORE 12 (6X WK.)
Via Alfana 39, Rome, 00191, Italy; tel (39) 06 332 2811; fax 333 1997
Circ.: 48,000
Dir. – Enzo Caretti
Ed. in Chief – Mario Caretti

PAESE SERA (D)
Viale Francheschini 56, Rome, 00100, Italy; tel (39) 06 407 2922
Circ.: 130,988
Dir. – Arnaldo Agostini
Mng. Ed. – Silvano Rizza

AVANTI (M-6X WK.)
Via Tomacelli 146, Rome, 00186, Italy; tel (39) 06 687 8268
Circ.: 83,000
Dir. – Ugo Intini
Dir. – Roberto Villeti
Asst. Dir. – Francesco Gozzano
Ed. in Chief – Vito Raponi

SECOLO D'ITALIA (6X WK.)
Serota 39, Rome, 00187, Italy; tel (39) 06 683 3889; fax 686 1598
Circ.: 40,000
Dir. – Aldo Giorleo
Ed. in Chief – Gennaro Malgieri

L'UMANITA (D)
Via degli Scialija 6, Rome, 00186, Italy; tel (39) 06 6830 0300; fax 6830 0884
Circ.: 50,000
Dir. – Ugo Gaudenzi Asinelli

LA VOCE REPUBBLICANA (D)
Piazza dei Caprettari 70, Rome, Italy; tel (39) 06 687 5297; fax 6880 2990
Dir. – Giorgio La Malfa
Ed. in Chief – Luca Paci

SASSARI

LA NUOVA SARDEGNA (M) EST. 1892
Predda Niedda Sardegna, Sassari, 07100, Italy; tel (39) 079 222 400; fax 267 4086; e-mail lanuovasardegna@lanuovasardegna.it; web site www.lanuovasardegna.it

Circ.: 74,142
Pres. – Carlo Benedetti
Mgr. – Stefano DelRe

SIENA

LA GAZZETTA DI SIENA (D)
Via Tolomei 5, Siena, 53100, Italy; tel (39) 0577 750 472
Dir. – Paolo Farneti
Ed. in Chief – Stefano Bisi

SYRACUSE

IL DIARIO DI SIRACUSA (6X WK.)
Via M. Politi Laudien 7, Syracuse, 96100, Italy; tel (39)
Mng. Ed. – Enzo Bonifazi

TARANTO

CORRIERE DEL GIORNO (D) EST. 1947
Piazza Immacolata 30, Taranto, 74100, Italy; tel (39) 099 455-3111; fax 453-8322; e-mail cdg@corgiorno.it; web site www.corgiorno.it
Circ.: 12,000
MD – Antonio Biella
Ed. in Chief – Mario D'Anzi

QUOTIDIANO DI TARANTO (D)
Via Acclavio 24, Taranto, 74100, Italy; tel (39) 099 459 5299
Circ.: 4,500
Dir. – Vittorio Bruno Stamerra
Dir. – Antonio Maglio
Ed. in Chief – Pierangelo Putzolu

TORINO

LA STAMPA (M-6X WK.) EST. 1867
Via Carlo Marenco 32, Torino, 10126, Italy; tel (39) 011 655 8111; fax 656 8187; e-mail direzionegenerale@lastampa.it; web site www.lastampa.it
Circ.: 536,233
Advertising: Publicitas.
Pres. – Giovanni Agnelli
Vice Pres. – Vittorio Caissotti di Chiusano
Vice Pres. – Umberto Cuttica
Mgr. – Gianni Riotta
Mgr. – Marcello Sorgi

TRENT

L'ADIGE (M-6X WK.)
Via Missioni Africane 17, Trent, 38100, Italy; tel (39) 0461 886 111; fax 886 263; web site www.ladige.it
Circ.: 26,720
Pres. – Sergio Gelmi di Caporiacco

TREVISO

LA TRIBUNA DI TREVISO (D) EST. 1978
Corso del Popolo 42, Treviso, 31100, Italy; tel (39) 0422 417 611; fax 579 212; e-mail cronaca@tribunatreviso.it; web site www.tribunatreviso.it
Circ.: 21,405
Ed. – Sandro Moser

TRIESTE

IL PICCOLO (M) EST. 1881
Via Guido Reni 1, Trieste, 34123, Italy; tel (39) 040 373 3111; fax 373 3243; e-mail segreteria.redazione@ilpiccolo.it; web site www.ilpiccolo.it
Circ.: 58,385
Dir. – Paolo Possamai
Mktg. Mgr. – Fabio Zbeochen

PRIMORSKI DNEVNIK (6X WK.)
Via Montecchi 6, Trieste, 34100, Italy; tel (39) 040 779 6600; fax 772 418; e-mail redakcija@primorski.eu; web site www.primorski.eu
Circ.: 10,750
Dir. – Dusan Udovic
Adv. Mgr. – Paolo Mahorcic

TURIN

STAMPA SERA (M&E)
Via Marenco 32, Turin, 10126, Italy; tel (39) 011 656 8111; fax 655 306; web site www.lastampa.it
Dir. – Luca Bernardelli
Vice Dir. – Carlo Bramardo
Ed. in Chief – Ernesto Marenco

TUTTOSPORT (D)
Corso Svizzera 185, Turin, 10149, Italy; tel (39) 011 77731; fax 777 3483; e-mail fegred@tuttosport.com; web site www.tuttosport.com
Circ.: 171,249
Dir. – Paolo DePaola

UDINE

MESSAGGERO VENETO (M) EST. 1946
Viale Palmanova 290, Udine, 33100, Italy; tel (39) 0432 5271; fax 523 072; e-mail direzione@messeggeroveneto.it; web site www.messaggeroveneto.it
Circ.: 62,172
Dir. – Andrea Filippi

VARESE

LA PREALPINA (D)
Viale Tamagno 13, Varese, 21100, Italy; tel (39) 0332 275 700; fax 275 701; e-mail prealpina.varese@prealpina.it; web site www.prealpina.it
Circ.: 37,700
Dir. – Geancarlo Angeler
Ed. in cheif – Roberto Ferrario

VENICE

IL GAZZETTINO (D) EST. 1887
Via Torino 110, Venice, 30172, Italy; tel (39) 041 665 111; fax 665 386; web site www.gazzettino.it
Circ.: 179,523
Dir. – Roberto Papetti

LA NUOVA VENEZIA (D) EST. 1984
Campo San Lio Castello 5620, Venice, 30122, Italy; tel (39) 041 240 3111; fax 958 856; e-mail nuovavenezia@nuovavenezia.it; web site www.nuovavenezia.it
Circ.: 14,868
Pres. – Carlo Caracciolo

VERONA

L'ARENA (D) EST. 1866
Viale del Lavoro 11, San Martino Buon Albergo, Verona, 37036, Italy; tel (39) 045 809 4000; fax 994 527; e-mail diffusione@larena.it; web site www.larena.it
Circ.: 63,021
Dir. – Maurizio Attanio

VICENZA

IL GIORNALE DI VICENZA (D) EST. 1943
Via Enrico Fermi 205, Vicenza, 36100, Italy; tel (39) 0444 396 311; fax 570 117; web site www.ilgiornaledivicenza.it
Circ.: 53,518
Pres. – Luigi Righetti
Vice Pres. – Arrigo Armellini
Vice Pres. – Silvio Fortuna
Vice Pres. – Giuseppe Parolini

VITERBO

CORRIERE DI VITERBO (D)
Via Luigi Rossi Danielli, Viterbo, 01100, Italy; tel (39) 0761 344 990; fax 344 657; web site www.corriereviterbo.it
Circ.: 5,500
Dir. – Sebastiano Botta

KAZAKHSTAN

ALMA-ATA

DIDAR KAZAKHSTAN
110 Zhiber Zholey, Alma-Ata, 480004, Kazakhstan; tel (73) 272 650 166
Ed. in Chief – Ascar Esmakhanov

KAZAKHSTANSKAYA PRAVDA (5X WK.)
39 ul. Gogolya, Alma-Ata, 480044, Kazakhstan; tel (73) 72 630 586; e-mail kazpravda@kaznet.kz; web site www.kazpravda.kz
Ed. in Chief – V. Mikhailov

LENINSHIL ZHAS (5X WK.)
50 ul. Gorykogo, Alma-Ata, 480044, Kazakhstan; tel (73)
Ed. – U. Kalizhanov

YEGEMEN KAZAKHSTAN (6X WK.)
39 ul. Gogolya, Alma-Ata, Kazakhstan; tel (73) 72 632 546
Circ.: 72,000
Ed. in Chief – N. Orazalin

ALMA-ATA

KHALYK KENESI (5X WK.)
64 Zhibek Zholy, Alma-ata, 480002, Kazakhstan; tel (73) 72 331 085
Ed. in Chief – Zh Kenzhalin

ALMATY

EXPRESS K (5X WK.)
6 Abdullin St, Almaty, 050044, Kazakhstan; tel (7) 27 259 6000; fax 259 6001; e-mail daily@express-k.kz; web site www.express-k.kz
Ed. in Chief – Mark Aisberg

KYRGYZSTAN

BISHKEK

KYRGYZ TUUSU (5X WK.)
Abdymomunova 193, Bishkek, Kyrgyzstan; tel (7) 12 224 509
Ed. – Abdilamit Matisakov

SLOVO KYRGZSTANA (D-6X WK.)
Abdymomunova 193, Bishkek, 720013, Kyrgyzstan; tel (7) 12 225 392
Circ.: 111,000
Ed. – Aleksandr I. Malevany

SOVETIK KYRZYSTAN (6X WK.)
193 ul. Kirova, Bishkek, 720013, Kyrgyzstan; tel (7) 12
Circ.: 162,625
Ed. – T. Ishemkulov

VECHERNII BISHKEK (D-5X WK.)
Ul. Usenbaeva 2, Bishkek, 720021, Kyrgyzstan; tel (996) 312 682 121; fax 680 268; web site www.vb.kg
Circ.: 51,500
Ed. in Chief – Kuzmin Gennadi

LATVIA

RIGA

BIZNES I BALTJA (6X WK.)
3 Balasta dambis, Riga, LV1081, Latvia; tel (371) 2 465 875; fax 465 922
Circ.: 19,000
Dir. – Jurijs Aleksejevs
Adv. Mgr. – Inara Baubule
Ed. in Chief – Vladimirs Gurovs

DIENA (6X WK.)
Mukusalas iela 41, Riga, LV1004, Latvia; tel (371) 2 706 3100; fax 706 3169; e-mail diena@diena.lv; web site www.diena.lv
Circ.: 110,000
Ed. in Chief – Sarmite Elerte

LABRIT (D)
Balasta dambis 3, Riga, LV1081, Latvia; tel (371) 2 246 2496; fax 246 2291
Circ.: 36,000
Ed. in Chief – Ivars Busmanis

NEATKARIGA RITA AVIZE (D)
Balasta dambis 3, Riga, LV1081, Latvia; tel (371) 2 246 2496; fax 246 2291
Circ.: 30,000
Ed. in Chief – Lato Lapsa

RIGA BALSS (5X WK.)
Balasta dambis 3, Riga, LV1081, Latvia; tel (371) 2 246 3842; fax 786 0070
Ed. in Chief – Valda Krumina

SM-SEGODNA (5X WK.)
Balasta dambis 3, Riga, LV1081, Latvia; tel (371) 2 246 8383; fax 246 8287
Circ.: 65,000
Ed. in Chief – Aleksandr Blinov

SOVIETSKAYA LATVIYA (6X WK.)
3 Balasta Dambis, Riga, LV1081, Latvia; tel (371)
Circ.: 71,300
Ed. – A.E. Visilyonok

VAKARA ZINAS (E)
Bezdeligu iela 12, Riga, LV1007, Latvia; tel (371) 2 261 7595; fax 261 2383
Circ.: 53,000
Ed. in Chief – Ainis Saulitis

LIECHTENSTEIN

SCHAAN

LIECHTENSTEINER VOLKSBLATT (6X WK.)
Im alten Riet 103, Schaan, 9494, Liechtenstein; tel (423) 237 5151; fax 237 5155; e-mail redaktion@volksblatt.li; verlag@volksblatt.li; inserate@volksblatt.li; abo@volksblatt.li; web site www.volksblatt.li
Circ.: 9,000
Proprietor – Dani Segel
Ed. in Chief – Tino Quaderer

VADUZ

LIECHTENSTEINER WOCHENZEITUNG (WEEKLY)
Lova Center, Vaduz, 9490, Liechtenstein; tel (423) 236 1692; fax 236 1699; e-mail info@medienhaus.li; web site www.liewo.li
Circ.: 5,000
Last Audit: March 29, 2010
Dir. – Daniel Quaderer
Ed. – Michael Winkler

LIECHTENSTEINER VATERLAND (D-6X WK.)
Austrasse 81, Vaduz, 9490, Liechtenstein; tel (423) 236 1616; fax 236 1617; e-mail redaktion@vaterland.li; info@medienhaus.li; inserate@vaterland.li; abo@vaterland.li; web site www.vaterland.li
Circ.: 9,584
Pub. – Daniel Quaderer
Ed. – Gunther Fritz

LITHUANIA

KAUNAS

KAUNO DIENA (D)
Vytauto pr. 27, Kaunas, 3687, Lithuania; tel (370) 7 302 250; fax 423 404; e-mail redakcija@kaunodiena.lt; web site www.kaunodiena.lt
Circ.: 57,000
Ed. in Chief – Tekle Maciuliene

VILNIUS

RESPUBLIKA (D-6X WK.)
A. Smetonos 2, Vilnius, 2600, Lithuania; tel (370) 2 223 112; fax 223 538
Circ.: 55,000
Ed. in Chief – Vitas Tomkus

LIETUVOS AIDAS (D-5X WK.)
Gedimino pr. 2, Vilnius, 2000, Lithuania; tel (370) 5 212 4876; fax 212 4876; e-mail centr@aidas.lt; web site www.aidas.lt
Circ.: 20,000
Ed. – Algirdas Pilvelis

LIETUVOS RYTAS (6X WK.)
Gedimino pr. 12A, Vilnius, 2001, Lithuania; tel (370) 5 274 3666; fax 274 3799; e-mail daily@lrytas.lt; web site www.lrytas.lt
Last Audit: March 22, 2010
Adv. Mgr. – Kavaliaus Kiene
Ed. in Chief – Gedvydas Vainauskas

LUXEMBOURG

ESCH-SUR-ALZETTE

TAGEBLATT/ZEITUNG FIR LETZEBUERG (M-6X WK.)
44 rue du Canal, Esch-sur-Alzette, L-4050, Luxembourg; tel (352) 547 1311; fax 547 130; e-mail redaktion@tageblatt.lu; tageblatt@telephonie.lu; web site www.tageblatt.lu
Circ.: 29,469
Adv. Mgr. – Vivian Porta
Ed. in Chief – Alvin Sold

LUXEMBOURG

D'LETZEBURGER LAND EST. 1954
BP 2083, Luxembourg, L-1020, Luxembourg; tel (352) (352) 485757; fax (352) 496309; e-mail land@land.lu; web site www.land.lu
Circ.: 6,500
General manager – Romain Hilgert

LUXEMBURGER WORT (6X WK.)
2 rue Christophe Plantin, Luxembourg, L-2988, Luxembourg; tel (352) 49931; fax 499 3726; e-mail wort@wort.lu; online.redaktion@wort.lu; web site www.wort.lu
Circ.: 81,000
Last Audit: January 10, 2007
Adv. Mgr. – Ludeveci Pattrick
Ed. in Chief – Glasanar Marc

LE REPUBLICAIN LORRAIN (M)
BP 2211, Luxembourg, L-1022, Luxembourg; tel (352) (352) 447744; fax (352) 452525
Circ.: 15,000
Pub./Ed. – V. Demange

LETZEBUERGER JOURNAL (M-5X WK.)
BP 2101, Luxembourg, L-1021, Luxembourg; tel (352) 493 033; fax 492 065; e-mail journal@journal.lu; web site www.journal.lu
Circ.: 13,500
Ed. in Chief – Claude Karger

LUXEMBOURG NEWS
31 allee Scheffer, Luxembourg, L-2520, Luxembourg; tel (352) (352) 4994501; fax (352) 470056

REVUE
1 rue J-P-Brasseur, Luxembourg, L-1258, Luxembourg; tel (352) 498 1811
Circ.: 29,078
Ed. in Chief – Yolande Kieffer

TELECRAN (WEEKLY)
BP 1008, Luxembourg, L-1010, Luxembourg; tel (352) (352) 4993500; fax (352) 4993590; e-mail telecran@isp.lu
Circ.: 45,000
Mng. Ed. – Fern Morbach

ZEITUNG VUM LETZEBURGER VOLLEK (5X WK.)
3 Rue Zenun Behnrht, Luxembourg, L-1143, Luxembourg; tel (352) 446 066; fax 446 066; e-mail info@zlv.lu; web site www.zlv.lu
Circ.: 8,000
Ed. – Ali Huckast

MACEDONIA

SKOPJE

BIRLIK
Mito Hadzivasilev Jasmine, Skopje, 91000, Macedonia; tel (389) 2 311 1146; fax 322 5560
Ed. in Chief – Drita Karahasan

DNEVNIK (D)
Dame Gruev 14, Skopje, Macedonia; tel (389) 2 127 047; web site www.dnevnik.com.mk
Ed. in Chief – Branko Geroski

FLAKA E VELLAZERIMIT
Mito Hadzivasilev bb, Skopje, 91000, Macedonia; tel (389) 91 112 025; fax 224 829
Circ.: 4,000
Ed. in Chief – Abdul-hadi Zulfiqari

NOVA MAKEDONIJA (M)
Mito Hadzivasilev bb, Skopje, 91000, Macedonia; tel (389) 91 113 586; fax 119 416
Circ.: 25,000
Dir. – Pande Kolemisevski

VECER (E)
Mito Hadzivasilev bb, Skopje, 91000, Macedonia; tel (389) 2 111 537; fax 238 329
Circ.: 29,200
Ed. in Chief – Stojan Nasev

MALTA

PIETA, HAMRUN

IN-NAZZJON (D)
Herbert Ganado St., Pieta, Hamrun, HMR 08, Malta; tel (356) 2124 3641; fax 2124 3640; e-mail news@media.link.com.mt; web site www.nazzjon.com.mt
Circ.: 20,000
Ed. – Alex Attard

VALLETTA

IT-TORCA (WEEKLY)
Union Press, A 41, Marsa Indstrial Estate, Marsa, Valletta, HMR 15, Malta; tel (356) 21244557; fax 21242995; e-mail ian@unionprint.com.mt
Circ.: 30,000
Ed. – Alfred Briffa

L'ORIZZONT (D)
Union Press Co., A 41 Industrial Estate, Valletta, HMR 15, Malta; tel (356) 2124 4557; fax 2124 2995; e-mail ian@unionprint.com.mt
Circ.: 25,000
Ed. – Frans Ghirxi

THE SUNDAY TIMES (S)
341 Saint Paul St., Valletta, VLT 07, Malta; tel (356) 21241465; fax 21241336; web site www.timesofmalta.com
Ed. – Laurence Grech

THE TIMES (DS)
341 Saint Paul St., Valletta, VLT 1211, Malta; tel (356) 2559 4100; fax 2559 4116; e-mail sport@timesofmalta.com; web site www.timesofmalta.com
Adv. Mgr. – Alex Galean
Ed. – Ray Bugeja

VALLETTA, SLIEMA

THE MALTA INDEPENDENT (DS)
Standard House, Birkirkara Hill, St. Julian's, Valletta, Sliema, STJ 09, Malta; tel (356) 2134 5888; fax 2134 4860; e-mail info@independent.com.mt; web site www.independent.com.mt
Ed. in Chief – David Lindsey
Ed. in Chief (d) – Michael Carabott
News Room Mgr. – Stephen Calleja

MOLDOVA

CHISINAU

NEZAVISIMAYA MOLDOVA (5X WK.)
str. Puskin 22, Chisinau, 2612, Moldova; tel (373) 22 233 605; fax 233 141; e-mail tis@nm.mld.net.com; web site www.nm.md
Circ.: 60,692
Ed. – Boris Marian

KISHINEV

MOLDOVA SUVERANA (D)
str. Puskin 22, Kishinev, 2012, Moldova; tel (373) 22 233 196; fax 233 538; e-mail cotidian@moldova-suverana.md; web site www.moldova-suverana.md
Circ.: 105,000
Ed. in Chief – John Berlinski

TINERIMYA MOLDOVEI/MOLODEZH MOLDOVY (3X WK.)
., Kishinev, Moldova; tel (373)
Circ.: 16,486
Ed. – V. Botnaru

TRUDOVOI TIRASPOL
25 October Str. 101, Kishinev, Moldova; tel (373) 22 230 412
Circ.: 7,500
Ed. – Dima Kondratovich

VIATA SATULUI (3X WK.)
str. Puskin 22, Casa presei 4th Flr., Kishinev, 2612, Moldova; tel (373) 22 230 368
Circ.: 50,000
Ed. – V.S. Spiney

MONACO

MONACO

MONACO-MATIN (D)
214, Route de Grenoble, Monaco, 06290, Monaco; tel (377) 4 9318 2838; fax 104 399; e-mail redacchef@nicematin.fr; web site www.nicematin.com
Pres. – Michel Comboul
Sales Mgr. – Laurence Genevet
Ed. in Chief – Dominique Dabin

NETHERLANDS

ALKMAAR

NOORDHOLLANDS DAGBLAD (6X WK.)
PO Box 2, Alkmaar, 1800 AA, Netherlands; tel (31) 72 519 6196; fax 512 6183; e-mail directie@hdcmedia.nl; web site www.hdcmedia.nl
Circ.: 230,000
Mktg. Mgr. – Dorine Buys
Ed. – Geert Ten Dam

ALPHEN AAN DEN RIJN

RIJN EN GOUWE (6X WK.)
PO Box 1, Alphen aan den Rijn, 2400 AA, Netherlands; tel (31) 172 487 444; fax 487 408
Circ.: 30,000
CEO – R.M. de Koning
Adv. Mgr. – C.A.C. Nieuwenhuizen
Ed. – L.M. Heskes

AMSTERDAM

DE TELEGRAAF (M)
PO Box 376, Amsterdam, 1000 EB, Netherlands; tel (31) 20 585 9111; fax 585 4130; web site www.telegraaf.nl
Circ.: 776,000
CEO – A.J.M. Boerma
Adv. Mgr. – F. Volmer
Ed. – S. Paradis

HET FINANCIEELE DAGBLAD (6X WK.)
PO Box 216, Amsterdam, 1000 AE, Netherlands; tel (31) 20 592 8888; fax 592 8800; e-mail info@fd.nl; content@fd.nl; web site www.fd.nl
Circ.: 60,000
CEO – Jacques Kuijf
Ed. – Ulko Jonker

DE VOLKSKRANT (M-6X WK.)
PO Box 2104, Amsterdam, 1000 CC, Netherlands; tel (31) 20 562 9111; fax 668 1389; e-mail holding@persgroep.nl; web site www.persgroep.nl
Circ.: 260,000
Last Audit: March 23, 2010
Adv. Mgr. – Wouter Cander Meulen
Ed. – P.I. Broertjes

TROUW (M-6X WK.)
PO Box 859, Amsterdam, 1000 AW, Netherlands; tel (31) 20 562 9111; fax 668 0389; e-mail redactie@trouw.nl; web site www.trouw.nl
Circ.: 117,000
Ed. – William Schoen

NRC HANDELSBLAD (E-6X WK.)
PO Box 3372, Amsterdam, 1001 AD, Netherlands; tel (31) 20 562 9111; fax 668 6967; e-mail nrc@nrc.nl; web site www.nrc.nl
Circ.: 262,000
Ed. in Chief – Birgig Donker

HET PAROOL (E-6X WK.)
PO Box 433, Amsterdam, 1000 AK, Netherlands; tel (31) 20 558 4444; fax 558 4464; web site www.parool.nl
Circ.: 87,000
Adv. Mgr. – Micheal Bergman
Ed. – Barbara Zambeukering
Prodn. Mgr. – Justin Vin Ses

APELDOORN

ARNHEMSE COURANT (E)
Laan van Westenenk 4, Apeldoorn, 7300 AZ, Netherlands; tel (31) 55 538 8888; fax 538 8500; e-mail info@wegener.nl; web site www.wegener.nl
Circ.: 31,400
Ed. – G. Dielessen

REFORMATORISCH DAGBLAD (E)
PO Box 613, Apeldoorn, 7300 AP, Netherlands; tel (31) 55 539 0222; fax 541 7450; e-mail bvisser@refdag.nl; web site www.reformatorischdagblad.nl
Circ.: 59,000
CEO – B. Visser
Adv. Mgr. – J.K. van Klaveren

APELDOORNSE COURANT (M-6X WK.)
PO Box 99, Apeldoorn, 7300 AB, Netherlands; tel (31) 55 538 8388; fax 538 8333; web site www.destentor.nl; www.wegener.nl
Circ.: 159,000
Ed. – Alex Engbeers

BARNEVELD

BARNEVELDSE KRANT (E-6X WK.)
PO Box 67, Barneveld, 3771 AM, Netherlands; tel (31) 342 494 911; fax 413 141; e-mail t.roskam@bdu.nl; web site www.bduuitgeverij.nl
Circ.: 11,000
Co-CEO – C.R. Rebel
Co-CEO – T. Roskam
Adv. Mgr. – R.C. Houweling
Ed. – W. Vonk

NEDERLANDS DAGBLAD (6X WK.)
PO Box 111, Barneveld, 3770 AC, Netherlands; tel (31) 342 411 711; fax 411 611; e-mail redactie@nd.nl; web site www.nd.nl
Circ.: 35,000
Last Audit: November 23, 2011
MD – Den Gort
Adv. Mgr. – Z. Koops
Mktg .Mgr. – Ten Heuw
Ed. – P.A. Bergwerff

BREDA

BN DESTEM (M)
PO Box 3229, Breda, 4800 MB, Netherlands; tel (31) 76 5312 311; fax 5312 355; web site www.bndestem.nl
Circ.: 56,800
Ed. – John Bes

BN DE STEM (M)
PO Box 3229, Breda, 4800 MB, Netherlands; tel (31) 76 531 2161; fax 531 2212; web site www.bnstem.nl
Circ.: 140,000
CEO – A.A.M. Verrest

DELFT

DELFTSCHE COURANT/WESTLANDSCHE COURANT
PO Box 18, Delft, 2600 AA, Netherlands; tel (31) 15 126700; fax 135987

DEN HAAG

HAAGSCHE COURANT (E-6X WK.)
PO Box 16050, Den Haag, 2500 AA, Netherlands; tel (31) 70 319 0911; fax 390 6447; e-mail service@ad.nl; web site www.haagschecourant.nl
Circ.: 117,000

DEVENTER, OVERIJSSEL

DEVENTER DAGBLAD (M)
PO Box 18, Deventer, Overijssel, 7400 AA, Netherlands; tel (31) 570 686 432; e-mail deventer@destentor.nl; web site www.destentor.nl
Circ.: 34,849
Ed. – Alex Engbers
Mktg. Mgr. – Rokeas Rikars

GELDERS-OVERIJSSELSE COURANT/ZUTPHENS DAGBLAD
PO Box 18, Deventer, Overijssel, 2600 AA, Netherlands; tel (31) 5700 48350
Circ.: 20,725

DORDRECHT

DE DORDTENAAR (M)
PO Box 54, Dordrecht, 3300 AB, Netherlands; tel (31) 78 632 4705; fax 632 4729; e-mail service@ad.nl; web site www.ad.nl
Circ.: 31,000
CEO – Vander Heyden
Ed. – Coonie Cahey

EINDHOVEN

EINDHOVENS DAGBLAD (6X WK.)
PO Box 534, Eindhoven, 5600 AM, Netherlands; tel (31) 40 233 6336; fax 233 6954; e-mail opinie@ed.nl; web site www.ed.nl
Circ.: 120,000
Ed. in Chief – Henk Vanweert

EMMEN

EMMER COURANT
PO Box 5, Emmen, 7800 AA, Netherlands; tel (31) 5916 18600
Circ.: 29,459

ENSCHEDE

DAGBLAD TUBANTIA/TWENTSCHE COURANT (M)
PO Box 28, Enschede, 7500 AA, Netherlands; tel (31) 53 484 2842; fax 484 2200; web site www.tctubantia.nl
Circ.: 136,000
Ed. in Chief – G. Dijkstra
Mng. Ed. – Andre Vish

TWENTSCHE COURANT (M)
PO Box 28, Enschede, 7500 AA, Netherlands; tel (31) 53 484 2842; fax 484 2706; e-mail redactieonline@tubantia.wegener.nl; web site www.tctubantia.nl
Circ.: 49,100
Ed. in Chief – Andre Vis
Adv. Mgr. – Bert Bodde

GOES

PROVINCIALE ZEEUWSE COURANT (6X WK.)
PO Box 31, Goes, 4460 AA, Netherlands; tel (31) 113 315 500; fax 315 509; e-mail redactie@pzc.nl; web site www.pzc.nl
Circ.: 63,000
Ed. – Peter Jansen

GRONINGEN

DAGBLAD VAN HET NOORDEN (M-6X WK.)
PO Box 60, Groningen, 9700 MC, Netherlands; tel (31) 50 584 4106; fax 584 4109; web site www.dvhn.nl
Circ.: 150,000
CEO – Jan De Roos
Dir. – Gijs Lensink

DRENTS GRONINGSE DAGBLADEN (6X WK.)
PO Box 60, Groningen, 9700 MC, Netherlands; tel (31) 50 584 4444; fax 584 4408
Circ.: 150,000
Ed. – P. Sijpersma

HAARLEM, NORTH HOLLAND

HAARLEMS DAGBLAD (M-6X WK.)
PO Box 507, Haarlem, North Holland, 2003 PA, Netherlands; tel (31) 88 824 1210; fax 824 1212; e-mail desmaak@hvcmedia.nl; web site www.haarlemsdagblad.nl
Circ.: 61,300
Ed. in Chief – Bill Meyer
Ed. – William Spierdigk

HILVERSUM, NORTH HOLLAND

DE GOOI EN EEMLANDER (E)
PO Box 15, Hilversum, North Holland, 1200 AA, Netherlands; tel (31) 35 6257911; fax 6257246
Circ.: 52,500
Ed. – H. van Zenderen

HOUTEN

AMERSFOORTSE COURANT/UTRECHTS NIEUWSBLAD (M)
PO Box 500, Houten, 3990 DM, Netherlands; tel (31) 30 639 9911; fax 639 9937; e-mail un.redactie@ad.nl; lezersservice@ed.nl; web site www.wegener.nl
Circ.: 99,000
Ed. – A. Kalmann

HOUTEN, UTRECHT

UTRECHTS NIEUWSBLAD/DAGBLAD RIVERENLAND (M-6X WK.)
PO Box 500, Houten, Utrecht, 3990 DM, Netherlands; tel (31) 30 639 9911; fax 639 9920; web site www.ad.nl
Circ.: 145,300
Ed. in Chief – Arjeh Kalmann

LEEUWARDEN

FRIESCH DAGBLAD (6X WK.)
PO Box 412, Leeuwarden, 8901 BE, Netherlands; tel (31) 58 298 7600; fax 298 7666; e-mail t.milgen@friesch-dagblad.nl; web site www.friesch-dagblad.nl
Circ.: 17,000
Adv. Mgr. – Gloria Dijkstra
Ed. – L. Kooistra
Mktg. Mgr. – Bart Venderkooi

LEEUWARDER COURANT (6X WK.)
PO Box 394, Leeuwarden, 8901 BD, Netherlands; tel (31) 58 284 5845; fax 284 5829; e-mail info@lc.nl; web site www.lc.nl
Circ.: 85
editor in chief – Hans Snijder

LEIDEN, SOUTH HOLLAND

LEIDSE COURANT (E)
PO Box 11, Leiden, South Holland, 2300 AA, Netherlands; tel (31) 71 5122244; fax 5134941
Circ.: 9,967

Ed. – J.W.C. Leune

LEIDSCH DAGBLAD (6X WK.)
PO Box 54, Leiden, South Holland, 2300 AB, Netherlands; tel (31) 71 535 6356; fax 535 6415; e-mail stadsredactie@leidschdagblad.nl; web site www.leidschdagblad.nl
Circ.: 50,227
Ed. – J.G.C. Majoor

MAASTRICHT, LIMBURG

DAGBLAD VOOR NOORD-LIMBURG (M)
PO Box 1056, Maastricht, Limburg, 5900 AB, Netherlands; tel (31) 77 551 234; fax 519 533
Circ.: 53,909
Ed. – J.L.L. Wijnen

DE LIMBURGER (M-6X WK.)
Duboisdomein 30, Maastricht, Limburg, 6229 GT, Netherlands; tel (31) 43 350 2000; fax 350 1899; e-mail redactie@limburger.nl; web site www.limburger.nl
Circ.: 144,746
Dir. – H. Straat
Ed. in Chief – G.H. Vogelaar

NIJMEGEN

DE GELDERLANDER (M-6X WK.)
PO Box 36, Nijmegen, 6500 DA, Netherlands; tel (31) 24 365 0611; fax 365 0209; web site www.gelderlander.nl
Circ.: 193,000
Dir. – Stef Rietbergen
Adv. Mgr. – Albert Smeinc

PURMEREND, NORTH HOLLAND

NIEUWE NOORDHOLLANDSE COURANT (E)
PO Box 14, Purmerend, North Holland, 1440 AA, Netherlands; tel (31) 299 432071; fax 430205
Circ.: 10,986
Ed. – H. Lansdaal

ROOSENDAAL EN NISPEN, NORTH BRABANT

BRABANTS NIEUWSBLAD (M)
PO Box 1052, Roosendaal en Nispen, North Brabant, 4700 BB, Netherlands; tel (31) 557 8888; fax 557 8149
Circ.: 55,000
Ed. – Gerrit Bielderman

ROTTERDAM

ALGEMEEN DAGBLAD (6X WK.)
PO Box 8983, Rotterdam, 3009 AT, Netherlands; tel (31) 10 406 7211; fax 406 6969; web site www.ad.nl
Circ.: 490,000
Adv. Mgr. – Jan Candemarel
Ed. in Chief – Peter Dejong

ROTTERDAMS DAGBLAD (M & E-6X WK.)
PO Box 8759, Rotterdam, 3009 AT, Netherlands; tel (31) 10 400 4400; fax 412 8509; e-mail nieuwsdienst@ad.nl; web site www.ad.nl
Circ.: 400,000
Adv. Mgr. – Jan Vandernmarel
Ed. in Chief – Peter Dejonge

ROTTERDAM, SOUTH HOLLAND

ROTTERDAMS NIEUWSBLAD (E)
PO Box 1162, Rotterdam, South Holland, 3000 BD, Netherlands; tel (31) 10 4004400; fax 4128449
– J. Prins
– J.R. SoetenhorstEd.s

HET VRIJE VOLK (6X WK.)
PO Box 1162, Rotterdam, South Holland, 3000 BD, Netherlands; tel (31) 10 406 7211; fax 406 6410; web site www.rotterdamsdagblad.nl
Circ.: 153,615

S-HERTOGENBOSCH

BRABANTS DAGBLAD (M-6X WK.)
PO Box 235, S-Hertogenbosch, 5201 HB, Netherlands; tel (31) 73 615 7157; fax 615 7357; e-mail redactie@brabantsdagblad.wegener.nl; web site www.brabantsdagblad.nl
Circ.: 153,300
CEO – M. Paans
Ed. – A. Bessengleng

SITTARD

LIMBURGS DAGBLAD (M-6X WK.)
Mercator 3, Sittard, 6135 KW, Netherlands; tel (31) 46 411 6300; e-mail lezersservice@mgl.nl; web site www.limburger.nl
Circ.: 79,800
Dir. – Johan Boermann
Adv. Mgr. – Roger Scholtes

THE HAGUE

NEDERLANDS STAATSCOURANT (E)
PO Box 20025, The Hague, 2500 EA, Netherlands; tel (31) 70 378 9911; fax 385 4321; e-mail info@sdu.nl; sdu@sdu.nl; web site www.sdu.nl
Circ.: 10,000
Co-CEO – L. Jongsma
Co-CEO – S. Van Oostrom
Ed. – W.M.C. de Jong
Prodn. Mgr. – M.O.D. Scholten

ZWOLLE, OVERIJSSEL

ZWOLSE COURANT (M)
Assendorperdijk 7, Zwolle, Overijssel, 8000 AA, Netherlands; tel (31) 38 455 9455; fax 421 9453; e-mail info@wegener.nl; web site www.wegener.nl
Circ.: 70,400
Ed. – J. Bartelds

NORWAY

ALESUND

SUNNMORSPOSTEN (M-6X WK.)
Boks 123, Alesund, 6001, Norway; tel (47) 7012 0000; web site www.smp.no
Circ.: 37,918
Adv. Mgr. – Engrid Sperre
Ed. – Hanna Relling Berg

ALTA

ALTAPOSTEN (6X WK.)
PO Box 1193, Alta, 9501, Norway; tel (47) 7845 6700; fax 7845 6740; web site www.altaposten.no
Circ.: 5,198
Ed. in Chief – Rolf Edmund Lund

ARENDAL

AGDERPOSTEN (M-6X WK.)
PO Box 8, Arendal, 4801, Norway; tel (47) 3700 3700; fax 3700 3838; e-mail agderposten@agderposten.no; web site www.agderposten.no
Circ.: 25,660
Ed. – Stein Gauslaa

ASKIM

OEVRE SMAALENENE (6X WK.)
Torget 12, Askim, 1830, Norway; tel (47) 6981 6100; fax 6988 6084; e-mail smaa@online.no; web site www.smaalenene.no
Circ.: 13,500
Ed. in Chief – Jarle Bentzen
Adv. Mgr. – Kari Ann

BERGEN

BERGENS ARBEIDERBLAD (M-7X WK.)
Chr. Michelsens Gate 4, Bergen, 5001, Norway; tel (47) 5523 5000; fax 5531 0030; e-mail internett@ba.no; web site www.ba.no
Circ.: 23,875
Adv. Mgr. – Kjersti Rassmussen
Ed. – Anders Nyland

BERGENS TIDENDE (DS)
PO Box 7240, Bergen, 5020, Norway; tel (47) 05500 05500; fax 5521 4870; e-mail bt@bt.no; web site www.bt.no
Circ.: 90,000
Advertising: Publicitas.
Editor in Chief – Trine Eilertsen
CEO – Sondre Gravir

BERGENSAVISEN (D)
PO Box 824, Bergen, 5807, Norway; tel (47) 5523 5000; fax 5531 0030; e-mail internett@ba.no; web site www.ba.no
Circ.: 28,000
Ed. in Chief – Olav Terje Bergo
Ed. in Chief – Anders Nyland
Adv. Mgr. – Kjersti Rasmussen

BILLINGSTAD (M-5X WK.)
PO Box 133, Bergen, 1361, Norway; tel (47) 5698 6901; fax 5698 0919
Circ.: 31,720

DAGEN (E-6X WK.)
PO Box 2394, Bergen, 5824, Norway; tel (47) 4777 3775; fax 5555 9720; e-mail idag@dagenmagazinet.no; web site www.dagen.no
Circ.: 12,351
Ed. in Chief – Odd Sverre Hove

FISKAREN (M-2X WK.)
PO Box 4053, Bergen, 5023, Norway; tel (47) 5521 3321; fax 5531 8201
Circ.: 10,000
Mgr. – Jan L. Larsen
Ed. – Nils Torsvik

GULA TIDEND
PO Box 250, Bergen, 5001, Norway; tel (47) 5523 0330; fax 5590 2436
Circ.: 4,111
Ed. – Gunnar Wiederstrom

BILLINGSTAD

BUDSTIKKE (E-MON-FRI; M-SAT)
PO Box 133, Billingstad, 1361, Norway; tel (47) 6677 0000; fax 6677 0011; web site www.budstikka.no
Circ.: 27,000
Adv.Mgr. – Terje Tamberj
Ed. in Chief – Andreas Gjolme

BODO

AVISA NORDLAND (M-6X WK.)
Storgata 38, Bodo, 8002, Norway; tel (47) 7550 0000; fax 7550 5190; e-mail annonse@an.no; web site www.an.no
Circ.: 24,500
Ed. – Jan-Eirik Hanssen
Adv. Mgr. – Gan Braastad

MEDIA-NOR AS (D-6X WK.)
PO Box 244, Bodo, 8001, Norway; tel (47) 7550 5170; fax 7550 5180

NORDLANDSPOSTEN (M-6X WK.)
PO Box 44, Bodo, 8001, Norway; tel (47) 7552 8460; fax 7552 7200
Circ.: 20,238
Mgr. – Iver Hammeren
Mktg. Mgr. – Turid Anderson

BRANDBU

HADELAND (M-4X WK.)
PO Box 85, Brandbu, 2760, Norway; tel (47) 0633 4120; fax 0633 5144
Circ.: 7,694
Mgr. – Ole Hamstad
Adv. Mgr. – Torgeir Sater
Ed. – Marit Ascheoug

BROENNOEYSUND

BROENNOEYSUND AVIS (M-5X WK.)
Boks 38, Broennoeysund, 8901, Norway; tel (47) 7501 8400; fax 7501 8413; e-mail desk@ba-avis.no; web site www.ba-avis.no
Circ.: 4,900
Adv. Mgr. – Frode Nordmark
Ed. – Anita Gustavsn

DRAMMEN

DE FIRE NESTE (D-6X WK.)
PO Box 7032, Drammen, 3007, Norway; tel (47) 3282 6190; fax 3220 4210
Circ.: 442,000

DRAMMENS TIDENDE OG BUSKERUDS BLAD A/S (D)
PO Box 7033, Drammen, 3007, Norway; tel (47) 3220 4000; fax 3220 4061; e-mail redaksjonen@dt.no; sentralbord@dt.no; web site www.dt.no
Circ.: 39,000
Adv. Mgr. – Svein Aas
Ed. – Geir Arne Bore

FREMTIDEN (M-6X WK.)
PO Box 7013, Drammen, 3007, Norway; tel (47) 3282 3580; fax 3282 3600
Circ.: 17,138
Ed. – Knut S. Evensen

DROEBAK

AKERSHUS AMTSTIDENDE (M-5X WK.)
PO Box 12, Droebak, 1441, Norway; tel (47) 6490 5400; fax 6493 3744; e-mail kundesenter@amta.no; web site www.amta.no
Circ.: 8,822
Ed. – Mortan Oby

EIDSVOLL

EIDSVOLD BLAD/ULLENSAKER BLAD (5X WK.)
PO Box 130, Eidsvoll, 2081, Norway; tel (47) 6392 2700; fax 6396 4976; e-mail redaksjon@eub.no; web site ^www.eub.no
Circ.: 8,252
Ed. in Chief – Terje Granerud

ELVERUM

OESTLENDINGEN/HAMAR/OESTLENDINGEN SOLOER-ODAL (M-6X WK.)
Gaarderbakken 3, Elverum, 2406, Norway; tel (47) 6243 2400; fax 6243 2421; e-mail redaksjonen@ostlendingen.no; web site www.ostlendingen.no
Circ.: 26,338
Adv. Mgr. – Knut Wold
Ed.in Cheif – Nils Kristian Myhre

FAGERNES

VALDRES (M-4X WK.)
PO Box 54, Fagernes, 2901, Norway; tel (47) 6136 4200; fax 6136 4251; web site www.avisa-valdres.no
Circ.: 10,098
Mgr. – Kari Slaattelid

FARSUND

FARSUNDS AVIS (M-6X WK.)
PO Box 23, Farsund, 4551, Norway; tel (47) 3839 5000; fax 3839 2086; e-mail redrksaun@favis.no; web site www.favis.no
Circ.: 5,836
Gen.Mgr. – Svenune Genfen

FINNSNES

TROMS FOLKEBLAD (D)
PO Box 308, Finnsnes, 9305, Norway; tel (47) 7785 2000; fax 7785 2030; web site www.folkebladet.no
Circ.: 7,000
Mgr. – Rolf A. Erstad

FLOROE

FIRDAPOSTEN
PO Box 38, Floroe, 6901, Norway; tel (47) 5775 7300; fax 0571 4313
Circ.: 5,960
Adv. Mgr. – Malvin Horne
Mgr./Ed. – Erik Stephansen

FOERDE

FIRDA (6X WK.)
PO Box 160, Foerde, 6801, Norway; tel (47) 5783 3333; fax 5720 5312; e-mail redaksjon@firda.no; web site www.firda.no
Circ.: 13,166
Mgr. – Dag Solheim
Adv. Mgr. – Herald Setre

FREDRIKSTAD

FREDRIKSTAD AVISA DEMOKRATEN (3X WK.)
PO Box 83, Fredrikstad, 1601, Norway; tel (47) 6936 8000; fax 6936 8020; web site www.demokraten.no
Circ.: 11,285
Mgr. – Oyvind Tveter

FREDRIKSTAD BLAD (D)
PO Box 143, Fredrikstad, 1606, Norway; tel (47) 46 80 77 77; fax 6931 9312; e-mail tips@f-b.no; web site www.f-b.no
Circ.: 22,138
Ed. in Chief – Erling Omvik

GJOVIK

OPPLAND ARBEIDERBLAD (M-6X WK.)
PO Box 24, Gjovik, 2801, Norway; tel (47) 6118 9300; fax 6117 9856; e-mail redaksgonen@oa.no; web site www.oa.no
Circ.: 25,000
Adv. Mgr. – Oynyind Ludyigsen
Ed. in Chief – Jens O. Jensen

SAMHOLD (M-6X WK.)
PO Box 22, Gjovik, 2801, Norway; tel (47) 6117 0000; fax 6117 7451
Circ.: 6,700
Mktg. Mgr. – Tom Torkehagen

HALDEN

HALDEN ARBEIDERBLAD (M-6X WK.)
PO Box 113, Halden, 1751, Norway; tel (47) 6921 5600; fax 6921 5602; e-mail redaksjonen@ha-halden.no; web site www.hahalden.no
Circ.: 9,500
Mgr. – Ammegrethe Kolstad
Adv. Mgr – Monica Mordbroden

HAMAR

HAMAR ARBEIDERBLAD (M-6X WK.)
PO Box 262, Hamar, 2301, Norway; tel (47) 02318; fax 6251 9555; e-mail ha-torget@hanett.no; web site www.ha-nett.no
Circ.: 28,000
Ed. – Rolv Amdal

HEDMARK/OPPLAND SAMKJOERINGEN (M-6X WK.)
PO Box 443, Hamar, 2301, Norway; tel (47) 6253 2211; fax 0653 3609

HAMMERFEST

FINMARK DAGBLAD (M-6X WK.)
Salsgata 16, Hammerfest, 9600, Norway; tel (47) 7842 8600; fax 7842 8639; e-mail redaksjonen@fd.no; web site www.fd.no
Circ.: 11,750
Ed. in Chief – Erik Palm

HARSTAD

HARSTAD TIDENDE (M-6X WK.)
PO Box 85, Harstad, 9400, Norway; tel (47) 7701 8060; fax 7701 8005; e-mail redaksjonen@harstad-tidende.no; web site www.harstad-tidende.no
Circ.: 15,556
Ed. – Board Necaelsan

HAUGESUND

HAUGESUNDS AVIS (M-6X WK.) EST. 1895
PO Box 2024, Haugesund, 5504, Norway; tel (47) 5272 0000; fax 5272 0444; e-mail redaksjonen@h-avis.no; web site www.h-avis.no
Circ.: 29,000
MD – Jan Tore Hamnoy
Ed. – Paal A. Berg

HOEYANGER

SOGN DAGBLAD (M-6X WK.)
PO Box 129, Hoeyanger, 5901, Norway; tel (47) 0571 2933; fax 0571 2917
Circ.: 5,476
Ed. – Norvald Stedje
Mgr. – Jarle Oren
Adv. Mgr. – Odd Rune Forsund

HORTEN

GJENGANGEREN (M-6X WK.)
PO Box 85, Horten, 3191, Norway; tel (47) 3302 0020; fax 3302 0030; e-mail redaksjonen@gjengangeren.no; web site www.gjengangeren.no
Circ.: 6,285
Adv. Mgr – Alrsalill Endrasan

KONGSBERG

LAAGENDALSPOSTEN (M-6X WK.) EST. 1903
Stasjonsbakken 3, Kongsberg, 3611, Norway; tel (47) 3277 1000; fax 3273 6950; e-mail redaksjonen@laagendalsposten.no; web site www.laagendalsposten.no
Circ.: 9,511
Ed. – Jorn Steinmoen

KONGSVINGER

GLOMDALEN (M-6X WK.) EST. 1885
Box 757, Kongsvinger, 2204, Norway; tel (47) 6288 2500; fax 6288 2501; web site www.glomdalen.no
Circ.: 22,557
Chief Editor – Eivind Lid
Managing director – Bangsund Leif

KRAGEROE

KRAGEROE BLAD EST. 1844
PO Box 55, Krageroe, 3771, Norway; tel (47) 3598 6700; e-mail sentralbord@kv.no; web site www.kv.no
Circ.: 4,200
Editor in Chief and General Manager – Tone Storseth

VESTMAR
PO Box 85, Krageroe, 3771, Norway; tel (47) 3598 1241; fax 3598 0983
Mgr. – Hans Ch Paus-Knudsen

KRISTIANSAND

FAEDRELANDSVENNEN (M-6X WK.)
PO Box 369, Kristiansand, 4664, Norway; tel (47) 3811 3000; fax 3811 3201; e-mail 03811@fvn.no; web site www.fvn.no
Circ.: 50,000
Ed. – Lars Erik Torjussen

KRISTIANSUND

TIDENS KRAV (6X WK.)
PO Box 8, Kristiansund, 6501, Norway; tel (47) 7157 0000; fax 7167 9666; web site www.tk.no
Circ.: 16,049
Ed. in Chief – Tore Dyrnes

LARVIK

OSTLANDS-POSTEN (E-6X WK.)
PO Box 5, Larvik, 3285, Norway; tel (47) 3316 3000; web site www.op.no
Circ.: 14,087
Dir. – Are Stokstad

LEIKANGER

SOGN AVIS (M-5X WK.)
PO Box 3, Leikanger, 6861, Norway; tel (47) 5765 6000; fax 5765 3543; e-mail redaksjon@sognavis.no; web site www.sognavis.no
Circ.: 10,900
Ed. – Jan Inge Fardal

LILLEHAMMER

GUDBRANDSDOLEN DAGNINGEN (M-6X WK.)
PO Box 954, Lillehammer, 2604, Norway; tel (47) 6122 1000; fax 612 60960; web site www.gd.no
Circ.: 12,441
Ed. – Kristian Skullerud

GUDBRANDSDOLEN LILLEHAMMER TILSKUER (M-6X WK.)
PO Box 954, Lillehammer, 2601, Norway; tel (47) 6128 9833; fax 6126 0960
Circ.: 30,018
Ed. in Chief – Asbjorn Ringen

LILLESTROM

ROMERIKES BLAD (M) EST. 1902
PO Box 235, Lillestrom, 2001, Norway; tel (47) 6380 5050; e-mail redaksjonen@rb.no; web site www.rb.no
Circ.: 33,364
Ed. in Chief – Thor Woje

MANDAL

LINDESNES (M-6X WK.)
PO Box 41, Mandal, 4501, Norway; tel (47) 3827 1000; fax 3827 1002; web site www.l-a.no
Circ.: 6,700
Adv. Mgr. – Per Didriksen
Ed. – Kare M. Hansen

MELHUS

TROENDERBLADET (M-4X WK.)
PO Box 160, Melhus, 7084, Norway; tel (47) 7287 8370; fax 7287 8371; e-mail tronderbladet@tronderbladet.no; web site www.tronderbladet.no
Circ.: 6,000

MO

RANA BLAD (M-6X WK.)
PO Box 55, Mo, 8601, Norway; tel (47) 7512 5500; fax 7512 5540; e-mail redaksjonen@ranablad.no; web site www.ranablad.no
Circ.: 11,332
Ed. in Chief – Kirsti Nielsen

MOLDE

ROMSDALS BUDSTIKKE (M-6X WK.)
PO Box 2100, Molde, 6402, Norway; tel (47) 7125 0000; fax 7125 0011; e-mail tips@rbnett.no; web site www.rbnett.no
Circ.: 18,456
Ed. – Richard Nergaard

MOLDE, MOLDEGARD

FYLKET
PO Box 2012, Molde, Moldegard, 6401, Norway; tel (47) 7125 1088; fax 7125 1442
Circ.: 3,079
Mgr./Ed. – Lars Steinar Anses

MOSJOEEN

HELGELAND ARBEIDERBLAD (M-6X WK.)
Fearnleysgate 23, Mosjoeen, 8654, Norway; tel (47) 7511 3600; e-mail vaktsjef@helgeland-arbeiderblad.no; web site www.helgeland-arbeiderblad.no
Circ.: 9,741
Ed. – Geir Glad

MOSS

MOSS AVIS (D)
PO Box 248-250, Moss, 1501, Norway; tel (47) 4690 7777; fax 6920 5002; web site www.moss-avis.no
Circ.: 15,000
Ed. – Jan Tollefsen

NAMSOS

NAMDALS-AVISA A/S (M-6X WK.)
PO Box 100, Namsos, 7801, Norway; tel (47) 7421 2100; fax 7421 2101; e-mail annonse@namdalsavisa.no; web site www.namdalsavisa.no
Circ.: 12,538
Ed. – Sveim Karlsen
News Ed, – Lars Morkved

NORDTROENDEREN OG NAMDALEN (M-6X WK.)
PO Box 10, Namsos, 7801, Norway; tel (47) 0777 2955
Circ.: 3,500
Mgr. – Arnt Farbu
Adv. Mgr. – Bjoern Hyrrold

NARVIK

FREMOVER (M-6X WK.)
PO Box 324, Narvik, 8504, Norway; tel (47) 7695 0000; fax 7695 0030; e-mail redaksjon@fremover.no; web site www.fremover.no
Circ.: 10,857
Gen. Mgr. – Rogar Bargarsen

NORSK LYSINGSBLAD (D-6X WK.)
PO Box 177, Narvik, 8501, Norway; tel (47) 7695 0550; fax 7695 0580
Circ.: 12,000

OFOTENS TIDENDE
PO Box 283, Narvik, 8501, Norway; tel (47) 0824 1526; fax 0824 5360

ORKANGER

SOER-TROENDELAG (M-5X WK.)
Orkdalsveien 57, Orkanger, 7300, Norway; tel (47) 7248 7500; fax 7248 7506; e-mail service-senter@avisa-st.no; web site www.avisa-st.no
Circ.: 7,238
Ed. in Chief – Anders Morkem

OSLO

A-MAGASINET
PO Box 1178, Oslo, 0107, Norway; tel (47) 2286 3000; fax 2242 1593

AFTENNUMMER (E-5X WK.)
PO Box 1, Oslo, 0051, Norway; tel (47) 2286 3000; fax 2282 4130; e-mail service@aftenposten.no; web site www.aftenposten.no
Circ.: 267,809
Advertising: Publicitas.
Mng. Dir. – Lars Erik Torjussen
Adv. Mgr. – Knutfredrek Lramsead
Ed. in Chief – Hilde Haudsrjerd

AFTENPOSTEN (M&ES)
PO Box 1, Oslo, 0051, Norway; tel (47) 2286 3000; fax 2286 3800; e-mail aftenposten@aftenposten.no; service@aftenposten.no; web site www.aftenposten.no
Mng. Dir. – Lars Erik Torjussen
Ed. in Chief – Hilde Haugsgjerd

DAGBLADET (D)
PO Box 1184 Sentrum, Oslo, 0107, Norway; tel (47) 2400 1000; fax 2400 0200; web site www.dagbladet.no
Circ.: 204,850
Group: Berner Gruppen AS
Ed. in Chief – Lars Helle

DAGENS NAERINGSLIV (M-6X WK.)
PO Box 1182 Sentrum, Oslo, 0107, Norway; tel (47) 2200 1000; e-mail tips@dn.no; web site www.dn.no
Circ.: 60,027
Advertising: Publicitas.
Ed. – Amung Djqde

DAGSAVISEN (M-6X WK.)
PO Box 1183 Sentrum, Oslo, 0107, Norway; tel (47) 8153 4000; e-mail dagsavisen@kundesenter.com; nettredaksjonen@dagsavisen.no; tipset@dagsavisen.no; web site www.dagsavisen.no
Circ.: 51,786
Adv. Mgr. – Anders Brisa
Foreign Ed. – Kaia Storvik

FINANSAVISEN (6X WK.)
PO Box 724, Oslo, 0214, Norway; tel (47) 2329 6300; fax 2329 6301; web site www.hegnar.no
Circ.: 11,000
Ed. – Trygve Hegnar

FOLKET
Moellergt. 38, Oslo, 0179, Norway; tel (47) 2211 5510
Mgr./Ed. – Inge Groesland

FOLKETS FRAMTID
Ovre Slottsgate 18/20, Oslo, 0157, Norway; tel (47) 2310 2820; fax 2310 2828
Circ.: 8,778
Mgr. – Kjell Mathiesen
Ed. – Odd Hagen

KLASSEKAMPEN (M-6X WK.)
PO Box 9257, Oslo, 0134, Norway; tel (47) 2205 9500; fax 2205 9587; web site www.klassekampen.no
Circ.: 10,042
Pub. – Braanen Bjorgulv

NATIONEN (6X WK.)
PO Box 9390 Gronland, Oslo, 0135, Norway; tel (47) 2131 0000; fax 2131 0090; e-mail desk@nationen.no; web site www.nationen.no
Circ.: 26,000
Last Audit: March 22, 2010
Ed. in Chief – Mari Velsand
News Desk Ed. – Michael Brondbo

NY TID (WEEKLY)
S□rkedalsveien 10 A, Oslo, N-0055, Norway; tel (47) 2308 0580; fax 2308 0581
Circ.: 8,500
Mgr./Ed. – Gunnar Ringheim

VART LAND (M-6X WK.)
PO Box 1180 Sentrum, Oslo, 0107, Norway; tel (47) 2231 0310; fax 2231 0305; e-mail sentral@vl.no; annonse@vartland.no; web site www.vl.no
Circ.: 26,000
Ed. – Helge Simonnen

VERDENS GANG (D)
PO Box 1185 Sentrum, Oslo, 0107, Norway; tel (47) 2200 0000; fax 2242 6689; e-mail annonser@vg.no; web site www.vg.no
Ed. in Chief – Bernt Olufsen

RJUKAN

RJUKAN ARBEIDERBLAD (D-5X WK.)
PO Box 63, Rjukan, 3661, Norway; tel (47) 3508 0050; fax 3509 1038
Circ.: 2,614
Ed. – Kjell Gunnar Dahle
Mgr. – Terje Paulsen

SANDEFJORD

SANDEFJORDS BLAD (M-6X WK.)
PO Box 143, Hasle, Sandefjord, 3202, Norway; tel (47) 3342 2000; fax 3342 2044; e-mail redaksjonen@sb.no; web site www.sb.no
Circ.: 15,000
Dir. – Jan Roaldseth

SARPSBORG

SARPSBORG ARBEIDERBLAD (M-6X WK.)
PO Box 83, Sarpsborg, 1701, Norway; tel (47) 6911 1111; fax 6911 1074; e-mail sa@sa.no; web site www.sa.no
Circ.: 17,000
Ed. – Eirik Moe

SENTRUM

RINGERIKES BLAD (M-6X WK.)
PO Box 68, Sentrum, 3502, Norway; tel (47) 3217 9500; fax 3217 9501; web site www.ringblad.no
Circ.: 13,453
Ed. – Tore Roland

SKI

OESTLANDETS BLAD (E-6X WK.)
PO Box 3110, Ski, 1402, Norway; tel (47) 6485 5000; fax 6485 5050; web site www.oblad.no
Circ.: 18,217
Ed. – Siri Zachariassen

SKIEN

TELEMARK ARBEIDERBLAD (M-6X WK.)
PO Box 2833, Skien, 3702, Norway; tel (47) 3558 5500; fax 3553 0590; web site www.ta.no
Circ.: 21,000
Ed. in Chief – Ove Mellingen

TELEMARKSAVISA A/S (M-6X WK.)
PO Box 2833, Kjorbekk, Skien, 3702, Norway; tel (47) 3558 5500; fax 3553 0021; e-mail dag.reiersen@ta.no; web site www.ta.no
Circ.: 23,000
Ed. in Chief – Ove Mellingen

VARDEN (M-6X WK.)
PO Box 2873, Skien, 3702, Norway; tel (47) 3554 3000; fax 3554 3087; e-mail info@varden.no; redaksjonen@varden.no; web site www.varden.no
Circ.: 38,000
Ed. in Chief – Lars Kise

SORTLAND

BLADET VESTERALEN (5X WK.)
PO Box 33, Sortland, 8401, Norway; tel (47) 7611 0900; e-mail red@blv.no; web site www.blv.no
Circ.: 10,582
Ed. in Chief – Karl-Einar Nordahl

VESTERALEN (M-5X WK.)
PO Box 33, Sortland, 8401, Norway; tel (47) 7611 0900; fax 7611 0891; web site www.blv.no
Circ.: 10,334
Ed. in Chief – Willy Vaestaz
Mktg. Mgr. – Karl Inar

STAVANGER

ROGALANDS AVIS (M-6X WK.)
PO Box 233, Stavanger, 4001, Norway; tel (47) 5182 2000; fax 5182 2150; e-mail redaksjon@rogalandsavis.no; web site www.rogalandsavis.no
Circ.: 12,000
Ed. in Chief – Harald Minge
Ed. in Chief – Bjorn Sabo
Adv. Mgr. – Raymond Lind

STAVANGER AFTENBLAD (M-6X WK.)
PO Box 229, Stavanger, 4001, Norway; tel (47) 5150; fax 5193 8976; e-mail privatannonser@aftenbladet.no; abonnement@aftenbladet.no; web site aftenbladet.no
Circ.: 72,000
Ed. – Tom Hetland

STEINKJER

TROENDER-AVISA (M-6X WK.) EST. 1952
PO Box 2590, Steinkjer, 7738, Norway; tel (47) 7412 1200; fax 7412 1211; e-mail redaksjonen@tronderavisa.no; annonse@tronderavisa.no; web site www.tronderavisa.no
Circ.: 23
CEO – Arve Loeberg

STORD

SUNNHORDLAND (5X WK.)
PO Box 100, Stord, 5401, Norway; tel (47) 5345 0000; fax 5345 0001; web site www.sunnhordland.no
Ed. – Magne Kydland

SVOLVAER

LOFOTPOSTEN (M-6X WK.)
Avisgt 15, Svolvaer, 8305, Norway; tel (47) 7606 7800; fax 7607 0009; e-mail red@lofotposten.no; web site www.lofotposten.no
Circ.: 12,400
Ed. in Chief – Jan Eivind Fredly

TONSBERG

TONSBERGS BLAD (M-6X WK.)
PO Box 2003 Postterminalen, Tonsberg, 3103, Norway; tel (47) 3337 3000; e-mail redaksjonen@tb.no; web site www.tb.no
Circ.: 32,825
Ed. in Chief – Haon Borud
Adv. Mgr. – Roar Kirkvold

TROMSOE

NORDLYS (6X WK.)
PO Box 2515, Tromsoe, 9272, Norway; tel (47) 7762 3500; fax 7762 3501; e-mail ny-heter@nordlys.no; firmapost@nordlys.no; annonse@nordlys.no; web site www.nordlys.no
Circ.: 30,924
Ed. – Hans Kristian Amundsen

TROMSOE (M-6X WK.)
PO Box 1028, Tromsoe, 9260, Norway; tel (47) 7764 0600; fax 7764 0601; e-mail ny-heter@itromso.no; web site www.itromso.no
Circ.: 10,500
Ed. in Chief – Jonny Hansen

TRONDHEIM

ADRESSEAVISEN (M-6X WK.)
PO Box 6070, Trondheim, 7003, Norway; tel (47) 7250 0000; fax 7250 1500; e-mail redak-sjonen.faxmottak@adresseavisen.no; web site www.adresseavisen.no
Advertising: Publicitas.
Ed. – Gunnar Flikke

ARBEIDER-AVISA (6X WK.)
PO Box 5440, Trondheim, 7002, Norway; tel (47) 0792 1122; fax 0792 1410
Circ.: 15,300
Mgr. – Randi Rasmussen

VADSOE

FINNMARKEN (M-6X WK.)
PO Box 616, Vadsoe, 9811, Norway; tel (47) 7895 5500; fax 7895 5555; e-mail desk@finnmarken.no; web site www.finn-marken.no
Circ.: 7,155
Ed. – Kari Karstensen

POLAND

BIALYSTOK

KURIER PORANNY (M-6X WK.)
ul. Swietego Mikolaja 1, Bialystok, 15-424, Poland; tel (48) 85 748 9532; fax 754604; e-mail online@poranny.pl; web site www.po-ranny.pl
Ed. in Chief – Peter Waseakowke
Exec. Ed. – Barbara Likowska-Matys

GAZETA WSPOLCZESNA (M)
ul. sw. Mikolaja 1, Bialystok, 15-419, Poland; tel (48) 85 748 7474; fax 748 7473; web site www.wspolczesna.pl
Circ.: 35,000
Ed. in Chief – Konrad Kruszewski

KURIER PODLASKI (M)
ul. Suraska 4, Bialystok, 15-950, Poland; tel (48) 85 436715; fax 28152
Circ.: 30,000
Ed. in Chief – Andrzej Rozalski

BIELSKO BIALA

DZIENNIK BESKIDZKI (D)
3 Maja 1, Bielsko Biala, 43-300, Poland; tel (48) 85 22617; fax 27287
Circ.: 30,000
Ed. in Chief – Andrzej Otczyk

BYDGOSZCZ

EXPRESS BYDOGSKI (6X WK.)
ul. Warszawska 13, Bydgoszcz, 85-058, Poland; tel (48) 52 322 2615; fax 322 3389; web site www.express.bydgoski.pl
Circ.: 16,000
Mgr. – Tomasz Wojciekewecz
Ed. – Mariusz Zaluski

ILUSTOWANY KURIER POLSKI (E)
ul. Marszalka Focha 16, Bydgoszcz, 85-950, Poland; tel (48) 52 375 1000; fax 322 1998
Circ.: 40,000
Ed. in Chief – Marek Fascizewski

GAZETA POMORSKA (6X WK.)
ul. Zamoyskiego 2, Bydgoszcz, 85-063, Poland; tel (48) 52 326 3100; fax 322 1542; e-mail gp.redakcja@gpmedia.pl; web site www.pomorska.pl
Ed. – Wotecd Potocke

DZIENNIK WIECZORNY
ul. Dworcowa 110, Bydgoszcz, 80-010, Poland; tel (48) 52 224600; fax 227117
Circ.: 30,000
Ed. in Chief – Andrzej Bialoszycki
Exec. Ed. – Jerzy Derenda

CZESTOCHOWA

DZENNIK CZESTOCHOWSK-24 GODZINY (D)
Czestochewa 17, Czestochowa, 42-200, Poland; tel (48) 44686; fax 49681
Circ.: 10,000
Pub. – Spotka Drogowiec
Ed. in Chief – Marian Piotr Rawinis
Exec. Ed. – Emilia Zapata

ZYCIE CZESTOCHOWY (D)
ul. Kopernika 8, Czestochowa, 42-200, Poland; tel (48) 34 374 0670; fax 374 0870; e-mail reklama@zycie.czest.pl; web site www.zycie.czest.pl

GDANSK

GLOS WYBRZEZA (D)
ul. Targ Drzewny 3/7, Gdansk, 80-886, Poland; tel (48) 58 3011572
Circ.: 50,000
Ed. in Chief – Marek Formola

DZIENNIK BALTYCKI (M-6X WK.)
ul. Targ Drzewny 3/7, Gdansk, 80-886, Poland; tel (48) 58 301 2651; fax 301 3340
Circ.: 80,000

WIECZOR WYBRZEZA (E)
ul. Targ Drzewny 3/7, Gdansk, 80-886, Poland; tel (48) 58 314250
Circ.: 220,000
Advertising: Nielsen Communications.
Ed. in Chief – Edmund Szczeslak

GAZETA GDANSKA (D)
ul. Targ Drzewny 3/7, Gdansk, 80-886, Poland; tel (48) 58 311864; fax 310971
Circ.: 30,000
Ed. in Chief – Marek Formela
Exec. Ed. – Dariusz Chabior

GOSTYN

WIECZOR (E)
Starogostynska 10, Gostyn, 63-800, Poland; tel (48) 65 572 0566
Circ.: 35,000
Ed. in Chief – Krzysztof Kuzniewski
Exec. Ed. – Beata Netz

KATOWICE

DZIENNIK ZACHODNI (M)
ul. Mlynska 1, Katowice, 40-953, Poland; tel (48) 32 358 2100; e-mail dziennik@dz.com.pl
Circ.: 510,000
Ed. in Chief – Elzibieta Kazibut

GAZETA KATOWICKA (D)
Plac Oddz. Mlodziezy Powstanczej 1, Katowice, 46-061, Poland; tel (48) 3 2512130; fax 2517084

KURIER ZACHODNI (D)
ul. Opolska 1/6, Katowice, 40-084, Poland; tel (48) 3 2539314
Circ.: 25,000

TRYBUNA SLASKA (M-EX S)
ul. Mlynska 1, Katowice, 40-098, Poland; tel (48) 3 21539763; fax 21537997
Ed. – Tadeusz Biedzki

SPORT (D)
ul. Mlynsksa 1, Katowice, 40-953, Poland; tel (48) 3 539995; fax 537138
Circ.: 100,000
Ed. in Chief – Adam Barteczko
Exec. Ed. – Lidia Nowakowa

KIELCE

ECHO DNIA (6X WK.)
skr. poczt. 12, Kielce, Poland; tel (48) 41 349 5353; fax 368 2218; e-mail listy@echodnia.eu; web site www.echodnia.eu
Circ.: 20,000
Ed. in Chief – Stanislaw Wrobel

SLOWO LUDU (M-EX S)
ul. Targowa 18/12, Kielce, 25-250, Poland; tel (48) 41 (48-41) 42480; fax (48-41) 46979
Ed. in Chief – Krzysztof Falkiewicz

GAZETA KIELECKA-24 GODZINY (D)
ul. Zlota 3, 25-015, Kielce, 40-098, Poland; tel (48) 41 345 1440; fax 345 1045; web site www.drogowiec.kielce.pl
Circ.: 30,000
Exec. Ed. – Maria Modrek
Exec. Ed. – Andrzej Mackowski
Ed. in Chief – Anna Krawiecka

KOSZALIN

GONIEC POMORSKI (D)
ul. Grun Waldzka 8/10, Koszalin, 75-24, Poland; tel (48) 94 340 5955
Circ.: 35,000
Ed. in Chief – Jerzy Banasiak
Exec. Ed. – Katarzyna Rychiewicz
Exec. Ed. – Pawel Nikiel

GLOS KOSZALINSKI (6X WK.)
ul. Mickiewicza 24, Koszalin, 75-502, Poland; tel (48) 94 347 3599; fax 347 3540; e-mail online@gk24.pl; web site www.gk24.pl
Circ.: 50,000
Dir. – Krzysztof Natecz

KRAKOW

ECHO KRAKOWA (E)
ul. Wielopole 1, Krakow, 31-072, Poland; tel (48) 12 4224678
Ed. – Witold Grzybowski

GAZETA W KRAKOWIE (D)
ul. Szewska 5, Krakow, 31-009, Poland; tel (48) 12 629 5403; fax 629 5266; e-mail redakcja@krakow.agora.pl; web site www.miasta.gazeta.pl/krakow; www.gazeta.pl
Ed. in Chief – Yousuf Stachow
Sales Dir. – Mariusz Piotrowski

TEMPO (D)
ul. Wielopole 1, Krakow, 31-072, Poland; tel (48) 12 222960; fax 222960
Circ.: 140,000
Ed. in Chief – Ryszard Niemec
Exec. Ed. – Marian Grzegorz Nowak

GAZETA KRAKOWSKA (6X WK.)
Al. Pokoju 3, Krakow, 31-548, Poland; tel (48) 12 688 8100; fax 688 8109; web site www.gk.pl
Ed. – Tomasz Lachowicz

DZIENNIK POLSKI (M-6X WK.)
ul. Wielopole 1, Krakow, 31-072, Poland; tel (48) 12 619 9148; fax 619 9149; e-mail redakcja@dziennik.krakow.pl; web site www.dziennik.krakow.pl
Circ.: 34
Ed. in Chief – Piotr Legutko
Vice editor in Chief – Marcin Baran

LESZNO

DZIENNIK INFORMACYJNY (D)
ul. Slowianska 63, Leszno, 64-100, Poland; tel (48) 65 529 2540; fax 529 2540
Circ.: 18,000
Exec. Ed. – Halina Siecinska

LODZ

DZIENNIK LODZKI (6X WK.)
ul. ks. Skorupki 17/19, Lodz, 90-532, Poland; tel (48) 42 630 3565; fax 637 7364; e-mail dziennik@dziennik.lodz.pl; web site polska-times.pl/dzienniklodzki
Ed. in Chief – Robert Sakowski

EXPRESS ILUSTROWANY (M-6X WK.)
ul. ks. hm. I. Skorupki 17/19, Lodz, 90-532, Poland; tel (48) 42 630 3583; e-mail ex-press@express.lodz.pl; web site www.ex-press.lodz.pl; www.polskapresse.pl
Circ.: 370,000
Advertising: Nielsen Communications.
Dir., Adv. Sales – Michal Frontczak
Ed. in Chief – Marcin Kowalczyk

GAZETA LODZKA (D)
ul. Piotrkowska 45, Lodz, 90-410, Poland; tel (48) 42 321935; fax 337320

GLOS PORANNY (D)
skr. poczt. 12, Lodz, 90-113, Poland; tel (48) 42 366785; fax 334171
Circ.: 52,000
Ed. in Chief – Gustaw Romanowski
Exec. Ed. – Jadwiga Rybicka-Dzikowi

WIADOMOMOSCI DNIA (D)
ul. Piotrkowska 175, Lodz, 90-447, Poland; tel (48) 42 374688; fax 361153
Circ.: 150,000
Ed. in Chief – Ewa Kluczkowska
Exec. Ed. – Elzbieta Sokolowska

LUBLIN

A-STOP (D)
Al. Krolewska 15, Lublin, 20-109, Poland; tel (48) 81 28160
Ed. in Chief – Tomasz Orlowski

GAZETA W LUBLINIE (D)
ul. Krakowskie Przedmiescie 39/9, Lublin, 20-076, Poland; tel (48) 81 537 9021; web site lublin.gazeta.pl
Ed. in Chief – Margaret Bielecka Holda

DZIENNIK LUBELSKI (D)
ul. Zana 38C, Lublin, 20-601, Poland; tel (48) 81 558000; fax 558010
Ed. – Alojzy Leszek Gzella

KURIER LUBELSKI (E-6XWK.)
ul. 3 Maja 14, Lublin, 20-078, Poland; tel (48) 81 532 6634; fax 446 2830; web site www.archiwum.kurierlubelski.pl
Ed. in Chief – Koerarz Kireowz

SZTANDAR LUDU (M)
Al. Raclawickie 1, Lublin, 20-059, Poland; tel (48) 81 23234
Circ.: 114,000
Ed. in Chief – Tadeuz Fita

OLSZTYN

DZIENNIK POJEZIERZA (D)
Al. 1 Marszalka Jozefa PIlsudskiego 54a, Olsztyn, 10-557, Poland; tel (48) 889 336140; fax 333751
Circ.: 30,000
Ed. in Chief – Pawel Krupa

GAZETA OLSZTYNSKA (6X WK.)
ul. Tracka 5, Olsztyn, 10-364, Poland; tel (48) 89 539 7700; fax 539 7476; web site www.gazetaolsztynska.pl
Ed. in Chief – Tomasz Srutkowski

OPOLE

NOWA TRYBUNA OPOLSKA (M-6X WK.)
ul. Powstancow Slaskich 9, Opole, 45-086, Poland; tel (48) 77 443 2522; fax 443 2540; e-mail ogloszenia@nto.pl; web site www.nto.pl
Circ.: 80,000
Pres. – Marian Szczurek

POZNAN

DZIENNIK POZNANSKI (D)
ul. Mlynska 5, Poznan, 61-729, Poland; tel (48) 61 523681; fax 525879
Circ.: 40,000
Exec. Ed. – Zdzislaw Narbuntowicz
Exec. Ed. – Marek Nowak
Ed. in Chief – Konrad Napierala

GAZETA WYBORCZA (D)
27 Grodnia No.3, Poznan, 61-737, Poland; tel (48) 61 855 2233; fax 853 6779; e-mail czytelnicy@poznan.agora.pl; web site www.gazeta.pl; poznan.agora.pl
Circ.: 160,000
Ed. – Wlodzimierz Bogaczk

GAZETA POZNANSKA (6X WK.)
ul. Grunwaldzka 19, Poznan, 60-782, Poland; tel (48) 61 869 4196; fax 860 6115; e-mail redakcja@glos.com; web site www.gloswielkopolski.pl
Ed. in Chief – Adam Pawlowski

GLOS WIELKOPOLSKI (D)
ul. Grunwaldzka 19, Poznan, 60-782, Poland; tel (48) 61 869 4100; fax 860 6115; web site www.gloswielkopolski.pl
Ed. in Chief – Adam Pawlowski

EXPRESS POZNANSKI (E)
ul. Grunwaldzka 19, Poznan, 60-959, Poland; tel (48) 61 866 1443; fax 866 5848
Circ.: 50,000
Ed. in Chief – Dariusz Nowaczyk
Exec. Ed. – Kazimierz Orlewicz
Exec. Ed. – Bogna Kisiel

RADOM

DZIENNIK RADOMSKI-24 GODZINY (D)
ul. Stowackiego 1, Radom, 26-600, Poland; tel (48) 48 27995; fax 29091
Circ.: 12,000
Ed. in Chief – Marek Oleszuk

RZESZOW

NOWINY WIECZORNE (D)
ul. Lisa Kuli 19, Rzeszow, 35-959, Poland; tel (48) 17 37143
Circ.: 15,000
Ed. in Chief – Jan Stepek
Exec. Ed. – Jan Filipowicz

NOWINY (M-7X WK.)
Unii Lubelskiej 3, Rzeszow, 35-959, Poland; tel (48) 17 628471; fax 628836
Ed. in Chief – Jan Musial

A-Z DZIENNIK OBYWATELSKI (D)
Pl. Wolnosci 2, Rzeszow, 35-061, Poland; tel (48) 17 39491; fax 33749
Circ.: 30,000
Exec. Ed. – Marek Wojcik
Exec. Ed. – Danuta Majko
Ed. in Chief – Andrzej Potocki

SZCZECIN

GAZETA NA POMORZU (D)
Al. Wojska Polskiego 52, Szczecin, 71-477, Poland; tel (48) 91 533004; fax 38028

KURIER SZCZECINSKI (M-5X WK.)
Pl. Holdu Pruskiego 8 skr. poczt., Szczecin, 70-550, Poland; tel (48) 91 442 9170; fax 442 9190; web site www.kurier.szczecin.pl
Circ.: 40,000
Ed. in Chief – Anna Wieckowska-Machay
Exec. Ed. – Bernard Ziolkiewicz

GLOS SZCZECINSKI (D)
Biuro Ogloszen, Szczecin, 70-550, Poland; tel (48) 91 481 3305; fax 433 4864; web site www.glosszczecinski.com.pl
Dir. – Elzbieta Zawadzka

TORUN

NOWOSCI (D)
St. Podmurna 31, Torun, 87-100, Poland; tel (48) 56 611 8100; fax 611 8199; e-mail redakcja@nowosci.com.pl; web site www.nowosci.com.pl
Circ.: 55,000
Chrmn. – Tomasz Wojciekiewicz
Ed. in Chief – Andrzej Szmak
Exec. Ed. – Stanislaw Frankowski
Exec. Ed. – Przemyslaw Luczak

WALBRZYCH

EXPRESS SUDECKI (D)
Pl. Magistracki 3, Walbrzych, 58-300, Poland; tel (48) 26925
Circ.: 25,000
Ed. in Chief – Wojciech Romanowski
Exec. Ed. – Iwona Rubin

WARSAW

GAZETA WYBORCZA (D)
ul. Czerska 8/10, Warsaw, 00-732, Poland; tel (48) 22 555 6001; fax 555 4780; e-mail redakcja_portalu@agora.pl; web site www.gazeta.pl
Ed. in Chief – Adam Michnik

GLOB 24 (D)
ul. Konstrukurska 3A, Warsaw, 02-673, Poland; tel (48) 22 435001; fax 488254
Circ.: 100,000
Ed. in Chief – Dobrochna Kedzierska
Exec. Ed. – Krzyszlof Rozum

SLOWO POWSZECHNE (D)
ul. Mokotowska 43, Warsaw, 00-551, Poland; tel (48) 22 297767; fax 6286739
Circ.: 157,000
Ed. in Chief – Anna Borowska

NOWY SWIAT (PISMO CODZIENNE DLA WSZYSTKICH SFER) (D)
ul. Bialobrzeska 53, Warsaw, 02-325, Poland; tel (48) 22 6583230; fax 6583171
Circ.: 120,000
Ed. in Chief – Andrzej Karnkowski
Exec. Ed. – Antoni Bartkiewicz

NOWA EUROPA (D)
ul. Miedziana 11, Warsaw, 00-958, Poland; tel (48) 22 206161; fax 206161
Circ.: 40,000
Ed. in Chief – Witold Gadomski

POLSKA ZBROJNA (D)
ul. Grzybowska 77, Warsaw, 00-950, Poland; tel (48) 22 6204293; fax 6242273
Circ.: 50,000
Ed. in Chief – Jerzy Slaski

RZECZPOSPOLITA (6X WK.)
Prosta Office Ctr., ul. Prosta 51, Warsaw, 00-838, Poland; tel (48) 22 628 3401; fax 628 0588; web site www.rzeczpospolita.pl
Circ.: 280,000
Ed. in Chief – Pawel Lisicki

GAZETA MLODYCH (D)
ul. Nowy Zjazd 1, Warsaw, 00-304, Poland; tel (48)
Circ.: 49,000
Ed. in Chief – Witold Wisniewski

SZTANDAR MLODYCH (M)
ul. Wspolna 61, Warsaw, 00-687, Poland; tel (48) 22 388 1612; fax 388 1613; e-mail info@mediatel.pl; web site www.mediatel.p
Circ.: 250,000
Pres. – Zbigniew Kazismierczak

SWIAT MLODYCH (D)
Mokotowska 24, Warsaw, 00-561, Poland; tel (48) 22 6285618; fax 292142
Circ.: 62,000
Ed. in Chief – Jaroslaw Machowiak

TRYBUNA (D-EX S)
ul. Miedziana 11, Warsaw, 00-835, Poland; tel (48) 22 389 8800; fax 389 8870; web site www.trybuna.com.pl
Ed. in Chief – Wieslaw Debski

DZIENNIK LUDOWY (D)
ul. Grzybowska 4-8, Warsaw, 00-139, Poland; tel (48) 22 200251
Circ.: 152,000
Ed. in Chief – Janusz Tarniewski

ZOLNIERZ WOLNOSCI (M)
ul. Grzybowska 77, Warsaw, 00-950, Poland; tel (48) 22 201 227
Circ.: 123,000
Ed. in Chief – Zdzislaw Janos

ZYCIE WARSZAWY (M&E)
ul. Armii Ludowej 3/5, Warsaw, 00-575, Poland; tel (48) 22 6256990; fax 6252426; e-mail zycie@zw.com.pl; web site www.zw.com.pl
Ed. in Chief – Andrzej Bober

WARSZAWA

RYNKI ZAGRANICZNE (D)
ul. Kopernika 30, Warszawa, 00-336, Poland; tel (48) 22 826 4311; fax 828 6713; e-mail rynki@rynkizagraniczne.pl; web site www.rynkizagraniczne.pl
Circ.: 10,000
Ed. in Chief – Andrzej Zielinski

TELEGAZETA (D)
ul. J.P. Woronicza 17, Warszawa, 00-999, Poland; tel (48) 22 5476 705; fax 547 3077; web site www.tvp.com.pl
Ed. in Chief – Czeslaw Berenda

EXPRESS WIECZORNY (E)
ul. Wiejska 13/3, Warszawa, 00-480, Poland; tel (48) 22 862 3353; fax 499 6481; e-mail redakcja@exmedia.pl; web site www.ew.exmedia.pl
Ed. in Chief – Janusz Szostak

WARZAW

OBSERWATOR CODZIENNY (D)
ul. Solec 22, Warzaw, 00-410, Poland; tel (48) 22 6253101; fax 6250068
Circ.: 120,000
Ed. in Chief – Damian Kolbarczyk
Exec. Ed. – Jan Cywinski

PRZEGLAD SPORTOWY (5X WK.)
PO Box 181, Warzaw, 02-017, Poland; tel (48) 22 6289116; fax 6218697
Circ.: 110,000
Ed. – Maciej Polkowski

WROCLAW

GAZETA DOLNOSLASKA (D)
ul. Krupnicza 13, Wroclaw, Poland; tel (48) 71 38126; fax 448450

WIECZOR WROCLAWIA (E)
skr. poczt. 1003, Wroclaw, 50-010, Poland; tel (48)
Circ.: 30,000
Ed. in Chief – Roman Rubin
Exec. Ed. – Jadwiga Jakubek

SLOWO POLSKIE (MD)
Sprzegomskia 42A, Wroclaw, 33-611, Poland; tel (48) 71 374 8115; fax 374 8101
Circ.: 90,000
Ed. – Agmieszki Niczewski

GAZETA ROBOTNICZA (D)
ul. Podwale 62, Wroclaw, 50-010, Poland; tel (48) 71 335756; fax 335756
Ed. – Andrzej Bulat

ZIELONA GORA

GAZETA LUBUSKA (D)
PO Box 120, Zielona Gora, 65-042, Poland; tel (48) 68 324 8800; fax 324 8824; e-mail redakcja@gazetalubuska.pl; web site www.gazetalubuska.pl
Ed. – Iwona Zielinska

PORTUGAL

ANGRA DO HEROISMO, AZORES

DIARIO INSULAR (M)
Avda. Infante D. Henrique 1, Angra do Heroismo, Azores, 9700, Portugal; tel (351) 295 401 050; fax 214 246; e-mail np21na@mail.telepac.pt; diopiniao@diarioinsular.com; web site www.diarioinsular.com
Circ.: 3,200
Dir. – Jose Lourenco

BEJA

DIARIO DO ALENTEJO (D)
Praca da Republica 43, Beja, Portugal; tel (351)
Circ.: 15,000
Pub. – Dr. Joao Paulo Marcelo Velez

JORNAL DO ALENTEJO (E)
Avda. Miguel Fernandes 23, Beja, 7800, Portugal; tel (351)
Pub. – Louis Asilio Caeito

BRAGA

CORREIO DO MINHO (M)
Praceta do Magisterio, 34 Maximinos, Braga, 4700-236, Portugal; tel (351) 253 309 500; fax 309 526; web site www.correiodominho.com
Circ.: 1,573
– Antonio Costa Guimaraes
– Prulr NrntaehrDir.s

DIARIO DO MINHO (M)
Rua de Santa Margarida 4A, Braga, 4709, Portugal; tel (351) 253 609 460; fax 609 465; e-mail geral@diariodominho.pt; web site www.diariodominho.pt
Circ.: 10,000
Dir. – Jose Miguel Pereira
Ed. in Chief – Damiao Pereira

COIMBRA

DIARIO DE COIMBRA (D)
Rua Adriano Lucas 3020, Coimbra, 3000, Portugal; tel (351) 239 499 999; fax 499 991; e-mail publicidade@diariocoimbra.pt; web site www.diariocoimbra.pt
Circ.: 9,000
Mng. Dir. – Adriano Mario Lucas

CORREIO DE COIMBRA (D)
Blvd. S. Jose 2, Coimbra, 30-49, Portugal; tel (351) 239 718 167
Pub. – Antonio Duarte Almeida

COVE OF THE HERO¡SMO

A UNIAO (M)
Pink St. N. 19, Cove of the Hero¡smo, 9700-171, Portugal; tel (351) 295 214 275; fax 214 030; e-mail auniao@auniao.com; web site www.auniao.com
Circ.: 1,500
Dir. – Manuel Carlos

EVORA

NOTICIAS D' EVORA (M)
Rua do Raimundo 41-43, Evora, 7002, Portugal; tel (351) 62 22348
Circ.: 3,000
Dir. – Rosa Souto Armas

DIARIO DO SUL (6X WK.)
Apdo. Postal 37, Evora, 7001, Portugal; tel (351) 266 730 410; fax 730 411; e-mail diariodosul@diariodosul com.pt; publicidade@diariodosul.com.pt; web site www.diariodosul.com.pt
Circ.: 8,500
MD – Manuel Madeira Picarra
Mng. Ed. – Manuel MadeiraPicarra

FUNCHAL

ECO DO FUNCHAL (D)
Travessa dos Freitos 10-14, Funchal, Portugal; tel (351)
Pub. – Rogerio Margues Caldeira

DIARIO DE NOTICIAS DO FUNCHAL (M)
Rua Dr. Fernao de Ornelas 56-3, Funchal, 9054-514, Portugal; tel (351) 291 202 300; fax 202 306; e-mail internet@dnoticias.pt; web site www.dnoticias.pt
Circ.: 16,353
Dir. – Jose Bettencourt da Camara

JORNAL DA MADEIRA (M)
Rua Dr. Fernao de Ornelas 35, Funchal, 9054-528, Portugal; tel (351) 291 210400; fax 210401; web site www.jornaldamadeira.pt
Circ.: 8,000
Dir. – Henrique Correia

GUARDA

DIARIO DA GUARDA (D)
Centro Comercial Garden, Loja 46, Guarda, 6300-752, Portugal; tel (351) 271 083 978; fax 084 019; e-mail diariodaguarda@netvisao.pt

HORTA, FAIAL

CORREIO DA HORTA (E)
Rua Ernesto Rebelo 5, Horta, Faial, Portugal; tel (351)
Circ.: 1,020
Dir. – Fernando Faria Ribeiro

O TELEGRAFO (M)
Rua Conselheiro Medeiros 30, Horta, Faial, Portugal; tel (351)
Circ.: 1,850
Dir. – Rogerio da Silva Goncalves

LEIRIA

DIARIO DE LEIRIA (M-5X WK.)
Edificio Maringa R. S. Francisco n.7 4 E, Leiria, 2400, Portugal; tel (351) 244 000 030; e-mail diarioleiria@diarioleiria.pt; web site www.diarioleiria.pt
Circ.: 3,500
Dir. – Adriano Calle Lucas

LISBON

DIARIO POPULAR (E-EX S)
Rua Luz Soriano 67, Lisbon, 1200, Portugal; tel (351) 21 347 6281
Circ.: 62,000
Dir. – D. Rodolfo Iriarte
Ed. in Chief – Carlos Morgado

DIARIO DE NOTICIAS (MS)
Avda. da Liberdade 266, Lisbon, 1250, Portugal; tel (351) 213 187 500; fax 187 515; e-mail dnot@dn.pt; web site www.dn.pt
Advertising: Publicitas.
Dir. – Joao Marcelino

EXPRESSO (WEEKLY)
Rua Duque de Palmela 37-3 Dto., Lisbon, 1296, Portugal; tel (351) 21 454 4000; fax 3543858
Circ.: 160,000
Dir. – Jose Antonio Paula Saraiva

JOURNAL DE O DIA (M)
Praceta da Tabaqueira Lote A 5, Porta B, Matinha, Lisbon, 1900, Portugal; tel (351) 1 8583421; fax 8584421
Circ.: 49,300
Dir. – Adelino Alves

O DIARIO (D)
Rua de S Bernardo 14-2, Lisbon, 1200, Portugal; tel (351) 21 842 9830
Circ.: 29,000
Pub. – Antonio Alberto Alves Pereira Borja

CORREIO DA MANHA (M)
Avda. Joao Crisostomo 72, Lisbon, 1069-043, Portugal; tel (351) 21 3307741; fax 3540643; e-mail redaccaocm@mail.telepac.pt; luisbcm@mail.telepac.pt; web site www.correiomanha.pt
Circ.: 85,000
Chrmn. – Paul Fernandez

PUBLICO (D)
Rua Amilcar Cabral, Lote 1, Quinta do Lambert, Lisbon, 1700, Portugal; tel (351) 21 750 1189; fax 758 7638; e-mail publico@publico.pt; web site www.publico.pt
Circ.: 75,000
Dir. – Jose Manuel Fernandes

A CAPITAL (E)
Avda. Infante D. Henrique 334, Lisbon, 1800, Portugal; tel (351) 21 8542000; fax 8530732
Circ.: 40,000
Dir. – Elena Sanches Osorio

PONTA DEL GADA

CORREIO DOS ACORES (M)
Rua Dr. Joao Francisco de Sousa 14, Ponta del Gada, 9500, Portugal; tel (351) 96 24218; fax 26119
Circ.: 4,460
Dir. – Jorge do Nascimento Cabral

DIARIO DOS ACORES (6X WK.)
Rua Diario dos Acores 11, Ponta del Gada, 9500, Portugal; tel (351) 296 284 355; fax 284 840; e-mail jornal@diariodosacores.pt; web site www.diariodosacores.pt
Circ.: 2,380
CEO – Americo Viveisrros
MD – Paulo Viveiros
Ed. – Manuel Moniz

ACORIANO ORIENTAL (M)
Rua Dr. Bruno Tarares Carreiro 36, Ponta del Gada, 9500, Portugal; tel (351) 96 202800; fax 202826
Circ.: 6,000
Dir. – Gustavo Moura

PORTO

DIARIO INFORMADOR (D)
Rua Elisio Melo 28, Porto, Portugal; tel (351)

O COMERCIO DO PORTO (MS)
Rua Fernandes Tomas 352-7, Porto, 4000, Portugal; tel (351) 22 563571; fax 575095
Circ.: 30,295
Dir. – Luis de Carvalho

O PRIMEIRO DE JANEIRO (M-5X WK.)
Rua das Oliveirinhas, 36-1§, Porto, 4000, Portugal; tel (351) 22 010 9130; fax 010 9966; e-mail geral@oprimeirodejaneiro.pt; web site www.oprimeirodejaneiro.pt
Circ.: 20,200
Dir. – Carlos Moura

JORNAL DE NOTICIAS (M)
Rua Goncalo Cristovao 195, Porto, 4052, Portugal; tel (351) 22 209 6111; fax 209 6140; e-mail noticias@noticias.pt; jndt@noticias.pt; web site www.jnoticias.pt
Circ.: 90,000
Dir. – Jose Leite Pereira

VISEU

DIARIO VISEU (5X WK.)
Rua Alex Andre Herculano 198, Viseu, 3510, Portugal; tel (351) 232 000 030; fax 000 032; e-mail diarioviseu@diariodeviseu.pt; web site www.diariodeviseu.pt; www.diarioregional.pt
Ed. – Sandra Rodregues

ROMANIA

ARAD

ADEVARUL (D)
Piata Presei Libere 1, ARAD, 031701, Romania; tel (40) 407 7609; fax 407 7602; web site www.adevarulonline.ro
Circ.: 53,000
Dir. – Dorel Zavoianu

ARAD, ARAD

JELEN (D)
81 Revolutiei Blvd., Arad, Arad, 2900, Romania; tel (40) 57 219804
Adv. Mgr. – Janos Boros
Ed. in Chief – Janos Irhazi

ARGES, PITESTI

ARGESUL LIBER (D)
Str. Dija 7a, Arges, Pitesti, Romania; tel (40) 248 217704; fax 210060; e-mail argesul@gmail.com; web site www.ziarulargesul.ro
Mgr. – Mikai Gjoulosku
Ed. in Chief – Gabriel Likandru

BACAU, BACAU

DESTEPTAREA (D)
41 Alecsandri Vasile St., Bacau, Bacau, 5500, Romania; tel (40) 234 511 272; fax 523 515; e-mail office@desteptarea.ro; dsa@desteptarea.ro; publicitate@desteptarea.ro; comercial@desteptarea.ro; web site www.desteptarea.ro
Circ.: 50,000
Mgr. – Narcisa Fecioru
Ed. in Chief – Nelu Brosteanu

BAIA MARE, MARAMURES

GRAIUL MARAMURESULUI (D)
25 Bucuresti Blvd., Baia Mare, Maramures, 4800, Romania; tel (40) 262 221 017; fax 227 880; e-mail graiul@graiul.ro; web site www.graiul.ro
– George Serban
– Parjya GhaoghagEd. in Chiefs

BIHOR, ORADEA

BIHARI NAPLO (D)
25 Sirul Canonicilor St., Bihor, Oradea, 3700, Romania; tel (40) 59 412581; fax 415450; web site www.biharinaplo.ro
Ed. in Chief – Tompa Z. Mihaly

CRISANA (D) EST. 1945
3 Aleea Emanoil Gojdu, Bihor, Oradea, Romania; tel (40) 259 413606; fax 417 421; e-mail crisana@rdsor.ro; web site www.crisana.ro
Ed. in Chief – Dan Matea

JURNALUL BIHOREAN (D)
4 Piata 1 Decembrie, Bihor, Oradea, 3700, Romania; tel (40) 59 135497; fax 136639

BOTOSANI, BOTOSANI

GAZETA DE BOTOSANI
Blvd. Mihai Eminescu 91, Botosani, Botosani, 6800, Romania; tel (40) 31 851106
Ed. in Chief – Gheorghe Zanea

BRASOV

INCOTRO BRASOVUL (D)
58 Calea Calarasilor, Brasov, Romania; tel (40) 68 94631740
Ed. in Chief – Chinea Mitrea

LIBERTATRA (D)
1 Piata Independentei, Brasov, Romania; tel (40) 68 (40-68) 94635943
Dir./Ed. in Chief – Rodica Oana

BRASOV, BRASOV

BUNA ZIUA BRASOV (D)
Centrul de afaceri Roland, Brasov, Brasov, 2200, Romania; tel (40) 368 413 641; fax 413 640; e-mail bzb@bzb.ro; web site www.bzb.ro
Circ.: 30,000
Mng. Ed. – Mirela Leonte

GAZETA DE TRANSILVANIA (D-6X WK.)
3 Sadoveanu M St., Brasov, Brasov, 2200, Romania; tel (40) 268 472 099; fax 475 604; e-mail gazeta.transilvania@brasovia.ro; web site www.gtbv.ro
Ed. in Chief – Eduard Huidan

BUCHAREST

ADEVARUL (6X WK.)
1 Piata Presei Libere, Bucharest, 71341, Romania; tel (40) 21 407 7609; fax 407 7602; web site www.adevarul.ro
Circ.: 85,000
Ed. in Chief – Laurentiu Dragotescu

AZI (D)
39A Calea Victoriei, Bucharest, 010062, Romania; tel (40) 21 314 1998; e-mail redactie@azi.ro; web site www.azi.ro
Ed. in Chief – Ruxandra Negrea

COTIDIANUL (D-EX S)
Calea Plevnei 114, Bucharest, 77107, Romania; tel (40) 21 311 4061; fax 311 4075; e-mail abonamente@cotidianul.ro; web site www.cotidianul.ro
Dir. – Calin Husar

CRONICA ROMANA (D)
Piata Presei Libere, nr. 1, corp C, etaj 1, Bucharest, OP - 33, Romania; tel (40) 21 317 9165; fax 317 9169; e-mail cronica@rdsmail.ro; economic@cronicaromana.ro; secretariat@cronicaromana.ro; sport@cronicaromana.ro; web site www.cronicaromana.ro
Circ.: 29,000
Mktg. Mgr. – Dan Mihalache
Ed. in Chief – Dragos Moldovan

CURIERUL NATIONAL (D)
Cristian Popisteanu St. nr. 2-4, Bucharest, 70109, Romania; tel (40) 21 599 5500; fax 312 1300; web site www.curierulnational.ro
Circ.: 55,000
Dir. – Valentin Paunescu
Ed. in Chief – Stefan Radeanu

EVENIMENTUL ZILEI (D)
Dimitrie Pompeiu 6, Bucharest, 020337, Romania; tel (40) 21 202 2000; fax 202 2001; e-mail officeredactee@evz.ro; web site www.evz.ro
Circ.: 38,000
Creative Dir. – Felix Gregory
Ed. in Chief – Vlad Macovei

GAZETA SPORTURILOR (D)
St. Dionisie Lupu No 64-66, Bucharest, 70139, Romania; tel (40) 21 406 6507; fax 406 6584; e-mail gazeta@gsp.ro; contact@gsp.ro; web site www.gsp.ro
Ed. in Chief – Catalin Tolontan

JURNALUL NATIONAL (6X WK.)
Pta Presei Libere nr. 1, Bucharest, 71544, Romania; tel (40) 21 318 2037; fax 318 2035; web site www.jurnalul.ro
Circ.: 70,000
Dir. – Marius Tuca

LIBERTATEA (D)
Bulevardul Dimitrie Pompeiu nr. 6, sector 2, Bucharest, Romania; tel (40) 21 203 0885; fax 404 3099; web site www.libertatea.ro
Circ.: 75,000
Mgr. – Ana Nita

ROMANIA LIBERA (D-EX S)
Narvatraean 3, Bucharest, 031041, Romania; tel (40) 21 202 8100; fax 202 8143; e-mail politica@romanialibera.ro; web site www.romanialibera.com
Circ.: 100,000
Exec. Dir. – Petre Mihai Bacanu

ROMANIAI MAGYAR SZO (D)
1 Piata Presei Libere, Bucharest, 013701, Romania; tel (40) 21 223 1510; fax 223 1520; e-mail rmsz@com.pcnet.ro; web site maszol.ro
Ed. in Chief – Gyarmath Janos

TINERETUL LIBER (D-5X WK.)
1 Piata Presei Libere, Bucharest, 71341, Romania; tel (40) 1 2225040; fax 2223313
Ed. in Chief – Aristotel Bunescu

BUCURESTI

ALLGEMEINE DEUTSCHE ZEITUNG FÃ&POUND;R RUMÃ&POUND;NIEN (D)
Piata Presei Libere 1, Bucuresti, 013701, Romania; tel (40) 021 317 89 16; e-mail verlag@adz.ro; web site www.adz.ro
Marketing and Media Relations – Ioana Moldovan

BUZAU

BRIGADA 24 (D)
28 Garii Blvd., Buzau, Romania; tel (40) 38 7436045
Dir. – Constantin Niculescu
Ed. in Chief – Ion Nicolae

MUNTENIA
3 Chiristigii St., Buzau, 5100, Romania; tel (40) 38 58412524

OPINIA (D)
3 Chiristigii St., Buzau, 5100, Romania; tel (40) 238 711 063; fax 412 764; e-mail opinia@buzau.ro; web site www.opiniabuzau.ro
Adv. Mgr. – Beatrice Vergu

CLUJ-NAPOCA

ADEVARUL DE CLUJ (D)
16 Napoca St., Cluj-Napoca, 3400, Romania; tel (40) 264 593 642
Circ.: 200,000
Ed. in Chief – Ilie Calian

CLUJ-NAPOCA, CLUJ

SZABADSAG (D-EX S)
PO Box 340, Cluj-Napoca, Cluj, 400009, Romania; tel (40) 264 596 621; fax 597 206; e-mail office@szabadsag.ro; web site www.szabadsag.ro.
Circ.: 12,000
Ed. in Chief – Ã©jvÂ ri IldikÂ¢

CONSTANTA

CUGET LIBER (D)
5 Bratianu IC Blvd., Constanta, 900711, Romania; tel (40) 241 582 130; fax 582 125; e-mail office@cugetliber.ro; web site www.cugetliber.ro
Dir. – Robert Bak

CONSTANTA, CONSTANTA

TELEGRAF (D)
10 Dragos Voda St., Constanta, Constanta, 8700, Romania; tel (40) 16 616123; fax 615872

CRAIOVA, DOLJ

CUVANTUL LIBERTATII (D-EX S)
Nikoliscue Plocha 22 A, Craiova, Dolj, 200733, Romania; tel (40) 722 208 585; web site www.cvlpress.ro
Circ.: 40,000
Ed. in Chief – Nircha Kansir
Ed. – Rusan Karnen

GAZETA DE SUD (D)
Str. Campia Islaz. 97A, Craiova, Dolj, Romania; tel (40) 251 413 100; fax 410 565; e-mail office@gds.ro; web site www.gds.ro
Circ.: 21,660
Adv. Mgr. – Christina Obrea
Adv. Mgr. – Florin Antonie
Ed. in Chief – Ina Voinea
Deputy Chief Ed. – Valentin Tudor

DEVA, HUNEDOARA

CUVANTUL LIBER (D-5X WK.)
22 Decembrie N0.37 A, Deva, Hunedoara, 330166, Romania; tel (40) 254 211 269; fax 218 061; web site www.huon.ro; www.cuvantul-liber.ro
Circ.: 25,000
Ed. in Chief – Adrian Salagean

DROBETA TURNU SEVERIN, MEHEDINTI

DATINA (D)
Str. Traaan 89, Drobeta Turnu Severin, Mehedinti, 1500, Romania; tel (40) 978 119950
Ed. in Chief – Gheorghe Buretea

GALATI

VIATA LIBERA (D) EST. 1991
68 Domneasca St., Galati, 800215, Romania; tel (40) 236 460 620; fax 471 028; e-mail sec@viata-libera.ro; web site www.viata-libera.ro
Dir. – Cristina Cocu
Adv. Mgr. – Mioara Manaila

GORJ

GORJANUL (D)
15 Str. Constantin Brancusi, Gorj, 1400, Romania; tel (40) 253 212 072; e-mail gorjanul@intergorj.ro
Ed. in Chief – Victor Buneci

IASI

EVENIMENTUL (6X WK.)
4 Stefan cel Mare St., Iasi, 6600, Romania; tel (40) 232 246 000; fax 246 002; e-mail contact@evenimentul.ro; web site www.evenimentul.ro
Ed. – Catalin Nistor

ZIARUL DE IASI (6X WK.) EST. 1991
5 Smirdan St., Iasi, 700399, Romania; tel (40) 232 271 333; fax 270415; e-mail redactie@ziaruldeiasi.ro; web site www.ziaruldeiasi.ro
Circ.: 10,000
Last Audit: March 23, 2010
Mktg. Asst. – Magdlaena Oladru
Ed. in. Chief – Constantine Hrettac

MIERCUREA CIUC, HARGHITA

ADEVARUL HARGHITEI (M-4X WK.)
45 Leticeni St., Miercurea Ciuc, Harghita, 530190, Romania; tel (40) 266 371 065; fax 371 805; e-mail informatiahr@gmail.com; web site www.informatiahr.go.ro
Circ.: 3,000
Last Audit: March 23, 2010
Adv. Mgr. – Maria Tef
Ed. in Chief – Michael Groza

HARGHITA NEPE (6X WK.)
45 Sfantului Duh St., Miercurea Ciuc, Harghita, 4100, Romania; tel (40) 266 372 633; fax 372 633; e-mail office@hargitanepe.ro; web site http://www.hhrf.org/hargitanepe; www.honline.ro
– KozÂ n IstvÂ n
– Siroin StephenEd. in Chiefs

NEAMT

CEAHLAUL (D)
14 Al. Tiparului, Neamt, 5600, Romania; tel (40) 233 225 055; fax 225 282; web site www.ziarulceahlaul.ro
Circ.: 20,000
Dir. – Vasile Tudose

PLOIESTI, PRAHOVA

PRAHOVA (D)
2 Republicii Blvd., Ploiesti, Prahova, 2000, Romania; tel (40) 44 141 245; fax 111 206
Circ.: 17,000
Ed. in Chief – Dumitru Carstea

RESITA, CARAS-SEVERIN

TIMPUL (D)
7 Piata Republicii St., Resita, Caras-Severin, 1700, Romania; tel (40) 55 416709
Ed. in Chief – Gheorghe Jurma

SATU-MARE

UNIVERS SATMAREAN (D)
39 Corvinilor St., Satu-Mare, 3900, Romania; tel (40) 61 737278

SEPSISZENTGYORGY, COVASNA

HAROMSZEK (6X WK.)
Sajto utca 8/A, Sepsiszentgyorgy, Covasna, 520064, Romania; tel (40) 267 351 504; fax 351 135; e-mail hpress@3szek.ro; web site www.3szek.ro
Circ.: 15,000

Ed. in Chief – Farkas Arpad

SIBIU

EVENIMENTUL SIBIAN (D)
Strada Alexandru Vlahuta 9A, Sibiu, 2400, Romania; tel (40) 269 447 763
Ed. in Chief – Traian Suciu

RONDUL (D)
12 N. Balcescu St., Sibiu, 2400, Romania; tel (40) 69 218133; fax 210102

TRIBUNA (D)
Str. George Cosbuc Nr. 38, Sibiu, 550013, Romania; tel (40) 269 801 054; fax 214 141; web site www.tribuna.ro
Circ.: 40,000
Ed. in Chief – Mercar Bitu
Adv. Mgr. – Sorin farac

SLATINA, OLT

GLASUL ADEVARULUI (D)
Str. Filimon Sarbu 5, Slatina, Olt, 0500, Romania; tel (40) 44 22131

STANTU GHGEORGHE, COVASNA

CUVANTUL NOU (D-5X WK.)
8 Pietei St., Stantu Ghgeorghe, Covasna, 4000, Romania; tel (40) 267 352 210
Ed. in Chief – Dumitru Manolachescu

SUCEAVA

CRAI NOU (D)
Str. Mihai Viteazul nr. 32, Suceava, 720059, Romania; tel (40) 230 214 723; fax 214 723; e-mail contact@crainou.ro; crainou@gmail.com; web site www.crainou.ro
Last Audit: November 23, 2011
Ed. in Chief – Teodorescu Dumitru

TARGU MURES, MURES

CUVANTUL LIBER (D)
9 Gheorghe Doja St., Targu Mures, Mures, 4300, Romania; tel (40) 265 266 629; web site www.cuvantul-liber.ro
Ed. in Chief – Lazar Ladariu

NEPUJSAG (6X WK.)
9 Gheorghe Doja St., Targu Mures, Mures, 4300, Romania; tel (40) 265 268 273; fax 266 270; e-mail nepujsag@e-nepujsag.ro; web site www.e-nepujsag.ro
Ed. in Chief – Nagy Miklos Kund

TIMISOARA

AGENDA (D)
Emanoil Ungureanu Nr. 3, Timisoara, 300088, Romania; tel (40) 256 495 195; e-mail office@agenda.ro; web site www.agenda.ro
Circ.: 4,500
Dir. – Zoltan Kovacs
Adv. Mgr. – Loradana Rosu

NEUE BANATER ZEITUNG (D)
16 Decembrie Blvd., Timisoara, 1900, Romania; tel (40) 256 15317
Ed. in Chief – Gerhard Binder

RENASTEREA BANATEANA (D)
8 Revolutiei Blvd., Timisoara, Romania; tel (40) 256 359 777; fax 490 370; e-mail renasterea@renasterea.ro; web site www.renasterea.ro
Circ.: 50,000
Ed. in Chief – Adrian Pop

TIMISOARA, TIMIS

REALITATEA BANATEANA (D)
21-23 Stefan Cel Mare St., Timisoara, Timis, 1900, Romania; tel (40) 56 133563; fax 196647

TIMISOARA (D)
37A Brediceanu St., Timisoara, Timis, 1900, Romania; tel (40) 56 123401; fax 146170
– George Serban
– Lucian Vasile SzaboDir.s

TULCEA

DELTA (D-5X WK.)
4 Spitalului St., Tulcea, 8800, Romania; tel (40) 5 12406; fax 16616
Ed. in Chief – Neculai Amihulesei

V LCEA

CURIERUL DE VALCEA (D-5X WK.)
Carol I 19, V□lcea, 240591, Romania; tel (40) 250 732 325; fax 732 326; e-mail office@curierul.ro; web site www.curierul.ro
Circ.: 3,000
Dir. – Ioan Barbu
Adv. Mgr. – Alene Dudoroeu

ZALAU, SALAJ

GRAIUL SALAJULUI (D)
Piata Unirii 7, Zalau, Salaj, 4700, Romania; tel (40) 99 614120
Ed. in Chief – Ioan Lupa

RUSSIA

MOSCOW

SOVIETSKI SPORT (D-EX MON.)
8 ul. Arkhipova, Moscow, 101913, Russia; tel (7) 095 924 7428
Circ.: 495,000
Ed. – V.G. Kudryavtsev

IZVESTIYA (D-EX S)
K-6, st. Florida 18, Bldg. 1, Moscow, 127994, Russia; tel (7) 495 650 0581; e-mail info1@izvestia.ru; web site www.izvestia.ru
Circ.: 415,120
Ed. in Chief – Vladimir Mamontov

KRASNAYA ZVEZDA (5X WK.)
38 Khoroshevskoye Shosse, Moscow, 123826, Russia; tel (7) 495 941 2158; fax 941 4057; web site www.redstar.ru
Circ.: 70,000

KURANTY (D-5X WK.)
15 ul. Novyi Arbat, Moscow, 103009, Russia; tel (7) 495 2022414; fax 2022590
Circ.: 65,000
Ed. in Chief – Anatolii Pankov

LESNAYA GAZETA (D)
25 Oktyabyra GSP, Moscow, 103645, Russia; tel (7) 495 9211260

LZ-NARODNAYA GAZETA (D-EX MON.)
7 ul. 1905 Goda, Moscow, 123847, Russia; tel (7)

GUDOK (5X WK.)
Old Basmannaya St., 38 / 2, Bldg. 3, Moscow, 105066, Russia; tel (7) 495 262 9916; e-mail gudok@css-rzd.ru; welcome@gudok.ru; web site www.gudok.ru
Circ.: 500,000
Ed. in Chief – Vladmir Zmeyushenko

MOSKOVSKAYA PRAVDA (6X WK.)
7 ul. 1905 Goda, Moscow, 123846, Russia; tel (7) 495 259 8233; fax 259 6360; e-mail newspaper@mospravda.ru; web site www.mospravda.ru
Circ.: 300,000
Ed. – Shod Muladzhanov

MOSKOVSKII KOMSOMOLETS (6X WK.)
7 ul. 1905 Goda, Moscow, 123995, Russia; tel (7) 495 250 7272; fax 259 4639; e-mail info@mk.ru; web site www.mk.ru
Circ.: 2,035,049
Ed. in Chief – Andrei Vorontsov

NEZAVISIMAYA GAZETA (5X WK.)
13 ul. Myasnitskaya, Moscow, 10100, Russia; tel (7) 495 645 5428; fax 975 2346; e-mail info@ng.ru; web site www.ng.ru
Advertising: The Cal Hart Co.
Ed. in Chief – Konstantin Remchukov

RABOCHAYA TRIBUNA (D-EX MON.)
24 ul. Pravdy, Moscow, 125869, Russia; tel (7) 495 257 9313; fax 973 2002
Circ.: 150,000
Ed.-in Chief – Viktor Andriyanov

ROSSIISKAYA GAZETA (D-EX S)
24 ul. Pravdy, Moscow, 125881, Russia; tel (7) 495 775 3113; web site www.rg.ru
Circ.: 439,700
Ed. in Chief – Anatoly Yurkov

SELSKAYA ZHIZN (3X WK.)
24 ul. Pravdy, Moscow, 125869, Russia; tel (7) 095 2575151; fax 2575839
Circ.: 102,000
Ed. in Chief – M. Sharov

SOVETSKAYA ROSSIYA (3X WK.)
24 ul. Pravdy, Moscow, 125993, Russia; tel (7) 495 257 5300; fax 200 2290; e-mail info@rednews.ru; web site www.rednews.ru
Circ.: 300,000
Ed. – Viktor Chikin

STROITELNAYA GAZETA (6X WK.)
Olkhovskaya Ul., 45, Str. 1, Moscow, 125885, Russia; tel (7) 495 755 9557; fax 755 9557; e-mail stroygaz@mtu-net.ru; web site www.stroygaz.ru
Circ.: 360,000
Ed. in Chief – Peter Degtyare

VECHERNYAYA MOSKVA (5X WK.)
7 ul. 1905 Goda, Moscow, 123995, Russia; tel (7) 499 259 8391; fax 256 5550; e-mail post@vm.ru; web site www.vm.ru
Chrmn. – Vladimir Zubkov

SAINT PETERSBURG

NEVSKOYE VREMYA (6X WK.)
St. Petersburg ul. Bol. Morskaya 47, Saint Petersburg, 190000, Russia; tel (7) 812 315 5050; fax 312 2078
Circ.: 100,000
Ed. in Chief – V. Chichin

VECHERNIY PETERSBURG (E)
ul. Fontanka 59, Saint Petersburg, 191023, Russia; tel (7) 891 3118988; fax 3143105
Circ.: 135,628
Ed. in Chief – Vladimir Gronskii

SMENA (6X WK.)
ul. Fontanka 59, Saint Petersburg, 191023, Russia; tel (7) 812 210 8052; fax 311 0957; web site www.smena.ru
Circ.: 100,285
Ed. in Chief – Leonid Davydov

SANKT-PETERBURGSKIYE VEDOMOSTI (5X WK.)
Marat 25, Saint Petersburg, 191025, Russia; tel (7) 812 325 3100; fax 764 4840; e-mail post@spbvedomosti.ru; web site www.spbvedomosti.ru
Circ.: 125,000
Ed. in Chief – Dmitry Sherih

VLADIVOSTOK

KRASNOYE ZNAMYE (D)
Leninskaya 43, Vladivostok, Russia; tel (7)
Ed. – V.G. Chukhlantsev

RYGSVEGUR 3

KLAKSVIK

NORDLYSID (WEEKLY)
PO Box 58, Klaksvik, 710, Rygsvegur 3; tel (298) 456 285; fax 456 498; e-mail nordpres@post.olivant.fo; info@nordlysid.fo; web site www.nordlysid.fo
Circ.: 1,200
Ed. – Oliver Joensen

SAN MARINO

SAN MARINO

IL NUOVO TITANO (D)
Via G. Ordelaffi 46, San Marino, 47890, San Marino; tel (378) 902016; fax 906438
Circ.: 1,300
Pub. – Augusto Zonzini

LA SCINTILIA (D)
Via Sentier Rosso, 1, San Marino, San Marino; tel (378) 549 991199
Pub. – Georges Santi

NOTIZIARIO (D)
Segreteria Esteri-Contrada Omerelli, San Marino, San Marino; tel (378)
Ed. in Chief – Pier Roberto De Biagi

RISCOSSA SOCIALISTA (D)
Via Della Tana 117, San Marino, San Marino; tel (378)
Pub. – Mauro Busignani

SAN MARINO (D)
Via delle Scalette 6, San Marino, 47890, San Marino; tel (378) 549 991193; fax 992694
Ed. in Chief – Carlo Franciosi

SERBIA

BELGRADE

POLITIKA (E)
Makedonska 29, Belgrade, 11000, Serbia; tel (381) 11 330 1617; fax 337 3419; web site www.politika.rs
Circ.: 300,000

Dir. – Werner Herics

PRIVREDNI PREGLED (M)
Marsala Birjuzova 3, Belgrade, 11000, Serbia; tel (381) 11 328 2888
Circ.: 15,000
Ed. in Chief – Dusan Djordjevic

BORBA (M-EX S)
Trg Nikole Pasica 7, Belgrade, 11000, Serbia; tel (381) 11 339 8020; fax 339 8376; e-mail borba@bitsyu.net
Circ.: 85,000
Ed. in Chief – Nebojsa Nedeljkovic

NOVI SAD, VOJVODINA

MAGYAR SZO (M)
Vojvode Misica 1, Novi Sad, Vojvodina, 21000, Serbia; tel (381) 21 457 244; web site www.magyarszo.com
Circ.: 25,590
Dir. – Barta Zoltan
Ed. in Chief – Peter Kokae

SLOVAKIA

BANSKA BYSTRICA

SMER DNES (D)
Cs. armady 26, Banska Bystrica, 97401, Slovakia; tel (421) 88 43343; fax 43341
Circ.: 20,000
Ed. in Chief – Juraj Kucera

BRATISLAVA

NOVY SLOVAK (D)
PO Box 254, Bratislava, 81499, Slovakia; tel (421) 7 67239; fax 67042
Circ.: 18,000
Ed. in Chief – Peter Skultety

MERIDIAN (D)
Sturova 4, Bratislava, 81580, Slovakia; tel (421) 2 53087; fax 55154
Circ.: 5,000
Ed. in Chief – Miroslav Jaslovsky

NARODNA OBRODA (M-EX S)
Mickiewiczova 1, Bratislava, 81005, Slovakia; tel (421) 2 5923 3500; e-mail redakcia@narodnaobroda.sk; admin@bitmedia.sk; extro@savba.sk; web site www.narodnaobroda.sk
Circ.: 28,000
Ed. in Chief – Stefan Mesaros

NOVY CAS (M)
Gorkeho 5, Bratislava, 81278, Slovakia; tel (421) 7 363070; fax 363104
Circ.: 230,000
Ed. in Chief – Zuzana Rackova

PRAVDA (M)
Trnavska cesta 39/A, Bratislava, 831 04, Slovakia; tel (421) 2 4959 6959; fax 4959 6102; e-mail pravda@pravda.sk; inzercia@pravda.sk; web site www.pravda.sk
Circ.: 165,000
Key Accts. Mgr. – Michal Jaros
Sales Devel. Mgr. – Robert Nahalka
Ed. in Chief – Juraj Porubsky
Online Ed. – Jaroslav Matyas

HLAS L'UDU (M)
Pribinova 21, Bratislava, 81109, Slovakia; tel (421) 7 50634337; fax 325544
Circ.: 22,000
Ed. in Chief – Pavol Dinkav

ROL'NICKE NOVINY (D)
Dobrovicova 12, Bratislava, 81378, Slovakia; tel (421) 7 368449; fax 321282
Circ.: 20,000
Ed. in Chief – Juraj Sestak

SLOVENSKY DENNIK (D)
Martanovicova 25, Bratislava, 81932, Slovakia; tel (421) 7 50545; fax 53061
Circ.: 27,000
Ed. in Chief – Anton Balaz

SME (D)
Mytna 33, Bratislava, 81005, Slovakia; tel (421) 7 498726; fax 498306
Circ.: 50,000

SMENA (D)
Dostojevske-ho rad 1, Bratislava, 81924, Slovakia; tel (421) 7 490255; fax 58655
Circ.: 80,000
Ed. in Chief – Gabriela Baranovicova

SPORT (D)
Svatoplukova 2, Bratislava, 81923, Slovakia; tel (421) 7 60053; fax 211380
Circ.: 85,000
Ed. in Chief – Zdeno Simonides

SZABAD UJSAG (WEEKLY)
P.O.Box 11. 82011, Bratislava, 81499, Slovakia; tel (421) 2 333012; fax 330519
Circ.: 40,000
Ed. in Chief – Geza Szabo

PRACA (D)
Odborarske nam. 3, Bratislava, 81499, Slovakia; tel (421) 7 50239316; fax 55422985; e-mail redakcia@praca.sk; web site www.praca.sk
Circ.: 80,000

VECERNIK (E)
Pribinova 25, Bratislava, 81916, Slovakia; tel (421) 7 325085; fax 2104521
Circ.: 30,000
Ed. in Chief – Martin Podstupka

BRATISLAVA 1

UJ SZO (D) EST. 1948
Lazaretska 12, Bratislava 1, 81108, Slovakia; tel (421) 2 5923 3421; e-mail redakcia@ujszo.com; web site www.ujszo.com
Circ.: 42,000
Ed. in Chief – Molnar Norbert

BRATISLAVA 111

REPUBLIKA (D)
Pribinova 25, Bratislava 111, 81928, Slovakia; tel (421) 2 5921 0111; fax 5296 3405; web site www.tasr.sk
Circ.: 50,000
Ed. in Chief – Marian Kolar

KOSICE

KOSICKY VECER (D)
Trieda SNP 24, Kosice, 04297, Slovakia; tel (421) 95 429820; fax 421214
Circ.: 25,000
Ed. in Chief – Mikulas Jesensky

LUC (D)
B. Nemcovej 32, Kosice, 04262, Slovakia; tel (421) 95 6332117; fax 359090
Circ.: 15,000
Ed. in Chief – Edita Pacajova Kardosova

SLOVENSKY VYCHOD (D)
Letna 45, Kosice, 04266, Slovakia; tel (421) 95 53979; fax 53950
Circ.: 30,000
Ed. in Chief – Dusan Klinger

PRESOV

PRESOVSKY VECERNIK (D)
Jarkova 4, Presov, 08001, Slovakia; tel (421) 91 724563; fax 723398
Circ.: 13,000
Ed. in Chief – Peter Licak

SLOVENIA

LJUBLJANA

DELO (M)
Dunajska 5, Ljubljana, 1509, Slovenia; tel (386) 1 473 600; fax 473 7519; e-mail delo@delo.si; web site www.delo.si
Circ.: 90,000
Mktg. Mgr. – Katrena Ferko

DNEVNIK (6X WK.)
Kopitarjeva 2 & 4, Ljubljana, 1510, Slovenia; tel (386) 1 308 2450; fax 308 2309; web site www.dnevnik.si
Circ.: 62,000
Adv. Mgr. – Nives Ros
Ed. in Chief – Suzana Rankov

SLOVENEC (M-EX S)
PO Box 59, Ljubljana, 1509, Slovenia; tel (386) 61 320841; fax 319751
Mng. Ed. – Joze Mlakar

SLOVENSKE NOVICE (D)
Dunajska 5, Ljubljana, 1000, Slovenia; tel (386) 1 473 7502; fax 473 7504; e-mail internet@delo.si; web site www.delo.si
Circ.: 80,000
Ed. in Chief – Marjan Bauer

MARIBOR

VECER (6X WK.)
Svetozarevska 14, Maribor, 2504, Slovenia; tel (386) 2 235 3500; fax 235 3368; web site www.vecer.si
Circ.: 70,000
Ed. in Chief – Milan Predan

SPAIN

ALBACETE

LA VERDAD DE ALBACETE (D)
Pza. Catedral, 6, Albacete, 02002, Spain; tel (34) 967 219350; fax 210781; web site www.laverdad.es
Dir. – Eduardo San Martin Montilla

LA TRIBUNA DE ALBACETE (D)
Paseo de la Cuba 14, Albacete, 02005, Spain; tel (34) 967 191 000; fax 240 386; e-mail publicidad@latribunadealbacete.es; web site www.latribunadealbacete.es
Ed. in Chief – Carlos Zuloaga Lopez
Ed. – Antonio Cordoba
Ed. – Antonio Diaz
Ed. – Cristobal Guzman
Ed. – Esther Perez
Ed. – Irene Soriano
Ed. – Juan Carrizo

ALCAL DE HENARES

DIARIO DE ALCALA (D)
Plaza de Navarra 3, 1. o. C y D, Alcal de Henares, 28804, Spain; tel (34) 91 889 4162; fax 889 4162; e-mail redaccion@diariodelhenares.com; web site www.diariodelhenares.com
Dir. – Antonio R. Naranjo
Ed. in Chief – Pedro Perez Honojos

ALCOBENDAS, MADRID

YA (D)
Valportillo Primera, 11, Alcobendas, Madrid, 28100, Spain; tel (34) 1 6234100; fax 6234171
Circ.: 75,441
Dir. – Rafael Gonzalez Rodriguez
Ed. in Chief – Jose Vilamor
Ed. in Chief – Carlos Aganzo
Ed. in Chief – Julio Riquelme
Ed. in Chief – Carlos Cernuda
Ed. in Chief – Juan Balboa

ALCOY

CIUDAD DE ALCOY (5X WK.)
Avda. Pte. Sant Jordi 8 y 10, Alcoy, 03803, Spain; tel (34) 96 652 1548; fax 652 1551; e-mail ciudad@elperiodico.com; web site www.ciudaddealcoy.com
Ed. – Graficas Ciudadsa
Adv. Mgr. – Manuel Valls

ALGECIRAS, CADIZ

EUROPA SUR (D)
Calle Muro, 3 CP, Algeciras, Cadiz, 11201, Spain; tel (34) 956 588250; fax 631167; web site www.europasur.com
Pres. – Jose Joly Martinez de Salazar
Gen. Dir. – Javier Moyano
Gen. Dir. – Tomas Valiente
Dir. – Jorge Bezares Bermundez

ALICANTE

INFORMACION (D)
Avda. Doctor Rico 17, Apdo. 214, Alicante, 03005, Spain; tel (34) 965 98 9100; fax 98 9162; e-mail publicidad@diarioinformacion.com; web site www.diarioinformacion.com
Dir., Information – Juan Ranon Jil

LA VERDAD DE ALICANTE (D)
Avda. Oscar Espl 4, bajo 5, Alicante, 03003, Spain; tel (34) 96 592 2282; fax 592 2248; e-mail alicante.lv@laverdad.es; web site www.laverdad.es/alicante
Chief Ed. – Ramon Gomez Carrion

ALMERIA

LA CRONICA DEL AMERIA (D)
Andalucia 8, Almeria, 04007, Spain; tel (34) 950 276511; fax 271683
Circ.: 1,375
Dir. – Joaquin Abad Rodriguez
Ed. in Chief – Francisco Venegas Alonso
Ed. in Chief – Jose Manuel Bretones
Ed. in Chief – Maria del Mar Zobaran

LA VOZ DE ALMERIA (M)
Avda. del Mediteraneo 159, Almeria, 04006, Spain; tel (34) 950 181818; fax 151944; e-mail info@lavozdealmeria.com; lavoz@lavozdealmeria.com; web site www.lavozdealmeria.com
Circ.: 7,737
Dir. – Pedro Manuel de la Cruz Alonso

Ed. – Jose Luis Martinez

ANDOAIN, GUIPUZCOA

EUSKALDUNON EGUNKARIA (D)
Martin Ugalde kultur Parkea, Andoain, Guipuzcoa, 20140, Spain; tel (34) 943 300 600; fax 300 600; e-mail egunkaria@egunkaria.info; web site www.egunkaria.info
MD – Martxelo Otamendi

ARRECIFE LANZAROTE, LAS PALMAS

LA VOZ DE LANZAROTE (D)
Canalejas 2, 2.o izq., Arrecife Lanzarote, Las Palmas, 35500, Spain; tel (34) 928 812 285; fax 814 225; web site www.lavozdelanzarote.com
Dir. – Esabel Lusarrata

ASTORGA, LEON

EL FARO ASTORGANO (D)
Manuel Gullon 3-5, Astorga, Leon, 24700, Spain; tel (34) 987 617 012; fax 617 025; e-mail elfaro@astorga.com; web site www.astorga.com
Circ.: 2,747
Dir. – Isidro Martinez Rodriguez

AVILA

EL DIARIO DE AVILA (M)
Rio Cea, 1 Nave 20, Avila, 05004, Spain; tel (34) 920 351 852; fax 351 853; e-mail redaccion@diariodeavila.es; web site www.diariodeavila.es
Circ.: 8,000
Dir. – Jose Manuel Serrano Alvarez
Asst. Dir. – Juan Carlos Fernandez Aganzo

AVILES, ASTURIAS

LA VOZ DE AVILES (D)
La Camara 47, Aviles, Asturias, 33402, Spain; tel (34) 985 520 056; fax 569 899; e-mail redaccaoin.av@lavozdeaviles.es; web site www.elcomerciodigital.com
Circ.: 17,092
Dir. – Jose Maria Urbano

BADAJOZ

HOY-DIARIO DE EXTREMADURA (D)
Carretera de Madrid-Lisboa 22, Badajoz, 06008, Spain; tel (34) 924 214 300; fax 205 320; e-mail hoyredaccion@audinex.es; web site www.hoy.es
Circ.: 18,015
Dir. – Teresiano Rodriguez Nunez
Asst. Dir. – Manuel Garcia Carmona
Chief Ed. – Juan Domingo Fernandez Gomez
Chief Ed. – Manuel Lopez Garcia
Chief Ed. – J. Joaquin Rodriguez Lara
Chief Ed. – Luis A. Ruiz de Gopegui y Santoyo

BADALONA, BARCELONA

EL PUNT BARCELONES NORD (D)
Tapies Str. 2, Badalona, Barcelona, 08001, Spain; tel (34) 93 972 186 400; fax 227 6606; web site www.elpunt.cat
MD – Sara Munoz

BARCELONA

ABC (DS)
Paseo De Gracia 84, Barcelona, 8008, Spain; tel (34) 93 272 1610; fax 226 3750; web site www.abc.es
Dir. – Francisco Perez Bretel

BOLENTIN DE BOLSA 16 BARCELONA (D)
San Gervasio 8, entlo., Barcelona, 08022, Spain; tel (34) 93 418 4779; fax 418 4251
Dir. – Rafael Rubio Gomez-Caminero

AVUI (D)
Enrique Ganados 84, Barcelona, 08008, Spain; tel (34) 93 316 3900; fax 316 3936; e-mail pub@avui.cat; web site www.avui.cat
Circ.: 50,000
Pres. – Vicent Sanchis
Ed. – Lluis Martinez

DIARI QUATRE GATS (D)
SUquia 1, Barcelona, 08003, Spain; tel (34) 93 608691260; fax 3102941
Dir. – Ruben Adri n Valenzuela

DIARIO MARITIMAS (5X WK.)
P. o. de Colon 24, Barcelona, 08002, Spain; tel (34) 93 301 5516; fax 318 6645; e-mail men-car@men-car.com; web site www.men-car.com
Mng. Dir. – Juan Cardona Delclos

EL PERIODICO DE CATALUNYA (DS)
Consell de Cent 425-427, Barcelona, 08009, Spain; tel (34) 93 265 5353; fax 484 6517; e-mail online@elperiodico.com; web site www.elperiodico.es
Intl Adv./Sales – Andree Mangar
Ed. in Chief – Enrique Hernandez

EL MUNDO DE CATALUNYA (D)
Passeig Gr□cia 11, Barcelona, 08007, Spain; tel (34) 93 496 2400; fax 496 2408; e-mail catalunya@elmundo.es; web site www.elmundo.es
Director – Alex Salmon

EL PAIS (D)
Conseio Canto 341, Barcelona, 08007, Spain; tel (34) 93 401 0500; fax 401 0631; e-mail publicidad@elpais.es; web site www.elpais.es/elpais.htm
Ed. in Chief – Milagros Perez Oliva

LA VANGUARDIA (DS)
Diagonal 477, Barcelona, 08001, Spain; tel (34) 93 481 2624; fax 270 4349; e-mail digital@vanguardia.es; web site www.lavanguardia.es
Dir. – Jose Antich
Asst. Dir. – Alfredo Abian Munoz
Asst. Dir.-Art – Carlos Perez de Rozas
Asst. Dir.-Information – Rafael Jorba Castellvi
Asst. Dir.-Information – Enric Juliana Ricart
Asst. Dir.-Information – Rosa Paz Macazaga
Chief Ed.-Int'l – Pau Baquero

NOU DIARI BARCELONA
Tamarit 155, Barcelona, 08015, Spain; tel (34) 93 5424200; fax 5424201
Dir. – Pasqual Llongueras Arola

EL OBSERVADOR (D)
Sector C. Calle D. Poligono Industrial Zona Franca, Barcelona, 08040, Spain; tel (34) 93 263 0304; fax 263 1679
Circ.: 76,000
Dir. – Enric Canals

DIARI DE BARCELONA (D)
Placa d'en Tisner, 1, Barcelona, 08018, Spain; tel (34) 93 506 4200; fax 506 4201; e-mail diari@diaridebarcelona.com; web site www.diaridebarcelona.com
Ed. – Rafael Lujan

EL VIGIA (5X WK.)
Pg. de la Zona Franca, 137-139, 1. Local 10, Barcelona, 08038, Spain; tel (34) 93 393 2323; fax 393 2325; web site www.elvigia.com
Ed./Dir – Aitor Zieco

BILBAO, VIZCAYA

DEIA (D)
Camino de Capuchinos 6, Bilbao, Vizcaya, 48004, Spain; tel (34) 94 459 9100; fax 459 9121; e-mail infodeia@deia.com; web site www.deia.com/es/
Circ.: 50,018
Dir. – Juan Jose Banos Loinaz
Asst. Dir. – Xabier Lapitz Gonzalez
Chief Ed. – Maria Jesus Gandariasbeitia de la Torre
Chief Ed. – Angel Ruiz de Azua
Chief Ed. – Felix Macua Zugasti

EL CORREO ESPANOL/EL PUEBLO VASCO (M)
Pintor Losada 7, Bilbao, Vizcaya, 48004, Spain; tel (34) 94 487 0100; fax 487 0111; e-mail info@diario-elcorreo.es; web site www.diario-elcorreo.es
Circ.: 123,123
Asst. Dir. – Jose Miguel Santamaria
Chief Ed.-Nat'l – Mikel Iturralde Lazaro
Chief Ed.-Int'l – Jose Luis Penalva Abrisqueta
Chief Ed.-Opinion – Pedro Ontoso Soto
Chief Ed.-Economics – Manuel Arroyo Anaya
Chief Ed.-Society/Culture – Cesar Coca Garcia
Chief Ed.-Sports – Oscar Alonso Herran
Chief Ed. – Javier Trigueros

EL MUNDO DEL PAIS VASCO (D)
Camino de cetuphinos de basurto 2, Bilbao, Vizcaya, 48013, Spain; tel (34) 94 473 9100; fax 473 0208; e-mail elmundo@elmundo.com; web site www.elmundo.com
Dir. – Josean Izarra
Asstistant Dir. – Montse Ramirez

BURGOS

DIARIO DE BURGOS (DS)
Avda. Castilla y Leon 62, Burgos, 09002, Spain; tel (34) 947 268 375; fax 27 72 19; web site www.diariodeburgos.es
Ed. in Chief – Antonio Jose Mencia Gullon

DIARIO 16 BURGOS (D)
Maese Calvo 1, bajo, Burgos, 09002, Spain; tel (34) 947 204 616

CACERES

PERIODICO EXTREMADURA (M)
Doctor Maranon 2, local 7, Caceres, 10002, Spain; tel (34) 927 620 600; fax 620 618; web site www.elperiodicoextremadura.com
Circ.: 8,933
Dir. – Antonio Tinoco Ardila
Asst. Dir. – Jose Ramon Gonzalez Valdivia
Ed. in Chief – Jose Luis Guerra Iglesias

CADIZ

DIARIO DE CADIZ (DS)
Avda. de El Puerto, 2 Ed., Fenix CP, Cadiz, 11007, Spain; tel (34) 956 29 79 00; fax 224 883; e-mail redaccion@diariodecadiz.com; web site www.diariodecadiz.es
Circ.: 28,112
Dir. – Jose Joaquin Leon Morgado
Assistant Dir.-Gen. Information – Antonio Perez Sauci
Assistant Dir. – Juan Joly Palomino
Assistant Dir. – Juan Jose Tellez Rubio
Art Dir. – Ignacio Valdes Merello
Assistant Dir. – Pablo Joly Palomino
Chief Ed. – Jose Manuel Otero Bada
Chief Ed. – Lalia Gonzalez Santiago
Chief Ed. – Francisco Perea Marques
Chief Ed. – Ignacio de la Varga Perez
Manuel Munoz Fossati

INFORMACION CADIZ (D)
Ancha 5, 1. o., Cadiz, 11001, Spain; tel (34) 956 220805; fax 221291
Dir. – Joaquin Ladron de Guevara

CARTAGENA, MURCIA

LA OPINION DE CARTAGENA (D)
Plaza del Ayuntamiento s/n, Cartagena, Murcia, 30201, Spain; tel (34) 968 525 505; fax 528 219; e-mail laopiniondecartagena@ebi.es
Circ.: 8,415
Dir. – Pedro Garcia Raja

LA VERDAD DE CARTAGENA (D)
Plz. De Castellini, 4, Cartagena, Murcia, 30201, Spain; tel (34) 968 504 400; fax 528 616; web site www.laverdad.es
Circ.: 47,143
Contact – Pilar Barreiro

CASTELLON

CASTELLON DIARIO (D)
Apdo. Postal 505, Castellon, 12080, Spain; tel (34) 964 209 598; fax 243 650
Circ.: 4,230
Dir. – Juan Enrique Molina
Ed. in Chief – Christina Rodriguez Schillhofer

MINI DIARIO CASTELLON (D)
San Vicente 11, 2.o, Castellon, 12002, Spain; tel (34) 964 257 789; fax 257 119
Dir. – Pedro Sanchez Garcia
Ed. in Chief – Ana Salvador Perez

MEDITERRANIO (D)
Carretera de Almazora s/n, Castellon, 12005, Spain; tel (34) 964 349 500; fax 349 506; e-mail sistemas@mediterraneo.elperiodico.com; mediterraneo@elperiodico.com; web site www.elperiodicomediterraneo.com
Circ.: 9,309
Dir. – Jose Luis Valencia Larraneta
Prodn. – Jose luis Marin

CASTILLA-LA-MANCHA

ABC (D)
Alfonso XII 7, bajo A, Toledo, Castilla-La-Mancha, 45002, Spain; tel (34) 925 212206; fax 212820; e-mail info@abc.es; web site www.abc.es/index.html

LANZA (D)
Alferez Provisional 1, Toledo, Castilla-La-Mancha, 45001, Spain; tel (34) 925 254 713; fax 254 391
Dir. – Jose Antonio Casado Corrales

YA (D)
Nuncio Viejo 3, 2.o. A, Toledo, Castilla-La-Mancha, 45002, Spain; tel (34) 925 211 154; fax 211 351

CEUTA, CADIZ

EL FARO DE CEUTA (D)
Sargento Mena 8, Ceuta, Cadiz, 51001, Spain; tel (34) 956 524 149; fax 524 147; e-mail ceuta@grupofaro.es; web site www.elfaroceutamelilla.es
Chief Ed. – Carmen Echarri

CIUDAD REAL

LA TRIBUNA DE CIUDAD REAL (D)
C/ Pedro Munoz 3, Ciudad Real, 13005, Spain; tel (34) 926 215 301; fax 215 145; e-mail redaccion@diariolatribuna.com; web site www.diariolatribuna.com; www.ogd.com
Ed. – Mendez Pozo

LANZA-CIUDAD REAL (D)
Ronda del Carmen, s/n, Ciudad Real, 13002, Spain; tel (34) 926 274 692; fax 274 745; e-mail redaccion@lanzadigital.com; web site www.lanzadigital.com
Circ.: 9,000
Last Audit: March 31, 2010
MD – Laura Espinar Sanchez
Asst. Dir. – Raul Gratacoa Santacruz

CORDOBA

CORDOBA (D)
Ingeniero Juan de la Cierva 18, Cordoba, 14013, Spain; tel (34) 957 420 302; fax 204 648; e-mail cordoba1@elperiodico.es; cordoba2@elperiodico.es; web site www.diariocordoba.com
Circ.: 18,660
Ed. in Chief – Francisco Luis Cordoba

CORDOVILLA

DIARIO DE NAVARRA (DS)
Carretera Zaragoza s/n., Cordovilla, 31191, Spain; tel (34) 948 236 050; fax 150 320; e-mail redaccion@diariodenavarra.es; web site www.diariodenavarra.es
Dir. – Luis Colina Lorda

CUENCA

EL DIA DE CUENCA (D)
Poligono El Cantorral 13, Cuenca, 16004, Spain; tel (34) 969 240 423; fax 225 351; e-mail diadecuenca@citelan.es
Circ.: 5,500
Dir. – Santiago Mateo Sahuquillo

NUEVO DIARIO (D)
Calderon de la Barca 14, Cuenca, 16001, Spain; tel (34) 969 230 404
Dir. – Inmaculada Cruz Salcedo

EL PUERTO DE SANTA MARIA, CADIZ

INFORMACION EL PUERTO (D)
Aurora 11, 1.o. local 7, El Puerto De Santa Maria, Cadiz, 11500, Spain; tel (34) 956 860 367; fax 540 683; e-mail elpuerto@publicacionesdelsur.net
Ed. in Chief – Josefina Escudero Marquez

ELCHE, ALICANTE

HOY DE LA PROVINCIA DE ALICANTE
Poligono Industrial Altabix, Elda 35, Elche, Alicante, 03203, Spain; tel (34) 96 545 6875; fax 545 6519
Dir. – Vicente Marco Valladolid
Ed. in Chief – Fernando Marti Molina

LA VERDAD DE ELCHE (D)
Hospital 16, Elche, Alicante, 03203, Spain; tel (34) 96 545 2843; fax 542 0548; e-mail elche.lv@laverdad.es; web site www.laverdad.es
Dir. – Gaspar MaciÂ
Dir. – Alberto Avuirre
Mktg. Mgr. – Gose Manuel

FORNELLS DE LA SELVA, GIRONA

DIARI DE GIRONA (D)
Passeig General Mendoza 2, Fornells de la Selva, Girona, 17002, Spain; tel (34) 972 202 066; fax 202 005; e-mail diaridegirona@epi.es; web site www.diaridegirona.cat
Circ.: 6,208
Dir. – Jordi XargayÂ¢ i Teixidor

GERONA

NOU DIARI GIRANA (D)
Ultonia 10-12, Gerona, 17002, Spain; tel (34) 972 409300; fax 409301
Dir. – Josep Gil Franquesa
Ed. in Chief – Josep Mir Hurtado

GIJON, ASTURIAS

EL COMERCIO (D)
Calle del Diario El Comercio 1, Gijon, Asturias, 33207, Spain; tel (34) 98 517 9800; fax 534 0955; e-mail elcomercio@elcomercio-sa.es; web site www.elcomercio-sa.es
Circ.: 34,000
Pub. – Ina Inigonorieja
Ed. in Chief – Marcelino Gonzalez Menendez
Ed. in Chief – Ruben Espiniella Castro

GIRONA

EL PUNT COMARQUES GIRONNES (M-6X WK.)
Santa Eugenia, 42, Girona, 17005, Spain; tel (34) 972 186 400; fax 186 420; e-mail elpuntdigital@elpunt.com; web site www.elpunt.com
Circ.: 15,350
Dir. – John Valley

GRANADA

CRONICA DE GRANADA
Avda. de Andalucia s/n, Edificio Simoa Bajo 2, Granada, 18005, Spain; tel (34) 958 800626; fax 800946
Dir. – Joaquin Abad Rodriguez
Ed. in Chief – Rafael Martos

HERNANI, GUIPUZCOA

EGIN (D)
Poligono Eciago 10B, Hernani, Guipuzcoa, 20120, Spain; tel (34) 943 554712; fax 553494
Dir. – Melchior S iz-Pardo
Ed. in Chief – Mertxe Aizpurua
Ed. in Chief – Inaki Iriondo
Ed. in Chief – Juan Carlos Elorza
Ed. in Chief – Martin Garitano
Ed. in Chief – Fermin Munarriz

HEUSCA

DIARIO DEL ALTOARAGON (D)
Ronda Estaci¢n 4, Heusca, 22005, Spain; tel (34) 974 215 656; fax 215 657; e-mail redaccion@diariodelaltoaragon.es; web site www.diariodelaltoaragon.es
Circ.: 4,518
MD – Antonio Angulo Aragus
Ed. in Chief – Javier Garcia Anton

HUARTE, NAVARRA

DIARIO DE NOTICIAS (D)
Poligono Areta Huarte, s/n, Huarte, Navarra, 31620, Spain; tel (34) 948 332 533; fax 332 518; e-mail redaccion@noticiasdenavarra.com; web site www.noticiasdenavarra.com
Circ.: 12,673
Dir. – Aoseva Sranpanaria
Chief Ed. – Felix Monreal Nuin

DIARIO NOTICIAS (D)
Altzutzate 8, Poligono Industrial Areta, Huarte, Navarra, 31620, Spain; tel (34) 948 332 533; fax 332 518; e-mail cad@noticiasdenavarra.com; local@noticiasdenavarra.com; politica@noticiasdenavarra.com; economia@noticiasdenavarra.com; web site www.noticiasdenavarra.com
Circ.: 8,810
Dir. – Joseba Santamaria

HUELVA

ABC (D)
Martin Alonso PinzOn 23, Huelva, 21003, Spain; tel (34) 959 334 555; fax 261 022; e-mail info@abc.es; web site www.abc.es
Ed. in Chief – Jose Cejudo Hidalgo

HUELVA INFORMACION (D)
Isaac Albeniz, 1, Huelva, 21001, Spain; tel (34) 959 281139; fax 260608; e-mail redaccion@huelvainformacion.es; web site www.huelvainformacion.es
Circ.: 7,047
Editorial Dir. – Fernando Merchan Alvarez
Chief Ed. – Antonio Peinazo Pleguezuelos

HUESCA

HERALDO DE HUESCA (D)
Coso Bajo 28, Huesca, 22001, Spain; tel (34) 974 239 000; fax 239 005; web site www.heraldo.es
Pres. – Antonio Cosculluela Bergua
Dir. – Santigo Mendive

IBIZA, BALEARES

DIARIO DE IBIZA (D)
Avda. de la Paz, Ibiza, Baleares, 07800, Spain; tel (34) 971 190 000; fax 190 321; e-mail diariodeibiza@epi.es; web site www.diariodeibiza.es
Circ.: 12,000
Dir. – Joan Serra Tur
Mktg. Mgr. – Juan Suerez

JAEN

JAEN (D)
PO Box 81, Jaen, 23009, Spain; tel (34) 953 211 111; fax 211 125; e-mail diariojaen@interbook.net; web site www.diariojaen.es
Circ.: 7,466
Dir. – Juan Espejo Gonzalez

JEREZ DE LA FRONTERA

ABC
Hornos 3, Jerez de la Frontera, 11403, Spain; tel (34) 956 340007; fax 345832; e-mail info@abc.es; web site www.abc.es
Ed. in Chief – Antonio Castro Caro

INFORMACION JEREZ (D)
Parque Empresarial Investigacion D-11, Jerez de la Frontera, 11407, Spain; tel (34) 956 319 834; fax 318 159
Dir. – Juan Manuel Garro Rementeria

JEREZ DE LA FRONTERA, CADIZ

DIARIO DE JEREZ (D)
Patricio Garvey, s/n, Jerez de la Frontera, Cadiz, 11402, Spain; tel (34) 956 321 411; fax 320 011; e-mail redaccion@diariojerez.es; web site www.diariodejerez.com
Circ.: 10,265
Ed. in Chief – Jose Martinez De Salakar

INFORMACION JEREZ (D)
Calle de la investigacion mparcela D11, Jerez de la Frontera, Cadiz, 11407, Spain; tel (34) 956 167 300; fax 90 170 6501; e-mail jerez@publicacionesdelsur.net; web site www.andaluciainformacion.es
Dir. – Jose Antonio Mallou DÂ¡az
Adv. Mgr. – Jose Maria Sosa

LA CORUNA

LA VOZ DE GALICIA (D)
Avda. de la Prensa, 84-85. Poligono de Sabon., La Coruna, 15006, Spain; tel (34) 981 180 180; fax 180410; e-mail redac@lavoz.com; web site www.lavozdegalicia.es
Dir. – Bieito Rubido
Asst. Dir.-Organization – Francisco Rios Alvarez
Asst. Dir.-Information – Xose Luis Vilela Conde
Chief Ed. – Arturo Lezcano Fernandez
Chief Ed. – Leoncio Gonzalez Dominguez
Chief Ed. – Cesar Casal Gonzalez
Chief Ed. – Xurxo Lobato Sanchez
Chief Ed. – Alfredo Vara Fernandez
Chief Ed. – Jose Benito Calvo Rego
Chief Ed. – Fernando Hidalgo Urizar
Fernando Rodriguez Ojea

LA LINEA DE LA CONCEPCION, CADIZ

AREA CAMPO DE GILBRALTAR Y COSTA DEL SOL (D)
Gibraltar 13, La Linea de la Concepcion, Cadiz, 11300, Spain; tel (34) 956 690 620; fax 763 050; e-mail gerente@grupodiarioarea.info; web site www.grupodiarioarea.info
Dir. – Jose Antonio Gomez Amado
Chief Ed. – Jose Correa Torres

LAS PALMAS DE GRAN CANARIA, CANARY ISLANDS

LA GACETA DE LAS PALMAS
Alcade Jose Ramirez Bethencourt 18, Las Palmas de Gran Canaria, Canary Islands, 35004, Spain; tel (34) 928 302600
Dir. – Jorge Batista Prats

LAS PALMAS DE GRAN CANARIA, LAS PALMAS

CANARIAS 7 (D)
Profesor Lozano 7, Urbanizacion El Sebadal, Las Palmas de Gran Canaria, Las Palmas, 35008, Spain; tel (34) 928 301 301; fax 301 302; e-mail redaccion@canarias7.es; web site www.canarias7.es
Circ.: 12,194
– Vicente Llorca Llinares
– Francisco Suarez AlamoAsst. Dir.s

DIARIO DE LAS PALMAS (E-EX S)
Alcade Ramirez Bethencourt 8, Las Palmas

de Gran Canaria, Las Palmas, 35003, Spain; tel (34) 928 479 448; fax 479 421; e-mail diario@editorialprensacanaria.es; web site www.diariodelaspalmas.com
Circ.: 11,545
Dir. – Santiago Betancor Brito
Asst. Dir. – Amado Moreno Suarez
Ed. in Chief – Rafael Gonzalez Morera
Ed. in Chief – Cristobal Rodriguez Rodriguez
Sports – Jose Miguel Santana Hernandez
Chief, Info – Miguel Luis Barrera Ventura

LA PROVINCIA (M)
Alcade Ramirez Bethencourt 8, Las Palmas de Gran Canaria, Las Palmas, 35003, Spain; tel (34) 928 479 410; fax 479 475; e-mail laprovincia@editorialprensacanaria.es; web site www.la-provincia.com
Circ.: 38,537
Dir. – Angel Tristan Pimienta

LEON

DIARIO DE LEON (D)
Carretera de Leon-Astorga, Km. 4, 6 Trobajo del Ca, Leon, 24010, Spain; tel (34) 987 840 300; fax 840 340; e-mail diariodeleon@lesein.es; web site www.diariodeleon.com
Circ.: 5,743
MD – Fernando Aller Gonzalez
Asst. Dir. – Rafael Blanco Fernandez
Ed. in Chief – Susana Vergara

LA CRONICA 16 DE LEON (D)
Moises De Leon 49, Leon, 24006, Spain; tel (34) 987 212 512; fax 213 152; web site www.la-cronica.net
Circ.: 8,700
Dir. – Estrada Liebana
Vice Pres. – Martinez Parra

LLEIDA

LA MANANA-DIARI DE PONENT (D)
Apdo. Postal 11, Lleida, 25080, Spain; tel (34) 973 241 399; fax 205 810; e-mail manyana@lleida.net; web site www.lamanyana.cat
Circ.: 7,510
Dir. – Jordi Perez Ansotegui

NOU DIARI LLEIDA (D)
Pallars 4, Lleida, 25004, Spain; tel (34) 973 700 500; fax 700 507
Circ.: 14,000
Dir. – Ramon Badia Vidal
Ed. in Chief – Joan Tort

SEGRE (DS)
Del Riu 6, Lleida, 25007, Spain; tel (34) 973 248 000; fax 246 031; e-mail comunicacio@segre.com; web site www.segre.com
Circ.: 16,000
Mng. Dir. – Juan Cal Sanchez
Dir. – Jose Carlos Miranda Ester

LOGRONO, LA RIOJA

LA RIOJA (M-6X WK.)
Apdo. Postal 28, Logrono, La Rioja, 26002, Spain; tel (34) 941 279 130; fax 279 106; e-mail redaccion@larioja.com; web site www.larioja.com
Circ.: 12,305
Dir. – Jose Luis Prusen de Blas
Ed. in Chief – Luis Saez Angulo
Ed. in Chief – Jose Antonio del Rio Sacristan

LA VOZ 16 DE LA RIOJA
Marques de Murrieta 22, entlo., Logrono, La Rioja, 26005, Spain; tel (34) 941 211 000
Dir. – Jose Luis Lloret Diez

LOS MAJUELOS, SANTA CRUZ DE TENERIFE

LA GACETA DE CANARIAS (D)
C/G¢ngora, 4, Los Majuelos, Santa Cruz de Tenerife, 38108, Spain; tel (34) 922 821 698; fax 821 460; web site www.lagacetadecanarias.net
Dir. – Juan Martinez Novo

LUGO

EL PROGRESO (D)
Ribadeo, 5, Lugo, 27001, Spain; tel (34) 982 298 100; fax 298 102; e-mail correo@elprogresso.es; web site www.elprogreso.es
Circ.: 13,177
– Jose Maria Vilabrille
– Tito Dieguez SanchezChief Ed.s

LUGONES-SIERO

EL PERIODICO-LA VOZ DE ASTURIAS (D)
Calle La Lila No. 6, Lugones-Siero, 33003, Spain; tel (34) 98 5101500; fax 5101505; e-mail vozredaccion@elperiodico.com; web site www.elperiodico.com
Circ.: 12,000
Dir. – Luis Mugueta San Martin
Asst. Dir. – Luis Miguel Rebustiello
Ed. in Chief – Angel Falcon Martinez
Ed. in Chief – Jose Garcia-Carreno

MADRID

ABC (D)
C/Juan Ignacio Luca de Tena, 7, Madrid, 28027, Spain; tel (34) 91 3399559; fax 3399661; e-mail spromozionez@abc.es; web site www.abc.es
Ed. – Jose Antonio Zarzalejos

ABC (DS)
Juan Ignacio Luca de Tena 7, Madrid, 28027, Spain; tel (34) 91 339 9000; fax 320 3620; e-mail info@abc.es; web site www.abc.es
Dir. – Jose Antonio Zarzalejos
Asst. Dir. – Santiago Castelo
Asst. Dir. – Fernando R. Lafuente
Asst. Dir. – Alberto Perez
Gen. Mgr. – Jose Luis Romero
Culture Ed. – J.G. Calero
Economics Ed. – Fernando Cortes
Int'l Ed. – Manuel Erice Oronoz
Nat'l Ed. – A. Martinez
Society Ed. – John Fernandez-Cuesta
J.M. Mata

AS (DS)
Albasanz. 14-4, Madrid, 28037, Spain; tel (34) 91 375 2500; fax 375 2558; web site www.as.com
MD – Alfredo Relano Estape

DELEGACION MADRID (D)
Oquendo 23, bajos, Madrid, 28006, Spain; tel (34) 91 4110107
– Jose M. Brunet
– Mariano GuindalEd. in Chiefs

DIARIO 16 (DS)
Capitan Haya 1, planta 8. a., Madrid, 28020, Spain; tel (34) 91 343 4434; fax 343 4414; web site www.diario16.es
Pres. – Santiago Rey Fernandez-LaTorre
Ed. in Chief – Ricardo de Querel
Ed. in Chief – Gonzalo Barene
Art Dir. – Lorena Canamere

EL BOLETIN DE LA TARDE (5X WK.)
Cocepcion Jeronima 24, 1st Fl., Madrid, 28012, Spain; tel (34) 91 319 7000; fax 319 5831; e-mail elboletin@tsai.es; redaccion@elboletin.com; web site www.elboletin.com
Dir. – Carlos Humanes

EL MUNDO (DS)
Pradillo 42, Madrid, 28002, Spain; tel (34) 91 586 4700; fax 586 4848; web site www.elmundo.es
MD – Pedro J. Ramirez Codina

EL PAIS (DS)
Miguel Yuste 40, Madrid, 28037, Spain; tel (34) 91 330 1000; fax 304 8766; e-mail publicidad@elpais.es; digital@elpais.es; web site www.elpais.es
Pres. – Ignacio Polanco
CEO – Juan Luis Cebrian
COO – Jose Angel Garcia Olea

IBERIAN DAILY SUN (D)
Zurbano 74, Madrid, 28010, Spain; tel (34) 91 4427689; fax 4427854
Circ.: 5,524
Dir. – Miguel Serra Megraner

LA INFORMACION DE MADRID (D)
Francisco Sancha 4, Madrid, 28034, Spain; tel (34) 91 3346100; fax 3346148
Dir. – Manuel Marlasca

MARCA (D)
Ave. de San Luis, 25-27, Madrid, 28033, Spain; tel (34) 91 4435000; fax 4436959; e-mail marca@marca.com; web site www.marca.com
MD – Oscar Campillo

MAHON, BALEARIC ISLANDS

MENORCA (D)
Avda. Central 5, Mahon, Balearic Islands, 07714, Spain; tel (34) 971 351 600; fax 351 983; e-mail redaccion@menorca.info; web site www.menorca.net
Circ.: 4,200
Pres. – Jose Guillermo Diaz
Dir. – Joan Bosco Marques Bosch
Mgr. – Xavier Segui Puntas
Ed. in Chief – Juan Carlos Ortego Elvira

MALAGA

DIARIO 16 MALAGA (D)
Compisitor Lemhber, 9 Edificio Jabega, Malaga, 29007, Spain; tel (34) 95 261 3311
Dir. – Juan de Dios Mellado Morales
Ed. in Chief – Tomas Mayoral Gonzalez

EL SOL DEL MEDITERRANEO (D)
Carretera de Azucarera-Intelhorce 24, Malaga, 29004, Spain; tel (34) 95 223 3500; fax 223 9911
Dir. – Antonio Sanchez Morillaa

LA GACETA DE MALAGA (D)
Puerta del Mar 5-7, 1A y 2A, Malaga, 29005, Spain; tel (34) 95 2218858; fax 2218819

LA VOZ DE MELILLA (D)
Cervantes 2, 1.o., Malaga, 29801, Spain; tel (34) 95 267 0690; fax 267 0689
Dir. – Jose M. Navarro Gil

SUR (M-6X WK.)
Avda. Muelle de Heredia, 20-1-4, Malaga, 29001, Spain; tel (34) 95 264 9600; fax 227 9508; e-mail surdigital@diariosur.es; redaccion@diariosur.es; web site www.diariosur.es
MD – Jose Antonio Frias Ruiz
Pub. – Pedro Luis Gomez Carmona

MANRESA, BARCELONA

REGIO 7 INFORMATIVO INTERCOMARCAL (D)
Sant Antoni Maria Claret, 32, Manresa, Barcelona, 08240, Spain; tel (34) 93 877 2233; fax 874 0352; e-mail regio7@regio7.cat; web site www.regio7.cat
Dir. – Mark Narce

MELILLA

MELILLA HOY (D)
Poligono SEPES, Naves A-1 y A-2, Melilla, 52006, Spain; tel (34) 95 269 0000; fax 267 9385; e-mail redaccion@melillahoy.es; web site www.melillahoy.es
Dir. – Mustafa Hamed
Mktg. Mgr. – Amialia Ruiz

MELILLA, MALAGA

EL TELEGRAMA DE MELILLA (D)
Poligono El Sepes, Calle La Espiga, nave A-8, Melilla, Malaga, 52006, Spain; tel (34) 95 269 1384; fax 269 1469; web site www.eltelegrama.com
Dir. – Juan Carlos Heredia

MESOIRO, LA CORUNA

EL IDEAL GALLEGO (D)
Poligono de Pocomaco, Parcela C-12, Mesoiro, La Coruna, 15190, Spain; tel (34) 981 173 040; fax 299 327; e-mail elidealgallego@elidealgallego.com; web site www.elidealgallego.com
Circ.: 10,000
MD – Manuel Ferreiro Regueiro
Adv. Mgr. – Jose Manuel

MURCIA

LA VERDAD DE MURCIA (DS)
Camino Viejo de Monteagudo-Edificio La Verdad, Murcia, 30160, Spain; tel (34) 968 369 100; fax 369 147; e-mail lectores@laverdad.com; web site www.la-verdad.com
Dir. – Eduardo San Martin Montilla

DIARIO 16 DE MURCIA (D)
Cartagena 4, Murcia, 30002, Spain; tel (34) 968 221542; fax (34-968) 221926
Ed. in Chief – Jose Antonio Montesinos Agullo
Gen. Dir. – Jose Alfonso Orrico Martinez

LA OPINION DE MURCIA (D)
Plaza Condestable 3, Murcia, 30009, Spain; tel (34) 968 286 568; fax 281 538; web site www.laopiniondemurcia.es
Circ.: 8,400
Dir. – Paloma Reverte de Luis
Asst. Dir. – Javier Soto Andrados
Ed. in Chief – Jose Angel Ceron Garcia

ORENSE

LA REGION (M-6X WK.)
Poligono Industrial San Cibr n de Vinas, C/4, Orense, 32091, Spain; tel (34) 988 383 838; fax 242 010; e-mail info@laregion.es; web site www.laregion.net
Dir. – Pastoriza Xose Martinez
Asst. Dir. – Miguel Sanchez Lopez

OURENSE

LA REGION INTERNACIONAL (D)
Pol. San Ciprian de Vinas, C. 4, Ourense, 32901, Spain; tel (34) 98 860 0150; fax 256 633; e-mail lri@laregion.net; web site www.laregioninternacional.com
Dir. – Sose Pastorica
Ed. – Jose Luis Outeirino Rodrguez

OVIEDO, ASTURIAS

LA NUEVA ESPANA (D)
Calvo Sotelo, 7, Oviedo, Asturias, 33007, Spain; tel (34) 98 527 9700; fax 527 9704; e-mail pam@lne.es; web site www.lne.es
Dir. – Andelels Rivero
Asst. Dir. – Alberto Menendez
Asst. Dir. – Evelio Gonzalez Palacio

PALENCIA

ALERTA DE PALENCIA (D)
Valentin CalderOn 4, Palencia, 34001, Spain; tel (34) 979 750700; fax 750666
Dir. – Juan Luis Fernandez Vega
Ed. in Chief – Gonzalo Romero de la Villa

EL DIARIO PALENTINO/EL DIA DE PALENCIA (D)
Mayor 67, Palencia, 34001, Spain; tel (34) 979 744 822; fax 743 360
Circ.: 10,000
Dir. – Mariano Valero Gutierrez Carlon
Chief Ed. – Gonzalo Ortega Aragon
Asst. Dir. – Guillermo Alonso Balbas

PALMA DE MALLORCA, BALEARES

BALEARS (D)
Paseig de Mallorca 9A, Palma de Mallorca, Baleares, 07011, Spain; tel (34) 971 788 300; fax 455 740; e-mail master@diaridebalears.com; web site www.dbalears.cat
Pres. – Pedro Serra

DIARIO BALEARES (D)
Paseo Mallorca 9a, Palma de Mallorca, Baleares, 07011, Spain; tel (34) 971 788 300; fax 455 740; e-mail master@diaridebalears.com; web site www.gruposerra.com
Ed. – Pere A. Serra Bauza

DIARIO DE MALLORCA (DS)
Puerto Rico 15, Poligono de Levante, Palma de Mallorca, Baleares, 07006, Spain; tel (34) 971 170 300; fax 170 301; e-mail diariomallorca@diariodemallorca.es; web site www.diariodemallorca.es
Dir. – Jose Eduardo Iglesias Barca

MAJORCA DAILY BULLETIN (M-6X WK.)
Paseo Mallorca 9A, Palma de Mallorca, Baleares, 07011, Spain; tel (34) 971 788 400; fax 719 706; web site www.majorcadailybulletin.es
Asst. Dir. – Irene Taylor
Ed. – Jason Moore
Ed. – Miguel Serra
Ed. – Ray Fleming

ULTIMA HORA (E-EX S)
Paseo Mallorca 9A, Palma de Mallorca, Baleares, 07011, Spain; tel (34) 971 788 300; fax 454 190; web site www.ultimahora.es
Dir. – Pedro Comas Barcelo

PALMA DE MALLORCA, BALEARIC ISLANDS

EL MUNDO/EL DIA DE BALEARES (D)
Avda. 16 de Julio 75 (Poligono Son Castello), Palma de Mallorca, Balearic Islands, 07009, Spain; tel (34) 971 767 600; fax 767 656; e-mail correo@elmundo-eldia.com; web site www.elmundo-eldia.com
Circ.: 18,000
Pres. – Paolo. G Carrer
Dir. – Pedro J. Ramirez

PELIGROS, GRANADA

IDEAL (D)
C/ Huelva 2, Polygon of ASEGRA, Peligros, Granada, 18210, Spain; tel (34) 958 809 809; web site www.ideal.es
Circ.: 40,000
Dir. – Eduardo Peralta de Ana

PENACASTILLO, CANTABRIA

ALERTA DE CANTABRIA (DS)
1.o. de Mayo, s/n., Penacastillo, Cantabria, 39011, Spain; tel (34) 942 320 033; fax 321 146; e-mail directorgeneral@eldiarioalerta.com; marketing@eldiarioalerta.com; web site www.eldiarioalerta.com
Ed. in Chief – Jose Ramon Diaz Rivas
Ed. – Ciriaco Diaz Porras

PONTEVEDRA

DIARIO DE PONTEVEDRA (D)
Rua Lepanto 5, Pontevedra, 36002, Spain; tel (34) 986 011 100; web site www.diariodepontevedra.com
Dir. – Jose Luis Adrio Poza

REUS, TARRAGONA

NOU DIARI REUS (D)
Roser 4, Reus, Tarragona, 43201, Spain; tel (34) 77 759800; fax 759801
Dir. – Xavier Abello Tomas

SABADELL, BARCELONA

EL 9 NOU DEL VALLES OCCIDENTAL
Sant Llorenc 23, 2.o B, Sabadell, Barcelona, 08202, Spain; tel (34) 93 7277 910; fax 7279 120
Dir. – Dolors Altarriba
Assistant Dir. – Joan Rueda

DIARI DE SABADELL (5X WK.)
Sant Quirze 37-41, 2.o., Sabadell, Barcelona, 08201, Spain; tel (34) 93 726 1100; fax 727 0865; e-mail redaccio@diarisabadell.com; web site www.diarisabadell.com
Circ.: 7,164
Dir. – Ramon Rodriguez Zorrilla
Chief Dir. – Maties Serracant Clermont
Chief Dir. – Nomagroma Gamell
Chief Ed. – Josep Mercade Mateu
Assistant Dir. – Angel Diez Tierno
Chief Ed. – Manuel Moreno Izquierdo

SALAMANCA

LA GACETA REGIONAL DE SALAMANCA (M-6X WK.)
Avda. de Los Cipreses 81, Salamanca, 37004, Spain; tel (34) 923 125 252; fax 256 155; web site www.lagacetadesalamanca.com
Dir. – Inigo Dominguez de Calatayud
Asst. Dir. – Juan Antonio Garcia Iglesias

EL ADELANTO (D)
Gran Via 56, Salamanca, 37001, Spain; tel (34) 923 280 228; fax 280 261; e-mail eladelanto@eladelanto.com; web site www.eladelanto.com
Dir. – Åμngel Carreras

TRIBUNA DE SALMANCA (D)
Canon de Rio Lobos (Poligono Montalvo II), Salamanca, 37008, Spain; tel (34) 923 191 111; fax 191 152; e-mail info@tribuna.net; web site www.tribuna.net
Dir. – Puri Contreras

SAN FERNANDO, CADIZ

INFORMACION SAN FERNANDO (D)
San Nicols 34, San Fernando, Cadiz, 11100, Spain; tel (34) 956 800 193; fax 591 510
Ed. – Anthonio Atelnza

SAN SEBASTIAN, GUIPUZCOA

EL DIARIO VASCO (D)
Camino de Portuetxe 2, Barrio Ibaeta, San Sebastian, Guipuzcoa, 20009, Spain; tel (34) 943 410 700; fax 410 813; e-mail korta@diariovasco.com; web site www.diariovasco.com
Circ.: 80,714
Dir. – Jose Gabriel Mujika

SANTA CRUZ DE TENERIFE

DIARIO DE AVISOS (M-6X WK.)
Salamanca 5, Santa Cruz de Tenerife, 38006, Spain; tel (34) 922 290 669; fax 241 039; e-mail info@teideradio.com; web site www.diariodeavisos.com
Circ.: 12,000
Dir. – Leopoldo Fernandez Cabeza de Vaca
Asst. Dir. – Manuel Iglesia Garcia
Asst. Dir. – Enrique Rey Petti
Chief Ed. – Jose Luis Lloret Diez de Rivera

EL DIA (MD)
Avda. Buenos Aires 71, Santa Cruz de Tenerife, 38005, Spain; tel (34) 922 238 300; fax 214 247; e-mail produccion@eldia.es; web site www.eldia.es
Circ.: 25,779
Dir. – Jose Rodriguez Ramirez

SANTA CRUZ DE TENERIFE, CANARY ISLANDS

JORNADA DEPORTIVA (D)
Avda. Buenos Aires 71, Santa Cruz de Tenerife, Canary Islands, 38005, Spain; tel (34) 922 238 300; fax 200 229
MD – Jose Rodriguez Ramirez

SANTANDER

EL NORTE (D)
Miestgelvalle 5, Santander, 39008, Spain; tel (34) 942 230 000; fax 31017
MD – Victor Gijon Penas

SANTANDER, CANTABRIA

EL DIARIO MONTANES (D)
Calle La Prensa s/n, La Albericia, Santander, Cantabria, 39012, Spain; tel (34) 942 354 000; fax 341 806; e-mail eco.dm@eldiariomontanes.es; web site www.eldiariomontanes.es
Dir. – Manuel Angel Castaneda Perez
Asst. Dir. – Jose Emilio Pelayo Valdeolivas
Ed. in Chief – Jose Ramon San Juan Jimenez
Ed. in Chief – Jesus Martinez Teja
Ed. in Chief – Jose Luis Ramos Arguelles
Ed. in Chief – Jesus Maria Serrera Ranero

SANTIAGO DE COMPOSTELA, LA CORUNA

EL CORREO GALLEGO (M-6X WK.)
Preguntoiro 29, Santiago de Compostela, La Coruna, 15704, Spain; tel (34) 981 543 700; fax 543 701; e-mail ocorreo@tsai.es; web site www.elcorreogallego.es
Dir. – Jose Manuel Rey Novoa
Asst. Dir. – Victor Tobio Barreira
Asst. Dir. – Caetano Diaz Vidal
Asst. Dir. – Xoan Salgado Fernandez
Asst. Dir. – Luis Pousa Merens
Asst. Dir. – Jose A. Perez Docampo
Ed. in Chief – Demetrio Pelaez Casal
Ed. in Chief – Xavier Cea Otero

SEGOVIA

EL ADELANTADO DE SEGOVA (6X WK.)
Calle Morillo, 7 (near Botanic Gardens), Segovia, 40002, Spain; tel (34) 921 437 261; fax 442 432; e-mail adelantado@eladelantado.com; web site www.adelantado-sg.es
Circ.: 5,000
Dir. – Carlos Herranz Cano

SEVILLA

ABC (D)
Avenida Albert Einstein 10, s/n. Isla de la Cartuja, Sevilla, 41092, Spain; tel (34) 95 448 8600; fax 448 8601; e-mail info@abc.es; web site www.abc.es
Circ.: 56,692
Mng. Dir. – Greg Avarra

EL CORREO DE ANDALUCIA (M-6X WK.)
Am□rico Vespucio 39. Isla de la Cartuja., Sevilla, 41092, Spain; tel (34) 95 448 8500; fax 446 2881; e-mail redaccion@correoandalucia.es; web site www.correoandalucia.com
Circ.: 27,000
Pres. – Jose Rodriguez

SORIA

DIARIO DE SORIA (D)
Morales Contreras 2, bajo, Soria, 42003, Spain; tel (34) 975 212 008; fax 221 504; e-mail diariosoria@maptel.es; web site www.diariodesoria.com
Ed. in Chief – Pilar Perez Soler

SORIA 7 DIAS (D)
The Col 17, Soria, 42002, Spain; tel (34) 975 233 607; fax 229 211; e-mail soriaredaccion@heraldo.es; web site www.heraldodesoria.es
Dir. – Esther Guerrero Gijon

TALAVERA DE LA REINA

LA VOZ DE TAJO (D)
Banderas de Castilla 2 (entreplanta), Talavera de la Reina, 45600, Spain; tel (34) 25 812400; fax 812454
Circ.: 10,000
Ed. in Chief – Joaquin Menendez del Rio

TARRAGONA

DIARI DE TARRAGONA (M-6X WK.)
Avinguda Roma 11, Tarragona, 43005, Spain; tel (34) 977 299 720; fax 223 013; e-mail diari@diaridetarragona.com; web site www.diaridetarragona.com
Circ.: 12,000
Dir. – Josep Correal

NOU DIARI TARRAGONA (D)
Avda. Presideny Companys 14, Tarragona, 43005, Spain; tel (34) 77 223377; fax 245092
Dir. – Joseph Garriga Argente

TERRASSA, BARCELONA

DIARI DE TERRASSA (5X WK.) EST. 1977
CA DE VINYALS 61, Terrassa, Barcelona, 08221, Spain; tel (34) 93 728 3700; fax 728 3719; e-mail anuncios@diariterrassa.es; web site www.diarideterrassa.es
Circ.: 65
Last Audit: November 23, 2011
Dir. – Anna Munoz Nunez
Asst. Dir. – Pedro Millan Reyes
Ed. in Chief – Julian Sanz

EL 9 NOU DEL VALLES OCCIDENTAL
Doctor Ulles 2a, 1r., Terrassa, Barcelona, 08224, Spain; tel (34) 93 7806633; fax 7883759
Dir. – Dolors Altarriba
Asst. Dir. – Joan Rueda

TERUEL

DIARIO DE TERUEL (D)
Avda. de Sagunto 27, Teruel, 44002, Spain; tel (34) 978 617 086; e-mail redaccion@diariodeteruel.net; web site www.diariodeteruel.net
Circ.: 2,800
MD – Juan Jose Francisco Valero

TOLEDO

ABC (DS)
Barriorey No.9, Toledo, 45001, Spain; tel (34) 925 284 407; fax 252 920; e-mail toledo@abc.es; web site www.abc.es
Circ.: 7,000
Dir. – Antonio Gonzalez Jerez

DIARIO 16 (D)
Pasaje de Mayoral 2 (Multicines Maria Cristina), Toledo, 45003, Spain; tel (34) 925 228100; fax 228114
Ed. in Chief – Joaquin Menendez del Rio

EL DIA DE TOLEDO (D)
Cuesta de Carlos V, 4-3Â§ izqda, Toledo, 45001, Spain; tel (34) 925 221 400; fax 214 065; web site www.eldiaencastillalamancha.com/to/
Circ.: 3,500
Mng. Dir. – Santiago Mateo Sahuquillo

LA VOZ DEL TAJO (D)
Calle Trinidad 47 - Mezzanine A, Toledo, 45600, Spain; tel (34) 925 722 151; fax 722 149; e-mail lavozdeltajo@lavozdeltajo.com; web site www.lavozdeltajo.com
Dir. – Segundo Marino Vasquez

YA (D)
Nuncio Viejo 3, 2.o. A, Toledo, 45002, Spain; tel (34) 925 211150; fax 211351
Ed. in Chief – Miguel Angel Larriba Terrell

VALENCIA

ABC (DS)
Plaza del Ayuntamiento 19, 9. A y B, Valencia, 46002, Spain; tel (34) 96 353 0237; fax 351 37 69; e-mail valencia@abc.es; web site www.abc.es
Dir. – Isaac Blasco

DIARIO 16 COMUNIDAD VALENCIA (D)
Cronista Carreres 9, 5.o. B-C, Valencia, 46003, Spain; tel (34) 96 3511442; fax 3512809
Ed. in Chief – Vicente Orti Hernandez

LEVANTE-EL MERCANTIL VALENCIANO (D)
Traginers 7, Valencia, 46014, Spain; tel (34) 96 399 2200; fax 399 2276; e-mail levante-emv@epi.es; web site www.levante-emv.com
Dir. – Fearne Belda
Pres./Ed. in Cheif – Francisco Mall

LAS PROVINCIAS (DS)
Poligono Industrial Vara de Quart, Calle Gremis 1, Valencia, 46014, Spain; tel (34) 96 350 2211; fax 354 6014; e-mail cartas@lasprovincias.es; web site www.lasprovincias.es
Dir. – Francisco Perez Puche

MINI DIARIO VALENCIA (D)
Street Jesus, 40-1, Valencia, 46007, Spain; tel (34) 96 346 2624; fax 346 2620; e-mail publicidad@minidiario.com
Dir., Finance – Ignacio Pedrosa

VALENCIA MARITIMA (5X WK.)
Doctor J.J. Domine 5, 1, Valencia, 46011, Spain; tel (34) 96 316 4515; fax 367 8555; web site www.veintepies.com
Circ.: 2Cristina Saiz

VALLADOLID

ABC (DS)
Santiago 19, Valladolid, 47001, Spain; tel (34) 983 373 211; fax 374 090; e-mail valladolid@abc.es; web site www.abc.es
Circ.: 15,000
– Lasael Daniel
– Jose Lucas MartinEd. in Chiefs

EL MUNDO DE VALLADOLID (D)
Avda. de Burgos 33, Valladolid, 47009, Spain; tel (34) 983 421 700; fax 421 717; e-mail redaccion.valladolid@el-mundo.es; web site www.elmundo.es
Dir. – Bidal Arranz
Asst. Dir. – Julian Ballestero Chillon

EL NORTE DE CASTILLA (DS)
Vazquez de Menchaca 8-10, Poligono de Argales, Valladolid, 47008, Spain; tel (34) 983 412 100; fax 412 111; e-mail norte@nortecastilla.es; ncdigital@nortecastilla.es; redaccion.nc@nortecastilla.es; web site www.nortecastilla.es
Circ.: 35,000
Mng. Dir. – Ignacio Berez
Ed. in Chief – Isabel Fernandez Barbadillo
Ed.in Chief – Carlos Ajanzo
Ed. in Chief – Fernando Bravo Santos
Ed. in Chief – Francisco Fernandez Bernardo

VIGO, PONTEVEDRA

ATLANTICO DIARIO (D)
Camelias 104, Vigo, Pontevedra, 36211, Spain; tel (34) 986 208 686; fax 201 269; e-mail atlantico@atlantico.net; web site www.atlantico.net
Circ.: 5,400
Dir. – Julio Rodriguez Gonzalez
Administrator – Marisol Pereiro

DIARIO 16 DE GALICIA (D)
Alcalde Lavadores 124, Vigo, Pontevedra, 36214, Spain; tel (34) 986 375200; fax 375631
Circ.: 50,000
Ed. in Chief – Alberto Alonso Gallego
Dir. – Manuel Quintero
Advertising – Miguel Angel Lavandeira

FARO DE VIGO (D)
Avenida Redondela 9-11, Vigo, Pontevedra, 36320, Spain; tel (34) 986 814 600; fax 814 615; e-mail local.faro@epi.es; web site www.farodevigo.es
Circ.: 36,800
Mktg. Mgr. – Victoria Ieleseas
Ed. – Jesus Portela Medrano

ZAMORA

LA OPINION-EL CORREO DE ZAMORA (D)
Rua de los Francos 20, Zamora, 49001, Spain; tel (34) 980 534 759; fax 513 552; web site www.laopiniondezamora.es
Circ.: 6,400
Deputy Dir. – Francisco Garcia Alonso
Dir. – Marisol Lopez

ZARAGOZA

ABC (D)
San Jorge 10, entlo., Zaragoza, 50001, Spain; tel (34) 976 290 061; fax 290 037; e-mail zaragoza@abc.gr; web site www.abc.es
Dir. – Manuel Trillo

DIARIO 16 ARAGON (D)
Avda. Cataluna 17, Zaragoza, 50014, Spain; tel (34) 976 396767; fax 294069

EL DIA (D)
Poligono El Portazgo, Km. 2400, Nave 24, Zaragoza, 50011, Spain; tel (34) 976 703500; fax 319006

EL EBRO ECONOMICO (D)
Poligono Argualas, s/n, Zaragoza, 50012, Spain; tel (34)
Dir. – Jose Luis Andres Lacasa

EL NUEVO DIA DE ARAGON (D)
Poligono Argualas, s/n, Zaragoza, 50012, Spain; tel (34) 976 703500; fax 319006
Dir. – Manuel Gracia Alonso

EL PERIODICO DE ARAGON (D)
Hernan Cortes 37, Zaragoza, 50005, Spain; tel (34) 976 700 400; fax 700 462; e-mail eparagon@elperiodico.com; web site www.elperiodico.es
Dir. – Jaime Armengol Cardiel
Asst. Dir. – Nicolas Espada
Chief Ed. – Juan Carlos Garcia de Frutos

HERALDO DE ARAGON (D)
Paseo de la Independencia 29, Zaragoza, 50001, Spain; tel (34) 976 765 000; fax 765 003; e-mail redaccion1@heraldo.es; web site www.heraldo.es
Circ.: 62,262
Dir. – Antonio Bruned Mompeon
Asst. Dir. – Jesus Frago Perez
Asst. Dir. – Jose Luis Trasobares Gavin
Chief Ed. – Alejandro Lucea Labuena
Chief Ed. – Jose Carlos Arnal Losilla
Chief Ed. – Luis Garcia Bandres
Chief Ed. – Encarna Samitier Lain

SWEDEN

ARBOGA

ARBOGA TIDNING (M-5X WK.)
Stortatan 28 B, Arboga, 73246, Sweden; tel (46) 589 85710; fax 85701; e-mail bjorn.johansson@ingress.se; web site www.ingress.se
Ed. in Chief – Jan-Erik Eriksson

AVESTA

AVESTA-TIDNING (D)
PO Box 163, Avesta, 77424, Sweden; tel (46) 226 86400; fax 86419; e-mail at.redaktionen@ingress.se; web site avestatidning.com
Circ.: 7,300
Dir. – Goran Lundberg
Ed. – Jan-Erik Eriksson
Adv. Mgr. – Rene Hustasffon

BOLLNAS

LJUSNAN (M-6X WK.)
PO Box 1059, Bollnas, 82112, Sweden; tel (46) 278 27500; fax 27519; web site www.ljusnan.se
Circ.: 15,000
Mng. Ed. – Ruben Jacobson

BORAS

BORAS TIDNING (M-D)
Allegatan 67, Boras, 50185, Sweden; tel (46) 33 700 0700; fax 101 436; e-mail redaktionen@bt.se; web site www.bt.se
Circ.: 47,000
Circ. Mgr. – Hakan Palmborg
Ed. – Jan Ojmertz

BORLANGE

BORLANGE TIDNING (D-6X WK.)
PO Box 29, Borlange, 78121, Sweden; tel (46) 243 25000; fax 11615
Circ.: 9,900
Mng. Dir. – Lennart Bengtsson

EKSJO

SMALANDS-TIDNINGEN (6X WK.)
PO Box 261, Eksjo, 57523, Sweden; tel (46) 381 13200; fax 17145; e-mail bo.eklund@smt.se; web site www.smt.se
Circ.: 18,700
MD – Bo Eklund

ENKOPING

ENKOPINGS-POSTEN (6X WK.)
PO Box 918, Enkoping, 74525, Sweden; tel (46) 171 414 600; fax 440 402; e-mail redaktionen@eposten.se; annonser@eposten.se; web site www.eposten.se
Circ.: 10,000
Ed. in Chief – Thomaz Andersson

ESKILSTUNA

ESKILSTUNA-KURIREN MED STRENGNAS TIDNING (6X WK.)
PO Box 120, Eskilstuna, 63102, Sweden; tel (46) 16 156 000; fax 156 248; e-mail redaktion@ekuriren.se; web site www.ekuriren.se
Circ.: 33,300
Mng. Dir. – Soren axelsson

FOLKET (M-6X WK.)
redaktionen@folket.se, Eskilstuna, 63105, Sweden; tel (46) 16 177 500; web site www.folket.se
Circ.: 15,409
Mktg. Dir. – Anders Boberg
Marie Hillblom

FALKENBERG

HALLANDS NYHETER (6X WK.)
Storgatan 22, Falkenberg, 31181, Sweden; tel (46) 346 29000; fax 29120; e-mail redaktionen@hn.se; web site www.hn.se
Circ.: 32,000
MD – Boine Getertz

FALKOPING

FALKOPINGS TIDNING (6X WK.)
Landbogatan 4, Falkoping, 52182, Sweden; tel (46) 515 670 400; e-mail debatt@vgt.se; web site www.falkopingstidning.se
Circ.: 13,700
MD – Sven Wedell
Ed. in Chief – Morgan Ahlberg
Contact – Borje Johansson

FALUN

DALA-DEMOKRATEN (6X WK.)
PO Box 825, Falun, 79129, Sweden; tel (46) 23 47500; fax 29115; e-mail redaktion@daladem.se; web site www.dalademokraten.es
Circ.: 20,000
Ed. in Chief – Goran Greider

FALU KURIREN (M-6X WK.)
PO Box 265, Falun, 79126, Sweden; tel (46) 23 93500; fax 93518; e-mail annonser@dt.se; web site www.dt.se
Circ.: 29,400
CEO – Tar Sagerstrom
Adv. Mgr – Peter Karlsson

GAVLE

ARBETARBLADET (D)
PO Box 287, Gavle, Sweden; tel (46) 26 159 300; fax 185 270; e-mail redaktionen@arbetarbladet.se; web site www.arbetarbladet.se
Circ.: 30,000
Pub. – Sven Johansson
Ed. – Kennet Lutti

GEFLE DAGBLAD (D)
PO Box 367, Gavle, 80105, Sweden; tel (46) 26 159 500; fax 159 710; e-mail familje@gd.se; web site www.gd.se
Circ.: 30,800
Ed. – Christina Vad Scautt

GOTEBORG

GOTEBORGS-POSTEN (D)
Polhemsplatsen 5, Goteborg, 40502, Sweden; tel (46) 31 624 000; e-mail redaktion@gp.se; web site www.gp.se
Circ.: 500,000
Advertising: Publicitas.
Ed. in Chief – Thomas Brunegard

GT (GOTEBORG TIDNINGEN) (E-7X WK.)
PO Box 417, Goteborg, 40126, Sweden; tel (46) 31 725 9000; fax 725 9201; web site www.gt.se
Ed. in Chief – Lars Maslund

IDAG VAST (7X WK.)
PO Box 417, Goteborg, 40126, Sweden; tel (46) 31 639000; fax 528350
Advertising: Publicitas.
Mng. Dir. – Tommy Carlsson
Ed. – Bengt Hansson
Adv. Mgr. – Torbjoern Wittstroem

HALMSTAD

HALLANDSPOSTEN (MS)
PO Box 144, Halmstad, 30181, Sweden; tel (46) 35 147 500; fax 147 688; e-mail info@hallandsposten.se; hp@hallandsposten.se; web site www.hallandsposten.se
Circ.: 32,200
MD – Goran Johansson
Ed. – Sverker Emanuelsson

HASSLEHOLM

NORRA SKANE (M-6X WK.)
Vapnaregatan 6, Hassleholm, 28181, Sweden; tel (46) 451 745 000; e-mail chefred@nsk.se; web site www.nsk.se
Circ.: 23,000
Ed. in Chief – Johan Hammarqvist

HEDEMORA

SODRA DALARNES TIDNING (6X WK.)
PO Box 42, Hedemora, 77600, Sweden; tel (46) 225 12100; fax 15900
Circ.: 6,300
Mng. Dir. – Lennart Bengtsson

HELSINGBORG

HELSINGBORGS DAGBLAD (MS)
Vasatorpsvagen 1, Helsingborg, 25108, Sweden; tel (46) 42 489 9000; fax 489 9165; e-mail helsingborg@hd.se; redaktionen@hd.se; web site www.hd.se/default.ssi
Circ.: 49,500
Dir. – Lars Svensson

NORDVASTRA SKANES TIDNINGAR (M)
Vasatorpsvagen 1, Helsingborg, 25183, Sweden; tel (46) 431 84000; e-mail nyhetsbordet@nst.se; web site www.nst.se; www.hd.se
Circ.: 42,400
MD – Lars Svensson

HUDIKSVALL

HUDIKSVALLS TIDNING (MED HALSINGLANDS TIDNING) (M-6X WK.)
PO Box 1201, Hudiksvall, 82415, Sweden; tel (46) 650 35555; fax 35560; e-mail redaktion@ht.se; web site www.ht.se
Circ.: 16,000
Mng. Dir. – Ruben Jacobsson
Ed. – Mats Tamvall

JONKOPING

JONKOPINGS-POSTEN/SMALANDS ALLEHANDA (6X WK.)
Skolgatan 24, Jonkoping, 55180, Sweden; tel (46) 36 304 050; fax 126 111; e-mail red@jonkopingsposten.sa; web site www.jonkopingsposten.sa
Circ.: 40,000
MD – Lovisa Hamrin

KALMAR

OSTRA SMALAND/NYHETERNA (6X WK.)
PO Box 612, Kalmar, 39126, Sweden; tel (46) 480 61334; fax 87545; e-mail familjered@ostrasmaland.se; web site www.ostran.se
Circ.: 15,000
Dir. – Karin Mattffon
Ed. in Cheif – Luf Carlsson
Ed. – Jan G. Andersson

BAROMETERN MED OSKARSHAMNS-TIDNINGEN (6X WK.)
Sodra Langgatan 33, Kalmar, 39188, Sweden; tel (46) 480 59100; fax 59131; web site www.barometern.se
Circ.: 48,500
Pres. – Gunilla Andreasson

KARLSKOGA

KARLSKOGA TIDNING (6X WK.)
PO Box 105, Karlskoga, 69127, Sweden; tel (46) 586 721 300; fax 58050; web site www.karlskogatid.se
Circ.: 11,241
Adv. Mgr. – Eric Wahlstlom
Ed. in Chief – Jonas Klint

KARLSKRONA

BLEKINGE LANS TIDNING (MED. SOLVEBORGS TIDNINGEN) (M-6X WK.)
Landbrogatan 15, Karlskrona, 37189, Sweden; tel (46) 455 77000; fax 19120; web site www.blt.se
Circ.: 35,400
Ed. – Justin Orman
Mktg. Mgr. – Merlene Danelson

SYDOSTRA SVERIGES DAGBLAD (M-6X WK.)
Landbrogatan 17, Karlskrona, 37188, Sweden; tel (46) 455 19000; fax 82237
Circ.: 18,000
Ed. – Anders Hagquist

KARLSTAD

NYA VERMLANDS-TIDNINGEN (M-6X WK.)
PO Box 28, Karlstad, 65102, Sweden; tel (46) 54 199 000; fax 199 600; e-mail redaktion@nwt.se; info@nwt.se; web site www.nwt.se
Circ.: 59,500
Ed. – Staffan Ander

VARMLANDS FOLKBLAD (M-6X WK.)
PO Box 67, Karlstad, 65103, Sweden; tel (46) 54 175 506; fax 175 599; web site www.vf.se
Circ.: 25,300
Ed. – Perolov Olsson

KATRINEHOLM

KATRINEHOLMS-KURIREN (M-6X WK.)
PO Box 111, Katrineholm, 64122, Sweden; tel (46) 150 72800; fax 53900; e-mail redaktion@kkuriren.se; web site www.kkuriren.se
Circ.: 13,000
Ed. – Krister Wistbacka

KOPING

BARGSLAGSBLADET (6X WK.)
PO Box 120, Koping, 73123, Sweden; tel (46) 221 36550; fax 36580; web site www.vlt.se
Circ.: 15,500
Mng. Dir. – Bengt Larsson

KRISTIANSTAD

KRISTIANSTADSBLADET (6X WK.)
Hornet Nya Boulevarden, Kristianstad, 29184, Sweden; tel (46) 44 185 500; fax 185 515; e-mail kb@kristianstadsbladet.se; web site www.kristianstadsbladet.se
Circ.: 29,900
Ed. in Chief – Lasse Bernfalk

LAHOLM

LAHOLMS TIDNING (M-6X WK.)
Tradgardsgatan 13, Laholm, 31230, Sweden; tel (46) 430 73700; fax 13532; e-mail lt@laholmstidning.se; web site www.laholmstidning.se
Circ.: 4,700
Ed. – Mona Davidsson

LIDKOPING

NYA LANS-TIDNINGEN (3X WK.)
Stenportsgatan 14, Lidkoping, 531 81, Sweden; tel (46) 510 89700; fax 89796; e-mail post@nlt.se; web site www.nlt.se
Circ.: 25,900
Ed. – Lennart Horling

LINKOPING

OSTGOTEN (6X WK.)
PO Box 330, Linkoping, 58103, Sweden; tel (46) 13 249400; fax 141194
Circ.: 5,800
Mng. Dir. – Janne Berglund
Ed. in Chief – Mark Olson

OSTGOTA CORRESPONDENTEN (M-6X WK.)
Badhusgatan 5, Linkoping, 58189, Sweden; tel (46) 13 280 250; fax 280 324; e-mail privatannons@corren.se; web site www.corren.se
Circ.: 66,300
Pub. – Ola Sigvardsson
News Mgr. – Anna-Karin Thorstensson

LJUNGBY

SMALANNINGEN (5X WK.)
PO Box 304, Ljungby, 34126, Sweden; tel (46) 372 69201; web site www.smalanningen.se
Circ.: 14,623
Ed. in Chief – Christer Gustafsson

LJUSDAL

LJUSDALS-POSTEN (E-6X WK.)
PO Box 707, Ljusdal, 82725, Sweden; tel (46) 651 13360; fax 585 060; web site www.ljp.se
Circ.: 7,000
Adv. Mgr. – Tony Bergstrom
Ed. in Chief – Anders Ingvarsson

LUDVIKA

NYA LUDVIKA TIDNING (M-6X WK.)
Carlavagen 21, Ludvika, 77130, Sweden; tel (46) 240 88200; fax 88230
Circ.: 10,400
Ed. in Chief – Karin Rosencrantz Bergdahl

LULEA

NORRBOTTENS-KURIREN (6X WK.)
PB 97181, Lulea, Sweden; tel (46) 920 262900; fax 37628; web site www.kuriren.nu
Circ.: 30,700
Ed. in Chief – Sture Bergmam

NORRLANDSKA SOCIALDEMOKRATEN (M-6X WK.)
Robertsviksgatan 5, Lulea, 97183, Sweden; tel (46) 920 36000; fax 89210; web site www.nsd.se
Circ.: 40,000
Ed. – Lennart Hakansson

LYSEKIL

LYSEKILSPOSTEN (E-4X WK.)
Rosviksgatan 9, Lysekil, 45300, Sweden; tel (46) 523 14050; fax 667 098; web site www.lysekilsposten.se
Circ.: 4,000
MD/Ed. in Chief – Helge Gustafzon

MALMO

IDAG SYG (ES)
Idag AB, Malmo, 20526, Sweden; tel (46) 40 281732; fax 939567

KVALLSPOSTEN (ES)
Sodergatan 24, Malmo, 20526, Sweden; tel (46) 40 602 0100; e-mail redaktionen@kvp.se; web site www.kvp.se
Circ.: 62,900
Ed. /Pub. – Lars Mohlin

SKANSKA DAGBLADET (M)
PO Box 165, Malmo, 20121, Sweden; tel (46) 40 660 5500; e-mail redaktion@skd.se; web site www.skanskan.se
Circ.: 29,400
Adv. Mgr. – Henerik Olsson
Ed. – Jan A. Johansson

SYDSVENSKA DAGBLADET (MS)
Krusegatan 19, Malmo, 20505, Sweden; tel (46) 40 281 200; fax 935 475; e-mail sydsvenskan@sydsvenskan.se; web site www.sydsvenskan.se
Circ.: 119,400
Advertising: Publicitas.
– Per Ohlsson
– Jan WifstrandEd.s

SYDSVENSKAN (MS)
Krusegaten 19, Malmo, 20505, Sweden; tel (46) 40 280 000; fax 935 475; e-mail sydsvenskan@sydsvenskan.se; web site www.sydsvenskan.se
Ed. in Chief – Daniel SandstrÅ£m

MARIESTAD

MARIESTADS-TIDNINGEN (M-5X WK.)
PO Box 242, Mariestad, 54223, Sweden; tel (46) 501 68700; fax 77558; web site www.mariestadstidningen.se
Circ.: 14,100
Adv. Mgr. – Tumas Semrin
Ed. in Chief – Karin Eriksson

MOTALA

MOTALA TIDNING MED VADSTENA TIDNING (M-6X WK.)
Industrigatan 9, Motala, 59135, Sweden; tel (46) 141 223 600; e-mail mt@motalatidning.se; web site www.motalatidning.se
Circ.: 13,000
MD – Uls Johansson

NORRKOPING

NORRKOPINGS TIDNINGAR (6X WK.)
Stohagsgatan 2, Norrkoping, 60183, Sweden; tel (46) 11 200 000; fax 200 140; e-mail redaktionen@nt.se; web site www.nt.se
Circ.: 48,100
Dir. – Lennart Foss
Ed. – Charli Nilsson

FOLKBLADET (6X WK.)
Storgatan 6, Norrkoping, 60184, Sweden; tel (46) 11 100 000; e-mail redaktion@folkbladet.se; web site www.folkbladet.se
Circ.: 18,000
Ed. in Chief – Christer Sandberg

NORRTALJE

NORRTALJE TIDNING (5X WK.)
Tibeliusgatan 1, Norrtalje, 76184, Sweden; tel (46) 176 79500; fax 10103; web site www.norrteljetidning.se
Circ.: 14,800
Ed. – Robert Johnsson

NYKOPING

SODERMANLANDS NYHETER (6X WK.)
St. Annegatan 3, Nykoping, 61179, Sweden; tel (46) 155 76700; fax 268 682; e-mail webmaster@sn.se; web site www.sn.se
Circ.: 25,300
Ed. – Goran Carstorp

OREBRO

BERGSLAGSPOSTEN (DS)
N Strandgatan 5, Orebro, 70192, Sweden; tel (46) 19 155 000; fax 105 290; e-mail webb@na.se; web site www.na.se
Circ.: 62,600
MD – Juan Sa Fanstrand
Ed. in Chief – Ulf Juansson
Mktg. Mgr. – Marie Alstrom

KARLSKOGA-KURIREN (6X WK.)
N Strandgatan 5, Orebro, 701 92, Sweden; tel (46) 19 155 000; e-mail info@nakoncernen.se; web site www.nakoncernen.se; www.karlskoga-kuriren.se
Circ.: 15,841
Mng. Dir. – Jerry Wiklund
Ed. in Chief – Helle Klein

NERIKES ALLEHANDA (D)
Norra Strandgatan 5, Orebro, 70192, Sweden; tel (46) 19 155 000; fax 120 383; e-mail na@na.se; web site www.na.se
Circ.: 62,600
Adv. Mgr – Magnus Lovang
Ed. in Chief – Wolf Johansson

ORNSKOLDSVIK

ORNSKOLDSVIKS ALLEHANDA (M-6X WK.)
PO Box 110, Ornskoldsvik, 89123, Sweden; tel (46) 660 295 500; fax 81907; web site www.allehanda.se
Circ.: 21,200
Mgr. – Anders Kallstrom
Ed. in Chief – Zimmit Nrslumb

TIDNINGEN ANGERMANLAND (M-6X WK.)
Box 110, Ornskoldsvik, 891 23, Sweden; tel (46) 660 295500; web site www.allehanda.se
Circ.: 16,060
Editor in Chief – Jimmie Naslund

OSKARSHAMN

OSKARSHAMNS - TIDNINGEN (6X WK.)
PO Box 992, Oskarshamn, 57224, Sweden; tel (46) 480 59 100; fax 59 111; web site www.ot.se
Circ.: 44,500
Mgr. – Lesa Lendan
Adv. Mgr. – Peter Kennander

OSTERSUND

LANSTIDNINGEN (M-6X WK.)
Kyrkgatan 52, Ostersund, 83189, Sweden; tel (46) 63 155 500; fax 155 595; e-mail redaktionen@ltz.se; web site www.ltz.se
Circ.: 17,000
Mgr. Dir. – Bjorn Hemmingsson
Ed. – Peter Swedenmark

OSTERSUNDS-POSTEN (M-6X WK.)
PO Box 720, Ostersund, 83128, Sweden; tel (46) 63 161 600; fax 105802; e-mail info@op.se; web site www.op.se
Circ.: 27,100
Ed. – Goran Henriksson

PITEA

PITEA-TIDNINGEN (M-6X WK.)
PO Box 193, Pitea, 94124, Sweden; tel (46) 911 64500; fax 64599; e-mail redaktionen@pitea-tidningen.se; web site www.pitea-tidningen.se
Circ.: 16,000
Ed. – Matt Ilelga
Mktg. Mgr. – Maria Lundkvist

SALA

SALA ALLEHANDA-OSTRA LANSTIDNINGEN (6X WK.)
PO Box 303, Sala, 73325, Sweden; tel (46) 224 56100; fax 56135; e-mail sa.info@ingress.se; web site www.vlt.se
Circ.: 10,700
Dir. – Goran Lundberg
Ed. in Chief – Jan-Erik Eriksson

SKARA

SKARABORGS LANS TIDNING (M-6X WK.)
Skaraborgsg. 17, Skara, 53230, Sweden; tel (46) 511 770 197; fax 770 199; web site www.skaraborgslanstidning.se
Circ.: 20,100
Ed. in Chief – Morgan Ahlberg

SKELLEFTEA

NORRA VASTERBOTTEN (6X WK.)
PO Box 58, Skelleftea, 93121, Sweden; tel (46) 910 57700; fax 57719; e-mail redaktion@norran.se; norran@norran.se; web site www.norran.se
Circ.: 29,000
Ed. – Anette Novak
Adv. Mgr. – Robert Erannstrom

SKOVDE

SKOVDE NYHETER (SKARABORGS TIDNINGEN) (M-6X WK.)
PO Box 409, Skovde, 54128, Sweden; tel (46) 500 770 200; fax 444 490; web site www.skovdenyheter.se
Circ.: 26,600
MD – Hans Moree
Ed. in Chief – Christer Svensson

SKOVDE, ERLING EKELUND

SKARABORG LANS ALLEHANDA (M-6X WK.)
PO Box 407, Skovde, Erling Ekelund, 54128, Sweden; tel (46) 500 467 500; fax 480 582; e-mail kundtjanst@sla.se; web site www.sla.se
Circ.: 23,700
Ed. – Mans Johnson

SODERHAMN

HALSINGE KURIREN (6X WK.)
PO Box 514, Soderhamn, 82627, Sweden; tel (46) 270 74000; fax 12807
Circ.: 11,600
Ed. – Ruben Jacobsson

SODERTALJE

LANSTIDNINGEN (6X WK.)
Storgatam 3-5, Sodertalje, 15182, Sweden; tel (46) 8 5509 2100; fax 5509 2178; e-mail redaktion@lt.se; web site www.lt.se
Circ.: 15,000
Ed. – Thomas Carlsson

STENUNGSUND, LYSEKIL

STENUNGSUNDS-POSTEN MED ORUST-TJORN (4X WK.)
PO Box 93, Stenungsund, Lysekil, 45322, Sweden; tel (46) 5231 4050; fax 523 667 098; e-mail redaktion@stenungsund-sposten.se; web site www.stenungsund-sposten.se
Circ.: 3,200
Ed. in Chief – Helge Gustafzon

STOCKHOLM

DAGEN (4X WK.)
Carpentry 4, Stockholm, 10536, Sweden; tel (46) 8 619 2400; fax 619 6051; e-mail info@dagen.se; publicopinion@dagen.se; web site www.dagen.se
Circ.: 18,200
Ed. – Elisabeth Sandlund

DAGENS INDUSTRI (M-6X WK.)
Torsgatan 21, Stockholm, 11390, Sweden; tel (46) 8 5736 5000; fax 5736 5220; e-mail info@di.se; web site www.di.se
Circ.: 102,000
Group: Bonnier AB
Advertising: Nielsen Communications.
Ed. in Chief – Peter Fellman

DAGENS NYHETER (MS)
Gjorwellsgatan 30, Marieberg, Stockholm, 10515, Sweden; tel (46) 8 738 1000; fax 738 2190; web site www.dn.se
Circ.: 361,600
Advertising: Publicitas.
Ed. – Guneilla Herligz

FINANS TIDNINGEN (5X WK.)
PO Box 70347, Stockholm, 10723, Sweden; tel (46) 8 5062 4500; fax 149 930; e-mail webmaster@fti.se; web site www.fti.se
Circ.: 9,200
Mng. Dir. – Frederick Rudback
Ed. in Chief – Jon Asberg
Ed. – Knut Carlgvist
Ed. – Tommy Borglund

EXPRESSEN (D)
Gjorwellsgatan 30, Stockholm, 10516, Sweden; tel (46) 8 738 3000; fax 619 0450; e-mail tips@expressen.se; web site www.expressen.se
Circ.: 374,200
Advertising: Publicitas.
Ed. in Chief/Pub. – Thomas Mattson

METRO (5X WK.)
PO Box 45075, Stockholm, 10430, Sweden; tel (46) 8 402 2030; e-mail redaktionen@metro.se; web site www.metro.se
Circ.: 252,000
CEO – Per Mikael Jensen
Pub. – Per Gunne
Mng. Dir. – Andreas Ohlson

POST-OCH INRIKES TIDNINGAR (5X WK.)
PO Box 49031, Stockholm, 10028, Sweden; tel (46) 8 5088 2913; fax 5088 2971; e-mail red@poit.org; web site www.poit.org

Circ.: 3,000
MD – Rolf Backlund
Ed. in Chief – Hans Holm

SVENSKA DAGBLADET (DS)

Master Samuelsgatan 56, Stockholm, 10517, Sweden; tel (46) 8 135 000; fax 135 140; e-mail synpunkt@svd.se; web site www.svd.se
Circ.: 187,600
Ed. in Chief – Lena K Samuelsson

STOCKHOLM, GLOBEN

AFTONBLADET (ES)

Arenavagen 63, Stockholm, Globen, 10518, Sweden; tel (46) 8 725 2000; fax 600 0177; e-mail ettan@aftonbladet.se; 71000@aftonbladet.se; web site www.aftonbladet.se
Circ.: 381,200
Ed. – Jan Helin
Adv. Mgr. – Anna Ericson

SUNDSVALL

DAGBLADET/NYA SAMHALLET (6X WK.)

PO Box 446, Sundsvall, 85106, Sweden; tel (46) 60 663 500; fax 127 823; e-mail kundtjanst@dagbladet.se; web site www.dagbladet.se; www.dagbladet.nu
Circ.: 11,300
Ed. – Ake Hardfeldt

SUNDSVALLS TIDNING (D)

Tradgardsgatan 27-29, Sundsvall, 85172, Sweden; tel (46) 60 197 000; fax 122 212; web site www.st.nu
Circ.: 30,000
Last Audit: March 22, 2010
Ed. in Chief – Kjell Carnbro
Adv.Mgr – Lars Nylen

TIDAHOLM

VASTGOTA-BLADET (6X WK.)

Villagatan 1, Tidaholm, 52202, Sweden; tel (46) 502 770 300; fax 770 349; web site www.vastgotabladet.se
Circ.: 3,500
Gen Mgr. – Lotta Hjarne
Ed. in Chief – Morgan Ahlberg

TRANAS

TRANAS-POSTEN (M-6X WK.)

PO Box 1020, Tranas, 57328, Sweden; tel (46) 140 385 570; fax 12111
Circ.: 2,800
Pub./Ed. – Jan Justegard

TRELLEBORG

TRELLEBORGS ALLEHANDA (M-6X WK.)

PO Box 73, Trelleborg, 23121, Sweden; tel (46) 410 54500; fax 17100; web site www.trelleborgsallehanda.se
Circ.: 11,000
Ed. in Chief – Margaretha Engstrom

TROLLHATTAN

TTELA (M-6X WK.)

PO Box 54, Trollhattan, 46122, Sweden; tel (46) 520 422600; fax 10127; e-mail redaktionen@ttela.se; web site www.ttela.se
Circ.: 17,300
Group: Mediebolaget Västkusten Stampen
executive director – Tommy Hermansson

Editor-in-chief – Morgan Ahlberg

TROLLH TTAN

TTELA (6X WK.) EST. 2004

Box 54, Trollh□ttan, 46122, Sweden; tel (46) 520 422600; e-mail redaktion@ttela.se; web site ttela.se
Circ.: 14,300
Group: Mediebolaget Västkusten
Executive Director – Tommy Hermansson

UDDEVALLA

BOHUSLANINGEN MED DALS DAGBLAD (M-6X WK.)

Norra Drottninggatan 19-21, Uddevalla, 45183, Sweden; tel (46) 522 99000; fax 511 888; e-mail redaktionen@bohuslaningens.se; web site www.bohuslaningen.se
Circ.: 32,400
Ed. – Ingalill Yusupov

UMEA

VASTERBOTTENS FOLKBLAD (M-6X WK.)

PO Box 3164, Umea, 90304, Sweden; tel (46) 90 170 000; fax 170 250; e-mail redioeionen@folkbladt.nu; web site www.folkbladet.nu
Circ.: 20,600
Ed. in Chief/ Adv. Mgr. – Ronald Edlund

VASTERBOTTENS-KURIREN (M-6X WK.)

Forradsvagen 9, Umea, 90170, Sweden; tel (46) 90 151 177; fax 774 647; e-mail info@vk.se; web site www.vk.se
Circ.: 41,500
Ed. in Chief – Torbjorn Bergmark

UPPSALA

UPSALA NYA TIDNING (D)

PO Box 36, Uppsala, 75103, Sweden; tel (46) 18 478 1000; fax 692 594; e-mail prenumerera@unt.se; web site www.unt.se
Circ.: 64,400
CEO – Dan Lannero
Ed. – Lars Nilsson

VARNAMO

VARNAMO NYHETER (M-4X WK.)

Storgatsbacken 13, Varnamo, 33184, Sweden; tel (46) 370 300 600; web site www.varnamonyheter.se
Circ.: 19,200
Mng. Dir. – Maths Berggren
Adv. Mgr. – Stefan Berdh
Ed. in Chief – Lars Alkner

VASTERAS

VESTMANLANDS LANS TIDNING (M-6X WK.)

PO Box 3, Vasteras, 72103, Sweden; tel (46) 21 199 000; fax 199 060; e-mail nyheter@vlt.se; web site www.vlt.se
Circ.: 42,200
Dir. – Juan FarnStrand
Mng. Ed. – Martin Enberg

VASTERVIK

VASTERVIKS-TIDNINGEN (M-6X WK.)

Stora Torget 2, Vastervik, 59382, Sweden; tel (46) 490 66600; fax 66699; e-mail vt.red@vt.se; web site www.vt.se
Circ.: 14,000
Ed. in Chief – Charli Nilsson

VAXJO

SMALANDSPOSTEN (M-6X WK.)

Smalandsposten, Linnegatan 2, Vaxjo, 35170, Sweden; tel (46) 470 770 500; web site www.smp.se
Circ.: 41,500
Adv. Mgr. – Mmaria Churesson
Ed. – Magnus Karlsson

VETLANDA

VETLANDA-POSTEN (6X WK.)

PO Box 63, Vetlanda, 57421, Sweden; tel (46) 383 763 210; fax 763 210; e-mail vetlandared@smt.se; web site www.vetlanda-posten.se
Circ.: 10,448
Ed. in Chief – Mari Ermeland

VIMMERBY

VIMMERBY TIDNING/KINDA-POSTEN (M-6X WK.)

Stangagatan 46, Vimmerby, 59880, Sweden; tel (46) 492 16000; fax 10102; e-mail redaktion@vimmerbytidning.se; web site www.vimmerbytidning.com
Circ.: 11,600
Ed. in Chief – Bengt Ingemarsson

VISBY, GOTLAND COUNTY

GOTLANDS TIDNINGAR (M-6X WK.)

PO Box 1223, Visby, Gotland County, 62123, Sweden; tel (46) 498 202 500; fax 215080; e-mail redaktion@gotlandstidningar.se; web site www.helagotland.se
Circ.: 13,600
MD. – Marie Ahlgren
Ed. in Chief – Ulf Hammarlund
Ed. in Chief – Hakan Ericsson
Mktg. Mgr – Rolf Wahlgren

GOTLANDS ALLEHANDA (6X WK.)

PO Box 1284, Visby, Gotland County, 62123, Sweden; tel (46) 498 202 550; fax 202 597; e-mail redaktion@gotlandsallehanda.se; web site www.helagotland.se
Circ.: 12,400
MD – Lars Herlin

YSTAD

YSTADS ALLEHANDA (M-6X WK.)

Lilla Norregatan 9, Ystad, 27181, Sweden; tel (46) 411 557 800; fax 13955; web site www.ystadsallehanda.se
Circ.: 24,100
Ed. in Chief – Margaretha Engstrom

SWITZERLAND

ALTDORF

NEUE URNER ZEITUNG (D.)

Herrengasse 2, Altdorf, 6460, Switzerland; tel (41) 41 874 2160; fax 874 2161; e-mail redaktion@neue.ch; redaktion@zisch.ch; web site www.zisch.ch
Circ.: 4,100
Ed. in Chief – Bruno Arnold
Gen. Mgr. – Thomas Bornhauser

NEUE URNER ZEITUNG (D-6X WK.)

Hofligasse 3, Altdorf, 6460, Switzerland; tel (41) 41 874 2160; fax 874 2161; web site www.zisch.ch
Circ.: 3,500
Ed. in Chief – Bruno Arnold

ALTSTAETTEN, ST. GALLEN

RHEINTALISCHE VOLKSZEITUNG (6X WK.)

PF 9450, Altstaetten, St. Gallen, 9001, Switzerland; tel (41) 71 757 7555; fax 757 7545; e-mail redaktion@rva.ch; web site www.rva.ch
Circ.: 5,700
Ed. in Chief – Rene Jaan

APPENZELL

APPENZELLER VOLKSFREUND (4X WK.)

Engelgasse 3, Appenzell, 9050, Switzerland; tel (41) 71 788 3000; fax 788 5021; web site www.dav.ch
Circ.: 5,300
Ed. in Chief – Markus Rusch

ARBON, THURGAU

TAGBLATT THURGAU (6X WK.)

Romanshornerstrasse 36, Arbon, Thurgau, 9320, Switzerland; tel (41) 71 447 6060; fax 447 6070; web site www.tagblatt.ch
Circ.: 15,900
Ed. in Chief – Christian Kunn

BADEN

AARGAUER ZEITUNG (6X WK.)

Stadtturmstrasse 19, Baden, 5401, Switzerland; tel (41) 58 200 5858; fax 200 5859; web site www.aargauerzeitung.ch
Circ.: 15,000
Ed. in Chief – Peter Buri

BASEL, BASEL-STADT

BASLER ZEITUNG (6X WK.)

Hochbergerstrasse 15, Basel, Basel-Stadt, 4002, Switzerland; tel (41) 61 639 1111; fax 631 1582; e-mail redaktion@baz.ch; web site www.baz.ch
Circ.: 114,686
Advertising: Publicitas.
Mng. Ed. – M. Hicklin

BELLINZONA, TICINO

LA REGIONE (6X WK.)

via Ghiringhelli 9, Bellinzona, Ticino, 6500, Switzerland; tel (41) 91 821 1121; fax 821

1122; e-mail info@laregione.ch; web site www.laregione.ch
Circ.: 30,538
Ed. in Chief – Matteo Caratti
Ed. – Giacomo Salvioni

BERN

BERNER ZEITUNG BZ (6X WK.)
Nordring/Dammweg 9, Bern, 3001, Switzerland; tel (41) 31 330 3111; fax 330 3730; e-mail werbung@espace.ch; web site www.bernerzeitung.ch
Circ.: 131,515
Ed. – Michael Hug

BERNE

DER BUND (6X WK.)
Dammweg 9, Berne, 3001, Switzerland; tel (41) 31 385 1111; fax 385 1112; e-mail derbund@derbund.ch; web site www.derbund.ch
Circ.: 50,000
Advertising: Publicitas.
CEO – Ueli Eckstein
Ed – Artur Vogel

BERNECK ST. GALLEN

DER RHEINTALER (6X WK.)
Hafnerwisenstrasse 1, Berneck St. Gallen, 9442, Switzerland; tel (41) 71 747 2222; fax 747 2220; e-mail rdv@rdv.ch; web site www.rdv.ch
Circ.: 11,023
Gen. Mgr. – Rene Wuffli

BIEL

BIELER TAGBLATT (6X WK.)
Longfeldweg 135, Biel, 2501, Switzerland; tel (41) 32 321 9111; fax 321 8338; e-mail btredaktion@bielnews.ch; web site www.bielertagblatt.ch
Circ.: 33,281
Pub. – W. Gassman

BIENNE

JOURNAL DU JURA (6X WK.)
Case postale 624, Bienne, 2501, Switzerland; tel (41) 32 321 9000; fax 321 9009; e-mail redactionjj@journaldujura.ch; web site www.journaldujura.ch
Circ.: 13,131
Ed. in Chief – Stephane Devaux
Mktg. Mgr. – Martin Burki

BISCHOFSZELL, THURGAU

BISCHOFSZELLER ZEITUNG (6X WK.)
Grabenstrasse 1, Bischofszell, Thurgau, 9220, Switzerland; tel (41) 71 4221921; fax 4221988
Circ.: 3,790
Ed. in Chief – Dr. Peter Forster

BISCHOFSZELLER NACHRICHTEN (6X WK.)
Bahnhofstrasse 1, Bischofszell, Thurgau, 9220, Switzerland; tel (41) 71 4222533; fax 4222344
Circ.: 900
Ed. in Chief – Esther Simon

BRIG, VALAIS/WALLIS

WALLISER BOTE (MIT WALLISER SPIEGEL) (6X WK.)
Furkastrasse 21, Brig, Valais/Wallis, 3900, Switzerland; tel (41) 27 922 9988; fax 922 9989; e-mail info@walliserbote.ch; web site www.walliserbote.ch
Circ.: 26,727Thomas

BUCHS, ST. GALLEN

WERDENBERGER UND OBERTOGGENBURGER (6X WK.)
Bahnhofstr. 14, Buchs, St. Gallen, 9471, Switzerland; tel (41) 81 750 0202; fax 750 0209; e-mail info@buchsmedien.ch; web site www.w-und-o.ch
Circ.: 10,000
Ed. in Chief – Thomas Schwizer

BULACH, ZURICH

NEUES BULACHER TAGBLATT (6X WK.)
Bahnhofstrasse 44, Bulach, Zurich, 8180, Switzerland; tel (41) 44 8601414; fax 8605114
Circ.: 6,200
Ed. in Chief – Dr. Hans Ulrich Graf

BURGDORF, BERN

BURGDORFER TAGBLATT (5X WK.)
Postfach 496, Burgdorf, Bern, 3400, Switzerland; tel (41) 34 222256; fax 234801
Circ.: 3,100
Ed. in Chief – Werner Zuber
Ed. – Christine Kunzler

CHUR, GRAUBUENDEN/GRISONS

BUNDNER TAGBLATT (6X WK.)
Commireicil. 22, Chur, Graubuenden/Grisons, 7000, Switzerland; tel (41) 81 255 5050; fax 255 5123; web site www.suedostschweiz.ch
Circ.: 12,826
Ed. – Hanstitir Librunint

CHUR, GRAUBUNDEN/GRISONS

DIE SU DOSTSCHWEIZ (D)
Comercialstrasse. 22, Chur, Graubunden/Grisons, 7007, Switzerland; tel (41) 81 255 5050; fax 255 5100; e-mail zentral.redaktion@suedostschweiz.ch; web site www.suedostschweiz.ch
Circ.: 139,568
Ed. – Andrea Masucger
Susanne Ledrunent-Adv. Mgr. – Susanne Ledrunent

DELEMONT, JURA

LE QUOTIDIEN JURASSIEN (6X WK.)
Route de Courroux 6, Delemont, Jura, 2800, Switzerland; tel (41) 32 421 1919; fax 421 1890; e-mail democrate@bluewin.ch; web site www.democrate.ch; www.lqj.ch
Circ.: 24,900
Dir. – Michel Voisard

DIELSDORF

ZURCHER UNTERLANDER (6X WK.)
Training race 12, Dielsdorf, 8157, Switzerland; tel (41) 44 8548282; fax 8530690; e-mail redaktion@zuonline.ch; web site www.zuonline.ch
Circ.: 17,900
Bus. Mgr. – E. Herkenrath
Ed. in Chief – Christine Fivian
Ed. – C. Schonz

DIETIKON

LIMMATTALER TAGBLATT (D)
Postfach 504, Dietikon, 8953, Switzerland; tel (41) 58 200 5777; fax 200 5758; e-mail redaktion@limmattalerzeitung.ch
Circ.: 10,500
Ed. in Chief – Daniel Winter

EINSIEDELN, SCHWYZ

EINSIEDLER ZEITUNG (6X WK.)
PF 48, Einsiedeln, Schwyz, 8842, Switzerland; tel (41) 55 532220; fax 535061
Circ.: 2,977
Ed. in Chief – Oskar Hiestand
Bus. Mgr. – J. Thali

FLAWIL, ST. GALLEN

DER VOLKSFREUND/WILER ZEITUNG/GOSSAUER ZEITUNG (6X WK.)
Burgauerstrasse 50, Flawil, St. Gallen, 9230, Switzerland; tel (41) 71 394 9696; fax 393 8382; e-mail info@dfag.ch; web site www.dfag.ch
Circ.: 10,473
Ed. – Guido Bertuzzi

FRAUENFELD, THURGAU

THURGAUER VOLKSZEITUNG (6X WK.)
PF 982, Frauenfeld, Thurgau, 8500, Switzerland; tel (41) 54 7211845; fax 7222268
Circ.: 3,000
Bus. Mgr. – U. Herberger

THURGAUER ZEITUNG (6X WK.)
Promenadenstrasse 16, Frauenfeld, Thurgau, 8501, Switzerland; tel (41) 52 723 5511; fax 721 0002; web site www.thurgauerzeitung.ch
Circ.: 31,866
MD – Ursula Fraefel

FRIBOURG

LA LIBERTE (6X WK.)
Blvd. Perolles 42, Fribourg, 1700, Switzerland; tel (41) 26 426 4411; fax 426 4400; e-mail redaction@laliberte.ch; web site www.laliberte.ch
Circ.: 40,000
Ed. – Louis Ruffieux
Mktg. Mgr. – Nancy Zurcher

FRIBOURG, FREIBURG

FREIBURGER NACHRICHTEN (6X WK.)
Bahnhofplatz 5, Fribourg, Freiburg, 1700, Switzerland; tel (41) 26 347 3076; fax 426 4740; e-mail fn.verlag@freiburger-nachrichten.ch; web site www.freiburger-nachrichten.ch
Circ.: 16,131
Ed. – Gilbert Buahler
Adv. Mgr. – Naghalea Bosuschbacher

GENEVA

JOURNAL DE GENEVE ET GAZETTE DE LAUSANNE (6X WK.)
Case Postale 5160, Geneva, 1211-11, Switzerland; tel (41) 22 8198888; fax 8198989
Circ.: 29,500
Advertising: Publicitas.
Bus. Mgr. – Marian Stepczynski
Ed. in Chief – Antoine Maurice
Ed. in Chief – P. Garein

LE COURRIER (6X WK.)
Rue de la Truite 3, Geneva, 1211, Switzerland; tel (41) 22 809 5555; fax 809 5567; e-mail lecteurs@lecourrier.ch; web site www.lecourrier.ch
Circ.: 10,000
Ed. in Chief – Fabio Lo Verso
Assoc. Ed. – Rachad Armanios

TRIBUNE DE GENEVE (M)
11 rue des Rois, Geneva, 1204, Switzerland; tel (41) 22 322 4000; fax 781 0107; e-mail news@tdg.ch; web site www.tdg.ch
Circ.: 78,000
Advertising: Publicitas.
Ed. – Pierre Ruetschi

GLARUS

GLARNER NACHRICHTEN (6X WK.)
PF 366, Glarus, 8750, Switzerland; tel (41) 55 640 1921; fax 640 6440
Circ.: 10,976

HALLAU, SCHAFFHAUSEN, FRONHOF

KLETTGAUER ZEITUNG/SCHAFFHAUSERLAND
., Hallau, Schaffhausen, Fronhof, Switzerland; tel (41) 52 6813129; fax 6814006
Circ.: 2,908
Ed. – Fritz Gruninger

HERISAU, AARGAU

APPENZELLER ZEITUNG (6X WK.)
Kasernenstrasse 64, Herisau, Aargau, 9100, Switzerland; tel (41) 71 354 6474; fax 354 6475; e-mail redaktion@appon.ch; web site www.appon.ch
Circ.: 14,500
Pub. – Marcel Steiner
Adv. Mgr. – Monika Egli

INTERLAKEN, BERN

OBERLANDISCHES VOLKSBLATT OV (6X WK.)
Bahnhofstr. 15, Interlaken, Bern, 3800, Switzerland; tel (41) 36 232370; fax 224041
Circ.: 10,900
Ed. in Chief – Ueli Fluck
Ed. – Peter Schmid
Ed. – Sandro Hugli
Ed. in Chief – A. Karlen

KREUZLINGEN, THURGAU

THURGAUER VOLKSFREUND MIT TAGESSPIEGEL (6X WK.)
Zelgstrasse 1, Kreuzlingen, Thurgau, 8280, Switzerland; tel (41) 71 686 5252; fax 686 5251
Circ.: 9,000
Bus. Mgr. – P. Ruckstuhl

KRONBUHL

RORSCHACHER ZEITUNG (6X WK.)
Hofstestr.14, Kronbuhl, 9302, Switzerland; tel (41) 71 292 2929; fax 292 2938
Circ.: 3,400
Ed. in Chief – Edgar Oehler
Exec. Ed. – Dr. Roland Mattes

LA CHAUX-DE-FONDS , NEUCHATEL

L'IMPARTIAL (6X WK.)
Rue Neuve 14, La Chaux-de-Fonds , Neuchatel, 2300, Switzerland; tel (41) 32 910 2001; fax 910 2009; e-mail info@lexpress.ch; web site www.arcinfo.ch
Circ.: 26,951
Ed. in Chief – Nicolas Willemin

LACHEN

MARCH-ANZEIGER (5X WK.)
Alpenblickstrasse 26, Lachen, 8853, Switzerland; tel (41) 55 451 0888; fax 451 0889; web site www.marchanzeiger.ch
Ed. in Chief – Stephen Gruter

LANGENTHAL, BERN

BERNER RUNDSCHAU/LANGENTHALER TAGBLATT (D)
Schulhausstrasse 2a, Langenthal, Bern, 4900, Switzerland; tel (41) 62 919 5023; fax 919 5043; e-mail info@mzbern.ch; web site www.a-z.ch
Circ.: 50,000
Ed. – Fox Shield
Adv. Mgr. – Walter Reiser

LAUSANNE

L'AGEFI (5X WK.)
PO Box 5031, Lausanne, 1002, Switzerland; tel (41) 21 331 4141; fax 331 4110; e-mail agefi@agefi.com; web site www.agefi.com
Circ.: 8,000
Dir. – Eric Valette
Mktg. Mgr. – Patrica Kung

LAUSANNE, VAUD

24 HEURES (6X WK.)
Case Postale 585, Lausanne, Vaud, 1001, Switzerland; tel (41) 21 349 4444; fax 349 4419; e-mail 24heures@edipresse.ch; web site www.24heures.ch
Circ.: 91,096
Advertising: Publicitas.
Pub. – Eric Hoesli
Ed. – Thierry Meyer

LE MATIN (DS)
Case Postale 1095, Lausanne, Vaud, 1001, Switzerland; tel (41) 21 349 4545; fax 349 4929; e-mail lematin@edipresse.ch; web site www.lematin.ch
Redactrice – Ariane Dayer
Mktg. Dir. – Patrice Matthey

LE NOUVEAU QUOTIDIEN (5X WK.)
78 chemin de Montelly, Lausanne, Vaud, 1007, Switzerland; tel (41) 21 6262524; fax 6262523
Circ.: 38,100
– Jacques Pilet
– Joalle Kuntz
– X. Pellegrini
– J.J. RothEd. in Chiefs

NOUVELLE REVUE ET JOURNAL POLITIQUE (D)
Ave. Ruchonnet 15, Lausanne, Vaud, 1001, Switzerland; tel (41) 21 340 0011; fax 340 0030
Circ.: 6,790
Ed. in Chief – Martine Bailly

LIESTAL, BASELLAND

BASELLANDSCHAFTLICHE ZEITUNG (D)
Rheinstrasse 3, Liestal, Baselland, 4410, Switzerland; tel (41) 61 927 2600; fax 921 2268; web site www.bz-ag.ch
Circ.: 69,000
Ed. in Chief – Franz C. Widmer

LUCERNE, LUZERN

LUZERN HEUTE (5X WK.)
Denkmalstr. 2, Lucerne, Luzern, 6000, Switzerland; tel (41) 8 4104481; fax 4121055; e-mail luheu@centralnet.ch; web site www.centralnet.ch/luheu
Circ.: 3,000
Ed. in Chief – Sandra Baumeler
Bus. Mgr. – T. Demuth

NEUE LUZERNER ZEITUNG (6X WK.)
Maihofstrasse 76, Lucerne, Luzern, 6002, Switzerland; tel (41) 41 429 51 51; fax 429 51 81; e-mail redaktion@luzernerzeitung.ch; web site www.zisch.ch
Circ.: 130,315
Chief-Editor – Thomas Bornhauser

LUGANO, TICINO

GIORNALE DEL POPOLO (6X WK.)
Via San Gottardo 50, Casella postale 233, Lugano, Ticino, 6903, Switzerland; tel (41) 91 910 3565; fax 922 3805; e-mail lugano@gdp.ch; web site www.gdp.ch
Circ.: 26,485
Bus. Mgr. – F. Balmelli
Mktg. Mgr. – Angelo Paglarini

LUZERN

NEUE NIDWALDNER ZEITUNG (6X WK.)
Maihofstrasse 76, Luzern, 6002, Switzerland; tel (41) 41 429 51 51; e-mail redaktion@luzernerzeitung.ch; web site www.luzernerzeitung.ch
Circ.: 18,000
Ed. in Chief – Thomas Bornhauser

MELS, ST. GALLEN

SARGANSERLANDER (5X WK.)
Zachaustrasse 50, Mels, St. Gallen, 8887, Switzerland; tel (41) 81 723 3761; fax 723 7018; e-mail h.gmur@sarganserlander.ch
Circ.: 10,272
Ed. in Chief – Heinc Gmur

MONTREUX, VAUD

LA PRESSE (6X WK.)
22 Ave. des Planches, Montreux, Vaud, 1820, Switzerland; tel (41) 21 966 8181; fax 966 8182
Circ.: 22,893
Ed. in Chief – Pierre-Alain Luginbuhl

MUZZANO, TICINO

CORRIERE DEL TICINO (6X WK.)
Via Industria, Muzzano, Ticino, 6933, Switzerland; tel (41) 91 960 3131; fax 968 2779; e-mail cdt@cdt.ch; web site www.cdt.ch
Circ.: 37,000
Advertising: Publicitas.
Ed. – Giancarlo Dillena

NEUCHATEL

L'EXPRESS (6X WK.)
Case Postale 22, Neuchatel, 2001, Switzerland; tel (41) 32 723 5300; fax 723 5219; e-mail info@lexpress.ch; web site www.arcinfo.ch
Circ.: 31,708
Group: Reseau Select/Select Network
MD – Fabien Wolfrath

NYON, VAUD

LE QUOTIDIEN DE LA COTE (5X WK.)
Route Dustrnd 6H, Nyon, Vaud, 1256, Switzerland; tel (41) 22 994 4111
Circ.: 9,000
Ed. in Chief – Jacques Richard

OLTEN, SOLOTHURN

OLTNER TAGBLATT (6X WK.)
Ziegelfeldstrasse 60, Olten, Solothurn, 4600, Switzerland; tel (41) 62 324141; fax 322154
Circ.: 21,147
Ed. in Chief – Kurt Schibler
Ed. in Chief – K. Schibler
Ed. in Chief – B. Nutzi
Bus. Mgr. – A. Tabeling

SOLOTHURNER NACHRICHTEN (6X WK.)
Ziegelfeldstrasse 60, Olten, Solothurn, 4600, Switzerland; tel (41) 62 762808; fax 762917
Circ.: 2,853
Ed. in Chief – W. Knusel

RAPPERSWIL

LINTH ZEITUNG (6X WK.)
Postfach 1437, Rapperswil, 8640, Switzerland; tel (41) 55 220 4242; fax 220 4243; e-mail redaktion.opersee@zsz.ch; web site www.zsz.ch
Circ.: 13,800
Dir. – Michael Kaspar

RORSCHACH, ST. GALLEN

OSTSCHWEIZER TAGBLATT (6X WK.)
Signalstrasse 15, Rorschach, St. Gallen, 9400, Switzerland; tel (41) 71 8414345; fax 8414233
Circ.: 7,800
Pub. – Urs Lanz

SAINT GALLEN

OSTSCHWEIZER AZ (5X WK.)
PF 221, Saint Gallen, 9008, Switzerland; tel (41) 71 2457777; fax 2447701
Circ.: 3,600
– Jurg Bareiss
– Michael WaltherEd.s

DIE OSTSCHWEIZ (6X WK.)
Oberer Graben 8, Saint Gallen, 9001, Switzerland; tel (41) 71 308580
Circ.: 21,642
Bus. Mgr. – Dr. E. Dahler
Ed. in Chief – S. Luchinger
Mng. Ed. – H. Stadelmann

ST GALLER TAGBLATT (6X WK.)
Furstenlandstrasse 122, Saint Gallen, 9001, Switzerland; tel (41) 71 272 7888; fax 272 7475; web site www.tagblatt.ch
Circ.: 93,450
Ed. – Gottlieb Hoepli

SARGANS, ST. GALLEN

OBERLANDER TAGBLATT (6X WK.)
Schwefeldbadplatz, Sargans, St. Gallen, 7320, Switzerland; tel (41) 36 7234022; fax 7233003
Circ.: 1,572
Ed. – J. Gadient

SCHAFFHAUSEN

SCHAFFHAUSER NACHRICHTEN (6X WK.)
Vordergasse 58, Schaffhausen, 8000, Switzerland; tel (41) 52 633 3111; fax 633 3401; e-mail neininger@shn.ch; web site www.shn.ch
Circ.: 26,000
Ed. in Chief – Norbert Neininger

SCHAFFHAUSER AZ (6X WK.)
Webergasse 39, Schaffhausen, 8201, Switzerland; tel (41) 52 633 0833; fax 633 0834; e-mail sh-az@bluewin.ch; web site www.schaffhauseraz.ch
Circ.: 3,000
Ed. in Chief – Bea Hauser

SCHWYZ

BOTE DER URSCHWEIZ (D)
Schmiedgasse 7, Schwyz, 6431, Switzerland; tel (41) 41 819 0809; fax 819 0853; web site www.bote.ch
Circ.: 15,600
Ed. in Chief – Josias Clavadetscher

NEUE SCHWYZER ZEITUNG (6X WK.)
Bahnofstrasse 14, Schwyz, 6430, Switzerland; tel (41) 43 811 3333; fax 811 7428
Circ.: 3,600
Ed. – B. Schnuriger

SION, VALAIS

NOUVELLISTE (6X WK.)
rue de l'Industrie 13, Sion, Valais, 1950, Switzerland; tel (41) 27 329 7511; fax 329 7578; e-mail redaction@nouvelliste.ch; web site www.nouvelliste.ch
Circ.: 42,066
Ed. – Joan Bonnard

SOLOTHURN

SOLOTHURNER ZEITUNG (D)
PF 848, Solothurn, 4501, Switzerland; tel (41) 32 624 7111; fax 624 7444; e-mail info@vsonline.ch; web site www.szonline.ch
Circ.: 47,400
Ed. in Chief – Theodor Eckert

STAFA, ZURICH

ZURICHSEE-ZEITUNG (5X WK.)
Seestrasse 86, Stafa, Zurich, 8712, Switzerland; tel (41) 44 928 5555; fax 928 5520; e-mail redaktion.staefa@zsz.ch; web site www.zsz.ch

Circ.: 53,000
Ed. in Chief – Benjamin Geiger
Ed. – Michael Kaspar

SULGEN

THURGAUER ANZEIGER (6X WK.)
Sulgen, Switzerland; tel (41) 72 421414; fax 424179
Circ.: 2,500
Ed. – Roman Salzmann

TEUFEN, AARGAU

APPENZELLER TAGBLATT (6X WK.)
Hauptstr. 39, Teufen, Aargau, 9053, Switzerland; tel (41) 41 3350933; fax 3350939
Circ.: 5,240
Ed. – W. Meier

THUN

BERNER OBERLANDER (6X WK.)
Rampenstr. 1, Thun, 3602, Switzerland; tel (41) 33 225 1530; fax 225 1500; e-mail redaktion-tt@bom.ch; web site www.berner-oberlaender.ch
Circ.: 20,891
Pub. – G. Maurer
Bus. Mgr. – Konrad Maurer

THUN, BERN

THUNER TAGBLATT (6X WK.)
Rampenstrasse 1, Thun, Bern, 3602, Switzerland; tel (41) 33 225 15 55; fax 225 15 00; web site tt.bernerzeitung.ch/schweiz
Circ.: 18,759
CEO – Konrad Maurer

USTER, ALTDORF

ANZEIGER VON USTER (6X WK.)
Oberlandstrasse 100, Uster, Altdorf, 8610, Switzerland; tel (41) 44 905 7900; fax 905 7901; web site www.zo-online.ch
Circ.: 11,524
Ed. in Chief – Christain Brandly

USTER, ZURICH

DIE REGIONALZEITUNG
Imkerstrasse 4, Uster, Zurich, 8610, Switzerland; tel (41) 44 940 4747
Circ.: 11,500
– Gabriella Hofar Reinhard
– F. Muller
– B. LamparskyEd. in Chiefs

UZNACH

SUEDOSTSCHWEIZ (D)
Zwinglistrasse 6, Uznach, 8730, Switzerland; tel (41) 55 285 9100; fax 285 9111; e-mail redaktion-ga@suedostschweiz.ch; web site www.suedostschweiz.ch
Circ.: 3,900
Ed. in Chief/Adn. Mgr. – Andrea Masueter

WAEDENSWIL, ZURICH

ALLGEMEINER ANZEIGER VOM ZURICHSEE (5X WK.)
PF 48, Waedenswil, Zurich, 8820, Switzerland; tel (41) 44 7814742; fax 7814272
Circ.: 5,671
Ed. in Chief – Recco Doppeler

WEINFELDEN, THURGAU

THURGAUER ZEITUNG (6X WK.)
Schutzenstrasse 15, Weinfelden, Thurgau, 8570, Switzerland; tel (41) 52 723 5757; fax 723 5926
Circ.: 7,500
Ed. in Chief – Urs Luedi

WETZIKON, ZURICH

ZURCHER OBERLANDER (6X WK.)
PF 1428, Wetzikon, Zurich, 8620, Switzerland; tel (41) 44 933 3333; fax 932 3232; web site www.zo-online.ch
Circ.: 37,040
CEO – Peter Edelmann
Pub. – Konrad Mueller

WIL, ST. GALLEN

NEUES WILER TAGBLATT (6X WK.)
PF 374, Wil, St. Gallen, 9500, Switzerland; tel (41) 71 9115307; fax 9116343
Circ.: 2,800
Ed. in Chief – Matthias Unseld

WINTERTHUR, ZURICH

DER LANDBOTE (M-6X WK.)
PF 8401, Winterthur, Zurich, 8401, Switzerland; tel (41) 52 266 9901; fax 266 9911; e-mail redaktion@landbote.ch
Circ.: 45,000
Ed. – Colette Gradwohl

WEINLANDER TAGBLATT (6X WK.)
PF 281, Winterthur, Zurich, Switzerland; tel (41) 52 317 3143; fax 317 1243
Circ.: 24,116
– A. Wegmann
– R. SpalingerEd. in Chiefs

WINTERTHURER AZ (6X WK.)
PF 1254, Winterthur, Zurich, 8401, Switzerland; tel (41) 52 2126121; fax 2127507
Circ.: 4,100
Ed. in Chief – M. Koch
Bus. Mgr. – B. Ott

YVERDON, VAUD

JOURNAL DU NORD VAUDOIS (6X WK.)
Ave. Haldimand 4, Yverdon, Vaud, 1401, Switzerland; tel (41) 24 231151; fax 210996
Ed. in Chief – Jacques-Antoine Lombard
Ed. – Pierrette Roulet-Grin

ZOFINGEN, AARGAU

ZOFINGER TAGBLATT (6X WK.)
Vordere Hauptgasse 33, Zofingen, Aargau, 4800, Switzerland; tel (41) 62 745 9350; fax 745 9419
Circ.: 16,815
Ed. – Baet Kefchhofer

ZUG

NEUE ZUGER ZEITUNG (D-6X WK.)
Bundesplatz 14, Zug, 6301, Switzerland; tel (41) 42 7111626; fax 7112137
Circ.: 8,014
Ed. in Chief – Werner Steinmann
Ed. – Niklaus Zeier
Ed. – Ronald Schenkel
Ed. – Annemarie Setz

ZUGER NACHRICHTEN (6X WK.)
PF 364, Zug, 6301, Switzerland; tel (41) 41 211626; fax 212137
Circ.: 26,905
Ed. in Chief – Dieter Mittler

ZURICH

BLICK (6X WK.) EST. 1959
Dufourstrasse 23, Zurich, 8008, Switzerland; tel (41) 44 259 6262; fax 259 6665; e-mail redaktion@blick.ch; web site www.blick.ch
Circ.: 270,000
CEO – Caroline Thoma

DAZ (D-5X WK.)
PF 926, Zurich, 8021, Switzerland; tel (41) 44 295 9252; fax 291 2224
Circ.: 5,200
Bus. Mgr. – P. Weishaupt
Ed. in Chief – Matthias Ersinger
Ed. – Koni Loepfe
Ed. – Judith Anna Stofer
Mng. Ed. – Susanna Hubscher

NEUE ZURCHER ZEITUNG (6X WK.)
Falkenstrasse 11, Zurich, 8008, Switzerland; tel (41) 44 258 1111; fax 252 1329; e-mail redaktion@nzz.ch; web site www.nzz.ch
Circ.: 158,167
Advertising: Publicitas.
Ed. in Chief – Marcus Stillman

TAGES-ANZEIGER ZURICH (D-EX S)
Werdstrasse 21, Zurich, 8021, Switzerland; tel (41) 44 248 4411; fax 248 4471; web site www.tages-anzeiger.ch
Circ.: 210,000
Advertising: Publicitas.
Pub. – Rolf Bollmann
Ed. in Chief – Markus Eisenhut
Ed. in Chief – Andreas Strehle

TAJIKISTAN

DUSHANBE

NARODNAYA GAZETA (3X WK.)
16,Sherozi Ave., Dushanbe, 734018, Tajikistan; tel (992) 372 330825
Ed. – Nikolai Nikolaiyevich

TURKMENSKAYA ISKRA (6X WK.)
20 ul. Atabaeva, Dushanbe, 744604, Tajikistan; tel (992) 372
Circ.: 62,946
Ed. – V.V. Slushny

UKRAINE

CRIMEA

KRYMSKAYA GAZETA (D-5X WK.)
35 Sverdlova St., Yalta, Crimea, 334200, Ukraine; tel (7) 654 325559
Circ.: 60,000
Pub. – K. Kinelyev

DONETSK

DONBASS (D)
vul. Artema 80a, Donetsk, 340055, Ukraine; tel (380) 62 311 6610; web site www.donbass.dn.ua
Circ.: 39,000
Ed. in Chief – Alexander Brizh

KHARKIV

SLOBODSKIY KRAY
247 Moskovskki Prospect, Kharkiv, 310302, Ukraine; tel (7) 572 924309
Circ.: 102,000

KIEV

RABOCHAYA GAZETA (E-5X WK.)
Peremohy pr. 50, Kiev, 252047, Ukraine; tel (380) 44 2243301; fax 4460298
Circ.: 176,000
Ed. in Chief – Evelina V. Babenko-Pivtoradni

URYADOVIY KURYER (5X WK.)
vul. Sadova 1/14, Kiev, 252008, Ukraine; tel (7) 44 2931295
Circ.: 200,000
Ed. in Chief – Mykhailo SoroKa

KIEV, UKRAINE

DEMOKRATYCHNA UKRAINA (5X WK.)
50 pr. Peremohy, Kiev, Ukraine, 252047, Ukraine; tel (7) 44 4418333
Circ.: 311,300
Ed. – Oleksandr Pobigai

HOLOS UKRAINY (5X WK.)
vul. Nesterov 4, Kiev, Ukraine, 252047, Ukraine; tel (7) 44 4418823; fax 2247254
Circ.: 768,000
Ed. – Serhiy Pravdenko

NEZAVISIMOST (2X WK.)
Peremohy pr. 50, Kiev, Ukraine, 252047, Ukraine; tel (380) 44 4418578; fax 2242285
Circ.: 228,000
Ed. in Chief – Volodymyr Kuleba

PRAVDA UKRAINY (5X WK.)
Peremohy pr. 50, Kiev, Ukraine, 252047, Ukraine; tel (380) 44 4418534
Circ.: 358,300
Ed. in Chief – Olha Pronina

PROFAPSLKOVA HAZETA (WEEKLY)
2 Maidan Nezalezhnosti, Kiev, Ukraine, 252001, Ukraine; tel (380) 44 2280162
Ed. – O. Husyen

ROBITNYCHA HAZETA (5X WK.)
Peremohy pr. 50, Kiev, Ukraine, 252047, Ukraine; tel (7) 44 2243301; fax 4460298
Circ.: 155,000
Ed. in Chief – Evelina V. Babenko-Pivtoradni

UKRAINA-BIZNES
26g Lenin St., Kiev, Ukraine, Ukraine; tel (7) 44 2253260

VECHIRNIY KYIV (5X WK.)
vul. Marshala Hrechka 13, Kiev, Ukraine, 252136, Ukraine; tel (380) 44 434 6109; fax 443 9609; e-mail office@vechirka.kiev.ua; web site www.vechirka.kiev.ua
Circ.: 90,000
Ed. in Chief – Vitaliy Karpenko

LUGANSK

LUGANSKAJA PRAVDA
1-B Lermontov St., Lugansk, 348022, Ukraine; tel (7) 642 536130
Circ.: 190,000

LVIV

VYSOKIY ZAMOK (5X WK.)
ul.Vladimira Great 2, Lviv, 79026, Ukraine; tel (380) 322 374 731; e-mail info@wz.lviv.ua; web site www.wz.lviv.ua
Circ.: 90,000
Ed. in Chief – Natalia Baluk

ODESSA

ODESKI VISTI (4X WK.)
83 Sverdlov St., Odessa, 270107, Ukraine; tel (7) 482 284367

UZBEKISTAN

TASHKENT

KHALK SUZI (5X WK.)
ul. Matbuotchilar 32, Tashkent, 700000, Uzbekistan; tel (998) 71 133 1522
Circ.: 52,000
Ed. – Jarddros S

NARODNOYE SLOVO (WEEKLY)
ul. Matbuotchilar 19, Tashkent, 700000, Uzbekistan; tel (7) 3711 331522
Circ.: 21,000
Ed. – Anwar Jurabayev

SOVET UZBEKISTONI (6X WK.)
32 ul. Leningradskaja, Tashkent, 700083, Uzbekistan 7
Ed. – L. Kayumov

TASHKENT, UZBEKISTAN

PRAVDA VOSTOKA (5X WK.)
ul. Matbuotchilar 32, Tashkent, Uzbekistan, 700000, Uzbekistan; tel (998) 71 133 7098; fax 133 5633; e-mail pvbox@mail.ru; web site www.pv.uz
Circ.: 35,000
Ed. – Abbas Hon Usmanov

VATICAN CITY

L'OSSERVATORE ROMANO (D-EX MON.)
Vatican City, 00120, Vatican City; tel (39) 06 6988 3461; fax 6988 3675; e-mail ornet@os-srom.va; web site www.vatican.va
Circ.: 70,000
Ed. in Chief – Giovanni Maria Vian
Mktg. Mgr. – Anna Lisa Cipollone

YUGOSLAVIA

BELGRADE

POLITIKA EKSPRES (E)
Makedonska 29, Belgrade, 11000, Yugoslavia; tel (381) 11 325630
Circ.: 76,000
Ed. in Chief – Mile Kordic

VECERNJE NOVOSTI (M)
Trg Nikole Pasica 7, Belgrade, 11000, Yugoslavia; tel (381) 11 302 8000; e-mail oliv-erap@novosti.rs; web site www.novosti.rs
Circ.: 169,000
Ed. in Chief – Manojlo Manjo Vukotic

NOVI SAD, VOJVODINA

DNEVNIK (M)
Bulevar 81, Novi Sad, Vojvodina, 21000, Yugoslavia; tel (381) 21 662 1555; web site www.dnevnik.co.yu
Circ.: 61,000
Adv. Mgr. – Sbedozar Krranovic
Ed. In Cheif. – Aleksandar Deigulgskij

PRISTINA

JEDINSTVO (M)
Srpskih Vladara 41, Pristina, 38000, Yugoslavia; tel (381) 38 29090
Circ.: 6,090
Ed. in Chief – Dragan Malovic

NAMUR, NAMUR

LA WALLONE (D)
Rue J. B. de Marne 30, Namur, Namur, 5000 (32-81) 2600052; fax (32-81) 2600070
Pub. – Laurence Hottart

STUTTGART

FILDER-ZEITUNG (6X WK.) EST. 1946
PO Box 104452, Stuttgart, 70039; tel (49) 711 72050; e-mail cvd@stn.zgs.de; web site www.stuttgarter-nachrichten.de
Circ.: 10,200
Last Audit: November 23, 2011
– Dr. Richard Rebmann
– Dr. Richard RebmannCEOs

NEWSPAPERS OF THE MIDDLE EAST

BAHRAIN

MANAMA

AL AYAM (D)
N/APO Box 3232, Manama, Bahrain; tel (973) 1772 7111; fax 1772 9009; e-mail alayam@batelco.com.bh; web site www.alayam.com
Circ.3,700@RecordBodyIndent:Chrmn. – Nabil Yaqub Al-Hamer

AL ADHWAA
N/APO Box 250, Manama, Bahrain; tel (973) 293166
Circ.@RecordBodyIndent:Chrmn. – Raid Mahmoud Al-Mardi
Ed. in Chief – Muhammad Qassim Shirawi

GULF DAILY NEWS (D)
N/APO Box 5300, Manama, Bahrain; tel (973) 1762 0222; fax 1762 2141; e-mail gdn1@batelco.com.bh; web site www.gulf-daily-news.com
Circ.50,000@RecordBodyIndent:Pub. – Anwar Abdul Rahman
Ed. in Chief – George Williams
Deputy Ed. – Les Horton

AKHBAR AL KHALIJ (D)
N/APO Box 5300, Manama, Bahrain; tel (973) 1762 0111; fax 1762 1566; web site www.akhbar-alkhaleej.com
Circ.35,000
Last Audit: March 23, 2010@RecordBodyIndent:Chrmn. – Anwar Mohammad Abdul Rahman
Adv. Mgr. – Abdul Majeed
Advertising: AdMarket Int'l.

AKHBAR AL BAHRAIN (D)
N/APO Box 253, Manama, Bahrain; tel (973)
Circ.

AL BAHRAIN
N/APO Box 253, Manama, Bahrain; tel (973) 681555
Circ.4,000

AL JARIDA AL RASMIYA
N/APO Box 253, Manama, Bahrain; tel (973) 1787 1712
Circ.

SADA AL USBOU
N/APO Box 549, Manama, Bahrain; tel (973) 1729 1234; fax 1729 0507
Circ.@RecordBodyIndent:Owner/Ed. in Chief – Ali Sayyar

IRAN

ESFAHAN

RAHNEJAT (D)
N/ADarvazeh Dowlat, Esfahan, Iran; tel (98)
Circ.@RecordBodyIndent:Pub. – N. Rahnejat

KERMAN

ANDESHA (D)
N/APO Box 77, Kerman, Iran; tel (98)
Circ.

MASHHAD

KHORASSAN (D)
N/A14 Zohre St., Mobarezan Ave., Mashhad, Iran; tel (98)
Circ.40,000@RecordBodyIndent:Pub. – M.S. Tehrnian

SHIRAZ

BAHARI IRAN (D)
N/AKhayaban Khayam, Shiraz, Iran; tel (98) 71 33738
Circ.

TEHRAN

ABRAAR-E-VARZESHI (D)
N/A26 Shahid Denesh Kian Alley, Valiassr Ave., Tehran, Iran; tel (98) 21 8848274; fax 891215
Circ.@RecordBodyIndent:Pub./Mng. Dir. – Seyyed Mohammad Safizadeh

ABRAR (M)
N/A26 Shahid Denesh Kian Alley, Below Zartasht St., Tehran, Iran; tel (98) 21 8848270; fax 8849200; web site www.abrarnews.com
Circ.75,000

AKHBAAR (D)
N/APO Box 14185-481, Tehran, Iran; tel (98) 21 658095; fax 658272
Circ.

ALIK (D)
N/APO Box 1365-953, Tehran, 11357, Iran; tel (98) 21 8876 8567; fax 8876 0994; e-mail alikmail@hyenet.ir; web site www.alikon-line.com
Circ.3,400@RecordBodyIndent:Pub. – A. Ajemian

JOURNAL DE TEHERAN (D)
N/AKhayyam Ave., Tehran, Iran; tel (98)
Circ.8,000

KHORASSAN (D)
N/A14 Zohre St., Mobarezan Ave., Tehran, Iran; tel (98)
Circ.40,000

TEHERAN TIMES (D)
N/APO Box 14155-4843, Tehran, Iran; tel (98) 21 8800 7889; fax 8800 9768; e-mail info@tehrantimes.com; web site www.tehrantimes.com
Circ.7,700@RecordBodyIndent:Mng. Dir. – Parviz Esmaeili

ETTELA'AT (E)
N/AMirdamad Ave., South Naft St., Ettela'at Publishin, Tehran, 15499, Iran; tel (98) 21 29999; fax 2258022; e-mail bijan@ettelaat.com; email@ettelaat.com; web site www.ettelaat.com
Circ.500,000@RecordBodyIndent:Ed. – Seyyed Mahmud Doaei

KAYHAN (E-6X WK.)
N/AFerdowsi Ave., Tehran, Iran; tel (98) 21 311 2730; fax 390 6844; e-mail kayhan@kayhannews.ir; web site www.kayhannews.ir
Circ.350,000@RecordBodyIndent:Ed. in Chief – Hossein Shariatmadari

AD DUSTOUR (D)
N/APO Box 591, Amman, Jordan; tel (962) 6 566 4153; fax 566 7170; e-mail addustour@addustour.com; web site www.addustour.com
Circ.100,000@RecordBodyIndent:Mgr. – Wnabeel Sharif
Ed. – Nabil Ash-Sharif

SAWT ASH-SHAAB (M)
N/APO Box 3037, Amman, Jordan; tel (962) 6 5667101; fax 5667993
Circ.30,000@RecordBodyIndent:Ed. in Chief – Hashem Khaisat

KUWAIT

AL-KUWAIT

AL ANBA'A (D)
N/APO Box 23915, Al-Kuwait, 13100, Kuwait; tel (965) 483 4772; fax 483 7914; web site www.alanba.com.kw
Circ.106,827@RecordBodyIndent:Ed. in Chief – Bibi Khalid Al-Marzooq
Advertising: AdMarket Int'l.

AL JAMEHEER (D)
N/APO Box 21162, Safat, Al-Kuwait, Kuwait; tel (965) 263 8308
Circ.83,000

AL-QABAS (D)
N/APO Box 21800, Al-Kuwait, 13078, Kuwait; tel (965) 481 2134; fax 481 0469; e-mail info@alqabas.com.kw; web site www.alqabas.com.kw
Circ.79,700@RecordBodyIndent:Gen. Mgr. – Fouzan Al-Fares
Ed. – Weeled An Muos

AL-SEYASSAH (D)
N/APO Box 2270, Al-Kuwait, 13023, Kuwait; tel (965) 481 6326; fax 483 3628; web site www.alseyassah.com
Circ.49,000@RecordBodyIndent:Ed. in Chief – Ahmed Abd Al-Aziz Al-Jarallah

AR RESSALEH (WEEKLY)
N/APO Box 2490, Al-Kuwait, Kuwait; tel (965)
Circ.@RecordBodyIndent:Ed. – Jassim Mubarak

ARAB TIMES (M)
N/APO Box 2270, Al-Kuwait, 13023, Kuwait; tel (965) 481 3566; fax 481 8267; e-mail arabtimes@arabtimesonline.com; web site www.arabtimesonline.com
Circ.41,922
Group: Publicitas North America, Inc.@RecordBodyIndent:Ed. in Chief – Ahmad Abd Al-Aziz Al-Jarallah
Mng. Ed. – Taduz Karwaki

AL-WATAN (M)
N/APO Box 1142, Al-Kuwait, 13012, Kuwait; tel (965) 484 0950; fax 483 5426; e-mail alwatanart@alwatan.com.kw; sports@alwatan.com.kw; web site www.alwatan.com.kw
Circ.110,000
Last Audit: March 23, 2010@RecordBodyIndent:Adv. Mgr. – Abdukader Aljassin
Ed. in Chief – Hussan Fathi

AR-RA'I AL-'AAM (M)
N/APO Box 695, Al-Kuwait, 13007, Kuwait; tel (965) 4813134; fax 4849298
Circ.86,900@RecordBodyIndent:Ed. in Chief – Jassem Boodi

AL-KUWAIT, SAFAT

KUWAIT TIMES (D)
N/APO Box 1301, Al-Kuwait, Safat, 13014, Kuwait; tel (965) 483 3199; fax 483 5621; e-mail info@kuwaittimes.net; web site www.kuwaittimes.net
Circ.43,000
Last Audit: March 23, 2010@RecordBodyIndent:Ed. in Chief – Abd Al-Rahman Alyan

LEBANON

BEIRUT

AL-LIWA' (D)
N/APO Box 112402, Beirut, Lebanon; tel (961) 1 735 749; fax 735 742; web site www.aliwaa.com
Circ.15,000@RecordBodyIndent:Ed. – Salah Salam

AL ANWAR (M) Est. 1959
N/APO Box 11-1038, Beirut, Lebanon; tel (+ 961) 5 +961 4 456 375; e-mail alanwar@alanwar.com.lb; web site www.alanwar.com
Circ.58,675@RecordBodyIndent:Founder – Said Freiha
Chrmn. – Issam Freiha
Gen. Mgr. – Bassam Freiha
Deputy Gen. Mgr. – Elham Freiha
Ed. in Chief – Rafic Khoury
Ed. in Chief – Michel Raad
Mng. Ed. – Fouad Daaboul

AL-BAYRAK (D)
N/APO Box 165612, Beirut, Lebanon; tel (961) 1
Circ.@RecordBodyIndent:Pub./Ed. – Melhem Karanz

AL HAYAT (D)
N/APO Box 11-1242, Beirut, Lebanon; tel (961) 1 987 990; fax 983 995; e-mail information@alhayat.com; web site www.daralhayat.com
Circ.31,034
Last Audit: March 23, 2010@RecordBodyIndent:Gen. Mgr. – Raja Rassi
Ed. in Chief – Ghassan Charbel

AL-NA'AR
N/A2014 5401, Beirut, Lebanon; tel (961) 1 9611994888
Circ.77,595

AL-SHARQ (D)
N/ACenter Anis Assaf, Beirut, Lebanon; tel (961) 1
Circ.36,000@RecordBodyIndent:Pub. – Aouni El-Kaake
Ed. – Nouriddin Madoud
Pub. – Albert Freiha

AL-BILAL (D)
N/APO Box 113-5554, Beirut, Lebanon; tel (961)
Circ.@RecordBodyIndent:Pub. – Afif Chams

AN-NIDA (D)
N/APO Box 4744, Beirut, Lebanon; tel (961)
Circ.10,000@RecordBodyIndent:Ed. – Karim Mroue

AS-SAFIR (6X WK.) Est. 1974
N/APO Box 113/5015, Beirut, Lebanon; tel (961) 1 350 005; fax 349 430; e-mail coordinator@assafir.com; mail@assafir.com; web site www.assafir.com
Circ.50,000@RecordBodyIndent:Exec. Ed. – Moetaz Midani
Ed. – Talal Salman

AYK (D)
N/APO Box 2623, Beirut, Lebanon; tel (961)
Circ.

DAILY STAR (D)
N/AMarine Tower, 6th Flr., rue de La Ste Famille Gema, Beirut, Lebanon; tel (961) 1 587 277; fax 561 333; web site www.dailystar.com.lb
Circ.10,000@RecordBodyIndent:Pub./Ed. in Chief – Jamil K. Mroue
Pub. Asst – Rola Hagdag
Circ. Mgr. – Salem Gaccak
Ed. – Hanna Anbar

AL-AMAL (M)
N/APO Box 959, Beirut, Lebanon; tel (961) 1 382992
Circ.35,000@RecordBodyIndent:Ed. in Chief – Elias Rababi

AL-AHRAR (D)
N/APO Box 165600, Beirut, Lebanon; tel (961) 3 961 020
Circ.15,000@RecordBodyIndent:Contact – Ribal Zuwein

LE REVEIL (M)
N/APO Box 11-8383, Beirut, Lebanon; tel (961) 1 890700
Circ.10,000@RecordBodyIndent:Ed. in Chief – Jean Shami
Dir. – Raymond Daou

LE SOIR (E)
N/APO Box 1470, Beirut, Lebanon; tel (961)
Circ.16,500@RecordBodyIndent:Dir. – Dikran Tosbath
Ed. – Andre Kecati

L'ORIENT/LE JOUR (M)
N/ABP 11-2488, Beirut, Lebanon; tel (961) 1 05 956 444; fax 05 957 444; e-mail administration@lorientlejour.com; redaction@lorientlejour.com; web site www.lorientlejour.com
Circ.15,000@RecordBodyIndent:Pres. – Michel Edde
MD – Nayla de Freige
Ed. in Chief – Nagib Aoun
Columnist/Adv. CEO – Issa Goraieb

AN-NAHAR (MS)
N/APO Box 20145401, Beirut, 20145401, Lebanon; tel (961) 199 4888; fax 199 6777; web site www.annahar.com.lb
Circ.77,595@RecordBodyIndent:Pub./Pres. – Ghassan Tueni
Ed. in Chief – Francois Akl

OMAN

CAPITAL AREA

AL ADWAA (WEEKLY)
N/APO Box 580, Muscat City, Capital Area, 113, Oman; tel (968) 704353; fax 798187
Circ.15,600@RecordBodyIndent:Ed. in Chief – Habib Muhammad Nasib

AL NAHDA
N/APO Box 979, Muscat City, Capital Area, Oman; tel (968) 713934
Circ.11,000

OMAN DAILY NEWSPAPER (D)
N/APO Box 6002, Ruwi City, Capital Area, 112, Oman; tel (968) 701555
Circ.15,560@RecordBodyIndent:Ed. in Chief – Habib Muhammad Nasib

AL-WATAN (D)
N/APO Box 643, Muscat City, Capital Area, 113, Oman; tel (968) 591919; fax 591280; e-mail alwatan@gto.net.om
Circ.32,500@RecordBodyIndent:Ed. in Chief – Muhammad Bin Sulayman At-Tai

MUSCAT

OMAN DAILY OBSERVER (D)
N/APO Box 974, Muscat, 113, Oman; tel (968) 2469 9170; fax 2469 9643; web site www.omanobserver.com
Circ.22,000@RecordBodyIndent:Ed. in Chief – Ibrahim Bin Saif Al Hamdani

RUWI CITY

TIMES OF OMAN (D)
N/APO Box 770, Ruwi City, 112, Oman; tel (968) 24 814 154; fax 813 153; e-mail online@timesofoman.com; timesofoman@gmail.com; web site www.timesofoman.com
Circ.15,000@RecordBodyIndent:Mng. Dir. – Ahammed Az-Zedjali
Circ. Mgr. – Vinud Panikiker

QATAR

DOHA

DAILY NEWS BULLETIN (D)
N/APO Box 3299, Doha, Qatar; tel (974) 445 0451; fax 442 7810; web site www.qnaol.net
Circ.@RecordBodyIndent:Ed. in Chief – Ahmed Jassem Al-Hamar

AL ARAB (D)
N/APO Box 6334, Doha, Qatar; tel (974) 325874; fax 440016
Circ.25,000@RecordBodyIndent:Pub. – Abdullah Hussain Naama
Ed. – Khalid Abdallah Naama

AL-SHARQ (D)
N/APO Box 3488, Doha, Qatar; tel (974) 455 7840; fax 455 7862; e-mail alsharqadv@qatar.net.qa; web site www.alsharq.com
Circ.39,000@RecordBodyIndent:Gen. Mgr. – Abdul Latif Al-Mahmoud

AL WATTAN (D)
N/APO Box 22345, Doha, Qatar; tel (974) 465 2244; fax 466 4206; e-mail alwatan_adv@yahoo.com; web site www.alwatan.com
Circ.@RecordBodyIndent:Ed. in Chief – Ahmad Ali Al-Abdullah

AR-RAYAH (D)
N/APO Box 3464, Doha, Qatar; tel (974) 446 6555; fax 350 476; e-mail edit@raya.com; web site www.raya.com
Circ.25,000@RecordBodyIndent:Mgr. – Mohammed Shahta
Ed – Salihbin Afssanelkwary

DOHA, QATAR

DAILY GULF TIMES & WEEKLY GULF TIMES (M)
N/APO Box 533, Doha, Qatar, Qatar; tel (974) 435 0478; fax 435 0474; e-mail editor@gulf-times.com; web site www.gulf-times.com
Circ.15,000@RecordBodyIndent:Mng. Ed. – Neil Cook

KAYHAN INTERNATIONAL (M-6X WK.)
N/AFerdowsi Ave., Tehran, Iran; tel (98) 21 311 2730; fax 390 6844; e-mail kayhan@kay-hannews.ir; web site www.kayhannews.ir
Circ.@RecordBodyIndent:Mng. Ed. – Hossein Shariatmadari

TEHRAN, ISLAMIC REPUBLIC OF IRAN

IRAN NEWS (D)
N/APO Box 15875-8551, Tehran, Islamic Republic of Iran, Iran; tel (98) 21 425 3450; fax 425 3478; e-mail info@irannewsdaily.com; web site www.irannewsdaily.com
Circ.@RecordBodyIndent:MD – Mohammad Soltanifar

BAGHDAD

AL-JUMHURIYA (D)
N/APO Box 491, Baghdad, Iraq; tel (964) 1 416 9341; fax 416 1875
Circ.150,000@RecordBodyIndent:Ed. in Chief – Sami Mahdi

BABIL
N/APO Box 5922, Baghdad, Iraq; tel (964) 1 8862008
Circ.@RecordBodyIndent:Ed. – Uday Saddam Hussain

AL-IRAQ (D)
N/APO Box 5717, Baghdad, Iraq; tel (964) 1 7186580; fax 7186583
Circ.30,000@RecordBodyIndent:Ed. in Chief – Salahudin Saeed

BAGHDAD OBSERVER (M-6X WK.)
N/APO Box 624, Baghdad, Iraq; tel (964) 1 416 9341
Circ.22,000@RecordBodyIndent:Ed. in Chief – Naji al-Hadithi

ATH-THAWRA (M)
N/APO Box 2009, Baghdad, Iraq; tel (964) 7196161; fax 7196818
Circ.250,000@RecordBodyIndent:Ed. in Chief – Hameed Saeed

HAWKARI
N/AKurdish Cultural & Publishing House, Baghdad, Iraq; tel (964) 1 425 1846
Circ.@RecordBodyIndent:Ed. – Badr Khan al-Sindi

AL-BAGTH AL-RIYADI
N/APO Box 5922, Baghdad, Iraq; tel (964) 1 8862008
Circ.@RecordBodyIndent:Ed. – Salman Ali

AL-QADISIYA
N/AHai Al-Tashri, Baghdad, Iraq; tel (964) 7765191
Circ.

ISRAEL

HAIFA

AL-ITTIHAD (D)
N/APO Box 104, Haifa, Israel; tel (972) 4 511296; fax 511297
Circ.@RecordBodyIndent:Ed. in Chief – Nazir Mjalli Zubiedat

JERUSALEM

HAMODI'A (MS)
N/APO Box 1306, Jerusalem, Israel; tel (972) 2 538 9255; fax 500 3384; e-mail english@hamodia.co.il; web site www.hamodia.com
Circ.7,000@RecordBodyIndent:– M.A. Druck – H.M. KnopfEd.s

AL-ALMUWAKAF
N/APO Box 21592, Jerusalem, Israel; tel (972) 2 851176
Circ.

AL ANBA (M)
N/APO Box 428, Jerusalem, Israel; tel (972) 2
Circ.10,000@RecordBodyIndent:Ed. in Chief – Ovadia Danon

AL-BAIDER AL-SIASI
N/A3 Al-Rashid, Jerusalem, Israel; tel (972) 2 851176
Circ.

AL-FAJR (WEEKLY)
N/APO Box 19315, Jerusalem, Israel; tel (972) 2 271649; fax 273521
Circ.28,000@RecordBodyIndent:Ed. in Chief – Manna Siniora

AL-QUDS (D)
N/APO Box 19788, Jerusalem, Israel; tel (972) 2 627 2663; fax 585 5003; e-mail alquds@p-ol.com; web site www.alquds.com
Circ.60,000@RecordBodyIndent:Ed. – M. Abu-Zuluf
Adv. Mgr. – Ani Abbasi

AL-SHA'AB (D)
N/APO Box 19154, Jerusalem, Israel; tel (972) 2 289881
Circ.

BAHAMANE
N/AArmy Post 01013, IDF, Jerusalem, Israel; tel (972) 2 4211364; fax 4211363
Circ.

EREV SHABBAT
N/APO Box 81, Jerusalem, Israel; tel (972) 2 551620; fax 537527
Circ.

HAMACHANE HAHAREDI
N/APO Box 5783, Jerusalem, Israel; tel (972) 2 380407; fax 385582
Circ.

HAMODI'A (D)
N/APO Box 1306, Jerusalem, Israel; tel (972) 3 579 2490; e-mail english@hamodia.co.il; web site www.hamodia.com
Circ.@RecordBodyIndent:Ed. in Chief – Yizchak Knop

JERUSALEM POST (D-6X WK.)
N/APO Box 81, Jerusalem, 91000, Israel; tel (972) 2 531 5612; fax 538 9527; e-mail jpedt@jpost.com; web site www.jpost.com
Circ.42,000@RecordBodyIndent:Ed. in Chief – David Horovitz
Adv. Mgr. – Amanda Kuperman

LA SEMANA (D)
N/APO Box 2427, Jerusalem, Israel; tel (972) 2 664 637; fax 290 774
Circ.

NAZARETH

AL-SINARA
N/APO Box 148, Nazareth, Israel; tel (972) 6 555750; fax 578092
Circ.

RISHON LE-ZION

GLOBES (D)
N/APO Box 5126, Rishon Le-Zion, 75150, Israel; tel (972) 3 953 8787; fax 951 7297; e-mail editor@globes.co.il; web site www.globes.co.il
Circ.36,000@RecordBodyIndent:Ed. in Chief – Haggai Golan

TEL-AVIV

A'AOURORA (D)
N/APO Box 18066, Tel-Aviv, Israel; tel (972) 3 5462785; fax 5469977
Circ.

CHADSHOT HASPORT (M)
N/APO Box 20011, Tel-Aviv, 61200, Israel; tel (972)
Circ.27,000

HA'ARETZ (D-6X WK.)
N/APO Box 233, Tel-Aviv, 61001, Israel; tel (972) 3 512 1750; fax 681 0012; e-mail contact@haaretz.co.il; iht@haaretz.co.il; international@haaretz.co.in; web site www.haaretzdaily.com; www.haaretz.com
Circ.65,000@RecordBodyIndent:Pub. – Amos Schocken
Dir. – Moshe Cohen
Mng. Dir. – Yossi Warshavski
Circ. Mgr. – Yoram Ilan
Dep. Ed. – Aluf Ben
Ed. in Chief – David Landau
Prodn. Mgr. – Eran Gez
Advertising: Israel Communications Inc.; Publicitas.

HADASHOT (M-6X WK.)
N/A108 Yigal Alon St., Tel-Aviv, 67801, Israel; tel (972) 3 512 0555; fax 562 3084
Circ.@RecordBodyIndent:Pub./Dir. – Roni Aran
Ed. – Yoel Esteron
Adv. Dir. – Samuel Segal

HAOLAM HAZEH (E)
N/A2 Chomah U'migdal, Tel-Aviv, Israel; tel (972) 3 5376844; fax 5376811
Circ.

LETZTE NYESS (M)
N/APO Box 28034, Tel-Aviv, Israel; tel (972) 3 35816
Circ.23,000@RecordBodyIndent:Ed. in Chief – S. Himmelfarb

ISRAELSKI FAR TRIBUNA (M)
N/A113 Givat Herzl St., Tel-Aviv, Israel; tel (972) 3 3700
Circ.6,000@RecordBodyIndent:Ed. – D. Amarillo

LATZA NEISS (D)
N/A52 Harakevet St., Tel-Aviv, Israel; tel (972) 3 370011; fax 5371921
Circ.

LE JOURNAL D'ISRAEL (M)
N/APO Box 28330, Tel-Aviv, Israel; tel (972) 3 33188
Circ.10,000@RecordBodyIndent:Ed. in Chief – J. Rabin

MA'ARIV VREMIA (D)
N/A2 Cartebach, Tel-Aviv, 67132, Israel; tel (972) 3 563 8795; fax 561 0614; e-mail ads@maariv.co.il; web site www.maariv.co.il
Circ.160,000@RecordBodyIndent:Ed. – Dankner Amnon

YOM-YOM (M)
N/APO Box 1194, Tel-Aviv, Israel; tel (972)
Circ.2,500@RecordBodyIndent:Ed. – Nachman Pavian

MABAT (M)
N/A8 Amazger St., Tel-Aviv, 67218, Israel; tel (972) 3 537 1016
Circ.7,000@RecordBodyIndent:Ed. – S. Yarkoni

MA'ARIV EVENING (D-6X WK.)
N/A2 Carlebach St., Tel-Aviv, 61200, Israel; tel (972) 3 563 2111; fax 561 0614; web site www.nrg.co.il
Circ.160,000@RecordBodyIndent:Pub. – Offer Nimrodi
Advertising: Israel Communications Inc.; Publicitas.

NASHA STRANA (M)
N/A52 Harakeret St., Tel-Aviv, 67770, Israel; tel (972) 3 370011; fax 5371921
Circ.35,000@RecordBodyIndent:Ed. – S. Himmelfarb

NOWINY KURIER (M)
N/A52 Harakevet St., Tel-Aviv, Israel; tel (972)
Circ.@RecordBodyIndent:Ed. – S. Himmelfarb

SHE'ARIM (M)
N/APO Box 11044, Tel-Aviv, Israel; tel (972) 3 242 126
Circ.5,000

SHA'AR (M)
N/A52 Harakevet St., Tel-Aviv, 64284, Israel; tel (972) 3 5286141
Circ.@RecordBodyIndent:Ed. – Y. Kena'an

TRIBUNA (M)
N/A113 Givat Herzl, Tel-Aviv, Israel; tel (972)
Circ.4,500

UJ KELET (M)
N/A49 Tchlenor St., Tel-Aviv, 61351, Israel; tel (972) 3 537 2868
Circ.20,000@RecordBodyIndent:Ed. – D. Drory

VIATA-NOASTRA (M)
N/APO Box 28397, Tel-Aviv, 61283, Israel; tel (972) 3 537 2059; fax 537 6166; e-mail erancourt@shani.co.il
Circ.30,000@RecordBodyIndent:Ed. – George Edri

YEDIOTH AHARONOTH (E-6X WK.)
N/A2 Yehuda & Noah Mozes St., Tel-Aviv, 61000, Israel; tel (972) 3 608 2222; fax 695 3950; web site www.ynet.co.il
Circ.300,000@RecordBodyIndent:Ed. in Chief – Shilo De beer

YIDDISCHE ZEITUNG (D)
N/A52 Harakevet St., Tel-Aviv, Israel; tel (972) 3 370011; fax (972-3) 5371921
Circ.

JORDAN

AMMAN

JORDAN TIMES (6X WK.)
N/APO Box 6710, Amman, 11118, Jordan; tel (962) 6 560 0800; fax 569 6183; e-mail jotimes@jpf.com.jo; web site www.jordantimes.com
Circ.15,000@RecordBodyIndent:Ed. in Chief – Samir Barhoum
Mng. Ed. – Ica Wahbeh
Advertising: AdMarket Int'l.; The N DeFilippes Corp.

AL RAI (D)
N/APO Box 6710, Amman, Jordan; tel (962) 6 566 7171; fax 560 7309; e-mail alrai@jpf.com.jo; web site www.alrai.com
Circ.105,000@RecordBodyIndent:Ed. in Chief – Abdul Wahab Zegelat
Adv. Mgr. – Naim Alhorani
Advertising: AdMarket Int'l.; The N DeFilippes Corp.

SAUDI ARABIA

DAMMAM

AL-YAUM (M-6X WK.)
N/APO Box 565, Dammam, 31421, Saudi Arabia; tel (966) 3 858 0800; fax 858 8777; e-mail mail@alyaum.com; web site www.alyaum.com
Circ.50,000@RecordBodyIndent:Chrmn. – Abdul Hazeez Mohammed Alhokail
Gen. Mgr. – Saleh Ali Al Humaidan

JEDDAH

AL-BILAD (M)
N/APO Box 7095, Jeddah, 21462, Saudi Arabia; tel (966) 2 671 1000; fax 671 1222
Circ.66,210@RecordBodyIndent:Ed. in Chief – Quinan Al-Ghomdi

AL-HAYAT (D)
N/APO Box 13676, Jeddah, 21414, Saudi Arabia; tel (966) 2 653 4426; fax 652 0151; e-mail information@alhayat.com; web site www.alhayat.com
Circ.@RecordBodyIndent:Ed. in Chief – Ghassan Sharbal

AL-MADINA AL-MUNAWARA (D)
N/APO Box 807, Jeddah, 21421, Saudi Arabia; tel (966) 2 671 2100; fax 671 1877; web site www.almadina.com
Circ.46,370@RecordBodyIndent:Ed. – Fahad Hassan Al-Agran
Advertising: Marston Webb & Associates.

SAUDI GAZETTE (D)
N/APO Box 5576, Jeddah, 21432, Saudi Arabia; tel (966) 2 676 0000; fax 672 7621
Circ.676,000
Last Audit: December 27, 2006@RecordBodyIndent:Ed. in Chief – Ahmad Al-Youssuf

OKAZ (M)
N/APO Box 5576, Jeddah, 21432, Saudi Arabia; tel (966) 2 676 0000; fax 672 4277; web site www.okaz.com.sa
Circ.107,614@RecordBodyIndent:Ed. in Chief – Abdul Hajim

ARAB NEWS (M)
N/APO Box 10452, Jeddah, 21433, Saudi Arabia; tel (966) 2 639 1888; fax 639 3223; e-mail letters@arabnews.com; arabnews@arabnews.com; web site www.arabnews.com
Circ.110,000@RecordBodyIndent:Ed. in Chief – Khaled A. Almaeena
Advertising: Attache Inc.

URDU NEWS (D)
N/APO Box 4556, Jeddah, 21412, Saudi Arabia; tel (966) 2 639 1888
Circ.30,000@RecordBodyIndent:Ed. in Chief – Tariq Miskath

MECCA

AN-NADWAH (D)
N/APO Box 5803, Mecca, Saudi Arabia; tel (966) 2 520 0111; fax 520 3055
Circ.35,000@RecordBodyIndent:Ed. – Dr. Abd Ar-Rahman Al-Harthi

RIYADH

AL-JAZIRAH (E)
N/APO Box 354, Riyadh, 11411, Saudi Arabia; tel (966) 1 4419999; fax 4413826
Circ.94,000@RecordBodyIndent:Ed. in Chief – Muhammad Abd Al-Aziz Aba Hussein
Gen. Dir. – Abd Ar-Rahman Bin Fahd Ar-Rashad

AL-MASSAIYAH (D)
N/APO Box 354, Riyadh, 11411, Saudi Arabia; tel (966) 1 4021440; fax 4021795
Circ.

AR-RIYADH (M)
N/APO Box 2943, Riyadh, 11476, Saudi Arabia; tel (966) 1 442 0000; fax 441 7417; web site www.arriyadh.com
Circ.150,000@RecordBodyIndent:Pub. – Ahmed Al-Houshan
Ed. – Turki A. As-Sudari

ASHARQ ALAWSAT (M)
N/APO Box 53108, Riyadh, 11583, Saudi Arabia; tel (966) 1441 9933; web site www.asharqalawsat.com
Circ.224,992@RecordBodyIndent:Ed. – Tariq Hameed
Advertising: Attache Inc.

RIYADH DAILY NP (M)
N/APO Box 2943, Riyadh, 11476, Saudi Arabia; tel (966) 1 441 7544; fax 441 7116
Circ.50,000@RecordBodyIndent:Ed. in Chief – Tala't Warfa
Advertising: The N DeFilippes Corp.

SYRIA

ALEPPO

ASH SHABAB (M)
N/ARue At-Tawil, Aleppo, Syria; tel (963)
Circ.9,000@RecordBodyIndent:Ed. – Muhammad Talas

BARQ ASH SHIMAL (M)
N/ARue Aziziyah, Aleppo, Syria; tel (963)
Circ.6,400@RecordBodyIndent:Ed. – Maurice Djandji

DAMASCUS

AL JAMAHIR AL ARABIA (M)
N/ABP 2448, Damascus, Syria; tel (963) 21 214 309; fax 214 308
Circ.10,000@RecordBodyIndent:Ed. in Chief – Mortada Bakach

AL FIDA' (M)
N/ABP 2448, Damascus, Syria; tel (963) 11 225 219
Circ.4,000@RecordBodyIndent:Ed. – A. Aulwani

AL OROUBAT (M)
N/ABP 2448, Damascus, Syria; tel (963) 11 225219
Circ.5,000@RecordBodyIndent:Ed. – Ameod Khuly

ATH THAWRA (M)
N/ABP 2448, Damascus, Syria; tel (963) 11 221 0850; fax 221 6851
Circ.40,000@RecordBodyIndent:Ed. – Asaab Aboud

AL BAATH (M)
N/ABP 9389, Damascus, Syria; tel (963) 11 662 2142; fax 662 2140; web site www.albaath.news.sy
Circ.40,000@RecordBodyIndent:Adv. Mgr. – Muein Mustafa
Ed. in Chief – Mohammad Kanaisy

SYRIA TIMES (D)
N/APO Box 5452, Damascus, Syria; tel (963) 11 213 1100; fax 224 6860; e-mail syria-times@tishreen.news.sy; tnp@mail.sy; web site www.tishreen.info
Circ.3,000@RecordBodyIndent:Ed. in Chief – Mohammad Agha

TISHRIN (D)
N/APO Box 5452, Damascus, Syria; tel (963) 11 213 1100; fax 224 6860; e-mail tnp@mail.sy; web site www.tishreen.info
Circ.50,000@RecordBodyIndent:Ed. in Chief – M. Kheir Wadi

TURKEY

ADANA

BUGUN (D)
N/ASun Sinemasi Sokagi, Adana, Turkey; tel (90)
Circ.@RecordBodyIndent:Pub. – Onay Bilgin

CUMHURIYET (D)
N/AInonu Caddesi 5 Sokak Aksogan Is HanÃ£Â£ Kat:1 Seyhan, Adana, 01010, Turkey; tel (90) 322 363 1211; fax 363 1215; e-mail adana@cumhuriyet.com.tr; web site www.cumhuriyet.com.tr
Circ.@RecordBodyIndent:Pub. – Ilhan Selcuk

FOTOSPOR (D)
N/ACeyhan Yolu 5-Km. Yuregir, Adana, Turkey; tel (90)
Circ.@RecordBodyIndent:Pub. – Birol Nadir

GUNES (D)
N/ASakarya Mah. Turhan Cemal Berigel BulvarÃ£Â£, No:212, Adana, Turkey; tel (90) 322 436 0310; web site www.gunes.com
Circ.@RecordBodyIndent:Pub. – Asil Nadir

GUNAYDIN (D)
N/ACeydan Yolu 5-Km., Adana, Turkey; tel (90)
Circ.386,000@RecordBodyIndent:Pub. – Asil Nadir

HURRIYET (D)
N/ACeyhan Karayolu 5-Km., Adana, Turkey; tel (90) 322 459 6644; web site www.hurriyet.com.tr
Circ.@RecordBodyIndent:Pub. – Erol Simavi

MILLIYET (D)
N/AAtaturk Caddesi Toren Apt., Kat:3, Adana, Turkey; tel (90) 212 505 6111; fax 677 0372
Circ.@RecordBodyIndent:Pub. – Aydin Dogan

SABAH (D)
N/ACinarli Mah. 126, Sokak No. 4, Adana, Turkey; tel (90)
Circ.700,000@RecordBodyIndent:Pub. – Dinc Bilgin

TERCUMAN (D)
N/AIstiklal Mah. 190, Sokak No. 27, Adana, Turkey; tel (90)
Circ.@RecordBodyIndent:Pub. – Kemal Ilicak

TURKIYE (D)
N/AC. Gursel Caddesi, No. 21, Adana, Turkey; tel (90) 322 359 4959; web site www.turkiyegazetesi.com.tr
Circ.@RecordBodyIndent:Pub. – Enver Oren

ZAMAN (D)
N/ASaydam, Caddesi 46-1, Sokak No. 2, Adana, Turkey; tel (90)
Circ.@RecordBodyIndent:Pub. – Alaeddin Kaya

ANKARA

BUGUN (D)
N/AKarum is Merkezi; Kat:6, Kavaklidere, Ankara, Turkey; tel (90) 312 436 4700; fax 436 4720; web site www.bugun.com.tr
Circ.@RecordBodyIndent:Ed. – Murat Gelik

CUMHURIYET (D)
N/AAtaturk Bulvari, No. 125, Kat:4, Bakalikar, Ankara, Turkey; tel (90) 312 419 5020; fax 419 5027
Circ.@RecordBodyIndent:Pub. – Nadir Nadi

DUNYA (D)
N/AKaranfil Sokak 43/6 Kizilay, Ankara, Turkey; tel (90) 212 629 0846; fax 440 2424; web site www.dunyagazetesi.com.tr
Circ.@RecordBodyIndent:Pub. – Nezih Demirkent

FOTOSPOR (D)
N/ARuzgarli, Sokak No. 34/1, Ulus, Ankara, Turkey; tel (90) 312 3091015; fax 3091022
Circ.@RecordBodyIndent:Pub. – Birol Nadir

GUNES (D)
N/ACinnah Cad. 15 , Cankaya, Ankara, Turkey; tel (90) 312 467 5000; fax 467 3564; web site www.gunes.com
Circ.@RecordBodyIndent:Ed. in Chief – Sercar Turbut

MEYDAN (D)
N/ANevzat Tandogan Caddesi 8, Asagi Ayranci, Ankara, 06540, Turkey; tel (90) 312 472100; fax 475500
Circ.

MILLI GAZETE (D)
N/AZiya Bey, Sokak 10/2-4, Balgat, Ankara, Turkey; tel (90) 312 287 2745; fax 285 2816; e-mail ankara@milligazete.com.tr; web site www.milligazete.com.tr
Circ.@RecordBodyIndent:Dir. – Nezir Aydin

MILLIYET (D)
N/ANeyzat Tandogan, Caddesi 8, Asagi Ayranci, Ankara, Turkey; tel (90) 312 419 1400; fax 417 3878; web site www.milliyet.com.tr
Circ.@RecordBodyIndent:Pub. – Aydin Dogan

ORTADOGU (D)
N/AAtatÃ£Â£rk BulvarÃ£Â£ 223/15 KavaklÃ£Â£dere, Ankara, Turkey; tel (90) 312 427 3438; fax 427 3438; e-mail haber@ortadogugazetesi.net; web site www.ortadogugazetesi.net
Circ.@RecordBodyIndent:Ed. – Orhan Karatas

SABAH (D)
N/AIran Caddesi Karum is Merkez, Kat:6, Kavaklidere, Ankara, Turkey; tel (90) 312 4685050; fax 4266365
Circ.@RecordBodyIndent:Pub./Owner – Dinc Bilgin

TAN (D)
N/AIstanbul, Caddesi Gayret Sokak No. 2, Ulus, Ankara, Turkey; tel (90)
Circ.@RecordBodyIndent:Pub. – Asil Nadir

TERCUMAN (D)
N/ACinnah Cad 15, Cankaya, Ankara, Turkey; tel (90) 312 4674 044748; fax 467 0449; web site www.tercuman.com.tr
Circ.@RecordBodyIndent:Gen. Mgr. – Nermi Karacabeyli

TURKIYE TICARET SICILI (D)
N/AKaranfil Sok 56, Bakanliklar, Ankara, Turkey; tel (90) 312 218 2000; fax 425 8173; e-mail ttsgmd@tobb.org.tr; web site www.ticaretsicil.gov.tr
Circ.@RecordBodyIndent:Pub. – Kemal Cirak

ULUS
N/ARuzgarli Gazret, Sokak No. 2, Ulus, Ankara, Turkey; tel (90) 312 212 5353; fax 310 3731

Circ. @RecordBodyIndent:Owner – Omer Erdal Yilmaz
Ed. in Chief – Sedat Yazicioglu

GUNAYDIN-TAN (D)
N/ARuzgarli Gayret, Sokak No. 2, Ulus, Ankara, Turkey; tel (90) 312 312 6222; fax 311 6055
Circ. @RecordBodyIndent:Pub. – Asil Nadir

YENI ASIR (D)
N/ASogutozu Caddesi Cogutozu Ic Nerkezi, No 14, Ankara, Turkey; tel (90) 312 292 5050; e-mail yasir@yeniasir.com.tr; web site www.yeniasir.com.tr
Circ. @RecordBodyIndent:Ed. – Ismet Berkan

YENI NESIL (D)
N/AAtaturk Bul. Atahan, No. 117/31, Bakanliklar, Ankara, Turkey; tel (90) 312 4415000
Circ. 80,000@RecordBodyIndent:Pub. – Bekir Berk

ZAMAN (D)
N/AZiyabey Cad. 4 Sok. 14, Balgat, Ankara, Turkey; tel (90) 312 284 7284; fax 284 8640; web site www.todayszaman.com
Circ. 800,000@RecordBodyIndent:Ankara Rep. – Kaerim Balzi
Adv. Mgr. – Sabahattin Surmen

BURSA

DUNYA (5X WK.)
N/AAtatÃ£Â£rk Cad.23 SelÃ£Â£uk Mah. Ali Haydar Apt.Daire:3, Bursa, Turkey; tel (90) 224 223 2481; fax 221 1579; e-mail bursa@dunyagazetesi.com; web site www.dunyagazetesi.com.tr
Circ. @RecordBodyIndent:Ed. in Chief – Didem Demirkent
Contact – Omer Faruk Ciftci

ZAMAN (D)
N/AAtaturk Caddesi Koruyucu Ishani, Kat:5, Bursa, Turkey; tel (90) 224 223 6363; web site www.zaman.com.tr
Circ. @RecordBodyIndent:Pub. – Alaeddin Kaya

CANKAYA, ANKARA

HURRIYET DAILY NEWS (D)
N/ASogutozu Mahallesi Dumlupinar Bulvari No. 102-06510, Cankaya, Ankara, Turkey; tel (90) 312 207 0090; fax 207 0094; e-mail tdn@tdn.com.tr; web site www.hurriyet.com
Circ. @RecordBodyIndent:Mgr. – Zergen Bemertes
Ed. – David Judson

DIYARBAKIR

MILLIYET
N/AFeray Apt., Kat:1, Diyarbakir, Turkey; tel (90)
Circ. @RecordBodyIndent:Pub. – Aydin Dogan

ERZURUM

HURRIYET (D)
N/AGezkoy Cikisi Organize Sanayi Bolgesi, Erzurum, Turkey; tel (90)
Circ. @RecordBodyIndent:Pub. – Erol Simavi

MILLIYET (D)
N/AMuratpasa Mah. ismet pasa, Caddesi No. 4/3, Erzurum, Turkey; tel (90) 212 505 6111; web site www.milliyet.com.tr
Circ. @RecordBodyIndent:Pub. – Aydin Dogan
Adv. Mgr – Yikki Habis

TURKIYE (D)
N/ACumhuriyet Caddesi Ozel Idare Ticaret Sitesi, Kat:, Erzurum, Turkey; tel (90) 442 235 5757; fax 235 8148; web site www.turkiyegazetesi.com.tr
Circ. @RecordBodyIndent:Pub. – Enver Oren

ISTANBUL

AYDINLIK
N/AIstiklal Caddesi, Deva CÃ£Â£kmazÃ£Â£d; 7/3, Istanbul, Turkey; tel (90) 212 251 5122; fax 251 5122; web site www.aydinlik.com.tr
Circ. @RecordBodyIndent:Pub. – Mehmet Sabuncu
Adv Mgr. – Nuri Itihtardes

BUGUN (D)
N/AMedya Plaza Basin Ekspres Yolu, Gunesli, Istanbul, 34540, Turkey; tel (90) 212 448 8000; fax 216 2194; web site www.bugun.com.tr
Circ. 184,884@RecordBodyIndent:Owner/Pub. – Onay Bilgin

CUMHURIYET (M)
N/AProf. Nurettin Mazhar Oktel Sokak No:2 Sisli, Istanbul, 34381, Turkey; tel (90) 212 343 7274; fax 343 7264; e-mail postakutusu@cumhuriyet.com.tr; web site www.cumhuriyet.com
Circ. 80,000@RecordBodyIndent:Pub. – Yenigun Hadarajansi
Ed. in Chief – Ibrahim Yilbiz

CUMHURIYET (D)
N/ACumhuriyet Daily Sisli, Istanbul, Turkey; tel (90) 212 343 7274; fax 343 7264; web site www.cumhuriyet.com.tr
Circ. @RecordBodyIndent:Adv. Mgr. – Ozlem Ayden
Ed. in Chief – Ibrahim Yildiz
Head Columnist – Alhal Selcuk

DUNYA (6X WK.)
N/AYil Mahallesi 100, Istanbul, 34440, Turkey; tel (90) 212 440 2424; fax 629 0846; e-mail dunya@dunya-gazette.com.tr; web site www.dunya.com
Circ. @RecordBodyIndent:Ed. in Chief – Didem Demirkent

FOTOMAC (D)
N/ABarbaros Bulvari No. 125, Istanbul, 34540, Turkey; tel (90) 212 354 3774; fax 354 3557
Circ. 150,000@RecordBodyIndent:Ed. – Tahsin Sezer

FOTOSPOR (D)
N/AEkspress Basin Yolu Kavsagi, Matbaacilar Sitsei, G, Istanbul, 34540, Turkey; tel (90) 212 652 5094
Circ. 215,000@RecordBodyIndent:Pub. – Birol Nadir
Ed. in Chief – Ersan Celik

GUNES (D)
N/ATuranli, Sokak No. 20, Beyazit, Istanbul, Turkey; tel (90) 212 516 6600; fax 517 1990; web site www.gunes.com
Circ. 84,000@RecordBodyIndent:Pub. – Asil Nadir
Ed. in Chief – Ertugrul Ozkok

GUN
N/AMedya Plaza, Gunesli, Istanbul, 34540, Turkey; tel (90) 212 5504810; fax 5028340
Circ. @RecordBodyIndent:Owner – Ali Karacan
Ed. in Chief – Selahattin Duman

HURRIYET (D)
N/AHurriyet Media Towers, Istanbul, 06690, Turkey; tel (90) 212 677 0000; fax 677 0340; e-mail interneteditor@hurriyet.com.tr; web site www.hurriyet.com.tr
Circ. 6,000
Group: Admarket International (Div. of Marcom International, Inc.)@RecordBodyIndent:Adv. Mgr. – Nilgun Cetin
Ed. in Chief – David Judson

HURRIYET (M)
N/AMedya Towers, Gunesli, Istanbul, 34212, Turkey; tel (90) 212 677 0000; fax 677 0846; web site www.hurriyet.com.tr
Circ. 542,797@RecordBodyIndent:Ed. in Chief – Enis Berberoglu

MEYDAN (D)
N/AYuzyil Mahallesi, Mahmutbey Viyadugu Alti, Ikitell, Istanbul, 34410, Turkey; tel (90) 216 556 9000
Circ. @RecordBodyIndent:Owner – Refik Aras
Ed. – Ufuk Guldemir

MILLI GAZETE (D)
N/ACayhane Sok 1, Istanbul, 34040, Turkey; tel (90) 212 567 4775; fax 567 4024
Circ. @RecordBodyIndent:Ed. in Chief – Ekrem Kiziltas

MILLIYET (D)
N/ADogan Medya Center, Bagcilar, Istanbul, 34554, Turkey; tel (90) 212 505 6111; fax 505 6233; e-mail webadmin@milliyet.com.tr; web site www.milliyet.com.tr
Circ. @RecordBodyIndent:Pub. – Aydin Dogan

YENI NESIL (D)
N/A19 MayÃ£Â£s Mah. Inonu Cad. Samli Apartment No.87 D-13, Istanbul, Turkey; tel (90) 216 445 7332; fax 410 7339
Circ. 80,000@RecordBodyIndent:Ed. in Chief – Umit Simsek

ORTADOGU (D)
N/AFabrikalar Caddesi, No. 1 Besyol, Istanbul, 34630, Turkey; tel (90) 212 425 3650; fax 624 5329; e-mail haber@ortadogugazetesi.net; web site www.ortadogugazetesi.net
Circ. @RecordBodyIndent:Pub. – Zeki Saracogiu

SABAH (D)
N/AMedya Plaza Basin Ekspres Yolu, Gunesli, Istanbul, 34540, Turkey; tel (90) 212 550 4810; web site www.sabah.com.tr
Circ. @RecordBodyIndent:Pub./Owner – Dinc Bilgin
Ed. – Zafer Mutlu

TAN (D)
N/AAlaykosku, Caddesi Eryilmaz, Sokak No. 13, Cagalog, Istanbul, Turkey; tel (90) 212 5120050; fax 5265013
Circ. 170,000@RecordBodyIndent:Pub. – Asil Nadir
Ed. in Chief – Fikret Ercan

TERCUMAN (D)
N/ASercekale, Sok 4, Istanbul, 34370, Turkey; tel (90) 212 5017505; fax 5446562
Circ. @RecordBodyIndent:Owner/Pub. – Sedat Colak
Ed. in Chief – Nazif Okumus

TURKISH DAILY NEWS (D)
N/AHurriyet Media Towers, Gunesli, Istanbul, Turkey; tel (90) 212 449 6035; fax 449 6014
Circ. 9,000@RecordBodyIndent:CEO – Vuslat Dogan
Ed. – David Judson

TURKIYE (D)
N/AYenibosna, Istanbul, 34410, Turkey; tel (90) 212 513 9900; fax 513 6857; e-mail info@tg.com.tr; web site www.turkiyegazetesi.com.tr
Circ. 9,000@RecordBodyIndent:Ed. – Nuhalea Erej

GUNAYDIN-TAN (D)
N/AAlaykosku, Caddesi Eryilmaz Sok 13, Cagaloglu, Istanbul, Turkey; tel (90) 216 585 9499
Circ. 386,000@RecordBodyIndent:Ed. in Chief – Seckin Turesay

YENI ASIR (D)
N/AAtakan, Sokak No. 14, Mecidiyekoy, Istanbul, Turkey; tel (90) 212
Circ. @RecordBodyIndent:Pub. – Dinc Bilgin

ZAMAN (D)
N/AFevzi Cakmak Mah. A. Taner Kislali Cad. 6, Istanbul, 34194, Turkey; tel (90) 212 454 1444; fax 454 1497; e-mail customer@todayszaman.com; web site www.zaman.com.tr
Circ. 6,000@RecordBodyIndent:Gen. Dir. – Ekren Dumanli
Adv. Mgr. – Hakan Dikmen

IZMIR

BUGUN (D)
N/AGaziosmanpasa Bul. No. 5, Izmir, Turkey; tel (90)
Circ. @RecordBodyIndent:Pub. – Onay Bilgin

DUNYA (6X WK.)
N/ACumhuriyet Bul. Elcin Ishani, No. 118, Kat:2, Izmir, Turkey; tel (90) 232 446 8819
Circ. @RecordBodyIndent:Ed. in Chief – Didem Demirkent

FOTOSPOR (D)
N/AVali Kazim Dirik Caddesi, No. 13, Izmir, Turkey; tel (90)
Circ. @RecordBodyIndent:Pub. – Birol Nadir

GUNAYDIN (D)
N/AMurselpasa Bul., No. 161, Izmir, Turkey; tel (90)
Circ. @RecordBodyIndent:Pub. – Asil Nadir

GUNES (D)
N/AAnkara AsfaltÃ£Â£, No:64/1 Turkcell Plaza, Bornova, Izmir, Turkey; tel (90) 232 435 1717; fax 462 6057; web site www.gunes.com
Circ. @RecordBodyIndent:Head – Mehmet Bulent Ergin

HURRIYET (D)
N/ASehit Fethi Bey Caddesi, No. 53, Izmir, Turkey; tel (90)
Circ. @RecordBodyIndent:Pub. – Erol Simavi

MILLIYET (D)
N/ASehit Plaza Bey Caddesi, No. 18 K Plaza, 5th Fl., Izmir, Turkey; tel (90) 232 464 2000; fax 464 1402; web site www.milliyet.com.tr
Circ. @RecordBodyIndent:Pub. – Aydin Dogan

SABAH (D)
N/AGazi Osman Pasa Bulvari, No. 5, Cankaya, Izmir, Turkey; tel (90) 216 585 9100; fax 354 3469; web site www.sabah.com.tr
Circ. 700,000@RecordBodyIndent:Pub. – Dinc Bilgin
Adv. Mgr. – Drdal Fafak

TAN (D)
N/AMurselpasa Bul., No. 61, Izmir, Turkey; tel (90)
Circ. @RecordBodyIndent:Pub. – Asil Nadir

TERCUMAN (D)
N/A1371, Sokak No. 5/2, Cankaya, Izmir, Turkey; tel (90)
Circ. @RecordBodyIndent:Pub. – Kemal Ilicak

TURKISH DAILY NEWS (D)
N/ASehitler Cad.No:16/1, Izmir, Turkey; tel (90) 232 464 2607; fax 464 2999; e-mail tdnizm@tdn.com.tr
Circ. 15,000@RecordBodyIndent:Ed. – David Yasir

TURKIYE (D)
N/A1479, Sokak No. 9, Alsancak, Izmir, Turkey; tel (90)
Circ. @RecordBodyIndent:Pub. – Enver Oren

YENI ASIR (D)
N/AGaziosmanpasa Bulvari No: 5, Cankaya,

Izmir, 35210, Turkey; tel (90) 232 441 5000; fax 483 4141; e-mail info@yeniasir.com.tr; web site www.yeniasir.com.tr
Circ.@RecordBodyIndent:Pub./Owner – Dinc Bilgin
Adv. Mgr. – Turiy Aritin
Mng. Ed. – Aydin Bilgin

ZAMAN (D)
N/AAkbeniz sk. No. 31-1343 SK, Izmir, Turkey; tel (90) 232 483 6003; fax 446 8836; web site www.zaman.com; www.todayszaman.com
Circ.800,000@RecordBodyIndent:Pub. – GÃ£ray Demir
Adv. Mgr. – Adem Kurt

KAYSERI

MILLIYET (D)
N/AIstasyan Caddesi Tapinc Han, Kat:3, Kayseri, Turkey; tel (90); web site www.milliyet.com.tr
Circ.@RecordBodyIndent:Pub. – Aydin Dogan

SAMAUN

MILLIYET (D)
N/A19 Mayis Mah. Hurriyet, Sokak No. 8, Kat:3, Samaun, Turkey; tel (90)
Circ.@RecordBodyIndent:Pub. – Aydin Dogan

YENIBOSNA

MILLI GAZETE (D)
N/ACemal Ulusoy Cd. No: 35, Yenibosna, Turkey; tel (90) 212 697 1000; fax 693 1801; e-mail milli@milligazete.com.tr; web site www.milligazete.com.tr
Circ.@RecordBodyIndent:Pub. – Omer Yukselozek

UNITED ARAB EMIRATES

DU BAI

INTERNATIONAL PRINTING PRESS (D)
Est. 1976
N/APO Box 5266, DU BAI, UNITED ARAB EMIRATES; tel (+971) +971 4 +971 4 2667131; fax +971 4 2660163; e-mail ippdubai@emirates.net.ae; web site ippdubai.com
Circ.8,000

UNITED ARAB EMIRATES

ABU DHABI

AL FAJR (D)
N/APO Box 505, Abu Dhabi, United Arab Emirates; tel (971) 2 448 8300; fax 448 8436; e-mail fajrnews@emirates.net.ae
Circ.28,000@RecordBodyIndent:Adv. Mgr. – Sherif Al Bassel
Mng. Ed. – Obaid Al-Mazroui

AL-ITTIHAD (D)
N/APO Box 40401, Abu Dhabi, United Arab Emirates; tel (971) 2 641 1440; fax 641 4184; web site www.alittihad.ae
Circ.58,000@RecordBodyIndent:GM – Juma Magar Alnumi
Advertising: Marston Webb & Associates.

EMIRATES NEWS (MS)
N/APO Box 791, Abu Dhabi, United Arab Emirates; tel (971) 2 451466; fax 453662; e-mail emrtnews@emirates.net.ae
Circ.21,150@RecordBodyIndent:Chrmn. – Sheikh Abdullah Bin Zayed An-Nahyan
Mng. Ed. – Peter Hellyer
Advertising: AdMarket Int'l.

GULF NEWS (D)
N/APO Box 7441, Abu Dhabi, United Arab Emirates; tel (971) 2 634 5144; e-mail gulfnews@emirates.net.ae
Circ.@RecordBodyIndent:Mng. Dir./Ed. in Chief – Obaid Humaid Al Tayer
Adv. Mgr. – Duleep George

AL-WAHDAH (D)
N/APO Box 2488, Abu Dhabi, United Arab Emirates; tel (971) 2 448 8400; fax 448 8937; e-mail alwahdah@emi.ae
Circ.20,000@RecordBodyIndent:Owner – Rashid Aweidha
Gen. Mgr. – Khalifa Al-Mashwi
Adv. Mgr. – Ahmed Mawed
Ed. in Chief – Khalid Minishi

KHALEEJ TIMES (D)
N/APO Box 3082, Abu Dhabi, United Arab Emirates; tel (971) 2 633 7666; fax 634 4339; e-mail news@khaleejtimes.com; web site www.khaleejtimes.com
Circ.100,000@RecordBodyIndent:Bureau Chief – Hassan Raafat
Deputy Bureau Chief – Mohammad Abdul-Qudoos

DUBAI

AL-BAYAN (D)
N/APO Box 2710, Dubai, United Arab Emirates; tel (971) 4 344 4400; fax 344 5257; e-mail bayan@albayan.ae; web site www.albayan.ae
Circ.32,651@RecordBodyIndent:Gen. Mgr. – Zaan Haheen
Ed. – Daen Shaheen

AL FAJR (D)
N/APO Box 10630, Dubai, United Arab Emirates; tel (971) 4 221 7155; fax 221 0070; e-mail fajrnews@emirates.net.ae
Circ.22,000@RecordBodyIndent:Ed. in Chief – Obeid Al-Mazroui

AL-ITTIHAD (D)
N/APO Box 3446, Dubai, United Arab Emirates; tel (971) 4 332 2221; fax 331 1222; web site www.alittihad.ae
Circ.@RecordBodyIndent:Ed. in Chief – Moza Matar

GULF NEWS (D)
N/APO Box 6519, Dubai, United Arab Emirates; tel (971) 4 344 7100; fax 344 3108; e-mail gulfnews@emirates.net.ae; web site www.gulfnews.com
Circ.91,534@RecordBodyIndent:Mktg. Dir. – Duleep George
Circ. Mgr. – R.V. Dhar
Circ. Mgr. – Sanjay Malik
Ed. in Chief – Abdul Hameed Ahmed
Ed. – Francis Matthew
Administrative Ed. – Jumana Al Etamim
Prodn. Mgr. – Michael Condon

AL WAHDA (D)
N/APO Box 2488, Dubai, United Arab Emirates; tel (971) 4 474121
Circ.20,000@RecordBodyIndent:– Rashed Aweidha
– Dar Al-WahdaPub.s

KHALEEJ TIMES (D)
N/APO Box 11243, Dubai, United Arab Emirates; tel (971) 4 338 4545; fax 338 2238; web site www.khaleejtimes.com
Circ.90,000@RecordBodyIndent:Dir. Mktg. – Arun Qureshi
Associate Ed. – Patrick Michael

MATHRUBHUMI (D)
N/APO Box 11243, Dubai, United Arab Emirates; tel (971) 4 338 3535; fax 338 3345; e-mail kteditor@emirates.net.ae; web site www.khaleejtimes.com
Circ.

SHARJAH

AL-ITTIHAD (D)
N/APO Box 1777, Sharjah, United Arab Emirates; tel (971) 6 556 6678; fax 556 6679; web site www.alittihad.ae
Circ.@RecordBodyIndent:Adv. Mgr. – Saif Al-Shamici
Ed. in Chief – Majit Al-Haz

AL KHALEEJ (D)
N/APO Box 30, Sharjah, United Arab Emirates; tel (971) 6 577 7777; web site www.alkhaleej.ae
Circ.85,000@RecordBodyIndent:Pub. – Taryam Omran
Adv. Mgr. – Faraj Yassine
Ed. in Chief – Mohammed Banjak

YEMEN

ADEN

ADEN NEWS BULLETINS
N/APO Box 1166, Tawahi, Aden, Yemen; tel (967) 2
Circ.

AR-RABI ASHAR MIN UKTUBAR (M-EX SAT.)
N/APO Box 4227, Crater, Aden, Yemen; tel (967)
Circ.20,000@RecordBodyIndent:Editorial Dir. – Farouq Mustafa Rifat
Ed. in Chief – Muhammad Hussain Muhammad

SANA

ASH SHURA (WEEKLY)
N/APO Box 15114, Sana, Yemen; tel (967) 1 213584; fax 213468; e-mail shoura@y.net.ye
Circ.15,000@RecordBodyIndent:Ed. – Abdallah Sa'ad

ATH THAWRA (D)
N/APO Box 2195, Sana, Yemen; tel (967) 1 262 626; fax 274 139
Circ.110,000@RecordBodyIndent:Ed. – Muhammad Az-Zorkah

YEMEN TIMES (WEEKLY)
N/APO Box 2579, Sana, Yemen; tel (967) 1 268 661; fax 268 276; e-mail info@yementimes.com; web site www.yementimes.com
Circ.20,000@RecordBodyIndent:Pub. – Nadia Abdulaziz Al Saqqaf
Adv. Mgr. – Rasheed Ali Abdulwahid
Ed. – Mohamed Khader

TAIZ

AL JUMHURIYA (D)
N/ATaiz Information Office, Taiz, Yemen; tel (967) 4 216748
Circ.100,000

NEWSPAPERS OF AFRICA

ALGERIA

ALGIERS

ALGERIE-ACTUALITE (WEEKLY)
2 rue Jacques Cartier, Algiers, 16000,Algeria; tel (213) 2 635420
Circ.: 250,000
Advertising: Mouni Berrah.
Dir. – Kamel Belkacem

AL-MOUDJAHID (D)
20 rue de la Liberte, Algiers,Algeria; tel (213) 21 737 806; fax 739 043; e-mail info@elmoudjahid.com; website www.elmoudjahid-dz.com
Circ.: 392,000
Mng. Dir. – Abdelmadjid Cherbal

ACH-CHA'AB (D)
1 pl. Maurice Audin, Algiers,Algeria; tel (213) 2 259 5698
Dir. – Kamel Avache

LE JEUNE INDEPENDANT (6X WK.)
1, rue Bachir-Attar, place du 1er-Mai, Algiers, 16016,Algeria; tel (213) 21 670 749; fax 670 746; e-mail direction@jeune-independant.com; website www.jeune-independant.net
Ed. – Naima Nefles Boulares
Adv. Mgr. – Aluache Amene

CONSTANTINE

AN-NASR (D)
BP 388, Constantine,Algeria; tel (213) 4 939216
Circ.: 340,000
Ed. – Abdullah Guettat

ORAN

AL-JOUMHOURIA (D)
6, rue Bensenouci Hamida, Oran,Algeria; tel

(213)
Circ.: 20,000
Ed. – Boukhalfa Benameur

ANGOLA

LUANDA

ABC DIARIO DE ANGOLA (E)
Estrada de Catete, Luanda,Angola; tel (244) 2
Circ.: 8,500
Adv. Mgr. – M. Oliveira

DIARIO DA LUANDA (M)
CP 1290, Luanda,Angola; tel (244)
Circ.: 18,000
Adv. Mgr. – Filipe Amado

DIARIO DA REPUBLICA (D)
CP 1306, Luanda,Angola; tel (244)

O JORNAL DE ANGOLA (MS)
CP 1312, Luanda,Angola; tel (244) 2 338947; fax 333342
Circ.: 41,000
Gen. Dir. – Luis Fernando

PROVINCIA DE ANGOLA (D)
18/24 rua Salvador Correia, Luanda,Angola; tel (244)
Circ.: 35,000
Adv. Mgr. – R.C. de Freitas

BENIN

COTONOU

EHUZU (D)
BP 1210, Cotonou,Benin; tel (229) 21 313681
Circ.: 12,000
Pub./Dir. – Maurice Chabi

L'OPINION
BP 1268, Cotonou,Benin; tel (229) 331385

LA GAZETTE DU GOLFE (WEEKLY)
BP 03-1624, Cotonou,Benin; tel (229) 313558; fax 300199
Circ.: 18,000
Dir. – Ismael Y. Soumanou
Ed. – Karim Okanla

LE FORUM DE LA SEMAINE (WEEKLY)
BP 04-0301, Cotonou,Benin; tel (229) 302623; fax 305391
Dir. – Franck Agbanglan

TAM-TAM EXPRESS (EVERY OTHER WEEK)
BP 2302, Cotonou,Benin; tel (229) 301205; fax 303975
Circ.: 8,000
Dir. – Denis Hodonou

BOTSWANA

GABORONE

BOTSWANA ADVERTISER (WEEKLY)
BP 130, Gaborone,Botswana; tel (267) 391 4788

THE BOTSWANA GAZETTE (WEEKLY)
BP 1605, Gaborone,Botswana; tel (267) 31 312833; fax 312833
Circ.: 16,000

BOTSWANA DAILY NEWS/DIKGANG TSA GOMPIENO (D-5X WK.)
Private Postbag 0060, Gaborone,Botswana; tel (267) 31 352541; website www.dailynews.gov.bw
Circ.: 50,000
Ed. – L. Leshaga

MMEGI WA DIGMANG (WEEKLY)
Private Bag BR50, Gaborone,Botswana; tel (267) 31 374784; fax 305508; e-mail mmegi2@inet.co.bw
Circ.: 24,000
Ed. – Metlhaitsile Leepile

BOTSWANA GUARDIAN (WEEKLY)
BP 1641, Gaborone,Botswana; tel (267) 31 352556; fax 374381
Circ.: 17,673
Ed. – Keto Segwai

BURKINA FASO

OUAGADOUGOU

CAREFOUR AFRICAIN
BP 507, Ouagadougou, 01,Burkina Faso; tel (226)

DUNIA (D)
BP 3013, Ouagadougou, 01,Burkina Faso; tel (226)

L'OBSERVATEUR (M)
BP 584, Ouagadougou, 01,Burkina Faso; tel (226) 332 705; fax 314 579; e-mail lobservateur@zcp.bf; website www.lobservateur.bf
Circ.: 8,000
Dir. – Edouard OuÂ£draogo

BULLETIN QUOTIDIEN D'INFORMATION (M)
BP 507, Ouagadougou, 01,Burkina Faso; tel (226)
Circ.: 1,500
Dir. – Hubert Bazie
Ed. – Pierre-Clavier Tassembedo

LE PAYS (D)
BP 4577, Ouagadougou, 01,Burkina Faso; tel (226) 50 554 160; fax 360 378; e-mail ed.lepays@cenatrin.bf; website www.lepays.bf
Circ.: 4,000
MD – Sigue Jeremie Boureima

NOTRE COMBAT (D)
BP 507, Ouagadougou, 01,Burkina Faso; tel (226)

OBSERVATEUR PAALGA (D)
BP 584, Ouagadougou, 01,Burkina Faso; tel (226) 305 575; fax 314 579; e-mail lobservateur@zcp.bf; lobs@fasonet.bf; website www.lobservateur.bf
Circ.: 8,000
Dir. – Edouard Ouedraogo

SIDWAYA (6X WK.)
BP 507, Ouagadougou, 01,Burkina Faso; tel (226) 5030 6307; fax 5031 0362; e-mail ouedro1@yahoo.fr; website www.sidwaya.bf
Circ.: 3,000
Ed. in Chief – Daouda Emile Ouedraogo

BURUNDI

BUJUMBURA

BURUNDI CHRETIEN (WEEKLY)
BP 232, Bujumbura,Burundi; tel (257)

LE RENOUVEAU DU BURUNDI (D-EX MON.)
BP 2870, Bujumbura,Burundi; tel (257)
Circ.: 20,000
Dir. – Jean Nzeyimana

UBUMWE (WEEKLY)
BP 1400, Bujumbura,Burundi; tel (257) 2 23929
Circ.: 20,000

CAMEROON

DOUALA

THE HERALD (WEEKLY)
BP 3659, Douala,Cameroon; tel (237) 315522; fax 318161
Circ.: 8,000
Dir. – Dr. Boniface Forbin

LA DETENTE
BP 8373, Douala,Cameroon; tel (237)
Circ.: 20,000
Gen. Mgr. – Samuel Eleme

LA GAZETTE (2X WK.)
BP 5485, Douala,Cameroon; tel (237)
Circ.: 35,000
Ed. – Abobel Karimou

LA NOUVELLE EXPRESSION (5X WK.)
BP 15333, Douala,Cameroon; tel (237) 343 2227; fax 343 2669; e-mail lanouvelleexpression2005@yahoo.fr; website www.lanouvelleexpression.net
Circ.: 35,000
Ed. – Severin Tchounkeu

LA VISION
BP 8454, Douala,Cameroon; tel (237) 430839; fax 430265
Circ.: 20,000
Gen. Mgr. – Edouard Kingue

LE MESSAGER (3X WK.)
BP 5925, Douala,Cameroon; tel (237) 342 0214
Circ.: 39,000
Mng. Ed. – Pius Njawe

LE MONT-CAMEROUN
BP 3979, Douala,Cameroon; tel (237)
Pub. – Issac-Desire Boundja

LE TEMPS
BP 12931, Douala,Cameroon; tel (237) 433119
Circ.: 15,000
Gen. Mgr. – Benjamin Malake

YAOUNDE

AFRIQUE EN DOSSIERS (D)
BP 1715, Yaounde,Cameroon; tel (237) 3
Dir. – Ebongue Soelle

CAPE VERDE

PRAIA

BOLETIM OFICIAL DA REPUBLICA DE CABO VERDE (WEEKLY)
CP 113, Praia,Cape Verde; tel (238) 614150

BOLETIM INFORMATIVO (WEEKLY)
CP 126, Praia,Cape Verde; tel (238)
Circ.: 1,500

NOVO JORNAL CABO VERDE (2X WK.)
CP 118, Praia,Cape Verde; tel (238) 613989; fax 613829
Circ.: 5,000
Ed. – Lucia Dias

A SEMANA (WEEKLY)
CP 36C, Praia,Cape Verde; tel (238) 613950; fax 632271; e-mail asemana@mail.cvtelecom.cv; website www.asemana.publ.cv
Circ.: 5,000
Ed. – Filomena Silva

CENTRAL AFRICAN REPUBLIC

BANGUI

BANGUI CENTRAFRIC PRESS (D)
BP 1290, Bangui,Central African Republic; tel (236)

CHAD REPUBLIC

N'DJAMENA

INFO-TCHAD (D)
BP 670, N'Djamena,Chad Republic; tel (235) 51 5867

N'DJAMENA HEBDO (WEEKLY)
BP 760, N'Djamena,Chad Republic; tel (235) 51 5314; fax 1498; e-mail ndjh@intnet.td
Ed. in Chief – Dieudonne Djonabaye

TCHAD ET CULTURE
BP 907, N'Djamena,Chad Republic; tel (235) 51 4142
Dir./Pub. – Jean Geli
Ed. in Chief – Sabine Laplane

CONGO

BUKAVU

CENTRE-AFRIQUE (E)
BP 379, Bukavu,Congo; tel (242)
Adv. Mgr. – M. van Leeuwan

KINSHASA

COURRIER D'AFRIQUE (M-EX S)
BP 4826, Kinshasa,Congo; tel (242)
Circ.: 15,000
Adv. Mgr. – G. Makosso

ELIMA (E)
BP 11498, Kinshasa,Congo; tel (242) 77332
Dir./Ed. in Chief – Essolomwa Nkoy Ea Linganga

KINSHASA, LIMETE

SALONGO (M)
BP 601, Kinshasa, Limete,Congo; tel (243) 12 77367
Circ.: 10,000

KISANGANI

LE STANLEYVILLOIS (E)
BP 6, Kisangani,Congo; tel (242)
Pub. – Georges Hensenne

KISANGANI, HAUT-ZAIRE

BOYOMA (D)
BP 982, Kisangani, Haut-Zaire,Congo; tel (242)
Dir./Ed. – Badriyo Rova Rovatu

LUBUMBASHI, SHABA

MJUMBE (D)
BP 2474, Lubumbashi, Shaba,Congo; tel (242) 2 25348
Dir./Ed. – Tshimanga Koya Kakona

LUBUMBASHI-SHABA

L'ESSOR DU ZAIRE (M)
BP 525, Lubumbashi-Shaba,Congo; tel (242)
Circ.: 10,000
Ed. – Mikola Jack
Adv. Mgr. – Jacques Kote Tshilembe

LA DEPECHE (D)
BP 2474, Lubumbashi-Shaba,Congo; tel (242)
Circ.: 20,000
Adv. Mgr. – A. Tumba

TAIFA (WEEKLY)
BP 884, Lubumbashi-Shaba,Congo; tel (242)
Ed. – Lwambwa Milambu

DEMOCRATIC REPUBLIC CONGO

BRAZZAVILLE

ACI (D)
BP 2144, Brazzaville,Democratic Republic Congo; tel (243) 830591
Circ.: 1,000

COURRIER D'AFRIQUE (D)
BP 2027, Brazzaville,Democratic Republic Congo; tel (243)

ETUMBA (WEEKLY)
BP 23, Brazzaville,Democratic Republic Congo; tel (243) 811389
Circ.: 8,000

JOURNAL DE BRAZZAVILLE (D)
BP 132, Brazzaville,Democratic Republic Congo; tel (243)
Pub. – M.J. Devoue

JOURNAL OFFICIAL DE LA REPUBLIQUE DU CONGO (D)
BP 58, Brazzaville,Democratic Republic Congo; tel (243)

MWETI (D)
BP 991, Brazzaville,Democratic Republic Congo; tel (243) 811087
Circ.: 7,000
Dir. – Matongo Aveley
Ed. in Chief – Hubert Madouaba

POINTE-NOIRE

L'EVEIL DE POINTE-NOIRE (D)
BP 66, Pointe-Noire,Democratic Republic Congo; tel (243)

DJIBOUTI

DJIBOUTI (CAPITAL CITY)

LA NATION DE DJIBOUTI (WEEKLY)
BP 32, Djibouti (Capital city),Djibouti; tel (253) 352201; fax 353937
Circ.: 4,300
Dir. – Ismael H. Tani

EGYPT

ALEXANDRIA

AL-ITTIHAD AL-MISRI (E)
13 Sharia Sidi Abd ar-Razzak, Alexandria,Egypt; tel (20)
Dir. – Hassan Maher Farag

AS SAFEER (E)
4 Sharia as-Sahafa, Alexandria,Egypt; tel (20)
Ed. – Mustafa Sharaf

BAREED ACH-CHARIKAT (E)
BP 813, Alexandria,Egypt; tel (20)
Circ.: 15,000
Ed. – S. Beneducci

LA REFORME (D)
8 Passage Sherif, Alexandria,Egypt; tel (20)

LE JOURNAL D'ALEXANDRIE (E)
1 Sharia Rolo, Alexandria,Egypt; tel (20)
Ed. – Charles Arcache

TACHYDROMOS-EGYPTOS (M)
4 Sharia Zangarol, Alexandria,Egypt; tel (20) 3 35650
Circ.: 2,000
Pub. – Penny Koutsoumis
Ed. – Dinos Koutsoumis

CAIRO

AKHBAR AL YAUM/AL AKHBAR (WEEKLY)
6 Sharia as-Sahafa, Cairo,Egypt; tel (20) 2 758888; fax 745888
Circ.: 1,158,000
Chrmn./Ed. in Chief – Ibrahim Abu Sadah

AL AHRAM (D)
Sharia al-Galaa, Cairo, 11511,Egypt; tel (20) 2 2770 4781; fax 2578 6023; website www.ahram.org.eg
Advertising: Publicitas.
Chrmn. – Morsi Adalla

AL HAYAT (D)
1 Latin America St., Garden City, Cairo,Egypt; tel (20) 2 3546646; fax 3546646

AL KORA WAL MALACEB
24-26 Sharia Zakaria Ahmad, Cairo,Egypt; tel (20) 02
Circ.: 95,000
MD – Abdel Hamid Hamrouch
Ed. – Hamdi El Nahas

AL MISSA' (E)
111-115 Ramsis St., Cairo,Egypt; tel (20) 22 578 1010; fax 578 4747; e-mail gazette-editor@hotmail.com; website www.gom.com.eg
Circ.: 405,000
Ed. in Chief – Ramadan Abdel Kader

AL GOUMHOURIYA (D)
111-115 Ramses St., Cairo,Egypt; tel (20) 2 578 1010; fax 578 4747
Circ.: 900,000
Chrmn. – Mohammad Abou Al-Hadid
Ed. – Mohammed Ali Ibrahim

AREV (E)
3 Sharia Sulayman Halabi, Cairo,Egypt; tel (20) 2 754703
Ed. – Avedis Yapoudjian

EGYPTIAN GAZETTE (M)
24-26 Sharia Zakaria Ahmad, Cairo,Egypt; tel (20) 2 578 1010; fax 578 4747; e-mail webmaster@egy.com; website www.egy.com
Circ.: 40,000
Ed. in Chief – Muhammad Ali Ibrahim

EGYPTIAN MAIL (WEEKLY)
24-26 Sharia Zakaria Ahmad, Cairo,Egypt; tel (20) 2 751511
Circ.: 40,000
Ed. in Chief – Muhammad Ali Ibrahim

LE JOURNAL D'EGYPTE (MS)
1 Sharia Borsa Guedida, Cairo,Egypt; tel (20)
Circ.: 72,000
Gen. Mgr. – Lita Gallad
Ed. in Chief – Muhammad Rachad

LE PROGRES EGYPTIEN/LE PROGRES DIMANCHE (MS)
Ramses St. 111-115, Cairo,Egypt; tel (20) 2 578 1010; fax 578 4747; e-mail ask@progres.net.eg; website www.progres.net.eg
Circ.: 30,000
Ed. in Chief – Ahmed El-Bardissi

PHOS (M)
14 Sharia Zakaria Ahmad, Cairo,Egypt; tel (20)
Circ.: 20,000
Ed. – S. Pateras
Mgr. – Basile A. Pateras

EQUATORIAL GUINEA

BATA

EGYPTIAN MAIL
24-26 Sharia Zakaria Ahmed St., Al Tahrir, Bata,Equatorial Guinea; tel (240) 8 7466

POTO POTO (D)
Apdo. Postal 236, Bata,Equatorial Guinea; tel (240)
Pub. – Francisco de Anta Franco

ETHIOPIA

ADDIS ABABA, SHEWA

YEZAREITU ETHIOPIA (WEEKLY)
BP 30232, Addis Ababa, Shewa,Ethiopia; tel (251)
Circ.: 30,000
Ed. in Chief – Imiru Worku

ADDIS ZEMEN (M-EX MON.)
BP 30232, Addis Ababa, Shewa,Ethiopia; tel (251) 11 569 883; fax 569 862; e-mail ethpress@ethionet.et; website www.ethpress.gov.et
Circ.: 40,000
Ed. in Chief – Merid Bekele

ETHIOPIAN HERALD (M)
BP 30701, Addis Ababa, Shewa,Ethiopia; tel (251) 11 119050
Circ.: 37,000
Ed. in Chief – Kiflom Hadgoi

ASMARA, ERITREA

ASMARA HEBRET/AL WADHA (D)
BP 247, Asmara, Eritrea,Ethiopia; tel (251)
Circ.: 4,000
Ed. in Chief – Gurgia Tesfaselassie

QUOTIDIANO ERITREO (D)
BP 247, Asmara, Eritrea,Ethiopia; tel (251)

GABON

LIBREVILLE

GABON-MATIN (D)
BP 168, Libreville,Gabon; tel (241)
Circ.: 18,000
Mgr. – Hilarion Vendany

L'UNION (D)
BP 3849, Libreville,Gabon; tel (241) 732 184; fax 738 326
Circ.: 40,000

MD – Albert Yangari

GABON D'AUJOURD'HUI (WEEKLY)
BP 750, Libreville,Gabon; tel (241)

GAMBIA

BANJUL

THE GAMBIA DAILY (M-3X WK.)
Dept. of Information, 14 Daniel Goddard St., Banjul,Gambia; tel (220) 225060; fax 227230; e-mail gamna@gamtel.ga; website www.gambia.dk/press
Circ.: 500
Ed. – Alieu F. Sagnia

THE DAILY OBSERVER (D-5X WK.)
PMB 131, Banjul,Gambia; tel (220) 441 4425; fax 449 6878; website www.observer.gm
Circ.: 2,000
Advertising: Kenneth Y Best.
Ed. – Baba Galleh Jallow

THE FOROYAA (WEEKLY)
BP 2306, Banjul,Gambia; tel (220) 393177; fax 393177; e-mail online@foroyaa.gm; website www.foroyaa.gm
Circ.: 1,500
– Sam Sarr
– Halifa Sallah
– Sidia JattaEd.s

THE GAMBIA NEWS & REPORT (WEEKLY)
BP 976, Banjul,Gambia; tel (220) 391691; fax 392866
Circ.: 1,500
Ed. in Chief – Momodou L. Gaye

THE POINT (M-5X WK.)
PO Box 66, Banjul,Gambia; tel (220) 449 7441; fax 449 7442; e-mail thepoint13@yahoo.com; thepoint@hotmail.com; website www.thepoint.gm
Circ.: 4,000
Pub. – Pap Saine
Ed. – Ebrina Sawaneh

GHANA

ACCRA

ECHO (WEEKLY)
BP 5288, Accra,Ghana; tel (233)
Circ.: 40,000
Mng. Ed. – M.K. Frimpong

EVENING NEWS (WEEKLY)
BP 7505, Accra,Ghana; tel (233) 21 229416
Circ.: 30,000
Mng. Ed. – Osei Poku

GRAPHIC SPORTS (WEEKLY)
BP 742, Accra,Ghana; tel (233) 21 228911; e-mail graphic@ghana.com; website www.graphic.com.gh
Circ.: 60,000
Ed. – Joe Aggrey

DAILY TELEGRAPH (M-EX S)
BP 742, Accra,Ghana; tel (233) 21 684 001; fax 234754; e-mail info@graphicghana.com; website www.graphicghana.com
Circ.: 10,000
Adv. Mgr. – W.J. Cooke

THE MIRROR (WEEKLY)
BP 742, Accra,Ghana; tel (233) 21 228911; fax 669886; e-mail graphic@ghana.com; website www.graphic.com.gh
Circ.: 90,000
Ed. – E.N.V. Provencal

DAILY GRAPHIC (D)
BP 742, Accra,Ghana; tel (233) 21 684001; fax 234754; e-mail info@graphicghana.com; website www.graphicghana.com
Circ.: 100,000
Ed. in Chief – Elvis Aryeh

THE GHANAIAN TIMES (M-EX S)
BP 2638, Accra,Ghana; tel (233) 21 228 242; fax 220 733; e-mail info@newtimes.com.gh; website www.newtimes.com.gh
Circ.: 40,000
Ed. – Enimil Ashon

WEEKLY SPECTATOR (WEEKLY)
BP 2638, Accra,Ghana; tel (233) 21 228282; fax 229398
Circ.: 165,000
Ed. – Willie Donkor

THE GHANAIAN CHRONICLE (WEEKLY)
General Portfolio Ltd., Private mail bag, Accra,Ghana; tel (233) 21 222319; fax 232608; e-mail chronicl@africaonline.com.gh; website www.ghanaian-chronicle.com
Circ.: 60,000
Ed. – Ato Kobbie

KUMASI

THE PIONEER (WEEKLY) Est. 1939
BP 325, Kumasi,Ghana; tel (233) 51 2204
Circ.: 100,000
Ed. – Johnson Gyampoh

GUINEA

CONAKRY

FONIKE
BP 341, Conakry,Guinea; tel (224)
Dir. – Ibrahima Kalil Diare

GUINEA-BISSAU

BISSAU

VOZ DA GUINE (D)
UNKNOWN, Bissau,Guinea-Bissau; tel (245)
Circ.: 6,000

IVORY COAST

ABIDJAN

IVOIR 'SOIR (E-5X WK.)
01 BP 1807, Abidjan, 01,Ivory Coast; tel (225) 219578; fax 372545
Circ.: 50,000
Advertising: AdMarket Int'l.
Gen. Dir. – Michel Kouame

FRATERNITE-MATIN (M-EX S)
01 BP 1807, Abidjan, 01-RCI,Ivory Coast; tel (225) 20 370 666; e-mail regieweb@fratmat.info; website www.fratmat.info
Circ.: 80,000
Gen. Dir. – Michel Kouame

KENYA

NAIROBI

CHEMSHA BONGO
BP 57657, Nairobi,Kenya; tel (254)

DAILY NATION (D)
PO Box 49010, Nairobi,Kenya; tel (254) 20 328 8000; fax 328 8995; e-mail bdnewsdesk@nation.co.ke; website www.nation.co.ke
Circ.: 170,000
CEO – Linus Gitahi
Adv. Mgr. – Michael Ngugi
Ed. Dir. (Grp.) – Joseph Odindo

KENYA LEO (D)
PO Box 30958, Nairobi,Kenya; tel (254) 2 337798
Mng. Ed. – Job Mutungi

KENYA TIMES (M)
PO Box 30958, Nairobi,Kenya; tel (254) 20 652 372; fax 218 809
Circ.: 52,000
Ed. in Chief – John Khakhudu Agunda

TAIFA LEO (M-EX S)
PO Box 49010, Nairobi,Kenya; tel (254) 20 211 448; fax 213 946; website www.nationmedia.com
Circ.: 57,000
Ed. – Robert Mwangi

THE STANDARD (M-EX S)
PO Box 30080, Nairobi,Kenya; tel (254) 20 322 2111; fax 214 467; e-mail editorial@eastandard.net; website www.eastandard.net
Circ.: 200,000
Grp. Mng. Dir. – John Bundotich

THE STANDARD ON SUNDAY (S)
PO Box 30080, Nairobi,Kenya; tel (254) 2 540280; fax 553939
Circ.: 90,000
Mng. Ed. – Esther Kamweru

SUNDAY NATION
PO Box 49010, Nairobi,Kenya; tel (254) 2 3208 8000; fax 214 531; website www.nationmedia.com
Circ.: 170,000
Mng. Ed. – Bernard Nderitu

SUNDAY TIMES
PO Box 30958, Nairobi,Kenya; tel (254) 2 337798
Ed. – Robert Otani

LESOTHO

MASERU

MAKATOLLE (WEEKLY)
PO Box 111, Maseru, 100,Lesotho; tel (266)
Circ.: 2,000
Ed. – Mohaila Mohale

LENTSOE LA BASOTHO (WEEKLY)
PO Box 353, Maseru, 100,Lesotho; tel (266) 323561; fax 310003
Circ.: 14,000
Ed. – Lebenya Kamliso

LESOTHO TODAY (WEEKLY)
PO Box 36, Maseru, 100,Lesotho; tel (266) 323586; fax 310003
Circ.: 7,000
Ed. – T. Tsepane

MOAFRIKA
BP 7234, Maseru, 100,Lesotho; tel (266)
Circ.: 3,500
Pub./Adv. Mgr. – Thabang Khalieli

MOHLANKA
BP 124, Maseru, 100,Lesotho; tel (266)
Circ.: 6,000
Ed./Adv. Mgr. – C.S. Maboloka

MPHATLATSANE (D)
BP 7066, Maseru, 100,Lesotho; tel (266)
Circ.: 4,000
Ed./Adv. Mgr. – Ms. Mamello Morrison

MAZENOD

MOELETSI OA BASOTHO (WEEKLY)
PO Box 18, Mazenod, 160,Lesotho; tel (266) 350254
Circ.: 20,000
Ed. – Rev. M. Khutlang

MORIJA

LESELINYANA LA LESOTHO (EVERY OTHER WEEK)
PO Box 7, Morija, 190,Lesotho; tel (266) 360244; fax 360005
Circ.: 15,000
Ed./Adv. Mgr. – Aaron B. Thoalane

LIBERIA

MONROVIA, MONTSERRADO

DAILY OBSERVER (M-5X WK.) Est. 1981
PO Box 1858, Monrovia, Montserrado, 1000-10,Liberia; tel (231) 6472772; website www.liberianobserver.com
Circ.: 30,000
Ed. in Chief – Stanton B. Peabody

FOOTPRINTS TODAY (DS)
PO Box 3496, Monrovia, Montserrado,Liberia; tel (231)

LIBERIAN AGE (M)
PO Box 9031, Monrovia, Montserrado,Liberia; tel (231)
Circ.: 4,000

NEW LIBERIAN (D-EX WED.)
PO Box 9021, Monrovia, Montserrado,Liberia; tel (231)
Ed. in Chief – J. Emmanuel Zehkpehge Bowier

SUN TIMES (D)
PO Box 2475, Monrovia, Montserrado,Liberia; tel (231)

LIBYA

TRIPOLI

AL-FAJR AL-JADID (D)
PO Box 2303, Tripoli,Libya; tel (218) 21 333 7106; website www.alfajraljadeedeng.com
Circ.: 40,000
Ed. – Ali Mahmaud Mariya

AL-JIHAD (D)
2 Sharia Jama Syala, Tripoli,Libya; tel (218)
Ed. – Ali Al-Mahdi

LIBYAN PRESS REVIEW (D)
PO Box 2461, Tripoli,Libya; tel (218) 21 42781

MADAGASCAR

ANTANANARIVO

IMONGO VAOVAO (D)
BP 7014, Antananarivo, 101,Madagascar; tel (261) 2 2221053
Circ.: 10,000
Dir. – Clement Ramamonjisoa

MARESAKA (D)
12 Ialana Ratsimba John, Isotry, Antananarivo, 101,Madagascar; tel (261) 2 2223568
Circ.: 5,000
Ed. – M. Ralaiarijaona

MIDI-MADAGASIKARA (D)
BP 1414 Ankorondrano, Antananarivo, 101,Madagascar; tel (261) 20 226 9779; fax 222 7351; e-mail midi@midi-madagasikara.mg ; contact@midi-madagasikara.mg; website www.midi-madagasikara.mg
Circ.: 25,500
Gen. Mgr. – Juliana Andriambelo Rakotoarivelo
Editorial Dir. – Stephane Jacob
Ed. in Chief – Zo Rakotoseheno

ATRIKA (D)
BP 271, Antananarivo,Madagascar; tel (261) 2 22220
Circ.: 13,000

MALAWI

BLANTYRE

MALAWI NEWS (WEEKLY)
Private Bag 39, Blantyre,Malawi; tel (265) 671566; fax 671114
Circ.: 30,000
Ed. – Dr. K. Lipenga

DAILY TIMES (M-5X WK.) Est. 1895
Private Bag 39, Blantyre,Malawi; tel (265) 871 181; fax 671233; e-mail dailytimes@bnltimes.com; website www.bnltimes.com
Circ.: 22,000Brian Ligomeka
Ed. in Chief – Charles Simango

COMPUTER MONITOR (D)
PO Box 2521, Blantyre,Malawi; tel (265) 623863; fax 623289
Owner – Richard Stambuli

MICHIRU SUN (D)
PO Box 90143, Blantyre,Malawi; tel (265) 641671; fax 645095
Owner/Mng. Ed. – Edward Chitsulo
Owner – Gray Mang'Anda

THE NATION (WEEKLY)
PO Box 30403, Blantyre,Malawi; tel (265) 1 674208; fax 674343
Ed. – Ken Lipanga

THE NEW EXPRESS (WEEKLY)
PO Box 30717, Blantyre,Malawi; tel (265) 624168
Owner/Ed. – Willie Zingani
Ed. – Felix Mponda

THE INDEPENDENT (WEEKLY)
PO Box 2094, Blantyre,Malawi; tel (265) 624915; fax 624330; e-mail jayzedkay@yahoo.com
Circ.: 10,000
Owner – Zeenat Karim
Ed. in Chief – Janet Karim

U.D.F. NEWS (D)
PO Box 3052, Blantyre,Malawi; tel (265) 643245

BVUMBWE

THE ENQUIRER (D)
PO Box 110, Bvumbwe,Malawi; tel (265) 675229

MALI

BAMAKO

BULLETIN QUOTIDIEN (M)
BP 46, Bamako,Mali; tel (223) 222 5036; fax 222 2120; e-mail ccim@cefip.com; website www.lamaisondelafrique.com/ecci_mali.html
Ed. – Malle Ousmane

LES ECHOS
BP 2043, Bamako,Mali; tel (223) 229 6289; fax 229 7639; e-mail jamana@jamana.org; infos@jamana.org; website www.jamana.org
Circ.: 25,000
Mng. Dir. – Hamidou Konate
Ed. in Chief – Aboubacar Salif Diarra

L'ESSOR-LA VOIX DU PEUPLE (D)
BP 141, Bamako,Mali; tel (223) 224797
Circ.: 3,500
Ed. – Souleymane Drabo

JOURNAL OFFICIEL DE LA REPUBLIQUE DU MALI
BP 1463, Bamako,Mali; tel (223)

MAURITANIA

NOUAKCHOTT

ACH-CHABB (D)
BP 371, Nouakchott,Mauritania; tel (222) 252 916; fax 255 520; website www.ami.mr
Gen. Dir. – Mohamed El-Hafed Ould Maham

MAURITIUS

PORT LOUIS

CHINA TIMES (D)
PO Box 325, Port Louis,Mauritius; tel (230) 240 3067; fax 217 4013
Circ.: 3,000
MD – Lim Kin Sing
Ed. – Liu Jin Guo

THE NEW NATION (M)
PO Box 647, Port Louis,Mauritius; tel (230)
Circ.: 15,000
Pub./Ed. – Jugdish Joypaul
Adv. Mgr. – Raveen Kreshwan Singh

L'EXPRESS (DS)
3 rue Brown Sequard, Port Louis,Mauritius; tel (230) 206 8400; fax 247 1010; e-mail sentinelle@intnet.mu; website www.lexpress.mu
Circ.: 35,000
Dir. – Jean-Claude De L'Estrac
Prodn. Mgr. – Edgar Adolphe

LE MAURICIEN (E-6X WK.)
PO Box 7, Port Louis,Mauritius; tel (230) 2078200; fax 208 7059; e-mail redaction@lemauricien.com; website www.lemauricien.com
Circ.: 35,000
Insert rate: stefr@intnet.mu
Advertising: stefr@intnet.mu
Dir. – Jacques Rivet
Ed. in Chief – Gben Sendque

LE NOUVEAU MILITANT (WEEKLY)
21 Poudriere St., Port Louis,Mauritius; tel (230) 2126553; fax 2082291
Circ.: 5,000
Ed. in Chief – J. Raumiah

ADVANCE (D-EX S)
5 Dumat St., Port Louis,Mauritius; tel (230)
Circ.: 10,000
Adv. Mgr. – Roger Merven

NEW CHINESE COMMERCIAL PAPER (D)
12 Arsenal St., Port Louis,Mauritius; tel (230)

SUN (D)
31 Edith Cavell St., Port Louis,Mauritius; tel (230) 212 4820; fax 208 9517
Ed. in Chief – Subash Gobin

MAYOTTE ISLAND

MAMOUDZOU

LE JOURNAL DE MAYOTTE
BP 181, Mamoudzou, 97600,Mayotte Island; tel (269) 611 695; fax 610 388
Circ.: 15,000
Pub. – Martial Henry
Adv. Mgr. – Brigitte Kern

MOROCCO

CASABLANCA

AL BAYANE (D)
BP 13152, Casablanca,Morocco; tel (212) 2 307882
Circ.: 5,000
Dir. – Ismail Alaoui

AL ITTAHID AL ICHTIRAKI (D)
33 Zenkh Prince Abdul Qadir, Casablanca, 05,Morocco; tel (212) 22 619 400; fax 619 405; e-mail Ail@menara.ma; website www.alittihad.press.ma
Circ.: 110,000
Dir. – Mohamed Elyazghi

AL MASSIRA AL KHADRA (D)
33 rue Mohammad Smiha, Casablanca,Morocco; tel (212) 2 75043

BAYANE AL YOUM (D)
B.P. 13152, Casablanca,Morocco; tel (212) 22 449 979; fax 4925 44022; website www.bayanealyaoume.ma
Dir. – Ali Yata

LE MATIN DU SAHARA ET DU MAGHREB (M)
17, Rue Othmane Ben Affane, Casablanca,Morocco; tel (212) 22 489 100; fax 203 048; website www.lematin.ma
Circ.: 100,000
Dir. – Mohamed Jouahri

MAROC-SOIR (E)
34 rue Muhammad Smiha, Casablanca,Morocco; tel (212) 2 268860; fax 262969
Circ.: 50,000
Dir. – Drissi El-Alami

RISSALAT AL OUMMA (D)
158 Ave. des Forces Armees Royales, Casablanca,Morocco; tel (212) 2 901925
Circ.: 7,000
Dir. – Muhammad Alaoui Muhammadi

RABAT

AL ALAM (D)
BP 141, Rabat,Morocco; tel (212) 37 293 002; fax 292 639; e-mail alalam@alalam.ma; website www.alalam.ma
Circ.: 100,000
Dir. – Abdul Jabbar Suhaimi

AL HARAKA (WEEKLY)
8 Sahat al-Alaouiyine, Rabat,Morocco; tel (212) 7 764493
Dir. – Ali Alaoui

AL ITTIHAD AL-ICHTIRAKI (D)
10 Zenkh Zahleh, Rabat,Morocco; tel (212) 3772 2491; fax 3770 4619; e-mail contact@alittihadalichtiraki.press.ma; website www.alittihad.press.ma
Circ.: 25,000

AL MAGHRIBI (WEEKLY)
113 Ave. Allal ben Abdallah, Rabat,Morocco; tel (212) 37 768139
Circ.: 15,000
Dir. – Abdallah Al-Hanani

AL MITHAQ AL WATANI (D)
BP 469, Rabat,Morocco; tel (212) 37 722709; fax 722765
Circ.: 15,000
Dir. – Med Auajjar

AN-NIDAL AD-DIMOKRATI (D)
18 rue de Tunis, Rabat,Morocco; tel (212) 37 730 3754
Dir. – Muhammad Arsalane Al-Jadidi

ANOUAL (WEEKLY)
BP 1385, Rabat,Morocco; tel (212) 7 726733; fax 738259
Dir. – Abd Al-Latif Aouad

L'OPINION (M)
Ave. Hassan II, Lotissment Vita, Rabat,Morocco; tel (212) 37 293 002; fax 283 887; e-mail lopinion@lopinion.ma; website www.lopinion.ma
Circ.: 60,000
Dir. – Muhammad Idrissi Kaitouni

LA TRIBUNE POPULAIRE
12 rue Al Mariniyine, Rabat,Morocco; tel (212) 7 730808
Dir. – Soulahi Bouzekri

AL-ANBA'A (D)
21 rue Patrice Lumumba, Rabat,Morocco; tel (212) 7 724644; e-mail webmaster@mincom.gov.ma; website www.mincom.gov.ma/alanbaa
Circ.: 15,000
Pub./Dir. – Ahmad Al-Yaakoubi

MOZAMBIQUE

BEIRA

DIARIO DE MOZAMBIQUE (D)
CP 81, Beira,Mozambique; tel (258) 3 322501
Circ.: 16,000
Dir. – Ezequiel Ambrosio
Ed. – Faruco Sadique

MAPUTO

DEMOS
CP 2011, Maputo,Mozambique; tel (258) 1 430870; fax 430869
Dir. – Noe Dimande
Ed. – Elias Cossa

DESAFIO
CP 327, Maputo,Mozambique; tel (258) 1 431026; fax 431726
Circ.: 40,000
Ed. – Jorge Matine

DOMINGO (WEEKLY)
CP 327, Maputo,Mozambique; tel (258) 1 431026; fax 431027
Circ.: 25,000
Dir. – Jorge Matine
Pub. – Benjamin Faduco
Ed. – Moises Mabunda

NOTICIAS (MS)
CP 327, Maputo,Mozambique; tel (258) 1 420119; fax 420575
Circ.: 33,000
Dir. – Bernardo Mavanga
Ed. – Hilario Cossa

SAVANA (WEEKLY)
CP 73, Maputo,Mozambique; tel (258) 1 429180; fax 428799; e-mail info@sadirectory.co.za; website www.sadirectory.co.za/mediacoop
Dir. – Kok Nam
Ed. – Salomao Moyoana

NAMIBIA

WALVIS BAY

NAMIB TIMES (2X WKLY)
PO Box 706, Walvis Bay,Namibia; tel (264) 64 205 854; fax 204 813; e-mail ntimes@iway.na; design@iway.na; website www.namibtimes.netLast Audit: March 26, 2010
Ed. In Cheif – Floris Steenkamp

WINDHOEK

DIE REPUBLIKEIN (D) Est. 1978
PO Box 3436, Windhoek, 9000,Namibia; tel (264) 61 2972000; fax 223721; e-mail republikein@republikein.com.na; website www.republikein.com.na
Ed. (acting) – Christo Retief

THE NAMIBIAN (5X WK.)
PO Box 20783, Windhoek,Namibia; tel (264) 61 279 600; fax 279 602; e-mail info@namibian.com.na; webmaster@namibian.com.na; website www.namibian.com.na
Mng. Ed. – Daoud Vriea
Ed. – Gwen Lister

ALLGEMEINE ZEITUNG (D-5X WK.)
PO Box 2127, Windhoek, 9000,Namibia; tel (264) 61 230331; fax 220225; e-mail aznews@iafrica.com.na; website www.allgemeine-zeitung.de
Ed. in Chief – Eberhard Hofmann

TEMPO (S)
PO Box 1794, Windhoek, 9000,Namibia; tel (264) 61 225 822; fax 223 110
Circ.: 11,000
Ed. – Des Erasmus

NIGER REPUBLIC

NIAMEY

AL FAZAR
rue du Paon, Niamey,Niger Republic; tel (227) 733054; fax 760023
Circ.: 1,500
Pub. – Djibo Karama

ANFANI (WEEKLY)
BP 2096, Niamey,Niger Republic; tel (227) 740052; fax 740052; e-mail anfani@intnet.ne
Circ.: 3,000
Pub. – Grmah Boucar

LA TRIBUNE DU PEUPLE (WEEKLY)
BP 2624, Niamey,Niger Republic; tel (227) 733428
Circ.: 3,000
Mng. Ed. – Ibrahim Hamidou

LE PAON AFRICAIN (WEEKLY)
BP 10381, Niamey,Niger Republic; tel (227) 753698; fax 740023
Circ.: 2,000
Dir./Ed. – Moustapha Diop

LE REPUBLICAIN (WEEKLY)
BP 12015, Niamey,Niger Republic; tel (227) 734798; fax 734142
Circ.: 3,000
Dir. – Mamane Abou

LE SAHEL HEBDO
PO Box 368, Niamey,Niger Republic; tel (227) 722020
Circ.: 3,500
Ed. in Chief – Adamou Garba

LE SAHEL (D)
BP 13182, Niamey,Niger Republic; tel (227) 20 733 487; fax 733 090; e-mail onep@intnet.ne; website ^www.lesahel.ne
Circ.: 5,000
Pub. – Ali Ousseini
Pub. Dir. – Saedou Daoura
Mktg. Dir. – Morou Hamadu

LE SAHEL DIMANCHE (WEEKLY)
BP 13182, Niamey,Niger Republic; tel (227) 733486; fax 733090
Circ.: 3,000
Dir. – Ali Ousseini

NIGERIA

BENIN CITY

NIGERIAN OBSERVER (M)
PMB 1334, Benin City,Nigeria; tel (234) 52 240 050; e-mail info@nigerianobservernews.com; website www.nigerianobservernews.com
Circ.: 150,000
Ed. – Tony Ikeakanam

CALABAR, CROSS-RIVER

NIGERIAN CHRONICLE (M)
17-19 Barracks Rd., Calabar, Cross-River,Nigeria; tel (234) 87 232 320
Circ.: 50,000
Ed. – Unimke Nawa

ENUGU, ANAMBRA & ENUGU STATES

SATELLITE (D)
PO Box 9429, Enugu, Anambra & Enugu States,Nigeria; tel (234)

DAILY STAR/EVENING STAR (M&E)
PO Box 1139, Enugu, Anambra & Enugu States,Nigeria; tel (234) 42 253 561
Ed. – Josef Bel-Molokwu

IBADAN, OYO

NIGERIAN TRIBUNE (D)
PO Box 78, Ibadan, Oyo,Nigeria; tel (234) 1 231 3406; website www.tribune.com.ng
Circ.: 109,000
Ed. – Folu Olamiti

THE INDEPENDENT (D)
PO Box 5109, Ibadan, Oyo,Nigeria; tel (234)
Circ.: 13,000
Ed. – Rev. F.B. Cronin-Coltsman

IMOLE OWURO (D)
PO Box 5239, Ibadan, Oyo,Nigeria; tel (234)

IBADAN, OYO STATE

DAILY SKETCH/EVENING SKETCH/SUNDAY SKETCH (MS)
PO Box 5067, Ibadan, Oyo State,Nigeria; tel (234) 2 414851
Chrmn. – Ronke Okusanya
Ed. – Ademola Idowu
Ed. (Sunday Sketch) – Obafemi Oredein

ILORIN, KWARA & KOGO STATES

NIGERIAN HERALD (M)
PO Box 1369, Ilorin, Kwara & Kogo States,Nigeria; tel (234) 31 220 506; fax 220 506
Circ.: 25,000
Ed. – Razak El-Alawa

JOS, PLATEAU

NIGERIAN STANDARD/SUNDAY STANDARD (MS)
PO Box 2112, Jos, Plateau,Nigeria; tel (234)
Circ.: 100,000
Ed. – Sale Iliya

KADUNA SOUTH, KADUNA

NEW DEMOCRAT (D)
PO Box 4457, Kaduna South, Kaduna,Nigeria; tel (234) 62 231907
Circ.: 100,000
Ed. – Abdulhamid Babatunde

KADUNA, KADUNA

GASKIYA TA FI KWABO (M-3X WK.)
PO Box 254, Kaduna, Kaduna,Nigeria; tel (234) 62 201420
Ed. – Abdul-Hassan Ibrahim

NEW NIGERIAN (M)
PO Box 254, Kaduna, Kaduna,Nigeria; tel (234) 62 201420; website www.newnigeriannews.com
Circ.: 80,000
Pub. – Inuwa Jibirin
Chrmn. – Prof. Tekena Tamuno

THE REPORTER (D)
Kaduna South, Kaduna, Kaduna,Nigeria; tel (234)
Mng. Dir. – Muhammed Sulaiman

KANO

TRIUMPH (D)
PO Box 3155, Kano,Nigeria; tel (234) 64 633 875; fax 630 273; website www.triumphnewspapers.com
Ed. in Chief – Mahmoud Adnan Audi

LAGOS

AMANA (D)
PO Box 4483, Ikeja, Lagos,Nigeria; tel (234) 1 713595335

DAILY EXPRESS (D)
PO Box 163, Lagos,Nigeria; tel (234)
Circ.: 20,000
Ed. (acting) – Alhaji Ahmed Alao

NATIONAL CONCORD (M)
PO Box 4483, Ikeja, Lagos,Nigeria; tel (234) 1 9010109
Circ.: 200,000
Pub. – Chief M. K. O. Abiola
Ed. – Nsikak Essien

DAILY TIMES/SUNDAY TIMES/EVENING TIMES (DS)
PO Box 21340, Ikeja, Lagos,Nigeria; tel (234) 1 497 7280; fax 497 7284
Admission – Innocent Okparadike
Ed.(Sunday Times) – Dupe Ajayi

THE GUARDIAN
PO Box 1217, Oshodi, Lagos,Nigeria; tel (234) 1 452 9184; fax 493 1797; e-mail letters@ngrguardiannews.com
Circ.: 80,000
Ed. – Emeka Izeze

THE PUNCH (DS)
PO Box 21204, Onipetsi, Ikeja, Lagos,Nigeria; tel (234) 803 325 9593; e-mail infoadvert@punchontheweb.com; website ^www.punchng.com
Circ.: 150,000
Adv. Mgr. – Remi Ofakunrin

UDORAN (D)
unknown, Lagos,Nigeria; tel (234)

OSHODI, LAGOS

DAILY CHAMPION/SUNDAY CHAMPION (D)
PO Box 2276, Oshodi, Lagos,Nigeria; tel (234) 1 452 5983; fax 452 4421; e-mail info@champion.com.ng; website www.champion.com.ng
Circ.: 150,000
Ed. – Seyi Fasugba

OWERRI

NIGERIAN STATESMAN/SUNDAY STATESMAN (DS)
PO Box 1095, Owerri,Nigeria; tel (234) 83 230099
Ed. – Edube Wadibia

OWERRI, IMO

DAILY NATION (M)
43 Okigwe Rd., Aba, Owerri, Imo,Nigeria; tel (234)
Ed. – Gab Okafor

PORT HARCOURT, RIVERS

NIGERIAN STAR (D)
PO Box 73, Port Harcourt, Rivers,Nigeria; tel (234)

NIGERIAN TIDE/SUNDAY TIDE (MS)
PO Box 5072, Port Harcourt, Rivers,Nigeria; tel (234) 084 230 298; e-mail contact@thetidenews.com; website www.thetidenewsonline.com
Circ.: 30,000
Ed. – Celesbin Ogolo

REUNION ISLAND

LE PORT

TEMOIGNAGES (D)
BP 192, Le Port, 97465,Reunion Island; tel (262) 211 307; e-mail temoignages@wanadoo.fr; website www.temoignages.re
Circ.: 6,000
Ed. – Alain Witz

SAINT-DENIS

JOURNAL DE L'ILE DE LA REUNION (E)
BP 166, Saint-Denis, 97463,Reunion Island; tel (262) (262) 904676; fax 904601; e-mail info@jir.fr; website www.jir.fr
Circ.: 26,000
Dir. – Bruno Hervieu

LE REUNIONNAIS
190, rue des Deux-Canons, Saint-Denis, 97490,Reunion Island; tel (262) 287777; fax 282816
Ed. in Chief – Jean Noel Fortier

QUOTIDIEN DE LA REUNION (D)
BP 303, Saint-Denis, 97712,Reunion Island; tel (262) 921 517; fax 284 360
Circ.: 30,000
Dir. – Maximin Chane-Ki-Chune

RWANDA

KIGALI

ARP (D)
PO Box 83, Kigali,Rwanda; tel (250); website www.orinfor.gov.rw
Circ.: 100,000

LA RELEVE (MTHLY)
BP 83, Kigali,Rwanda; tel (250) 75665
Circ.: 1,700
Dir. – Christophe Mfizi

IMVAHO (WEEKLY)
BP 83, Kigali,Rwanda; tel (250) 75724; website www.orinfor.gov.rw
Circ.: 51,000

SAINT HELENA

JAMESTOWN

ST. HELENA NEWS (WEEKLY)
St. Helena Information Office, Broadway House, Jamestown,Saint Helena; tel (290) 2612; fax 2802; e-mail info.office@atlantis.co.ac
Circ.: 1,500
Ed. – John Drummond

SENEGAL

DAKAR

LE SOLEIL (D)
BP 92, Dakar,Senegal; tel (221) 859 5932; fax 832 0886; website www.lesoleil.sn
Circ.: 45,000
Ed. in Chief – Ibrahima Mbodj

SUD QUOTIDIEN (D)
BP 4130, Dakar,Senegal; tel (221) 822 5393; website www.sudonline.sn
Circ.: 30,000
Ed. – Abdoulaye Ndiaga Sylla

SEYCHELLES ISLAND

VICTORIA, MAHE

THE SEYCHELLES NATION (6X WK.)
PO Box 800, Victoria, Mahe,Seychelles Island; tel (248) 225 775; fax 321 006; e-mail nation@seychelles.net; website www.nation.sc
Circ.: 3,500
Dir. – Abdula Sylla
Ed. – Abdulla Sylla

SIERRA LEONE

FREETOWN

DAILY MAIL (M)
PO Box 53, Freetown,Sierra Leone; tel (232) 22 223191; website www.sierraleonedailymail.com
Circ.: 10,000
Ed. – Aiah Martin Mondeh

NEW SHAFT (D)
60 Old Railway Line, Brookfields, Freetown,Sierra Leone; tel (232) 22 241093
Circ.: 10,000
Ed. – Franklin Bunting-Davies

WE YONE
89 Fort St., Freetown,Sierra Leone; tel (232)
Ed. – Sam Metzeger

WEEKEND SPARK (WEEKLY)
7 Lamina Sankoh St., Freetown,Sierra Leone; tel (232) 22 223397
Circ.: 20,000
Ed. – Rowland Martyn

SOMALIA

MOGADISHU

THE COUNTRY (D)
PO Box 1178, Mogadishu,Somalia; tel (252) 1 21206

HORSEED (WEEKLY)
PO Box 1178, Mogadishu,Somalia; tel (252) 1 21206

HEEGAN (WEEKLY)
PO Box 1178, Mogadishu,Somalia; tel (252) 1 21206
Ed. – Mohamoud M. Afrah

XIDDIGTA OKTOBAR (D)
PO Box 1178, Mogadishu,Somalia; tel (252) 61 21206

SOUTH AFRICA

AUCKLAND PARK, JOHANNESBURG

BEELD (M-6X WK.)
PO Box 333, Auckland Park, Johannesburg, 2006,South Africa; tel (27) 11 713 9000; fax 713 9956; e-mail nuus@beeld.com; website www.beeld.com
Bus. Mgr. – John Vosloo
Adv. Mgr. – Margaretha Bloysen
Ed. – Tim Du Plessis

BLOEMFONTEIN

DIE VOLKSBLAD (M-6X WK.)
PO Box 267, Bloemfontein, 9300,South Africa; tel (27) 51 404 7600; fax 430 6949; website www.volksblad.com
Ed. – Ainsley Moos

CAPE TOWN

CAPE ARGUS (D)
PO Box 56, Cape Town, 8000,South Africa; tel (27) 21 488 4911; fax 488 4156; e-mail argusnews@inl.co.za; website www.capeargus.co.za; www.inl.co.za
Circ.: 60,000Last Audit: March 25, 2010
Display Adv. Mgr. – Peter Knutsen
Ed. – Chris Whitfield

THE CAPE TIMES (5X WK.)
PO Box 56, Cape Town, 8000,South Africa; tel (27) 21 488 4911; fax 488 4744; e-mail ctnews@inl.co.za; website www.capetimes.co.za
Circ.: 53,000
Ed. – Alide Dannoin

CAPE TOWN, WESTERN CAPE

DIE BURGER (M-6X WK.)
PO Box 2771, Cape Town, Western Cape, 8000,South Africa; tel (27) 21 406 2222; fax 406 3826; e-mail dbnred@dieburger.com; website www.dieburger.com
Adv. Mgr. – Evan Smith
Ed. – Henry Jeffreys

DURBAN, KWAZULU & NATAL

SUNDAY TRIBUNE (WEEKLY)
PO Box 47549, Durban, Kwazulu & Natal, 4023,South Africa; tel (27) 31 3082100; fax 3082715; e-mail tribnews@nn.independent.co.za
Circ.: 113,000
Ed. – Peter Davis

THE DAILY NEWS (5X WK.)
PO Box 47549, Durban, Kwazulu & Natal, 4023,South Africa; tel (27) 31 308 2100; fax 308 2111; e-mail alan.dunn@inl.co.za; website www.iol.co.za
Ed. – Alan Dunn
Mktg. Mgr. – Phillida Ellis

POST (WEEKLY)
PO Box 733, Durban, Kwazulu & Natal, 4000,South Africa; tel (27) 31 3082400; fax 3082427; e-mail post@nn.independent.co.za
Circ.: 42,203

ILANGA (2X WK.)
PO Box 2159, Durban, Kwazulu & Natal, 4000,South Africa; tel (27) 31 3094350; fax 3093489; e-mail cindyd@nu.independent.co.za; website www.ilanganews.co.za
Circ.: 117,000
Ed. – Amos Maphumulo

UMAFRIKA (WEEKLY)
PO Box 11002, Durban, Kwazulu & Natal, 3601,South Africa; tel (27) 31 7002720; fax 7003707; e-mail umafrika@futuredbn.co.za; website www.umafrika.co.za
Circ.: 60,000
Ed. – M.J. Khuzwayd

EAST LONDON, EASTERN CAPE

DAILY DISPATCH (M-EX S)
PO Box 131, East London, Eastern Cape, 5200,South Africa; tel (27) 43 702 2000; fax 743 5159; e-mail news@dispatch.co.za; website www.dispatch.co.za
Circ.: 39,000
Adv. Mgr. – Lieso Elias
Ed. in Chief – Phylicia Oppelt

GREYVILLE

THE MERCURY (5X WK.) Est. 1852
PO Box 47549, Greyville, 4023,South Africa; tel (27) 31 308 2300; fax 308 2333; e-mail mercletter@inl.co.za; mercnews@inl.co.za; website ^www.iol.co.za ; www.themercury.co.za
Circ.: 33,640
Insert rate: 2-4 pages R722 ex vat
Ed – Angela Quintal
Joint GM: Revenue – Brian Porter
Adv. Mgr. – Mariam Rahiman
Joint GM: Finance – Greg le Roux

JOHANNESBURG, PWV

THE SOWETAN (D)
PO Box 6663, Johannesburg, PWV, 2000,South Africa; tel (27) 11 471 4000; fax 474 8834; website www.sowetan.co.za
Ed. – Thabo Leshico

THE CITIZEN (M-6X WK.)
PO Box 43069, Johannesburg, PWV, 2000,South Africa; tel (27) 11 248 6000; e-mail citizen@citizen.co.za; website www.citizen.co.za
Ed. in Chief – Martin Williams

CITY PRESS (WEEKLY)
PO Box 3413, Johannesburg, PWV, 2000,South Africa; tel (27) 11 4021632; fax 4026662
Circ.: 259,374
Ed. in Chief – Khulu Sibiya

MAIL & GUARDIAN (WEEKLY)
PO Box 32362, Johannesburg, PWV, 2017,South Africa; tel (27) 11 403 7111; fax 403 1025; e-mail manoim@e-mg.co.za; website www.mg.co.za/mg
Circ.: 30,000
CEO – Mike Martin
Ed. – Phillip van Niekerk
Deputy Ed. – Rehana Rossouw
Adv. Mgr. – Marie van der Walt

THE NEW NATION (WEEKLY)
PO Box 10674, Johannesburg, PWV, 2001,South Africa; tel (27) 11 (27-11) 3332722; fax 3332733
Circ.: 64,000
Ed. – Zwelakhe Sisulu

RAPPORT (WEEKLY)
PO Box 8422, Johannesburg, PWV, 2000,South Africa; tel (27) 11 4022620; fax 4026163
Circ.: 353,000
Ed. – Izak de Villiers

THE STAR/WEEKEND STAR (D)
PO Box 1014, Johannesburg, PWV, 2000,South Africa; tel (27) 11 633 9111; fax 836 8398; website www.thestar.co.za
Pub. – Gavin Reilly
Asst. to CEO – Shirley Chetty
Ed. – Moegsien Williams

FINANCIAL MAIL (WEEKLY)
4 Biermann Ave., Rosebank, Johannesburg, PWV, 2196,South Africa; tel (27) 11 2803000; fax 2805800
Circ.: 33,000
Ed. – Peter Bruce

BUSINESS DAY (M)
4 Biermann Ave., Johannesburg, PWV, 2196,South Africa; tel (27) 11 2803000; fax 2805505
Circ.: 41,000
Ed. – Jim Jones

SUNDAY TIMES (S)
PO Box 1742, Johannesburg, PWV, 2132,South Africa; tel (27) 11 2805102; fax 2805111
Circ.: 458,000
Ed. – Mike Robertson

KIMBERLEY, NORTHERN CAPE

DIAMOND FIELDS ADVERTISER (5X WK.)
PO Box 610, Kimberley, Northern Cape, 8300,South Africa; tel (27) 53 832 6261; fax 832 1141; e-mail johan.duplessis@inl.co.za; website www.iol.co.za
Circ.: 8,000
Ed. – Johan Du Plessis
Adv. Mgr. – Rudi Ferreira

KING WILLIAMSTON, EASTERN CAPE

IMVO ZABANTSUNDU (WEEKLY)
PO Box 190, King Williamston, Eastern Cape, 5600,South Africa; tel (27) 433 23550; fax 33865
Circ.: 31,000
Gen. Mgr. – Will Ferreira
Ed. – W. Mnyikizo

PIETERMARITZBURG

NATAL WITNESS (M-EX S)
PO Box 362, Pietermaritzburg, 3200,South Africa; tel (27) 33 355 1111; fax 355 1122; website ^www.witness.co.za
Circ.: 28,000
Ed. – J. Conyngham
Adv. Mgr. – Fred Smithdorf

PORT ELIZABETH, EASTERN CAPE

THE HERALD (M-5X WK.)
PO Box 6071, Port Elizabeth, Eastern Cape, 6000,South Africa; tel (27) 41 504 7911; fax 585 4966; e-mail heraldletters@avusa.co.za; website www.herald.co.za
Circ.: 30,000
Adv. Mgr – Afhley Poobalan
Ed. In Cheif – Jeremoy McCabe

POST/WEEKEND POST (MSAT.)
19 Baakens St., Port Elizabeth, Eastern Cape, 6000,South Africa; tel (27) 41 504 7911; fax 554 966; website ^www.weekendpost.co.za
Ed. in Chief – Jeremy McCabe

PRETORIA, PWV

THE PRETORIA NEWS (M-6X WK.)
216 Vermeulen St., Pretoria, PWV, 0002,South Africa; tel (27) 12 300 2000; fax 328 7166; e-mail pta.newsdesk@inl.co.za; website www.pretorianews.co.za
Ed. – Zingisa Mkhuma

SANDTON

FINANSIES & TEGNIEK (MTHLY)
PO Box 786466, Sandton, 2146,South Africa; tel (27) 11 8847676; fax 8840851
Circ.: 25,791
Pub. – G.L. Marais

SUDAN

KHARTOUM

AL AYAM (D-EX SAT.)
PO Box 303, Khartoum,Sudan; tel (249) 1178 2672; fax 1178 2619; e-mail ayam@alayaam.net; website www.alayaam.net
Circ.: 200,000
Pub. – Beshir M. Said
Pub. – Dar Al Ayam
Ed. – Mahagoub Mohmed Salih

AL SIASA (D-EX S)
PO Box 3130, Khartoum,Sudan; tel (249)
Circ.: 60,000
– Dr. Khalio Farah
– Dar El SiasaPub.s

AL SUDANI (D-EX FRI.)
unknown, Khartoum,Sudan; tel (249); website www.alsudani.info
Circ.: 305,000
Ed. – Mahagoub M. Elhassan Irwa

SUDAN STANDARD (D)
PO Box 2651, Khartoum,Sudan; tel (249)

SWAZILAND

MBABANE

TIMES OF SWAZILAND (D)
PO Box 156, Mbabane,Swaziland; tel (268) 404 2211; fax 404 2438; e-mail subeditor@times.co.sz; website www.times.co.sz
Circ.: 25,000
Mng. Ed. – Mbongeni Mbingo
Pub. – Paul Loffley

SWAZI OBSERVER (D)
PO Box A385, Mbabane,Swaziland; tel (268) 404 9797; fax 404 5503; e-mail chiefeditor@observer.org.sz; info@observer.org.sz; website www.observer.org.sz
Circ.: 11,000
Ed. in Chief – Musa Ndlangamandla

TANZANIA

DAR ES SALAAM

UHURU/MZALENDO (M)
PO Box 9221, Dar Es Salaam,Tanzania; tel (255) 51 182224; fax 185065; e-mail uhuru@intafrica.com
Mng. Ed. – Saidi Nguba

DAILY NEWS (DS)
PO Box 9033, Dar Es Salaam,Tanzania; tel (255) 22 211 0595; fax 213 5239; e-mail newsdesk@dailynews-tsn.com; website www.dailynews-tsn.com
Mng. Ed. – Gabby Muya

ZANZIBAR

KIPANGA (D)
PO Box 199, Zanzibar,Tanzania; tel (255)

TOGO

LOME

JOURNAL OFFICIEL DE LA REPUBLIQUE DU TOGO (D)
BP 891, Lome,Togo; tel (228) 213718; fax 213163

TOGO-PRESSE (D)
Fifth Ave. Leopold Sedar Senghor, Lome,Togo; tel (228) 221 6108; fax 222 1489; e-mail editogo@cafe.tg; website www.editogo.tg
Circ.: 15,000
Dir. – Prosper Kokou
Dir. – Wolah Amabley
Ed. in Chief – Kokou Edina Logo

TUNISIA

TUNIS

ACH-CHOUROUK (WEEKLY)
10 rue ach-Cham, Tunis, 1002,Tunisia; tel (216) 71 834000; fax 830337
Circ.: 110,000
Dir. – Slaheddine Al-Amri

AL-AMAL (D)
15 rue 2 Mars 1934, Tunis,Tunisia; tel (216) 1 264899
Circ.: 50,000
Advertising: Int'l Media Service.
Dir. – Hucine Maghrebi

AS-SAHAFA (D)
6 rue Ali Bach-Hambra, Tunis,Tunisia; tel (216) 71 341 066; fax 349 720; e-mail contact@lapresse.tn; website www.lapresse.tn
Pub. – Mohamed Mahfoudh
Ed. in Chief – Jamel Karmaoui

ERRAI EL-AM (D)
10 rue IBW Khaldoun, Tunis, 1001,Tunisia; tel (216) 1 334688; fax 337048
Pub. – Abdejelil Dammak
Ed. in Chief – Salah Hajja

L'ACTION (M-4X WK.)
15 rue 2 Mars 1934, Tunis,Tunisia; tel (216) 1 264899
Advertising: Int'l. Media Service.
Dir. – Mustapha Masmoudi

LA PRESSE DE TUNISIE (M-EX MON.)
6 rue Ali Bach-Hamba, Tunis, 1000,Tunisia; tel (216) 71 341 066; fax 349 720; e-mail contact@lapresse.tn; website www.la-presse.tn
Circ.: 40,000
Dir. – Zohra Venrondhand

LE RENOUVEAU (M)
8 rue de Rome, Tunis, 1000,Tunisia; tel (216) 1 352 168; website www.tunisieinfo.com/LeRenouveau
Circ.: 23,000
Ed. – M. Nejib Ouerghi

LE TEMPS (D)
BP 441, 1004-El Menzah, Ave. du 7 Novembre, Tunis,Tunisia; tel (216) 71 238 222; fax 232 761; e-mail letemps@gnet.tn; website www.letemps.com.tn
Circ.: 42,000
Gen. Mgr. – R. Cheikhrouhou

TUNIS,

AS-SABAH (D)
BP 441, Tunis,, 1004-El Menzeh,Tunisia; tel (216) 7123 8222; fax 7123 2761; e-mail info@assabah.com.tn; website www.assabah.com.tn
Circ.: 50,000
Founder – Habib Cheikhrouhou
Pres. – Fatima Bakir Cheikhrouhou

UGANDA

KAMPALA

THE MONITOR (D) Est. 1992
PO Box 12141, Kampala,Uganda; tel (256) 417 744100; fax 232 369; website www.monitor.co.ug
Circ.: 24,600
Mng. Ed. – Daniel Kalinaki
Cir. Mgr. – Justus Katungi

MUNNO (D)
PO Box 4027, Kampala,Uganda; tel (256) 41 233571
Circ.: 15,000
Ed. – Anthony Ssekweyama

NEW VISION (D)
PO Box 9815, Kampala,Uganda; tel (256) 414 337 000; fax 235 843; e-mail news@newvision.co.ug; website www.newvision.co.ug
Ed. in Chief – Barbara Kaija

ZAMBIA

LUSAKA

THE POST (D)
PO Box 352, Lusaka, 10101,Zambia; tel (260) 1 226 027; fax 229 271; e-mail post@zamnet.zm; website www.postzambia.com
Circ.: 40,000
Ed. in Chief – Fred M'membe
Adv. Mgr. – Ingrid Kunda

LUSAKA, ZAMBIA

TIMES OF ZAMBIA/SUNDAY TIMES OF ZAMBIA (MS)
PO Box 30394, Lusaka, Zambia,Zambia; tel (260) 1 229 076; fax 227 348; e-mail tozim-ages@yahoo.com; website ^www.times.co.zm
Ed. (Sunday) – Arthur Simuchoba

ZAMBIA DAILY MAIL (D)
PO Box 31421, Lusaka, Zambia,Zambia; tel (260) 96 122 7793; website www.daily-mail.co.zm
Circ.: 40,000
Mng. Ed. – Evans Milimo

ZIMBABWE

BULAWAYO

THE CHRONICLE (M-EX S)
PO Box 585, Bulawayo,Zimbabwe; tel (263) 9 888 8719
Circ.: 74,032
Ed. – Geoffrey Nyarota

SUNDAY NEWS (S)
PO Box 585, Bulawayo,Zimbabwe; tel (263) 9 540071; fax 540084
Circ.: 66,171
Ed. – E. Machirori

HARARE

ZIMBABWE GOVERNMENT GAZETTE (WEEKLY)
PO Box 8062, Harare,Zimbabwe; tel (263) 4 724215
Ed. – L. Takawira

THE HERALD/THE SUNDAY HERALD (DS)
PO Box 396, Harare,Zimbabwe; tel (263) 4 795 771; fax 791 311; e-mail theherald@zimpapers.co.zw; website www.theherald.co.zw
Circ.: 122,166
Ed. – William Chikoto
Adv. Mgr. – Munyaradzi Haatenzi

NEWSPAPERS OF ASIA AND THE FAR EAST

AFGHANISTAN

BAGHLAN

ETTEHADI-BAGHLAN (D)
Baghlan, Afghanistan; tel (93)
Circ.: 1,200
Ed. in Chief – Shafiqullah Moshfeq

BOST

HELMAND (M-2X WK.)
Bost, Afghanistan; tel (93)
Circ.: 1,700
Ed. in Chief – M. Omer Farhat Balegh

FAIZABAD

BADAKHSHAN (M)
Faizabad, Afghanistan; tel (93)
Circ.: 3,000
Ed. in Chief – Hadi Rostaqi

FARAH

SEISTAN (D)
Farah, Afghanistan; tel (93)
Circ.: 1,800
Ed. in Chief – M. Anwar Mahal

GHAZNI, PARWAN

SANAE (D)
Ghazni, Parwan, Afghanistan; tel (93)
Circ.: 1,700
Ed. in Chief – G. Sakhi Eshanzada

HERAT

ITTIFAK ISLAM (M)
Herat, Afghanistan; tel (93)
Circ.: 2,500

JALALABAD

NENGAHAR (WEEKLY)
Jalalabad, Afghanistan; tel (93)
Circ.: 1,500
Ed. in Chief – Karim Hashimi

KABUL

HAQIQAT-E-ENQELAB-E-SAUR (D)
PO Box 1949, Kabul, Afghanistan; tel (93)
Circ.: 50,000

HEWAD (D)
Kabul, Afghanistan; tel (93) 26851
Circ.: 12,200
Ed. in Chief – Amir Afghanpur

ANIS (E)
Kabul, Afghanistan; tel (93)
Circ.: 25,000
Ed. in Chief – Mohammad S. Kharnikash

NEW KABUL TIMES (M)
PO Box 983, Kabul, Afghanistan; tel (93) 61847
Circ.: 5,000
Group: ANA Ad Services, Inc. (Arizona Newspaper Association)
Ed. in Chief – M. Seddiq Rahpoe

MAZAR-I-SHARIF

BEDAR (M)
Mazar-I-Sharif, Afghanistan; tel (93)
Circ.: 2,500
Ed. in Chief – Rozeq Fani

PAKTIA

WOLANGA (D)
Paktia, Afghanistan; tel (93)
Circ.: 1,500
Ed. in Chief – M. Anwar

QANDAHAR

TULU-I-AFGHAN (D)
Qandahar, Afghanistan; tel (93)
Circ.: 1,500
Ed. in Chief – Taher Safeq

BANGLADESH

CHITTAGONG

DAILY BURBOKONE (D)
Book Society Bldg., Jubli Rd., Chittagong, 4000, Bangladesh; tel (880) 31 212476
Circ.: 28,875
Pub. – MD. Yusuf Chowdhury
Ed. – Taslim Uddin Chowdhury

DAILY LIFE (D)
100 E. Nasirabad, Chittagong, Bangladesh; tel (880) 31 651 122; fax 651 144; e-mail life@arife.net
Circ.: 16,065
Pub. – Arife Islam

DAINIK AZADI (M)
9 CDA, C/A, Momin Rd., Chittagong, 4000, Bangladesh; tel (880) 31 612 380; fax 612 381; e-mail azadi@dainikazadi.net
Circ.: 13,000
Pub. – Abdul Malek

DAINIK NAYA BANGLA (D)
101 Momin Rd., Chittagong, 4000, Bangladesh; tel (880) 31 202 816
Circ.: 12,000
Ed. – Abdullah Al-Sagir

PURBA TARA (D)
390 Sirajuddohla Rd., Chittagong, Bangladesh; tel (880) 226356
Circ.: 4,003
Pub./Ed. – M.M. Afzal Matin Siddiquie

ZAMANA (M)
Razar Dewry, 2nd Ln., Chittagong,

Bangladesh; tel (880) 31 226288
Circ.: 17,000
Ed. – Moyeenul Alam

DHAKA

BANGLADESH OBSERVER (M)
Observer House, 33 Toyenbee Circular Rd., Motijheel, Dhaka, 1000, Bangladesh; tel (880) 2 955 5105; fax 956 2243; e-mail observer@dhaka.net
Circ.: 43,000
Chrmn. – Manzoor A. Chowdhury
Pub. – Nargis Rahman
Advisor, Adv. Dept. – A.M. Moffazzal
Ed. – Iqbal Sobhan Chowdhury

DAINIK SANGRAM (D)
423 Elephant Rd., Baramaghbazar, Dhaka, 1217, Bangladesh; tel (880) 2 933 0579; web site www.dailysangram.com
Circ.: 45,000
Chrmn. – Mohammad Younus
Ed. – Abdul Asad

BANGLADESH TIMES (M)
One Rajuk Ave., Dhaka, 1000, Bangladesh; tel (880) 2 233 195
Circ.: 35,000
Ed. – Aeru Yakub-Ahsan

BANGLAR BANI (D)
81 Motijheel C/A, Dhaka, 1000, Bangladesh; tel (880) 2 237548
Circ.: 20,000
Ed. – Sheikh Fazlul Karim Salim

DAILY SHAKTI (D)
165/1, DIT Extension Rd., Dhaka, 1203, Bangladesh; tel (880) 2 405 535
Circ.: 16,510
Adv. Mgr. – M.D. Liaquat Ali
Ed. – A.Q.M. Zainul Abedin

DAILY STAR (D) Est.1991
64-65 Kazi Nazrul Islam Avenue, Dhaka, 1215, Bangladesh; tel (880) 2 9144330; fax 812 5155; e-mail editor@thedailystar.net; web site www.thedailystar.net
Circ.: 30,000
Group: Media World Limited
Editor and Publisher – Mahfuz Anam

DAINIK BANGLA (M)
1 Rajuk Ave., Dhaka, 1000, Bangladesh; tel (880) 2 864748; fax 867328
Circ.: 65,000

DAINIK INQILAB (D)
2/1 Ramkrishna Mission Rd., Dhaka, 1203, Bangladesh; tel (880) 2 712 2771; fax 712 2722; e-mail inqilab08@dhaka.net; web site www.dailyinqilab.com
Circ.: 180,025
Ed. – A.M.M. Bahauddin

DAINIK JANATA (D)
24 Aminbagh, Shanti Nagar, Dhaka, 1217, Bangladesh; tel (880) 2 400498
Circ.: 20,090
Ed. – Dr. M. Asadur Rahman

DAINIK KHABAR (D)
137 Shanti Nagar, Dhaka, 1217, Bangladesh; tel (880) 2 406601
Circ.: 18,000
Pub./Ed. – Mizanur Rahman Mizan

DAINIK KISHAN (D)
309 Outer Circular Rd., Dhaka, 1217, Bangladesh; tel (880) 2 600360; fax 883543
Circ.: 6,030
Pub./Ed. – Kazi A. Qader
Adv. Mgr. – Abdur Razzak

ITTEFAQ (M)
1 Ramkrishna Rd., Dhaka, 1203, Bangladesh; tel (880) 2 256075; fax 865776; e-mail webguru@daily-ittefaq.com; web site www.ittefaq2.com
Circ.: 200,000
Pub./Ed. – Anwar Hussain Manju

DAINIK DINKAL (D)
441/1 Tejguan Industrial Area, Dhaka, 1208, Bangladesh; tel (880) 2 988 1118; e-mail dinkalnews@gmail.com; web site www.daily-dinkal.com
Circ.: 60,000Last Audit: March 24, 2010
Pub. – Tarique Rahman
Ed. – Hafizur Rahman

MORNING SUN (D)
15/1 South Kamalapur, Dhaka, 1000, Bangladesh; tel (880) 2 400907; fax 831618
Circ.: 18,125
– Leena Islam
– Atiqul IslamPub.s

NEW NATION (D)
1 Ramkrishna Mission Rd., Dhaka, 1203, Bangladesh; tel (880) 2 712 2654; fax 712 2650; e-mail info@nation-online.com; web site www.nation-online.com; www.ittefaq.com
Circ.: 20,000
Pub. – Mainul Hosein
Ed. – Mustafa Kamal Majumdar

SANGBAD (M)
36 Purana Paltan, Dhaka, 1000, Bangladesh; tel (880) 2 955 8160; fax 955 8900; e-mail sangbad@gononet.com; web site sangbad.com.bd
Circ.: 71,050
Ed. – Ahmadul Kabir

SANGRAM (D)
423 Bara Maghbazar, Elephant Rd., Dhaka, 1217, Bangladesh; tel (880) 2 831 5094; fax 840 7874; e-mail dsangram@gmail.com

DINAJPUR

DAINIK UTTARA (D)
Bahadur Bazar, Dinajpur Town, Dinajpur, Bangladesh; tel (880) 531 4326
Circ.: 8,500
Pub./Ed. – Prof Muhammad Mohsin
Adv. Mgr. – Komol Sen

JESSORE

RUNNER (D)
Pyari Mohan Das Rd., Bejpara, Jessore, Bangladesh; tel (880) 421 6943
Circ.: 2,000
Pub. – Rabeya Khatun
Ed. – R.M. Saiful Alam Mukul

SPHULINGA (D)
Amin Villa, P-5 Housing Estate, Jessore, Bangladesh; tel (880) 421 86433
Circ.: 3,050
Pub./Ed. – Mia A. Sattar

THINKANA (D)
1/1 W Goal Chamet, Jessore, Bangladesh; tel (880) 421 3086
Circ.: 3,150
Pub./Ed. – Abdul Hussain Mir

KHULNA

DAILY TRIBUNE (M)
38 Iqbal Nagar Mosque Ln., Khulna, 9100, Bangladesh; tel (880) 41 722 251; fax 721 013
Circ.: 22,000
Pub. – Liaquat Ali
Ed. – Ferdousi Ali

DAINIK PURBANCHAL (D)
38 Iqbal Nagar Mosque Ln., Khulna, 9100, Bangladesh; tel (880) 41 722 251; fax 721 013; e-mail info@purbanchal.com; web site www.purbanchal.com
Circ.: 42,960
Pub. – Alhaj Liaquat Ali
Adv. Mgr. – Zakir Hossain

JANABARTA (D)
5 Babu Khan Rd., Khulna, Bangladesh; tel (880) 41 21075
Circ.: 4,000
Pub./Ed. – Syed Sohrab Ali

PROBAHO (D)
2 Raipara Cross Rd., Khulna, Bangladesh; tel (880) 41 23650
Circ.: 3,000
Pub./Ed. – Ashraful Hoque

DAINIK PURBANCHAL (D)
38 Iqbal Nagar Mosque Rd., Khulna, 9100, Bangladesh; tel (880) 41 722 251; fax 721 013
Circ.: 3,000
Ed. – Alhaj Liaquat Ali

RAJSHAHI

DAINIK BARTA (M)
Natori Rd., Razi Villa, Rani Bazar, Rajshahi, 6100, Bangladesh; tel (880) 2699
Circ.: 3,000
Pub. – Advocate Kamrul Monir
Ed. – Mir Mahbub Ali

RAJSHAHO

RAJSHAHI BARTA (D)
Natore Rd., Shaheib Bazar, Rajshaho, Bangladesh; tel (880) 721
Circ.: 1,120
Pub./Ed. – M.D. Abdus Shamed

BHUTAN

THIMPHU

KUENSEL (WEEKLY)
PO Box 204, Thimphu, Bhutan; tel (975) 23043; fax 22975; e-mail editor@kuensel.com; web site www.kuensel.com
Circ.: 11,162
Ed. in Chief – Kinley Dorji
Ed. (Nepali) – R.N. Mishra

BRUNEI DARUSSALAM

BANDAR SERI BEGAWAN

BORNEO BULLETIN (D)
Locked Bag 2, MPC (Old Airport Rd, Berakas), Bandar Seri Begawan, 3510, Brunei Darussalam; tel (673) 2 453 388; fax 451 461; e-mail brupress@brunet.bn; web site www.borneobulletin.com.bn
Ed. – Charles Rex De Silva

CAMBODIA

PHNOM PENH

CAMBODIA DAILY (6X WK.)
Villa129, St. 228, Phnom Penh, Cambodia; tel (855) 23 426 602; fax 426 573; e-mail editor@cambodia.daily.com
Circ.: 2,000
Pub. – Bernard Krisher

REAKSMEI KAMPUCHEA (D)
474 Monivong Blvd., Phnom Penh, Cambodia; tel (855) 23 362 881; fax 332 472
Circ.: 15,000
Ed. in Chief – Pen Samitthy

CHINA

AMOY

XIAMEN RIBAO (D)
46 Sentian Rd., Amoy, China; tel (86)
Circ.: 100,000

BEIJING

GONGREN RIBAO (D)
Liupukang, Andingmen Wai, Beijing, 100718, China; tel (86) 10 64211561; fax 64214890
Circ.: 2,500,000
Dir./Ed. in Chief – Qu Zugeng

BEIJING RIBAO (D)
34 Xi Biaobei Hutong, Dongdan, Beijing, 100734, China; tel (86) 10 8520 4626; web site www.bjd.com.cn
Circ.: 700,000
Dir. – Wan Yunlai
Ed. in Chief – Liu Hushan

BEIJING WANBAO (ES)
34 Xi Biaobei Hutong, Dongdan, Beijing, 100743, China; tel (86) 10 8520 1155; fax 8520 1978; web site www.bjd.com.cn
Circ.: 800,000
Ed. – Zhang Bi

BEIJING WANBAO (D)
34 Xibiaobei Hutong, Dongdan, Beijing, China; tel (86) (86-1) 553431
Circ.: 1,000,000

CANKAO (D)
20 Guo Hui Jie, Beijing, China; tel (86)

JIEFANGJUN RIBAO (D)
Beijing, China; tel (86)
Circ.: 800,000
Dir. – Major Gen. Sun Zhongtong
Ed. in Chief – Yu Shunchang

GUANGMING RIBAO (D)
106 Yongan Lu, Beijing, 100050, China; tel (86) 10 6301 7788
Circ.: 920,000
Ed. in Chief – Wang Chen

JINGJI RIBAO (D)
Two Bai Zhi Fang Dong Jie, Beijing, 100054, China; tel (86) 10 63559988; fax 63539408
Circ.: 1,200,000
Ed. in Chief – Ai Feng

NONGMIN RIBAO (D-6X WK.)
Shilipu Beli, Chao Yang Qu, Beijing, 100025, China; tel (86) 10 65005522; fax 65071154
Circ.: 1,000,000

Dir. – Sun Yongren
Ed. in Chief – Zhang Dexiu

RENMIN RIBAO (D)
2 Jin Tai Xi Lu, Chao Yang Men Wai, Beijing, 100733, China; tel (86) 10 6536 8977; fax 6536 8979; web site www.people.com.cn
Circ.: 240,000
Pres. – Yannong Zhang
Ed. in Chief – Heng Quan Wu

ZHONGGUO QINGNIAN BAO (D)
2 Haiyuncang, Dong Zhi Men Nei, Beijing, 100702, China; tel (86) 10 64032233; fax 64033792
Circ.: 1,000,000
Dir./Ed. in Chief – Xu Zhuqing

ZHONGGUO RIBAO (6X WK.)
15 Huixin Dongjie, Chao Yang Qu, Beijing, 100029, China; tel (86) 10 6499 5000; fax 6491 8377; e-mail cdweb@chinadaily.net; web site www.chinadaily.com.cn
Circ.: 150,000
Ed. – Ling Zhu

CHANGCHUN, JILIN

JILIN RIBAO (D)
68 Stalin St., Changchun, Jilin, China; tel (86)
Circ.: 500,000
Ed. in Chief – Yi Hongbin

CHANGSHA, HUNAN

HUNAN RIBAO (D)
18 Furong Zhong Lu, Changsha, Hunan, 410071, China; tel (86) 731 4312999; fax 4314029
Dir./Ed. in Chief – Jiang Xianli

CHENGDU, SZECHUAN

CHONGQING RIBAO (D)
19 South Quing Yung St., Chengdu, Szechuan, 610017, China; tel (86) 664501; fax 666597
Circ.: 700,000

SICHUAN RIBAO (D)
70 Hongxing Zhong Lu, Erduan, Chengdu, Szechuan, 610012, China; tel (86) 28 675 8900; fax 666 5035
Circ.: 8,000,000
Ed. – Yao Zhineng

FUJIAN, FU KIEN

FUJIAN RIBAO (D)
Hualin Lu., Fuzhou, Fujian, Fu Kien, China; tel (86) 591 8709 5114; web site http://202.101.139.129/fujian_w/news/fjrb/gb/
Circ.: 600,000
Dir. – Huang Shiyun
Ed. in Chief – Huang Zhongsheng

GUANGZHOU, GUANGDONG

GUANGDONG NONGMIN RIBAO (D)
Guangzhou, Guangdong, China; tel (86)
Circ.: 20,000

GUANGZHOU, GUANGZHOU

GUANGXI RIBAO (D)
Minzhu Rd., Guangzhou, Guangzhou, China; tel (86)
Circ.: 650,000
Ed. in Chief – Li Mingde

GUANGZHOU RIBAO (D)
10 Dongle Lu, Renmin Zhonglu, Guangzhou, Guangzhou, 510121, China; tel (86) 20 8188 7294; fax 8186 2022; e-mail gzdaily@public.guangzhou.gd.cn; web site www.dayoo.com
Circ.: 600,000
Dir. – Dai Yucqing

NANFANG RIBAO (D)
289 Guangzhou Da Lu, Guangzhou, Guangzhou, 51061, China; tel (86) 20 8737 3474; fax 8737 5806; web site nf.nfdaily.cn
Circ.: 1,000,000
Dir. – Li Mengyu
Ed. in Chief – Fan Yijin

SHENZHEN SPECIAL ZONE HERALD (D)
1 Shen South Blvd., Guangzhou, Guangzhou, China; tel (86)

YANGCHENG WANBAO (E)
733 Dongfeng Dong Lu, Guangzhou, Guangzhou, 510085, China; tel (86) 20 8713 3591; fax 8776 5103; e-mail ycwbic@ycwb.com.cn; web site www.ycwb.com.cn
Circ.: 1,300,000
Pres. – Liang Guo Piao
Mgr. – Lin Zhi Pong

GUIYANG, GUIZHOU

GUIZHOU RIBAO (D)
Guiyang, Guizhou, China; tel (86) 851 662 5107
Circ.: 300,000
Ed. in Chief – Liu Xuezhu

HANGZHOU, ZHEJIANG

HANGZHOU RIBAO (D)
4 Guohuo Rd., Hangzhou, Zhejiang, China; tel (86) 218 868
Circ.: 200,000

ZHEJIANG RIBAO (D)
Unknown, Hangzhou, Zhejiang, China; tel (86); e-mail webmaster@zjnews.com.cn; web site www.zjdaily.com.cn
Circ.: 700,000
Ed. in Chief – Jiang Ping

HARBIN, HEILONGJIANG

HEILONGJIANG RIBAO (D)
Unknown, Harbin, Heilongjiang, China; tel (86)
Circ.: 500,000
Ed. in Chief – Jia Shixiang

JINAN, SHANDONG

DAZHONG RIBAO (D)
46 Jinshi Lu, Jinan, Shandong, 250014, China; tel (86) 531 2968911; fax 2962450
Circ.: 550,000
Dir. – Liu Xuede
Ed. in Chief – Liu Guangdong

KUMMING, HUNAN

HUNAN RIBAO (D)
Kumming, Hunan, China; tel (86)
Circ.: 300,000

NANJING, JIANGSU

XINHUA RIBAO (D)
55 Zhongshan Lu, Nanjing, Jiangsu, 210005, China; tel (86) 21 741757; fax 741023
Circ.: 900,000
Ed. in Chief – Zhou Zhengrong

NANNING, GUANGXI ZHUANGZU

GUANGXI RIBAO (D)
Minzhu Rd., Nanning, Guangxi Zhuangzu, China; tel (86) 771 569 0137; fax 569 0137
Circ.: 400,000
Pub./Ed. in Chief – Yang Zhiqing

SHANGHAI

JIEFANG RIBAO (D)
300 Han Kou Lu, Shanghai, 200001, China; tel (86) 21 6352 1111; fax 6351 6517; web site www.jfdaily.com.cn
Circ.: 1,000,000
Ed. in Chief – Yong Siong Nao

WENHUI BAO (D)
50 Huqiu Lu, Shanghai, 200002, China; tel (86) 21 63211410; fax 63230198
Circ.: 1,700,000
Ed. in Chief – Shi Junsheng

XIN MIN WAN BAO (D)
839 Yan An Zhong Lu, Shanghai, 200040, China; tel (86) 21 6279 1234; fax 5292 1234; web site www.xmwb.com.cn
Circ.: 1,800,000
Ed. in Chief – Bao Ping Hen

SHENGYANG, LIAONING

LIAONING RIBAO (D)
1 Er Sangjing St., Shengyang, Liaoning, China; tel (86) 472746; web site www.lnd.com.cn
Circ.: 600,000
Dir. – Zhu Shiliang
Ed. in Chief – Xie Zhengqian

TIANJIN, HEPING QU

TIANJIN RIBAO (D)
873 Dagu Nan Lu, Heri Qu, Tianjin, Heping Qu, 300211, China; tel (86) 22 2820 1211; fax 2820 1343; web site www.tianjindaily.com.cn
Circ.: 600,000
Dir. – Qiu Yunsheng
Ed. in Chief – Wu Bingjing

WUHAN, HUBEI

HUBEI RIBAO (D)
65 Huangli Lu, Wuhan, Hubei, 430077, China; tel (86) 27 6833522; fax 6813989
Circ.: 800,000
Dir. – Lu Jian
Ed. in Chief – Yang Renben

XI'AN, SHAANXI

SHAANXI RIBAO (D)
Xi'an, Shaanxi, China; tel (86)
Circ.: 500,000
Pres./Ed. in Chief – Qian Guozheng

ZHENGZHOU, HAINAN

HAINAN RIBAO (D)
7 Xinhua Nan Lu,, Zhengzhou, Hainan, 570001, China; tel (86) 898 6681 0731; web site www.hndaily.com.cn
Circ.: 100,000
Ed. in Chief – Vhong Ye Chang

HONG KONG

HONG KONG

ASAHI SHIMBUN (D)
2607 Shell Tower, Time Square, Hong Kong, Hong Kong; tel (852) 2806 2126; fax 2806 2079; web site www.asahi.com
Ed. – Atushi Okugera

THE AUSTRALIAN
15 New Eastern Terr., 3/F, Causeway Bay, Hong Kong, Hong Kong; tel (852) 2887 9492; fax 2571 4320; web site www.theaustralian.news.com.au

BOSTON GLOBE
88 Kennedy Rd., Flat A2, 1/F, Wanchai, Hong Kong, Hong Kong; tel (852) 25916786; fax 25916790

CHINA DAILY NEWS
1118 King's Rd., 20C, Block 5, Kornhill Garden, Hong Kong, Hong Kong; tel (852) 28858609
Ed. – Liu Dizhong

CHING PAO (M)
3/F 141 Queen's Rd. East, Hong Kong, Hong Kong; tel (852) 25273836
Circ.: 120,000
Ed. – Mok Kong

CHIU YIN PAO (M)
458-460 Lockhart Rd., Hong Kong, Hong Kong; tel (852) 28919361
Circ.: 30,000
Ed. – Kwong Lai

CHOSUN DAILY (6X WK.)
21st Fl. Flat C. Pine Chosun, Hong Kong, Hong Kong; tel (852) 2591 0150; fax 2591 0569
Bureau Chief – Edward Song

CHUNICHI SHIMBUN & TOKYO SHIMBUN
Fortress MTR Tower, 238 King's Rd., North Point, Hong Kong, Hong Kong; tel (852) 25107907; fax 25033057

DAILY COMMODITY QUOTATIONS (M)
2 Moon St., F, Ground Floor, Hong Kong, Hong Kong; tel (852)
Circ.: 12,000
Ed. – Edward Ip

DAILY TELEGRAPH
Evergreen Villa, 43 Stubbs Rd., D1, 4th Flr., Hong Kong, Hong Kong; tel (852) 25732800; fax 25733004
Group: Publicitas North America, Inc.

DIENA
31 Perth St., Apartment 2C, Homantin, Kowloon, Hong Kong, Hong Kong; tel (852) 27610890; fax 27610890

THE DONG-A ILBO
Korea Centre, 119-120 Connaught Rd., Room 1704, Hong Kong, Hong Kong; tel (852) 25444652; fax 25415381

EASTERN EXPRESS (M)
Oriental Press Centre, 7 Wang Tai Rd.,

Kowloon Bay, Hong Kong, Hong Kong; tel (852) 2707 1111; fax 2707 1122
Circ.: 40,000
Ed. in Chief – Michael Chugani
Mng. Ed. – Jack Beattle

EL MERCURIO
First Pacific Bank Centre, 51-57 Gloucester Rd., Hong Kong, Hong Kong; tel (852) 25270777; fax 25271607

EVENING STANDARD
23 Plantation Rd., 1/F, The Peak, Hong Kong, Hong Kong; tel (852) 28494800; fax 28494811
Group: Brydson Global Media Sales

GOLDEN PAO (M)
N Point Industrial Bldg., 13/F, Flat B, Hong Kong, Hong Kong; tel (852)
Circ.: 60,000
Pub. – Wong Chun Lung

THE GUAURDIAN
Kingsfield Tower, 73 Bonham Rd., Flat A1, 25/F, Hong Kong, Hong Kong; tel (852) 28573431; fax 25170258

HELSINGIN SANOMAT
8B Ying Yin Mansion, 50-52 Western St., Hong Kong, Hong Kong; tel (852) 25481435; fax 25481358

HONG KONG COMMERCIAL DAILY (D)
1/F, 499 King's Rd. North Point, Hong Kong, Hong Kong; tel (852) 2590 5322; fax 2565 5456; e-mail hkness@hkcd.com.hk; web site www.hkcd.com.hk
Circ.: 120,000
Ed. in Chief – Cheng Xi Tian

HONG KONG DAILY NEWS (D)
Hong Kong Industrial Bldg., 17/F,, Hong Kong, Hong Kong; tel (852) 2855 5111; fax 2816 9012
Circ.: 90,000
Ed. in Chief – Kaiwing Ip

HONG KONG ECONOMIC JOURNAL (M)
Est.1973
North Point Industrial Bldg., 22/F, 499 King's Rd., Hong Kong, Hong Kong; tel (852) 2856 7567; fax 2811 1070; e-mail enquiry@hkej.com; web site www.hkej.com
Circ.: 70,000
Ed. – Shan-muk Lam

HONG KONG ECONOMIC TIMES (6X WK.)
Est.1988
8/F Kodak House II, 321 Java Road, North Point, Hong Kong, Hong Kong, Hong Kong; tel (852) 2880 2888; fax 2880 5111; e-mail info@hket.com; web site www.hket.com
Circ.: 64,565
Group: HONG KONG ECONOMIC TIMES HOLDINGS LTD

HONG KONG PEOPLE'S DAILY (M)
Aik San Industrial Bldg., 1/F, Block B, Hong Kong, Hong Kong; tel (852) 28111763; fax 28112196
Exec. Ed. in Chief – Kam-hung Ng
Ed. in Chief – Winston Chou

HONG KONG POST (D)
Washington Plaza, 230-230A Wanchai Rd., 12/F, Hong Kong, Hong Kong; tel (852) 28339021; fax 25725315
Circ.: 10,000
Adv. Mgr. – Danny Hau
Sales Mgr. – T. Sano

HONG KONG TIMES (M)
64-66 Gloucester Rd., Hong Kong, Hong Kong; tel (852) 25279321; fax 25295480
Circ.: 60,000
Pub. – Ta-kai King
Ed. in Chief – Yuk-ting Ng
Mng. Ed. – Kam Tung
Adv. Mgr. – Timothy Mak

HUANAN JINGJI JOURNAL (M)
Culturecom Centre, 8/F, 47 Hung To Rd., Kwun Tong, Hong Kong, Hong Kong; tel (852) 2950 8700; fax 2345 1966
Ed. in Chief – Shing To
Ed. – Joe Law

HUNG LOOK DAILY NEWS (D)
30-32 D'Aguilar St., 10th Floor, Hong Kong, Hong Kong; tel (852)
Circ.: 50,000
Ed. – Yam Tat-Nin

THE INDEPENDENT
Sceneway Gardens, Flat 2A, Block 12, Lam Tin, Hong Kong, Hong Kong; tel (852) 23488381; fax 23488381

INTERNATIONAL HERALD TRIBUNE (M-EX S)
1201 K Wah Ctr., Hong Kong, Hong Kong; tel (852) 2922 1188; fax 2922 1190; e-mail iht@iht.com; web site www.iht.com
Pub. – Stephen Dunbar-Johnson
Deputy Mng. Ed. – Philip McClellan

JOCKEY DAILY NEWS (D)
2 Hok Yuen St. East, Ste. 5, Hilder Ctr., Hung Hom, Hong Kong, Hong Kong; tel (852)
Circ.: 80,000
Ed. – Kenneth Liang
Adv. Sales Mgr. – McVicar Wong

JOURNAL OF COMMERCE
U.T.C., 3-5 Arbuthnot Rd., Rm. 2404, Central, Hong Kong, Hong Kong; tel (852) 28100056; fax 25371652

KAM YEH PAO (E)
6-16 Tin Lok Lane, Block B, 1st Flr., Hong Kong, Hong Kong; tel (852)
Ed. – Allan Fong

THE KOREA ECONOMIC DAILY
27A Tsui Kung Mansion, Hong Kong, Hong Kong; tel (852) 28851677; fax 25670741

LA VANGUARDIA
41E Seabird Ln., Discovery Bay, Hong Kong, Hong Kong; tel (852) 29878340; fax 29879208

LIANHE ZAOBAO (D)
Unit 1308, 13/F Lippo Centre, Tower Two, 89 Queensway, Hong Kong, Hong Kong; tel (852) 2524 6191; fax 2524 7394; e-mail zbhk01@netvigator.com; web site www.zaobao.com.sg
Group: Publicitas North America, Inc.
Ed. in Chief – Yip Yui Man

LIBERATION
Pioneer Ct., 17 Ventris Rd., Flt. 12B Happy Valley, Hong Kong, Hong Kong; tel (852) (852) 28080489; fax (852) 28080549

LOS ANGELES TIMES
66 MacDonnell Rd., Flat 8B, Hong Kong, Hong Kong; tel (852) 25251795; fax 25216015

MAINICHI SHIMBUN
Mainichi Bureau, 6 Glenealy, Flat 6A, Central, Hong Kong, Hong Kong; tel (852) 25245646; web site http://mdn.mainichi.co.jp/

MINAMI-NIPPON SHIMBUN
1 King's Rd., Flat A, 34/F, Hong Kong, Hong Kong; tel (852) 25701303; fax 28060892

MING PAO DAILY NEWS (M)
Blk. A, Ming Pao Industrial Ctr., 15/F,, Hong Kong, Hong Kong; tel (852) 2595 3111; fax 2898 2534; e-mail mingpao@mingpao.com; web site www.mingpao.com
Circ.: 84,217
Ed. in Chief – Paul Cheung

MING TANG YAT PAO (M)
196 Tsat Tse Mui Rd., 3rd Flr., Hong Kong, Hong Kong; tel (852)
Circ.: 45,000
Ed. – Fong Leung

MORGENAVISEN JYLLANDS-POSTEN
41 Barker Rd., Flat 1B, Hong Kong, Hong Kong; tel (852) 28496430; fax 28496408

THE MORNING NEWS (M)
Aik San Factory Bldg., 14/C, 14 Westland Rd., Hong Kong, Hong Kong; tel (852) 2564 0131; fax 2565 5408
Pub./Chief Ed. – Kin-bong Wai

HSIN WAN PAO (E)
342 Hennessy Rd., Wanchai, Hong Kong, Hong Kong; tel (852) 28911604; fax 28382307
Circ.: 90,000
Pub. – Fei Yi Ming
Ed. in Chief – Chao Tse-Lung
Adv. Mgr. – B.L. Lam

THE OBSERVER
Beverly Court, 6D, Shiu Fai Terrace, 2C, Hong Kong, Hong Kong; tel (852) 25731994; fax 25732533

ORIENTAL DAILY NEWS (6X WK.)
Oriental Press Centre, Wang Tai Rd., Kowloon Bay, Hong Kong, Hong Kong; tel (852) 2795 1111; fax 2754 1633
Circ.: 650,000
Chrmn. – C.F. Ma
Pub. – Shun-Choi Lam
Ed. in Chief – Ma Kai Lun

WAH KIU MAN PO (E)
Morning Post Bldg., 28 Tong Chong St., 6/F, Hong Kong, Hong Kong; tel (852) 25654812; fax 25611774
Circ.: 58,000
Ed. – Shiu-chiu Chan
Adv. Dir. – Shum Wai

WAH KIU YAT PO (M)
110 Hollywood Rd., Hong Kong, Hong Kong; tel (852) 25491181; fax 25590406
Circ.: 125,000
Pub. – Choi-sang Shum
Ed. in Chief – N.G. Kwok-kai
Adv. Mgr. – Ta Kam-sang

POPULAR DAILY (M)
Kingston Bldg., 6/F, Block 4, 2-4 Kingston St., Hong Kong, Hong Kong; tel (852) 28901763; fax 25770737
Pub. – Ji Kon
Ed. in Chief – Leung Fong
Ed. – Chi-chun Chan

SANG PO (M)
N. Point Industrial Bldg., 13/F, King's Rd., Blk 4, Hong Kong, Hong Kong; tel (852)
Circ.: 10,000
Pub./Ed. – Wong Chun Lung

THE SANKEI SHIMBUN
Dragon Court, 6 Dragon Terr., Flat 4, 8/F, Block B, Hong Kong, Hong Kong; tel (852) 2578 6062; fax 2887 9600

SENG WENG EVENING NEWS (E)
198 Tsat Tsz Mui Rd., 5/F, Hong Kong, Hong Kong; tel (852) 25644367; fax 25658987
Circ.: 60,000
Ed. – Wong Long-Chau

SHENZHEN HONG KONG ECONOMIC TIMES (M)
Sing Tao Bldg., 5/B, 1 Wang Kwong Rd., Hong Kong, Hong Kong; tel (852) 27075701; fax 23181764
Exec. Ed. in Chief – Kai-woon Lee

SING PAO DAILY NEWS (M)
3/F CWG Bldg., 3A Kung Ngam Village Rd., Shaukeiwan, Hong Kong, Hong Kong; tel (852) 2570 2201; fax 2887 0348; e-mail localnews@singpao.com.hk; web site www.singpao.com
Circ.: 229,250
Adv. Mgr. – Rossetti It
Ed. in Chief – Ngai Kai Kwong

SING TAO EVENING POST (E)
Sing Tao Bldg., 3/F, Block A, 1 Wang Kwong Rd., Hong Kong, Hong Kong; tel (852) 27982323; fax 27953007
Ed. in Chief – Ms. Irene Shuk-wai Sung
Mng. Ed. – Yick-Kwan Tang

SING TAO JIH PAO (D)
Sing Tao Bldg., 3Tung Wong Rd., Hong Kong, Hong Kong; tel (852) 2798 2898; fax 2795 3017
Ed. in Chief – Siu Saiwo

SING TAO LI CHUNG (D)
Sing Tao News Corp Bldg., 3/F, 3 Tung Wong Rd., Hong Kong, Hong Kong; tel (852) 2798 2556; fax 2795 3022
Circ.: 125,000
Dir. – Aw Sian
Adv. Mgr. – Roddy Yu
Circ. Mgr. – Newman Leung
Ed. – Kam-hung Lee

SOUTH CHINA MORNING POST (M)
Morning Post Ctr., 22 Dai Fat St., Tai Po Ind. Est., Hong Kong, Hong Kong; tel (852) 2680 8888; fax 2661 6984; e-mail info@scmp.com; web site www.scmp.com
Circ.: 104,000
Adv. Mgr. – Elsie Cheung
Ed. – Reginald Chua

SUNDAY HONG KONG STANDARD (S)
Sing Tao Bldg., 4/F, 1 Wang Kwong Rd., Kowloon Bay, Hong Kong, Hong Kong; tel (852) 2798 2801; fax 2795 3009
Ed. in Chief – David Wong

SUNDAY MORNING POST (S)
South China Morning Post Bldg., Tong Chong St.,, Hong Kong, Hong Kong; tel (852) 25652254; fax 25651423
Ed. – Mrs. Ann Quon

SYDNEY MORNING HERALD
Citicorp Centre, 18 Whitfield Rd., 25/F, Hong Kong, Hong Kong; tel (852) 25084384; fax 28179187

TA KUNG PAO (M)
1st Fl. Kodak House, 39 Healthy St. East 2, North Point, Hong Kong, Hong Kong; tel (852) 2575 7181; fax 2834 5104; e-mail tkp@takungpao.com; web site www.takungpao.com
Circ.: 150,000
Adv. Mgr. – Sonic Ma
Ed. – Kokan Tsang
Ed. – Sam Wan

TAIWAN SHIN WEN PAO
Kornhill Garden, 1118 Quarry Bay, 20C, Block 5, Hong Kong, Hong Kong; tel (852) 2885 8609; fax 2898 8023

TARGET FINANCIAL SERVICE (5X WK.)
Ste. 2901, 29/F Bank Of America Tower, 12 Harcourt Rd. Central, Hong Kong, Hong Kong; tel (852) 2573 0379; fax 2838 1597; e-mail info@targetnewspapers.com; web site www.targetnewspapers.com
Circ.: 100,000
CEO – Zhang Fan

THE STANDARD (M)
3/F, Sing Tao News Corporation Bldg., Hong Kong, Hong Kong; tel (852) 2798 2798; fax 2795 3009; web site www.thestandard.com.hk
Circ.: 55,000
Ed. in Chief – Ivan Tong
Adv. Mgr. – Irene Chan

THE TIMES
Two Old Peak Rd., Flat 23B, Hong Kong, Hong Kong; tel (852) 2530 2949; fax 2530 2944

TIMES OF INDIA
Peak Rd., G-S, Black A, 3E, Hong Kong, Hong Kong; tel (852) 29811204
Group: Admarket International (Div. of Marcom International, Inc.)

TIN FUNG DAILY NEWS (M)
265-267 Queen's Rd. East, 1st Flr., Block B, Hong Kong, Hong Kong; tel (852)
Ed. – Chan Chi-shing

TIN TIN DAILY NEWS (M)
Culturecom Centre, 10/F, 47 Hung To Rd., Hong Kong, Hong Kong; tel (852) 29507307; fax 8
Pub. – Sai-chu Ho
Exec. Chief Ed. – King-bun Louie

TIN TIN YAT PO (M)
Culturecom Centre, 10/F, 47 Hung To Rd., Kwun Tong, Hong Kong, Hong Kong; tel (852) 2950 7300; fax 2345 2285
Circ.: 199,258
Ed. in Chief – Ip Kai-Wing

TIN WONG EVENING NEWS (E)
25-33 Johnston Rd., 15/F., Flat C, Hong Kong, Hong Kong; tel (852) 25293577; fax 28657452
Pub. – Chi-mou Yui
Gen. Mgr. – Pui-ying Hue

TODAY NEWS (D)
657 King's Rd., North Point, Hong Kong, Hong Kong; tel (852)
Circ.: 12,000
Pub. – Won Chun Hing

TORONTO STAR
21 Headland Dr., Discovery Bay, Hong Kong, Hong Kong; tel (852) 29874348; fax 29874317
Group: American Publishers Representatives Ltd.

TRUTH DAILY (E)
29 Gage St., 1st Flr., Hong Kong, Hong Kong; tel (852)
Ed. – Luk Koon-Cheung

TSAO PAO (M)
657 King's Rd., 1st Flr., Flat C, North Point, Hong Kong, Hong Kong; tel (852)
Circ.: 28,000
Ed. – Chun-Keung Wong

VANCOUVER SUN
76 Kennedy Rd., Flat 3101, Hong Kong, Hong Kong; tel (852) 25720146; fax 28360955
Group: CanWest Media Sales

VILLA VERDE POST (M)
123 Hennessy Rd., Causeway Bay, Hong Kong, Hong Kong; tel (852)
Circ.: 25,000
Pub. – Cheng Fei Hong
Ed. – Kam-Pei Fung

WALL STREET JOURNAL (D)
25/F Central Plz., 18 Harbour Rd., Hong Kong, Hong Kong; tel (852) 2573 7121; fax 2834 5291; e-mail editor@wsj.com; web site www.wsj-asia.com
Mng. Ed. – Christine Glancey

WEN WEI PO (D)
Tin Wan Praya Rd., Aberdeen, Hing Wai Ctr. 7 2-4 F, Hong Kong, Hong Kong; tel (852) 2873 8090; web site www.wenweipo.com
Circ.: 180,000
MD – Chang Yun-Feng
Ed. in Chief – Liu Zai-Ming

WORLD DAILY NEWS (M)
N. Point Industrial Bldg., 4/F, Block B,, Hong Kong, Hong Kong; tel (852) 2563 5141; fax 2565 9675
Circ.: 40,000
Ed. – Lo Siuman

YEDIOT ACHARONOT
Hong Kong Univ. of Science & Technology, Tower 1, Hong Kong, Hong Kong; tel (852) 23588262

YOMIURI SHIMBUN
Windsor House, 311 Gloucester Rd., Room 3506, Hong Kong, Hong Kong; tel (852) 2882 1392; fax 2576 5236
Group: Marston Webb International

SHAUKEI WAN

SING TAO DAILY (D)
74 Sing News Corporation Bldg. 3 Tung Wong Rd.;, Shaukei wan, Hong Kong; tel (852) 2798 2323; fax 2795 3022; e-mail stltor@singtaotor.com; web site www.singtao.com
Ed. in Chief – Siu Saiwo

WAN CHAI

WALL STREET JOURNAL ASIA (5X WK.)
25th Fl., Center Plz., 18 Harbour Rd., Wan Chai, Hong Kong; tel (852) 2573 7121; fax 2503 1549; e-mail letters@wsj.com; web site www.wsj-asia.com
Circ.: 59,309
Ed. in Chief – Almar Latour

INDIA

AGARTALA, TRIPURA

DAINIK GANADOOT (D)
Palace Compound, Agartala, Tripura, 799-001, India; tel (91) 381 232 5018; fax 232 4157; e-mail ganadoot@sancharnet.in
Circ.: 42,500
Ed. – Sushil Chaudhuri

AGARTALA, TRIPURA WEST

DAINIK SAMBAD (D)
PO Box 2, Agartala, Tripura West, 799-001, India; tel (91) 381 232 2340; fax 232 4845; e-mail dainikphoto@yahoo.com; web site dainiksambad.net
Circ.: 70,000
Pub. – Pradip Datta Bhowmick
Ed. – Paramita Livingstone

AGRA, UTTAR PRADESH

AMAR UJALA (DS)
Sikandra Rd., Agra, Uttar Pradesh, 282-007, India; tel (91) 562 260 1600; fax 260 2181; web site www.amarujala.com
Adv. Mgr. – Rajesh Baghel
Ed. – Rajendra Tripathi

SAINIK (D)
4-A John's Bungalow, Jeoni Mandi, Agra, Uttar Pradesh, 282-004, India; tel (91) 562 72996
Circ.: 14,817
Mng. Ed. – D.D. Paliwal
Adv. Mgr. – R.L. Sharma

VIKAS SHEEL BHARAT (D)
Transport Nagar, Agra, Uttar Pradesh, India; tel (91) 562 72944
Circ.: 25,076
Pub. – M.R. Aggarwal

AHMEDABAD, GUJARAT

THE TIMES OF INDIA (MS)
PO Box 4046, Ahmedabad, Gujarat, 380-009, India; tel (91) 79 2658 3758; fax 2658 3758; web site www.timesofindia.indiatimes.com
Circ.: 50,774
Ed. – Bharat Desai

HINDU (M)
Purneshwar Chambers, 2nd floor, Opp. Dinesh Hall, Ahmedabad, Gujarat, 380-004, India; tel (91) 79 2754 5966; fax 2754 5977
Circ.: 35,790
Adv. Mgr. – Manohar Varyani
Ed. – Kishan Varyani

INDIAN EXPRESS (MS)
3rd Fl. Sambhav House, Ahmedabad, Gujarat, 380-015, India; tel (91) 79 2687 3941; fax 2687 3950; web site www.expressindia.com
MD – Vivek Goenka
Ed. in Chief – Shekhar Gupta

JAI HIND (D)
Jai Hind Press Bldg., Navrangpura Ashram Rd., Ahmedabad, Gujarat, 380 009, India; tel (91) 79 2658 1051; fax 2658 7681; e-mail info@jaihinddaily.com; web site www.jaihinddaily.com
Circ.: 11,364
Mng. Ed. – Y.N. Shah

GUJARAT SAMACHAR (D)
Gujarat Samachar Bhavan, Khanpur, Ahmedabad, Gujarat, 380-001, India; tel (91) 79 3041 0000; fax 2550 2000; web site www.gujaratsamachar.com
Circ.: 400,000
Mng. Ed. – Shreyans Shah

PRABHAT (M)
PO Box 121, Ahmedabad, Gujarat, 380-001, India; tel (91) 22196
Circ.: 47,000
Pub./Ed. – R.K. Kothari
Adv. Mgr. – R.R. Kothari

SANDESH (M)
Sandesh Bhavan, Lad Society Rd. Vastrapur, Ahmedabad, Gujarat, 380 054, India; tel (91) 79 4000 4000; fax 4000 4242; e-mail sandesh@sandesh.com; web site www.sandesh.com
Chrmn./MD – Falgunbhai C. Patel

WESTERN TIMES (D)
Western House, Sudama Resort Bldg., Ahmedabad, Gujarat, 380-006, India; tel (91) 79 2657 6738; fax 2657 7421; e-mail gujarati@westerntimes.co.in; web site www.westerntimes.co.in
Adv. Mgr. – D.M. Patel
Mng. Ed./Ed. in Chief – Nikunj Patel

AHMEDNAGAR, MAHARASHTRA

KESARI (M)
Unknown, Ahmednagar, Maharashtra, India; tel (91)
Circ.: 11,654

AJMER, RAJASTHAN

DAINIK NAVAJYOTI (D)
PO Box 72, Ajmer, Rajasthan, India; tel (91) 145 242 9516; fax 242 5873; e-mail njaj@datainfosys.net; web site www.naitindia.com
Circ.: 108,000
Ed. in Chief – Durga Prasad Chaudhary

HINDU (D)
PO Box 83, Ajmer, Rajasthan, 305-001, India; tel (91) 21019
Pub./Ed. – Kishan Varyani

NYAYA (M)
PO Box 150, Ajmer, Rajasthan, India; tel (91) 21632
Circ.: 170,164
Pub./Ed. – V.D. Sharma
Adv. Mgr. – V.K. Sharma

AKOLA, MAHARASHTRA

MATRIBHUMI (M)
PO Box 32, Akola, Maharashtra, 444-001, India; tel (91) 3839; web site www.mathrubhumi.com
Circ.: 9,673
Pub./Ed. – Kamal K. Biyani

ALIGARH, UTTAR PRADESH

JANTAYUG (M)
Gandhi Marg, Aligarh, Uttar Pradesh, India; tel (91)
Circ.: 21,000
Pub./Ed. – Gauri Shankar
Adv. Mgr. – S.C. Kulshrestha

ALLAHABAD, UTTAR PRADESH

NORTHERN INDIA PATRIKA (M)
10 Edmonstone Rd., Allahabad, Uttar Pradesh, 211-001, India; tel (91) 532 52665
Circ.: 49,268
Ed. – Manas Mukal Das
Ed. in Chief – Tushar Kanti Ghosh

AMRITA PRABHAT (M)
10 Edmonstone Rd., Allahabad, Uttar Pradesh, 211-001, India; tel (91) 532 600654
Ed. – Tamal Kanti Ghosh

BHARAT (M)
3 Leader Rd., Allahabad, Uttar Pradesh, 211-001, India; tel (91)
Circ.: 15,000
Pub./Ed. – Santosh Tiwari
Adv. Mgr. – L.M. Tipathi

AJ (MS)
Unknown, Allahabad, Uttar Pradesh, India; tel (91)
Circ.: 29,612

MAYA (D)
281 Muthiganj, Allahabad, Uttar Pradesh, 211-003, India; tel (91) 532 53681
Circ.: 237,366
Ed. in Chief – Aloke Mitra
Adv. Mgr. – Priya Raj

AMRAVATI, MAHARASHTRA

MATRIBHUMI (M)
Unknown, Amravati, Maharashtra, India; tel (91)
Circ.: 3,212

ANAND, GUJARAT

NAYA PADKAR (D)
Station Rd., Sathi Estate, Anand, Gujarat, 388-001, India; tel (91) 2692 253 440; fax 204 114; e-mail nayapadkar@gmail.com
Circ.: 16,787
Mng. Ed. – D.C. Patel

AURANGABAD, MAHARASHTRA

MARATHWADA (MS)
PO Box 22, Sanmitra Colony, Aurangabad, Maharashtra, 431-001, India; tel (91) 4845
Circ.: 13,679
Gen. Mgr. – K.S. Deshpande
Ed. – A.K. Bhalerao
Adv. Mgr. – V.S. Apsingekar

DAINIK LOKMAT (DS)
Lokmat Bhavan, MIDC Jalna Rd., Aurangabad, Maharashtra, 431-010, India; tel (91) 240 248 5301; fax 248 4130; e-mail dainiklokmat@sancharnet.in; web site www.lokmat.com
Circ.: 72,064
Ed. in Chief – S. Wagholikar

BANGALORE, KARNATAKA

ANDHRA PRABHA (MS)
One Queen's Rd., Bangalore, Karnataka, 560-001, India; tel (91) 80 286 6893
Circ.: 15,989
MD – Mrs. Saroj Goenka
Adv. Mgr. – M. Nagarajan

THE ECONOMIC TIMES (MS)
S & B Towers, 2nd Flr., 88 MG Rd., Bangalore, Karnataka, 560-001, India; tel (91) 80 2839 9868; fax 2555 9368; web site www.economictimes.com
Circ.: 50,000
Mgr. – Sunil Rajshekhar

THE TIMES OF INDIA (DS)
S & B Towers, 1st and 2nd Fl., 40/1 MG Rd., Bangalore, Karnataka, 560 001, India; tel (91) 80 2555 0000; fax 2558 6617; web site www.timesofindia.com
Circ.: 500,000
VP. – CG Varguese

DAILY SALAR (D)
69 Ameen Tower Hosur Rd., Bangalore, Karnataka, 560-027, India; tel (91) 80 2227 5115; fax 2223 2309; e-mail dailysalarbangalore@gmail.com
Ed. in Chief – B. Shaik Ali

DAILY THANTHI (D)
54/1, 70th Cross, 5th Block, Rajaj iNagar, Bangalore, Karnataka, 560-010, India; tel (91) 80 2330 2698; fax 2315 3467; web site www.dailythanthi.com
Circ.: 23,492Kotta

DINA SUDAR (ES)
11/2 Queen's Rd., Bangalore, Karnataka, 560 052, India; tel (91) 80 2286 6213; fax 2286 8484; e-mail dinasudar@dinasudar.co.in; web site www.dinasudar.co.in
Gen. Mgr. – B.T. Amudhan

KANNADA PRABHA (MS)
1 Queen's Rd., Bangalore, Karnataka, 560-001, India; tel (91) 80 2286 6893; fax 2286 6617; e-mail info@kannadaprabha.com; web site www.kannadaprabha.com
Circ.: 150,000
Ed. – Shiva Subramanya

INDIAN EXPRESS (MS)
1 Queen's Rd., Bangalore, Karnataka, 560-001, India; tel (91) 80 2286 6893; fax 2286 6617; web site www.indianexpress.com
Circ.: 329,200
Pub. – Shankaran Nair
Ed. – Ravi Joshi

JANAVANI (E)
25 Sheshadri Rd., Gandhi Nagar, Bangalore, Karnataka, India; tel (91)
Circ.: 63,000
Pub./Ed. – M.D. Nataraj
Adv. Mgr. – M. Mallikarjun

SANJEVANI (D)
11/2 Queen's Rd., Bangalore, Karnataka, 560-052, India; tel (91) 80 2286 8882; fax 2286 8484; e-mail svani@sanjevani.com; web site www.sanjevani.com
Mng. Dir. – B.T. Amuthan

THE HINDU (D)
19 & 21 Bhaghwan Mahaveer Rd., Bangalore, Karnataka, 560-001, India; tel (91) 80 2286 8553; fax 2286 4052; e-mail letters@thehindu.co.in; web site www.hinduonnet.com
Circ.: 68,000
Mgr. – N. Rajashekar
Ed. – Parvathi Menon

DECCAN HERALD (D)
PO Box 5331, Bangalore, Karnataka, 560-001, India; tel (91) 80 2588 0151; fax 2588 0523; e-mail decnet@blr.vsnl.net.in; web site www.deccanherald.com
Pub. – S.V. Srinivasan
Ed. in Chief – K.N. Thilak Kumar

PRAJAVANI (D)
PO Box 5331, 75 Mahatma Gandhi Rd., Bangalore, Karnataka, 560-001, India; tel (91) 80 2588 0000; fax 2588 0165; e-mail editor@decanherald.co.in; web site www.prajavani.net
Ed. in Chief – K.N. Thilak Kumar

BAREILLY, UTTAR PRADESH

AMAR UJALA (D)
19 Civil Lines, Shahjhanbur Rd., Bareilly, Uttar Pradesh, 243-005, India; tel (91) 581 256 2843; fax 256 2765; web site ^www.amarujala.com
Circ.: 110,000
Ed. – Prabhat Singh

BARODA, GUJARAT

GUJARAT SAMACHAR (D)
Gujarat Samachar Press, Bahucharaji Mandir Rd., Karelibaug, Baroda, Gujarat, 390 018, India; tel (91) 265 246 2324; fax 246 4849; e-mail editor@gujaratsamachar.com; web site www.gujaratsamachar.com
Circ.: 220,000
Ed. – Hiren Antani

LOKASATTA-JANASATTA (D)
Lokasatta Karyala, Nagarwada, Baroda, Gujarat, 390-001, India; tel (91) 265 242 6221; fax 243 2210
Circ.: 41,240
Pub. – Kiran Vadodaria
Ed. – Hardev Giri

BELGAUM, KARNATAKA

KANNADAMMA (D)
2003 Ganapati Galli, Belgaum, Karnataka, 590-002, India; tel (91) 831 28850; web site www.kannadamma.net
Adv. Mgr. – Shri M. S. Suldhal

TARUN BHARAT (D)
3524 Narvekar St., Belgaum, Karnataka, 590-002, India; tel (91) 831 240 4335; fax 242 8603; e-mail tarunad@rediffmail.com; web site www.tarunbharat.com
Circ.: 175,000
Pub. – Kiran D. Thakur
Adv. Mgr. – Roma Thakur

BHAVNAGAR, GUJARAT

SAURASHTRA SAMACHAR (D)
Balwantrai Mehta Rd., Bhavnagar, Gujarat, 364-001, India; tel (91) 278 242 2577; fax 242 8811; e-mail saurashtrasamachar@vsnl.net; web site www.saurashtrasamachar.net
Circ.: 43,000Last Audit: December 26, 2006
Adv. Mgr. – T.C. Shah
Ed. – Prathap Shah

BHOPAL

NAVA BHARAT (D)
3 Indira Complex, Ramgopal Maheshwari Marg, Bhopal, 462-011, India; tel (91) 755 255 1412; fax 255 0622; e-mail contact@navabharat.com; navabharatbhopal@gmail.com; web site www.navabharat.net
Circ.: 25,389
– Wilfred D'Souza
– Vinay AwasthyMgr.s

BHOPAL, MADHYA PRADESH

DAILY JAGRAN (M)
33 Muharana Pratap Nagar, Bhopal, Madhya Pradesh, 462-001, India; tel (91) 755 429 2000; fax 429 2218
Circ.: 61,191
Ed. – Rajiv Mohan Gupta

DAINIK ALOK (D)
Alok Bhawan, Tallaiya, Bhopal, Madhya Pradesh, 462-001, India; tel (91) 755 73564
Circ.: 13,391
Pub. – Sanjay Sharma
Adv. Mgr. – P.N. Premi

DAINIK MADHYADESH (M)
462 Madhya Marg, Bhopal, Madhya Pradesh, India; tel (91)
Circ.: 20,000
Pub. – Inder Narain Dube
Ed. – V.N. Sharma

MADHYA PRADESH CHRONICLE (D)
Nava Bharat Prakashan, Bhopal, Madhya Pradesh, India; tel (91) 755 301 0585; e-mail editor@centralchronicle.com; web site www.centralchronicle.com
Circ.: 172,979
Pub. – P.K. Maheshwari

THE HITAVADA (D)
Gangotri Complex, Central T.T. Nagar, Bhopal, Madhya Pradesh, 462-003, India; tel (91) 755 24820
Circ.: 16,993
Mng. Dir./Ed. – Beni Madhav Tiwari

DAINIK BHASKAR (D)
6 Dwarka Sadan, Habibganj Rd., M. P. Nagar, Bhopal, Madhya Pradesh, 462-011, India; tel (91) 755 398 8884; fax 270 466; e-mail editorbhaskar@bhaskar.com; web site www.bhaskar.com
Circ.: 150,000
Chrmn. – Ramesh Chandra Agarwal

BHUBANESWAR, ORISSA

DHARITRI (M)
B-26 Industrial Estate, Bhubaneswar, Orissa, 751-010, India; tel (91) 674 258 0102; fax 258 6854; web site www.dharitri.com
Ed. – Tathagata Satpathy
Dir. Mktg. – Himanshu Hota

SAMBAD (D)
A/62 Nayapalli, Bhubaneswar, Orissa, 751-003, India; tel (91) 674 256 1108; fax 256 2914; e-mail sambad@aol.com; srp@orissasambad.com; web site www.orissasambad.com
Circ.: 59,962
Pub. – B.K. Patnaik
Ed. – S.R. Patnaik

PRAGATIVADI (D)
178-B, Mancheswar Industrial Estate, Bhubaneswar, Orissa, 751-010, India; tel (91) 674 309 6642; fax 258 5081; e-mail pragativadi@pragativadi.com; pragativadi@yahoo.com; web site www.pragativadi.com
Ed. – Samahit Bal

DINALIPI (D)
A/69 Industrial Area, Unit-III, Bhubaneswar, Orissa, 751-001, India; tel (91)
Circ.: 24,170
Ed. – Satya Mohapatra

SWARAJYA (M)
561 Shaeed Nagar Rd., Bhubaneswar, Orissa, 751-007, India; tel (91)
Circ.: 11,000
Pub. – R.N. Behara
Ed. – B.C. Mohanty
Adv. Mgr. – N.P. Khilar

BHUJ, GUJARAT

KUTCHMITRA (MS)
Kutchmitra Bhavan, Near Indirabai Park, Bhuj, Gujarat, 370 001, India; tel (91) 2832 252 090; fax 250 271; e-mail kutchmitra@yahoo.com; web site www.kutchmitradaily.com
Circ.: 46,000
Mgr. – Shailesh Hansraj Kansara
Ed. – Kirtin Jayant Khatri
Mng. Ed. – Kundan Vyas

BIJNOR, UTTAR PRADESH

BIJNOR TIMES (D)
Bijnor Times Rd., Bijnor, Uttar Pradesh, 246-701, India; tel (91) 1342 262 603; fax 262 602
Circ.: 22,000
Pub. – Chandramani Raghuvanshi
Bus. Mgr. – Vipen Bharatwaj
Adv. Mgr. – S.M. Raghuwanshi

UTTAR BHARAT TIMES (D)
Court Rd., Bijnor, Uttar Pradesh, 246-701, India; tel (91) 864364
Pub. – Paresh Kumar Kashyap
Ed. – R.P.S. Kashyap
Adv. Mgr. – S. Devi

BIKANER, RAJASTHAN

RAJASTHAN PATRIKA (MS)
Bikaner, Rajasthan, India; tel (91)
Circ.: 14,489

BILASPUR, MADHYA PRADESH

NAVA BHARAT (D)
PO Box 897, Bilaspur, Madhya Pradesh, 495-001, India; tel (91) 7752 230 591; fax 224 563
Circ.: 21,293
Ed. in Chief – Vasanth Gupta

BOMBAY, MAHARASHTRA

NAVBHARAT TIMES (MS)
Dr. Dadabhai Naoroji Rd., Bombay, Maharashtra, 400-001, India; tel (91) 22 6635 3535; web site www.timesofindia.com
Ed. – S.P. Tripathy
Adv. Mgr. – Bhaskar Das

HINDUSTAN (M)
19-21 Ambalal Doshi Marg, Fort, Bombay, Maharashtra, 400-023, India; tel (91) 22 273043
Circ.: 8,054
Ed. – Tirath G. Sabhani
Adv. Mgr. – R.H. Advani

BOMBAY SAMACHAR (D)
Red House, Sayed Brelvi Rd., Bombay, Maharashtra, 400-001, India; tel (91) 22 2204 5532; fax 2204 1501; e-mail samachar.bombay@gmail.com; web site www.bombaysamachar.com
Circ.: 100,000
Ed. – Pinky Dalal

THE DAILY (D)
Asia Publishing House, Mody Bay Estate, Calicut St, Bombay, Maharashtra, 400-038, India; tel (91) 22 2653104; fax 2619773
Circ.: 41,100
Ed. – Rajiv Bajaj

EVENING NEWS OF INDIA (E)
PO Box 213, Bombay, Maharashtra, 400-001, India; tel (91)
Circ.: 12,923
Mgr. Dir. – Dr. Ram S. Tarneja
Ed. – Girilal Jain
Adv. Dir. – G.R. Warrier

SAMAKALEEN (D)
Express Towers, Nariman Point, Bombay, Maharashtra, 400-021, India; tel (91) 22 2471 7677; fax 2471 7636
Circ.: 48,224
Ed. – Ganek Shah

JAM-E-JAMSHED (M)
Ballard House, Adi Marzban Path, Ballard Estate, Bombay, Maharashtra, 400-038, India; tel (91) 22 2269 2572; fax 2271 4747
Circ.: 10,000
Pub. – Rusi Adi Dhondy
Adv. Mgr. – Vera A. Dhondy

MUMBAI TARUN BHARAT (D)
A/36 Shriram Industrial Estate, G.D. Ambekar Marg, Wadala, Bombay, Maharashtra, 400-031, India; tel (91) 22 2207 8876; fax 2207 0416
Ed. – Dilip Krambelkar

QUAMI AWAZ (MS)
35 Jolly Maker Chamber II, 225 Nariman Point, Bombay, Maharashtra, 400-021, India; tel (91)
Ed. – Ishrat Ali Siddiqui
Adv. Mgr. – P.S.K. Singh

DAILY SAKAL/SUNDAY SAKAL (MS)
Dr. N B Parvlekar Marg, Bombay, Maharashtra, 400-025, India; tel (91)

SANJ TARUN BHARAT (D)
160 Dr. Dadabhai Naoroji Rd., 1st Flr., Fort, Bombay, Maharashtra, 400-001, India; tel (91)
Ed. – Chittaranjan D. Pandit
Adv. Mgr. – R.V. Mulye

SUNDAY OBSERVER (S)
121-127 MG Rd., Bombay, Maharashtra, India; tel (91) 22 270621
Ed. in Chief – Rahul Singh

MADHYANTAR (D)
Salva Chambers, 40 Cawasji Patel St., Fort, Bombay, Maharashtra, 400-023, India; tel (91) 22 2044381
Circ.: 17,027
Pub./Ed. – R.M. Bhutta
Adv. Mgr. – S. Chandrashekhar

CALCUTTA

AMRITA BAZAR PATRIKA (M)
41/A Acharya J. C. Bose Rd., Calcutta, 700-017, India; tel (91) 33 2222 9784; fax 2245 2785
Circ.: 128,101
Pub. – Tulsi Kanti De Biswas
Adv. Mgr. – P.K. Sen
Ed. – Tushar Kanti Ghosh

RAVIVAR
6 Prafulla Sarkar St., Calcutta, 700-001, India; tel (91) 33 2260 0198; fax 2225 3243
Circ.: 36,411
Ed. – Aveek Sarkar

SUNDAY (S)
6 Prafulla Sarkar St., Calcutta, 700-001, India; tel (91) 33 2260 0198; fax 2225 3243
Ed. – Vir Sanghvi

HINDUSTAN STANDARD (E)
PO Box 2536, Calcutta, 700-001, India; tel (91) 33 2260 0428; fax 2225 3140; e-mail anandabazar@abpmail.com; web site www.anandabazar.com
Circ.: 6,000
Ed. – Aveek Sarkar

AWAZ (D)
138 Biplabi Rash Behari Basu Rd., Calcutta, 700-001, India; tel (91) 33 2243 3073
Pub. – D.N. Singh
Ed. – Brahmdeo S. Sharma

DAINIK BASUMATI (M)
166 B.B.Ganguly St., Calcutta, 700-012, India; tel (91) 33 2350 9462
Circ.: 27,273
Adv. Mgr. – Binoy Chakrabarti
Ed. – Buddhadeb Ghosh

SATYAJUG (M)
13 Prafulla Sarkar St., Calcutta, 700-072, India; tel (91) 33 2212 6500; fax 2212 7308; e-mail satyajug_2000@yahoo.com
Circ.: 38,000
Mng. Dir. – Chitta Devnath

CALCUTTA, WEST BENGAL

BHARAT KATHA (D)
83 B. K. Paul Ave., Calcutta, West Bengal, 700-005, India; tel (91)
Circ.: 18,978
Ed. – Narayan Basu

PAIGAM (D)
26/1 Market St., Calcutta, West Bengal, 700-087, India; tel (91) 33 246040
Circ.: 14,151
– Momarzad Ali
– Morzina TarafdarPub.s

ROOPLEKHA (M)
9 Lenin Sarani St., Calcutta, West Bengal, 700-013, India; tel (91)
Circ.: 36,783
Pub. – B.K. Shah
Ed. – B.L. Shah

CALICUT

CALICUT TIMES (D)
MCM Bldg., 13/174 NR, Kammathi Ln., Calicut, 673-001, India; tel (91) 495 270 0884
Pub. – M. Joy Verghese
Mgr. – K.V. Kunhammea
Ed. – Jacob Roy

CALICUT, KERALA

DESHABHIMANI (M)
11/127 Convent Rd., Calicut, Kerala, 673-032, India; tel (91) 495 236 6178; fax 236 5883; e-mail calicut@deshabhimani.com; dclt@gmail.com; web site www.deshabhimani.com
Circ.: 61,595
Pub – E.P. Jayarajan
Ed. – V.V. Dakshinamoorthy

KERALA KAUMUDI (DS) Est.1984
19/110 B Ward 28 Thondayad Nellicode, Calicut, Kerala, 673-016, India; tel (91) 495 235 6623; fax 235 4129; web site keralakaumudi.com
Mng. Ed. – Deepu Ravi
Adv. Mgr. – K.V. Ritesh
Circ. Mgr. – N.K. Prafoon

MALAYALA MANORAMA (MS)
PO Box 187, Calicut, Kerala, 673-011, India; tel (91) 495 276 6425; fax 276 0660; e-mail customersupport@mm.co.in; web site www.malayalamanorama.com
Circ.: 1,761,000
Ed. – P.J. Joshua

MATHRUBHUMI (MS) Est.1923
PO Box 46, Calicut, Kerala, 673-001, India; tel (91) 495 236 6655; fax 236 6656; e-mail mbiclt@mpp.co.in; web site www.mathrubhumi.com
Adv.Mgr. – K.P. Narayanan
Ed. – M. Keshava Menon
Mng. Ed. – P.V. Chandran

CHANDIGARH

INDIAN EXPRESS (MS)
PO Box 623, Chandigarh, India; tel (91) 172 502 4444; fax 502 4422; web site www.indianexpress.com; www.expressindia.com
Circ.: 53,128
Ed. – Vipin Pubby

THE TRIBUNE (D)
Sector 29-C, Chandigarh, 160-030, India; tel (91) 172 265 1291; fax 265 7149; e-mail letters@tribuneindia.com; web site www.tribuneindia.com
Circ.: 203,900
Ed. in Chief – Raj Chengappa
Adv. Mgr. – Dilbar Ali

DAINIK TRIBUNE (M)
Sector 29-C, Chandigarh, 160-030, India; tel (91) 172 265 5066; fax 265 1291; e-mail news@tribuneindia.com; web site www.tribuneindia.com
Circ.: 33,797
Ed. in Chief – H.K. Dua
Ed. – M.K. Kaushal

PUNJABI TRIBUNE (D)
Sector 29-C, Chandigarh, 160-030, India; tel (91) 172 265 1291; fax 265 7149; web site www.tribuneindia.com
Circ.: 57,441
Adv. Mgr. – Dilbar Khan
Ed. in Chief – Raj Chengappa

CHENNAI

ALAI OSAI (M)
A-84, 3rd St., Anna Nagar, Chennai, 600-102, India; tel (91) 44
Circ.: 37,000
Pub. – Velur D. Narayanan
Ed. – S. Sambathi
Adv. Mgr. – K.S. Srinvasan

ANDHRA PRABHA (MS)
Express Estates, Mount Rd., Chennai, 600-002, India; tel (91) 44 2846 1889; fax 2846 1830; e-mail info@andhraprabha.com; web site www.andhraprabha.com
Circ.: 3,615

DINASARI (D)
29 Police Commissioners Office Rd., Chennai, 600-008, India; tel (91) 44 256 2738
Circ.: 65,739
Pub. – S. James Fredrick

THE HINDU (MS) Est.1878
The Hindu, Chennai, 600002, India; tel (91) 44 28576300; fax 28415325; web site www.thehindu.com
Circ.: 16,886
Group: Kasturi & Sons Limited
Ed. – N. Ravi
Sr. Assoc. Ed. – Harish Khare

MAIL (E)
Mail Bldg., 210 Mount Rd., Chennai, 600-002, India; tel (91) 44
Circ.: 10,000
Pub. – R.K. Anantharaman
Ed. – V.P.V. Rajan

MAKKAL KURAL (E)
1 Main Rd., United India Colony, Chennai, 600-024, India; tel (91) 44 2483 5588
Circ.: 39,000
Pub./Ed. – M. Shanmugavel
Adv. Mgr. – K. Sitharanjan

MALAI MURASU (E)
712 Anna Salai, Thousand Lights, Chennai, 600-006, India; tel (91) 44 2854 0798; fax 2852 5685
Circ.: 21,668
Pub./Ed. – V. Ramasamy
Adv. Mgr. – R. Swaminathan

MURASOLI (M)
93 Kodambakkam High Rd., Chennai, 600-034, India; tel (91) 44 2827 0140; fax 2821 7515; web site www.murasoli.in
Circ.: 54,000
Ed. – S. Selvam

SWADESMITRAN (D)
2 Vembuliamman Koli St., Chennai, 600-092, India; tel (91) 44 242 0504
Circ.: 3,529
Ed. – Sri K. Porko

THANTHI (D)
46 E. V. K. Sampath Rd., Chennai, 600-007, India; tel (91) 44 231 331
Circ.: 297,797
Pub./Ed. – R. Thiruvadi

CHENNAI, TAMIL NADU

ANNA (E)
62 Officers Colony, Chennai, Tamil Nadu, 600-029, India; tel (91) 44 242 9074
Circ.: 54,694
Pub./Ed. – K. Ravindram
Adv. Mgr. – A.P. Padmanabhan

DINAMANI (MS)
29,Ambattur Industrial Estate, 2nd Main Rd., Chennai, Tamil Nadu, 600-058, India; tel (91) 44 2345 7601; fax 2345 7619; e-mail info@dinmani.com; web site www.newindpress.com
Circ.: 178,232
Ed. – Vaithya Nathan
Adv. Mgr. – Sathya Narayanan

INDIAN EXPRESS (MS)
37/C 2nd Fl., Whites Rd., Royapettah, Chennai, Tamil Nadu, 600-014, India; tel (91) 44 2854 3031; fax 2854 3035; web site www.expressindia.com
Ed. in Chief – Shekhar Gupta
Mng. Ed. – Vivek Goenka

FINANCIAL EXPRESS (M)
Second Fl., Whites Rd., Chennai, Tamil Nadu, 600-014, India; tel (91) 44 2854 3031; fax 2854 3035; web site www.expressindia.com
Circ.: 6,446
Ed. – Shekar Gupta
Mng. Ed. – Vivek Goenka

DINAKARAN (D)
No. 229 Kutchery Rd., Mylapore, Chennai, Tamil Nadu, 600-004, India; tel (91) 44 4220 9191; e-mail dinakaran@dinakaran.com; dotcom@dinakaran.com; murasu@giasmd01.vsnl.net.in;

dinakarannew@gmail.com; web site www.dinakaran.com
Chrmn. – Kalanidhi Maran

THE HINDU (M)
Kasturi Bldg., 859/860 Anna Salai, Chennai, Tamil Nadu, 600-002, India; tel (91) 44 2841 3344; fax 2853 5325; e-mail thehindu@indiaserver.com; thehindu@vsnl.com; web site www.hinduonline.com
Ed. – N. Ravi

DINAMALAR (MS)
219 Anna Salai, Chennai, Tamil Nadu, 600-002, India; tel (91) 44 2855 5783; fax 2859 2815; web site www.dinamalar.com
Circ.: 129,235
Ed. – R. Krishnamoorthy

DAILY THANTHI (MS)
86 EVK Sampath Rd., Chennai, Tamil Nadu, 600-007, India; tel (91) 44 2661 8661; fax 2661 8797; e-mail marketing@dt.co.in; advt-thanthi@yahoo.com; web site www.dailythanthi.com
Circ.: 370,000
Ed. – K. Sunderashan

COCHIN, KERALA

DESHABHIMANI (M)
Deshabhimani Rd.,, Cochin, Kerala, 682 017, India; tel (91) 484 253 1888; fax 253 0006; e-mail kochi@deshabhimani.com; web site www.deshabhimani.com
Gen. Mgr. – E.T. Jayarajan
Ed. – Dr. V. Krishnamurthy

THE FINANCIAL EXPRESS (7X WK.)
Est.1973
Ground Flr., Sankoorikal Bldg., Kadavanthara Rd., Cochin, Kerala, 682-017, India; tel (91) 484 234 3269; fax 234 3153; e-mail iemvkob@vsnl.net; web site www.indianexpress.com
Circ.: 3,750
Principal Correspondent – Rajesh Ravi
Ed. – M.K. Venu

MALAYALA MANORAMA (MS)
PO Box 4278, Cochin, Kerala, 682-036, India; tel (91) 481 231 6245; fax 231 6549; web site www.manoramaonline.com
News Ed. – P.J. George

THE WEEK (S)
Manorama Bldg., Panampilly Nagar Ernakulam, Cochin, Kerala, 682-016, India; tel (91)
Circ.: 63,662

THE MATHRUBHUMI (MS)
PO Box 1851, Cochin, Kerala, 682-017, India; tel (91) 484 253 0531; fax 253 0729; e-mail mbichn@mpp.co.in; web site www.mathrubhumi.com
Circ.: 155,159
Pub. – V. Bhaskara Menon

JANMABHUMI (D)
Perandur Rd., Cochin, Kerala, 682-026, India; tel (91) 484 321 9926; fax 240 9817
Ed.-in-Cheif – Hari S. Kartha
Adv. Mgr. – P. Sajeev

VEEKSHANAM (MS)
Kaloor Cross Rd., Cochin, Kerala, 682-018, India; tel (91) 484 236 7926
Circ.: 33,000
Pub. – A.C. Jose
Adv. Mgr. – V. Ramachandran
Ed. – C.P. Sreedharan

COIMBATORE, TAMIL NADU

THE HINDU (MS)
19 & 20 A.T.T. Colony, L.I.C. Rd., Coimbatore, Tamil Nadu, 641-018, India; tel (91) 422 221 3603; fax 221 3176; e-mail apollo@thehindu.co.in; web site www.hinduonline.com
Circ.: 85,000
Ed. – Sathya Moorthy
Adv. Mgr – Venkatesh Natarajan

DAILY THANTHI (MS)
766, Avinashi Rd., Coimbatore, Tamil Nadu, 641-018, India; tel (91) 422 221 5545; fax 221 8592; e-mail support@dt.co.in; web site www.dailythanthi.com
Circ.: 100,000
Mgr. – N. Ranganathan
Adv. Mgr. – Ravi Kumar
Ed. in Chief – J. Jeyaraj

CUDDALORE, TAMIL NADU

DAILY THANTHI (MS)
7, Imperial Rd., Cuddalore, Tamil Nadu, India; tel (91) 4142 224 901; fax 235 541
Circ.: 19,813
Mgr. – Selva Raj

CUTTACK

NEWS OF THE WORLD (D)
Kaligali, Cuttack, India; tel (91) 671
Circ.: 19,000
Pub. – Kala o Sahitya Bikash
Ed. – N.K. Mohapatra
Adv. Mgr. – T. Mohapatra

CUTTACK, ORISSA

PRAJATANTRA (E)
Prajatantra Bldg., Behari Baug, Cuttack, Orissa, 753-002, India; tel (91) 671 250 8111; fax 260 7111
Ed. – Bhartruhari Mahtab

THE SAMAJ (D)
Gopabandhu Bhavan, Buxi Bazar, Cuttack, Orissa, 753-001, India; tel (91) 671 230 1598; fax 230 7617; e-mail samaj@orissanews.com; web site www.thesamaja.com
Circ.: 121,600
Exec. Ed. – Sarat Misra

DELHI

DAILY JATHE DAR (M)
14 Shidipura St., Delhi, 110-002, India; tel (91) 11
Circ.: 13,000
Ed. – Bir Inder Singh
Adv. Mgr. – S.J. Singh

DELHI/NEW DELHI

SARITA (EVERY OTHER WEEK)
Delhi Press Bldg, E-3 Jhandewala Estate, Rani Jhan, Delhi/New Delhi, 110-055, India; tel (91) 11 7526311; fax 7525020
Circ.: 167,900
Ed. – Vishwa Nath

NATIONAL HERALD (MS)
Herald House, 5A Bahadurshah Zafar Marg, New Delhi, Delhi/New Delhi, 110-002, India; tel (91) 11 3319014; fax 3313458
Circ.: 36,160
Ed. in Chief – K.V.S. Rama Sarma

PATRIOT (MS)
PO Box 727, Delhi/New Delhi, 110-002, India; tel (91) 11 3311056
Circ.: 33,000
Pub. – A.K. Painuli
Ed. – R.K. Misra
Adv. Mgr. – Suven Mukherjee

VIRARJUN (M)
5 Mathura Rd., New Delhi, Delhi/New Delhi, 110-002, India; tel (91)
Circ.: 27,000
Pub. – Anil Narendra
Ed. – K. Narendra

DHANBAD, BIHAR

AWAZ (M)
Hari Mandir Rd., Dhanbad, Bihar, 826-001, India; tel (91)
Circ.: 88,136
Pub. – D.N. Singh
Ed. – Brahmdeo S. Sharma
Adv. Mgr. – S. Keskar

ERNAKULAM

KERALA TIMES (D)
PO Box 1929, Ernakulam, 682-018, India; tel (91) 484 235 2696
Circ.: 20,739
Pub. – K.V. Joseph
Ed. – P.M. Jussay

ERODE, TAMIL NADU

DINAMALAR (D)
51/37 Thiruvika St., Erode, Tamil Nadu, 638 009, India; tel (91) 424 227 1661; fax 227 0688; e-mail dinamalarnews@gmail.com
Mng. Ed. – S. Kannapan

GORAKHPUR, UTTAR PRADESH

SWATANTRA CHETNA (D)
Shahmaroof, Gorakhpur, Uttar Pradesh, 273-001, India; tel (91) 5568 229 173; fax 229 173
Circ.: 10,341
Bureau Chief – Brijesh Chand Sharma

DAILY JAGRAN (D)
23 Civil Lines, Gorakhpur-1, Gorakhpur, Uttar Pradesh, India; tel (91) 551 233 3085; fax 233 8699
Circ.: 44,572
Ed. – Shailendra Mani Tripathi

AJ (MS)
Unknown, Gorakhpur, Uttar Pradesh, India; tel (91)
Circ.: 41,522

GUJARAT, RAJKOT

SANJ SAMACHAR (D-EX S)
Opp. Sharda Baug, Gujarat, Rajkot, 360-001, India; tel (91) 281 304 8021; fax 244 8677
Circ.: 38,906
Ed. – Pradeep Shah

GUWAHATI, ASSAM

ASSAM EXPRESS (M)
Uzan Bazar, Bhuban Rd., Guwahati, Assam, 781-001, India; tel (91)
Circ.: 8,000
Pub. – S. Bijoy Singh
Ed. – Jiba Kanta Gogoi
Adv. Mgr. – Biren Sarma

DAINIK ASAM (D)
Tribune Bldg., Maniram Dewan Rd., Chandmari, Guwahati, Assam, 781-003, India; tel (91) 361 266 1356; fax 266 0594; e-mail info@assamtribune.com
Mng. Dir. – P.G Baruah

ASSAM TRIBUNE (M)
Tribune Bldg., Maniram Dewan Rd., Chandmari, Guwahati, Assam, 781-003, India; tel (91) 361 266 1356; fax 266 0594; e-mail info@assamtribune.com; web site www.assamtribune.com
Circ.: 56,000
Mgr./Dir./Ed. – P.G. Baruah

GWALIOR

SWADESH (M)
53 Jayendraganj, Gwalior, 474-009, India; tel (91) 751 24370
Circ.: 20,960
Ed. – Shri Rajendra Sharma

GWALIOR, MADHYA PRADESH

AACHARAN (D)
Aacharan Building, Jhansi Rd., Gwalior, Madhya Pradesh, 474-001, India; tel (91) 751 401 1560; fax 401 1560
Circ.: 21,209
Ed. – Anwar Hussain Qureshi

DAINIK BHASKAR GWALIOR (D)
Bhaskar Lane, Jayendraganj, Gwalior, Madhya Pradesh, 474-009, India; tel (91) 751 232 3966
Circ.: 105,000
Ed. – Hari Mohan Sharma

DAINIK NIRANJAN (M)
Jinsi Nala, No. 1, Gwalior, Madhya Pradesh, 474-001, India; tel (91) 22237
Circ.: 16,142
Pub./Ed. – Smt. Ram Sumarini Saxena
Adv. Mgr. – P.V. Khirwadkar

NAV PRABHAT (D)
Shree Bhawan, Sarafa Rd., Gwalior, Madhya Pradesh, 474-001, India; tel (91)
Circ.: 16,000
Ed. – C.M. Nagory
Adv. Mgr. – Uttam Kumar Dubey

HUBLI-DHARWAR, KARNATAKA

SAMYUKTA KARNATAKA (MS)
Koppikar Rd., Hubli-Dharwar, Karnataka, 580-020, India; tel (91) 64858
Mng. Ed. – K. Shama Rao

HYDERABAD

ANDHRA PRABHA (D)
Door No 6-3-4, Prem Nagar, Bangara Hills, Hyderabad, 500-039, India; tel (91) 40 2332 0519; fax 2332 6478; e-mail info@andhraprabha.com; web site www.andhraprabha.com
Circ.: 30,000
Ed. – Vijaya Babu

MUNSIF (D)
5-9-62, Khan Lateef Khan Estate, F.M.C Rd., Hyderabad, 500-001, India; tel (91) 40 6666 0006; fax 6678 7786; e-mail munsifdaily@eth.net; web site www.munsifdaily.com
Circ.: 10,582
Ed. in Chief – Khan Lateef Mohamed Khan

EENADU (MS)
Eenadu Complex, Hyderabad, 500-082, India; tel (91) 40 2331 8181; fax 2331 8555; e-mail feedback@eenadu.net; web site www.eenadu.net
Ed. in Chief – Ramoji Rao

HYDERABAD, ANDHRA PRADESH

SIASAT DAILY (E)
Jawaharlal Nehru Rd., Hyderabad, Andhra Pradesh, 500-001, India; tel (91) 40 2474 4180; fax 2460 3188; e-mail siasat@hd1.vsnl.net.in; contact@siasat.com
Circ.: 45,874
Adv. Mgr. – Aslam Khan
Ed. – Zahid Ali Khan

ANDHRA PATRIKA (M)
Hill Fort Palace Annex, Hyderabad, Andhra Pradesh, 500, India; tel (91)
Circ.: 22,486
Pub. – S. Nageswara Rao
Mng. Dir. – S. Radhakrishna
Adv. Mgr. – K. Rama Chandraiah

CITIZEN'S EVENING (E)
365-A-Bakaram, Hyderabad, Andhra Pradesh, 500-002, India; tel (91)
Circ.: 23,735
Mng. Ed. – S. Ramesh

DECCAN CHRONICLE (D)
36 Sarojini Devi Rd., Hyderabad, Andhra Pradesh, 500-003, India; tel (91) 40 7803930; fax 7805256; e-mail deccan@hd1.vsnl.net.in; web site www.deccan.com
Circ.: 126,700
Ed. in Chief – M.J. Akbar
Ed. – A.T. Jayanti

INDIAN EXPRESS (MS)
6-3-1186, Flat 2, Begumpad, Hyderabad, Andhra Pradesh, 500-016, India; tel (91) 40 2341 3908; fax 2341 4282; e-mail hyd@epmltd.com; web site www.epmltd.com
Circ.: 33,022
Gen. Mgr. – Ramakrishna Rao

THE HINDU (D)
6-3-879 & 879-B Begumpet Public Rd., Hyderabad, Andhra Pradesh, India; tel (91) 40 2340 3903; fax 2340 2902; e-mail reddy@thehindu.co.in; web site www.thehindu.com
Circ.: 73,949
Ed. – S. Nagesh Kumar

NEWSTIME (D)
6-3-570 Somajiguda, Hyderabad, Andhra Pradesh, 500-482, India; tel (91) 40 2331 8181; fax 318555
Circ.: 60,000
Ed. – Ramoji Rao

RAHNUMA-E-DECCAN (M)
5-3-831, Goshamahal, Hyderabad, Andhra Pradesh, 500-012, India; tel (91) 40 4732225; fax 4616991
Circ.: 20,000
Gen. Mgr. – Mir Ali Hyder Hussaini
Ed. in Chief – Syed Vicaruddin

TARAKA PRABHA (D)
1-2-593/37 Gangamahal Colony, Hyderabad, Andhra Pradesh, 500-029, India; tel (91)
Pub. – K. Ramakrishna Prasad

UDAYAM (D)
7/1 Azamabad Industrial Area, Hyderabad, Andhra Pradesh, 500-020, India; tel (91) 40 2766 0020
Circ.: 45,825
Ed. in Chief – D.N. Rao

INDORE, MADHYA PRADESH

INDORE SAMACHAR (M)
PO Box 228, Indore, Madhya Pradesh, 452 003, India; tel (91) 731 243 4701; fax 243 2390
Circ.: 7,000
Pub. – Suresh Sheth
Adv. Mgr. – R.P. Rathore
Ed. in Chief – Sohan Mehra

NAIDUNIA (M)
60/1 Babu Labhchand Chhajlani Marg, Indore, Madhya Pradesh, 452-009, India; tel (91) 731 276 3111; fax 276 3120; e-mail editor@naidunia.com; web site www.naidunia.com
Circ.: 122,378
Ed. in Chief – Abhay Chhajlani
Adv. Mgr. – Manish Sharma

DAINIK BHASKAR (D)
4/54 Press Complex, Agra Bombay Rd., Indore, Madhya Pradesh, 452-008, India; tel (91) 731 398 8884; fax 307 2543; web site www.bhaskar.com
Circ.: 58,173
Ed. – Rajendra Tiwari

DAINIK JAGRAN (D)
302 Appolo Sq., Jagrwala Chaurasa, Indore, Madhya Pradesh, 452-001, India; tel (91) 731 391 8190; fax 391 8189
Circ.: 13,000
Pub. – Madhan Mohan Gupta

FREE PRESS (DS)
3/54 Press Complex, Mumbai-Agra Rd., Indore, Madhya Pradesh, 452-008, India; tel (91) 731 255 5112; fax 255 8555; e-mail fpindore@gmail.com; fpindore@rediffmail.com; freepres@sancharnet.in; web site ^www.freepressjournal.in
Circ.: 10,085
Pub. – Praveen Nagar
Ed. – Deepak Shinde
Adv.Mgr – Mahinder Singh Khmchi

NAVA BHARAT (D)
6/54 Firoz Gandhi Press Complex, A. B. Rd., Indore, Madhya Pradesh, 452-008, India; tel (91) 731 320 5901; fax 255 7715
Circ.: 10,068
Ed. – Kranti Chaturvedi

SWADESH (M)
PO Box 86, Indore, Madhya Pradesh, 452-004, India; tel (91) 731 33277
Circ.: 20,000
Ed. – Prakash Bohra
Adv. Mgr. – Vinayak Raut

JABALPUR, MADHYA PRADESH

DAINIK BHASKAR (M)
581 South Civil Lines, Jabalpur, Madhya Pradesh, 482001, India; tel (91) 761 260 1352; fax 260 3290; e-mail dainikbhaskar@mantrafreenet.com; web site www.bhaskar.com
Circ.: 25,142
Pub. – B.D. Agarwal

NAVA BHARAT (D)
PO Box 67, Napier Town, Jabalpur, Madhya Pradesh, India; tel (91) 761 245 0699; fax 254 1442
Circ.: 171,920
Ed. – Abi Manoj

YUGADHARMA (D)
Shrinath Ki Talaiya, Jabalpur, Madhya Pradesh, 482-002, India; tel (91) 26486
Circ.: 6,558
Pub. – Shri M. T. Pingle
Ed. – R.P. Tiwari

JAIPUR, RAJASTHAN

ADHIKAR Est.1956
Laxminagar, Esi Hospital, Ajmer Rd., Jaipur, Rajasthan, 302-006, India; tel (91) 141 245 0604; fax 245 0604; e-mail adhikarpatrika@yahoo.com
Pub. – Vishnu Sharma

NAVAJYOTI (M)
PO Box 132, Jaipur, Rajasthan, 302-006, India; tel (91) 141 220 6661; fax 220 6673; web site www.dainiknavajyoti.com
Circ.: 130,000
Pub./Ed. – Deen Bandhu Chaudhary
Adv. Mgr. – Arvind Agauwal

RAJASTHAN PATRIKA (D)
Kesargarh, Jawaharlal Nehru Marg, Jaipur, Rajasthan, 302-004, India; tel (91) 141 300 5662; fax 256 6011; e-mail info@rajasthanpatrika.com; web site www.rajasthanpatrika.com
Ed. – Gulab Kothari

RAJASTHAN PATRIKA (D)
Kesargarh, Jawahar Lal Nehru Marg, Jaipur, Rajasthan, 302-004, India; tel (91) 141 256 1582; fax 256 6011; e-mail info@rajasthanpatrika.com; web site www.rajasthanpatrika.com
Circ.: 3,148
Ed. in Chief – Gulab Kothari

JALANDHAR, PUNJAB

PUNJAB KESARI (DS)
Civil Lines, Jalandhar, Punjab, 144-001, India; tel (91) 181 306 7200; fax 228 0111; e-mail sales@punjabkesari.com ; contact@thepunjabkesari.com; web site www.punjabkesari.in
Ed. in Chief – Vijay Kumar Chopra
Ed. – Avinash Chopra

AKALI PATRIKA (D)
26 Chahar Bagh, Jalandhar, Punjab, 144-001, India; tel (91) 181 245 6579; fax 228 4694; e-mail akalipatrika@gmail.com; web site ^www.dailyakalipatrika.com
Circ.: 35,000
Pub. – R.S. Sodhi
Ed. – Ratnesh Sodi
Adv. Mgr. – P.L. Vig

JALGAON, MAHARASHTRA

JANASHAKTI (D)
Janashakti Karyalayla 200, Navipeth, Jalgaon, Maharashtra, 425-001, India; tel (91) 257 3842
Pub./Ed. – Bhuta Patil
Adv. Mgr. – W.W. Kulkarni

LOKMAT (D)
PO Box 73, Lokmat Bhavan, C-19, Addl. MIDC Area, Jalgaon, Maharashtra, 425-003, India; tel (91) 257 227 3015; fax 227 3012; e-mail lokmat@bom2.vsnl.net.in; web site www.lokmat.com; www.lokmat.net
Circ.: 125,000
Ed. – Sudhir Mahajan
Adv. Mgr. – Sandeep Tripathi

JAMBALPUR, MADHYA PRADESH

DESH BANDHU (M)
625 Gandhi Marg, Jambalpur, Madhya Pradesh, 482-002, India; tel (91)
Circ.: 6,000
Pub./Ed. – M.R. Surjan
Adv. Mgr. – H.K. Misra

NAVEEN DUNIA (M)
2566 Wright Town, Jambalpur, Madhya Pradesh, 482-002, India; tel (91) 24703
Circ.: 22,421
Pub. – S.K. Patel
Ed. – Brij Vilas Shukla
Adv. Mgr. – V.S. Bele Gutamganj

JAMSHEDPUR, BIHAR

AMRITA BAZAR PATRIKA (M)
Ulyan Kadma, Jamshedpur, Bihar, India; tel (91) 657
Circ.: 15,772

UDITVANI (D)
Jugsalai, Jamshedpur, Bihar, 831-006, India; tel (91) 27387
Pub./Ed. – Radhe Shyam Agrawal
Adv. Mgr. – S. Dass

JHANSI, UTTAR PRADESH

DAILY JAGRAN (MS)
Jagran Bhavan, 362, Civil Lines, Jhansi, Uttar Pradesh, 480-002, India; tel (91) 510 233 0022; fax 233 0011
Circ.: 26,512
Pub. – Rajendra Gupta

DAINIK VISHWA PARIWAR (D)
34 Chandra Sekhar Azad, Jhansi, Uttar Pradesh, 284-002, India; tel (91) 510 244 0099
Circ.: 14,425
Pub. – K.C. Jain
Ed. – J.K. Jain

JODPHUR, RAJASTHAN

JALTE DEEP (M)
Jalte Deep Bhawan, Jalori Gate, Jodphur, Rajasthan, 342-003, India; tel (91) 291 261 2900; fax 243 4896; e-mail jaltedeep@gmail.com; info@manak.org; web site ^www.manak.org
Circ.: 85,000
Ed. – Padam Mehta
Adv. Mgr. – Ashish Mehta

JANGAN (M)
Near Anand Cinema, Jodphur, Rajasthan, 342-001, India; tel (91) 291 28216
Circ.: 15,000
Pub./Ed. in Chief/Adv. Mgr. – Manak M. Chopra

RAJASTHAN PATRIKA (D)
Manji Ka Hatha, Jodphur, Rajasthan, 342-006, India; tel (91) 291 5109 935; fax 5109 901; e-mail info@rajasthanpatrika.com; web site www.rajasthanpatrika.com
Ed. – Daulat Singh Chouan

JORHAT, ASSAM

DAINIK JANAMBHUMI (M)
Tulasi Narayan Sharma Path, Jorhat, Assam, 785-001, India; tel (91) 376 232 0033; fax 232 1713; e-mail editordj@sify.com; web site ^www.dainikjanambhumi.co.in
Circ.: 50,359
Ed. – Hemanta Barman
Adv. Mgr. – Minhazuddin Firas

JULLUNDUR, PUNJAB

AJIT (M)
Ajit Bhavan, Nehru Garden Rd., Jullundur, Punjab, 144-001, India; tel (91) 181 245 5961; fax 245 5960; e-mail ajit@jla.vsnl.net.in; web site www.ajitjalandhar.com
Circ.: 342,569
Circ. Mgr. – Gurmit Singh
Ed. in Chief – Barjinder Singh

DAILY MILAP (DS)
Milap Rd., Jullundur, Punjab, India; tel (91); e-mail yogi@milap.com; web site www.milap.com

Circ.: 24,039
Pub. – Punam Suri
Ed. in Chief – Navin Suri

JAG BANI (D)
Hind Samachar Bldg., Civil Lines, Jullundur, Punjab, 144-001, India; tel (91) 181 228 0104; fax 228 0113
Pub. – Vijay Kumar Chopra
Ed. – Avinash Chopra

HIND SAMACHAR (D)
Civil Lines, Jullundur, Punjab, 144-001, India; tel (91) 181 221 2121; fax 228 0113; e-mail news@punjavkesari.com
Pub. – Vijaya Kumar Chopra
Ed. – Avinash Chopra

PRATAP DAILY (M)
Nehru Garden Rd., Jullundur, Punjab, 144-001, India; tel (91)
Circ.: 9,669
Pub. – Chander Mohan

VIR PRATAP (M)
Pratap Bhavan, Nehru Garden Rd., Jullundur, Punjab, 144-001, India; tel (91)
Circ.: 34,000
Dir./Adv. Mgr. – Chandar Mohan
Ed. – Lalit Mohan

KANNUR RD., KERALA

CHANDRIKA DAILY (D)
PO Box 64, Kannur Rd., Kerala, 673002, India; tel (91) 495 276 6032; fax 276 5950; e-mail knr@chandrika.net
Circ.: 31,735
Ed. – M. I. Thangal

KANPUR, UTTAR PRADESH

AJ (DS)
79/75 Bans Mandi, Kanpur, Kanpur, Uttar Pradesh, 208-001, India; tel (91) 512 60686
Circ.: 53,624
Dir. – Poonam Gupta
Ed. – S.V. Gupta

DAILY JAGRAN (MS)
Jagran Bldg., 2 Sarvodaya Nagar, Kanpur, Uttar Pradesh, 208-005, India; tel (91) 512 221 6163; fax 221 8791; e-mail jpl@jagran.com; web site www.jagran.com
Ed. – Sanjay Gupta
Adv. Mgr. – Shailendra Jaitely

GANESH (D)
117 Pandu Nagar, Kanpur, Uttar Pradesh, 208, India; tel (91)
Circ.: 14,000
Pub. – K.N. Tripathi
Adv. Mgr. – Sharad Avasthi

DAINIK JAGRAN (D)
2 Sarvodaya Nagar, Kanpur, Uttar Pradesh, 208-005, India; tel (91) 512 221 6562; fax 221 6972; e-mail jagran@lw1.vsnl.net.in; web site www.jagran.com
Circ.: 409,477
Mng. Dir. – M. Mohan Gupta
Adv. Mgr. – Shailesh Gupta

LOK BHARTI (D)
White House, Yasoda Nagar, Kanpur, Uttar Pradesh, 208-011, India; tel (91) 512 263 5007; fax 263 5007
Circ.: 14,657
Ed. in Chief – Anam Pandey

SIYASIT JADID (M)
PO Box 418, Kanpur, Uttar Pradesh, 208-001, India; tel (91)
Circ.: 11,000
Pub. – M. Ishaq Ilmi
Ed. – Khan Ghufran Zahidi

VISHWAMITRA (M)
128 Mahatma Gandhi Rd., Kanpur, Uttar Pradesh, 208-001, India; tel (91)
Pub./Ed. – Kanak Chandra Agrawalla
Adv. Mgr. – P. Chandra Agrawalla

VYAPAR SANDESH (D)
359 Harishgant Rail Bazar, Kanpur, Uttar Pradesh, 208-001, India; tel (91) 512 232 0312; e-mail vyaparsandesh@gmail.com
Circ.: 33,000
Adv. Mgr. – Suresh Sharma

KOLHAPUR

SATYAWADI (M)
Kolhapur, 416002, India; tel (91)
Circ.: 23,000
Pub./Ed./Adv. Mgr. – Shri Suresh B. Patil

KOLHAPUR, MAHARASHTRA

PUDHARI (D)
2318, C. Ward, Bhausingji Rd., Kolhapur, Maharashtra, 416-002, India; tel (91) 231 254 3112; fax 254 3124; e-mail kolhapur@pudhari.in; web site www.pudhari.com
Ed. – P.G. Jadhav

KOLHARPUR, MAHARASHTRA

SAKAL/SUNDAY SAKAL (M)
1466 C ward, Heda Chambers, Konda Ln., Laxmipuri, Kolharpur, Maharashtra, 416011, India; tel (91) 230 246 8383; fax 264 4790; web site www.esakal.com
– Shriram Pawar
– Rajan GuneAdv. Mgr.s

KOLKATA, WEST BENGAL

AAJKAAL (MS)
B P-7, Sector-5, Bidhannagar, Kolkata, West Bengal, 700-091, India; tel (91) 33 3011 0800; fax 2367 5503; e-mail aajkaal@cal.vsnl.net.in; web site www.aajkaal.net
Ed. in Chief – Ashok Dasgupta
Adv. Mgr. – Pradeep Dasgupta

AKKAS DAILY (D) Est.1966
PO Box 7825, Kolkata, West Bengal, 700-012, India; tel (91) 33 2211 1187; fax 2211 7523; e-mail akkas@cal3.vsnl.net.in
Circ.: 66,185
Pub. – Karim Raza Monghyri
Adv. Mgr. – Arup Majumdar

THE TELEGRAPH (D)
6 Prafulla Sarkar St., Kolkata, West Bengal, 700-001, India; tel (91) 33 2260 0198; fax 2234 8244; web site www.telegraphindia.com
Circ.: 234,500
Ed. – Aveek Sarkar

ANANDA BAZAR PATRIKA (M)
6 Prafulla Sarkar St., Kolkata, West Bengal, 700-001, India; tel (91) 33 2221 6600; fax 2225 32412; e-mail anandabazar@abp-mail.com; web site www.anandabazar.com
Ed. – Aveek Sarkar

AZAD HIND (D)
25 Eden Hospital Rd., Kolkata, West Bengal, 700-073, India; tel (91) 33 2237 3785; fax 2212 6557; e-mail azadhinddaily@hotmail.com
Circ.: 19,000
Pub./Ed. – Ahmad Malihabadi
Adv. Mgr. – Anwar Saeed

BARTAMAN (D)
6, J.B.S. Haldan Ave., Kolkata, West Bengal, 700-105, India; tel (91) 33 2300 0110; fax 2323 4430
Circ.: 400,000
Ed. – Suba Dutta

THE ECONOMIC TIMES (MS)
105/7A S. N. Banerjee Rd., Kolkata, West Bengal, 700-014, India; tel (91) 33 2244 4244; fax 2244 1400; web site www.economictimes.com
Circ.: 17,675
Mgr. – Bhaskar Das
Ed. – Kingshuk Mukherjee

DAINIK CHHAPTE-CHHAPTE (D)
26-C, Creek Row, Kolkata, West Bengal, 700-014, India; tel (91) 33 2246 1488; fax 2246 8056
Circ.: 85,000
Pub./Ed. – Bishambhar Newar

NAVI PARBHAT (M)
264 -M, Bepin Behari, Kolkata, West Bengal, 700-012, India; tel (91) 33 2237 5068; fax 2237 5068
Circ.: 12,000
Circ. Mgr. – K. Singh
Ed. – S.R.S. Dharni

ROZANA HIND (M)
4A Hide Ln., Kolkata, West Bengal, 700-073, India; tel (91) 33 2237 4638; fax 2237 4638
Circ.: 17,500
Ed. – Mohammed Jallaluddin
Adv. Mgr. – Vishwanath Bhattacharya

SANMARG (M)
160/B Chittaranjan Ave., Kolkata, West Bengal, 700-007, India; tel (91) 33 3061 5000; fax 2241 5087; e-mail sanmarg@sanmarghindi.com; sanmarghindi@gmail.com; web site www.sanmarghindi.com
Circ.: 69,140
Ed. – H. R. Pande

THE STATESMAN (M)
Statesman House, 4 Chowringhee Sq., Kolkata, West Bengal, 700-001, India; tel (91) 33 2212 7070; fax 2212 6181; e-mail calaaa12@giascl01.vsnl.net.in; thestatesman@vsnl.com; web site www.thestatesman.net
Circ.: 148,382
Mng. Dir. – Ravindra Kumar

KOTA, RAJASTHAN

JANNAYAK (D)
Jannayak Bhawan Rd., Kota, Rajasthan, 327-001, India; tel (91) 27344
Circ.: 28,585
Pub./Ed. – Bhanwar Sharma Atal
Adv. Mgr. – Omvir Sharma

RAJASTHAN PATRIKA (D)
25, Small Scale Industrial Area, Kota, Rajasthan, 324 007, India; tel (91) 744 3940 4142; fax 2366 177; e-mail rpkota@patrika.com; info@rajasthanpatrika.com; web site www.rajasthanpatrika.com
Circ.: 125,000
Mgr. – Ajay Thomas
Ed. – Rakesh Gandhi

KOTTAYAM, KERALA

DEEPIKA (D) Est.1887
PO Box 7, Kottayam, Kerala, 686-001, India; tel (91) 481 301 2001; fax 301 2222; e-mail deepika@md2.vsnl.net.in; web site www.deepika.com
Chrmn – Francis Cleetus
Ed. in Chief – Alexander Caikada

MALAYALA MANORAMA (D)
PO Box 26, Kottayam, Kerala, 686-001, India; tel (91) 481 256 3646; fax 256 5398; e-mail editor@malayalamanorama.com; customersupport@mm.co.in; web site www.malayalamanorama.com
Circ.: 1,013,590
Mng. Dir./Ed. – Mammen Mathew
Ed. in Chief – K.M. Mathew

LUCKNOW

AMRITA PRABHAT (M)
Lucknow, Uttar Pradesh, India; tel (91) 522 608 901; fax 605 394
Circ.: 25,754

NATIONAL HERALD (M)
1 Bisheshwar N. Rd., Lucknow, 226-001, India; tel (91) 522 228 6996
Circ.: 73,419
Ed. in Chief – K.V.S. Rama Sharma
Asst. Ed. – H. K. Gaur

QUAMI AWAZ (M)
1 Bisheswar North Rd., Lucknow, 226-001, India; tel (91) 522
Mgr. – D.B. Tandon
Adv. Mgr. – P.S.K. Singh
Ed. – Ishrat Ali Siddiqui

NAVJIVAN (M)
PO Box 122, Lucknow, 226-001, India; tel (91) 522 222 0471
Circ.: 11,326
Chrmn./Ed. – Yashpal Kapoor

LUCKNOW, UTTAR PRADESH

NORTHERN INDIA PATRIKA (MS)
51, Officers Hostel, Lucknow, Uttar Pradesh, 226-001, India; tel (91) 522 239 1442; fax 260 6546
Circ.: 59,212
Pub. – Shibendra Kumar De Biswas
Pub. – D.K. Gupta
Ed. – Sunil Bose

SWATANTRA BHARAT (M)
2nd Fl., Suraj Deep Complex, 1 Jopling Rd., Lucknow, Uttar Pradesh, 226-001, India; tel (91) 522 220 6440; fax 220 9426; e-mail sbharats@satyam.net.in; info@swtantrabharat.com; web site www.swatantrabharat.com
Chrmn./ MD/ Ed. – K.K. Srivastava
Mktg. Mgr. – Vijay Roy

THE PIONEER (M)
20 Vidhan Sabha Marg, Lucknow, Uttar Pradesh, 226-001, India; tel (91) 522 234 6445; fax 234 5582; e-mail info@dailypioneer.com; feedback@dailypioneer.com; web site www.dailypioneer.com
Circ.: 86,000
Pub. – Dipak Mukerji
Adv. Mgr. – Sunil Kumar
Ed. – Chandan Mitra

LUDHIANA, PUNJAB

TARJMAN (E)
47/49 Kailash Cinema Market, Civil Lines, Ludhiana, Punjab, India; tel (91) 161 222 764
Circ.: 17,525
Pub. – Amardass Bhatia
Gen. Mgr. – Ashwari Kumar

DAILY ROHJAN (D)
Deepak Cinema Rd., Ludhiana, Punjab, 141-008, India; tel (91) 161 220 622
Circ.: 11,270
Pub./Ed. – Shri Sunil Sharma

MADURAI

ATHIRSTAM (D)
9/3-D/1 Dindigul Main Rd., Madurai, 625-001, India; tel (91) 452 266 2185; fax 266 0977; e-mail athirstam@yahoo.com; athirstam@vsnl.net.in
Circ.: 30,020
Pub. – S. Manimaran
Adv. Mgr. – M. Elango

MADURAI, TAMIL NADU

DINAKARAN (D)
2/2 Melur Main Rd., Madurai, Tamil Nadu, 625-107, India; tel (91) 452 244 5152; web site www.dinakaran.com
Ed. – Kanda Velu

INDIAN EXPRESS (MS)
Express Press 1/2 A , Samiyar Thoppu, Ramnad High Rd., Madurai, Tamil Nadu, 625-009, India; tel (91) 452 231 0445; fax 231 1200; web site www.indianexpress.com
Circ.: 272,670
Mktg. Mgr. – Joel Martin
Ed. in Chief – R. Sunderasan

DINAMANI (MS)
1/2 A Samiyar Thoppu,, Madurai, Tamil Nadu, 625-009, India; tel (91) 452 2310 445; e-mail info@dinamani.com; web site www.dinamani.com
Asst. Mktg. Mgr. – Dilip Kumar
Ed. – R. Vaidhyanathan
Deputy News Ed. – Siva Perumal

THE HINDU (MS)
Unknown, Madurai, Tamil Nadu, India; tel (91)
Circ.: 56,498

DINAMALAR (MS)
Dinamalar Ave., Madurai, Tamil Nadu, 625-010, India; tel (91) 452 238 0904; fax 238 0907; e-mail dmrmdu@dinamalar.in; web site www.dinamalar.com
Circ.: 42,906
Adv. Mgr. – S. Balachandran
Ed. in Chief – Ramesh Kumar

DAILY THANTHI (D)
1 Central Bus Stand Rd., Madurai, Tamil Nadu, 625-001, India; tel (91) 452 233 8529; e-mail thanthaimd@gmail.com; web site www.dailythanthi.com
Circ.: 31,175
Ed. – K. Sunderashan

MANGALORE, KARNATAKA

MUNGARU (D)
J. V. Bldg., Hampankatta, Mangalore, Karnataka, 575-001, India; tel (91) 32411
Circ.: 31,530
Ed. – V. Raghurama Shetty

NAVABHARATH (M)
PO Box 706, Mangalore, Karnataka, 575-003, India; tel (91)
Circ.: 12,000
Pub./Ed. – Sanjiv V. Kudva
Adv. Mgr. – F. Fakeer

MANIPAL, KARNATAKA

UDAYAVANI (D)
4th Fl. Udayavani Bldg., Press Corner, Manipal, Karnataka, 576104, India; tel (91) 820 257 1151; fax 257 0563; e-mail udayavanionline@manipalmedia.com; web site www.udayavani.com
CEO – Vinod Kumar
Ed. – Balakrishna Holla

MUMBAI

FREE PRESS JOURNAL (D)
Free Press House, Free Press Journal Marg., 215, Nariman Point, Mumbai, 400-021, India; tel (91) 22 2285 3335; fax 2285 3341; web site www.freepressjournal.in
Circ.: 100,000
Adv. Mgr. – V. Mahalingam
Ed. – S.S. Thawan
Mng. Ed. – G.L. Lakhotia

NAVAKAL (D)
13 Shenviwadi, Khadilkar Rd., Girgaun, Mumbai, 400-004, India; tel (91) 22 2386 0987; fax 2386 0989; e-mail navakal@vsnl.com
Circ.: 210,000
Ed. – Jaishree Khadilkar Pandey

MUMBAI, MAHARASHTRA

MAHARASHTRA TIMES (MS)
PO Box 213, Mumbai, Maharashtra, 400-001, India; tel (91) 22 6635 3535; fax 2273 1144; web site www.timesgroup.com
Ed. in Chief – Bharat Kumar Raut

THE ECONOMIC TIMES (M)
Economic Times, Times of India Bldg., Dr. Dadabhai Naoroji Rd., Mumbai, Maharashtra, 400-001, India; tel (91) 22 6635 3535; fax 2273 1364; web site www.economictimes.com
Circ.: 336,059
Exec. Ed. – Rahul Joshi

THE TIMES OF INDIA (M)
The Times of India Bldg., Dr. Dadabahai Naoroji Rd, Mumbai, Maharashtra, 400-001, India; tel (91) 22 6635 3535; fax 2273 1784; e-mail webmaster@timesofindia.com; toieditorial@timesgroup.com; web site www.timesofindia.com
Circ.: 4,100,000
MD – Vineet Jain
Ed. – Jaideet Bose

FINANCIAL EXPRESS (M)
Express Towers, Nariman Point, Mumbai, Maharashtra, 400-021, India; tel (91) 22 2471 7677; fax 2285 6323; e-mail iemumbai@express.indexp.co.in
Circ.: 30,448
Ed. – Saurav Mazumdar

INDIAN EXPRESS (M)
Express Towers, Nariman Point, Mumbai, Maharashtra, 400-021, India; tel (91) 22 2202 2627; fax 2283 5726; e-mail feedback@indiaexpress.com; web site www.expressindia.com
Ed. – Sekar Gupta
Circ. Mgr. – Ronak Ali Akbar

LOKASATTA (MS)
Express Tower, 1st/2nd Fl., Mumbai, Maharashtra, 400-012, India; tel (91) 22 2202 2627; fax 2284 6277; web site www.expressindia.com
Adv. Mgr. – Anuradha Agarwal
Ed. – Kumar Ketkar

FREE PRESS BULLETIN (D)
Free Press House, 215 Nariman Point, Mumbai, Maharashtra, 400-021, India; tel (91) 22 2285 3335; fax 2285 3341; e-mail mail@stj.co.in; web site www.freepressjournal.in
Circ.: 15,818
Mng. Dir. – Jai Kumar Karnani
Ed. – G.L. Lakhodia

JANMABHOOMI (D)
PO Box 62, Mumbai, Maharashtra, 400-001, India; tel (91) 22 2287 0831; fax 2287 4097; e-mail info@janmabhoominewspapers.com; jbhoomi@yahoo.com; web site ^www.janmabhoominewspapers.com
Circ.: 58,214
Ed. – Kundan Vyas
Adv. Mgr. – Deepak Bhatt

GUJARAT SAMACHAR (D)
Gala No. 337/340, Shah & Nahar Industrial Estate, Lower Parel, Mumbai, Maharashtra, 400-013, India; tel (91) 22 2492 1640; fax 2267 4382; web site www.gujaratsamachar.com
Circ.: 1,542,115
MD – Bahubali Shah
Ed. – Shreyans Shah
Adv. Mgr. – Nirmam Shah

INQUILAB (D)
156 D. J. Dadajee Rd., Tardeo, Mumbai, Maharashtra, 400-034, India; tel (91) 22 2419 7171; fax 2414 3171; e-mail inquilab@mid-day.com; web site www.inquilab.com
Circ.: 28,800
Ed. – Shaib Latif

MID-DAY/SUNDAY MID-DAY (DS)
Peninsula Center, Dr. S.S. Rao Rd., Parel, Mumbai, Maharashtra, 400-002, India; tel (91) 22 2419 7171; fax 2414 3171
Ed. – Shishir Joshi

NAVSHAKTI (D)
Free Press House, 215 Nariman Point, Mumbai, Maharashtra, 400-021, India; tel (91) 22 2287 4566; fax 2287 4688; e-mail mail@fpj.co.in; web site ^www.prepress.com
Ed. – Prakash Kulkarni

PRAVASI (D)
Janmabhoomi Bhavan, Janmabhoomi Marg, Fort, Mumbai, Maharashtra, 400-001, India; tel (91) 22 2287 0831; fax 2287 4097; web site www.janmabhoominewspapers.com
Circ.: 27,700
Ed. – Kundan Vyash
Adv. Mgr. – Deepak Bhatt

NAGPUR, MAHARASHTRA

DAINIK MAHASAGAR (D)
Tekdi Rd., Sitabuldi, Nagpur, Maharashtra, 440-012, India; tel (91) 712 49501
Pub./Ed. – Shrikrishna Chandak
Adv. Mgr. – Kishor Inamdar

LOKMAT (D)
PO Box 216, Nagpur, Maharashtra, 440-012, India; tel (91) 712 242 3527; fax 243 5666; e-mail lokmat@bom2.vsnl.net.in; web site onlinenews1.lokmat.com; www.lokmat.com
Ed. in Chief – Vijay Darda
Adv. Mgr. – Ashok Jain

MAHAVIDRABHA (D)
Kamgar Bhavan, Kamgar Sq., Nagpur, Maharashtra, 440-003, India; tel (91) 712 274 4547; fax 243 0596
Circ.: 12,512
Ed. – Kranti Keshavrao Nalamwar

NAVA BHARAT (D)
Nava Bharat Bhavan, Shatrapathi Sq., Nagpur, Maharashtra, 440-015, India; tel (91) 712 228 4001; fax 228 4000; e-mail navabharat@tataone.in; web site www.navabharat.net
Adv. Mgr. – B N Naseri
Ed. – Vinod Maheswari

NAGPUR PATRIKA (DS)
37 Farmland, Ramdaspeth, Nagpur, Maharashtra, 440-010, India; tel (91) 712 34780
Circ.: 20,398
Ed. – Chandra Shekhar Phadnis

NAGPUR TIMES (MS)
37 Farmland, Ramdaspeth, Nagpur, Maharashtra, 440-010, India; tel (91) 712 535071; fax 543782
Mng. Ed. – Dr. Shrikant Jichkar

HITAVADA (D)
Pandit Jawaharlal Nehru Marg, Wardha Rd., Nagpur, Maharashtra, 440-012, India; tel (91) 712 242 4245; fax 243 5039; e-mail hitavada_ngp@sancharnet.in; web site ^www.hitavadaonline.com
Adv. Mgr. – Susheem Koley
Ed. in Chief – Vijay Phanshikar
Mng. Ed. – Banwarilal Purohit

TARUN BHARAT (MS)
28 Farmland, Ramdaspeth, Nagpur, Maharashtra, 440-010, India; tel (91) 712 525052
Ed. – L.T. Joshi

YUGADHARMA (M)
28 Farmland, Ramdas Peth, Nagpur, Maharashtra, 440-010, India; tel (91)
Circ.: 31,000
Pub. – Ramlal Pandey
Ed. – D.S. Potnis

NASHIK, MAHARASHTRA

DESHDOOT/SUNDAY DESHDOOT (DS)
New Congress House, MG Rd., Nashik, Maharashtra, India; tel (91) 253 257 5716; fax 257 0938
Ed. in Chief – Nandakumar Teni

NASIK, MAHARASHTRA

GAVAKARI (MS)
NR. ST Stand, Hiralal Towers, A-P & Tal-Sinnar, Nasik, Maharashtra, 422103, India; tel (91) 2551 0253 2508945; fax 222 578; e-mail gavakari@rediffmail.com
Circ.: 30,720
Ed. – D.S. Potnis

SARWAMAT (D)
New Congress House, MG Rd., Nasik, Maharashtra, 422 001, India; tel (91) 2557 222 888; fax 570 338
Circ.: 10,905
Pub. – V.R. Deshmukh

NAVI MUMBAI, MAHARASHTRA

MUMBAI SAKAL (D)
Sakal Bhavan. Plot 42 B, Navi Mumbai, Maharashtra, 400-614, India; tel (91) 22 6684 3000; fax 2757 4280; e-mail sakal@vsnl.in; web site www.esakal.com
Ed. – Sunil Patrudkar

NEW DELHI

AL JAMIAT (D)
1502 Jamiat Bldg., Qasim Jan St., New Delhi, 110-006, India; tel (91) 11
Pub. – Maulana Asraul
Adv. Mgr. – Mohammad Hassain

QUAMI AWAZ (MS)
Herald House 5A, Bahadurshah Zafar Marg, New Delhi, 110-002, India; tel (91) 11 6535 1198; fax 2331 3458
Dir. – K.C. Khanna
Ed. in Chief – Mohan Charagi

THE TIMES OF INDIA (MS)
Times House, 4th Fl., 7 Bahadurshah Zafar Marg, New Delhi, 110 103, India; tel (91) 11 2330 2000; fax 2332 3346; web site www.timesofindia.com
Ed. in Chief – Jaideep Bose

THE ECONOMIC TIMES (MS)
7 Bahadurshah Zafar Marg, New Delhi, 110 103, India; tel (91) 11 2330 2000; fax 2332 3346; web site www.economictimes.com
Ed. in Chief – Rahul Joshi
Adv.Mgr – Nidhi Sharma

NAVBHARAT TIMES (MS)
7 Bahadurshah Zafar Marg, New Delhi, 110 002, India; tel (91) 11 2330 2000; fax 2332 3346; web site www.navbharattimes.indiatimes.com
Circ.: 418,500
Ed. in Chief – Madhusudan Anand

SANDHYA TIMES (E-EX S)
7 Bahadurshah Zafar Marg, New Delhi, 110-002, India; tel (91) 11 2330 2000; fax 2332 3346; web site www.timesofindia.com
Ed. in Chief – Arindam Sengupta

BUSINESS STANDARD (MS)
Nehru House, 4, Bahadur Shah Zafar Marg, New Delhi, 110-001, India; tel (91) 11 2372 0202; fax 2372 0201; e-mail editor@business-standard.com; web site www.business-standard.com
Circ.: 120,000
Ed. in Chief – Sanjaya Baru
Gen. Mgr. – Rajesh Mendiratta

DAILY MILAP (MS)
8-A Bahadurshah Zafar Marg, New Delhi, 110-002, India; tel (91) 11 2331 7737; fax 2331 9166; e-mail editor@milap.com; yogi@milap.com; web site www.milap.com
Circ.: 31,250
Mng. Ed. – Punam Suri
Ed. in Chief – Navin Suri
Adv. Mgr – K.L. Khanna

DAILY PRATAP Est.1919
Pratap Bhawan, 5 Bahadurshah Zafar Marg, New Delhi, 110-002, India; tel (91) 11 2331 7938; fax 4150 9555; e-mail dailypratap@gmail.com; web site ^www.dailypratap.com
general manager – syed mohammed mohsin
Ed. – K. Narendra
Adv. Mgr. – Mahendra Singh

PUNJAB KESARI (DS)
Romesh Bhavan, 2 Printing Press Complex, New Delhi, 110-052, India; tel (91) 11 3071 2200; fax 2719 4470; e-mail feedback@punjabkesari.com
– Vijay Kumar Chopra
– Ashwini Kumar ChopraEd.s

THE HINDUSTAN TIMES (M)
18/20 Kasturba Gandhi Marg, New Delhi, 110-001, India; tel (91) 11 2336 1234; fax 6656 1270; e-mail feedback@htclassifieds.biz; web site www.hindustantimes.com
Bus. Head/Circ/SEAL – Venky Venkatesh
Ed. in Chief – Sanjoy Narayan
Mng. Ed. – Samar Halarnkar

HINDUSTAN TIMES EVENING NEWS (D)
18/20 Kasturba Gandhi Marg, New Delhi, 110-001, India; tel (91) 11 2336 1234; fax 2370 4600; e-mail feedback@hindustantimes.com; web site www.hindustantimes.com
Circ.: 5,628
Ed. in Chief – Sanjoy Narayan

HINDUSTAN HINDI (D)
18/20 Kasturba Gandhi Marg, New Delhi, 110-001, India; tel (91) 11 2336 1234; fax 6656 1270; e-mail feedback@hindustantimes.com; web site www.hindustantimes.com
Circ.: 98,900
Ed. – Shashi Shekhar

FINANCIAL EXPRESS (D)
9-10 Bahadurshah Zafar Marg, New Delhi, 110-002, India; tel (91) 11 2370 2145; fax 2370 2141; e-mail feletters@expressindia.com; web site www.indianexpress.com; www.financialexpress.com
Ed. in Chief – Shekhar Gupta

INDIAN EXPRESS (D)
9-10 Bahadurshah Zafar Marg, Express Bldg., ITO, New Delhi, 110-002, India; tel (91) 11 2370 2145; fax 2370 2141; e-mail feedback@expressindia.com; web site www.expressindia.com
Circ.: 130,000
Ed. in Chief – Shekhar Gupta
Mng. Ed. – Vivek Goenka

JANYUG (D)
5E Rani Jhansi Rd., New Delhi, 110-055, India; tel (91)
Circ.: 14,000
Pub. – Mukhtar Ahmed Khan
Ed. – H.K. Vyas
Adv. Mgr. – OM. A. Khan

PIONEER (D)
Link House, 3 Bahadurshah Zafar Marg, New Delhi, 110-002, India; tel (91) 11 2375 5271; fax 2375 5275; e-mail pioneer@del2.vsnl.net.in; info@dailypioneer.com; web site www.dailypioneer.com
Circ.: 125,000
Ed. – Chandan Mitra
Mktg. Mgr. – Aparna Sen

THE STATESMAN (MS)
Statesman House 148, New Delhi, 110-001, India; tel (91) 11 2331 5911; fax 2331 5295; e-mail sman@nde.vsnl.net.in; delhistatesman@yahoo.com; web site www.thestatesman.net
Circ.: 172,300
Ed. – Ravindra Kumar

TEJ (MS)
8-B Bahadurshah Zafar Marg, New Delhi, 110 002, India; tel (91) 11 2373 1750; fax 2331 7499
Circ.: 10,000
Mng. Dir./Ed. – Vishwa Bandhu Gupta

VYAPAR BHARATI (D)
WZ - 48, 1st fl., Shakurpur Village, Opp. M-Block Market, Shakurbasti, New Delhi, 110-034, India; tel (91) 11 2715 7052; fax 2710 8686; e-mail info@vyaparbharti.com; vyapar_bharati@mantraonline.com
Circ.: 12,134
MD – Ramvir Singh Raghav

NOIDA, UTTAR PRADESH

JANASATTA (DS)
A 8, Sector 7, Noida, Uttar Pradesh, India; tel (91) 120 247 0700; fax 247 0753
Adv. Mgr. – Sanjay Puri
Ed. in Chief/Advisor – Prabhash Joshi
Ed. – Om Thanvi

ORAI, UTTAR PRADESH

DAINIK KARMYUG PRAKASH (D)
76 Gopal Ganj, Orai, Uttar Pradesh, 285-001, India; tel (91)
Circ.: 17,300
Pub. – R.C. Gupta

KARMYUG PRAKASH (M)
76 Gopal Ganj, Orai, Uttar Pradesh, 285-001, India; tel (91)
Circ.: 20,000
Pub./Ed. – R.C. Gupta
Adv. Mgr. – D.U. Gupta

PANAJI, PANJIM

GOMANTAK (M)
Gomantak Bhavan, St. Inez, Panaji, Panjim, 403-001, India; tel (91) 832 242 2701; fax 242 2700; e-mail gomantak@bom2.vsnl.net.in; gomtimes@sacharnet.in; web site www.esakal.com
Adv. Mgr. – Subash Naik
Ed. – Suresh Naik

NAVHIND TIMES (M)
PO Box 161, Navhind Bhavan, Rua Ismail Gracias, Panaji, Panjim, 403-001, India; tel (91) 832 665 1111; fax 222 4258; e-mail navhind@navhindtimes.com; web site www.navhindtimes.com
Circ.: 25,983
Adv. Mgr. – V.Y. Kalangutkar
Ed. in Chief – Arun Sinha

RASHTRAMAT (MS)
PO Box 109, Panaji, Panjim, 403-601, India; tel (91)
Circ.: 8,400
Mng. Dir. – S.P. Madkaiker
Ed. – Chandrakant S. Keni
Pub. – Nav-Gaomant Prakashan

PATNA, BIHAR

JANASHAKTI (D)
PO Box 124, Patna, Bihar, 800-001, India; tel (91)
Circ.: 41,212
Pub. – Shyam Nandan Prasad Singh
Ed. – Upendra Nath Mishra
Adv. Mgr. – Narendra K. Singh
Pub. – Navchetan Samiti

INDIAN NATION (M)
Mazharul Haque Path, Patna, Bihar, 800-001, India; tel (91) 612 233015; fax 222350
Ed. – Harishankar Dwivedi

PRADEEP (M)
PO Box 43, Patna, Bihar, 800 001, India; tel (91) 612 23413
Circ.: 33,110
Pub. – B.P. Jhunjhunwala
Ed. – Paras Nath Singh
Adv. Mgr. – A.S. Raghunath

QUAMI AWAZ (MS)
Shyam Sadan Annexe, Exhibition Rd., Patna, Bihar, India; tel (91)
Mgr. – J.N. Jha

AATMA KATHA (D)
Sandesh Bhavan, Sinha Library Rd., Patna, Bihar, 800-001, India; tel (91)
Circ.: 21,450
Pub. – Arun Kumar
Adv. Dir. – Maheshwar Jha

THE SEARCHLIGHT (M)
PO Box 43, Buddha Marg, Patna, Bihar, 800-001, India; tel (91)
Circ.: 22,741
Pub. – B.P. Jhunjhunwala
Ed. – R.K. Mukker

AJ (D)
Tajer, Patna, Bihar, 800-001, India; tel (91) 612 223 5072; fax 223 5076
Circ.: 90,607
Ed. – Shardul Vikram Gupta

VISHWABANDHU (M)
Braj Kishore, Patna, Bihar, 800-001, India; tel (91)
Circ.: 14,000
Pub. – Raghunandan Singh
Ed. – Avadh Kishore Singh

PUNE, MAHARASHTRA

AAJ KA ANAND (D)
Aaj ka Anand Bldg., 365/6 Shivajinagar, Pune, Maharashtra, 411-005, India; tel (91) 20 2553 8835; fax 2553 3224; e-mail aajkaanand@yahoo.com; info@aajkaanandpapers.com; web site www.aajkaanandpapers.com
Circ.: 150,000
Ed. in Chief – Shyam G. Agarwal

PRABHAT (D)
303 Narayan Peth, Pune, Maharashtra, 411-030, India; tel (91) 20 2445 4841; fax 2445 0979; e-mail dailyprabhat@gmail.com; web site www.eprabhat.com
Circ.: 27,618
Pub. – Anand Gandhi
Ed. – Arun Tori

INDIAN EXPRESS (MS)
Aurors Tower, West Wing, 2nd Fl., Camp, Pune, Maharashtra, 411-001, India; tel (91) 20 2613 1541; fax 2613 1547; web site www.expressindia.com
Ed. – Vinod Mathew Jacob

KESARI (D)
Tilak Wada, 568 Narayan Peth, Pune, Maharashtra, 411-030, India; tel (91) 20 2445 9051; fax 2445 1677
Circ.: 122,000
Mgr. – Tilak Deepak

TARUN BHARAT (MS)
PO Box 598, Pune, Maharashtra, 411-030, India; tel (91) 212 441752
Circ.: 53,446
Pub. – L.D. Kane
Ed. – M.R. Kulkarni
Adv. Mgr. – V.V. Atre

SAKAL/SUNDAY SAKAL (D)
595 Budhwar Peth, Pune, Maharashtra, 411-002, India; tel (91) 20 5603 5500; fax 2445 0583; e-mail sakal@giaspn01.vsnl.net.in; web site www.esakal.com
Chm. – Pratap Pawar
Mktg. Mgr – Sailesh Patel
Cir. Mgr. – Sanjay Pandey
Ed. in Chief – Suresh Chandra Pandey

SAKAAL TIMES (D)
Plot 27 Narveer Tanaji Wadi, Shivaji Nagar, Pune, Maharashtra, 411-005, India; tel (91) 20 2551 3872; fax 2560 2200; web site www.sakaaltimes.com
Circ.: 19,150
Owner – Abhijeet Pawar

VISHAL SAHYADRI (M)
Sahyadri Sadan, Tilak Rd., Pune, Maharashtra, 411-030, India; tel (91) 20 2433 7020
Circ.: 20,000
Ed. – A.V. Patel
Adv. Mgr. – M.G. Ranadive

RAIPUR

YUGADHARMA (M)
Civil Lines, City Station, Raipur, 492-001, India; tel (91) 771 25361
Circ.: 6,500
Ed. – Shri K.M. Jain

RAIPUR, MADHYA PRADESH

NAVA BHARAT (D)
Ragdandgh Madhian, Raipur, Madhya Pradesh, India; tel (91) 771 253 5544; fax 253 5555
Ed. – Anil Prakash

DESHBANDHU (D)
Deshbandhu Complex, Ramsagarpara Layout, Raipur, Madhya Pradesh, 492-001, India; tel (91) 771 229 2011; fax 503 3116; e-mail deshbandraipur@gmail.com; web site www.deshbandhu.co.in
Ed. in Chief – Lalit Surjan
Vice Pres. – Sri Sharat Jain

AMRIT SANDESH (D)
Jawaharlal Nehru Marg Main Rd., Raipur, Madhya Pradesh, 492-001, India; tel (91) 771 253 5767; fax 223 3304
Circ.: 26,232
Gen. Mgr. – Rajkumar Sahoo
Ed. in Chief – Govindlal Vora

RAJKOT, GUJARAT

JAI HIND (D)
PO Box 59, Jai Hind Press Bldg., Babubhai Shah Marg, Rajkot, Gujarat, 360-001, India; tel (91) 281 244 0511; fax 244 8677; e-mail jaihind@satyam.net.in
Adv. Mgr. – Pradeep Josh
Ed. – Y.N. Shah

LOKASATTA-JANASATTA (D)
Janasatta Karyalaya, Sadar, Rajkot, Gujarat, 360-001, India; tel (91) 281 305 1021; fax 246 0186
Circ.: 19,538
Ed. – N.M. Kariya

PHULCHHAB (MS)
Phulchhab Bhavan, Phulchhab Chowk, Rajkot, Gujarat, 360-001, India; tel (91) 281 244 4611; fax 247 9444
Circ.: 90,730
Ed. – Naran Bhai Parmar

SHRI NUTAN SAURASHTRA (M)
PO Box 85, Rajkot, Gujarat, 360-001, India; tel (91) 47047
Circ.: 13,000
Pub. – K.J. Rawal
Ed. – H.J. Rawal
Adv. Mgr. – N.J. Rawal

RANCHI, JHARKHAND

RANCHI EXPRESS (D)
55 Baralal St., Ranchi, Jharkhand, 834-001, India; tel (91) 651 220 5448; fax 220 6213; e-mail rexpress@gmail.com; rncexpress@yahoo.com; web site www.ranchiexpress.com
Circ.: 74,800
Circ. Mgr. – Manish Maroo
Ed. – Balbir Dutt

BIHAR SAMACHAR PATRA PVT LTD
Est.1984
Plot No 15/16 Namkoon Industrial Area, Ranchi, Jharkhand, India; tel (91) 651 226 0668; fax 246 1924; e-mail ranchi_aj@yahoo.comLast Audit: December 28, 2006
Resident Editor - Manager – Amit Agarwal
Ed. – Dilip Srivastu Nilu

REWA, MADHYA PRADESH

BANDHAVIYA SAMACHAR (M)
Surya Kiran, Kalamandir Rd., Rewa, Madhya Pradesh, India; tel (91)
Circ.: 9,000
Pub. – Rakesh Prasad Mishra
Ed. – Madhava Prasad Mishra
Adv. Mgr. – H. Prasad Mishra

SALEM, TAMIL NADU

DAILY THANTHI (MS)
Unknown, Salem, Tamil Nadu, India; tel (91)
Circ.: 20,560

SANGLI, MAHARASHTRA

LOKMANYA TRUST Est.1986
67-70 Industrial Estate, Sangli, Maharashtra, India; tel (91) 0233 231 0737 & 2310838; fax 231 0846; e-mail sanglikesari@rediffmail.com
MANAGER – Manohar Peshave
Ed. – Deepak Tilak

SATNA, MADHYA PRADESH

DESH BANDHU (MS)
Khermai Rd., Satna, Madhya Pradesh, India; tel (91)
Circ.: 15,750

SECUNDERABAD, ANDHRA PRADESH

ANDHRA BHOOMI (D)
36 Sarojini Devi Rd., Secunderabad, Andhra Pradesh, 500-003, India; tel (91) 40 2780 3930; fax 2771 8139; e-mail bhoomi@deccanmail.com; web site www.andhrabhoomi.com
Circ.: 1,379,091
Owner – T. Venkatram Reddy
Ed. – A.T Jayanti

DECCAN CHRONICLE (D)
36 Sarojini Devi Rd., Secunderabad, Andhra Pradesh, 500-003, India; tel (91) 40 2780 3930; fax 2780 5256; e-mail deccan@hdl.vsnl.net.in; info@deccanmail.com; web site www.deccan.com
Circ.: 500,000
Pub. – Venkattram Reddy
Ed. – A.T. Jayanthi

SHOLAPUR, MAHARASHTRA

KESARI (MS)
Unknown, Sholapur, Maharashtra, India; tel (91)
Circ.: 19,257

SANCHAR (M)
Industrial Estate, Hotgi Rd., Sholapur, Maharashtra, 413-003, India; tel (91)
Circ.: 17,852
Pub./Ed. – R.M. Vaidya
Adv. Mgr. – M.M. Kadadi

SHRIRAMPUR, MAHARASHTRA

SARWAMAT (DS)
3366 Somani Bldg., Ward No. 7, Shrirampur, Maharashtra, India; tel (91)
Circ.: 13,165

SURAT, GUJARAT

GUJARATMITRA & GUJARATDARPAN (MS)
Gujaratmitra Press, Chowk Bazaar, Sonifilia, Surat, Gujarat, 395-003, India; tel (91) 261 259 9992; fax 259 9990; e-mail gujaratmitrasurat@yahoo.com; web site www.gujaratmitra.in
Circ.: 86,254
Adv. Mgr. – Ramesh Parmar
Ed. – B.P. Reshamwala

GUJARAT SAMACHAR (M)
Unknown, Surat, Gujarat, India; tel (91)
Circ.: 54,841

PRATAP (DS)
PO Box 242, Surat, Gujarat, 395-003, India; tel (91) 261 (91-261) 23252
Circ.: 13,010
Pub./Ed. – Jagdish Shah
Adv. Mgr. – K.D. Shukla

TIRUCHIRAPALLI, TAMIL NADU

DINAMALAR (D)
PO Box 43, Tiruchirapalli, Tamil Nadu, India; tel (91) 431 246 0272; web site www.dinamalar.com
Ed. – R. Ramasubbu

DAILY THANTHI (D)
130 Bharathiyar Salai, Tiruchirapalli, Tamil Nadu, India; tel (91) 431 240 1562; fax 241 1731; web site www.dailythanthi.com
Circ.: 75,000
– Kotta Sami
– Guna SinghEd.s

TIRUNELVELI, TAMIL NADU

DAILY THANTHI (D)
27 Madurai Rd., Tirunelveli, Tamil Nadu, 627-001, India; tel (91) 462 233 3356; fax 233 7279; e-mail dailythanthi@yahoo.co.in; web site www.dailythanthi.com
Circ.: 24,496
Pub – V Sundaresan
Ed. Muthunayagam

DINAMALAR (D)
PO Box 4, Vannarpettai, Madurai Rd., Tirunelveli, Tamil Nadu, 627-003, India; tel (91) 462 250 1971; fax 250 1975; e-mail dinamalarnet@yahoo.co.in; web site www.dinamalar.com
Ed. – R Venkatapathy

TIRUPATI, ANDHRA PRADESH

EENADU (MS)
Unknown, Tirupati, Andhra Pradesh, India; tel (91)
Circ.: 39,144

TRICHUR, KERALA

THE EXPRESS (D)
West Port, Adiyat Lane, Trichur, Kerala, India; tel (91) 487 233 2108; fax 242 7948
Circ.: 51,083
Ed. – K. Balakrishnan

DEEPIKA (D) Est.1992
Velinnunr Post, Trichur District, Trichur, Kerala, 680-021, India; tel (91) 487 242 1596; fax 242 4231; web site www.deepika.com
Circ.: 50,785
Ed. in Chief – Alexander Paikada
Resident Manager – Varghese Pathadan

TRIVANDRUM (THIRUVANANTHAPURAM), KERALA

KERALA KAUMUDI (D) Est.1911
PO Box 77, Pettah, Trivandrum (Thiruvananthapuram), Kerala, 695-024, India; tel (91) 471 246 1050; fax 2454647; e-mail sreeni@giasmd01.vsnl.net.in; desk@keralakaumudi.com; web site www.keralakaumudi.com
Pub. – M.S. Ravi
Ed. in Chief – M.S. Mani
Ravi Deepu

TRIVANDRUM, KERALA

MALAYALA MANORAMA (MS)
Unknown, Trivandrum, Kerala, India; tel (91); web site www.manoramaonline.com

THE MATHRUBHUMI (D)
Vanchiyoor, Mathrubhumi Rd., Trivandrum, Kerala, 695-008, India; tel (91) 471 246 1617; fax 246 2045; web site www.mathrubhumi.com
Circ.: 108,330
MD – M.P. Veerendra Kumar
Ed. – K. Gopalakrishnan

UDAIPUR, RAJASTHAN

JAI RAJASTHAN (M-D)
Sector No. 11, Sahibagh, Udaipur, Rajasthan, 313002, India; tel (91) 294 248 7066; fax 248 7066; e-mail mail@jairajasthan.com; web site www.jairajasthan.com
Circ.: 43,800
Ed. in Chief – Shailesh Vyas

RAJASTHAN PATRIKA (D)
Sunderwas Old Station Rd., Udaipur, Rajasthan, 313-001, India; tel (91) 294 249 2002; fax 249 1491; e-mail info@rajasthanpatrika.com; web site www.rajasthanpatrika.com
Ed. – Rakesh Gandhi

VARANASI, UTTAR PRADESH

DAILY JAGRAN (D)
321 Purana GT Rd., Natesar, Varanasi, Uttar Pradesh, 221-002, India; tel (91) 542 250 3180; fax 250 2795
Ed. – Virendra Kumar Gupta

JANAVARTA (D)
52/82, Shakari Bhawan Nadesar, Varanasi, Uttar Pradesh, 221-002, India; tel (91) 542 42844
Circ.: 15,000
Ed. – Ishwar D. Mishra

AJ (MS)
Aj Bhavan, Sant Kabir Rd., Kabirchaura, Varanasi, Uttar Pradesh, 221-001, India; tel (91) 542 239 3981; fax 239 3989
Circ.: 120,575
Circ. Mgr. – Suresh Singh
Ed. – Shardul Vikram Gupta

SANMARG (D)
Tulsi Mandir, Bhadaini, Varanasi, Uttar Pradesh, 221-001, India; tel (91) 542 231 3590; fax 231 4278; e-mail sanmargvsnl@satyam.net.in; web site www.sanmarg.in
Circ.: 30,000
Pub. – Veer Bhadra Mishra
Adv. Mgr. – Ashok Pandey
Ed. – Anand Bahadhur Singh

VELLORE, TAMIL NADU

DAILY THANTHI (D)
35 Arcot Rd., Vellore, Tamil Nadu, 632004, India; tel (91) 416 222 2401; fax 222 2302; web site www.dailythanthi.com
Circ.: 16,445
Mgr. – T. Balasubramaniam
Ed. – C. Jayaraman

VIJAYAWADA, ANDHRA PRADESH

ANDHRA JYOTI (DS)
Andhra Jyoti Bldg., Donka Rd., Padamada, Vijayawada, Andhra Pradesh, 520-010, India; tel (91) 866 255 0127; fax 255 1280; web site www.andhrajyothy.com
Circ.: 78,600
Branch Mgr. – V. Murali
Ed. in Chief – Ramachandra Murthy

ANDHRA PRABHA (D)
56-5-1/2 High School Rd., Vijayawada, Andhra Pradesh, 520010, India; tel (91) 866 247 5258; fax 247 4112; e-mail newxpres@vsnl.com; web site www.andhraprabha.com
Ed. in Chief – Vijay Babu

INDIAN EXPRESS (MS)
29-28-39, Dasari Vari St., Suryarao Pet, Vijayawada, Andhra Pradesh, 520-002, India; tel (91) 866 244 4161; fax 244 4262
Circ.: 329,215
Ed. – P.V. Krishna Rao

ANDHRA PATRIKA (D)
PO Box 534, Gandhinagar, Vijayawada, Andhra Pradesh, 520-003, India; tel (91) 866 61247
Ed. – S. Radhakrishna

EENADU (D)
401 AA Patamatalanka, Vijayawada, Andhra Pradesh, 520-010, India; tel (91) 866 249 4900; fax 247 0000; e-mail response@eenadu.net ; feedback1@eenadu.net; web site www.eenadu.net
Circ.: 91,735
Gen. Mgr. – A. Durgaprasad

VISALAANDHRA (DS)
Book Publishing House, Carl Marx Rd., Vijayawada, Andhra Pradesh, 520-002, India; tel (91) 866 243 1301; fax 243 1780
Ed. – Edupugandi Nagaswara Rao

VISHAKAPATNAM, ANDHRA PRADESH

EENADU (MS)
Vishakapatnam, Andhra Pradesh, India; tel (91)
Circ.: 39,754

VISHAPATNAM, ANDHRA PRADESH

ANDHRA PRABHA (MS)
Indian Express office, Vishapatnam, Andhra Pradesh, India; tel (91) 891 657 5072
Circ.: 7,870

VIZIANAGARAM, ANDHRA PRADESH

INDIAN EXPRESS (MS)
Unknown, Vizianagaram, Andhra Pradesh, India; tel (91)
Circ.: 16,130

INDONESIA

BALIKPAPAN, EAST KALIMANTAN

HARIAN PAGI MANUNTUNG (D)
Jl. Jenderal Sudirman, RI XVI/82, Balikpapan, East Kalimantan, Indonesia; tel (62) 542 736 459; fax 730 353; e-mail redaksi@kaltimpost.net
Circ.: 12,000

BANDA ACEH, ACEH

ACEH POST (M)
Jl. Perdagangan, No. 11, Banda Aceh, Aceh, Indonesia; tel (62)
Circ.: 18,000
– Syamsul Kahar
– Tia HusphiaEd.s

BANDJARMASIN

BANJARMASIN POST (M)
Gedung HJ Djok Mentaya, Bandjarmasin, 70111, Indonesia; tel (62) 511 335 4370; fax 436 6123; web site www.indomedia.com/bpost
Circ.: 50,000
Ed. in Chief – Rusdi Effemdi

BANDUNG, WEST JAVA

BANDUNG POST (D)
Jalan Lodaya, 38A, Bandung, West Java, 40264, Indonesia; tel (62) 22 305124; fax 302882
Dir. – Ahmad Jusacc
Ed. in Chief – Ahmad Saelan

BERITA HARIAN
Jl. Terusan Rajawali, No. 160, Bandung, West Java, Indonesia; tel (62)

GALA MEDIA (D)
Jl. Asia-Afrika, 84 Atas, Bandung, West Java, Indonesia; tel (62) 22 445936
Circ.: 25,000
Dir. – H. Syamsuyar Adnan
Ed. – Aria Pandji

GALURA KORAN SUNDA (D)
Jl. Asia-Afrika, No. 77, Bandung, West Java, Indonesia; tel (62) 22 (62-22) 444269

MANDALA (D)
Jend. Gatot Subroto, No. 42, Bandung, West Java, Indonesia; tel (62)
Pub. – Krisna Harahap

PIKIRAN RAKYAT (M)
PO Box 219, Bandung, West Java, 40111, Indonesia; tel (62) 51216; e-mail info@pikiran-rakyat.com; dwi@pikiran-rakyat.com; web site www.pikiran-rakyat.com
Circ.: 150,000
Dir. – Soeharmono Tjitroseowarno
Ed. – Bram Mucharam Darmaprawira
Mktg. Dir. – Dalius Achyar Supriyadi

BANJARMASIN, SOUTH KALIMANTAN

GAWI MANUNTUNG (D)
Jalan Pangeran Samudra, 97B, Banjarmasin, South Kalimantan, Indonesia; tel (62) 511 2701
Circ.: 5,000
Mgr./Ed. – M. Ali Sri Indradjaya

MEDIA MASYARAKAT HARIAN (M)
Jalan Pangeran Samudra, 99 Baamang Tengah II/170, Banjarmasin, South Kalimantan, Indonesia; tel (62) 511 3701
Circ.: 15,000
Ed. – Syahran R. Anang Adenansi

DENPASAR, BALI

HARIAN PAGI UMUM (D)
Jalan Kepudang 67A, Denpasar, Bali, 80232, Indonesia; tel (62) 361 225 764; fax 227 418; e-mail balipost@indo.net.id
Circ.: 50,000
Ed. – K. Nadha

NUSA TENGGARA (D)
Jalan Hayam Wuruk, No. 110, Denpasar, Bali, Indonesia; tel (62) 361 25249
Circ.: 13,000
Editorial Dir. – Jimmy Z. Zaputan

JAKARTA, JAVA

BERITA BUANA (M)
Jalan Tahah Abang Dua 33-35, Jakarta, Java, 10110, Indonesia; tel (62) 21 5487175; fax 5491555
Circ.: 150,000
Pub. – H. Darajad
Pub. – M. Soewignjo
Ed. – Sukarno H. Wibowo
Adv. Mgr. – Nurul Iman

BERITA JAYAKARTA (D)
Jalan Otto Iskandardinata, III/30, Jakarta, Java, Indonesia; tel (62)

BERITA YUDHA (D)
Jalan Letjenderal Haryono MT22, Jakarta, Java, Indonesia; tel (62) 21 8298331
Circ.: 50,000
Dir. – Bagyo Purwantho
Ed. – Sugeng Widjala

BISNIS INDONESIA (D)
Khmas Mansur 7, Jakarta, Java, Indonesia; tel (62) 21 5790 1023; e-mail pda_bisnis@bisnis.co.id; web site www.bisnis.co.id
Circ.: 60,000
Ed. – H. Sukamdani S. Gitosardjono

ANGKATAN BERSENJATA (M)
CTC Bldg., Jalan Kramat Raya 94, 3rd Flr., Jakarta, Java, Indonesia; tel (62) 46071; fax 366870
Circ.: 52,000
Pub. – Emir H. Mungaweang
Ed. – M. Hilmy Naustion

INDONESIA TIMES (M)
Jalan Pulo Lentut 12, Jakarta, Java, 10012, Indonesia; tel (62) 21 461 1280; fax 375 012; e-mail indotimes@indocon.com
Circ.: 35,000
Ed. – Tribuana Said

INDONESIAN OBSERVER (M)
Redtop Sq., Block C-7, Jalan Pecenongan 72, Jakarta, Java, 10120, Indonesia; tel (62) 21 350 0155; fax 350 2417; e-mail indonesian-observer@indoexchange.com; web site www.indoexchange.com/indonesian-observer
Circ.: 25,000
Pub. – Herawati Diah
Adv. Mgr. – Muslich Aliehoesin

JAKARTA POST (D)
PO Box 85, Jakarta, Java, 11001, Indonesia; tel (62) 21 530 0478; fax 530 9066; e-mail editorial@thejakartapost.com; web site www.thejakartapost.com
Circ.: 55,000
Deputy Chief Ed. – Meidyatama Suryodiningrat
Mng. Ed. – Riyadi Suparno
Mng. Ed. – Ati Nurbaiti
Mng. Ed. – Primastuti Handayani

KOMPAS (M)
Gedung Kompas Gramedia, Unit II Lt. 5, Jl. Palmerah Selatan No. 22 - 28, Jakarta, Java, 10270, Indonesia; tel (62) 21 535 0388; fax 536 0678; e-mail kompas@kompas.com; redaksikcm@kompas.com; redaksikcm@kompas.co.id; web site www.kompas.com
Circ.: 523,453
Pub. – Jakob Oetama

LENSA GENERASI (D)
AKA Bldg., Jalan Bangka, No. 11/2, Jakarta, Java, Indonesia; tel (62)
Dir. – Aggi Tjetje

MERDEKA (M)
Jalan Raya Kebayoran Lama 17, Jakarta, Java, 12210, Indonesia; tel (62) 21 5556059; fax 5556063
Circ.: 130,000
Dir./Ed. in Chief – B.M. Diah

SUARA RAKYAT MEMBANGUN (M)
Jalan Bangka Raya, No. 11/2, Kebayoran Baru, Jakarta, Java, Indonesia; tel (62)
Circ.: 100,000
Ed. – Sjamsul Basri
Adv. Mgr. – Imran Sidik

PELITA (M)
Jalan Jenderal Sudirman 65, Jakarta, Java, 10310, Indonesia; tel (62) 21 332 558
Circ.: 80,000
Ed. – Akbar Tanjung

POS KOTA (D)
Yayasan Antar Kota, Jalan Gajah Mada 100, Jakarta, Java, 10130, Indonesia; tel (62) 21 633 4702; fax 634 0252; e-mail redaksi@poskota.co.id; web site www.poskota.co.id
Circ.: 500,000
Ed. – Syamsir Basbiam

REPUBLIKA (D)
Jalan Warung Buncit Raya 37, Jakarta, Java, 12510, Indonesia; tel (62) 21 426 3333; fax 780 0420; web site www.republika.co.id
Ed. in Chief – Ikhwanulkisam Shuri

SINAR PAGI (M)
Jalan Letjenderal Haryono MT22, Selatan, Jakarta, Java, Indonesia; tel (62) 21 828 1044
Circ.: 15,000
Dir. – Jimmy Juneato
Ed. – Charly T. Siahaan

SUARA PEMBARUAN (D)
PO Box 260, Jakarta, Java, 13630, Indonesia; tel (62) 21 801 4077; fax 809 1652; e-mail pembaru@suarapembaruan.com; web site www.suarapembaruan.com
Circ.: 250,000
Ed. – Willy Hangguman

JAYAPURA, IRIAN JAYA

CENDERAWASIH (D)
Jalan Irian, No. 11, Jayapura, Irian Jaya, Indonesia; tel (62)
– J.M. Simatupang
– T. SeriwaDir.s

JOGJAKARTA, JAVA

BERITA NASIONAL (M)
M T Haryono, No. 15, Jogjakarta, Java, Indonesia; tel (62) 274 62643
Circ.: 15,000
Ed. – Mustafa W. Hasjim

KEDAULATAN RAKYAT (M)
Jalan P. Mangkubumi, No. 40-42, Jogjakarta, Java, Indonesia; tel (62) 274 65685; fax 63125
Circ.: 72,000
Mgr. – Soemadi M. Wononito
Ed. – Iman Sutrisno

LAMPUNG, SUMATRA

LAMPUNG POST (D)
Soekarno Hatta No. 108, Rajabasa, Lampung, Sumatra, Indonesia; tel (62) 721 783 693; fax 783 598; web site www.lampungpost.com
MD – Surya Paloh

MANADO, NORTH SULAWESI

CAHAYA SIANG
Jalan Kembang II 2, Manado, Manado, North Sulawesi, 95114, Indonesia; tel (62) 431 61054; fax 63393
Circ.: 12,000
Ed. – Lanny Politan

MEDAN, NORTH SUMATRA

ANALISA (M)
Jalan Jenderal A. Yani 37-43, Medan, North Sumatra, Indonesia; tel (62) 61 326 655; fax 514 031
Circ.: 75,000
Ed. – H. Soffyan

BUKIT BARISAN (D)
Jalan Lahat, No. 11, Medan, North Sumatra, Indonesia; tel (62)
Circ.: 10,000

MIMBAR UMUM (M)
Jalan Riau, No. 79, Medan, North Sumatra, Indonesia; tel (62) 61 517807
Circ.: 55,000
Pub. – H. Fauzi Lubis
Ed. – Mohd Lud Lubis

SINAR INDONESIA BARU (D)
Jalan Brigjenderal Katamso No. 66 AB, Medan, North Sumatra, 20151, Indonesia; tel (62) 61 451 6530; fax 453 8150; web site www.hariansib.com
Pub./Ed. in Chief – G.M. Panggabean

SINAR PEMBANGUNAN HARIAN UMUM (M)
Jalan Mayjen Sutoyo, Siswomiharjo, No. 107-109, Medan, North Sumatra, Indonesia; tel (62)
Circ.: 10,000
Ed. – Ibrahim Sinik

MENADO, NORTH SULAWESI

MANADO POST (D)
Jalan Yos Sudarso 73, Menado, North Sulawesi, Indonesia; tel (62) 431 855 558; fax 840 763; web site www.mdopost.com
Circ.: 22,000
Ed. in Chief – Suhendro Boroma

PADANG, WEST SUMATRA

HALUAN (D)
Jalan Damar 59 C/F, Padang, West Sumatra, Indonesia; tel (62) 751 31660
Circ.: 40,000
Pub. – Kasoema Bim R. Hoesin
Ed. in Chief – Rivai Marlaut

SINGGALANG (M)
Jalan Veteran, No. 17, Padang, West Sumatra, Indonesia; tel (62) 751 25001
Circ.: 20,000
Pub./Ed. – Basril Djabar

PALANGKARAYA, CENTRAL KALIMANTAN

PALANGKARAYA POS (D)
Jalan Jend A. Yani, Blok C, Palangkaraya, Central Kalimantan, Indonesia; tel (62) 751 21055
– D.A. Dharmo
– Siun IhilDir.s

PALEMBANG, SOUTH SUMATRA

BERITA EXPRESS (D)
Jend Sudirman, No. 24, Palembang, South Sumatra, Indonesia; tel (62) 711 27258

GARUDA POST (D)
Jl Jend Sudirman 2841 C, Palembang, South Sumatra, 30129, Indonesia; tel (62) 711 357 783
Pub. – H. Rivolis

SUARA RAKYAT SEMESTA (D)
Jalan K.H. Ashari 52, Palembang, South Sumatra, Indonesia; tel (62) 711 22956
Circ.: 10,000
Pub./Ed. – Djadil Abdullah

PONTIANAK, WEST KALIMANTAN

AKCAYA (M)
Nusa Indah Bl, No. B-62, Pontianak, West Kalimantan, Indonesia; tel (62) 561 34595
Circ.: 10,000
Pub./Ed. – Yacob Mochsin

SEMARANG, CENTRAL JAVA

BAHARI MINGGUAN UMUM (D)
Jalan Sekayu Raya, No. 261, Semarang, Central Java, Indonesia; tel (62) 24 289515
Pub. – Yulistyo Suyatno

TO O NIPPO (M & E)
Jalan Pandanaran 30, Semarang, Central Java, 50241, Indonesia; tel (62) 24 841 2600; web site www.suaramerdeka.com
Circ.: 235,000
Ed. – S.H. Suwarno

KARTIKA (M)
Jalan Pemuda, No. 145, Semarang, Central Java, Indonesia; tel (62) 24 23991
Circ.: 10,000
Ed. – M. Soebagio

SURABAYA, EAST JAVA

HARIAN PAGI MEMORANDUM (D)
Jalan Karas Acung 45, Surabaya, East Java, Indonesia; tel (62) 31 828 9999
Circ.: 190,000
Adv. Mgr. – Zaman Syah

JAWA POS (D)
Jl. Ahmad Yani 88, Surabaya, East Java, 60234, Indonesia; tel (62) 31 828 3333; fax 828 5555; e-mail editor@jawapos.co.id; web site www.jawapos.co.id
Circ.: 120,000
CEO – Ratna Dewi
Ed. – Azrul Ananda

KARYA DARMA (D)
Jemursari Selatan IV, Kav. 20-22, Surabaya, East Java, Indonesia; tel (62) 31 567 9231
Circ.: 30,000
Pub. – Agil H. Ali

SUARA INDONESIA (D)
Jalan Roden Saleh, No. 8, Surabaya, East Java, Indonesia; tel (62) 31 46566
Circ.: 8,000
Dir. – Aco Manafe

SURABAYA POST (E)
Jalan Taman Ade Irma Nasution 1, Surabaya, East Java, Indonesia; tel (62) 31 45394; fax 519585; e-mail sbypost@server.indo.net.id
Circ.: 115,000
Pub. – Tuty Azis
Ed. – Imam Pujono

TELUKBETUNG, SUMATRA

TAMTAMA (D)
Jalan Veteran, No. 154A, Telukbetung, Sumatra, Indonesia; tel (62)
– J. Koesri
– Bachtiar JalilDir.s

UJUNG PANDANG, SOUTH SULAWESI

GEMA (D)
Jalan Jend A. Yani, No. 13 (Atas), Ujung Pandang, South Sulawesi, Indonesia; tel (62)
– H.A. Zaiyani
– Henky Jonas
– M.N. SamDir.s

PEDOMAN RAKYAT (M)
Jalan H. A. Mappanyukki 28, Ujung Pandang, South Sulawesi, Indonesia; tel (62) 411 83344
Circ.: 30,000
Ed. – M. Basir

UJUNG PANDANG POST
Ujung Pandang, South Sulawesi, Indonesia; tel (62)
Circ.: 8,000
Ed. – Alwi Hamid

JAPAN

AKITA, TOHOKU

THE AKITA SAKIGAKE SHIMPO (M&E)
1-1, San-no-rinkai-cho, Akita, Tohoku, 010-8601, Japan; tel (81) 18 888 1800; fax 866 9285; web site www.sakigake.co.jp
Chrmn. – Nopqo Satou
Pres. – Naoki Otssawara
Ed. – Koyokacu Shishito

AOMORI, TOHOKU

TO-O NIPPO (M&E)
Wholesaler 3-chome 89, Aomori, Tohoku, 030-0180, Japan; tel (81) 177 391 111; web site www.toonippo.co.jp
Adv. Mgr. – Katuyuki Siono
Ed. – Seiji Narumi

ASAHIKAWA CITY, HOKKAIDO

HOKKAIDO SHIMBUN (D)
10, Shijo-dori, Asahikawa City, Hokkaido, 070-8720, Japan; tel (81) 166 232 111; e-mail info@hokkaido-np.co.jp; web site www.hokkaido-np.co.jp
Pres. – Kikuti Ikuo
Asahikawa Head Officer – Toshiko Okuda

HOKKAI TIMES (M)
13, 6-jo, Asahikawa City, Hokkaido, 070-0036, Japan; tel (81) 166 234171
Circ.: 52,885
Asahikawa Head Officer – Ryoji Kikuchi

CHIBA, KANTO

CHIBA NIPPO (M)
4-14-10, Chuo, Chuo-ku, Chiba, Kanto, 260-0013, Japan; tel (81) 43 222 9211; fax 222 3040; e-mail c-nippon@j-link.ne.jp; web site www.chibanippo.co.jp
Circ.: 189,597
Pres. – Yasuhidea Kada

FUKUI, HOKURIKU

FUKUI SHIMBUN (D)
Fukui 56, Fukui, Hokuriku, 910-8552, Japan; tel (81) 776 575 111; e-mail fprs@fukuishimbun.co.jp; web site www.fukuishimbun.co.jp
Circ.: 201,577
Pres. – Kosuke Yoshida
Bus. Dir. – Shuichi Sano
Mng. Ed. – Mitsushi Asano

NIKKAN KENMIN FUKUI (D)
3-1-8, Ohte, Fukui, Hokuriku, 910, Japan; tel (81) 776 288 611; web site www.chunichi.co.jp/kennin-fukui
Circ.: 40,000
Pres. – Tamotsu Ogawara
Ed. – Bungo Shirai

FUKUOKA CITY

YOMIURI SHIMBUN (D)
Akasaks 1-16-5, Fukuoka City, 810-8581, Japan; tel (81) 93 531 5131; web site www.yomiuri.co.jp/kyushu
Pres. – Atseushi Kojima

FUKUOKA, KYUSHU

DEMPA SHIMBUN (5X WK.)
2-13-23, Hakata-eki-mae, Haka-ta-ku, Fukuoka, Kyushu, 812, Japan; tel (81) 92 431 7411
Pres. – Tetsuo Hirayama

KYUSHU SPORTS (M)
Fukuoka Tenjin Center Bldg., 2-14-8, Tenjin-cho, C, Fukuoka, Kyushu, 810-0001, Japan; tel (81) 92 751 8201; web site ^www.tokyo-sports.co.jp
Circ.: 471,740
Kyushu Head Officer – Hiroshi Mitomi

NIHON KEIZAI SHIMBUN (M&E)
2-16-1, Hakata-eki-Higashi, Hakata-ku, Fukuoka, Kyushu, 812-8666, Japan; tel (81) 92 473 3300; e-mail ewbmstr@nikkei.co.jp; web site e.nikkei.com
Dir. – Tamizo Suzuki

NISHI-NIPPON SHIMBUN (D)
1-4-1, Tenjin, Chuo-ku, Fukuoka, Kyushu, 810-8721, Japan; tel (81) 92 711 5555; fax 711 5421; e-mail media@nishinippon.co.jp; web site www.nishinippon.co.jp
Pres. – Hikaru Shimizu
Bd. Dir./Adv. Dir. – Seiichi Harada
Bd. Dir./Circ. Dir. – Jun-ichi Ichimura
Bd. Dir./Mng. Ed. – Takamichi Tamagawa
Exec. Dir./Gen. Affairs Dir. – Masanobu Shimizu
Exec. Dir.-Bus. – Akishige Tada
Bus. Dir. – Hiroshi Oyama
Chief Editorial Writer – Iwao Yamamoto

NISHI NIPPON SPORTS (M)
1-4-1, Tenijin, Chuo-ku, Fukuoka, Kyushu, 810, Japan; tel (81)

FUKUSHIMA, TOHOKU

FUKUSHIMA MIMPO (M&E)
13-17, Ota-machi, Fukushima, Tohoku, 960-8602, Japan; tel (81) 245 314 111; e-mail kokoku@mimpo.np.jp; web site www.minpo.jp
Chrmn. – Tsutomu Hanada
Pres. – Seiichi Watanabe
Vice Pres. – Hidenori Watanabe

FUKUSHIMA MINYU (D)
4-29, Yanagimachi, Fukushima, Tohoku, 960-8648, Japan; tel (81) 24 523 1191; fax 515 3491; web site www.minyu-net.com
Ed. in Chief – Yukio Yagimuma

GIFU, CHUBU

GIFU SHIMBUN (D)
10, Imakomachi, Gifu, Chubu, 500-8577, Japan; tel (81) 58 264 1151
Pres. – Mikio Sugiyama
Mng. Dir. – Yoshinori Kanayama
Mng. Dir. – Tadahiro Watanabe
Circ. Dir. – Jiro Hikasa

HACHINOHE, TOHOKU

DAILY TOHOKU (D)
1-3-12, Shiroshita, Hachinohe, Tohoku, 031-8601, Japan; tel (81) 178 445 111
Circ.: 106,081
Pres. – Miyuma Uichi
MD – Takehana Koji
Gen. Affairs Dir. – Tokuju Yoshida
Adv. Dir. – Kenji Endo
Bd. Dir./Circ. Dir. – Katsuyoshi Joshita
Chief Editorial Writer – Tatsuo Hosogoe
Bd. Dir./Mng. Ed. – Uichi Izumiyama

HAKODATE, HOKKAIDO

HOKKAIDO SHIMBUN (D)
31-3, Goryokaku-cho, Hakodate, Hokkaido, 040-8688, Japan; tel (81) 138 325 112; fax 325 119; e-mail info@hokkaido-np.co.jp; web site www.hokkaido-np.co.jp
Mgr. – Hainichi Harada

HAMAMATSU CITY, CHUBU

CHUNICHI SHIMBUN (D)
45, Yakushin-cho, Hamamatsu City, Chubu, 435-8555, Japan; tel (81) 53 421 7711; fax 421 5561; web site ^www.chunichi.co.jp
Ed. – Satzo Sato

HIROSAKI, TOHOKU

MUTSU SHIMPO (M)
2-1, Shimo-shirogane-cho, Hirosaki, Tohoku, 036-8356, Japan; tel (81) 172 343 111; fax 323 238; web site www.mutusinpou.co.jp
Circ.: 53,500
Pres. – Tokuhiro Shimoyama
Circ. Dir. – Tsutomu Kasai

HIROSHIMA, CHUGOKU

CHUGOKU SHIMBUN (D)
7-1, Dobashi-cho, Naka-ku, Hiroshima, Chugoku, 730-8677, Japan; tel (81) 82 236 2111; fax 236 2456; e-mail denshi@hiroshima-cdas.or.jp; web site www.chugoku-np.co.jp
Ed. in Chief – Osamu Kanashige
Chrmn. – Jiro Yamamoto

ICHINOSEKE CITY, TOHOKU

IWATE NICHI-NICHI SHIMBUN (M)
60, Minamishi-machi, Ichinoseke City, Tohoku, 021-8686, Japan; tel (81) 191 265114; e-mail iwanichi@iwanichi.co.jp; web site www.isop.ne.jp/iwanichi
Circ.: 59,697
Adv. Dir. – Masahiro Chiba
Circ. Dir. – Seishi Abe
Mng. Ed. – Seiichi Watanabe

ISHIGAKI, KYUSHU

YAEYAMA MAINICHI SHIMBUN (D)
614 Tonoshiro, Ishigaki, Kyushu, 907-0004, Japan; tel (81) 9808 22121; fax 21150; web site www.y-mainichi.co.jp
Circ.: 14,500
Pres. – Choyu Itosu
Bd. Dir./Adv. Dir. – Kiyotaka Nakama
Bd. Dir./Mng. Ed. – Yoshio Uechi

ISHINOMAKI CITY, TOHOKU

ISHINOMAKI SHIMBUN (E)
2-1-28, Sumiyoshi-machi, Ishinomaki City, Tohoku, 986-0821, Japan; tel (81) 225 223201
Circ.: 13,000
Pres./Mng. Ed. – Motomi Wada
Bus. Mgr. – Minoru Wada
Adv. Mgr. – Kosho Motoki
Sales Mgr. – Yoji Abe

IZUMO, CHUGOKU

SHIMANE NICNI-NICHI SHIMBUN (E)
545, Satogata-cho, Izumo, Chugoku, 693-0064, Japan; tel (81) 853 236760
Circ.: 25,656
Owner/Ed./Bus. Dir. – Kosuke Kikuchi
Pres./Gen. Affairs Dir. – Emiko Kikuchi
Bd. Dir./Adv. Dir. – Keiichi Kanda
Bd. Dir./Bus. Dir. – Joji Yamada
Bd. Dir./Circ. Dir. – Kokichi Mishima
Bd. Dir./Mng. Ed. – Toyomi Hino
Bd. Dir./Mng. Ed. – Shinji Horii

KAGOSHIMA, KYUSHU

KAGOSHIMA SHIMPO (M)
7-28, Jonan-cho, Kagoshima, Kyushu, 892-8551, Japan; tel (81) 99 2262100
Circ.: 39,798
Chrmn. – Hisamasa Sakomizu
Pres. – Ryogo Suzuki
Bd. Dir./Adv. Dir. – Hiroyuki Shinnishi
Bd. Dir./Gen. Affairs Dir. – Hitoshi Uemura
Bd. Dir./Mng. Ed. – Junsuke Kinoshita
Mng. Dir./Circ. Dir. – Satoru Nakamura
Chief Editorial Writer – Hisao Fukumitsu

MINAMI-NIPPON SHIMBUN (M)
1-9-33 Yojiro, Kagoshima-shi, Kagoshima, Kyushu, 890-8603, Japan; tel (81) 99 813 5001; fax 813 5411; e-mail webmaster@373news.com; web site 373news.com/index.phpLast Audit: March 24, 2010
Ed. in Chief – Naohumi Sakasegawa

KANAZAWA CITY, HOKURIKU

HOKKOKU SHIMBUN (M&E)
2-5-1, Korinbo, Kanazawa City, Hokuriku, 920-8588, Japan; tel (81) 76 2632111; e-mail admin@hokkoku.co.jp; web site www.hokkoku.co.jp
Pres./Ed. in Chief – Hidekazu Tobita
Exec. Dir. – Minoru Kita
Mng. Dir. – Motoi Takazawa
Adv. Dir. – Shin-ichiro Miyamura
Circ. Dir. – Yoshio Yamamoto
Mng. Ed. – Hajime Murahama
Chief Editorial Writer – Kiyoji Hori

HOKURIKU CHUNICHI SHIMBUN (M&E)
3-20, Minanicho, Kanazawa City, Hokuriku, 920-8573, Japan; tel (81) 76 261 3111; fax 265 7490; web site www.chunichi.co.jp/hokuriku
Mgr. – Itou Koji

KITA-KYUSHU, KYUSHU

ASAHI SHIMBUN (M&E)
1-12-1, Sunatsu, Kokurakita-ku, Kita-Kyushu, Kyushu, 802-8588, Japan; tel (81) 93 563 1131; fax 563 1173; e-mail newsroom@emb.asahi-np.co.jp; web site www.asahi.com
Bd. Dir./Seibu Head Officer – Kiyomasa Habara
Mng. Ed. – Osamu Owa

KITAKYUSHU, KYUSHU

MAINICHI SHIMBUN (D)
13-1, Kon-ya-machi, Kokurakita-ku, Kitakyushu, Kyushu, 802-8651, Japan; tel (81) 93 541 3131; e-mail webmaster@mainichi.co.jp; web site www.mainichi.co.jp
Mng. Dir./Seibu Head Officer – Akio Kaminishi
Mng. Ed. – Yoshitaka Nagamori

KOBE, KINKI

DAILY SPORTS (M)
1-5-7, Higashikawasaki-cho, Chuo-ku, Kobe, Kinki, 650-0044, Japan; tel (81) 78 362 7100
Pres. – Kaoru Takashi
Exec. Dir. – Minoru Inoue
Mng. Dir./Advertising/Tokyo Head Officer – Yoshihiko Shimomura
Mng. Dir./Mng. Ed. – Hirohisa Karuo
Adv. Dir. – Tsuyoshi Kumano
Circ. Dir. – Naoto Hamada

KOBE SHIMBUN (D)
1-5-7, Higashikawasaki-cho, Chuo-ku, Kobe, Kinki, 650-8571, Japan; tel (81) 78 362 7100; fax 360 5501; web site www.kobe-np.co.jp
Pres. – Kaoru Takashi

KOCHI, SHIKOKU

KOCHI SHIMBUN (M&E)
3-2-15, Honmachi, Kochi, Shikoku, 780-8572, Japan; tel (81) 888 222 111; fax 738 119; e-mail master@kochinews.co.jp; web site www.kochinews.co.jp
Pres. – Toshio Iwai
Chrmn. – Shoroku Hashii
Bd. Dir. – Toshiaki Ogasawara
Bd. Dir. – Kengo Fujito
Gen. Affairs Dir. – Ken-ichi Okada
Assoc. Dir./Chief Editorial Writer – Hiroshi Okubo
Adv. Dir. – Shin-ichi Kusunose

KOFU CITY, CHUBU

YAMANASHI NICHI-NICHI SHIMBUN (M)
2-6-10, Kitaguchi, Kofu City, Chubu, 400-8515, Japan; tel (81) 552 313 000; fax 251 4311; e-mail staff@sannichi-ybs.co.jp; web site www.sannichi.co.jp
Circ.: 210,000
Pres. – Eiichi Noguchi

KUMAMOTO, KYUSHU

KUMAMOTO NICHI-NICHI SHIMBUN (M&E)
172, Yoyasu-machi, Kumamoto, Kyushu, 860-8506, Japan; tel (81) 96 361 3111; e-mail staff@kumanichi.co.jp; web site www.kumanichi.com
Chrmn. – Mitsuya Nagano
Pres. – Eiichi Izu
Bus. Dir. – Toshiki Hashimoto
Mng. Dir. – Takeshi Kakiyama
Mng. Dir. – Keisuke Hisano
Gen. Affairs Dir. – Hideo Uemura
Adv. Dir. – Shunsaku Goto
Circ. Dir. – Masaji Nogata
Mng. Ed. – Hiroshi Kawarabata
Chief Editorial Writer – Michio Nakamura

KUSHIRO, HOKKAIDO

HOKKAIDO SHIMBUN (D)
11-5, Kurogane-cho, Kushiro, Hokkaido, 085-8655, Japan; tel (81) 154 222 121; fax 312 711; e-mail info@hokkaido-np.co.jp; web site www.hokkaido-np.co.jp
– Yoshiaki Matusoka
– Kenji SagawaKushiro Head Officers

KUSHIRO SHIMBUN (M)
7-3, Kurogane-cho, Kushiro, Hokkaido, 085-8650, Japan; tel (81) 154 221 111; fax 220 050; web site www.news-kushiro.jp/index.php
Circ.: 56,095
Gen. Affairs Dir. – Masanori Takahashi
Adv. Dir. – Yukihiro Yamamoto
Mng. Ed. – Yutaka Ito

KYOTO, KINKI

KYOTO SHIMBUN (D)
239 Shoshoimachi, Ebisugawa-Kitairu, Karasuma-dori, Kyoto, Kinki, 604-8577, Japan; tel (81) 75 241 5430; fax 252 5454; e-mail kpdesk@mb.kyoto-np.co.jp; web site www.kyoto-np.co.jp
Pres. – Osamu Saito
Exec. Dir./Circ. – Shiyouzou Masuda
Gen. Affairs Mgr. – Keniti Terai

MAEBASHI, GUNMA

JOMO SHIMBUN (D)
1-50-21, Furuichi-machi, Maebashi, Gunma, 371-8666, Japan; tel (81) 27 254 9977; web site www.raijin.com
Circ.: 310,139
Pres. – Kozo Takahashi
Assoc. Dir./Gen. Affairs Dir. – Yukio Kitamura
Ed. in Chief – Hagi Wara

MATSUE, CHUGOKU

SAN-IN-CHUO SHIMPO (M)
383, Tono-machi, Matsue, Chugoku, 690-8668, Japan; tel (81) 852 323 440
Circ.: 171,899
Pres. – Tsunemasa Yamane

MATSUMOTO, CHUBU

SHINANO MAINICHI SHIMBUN (M&E)
2-10, Miyata, Matsumoto, Chubu, 399-8711, Japan; tel (81) 263 252 151; fax 272 050; e-mail m-houdo@shinmai.co.jp; web site www.shinmai.co.jp
Dir. – Masahisa Tsunekawa

MATSUYAMA, SHIKOKU

EHIME SHIMBUN (M)
1-12-1, Ote-machi, Matsuyama, Shikoku, 790-8511, Japan; tel (81) 89 935 2111; fax 941 8108; web site www.ehime-np.co.jp
Pres. – Rurio Imai

Exec. Dir. – Takuo Nomoto

MITO, KANTO

IBARAKI SHIMBUN (M)
2-15, Kitami-cho, Mito, Kanto, 310-8686, Japan; tel (81) 29 221 3121; e-mail iba-news@mbf.sphere.ne.jp; web site www.sphere.ne.jp/iba-news
Circ.: 118,277
Pres. – Takashi Kotabe
Bd. Dir./Mng. Ed. – Yoshio Saito

MIYAZAKI, KYUSHU

MIYAZAKI NICHI-NICHI SHIMBUN (M)
1-1-33, Takachiho-dori, Miyazaki, Kyushu, 880-8570, Japan; tel (81) 985 269 315; e-mail info@the-miyanichi.co.jp; web site www.the-miyanichi.co.jp
Circ.: 236,489
Pres. – Riichiro Miyake
Bd. Dir. – Kazuhiro Watanabe
Adv. Dir. – Kunihiko Yuasa
Circ. Dir. – Takashi Mizoguchi
Mng. Ed. – Masaaki Minamimura
Chief Editorial Writer – Takehiko Zushi

MORIOKA CITY, TOHOKU

IWATE NIPPO (D)
3-7, Uchimaru, Morioka City, Tohoku, 020-8622, Japan; tel (81) 19 653 4111; e-mail center@iwate-np.co.jp; web site www.iwate-np.co.jp
Pres. – Hiroshi Miura
Bus. Dir. – Atsuhiro Miyamori

MURORAN, HOKKAIDO

MURORAN MIMPO (D)
1-3-16, Honcho, Muroran, Hokkaido, 051-8550, Japan; tel (81) 143 225 121; fax 233 744
Exec. Dir. – Tomizo Murakami
MD – Takeo Sumitomo

NAGANO, CHUBU

SHINANO MAINICHI SHIMBUN (D)
657, Minamiagata-machi, Nagano, Chubu, 380-8546, Japan; tel (81) 26 236 3000; fax 236 3197; e-mail center@shinmai.co.jp; web site www.shinmai.co.jp
Adv. Mgr. – Furukawa Kazuo
Ed. in Chief – Watanabe Higehisa

SHINANO MAINICHI SHIMBUN (M&E)
657, Minamiagata-machi, Nagano, Chubu, 380-8546, Japan; tel (81) 26 236 3000; e-mail center@shinmai.co.jp; web site www.shinmai.co.jp
Pres. – Kensuke Kosaka
Bd. Dir./Adv. Dir. – Hisatada Tateiwa
Bd. Dir./Chief Editorial Writer – Takaharu Hanajima
Bd. Dir./Circ. Dir. – Hiromu Iwamoto
Bd. Dir./Mng. Ed. – Seiichi Inomata
Bus. Dir. – Kenjiro Kida
Gen. Affairs Dir. – Shigekazu Nakamura

NAGASAKI, KYUSHU

NAGASAKI SHIMBUN (M)
3-1, Mori-machi, Nagasaki, Kyushu, 852-8601, Japan; tel (81) 95 844 2111; fax 844 2106; web site www.nagasaki-np.co.jp
Circ.: 200,154
Gen. Affairs Dir. – Tadahiro Motomura

NAGOYA, CHUBU

ASAHI SHIMBUN (D)
1-3-3, Sakae, Naka-ku, Nagoya, Chubu, 460-8488, Japan; tel (81) 52 231 8131; e-mail newsroom@emb.asahi-np.co.jp; web site www.asahi.com
Nagoya Head Officer – Sumitsugu Kajihara

CHUKYO SPORTS (E)
4th Fl., CKO Insatsu Bldg., 4-3-19 Ki, Kita-ku, Nagoya, Chubu, 460-0847, Japan; tel (81) 52 982 1911
Circ.: 289,430
Chukyo Head Officer – Osamu Suetsugu

CHUNICHI SHIMBUN (M&E)
1-6-1, San-no-maru, Naka-ku, Nagoya, Chubu, 460-8511, Japan; tel (81) 52 201 8811; fax 231 0628; e-mail shakai@chunichi.co.jp; web site www.chunichi.co.jp
Chrmn. – Hirohiko Oshima
Pres. – Bungo Shirai
Vice Pres. – Isamu Koyama
Exec. Dir./Circ. – Hisashi Kushida
Bd. Dir./Chief Editorial Writer – Toshihiko Uji
Bd. Dir./Ed. – Kunihiro Takaba
Mng. Dir./Advertising – Torao Oshima
Mng. Dir. Bus. – Shinsuke Yoshimura

CHUNICHI SHIMBUN (M&E)
1-6-1, San-no-maru, Naka-ku, Nagoya, Chubu, 460-8511, Japan; tel (81) 52 201 8811
Mng. Ed. – Nobuaki Koide
Chief Editorial Writer – Satoru Tajima

CHUNICHI SPORTS (E)
1-6-1, San-no-maru, Naka-ku, Nagoya, Chubu, 460-8511, Japan; tel (81) 52 201 8811; fax 242 8051
Chunichi Sports Head Officer – Takashi Emahara

MAINICHI SHIMBUN (D)
4-7-35, Meieki, Nakamura-ku, Nagoya, Chubu, 450-8651, Japan; tel (81) 52 527 8000; web site www.mainichi.co.jp
Chubu Head Officer – Hiroto Sasaki
Mng. Ed. – Noritaka Kamiya

CHUBU KEIZAI SHIMBUN (D)
4-4-12, Meieki, Nakamura-ku, Nagoya, Chubu, 450-8561, Japan; tel (81) 52 561-5213; fax 561 5247; web site www.chukei-news.co.jp
Circ.: 96,000
Pres. – Kato Sho
Pub. Dir. – Hidekazu Okada
Adv. Dir. – Toyoaki Takada
Chief Editorial Writer – Masahiro Oohashi
Mng. Ed. – Norimitsu Inagaki

NAGOYA TIMES (D)
1-3-10, Marunouchi, Naka-ku, Nagoya, Chubu, 460-8530, Japan; tel (81) 52 231 1331
Circ.: 146,137
Ed. in Chief – Mitsuo Saito

NIHON KEIZAI SHIMBUN (D)
4-16-33 Sakae, Naka-ku, Nagoya, Chubu, 460-8366, Japan; tel (81) 52 243 3350; e-mail ecntct@nikkei.co.jp; web site www.nikkei.com
Ed. – Akahiko NiYamoto

YOMIURI SHIMBUN (M)
1-17-6, Sakae, Naka-ku, Nagoya, Chubu, 460-8470, Japan; tel (81) 52 211 0017; web site www.yomiuri.co.jp
Circ.: 194,884
Pres. – Tsuneo Watanabe
Exec. Dir./Chubu Head Officer – Haruo Takano
Bd. Dir./Bus. Dir. – Tadao Matsumoto
Mng. Ed. – Yukio Isahaya

NAHA (OKINAWA I.), KYUSHU

RYUKYU SHIMPO (M)
1-10-3, Izumisaki, Naha (Okinawa I.), Kyushu, 900-8525, Japan; tel (81) 98 865 5111; fax 861 0100; e-mail info@ryukyushimpo.co.jp; web site www.ryukyushimpo.co.jp
Chief – Nakada Seiki
Pres. – Pomokadu Takamine
Pres. – Hisatoshi Takehara
Ed.in Chief – Tomomita Jumichi
Mng. Ed. – Tomokazu Takamine

OKINAWA TIMES (M)
2-2-2, Kumoji, Naha (Okinawa I.), Kyushu, 900-8678, Japan; tel (81) 98 860 3582; fax 860 3435; web site www.okinawatimes.co.jp
Pres. – Masao Kishimoto
Ed. – Toro Uehara

NARA, KINKI

NARA SHIMBUN (D)
2-4 Hokkeji-cho, Nara, Kinki, 630-8686, Japan; tel (81) 742 261 331; fax 225 013
Circ.: 118,064
Mng. Dir. – Haruo Amari

NAZE, KYUSHU

NANKAI NICHI-NICHI SHIMBUN (M)
10-3, Nagahama-cho, Naze, Kyushu, 894-8601, Japan; tel (81) 997 532 121; web site www.nankainn.com
Circ.: 23,993
Pres. – Michio Murayama
Tokyo Head Officer – Yasuo Maki
Ed. in Chief – Terumi Matsui

NIIGATA, HOKURIKU

NIIGATA NIPPO (M&E) Est.1942
772-2 Zenku, Niigata, Hokuriku, 950-1189, Japan; tel (81) 25 378 9111; web site www.niigata-nippo.co.jp
Pres. – Sachio Igarashi
Bd. Dir./Mng. Ed. – Gen Hoshino

NOSHIRO, TOHOKU

HOKUU SHIMPO (D)
3-2, Nishi-dori-machi, Noshiro, Tohoku, 016-0891, Japan; tel (81) 185 543 150
Circ.: 31,470
Pres. – Yasumasa Yamaki

OBIHIRO, HOKKAIDO

TOKACHI MAINICHI SHIMBUN (D)
8-2, Higashi, 1-jo-minami, Obihiro, Hokkaido, 080-8688, Japan; tel (81) 155 222 121; fax 252 700; e-mail info@kachimai.co.jp; web site www.tokachi.co.jp
Circ.: 88,134
Pres. – Hiroshi Hayashi

OITA, KYUSHU

OITA GODO SHIMBUN (D)
3-9-15, Funai-machi, Oita, Kyushu, 870-8605, Japan; tel (81) 97 536 2121; fax 538 9674; web site www.oita-press.co.jp
Pres. – Takeshi Nagano
Vice Pres. – Keiichi Nagano

OKAYAMA, CHUGOKU

OKAYAMA-NICHI-NICHI-SHIMBUN (D)
3-30 Banzan-cho,, Okayama, Chugoku, 700-8678, Japan; tel (81) 86 231 4211; web site www.okanichi.co.jp
Circ.: 45,000
Pres. – Masaaki Matu
MD – Takashi Ando

SANYO SHIMBUN (M&E)
2-1-1, Yanagi-machi, Okayama, Chugoku, 700-8634, Japan; tel (81) 86 803 8008; e-mail s-net@mxa.mesh.ne.jp; web site www.sanyo.oni.co.jp
Pres. – Takamasa Koshimune
Bus. Dir. – Kuniaki Fujii
Mng. Dir. – Takashi Kaneki
Mng. Dir./Gen. Affairs Dir. – Tetsuhiko Okura
Adv. Dir. – Masaki Matsuva
Circ. Dir. – Manabu Fujita
Chief Editorial Writer – Seiichi Yasuda

OSAKA

YUKAN FUJI (E)
Osaka, Japan; tel (81)
Circ.: 298,648
Osaka Head Officer – Motohisa Saeki
Mng. Dir./Head Officer – Tomio Saito
Advertising/Circ. Dir. – Katsuzo Mori
Mng. Ed. – Masami Kato

OSAKA BAKUROMACHI

OSAKA NICHI-NICHI SHIMBUN (E)
No. 6 No. 8, 2-chome, Chuo-ku, Osaka Bakuromachi, Japan; tel (81) 6 6241 7872; fax 6120 1811; e-mail osaka@nnn.co.jp; web site www.nnn.co.jp
Circ.: 225,000
Adv. Mgr. – Satoshi Kadoaaki
Ed. – Hiroshi Hatayama

OSAKA, OSAKA

ASAHI SHIMBUN (D)
3-2-4, Nakanoshima, Kita-ku, Osaka, Osaka, 530-8211, Japan; tel (81) 6 6231 0131; web site www.asahi.com
Ed. – Yoshifumi Otsuao

DAILY SPORTS (D)
1-10-8, Edobori, Nishi-ku, Osaka, Osaka, 550-0002, Japan; tel (81) 6 6447 1821; fax 6447 0195
Circ.: 300,219
Ed. – Miya Moto

DEMPA SHIMBUN (D)
3-2-4, Nakanoshima, Kita-Ku, Osaka, Osaka, 530-8211, Japan; tel (81) 6 6203 3361; fax 6227 5153; web site www.dempa.com
Pres. – Tetsuo Hirayama
Ed. – Hidetsuna Sasaki

HOCHI SHIMBUN (M)
2-22-17, Honjo-Nishi, Kita-ku, Osaka, Osaka, 531-8558, Japan; tel (81) 6 7732 2311; web site www.yomiuri.co.jp/hochi/
Circ.: 438,417
Vice Pres./Osaka Head Officer – Eiji Tomita
Mng. Dir./Adv. Dir. – Munesuke Seki
Mng. Dir./Circ. Dir. – Naofumi Sugimoto
Mng. Ed. – Masahito Gotoda

MAINICHI SHIMBUN (M&E)
3-4-5, Umeda, Kita-ku, Osaka, Osaka, 530-8251, Japan; tel (81) 6 6346 8392; fax 6346 8383; e-mail osaka@mdx.mainichi.co.jp; web site www.mainichi.co.jp
Pres./Osaka Head Officer – Asahina Utaka

NIHON KEIZAI SHIMBUN (D)
1-1-1, Otemae, Chuo-ku, Osaka, Osaka,

540-8488, Japan; tel (81) 6 6943 7111; e-mail ecntct@nikkei.co.jp; web site www.nikkei.co.jp/enews
Circ. Dir. – Hiroshi Kikuchi

NIKKAN SPORTS (M)
5-92-1, Hattori-Kotobukicho, Toyonaka, Osaka, Osaka, 561-8585, Japan; tel (81) 6 6867 2811; web site www.nikkansport.com/osaka
Circ.: 523,120
Pres. – Tadashi Nakai
Assoc. Dir./Adv. Dir. – Akira Asahara
Circ. Dir. – Yoshihiro Kawabata
Mng. Ed. – Katsuo Furukawa

OSAKA SHIMBUN (E)
2-4-9, Umeda, Kita-ku, Osaka, Osaka, 530-8279, Japan; tel (81) 6 63431221; web site www.osakanews.com
Circ.: 87,633
Pres. – Yukio Tsujimoto
Exec. Dir. – Hiroyuki Katsumi
Bd. Dir./Advertising/Circ. Dir. – Yoshiyasu Ishii
Bd. Dir./Mng. Ed. – Kaoru Yura
Tokyo Head Officer – Isoshi Yoshino

OSAKA SPORTS (E-EX S)
Takaichi Sakai, Osaka, Osaka, 590-0902, Japan; tel (81) 7 2222 7701; fax 2227 4450; e-mail dai-ad@tokyo-sports.co.jp; web site www.tokyo-sports.co.jp
Circ.: 470,660
Osaka Head Officer – Kazuomi Tanaka

SANKEI SHIMBUN (D)
2-1-57 Minatomachi, Osaka, Osaka, 556-8660, Japan; tel (81) 6 6633 1221; fax 6633 0359; e-mail desk@people.or.jp; webmaster@sankei.co.jp; web site www.sankei.co.jp
Dir. – Akimasa Negishi

SANKEI SPORTS (M)
2-4-9, Umeda, Kita-ku, Osaka, Osaka, 530-8277, Japan; tel (81)
Circ.: 552,519
Mng. Dir./Osaka Head Officer – Tomio Saito
Advertising/Circ. Dir. – Jin-emon Akahori
Mng. Ed. – Masaki Yoshida

SPORTS NIPPON (D)
3-4-5, Umeda, Kita-ku, Osaka, Osaka, 530-8278, Japan; tel (81) 6 6346 8500; e-mail jtoto-o@sponichi.co.jp; web site www.sponichi.co.jp
Circ.: 920,000
Pres. – Susumu Yamamoto

NIHON KOGYO SHIMBUN (M)
2-4-9, Umeda, Kita-ku, Osaka, Osaka, 530-8277, Japan; tel (81) 6 6343 1221
Circ.: 148,532
Dir. – Atsushi Tateyama

THE MAINICHI DAILY NEWS (M)
3-4-5, Umeda, Kita-ku, Osaka, Osaka, 530-8251, Japan; tel (81) 6 6346 8392; fax 6346 8383; e-mail osaka@mdx.mainichi.co.jp; web site www.mainichi.co.jp
Mng. Ed. – Katsuya Fukunaga

YOMIURI SHIMBUN (D)
5-9, Nozaki-cho, Kita-ku, Osaka, Osaka, 530-8551, Japan; tel (81) 6 6366 1896; e-mail webmaster@yomiuri.co.jp; web site www.yomiuri.co.jp
Pres. – Jin Nakamura
Adv. Mgr. – Jun Morimoto
Ed. in Chief – Koichi Kishsinto

SAGA, KYUSHU

SAGA SHIMBUN (D)
3-2-23, Tenjin, Saga, Kyushu, 840-8585, Japan; tel (81) 952 282 111; fax 295 760; e-mail webmaster@saga-s.co.jp; web site www.saga-s.co.jp
Circ.: 138,154
Pres. – Seiichiro Nakao

Gen. Affairs Dir. – Shigeru Yoshida
Circ. Dir. – Hidenori Nakamuta
Chief Editorial Writer – Tamio Sakai
Mng. Ed. – Teruhiko Washizaki

SAITAMA CITY, KITA-KU

SAITAMA SHIMBUN (D)
2-282-3, Yoshino-cho, Saitama City, Kita-ku, 331-8686, Japan; tel (81) 48 795 9930; fax 653 9020; e-mail info@saitama-np.co.jp; web site www.saitama-np.co.jp
Circ.: 160,964
Pres. – Akira Maruyama
Gen. Mgr. – Yoshimasa Takayama

SAPPORO, HOKKAIDO

ASAHI SHIMBUN (D)
1-1-1, Kita-2 jo-nishi, Chuo-ku, Sapporo, Hokkaido, 060-8602, Japan; tel (81) 11 281 2131; e-mail newsroom@emb.asahi-np.co.jp; web site www.asahi.com
Hokkaido Office Dir. – Koji Isomatsu
Ed. in Chief – Yoichi Funabashi

DOSHIN SPORTS (D)
3-6, Odori-Nishi, Chuo-ku, Sapporo, Hokkaido, 060-8711, Japan; tel (81) 11 241 1230; fax 251 7587
Circ.: 142,451
Pres. – Tuyosi Hama

HOCHI SHIMBUN (D)
4-1, Nishi, Kita-yojo, Chuo-ku, Sapporo, Hokkaido, 60, Japan; tel (81) 11 251 3671; fax 251 2312
Vice Pres./Hokkaido Head Officer – Tsutomu Ikeda

MAINICHI SHIMBUN (D)
6-1, Nishi, Kita-4 jo-nishi, Chuo-ku, Sapporo, Hokkaido, 060-8643, Japan; tel (81) 11 221 4141; fax 281 5164; web site www.mainichi.co.jp
Ed. – Youiti Evada

NIHON KEIZAI SHIMBUN (D)
7-3, Kita-1 jo-nishi, Chuo-ku, Sapporo, Hokkaido, 060-8621, Japan; tel (81) 11 281 3211; e-mail ecntct@nikkei.co.jp; web site www.nikkei.co.jp/enews
Circ.: 60,373
Sapporo Head Officer – Fumisato Ebihara

NIKKAN SPORTS (D)
3-1-30, Kita 3-jo-higashi, Chuo-ku, Sapporo, Hokkaido, 060-0033, Japan; tel (81) 11 242 3900; fax 272 1754; web site www.kita-nikkan.co.jp
Circ.: 160,199
Bus. Mgr. – Yoshitaka Suzuki
Bus. Employment Asst. – Yuriko Suzawara

HOKKAI TIMES (M)
10-6, Nishi, Minami-Ichijo, Sapporo, Hokkaido, 060-8701, Japan; tel (81)
Circ.: 115,430
Owner – Tonezo Yamazaki

HOKKAI TIMES (M)
10-6, Nishi, Minami-Ichijo, Chuo-ku, Sapporo, Hokkaido, 060-8701, Japan; tel (81) 11 231 0131
Circ.: 62,650
Pres. – Koichi Fujino
Advertising/Bus. Mgr. – Toshinori Chiba
Exec. Dir./Ed. – Koki Ito
Mng. Ed.-Adv./Bus. – Shiro Kitsunai
Sales Mgr. – Jun-ichi Kato
Chief Editorial Writer – Tadaaki Azuma

HOKKAIDO SHIMBUN (D)
3-6, Odori-Nishi, Chuo-ku, Sapporo, Hokkaido, 060-8711, Japan; tel (81) 11 221 2111; fax 210 4965; e-mail info@hokkaido-np.co.jp; web site www.hokkaido-np.co.jp
Chrmn. – Ikuo Kikuchi

Exec. Dir. – Nobuaki Suga

HOKKAIDO SHIMBUN (M&E)
3-6, Odori-Nishi, Chuo-ku, Sapporo, Hokkaido, 060-8711, Japan; tel (81) 2212111; fax 2104965; e-mail info@hokkaido-np.co.jp; web site www.hokkaido-np.co.jp

YOMIURI SHIMBUN (D)
4-1, Kita 4-jo-nishi, Chuo-ku, Sapporo, Hokkaido, 060-8656, Japan; tel (81) 11 242 3111; fax 242 5627; web site www.yomiuri.co.jp
Adv. Mgr. – Norikavu Takagi
Ed. – Yamakoshi Takashi

SENDAI CITY, TOHOKU

KAHOKU SHIMPO (D)
1-2-28, Itsutsubashi, Aoba-ku, Sendai City, Tohoku, 980-8660, Japan; tel (81) 22 211 1111; fax 224 7947; e-mail kahoku@po.kahoku.co.jp; web site www.kahoku.co.jp
Owner – Kazuo Ichiriki
Bd. Dir. – Toru Suginome
Bd. Dir. – Masahiko Ichiriki
Bd. Dir. – Masaaki Otsuka
Mng. Dir.-Bus. – Keiichi Koizumi
Mng. Dir. – Kohei Kumagai
Mng. Dir. – Kuninori Aizawa
Bus. Dir. – Toru Hirama
Adv. Dir. – Kunio Sato
Chief Editorial Writer – Shoichi Shinohara

SHIMONOSEKI, CHUGOKU

YAMAGUCHI SHIMBUN (D)
1-1-7, Higashi-Yamato-cho, Shimonoseki, Chugoku, 750-8506, Japan; tel (81) 832 663 211; fax 665 344; web site www.minato-yamaguchi.co.jp
Circ.: 82,500
Ed. – Matsumi Matsushita

SHIZUOKA, CHUBU

SHIZUOKA SHIMBUN (M&E)
3-1-1, Toro, Shizuoka, Chubu, 422-8033, Japan; tel (81) 54 284 8900; fax 284 8994; e-mail webmaster@sbs-np.co.jp; web site www.shizuokaonline.com
Sec. – Yuko Okada
Pres. – Jun Matsui
Exec. Dir. – Shigeru Oishi
Bd. Dir./Adv. Dir./Circ. Dir. – Yoshiro Sugita
Bd. Dir./Bus. Dir. – Yasuhide Ikeda
Bd. Dir./Circ. Dir – Takashi Ishiyama
Mgr – Poru Yamashita
Mng. Dir. – Toshihiro Kitamura
Ed. in chief – Go Oagishi

SUWA, CHUBU

NAGANO NIPPO (M)
3-1323-1, Takashima, Suwa, Chubu, 392-8611, Japan; tel (81) 266 522 000; fax 588 895; e-mail info@nagano-np.co.jp; web site www.nagano-np.co.jp
Circ.: 47,676
Dir./Advisor – Hama Keisuke
Pres. – Hideyuki Saku
Toyko Head Officer – Mitsuko Oishi
Adv. Bus. Dir. – Sakata Kazuo
Sr. Mng. Ed. – When Yoshiro Ban
Opns. Dir. – Keigo Ota

TAKAMATSU CITY, SHIKOKU

SHIKOKU SHIMBUN (M)
15-1, Nakano-cho, Takamatsu City, Shikoku, 760-8572, Japan; tel (81) 87 833 1111; fax 833 8218; e-mail hostmaster@shikoku-np.co.jp; web site www.shikoku-np.co.jp
Circ.: 208,376
Owner/Chrmn. – Takushi Hirai
Pres. – Ryuji Hirai
Exec. Officer – Kozo Tsuzuki
Exec. Officer – Shigeru Tanaka
Adv. Dir. – Yoshine Yoshida

TAKAOKA CITY, HOKURIKU

YOMIURI SHIMBUN (D)
4-5, Shimonoseki-machi, Takaoka City, Hokuriku, 933-8543, Japan; tel (81) 766 266 833; e-mail webmaster@yomiuri.co.jp; web site www.yomiuri.co.jp
Hokuriku Head Officer – Kazuo Komatsuzaki

TANABE CITY, AKITSU TOWN MINPO

KII MINPO (E)
100, Wakayama, Tanabe City, Akitsu Town Minpo, 646-8660, Japan; tel (81) 739 227 171; e-mail agara-km@mb.aikis.or.jp; web site www.agara.co.jp
Circ.: 38,101
Pres. – Yohachiro Koyama
Bd. Dir./Gen. Affairs Dir. – Takeo Shiki
Bd. Dir./Mng. Ed. – Soichi Tanikawa

TOKUSHIMA CITY, SHIKOKU

TOKUSHIMA SHIMBUN (M&E)
2-5-2, Naka-Tokushima-cho, Tokushima City, Shikoku, 770-8572, Japan; tel (81) 88 655 7373; e-mail jouhou@topics.or.jp; web site www.topics.or.jp
Bd. Dir. – Hiroshi Matsumura
Bus. Dir. – Takami Tokumae
Adv. Dir. – Hisashi Miura
Circ. Dir. – Isao Takeda

TOKYO

ASAHI EVENING NEWS (E)
5-3-2 Tsukiji, Chuo-ku, Tokyo, 104-8011, Japan; tel (81) 3 5541 8538; fax 5540 7646; e-mail iht-asahi@asahi.com; web site www.asahi.com
Circ.: 38,800
MD – Nobuo Watali

ASAHI SHIMBUN (M&E)
5-3-2, Tsukiji, Chuo-ku, Tokyo, 104-8011, Japan; tel (81) 3 3545 0131; e-mail newsroom@emb.asahi-np.co.jp; web site www.asahi.com
Gen. Mgr. – Shinichi Yoshida

ASAHI SHIMBUN (D)
5-3-2, Tsukiji, Chuo-ku, Tokyo, 104-8011, Japan; tel (81) 3 3545 0131; fax 5541 8565; e-mail newsroom@emb.asahi-np.co.jp; web site www.asahi.com
Owner – Michiko Murayama
Owner – Shoichi Ueno
Gen. Mgr. – Shin-ichi Yoshida

DAILY SPORTS (M)
2-14-8 Kiba Koto Ward, Tokyo, 135-8566, Japan; tel (81) 50 3383 2520; web site www.daily.co.jp
Circ.: 174,414
Dir. – Takashi Yamaki

DEMPA SHIMBUN (5X WK.)
1-11-15, Higashi Gotanda, Shinagawa-ku, Tokyo, 141-8790, Japan; tel (81) 3 3445 6111; fax 3447 4666; web site www.dempa.net
Circ.: 298,000
Ed. in Chief – Tetsuo Hirayama

HOCHI SHIMBUN (M)
4-6-49, Kohnan Minato-ku, Tokyo, 108-8485, Japan; tel (81) 3 5479 1111; web site www.yomiuri.co.jp/hochi/home.htm
Circ.: 670,892
Pres. – Masaru Fushimi
Bd. Dir./Bus. Dir. – Ryozo Koto
Bd. Dir./Gen. Affairs Dir. – Hisao Suda
Bd. Dir./Circ. Dir. – Akira Osada
Adv. Dir. – Haruyasu Moriya
Mng. Ed. – Tatsue Aoki

NIHON KAIJI SHIMBUN (D)
5-19-2, Shimbashi, Minato-ku, Tokyo, 105-0004, Japan; tel (81) 3 3436 3221; e-mail tokyo@jmd.co.jp; web site www.jmd.co.jp
Circ.: 50,000
Pres. – Takaaki Oyama
Bus. Dir. – Osami Endo
Adv. Mgr. – Masahito Hata
Ed. in Chief – Igsuro Sujimoto

JAPAN TIMES (D)
5-4, Shibaura 4-chome, Minato-ku, Tokyo, 108-8071, Japan; tel (81) 3 3453 5312; fax 3453 5456; web site www.japantimes.co.jp
Circ.: 58,380
Chrmn./Pub. – Toshiaki Ogasawara
Admin. Dir. – Motoi Nishmatsu
Managing editor – Takashi Kitazume
President – Yukiko Ogasawara
Head Adv. – Okada Keisuke

MAINICHI SHIMBUN (D)
1-1-1, Hitotsubashi, Chiyoda-ku, Tokyo, 100-8051, Japan; tel (81) 3 3212 0321; e-mail webmaster@mainichi.co.jp; web site www.mainichi.co.jp
Exec. Dir./Tokyo Head Officer – Yutaka Asahana
Bd. Dir./Mng. Ed. – Masato Kitamura

THE MAINICHI DAILY NEWS (D)
1-1-1, Hitotsubashi, Chiyoda-ku, Tokyo, 100-8051, Japan; tel (81) 3 3212 0321; fax 3211 2509; e-mail webmaster@mainichi.co.jp; web site www.mainichi.co.jp
Circ.: 48,000
Mng. Ed. – Hiroshi Takahashi

MAINICHI SHIMBUN (M&E)
1-1-1, Hitotsubashi, Chiyoda-ku, Tokyo, 100-8051, Japan; tel (81) 3 3212 0321; fax 3211 3598; web site www.mainichi.co.jp
Pres. – Yutoka Asahima
Chmn. – Masato Kipamura
Ed. in Chief – Yoshiuki Ito

NAIGAI TIMES (D)
2-14-11 Shintomi, Chuo-ku, Tokyo, 104-0041, Japan; tel (81) 3 3552 4587; fax 3552 4588; e-mail bunsha@naigai-times.net
Circ.: 298,000
Pres./CEO – Koji tail Kaori
Vice Pres. – Masahiro Morita

NIHON NOGYO SHIMBUN (M)
2-3, Akihabara, Taito-ku, Tokyo, 110-8722, Japan; tel (81) 3 5295 7403; fax 5295 7459; e-mail keiei-kikaku@agrinews.co.jp; web site www.agrinews.co.jp
Circ.: 405,794
Chrmn. – Katsuji Tanabe
Vice Chrmn. – Takao Tokorodani
Exec. Dir. – Nobuo Kanai
Councillor – Katsutoshi Futagami
Gen. Affairs Dir. – Tetsuro Sugawara
MD – Kuniyuki Murakami
MD – Atsushi Matsuzawa
Adv. Dir. – Seiichi Kiryu
Mng. Ed. – Yasunori Inoue
Chief Editorial Writer – Kiyoshi Hayakawa

NIHON KEIZAI SHIMBUN (M&E-D)
1-3-7 Ote-machi, Chiyoda-ku, Tokyo, 100-8066, Japan; tel (81) 3 3270 0251; fax 5255 2640; e-mail ecntct@nikkei.co.jp; index@nex.nikkei.co.jp; web site www.nikkei.co.jp/enews
Staff writer – Shinya Oshino

NIHON SEN-I SHIMBUN (M)
Horidomecho, Toshihiko 1-6-5 Round 4, Tokyo, 103-0024, Japan; tel (81) 3 5649 8711; fax 5649-8717; e-mail nissen@nissen-media.com; web site www.nissenmedia.com
Circ.: 143,060
Adv. Mgr. – Tatsuo Kato
Ed. in Chief – Oka Zaki

NIKKAN SPORTS (M)
3-5-10, Tsukiji, Chuo-ku, Tokyo, 104-8055, Japan; tel (81) 3 5550 8888; web site www.nikkansports.com
Circ.: 992,230
Pres. – Kazuyuki Kawata
MD – Shigeaki Ota

NOZEI TSUSHIN (D)
3-8-4, Minami-Ikebukuro, Toshima-ku, Tokyo, 171-8558, Japan; tel (81) 3 3971 0111; web site www.np-net.co.jp
Pres. – Nobuya Aida
Mng. Dir./Ed. – Yoji Aida

SANKEI SHIMBUN (D)
1-7-2, Ote-machi, Chiyoda-ku, Tokyo, 100-8077, Japan; tel (81) 3 3231 7111; fax 3275 8994; e-mail desk@people.or.jp; webmaster@sankei.co.jp; web site www.sankei.co.jp
Pres. – Nagayoshi Sumida
MD – Nobuyuki Yoshida

SANKEI SHIMBUN (D)
1-7-2, Ote-machi, Chiyoda-ku, Tokyo, 100-8077, Japan; tel (81) 3 3231 7111; fax 3275 8994; web site www.sankei.co.jp
MD – Nagayoshi Sumida
Advisor – Shigeaki Hazama

SANKEI SPORTS (M)
1-7-2, Ote-machi, Chiyoda-ku, Tokyo, 100-8077, Japan; tel (81) 3 3231 7111; web site www.sanspo.com
Circ.: 815,215
Mng. Dir./Head Officer – Tomio Saito
Mng. Ed. – Yukio Inada

SPORTS NIPPON (D)
2-1-30, Ecchujima, Koto-ku, Tokyo, 135-8735, Japan; tel (81) 3 3820 0700; fax 3820 0669; web site www.sponichi.co.jp
Circ.: 931,687
Pres – Susumu Yamamoto
Sec – Kayo Yoshida
Bd. Dir. – Nobuyoshi Ide
Bus. Dir. – Shigeo Hojo
Gen. Affairs Dir. – Hisashi Matsumura
Circ. Dir. – Kazumasa Tamagawa
Mng. Ed. – Susumu Komuro

STARS AND STRIPES (D)
7-23-17 Roppongi, Minato-ku, Tokyo, 106-0032, Japan; tel (81) 3 3404 9428; fax 3408 8936; e-mail marketing@pstripes.osd.mil; web site www.pstripes.com
Exec. Ed. – Robert P. Grindstaff
Mng. Ed. – Doug Clawson

NIHON KOGYO SHIMBUN (M-EX S)
1-7-2, Ote-machi, Chiyoda-ku, Tokyo, 100-8125, Japan; tel (81) 3 3273 6184; fax 3241 4999; web site www.sankeibiz.jp
Circ.: 1,053,000
Asst. Dir. – Aray Kajunori
Adv. Mgr. – Kiyoshi Kuwahara

NIKKAN KOGYO SHIMBUN (M)
14-1, Nihombashi Koami-cho, Chuo-ku, Tokyo, 103-8548, Japan; tel (81) 3 5644 7221; fax 3222 7028; web site www.nikkan.co.jp
Circ.: 533,145
Pres. – Taihei Kanno
Chrmn. – Toshio Fujiyoshi
Bd. Dir./Adv. Dir. – Ayao Kawahara
Bd. Dir./Bus. Dir. – Kiyoaki Hirotani
Bd. Dir. – Seishi Muramoto
Bd. Dir. – Hideo Watanabe
Chief Editorial Writer – Shunroku Saito

SUISAN KEIZAI SHIMBUN (5X WK.)
6-8-19, Roppongi, Minato-ku, Tokyo, 106-0032, Japan; tel (81) 3 3404 6531; fax 3444 0863; web site www.suikei.co.jp
Circ.: 61,000
Pres. – Nagiko Yasunari
Mng. Dir./Mng. Ed. – Koshi Torinoumi
Adv. Mgr. – Nakashima Masaki
Mng. Ed. – Norimoto Jyozaki

TOKYO CHUNICHI SPORTS (D)
2-1-4, Uchisaiwai-Cho, Shiyoba-Ku,, Tokyo, 100-8505, Japan; tel (81) 3 6910 2211; web site www.chunichi.co.jp
Circ.: 323,951
Ed. in Chief – Kazuo Nishiyama

TOKYO SHIMBUN (D)
2-1-4 Uchisaiwai-cho,, Tokyo, 100-8505, Japan; tel (81) 3 6910 2211; fax 3595 6915; e-mail webmaster@tokyo-np.co.jp; taiko@tokyo-np.co.jp; web site www.tokyo-np.co.jp
Tokyo Head Officer – Torao Oshima

TOKYO SPORTS (E)
2-1-30, Ecchujima, Koto-ku, Tokyo, 135-8721, Japan; tel (81) 3 3820 0821; fax 3820 0829; web site www.tokyo-sports.co.jp
Circ.: 534,100
Pres. – Tsuneo Tachikawa
Bd. Dir./Advertising/Gen. Affairs Dir. – Kunii Makino
Bd. Dir./Circ. Dir. – Katsuhisa Higuchi
Bd. Dir./Mng. Ed. – Yasuo Sakurai

THE DAILY YOMIURI (D)
1-7-1, Ote-machi, Chiyodo-ku, Tokyo, 100-8055, Japan; tel (81) 3 3242 1111; fax 3217 8247; e-mail dy@yomiuri.com; web site www.yomiuri.co.jp/dy/
Circ.: 30,000
Mng. Ed. – Shini Chiano

YOMIURI SHIMBUN (D)
1-7-1, Otemachi, Chiyoda-ku, Tokyo, 100-8055, Japan; tel (81) 3 3242 1111; e-mail webmaster@yomiuri.co.jp; web site www.yomiuri.co.jp
Pub. – Toru Shoriki

YOMIURI SHIMBUN (M&E)
1-7-1, Otemachi, Chiyoda-ku, Tokyo, 100-8055, Japan; tel (81) 3 3242 1111; web site www.yomiuri.co.jp
Chrmn. – Ken-ya Mizukami
Vice Pres. – Hitoshi Uchiyama
Bd. Dir./Gen. Affairs Dir. – Koji Takada
Bd. Dir. – Shoichi Oikawa
Bus. Dir. – Katsuhiro Yago
Mng. Dir. – Yoshio Matsui
Mng. Dir. – Yasuo Itagaki
Mng. Dir. – Naoki Ogino
Ed. In Chief – Tsuneo Watanabe
Exec. Ed. – Yoshinori Horikawa

TOMAKOMAI, HOKKAIDO

TOMAKOMAI MIMPO (D)
3-1-8, Wakakusa-cho, Tomakomai, Hokkaido, 053-8611, Japan; tel (81) 144 325 311; fax 326 386; e-mail henshu@tomamin.co.jp; web site www.tomamin.co.jp
Circ.: 60,676
Ed. in Chief – Tomoharu Miyamoto

TOTTORI, CHUGOKU

NIHONKAI SHIMBUN (D)
2-137, Tomiyasu, Tottori, Chugoku, 680-8688, Japan; tel (81) 857 212 888; fax 212 891; e-mail info@nnn.co.jp; web site www.nnn.co.jp
Circ.: 166,530
Owner/Pres. – Toshikata Yoshioka

TOYAMA, HOKURIKU

KITANIPPON SHIMBUN (D)
2-14, Azumi-cho, Toyama, Hokuriku, 930-8680, Japan; tel (81) 76 445 3300
Pres. – Ryuzo Ueno

TOYAMA SHIMBUN (M)
5-1, Ote-machi, Toyama, Hokuriku, 930-8520, Japan; tel (81) 76 491 8111; e-mail admin@hokkoku.co.jp; web site www.toyama.hokkoku.co.jp
Circ.: 42,988
Bus. Dir. – Chiaki Komatsu
Mng. Ed. – Sachio Miyamoto

TOYOHASHI CITY, CHUBU

HIGASHI-AICHI SHIMBUN (D)
62, Torinawate, Shinsakae-machi, Toyohashi City, Chubu, 441-8666, Japan; tel (81) 532 323 111; fax 323 115; e-mail hensyu@higashi.co.jp
Circ.: 52,300
Pres. – Keigo Fujimura
Circ. Dir. – Akhiro Kojima
Mng. Ed. – Haruo Inoue
Ed. – Akira Honda

TSU, KINKI

ISE SHIMBUN (M)
34-6, Honmachi, Tsu, Kinki, 514-0831, Japan; tel (81) 592 240 003; e-mail mail@isenp.co.jp; web site www.isenp.co.jp
Circ.: 100,550
Pres. – Senzo Kobayashi
Adv. Mgr. – Kaoroi Iwawaki
Ed. – Fujio Yamamoto

TSUCHIURA, KANTO

JOYO SHIMBUN (M)
2-7-6, Manabe, Tsuchiura, Kanto, 300-0051, Japan; tel (81) 298 211 780; fax 211 689; e-mail info-02@joyo-net.com; web site www.tsukuba.com
Circ.: 20,731
Mng. Ed. – Cakahide Sonabe
Pres – Hiroshi Kikuta

TSURUOKA, TOHOKU

SHONAI NIPPO (D)
8-29, Baba-cho, Tsuruoka, Tohoku, 997-8691, Japan; tel (81) 235 221 480; web site www.shonai-nippo.co.jp
Circ.: 22,500
Pres. – Masayuki Hashimoto

UBE, CHUGOKU

UBE JIHO (E)
3-6-1, Kotobuki-machi, Ube, Chugoku, 755-8557, Japan; tel (81) 836 311511
Circ.: 42,550
Pres. – Fumio Tokuda
Bd./Gen. Affairs/Circ. Dir. – Hiromi Uchida
Mng. Dir./Ed./Chief Editorial Writer – Kazuya Waki
Adv. Dir. – Setsuo Tagaya

UTSUNOMIYA, KANTO

SHIMOTSUKE SHIMBUN (D)
1-8-11, Showa, Utsunomiya, Kanto, 320-8686, Japan; tel (81) 28 625 1111; fax 650 1500; e-mail media@shimotsuke.co.jp; web site www.shimotsuke.co.jp
Circ.: 308,260

Bd./Adv. Dir. – Hideyuki Satoyoshi
Bd./Gen. Affairs Dir. – Isao Sawamura
Mng. Dir./Ed. in Chief – Eisuke Toda
Bus. Dir. – Mitsuhiko Yanagida
Circ. Dir. – Hironobu Sekine
Mng. Ed. – Satoshi Sotome
Chief Editorial Writer – Tadataka Shinkawa

YAMAGATA, TOHOKU

YAMAGATA SHIMBUN (D)
2-5-12, Hatagomachi, Yamagata, Tohoku, 990-8550, Japan; tel (81) 23 622 5271; e-mail info@yamagata-np.jp; web site www.yamagata-np.co.jp
Owner – Yusuke Kurosawa

YOKOHAMA CITY, KANTO

KANAGAWA SHIMBUN (M)
2-23 Ota-machi, Naka-ku, Yokohama City, Kanto, 231-8445, Japan; tel (81) 45 227 1111; fax 227 0900; web site www.kanaloco.jp
Circ.: 238,541
Pres. – Kenji Hotta
Vice Pres. – Junichi Saito
Ed. – Shinichiro Shinohara

YONEZAWA CITY, TOHOKU

YONEZAWA SHIMBUN (D)
3-3-7, Monto-cho, Yonezawa City, Tohoku, 992-0039, Japan; tel (81) 238 224 411; fax 245 554
Circ.: 13,750
Pres. – Yukio Seino

LAOS

VIENTIANE

KHAO SAN PATHET LAO
BP 310, Vientiane, Laos; tel (856) 21 215780
Circ.: 1,200
Gen. Dir. – Bounteng Vongsay

VIENTIANE TIMES (D)
PO Box 5723, Vientiane, Laos; tel (856) 21 251619; fax 216365; e-mail vttimes@hotmail.com; info@vientianetimes.org.la; web site www.vientianetimes.org.la
Circ.: 3,000
Ed. in chief – Savankhon Rasmountry

PASASON (5X WK.)
BP 110, 80 rue Sethathirath, Vientiane, Laos; tel (856) 21 212 466; fax 212 407
Circ.: 28,000
Ed. – Bounlathonu Thantilome

VIENTIANE MAI (D)
BP 989, Vientiane, Laos; tel (856) 21 212 623; fax 215 989; e-mail admin@vientianemai.net; web site www.vientianemai.net
Circ.: 2,500
Ed. (acting) – Sichane Sichane

MACAU

MACAU

BOLETIM DIARIO DE INFORMACAO (D)
Rua da Praia Grande 31, Macau, Macau; tel (853)
Ed. – Rogerio Beltrao Coelho

CHENG POU (D)
Av Praia Grande 63-67, Macau, Macau; tel (853) 2896 5976
Dir. – Kung Su Kan
Ed. in Chief – Cheng Pui

COMERCIO DE MACAU
9-4-D, Rua da Praia Grande, Macau, Macau; tel (853) 310428

DIARIO DE MACAU (D)
37 Ave. Infante D. Henrique, Macau, Macau; tel (853)
Ed. – Leonel Borralho

EXPRESSO DO ORIENTE
6-8, Rua do Chunambeiro, Edif. Keng Fai, 60C, Macau, Macau; tel (853) 566395; web site www.expressodooriente.com

GAZETA MACAENSE (D)
Rua de S. Clara, Edif. Ribeiro, Macau, Macau; tel (853) 575626

JORNAL DE MACAU (D)
PO Box 945, Macau, Macau; tel (853) 329270; fax 573277
Circ.: 2,000
Ed. – Joao Fernandes

O CLARIM (WEEKLY)
26-A, Rua Central, Macau, Macau; tel (853) 28573860; fax 85328307867; e-mail clarim@macau.ctm.net
Director – Albino Bento Pais

OU MUN IAT POU (D)
Rua Pedro Nolasco da Silva 37, Macau, Macau; tel (853) 2837 1688; fax 2833 1998; web site www.macaodaily.com
Circ.: 100,000
Chm. – Lei Seng Chun
Dir. – Lei Pang Chu

SENG POU (D)
Travessa da Caldeira Nine, Macau, Macau; tel (853) 938387; fax 388192
Ed. in Chief – Tou Man Kam
Dir. – Kuok Kam Seng

SI MAN POU (D)
Rua dos Pescadores,Edif. Ind. Oceano,Bl. 11,2/F-B, Macau, Macau; tel (853) 722 111; fax 722 133
Circ.: 12,000
Dir. – Kuok Su Peng

TAI CHUNG POU (D)
Rua Dr. Lourenco P Marques 7a, 2/F, Macau, Macau; tel (853) 2893 9888; fax 2893 4114; e-mail taichungpou@gmail.com; web site taichungpou.blogspot.com
Circ.: 16,000
Dir. – Vong U Kong
Ed. in Chief – Sou Kim Keong

TRIBUNA DE MACAU (D)
Av. Almeida Ribeiro, 99, Macau, Macau; tel (853) 2837 8057; fax 2833 7305; e-mail jtm@yp.com.mo; web site www.jtm.com.mo
Circ.: 3,000
Ed. – Jose Rocha Dinis

VA KIO POU (D)
Rua da Alfandega 69, Macau, Macau; tel (853) 2834 5888; fax 2851 0351; e-mail vakiopou@macau.ctm.net; web site www.jornalvakio.com
Mng. Dir. – Chiang Sao Meng

MALAYSIA

CHERAS

UTUSAN ZAMAN (D)
Level 7 Menara PGRM, Cheras, 56100, Malaysia; tel (60) 3 9287 7777; fax 9282 7751; e-mail online@utusan.com.my; corporate@utusan.com.my; web site www.utusangroup.com.my
Circ.: 11,782
Ed. – Mustafa Fadula Suhaimi

KOTA KINABALU, SABAH

ASIA TIMES (D)
PO Box 11280, Kota Kinabalu, Sabah, 88814, Malaysia; tel (60) 88 429 159; fax 420 902; e-mail atimes@tm.net.my; web site www.atimes.com
Circ.: 14,278
Ed. – Lai Su Chon

BORNEO MAIL (D)
1 Jalan Bakau, 1st Flr., off Jalan Gaya, Kota Kinabalu, Sabah, 88999, Malaysia; tel (60) 88 238001; fax 238002
Circ.: 14,610
Ed. in Chief – George Kanavathi
Ed. – Amin Muin
Ed. – Frankie Inoh

DAILY EXPRESS (D)
PO Box 10139, Kota Kinabalu, Sabah, 88801, Malaysia; tel (60) 88 238 666; fax 238 611; e-mail advertisement@dailyexpress.com.my; web site www.dailyexpress.com.my
Circ.: 25,520
Ed. in Chief – Sardathisa James
Dir. – Clement Yeh

HWA CHIAW JIT PAO (D)
PO Box 10139, Kota Kinabalu, Sabah, 88801, Malaysia; tel (60) 88 52165
Circ.: 28,000
Ed. – Hii Yuk Seng

NEW STRAITS TIMES (D)
Ground Gloor, Lot 53A, Block I, KK Times Square, Kota Kinabalu, Sabah, 88100, Malaysia; tel (60) 88 487657; fax 487523; e-mail nstsabah@gmail.com; web site www.nst.com.my
Adv. Mgr. – Kimsoi Lodunis
Regional Head/Bureau Chief – Datuk Joniston Bangkuai

SABAH SHI PAO/WAN PAO (D)
PO Box 11500, Kota Kinabalu, Sabah, 88816, Malaysia; tel (60) 88 244313; fax 249666
Circ.: 8,000
– Siva Kumar
– Liaw Thien LoiEd. in Chiefs

SABAH TIMES (D)
PO Box 15141, Kota Kinabalu, Sabah, 88861, Malaysia; tel (60) 88 230 055; fax 231 155
Circ.: 30,000
Ed. in Chief – Ch'ng Voon Heng

SEH HWA DAILY NEWS (D)
PO Box 14210, Kota Kinabalu, Sabah, 88848, Malaysia; tel (60) 88 421 717; fax 431 779
Ed. in Chief – Toh Chee Kong

KUALA LUMPUR

BUSINESS TIMES (M)
31 Jalan Riong, Kuala Lumpur, 59100, Malaysia; tel (60) 3 2282 2628; fax 2282 5424; web site www.nstp.com.my
Circ.: 15,000
Adv. Mgr. – Badrul Hisham
Ed. in Chief – Mustapha Kamal
Exec. Ed. – Mustapha Kamil
News Ed. – Francis Fernandez

CHINA PRESS (M)
80 Jalan Riong, Kuala Lumpur, 59100, Malaysia; tel (60) 3 2828208; fax 2825327
Circ.: 210,000
Ed. – Poon Chau Huay
Gen. Mgr. – Ng Beng Lye

HARAKAH (D)
28A, Jalan Pahang Barat, off Jalan Pahang, Kuala Lumpur, 53000, Malaysia; tel (60) 3 4021 3343; fax 4021 2422; e-mail hrkh@pc.jaring.my; web site www.harakahdaily.net
Ed. in Chief – Mohammad Mokhtarrozaidi

KUMPULAN AKHBAR WATAN SDN BHD (D)
No. 23-1, Jalan 9A/55A , Taman Setiawangsa, Kuala Lumpur, 54200, Malaysia; tel (60) 3 4252 3040; fax 452 3043
Ed. – Zahari B. Affandi
Dir. – Clement Yeh

MALAYSIAN NANBAN (D)
544-3, Batu Complex, off Jalan Ipoh, Kuala Lumpur, 51200, Malaysia; tel (60) 3 6251 5984; fax 6259 1617; e-mail news@nanban.com.my; web site www.nanban2u.com
Ed. in Chief – M. Malayandy

NEW STRAITS TIMES & NEW SUNDAY TIMES (MS)
31 Jalan Riong, Kuala Lumpur, 59100, Malaysia; tel (60) 3 2282 3322; fax 2282 4482; e-mail news@nstp.com.my; web site www.nstp.com.my
Adv. Sales Dir. – Badrul Hisham
Mng. Ed. (Grp.) – Zainul Arifin Mohammed Isa

MALAY MAIL (E)
31 Jalan Riong, Kuala Lumpur, 59100, Malaysia; tel (60) 3 7947 2288; fax 7947 2323; e-mail mmnews@mmail.com.my; web site www.mmail.com.my
Circ.: 100,000Last Audit: March 30, 2010
Adv. Mgr. – Fabian Mesan Selva
Exec. Ed. – Yushaimi Yahaya
Ed. – Khirudin Attan

SUNDAY MAIL (S)
31 Jalan Riong, Kuala Lumpur, 59100, Malaysia; tel (60) 3 2282 2328; fax 2282 4482
Circ.: 75,641
Ed. – Joachim S.P. Ng

BERITA HARIAN (MS)
31 Jalan Riong, Kuala Lumpur, 59100, Malaysia; tel (60) 3 2282 2323; fax 2282 2425
Circ.: 350,000
Adv. Mgr. – Badrul Hishan Mahzan
Ed. – Datuk Mior Kamarul Baid

SHIN MIN DAILY NEWS (MS)
31 Jalan Riong, Bangsar, Kuala Lumpur, 59100, Malaysia; tel (60) 3 2826363; fax 2821812
Ed. in Chief – Cheng Song Huat

TAMIL NESAN (MS)
C/O 3rd Fl., Menara Manikavasagam, Kuala Lumpur, 50350, Malaysia; tel (60) 3 6184 1818; fax 6187 1818; web site www.tamilnesan.com.my
Mng. Dir. – Vell Paari
Ed. – K. Padma

UTUSAN MALAYSIA (M)
46M Jalan Lima, off Jalan Chan Sow Lin, Kuala Lumpur, 55200, Malaysia; tel (60) 3 9221 7055; fax 9222 7876; e-mail corp-comm@utusan.com.my; online@utusan.com.my; web site www.utusan.com.my
Circ.: 240,000
Ed. in chief – Abdul Aziz

KUCHING, SARAWAK

BERITA PETANG SARAWAK (4X WK.)
PO Box 1315, Kuching, Sarawak, 93726, Malaysia; tel (60) 82 480 771; fax 489 006
Circ.: 12,000
Ed. in Chief – Hwang Yu Chai

BORNEO BULLETIN (D)
Lot 250, Tingkat 1, Jalan Haji Taha, Kuching, Sarawak, 93400, Malaysia; tel (60) 82 426309; fax 419069
Ed. in Chief – Ketua Penyunting

INTERNATIONAL TIMES (D)
PO Box 1158, Kuching, Sarawak, 93724, Malaysia; tel (60) 82 482 215; fax 480 996
Circ.: 37,000
Asst. Mgr. – Lee Han Thiaw
Ed. in Chief – Lee Fook Onn

THE NEW STRAITS TIMES (D)
Lot 8130, Section 64, 104 Lorong , Datuk Abang, Abdul Rahim 10, Kuching, Sarawak, 93450, Malaysia; tel (60) 82 481 876; e-mail general@nstp.com.my; web site www.nstp.com.my
Bureau Chief – Sulok Tawie

THE PEOPLE'S MIRROR (D)
PO Box 3025, Kuching, Sarawak, 93990, Malaysia; tel (60) 82 360030; fax 363278
Circ.: 24,990
Ed. in Chief – B.R. Adai

UTUSAN SARAWAK (D)
PO Box 138, Kuching, Sarawak, 93100, Malaysia; tel (60) 82 424 411; fax 415 024
Circ.: 32,292
Ed. – William Chan

THE SARAWAK TRIBUNE/SUNDAY TRIBUNE (MS)
Lot 231, Jalan Nipah, off Abell, Kuching, Sarawak, 93100, Malaysia; tel (60) 82 424 411; fax 420 358; e-mail tribune@po.jaring.my; web site tribune.my
Circ.: 29,598
Ed. – Francis Siah

CHINESE DAILY NEWS (DS)
Lot 164-165, Jalan Sungei Padungan, Kuching, Sarawak, 93754, Malaysia; tel (60) 82 233888; fax 233399
Circ.: 10,406
Ed. – T.T. Chow

MIRI, SARAWAK

THE MIRI DAILY NEWS (D)
PO Box 377, Miri, Sarawak, 98007, Malaysia; tel (60) 85 656 666; fax 662 882; web site www.eunited.com.my
Circ.: 22,431
Mng. Dir. – Sim Yong Liang
Ed. – Lau Kung King

SEE HUA DAILY NEWS/BERHAD
Lot 433, Sg. Merah Town District, Sg Antu Industri, Miri, Sarawak, 96000, Malaysia; tel (60) 85
Circ.: 48,809
Pub. – Wong Keh Huong
Ed. in Chief – Ho Bu Tin

PENANG, GEORGETOWN

KWONG WAH YIT POH (MS)
19 Presgrave St., Penang, Georgetown, 10300, Malaysia; tel (60) 4 2612312; fax 2615407
Ed. in Chief – Sze Toh Tgam

PETALING JAYA

NANYANG SIANG PAU (MS)
19 Jalan Semangat, Petaling Jaya, 46200, Malaysia; tel (60) 3 7650 8666; fax 7872 6900; web site www.nanyang.com
Pub. – NanYang Siang Pau
Ed. in Chief – Chong Choong Nam

SIN JEW JIT PHO (D)
19 Jalan Semangat,, Petaling Jaya, 46200, Malaysia; tel (60) 3 7958 7777; web site www.sinchew-i.com
Deputy Exe. Ed. in Chief – Kuik Cheng Kang

PETALING JAYA, SELANGOR

CHINA PRESS (D)
40 Jalan Lima, Melalui Jalan Chan San Lein, Petaling Jaya, Selangor, 5520, Malaysia; tel (60) 3 2214323; fax 2214310
Circ.: 126,271
Ed. – Wong Ah Lek
Gen. Mgr. – Bernard Chow

NEW LIFE POST (EVERY OTHER WEEK)
80m Jalan SS21/39, Damansara Utama, Petaling Jaya, Selangor, 47400, Malaysia; tel (60) 7571833; fax 7181809
Circ.: 231,000
Ed. – Low Beng Chee

SIN CHEW JIT POH (MS)
19 Jalan Semangat, Petaling Jaya, Selangor, 46200, Malaysia; tel (60) 3 603-79658888; fax 603-79570527
Ed. in Chief – Liew Chen Chuan

THE STAR/SUNDAY STAR (MS)
Level 7 Menara Star, 15 Jln 16/11, Petaling Jaya, Selangor, 46350, Malaysia; tel (60) 3 7967 1388; fax 7955 4039; e-mail msd@thestar.com.my; web site www.thestar.com.my
Exec. Deputy Chm. – Datuk Clement Hii
Ed. in Chief – Datuk Wongchun Wai
News Ed. – Leong Shen-Li

MALAYAN THUNG (PAU TONG BAO) (D)
Jalan 13/6, Petaling Jaya, Selangor, 46200, Malaysia; tel (60) 3 57911; fax 7577798
Circ.: 62,000
Pub. – Stephen Tan
Ed. in Chief – Ng Ho Peng
Gen. Mgr. – Goh Tuch Hai
Adv. Mgr. – Chin Kon Wen

THINA MARASU
123, Batu 1, Jalan Ipoh, Petaling Jaya, Selangor, 51200, Malaysia; tel (60) 3 4439291; fax 4435292
Circ.: 25,000

PULAU PINANG

GUANG MING DAILY (D)
67 Jales Mcalister, Pulau Pinang, 10400, Malaysia; tel (60) 4 222 6685; fax 222 6700; e-mail editorial-pg@guangming.com.my; web site www.guangming.com.my
Sr. Adv. Mgr – Cheahehin Wah
Ed. – Chonchau Huay

SANDAKAN, SABAH

MERDEKA DAILY NEWS (M)
Lot 23, Hockseng Industry, Batu 1 1/2, Jalan Utara, Sandakan, Sabah, 90000, Malaysia; tel (60) 89 213 704; fax 275 537
Circ.: 1,500Last Audit: March 29, 2010
Adv. Mgr. – Daymong Tang
Ed. in Chief – Fung Kon Shing

SANDAKAN JIH PAO (D)
PO Box 337, Sandakan, Sabah, 90007, Malaysia; tel (60) 89 212 566; fax 212 570
Circ.: 4,971
Ed. in Chief – Lim Yee Boo

SHAH ALAM

KUMPULAN KARANGKRAF SDN BHD (D)
Lot 2, Jalan Sepana 15/3, Ofdf Persiaran Selangor, Seksyen 15, Shah Alam, 40200, Malaysia; tel (60) 3 5101 3888; fax 5101 3601; web site www.karangkraf.com
Ed. in Chief – Hishamuddin B. Hj Yaacub

SIBU, SARAWAK

THE BORNEO POST (M)
PO Box 20, Sibu, Sarawak, 96000, Malaysia; tel (60) 84 332 055; fax 321 255
Circ.: 60,000
MD – Lau Hui Siong
Ed. – Nguoi How Yieng

MALAYSIA DAILY NEWS (M)
PO Box 237, 7 Island Rd., Sibu, Sarawak, 96009, Malaysia; tel (60) 84 320 540; fax 339 019
Circ.: 22,735
Ed. – Wong Seng Kwong

SARAWAK SIANG PAO (M)
4 Ole St., SAR, Sibu, Sarawak, Malaysia; tel (60)
Circ.: 5,000

SEE HUA DAILY NEWS (M)
PO Box 20, Sibu, Sarawak, 96000, Malaysia; tel (60) 84 332 055; fax 321 255
Circ.: 80,000
Ed. in Chief – Ling Kuo Kiong

TAWAU

TAWAU MORNING POST (D)
PO Box 102, Tawau, 91007, Malaysia; tel (60) 89 712 850; fax 711 855; e-mail mg-post@tm.net.my
Circ.: 7,261
Ed. – Wong Cortor

MALDIVES

MALE

AAFATHIS (D)
Silver Star 4, Handhuvaree Higun, Male, Maldives; tel (960) 328730; fax 328906
Circ.: 300
Owner – Abbas Ibrahim
Ed. – Abdul Sattar

MAURITIUS

PORT LOUIS

CHINESE DAILY NEWS (E)
PO Box 316, Port Louis, Mauritius; tel (230) 240 0472
Circ.: 5,000
Ed. in Chief – Wong Yuen Moy

MONGOLIA

ULAANBAATAR

UNEN
Baga toiruu 37, Ulaanbaatar, 11, Mongolia; tel (976) 11 323 223; fax 323 223
Ed. Gandat

ULAN BATAR

ARDYN ERH (D)
Ikh Toyruu, Ulan Batar, 20, Mongolia; tel (976) 11 313 403; fax 313 403
Circ.: 77,500
Ed. in Chief – Jambalyn Myagmarsuren

MYANMAR

MANDALAY

THE HANTHAWADDY (M)
PO Box 1025, Mandalay, Myanmar; tel (95)
Circ.: 23,000
Ed. – U. Win Tin

YANGON

MYANMAR ALIN (M)
PO Box 21, Yangon, Myanmar; tel (95) 1 250 777
Circ.: 400,000
Ed. in Chief – U. Soe Myint

LOKTHA PYITHU NAYZIN (M)
PO Box 40, Yangon, Myanmar; tel (95) 1 282 777; web site www.myanmar.com/newspaper/kyaymon/index.html
Ed. – Itla Myaing

KYEMON (D)
PO Box 819, Yangon, Myanmar; tel (95) 1 282 777
Circ.: 100,000

THE NEW LIGHT OF MYANMAR (M)
22-30 Strand Rd., Yangon, Myanmar; tel (95) 1 297 028; web site www.myanmar.com
Circ.: 14,000
Ed. in Chief – U. Kyaw Min

BOTAHTAUNG (D)
PO Box 539, Yangon, Myanmar; tel (95) 1 274310
Circ.: 96,000

NEGARA BRUNEI DARUSSALAM

LAPANGAN TERBANG LAMA, BERAKAS

PELITA BRUNEI (WEEKLY)
Dept. of Information, Prime Minister's Office, Ist, Lapangan Terbang Lama, Berakas, BB3510, Negara Brunei Darussalam; tel (673) 2 383 941; fax 381 004; e-mail pelita@brunet.bn
Circ.: 45,000
Ed. – Timbang Bin Bakar

NEPAL

BHAIRAWA, LUMBINI ANCHAL

DAINIK NIRNAYA (D)
Ward 6, Bhairawa, Lumbini Anchal, Nepal; tel (977) 71 540 245
Ed. – Pratap Kumar Bhattachan

BIRATNAGAR, KOSI ANCHAL

GHATNA (D)
Biratnagar, Kosi Anchal, Nepal; tel (977)
Ed. – Keshav Prasad Aacharya

JANAVART (D)
Biratnagar, Kosi Anchal, Nepal; tel (977)
Ed. – Kosh Raj Regmi

NIRMAN (D)
Biratnagar, Kosi Anchal, Nepal; tel (977)
Ed. – Suresh Kumar Adhikari

KATHMANDU

THE COMMONER (M)
PO Box 203, Kathmandu, Nepal; tel (977) 1 425 9136; e-mail thecommoner@hotmail.com
Circ.: 7,000

DAILY NEWS (E)
PO Box 171, Kathmandu, 9900, Nepal; tel (977) 1 4223131; fax 4279544; e-mail mrshakya@wlink.com.np
Circ.: 13,500
Pub. – Subha Luxmi Sakya
Ed. in Chief – Manju Ratna Sakya

DAINIK NEPAL (D)
Anu Printing Press, 5/82 Jhochhen, Kathmandu, Nepal; tel (977)
Circ.: 1,000
Pub./Ed. – Indra Kant Mishra

DAINIK NIRNAYA (D)
Bhairawa, Kathmandu, Nepal; tel (977) 1 4200119
Ed. – Pratap Kumar Bhattachar

GLIMPSE (D)
Dilli Bazar, Kathmandu, Nepal; tel (977)
Ed. – Madan Raj Subedi

THE RISING NEPAL (D)
PO Box 23, Kathmandu, Nepal; tel (977) 1 424 4437; fax 424 4428; web site www.gorkhapatra.org.np
Circ.: 20,000
Ed. in Chief – Puskar Mathema

HIMALI BELA (M)
Bhawani Printing Press, Tripureshor, Kathmandu, Nepal; tel (977)
Circ.: 2,000
Ed. – S.S. Rajbhandari

JANA JIVAN (E)
Gorakha Printers, Rani Pokhari, Kathmandu, Nepal; tel (977)
Circ.: 1,000
Pub./Ed. – Sitaram Bhandari

JANADOOT (E)
Ga-2, 549, Kamal Pokhari, Kathmandu, Nepal; tel (977) 1 441 0284; fax 441 2501
Circ.: 6,500
Ed. – Govinda Biyogi

THE KATHMANDU POST (D)
Subbhi Nagar, Kathmandu, Nepal; tel (977) 1 448 0100; fax 446 6320; e-mail corporate@kantipur.com.np; web site www.ekantipur.com
Circ.: 40,000
Ed. – Prateek Pradhan

KANTIPUR DAILY
Subbhi Nagar, Kathmandu, Nepal; tel (977) 1 448 0100; fax 446 6320; e-mail corporate@kantipur.com.np; web site www.ekantipur.com
Circ.: 8,000
Ed. in Chief – Narayan Wagle

GORKHAPATRA (D)
PO Box 876, Kathmandu, Nepal; tel (977) 1 422 4839; fax 425 9429; e-mail feedback@mos.com.np; web site www.nepalnews.com
Circ.: 75,000
Gen Mgr. – Divesh Rana
Ed. in Chief – Krishna Bhakta Shrestha

NABIN KHABAR
Gokhale, Kathmandu, Nepal; tel (977)
Circ.: 3,000

NAYA NEPAL (D)
Kilagal Tole, Kathmandu, Nepal; tel (977)
Circ.: 3,000
Ed. – Gowinda Pradhan

NAYA SANDESH (D)
Maitideri, Kathmandu, Nepal; tel (977)
Circ.: 8,000
Pub./Ed. – Ramesh Nath Pandey

NEPAL BHASA PATRIKA (D)
Kel Tole, Kathmandu, Nepal; tel (977)
Circ.: 850
Ed. – Malla K. Sunder

NEPAL SAMACHAR (E)
Sagarmatha Press, Ramshah Path, Kathmandu, Nepal; tel (977)
Circ.: 1,000
Ed. – Narendra Bilas Pandey

NEPAL TIMES (M)
Maruhiti, Kathmandu, Nepal; tel (977)
Circ.: 3,000
Pub./Ed. – Chandra Lal Jha

THE NEPALI HINDI DAILY (D)
PO Box 49, Kathmandu, Nepal; tel (977) 1 443 6584; fax 443 5931
Circ.: 40,000
Pub. – Uma Kant Das
Ed. in Chief – Vijoy Kumar Das

SAHI AAWAZ (E)
Bhotebahal, Kathmandu, Nepal; tel (977)
Circ.: 500
Pub./Ed. – Surya Lal Pidit

SAMAJ (E)
National Printing Press, Dilli Bazar, Kathmandu, Nepal; tel (977)
Circ.: 5,000
Ed. – Mani Raj Upadhyaya

SAMALOCHANA
PO Box 4910, Kathmandu, Nepal; tel (977)

SAMAYA (E)
Kamal Press, Ramshah Path, Kathmandu, Nepal; tel (977)
Circ.: 18,000
Ed. – Manik Lal Shrestha

SWATANTRA SAMACHAR (D)
Vina Bhandranalya, Chhetrapati, Kathmandu, Nepal; tel (977)
Circ.: 2,000
Ed. – Madan Dev Sharma

THE MOTHER LAND (D)
PO Box 1184, Kathmandu, Nepal; tel (977)
Circ.: 5,000
Ed. – Manindra Raj Shrestha

THE NEW HERALD (M)
Maitidevi, Kathmandu, Nepal; tel (977)
Circ.: 4,000
Pub./Ed. – Ramesh Nath Pandev

NORTH KOREA

PYONGYANG

RODONG CHONGNYON (D-6X WK.)
Pyongyang, North Korea; tel (850)
Ed. in Chief – Ri Jong Gi

RODONG SINMUN (D)
Pyongyang, North Korea; tel (850)
Circ.: 1,500,000
Ed. in Chief – Choe Chil Nam

JOSON INMINGUN (D)
Pyongyang, North Korea; tel (850)
Ed. in Chief – Kim Tok Hyon

MINJU CHOSON (6X WK.)
Pyongyang, North Korea; tel (850)
Circ.: 200,000
Ed. in Chief – Kim Jong Suk

PAKISTAN

ABBOTTABAD

FUTURE (D)
Kawai House, Mansehra, Abbottabad, Pakistan; tel (92)
– Ghulan Jan Khan
– Tahir KhailiEd.s

MUSTAQBAL (D)
Kawai House, Mansehra, Abbottabad, Pakistan; tel (92)
– Ghulam Jan Khan
– Tahir KhailiEd.s

BAHAWALPUR, BAHAWALPUR DIVISION

AFTAB-E-MASHRIQ (D)
Mohalla Kajal Pura, Punjab, Bahawalpur, Bahawalpur Division, Pakistan; tel (92) 621
Ed. – Arshad Hayat

DASTOOR (D)
4-A, 796-R Zanana Hospital Rd., Punjab, Bahawalpur, Bahawalpur Division, Pakistan; tel (92)
Ed. – Mumtaz Zaman

KAINAT (D)
Near Eidgah Rd., Punjab, Bahawalpur, Bahawalpur Division, Pakistan; tel (92)
Ed. – Waliullah Ohad

KARWAN (D)
Ahmed Nagar, Punjab, Bahawalpur, Bahawalpur Division, Pakistan; tel (92)
Ed. – Syed Ali Ahmed

MAGHRABI PAKISTAN (D)
16 McLeod Rd., Punjab, Bahawalpur, Bahawalpur Division, Pakistan; tel (92)
Ed. – Sh M. Shafaat
Adv. Mgr. – Syed Jobal Bukhar

MASHAL (D)
Mohallah Dinpura, Victoria Hospital, Punjab, Bahawalpur, Bahawalpur Division, Pakistan; tel (92)
Ed. – Majeeb Hashmi

NAWA-E-NORAZ (D)
Setellete Town, Punjab, Bahawalpur, Bahawalpur Division, Pakistan; tel (92)
Ed. – Sufia Sultan

NIDA-E-WAQT (D)
Mohallah Shah Fatah Khan, Punjab, Bahawalpur, Bahawalpur Division, Pakistan; tel (92)
Ed. – Zafar Khan

PARA (D)
Circular Rd., Punjab, Bahawalpur, Bahawalpur Division, Pakistan; tel (92)
Ed. – Qamar Malik

REHBAR (D)
Jamil Market, Circular Rd., Bahawalpur, Bahawalpur Division, Pakistan; tel (92) 621 4372
Circ.: 9,970
Ed. in Chief – Malik Mohammad Hayat

SUTLEJ (D)
Zanana Hospital Rd., Punjab, Bahawalpur, Bahawalpur Division, Pakistan; tel (92)
Ed. – Fazal Hameed Ahmed

TABEER (D)
Bahawalpur, Punjab, Bahawalpur, Bahawalpur Division, Pakistan; tel (92)
Ed. – Khalid Zamir

BAHAWALPUR, BAHAWALPUR, PUNJAB

SADA-E-PAKISTAN (D)
Bahawalpur, Bahawalpur, Punjab, Pakistan; tel (92)
Ed. – Rana Abdul Saleem

FAISALABAD, FAISALABAD DIV.

AL-KHABAR (D)
Akbar Manzil, Amin Pura Bazar, Punjab, Faisalabad, Faisalabad Div., Pakistan; tel (92) 41
Ed. – Younas Rana

AL-NAQEEB (D)
6-Kutchery Bazar, Punjab, Faisalabad, Faisalabad Div., Pakistan; tel (92) 41 262 4102; fax 261 8283
Ed. – Asghar Ali Jahangir

AMAN (D)
Council House, Kutchery Bazar, Punjab, Faisalabad, Faisalabad Div., Pakistan; tel (92) 41; web site www.dailyaman.com.pk
Ed. – Arshad Khalid

FAISALABAD, FAISALABAD DIVISION

ASIA TIMES (D)
Wakinanwali Gali, Chiniot Bazar, Office Daily Aila, Faisalabad, Faisalabad Division, Pakistan; tel (92)
Ed. – Anayat-ullah Qadir

AWAM (D)
Tawakal Bldg., Kutchery Bazar, Punjab, Faisalabad, Faisalabad Division, Pakistan; tel (92)
Ed./Adv. Mgr. – Zaheer Qureshi

AYYAM (D)
Council House, Kutchery Bazar, Punjab, Faisalabad, Faisalabad Division, Pakistan; tel (92)
Ed. – Adbul Sattar Javed

BUSINESS REPORT (D)
Railway Rd., Faisalabad, Faisalabad Division, Pakistan; tel (92) 41 255 0332
Circ.: 26,000
Ed. – Abdul Rashid Ghazi

CHENAB (D)
Bismillah Market, Wakilen St., Punjab, Faisalabad, Faisalabad Division, Pakistan; tel (92)
Ed. – Mustafa Malik

COMMERCE (D)
Railway Rd., Punjab, Faisalabad, Faisalabad Division, Pakistan; tel (92)
Ed. – Javaid Iqbal

DAILY NEWS (D)
Medicine Market, Chiniot Bazar, Punjab, Faisalabad, Faisalabad Division, Pakistan; tel (92)
Ed. – Munir A. Pervaiz

DAILY REPORT (D)
Aminpura Bazar, Punjab, Faisalabad, Faisalabad Division, Pakistan; tel (92)
Ed. – Dr. Nazir Ahmed

FARHAN (D)
A1-Khayam Hotel Bldg., Punjab, Faisalabad, Faisalabad Division, Pakistan; tel (92)
Ed. – Ramzan Pervaiz

FOOTPATH (D)
Rehman Bldg., Kutchery Bazar, Punjab, Faisalabad, Faisalabad Division, Pakistan; tel (92)
Ed. – Malik Ehsanul Haq

GHAREEB (D)
Kutchery Bazar, Punjab, Faisalabad, Faisalabad Division, Pakistan; tel (92)
Ed. – Tanveer Shaukat

LIAQUAT (D)
Kotwali Rd., Punjab, Faisalabad, Faisalabad Division, Pakistan; tel (92)
Ed. – Haji Abdul Ghani

MILLAT (D)
F-159 B. Circular Rd., Punjab, Faisalabad, Faisalabad Division, Pakistan; tel (92)
Ed. – Sajid Aleem

MUBASSAR (D)
Kutchery Bazar, Punjab, Faisalabad, Faisalabad Division, Pakistan; tel (92) 41 23819
Ed. – Ijaz Batalvi

NASEER (D)
Ayub Plaza, Kutchery Bazar, Punjab, Faisalabad, Faisalabad Division, Pakistan; tel (92)
Ed. – Sh Naseer

PAIGHAM (D)
Kutchery Bazar, Punjab, Faisalabad, Faisalabad Division, Pakistan; tel (92) 41 263 1321
Circ.: 20,000
Ed. – Syed Muhammad Munir

PUNJAB NEWS (D)
PO Box 419, Kutchery Bazar, Faisalabad, Faisalabad Division, Pakistan; tel (92) 41 263 3102
Circ.: 20,000
Ed. in Chief – Pervaiz Pasha
Mng. Ed. – Javaid Himyarite

SHAHKAR (D)
Awaz Market, Wakeelan St., No. 7 Chiniot Bazar, Pu, Faisalabad, Faisalabad Division, Pakistan; tel (92)
Ed. – Raies Ahmed Khalid

SORTEHAL (D)
Chirag Bldg., Chiniot Bazar, Punjab, Faisalabad, Faisalabad Division, Pakistan; tel (92)
Ed. – Khalid Mahmood

TARJUMAN (D)
Kutchery Bazar, Punjab, Faisalabad, Faisalabad Division, Pakistan; tel (92)
Ed. – Shahbaz Chaudhry

TIJARATI REHBAR (D)
Kutchery Bazar, Punjab, Faisalabad, Faisalabad Division, Pakistan; tel (92) 41 262 5524
Ed. – Atiq-ur Rehman

GUJRANWALA

TIJARAT (D)
Pasban Plz., G.T. Rd., Gujranwala, Pakistan; tel (92) 55 421 1688
Circ.: 15,000
Ed. – Jamil Akthar

TOHFA (D)
Gondwala Rd., Punjab, Gujranwala, Pakistan; tel (92) 221 84221
Ed. – M. Sarwar Chaudhary

HYDERABAD, HYDERABAD DIVISION

AFTAB (D)
Risala Rd., nr Circular Bldg., Hyderabad, Hyderabad Division, Pakistan; tel (92) 221 24358
Ed. – Sheikh Ali Mohammad

BASHARAT (D)
Sharah-e-Quaid-e-Azam, Sind, Hyderabad, Hyderabad Division, Pakistan; tel (92) 221 23791
Ed. – Syed Musharaf Razajafri

THE DAILY JOURNAL (D)
Near New Famous Printers, Holmstead Hall Charhi, S, Hyderabad, Hyderabad Division, Pakistan; tel (92)
Ed. – Muhammad Akhlaque

FATEH ISLAM (D)
Tilak Incline, Sind, Hyderabad, Hyderabad Division, Pakistan; tel (92) 221 23625
Ed. – Akhtar Hussain Kamal

IBRAT (D)
Ibrat Building, Gadi Khata,, Hyderabad, Hyderabad Division, Pakistan; tel (92) 22 272 8703; fax 278 1879; e-mail ibrat@hyd.paknet.com.pk; web site www.dailyibrat.com
Mng. Ed. – Qazi Asad Abid

INDUS TRIBUNE (D)
Ibrat Bldg., Gari Khata, Sind, Hyderabad, Hyderabad Division, Pakistan; tel (92)
Ed. – Kazi Asad Abid

KAWISH (D)
PO Box 43, Hyderabad, Hyderabad Division, Pakistan; tel (92) 22 278 0525; fax 263 6448; e-mail kawish12@yahoo.com; web site www.dailykawish.com
Circ.: 150,000
Adv. Mgr. – Saif Samjo
Circ. Mgr. – Muhammad Ismail Khan
Ed. in Chief – Muhammad Ali Qazi

KHADIM-E-WATEN (D)
B-2, Civil Lines, Hyderabad, Hyderabad Division, Pakistan; tel (92) 22 278 0026; fax 278 4632
Ed. – Mushtaq Ahmad

MEHRAN (D)
Kingiri Press, Habib Ave., Sind, Hyderabad, Hyderabad Division, Pakistan; tel (92) 22 278 2734; fax 278 3972; e-mail dailymehran@hotmail.com; web site www.dailymehran.com
Ed. in Chief – Sakir Anthar Makairo

PASBAN (D)
Pasban Press, Gari Khata, Sind, Hyderabad, Hyderabad Division, Pakistan; tel (92) 22 272 0677; fax 278 0556
Ed. – Akbar Ali Shah

THE SAFEER (D)
Sind Printing & Publishing House, Gari Khata, Sind, Hyderabad, Hyderabad Division, Pakistan; tel (92)
Ed. – Qazi Muhammad Ali

SINDH OBSERVER (D)
PO Box 43, Hyderabad, Hyderabad Division, Pakistan; tel (92) 221 23702
Ed. – Aslam Akber Kazi

SINDH TODAY (D)
49-Circular Bldg., Sind, Hyderabad, Hyderabad Division, Pakistan; tel (92)
Ed. – Muhammad A. Hassan

ZAMIN (D)
152/8-E Latifabad, Sind, Hyderabad, Hyderabad Division, Pakistan; tel (92)
Ed. – Muhammad Ali Khalid

HYDERABAD, SINDH

SINDH NEWS (D)
B-41 Nasim Nagar Phase-1, Hyderabad, Sindh, Pakistan; tel (92) 221 265 6525; e-mail info@thesindh.com; web site www.thesindh.com
Circ.: 10,000
Ed. – Kazi Saeed Akbar

ISLAMABAD

DEYANAT (D)
Flat No. 1, Plot No. 16, Zeshan Plaza, Islamabad, Pakistan; tel (92)
Ed. – Najmuddin Najmuddin

INQILAB (D)
Ali Akbar House, G-8, Islamabad, Pakistan; tel (92)
Ed. – Zahid Malik

ISLAMABAD OBSERVER (D)
PO Box 20, Islamabad, Pakistan; tel (92)
Ed. – Habib Hayat

JIHAD (D)
H St., No. 398, St. No. 4.3, G-9/1, Islamabad, Pakistan; tel (92)
Ed. – Sharif Farooq

MARKAZ (D)
Buland Markaz, 33-Blue Area, Islamabad, Pakistan; tel (92)
Ed. – Khurshid Ahmed Khan

THE MUSLIM (D)
9-Hameed Chambers, Aabpara, Islamabad, Pakistan; tel (92) 51 277479; fax 277485
Circ.: 22,000
Ed. – Salamat Ali
Chief Exec. – Hasan Pooya

THE NATION (D)
Nawa-i-Waqt House, Zero Point, Islamabad, Pakistan; tel (92) 51 220 2642; e-mail editorisd@nation.com.pk; web site nation.com.pk
Circ.: 14,500
Group: Reseau Select/Select Network
Chief Supporter – Afzal Bajwa
Ed. in Chief – Najeeb Mizami

NAWA-I-PAKISTAN (D)
H St., No. 15, St. No. 22, F-8/2, Islamabad, Pakistan; tel (92)
Ed. – Shabaz Ali

PAKISTAN (D)
Civic Centre, Islamabad, Pakistan; tel (92)
Ed. – Abdul Rashid

PAKISTAN OBSERVER (D)
Ali Akbar House, G-8 Markaz, Islamabad, 44870, Pakistan; tel (92) 51 285 2027; fax 226 2258; e-mail observer@pakobserver.net; web site www.pakobserver.net
Ed. in Chief – Zahid Malik

PAKISTAN TIMES (D)
Post Box 2008 GPO, Islamabad, 44000, Pakistan; tel (92) 300 512 3000; fax 410 0078; e-mail editor@pakistantimes.net; web site www.pakistantimes.net
Adv. Mgr. – Maria Khan
Ed. in Chief – Mumtaz Hamid Rao

JACCOBABAD

NAWA-E-SINDH (D)
Nawa-e-Sindh Press, Old Municipality, Sind, Jaccobabad, Pakistan; tel (92) 721 2233
Ed. – Mumtaz Ali Mangrid

SARANG (D)
Quaid-e-Azam Rd., Sind, Jaccobabad, Pakistan; tel (92) 2146
Ed. – Tariq Latif

SHAHADAT (D)
Shah Bhitai Bazar, Sind, Jaccobabad, Pakistan; tel (92)
Ed. – Syed Nazar Abbas Bukhari

SITARA-E-SINDH (D)
Old Municipal Bldg., Sind, Jaccobabad, Pakistan; tel (92)
Ed. – Ali Sher Afridi

JHANG

UROOJ (D)
Shaheed Rd., Punjab, Jhang, Pakistan; tel (92) 2118
Ed. – Khalid Mahmood

KARACHI

ACTION (D)
Ahmed Chamber, Billmoria St., I. I. Chundrigar Rd., Karachi, Pakistan; tel (92) 21 262 8015; fax 263 9577; e-mail thair@cyber.net.pk
Ed. in Chief – Mushtaq Ahmed Qureshi

ADVANTAGE (D)
447-4th Flr., Sunny Plaza, Hasrat Mohani Rd., Sind, Karachi, Pakistan; tel (92) 21
Ed. – Najamuddin Shaikh

AILAN (D)
303-Rainbow Centre, Saddar, Sind, Karachi, Pakistan; tel (92) 21 714636
Ed. – Dr. Muhammad Nawaz Khan

AKHBAR-E-NAU (D)
9-E-553, Orangi Town, Sind, Karachi, Pakistan; tel (92) 21

Ed. – Syed Jamil Ragbhi

AKHBAR-E-WATAN (MTHLY)
Plot C 119-E, 9 Commercial St., Karachi, Pakistan; tel (92) 21 588 6071
Circ.: 43,000
Mng. Ed. – Munir Hussain

AMN (D)
PO Box 1020, Karachi, 74200, Pakistan; tel (92) 21 263 4451; fax 263 4454; web site www.amn.com.pk
Ed. – Ajmal Dehlvi

JASARAT (M)
3rd Fl. Syed House, Karachi, 74200, Pakistan; tel (92) 21 263 9039; fax 262 9344; e-mail jasarat@cyber.net.pk; web site www.jasarat.com
Circ.: 50,000
Ed. – Ahtar Hashmi

BHUTTO TIMES (D)
C/2-II, Ayaz Town, Gulshan-e-Iqbal, Sind, Karachi, Pakistan; tel (92)
Ed. – Shahzada Alamgir

BUSINESS RECORDER (D)
531 Business Recorder Rd., Karachi, 74550, Pakistan; tel (92) 21 225 0311; fax 222 8644; e-mail editor@brecorder.com; web site www.brecorder.com
Circ.: 18,000
Ed. – Wamiq Zuberi

DAHAISAR (D)
F-1/13-B, C-3/iv, Gulshan-e-Iqbal, Sind, Karachi, Pakistan; tel (92)
Ed. – Shah Muhammad Sheikh

THE DAILY MALL (D)
24/1 Khayabane Shaheen Phase IV, Defence Housing S, Karachi, Pakistan; tel (92)
Ed. – Anwer Hassan Mooraj

DEYANET (D)
4th Fl. Alwaris Ctr, I.I. Chandigarh Rd., Karachi, 74200, Pakistan; tel (92) 21 263 1555; fax 263 1999
Ed. – Shahbuddin Shaikh

EVENING TIMES (D)
92 Habib Chambers, nr Civic Centre, Main Universit, Karachi, Pakistan; tel (92) 21 423052
Ed. – Tanvi Kazmi

RIYASAT (D)
191-Altaf Hussain Rd., New Challi, Sind, Karachi, Pakistan; tel (92)
– Pirzada Syed
– Inquilab MatriEd.s

FRONTIER POST (D)
402-I-I Chundrigarh Rd., Karachi, Pakistan; tel (92) 21 263 4907; fax 263 4908; web site www.thefrontierpost.com
Mktg. Mgr. – Sher Afzal
Chief Ed. – Rahmat Shah Afridi
Mng. Ed. – Jalil Afridi
Ed. – Mahmood Afridi

GHAREEB AWAM (D)
36/3 Masood Chambers, M.A. Jinnah Rd., Sind, Karachi, Pakistan; tel (92)
Ed. – Farrukh Kamal Hussain

GUARDIAN (D)
Falak (Pvt.) Ltd. Press, 191 Altaf Hussain Rd., Si, Karachi, Pakistan; tel (92)
Group: Charney/Palacios & Co.
– Pirzada Syed
– Inquilab MatriEd.s

HILAL-E-PAKISTAN (D)
Court View Bldg., 2nd Flr., M. A. Jinnah Rd., Karachi, 74200, Pakistan; tel (92) 21 262 4997; fax 221 2096
Circ.: 15,000
Ed. – Iqbal Dalsab

HOT NEWS (D)
C-3 Darakshan-Villa, Defence IV, Clifton, Sind, Karachi, Pakistan; tel (92)
Ed. – Shahnaz Tariq

INQILAB (D)
Grand Hotel Bldg., I.I. Chundrigar Rd., Sind, Karachi, Pakistan; tel (92) 21 219337
Circ.: 10,000
Ed. – Syed Majid Ali

JAMHOOR (D)
Central-55, Yousuf Plaza, F.B. Area, Sind, Karachi, Pakistan; tel (92) 21 679660
Ed. – Kabir Ahmed Pirzada

JANG (D)
Printing House, I.I. Chundrigar Rd, Karachi, 74200, Pakistan; tel (92) 21 263 7111; fax 263 4395; e-mail editorjang@jang.com.pk; web site www.jang-group.com
Circ.: 750,000
Pub. – Mir Javed-ur-Rehman
Exec. Dir. – Ziauddin T. Kisat
Adv. Mgr. – Shahrukh Hasan
Ed. in Chief – Mir Shakil-ur-Rahman

KAMRAN (D)
Ms. Printers, 84-85 Hockey Stadium, Sind, Karachi, Pakistan; tel (92)
Ed. – Muhammad Ishaq Khan

KHYBER POST (D)
706 Panorama Centre, Sind, Karachi, Pakistan; tel (92)
Ed. – Shukat Javeed

THE LEADER (D)
606 Shawn Circle, Karachi, Pakistan; tel (92) 21 582 0801; fax 586 2206
Circ.: 11,751
Ed. – Nafees Naeem

MASHRIQ EVENING SPECIAL (E)
2nd Floor, Jubilee Mansion, Karachi, Pakistan; tel (92) 21 273 5118; fax 272 3869
Ed. – Muhammad Ahmed

MAZDUR (D)
Spencer Bldg, I.I. Chundrigar Rd., Karachi, Pakistan; tel (92) 21 215 025
Ed. – Mohammad Anwar Bin Abbas

MUSAWAT (D)
People's House, Shireen Jinnah Colony, Sind, Karachi, Pakistan; tel (92)
– Achchi Memon Kasbati
– Syed BadruddinEd.s

THE MUSLIM (D)
Spencer's Bldg., 1st Flr., I.I. Chundrigar, Sind, Karachi, Pakistan; tel (92)
Ed. – Ali Hasan Khan

NAI ROSHNI (D)
546, A-5, Gulshan-e-Iqbal, Sind, Karachi, Pakistan; tel (92)
Ed. – Syed Mehboob Ali

MORNING NEWS (MS)
PO Box 2804, Karachi, Pakistan; tel (92) 21 210 3949
Ed. – Amanullah Hussain
Adv. Mgr. – Rai Faroog Azal

NATIONAL TIMES (D)
A-3, Kahkashan APTS. Block-7, Clifton, Sind, Karachi, Pakistan; tel (92) 21
Ed. – H.B. Khokhar

NAWA-E-WAQT (D)
Khayaban-e-Shamsheer, Phase V, Karachi, Pakistan; tel (92) 21 111 222 007; fax 585 4932; e-mail editor@nawaiwaqt.com.pk; web site www.nawaiwaqt.com.pk
Circ. Mgr. – Abdul Wahab Khan
Ed. – Saeed Khawar

NEWS EXPRESS (D)
5-F, 16-Orangi Town, Sind, Karachi, Pakistan; tel (92)
Ed. – Noor Ahmed Anjum

NEWS & NEWS (D)
C-3, Darakshan Villas, Phase 1V, Defence Cliftion,, Karachi, Pakistan; tel (92)
Ed. – Shahnaz Tariq

NEWS TIMES (D)
1710-Muhammadabad, Gulbahar, Sind, Karachi, Pakistan; tel (92) 21 218566
Ed. – Samiullah Alias Sami Jawed

THE OBSERVER (D)
21 Sector-14/b, Nolli Karrchi Sind, Karachi, Pakistan; tel (92)
Group: Joseph Jacobs Organization
Ed. – Ghulam Rabbani

MILLAT (D)
3rd Fl. Saify Market, Shahra-e-liaqat, Karachi, Pakistan; tel (92) 21 221 9022; fax 221 1764; web site www.millatgujarati.com
Circ.: 22,550
Ed. – Inquilab Matri

PAKISTAN EXPRESS (D)
A-81, Block No. 9-PECHS, Sind, Karachi, Pakistan; tel (92)
Ed. – Mijan Mujibur Rahman

DAWN (D)
Haroon House, Dr. Ziauddin Ahmed Rd., Karachi, 74200, Pakistan; tel (92) 21 111 444 777; fax 568 4229; e-mail webmaster@dawn.com; web site www.dawn.com
Circ.: 80,000
CEO – Hameed Haroon
Pub. – Hoshang Master
Dir. Mktg. – Masood Hamid
Dir. Circ. – Niloufer Patel
Ed. – Abbas Nasir

THE WATAN (E-EX FRI.)
Haroon House, Dr. Ziauddin Ahmed Rd., Karachi, Pakistan; tel (92) 21 1114 44777
Circ.: 12,000
Ed. – M. Ilyas Gadit

HURRIYET (M)
Saifee House, Dr. Ziauddin Ahmed Rd., Karachi, 74000, Pakistan; tel (92) 21 1114 44777
Circ.: 600,000
Ed. in Chief – Farhat H. Rizvi

THE STAR (E)
Haroon House, Dr. Ziauddin Ahmed Rd., Karachi, Pakistan; tel (92) 21 1114 44777; fax 568 9892
Circ.: 38,000
Pub. – G.A. Mirza

THE PAKISTAN PEOPLE'S DAILY (D)
706-Panorama Centre, Saddar, Sind, Karachi, Pakistan; tel (92)
Ed. – Tariq Ishaq Mirza

THE PARLIAMENT (D)
1013 Qasimabad, Karachi, Pakistan; tel (92) 21 422030
Ed. in Chief – Farrugh Ahmad Siddiq

THE PEOPLE (D)
People's House, Shireen Jinnah Colony, Sind, Karachi, Pakistan; tel (92)
Ed. – Syed Badruddin

PEOPLE'S TIMES (D)
14-Abuzar Sq., Block-N, North Nazimabad, Sind, Karachi, Pakistan; tel (92)
Ed. – Muhammad Munzir Jafri

QAUMI AKHBAR (D)
14 Ramzan Chambers, Dr. Billmoria St., I. I. Chundrigar Rd., Karachi, 74200, Pakistan; tel (92) 21 263 3382; fax 263 5774; e-mail qaumi@hotmail.com; web site www.quamiakhbar.com
Gen. Mgr. – Zuhair Mote
Ed. – Ilyas Shakir

QUMI MILAP (D)
14/6, 5-C, Paposhnagar, Nazimabad No. 5, Sind, Karachi, Pakistan; tel (92)
Ed. – Muhammad Akhtar Shad

QURBANI (D)
Lakhi Gate Shikarpur, Sind, Karachi, Pakistan; tel (92)
Ed. – Ghulam Rasool Memon

SAVERA (D)
108-Adam Arcade, Shaheed-e-Millat Rd., Karachi, Pakistan; tel (92) 21 419616
Ed. – Rukhsana Saham Mirza

SUB-KA-AKHBAR (D)
C-3, Darkshan Villa, Phase IV, Defence Housing Aut, Karachi, Pakistan; tel (92)
Ed. – Shehnaz Tariq

SURAT (D)
46/A, Yousuf Plaza, F.B. Area, Sind, Karachi, Pakistan; tel (92)
Ed. – Syed Wajahat Ali

THE NEWS INTERNATIONAL (D)
PO Box 52, Karachi, Pakistan; tel (92) 21 263 7111; fax 241 8344; e-mail editor.internet@janggroup.com.pk; web site www.janggroup.com
Ed. in Chief – Mir Shakil Rahman

TODAY (D)
B-7, Gulshan-e-Zubeda, Block-E-North, Nazimabad, S, Karachi, Pakistan; tel (92)
Ed. – Syed Mazahir Hussain

TODAY SPECIAL (D)
35 M.A. Jinnah Rd., 2nd Flr., Aurangzeb Market, Si, Karachi, Pakistan; tel (92)
Ed. – Muhammad Babar Faisal

THE TRIBUNE (D)
Camp Office 502-Kashif Centre, Sind, Karachi, Pakistan; tel (92)
Ed. – Agha Saddaruddin Ismaili

WOMEN DAILY (D)
Recorder House, 351-Business Recorder Rd., Sind, Karachi, Pakistan; tel (92)
Ed. – Muhammad Ahmed Zuberi

LAHORE

AFAQ (D)
22-Abbot Rd., Punjab, Lahore, Pakistan; tel (92) 42
Ed. – Shaukat H. Shaukat

NAWA-E-SEHAR (D)
15-Anarkali, Punjab, Lahore, Pakistan; tel (92)
Ed. – H.M. Hassan

ZAMAN (D)
unknown, Lahore, Pakistan; tel (92)

LAHORE, LAHORE

JANG LAHORE (M)
PO Box 609, Lahore, Lahore, Pakistan; tel (92) 42 636 7480; fax 636 4280; e-mail thenewslhr@hotmail.com; web site www.janggroup.com
Circ.: 1,200,000
Ed. in Chief – Shakeer Ur-Rehman

LAHORE, LAHORE DISTRICT

AAJ KA AKHBAR (D)
H No. 1, St. 10, Tajpura, Punjab, Lahore, Lahore District, Pakistan; tel (92) 42
Ed. – Mohammad Abbas Athar

AAJ KAL (WEEKLY)
118-A, Garden Town, Punjab, Lahore, Lahore District, Pakistan; tel (92) 42
Ed. – Khaled Ahmed

AFTAB (D)
19 A Abbot Rd., Lahore, Lahore District, Pakistan; tel (92) 42 630 2185; fax 627 1260; e-mail info@aftabdaily.com; web site www.aftabdaily.com
Adv. Mgr. – Mohsin Mumtaz
Ed. in Chief – Mumtaz Tahir

AILAN (D)
Office Daily Ailan, Lahore, Lahore District, Pakistan; tel (92) 42

AILAN-E-JNG (D)
77-Nisbat Rd., Punjab, Lahore, Lahore District, Pakistan; tel (92) 42
Ed. – Shahzada Alamgir

ALAM GIR (D)
Shah Din Bldg., Punjab, Lahore, Lahore District, Pakistan; tel (92)
Ed. – Tahir Javaid

AWAZ-E-JEHAN (D)
16 Sir Adha Khan Rd., Lahore, Lahore District, Pakistan; tel (92) 42 636 7480; fax 630 9451
Ed. – Khalid Saruqi

AZADI
29-Railway Rd., Punjab, Lahore, Lahore District, Pakistan; tel (92) 42 56725
Ed. – Sh Riazuddin

BALAGHAT (D)
57-Badami Bagh, Punjab, Lahore, Lahore District, Pakistan; tel (92)
Ed. – Syed Munawar Hussain

BHUTTO TIMES (D)
77-Nisbat Rd., Punjab, Lahore, Lahore District, Pakistan; tel (92)
Ed. – Shahzada Alamgir

BUSINESS VOICE (D)
8-Abbot Rd., Punjab, Lahore, Lahore District, Pakistan; tel (92)
Ed. – Siddiq Azher

CHONAN (D)
7-Nadirabad, Punjab, Lahore, Lahore District, Pakistan; tel (92)
Ed. – Muhammad Ikram

DAILY MUSAWAAT (D)
Sir Agha Khan Davis Rd., Lahore, Lahore District, Pakistan; tel (92) 42 637 1836; fax 631 0119; e-mail pbpisfl@brail.net.tk; web site dailymusawaat.com
Ed. in Chief – Syed Sajjad Bukhari

DAILY PAKISTAN (D)
41 Jail Rd., Lahore, Lahore District, Pakistan; tel (92) 42 757 6302; fax 756 1116; e-mail editorweb@dailypak.com; web site www.dailypak.com
Adv. Mgr. – UmerMujib Shami
Ed. in Chief – Mujibl-Ur-Rahman Shami

DASTAK (D)
14-D Manzoor Plaza, Blue Area, Lahore, Lahore District, Pakistan; tel (92)
Ed. – Afzal Shahid

EXPRESS (D)
43/16-Main Gulberg, Punjab, Lahore, Lahore District, Pakistan; tel (92)
Ed. – Mir Javaid Rehman

FINANCIAL TIMES (D)
16-Temple Rd., Punjab, Lahore, Lahore District, Pakistan; tel (92)
Ed. – Tariq Majid Ch

PAKISTAN TIMES (D)
PO Box 223, Lahore, Lahore District, Pakistan; tel (92) 42 7226271; fax 7223766
Circ.: 50,000
Ed. in Chief – Nasim Ahmad

HAJUM (D)
H No. 4, St. 1, Sanda Rd., Punjab, Lahore, Lahore District, Pakistan; tel (92)
Ed. – Khalique Ahmed

HAYAT NAU (D)
416-Jahanzeb Block, Allama Iqbal Town, Punjab, Lahore, Lahore District, Pakistan; tel (92)
Ed. – Israrul Haq

JANG DAILY (D)
13 Sir Agha Khan Rd., Lahore, Lahore District, Pakistan; tel (92) 42 637 1340; fax 630 9764; e-mail sales@jang.com.pk; web site www.jang.com.pk
Adv. Mgr. – Yunus Arain
Ed. in Chief – Mir Shakil-ur-Rahman

ISHARA (D)
Degree College, Chowk Near Asghar Mall, Punjab, Lahore, Lahore District, Pakistan; tel (92)
Ed. – Muhammad Noor Tahir

JAHAN NUMA (D)
18-Beadon Rd., Punjab, Lahore, Lahore District, Pakistan; tel (92)
Ed. – Tariq Farooq

JUBLEE (D)
91/K Zafarul Haq Rd., Punjab, Lahore, Lahore District, Pakistan; tel (92)
Ed. – Syed Qaisara Sherazi

KARKUN (D)
Crown Arcade, Crown Cemina, Ghari Shahoo, Punjab, Lahore, Lahore District, Pakistan; tel (92)
Ed. – Ayyub Sarwar Khan

MADAM (D)
29-Main Rd., Samnabad, Punjab, Lahore, Lahore District, Pakistan; tel (92)
Ed. – Anwar Ul Haq

MAHGRIBI PAKISTAN (D)
20 Beadon Rd., Lahore, Lahore District, Pakistan; tel (92) 42 53490
Circ.: 3,000
Ed. – M. Shafaat

MEDIA NEWS (D)
Ferozepur Rd., Punjab, Lahore, Lahore District, Pakistan; tel (92)
Ed. – S.A. Khan Durrani

THE NATION (D)
PO Box 1815, Lahore, Lahore District, 54000, Pakistan; tel (92) 42 636 7580; fax 636 7005; e-mail editor@nation.pk.com; web site www.nation.com.pk
Circ.: 48,000
Chrmn. – Majeed Nizami
Ed. – Arif Nizami

NATIONAL VOICE (D)
336-Rehmanpura, Punjab, Lahore, Lahore District, Pakistan; tel (92)
Ed. – Syed Azhar-ul-Hasan

NAWA-I-WAQT (M)
4 Shaarey Fatima Jinnah, Lahore, Lahore District, 54000, Pakistan; tel (92) 42 636 7580; fax 636 7005; e-mail editor@nawaiwaqt.com.pk; web site www.nawaiwaqt.com.pk
Circ.: 560,000
Circ. Mgr. – Istikhar Shah
Ed. – Majid Nizami

NEWS (D)
13-Davis Rd., Punjab, Lahore, Lahore District, Pakistan; tel (92)
Ed. – Hussain Naqi

NEWS SPECIAL (D)
139-Islamia St., McLeod Rd., Punjab, Lahore, Lahore District, Pakistan; tel (92)

NIDA-E-SADAQAT (D)
16 Ratigun Rd., Punjab, Lahore, Lahore District, Pakistan; tel (92)
Ed. – Syed Abbas Anwar

PUNJAB CHRONICLE (D)
107/2 Allama Iqbal Rd., Punjab, Lahore, Lahore District, Pakistan; tel (92)
Ed. – Zia ul-Islam

SAADAT (D)
Fazal Bldg., Cooper Rd., Punjab, Lahore, Lahore District, Pakistan; tel (92) 42 310580
Circ.: 40,000
Ed. – Kahlil ur-Rehman

SACHCHAI (D)
19 Akbar St., Punjab, Lahore, Lahore District, Pakistan; tel (92)
Ed. – Muhammad Khalil

SADAQAT (D)
7/45 Beadon Rd., Punjab, Lahore, Lahore District, Pakistan; tel (92)
Ed. – Naveed Iqbal Qureshi

SAKAB (D)
15 Shahrah-e-Quaid-e-Azam, Punjab, Lahore, Lahore District, Pakistan; tel (92)
Ed. – Farid Haqe Zaidi

SALAB (D)
15 The Mall, Punjab, Lahore, Lahore District, Pakistan; tel (92)
Ed. – Farid Haq

SEERAT (D)
Ujala Press, Athurtan Rd., Punjab, Lahore, Lahore District, Pakistan; tel (92)
Ed. – Mian M. Ismael

SHER-E-PAKISTAN (D)
6/C Data Darbar Market, Punjab, Lahore, Lahore District, Pakistan; tel (92)
Ed. – Mir Israr Chouhan

SIYASAT (D)
Cooper Rd., Punjab, Lahore, Lahore District, Pakistan; tel (92)
Ed. – Asar Chohan

TIJARAT (D)
14 Abbot Rd., opp. Nishat Cinema, Lahore, Lahore District, Pakistan; tel (92)
Ed. – Jamil Athar

THE TRIBUNE (D)
8-A Sharif Colony, Gulberg, Punjab, Lahore, Lahore District, Pakistan; tel (92)
Ed. – Sikandar Shaheen

URDU TIMES (D)
Shahzeb Market, Cooper Rd., Punjab, Lahore, Lahore District, Pakistan; tel (92)
Ed. – Bashir A. Sheikh

WAQT (D)
2-B Shah Alam Market, Punjab, Lahore, Lahore District, Pakistan; tel (92) 42 228736
Ed. – Khawaja Nazir Butt

WIFAQ (D)
6-A Waris Rd., Lahore, Lahore District, Pakistan; tel (92) 42 302862
Ed. – Mostafa Sadiq

WORLD TODAY (D)
43/16 Main Gulberg, Punjab, Lahore, Lahore District, Pakistan; tel (92)
Ed. – Mir Javid

LARKANA

AGWAN (D)
Office Daily Agwan, Sind, Larkana, Pakistan; tel (92)

LASBELLA

DAILY INTEKHAB (D)
Lasbella, Balochistan, Lasbella, Pakistan; tel (92) 81 282 1448; fax 283 5271; e-mail intekhab@cyber.net.pk; web site www.dailyintekhab.com.pk
Ed. – Anwar Sajidi

MANSEHRA

FUTURE (D)
Kawai House, Mansehra, Mansehra, Pakistan; tel (92)
Ed. – Ghulam Jankhan Tahir Khaili

MASTUNG

HIMMAT (D)
Mastung, Pakistan; tel (92)
Ed. – Kausar Hussain

MULTAN

AFTAB (D)
Bagh Lang-e-Khan Rd., Nr. Children Hospital, Multan, Pakistan; tel (92) 61 454 6080; fax 478 6083; web site www.aftabdaily.com
Publication Mgr. – Mirza Arshad
Ed. in Chief – Asad Mumtaz

MULTAN CITY

HAQ (D)
28 Hassan, Parwana Colony, Punjab, Multan City, Pakistan; tel (92)
Ed. – Qaisar Malik

MULTAN CITY, MULTAN DISTRICT

ADAL (D)
PO Box 124, Multan City, Multan District, Pakistan; tel (92) 61 454 0301; fax 454 0201
Ed. – Jalal Rabbani

AILAN HAQ (D)
Pul Shahwala Baher Gate, Punjab, Multan City, Multan District, Pakistan; tel (92) 61
Ed. – Muhammad Ali

AKHBAR-E-MILLAT (D)
Abdali Rd., Punjab, Multan City, Multan District, Pakistan; tel (92) 61 73766
Ed. – Rana Muhammad Aslam

ELAN (D)
1902/W-7 Mohni Buri Babar St., Purana Dangal, Punj, Multan City, Multan District, Pakistan; tel (92)
Ed. – Abdul Rehman Malik

HARARAT (D)
131/A Purana Bahawalpur Rd., 1st Flr., Punjab, Multan City, Multan District, Pakistan; tel (92)
Ed. – Nazir Ahmed

HIJRAT (D)
Mahlem Press Bldg., Multan City, Multan District, Pakistan; tel (92)
Ed. – Khalil Bhatti

NAWA-E-MULTAN (D)
Near Beef Market, Opp. Haram Gate, Punjab, Multan City, Multan District, Pakistan; tel (92)
Ed. – Khalil Bhatti

QUAMI AWAZ (D)
PO Box 585 GPO Multan, Multan City, Multan District, Pakistan; tel (92) 61 400 0066; fax 454 0885; e-mail qaumiaawaz@raeeinternational.com; info@raeeinternational.com; web site www.raeeinternational.com
Ed. – Nasheed Raee

SUNG-E-MEEL (D)
Hassan Parwana Rd., Punjab, Multan City, Multan District, Pakistan; tel (92)
Ed. – M.R. Roohani

MULTAN CITY, PUNJAB

NAWA-E-WAQT (D)
63-A Astali Rd., Multan City, Punjab, Pakistan; tel (92) 61 454 5571; fax 458 0958
Ed. – Abdul Jabbar Mukti

PESHAWAR

DAWN (D)
State Life Bldg, First Fl, Peshawar Cantt.,, Peshawar, Pakistan; tel (92) 91 527 9974; fax 527 9976; e-mail peshawar@dawn.com; web site www.dawn.com
Mktg. Exec. – Muhammad Hassan
Ed. – Mohammed Ismail

PESHAWAR, PESHAWAR DISTRICT

AL FALAH (D)
Al Falah Bldg., Saddar Rd., Peshawar, Peshawar District, Pakistan; tel (92) 521 73783
Circ.: 8,000
Ed. – S. Abdullah Shah

AL JAMIAT-E-SARHAD (D)
Kocha Gilania Chakagali, Karimpura, Peshawar, Peshawar District, Pakistan; tel (92) 521 212093
Ed. in Chief – S. Muhammad Hassan Gilani

ALAKHBAR (D)
Bazar Kalan Tehsil, Peshawar, Peshawar District, Pakistan; tel (92) 91 256 5048; fax 256 5841; web site www.alakhbar.com.pk
Ed. – Khurshid Amed

ALHAQ (D)
Islamia Club Bldg., Khyber Bazar, Peshawar, Peshawar District, Pakistan; tel (92) 521 2131
Ed. – Bashir Tabasum

AWAZ (D)
Cantonment Plaza, Arbab Rd., Sadar, Peshawar, Peshawar District, Pakistan; tel (92) 521 271195
Mng. Ed. – Ali Raza Malik

AZME NAU (D)
Kuku Bldg., Ghenl Ghar, Peshawar, Peshawar District, Pakistan; tel (92) 521 214 293
Ed. – Khawaja Imran

BAGRAM (D)
Bazar Kalan Tehsil, Peshawar, Peshawar District, Pakistan; tel (92) 521 213076
Ed. – Khurshid Ahmed

FRONTIER POST (D)
PO Box 1161, Peshawar, Peshawar District, Pakistan; tel (92) 521 570 3687; fax 527 9683; e-mail tfpost@brain.net.pk; web site www.thefrontierpost.com
Ed. in Chief – Rahmat Shah Afridi
Ed. – Mahmood Afridi

HAMARA PAKISTAN (E)
Mohammed Ali Johar Rd., Peshawar, Peshawar District, Pakistan; tel (92)
Ed. – Ghulam Ghaus Sehrai
Adv. Mgr. – Mohammad Ali Tariq

HAQEEQAT (D)
20 Islamia Club Bldg., Peshawar, Peshawar District, Pakistan; tel (92) 521 213141

INQILAB (D)
Bazar Kalan, Peshawar, Peshawar District, Pakistan; tel (92) 213076
Ed. – Khurshid Ahmad

IRRUM (D)
20 Islamia Club Bldg., Peshawar, Peshawar District, Pakistan; tel (92) 521 213141

JIDDAT (D)
Rehman Baba Colony, Peshawar, Peshawar District, Pakistan; tel (92) 521 221 3081; fax 221 1921
Ed. in Chief – Syed Qaiser Rizvi

NISHAN-I-HAIDER (D)
Rehman Baba Colony, Peshawar, Peshawar District, Pakistan; tel (92) 521 211921
Ed. – Qasir Rizvi

QUAID (D)
20 Islamia Club Bldg., Peshawar, Peshawar District, Pakistan; tel (92) 521 210574
Ed. – Naeem Sarhadi

RAHAT (D)
Chowk Yadgar, Peshawar, Peshawar District, Pakistan; tel (92)
Ed. – Zabuir Kazmi

SANG (D)
Fancy Market Bazar Kalan, Peshawar, Peshawar District, Pakistan; tel (92) 521 213735
Ed. – S. Nazli

SARHAD (D)
Asad Anwar Colony, Gul Bahar, Peshawar, Peshawar District, Pakistan; tel (92) 91 257 0743; fax 257 0743; e-mail sarhad@brain.net.pk
Pub. – Zahid Hafeez
Ed. – Hafeez Ulfat

SHAHBAZ (D)
Nazar Bagh Flats, Grand Trunk Rd., Peshawar, Peshawar District, Pakistan; tel (92) 521 220188; fax 216483
Ed. in Chief – Begum Naseem Wali Khan

TARJUMAN-E-AFGHAN (D)
Azmat Bldg., Chowk Yadgar, Peshawar, Peshawar District, Pakistan; tel (92) 521 61548
Ed. – Javed Akhtar
Adv. Mgr. – Abdul Hamid Mufti

WAHDAT (D)
Gulbahar 8-Nishter Abad Road, Peshawar, Peshawar District, Pakistan; tel (92) 91 221 4034; fax 221 4321; web site www.wahdat-daily.com
Ed. in Chief – Peer Syed Surfid Shah

WATTAN (D)
10 Nazar Bagh Flats, Peshawar, Peshawar District, Pakistan; tel (92)
Ed. – Bari Malik

QUETTA, QUETTA DIVISION

BALOCHISTAN TIMES (D)
Standard Complex, Mission Rd., Quetta, Quetta Division, Pakistan; tel (92) 81 283 7724; fax 282 3354
Pub. – Syed Fasih Iqbal
Mgr. – Anwar Hussain

BOLAN-E-JADEED (D)
Near Bohra Thana Rd., Quetta, Quetta Division, Pakistan; tel (92) 81 73340
Ed. – Nusrat Hussain

EITEMAD (D)
Jinnah Rd., Quetta, Quetta Division, Pakistan; tel (92) 81 71124
Ed. – Javed Ahmed

JANG (D)
Jamiat Rai Rd., Quetta, Quetta Division, Pakistan; tel (92) 81 73064; fax 70515
Circ.: 21,000
Pub. – Mir Javed-ur-Rahman
Ed. – Habibur Rehman
Ed. – Majeud Asghat

MASHRIQ (D)
Dr. Shar Mahammad Rd., Quetta, Quetta Division, Pakistan; tel (92) 81 282 1626
Ed. – Saeed Kamran Mumtaz

MEEZAN (D)
Meezan Chambers, Mecongi Rd., Quetta, Quetta Division, Pakistan; tel (92) 81
Ed. – Jamilur Rehman

NARA-E-HAQ (D)
Mecongi Rd., Quetta, Quetta Division, Pakistan; tel (92) 81 283 0963
Ed. – Iftikhar Yousaf

SHAL (D)
Al-Syed Bldg., Jinnah Rd., Quetta, Quetta Division, Pakistan; tel (92)
Ed. – Abdul Haque

TAMEER-E-BALOCHISTAN (D)
Al-Syed Bldg., Jinnah Rd., Quetta, Quetta Division, Pakistan; tel (92)
Ed. – M. Noor Ahmed Baloch

ZAMANA (D)
Jinnah Rd., Quetta, Quetta Division, Pakistan; tel (92) 81 282 1120; fax 527 5393
Circ.: 5,000
Ed. – Syed Fasih Iqbal

RAHIMYAR KHAN

IBADAT (D)
Shah Jahan Bldg., Rahim Yar Khan Railway Rd., Punj, Rahimyar Khan, Pakistan; tel (92)
Ed. – Muhammad Aslam Khan

ISRAR
8/P Gulran Usmania, Punjab, Rahimyar Khan, Pakistan; tel (92)
Ed. – Muhammad Israrul Haqe

SHAHADAT (D)
Shahi Rd., Punjab, Rahimyar Khan, Pakistan; tel (92)
Ed. – Zia-ullah Khan

TAKMEEL-E-PAKISTAN (D)
Rahim Yar Khan, Rahimyar Khan, Pakistan; tel (92)
Ed. – Munawar Naqvi

WIFAQ (D)
112 Bano Bazar, Punjab, Rahimyar Khan, Pakistan; tel (92) 731
Ed. – Wiqar Mustafa

RAWALPINDI, RAWALPINDI

JANG RAWALPINDI (M)
PO Box 30, Rawalpindi, Rawalpindi, Pakistan; tel (92) 51 596 2444; fax 596 2271; web site www.jang.com.pk
Adv. Mgr. – Raja Aziz
Ed. – Mir Khalil-ur-Rahman

RAWALPINDI, RAWALPINDI DIVISION

DAILY JANG (M)
44 S. Marree Rd., Al Rehman Bldg., Rawalpindi, Rawalpindi Division, 56000, Pakistan; tel (92) 51 596 2444; fax 596 2277; web site www.jang.com.pk
Circ.: 65,000
Ed. – Mir Javed-ur-Rehman

DAILY WIFAQ (D)
7/a C/A, Satellite Town, Rawalpindi, Rawalpindi Division, Pakistan; tel (92)
Ed. – Mustafa Sadiq

HAIDER (D)
1901-M Murree Rd., Punjab, Rawalpindi, Rawalpindi Division, Pakistan; tel (92)
Ed. – Ijaz Butt

JURAT (D)
125-N Circular Rd., Punjab, Rawalpindi, Rawalpindi Division, Pakistan; tel (92) 51 553 2761; fax 555 1654
Adv, Mgr. – Imran Athar
Ed. in Chief – Jamil Athar

MILLAT NEWS (D)
J-259 Liaquat Chowk, Murree Rd., Punjab, Rawalpindi, Rawalpindi Division, Pakistan; tel (92)
Ed. – Asar Ali Chauhan

NAWA-E-WAQT (M)
Al-Mir Bldg., Bank Rd., Punjab, Rawalpindi, Rawalpindi Division, Pakistan; tel (92) 51 2773614
Circ.: 3,000
Pub. – Majid Nizami
Ed. – Tariq Warsi

SAHIWAL

JAMHOORISTAN (D)
Stadium Chowk, Railway Rd., Punjab, Sahiwal, Pakistan; tel (92)
Ed. – Pervaiz Ahmed Kharal

PAIGHAM (D)
120 Civil Line Rd., Punjab, Sahiwal, Pakistan; tel (92) 40 446 7677
Ed. – S.M. Munir

SARGODHA, RAWALPINDI DIVISION

AZADI
Block 14, Kutchery Bazar, Punjab, Sargodha, Rawalpindi Division, Pakistan; tel (92)
Ed. – Ashiq Jafri

NIZAM-E-NAU (D)
Kutchery Bazar, Punjab, Sargodha, Rawalpindi Division, Pakistan; tel (92)
Ed. – Mukhtar Younas

SHOLA (D)
9-Jauhar Colony, Punjab, Sargodha, Rawalpindi Division, Pakistan; tel (92) 451 2982
Ed. – Mir Khalid Mahmood

TIJARAT (D)
Kutchery Bazar, Punjab, Sargodha, Rawalpindi Division, Pakistan; tel (92) 48 374 1283; fax 374 1383
Ed. – Malik Aamer Afzal

WIFAQ (D)
Aminpur Bazar, Punjab, Sargodha, Rawalpindi Division, Pakistan; tel (92) 48 374 0762
Ed. – Moazam Tauseef

SUKKUR

DEYANAT (D)
C 416 Upper Queens Rd., Sind, Sukkur, Pakistan; tel (92) 71 561 6354
Ed. – Najmuddin Shaikh

SUKKUR, KHAIRPUR DIVISION

BAYAN (D)
C-488/1 Wallice Rd., Sind, Sukkur, Khairpur Division, Pakistan; tel (92) 71 83289
Ed. – Attaullah Khan

MAGHRIBI PAKISTAN (D)
Mehran Markaz, Sukkur, Khairpur Division, Pakistan; tel (92) 71 85642
Ed. – M. Shafaat

NAWA-E-INQILAB (D)
Queens Rd., Sind, Sukkur, Khairpur Division, Pakistan; tel (92) 71 4783
Ed. – Inamur Rehman

NIJAAT (D)
PO Box 70, Sukkur, Khairpur Division, Pakistan; tel (92) 71 6304
Ed. – Mukhdoom Muhammad Rafiqu

YADGAR (D)
Office Daily Yadgar, Mehran Centre, Sind, Sukkur, Khairpur Division, Pakistan; tel (92) 71 84238
Ed. – Javed Ashfaq

SUKKUR,SINDH, PAKISTAN

KALEEM (D) Est.1948
PO Box 88, Sukkur,Sindh, Pakistan, Pakistan; tel (92) 71 562 7833-5622086; fax 562 2087
Ed. in Chief – Javed Mehr Shamsi

PHILIPPINES

CEBU CITY

CEBU ADVOCATE (M)
158 Padilla St., Cebu City, Philippines; tel (63) 32 93737
Circ.: 4,000
Pub. – Danny Gonzales
Ed. – Elma C. Avellanosa

CEBU DAILY TIMES
F. Gonzales St., Cebu City, Philippines; tel (63)
Pub. – Edgardo Mongaya
Ed. – Wilfredo Veloso

MORNING TIMES (D-EX MON.)
PO Box 51, Cebu City, Philippines; tel (63) 32 77032
Circ.: 4,000
Pub./Ed. – Pedro D. Calomarde

REPUBLICAN NEWS (D-EX MON.)
57-59 Colon St., Cebu City, Philippines; tel (63)
Circ.: 12,175
Pub. – Dioscoro B. Lazaro
Ed. – Jose G. Logarte

SUN-STAR DAILY (D)
Sun Star Bldg., P del Rosario and Don Pedro Cui St, Cebu City, 6000, Philippines; tel (63) 32 254 6100; fax 253 7256; web site www.sunstar.com.ph
Chrmn. – Jesus P. Garcia
Ed. in Chief – Nini B. Cabaero
Mng. Ed. – Marlen D. Limpag
News Ed. – Bong O. Wenceslao

THE FREEMAN (M)
107-109 V. Gulles St., Cebu City, Philippines; tel (63); e-mail freeman@mozcom.com; online_ed@thefreeman.com; web site thefreeman.com
Circ.: 6,500
Ed. – Pachico A. Seares

DAVAO CITY

DAILY FORUM (D)
153 Pichon St., Davao City, Philippines; tel (63) 82 300 0854
Pub. – Doreta A. Flaviano

DAVAO STAR
230 Solas, Aquarius St., Davao City, Philippines; tel (63)
Pub. – Jose M. Santes

DIGOS TIMES
Digos, Davao del Sur, Davao City, Philippines; tel (63)
Pub. – Bievenida Sacada

MINDANAO DAILY MIRROR (D)
270 R. Magsaysay Ave., Davao City, Philippines; tel (63) 82 227 2874; fax 227 9347; web site www.dailymirror.net.ph
Circ.: 20,000Last Audit: March 23, 2010
Circ. Mgr. – Shirluy Dominzuez
Ed. – Marietta Siongco

MINDANAO MAIL
Lozano Bldg., Rm. 183, C.M. Recto Ave., Davao City, Philippines; tel (63)
Ed. – Angelo M. Abarico

MINDANAO MIRROR BULLETIN
270 Magsaysay Ave., Davao City, Philippines; tel (63) 82 227 5716; e-mail mirror1@skyinet.net; web site www.dailymirror.net.ph
Pub. – Teresita F. Basilio

MINDANAO TIMES (M)
C.M. Recto Ave., Davao City, Philippines; tel (63) 82 300 0854; web site www.mindanaotimes.net
Circ.: 10,000
Adv. Mgr. – Jingo Camomot
Ed. in Chief – Amalia Bandiola-Cabusao

PEOPLE'S FORM
153 Pichon St., Davao City, Philippines; tel (63)
Pub. – Rogelio J. Flaviano

SAN PEDRO EXPRESS
Covern Trade Bldg., Gen. Luna St., Davao City, Philippines; tel (63)
Pub. – Leoniloa G. Claudio

VOICE OF ISLAM (MTHLY)
PO Box 407, Davao City, Philippines; tel (63) 82 83168
Pub./Ed. – Muhammad Al'Rashid Al Hajj

MAKATI CITY

THE JOURNAL (D)
6th Floor Universal Re Building, Legaspi Village, Makati City, Philippines; tel (63) 2 813 5238; fax 840 1369; e-mail journal@skyinet.net; web site www.journal.com.ph
Ed.- in- Chief – Manuel C. Villa Real

PHILIPPINE DAILY INQUIRER (D)
PO Box 2353, Makati City, 1263, Philippines; tel (63) 2 897 8808; fax 897 4793; e-mail feedback@inquirer.com.ph; web site www.inquirer.com.ph
Circ.: 250,000
Chrmn. – Marixi R. Prieto
Ed. – Leticia J. Magsonoc

PEOPLES JOURNAL (M)
6th Fl. Universal-Re Bldg.,, Makati City, Philippines; tel (63) 2 892 3052; fax 840 1369; e-mail journal@journal.com.ph; web site www.journal.com.ph
Circ.: 111,457
Ed. in Chief – Augusto Villanueva

PEOPLE TONIGHT (D)
6th Fl. Universal-Re Bldg.,, Makati City, Philippines; tel (63) 2 892 3052; fax 527 4629; e-mail journal@journal.com.ph; web site www.journal.com.ph
Circ.: 500,000
Ed. in Chief – Augusto Villanueva

TALIBA (D)
6th Fl. Universal-Re Bldg.,, Makati City, Philippines; tel (63) 2 892 3052; fax 527 4624; e-mail journal@journal.com.ph; web site www.journal.com.ph
Circ.: 229,000Last Audit: December 28, 2006
Ed. in Chief – Agusto Villanueva

MANILA

CHINA TOWN NEWS (M)
429 Nueva St., Binondo, Manila, Philippines; tel (63) 2
Circ.: 20,000
Pub. – Bangong Dina
Ed. in Chief – Jose Locsin

ANG FILIPINO NGAYON (M-EX S)
202 Railroad St., cnr 13th St., Port Area, Manila, Philippines; tel (63) 2 401871; fax 5224998
Circ.: 286,452
Pub./Ed. – Jose Buhain

ANG PAHAYAGANG MALAYA (D)
70 Serrano Laktaw, Manila, Philippines; tel (63)
Circ.: 165,000

TEMPO (M)
Muralla corner Recoletos Sts., Intramuros, Manila, Philippines; tel (63) 2 527 8121; fax 527 7510; web site www.mb.com.ph; www.tempo.com.ph
Circ.: 230,000
Ed. in Chief – Robert Roque

BALITA (M)
PO Box 769, Manila, Philippines; tel (63) 2 527 8121; fax 527 7534; web site www.mb.com.ph
Circ.: 151,000
Pub. – Hermogenes P. Pobre
Ed. in Chief – Cris J. Icban

MANILA BULLETIN (D)
PO Box 769, Manila, Philippines; tel (63) 2 527 8121; fax 527 7511; e-mail bulletin@mb.com.ph; web site www.mb.com.ph
Pres./Pub. – Hermogenes Pobre
Ed. in Chief – Cris J. Icban
Ed. – Vicente Edgardo Bartilad

BUSINESS STAR (5X WK.)
202 Railroad St., cnr 13th St., Port Area, Manila, Philippines; tel (63)
Pub./Ed. – Gabriel V. Manalac

BUSINESS WORLD NEWSPAPER (5X WK.)
95 Balete Drive Extension, New Manila, Quezon City, Manila, 1112, Philippines; tel (63) 2 535 9923; fax 535 9926; e-mail editor@bworld.com.ph; web site www.bworldonline.com
Circ.: 66,000Last Audit: March 23, 2010
Chrmn. – Vergel O. Santos
Ed. in Chief – Arnold Belleza
Mng. Ed. – Wilfredo G. Reyes

EVENING POST (E)
20th St. & Bonifacio Dr., Port Area, Manila, Philippines; tel (63) 2 481234
Circ.: 90,000

EVENING STAR (E-EX S)
Philippines Today Inc., 202 Railroad St., Manila, Philippines; tel (63) 2 401871
Pub. – Betty Go-Belmonte
Ed. in Chief – Luis D. Beltran

FINANCIAL TIMES OF MANILA (D)
Times Journal Bldg., Railroad St., cnr 19th St., Manila, Philippines; tel (63)

HEADLINE (D)
Vista Cinema Bldg., 2nd Flr., Recto Ave., Manila, Philippines; tel (63) 2 478661; fax 478668
Circ.: 105,000
Pub. – Juan P. Dayang

HERALD TRIBUNE (D)
V. Esguerra II Bldg., 140 Amorsolo St., Manila, Philippines; tel (63) 2 853711
Pres. – Amada Valino

TODAY (D)
1666 EDSA car. Escuela, Macrina Bldg., Manila, Philippines; tel (63) 2 818 6133 1844
Circ.: 106,000
Ed. in Chief – Teodoro L. Locsin

MANILA CHRONICLE (M)
371a Bonifacio Dr., Port Area, Manila, Philippines; tel (63) 2 810 6941
Circ.: 162,000
Chrmn. – Roberto T. Villanueva
Ed. in Chief – Amando Doronila

THE MANILA TIMES (M)
371 A. Bonifacio Dr., Port Area, Manila, Philippines; tel (63) 2 834 0509; fax 301 9552; e-mail business@manilatimes.net; web site www.manilatimes.net
Circ.: 194,000
Circ. Mgr. – Arlan Campos
Ed. in Chief – Rene Q Bas

ABANTE (M)
PO Box 3145, Manila, Philippines; tel (63) 2 527 4480; web site www.abante.com.ph
Circ.: 350,000
Pub. – Allen A. Macasaet
Adv. Mgr. – Ron Tamayo

NEWS TODAY (M)
PO Box 4245, Manila, Philippines; tel (63)
Circ.: 35,000
Ed. in Chief – Augusta B. Villanueva

OBSERVER (D)
Times Journal Bldg., Railroad St., cnr 19th St., Manila, Philippines; tel (63) 2 487511
Circ.: 60,000
Group: Admarket International (Div. of Marcom International, Inc.)
Ed. – Yen Makabenta

MANILA EVENING POST (E)
Oriental Media Inc., 20th St., Port Area, Manila, Philippines; tel (63) 2 481234
Circ.: 90,000
Ed. – Kerima P. Tuvera

ORIENT NEWS (D)
Times Journal Bldg., Railroad St., cnr 19th St.,, Manila, Philippines; tel (63) 2 472694
Circ.: 26,000

PEOPLE'S BAGONG TALIBA (6X WK.)
6th Fl. Universalre Bldg, 106 Basborosee Corner, Manila, Philippines; tel (63) 2 89230 52258; fax 840 1369; e-mail nt@journal.com.ph ; veliba@journal.com.ph; web site www.journal.com.ph
Circ.: 508,000
Ed. in Chief – Augusto B Villlenuev
Ed. – LBP Manzano
News Ed. – Ederlina R Calso
Editorial consultant – Manuel H Ces
Assoc. Ed. – Denis S Fetalino

MALAYA (D)
Leyland Bldg., Railroad St., Corner 20th St., Manila, 1018, Philippines; tel (63) 2 339 3324; fax 527 7240; e-mail malayanews@yahoo.com; web site www.malaya.com.ph
Circ.: 175,000
Ed. in Chief – Joy C. de los Reyes

PHILIPPINE DAILY GLOBE (M)
Nova Communications Inc., 2nd Flr., Rudgen Bldg., Manila, Philippines; tel (63) 2 6730496
Circ.: 40,000
Pub. – Benjamin C. Ramos
Ed. in Chief – Yen Makabenta

PEOPLE'S JOURNAL (D)
Times Journal Bldg., Railroad St., cnr 19th St., Manila, Philippines; tel (63) 2 527 8421; fax 527 4629; web site www.journal.com.ph
Circ.: 219,000
Ed. in Chief – Augusto Villanueva

PHILIPPINE STAR (D)
13th Corner Railroad St., Port Area, Manila, 1016, Philippines; tel (63) 2 527 7901; fax 527 5820; e-mail info@philstar.com; web site www.philstar.com
Circ.: 275,000
Pres. – Miguel G. Belmonte
Exec. Vice Pres. – Grace Glory Go
Ed. in Chief – Issac G. Belmonte

MANILA STANDARD (M)
Elizalde Bldg., Ayalda Ave., 4th Fl., Manila, Philippines; tel (63) 2 163893
Pub. – Rodolfo T. Reyes
Ed. in Chief – Alejandro del Rosario

THE MAKATI BUSINESS DAILY (D)
429 Mueva St., Manila, Philippines; tel (63)
Pub./Ed. – Veronica T. Velosoyap

UNIVERSAL DAILY NEWS (M)
Traders Bldg., 275 Juan Luna St., 2nd Flr., Manila, Philippines; tel (63)
Circ.: 5,000
Ed. – Eddie Lee
Adv. Mgr. – Henry Sy

WORLD NEWS (D)
549 T. Pinpin St., Binondo, Manila, Philippines; tel (63) 2 402751
Circ.: 35,000
Pub. – Florencio Mallare
Ed. in Chief – Go Eng Guan
Adv. Mgr. – Joseph Ong

METRO MANILA

DAILY TRIBUNE (D)
The Penthouse Suites, GLC Bldg., Metro Manila, Philippines; tel (63) 2 521 5577; web site www.tribune.net.ph
Circ.: 35,000
Pub. – Ninez Cacho-Olivares

SINGAPORE

SINGAPORE

LIANHE ZAOBAO (M) Est.1923
1000 Toa Payoh N., Singapore, 318994, Singapore; tel (65) 6319 6319; fax 6319 8119; web site www.zaobao.com
Circ.: 205,158Last Audit: November 23, 2011
Group: Singapore Press Holdings Limited
Editor, Lianhe Zaobao – Goh Sin Teck

LIANHE WANBAO (ES)
News Centre, 82 Genting Ln., Singapore, 349567, Singapore; tel (65) 6319 6319
Circ.: 85,500
Ed. – Chua Chim Kang

SHIN MIN DAILY NEWS (E)
1000 Toa Payoh N., News Centre, Singapore, 318994, Singapore; tel (65) 6319 2269; fax 6319 8166; e-mail shinmin@sph.com.sg; web site www.sph.com.sg
Circ.: 120,126
Ed. – Koh Lin Hoe

BUSINESS TIMES (M-EX S)
1000 Toe Peyoh N., Singapore, 318994, Singapore; tel (65) 6319 1050; fax 6319 8282; e-mail btnews@sph.com.sg; sphcorp@sph.com.sg; web site www.sph.com.sg
Circ.: 36,000
Ed. – Alvin Tay

NANYANG XINGZHOU (M)
307 Alexandra Rd., Singapore, Singapore; tel (65) 635555
Ed. – Loy Teck Juan
Mktg. Mgr. – Lee Cheok Yew
Adv. Mgr. – Teo Hankim

THE NEW PAPER (MS)
1000 Toa Payoh N., Singapore, 318 994, Singapore; tel (65) 6319 6319; fax 6319 8266; e-mail tnp@sph.com.sg; web site www.sph.com.sg
Circ.: 121,000
Ed. – Dominic Nathan
Deputy Ed. – Melvin Derpal Singh

SUNDAY TIMES (S)
1000 Toa Payoh N., Singapore, 318 994, Singapore; tel (65) 6319 6319; fax 6319 8282; e-mail sphcorp@sph.com.sg; web site www.sph.com.sg
Circ.: 387,000
Ed. in Chief – Cheong Yip Seng
Ed. – Leslie Fong

STRAITS TIMES (M) Est.1984
1000 Toa Payoh N., Singapore, 318994, Singapore; tel (65) 6319 6319; fax 6319 8150; e-mail sphcorp@sph.com.sg
Circ.: 392,611
Group: Singapore Press Holdings Ltd

STRAITS TIMES (D)
1000 Toa Payoh N., News Centre, Singapore, 318994, Singapore; tel (65) 6319 5397; fax 6319 8282; e-mail stonline@sph.com.sg; stlocal@sph.com.sg; web site www.straitstimes.com
Circ.: 352,000Last Audit: March 24, 2010
Group: Dow Jones International Marketing Services
Mktg. Mgr. – Leslie Fong
Ed. in Chief – Patrick Daniel
Ed. – Han Fook Kwang

BERITA HARIAN (M)
1000 Toa Payoh N., News Centre, Singapore, 318994, Singapore; tel (65) 6319 6319; fax 63198252; web site www.stpress-books.com.sg
Circ.: 60,000
Group: Singapore Press Holdings Limited
Executive Director – Shirley Hew
Ed. – Han Fook Kwang

TAMIL MURASU (MS)
82 Genting Ln. No. 06-07, Singapore, 349567, Singapore; tel (65) 6388 3838; fax 6341 7195; web site www.tamilmurasu.com.sg
Adv. Mgr – Karunanidhi Jeevaratnam
Ed. – M. Nirmala

USA TODAY (D)
7500A Beach Rd., Singapore, Singapore; tel (65) 2972933; fax 2965446

SOUTH KOREA

ANSAN, KYONGGI

KYUNGIN MAEIL SHINMUN (M)
1028, Sonpu-Dong, Ansan, Kyonggi, South Korea; tel (82) 345 863411
Pres. – Yon-Sok Shin
Mng. Ed. – Han-Sik Kang
Adv. Mgr. – Song-Kyun O

CHANGWON, KYONGSANG

KYUNGNAM SHINMUN (E)
100-5, Shinwol-dong, Changwon, Kyongsang, South Korea; tel (82) 551 832211; fax 832227
Circ.: 159,728
Pres. – Kim Dong-Kyu
Ed. – Park Sung-Kwan

CHEJU

CHE MIN ILBO (D)
290-64, Yon-dong, Cheju, 690-170, South Korea; tel (82) 64 741 3111; fax 743 9530
Pres. – Myong-Pyo Hong
Adv. Mgr. – Tok-Nam Kim
Mng. Ed. – Chong-Hung Kang

CHEJU DAILY NEWS (D)
2324-6, Yon-dong, Cheju, South Korea; tel (82) 64 740 6114; fax 742 2004; e-mail cjnews@chejunews.co.kr; web site www.chejunews.co.kr
Circ.: 32,150
Pres. – Kim Dae-Sung

HALLA ILBO (6X WK.)
568-1, Samdo 1-dong, Cheju, South Korea; tel (82) 64 750 2114; fax 750 2520; web site www.hallailbo.co.kr
Ed. in Chief – Kim Yin pae

CHINJU, KYONGSANG

SHIN KYUNGNAM ILBO (M)
237-4, Sangpyong-dong, Chinju, Kyongsang, South Korea; tel (82) 55 751 1000; fax 757 1722
Pres. – Hung-Chi Kim
Ed. – Nak-Ryul Song
Mng. Ed. – Yong-Jin Park

CHONGJU, CHUNGCHONG

CHUNGCHONG DAILY NEWS (M)
304, Sachang-dong, Hungduk-ku, Chongju, Chungchong, South Korea; tel (82) 43 279 5011; fax 279 5050; web site www.cctimes.co.kr
Circ.: 38,020
Pres. – Ahn Byung-Sup
Ed. – Ahn Chie-Young

JOONG-BU MAEIL (M)
150-1, Shinpong-Dong, Hungtok-gu, Chongju, Chungchong, South Korea; tel (82) 431 2752001
Pres. – Sung-Chae Lee
Mng. Ed. – Yong-Hoe Kim

CHONJU, CHOLLA

CHOLLA ILBO (M)
748-3, 3-ga, Ua-dong, Tokchin-gy, Chonju, Cholla, South Korea; tel (82) 652 537111
Pres. – On-Song Hwang
Mng. Ed. – Chong-Kyu Chong

CHONBUK DOMIN ILBO (M)
207-10, 2-ka, Tokchin-dong, Tokchin-ku, Chonju, Cholla, South Korea; tel (82) 63 251 7216; fax 251 6218; web site www.domin.co.kr
Pres. – Lim Byoung-Chan
Mng. Ed. – Yang Chae-Suk

CHONBUK ILBO (D)
710-5, Kumam-dong, Tokchin-ku, Chonju, Cholla, South Korea; tel (82) 63 250 5500; fax 250 0090; web site www.jjan.co.kr
Ed. – Choi Pong Sung

CHUNCHEON, GANGWON

KANGWON ILBO (E)
31 Jungang-no, Chuncheon, Gangwon, South Korea; tel (82) 33 258 1000; fax 252 5884; web site www.kwnews.co.kr
Circ.: 58,381
Pres. – Cho Sung
Ed. – Cho Kwang

DAEGU

MAEIL SHINMUN (M-6X WK.)
71, 2-ka, Kyesan-dong, Chung-ku, Daegu, South Korea; tel (82) 53 255 5001; fax 255 8902; e-mail imaeil@msnet.co.kr; web site www.imaeil.com
Circ.: 300,000
Ed. – Chang Ryong

DAEJEON

TAEJON MAEIL SHINMUN (E)
400 Kalma-dong So-ku Daejeon, Daejeon, South Korea; tel (82) 42 521 5530; fax 380 7159
Circ.: 90,087
Pres. – Namjin Jung
Ed. – Kwang Hi Lee

INCHON

INCHON ILBO (D)
18-1, 4-ka, Hang-dong, Chung-ku, Inchon, South Korea; tel (82) 32 452 0114; fax 763 8822; web site news.itimes.co.kr
Mgr. – Tang Sain
Ed. – Park Young Jin

KIHO ILBO (D)
1, 1-ga, Chungang-dong, Chung-gu, Inchon, South Korea; tel (82) 32 761 0001
Pres. – Kang-Hun So
Ed. – Kim Jung Tae

KWANGJU, GWANGIU

CHONNAM MAEIL SHINMUN (E)
183-2, 5-ga, Kumnam-no, Tong-ku, Kwangju, Gwangiu, South Korea; tel (82) 62 234 0540
Pres. – U-Chun Kim
Mng. Ed. – Hui-Taek Choe

CHUNNAM ILBO (D)
700-5, Chunghung-dong, Puk-ku, Kwangju, Gwangiu, South Korea; tel (82) 62 527 0015; fax 527 3320
Pres. – Lee Jung-Il

KWANGJU ILBO (D)
1, 1-ka, Kumnam-no, Tong-ku, Kwangju, Gwangiu, South Korea; tel (82) 62 222 8111; fax 227 9500; e-mail kwangju@kwangju.co.kr; web site www.kwangju.co.kr
Ed. – Kim Dae-jung

MOODEUNG ILBO (D)
699-2, Chunghung-Dong, Puk-ku, Kwangju, Gwangiu, South Korea; tel (82) 62 606 7760; e-mail root@honam.co.kr
Pres. – Chun Young Chung

MASAN, KYONGSANG

DONGNAM ILBO (D)
2-3, 3-ga, Chungang-dong, Happo-gu, Masan, Kyongsang, South Korea; tel (82) 551 211300
Pres. – In-Tae Kim
Ed. in Chief – Chi-Sok Kim

KYUNGNAM DAILY NEWS (E)
100-5, Shinwol-Dong, Changwon, Masan, Kyongsang, South Korea; tel (82) 55 283 2211
Ed. – Aeeson Bok

PUCHON, KYONGGI

SOODOKWON ILBO (D)
1029-21, Hokye, 1-Dong, Tongan-ku, Puchon, Kyonggi, South Korea; tel (82) 361 589060
Pres. – Chae-Chung Kim
Ed. in Chief – Yong-Ho Son

PUSAN

HAHNGDO ILBO (M)
1637-1, Yonsan 2-dong, Tongrae-gu, Pusan, South Korea; tel (82) 51 8630071
Pres. – In-Su Kim
Adv. Mgr. – Ki-To Nam

KOOKJE DAILY NEWS (E-6X WK.)
76-2, Geoje-dong, Yonje-Ku, Pusan, 611-702, South Korea; tel (82) 51 500 5114; fax 500 5123; web site www.pusannews.co.kr
Pres. – Khawn Myoung-Vo

PUSAN ILBO (D)
1-10, Sujong-dong, Dong-ku, Pusan, 601-738, South Korea; tel (82) 51 461 4114; fax 463 8880; e-mail webmaster@pusanilbo.co.kr; web site www.pusanilbo.co.kr
Circ.: 427,000
Pres. – Kim Jong Lyus

PUSAN MAEIL SHINMUN (D)
1637-1, Yonsan-2-dong, Tongrae-gu, Pusan, South Korea; tel (82) 51 8630071
Pres. – In-Hyong Lee
Ed. in Chief – Chae-Kun Song

SEOUL

CHOSUN ILBO (M)
61, 1-ka, Taepyong-no, Chung-ku, Seoul, 100-756, South Korea; tel (82) 2 724 5114; fax 724 5018; web site www.chosun.com
Circ.: 1,960,000
Pub. – Yong Sik Pyun
Circ. Mgr. – Joo Lee Hyeok
Ed. in Chief – Joon Ho Hong

DAILY INDUSTRIAL NEWS (D)
1, 2-ga, Myong-dong, Chung-gu, Seoul, South Korea; tel (82) 2 7740091

DONG-A ILBO (D)
139-1, 3-ka, Chungchon-no, Sodaemun-ku, Seoul, 110, South Korea; tel (82) 2 360 0316; fax 360 0329; e-mail newsroom@dong.com; web site www.donga.com
Circ.: 2,150,000
Pres. – Jae-ho Kim

FINANCIAL & SECURITIES DAILY (D)
86-4, Songsan-dong, Mapo-gu, Seoul, South Korea; tel (82) 2 3388833

HAN-JOONG DAILY NEWS (M)
91-1, 2-ka, Myong-dong, Chung-ku, Seoul, South Korea; tel (82) 7762801; fax 7782803
Circ.: 5,000
Pres. – Su-Tong Kang
Mng. Dir. – Chung-Son Lee
Mng. Ed. – Chun-Saeng Im

SEOUL KYUNGJE SHINMUN (D)
Chung-gu Choongmuro St. 4, Seoul, South Korea; tel (82) 2 724 2450; fax 730 9092; web site www.sed.co.kr
Circ.: 500,000
Pres. – Jong-Gun Lin
Ed.-in-Cheif – Jong-Hwan Lee

HANKOOK ILBO (6X WK.)
118, Jungko, Namdae moon Rd. 2ga, Seoul, South Korea; tel (82) 2 724 2325; fax 732 4124; e-mail webmaster@hk.co.kr; web site www.hankooki.com
Circ.: 200,000Last Audit: March 29, 2010
Pres. – Chang Chae-Keun
Ed. – Lee Jong-Sung

KOREA TIMES (6X WK.)
43, Chungmuro 3-ga, Chung-ku, Seoul, 100-013, South Korea; tel (82) 2 724 2343; fax 736 4061; web site www.koreatimes.co.kr
Circ.: 200,000
Pres. – Park Moo Jong
Adv. Mgr. – Jake J. Nho

HANKYOREH SHINMUN (D)
116-25, Kongdok-dong, Mapo-ku, Seoul, 121-020, South Korea; tel (82) 2 710 0114; web site www.hani.co.kr
Circ.: 500,000
Ed. in Chief – O. Hyan

JEIL ECONOMIC DAILY (M)
40-1, 3-ka, Hangang-no, Yongsan-ku, Seoul, 140-013, South Korea; tel (82) 2 7921131; fax 7921130
Pres. – Hwang Myung-Soon
Ed. in Chief – Lee Soo-Sam

JOONG-ANG ILBO (D)
7, Soonhwa-dong, Chung-ku, Seoul, 100-759, South Korea; tel (82) 2 751 5114; fax 751 5404; e-mail feedback@joongang.co.kr
Circ.: 2,020,000
Pres./Pub. – Seok-Hyun Hong
Ed. in Chief – Song Jin Hyuk
Ed. – Lee Ji Hoon
Mng. Ed. – Nam Kyu Han

KOOK-MIN ILBO (E)
371-16, Shinsu-dong, Mapo-ku, Seoul, South Korea; tel (82) 2 7054114; fax 7054116; web site www.kookminilbo.co.kr
Pres. – Cha Il-Suk

KOREA DAILY (D)
55-1, 2-ga, Chongno, Chongno-gu, Seoul, South Korea; tel (82) 2 (82-2) 2796621

KOREA ECONOMIC DAILY (M-6X WK.)
441, Chungnim-dong, Chung-ku, Seoul, 100-791, South Korea; tel (82) 2 360 4114; fax 312 6610; e-mail inter@hankyung.com; web site www.hankyung.com
Circ.: 520,000
Group: Admarket International (Div. of Marcom International, Inc.)
Pres. – Shin Sang Min
Ed. – Kim Jeong Ho

KOREA HERALD (M) Est.1953
1-17, Jeong-Dong, Jung-gu, Seoul, 100-120, South Korea; tel (82) 2 727 0205; fax 727 0670; e-mail subscribe@heraldm.com; web site www.koreaherald.co.kr
Circ.: 50,000Last Audit: March 23, 2010
Group: Admarket International (Div. of Marcom International, Inc.)
Mng.Ed. – Shiyong Chon
CEO&publisher – Byung-chang Yoo
Chief editorial writer – Nam-hyun Choi

KYUNG-HYANG SHINMUN (M-EX S)
22, Chong-dong, Chung-ku, Seoul, 100-702, South Korea; tel (82) 2 3701 1114; fax 735 6140
Circ.: 500,000Last Audit: March 23, 2010
Pres. – Song Young Seong

MAEIL KYUNGIE SHINMUN (E)
30, 1-Ga, Pil-dong, Jung-gu, Seoul, 100-728, South Korea; tel (82) 2 2000 2114; fax 2000 2109; e-mail ceo@mk.co.kr; web site www.mk.co.kr
Circ.: 235,000
Chairman & Publisher – Dae-whan CHANG

MINJU DAILY NEWS (M)
44-37, Youido-dong, Yongdungpo-gu, Seoul, South Korea; tel (82) 2 6321981
Pres./Adv. Mgr. – Yong-Su Kim

SEGYE TIMES (D)
63-1, 3-ka, Hangang-no, Yongsan-ku, Seoul, South Korea; tel (82) 2 799 4114; fax 799 4520; e-mail webman@segye.com; web site www.segye.com
Pres. – Hwang Hwan-Chai
Ed. – Mok Jung-Gyum

SEOUL SHINMUN (M)
25, 1-ka, Taepyong-no, Chung-ku, Seoul, South Korea; tel (82) 2 724 5542; fax 721 5849; web site www.seoul.co.kr
Circ.: 700,000
Pub./Pres. – Son Chu-Hwan
Mng. Ed. – Lee Dong-Hwa

SPORTS CHOSUN (M)
61, 1-ka, Taepyong-no, Chung-ku, Seoul, South Korea; tel (82) 2 724 6114; fax 724 6979; web site www.sportschosun.com
Circ.: 400,000
Adv. Mgr. – Nam Kyu Park
Ed. in Chief – Bang Sang-Hoon

THE HERALD BUSINESS (M)
1-17, Jeong-Dong, Jung-gu, Seoul, 100-120, South Korea; tel (82) 2 727 0114; fax 727 0661; web site www.heraldm.com
Circ.: 300,000
Mng. Ed. – Yoon Young Chang

SUWON

KYEONGIN ILBO (M)
1122 Ingyetong Palgu, Suwon, South Korea; tel (82) 31 231 5114; fax 232 1231; web site www.kyeongin.com
Circ.: 127,900
Ed. in Chief – Kim Hwa-Yang

SUWON, KYONGGI

JOONG BOO ILBO (D)
1036-2, Ingye-dong, Paltal-gu, Suwon, Kyonggi, South Korea; tel (82) 31 230 2115; fax 233 3014; e-mail sahb2@joongboo.com; web site www.joongboo.com
Ed. in Chief – Chin-Yong Lee

KYEONGGI ILBO (E)
452-1, Songjuk-dong, Changan-ku, Suwon, Kyonggi, South Korea; tel (82) 31 250 3333; fax 250 3306; e-mail webmaster@kgib.co.kr; web site www.kgib.co.kr
Chrmn. – Shin Son-Chol
Mng. Ed. – Lee Chin-Yong

KYEONGIN ILBO (D)
1122-11,Inkye-Dong,Paldal-Gu, Suwon, Kyonggi, South Korea; tel (82) 31 231 5114; fax 231 5236; web site www.kyeongin.com
Circ.: 127,900
Chrmn. – Song Kwang-Suc
Mng. Ed. – Kim Hwa-Yang

TAEJON

TAEJON DAILY NEWS (D)
1-135, Munhwa-dong, Chung-ku, TAEJON, South Korea; tel (82) 42 251 3311; fax 254 3323; web site www.daejonilbo.com
Chrmn – Soo Yong-Shin
Planning Mgr. – Sang Hyeon

TAEGU

DAEGU ILBO (5X WK.)
177, N-10, Tung-Fong, Chung-gu, Taegu, South Korea; tel (82) 53 757 5700; fax 757 5788; e-mail ysw@idaegu.com; web site www.idaegu.com
Pub. – Lee Taeyeol
Sec. – Chang Nkyeongneun
Ed. – Han Guk-Sun

KYUNG BUK ILBO (E)
286-2, Hyomok-dong, Tong-gu, Taegu, South Korea; tel (82) 53 741 2222
Pres. – Hong-Sok Ko
Adv. Mgr. – Chu-Yong Pak
Mng. Ed. – Chong-Hwa Yu

YEONGNAM ILBO (D)
111, Shinchon-dong, Tong-Ku, Taegu, 701750, South Korea; tel (82) 53 756 8001; fax 756 9011; e-mail master@yeongnam.co.kr; web site www.yeongnam.co.kr
Asst. Mgr. – Kim Sang-Kin

TAEJON

JUNGDO ILBO (E)
274-7, Kalma-dong, Suh-ku, Taejon, South Korea; tel (82) 42 220 1114; fax 220 1188; web site www.joongdoilbo.co.kr
Chrmn. – Lee Sung-Yol
Mng. Ed. – Sung Ki-Hoon

ULSAN, KYONGSANG

KYUNGSANG ILBO (D)
299-10, Mugo-dong, Nam-gu, Ulsan, Kyongsang, South Korea; tel (82) 522 241 001; fax 241 030
Ed. – Tung Nyungsuk

YOCHON, CHOLLA

HANNAM DAILY NEWS (E)
44-3, Hak-dong, Yochon, Cholla, South Korea; tel (82) 65843501
Pres. – Chong-Kyun Chong
Mng. Ed. – Chung-Hong Yun
Adv. Mgr. – Chang-Hyon Kim

SRI LANKA

COLOMBO

LAKJANATHA (E-5X WK.)
Janata Lake House, D.R. Wijewardene Mawatha, Colombo, 10, Sri Lanka; tel (94) 11 242 9231; fax 242 9329; e-mail lakjanatha@lakehouse.lk; web site www.lakehouse.lk
Circ.: 15,000
Ed. in Chief – Sujeewa Dissanayaka

SILUMINA (WEEKLY)
PO Box 248, Colombo, 10, Sri Lanka; tel (94) 11 242 9269; fax 242 9260; web site www.silumina.lk
Circ.: 254,000
Ed. – W.B. Mettananda

THINAKARAN (MS)
Lake House, D.R. Wijewardene Mawatha, Colombo, 10, Sri Lanka; tel (94) 11 242 9429; web site www.dailynews.lk
Adv. Mgr. – WWS Preethiaith
Ed. in Chief – Siva Subramaniam

DAILY NEWS (M-EX S)
35 D R Wijewardena Mawatha, Colombo, 10, Sri Lanka; tel (94) 11 242 1181; fax 242 9210; web site www.dailynews.lk
Circ.: 65,000

Ed. Dir. – Nihal Raenaike
Ed. in Chief – Jayatilleke Desilva
Sr. Associate Ed. – Pramod Desilva

DINAMINA (M-EX S)
PO Box 248, Colombo, 10, Sri Lanka; tel (94) 11 242 9261; fax 242 9260; web site www.dinamina.lk
Circ.: 140,000
Ed. in Chief – Mahinda Abaysundara

OBSERVER (ES)
PO Box 248, Colombo, 10, Sri Lanka; tel (94) 1 242 9429; web site www.lanka.net/lakehouse
Ed. – Ajith Samaranayake

DAWASA (M)
PO Box 226, Colombo, 12, Sri Lanka; tel (94) 1 23864
Circ.: 108,000
Ed. – Rohana Gamage

DINAKARA (M)
95 Maligakanda Rd., Colombo, 10, Sri Lanka; tel (94) 1 595754
Circ.: 12,000
Ed. – Mulen Perera

MITHRAN VARAMALAR (WEEKLY)
185 Grandpass Rd., Colombo, 14, Sri Lanka; tel (94) 1 320881; fax 448205; e-mail virakesari@lanka.com.lk
Circ.: 29,000
Ed. – P. Suriyakumary
Mng. Dir. – M.G. Wenceslaus

VIRAKESARI (MS)
PO Box 160, Colombo, 14, Sri Lanka; tel (94) 11 232 7827; fax 532 2740; web site www.virakesari.lk
Ed. in Chief – V. Devaraja

SUN (D)
PO Box 226, Colombo, 12, Sri Lanka; tel (94) 1 23864
Circ.: 59,400
Ed. – Rex De Silva

THE ISLAND/THE ISLAND SUNDAY EDITION (DS)
PO Box 133, Colombo, 13, Sri Lanka; tel (94) 11 249 7567; fax 249 7543; e-mail island@lanka.com.lk; web site www.island.lk
Ed. in Chief – Manik de Silva

DIVAINA (MS)
PO Box 133, Colombo, 13, Sri Lanka; tel (94) 1 324 001; fax 448 103
Circ.: 100,000
Ed. in Chief – Upali Tennakoon

DAILY LANKADEEPA (D)
8 Hunupitiya Cross Rd., Colombo, 2, Sri Lanka; tel (94) 11 423 920; fax 231 4651; web site www.lankadeepa.lk
Circ.: 259,172
Ed. in Chief – Siri Ransinghe

JAFFNA

EELAMURASU (D)
140 Navalar Rd., Jaffna, Sri Lanka; tel (94) 21 22389
Pub. – M. Amirthalingam

EELANADU (M)
PO Box 49, Jaffna, Sri Lanka; tel (94) 21 22389
Circ.: 15,000
Ed. – M. Sivanantham
Chrmn. – S. Raveenthiranathan

TAIWAN

BEIJING

THE PEOPLE'S DAILY
Chaoyang Dist., West, Beijing, 100733, Taiwan; tel (852) 2308 7910; e-mail kf@peopledaily.com.cn; web site www.people.com.cn
Group: Brydson Global Media Sales
Ed. in Chief – Cao Hong Liang

CHENGUANG

THE COMMONS DAIRY (D)
31 Third Rd., Chenguang, Taiwan; tel (886) 7 336 3131; fax 336 3604
Circ.: 30,000Last Audit: December 28, 2006
Pub. – Jui-Paio Lee
Ed. – Hwang Yeh

HUALIEN

KENG SHENG DAILY NEWS (D)
36 Wuchuan St., Hualien, Taiwan; tel (886) 38 340 131; fax 341 406
Circ.: 50,000
Pub. – Leater Hsing
Ed. – Chen Hsing

KAOHSIUNG

CHINA DAILY
1366 Chunghua 5th Rd., Kaohsiung, Taiwan; tel (886) 7 3332203; fax 3349557
Group: Admarket International (Div. of Marcom International, Inc.)
Pub. – H.H. Liu
Chrmn. – Wen-Hsia Lee

CHINA EVENING NEWS (E)
71 Linhai St., Fengshan, Kaohsiung, Taiwan; tel (886) 7 8122525
Circ.: 60,000
Pub. – Lai Jung Tsen

MIN CHUNG DAILY NEWS (M)
180 Minchuan, 2nd Rd., Kaohsiung, Taiwan; tel (886) 3363131; fax 3363604
Circ.: 148,000
Pub. – Lee Jer-Lang
Ed. – Lee Wang-Tai

PACIFIC DAILY NEWS (M)
13 Yencheng St., Kaohsiung, Taiwan; tel (886) 7 5316131; fax 5215993
Chrmn. – C.C. Chen
Pub. – K.P. Cheng

TAIWAN HSIN WEN DAILY NEWS (M)
249 Chung Cheng 4th Rd., Kaohsiung, Taiwan; tel (886) 7 295 8951
Pub. – Chao Li-Nien
Ed. – Hsieh Tsung-Min

TAIWAN TIMES (M)
110 Chung Shan 1st Rd., Kaohsiung, Taiwan; tel (886) 7 215 5666; fax 215 0264
Circ.: 148,000
Pub. – Wang Yuh-Chen
Ed. – Hwang Dong-Lieh

KINMEN, QUEMOY

KINMEN DAILY NEWS (M)
Chin Hu Village, Kinmen, Quemoy, Taiwan; tel (886) 8 232874
Circ.: 5,000
Pub. – Chen Shoei-Tzoy
Ed. – Yang Cherng-Yeh

MATSU

MATSU DAILY NEWS (M)
1 Jenai Village, Nankan Hsiang, Matsu, Taiwan; tel (886) 8 362276
Pub. – Hwang Nan-Tung
Ed. – Yu Chang-Chao

PENGHU, PESCADORES

CHIEN KUO DAILY NEWS (M)
36 Min Sheng Rd., Makung, Chen, Penghu, Pescadores, Taiwan; tel (886) 6 9272675; fax 9273618
Circ.: 15,000
Pub. – Kuo Chung
Ed. – Lu Kuo-Hsiung

TAICHUNG

CHUNG KUO DAILY NEWS
147-10 Chungching Rd., Taichung, Taiwan; tel (886) 4 (886-4) 2922108

DAILY FREE PRESS (E)
402-12 Peitun Rd., Taichung, Taiwan; tel (886)
Circ.: 20,000
Pub. – E-M Wu
Ed. – Hsin-Chang Tsai

TAIWAN DAILY NEWS (M)
361 Wen Shin Rd., Section 3, Taichung, Taiwan; tel (886) 4 2295 8511; fax 2295 6163
Circ.: 250,000
Pub. – Anthony Chiang

TAINAN

CHINA DAILY NEWS (D)
57 Hsi Hwa St., Tainan, Taiwan; tel (886) 6 229 6381; fax 220 1804
Circ.: 670,000
Ed. – Tien Shing Chan

TAIPEI

CENTRAL DAILY NEWS (M)
260 Pa Teh Rd., Section 2, Taipei, Taiwan; tel (886) 2 27765368; fax 27775835
Circ.: 600,000
Pub./Ed. in Chief – Huang Huitsen

CHAO JAN TIMES (M)
139 Nanchang Rd., 2nd Flr., Section 2, Taipei, Taiwan; tel (886)
Pub. – Pao-Hai Yuan
Ed. – Ho-Chien Li

THE CHILDREN'S DAILY NEWS (M)
6F, 38 Fuhsing North Rd., Taipei, Taiwan; tel (886) 2 771 6622; fax 775 5769
Pub. – Hung-Tien Lin
Ed. – Hua-Jung Wang

CHINA MORNING NEWS (M)
16 Nanking East Rd., 7th Flr.-5, Section 1, Taipei, Taiwan; tel (886) 2 5231545
Pub./Ed. – Hung Te-Jung

CHINA NEWS (M)
10th Fl., 41 Tung Hsing St., Taipei, Taiwan; tel (886) 2 2351 7666; fax 2351 5330; e-mail chinews@tpts1.seed.net.tw; supplements@etaiwannews.com; web site www.etaiwannews.com
Circ.: 180,000
Chrmn./Pub. – Simone Wei
Mng. Ed. – Anthony Lawrance

CHINA DAILY NEWS (M)
10/F, 109-1, Tung Hsing St., Taipei, Taiwan; tel (886) 6 229 6381; fax 220 1804; e-mail cdns@ms1.hinet.net; web site www.cdns.com.tw
Circ.: 100,000
Pub. – Simone Wei

CHINA POST (D) Est.1952
8 Fu Shun St., Taipei, 104, Taiwan; tel (886) 2 2596 9971; fax 2595 7962; e-mail cpost@msl.hinet.net; info@mail.chinapost.com.tw; web site www.chinapost.com.tw
Circ.: 180,000
Pub./Ed. – Jack Huang

CHINA TIMES EXPRESS (E)
132 Da Le St., Taipei, Taiwan; tel (886) 2 23087111; fax 23048138
Circ.: 400,000
Chrmn. – Yu Chi-Chung
Pub. – Alice Yu
Ed. – Lin Kuo-Ching

CHINA TIMES (MS)
132 Da Le St., Taipei, Taiwan; tel (886) 2 2308 7111; e-mail service@it.chinatimes.com.tw; web site www.chinatimes.com.tw
Circ.: 1,200,000
Ed. in Chief – Wang Mei Yu

CHUNG CHENG PAO (M)
34/2 Twelve Chang Rd., Taipei, Taiwan; tel (886)
Circ.: 50,000
Pub. – Ruey-Hauh Lee
Ed. – Chein-Min Hsiao

COMMERCIAL TIMES (D)
132 Da Le St., Taipei, Taiwan; tel (886) 2 2308 7111; fax 2308 4708
Circ.: 250,000
Pub. – Yu Chi-Cheng
Ed. in Chief – Jimmy Chang

DA-MIN NEWS
5F, 18, Alley 1, Ln. 768, Paleh Rd., Section 4, Taipei, Taiwan; tel (886) 2 7885570; fax 7864782
Pub. – Pal-Hsun Liu
Chrmn. – Tsai-Wang Lan

LES ECHOS
2 Tientsin St., Taipei, Taiwan; tel (886) 2 3228718; fax 3568233
Pub. – Arthur lap

ECONOMIC DAILY NEWS (MS)
555 Chung Hsiao East Rd., Section 4, Taipei, 10516, Taiwan; tel (886) 2 2768 1234; fax 2746 3550; e-mail news@udn.com; web site www.udnnews.com.tw
Circ.: 356,000
Pub. – Wang Pi-Ly
Ed. – Lu Shih Hsiang

FINANCE AND ECONOMIC TIMES (M)
7F, 61 Roosevelt Rd., 7th Flr., Section 1, Taipei, Taiwan; tel (886) 2 3221772; fax 3221776
Pub. – Hsi-Kuang Yuan
Ed. – Tien-Ming Yuan

FORTUNE DAILY NEWS
6F, 20, Alley 1, Ln. 768, Pateh Rd., Section 4, Taipei, Taiwan; tel (886) 2 7820005; fax 7820426
Pub./Dir. – C.T. Hsu

THE GREAT NEWS (M)
216 Chen Teh Rd., Section 3, Taipei, Taiwan; tel (886) 2 2597 3111
Circ.: 310,000
Pub. – Chen Che-Chia

GWOYEU RYHBAW (D)
2-10, Fuchow St., Taipei, Taiwan; tel (886) 2 2392 1133; fax 2341 0203; e-mail feedback@mail.mdnkids.com; web site

www.mdnkids.com
Pub. – Lin Liang

THE HERALD NEWS (M)
203 Chunghsiao West Rd., 3rd Flr., Section 1, Taipei, Taiwan; tel (886) 2 3112951
Pub./Ed. – C.C. Lee

INDEPENDENCE EVENING POST (E)
15 Chi Nan Rd., Section 2, Taipei, Taiwan; tel (886) 2 2351 9621; fax 2341 9054
Circ.: 307,071
Pub. – Chen Tsen-Huei
Ed. – Lee Sen-Hong

INDEPENDENCE MORNING POST (M)
15 Chi Nan Rd., Section 2, Taipei, Taiwan; tel (886) 2 2351 9621; fax 2351 4219
Circ.: 310,087
Pub. – Kuo Cheng-Chau
Ed. – Su Jeng-Ping

KING LIGHT (M)
10 Chungking South Rd., B Flr., Section 1, Taipei, Taiwan; tel (886)
Pub./Ed. – Owen Zou

MANDARIN DAILY NEWS (M)
4 Foo Chou St., Taipei, Taiwan; tel (886) 2 2392 1133; e-mail feedback@mail.mdnkids.com; web site www.mdnkids.com
Pub. – Lin Liang

MANDARIN TIMES
38 Nan King Rd., 9th Flr., Rm. G, Section 2, Taipei, Taiwan; tel (886) 2 561 1592
Pub. – C.C. Lee

MIN SHEN PAO
555 Chung Hsiao East Rd., Section 4, Taipei, Taiwan; tel (886) 2 2768 1234; fax 2756 0955
Chrmn. – Pi-Cheng Wang
Pub. – Shaw-lan Wang

MIN SHENG DAILY (D)
555 Chung Hsiao East Rd., Section 4, Taipei, Taiwan; tel (886) 2 2768 1234; fax 2746 3571; e-mail news@udn.com; web site www.udn.com
Circ.: 556,639
Pub. – Wang Shaw-Lan
Ed. in Chief – Gloria Hsu Rong-Hun

TAIPEI JOURNAL (WEEKLY)
Two Tianjin St., Taipei, 10051, Taiwan; tel (886) 2 2397 0180; fax 2356 8233; e-mail ttonline@mail.gio.gov.tw; web site http://taiwantoday.tw
Group: Government Information Office, R.O.C.(Taiwan)Philip Yang

TAIWAN HSIN SHENG PAO (M)
12th Flr., 110 Yengping South Rd., Taipei, Taiwan; tel (886) 2 2311 7000; fax 2311 5319
Circ.: 460,000
Pub. – Su Yu-Chen
Ed. – Wann Tsu

TAIWAN LIH PAO (M)
1 Ln. 17, Sector 1, Mu-Cha Rd., Taipei, 116, Taiwan; tel (886) 3 2236 7116; fax 2236 7116; web site www.shu.edu.tw
Pub./Dir. – Lu-Hsi Cheng
Chrmn. – Ming-Hsun Yeh

TATUNG TIMES (M)
45 Antung St., 10th Flr.-7, Taipei, Taiwan; tel (886)
Pub./Ed. – Li-Ping Cheng

TRADERS EXPRESS
333 Keelung Rd., 8th Fl., Section 1, Taipei, Taiwan; tel (886) 2 2725 5200; fax 2757 6828; e-mail e-member@taitra.org.tw; web site www.taiwantrade.com.tw
Ed. in Chief – C.J. Hsu

UNIFICATION DAILY (M)
70 Nanchang Rd., 9th Flr.-1, Section 2, Taipei, Taiwan; tel (886)
Pub./Ed. – Hsai-Chou Peng

UNITED DAILY NEWS (D)
555 Chung Hsiao East Rd., Section 4, Taipei, 10516, Taiwan; tel (886) 2 2746 3533; fax 2546 3570; web site www.udn.com
Circ.: 1,200,000
Pub. – Wang Shaw-Lan
Ed. – Suang Huang

WEALTH NEWS
11F, 52 Nanking East Rd., 7th Flr., Section 1, Taipei, Taiwan; tel (886) 2 551 2561; fax 531 6438
Pres./Pub. – Y.H. Chiu
Dir. – W.H. Sun

WORLD TRIBUNE (M)
342 Keeling Rd., 9th Fl., Section 1, Taipei, Taiwan; tel (886) 2 723 1791
Pub./Ed. – Huai-Hsuan Chung

YOUTH DAILY NEWS (M)
3 Hsinyi Rd., Section 1, Taipei, Taiwan; tel (886) 2 23222722
Pub. – Tien Tuan-Yuan
Ed. – Chiao Cheng-Chong

TAIPEI (MUNICIPALITY)

UNITED EVENING NEWS (D)
555 Chung Hsiao East Rd., Section 4, Taipei (Municipality), Taiwan; tel (886) 2 2746 3533; fax 2746 3570; web site www.udn.com
Ed. – Iping Fu

TAIPEI CITY

LIBERTY TIMES (E)
Lakes Rd. 399, Taipei City, 11492, Taiwan; tel (886) 2 2656 2828; fax 2656 1099; e-mail letters@taipeitimes.com; web site www.taipeitimes.com; www.libertytimes.com.tw
Circ.: 500,000
Pub. – Yen Wen-Shun
Ed. in Chief – Lin Jian-Lian

TOUNAN

TAIWAN JUSTICE DAILY NEWS
1 Kunglun Rd., Tounan, Taiwan; tel (886) 5 596 0626; fax 596 0629
Pub. – Wu-Sheng Hsu
Chrmn. – Hsiao-Tien Wu

THAILAND

BANGKOK

DAILY MIRROR (E)
15/8 Lardprao, Bangkok, 501124, Thailand; tel (66) 2 5380220; fax 5301826
Circ.: 60,000
Pub./Ed. – Yingpan Manasikavn

KHAO PANICH (D)
22/27 Thanon Ratchadaphisek, Bangkok, 10900, Thailand; tel (66) 2 5115066
Circ.: 30,000
Pub./Ed. – Samruane Sumphandharak

DAILY TIMES (M)
60 Sukumvit Soi 42, Kluey Nam Thai, Bangkok, Thailand; tel (66) 2 392 5021
Circ.: 10,000
Pub./Ed. – Chote Maneenoi
Adv. Mgr. – Van Chalerm

KIATTIYOS (M)
25 Prachathiprathai Rd., Bangkok, Thailand; tel (66)
Circ.: 5,000
Pub./Ed. – Phajon Pinthuyothin

KHOA SOD DAILY NEWSPAPER (D)
12 Tethsaban-naremern Rd., Prachanivate 1, Bangkok, 10900, Thailand; tel (66) 2 5800021; fax 5899112
Circ.: 120,000

KROHLEK (E)
499/9 Petchburi Rd, Ratchthevi, Phyathai, Bangkok, Thailand; tel (66)
Circ.: 8,000
Pub./Ed. – Sangwian Soodrak

KRUNGTHEB VICHARN (M)
1111-2 Soi Thinnakorn, Phyathai Rd., Bangkok, Thailand; tel (66)
Circ.: 1,500
Pub./Ed. – Kongkiat Na Ranong

MATICHON DAILY NEWSPAPER (M)
12 Thanon Thedsaban Naruban, Prachanivate 1, Chatu, Bangkok, 10900, Thailand; tel (66) 2 589 0020; fax 589 7049; web site www.matichon.co.th
Circ.: 180,000
Ed. – Wipa Sukkit

NAEW NA (D)
96 Moo 3, Vibhavadi Rangsit Rd., Bangkok, 10210, Thailand; tel (66) 2 521 4127; e-mail naewna@naewna.com; naewna@yahoo.com; contac@naewna.com; web site www.naewna.com
Circ.: 200,000
Ed. – Tarinya Tshansavak

THE NATION (M)
44 Moo 10 Bang Na-Trat, Km. 4.5, Bang Na district, Bangkok, 10260, Thailand; tel (66) 2 316 5900; fax 317 2071; e-mail bangna@nation.nationgroup.com; info@nationgroup.com; web site www.nationmultimedia.com
Chrmn. – Thanachai Theerapatvong
Vice Chrmn. – Thanachai Santichaikul
CFO – Vanchai Sriherunrusmee
Ed. in Chief – Suthichai Yoon
Ed. – Pana Janviroj
Mng. Ed. – Kavi Chongkittavorn
Deputy Mng. Ed. – Tulsathit Taptim
Deputy Mng. Ed. – Sorrayuth Suthassanachinda
Deputy Mng. Ed. – Francesco Delfino
Contributing Ed. – Sopon Onkgara
Chief Sub-Ed. – Richard Valendares

BAAN MUANG (M)
1 Soi Pluem-Manee, Thanon Vibhavadi Rangsit Rd., Bangkok, 10900, Thailand; tel (66) 2 513 0230; fax 513 3106
Ed. in Chief – Bhalow Chun Suk Ki

THAI CHONG DAILY NEWS (M)
970/31 Charoenkrung, Talad Noi, Bangkok, 10100, Thailand; tel (66)
Circ.: 10,000
Pub./Ed. – Arunee Ammarjbundit

PALANG CHON (M)
275 Krungthep-Nonth, Bangkok, Thailand; tel (66) 2 5859852
Circ.: 2,000
Pub./Ed. – Phoomchai Inthapanti

PHAYA CRUT (M)
72 Soi Woranpong Samsen Rd., Bangkok, Thailand; tel (66)
Circ.: 100,000
Pub. – Wandee Thongprapa
Ed. – Wason Thonvisud

PHNOM PENH POST (WEEKLY)
PO Box 12-1074, Bangkok, 10121, Thailand; tel (855) 23 426568; fax 428309; e-mail michael.pppost@worldmail.com.kh; web site www.phnompenhpost.com
Mng. Dir. – Kathleen Hayes
Adv. Mgr. – James Whittle
Pub./Ed. in Chief – Michael Hayes
Mng. Ed. – Peter Sainsbury
Prodn. Ed. – John Treizse
Prodn. Mgr. – Peter Huttenmoser

BANGKOK POST (D)
Bangkok Post Bldg., 136 Na Ranong Rd., Klong Toey, Bangkok, 10110, Thailand; tel (66) 2 240 3700; fax 240 3666; web site www.bangkokpost.co.th; www.postpublishing.co.th
Circ.: 56,750
Ed. – PattnaPong Chantianont Wong

PRACHA CHANG DAILY NEWS (D)
30/2 Soi Naphasap Yaek One Sukhumvit Road Klongton Klongtoey, Bangkok, 10100, Thailand; tel (66) 2 661 2517; fax 661 5189
Pub. – Preeda Hetrakool

MORNING EXPRESS (M)
242 Ammuay Songkram Rd., Bangkok, Thailand; tel (66)
Circ.: 10,000
Dir./Ed. – Usum Nimmanhemindra

SAI KLANG (5X WK.)
163/52 Prapinklao Rd., Bangkok, 10700, Thailand; tel (66) 2 423 0317; fax 433 7787; web site www.saiklang.com
Circ.: 10,000
Pub. – Suvit Phadermchit

DAO SIAM (M)
60 Mansion 4, Thanon Rajdamnern, Bangkok, 10200, Thailand; tel (66) 2 2226001; fax 2226885
Circ.: 120,000
Pub./Ed. – Santi Untrakarn

DAILY NEWS (M)
1/4 Thanon Vibhavadi Rangsit, Bangkok, Thailand; tel (66) 2 561 1456; fax 561 1343; web site www.dailynews.co.th
Ed. – Pracha Hetrakul

SIAM RATH (E)
12 Mansion Six, Thanon Rajdamnern, Bangkok, 10200, Thailand; tel (66) 2 224 1952; fax 224 1982
Circ.: 150,000
Ed. – Assiri Thammachot

SIAM TIMES (M)
192/8-9 Soi Voraphong, Visuthikasat Rd., Bangkok, Thailand; tel (66) 2 2817422
Circ.: 5,000
Pub. – Nerong Charusophon

SIANG PUANG CHON (M)
52/3-8 Banpanthom Ln., Prasumen, Bangkok, Thailand; tel (66) 2 2811076
Circ.: 93,000
Dir./Ed. – Ruang-nam Ruang-Vooth

SIRINAKORN (M)
108 Suapa Rd., Bangkok, Thailand; tel (66) 2 221 4181; fax 225 4073
Circ.: 80,000
Dir. – Prasert Areeves
Ed. – Prasil Sirivareeves

NEW CHINESE DAILY NEWS (M)
1022-1030 Thanon Charoenkrung, Talad Noi, Bangkok, Thailand; tel (66) 2 234 0684; fax 234 0684
Circ.: 72,000
Dir. – Kriet Leephone
Ed. – Pusadee Keetaworanart

PIMTHAI (M)
163/54 Phrapinklao, Bangkok, Thailand; tel (66) 2 433 5997
Circ.: 10,000
Pub./Ed. – Chamnong Khumpairoj

TAWAN SIAM (M)
72 Soi Worapong, Samsen Rd., Bangkok, Thailand; tel (66)
Circ.: 97,000

Dir. – Wandee Thongprapa
Ed. – Charlerm Siboonrveng

TEP SIAM (M)
120 Charoenkrung Rd., Bangkok, Thailand; tel (66)
Circ.: 2,000
Pub./Ed. – Angun Saardsaengthong

THAI (M)
423-425 Thanon Chao Khamrop, Bangkok, Thailand; tel (66) 2 2233175
Circ.: 4,000
Pub./Ed. – Vichien Mana-Natheethoratham

THAI SHANG YIG PAO (E)
877-879 Charoenkrung Rd., Bangkok, 10100, Thailand; tel (66) 2 236 9172; fax 238 5286
Circ.: 85,000
Adv. Mgr. – Samnuk Kyayatanokij
Ed. – Chart Payonitikarn

TONG HUA DAILY NEWS (D)
877/879 Thanon Charoenkrung, Talad-Noi, Bangkok, 10100, Thailand; tel (66) 2 236 9172; fax 238 5286
Circ.: 85,000
MD – Sakorn Kyavatanaki
Ed. – Chart Payonithikarn

UNIVERSAL DAILY NEWS (D)
21/1 New Rd., Bangkok, Thailand; tel (66) 2 221 3411; fax 224 4745; web site www.uniteddaily.com
Circ.: 25,000
Ed. – Lin Shin Shung

THAI RATH (M)
1 Viphavadirangsit Rd., Bangkok, 10900, Thailand; tel (66) 2 272 1030; fax 272 1324; e-mail newmedia@thairath.co.th; web site www.Thairath.co.th
Circ.: 10,000,000
Ed. – Pithoon Sunthorn

VISNEWS (D)
72 Soi Vorapong, Samson Rd., Bangkok, Thailand; tel (66) 2 2820643

BANGKOK WORLD (E)
U-Chuliang Foundation Bldg., 968 Rama IV Rd., 3rd Floor, Bangkok, Thailand; tel (66)
Circ.: 12,000
Ed. – Anussorn Thavisin
Mktg. Dir. – Prasit Maekwatana

KLONG TOEY, BANGKOK

SIAM POST (D)
136 Na Ranong Rd., Klong Toey, Bangkok, 10110, Thailand; tel (66) 2 240 3700; fax 240 3791; web site www.bangkokpost.com
Circ.: 60,000
Mng. Dir. – Paisal Sricharatchanya

UNITED KINGDOM

LONDON,

LLOYD'S OF LONDON PRESS (5X WK.)
Est.1734
Guardian House, 4th Floor, 119 Farringdon Road, London, , EC1R 3DA, United Kingdom; tel (0044) 020 701 75445; e-mail info@lloydslist.com; web site www.lloydslist.com
Editor, Lloyd's List – Richard Meade
Editor and Chief, Lloyd's List Asia – Tom Leander
Head of Marketing, Lloyd's List – Louise Challoner

VIETNAM

HANOI

QUAN DOI NHAN DAN (D)
7 Phan Dinh Phung St., Hanoi, Vietnam; tel (84) 4 747 1029; fax 747 4913; web site www.qdnd.vn
Circ.: 60,000
Ed. in Chief – Le Phuc Nguyen

NHAN DAN (D)
71 Hang Trong St., Hanoi, Vietnam; tel (84) 4 3825 4231; fax 3825 5593; e-mail toasoan@nhandan.org.vn; web site www.nhandan.com.vn
Circ.: 200,000
Ed. in Chief – Dinh The Huynh

HANOI MOI (D)
44 Le Thai To Ave., Hanoi, Vietnam; tel (84) 4 3825 3067; fax 3828 7327; web site www.hanoimoi.com.vn
Circ.: 50,000Last Audit: March 23, 2010
Ed. in Chief – Ho Quing Loi

HO CHI MINH CITY

SAI GON GIAI PHONG (D)
432 Nguyen Thi Minh Khai, Ho Chi Minh City, Vietnam; tel (84) 8 839 5942; e-mail sggponline@sggp.org.vn; web site www.sggp.org.vn
Circ.: 100,000
Ed. in Chief – Vuong Trong

NEWSPAPERS OF AUSTRALIA AND NEW ZEALAND

AUSTRALIA

ADELAIDE

SUNDAY MAIL (S)
9th Flr., 121 King William St., Adelaide, 5001, Australia; tel (61) 8 82062000; fax 82063646
Circ.: 342,210
Ed. – Kerry Sullivan
Advertising28.05 casual rate.

THE ADELAIDE ADVERTISER (M-6X WK.)
GPO Box 339, Adelaide, 5001, Australia; tel (61) 8 8206 2220; fax 8206 3669; web site www.adelaidenow.com.au
Circ.: 199,689
Ed. – Melvin Mansell
Advertising20.25 casual rate (mon.-fri.); 24.95 casual rate (sat.).

THE AUSTRALIAN (M-6X WK.)
GPO Box 339, Adelaide, 5001, Australia; tel (61) 8 8206 2686; fax 8206 3688; e-mail sa@theaustralian.com.au; web site www.theaustralian.com.au
Ed. in Chief – Chris Mitchell
Ed. – Paul Whittaker

THE ADELAIDE NEWS (E-5X WK.)
GPO Box 339, Adelaide, 5001, Australia; tel (61) 8 8206 2729; fax 8206 3688; e-mail tiser@adv.newsltd.com.au
Circ.: 143,418
Adv. Mgr. – John Goidan
Ed. – Melvin Minsaoo

BALLARAT

THE BALLARAT COURIER (M-6X WK.)
110 Creswick Rd., Ballarat, VIC, 3350, Australia; tel (61) 3 5320 1200; fax 5333 1651; e-mail inquiries@thecourier.com.au; web site www.thecourier.com.au
Circ.: 20,000
Chief of Staff – Chloe Biggin
Ed. – Angela Carey
Advertising6.95 casual rate (mon.-fri.); 7.65 casual rate (sat.).

BATHURST

WESTERN ADVOCATE (M-EX S.)
PO Box 11, Bathurst, 2795, Australia; tel (61) 2 6331 2611; fax 6332 2709; e-mail mail.westernadvocate@ruralpress.com; web site www.westernadvocate.com.au
Circ.: 27,200
Last Audit: March 23, 2010
Advisor – Andrew Naanahan
Ed. – Murray Nicholls
Advertising5.29 casual rate.

BENDIGO

BENDIGO ADVERTISER (M-6X WK.)
PO Box 61, Bendigo, 3550, Australia; tel (61) 3 5434 4400; fax 5434 4440; web site bendigo.yourguide.com.au
Circ.: 15,231
Gen Mgr – Mirgot Filconer
Ed. – Peter Kennedy
Advertising5.95 casual rate.

BRISBANE

THE AUSTRALIAN (M-6X WK.)
GPO Box 2145, Brisbane, 4001, Australia; tel (61) 7 3666 7465; fax 3666 7499; e-mail queensland@theaustralian.com.au; web site www.theaustralian.news.com.au
Ed. in Chief – Chris Mitchell

THE COURIER-MAIL (M-6X WK.)
GPO Box 130, Brisbane, 4001, Australia; tel (61) 7 800 630 130; fax 3666 6696; e-mail subscriptions@thecouriermail.com.au; web site www.thecouriermail.com.au
Circ.: 600,000
Ed. – David Fagan
Advertising38.25 casual rate (mon.-fri.); 48.30 casual rate (sat.).

THE DAILY SUN (E-EX WKND.)
GPO Box 222, Brisbane, 4001, Australia; tel (61) 7 2533333; fax 2533103
Circ.: 121,872
Pub. – F. Moore
Ed. – Mike Quirk
Adv. Mgr. – Bill Stephens

SUNDAY SUN (S)
GPO Box 222, Brisbane, 4001, Australia; tel (61) 7 2533333; fax 2533103
Circ.: 352,115
Pub. – F. Moore
Adv. Mgr. – B. Stephens

BRISBANE, QLD

THE SUNDAY MAIL (S)
GPO Box 130, Brisbane, Qld, 4001, Australia; tel (61) 7 3666 6127; fax 3252 6691
Circ.: 598,065
Editor, The Courier-Mail – Michael Crutcher

BROADWAY

GREEK HERALD (D)
PO Box 146, Broadway, 2007, Australia; tel (61) 2 9660 2033; fax 9669 2302; e-mail greek@foreignlanguage.com.au
Circ.: 25,530
Pub. – Theo Skalkos
Ed. – Michael Mystakidis

BROKEN HILL

BARRIER DAILY TRUTH (M-EX S.)
Est.1908
PO Box 453, Broken Hill, 2880, Australia; tel (61) 8 8087 2355; fax 8088 5066; e-mail inquiries@bdtruth.com.au; web site www.bdtruth.com.au
Circ.: 6,000
Gen. Mgr. – John Casey
Adv. Mgr. – Peter R. Keenan
Ed. – David Pearce
Advertising6.00 casual rate.

BUNDABERG

NEWS-MAIL (M-6X WK.)
PO Box 3006, Bundaberg, QLD, 4670, Australia; tel (61) 7 4153 8555; fax 4153 1028; web site www.news-mail.com.au
Circ.: 12,842
Adv. Mgr. – Bruce Partridge
Circ. Mgr. – Lisa Prowd
Ed. – Christina Ongley
Advertising7.90 casual rate.

BURNIE

THE ADVOCATE (M-6X WK.)
PO Box 63, Burnie, 7320, Australia; tel (61) 3 6440 7409; fax 6440 7461; e-mail news@theadvocate.com.au; web site www.theadvocate.com.au
Circ.: 25,189
Ed. – Jason Puadia

THE WEEKENDER
PO Box 63, Burnie, 7320, Australia; tel (61) 3 6440 7409; web site www.theadvocate.com.au
Circ.: 13,671
Ed. – D.J. Cherry
Adv. Mgr. – P. Sproule

CABRAMATTA

CHIEU DUONG (5X WK.)
PO Box 64, Cabramatta, NSW, 2166, Australia; tel (61) 2 9725 6444; fax 9725 6446; e-mail email@chieuduong.com.au; web site www.chieuduong.com.au
Circ.: 55,000
Ed. in Chief – Nhat Giang

CAIRNS

CAIRNS POST (M-6X WK.)
PO Box 126, Cairns, 4870, Australia; tel (61) 7 4052 6666; fax 4052 6630; e-mail enquiries@tcp.newsltd.com.au; web site www.cairnspost.com.au
Circ.: 26,945
Last Audit: March 21, 2010
Gen. Mgr. – Nick Tromps
Adv. Mgr. – Tracy Couper
Ed. – Andrew Webster
Advertising7.20 casual rate (mon.-fri.); 7.92 casual rate (sat.).

F.N.Q. SUNDAY (S)
PO Box 126, Cairns, 4870, Australia; tel (61) 7 4052 6666; fax 4052 6630; e-mail enquiries@tcp.newsltd.com.au; web site www.cairnspost.com.au
Circ.: 28,500

CANBERRA

THE CANBERRA TIMES (D)
PO Box 7155, Canberra, 2610, Australia; tel (61) 2 6280 2122; fax 6280 2282; e-mail media.release@canberratimes.com.au; web site www.canberratimes.com.au
Circ.: 34,000; 72,008(sat); 40,488(sun)
Last Audit: March 21, 2010
Ed. – Rod Quinn

THE AUSTRALIAN (D)
Ste. 117, Press Gallery, Parliament House, Canberra, 2600, Australia; tel (61) 2 6270 7000; fax 6270 7071; e-mail act@theaustralian.com.au; web site www.theaustralian.news.com.au
Ed. in Chief – Chris Mitchell
Ed. – Paul Whittaker

COFFS HARBOUR

THE ADVOCATE (6X WK.)
PO Box 534, Coffs Harbour, 2450, Australia; tel (61) 2 6652 2522; e-mail advocate@coffscoastadvocate.com.au; web site www.coffscoastadvocate.com.au
Circ.: 20,000
Gen Mgr. – Craig Frost
Ed. – Brent Rees
Advertising7.05 casual rate.

DARWIN

SUNDAY TERRITORIAN (S)
PO Box 1300, Darwin, NT, 0801, Australia; tel (61) 8 89449900; fax 89816045
Circ.: 26,437
Ed. – David Coren

NORTHERN TERRITORY NEWS (D)
PO Box 1300, Darwin, NT, 0801, Australia; tel (61) 8 8944 9900; fax 8981 3693; e-mail online@ntn.newsltd.com.au; web site www.ntnews.com.au
Circ.: 24,000; 31,000(sat); 24,000(sun)
Gen. Mgr. – Evin Hannah
Adv. Dir. – Cecilia Quek
Ed. – Julian Ricci
Circ. Mgr. – Jason McCormick

DUBBO

DAILY LIBERAL (M-6X WK.)
PO Box 311, Dubbo, 2830, Australia; tel (61) 2 6883 2900; fax 6882 5898; e-mail mail.liberal@ruralpress.com; web site www.dailyliberal.com.au
Circ.: 35,517
Pub./Ed. – Aaron Likan
Adv. Mgr. – Annissa Shean
Circ. Mgr. – Elizabeth Tarry
Advertising7.00 casual rate.

GEELONG

THE ECHO (D)
PO Box 91, Geelong, 3220, Australia; tel (61) 3 5220 5700; fax 5220 5799; e-mail echo@geelongadvertiser.com.au
Ed. – Gavin Whyte

GEELONG ADVERTISER (M-6X WK.)
PO Box 91, Geelong, 3220, Australia; tel (61) 3 5227 4300; fax 5227 4330; e-mail reception@geelongadvertiser.com.au; web site www.geelongadvertiser.com.au
Circ.: 26,024
Gen. Mgr. – Mark Jirdy
Ed. – Steele Killon
Advertising8.10 casual rate.

GEELONG NEWS (D)
PO Box 91, Geelong, 3220, Australia; tel (61) 3 N/A
Ed. – Gavin Whyte

GERALDTON

GERALDTON GUARDIAN (E-4X WK.)
PO Box 128, Geraldton, 6531, Australia; tel (61) 8 9956 1000; fax 9956 1030; web site www.geraldtonguardian.com.au
Gen. Mgr. – Malcolm Smith
Adv. Mgr. – Grege Stephen
Ed. – Charles Jenkinson
Prodn. Mgr. – Joe Criddle

GLADSTONE

THE GLADSTONE OBSERVER (M-6X WK.)
PO Box 351, Gladstone, 4680, Australia; tel (61) 7 4970 3030; e-mail newsroom@gladstoneobserver.com.au; administration@gladstoneobserver.com.au; web site www.gladstoneobserver.com.au
Circ.: 7,512
Gen. Mgr. – Carl Carter
Adv. Mgr. – Philip Clynes
Ed. – Meredith Papavasiliou
Advertising5.00 casual rate.

GOULBURN

GOULBURN POST (M-6X WK.)
PO Box 152, Goulburn, 2580, Australia; tel (61) 2 4827 3500; e-mail class.goulburnpost@ruralpress.com; web site www.goulburn.yourguide.com.au
Ed. – John Thistleton
Advertising7.60 casual rate.

GRAFTON

THE DAILY EXAMINER (M-6X WK.)
PO Box 271, Grafton, NSW, 2460, Australia; tel (61) 2 6643 0500; fax 6642 7156; e-mail newsroom@dailyexaminer.com.au; web site www.dailyexaminer.com.au
Circ.: 7,751
Gen. Mgr. – Judy Lewis
Adv. Mgr. – Nick Inmon
Ed. – David Cincrost
Advertising6.25 casual rate.

GRIFFITH

THE AREA NEWS
Corner of Ulong and Olympic St., Griffith, 2680, Australia; tel (61) 2 6962 1733; fax 6964 1844; e-mail news@dailyadvertiser.com.au; web site www.areanews.com.au
Circ.: 3,545
Adv. Mgr. – Lyn Uruuhart
Ed. – Daniel Johns

GYMPIE

THE GYMPIE TIMES (M-5X WK.)
PO Box 394, Gympie, 4570, Australia; tel (61) 7 5482 1011; fax 5480 4204; e-mail counter@gympietimes.com.au; web site www.gympietimes.com.au
Circ.: 5,501
Gen. Mgr. – Andrew Smith
Adv. Mgr. – Tracey McKean
Circ. Mgr. – Deb Rowlands
Ed. – Nev McHarg
Prodn, Mgr. – Sharmaine Gear
Advertising6.70 casual rate.

HAYMARKET

THE AUSTRALIAN CHINESE DAILY (M-6X WK.)
PO Box K525, Haymarket, 1240, Australia; tel (61) 2 9261 3033; fax 9261 3525; e-mail info@aucd.com.au
Circ.: 20,000
Ed. – Daniel Tong
Advertising3.00 casual rate (mon.-fri.); 3.70 casual rate (sat.).

CHINESE HERALD (6X WK.)
PO Box K65, Haymarket, 2000, Australia; tel (61) 2 9281 2988; fax 9281 8328; e-mail info@ausdaily.com.au; enquiry@ausdaily.com.au; web site www.1688.com.au
Circ.: 20,000
Pub. – Roger Huang

SING TAO JIH PAO (D)
PO Box K351, Haymarket, 2000, Australia; tel (61) 2 9264 7876; fax 9267 6567; web site www.singtaonewscorp.com
Circ.: 30,000
Dir. – Sally Aw Sian
Ed. – Patrick Poon

HERVEY BAY

CHRONICLE (M-6X WK.)
PO Box 217, Hervey Bay, 4655, Australia; tel (61) 7 4120 1000; fax 4120 1043; web site www.frasercoastchronicle.com.au
Circ.: 10,100
EDITOR – Peter Chapman
Advertising7.82 casual rate.

HOBART

THE SUNDAY TASMANIAN (S)
91-93 Macquarie St., Hobart, 7000, Australia; tel (61) 3 62300622; fax 62300711; e-mail mercuryedletter@dbl.newsltd.com.au
Circ.: 53,449
Ed. – Ian McCausland
Mng. Dir. – Rex Gardner
Advertising13.30 casual rate.

THE MERCURY (D)
93 Macquarie St., Hobart, 7000, Australia; tel (61) 3 6230 0622; fax 6230 0766; web site www.themercury.com.au
Circ.: 45,210
Mng. Dir. – Rex Gardner
Adv. Dir. – Michael Moffitt
Mgr., Mktg. – Marian Maclachlan
Circ. Mgr. – Bill Roe
Ed. – Garry Bailey
Advertising14.80 casual rate (mon.-fri.); 16.75 casual rate (sat.).

THE AUSTRALIAN (M-6X WK.)
49 Salamanca Pl., Hobart, 7000, Australia; tel (61) 3 6224 2196; fax 6224 2164; web site www.theaustralian.news.com.au
Ed. in Chief – Chris Mitchell
Tasmanian Correspondent – Den Holm

IPSWICH

THE QUEENSLAND TIMES (M-6X WK.)
PO Box 260, Ipswich, 4305, Australia; tel (61) 7 3817 1717; fax 3817 1775; e-mail qt@qt.com.au; web site www.qt.com.au
Circ.: 13,348
Gen. Mgr. – Steve Portas
Adv. Mgr. – Paul Young
Ed. – Stuart Sherwin
Advertising10.75 casual rate (mon.-fri.); 11.80 casual rate (sat.).

KALGOORLIE

KALGOORLIE MINER (M-6X WK.)
Est.1895
PO Box 10392, Kalgoorlie, 6430, Australia; tel (61) 8 9022 0555; e-mail news@kalminer.com.au; web site www.kalminer.com.au
Circ.: 5,500; 8,700(sat)
Group: The West Australian
General Manager – Tracee Relph
Editor – Anne Skinner
Front Office Manager – Stacey Strong
Senior Sales Excutive – Jannice Ward
Production Manager – Genine Werner
Circulation & Administration Manager – Bianca Hopkinson
Deputy Editor – Carmel Puckett
Accountant – Malcolm Hamilton
Advertising7.01 casual rate (mon.-fri.); 7.41 casual rate (sat.).

LAUNCESTON

THE SUNDAY EXAMINER (S)
PO Box 99A, Launceston, 7250, Australia; tel (61) 3 6336 7111; fax 6334 7328; e-mail mail@examiner.com.au; web site www.examiner.com.au
Circ.: 42,000
Ed. – Rod J. Scott
Advertising13.10 casual rate.

THE EXAMINER (D)
PO Box 99, Launceston, 7250, Australia; tel (61) 3 6336 7111; fax 6334 7328; e-mail mail@examiner.com.au; admin@examiner.com.au; web site www.examiner.com.au
Circ.: 50,000
Adv. Mgr. – Joel Brewer
Circ. Mgr. – Rob King

Ed. – Fiona Reynolds
Advertising13.10 casual rate (mon.-fri.); 14.45 casual rate (sat.).

LISMORE

THE NORTHERN STAR (M-6X WK.)
PO Box 423, Lismore, 2480, Australia; tel (61) 2 6620 0500; fax 6620 0577; web site www.northernstar.com.au
Circ.: 20,968
Gen. Mgr. – Paul Spotswood
Sales Adv. Mgr. – Janet Bowden
Brand Sales Mgr. – Kellie Creighton
Ed. – David Kirkpatrick
Advertising10.65 casual rate (mon.-fri.); 11.75 casual rate (S).

MACKAY

THE DAILY MERCURY (M-6X WK.)
Mercury House, 38-40 Wellington St., Mackay, 4740, Australia; tel (61) 7 4957 0444; fax 4953 4009; e-mail news@dailymercury.com.au; web site www.dailymercury.com.au
Circ.: 16,045; 19,839(sat)
Group: APN NEWS AND MEDIA
GENERAL MANAGER – DARREN MCVEAN

MAITLAND

MAITLAND MERCURY (E-5X WK.)
PO Box 222, Maitland, NSW, 2320, Australia; tel (61) 2 4931 0100; fax 4933 8087; e-mail mail.mercury@ruralpress.com; web site www.maitlandmercury.com.au
Circ.: 5,505
Gen. Mgr. – Peter Kennett
Ed. – Tick Ner
Advertising7.45 casual rate.

MANLY

THE MANLY DAILY (D-5X WK.)
26 Sydney Rd., Manly, 1655, Australia; tel (61) 2 9977 3333; fax 9977 2831; web site www.manlydaily.com.au
Circ.: 90,000
Ed. – Luke Mcilveen
Advertising9.65 casual rate.

MAROOCHYDORE

SUNSHINE COAST DAILY (D) Est.1980
PO Box 56, Maroochydore, 4558, Australia; tel (61) 7 5430 8000; fax 5443 5150; e-mail community@thedaily.com.au; web site www.sunshinecoastdaily.com.au
Circ.: 20,603
Last Audit: March 22, 2010
Group: APN Australian Regional Media
Gen. Mgr. – Paul Kent
Ed. in Chief – Mark Furler
Adv. Mgr. – Nigel Irving

MELBOURNE

THE AGE (D)
PO Box 257C, Melbourne, 3001, Australia; tel (61) 3 9600 4211; fax 13006 66499; e-mail inquiries@theage.com.au; web site www.theage.com.au
Circ.: 197,000; 308,000(sat)
Ed. in Chief – Paul Ramadge

SUNDAY AGE (S)
250 Spencer St., Melbourne, 3000, Australia; tel (61) 3 96004211; fax 96021856
Circ.: 220,000
Pub. – Steve Harris
Ed. – Michael Gawenda
Advertising24.50 casual rate.

THE SUN NEWS-PICTORIAL (M-6X WK.)
44-74 Flinders St., Melbourne, 3000, Australia; tel (61) 3 9292 2000
Ed. – Colin Duck
Adv. Mgr. – Ian Rose

THE HERALD SUN (D-6X WK.)
PO Box 14999, Melbourne, 8001, Australia; tel (61) 3 9292 2000; fax 9292 2112; e-mail helpline@heraldsun.com.au; news@heraldsun.com.au; web site www.heraldsun.news.com.au
Circ.: 575,317
Adv. Mgr. – Sean Atkinson
Ed. in Chief – Phil Gardner
Advertising70.50 casual rate (mon.-fri.); 63.00 casual rate (sat.).

THE AUSTRALIAN (M-6X WK.)
PO Box 14740, Melbourne, 8001, Australia; tel (61) 3 9292 2888; fax 9292 2803; e-mail victoria@theaustralian.com.au; web site www.theaustralian.news.com.au
Ed. in Chief – Chip Lejrand
Ed. – Christopher Dora

SUNDAY OBSERVER (S)
45-50 Porter St., Prahran, Melbourne, 3181, Australia; tel (61) 3 525555
Circ.: 91,545
Pub. – Leigh Garwood
Ed. – Jim Lawrence

MILDURA

SUNRAYSIA DAILY (M-6X WK.)
PO Box 1400, Mildura, 3502, Australia; tel (61) 3 230211; fax 234817
Pub. – W.R. Lanyon
Ed. – Kevin Boyle
Adv. Mgr. – Malcolm J. Goodieson
Gen. Mgr. – Des Morris
Advertising4.55 casual rate.

MOUNT GAMBIER

BORDER WATCH (4X WK.) Est.1861
PO Box 309, Mount Gambier, 5290, Australia; tel (61) 8 8724 1555; fax 8724 1551; e-mail scoop@borderwatch.com.au; web site www.borderwatch.com.au
Circ.: 8,750
Gen. Mgr. – Tim Lewis
Ed. – Jason Wallace
Circ. Mgr. – Demi Ploenges
Advertising8.00 casual rate.

MOUNT ISA

THE NORTH WEST STAR (M-5X WK.)
PO Box 777, Mount Isa, QLD, 4825, Australia; tel (61) 7 4743 3355; fax 4743 9789; e-mail admin@starnews.com.au; web site ^www.northweststar.com.au
Circ.: 4,183
Gen. Mgr. – Peter Baldwin
Ed. – Tahnee Watson
Advertising6.44 casual rate.

MURWILLUMBAH

TWEED DAILY NEWS (M-6X WK.)
PO Box 6336, Murwillumbah, 2486, Australia; tel (61) 7 5524 6400; web site www.tweednews.com.au
Circ.: 7,204
Gen. Mgr. – Alisdair McLean
Adv. Mgr. – Kevin Wheitley
Ed. – Natlie Gauld
Advertising4.95 casual rate.

NEWCASTLE

THE NEWCASTLE HERALD (M-6X WK.)
28-30 Bolton St., Newcastle, 2300, Australia; tel (61) 2 4979 5000; web site www.theherald.com.au
Circ.: 51,000
Gen. Mgr. – Julie Ainsworth
Adv. Sales Mgr. – Jason King
Ed. – Roger Brock

NOWRA

SOUTH COAST (MON, WED, FRI)
PO Box 106, Nowra, 2541, Australia; tel (61) 2 4421 9123; fax 4421 8160; web site www.southcoastregister.com.au
Circ.: 45,600
Adv. Mgr. – Nick Beale
Ed. – John Hanscombe
Advertising5.45 casual rate.

ORANGE

CENTRAL WESTERN DAILY (M-6X WK.)
PO Box 321, Orange, 2800, Australia; tel (61) 2 6391 2900; fax 6362 9679; e-mail mail.cwd@ruralpress.com; web site www.centralwesterndaily.com.au
Circ.: 5,863
Last Audit: March 22, 2010
Gen. Mgr. – Andrew Meenahan
Ed./Mng. Ed. – Tony Rheid
Advertising5.65 casual rate.

PERTH

THE AUSTRALIAN (M-6X WK.)
34 Stirling St., Perth, 6000, Australia; tel (61) 8 9326 8412; fax 9325 9217; e-mail news@theaustralian.com.au; wa@theaustralian.com.au; web site www.theaustralian.news.com.au
Ed. – Paul Whittaker

SUNDAY TIMES (S)
34 Stirling St., Perth, 6000, Australia; tel (61) 8 9326 8326; fax 9221 1121; web site www.sundaytimes.news.com.au
Adv. Mgr. – David Perrins
Mktg. Servs. Mgr. – Janine Mayger
Ed. – Brett McCarthy

THE WEST AUSTRALIAN (D-6X WK.)
PO Box D162, Perth, 6001, Australia; tel (61) 8 9482 3111; fax 9482 3177; e-mail editor@wanews.com.au; web site au.news.yahoo.com/thewest
Circ.: 198,211
Last Audit: March 22, 2010
Ed. – Brett McCarthy
Advertising31.50 casual rate (sat.); 22.80 casual rate (mon.-fri.).

PYRMONT

AUSTRALIAN FINANCIAL REVIEW (D-6X WK.)
1 Darling Island Rd., Pyrmont, 2009, Australia; tel (61) 2 9282 2512; fax 9282 2484; web site www.afr.com
Circ.: 90,000
Adv. Mgr. – Phil Gallagher
Ed. in Chief – Michael Gill
Ed. Dir. – Glenn Burge
Advertising41.20 casual rate.

ROCKHAMPTON

THE MORNING BULLETIN (M-6X WK.)
PO Box 397, Rockhampton, QLD, 4700, Australia; tel (61) 7 4930 4222; fax 4930 4360; e-mail tmbully@capnews.com.au; web site www.themorningbulletin.com.au
Circ.: 25,000
Last Audit: March 23, 2010
Gen. Mgr. – Simon Irwin
Ed. – Frazer Pearce
Advertising8.00 casual rate.

SHEPPARTON

THE SHEPPARTON NEWS (M-5X WK.)
PO Box 204, Shepparton, 3632, Australia; tel (61) 3 5831 2312; fax 5831 2059; e-mail n/a; web site www.sheppnews.com.au
Circ.: 10,156
Ed. – Richard Bryce
Chief Executive Officer – Damian Trezise
Advertising5.70 casual rate.

SOUTHBANK

THE SUNDAY HERALD SUN (S)
HWT Tower, 40 City Rd., Southbank, 3006, Australia; tel (61) 3 92922000; fax 92922080; e-mail sundayhs@hwt.newsltd.com.au
Circ.: 500,000
Ed. – Alan Howe
Advertising47.50 casual rate.

SOUTHPORT

THE GOLD COAST BULLETIN (6X WK.)
PO Box 1, Southport, 4215, Australia; tel (61) 7 5584 2000; fax 5539 3950; web site www.goldcoast.com.au
Circ.: 42,515
MD – Steve Haward
Circ. Mgr. – Michael Horvath
Ed. in Chief – Dean Gould
Prodn. Mgr. – Andrew Nightingale
Advertising13.42 casual rate (mon.-fri.); 17.60 casual rate (sat.).

SURRY HILLS

THE AUSTRALIAN (M-6X WK.)
PO Box 4245, Surry Hills, 2010, Australia; tel (61) 2 9288 3000; fax 9288 2250; e-mail nsw@theaustralian.com.au; web site www.theaustralian.news.com.au
Circ.: 122,500; 311,000(sat)
Chief of Staff – David King
Ed. – Paul Whittiken
Advertising29.90 casual rate (mon.-fri.); 56.00 casual rate (sat.).

SYDNEY

THE SYDNEY MORNING HERALD (M-6X WK.)
PO Box 506, Sydney, 2001, Australia; tel (61) 2 9282 2833; fax 9282 3253; e-mail smh@access.fairfax.com.au; newsdesk@smh.com.au; web site www.smh.com.au
Circ.: 225,861; 381,217(sat)
Ed. – Peter Fray
Advertising67.70 casual rate (mon.-fri.); 85.45 casual rate (sat.).

THE SUN HERALD (S)
PO Box 506, Sydney, 2001, Australia; tel (61) 2 9282 2822; fax 9282 2151
Circ.: 613,000
Ed. – Simon Dulhunt
Advertising68.90 casual rate.

SUNDAY TELEGRAPH (S)
2 Holt St., Sydney, 2010, Australia; tel (61) 2 9288 3000; fax 9288 2300; web site www.dailytelegraph.com.au
Ed. – Neil Breen
Advertising75.00 casual rate.

DAILY TELEGRAPH (6X WK.)
2 Holt St., Surry Hills, Sydney, 2010, Australia; tel (61) 2 9288 3000; fax 9288 2300; web site www.dailytelegraph.com.au
Circ.: 500,000
Ed. – Gary Linnell
Advertising59.28 casual rate (mon.-fri.); 48.03 casual rate (sat.).

DAILY COMMERCIAL NEWS (M-5X WK.)
PO Box 1552, Sydney, 2001, Australia; tel (61) 2 99368700; fax 99368769; e-mail dcrisp@dcn.com.au
Ed. – Dale Crisp
Advertising11.90 casual rate.

TAMWORTH

THE NORTHERN DAILY LEADER (M-6X WK.)
PO Box 525, Tamworth, NSW, 2340, Australia; tel (61) 2 6768 1200; fax 6766 5810; e-mail mail.ndl@ruralpress.com; web site www.northerndailyleader.com.au
Circ.: 10,453; 16,000(sat)
Last Audit: March 22, 2010
Ed. – David Elooey
Advertising7.70 casual rate.

TOOWOOMBA

THE CHRONICLE (D-EX S)
PO Box 40, Toowoomba, 4350, Australia; tel (61) 7 4690 9300; e-mail production@thechronicle.com.au; web site www.thechronicle.com.au
Circ.: 22,808; 30,270(sat)
Ed. – Hieve Etwell
Adv. Mgr. – Markeeta Hatherell
Advertising8.25 casual rate.

TOWNSVILLE

TOWNSVILLE BULLETIN (M-6X WK.)
PO Box 587, Townsville, 4810, Australia; tel (61) 7 4722 4405; fax 4722 4515; e-mail circulation@nqn.newsltd.com.au; web site www.townsvillebulletin.com.au
Circ.: 35,000
Ed. – Peter Gleeson
Advertising10.66 casual rate (mon.-fri.); 12.00 casual rate (sat.).

ULTIMO

THE INDEPENDENCE DAILY (D-6X WK.)
141 Broadway, Ultimo, 2007, Australia; tel (61) 2 9211 4611; fax 9212 2451
Ed. – Mr. Yuan-hui Hu
Adv. Mgr. – Michael Pun
Advertising6.00 casual rate.

WAGGA WAGGA

THE DAILY ADVERTISER (M-6X WK.)
PO Box 35, Wagga Wagga, 2650, Australia; tel (61) 2 6938 3300; e-mail news@dailyadvertiser.com.au; web site www.dailyadvertiser.com.au
Circ.: 14,406
Adv. Mgr. – Allan Rives
Ed. – Paul Mcloughlin

WARRNAMBOOL

THE STANDARD (M-6X WK.)
PO Box 419, Warrnambool, 3280, Australia; tel (61) 3 5563 1800; fax 5563 1880; web site www.the.standard.net.au
Circ.: 13,234
Sub Ed – Ian Pech
Adv. Mgr. – Wayne Cashion
Advertising5.70 casual rate.

WARWICK

DAILY NEWS (M-6X WK.)
PO Box 358, Warwick, 4370, Australia; tel (61) 7 4660 1312; fax 4661 9191; web site www.warwickdailynews.com.au
Circ.: 3,218
Adv. Mgr. – Phill LaPetit
Ed. in Chief – Peter Read
Ed. – Jeremy Llirs
Advertising6.95 casual rate.

WODONGA

THE BORDER MAIL (6X WK.)
PO Box 491, Wodonga, 3689, Australia; tel (61) 02 6024 0555; fax 6024 0604; e-mail newsroom@bordermail.com.au; web site www.bordermail.com.au
Circ.: 27,000; 83,000(sat)
Nat'l Adv. Mgr. – Darryl Star

WOLLONGONG

ILLAWARRA MERCURY (M-6X WK.)
PO Box 1215, Wollongong, 2500, Australia; tel (61) 2 4221 2333; fax 4221 2338; e-mail info@illawarramercury.com.au; web site www.illawarramercury.com.au
Circ.: 35,474
Adv. Mgr. – Amanda Watson
Circ. Mgr. – Grant Bonner
Ed. – Staurt Howie
Advertising16.72 casual rate (mon.-fri.); 18.10 casual rate (sat.).

NEW ZEALAND

ASHBURTON

ASHBURTON GUARDIAN (E-6X WK.) Est.1879
PO Box 77, Ashburton, New Zealand; tel (64) 3 307 7970; e-mail report@theguardian.co.nz; web site www.ashburtonguardian.co.nz
Circ.: 5,200
Managing Director – Bruce Bell

AUCKLAND

THE NEW ZEALAND HERALD (M-D)
PO Box 32, Auckland, New Zealand; tel (64) 9 379 5050; web site www.nzherald.co.nz
Circ.: 210,910
Ed. in Chief – Tim Merphy
Adv. Mgr. – Matthew Herry
Adv. Mgr. – Dean Louden

AUCKLAND CITY HARBOUR NEWS
Private Bag 41906, Auckland, New Zealand; tel (64) 9 8496060
Ed. – Isabell Speck

BAYS AND REMUERA TIMES
PO Box 38-189, Auckland, New Zealand; tel (64) 9 5380050
Ed. – Barbara Weil

CENTRAL LEADER
Private Bag 41906, Auckland, New Zealand; tel (64) 9 8496060
Ed. – Isabell Speck

DRIVETIMES
PO Box 8970, Auckland, New Zealand; tel (64) N/A
Ed. – Ray Willmott

EAST AND BAYS COURIER
Private Bag 92815, Auckland, New Zealand; tel (64) 9 5251133
Ed. – Laura Basham

EASTERN COURIER
PO Box 38-312, Auckland, New Zealand; tel (64) 9 5359660
Ed. – Duncan Pardon

SUNDAY NEWS (S)
PO Box 1327, Auckland, New Zealand; tel (64) 9 302 1300; fax 358 3003; e-mail editor@sunday-news.co.nz; web site www.fairfaxnz.co.nz
Circ.: 110,136
Mng. Dir. – Terry Quinn
Adv. Mgr. – Dwayne Alexander
Ed. – Clive Nelson

SUNDAY STAR-TIMES (S)
PO Box 1409, Auckland, New Zealand; tel (64) 9 302 1300; fax 366 4670; e-mail feedback@star-times.co.nz; web site www.stuff.co.nz
Circ.: 203,901
Mng. Dir. – Terry Quinn
Adv. Mgr. – Dwayne Alexander
Ed. – Cate Brett

FLASH
PO Box 1327, Auckland, New Zealand; tel (64) 9 3021310; fax 3664565
Ed. – Bob Lovett

HOWICK AND PAKURANGA
PO Box 38-189, Auckland, New Zealand; tel (64) 9 5380050
Ed. – Mike Smith

MANUKAU COURIER
PO Box 76-400, Auckland, New Zealand; tel (64) 9 2624700
Ed. – Peter Tiffany

NATIONAL BUSINESS REVIEW (WEEKLY)
PO Box 1734, Auckland, 1015, New Zealand; tel (64) 9 307 1629; fax 307 5129; e-mail editor@nbr.co.nz; web site www.nbr.co.nz
Circ.: 14,200
Ed. in Chief – Nevil Gibson
Ed. at Large – Graeme Hunt
Adv. Mgr. – Di Driver
AdvertisingMarston Webb & Associates.

THE NEW ZEALAND LISTENER (WEEKLY)
PO Box 90-783, Auckland Mail Centre, Auckland, New Zealand; tel (64) 9 373 9400; fax 373 9406; web site www.listener.co.nz
Circ.: 96,000
Ed. – Paul Little

NORTH HARBOUR NEWS
PO Box 494, Auckland, New Zealand; tel (64) 9 4157430
Ed. – Elizabeth Mahoney

NORWEST NEWSBRIEF
PO Box 46, Auckland, New Zealand; tel (64) 9 4128589; fax 4127806
Ed. – Geoff Dobson

PAPAKURA COURIER
PO Box 76-400, Auckland, New Zealand; tel (64) 9 2624700
Ed. – Peter Tiffany

WESTERN LEADER
John Henry Centre, 12 Pioneer St., Henderson, Auckland, New Zealand; tel (64) 9 8370340
Ed. – Wally Thomas

BLENHEIM

THE MARLBOROUGH EXPRESS (E-5X WK.) Est.1866
PO Box 242, Blenheim, 7240, New Zealand; tel (64) 3 5208900; fax 5208911; e-mail mailbox@marlexpress.co.nz; web site www.marlexpress.co.nz
Circ.: 10,173
General Manager – Vanessa Watson
Editor – Stephen Mason
Adv. Mgr. – Vanessa Watson
AdvertisingOpen inch rate $5.97

CHRISTCHURCH CITY

THE PRESS (6X WK.)
Private Bag 4722, Christchurch City, New Zealand; tel (64) 3 379 0940; fax 364 8496; e-mail management@press.co.nz; news.sales@press.co.nz; subscribe@press.co.nz; web site www.press.co.nz
Circ.: 91,111
Ed. – Andrew Holden
Mng. Dir. – Andrew Boyle
Adv. Mgr. – Mark Ross
Circ. Mgr. – John Parry
AdvertisingOpen inch rate $10.76 (montues, thur-fri); 11.65 (wed); 13.73 (sat)

DANNEVIRKE

EVENING NEWS (E-6X WK.)
16 -18Gordon St., Dannevirke, New Zealand; tel (64) 6 374 7081; fax 374 9353; web site www.wilsonandhorton.co.nz
Circ.: 2,174
Ed. – Cristine McKay

DUNEDIN

OTAGO DAILY TIMES (6X WK.)
PO Box 517, Dunedin, New Zealand; tel (64) 3 477 4760; fax 474 7420; e-mail corporate@alliedpress.co.nz; circulation@alliedpress.co.nz; accounts@alliedpress.co.nz; web site www.alliedpress.co.nz
Circ.: 44,546
Managing Director – Julian C. S. Smith
Adv. Mgr. – Paul Dwyer
Ed – Murray Kirkness

DUNEDIN CITY

DUNEDIN STAR WEEKENDER (S)
PO Box 517, Dunedin City, New Zealand; tel (64) 3 (64-3) 4774760; fax (64-3) 4747426; e-mail star@alliedpress.co.nz
Circ.: 43,000
Mng. Ed. – Jeff Whyte
Adv. Sales – Jan McKenzie

THE NEW ZEALAND TABLET (WEEKLY)
PO Box 1285, Dunedin City, New Zealand; tel (64) 3 4778010; fax 4778245
Ed. – Fr. J.M. Hill

GISBORNE CITY

GISBORNE HERALD (6X WK.)
PO Box 1143, Gisborne City, New Zealand; tel (64) 6 869 0600; fax 869 0643; e-mail info@gisborneherald.co.nz; web site www.gisborneherald.co.nz
Circ.: 8,573
Mng. Dir. – Michael Muir
Editor – Jeremy Muir
Advertising Manager – Glenda Stokes
Adv. Mgr. – Glenda Starkes
Ed. – Iain Gillies

GORE

THE ENSIGN (E)
PO Box 182, Gore, New Zealand; tel (64) 3 2089280; fax 2089594; e-mail ensign@alliedpress.co.nz; web site www.alliedpress.co.nz
Circ.: 3,171
Pub./Ed. – W. Kornet
Adv. Mgr. – Graham Avery

NEWSLINK (WEEKLY)
PO Box 66, Gore, New Zealand; tel (64) 3 209 0108; fax 208 4656; e-mail newspapersales@stl.co.nz
Ed. – Catherine Ladbrook

GREYMOUTH

THE GREYMOUTH EVENING STAR (6X WK.)
PO Box 3, Greymouth, 7840, New Zealand; tel (64) 3 768 7121; fax 768 6205; e-mail office@greystar.co.nz; web site www.greystar.co.nz
Circ.: 4,054
GM – John Goulding

HAMILTON CITY

WAIKATO TIMES (6X WK.)
PO Box 3086, Hamilton City, New Zealand; tel (64) 7 849 6180; fax 849 9554; web site www.stuff.co.nz
Circ.: 40,972
Adv. Mgr. – Delwyn Knight
Ed. – Bryce Johns

HAWERA

HAWERA STAR (E)
PO Box 428, Hawera, New Zealand; tel (64) 6 2785139; fax 2785458
Circ.: 13,452
Ed. – Mary Davis

INVERCARGILL CITY

THE SOUTHLAND TIMES (6X WK.)
PO Box 805, Invercargill City, 9840, New Zealand; tel (64) 3 218 1909; fax 214 9905; e-mail executive@stl.co.nz; win@stl.co.nz; web site www.stuff.co.nz
Circ.: 29,928
Ed. – Fred Tulett

KAIKOHE

NORTHERN NEWS (M-2X WK.) Est.1919
PO Box 1, Kaikohe, New Zealand; tel (64) 9 405 2040; fax 401 2129; e-mail northern.news@icn.co.nz; web site www.northernnews.co.nz
Circ.: 6,122
Northern Regional Manager – Lynne Popham
Editor – Malcolm McMillan
Mng. Dir. – Greg Phillips

LEVIN

HOROWHENUA KAPITI CHRONICLE (E)
PO Box 547, Levin, New Zealand; tel (64) 3 368 5109; fax 368 2366; e-mail levin_chronicle@wilsonandhorton.co.nz
Circ.: 3,950
Adv. Mgr. – Bryan Snaith
Ed. – Geoff Mead

LOWER HUTT

HUTT NEWS
PO Box 30-029, Lower Hutt, New Zealand; tel (64) 4 5702040; fax 5665485
Pub. – Trevor Howes
Ed. – Simon Edwards

KAPI MANA NEWS/NORWESTER
PO Box 50-012, Lower Hutt, New Zealand; tel (64) 4 2378118; fax 2378552
Ed. – R. Olsen

KAPITI NEWSPAPER
PO Box 110, Lower Hutt, New Zealand; tel (64) 4 2972996; fax 2982073
Ed. – Richard Woodd

UPPER HUTT LEADER
PO Box 40-001, Lower Hutt, New Zealand; tel (64) 4 5289654; fax 5283021
Ed. – Rosemary McLennan

MASTERTON

WAIRARAPA NEWS (WEEKLY)
PO Box 87, MASTERTON, New Zealand; tel (64) 6 3705690; fax 3705699
Circ.: 7,585
Ed. – Eric Turner

MASTERTON

WAIRARAPA TIMES-AGE (E-6X WK.)
PO Box 445, Masterton, 5940, New Zealand; tel (64) 6 378 9999; fax 378 2371; e-mail office@age.co.nz; web site www.times-age.co.nz
Circ.: 7,585
Mng. Dir. – Windy Morrison
Adv. Mgr. – Frrah Figgins
Ed. – Dave Sanduel

MORRINSVILLE

PIAKO POST
27-31 Canada St., Morrinsville, New Zealand; tel (64) 7 8897099; fax 8896572
Ed. – Ian Harrop

NAPIER CITY

DAILY TELEGRAPH (E)
PO Box 343, Napier City, New Zealand; tel (64) 6 8354488; fax 8344679; e-mail gm@telegraph.co.nz; web site www.hawkesbaytoday.co.nz
Circ.: 15,530
Gen. Mgr. – J.A. Silvester
Ed. – L.H. Pierard

NELSON CITY

THE NELSON MAIL (E-6X WK.)
PO Box 244, Nelson City, New Zealand; tel (64) 3 548 7079; fax 546 2802; e-mail nml@nelsonmail.co.nz; web site www.nelsonmail.co.nz
Circ.: 18,312
Mng. Dir. – Craig Dennis
Adv. Mgr. – Rob Whittaker
Ed. – Paul Mcintyra
Reporter – Bill Moore

NEW PLYMOUTH CITY

TARANAKI DAILY NEWS (M-6X WK.)
PO Box 444, New Plymouth City, New Zealand; tel (64) 6 758 0559; fax 758 4653; web site www.stuff.co.nz
Circ.: 26,687
Mng. Dir. – Mike Brewer
Adv Mgr – Mett Surjanor
Ed. – Lance Girling-Butcher

NORTH TARANAKI MIDWEEK (WED.)
PO Box 444, New Plymouth City, 4340, New Zealand; tel (64) 6 758 0559; fax 759 0814; web site www.taranakidailynews.co.nz
Adv. Mgr. – Matt Surgenor
Ed. – Gordon Brown

NORTH HASTINGS CITY

HAWKE'S BAY TODAY (E-5X WK; M-SAT.)
PO Box 180, North Hastings City, 4201, New Zealand; tel (64) 6 873 0800; fax 873 0812; e-mail news@hbtoday.co.nz; web site www.hbtoday.co.nz
Circ.: 30,079
Ed. – Louis Pierard

OAMARU

THE OAMARU MAIL (E-5X WK.)
PO Box 343, Oamaru, New Zealand; tel (64) 3 434 9970; fax 433 0549; e-mail news@oamarumail.co.nz; web site www.oamarumail.co.nz
Circ.: 3,464
Last Audit: November 23, 2011
Gen. Mgr. – Tony Neilson
Ed. – Sally Brooker

PALMERSTON NORTH CITY

MANAWATU STANDARD (E-6X WK.)
PO Box 3, Palmerston North City, New Zealand; tel (64) 6 356 9009; fax 350 9545; web site www.stuff.co.nz; www.manawatustandard.co.nz
Circ.: 30,357
Ed. – Michael Cummings

FIELDING HERALD
PO Box 3, Palmerston North City, New Zealand; tel (64) N/A
Ed. – Ann Kilduff

RANGITIKEI MAIL
289 Broadway, Marton, Palmerston North City, New Zealand; tel (64) 6 327-8671
Ed. – Ann Kilduff

THE TRIBUNE
PO Box 3, Palmerston North City, New Zealand; tel (64) 6 350 9555; e-mail tribune@msl.co.nz
Ed. – Ann Kilduff

PUKEKOHE

FRANKLIN COUNTY NEWS (2X WKLY)
PO Box 14, Pukekohe, New Zealand; tel (64) 9 237 0400; web site fairfaxmedia.newspaperdirect.com
Sls. Mgr. – Sonia Tate
Ed. – John Brown

PUKEKOHE WEEKEND
PO Box 14, Pukekohe, New Zealand; tel (64) 9 2384179; fax 2389744
Ed. – H. Danes

ROTORUA

THE DAILY POST (6X WK.)
PO Box 1442, Rotorua, New Zealand; tel (64) 7 348 6199; fax 346 0153; web site www.dailypost.co.nz
Circ.: 11,979
Gen Mgr. – Greg Alexander

RURAL REVIEW
PO Box 2344, Rotorua, New Zealand; tel (64) 7 N/A
Ed. – Rod Hall

DAILY POST (M-6X WK.)
PO Box 1442, Rotorua, New Zealand; tel (64) 7 348 6199; fax 348 0220; e-mail editor@dailypost.co.nz; web site www.dailypost.co.nz
Circ.: 12,500
Gen. Mgr. – Craig Alexander
Adv. Mgr. – Margaret Turner
Ed. – Kim Gillespie

TAUPO

TAUPO TIMES
Heu Heu St., Taupo, New Zealand; tel (64) 7 3789060; fax 3780247
Ed. – Helen Faville

TAURANGA CITY

BAY OF PLENTY TIMES (6X WK.)
Private Bag 12002, Tauranga City, New Zealand; tel (64) 7 578 3059; fax 577 3152; web site www.bayofplentytimes.co.nz
Circ.: 23,285
Gen. Mgr. – David Mackenzia
Ed. – Cott Inglis

HAURAKI HERALD
PO Box 363, Tauranga City, New Zealand; tel (64) 7 868 8850; fax 868 8265
Ed. – Eric Toplis

TE PUKE

TE PUKE TIMES
PO Box 260, Te Puke, New Zealand; tel (64) 7 5737078; fax 5736012
Ed. – John McMenamin

TIMARU CITY

THE TIMARU HERALD (E-6X WK.)
PO Box 46, Timaru City, New Zealand; tel (64) 3 684 4129; fax 688 1042; e-mail editor@timaruherald.co.nz; web site www.timaruherald.co.nz
Circ.: 14,360
Gen Mgr. – Chris McAuslin
Adv. Mgr. – Kelvin Iysin
Ed. – David King

TOKOROA

SOUTH WAIKATO NEWS
PO Box 89, Tokoroa, New Zealand; tel (64) 7 8869159; fax 8865347
Ed. – Allan Winter

WANGANUI CITY

WANGANUI CHRONICLE (M-6X WK.)
PO Box 433, Wanganui City, New Zealand; tel (64) 6 349 0710; fax 349 0721; e-mail news@wanganuichronicle.co.nz; web site www.wanganuichronicle.co.nz
Circ.: 14,000
Gen. Mgr. – Andy Jarden
Adv. Mgr. – Donna Wallace
Ed. – Ross Pringle

WELLINGTON

THE DOMINION POST (M-EX S)
PO Box 3740, Wellington, New Zealand; tel (64) 4 474 0222; fax 474 0350; e-mail emailads@dompost.co.nz; display@dompost.co.nz; web site www.dompost.co.nz
Circ.: 175,000
Adv. Mgr. – Cheryl Kortink
Ed. – Bernadette Courtney

WELLINGTON CITY

CONTACT
PO Box 3740, Wellington City, New Zealand; tel (64) N/A
Ed. – Judy Bradwell

WESTPORT

THE WESTPORT NEWS (E-5X WK.)
Est.1871
171 Palmerston St., Westport, New Zealand; tel (64) 3 789 7319; fax 789 7203; e-mail westportnews@westportnews.co.nz; web site www.westportnews.co.nz
Circ.: 2,200
Managing direcctor MD – Colin Warren

WHANGAREI CITY

THE NORTHERN ADVOCATE (E-6X WK.)
PO Box 210, Whangarei City, New Zealand; tel (64) 9 438 2399; fax 430 6800; e-mail daily@northernadvocate.co.nz; web site www.northernadvocate.co.nz
Circ.: 15,112
Mng. Dir. – John Henton
Ed. – Tony Verdon

NEWSPAPERS OF THE PACIFIC OCEAN TERRITORIES

AMERICAN SAMOA

PAGO PAGO

SAMOA JOURNAL & ADVERTISER (WEEKLY)
PO Box 3986, Pago Pago, AS 96799, American Samoa; tel (684) 6332399
Ed. – Michael Stark

SAMOA NEWS (6X WK.)
PO Box 909, Pago Pago, AS 96799, American Samoa (684) 633-5599; fax (684) 633-4864; e-mail news.newsroom@samoatelco.com; web site www.samoanews.comCirc.: 4,500
Gen. Mgr. – Terry auvaa
Pub. – Vera Annesley

COOK ISLANDS

RAROTONGA

COOK ISLANDS NEWS (6X WK.)
PO Box 15, Avarua, Rarotonga, Cook Islands; tel (682) 22999; fax 25303; e-mail editor@cookislandnews.com; web site www.cookislandnews.comCirc.: 2,000
Ed. – John Woods

FIJI

SUVA

FIJI TIMES (D)
177 Victoria Parade, Suva, Fiji; tel (679) 330 4209; fax 330 1521; e-mail timesnews@fijitimes.com.fj; web site www.fijitimes.com-Circ.: 25,000
Gen. Mgr. – Ann Fussell
Ed. in Chief – Metani Rika
Advertising: f$0.60 including VAT.

VATUWAQA, SUVA

FIJI DAILY POST (6X WK.)
19 Ackland St., Viria East Industrial Subdivision, Vatuwaqa, Suva, Fiji; tel (679) 327 5177; fax 327 5179; e-mail info@fijidailypost.com; web site www.fijidailypost.com-Circ.: 9,000
Ed. – Mesake Koroi

FRENCH POLYNESIA

PAPEETE

LE JOURNAL DE TAHITI (D)
BP 6000, Papeete, French Polynesia; tel (689) N/A

LES NOUVELLES DE TAHITI (D)
BP 1757, Place de la Cathedrale, Papeete, French Polynesia; tel (689) 464 343; fax 464 350; web site www.lesnouvelles.pfCirc.: 18,500
Pub. – Philippe Hersant
Pub. Dir. – Frederic Aurand
Ed. – Muriel Pontarollo

SOCIETE OCEANIENNE DE COMMUNICATION (D)
BP 50, Papeete, French Polynesia; tel (689) 424 343; fax 426 907
Ed. in Chief – Daniel Pardon

TAHITI BULLETIN (D)
BP 912, Papeete, French Polynesia; tel (689) N/A

GUAM

HAGATNA

PACIFIC DAILY NEWS/SUNDAY NEWS (MS)
244 Archbishop Flores St., Hagatna, GU 96932, Guam (671) 472-1736; fax (671) 472-1512; e-mail enery@guam.gannett.com; web site www.guampdn.comCirc.: 26,000
Pub. – Rindraty Celes Limtiaco
Advertising: Landon Associates Inc.

MARSHALL ISLANDS

MAJURO

THE MASHALL ISLANDS JOURNAL (WEEKLY) Est. 1970
PO Box 14, Majuro, MH 96960, Marshall Islands; tel (692) 625-3251; fax 625-3136; e-mail journal@ntamar.netCirc.: 3,000
Pub. – Joe Murphy
Ed. – Giff Johnson

MINISTRY OF FOREIGN AFFAIRS
Office of the Chief Secretary, Marshall Islands Go, Majuro, MH 96960, Marshall Islands; tel (692) 625 3143
Ed. – Giff Johnson

NEW CALEDONIA

NOUMEA

LA FRANCE AUSTRALE (D)
13 Nes Grneseour, Noumea, New Caledonia; tel (687) 274444

LA PRESSE CALEDONIENNE (D)
14, rue Sebastopol, Noumea, New Caledonia; tel (687) 285055

LES NOUVELLES CALEDONIENNES (D)
41-43 rue de Sebastopol, Noumea, New Caledonia; tel (687) 272 584; fax 281 627; e-mail lnc@canl.ncCirc.: 18,500
Pub. – Philippe Hersant
Dir. – Benoit Luizet
Ed. in Chief – Didier Fleaux

NIUE

ALOFI

MEDIA SERVICES NIUE OFFICE OF COMMUNITY AFFAIRS (WEEKLY)
PO Box 67, Alofi, Niue; tel (683) N/A
Asst. Ed. – Patrick Lino

NORFOLK ISLAND

NORFOLK ISLAND

THE NORFOLK ISLANDER (WEEKLY)
Greenways Press, Norfolk Island, 2899, Norfolk Island; tel (672) 22159; fax 22948
Owner – Tim Lloyd
Ed. – Tom Lloyd

PAPUA NEW GUINEA

BOROKO, NCD

NIUGINI NIUS & WEEKENDER (5X WK.)
PO Box 3019, Boroko, NCD, Papua New Guinea; tel (675) 325 2177
Ed. – Yehiura Hriehwazi

THE NATIONAL (D)
PO Box 6817, Boroko, NCD, Papua New Guinea; tel (675) 324 6888; fax 325 2764; e-mail national@online.net.pgCirc.: 20,000
Ed. – Daniel Korimbao

PORT MORESBY

PAPUA NEW GUINEA POST-COURIER (M)
PO Box 85, Port Moresby, Papua New Guinea; tel (675) 309 1000; fax 321 2721; e-mail postcourier@spp.com.pg; web site www.postcourier.com.pgCirc.: 30,484
Ed. – Oseah Philemon

SAIPAN

SAIPAN ISLAND

THE MARIANAS REVIEW (WEEKLY)
PO Box 1074, Saipan Island, MP 96950, Saipan; tel (670) 234 7160
Owner/Pub. – Luis C. Benavente
Ed. – Ruth L. Tighe

SOLOMON ISLANDS

HONIARA, GUADALCANAL

GOVERNMENT INFORMATION SERVICES (MTHLY)
PO Box 718, Honiara, Guadalcanal, Solomon Islands; tel (677) 21300; fax 20401
Ed. in Chief – Thomas Kivo

SOLOMON STAR (D)
PO Box 255, Honiara, Guadalcanal, Solomon Islands; tel (677) 22062; fax 25290; e-mail solstar@solomon.com.sb; web site www.solomonstarnews.comCirc.: 5,000
Pub. – John Lamani

SOLOMON VOICE (WEEKLY)
PO Box 1235, Honiara, Guadalcanal, Solomon Islands; tel (677) 20116; fax 20090
Ed. – John Asipara

TONGA

NUKU'ALOFA

GOV'T OF TONGA (WEEKLY)
PO Box 197, Nuku'Alofa, Tonga; tel (676) 23302
Ed. – Paua Manuatu

TUVALU

FUNAFUTI

TUVALU ECHOES (MTHLY)
Broadcasting & Information Office, Vaiaku, Funafuti, Tuvalu; tel (688) 20138; fax 20732Circ.: 250
Ed. – Vaiatoa Uale

VANUATU

PORT VILA

VANUASCOPE
PO Box 711, Port Vila, Vanuatu; tel (678) N/A
Ed. in Chief/Adv. Mgr. – Patrick Decloitre

VANUATU INFORMATION DEPT
Private Bag 049, Port Vila, Vanuatu; tel (678) 22999
Ed. in Chief/Adv. Dir. – Kaltan Ayong

VANUATU NEWS Est. 2000
PO Box 637, Port Vila, Vanuatu; tel (678) 7743532; e-mail publisher@news.vu; web site www.news.vu
Pub. – Marke Lowen

NEWSPAPERS OF THE CARIBBEAN REGION

ANGUILLA

THE VALLEY

THE VANTAGE NEWSPAPER
PO Box 72, The Valley, Anguilla; tel (264)
Ed./Adv. Mgr. – James Fleming

ANTIGUA AND BARBUDA

ST. JOHN'S

OUTLET (WEEKLY)
PO Box 493, ST. JOHN'S, Antigua and Barbuda; tel (268) 4624425; fax 4620438
Ed. – Tim Hector
Advertising: AdMarket Int'l.; Charney/Palacios & Co. Inc.

SAINT JOHN'S

SENTINEL
PO Box 270, Saint John's, Antigua and Barbuda; tel (268) 4625000; fax 4624084
Ed. – Norman (Gus) Thomas

SAINT JOHNS

THE WORKER'S VOICE (WEEKLY)
PO Box 1281, Saint Johns, Antigua and Barbuda; tel (1) 268 462 0090
Ed. – Noel Thomas

WHAT'S HAPPENING
PO Box 1477, Saint Johns, Antigua and Barbuda; tel (1) 268 462 1918

THE NATION
Cnr. Factory Road & Carnival Gardens, Saint Johns, Antigua and Barbuda; tel (268) 4620010
Ed. – George Joseph

ARUBA

ORANGESTAD

MATUTINO CORANT (6X WK.)
Newtonstraat 14, Orangestad, Aruba; tel (297) 8 28628; fax 34834
Dir. – Stanley Arends
Pub. – Albertico Arends

ORANJESTAD

THE ARUBA GAZETTE (6X WK.)
Dakota Shopping Paradise Fergusonstraat, Oranjestad, Aruba; tel (297) 583 6755
Pub. – Edvin Irausquin

ULTIMO NOTICIA (6X WK.)
Dominicanessenstraat, No. 17, Oranjestad, Aruba; tel (297) 8 96244
Ed. – Norma Erasmus

ARUBA TODAY/BON DIA ARUBA (6X WK.)
Weststraat 22, Oranjestad, Aruba (297) 582-7800; fax (297) 582-7044; e-mail comment@bondia.com; news@arubatoday.com; web site www.bondia.com; www.arubatoday.com
Circ. 20,000
Gen. Mgr. – Grace Mary Maduro
Sales Exec. – Marijke Croes
Ed. in Chief – Julia C. Renfro

BEURS EN NIEUWSBERICHTEN (6X WK.)
Bachstraat 6, Oranjestad, Aruba; tel (297) 8 21465
Ed. – E. Lacle

DIARIO (6X WK.)
PO Box 577, Engelandstraat 29, Oranjestad, Aruba (297) 582-6747; fax (297) 582-8551; e-mail arubadaily@yahoo.com ; info@diario.aw; web site www.diarioaruba.com
Circ. 15,000
Ed. in Cheif – Jossy M. Mansur
Advertising: Charney/Palacios & Co.

EXTRA (6X WK.)
Dominicanessenstraat 17, Oranjestad, Aruba; tel (297) 8 34034; fax 21639
Dir. – C. Franken

MATUTINO DI NOS (6X WK.)
J.G. Emanstraat, No. 68, Oranjestad, Aruba; tel (297)
Pub./Ed. – Jacobo Arends

MERIDIANO (6X WK.)
Wilhelminastratt, No. 88, Oranjestad, Aruba (297) 582-2207; fax (297) 582-1639
Ed. – Jubi Naar
Pub. – Jossy Mansur

THE NEWS (6X WK.)
PO Box 300, Italiestraat 5, Oranjestad, Aruba (297) 582-4725; fax (297) 588-9430; e-mail thenewsaruba@setarnet.aw
Circ. 8,228
Pub. – Sir Gerardus J. Schouten
Advertising: AdMarket Int'l.; Charney/Palacios & Co.

AMIGOE (6X WK.)
PO Box 323, Oranjestad, Aruba (297) 582-4333; fax (297) 582-2368; e-mail directie@amigoearuba.aw
Circ. 12,000
Gen. Mgr. – Willem Dacosta Gomez

LA PRENSA (6X WK.)
PO Box 566, Oranjestad, Aruba; tel (297) 8 21199; fax 28634
Ed. – Thomas C. Pietersz

POS CKIKITO

NOBO ARUBA (6X WK.)
Pos Ckikito, No. 3-D, Pos Ckikito, Aruba; tel (297) 8 9673500
Ed. – Meredith Carrion-Koolman

BAHAMAS

FREEPORT

THE FREEPORT NEWS (6X WK.)
PO Box F-40007, Freeport, Bahamas (242) 352-8322; fax (242) 351-3449; web site freeport.nassauguardian.net
Circ. 4,000
Ed. – Oswald Brown

NASSAU

THE NASSAU GUARDIAN (6X WK.)
PO Box N-3011, Nassau, Bahamas (242) 328-8943; fax (242) 328-8943; web site www.thenassauguardian.com
Circ. 14,100
Pres. – Anthony Ferguson
Mng.Ed. – Erica Wells
Advertising: AdMarket Int'l.; The N DeFilippes Corp.

NASSAU DAILY TRIBUNE (D-5X WK.)
Est. 1903
PO Box N-3207, Shirley St., Nassau, Bahamas; tel (242) (242) 322-1986; fax (242) 328-2398; e-mail tribune@tribunemedia.com; web site www.tribune242.com
Circ. 12,000
Pub./Ed. – Eileen Dupuch Carron
Gen. Mgr. – Robert Carron
Advertising: The Cal Hart Co.

BARBADOS

BRIDGETOWN

BARBADOS ADVOCATE/SUNDAY ADVOCATE-NEWS (D)
PO Box 230, Fontabelle, Bridgetown, BD 11000, Barbados (246) 467-2000; fax (246)

434-2300; web site www.barbadosadvocate.com
Circ. 15,000; 25,000(sun)
Adv. Mgr. – Sandra Clarke
Advertising: AdMarket Int'l.

THE DAILY NATION/THE WEEKEND NATION/THE SUNDAY SUN (D)
PO Box 1203, Bridgetown, BB11000, Barbados (246) 430-5400; fax (246) 427-6968; e-mail nationnews@sunbeach.net; web site www.nationnews.com
Circ. 78,000; 55,000(sun)
Last Audit: March 29, 2010
Pub. – Vivian Anne Gittens
Adv Mgr. – Paulette Jones
Advertising: Charney/Palacios Co.

BERMUDA

HAMILTON

BERMUDA SUN
PO Box HM 1241, Hamilton, HMFX, Bermuda; tel (441) 2953902; fax 2925597; e-mail bdasun@mail.ibl.bm; web site www.bermudasun.bm
Pub. – Randy French
Bus. Mgr. – Andrea Brown
Mgr.-Creative Servs. – Tamara McKee
Opns. Mgr. – Gerald Collins
Adv. Mgr. – Lisa Arrowsmith
Ed. – Tony McWilliam
Deputy Ed. – Bob Amesse
Advertising: AdMarket Int'l.

BERMUDA TIMES
9 Burnaby St., Hamilton, HMDX, Bermuda; tel (1) 441 292 2596; fax 295 8771
Pub. – Ewart F. Brown
Ed. – K. Murray Brown
Adv. Mgr. – Rennie Rowling

ROYAL GAZETTE/MID OCEAN NEWS (6X WK.)
PO Box 1025, Hamilton, HMDX, Bermuda (441) 295-5881; fax (441) 295-9813; web site www.theroyalgazette.com
Circ. 14,500
Gen. Mgr. – Keith Jensen
Circ. Mgr. – Delmonte Davis
Ed. in Chief – William J. Zuill
Advertising: Charney/Palacios & Co.

BRITISH VIRGIN ISLANDS

ROAD TOWN, TORTOLA ISLANDS

THE BVI BEACON (WEEKLY)
PO Box 3030, Road Town, Tortola Islands, British Virgin Islands; tel (284) 4943767; fax 4946267; e-mail bvibeacn@caribsurf.com
Adv. Mgr. – Cromwell B. Smith
Owner/Ed./Adv. Mgr. – Linnell M. Abbott
Advertising: AdMarket Int'l.

SAINT CROIX

ST. CROIX AVIS (M)
La Grande Princesse, Christiansted, Saint Croix, 00820, British Virgin Islands; tel (284) (809) 7732300; fax (809) 7735511
Owner/Pub. – Rena Broadhurst-Knight
Ed. – Wynn Brant
Adv. Mgr. – Lesa Fisher
Advertising: AdMarket Int'l.; Charney/Palacios & Co.; The N DeFilippes Corp.

DAILY NEWS (D)
4006 Estate Diamond, Saint Croix, 00802, British Virgin Islands (340) 773-4425; fax (340) 773-1621; e-mail dailynews@vipowernet.net; web site www.virginislandsdailynews.com
Circ. 18,500
Group: U.S. Suburban Press, Inc.
Pub. – Jason Robbins
Adv. Dir. – Kevin Downey
Exec. Ed. – Lowe Davis

SAINT THOMAS

VIRGIN ISLANDS DAILY NEWS (M)
9155 Estate Thomas, Saint Thomas, VI, 00802, British Virgin Islands (340) 774-8772; fax (340) 776-0740; e-mail dailynews@vipowernet.net; web site www.virginislandsdailynews.com
Circ. 15,560
Pub. – Jason Robbins
Adv. Dir. – Kevin Downey
Advertising: AdMarket Int'l.; The N DeFilippes Corp.; Landon Associates Inc.

TORTOLA

THE ISLAND SUN (WEEKLY)
PO Box 704, 9 Wailing Rd., Road Town, Tortola, British Virgin Islands; tel (284) (284) 494-2476; fax (284) 494-3510; e-mail issun@candwbvi.com; issun@caribsurf.com; web site www.islandsun.com
Ed. – Vernon W. Pickering
Adv. Mgr. – Delseita (Peggy) Carney

CAYMAN ISLANDS

GEORGE TOWN, GRAND CAYMAN

CAYMANIAN COMPASS (M-5X WK.)
PO Box 1365, George Town, Grand Cayman, KY1-1108, Cayman Islands (345) 949-5111; fax (345) 949-7675; web site www.caycompass.com
Circ. 9,500
Pub. – Brian Uzzell
Ed. – Tammie Chisholm

COMMONWEALTH OF DOMINICA

ROSEAU

THE CHRONICLE Est. 1995
P O BOX 1724, Roseau, Commonwealth of DOMINICA (767) 448-7887; fax (767) 448-0047; e-mail thechronicle@cwdom.dm
Group: The Chronicle Company Ltd.
General Manager / Editor – Gwendolyn Evelyn

CUBA

BAYAMO

LA DEMAJAGUA (D)
Amado Estevez, esq. Calle 10, Rpto. R Reyes, Bayamo, Cuba; tel (53) 424 221; e-mail cip225@cip.etecsa.cu; web site www.lademajagua.co.cu
Dir. – Pedro Mora Estrada

CAMAGUEY

ADELANTE (M-4X WK.)
Cisneros 306, Camaguey, 70100, Cuba; tel (53) 32 284 630; e-mail adelante@caonao.cmw.inf.cu; web site www.adelante.cu
Dir. – Evaristo Sardinas Vera
Ed. in Chief – Mabel Guerra GarcÃ¡a

CIEGO DE AVILA

EL INVASOR (D)
Avenida de los deportes s/n, Ciego de Avila, 65395, Cuba; tel (53) 25125; e-mail cip221@cip.enet.cu; web site www.invasor.islagrande.cu
Dir. – Migdalia Utrera Pena

CIENFUEGOS

CINCO DE SEPTIEMBRE (D)
Avenida 54 No. 3516, e/. 35 y 37, Cienfuegos, 55100, Cuba; tel (53) 43 522 144; web site www.5septiembre.cu
Circ. 18,000
Dir. – Alina Rosell Chong

GUANTANAMO

VENCEREMOS (D)
Ave Che Guevara, Guantanamo, 95400, Cuba; tel (53) 325 424; e-mail cip227@cip.enet.cu; web site www.venceremos.co.cu
Dir. – Elizabeth Santiesteban PÃ£rez
Ed. – Raisa MartÃ¡n Lobo

HAVANA

JUVENTUD REBELDE (D)
PO Box 6344, Havana, 10698, Cuba; tel (53) 7 882 0155; fax 833 8959; e-mail jrebelde@teleda.get.cma.net; cida@jrebelde.cip.cu; web site www.juventudrebelde.co.cu
Circ. 250,000
Dir. – Rogelio Polanco Fuentes

LOS TRABAJADORES (D)
Gen. Suarez y Territorial, Plaza de la Revolucion, Havana, 10698, Cuba; tel (53) 7 555 927; fax 555 927; e-mail digital@trabaja.cip.cu; web site www.trabajadores.co.cu
Dir. – Jorge Luis Canela Ciurana

GRANMA INTERNACIONAL (MS)
Apdo. 6187, Havana, 10699, Cuba; tel (53) 7 813333; fax 335176; e-mail redac@granmai.get.cma.net; web site www.granma.cubaweb.cu
Dir. – Frank Aguero Gomez

TRIBUNA DE LA HABANA (WEEKLY)
Territorial y General SuÃ£Â rez, Plaza de la RevoluciÃ£Â¢n, Havana, Cuba; tel (53) 881 8021; e-mail redac@tribuna.cip.cu; web site www.tribuna.islagrande.cu
Dir. – Angel Zuniga Suarez

HOLGUIN

AHORA (D)
Salida a San Germ n y Circunvalacion, Holguin, Cuba; tel (53) 24 425 707; web site www.ahora.cu
Dir. – Radobaldo Martinez Perez

ISLA DE LA JUVENTUD

VICTORIA (D)
Carretera La Fe Km 1 y Medio S/N. Nueva Gerona, Isla De La Juventud, 25500, Cuba; tel (53) 46 324 868; e-mail cip228@cip.enet.cu; web site www.victoria.co.cu
Dir. – Sergio Rivero Carrasco

MATANZAS

GIRON (D)
Avda. Camilo Cienfuegos No. 10505 P. Nuero, Matanzas, Cuba; tel (53) 245 657; web site www.giron.co.cu
Dir. – Clovis Ortega CastaÂ¤eda

PINAR DEL RIO

GUERRILLERO (D)
Colon esq. Delicias y Adela Azcuy, Pinar Del Rio, Cuba; tel (53) 2623
Dir. – Ronald Suarez

SANCTI SPIRITUS

ESCAMBRAY (D)
Adolfo del Castillo 10, Sancti Spiritus, Cuba; tel (53) 41 23003; e-mail cip220@cip.enet.cu; web site www.escambray.cu
Dir. – Aramis Arteaga Perez

SANTA CLARA

VANGUARDIA (D)
Calle CÃ£Â£spedes 5, entre PlÃ£Â cido y Maceo, Santa Clara, 50100, Cuba; tel (53) 222 090; e-mail cip218@cip.enet.cu; web site www.vanguardia.co.cu
Circ. 24,000
Dir. – F. A. Chang

SANTIAGO DE CUBA

SIERRA MAESTRA (WEEKLY)
Avenida de los Desfiles S/N, Santiago De Cuba, Cuba; tel (53) 651 751; e-mail cip226@cip.enet.cu; web site www.sierramaestra.cu
Dir. – Arnaldo Clavel Carmenaty

TUNAS

VENTISEIS (D)
Avda. Carlos J. Finley, Las Tunas, Tunas, Cuba; tel (53)
Dir. – Jose Infantes Reyes

DOMINICAN REPUBLIC

ROSEAU

DOMINICA OFFICIAL GAZETTE (WEEKLY)
Government Printery, Roseau, Dominican Republic; tel (809) 448 2401

SANTIAGO DE LOS CABALLEROS

LA INFORMACION (6X WK.) Est. 1915
Apdo. Postal 237, Santiago de los Caballeros, Dominican Republic (809) 583-7281; fax (809) 581-7770; e-mail e.informacion@codetel.net.do; web site www.lainformacion.com.do
Circ. 15,000
Pres. – Priamo A. Rodriquez Castillo
Gen. Mgr. – Jose E. Souffront
Ed. – Fernando A. Perez Memem

SANTO DOMINGO

DIARIO LAS AMERICAS (D)
Avda. Tiradentes, Santo Domingo, Dominican Republic; tel (809) 5664577

HOY (M) Est. 1981
Avda. San Martin, No. 236, Santo Domingo, Dominican Republic (809) 565-5581; web site www.hoy.com.do
Circ. 40,000
Pres. – Jose A. Moreno
Gen. Mgr. – Juan Carlos Camino
Adv. Sales Mgr. – Rafael Reyes Bisono
Ed. – Bienvenido Alvarez Vega
Advertising: Charney/Palacios & Co.

LISTIN DIARIO (M) Est. 1889
Calle Paseo de los Periodistas No. 52, Santo Domingo, Dominican Republic (809) 686-6688; fax (809) 686-6595; web site www.listin.com.do
Circ. 88,000
Pres. – Ramon Baez Figueroa
Gen. Mgr. – Jose Miguel Baez Figueroa
Sales Mgr. – Lourdes Polanco
Ed. – Miguel Franjul
Prodn. Mgr. – Fabio Ortiz
Advertising: Charney/Palacios & Co.

LA NACION
PO Box 20213, Santo Domingo, Dominican Republic; tel (809) 537 2444; fax 537 4865; e-mail editor@lanacion.net
Pres. – Jose Miguel Vaz Figueroa
Dir. – Vonaperte Grutreaux Pineyro
Ed. in Chief – Christian Jimenez
Dir.-Opns. – David Castillo
Prodn. Mgr. – Juan H. Galvez

EL SOL (M)
Carretera S nchez, Km. 6 1/2, Santo Domingo, Dominican Republic (809) 532-9511
Gen. Dir. – Miguel Angel Cedeno
Pres. – Quiterio Cedeno

LA NOTICIA (ES)
Julio Verne 14, Santo Domingo, Dominican Republic (809) 535-0185
Pres. – Jose A. Brea Pena
Dir. – Bolivar Bello

EL SIGLO (5X WK.)
PO Box 20213, Santo Domingo, Dominican Republic (809) 518-4035; e-mail elsiglo@elsiglord.com
Pres. – Jose Miguel Baez Figueroa
Exec. Dir. – Osvaldo Santana
Admin. – Jesus A. Diaz
Prodn. Dir. – Juan H. Galvez

ULTIMA HORA (E) Est. 1970
Apdo. Postal 1455, Santo Domingo, Dominican Republic; tel (809) 688-3361; fax 688-3019; e-mail uh.redacc@codetel.net.do; web site www.codetel.net.do/ultimahora
Pres. – Eduardo Pellerano Nadal
Gen. Mgr. – Ernesto Vitienes
Sales Mgr. – Lourdes Polanco
Editorial Dir. – Ruddy L. Gonzalez
Prodn. Mgr. – Fabio Ortiz
Advertising: Charney/Palacios & Co.

EL CARIBE (D)
Apdo. Postal 416, Santo Domingo, Dominican Republic (809) 200-5338; fax (809) 544-4003; e-mail editora@ecaribe.com.do
Circ. 10,000
Pres. – Rafael del Toro
Adv. Mgr. – Virginia Pagan

LA INFORMACION
Maximo Gomez, No. 16-18, Santo Domingo, Dominican Republic; tel (1) 809 583 7281
Ed. – Andriano Miguel Teyada

EL NUEVO DIARIO (6X WK.)
Avenida Francia No. 41, Santo Domingo, Dominican Republic (809) 687-7450; fax (809) 687-3205; e-mail redaccionnd@verizon.net.do; redaccionnd@gmail.com; web site www.elnuevodiario.com.do
Circ. 10,000
Dir. – Persio Maldonado

EL NACIONAL (ES)
Av. San MartÃ£Â¡n 236, Santo Domingo, Dominican Republic (809) 565-5582; fax (809) 565-4190; web site www.elnacional.com.do
Circ. 45,000
Dir. – Mario Alvarez Dugan
Advertising: AdMarket International; Charney Palacios & Co.; The N DeFilippes Corp.

GRENADA

SAINT GEORGES

GOVERNMENT GAZETTE (WEEKLY)
Prime Minister's Office, Saint Georges, Grenada; tel (473)

THE INFORMER
Market Hill, St. George's, Saint Georges, Grenada; tel (473) 1530
Ed. – Carla Briggs

THE GRENADIAN VOICE
PO Box 633, Saint Georges, Grenada; tel (473) 440-3983; fax 440-4117; e-mail gvoice@caribsurf.com; web site www.spiceisle.com/gvoice
Pub./Mng. Ed. – Leslie Pierre

GUADELOUPE

POINTE-A-PITRE

FRANCE-ANTILLES (D)
BP 658, Pointe-A-Pitre, 97159, Guadeloupe; tel (590) 902525; fax 917831
Dir. – Francois Mercader

HAITI

PORT-AU-PRINCE

L' UNION (D)
BP 409, Port-Au-Prince, Haiti; tel (509)
Dir. – Pierre Clitandre

LE MATIN (M-5X WK.)
3, Rue Goulard Petion-Ville, Port-Au-Prince, Haiti; tel (509) 2256 4456; e-mail info@lematinhaiti.com; web site www.lematinhaiti.com
Circ. 5,000
Group: Charney/Palacios & Co.
– David Jeanty
– Joseth Etienne ReneMgr.s

LE NOUVELLISTE (E)
BP 1316, 198 Centre St., Port-Au-Prince, Haiti (509) 224-2057; fax (509) 224-2061; e-mail administration@lenouvelliste.com; web site www.lenouvelliste.com
Circ. 6,000
Group: CanWest Media Sales
Dir. – Max E. Chauvet

PANORAMA (6X WK.)
27 rue du Peuple, Port-Au-Prince, Haiti; tel (509)
Pub./Ed. – Paul Blanchet

JAMAICA

KINGSTON

THE JAMAICA GLEANER (D) Est. 1834
PO Box 40, Kingston, Jamaica (876) 922-3400; fax (876) 922-6223; web site www.jamaica-gleaner.com
Circ. 259,000
Chairman – Oliver Clarke
Editor. – Garfield Grandison
Managing Director – Christopher Barnes
Advertising: AdMarket Int'l.; Charney/Palacios & Co. Inc.

THE DAILY STAR (5X WK.)
7 North St., Kingston, Jamaica (876) 922-3400; fax (876) 922-6223; e-mail feedback@jamaica-gleaner.com; web site www.jamaica-gleaner.com
Circ. 40,000
Dir. – Oliver Clarke

THE JAMAICA HERALD (D)
29 Molynes Rd., Kingston, 10, Jamaica; tel (1) 876 906 7572; fax (809) 9687722
Mng. Ed. – Franklin McKnight

MARTINIQUE

FORT-DE-FRANCE

AUJOURD'HUI DIMANCHE (WEEKLY)
Presbytere de Bellevue, Fort-De-France, 97200, Martinique; tel (596) 714897
Dir. – Pere Gauthier

FRANCE-ANTILLES (D)
pl. Stalingrad, Fort-De-France, 97200, Martinique; tel (596) 590883; fax 602996
Dir. – Henri Merle

MONTSERRAT

PLYMOUTH

MONTSERRAT NEWS
PO Box 888, Plymouth, Montserrat; tel (664) 4918888
Owner/Ed. – J.D. Fenton

MONTSERRAT REPORTER (WEEKLY)
PO Box 215, Plymouth, Montserrat; tel (664) 491 4715; fax 491 2430; e-mail editor@themontserratreporter.com; web site www.themontserratreporter.com
Ed. – Dave Fenton

NETHERLANDS ANTILLES

KORSOU

EXTRA (6X WK.)
Recto Zwijssenstraat 24, Korsou, Netherlands Antilles; tel (599) 9 462 4595; fax 462 7575; web site www.extra.an
Circ. 20,000
Dir. – R. Yrausquin
Adv. Mgr. – Calos Mamotas
Advertising: Extra Productions NV.

SAINT MAARTEN

THE CHRONICLE (D)
PO Box 488, Saint Maarten, Netherlands Antilles; tel (599) 5 25462
Pub. – Roger F. Snow
Ed. – Mary J. Hellmund
Adv. Mgr. – Irene Morris

THE NEWS (M-5X WK.)
Italiestraat, No. 5, Saint Maarten, Netherlands Antilles; tel (599)
Pub. – G.J. Schouten
Ed. – B. Bennett

WILLEMSTAD, CURACAO

AMIGOE DI CURACAO (6X WK.)
PO Box 577, Willemstad, Curacao, Netherlands Antilles; tel (599) 9 767 2000; e-mail amigoe@amigoe.com; web site www.amigoe.com
Circ. 10,000
Dir. – Ernest Foges

NOBO (D-EX S)
PO Box 323, Willemstad, Curacao, Netherlands Antilles; tel (599) 9 4673500; fax 4672783
Ed. – Carlos Daantje
Advertising: AdMarket Int'l.

BEURS EN NIEUWSBERICHTEN (E)
PO Box 741, Willemstad, Curacao, Netherlands Antilles; tel (599) 9 465 4544; fax 465 3411
Ed. – Lauren Schenk
Advertising: Charney/Palacios & Co.

LA PRENSA (6X WK.) Est. 1928
W.I. Compagniestraat No. 41, Willemstad, Curacao, Netherlands Antilles; tel (599) 9 462 3878; fax 462 5983; e-mail laprensa@laprensacur.com; web site

www.laprensacur.com
Circ. 10,750
Dir. – R. Irausquin

PUERTO RICO

SAN JUAN

EL VOCERO DE PUERTO RICO (6X WK.)
PO Box 9067515, San Juan, PR, 00906-7515, Puerto Rico (787) 721-2300; fax (787) 722-0131; e-mail suopinion@vocero.com; web site www.vocero.com
Circ. 136,000
Pres. – Miguel Roca
Advertising: AdMarket Int'l.; The N DeFilippes Corp.

EL NUEVO DIA (M)
Apartado 9067512, San Juan, PR, 00906-7512, Puerto Rico (787) 641-8000; fax (787) 641-3111; e-mail laferre@elnuevodia.com; web site www.elnuevodia.com; www.endi.com
Circ. 203,153
Pres. – Maria Eugenia Ferre
Ed. – David Colon
Advertising: Charney/Palacios & Co.

PERIODICO CLARIDAD
Urb. Santa Rita, 57 Calle BorinqueÃ£Â¤a, San Juan, PR, 00909-2732, Puerto Rico; tel (787) 777-0534; fax 777 0537; e-mail info@claridad-puertorico.com; web site www.claridadpuertorico.com
Dir. – Manolo Coss

SAINT KITTS

BASSETERRE

DEMOCRAT (WEEKLY)
PO Box 30, Basseterre, Saint Kitts; tel (1) 869 4652091; fax 4650857
Ed. – FitzRoy P. Jones
Dir. – Captain J. L. Wigley
Advertising: AdMarket Int'l.; Charney/Palacios & Co.

THE LABOUR SPOKESMAN (2X WK.)
PO Box 239, Basseterre, Saint Kitts; tel (869) 4652229; fax 4669866
Ed. – Dawud Byron
Mgr. – Walford Gumbs

SAINT LUCIA

CASTRIES

CRUSADER (WEEKLY)
19 St. Louis St., Castries, Saint Lucia; tel (758) 4522203
Ed. – George Odlum

ST. LUCIA STAR (TWICE WEEKLY)
PO Box 1146, Castries, Saint Lucia; tel (758) 450-7827; fax 450-8694; e-mail slustar@candw.lc; starpub@candw.lc; web site www.stluciastar.com
Owner/Pub./Ed. – Rick Wayne
Owner/Mng. Dir. – Mae Wayne
Advertising: AdMarket Int'l.

VOICE OF SAINT LUCIA (2X WK.)
PO Box 104, Castries, Saint Lucia; tel (758) 4522590; fax 4531453
Ed. – Guy Ellis
Adv. Mgr. – Simone Gustave
Advertising: AdMarket Int'l.; Charney/Palacios & Co.

SAINT PIERRE AND MIQUELON

SAINT-PIERRE

L'ECHO DES CAPS (WEEKLY)
BP 4213, Saint-Pierre, 97500, Saint Pierre and Miquelon; tel (508) 414101; fax 414933; e-mail echohebd@cancom.net
Dir. – Albert Pen
Dir. – Nadege LeSenechal
Ed. – Didier Gil

TRINIDAD

BARATARIA

SUNDAY PUNCH (WEEKLY)
9th Ave. & 9th St., Barataria, Trinidad; tel (1) 868 (809) 6741692; fax (809) 6743228
Ed. – Anthony Alexis
Pub. – Daniel Chookolingo

TRINIDAD & TOBAGO MIRROR (2X WK.)
9th Ave. & 9th St., Barataria, Trinidad; tel (1) 868 (809) 6741692; fax (809) 6743228
Pub. – Daniel Chookolingo
Ed. – Ken Ali
Ed. – Keith Shepherd

CUREPE

THE BOMB (WEEKLY)
Southern Main Rd. & Clifford St., Curepe, Trinidad; tel (1) 868 (809) 6452744
Ed. – Kit Roxburgh

THE WEEKEND HEAT (WEEKLY)
Southern Main Rd. & Clifford St., Curepe, Trinidad; tel (1) 868 645 2744
Ed. – Stan Mora

PORT-OF-SPAIN

TRINIDAD EXPRESS/SUNDAY EXPRESS (D)
PO Box 1252, Port-Of-Spain, Trinidad (868) 623-1711; fax (868) 625-8897; e-mail express@trinidadexpress.com; web site www.trinidadexpress.com
Circ. 51,000
Ed. – Omatie Lyder

PORT-OF-SPAIN

NEWSDAY (D)
23A Chacon St., Port-of-Spain, Trinidad (868) 623-2459; fax (868) 625-8362; e-mail newsday@newsday.co.tt; web site www.newsday.co.tt
Circ. 25,000
CEO – Therese Mills
Office Mgr. – Christina Lumywai

EVENING NEWS (E-5X WK.)
PO Box 122, Port-of-Spain, Trinidad; tel (1) 868 623 8870; fax 625 7211
Ed. – Lenn Chongsing
Adv. Mgr. – Dennis Cumming
Advertising: Charney/Palacios & Co.

TRINIDAD EVENING NEWS (E-EX WKND.)
PO Box 122, Port-of-Spain, Trinidad; tel (1) 868 623 8870; fax 625 7211
Pub. – Mark A. Conyers
Ed. – C. Delph

TRINIDAD GUARDIAN/SUNDAY GUARDIAN (D)
PO Box 122, Port-of-Spain, Trinidad (868) 623-8870; fax (868) 625-7211; e-mail letters@ttol.co.tt; web site www.guardian.co.tt
Circ. 55,000; 70,000(sat); 56,000(sun)
Dir. – Grenfell Kissoon
Gen. Mgr. – Douglas Wilson
Advertising: AdMarket Int'l.; Charney/Palacios & Co.

SAN JUAN

THE BLAST (WEEKLY)
5-6 Hingoo Ln., El Socorro, San Juan, Trinidad; tel (868) 674 4414; fax 675 0049
Ed. – Zaid Mohammed

TURKS AND CAICOS ISLANDS

PROVIDENCIALES

TURKS AND CAICOS SUN Est. 2005
Suite # 5 Airport Hotel Plaza, Providenciales, Turks and Caicos Islands; tel (649) 649-946-8542; fax 649-941-3281; e-mail sun@suntci.com; web site www.suntci.com

TURKS AND CALCOS ISLANDS

GRAND TURK, GRAND TURK ISLANDS

TURKS AND CAICOS NEWS
PO Box 52, Grand Turk, Grand Turk Islands, Turks and Calcos Islands; tel (649) 9464664; fax 9464661; e-mail tcnews@tcway.tc
Adv. Mgr. – Blythe Dunacason
Advertising: Charney/Palacios & Co.

NEWSPAPERS OF THE CENTRAL AMERICAS AND MEXICO

BELIZE

BELMOPAN

GOVERNMENT GAZETTE (WEEKLY)
Government Printery, Power Ln., BELMOPAN, Belize; tel (501) 8 22127

BELIZE CITY

AMANDALA (WEEKLY)
3304 Partridge St., Belize City, Belize; tel (501) 202 4477; fax 4702; e-mail russell@btl.net; web site www.belizemall.com/amandala
Circ.:45,000
Group: Brydson Global Media Sales
Ed. – Evan X. Hyde
Ad Rate: The Cal Hart Co.

THE BELIZE TIMES (WEEKLY)
3 Queen St., Belize City, Belize; tel (501) 2 (501-2) 35556; fax 31940; e-mail belizetime@btl.net; web site www.belizetimes.bz
Circ.:6,000
Ed. – Michael Rudon
Mgr. – Florita P. Gidwani
Reporter – Gaspar R. Ken

THE PEOPLE'S PULSE (WEEKLY)
7 Tanoomah St., Belize City, Belize; tel (501) 2 77035; fax 76012
Circ.:5,000
Ed. – Richard Stuart

THE REPORTER (WEEKLY)
147 cnr Allenby and West Sts., Belize City, Belize; tel (501) 2 72503; fax 78118
Ed. – Harry Lawrence

BELMOPAN

BELIZE TODAY (MTHLY)
Belize Information Service, East Block, Belmopan, Belize; tel (501) 8 22159; fax 23242
Circ.:17,000
Ed. – Miguel H. Hernandez

COSTA RICA

SAN JOSE

THE TICO TIMES (WEEKLY) Est.1956
Avda. 8, Calle 15, SAN JOSE, 1000, Costa Rica; tel (506) (506)2 2581558; fax (506)2 2336378; e-mail info@ticotimes.net; web site www.ticotimes.net
Circ.:23,000
Group: The Tico Times S.A.
Owner/Publisher – Dery Dyer

SAN JOSE

AL DIA (D) Est.1992
Apdo. Postal 7-0270-1000, San Jose, Costa Rica; tel (506) 247 4647; fax 247 4665; e-mail redaccion@aldia.co.cr; web site www.aldia.co.cr
Circ.:65,000
Dir. – Edgar Fonseca

BOLETIN JUDICIAL (D)
La Uruca, San Jose, Costa Rica; tel (506) 2315222
Circ.:2,500
Dir. – Isais Castro Vargas

LA NACION (D) Est.1946
Apdo. Postal 10138-1000, San Jose, Costa Rica; tel (506) 2247 4747; fax 2247 5022; web site www.nacion.com
Circ.:125,000
Dir. – Yanancy Noguera
Ad Rate: Charney/Palacios & Co. Inc.

LA PRENSA LIBRE (E) Est.1889
Calle 4, Avda. 4, San Jose, Costa Rica; tel (506) 2223 6666; fax 2223 4671; e-mail plibre@prensalibre.co.cr; web site www.prensalibre.co.cr
Circ.:56,000
Pres. – William GÃ£Â¢mez Vargas
Sub. Dir. – Iary GÃ£Â¢mez Quesada

LA REPUBLICA (6X WK.) Est.1950
Apdo. Postal 2130-1000, San Jose, Costa Rica; tel (506) 2522 3300; fax 2257 0401; e-mail redccion@larepublica.net; web site www.larepublica.net
Pres. – Fred Blaser
Gen Mgr. – Fred Anton
Dir. – Luis Munoz
Ad Rate: Hollinger, Inc.

DIARIO EXTRA (M) Est.1978
Avda. 4, Calle 4, Edif. Borrase, San Jose, Costa Rica; tel (506) 2547-9300; fax 2223 6101; e-mail rrhh@grupoextra.com; web site www.diariextra.com
Circ.:200
Gerente Genaeral – Iary gomez
Ad Rate: 1904370

EL SALVADOR

CUSCATLAN, LA LIBERTAD

LA PRENSA GRAFICA (M-6X WK.)
Blvd. Santa Elena entre Calle Conchagua y Izalco, Cuscatlan, La Libertad, El Salvador; tel (503) 2241 2000; e-mail comercializacion@laprensa.com.sv; web site www.laprensa.com.sv
Circ.:112,800
Group: Charney/Palacios & Co.
News Editor – Gabriel Trillos
Prodn. Mgr. – Cristina de Lopez

SAN SALVADOR

CO LATINO (E)
23a Avda. Sur 225, San Salvador, El Salvador; tel (503) 710671; fax 710971; e-mail colatino@es.com.sv
Circ.:15,000
Pres. – Manuel Toledo Canas
Ed. – Francisco Elias Valencia
Prodn. Mgr. – Rogelio Ramos

EL DIARIO DE HOY
11 Calle Oriente 271, San Salvador, El Salvador; tel (503) 710100; fax 712040; web site www.elsalvador.com
Circ.:115,000
Group: Charney/Palacios & Co.
Pres. – Enrique Altamirano Madriz
Gen. Mgr. – Roberto Herodier
Sales Mgr. – Marta Barrera
Ed. – Fabricio Altamirano Basil
Prodn. Mgr. – Javier Jimenez

DIARIO OFICIAL
4a Calle Poniente 829, San Salvador, El Salvador; tel (503) 219101
Circ.:2,100
Dir. – Lud Dreikorn Lopez

EL MUNDO
2 Ave. Norte 211, San Salvador, El Salvador; tel (503) 714400; fax 714342
Pres. – Juan Jose Borja Nathan
Ed. – Ricardo Chacon
Gen. Mgr. – Arturo Arguello Oertel

LA NOTICIA (E-6X WK.)
Edif. Espana, Avda. Espana 321, San Salvador, El Salvador; tel (503) 227906; fax 711650
Circ.:30,000
Dir. – Carlos Samayoa Martinez

GUATEMALA

GUATEMALA CITY

IMPARCIAL
7a Calle 10-54, Zona 1, GUATEMALA CITY, Guatemala; tel (502) 2514723
Circ.:25,000

GUATEMALA

PRENSA LIBRE (E) Est.1951
13 calle 9-31 zona 1, Edif. Prensa Libre, Guatemala, Guatemala, 00101, Guatemala; tel (502) 2412 5000; e-mail webmaster@prensalibre.com.gt; web site www.prensalibre.com
Circ.:134,000
Editorial Director – MIGUEL MENDEZ

GUATEMALA CITY

EL GRAFICO
14a Avda. 4-33, Zona 1, Guatemala City, Guatemala; tel (502) (502-2) 2514869; fax (502-2) 2510014
Circ.:60,000
Dir. – Rodrigo Carpio Arrivillaga
Ad Rate: Charney/Palacios & Co. Inc.

DIARIO DE CENTRO AMERICA
18a Calle 6-72, Zona 1, Guatemala City, Guatemala; tel (502) 224418
Dir. – Luis Mendiz bal

LA HORA Est.1920
9a Calle A, No. 1-56, Zona 1, Guatemala City, Guatemala; tel (502) 2423 1800 PBX; fax 2423 1837; e-mail lahora@lahora.com.gt; web site www.lahora.com.gt
Circ.:15,000
Pres./CEO – Oscar Clemente Marroquin
Dir. – Pedro Pablo Marroquin
Chief Ed. – Mario Cordero

LA REPUBLICA
13 Calle, No. 8-41, Zona 10, Guatemala City, Guatemala; tel (502) (502-2) 343843; fax (502-2) 343740
Pub./Gen. Dir. – Gonzalo Marroquin Godoy
Sales Mgr. – Manuel Ju rez Montenegro
Exec. Dir. – Luis Marroquin Godoy
Ed. in Chief – Mario Recinos Lima
Chief of Info. – Mario R. Sierra

PRENSA LIBRE
13a Calle 9-31, Zona 1, Guatemala City, 01001, Guatemala; tel (502) 2412 5000; fax 2251 8768; e-mail econtrer@infovia.com.gt; web site www.prensalibre.com
Circ.:110,000
Last Audit: December 30, 2010
Pres. – Edgar Contreras Molina
Gen. Mgr. – Luis Enrique Solorzano
Sales Mgr. – Enrique Cordon
Ed. – Gonzalo Marroquin Godoy
Prodn. Mgr. – Lazaro Urizar
Ad Rate: Charney/Palacios & Co. Inc.

SIGLO VEINTIUNO
14 Avda. 4-33 Zona 1, Guatemala City, Guatemala; tel (502) 2423 6100; fax 2423 6347; web site www.sigloxxi.com
Circ.:56,000
Pres. – Alvaro Castillo Monge
Circ. Mgr. – Lejandro Traemer

HONDURAS

SAN PEDRO SULA

DIEZ
Bo Guamilito, 3 Ave 6-7 Calle N.O.,, San Pedro Sula, Honduras; web site www.elheraldo.hn
Circ.:27,767
Last Audit: June 30, 2010Fernando Berrios

EL HERALDO
Bo Guamilito, 3 Ave 6-7 Calle N.O.,, San Pedro Sula, Honduras; web site www.elheraldo.hn
Circ.:30,712
Last Audit: June 30, 2010Fernando Berrios

LA NACION (M)
Edif. San Miguel, Calle Los Horcones, San Pedro Sula, 1359, Honduras; tel (504) 511961; fax 510511
Pres. – Antonio Handal
Gen. Mgr. – Juan Jose Aguirre
Sales Mgr. – Julian Cruz

LA PRENSA
Bo Guamilito, 3 Ave 6-7 Calle N.O.,, San Pedro Sula, Honduras; web site www.elheraldo.hn
Circ.:51,250
Last Audit: June 30, 2010Fernando Berrios

LA PRENSA (MS)
3 Ave. 6-7 Calle N.O., No. 34, San Pedro Sula, Honduras; tel (504) 553 3101; fax 553 4020; e-mail jcanla@laprensa.hn; web site www.laprensahn.com
Circ.:62,000
Dir. – Jose Francisco
Ad Rate: Charney/Palacios & Co. Inc.

SAN PEDRO SULA, CORTES

TIEMPO (M)
Apdo. Postal 450, San Pedro Sula, Cortes, Honduras; tel (504) 553 3388; fax 552 6760; web site www.tiempo.hn
Circ.:30,000
Pres. – Carlos Rosenthal
Dir. – Manuel Gamero
Prodn. Mgr. – Leonel Mejia

TEGUCIGALPA

EL PERIODICO (M)
Carretera al Batallon, Tegucigalpa, Honduras; tel (504) 343 086; fax 343 090
Pres. – Emin Abufele
Ed. – Oscar Armando Martinez

LA TRIBUNA (D)
Apdo. Postal 1501, Tegucigalpa, Honduras; tel (504) 234 2673; fax 234 3050; e-mail tribuna@latribuna.hn; web site www.latribuna.hn
Circ.:20,000
Pres. – Carlos Roberto Flores
Gen. Mgr. – Manuel Acosta Medina
Ed. – Adan Elvir Flores
Ad Rate: Charney/Palacios & Co. Inc.

TEGUCIGALPA, CENTRAL DISTRICT

EL HERALDO (M)
Avda. los Proceres, Frente Instituto del Torax, Tegucigalpa, Central District, Honduras; tel (504) 366000; fax 210778
Circ.:30,000
Pres. – Jorge Canahuati Larach
Sales Mgr. – Maria Angelica Hazza
Ed./Dir. – Jose Francisco Morales Calix
Prodn. Mgr. – Ronny Marini

MEXICO

ACAPONETA, NAYARIT

EL ECO DE NAYARIT
Allende 12, Poniente, Acaponeta, Nayarit, Mexico; tel (52) 325 20286
Mng. Dir. – Antonio Saizar Quintero

ACAPULCO, GUERRERO

AVANCE (D)
Avda. Costera Miguel Aleman, No. 187, Acapulco, Guerrero, Mexico; tel (52) 744 821097
Pub. – Fernando Alcala Perez
Adv. Mgr. – Emilia Montero

DIARIO DE ACAPULCO (D)
J. Ruiz de Alarcon, No. 2, Acapulco, Guerrero, Mexico; tel (52) 744 822908
Circ.:6,500
Pub. – Alfredo G. Lobato Castro

DIARIO DEL PACIFICO
5 de Mayo No. 74, Col. Centro, Acapulco, Guerrero, 39300, Mexico; tel (52) 736 822375; fax 482-9047
Pres./Owner – Arturo Caballero Vela
Ed. – Alfredo Bello Bastor

DIARIO DIECISIETE (M)
Calzada Pie de la Cuesta, No. 90, Esquina Revoluci, Acapulco, Guerrero, 39580, Mexico; tel (52) 736 831670; fax 837802
Circ.:27,000

Chrmn. – Fernando Navarrete Magdaleno
Gen. Dir. – Prof. Victor Manuel Garcia Garcia
Assistant Dir. – Miguel Angel Mata Mata
Mgr. – J. Francisco Medina Rivera
Ad Rate: 27.00.

EL GRAFICO (M)
Nicolas Bravo y E. Mendoza Local 1, Acapulco, Guerrero, Mexico; tel (52) 744 830210; web site www.elgrafico.com
Circ.:15,000
Dir. – Jose M. Severiano Gomez

EL SOL DE GUERRERO (D-EX MON.)
Calle Prof. Silvestre Gomez Hernandez No. 4, Acapulco, Guerrero, Mexico; tel (52) 744 482 1250; fax 482 2550
Circ.:19,000
Dir./Gen. Mgr. – Alejandro E. Valdez Pineiro
Ad Rate: 25.00.

LA OPINION (M)
Nicolas Bravo, No. 4-8, Acapulco, Guerrero, Mexico; tel (52) 744 837112
Circ.:4,000
Pub. – Juan Lopez Garcia

LA VERDAD DE GUERRERO
5 de Mayo, No. 73-H, Acapulco, Guerrero, Mexico; tel (52) 744 820610
Dir. – Reynol Gomez Escalera

NOVEDADES DE ACAPULCO (MS)
Avda. Costera M. Aleman, No. 258 CP, Acapulco, Guerrero, 39300, Mexico; tel (52) 744 851155; fax 860466; e-mail editor@aca-novenet.com.mx; buzon@aca-novenet.com.mx; web site www.aca-novenet.com.mx
Pres./Gen. Dir. – Romulo O'Farrill
Exec. Mgr. – Andres Garcia Lavin
Mgr. – J. Mario Bustos Garcia
Adv. Mgr. – Juan Oms Davila
Ad Rate: 29.00.

EL SOL DE ACAPULCO (M)
Ave. Costera Miguel Aleman, No. 250, Francc. Hornos Insurgentes, Acapulco, Guerrero, 39350, Mexico; tel (52) 744 854330; fax 868940; e-mail solaca@oem.com.mx; web site www.oem.com.mx
Circ.:20,000
Gen. Mgr. – Javier Soriano Guerrero
Sales Mgr. – Javier Cagigas Gurza
Ed./Dir. – Eloina Lopez Cano

REVOLUCION (M)
Comonfort 3, Acapulco, Guerrero, Mexico; tel (52) 744 834780
Circ.:15,000
Dir. – Rodrigo Huerta Pegueros

TRIBUNA (E)
J. Ruiz de Alarcon, No. 2, Acapulco, Guerrero, Mexico; tel (52) 744
Pub. – Alfredo G. Lobato Castro

TROPICO (M)
Nicolas Bravo, No. 17, Centro, Acapulco, Guerrero, 39300, Mexico; tel (52) 744 845429; fax 845429
Circ.:20,000
Pres. – Raul Perez Garcia
Gen. Mgr. – Andres Perez Garcia
Sales Mgr. – Arturo Jimenez
Ed./Dir. – Jaime Garcia Guillen

ULTIMA HORA (M)
Calle Progreso No. 17 Col. Centro, Acapulco, Guerrero, 39300, Mexico; tel (52) 744 822375; fax 800009
Pres. – Amalia Leticia Zamora Marroquin
Gen. Mgr. – Ernesto Caballero Zamora
Sales Mgr. – Josefina Santiago Hernandez
Ed./Dir. – Fulgencio Ramirez Lozano

ULTIMAS NOTICIAS (M)
Nicolas Bravo, No. 25, Acapulco, Guerrero, Mexico; tel (52) 744 834497
Circ.:12,000
Pub. – Reemberto Valdez Ortega
Adv. Mgr. – Blanca P. de Valdez

AGUA PRIETA, SONORA

EL SOL DE AGUA PRIETA (D)
DELETE, Agua Prieta, Sonora, Mexico; tel (52) 633 338-0041

LA VERDAD DE AGUA PRIETA (WED)
Calle 8 y Avda. 30 y 30, No. 3031, Agua Prieta, Sonora, 84200, Mexico; tel (52) 633 331 0097; fax 331 0097
Circ.:2,500
Director – Fernando lomares

AGUASCALIENTES

EL SOL DEL CENTRO (M)
Madero No. 460, Zona Centro, Aguascalientes, 20000, Mexico; tel (52) 449 915 2323; fax 918 2239; e-mail publicidad@elsoldelcentro.com.mx; web site www.oem.com.mx/elsoldelcentro
Circ.:22,000
Pres. – Mario Vazquez Rana

AGUASCALIENTES, AGUASCALIENTES

EL HERALDO (MS)
Jose Maria Chavez, No. 120, Aguascalientes, Aguascalientes, 20230, Mexico; tel (52) 449 915 3223; fax 918 2220; web site heraldoags.com
Circ.:10,500
Pres. – Mauricio Bercun Melnic
Sales Mgr. – Yolando Martinez
Ed. – Jose Asuncion Gutierrez Padilla

HIDROCALIDO (D)
Quinta Avenida 101, fracc. Las Am□ricas, Aguascalientes, Aguascalientes, 20230, Mexico; tel (52) 449 910 6330; fax 978 2888; web site www.hidrocalidodigital.com
Circ.:30,000
Pres./CEO – Augustine Morales Padilla
Asst. Gen. Mgr. – Dr. Ramon Morales Agustin Pena
Adv. Mgr. – Humberto Villalobos Gonzalez
Ad Rate: 18.00.

OPINION DE AGUASCALIENTES (D)
Juan de Montoro y Cosio, Aguascalientes, Aguascalientes, Mexico; tel (52) 449 63411
Circ.:20,000
Pub. – Gustavo A. Lomelin Guerra
Adv. Mgr. – Salvador Noriega

ALTOS

AM DE SAN FRANCISCO (M)
Venustiano Carranza 126, Altos, CP 36600, Mexico; tel (52) 476 743 6099; fax 743 0336; e-mail guanajuato@am.com.mx; web site www.am.com.mx
Gen. Dir. – Enrique Gomez Orozco
Dir., Local – Enrique Rangel
Ad Rate: 9.00.

APATZINGAN, MICHOACAN

EL DIARIO (M)
Pedro Jose Bermeo, No. 10, Apatzingan, Michoacan, Mexico; tel (52) 453 40493
Circ.:10,000
Pub. – Carlos Urena

LA OPINION DE APATZINGAN (D)
Esteban Vaca Calderon No. 170, Col. Centro, Apatzingan, Michoacan, 60600, Mexico; tel (52) 453 534 0082; fax 534 1289; e-mail opinionapatzingan@gmail.com; laopinionapat@yahoo.com.mx; web site www.laopiniondeapatzingan.com
Circ.:10,000
Dir. – Jayma Mirquez Rochyn
Mgr. – Carlos Andrede Garcia

MOMENTO DE MICHOACAN (D)
Manuel Doblado, No. 174, Apatzingan, Michoacan, Mexico; tel (52) 453 40812
Dir. – Eleazar Carillo Quezada

NUEVO DIA (M)
Avda. Constitucion, No. 85, Sur, Apatzingan, Michoacan, Mexico; tel (52) 453 41695
Circ.:10,000
Group: Charney/Palacios & Co.
Pub. – Herminio Angeles Magallon
Adv. Mgr. – Alejandro T. Angeles Fernandez

TIEMPO DE APATZINGAN (D-6X WK.)
Avda. 22 de Octubre 870, Varillero, Apatzingan, Michoacan, 60600, Mexico; tel (52) 453 40491; fax 40491
Ed./Dir. – Felipe Arturo Ibanez Torres

APIZACO, TLAXCALA

LA VOZ DE APIZACO (D)
Josefa Ortiz de Dominguez, No. 711, Sur, Apizaco, Tlaxcala, Mexico; tel (52) 241 23937
Gen. Dir. – Roman Sanchez Araoz

AUTLAN, JALISCO

NUEVA EPOCA
Guadalupe Victoria, No. 173, Autlan, Jalisco, Mexico; tel (52) 317 21540

CABORCA, SONORA

NORTE DE CABORCA (D)
Calle 12 s/n, Caborca, Sonora, Mexico; tel (52) 637 21606
Gen. Dir. – Francisco Moreno Bustamante

CAMPECHE, CAMPECHE

DIARIO DE CAMPECHE (M)
Niebla, No. 4, Fraccionamiento 2000, Campeche, Campeche, Mexico; tel (52) 981
Circ.:10,000
Pub. – Jose Luis llovera Baranda

EDICIONES DE CAMPECHE
DELETE, Campeche, Campeche, Mexico; tel (52) 981 11414
Dir. – Virgilio Soberanis Rodriquez

EL SUR Est.1994
Allende No. 23 Col. San Roman, Campeche, Campeche, 24040, Mexico; tel (52) 981 60234; fax 63176; e-mail elsur@elsur.com.mx; web site www.elsur.com.mx
Circ.:10,000
– Jorge Rueda Coba
– Luis MartinezSr.s
Ad Rate: 20.70.

NOVEDADES DE CAMPECHE (D)
Avda. Ruiz Cortines S/N, Prolongacion 49-B, Campeche, Campeche, 24010, Mexico; tel (52) 981 11050; fax 64294; e-mail novcam@cancun.novenet.com.mx
Circ.:40,000
Pres. – Felix Ayuso Centurion
Sales Mgr. – Emilio Padilla Sanchez
Ed./Dir. – Lazaro Briceno Perez
Prodn. Mgr. – Ricardo Calderon Puerto

TRIBUNA DE CAMPECHE (M)
Tamaulipas No. 15-B, Col. Santa Ana, Campeche, Campeche, 24050, Mexico; tel (52) 981 816 0979; fax 816 6658; e-mail tribuna@tribunacampeche.com; web site www.tribunacampeche.com
Circ.:20,000
Pres. – Jorge Luis Gonzalez Valdez
Gen. Mgr. – Irma Yolanda Carmona de Sanchez

CANANEA, SONORA

NORTE DE CANANEA (D)
Avda. Obregon, No. 92, Cananea, Sonora, Mexico; tel (52) 622 20432
Gen. Dir. – Francisco Moreno Bustamante

CANCUN, QUINTANA ROO

CANCUN NEWS (D)
Col. Super Manzana 64, Cancun, Quintana Roo, 77500, Mexico; tel (52) 998 840 639; fax 840 833
Circ.:12,000
Founder – Othon Arroniz Baez
Gen. Dir. – Clementina de la Huerta de Arroniz
Adv. Mgr. – Marisol Arroniz de Marquez
Ad Rate: 15.14.

CARIBBEAN REPORT (M)
Avda. Chichen-Itza, No. 51, Retorno 7 Ceibo, Cancun, Quintana Roo, Mexico; tel (52) 998
Circ.:5,000
Pub. – Victor Hugo de la Cadena
Ed. – Rogelio Rodriguez Gonzalez

DIARIO DEL CARIBE (MS)
Avda. Xel-Ha, No. 67, Cancun, Quintana Roo, Mexico; tel (52) 998 830007
Circ.:14,000
Pub. – Federico de Leon
Adv. Mgr. – Vicente Lopez Torres

EL MUNDO DE CANCUN (D)
Col. Super Manzana, Cancun, Quintana Roo, 77500, Mexico; tel (52) 998 8840639; fax 8840833
Circ.:10,000
Gen. Dir. – Clementina de la Huerta de Arroniz
Administrative Dir. – Monica Almudena Arroniz
Ed. – Auricela Castro Garcia

NOVEDADES DE QUINTANA ROO (DS)
Calle Pecari, No. 37, Retorno 2, Supermanzana 20, M6, Cancun, Quintana Roo, 77500, Mexico; tel (52) 998 881 5959; fax 881 5946; e-mail novenet@cancun.novenet.com.mx; clasificados@novenet.com.mx; web site www.sipse.com
Pres. – Gerardo Garcia Damboa
Gen. Mgr. – Hector Chavec
Adv. Mgr. – Mauricio Acuna Gonzalez
Editorial Dir. – Cesar MuÃ¤oz
Ad Rate: 27.00.

POR ESTO! (M)
Manzana 63 Lote 62 Esq. Chichen Itza, Cancun, Quintana Roo, 77500, Mexico; tel (52) 998 867870
Gen. Dir. – Mario Renato Menendez Rodriguez
Adv. Coord. – Edgar Morales
Ad Rate: 30.00.

CELAYA, GUANAJUATO

AM (M)
Blvd. Adolfo Lopez Mateos, No. 1237, Ote. Col. Jardines, Celaya, Guanajuato, 38080, Mexico; tel (52) 461 26171; fax 28553; e-mail amcelaya@celaya.podernet.com.mx
Circ.:10,000
Owner/Pres. – Enrique Gomez Orozco

Gen. Mgr. – Mauricio Paredes
Ed./Dir. – Pedro Pablo Tejada

EL SOL DEL BAJIO (MS)
Boulevard Adolfo Lopez Mateos 1019 Col. Revival, Celaya, Guanajuato, 38060, Mexico; tel (52) 461 598 5300; fax 612 0505; e-mail solcel@oem.com.mx; publicidad@elsoldelbajio.com.mx; web site www.oem.com.mx
Circ.:21,840
Pres. – Mario Vazquez Rana
Gen. Mgr. – Miguel Angel Chico Herrera

CERRADA, DISTRITO FEDERAL

UNO MAS UNO (M)
Retorno de Corregio 12, Cerrada, Distrito Federal, Mexico; tel (52) 55
Circ.:70,000
Pub. – Manuel Becerea Acosta
Adv. Mgr. – Jose Bermudez Gomez

CHETUMAL, QUINTANA ROO

DIARIO DE QUINTANA ROO (M) Est.1985
Tampico Calzada No. 615, Esq Ignacio Comonford, Chetumal, Quintana Roo, 77018, Mexico; tel (52) 983 832 4587; fax 892 5317; e-mail publicidad@dqr.com.mx; web site www.dqr.com.mx
Circ.:17,000
Chrmn., Administrative council – Luis Antonio Contreras Castillo
Adv. Mgr. – Manuel Villanueva Enriquez
Ed. – Elder Alberto Vega MartÂ¡nez

NOVEDADES (M)
Carmen Ochoa de Merino, Esquina Heroes, Chetumal, Quintana Roo, Mexico; tel (52) 983 20075
Circ.:16,000
Pub. – Romulo O'Farrill
Adv. Mgr. – Wilberth Boeta

CHIHUAHUA

EL HERALDO (M)
Av. Universidad 2507, Col. San Felipe, Chihuahua, CP 31240, Mexico; tel (52) 656 432-3802; fax 432 3855; e-mail publicidad@elheraldodechihuahua.com.mx; contactanos@elheraldodechihuahua.com.mx; web site www.oem.com.mx
Circ.:10,000
Pres. – Mario Vazquez Rana

CHIHUAHUA, CHIHUAHUA

DIARIO DE CHIHUAHUA (D) Est.1985
Ave. Universidad No. 1900, col. San Felipe, Chihuahua, Chihuahua, 31210, Mexico; tel (52) 614 429 0700; fax 429 0790; web site www.diario.com.mx
Circ.:25,000
Owner – Osvaldo Rodriguez Borunda

INDICE (E)
Avda. Aldama, No. 413, Chihuahua, Chihuahua, Mexico; tel (52) 614 24535
Circ.:17,000
Pub. – Rosalba Torres de Gallardo
Adv. Mgr. – Lauro Gomez Arteaga

NORTE
Adva. Juarez, No. 6689, Chihuahua, Chihuahua, Mexico; tel (52) 614 170250
Circ.:40,000
Pres. – Oscar A. Cantu
Gen. Dir. – Alberto Riva Palacio

NOVEDADES DE CHIHUAHUA (D)
Avda. Revolucion, No. 501, Chihuahua, Chihuahua, Mexico; tel (52) 614 163385
Circ.:32,000
Dir./Ed. – Gerardo Santoyo
Dir. – Rodolfo Javier Figueroa Cardona

EL HERALDO DE LA TARDE (E-EX S)
Avda. Universidad No. 2507, Col. San Felipe, Chihuahua, Chihuahua, 31240, Mexico; tel (52) 614 432-3802; fax 432 3855; e-mail heraldo@buzon.online.com.mx; publicidad@elheraldodechihuahua.com.mx; contactanos@elheraldodechihuahua.com.mx; web site www.oem.com.mx
Circ.:21,000
Pres. – Mario Vazquez Rana
Ad Rate: Charney/Palacios & Co.

EL HERALDO DE CHIHUAHUA (D)
Avda. Universidad No. 2507, Col. San Felipe, Chihuahua, Chihuahua, 31240, Mexico; tel (52) 614 432 3802; fax 432 3855; e-mail publicidad@elheraldodechihuahua.com.mx; web site www.elheraldodechihuahua.com.mx
Circ.:68,000
Pres. – Mario Vazquez Rana
Ad Rate: Charney/Palacios & Co.

CHILPANCINGO, GUERRERO

AVANCE (D)
Cuauhtemoc y Corregidora, Chilpancingo, Guerrero, Mexico; tel (52) 747 22553
Pub. – Fernando Alcala Perez

DIARIO DE GUERRERO (D-6X WK.)
Ave. Insurgentes No. 2, Col. Morelos, Chilpancingo, Guerrero, 39010, Mexico; tel (52) 747 22888; fax 23777; e-mail diaguero@dns.pentrinex.com.mx
Circ.:12,000
Pres. – Arturo Mundo Catalan
Ed./Dir. – Ernesto Orea Garcia

ECOS DE GUERRERO (M)
Ave. Insurgentes No. 7, Col.Ruffo Figueroa, Chilpancingo, Guerrero, 39060, Mexico; tel (52) 747 472 5607; fax 472 5607
Pres. – Raul Arriaga Rodriguez
Ed. – Silce Campos Najera

PUEBLO (D)
Plazuela de San Francisco, No. 19-C,, Barrio de San Francisco, Chilpancingo, Guerrero, 39000, Mexico; tel (52) 747 471 3664; e-mail puebloguerrero@yahoo.com.mx; pueblo@hotmail.com
Circ.:15,000
Pres. – Gustavo Salazar Adame
Sales Mgr. – Rafael Ramirez Valdes

EL SOL DE CHILPANCINGO (M)
Avda. Guerrero No. 48, Col. Centro, Chilpancingo, Guerrero, 39000, Mexico; tel (52) 747 472 2112; web site www.elsoldechilpancingo.com.mx
Circ.:15,000
Pres. – Pedro Julio Valdez Vilchis

EXPRESION POPULAR (D)
Emiliano Zapata No. 25, Col. Centro, Chilpancingo, Guerrero, 39000, Mexico; tel (52) 747 12826; fax 12826
Pres. – Fredy Roman Roman
Ed./Dir. – Olivia Carbajal Uribe

EL SOL DE GUERRERO (D)
Chinacos, No. 4, Chilpancingo, Guerrero, Mexico; tel (52) 747 22550
Dir. Gen. – Alejandro Valdaz Pineiro

LA TARDE (D)
Ave. Alvarez Norte No. 48, Col. Centro, Chilpancingo, Guerrero, 39000, Mexico; tel (52) 747 22865; fax 22865
Ed./Dir. – Reemberto Valdez Vilchis

VERTICE (D)
Nicolas Bravo No. 13 Ctr., Chilpancingo, Guerrero, 39000, Mexico; tel (52) 747 25494; fax 472 2001; web site www.verticediario.com
Pres./Dir. – Miguel Angel Castorena Tenorio

CINTALAPA, CHIAPAS

ECOS DEL VALLE (D)
Blvd. Cintalapa, No. 75 M200, Cintalapa, Chiapas, 30400, Mexico; tel (52) 968 684 3528; fax 684 3528; e-mail ecosdelvalle@hotmail.com; web site www.ecosdelvalle.com
Pres. – Jorge A. Gonzalez
Gen. Mgr. – Rene Ramirez Ramos
Sales Mgr. – David Montero Montero
Ed./Dir. – Leopoldo Gonzalez Calymayor

CIUDAD ACUNA, COAHUILA

EL COAHUILENSE
2 de Abril, No. 755, Ciudad Acuna, Coahuila, Mexico; tel (52) 877
Circ.:8,000
Pub. – Rogelio Castaneda Guerrero

EL ECO
Allende Norte, No. 250, Ciudad Acuna, Coahuila, Mexico; tel (52) 877 22933; fax 21250
Circ.:8,500
Gen. Dir. – Enrique V. Castaneda

CIUDAD ALTAMIRANO, GUERRERO

EL CALENTANO (M)
Independencia Oriente, No. 14, Ciudad Altamirano, Guerrero, 40660, Mexico; tel (52) 464 2946; fax 22946
Circ.:8,000
Dir. Gen. – Urbano Delgado Castaneda
Dir. – Ernesto Castro Sagardez
Mgr. – Jorge Jaimes Salgado
Ed. – Gerardo Delgado Castaneda
Ad Rate: 5.00.

CIUDAD CUAUHTEMOC, CHIHUAHUA

DIARIO DE CUAUHTEMOC (D)
Calle 3a, No. 273, Ciudad Cuauhtemoc, Chihuahua, Mexico; tel (52) 158 26965
Dir. – Elias Montanez Alvarado

CIUDAD CUAUTHEMOC, CHIHUAHUA

NOVEDADES DE CUAUHTEMOC (D)
Morelos y Calle 17, Altos, Ciudad Cuauthemoc, Chihuahua, Mexico; tel (52) 158 22447
Dir. – Rodolfo Javier Figueroa Cardona

CIUDAD HIDALGO, MICHOACAN

EL CLARIN
Leandro Valle No. 12, Col. Centro, Ciudad Hidalgo, Michoacan, 61100, Mexico; tel (52) 786 154 1289; fax 154 1289; e-mail elclarindiario@hotmail.com
Ed. – Hector Edmundo Tinajero Gonzalez

CIUDAD JUAREZ, CHIHUAHUA

CORREO
20 de Noviembre y Saltillo, Ciudad Juarez, Chihuahua, Mexico; tel (52) 656
Circ.:18,000
Pub. – A.Q. Gutierrez
Adv. Mgr. – Arturo Rivera Olivas

DIARIO DE LA MANANA (M)
Justo Sierra, No. 485, Norte, Ciudad Juarez, Chihuahua, Mexico; tel (52) 656
Circ.:27,500
Pub. – Salvador Holguin Gutierrez
Adv. Mgr. – Gloria Leticia Escarcega

DIARIO DE JUAREZ (D)
Paseo Triunfo de la Republica, 3505 Zona Pronaf, Ciudad Juarez, Chihuahua, 32310, Mexico; tel (52) 656 629 1900; fax 629 1954; e-mail djuarez@diario.com.mx; web site www.diario.com.mx
Pres. – Osvaldo Rodriguez Borunda
Gen. Mgr. – Noah Rodriguez Avila
Adv. Mgr. – Osvaldo Rodriguez Jimenez
Ed. – Oscar Vazquez
Ad Rate: 40.00 (m); 47.00 (S).

EL NORTE DE CIUDAD JUAREZ (M)
Avda. Valle de Juarez, No. 6689, San Lorenzo, Ciudad Juarez, Chihuahua, 32320, Mexico; tel (52) 656 170250
Circ.:26,000
Pres. – Oscar A. Cantu
Dir. Gen. – Luis Silva Garcia
Adv. Mgr. – Karla Sanchez
Ad Rate: 30.00.

EL FRONTERIZO (MS)
Ignacio Mejia 1079 y 5 de Mayo, Ciudad Juarez, Chihuahua, 32230, Mexico; tel (52) 656 615 1604; web site www.elfronterizo.com.mx
Circ.:24,600
Dir. – Alma Leticia Landavazo Carrillo
Pres./Gen. Dir. – Mario Vazquez Rana
Mgr. – Jaime Gutierrez Melchor
Adv. Mgr. – Carla Sanchez Chavez

EL MEXICANO (E-EX S)
Ramon Corona y Galeana, No. 301 Centro, Ciudad Juarez, Chihuahua, 32230, Mexico; tel (52) 656 612 1023; e-mail publicidad@periodicoelmexicano.com.mx; web site www.oem.com.mx/elmexicano
Circ.:15,000
Pres. – Mario Vazquez Rana

CIUDAD MANTE, TAMAULIPAS

EL TIEMPO DE CIUDAD MANTE (M)
Galeana, No. 109, Norte, Ciudad Mante, Tamaulipas, 89800, Mexico; tel (52) 123 21555
Circ.:30,000
Pres./Dir. Gen. – Gabriel Puga Tovar
Dir. – Jose Gonzalez Alvarado
Ad Rate: 30.00.

ECO DEL MANTE (E)
Galeana, No. 212, Sur, Ciudad Mante, Tamaulipas, Mexico; tel (52) 831
Circ.:6,000
Pub. – Cesar Arturo Cervantes Gomez

EL DIARIO DE CIUDAD MANTE (D)
Canales y Anahuac, Ciudad Mante, Tamaulipas, Mexico; tel (52) 831 (52-123) 23431
Dir. – Paulino Ramirez Ju rez

LA EXTRA (D)
Canales, No. 307, Poniente, Ciudad Mante, Tamaulipas, Mexico; tel (52) 831

CIUDAD MIGUEL ALEMAN, TAMAULIPAS

EL TIEMPO DE CIUDAD MIGUEL ALEMAN (D-6X WK.)
Insurgentes, No. 170, Ciudad Miguel Aleman, Tamaulipas, 88300, Mexico; tel (52) 897 20754; fax 20482

Circ.:12,000
Dir. – Mariano Bueno Gil
Ad Rate: 11.35.

CIUDAD NEZAHUALCOYOTL, MEXICO

LAS NOTICIAS DE ULTIMA HORA (D)
Calle 9, No. 86, Col. Las Aguilas, Ciudad Nezahualcoyotl, Mexico, Mexico; tel (52) 79 36624; fax 36624
Dir. Gen. – Federico Zavalza Ramirez
Dir./Ed. – Ignacio del Castillo Diaz

CIUDAD OBREGON, SONORA

DIARIO DEL YAQUI (M)
Ciudad Obregon, Sonora, Ciudad Obregon, Sonora, 85000, Mexico; tel (52) 644 52332; fax 45990
Circ.:25,000
Founder – Jesus Corral Ruiz
Gen. Mgr. – Jesus Javier Ruiz Garcia
Ad Rate: 25.00.

EXTRA DE LA TARDE (E)
Ciudad Obregon, Sonora, Ciudad Obregon, Sonora, Mexico; tel (52) 644
Circ.:12,000
Pub. – Heriberto Leon Pena
Adv. Mgr. – Lilia Torres Morgan

TRIBUNA DEL YAQUI (M)
Durango y Guadalupe Victoria 903 Sur, Ciudad Obregon, Sonora, 85160, Mexico; tel (52) 644 416 5100; fax 416 3511; e-mail tribuna@tribuna.com.mx; lector@tribuna.com.mx; web site www.tribuna.com.mx
Circ.:35,000
Pres. – Faustino Felix Escalante
Gen. Mgr. – Gabriel Roberto Monteverde
Ed. Dir. – Faustino Felix Chavez
Sports Ed. – Arturo Garcia
Prodn. Mgr. – Silveria Cruz Rodriguezr

CIUDAD SATELITE, MEXICO

OBJECTIVO (WEEKLY)
Lago Como, No. 124, An huac, Ciudad Satelite, Mexico, 11320, Mexico; tel (52) 250 3088; fax 3949
Founder/Dir. Gen. – Benigno Vazquez Olazo

CIUDAD VALLES, SAN LUIS POTOSI

DIARIO DE LAS HUASTECAS (D)
Ciudad Valles, San Luis Potosi, Ciudad Valles, San Luis Potosi, Mexico; tel (52) 138 (52-138) 21655
Dir. Gen. – Esteban Lopre Cardenas

DIARIO DE VALLES (M)
Taninul, No. 5, Fraccionamiento Las Lomas, Ciudad Valles, San Luis Potosi, Mexico; tel (52) 138 (52-138) 21558
Circ.:4,000
Dir. Gen. – Jose Angel de la Garza Gonzalez

LA EXTRA (D)
Acapulco y Ferrocarril, Ciudad Valles, San Luis Potosi, Mexico; tel (52) 138 (52-138) 21764
Dir. – Ricardo Figueroa Sanchez

OPINION (M)
Venustiano Carretera, No. 433, Ciudad Valles, San Luis Potosi, Mexico; tel (52) 444
Circ.:10,000
Pub. – Ignacio A. Rosillo

EL SOL DE LA HUASTECA (M)
Avda. Juarez y Pedro A. Santos, Ciudad Valles, San Luis Potosi, Mexico; tel (52) 481
Circ.:10,000
Pub. – Florencio Ruiz de la Pena

CRONICA (M)
Calle Las Damas, Esquina Mali, Fraccionamiento Val, Ciudad Valles, San Luis Potosi, 79020, Mexico; tel (52) 138 11877
Circ.:10,000
Dir. Gen. – Dr. Alfonso Cruz Sahagun
Ad Rate: 6.10.

LA VOZ DE LA HUASTECA (D)
Clavel 10, Col. Doraceli, Ciudad Valles, San Luis Potosi, Mexico; tel (52) 138 20561
Dir. – David Flores Guzman

CIUDAD VICTORIA, TAMAULIPAS

EL EDITOR
Ciudad Victoria, Tamaulipas, Ciudad Victoria, Tamaulipas, Mexico; tel (52) 834
Circ.:4,000
Pulbisher – Gildo R. Garza

EL DIARIO
Ciudad Victoria, Tamaulipas, Ciudad Victoria, Tamaulipas, 87000, Mexico; tel (52) 834 318 2460; fax 318 2463; e-mail redaccion@eldiariodevictoria.com.mx; web site www.eldiariodevictoria.com.mx
Circ.:39,000
Ed. – Francisco Filizola Gonzalez

EL MERCURIO (M)
Matamoros No. 301, Oriente, Ciudad Victoria, Tamaulipas, 87000, Mexico; tel (52) 834 172 5200; web site www.elmercurio.com.mx
Circ.:42,000
Pres. – Antonio Villarreal Saldivar
Gen. Mgr. – Ricardo Villarreal Rodriguez
Ed./Dir. – Noe Rodriguez Martinez

LA EXTRA (D)
Matamores, No. 301, Otem n, Ciudad Victoria, Tamaulipas, Mexico; tel (52) 834
Circ.:8,000
Pub. – Jose Villarreal Caballero

EL GRAFICO (D)
Zaragoza No. 1525, Col. Centro, Ciudad Victoria, Tamaulipas, 87000, Mexico; tel (52) 131 22364; fax 27321; e-mail elgrafico@infosel.net.mx; web site www.elgraficotam.com.mx
Pres. – Jose Guadalupe Diaz Martinez

NUEVAS NOTICIAS DE TAMAULIPAS (D)
Calle Hidalgo 21 y 22, No. 561, Ciudad Victoria, Tamaulipas, 87000, Mexico; tel (52) 131 22143; fax 25232
Circ.:30,000
Dir. Gen. – Antonio Villarreal Saldivar
Dir. – Ricardo Gonzalez De La Vina
Adv. Mgr. – Jorge Othon Rocha
Ad Rate: 5.00.

LA VERDAD DE TAMAULIPAS
21 y 22 Hidalgo No. 561, Ciudad Victoria, Tamaulipas, 87000, Mexico; tel (52) 834 312 5118; fax 312 5232; web site www.laverdad.com.mx
Circ.:30,000
Dir. Gen. – Guillermo Villarreal Caballero
Ed. – Javier Terrazas Barraza
Ad Rate: 16.00.

CIUDAD DEL CARMEN, CAMPECHE

TRIBUNA DEL CARMEN (M)
Calle 31 por 32 Altos, Ciudad del Carmen, Campeche, 24100, Mexico; tel (52) 938 382 2394; fax 382 2338; web site www.tribunacampeche.com
Circ.:50,000
Pres. – Jorge Luis Gonzalez Valdez
Sales Mgr. – Pedro Jose Espinoza
Ed. – Sixto Sosa Barrera

COATZACOALCOS, VERACRUZ

DIARIO DE SOTAVENTO (M)
La Llave, No. 103, Coatzacoalcos, Veracruz, Mexico; tel (52) 921 20318
Circ.:15,000
Pub. – Alfonso Grajales
Adv. Mgr. – Hilda Lara Alvarez

DIARIO DEL ISTMO (M)
Avda. Hidalgo, No. 1115, Col. Centro, Coatzacoalcos, Veracruz, 96400, Mexico; tel (52) 921 211 8000; fax 211 8008; web site www.diariodelistmo.com
Circ.:64,600
Dir. Gen. – Hector Robles Barajas
Adv. Mgr. – Solorsano Ortega
Ad Rate: 15.25.

NOTICIAS (D)
Avda. Hidalgo, No. 1115, Coatzacoalcos, Veracruz, 96400, Mexico; tel (52) 921 (52-921) 48802
Circ.:30,000
Dir. – Hector Zaragoza Lopez
Ed. in Chief – Natalio Bernal Amador

COLIMA

EL DIARIO DE COLIMA (D)
Av 20 de Noviembre No. 580, Colima, 28060, Mexico; tel (52) 312 312 0111; fax (312) 316-1800; web site www.diariodecolima.com
Circ.:25,000
Founder – Manuel Sanchez Silva
Dir. – Hector Sanchez De la Madrid
Sales Mgr. – Melissa Nohemi Aguilar Venegas
Ad Rate: 18.75.

COLIMA, COLIMA

EL COMENTARIO (M-EX S)
Gildardo Gomez, No. 66, Colima, Colima, 28000, Mexico; tel (52) 312 22 440; fax 22 440; e-mail comenta@venus.ucol.mx; web site elcomentario.ucol.mx
Circ.:1,500
Dir. Gen. – Victor M. de Santiago
Ad Rate: 14.00.

ECOS DE LA COSTA (M)
Gabino Barreda, No. 452, Colima, Colima, 28000, Mexico; tel (52) 312 128040; fax 142829; e-mail ecos01@volcan.ucol.mx; web site www.ecosdelacosta.com.mx
Circ.:22,000
Pres. – Armando Martinez De La Rosa
Sales Mgr. – Hugo Fernandez
Ed./Dir. – Manolo Delgado

EL INDEPENDIENTE DE COLIMA (D)
Libertad, No. 264, Colima, Colima, 28000, Mexico; tel (52) 312 40 150; fax 40 201
Circ.:28,000
Dir. Gen. – Gabriel Macias Becerril
Admin. – Leonel C. Lozano Baltazar

EL IMPARCIAL (D-EX S)
Gregorio Torres Quintero No. 113, Col. Centro, Colima, Colima, 28000, Mexico; tel (52) 312 312 1239; fax 312 1239; e-mail lector@elimparcial.com; web site www.elimparcial.com
Circ.:13,000
Pres. – Carlos Manuel Zepeda Rosas

EL MUNDO DESDE COLIMA (D)
Independencia No. 131, Col. Centro, Colima, Colima, 28000, Mexico; tel (52) 312 313 5570; fax 312 3353; e-mail elmundo@hotmail.com
Circ.:25,000
Pres. – Manuel Sanchez de la Madrid
Sales Mgr. – Maria de la Cruz Estrada

CORDOBA, VERACRUZ

DIARIO 2001 (D)
Calle 9, No. 311, Cordoba, Veracruz, Mexico; tel (52) 271

ABC CORDOBA (D)
Avda. 3, No. 1504, Col. Centro, Cordoba, Veracruz, 94500, Mexico; tel (52) 271 43551
Circ.:10,000
Dir. Gen. – Alfredo Rios Hernandez

EL MUNDO DE CORDOBA (M)
Ave. 3 No. 1102 Altos 1, Zona Industrial, Cordoba, Veracruz, 94690, Mexico; tel (52) 271 143521; fax 126777; e-mail mundo@cordoba.rp.com.mx; web site www.elmundodecordoba.com
Circ.:25,000
Pres. – Clementina de la Huerta de Arroniz
Sales Mgr. – Trinidad Vargas
Ed./Dir. – Raul Gil Arroniz de la Huerta

EL SOL DEL CENTRO (M)
Calle 9 No. 311, Col. Centro, Cordoba, Veracruz, 94500, Mexico; tel (52) 271 25212; fax 40377; e-mail info@oem.com.mx; web site www.oem.com.mx
Circ.:15,000
Pres. – Mario Vazquez Rana
Gen. Mgr. – Jose Antonio Sagasti Redondo
Sales Mgr. – Juan Contreras Lara
Ed./Dir. – Jose de Jesua Algarin Duran

EL SOL DE ORIZABA (D)
Sur 5, entre 2 Ote y 4, Cordoba, Veracruz, 94500, Mexico; tel (52) 271 59631
Circ.:12,000

EL SOL DE LA TARDE (E-EX S)
Calle 9, No. 31, Cordoba, Veracruz, 94500, Mexico; tel (52) 271 22750; fax 20389
Circ.:10,000
Pub. – Eduardo G. Valdez

CUAULTA, MORELOS

EL SOL DE CUAUTLA (MS)
Calle Fin del Rul No. 5, Col. Centro, Cuaulta, Morelos, 62740, Mexico; tel (52) 735 354 2252; e-mail publicidad@elsoldecuernavaca.com.mx; web site www.oem.com.mx/elsoldecuautla
Circ.:12,000
Pres. – Mario Vazquez Rana
Dir. – Emilio GonzÂ lez Anguiano

CUAUTLA, MORELOS

POLIGRAFO
2 de Mayo, No. 25, Cuautla, Morelos, Mexico; tel (52) 735
Circ.:8,000
Pub. – Enrique Romano Hernandez
Adv. Mgr. – Faustino Romano

CUERNAVACA, MORELOS

AVANCE (D)
Galeana, No. 2213, Cuernavaca, Morelos, Mexico; tel (52) 777 122238
Circ.:10,000
Pub. – Alfonso Garcia

DIARIO DE MORELOS (M)
Morelos Sur No. 817, Cuernavaca, Morelos, 62000, Mexico; tel (52) 777 (52-73) 185086
Circ.:47,000
Gen. Dir. – Federico Bracamontes
Gen. Mgr. – Augustin Arana
Dir.-Local – Jorge Mejia Lara
Local Mgr. – Jorge Reynoso Mangino
Adv. Mgr. – Jesus Izaguirre Mora
Ad Rate: 30.00.

EL FINANCIERO (M-EX WKND.)
Avda. A. Lopez Mateos, No. 102-A, Col. El Vergel, Cuernavaca, Morelos, 62400, Mexico; tel (52) 777 3183594; fax 3184995; e-mail contacto@elfinanciero.com.mx; web site www.elfinanciero.com.mx
Owner/Pres. – Rogelio Cardenas Sarmiento
Pres. – Guillermo Sanchez Fabian
Ed./Dir. – Manuel deJesus Duran Valdivia

EL MUNDO (D)
Degollado 104, Cuernavaca, Morelos, Mexico; tel (52) 777 180336
Dir. – Andres Alberdi Aburto

EL REGIONAL DEL SUR (6X WK.)
Avda. Lazaro Cardenas, No. 494, Col. Jiquilpan, Cuernavaca, Morelos, 62170, Mexico; tel (52) 777 313 0507; fax 313 2893; e-mail publicidadelregionaldelsur@yahoo.com.mx,; web site www.elregional.com.mx
Pres. – Eolo Ernesto Pacheco Rodriguez
Ed. – Carlos Gallardo Sanchez
Mng. Ed. – Minerva Delgado Torres

EL RENOVADOR (D)
Rayon 2-1, Cuernavaca, Morelos, Mexico; tel (52) 731 84914
Dir. – Rodolfo Barrera Gutierrez

LA UNION DE MORELOS (M) Est.1990
Avda. Vicente Guerrero, No. 777, Col. Tezontepec C, Cuernavaca, Morelos, 62250, Mexico; tel (52) 777 114634; fax 114760; e-mail uniomor@infosel.net.mx; web site www.launion.com.mx
Circ.:20,000
Pres./Gen. Dir. – Mario Estrada Elizondo
Asst. Gen. Dir. – Ricardo Estrada Gonzalez
Gen. Mgr. – Arnoldo Sanchez Rosales
Ad Rate: 35.00.

LA VOZ (M)
Salazar, No. 107, Cuernavaca, Morelos, Mexico; tel (52) 777 120120
Circ.:7,000
Gen. Dir. – Jose Gutierrez Sandoval

OPINION (D)
Jardin Juarez, No. 7-104, Edificio Bellavista, Cuernavaca, Morelos, Mexico; tel (52) 777
Dir. – Sergio Parra Roman

EL SOL DE CUERNAVACA (D)
Galeana No. 125, Col. Las Palmas, Cuernavaca, Morelos, 62050, Mexico; tel (52) 777 314 2733; fax 318 3331; e-mail publicidad@elsoldecuernavaca.com.mx; oemenlinea@oem.com.mx; web site www.oem.com.mx/elsoldecuernavaca
Circ.:14,000
Pres. – Mario Vazquez Rana

CULIACAN, SINALOA

EL DEBATE DE CULIACAN (MS)
Madero, No. 556, Poniente, Culiacan, Sinaloa, 80000, Mexico; tel (52) 667 166353; fax 157131; e-mail redaccion@debate.com.mx; pubcul@debtel.com.mx; web site www.debate.com.mx
Mgr./Dir. – Jose Isabel Ramos Santos
Adv. Dir. – Armando X. Lopez Angulo
Dir. – Rosario I. Oropeza
Ad Rate: 26.00.

EL DIARIO DE CULIACAN (M)
Rosales, No. 167, Oriente, Culiacan, Sinaloa, 80000, Mexico; tel (52) 667 130947; e-mail info@debate.com.mx; web site www.debate.com.mx
Circ.:25,000
Pub. – Gonzalo R.A. Valdez

EL DIARIO DE SINALOA (M)
Rosales, No. 167, Oriente, Culiacan, Sinaloa, 80000, Mexico; tel (52) 667 130947; fax 154600
Circ.:46,000
Pres. – Miguel Valle Campos

LA HORA DE SINALOA (M)
Blvd. Francisco I. Madero, No. 490-B, Poniente, Culiacan, Sinaloa, 80000, Mexico; tel (52) 667 168840
Circ.:8,000
Pres./Gen. Dir. – Silvino Silva Lozano
Ad Rate: 8.00.

NORESTE CULIACAN (MS)
Angel Flores, No. 282, Oriente Centro, Culiacan, Sinaloa, 80000, Mexico; tel (52) 667 132100; fax 139761
Gen. Dir. – Maunel J. Clouthier
Ed. – Jose Refugio Haro
Adv. Mgr. – Ana Cecilia Castro Castro
Ad Rate: 29.00.

EL SOL DE SINALOA (M)
Leyva Solano and Gabriel Blvd. 320 Corona, Culiacan, Sinaloa, 80000, Mexico; tel (52) 667 713 6590; e-mail publicidad@elsoldesinaloa.com.mx; web site www.oem.com.mx/elsoldesinaloa
Circ.:20,000
Pres. – Mario Vazquez Rana
Dir. – Maria De Luis Anells

EL SOL DE CULIACAN (E-EX S)
Blvd. Leyva Solano y Corona No. 320, Col. Centro, Culiacan, Sinaloa, 80000, Mexico; tel (52) 667 131621; fax 131597; e-mail solcul@oem.com.mx; web site www.oem.com.mx/solcul
Circ.:10,750
Pres. – Mario Vazquez Rana
Gen. Mgr. – Jose Carlos Rodriguez Terron
Sales Mgr. – Guadalupe Gaxiola
Ed./Dir. – Jorge Luis Tellez

DELICIAS, CHIHUAHUA

DIARIO DE DELICIAS (MS)
Avda. 6ta. y Calle 4ta., Sur, Delicias, Chihuahua, 33000, Mexico; tel (52) 147 45555; fax 45656; e-mail delicias@diarioch.com.mx; diario_del@infosel.com.mx; web site www.diario.com.mx
Circ.:3,000
Pres. – Ruben Valles Mata
Sales Mgr. – Juan Carlos Anota
Ed./Dir. – Genaro Fuentes V'lez

EL HERALDO DE DELICIAS (M)
Avda. Rio Chuviscar, Oriente No. 201, Esquina Avda, Delicias, Chihuahua, 33000, Mexico; tel (52) 147 25629; fax 25626; web site www.online.com.mx/elheraldo
Circ.:5,000
Pres./Gen. Dir. – Mario Vazquez Rana
Dir. – Javier Contreras
Coord. – Edgar Itamar Rivera Garcia
Ad Rate: 14.00.

DURANGO

LA EPOCA (M)
Blvd. Aleman y Calle Santiago Papasquiaro ZI, Gome, Durango, Mexico; tel (52) 171 29180; fax 27944
Circ.:10,000
Gen. Dir. – Jose Gonzalez Cantu

DURANGO, DURANGO

EL SIGLO DE DURANGO (M)
Hildalgo, No. 419 Sur, Centro, Durango, Durango, 34000, Mexico; tel (52) 618 125058; fax 125050; e-mail durango@elsiglo.com.mx; web site www.elsiglodedurango.com.mx
Pres. – Antonio Irazoqui de Juambelz
Gen. Mgr. – Miguel Angel Ruelas
Ed./Dir. – Alfonso Gonzalez Karg

EL SOL DE LA LAGUNA (M)
Zaragoza, No. 202, Sur, Durango, Durango, Mexico; tel (52) 618 142845
Circ.:15,000
Pub./Gen. Dir. – Daniel Ramos Nava
Ed. in Chief – Joaquin Maldonado
Ed. in Chief – Gomez Palacio
Adv. Mgr. – Angel Gomez Silva

IMPULSO (D)
Excampo Deportivo, No. 3, Durango, Durango, Mexico; tel (52) 618 120962
Dir. – Jesus Asef Rodriguez

MERIDIANO (E-EX S)
Juarez, No. 110, Sur, Durango, Durango, Mexico; tel (52) 618
Circ.:10,000
Pub. – Salvador Nava Rodriguez

NORTE (M)
Hidalgo, No. 117, Sur, Durango, Durango, Mexico; tel (52) 618
Circ.:28,000
Dir. – Alfonso Bautista

DIARIO DE DURANGO (E-EX S)
Negrete No. 903, Poniente, Durango, Durango, 34000, Mexico; tel (52) 618 115010; fax 115742; e-mail soldgo@ocnanet.com.mx; web site www.oem.com.mx
Circ.:23,000
Pres. – Juan Alvarez Montes
Sales Mgr. – Andres Montesinos Celis
Ed./Dir. – Guillermo Carreon

EL SOL DE DURANGO (D)
Negrete No. 903 Poniente, Durango, Durango, 34000, Mexico; tel (52) 618 811 5742; fax 813 3396; e-mail publicidad@elsoldedurango.com.mx; web site www.oem.com.mx/elsoldedurango
Circ.:36,000
Pres. – Juan Alvarez Montes

PROVINCIA (D)
Rebote, No. 929, Durango, Durango, Mexico; tel (52) 618 123541; fax 118895
Dir. – Agapito Salazar

SATURNO (D)
Constitucion, No. 415, Norte, Durango, Durango, Mexico; tel (52) 618
Circ.:13,000
Pub. – Oscar Hiram Herrera Munoz

VICTORIA DE DURANGO (D)
Pino Suarez, No. 801, Oriente Col. Ctr., Durango, Durango, 34000, Mexico; tel (52) 618 817 0330; fax 817 9244; web site www.periodicovictoria.com.mx
Dir. Gen – Jorge C. Mojica Vargas
Circ. Mgr. – Ulpiano R. Sortillon Tena
Ed. – Mariano Cervantes Pizarro

LA VOZ DE DURANGO (MS)
Calle Juarez No. 110 Sur, Col. Centro, Durango, Durango, 34000, Mexico; tel (52) 618 812 9911; fax 129 446; e-mail lavozdedurango@yahoo.com.mx; web site www.lavozdedurango.com
Circ.:36,000
Dir. – Juan G. Nava Stenner
Asst. Dir. – Edgar Gurrola

ENSENADA, BAJA CALIFORNIA

ABC (M)
Blancarte, No. 369-4, Ensenada, Baja California, Mexico; tel (52) 646 40318; fax 81277
Pub./Gen. Mgr. – Francisco Guerrero
Dir. – Ernesto Paredes Villegas

FRESNILLO, ZACATECAS

LA VOZ DE FRESNILLO (M-EX S)
Ave. Garcia Salinas No. 119, Col. Centro, Fresnillo, Zacatecas, 99000, Mexico; tel (52) 493 26771; fax 26771
Circ.:12,000
Pres. – Fernando Frias Salcedo
Ed./Dir. – Mario Alberto Castaneda Banuelos

GUADALAJARA, JALISCO

EL DIARIO DE GUADALAJARA (M)
Lopez Mateos, Norte, No. 249, esq. Avda. Mexico, Guadalajara, Jalisco, 44940, Mexico; tel (52) 33 6162278
Circ.:60,000
Pres./Gen. Dir. – Luis A. Gonzalez Becerra

EL FINANCIERO (M-EX WKND.)
Zaragoza No. 376, Col. Artesanos, Guadalajara, Jalisco, 44290, Mexico; tel (52) 33 613-7831; fax 658-1798; e-mail financ@vinet.com.mx
Circ.:12,000
Owner – Rogelio Cardenas Sacmiento
Pres. – Guillermo Sanchez Fabian
Sales Mgr. – Francisco Javier Badiola Contreras
Ed./Dir. – Salvador Maldonado

EL INFORMADOR (MS)
Calle Independencia No. 300, Col. Centro, Guadalajara, Jalisco, 44100, Mexico; tel (52) 333 614-6340; fax 614-4653; e-mail diario@informador.com.mx; web site www.informador.com.mx
Circ.:46,000
Pres. – Jorge Alvarez del Castillo Zuloaga
Gen. Mgr. – Ramon Munguia Duenas
Sales Mgr. – Fernando Ibarra
Ed./Dir. – Carlos Alvarez del Castillo Gregory

EL JALISCIENSE (M)
Avda. Rio Nilo, No. 2003, Lomas del Paradero Secto, Guadalajara, Jalisco, 44840, Mexico; tel (52) 33 6394445; fax 6393675
Circ.:30,000
Gen. Dir. – Alfredo Perez Diaz

LET'S ENJOY
Avda. Nino Obrero, No. 706, Chapalita CP, Guadalajara, Jalisco, Mexico; tel (52) 33 6215201

EL SOL DE GUADALAJARA (E-EX S)
Calzada Independencia Sur No. 324, Guadalajara, Jalisco, 44100, Mexico; tel (52) 33 613-0690; fax 613-6274; web site www.oem.com.mx
Pres. – Mario Vazquez Rana
Ed./Dir. – Ricardo del Valle del Peral

EL OCCIDENTAL (MS)
Calzada Independencia Sur No. 324, Guadalajara, Jalisco, 44100, Mexico; tel (52) 33 3613 0690; e-mail publicidad@eloccidental.com.mx; oemenlinea@oem.com.mx; web site www.oem.com.mx
Circ.:40,000
Pres. – Mario Vazquez Rana
Chief Information – VÃ¡ctor Manuel Chavez Ogazon
Ed. – Javier Valle Chavez
Ad Rate: Charney/Palacios & Co.

SIGLO 21 (M)
Avda. Washington 250A, Guadalajara,

Jalisco, 44440, Mexico; tel (52) 33 36500561; fax 36500433; e-mail siglo21@foreigner.class.udg.mx; web site www.s21.com.gt
Circ.:34,646
Dir. – Jorge Zepeda
Pres. – Alfonso Dau

TABLOIDE (D)
Tamaulipas, No. 1293, Guadalajara, Jalisco, Mexico; tel (52) 33 624 1313
Dir. – Miguel Ochoa de la Mora

TIEMPO DE JALISCO (M&E)
Cerro Viejo, No. 1200, Col. Lomas de Independencia, Guadalajara, Jalisco, Mexico; tel (52) 33 6378981

OCHO COLUMNAS (D)
Avda. Patria No. 1201 Lomas del Valle, Cuidad Universitaria, Guadalajara, Jalisco, 45129, Mexico; tel (52) 333 641-9708; fax 641-8963; e-mail ocho@foreigner.class.udg.mx; web site www.ochocolumnas.com.mx
Circ.:40,000
Pres. – Gonzalo Leano Reyes
Gen. Mgr. – Carlos Peregrina Barajas
Sales Mgr. – Pieiro Vega
Ed./Dir. – Rafael Rodriguez Lopez
Prodn. Mgr. – Pablo Horak Cruz

GUADALUPE, ZACATECAS

IMAGEN (M)
Calzada Revolucion No. 24, Col. Tierra y Libertad, Guadalupe, Zacatecas, 98600, Mexico; tel (52) 492 923 8898; e-mail buzon@imagenzac.com.mx; web site www.imagenzac.com.mx
Pres. – Alfredo Jimenez De Sandi
Ad Rate: 30.00.

GUAMUCHIL, SINALOA

EL AVANCE DE GUAMUCHIL (M)
Benito Juarez, No. 64, Norte, Guamuchil, Sinaloa, Mexico; tel (52) 673 20426
Circ.:9,000
Ed. – Romano Lanciani
Pub. – Aureliano Perez

EL DEBATE (MS)
Silverio Trueba y 22 de Diciembre, Guamuchil, Sinaloa, 81400, Mexico; tel (52) 67373 25150; fax 25154; e-mail info@debate.com.mx
Circ.:2,822
Gen. Mgr. – Jose Isabel Ramos Santos
Ed./Dir. – Benjamin Bojorquez

EL INFORMADOR (D)
Mina 239 Sur, Guamuchil, Sinaloa, Mexico; tel (52) 674
Circ.:12,000
Pub. – Jose Betancourt Gomez

NOROESTE
Agustina Ramirez, No. 66, Sur, Guamuchil, Sinaloa, 81400, Mexico; tel (52) 673 320220; fax 324085; e-mail webmaster@noroeste.com.mx; web site www.noroeste.com.mx
Circ.:3,000
Sales Mgr. – Ana Cecilia Castro
Ed./Dir. – Armando Ojeda Camacho
Ad Rate: 26.00.

GUANAJUATO, GUANAJUATO

AM GUANAJUATO (D)
Cantarranas no 5, Int no 1, Numero 16 Interior 3, Guanajuato, Guanajuato, 36000, Mexico; tel (52) 473 732 7727; fax 732 5697; web site www.am.com.mx
Dir. Gen. – Enrique Gomez Orozco
Gen. Mgr. – Josephine Palomino
Adv. Mgr. – Sergio Pablo Tejada

CONTACTO
Plaza de Guanajuato, No. 49, 1er. Piso, Guanajuato, Guanajuato, 36000, Mexico; tel (52) 473

DIARIO DE GUANAJUATO (M)
Hotel Castillo, Guanajuato, Guanajuato, Mexico; tel (52) 473 6120818
Circ.:78,000
Pub. – Carlos Loret de Mola
Adv. Mgr. – Arturo Joel Padilla

EL NACIONAL (M)
Carretera Guanajuato-Juventud Rosas, Km. 9.5, Guanajuato, Guanajuato, Mexico; tel (52) 473 (52-473) 31266; fax 31288
Circ.:60,000
Gen. Dir. – Arnoldo Cuellar Ornelas
Ad Rate: 22.50.

GUASAVE, SINALOA

EL DEBATE (MS)
Cuauhtemoc, No. 52, Guasave, Sinaloa, 81000, Mexico; tel (52) 687 23940; fax 21530; e-mail info@debate.com
Circ.:3,842
Gen. Mgr. – Jose Isabel Ramos Santos
Sales Mgr. – Ramon Francisco Cota Felix
Ed./Dir. – Moises Garcia Castro

EL GUASAVENSE (D-6X WK.)
Vicente Guerrero, No. 110, Guasave, Sinaloa, 81000, Mexico; tel (52) 687 21350; fax 22350
Circ.:25,000
Pres. – Francisco Echavarria Salazar

EL REGIONAL (D)
Cesar Aguilar Lopez, No. 18, Guasave, Sinaloa, 81000, Mexico; tel (52) 687 22976; fax 20970
Gen. Dir. – Romualdo Ruiz

LA OPINION DEL VALLE (E)
Colon, No. 673 Bis, Guasave, Sinaloa, Mexico; tel (52) 687 20039
Circ.:13,000
Pub. – Ramon Hernandez Rubio

GUAYMAS, SONORA

EL DIARIO (E-EX S)
Calle 18 y Avda. Adolfo de la Huerta, Guaymas, Sonora, Mexico; tel (52) 622 220028
Circ.:4,500
Pub. – Alejandro Ramirez Cisneros
Adv. Mgr. – Bernardo Gastelum

EL ECO (M)
Blvd. Garcia Lopez, s/n, Guaymas, Sonora, Mexico; tel (52) 622
Circ.:13,000
Pub. – Jose G. Rodriguez

EL FINANCIERO (M-EX WKND.)
Privada Inalambrica, No. 26, Col. San Benito, Guaymas, Sonora, 83190, Mexico; tel (52) 622 101963; fax 101962
Circ.:10,000
Dir. – Rogelio Cardenas Sarmiento

LA GACETA (WEEKLY)
Avda. A. L. Rodriguez y Calle 16, Guaymas, Sonora, 85460, Mexico; tel (52) 622 27879
Dir. – Miguel Escobar Valdez

LA VOZ DEL PUERTO (M)
Calle 10 Ave. No. 142, Col. Centro, Guaymas, Sonora, 85400, Mexico; tel (52) 622 42184; fax 24117; e-mail lavoz@tetakawi.net.mx; web site www.lavozdelpuerto.com.mx
Circ.:10,000
Owner/Pres. – Gilberto Felix Escalante
Gen. Mgr. – Jose Regino Borquez Felix
Sales Mgr. – Enrique Rodriguez
Ed./Dir. – Jose Luis Borquez Rivas

HERMOSILLO, SONORA

EL FINANCIERO (D)
Pedro Moreno No. 35 Col. Centenario, Hermosillo, Sonora, 83000, Mexico; tel (52) 662 101 963; fax 101 962; e-mail contacto@elfinanciero.com.mx; web site www.elfinanciero.com.mx
Circ.:8,500
Owner/Pres. – Rogelio Cardenas Sarmiento

EL IMPARCIAL (MS)
Sufragio Efectivo y Mina No. 71, Hermosillo, Sonora, 83000, Mexico; tel (52) 662 213 2281; fax 217 4483; web site www.elimparcial.com
Circ.:33,610
Pres./CEO – John F. Healy
Gen Mgr. – Luis Alejandro Bernal
Reporter – Sebastian Moreno
Dir., Opns – Jorge Castro Toulouse

EL NACIONAL (D)
Morelia 10 y Manuel Gonzalez, Hermosillo, Sonora, Mexico; tel (52) 662 134153
Dir. – Jose Angel Calderon Trujillo

EL SONORENSE (M)
Blvd. Transversal y Royal Fraccionamiento Col. Los, Hermosillo, Sonora, 83060, Mexico; tel (52) 662 135757
Circ.:40,000
Gen. Dir. – Fortino Leon Ahumada

HERMOSILLO FLASH (D)
Blvd. Rodriguez, No. 26-B, Hermosillo, Sonora, Mexico; tel (52) 662 127065
Dir. – Eduardo Gomez Torres

INFORMACION DE HERMOSILLO (D)
Colima, No. 52, Hermosillo, Sonora, Mexico; tel (52) 662 134800
Circ.:15,000
Pub. – Abelardo Casanova Labrada
Adv. Mgr. – Myrna Gamez

OPINION (M)
Rama Blanca, No. 32-By Periferico, Oriente, Hermosillo, Sonora, 83010, Mexico; tel (52) 662 158700; fax 158567
Circ.:15,000
Gen. Dir. – Jose Luis Hernandez Salas
Gen. Mgr. – Joel Valdez Campos
Ad Rate: 9.95.

PRIMERA PLANA (D)
Revolucion, No. 14, Hermosillo, Sonora, 83000, Mexico; tel (52) 662 145600; fax 145600; e-mail authentic@son1.telmex.net.mx
Ed./Dir. – Francisco Javier Ruiz Quirrin

HUIXTLA, CHIAPAS

EL INFORMADOR (D-6X WK.)
Calle Guerrero Poniente, No. 4-B, Huixtla, Chiapas, 30640, Mexico; tel (52) 964 20873; fax 20873

IGUALA, GUERRERO

DIARIO 21 (M-EX S)
Av. Bandera Nacional No. 46, Iguala, Guerrero, 40000, Mexico; tel (52) 733 332 0400; fax 332 0054; e-mail diario21@prodigy.net.mx; web site www.diario21.com
Circ.:5,000
Owner/Pres. – Jorge Albarran Jaramillo
Gen. Mgr. – Ninfa Mendoza Barrera
Sales Mgr. – Reyna Elizabeth Rodriguez Monroy

VANGUARDIA (M)
Periferico Norte, Iguala, Guerrero, 40020, Mexico; tel (52) 733 29332
Dir. – Mario Delgado Castaneda
Ed. – Gerardo Delgado Casteneda
Ad Rate: 5.00.

IRAPUATO, GUANAJUATO

EL CENTRO (MS)
Blvd. Diaz Ordaz, No. 132 Sur, Irapuato, Guanajuato, 36500, Mexico; tel (52) 462 273896; fax 270831; e-mail el_centro@infosel.net.mx
Circ.:30,000
Pres. – Felix Arredondo Ortega

EL DIARIO DE LA TARDE (D)
Reforma, No. 432, Irapuato, Guanajuato, Mexico; tel (52) 462 62139
Mng. Dir. – Eugenio Albo Moreno

EL SOL DE LA TARDE (E)
Avda. de la Reforma, No. 432, Poniente, Irapuato, Guanajuato, 36650, Mexico; tel (52) 462 62139
Circ.:15,000

GUANAJUATO (D)
Donato Guerra, No. 249, Irapuato, Guanajuato, Mexico; tel (52) 462 61917
Circ.:4,000
Pub. – Armando Calderon

EL SOL DE IRAPUATO (MS)
Avda. de la Reforma, 432 Poniente, Fracc. Gamez, Irapuato, Guanajuato, 36650, Mexico; tel (52) 462 624 1848; e-mail publicidad@elsoldeirapuato.com.mx; oemenlinea@oem.com.mx; web site www.oem.com.mx
Circ.:34,000
Pres. – Mario Vazquez Rana
Dir. – Alejandro Herrera Sanchez

JACONA, MICHOACAN

EL DIARIO DE ZAMORA (M-EX MON.)
Damian Carmona y Alvaro Obregon 82, Col. Centro, Jacona, Michoacan, 59800, Mexico; tel (52) 351 516 0926; fax 516 0926; web site www.diariozamora.com
Circ.:10,000
Dir. Gen. – Jaime Ochoa Ceja
Ad Rate: 30.00.

EL HERALDO MICHOACANO (D)
Morelos, No. 93, Jacona, Michoacan, Mexico; tel (52) 351 26829
Dir. – Epifanio Torres Padilla

JALAPA, VERACRUZ

GRAFICO DE XALAPA (M)
Ursulo Galvan, No. 31, Jalapa, Veracruz, 91000, Mexico; tel (52) 228 183586; fax 183146
Circ.:35,000
Asst. Adv. Dir. – Eva Laura Medrano de Garcia
Gen. Dir. – Jose Luis Poceros
Asst. Dir.-Adm. – Claudia Zuniga Ortega
Ad Rate: 18.00.

MUNDO DE XALAPA (M)
Dr. R. Lucia 77, Jalapa, Veracruz, 91000, Mexico; tel (52) 228 175652
Circ.:12,000
Pub. – Ernesto Rizzo Murrieta

EL SOL VERACRUZANO (M)
Avda. Avila Camacho No. 3, Jalapa, Veracruz, 91000, Mexico; tel (52) 228 83000; fax 877100

Circ.:12,000
Pres. – Mario Vazquez Rana
Ed./Dir. – Jose Valencia Sanchez

POLITICA (D)
Avda. Revolucion, No. 11-202, Jalapa, Veracruz, Mexico; tel (52) 228 189191
Gen. Dir. – Leodegario Gutierrez

PUNTO Y APARTE (D)
Juarez, No. 79, Jalapa, Veracruz, Mexico; tel (52) 228 8178228; fax 8187115
Dir. – Froylan Lopez Cancela

JIQUILPAN, MICHOACAN

EL VIGIA DE LA CIENEGA DE CHAPALA (D)
Cuauhtemoc, No. 80, Jiquilpan, Michoacan, Mexico; tel (52) 353 20606
Gen. Dir. – Jose Luis Arceo Galvez

JUCHITAN DE ZARAGOZA, OAXACA

ENLACE DE OAXACA (D)
Dr. Roque Robles 6 Barrio Lima, Juchitan De Zaragoza, Oaxaca, Mexico; tel (52) 971
Gen. Dir. – Armando Santibanez Olivera

LA PAZ, BAJA CALIFORNIA SUR

DIARIO PENINSULAR Est.1990
Reforma No. 1355, La Paz, Baja California Sur, 23040, Mexico; tel (52) 612 55580; fax 122-8715; e-mail peninsul@bcs1.telmex.net.mx
Circ.:5,000
Pres. – Salvador Estrada Pinuelas
Gen. Mgr. – Rosario Felix Alvarado
Sales Mgr. – Maria del Carmen Rios Meza
Ed. – Francisco Araus Carrizales
Prodn. Mgr. – Jose Luis Gonzalez

LA PAZ, BAJA CALIFORNIA SUR

AVANTE
Abasalo y Cuauhtemoc, La Paz, Bajo California Sur, Mexico; tel (52) 112 53297; fax 25990
Circ.:6,000
Pres. – Jose Alfredo Carballo Ruiz
Sales Mgr. – Rommel H. Carballo Ruiz
Ed./Dir. – Alfredo Carballo Cota
Prodn. Mgr. – Arturo Gonzalez

EL TIEMPO DE LA PAZ (M)
Heroes de Independencia, No. 954, N, La Paz, Bajo California Sur, Mexico; tel (52) 112 22163
Circ.:13,000
Pub. – Octavio Hernandez

LA EXTRA (D-6X WK.)
La Paz, Bajo California Sur, La Paz, Bajo California Sur, 23000, Mexico; tel (52) 112 25386; fax 54828; e-mail laextra@lapaz.cromwell.com.mx
Circ.:17,000
Gen. Mgr. – Bernardo Flores
Ed./Dir. – Daniel Roldan Zimbron

LA VOZ (D)
Marquez de Leon, Carranza y Olachea, La Paz, Bajo California Sur, 23000, Mexico; tel (52) 112 54505; fax 54505
Ed./Dir. – Adan Garcia Rosales

SUDCALIFORNIANO (M)
Constitucion, No. 706, La Paz, Bajo California Sur, 23000, Mexico; tel (52) 612 122 0144; e-mail publicidad@elsudcaliforniano.com.mx; web site www.elsudcaliforniano.com.mx
Circ.:20,000
Pres. – Mario Vazquez Rana

ULTIMAS NOTICIAS (M-EX MON.)
Belisario Dominguez, No. 291, La Paz, Bajo California Sur, 23000, Mexico; tel (52) 112 20775; fax 27385
Sales Mgr. – Arturo Sotelo Salgado
Ed./Dir. – Tere Osuna Rivera

LA PIEDAD, MICHOACAN

AM LA PIEDAD (M)
Centro Comercial Plaza, Local 37, sobre Blvd. Lazaro Cardenas, La Piedad, Michoacan, 59300, Mexico; tel (52) 352 229560; fax 229530
Owner/Pres. – Enrique Gomez Orozco
Sales Mgr. – Antonio Leon Vasquez
Ed./Dir. – Mayra Orozco
Ad Rate: 9.00.

DESPERTAR (D)
Reforma, Eso. Pino Suarez, La Piedad, Michoacan, 59300, Mexico; tel (52) 352 20032; fax 23662; web site www.despertardelsur.com
Circ.:10,000
Dir. – Marco Antonio Avina Martinez

EL CRUZADO DE LA PIEDAD (D)
Hidalgo, No. 190, La Piedad, Michoacan, Mexico; tel (52) 352 23434
Dir. – Roberto Murillo Lara

VIDA DE LA PIEDAD (M)
Matamoros, No. 100, La Piedad, Michoacan, Mexico; tel (52) 352 21242
Circ.:12,000
Pub. – Rafael Rodriguez Salgado
Ed. – Salvador Plascencia
Adv. Mgr. – Crescencio Abarca Melgoza

LAGOS DE MORENO, JALISCO

PROVINCIA (D)
Lic. Primo de Vedad 133-13, Lagos De Moreno, Jalisco, Mexico; tel (52) 474 21174
Dir. – Alfredo Hernandez Martin del Campo

LAZARO CARDENAS, MICHOACAN

EL DIARIO DE LAZARO CARDENAS (M)
Lazaro Cardenas, Michoacan, Lazaro Cardenas, Michoacan, 60950, Mexico; tel (52) 743 71681; fax 71681
Circ.:12,000
Dir. – Rogelio Rodriguez Gonzalez

EL QUIJOTE (D)
Autonomia Universitaria, No. 41-C, Lazaro Cardenas, Michoacan, Mexico; tel (52) 743 27722
Dir. – Raul Macias Reyes

LEON, GUANAJATO

OPINION DE LEON (M)
Miguel Cervantes Saavedra, No. 201, Leon, Guanajato, Mexico; tel (52) 477 162566
Circ.:20,000
Pub. – Gustavo A. Leomelin Guerra

LEON, GUANAJUATO

AM DE LEON (MS)
Blvd. Adolfo Lopez Mateos No. 3601 Ote., Col. San Isidro, Leon, Guanajuato, 37000, Mexico; tel (52) 477 711 5051; fax 711 4535; e-mail perioam@infosel.net.mx
Circ.:27,800
Gen. Mgr. – Josefina Palomino

AM (D)
Prol. Calzada de los Heroes 208, Leon, Guanajuato, 37500, Mexico; tel (52) 477 788 2100; fax 788 2101; web site www.am.com.mx
Dir. – Enrique Gomez

CONTACTO DE GUANAJUATO (D)
Leon, Guanajuato, Leon, Guanajuato, Mexico; tel (52) 477 162757; fax 169600
Pres. – Luis Torres Martinez
Gen. Dir. – Juan I. Morales Castaneda

CONTACTO DE LEON (D)
Blvd. Cerrito de Jerez, No. 103 y Lopez Mateos, Or, Leon, Guanajuato, Mexico; tel (52) 477 162757; fax 169600
Circ.:50,000
Pres. – Luis Torres Martinez
Gen. Dir. – Juan I. Morales Castaneda

EL HERALDO DE LEON (MS)
Hermanos Aldama No. 222, Col. Centro, Leon, Guanajuato, 37530, Mexico; tel (52) 477 713 1130; fax 714 3464; e-mail heraldoleon@heraldo-adi.com.mx; web site www.heraldo-adi.com.mx
Circ.:19,300
Ed. in Chief – Benjamin Cordero
Ed. – Enrique Rangel

NOTICIAS VESPERTINAS (E-EX S)
Ave. Madero No. 312, Leon, Guanajuato, 37000, Mexico; tel (52) 477 716 8290; fax 716 8299; web site www.oem.com.mx
Circ.:17,000
Ed. – Ramiro Munoz

EL SOL DE LEON (MS)
Ave. Madero No. 312, Leon, Guanajuato, 37000, Mexico; tel (52) 477 716 8297; fax 714 0955; e-mail publicidad@elsoldeleon.com.mx; mdealba@hotmail.com; web site www.oem.com.mx/elsoldeleon
Circ.:36,000
Pres. – Mario Vazquez Rana

LOS MOCHIS, SINALOA

ASI ES LA POLITICA (D)
Los Mochis, Sinaloa, Los Mochis, Sinaloa, Mexico; tel (52) 668 57310
Dir. – Ramiro Valenzuela Medina

EL SOL DE LOS MOCHIS (M)
Prof. Marcial Ordonez, No. 118, Poniente Centro, Los Mochis, Sinaloa, 81200, Mexico; tel (52) 668 185175; e-mail info@oem.com.mx; web site www.oem.com.mx
Circ.:6,000
Pres./Gen. Dir. – Mario Vazquez Rana
Mgr. – Raul Rivera Haro
Adv. Mgr. – Mercedes Nunez Lugo
Ad Rate: 15.00.

EL DEBATE
Ave. Obregon No. 8 Poniente, Los Mochis, Sinaloa, 81200, Mexico; tel (52) 668 158040; fax 157678; e-mail info@debate.com.mx; web site www.debate.com.mx
Circ.:15,000
Pres./Gen. Mgr. – Jose Isabel Ramos Santos
Sales Mgr. – Juan Jose Medina Ortiz
Ed./Dir. – Jaime Perez Rocha

LA OPINION DEL PACIFICO (D)
Avda. Gabriel Leyva y Callejon Rubi, Los Mochis, Sinaloa, Mexico; tel (52) 668 (52-68) 80264; fax (52-68) 80263
Circ.:36,000

LAS NOTICIAS (M)
Guillermo Prieto y G. Victoria, Los Mochis, Sinaloa, 81200, Mexico; tel (52) 668 20749
Gen. Mgr. – J. Elias Chavez
Ad Rate: 5.50.

TRIBUNA DE SINALOA (D)
Blvd. Rosales y Juarez, Los Mochis, Sinaloa, Mexico; tel (52) 668 50001
Dir. – Melchor Angulo Castro

LOS REYES, MICHOACAN

PRESENCIA (D)
Rayon, No. 74, Los Reyes, Michoacan, Mexico; tel (52) 354 20001
Dir. – Jesus Chavez Andrade

MANZANILLO, COLIMA

EL CORREO DE MANZANILLO (M)
Avda. Juarez 143, Locales 6 y 8 (Pasaje Oscarana), Manzanillo, Colima, 28200, Mexico; tel (52) 314 (52-3) 328040; fax 324779
Circ.:15,500
Dir. – Miguel De la Mora Anguiano
Regl. Dir. – Victor De Santiago Fuentes
Assistant Dir. – Sergio Venancio Osegueda
Ad Rate: 18.00.

MATAMOROS, TAMAULIPAS

EL MANANA (M)
Calle 2 y Gonzalez, Matamoros, Tamaulipas, 87300, Mexico; tel (52) 868 123501
Circ.:20,000
Gen. Dir. – Heriberto Deandar Robinson
Ed. – Orlando Deandar Martinez
Ed. – Heriberto Deandar Martinez
Ad Rate: 19.00.

EL BRAVO (M)
Primera y Morelos No. 129, Col. Centro, Matamoros, Tamaulipas, 87300, Mexico; tel (52) 868 160848; fax 162007; e-mail elbravo@riogrande.net.mx
Circ.:60,000
Pres. – Jose Carretero Balboa
Sales Mgr. – Emma Rosa Sanchez Huhn
Ed./Dir. – Edgardo Montiel Govea

EL GRAFICO
Matamoros, Tamaulipas, Matamoros, Tamaulipas, Mexico; tel (52) 891 21792
Circ.:10,000
Pub. – Victor Manuel Gonzalez Rubio

EL VESPERTINO (D)
Calle 12, No. 17, Matamoros, Tamaulipas, Mexico; tel (52) 868

EXPRESION (5X WK.)
Matamoros, Tamaulipas, Matamoros, Tamaulipas, 87457, Mexico; tel (52) 868 817 9555; fax 817 3307; e-mail xpresion@progidy.net.mx; xpresionenred@gmail.com; web site www.expresionenred.com
Circ.:2,000
Ed. – Miguel Garay Avila

PM DE EL BRAVO (E)
Morelos y Primera, No. 129, Matamoros, Tamaulipas, 87300, Mexico; tel (52) 868 160848; fax 163848
Circ.:40,000
Pres. – Jose Carretero Balboa
Ed./Dir. – Manuel Martinez Orozco

PRENSA DE MATAMOROS (M)
Guerrero, No. 71-A, Matamoros, Tamaulipas, Mexico; tel (52)
Circ.:10,000
Pub. – Antonio Manzur Maron

PRENSA LIBRE (D)
Gonzalez 1 y 1, No. 29, Matamoros, Tamaulipas, Mexico; tel (52) 868 2230 1384
Dir. – Ruben Herrera Ramos

MATEHUALA, SAN LUIS POTOSI

MOMENTO (MS)
Zenon Fernandez y Leandro Valle, Matehuala, San Luis Potosi, Mexico; tel (52) 488
Circ.:15,000
Pub. – Alejandro Leal Tovias
Adv. Mgr. – Mateo Seguro Leon

MAZATLAN, SINALOA

ACUACULTURA INTERNACIONAL
Apdo. Postal 343, Mazatlan, Sinaloa, Mexico; tel (52) 669 841668; fax 836711

NOTICIAS DEL SOL (E-EX S)
Avda. Miguel Alem n y Benito Juarez, Mazatlan, Sinaloa, 82000, Mexico; tel (52) 669 890244; fax 821998
Circ.:17,000
Pres./Gen. Dir. – Mario Vazquez Rana
Dir. – Jose Angel Sanchez Lopez
Mgr. – Idelfonso Manuel Aviles Montoya
Ad Rate: 3.00.

EL SINALOENSE (M)
Carnaval y Playa Rosarito, s/n Fraccionamiento Pla, Mazatlan, Sinaloa, Mexico; tel (52) 669 826799; fax 826768
Circ.:12,000
Founder – Blas Rojo Lira
Gen. Dir. – Jose Nilo Rojo Robles
Ad Rate: 7.00.

NOROESTE (6X WK.)
Av. Benemerito de las Americas 708, Fraccionamiento Campo Bello, Mazatlan, Sinaloa, 82010, Mexico; tel (52) 669 915 5200; fax 915 5231; web site www.noroeste.com.mx
Circ.:26,000
Sales Mgr. – Elizabeth Peraca
Ed. – Joel Diaz Fonseca

EL DEMOCRATA SINALOENSE (M)
Gaviotas, No. 610, Mazatlan, Sinaloa, 82010, Mexico; tel (52) 669 854209; fax 815608
Circ.:8,500
Pres. – Quirino Ordaz Coppel
Ed./Dir. – Roberto Ruiz

EL SOL DEL PACIFICO (MS)
Avda. Miguel Aleman No. 312, Fracc. Playa Sur, Mazatlan, Sinaloa, 82040, Mexico; tel (52) 669 80922; fax 812243; e-mail solmaz@red.2000.com.mx; solmaz@oem.com.mx; web site www.oem.com.mx/solmaz
Circ.:36,000
Pres. – Mario Vazquez Rana
Sales Mgr. – Patricia Sanchez
Ed./Dir. – Osvaldo Bernal Lozolla

MERIDA, YUCATAN

DIARIO DE YUCATAN (MS)
Calle 60, No. 521, Merida, Yucatan, 97000, Mexico; tel (52) 999 942 2222; fax 942 2203; web site www.yucatan.com.mx
Asst. Dir. – A. Ruben Menendez Navarrete
Gen. Mgr. – Carlos R. Menendez Navarrete
Adv. Mgr. – A. Rueben Menendez Antunano
Circ. Mgr. – Olegario Moguel
Ed. – Louis Alverato Gonzalez
Ad Rate: 37.00 (m); 40.00 (S).

EL FINANCIERO
Carretera Merida-Uman Km, 9 Ampliacion Industrial, Merida, Yucatan, 97288, Mexico; tel (52) 999 462222; fax 462223; e-mail finan@yuc1.telmex.net.mx; web site www.elfinanciero.com.mx
Circ.:5,000
Owner/Pres. – Rogelio Cardenas Sarmiento
Sales Mgr. – Gerardo Duran
Ed./Dir. – Noel Quizas Fontanez

NOVEDADES DE YUCATAN (MS)
Calle 62, No. 514-A, Col. Centro, Merida, Yucatan, 97000, Mexico; tel (52) 999 924 9885; fax 924 1777; e-mail nmerida@cancun.novenet.com
Circ.:25,000
Group: Charney/Palacios & Co.
Gen. Mgr. – Gerardo Garcia Gamboa
Ed./Dir. – Alvaro Luis Mendez
Ad Rate: 24.00.

POR ESTO (MS)
Calle 60, No. 578 Col. Centro, Merida, Yucatan, 97000, Mexico; tel (52) 999 930 2760; fax 924 8420; e-mail poresto@prodigy.com.net.mx; publicidad-merida@gmail.com; redaccion@poresto.net; web site www.poresto.net
Pres. – Mario Renato Menendez Rodriguez
Gen. Mgr. – Hernan R. Menendez Rodriguez
Sales Mgr. – Ileana Menendez
Ed. – Miguel Menendez Cameron

DIARIO DEL SURESTE (MS)
Calle 60, No. 532, Merida, Yucatan, 97000, Mexico; tel (52) 999 237393; fax 237393
Gen. Dir. – Gaspar Villanueva
Ed. in Chief – Marcos Heredia Perez
Ad Rate: 13.50.

TRIBUNA DE YUCATAN (M)
Calle 61, No. 524-B, Col. Centro, Merida, Yucatan, 97000, Mexico; tel (52) 999 923 6459; fax 923 8010; web site www.tribunacampeche.com
Dir. – Thomas Martin

MEXICALI, BAJA CALIFORNIA NORTE

ABC DE MEXICALI (D)
Plaza Cholula, No. 1095-D Centro, Civico, Mexicali, Baja California Norte, Mexico; tel (52) 686 571544
Dir. – Franti E. Canales

NOVEDADES DE BAJA CALIFORNIA (D)
Avda. Heroes de la Patria, No. 952, Centro Civico, Mexicali, Baja California Norte, 21000, Mexico; tel (52) 686 574 801
Circ.:45,000
Gen. Dir. – Adolfo Sanchez

LA CRONICA (MS)
Avda. Heroes de la Patria No. 952, Centro Civico, Mexicali, Baja California Norte, 21000, Mexico; tel (52) 686 557 4801; fax 557 0424; e-mail comentarios@lacronica.com; web site www.lacronica.com
Circ.:12,000
Pres./CEO – Juan Fernando Healy Loera
Sales Mgr. – Norma M. Lira Teran
Ed. – Adolfo Sanchez Rodriguez
Ed. – Carlos Lima
Prodn. Mgr. – Jose Antonio Lujano

LA VOZ DE LA FRONTERA (MS)
Ave. Madero No. 1545, Mexicali, Baja California Norte, 21100, Mexico; tel (52) 686 5534545; fax 55536912; e-mail lavoz@oem.com.mx; web site www.oem.com.mx/lavoz
Circ.:67,000
Pres. – Mario Vazquez Rana
Gen. Mgr. – Mario Valdes Hernandez
Sales Mgr. – Sonia Sepulveda Morales
Ed./Dir. – Felipe de Jesus Lopez Rodriguez

EL CENTINELA (E)
Avda. Cristobal Colon No. 1512, Col. Nueva, Mexicali, Baja California Norte, 21100, Mexico; tel (52) 686 5534545; fax 5539612; e-mail lavoz@telnor.net; lavoz@oem.com.mx; web site www.oem.com.mx
Circ.:17,000
Pres. – Felipe de Jesus Lopez Rodriguez
Gen. Mgr. – Mario Valdes Hernandez
Sales Mgr. – Sonia Sepulveda Morales
Ed./Dir. – Jose Luis Mendoza

MEXICO CITY

DIARIO DE MEXICO (M)
Chimalpopoca, No. 38, Col. Obrera, Mexico City, 06800, Mexico; tel (52) 55 5442 6500; fax 5442 6503; e-mail redaccion@diariodemexico.com.mx; web site www.diariodemexico.com.mx
Circ.:76,000
Pres. – Federico Bracamontes Galvez
Ad Rate: 15.00.

EL SOL DE MEXICO (D)
Guillermo Prieto No. 7, Col. San Rafael, Mexico City, 06470, Mexico; tel (52) 55 5566 1511; fax 5546 6096; e-mail oemenlinea@oem.com.mx; web site www.oem.com.mx/elsoldemexico
Circ.:3,000
Pres. – Mario Vazquez Rana

MEXICO CITY, DISTRITO FEDERAL

CINE MUNDIAL (D)
Avda. Cuauhtemoc 16, Col. Doctores, Mexico City, Distrito Federal, 06720, Mexico; tel (52) 55 5578-5244; fax 5761-7384
Ed./Dir. – Carlos Santa Ana Alvarez

UNO MAS UNO (M)
Primer Retorno de Correggio, No. 12, Mexico City, Distrito Federal, 03720, Mexico; tel (52) 55 5639911; fax 5988821
Pres./Gen. Dir. – Manuel Alonso Munoz
Dir. – Rafael Cardona
Vice Pres./Dir. – Manuel Alonso Coratella
Gen. Mgr. – Fernando Garcia Priego
Ad Rate: 20.70.

EL ECONOMISTA (5X WK.)
Avda. Coyoacan 515, Calle del Valle, Mexico City, Distrito Federal, 03100, Mexico; tel (52) 55 5326 5454; fax 5682 9070; e-mail internet@eleconomista.com.mx; web site www.eleconomista.com.mx
Circ.:37,163
Pres. – Jorge Nacer Gober
Dir. Gen. – Marco Antonio Mares
Ed. – Luis Miguel Gonzalez
Dir., Opns – Alfredo Hernandez
Ad Rate: Charney/Palacios & Co.

EL FINANCIERO (M-5X WK.)
Lago Bolsena No. 176, Col. Anahuac (Pensil), Mexico City, Distrito Federal, 11320, Mexico; tel (52) 55 5227 7600; fax 5255 1799; e-mail contacto@elfinanciero.com.mx; web site www.elfinanciero.com.mx
Circ.:40,000
Owner/Pres. – Rogelio Cardenas Sarmiento
Ed. – Alejandro Ramos
Ad Rate: Charney/Placios & Co.

EL HERALDO DE MEXICO (MS)
Dr. Lucio y Dr. Velasco, Col. Doctores, Mexico City, Distrito Federal, 06720, Mexico; tel (52) 55 5578 7022; fax 5578 9824; e-mail heraldo@iwm.com.mx; web site www.heraldo.com.mx
Circ.:7,000
Pres. – Gabriel Alarcon Velazquez

EL NACIONAL (MS)
Ignacio Mariscal 25, Col. Tabacalera, Mexico City, Distrito Federal, 06030, Mexico; tel (52) 55 5354613; fax 7055615; e-mail buzon@condor.dgsca.unam.mx
Circ.:210,000
Gen. Dir. – Enriqueta Cabrera
Mng. Ed. – Gabriela Ortega
Dir. – Hector M. Ezeta Gomez Portugal
Ad Rate: 16.40.

EL UNIVERSAL (D)
Mexico City, Distrito Federal, Mexico City, Distrito Federal, 06040, Mexico; tel (52) 55 5709 1313; fax 5510 1269; e-mail redaccio@aguila.el-universal.com.mx; ventas@eluniversal.com.mx; web site www.el-universal.com.mx
Circ.:170,000
Group: Latin Admerica, Inc.
CEO – Juan Francisco Ealy Ortiz
Ed. – Jorge Zepeda Patterson
Ad Rate: Charney/Palacios & Co.

LA JORNADA (D)
Ave. Cuauhtemoc 1236 Colonia Santa Cruz Atoyac, Mexico City, Distrito Federal, 03310, Mexico; tel (52) 559 183 0300; fax 5682 9369; web site www.jornada.unam.mx
Circ.:35,000
Pres. – Nacai Jorge
Gen. Mgr. – Grosenor Rlyes
Sales Mgr. – Ardo Reos

LA AFICION (MS)
Ignacio Mariscal No. 23, Col. Tabacalera, Mexico City, Distrito Federal, 06030, Mexico; tel (52) 55 5514 04900; fax 5592 7400
Gen. Mgr. – Christian Ramirez Reyna
Gen. Dir. – Juan Francisco Ealy Ortiz
Ed./Dir. – Angel Trinidad Ferreira

THE NEWS (M)
Balderas No. 87 Colonia Centro, Mexico City, Distrito Federal, 06040, Mexico; tel (52) 55 55185490; fax 5521-6339; web site www.thenewsmexico.com
Circ.:30,000
Pres. – Romulo O'Farrill
Gen. Mgr. – Jose Antonio O'Farrill Avila
Ed./Dir. – Daniel Parkinson

NOVEDADES (MS)
Balderas No. 87, esq. Morelos Centro, Mexico City, Distrito Federal, 06040, Mexico; tel (52) 55 5185490
Pres./Gen. Dir. – Don Romulo O'Farrill
Vice Pres. – Jose Antonio O'Farrill Avila
Ad Rate: 20.00.

ESTO (D)
Guillermo Prieto, No. 7, Col. San Rafael, Mexico City, Distrito Federal, 06470, Mexico; tel (52) 55 5566 1511; fax 5535 5560; e-mail oemenlinea@oem.com.mx; web site www.oem.com.mx
Circ.:150,000
Pres. – Mario Vazquez Rana
Dir. – Carlos Trapaga Barrientos
Asst. Dir., Sales/Mktg. – Jesus Ernesto Cobos Balderas

LA PRENSA (D)
Basilio Vadillo No. 40, Col. Tabacalera, Mexico City, Distrito Federal, 06030, Mexico; tel (52) 55 5228 9977; e-mail oemenlinea@oem.com.mx; web site www.la-prensa.com.mx
Circ.:275,000
Pres. – Mario Vazquez Rana
Dir. – Mauricio Ortega Camberos
Gen. Mgr. – Ignacio Ibarra Pescador

OVACIONES (M&E)
Lago Zirahuen No. 279, Col. Anahuac, Mexico City, Distrito Federal, 11320, Mexico; tel (52) 55 5328 0700; fax 5328 0770; web site www.ovaciones.com
Circ.:50,000
Pres. – Miguel Angel Couchonnal Miranda
Gen. Mgr. – Octavio Mota
Sales Mgr. – Ramon Mayaudon
Ed. – Juan Bustillos Orozco
Prodn. Mgr. – Hugo R. Paez Miramontes
Ad Rate: 7.30 (m-tues.-S); 9.60 (e).

REFORMA (D)
Avda. Mexico Coyoacan, No. 40, Col. Santa

Cruz Ato, Mexico City, Distrito Federal, 03310, Mexico; tel (52) 55 5628 7100; fax 5628 7189; e-mail nacional@reforma.com.mx; web site www.reforma.com
Circ.:126,000
Dir. – Alejandro Junco de la Vega Elizondo
Gen. Mgr. – Ricardo Junco Garza
Mktg. Mgr. – Gerardo Lara
Ed. Coord. – Luis De Uriarte Guerrero
Ed. – Victor German
Ad Rate: Charney/Palacio & Co.

TRIBUNA (M)
Bahia de San Hipolito, No. 56, Col. Veronica Anzures, Mexico City, Distrito Federal, 11300, Mexico; tel (52) 55 5260 0583; fax 5260 0695; e-mail tribuna@df1.telmex.mx
Circ.:40,000
Pres. – Miguel Angel Morales Carillo
Gen. Mgr. – Pedro Eschaverri
Ed./Dir. – Arnoldo Saenz Ramirez

ULTIMAS NOTICIAS DE EXCELSIOR (E-EX WKND.)
Paseo de la Reforma No. 10, Mexico City, Distrito Federal, 06600, Mexico; tel (52) 55 662200; fax 660223
Circ.:9,000
Pres. – Patricia Guevara

EL UNIVERSAL GRAFICO (5X WK.)
Bucareli No. 8, Centro, Mexico City, Distrito Federal, 06040, Mexico; tel (52) 55 5709 1313; fax 5237 0877; e-mail ventas@eluniversal.com.mx; web site www.eluniversal.com.mx
Circ.:105,000
Pres. – Juan Francisco Ealy Ortiz

MONCLOVA, COAHUILA

LA VOZ DE MONCLOVA (M)
Guatemala y Allende, Col. Guadalupe, Monclova, Coahuila, 25750, Mexico; tel (52) 866 333254; fax 332962
Circ.:20,000
Pres. – Salvador Kamar Apud
Ad Rate: 16.95.

EL DIA (M)
Avda. Venustiano Carranza, No. 224, Oriente, Monclova, Coahuila, Mexico; tel (52) 866 333542
Circ.:6,000
Pub. – Jorge Zertuche Tenorio

LA OPINION (M)
Allende y Guatemala, Monclova, Coahuila, Mexico; tel (52) 866 333253
Circ.:15,000
Pub. – Mario Garay

LA VOZ DE COAHUILA (D)
Guatemala y Allende, Col. Guadalupe, Monclova, Coahuila, 25750, Mexico; tel (52) 866 633 2994; fax 633 2962; e-mail editorial@lavozmva.com
Circ.:5,000
Owner/Pres. – Salvador Kamar Apud

EL TIEMPO (M)
Calle de la Ermita No. 318, Col. Nueva Rosita, Monclova, Coahuila, 25700, Mexico; tel (52) 866 320067; fax 320048; e-mail eltiempo@infosel.net.mx
Circ.:46,000
Owner/Pres. – Alfonso Zabaleta Margain
Gen. Mgr. – Maria Eugenia Lopez Saldana
Sales Mgr. – Esperanza Ramirez Granados
Ed./Dir. – Fidel Ortiz

VANGUARDIA (M)
Francisco I Madero, No. 611, Monclova, Coahuila, 25750, Mexico; tel (52) 866 353060; fax 333283
Circ.:9,000
Owner/Pres. – Armando Castilla Sanchez
Ed./Dir. – Oscar Medrano Sanchez

MONTERREY, NUEVO LEON

ABC (MS)
Platon Sanchez, No. 411, Sur, Monterrey, Nuevo Leon, 64000, Mexico; tel (52) 81 34480
Circ.:75,000
Pres./Gen. Dir. – Gonzalo Estrada Cruz
Editorial Dir. – Gonzalo Estrada Torres
Ad Rate: 17.00 (m); 20.00 (S).

CAMBIO
15 de Mayo, No. 455, Poniente Mexico, Monterrey, Nuevo Leon, Mexico; tel (52) 722 3454410; fax 3455642
Circ.:20,000
Gen. Dir. – Guillermo Salinas Trevino
Pres. – F. Javier Sanchez Campuzano
Ad Rate: 17.20.

TRIBUNA DE MONTERREY (M)
Isaac Garza, No. 200, Oriente, Monterrey, Nuevo Leon, 64000, Mexico; tel (52) 81 3755576; fax 3744467
Circ.:23,000
Dir. – Francisco Cerda Munoz
Mgr. – Jose Saul Homero Hernandez Ayala
Pres./Gen. Dir. – Mario Vazquez Rana

EL SOL VESPERTINO (D)
Washington, No. 629 Oriente, Monterrey, Nuevo Leon, 64000, Mexico; tel (52) 81 345 3388; fax 343 2476
Editorial Dir. – Ramon Alberto Garza
Exec. Dir. – Rodolfo Junco de la Vega

EL FINANCIERO (M)
Monterrey, Nuevo Leon, Monterrey, Nuevo Leon, 64790, Mexico; tel (52) 81 357-0077; fax 357-8880; e-mail contacto@elfinanciero.com.mx; web site www.elfinanciero.com.mx
Circ.:9,750
Owner/Pres. – Rogelio Cardenas Sarmiento
Ed./Dir. – Alberto Tovar Castro

EL MUNDO DE LAS ESTRELLAS (D)
Eugenio Garza, No. 2245, Sur, Col. Roma, Monterrey, Nuevo Leon, Mexico; tel (52) 81 3592525
Gen. Dir. – Francisco A. Gonzalez Sanchez

EL NORTE (MS)
Washington Oriente, No. 629, Monterrey, Nuevo Leon, 64000, Mexico; tel (52) 81 8150 8100; fax 8345 0264; e-mail marpha.tarvino@elnorte.com; web site www.elnorte.com
Pres. – Alejandro Junco de la Vega
Gen. Mgr. – Ricardo Junco Garza
Sales Mgr. – Carlos Ortiz Lozano

EL PORVENIR (MS) Est.1919
Galeana No. 344 Sur, Monterrey, Nuevo Leon, 64000, Mexico; tel (52) 81 8340 8239; fax 8340 8008; e-mail editorial@prodigy.net.mx; web site www.elporvenir.mx
Circ.:60,000
CEO – Jose Gerardo Cantu
Gen. Mgr. – Lucila Cruz Segueda
Ed. – Rolando Macias Bermudes

EL TIEMPO (E)
Avda. Colon, No. 101, Poniente, Monterrey, Nuevo Leon, Mexico; tel (52) 81 3750226
Circ.:20,000
Pub. – Alberto Escamilla Gonzalez
Ed. – Eduardo Martinez Celis

LA MONEDA (D-5X WK.)
Roma No. 220, Col. Mirador, Monterrey, Nuevo Leon, 64000, Mexico; tel (52) 81 310-6258; fax 310-6528
Pres. – Archibaldo Rullan Dominguez

EXTRA (E-EX S)
Eugenio Garza Sada, No. 2245, Sur, Col. Roma, Monterrey, Nuevo Leon, 64700, Mexico; tel (52) 813 359-2525; e-mail diariomty@hotmail.com
Circ.:55,000
Pres. – Francisco A. Gonzalez
Gen. Mgr. – Enrique Gomez Junco
Ed./Dir. – Jorge Villegas

METRO (M)
Washington Ote., No. 629, Monterrey, Nuevo Leon, 64000, Mexico; tel (52) 818 345 3388; fax 343 2476
Circ.:90,153
Pres. – Alejandro Junco
Mktg. Asst. – Francisco Sanchez

MAS NOTICIAS/MAS DEPORTES (MS)
Eugenio Garza Sada, No. 2245, Sur, Col. Roma, Monterrey, Nuevo Leon, 64700, Mexico; tel (52) 81 1505500
Circ.:75,000
Founder/Pres. – Jesus D. Gonzalez
Pres. – Francisco A. Gonzalez
Gen. Dir. – Federico Arreola
Vice Pres.-Info – Hector Benavides
Gen. Dir.-Opns. – Gilberto Luna
Gen. Mgr.-Mex. Div. – Francisco Somohano Diaz
Vice Pres.-Advertising – Enrique Gomez Junco
Adv. Dir. – Gerardo M. Flores
Ad Rate: 38.40 (d); 43.00 (S).

EL DIARIO DE MONTERREY (M)
Eugenio Garza Sada, No. 2245, Sur, Col. Roma, Monterrey, Nuevo Leon, 64700, Mexico; tel (52) 81 1505500
Circ.:80,000
Founder/Pres. – Jesus D. Gonzalez
Pres. – Francisco A. Gonzalez
Vice Pres.-Info – Hector Benavides
Gen. Dir. – Federico Arreola
Gen. Dir.-Opns. – Gilberto Luna
Gen. Mgr.-Mex. Div. – Francisco Somohano Diaz
Vice Pres.-Adv. – Enrique Gomez Junco
Adv. Dir. – Gerardo M. Flores

LA RAZON (M)
Monterrey, Nuevo Leon, Monterrey, Nuevo Leon, 64700, Mexico; tel (52) 813 425403; fax 429698
Circ.:6,000
Owner/Pres. – Francisco Tijerina Gonzalez
Gen. Mgr. – Hernan Macias
Ed./Dir. – Oscar Perez Hernandez

EL SOL (E-EX S)
Washington, Oriente No. 629, Monterrey, Nuevo Leon, 64000, Mexico; tel (52) 818 345 5100; fax 343 2476
Circ.:45,000
Pres. – Alejandro Junco
Dir. – Ramon Alberto Garza
Adv. Dir. – Ricardo Junco

MORELIA, MICHOACAN

CRONICA (D)
Morelia, Michoacan, Morelia, Michoacan, Mexico; tel (52) 443 52851; web site www.cronica.com.mx/cronica
Dir. – Enrique Ibarra Carreon

DIARIO DE MORELIA
Abasolo 707, Morelia, Michoacan, Mexico; tel (52) 443 20850
Circ.:12,000
Pub. – Miguel Sanchez Vargas

HERALDO MICHOACANO (E)
Morelia, Michoacan, Morelia, Michoacan, 58000, Mexico; tel (52) 443
Circ.:23,000
Pub. – Humberto Hernandez Pimentel

NOTICIAS DE MORELIA (M-EX S)
Avda. del Periodismo, No. 2001, Morelia, Michoacan, 58000, Mexico; tel (52) 443
Circ.:37,000
Gen. Dir. – Humberto Hernandez Pimentel
Ad Rate: 7.80.

EL SOL DE MORELIA (MS)
Madero Oriente No. 783, Morelia, Michoacan, 58000, Mexico; tel (52) 443 313 2568; fax 313 2408; e-mail solmor@oem.com.mx; solmordi@mail.giga.com; web site www.oem.com.mx/elsoldemorelia
Circ.:20,000
Pres. – Mario Vazquez Rana

PRESENCIA DE MICHOACAN
Andador Bernardo Arreola, No. 92, Morelia, Michoacan, Mexico; tel (52) 443 31130; fax 32605
Dir. – Javier Lozano Solis

REFORMA (D)
Caltzontzin, No. 184, Fraccionamiento, Rancho del, Morelia, Michoacan, Mexico; tel (52) 443 41767
Circ.:9,000
Dir. – Gilberto Chavez Valencia

CAMBIO DE MICHOACAN (M)
Morelia, Michoacan, Morelia, Michoacan, 58170, Mexico; tel (52) 443 266278
Circ.:40,000
Pub. Rel. – Eleazar Zizumbo Gerrera
Ch. of Info – Arturo Familiar Arteaga
Ed. in Chief – Jaime Martinez Ochoa
Pres./Gen. Dir. – Vicente Godinez Zapien
Dir. – Andres Resillas Mejia
Ad Rate: 27.00.

TIEMPO DE MORELIA (D)
Corregidora, No. 610, Morelia, Michoacan, Mexico; tel (52) 443 39071
Dir. – Francisco Javier Gonzalez Pizano

LA VOZ DE MICHOACAN (MS)
Ave. Periodismo Jose Tocaven Lavin No. 1270, Col. Agustin Arriaga, Morelia, Michoacan, 58190, Mexico; tel (52) 443 273712; fax 273726; web site www.voznet.com.mx
Sales Mgr. – M. Benitez
Ed./Dir. – Miguel Medina Robles

MOROLEON, GUANAJUATO

EL INFORMADOR (D)
Pipila, No. 154, Moroleon, Guanajuato, Mexico; tel (52) 466 70446
Gen. Dir. – Jose G. Gonzalez

NAUCALPAN DE JUAREZ, MEXICO

EL SOL DEL VALLE DE MEXICO (MS)
Urbina, No. 65, Naucalpan de Juarez, Mexico, Mexico; tel (52)
Circ.:28,000
Pub. – Luis Jasso

NAVOJOA, SONORA

NUESTRO TIEMPO (M)
Morelos, No. 711, Poniente, Navojoa, Sonora, 85800, Mexico; tel (52) 642 22195; fax 21464
Circ.:25,000
Pres./Ed. – Alejandro Gonzalez Izabal
Gen. Dir. – Sergio R. Padilla Solano
Ad Rate: 12.50.

EL INFORMADOR DEL MAYO (M)
Rayon y Jesus Salido, Col. Centro, Navojoa, Sonora, 85800, Mexico; tel (52) 642 20983; fax 20587; e-mail informa@cybernet.com.mx
Circ.:35,000
Pres. – Gerardo Armenta Balderrama
Sales Mgr. – Jesus Garcia Perez
Ed./Dir. – Esteban Rodriguez Salazar

LA VOZ DEL PUEBLO (D)
Rincon, No. 504, Norte, Navojoa, Sonora, Mexico; tel (52) 642 21777

Dir. – Rogelio Altamirano Sanchez

NOGALES, SONORA

ACCION (E)
Ingenieros, No. 30, Nogales, Sonora, Mexico; tel (52) 631 22287
Circ.:5,000
Pub. – Jose Ramon Velasco Beruben

DIARIO DE NOGALES (E)
Nogales, Sonora, Nogales, Sonora, 84000, Mexico; tel (52) 631 313-0534; fax 314-3330; e-mail diario@internexos.net
Circ.:10,000
Pres. – Imelda Gomez Espinoza
Ed. – Carlos de la Isla Ortiz

EL CENTINELA (E)
Nogales, Sonora, Nogales, Sonora, Mexico; tel (52) 631 26340
Circ.:8,000
Pub. – Jesus Orozco Morales
Adv. Mgr. – Maricruz Quijada Chavarin

LA VOZ DEL NORTE (M)
Periferico Norte, s/n, Nogales, Sonora, 84000, Mexico; tel (52) 631 27171; fax 25900
Circ.:20,000
Pres. – Arnoldo Ahumada Barrera
Dir. – Hugo Penoc Rico

NUEVA ROSITA, COAHUILA

EL DEMOCRATA (D)
Reforma, No. 125, Nueva Rosita, Coahuila, Mexico; tel (52) 861
Circ.:12,000
Pub. – Francisco Baltazaar Garcia

NUEVO LAREDO, TAMAULIPAS

EL CORREO (E-EX S)
Gonzalez No. 2409, Col. Centro, Nuevo Laredo, Tamaulipas, 88000, Mexico; tel (52) 867 128444; fax 128221; e-mail eldiario@nld.bravo.net
Circ.:17,500
Pres. – Ricardo David Villarreal Marroquin
Ed./Dir. – Ruperto Villarreal Montemayor

EL MANANA (MS)
Juarez No. 1920, Col. Juarez, Nuevo Laredo, Tamaulipas, 88209, Mexico; tel (52) 867 711 9999; fax 714 8797; e-mail elmanana@elmanana.com.mx
Circ.:27,000
Pres. – Ninfa Deandar Martinez

EL SOL DE NUEVO LAREDO (E)
Guatemala, No. 1737, Nuevo Laredo, Tamaulipas, Mexico; tel (52) 867
Circ.:10,000
Pub. – Raul Cuellar Garcia
Adv. Mgr. – Jose Gonzalez Rodriguez

EL DIARIO DE NUEVO LAREDO (MS)
Gonzalez, No. 2409, Nuevo Laredo, Tamaulipas, 88000, Mexico; tel (52) 867 712 8444; e-mail publicidad@diario.net; web site www.diario.net
– Marco G. Villareal Marroquin
– Leonardo HerradoEd.s
Ad Rate: 34.00.

OAXACA, OAXACA

EL IMPARCIAL (M)
Armenta y Lopez No. 312, Col. Centro, Oaxaca, Oaxaca, 70610, Mexico; tel (52) 951 516 9024; fax 514 7020; e-mail impaorax@prodigy.net.mx; web site www.imparcialenlinea.com
Circ.:30,000
Dir. – Benjamin Fernandez Pichardo
Ad Rate: Charney/Palacios & Co.

EL NUEVO INFORMADOR (M)
Guerrero, No. 1001, Oaxaca, Oaxaca, Mexico; tel (52) 951 65705
Circ.:20,000
Gen. Dir. – Evaristo Martinez Lopez

EL OBSERVADOR
Abasolo No. 518, Col. Centro, Oaxaca, Oaxaca, 68000, Mexico; tel (52) 951 59998; fax 59998
Pres. – Socorro Zuniga Viuda de Loyo
Ed./Dir. – Daniel Vazquez Aquino

EL SOL DE OAXACA (D)
Avda. Independencia, No. 1405-A, Oaxaca, Oaxaca, 68000, Mexico; tel (52) 951 54847; fax 60925
Circ.:18,500
Gen. Dir. – Ana Gloria Villicana Jimenez

LA OPINION (M)
Oaxaca, Oaxaca, Oaxaca, Oaxaca, Mexico; tel (52) 951 67079
Circ.:15,000
Pub. – Manuel Humberto Siordia

NOTICIAS (M)
Oaxaca, Oaxaca, Oaxaca, Oaxaca, 68000, Mexico; tel (52) 951 54989; fax 551448; e-mail noticias@noticias-oax.com.mx; web site www.noticias-oax.com.mx
Circ.:30,000
Pres. – Ericel Gomez Nucamendi
Gen. Mgr. – Luis Lagunas Aragon
Sales Mgr. – Juan Alejandro de la Huerta Ramos
Ed. Dir. – Ismael Sanmartin Hernandez
Prodn. Mgr. – Alejandro Gomez Moreno

EL EXTRA
Abasolo, No. 119, Oaxaca, Oaxaca, 68000, Mexico; tel (52) 951 60221; fax 64590
Circ.:15,000
Gen. Dir. – Hector Puega Ramirez Leyva
Gen. Mgr. – Carlos Ramirez Leyva
Pub. Rel. – Alberto Ramirez Leyva
Ad Rate: 30.00.

EL SUR (M)
Emilio Carranza, No. 820, Col. Reforma, Oaxaca, Oaxaca, 68050, Mexico; tel (52) 951 34541; fax 52688
Circ.:25,000
Pres. – Rosa Maria Sanchez Montiel
Ed./Dir. – Jose Martinez Bastida

ORIZABA, VERACRUZ

EL SOL DE ORIZABA (M)
Avda. Colon, Poniente, No. 303, Orizaba, Veracruz, 94300, Mexico; tel (52) 1227 725 5646; e-mail info@oem.com.mx; web site www.oem.com.mx
Circ.:20,000
Pres. – Mario Vazquez Rana
Sales Mgr. – Doris Elvia Saldana
Adv. Mgr. – Rogelio Romero Cruz

EL MUNDO DE ORIZABA (M)
Oriente 6, No. 126 Centro, Orizaba, Veracruz, 94300, Mexico; tel (52) 272 56814
Circ.:25,000
Gen. Dir. – Clementina de la Huerta de Arroniz
Editorial Dir. – Raul Gil Arroniz de la Huerta
Advertising – Angelina Sanchez Bautista
Dir., Adm. – Monica Arroniz de Argudin
Ad Rate: 13.00.

PACHUCA, HIDALGO

AVANZANDO (D)
Matamoros No. 212, Pachuca, Hidalgo, 42000, Mexico; tel (52) 771 145863; fax 152977; e-mail avanhgo@prodigy.net.mx; web site www.galeon.com/avanzando
Pres. – Gabriela Rodriguez Torres
Ed./Dir. – Juan Sanchez Cabrera

EL HIDALGUENSE (D)
Avda. Heroico Coleigo Militar, No. 51-3, Pachuca, Hidalgo, Mexico; tel (52) 771 123707

EL NUEVO DIA (D)
Avda. Revolucion No. 1109, Pachuca, Hidalgo, Mexico; tel (52) 771 131991
Gen. Dir. – Marco Antonio Gonzalez Pineda

NUEVO GRAFICO (D)
Guerrero, No. 1106-7 Col. Centro, Pachuca, Hidalgo, 42000, Mexico; tel (52) 771 152923; fax 151018
Pres. – Julio Jose Galvez Mendez
Gen. Mgr. – Julio Alejandro Galvez Rodriguez
Sales Mgr. – Norma Angelica Ruiz Galvez
Ed./Dir. – Norma Lliana Galvez Rodriguez
Prodn. Mgr. – Juan Morales Ruiz

NUEVO HIDALGO (D)
Arista, No. 207, Pachuca, Hidalgo, Mexico; tel (52) 771 150058
Gen. Dir. – Maria Thalia Sanchez Richardos

EL SOL DE HIDALGO (D)
Matamoros 508, Col. Centro, Pachuca, Hidalgo, 42000, Mexico; tel (52) 771 715 0027; e-mail publicidad@elsoldehidalgo.com.mx; web site www.oem.com.mx/elsoldehidalgo
Circ.:49,000
Pres. – Mario Vazquez Rana
Adv. Mgr. – Eva Pineva
Circ. Mgr. – Soldad Tillis

PARRAL, CHIHUAHUA

EL SOL DE PARRAL (M)
Colegio, No. 20, Parral, Chihuahua, 33800, Mexico; tel (52) 627 522 5250; fax 522 1897; e-mail publicidad@elsoldeparral.com.mx; web site www.oem.com.mx/elsoldeparral
Circ.:12,000
Pres./Gen. Dir. – Mario Vazquez Rana

EL CORREO (E)
Avda. 20 de Noviembre, No. 7, Parral, Chihuahua, Mexico; tel (52) 627
Circ.:10,000
Pub. – Ruben Rocha Chavez

EL MONITOR (M)
Calle del Cerre, No. 34, Parral, Chihuahua, 33800, Mexico; tel (52) 152 20979; fax 27640
Circ.:20,000
Dir. – Luis Salayandia Saenz

PATZCUARO, MICHOACAN

AVANCE (D)
Serrato, No. 32, Patzcuaro, Michoacan, Mexico; tel (52) 454 21933
Dir. – Susana Alcala Dominguez

CRITICA REGIONAL (D)
Patzcuaro, Michoacan, Patzcuaro, Michoacan, Mexico; tel (52) 454 20432
Dir. – Lucio Herrera Alonso

PIEDRAS NEGRAS, COAHUILA

LA VOZ DEL NORTE (M)
Piedras Negras, Coahuila, Piedras Negras, Coahuila, Mexico; tel (52) 878
Circ.:25,000
Pub. – Juan Antonio Guajardo Coss
Adv. Mgr. – Isidro Pena Guajardo

LA EXTRA DE ZOCALO (E)
Cuauhtemoc, No. 714, Norte, Piedras Negras, Coahuila, Mexico; tel (52) 878 23990
Circ.:11,500
Dir. – Francisco Juaristi Septien
Adv. Mgr. – Jose Luis Rosales
Ed. in Chief – Paul Garza

EL DIARIO (M)
Piedras Negras, Coahuila, Piedras Negras, Coahuila, 26000, Mexico; tel (52) 878 20910; fax 20538
Circ.:45,000
Ed./Dir. – Hugo H. Martinez Tijerina

POZA RICA

EL DIARIO NORTE DE POZA RICA (D)
Avda. Juarez, No. 103, Col. Tajin, Poza Rica, 93320, Mexico; tel (52) 782 37750; fax 27729
Circ.:8,000
Founder – Dr. Othon Arroniz Baez
Gen. Dir. – Clementina de la Huerta de Arroniz
Dir. – Raul Gil Arroniz de la Huerta
Adv. Mgr. – Marisol Arroniz de M rquez
Ad Rate: 5.40.

POZA RICA, VERACRUZ

DOCE HORAS (E)
Blvd. Adolfo Ruiz Cortinez, No. 613, Poza Rica, Veracruz, Mexico; tel (52) 782
Circ.:18,000
Pub. – Federico Hernandez Leon
Ed. in Chief – Juan Garcia Sanchez

HOY EN POZA RICA
5 de Mayo, No. 200, Col. Tajin, Poza Rica, Veracruz, 93330, Mexico; tel (52) 782 29506; fax 29506
Circ.:10,000
Dir./Gen. Mgr. – Juan Arenas Ramirez
Asst. Dir. – Guillermo Arenas Ramos
Advertising – Carlos Arenas Ramos
Ed. in Chief – Mario Noriega Villanueva
Ad Rate: 14.00.

LA OPINION (M)
M. Arista No. 209, Col. Tajin, Poza Rica, Veracruz, 95330, Mexico; tel (52) 782 20196; fax 42124; e-mail redaccion@laopinion.com.mx; web site www.laopinion.com.mx
Circ.:32,000
Owner/Pres. – Raul Gibb Guerrero
Sales Mgr. – Ernesto Mercado
Ed./Dir. – Abel Andrade

EL MUNDO DE POZA RICA (M)
Ave. 6 Norte No. 40, Poza Rica, Veracruz, 93200, Mexico; tel (52) 782 20017
Circ.:27,000
Owner/Pres. – Antonio Manzur Maron

PUEBLA, PUEBLA

ABC (D)
Calzada Manantiales No. 14, Carretera Federal Mexico-Puebla km 127, Puebla, Puebla, 72760, Mexico; tel (52) 222 285-0206; fax 285-0208
Pres. – Angel Garcia Lopez
Ed./Dir. – Miguel Angel Garcia Munoz

CAMBIO
Puebla, Puebla, Puebla, Puebla, 72000, Mexico; tel (52) 222 465080; fax 329305; web site www.diariocambio.com
Ed./Dir. – Gabriel Sanchez Andraca

DIARIO DE PUEBLA
4 Norte No. 208, Col. Centro, Puebla, Puebla, 72000, Mexico; tel (52) 222 232 4424; fax 232 4424

Pres. – Gilberto Cruz Flores
Ed. – Jaime Osorio Ruiz

EL FINANCIERO
Puebla, Puebla, Puebla, Puebla, 72000, Mexico; tel (52) 222 461441; fax 463133; e-mail contacto@elfinanciero.com.mx; web site www.elfinanciero.com.mx
Circ.:11,000
Owner/Pres. – Rogelio Cardenas
Sales Mgr. – Jose Emilio Pastor
Ed./Dir. – Alma Norma Lopez
Ad Rate: 43.74.

EL HERALDO (M)
Calle 8, Oriente, No. 216 Centro, Puebla, Puebla, 72000, Mexico; tel (52) 222 246 1840; fax 246 3949; e-mail puebla@heraldo.com.mx; web site www.heraldo.com.mx
Pres. – Sergio Reguero Placeres
Ed. – Arnaldo Fernandez Gonzaez

LA OPINION (D)
3 Oriente, No. 1207, Puebla, Puebla, 72000, Mexico; tel (52) 222 242 1682; fax 232 7772; web site www.opinion.com.mx
Circ.:15,000
Pres. – Oscar Lopez Morales
Ed. – Rafael Tellez

LA OPINION DE PUEBLA (D)
Avda. Luis Sanchez Ponton No. 414, Zona Dorada, Puebla, Puebla, 72000, Mexico; tel (52) 222 2432631; fax 2400976
Circ.:15,000
Pres. – Manuel Sanchez Ponton
Ed./Dir. – Oscar Lopez Morales

MOMENTO
7 Oriente, No. 406, Centro Historico, Puebla, Puebla, 72000, Mexico; tel (52) 222 424337; fax 421935; e-mail madek@pue1.telmex.net.mx
Pres. – Baraquiel Alatriste Montoto
Ed./Dir. – Rafael Velasco Oliver

LA VOZ DE PUEBLA (E-EX S)
3 Oriente, No. 201, Puebla, Puebla, 72000, Mexico; tel (52) 222 424560; fax 460869; e-mail solger@prodigy.net.mx; elsolpue@spersa.com.mx; web site www.oem.com.mx
Circ.:17,000
Pres. – Mario Vazquez Rana
Sales Mgr. – Juan Silva Cepeda
Ed./Dir. – Josefina Sarate

EL SOL DE PUEBLA (MS)
Avda. 3, Oriente, No. 201, Puebla, Puebla, 72000, Mexico; tel (52) 222 514 3300; fax 242 4560; e-mail solpue@oem.com.mx; web site www.oem.com.mx/elsoldepuebla
Circ.:67,000
Pres. – Mario Vazquez Rana

PUERTO VALLARTA, JALISCO

MERCURIO (M)
Avda. Las Torres, No. 120, Fraccionamiento Los Sau, Puerto Vallarta, Jalisco, 48320, Mexico; tel (52) 322 40266; fax 40356
Circ.:9,000
Pres./Gen. Dir. – Juan de Dios De la Torre Valencia
Ad Rate: 11.00.

MERIDIANO (M)
Morelos, No. 800, Puerto Vallarta, Jalisco, 48300, Mexico; tel (52) 322 223-2972; e-mail meridian@pvnet.com.mx; web site www.meridiano.com.mx
Circ.:30,000
Pres. – Juan Moises Serna Madariaga
Sales Mgr. – Fernando Acosta Camacho
Ed./Dir. – Jose Acevabas

NOTICIAS DEL PUERTO (D)
Puerto Vallarta, Jalisco, Puerto Vallarta, Jalisco, Mexico; tel (52) 322 21890
Gen. Dir. – Rafael de la Cruz Corona

TRIBUNA DE LA BAHIA (M)
Puerto Vallarta, Jalisco, Puerto Vallarta, Jalisco, 48380, Mexico; tel (52) 322 31302; fax 24361
Circ.:7,000
Pres. – Procoro Hernandez Oropeza
Ed./Dir. – Francisco Quezeda Hernandez

VALLARTA OPINA (M)
Puerto Vallarta, Jalisco, Puerto Vallarta, Jalisco, 48310, Mexico; tel (52) 322 42829; fax 41186; e-mail vtaopina@puerto-vallarta.com.mx; web site www.vallartaopina.net
Circ.:30,000
Owner/Pres. – Luis Reyes Brambila
Gen. Mgr. – Alejandro Reyes Brambila
Sales Mgr. – Aracely Parra
Ed./Dir. – Eduardo Garcia

QUERETARO, QUERETARO

DIARIO DE QUERETARO (MS)
General Escobedo, Poniente, No. 65, Queretaro, Queretaro, 76000, Mexico; tel (52) 442 120852; e-mail diarioqro@ciateq.mx; web site www.oem.com.mx/diariodequeretaro
Circ.:35,000
Pres./Gen. Dir. – Mario Vazquez Rana
Mgr./Dir. – Luis Roberto Amieva Perez
Adm. Mgr. – Carlos Campos Diaz
Adv. Mgr. – Jose Juan Rodriguez Ferruzquia
Ad Rate: 12.00.

EL SOL DE QUERETARO (E)
General Escobedo, Poniente, No. 65, Queretaro, Queretaro, 76000, Mexico; tel (52) 442 121300; fax 130355
Circ.:8,000
Pres./Gen. Dir. – Mario Vazquez Rana
Mgr./Dir. – Luis Roberto Amieva Perez

EL FINANCIERO (M-EX WKND.)
Queretaro, Queretaro, Queretaro, Queretaro, 76040, Mexico; tel (52) 442 212-2982; fax 212-2832; e-mail contacto@elfinanciero.com.mx; web site www.elfinanciero.com.mx
Circ.:5,500
Owner/Pres. – Rogelio Cardenas Sarmiento
Gen. Mgr. – Jesus Montero Oropeza

NOTICIAS (M)
Queretaro, Queretaro, Queretaro, Queretaro, 76000, Mexico; tel (52) 442 212-5888; fax 214-3821; e-mail noticiasqro@prodigy.net.mx; web site www.noticias.com.mx
Circ.:23,000
Owner/Pres. – Rogelio Garfias Ruiz
Gen. Mgr. – Maria Eugenia Rico Hernandez
Sales Mgr. – Laura Garfias Torres
Ed./Dir. – Antonia Sanchez Hernandez
Prodn. Mgr. – Manuel Ramirez Espinoza

RAMOS ARIZPE, COAHUILA

VANGUARDIA (M)
Calle Ocampo, esquina Calle Juarez, Ramos Arizpe, Coahuila, Mexico; tel (52)
Circ.:6,000
Pub. – Armando Castilla Sanchez
Adv. Mgr. – Angel Vela Rios

REYNOSA, TAMAULIPAS

VALLE DE NORTE (M-EX S)
Reynosa, Tamaulipas, Reynosa, Tamaulipas, Mexico; tel (52) 899 238355; fax 238572
Circ.:10,000
Gen. Dir. – Fernando J. De Luna Leal
Ad Rate: 8.25.

EL MANANA DE REYNOSA (M)
Prof. Lauro Aguirre con Matias Canales, Reynosa, Tamaulipas, 88620, Mexico; tel (52) 899 251293
Circ.:65,000
Pres. – Orlando Deandar Martinez
Gen. Dir. – Heriberto Deandar Martinez
Ad Rate: 25.59.

NOTICIAS (M)
Reynosa, Tamaulipas, Reynosa, Tamaulipas, 88500, Mexico; tel (52) 899 230090
Circ.:36,000
Mng. Dir. – Mario Lucio Martinez Garcia

PRENSA DE REYNOSA (M)
Reynosa, Tamaulipas, Reynosa, Tamaulipas, 88500, Mexico; tel (52) 899 223515; fax 223823; e-mail prensare@tamps1.telmex.net.mx
Circ.:60,000
Pres. – Felix Mario Garza Elizondo
Ed./Dir. – Daniel Ulloa Campos

ULTIMA HORA (E)
Avda. Aguascalientes, No. 680, Sur, esq. Nuevo Leo, Reynosa, Tamaulipas, 88630, Mexico; tel (52) 899 234112
Gen. Dir. – Isauro Rodriguez Garza
Editorial Dir. – Angel Virgen Alvarado
Ed. – Waldo Rodriguez Valenzuela

RIO VERDE, SAN LUIS POTOSI

LA OPINION (M)
Venustiano Carranza, No. 433, Rio Verde, San Luis Potosi, Mexico; tel (52) 487
Circ.:20,000
Pub. – Ignacio A. Rosillo

EL SOL DEL RIO VERDE (MS)
Calle Dr. Gallardo, No. 2-B, Rio Verde, San Luis Potosi, Mexico; tel (52) 481 21111
Circ.:3,000
Pub. – Florencio Ruiz de la Pena

SABINAS, COAHUILA

LA VOZ DE SABINAS (M)
Madero No. 422, Sabinas, Coahuila, 26700, Mexico; tel (52) 861 22301
Circ.:5,000
Pres. – Jose Luis de la Luna Abrego
Ed./Dir. – Fidel Ortiz Morales

PRESENTE (M)
Labradores, No. 416, Sabinas, Coahuila, Mexico; tel (52) 861 21057
Circ.:10,000
Pub. – Enrique V. Castaneda

VANGUARDIA DE SABINAS (D)
Sabinas, Coahuila, Sabinas, Coahuila, Mexico; tel (52) 861 30957
Gen. Dir. – Ruben Mena
Dir. – Natalia M. de Mena

SAHUAYO, MICHOACAN

PROVINCIA
Sahuayo, Michoacan, Sahuayo, Michoacan, Mexico; tel (52) 353 20400
Dir. – Luis Amerzcua Arceo

SALAMANCA, GUANAJUATO

EL SOL DE LA TARDE (E)
S nchez Torrado, No. 202, Esquina Morelos, Salamanca, Guanajuato, 36700, Mexico; tel (52) 464 82428; fax 80064
Circ.:9,000
Dir. – Eugenio Albo Moreno

EL SOL DE SALAMANCA (MS)
Faja de Oro 800, Salamanca, Guanajuato, 36700, Mexico; tel (52) 464 647 2624; e-mail publicidad@elsoldesalamanca.com.mx; web site www.elsoldesalamanca.com.mx
Circ.:15,800
Pres. – Mario Vazquez Rana

TRIBUNA (M)
Salamanca, Guanajuato, Salamanca, Guanajuato, 36700, Mexico; tel (52) 464 83922; fax 83922
Circ.:10,000
Pres./Gen. Dir. – Ramon Lopez Diaz

SALINA CRUZ, OAXACA

EL IMPARCIAL DEL ISTMO (M)
Ave. Tapico No. 22, Salina Cruz, Oaxaca, 70610, Mexico; tel (52) 971 714 2080; fax 714 0513; e-mail imparcial_istmo@hotmail.com; web site www.imparcialenlinea.com
Circ.:20,000
Pres. – Benjamin Fernandez Pichardo

SALTILLO, COAHUILA

EXTRA! DIARIO DE LA TARDE (E-EX S)
Saltillo, Coahuila, Saltillo, Coahuila, 25280, Mexico; tel (52) 844 153041
Circ.:15,212
Editorial Dir. – Oscar Medrano Sanchez
Asst. Editorial Dir. – Lucia Rosa Teissier de Galindo
Ad Rate: 12.00.

EL DIARIO DE COAHUILA (M)
Saltillo, Coahuila, Saltillo, Coahuila, 25260, Mexico; tel (52) 844 438 8100; fax 438 8174; e-mail criterio@prodigy.net.mx; web site www.eldiariodecoahuila.com.mx
Circ.:16,000
Pres. – Luis Horacio Salinas Aguilera
Sports Ed. – Raul Chavez Alustiza
Editorial Dir. – HÂ£ctor L. Chapa GarcÂ¡a

EL HERALDO DE SALTILLO Est.1937
Ave. Abasolo Norte No. 228, Col. Centro, Saltillo, Coahuila, 25000, Mexico; tel (52) 844 148438; fax 148874; e-mail eco_heraldo@terra.com.mx; web site www.elheraldodesaltillo.mx
Owne/Pres. – Francisco J. de la Pena Davilla
Gen. Mgr. – Alicia de la Pena De Leon
Ed./Dir. – Eduardo de la Pena Davila

EL INDEPENDIENTE (M)
Saltillo, Coahuila, Saltillo, Coahuila, Mexico; tel (52) 844 148286
Circ.:10,000
Gen. Dir. – Jorge A. Estrada Garcia

EL SOL DE SALTILLO (D)
Cuauhtemoc, No. 349, Sur, Saltillo, Coahuila, Mexico; tel (52) 844 122692; fax 121101
Gen. Dir. – David Brondo Garcia

EL SOL DEL NORTE (M)
Saltillo, Coahuila, Saltillo, Coahuila, 25000, Mexico; tel (52) 844 122692; fax 121101
Circ.:12,000
Pres. – Mario Vazquez Rana
Ed./Dir. – Jose Concepcion Hernandez
Ad Rate: International Newspapers.

VANGUARDIA (MS)
Blvd. Venustiano Carranza No. 1918, Col. Republic, Saltillo, Coahuila, 25280, Mexico; tel (52) 844 450 1000; fax 415 3321; e-mail hola@vanguardia.com.mx; vanlider@vanguardia.com.mx; web site www.vanguardia.com.mx
Circ.:16,000
Dir. – Armando Castilla Galindo

Ad Rate: International Newspapers.

ZOCALO (M)
Blvd. Venustiano Carranza, Saltillo, Coahuila, 5280, Mexico; tel (52) 844 438-1800; e-mail web@zocalo.com.mx; web site www.zocalo.com.mx
Circ.:48,300
Group: Grupo Zócalo
Pres. – Francisco Juaristi Santos
Luis Eduardo Mendoza
Francisco Linan
José David Juaristi

ZOCALO (D) Est.1965
Blvd. Venustiano Carranza 5280, Saltillo, Coahuila, 5280, Mexico; tel (52) 844 438 1800; fax 438 1801; e-mail correo@zocalo.com.mx; web site www.zocalo.com.mx
Circ.:22,000
Presidente y Director General – Francisco Juaristi

SALVATIERRA, GUANAJUATO

EL SOL DEL SUR DEL BAJIO (M)
Guillermo Prieto, No. 328-B, Salvatierra, Guanajuato, 38900, Mexico; tel (52) 466 21569
Circ.:8,000
Mng. Dir. – Miguel Angel Chico Herrera
Pres./Gen. Dir. – Mario Vazquez Rana

SAN ANDRES TUXTLA, VERACRUZ

EL DIARIO DE LOS TUXTLAS (MS)
Avda. Tampico, No. 22, Esquina Manzanillo, San Andres Tuxtla, Veracruz, 70610, Mexico; tel (52) 294 (52-294) 40513
Circ.:25,000
Gen. Dir. – Benjamin Fernandez Pichardo
Dir. – Guillermo Soto Bejarano
Ad Rate: 7.15.

SAN FRANCISCO DE CAMPECHE

CRONICA (M)
Privada de la 14 No. 5 Colonia San Rom n, San Francisco de Campeche, 24040, Mexico; tel (52) 981 811 5067; fax 816 8920; e-mail contacto@cronicacampeche.com; web site www.cronicacampeche.com
Circ.:7,000
Pres. – Virgilio S. Soberanis Rodriguez

SAN JUAN DEL RIO, QUERETARO

EL SOL DE SAN JUAN DEL RIO (M)
San Juan Del Rio, Queretaro, San Juan Del Rio, Queretaro, 78000, Mexico; tel (52) 427 272 0556; e-mail publicidad@elsoldesanjuandelrio.com.mx; oemenlinea@oem.com.mx; web site www.oem.com.mx
Circ.:9,000
Pres. – Mario Vazquez Rana
Dir. – Sergio Arturo Venegas Alarcon

SAN LUIS POTOSI,

EL HERALDO
Villerias No. 305, Col. Centro, San Luis Potosi,, 78000, Mexico; tel (52) 444 812 2684; fax 812 2081; e-mail direccion@elheraldoslp.com.mx; redaccion111@elheraldoslp.com.mx; sociales@elheraldoslp.com.mx; web site www.elheraldoslp.com.mx
Circ.:27,000
Pres. – Alejandro Villasana Mena
Prodn. Mgr. – Rodrigo Villasana Mena
Ed. in Chief – Aurelio Ventura

SAN LUIS POTOSI, SAN LUIS POTOSI

LA OPINION (D)
Venustiano Carranza, No. 433, San Luis Potosi, San Luis Potosi, Mexico; tel (52) 444 120049
Circ.:25,000
Pub. – Ignacio A. Rosillo

EL SOL DE SAN LUIS (MS)
San Luis Potosi, San Luis Potosi, San Luis Potosi, San Luis Potosi, 78000, Mexico; tel (52) 444 812 6713; e-mail publicidad@elsoldesanluis.com.mx; oemenlinea@oem.com.mx; web site www.oem.com.mx
Circ.:40,000
Pres. – Mario Vazquez Rana
Dir. – Jose Angel Martinez Limon

PULSO (M)
San Luis Potosi, San Luis Potosi, San Luis Potosi, San Luis Potosi, 78000, Mexico; tel (52) 444 812 7512; fax 812 3525; e-mail pulso@slp.intermex.com.mx; web site www.pulsoslp.com.mx
Circ.:60,000
Last Audit: April 1, 2010
Pres. – Miguel F. Valladares Garcia
Gen. Mgr. – Bablo Bllladares
Adm. Dir. – Elmma Dorres
Asst. Dir. – Rosy Dominguez
Prom. Mgr. – Jose Luis Hernandez Medina
Adv. Mgr. – Rogelio Catano Barrera
Ed. – Marta Rangel
Ed. – Armando Acosta

SAN LUIS HOY (M)
San Luis Potosi, San Luis Potosi, San Luis Potosi, San Luis Potosi, 78000, Mexico; tel (52) 444 810 0100; fax 810 0100; web site www.sanluishoy.com.mx
Circ.:16,000
Pres. – Valladares Pablo
Ed. Coord. – Marta Torres
Ed. Coord. – Averiana Ocsoa
Ed. Coord. – Armando Acosta

SAN LUIS RIO COLORADO, SONORA

TRIBUNA DE SAN LUIS (D)
Avda. Juarez y Calle 11, No. 1017, Col. Comercial, San Luis Rio Colorado, Sonora, 83400, Mexico; tel (52) 653 534 2542; fax 534 3274; e-mail publicidad@tribunadesanluis.com.mx; web site www.oem.com.mx/tribunadesanluis
Circ.:14,000
Pres/Owner – Mario Vazquez Rana

TACAMBARO, MICHOACAN

AVANZADA (D)
Fray Alonso de la Veracruz, No. 58, Tacambaro, Michoacan, Mexico; tel (52) 454 60027
Dir. – Servio Tulio Gutierrez Venegas

PIONERO
Tacambaro, Michoacan, Tacambaro, Michoacan, Mexico; tel (52) 459
Dir. – Margarita Tapia Quintana

TAMPICO, TAMAULIPAS

EL CORREO (D)
Tampico, Tamaulipas, Tampico, Tamaulipas, Mexico; tel (52) 833
Pub. – Antonio M. Maron

EL DIARIO DE TAMPICO (M)
Tampico, Tamaulipas, Tampico, Tamaulipas, 89120, Mexico; tel (52) 833 12134570
Circ.:54,000
Pres. – Antonio Manzur

EL HERALDO DE TAMPICO (MS)
Venustiano Carranza, No. 801, Poniente, Tampico, Tamaulipas, Mexico; tel (52) 833 128260
Circ.:95,000
Pub. – Mauricio Bercun
Adv. Mgr. – Faustino Paredes

EXTRA
Altamira, No. 800, Pte., Tampico, Tamaulipas, 89000, Mexico; tel (52) 833 12190395; fax 12123304; e-mail diario@diariodetampico.com; web site www.diariodetampico.com
Circ.:15,000
Pres. – Maria Eugenia Gonzalez Ramos
Sales Mgr. – Jorge Vela
Ed./Dir. – Jose Antonio Suarez

EL MUNDO (MS)
Ejercito Nacional, No. 201, Col. Guadalupe, Tampico, Tamaulipas, 89120, Mexico; tel (52) 833 134978; fax 134570; e-mail mundo@interxcable.net.mx
Pres. – Antonio Manzur Maron

EL SOL DE LA TARDE
Tampico, Tamaulipas, Tampico, Tamaulipas, 89000, Mexico; tel (52) 833 123535; fax 126821; e-mail soltam@oem.com.mx; web site www.oem.com.mx
Circ.:37,000
Pres. – Mario Vazquez Rana
Gen. Mgr. – Ruben Diaz de la Garza
Sales Mgr. – Leobardo Oueblo
Ed./Dir. – Agustin Jimenez Hernandez

EL SOL DE TAMPICO
Tampico, Tamaulipas, Tampico, Tamaulipas, 89000, Mexico; tel (52) 833 212 1067; fax 212 6821; e-mail publicidad@elsoldetampico.com.mx; oemenlinea@oem.com.mx; web site www.oem.com.mx
Circ.:77,000
Pres. – Mario Vazquez Rana
Dir. – Agustin Jimenez Hernandez

TAPACHULA, CHIAPAS

NOTICIAS DE CHIAPAS
Tapachula, Chiapas, Tapachula, Chiapas, 30700, Mexico; tel (52) 962 63288; fax 68310; e-mail notichis@tapachula.podernet.com.mx; web site www.noticiasdechiapas.com.mx
Circ.:5,000
Pres. – Carlos Correa Leo
Gen. Mgr. – Yolanda Gonzalez de Correa
Ed./Dir. – Ernesto Lopez Quintero

EL SOL DEL SOCONUSCO
Tapachula, Chiapas, Tapachula, Chiapas, 30700, Mexico; tel (52) 962 64360
Circ.:8,000
Gen. Dir./Ed. – Nahum Gomez Grajales
Ad Rate: 19.00.

SUR DE MEXICO (D-6X WK.)
Ave. Centro Poniente, No. 36, Tapachula, Chiapas, 30700, Mexico; tel (52) 962 65599; fax 65306
Circ.:5,000
Owner/Pres. – Augusto Enrique Villareal Quezada
Gen. Mgr. – Eduardo A. Villareal
Ed./Dir. – Jorge Barajas Hernandez

SURESTE
Tapachula, Chiapas, Tapachula, Chiapas, 30799, Mexico; tel (52) 962 68406
Circ.:30,000
Editorial Dir. – Sergio Gutierrez Vargas
Adm. Dir. – Jose M. Pina Gonzalez

TAPACHULA, CHIS

DIARIO DEL SUR (M)
Segunda Calle Pte. 4, Col. Centro, Tapachula, Chis, 30700, Mexico; tel (52) 962 626 2370; fax 626 4301; e-mail oescamilla@diariodelsur.com.mx; publicidad@diariodelsur.com.mx; web site www.oem.com.mx
Gen. Mgr. – Roberto Tapia
Ad Rate: 21.00.

TAXCO, GUERRERO

DIARIO DE TAXCO (M)
Morelos, No. 37-A, Int. 5 CP, Taxco, Guerrero, 40289, Mexico; tel (52) 762 23950
Circ.:15,000
Gen. Dir. – Urbano Delgado Castaneda
Dir. – Agustin Mazon Barrera
Mgr. – Alfredo Desentis Ruiz
Ad Rate: 22.00.

TECOMAN, COLIMA

MONITOR DE COLIMA
Antonio Montes, No. 27, Sur, Tecoman, Colima, Mexico; tel (52) 332 42350
Dir. – Tranquilino Contreras Renteria

TEHUACAN, PUEBLA

EL MUNDO DE TEHUACAN (M)
Tehuacan, Puebla, Tehuacan, Puebla, 75700, Mexico; tel (52) 238 382 2691; fax 382 2620; web site www.elmundodetehuacan.com
Circ.:15,000
Pres. – Clementina de la Huerta de Arroniz
Ed./Dir. – Raul Gil Arroniz de la Huerta

EL SOL DE TEHUACAN (M)
Avda. Independencia, Pte. 227 Altos, Tehuacan, Puebla, 75700, Mexico; tel (52) 238 232 6028; fax 382 6557; e-mail publicidad@elsoldepuebla.com.mx; web site www.oem.com.mx/elsoldetehuacan
Circ.:9,000
Chief Ed. – Wendy Sanchez

LA ESCOBA (M)
1 Norte, No. 212, Tehuacan, Puebla, Mexico; tel (52) 238 21044
Circ.:10,000
Gen. Dir. – Daniel Gamez Andrade

TEPIC, NAYARIT

DIARIO DEL PACIFICO (D)
Avda. Mexico, No. 189, Sur, Tepic, Nayarit, Mexico; tel (52) 311 131899
Gen. Dir. – Emilio Valdez Hernandez

EL OBSERVADOR (M)
Tepic, Nayarit, Tepic, Nayarit, 63000, Mexico; tel (52) 311 124309; fax 124309
Circ.:55,000
Mng. Dir. – Fernando Gutierrez Pinedo
Pres./Gen. Dir. – Luis Arturo Gonzalez Becerra
Mgr. – Jose Iniguez Nunez
Adv. Mgr. – Francisco Ortiz
Ad Rate: 18.00.

EL PUEBLO
13 de Septiembre, No. 33, Tepic, Nayarit, Mexico; tel (52) 311

EL SOL DE TEPIC (M-EX S)
Zacatecas, Sur, No. 148, Altos, Tepic, Nayarit, Mexico; tel (52) 311 136581
Circ.:10,000
Gen. Dir. – Prof. Guillermo E. Rodriguez Jimenez
Ed. in Chief – Oziel Rosas Nunez
Ad Rate: 5.80.

EXPRESS (D)
Ejido No. 251, Col. H. Casas, Tepic, Nayarit, 63000, Mexico; tel (52) 311 160916; fax 126731; e-mail express@foreigner.com.mx; web site www.periodicoexpress.com.mx
Circ.:13,200
Group: Charney/Palacios & Co.
Pres. – Edgar Rafael Arellano Ontiveros
Gen. Mgr. – Edith Cecilia Jimenez Sanchez
Sales Mgr. – Carlos Alberto Lopez Ramos
Ed./Dir. – Carmen Georgina Martinez

LA VOZ DE NAYARIT (D)
Zacatecas, No. 224, Norte, Tepic, Nayarit, Mexico; tel (52) 311 120503
Gen. Dir. – Marco Antonio Casillas

MERIDIANO (M)
Emiliano Zapata, No. 73, Pte., Tepic, Nayarit, 63000, Mexico; tel (52) 311 214 3809; fax 212 6731; e-mail meridiano@tepic.megared.net.mx
Circ.:60,000
Pres. – David Alfaro
Ed./Dir. – Guillermo Aguirre

NOVEDADES (D)
Avda. Insurgentes, No. 170, Poniente, Tepic, Nayarit, Mexico; tel (52) 311

PRENSA LIBRE (D)
Tepic, Nayarit, Tepic, Nayarit, Mexico; tel (52) 311
Group: Charney/Palacios & Co.
Pub. – Jose Gonzalez Reyna
Adv. Mgr. – Ignacia Lopez Ramirez

REALIDADES (M-6X WK.)
Tepic, Nayarit, Tepic, Nayarit, 63000, Mexico; tel (52) 311 214 0657; fax 214 0657; web site www.periodicorealidades.com
Pres. – Hugo Rodriguez Jimenez

EL TIEMPO DE NAYARIT
Tepic, Nayarit, Tepic, Nayarit, 63170, Mexico; tel (52) 311 2135333; fax 2135333
Ed./Dir. – Antonio Garcia Hernandez

ULTIMAS NOTICIAS DE NAYARIT (D)
Tepic, Nayarit, Tepic, Nayarit, Mexico; tel (52) 311 121634
Gen. Dir. – Cesar A. Renteria Velazquez

TIJUANA, BAJA CALIFORNIA

DIARIO 29 (M)
Tijuana, Baja California, Tijuana, Baja California, 22320, Mexico; tel (52) 664 340084; fax 340083
Circ.:40,000
Gen. Dir. – Virgilio Munoz
Editorial Dir. – Rogelio Lozoya Godoy

EL SOL DE TIJUANA (D)
Tijuana, Baja California, Tijuana, Baja California, 22320, Mexico; tel (52) 664 634 3232; fax 634 2234; e-mail publicidad@elsoldetijuana.com.mx; web site www.oem.com.mx/elsoldetijuana
Circ.:50,000
Dir. – Arturo Gonzalez Perez

SEGUNDA EDICION (E-EX S)
Tijuana, Baja California, Tijuana, Baja California, 22450, Mexico; tel (52) 664 104 2400; fax 104 2401; e-mail dgeneral@elmexicano.info; web site www.elmexicano.info
Circ.:45,000
Pres. – Eligio Valencia Roque
Sales Mgr. – Jorge Bautizta
Ed./Dir. – Enrique Sanchez Diaz

TIJUANA, BAJA CALIFORNIA NORTE

ABC
Aguas Caliente, No. 2700, Col. Cacho, Tijuana, Baja California Norte, 22150, Mexico; tel (52) 664 840971
Circ.:50,000
Gen. Mgr. – Rafael A. Martinez

BAJA CALIFORNIA (M)
Tijuana, Baja California Norte, Tijuana, Baja California Norte, 22450, Mexico; tel (52) 664 235022; fax 235030
Circ.:55,000
Gen. Dir. – Marco Antonio Blasquez Salinas
Ad Rate: 19.50.

EL MEXICANO (M)
Tijuana, Baja California Norte, Tijuana, Baja California Norte, 22540, Mexico; tel (52) 664 104 2400; fax 104 2401; e-mail elmextj@telnor.net; web site www.el-mexicano.com.mx
Circ.:48,000
Gen. Mgr. – Eligio Valencia Roque
Dir. – Eligio Valencia Alonso
Adv. Mgr. – Jose Gomez
Ed. – Enrique Sanchez Diaz

ULTIMAS NOTICIAS (E)
Carretera al Aeropuerto Alamar, Tijuana, Baja California Norte, Mexico; tel (52) 664 868001
Circ.:45,000
Pub. – Jose de Jesus Rios
Adv. Mgr. – Salvador Rueda Badillo

TLANEPANTLA, MEXICO

AVANCE (DS)
Tlanepantla, Mexico, Tlanepantla, Mexico, Mexico; tel (52) 56 58125
Circ.:20,000
Pub. – Jose O'Farrill Larranaga

TLAXCALA, TLAXCALA

EL SOL DE TLAXCALA (M)
Tlaxcala, Tlaxcala, Tlaxcala, Tlaxcala, 90070, Mexico; tel (52) 246 462 0756; e-mail publicidad@elsoldetlaxcala.com.mx; web site www.oem.com.mx/elsoldetlaxcala
Circ.:15,000
Dir. – MÂ ximo HernÂ ndez Cervantes
Sales Mgr. – Antonia Perez Perez
Ed. – Sergio E. DÂ¡az DÂ¡az

TOLUCA

EL SOL DE TOLUCA (D)
Toluca, Toluca, 50050, Mexico; tel (52) 722 214 7077; fax 215 0340; e-mail publicidad@elsoldetoluca.com.mx; oemenlinea@oem.com.mx; web site www.oem.com.mx
Circ.:42,000
Pres. – Mario Vazquez Rana
Dir. – Rafael Vilchis

TOLUCA, ESTADO DE MEXICO

RUMBO
Allende, Sur, No. 205, Toluca, Estado de Mexico, 50050, Mexico; tel (52) 722 216 0270; fax 214 1523
Circ.:10,800
Owner/Pres. – Luis Maccise Uribe
Ed. – Manual Pelaez Najera

TOLUCA, MEXICO

AMANECER (D)
Toluca, Mexico, Toluca, Mexico, 50130, Mexico; tel (52) 722 134 0000; fax 219 2728; e-mail amanecer@mail.diarioamanecer.com.mx; web site www.diarioamanecer.com.mx
Pres. – Naim Libien Kaui
Ed./Dir. – Juan Lopez Cruz

ABC (M)
Avda. Hidalgo Oriente No. 1339 CP, Toluca, Mexico, 50000, Mexico; tel (52) 722 178846; e-mail miled1@mail.miled.com; web site www.miled.com
Dir. – Guillermo Padilla Cruz
Pres./Ed. – Miled Libien Kaui
Gen. Dir. – Miled Libien Santiago
Gen. Mgr. – Gabriela Libien Santiago
Advertising – Claudia Libien Santiago

EL DIARIO
Allende Sur No. 205, Col. Centro, Toluca, Mexico, 50000, Mexico; tel (52) 722 276 0700; fax 276 0703; e-mail eldiario@netspace.com.mx; web site www.diariodetoluca.com.mx
Circ.:22,800
Prodn. Mgr. – Ignacio Naime

EL FINANCIERO (M)
Toluca, Mexico, Toluca, Mexico, 50000, Mexico; tel (52) 722 147053; fax 134532; e-mail contacto@elfinanciero.com.mx; web site www.elfinanciero.com.mx
Circ.:5,700
Group: Admarket International (Div. of Marcom International, Inc.)
Owner/Pres. – Rogelio Cardenas Sarmiento
Sales Mgr. – Guillermo Chavez

EL HERALDO DE TOLUCA (M)
Toluca, Mexico, Toluca, Mexico, 50150, Mexico; tel (52) 722 174913; fax 122535; e-mail editotol@edomex1.telmex.net.mx
Sales Mgr. – Enrique Alzcazar
Ed./Dir. – Alberto Barraza Sanchez
Ad Rate: 8.58.

EL MANANA (M)
Toluca, Mexico, Toluca, Mexico, 50070, Mexico; tel (52) 722 179646; fax 178402; e-mail miled1@mail.miled.com; web site www.miled.com
Circ.:65,000
Pres. – Miled Libien Kaui
Sales Mgr. – Claudia Libien Santiago
Ed./Dir. – Santos Sanchez Albarrin
Prodn. Mgr. – Guillermo Padilla Cruz

EL VESPERTINO (E-EX S)
Avda. Hidalgo Oriente No. 1339, Toluca, Mexico, 50070, Mexico; tel (52) 722 2179646; fax 2178868; web site www.miled.com
Circ.:25,000
Pres. – Miled Libien Kaui
Sales Mgr. – Claudia Libien Santiago
Ed./Dir. – Francisco Quezada

EXTRA DE EL SOL (E-EX S)
Santos Degollado, No. 105, Toluca, Mexico, 50050, Mexico; tel (52) 722 150340; fax (52-72) 147441
Circ.:17,000
Pres. – Mario Vazquez Rana
Gen. Mgr. – Napoleon Galvan
Ed./Dir. – Rafael Vilchis

TORREON, COAHUILA

LA OPINION DE LA TARDE (E-EX S)
Blvd. Independencia, No. 1492, Oriente, Torreon, Coahuila, 27010, Mexico; tel (52) 871 7133-198
Circ.:20,000
Pub. – V.M. Guillermo Jaramillo
Pres. – Francisco A. Gonzalez
Gen. Dir. – Jorge Villegas
Pres. – Jesus D. Gonzalez
Adv. Dir. – Enrique Gomez Junco
Gen. Mgr.-Mex. Div. – Francisco Somohano Diaz
Ad Rate: 9.00.

EL SIGLO DE TORREON (MS)
Avda. Matamoros, No. 1056, Poniente, Torreon, Coahuila, 27000, Mexico; tel (52) 871 17128600; fax 17124500; e-mail elsiglo@elsiglodetorreon.com.mx; web site www.elsiglodetorreon.com.mx
Circ.:38,000
Pres. – Antonio Irazoqui y de Juambelz
Asst. Pub. – Alfonzo Gonzalez Karg y de Juamblez
Gen. Mgr. – Miguel Angel Ruelas Talamantes
Sales Mgr. – Sandra Luz Garcia Avalos
Ed./Dir. – Sergio Enrique Guajardo Adame
Asst. Dir. – Alfonso Gonzalez Karg y De Juambelz
Opns. Dir. – Enrique Irazoqui Morales

NOTICIAS DEL SOL DE LA LAGUNA (MD)
Torreon, Coahuila, Torreon, Coahuila, 27350, Mexico; tel (52) 871 716 4040; fax 716 4150; e-mail publicidad@noticiasdelsoldelalaguna.com.mx; oemenlinea@oem.com.mx; web site www.oem.com.mx
Circ.:17,000
Dir. – Gustavo Flores Acosta

VANGUARDIA LAGUNA (M)
Matamoros, No. 1018, Poniente, Torreon, Coahuila, Mexico; tel (52) 871
Circ.:40,000
Pub. – Oscar Medrano Sanchez
Adv. Mgr. – Gustavo Valdez Ramirez

TULA, HIDALGO

LA REGION (D)
Leandro Valle, No. 118, Tula, Hidalgo, Mexico; tel (52) 773 20324
Circ.:6,000
Pub. – Francisco Tovar Perez

TULANCINGO, HIDALGO

EL SOL DE TULANCINGO (MS)
Tulancingo, Hidalgo, Tulancingo, Hidalgo, 46000, Mexico; tel (52) 775 753 5800; e-mail publicidad@elsoldehidalgo.com.mx; web site www.oem.com.mx/elsoldetulancingo
Circ.:12,000
Pres. – Mario Vazquez Rana
Dir. – Fausto Marin Tamayo

TUXPAM, VERACRUZ

LA VOZ DE LA HUAXTECA (M-EX S)
Tuxpam, Veracruz, Tuxpam, Veracruz, 92800, Mexico; tel (52) 783 41160; fax 46438
Circ.:24,000
Owner/Pres. – Calixto A. Mazan Ferrer

TUXPAN, NAYARIT

CORREO DEL PACIFICO (D)
Juarez y Lerdo, Tuxpan, Nayarit, Mexico; tel (52) 323 20300
Gen. Dir. – Arturo Flores Mejia

TUXPAN, VERACRUZ

DIARIO DE TUXPAM (M)
Tuxpan, Veracruz, Tuxpan, Veracruz, 92800, Mexico; tel (52) 783 46248; fax 46247

Circ.:16,000
Founder – Dr. Othon Arroniz Baez
Gen. Dir. – Clementina de la Huerta de Arroniz
Editorial Dir. – Miguel Angel Cristiani
Adv. Mgr. – Marisol Arroniz de Marquez
Ad Rate: 7.81.

LA TRIBUNA (M)
Tuxpan, Veracruz, Tuxpan, Veracruz, Mexico; tel (52) 783
Circ.:11,000
Pub. – Carlos Rodriguez

TUXTLA GUTIERREZ, CHIAPAS

AMBAR
3a. Poniente, No. 170, Sur, Tuxtla Gutierrez, Chiapas, Mexico; tel (52) 961 35376
Gen. Dir. – Juan Balboa Cuesta

CHIAPAS LIBRE (D)
Tuxtla Gutierrez, Chiapas, Tuxtla Gutierrez, Chiapas, Mexico; tel (52) 961 10676
Gen. Dir. – Julio Barrera Gordillo

EL DIA
Tuxtla Gutierrez, Chiapas, Tuxtla Gutierrez, Chiapas, Mexico; tel (52) 961
Circ.:2,000

EL HERALDO DE CHIAPAS
Tuxtla Gutierrez, Chiapas, Tuxtla Gutierrez, Chiapas, Mexico; tel (52) 961 21682; web site www.oem.com.mx/elheraldodechiapas
Circ.:18,000
Gen. Dir. – Mario Maturana Lopez
Dir. – Hubert Ochoa Ramirez

EL OBSERVADOR DE LA FRONTERA SUR
9a. Sur, No. 2203, Oriente, Tuxtla Gutierrez, Chiapas, Mexico; tel (52) 961 29067; fax 37431
Gen. Dir. – Francisco J. Ramirez Solis

EL PLANETA DE CHIAPAS (D-6X WK.)
1a. Avda. No. 1036, Sur, Poniente, Tuxtla Gutierrez, Chiapas, 29000, Mexico; tel (52) 961 23829; fax 11344
Circ.:17,000
Dir. – Rafael Revueltas Marin
Ad Rate: 5.50.

EL SOL DE CHIAPAS
4a. Calle Poniente, Norte No. 373, Tuxtla Gutierrez, Chiapas, 29000, Mexico; tel (52) 961 132198; fax 132198; e-mail nunez-diaz@infosel.net.mx
Ed./Dir. – Gonzalo Nunez de Leon

EL SOL DE TUXTLA GUTIERREZ (DS)
4a. Calle Poniente, No. 221, Norte, Tuxtla Gutierrez, Chiapas, Mexico; tel (52) 961
Circ.:15,000
Pub. – Francisco Nunez Lopez

ES! DIARIO POPULAR
Tuxtla Gutierrez, Chiapas, Tuxtla Gutierrez, Chiapas, 29000, Mexico; tel (52) 961 20595; fax 20595
Circ.:28,000
Dir. – Alfonso Macias Grajales Burguete
Founder – Gervasio Macias Grajales Gomez
Ad Rate: 17.50.

LA EXTRA (D)
4a. Poniente y 1a. Norte, Tuxtla Gutierrez, Chiapas, Mexico; tel (52) 961 20219
Gen. Dir. – Francisco Nunez Lopez
Adv. Dir. – Gonzalo Nunez de Leon

LA TRIBUNA
Tuxtla Gutierrez, Chiapas, Tuxtla Gutierrez, Chiapas, 29000, Mexico; tel (52) 961 22206
Circ.:10,000
Pres. – Gustavo Cancino Montesinos
Gen. Mgr. – Carlos Cancino Montesinos
Sales Mgr. – Fabiola Cancino Culebro
Ed. – Humberto Trejo Gomez

LA VERSION
2a. Oriente Sur, No. 350, Tuxtla Gutierrez, Chiapas, Mexico; tel (52) 961 23204
Gen. Dir. – Ciro Antonio Jimenez Rodriguez
Dir. – Luis Castillo Peralta

LA VOZ DEL SURESTE
5ta. Ave. Norte Poniente, No. 1412, Tuxtla Gutierrez, Chiapas, 29000, Mexico; tel (52) 961 32921; fax 31487; e-mail edilavoz@chis1.telmex.net.mx; web site diariolavozdelsureste.com
Circ.:12,000
Pres. – Roberto Coello Trejo
Ed./Dir. – Higinio Garcia Mendoza

NUMERO UNO
1a. Avda. Norte, y 2a. Calle, Oriente, Tuxtla Gutierrez, Chiapas, Mexico; tel (52) 961 11324; fax 28136
Circ.:15,000
Pres./Gen. Dir. – Jaime Fernandez Armendariz

CUARTO PODER
3a. Poniente, Norte No. 141 CP, Tuxtla Gutierrez, Chiapas, 29000, Mexico; tel (52) 961 14014; fax 25242; web site www.cuartopoder.com.mx
Circ.:30,000
Gen. Dir. – Conrado de la Cruz Jimenez
Adv. Dir. – Conrado de la Cruz Morales
Ad Rate: 31.00.

URUAPAN, MICHOACAN

DIARIO DE MICHOACAN (M-6X WK.)
Uruapan, Michoacan, Uruapan, Michoacan, 60120, Mexico; tel (52) 452 37303; fax 40072
Circ.:13,000
Gen. Dir. – Felipe Arturo Ibanez Torres
Gen. Mgr. – Ulises Ibanez Torres
Ad Rate: 4.00.

EL CRUZADO (4X WK.)
Privada Lerdo de Tejada, No. 26, Uruapan, Michoacan, 60040, Mexico; tel (52) 452 34488
Gen. Dir. – Roberto Murillo Rocha
Ad Rate: 7.80.

LA OPINION DE MICHOACAN (MD)
Uruapan, Michoacan, Uruapan, Michoacan, 60040, Mexico; tel (52) 452 523 0951; fax 523 8989; e-mail opinion@ulter.net
Circ.:18,000
Pres. – Enrique Alcazar Ramirez

VERACRUZ, VERACRUZ

DIARIO DE VERACRUZ (D)
Veracruz, Veracruz, Veracruz, Veracruz, Mexico; tel (52) 229 51055
Circ.:20,000
Pub. – Ruben Pabello Acosta

HOY LA NACION (M)
Veracruz, Veracruz, Veracruz, Veracruz, 91700, Mexico; tel (52) 229 315624
Circ.:30,000
Gen. Dir. – Fernando De La Miyar Barrios
Ad Rate: 6.00.

LA NOTICIA (M)
Holtzunger, No. 76, Veracruz, Veracruz, 91700, Mexico; tel (52) 229 344398
Circ.:18,500
Gen. Dir. – Apolonio Gamboa Gonzalez

LA TARDE
16 de Septiembre y Arista, Veracruz, Veracruz, 91700, Mexico; tel (52) 229 311745; fax 315804
Pres. – Bertha Malpica de Ahued
Ed. – Guillermo Ingram Garcia

LA VOZ DE VERACRUZ (M)
Veracruz, Veracruz, Veracruz, Veracruz, Mexico; tel (52) 229
Circ.:35,000
Pub. – Manuel Bravo Malpica

NOTIVER (M)
Francisco Canal y Gomez Farias, s/n, Veracruz, Veracruz, 91700, Mexico; tel (52) 229 310013; fax 316146; e-mail notiver@infosel.net.mx
Circ.:38,000
Dir. – Alfonso Salces
Ad Rate: 25.00.

EL SOL DE VERACRUZ (MS)
Veracruz, Veracruz, Veracruz, Veracruz, Mexico; tel (52) 229 45520
Circ.:21,000
Pub. – Wilbur Patron
Adv. Mgr. – Hector Noguera Trujillo

VILLAFLORES, CHIAPAS

EL FRAYLESCANO (D)
Belisario Dominguez, No. 198, Col. Bienestar Socia, Villaflores, Chiapas, Mexico; tel (52) 961 29919
Dir. – Julio Archila Gomez

VILLAHERMOSA, TABASCO

AVANCE (M)
Avda. Mexico, No. 6, Col. Del Bosque, Villahermosa, Tabasco, 86160, Mexico; tel (52) 993 514400; fax 510311; e-mail davance@nexus.net.mx
Circ.:10,000
Owner/Pres. – Ignacio Cobo Gonzalez
Gen. Mgr. – Mario Valdez
Sales Mgr. – Leticia Murillo Leon
Ed./Dir. – Miguel Angel Moreno Cota

DIARIO DE TABASCO (M)
Villahermosa, Tabasco, Villahermosa, Tabasco, Mexico; tel (52) 993 121715
Circ.:5,000
Pub. – Erwin Macario Rodriguez

EL VESPERTINO DE PRESENTE (E)
Jose Pages Llergo 116, Sanchez Magallanes, Villahermosa, Tabasco, 86040, Mexico; tel (52) 993 312 1775; fax 312 3493
Ed./Dir. – Jorge Fausto Calles Broca

NOVEDADES DE TABASCO (M)
Ave. Adolfo Ruiz Cortines y Paseo Tabasco, Col. Tabasco, Villahermosa, Tabasco, 20000, Mexico; tel (52) 993 154031; fax 154031; e-mail admin@tnet.net.mx
Circ.:32,000
Pres. – Federico Bracamontes Galves
Sales Mgr. – Alfonso Izaguirre Diaz
Ed./Dir. – Sergio Anaya

PRESENTE (M)
Villahermosa, Tabasco, Villahermosa, Tabasco, 86040, Mexico; tel (52) 993 312 1775; fax 312 2851; web site www.diariopresente.com.mx
Circ.:38,000
Pres. – Jorge Fausto Calles Broca
Ed. – Salvador Fernandez
Prodn. Mgr. – Carlos Pineda
Ad Rate: 27.00.

PRESENTE DE LA CHONTALPA (M)
Jose Pages Llergo s/n, Esquina Sanchez Magallanes, Villahermosa, Tabasco, 86040, Mexico; tel (52) 993 121755; fax 143493
Pub./Mng. Dir. – Jorge Fausto Calles Broca
Ad Rate: 19.13.

TABASCO HOY (M)
Avda. de los Rios, No. 206, Villahermosa, Tabasco, 86035, Mexico; tel (52) 993 163333; fax 160320; e-mail tabhoy@nexus.net.mx; web site www.tabascohoy.com.mx
Circ.:52,302
Pres. – Miguel Canton Zetina
Gen. Mgr. – Javier Perez Campos
Sales Mgr. – Alejandro Campos Beltran
Ed./Dir. – Rafael Santiago Campos
Prodn. Mgr. – Raul Villalvazo Zepeda

XALAPA, VERACRUZ

DIARIO DE XALAPA (M) Est.1943
Ave. Avila Camacho No. 3, Col. Centro, Xalapa, Veracruz, 91000, Mexico; tel (52) 228 818 3000; fax 817 7100; e-mail sgg@xal.megared.net.mx; web site www.diariodexalapa.com.mx; www.oem.com.mx/diariodexalapa
Circ.:40,000
Pres. – Mario Vasquez Rana

XALISCO, NAYARIT

DIARIO 13 (D)
Xalisco, Nayarit, Xalisco, Nayarit, Mexico; tel (52)
Gen. Dir. – Andres Gonzalez Reyna

ZACAPU

ZACAPU EN MARCHA (D)
Felix Acosta, No. 23, Zacapu, Mexico; tel (52) 456 31383
Dir. – Arturo Velasquez Rivera

ZACAPU, MICHOACAN

REALIDAD (D)
Felix Acosta, No. 25, Zacapu, Michoacan, Mexico; tel (52) 456 31383
Dir. – Arturo Velasquez Rivera

ZACATECAS, ZACATECAS

MOMENTO
Alameda No. 440 Centro, Zacatecas, Zacatecas, 98000, Mexico; tel (52) 492 23425; fax 29011; e-mail momento@academo1.zac.itesm.mx; web site www.itesm.mx/momento
Circ.:30,000
Pres. – Samuel Molina de la Torre
Gen. Mgr. – Flor de Maria Gutierrez Raigosa
Ed./Dir. – Francisco Martinez

OPINION DE ZACATECAS (M)
Avda. Gonzalez Ortega, No. 101, Zacatecas, Zacatecas, Mexico; tel (52) 492 25032
Circ.:20,000
Pub. – Gustavo A. Lomelin Guerra
Adv. Mgr. – Salvador Noriega

EL HERALDO (M)
Enrique Estrada, No. 104, Zacatecas, Zacatecas, 98000, Mexico; tel (52) 492 24719; e-mail heraldo@orb.org.mx
Circ.:40,000
Owner/Pres. – Rodrigo Villasana Lopez

LA VOZ DEL PUEBLO (E)
Jardin Hidalgo, No. 606, Zacatecas, Zacatecas, Mexico; tel (52) 492
Circ.:10,000
Pub. – R. de Jesus Luna Martinez
Adv. Mgr. – Rafaela Miranda Moreno

EL SOL DE ZACATECAS (MS)
Zacatecas, Zacatecas, Zacatecas, Zacatecas, 98045, Mexico; tel (52) 492 922 6583; e-mail publicidad@elsoldezacatecas.com.mx; contactanos@elsoldezcatecas.com.mx; web site www.oem.com.mx/elsoldezacatecas

Circ.:45,000
Pres. – Mario Vazquez Rana
Dir. – Salvador del Hoyo Bramasco

ZAMORA, MICHOACAN

EL HERALDO DE ZAMORA (M)
Zamora, Michoacan, Zamora, Michoacan, 59600, Mexico; tel (52) 351 512 1356; fax 21356
Circ.:20,000
Pres. – Efrain Gonzalez Nunez

LA VOZ DE ZAMORA (D)
Zamora, Michoacan, Zamora, Michoacan, Mexico; tel (52) 351 21560
Circ.:12,000
Pub. – Miguel Valencia Mora

EL SOL DE ZAMORA (M)
Morelos 353 Altos, Zona Centro, Zamora, Michoacan, 59600, Mexico; tel (52) 351 24180; fax 53360; e-mail publicidad@elsoldezamora.com.mx; web site www.oem.com.mx/elsoldezamora
Circ.:16,000
Pres. – Mario Vazquez Rana

Z DE ZAMORA (D-EX MON.)
Zamora, Michoacan, Zamora, Michoacan, Mexico; tel (52) 351 54489; fax 54489
Mgr./Dir. – David Nino Zavala
Ad Rate: 12.00.

ZIHUATANEJO

EL DIARIO DE ZIHUATANEJO (M-6X WK.)
Paseo del Palmar s/n Col. La Madera, Zihuatanejo, Mexico; tel (52) 755 554 3864
Circ.:5,000
Dir. – Edber Arturo Garcia Alvarez
Ad Rate: 20.00.

ZIHUATANEJO, GUERRERO

DIARIO DE ZIHUATANEJO (M) Est.1971
Ave. Paseo del Palmar No. 115, Fracc. La Madera, Zihuatanejo, Guerrero, Mexico; tel (52) 755 554 3864; e-mail zihua@cdnet.com.mx
Circ.:8,500
Pres. – Edber Arturo Garcia Alvarez

ZITACUARO, MICHOACAN

LA VERDAD (D)
Zitacuaro, Michoacan, Zitacuaro, Michoacan, 61500, Mexico; tel (52) 715 153 1310; fax 153 1310; e-mail laverdadmich@prodigy.net.mx
Circ.:10,000
Exec. Dir. – Blanca Estela Rueda Cazares
Ad Rate: 18.60.

NICARAGUA

MANAGUA

EL NUEVO DIARIO (M)
Pista Pedro Joaquin Chamorro, Km 4 Carretera Norte, Managua, Nicaragua; tel (505) 2 491 190; fax 490 700; e-mail info@elnuevodiario.com.ni; web site www.elnuevodiario.com.ni
Circ.:30,000
Pres./Owner – Xavier Chamorro Cardenal
Sales Mgr. – Ana Maria Chamorro Lang
Ed. – Danilo Aguirre Solis

LA PRENSA (M)
Km. 4 1/2, Carretera Norte, Managua, Nicaragua; tel (505) 2 255 6767; fax 496 928; e-mail info@laprensa.com.ni; web site www.laprensa.com.ni
Circ.:37,000
Pres. – Jaime Chamorro Cardenal
Gen. Mgr. – Hugo Holmann Chamorro
Ad Rate: Charney/Palacios & Co. Inc.

LA TRIBUNA (M)
De donde fue la Pepsi, 2 1/2 cuadras al lago, Managua, Nicaragua; tel (505) 2 482 416; fax 483 269; e-mail tribuna@latribuna.com.ni
Pres./Dir. – Haroldo J. Montealegre
Gen. Mgr. – Mario Gonzalez

PANAMA

PANAMA CITY

LA PRENSA (D)
Panama City, Panama City, Panama; tel (507) 222 1222; fax 221 7328; web site www.prensa.com
Circ.:40,000
Dir. – Ciesca Salzaro

CRITICA LIBRE (D)
Via Ricardo J. Alfaro, al lado de la USMA, Panama City, 9A, Panama; tel (507) 230 7777; fax 230 7774; e-mail redaccion-critica@epasa.com; web site www.epasa.com
Circ.:40,000
Pres. – Rosario Arias de Galindo
Dir. – Juan Pritsiolas
Gen. Mgr. – Francisco Arias Vallarino

EL PANAMA AMERICA (M)
Ave. Ricardo J. Alfaro, al lado de la USMA, Panama City, 9-A, Panama; tel (507) 230 7777; fax 230 7773; web site www.epasa.com
Circ.:40,000
Pres. – Francisco Arias Vallarino
Sales Mgr. – Rosario Arias de Gallindo

LA ESTRELLA DE PANAMA (M)
Calle Alejandro A. Duque G., Panama City, Panama; tel (507) 204 0000; fax 227 2394; e-mail periodistas@laestrella.com.pa; web site www.laestrella.com.pa
Group: Charney/Palacios & Co.
Dir. – Gerardo Berroa Loo
Gen. Mgr. – Juan Luis Correa
Ad Rate: Charney/Palacios & Co. Inc.; AdMarket Int'l.

EL EXPRESSO (D)
Panama City, Panama City, Panama; tel (507) 237 313; fax 691 026
Circ.:1,500
Dir. – Marcel Ho
Ed. – Liu Gan

HOY (M)
Condominio Anayansi, Avda. Chile y Calle 38, Local, Panama City, Panama; tel (507) 251 666; fax 270 740
Circ.:12,000
Pres./Dir./Ed. – Eduardo Vallarino
Gen. Mgr. – Sergio A. Rodriguez Montes de Oca
Admin. Mgr. – Mayre de Calvo
Ed. in Chief – Euclides M. Corro

EL SIGLO (M)
Via Frangipani, Calidonia, Panama City, 9a, Panama; tel (507) 204 0000; fax 227 0238; e-mail sdigital@elsiglo.com; web site www.elsiglo.com
Circ.:42,000
Pres. – Ebrahim Asvat

NEWSPAPERS OF SOUTH AMERICA

ARGENTINA

ARRECIFES, PROV. DE BUENOS AIRES

ACCION (D)
Santiago H. Perez 664, Arrecifes, Prov. de Buenos Aires, 2740, Argentina; tel (54) 11
Dir. – Ruben Luis Blanco

ARRECIFES, PROVINCIA DE BUENOS AIRES

ARRECIFES (D)
R. Gutierrez 631, Arrecifes, Provincia de Buenos Aires, 2740, Argentina; tel (54) 11
Dir. – Horacio A. Bancalari

EL PROGRESO (M)
Vincente Lopez y Planes 62, Arrecifes, Provincia de Buenos Aires, 2740, Argentina; tel (54) 11
Dir. – Tomas Jauregui

AVELLANEDA, PROVINCIA DE BUENOS AIRES

LA CIUDAD (M)
La Madrid 125, Avellaneda, Provincia de Buenos Aires, 1870, Argentina; tel (54) 1 222-5402; fax 222-6705
Pres. – Leonor Uriarte
Gen. Mgr. – Eugenio Limongi
Adv. Mgr. – Leonardo Prego
Ed. – Alejandra Persico

DIARIO POPULAR (M)
Beguiristain 182, Avellaneda, Provincia de Buenos Aires, 1872, Argentina; tel (54) 11 4204 2778; fax 4205 2376; e-mail redaccion@diariopopular.com; web site ^www.diariopopular.com
Circ.: 140,000
Dir – Francisco Fascetto
Adv. Mgr. – Mariano Leuctti

LA CALLE (D)
Monseror Piaggio 136, Avellaneda, Provincia de Buenos Aires, 1870, Argentina; tel (54) 11
Dir. – Nestor Luis Santos

AZUL, PROVINCIA DE BUENOS AIRES

EL TIEMPO (M)
Calles Burgos y Belgrano, Azul, Provincia de Buenos Aires, 7300, Argentina; tel (54) 2281 422 814; fax 422 2397; e-mail eltiempo@satlink.com.ar; web site www.diarioeltiempo.com.ar
Gen. Mgr. – Alfredo Fernando Ronchetti
Adv. Mgr. – Victoriano Raul Irigoyen
Ed. – Alfredo Carlos Ronchetti
Prodn. Mgr. – Marta Marcela Ronchetti

BAHIA BLANCA, PROVINCIA DE BUENOS AIRES

LA NUEVA PROVINCIA (MS)
Sarmiento 64, Bahia Blanca, Provincia de Buenos Aires, 8000, Argentina; tel (54) 291 459 0000; fax 550 938; e-mail info@lanueva.com.ar; web site www.lanueva.com.ar
Circ.: 42,000
Pres. – Diana Julio de Massot
Mktg. Mgr. – Jose Omar Trillini
Ed. – Domingo Marra

BALCARCE, PROVINCIA DE BUENOS AIRES

DIARIO EL LIBERAL (M)
Mitre 672, Balcarce, Provincia de Buenos Aires, 7620, Argentina; tel (54) 542 662 4036; fax 662 3222
Circ.: 3,000
Gen. Mgr. – Luis Mario Pollio
Adv. Mgr. – Juan Pedro Panaggio
Ed. – Jose Raul Pollio

BENITO JUAREZ, PROVINCIA DE BUENOS AIRES

EL FENIX (M)
Ave. Libertad 50, Benito Juarez, Provincia de Buenos Aires, 7020, Argentina; tel (54) 2292 451277; web site www.elfenixdigital.com
Pres. – Hugo Alberto Beain
Adv. Mgr. – Stella Maris Infantino
Ed. – Luis Laureano Fernandez
Prodn. Mgr. – Beatriz Rodriguez

BOLIVAR, PROVINCIA DE BUENOS AIRES

LA MANANA (M)
Venezuela 159, Bolivar, Provincia de Buenos Aires, 6550, Argentina; tel (54) 3 14-7376
Ed. – Oscar C. Cabreros

BRAGADO, PROVINCIA DE BUENOS AIRES

EL CENSOR (M)
Avda. General Paz 1269, Esq. Nunez, Bragado, Provincia de Buenos Aires, 6440, Argentina; tel (54) 3 423-0282; fax 423-0996
Ed. – Juan Jose Devenutto

LA VOZ DE BRAGADO (M)
Isidro Suarez 326, Bragado, Provincia de Buenos Aires, 6640, Argentina; tel (54) 342 30200; fax 30200
Circ.: 4,800
Gen. Mgr. – Martin Soto
Prodn. Mgr. – Esteban Allignani

BUENOS AIRES

BUENOS AIRES HERALD LTDA. S.A. (D)
Azopardo 455, Buenos Aires, 1107, Argentina; tel (54) 11 4349 1524; fax 4349 1524; web site www.buenosairesherald.com
Advertising: AdMarket Int'l.; The N DeFilippes Corp.
Pres. – Orlando Vignatti
Ed. – Peter Johnson

CLARIN (M)
Avda. Belgrano 671, Buenos Aires, 1092, Argentina; tel (54) 11 4334-2334; fax 4334-2330; e-mail comerc@pagina12.com.ar; web site www.pagina12.com
Pres. – Fernando Sokolowicz
Gen. Mgr. – Hugo Soriani
Ed. – Ernesto Tiffemberg

CLARIN (MS)
Tacuari 1846, Buenos Aires, 1193, Argentina; tel (54) 11 4309 7500; fax 4309 7635; e-mail lectores@clarin.com.ar; web site www.clarin.com.ar
Advertising: Charney/Palacios & Co.; The N DeFilippes Corp.
Pres. – Ernestina L. Herrera de Noble
Gen. Mgr. – Hector M. Aranda
Sales Mgr. – Alberto Pazos
Ed. – Roberto Guareschi
Prodn. Mgr. – Santos Casalnuovo

EL CRONISTA (5X WK.)
Paseo Colon 740/6, Buenos Aires, 1063, Argentina; tel (54) 11 4121 9300; fax 4121 9301; e-mail publicidad@cronista.com; web site www.cronista.com.ar
Circ.: 65,000
Advertising: AdMarket Int'l.; Martin Media Communications; The N DeFilippes Corp.
Ed. – Fernando Gonzalez

EDITORIAL AMFIN S.A. (5X WK.)
Avda. Paseo Colon 1196, Buenos Aires, 1063, Argentina; tel (54) 11 4349 1500; fax 4349 1505; e-mail redaction@ambito.com.ar; web site www.ambitoweb.com
Circ.: 115,000
Advertising: Charney/Palacios & Co. Inc.; The N DeFilippes Corp.
Pub. – Mario Coschica
Ed. – Mario Cordo

EDITORIAL SARMIENTO (M&ES)
Avda. Juan de Garay 140, Capital Federal, Buenos Aires, 1063, Argentina; tel (54) 11 4361 1001; fax 4361 4237; web site www.cronica.com.ar
Dir. – Mario Alberto Fernandez

EL ACCIONISTA (D)
San Martin 50, E.P. Of. 6/7, Buenos Aires, 1004, Argentina; tel (54) 11 4331 1883; fax 4331 1883; e-mail info@diarioelaccionista.com.ar; patricia@diarioelaccionista.com.ar; web site www.diarioelaccionista.com.ar
Owner/Dir./Ed. – Roberto Garibaldi
Adv. Mgr. – Beironica Rodriegz

EL CRONISTA COMERCIAL S.A. (M-6X WK.) Est. 1908
Paseo Col□n 746, Buenos Aires, C1063ACU, Argentina; tel (54) 11 41219300; fax 41219301; web site www.cronista.com
Pub. – Hugo Perojo

LA NACION (D)
Bouchard 557, Buenos Aires, 1106, Argentina; tel (54) 11 4319 1600; fax 4319 1656; web site www.lanacion.com
Circ.: 160,000
Advertising: Charney/Palacios & Co.
Pres. – Julio Saquier
Ed. – Bartolome Mitre

LA PRENSA (D)
Azopardo 715, Buenos Aires, 1107, Argentina; tel (54) 11 4349 1000; fax 4349 1097; e-mail informaciongeneral@laprensa.com.ar; web site www.laprensa.com.ar
Circ.: 32,000
Pres. – Florencio Aldrey Iglesias
Adv. Mgr. – Elsa Alonso

PUBLIEXITO S.A. (M)
Estrada 1969 Avellaneda, Buenos Aires, 1872, Argentina; tel (54) 11 4204 2778; fax 4813 2009; web site www.popularonline.com.ar
Circ.: 145,000
Dir. – Eduardo Tucci

LA RAZON (6X WK.)
Ituzaingo 647, Buenos Aires, 1141, Argentina; tel (54) 11 4309 6000; fax 4309 6088; e-mail admpubli@larazon.com.ar; web site www.larazon.com.ar
Circ.: 62,000
Gen. Mgr. – Roberto Conde
Ed. – Luis Vinker

CAMPANA, PROVINCIA DE BUENOS AIRES

LA DEFENSA POPULAR (M-6X WK.)
Becerra 834, Campana, Provincia de Buenos Aires, 2804, Argentina; tel (54)

CANADA DE GOMEZ, PROVINCIA DE SANTA FE

ESTRELLA (M-5X WK.)
Lavalle 1140, Canada de Gomez, Provincia de Santa Fe, 2500, Argentina; tel (54)
Pub. – Jose Antonio Ramacciotti

CAPITAL FEDERAL, BUENOS AIRES

INDUGRAF S.A. (M)
Sanchez de Loria 2251, Capital Federal, Buenos Aires, 6450, Argentina; tel (54) 114 911 7374; fax 912 3613; e-mail info@indugraf.com.ar; web site www.indugraf.com.ar
Circ.: 8,500
Ed. – Robert E. Rossi

CARLOS CASARES, PROVINCIA DE BUENOS AIRES

EL ARGENTINO (D)
Colon 146, Carlos Casares, Provincia de Buenos Aires, 6530, Argentina; tel (54) 2241 423 453; fax 422 944; web site www.elargentino.com
Pub. – Dario E. Cuence

EL IMPARCIAL
Libres del Sur 98, Carlos Casares, Provincia de Buenos Aires, 6530, Argentina; tel (54)
Pub. – Fernando R. Pieske

CATAMARCA, PROVINCIA DE CATAMARCA

LA UNION (M)
San Martin 671, Catamarca, Provincia de Catamarca, 4700, Argentina; tel (54) 383 434-6666; fax 343-0219; e-mail redaccion@launiononline.com.ar; web site www.catamarca.com/launion
Circ.: 3,000
Ed. – Cesar Atilio Molas

CHIVILCOY, PROVINCIA DE BUENOS AIRES

LA CAMPANA (D)
Avda. Villarino 137, Chivilcoy, Provincia de Buenos Aires, 6620, Argentina; tel (54) 2346 424 280; fax 420 993; e-mail diario@dechivilcoy.com.ar; web site www.dechivilcoy.com.ar
Circ.: 5,000
Pres. – Claudia C. Roger
Ed. – Aclides Oscar Decunta

LA RAZON DE CHIVILCOY S.A. (D)
Sarmiento 74, Chivilcoy, Provincia de Buenos Aires, 6620, Argentina; tel (54) 2346 430 722; fax 434 900; e-mail larazon@chivilcoy.com.ar; web site www.larazondechivilcoy.com.ar
Circ.: 5,000
Pres. – Alberto Monaco
Ed. – Ruben Diego Cavagna

CITY OF BUENOS AIRES

ACCION NACIONAL (D)
Uruguay 988, 3er piso, City of Buenos Aires, 1015, Argentina; tel (54) 11
Dir./Ed. – Luis Alberto Rodriguez

ALEMANN S.R.I. (D)
25 de Mayo 626, City of Buenos Aires, 1002, Argentina; tel (54) 11 4311 9561; fax 4311 5798
Circ.: 20,000

ARMENIA (D)
El Salvador, City of Buenos Aires, 4627, Argentina; tel (54) 11
Circ.: 3,000
Pub. – Jose Oghoulian

BOLETIN OFICIAL DE LA REPUBLICA ARGENTINA (5X WK.)
Suipacha 767, Capital Federal, City of Buenos Aires, 1008, Argentina; tel (54) 11 4322 3982; fax 4394 4423; web site www.boletinoficial.gov.ar
Circ.: 15,000
Dir. – Jorge Etuardo Feijoo

CONVICCION (M)
Red. Luzuriaga 1700, City of Buenos Aires, Argentina; tel (54) 11
Pub. – Hugo Ezequiel Lezama

EL BARRIO (M)
Terreno 14, 8vo. D, City of Buenos Aires, 1406, Argentina; tel (54) 11
Dir./Ed. – Nereida Tadich

EL CIVISMO (D)
Dr. Muniz, 654, City of Buenos Aires, Argentina; tel (54) 11
Pub. – Maria M. Marquez de Gigante

FREIE PRESSE (MS)
Viamonte 369, City of Buenos Aires, 1053, Argentina; tel (54) 11
Circ.: 5,000
Pub. – Ricardo L. Bach Cano

LA PRENSITA (D)
H. Irigoyen 818. (T. Lomas), City of Buenos Aires, Argentina; tel (54) 11 420 015; fax 430 111; e-mail prensita@teletel.com.ar
Pub. – Andres M. Pocchiola

LA PROVINCIA (D)
San Maria de Oro 889, City of Buenos Aires, Argentina; tel (54) 11
Pub. – Juan R. Salomon

LA VOX (D)
Tabare 1641, City of Buenos Aires, 1437, Argentina; tel (54) 11 49223800
Pub. – Vincente Leonides Saadi

PRENSA ECONOMICA
Rivadavia 926, p5, City of Buenos Aires, 1002, Argentina; tel (54) 11 437 6020

CITY OF BUNEOS AIRES

TIEMPO ARGENTINO S.A. (D)
Lafayette 1910, City of Buneos Aires, 1286, Argentina; tel (54) 11 4281929
Circ.: 75,000
Ed. – Tomas Leona

COLON

LA VOZ DE COLON (E)
Calle 18, No. 713, Colon, Argentina; tel (54) 2473 422 020; web site www.vozdecolon.com.ar
Pub. – Jaime Juan Orpella

COMODORO RIVADAVIA, PROVINCIA DE CHUBUT

CRONICA (M)
Namuncura 122, No. 550, Comodoro Rivadavia, Provincia de Chubut, 9000, Argentina; tel (54) 297 447 1200; fax 447 1780; e-mail diariocronica@diariocronica.com.ar; web site www.diariocronica.com.ar
Circ.: 18,000
Dir. – Diego Zamit

INSTITUTO DE CULTURA (D)
Rivadavia 1275, Comodoro Rivadavia, Provincia de Chubut, Argentina; tel (54)
Pub. – Silvia S. de Pereda

EL PATAGONICO (M)
Sarmiento 569, Comodoro Rivadavia, Provincia de Chubut, 9000, Argentina; tel (54) 297 446 2728; fax 447 2160; e-mail redaccion@elpatagonico.net; web site www.elpatagonico.net
Pres. – Rodolfo Abel Perez

CONCEPCION DEL URUGUAY, ENTRE RIOS

HOY
Eva Peron 221, Concepcion del Uruguay, Entre Rios, 3260, Argentina; tel (54)
Dir./Ed. – Roberto Roman Farabello

CONCEPCION DEL URUGUAY, PROVINCIA DE ENTRE RIOS

LA CALLE (M)
Moreno 139, Concepcion del Uruguay, Provincia de Entre Rios, 3260, Argentina; tel (54) 442 425 614; fax 422 059
Circ.: 6,000
Pres. – Ricardo Saenz Valiente
Gen. Mgr. – Hector Lovisa
Adv. Mgr. – Jaime Mir
Ed. – Daniel Libardi

CONCORDIA, PROVINCIA DE ENTRE RIOS

CONCORDIA (M)
San Martin 119, Concordia, Provincia de Entre Rios, 3200, Argentina; tel (54)
Dir. – F.J. Garay

COOPERATIVA DE TRABAJO OBRERA (M)
Concejal Veiga 777, Concordia, Provincia de Entre Rios, 3200, Argentina; tel (54) 345 421 0332; fax 422 4018; e-mail correo@diarioelsol.com.ar; web site www.diarioelsol.com
Circ.: 6,000
Pres. – Luis A. Mazurier

EL HERALDO (E)
Quintana 42, Concordia, Provincia de Entre Rios, 3200, Argentina; tel (54) 345 421-5304; fax 421-5397; e-mail redaccion@elheraldo.com.ar; web site www.elheraldo.com.ar
Circ.: 10,000
Pres. – Carlos Liebermann
Ed. – Graciela Liebermann

CORDOBA, PROVINCIA DE CORDOBA

COMERCIO Y JUSTICIA (M)
F□lix Paz 310, Cordoba, Provincia de Cordoba, 5000, Argentina; tel (54) 351 488 0088; fax 488 0088; web site www.comercioyjusticia.com.ar
Circ.: 5,800
Pres. – Carlos Ableola

SOCIEDAD ED. CORDOBA S.A. (E)
Santa Rosa 167, Cordoba, Provincia de Cordoba, 5000, Argentina; tel (54) 351 422072
Circ.: 25,000
Adv. Mgr. – Jose Maria Lopez Bravo

LA VOZ DEL INTERIOR (D)
Avda. Monsenor Pablo Cabrera 6080, Cordoba, Provincia de Cordoba, 5000, Argentina; tel (54) 351 475 7200; fax 475 7114; e-mail lavoz@lavozdelinterior.com.ar; web site www.lavozdelinterior.com.ar
Circ.: 100,000
Group: Brydson Global Media Sales
Pres. – Marisa Failla de Garcia Remonda
Pub. – Sergio Sutto
Gen. Mgr. – Osvaldo A. Salas
Adv. Mgr. – Benjamin E. Ferreyra
Ed. – Franco Piccato
Prodn. Mgr. – Luis Sentana

CORONEL BORREGO, PROVINCIA DE BUENOS AIRES

LA VOZ (D)
Avda. San Martin 619, Coronel Borrego, Provincia de Buenos Aires, Argentina; tel (54)
Pub. – Roberto A. Vecchi

CORONEL PRINGLES, PROVINCIA DE BUENOS AIRES

EL ORDEN (M)
Avda. Leandro N. Alem 1025, Coronel Pringles, Provincia de Buenos Aires, 7530, Argentina; tel (54) 2922 42-1857; fax 42-1857
Pub. – Raul Hector Cejas

CORONEL SUAREZ, PROVINCIA DE BUENOS AIRES

EDITORIAL EL IMPARCIAL (D)
Sarmiento 275, Coronel Suarez, Provincia de Buenos Aires, 7540, Argentina; tel (54)
Circ.: 3,000
Pub. – Pablo A. Garcia Plandolit

CORRIENTES, PROVINCIA DE CORRIENTES

EPOCA (D)
Hipolito Yrigoyen 835, Corrientes, Provincia de Corrientes, 3400, Argentina; tel (54) 3783 424 919; fax 433 966; e-mail contacto@diarioepoca.com; web site www.diarioepoca.com
Dir. – Alfredo Zacarias

JUAN FRANCISCO TORRENT Y HERMANOS (E)
Avda. 25 de Mayo 345, Corrientes, Provincia de Corrientes, Argentina; tel (54) 3783 422 069
Circ.: 4,000
Pub./Ed. – Juan Francisco Torrent

EL LITORAL (M)
Hipolito Yrigoyen 990, Corrientes, Provincia de Corrientes, 3400, Argentina; tel (54) 3783 411 524; fax 422 227; e-mail el-litoral@compunort.com.ar; web site www.corrientes.com.ar/el-litoral/
Pres. – Carlos A. Romero Feris
Gen. Mgr. – Pedro J. Gonzalez
Ed. – Carlos Gelmi

DOLORES, PROVINCIA DE BUENOS AIRES

EL NACIONAL (D)
Rico y Avda. del Valle, Dolores, Provincia de Buenos Aires, 7100, Argentina; tel (54)
Circ.: 3,200
Group: Charney/Palacios & Co.
Dir. – Gustavo M. Conti

EL TRIBUNO (E)
Castelli y Avda. del Valle, Dolores, Provincia de Buenos Aires, 7100, Argentina; tel (54) 2245 442 471; fax 442 471; e-mail tribuno@fairweb.com.ar
Pres. – Maria Dolores E. de Conti
Ed. – Ricardo Conti

ESQUEL, PROVINCIA DE CHUBUT

ESQUEL (M)
Rivadavia 979, Esquel, Provincia de Chubut, 9200, Argentina; tel (54)
Circ.: 3,200
Pub. – Carlos Juan Azparen

EL OESTE
Roca 659, Esquel, Provincia de Chubut, 9200, Argentina; tel (54) 2945 45-0396; fax 45-0396; e-mail eloeste@teletel.com.ar; web site www.cpatagonia.com/eloeste
Ed. – Jose Agustin Moran

FORMOSA, PROVINCIA DE FORMOSA

EL DIARIO (M)
Pederna 1212, Formosa, Provincia de Formosa, Argentina; tel (54)
Pub. – H.M. Perez

LA OPINION (E-EX S)
San Martin 682, Formosa, Provincia de Formosa, Argentina; tel (54)
Circ.: 3,000
Pub. – E.R. Saa

LA VICTORIA (D)
Entre Rios 8, Formosa, Provincia de Formosa, Argentina; tel (54)
Pub. – Jorge A. Castro

LA MANANA (M)
Dean Funes 950, Formosa, Provincia de Formosa, 3600, Argentina; tel (54) 3717 430 868; fax 430 865; e-mail lamanana@arnet.com.ar
Circ.: 15,000
Pres. – Hugo Alberto Read
Gen. Mgr. – Jose Antonio Read
Ed. – Enrique H. Read

NUEVO DIARIO (D)
25 de Mayo 52, Formosa, Provincia de Formosa, 3600, Argentina; tel (54) 3717 422 9995; web site www.nuevodiariodesalta.com.ar
Dir. – NÂ£stor Arnaldo Gauna

GENERAL BELGRANO, PROVINCIA DE BUENOS AIRES

EL MANGRULLO (D)
Guido 650, General Belgrano, Provincia de Buenos Aires, 7223, Argentina; tel (54)
Dir. – Hector A. Carricaburu Carou

GENERAL PAZ, PROVINCIA DE BUENOS AIRES

LA PALABRA (D)
Vivot y Ceijas, General Paz, Provincia de Buenos Aires, 1987, Argentina; tel (54)
Pub. – Hector A. Carricaburu Carou

GENERAL PICO, PROVINCIA DE LA PAMPA

LA REFORMA (D)
Belgrano 627, General Pico, Provincia de La Pampa, 6360, Argentina; tel (54) 2302 421 854; fax 422 768; e-mail lareforma@infovia.com.ar; web site www.lareformaonline.com.ar
Circ.: 6,000
Dir. – Arnaldo Cesar Matilla

GENERAL ROCA, PROVINCIA DE RIO NEGRO

RIO NEGRO (D)
9 de Julio 733, General Roca, Provincia de Rio Negro, 8332, Argentina; tel (54) 2941 439 300; fax 423 915; web site www.rionegro.com.ar
Circ.: 40,000
Dir. – Kulio Raul Rajneri
Asst. Dir. – Nelida Rajneri de Gamba
Ed. – Italo Pisani

GENERAL SARMIENTO, PROVINCIA DE BUENOS AIRES

LA VOZ DE GENERAL SARMIENTO (M)
Misiones 698, General Sarmiento, Provincia de Buenos Aires, 1663, Argentina; tel (54)
Pub. – Roberto Campos

GOYA, PROVINCIA DE CORRIENTES

PRIMERA HORA (M)
Alvear 391, Goya, Provincia de Corrientes, 3450, Argentina; tel (54) 3777 42-2868; fax 42-2868
Circ.: 116,201
Last Audit: September 30, 2011
Dir. – Abelardo Palisa

GUALEGUAY, PROVINCIA DE ENTRE RIOS

EL DEBATE-PREGON (M)
Islas Malvinas 170, Gualeguay, Provincia de Entre Rios, 2840, Argentina; tel (54) 444 23115; fax 23115
Pres. – Alberto M. Lagrenade
Ed. – Cayetano Dalvano

EL SUPREMO (M)
Avda. 25 de Mayo 569, Gualeguay, Provincia de Entre Rios, 2840, Argentina; tel (54)
– Miguel A. Nefia
– Roberto MartinezDir.s

GUALEGUAYCHU, PROVINCIA DE ENTRE RIOS

EL ARGENTINO (M)
9 de Julio 45, Gualeguaychu, Provincia de Entre Rios, 2820, Argentina; tel (54) 3446 427 027; fax 426 164; e-mail diario@diarioelargentino.com.ar; web site www.diarioelargentino.com
Circ.: 7,200
Gen. Mgr. – Elsa Courtet de Barcia
Ed. – Maria Teresa de Suilar

EL DIA (D)
Jose M. Neyra 75, Gualeguaychu, Provincia de Entre Rios, 2820, Argentina; tel (54) 221 425 0101; e-mail editor@eldia.com; web site www.eldia.com.ar
Ed. – Raul Kraiselburd

JOSE INGENIEROS, PROVINCIA DE BUENOS AIRES

EL MANGRULLO (D)
Jose Ingenieros, Provincia de Buenos Aires, Argentina; tel (54)
Pub. – Hector A. Carricaburu Carou

JOSE INGENIEROS (D)
Rotarismo Argentino 1992, Jose Ingenieros, Provincia de Buenos Aires, 1778, Argentina; tel (54)
Pub. – Alba Gomez

JUNIN, PROVINCIA DE BUENOS AIRES

DEMOCRACIA (E)
Rivadavia 436, Junin, Provincia de Buenos Aires, 6000, Argentina; tel (54) 362 44 4408; fax 44 4408; e-mail democracia@pampeana.com
Circ.: 7,000
Ed. – Hector Lebensohn

LA VERDAD (M)
Roque Saenz Pena 167, Junin, Provincia de Buenos Aires, 6000, Argentina; tel (54) 2362 443 465; fax 443 474; e-mail laverdad@satlink.com; web site www.laverdadonline.com/Portada.asp
Circ.: 10,000
Ed. – Armando Rosido

LA LUCILA, PROVINCIA DE BUENOS AIRES

EL PARQUE (D)
J.M. Estrada 3608, La Lucila, Provincia de Buenos Aires, 1636, Argentina; tel (54)
Dir. – Hector Rostro

LA PLATA, BUENOS AIRES

EL DIA (D)
Diagonal 80, No. 815, La Plata, Buenos Aires, 1900, Argentina; tel (54) 221 425 0101; fax 423 2996; e-mail laciudad@eldia.com; lectores@eldia.com; web site www.eldia.com.ar
Circ.: 55,000
Gen. Mgr. – Griselda Piaggio
Ed. – Raul Kraiselburd

LA RIOJA, PROVINCIA DE LA RIOJA

EL SOL (E)
Avda. 25 de Mayo 76, La Rioja, Provincia de La Rioja, 5300, Argentina; tel (54)
Dir. – Tomas N. Alvarez Saavedra

EL INDEPENDIENTE (M)
Avda. 9 de Julio 223, La Rioja, Provincia de La Rioja, 5300, Argentina; tel (54) 3822 421-000; fax 422-850; e-mail independ@satlink.com; web site www.el-independente.com.ar
Circ.: 6,000
Ed. – Lucio del Carmen Cordoba

LANUS OESTE, PROVINCIA DE BUENOS AIRES

PREGON (M)
Amancio Alcorta 436, Lanus Oeste, Provincia de Buenos Aires, 1824, Argentina; tel (54) 1 241 2039; fax 982 8928
Circ.: 10,000
Pres. – Jose Maria Vasquez
Gen. Mgr. – Elena Oliveri
Adv. Mgr. – Cecilia Barat
Ed. – Horacio Jose Casco Farina
Prodn. Mgr. – Enrique Carral

LOMAS DE ZAMORA, PROVINCIA DE BUENOS AIRES

LA UNION (MS) Est. 1897
Ave. Hipolito Yrigoyen 9265, Lomas De Zamora, Provincia de Buenos Aires, 1832, Argentina; tel (54) 11 4243 0239; fax 4243 8287; e-mail info@launion.com.ar; web site www.launion.com.ar
Circ.: 12,000
Dir./Ed. – Ana Maria Wosco

LOMAS DEL MIRADOR, PROVINCIA DE BUENOS AIRES

EL CENSOR DEL OESTE (D)
Bolivar, Lomas Del Mirador, Provincia de Buenos Aires, 2782, Argentina; tel (54) 11
Pub. – Ricardo D. Victorero

MAR DEL PLATA, PROVINCIA DE BUENOS AIRES

LA CAPITAL (M)
Avda. Champagnat 2551, Mar del Plata, Provincia de Buenos Aires, 7600, Argentina; tel (54) 223 493 8002; fax 478 1038; e-mail diario@lacapitalnet.com.ar; web site www.lacapitalnet.com.ar
Circ.: 32,000
Ed. in Chief – Oscar LardizÂ bal

EDITORIAL EL ATLANTICO S.A. (D)
Simon Bolivar 2975, Mar del Plata, Provincia de Buenos Aires, 7600, Argentina; tel (54) 223 495 0783; fax 495 7503
Circ.: 20,000
Pres. – Omar Jose Pomero
Gen. Mgr. – Luis E. Martinez Tecco
Ed. – Oscar A. Gastiarena
Prodn. Mgr. – Luis Trotta

MENDOZA, PROVINCIA DE MENDOZA

DIARIO LOS ANDES HERMANOS CALLE S.A. (MS)
Avda. San Martin 1049, Mendoza, Provincia de Mendoza, 5500, Argentina; tel (54) 261 420 2222; fax 449 1240; e-mail ciabsas@losandes.com.ar; web site www.losandes.com.ar
Circ.: 107,000
Gen. Mgr. – Miguel Bauza
Ed. – Arturo Guardiola
HR – Martin Perez

EL ANDINO (E)
San Martin 1049, Mendoza, Provincia de Mendoza, 5500, Argentina; tel (54) 261
Circ.: 2,128
Pub. – Elcira Videla de Azevedo

LA VICTORIA (D)
Entre Rios 78, Mendoza, Provincia de Mendoza, Argentina; tel (54)
Pub. – Jorge A. Castro

PRENSA DEL OESTE (M)
San Martin 947, Mendoza, Provincia de Mendoza, 5500, Argentina; tel (54) 261 (54-261) 241064
Circ.: 23,000
Dir. – Jose Llopart

MERCEDES, PROVINCIA DE BUENOS AIRES

EL OESTE (M)
Calle 33, Mercedes, Provincia de Buenos Aires, 6600, Argentina; tel (54)
Circ.: 2,500
– Teobaldo Bustos Barrando
– Marcelo Bustos BarrandoDir.s

IMPULSO (D)
Avda. Mitre 538, Mercedes, Provincia de Buenos Aires, 6600, Argentina; tel (54)
Pub. – Eduardo L. Estrada Dubor

LA HORA (M)
Calle 18, No. 905, Mercedes, Provincia de Buenos Aires, 6600, Argentina; tel (54)
Circ.: 4,000
– Juan M. Spalla
– E. Pardos
– B. PonceDir.s

MORENO, PROVINCIA DE BUENOS AIRES

LA OPINION (M)
Independencia 977, Moreno, Provincia de Buenos Aires, 1744, Argentina; tel (54)
Dir. – Juan Carlos Lacusta

NAVARRO, PROV. DE BUENOS AIRES

AMANECER NUEVA EPOCA (D)
Calle 22, No. 500, Navarro, Prov. de Buenos Aires, 6605, Argentina; tel (54) 2272 420 365
Ed. – Nestor O. Benitez

NECOCHEA, PROVINCIA DE BUENOS AIRES

ECOS DIARIOS (MS)
Calle 62, No. 2486, Necochea, Provincia de Buenos Aires, 7630, Argentina; tel (54) 2262 430 754; fax 424 114; e-mail ecosventas@infovia.com.ar; web site www.ecosdiarios.com.ar
Circ.: 7,000
Pres. – Guillermo Anibal Ignacio
Ed. – Jorge Ignacio
Prodn. Mgr. – Andres Ignacio

NOGOYA, PROVINCIA DE ENTRE RIOS

ACCION (M)
Caseros 989, Nogoya, Provincia de Entre Rios, 3150, Argentina; tel (54) 21620
Dir. – Luis Miguel Etchevehere

LA TARDE (D)
Junin 469, Nogoya, Provincia de Entre Rios, 3150, Argentina; tel (54)
Dir. – Salvador Solorzano

NUEVE DE JULIO, PROVINCIA DE BUENOS AIRES

EL 9 DE JULIO (E)
Avda. Vadia 774, Nueve De Julio, Provincia de Buenos Aires, 6500, Argentina; tel (54) 11 432 532
Dir./Ed. – Antonio Aita

EL ORDEN (M)
Mendoza 351, Nueve De Julio, Provincia de Buenos Aires, 6500, Argentina; tel (54)
Pub. – Abel Rodriguez

OLAVARRIA, PROVINCIA DE BUENOS AIRES

EL POPULAR (D)
Vicente Lopez 2626, Olavarria, Provincia de Buenos Aires, 7400, Argentina; tel (54) 2284 420 671; fax 420 671; e-mail diario@elpopular.com.ar; web site www.diarioelpopular.com.ar
Circ.: 12,000
Adv. Mgr. – Maria Cecilia Botta
Prodn. Mgr. – Jorge Gabriel Botta

PARANA, PROVINCIA DE ENTRE RIOS

EL DIARIO (M)
Urquiza y Buenos Aires, Parana, Provincia de Entre Rios, 3100, Argentina; tel (54) 343 423 1000; fax 431 9104; e-mail info@eldiario.com.ar; web site www.eldiario.com.ar
Circ.: 28,000
Gen. Mgr. – Dario Codno
Prodn. Mgr. – Arturo R. Etchevehere

PERGAMINO, PROVINCIA DE BUENOS AIRES

LA OPINION (M)
San Nicolas 399, Pergamino, Provincia de Buenos Aires, 2700, Argentina; tel (54) 2477 423 400; fax 417 758; e-mail laopinion@bbt11.com.ar; web site www.laopinion-pergamino.com.ar
Dir. – Hugo E. Apesteguia

EL TIEMPO
San Nicolas 29, Pergamino, Provincia de Buenos Aires, 2700, Argentina; tel (54) 2477 42-4665; fax 42-4665
Gen. Mgr. – Pedro Osvaldo Rivero

POSADAS, PROVINCIA DE MISIONES

EL TERRITORIO (MS)
Ruta 12 y H. Perez, No. 382, Posadas, Provincia de Misiones, 3300, Argentina; tel (54) 3752 452-100; fax 453-620; e-mail elterritorio@elterritorio.com.ar
Circ.: 18,000
Pres. – Herminia E.P. de Perez
Gen. Mgr. – Carlos A. Lopez
Ed. – Stuart Navajas McNeil

PUERTO DESEADO, PROVINCIA DE BUENOS AIRES

EL ORDEN (D)
Don Bosco 1055, Puerto Deseado, Provincia de Buenos Aires, Argentina; tel (54)
Pub. – Jose A. Rodriguez

QUILMES, PROVINCIA DE BUENOS AIRES

PERSPECTIVA SUR
Alvear 780, Quilmes, Provincia de Buenos Aires, 1878, Argentina; tel (54) 257-1182
Ed. – Raul David Caballero

EL SOL S.A. (M-6X WK.)
Hipolito Yrigoyen 122, Quilmes, Provincia de Buenos Aires, 1878, Argentina; tel (54) 11 4257 6325; fax 4257 6325; e-mail elsol@elsolquilmes.com.ar; web site www.elsolquilmes.com.ar
Circ.: 10,000
Pres. – Rodrigo Ghisani
Ed. – Carlos Bottaso
Adv. Mgr. – Andrea Guarneri

RAFAELA, PROVINCIA DE SANTA FE

BUFFELLI Y ACTIS S.A. (D)
Lavalle 153/71, Rafaela, Provincia de Santa Fe, 2300, Argentina; tel (54) 3492 426 821; fax 427 821; e-mail diario@laopinion-rafaela.com.ar; web site www.laopinion-rafaela.com.ar
Circ.: 4,000
Pres. – Miguel J. Buffelli
Ed. – Roberto Actis

RAUCH, PROVINCIA DE BUENOS AIRES

EL MUNICIPIO (M)
Alem 83, Rauch, Provincia de Buenos Aires, 7203, Argentina; tel (54)
Dir. – Julio Gonzalez

RAWSON, PROVINCIA DE SAN JUAN

DIARIO LA TARDE (D) Est. 3 (three)
Orzali 1173 (Oeste), Rawson, Provincia de San Juan, 5425, Argentina; tel (54) 264 4284213; web site www.diariolatarde.com.ar
Circ.: 9,000
Pub. – Cristobal Carbajal
Mng. Dir. – Armando Guevara

RESISTENCIA, PROVINCIA DE CHACO

EDITORIAL CHACO S.A. (D)
Carlos Pellegrini 744, Resistencia, Provincia de Chaco, 3500, Argentina; tel (54) 3722 429 681; e-mail m_diaz@diarionorte.com; web site www.diarionorte.com
Circ.: 2,700
CEO – Ruden Picevra
Gen. Mgr. – Oscar Romero
Adv. Mgr. – Norma Trabalon
Ed. – Miguel A. Fernandez

EL TERRITORIO
Casilla Correo 320, Resistencia, Provincia de Chaco, Argentina; tel (54) 3722
Circ.: 15,000
Pub./Dir. – Raul Andres Aguirre
Ed. in Chief – Reynaldo A. Martinez

RIO CUARTO, PROVINCIA DE CORDOBA

EDITORIAL FUNDAMENTO S.A. (D)
Rivadavia 180, Rio Cuarto, Provincia de Cordoba, 5800, Argentina; tel (54) 358 464 9300; fax 464 9300; e-mail puntal@puntal.com.ar; web site www.puntal.com.ar
Circ.: 14,000
Ed. – Carlos Gamond

LA CALLE (M)
Sobremonte 743, Rio Cuarto, Provincia de Cordoba, Argentina; tel (54)
Circ.: 6,000
Pub. – Francisco Savino

RIO GALLEGOS, PROVINCIA DE SANTA CRUZ

LA OPINION AUSTRAL (M)
Zapiola 25, Rio Gallegos, Provincia de Santa Cruz, 9400, Argentina; tel (54) 2966 420 185; fax 420 029; web site www.laopinionaustral.com
Pres. – Hector Mario Perincioll

RIO GRANDE, PROVINCIA DE SANTA CRUZ

LA CIUDAD NUEVA (D)
Ameghino 626, Rio Grande, Provincia de Santa Cruz, Argentina; tel (54)
Pub. – Leonor Maria Pinero

RIO TERCERO, PROVINCIA DE CORDOBA

CRONICA (S)
Sgto. Cabral 142, Rio Tercero, Provincia de Cordoba, 5850, Argentina; tel (54)
Pub. – Jose Maria Lioy

ROJAS, PROVINCIA DE BUENOS AIRES

LA VOZ DE ROJAS (D)
Leandro N. Alem 472, Rojas, Provincia de Buenos Aires, 2705, Argentina; tel (54) 4 75-3668; fax 75-3668
Ed. – Carlos A. Rodriguez

ROSARIO, PROVINCIA DE SANTA FE

LA CAPITAL (MS)
Sarmiento 763, Rosario, Provincia de Santa Fe, 2000, Argentina; tel (54) 341 420-1100; fax 420-1114; e-mail informat@lacapital.com.ar
Circ.: 65,000
Pres. – Carlos Maria Lagos
Gen. Mgr. – Juan S. Alvarez
Adv. Mgr. – Daniel Depaola
Ed. – Eduardo Luis Lagos

SALTA, PROVINCIA DE SALTA

CRONICA DEL NOA (D)
Espana 478, Salta, Provincia de Salta, Argentina; tel (54)

EL TRIBUNO (M)
Avda. Ex Combatienes del Malvinas 3890, Salta, Provincia de Salta, 4400, Argentina; tel (54) 387 424-0000; fax 424-6240; e-mail redaccion@eltribuno.com.ar
Circ.: 32,000
Pres. – Vicenta Di Gangi de Romero
Gen. Mgr. – Miguel Angel Ruiz
Adv. Mgr. – Irene Mintzer
Ed. – Roberto Eduardo Romero
Prodn. Mgr. – Bernardo Costa

SALTO, PROVINCIA DE BUENOS AIRES

EL NORTE (D)
Buenos Aires 636, Salto, Provincia de Buenos Aires, 2741, Argentina; tel (54)
Pub. – Jorge Nahara

SAN CARLOS DE B-ARILOCHE, PROVINCIA DE RIO NEGRO

DIARIO LA ULTIMA (M)
Pje. Gutierrez 101, San Carlos de Bariloche, Provincia de Rio Negro, Argentina; tel (54)
Pub. – Jose Antoni Jalil

SAN FRANCISCO DEL VALLE DE CATAMARCA, PROVINCIA DE

EL SOL
Esq. 551, San Francisco del Valle de Catamarca, Provincia de, 4700, Argentina; tel (54)
Pub. – T. Alvarez Saavedra

SAN FRANCISCO, PROVINCIA DE CORDOBA

LA VOZ DE SAN JUSTO S.R.L. (M)
9 de Julio 2001, San Francisco, Provincia de Cordoba, 2400, Argentina; tel (54) 356 424-5544; fax 442-4121; e-mail sanjusto@solsoft.com.ar; web site www.lavozdesanjusto.com.ar
Circ.: 7,500
Gen. Mgr. – Norberto Zorzi
Adv. Mgr. – Juan Jose Caset
Ed. – Elly V. Martinez de Cottani

SAN ISIDRO, PROVINCIA DE BUENOS AIRES

CARTA ABIERTA
Avda. ItuzaingO 632, San Isidro, Provincia de Buenos Aires, 1642, Argentina; tel (54)
Dir./Ed. – Jaime A. Smart

COSTA NORTE
Primera Junta 58, San Isidro, Provincia de Buenos Aires, 1642, Argentina; tel (54)
Dir./Ed. – Leonardo DiPetro Paolo

SAN JUAN, PROVINCIA DE SAN JUAN

FRANCISCO SALVADOR MONTES S.A. (D)
Mendoza 380 Sur, San Juan, Provincia de San Juan, 5400, Argentina; tel (54) 264 429 0033; fax 429 0004; web site www.diariodecuyo.com.ar
Circ.: 26,000
Dir. – Francisco J. Montes

SAN JUSTO, PROVINCIA DE BUENOS AIRES

EL INFORMATIVO (M)
Dr. 1, Arieta 2789, San Justo, Provincia de Buenos Aires, 1754, Argentina; tel (54)
Pub. – Ana Maria Policastro

SAN LUIS, PROVINCIA DE SAN LUIS

EL DIARIO DE LA REPUBLICA (M)
Junin 741, San Luis, Provincia de San Luis, 5700, Argentina; tel (54) 2652 422 037; fax 422 037; web site www.eldiariodelarepublica.com
Circ.: 12,000
Pres. – Alberto Jose Rodriguez
Adv. Mgr. – Sonja Martinez
Ed. – Jorge Saporiti
Prodn. Mgr. – Mario Omar La Torre

EL DIARIO DE SAN LUIS (D)
Pedemera 1212, San Luis, Provincia de San Luis, 5700, Argentina; tel (54)
Dir. – Edgardo L. Cordera

LA OPINION (E)
Aysoucho 1257, San Luis, Provincia de San Luis, 5700, Argentina; tel (54)
Circ.: 3,000
Dir. – Eduardo Rodriguez Saa

SAN MARTIN, PROVINCIA DE BUENOS AIRES

EL MUNICIPIO (M)
Pueyrredon 414, San Martin, Provincia de Buenos Aires, 1650, Argentina; tel (54)
Dir. – Diego R. Gomez

LA RECONQUISTA (D)
Calle 93, No. 1841, San Martin, Provincia de Buenos Aires, 1650, Argentina; tel (54)
Dir. – Manuel G. Morillo

SAN MIGUEL DE TUCUMAN, PROVINCIA DE TUCUMAN

EL TRIBUNO (M)
Belgrano 645, San Miguel de Tucuman, Provincia de Tucuman, Argentina; tel (54)
Pub. – Emma Barcena de Gronda

LA GACETA (MS)
Mendoza 654, San Miguel de Tucuman, Provincia de Tucuman, 4000, Argentina; tel (54) 381 484 2200; fax 484 2237; e-mail redaccion@lagaceta.com.ar; web site www.lagaceta.com.ar
Circ.: 85,000
Gen. Mgr. – Jose Pochat Alurralde
Adv. Mgr. – Carlos Lopez Nieves
Ed. – Guillermo Garcia Hamilton
Tech. Dir – Jose Blanco

LA TARDE
Mendoza 654, San Miguel de Tucuman, Provincia de Tucuman, 4000, Argentina; tel (54) 381 4219260
Dir. – Daniel Alberto Dessein

SIGLO XXI S.A. (D)
Mabau 70, San Miguel de Tucuman, Provincia de Tucuman, 4000, Argentina; tel (54) 381 430 1010; e-mail redaccion@elsiglo.com.ar
Circ.: 12,000
Sales Mgr. – Carlos Miranda

SAN NICOLAS, PROVINCIA DE BUENOS AIRES

EL LITORAL (D)
San Martin 2651-59, San Nicolas, Provincia de Buenos Aires, 3000, Argentina; tel (54) 41 20101
Circ.: 40,000

HOY (D)
1.o. de Mayo 2820, San Nicolas, Provincia de Buenos Aires, 3000, Argentina; tel (54) 41
Circ.: 30,000

EL NORTE (M)
Francia 64, San Nicolas, Provincia de Buenos Aires, 2900, Argentina; tel (54) 02461 422 112; e-mail el-norte@el-norte.com.ar; web site www.el-norte.com.ar
Circ.: 8,000
Pres. – Sebastian Zeulgaray
Gen. Mgr. – Roberto Flores
Ed. – Haroldo T. Zuelgaray

SAN RAFAEL, PROVINCIA DE MENDOZA

EL COMERCIO (M)
Avda. Mitre 327, San Rafael, Provincia de Mendoza, Argentina; tel (54)
Pub. – Manuel E. Butti

LA CAPITAL (D-EX S)
Bdo. de Irigoyen 236, San Rafael, Provincia de Mendoza, Argentina; tel (54)
Pub. – Raul A. Morales

SAN SALVADOR DE JUJUY, PROVINCIA DE JUJUY

PREGON (D)
Belgrano 545, San Salvador de Jujuy, Provincia de Jujuy, 4600, Argentina; tel (54) 388 423 6200; fax 423 6200; e-mail pregon@imagine.com.ar; web site www.pregon.com.ar
Circ.: 15,000
Ed. – Annuar Orce

SAN SALVADOR DE JUJUY, PROVINCIA DE SAN SALVADOR DE JUJUY

EL TRIBUNO DE JUJUY (D)
Belgrano 306, San Salvador de Jujuy, Provincia de San Salvador de Jujuy, 4600, Argentina; tel (54) 3882 437 800; e-mail tribunojujuy@cootepal.com.ar
Circ.: 3,300
Gen. Mgr. – Veronica Castro
Ed. – Ricardo Tezanos Pinto

SANTA FE, PROVINCIA DE SANTA FE

EDICION (D)
9 de Julio 889, Santa Fe, Provincia de Santa Fe, Argentina; tel (54) 42
Pub. – Emilio Cesar Adobato

EL IMPARCIAL (MS)
Avda. General Paz 6301, Santa Fe, Provincia de Santa Fe, 3000, Argentina; tel (54) 42
Circ.: 10,000
Dir. – Raul S. Capoccetti

HOY (D)
1.o. de Mayo 2820, Santa Fe, Provincia de Santa Fe, 3000, Argentina; tel (54)
Circ.: 30,000

EL LITORAL S.R.L. (D)
Avda. 25 de Mayo 3536, Santa Fe, Provincia de Santa Fe, 3000, Argentina; tel (54) 342 450 2500; e-mail litoral@litoral.com; web site www.ellitoral.com
Circ.: 37,000
Pres. – Gustavo Jose Vittori
Adv. Mgr. – Enrique Llapur

SANTA ROSA, PROVINCIA DE LA PAMPA

LA ARENA (M)
Bartolome Mitre 339, Santa Rosa, Provincia de La Pampa, 6300, Argentina; tel (54) 3546 433-733; fax 433-733; e-mail arena@cpsarg.com; web site www.arena.com.ar
Circ.: 12,000
Pres. – Rosalba D'Atri de Santesteban
Adv. Mgr. – Antonio Mario D'Atri
Ed. – Saul Hugo Santesteban
Prodn. Mgr. – Dario Casais

EL DIARIO
Avda. San Martin y 25 de Mayo, Santa Rosa, Provincia de La Pampa, 6300, Argentina; tel (54) 2954 411-117; fax 431-400; e-mail eldiario@infovia.com.ar; web site www.eldiariolp.com.ar
Ed. – Jorge Ricardo Nemesio

LA CAPITAL (M)
Pellegrini 126, Santa Rosa, Provincia de La Pampa, 6300, Argentina; tel (54) 954
Pub. – Angel Ortiz

SANTIAGO DEL ESTERO

EDITORIAL EL LIBERAL S.R.L. (D)
Libertad 263, Santiago del Estero, 4200, Argentina; tel (54) 385 422 4400; fax 422 4538; e-mail direccion@elliberal.com.ar; web site www.elliberal.com.ar
Circ.: 22,000
Dir. – Gustavo Vittori

SANTOS LUGARES, PROVINCIA DE BUENOS AIRES

EL MATUTINO (M)
Pablo Giorello 1688, Santos Lugares, Provincia de Buenos Aires, 1676, Argentina; tel (54)
Dir. – Remagio M. Amaya

TANDIL

EL ECO DE TANDIL (D)
H. Yrigoyen 799, Tandil, Argentina; tel (54) 2293 425 232; fax 430 900; e-mail info@ecocontrol.com.ar; web site www.eleco.com.ar
Circ.: 7,000
Gen. Mgr. – Ricardo Oscar Fortunato
Ed. – Rogelio Rotonda

EDITORA INDEPENDENCIA (D)
Tandil, Argentina; tel (54)

TANDIL, PROVINCIA DE BUENOS AIRES

NUEVA ERA (D)
General Rodriguez 445, Tandil, Provincia de Buenos Aires, 7000, Argentina; tel (54) 2293 422 085; fax 342 085; e-mail nuevaera@infovia.com.ar
Circ.: 2,000
Ed. – Anibal Filippini
CEO – Jose Filippini

TIGRE, PROVINCIA DE BUENOS AIRES

FOMENTO (MS)
Hipolito Yrigoyen 707, Tigre, Provincia de Buenos Aires, 1648, Argentina; tel (54) 4740 2318
Pub. – Enrique Innocensi

TRELEW, PROVINCIA DE CHUBUT

DIARIO JORNADA (D)
Hipolito Yrigoyen 583, Trelew, Provincia de Chubut, 9100, Argentina; tel (54) 2965 421 010; fax 437 409; e-mail redaccion1@diariojornada.com; web site www.diariojornada.com.ar
Circ.: 10,000
Last Audit: November 20, 2006
Ed. – Carlos Juagardo

IMPRESORA CHUBUTENSE S.A. (M)
9 de Julio 329, Trelew, Provincia de Chubut, 9100, Argentina; tel (54) 2965 434 802; fax 420 799; e-mail elchubut@internet.siscotel.com; web site www.diarioelchubut.com.ar
Circ.: 17,500
Dir. – Alejandro Cagnoli

TRENQUE LAUQUEN, PROVINCIA DE BUENOS AIRES

LA OPINION (M)
Avda. General Roca 752, Trenque Lauquen, Provincia de Buenos Aires, 6400, Argentina; tel (54) 2392 430 441
Circ.: 4,500
Ed. – Mariela Nazar

TRES ARROYOS, PROVINCIA DE BUENOS AIRES

MACIEL HERMANOS S.A.E.C.I. (M)
Avda. San Martin 991, Tres Arroyos, Provincia de Buenos Aires, 7500, Argentina; tel (54) 2983 430 680; fax 430 682; e-mail redaccion@lavozdelpueblo.com.ar; web site www.lavozdelpueblo.com.ar
Circ.: 3,200
Pres. – Enrique Maciel
Prodn. Mgr. – Alberto Jorge Maciel

VEINTICINCO DE MAYO, PROVINCIA DE BUENOS AIRES

LA MANANA (M)
Rafael Salerno (11) 457, Veinticinco de Mayo, Provincia de Buenos Aires, 6660, Argentina; tel (54) 345 2227; fax 2883; e-mail lamanana@ciudad.com.ar; web site www.lamanana.com.ar
Circ.: 4,700
Pres. – Anibal Ruben Borda
Gen. Mgr. – Ana Lina Dithurbida
Adv. Mgr. – Lilia P. Otero
Ed. – Alberto Eduardo Rocha
Prodn. Mgr. – Rodolfo J. Pirotta

VICENTE LOPEZ, PROVINCIA DE BUENOS AIRES

LA RIBERA (D)
PO Box A, Vicente Lopez, Provincia de Buenos Aires, 1638, Argentina; tel (54)
Ed. – Alejandro Vincente Chiodi

VICTORIA, PROVINCIA DE ENTRE RIOS

CRISOL (D)
Las Piedras 63, Victoria, Provincia de Entre Rios, 3153, Argentina; tel (54)
Dir. – Arturo J. Etchevehere

LA MANANA (M)
Italia 568, Victoria, Provincia de Entre Rios, 3153, Argentina; tel (54) 3436 42 1113; fax 42 1113; e-mail lamanana@arnet.com.ar
Circ.: 1,000
Last Audit: November 20, 2006
Ed. – Gracia Jaroslavsky

VILLA DOLORES, PROVINCIA DE CORDOBA

DEMOCRACIA (D)
Lib. Urquiza 101, Villa Dolores, Provincia de Cordoba, 5870, Argentina; tel (54)
Dir. – Oscar A. Tello

VILLA MARIA, PROVINCIA DE CORDOBA

EL DIARIO DEL SUR DE CORDOBA (E)
Blvd. Espana 125, Villa Maria, Provincia de Cordoba, 5900, Argentina; tel (54) 53 453-3851; fax 453-4182
Pres. – Hugo Horacio Las Heras
Adv. Mgr. – Paola P. Santunione

VILLA MERCEDES, PROVINCIA DE SAN LUIS

IMPULSO (M)
Avda. Mitre 538, Villa Mercedes, Provincia de San Luis, 5730, Argentina; tel (54)
Circ.: 9,500
Pub. – Eduardo Luis Estrada Dubor

VILLAGUAY, PROVINCIA DE ENTRE RIOS

EMILIO SURRA Y HIJOS S.R.L. (E)
San Martin 368, Villaguay, Provincia de Entre Rios, 3240, Argentina; tel (54) 455 21204; fax 22391
Circ.: 3,800
Gen. Mgr. – Nelly R. Surra de Carulla
Dir./Ed. – Juan Carlos Surre
Prodn. Mgr. – Felix Gaston Surra Munoz

EL PUEBLO (6X WK.)
San Martin 360, Villaguay, Provincia de Entre Rios, 3240, Argentina; tel (54) 3455 421 204; fax 421 204; e-mail info@elpueblo.com.ar
Circ.: 2,500
Gen. Mgr. – Nelly Ruth Surra de Carulla
Ed. – Orfilia Munoz de Surra
Prodn. Mgr. – Felix Gaston Surra

ZAPALA, PROVINCIA DE MISIONES

ECOS CORDILLERANOS (D)
Ivorquis 120, Zapala, Provincia de Misiones, Argentina; tel (54)
Circ.: 4,200
Pub. – Manuel Vega

ZARATE

GRUPO SERPEIN S.A. (D)
Decano del Norte Bonaerense, Zarate, 2800, Argentina; tel (54) 3487 432 002; fax 441 142; e-mail info@eldebate.com.ar; web site www.eldebate.com.ar
Pres. – Daniel Armando Vogel
Gen. Mgr. – Maria Christina Romano

ZARATE, PROVINCIA DE BUENOS AIRES

EL PUEBLO (E)
Castelli 900, Zarate, Provincia de Buenos Aires, 2800, Argentina; tel (54)
Circ.: 4,000
Pub. – Ruque F. de Paolo
Adv. Mgr. – Jorge de Paolo

LA VOZ DE ZARATE (D)
Alte. Brown 742, Zarate, Provincia de Buenos Aires, 2800, Argentina; tel (54) 3487 420 855; e-mail lavoz@arnet.com.ar
Ed. – Virginia de Paolo

BOLIVIA

COCHABAMBA

OPINION (M)
General Acha 0252, PO Box 287, Cochabamba, Bolivia; tel (591) 42 5-4402; fax 1-5121; e-mail publicidad@opinion-bo.com; web site www.opinion-bo.com
Pres. – Edwin Tapia Frontanilla
Gen. Mgr. – Graciela Mendez de Escobar
Adv. Mgr. – Patricia Bonuccelli
Ed. – Federico Sabat Lara
Prodn. Mgr. – Jose Luis Colque

LOS TIEMPOS (M)
Plaza Quintanilla Norte, PO Box 525, Cochabamba, Bolivia; tel (591) 42 254563; fax 5-4577; e-mail redaccion@grupocanales.com; web site www.lostiempos-bolivia.com
Circ.: 19,000
Pres. – Carlos Canelas
Gen. Mgr. – Gonzalo Canelas
Ed. – Alfonso Canelas
Prodn. Mgr. – Eduardo Canelas

LA PAZ

AURELIOS S.R.L. (E)
Edif. Almirante Grau 672, PO Box 1628, La Paz, Bolivia; tel (591) 2 248-8163; fax 248-7487; e-mail cartas@jornadanet.com; web site www.jornadanet.com
Pres. – Jaime Rios Chacon
Adv. Mgr. – Vanessa Grace Rios Aranda
Ed. – Jenny Rodriguez Aranibar

EL DIARIO (M)
Calle Loayza 118, La Paz, Bolivia; tel (591) 2 233 2233; fax 236 3846; e-mail redinfo@eldiario.net; web site www.eldiario.net
Advertising: Charney/Palacios & Co. Inc.
Gen. Mgr. – Jorge Carrasco Jahnsen

GRUPO GARAFULIC (M)
Colinas de Santa Rita, La Paz, 13100, Bolivia; tel (591) 2 277 1415; fax 277 0908; e-mail larazon@la-razon.com; web site www.la-razon.com
Advertising: Charney/Palacios & Co. Inc.
Dir. – Juan Carlos Rocha ChavarrÃ¡a

HOY (M)
Pasaje Carrasco 1718, Miraflores, La Paz, Bolivia; tel (591) 2 244 154; fax 244 147; e-mail hoy@wara.bolnet.bo
Pres. – Samuel Doria Medina
Gen. Mgr. – Hernan Solares
Sales Mgr. – Cinthia Yanez
Ed. – Hernan Paredes Munoz

PRESENCIA (M)
Avda. Mariscal Santa Cruz 2150, Edif. Esperanza, PO Box 3276, La Paz, Bolivia; tel (591) 2 233-1717; fax 233-1206; e-mail comercial@presenciabolivia.com; web site www.presenciabolivia.com
Circ.: 20,000
Pres. – Edmundo Abastoflor
Gen. Mgr. – Jose Luis Laguna
Adv. Mgr. – Hugo Monasterios
Ed. – Mario Frias Infante
Prodn. Mgr. – Rafael Fernandez

SOCIEDAD DE RESPONSABILIDAD LTDA.
Coroico, No. 1441, La Paz, Bolivia; tel (591) 2 525 0780; fax 525 0782
Pres. – Carlos Cardona
Gen. Mgr. – Edgar Fernandez
Dir./Ed. – Dante Escobar

ULTIMA HORA (M)
Avda. Camacho 1372, PO Box 5920, La Paz, Bolivia; tel (591) 2 39-2115; fax 39-2139; e-mail uhora@caoba.entelnet.bo; web site ns.megatron-bo.net/inter/Ultima_Hora.htm
Circ.: 15,000
Pres. – Alvaro Velasco
Gen. Mgr. – Miguel Lopez
Adv. Mgr. – Juan Pasden
Ed. – Victor Toro
Prodn. Mgr. – Gonzalo Campuzano

ORURO, ORURO

LA PATRIA (M) Est. 1919
PO Box 48, Oruro, Oruro, Bolivia; tel (591) 2 525 0780; fax 525 0782; e-mail info@lapatria.com.bo; web site www.lapatriaenlinea.com
Circ.: 6,000
Pres./Ed. – Marcelo Miralles Bova
Prodn. Mgr. – Eduardo Rodriguez Cordova

POTOSI

ASOCIACION DE PERIODISTAS POTOSINOS
Casilla Correo 394, Potosi, Bolivia; tel (591) 62 26906; fax 24005
Pres./Dir./Ed. – Crisologo ALeman Almendras
Gen. Mgr. – Oscar Vargas
Sales Mgr. – Julio Mujica

SANTA CRUZ DE LA SIERRA

EDITORIAL ORIENTE (M)
Avda. El Trompillo 1144 entrada Av. San Aurelio, Santa Cruz De La Sierra, Bolivia; tel (591) 3 538000; e-mail web@eldeber.com.bo; web site www.eldeber.com.bo
Circ.: 35,000
Dir. – Pedro Rivero Mercado
Mng. Ed. – Guillermo Rivero Jordan

SANTA CRUZ DE LA SIERRA, SANT CRUZ

CHAMBER OF COMMERCE & INDUSTRY (D)
Parque Industrial 7, Santa Cruz de la Sierra, Sant Cruz, Bolivia; tel (591) 33 464 646; fax 463 322; web site www.elmundo.com.bo
Circ.: 15,000
Pres. – Ronald Paz
Adv. Mgr. – Nadia Eid

SANTA CRUZ DE LA SIERRA, SANTA CRUZ

EL DIA (M)
Casilla de correos 5344, Santa Cruz de la Sierra, Santa Cruz, Bolivia; tel (591) 33 343 4040; fax 343 4041; e-mail nuevodia@elnuevodia.com; eldia@eldia.com.bo; web site www.el-nuevodia.com
Circ.: 12,500
Dir. – Eduardo Bowles

SUCRE

GRUPO CANELAS (D)
Casilla Postal 242, Sucre, Bolivia; tel (591) 4 644 3202; fax 646 0152; e-mail info@correodelsur.net; web site www.correodelsur.com
Pres. – Gonzalo Canelas Tardio
Gen. Mgr. – Julio Auza Anglarill
Editorial Dir. – Antonio Dipp Mukled

SUCRE, CHUQUISACA

PAGINA 20 (M)
Nicolas Ortiz 70, PO Box 867, Sucre, Chuquisaca, Bolivia; tel (591) 64 4-0752; fax 4-0752
Gen. Mgr. – Gladys Bernal Cardenas
Ed. – Vicente Davila Velasquez

BRAZIL

AMERICANA, SAO PAULO

EMPRESA EDITORA O LIBERAL LTD. (D)
Rua Padre Manoel da Nobrega, No. 154, Americana, Sao Paulo, 13470, Brazil; tel (55)
Circ.: 7,000
Pub. – Jessyr Bianco

ANDRADINA, SAO PAULO

EDITORA O JORNAL DA REGIAO LTD. (D)
Rua Ceara, No.1353, Andradina, Sao Paulo, 16900, Brazil; tel (55) 11 722 3797; fax 722 3366; e-mail editorajr@andranet.com.br
Circ.: 7,000
Pub. – Isael Soares Fernandes

ARACAJU, SERGIPE

GAZETA DE SERGIPE (M) Est. 1956
Ave. Juscelino Kubitschek, 396-A, Aracaju, Sergipe, 49070-400, Brazil; tel (55) 79 211-8833; fax 211-8808; e-mail gazetase@netdados.com.br
Circ.: 15,000
Pres. – Maria Helena Silva Dantas
Adv./Sales Mgr. – Rodrigo Carvalho
Ed. – Diogenes Brayner

ARACATUBA, SAO PAULO

EDITORA FOLHA DA REGIAO DA ARACATUBA LTD. (D)
Rua Joaquim Fernandes, 445 jardim Nova Iorque, Aracatuba, Sao Paulo, 16018-280, Brazil; tel (55) 18 3636 7774; fax 3636 7702; e-mail folha@folhaderegiao.com.br; web site www.folhadaregiao.com.br
Circ.: 15,000
Pub. – Genilson Senche
Mgr. – Maria Antonio Danio
Ed. – Aine Selviano

EDITORA GRAFICA JORNAL A COMERCA LTD. (D)
Rua Marechal Deodora, No. 433, Aracatuba, Sao Paulo, 16100, Brazil; tel (55)
Circ.: 9,000
Pub. – Paulo Alcides Jorge

ARARAQUARA, SAO PAULO

DIARIO DA ARARAQUARENSE (D)
Rua 9 de Julho, No. 504, Araraquara, Sao Paulo, 14800, Brazil; tel (55)
Circ.: 5,000
Pub. – Roberto Barbieri

EMPRESA O IMPARCIAL LTD. (D)
Avda. Jose Bonifacio, No. 715, Araraquara, Sao Paulo, 14800, Brazil; tel (55)
Circ.: 8,000
Pub. – Paulo de Arruda Correada Silva

ASSIS, SAO PAULO

EMPRESA EDITORA DE JORNAIS REGIONAL LTD. (D)
Rua Rangel Pestana, No. 2, Assis, Sao Paulo, 19800, Brazil; tel (55)
Circ.: 2,000
Pub. – Nelson de Souza

EMPRESA JORNALISTICA VOZ DE TERRA LTD. (D)
Avda. Rui Barbosa, No. 1291, Assis, Sao Paulo, 19800, Brazil; tel (55)
Circ.: 6,500
Pub. – Egidio Coelho da Silva

AVARE, SAO PAULO

O AVARE (M)
Praca Juca Novaes, 227, Avare, Sao Paulo, 18700-000, Brazil; tel (55) 14 721-1021; fax 722-0360
Ed. – Luiz A.V. de Freitas

BAGE, RIO GRANDE DO SUL

EMPRESA GRAFICA DO CORREIO DO SUL LTD. (M)
Avda. 7 de Setembro, No. 664, Bage, Rio Grande do Sul, 96400, Brazil; tel (55) 53 242 1386; web site www.correiodosul.com.br
Circ.: 3,500
Pub. – Mario Nogueira Lopes

BAG /RS

CORREIO DO SUL (M)
Gal Netto, 32, Bag□/RS, 37006-000, Brazil; tel (55) 3242 1386; fax 3242 1386
Circ.: 10,000
Ed. – Antonio Carlos Medes Campos

BAIRRO SANTA MARIA

GAZETA DE VARGINHA (M) Est. 1967
Av. dos Imigrantes, 445, Bairro Santa Maria, 37100-010, Brazil; tel (55) 35 3221 4668; fax 3221 4845; e-mail gazetavga@varginha.com.br; web site www.varginhaonline.com.br
Ed. – Sergio F. de Avelar

BARRA MANSA, RIO DE JANEIRO

MAPA PUBLICIDADE LTD. (D)
Avda. Dario Aragao, No. 837, Barra Mansa, Rio de Janeiro, 27400, Brazil; tel (55)
Circ.: 8,000
Pub. – Geraldo Almeida Pancardes

BARRETOS, SAO PAULO

O DIARIO (M) Est. 1969
Praca Joel Waldo, 1, Barretos, Sao Paulo, 14781-574, Brazil; tel (55) 17 322-1090; fax 322-2633
Pres. – Luiz Antonio Montero de Barros

BAURU, SAO PAULO

EMPRESA GRAFICA E EDITORA BAURU (D)
Praca D. Pedro II, No. 2-77, Bauru, Sao Paulo, 17015, Brazil; tel (55)
Circ.: 10,000
Pub. – Zarcillo R. Barbosa

JORNAL DA CIDADE DE BAURU LTD. (D)
Rua Xingu, No. 4-44, Bauru, Sao Paulo, 17013903, Brazil; tel (55) 14 3104 3104; fax 3104 3115; e-mail anunciof@jcnet.com.br; web site www.jcnet.com.br
Pub. – Gifell Hilario

Dir. – Renato Zaiden

BELEM, PARA

DELTA PUBLICIDADE S.A. (D)
Avda. 25 de setembro, No. 2473, Belem, Para, 66093-000, Brazil; tel (55); e-mail denispb@libnet.com.br; web site www.oliberal.com.br
Circ.: 110,000
Pub. – Denis Paes Barreto

EDITORA O ESTADO DO PARA (D)
Rua Gaspar Viana, No. 773, Belem, Para, 66000, Brazil; tel (55)
Circ.: 24,000
Pub. – Avertano Barreto da Rocha
Ed. – Walmir Botelho

BELO HORIZONTE, MINAS GERAIS

DIARIO DE MINAS (M)
Rua Francisco Salles, 540, Belo Horizonte, Minas Gerais, 30150-220, Brazil; tel (55) 31 213-1210; fax 224-3359
Circ.: 50,000
Pres. – Aurelio Flores Carone
Ed. – Joao M. Tejeira

ESTADO DE MINAS (M)
Rua Goias, 36 - Centro, Belo Horizonte, Minas Gerais, 30190-030, Brazil; tel (55) 31 237-5000; fax 237-5070; e-mail jbosco@uai.com.br; web site www.jbosco.uai.com.br
Circ.: 170,000
Pres. – Camilo Teixeira da Costa
Gen. Mgr. – Luis Antonio Mendes
Sales Mgr. – Gino Muria
Sales Mgr. – Cyro Siqueira
Ed. – Edison Zenobrio

ESTADO DE MINAS S.A. (E)
Rua Goias 36, Belo Horizonte, Minas Gerais, 30190, Brazil; tel (55) 31 2732322; fax 2734400
Gen. Dir. – Paulo C. de Araujo

JORNAL DE MINAS S.A. (5X WK.)
Avda. Francisco Sales, No. 536, Belo Horizonte, Minas Gerais, 30150, Brazil; tel (55) 32 3373 2552; e-mail jornaldeminas@city10.com.br; web site www.jornaldeminas.com.br
Pub. – Alfonso Araujo Paulino

BIRIGUI, SAO PAULO

JORNAL DIARIO DE BIRIGUI LTD. (D)
Rua Saudades, No. 1395, Birigui, Sao Paulo, 16200, Brazil; tel (55)
Circ.: 2,000
Pub. – Geraldo Silvero

O NOROESTINO LTD. (D)
Rua Santos Dumont, No. 74, Birigui, Sao Paulo, 16200, Brazil; tel (55)
Circ.: 1,000
Pub. – Leonardo Sabioni

BLUMENAU, SANTA CATARINA

EMPRESA EDITORA JORNAL DE SANTA CATARINA LTD. (D)
Rua Sao Paulo 1120, Blumenau, Santa Catarina, 89010, Brazil; tel (55) 473 266411; e-mail redacao@santa.com.br; web@santa.com.br
Circ.: 25,000
Dir. – Paulo A. Malbu

BOA VISTA, RORAIMA

FOLHA DE BOA VISTA (M) Est. 1983
Rua Lobo D'Almado, 21 - Sao Francisco, Boa Vista, Roraima, 69050-500, Brazil; tel (55) 95 623-8806; fax 623-8803; e-mail folhabv@technet.com.br; web site www.folhabv.com.br
Pres. – Getulio Alberto de Souza Cruz
Gen. Mgr. – Nazare Cruz
Sales Mgr. – Paula Cruz
Ed. – Cavilio Pires

BRAGANCA PAULISTA, SAO PAULO

BRAGANCA JORNAL DIARIO (D)
Av. Antonio Pires Pimentel, 937 - Sala 2, Braganca Paulista, Sao Paulo, 12900, Brazil; tel (55) 11 4033-1094; e-mail paulo@bjd.com.br; web site www.bjd.com.br
Circ.: 4,200
Pub. – Omair Fagundes de Oliveira

BRASILIA, FEDERAL DISTRICT

DIARIO DE BRASILIA (D)
Avda. W-3, Quadro 503, Brasilia, Federal District, Brazil; tel (55)
Circ.: 18,000
Pub. – Dyrno Pires Ferreira

J CAMARA E IRMAOS S.A. (D)
SIG Trecho 1, Lotes 585/645, Brasilia, Federal District, 70610-400, Brazil; tel (55) 61 225 2515
Circ.: 25,000
Advertising: Charney/Palacios & Co. Inc.
Gen. Dir. – Fernando Coma

S.A. CORREIO BRASILIENSE (MS)
SIG Quandra 2 Lotes 300/340, Brasilia, Federal District, 70610-901, Brazil; tel (55) 3211314; fax 3212856
Circ.: 30,000
Advertising: The N DeFilippes Corp.
Gen. Dir. – Paulo C. de Araujo

CACERES, MATO GROSSO

CORREIO CACERENSE (D)
Rua General Osorio, No. 363, Caceres, Mato Grosso, 78700, Brazil; tel (55)
Circ.: 2,000
Pub. – Alvisio Coelho Barros

CAMPINA GRANDE, PARAIBA

DIARIO DA BORBOREMA (M) Est. 1957
Rua Venacio Neiva, 198 - Centro, Campina Grande, Paraiba, 58200-060, Brazil; tel (55) 83 3241 2053; fax 3241 2541; e-mail db@db.com.br
Circ.: 5,000
Pub. – Nereu Gusmao Bastos

EDITORA JORNAL DA PARAIBA S.A. (D)
Rua Major Juvino do O, No. 81, Campina Grande, Paraiba, 58100, Brazil; tel (55); e-mail jpb@openline.com.br; web site www.openline.com.br/~jpb
Circ.: 12,000
Pub. – Jose Carlos da Silva

CAMPINAS, SAO PAULO

CORREIO POPULAR (D) Est. 1927
Rua Conceicao, 124 - Centro, Campinas, Sao Paulo, 13010-902, Brazil; tel (55) 19 3736 3200; fax 3736 3186; e-mail cpopular@cpopular.com.br; web site www.cpopular.com.br
Circ.: 60,000
Pres. – Sylvino de Godoy Neto

EMPRESA JORNALISTICA EDITORA REGIONAL LTD. (D)
Rua Cezar Bierrenbach, No. 67, Campinas, Sao Paulo, 13015, Brazil; tel (55)
Circ.: 25,000
Pub. – Maria Beatriz C. de Carvalho Moreira

CAMPO GRANDE, MATO GROSSO

CORREIO DO ESTADO (M) Est. 1952
Ave. Calogeras, 356 - Centro, Campo Grande, Mato Grosso, 79004-380, Brazil; tel (55) 67 742-6090; fax 742-5681; e-mail adm@correiodoestado.com.br; web site www.correiodoestado.com.br
Pres. – Jose Barbosa Rodrigues
Gen. Mgr. – Vilma Gutierres Leite
Ed. – Antonio Joao Rodrigues

DIARIO DA SERRA (M)
Rua Eng. Roberto Mange, 849, Campo Grande, Mato Grosso, 79005-420, Brazil; tel (55) 67 721 3030; fax 721 3020
Circ.: 6,000
Pres. – Antonio Joao Hugo Rodrigues
Adv./Sales Mgr. – Nidia Oliveira dos Santos
Ed. – Oscar Ramos Gaspar

JORNAL DA MANHA (D)
Avda. Afonso Pena, No. 1408, Campo Grande, Mato Grosso, 79100, Brazil; tel (55)
Circ.: 6,000
Pub. – Francisco Pedro Godoy

PATROPI-JORNAL DA ZONA OESTE
Rua Aurelio de Figueiredo 115, Grupo 210, Campo Grande, Mato Grosso, Brazil; tel (55) 3944450; fax 3944450

CAMPOS, RIO DE JANEIRO

A NOTICIA (D)
Avda. 7 de Setembro, Campos, Rio de Janeiro, 28100, Brazil; tel (55)
Circ.: 7,000
Pub. – Herve Salgado Rodrigues

PLENA EDITORA GRAFICA LTD. (D)
Rua Carlos de Lacerda, No. 75, Campos, Rio de Janeiro, 28100, Brazil; tel (55)
Pub. – Aluysio dos Santos Abreu

CASCAVEL, PARANA

EDITORA O PARANA LTD. (D)
Rua Pernambuco, No. 1592, Cascavel, Parana, 85800, Brazil; tel (55)
Circ.: 12,000
Pub. – J.M. Scanagatta

CATANDUVA, SAO PAULO

A CIDADE (D)
Rua 13 de Maio, No. 248, Catanduva, Sao Paulo, 15800, Brazil; tel (55)
Circ.: 6,000
Pub. – Nair de Frietas

EMPRESA DE PUBLICIDADE CATANDUVA LTD. (D)
Rua Para, No. 147, Catanduva, Sao Paulo, 15800, Brazil; tel (55) 17 3531 1000; e-mail presidencia@fm.com.br
Circ.: 3,000
Pub. – Jose Gerson de Camargo Gabas

CORUMBA, MATO GROSSO

DIARIO DA MANHA
Rua Cabral, 1121, Corumba, Mato Grosso, 79300-090, Brazil; tel (55) 67 231-3535
Pres. – Valdemar Baiaroski

JORNAL O MOMENTO (D)
Rua Delamare, No. 1380, Corumba, Mato Grosso, 79300, Brazil; tel (55)
Circ.: 6,000
Pub. – Nelson Dias de Rosa

CRUZ ALTA, RIO GRANDE DO SUL

EMPRESA JORNALISTICA PLANALTO MEDIO LTD. (D)
Avda. Pres. Vargas, No. 892, Cruz Alta, Rio Grande do Sul, 98100, Brazil; tel (55)
Circ.: 5,000
Pub. – Riograndino Portes Abreu

CUIABA, MATO GROSSO

EDITORA CUIABA LTD. (D)
Rua Cursino do Amarante, No. 881, Cuiaba, Mato Grosso, 78000, Brazil; tel (55)
Circ.: 8,000
Pub. – Pedro Rocha Juca

IMPRENSA RIBEIRO (D)
Rua 13 de Junho, No. 431, Cuiaba, Mato Grosso, 78000, Brazil; tel (55) 65
Circ.: 120,000
Pub. – Emanuel Ribeiro Daubian

JORNAL DO DIA (M) Est. 1979
Rua Pontes e Lacerda, Qd..98, Cuiaba, Mato Grosso, 78068-420, Brazil; tel (55) 65 361-5838; fax 361-5838
Pres. – Benedito A. Ferraz

CUIABA, MATTO GROSSO

IMPRENSA OFICIAL (DS)
Avda. XV de Novembro, No. 207, Cuiaba, Matto Grosso, 7800, Brazil; tel (55)
Pub. – Iris Capile de Oliveira

CURITIBA, PARANA

A TRIBUNA DO PARANA (D)
Rua Joao Tschannerl 800, Curitiba, Parana, 80820-010, Brazil; tel (55) 41 3358811; fax 3352838
Circ.: 15,000
Pres. – Paulo Cruz Pimentel

DIARIO POPULAR (M)
Rua 15 de Novembro, 1190, Curitiba, Parana, 80060, Brazil; tel (55) 41 3362 2233; fax 3264 4681; e-mail diario@diariopopular.com.br; web site www.diariopopular.com.br
Pub. – Abdo Aref Kudri

EDITORA GAZETA DO POVO LTD. (D)
Praca Carlos Gomes 4, Curitiba, Parana, 80010, Brazil; tel (55) 41 322 4445; fax 225 6848
Circ.: 40,000
Pres. – Francisco Cunha Pereira

EDITORA JORNAL DO ESTADO LTD. (D)
Rua Dr. Roberto Barroso, 22, Curitiba, Parana, 80520, Brazil; tel (55) 413 350 6600; fax 350 6650; e-mail comercial@jornaldoestado.com.br; web site www.bemparana.com.br
Dir. – Rodrigo Barrozo

EDITORA O ESTADO DE PARANA LTD. (M)
Rua Joao Tschannerl 800, Curitiba, Parana, 80820-000, Brazil; tel (55) 41 358811; fax 3352838
Circ.: 15,000
Pres. – Paulo Cruz Pimentel

JORNAL INDUSTRIA E COMERCIO DO PARANA
Travesa Itare, No. 52, Curitiba, Parana, 80000, Brazil; tel (55) 41; e-mail jinduscom@ativanet.com.br; web site www.ativanet.com.br/jinduscom.htm

DIVINOPOLIS, MINAS GERAIS

JORNAL AGORA (M) Est. 1971
Ave. 1o de Junho, 708, Divinopolis, Minas Gerais, 35000, Brazil; tel (55) 37 222-6969; fax 222-6969; e-mail jagora@jagora.com.br; jagora@div.globalsite.com.br; web site www.jagora.com.br
Pres. – Pedro Magalhaes de Faria
Gen. Mgr. – Marcelo Henrique Faria
Ed. – Sonia Terra de Faria

DOURADOS, MATO GROSSO DO SUL

FOLHA DE DOURADOS (M)
Rua Tiete, 520, Dourados, Mato Grosso do Sul, 79814-410, Brazil; tel (55) 67 421-7843
Pres. – Theodorico Luiz Viegas

O PROGRESSO (M)
Ave. Presidente Vargas, 447, Dourados, Mato Grosso do Sul, 79804-030, Brazil; tel (55) 67 421 4123; fax 421 1911; e-mail progresso@zaz.com.br; web site www.progresso.com.br
Circ.: 5,400
Pres. – Adiles do Amaral Torres
Sales Mgr. – Diogo Teotonio de Almeida

FERNANDOPOLIS, SAO PAULO

EDITORA FREITAS FERREIRA LTD. (D)
Rua Rio de Janeiro, No. 417, Fernandopolis, Sao Paulo, 15600, Brazil; tel (55)
Circ.: 2,600
Pub. – Jose de Freitas

FLORIANOPOLIS, SANTA CATARINA

A GAZETA (D)
Rua Conselheiro Mafra, No. 51, Florianopolis, Santa Catarina, 88010, Brazil; tel (55) 482 225592
Circ.: 4,000
Pub. – J.M. Fereira

EMPRESA EDITORA O ESTADO LTD. (D)
Rodovia SC-401, Km. 3, Florianopolis, Santa Catarina, 88030, Brazil; tel (55) 482 3888888; fax 3800711
Circ.: 20,000
Pres. – Jose Matusalem Comelli

FORTALEZA, CEARA

EDITORA VERDES MARES LTD.
Praca da Imprensa, Fortaleza, Ceara, 60170, Brazil; tel (55) 85 266-9773; web site www.diariodonordeste.com.br
Circ.: 35,000
Ed. – Francisco Bilas

EMPRESA JORNALISTICA O POVO LTD. (E)
Avda. Aguanambi 282, Fortaleza, Ceara, 60055, Brazil; tel (55) 85 2119666; fax 2315792; web site www.opovo.com.br
Circ.: 20,000
Pres. – Democrito Rocha Dummar

TRIBUNA DO CEARA (M) Est. 1957
Ave. Desembargador Moreira, 2900, Fortaleza, Ceara, 60170-025, Brazil; tel (55) 85 247-3000; fax 272-2799; e-mail tribuna@baydenet.com.br
Circ.: 15,000
Pres. – Jose Afonso Sancho
Ed. – Erivelto de Souza

FRANCA, SAO PAULO

EMPRESA FRANCA EDITORA DE JORNAIS REVISTAS LTD. (D)
Rua Ouvidor Freire, No. 1986, Franca, Sao Paulo, 14400, Brazil; tel (55)
Circ.: 10,000
Pub. – Jose Correra Neves

GOIANIA, GOIAS

JAIME CAMARA E IRMAOS S.A. (D)
Rua Thomas Edson Q7, Setor Serrinha, Goiania, Goias, 74835-130, Brazil; tel (55) 62 2501000; fax 2411018; web site www.opopular.com.br
Circ.: 65,000
Pres. – Jaime Camara

GOVERNADOR VALADARES, MINAS GERAIS

EQUSA EDITORA E GRAFICA UNIAO S.A. (D)
Rua Barbara Heliodoro, No. 231, Governador Valadares, Minas Gerais, 35010, Brazil; tel (55)
Circ.: 5,000
Pub. – Oswaldo Alcantara

GUARULHOS, SAO PAULO

EMPRESA JORNALISTICA FOLHA METROPOLITANA S.A. (D)
Praca Tereza Cristina, No. 21, Guarulhos, Sao Paulo, 70000, Brazil; tel (55)
Circ.: 8,000
Pub. – Paschoal Thomeu

ILHEUS, BAHIA

EDITORA DIARIO DA MANHA LTD. (E)
Rua Marques de Paranaqua, No. 9, Ilheus, Bahia, 45660, Brazil; tel (55)
Pub. – Eduardo Jose Nascimento Cardoso

EDITORA DIARIO DA MANHA LTD. (D)
Rua Maria Quiteria, No. 75, Ilheus, Bahia, 45660, Brazil; tel (55)
Circ.: 2,000
Pub. – Diamentino Correra da Cruz

IPATINGA, MINAS GERAIS

EDITORA DIARIO DA MANHA LTD. (D)
Rua Diamantia, No. 160, Ipatinga, Minas Gerais, 35160, Brazil; tel (55)
Circ.: 3,000
Pub. – Jose Rodrigues do Amaral

ITABUNA, BAHIA

EMPRESA DE DIVULGACAO SULBAHIANO S.A. (D)
Avda. Princeza Izabel, No. S/N, Itabuna, Bahia, 45600, Brazil; tel (55)
Circ.: 5,000
Pub. – Paulo Simoes Machada

ITAPEVA, SAO PAULO

TRIBUNA SUL PAULISTA (D)
Rua Prof. Rivadavia M. Junior, No. 103, Itapeva, Sao Paulo, 18400, Brazil; tel (55)
Circ.: 4,000
Pub. – Jandir Abreu Gonzaga

ITATIBA, SAO PAULO

JORNAL DE ITATIBA (M) Est. 1973
Rua Cel. Camilo Peres, 368, Itatiba, Sao Paulo, 13250-907, Brazil; tel (55) 11 4524 0507; fax 4524 0115; e-mail redacao@ji.com.br; web site www.ji.com.br
Ed. – Manuel Hopesto

ITUIUTABA, MINAS GERAIS

JORNAL CIDADE DE ITUIUTABA LTD. (D)
Rua 18, No. 923, Ituiutaba, Minas Gerais, 38300, Brazil; tel (55)
Circ.: 5,000
Pub. – Jargas T. Gomes

JAU, SAO PAULO

COMERCIO DO JAHU (M) Est. 1908
Rua Mal Bittencourt, 320, Jau, Sao Paulo, 17201-430, Brazil; tel (55) 14 2104 2100; fax 621-2000
Pres. – Mima Cury Bauab
Sales Mgr. – Angela Cristina Lima do Am
Ed. – Raul Bauab Filho

JOAO PESSOA, PARAIBA

O NORTE (M)
Ave. Pedro II, 899 - Centro, Joao Pessoa, Paraiba, 58013-420, Brazil; tel (55) 83 4009 5000; fax 222 2541; e-mail editor@jornalonorte.com.br; web site www.jornalonorte.com.br
Circ.: 5,000
Gen. Mgr. – Cecilio fonseca
Sales Mgr. – Carlos Alexandre Malteze
Ed. – Luiz Carlos de Sousa
Prodn. Mgr. – Walkiria Fonseca

UNIAO CIA. EDITORA (D)
Est. Br. 101, Km. 03, District Industrial, Joao Pessoa, Paraiba, 58070, Brazil; tel (55)
Circ.: 5,000
Pub. – Aluysio Moura

JOINVILLE, SANTA CATARINA

A NOTICIA (M) Est. 1924
Rua Cacador, No. 112 - Atiradores, Joinville, Santa Catarina, 89203-610, Brazil; tel (55) 47 3431 9000; fax 3433 9100; e-mail anoticia@an.com.br; web site www.an.com.br
Circ.: 60,000
Adv. Mgr. – Henrique de Carvalho
Sales Mgr. – Helmut Kleczewski
Ed. – Luis Meneghim

JUIZ DE FORA, MINAS GERAIS

ESDEVA EMPRESA GRAFICA LTD. (D)
Av. Getulio Vargas, 387, Juiz De Fora, Minas Gerais, 36015, Brazil; tel (55) 32 3215 4555; fax 3215 6080; e-mail balcaocentro@tribunademinas.com.br; web site www.tribunademinas.com.br
Circ.: 15,000
Mng. Ed. – Marcos Neves
Exec. Ed. – Denise Goncales
Gen. Ed. – Paulo Cesar Magela

JUNDIAI, SAO PAULO

EDITORA JUNDIAI LTD. (D)
Rua Barao de Jundiai, No. 374, Jundiai, Sao Paulo, 13200, Brazil; tel (55)
Circ.: 14,500
Pub. – Tobias Muzaiel

EDITORA PANORAMA LTD. (D)
Rua Coronel Leme da Fonseca, No. 344, Jundiai, Sao Paulo, 13200, Brazil; tel (55)
Circ.: 13,000
Pub. – Gustavo Leopoldo Maryssael de Campos

LAGES, SANTA CATARINA

CORREIO LAGEANO (M) Est. 1939
Caixa Postal 59, Lages, Santa Catarina, 88502-000, Brazil; tel (55) 49 3221 3311; fax 3221 3310; e-mail jcl1@matrix.com.br; web site www.correiolageano.com.br
Circ.: 5,000
Ed. – Maiuro Maciel

LAJEADO, RIO GRANDE DO SUL

O INFORMATIVO DO VALE (M)
Ave. Benjamin Constant, 2197, Lajeado, Rio Grande do Sul, 95900-000, Brazil; tel (55) 51 714-1144; fax 714-1144
Circ.: 6,000
Ed. – Osvaldo Carlos Van Leeuwen

LIMEIRA, SAO PAULO

GAZETA DE LIMEIRA (M)
Rua Sen. Vergueiro, 319, Limeira, Sao Paulo, 13480-000, Brazil; tel (55) 19 3404 3700; e-mail gazeta@limeira.com.br; web site www.gazetadelimeira.com.br
Circ.: 6,000
Pres. – Robert Lucato

LONDRINA, PARANA

EMPRESA JORNALISTICA FOLHA DE LONDRINA LTD. (D)
Rua Piaui 241, Londrina, Parana, 86010, Brazil; tel (55) 432 242020; fax 211051
Circ.: 40,000
Pres. – Joao Milanez

MACEIO, ALAGOAS

JORNAL DE ALAGOAS (DS)
R. Cons. Lourenco de Albuquerque, No. 115, Maceio, Alagoas, 57000, Brazil; tel (55) 82 2121 3888; e-mail redacao@tribunadealagoas.com.br; web site www.tribunadealagoas.com.br
Dir. – Geraldo Lessa

JORNAL GAZETA DE ALAGOAS LTD. (D)
Avda. Durval de Goes Monteiro, Maceio,

Alagoas, 57000, Brazil; tel (55); e-mail gazn01@nornet.com.br
Circ.: 12,000
Pub. – Fernando Collor de Mello

K.P. ASSUNCAO JORNAL DE HOJE (D)
Rua Barao de Alagoas, No. 160, Maceio, Alagoas, 57000, Brazil; tel (55)
Circ.: 5,000
Pub. – Dauntenorio de Oliveira

MANAUS

EMPRESA JORNAL DO COMERCIO S.A. (M)
Ave. Tefe 3025, Manaus, 69078, Brazil; tel (55) 92 2101 5500
Circ.: 25,000
Pub. – Guilherme Filva

MANAUS, AMAZONAS

EDITORA ANA CASSIA LTD. (D)
Avda. Djalma Batista, No. 2010, Manaus, Amazonas, 69000, Brazil; tel (55) 92
Circ.: 10,000
Pub. – Cassiano Cirilo Anuniacato
Adv. Mgr. – Cassiano Filho
Ed. – Pilinio Valerio

EDITORA GARCIA LTD. (D)
Estrada do Contorno, No. S/N, Manaus, Amazonas, 69000, Brazil; tel (55) 92
Circ.: 12,000
Pub. – Francisco Garcia Rodrigues
Ed. – Raimundo Nonato Cardosa

EMPRESA DE JORNAIS CALDERARO (MS)
Avda. Andre Araujo, Km. 3, Manaus, Amazonas, 69060, Brazil; tel (55) 92 6422000; fax 6421501; e-mail jornal@acritica.com.br; web site www.acritica.com.br
Circ.: 19,000
Advertising: Charney/Palacios & Co. Inc.
Dir. – Umberto Caderaro

EMPRESA DE JORNAL DO COMERCIO LTD. (M)
Avda. Santa Cruz Mackado, No. 170A, Manaus, Amazonas, 69000, Brazil; tel (55) 92 2373218
Circ.: 5,000
Pub. – Selma Bonfim Silva
Ed. – Guilherme Gadelha

MARILIA, SAO PAULO

JORNAL DA MANHA REGIONAL (M) Est. 1981
Rua 15 de Novembro, 883, Marilia, Sao Paulo, 17500-050, Brazil; tel (55) 144 22-2400; fax 22-2488
Pres. – Wanderley Rossilho D'Avila
Ed. – Jocelyn M. de Oliveira

JORNAL DO COMERCIO (M) Est. 1956
Rua 9 de Julho, 1440, Marilia, Sao Paulo, 17500-050, Brazil; tel (55) 14 433-1022
Circ.: 6,000
Pres. – Antonio C. Alves

MARINGA, PARANA

EDITORA CENTRAL LTD. (D)
Avda. Maua, No. 1988, Maringa, Parana, 87050, Brazil; tel (55)
Circ.: 8,000
Pub. – Franklin Vierira da Silva

EDITORA EDIMAR LTD. (D)
Avda. Bento Munhoz da Rocha Netto, No. 1318, Maringa, Parana, 87030, Brazil; tel (55)
Circ.: 10,000
Pub. – Dr. Jerdellicio Barbosa

MAR¡LIA

JORNAL DA MANHA (D)
PO Box 215, Mar¡lia, 17500-050, Brazil; tel (55) 143 422-2400; fax 422-2488; e-mail jmanha@terra.com.br
Circ.: 8,000
Pub. – Gustavo Horst

MOGI DAS CRUZES, SAO PAULO

DIARIO DE MOGI EMPRESA JORNALISTICA S.A. (6X WK.)
Rua Ricardo Vilela, No. 586, Mogi Das Cruzes, Sao Paulo, 8700, Brazil; tel (55) 11 4798 9000; fax 4798 9016; e-mail diario@odiariodemogi.com.br; web site www.odiariodemogi.com.br
Circ.: 15,000
Pub. – Tirreno Dasambiagio

MONTES CLAROS, MINAS GERAIS

DIARIO DE MONTES CLAROS (M) Est. 1979
Rua Antonio Rodrigues, 36 - S. Jose, Montes Claros, Minas Gerais, 39400-001, Brazil; tel (55) 38 3221 7008; fax 3221 2337
Ed. – Mario Augusto Bermamm Oliva

GRAFICA JORNAL DE MONTES CLAROS LTD. (D)
Avda. Dulce Sarmento, No. 397, Montes Claros, Minas Gerais, 39400, Brazil; tel (55)
Circ.: 15,000
Pub. – Oswaldo Alves Antunes
Ed. – Waldyr de Senna Batista

JORNAL DO NORTE
Ave. Mestra Fininha, 755, Montes Claros, Minas Gerais, 39401-074, Brazil; tel (55) 38 221-1616; fax 221-1616
Pres. – Americo Martins Filho

MOSSORO, RIO GRANDE DO NORTE

GAZETA DE OESTE (M) Est. 1977
Ave. Cunha da Mota, 96 Centro, Mossoro, Rio Grande do Norte, 59600-160, Brazil; tel (55) 84 321-6214; fax 321-3203; e-mail gazeta@nextway.com.br; web site www.gazetadoeste.com.br
Circ.: 5,000
Gen. Mgr. – Maria Emilia Lopes Pereira
Adv./Sales Mgr. – Jose Nilton da Silva
Ed. – Francisco Caninde Queiroz e Silva
Prodn. Mgr. – Leonidas Pereira de Paula Terceiro

O MOSSOROENSE (M) Est. 1872
Travessa O Mossoroense, 42, Centro, Mossoro, Rio Grande do Norte, 59600-730, Brazil; tel (55) 84 315 3200; fax 321 6098; e-mail diretor@omossoroense.com.br; web site www.uol.com.br/omossoroense
Pres. – Alvanilson Carlos
Ed. in Chief – Emerson Linhares
Ed. – Pedro Carlos

NATAL, RIO GRANDE DO NORTE

COMPANHIA EDITORA DO RIO GRANDE DO NORTE (D)
Avda. Junqueira Aires, No. 355, Natal, Rio Grande do Norte, 59000, Brazil; tel (55) 84
Circ.: 2,000
Pub. – Marcelo Fernandes de Oliveira

EDITORA O DIARIO S.A. (DS)
Avda. Deodoro, No. 245, Natal, Rio Grande do Norte, 59000, Brazil; tel (55)
Pub. – Luiz Maria Alves

EMPRESA JORNALISTICA TRIBUNA DO NORTE S.A. (M)
Travesa Nizia Floresta, No. 100, Natal, Rio Grande do Norte, 59000, Brazil; tel (55)
Circ.: 20,000
Pub. – Aluizio Alves
Ed. – Dorian Jorge Freire

IMPRENSA OFICIAL (D)
Avda. Junqueira Aires, No. 355, Natal, Rio Grande do Norte, 59000, Brazil; tel (55) 8423748
Circ.: 1,500
Pub. – Marcelo Fernandes de Oliveira

NITEROI, RIO DE JANEIRO

EDITORA ESQUENA LTD. (D)
Rua Barao do Amazonas 31, Niteroi, Rio de Janeiro, 24210, Brazil; tel (55) 21 7191886
Circ.: 18,000
Gen. Dir. – Jourdan Amora

EDITORA FLUMINESE LTD. (M)
Rua Visconde de Itaborai 184, Niteroi, Rio de Janeiro, 24030, Brazil; tel (55) 21 7193311; fax 7196344
Circ.: 80,000
Dir. – Alberto Francisco Torres

NOVA IGUACU, RIO DE JANEIRO

GRAFICA E EDITORA JORNALISTICA DE HOJE LTD. (D)
Rua Kennedy, No. 101, Nova Iguacu, Rio de Janeiro, 26260, Brazil; tel (55)
Circ.: 80,000
Pub. – Walcir Alemeida

NOVO HAMBURGO, RIO GRANDE DO SUL

GRUPO EDITORIAL SINOS S.A. (D)
Avda. Coronel Federico Linck, No. 71, Novo Hamburgo, Rio Grande do Sul, 93330, Brazil; tel (55)
Circ.: 22,000
Pub. – Mario A. de Paula Gusmao

OURINHOS, SAO PAULO

EMPRESA EDITORA JORNAIS DE OURINHOS LTD. (D)
Rua Euclides da Cunha, No. 80, Ourinhos, Sao Paulo, 19900, Brazil; tel (55)
Circ.: 4,600
Pub. – Benedito da Silva Ecoy

PARAIBA DO SUL, RIO DE JANEIRO

JORNAL DE PARAIBA DO SUL (M) Est. 1967
Rua Dr. Saturnino Braga, 104, Paraiba Do Sul, Rio de Janeiro, 25850-000, Brazil; tel (55) 24 263-2081; fax 263-2081
Pres. – Esmail Texeira de Abreu
Ed. – Victor Augusto L. de Abreu

PARANAGUA, PARANA

ANASTACIO E ANASTACIO (D)
Rua Mar Alberto de Abreu, No. 140, Paranagua, Parana, 83200, Brazil; tel (55)
Circ.: 1,000
Pub. – N. Miguel Anastacio Netto

PARANAVAI, PARANA

DIARIO NOROESTE (M) Est. 1955
Ave. Parana, 1100, Paranavai, Parana, 87705-140, Brazil; tel (55) 44 423-2626; fax 423-2186
Pres. – Euclides Bogoni
Ed. – Saul Bogoni

PASSO FUNDO, RIO GRANDE DO SUL

EMPRESA JORNALISTICA DIARIO DA MANHA LTD. (D)
Avda. 7 de Septembre, No. 909, Passo Fundo, Rio Grande do Sul, 99100, Brazil; tel (55)
Circ.: 5,500
Pub. – Dyogenes Auildo Martins Pinto

O NACIONAL (M) Est. 1925
Ave. Sete de Setembro, 481, Passo Fundo, Rio Grande do Sul, 99010-121, Brazil; tel (55) 54 313 6266; fax 313 6133; e-mail redacao@onacional.com.br; web site www.onacional.com.br
Circ.: 6,000
Pres. – Mucio de Castro Filho
Ed. – Luiz Carlos Schneider

PELOTAS, RIO GRANDE DO SUL

GRAFICA DIARIO POPULAR LTD. (D)
Rua 15 de Novembro, No. 718, Pelotas, Rio Grande do Sul, 96015, Brazil; tel (55) 532 255 566; web site www.diariopopular.com.br
Circ.: 6,000
Pub. – Ruy Faria de Queiroz
Dir. – Clayr Lobo Rochefort

PETROPOLIS, RIO DE JANEIRO

DIARIO DE PETROPOLIS (M) Est. 1954
Ave. Epitacio Pessoa, 84/100, Petropolis, Rio de Janeiro, 25610-010, Brazil; tel (55) 24 243-3189; fax 231-1389; web site www.tribuna.com.br
Circ.: 4,000
Pres. – Paulo Antonio Carneiro Dias
Gen. Mgr. – Manoel Carneiro
Ed. – Ricardo Goothuzem

TRIBUNA DE PETROPOLIS (M) Est. 1902
Rua Alencar Lima, 26, Petropolis, Rio de Janeiro, 25620-050, Brazil; tel (55) 21 237-5122; fax 242-7549; web site www.e-tribuna.com.br
Circ.: 12,000
Pres. – Francisco de Orleans e Braganca
Ed. – Francisco Carlos de Andrade

PIRACICABA, SAO PAULO

EMPRESA O DIARIO LTD. (D)
Rua Sao Jose, No. 844, Piracicaba, Sao Paulo, 13400, Brazil; tel (55)
Circ.: 8,000
Pub. – Cecilio Elias Netto

JORNAL DE PIRACICABA (M) Est. 1900
Ave. Comendador Luciano Guidotti, 2525, Piracicaba, Sao Paulo, 13424-540, Brazil; tel

(55) 19 430-4000; fax 430-4001; e-mail jp@jpjornal.com.br; web site www.jpjornal.com.br
Pres. – Antonietta Rosalina da Cunha Losso Pe
Ed. – Lourenco Jorge Tayar

TRIBUNA PIRACICABANA JORNAL E GRAFICA LTD. (D)
Rua Tiradentes, 647 - Centro, Piracicaba, Sao Paulo, 13400, Brazil; tel (55) 19 2105 8555; e-mail tribuna@tribunatp.com.br; web site www.tribunatp.com.br
Circ.: 1,500
Pub. – Evaldo A. Vincente

POCOS DE CALDAS, MINAS GERAIS

DIARIO DE POCOS DE CALDAS (D)
Rua Santa Catarina, No. 715, Pocos De Caldas, Minas Gerais, 37700, Brazil; tel (55)
Circ.: 1,600
Pub. – Trajano Barroco

EMPRESA JORNALISTICA POCOS DE CALDAS LTD. (D)
Avda. Joao Pineheiro, No. 177, Pocos De Caldas, Minas Gerais, 37700, Brazil; tel (55)
Circ.: 3,000
Pub. – Cedio Alves de Morais

PONTA PORA, MATO GROSSO

JORNAL DA PRACA (M)
Rua Rio Branco, 287, Ponta Pora, Mato Grosso, 79900-000, Brazil; tel (55) 67 431-2160; fax 431-2234
Ed. – Joao N. de Oliveira

PORTO ALEGRE, RIO GRANDE DO SUL

CIA. JORNALISTICA (D)
Avda. Joao Pessoa, No. 1282, Porto Alegre, Rio Grande do Sul, 90040, Brazil; tel (55)
Circ.: 30,000
Pres. – Zaida Jayme Jarros
Editorial Dir. – Homero Guerreiro
Adv. Dir. – Sepe Tiaraju Matzenbacher
Pub. – J.C. Jarros

EMPRESA JORNALISTICA CALDAS JUNIOR LTD. (DS)
Avda. Caldas Junior, No. 219, Porto Alegre, Rio Grande do Sul, 90000, Brazil; tel (55) 51 3215 6100; e-mail correio@cpovo.net; web site www.correiodopovo.com.br
Dir. – Breno Caldas

IMPRENSA OFICIAL (D)
Rua Cel. Aparicip Borges, No. 2199, Porto Alegre, Rio Grande do Sul, 90630, Brazil; tel (55) 513 288 9700; web site www.corag.com.br
Circ.: 5,000
Pub. – Antonio Setembrino de Mesquita

ZERO HORA (D) Est. 1964
Ave. Ipiranga, 1075, Porto Alegre, Rio Grande do Sul, 90169-900, Brazil; tel (55) 51 3218 4400; fax 3218 4795; e-mail editorias@zerohora.com.br; web site www.zerohora.com.br
Circ.: 270,000
Advertising: The N DeFilippes Corp.
Pres. – Nelson Pacheco Sirotsky
Ed. in Chief – Marta Gleich
Ed. in Chief – Ricardo Stefenelli

PORTO VELHO, RONDONIA

EMPRESA ALTO MADEIRA (D)
Avda. Costa E. Silva, No. S/N, Porto Velho, Rondonia, 78900, Brazil; tel (55)
Circ.: 3,000
Pub. – Epaminondas Barahuna

JORNAL O ESTADO (D)
Avda. Duque de Caxias, No. 1523, Porto Velho, Rondonia, 78900, Brazil; tel (55)
Circ.: 12,000
Pub. – Mario Calixto Filho

PRESIDENTE PRUDENTE, SAO PAULO

EDITORA IMPRENSA LTD. (D)
Rua Siqueira Campos, No. 600, Presidente Prudente, Sao Paulo, 19100, Brazil; tel (55)
Circ.: 13,000
Pub. – Dr. Deodato da Silva

RECIFE, PERNAMBUCO

DIARIO DE PERNAMBUCO (M)
Praca Independencia, 12, Recife, Pernambuco, 50010-902, Brazil; tel (55) 81 3425 7666; fax 424 2527; e-mail diario@dpnet.com.br; web site www.dpnet.com.br
Circ.: 90,000
Pres. – Paulo Cabral de Araujo
Ed. – Gladstone Vieira Belo

GRAFICA EDITORA DO RECIFE S.A. (D)
Rua do Imerador Dom Pedro II, No. 227, Recife, Pernambuco, 50000, Brazil; tel (55)
Circ.: 12,000
Pub. – Benita Fernandes de Gouveia

RIBEIRAO PRETO, SAO PAULO

A CIDADE (M)
Rua Sao Sebastiao, No. 610, Ribeirao Preto, Sao Paulo, 14014-040, Brazil; tel (55) 16 634-2549; fax 625-0336
Circ.: 12,000
Pres. – Jandyra de Camargo Moquenco
Ed. – Juracy L. de Campos

DIARIO DA MANHA
Rua Duque de Caxias 179, Ribeirao Preto, Sao Paulo, 14015, Brazil; tel (55) 16 6340909
Circ.: 17,000
Dir. – Paulo M. Santanna

EDITORA COSTABILE ROMANO LTD. (D)
Rua Americo Brasiliense, No. 140, Ribeirao Preto, Sao Paulo, 14010, Brazil; tel (55)
Circ.: 15,000
Pub. – Marcelino Romano Machado

RIO BRANCO, ACRE

EMPRESA O RIO BRANCO LTD. (D)
Avenida Cear 2804 - Edificio Cristiano M de Assis - Centro, Rio Branco, Acre, 69900-460, Brazil; tel (55) 68 226-1019; e-mail direcao@oriobranco.com.br; web site www.oriobranco.com.br
Circ.: 2,000
Pub. – Jose Chalub Leite

RIO CLARO, SAO PAULO

DIARIO DO RIO CLARO LTD. (D)
Avda. Dois, No. 1068, Rio Claro, Sao Paulo, 13500, Brazil; tel (55)
Circ.: 7,500
Pub. – Geraldo Zanello

JORNAL CIDADE (M) Est. 1934
Ave. Cinco, 283 Centro, Rio Claro, Sao Paulo, 13500-380, Brazil; tel (55) 19 534-5511; fax 534-5511; e-mail alinejc@uol.com.br
Circ.: 4,500
Pres. – Aline Magalhaes Ceron
Gen. Mgr. – Djalma Lautenschlager
Ed. – Jose Roberto Santana

JORNAL DE RIO CLARO (M) Est. 1982
Rua 1, 861 - Centro, Rio Claro, Sao Paulo, 13500-040, Brazil; tel (55) 19 3526 1000; e-mail jornalrclaro@linkway.com.br; web site http://jornalrclaro.linkway.com.br
Pres. – Evanilton Sergio Castanho

RIO DE JANEIRO

DIARIO DAS CONCORRENCIAS (M) Est. 1939
Rua Leandro Martins, 20, Rio De Janeiro, 20080-70, Brazil; tel (55) 21 263-5840; fax 263-5840
Pres. – Rosselita F. de Lima

EDITORA E IMPRESSORA DE JORNAIS E REVISTAS S.A. (MS)
Rua Riachuelo 359, Rio De Janeiro, 20235, Brazil; tel (55) 21 2728000; fax 5071038
Pres. – Antonio Ary de Carvalho

EDITORA TRIBUNA DO IMPRENSA S.A. (E)
Rua do Lavradio, No. 98, Rio De Janeiro, 20230, Brazil; tel (55) 21 2526040
Circ.: 12,000
Pub. – Nice Lourdes Garcia Brant

JORNAL DO BRASIL (D) Est. 1891
Paulo de Frontin 568, Rio De Janeiro, 20261, Brazil; tel (55) 21 2101 4000; fax 2101 4488; e-mail jb@jb.com.br; web site jbonline.terra.com.br
Circ.: 196,000
Advertising: Charney Palacios & Co.
Ed. – Amateur Mello

JORNAL DO COMERCIO (M) Est. 1827
Rua do Livramento, 189/74, Rio De Janeiro, 20221-191, Brazil; tel (55) 21 2223 8551; fax 2223 8604; e-mail jornaldocommercio@jcom.com.br; web site www.jornaldocommercio.com.br
Circ.: 40,000
Pres. – Mauricio Ginepi
Gen. Mgr. – Nelson Gimenez
Ed. – Antonio Calegari

JORNAL DOS SPORTS (M) Est. 1931
Rua Pereira de Almeida, 88, Rio De Janeiro, 20260-000, Brazil; tel (55) 21 2221 2926; fax 2509 1101; e-mail confidenc@uol.com.br
Circ.: 150,000
Ed. – Carlos Antonio Campos Macedo

O GLOBO (MS)
Caixa Postal 1090, Rio De Janeiro, 20233-900, Brazil; tel (55) 21 5345000; fax 5345510; web site www.oglobo.com.br
Group: Multimedia, Inc.
Advertising: The N DeFilippes Corp.
Dir. – Francisco Graell

SAO MARCELO DE PUBLICACOES LTDA. (MS)
Rua do Resende, 65, Rio De Janeiro, Brazil; tel (55)
Circ.: 28,600
Pub. – Giberto Huber
Ed. – Mauro Salles

RIO GRANDE, RIO GRANDE DO SUL

ORGANIZACOES RISUL (D)
Rua Aquidabam, No. 695, Rio Grande, Rio Grande do Sul, 96200, Brazil; tel (55)
Circ.: 2,500
Pub. – Germano Torales Leite

SALVADOR, BA

A TARDE (E) Est. 1912
Ave. Tancredo Neves, 1092 - Caminho das Arvores, Salvador, BA, 41822-900, Brazil; tel (55) 71 200-1234; fax 340-8714; e-mail atarde@atarde.com.br; web site www.atarde.com.br
Circ.: 125,000
Pres. – Renato Simoes
Gen. Mgr. – Edivaldo Machado Boaventura
Ed. – Sylvio Simoes

SALVADOR, BAHIA

EMPRESA BAIANA DE JORNALISMO (A MEMBER OF REDE BAHIA DE COMUNICACAO) (D)
Avda. Luiz Viana Filho, s/n, Centro Executivo da B, Salvador, Bahia, 41736-900, Brazil; tel (55) 71 3709700; fax 3709788; e-mail redacao@correiodabahia.com.br; web site www.correiodabahia.com.br
Ed. – Demostenes Teixeira

EMPRESA EDITORA A TARDE S.A. (MS)
R. Prof. Milton Cayres De Brito 204, Salvador, Bahia, 41822-900, Brazil; tel (55) 713 340 8800; fax 340 8712; web site www.atarde.com.br
Pub. – Egivaldo Boabentuda

INFORME DO EMPRESARIO (M) Est. 1970
Rua Portugal, 11-5 andar, Salvador, Bahia, 40015-000, Brazil; tel (55) 71 242-8363; fax 243-2645
Ed. – Afranio E. Correa

JORNAL DA BAHIA (MS)
Rua Peruvia Carneiro 220, Salvador, Bahia, 41100, Brazil; tel (55) 71 3842919; fax 3845726
Circ.: 20,000
Pres. – Mario Kertesz

TRIBUNA DA BAHIA (M) Est. 1969
Rua Djalma Dutra, 121, Salvador, Bahia, 40256-900, Brazil; tel (55) 71 3321 2161; fax 3321 5322; e-mail tribunadabahia@tribunadabahia.com.br; web site www.tribunadabahia.com.br
Pres. – Walter Pinheiro

SANTA MARIA, RIO GRANDE DO SUL

JORNAL A RAZAO (D)
Rua Serafim Valandro, No. 1284, Santa Maria, Rio Grande do Sul, 97100, Brazil; tel (55) 3220 2100; fax 3220 2110; e-mail arazao@arazao.com.br; web site www.arazao.com.br
Circ.: 3,000
Dir. – Alexandre De Grandi

SANTANA DO LIVRAMENTO, RIO GRANDE DO SUL

EDITORA FOLHA POPULAR S.A. (D)
Vasco Alves, No. 423, Santana Do Livramento, Rio Grande do Sul, 97570, Brazil; tel (55)
Pub. – Jose Getulio M. Pereira

SANTO ANDRE, SAO PAULO

DIARIO DO GRANDE ABC (M) Est. 1958
Rua Catequese, 562 - Bairro Jardim, Santo Andre, Sao Paulo, 09090-900, Brazil; tel (55) 11 4435 8100; fax 4435 8250; e-mail secretaria@dgabc.com.br; web site www.dgabc.com.br
Circ.: 50,000
Ed. – Lola Nicolas

SANTOS, SAO PAULO

EMPRESA FOLHA DA MANHA LTD. (D)
Rua do Comercio, No. 32, Santos, Sao Paulo, 11100, Brazil; tel (55)
Circ.: 40,000
Pub. – Octavio Frias de Oliveira

A TRIBUNA (M)
Rua General Camara 90-94 - Centro, Santos, Sao Paulo, 11010-903, Brazil; tel (55) 13 2102 7151; fax 3219 4394; e-mail atribuna@atribuna.com.br; admjornal@atribuna.com.brComercial; web site www.atribuna.com.br
Circ.: 33,000
Ed. in Chief – Wilson Marini

SAO CARLOS, SAO PAULO

A TRIBUNA (D)
Rua Conde do Pinhal, No. 2443, Sao Carlos, Sao Paulo, 13560, Brazil; tel (55)
Circ.: 6,000
Pub. – Celso Luiz Guimeres Keppe

EMPRESA JORNALISTICA DECISAO LTD. (D)
Rua Dona Alexandria, No. 1090, Sao Carlos, Sao Paulo, 13560, Brazil; tel (55)
Circ.: 3,000
– J. Sigueira
– P.E.D. Duarte
– Rubens BettingPub.s

EMPRESA O IMPERIAL LTD. (D)
Avda. Dr. Jose Pereira LOpes, No. 188, Sao Carlos, Sao Paulo, 13560, Brazil; tel (55)
Circ.: 7,000
Pub. – Paulo de Arruda Correra da Silva

SAO GONCALO, RIO DE JANEIRO

O SAO GONCALO (M) Est. 1931
Rua Yolanda Saad Abuzaid, 150 Grupo 917-Alcantara, Sao Goncalo, Rio de Janeiro, 24710-460, Brazil; tel (55) 21 2601 7272; fax 2601 3965; e-mail redacao@jornalsg.com.br; web site www.jornalsaogoncalo.com.br
Circ.: 5,000
Pres. – Cezar Augusto de Mattos
Sales Mgr. – Marcia Vianna de Mattos
Ed. – Cecilia Ma. Vianna de Mattos Pereira

SAO JOAO DEL REI, MINAS GERIAS

JORNAL DO POSTE
Rua Santa Teresa, 09 - Centro, Sao Joao Del Rei, Minas Gerias, 36300-000, Brazil; tel (55) 32 371-1875
Ed. – Claudio Monteiro

SAO JOSE DO RIO PRETO, SAO PAULO

A NOTICIA (D)
Rua General Glicerio, No. 2023, Sao Jose Do Rio Preto, Sao Paulo, 15100, Brazil; tel (55)
Circ.: 8,000
Pub. – Fausto Gomes

DIARIO DA REGIAO (M) Est. 1950
Rua Delegado Pinto de Toledo, 2844 - Centro, Sao Jose Do Rio Preto, Sao Paulo, 15010-500, Brazil; tel (55) 17 2139 2000; fax 2139 2049; e-mail diario@diarioweb.com.br; web site www.diarioweb.com.br
Circ.: 31,000
Pres. – Norberto Buzzini

FOLHA DE RIO PRETO (D)
Rua Coronel Spindola Castro, No. 3562, Sao Jose Do Rio Preto, Sao Paulo, 15100, Brazil; tel (55)
Circ.: 6,000
Pub. – Jose Barbar Cury

SAO JOSE DOS CAMPOS, SAO PAULO

JAC EDITORA LTD. (D)
Rua Sao Paulo, No. 217, Sao Jose Dos Campos, Sao Paulo, 12215, Brazil; tel (55)
Circ.: 9,600
Pub. – Jose Cristovao Ribeiro Cursino

O VALEPARAIBANO (DS)
Estrada Velha Rio Sao Paulo, Sao Jose Dos Campos, Sao Paulo, 3755, Brazil; tel (55)
Circ.: 50,000
Pub. – Ferdinando Salerno

SAO LUIS, MARANHAO

EMPRESA PACOTILHA LTD. (D)
Rua Afonso Pena 46, Sao Luis, Maranhao, 65000, Brazil; tel (55) 98 2225120; fax 2225120
Circ.: 5,000
Gen. Dir. – Pedro Batista Freire

GRAFICA ESCOLAR S.A. (D)
Avda. Ana Jansen, Sao Luis, Maranhao, 65000, Brazil; tel (55); e-mail adriana@mirante.com.br; web site www.mirante.com.br/oestado
Circ.: 5,000
Pub. – Humberto de Almeida Castro
Ed. in Chief – Ademir Santos
Adv. Mgr. – Evilson Almeida

JORNAL PEQUENO (D)
Rua Formosa, No. 171, Sao Luis, Maranhao, 65000, Brazil; tel (55) 98
Circ.: 6,000
Pub. – J.M. Ferreira

SAO PAULO

DIARIO DO COMERCIO (M) Est. 1932
51 Boa Vista St., 6th Fl., Sao Paulo, 01014-911, Brazil; tel (55) 11 3244 3322; fax 3244 3046; e-mail psteza@docomercio,com.br; web site www.docomercio.com.br
Circ.: 35,000
Ed. in Chief – Jose Guillermo Rodrigues Ferreira

EMPRESA JORNALISTICA DIARIO POPULAR LTD.
Rua Major Quedinho, No. 28, Sao Paulo, Brazil; tel (55) 11 713-1973

FOLHA DE SAO PAULO (M) Est. 1921
Alameda Barao de Limeira, 425 - Campos Eliseos, Sao Paulo, 01202, Brazil; tel (55) 11 3224 3222; fax 3223 1644; e-mail folha@uol.com.br; web site www.uol.com.br/fsp/
Circ.: 1,200,000
Group: Brydson Global Media Sales
Advertising: Charney/Palacios and Co.
Editorial Dir. – Octavio Frias

JORNAL DA MANHA (M) Est. 1975
Av. Ipiranga, 1251, Sao Paulo, 01039-906, Brazil; tel (55) 11 227-2857; fax 227-2857
Pres. – Gecia P. Sotomayor
Sales Mgr. – Mauro Morales Baessa
Ed. – Carlos Henrique Bastos Duarte

NOTICIAS POPULARES (M) Est. 1963
Alameda Barao de Limeira, 425, Sao Paulo, 01202-900, Brazil; tel (55) 11 224-3222; fax 224-4224; e-mail np@uol.com.br; web site www.folha.com.br/hp
Circ.: 100,000
Pres. – Pedroo Pinciroli
Sales. Mgr. – Antonio Carlos de Moura
Ed. – Eliane Silva

O ESTADO DE SAO PAULO S.A. (E-EX S)
Rua Peixoto Gomidi 671, Sao Paulo, 01409, Brazil; tel (55) 11 284-1944; fax 289-3548
Advertising: The N DeFilippes Corp.
Dir. – R. Mesquita

POPULAR DA TARDE (E)
Rua Major Quedinho, No. 28, Sao Paulo, 01050, Brazil; tel (55)
Circ.: 110,000
Pub. – Rodrigo Soares

VISAO/REVISTA
Rua Alfonso Celso 143, Sao Paulo, Brazil; tel (55) 11 239 4333

SAO PAULO, SAO PAULO

ASSOCIACAO COMERCIAL DE SAO PAULO (M)
Rua Boa Vista, No. 51, Sao Paulo, Sao Paulo, 10140, Brazil; tel (55) 11 3244 3322; fax 3244 3046; e-mail dcomercio@acsp.com.br; web site www.dcomercio.com.br
Circ.: 25,000
Pub. – Alencar Burti

BRASILTURIS JORNAL
Avda. Pacaembu 1400, Sao Paulo, Sao Paulo, Brazil; tel (55) 11 8856811

CIA. PAULISTA EDITORA DE JORNAIS (D-EX MON.)
Al. Barao de Limeira 425, Sao Paulo, Sao Paulo, 01202, Brazil; tel (55) 11 2200011
Advertising: Charney/Palacios & Co. Inc.
Gen. Mgr. – Renato Castanhari

DCI-EDITORA JORNALISTICA S.A. (M)
Rua Alvaro de Carvalho 354, Sao Paulo, Sao Paulo, 01050-020, Brazil; tel (55) 11 256-5011; fax 258-1989
Circ.: 50,000
Pres. – Hamilton Lucas de Olveira

EDITORA BRAZIL-POST (D)
CP 6401, Sao Paulo, Sao Paulo, 01064-970, Brazil; tel (55) 11 5589 2917; fax 5581 1442; e-mail brasilpost@brasilpost.com.br; web site www.brasilpost.com.br
Pub. – Ursula Dormien
Adv. Mgr. – K.D. Dormien

EMPRESA FOLHA DE MANHA S.A. (E)
Al. Barao de Limeira, No. 425, Sao Paulo, Sao Paulo, 01290, Brazil; tel (55) 11
Circ.: 90,000
Ed. in Chief – Antonio Aggio

EMPRESA JORNALISTICA DIARIO POPULAR S.A. (E)
Rua Major Quedinho 28, 1-6 andares, Sao Paulo, Sao Paulo, 01050, Brazil; tel (55) 11 2582133; fax 2561627; web site www.diariopopular.com.br
Circ.: 90,000
Dir. – Ricardo Gural de Sabeya

O ESTADO DE SAO PAULO S.A. (MS)
Avda. Eng. Caetano Alvares 55, Sao Paulo, Sao Paulo, 02550, Brazil; tel (55) 11 8562122; fax 2662206; web site www.estado.com.br
Circ.: 491,070
Advertising: The N DeFilippes Corp.
Pub. – Jose Vieira de Carvalho Mesquita
Dir. – Francisco Mesquita Neto

SOROCABA, SAO PAULO

CRUZEIRO DO SUL (M) Est. 1903
Ave. Engro. Carlos Reinaldo Mendes, 2.800, Sorocaba, Sao Paulo, 18013-280, Brazil; tel (55) 15 3224-5100; fax 3228-1888; web site www.jcruzeiro.com.br
Circ.: 30,000
Pub. – F.S. de Oliveira Camargo
Ed. – Djalma L. Benette

JORNAL E EDITORA LTD. (D)
Rua da Penha, No. 609, Sorocaba, Sao Paulo, 18010, Brazil; tel (55)
Circ.: 17,000
Pub. – Fernando de Lucas Neto

SUMARE, SAO PAULO

COMUNICACAO JORNAL (M) Est. 1976
Av. Luiz Frutuoso, 534, Sumare, Sao Paulo, 13170-260, Brazil; tel (55) 19 273-1370; fax 273-1370
Ed. – Izabel M. Ferreira

TAQUARITINGA, SAO PAULO

CIDADE DE TAQUARITINGA (D)
Rua Marechal Deodoro, No. 1131, Taquaritinga, Sao Paulo, 15900, Brazil; tel (55)
Circ.: 4,000
Pub. – Joao Atello

TAUBATE, SAO PAULO

DIARIO DE TAUBATE (M)
Rua Dr. Souza Alves, 844, Taubate, Sao Paulo, 12020-030, Brazil; tel (55) 12 232-2480
Ed. – Neva T. Rodrigues

A VOZ DO VALE DO PARIABO (M)
Rua Dr. Emilio Winther, No. 79, Taubate, Sao Paulo, 12030-000, Brazil; tel (55) 12 232-3176; fax 232-3176
Circ.: 5,000
Ed. – Waldemar Duarte

TERESINA, PIAUI

EDITORA GRAFICA RIJORA LTD. (M)
Rua Lisandro Nogueira, No. 870, Teresina, Piaui, 64000, Brazil; tel (55)
Circ.: 3,000
Pub. – Jose Ribomar Oliveira

JORNAL DO PIAUI (M) Est. 1951
Rua Arlindo Nogueira, 505, Teresina, Piaui, 64001-230, Brazil; tel (55) 86 222-8244
Pres. – Maria E. Ferreira Diniz

JORNAL O DIA (D)
Rua Governador Arturo de Vasconcelos, No. 131, Teresina, Piaui, 64000, Brazil; tel (55)
Circ.: 10,000
Pub. – Otavio Miranda

TERESOPOLIS, RIO DE JANEIRO

GAZETA DE TERESOPOLIS (M) Est. 1970
Rua Darcy Menezes de Aragao, 51, Teresopolis, Rio De Janeiro, 25963-160, Brazil;

tel (55) 21 742-1822
Ed. – Viviano Leite de Castro

TOLEDO, PARANA

JORNAL DO OESTE (M) Est. 1984
Av. Parigot de Souza, 2926, Toledo, Parana, 85904-270, Brazil; tel (55) 45 252 3222; fax 252 3222
Pres. – Joao Kreuz
Ed. – Luiz Alberto Costa

TRES RIOS, RIO DE JANEIRO

ENTRE RIOS JORNAL (M) Est. 1935
Rua Padre Conrad 67 -Center, Tres Rios, Rio de Janeiro, 25804-090, Brazil; tel (55) 24 2252 0855; fax 252 1391; web site www.entreriosjornal.com.br
Dir./Pres. – Joseph Bridges Nada de Souza
Ed. – Daniel Vizeu

TUPA, SAO PAULO

FOLHA DO POVO (M) Est. 1956
Rua Caetes, 587, Tupa, Sao Paulo, 17601-150, Brazil; tel (55) 14 442-5944; fax 442-6784
Circ.: 4,000
Ed.. – Carlos Marques Pereira

UBERABA, MINAS GERAIS

JORNAL DA MANHA (6X WK.)
Av Dr. Fidelis Reis, 820 - Centro, Uberaba, Minas Gerais, 38100, Brazil; tel (55) 34 3331 7900; fax 3321 8200; e-mail jmonline@jmonline.com.br; web site www.jmonline.com.br
Circ.: 5,000
Pub. – Joaquim dos Santos Martins

UBERLANDIA, MINAS GERAIS

CORREIO DE UBERLANDIA (M) Est. 1938
Ave. Jose andraus Gassani, 4555, Uberlandia, Minas Gerais, 38402-324, Brazil; tel (55) 34 218-7888; fax 218-7811; e-mail correio@triang.com.br; web site www.jornalcorreio.com.br
Circ.: 12,000
Pres. – Luiz Alberto Garcia
Sales Mgr. – Adilson Colucci
Ed. – Mauricio Ricardo Quirino

O TRIANGULO (M) Est. 1928
Ave. Floriano Peixoto, 2023 Barrio Aparecida, Uberlandia, Minas Gerais, 38406-050, Brazil; tel (55) 34 212-2900; fax 212-2131; e-mail otriang@triang.com.br
Circ.: 10,000
Pres. – Fabiano Fideles
Ed. – Ademir Reis

UMUARAMA, PARANA

A TRIBUNA DO POVO (M) Est. 1973
Rua Piuna, 4150 Centro, Umuarama, Parana, 87501-050, Brazil; tel (55) 44 3056 6050; fax 3622 2818; e-mail redacao@atribunaonline.com.br; web site www.atribunaonline.com.br
Pres. – Walter Sucupira
Gen. Mgr. – Walter L.N. Sucupira
Ed. – Silvio Luiz Ribeiro da Silva

UMUARAMA ILUSTRADO (M) Est. 1973
Ave. Tiradentes, 2680, Umuarama, Parana, 87505-090, Brazil; tel (55) 44 3621 2500; fax 3621 2545; e-mail umuarama@ilustrado.com.br; web site www.ilustrado.com.br
Pres. – Ilidio Coelho Sobrinho

VITORIA DA CONQUISTA, BAHIA

TRIBUNA DO CAFE (M) Est. 1973
Rua Ernesto Dantas, 170 Cj. 207, Vitoria Da Conquista, Bahia, 45100-000, Brazil; tel (55) 73 421-2107; fax 422-5036
Circ.: 5,000
Pub. – Isnard Vasconcelos

VITORIA, ESPIRITO SANTO

A GAZETA (M)
Rua Chafic Murad 902 - Bento Ferreira, Vitoria, Espirito Santo, 29050-901, Brazil; tel (55) 27 3321 8333; fax 3223 1525; e-mail aure@redegazeta.com.br; web site www.gazetaonline.com.br
Circ.: 87,000
Pres. – Maria Antonietta Queiroz Lindenberg

JORNAL DE CIDADE (D)
Avda. Cezar Hilal 905, Ed. Caribe, Vitoria, Espirito Santo, Brazil; tel (55) 27 2253826
Circ.: 10,000
Pub. – Djalma Juarez Magalhaes

VOTUPORANGA, SAO PAULO

DIARIO DE VOTUPORANGA (M) Est. 1949
Praco dos Expedicionarios, 44 - Centro, Votuporanga, Sao Paulo, 15500, Brazil; tel (55) 17 3422 3322; e-mail diario.votup@votuporanga.com.br; web site www.diariodevotuporanga.com.br
Dir. – Danilo LiÂ£vana de Camargo

CHILE

ANGOL

DIARIO RENACER (D)
Vergara 367, Angol, Chile; tel (56) 45 717 409; fax 718 885; e-mail diariore.nacer001@chinet.cl; web site www.renacerdeangol.cl
Dir. – Pablo Sandoval Jara

ANTOFAGASTA

LA ESTRELLA DEL NORTE (E)
Manuel Antonio Matta 2112, Antofagasta, Chile; tel (56) 55 453 600; fax 453 602; e-mail director@estrellanorte.cl; web site www.estrellanorte.cl
Circ.: 10,000
Gen. Mgr. – Jorge Leiva Concha
Ed. – Sergio Montivero Bruno

EL MERCURIO DE ANTOFAGASTA (D)
Manuel Antonio Matta 2112, Antofagasta, Chile; tel (56) 55 453 666; fax 453 602; web site www.elmercurio.cl; www.mercurioantofagasta.cl
Circ.: 20,000
Pres. – Augustin Edwards Eastman

ARAUCO

CELARAUCO (M)
Pedro de Valdivia, No. 80, Arauco, Chile; tel (56)
Dir. – Adalia Valencia Fuentealba

ARICA

ARICA EN MARCHA (M)
Avda. 7 de Junio, No. 188, Arica, Chile; tel (56)
Dir. – Nelson Torres Otarola

LA ESTRELLA DE ARICA (D) Est. 1976
San Marcos 580, Arica, Chile; tel (56) 58 352 828; fax 200 290; web site www.estrellaarica.cl
Circ.: 10,000
Pres. – Augustin Edwards Eastman
Dir. – Reinaldo Neira Ruiz

ILUSTRE MUNICIPALIDAD DE ARICA (D)
Casilla 07, Arica, Chile; tel (56) 58 206 200; fax 232 203; web site www.municipalidaddearica.cl
Circ.: 10,000
Pres. – Ivan Paredes Fierro
Gen. Mgr. – Jorge Backit Meza
Ed. – Manuel O. Flores Pina
Prodn. Mgr. – Hector Donoso Cortez

LA DEFENSA (D)
Avda. 18 de Septiembre, No. 470, Arica, Chile; tel (56)
Dir. – Juan Carlos Poli Iglesias

BULNES

LA OPINION (M)
Federico Errazuriz, No. 92, Bulnes, Chile; tel (56)
Dir. – Juan Luis Ramirez

CALAMA

LA ESTRELLA DEL LOA (M)
Sotomayor No. 2025, Calama, Chile; tel (56) 56 212535; fax 364251
Circ.: 4,000
Dir. – David Doll Pinto

EL MERCURIO DE CALAMA (DS)
Albaroa 2051, Calama, Chile; tel (56) 56 264815; fax 251710
Gen. Mgr. – Rodrigo Alvarez
Ed. – Mauricio Rivas Alvear

CAUQUENES

EL INDEPENDIENTE (M)
Antonio Varas, No. 150, Cauquenes, Chile; tel (56)
Dir. – Luis Bascur

CHILLAN

LA DISCUSION (D)
Calle 18 de Septiembre 721, Chillan, Chile; tel (56) 42 212 650; fax 213 578; e-mail impresora@ladiscusion.cl; web site www.ladiscusion.cl
Circ.: 8,500
Ed. – Tito Castillo

LA COMUNA (D)
Municipalidad de Chillan, Chillan, Chile; tel (56)
Dir. – Carlos Bastias Fuentes

CONCEPCION

EL SUR (M)
Casilla 8-C, Concepcion, Chile; tel (56) 41 235825; fax 235825; e-mail director@diarioelsur.cl
Circ.: 20,000
Advertising: AdMarket Int'l.
Gen. Mgr. – Aurelio Maria Lamas
Sales Mgr. – Ricardo Brain
Ed. – Ricardo Hepp Kuschel
Prodn. Mgr. – German Kuchartt

CONSTITUCION

EL MAULE (D)
Freire, No. 792, Constitucion, Chile; tel (56)
Dir. – Orlando Ilufi Coloma

COPIAPO

CHANARCILLO (M)
Los Carreras, No. 801, Copiapo, Chile; tel (56) 52 219 044; e-mail chanarcillo@enteinet.net; web site www.chanarcillo.cl
Pres. – Alberto Bichara Nicolas

PANORAMA UDA (M)
Avda. Kennedy, No. 485, Copiapo, Chile; tel (56)
Dir. – Juan Iglesias Diaz

VISION DE ATACAMA (M)
Edif. Alborada, Los Carrera S/No., 1er. piso, Copiapo, Chile; tel (56)
Dir. – Felipe Berstein Jimenez

COPIAPO, ATACAMA

ATACAMA (M)
O'Higgins 401, Copiapo, Atacama, Chile; tel (56) 52 212255; fax 213094
Dir. – Samuel Salgado Godoy

COYHAIQUE

EL DIARIO DE AYSEN (D)
21 de Mayo, No. 410, Coyhaique, Chile; tel (56) 67 234850; fax 670016; e-mail dptoprensa@diarioaysen.co.cl; web site www.diarioaysen.co.cl
Dir. – Aldo Marchesse

CURICO

CURICO AVANZA (M)
Carmen S/No., Curico, Chile; tel (56)
Dir. – Sergio Correa de la Cerda

EMPRESA PERIODISTICA CURICO LTD. (D)
Merced 373, Curico, Chile; tel (56) 75 310 453; fax 311 924
Circ.: 4,000
Pres. – Carlos Lazcano Alfonso
Gen. Mgr. – Manuel Massa Mautino

EL SALVADOR

ANDINO (M)
Avda. El Tofo, No. 531, El Salvador, Chile; tel (56)
Dir. – Pedro Serazzi Ahumada

GRANEROS

EL ESFUERZO (M)
Riquelme, No. 559, Corvi Norte, Graneros,

Chile; tel (56)
Dir. – Sergio Faundez Gaete

ILLAPEL

LA OPINION DEL NORTE (D)
Casilla 365, Illapel, Chile; tel (56)
Dir. – Katarina Fauda Vega

LA VOZ DE CHOAPA (D)
Constiticion, No. 371, Illapel, Chile; tel (56)
Dir. – Humberto Villarroel

IQUIQUE

EL PAMPINO (M)
Baquedano, No. 898, Iquique, Chile; tel (56)
Dir. – Hector Rojas Cabrera

LA ESTRELLA DE IQUIQUE (M)
Luis Uribe 452, Iquique, Chile; tel (56) 57 399 313; fax 399 388; e-mail suscripciones@estrellaiquique.cl; web site www.estrellaiquique.cl
Circ.: 10,000
Pres. – Augustin Edwards
Gen. Mgr. – Oscar Cofre
Ed. in Chief – Caupolican Marquez

LA LIGUA

LA RAZON (M)
Portales S/N, La Ligua, Chile; tel (56) 33 711414
Dir. – Carmen Pinonez Tapia

LA SERENA

EL DIA (M)
Brasil 431, La Serena, Chile; tel (56) 51 200 453; fax 219 599; web site www.diarioeldia.com.cl
Circ.: 11,800
Pres. – Antonio Puga Rodriguez
Gen. Mgr. – Jorge Beltra
Ed. – Sergio Barraza Lazo

LAS CONDES

EDICIONES FINANCIERAS S.A. (M)
San Crescente 81, Piso 2, Las Condes, Chile; tel (56) 2 339 1070; fax 231 3340; web site www.df.cl
Circ.: 20,000
Advertising: AdMarket Int'l.; The N DeFilippes Corp.
Pres. – Baltazar Sanchez
Gen. Mgr. – Eduardo Pooley
Ed. – Guillermo Turner
Prodn. Mgr. – Victoria Vodanovic

LINARES

EL HERALDO (D)
Kurt Moller, No. 75, Linares, Chile; tel (56) 73 210 069; fax 210 069; web site www.diarioelheraldo.cl
Dir. – Nadia Yanez

MI PROVINCIA (M)
Gobernacion Provincial, Linares, Chile; tel (56)
Dir. – Sergio Hernandez Carrasco

LOS ANDES

EL ANDINO (D)
Santa Rosa, No. 442, Los Andes, Chile; tel (56)
Dir. – Luis Rios Munoz

LOS ANGELES

EMPRESA PERIODISTICA BIO BIO LTD. (6X WK.)
Calle Colo-Colo 464, Los Angeles, Chile; tel (56) 43 311 040; fax 314 987; web site www.diariolatribuna.cl
Pres. – Cirilo Guzman de la Fuente
GM – Silvia Manriquez
Dir. – Juan Diaz Hernandez

MOLINA

EL LONTUE (M)
Quecherreguas, No. 1644, Molina, Chile; tel (56)
Dir. – Mercedes Reyes

LA RAZON (D)
Quecherreguas, No. 1631, Molina, Chile; tel (56)
Dir. – Augosto Trivino Diaz

OSORNO

DIARIO 24 HORAS (D)
Ramirez, No. 951, Osorno, Chile; tel (56) 64 2300

SOCIEDAD PERIODISTA ARAUCANIA S.A. (M)
Avda. Bernardo O'Higgins 870, Osorno, Chile; tel (56) 64 222 300; fax 222 316; e-mail rvenegas@australosorno.cl; web site www.australosorno.cl
Circ.: 6,500
Pres. – AgustÂ¡n Edwards Eastman
Gen. Mgr. – Rene Venegas Ruz
Ed. – Alex Trautmann Fuentealba

OVALLE

SOCIEDAD PERIODISTA LA PROVINCIA (D)
Libertad, No. 435, Ovalle, Chile; tel (56)
Circ.: 5,000
Dir. – Mario Banic Illanes

PARRAL

LA PRENSA (D)
Anibal Pinto, No. 615, Parral, Chile; tel (56)
Dir. – Alfonso Candia Barras

PEUMO

EL PROGRESO DE CACHAPOAL (D)
Carlos Walker Martinez, No. 464, Peumo, Chile; tel (56)
Dir. – Gustavo Fuentes Miranda

PICHILEMU

EL PICHILEMO (M)
Casilla, No. 37, Pichilemu, Chile; tel (56)
Dir. – Washington Saldias

PUERTO MONTT

EL LLANGUIHUE (M)
Casilla 1047, Puerto Montt, Chile; tel (56) 65 255115; fax 255114
Circ.: 6,500
Gen. Mgr. – Littre Medina Quiroga
Ed. – Ernesto Montalva Rencoret

SOCIEDAD PERIODISTA ARAUCANIA (D)
San Felipe, No. 129, Puerto Montt, Chile; tel (56)
Dir. – Edmundo Espinoza Aparico

PUERTO VARAS

SOCIEDAD PERIODISTA ARAUCANIA (D)
Del Salvador, No. 560, Puerto Varas, Chile; tel (56) 25
Dir. – Rosendo Alvarez Araneda

PUNTA ARENAS

EMPRESA PUBLICIDAD DE LA PRENSA AUSTRAL LTD. (E)
Casilla 9-D, Punta Arenas, Chile; tel (56) 61 204 000; web site www.laprensaaustral.cl
Circ.: 6,000
Dir. – Alexandro Toro
Adv. Mgr. – Francisco Karelovic Car

LA PRENSA AUSTRAL (6X WK.)
Casilla 9-D, Punta Arenas, Chile; tel (56) 61 204 000; fax 247 406; e-mail director@laprensaaustral.cl; web site www.prensaaustral.com
Circ.: 8,000
Dir. – Alejandro Toro
Gen. Mgr. – Francisco Karelovic
Ed. – Poly Rain
Prodn. Mgr. – Carlos Caseres

QUILLOTA

EL OBSERVADOR (D)
La Concepci¢n 277, Casilla 1-D, Quillota, Chile; tel (56) 33 342 209; fax 311 417; web site www.diarioelobservador.cl
Pres. – Roberto Silva Bijit

RANCAGUA

EL HERALDO (D)
Avda. Los Proceres, Rancagua, Chile; tel (56)
Group: Brydson Global Media Sales
Dir. – Francisco Morales

EL RANCAGUINO (D)
O'Carroll 518, Rancagua, Chile; tel (56) 72 230345; fax 221483; e-mail diarioel.ranca001@chilnet.cl
Circ.: 10,000
Gen. Mgr. – Fernando Reyes
Ed. – Hector Gonzalez Valenzuela

EL TENIENTE (M)
Millan, No. 240, Rancagua, Chile; tel (56)
Dir. – Jose Aranguiz Fuenzalida

RENGO

EL RENGUINO (D)
Pasaje Fresia No. 145, Pob. 2, Rengo, Chile; tel (56)
– Lillo Valenzuela
– Hugo PenaDir.s

SAN ANTONIO

OASIS (M)
Pedro Montt, No. 40, San Antonio, Chile; tel (56)
Dir. – Franco Belmonte

PROA REGIONAL (D)
Sanfuentes 1677, San Antonio, Chile; tel (56) 35 236 033; e-mail info@elproa.cl; web site www.elproa.cl
Dir. – Edmund Guerra Galaz

SAN CARLOS

EL COMERCIO (M)
Serrano, No. 424, San Carlos, Chile; tel (56)
Dir. – Mirthala Navarro

SAN FELIPE

EL TRABAJO (D)
Salinas, No. 348, San Felipe, Chile; tel (56) 34 343 170; fax 343 173; e-mail diaro@eltrabajo.cl; web site www.eltrabajo.cl
Dir. – Margo Yuri Ceballos

SAN FERNANDO

EL COLCHAGUINO (D)
Manuel Rodriguez, No. 917, San Fernando, Chile; tel (56)
Dir. – Enrique Fuentes

LA REGION (D)
Bernardo O' Higgins, No. 564, San Fernando, Chile; tel (56) 65 271 1859; fax 271 1743; e-mail diariola.regio001@chilnet.cl
Gen. Mgr. – Simon Martinez Perez

SAN JAVIER

LA TRIBUNA (D)
Sargento Aldea, No. 2568, San Javier, Chile; tel (56) 73 760 330
Dir. – Gustavo Prado Santos

SAN VINCENTE DE TAGUA-TAGUA

LA LIBERTAD (D)
Carlos Walker Martinez, No. 128, San Vincente De Tagua-Tagua, Chile; tel (56)
Dir. – Octavio Castro Ruiz

LA REGION (M)
Carmen Gallegos, No. 174, San Vincente De Tagua-Tagua, Chile; tel (56)
Dir. – Juan Carlos Ramirez Paredes

SANTA CRUZ

EL CONDOR (D)
R. Casanova, No. 186, Santa Cruz, Chile; tel (56)
Dir. – Aguiles de la Fuente

SANTIAGO

AMERICA ECONOMIA
Carlos Antunez 1934, Santiago, Chile; tel (56) 2 290 9400; fax 341 5687
Ed. – Filipe Aldueto

DIARIO OFICIAL (D)
Agustinas 1269, Santiago, Chile; tel (56) 2 688 8320; fax 698 2222; e-mail info@diariooficial.cl; suscripciones@diariooficial.cl; web site www.diariooficial.cl
Pres. – Florencio Ceballo Bustos

EL MERCURIO (D)
Casilla 13-D, Santiago, Chile; tel (56) 2 330 1111; fax 228 9289; e-mail redaccion@mercurio.cl; web site www.elmercurio.cl

Circ.: 112,000
Advertising: Charney/Palacios & Co. Inc.
Pres. – Augustin Edwards Eastman
Adv. Mgr. – Roberto Massiff
Prodn. Mgr. – Rodolfo Alvarez Rapapart

EL MERCURIO S.A. (D)
Bellavista 0112, Providencia, Santiago, Chile; tel (56) 2 730 3000; fax 730 3357; e-mail ultimas.noticias@lun.cl; web site www.lun.cl
Circ.: 120,000
Advertising: Charney/Palacios & Co.
Pres. – Agustin Edwards Eastman

EL MERCURIO S.A. (D)
Avda. Santa Maria 5542, Casilla 13-D, Santiago, Chile; tel (56) 2 330 1111; e-mail redaccion@lasegunda.cl; web site www.lasegunda.cl
Circ.: 25,000
Advertising: Charney/Palacios & Co.
Pres. – Augustin Edwards Eastman
Dir. – Tilar Vergara

ESTRATEGIA (M)
Rafael Canas 114, Santiago, Chile; tel (56) 2 655 6228; fax 655 6439; e-mail egesteon@reuna.cl; web site www.estrategia.cl
Gen. Mgr – Victor Manuel Ojeda Mendez
Sales Mgr. – Francisco Ojeda Gonzalez
Ed. – Alexandra Cfiguero

INVERSIONES PERIODISTICAS Y PUBLICITARIAS (M)
Casilla 50360, Santiago, Chile; tel (56) 2 6384444; fax 6381105
Circ.: 40,000
Pres. – Fernando Molina Vallejo
Dir./Ed. – Alberto Coddou Claramont
Gen. Mgr. – Ignacio Cardenas Equella
Prodn. Mgr. – Julio Palacios Gamboa

LA CUARTA (M)
Diagonal Vicuna Mackenna 2004, Santiago, Chile; tel (56) 2 555 0034; fax 556 8727; e-mail lacuarta@copesa.cl; web site www.lacuarta.cl
Gen. Mgr. – Juan Carlos Larrain Wormald
Ed. – Diozel Perez Vergara

LA PRENSA AUSTRAL
Dr. Sotero del Rio, No. 326/8 piso, Santiago, Chile; tel (56) 2 721446; fax 6966922

LA NACION (M)
Augustinas 1269, Casilla 81-D, Santiago, Chile; tel (56) 2 787 0100; fax 698 1059; e-mail nacion01@reuna.cl; web site www.lanacion.cl
Advertising: AdMarket Int'l.
Pres. – Sergio Granados Aguilar
Gen. Mgr. – Gustavo Rivera Urrutia
Ed. – Jaime Lopez
Prodn. Mgr. – Pablo de la Maza Burgos

LA TERCERA (D)
Vicuna Mackenna 1962, Santiago, Chile; tel (56) 2 550 7000; fax 550 7999; e-mail latercera@latercera.cl; web site www.tercera.cl
Circ.: 180,000
Dir. – Cristian Bofill Rodriguez

TALCA

LA MANANA DE TALCA (D) Est. 1906
4 Sur 1016, Talca, Chile; tel (56) 71 237 200; fax 237 199
Circ.: 10,000
Dir. – Gustavo Cid

TEMUCO

SOCIEDAD PERIODISTICA ARAUCANIA S.A. (M)
Casilla 1-D, Temuco, Chile; tel (56) 45 292 929; fax 232 656; web site www.australtemuco.cl
Circ.: 20,000
Dir. – Jose Manuel Avarez
Sales Mgr. – Eleazar Jaramillo

TOCOPILLA

LA PRENSA (M)
Bolivar 1244, Tocopilla, Chile; tel (56) 55 813 036
Dir. – Sergio Montivero Bruna

TRAIGUEN

EL COLONO (D)
Lagos, No. 733, Traiguen, Chile; tel (56)
Dir. – Javier Alberto Brito Munita

VALDIVIA CITY

EL CORREO DE VALDIVIA (D)
Casilla 15-D, Valdivia City, Chile; tel (56)
Circ.: 12,000
Dir. – Patricio Gomez Couchet

VALPARAISO

EL MERCURIO DE VALPARAISO (M)
Casilla 57-V, Valparaiso, Chile; tel (56) 32 264264; fax 264227; e-mail cartasdirector@mercuriovalp.cl; web site www.mercuriovalp.cl
Circ.: 65,000
Advertising: AdMarket Int'l.; Charney/Palacios & Co. Inc.
Pres. – Augustin Edwards Eastman
Gen. Mgr. – Gaston Montes Martinez
Sales Mgr. – Juan Carlos Encina Undurraga
Ed. – Marco Antonio Pinto Zespeda

EMPRESA EL MERCURIO S.A.P. (E)
Casilla 57-V, Valparaiso, Chile; tel (56) 32 264230; fax 264241; e-mail estrell@entelchile.net
Dir. – Alfonso Castagneto

VICTORIA

LAS NOTICIAS (D)
Avenida Suiza, No. 895, Victoria, Chile; tel (56) 45 841 543; e-mail administracion@lasnoticiasdevictoria.cl; diariolasnoticias@gmail.com; web site www.lasnoticiasdevictoria.cl
Circ.: 8,000
Dir. – Transito Bustamente Molina

VILLA ALEMANA

EL VILLALEMANINO (D)
Santiago, No. 655, Oficina 5-A, Villa Alemana, Chile; tel (56)
Dir. – Juan Guillermo Casanova Carrillo

YUMBEL

LA PRENSA (D)
Bernardo O'Higgins, No. 725, Yumbel, Chile; tel (56) 2221222; fax 2249646
Dir. – Mario Rocha Osses

COLOMBIA

ARMENIA

DIARIO DEL QUINDIO (D)
Carrera 13-26-14, Armenia, Colombia; tel (57) 67 411111
Pub. – Hernan Barberi Cano

ARMENIA, QUINDIO

LA CRONICA DEL QUINDIO (M) Est. 1991
Apdo. Aereo 1667, Armenia, Quindio, Colombia; tel (57) 6 741 1030; e-mail cronica@armenia.multi.net.co; web site www.cronicadelquindio.com
Circ.: 18,000
Pres. – Omar Giraldo Ramirez
Gen. Mgr. – Carlos Alfonso Rodriguez Orozco
Sales Mgr. – Carlos Fabio Alvarez Angel
Editorial Dir. – Rodrigo Gomez Jaramillo

BARRANQUILLA, ATLANTICO

EL HERALDO LTD. (M) Est. 1933
Calle 53B, No. 46-25, Barranquilla, Atlantico, Colombia; tel (57) 5 371 5000; fax 371 5094; e-mail elheraldo@metrotel.net.co; web site www.elheraldo.com.co
Circ.: 70,000
Advertising: Charney/Palacios & Co. Inc.
Gen. Mgr. – Alberto Mario Pumarejo
Sales Mgr. – Maria Emilia de la Rosa
Editorial Dir. – Juan B. Fernandez Renowitzky
Prodn. Mgr. – Gerardo Olmos

ESPER EDITORES S.A. (M)
Carrera 53, No. 55-166, Barranquilla, Atlantico, Colombia; tel (57) 5 831-1517; e-mail libertad@metrotel.net.co; web site www.lalibertad.com.co
Editorial Dir. – Roberto Esper

BOGOTA

EL ESPECTADOR (COMUNICAN S.A.) (MS)
Avenida El Dorado No. 69 - 76, Bogota, Colombia; tel (57) 1 423 2300; fax 220 0743; e-mail redactor@elespectador.com; editorweb@elespectador.com; web site www.elespectador.com
Circ.: 100,000
Advertising: AdMarket Int'l.; Charney/Palacios & Co. Inc.; The N DeFilippes Corp.
Ed. Gen. – Leonardo RodrÂ¡guez

BOGOTA, COLOMBIA

DIARIO 5 P.M.
Carrera 40, No. 16-24, Bogota, Colombia, Colombia; tel (57) 1 2692111
Dir. – Luis Guillermo Velez Trujillo

EDITORA SUPERNOVA (M)
Apdo. Aereo 9390, Bogota, Colombia, Colombia; tel (57) 1 2159707; fax 2159467
Circ.: 38,000
Pres. – Misael Pastrana Borrero
Pub./Ed. – Juan Carlos Pastrana Arango
Gen. Mgr. – Jaime Pastrana

BOGOTA, D.C.

EDITORIAL EL TIEMPO LTD. (D) Est. 1911
Avda. El Dorado, No. 59-70, Bogota, D.C., Colombia; tel (57) 1 294 0100; fax 410 5088; e-mail enrsan@eltiempo.com.co; web site www.eltiempo.com.co
Advertising: Charney/Palacios & Co.
Pres. – Edwardo Santos
Gen. Mgr. – Jaime Gaez Mondragon

J ARDILA C & CIA (M) Est. 1965
Apdo. Aereo 80111, Bogota, D.C., Colombia; tel (57) 1 410-5066; fax 410-4595
Pres. – Hellen Sierra Jerez
Gen. Mgr. – Pablo Ardila Sierra
Editorial Dir. – Jamie Ardila Casamitjana

LA REPUBLICA (M) Est. 1953
Apdo. Aereo 034208, Bogota, D.C., Colombia; tel (57) 1 413 5077; fax 413 0013; e-mail diario@la-republica.com.co; web site www.larepublica.com.co
Circ.: 55,000
Advertising: Charney/Palacios & Co.
Pres. – Jorge Emilio Sierra Montoya
Gen. Mgr. – Ricardao Morales Casas
Sales Mgr. – Maria Leonor Willis
Editorial Dir. – Francisco Rodriquez
Prodn. Mgr. – Juan Carlos Hernandez

SOCIEDAD ANONIMA (M) Est. 1936
Apdo. Aereo 5452, Bogota, D.C., Colombia; tel (57) 1 410-5066; fax 410-4595; e-mail sredacc@cc-net.net; web site www.elsiglo.com.co
Gen. Mgr. – Mario Rodriguez Pinzon
Sales Mgr. – Rafael Payan Villamizar
Editorial Dir. – Juan Pablo Uribe

BUCARAMANGA, SANTANDER

COMUNICACIONES MELODIA EL FRENTE S.A. (M) Est. 1942
Apdo. Aereo 665, Bucaramanga, Santander, Colombia; tel (57) 7 642 5369; fax 630 5050
Circ.: 10,000
Owner/Pres. – Rafael Serrano Prada
Gen. Mgr. – Antonio Maria Rueda Prada
Sales Mgr. – Juana Isabel Serrano Prada
Editorial Dir. – Felix Acelas Mejia

VANGUARDIA LIBERAL (M) Est. 1919
Calle 34, No. 13-42, Bucaramanga, Santander, Colombia; tel (57) 7 680 0700; fax 630 2443; e-mail publicidadccp@gmail.com; web site www.vanguardia.com
Circ.: 48,000
Owner/Gen. Mgr. – Alejandro Galvis Ramirez

CALI

EL PAIS LTDA. (M) Est. 1950
Carrera 2, No. 24-46, Cali, Colombia; tel (57) 2 685 7000; fax 685 7070; e-mail diario@elpais.com.co; web site www.elpais.com.co
Circ.: 60,000
Advertising: Charney/Palacios & Co.
Owner – MarÂ¡a Elvira DomÂ¡nguez

NUEVO DIARIO OCCIDENTE (M) Est. 1961
Centro Comercial Chipichape Bod 2., Cali, Colombia; tel (57) 2 680 2002; fax 680 2002; web site www.diariooccidente.com.co
Circ.: 25,000
Gen. Mgr. – Sergio Santa Sandoval

CALI, VALLE DEL CAUCA

EL CALENO (D)
Calle 25, No. 3-20, Cali, Valle del Cauca,

Colombia; tel (57) 2 893500
Pub. – Mauricio Montejo
Ed. – Oscar Hincape

EL CRISOL (M)
Carrera 1, No. 31-A-45, Cali, Valle del Cauca, Colombia; tel (57) 2 438 404
Circ.: 45,000

MERCEDES RINCON (MS)
Avda. de las Americas, No. 26BN-33, Cali, Valle del Cauca, Colombia; tel (57) 2 688 345
Circ.: 20,000
Pub. – Rodrigo Ospina Hernandez
Ed. – Claudio Ochoa Moreno

CARTAGENA, BOLIVAR

EL PERIODICO DE CARTAGENA
Apdo. Aereo 2221, Cartagena, Bolivar, Colombia; tel (57) 5 660 1127; fax 664 8797
Gen. Mgr. – Alvaro Gonzalez Fortich
Sales Mgr. – Claudia Marmolejo Carrasco
Dir./Ed. – Haroldo Calvo Stevenson

SOCIEDAD ANONIMA (D) Est. 1948
Pie del Cerro Calle 30 No. 17-36, Cartagena, Bolivar, Colombia; tel (57) 5 660 0383; fax 660 0382; e-mail director@eluniversal.com.co; web site www.eluniversal.com.co
Circ.: 30,000
Dir. – Edinson Alfaro
Sales Mgr. – Claudia Mendez

CUCUTA

LA OPINION (M) Est. 1960
Avda. 4, No. 16-12, Cucuta, Colombia; tel (57) 7 582 9999; e-mail editorweb@laopinion.com.co; web site www.laopinion.com.co
Gen. Mgr. – Patricia Monsalve
Ed. – Celmira Figueroa

CUCUTA, SANTANDER DEL NORTE

DIARIO LA FRONTERA (M) Est. 1951
Calle 14, No. 3-44, Cucuta, Santander Del Norte, Colombia; tel (57) 7 710 505; fax 710 505
Circ.: 25,000
Advertising: Nidia Maria Patino Estrada.
Owner/Pres. – Mario Javier Pacheco Garcia
Gen. Mgr. – Leovanny Chaparro Espitia
Sales Mgr. – Leonardo Gelvez
Editorial Dir. – Gustavo Rojas Perez
Prodn. Mgr. – Orlando Rodriquez

ENVIGABO

EMPRESA EL COLOMBIANO LTD. (D) Est. 1912
Carrera 48, No. 30 Sur-119, Envigabo, Colombia; tel (57) 4 331 5252; fax 335 9335; e-mail elcolombiano@elcolombiano.com.co; web site www.elcolombiano.com
Circ.: 90,000
Advertising: Charney/Palacios & Co. Inc.; The N DeFilippes Corp.
Gen. Mgr. – Luis Miguel de Bedout Hernandez
Dir. – Ana Mercedes Gomez Martinez
Ed. – Fransisco Jaramillo

HUILA, NEIVA

DIARIO DEL HUILA (D) Est. 1966
Calle 8A, No. 6-30, Huila, Neiva, Colombia; tel (57) 8 871 2458; fax 871 2453; e-mail prensa@diariodelhuila.com; web site www.diariodelhuila.com
Gen. Mgr. – Maximiliano Duque Rengifo
Editorial Dir. – Maria Rengifo de Duque

IBAGUE, TOLIMA

SOCIEDAD ANONIMA (D) Est. 1992
Carrera 6, No. 12-09, Ibague, Tolima, Colombia; tel (57) 8 261 0966; fax 263 3044; web site www.elnuevodia.com.co
Circ.: 28,000
Editorial Dir. – Antonio Melo Salazar

MANIZALES, CALDAS

EDITORIAL LA PATRIA S.A. (D) Est. 1921
Carrera 20, No. 46-35, Manizales, Caldas, Colombia; tel (57) 6 878 1700; fax 878 1778; e-mail lapatria@lapatria.com; web site www.lapatria.com
Circ.: 223
Insert rate: COP$ 370
Advertising: Charney/Palacios & Co.

MEDELLIN, ANTIOQUIA

GAVIRIA FAMILY GROUP (D)
Calle 53, No. 74-50, Medellin, Antioquia, Colombia; tel (57) 4 234 8657; fax 264 3729; e-mail elmundo@elmundo.com; web site www.elmundo.com
Pres. – Guillermo Gaviria Echeverri
Adv. Mgr. – Carlos Hoyos

NEIVA, HUILA

LA NACION (M) Est. 1994
Calle 11, No. 5-89, Neiva, Huila, Colombia; tel (57) 8 872 4200; fax 871 1716; web site www.lanacion.com.co
Dir. – Ricardo Areiza

PASTO, NARINO

EL DERECHO (M)
Calle 20, No. 26-20, Pasto, Narino, Colombia; tel (57) 277 2170
Circ.: 12,000
Pres. – Dr. Jose Elias Del Hierro
Dir. – Eduardo F. Mazuera

PEREIRA, RISARALDA

COMUNICADORES DEL RISARALDA LTD. (E) Est. 1975
Apdo. Aereo 3163, Pereira, Risaralda, Colombia; tel (57) 6 313 7676; fax 335 5187; e-mail webmaster@latarde.com.co; web site www.latarde.com
Circ.: 15,000
Owner – Alejandro Galvis Ramirez
Gen. Mgr. – Luis Fernando Baena Mejia
Ed. – Nancy Ocampo

EL DIARIO
Carrera 8, 15-38, Pereira, Risaralda, Colombia; tel (57) 63 357 585; fax 357 522; e-mail victoria@eccel.com
Pres. – Carlos Enrique Arango Medina
Gen. Mgr. – Carlos Ariel Jimenez Avellaneda
Sales Mgr. – Victoria Eugenia Jimenez Cardona
Editorial Dir. – Alberto Cardona Orozco
Prodn. Mgr. – Carlos Enrique Arango Duque

RR EDITORES RAMIREZ RAMIREZ LTD. (E)
Apdo. Aereo 2533, Pereira, Risaralda, Colombia; tel (57) 63 51 313; fax 342 897; e-mail eldiario@interco.net.co; jir@eldiario.com.co; web site www.eldiario.com.co
Circ.: 30,000
Financial Dir. – Javier Ignacio Ramirez Munera

POPAYAN, CAUCA

EDITORIAL EL LIBERAL S.A. (D) Est. 1938
Carrera 3, No. 2-60, Popayan, Cauca, Colombia; tel (57) 2 824 2418; fax 824 3888; e-mail liberal@emtel.net.co; web site www.elliberal.com.co
Circ.: 6,500
Pres. – Ana Maria Londono Riani

SANTA MARTA, MAGDALENA

EL INFORMADOR (D)
Calle 21, No. 5-06, Santa Marta, Magdalena, Colombia; tel (57) 56 234 771; web site www.el-informador.com
Circ.: 9,000
Dir. – Jose B. Vives

TUNJA, BOYACA

DIARIO DE BOYACA (D)
Calle 19, No. 11-31, Of. 203, Tunja, Boyaca, Colombia; tel (57) 87 422233
Circ.: 3,000
Gen. Dir. – Dr. Carlos H. Mojica

EL ORIENTE (D)
Calle 19, No. 9-35, Of. 1007, Tunja, Boyaca, Colombia; tel (57) 87 423360
Pub. – Luis Rodriguez Lopez

ECUADOR

AMBATO, TUNGURAHUA

EL HERALDO C.A. (M) Est. 1958
Casilla 18-01-43, Ambato, Tungurahua, Ecuador; tel (593) 3 241-2031; fax 241-2033
Circ.: 9,000
Pres. – Mons. Vicente Cisneros Duran
Gen. Mgr. – Jorge Castro Patino
Editorial Dir. – Wilson Olivos
Prodn. Mgr. – Alfonso Villavicencio

BABAHOYO

COMPANIA EDIRIOS S.A.
Casilla 127, BABAHOYO, Ecuador; tel (593) 5 730651; fax 273-0496
Pres. – Enrique Ponce Luque
Vice Pres. – Ricardo Ponce Noboa
Gen. Mgr. – Jorge Vaca Mosquera
Prodn. Mgr. – Oswaldo Moran Mena

BAHIA

EL GLOBO (D)
., Bahia, Ecuador; tel (593)
Circ.: 6,000
Pub. – Alberto Palan

CUENA, AZUAY

EL AUSTRAL (M) Est. 1987
Apdo. Postal 972, Cuena, Azuay, Ecuador; tel (593) 7 280-7486; fax 280-7547
Owner/Pres. – Rosalia Arteaga de Cordova

CUENCA, AZUAY

COMPANIA LTD. (M) Est. 1924
Casilla 01-60, Cuenca, Azuay, Ecuador; tel (593) 7 288 0110; fax 281 7266; e-mail redaccion@elmercurio.com.ec; web site www.elmercurio.com.ec
Circ.: 18,000
Pres. – Nicanor Merchan Luco
Gen. Mgr. – Doris Merchan
Sales Mgr. – Diana Aguilerra
Editorial Dir. – Roberto Vivar Reinoso
Prodn. Mgr. – Gilbert Amaya

EL TIEMPO CIA. LTD. (E) Est. 1955
Casilla 4909, Cuenca, Azuay, Ecuador; tel (593) 7 288 2551; fax 288 2555; e-mail eltiempo@cue.satnet.net; web site www.eltiempo.com.ec
Circ.: 15,000
Pres./Gen. Mgr. – Rene Toral Calle
Sales Mgr. – Fernando Toral Calle
Editorial Dir. – Felipe Heraande
Prodn. Mgr. – Ivan Toral Calle

GUAYAQUIL

COMPANIA ANONIMA EL UNIVERSO (D) Est. 1921
Casilla 09-01-0531, Guayaquil, Ecuador; tel (593) 4 249 0000; fax 249 2925; e-mail redaccion@eluniverso.com; elespecialista@eluniverso.com; web site www.eluniverso.com
Circ.: 143,000
Pres. – Carlos Perez Barriga
Gen. Mgr. – Leonard Teran Parral
Ed. – Gustavo Cortez

EDITORES Y IMPRESORES S.A.
9 de Octubre, No. 2202, Guayaquil, Ecuador; tel (593) 4 287891; fax 288348

ROBERTO ISAIAS DASSUM (M)
Casilla 5832, Guayaquil, Ecuador; tel (593) 4 280100; fax 285110
Circ.: 35,000
Dir. – Jorge E. Perez Pesantes

GUAYAQUIL, GUAYAS

CARLOS MANSUR (M) Est. 1983
Casilla 6366, Guayaquil, Guayas, Ecuador; tel (593) 4 232-0635; fax 232-0539; e-mail tecnico@telconet.net
Circ.: 60,000
Prez. – Carlos Mansur Perez
Gen. Mgr. – Carlos Manzur Sandoval
Sales Mgr. – Elsa Wong

EXTRA (M) Est. 1974
Casilla 5890, Guayaquil, Guayas, Ecuador; tel (593) 4 220 1100; fax 220 0291; e-mail garciam@granasa.com.ec; web site www.diarioextra.com
Circ.: 380,000
Group: Multimedia, Inc.
Pres. – Galo Martinez Merchan
Gen. Mgr. – Francisco Herrera
Sales Mgr. – Enrique Izquieta
Editorial Dir. – Maximo Garcia Pinargote

GR FICOS NACIONALES S.A. (M) Est. 1973
Casilla 5890, Guayaquil, Guayas, Ecuador; tel (593) 4 220 1100; fax 201 100; e-mail director@granasa.com.ec; web site www.diario-expreso.com
Circ.: 60,000

Pres. – Galo Martinez Merchan
Sales Mgr. – Jose Oruz
Prodn. Mgr. – Bolivar Ramirez

EL TELEGRAFO CA (D) Est. 1884
Avda. 10 de Agosto No. 601 y Boyaca, Guayaquil, Guayas, Ecuador; tel (593) 4 232 6500; fax 232 3265; e-mail redaccion@telegrafo.com.ec; web site www.telegrafo.com.ec
Dir. – Jamie Teran

IBARRA, IMBABURA

DIARIO DEL NORTE (M) Est. 1987
Casilla 210, Ibarra, Imbabura, Ecuador; tel (593) 2 295-5495; fax 295-2211; e-mail editores@imbanet.net
Circ.: 8,000
Pres. – Luis Alfredo Mejia Montesdeoca
Gen. Mgr. – Nelson Castillo Gallegos
Sales Mgr. – Nuevelle Andrade de Cevallos
Editorial Dir. – Pablo Jurado Moreno
Prodn. Mgr. – Marcelo Michilena

LA VERDAD (M) Est. 1944
Apdo. Postal 10-01-830, Ibarra, Imbabura, Ecuador; tel (593) 6 264-0335; fax 264-0194; e-mail laverdad@im.pro.ec
Circ.: 3,000
Gen. Mgr. – Roberto Morales
Editorial Dir. – Wilson Flores

LOJA

EL SIGLO (M) Est. 1982
Casilla 17-42-242, LOJA, Ecuador; tel (593) 7 275-0105; fax 275-9644
Circ.: 10,000
Owner – Jorge Piedra Armijos
Pres. – Luis Arturo Burneo
Gen. Mgr. – Ana Aguirre de Piedra
Editorial Dir. – Arcelio Tenorio Tinoco

LOJA

EL MUNDO S.A. (6X WK.) Est. 1979
Calle Azuay #14-32 entre Bol¡var y Sucre, edificio Godoy,, Loja, Ecuador; tel (593) 7 257 2003; fax 257 7202; web site www.cronica.com.ec
Gen. Mgr. – Ismael E. Betancourt
Dir. – Antonio Jaramillo

MACHALA, EL ORO

EDITORIAL DEL SUR LTDA (M) Est. 1983
Junin 104, entre Guabo y Kleber Franco., Machala, El Oro, Ecuador; tel (593) 7 293 0255; e-mail editorsur@eo.pro.ec
Circ.: 15,000
Pres. – Bolivar Prieto Calderon
Ed. – Ernesto Valle Lozano

GRAFICOS ORENSES C.A. (D) Est. 1964
Casilla 07-671, Machala, El Oro, Ecuador; tel (593) 7 293 0375
Circ.: 18,000
Pres. – Nicolas Castro Benitez
Gen. Mgr. – Jorge Castro Patino
Sales Mgr. – Ariosto Carchi
Editorial Dir. – Jamie Franco Mora
Prodn. Mgr. – Lauro Montufar

MANTA, MANABI

EL MERCURIO (M) Est. 1924
Casilla 13-4-780, Manta, Manabi, Ecuador; tel (593) 5 262-3273; fax 262-1000
Circ.: 20,000
Group: Admarket International (Div. of Marcom International, Inc.)
Pres. – Ricardo Delgado Abeiga
Gen. Mgr. – Marco Chalen
Editorial Dir. – Carlos Cedeno Mora

PORTOVIEJO

DIARIO MANABITA (MS)
Casilla 50, Portoviejo, Ecuador; tel (593) 5 653777
Circ.: 15,000
Owner/Dir./Ed. – Pedro Zambrano
Owner – Angela de Lopez

PORTOVIEJO, MANABI

SOCIEDAD ANONIMA (D) Est. 1934
Casilla 13-01-050, Portoviejo, Manabi, Ecuador; tel (593) 5 293 3777; fax 293 3151; e-mail redacc@eldiario.com.ec; web site www.eldiario.com.ec
Gen. Mgr. – MarÃ¡a Victoria Zambrano

QUEVEDO, LOS RIOS

CRUZ SEGOVIA FAMILY (M) Est. 1979
Malecon, No. 616, Quevedo, Los Rios, Ecuador; tel (593) 5 275 1572; fax 275 1572
Gen. Mgr. – Jamie Cruz Segovia
Sales Mgr. – Zoila de Cruz
Editorial Dir. – Kleber Cruz Campuzano

ECOS DE QUEVEDO (M) Est. 1963
14a. No. 204 y Bolivar, Quevedo, Los Rios, Ecuador; tel (593) 5 275 0444; fax 276 6223
Pres. – Jose Lubar
Ed. – Jose Laborde Ramirez

LA PALABRA (E) Est. 1989
Septima No. 439, Quevedo, Los Rios, Ecuador; tel (593) 5 275-3582
Owner/Pres. – Cesar Izquierdo Aguilera

QUITO

LA HORA (M) Est. 1982
Panamericana Norte Km. 3,5 y Nazareth, Quito, Ecuador; tel (593) 2 2475724; fax 2475723; e-mail webmaster@lahora.com.ec; web site www.lahora.com.ec
Circ.: 80,000
National President / Publisher – Francisco Vivanco Riofrio
Executive President – Francisco Vivanco Arroyo
Sales Mgr. – Gladis Vivanco
Editorial VP – Gabriela Vivanco

QUITO, PICHINCHA

COMPANIA ANONIMA EL COMERCIO (D) Est. 1906
Casilla 17-01-57, Quito, Pichincha, Ecuador; tel (593) 2 267 0999; fax 267 9810; e-mail redaccion@elcomercio.com; web site www.elcomercio.com
Advertising: El Comercio.
Gen. Dir. – Guadalupe Mantilla de Acquaviva

COMPANIA ANONIMA EL COMMERCIO (5X WK.) Est. 1938
Casilla 17-01-57, Quito, Pichincha, Ecuador; tel (593) 2 267 0999; fax 267 9810; web site www.ultimasnoticias.com.ve
Circ.: 60,000
Advertising: Charney/Palacios & Co.
Pres. – Guadalupe Mantilla de Acquaviva
Adv. Mgr. – Mantella Mosquara

EDIMPRES S.A. (D) Est. 1982
Avda. Mariscal Sucre OE6-116, Quito, Pichincha, Ecuador; tel (593) 2 249 0888; fax 249 1881; e-mail hoy@hoy.com.ec; web site www.hoy.com.ec
Pub. – Jaime Mantilla Anderson
VP., Adv. – Hernan Cueva

RIOBAMBA, CHIMBORAZO

EL ESPECTADOR (M) Est. 1972
Casilla 637, Riobamba, Chimborazo, Ecuador; tel (593) 3 296-0617; fax 296-3107
Circ.: 5,000
Pres. – Marcelo Roche Miranda
Gen. Mgr. – Vincente Limaico Andino
Sales Mgr. – Edwin Pombosa Junes
Editorial Dir. – Maritza Andino de Roche

EL LIBERTADOR (M) Est. 1984
Casilla 342, Riobamba, Chimborazo, Ecuador; tel (593) 3 296-5900
Pres. – Cesar Enrique Velez
Owner – Frank Velez

FRENCH GUIANA

CAYENNE

FRANCE-GUYANE (D)
17 Rue Lallouette, Cayenne, 97300, French Guiana; tel (594) 297 000; fax 297 022; e-mail france.guyane@media-antilles.fr
Circ.: 5,500
Dir. – Raymond Ozier Lafontaine

LA PRESSE DE GUYANE (D-4X WK)
BP 6012, Cayenne, 97300, French Guiana; tel (594) 295990
Circ.: 1,000
Dir. – Fabien Roubaud

GUYANA

GEORGETOWN

CATHOLIC STANDARD (WEEKLY)
PO Box 10720, Georgetown, Guyana; tel (592) 61540
Circ.: 10,000
Ed. – Colin Smith

GUYANA NATIONAL NEWSPAPERS LTD. (WEEKLY)
Congress Pl., Sophia, Georgetown, Guyana; tel (592) 2 67891
Circ.: 26,000
Ed. – Francis Williams

GUYANA NATIONAL NEWSPAPERS LTD. (D)
PO Box 11, Georgetown, Guyana; tel (592) 2 253 107; fax 75208; e-mail edit@guyana.net.gy; web site www.guyanachronicle.com
Advertising: AdMarket Int'l.; Charney/Palacios & Co. Inc.
Ed. in Chief – Mark Ramotar

NEW GUYANA CO. LTD. (2X WK.)
Lot 8, Industrial Estate, Ruimveldt, Georgetown, Guyana; tel (592) 2 62471; fax 62472; e-mail news@guyana.net.gy
Circ.: 25,000
Ed. – Janet Jagan

STABROEK NEWS (DS)
46-47 Robb St., Lacytown, Georgetown, Guyana; tel (592) 2 226 7206; fax 225 4637; e-mail stabroeknews@stabroeknews.com; web site www.stabroeknews.com
Ed. in Chief – David De Caires

PARAGUAY

ASUNCION

ABC COLOR (MS)
Yegros 745, Asuncion, Paraguay; tel (595) 2 141-5151; fax 1415 1329; e-mail azuccolillo@abc.com.py; web site www.abc.com.py
Circ.: 35,000
Advertising: Charney/Palacios & Co. Inc.
Pres. – Aldo Zuccolillo
Gen. Mgr. – Jorge Mendelson
Adv. Mgr. – Adolfo Rufo Medina
Ed. – Juan Luis Gauto

DIARIO POPULAR (D)
Avda. Mariscal Lopez 2948, Asuncion, Paraguay; tel (595) 21 603 400; fax 662 859; web site www.diariopopular.com.py
Pres. – Javier Pirovano Pena

EDITORIAL CONTINENTAL S.A. (MS)
Avda. Artigas y Brasilia, Asuncion, Paraguay; tel (595) 2 129-2721; fax 129-2841; e-mail director@diarionoticias.com.py; web site www.diarionoticias.com.py
Circ.: 50,000
Pres. – Eduardo Nicolas Bo
Gen. Mgr. – Jose Luis Pecci
Adv. Mgr. – Faustino Cabrera
Ed. – Celso Chavez
Prodn. Mgr. – Alejandro Mainero

PATRIA (M)
Calle Tacuari 443, Asuncion, Paraguay; tel (595) 21 92011
Circ.: 8,000
Dir. – Juan Ramon Chavez

ULTIMA HORA (M)
Avda. Benjamin Constant 658, Asuncion, Paraguay; tel (595) 21 496-261; fax 447-071; e-mail abreglia@uhora.com.py; web site www.uhora.com
Circ.: 40,000
Gen. Mgr. – Oscar Ferraro
Adv. Mgr. – Antonio Breglia
Mktg. Mgr. – Selene Rojas
Ed. – Demetrio Rojas Cardoso

PERU

AREQUIPA

AREQUIPA AL DIA (M)
Avda. Jorge Chavez 201, IV Centenario, Arequipa, Peru; tel (51) 54 21-5515; fax 21-7810
Pres. – Enrique Mendoza Nunez
Gen. Mgr. – Miguel Mendoza del Solar
Adv. Mgr. – Esperanza Mendoza del Solar
Ed. – Carlos Meneses Cornejo

CORREO DE AREQUIPA (D)
Calle Bolivar 204, Arequipa, Peru; tel (51) 54 203 993; fax 203 128; e-mail correoaqp@epensa.com.pe; web site

www.correoperu.com.pe
Circ.: 12,000
Gen. Mgr. – Mario Pautrat Calderon

EDITORIAL AREQUIPA S.A. (M)
Sucre 213, PO Box 35, Arequipa, Peru; tel (51) 54 211500; fax 213361
Circ.: 70,000
Pres. – Daniel Macedo Gutierrez
Ed. – Eduardo Laime Valdivia

MERCURIO AREQUIPA
Avda. Jorge Chavez 210, IV Centenario, Arequipa, Peru; tel (51) 54 215 515; fax 217 810

CHICLAYO, LAMBAYEQUE

LA INDUSTRIA (D)
Jr. Javier Prado Este 309 5to Piso, Chiclayo, Lambayeque, Peru; tel (51) 4422 11211; fax 0122 11211; e-mail chiclayo@laindustria.com.pe; web site www.laindustria.com
Circ.: 20,000
Pres. – Isabel Cerro de Burga
Gen. Mgr. – Maria Ofelia Cerro Moral

CHIMBOTE, ANCASH

DIARIO DE CHIMBOTE (M)
Jr. Huandoy Mz. A. Lt. 9, PO Box 136, Chimbote, Ancash, Peru; tel (51) 43 312 405; fax 311 148; e-mail diariodechimbote@yahoo.com; web site www.diariodechimbote.com
Pres. – Paula Olortegui de Pelaez
Gen. Mgr. – Wilfredo Pelaez Gularte
Ed. – Javier Pelaez Olortegui

CUZCO

EL COMERCIO (M)
Urb. Constanza B-11, Wanchaq, Cuzco, Peru; tel (51) 84 23-3352; fax 26-3931; e-mail comercio@telser.com.pe; web site www.telser.com.pe/elcomercio
Dir. – Abel Ramos Perea

EL OVALO -WANCHAQ -

EL SOL (M)
Av. Infancia, El Ovalo -Wanchaq -, Peru; tel (51) 84 239 783; web site www.diarioelsoldecusco.com
Dir. – Paulino Carlos Farfan

HUANCAYO

CORREO DE HUANCAYO (M)
Jiron Cusco 337, Huancayo, Peru; tel (51) 64 214 642; fax 233 811; web site www.correoperu.com.pe
Circ.: 9,000
Pres. – Enrique Agois Banchero
Gen. Mgr. – Mario Pautrat Banchero
Adv. Mgr. – Luis Meza
Ed. – Rodolfo Orosco

HUANCAYO, JUNIN

LA OPINION POPULAR (M)
Huancas 251, Huancayo, Junin, Peru; tel (51)
Pres. – Bernabe Suarez Palacios
Ed. – Jorge Suarez Osorio

HUANCHO

EL IMPARCIAL (M)
Avda. Grau 203, Huancho, Peru; tel (51) 34 32-4410; fax 32-3521
Pres. – Adan Manrique Romero
Adv. Mgr. – Jorge Portal Estrada
Ed. – Ana M. Adrianzen

ICA

LA OPINION (M)
Avda. Los Maestros 801, PO Box 186, Ica, Peru; tel (51) 56 235571
Group: U.S. Suburban Press, Inc.
Pres. – Gonzalo Tueros Ramirez
Ed. – Enrique Marticorena Estrada

LA VOZ DE ICA (D)
Castrovirreyna 191-193, Ica, Peru; tel (51) 56 232 112; fax 232 112; e-mail lavozica1918@yahoo.es
Dir. – Atilio Nieri Boggiano
Ed. – Mariella Mieri

IQUITOS, LORETO

EL MATUTINO (M)
Brasil 474, Iquitos, Loreto, Peru; tel (51) 65 23-5256; fax 23-4045
Ed. – Nelly Andrade

LIMA

AGOIS BANCHERO FAMILY (M)
Apdo. Postal 152, Lima, 1, Peru; tel (51) 1 225 5656; fax 475 8780; e-mail cmanrique@epensa.com.pe; web site www.ojo.com.pe
Circ.: 40,000
Pres. – Enrique Agois Paulsen
Gen. Mgr. – Luis Agois Banchero
Adv. Mgr. – Freddy Chirinos Castro
Ed. – Carlos A. Manrique Negron

AGOIS BANCHERO FAMILY (M)
PO Box 152, Lima, 1, Peru; tel (51) 14 75-6355; fax 75-8780; e-mail elbocon@epensa.com.pe; web site www.elbocon.com.pe
Circ.: 90,000
Pres. – Enrique Agois Paulsen
Gen. Mgr. – Luis Agois Banchero
Adv. Mgr. – Freddy Chirinos Castro
Ed. – Jorge Esteves Alfaro

AGOIS BANCHERO FAMILY (M)
PO Box 152, Lima, 1, Peru; tel (51) 1 476 1605; fax 475-8780; e-mail vramirez@epensa.com.pe; web site www.aja.com.pe
Circ.: 120,000
Pres. – Enrique Agois Paulsen
Gen. Mgr. – Enrique Agois Banchero
Adv. Mgr. – Freddy Chirinos Castro
Ed. – Victor Ramirez Canales

EL CALLAO (M)
Pedro Ruiz 141, Lima, Peru; tel (51) 14 651283
Pres. – Vittorio de Ferrari
Gen. Mgr. – Carlos Jimenez Horna
Adv. Mgr. – Esther Cherres
Ed. – Franco de Ferrari

CARETAS (WEEKLY)
Apdo. Postal 737, Lima, 100, Peru; tel (51) 1 4289490; fax 4262524; e-mail info@caretas.com.pe; web site www.caretas.com.pe
Circ.: 90,000
Ed. – Enrique Zileri Gibson

THE CERRO FAMILY (E)
Avda. Javier Prado Este, No. 309, piso 5, San Isid, Lima, Peru; tel (51) 1 221 1192; fax 221 1211; e-mail postmaster@induslim.com.pe
Circ.: 18,000
Pres. – Maria Ofelia Cerro Moral
Ed. Dir. – Luis Alfonso Burga Cerro
Gen. Mgr. – Isabel Cerro de Burga

EL CHINO
Jr. Yungay 820, Magdalena del Mar, Lima, Peru; tel (51) 12 63-9761; e-mail elchino@edsport.com.pe
Ed. – Owen Castillo

EL COMERCIO (M)
Gabriel Miro Quesada 300, Lima, 17, Peru; tel (51) 13 11 6500; fax 26 0810; e-mail amiroque@comercio.com.pe; web site www.elcomercioperu.com.pe
Circ.: 120,000
Advertising: Charney/Palacios & Co. Inc.
Pres. – Alejandro Miro Quesada Garland
Gen. Mgr. – Cesar Pardo-Figueroa
Ed. – Alejandro Miro Quesada Cisneros
Adv. Mgr. – Carlos Cabala

CORREO (MS)
Avda. Central, No. 480, Lima, Peru; tel (51) 1 414991; fax 401491
Circ.: 80,000
Pub. – Enrique Agois
Adv. Mgr. – Jorge E. Escudero
Ed. – Luis Agois Banchero

DEBATE
Gonzales Larranaga, No. 265, Lima, Peru; tel (51) 1 455237; fax 455946

EDITORA DEL ROSARIO S.A. (M)
Avda. Paseo de la Republica, No. 3101, 6to. piso, Lima, Peru; tel (51) 1 4222180
Dir./Ed. – Ivan Cortez Vargas
Gen. Mgr. – Cesar Villanueva Polo
Mng. Dir./Gen. Dir. – Carlos Castro Cruzado
Adv. Mgr. – Christian Villanueva

EL MUNDO (M)
Apdo. Postal 270077, Lima, Peru; tel (51) 1 4413635; fax 4429704
Pres. – Julio Vera Abad
Pub./Ed. – Blanca Rosales

EXPRESO (M)
Avda. Dos de Mayo 180, Miraflores, Lima, Peru; tel (51) 1 444 7088; e-mail publicidad@expreso.com.pe
Circ.: 50,000
Advertising: Charney/Palacios & Co. Inc.
Pres. – Manuel Alberto Ulloa van Peborgh
Gen. Mgr. – Alberto Villacorta
Adv. Mgr. – Carmen Oliva
Ed. – Veronica Becerra Estremadoyro
Prodn. Mgr. – Alejandro Hermoza

GESTION (M)
General Salaverry 156, Miraflores, Lima, 18, Peru; tel (51) 1 446-1554; fax 447-6569; e-mail gestion@gestion.com.pe; web site www.gestion.com.pe
Advertising: Charney/Palacios Co. Inc.
Pres. – Manuel Romero Caro
Gen. Mgr. – Oscar Romero Caro
Adv. Mgr. – Ada Ulloa Schiantarelli
Ed. – Alvaro Luis Mendez

HOY (M)
Jr. Camana 320, Lima, Peru; tel (51) 1 427 6455; fax 426 5678; e-mail direccion@hoyperu.com.pe
Ed. – Maritza Espinosa

LA MANANA S.R.L. (M)
Malecon Cisneros, No. 920, Miraflores, Lima, Peru; tel (51) 1 443988; fax 463489
Dir./Ed. – Luis Felipe Angell de Lama
Dir./Ed. – Maruja Valcarcel Acuna
Adv. Mgr. – Patricia Li-Carillo

LA PRENSA (D)
Jiron Union, No. 745, Lima, Peru; tel (51) 1 447 6830
Group: Charney/Palacios & Co.

LIBERO (M)
Jr. Camana 320, Lima, Peru; tel (51) 1 711-6000; fax 427 7253; e-mail lwebmaster@libero.com.pe; web site www.libero.com.pe
Pres. – Gustavo Mohme
Gen. Mgr. – Jose Samanez
Adv. Mgr. – Carlos Ganoza
Ed. – Gerardo Sosaya Saavedra

1+1 TODOS
Jiron Leoncio Prado, No. 800-806, Lima, Peru; tel (51) 1 44452863

OVACION (M)
Miguel Dasso, No. 139, 8vo. piso, San Isidro, Lima, Peru; tel (51) 1 4217403; fax 4405979
Dir.-Ed. – Micky Rospigliosi
Mng. Dir.-Gen. Dir. – Jose Luis Rospigliosi

PERUVIAN GOVERNMENT (D)
Avda. Alfonso Ugarte 873, Lima, Peru; tel (51) 1 315 0400; fax 424 0763; e-mail editoraperu@editoraperu.com.pe; web site www.elperuano.com.pe
Circ.: 27,000
Ed. – Carlos Manrique

EL POPULAR (M)
Jr. Camana 320, Lima, Peru; tel (51) 1 427 6455; e-mail popular@larepublica.com.pe; web site www.elpopular.com.pe
Circ.: 60,000
Pres. – Gustavo Mohme
Gen. Mgr. – Jose Samanez
Ed. – Felix Grijalba Sato

PYME (M)
Prolongacion Huanuco, No. 1711-203, La Victoria, Lima, Peru; tel (51) 1 4476830; fax 4474348
Pres. – Manuel Romero Caro
Vice Pres. – Alfredo Saldana Nunez

LA REPUBLICA (D)
Jr. Camana 320, Lima, Peru; tel (51) 1 711 6000; fax 711 6015; e-mail director@larepublica.com.pe; web site www.larepublica.com.pe
Circ.: 50,000
Pres. – Gustavo Mohme Seminario
Gen. Mgr. – Jose Samanez Acebo
Ed. – Carlos Castro Cruzado

REVISTA GENTE
Eduardo de Habich, No. 170, Miraflores, Lima, Peru; tel (51) 1 451747; fax 461173

SANTA ISABEL DEL PERU SCRL
Avda. Brasil, No. 3657, Lima, Peru; tel (51) 1 4619534
Dir./Ed. – Carlos Rojas Medina
Gen. Mgr. – Cesar Cortez Rivas
Adv. Mgr. – Luis Gonzalez Albujar

SINTESIS (M)
Avda. Aviacion 2760 San Borja, Lima, Peru; tel (51) 1 225-8501; fax 225-8502; e-mail sintesis@amauta.rcp.net.pe
Pres. – Boris Romero Accinelli
Gen. Mgr. – Roberto Matos Solorzano
Adv. Mgr. – Marina Zavala de Benza
Ed. – Boris Romero Ojeda

LIMA 14

EL SOL (M)
Avda. Trinidad Moran No. 821, Lima 14, 14, Peru; tel (51) 1 405 728; e-mail elsol@amauta.rcp.net.pe
Pres. – Andres Marsano Porras
Dir./Gen. Mgr. – Jorge Lazarte Conroy
Ed. – Victor Tipe Sanchez
Ed. – Jorge Sandoval
Ed. – Humberto Castillo
Ed. – Victor Caycho

PACASMAYO, LA LIBERTAD

ULTIMAS NOTICIAS (E)
2 de Mayo, Pacasmayo, La Libertad, Peru; tel (51) 44 522 060
Circ.: 3,000
Group: Brydson Global Media Sales
Dir. – Luis Alberto Ballena Sanchez

PIURA

CORREO DE PIURA (M)
Parque Industrial Manzana 247, Lote 6, Piura, Peru; tel (51) 73 303 744; fax 324 881; e-mail piurad@correoperu.com.pe; web site www.correoperu.com.pe
Pres. – Enrique Agois Banchero
Gen. Mgr. – Mario Pautrat Calderon
Ed. – Rolando Rodrich Arango

EL TIEMPO (D)
Ayacucho 751, Piura, Peru; tel (51) 73 325 141; fax 327 478; web site www.eltiempo.com.pe; www.eltiempo.pe
Circ.: 12,000
Pub. – Luz Maria Helguero
Ed. – Rosa Lavan

PUCALLPA, UCAYALI

DIARIO IMPETU (M)
Jr. 9 de Diciembre 599, Pucallpa, Ucayali, Peru; tel (51) 61 573 443; web site www.diario-impetu.com
Pres. – Fernando Sanchez Vela
Gen. Mgr. – Fidelia Rengifo de Sanchez
Adv. Mgr. – Juan Pablo Sanchez Rengifo
Ed. – Fernando Sanchez Rengifo

PUNO

LOS ANDES (D)
Casillo 110, Puno, Peru; tel (51) 51 352142; fax 352142
Circ.: 5,600
Pub. – Samuel Frisancho Pineda

TACNA

CORREO DE TACNA (M)
Calle Hipolito Unanue 636, Tacna, Peru; tel (51) 52 428-489; fax 211-015; e-mail correotac@epensa.com.pe; web site www.correoperu.com.pe
Circ.: 8,000
Pres. – Enrique Agois Banchero
Gen. Mgr. – Mario Paturat Romero
Ed. – Ruben Collazos Romero

TRUJILLO

LA INDUSTRIA (M)
Gamarra 443, Trujillo, Peru; tel (51) 44 295 757; e-mail redaccion@laindustria.com; web site www.laindustria.pe
Circ.: 20,000
Pres. – Eiavel Cerro de Burga
Gen. Mgr. – Isabel Cerro de Burga

TRUJILLO, LA LIBERTAD

SATELITE (6X WK.)
Jr. Gamarra 531, Trujillo, La Libertad, Peru; tel (51) 44 295 757; fax 295 757; web site www.laindustria.com/satelite
Circ.: 18,000
Pres. – Maria Ofelia Cerro Moral
Gen. Mgr. – Isabel Cerro de Burga
Ed. – Victor Hugo Paredes Dorian

SURINAME

PARAMARIBO

DE WARE TIJD (M-6X WK.)
PO Box 1200, Paramaribo, Suriname; tel (597) 472 823; fax 411 169; e-mail dwt@dwtonline.com; web site www.dwtonline.com
Circ.: 10,000
Ed. – Reginia Wagimin

DE WEST (E)
PO Box 176, Paramaribo, Suriname; tel (597) 473338; fax 470322
Circ.: 15,000
– G.R.H. Ferrier
– G.D.C. FindlayEd.s

OMHOOG (WEEKLY)
21 Gravenstraat, Paramaribo, Suriname; tel (597) 472 521; fax 473 904
Ed. – S. Mulder

URUGUAY

CANELONES

EL NOTICIOSO (D)
Jose Erodo, No. 258, Canelones, Uruguay; tel (598) 3322365; fax 3322365; e-mail copymap@adinet.com.uy
Pres. – Alberto Monserrat Reverdito
Dir. – Hector A. Montserrat
Gen. Mgr. – Diego Monserrat
Sales Mgr. – Gonzalo Monserrat
Ed. – Hector A. Monserrat
Prodn. Mgr. – Aldo Monserrat

EL PUEBLO (D)
Apdo. Postal 17, Canelones, Uruguay; tel (598)
Pub. – Juan C. Lanus

HOY CANELONES (D)
Tomas Berreta No. 207, Canelones, Uruguay; tel (598) 33 25950; fax 24386; e-mail hoycanelones@hoycanelones.com.uy; web site www.hoycanelones.com.uy
Pres. – Maria E. Boccardo de Britos
Ed. – Julio Britos Bide

COLONIA

LA COLONIA (D)
Gen Flores 2317, Colonia, Uruguay; tel (598)

FLORIDA

EL HERALDO S.A. (D) Est. 92
Independencia 827, Florida, 94000, Uruguay; tel (598) 435 22229; e-mail heraldo@adinet.com.uy; web site www.elheraldo,cin,uy
Circ.: 1,800
Director Responsable – Alvaro Riva Rey
Adv. Mgr. – Virginia Maoualr

MALDONADO

FORGOLD S.A. (M)
Michelini 815 Bis., Maldonado, 20000, Uruguay; tel (598) 42 35633; fax 35633; e-mail gallardo@adinet.com.uy
Circ.: 1,000
Pres. – Fernando Carlos Gallardo
Gen. Mgr. – Raul Guerra
Sales Mgr. – Ulbio Miranda
Ed. – Marta P. Rodriguez-Zanoni

MELO

EL DEBER CIVICO (D)
Calle Jose P. Varela 610, Melo, Uruguay; tel (598)

MERCEDES, SORIANO

ACCION (M)
Jose Artigas No. 352, Mercedes, Soriano, Uruguay; tel (598) 532 2236; fax 5327499; e-mail accion@internet.com.uv; web site www.sorianototal.com
Pres. – Fernando Fernandez Lasalvia
Ed. – Ruben Aunchayna Taruselli

CRONICAS (D)
Eusebio Gim□nez 695, Mercedes, Soriano, 75000, Uruguay; tel (598) 53 23642; fax 23652; e-mail cronicas@diariocronicas.com; web site www.diariocronicas.com
Ed. – Ricardo Nole Llaguno

MINAS, LAVALLEJA

LA UNION (6X WK.)
Florencio Sanchez 569, Minas, Lavalleja, Uruguay; tel (598) 44 22065; fax 24011; e-mail union@chasque.apc.org
Ed. – Sheobanna Cekongz

MONTEVIDEO

DIARIO OFICIAL (D)
Florida 1178, Montevideo, Uruguay; tel (598)
Dir. – Sra Zain Nassif De Zarumbe

EL DIARIO (E)
Camacua No. 589, Montevideo, 11000, Uruguay; tel (598) 2 9166336; fax 9930637; e-mail joterom@adinet.com.uy
Circ.: 170,000
Ed. – Jorge Otero

EL DIARIO ESPANOL (M)
Casilla 899, Montevideo, Uruguay; tel (598) 2 915 7389; fax 915 9545
Circ.: 20,000
Dir. – Carlos M. Reinante

EL PAIS (M)
Zelmar Michelini, No. 1287, Montevideo, 11100, Uruguay; tel (598) 2 901 1929; fax 902 7796; e-mail maguirre@elpais.com.uy; web site www.diarioelpais.com
Circ.: 110,000
Advertising: Charney/Palacios & Co. Inc.
Pres. – Daniel Scheck
Gen. Mgr. – Andrea Curcio
Sales Mgr. – Diego Beltran
Ed. – Martin Aguirre

GACETA COMERCIAL (M)
Juncal 1391, Montevideo, 11000, Uruguay; tel (598) 2 9165618; fax 9165619
Circ.: 4,500
Dir. – Milton Sans
Ed. – Pablo Sans

IMPRESORA POLO (D)
Rincon 541, Montevideo, Uruguay; tel (598)
Pub. – Danilo Arbilla

IMPRESORA POLO LTD. (M)
Paysandu 1179, Montevideo, Uruguay; tel (598) 2 902 0452; fax 902 0034; web site www.ultimasnoticias.com.uy
Circ.: 19,500
Dir. – Alvaro Giz

LA JUSTICIA URUGUAY (D)
25 de Mayo 555, Montevideo, 11000, Uruguay; tel (598) 2 915 7587; fax 915 9721
Dir. – Eduardo Albanell Mac Coll

LA MANANA (M)
Carlos Gardel No. 1062, Montevideo, 11000, Uruguay; tel (598) 2 902 0348; fax 902 1955
Ed. – Salvador Alaban Demare

LA PLATA (D)
Plaza Libertad 1164, Montevideo, Uruguay; tel (598)

MUNDO COLOR (E-EX S)
Cuareim 1287, Montevideo, 11800, Uruguay; tel (598)
Circ.: 4,500
Dir. – Daniel Herrera Lussich

LA REPUBLICA (D)
Avda. Garibaldi 2573, Montevideo, 11600, Uruguay; tel (598) 2 487 3565; fax 487 3824; e-mail redaccion@diariorepublica.com; web site www.diariorepublica.com
Pres. – Federico Fasano Mertens

VIDA MARITIMA (E)
Colon 1580, Montevideo, Uruguay; tel (598)

PAYSANDU

EL TELEGRAFO (M) Est. 1910
18 de Julio 1027, Paysandu, 60000, Uruguay; tel (598) 47223141; fax 47227999; e-mail correo@eltelegrafo.com; web site www.eltelegrafo.com
Circ.: 7,500
Director – Fernando Alberto Baccaro
Administrator – Enrique Baccaro

RIVERA

NORTE (D)
Avda. General San Martin 715, Rivera, Uruguay; tel (598)
Circ.: 2,200
Pub. – Rik J. Araujo

ROCHA, ROCHA

ECOS DEL ESTE (D-EX S)
Florencio Sanchez 94A, Rocha, Rocha, Uruguay; tel (598)
Circ.: 500
Pub. – Angel M. Pereyra

LA GACETA (D)
Calle Treinta y Tres 130, Rocha, Rocha, Uruguay; tel (598)
Circ.: 1,200
Pub. – Elio T. Sanchez

LA PALABRA (D)
19 de April 70, Rocha, Rocha, Uruguay; tel (598)
Pub. – Carlos N. Rocha
Dir./Ed. – Dr. Henio Palomera

SALTO

DIARIO CAMBIO (D)
Calle Brasil y Viera, Salto, Uruguay; tel (598) 473 33344; fax 32579; e-mail otlas@adinet.com.uy; web site www.diariocambio.com.uy
Gen. Mgr. – Julio Aguirrezabal
Sales Dir. – Pascual Perna
Ed. – Carlos F. Artia

EL PUEBLO (D)
Avda. 18 de Julio, No. 151, Salto, Uruguay; tel (598) 733 4133; web site www.diari-oelpueblo.com.uy
Circ.: 2,300
Pub. – Enrique A. Garcia
Dir./Ed. – Walter Martinez

EMPRESA POR LA PRENSA (E)
Calle Amorim 56, Salto, Uruguay; tel (598)
Circ.: 1,000
Pub. – Alfonso Cardoza
Adv. Mgr. – Maria Martinez
Dir./Ed. – Jose Pedro Cardozo

TRIBUNA SALTENA (MS)
Joaquin Suarez 71, Salto, Uruguay; tel (598)
Circ.: 3,000
Pub. – Modesto Llantada Fabini

SAN JOSE

AQUI ESTA (D)
Dr. B. de Bengoa, No. 440, San Jose, Uruguay; tel (598) 208 9059; fax 208 9059; e-mail aqui1952@adinet.com.uy
Pres. – Ariel Chabalgoity

SAN JOSE DE MAYO, SAN JOSE

LA MANANA Y EL DIARIO
Rio Negro 1028, San Jose De Mayo, San Jose, Uruguay; tel (598) 987047

VENEZUELA

ACARIGUA, PORTUGUESA

LALANO ADENTRO (M) Est. 1973
Avda. Eduardo Chollet, Acarigua, Portuguesa, Venezuela; tel (58) 55 21-1144; fax 21-2353
Pres. – Nestor Ramirez Paz

ANACO, PORTUGUESA

LA NOTICIA DE ORIENTE (D)
Peligro a Puente Republica, La Candelaria, Anaco, Portuguesa, Venezuela; tel (58) 8222253

ARAURE, PORTUGUESA

EL REGIONAL (M) Est. 1988
Vencedores de Araura, diagonal a la Manga de Coleo, Araure, Portuguesa, Venezuela; tel (58) 255 665 2253; fax 665 1466; e-mail nacionales@elregional.net.ve; politica@elregional.net.ve; deportes@elregional.net.ve; web site www.elregional.net.ve
Pres. – Juan Jose Briceno Guerrero

BARCELONA, ANZOATEGUI

EL NORTE (M) Est. 1989
Avda. Intercomunal Jorge Rodr¡guez, Barcelona, Anzoategui, Venezuela; tel (58) 281 286 2484; fax 286 2484; e-mail opinion@elnorte.com.ve; web site www.elnorte.com.ve
Ed. – Edgar Alfaro

BARINAS, BARINAS

EDITORIAL SABANA C.A. (M) Est. 1985
Avda. Andres Varela, Calles Plaza y 5 de Julio, Barinas, Barinas, Venezuela; tel (58) 73 2-6835; fax 2-8020
Circ.: 15,000
Pres. – Alberto Santeliz Melendez
Sales Mgr. – Pedro M. Ordonez
Editorial Dir. – Belkis Chacon
Prodn. Mgr. – Jorge Herrera

BARQUISIMETO

EL IMPULSO (D) Est. 1904
El Parque y Avda. Calle Juan Carmona, Barquisimeto, Venezuela; tel (58) 251 256 1111; fax 256 1129; web site www.elimpulso.com
Circ.: 47,000
Advertising: Proba International.
Pres. – Juan Manuel Carmona Perera
Sales Dir. – Carlos E. Carmona Palenzona
Ed. – Luis Rodriguez Moreno
Prodn. Mgr. – Carlos Guillen

BARQUISIMETO, LARA

EL INFORMADOR (M) Est. 1968
Edif. El Informador, Carrera 21, Barquisimeto, Lara, Venezuela; tel (58) 51 31-1811; fax 31-0624; e-mail informad@telcel.net.ve
Circ.: 45,000
Owner/Pres. – Eduardo Gomez Tamayo
Gen. Mgr. – Luis Navas
Sales Mgr. – Marisela Santana
Editorial Dir. – Alejandro Gomez Sigala

PUBLICACIONES OBELISCO C.A. (M) Est. 1995
Avda. Venezuela, No. 19-89, Barquisimeto, Lara, Venezuela; tel (58) 51 431-0246; fax 44-3046
Sales Mgr. – Clara Mazzarri

CARACAS

THE DAILY JOURNAL (M) Est. 1941
Avda. Principal De Boleita Norte, CARACAS, 1070, Venezuela; tel (58) 212 237 9644; fax 232 6831; web site www.thedailyjournalonline.com
Owner – Miguel Angel Villalba

CABIMAS, ZULIA

EL INFORMADOR (D)
Avda. Modedano, Urb. La Castellana, Centro Generen, Cabimas, Zulia, Venezuela; tel (58) 64 311811; fax 310624
Circ.: 35,000
Pub. – Edecio Gonzalez

CARACAS

BLOQUE DE ARMAS PUBLICACIONES (M) Est. 1969
Final Avda. San Martin y Avda. la Paz., Caracas, Venezuela; tel (58) 212 406 4233; fax 451 5097; e-mail opina@dearmas.com; web site www.meridiano.com.ve
Circ.: 150,000
Last Audit: March 23, 2010
Advertising: Carlos Obregon, Darmiven, Inc.
Vice Pres. – Andres de Armas
Dir. – Victor Lopez
Dir. – Graciano Cruz
Dir. Mktg. – Mirtin Dearmas
Sales Mgr. – Sernin Rodreguez
Prodn. Mgr. – Inaki Aznar

C.A ULTIMAS NOTICIAS (E) Est. 1958
Apdo. Postal 1192, Caracas, Venezuela; tel (58) 212 596 1911; fax 596 1478; e-mail cmundo@cadena-capriles.com; web site www.elmundo.com.ve
Circ.: 80,000
Group: Latin Admerica, Inc.
Advertising: Charney/Palacios & Co.
Pres. – Miguel Angel Capriles Lopez

DIARIO EL GLOBO (M)
Apdo. Postal 16415, Caracas, Venezuela; tel (58) 212 5764111; fax 5744353
Pres./Dir./Ed. – Jose Carta

EL DIARIO DE LA COSTA ORIENTAL (D)
Segunda Avda., Urb. Campos Alegre, Torre Credival, Caracas, Venezuela; tel (58) 2 2639350; fax 2636255

EQUIPO EDITOR (M)
Edif. San Marcos, Avda. San Martin, Caracas, Venezuela; tel (58)
Pub. – Pompeyo Marquez

GRUPO EDITORIAL PRODUCTO (D)
Apdo. Postal 88578, Caracas, Venezuela; tel (58) 212 7519846; fax 7519635

CARACAS, D.F.

COMUNICACIONES CORPORATIVES CCD, C.A. (M) Est. 1989
Apdo. Postal 14658, Caracas, D.F., 1011, Venezuela; tel (58) 212 576-9078; fax 572-5470; e-mail econohoy@telcel.net.ve
Circ.: 30,000
Advertising: Charney/Palacios & Co. Inc.
Pres. – Maria Di Mase Urbaneja
Sales Mgr. – Dulce Maria Estevez
Editorial Dir. – Cesar Salazar Cuervo
Prodn. Mgr. – Gustavo Molina

EDITORA EL NACIONAL S.A. (M) Est. 1943
Apdo. Postal 209, Caracas 10, Caracas, D.F., Venezuela; tel (58) 212 408-3111; fax 481-0548; e-mail jcalvo@el-nacional.com; web site www.el-nacional.com
Circ.: 100,000
Advertising: Charney/Palacios & Co.
Pres. – Jose Calvo Otero
Gen. Mgr. – Miguel Henrique Otero Castillo
Editorial Dir. – Argenis Martinez
Prodn. Mgr. – Luis Bonilla

EDITORIAL AMBOS MUNDOS C.A. (MS) Est. 1909
Avda. Urdaneta, esq. de Animas Edif. El Universal, Caracas, D.F., Venezuela; tel (58) 212 561-6016; fax 564-0067; e-mail mata@eud.com; web site www.eluniversal.com
Advertising: Charney/Palacios & Co. Inc.
Owner/Pres. – Andres Mata Osorio
Gen. Mgr. – Liliana Bachs
Sales Mgr. – Daniel Umana Parodi
Editorial Dir. – Miguel Angel Tortello

EDITORIAL SANTIAGO DE LEON (M) Est. 1973
Apdo. Postal 575 Carmelitas, Caracas, D.F., Venezuela; tel (58) 212 406-4111; fax 451-0762; e-mail imarquez@dearmas.com; web site www.2001.com.ve
Circ.: 100,000
Advertising: Carlos Obregon Darmiven, Inc.
Pres. – Andres de Armas
Sales Mgr. – Irene Gutierrez
Editorial Dir. – Israel Marquez
Mng. Ed. – Vladimir Lopez
News Ed. – Jose Campos Suarez
Prodn. Mgr. – Enrique Scott

EL GLOBO (M) Est. 1991
Avda. Principal de Mariperez, Transversal Colon, Caracas, D.F., Venezuela; tel (58) 212 577 3648; fax 574 4353; e-mail elglobo@infoline.wtfe.com
Circ.: 68,000
Group: Brydson Global Media Sales
Pres. – Nelson Mezerhane
Gen. Mgr. – Jose Luis Busgos
Sales Mgr. – Luz Marina Garcia
Editorial Dir. – Anibal J. Latuff
Prodn. Mgr. – Nelson Molina

EL NUEVO PAIS (M) Est. 1988
Apdo. Postal 14067, Caracas, D.F., Venezuela; tel (58) 2 541-5211; fax 545-9675; e-mail enpais@telcel.net.ve; web site www.enpais.com.ve
Group: Brydson Global Media Sales
Owner/Pres. – Rafael Poleo
Gen. Mgr. – Jesus Perez
Sales Mgr. – Graciela Requena
Editorial Dir. – Patricia Poleo

LA RELIGION (M) Est. 1890
Edif. Juan XXIII Torres a Madrices, Caracas, D.F., Venezuela; tel (58) 2 563-0600; fax 563-5583; e-mail lareligion@cantv.net; web site www.iglesia.org.ve/lareligion
Gen. Mgr. – Leonel Morin
Sales Mgr. – Heriberto Bustamante
Editorial Dir. – Jose Visconti

PUBLICACIONES CAPRILES (M) Est. 1941
Apdo. Postal 1192, Caracas, D.F., Venezuela; tel (58) 2 596-1911; fax 596-1433; web site www.ultimanoticias.com.ve
Circ.: 200,000
Advertising: Charney/Palacios & Co. Inc.
Pres. – Miguel Angel Capriles Lopez
Editorial Dir. – Eleazar Diaz Rangel

CARACAS. D.F.

REPORTE (M) Est. 1988
Torre Britanica piso 12 y Avda. B, Caracas. D.F., Venezuela; tel (58) 212 261-2141; fax 261-2141
Owner/Pres. – Tannuos F. Gerges
Sales Mgr. – Tibisay Garcia
Editorial Dir. – William Becerra

CARORA, LARA

EL DIARIO (M)
Calle 3, No. 10-69, Carora, Lara, Venezuela; tel (58) 5022222
Circ.: 16,000
Pub. – Lila de Herrera Oropeza
Adv. Mgr. – Pedro Claver Herrera
Ed. – Jesus Antonio Herrera

CARUPANO, SUCRE

DIARIO DE SUCRE (M) Est. 1986
Calle Juncal No. 170, Carupano, Sucre, Venezuela; tel (58) 93 432-0394; fax 431-2334
Editorial Dir. – Douglas Nassar

CIUDAD BOLIVAR, BOLIVAR

EL BOLIVARENSE (M) Est. 1957
Calle Igualdad No. 26, Ciudad Bolivar, Bolivar, Venezuela; tel (58) 85 2-4034; fax 2-4878
Circ.: 10,000
Sales Mgr. – Omaira Rodriguez
Editorial Dir. – Alvaro Natera

EL EXPRESO (M) Est. 1969
Paseo Gaspari c/c Democracia, Ciudad Bolivar, Bolivar, Venezuela; tel (58) 85 2-7908; fax 2-8401
Circ.: 20,000
Editorial Dir. – J.M. Guzman

J SUEGART & CIA. (E)
Apdo. Postal 65, Ciudad Bolivar, Bolivar,

Venezuela; tel (58) 85 20779
Circ.: 12,000
Pub. – G. Suegart
Ed. – Victor Barranco
Adv. Mgr. – Andres Bello

CIUDAD GUAYANA, BOLIVAR

EL GUAYANES (D)
Avda. Francisco de Miranda, Chacao, Ciudad Guayana, Bolivar, Venezuela; tel (58) 86 234250; fax 226844

CIUDAD OJEDA, ZULIA

EL REGIONAL DE ZULIA
Carretera N, Avda. Pal-Zona Industrial, Galpon 9, Ciudad Ojeda, Zulia, Venezuela; tel (58) 65 411395; fax 410565
Dir./Ed. – Adolfo Herrera

EL REGIONAL DEL ZULIA (M) Est. 1990
Avda. Principal Zona Industrial Edif. No. 9, Ciudad Ojeda, Zulia, Venezuela; tel (58) 65 41-1977; fax 41-0565; e-mail elregionalredac@iamnet.com; web site www.elregional.com
Pres. – Andres Finol Wardrop
Gen. Mgr. – Lendy Bermudez
Sales Mgr. – Jose Pina
Editorial Dir. – Adolfo Herrera
Prodn. Mgr. – Elkis Cardozo

CORO, FALCON

EL FALCONIANO (D)
Apdo. Postal 33, Coro, Falcon, Venezuela; tel (58) 68 517 543; fax (58-68) 512 275

LA MANANA (M) Est. 1952
Calle Zamora, No. 64-1, Coro, Falcon, Venezuela; tel (58) 68 51-8667; fax 51-5314
Circ.: 5,000
Pub. – Atilio Yanez Esis

CUMANA, SUCRE

DIARIO REGION (D)
Calle Bompland, Edif. Regio, Cumana, Sucre, Venezuela; tel (58) 268 911778

PROVINCIA (M) Est. 1968
Apdo. Postal 104, Cumana, Sucre, Venezuela; tel (58) 93 32-0736; fax 66-4920
Pub. – Ramon Yanez

REGION (M) Est. 1974
Avda. Bompland entre Calle Vela de Coro y Cordoba, Cumana, Sucre, Venezuela; tel (58) 93 321175; fax 31-0638
Pub. – Lois Marcan Barrios

EL TIGRE, ANZOATEGUI

ANTORCHA (M)
Avda. Francisco de Miranda, Edif. Antorcha, El Tigre, Anzoategui, Venezuela; tel (58) 83 35-2383; fax 35-3923
Circ.: 10,000
Pres. – Antonio M. Briceno Amparan
Gen. Mgr. – Manuel Briceno
Sales Mgr. – Aurora Valladares
Editorial Dir. – Juan Martinez

REPUESTOS PETROLEROS S.A. (M)
Avda. Fernandez Padilla-6-69, El Tigre, Anzoategui, Venezuela; tel (58) 83 359 027
Editorial Dir. – Luis Hurtado

GUANARE, PORTUGUESA

EL PERIODICO DE OCCIDENTE (M) Est. 1988
Apdo. Postal 1-D, Guanare, Portuguesa, Venezuela; tel (58) 57 530104; fax 531832
Sales Mgr. – Clara Mazzarri

GUARENAS, MIRANDA

LA VOZ DE GUARENAS (D) Est. 1965
Apdo. Postal 76399, Guarenas, Miranda, 1070, Venezuela; tel (58) 36 22-8817; fax 22-0851
Circ.: 50,000
Pres. – Jose Materan
Gen. Mgr. – Freddy Blanco
Editorial Dir. – Angel Urbina Machado

LOS TEQUES, MIRANDA

AVANCE Est. 1988
Final Calle Falcon No. 40, Los Teques, Miranda, Venezuela; tel (58) 32 4-7545; fax 31-4534
Editorial Dir. – Romulo Herrera

LA REGION (D)
Avda. Bolivar y Calle Junin, Edif. La Region, Los Teques, Miranda, Venezuela; tel (58) 32 311737; fax 311035
Gen. Mgr. – Alexandra Moreno

MARACAIBO, ZULIA

DIARIO PANORAMA C.A. (M) Est. 1914
Avda. 15, No 95-60, Maracaibo, Zulia, Venezuela; tel (58) 261 7256911; fax 725 6899; web site www.panodi.com
Circ.: 120,000
Advertising: Charney/Palacios Co. Inc.
Pres. – Esteban Pineda
Dir. – Roberto Baittiner
Dir. – Eduardo Ferrer

EL REGIONAL DE ZULIA (D)
Carretera N, Avda., Pal-Zona Industrial Galpon 9, Maracaibo, Zulia, Venezuela; tel (58) 261 29019; fax 920632

LA PRENSA ZULIANA (M)
Apdo. Postal 480, Maracaibo, Zulia, Venezuela; tel (58) 61 210176; fax 212861
Circ.: 77,000
Advertising: The N DeFilippes Corp.
Dir. – Samir Makarem Urdaneta

TIPOGRAFIA LA COLUMNA CA (M) Est. 1924
Apdo. Postal 420, Maracaibo, Zulia, Venezuela; tel (58) 61 22-3884; fax 22-7921; web site www.la-columna.com
Pres. – Alfredo Zambrano
Gen. Mgr. – Cecil Suarez
Editorial Dir. – Elvy Monzart Arraga
Prodn. Mgr. – Mercedes Marin

MARACAY

PUBLICACIONES CAPRILES (D) Est. 1973
Avda Bolivar, Edif. El Siglo, Maracay, Venezuela; tel (58) 243 554 2086; fax 554 5154; e-mail direccion@elsiglo.com.ve; web site www.elsiglo.com.ve
Circ.: 75,000
Pres. – Manuel Capriles

MARACAY, ARAGUA

EL ARAGUENO (M) Est. 1972
Calle 3ra. Oeste con Avda. 1ra., Maracay, Aragua, Venezuela; tel (58) 243 35-9018; fax 35-7866; e-mail shirleyb@latinmail.com; web site www.aragueno.com.ve
Circ.: 8,000
Sales Mgr. – Beatriz Miliani
Editorial Dir. – Mari Pia Ciafre

EL IMPARCIAL (D)
Avda. 10 de Diciembre, 46 Maracay, Maracay, Aragua, Venezuela; tel (58) 43 336178; fax 336178

EL PERIODICO (D)
Avda. Francisco de Miranda, Chacao, Maracay, Aragua, Venezuela; tel (58) 43 (58-43) 321338; fax 337110

MATURIN, MONAGAS

EL DIARIO (D) Est. 1965
Calle Bermudez y Carrera 3, Maturin, Monagas, Venezuela; tel (58) 91 42-9175; fax 42-9175
Group: Charney/Palacios & Co.
Pub. – J. Saragoza

EL ORIENTAL (M) Est. 1982
Calle Ascue con Sucre Edif. El Oriental, Maturin, Monagas, Venezuela; tel (58) 91 42-6339; fax 41-3856
Pub. – Gustavo Urbina

EL SOL DE MATURIN (M) Est. 1970
Urbanizacion Las Brisas a Pasaje 3 No. 35, Maturin, Monagas, Venezuela; tel (58) 91 41-4762; fax 41-2053
Pub. – Luis Guevara Monosalva

MERIDA

EDICIONES OCCIDENTE C.A. (M) Est. 1978
Avda. Fernandez Pena y Calle Rivas Devila, Ejido, Merida, Venezuela; tel (58) 999 21-3787; fax 21-3686; e-mail monsalve@telcel.net.ve; web site www.diariofrontera.com
Circ.: 80,000
Pres. – Alcides Monsalve
Gen. Mgr. – Alicia de Penaloza
Sales Mgr. – Elsi Rojas
Editorial Dir. – Adelfo Solarte Bullones
Prodn. Mgr. – Carlos Diaz

MERIDA, MERIDA

CORREO DE LOS ANDES (D)
Avda. Mohedano c/c Calle Blandin, Quinta No. 10, U, Merida, Merida, Venezuela; tel (58) 74 632270

EMPRESA EL VIGILANTE (M) Est. 1924
Avda. 5, No. 22-33, Merida, Merida, Venezuela; tel (58) 74 52-5510; fax 52-1839
Circ.: 3,000
Pres. – Monsignor Baltazar Enrique Porras Cardozo
Gen. Mgr./Sales Mgr. – Christian Gonzalez de Salas
Editorial Dir. – Monsignor Juan Maria Leonardi Villasmil
Prodn. Mgr. – Yban Pena

PORLAMAR, MARGARITA

EL SOL DE MARGARITA (M)
Calle Fermin con Charaima Sector Genoves, Porlamar, Margarita, Venezuela; tel (58) 295 264 5522; fax 264 5555; e-mail elsol@telcel.net.ve; web site www.elsoldemargarita.com.ve
Pres. – Ivan Cardozo Yanez
Ed. – Dany Fuentes Gonzalez

PORLAMAR, NUEVA ESPARTA

DIARIO CARIBAZO (M) Est. 1973
Calle Velazquez con calle Narvaez, Porlamar, Nueva Esparta, Venezuela; tel (58) 95 61-0713; fax 61-6567
Gen. Mgr. – Belkis Blondell de Pelaez
Editorial Dir. – Mario de Jesus Pelaez

PUERTO LA CRUZ, ANZOATEGUI

CORPORIENTE S.A. (D)
Avda. Casanove c/c Avda. Las Acacias, Sabana Grand, Puerto La Cruz, Anzoategui, Venezuela; tel (58) 81 665915

EL TIEMPO (M) Est. 1958
Av. Municipal, No. 153, Edif. Diario El Tiempo, Puerto La Cruz, Anzoategui, 6023, Venezuela; tel (58) 81 260 0600; fax 669 224; e-mail el.tiempo@eldish.net; web site www.eltiempo.com.ve
Circ.: 65,000
Pres. – Maria A. Marquez
Gen. Mgr. – Carmen Guevara
Sales Mgr. – Melida Leon
Editorial Dir. – Gioconda de Marquez

PUERTO ORDAZ, BOLIVAR

EDITORIAL RODERICK (M) Est. 1977
Urbanizacion Villa Colombia, Avda. Venezuela, Puerto Ordaz, Bolivar, Venezuela; tel (58) 86 23-4170; fax 22-5474; e-mail info@correodelcroni.com; web site www.correodelacroni.com
Circ.: 57,000
Owner – David Natera Febres
Pres./Gen. Mgr. – Luis Natera Febres
Sales Mgr. – Ramon Amparan
Editorial Dir. – Cruz Echeniquez
Prodn. Mgr. – Silverio Prieto

PUNTO FIJO, FALCON

MEDANO (D) Est. 1952
Peligro a Puente Republica, La Canelaria, Punto Fijo, Falcon, Venezuela; tel (58) 69 45-1487; fax 45-1487
Circ.: 4,000
Pub. – Rafael Martinez Hidalgo

SAN CARLOS, COJEDES

LAS NOTICIAS DE COJEDES (D) Est. 1988
Apdo. Postal 2201, San Carlos, Cojedes, Venezuela; tel (58) 58 330394; fax 331129
Pres. – Francisco Filardo
Editorial Dir. – Alfredo Bravo

SAN CRISTOBAL, TACHIRA

LA NACION (M) Est. 1968
Apdo. Postal 651, San Cristobal, Tachira, Venezuela; tel (58) 76 46-2367; fax 46-5178; e-mail lanacion@telcel.net.com; web site www.la-nacion.com.ve
Circ.: 30,000
Group: Brydson Global Media Sales
Pres. – Jesus Rodriguez
Gen. Mgr. – Gloria Nino de Cortez
Editorial Dir. – Jose Rafael Cortes Arvelo
Prodn. Mgr. – Hernan Vinasco

VANGUARDIA (M) Est. 1936
Avda. Andres Bello, Urb. San Bernandino, Edif. Nor, San Cristobal, Tachira, Venezuela; tel (58) 76 43-5555
Editorial Dir. – Enrique Delgado

SAN CRISTOBAL, TACHIRO

DIOCESE OF SAN CRISTOBAL (M) Est. 1924
Carrera 4a, No. 3-41, Edif. Diario Catolico, San Cristobal, Tachiro, Venezuela; tel (58) 276 43-2015; fax 43-4683
Circ.: 30,000
Pres. – Monsignor Marco Tulio Ramirez Roa
Gen. Mgr. – Marina Rivas Ostos
Sales Mgr. – Gladys Gamboa de Sanguino
Editorial Dir. – Monsignor Nelson Arellano Roja
Prodn. Mgr. – Josafat Somoza Chacon

PUEBLO (D)
Avda. Andres Bello, Urb. Los Palos Grandes, San Cristobal, Tachiro, Venezuela; tel (58) 76 445227

SAN FELIPE, YARACUY

POR QUE (D)
Avda. 8, Calle 7, San Felipe, Yaracuy, Venezuela; tel (58)
Circ.: 2,000
Pub. – Ricardo Proano

YARACUY AL DIA (M) Est. 1973
Avda. 7, No. 15-6, San Felipe, Yaracuy, Venezuela; tel (58) 54 31-3214; fax 44-1155
Circ.: 20,000
Pres. – Carloas J. Pinto
Gen. Mgr. – Petra Acosta de Pinto
Sales Mgr. – Aracelis Molina
Editorial Dir. – Salomon Escalona

SAN JUAN LOS MORROS, GUARICO

EL NACIONALISTA (M) Est. 1976
Avda. Los Llanos No. 5 y 7, San Juan Los Morros, Guarico, Venezuela; tel (58) 46 31-4437; fax 31-4437
Circ.: 17,000
Owner/Pres. – Parminio Gonzalez Arzola
Gen. Mgr. – Jose Zarpa
Sales Mgr. – Carmencita Castillo
Editorial Dir. – Leonardo Gonzalez
Prodn. Mgr. – Leopoldo Dib

VALENCIA, CARABOBO

CORPORACIN NOTI-LIBRE C.A. (D)
107-148 Av. Boyac entre Navas Sp¡nola y Flores, Valencia, Carabobo, Venezuela; tel (58) 241 850 1666; fax 850 1534; web site www.notitarde.com
Circ.: 53,000
Pres. – Ricardo Jose Degwitz Acosta
Ed. – Laurentzi Odriozola Echegaray

EL CARABOBENO (M) Est. 1933
Avenida Universidad, Edificio El Carabobeno, Valencia, Carabobo, Venezuela; tel (58) 41 672 918; fax 673 450; e-mail general@el-carabobeno.com; web site www.el-carabobeno.com
Circ.: 97,000
Advertising: Charney Palacios & Co.
Owner/Pres./Editorial Dir. – Eduardo Aleman Perez
Gen. Mgr. – Marcos Lopez Arocha
Sales Mgr. – Sandra Hernandez
Prodn. Mgr. – Lorenzo Araujo

EL ESPECTADOR (M)
Parcela 71, Galpon 4 Via Flor Amarilla, Valencia, Carabobo, Venezuela; tel (58) 41 78-3251; fax 37-9251
Editorial Dir. – Miguel Aguilar

EL REGIONAL (D)
Avda. Urdaneta, Valencia, Carabobo, Venezuela; tel (58)
Ed. – Aracelis Molina

LA CALLE (M) Est. 1988
Calle Colombia c/c Briceno Mendez, Edif. Taguanes, Valencia, Carabobo, Venezuela; tel (58) 241 57-4225; fax 58-4627
Gen. Mgr. – Enrique Ramirez
Editorial Dir. – Enrique Ramirez

PUBLICACIONES ANTON C.A. (D)
Santa Teresa y Cipreses, Valencia, Carabobo, Venezuela; tel (58)
Circ.: 5,000
Pub. – Guillermo Anton Santana
Ed – Jesus Muchacho Matheus

VALERA, TRUJILLO

CASA MUCHACHO HERMANOS C.A. (M) Est. 1978
Apdo. Postal 175, Valera, Trujillo, Venezuela; tel (58) 71 21-1811; fax 21-3289; e-mail dlandes@dlandes.com; web site www.dlandes.com
Circ.: 6,200
Pres. – Eladio Muchacho Unda
Gen. Mgr. – Alicia Paz Castellanos
Editorial Dir. – Antonio Ruiz Sanchez

EL TIEMPO (M) Est. 1958
Avda. Caracas Con Calle Buenos Aires, Valera, Trujillo, Venezuela; tel (58) 71 5-3656; fax 5-8677; e-mail buzon@eltiempo.com.ve
Circ.: 30,000

Section IV

News, Picture and Syndicate Services

NEWS, PICTURE AND SYNDICATE SERVICES

A

A & A – PO Box 543, Hazelwood, MO, 63042-0543, USA (314) 579-0215; fax (314) 579-0215; e-mail AaartWork@aol.com; web site www.AaartWork.com
Pres. – Elaine Sandra Abramson
Sr. Vice Pres. – Stan Abramson
Vice Pres.-Mktg./Sales – Mitchell Lee
Vice Pres.-Special Projects – Deborah Sue

ALM – 120 Broadway, 5th Fl., New York, NY, 10271, USA (212) 457-9400; web site www.incisivemedia.com
Pres./CEO – William L. Pollak
Sr. Vice Pres. – Jack Berkowitz
Vice Pres., Licensing/Bus. Devel. – Ellen Sigel
Editorial Dir. – Aric Press

Accuracy in Media – 4455 Connecticut Ave. NW, Ste. 330, Washington, DC, 20008, USA (202) 364-4401; fax (202) 364-4098; e-mail info@aim.org; web site www.aim.org
Chrmn. – Donald K. Irvine
Special Projects Dir. – Deborah Lambert
Exec. Secretary – Roger Aronoff

AccuWeather, Inc. – 385 Science Park Rd., State College, PA, 16803, USA (814) 235-8600; fax (814) 235-8609; e-mail sales@accuweather.com; info@accuwx.com; web site www.accuweather.com
President and Founder – Dr. Joel N. Myers
Exec. Vice Pres. – Barry Lee Myers
Sr. Vice Pres. – Elliot Abrams
Sr. Vice Pres. – Joseph P. Sobel
Sr. Vice Pres. – Evan A. Myers
Sr. Vice Pres. – Michael A. Steinberg
Vice Pres., New Media – James Candor
Mktg. Dir. – R. Lee Rainey
Sr. Sales Mgr. – Brian Kisslak
Mktg. Asst. – Felisha Dib
Vice President/Mktg. – Lee Rainey
Vice Pres. Sales – Brian Kisslack
Sr. Vice Pres. – Michael Steinberg
Dir., New Media Sales – Jim Candor

Acme Features Syndicate – 147 NE Yamhill St., Sheridan, OR, 97378, USA (503) 843-4555; fax (503) 843-4001; e-mail binky@acmefeatures.com
Editorial Dir. – Sondra Gatewood

Advertising Workshop – University of Oklahoma-Gaylord/AMC, Herbert School of Journalism & Mass Communication, Norman, OK, 73019, USA (405) 325-5209; fax (405) 325-7565; e-mail javery@ou.edu; web site www.ou.edu/gaylord
Self-Syndicator – Jim Avery
Staff Asst. – Kelly Storm

The Advice Goddess-Amy Alkon – 171 Pier Ave., Ste. 280, Santa Monica, CA, 90405, USA (310) 306-6160; e-mail adviceamy@aol.com; web site www.advicegoddess.com
Self-Syndicator – Amy Alkon
Vice Pres., Syndication – Lucy Furry

Agence France-Presse - Washington, DC – 1500 K St. NW, Ste. 600, Washington, DC, 20005, USA (202) 289-0700; fax (202) 414-0634; e-mail afp-us@afp.com; web site www.afp.com
Mktg./Sales Dir., North America – Gilles Tarot
Deputy Chief Ed. – Christophe Vogt
Sr. Mktg. Mgr. – Sue Mendives

Agence France-Presse - Montreal, QC – 180 rue Rene-Levesque St., Ste. 200, Montreal, QC, H2X 1N6, Canada (514) 288-2777; fax (514) 288-3506; e-mail afpcanada@afp.com; web site www.afp.com
Bureau Chief – Michel Matteau
Bureau Chief – Jacques Lemieux
Admin. – Susan Frohlich

EFE News Services - Madrid, Spain – Espronceda, 32, Madrid, 28003, Spain; tel (34 - 91) 346-7400; fax 441-0905
Pres. – Alexandro Grijelmo

EFE News Services - La Paz, Bolivia – Avda. Sanchez Lima, 2520. Edificio Anibal - MZ 01, La Paz, 7403, Bolivia; tel (591 - 2) 235-9837; fax 239-1441; e-mail efebol@entelnet.bo
Rep. – Soledad Alvarez

EFE News Services - Quito, Ecuador – Edificio Platinum Oficinas, piso 8 C. Carlos Padilla s/n, Quito, 4043, Ecuador; tel (593 - 2) 251-9466; fax 225-5769; e-mail redacquito@efe.com
Rep. – Enrique Ibanez

EFE News Services - Cairo, Egypt – 4 Mohamed Mazhar, 3 - apt. 5. Zamalek, Cairo, Egypt; tel (20 - 2) 738-0792; fax 361-2198
Rep. – Grace Augustine

EFE News Services - San Salvador, El Salvador – Condominio Balam Quitze, Local 17. 2. P. General Sta., San Salvador, El Salvador; tel (503 - 263 7063; fax 263 5281; e-mail elsalvador@acan-efe.com
Rep. – Laura Barros

EFE News Services - Paris, France – 10 rue St. Marc, Buro. 165, Paris, 75002, France; tel (33 - 1) 44 82 65 40; fax 40 39 91 78; e-mail paris@efe.com; web site www.efe.com
Rep. – Javier Alonso

EFE News Services - Athens, Greece – Marsalias 14-3, Athens, 10680, Greece; tel (30 - 1) 363-5626; fax 362-5922
Correspondent – Adriana Flores Borquez

EFE News Services - Algiers, Algeria – 4 Ave. Pasteur, 1st Fl., Algiers, 16000, Algeria; tel (213 - 2) 173 5680; fax 174 0456; e-mail javiergarcia@efe.com
Rep. – Javier Garcia

EFE News Services - Berlin, Germany – Schiffbauerdamm 40, Berlin, 10117, Germany; tel (49 - 30) 7262 62020; fax 7262 62030; e-mail berlin@efe.com
Rep. – Juan Carlos Barrena

EFE News Services - Guatemala City, Guatemala – 8 Ave. 8-56 Zone 1, Edif. 10-24, Segundo Nivel, Oficina 203, Guatemala City, Guatemala; tel (502 - 2) 51 94 84; fax 51 84 59; e-mail guatemala@acan-efe.com
Rep. – Carlos Arrazola

EFE News Services - Prague, Czech Republic – Ubriniveska 65, Prague, 10000, Czech Republic; tel (420 - 2) 67 31 36 20; fax 67 31 39 75
Correspondent – Miguel Fernandez Calvo

EFE News Services - Johannesburg, South Africa – 321 Main Rd., La Rocca, Unit E, 2021 Bryanston, Johannesburg, 2021, South Africa; tel (27 - 11) 463-1618; fax 463-5674
Rep. – Jose Maria Ortiz

EFE News Services - Santo Domingo, Dominican Republic – Ave. 27 Febrero, 54-5, Edif. Galerias Comerciales, Ste. 507, Santo Domingo, Dominican Republic (809) 567-7617; fax (809) 565-0308
Rep. – Jusus Sancsis

EFE News Services - Geneva, Switzerland – Bureau 49, Palas des Nations B, Ave. Paix, Geneva, 1211, Switzerland; tel (41 - 22) 724-6011 ext. 3765; fax 733-2041; e-mail ginebra@efe.com
Rep. – Virginia Hebrero

EFE News Services - Buenos Aires, Argentina – Av. Alicia Moreau de Justo 1720, Buenos Aires, 1107, Argentina; tel (54 - 11) 43 11 12 11; fax 43 12 75 18; e-mail redaccion@efe.com.ar
Rep. – Mar Marin

EFE News Services - Vienna, Austria – Rechte Wienzeile 51/16, Vienna, 1050, Austria; tel (43 - 1) 368 4174; fax 369 8842; e-mail viena@efe.com
Rep. – Ramon Santaularia

EFE News Services - Brussels, Belgium – Residence Palace, Rue de la Loi, 155, Brussels, 1040, Belgium; tel (32 - 2) 285-4831; fax 230-9319; e-mail bruselas@efe.com
Rep. – Jose Manuel Sanz

EFE News Services - Copenhagen, Denmark – Kronprinsensgade, 3 DK, Copenhagen, 1114, Denmark; tel (45 - 86) 33 32 54 20; fax 33 15 82 17
Rep. – Ruben Marcos

EFE News Services - Brasilia, Brazil – Praia de Botafogo 228, Sala 605 B - Centro, Empresarial Rio, Brasilia, 22359-900, Brazil; tel (55 - 212) 553 6355; fax 553 8823; e-mail rio@efebrasil.com.br
Rep. – Jaime Ortega

EFE News Services - Rio de Janeiro, Brazil – Praia de Botafogo, 228 Rm. 605 B, Rio de Janeiro, 22359-900, Brazil; tel (55 - 212) 553 63 55; fax 553 88 23; e-mail rio@efebrasil.com.br; web site www.efe.com
Rep. – Jaime Ortega

EFE News Services - Santiago, Chile – Almirante Pastene, 333 - office 502, Santiago, Chile; tel (56 - 2) 632-4946; fax 519-3912; e-mail redaccion@agenciaefe.tie.cl
Rep. – Manuel Fuentes

EFE News Services - Moscow, Russia – Ria Novosti International Press Center, Zubovski blvd. 4, Moscow, 119021, Russia; tel (7 - 495) 637 5137; fax 637 5137; e-mail efemos@gmail.com
Rep. – Miguel Bas

EFE News Services - Beijing, China – Julong Garden, 7-14 L. Xinzhongjie, 68 Dongcheng, Beijing, 100027, China; tel (86 - 10) 6553 1198; fax 6552 7861; web site www.efe.es
Rep. – Paloma Caballero

EFE News Services - Bogota, Colombia – Calle 67 No 7-35, Bogota, Colombia; tel (57 - 1) 321 48 55; fax 321 47 51; e-mail efecol@efebogota.com.co
Rep. – Esther Rebollo

EFE News Services - San Jose, Costa Rica – Avda., 10 Calles 19/21 n. 1912, Apanado 8.4930, San Jose, 1000, Costa Rica; tel (506 - 2222-6785; fax 2233-7681; e-mail costarica@acan-efe.com; web site Curridabat
Director – Nancy De Lemos

EFE News Services - Tunis, Tunisia – 126 rue de Yougoslavia, Tunis, 1000, Tunisia; tel (216 - 1) 33 14 97; fax 34 59 76
Rep. – Manuel Ostos Lopez

EFE News Services - Montevideo, Uruguay – Wilson Ferreira Aldunate 1294, Montevideo, 11100, Uruguay; tel (598 - 2) 902 03 38; fax 902 67 26; e-mail montevideo@efe.com
Rep. – Raul Cortes

EFE News Services - Havana, Cuba – Caclle 36 n. 110 entre 1. y3, Miramar Plz., Havana, 11300, Cuba; tel (53 - 7) 204 22 93; fax 204 22 72
Rep. – Mar Marin

EFE News Services - Caracas, Venezuela – Quinta Atlas Cumbres Esquina calles Coro y San Cristobal, Caracas, 1050, Venezuela; tel (58 - 212) 793-7618; fax 793 49 20
Rep. – Esther Borrell

EFE News Services - Belgrade, Yugoslavia – Gaspodar Javanova, 39-41/XI (Prvi Ulaz), Belgrade, 11000, Yugoslavia; tel (381 - 11) 62 32 44; fax 63 995 78
Rep. – Juan Fernandez Elornaga

EFE News Services - Tegucigalpa, Honduras – Col. Elvel, Segunda Calle, Apt. 2012, Tegucigalpa, Honduras; tel (504 - 231 1730; fax 231 1772; e-mail honduras@acan-efe.com
Rep. – German Reyes

EFE News Services - New Delhi, India – 72 Jor Bagh, 2nd Fl., New Delhi, 110003, India; tel (91 - 11) 2461-8092; fax 2461-5013; e-mail efedelhi@gmail.com
Rep. – Julia Rodriguez Arevalo

EFE News Services - Jerusalem, Israel – Hillel St. 18, 5th Fl., Office 3, Jerusalem, 91371, Israel; tel (972 - 2) 624 20 38; fax 624 20 56; e-mail administracion@efejerusalen.com; web site www.efe.com
Rep. – Alberto Masegosa

EFE News Services - Rome, Italy – Via dei Canestrari, 5-2, Rome, 00186, Italy; tel (39 - 06) 683-4087; fax 687-4918; e-mail eferoma@efe.it
Rep. – Carmen Postigo

EFE News Services - Tokyo, Japan – Kyodo Tshushin Kaikan, 9th Fl. 2.2.5, Toranomon Minato-Ku, Tokyo, 105, Japan; tel (81 - 3) 35 85 89 40; fax 35 85 89 48; e-mail efetokio@cello.ocn.ne.jp
Sec. – Yoko Kaneko
Rep. – Maribel Izcue
Rep. – Patricia Souza

EFE News Services - Rabat, Morocco – 14, rue de Kairoajne, Apt. 13, 5 ME (Angle rue d'Alger), Rabat, Morocco; tel (212 - 537) 723 218; fax 732 195; e-mail efe@menara.ma
Director – Javier Otazu
Rep. – Enrique Rubio

EFE News Services - Mexico City, Mexico – Lafayette, 69, Colonia Ave., Mexico City, 011590, Mexico; tel (52 - 55) 5545 8256; fax 5254 1412
Sales Mgr. – Alejandro Amezcua
Rep. – Manuel Fuentes

EFE News Services - Managua, Nicaragua – Garden City S-22, Managua, Nicaragua; tel (505 - 2) 49 11 66; fax 49 59 28; e-mail nicaragua@acan-efe.com
Rep. – Philadelphus Martinez

EFE News Services - Panama City, Panama – Avda. Samuel Lewis y Manuel Icaza. Edif. Comosa 22, Panama City, 0834 00749, Panama; tel (507 - 2) 23 90 14; fax 64 84 42; e-mail panama@acan-efe.com
Rep. – Hernan Martin

EFE News Services - Lima, Peru – Mauel Gonzalez Olaechea, 207, Lima, 27, Peru; tel (51 - 1) 441 24 22; fax 421 13 72; e-mail lima@efe.com
Rep. – Javier Otazu

EFE News Services - Manila, Philippines – Unit 1006, 88 Corporate Center, 141 Sedeno corner, Manila, 1227, Philippines; tel (63 - 2) 843 1986; fax 843 1973; e-mail manila@efe.com; web site www.efe.es
Bureau Chief – Miguel Frau Rovira
Ed. – Marco Zabaleta

EFE News Services - Warsaw, Poland – Sniadeckich 18 M 16, Warsaw, 00656, Poland; tel (48 - 22) 628-3912; fax 621-5989

Correspondent – Jorge Ruiz Lardizabal

EFE News Services - Lisbon, Portugal – Rua Castilho, 13 D, 5A, Lisbon, 1250 066, Portugal; tel (351 - 21) 351 39 30; fax 351 39 38; e-mail lisboa@efe.com
Rep. – Emilio Crespo

EFE News Services - Santurce, PR – Cobian's Plz., Of. 214, Santurce, PR, 00910 (787) 723-6023; fax (787) 725-8651; e-mail redacpr@est.es
Ed. – Alfonso Rodriguez

EFE News Services - London, United Kingdom – 299 Oxford St. 6th Fl., London, W1C 2DZ, United Kingdom; tel (44 - 20) 7493 7313; fax 7493-7114
Rep. – Joaquin Rabago

Agencia Prensa Internacional Inc. – 3501 W. 6th St., Los Angeles, CA, 90020, USA (323) 350-6365; fax (213) 388-0563; e-mail prensa@agenciapi.com; web site www.agenciapi.com
Media Mgr. – Javier Rojas
Ed. – Antonio Nava

The Agency – PO Box 139, Kings Park, NY, 11754, USA (631) 544-0705; e-mail cooksreviews@optonline.net
Ed. – Joel Cook

Dorothy Ahle Caricatures – 8 Grimshaw St., Malden, MA, 02148, USA (781) 321-8302; fax (781) 321-8302
Artist/Owner – Dorothy Ahle

All-Sports Publications – 72 Harvard Dr., Carmel, NY, 10512, USA (845) 225-7735; fax (845) 225-7735; e-mail gdales1680@aol.com
Vice Pres., Sales – Cris Dorier
Vice Pres., Mktg. – Marilyn Schnitter
Vice Pres. – George S. D'Alessandro
Vice Pres./Photo Ed. – G.S. D'Alessandro

Jonathon Alsop – 336 Washington St., Brookline, MA, 02445 6850, USA (617) 784-7150; fax (888) 833-9528; e-mail jalsop@invinoveritas.com; web site www.jonathonalsop.com; www.invinoveritas.com; www.bostonwineschool.com
Wine Writer/Self-Syndicator – Jonathon Alsop

AlterNet – 77 Federal St., San Francisco, CA, 94107, USA (415) 284-1420; fax (415) 284-1414; e-mail info@alternet.org; web site www.alternet.org
Pub./Exec. Ed. – Don Hazen
Bus. Mgr. – Leigh Johnson
Sr. Ed. – Tai Moses
Mng. Ed. – Davina Baum

Amanda y Rocinante – 50 School Rd., Bolton, CT, 06043, USA (860) 647-8266; fax (860) 647-8266; e-mail dhall@record-journal.com
Artist – Dorothy Hall
Writer – Resurreccion Espinosa

American Crossword Federation – PO Box 69, Massapequa Park, NY, 11762, USA (516) 804-0332; e-mail snpuzz@aol.com; web site www.stanxwords.com
Pres./Ed. in Chief – Stanley Newman
Vice Pres./Sales Dir. – Joseph Vallely

American Federation of Teachers – 555 New Jersey Ave. NW, Washington, DC, 20001, USA (202) 879-4400; fax (202) 879-4545; e-mail aftpres@aol.com; online@aft.org; web site www.aft.org
Pres. – Randi Weingarten
Sec./Treasurer – Antonia Portese
Exec. Vice Pres. – Lorretta Johnson

Ampersand Communications – 2311 S. Bayshore Dr., Miami, FL, 33133 4728, USA (305) 285-2200; e-mail amprsnd@aol.com; web site www.ampersandcom.com
Ed. – George Leposky
Mng. Partner – Rosalie E. Leposky

Anchored Dreams – 1301 Drier Pl., Highland Park, NJ, 08904, USA (732) 985-7613; e-mail azjaffe@optonline.net; az@azriela.com; web site www.azriela.com
Author/Self-Syndicator – Jaffe Azriela

And Sew On – PO Box 71, Martinsville, NJ, 08836, USA (908) 722-5676
Pres./Author – Alida Macor

Antique Detective Syndicate – 5808 Royal Club Dr., Boynton Beach, FL, 33437, USA (561) 364-5798; e-mail antique2@bellsouth.net
Pres./Writer – Anne Gilbert
Vice Pres./Writer – Jim Strawbridge

Antiques & Collectible Self-Syndicated Column – PO Box 597401, Chicago, IL, 60659, USA (773) 267-9773; e-mail thecapecod@aol.com; web site www.anitagold.com
Author/Creator/Owner – Anita Gold

Arrigoni Travel Syndication – 15 Rockridge Rd., Fairfax, CA, 94930, USA (415) 456-2697; fax (415) 456-2697; e-mail patarrigoni@comcast.net; web site www.travelpublishers.com
Pres. – Patricia Arrigoni

Arthur's International – 2613 High Range Dr., Las Vegas, NV, 89134, USA (702) 228-3731; e-mail arthurintl@aol.com
Pres. – Marvin C. Arthur

ArtistMarket.com – 35336 Spring Hill, Farmington Hills, MI, 48331 2044, USA (248) 661-8585; fax (248) 788-1022; e-mail info@artistmarket.com; web site www.artistmarket.com
CEO/Ed. – A. David Kahn

Artizans.com Syndicate – 11136 - 75 A St. NW, Edmonton, AB, T5B 2C5, Canada (780) 471-6112; fax (877) 642-8666; e-mail sales@artizans.com; support@artizans.com; web site www.artizans.com; www.dialanartist.com
Pres. – Malcolm Mayes

Ascher Features Syndicate – 214 Boston Ave., Egg Harbor Township, NJ, 08234 6923, USA (609) 927-1842
Pres. – Sidney Ascher
Sec./Treasurer – Evelyn Ascher

Ask Pippa – 194 Bain Ave., Toronto, ON, M4K 1G1, Canada (416) 463-0257; web site www.askpippa.ca
Self-Syndicator/Children's Science Columnist – Pippa B. Wysong

Associated Press, The – 19 Commerce Ct. W, Cranbury, NJ, 8512-9416

Associated Press, The – c/o The Press, Devins Ln., Pleasantville, NJ, 8232-4199

Associated Press, The – 2 Capital Plz., Ste. 400, Concord, NH, 3301-4911

Associated Press, The – Gazette-Journal Bldg., 955 Kuenzli Ln., Reno, NV, 89502-1160

Associated Press, The – 300 S. Fourth St., Ste. 810, Las Vegas, NV

Associated Press, The – 102 N. Curry St., Carson City, NV, 89703-4934

Associated Press, The – 909 N. 96 St., Ste. 104, Omaha, NE, 68114-2508

Associated Press, The – Lincoln Journal-Star Bldg., 926 P St., Lincoln, NE, 68508-3615

Associated Press, The – 825 Great Northern Blvd., Ste. 203, Helena, MT, 59601-3340

Associated Press, The – News-Leader Bldg., 651 N. Boonville Ave., Springfield, MO, 65806-1005

Associated Press, The – Post-Dispatch Bldg., 900 N. Tucker Blvd., Saint Louis, MO, 63101-1098

Associated Press, The – 215 W. Pershing Rd., Ste. 221, Kansas City, MO, 64108-4300

Associated Press, The – PO Box 272, Jefferson City, MO, 65102-272

Associated Press, The – 125 S. Congress St., Ste. 1330, Jackson, MS, 39201-3311

Associated Press, The – 75 King Blvd., Rm. B28, Saint Paul, MN, 55155-1601

Associated Press, The – Business & Tech Center, 511 11th Ave. S., Ste. 460, Minneapolis, MN, 55415-1536

Associated Press, The – 120 W. Front St., Traverse City, MI, 49684-2280

Associated Press, The – 215 S. Washington Sq., Ste. 120, Lansing, MI, 48933-1888

Associated Press, The – 300 River Pl., Ste. 2400, Detroit, MI, 48207-4260

Associated Press, The – 1391 Main St., Ste. 1020, Springfield, MA, 1103-1615

Associated Press, The – 184 High St., Boston, MA, 2110-3089

Associated Press, The – PO Box 648, Hagerstown, MD, 21741-648

Associated Press, The – 218 N. Charles St., Ste. 330, Baltimore, MD, 21201-4019

Associated Press, The – PO Box 2450, Annapolis, MD, 21404-1471

Associated Press, The – 75 Market St., Portland, ME, 4102

Associated Press, The – Box 126 Cross State Office Bldg., Rm. 106, Augusta, ME

Associated Press, The – 1515 Poydras St., Ste. 2500, New Orleans, LA, 70112-3723

Associated Press, The – PO Box 44395, Baton Rouge, LA, 70804-4395

Associated Press, The – PO Box 131, Pikeville, KY, 41502-131

Associated Press, The – Courier-Journal Bldg., 525 W. Broadway, Louisville, KY, 40202-2137

Associated Press, The – Herald-Leader Bldg., 100 Midland Ave., Lexington, KY, 40508-1999

Associated Press, The – State Capitol, Rm. 243, Frankfort, KY, 40601-3490

Associated Press, The – c/o Wichita Eagle, 825 E. Douglas Ave., Wichita, KS, 67202-3594

Associated Press, The – Statehouse Rm. 134 N, 300 SW Tenth St., Topeka, KS, 66612-1512

Associated Press, The – 103 E. College St., Ste. 208, Iowa City, IA, 52240-4014

Associated Press, The – Insurance Exchange Bldg., 505 5th Ave., Ste. 1000, Des Moines, IA, 50309-2315

Associated Press, The – 251 N. Illinois St., Ste 1600, Indianapolis, IN, 46204-1943

Associated Press, The – 300 E. Walnut St., Evansville, IN, 47713-1985

Associated Press, The – Carbondale Southern Illinoisan, 710 N. Illinois Ave., Carbondale, IL, 62901-1283

Associated Press, The – Press Room, State Capitol, Springfield, IL, 62704-1

Associated Press, The – Journal Star Bldg., 1 News Plz., Peoria, IL, 61643-3

Associated Press, The – 10 S. Wacker Dr., Ste. 2500, Chicago, IL, 60606-7407

Associated Press, The – Champaign News-Gazette Bldg., 15 Main St., Champaign, IL, 61820-3641

Associated Press, The – 101 S. Capitol Blvd., Boise, ID, 83702

Associated Press, The – 500 Ala Moana Blvd., Ste. 7-590, Honolulu, HI, 96813-4920

Associated Press, The – Centennial Tower, 101 Marietta St. NW, Ste. 2450, Atlanta, GA, 30303-2720

Associated Press, The – 126 N. Washington St., Albany, GA, 31701-2552

Associated Press, The – 9100 NW 36th St., Ste. 104, Miami, FL, 33178-2420

Associated Press, The – 336 E. College Ave., Ste. 301, Tallahassee, FL, 32301-1560

Associated Press, The – 501 N. Magnolia Ave., Ste. 1, Orlando, FL, 32801-1364

Associated Press, The – Pensacola News-Journal Bldg., Fl, 32574-2710

Associated Press, The – 9100 NW 36th St., Ste. 111, Miami, FL, 33178-2420

Associated Press, The – PO Box 327, Cape Canaveral, FL, 32920-327

Associated Press, The – 2021 K St. NW, 6th Fl., Washington, DC, 20006-1082

Associated Press, The – State Capitol, PO Box 934, Dover, DE, 19903-934

Associated Press, The – PO Box 6728, Stamford, CT, 6904-6728

Associated Press, The – 40 Sargent Dr., New Haven, CT, 6511-5939

Associated Press, The – 10 Columbus Blvd., 9th Fl., Hartford, CT, 6106-1976

Associated Press, The – 1444 Wazee St., Ste. 130, Denver, CO, 80202-1395

Associated Press, The – Civic Ctr. N., 675 N. First St., Ste. 1170, San Jose, CA, 95112-5118

Associated Press, The – 303 Second St., Ste. 680 N, San Francisco, CA, 94107-1327

Associated Press, The – Union-Tribune Bldg., 350 Camino de la Reina, San Diego, CA, 92108-3090

Associated Press, The – 1215 K St., Ste. 960, Sacramento, CA, 95814-3946

Associated Press, The – 221 S. Figueroa St., Ste. 300, Los Angeles, CA, 90012-2553

Associated Press, The – 5087 E. McKinley Ave., Fresno, CA, 93727-1965

Associated Press, The – 10810 Executive Center Dr., Ste. 308, Little Rock, AR, 72211-4377

Associated Press, The – Tucson Newspapers Inc., 4850 S. Park Ave., Tucson, AZ, 85726-6807

Associated Press, The – 1850 N. Central Ave., Ste. 640, Phoenix, AZ, 85004-3904

Associated Press, The – 319 Seward St., Ste. 12, Juneau, AK, 99801-1173

Associated Press, The – 750 W. 2nd Ave., Ste. 102, Anchorage, AK, 99501-2167

Associated Press, The – RSA Tower Bldg., 201 Monroe St., Ste. 1940, Montgomery, AL, 36104-3735

Associated Press, The – 401 N. Water St., Rm. 3058, Mobile, AL, 36602

Associated Press, The – 2200 4th Ave. N., Birmingham, AL, 35202-2553

Associated Press, The – 450 W. 33rd St., New York, NY, 10001

Associated Press, The – Florida Times-Union Bldg., 1 Riverside Ave., Jacksonville, FL, 32202-4984

Associated Press, The – 1117 Journalism Bldg., Philip Merrill College of Journalism, University of Maryland, College Park, MD, 20742-1

Associated Press, The – c/o Billings Gazette, 401 N. Broadway, Billings, MT, 59101-1274

Associated Press, The – 101 N. Fourth St. c/o Columbia Daily Tribune, Columbia, MO, 65201-4416

Associated Press, The – PO Box 9115, Savannah, GA, 31412-9115

Associated Press, The – 17291 Irvine Blvd., Ste. 263, Tustin, CA, 92780-2930

Associated Press, The – 309 Fellowship Rd., 2nd Fl., Mount Laurel, NJ, 8054-1233

Associated Press, The – c/o Palm Beach Post, 2751 S. Dixie Hwy., West Palm Beach, FL, 33405-1298

Associated Press, The – 7950 Jones Branch Dr., McLean, VA, 22107-1

Associated Press, The – c/o The Blade, 541 N. Superior St., Toledo, OH, 43660

Associated Press, The – 1611 S. Main St., Dayton, OH, 45409

Associated Press, The – 1103 Schrock Rd., Ste. 300, Columbus, OH, 43229-1179

Associated Press, The – 815 Superior Ave. E, Ste. 1203, Cleveland, OH, 44114-2768

Associated Press, The – c/o The Cincinnati Enquirer, 312 Elm St., Cincinnati, OH, 45202-2724

Associated Press, The – c/o The Forum, 101 Fifth St. N., Fargo, ND, 58102-4826

Associated Press, The – 707 E. Front Ave., Bismarck, ND, 58504-5646

Associated Press, The – 4800 Six Forks Rd., Ste. 210, Raleigh, NC, 27609-5245

Associated Press, The – 1100 S. Tryon St., Ste. 310, Charlotte, NC, 28203-4297

Associated Press, The – County Bldg., Room 237, 148 Martine Ave., White Plains, NY, 10601-3378

Associated Press, The – 666 Old Country Rd., Ste. 810, Garden City, NY, 11530-2019

Associated Press, The – The Syracuse Bldg., 224 Harrison St., Ste. 216, Syracuse, NY, 13202-3050

Associated Press, The – 55 Exchange St., Rochester, NY, 14614-2071

Associated Press, The – Press Bldg., 155 Michigan St. NW, Grand Rapids, MI, 49503-2353

Associated Press, The – 223 W. Colfax Ave., South Bend, IN, 46626-1001

Associated Press, The – 2039 Shattuck Ave., Ste. 306, Berkeley, CA, 94704-1150

Associated Press, The – 320 W. 25th St., Ste. 310, Cheyenne, WY, 82001-3005

Associated Press, The – Wausau Daily Herald Bldg., 800 Scott St., Wausau, WI, 54403-4951

Associated Press, The – 1011 E. Wisconsin Ave., Ste. 1925, Milwaukee, WI

Associated Press, The – 119 Martin Luther King Jr. Blvd., Ste. 422, Madison, WI, 53703-3379

Associated Press, The – 172 Hart Field Rd., Morgantown, WV, 26505-3755

Associated Press, The – c/o The Herald-Dispatch, 946 5th Ave., Huntington, WV, 25701-2004

Associated Press, The – 500 Virginia St. E, Ste. 1150, Charleston, WV, 25301-2135

Associated Press, The – 114 N. Fourth St., Yakima, WA, 98909-2707

Associated Press, The – 926 W. Sprague Ave., Ste. 682, Spokane, WA, 99201-4064

Associated Press, The – 3131 Elliott Ave., Ste. 750, Seattle, WA, 98121-1095

Associated Press, The – PO Box 607, Olympia, WA, 98507-607

Associated Press, The – 145 Campbell Ave., Ste. 520, Roanoke, VA, 24011-1215

Associated Press, The – 600 E. Main St., Ste. 1250, Richmond, VA, 23219-2440

Associated Press, The – 150 W. Brambleton Ave., Norfolk, VA, 23510-2075

Associated Press, The – 535 Stone Cutters Way, Ste. 102, Montpelier, VT, 5602-3795

Associated Press, The – 30 E. 100 S., Ste. 200, Salt Lake City, UT, 84111-1902

Associated Press, The – 301 Ave. E, San Antonio, TX, 78205-2006

Associated Press, The – c/o Lubbock Avalanche Journal, 710 Ave. J, Lubbock, TX, 79401-1808

Associated Press, The – 16945 Northchase Dr., Ste. 2110, Houston, TX, 77060-2151

Associated Press, The – c/o Valley Morning Star, 1310 S. Commerce St., Harlingen, TX, 78550-7799

Associated Press, The – Fort Worth Star-Telegram Bldg., Fort Worth, TX, 76101-1870

Associated Press, The – 300 N. Campbell Ave., El Paso, TX, 79901-1402

Associated Press, The – 4581 LBJ Frwy., Ste. 300, Dallas, TX, 75244-6002

Associated Press, The – 1005 Congress Ave., Ste. 995, Austin, TX, 78701-2469

Associated Press, The – 215 Centerview Dr., Ste. 110, Brentwood, TN, 37027-5246

Associated Press, The – Commercial Appeal Bldg., 495 Union Ave., Memphis, TN, 38101-3221

Associated Press, The – 2332 News-Sentinel Dr., Knoxville, TN, 37921-5761

Associated Press, The – 400 E. 11th St., Chattanooga, TN, 37402-4214

Associated Press, The – 330 N. Main Ave., Ste. 301, Sioux Falls, SD, 57104-6034

Associated Press, The – 124 S. Euclid Ave., Ste. 104, Pierre, SD, 57501-368

Associated Press, The – 1311 Marion St., Columbia, SC, 29201-3359

Associated Press, The – 211 King St., Ste. 205, Charleston, SC, 29401-3175

Associated Press, The – 10 Dorrance St., Providence, RI, 2903-2084

Associated Press, The – 119 S. Burrowes St., Ste. 607, State College, PA

Associated Press, The – 6 Gateway Ctr., Ste. 222, Pittsburgh, PA

Associated Press, The – 1835 Market St., Ste. 1700, Philadelphia, PA, 19103-2945

Associated Press, The – Main Capitol, E Fl., Rm. 526, Harrisburg, PA

Associated Press, The – State Office Bldg., Press Room, Salem, OR, 97310-1

Associated Press, The – 121 SW Salmon St., Ste. 1450, Portland, OR, 97204-2924

Associated Press, The – The Courier, 409 SE Seventh St., Grants Pass, OR, 97526-330

Associated Press, The – 315 S. Boulder Ave., Tulsa, OK, 74102-1770

Associated Press, The – 525 Central Park Dr., Ste. 202, Oklahoma City, OK, 73105-1703

Associated Press, The – Buffalo News, 1 News Plz., Buffalo, NY, 14240-2994

Associated Press, The – PO Box 7165, Capitol Sta., Albany, NY, 12224-165

Associated Press, The – 645 Albany-Shaker Rd., Albany, NY, 12211-10

Associated Press, The – Journal N. Bldg., 328 Galisteo St., Santa Fe, NM, 87501-2642

Associated Press, The – 5130 San Francisco Rd. NE, Ste. A, Albuquerque, NM, 87109-4640

Associated Press, The – 50 W. State St., Ste. 1114, Trenton, NJ, 8608-1220

Associated Press, The – 50 Park Pl., Ste. 800, Newark, NJ, 7102-4307

Associated Press, AP Newsfeatures – 450 W. 33rd St., New York, NY, 10001, USA (212) 621-1821; fax (212) 621-1852; e-mail info@apbookstore.com; web site www.apbookstore.com
Special Projects Dir. – Norm Goldstein

AP Images – 450 W. 33rd St., New York, NY, 10001, USA (212) 621-1720; fax (212) 621-1955; web site www.apimages.com
Vice Pres. – Ian Cameron

Atlantic Feature Syndicate – 16 Slayton Rd., Melrose, MA, 02176, USA (781) 665-4442; e-mail lynn@offthemarkcartoons.com; web site www.offthemark.com
Pres. – Mark Parisi
Mktg. Dir. – Lynn Reznick

Auto Digest Syndicate – 2684 34th St., Washougal, WA, 98671 9156, USA (831) 750-4805; fax (815) 550-1711; e-mail adigest@iname.com; web site www.iveho.com
Pres. – Bill Schaffer
Ed. – Barbara Schaffer

Auto How To's – PO Box M, Franklin, MA, 02038 0389, USA (508) 528-6211; fax (508) 528-6211
Glass/Automotive/Photo News Writer – J.A. Kruza

Autoeditor Syndication – 2314 Mar East St., Tiburon, CA, 94920, USA (415) 435-4541; e-mail brian@autoeditor.com; web site www.autoeditor.com
Ed./Pub. – Brian Douglas

AutoWriters Associates, Inc. (dba Motor Matters) – PO Box 3305, Wilmington, DE, 19804, USA (302) 998-1650; e-mail info@motormatters.biz; web site www.motormatters.biz
President – Connie Keane

Avanti NewsFeatures – 38550 Groesbeck Hwy., Clinton Township, MI, 48036, USA (586) 466-5944; fax (586) 466-5945; e-mail avanti1054@aol.com; macombobserver@aol.com; web site www.fracassanewsgroup.com
Editorial Dir./Columnist – Hawke Fracassa
Sr. Ed. – Dave Menard
Sr. Ed./Columnist – Michael Raveane
Family Columnist Ed. – Tracey Lee-Petri
Motor Homes Ed./Columnist – Marty Majchrzak
Music Columnist Ed. – Danielle Fracassa
Sports Ed./Columnist – Nick Meyer

B

Bankrate.com – 11760 US Hwy. 1, Ste. 200, North Palm Beach, FL, 33408, USA (561) 630-2400; fax (561) 625-4540; web site www.bankrate.com
Pres./CEO – Tom Evans
Sr. Vice Pres./Chief Revenue Officer – Donald M. Ross
Sr. Vice Pres., Finance/CFO – Robert J. DeFranco
Sr. Vice Pres./Chief Mktg./Commun. Officer – Bruce Zanca
Mktg. Dir. – Beth Planakis

Barbara Burtoff Syndicated Features – 4200 Massachusetts Ave. NW, Ste. 806, Washington, DC, 20016, USA (202) 966-0488; e-mail bbapartmentlife@aol.com; entertainingways@aol.com
Ed./Pub. – Barbara Burtoff

Buddy Basch Feature Syndicate – 720 West End Ave., Ste. 1612, New York, NY, 10025, USA (212) 666-2300
Pub. – Buddy Basch
Asst. to Pub. – Arlene Walters
Research – Peter Mallon
Photographer – Michael Flaster
Attorney – G. Godfrey, Esq.

Basic Chess Features – 102 Blatchley Rd., Windsor, NY, 13865, USA (607) 775-0587; e-mail slyman@tds.net
Pres. – Shelby Lyman

Beaver Creek Features – 3508 W. 151 St., Cleveland, OH, 44111 2105, USA (216) 251-1389; e-mail dnorman@bge.net
Artist/Owner – Dean Norman

Ron Bernthal – PO Drawer 259, Hurleyville, NY, 12747, USA; tel (1 - 1) (845) 292-3071; fax (845) 434-4806; e-mail rbern@sullivan.suny.edu; web site www.travelwritersmagazine.com/ronbernthal
Self-Syndicator, Travel/Historic Preservation Audio Programs – Ron Bernthal

Big Ring Media Team, Inc. – PO Box 231, Madison, IN, 47250 0231, USA (812) 265-6313; fax (812) 418-3368; e-mail info@bigringwriting.com; web site www.bigringwriting.com
Dir. – Richard Ries
Admin. Asst. – Julie Ries

Biofile – 995 Teaneck Rd., Unit 3N, Teaneck, NJ, 07666, USA (201) 833-2350; fax (201) 833-2350; e-mail mrbiofile@aol.com; web site www.thebiofile.com
Ed. – Mark (Scoop) Malinowski

Black Press Service, Inc. – 166 Madison Ave.,

New York, NY, 10016, USA (212) 686-6850; fax (212) 686-7308; e-mail news@blackradionetwork.com; web site www.blackradionetwork.com
Pres. – Jay R. Levy
Sales Mgr. – Peter Knight
Ed. – Roy Thompson
Assoc. Ed. – Bill Baldwin

Black Star Publishing Co., Inc. – 116 E. 27th St., New York, NY, 10016, USA (212) 679-3288; fax (212) 447-9732; e-mail sales@blackstar.com; research@blackstar.com; ben@blackstar.com; web site www.blackstar.com
Pres. – Ben Chapnick
Vice Pres. – John P. Chapnick

Bloomberg News – 1399 New York Ave., 11th Fl., Washington, DC, 20005

Bloomberg News – 27 Fl., Cheung Kong Ctr., 2 Queens Rd. Central, Hong Kong, Hong Kong

Bloomberg News – 1 Macquarie Pl., Level 36, Gtwy. 36, Sydney, NSW, 2000, Australia

Bloomberg News – Capital Square, 23 Church St., 12th Fl., Singapore, 49481, Singapore

Bloomberg News – Pierre 3., Ste., 101, San Francisco, CA, 94111

Bloomberg News – 100 Business Park Dr., Skillman, NJ, 8558

Bloomberg News – 161 Bay St., Ste. 4300, Toronto, ON, M5J 2S1, Canada

Bloomberg News – 111 S. Wacker Dr., Ste. 4950, Chicago, IL, 60606

Bloomberg News – 7 Rue Scribe, Paris, 75009, France

Bloomberg News – Neue Mainzer Strasse 75, Frankfurt, 60311, Germany

Bloomberg News – Yusen Bldg., 1st Fl., 2-3-2 Marunouchi, Tokyo, 100, Japan

Bloomberg News – 731 Lexington Ave., New York, NY, 10022

The Bookworm Sez, LLC – W5556 State Rd. 33, La Crosse, WI, 54601, USA (608) 782-2665; fax (608) 787-8222; e-mail bookwormsez@yahoo.com; bookwormsez@gmail.com; web site www.bookwormsez.com

Book Reviewer – Terri Schlichenmeyer

Bridge News – 3 World Financial Center, New York, NY, 10281

Bridge News – 15 Fetter Winchmore, London, ENG, EC4A 1BW, United Kingdom

Bridge News – 13 Fl., Kioicho Bldg. 3-12, Chiyoda-Ku, Tokyo, 1020094, Japan

Bridge News – 9900 W. 109th St., Ste. 200, Overland Park, KS, 66210

Bridge News – 3 World Financial Ctr., 28th Fl., New York, NY, 10281

Bridge News – 30 S. Wacker, Ste. 1810, Chicago, IL, 60606

Ashleigh Brilliant – 117 W. Valerio St., Santa Barbara, CA, 93101, USA (805) 682-0531; e-mail ashleigh@ashleighbrilliant.com; web site www.ashleighbrilliant.com
Pres. – Ashleigh Brilliant
Vice Pres. – Dorothy Brilliant

Broadcast News Limited, Halifax, NS, B3J 3J8, Canada (902) 423-5152
Legislative Reporter – Murray Brewster

Broadcast News Limited – The Press Gallery, Box 6000, Queen St., Fredericton, NB, E3B 5H1, Canada (506) 457-0746; fax (506) 457-9708
New Brunswick Correspondent – Kevin Bissett

Broadcast News Limited – 36 King St. E., Toronto, ON, M5C 2L9, Canada (416) 364-0321; fax (416) 364-8896; web site www.thecanadianpress.com
CFO – David Ross
Gen. Exec./Client Liaison – Terry Scott
Sales/Mktg. Dir. – Charles Messina
Sandra Clarke

Broadcast News Limited – 36 King St. E., Toronto, ON, M5C 2L9, Canada (416) 364-3172; fax (416) 364-1325
News Editor – Ellen Huebert

Broadcast News Limited – 1888 Brunswick St., Ste. 100, Halifax, NS, B3J 3J8, Canada (902) 422-9284; fax (902) 565-7588
Bureau Chief – Dean Beeby

Broadcast News Limited – 1050 rue Des Parlementaires, Bureau 207, Quebec City, QC, G1R 5A4, Canada (418) 646-5377; fax (418) 523-9686
Correspondent – Martin Ouellett

Broadcast News Limited – Rm. 335, Press Gallery, Regina, SK, S4S 0B3, Canada (306) 585-1024; fax (306) 585-1027

Saskatchewan Correspondent – Jay Branch

Broadcast News Limited – 165 Sparks St., Ste. 800, Ottawa, ON, K1P 5B9, Canada (613) 238-4142; fax (613) 232-5163
Bureau Chief – Robert Russo

Broadcast News Limited – PO Box 10109, 106th St., Ste. 504, Edmonton, AB, T5J 3L7, Canada (780) 428-6490; fax (780) 428-0663
Bureau Chief – Kathy Bell

Broadcast News Limited – Radio Rm. 012-F, BC Legislature, Parliament Bldg., Victoria, BC, V8V 1X4, Canada (250) 386-2552; fax (250) 356-9597
Legislative Reporter – Scott Sutherland

Broadcast News Limited – 215 St. Jacques W., Ste. 100, Montreal, QC, H2Y 1M6, Canada (514) 849-8008; fax (514) 282-6915
Quebec Correspondent – Peter Ray

Broadcast News Limited, Edmonton, AB, Canada (403) 427-2773
Contact – Jim MacDonald

Broadcast News Limited – 840 Howe St., Ste. 250, Vancouver, BC, V6Z 2L2, Canada (604) 687-1662; fax (604) 687-5040
Bureau Chief – Jill St. Louis

Broadcast News Limited – 386 Broadway Ave., Ste. 101, Winnipeg, MB, R3C 3R6, Canada (204) 988-1781; fax (204) 942-4788
Manitoba Correspondent – Steve Lambert

Business Newsfeatures – 417 Lexington Rd., Grosse Pointe Farms, MI, 48236, USA (313) 929 - 0800
Writer, Computer Columns – Robert H. Meyering
Ed. – Carl E. Meyering

Business Wire - Boston, MA – 2 Ctr. Plz., Ste. 500, Boston, MA, 02180, USA (617) 742-2760; fax (617) 742-2782; e-mail news@businesswire.com; web site www.businesswire.com
Pres./COO – Cathy Baron Tamraz

Business Wire - Cleveland, OH – 1001 Lakeside Ave., Ste. 1525, Cleveland, OH, 44114, USA (800) 769-0220; fax (800) 827-0237; web site www.businesswire.com
Midwest Reg. Mgr. – Jill Connor

Business Wire - Denver, CO – 1725 Blake St., Ste. 100, Denver, CO, 80202, USA (800) 308-0166; fax (303) 830-2442; web site www.businesswire.com
Vice Pres. – Dylan Frusciano

Business Wire - Los Angeles, CA – 12121 Wilshire Blvd., Ste. 1000, Los Angeles, CA, 90025, USA (800) 237-8212; fax (310) 820-7363; web site www.businesswire.com
Mgr., Southwest Reg. – Mike Iannuzzi
Nat'l Dir., Mktg. Programs – Tom Becktold

Business Wire - New York, NY – 40 E. 52nd St., 14th Fl., New York, NY, 10022, USA (800) 221-2462, (212) 752-9600; fax (212) 752-9698; web site www.businesswire.com
Vice Pres., New York Reg. – Phyllis Dantuono
Pres./CEO – Cathy Baron Tamraz

Business Wire - San Francisco, CA – 44 Montgomery St., 39th Fl., San Francisco, CA, 94104, USA (415) 986-4422; fax (415) 788-5335; e-mail news@businesswire.com; web site www.businesswire.comCathy Baron Tamraz
Co-Chief Opns. – Gregg Castano
Vice Pres., Global Media – news@businesswire.com Neil

C

Cagle Cartoons, Inc. – PO Box 22342, Santa Barbara, CA, 93121, USA (805) 969-2829; e-mail cari@cagle.com; web site www.caglecartoons.com
Pres./CEO – Daryl Cagle
Exec. Ed./Mktg. Dir. – Cari Dawson Bartley

Canadian Press, The - London, UK – 12 Norwich St., London, EC4A 1EJ, United Kingdom; tel (44 - 171) 353-6366; fax 583-4238
Bureau Chief – Helen Branswell

Canadian Press, The - Toronto, ON – 36 King St. E., Toronto, ON, M5C 2L9, Canada (416) 364-0321; fax (416) 364-0207; e-mail info@thecanadianpress.com; web site www.thecanadianpress.com
Chrmn. – John Honderich
Pres. – Eric Morrison
CFO – David Ross
Chief, Ontario Servs. – Wendy McCann
Vice Pres., Broadcasting – Terry Scott
Vice Pres., French Servs. – Jean Roy
Dir., HR – Paul Woods
Office Mgr. – Sharon Hockin
Exec. Dir. – Philipe Mercure

Canadian Press, The - Victoria, BC – Press Gallery, Rm. 360, Victoria, BC, V8V 1X4, Canada (250) 384-4912; fax (250) 356-9597; e-mail dirk.meissner@thecanadianpress.com; web site www.thecanadianpress.com
Correspondent – Dirk Meissner

Canadian Press, The - Winnipeg, MB – 386 Broadway Ave., Ste. 101, Winnipeg, MB, R3C 3R6, Canada (204) 988-1781; fax (204) 942-4788; e-mail info@thecanadianpress.com; web site www.thecanadianpress.com
Manitoba Correspondent – Steve Lambert

Canadian Press, The - Toronto, ON – CP Picture Service, 36 King St. E., Toronto, ON, M5C 2L9, Canada (416) 364-3172; fax (416) 364-1325; web site www.thecanadianpress.com
News Editor – Ellen Huebert

Canadian Press, The - Saint John's, NL – 139 Water St., Ste. 901, The Fortis Bldg., Saint John's, A1C 1B2, Canada (709) 576-0687; fax (709) 576-0049; web site www.thecanadianpress.com
Correspondent – Michelle MacAfee

Canadian Press, The - Regina, SK – Legislative Bldg., Press Gallery, Rm. 335, Regina, SK, S4S 0B3, Canada (306) 585-1024; fax (306) 585-1027; e-mail info@thecanadianpress.com; web site www.thecanadianpress.com
Correspondent – Stephanie Graham

Canadian Press, The - Fredericton, NB – Press Gallery, Legis. Bldg., Fredericton, NB, E3B 5H1, Canada (506) 457-0746; fax (506) 457-9708; web site www.thecanadianpress.com
Correspondent – Kevin Bissett

Canadian Press, The - Calgary, AB – 100 4th Ave. SW, Ste. 700, Calgary, AB, T2P 3N2, Canada (403) 543-7238; fax (403) 262-7520; e-mail calgary@thecanadianpress.com; web site www.thecanadianpress.com
National Correspondent – Bill Graveland

Canadian Press, The - Washington, DC – 1331 Pennsylvania Ave., Ste. 524, Washington, DC, 20004, USA (202) 638-3367; fax (202) 638-3369
Bureau Chief – Robert Russo

Canadian Press, The - Vancouver, BC – 840 Howe St., Ste. 250, Vancouver, BC, V6Z 2L2, Canada (604) 687-1662; fax (604) 687-5040; web site www.thecanadianpress.com
Bureau Chief – Wendy Cox

Canadian Press, The - Quebec City, QC – 1050 Des Parlementaires, Ste. 2, Quebec City, QC, G1R 5J1, Canada (418) 646-5377; fax (418) 523-9686; e-mail info@thecanadianpress.com; web site www.thecanadianpress.com
Bureau Chief – Michel Hebert

Canadian Press, The - Ottawa, ON – 165 Sparks St., Ste. 800, Ottawa, ON, K1P 5P7, Canada (613) 238-4142; fax (613) 238-4452; e-mail ottowa@thecanadianpress.com; web site www.thecanadianpress.com
Bureau Chief – Robert Russo

Canadian Press, The - Montreal, QC – 245 St. James St. W., Montreal, QC, H2Y 3J6, Canada (514) 849-3212; fax (514) 282-6915
Vice Pres.-French Serv. – Claude Papineau

Canadian Press, The - Halifax, NS – 1888 Brunswick St., Ste. 701, Halifax, NS, B3J 3J8, Canada (902) 422-8496; fax (902) 425-2675; web site www.thecanadianpress.com
Bureau Chief – Dean Beeby

Canadian Press, The - Edmonton, AB – Cornerpoint, 10109 106th St., Ste. 504, Edmonton, AB, T5J 3L7, Canada (780) 428-6490; fax (780) 428-0663; web site www.thecanadianpress.com
Bureau Chief – Heather Boyd

Canadian Press, The - Calgary, AB – 700-100 4th Ave. SW, Ste. 700, Calgary, AB, T2P 3N2, Canada (403) 5437237; fax (403) 262-7520; e-mail calgary@thecanadianpress.com
National Correspondent – Bill Graveland

Canadian Press, The - Montreal, QC – 215 St. Jacques St., Ste. 100, Montreal, QC, H2Y 1M6, Canada (514) 849-3212; fax (514) 282-6915; e-mail info@thecanadianpress.com; web site www.thecanadianpress.com
Pres. – Eric Morrison

Canadian Press, The - Toronto, ON – 1 Queen's Park Circle, Main Legislature Bldg., Toronto, ON, M7A 1Y7, Canada (416) 325-7843
Legislature Correspondent – Keith Leslie

Capital Connections – 1698 32nd St. NW, Washington, DC, 20007 2969, USA (202) 337-2044; fax (202) 338-4750; e-mail karen@karenfeld.com; web site www.karenfeld.com
Columnist/Owner – Karen Feld

Capitol News Service – 530 Bercut Dr., Ste. E, Sacramento, CA, 95811, USA (916) 445-6336; fax (916) 443-5871; e-mail editor@senior-spectrum.com; web site www.senior-spectrum.com

Career Source/Column – PO Box 85295, Hallandale, FL, 33008, USA (954) 647-5995; e-mail sgsilver2002@yahoo.com; sgsilver2002@lycos.com
Owner/Author – Sheryl Silver

Cartoon Resource – 3568 Cascade Rd. SE, Grand Rapids, MI, 49546, USA (616) 551-2238; e-mail andrew@cartoonresource.com; web site www.cartoonresource.com
Creative Dir. – Andrew Grossman
Mktg. Dir. – Nancy Terrell

Cartoonews, Inc. – 15 Central Park W., New York, NY, 10023, USA (212) 980-0855; fax (212) 980-1664; e-mail cartoonews@aol.com; luriestudios@aol.com; web site www.luriecartoon.com
Pres. – T.R. Fletcher
Vice Pres., Sales – L. Raymond
Admin. Dir. – Lisa Duval
Accountant/CPA – John Schmitt

Cartoonists & Writers Syndicate/Cartoon Arts International - Rancho Palos Verdes, CA – 28028 Lobrook Dr., Rancho Palos Verdes, CA, 90275, USA (212) 227-8666; fax (310) 541-9017; e-mail cwsmedia@cartoonweb.com; web site www.nytsyn.com/cartoons
Pres. – Jerry Robinson
Vice Pres./Ed. – Jens Robinson
Assoc. Ed. – Bojan Jovanovic

Cartoonists & Writers Syndicate/Cartoon Arts International - New York, NY – 67 Riverside Dr., Ste. 7A, New York, NY, 10024, USA (212) CARTOON (277-8666); e-mail cwss@cartoonweb.com; web site www.nytsyn.com/cartoons
Pres. – Jerry Robinson

Catholic News Service – 3211 Fourth St. NE, Washington, DC, 20017 1100, USA (202) 541-3250; fax (202) 541-3117; e-mail cns@catholicnews.com; web site www.catholicnews.com
Dir./Ed. in Chief – Tony Spence
General News Editor – Julie Asher
Features Editor – Edmond Brosnan
Library/Information Services – Katherine M. Nuss
Visual Media Manager – Nancy Wiechec

Chesstours – PO Box 1182, Reno, NV, 89504, USA (775) 786-3178; e-mail chesstours@cs.com
Author/Owner – Larry Evans

Chicago Tribune Press Service, Inc. – 2 Park Ave. 8th Fl., New York, NY, 10016

The Christian Science Monitor News Service – 210 Massachusetts Ave., Boston, MA, 02115, USA (617) 450-2000; fax (617) 450-7383; e-mail syndication@csmonitor.com; web site www.csmonitor.com
Bus. Mgr. – Dan Lawrence

City News Service, Inc. - Los Angeles, CA – 11400 W. Olympic Blvd., Ste. 780, Los Angeles, CA, 90064, USA (310) 481-0407; fax (310) 481-0416; e-mail citynews@pacbell.net; info@socalnews.com; web site www.socalnews.com
Pres. – Doug Faigin
Vice Pres. – Yet Lock
Bus. Mgr. – Frank Balderamma
Ed. – Lori Streifler
City Ed. – Marty Sauerzopf

City News Service, Inc. - Santa Ana, CA – Room 155, 10 Civic Center Plz., Santa Ana, CA, 92701, USA (714) 834-5794; fax (714) 836-7526; e-mail cnsoc@fdcglobal.net
Bureau Chief – Paul Anderson

City News Service, Inc. - San Diego, CA – 202 C St., Room MS 13A, San Diego, CA, 92101, USA (619) 231-9097; fax (619) 231-9633; e-mail fdrim@fdcglobal.net
Bureau Chief – Kelly Wheeler

Clarin Contenidos – Tacuari 1840, Buenos Aires, 1139, Argentina; tel (54 - 11) 4309-7216; fax 4309-7635; e-mail contenidos@clarin-contenidos.com.ar; web site www.clarin-contenidos.com.ar
– Matilde Sanchez
– Agustin Beltrame
– Leonardo Di Matteo
– Hernan DiMennaEd.s

The Classified Guys – 12 Bates Pl., Danbury, CT, 06812, USA (888) 712-7070; fax (815) 301-3377; e-mail comments@classifiedguys.com; web site www.classifiedguys.com
– Duane Holze
– Todd HolzeCo-Pres.s

Clear Creek Features – PO Box 3289, Grass Valley, CA, 95945, USA (530) 272-7176; e-mail clearcreekrancher@yahoo.com
Author/Self-Syndicator/Pub. – Mike Drummond

Collins Communications – 21-07 Maple Ave., Fairlawn, NJ, 07410, USA (201) 703-0911; fax (201) 703-0211; e-mail stepoutmag@aol.com; web site www.so-mag.com
Publisher – Lawrence Collins
Ed. – Chaunce Hayden

Communication International/National News – 1423 N. Orange Grove Ave., Los Angeles, CA, 90046, USA (323) 876-1668; fax (323) 876-1404; e-mail bonnie@bonniechurchill.com; web site www.bonniechurchill.com
Pres. – Hillary Bekins
Lead Columnist – Bonnie Churchill

Community Features – 1733 Dawsonville Hwy., Gainesville, GA, 30501, USA (770) 287-3798; fax (770) 287-0112; e-mail comm-feat@charter.net
– Christina Hollingsworth
– Bill JohnsonCo-Owners

ComputerUser – 220 S. 6th St., Ste. 500, Minneapolis, MN, 55402, USA (612) 339-7571; e-mail info@computeruser.com; web site www.computeruser.com
Ed. – Dan Heilman
Vice Pres., Publishing – Nathaniel Opperman

Congressional Quarterly, Inc. – 77 K Street NE, Washington, DC, 20002, USA 202-650-6500; fax 650-6741; web site www.cq.com
Editorial Director – Mike Mills
Sr Vice pres./CFO – Douglas Wallen
Sr. Vice Pres., Sales – Jim Gale
Executive Vice President and Managing Director – Keith White
SVP, Advertising – Mark Walters
SVP, legislative services and publisher – Meg Hargreaves
Vice President and Publisher, advocacy, state and transcripts
– Barkley Kern
Exec. Ed., News – Susan Benkelman

Consulate General of Sweden in New York – 1 Dag Hammarskjold Plz.,885 2nd Ave., 45th Fl., New York, NY, 10017-2201

Content That Works – 4410 Ste.101 N. Ravenswood Ave., Chicago, IL, 60640, USA (773) 728-8351; fax (773) 728-8326; e-mail info@contentthatworks.com; web site www.contentthatworks.com
CEO – Paul A. Camp
COO – Jenn Goebel
Vice Pres., Sales – Dan Dalton
Editorial Director – Mary Connors

Continental Features/Continental News Service, Inc. – 501 W. Broadway, Plz. A, PMB 265, San Diego, CA, 92101, USA (858) 492-8696; e-mail continentalnewsservice@yahoo.com; web site www.continentalnewsservice.com
Pres./Ed. in Chief – Gary P. Salamone

A.J. Cook – 6785 Slash Pine, Memphis, TN, 38119, USA (901) 754-8925; web site www.taxfables.com
Owner/Author – A.J. Cook

Copley News Service - Houston, TX – Apartado 268, POB 60326, Houston, TX, 77205, USA 55) 554-1658; fax 554-0584
Bureau Chief – S. Lynne Walker

Copley News Service - Sacramento, CA – Park Executive Bldg., 925 L St., Ste. 1190, Sacramento, CA, 95814, USA (916) 443-8181; fax (916) 443-1912
Bureau Chief – James P. Sweeney

Copley News Service - San Diego, CA – 123 Camino de la Reina, Ste. S-202, San Diego, CA, 92108, USA (310) 337-7003; fax (619) 297-0537; e-mail infofax@copleynews.com; web site www.copleynews.com
Pres./CEO – David C. Copley

Copley News Service - Springfield, IL – State Capitol, Pressroom, Springfield, IL, 62706, USA (217) 544-3666; fax (217) 544-9611
Bureau Chief – Dana Heupel

Copley News Service - Washington, DC – National Press Bldg., 529 14th St. NW, Rm. 1100, Washington, DC, 20045, USA (202) 737-6960; fax (202) 393-3643
Vice Pres./Bureau Chief – George E. Condon

Corbis – 250 Hudson St., New York, NY, 10013, USA (212) 375-7600; fax (212) 375-7700; web site www.corbis.com
Office Mgr. – Thomas Depuoz

Cox Newspapers, Inc. - Beijing, China – 33 Dongchang'an Jie, Beijing, 100004, China; tel (86 - 10) 6513-7766; fax 6513-7842
Asst. Mgr. – Martin Wan

Cox Newspapers, Inc. - Surrey, United Kingdom – PO Box 75, East Horsely, Surrey, KT246WA, United Kingdom; tel (44 - 148) 328-1432; fax 328-5135
European Correspondent – Bert Roughton

Cox Newspapers, Inc. - Mexico City, Mexico – Tlatetilpa #17 Casa C, Barrio San Lucas, Coyoacan, Mexico City, 04030, Mexico; tel (52 - 55) 549-7329; fax 549-2548
Mexico City Correspondent – Susan Ferriss

Cox Newspapers, Inc. - Jerusalem, Israel – 14 Nahshon St. Abu Tor, Jerusalem, 93548, Israel; tel (972 - 2) 672-2179; fax 672-2962
Middle East Correspondent – Larry Kaplow

Cox Newspapers, Inc. - Moscow, Russia – Dmitri Ulianova St. 16, Korpus 2, Apt. 264-265, Moscow, 117292, Russia; tel (7 - 495) 224-7148; fax 124-0712
Moscow Correspondent – Chuck Holmes

Crain News Service (includes Automotive News Syndicate) – 1155 Gratiot Ave., Detroit, MI, 48207 2997, USA (313) 446-6000; fax (313) 446-8030; e-mail info@crain.com; web site www.crain.com
Editorial Asst. – Dan Jones

Creative Circle Media Syndication – 52 Amaral St., East Providence, RI, 02915, USA (401) 455-1555; fax (401) 272-1150; e-mail info@creativecirclemedia.com; web site www.creativecirclemedia.com; www.adqic.com
President – Bill Ostendorf

Creative Comic Syndicate – 1608 South Dakota Ave., Sioux Falls, SD, 57105, USA (605) 336-9434; fax (605) 336-9434; web site www.creativecomics.net
Owner/Mgr. – Ken Alvine

Creators Syndicate – 5777 W. Century Blvd., Ste. 700, Los Angeles, CA, 90045, USA (310) 337-7003; fax (310) 337-7625; e-mail cre8ors@aol.com; info@creators.com; web site www.creators.com
Pres./CEO – Richard S. Newcombe
Nat'l Sales Dir. – Margo Sugrue
Sales Dir. – Mary Ann Veldman
Int'l Syndication – Marianne Sugawara
Office Mgr. – Teri Gao
Sales Administrator – Sheila Telle
Bus. Mgr. – Melissa Lin
Accounting Clerk – Jennifer Lee
Editorial Asst. – Jessica Burtch
Ed. – Anthony Zurcher

Cricket Communications, Inc. – PO Box 527, Ardmore, PA, 19003, USA (610) 924-9158; fax (610) 924-9159; e-mail crcktinc@aol.com
Pres./Pub. – Edwin Marks
Vice Pres./Ed. – Mark E. Battersby
Mng. Ed. – E. Arthur Stern

Critics, Inc. – 6724 Perimeter Loop Rd., Ste. 310, Dublin, OH, 43017, USA (614) 408-3865; e-mail comments@critics.com; web site www.critics.inc; www.kids-in-mind.com; www.mediascreen.com
Pub./Ed. – Aris T. Christofides
Commun. Dir. – Lori Pearson
Contributing Ed. – Teressa L. Elliott
Contributing Ed. – Wade R. Gossett
Bus. Mgr. – Ethan Cuhulinn

J.D. Crowe – PO Box 2488, Mobile, AL, 36652, USA (251) 219-5676; fax (251) 219-5799; e-mail jdcrowe@crowetoons.com; jdcrowe@press-register.com; web site www.crowetoons.com
Self-Syndicator, staff editorial cartoonist, Mobile Press-Register – J.D. Crowe

Crown Syndicate, Inc. – 3817 W. Parkmont Pl., Seattle, WA, 98199, USA (206) 285-1888
Pres. – L.M. Boyd
Vice Pres. – Patricia Boyd

D

DANY News Service – 420 E. 54th St., Ste. 21F, New York, NY, 10022, USA (212) 319 5090; fax (212) 319-5357; e-mail danynews@aol.com
Pres./Ed. – David Nydick

Dail Advertising Service – 1701 Wayne Memorial Dr., Goldsboro, NC, 27534, USA (919) 736-0447; fax (919) 736-0483; e-mail dailadvertising@bellsouth.net
Nat'l Rep. – Annette W. Dail

Daniel Kline Newspaper Column – 68 Sterling Dr., Newington, CT, 06111, USA (917) 523-3496; e-mail dan@notastep.com; web site DBKline.com
Columnist – Daniel Kline

Dateline Las Vegas – 7521 Crystal Forest Dr., Las Vegas, NV, 89117, USA (702) 228-9110
Author – Robert Macy

Davy Associates Media Features – 215 Avenida Del Mar, San Clemente, CA, 92672, USA (949) 498-0833; fax (949) 498-6573; e-mail jldavy@sbcglobal.net
Owner – James L. Davy

Deg Syndication – 25 columbus circle 55e, new york, NY, 10019, USA (212) 2090847; fax ; e-mail expert@deg.com; web site www.deg.com
Pres./Writer – Marisa D'Vari

Demko Publishing/Age Venture News Service – 19432 Preserve Dr., Boca Raton, FL, 33498 4818, USA (561) 866-8251; e-mail demko@ageventurenewsservice.com; newsdesk@ageventurenewsservice.com; demko@demko.com; web site www.demko.com; www.ageventurenewsservice.com
Gerontologist/Ed. – David J. Demko Ph.D.

Derus Media Service, Inc. – 7702 S. Cass Ave., Ste. 110, Darien, IL, 60561

Deutsche Presse-Agentur (dpa) – Schell 343 Ofc.

707, Apartado 18-1362, Lima 18 Miraflores, Peru

Deutsche Presse-Agentur (dpa) – Alberdi 733, 10 Piso 3, Edificio Ypacarai, ofc. 10, Asuncion, Paraguay

Deutsche Presse-Agentur (dpa) – 311-2, S01 24, 4th Fl., Sukhumvit Rd., Bangkok, 10110, Thailand

Deutsche Presse-Agentur (dpa) – Edificio 152, tercer piso, San Jose, Calle 11, Costa Rica

Deutsche Presse-Agentur (dpa) – Beijing, 100600, China

Deutsche Presse-Agentur (dpa) – Huerfanos 1373, Ofc. 502, Santiago, Chile

Deutsche Presse-Agentur (dpa) – Rua Abade Ramos, 65, Rio de Janeiro, 22641, Brazil

Deutsche Presse-Agentur (dpa) – Piso 9, ofc. 3, La Paz Dr., La Paz, 13885, Bolivia

Deutsche Presse-Agentur (dpa) – Blvd. Charlemagne 1, Bte. 17, International Press, Brussels, 1041, Belgium

Deutsche Presse-Agentur (dpa) – Villa 2788, Delmon Ave, Rd. 2772, Manama, Bahrain

Deutsche Presse-Agentur (dpa) – 36 Heath St., Mona Vale, NSW, 2103, Australia

Deutsche Presse-Agentur (dpa) – 1125 Corniche el Nil, 14th Fl., Maspero-Cairo, Egypt

Deutsche Presse-Agentur (dpa) – Bouchard 557, 5th Fl., Buenos Aires, 1106, Argentina

Deutsche Presse-Agentur (dpa) – 405 E. 42nd St., United Nations Bldg., Rm. L0219, New York, NY, 10017-3507

Deutsche Presse-Agentur (dpa) – Mittelweg 38, Hamburg, 20148, Germany

Deutsche Presse-Agentur (dpa) – Gunoldstr. 14, IPZ, Vienna, A-1199, Austria

Deutsche Presse-Agentur (dpa) – 40 Nazimuddin Rd., F 6/1, Islamabad, 44000, Pakistan

Deutsche Presse-Agentur (dpa) – Apartado 1550, Panama City 1, Panama

Deutsche Presse-Agentur (dpa) – Physician's Tower Bldg., PH, 1000 Ermita Manila, Philippines

Deutsche Presse-Agentur (dpa) – Ul. Saska 7a, 03-908 Warsaw, Poland

Deutsche Presse-Agentur (dpa) – Calle Lopez Landron 1509, Santurce, San Juan, Puerto Rico, 907

Deutsche Presse-Agentur (dpa) – Espronceda 32, 5th Fl., Madrid, 28003, Spain

Deutsche Presse-Agentur (dpa) – 10 Palais des Nations, Ste. 84, Geneva, 1211, Switzerland

Deutsche Presse-Agentur (dpa) – 1 Park Rd.,(Richmond 2092), Johannesburg-Braamfontein, 2092, South Africa

Deutsche Presse-Agentur (dpa) – 148 Angug-Dong, Jongro-Ku, Hae-Yung Bldg., 10th Fl., Seoul, 110, South Korea

Deutsche Presse-Agentur (dpa) – Petrske namesti 1/1186, Prague, 110 00, Czech Republic

Deutsche Presse-Agentur (dpa) – Bestekar Sokak 80/4, Ankara, Turkey

Deutsche Presse-Agentur (dpa) – Av. 18 de Julio 994, 4th Fl., Ofc. A, Montevideo, 11100, Uruguay

Deutsche Presse-Agentur (dpa) – Av. Fco. de Miranda, Centro Plz., Torre D, 11th Fl, Caracas, Venezuela

Deutsche Presse-Agentur (dpa) – 6H Seahorse Ln., Discovery Bay, Hong Kong, Hong Kong

Deutsche Presse-Agentur (dpa) – III Remetehegyi, UT 27, Budapest, H-1037, Hungary

Deutsche Presse-Agentur (dpa) – Istana Harmoni Apt., Unit 19J Komp Harmoni, Block B 26-27, Jakarta Pusat, 11000, Indonesia

Deutsche Presse-Agentur (dpa) – 1112 National Press Bldg. NW, Washington, DC, 20045

Deutsche Presse-Agentur (dpa) – Eisenhowerlaan 128, The Hague, 2517 KM, Netherlands

Deutsche Presse-Agentur (dpa) – Apartado Postal 3529, Managua, D.N., Nicaragua

Deutsche Presse-Agentur (dpa) – Avenida Cuauhtemoc 16, Colonia Doctores, Mexico City, 6720, Mexico

Deutsche Presse-Agentur (dpa) – Edificio Focsa, Apt. 2K, Calle 17 y M Vedado, Havana, Cuba

Deutsche Presse-Agentur (dpa) – Carrera 7 No. 17-02, Oficina 909, Apartado 044245, Bogota, Colombia

Deutsche Presse-Agentur (dpa) – Chester House, 1st Fl., Koinange St., Nairobi, Kenya

Deutsche Presse-Agentur (dpa) – 702 National Press Bldg., 150 Wellington, Ottawa, ON, K1P 5A4, Canada

Deutsche Presse-Agentur (dpa) – c/o HINA, Marulicev Trg 16, Zagreb, 4100, Croatia

Deutsche Presse-Agentur (dpa) – Nippon Press Center Bldg., 2-2-1 Uchisaiwaicho, Ste. 3F, Tokyo, 100, Japan

Deutsche Presse-Agentur (dpa) – Via della Mercede 55 Int. 15, Rome, 100187, Italy

Deutsche Presse-Agentur (dpa) – 30 Ibn Gvirol St., Tel Aviv, 64078, Israel

Deutsche Presse-Agentur (dpa) – 39 Golf Links, New Delhi, 110003, India

Deutsche Presse-Agentur (dpa) – 4a calle y 5a avenida, No. 405, officine 203, Tegucigalpa, Honduras

Deutsche Presse-Agentur (dpa) – Kreschtschalik 29, KW 33, Kiev, 252001, Ukraine

Deutsche Presse-Agentur (dpa) – Wohnung 210, Kutusowski Prospekt 7/4, Moscow, 121248, Russia

Deutsche Presse-Agentur (dpa) – 12 Calle 1-25, Zona 10, Ciudad de Guatemala, Guatemala

Deutsche Presse-Agentur (dpa) – 30 Old Queen St., London, ENG, SW1H 9HP, United Kingdom

Deutsche Presse-Agentur (dpa) – Miniati 1, Athens, GR 11636, Greece

Deutsche Presse-Agentur (dpa) – 30, rue St. Augustin, Paris, 75002, France

Deutsche Presse-Agentur (dpa) – Avenida Espana 225, Edificio Quan, San Salvador, El Salvador

Deutsche Presse-Agentur (dpa) – Edificio Atrium, ofc. S-7, Quito, Ecuador

Deutsche Presse-Agentur (dpa) – Store Kongensgade 14, Copenhagen K, DK 1460, Denmark

Deutsche Presse-Agentur (dpa) – 2 Vanda Cres., Singapore, 1128, Singapore

Sylvia Di Pietro – 55 W. 14th St., Ste. 4H, New York, NY, 10011, USA (212) 255-4059; fax (212) 633-6298; e-mail femalelitigator@yahoo.com
Self-Syndicator – Sylvia Di Pietro

Didato Associates – 106 Antler Ridge, Ossining, NY, 10562, USA (914) 923-1182; e-mail svd1@me.com
Principal/Ed. – Salvatore Didato
Exec. Ed. – Paul Hamway

Disability News Service – 13703 Southernwood Ct., Chantilly, VA, 20151-3345

Divorce Reality Group – 135 E. Bennett St., Ste. 29, Saline, MI, 48176, USA (734) 668-2001; fax (734) 668-1200; e-mail dell@divorcebalance.com; web site www.divorcepeers.com
Divorce Mediator – Dell Deaton

Doing Biz In – 1865 River Falls Dr., Roswell, GA, 30076, USA (770) 998-9911; e-mail thewritepublicist@earthlink.net; web site www.thewritepublicist.com
Creator/Writer – Regina Lynch-Hudson

Dork Storm Press/Shetland Productions – PO Box 45063, Madison, WI, 53744, USA (608) 222-5522; fax (608) 222-5585; e-mail john@kovalic.com; web site www.kovalic.com
Bus. Mgr. – Monica Valintinelli
Office Mgr. – Alexander Schiller
Ed. – Eleanor Williams
Assoc. Ed. – Becky Weiner

Dow Jones Newswires - Bogota, Colombia – Calle 93B No. 13-30 Oficina 301, Bogota, Colombia; tel (57 - 481-1785; fax 483-5623; e-mail datanewsdj@hotmail.com
Correspondent – Richard Sanders
Sales Exec. – Martha de Rengifo

Dow Jones Newswires - Brussels, Belgium – Blvd. Brand Whitlock 87, Brussels, 1200, Belgium; tel (32 - 2) 285-0130; fax 741 1429; e-mail dirk.geeraerts@dowjones.com; vanessa.stolk@dowjones.com
Rep. – Vanessa Stolk
Correspondent – Peter Greiff
Acct. Mgr. – Dirk Geeraerts

Dow Jones Newswires - Buenos Aires, Argentina – Leandro N. Alem 712, Piso 4, Buenos Aires, 1001, Argentina; tel (54 - 1) 4314-8788; fax 4311-0083; e-mail ana.delriccio@dowjones.com
Correspondent – Michelle Wallin
Sales Exec. – Ana Del-Riccio

Dow Jones Newswires - Frankfurt, Germany – Wilhem Leuschner Strasse 78, Frankfurt, D-60329, Germany; tel (49 - 69) 29 725 200; fax 29 725 222
Ed. – Fridrich Geiger

Dow Jones Newswires - Hong Kong, Hong Kong – 25F Central Plz., 18 Harbour Rd., Wanchai, Hong Kong, Hong Kong; tel (852 - 2573 7121; e-mail djnews.hk@dowjones.com; web site www.dowjones.com
Correspondent – Jeffrey Ng

Dow Jones Newswires - Kuala Lumpur, Malaysia – Ste. 21A-8-2, 8th Floor, Faber Imperial Ct., Jalan Sultan Ismail, Kuala Lumpur, 50250, Malaysia; tel (60 - 3) (65) 6415-4200; fax (65) 6225-8959; e-mail janet.leau@dowjones.com
Correspondent – Matthew Geiger
Acct. Mgr. – Janet Leau

Dow Jones Newswires - London, United Kingdom – E. Smithfield, London, E1W 1AZ, United Kingdom; tel (44 - 20) 726-7903; fax 726-7855; e-mail adam.howes@dowjones.com
Regl. Sales Mgr. – Adam Howes

Dow Jones Newswires - London, United Kingdom – Commodity Quay, E. Smithfield, London, E1W 1AZ, United Kingdom; tel (44 - 20) 3217 5233; fax 3217 5232; web site www.dowjones.com
Regl. Sales Mgr. – Adam Howes

Dow Jones Newswires - London, United Kingdom – 12 Norwich St., London, EC4A 1QN, United Kingdom; tel (44 - 227) 842-9550; fax 842-9551
Correspondent – Bhushan Bahree
Sales Mgr. – Sarah Money

Dow Jones Newswires - Madrid, Spain – Espronceda 32 1st Planta, Madrid, 28003, Spain; tel (34 - 91) 395-8120; fax 399-1930
Bureau Chief – Santiago Perez

Dow Jones Newswires - Manila, Philippines – Philamlife Tower, 19/F, 8767 Paseo de Roxas, Makati City, Manila, Philippines; tel (63 - 2) 574-616; fax 885-0293
Correspondent – Lilian Karununean

Dow Jones Newswires - Mexico City, Mexico – Av. Issac Newton No. 286, Piso 9, Col. Chapultepec Morales, Mexico City, 11560, Mexico 55) (52 5) 254-5581; fax (52 5) 254-7510
Correspondent – Peter R. Fritsch

Dow Jones Newswires - Milano, Italy – Via Burigozzo 5, Milano, 20122, Italy; tel (39 - 02) 7601-5386; fax 5821 9752
Correspondent – Jennifer Clark

Dow Jones Newswires - New York, NY – 1211 Avenue of the Americas, New York, NY, 10036 1198, USA 212-416-2400; fax 212-416-2410; e-mail spotnews@priority.dowjones.com; web site www.dowjones.com/newswires; www.djnewswires.com
Vice Pres./Gen. Mgr. – Tim Turner
Vice Pres., Sales/Mktg. – James Donoghue
Mng. Ed., Dow Jones Newswire Americas – Neal Lipschutz

Dow Jones Newswires - New York, NY – 335 Madison Ave., 7th Fl., New York, NY, 10036, USA (609) 520-4000; web site www.djnewswires.com
Correspondent – Gregory White

Dow Jones Newswires - Paris, France – 6-8 Boulevard Haussmann, Paris, 75009, France; tel (33 - 1) 7036 5502; fax 4017-1781; e-mail thierry.cadin@dowjones.com
Reg'l Sales Mgr. – Thierry Cadi
Correspondent – David Pearson

Dow Jones Newswires - Sao Paulo, Brazil – Rua Joaquim Floriano 488. 6 andar, Sao Paulo, 04534 002, Brazil; tel (55 - 11) 256-0520; fax 3044-2813; e-mail ana.gresenberg@dowjones.com
Correspondent – John Wright
Sales Exec. – Ana Gresenberg

Dow Jones Newswires - Singapore, Singapore – 10 Anson Rd., Ste. 32-09/10 Int'l Plz., Singapore, 079903, Singapore; tel (65 - 6415-4200; fax 6225-8959; e-mail hweekun.ho@dowjones.com
Correspondent – Lim Mui Khi
Regl. Sales Mgr. – Hwee-Kun Ho

Dow Jones Newswires - Stockholm, Sweden – Kungsgatan 12-14, Trapphus B, Plan 7, Stockholm, 11135, Sweden; tel (46 - 8) 118-440; fax 791-7202
Reg. Sales Mgr. – Isabel Ordonez

Dow Jones Newswires - Sydney, Australia – Level 10 56 Titt St., Sydney, 2000, Australia; tel (61 - 2) 8272 4600; fax 8272 4601; web site www.dowjones.com
Correspondent – Ian McDonald
Regl. Sales Mgr. – Tom Rustowski

Dow Jones Newswires - Tokyo, Japan – Marunouchi Mitsui Bldg. 1F, 2-2-2, Marunouchi Chiyoda-ku, Tokyo, 100 0004, Japan; tel (81 - 3) 5220 2730; fax 5220-2746; e-mail masashi.takeuchi@dowjones.com

Sales Mgr. – Masashi Takeuchi

Dow Jones Newswires - Washington, DC – 1025 Connecticut Ave. NW, Ste. 800, Washington, DC, 20036, USA (202) 862-9272; fax (202) 862-6621
Bureau Chief – Rob Wells

Dow Jones Newswires - Zurich, Switzerland – Sihlquai 253, Postfach 1128, Zurich, 8031, Switzerland; tel (41 - 43) 960 5870; fax 960 5701; e-mail sarah.money@dowjones.com; penny.greenwood@awp.ch
Sr. Acct. Mgr. – Penny Greenwood

DSEntertainment/North Shore Publishing – PO Box 318, Vermilion, OH, 44089, USA (440) 967-0293; fax (440) 967-0293; e-mail dave@northshorepublishing.com; dave@thecomedybook.com; web site www.thecomedybook.com; www.davelaughs.com; www.beatlesincleveland.com; www.northshorepublishing.com
Author/Award-Winning Humor Columnist – Dave Schwensen

Dunkel Sports Research Service – PO Box 133, Mount Vernon, VA, 22131, USA (202) 253-3899; e-mail dunkelratings@msn.com; web site www.dunkelindex.com
– Richard H. Dunkel Jr.
– Bob DunkelCo-Ed./Co-Owners

E

EFE News Services - Washington, DC – 529 14th St. NW Office No 1220, Washington, DC, 20045 1000, USA (202) 745-7692; fax (202) 393-4118; web site www.efe.es
Bureau Chief – Maria Luisa Azpiazu

EFE News Services - Washington, DC – 1220 National Press Bldg., 529 14th St. NW, Suite 529, Washington, DC, 20045, USA; tel (+1 - (202) 745-7692; fax (305) 262-7557; e-mail info@efeamerica.com; web site www.efe.com
Sales and Business Development Director – Rafael Carranza
Editorial Vice President - USA and Canada – José Manuel Sanz
Bureau Chief-Miami – Mar Gonzalo
Bureau Chief- New York – Elena Moreno
Marketing Coordinator – Marcela Romero
President – Alejandro Grijelmo
Vice Pres. – Maria Luisa Aspiazu

EFE News Services - Happy Valley, Hong Kong – 10A, Bonny View House, 63-85 Wong Nai Chung Rd., Happy Valley, Hong Kong; tel (852 - 28 08 01 99; fax 28 02 31 01
Correspondent – Antonia Gutierrez Almanzo r

EFE News Services - New York, NY – 25 W. 43rd St., Ste. 1114, New York, NY, 10036, USA (212) 867-5757; fax (212) 867-9074; web site www.efe.com
Bureau Chief – Elena Montero

ESPN/SportsTicker – 989 6th Ave., New York, NY, 10018, USA (212) 515-1298; fax (212) 515-1211; e-mail newsroom@pa-sportsticker.com; web site www.pa-sportsticker.com
Consumer Mktg./Commun. Mgr. – Adam Provost

Earth Talk: Questions & Answers About Our Environment – 28 Knight St., Norwalk, CT, 06851, USA (203) 854-5559/x106; fax (203) 866-0602; e-mail earthtalkcolumn@emagazine.com; web site www.emagazine.com/earthtalk/earthtalk_letter.html
Pub./Exec. Ed. – Doug Moss

East-West News Bureau – 531 Main St., Ste. 902, El Segundo, CA, 90245

Editor's Copy Syndicate – 3803 Pin Oaks St., Sarasota, FL, 34232, USA (704) 628-1994; fax (828) 628-0616; web site www.security-one.com/ecopy
Ed./Pub. – Edward H. Sims
Bus. Mgr. – Bente Christensen
Circ. Mgr. – Christian Sims

Elder Mirth – 13312 Shannondell Dr., Audubon, PA, 19403, USA (610) 728-5366; e-mail gb@sdlifestyle.com
Writer/Self-Syndicator – George L. Beiswinger

Karen M. Engberg, M.D. – 334 S. Patersons Ave., Ste. 120, Goleta, CA, 93111, USA (805) 682-8844; fax (805) 683-0149; e-mail kengbergmd@aol.com; web site www.jacksonmedicalgroup.com
Self-Syndicator – Karen M. Engberg, M.D.

Dr. Bee Epstein-Shepherd – PO Box 221383, Carmel, CA, 93922, USA (831) 625-3188; fax (831) 625-0611; e-mail drbeemm@aol.com; web site www.drbee.com
Mental Skills Coach/Writer – Dr. Bee Epstein-Shepherd

Europa Press News Service – Los Conquistadores 1700 Piso 2, Santiago, Chile

Exhibitor Relations Co. – 1262 Westwood Blvd., Los Angeles, CA, 90024, USA (310) 441-7400; fax (310) 475-0316; e-mail info@ercboxoffice.com; web site www.ercboxoffice.com
Pres. – Robert Bucksbaum
Box Office Analyst – Jeff Bock

F

FNA News – PO Box 11999, Salt Lake City, UT, 84147 0999, USA (801) 355-3336; e-mail rng2@utah.edu; web site www.fnanews.com
Mng. Ed. – Richard Goldberger
Energy Ed./Houston Bureau Chief – K. Rossi
Health/Wellness Ed./Los Angeles Bureau Chief – Connie Levy
Legal Affairs Ed. – Larry Long
Photo Bureau Chief – Matt D'Alessandro
Travel/Society Ed. – Cindy Richey
Technology Ed. – Marlon U. Stones
Washington Bureau Chief – Jenyfer Morris

Family Almanac – 420 Constitution Ave. NE, Washington, DC, 20002, USA (202) 544-5698; fax (202) 544-5699; e-mail marguerite.kelly@verizon.net; web site www.margueritekelly.com
Self-Syndicator – Marguerite Kelly

Family Features Editorial Syndicate, Inc. – 5825 Dearborne St., Mission, KS, 66202-2745, USA (913) 722-0055, (800) 800-5579; fax (913) 789-9228; e-mail support@familyfeatures.com, wmacdonald@familyfeatures.com; web site www.culinary.net; www.familyfeatures.com
Owner – Dianne Hogerty
President – Brian Agnes
Director of Media – Wendy MacDonald
Pres. – Dena Klein
CEO – Diane Hogerty

W.D. Farmer Residence Designer, Inc. – 5238 Rocky Hill Dr. SW, Lilburn, GA, 30047, USA (770) 934-7380; fax (770) 934-1700; e-mail wdfarmer@wdfarmerplans.com; vstarkey@wdfarmerplans.com; web site www.wdfarmer.com; www.wdfarmerplans.com/featurehomes; www.wdfplans.com
Designer – W.D. Farmer
Pres. – Vickie Starkey

Fashion Syndicate Press – PO Box 727, Woodstock, VT, 05091, USA (917) 749-8421; fax (212) 202-4604; e-mail fashionshowroom@yahoo.com; web site www.fashionsyndicatepress.com
Owner – Andres Aquino
Ed. – Elaine Hallgren
Prodn. Art Dir. – Justin Alexander

Feature Photo Service, Inc. – 320 W. 37th St., Ste. 301, New York, NY, 10018, USA (212) 944-1060; fax (212) 944-7801; web site www.featurephoto.com
Pres./CEO – Oren Hellner
Office Mgr. – Marla Edwards

Featurewell.com – 238 W. Fourth St., New York, NY, 10014, USA (212) 924-2283; e-mail featurewell@featurewell.com; sales@featurewell.com; contactus@featurewell.com; web site www.featurewell.com
Founder/CEO – David Wallis
CTO – Marc Deveaux

Financial Times – 1 Southwark Bridge, London, ENG, SE1 9HL, United Kingdom; tel (44 - 20) 7775 6248; fax 873-3070; e-mail synd.admin@ft.com; web site www.ft.com
Synd. Mgr. – Sophie deBrito
Picture Synd. – Richard Pigden

Ed Fischer Production – 2007 5th Ave. NE, Rochester, MN, 55906, USA (507) 281-5119
Self-Syndicator – Ed Fischer

Focus On Style – PO Box 532, Cooper Station, New York, NY, 10276 0532, USA (212) 473-8353; e-mail information@focusonstyle.com; web site www.sharonhaver.com; www.focusonstyle.com
Syndicated Columnist, Newspaper/Online – Sharon Haver

Food Nutrition Health News Service – 1712 Taylor St. NW, Washington, DC, 20011, USA (202) 723-2477; e-mail goody.solomon@verizon.net; web site www.fnhnews.com
Owner/Exec. Ed./Author – Goody L. Solomon

Fotopress Independent News Service International – 266 Charlotte St., Ste. 297, Peterborough, ON, K9J 2V4, Canada (705) 745-5770; fax (705) 745-9459; e-mail kubikjohn@fotopressnews.org; web site www.fotopressnews.org
Opns. Dir. – John M. Kubik
Accts. Administrator – Steven Brown
South America Journalist – Hugo Fernandez
Central America Photo Journalist – Vincent Delgado
North America Journalist – Elizabeth McKinney Bennett
North America Journalist – Frederick Brown
North America Journalist – Irene Clark
North America Journalist – Jarrett Dubois
North America Journalist – Barbara Jividen
North America Journalist – Jacquelyn Johnson
North America Journalist – Kevin G. Marty
North America Photographer – Lauren McFaul
Australia Artist – Peter Kozak
Africa Journalist – Mulenga Chola
Africa Journalist – Luis Managonde
Africa Photographer – Nariz Bhugaloo
United Kingdom Journalist – Gordon Irving
United Kingdom Journalist – Robert O'Connor
Japan Journalist – Edward Neilam
Japan Photo Journalist – Naohiro Kimura

The Funny Pages – 4185 Bonway Dr., Pensacola, FL, 32504, USA (850) 484-8622; fax (850) 484-8622; e-mail thejoker@thefunnypages.com; web site www.thefunnypages.com
Creator – Phillip A. Ryder

G

Gannett News Service - Baton Rouge, LA – 333 State Capitol Blvd, Baton Rouge, LA, 70804, USA (225) 342-7333
Bureau Chief – Mike Hasten

Gannett News Service - Albany, NY – 150 State St., Albany, NY, 12207, USA (518) 436-9781; fax (518) 436-0130
Bureau Chief – Joe Spector

Gannett News Service - Columbus, OH – 50 W. Broad St., Ste. 1615, Columbus, OH, 43215, USA (614) 224-4640; fax (614) 221-0781
Correspondent – Spencer Hunt

Gannett News Service - Harrisburg, PA – State Capital, News Room, Harrisburg, PA, 17105, USA (717) 783-3763; fax (717) 787-3941
Bureau Chief – Dan Nephin

Gannett News Service - McLean, VA – 7950 Jones Branch Dr., McLean, VA, 22108, USA (703) 854-6000; fax (703) 854-2152; e-mail candrews@gns.gannett.com; web site www.gannett.com
Office Mgr. – Marie Marino
Mng. Ed., Features/Graphics/Photography – Jeannette Barrett-Stokes
Mng. Ed., News – Phil Pruitt
Copy Desk Chief – Bev Winston
Asst. Copy Desk Chief – Michelle Washington
Regl. Ed. – Laura Rehrmann
Regl. Ed. – Val Ellicott
Regl. Ed. – Theresa Harrah
Regl./Database Ed. – Robert Benincasa
News/Sports/Technology Ed. – Craig Schwed
Photo Ed. – Jeff Franko
Special Projects Ed. – Linda Dono
Nat'l Correspondent, Defense/Security – John Yaukey
Nat'l Ed./Correspondent, Politics – Chuck Raasch
Sports Correspondent – Mike Lopresti
Regl. Correspondent, California/Nevada – Doug Abrahms
Regl. Correspondent, Colorado/Montana/Idaho – Faith Bremner
Regl. Correspondent, Delaware/Maryland/Vermont – Erin Kelly
Regl. Correspondent, Florida/Georgia – Larry Wheeler
Regl. Correspondent, Indiana/Illinois – Maureen Groppe

Gannett News Service - Sacramento, CA – 925 L St., Ste. 110, Sacramento, CA, 95814, USA (916) 446-1036; fax (916) 446-7326
Bureau Chief – Jake Henshaw

The Gelman Feature Syndicate – PO Box 399, Roscoe, NY, 12776, USA (607) 498-4700
Owner/Ed. – Bernard Gelman

German Press Agency – United Nations, 405 E. 42nd St., Ste. S-352, New York, NY, 10017, USA (212) 319-6626; fax (212) 753-6168; e-mail None; web site www.dpa.com
English Correspondent
United Nations and New York – J. Tuyet Nguyen

Get Fit with The World's Fittest Man – 201 W. 91st St., Ste. 5C, New York, NY, 10024, USA (917) 923-8968; e-mail info@joe-decker.com; web site www.joe-decker.com
Rep. – Eric Neuhaus
Author – Joe Decker

Gilchrist Features – 237 Hopmeadow St., Simsbury, CT, 06089, USA 860-651-4400; fax 860-651-6688; e-mail info@gilchristcartoonacademy.com; web site www.gilchristcartoonacademy.com
Self Syndicator – Guy Gilchrist

Glasserfide Directory – 10240 Camarillo St., Ste. 210, Toluca Lake, CA, 91602, USA (818) 769-4774
Pres./Ed. – Selma Glasser

Glenmoor Enterprise Media Group – 75 N. Main St., No. 203, Willits, CA, 95490, USA (707) 367-4608; fax (707) 459-6106; e-mail glenmoorent@yahoo.com
Gen. Mgr. – Ron C. Moorhead

Global Horizons – 1330 New Hampshire Ave. NW, Ste. 609, Washington, DC, 20036, USA (202) 966-8636; fax (202) 244-1242; e-mail edflattau@msn.com

Pres. – Edward Flattau
Ed. – Pam Ebert

Global Information Network – 146 W. 29th St., Ste. 7E, New York, NY, 10001 5303, USA (212) 244-3123; e-mail newsdesk@mind-spring.com; web site www.globalinfo.org
Exec. Dir. – Lisa Vives
News Ed. – Gabriel Packard
Webmaster – Chuck Newman

Globalvision News Network – PO Box 677, New York, NY, 10035, USA; tel (USA - (212) 246-0202; e-mail roc@globalvision.org; web site www.globalvision.org
Exec. Chrmn. – James H. Rosenfield
CEO/Ed. in Chief – Rory O'Connor
Vice Pres., News – Danny Schechter
Producer/Director – Glenn Beatty

Globe Photos, Inc. – 24 Edmore Lane South, West Islip, NY, 11795, USA (631) 661-3131; fax (631) 321-4063; e-mail requests@globephotos.com; web site www.globephotos.com
Pres. – Mary Beth Whelan
Vice Pres. – Raymond D. Whelan

Globe Syndicate – 499 Richardson Rd., Strasburg, VA, 22657 5236, USA (540) 635-3229; e-mail publisher@globesyndicate.com; web site www.globesyndicate.com
Ed./Pub. – Gavin Bourjaily
Asst. Pub./Assoc. Ed. – M.F. Bourjaily, III

Golf Publishing Syndicate – 2743 Saxon St., Allentown, PA, 18103, USA (610) 437-4982; e-mail k.gilbert24@hotmail.com
Pres. – Karl D. Gilbert

Dave Goodwin & Associates – 721 86th St., Miami Beach, FL, 33141-1115, USA (305) 865 0158; fax 305 865 1252; e-mail davegoodwi@aol.com
Author/Owner – Dave Goodwin
Writer – Ari Goodwin

Graham News Syndicate – 2770 W. Fifth St., Ste. G20, Brooklyn, NY, 11224, USA (718) 372-1920
Pres./Ed. in Chief – Paula Royce Graham
Correspondent – Lane W. Hall

The Green Thumb – 8656 Rte. 53, Naples, NY, 14512, USA (585) 374-5400
Ed. – George Abraham
Asst. Ed. – Katherine Abraham

H

Joe Harkins – 845 Bergen Ave., Ste. 385, Jersey City, NJ, 07306, USA (201) 985-2105; e-mail joe@travelthenet.com; web site www.travelthenet.com
Self-Syndicator – Joe Harkins

Have Fun at the Movies – 10017 Bushire Dr., Dallas, TX, 75229, USA 214-536-9399; fax (214) 559-4549; e-mail nreagan@aol.com
Columnist – Gail Reagan

Headbone Interactive – 2100 Geng Rd., Ste. 105, Palo Alto, CA, 94303, USA (650) 571-0100; fax (650) 813-0101; e-mail adsales@bonus.com; web site www.headbone.com; www.bonus.com
Vice Pres., Adv. Sales – Bryson Smith
Prodn. Mgr. – Endre Csaszar
Traffic Admin. – Jennifer Hunter

Healthy Living – PO Box 60443, Santa Barbara, CA, 93160 0443, USA (805) 683-3272; e-mail n.clancy@att.net; web site www.nicoleclancy.com
Pres. – Nicole Clancy

Healthy Minds – 3709 Crestbrook Rd., Birmingham, AL, 35223, USA (205) 969-2963; fax (205) 969-1972; e-mail wfleisig@hotmail.com
Writer/Self-Syndicator – Dr. Wayne Fleisig

Hearst News Service – 700 12th St. NW, Ste. 1000, Washington, DC, 20005, USA (202) 263-6400; fax (202) 263-6441
Senior Editor – Charles J. Lewis

Heart Tones – PO Box 30034, Kansas City, MO, 64112, USA (913) 433-3877; e-mail gloria@hearttones.com; web site www.hearttones.com
Pres./Founder – LMSW Thomas-Anderson, Gloria
Public Relations Director – Tracee Jackson
Webmaster and Graphics Specialist – Tammy Iroku

High Country News – 119 Grand Ave., Paonia, CO, 81428, USA (970) 527-4898; fax (970) 527-4897; e-mail hcnsyndicate@hcnsyndicate.org; web site www.hcn.org
Ed. in Chief – Jonathan Thompson
Syndicate Representative – JoeAnn Kalenak
Exec. Dir. – Paul Larmer

Hispanic Link News Service – 1420 N St. NW, Washington, DC, 20005, USA (202) 234-0280; fax (202) 234-4090; e-mail editor@hispaniclink.org; web site www.hispaniclink.org
Pub. – Carlos Ericksen-Mendoza
Capitol Hill Ed. – Patricia Guadalupe

Hollister Kids – 3 E. Wynnewood Rd., Wynnewood, PA, 19096 1917, USA (484) 829-0024; fax (484) 829-0027; e-mail contactus@hollisterkids.com; web site www.hollisterkids.com
Pres. – Kim Landry
Vice Pres. – Peter Landry
Art Dir. – Heidi Karl

Hollywood Inside Syndicate – PO Box 49957, Los Angeles, CA, 90049 0957, USA (818) 754-0751; fax (818) 754-0751; e-mail holywood@ez2.net; web site www.ez2.net/hollywood
Dir. – John Austin

Hollywood News Service – 13636 Ventura Blvd., Ste. 303, suite 303, Sherman Oaks, CA, 91423, USA (818) 986-8168; fax (818) 789-8047; e-mail editor@newscalendar.com; web site www.newscalendar.com
Ed. in Chief – Carolyn Fox
Mng. Ed. – Susan Fox

Home Improvement Time, Inc. – 7425 Steubenville Pke., Oakdale, PA, 15071 0247, USA (412) 787-2881; fax (412) 787-3233; e-mail info@homeimprovementtime.com; web site www.homeimprovementtime.com
Pres. – James A. Stewart, Jr.
Vice Pres. – Carole C. Stewart
Website Marketing Manager – Jeff Stewart

Hometown Content – 341 Cool Springs Blvd., Ste. 400, Franklin, TN, 37067, USA (615) 468-6000; fax (615) 468-6100; web site www.hometowncontent.com
Partner Services Coordinator – Tiffany Green

Rick Horowitz – 4014 N. Morris Blvd., Shorewood, WI, 53211, USA (414) 963-9333; e-mail rickhoro@execpc.com; web site www.huffingtonpost.com/rick-horowitz/
Self-Syndicator – Rick Horowitz
Webmaster – Charlie White

Hot Topics Publications, Inc. – PO Box 183, Wyncote, PA, 19095, USA (215) 635-1120; e-mail nie@hottopicshotserials.com; web site www.hottopicshotserials.com
Pres. – Deborah Carroll
Vice Pres. – Ned Carroll

Hurst Sports Media – 2740 N. Pine Grove Ave., Ste. 4C, Chicago, IL, 60614 6101, USA (773) 871-3918; e-mail hurstsportsmedia@yahoo.com; web site www.hurstsportsmedia.com
Owner/Ed./Columnist – Bob Hurst
Photographer – Mark Meckes

I

iMortgageGuide.com LLC – box 5795, Scottsdale, AZ, 85261, USA (480) 905-8000; fax (480) 905-8190; e-mail qualitycontrol@iMortgageguide.com; web site www.imortgageguide.com

Independence Feature Syndicate – 13952 Denver West Pkwy., Ste. 400, Golden, CO, 80401 3134, USA (303) 279-6536; fax (303) 279-4176; e-mail mike@i2i.org; web site www.independenceinstitute.org
President – Jon Caldara
Research Dir. – David Kopel

Inman News – 1100 Marina Village Pkwy., Ste. 102, Alameda, CA, 94501, USA (510) 658-9252; e-mail press@inman.com; web site www.inman.com
Mng. Ed. – Glenn Roberts, Jr.
Membership Coord. – Elaine Baker

International BusinessMan News Bureau – 535 5th Ave., 33rd Fl., New York, NY, 10185

International BusinessMan News Bureau – 241 W. 97th St., Ste. 7N, New York, NY

International News Agency – 2445 Pine Tree Dr., Ste. 20, Miami Beach, FL, 33140 4611, USA (305) 674-9746
Bureau Chief – C.H. Garvey
Exec. Ed. – R.J. Sherker
Ed. in Chief – T.M. Mosberg
Mng. Ed. – Mary Quinn
Arts Dept. – Donna Shaw
Bus. Dept. – Ed Dever
Charity Dept. – Ed Hayden
Food – Roz Shulin
Sports – Pat Simpson

International Photo News – 2902 29th Way, West Palm Beach, FL, 33407, USA (561) 683-9090; fax (561) 683-9090; e-mail jay@jaykravetz.com
– Jay N. Kravetz
– Cheryl DupreeEd.s

International Puzzle Features – 4507 Panther Pl., Charlotte, NC, 28269, USA (704) 921-1818; fax (704) 597-1331; e-mail publisher@cleverpuzzles.com; web site www.cleverpuzzles.com
Owner – Pat Battaglia

Interpress of London and New York – 90 Riverside Dr., Ste. 15B, New York, NY, 10024, USA (212) 873-0772; e-mail itpnyc@aol.com
Chief Ed. – Jeffrey Blyth

Ipol, Inc. – 41 John St., Ste. 4, Babylon, NY, 11702, USA (631) 661-3131; fax (631) 321-4063; e-mail requests@globephotos.com; web site www.globephotos.com
– Marybeth Whelan
– Raymond D. WhelanMgr.s

J

J Features – PO Box 70, Cohasset, MA, 02025 0070, USA (781) 383-9858; e-mail jfeatures@aol.com
Columnist – Chuck A. Jaffe
Syndicate Mgr. – Susan Biddle Jaffe

Gary James – 111 Shearin Ave., East Syracuse, NY, 13057, USA (315) 463-8348; e-mail garyjames111@hotmail.com; web site www.famousinterview.com; classicbands.com
Pres./Self-Syndicator – Gary James

Jandon Features – 53961 222nd St., Glenwood, IA, 51534, USA (712) 527-9517; e-mail don@riggenbach.info; web site www.midwestgardening.com
Mgr. – Don Riggenbach

JasonLove.com (Humor Features) – 165 N. Fifth St., Ste. 208, Port Hueneme, CA, 93041, USA (805) 271-9560; e-mail mail@jasonlove.com; web site www.jasonlove.com
Sole Proprietor – Jason Love
Office Mgr. – Yahaira Quintero
Agent – Philippe Marquis
Writer – Rima Rudner
Illustrator – Vladimir Stankovski
Illustrator – Jose Angel (Gogue) Rodriguez
Illustrator – Thaum Blumel

The Jerusalem Post Foreign Service – The Jerusalem Post Bldg., Jerusalem, 91000, Israel; tel (972 - 2) 5315666; fax 5389527; e-mail ads@jpost.co.il; web site www.jpost.comAlan D. Abbey
Mktg. Mgr. – Dori Shoshan Hiam
N. American Adv. Dir. – Hiam Simon

Jewish Telegraphic Agency, Inc. – 330 7th Ave., 17th Fl., New York, NY, 10001-5010

Jiji Press America Ltd. – 120 W. 45th St., Ste. 1401, New York, NY, 10036, USA (212) 575-5830; fax (212) 764-3950; e-mail edit@jijiusa.com; web site www.jiji.com
Pres. – Hiroshi Masuda

Journal Press Syndicate – 545 W. End Ave., Ste. 2C, New York, NY, 10024, USA (212) 580-8559; e-mail ijbnyc@aol.com
Ed. – Irwin J. Breslauer
Mng. Ed. – John Lynker
Automotive Ed. – Todd Lewis
Comics Ed. – William Kresse

Marion Joyce – 52 Sagamore Rd., Bronxville, NY, 10708, USA (914) 961-2020; fax (914) 793-3434
Pres. – Marion Joyce

K

Keister Williams Newspaper Services, Inc. – 1807 Emmet St., Ste. 6-B, Charlottesville, VA, 22901, USA (434) 293-4709; fax (434) 293-4884; e-mail ky@kwnews.com; web site www.kwnews.com
Pres./Treasurer – Walton C. (Ky) Lindsay
Vice Pres., Mktg. – Meta L. Nay
Admin. – Carol Lindsay
Pres. – Walton Lindsay

Keystone Pictures – 408 N. El Camino Real, San Clemente, CA, 92672, USA (949) 481-3747; fax (949) 481-3941; e-mail info@zumapress.com; web site www.zumapress.com
Dir. – Scott McKiernan

Kid Scoop – PO Box 1802, Sonoma, CA, 95476, USA (707) 996-6077; fax (707) 938-8718; e-mail thescoop@kidscoop.com; web site www.kidscoop.com
Pres./CEO – Vicki Whiting

King Features Syndicate – 300 W 57th St. 15th Fl., New York, NY, 10019 5238, USA (212) 969-7550; (800) 526-5464; fax (646) 280-1550; e-mail kfs-public-relations@hearst.com; web site www.kingfeatures.com
Pres. – T.R. Shepard, III
Vice Pres., Creative Services – Frank Caruso
Vice Pres., Gen. Mgr. – Keith McCloat
Vice Pres., North American Licensing – Ita Golzman
Vice Pres., Int'l Licensing – Cathleen Titus
Gen. Mgr., King Features Weekly Service – David Cohea
Dir., Adv./Pub. Rel. – Claudia Smith
Senior Sales Consultant/Printing & New England Newspaper Sales – Jack Walsh
Int'l Sales Mgr. – John Perry
Inside Sales Mgr. – Dennis Danko
Telemktg. Sales Rep. – Michael Mancino
Sunday Comics Mgr. – Jim Nolan
Syndication Sales Dir. – John Killian
SE Sales – Louis Albert
Sales Mgr., Western Region – Richard Heimlich

Promotions Director – Rose Croke
Editorial Dir., King Features Weekly Serv. – Jim Clarke
Mng. Ed./Dir., Publishing – Glenn Mott
Comics Editor – Brendan Burford
Director of Marketing – Mark Karlan
Director, Web Development – Michael G. Chan
Vice Pres., Worldwide Syndication Sales – George Haeberlein
Domestic Sales Coord. – Venetta Smith
Pres. – T.R. Shepard

King & Kango Komix & Illustrations – PO Box 7914, Vallejo, CA, 94590, USA (707) 704-2086; e-mail kango@pacbell.net; web site www.tuckyart.com
Pub. – Tucky McKey

Knight Ridder Newspapers – 12th St. NW, Ste. 1000, Washington, DC, 20005

Kyodo News International, Inc. – 747 3rd Ave. N., Ste. 1803, New York, NY, 10017, USA (212) 508-5440; fax (212) 508-5441; e-mail kni@kyodonews.com; web site www.kyodo.co.jp; www.kyodonews.com
Sales Mgr. – Daisuke Ota

L

Landmark Designs, Inc. – PO Box 5625, Eugene, OR, 97405, USA (541) 343-3029; e-mail orders@landmarkdesigns.com; web site www.landmarkdesigns.com; www.ldiplans.com
Chrmn./Pres. – W. Scott McAlexander

Alan Lavine, Inc. – 10199 Willow Ln., Palm Beach Gardens, FL, 34410, USA (561) 630-7112; e-mail mwliblav@aol.com
Chrmn./Pres. – Alan Lavine
Mktg. Mgr. – Gail Liberman

Legal & Word Briefs – 555 NE 15th St., Ste. 100, Miami, FL, 33132, USA (305) 372-0933; fax (305) 661-4359; e-mail jar@rrzlawyers.com; web site www.johnritter.us
Pres./Writer – John Ritter

Lester Syndicate – PO Box 1183, Cupertino, CA, 95015, USA (408) 257-9567
Pub. – Mary Lester
Exec. Ed. – William Lester

Levin Represents – 2402 Fourth St., Ste. 6, Santa Monica, CA, 90405, USA (310) 392-5146; fax (310) 392-3856; e-mail deblevin@aol.com; web site www.callahanonline.com
Pres. – Deborah Levin

Listening, Inc. – 152 S. Illinois St., Hobart, IN, 46342, USA (219) 947-5478; e-mail addup4@yahoo.com; web site listeninginc.com
Pres. – Patricia Work Bennett
Vice Pres. – Richard Bennett

Literary Features Syndicate – 92 East St., North Grafton, MA, 01536, USA (508) 839-4404; e-mail nick@gentlymad.com; web site www.literaryfeaturessyndicate.com
Pres. – Constance V. Basbanes
Mng. Ed./Columnist – Nicholas A. Basbanes

Glynda Lomax – P.O. Box 981, Princeton, TX, 75407, USA (580) 303-4381; e-mail glyndalomax@gmail.com; web site http://aboutlifecolumn.blogspot.com
Author – Glynda Lomax

L. A. Features Syndicate – 650 Winnetka Mews, Ste. 110, Winnetka, IL, 60093, USA (847) 446-4082; e-mail lafs@aol.com
Mng. Ed. – Alice O'Neill
Vice Pres.-Sales – A.V. Licht
Dir.-Sales – Mike Armstrong

M

Magnum Photos, Inc. – 151 W. 25th St., 5th Fl., New York, NY, 10001, USA (212) 929-6000; fax (212) 929-9325; e-mail photography@magnumphotos.com; web site www.magnumphotos.com
Cultural Projects Dir. – Mark Lubell

Making It Productions – 1018 Morningside Dr., Manhattan Beach, CA, 90266, USA (310) 379-5337; fax (310) 374-8431; e-mail krobinson@makingit.com; web site www.makingit.com
Cartoonist/Owner – Keith Robinson
Asst. – Lisa M. Dawson

Male Call – 721 Shore Acres Dr., Mamaroneck, NY, 10543, USA (914) 698-0721; e-mail lois.fenton@prodigy.net
Columnist/Advice, Men's Business & Social Dress Consultant/Men's Personal Shopper, Blogger – Lois Fenton

Mark-Morgan, Inc. – 10 Alpine Dr., Newnan, GA, 30263, USA (770) 253-5355
Pres. – Robert David Boyd
Sec./Treasurer – Rosalyn M. Boyd

Market News International – 40 Fulton St., 5th Fl., New York, NY, 10038, USA (212) 669-6400; fax (212) 608-3024; e-mail tony@marketnews.com; web site www.marketnews.com
Mng. Ed. – Tony Mace
Washington Bureau Chief – Denis Gulino
London Bureau Chief/European Ed. – Kevin Woodfield

Marks & Frederick Assoc., LLC – 206 Popham Road, Phippsburg, ME, 04562, USA (207) 389-2620; fax (207) 389-1882; e-mail tmarks@mfamedia.com
Pres. – Ted Marks

Masterfile (Stock Color Photo Library) – 3 Concord Gate 4th Fl., Toronto, ON, M3C 3N7, Canada (416) 929-3000; fax (416) 929-2104; e-mail info@masterfile.com; web site www.masterfile.com
Pres. – Steve Pigeon
Vice Pres., Sales/Mktg. – John McDonald
Infringement Researcher – Jack Seto

Mature Life Features – 3911 Kendall St., San Diego, CA, 92109, USA (858) 483-3412
Ed. in Chief/Financial Ed. – Cecil F. Scaglione
Book Ed. – Beverly Rahn Scaglione
Nat'l Affairs/Health Ed. – James B. Gaffney
Travel Ed. – Igor Lobanov

McClatchy-Tribune Information Services – 700 12th St. NW, Ste. 1000, Washington, DC, 20005, USA (202) 383-6095; e-mail mctsales@tribune.com; web site www.mctdirect.com; www.mct-international.com
Ed. – Jane Scholz
Photo Servs. Dir. – Harry Walker
MCT Graphics Dir. – Wes Albers
Dir., News Servs. – Fred Povey
Vice Pres., Global Sales – Walter F. Mahoney
MCT Sales Mgr. – Rick DeChantal

Meadowlands Media Group – 20 Nevins St., Rutherford, NJ, 07070, USA (201) 939-7875; fax (201) 896-8619; e-mail salfino@comcast.net; web site www.rotoaction.com
Pres. – Catherine Salfino
Columnist – Michael Salfino
Columnist – David Ferris

Media General News Service – 333 E. Franklin St., Richmond, VA, 23219, USA (804) 649-6000; fax (804) 819-1266; web site www.mgnewsservice.com
Vice Pres., Content – Donna M. Reed
Ed. – Guy Lucas

Media General Syndication Services – 418 N. Marshall St., Winston-Salem, NC, 27101, USA (800) 457-1156; fax (336) 727-7461; e-mail jsarver@wsjournal.com; web site www.mgnewsservice.com; www.starwatch.com
Rep. – Jodi Stephenson Sarver

The Media Maven – 33 Holidat Drive, Carrollton, GA, 30116, USA 404-210-5160; e-mail howardhopwood@yahoo.com; web site www.mediamaven.com
Self-Syndicator – Howard Hopwood

MIC Insurance Services – 170 Kinnelon Rd., Ste. 11, Kinnelon, NJ, 07405 2328, USA (973) 492-2828; fax 973-492-9068; web site www.micinsurance.com
Pres./Author – Irene C. Card
Sec./Treasurer/Author – Betsy Chandler

Megalo Media – PO Box 1503, New York, NY, 10021, USA (212) 861-8048; e-mail megalomedia@lawtv.com; web site www.megalomedia.biz; www.crossword.org
Pres. – J. Baxter Newgate
Ed./Vice Pres. – Sandy Applegreen
Assoc. Ed. – Paul Merenbloom
Puzzle Ed. – Arthur Wynne

Merrell Enterprises – 2610 Garfield St. NW, Washington, DC, 20008 4104, USA (202) 265-1925; fax (202) 265- 8721; e-mail jessemerrell@comcast.net; web site www.merrellenterprises.com
Pres. – Jesse H. Merrell
Exec. Vice Pres. – Margaret R. Miller

Metro Editorial Services – 519 8th Ave., 18th Fl., New York, NY, 10018, USA (212) 947-5100; fax (212) 714-9139; e-mail mes@metroemail.com; web site www.metroeditorialservices.com
Pres. – Robert Zimmerman
Vice Pres./Mktg. Dir. – Debra Weiss

Michaels News – W10236 Vaudriel Rd., Black River Falls, WI, 54615 5416, USA (715) 284-5638
Pres./Ed. – Marion Michaels

Midwest Features Syndicate – PO Box 259623, Madison, WI, 53725, USA (608) 274-8925; e-mail info@roadstraveled.com; web site www.midwestfeatures.com; www.roadstraveled.com
Columnist – Mary Bergin

Miko's Pacific News Service – 159 Reitter St., Stratford, CT, 06614, USA (203) 829-5613; e-mail bmiko@pacificdialogue.com; web site www.pacificdialogue.com
Ed. – Robert J. Miko

Military Update – PO Box 231111, Centreville, VA, 20120 1111, USA (703) 830-6863; e-mail tomphilpott@militaryupdate.com; web site www.militaryupdate.com
Self-Syndicator – Tom Philpott

Milligan Syndicate – 981 Longmeadow Ct., Barrington, IL, 60010, USA (847) 382-1593
– Molly Milligan
– Annie MilliganEd.s

Minding Your Business – 5317 Canary Ansas Dr., Kenner, LA, 70065, USA (504) 522-9392; fax (504) 523-2140; e-mail channing.hayden@lanyap.com; cfhjr@bellsouth.net
Self-Syndicator – Channing F. Hayden, Jr.

Morris News Service – 18 Capitol Sq. SW, Atlanta, GA, 30334

Mortgage News Company – 141 North Rd., Cromwell, CT, 06416, USA (860) 685-0082; fax (860) 613-0790; e-mail epeat@mortgagenews.com
Pres./Author – Earl Peattie

Moskowitz News and Learning Network – 83-09 Brevoort St., Kew Gardens, NY, 11415, USA (917) 916-4681; e-mail gavriael@aol.com; web site www.geocities.com/mnln2003/home/html
Pres./Ed./Columnist – Gary Moskowitz
Gen. Ed. – Betty Sebrow
Ed. – Stu Rosenberg
Human Relationships/Family Ed. – Brenda Shoshana Lukeman
Jewish History Ed. – Larry Domitch
Music Ed. – Shoshan Kaye
Photography Ed. – Yossi Tepper
Psychology Ed. – Rivka Bertiche
Science Ed. – Michael Meir
Arts Ed. – Raquel Fereres

Motor News Media Corp. – 3710 Capitol Circle, Suite F, Grimes, IA, 50111, USA (515) 986-1155; e-mail motornewsmedia@live.com; web site www.motornewsmedia.com
Pres./CEO – Kenneth J. Chester, Jr.

Mountain Media – 3172 N. Rainbow Blvd., Ste. 343, Las Vegas, NV, 89108, USA (702) 656-3285; e-mail vin@thelibertarian.us; web site www.thelibertarian.us
Pres./Ed. – Vin Suprynowicz
Pub. – Wayne P. Murray
Webmaster – Tyger Gilbert

Move, Inc. – 30700 Russell Ranch Rd., Westlake Village, CA, 91362, USA (805) 557-2300; fax (805) 557-2680; e-mail corporateinfo@move.com; web site www.move.com
Chrmn. – Joe F. Hanauer
CEO – W. Michael Long

Movie Choices for Kids – 160 W. 77th St., New York, NY, 10024, USA (212) 799-6416; web site www.moviechoicesforkids.com
Writer – Jean Joachim

N

NISyndication – 1 Virginia St., London, ENG, E98 1SY, United Kingdom; tel (44 - 207) 711 7888; fax 782 5353; e-mail enquiries@nisyndication.com; web site www.nisyndication.com
Grp. Pub. – Kate Morgan
Syndication Sales Mgr. – Tonia Mimai

NYT Graphics Service – 620 8th Ave., FL 9, New York, NY, 10018, USA (212) 556-4204; fax (212) 556-3535; e-mail nytnsphotos@nytimes.com; web site www.nytimages.com
Managing Editor/Images – Sergio Florez

NYT Photo Service – 620 8th Ave., 9th Fl., New York, NY, 10018, USA (212) 556-4204; fax (212) 556-3535; e-mail nytns@nytimes.com; web site www.nytimages.com
Dir., Photos/Graphics News Servs. – Sergio Florez

The Name Game International, Inc. – 401 SW 54th Ave., Plantation, FL, 33317, USA (954) 321-0032; fax (954) 321-8617; e-mail namegameco@aol.com
Pres. – Melodye Hecht Icart
Vice Pres., Sales/Dev. – Mitchell J. Free

Nasco Products Co. – 13810 Metcalf Ave., Apt. 12211, Overland Park, KS, 66223, USA (913) 897-3101; fax (913) 897-3101; e-mail normaschon@gmail.com
Vice Pres., Mktg. – Wendy Schonwetter
Ed. – Norma Schonwetter

National News Bureau – PO Box 43039, Philadelphia, PA, 19129, USA 215) (215) 849-9016; e-mail nnbfeature@aol.com; fashionnnb@aol.com; travelnnb@aol.com; foodandwinennb@aol.com; booksnnb@aol.com; web site www.nationalnewsbureau.com
Pub./Ed. in Chief – Harry Jay Katz
Fashion/Beauty/Lifestyles Ed. – Debra Renee Cruz
Features Ed. – Andy Edelman

New Car News Syndicate – 41 Quercus Circle, Little Rock, AR, 72223, USA (501) 425-9737; e-mail carnews@aol.com
Ed. in Chief – Bob Plunkett

New England News Service, Inc. – 66 Alexander Rd., Newton, MA, 02461, USA (617) 969-4102; e-mail nenewsnow@yahoo.com
Pres./CEO – Eleanor Gun
Bureau Chief – Milton J. Gun
Staff – Lee Ann Jacob
Staff – Eleanor Margolis

Staff – Howard Neal
Staff – Steve Richards
Staff – Kate Tattlebaum

New Living Syndicate – 99 Waverly Avenue , Suite 6D, Patchogue, NY, 11772, USA (631) 751-8819; e-mail charvey@newliving.com; web site www.newliving.com
Pub./Ed. in Chief – Christine Lynn Harvey

New Wave Syndication – PO Box 232, North Quincy, MA, 02171, USA (617) 471-8733
Pres./Pub./Ed. – Tim Lynch

New York Press Photographers Association – 225 E. 36th St., Ste. 1-P, New York, NY, 10016-3664

New York Times News Service – 620 8th Ave., New York, NY, 10018, USA; tel (1 - 212) 556-5162; e-mail nytsyn-northamerica@nytimes.com; web site www.nytsyn.com
Managing Editor News Services – Mitch Keller
Marketing Manager – Cheri Dannels
Director, Domestic Sales & Licensing – Stephanie Serino
Director, International Sales – Philippe Hertzberg
Regional Manager, Southern Region – Andrea Mariano
Regional Manager, Western Region & Canada – Roddy Salazar
Regional Manager, Eastern & Southeastern Region – Debra Weydert
Regional Director, Latin America, Mexico & the Caribbean – Isabel Amorim Sicherle
Regional Director, Northern, Eastern & Central Europe – Jodie Hopperton
Regional Director, Southern Europe, Middle East & Africa – Milena Trevisani
Regional Director, Asia Pacific – Whye-Ko Tan
Mktg. Mgr. – Tricia Kang

New York Times Syndicate – 620 8th Ave., New York, NY, 10018, USA; tel (1 - 212) 556-7201; e-mail nytsyn-paris@nytimes.com; web site www.nytsyn.com
Marketing Manager – Cheri Dannels
Director, Domestic Sales & Licensing – Stephanie Serino
Director, International Sales – Philippe Hertzberg
Regional Manager, Southern Region – Andrea Mariano
Regional Manager, Western Region & Canada – Roddy Salazar
Regional Manager, Eastern & Southeastern Region – Debra Weydert
Regional Director, Latin America, Mexico & the Caribbean – Isabel Amorim Sicherle
Regional Director, Northern, Eastern & Central Europe – Jodie Hopperton
Regional Director, Southern Europe, Middle East & Africa – Milena Trevisani
Managing Editor NYT Syndicate – Patti Sontag
Regional Director, Asia Pacific – Whye-Ko Tan
Pres. – Cristian Edwards
Vice Pres., Int'l/Editorial Devel. – Gloria Brown Anderson
Sales Exec., Western US – Mike Pearson
Sales Exec., US/Canadian One-Shots – Debra Weydert
Mktg. Mgr. – Tricia Kang

The News Item – 707 N. Rock St., Shamokin, PA, 17872, USA (570) 644-6397; fax (570) 648-7581; e-mail publisher@newsitem.com; web site www.newsitem.com
Pub. – Henry Nyce
Webmaster – Scott Griffiths

News USA, Inc. – 2841 Hartland Rd., Ste. 301, Falls Church, VA, 22043, USA (703) 734-6300; fax (703) 734-6314; e-mail info@newsusa.com, YB_ASSOC_CLIPART; web site www.newsusa.com
Pres./CEO – Richard D. Smith
Vice Pres., Sales – Richard Rothstein
Ed. – Jacob Maurer
IT Dir. – Scott Peters
Pub. – Rick Smith
CEO – Richard Smith
Sales Rep. – John Phillips

NewsCom – 700 12th St. NW, Ste. 1000, Washington, DC, 20005, USA (801) 584-3900; fax (202) 383-6190; e-mail sales@newscom.com; web site www.newscom.com
Gen. Mgr. – Bill Creighton
Sales Mgr. – Tom Bannon
IP Rel. Mgr. – Lily Cheung
Mktg. Dir. – Ericka Calvert

Newsfinder – 1700 E. Racine Ave., Waukesha, WI, 53186 6934, USA (262) 544-5252; fax (262) 544-0740; e-mail nf-support@newsfinder.com; web site www.newsfinder.com

Gen. Mgr. – Sandy Hamm
Admin. Mgr. – Morgan Butler, III
Acct. Mgr. – Linda Kalinowski

Newsletters Plus – 411 Palmer Ave., Aptos, CA, 95003, USA (831) 685-1932; e-mail hdomash@winninginvesting.com; web site www.winninginvesting.com; www.dividenddetective.com
Self-Syndicator – Harry Domash

Newslink Africa Ltd. – 7-11 Kensington High St., London, ENG, W8 5NP, United Kingdom; tel (44 - 171) 73683306; fax 79384168; e-mail newslinkafrica@adlink-int.demon.co.uk; web site www.adlinkint-newslinkafri.com
Mng. Ed. – Shamlal Puri
Deputy Ed. – S. Kumar
Deputy Ed. – Kimi Mamtora

Newspaper Enterprise Association (Div. of United Media) – 200 Madison Ave., New York, NY, 10016, USA (212) 293-8500; fax (212) 293-8600; web site www.comics.com; www.unitedfeatures.com
Pres./CEO – Douglas R. Stern
Sr. Vice Pres./Gen. Mgr. – Lisa Klem Wilson
Exec. Dir., Pub. Rel. – Mary Anne Grimes
Exec. Ed. – Suma CM
Sales/Admin. Mgr. – Carmen Puello
Regl. Sales Mgr. – Colette Cogley
Regl. Sales Mgr. – Ron O'Neal
Regl. Sales Mgr. – Jim Toler
Sales Mgr., Int'l/E-Rights – Emily Stephens
Reprint Rights Sales – Reprints Coord.

Newsportraits Syndicate – PO Box 564, Hackensack, NJ, 07602 0564, USA (201) 342-2985
Exec. Ed. – Y.L. Tiajcliff
Bus. Mgr. – Martin Sager

Nielsen Entertainment News Wire – 101 Federal St., Ste. 600, Boston, MA, 02110, USA (617) 478-5500; e-mail Donald.Gallagher@nielsen.com; web site www.nielsenenw.comDonald Gallagher
Features Ed. – Andrew Power

No Rodeo – 41 Ivy Hill Rd., Brewster, NY, 10509, USA (845) 279-2790; e-mail robtberardi@yahoo.com; web site www.preteenplanet.com
Creator/Owner – Robert Berardi

North America Syndicate – 300 W. 57th St., 15th Fl., New York, NY, 10019-5238, USA (212) 969-7550; fax (646) 280-1550; e-mail kfs-public-relations@hearst.com; web site www.kingfeatures.com
Pres. – T.R. Shepard, III
Vice Pres./Gen. Mgr. – Keith McCloat
Vice Pres., North American Licensing – Ita Golzman
Vice Pres., Int'l Licensing – Cathleen Titus
Syndication Sales Dir. – John Killian
Gen. Mgr., King Features Weekly Service – David Cohea
Senior Sales Consultant/Printing and New England Newspaper Sales – Jack Walsh
Adv./PR Dir. – Claudia Smith
Mng. Ed./Dir., Publishing – Glenn Mott
Promotions Director – Rose Croke
Int'l Sales Mgr. – John Perry
Inside Sales Mgr. – Dennis Danko
Inside Sales Rep – Michael Mancino
Sunday Comics Mgr. – Jim Nolan
Sales Mgr., Western Reg. – Richard Heimlich
Director, Web Development – Michael G. Chan
Comics Ed. – Brendan Burford
Domestic Sales Coordinator – Carin Bacchiocchi
Director of Marketing – Mark Karlan
Editorial Director, King Features Weekly Service – Jim Clarke
Vice Pres., Worldwide Syndication Sales – George Haeberlein
Mng. Dir., King Digital – John Soppe
Domestic Sales Coord. – Venetta Smith

North American Precis Syndicate, Inc. – 415 Madison Avenue Fl 12, New York, NY, 10017, USA (212) 867-9000; e-mail service@napsnet.com; printmedia@napsnet.com; web site www.napsnet.com
Pres./Exec. Ed. – Dorothy York
Vice Pres., Media Rel. – Gary Lipton
Ed. in Chief – Candace Lieberman

O

Oasis Newsfeatures, Inc. – PO Box 2144, Middletown, OH, 45042, USA (800) 245-7515; e-mail kwilliams@oasisnewsfeatures.com; web site www.oasisnewsfeatures.com
Exec. Ed. – Kevin Williams

Lona O'Connor – 10887 Old Bridgeport Ln., Boca Raton, FL, 33498, USA (561) 820-3471; e-mail lona_oconnor@pbpost.com; web site www.palmbeachpost.com
Author, journalist – Lona O'Connor

On The House Syndication, Inc. – 2420 Sand Creek Road, C-1318, Brentwood, CA, 94513, USA (925) 432-7246 x24; fax (925) 420-5690; e-mail info@onthehouse.com; web site www.onthehouse.com
Pres./Co-Host – James Carey
Vice Pres./Co-Host – Morris Carey
Affiliate Rel. Dir. – Sylvie Castaniada

One Voice Communications – 83 Midland Crescent SE, Calgary, AB, T2X 1N8, Canada; tel (001 - (800) 565-4661; fax (403) 313-9177; e-mail stuff@parentpreviews.com; web site www.parentpreviews.com
Pres./Sr. Reviewer – Rod Gustafson
Reviewer – Donna Gustafson
Reviewer – Kerry Bennett

OpEd Online – 7200 Wisconsin Ave., Ste. 601, Bethesda, MD, 20814

Tom & Joanne O'Toole, Travel Journalists/Photographers – 4603 Wood St., Willoughby, OH, 44094 5821, USA (440) 942-5455; e-mail traveljournalists@hotmail.com
Journalist/Photographer – Thomas J. O'Toole
Journalist – Joanne R. O'Toole

P

PR Newswire - Seattle, WA – 1001 4th Ave., Ste. 2138, Seattle, WA, 98154 1102, USA (800) 367-8555; fax (800) 927-6587; e-mail mediaservices@prnewswire.com; web site www.prnewswire.com
CEO – Ninan Chacko

PR Newswire - Washington, DC – The Homer Building, 601 13th St. NW, Ste. 560 S., Washington, DC, 20005 1794, USA (800) 378-7112; fax (202) 347-6606; e-mail mediaservices@prnewswire.com; web site www.prnewswire.com
CEO – Ninan Chacko

PR Newswire - Minneapolis, MN – 2 Meridan Crossing, Ste. 510, Minneapolis, MN, 55423, USA (800) 582-5154; fax (888) 776-6552; e-mail mediaservices@prnewswire.com; web site www.prnewswire.com
CEO – Ninan Chacko

PR Newswire - Philadelphia, PA – One Penn Ctr., 1617 JFK Blvd., Ste. 1665, Philadelphia, PA, 19103, USA (215) 568-6300; fax (888) 568-0898; e-mail mediaservices@prnewswire.com; web site www.prnewswire.com
CEO – Ninan Chacko

PR Newswire - Pittsburgh, PA – 436 Seventh Ave., Ste. 2917, Pittsburgh, PA, 15219, USA (888) 776-8563; fax (800) 341-4460; e-mail mediaservices@prnewswire.com; web site www.prnewswire.com
CEO – Ninan Chacko

PR Newswire - San Francisco, CA – 456 Montgomery St., 5th Fl., San Francisco, CA, 94104, USA (800) 334-6692; fax (800) 927-6587; e-mail mediaservices@prnewswire.com; web site www.prnewswire.com
CEO – Ninan Chacko

PR Newswire - New York, NY – 350 Hudson St., Ste. 300, New York, NY, 10014, USA (201) 360-6700; fax 800-793-9313; e-mail mediaservices@prnewswire.com; web site www.prnewswire.com
CEO – Ninan Chacko
Exec. Vice Pres./Chief Devel. Officer – Scott Mozarsky
CFO – Dave Wein
Exec. Vice Pres. – Ken Dowell
CIO – Jim Slattery
Sr. Vice Pres., Opns. – Dave Haapaoja
Vice Pres., Mktg./PR – Rachel Meranus

PR Newswire - Atlanta, GA – 950 E. Paces Ferry Rd., Ste. 2155, Atlanta, GA, 30326 1144, USA (800) 232-3998; fax (888) 776-0944; e-mail mediaservices@prnewswire.com; web site www.prnewswire.com
CEO – Ninan Chacko

PR Newswire - Washington, DC – 601 13th St. NW, Ste. 850, Washington, DC, 20005 1794, USA (201) 360-6270; fax (888) 776-0942; e-mail newsdesk@prnewswire.com; web site www.prnewswire.com
Audience Development – Christine Cube

PR Newswire - Chicago, IL – 111 East Wacker Dr., Ste. 900, Chicago, IL, 60601, USA (888) 776-6551; fax (888) 776-6552; e-mail prncs@prnewswire.com; web site www.prnewswire.com
CEO – Ninan Chacko

PR Newswire - San Diego, CA – 4445 Eastgate Mall, Ste. 200, San Diego, CA, 92121, USA (619) 232-4497; fax (619) 232-9304; e-mail mediaservices@prnewswire.com; web site www.prnewswire.com
CEO – Ninan Chacko

PR Newswire - New York, NY – 350 Hedson St. 3300, New York, NY, 10014-4504, USA (800) 207-1238; fax (800) 793-9313; e-mail mediaservices@prnewswire.com; web site www.prnewswire.com
CEO – Ninan Chako

PR Newswire - Los Angeles, CA – 865 S. Figueroa St., Ste. 2500, Los Angeles, CA, 90017 2565, USA (800) 321-8169; fax (800) 473-5152; e-mail mediaservices@prnewswire.com; web site www.prnewswire.com
CEO – Ninan Chacko

PR Newswire - Denver, CO – 1099 18th St., Ste. 2730, Denver, CO, 80202 1927, USA (800) 843-2495; fax (800) 473-5152; e-mail mediaservices@prnewswire.com; web site www.prnewswire.com
CEO – Ninan Chacko

PR Newswire - Cleveland, OH – 1375 E. 9th St., Ste. 3100, Cleveland, OH, 44114 1786, USA

(800) 826-3133; fax (800) 941-4460; e-mail mediaservices@prnewswire.com; web site www.prnewswire.com
CEO – Ninan Chacko

PR Newswire - Charlotte, NC – 212 S. Tryon St., Ste. 1380, Charlotte, NC, 28281 0001, USA (800) 998-9806; fax (888) 776-3975; e-mail mediaservices@prnewswire.com; web site www.prnewswire.com
CEO – Ninan Chacko

PR Newswire - Boston, MA – 141 Tremont St., 12th Fl., Boston, MA, 02111, USA (800) 866-8060; fax (800) 776-0946; e-mail mediaservices@prnewswire.com; web site www.prnewswire.com
CEO – Ninan Chacko

Pacific News Service – 275 Ninth St., San Francisco, CA, 94103

Pappocom – 3 Birch Ledge Rd., Glen, NH, 03838, USA (603) 383-6729; e-mail info@waynegouldpuzzles.com; web site www.waynegouldpuzzles.com
Dir. – Wayne Gould
Mgr. – Scott Gould

Paradigm News, Inc. – 500 Summer St., Ste. 404, Stamford, CT, 6901

Parent to Parent – 2464 Taylor Dr., Ste. 131, Wildwood, MO, 63040, USA (877) 236-7793 ; fax (636) 458 7688; e-mail editor@parenttoparent.com; web site www.parenttoparent.com
Owner – Jodie Lynn
Personal Assistant
Assistant Editor – Kyle Johnson

Parwell-Davis Features – 3741 N. 400 E., Lagro, IN, 46941 9664, USA (260) 563-8828; fax (260) 563-0706; e-mail parwell@email.com; web site parwell.hypermart.net
Pres./Chrmn. – P. Davis
Author/Illustrator/Cartoonist/Historian/Speaker – Richard J. Lynn

Passage Media – 1284 Main St., Crete, IL, 60417 2145, USA (708) 672-1300; e-mail culp@workwise.net; web site www.workwise.net; www.modbee.com/workwise
Dir. – Mildred L. Culp, Ph.D.

Peary Perry Enterprises – PO Box 202110, Austin, TX, 78720 2810, USA (512) 653-8454; e-mail pperry@austin.rr.com; web site www.pearyperry.com
Self-Syndicator/Columnist – Peary Perry

Pediatric Points – 5 Chain Bridge Dr., Newburyport, MA, 01950, USA (978) 476-9121; fax (978) 521-8372; e-mail pediatricpoints@comcast.net; web site www.carolynroybornstein.com
MD – Carolyn Roy-Bornstein

PhotoSource International – 1910 35th aVE ., Osceola, WI, 54020, USA (715) 248-3800; fax (715) 248-3800; e-mail info@photosource.com; psi2@photosource.com; web site www.photosource.com; www.search.photosource.com; www.photosourcefolio.com
Editorial Dir. – Jeri Engh

Piercy & Barclay Designers, Inc. – 6441 SW Wilbard St., Portland, OR, 97219, USA (800) 772-7225; fax (503) 245-3808; e-mail jcpclemens@yahoo.com; web site www.pbdesigners.com
Pres. – Janet Piercy

Plain Label Press – 1690 Carman Mill Dr., Ballwin, MO, 63021, USA (636) 207-9880; fax (636) 207-9880; e-mail mail@plainlabelpress.com; web site www.creativeonline.com/syndicate
Vice Pres./Mng. Ed. – Ed Chermoore
Submissions Ed. – Laura Meyer

Jack Posner Syndicate – 216 Ellesmere E., Century Village, Deerfield Beach, FL, 33442, USA (954) 427-8068
Self-Syndicator/Writer – Jack Posner

The Practical Pantry – 5 Prouty Dr., Veazie, ME, 04401 6961, USA (207) 947-9624; e-mail info@practicalpantry.com; web site www.practicalpantry.com
Writer – Tammy P. Olson
Consultant – Eric T. Olson

Prensa Latina – UN Secretarial Bldg., Rm. L240, New York, NY, 10017, USA 917-432-9961; e-mail plonu@mindspring.com; web site www.prensa-latina.cu
UN Correspondent – Carriba Victor

Press Associates, Inc. – 2605 P St. NW, Ste. A, Washington, DC, 20007, USA (202) 898-4825; e-mail press_associates@yahoo.com
Ed. in Chief – Mark J. Gruenberg
Ed. – Janet Brown
Cartoonist – Dick Belland
Accounting – Martha Turner

Press News Ltd. – 36 King St. E., Toronto, ON, M5C 2L9, Canada (416) 364-0321; fax (416) 364-9283; e-mail lora.dipoce@canadianpress.com; web site www.canadianpress.com
Gen. Mgr./Vice Pres., Broadcasting (CP) – Wayne Waldroff
Admin. Asst. – Lora DiPoce

Press News Syndicate – 2073 Gerritsen Ave., Brooklyn, NY, 11229, USA (718) 339-1417
Dir. – Martin Pine

Print Marketing Concepts, Inc. – 10590 Westoffice Dr., Ste. 100, Houston, TX, 77042, USA; tel (United States - (713) 780-7055; fax (713) 780-9731; e-mail rgoodpmc@aol.com; web site www.printmkt.com
Pres. – Sue Beck
Pres. – Sue Beck
Sr. Vice Pres. – Robin L. Good
Sr. Vice Pres. – Robin L. Good
Sr. Vice Pres., Nat'l Adv. Sales – Robin Good
Vice Pres. – Greg Wickliff
Vice Pres. – Greg Wickliff

Public Service News, Kenneth Ellman – PO Box 18, Newton, NJ, 07860, USA (973) 948-6961; fax (973) 948-2986; e-mail ke@kennethellman.com; web site http://www.jdsupra.com/profile/kennethellman/
Pub. – Kenneth Ellman

Punch In Travel, Food, Wine & Entertainment News Syndicate – 400 E. 59th St., Ste. 9F, New York, NY, 10022, USA (212) 755-4363; e-mail info@punchin.com; web site www.punchin.com
Pres./Mng. Ed. – Nancy Preiser
Contributing Writer – Betty Andrews
Contributing Writer – Bob Andrews
Contributing Writer – John Edwards
Contributing Writer – Bette Johns
Contributing Writer – Nina Lindt
Contributing Writer – Tom Weston

Puzzle Features Syndicate – 13615 Beverly Park Road, Suite A, Lynnwood, WA, 98087, USA (800) 292-4308; e-mail crosspuzz@aol.com
Ed. – Jackie Mathews

Pythia Press – 245 Bannerman Beach Ln., Santa Rosa Beach, FL, 32459, USA (850) 267-2461; fax (850) 267-0155; e-mail cnmsrbch@aol.com
Pres. – Ashley M. Conyers

Q

Q Syndicate – 11920 Farmington Rd., Livonia, MI, 48150, USA (734) 293-7200; fax (734) 293-7201; e-mail qsyndicate@pridesource.com; web site www.qsyndicate.com
Pres. – Susan Horowitz
CFO – Jan Stevenson
Ed. – Christopher Azzopardi

QuipTide.com – 426 Dehoff Canyon Rd., Half Moon Bay, CA, 94019, USA (650) 726-0316; fax (650) 726-0316; e-mail info@quiptide.com; web site www.quiptide.com
Humorist – Louie Castoria

R

RBH Food Safety/Education & Consultation – 10 Schlough Ct., Madison, WI, 53717, USA (608) 836-4505; fax (608) 836-4080; e-mail bhohlstein@aol.com
Independent Consultant/Author/Speaker – Rebecca Hohlstein

Rafferty Consulting Group – 45-775 Indian Wells Ln., Indian Wells, CA, 92210, USA (760) 776-9606; fax (760) 776-9608; e-mail info@raffertyconsulting.com; web site www.raffertyconsulting.com
Pres. – Renata J. Rafferty

James Raia – 122 43rd St., Sacramento, CA, 95819, USA (916) 508-5122; fax (916) 455-8389; e-mail james@byjamesraia.com; web site www.byjamesraia.com; www.montereypeninsula.org; www.golftribune.com; www.theweeklydriver.com
Self-Syndicator – James Raia

Red, White & True Mysteries – 2614 S. 24th St., Quincy, IL, 62305, USA (217) 653-7058; e-mail niemann7@aol.com; web site www.inventionmysteries.com; www.paulniemann.com; www.redwhiteandtruemysteries.com
Syndicated Columnist – Paul Niemann

Reel to Real Celebrity Profiles – 8643 N. Fielding Rd., Bayside, WI, 53217, USA (414) 352-7966; e-mail davereel@execpc.com; web site www.reeltoreal.com
– David Fantle
– Tom JohnsonCreator/Writers

Religion News Service – National Press Building, 529 14th Street NW, Suite 425, Washington, DC, 20045, USA (202) 463-8777; fax (202) 662-7154; e-mail info@religionnews.com; web site www.religionnews.com
Senior Editor – David E. Anderson
Editor-in-Chief – Kevin Eckstrom
Editorial/Publishing Consultant – Tracy Gordon
Production Editor – Adelle Banks
Associate Editor – Daniel Burke
National Correspondent – Lauren Markoe
Bus./Sales Mgr. – Claudia M. Sans Werner
Bus. Coord. – David Shaw

Werner Renberg – PO Box 496, Chappaqua, NY, 10514, USA (914) 241-2038; fax (914) 242-0470; e-mail werren@att.net

Self-Syndicator – Werner Renberg

Reuters – Standard Life Ctr., 121 King St. W., Ste. 2000, Toronto, ON, M5H 3T9, Canada

Reuters – 1333 H St. NW, Ste. 410, Washington, DC, 20005

Reuters – 575 High St., Ste. 400, Palo Alto, CA, 94301-1648

Reuters – 300 Blvd. Rene-Levesque W., Ste. 300, Montreal, QC, H3B1X9, Canada

Reuters – 1999 Bryan St., Ste. 1516, Dallas, TX, 75201

Reuters – Booth Bldg., 165 Sparks St., Ste. 400, Ottawa, ON, K1P 5B9, Canada

Reuters – 700 W. Pender St., Ste. 1405, Vancouver, BC, V6C 1G8, Canada

Reuters – 407 Second St. SW, Ste. 312, Calgary, AB, T2P2Y3, Canada

Reuters – Columbia Ctr., 701 5th Ave., Ste. 6770, Seattle, WA, 98104

Reuters – Summit Tower, 11 Greenway Plz., Ste. 1200, Houston, TX, 77046

Reuters – 633 W. Fifith St., Los Angeles, CA, 90071

Reuters – 88 Kearny St., San Francisco, CA, 94108

Reuters – 410 17th St., Ste. 1215, Denver, CO, 80202-4431

Reuters – 179 Allyn St., Ste. 305, Hartford, CT, 6103-1421

Reuters – 5201 Blue Lagoon Dr., Ste. 510, Miami, FL, 33126-2075

Reuters – 1355 Peachtree St., Atlanta, GA, 30309

Reuters – 311 S. Wacker Dr., Ste. 1200, Chicago, IL, 60606

Reuters – 22 Thomson Pl. Mail Stop 26T3, Boston, MA, 2210-8909

Reuters – 31500 Northwestern Hwy., Ste. 220, Farmington Hills, Detroit, MI, 48018

Reuters – 4800 Main St., Ste. 713, Kansas City, MO, 64112-2510

Reuters – 3 Times Sq., 17th Fl., New York, NY, 10036-6564

Reuters – United Nations, Rm. C316, New York, NY, 10017-3514

Reuters – 500 Pearl St., New York, NY, 10007

Reuters – 212 S. Tryong St., Charlotte, NC, 28281

Reuters – 1835 Market St., 11 Penn Ctr., Ste. 501, Philadelphia, PA, 19103

Reuters – Liberty Ctr., 1001 Liberty Ave., Ste. 501, Pittsburgh, PA, 15222

Reuters Media – 3 Times Sq., New York, NY, 10036, USA (646) 223-4000; fax (646) 223-4393; e-mail rosalina.thomas@thomsonreuters.com; web site reuters.com/newsagency
Vice Pres./Head of Sales - The Americas, Reuters News Agency, Thomson Reuters – Ms. Rosalina Thomas

Robertstock/Classicstock – 4203 Locust St., Philadelphia, PA, 19104, USA (215) 386-6300; fax (215) 386-3521; e-mail info@robertstock.com; web site www.robertstock.com; www.classicstock.com
Pres., Robertstock – H. Armstrong Roberts
Vice Pres., Sales – John Fitzpatrick
Vice Pres., Creative – Roberta Groves

The RoMANtic Syndicated Column – PO Box 1567, Cary, NC, 27512, USA (919) 701-9818; e-mail column@theromantic.com; web site www.theromantic.com
Writer – Michael Webb

Rothco Cartoons – 1531 53rd St., Brooklyn, NY, 11219 3961, USA (718) 853-5435
Mgr. – Steven Weiss

S

Got Influence? Publishing – 190 E. Dundee Rd., Barrington, IL, 60010, USA (847) 359-7860; e-mail info@GotInfluenceInc.com; web site www.GotInfluenceInc.com
Founder/Self-Syndicator/Columnist – Dan Seidman

Sam Mantics Enterprises – 3650 mockingbird drive, Vero Beach, FL, 329063, USA 772-492-9032; fax 772-492-9032; e-mail jancook@myvocabulary.com; web site www.syndicate.com; www.myvocabulary.com
Pres./Cartoon Ed. – Carey Orr Cook
Bus. Devel. – Jan Cook
Sr. Vice Pres., Mktg./Sales – Keith Cook
Internet/Web Ed. – Kylie Cook
Prodn. Mgr., Opns. – Brad Cook

Curt Schleier Reviews – 646 Jones Rd., River Vale, NJ, 07675, USA (201) 391-7135; e-mail writa1@verizon.net
Pres./Ed. – Curt Schleier

Schmidt Services, Inc. – 720 Creek Rd., Attica, NY, 14011, USA (585) 591-3010
Pres. – Stephen P. Schmidt

Schwadron Cartoon & Illustration Service – PO Box 1347, Ann Arbor, MI, 48106, USA (734) 665-8272; fax (734) 665-8272; e-mail schwaboo@comcast.net; web site www.schwadroncartoons.com
Ed. – Harley Schwadron
Sec. – Sally Booth

Scrambl-Gram, Inc. – 5225 W. Lakeshore Dr., Bldg. 340, Port Clinton, OH, 43452, USA (419) 734-2600; fax (419) 734-2868; e-mail info@scrambl-gram.com; web site www.scrambl-gram.com
Co-Owner – Slate Kessler
Sales/Promo. Dir. – Mary Elum Kessler
Adv. Mgr. – Scott Bowers

Scripps Howard News Service – 1090 Vermont Ave. NW, Ste. 1000, Washington, DC, 20005, USA (202) 408-1484; fax (202) 408-5950; web site www.shns.com
Ed./Gen. Mgr. – Peter Copeland
Chief Tech. Officer/Webmaster – David Johnson
Sales & Mktg. Contact/Sr. Vice Pres. & Gen. Mgr., United Media – Lisa Klem Wilson
Desk Ed. – Bob Jones
Sports Ed. – John Lindsay

Scripps-McClatchy Western Services – 1090 Vermont Ave., NW, Ste. 1000, Washington, DC, 20005-4965

Senior Wire News Service – 2377 Elm St., Denver, CO, 80207, USA (303) 355-3882; e-mail clearmountain@tde.com; web site www.seniorwire.net
Pub./Ed. – Allison St. Claire

Seriocomics Features – PO Box 9633, Fort Wayne, IN, 46899, USA (317) 858-0630; e-mail protista1@aol.com; seriocomics@comcast.net; web site www.seriocomics.com
– Richard Kolkman
– David ReddickCartoonists

ServiceQuality.US – 1063 Todos Santos Sta., Concord, CA, 94522 1063, USA (925) 798-0896; fax (925) 215-2320; e-mail support@servicequality.us; web site www.service-quality.com
Pres. – Dr. Jeffrey S. Kasper

Sharpnack, Joe – PO Box 3325, Iowa City, IA, 52244, USA (319) 512 9705; e-mail sharptoons@yahoo.com; web site www.sharptoons.com
Self-Syndicator – Joe Sharpnack

Silver Bird Travel Features – 414 Bee St., Apt. 8, Sausalito, CA, 94965, USA (415) 331-7700
Author – Kevin Keating
Lifestyle Ed. – Karen Beckner

Sipa News Service – 59 E. 54th St., New York, NY, 10022, USA (212) 759-5571; fax (212) 593-5194; e-mail sipa@sipausa.com; web site www.leadersmag.com
Chrmn./Ed. in Chief – Henry O. Dormann
Vice Pres./Exec. Ed. – Darrell Brown

Slightly Off! – 24730 Illini Dr., Plainfield, IL, 60544, USA (815) 439-1172; e-mail deb@slightlyoff.com; web site www.slightly-off.com
Author/Owner – Deb DiSandro

Small Talk – 74 Commonwealth Ave., Apt. 11, Boston, MA, 02116, USA (617) 267-1396; fax (509) 275-4252; e-mail info@eyeintheear.com; web site www.eyeintheear.com
Pres. – Laurence A. Kelly
Creative Dir. – Allan H. Kelly, Jr.

Elizabeth S. Smoots – 5735 27th Ave. NE, Seattle, WA, 98105 5511, USA; e-mail doctor@practicalprevention.com; web site www.practicalprevention.com
Self-Syndicator – Elizabeth S. Smoots MD

Southern California Focus – 1720 Oak St., Santa Monica, CA, 90405, USA (310) 452-3101; e-mail tdelias@aol.com
Author – Thomas Elias

Sovfoto/Eastfoto – 263 W. 20th St., Ste. 3, New York, NY, 10011, USA (212) 727-8170; fax (212) 727-8228; e-mail info@sovfoto.com; web site www.sovfoto.com
Dir. – Vanya Edwards

Spectrum Features – 2460 Second St., Bloomsburg, PA, 17815, USA (570) 784-2460; e-mail editor@greeleyandstone.com; web site www.walterbrasch.com
Ed. in Chief – Walter Brasch
Exec. Ed. – Rose Renn
Assoc. Ed. – Matt Gerber
Art/Prodn. Dir. – Mary Jayne Reibsome
Deputy Art/Prodn. Dir. – Nicole Clark
director of marketing – Diana Saavedra

The Sports Network (Div. of Computer Info. Network) – 2200 Byberry Rd., Hatboro, PA, 19040, USA (215) 441-8444; fax (215) 441-5767; e-mail kzajac@sportsnetwork.com; maureen@sportsnetwork.com; web site www.sportsnetwork.com
Pres./CEO – Mickey Charles
Vice Pres., Admin. – Rosalind C. Tucker
Sales Dir. – Ken Zajac
Content Devel. Dir. – Kevin Spiegel
Technical Opns. Dir. – Bruce Michaels
Director of Design and Web – Rob Dougherty
Director of Operations – Phil Sokol
Managing Editor – Jim Gillis

Sportsbuff Features – PO Box 197, Hamilton, MA, 01936, USA (978) 468-2632; e-mail sportsbuff.features@comcast.net
Ed. – Steve Ollove

Springer Foreign News Service – 500 5th Ave., Ste. 2800, New York, NY, 10110

Stadium Circle Features – 55 Broad St., Suite 13F, New York, NY, 10004, USA; tel (1 - (917) 267-2493; e-mail info@paperpc.net; web site www.paperpc.net; www.paperpc.com
Ed./Columnist – Robert S. Anthony

Stampede Features – 118 Texas Trail, Saratoga, WY, 82331, USA (307) 326-9852; fax (307) 326-9852; e-mail annpalen@mac.com
Pres. – Jerry Palen
Office Mgr. – Ann Palen

Stamping Grounds – 2 Escondido Cir., Ste. 183, unit183, Altamonte Springs, FL, 32701 4586, USA (407) 831-2359; e-mail joezoll183@aol.com
Author/Owner – Joseph Zollman

Starcott Media Services, Inc. – 6906 Royalgreen Dr., Cincinnati, OH, 45244, USA (513) 231-6034; e-mail dulley@dulley.com; contact@dulley.com; web site www.dulley.com
Pres. – James T. Dulley

State Net – 2101 K St., Sacramento, CA, 95816, USA (916) 444-0840; fax (916) 446-5369; e-mail info@statenet.com; web site www.statenet.com
– Laurie Stinson
– Jud ClarkPres.s

Straight Dope - Creative Loafing Media, Inc. – 11 E. Illinois St., Chicago, IL, 60611, USA (312) 828-0350; fax (312) 828-0305; e-mail cecil@straightdope.com; web site www.straightdope.com
Creator/Writer – Cecil Adams

Sun Features, Inc. – PO Box 368, Cardiff, CA, 92007, USA (760) 431-1660; e-mail jlk@sunfeatures.com; web site www.sunfeatures.com
Pres. – Joyce Lain Kennedy
Vice Pres. – Tim K. Horrell

Sun Media Corporation/Toronto Sun Syndicate Sales – 333 King St. E., Toronto, ON, M5A 3X5, Canada (416) 947-3123; fax (416) 947-2043; e-mail julie.kirsh@sunmedia.ca; web site www.sunmedia.ca
Electronic Information Dir. – Julie Kirsh
Asst. Mgr., News Research – Kathy Webb Nelson
Photo Reprint Sales – Jillian Goddard

Syndicated News Service – 232 Post Ave., Rochester, NY, 14619 1398, USA (800) 222-6000; fax (585) 328-7018; e-mail sns3@aol.com; sns1@compuserve.com; sns3@prodigy.com; sns1@msn.com
Ed./Pub. – Frank Judge
Assoc. Pub./Art Dir. – Mary Whitney
Chicago Bureau Dir. – Aljay Randall
New York Bureau Dir. – Louis Tesauro
Toronto Bureau Dir. – Sergio Navarretta
Administrative Ed. – Bryan Campbell
Assoc. Ed. – Paul Ferguson
Assoc. Ed. – David Gridley
Assoc. Ed. – Kate Linsner
Assoc. Ed. – Ken O'Brien
Children's Features Ed. – Jennifer Ferguson
Correspondent – Jim Kraus
Features Ed. – Peter Heinrich
Features Ed. – Sid Rosenzweig
Features Ed. – David D. Williams
Features Ed.-Toronto – Anna Greco
Food/Travel Ed. – Marcie VerPloeg
Photo Ed.-Toronto – Tony Moronne
Sr. Ed. – Doris Carey
Sports/Recreation Ed. – Devon Ferguson

Syndication Associates, Inc. – PO Box 400, Beaconsfield, QC, H9W 5T9, Canada (888) 684-0084; fax (514) 499-8050; e-mail info@greatplans.com; web site www.featuresonline.com
Pres. – David Moulton

T

TMS Specialty Products – 1271 Avenue of the Americas, Chicago, IL, 60611, USA (312) 527-8200; fax (312) 527-8256; web site www.tmsspecialtyproducts.com
Gen. Mgr. – Marco Buscaglia
Gen. Mgr. – Marco Buscaglia
Asst. Mgr. – Curtis Trammell
Asst. Mgr. – Curtis Trammell
Mng. Ed. – Mary Elson
Mng. Ed. – Mary Elson
Art Dir. – Todd Rector
Art Dir. – Todd Rector

TV Times/New England Motorsports Syndication – 27 Bayberry Dr., Sharon, MA, 02067, USA (781) 784-7857; fax (781) 784-7857; e-mail lmodestino@hotmail.com; web site http://wickedlocal.com/sportsextra/
Author – Lou Modestino

Taipei Economic & Cultural Office, Information Division - New York, NY – 1E 42nd St., 11th Fl., New York, NY, 10017 6904, USA; tel (002 - 212) (212) 557-5122; fax (212) 557-3043; e-mail roctaiwan@taipei.org; web site www.taipei.org
Contact – Ching Yi Ting

Taipei Economic & Cultural Office, Information Division - Washington, DC – 4201 Wisconsin Ave. NW, Washington, DC, 20016, USA (202) 895-1800; fax (202) 362-0862; e-mail tecroinsodc@tecro.us
Dir. – Vance Chang

Press Division, Taipei Economic and Cultural Office in Chicago – 180 N. Stetson Ave., 2 Prudential Plaza, 57th Fl., Ste. 5702, Chicago, IL, 60601, USA (312) 616-6716; fax (312) 616-1497
Exec. Press Officer – Virginia Sheng

Taming The Workplace – 3003 14th Ave., W., Ste. 201, Seattle, WA, 98119, USA (206) 284-9566; e-mail mrscribe@aol.com
Columnist – Eric L. Zoeckler

Tel-Aire Publications, Inc. – 2035 Royal Ln, Suite 202, Dallas, TX, 75229, USA 214-716-1979; fax 214-716-1979; e-mail mcgee-sales@tel-aire.com; web site www.tel-aire.com
Sales Mgr. – David A. McGee

Telegraph Media Group – 111 Buckingham Palace Rd., London, SW1W 0DT, United Kingdom; tel (44 - 20) 7931-2000; fax 7931 2867; e-mail info@telegraph.co.uk; syndication@telegraph.co.uk; web site www.telegraph.co.uk
Syndication Dir. – Sophie Hanbury

The Wild Side – 2222 Fish Ridge Road, Cameron, WV, 26033, USA (304) 686-2630; e-mail sshalaway@aol.com; web site http://scottshalaway.googlepages.com/
Nature Writer – Scott Shalaway

Think Glink Inc. – 165 N. Canal St., Ste. 1425, Chicago, IL, 60606, USA (312) 930-9370; fax (847) 835-3451; e-mail ilyce@thinkglink.com; web site www.thinkglink.com; www.lawproblems.com; www.expertrealestatetips.net
Pub. – Ilyce R. Glink
Ed. – Samuel J. Tamkin

This Modern World – PO Box 150673, Van Brent Station, Brooklyn, NY, 11215, USA (718) 768-2522; e-mail tomtomorrow@ix.netcom.com; web site www.thismodernworld.com
Creator – Dan Perkins

This Side of 60 – PO Box 332, North Newton, KS, 67117, USA (316) 283-2309; e-mail thisside60@aol.com; web site www.visit-snider.com
Self-Syndicator – Marie Snider

Voterama in Congress - Thomas Voting Reports – PO Box 363, Washington, VA, 22747, USA (202) 667-9760; e-mail info@voterama.info; web site www.voterama.info
Pub./Ed. – Mr. Richard G. Thomas
Copy Chief – Michael Lesparre

Torstar Syndication Services – One Yonge St., Toronto, ON, M5E 1E6, Canada (416) 869-4994 (Sales); fax (416) 869-4587; e-mail syndicate@torstar.com; web site www.torstarsyndicate.com; www.tsscontent.ca
Managing Director – Robin Graham
Sales Rep. – Ted Cowan
Account Information – Evi Docherty
Sales Asst. – Joanne MacDonald

Trade News Service (Fats And Oils) – 3701 Rte. 21 S., Canandaigua, NY, 14424 9020, USA (585) 396-0027; e-mail tns@rochester.rr.com; web site www.fats-and-oils.com
Sr. Ed. – Dennis C Maxfield

Travelin' Light – 4001 W. Kings Row St., Muncie, IN, 47304, USA (937) 423-3517; e-mail kelsey@travelin-light.com; web site www.travelin-light.com
Writer/Photographer – Kelsey Timmerman
Cartoonist – Geoff Hassing

Tribune Media Services – 202 West 1st St., Los Angeles, CA, 90012, USA
Dir., Features – Monica Skotnicki

Tribune Media Services Entertainment Products – 40 Media Dr., Queensbury, NY, 12804, USA (800) 833-9581; fax (518) 792-4414; e-mail cyung@tribune.com; web site www.tribunemediaentertainment.com
Exec. Dir., Newspapers – Cameron Yung
Gen. Mgr., Sales/Mktg. – Kathleen Tolstrup

Tribune Media Services, Inc. – 435 N. Michigan Ave., Ste. 1500, Chicago, IL, 60611, USA (312) 222-4444; fax (312) 222-8620; e-mail tmssales@tribune.com; web site www.tribunemediaservices.com; www.tmsfeatures.com; www.mctdirect.com; www.zap2it.com; www.tmsinternational.com; www.mct-international.com; www.mctcampus.com
Pres./CEO – David D. Williams
Ed., McClatchy-Tribune Information Services – Jane Scholz
Vice Pres., Licensing/New Market Devel. – Steve Tippie
Vice Pres., Finance – Mike Gart
Vice Pres., Entertainment Products – Jay Fehnel
Vice Pres., Sales, News/Features Worldwide, McClatchy-Tribune Information Services – Walter F. Mahoney
Vice Pres., HR – Alexa Bazanos
Vice Pres., News/Features, Bus. Devel. – John Zelenka
Dir., Opns./Technology, News/Features – Mike Fioritto
Int'l Sales Dir., News/Features, McClatchy-Tribune Information Services – Ryan Stephens
Editorial Dir., Zap2it.com – Rebecca Baldwin
Gen. Mgr., Sales/Mktg. for TV Products – Kathy Tolstrup
Dir., Mktg., News/Features Worldwide, McClatchy-Tribune Information Services – Jan Guszynski
Dir., US Syndication Sales – Scott Cameron
Sales Mgr., McClatchy-Tribune Information Services – Rick DeChantal
Nat'l Acct. Exec., McClatchy-Tribune Information Services – Ron Mendell
Mng. Ed., News/Features – Mary Elson

Tribune Media Services International – CityPoint 12 Floor, 1 Ropemaker Street, London, EC2Y 9HT, United Kingdom; tel (44 - (207) 588-7588; fax (207) 153-1188; web site www.tmsinternational .com
Dir., European Opns. – Pia Ingberg

Tribune Media Services International Syndication – Unit 1207, 12/F Tower 2 Silvercord Ctr., Kowloon, Hong Kong; tel (852 - 2901-8900; fax 2865-3238
Dir., Opns. – Eric McPherson

Trivia Guy by Guinness Holder – 282 Spring Dr., Spartanburg, SC, 29302, USA (864) 621-7129; fax (864) 583-9009; e-mail wc@triviaguy.com; trivguy@bellsouth.net; web site www.triviaguy.com
Trivia Guiness World Record Holder/Syndicated Columnist – Wilson Casey

U

U-Bild Newspaper Features – 3800 Oceanic Dr., Ste. 107, Oceanside, CA, 92056, USA (800) 828-2453; fax (760) 754-2356; e-mail ktaylor@u-bild.com; web site www.u-bild.com
Pres. – Kevin Taylor
Features Ed. – Jeffrey Reeves

United Feature Syndicate (Div. of United Media) – 200 Madison Ave., New York, NY, 10016, USA (800) 221-4816; fax (212) 293-8600; web site www.unitedfeatures.com; www.comics.com
Pres./CEO – Douglas R. Stern
Sr. Vice Pres./Gen. Mgr. – Lisa Klem Wilson
Exec. Dir., Pub. Rel. – Mary Anne Grimes
Exec. Ed. – Suma CM
Sales/Admin. Mgr. – Carmen Puello
Regl. Sales Mgr. – Colette Cogley
Regl. Sales Mgr. – Ron O'Neal
Regl. Sales Mgr. – Jim Toler
Customer Serv. Rep – Dawn Gregory
Sales Mgr., Int'l/E-rights – Emily Stephens
Reprint Rights Sales – Reprint Rights Coord
.

United Media/EW Scripps – 312 Walnut Street, Cincinnati, OH, 45202, USA (513) 977 3949; web site www.unitedfeatures.com
General Manager, United Media – Vincent Marciano

Universal Uclick – 1130 Walnut St., Kansas City, MO, 64106 2109, USA (816) 581-7500; e-mail salesdirector@amuniversal.com; web site www.universaluclick.com
Pres./Ed. – Lee Salem
Vice Pres., Acquisitions/Rights – John Glynn
Vice Pres./Mng. Ed. – Sue Roush
Vice Pres., Int'l Sales – Kerry Slagle
Vice Pres., Sales – John Vivona
Asst. Vice Pres., US/Canadian Non-Daily Newspapers – Jack Prahl
Licensing Dir. – Sarah DeCoursey
Permissions Dir. – Mary Suggett
Asst. Vice Pres., Sales, Western USA – Dave Mace
Sales Mgr., Eastern USA – John Schneider
Digital Rep., Western USA/Pagination Sales – Staci Hobson
Sales Admin., Eastern USA/Canada – Jan Flemington
Sales Admin., Western USA – Sally Hile
Digital Rep., Eastern USA – Mindy Williford

Universal Uclick International Divison – 1130 Walnut St., Kansas City, MO, 64106, USA (816) 581-7500; e-mail sales@amuniversal.com; web site www.amuniversal.com
Pres. – Kerry Slagle
Mng. Dir., Latin America – Milka Pratt

The Usual Suspects/Mystery Fiction Lineup – 705 S Milwaukee Ave., Libertyville, IL, 60048, USA 708-909-5809; fax 847-549-6855; e-mail bnicholas@specializedmediaservices.net; web site www.specializedmediaservices.net
Self-Syndicator – Betty Nicholas

W

Wagner International Photos, Inc. – 62 W. 45th St., 6th Fl., New York, NY, 10036 4208, USA (212) 944-7744; fax (212) 944-9536; e-mail larry@nycphoto.com; info@nycphoto.com; web site www.nycphoto.com
Adv. Mgr. – Larry Lettera
Chief Photographer – Jeff Connell

The Wall Street Journal Sunday – 1155 Ave. of the Americas, 6th Floor, New York, NY, 10036, USA (212) 597-5733; fax (212) 597-5633; e-mail steven.townsley@wsj.com; web site www.wsj.com
Vice Pres., Partner Businesses – Paul Bell
Dir., Sales – Steven Townsley
Ed. – David Crook

The Washington Monthly LLC – 1200 18th St. NW, Ste. 330, Washington, DC, 20036, USA (202) 955-9010; fax (202) 955-9011; e-mail services@washingtonmonthly.com; web site www.washingtonmonthly.com
Pres./Pub. – Diane Straus Tucker
VP, Operations & Marketing – Carl Iseli
VP Cir. – Claire Iseli
Founding Ed. – Charles Peters
Ed. in Chief – Paul Glastris
Business Manager – Nicole Dubowitz
Adv. Mgr. – Ashleigh Kenny

Washington Post News Service with Bloomberg News – 1150 15th St. NW, Washington, DC, 20071 0070, USA; tel (+1 - (202) 334-6173; fax (202) 334-5096; e-mail info@wpbloom.com; web site www.wpbinfo.com
Pres./Editorial Dir. – Al Leeds
Vice Pres./Gen. Mgr. – John W. Payne
Vice Pres./Treasurer – Bao N. Dang
Vice Pres., Mktg./Tech. – Robert S. Cleland
Mng. Ed., Washington – Kate Carlisle

The Washington Post Writers Group – 1150 15th St. NW, Washington, DC, 20071 9200, USA (202) 334-5375; fax (202) 334-5669; e-mail wpwgsales@washpost.com; web site www.postwritersgroup.com
Editorial Dir./Gen. Mgr. – Alan Shearer
Opns. Mgr. – Karen H. Greene
Sales Mgr., Spanish Language Servs. – Maria Gatti
Sales Rep., North America – Jennifer Ferrell
Mng. Ed. – James S. Hill
Comics Ed. – Amy Lago
Editorial Prodn. Mgr. – Richard Aldacushion
Mktg. Mgr. – Karisue Wyson

Watauga Consulting, Inc. – 192 Abbey Rd., Boone, NC, 28607, USA (828) 773-3481; e-mail info@supin.com; web site www.supin.com
Author/Consultant – Jeanne Supin

George Waters – PO Box 80974, San Marino, CA, 91118 8974, USA (626) 568-9894; e-mail george@georgewaters.net; web site www.georgewaters.net; www.TheWaBlog.com
Humor Columnist – George Waters

The Weather Underground, Inc. – 185 Berry St., Ste. 5501, San Francisco, CA, 94107, USA (415) 983-2602; fax (415) 543-5044; e-mail chuck@wunderground.com; web site www.wunderground.com
Pres. – Alan Steremberg
Office Mgr. – Brian Read
Vice Pres. Sales/Mktg. – Chuck Prewitt

Weather Underground, Inc., The – 185 Berry St., Ste. 5501, San Francisco, CA, 94107, USA (415) 543-5044; fax (415) 543-5044
Vice Pres., Sales/Mktg. – Chuck Prewitt

Whitegate Features Syndicate – 71 Faunce Dr., Ste. 1, Providence, RI, 02906, USA (401) 274-2149; e-mail webmaster@whitegatefeatures.com; staff@whitegatefeatures.com; web site www.whitegatefeatures.com
Pres./CEO – Ed Isaac
Vice Pres./Gen. Mgr. – Steve Corey
Office Mgr. – Mari Howard
Talent Dir./Special Projects Mgr. – Eve Green

Wieck Media – 12700 Park Central Dr., Ste. 510, Suite 510, Dallas, TX, 75251, USA (972) 392-0888; fax (972) 934-8848; e-mail info@wieck.com; web site www.wieck.com
Chrmn. – James Wieck
Pres. – Tim Roberts
Client Servs. Mgr. – Bobby Warren
Network Mgr. – Tommy Thedford
Sales Mgr. – Bill Pemberton

Wild Bill's Cartoon Show! – 179 Old Cement Rd., Lot 40B, Montoursville, PA, 17754, USA (570) 494-6789; fax (570) 368-7636; e-mail wildbill@wildbillsartshow.net; web site www.wildbillsartshow.net
Creator/Self-Syndicator – Bill Stanford

Wilson Internet Services – PO Box 308, Rocklin, CA, 95677 0308, USA (916) 652-4659; e-mail rfwilson@wilsonweb.com; web site www.wilsonweb.com/syndicate
Dir./Columnist – Dr. Ralph F. Wilson

Wingo, LLC – 12230 Forest Hills Blvd., Ste. 110J, Wellington, FL, 33414, USA (561) 379-2635; e-mail sat@wingopromo.com; web site www.wingopromo.com; www.amerimarketing.com
Pres. – Scott Thompson

Wireless Flash News, Inc. – 827 Washington St., San Diego, CA, 92103, USA (619) 220-7191; fax (619) 220-8590; e-mail newsdesk2@flashnews.com; web site www.flashnews.com
Mng. Ed. – Patrick Glynn
Sr. Ed. – Monica Garske
Sales/Mktg. Mgr. – David Louie

The Witzzle Co. – PO Box 866933, Plano, TX, 75086 1853, USA (972) 398-3897; fax (972) 398-8154; e-mail care@kaidy.com; web site www.mathfun.com
Owner/Pres. – Louis Y. Sher

Wombania – 249 Kensington Ave. N., Hamilton, ON, L8L 7N8, Canada (905) 544-6174; e-mail wombania@wombania.com; web site www.wombania.com; www.wombies.com; www.comics.wombania.com+
Owner/Cartoonist – Peter Marinacci
Ed. – R.L.B. Hartmann

World Features Syndicate – 5842 Sagebrush Rd., La Jolla, CA, 92037, USA (858) 456-6215; e-mail info@worldfeaturessyndicate.com; web site www.worldfeaturessyndicate.com
Sales Dir. – Tom Robbins
Ed. – Ronald A. Sataloff
Sr. Assoc. Ed./Columnist – Karl A. Van Asselt
Assoc. Ed. – Ernie A. Gomez

World Images News Service – 12570 Cavalier Dr, Woodbridge, VA, 22192, USA; tel (1 - (703) 986-0171; fax (703) 986-0171; e-mail bureauchief@winsphoto.com; web site www.winsphoto.com
CEO/Chief Photographer – Jack Sykes
Executive Dir – Debbie Randall
News Ed. – Robert H. Williams
Photo Ed. – Donna L. Southard

Worldwatch/Foreign Affairs Syndicate – 14421 Charter Rd., Ste. 5C, Jamaica, NY, 11435, USA (718) 591-7246; e-mail jjmcolumn@earthlink.net
Ed. – John J. Metzler

Y

YellowBrix – 500 Montgomery St., Ste. 700, Alexandria, VA, 22314, USA (703) 548-3300; fax (703) 548-9151; e-mail info@yellowbrix.com; web site www.yellowbrix.com
Founder/Pres./CEO – Jeffrey P. Massa
Adv. Mgr. – Tom Hargis

Z

ZUMA Press, Inc. – 408 N. El Camino Real, San Clemente, CA, 92672, USA (949) 481-3747; fax (949) 481-3941; e-mail info@zumapress.com; web site www.zumawire.com; www.zumapress.com
CEO/Founder – Scott McKiernan
News Dir./Picture Desk Mgr. – Ruaridh Stewart
Head of Licensing and Global Relations – John J Camarillo
CTO – Patrick Johnson
CFO – Julie Mason

NEWSPAPER COMIC SECTION GROUPS AND NETWORKS

United States and Canadian independent as well as syndicated comics section in which advertising may be scheduled for entire groups with one order.

Business Information Group – 12, Concorde Pl., Ste. 800, Toronto, ON, M3C 4J2, Canada; tel (416) 442-5600; fax (416) 510-5127; web site www.bizinfogroup.ca
Pres. – Bruce Creighton

Metro-Puck Comics Network - San Francisco, CA – 160 Spear St., Ste. 1875, San Francisco, CA, 94105, USA; tel (415) 227-8857; fax (415) 358-4659; web site www.metrosn.com
Sr. Vice Pres. – Ali Nazem

Metro-Puck Comics Network - Chicago, IL – 190 S. La Salle St. Ste. 1710, Chicago, IL, 60601, USA; e-mail getinfo@metrosn.com; web site www.metrosn.com
SVP Client Services – Tack Prashad
Sr. Vice Pres./Midwest Sales Dir. – Carl Berg

Metro-Puck Comics Network - New York, NY – 8 W. 38th St., 4th Fl., New York, NY, 10018, USA; tel (212) 689-8200; fax (212) 532-1710; e-mail getinfony@metrosn.com; web site www.metrosn.com
Pres./CEO – Phyllis Cavaliere
Exec. Vice Pres./COO – Michael Baratoff
Vice Pres., Finance/Admin. – Nili DeBono
Vice Pres., Client Servs./Information Servs. – Tack Prashad
Vice Pres./Eastern Adv. Dir. – Bill Huck
Included in the following newspapers: Akron (OH) Beacon Journal; Albuquerque (NM) Journal/Tribune; Allentown (PA) Morning Call; Atlanta (GA) Journal-Constitution; Austin (TX) American-Statesman; Bangor (ME) Daily News; Bay City (MI) Times; Beaumont (TX) Enterprise; Biloxi (MS) Sun Herald; Birmingham (AL) News; Bloomington (IN) Herald-Times; Boston (MA) Globe; Boston (MA) Herald; Brockton (MA) Enterprise; Camden (NJ) Courier-Post; Cedar Rapids (IA) Gazette; Charleston (SC) Post & Courier; Charlotte (NC) Observer; Chattanooga (TN) Times Free Press; Chicago (IL) Sun-Times; Chicago (IL) Tribune; Cincinnati (OH) Enquirer; Cleveland (OH) Plain Dealer; Colorado Springs (CO) Gazette; Columbus (GA) Ledger-Enquirer; Corpus Christi (TX) Caller-Times; Corsicana (TX) Daily Sun; Dallas (TX) Morning News; Danbury (CT) News-Times; Dayton (OH) Daily News; Daytona Beach (FL) News-Journal; Del Rio (TX) News-Herald; Detroit (MI) News & Free Press; El Paso (TX) Times; Elmira (NY) Star-Gazette; Erie (PA) Times-News; Fargo (ND) Forum; Flint (MI) Journal; Fort Lauderdale (FL) South Florida Sun-Sentinel; Fort Myers (FL) News-Press; Fort Worth (TX) Star-Telegram; Fresno (CA) Bee; Grand Rapids (MI) Press; Green Bay (WI) Press-Gazette; Greensboro (NC) News & Record; Greenville (SC) News; Hackensack (NJ) Record; Harrisburg (PA) Patriot-News; Hartford (CT) Courant; Honolulu (HI) Advertiser; Houston (TX) Chronicle; Indianapolis (IN) Star; Jackson (MS) Clarion-Ledger; Jackson (TN) Sun; Jacksonville (FL) Florida Times-Union; Knoxville (TN) News Sentinel; Kansas City (MO) Star; Lancaster (PA) Sunday News; Las Vegas (NV) Review Journal & Sun; Lewiston (ME) Sunday Sun-Journal; Little Rock (AR) Arkansas Democrat-Gazette; Long Island (NY) Newsday; Longview (TX) News-Journal; Los Angeles (CA) Times; Louisville (KY) Courier-Journal; Lowell (MA) Sun; Lubbock (TX) Avalanche-Journal; Macon (GA) Telegraph; Madison (WI) Wisconsin State Journal; Memphis (TN) Commercial Appeal; Merrillville (IN) Post-Tribune; Miami (FL) Herald; Milwaukee (WI) Journal Sentinel; Minneapolis (MN) Star Tribune; Mobile (AL) Press-Register; Modesto (CA) Bee; Monterey (CA) Monterey County Herald; Muncie (IN) Star Press; Munster (IN) Times; Muskegon (MI) Chronicle; Myrtle Beach (SC) Sun News; Nashville (TN) Tennessean; New Haven (CT) Register; New Orleans (LA) Times-Picayune; New York (NY) Daily News; Newark (NJ) Star-Ledger; Newport News (VA) Daily Press; Norfolk (VA) Virginian-Pilot; North Andover (MA) Eagle-Tribune; Oakland (CA) Tribune; Ontario (CA) Inland Valley Daily Bulletin; Pasadena (CA) Star-News; Philadelphia (PA) Inquirer; Phoenix (AZ) Arizona Republic; Pittsburgh (PA) Post-Gazette; Pittsburgh (PA) Tribune-Review; Pleasanton (CA) Tri-Valley Herald; Port Arthur (TX) News; Portland (ME) Maine Sunday Telegram; Portland (OR) Oregonian; Providence (RI) Journal; Pueblo (CO) Chieftain; Raleigh (NC) News & Observer; Reading (PA) Eagle; Richmond (VA) Times-Dispatch; Riverside (CA) Press-Enterprise; Roanoke (VA) Times; Rochester (NY) Democrat & Chronicle; Sacramento (CA) Bee; Saginaw (MI) News; Saint Louis (MO) Post-Dispatch; Saint Paul (MN) Pioneer Press; Saint Petersburg (FL) Times; San Antonio (TX) Express-News; San Bernardino (CA) County Sun; San Diego (CA) Union-Tribune; San Francisco (CA) Chronicle; San Jose (CA) Mercury News; San Mateo (CA) County Times; Santa
Ana (CA) Orange County Register; Santa Barbara (CA) News-Press; Santa Rosa (CA) Press Democrat; Savannah (GA) Morning News; Shreveport (LA) Times; South Bend (IN) Tribune; Springfield (IL) State Journal-Register; Springfield (MA) Republican; Springfield (OH) News-Sun; Staten Island (NY) Advance; Stockton (CA) Record; Tacoma (WA) News Tribune; Tampa (FL) Tribune and Times; Toledo (OH) Blade; Torrance (CA) Daily Breeze; Trenton (NJ) Times; Troy (NY) Record; Tulsa (OK) World; Waco (TX) Tribune-Herald; Washington (DC) Post; Waterbury (CT) Republican-American; West Palm Beach (FL) Palm Beach Post; White Plains (NY) Journal News; Wichita (KS) Eagle; White Plains (NY) Journal
Circ. 32,083,450 Sworn

Montana Newspaper Group – 401 N. 28th St., Billings, MT, 59101-1243, USA; tel (406) 657-1200; fax (406) 657-1350; e-mail drussiff@billngsgazette.com; web site www.billngsgazette.com
Pub. – Mike Gullidge
Adv. Dir. – Dave Worstell
Nat'l Adv. Coord. – Diana Russiff
Ed. – Steve Prosinski

Included in the following newspapers: Billings (MT) Gazette; Butte-Anaconda (MT) Montana Standard; Missoula (MT) Missoulian; Helena (MT) Independent-Record
Circ. 143,240 (Mon, Tues, Wed, Thur, Fri, Sat, Sun) ABC

Rio Grande Valley Group – 1310 S. Commerce St., Harlingen, TX, 78550, USA; tel (956) 430-6211; fax (956) 430-6231
Gen. Mgr. – Tyler Patton
Pub. – Douglas Hardie
Ed. – Paul Binz
Mktg. Dir. – Marcia Kitten
Gen. Mgr., Adv. – Marcia Bleier

Texarkana Gazette – 315 Pine St., Texarkana, TX, 75501, USA; tel (903) 794-3311; fax (903) 792-7183; web site www.texarkanagazette.com
Pub. – Buddy King
Office Mgr. – Janet Barnes
Adv. Sales Mgr. – Rick Meredith
Mktg. Dir. – Kirk Blair
Circ. Mgr. – Bobby Perry
Ed. – Les Minor
Mng. Ed. – Ethel Channon
City Ed. – Christy Busby
Editorial Page Ed. – Russell McDermott
Farm Reporter – Greg Bischof
Features Ed. – Judy Morgan
News Ed. – Andrea Miller
Photo Ed. – Evan Lewis
Religion Ed. – Rhonda Morrow
Sports Ed. – Louie Avery
Technical Serv. Administrator – Guy Wheatley
Prodn. Mgr., Mailroom – Thomas Leonti
Prodn. Mgr., Press – Sammy Lee
Pres. – Walter E. Hussman
Jr. – Walter E. Hussman

Group: Arkansas Press Services
Included in the following newspapers: El Dorado (AR) News Timesp; Hot Springs (AR) Sentinel-Record; Texarkana (AR-TX) Gazette
Circ. 30,812 (Mon, Tues, Wed, Thur, Fri, Sat, Sun) ABC

Wyoming Color Comic Group – 702 W. Lincoln Way, Cheyenne, WY, 82001, USA; tel (307) 634-3361; fax (307) 633-3189; web site www.wyomingnews.com
Vice Pres., Mktg./Opns. – Scott P. Walker
Nat'l Adv. Mgr. – Cynthia M. Marek
Included in the following newspapers: Cheyenne (WY) Wyoming Sunday Tribune-Eagle; Laramie (WY) Boomerang; Rawlins (WY) Times

NEWSPAPER DISTRIBUTED MAGAZINES AND TOTAL MARKET COVERAGE PUBLICATIONS

American Profile - Chicago, IL–500 N Michigan Ave. Ste 300, Chicago, IL, 60611; tel (312) 396-4090; web site www.americanprofile.com
– Andrea Blank
– Andrea BlankAdv. Coord.s

American Profile - Franklin, TN–341 Cool Springs Blvd., Ste. 400, Franklin, TN, 37067; tel (615) 468-6021; web site www.americanpub.com
– Frank Zier
– Frank ZierNashville/West Coast Assoc. Pub.s

American Profile - Los Angeles, CA–6255 Sunset Blvd., Ste. 705, Los Angeles, CA, 90028; tel (323) 467-5906; fax (323) 467-7180; web site www.americanprofile.com
Adv Sales Rep. – Debbie Siegel

American Profile - New York, NY–60 E. 42nd St., Ste. 1111, New York, NY, 10165; tel (212) 478-1900; fax (646) 865-1921; web site www.americanprofile.com
Sr. Vice Pres./Grp. Pub. – Amy Chernoff
Sr. Vice Pres./Grp. Pub. – Amy Chernoff
Adv. Dir. – Shannon Hay
Adv. Dir. – Shannon Hay
Assoc. Ed., Direct Response – Linda Rich
Assoc. Ed., Direct Response – Linda Rich

American Profile - Northville, MI–22185 Heatheridge Ln., Northville, MI, 48167; tel (248) 991-1810; web site www.americanprofile.com
– Jim Main
– Jim MainAuto Adv. Mgr.s

Metro Newspaper Advertising Services, Inc. Sunday Magazine Network - New York, NY–8 W. 38th St., New York, NY, 10018; tel (212) 689-8200; fax (212) 824-4386; e-mail pcav@metrosn.com; web site www.metrosn.com
CEO – Phyllis Cavaliere
Pres. – Michael Baratoff
Sr. Vice Pres., Client Servs. – Tack Prashad
Sr. Vice Pres., Eastern Adv. – Bill Huck
Vice Pres., Finance/Admin. – Nili DeBono

Member Newspapers: Boston (MA) Globe; Buffalo (NY) News; Chicago (IL) Tribune; Kansas City (MO) Star; Los Angeles (CA) Times; New York (NY) Daily News; New York (NY) Times; Philadelphia (PA) Inquirer; St. Louis (MO) Post-Dispatch; San Antonio (TX) Express-News; Seattle (WA) Times & Post-Intelligencer; Washington (DC) Post
Circ. 8,237,412; Sworn March 31, 2007

Metro Newspaper Advertising Services, Inc. Sunday Magazine Network - San Francisco, CA–160 Spear St., Ste. 1875, San Francisco, CA, 94105; tel (415) 227-8857; fax (415) 227-0995; web site www.metrosn.com
Sr. Vice Pres., Western Sales – Ali Nazem

Metro Newspaper Advertising Services, Inc. Sunday Magazine Network - Chicago, IL–190 S. La Salle St., Ste. 1710, Chicago, IL, 60603; tel (312) 372-9310; fax (312) 372-4174; e-mail getinfo@metrosn.com; web site www.metrosn.com
Adv. Dir., Midwest Sales Reg. – Tom Vorel

Moline/Rock Island/Quad City Metro Unit–1720 Fifth Ave., Moline, IL, 61265; tel (309) 764-4344; e-mail advertising@qconline.com; web site www.qconline.com
Adv. Dir. – Val Yazbec
Ed. – Jerry Taylor

Member Newspapers: Davenport (IL) Leader; Moline (IL) Dispatch; Rock Island (IL) Argus
Circ. 51,927; Estimate May 18, 2004

Parade Publications, Inc. - San Francisco, CA–50 Francisco St., Ste. 400, San Francisco, CA, 94133; tel (415) 955-8222; fax (415) 397-0562; e-mail sf_sales@parade.com; web site www.parade.com
Adv. Contact – Bill Murray

Parade Publications, Inc. - Norcross, GA–340 E.

Big Beaver Ctr., Ste. 150, Norcross, GA, 30092; tel (770) 394-2400; fax (770) 395-7086
– Lauren Miller
– Lauren MillerAdv. Contacts

Parade Publications, Inc. - Los Angeles, CA–6300 Wilshire Blvd., 10th Fl., Los Angeles, CA, 90048; tel (323) 965-3649; fax (323) 965-4971; web site www.parade.com
Acct. Dir. – Greg Hancock

Parade Publications, Inc. - New York, NY–711 3rd Ave., New York, NY, 10017-4014; tel (212) 450-7000; fax (212) 450-7287; web site www.parade.com
Vice Chrmn./COO – John L. Beni
Chrmn./CEO – Jack Haire
Pres. – Randy Siegel
Exec. Vice Pres., Adv. – Mike DeBartolo
Sr. Vice Pres., Newspaper Rel. – David Barber
Sr. Vice Pres., Mktg. – Jim Hackett
Pub. – Brett Wilson
Editorial Dir. – Maggie Murphy
Vice Pres., Commun. – Christie Emden
Circ. 33,000,000; Rate Base January 18, 2009

Parade Publications, Inc. - Bloomfield Hills, MI–100 W. Long Lake Rd., Ste. 114, Bloomfield Hills, MI, 48304; tel (248) 540-9820; fax (248) 540-9891; e-mail det_sales@parade.com; web site www.parade.com
Vice Pres., Adv. – Mike DeBartolo

Parade Publications, Inc. - Chicago, IL–401 N. Michigan Ave., Ste. 2900, Chicago, IL, 60611; tel (312) 661-1620; fax (312) 661-0776; e-mail chi_sales@parade.com; web site www.parade.com
Vice Pres./Mid-Western Mgr. – Eric Karaffa

Print Marketing Concepts, Inc.–10590 Westoffice Dr., Ste. 100, Houston, TX, 77042, USA; tel (713) 780-7055; fax (713) 780-9731; e-mail rgoodpmc@aol.com; web site www.printmkt.com
Pres. – Sue Beck
Pres. – Sue Beck
Sr. Vice Pres. – Robin L. Good
Sr. Vice Pres. – Robin L. Good
Sr. Vice Pres., Nat'l Adv. Sales – Robin Good
Vice Pres. – Greg Wickliff
Vice Pres. – Greg Wickliff

Relish - Chicago, IL–500 N. Michigan Ave., Ste. 300, Chicago, IL, 60611; tel (312) 396-4090; web site www.pubgroup.com
Adv. Coord. – Andrea Blank

Relish - Franklin, TN–341 Cool Springs Blvd., Ste. 400, Franklin, TN, 37067; tel (615) 468-6021; web site www.pubgroup.com
Nashville/West Coast Assoc. Pub. – Frank Zier

Relish - Los Angeles, CA–340 S. Cloverdale Ave., Ste. 206, Los Angeles, CA, 90036; tel (646) 658-0550; web site www.relishmag.com
Acct. Mgr. – Jamie Relis

Relish - New York, NY–60 E. 42nd St., Ste. 1111, New York, NY, 10165; tel (212) 478-1900; web site www.relishmag.com
Sr. Vice Pres./Grp. Pub. – Amy Chernoff
Adv. Dir. – Shannon Hay
Assoc. Ed., Direct Response – Linda Rich

Relish - Northville, MI–22185 Heatheridge Ln., Northville, MI, 48167; tel (248) 991-1810; web site www.relishmag.com
Auto Adv. Mgr. – Jim Main

Spotlight–250 Yonge St., Winston-Salem, NC, 27101; tel (800) 457-1156; fax (336) 727-7461; web site www.starwatch.com
Bus. Mgr. – Alan Cronk
Bus. Mgr. – Alan Cronk
Sales Agent – Jody Stephenson Sarver
Sales Agent – Jody Stephenson Sarver

Star Watch–418 N. Marshall St., Winston-Salem, NC, 27101; tel (336) 727-7406; fax (800) 430-0532; web site www.starwatch.com
Sales Agent – Jody Stephenson Sarver
Exec. Ed. – Alan Cronk

TMS Specialty Products–1271 Avenue of the Americas, Chicago, IL, 60611, USA; tel (312) 527-8200; fax (312) 527-8256; web site www.tmsspecialtyproducts.com
Gen. Mgr. – Marco Buscaglia
Gen. Mgr. – Marco Buscaglia
Asst. Mgr. – Curtis Trammell
Asst. Mgr. – Curtis Trammell
Mng. Ed. – Mary Elson
Mng. Ed. – Mary Elson
Art Dir. – Todd Rector
Art Dir. – Todd Rector
Note TMS Specialty Products provides articles and images suitable for use in advertorial sections, niche publications and other targeted media, as well as custom ordered content, including local and paginated products.

Tribune Media Services TV Log - New York, NY–220 E. 42nd St., Ste. 400, New York, NY, 10017; tel (212) 210-2867; fax (212) 210-2863; web site www.tms.tribune.com

Tribune Media Services TV Log - Santa Monica, CA–3340 Ocean Park Blvd., Ste. 1060, Santa Monica, CA, 90405; tel (310) 581-5011; fax (310) 581-8025; web site www.tms.tribune.com

Tribune Media Services TV Log - Chicago, IL–8 W. 38th St., Chicago, IL, 60611-4012; tel (312) 222-3394; web site Mail, Newsstand.David D.
Member Newspapers: Allentown (PA) Morning Call; Arlington (IL) Daily Herald; Athens (GA) Daily News & Banner Herald; Atlanta (GA) Journal & Constitution; Atlantic City (NJ) Press; Bakersfield (CA) Californian; Baltimore (MD) Sun; Bangor (ME) News; Beaver (PA) County Times; Belleville (IL) News-Democrat; Bellevue (WA) Journal American; Boston (MA) Globe; Boston (MA) Herald; Boulder (CO) Daily Camera; Bridgeport (CT) Connecticut Post; Bridgewater (NJ) Courier News; Buffalo (NY) News; Canton (OH) Repository; Charlotte (NC) Observer; Chicago (IL) Sun-Times; Chicago (IL) Tribune; Cleveland (OH) Plain Dealer; Columbia (SC) State; Columbus (OH) Dispatch; Dallas (TX) News; Dayton (OH) News; Daytona Beach (FL) News-Journal; Denver (CO) Post; Denver (CO) Rocky Mountain News; Detroit (MI) Free Press; Detroit (MI) News; Durham (NC) Sun; Evansville (IN) Courier & Press; Everett (WA) Herald; Fort Lauderdale (FL) Sun-Sentinel; Fort Myers (FL) News Press; Fort Worth (TX) Star-Telegram; Fresno (CA) Bee; Galveston (TX) Daily News; Gary (IN) Post-Tribune; Glens Falls (NY) Post Star; Greensburg (PA) Tribune Review; Hackensack (NJ) Bergen County Record; Hartford (CT) Courant; Houston (TX) Chronicle; Indianapolis (IN) Star; Jacksonville (FL) Florida Times-Union; Jersey City (NJ) Jersey Journal; Kansas City (MO) Star; Kenosha (WI) News; Little Rock (AR) Democrat-Gazette; Long Beach (CA) Press Telegram; Long Island (NY) Newsday; Los Angeles (CA) Daily Breeze; Los Angeles (CA) Daily News; Lowell (MA) Sun; Los Angeles (CA) Times; Macomb (IL) Daily Journal; Mesa (AZ) Tribune; Miami (FL) Herald; Milwaukee (WI) Journal Sentinel; Minneapolis (MN) Star Tribune; Modesto (CA) Bee; Morristown (NJ) Daily Record; New Haven (CT) Register; New York (NY) Daily News; New York (NY) Post; Newport News (VA) Daily Press; Norfolk (VA) Virginian Pilot; Oakland (MI) Press; Oklahoma City (OK) Oklahoman & Times; Omaha (NE) World-Herald; Orange County (CA) Register; Orlando (FL) Sentinel; Palm Springs (CA) Desert Sun; Pasadena (CA) Star News; Philadelphia (PA) Daily News; Philadelphia (PA) Inquirer; Pittsburgh (PA) Post-Gazette; Port Huron (MI) Times Herald; Quincy (MA) Patriot Leader; Racine (WI) Journal Times; Raleigh (NC) News & Observer; Reading (PA) Eagle; Riverside (CA) Press; Rome (GA) News Tribune; Sacramento (CA) Bee; Salt Lake City (UT) Deseret News; Salt Lake City (UT) Tribune; San Antonio (TX) Express News; San Francisco (CA) Chronicle; San Francisco (CA) Examiner; San Jose (CA) Mercury News; Springfield (MO) News-Leader; St. Louis (MO) Post-Dispatch; St. Paul (MN) Pioneer Press; St. Petersburg (FL) Times; Trenton (NJ) Times; Tucson (AZ) Arizona Star; Vancouver (WA) Columbian; Washington (DC) Post; Washington (DC) Times; West Palm Beach (FL) Post; Wichita (KS) Eagle; Wilkes Barre (PA) Times-Leader; Wilmington (DE) News Journal; Worcester (MA) Telegram & Gazette; Youngstown (OH) Vindicator;
Circ. 32,853,868; Estimate July 23, 1999

TVtimes–250 Yonge St., Toronto, ON, M5B 2L7, Canada; tel (416) 593-6556; fax (416) 593-7329; e-mail tvtimes3@canwest.com; web site www.canwest.com
Dir., Newspaper Sales – Quin Millar
Member Newspapers: Windsor (ON) Star; Victoria (BC) Times-Colonist; Vancouver (BC) Sun; Saskatoon (SK) Star Phoenix; Regina (SK) Leader Post; Prince George (BC) Citizen; Ottawa (ON) Citizen; Montreal (QC) Gazette; Medicine Hat (AB) News; Kamloops (BC) Daily News; Edmonton (AB) Journal; Calgary (AB) Herald; Winnipeg (BC) Free Press
Circ. 1,124,839; ABC September 30, 2007

USA WEEKEND - Chicago, IL–444 N. Michigan Ave., Ste. 200, Chicago, IL, 60611; tel (312) 321-7760; fax (312) 527-9659; e-mail mpobrien@usaweekend.com; web site business.usaweekend.com
– Michael O'Brien
– Michael O'BrienMidwest Adv. Dir.s

USA WEEKEND - McLean, VA–7950 Jones Branch Dr., McLean, VA, 22107; tel (703) 854-6262; fax (703) 854 2128; e-mail usaw@usaweekend.com; web site www.usaweekend.com
Group: Gannett Company Inc.
Pres./Pub. – Chuck Gabrielson
Pres./Pub. – Chuck Gabrielson
Bus./Finance – Ed Maxwell
Bus./Finance – Ed Maxwell
Sr. Vice Pres., Newspaper Rel. – Ed Graves
Sr. Vice Pres., Adv. – Rob Harrison
Dir., Newspaper Mktg. – Joan Graff
Sr. Vice Pres., Newspaper Rel. – Ed Graves
Dir., Newspaper Mktg. – Joan Graff
Reg'l Dir., Newspaper Rel.-East/Midwest – Taaz Williams
Reg'l Dir., Newspaper Rel.-South/Southeast – Charlie Williams
Reg'l Dir., Newspaper Rel.-East/Midwest – Taaz Williams
Vice Pres./Exec. Ed. – Jack Curry
Reg'l Dir., Newspaper Rel.-Midwest/West – Jason Luebke
Vice Pres., Prodn. – Ken Kirkhart
Reg'l Dir., Newspaper Rel.-South/Southeast – Charlie Williams
Sr. Acct. Exec. – Lisa Baker
Vice Pres./Exec. Ed. – Jack Curry
Vice Pres., Prodn. – Ken Kirkhart
Sr. Acct. Exec. – Perri Kowalsky
Editorial Coord. – Troy Artis
Senior VP/Advertising – Michael O'Brien
Sr. Acct. Exec. – Lisa Baker
Sr. Acct. Exec. – Perri Kowalsky

USA WEEKEND - Troy, MI–340 E. Big Beaver Ctr., Ste. 150, Troy, MI, 48083-1244; tel (248) 680-1220; fax (248) 680-2348; e-mail jchauvin@usaweekend.com; web site business.usaweekend.com
Adv. Mgr. – Jim Chauvin
Adv. Mgr. – Jim Chauvin
Acct. Exec. – Bill Huney
Acct. Exec. – Bill Huney

USA WEEKEND - Los Angeles, CA–10960 Wilshire Blvd., Ste. 1000, Los Angeles, CA, 90024; tel (310) 444-2141; fax (310) 444-9631; e-mail msarsha@usaweekend.com; web site business.usaweekend.com; www.usaweekend.comMichael Hurwitz

Vista - The Magazine for All Hispanics - Miami Beach, FL–6538 Collins Ave., Ste. 397, Miami Beach, FL, 33141-4694, USA; tel (305) 416-4644; fax (305) 416-4344; e-mail leslie.russell@vistamagazine.com; web site www.vistamagazine.com
Group: impreMedia
Ed. Dir. – Cathleen Farrell
Sales Director – Leslie Russell
Editor – Marissa Rodriguez
Acct. Mgr. – Leslie Russell
Member Newspapers: Albuquerque (NM) Tribune; Austin (TX) American Statesman; Brownsville (TX) Herald; Dallas (TX) Al Dia; Harlingen (TX) Valley Morning Star; Laredo (TX) Morning Times; Los Angeles (CA) La Opinion; McAllen (TX) The Monitor; Miami (FL) El Nuevo Herald; New York (NY) El Diario La Prensa; Phoenix (AZ) Arizona Republic; Santa Fe (NM) New Mexican; Tulare (CA) Advance Register; Visalia (CA) Times Delta
Circ. 513,030; ABC June 30, 2008
Note 6 editions, bi-monthly

Vista - The Magazine for All Hispanics - Pontiac, MI–91 N. Saginaw St., Ste. 206, Pontiac, MI, 48342-2165; tel (248) 557-7490; fax (248) 577-7499; e-mail jay@rpmassoc.com; web site www.vistamagazine.com
– Jay Gagen
– Jay GagenAcct. Mgr.s

Vista - The Magazine for All Hispanics - New York, NY–345 Hudson St., 13th Fl., New York, NY, 10014-4502; tel (212) 807-4773; fax (212) 807-4738; e-mail roxana.rivas@vistamagazine.com; web site www.vistamagazine.com
Acct. Mgr. – Roxana Rivas

Vista - The Magazine for All Hispanics - San Antonio, TX–112 Redwood St., San Antonio, TX, 78209; tel (210) 832-9976
Acct. Mgr. – Ruth Gonzales

Section V

Mechanical and Interactive Equipment, Supplies and Services

EQUIPMENT, SUPPLIES AND SERVICES COMPANIES SERVING THE NEWSPAPER INDUSTRY

A

AAA Press International
3160 N. Kennicott Ave., Arlington Heights, IL, 60004; tel (847) 818-1100; fax (800) 678-7983; e-mail info@aaapress.com; web site www.aaapress.com
Pres.–Jack Ludwig
Vice Pres., Sales/Mktg.–Mark Hahn
Industry: Cameras & Accessories; Circulation Equipment & Supplies; Equipment Dealers (New); Equipment Dealers (Used); Imagesetters; Plate Mounting & Register Systems; Press Accessories, Parts & Supplies; Presses: Flexographic; Proofing Systems; Rewinders

A & A Research
690 Sunset Blvd., Kalispell, MT, 59901; tel (406) 752-7857; fax (406) 752-0194; e-mail fireowl@in-tch.com
Pres.–Judith Doonan
Research Dir.–E.B. Eiselein
Industry: Market Research; Research Studies;

A-American Machine & Assembly (Press Parts Div.)
2620 Auburn St., Rockford, IL, 61101; tel (815) 965-0882; fax (815) 965-1049; e-mail sales@a-americanpressparts.com; web site www.a-americanpressparts.com
Pres.–Mark Keller
Vice Pres., Opns.–Tom Sweeney
Industry: Belts, Belting, V-Belts; Copper Plating Drums; Cutting Tools; Folder Knives; Gauges, Measuring; Maintenance, Plant & Equipment; Motors; Press Accessories, Parts & Supplies; Press Rebuilding; Web Width Changer

ABB Inc.
9011 Bretshire Dr., Dallas, TX, 75228; tel (214) 328-1202; web site www.abb/printing.com
Nat'l Sales/Mktg. Dir.–Jeff Gelfand
Industry: Drives & Controls; Press Control Systems; System Integration Services;

ABB, Inc. (Printing Systems)
16250 W. Glendale Rd., New Berlin, WI, 53151; tel (262) 785-3206; fax (262) 785-6295; web site www.abb.com/printing
Vice Pres.-Paper Drives Systems/Printing–Rick Hepperla
Nat'l Sales/Mktg. Dir.-Printing Systems–Jeffrey Gelfand
Mgr.-Sales Applications/Printing Drives Systems–Hans Wirth
Industry: Drives & Controls; Press Control Systems; System Integration Services

ABB Ltd.
Affolternstr. 44, PO Box 8131, Zurich, N/A, CH-8050, Switzerland; tel 41 43 317-7111; fax 41 43 317-4420; e-mail engage.abb@ch.abb.com; web site www.abb.com
CEO–Joseph Hogan
CFO–Michel Demare

ACS Capital
6633 Grapevine Hwy., Ste. 107, North Richland Hills, TX, 76081; tel (817) 284-3060; fax (817) 284-3061; e-mail leaseguy@waymark.net
Contact–Stuart Kelley

ADI/PDM Trade Group
PO Box 220, Slyvania, GA, 30467; tel (912) 564-2400; fax (912) 564-2402; e-mail jlmcd1492@aol.com; web site www.arc-doyle.com
Pres.–Jim McDonald
Industry: Computers: Storage Devices; Counting, Stacking, Bundling Machines; Feeding, Folding, Delivery Equipment; Folding Machines; Material Handling Equipment: Automatic Guided Vehicles; Material Handling Equipment: Palletizing Machines; Material Handling Equipment: Pallets & Palletizers; Presses: Flexographic; Solvent Recovery Systems

AEC, Inc.
1100 Woodfield Rd., Ste. 588, Schaumburg, IL, 60173; tel (847) 273-7700; fax (847) 273-7804; web site www.aecinternet.com
Pres.–Tom Breslin
Industry: Architects/Engineers (Includes Design/Construction Firms); Press Accessories, Parts & Supplies

AG Industries, Inc.
1 American Rd., Cleveland, OH, 44144; tel (216) 252-6737; fax (216) 252-6773; web site www.agifixtures.com
Mktg./Adv. Coord.–Sandy Saunders
Industry: Newspaper Dispensers (Mechanical/Electronic)

A-Korn Roller, Inc.
3545 S. Morgan St., Chicago, IL, 60609; tel (773) 254-5700; fax (773) 650-7355; e-mail a-kornroller@a-kornroller.com; web site www.a-kornroller.com
Pres.–Michael Koren
Industry: Roll Cleaning Equipment; Roll Coverings; Roller Grinders; Roller Grinding Services; Rollers; Rollers: Dampening;

APS Packaging Systems
PO Box 712, Fairfield, NJ, 07006; tel (973) 575-1040; fax (973) 575-6540; e-mail sales@apspackaging.net
Pres.–Henry Verbeke
Vice Pres., Sales–Eric Verbeke
Industry: Shrink Wrapping Equipment

ARC International
10955 Withers Cove Pike Dr., Charlotte, NC, 28278; tel (704) 588-1809; fax (704) 588-9921; web site www.arcinternational.com
Pres.–Mike Foran
Gen. Mgr.–Steven Wilkinson
Vice Pres., Cor. Sales–Steve Woodard
Industry: Cleaners & Solvents; Platemakers: Flexographic (Computer to Plate); Platemakers: Laser; Roll Coverings; Rollers

AWS, A Thermal Care Division
7720 N. Leigh Ave., Niles, IL, 60714-3491; tel 800-666-7470 ; fax 630-595-5433; e-mail info@thermalcare.com; web site www.awsintl.com
Vice Pres., Sales/Mktg.–Tom Benson
Mktg. Servs. Mgr.–Audrey Guidarelli
Industry: Circulation Equipment & Supplies; Ink Fountains & Accessories; Ink Pumping Systems; Press Accessories, Parts & Supplies

Aaro Roller Corp.
4338 11th St., Rockford, IL, 61109; tel (815) 398-7655; fax (815) 398-7669; web site www.aaroroller.com
Pres.–Rick Wilson
Vice Pres.–Jeff Wilson
Industry: Copper Plating Drums; Press Accessories, Parts & Supplies; Roller Grinding Services; Rollers; Rollers: Dampening

Abelson Communications, Inc.
15 Bramshott Ct., Ste. 204, Rockville Centre, NY, 11570; tel (516) 596-9610; fax (516) 620-2460; e-mail susank@abelson.com; web site www.abelson.com
Pres.–Glenn R. Abelson
Vice Pres.–Susan Kaplan
Industry: Computers: Hardware & Software Integrators; Consulting Services: Advertising; Consulting Services: Circulation; Consulting Services: Computer; Consulting Services: Marketing

AbitibiBowater Inc.
55 E. Camperdown Way, Greenville, SC, 29602; tel (864) 271-7733; fax (864) 282-9482; web site www.abitibibowater.com
Pres./CEO–David J. Paterson
Sr. Vice Pres./CFO–Bill Harvey
Vice Pres., Newsprint–C. Randy Ellington
Vice Pres., Purchasing–Larry Green
Industry: Newsprint

AbitibiBowater Inc.
1155 Metcalfe St., Ste. 800, Montreal, QC, H3B 5H2, Canada; tel (514) 875-2160; fax (514) 394-2223; e-mail info@abitibibowater.com; web site www.abitibibowater.com
Pres./CEO–David J. Paterson
Exec. Vice Pres., Int'l Opns./Cor. Devel.–William H. Sheffield
Exec. Vice Pres., North American Opns.–Pierre Rougeau
Vice Pres., Pub. Aff./Sustainability/Environment–Seth Kursman
Industry: Newsprint; Paper: Coated Groundwood Offset; Paper: Groundwood Specialties; Paper: Specialty Printing Paper

Abi Bow US Inc.
5020 Hwy. 11 S., Calhoun, TN, 37309-5249; tel (423) 336-2211; fax (423) 336-7950; web site www.abitibibowater.com
VP and General Manager–Joe Vaughn
Industry: Newsprint

AbitibiBowater Pulp and Paper Canada, Inc.
1000 de la Gauchetiere St. W, Ste. 2820, Montreal, QC, H3B 4W5, Canada; tel (514) 954-2100; fax (514) 954-2191; web site www.abitibibowater.com
Sr. Vice Pres./CFO–David Maffucci
Vice Pres.-Int'l Sales–William Morris
Vice Pres.-Domestic Sales–Randy Ellinston
HR–Shan Tal
Industry: Film & Paper: Duplicating; Film & Paper: Filters (Photographic); Newsprint; Photostat: Paper

Accraply, Inc.
3580 Holly Ln. N., Minneapolis, MN, 55447-1269; tel (763) 557-1313; fax (763) 519-9656; web site www.accraply.com
Vice Pres., Sales–Dave Hansen
Industry: Label Printing Machines

AccuDocs LLC
300 Oak Wood Ln., Hollywood, FL, 33020; tel (800) 810-2390; fax (954) 920-5442; web site www.accudocs.com
Vice Pres.-Sales–Diane Rose
Industry: Archiving Systems; Data Communication; Marketing Database Design and Implementation

ACCUFAST Package Printing Systems
120 Defreest Dr., Troy, NY, 12180; tel (518) 283-0988; fax (518) 283-0977; e-mail sales@accufastpps.com; web site www.accufastpps.com
Pres.–Ken St. John
Mgr.–Meg Flanigan
Industry: Label Printing Machines; Mailroom Systems & Equipment;

Acer America
333 W. San Carlos St., Ste. 1500, San Jose, CA, 95110; tel (408) 533-7700; fax (408) 533-4555; web site www.acer.com
Pres., Pan America Opns.–Rudi Schmidleithner
CFO–Ming Wang
Industry: Computers: Laptop & Portable

Acutech LLC
25831 Pierina Dr., Elkhart, IN, 46514, USA; tel (574) 262-8228; fax (574) 262-4289; web site www.acu-tech.net
Mng. Dir.–Joe Bella
Dave Bratton
Pat Kelsey
Sales Coord.–Jeff Pulaski
Industry: Plate Mounting & Register Systems

Adhesives Research, Inc.
PO Box 100, Glen Rock, PA, 17327; tel (717) 235-7979; fax (717) 235-8320; web site www.adhesivesresearch.com
Vice Pres., Commercial Devel.–George Cramer
Industry: Adhesives

AdMission Corp.
3000 Executive Pkwy. Ste. 150, San Ramon, CA, 94583; tel (925) 328-1200; fax (925) 328-0140; e-mail sales@admission.net; web site www.admissioncorp.com
Vice Pres., Engineering–Robert Dominy
Industry: System Integration Services

Adobe Systems, Inc.
345 Park Ave., San Jose, CA, 95110-2074, USA; tel (408) 536-6000; fax (408) 537-6000; web site www.adobe.com
Sr. Vice Pres., Global Mktg.–Ann Lewnes
Dir., Worldwide Adv.–Jennifer Reynolds

AdStar, Inc.
13428 Maxella Ave., Ste. 261, Marina del Rey, CA, 90929, USA; tel (310) 577-8255; fax (888) 872-7981; e-mail info@adstar.com; web site www.adstar.com
Pres./CEO–Leslie Bernhard
Exec. Vice Pres./CTO–Eli Rousso
Sr. Vice Pres./COO–Jeffrey Baudo
Industry: Data Communication; Electronic Ad Delivery; Interfaces; Newspaper Marketing; Publishing Systems; Software: Advertising (Includes Display; Classified)

Advance Graphics Equipment of York, Inc.
4700 Raycom Rd., Dover, PA, 17315; tel (717) 292-9183; fax (717) 292-0196; e-mail info@ageyork.com; web site www.ageyork.com
Sales Mgr.–Bill Stiles
Industry: Counting, Stacking, Bundling Machines; Cutters & Trimmers; Feeding, Folding, Delivery Equipment; Folding Machines; In-Line Trimming Systems; Inserting Equipment (Includes Stuffing Machines); Numbering Machines; Three Knife Trimmer; Web Press - Special Equipment

Advance Systems, Inc.
PO Box 9428, Green Bay, WI, 54308-9428; tel (920) 468-5477; fax (920) 468-0931; e-mail asi_sales@advancesystems.com; web site www.advancesystems.com
Pres.–William Henry
Office Mgr.–Chelly Pierquet
Sales/Mktg. Mgr.–Mike Sellers
Industry: Dryers: Film and Papers; Drying Systems

Advanced Control Technologies, Inc.
1515 Murex Dr., Naples, FL, 34102-5147; tel (239) 262-8400; fax (239) 262-8400; e-mail wstobb@yahoo.com; web site www.wsa-print.com
Pres.–Walter J. Stobb
Vice Pres.–Garth S. Ryan
Sec.–Lorraine Earle Ryan
Treasurer–Jean M. Stobb
Industry: Consulting Services: Equipment; Cutters & Trimmers; Press Control Systems; Web Press - Special Equipment

Advanced Graphic Systems (AGS)
19324 Iron Mountain Dr., Grass Valley, CA, 95949; tel (530) 268-0116; web site www.ags-gv.com
Pres.–Earl T. Price
Mktg.–Wayne Kaim
Industry: Computers: Local Area Network (LANS); Controls: Photo Electric; Flying Pasters; Reels & Tensions; Reels (Inlcudes Paper Reels); Telecommunications; Tension & Web Controls; Testing Instruments

Advanced Publishing Technology
123 S. Victory Blvd., Burbank, CA, 91502, USA; tel (818) 557-3035; fax (818) 557-1281; e-mail info@advpubtech.com; web site www.advpubtech.com
Pres.–David Kraai
Vice Pres.–Ken Barber
Vice Pres., Sales-Central US–Mike Seller
Industry: Software: Advertising (Includes Display; Classified); Software: Circulation; Software: Editorial; Software: Pagination/Layout; Software: Workflow Management/Tracking

Advanced Technical Solutions, Inc.
20 Main St., Acton, MA, 01720; tel (978) 849-0533; fax (978) 849-0544; e-mail info@atsusa.com; web site www.atsusa.com
Exec. Vice Pres.–Bill Page
Industry: Computers: Hardware & Software Integrators; Input & Editing Systems; Publishing Systems; Software: Advertising (Includes Display; Classified); Software: Circulation; Software: Editorial; Software: Press/Post Press

Advanced Telecom Services, Inc.
996 Old Eagle School Rd., Ste. 1105, Wayne, PA, 19087-1806, USA; tel (610) 688-6000; fax (610) 964-9117; e-mail sales@advancedtele.com; web site www.advancedtele.com
Regional Sales Manager–Scott Bronenberg
Industry: Telecommunications

Advantex Marketing International, Inc.
491 Eglinton Ave. W., 5th Fl., Toronto, ON, M5N 1A8, Canada; tel (416) 481-5657; fax (416) 481-5692; e-mail info@advantex.com; web site www.advantex.com
Pres.–Kelly Ambrose
Industry: Consulting Services: Circulation; Consulting Services: Marketing; Promotion Services

Advertising Checking Bureau, Inc.
2 Park Ave., 18th Fl., New York, NY, 10016-5675; tel (212) 684-3377; fax (212) 684-3381; e-mail sales@acbcoop.com; web site www.acbcoop.com
Pres./CEO–Brian T. McShane
Vice Pres., Nat'l Sales–John Portelli
Dir., Mktg.–Mindy Weissler
Industry: Library Retrieval Systems; Market Research; Research Studies;

Advertising Data Scan/Adspies.com
9125 Phillips Hwy., Jacksonville, FL, 32256; tel (904) 363-0016; fax (904) 363-8384; e-mail sales@adspies.com; web site www.adspies.com
Pres.–William Jones
Gen. Mgr./Controller–Judy Matt
Sales Mgr.–Chastity Campbell
Industry: Consulting Services: Advertising; Consulting Services: Marketing; Software: Advertising (Includes Display; Classified)

AECOM
303 E. Wacker Dr., Chicago, IL, 60601; tel (312) 373-7700; fax (312) 373-7710; web site www.aecom.com
Office Mgr.–Betty Hendricks
Industry: Architects/Engineers (Includes Design/Construction Firms); Consulting Services: Equipment; Consulting Services: Production;

Agfa, Inc.
100 Challenger Rd., Ridgefield Park, NJ, 07660-2108; tel (201) 440-2500; fax (201) 342-4742; web site www.agfa.com
Dir. Bus. Dev.–Sheila Nysko
Pres., N. American Bus.–Peter Wilkens
Dir. Mktg.–Deborah Hutcheson
Industry: Film & Paper: Filters (Photographic)

Agfa Monotype Corporation
985 Busse Rd., Elk Grove Village, IL, 60007-2400; tel (847) 718-0400; fax (847) 718-0500; e-mail steve.kuhlman@agfamonotype.com; web site www.agfamonotype.com
Mgr., Sales/Mktg.–Steve Kuhlman
Industry: Consulting Services: Computer; Software: Design/Graphics; Type, Fonts

Agile Enterprise
2 Commerce Dr., Ste. 105, Bedford, NH, 03110-6803; tel (603) 584-1777; fax (603) 584-1778; e-mail info@agileenterprise.com; web site www.agileenterprise.com
Dir. Technical Support–John Vins
Industry: Software: Editorial; Software: Pagination/Layout

AIM Group / Classified Intelligence
402 Spring Valley Rd., Altamonte Springs, FL, 32714-5845, USA; tel (407) 788-2780; fax 866-611-6551; e-mail info@aimgroup.com; web site www.aim-group.com
Founding principal–Peter M. Zollman
Editorial director–Jim Townsend
Europe Director–Katja Riefler
Asia-Pacific Director–Emma Sorenson
MD–Bruce Annan
Industry: Consulting Services: Advertising

Airloc Products
PO Box 269, Franklin, MA, 02038; tel (508) 528-0022; fax (508) 528-7555; e-mail airloc@ma.ultranet.com; web site www.airloc.com
Vice Pres., Mktg.–Micheal McTermott
Industry: Noise Control

AirSystems, Inc.
16528 Westgrove, Addison, TX, 75001; tel (972) 931-0711; fax (972) 250-2034; e-mail milton@ghosting.com; web site www.ghosting.com
Pres.–Milton Lemaster
Industry: Inks; Controllers: Press

Alar Engineering Corp.
9651 W. 196th St., Mokena, IL, 60448, USA; tel (708) 479-6100; fax (708) 479-9059; e-mail info@alarcorp.com; web site www.alarcorp.com
Pres.–Paula Jackfert
Vice Pres., Int'l Sales–Vickey Gorski
Sales Mgr.–Steve Gorski
Industry: Water Management Systems

Alaska Information Marketing (AIM)
6081 Yukon Rd., Anchorage, AK, 99516; tel (907) 277-9996; fax (907) 272-0010; e-mail akinfo@alaska.net
Pres.–Kevin Tubbs
Industry: Marketing Database Design and Implementation

Alcatel-Lucent
600 Mountain Ave., Murray Hill, NJ, 07974-0636; tel (908) 582-3000; fax (908) 582-2576; e-mail execoffice@alcatel-lucent.com; web site www.alcatel-lucent.com
CEO–Ben Verwaayen
Pres., Bell Labs–Jeong H. Kim

alfa CTP Systems LLC
10 Columbia Dr., Amherst, NH, 03031; tel (603) 689-1101; fax (603) 689-1190; e-mail info@alfactp.com; web site www.alfactp.com
Gen. Mgr.–Tony Ford
Industry: Imagesetters; Plates: Offset (Computer to Plate); Proofing Systems; Software: Pagination/Layout; Typesetters: Laser;

alfaQuest Technologies
2100 Golf Rd., Rolling Meadows, IL, 60008, USA; tel (847) 427-8800; fax (847) 427-8860; e-mail marketing@alfaquest.com; web site www.alfaquest.com
Pres.–Dennis E. Nierman
Sr. Vice Pres., Sales–John Lally
Dir., Opns.–Keith Roeske
Dir., Systems Tech.–Frank O'Hearn
Industry: Color Proofing; Computers: Hardware & Software Integrators; Imagesetters; Interfaces; Laser Printers; Multiplexers/Routers; Output Management and Preflight Software; Photo Archiving; Platemakers: Laser; Raster Image Processors;

All Systems Color, Inc.
2032 S. Alex Rd., Ste. A, West Carrollton, OH, 45449; tel (937) 859-9701; fax (937) 859-9709; e-mail steveo@allsystemscolour.com; web site www.allsystemscolour.com
CEO–George Dick
Gen. Mgr.–Steve Orf
Industry: Color Proofing; Color Seperation Scanners; Color Seperations, Positives; Prepress Color Proofing Systems

All Systems Go
2 Cedar St., Woburn, MA, 01801; tel (781) 932-6700; fax (781) 932-6711; e-mail info@allsysgo.com; web site www.allsysgo.com
Pres.–Richard Pape
Industry: Computers: Hardware & Software Integrators; Computers: Laptop & Portable; Computers: Storage Devices; Consulting Services: Advertising; Consulting Services: Circulation; Consulting Services: Computer; Consulting Services: Equipment; Consulting Services: Marketing; Imagesetters; Software: Design/Graphics

Alliance Rubber Co.
PO Box 20950, Hot Springs, AR, 71901; tel (501) 262-2700; fax (501) 262-3948; e-mail sales@alliance-rubber.com; web site www.alliance-rubber.com
Mktg. Servs. Mgr.–Joan Dennis
Industry: Circulation Equipment & Supplies

Allpress Equipment, Inc.
4524 Curry Ford Rd., PMB 533, Orlando, FL, 32812, USA; tel (407) 348-2202; fax (407) 201-8322; e-mail apreeq@aol.com
Pres.–Jennie M. Schofield
Industry: Adhesive Wax Coaters; Drives & Controls; Equipment Dealers (Used); Folder Knives; Ink Fountains & Accessories; Ink Pumping Systems; Inks; Presses: Offset; Rollers; Splicers, Automatic

ALLTEL Communications Products
PO Box 1622, Alpharetta, GA, 30009-1622; tel (770) 409-9169; fax (770) 446-8400; web site www.alltel.com
Mktg. Dir.–Debbie Burgess
Industry: Telecommunications

Alpha-Omega Color Graphics, Inc.
PO Box 38, Mount Morris, IL, 61054; tel (815) 734-6066; fax (815) 734-6078; e-mail alphagr839@aol.com; web site www.alphaomegacolor.com
Owner–Gary R. Mennenga
Industry: Electronic Ad Delivery; Film & Paper: Phototypesetting; Telecommunications; Trade Publications; Training: Design & Layout; Training: Pre Press

ALTA- Al Taber - PHA
530 Saddle Creek Cir., Roswell, GA, 30076-1034; tel (770) 552-1528; e-mail altaeq@aol.com; web site www.altagraphics.com
Pres.–Albert Taber
Industry: Equipment Dealers (New); Equipment Dealers (Used); Press Accessories, Parts & Supplies; Presses: Offset; Web Press - Special Equipment

Altair Corp.
350 Barclay Blvd., Lincolnshire, IL, 60069; tel 847-634-9540

Alteneder, Theo & Sons
439 Main St., Darby, PA, 19023; tel (610) 522-9444; fax (610) 522-9446
Pres.–Theodore Alteneder
Sec.–Susan Alteneder
Treasurer–Emily Alteneder
Industry: Composing Room Equipment & Supplies; Rules

Amergraph Corporation
520 Lafayette Rd., Sparta, NJ, 07871; tel (973) 383-8700; fax (973) 383-9225; e-mail sales@amergraph.com; web site www.amergraph.com
Pres.–Robert Lesko
Industry: Exposure Lamps; Film & Paper: Film Processing Machines; Ink Bleeding Equipment; Ink Pumping Systems; Offset Plate-Making Service & Equipment; Plate Exposure Units; Plate Processors; Platemakers: Offset (Computer to Plate); Processors: Film & Paper; Vacuum Frames

American Consulting Services
440 NE 4th Ave., Camas, WA, 98607; tel (800) 597-9798; fax (360) 833-4620; e-mail info@toma.com; web site www.toma.com
Pres.–Mark Rood
Industry: Consulting Services: Advertising

American Fidelity Assurance Co.
PO Box 25523, Oklahoma City, OK, 73125-0523; tel (405) 523-2000; web site www.afadvantage.com
Chrmn./CEO/Pres.–William B. Cameron
Div. Mktg. Mgr.–Bob Fleet
Industry: Insurance

American Graphic Arts, Inc.
PO Box 240, Elizabeth, NJ, 07206; tel (908) 351-6906; fax (908) 351-7156; web site www.agamachinery.com
Pres.–John Jacobson
Industry: Equipment Dealers (Used); Gluing Systems

American Ink Jet Corp.
13 Alexander Rd., Billerica, MA, 01821; tel (978) 670-9200; fax (978) 667-9200; e-mail info@amjet.com; web site www.amjet.com
Pres./CEO–Michael Andreottola
Industry: Inks

American International Communications, Inc.
5595 E. 7th St., Ste. 110, Long Beach, CA, 90804-4419; tel (562) 428-5811; fax (562) 428-7904; e-mail speedyon@aol.com
Pres./CEO–Paul Keever
Industry: Audiotex Systems & Software; Circulation Equipment & Supplies; Consulting Services: Circulation

American Newspaper Representatives
2075 W. Big Beaver Rd., Ste. 310, Troy, MI, 48084-3543; tel (248) 643-9910; fax (248) 643-9914; web site www.anrinc.net
Pres.–John Jepsen
Exec. Vice Pres./COO–Robert Sontag
Regl. Sales Mgr., Minneapolis–Melanie Cox
Industry: Consulting Services: Advertising

American Opinion Research
279 Wall St., Research Pk., Princeton, NJ, 08540; tel (609) 683-4035; fax (609) 683-8398; e-mail acasale@imsworld.com; web site www.imsworld.com
Chrmn./CEO–Tony Casale
Pres.–Lois Kaufman
Industry: Consulting Services: Advertising; Consulting Services: Circulation; Consulting Services: Editorial; Consulting Services: Marketing

American Roller Co.
1400 13th Ave., Union Grove, WI, 53182; tel (262) 878-2445; fax (262) 878-1932; e-mail info@americanroller.com; web site www.americanroller.com
Pres.–Charles Tasch
Vice Pres., Sales/Mktg.–Dan Cahalane
Industry: Roll Coverings; Rollers; Rollers: Dampening;

American Ultraviolet Co., Inc.
212 S. Mt. Zion Rd., Lebanon, IN, 46052; tel (765) 483-9514; fax (765) 483-9525; web site www.auvco.com
Sales Rep.–Jack Slattery
Industry: Press Accessories, Parts & Supplies

Anchor Paper Corp.
1111 jenkins Rd., Gastonia, NC, 28052-1158; tel (704) 867-3980; fax (704) 867-9487
Pres.–Sam B. Woods
Industry: Paper: Specialty Printing Paper

Anocoil Corporation
PO Box 1318, Rockville, CT, 06066-1318; tel (860) 871-1200; fax (860) 872-0534; web site www.anocoil.com
CEO–H.A. Fromson
Pres.–David Bujese
Vice Pres., Anocoil–Timothy A. Fromson
Vice Pres., Prodn.–Michael Fromson
Industry: Chemicals: Plate Processing; Plates: Offset (Computer to Plate); Plates: Offset (Conventional)

Anygraaf USA
5235 Westview Dr., Ste. 100, Frederick, MD, 21703-8397; tel (240) 379-6620; e-mail any-inc@anygraaf.com; web site www.anygraaf.com
Pres.–Andy Hunn
Industry: Proofing Systems

ANewStartGuy.com
1261 Mokulua Dr., Kailua, HI, 96734-3249; tel 8082630933; fax 8082630933-0210; e-mail anewstartguy@aol.com; agiftcardguy@aol.com; web site www.anewstartguy.com
President–Jerry Weinerth
Industry: Circulation Equipment & Supplies; Consulting Services: Circulation; Consulting Services: Marketing; Newspaper Marketing; Promotion Services; Subscription Fulfillment Software; Training: Design & Layout

Apple, Inc.
1 Infinite Loop, Cupertino, CA, 95014, USA; tel (408) 996-1010; fax (408) 996-0275; web site www.apple.com; www.musicfan.com
CEO/Dir.–Steven P. Jobs
Sr. Vice Pres., Worldwide Pdct. Mktg.–Philip W. Schiller

Applied Creative Technologies
660 Preston Forest Ctr., Ste. 214, Dallas, TX, 75230-2718; tel (214) 221-4224; fax (214) 340-5717; e-mail info@connexperts.com; questions@connexperts.com; web site www.connexperts.com
Pres.–Tim Wilde
Industry: Computers: Local Area Network (LANS); Interfaces

Applied Graphics Technologies
450 West 33rd St., New York, NY, 10001; tel (212) 716-6600; fax (212) 716-6700; e-mail hulon@ccm.agtnet.com; web site www.agtseven.com
Chrmn.–Fred Drasner
Pres./CEO–John Harris
Exec-Newspaper Digital Servs. Grp.–Heloisa Ulon
Industry: Photography: Digital/Electronic Cameras; 282; Telecommunications

Applied Industrial Machinery
1930 SE 29th St., Oklahoma City, OK, 73129; tel (405) 672-2222; fax (405) 672-2272
Pres.–Robert Gilson
Industry: Equipment Dealers (New); Feeding, Folding, Delivery Equipment; Folding Machines; In-Line Trimming Systems; Three Knife Trimmer; Web Press - Special Equipment

Applied Learning Corp.
1376 Glen Hardie Rd., Wayne, PA, 19087; tel (800) 866-2442; fax (610) 688-6866
Pres.–James J. Barrett
Industry: Consulting Services: Ergonomics; Training: Keyboard Operation

Aragon System Products
PO Box 1725, Horsham, PA, 19044; tel (888) 491-4420; fax (215) 441-9500; web site www.aragon-sp.com
CEO–Herbert Wuest
Industry: Mailroom Systems & Equipment; System Integration Services;

Arch Chemicals, Inc.
PO Box 10099, Mesa, AZ, 85216-0099; tel (480) 987-7000; web site www.archchemicals.com
Pres.–Mike Campbell
Dir., Sales–Mario Stanghellini
Vice Pres., Int'l Mktg.–Jim LaCasse
Industry: Acid Dispensing Systems; Chemicals: Plate Processing; Chemicals: Pressroom;

Arco Engineering, Inc. (Newspaper Div.)
3317 Gilmore Industrial Blvd., Louisville, KY, 40213; tel (502) 966-3134; fax (502) 966-3135; e-mail sales@arcoengineering.com; web site www.arcoengineering.com
Pres.–James Gunn
Industry: Belts, Belting, V-Belts; Equipment Dealers (New); Equipment Dealers (Used); Gauges, Measuring; Noise Control; Pasters; Reels & Tensions; Reels (Inlcudes Paper Reels); Scanners: Color B & W, Plates, Web; Tension & Web Controls

Arpac Group
9511 W. River St., Schiller Park, IL, 60176; tel (847) 678-9034; fax (847) 671-7006; e-mail info@arpacgroup.com; web site www.arpacgroup.com
Pres.–Michael Levy
Industry: Bundling and Tying Machines; Conveyors; Shrink Wrapping Equipment

Arrow Printing Co.
PO Box 2898, Salina, KS, 67402-2898; tel (785) 825-8124; fax (785) 825-0784; e-mail arrow@arrowprintco.com; web site www.arrowprintco.com
Pres.–Kent Fellers
Adv. Mgr.–Dennis Suelter
Industry: Consulting Services: Advertising; Offset Camera, Darkroom Equipment; Offset Plate Files; Photo Proofing Systems; Platemakers: Offset (Conventional); Plates: Offset (Conventional); Prepress Color Proofing Systems; Presses: Offset; Processors: Film & Paper; Scanners: Color B & W, Plates, Web

Artbeats
PO Box 709, Myrtle Creek, OR, 97457; tel (541) 863-4429; fax (541) 863-4547; e-mail info@artbeats.com; web site www.artbeats.com
Pres.–Phil Bates
COO–Laura Hollifield
Adv./Mktg. Mgr.–Julie Hill
Global Dist. Mgr.–Peggy Nichols
Dir., Tech.–Bob Hayes
Industry: Software: Design/Graphics

Ashcraft Consulting
PO Box 430209, Pontiac, MI, 48343; tel (248) 334-4329; fax (248) 334-2226; e-mail aconsultinginc@aol.com
Dir., Mktg.–Sheila Ashcraft
Industry: Consulting Services: Circulation; Consulting Services: Computer; Consulting Services: Editorial; Consulting Services: Financial; ;

Ashworth Brothers, Inc.
450 Armour Dale, Winchester, VA, 22601; tel (540) 662-3494; fax (540) 662-3150; web site www.ashworth.com
Vice Pres. Mktg–Joe Lackner
Mktg. Mgr.–Tim Jones
Industry: Belts, Belting, V-Belts; Conveyors;

ASTech InterMedia
999 18th St., Ste. 2240, Denver, CO, 80202-2442, USA; tel (303) 296-9966; fax (303) 296-9969; e-mail ter@astech-intermedia.com; web site www.smartfocus.com
Pres./CEO–Tom Ratkovich
Dir., Client Servs.–Tia Talbert
Industry: Consulting Services: Advertising; Consulting Services: Circulation; Consulting Services: Computer; Consulting Services: Marketing; Marketing Database Design and Implementation; Software: Circulation; Training: Sales & Marketing

'Ataboy, Inc.
111 Ridgewood Way, Burlington, NJ, 08016; tel (609) 387-4908; fax (609) 387-7165; web site www.ataboyinc.com
Pres.–Howard McBane
Industry: Consulting Services: Production; Conveyors; Counting, Stacking, Bundling Machines; Delivery Equipment; Equipment Dealers (Used); Presses: Offset; Produciton Control Systems; Reels & Tensions; Remanufactures Equipment; Training: Press Operation & Maintenance

Atex North America
5405 Cypress Center Dr., Ste. 200, Tampa, FL, 33609; tel (813) 739-1700; fax (813) 739-1710; e-mail sales_us@atex.com; web site www.atex.com
CEO–John Hawkins
CEO, Atex North America–Scott Rossler
Sales Mgr.–Malcom McGregory
Industry: Software: Advertising (Includes Display; Classified); Software: Business (Includes Administration/Accounting); Software: Circulation; Software: Editorial; Software: Pagination/Layout;

Atex North America
5 Burlington Woods, Ste. 100, Burlington, MA, 01803, USA; tel (781) 685-3240; fax (781) 685-3276; e-mail info@atex.com; web site www.atex.com
CEO–John Hawkins
CEO, North America–Scott Roessler
CEO, NEMEA–David Hall
CEO, Asia Pacific–Ross Wood
COO–Alan Reardon
Sr. Vice Pres./Chief Integration Officer–Peter Marsh
Sr. Vice Pres., Sales Americas–Malcolm McGrory
Industry: Software: Advertising (Includes Display; Classified); Software: Asset Management; Software: Circulation; Software: Editorial; Software: Pagination/Layout;

Atex North America
410 N. Wickham Rd., Melbourne, FL, 32935; tel (321) 254-5559; fax (321) 254-4392; e-mail adbase.support-services.us@atex.com; web site www.atex.com
CEO of North America–Scott Roessler
Vice Pres., Product Mgmt.–Lars Jiborn
Vice Pres., Mktg.–Steve Roessler
Industry: Consulting Services: Advertising; Software: Advertising (Includes Display; Classified); Software: Business (Includes Administration/Accounting);

Atlas Specialty Lighting
7304 N. Florida Ave., Tampa, FL, 33604; tel (813) 238-6481; fax (813) 238-6656; web site www.asltg2.com
Mgr.–Ralph Felten
Industry: Lighting Equipment

The Austin Company
6095 Parkland Blvd., Cleveland, OH, 44124; tel (440) 544-2600; fax (440) 544-2690; e-mail austin.info@theaustin.com; ne@theaustin.com; web site www.theaustin.com
Gen. Mgr.–Curt Miller
Vice Pres., Planning/Design–Duane Lofdahl
Sr. Vice Pres., Sales/Mktg. Gen. Mgr.–Michael G. Pierce
Sr. Newspaper Consultant–Michael Craft
Industry: Architects/Engineers (Includes Design/Construction Firms); Consulting Services: Equipment; Consulting Services: Financial; Consulting Services: Marketing; Consulting Services: Production; Mailroom Systems & Equipment; Maintenance, Plant & Equipment; Newsprint Handeling Equipment; Roll Handeling Equipment; System Integration Services

Auto-Grafica Corp.
184 Rivervale Rd., River Vale, NJ, 07675; tel (201) 594-0100; fax (201) 594-0099; e-mail agcorp4usa@aol.com
Pres.–Ruth C. Hall
Gen. Mgr.–Frank D'Ambrosio
Mgr.-Opns.–Steve Dritschel
Industry: Business Computers; Color Proofing; Computers: Hardware & Software Integrators; Equipment Dealers (New); Imagesetters; Plate Processors; Platemakers: Direct; Prepress Color Proofing Systems; Processors: Film & Paper; Scanners: Color B & W, Plates, Web

Autologic Information International
1050 Rancho Conejo Blvd., Thousand Oaks, CA, 91320-1794; tel (805) 498-9611; fax (805) 499-1167; e-mail abrunner@autologic.com; web site www.autologic.com
Pres.–Al Brunner
Vice Pres., Software Engineering–Ratan Bhaunani
Vice Pres., Mfg.–Doug Arlt
Dir., Americas Opns.–Jack Embree
Mktg. Mgr.–Tom LeJeune
Industry: Archiving Systems; Computers: Hardware & Software Integrators; Facsimilie/Fax Transmission Systems; Multiplexers/Routers; Platemakers: Direct; Platemakers: Flexographic (Computer to Plate); Publishing Systems; Scanners: Color B & W, Plates, Web; Software: Advertising (Includes Display; Classified); Software: Electronic Data Interchange; Typesetters: Laser

Automated Mailing Systems Corp.
PO Box 541326, Dallas, TX, 75354-1326; tel (972) 869-2844; fax (972) 869-2735; e-mail amsco@amscodallas.com; web site www.amscodallas.com
Vice Pres.–Scott Helsley
Mktg. Mgr–Thomas Helsley
Industry: Addressing Machines; Bundling and Tying Machines; Inserting Equipment (Includes Stuffing Machines); Mailroom Systems & Equipment; Strapping Machines

Automatic Newsstand, Inc. (ANI Promotions)
6 S. Parker Dr., Monsey, NY, 10952; tel (800) 229-9029; fax (845) 354-5401; e-mail ANIpromo@aol.com
Owner–Joel Roth
Vice Pres.–Robin Honig
Industry: Cameras & Accessories; News Wire Capture Systems; Newspaper Bags; Newspaper Dispensers (Mechanical/Electronic);

Ayers/Johanek Publication Design, Inc.
8230 Rolling Hills Dr., Bozeman, MT, 59715-9349; tel (406) 585-8826; fax (406) 585-8837; web site www.publicationdesign.com
Partner–John Johanek

Publication Design, Inc.
6449 Meadowview Terrace S., Zionsville, PA, 18092-2091, USA; tel (610) 928-1111; fax (610) 928-1110; web site www.publicationdesign.com
President–Robert Ayers
Industry: Art & Layout Equipment and Services

B

BASF Corporation
100 Campus Dr., Florham Park, NJ, 07932-1020; tel (973) 245-6000; fax (973) 245-6714; web site www2.basf.us
Chrmn.–J□rgen Hambrecht
CFO–Kurt Bock
Sr. Vice Pres./Gen. Counsel–David Stryker
Exec. Vice Pres./Pres., Chemicals/Plastics/Performance Pdcts.–Joe Breunig
Exec. Vice Pres.–Hans U. Engel

Grp. Vice Pres., Performance Chemicals–Gerry Podesta
Exec. Dir., Research–Andreas Kreimeyer
HR–Harald Schwager

BASF Corp.
12 Thompson Rd., East Windsor, CT, 06088; tel (860) 623-9901; fax (860) 623-4657; web site www.basf.com
HR–Allan Bailie
Industry: Adhesives

B E & K, Inc.
PO Box 2332, Birmingham, AL, 35201-2332; tel (205) 972-6000; fax (205) 972-6300; web site www.bek.com
Industry: Architects/Engineers (Includes Design/Construction Firms)

BEK Systems, Inc.
605 South BLVD, Oak Park, IL, 60302; tel (630) 248-4334; e-mail info@beksystems.com; web site www.beksystems.com
Pres.–Paul Englram
Industry: Ink Bleeding Equipment; Ink Fountains & Accessories; Ink Pumping Systems; Ink Recovery Systems; Offset Fountain Controls;

B.G. Industrial, Inc.
PO Box 429, Deer Park, TX, 77536; tel (281) 479-8393; fax (281) 479-8827; e-mail sales@bgitex.com
Pres.–Charles R. Greer
Vice Pres.–Ashley Brandon
Industry: Ink Controls, Computerized; Ink Pumping Systems; Ink Storage Tanks; Ink Tank Monitors;

B.H. Bunn Co.
2730 Drane Field Rd., Lakeland, FL, 33811; tel (800) 222-2866; fax (863) 686-2866; e-mail sales@bunntyco.com; web site www.bunntyco.com
Pres.–John R. Bunn
Corp. Sec.–Harriet Bunn
Industry: Bundling and Tying Machines; Strapping Machines;

BLK Ltd.
220 Hasting Ave,, Highland Park, IL, 60035; tel (847) 433-8311; fax (847) 433-8285; e-mail BLKLTD@aol.com
Pres.–L.W. Kosoglad
Newspaper Rep.–Leovard W. Kosoglad
Industry: Web Press - Special Equipment

B & L Machine & Design
PO Box 743, Effingham, IL, 62401; tel (217) 342-3918; fax (217) 342-2081; web site www.blmachinedesign.com
Pres.–Larry Hines
Mktg. Mgr.–Lara Westjohn
Prodn. Mgr., Mfg.–Jim Strange
Industry: Presses: Offset; Training: Press Operation & Maintenance

BMF Newspaper Accounting Systems
PO Box 1590, Temple, TX, 76503; tel (254) 778-8918; fax (254) 778-1832; e-mail bmfi@aol.com
Owner–Bill Frank
Mgr.–Marilyn Frank
Industry: Business Computers; Computers: Hardware & Software Integrators; Software: Advertising (Includes Display; Classified)

BST Pro Mark
650 W. Grand Ave., Ste. 301, Elmhurst, IL, 60126-1026; tel (630) 833-9900; fax (630) 833-9909; e-mail sales@bstpromark.com; web site www.bstpromark.com
Vice Pres., Mktg.–John Thome
Industry: Color Management Software; Color Registration; Color Viewing Equipment; Press Accessories, Parts & Supplies; Produciton Control Systems; Web Cleaners; Web Guides

Badger Fire Protection
944 Glenwood Station Ln., Ste. 303, Charlottesville, VA, 22911; tel (800) 446-3857; fax (800) 248-7809; e-mail vmodic@badgerfire.com; web site www.badgerfire.com
Sales/Mktg. Dir.–Alan Owens
Industry: Fire Protection

Baird Manufacturing
Hwy. 79 E., Clarendon, AR, 72029; tel (800) 682-2278
Industry: Cart Distribution Systems

Baldor Electric Co.
5711 R.S. Boreham Jr. St., Fort Smith, AR, 72901; tel (479) 646-4711; fax (479) 648-5752; e-mail charlie_hubbard@baldor.com; web site www.baldor.com
Chrmn./CEO–John McFarland
Pres./COO–Ronald E. Tucker
Cor. Commun. Dir.–Charles G. Hubbard
Vice Pres., Sales–Randy Colip
Vice Pres., Mktg.–Randy Breaux
Industry: Drives & ControlsMotors

Baldwin Americas Corp.
1210 North Swift Road, Addison, IL, 60101, USA; tel 630-595-3651; fax 630-595-5433; e-mail info@baldwintech.com; web site www.baldwintech.com
Vice President, Baldwin Americas Sales & Marketing–Donald Gustafson
Industry: Circulation Equipment & Supplies; Dampening Systems; Drying Systems; Environmental Control Systems; Fluid Handeling: Pressroom; Ink Controls, Computerized; Press Accessories, Parts & Supplies; Recirculators; Solvent Recovery Systems; Water Management Systems

Baldwin Oxy-Dry Americas
185 Hansen Ct., Ste. 120, Wood Dale, IL, 60191; tel (630) 595-3651; fax (630) 735-2325; e-mail info@oxydry.com; web site www.oxydry.com
Sales Contact–Denise Jabotte
Industry: Blanket Cleaner/Washer (Automatic); Drying Systems; Offset Prevention-Materials & Equipment; Press Accessories, Parts & Supplies; Solvent Recovery Systems;

Balemaster
980 Crown Ct., Crown Point, IN, 46307; tel (219) 663-4525; fax (219) 663-4591; e-mail sales@balemaster.com; web site www.balemaster.com
Sales Mgr.–Mike Connell
Industry: Baling Machines

Ed Baron & Associates, Inc.
PO Box 3203, Oakton, VA, 22124; tel (703) 620-1725; fax (703) 620-9037; e-mail edbaron@edbaron.com; web site www.edbaron.com
Pres.–Ed Baron
Industry: Consulting Services: Advertising; Consulting Services: Circulation; Consulting Services: Financial; Consulting Services: Marketing; Training: Sales & Marketing

Base-Line, Inc.
2001 N. Delany Rd., Gurnee, IL, 60031; tel (847) 336-8403; fax (847) 336-8624; e-mail custsvc@base-line.com; web site www.base-line.com
Owner–Howard Harper
Industry: Blue Line Grids; Chemicals: Plate Processing; Chemicals: Pressroom; Masking Materials; Offset Chemicals & Supplies; Offset Fountain Solutions; Offset Negative Masking Paper; Plastic Folders; Plate Cleaners; Plates: Offset (Conventional);

Base-Line, Inc.
744 Nina Way, Warminster, PA, 18974; tel (800) 566-2256; fax (215) 444-0906; web site www.base-line.com
Vice Pres., Sales/Opns., Jomac Pdcts.–Roger Colehower
Sales Mgr.–Jack Maltby
Industry: Chemicals: Pressroom; Chemicals: Roller Cleaning; Cleaners & Solvents; Dampening Systems; Offset Chemicals & Supplies; Roll Coverings; Press Accessories, Parts & Supplies; Rollers; Rollers: Dampening;

Baton Lock & Hardware Co., Inc.
14275 Commerce Dr., Garden Grove, CA, 92843; tel (714) 265-3636; fax (714) 265-3630; e-mail info@batonlockusa.com; web site www.batonlockusa.com
Pres.–Hwei Ying Chen
Industry: Calibration Software/Hardware

Baumer Electric Ltd.
122 Spring St., C-6, Southington, CT, 06489; tel (860) 621-2121; fax (860) 628-6280; e-mail sales.us@baumerelectric.com; web site www.baumerelectric.com/usa
Pdct. Mgr.–Jeremy Jones
Mrkt.–Kristian Santamaria
Industry: Controls: Photo Electric; Newspaper Couter; Totalizing Systems; Web Break Detector

Baumfolder Corp.
PO Box 728, Sidney, OH, 45365-0278; tel (937) 492-1281; fax (937) 492-7280; e-mail baumfolder@baumfolder.com; web site www.baumfolder.com
Pres./Sales Mgr.–Ulrik Nygaard
Vice Pres., HR–Janice A. Benanzer
Vice Pres., Opns.–Sam Pryor
Vice Pres., Engineering/Quality–Robert D. Kinson
Dir., Sales/Mktg.–Mark Pellman
Parts–Mike Scott
Servcs.–Mike Hawkey
Industry: Belts, Belting, V-Belts; Collating Equipment; Counting, Stacking, Bundling Machines; Cutters & TrimmersCutters & Trimmers; Delivery Equipment; Feeding, Folding, Delivery Equipment; Folding Machines; Inserting Equipment (Includes Stuffing Machines); Pumps (Air, Ink, Vacuum)

Baumuller
117 W. Dudley Town Rd., Bloomfield, CT, 06002; tel (860) 243-0232; fax (860) 286-3080; e-mail info@baumuller.com; web site www.baumuller.com
Industry: Motors

Charles Beck Machine Corp.
400 W. Church Rd., King of Prussia, PA, 19406-3185; tel (610) 265-0500; fax (610) 265-5627; e-mail info@beckmachine.com; web site www.beckmachine.com
Pres.–C. Arthur Beck
Industry: Conversion Equipment; Cutters & Trimmers; Equipment Dealers (New); Roll Converters

Beckart Environmental, Inc.
6900 46th St., Kenosha, WI, 53144; tel (262) 656-7680; fax (262) 656-7699; e-mail inbox@beckart.com; web site www.beckart.com
Pres.–Thomas M. Fedrigon
Mgr., Mktg./Sales–Dan Fedrigon
Industry: Wastewater Treatment

Behrens International Ltd.
1120 Colony Plz., Newport Beach, CA, 92660; tel (949) 706-1660; fax (949) 706-1626
Chrmn.–Stanley Behrens
Industry: Newsprint; Paper: Coated Groundwood Offset; Paper: Groundwood Specialties

Bruce Bell & Associates
PO Box 400, Canon City, CO, 81215; tel (719) 275-1661; fax (719) 275-1664; web site www.surview.com
Opns. Dir.–Terri Madigan
Director, Sales and Customer Service–G. Alain Chamot
Industry: Computers: Hardware & Software Integrators; Computers: Laptop & Portable; Consulting Services: Advertising; Consulting Services: Marketing; Software: Advertising (Includes Display; Classified)

Bell & Howell Scanners
760 S. Wolf Rd., Wheeling, IL, 60090; tel (847) 675-7600; fax (847) 423-7503; web site www.bellhowell.com
Pres.–George Marton
Industry: Mailroom Systems & Equipment; Publishing Systems

Bellatrix Systems, Inc.
1015 SW Emkay Dr., Bend, OR, 97702; tel (541) 382-2208; fax (541) 385-3277; e-mail frontoffice@bellatrix.net; web site www.bellatrix.com
President and CEO–Steve Morris
Sr. Vice Pres., Sales/Mktg.–William Raven
Industry: Circulation Equipment & Supplies; Newspaper Dispensers (Mechanical/Electronic);

Belt Corporation of America
253 Castleberry Industrial Dr., Cumming, GA, 30040; tel (770) 887-9725; fax (770) 887-4138; e-mail sales@beltcorp.com; web site www.beltcorp.com
Pres.–William C. Levensalor
Sales Mgr.–Rich Blais
Inside Sales Supvr.–Mike Bridges
Industry: Belts, Belting, V-Belts

Belting Industries Co., Inc.
PO Box 310, Kenilworth, NJ, 07033-0310; tel (908) 272-8591; fax (908) 272-3825; e-mail info@beltingindustries.com; web site www.beltingindustries.com
Chrmn.–Webb A. Cooper
Pres.–Scott Cooper
COO–Gene Hobson
Controller–Paul West
Sales Mgr.–Jeff Smith
Industry: Belts, Belting, V-Belts

Bender Machine, Inc.
2150 E. 37th St., Los Angeles, CA, 90058; tel (323) 232-1790; fax (323) 232-6456; e-mail info@bendermachine.com; web site www.bendermachine.com
Mktg. Mgr.–Bruce Perry
Acct. Mgr.–Doug Martin
Industry: Newsprint; Newsprint Handeling Equipment; Roller Grinders; Roller Grinding Services;

Berkshire/Westwood Graphics Group, Inc.
PO Box 1399, Holyoke, MA, 01041-1399; tel (413) 532-1735; fax (413) 532-6508; e-mail sales@bwgg.com
Pres.–Mike Sullivan
Retail Sales Mgr.–Bob Beavlac
Industry: Chemicals: Photographic; Chemicals: Plate Processing; Chemicals: Pressroom; Composing Room Equipment & Supplies; Equipment Dealers (New); Imagesetters; Offset Chemicals & Supplies; Plate Exposure Units; Plates: Offset (Conventional); Typesetters: Laser

C. Berky & Associates, Inc.
11750 Watercrest Lane, Boca Raton, FL, 33498, USA; tel (561) 212-1219; fax (561) 852-6482; e-mail pageboca@aol.com
Pres.–H. Charles Berky
Industry: Brokers & Appraisers

Berlee Vacuum Systems
54 Winter St., Holyoke, MA, 01040; tel (413) 538-8341; fax (413) 533-2709
Pres.–Bernard L. Adams
Sales Mgr.–James Garland
Industry: Lift Trucks

Berting Communications
6330 Woburn Dr., Indianapolis, IN, 46250; tel (800) 536-5408; fax (317) 849-5408; e-mail bob@bobberting.com; web site www.bobberting.com
Pres.–Bob Berting
Vice Pres.–Barbara Berting
Graphic Artist–Dan Cooper
Industry: Consulting Services: Advertising; Consulting Services: Marketing; Training: Sales & Marketing

BESCO Graphic Systems Corp.
35 E. Wacker Dr., Ste. 3500, Chicago, IL, 60601; tel (312) 220-0042; fax (312) 220-

0091
Chrmn. of the Bd.–Daniel Z. Tropp
Pres.–Lawrence B. Tropp
Exec. Vice Pres.–Pete Walsh
Exec. Vice Pres.–James Penney
Vice Pres.-Opns.–Dee Morse
Vice Pres.-Mktg.–Dan Guerrieri
Industry: Dampening Systems; Drying Systems; Photo Proofing Systems; Proofing Systems;

Beta Screen Corp.
707 Commercial Ave., Carlstadt, NJ, 07072; tel (201) 939-2400; fax (201) 939-7656; e-mail info@betascreen.com; web site www.betascreen.com
Pres.–Arnold Serchuk
Contact–Larry Goldberg
Industry: Calibration Software/Hardware; Color Proofing; Color Viewing Equipment; Dark Room Equipment; Densitometers; Gauges, Measuring; Layout Tables, Light Tables & Workstations; Optical Products; Static Eliminators; Tables (Dot, Etch, Opaquing, Register, Retouching, Stripping)

Bishamon Industries Corp.
5651 E. Francis St., Ontario, CA, 91761; tel (909) 390-0055; fax (909) 390-0060; e-mail info@bishamon.com; web site www.bishamon.com
Pres.–Wataru Sugiura
Vice Pres., Sales/Mktg.–Bob Clark
Industry: Mailroom Systems & Equipment; Material Handling Equipment: Vehicle Loading; Newsprint Handeling Equipment; Paper Handeling Equipment;

Chuck Blevins & Assoc.
8396 Northmapton Ct., Naple, FL, 34120-1687; tel 239 348 7897; fax (239) 348-7897; e-mail chuckblevins@aol.com; web site www.chuckblevins.com
Pres.–Chuck Blevins
Mktg. Mgr.–Janelle Piccola
Industry: Consulting Services: Equipment; Consulting Services: Ergonomics; Consulting Services: Production; Mailroom Systems & Equipment; Press Engineers

Blower Application Co., Inc.
PO Box 279, Germantown, WI, 53022; tel (262) 255-5580; fax (262) 255-3446; e-mail info@bloapco.com; web site www.bloapco.com
Pres.–John Stanislowski
CEO–Michael J. Young
Mgr., Sales–Ric Johnson
Industry: Cutters & Trimmers; In-Line Trimming Systems; Paper Shredders; System Installations;

Blue Heron Paper Co.
419 Main St., Oregon City, OR, 97045; tel (503) 650-4211; fax (503) 650-4512; e-mail customerservice@blueheronpaper.com.; web site www.blueheronpaper.com
Pres. / CEO–Michael A Siebers
Mgr., Sales/Mktg.–Jon E. Melkerson
Industry: Newsprint

Bob Ray & Associates, Inc.
3575 Morreim Dr., Belvidere, IL, 61008; tel (815) 547-9393; fax (815) 547-5572; e-mail chuck@bobray.com; web site www.bobray.com
Pres.–Chuck Britton
Vice Pres., Admin.–Nolen G. Lee
Vice Pres., Sales–John R. Steker
Technical Sales Mgr.–John F. Nicoli

Bodine Electric
2500 W. Bradley Pl., Chicago, IL, 60618; tel (773) 478-3515; fax (773) 478-3232; web site www.bodine-electric.com
Pres.–John Bodine
Industry: Motors

Boles, Morgan & Canino, Inc.
102 South Court St., Ste. 403, Florence, AL, 35630; tel (256) 740-8234; fax (256) 767-1600; e-mail deem@hiwaay.com
Pres.–Harold Van Morgan
Vice Pres.–Durelle Boles
Industry: Consulting Services: Equipment; Consulting Services: Financial; Consulting Services: Production;

Bosch Rexroth
5150 Prairie Stone Pkwy., Hoffman Estates, IL, 60192; tel (847) 645-3600; fax (847) 645-6201; web site www.boschrexroth-us.com
Pres./CEO–Berend Bracht
Industry: Press Control Systems

Bottcher America Corp.
4600 Mercedes Dr., Belcamp, MD, 21017; tel (410) 273-7000; fax (410) 273-7174; web site www.bottcher.com
Vice Pres., Mktg.–Wayne Porter
Industry: Rollers

Bottom Line Industries
9556 Cozycroft Ave., Chatsworth, CA, 91311; tel (800) 334-6044; fax (818) 700-8232
Pres.–Al Singer
Vice Pres.–Manny Singer
Purchasing Agent–Bonnie Bosworth
Industry: Computers: Hardware & Software Integrators

Bowe Bell + Howell
3791 S. Alston Ave., Durham, NC, 27713-1803; tel (847) 675-7600; fax (610) 266-4565; e-mail marketing@bowebellhowell.com; web site www.bowebellhowell.com
Pres–George Marton
Exec. Vice Pres.–Frank Gozzo
Vice Pres., Sales–Scott Turner
Industry: Mailroom Systems & Equipment

Brady & Paul Communications
7 Orange St., Newburyport, MA, 01950-2805; tel (978) 463-2255; e-mail brady-brady@aol.com; contact@johnbrady.info; web site www.bradyandpaul.com; www.johnbrady.info
Pres.–John Brady
Designer–Greg Paul
Industry: Art & Layout Equipment and Services; Consulting Services: Editorial;

Brainworks Software Development Corp.
100 S. Main St., Sayville, NY, 11782; tel (631) 563-5000; fax (631) 563-6320; e-mail info@brainworks.com; web site www.brainworks.com
Mgr.–John Barry
Industry: Pagination Systems; Software: Advertising (Includes Display; Classified); Software: Business (Includes Administration/Accounting); Software: Design/Graphics; Software: Editorial; Software: Pagination/Layout; System Integration Services

Brock Solutions U.S. Inc.
6221 Riverside Dr., Ste. 102, Irving, TX, 75039-3604; tel (972) 373-2500; fax (972) 444-0352; e-mail info@brocksolutions.com ; hr@brocksolutions.com; web site www.brocksolutions.com
Project Mgr.–Bill Mctuire
Industry: Addressing Machines; Consulting Services: Production;

Brodie System, Inc.
1539 W. Elizabeth Ave., Linden, NJ, 07036; tel (908) 862-8620; fax (908) 862-8632; web site www.brodiesystem.com
Pres.–Thomas W. Nielsen
Engineer–Nicholas Lloyd
Prodn. Mgr., Opns.–John Farrell
Plant Mgr.–Paul J. Kamage
Industry: Cylinder Repair; Ink Fountains & Accessories; Press Accessories, Parts & Supplies; Roller Grinding Services; Rollers; Rollers: Dampening;

Brown Mannschreck Business System
PO Box 7, Saint Joseph, MO, 64502; tel (816) 279-7425; fax (816) 387-8915
CEO–Steven Pitluck
Vice Pres., Sales–Cathie Wayman
Vice Pres.–Craig Greer

Brown's Web Press Service & Machine Shop
PO Box 326, Mexico, MO, 65265; tel (573) 581-6275; fax (573) 581-7278; e-mail lgbrown59@gmail.com
Pres.–L.G. Brown
Vice Pres.–Gena Brow
Industry: Cylinder Repair; Drives & Controls; Equipment Dealers (Used); Erectors & Riggers; Press Rebuilding; Press Repairs; Presses: Offset; Roller Grinding Services;

Bruno Knives USA
11516 W. 90th St., Overland Park, KS, 66214; tel (913) 648-8497; fax (913) 859-0334
Owner–Al Elton
Industry: Cutters & Trimmers; Folder Knives;

Buffalo Technology Inc.
11100 Metric Blvd., Ste. 750, Austin, TX, 78758; tel (512) 349-1580; fax (512) 339-7272; e-mail sales@buffalotech.com; web site www.buffalotech.com
PR–Jay Pechek
Industry: Computers: Hardware & Software Integrators; Computers: Local Area Network (LANS); Computers: Storage Devices;

Buhrs Americas, Inc.
2405 Xenium Ln. N., Ste. 100, Plymouth, MN, 55441; tel (763) 557-9100; fax (763) 557-9700; e-mail info.americas@buhrs.com; web site www.buhrs.com
Pres.–Michael Aumann
Industry: Automatic Plastic Bagging Equipment; Feeding, Folding, Delivery Equipment; Folding Machines; Inserting Equipment (Includes Stuffing Machines); Mailroom Systems & Equipment; Newspaper Couter; Software: Press/Post Press;

Bulbtronics
45 Banfi Plz., Farmingdale, NY, 11735; tel (631) 249-2272; fax (631) 249-6066; e-mail bulbs@bulbtronics.com; web site www.bulbtronics.com
Vice Pres., Sales–Lee Vestrich
Mgr., Mktg.–Beckie Mullin
Industry: Lighting Equipment

Burgess Industries, Inc.
2700 Campus Dr., Plymouth, MN, 55441; tel (763) 553-7800; fax (763) 553-9289; e-mail djburgess@burgessind.com; web site ^www.burgessind.com
Pres./CEO–Dennis Burgess
Nat'l Pdct. Mgr.–Joe Stein
Nat'l Sales Dir.–Richard Fream
Industry: Color Proofing; Color Registration; Controls: Exposure; Controls: Register; Light Integrators; Plate Bending Systems; Plate Mounting & Register Systems; Proofing Systems; Static Eliminators; Vacuum Frames

M.W. Burke & Associates, Inc.
73 Menlo Pl., Berkeley, CA, 94707; tel (925) 838-9070; fax (925) 838-4695; e-mail mw-burke@aol.com
Pres./Chrmn.–M.W. (Maury) Burke
Industry: Consulting Services: Advertising; Consulting Services: Circulation; Consulting Services: Production; Prepress Color Proof ing Systems;

Burnishine Products
25392 W. Park Ct, Lake Villa, IL, 60047; tel 847-356-2553; fax 847 356 3177; e-mail rgiza@burnishine.com; web site www.burnishine.com
Graphic Arts, Vice Pres.–Patty Vick
President–Roger Giza
Sr. Vice Pres., Sales–John Brennan
Industry: Offset Fountain Solutions; Plate Cleaners;

Burt Technologies, Inc.
32156 Castle Ct., Ste. 206, Evergreen, CO, 80439-9500; tel (303) 670-7731; fax (303) 670-0978; e-mail info@burtmountain.com; sales@burtmountain.com; support@burtmountain.com; web site www.burtmountain.com
Founder/Pres.–Jim Burt
CEO–Rich Burt
Accounts Mgr.–Mickey Waleski
Opns. Mgr.–Colleen Bynum
Industry: Computers: Hardware & Software Integrators; Inserting Equipment (Includes Stuffing Machines); Interfaces; Mailroom Systems & Equipment; Software: Press/Post Press; Training: Post Press

Busch, Inc.
516 Viking Dr., Virginia Beach, VA, 23452; tel (757) 463-7800; fax (757) 463-7407; e-mail marketing@buschusa.com; web site www.buschpump.com
Pres.–Charles Kane
Mktg. Specialist–Linda Katz
Industry: Pumps (Air, Ink, Vacuum)

The Business Scribe, Inc.
105 Randolph's Green, Williamsburg, VA, 23185; tel (757) 229-7752; e-mail halron8@yahoo.com; web site www.virginiahospitalitysuite.com
Pres.–Hal Gieseking
Industry: Consulting Services: Computer; Consulting Services: Editorial; Consulting Services: Marketing;

Butler Automatic
Campanelli Business Pk., 41 Leona Dr., Middleborough, MA, 02346; tel (508) 923-0544; fax (508) 923-0885; e-mail butler@butlerautomatic.com; web site www.butlerautomatic.com
Vice Pres., Engineering–John Clifford
Industry: Conveyors; Counting, Stacking, Bundling Machines; Cutters & Trimmers; Flying Pasters; Material Handling Equipment: Palletizing Machines; Pasters; Roll Handeling Equipment; Splicers, Automatic; Tension & Web Controls;

ByChrome Ltd.
PO Box 1486, Springfield, OH, 45501; tel (800) 645-8309; fax (800) 966-1077; e-mail sales@bychrome.com; web site www.bychrome.com
Gen. Mgr.–Matthew Harris
Industry: Chemicals: Photographic; Chemicals: Plate Processing; Film & Paper: Contact; Film & Paper: Duplicating; Film & Paper: Phototypesetting; Plates: Letterpress; Plates: Offset (Computer to Plate); Plates: Offset (Conventional);

CCI Europe, Inc.
3550 George Busbee Parkway NW, Kennesaw, GA, 30144, USA; tel (770) 420-1100; e-mail info@ccieurope.com; web site www.ccieurope.com
CEO–Dan Korsgaard
Vice Pres., Project Sales–Jorgen Valker
Vice Pres., Mktg.–Torben Juul
President, CCI US–Carsten Boe Jensen
Industry: Software: Advertising (Includes Display; Classified); Software: Asset Management; Software: Business (Includes Administration/Accounting); Software: Design/Graphics; Software: Editorial; Software: Electronic Data Interchange; Software: Pagination/Layout; Software: Workflow Management/Tracking; System Integration Services; Training: Keyboard Operation;

CCI Europe, Inc.-Georgia Branch
3550 George Busbee Pkwy., Ste. 300, Kennesaw, GA, 30144; tel (770) 420-1100; fax (770) 420-5588; e-mail info@ccieurope.com; web site www.ccieurope.com
Pres.–Carsten Boe Jensen
Sales–Jorgen Valkaer

C

CE Engineering
3121 Swetzer Rd., Ste. F, Loomis, CA, 95650; tel (916) 652-5263; fax (916) 652-5264; e-mail cesales@ceengineering.com; web site www.ceengineering.com
Pres.–E. Robert Waterhouse

CEO–Chris Ellsworth
Vice Pres.-European Opns.–Gary Hall
Mktg. Dir.–Kevin King
Industry: Computers: Hardware & Software Integrators; Consulting Services: Computer; Consulting Services: Editorial; Consulting Services: Equipment; Software: Advertising (Includes Display; Classified); Software: Editorial; Software: Electronic Data Interchange; Software: Pagination/Layout; System Installations; System Integration Services

CHF Foto Supply
70 Worth St., South Hackensack, NJ, 07606; tel (800) 774-5294; fax (201) 488-9033; e-mail chf@chffoto.com
–Charlie Wimpfheimer
–Michael GreenCo-Owners
Industry: Cameras & Accessories; Film & Paper: Filters (Photographic);

Ch2MHill Lockwood Greene
PO Box 491, Spartanburg, SC, 29304; tel (864) 578-2000; fax (864) 599-4117; e-mail lockwood@lg.com; web site www.lg.com
Contact–Monique Plumley
Industry: Architects/Engineers (Includes Design/Construction Firms); Material Handling Equipment: Automatic Guided Vehicles;

CK Optical Co., Inc.
4432 Via Pavion, Palos Verdes Estates, CA, 90274-1552; tel (310) 373-2141; e-mail carlbomhs@cox.net
Pres.–Herbert W. Carlbom
Industry: Cameras & Accessories; Lenses (Camera); Offset Camera, Darkroom Equipment; Research Studies;

CNI Corp.
394 Elm St., Milford, NH, 03055; tel (603) 673-6600; fax (603) 672-6633; e-mail sales@cnicorp.com; web site www.cnicorp.com
Pres.–John Dickinson
Scott Snow
Bill Suplee
Industry: Consulting Services: Production; Data Communication; Input & Editing Systems; Optical Character Recognition (OCR); Pagination Systems; Prepress Color Proofing Systems; Publishing Systems; Training: Keyboard Operation; Typesetters: Laser; Word Processing System;

Cachet Fine Art Photographic Paper
11661 Martens River Ste. D, Fountain Valley, CA, 92708; tel (714) 432-7070; fax (714) 432-7102; e-mail onecachet@aol.com; web site www.onecachet.com
Pres.–Ike Royer
Industry: Chemicals: Photographic; Dark Room Equipment; Film & Paper: Filters (Photographic);

Canadian Web Consultants Ltd.
57 Hiawatha Dr., Port Sydney, ON, P0B 1L0, Canada; tel (340) 643-2400; e-mail canadaoffice@cwc4webs.com; web site www.cwc4webs.com
Pres.–Stephen Tweddle
Vice Pres.–Michele Belanger
Office Mgr.–Lorraine Bell
Industry: Consulting Services: Equipment; Consulting Services: Production; Erectors & Riggers;

Canadian Web Consultants Ltd.
PO Box 687, Christiansted, St Croix, 00821; tel (340) 643-2399; fax (340) 718-7571; e-mail cariboffice@cwc4webs.com; web site www.cwc4webs.com
Pres.–Stephen Tweddle

Cannon Equipment
15100 Business Pkwy., Rosemount, MN, 55068; tel (800) 533-2071; fax (651) 322-1583; e-mail info@cannonequipment.com; web site www.cannonequipment.com
Pres.–Chuck Gruber
Nat'l Sales Mgr./Newspaper Handling Systems–Pat Geraghty
Industry: Cart Distribution Systems; Circulation Equipment & Supplies; Conveyors; Mailroom Systems & Equipment;

The Cannon Group, Inc.
5037 Pine Creek Dr., Westerville, OH, 43081-4849; tel (614) 890-0343; fax (614) 890-0467; e-mail sales@pdisaneck.com; web site www.newsbags.com
Pres.–Frank Cannon

Canon USA, Inc.
1 Canon Plz., Lake Success, NY, 11042-1198; tel (516) 328-5000; fax (516) 328-5009; e-mail mediacontact@cusa.canon.com; web site www.usa.canon.com
Pres./CEO, Canon U.S.A., Inc.–Yoroku Adachi
Exec. Vice Pres./Gen. Counsel Admin./Reg'l Opns.–Seymour Liebman
Sr. Vice Pres./Gen Mgr., Sales Mktg./Admin.–Tod D. Pike
Adv. Dir., Cameras/Camcorders, Dir., Mktg. Serv./Adv.–Rick Booth

Capco Machinery Systems, Inc.
PO Box 11945, Roanoke, VA, 24022; tel (540) 977-0404; fax (540) 977-2781; web site www.capcomachinery.com
Pres.–Edward E. West
Vice Pres., Finance–Amy S. West
Industry: Roller Grinders

Capita Technologies
17600 Gillette Ave., Irvine, CA, 92614-5702; tel (949) 260-3000; fax (949) 851-9875; e-mail sales@capita.com; web site www.capita.com
CEO–Charles Granville
Exec. Vice Pres., Techn./Opns.–Imelda Ford
Industry: Software: Pagination/Layout; System Integration Services;

Capital Track Co.
145 Lucas St., Columbus, OH, 43215; tel (614) 221-4110; fax (614) 225-9832; web site www.capitaltrack.com
Adv. Contact–Matt Caldwell
Industry: Consulting Services: Equipment; Newsprint Handeling Equipment; Paper Handeling Equipment; Roll Handeling Equipment;

Caprock Developments, Inc.
PO Box 95, Morris Plains, NJ, 07950, USA; tel (973) 267-9292; fax (973) 292-0614; e-mail info@caprockdev.com; web site www.caprockdev.com
President–Alan Schwartz
Industry: Densitometers; Exposure Lamps; Gauges, Measuring; Lighting Equipment; Offset Blanket Thickness Gauge; Optical Products; Paper Testing Instruments; Testing Instruments;

Cariweb Products
PO Box 1349, Harlingen, TX, 78551-1349; tel (956) 423-5766; fax (956) 748-3417; e-mail cariwebproducts@aol.com
Pres.–Jose Henderson
Industry: Tape Splicing Equipment

Carlson Design Construct
34 Executive Pk., Ste. 250, Irvine, CA, 92614; tel (949) 251-0455; fax (949) 251-0465; web site www.carlson-dc.com
Vice Pres., Mktg–Tom Ryan
Industry: Architects/Engineers (Includes Design/Construction Firms)

Carnfeldt America
PO Box 387, Fort Atkinson, WI, 53538; tel (920) 563-7279; fax (920) 563-4868; e-mail erin@carnfeldt.com; web site www.carnfeldt.com
Dir., Sales/Mktg.–Erin Hynum
Industry: Processors: Film & Paper

Cascade Corp.
PO Box 20187, Portland, OR, 97294-0187; tel (503) 669-6300; fax (800) 693-3768; web site www.cascorp.com
Chrmn.–C. Calvert Knudson
Pres./CEO–Robert C. Warren
Sr. Vice Pres.-Finance/CFO–Andy Anderson
Vice Pres., HR–Greg Anderson
Mgr.,Cust. Srvs–Todd Finney
Mgr., Customer Info Serv.–Eric Fioler
Industry: Material Handling Equipment: Truck Loaders; Paper Handeling Equipment;

Catalyst Paper Corp.
3600 Lysander Ln., 2nd Fl., Richmond, BC, V7B 1C3, Canada; tel (604) 247-4400; fax (604) 247-0512; e-mail contactus@catalystpaper.com; web site www.catalystpaper.com
President & CEO–Kevin J. Clarke
Pres.–Richard Garneau

Catalyst Paper (USA), Inc.
2101 4th Ave., Ste. 1950, Seattle, WA, 98121-2312; tel (206) 838-2070; fax (206) 838-2071; web site www.catalystpaper.com
Vice Pres./Gen. Mgr. Directory Paper–Paul Gordon
Sr. Vice Pres. Sales/Mktg.–Tom Crowley
Vice Pres./Gen. Mgr. Newsprint/ Int'l–Jim Bayles
Vice Pres./Gen. Mgr. Speciality Papers–Matt Stapleton
Dir., Mktg.–Stuart Allan
Industry: Newsprint; Paper: Coated Groundwood Offset; Paper: Groundwood Specialties; Paper: Specialty Printing Paper;

Celebro
151 W. Fourth St., Ste. 201, Cincinnati, OH, 45202, USA; tel (513) 665-3777; fax (513) 241-7219; e-mail info@celebro.com; web site www.gmti.com
Pres./CEO–Steve Fuschetti
Vice Pres., Celebro Opns.–Tom Foster
Dir., Implementation Servs.–Michael Hibert
Industry: Computers: Hardware & Software Integrators; Electronic Ad Delivery; Software: Advertising (Includes Display; Classified); Software: Electronic Data Interchange

Cenosis
4435 St. Martin Blvd. W., Laval, QC, H7T 1C6, Canada; tel (450) 682-8170; fax (450) 682-7104; e-mail info@cenosis.com; web site www.cenosis.com
Pres.–Jean Louis Bouthillette
Vice Pres., Bus. Devel.–Ted Markle
Sr. Analyst–Robert Parenteau
Industry: Software: Advertising (Includes Display; Classified); Software: Editorial; Software: Electronic Data Interchange; Software: Pagination/Layout;

Central Graphics
1302 Enterprise Dr., Romeoville, IL, 60446-1016; tel (630) 759-1696; fax (630) 759-1792; e-mail cgi@cgipressparts.com
Pres.–Jim Crivellone
Sales/Opns. Mgr.–Pat Murphy
Industry: Belts, Belting, V-Belts; Copper Plating Drums; Cylinder Repair; Equipment Dealers (Used); Folder Knives; Pin Register Systems; Press Accessories, Parts & Supplies; Presses: Offset; Roller Grinding Services; Rollers: Dampening;

ChannelNet
100 Shoreline Hwy., Bldg. B, Ste. 300, Mill Valley, CA, 94941-3653, USA; tel (415) 332-4704; fax (415) 332-1635; e-mail info@channelnet.com; web site www.softad.com; www.channelnet.com
Founder/CEO–Paula George Tompkins
CFO–Kevin Kelly
Sr. Dir., Professional Servs.–Mike Behr
Industry: Consulting Services: Advertising; Software: Advertising (Includes Display; Classified);

Chapel Hill Manufacturing Co.
PO Box 208, Oreland, PA, 19075; tel (215) 884-3614; fax (215) 884-3617; e-mail sales@chapelhillmfg.com; web site www.chapelhillmfg.com
Pres./Vice Pres., Mktg.–John Seeburger
Vice Pres., Sales–J. Robert Seeburger
Industry: Dampening Systems

Chemetron Fire Systems
4801 Southwick Dr., 3rd Fl., Matteson, IL, 60443; tel (708) 748-1503; fax (708) 748-2847; e-mail info@chemetron.com; web site www.chemetron.com
Mgr.–John Powers
Industry: Architects/Engineers (Includes Design/Construction Firms); Fire Protection; System Installations; System Integration Services; Telecommunications;

Chemical Management Technology, Inc.
3035 Bravo Ct., Orange Park, FL, 32065; tel (904) 276-3737; fax (904) 272-7751; e-mail 76103.1355@compuserve.com; web site www.cmt-enviro-serv.com
Pres.–Chuck Freeman
Industry: Solvent Recovery Systems

Church Rickards, Whitlock & Co., Inc.
10001 Roosevelt Rd., Westchester, IL, 60154; tel (708) 345-7500; fax (708) 345-1166; e-mail crwfred@aol.com
Pres.–Fred C. Hohnke
Regl. Mgr.–Daniel Demjanik
Reg. Mgr.–Tim Solt
Industry: Consulting Services: Circulation; Consulting Services: Human Resources; Insurance;

Circulation Development, Inc.
po box 6, wentzville, MO, 63385-0006, usa; tel (800) 247-2338; fax (800) 400-4453; e-mail increase@circulation.net; web site www.circulation.net
Chrmn.–Bill Wesa
Pres.–Jim Oden
Vice Pres.–Rob Oden
Mktg. Dir.–Carmen Salvati
Dir., Info. Servs.–David Wesa
Industry: Consulting Services: Circulation; Consulting Services: Marketing;

Circulation Solutions, Inc.
PO Box 1575, Auburn, AL, 36831; tel (334) 826-6847; fax (334) 826-6952; e-mail van@circulationsolutions.com; web site www.circulationsolutions.com
Pres.–Van Dozier
Sec.–Wyndol Smith
Industry: Circulation Equipment & Supplies; Consulting Services: Circulation; Newspaper Marketing;

Circulation III Promotions, Inc.
2636 Walnut Hill Ln., Ste. 257, Dallas, TX, 75229; tel (214) 352-1123; fax (214) 956-0876; e-mail jdinan@circulationiii.com; web site www.circulationiii.com
Owner/Pres.–John Dinan
Industry: Consulting Services: Circulation

Citiplate, Inc.
1600 Stewart Ave., Westbury, NY, 11590; tel (516) 484-2000; fax (516) 484-9778; e-mail mreynolds@citiplate.com; web site www.citiplate.com
Customer Serv. Mgr.–Marie Reynolds
Adv. Customer Info Serv.–Tony Morella
Industry: Chemicals: Plate Processing; Offset Chemicals & Supplies; Platemakers: Offset (Conventional); Plates: Offset (Conventional);

Claritas
9276 Scranton Rd., Ste. 300, San Diego, CA, 92121-7700; tel (858) 677-9634; fax (858) 550-5800; web site www.claritas.com
Dir., Public Rel.–Stephen Moore
Industry: Consulting Services: Marketing; Market Research; Newspaper Marketing;

Clark-Cutler-McDermoth Co. (Air-Loc Div.)
PO Box 260, Franklin, MA, 02038; tel (508) 528-0022; fax (508) 528-7555; e-mail airiloc@ma.ultranet.com; web site www.airloc.com
Vice Pres., Mktg.–James Imoni
Industry: Dampening Systems

Clark Material Handling Co.
700 Enterprise Dr., Lexington, KY, 40510; tel (859) 422-6400; fax (859) 422-6521 (Sales); web site www.clarkmhc.com
Pres.–Dennis Lawrence
Dir., HR–Sherry Myers

Industry: Equipment Dealers (New); Equipment Dealers (Used); Lift Trucks; Material Handling Equipment: Palletizing Machines; Material Handling Equipment: Pallets & Palletizers; Material Handling Equipment: Truck Loaders; Material Handling Equipment: Vehicle Loading;

Classifieds Plus, Inc.
6400 Main St., Williamsville, NY, 14221-5803, USA; tel (716) 250-6884; fax (716) 634-0574; web site www.classifiedsplus.com
CEO–Michael Stanek
Vice Pres., Sales–Richard J. Saunders
Executive Director–Dominick Bordonaro
Client Partnerships–Debra Chase
Industry: Consulting Services: Advertising

Clipper Belt Lacer Co.
1995 Oak Industrial Dr. NE, Grand Rapids, MI, 49505; tel (616) 459-3196; fax (616) 459-4976; web site www.flexco.com
Gen. Mgr.–Nancy Ayres
Treasurer–Bro Ballentine
Sales Mgr.–Dick Reynolds
Mktg. Mgr.–John H. Meulenberg
Pdct. Mgr.–Beth Miller
Industry: Belts, Belting, V-Belts; Cutting Tools;

Coast Graphic Supply
4721 Market St., Ste. 101, Ventura, CA, 93003; tel (805) 642-5585; fax (805) 642-2236; e-mail coastgraphic@earthlink.net; web site www.coastgraphicsupply.com
Pres.–James Cagnina
Industry: Chemicals: Plate Processing; Chemicals: Pressroom; Composing Room Equipment & Supplies; Densitometers; Film & Paper: Contact; Film & Paper: Phototypesetting;

Cold Jet, Inc.
9105 Milliken Ave., Rancho Cucamonga, CA, 91730-5509; tel (909) 481-6444; fax (909) 980-3885; e-mail info@coldjet.com; web site www.coldjet.com; www.dryiceblasting.com
Pres./CEO–Gene Cooke
Industry: Cleaners & Solvents

ColorVision, Inc.
5 Princess Rd., Lawrenceville, NJ, 08648; tel (609) 895-7430; fax (609) 895-8110; e-mail info@colovision.com; web site www.datacolor.com
Vice Pres. Mktg./Sales–Brian Levey
Industry: Software: Electronic Data Interchange

Colter Peterson
2000 Des Moines St., Des Moines, IA, 50317; tel (515) 276-4528; fax (515) 276-8324; e-mail sales@colterpeterson.com; web site www.colterpeterson.com
Mktg. Mgr.–Vince Payne
Industry: Cutters & Trimmers

Commodity Resource & Environment
116 E. Prospect Ave., Burbank, CA, 91502; tel (818) 843-2811; fax (818) 843-2862; e-mail info@creweb.com; web site www.creweb.com
Pres.–Larry Dewitt
Industry: Hazardous Waste Disposal Services; Silver Recovery

Communications Management Service, Inc.
30 Nutmeg Dr., Trumbull, CT, 06611; tel (203) 377-3000; fax (203) 377-2632; e-mail dan@bargainnews.com; web site www.bargainnews.com
Pres.–John F. Roy
Vice Pres.–Daniel F. Rindos
New Media Sales Dir.–Daniel Firoa
Industry: Consulting Services: Circulation; Consulting Services: Marketing; Newspaper Marketing;

Communications Service Co.
PO Box 643, Antioch, IL, 60002-0643; tel (847) 395-1231; fax (847) 395-1231
Pres.–Mark A. Mehaffey
Industry: Consulting Services: Advertising; Consulting Services: Circulation; ;

ComPlan Associates
3451 Fawnrun Dr., Cincinnati, OH, 45241-3856; tel (513) 769-1446
–Patricia Myers
–Alan FlahertyPrincipals
Industry: Consulting Services: Advertising; Consulting Services: Circulation; Consulting Services: Computer; Consulting Services: Editorial; Consulting Services: Equipment; Consulting Services: Financial; Consulting Services: Marketing; Consulting Services: Production;

Computer Talk Technology, Inc.
225 E. Beaver Creek Rd., Ste. 310, Richmond Hill, ON, L4B 3P4, Canada; tel (905) 882-5000; fax (905) 882-5501; e-mail info@icescape.com; web site www.computer-talk.com
Mktg. Dir.–Robert Moore
Pres./CEO–Mandle Cheung
Mktg. Mgr.–Lindsay Aitken
Industry: Software: Electronic Data Interchange; System Integration Services;

Computer Tree
1760 Jonestown Rd., Ste. 200, Winston-Salem, NC, 27103, USA; tel (336) 768-9820; fax (336) 760-3309; e-mail sales@computertree.com; bobyoungjr@computertree.com; web site http://www.computertree.com/index.html
Pres.–Bob Young
Vice President–Joe Young
Industry: Computers: Hardware & Software Integrators; Computers: Local Area Network (LANS); Consulting Services: Computer; Imagesetters; Pagination Systems; Publishing Systems; Software: Advertising (Includes Display; Classified); System Installations; System Integration Services; Training: Keyboard Operation;

Computerease Software, Inc.
379 Amherst St., Ste. 208, Nashua, NH, 03063; tel (603) 578-9780; fax (603) 598-3948; e-mail cez_berg@compuserve.com
Pres.–Carl Berg
Vice Pres.–Carol Berg
Industry: Input & Editing Systems; Publishing Systems; Software: Advertising (Includes Display; Classified); Software: Editorial; Software: Electronic Data Interchange; Software: Pagination/Layout; Telecommunications; Software: Electronic Data Interchange; System Integration Services;

Comtel Instruments Co.
39830 Grand River Ave., Ste. B1-A, Novi, MI, 48375; tel (248) 888-4730; fax (248) 888-4743; e-mail comtelcorp@comtel.com; web site www.comtel.com
Industry: Software: Electronic Data Interchange

Conley Publishing Systems
PO Box 478, Beaver Dam, WI, 53916; tel (920) 887-3731; fax (920) 887-0439; e-mail concept@conleynet.com; web site www.conleynet.com
Pres.–James E. Conley
Industry: Input & Editing Systems; Pagination Systems; Phototypesetting Fonts; Publishing Systems; Software: Advertising (Includes Display; Classified); Software: Design/Graphics; Software: Editorial; Software: Pagination/Layout; Typesetting Programs;

Consolidated Storage Cos.
225 Main St., Tatamy, PA, 18085-7059; tel 800-323-0801; fax 888-859-2121; e-mail info@equipto.com; web site www.equipto.com; www.consolidatedstoragecompanies.com
President–Robert Ammerman
Mktg. Lead–Brian Moretz
Industry: Cabinets; Computers: Storage Devices; Consulting Services: Equipment; Consulting Services: Ergonomics; Files, Storage; Storage Retrieval Systems

Continental Products
PO Box 760, Mexico, MO, 65265; tel (573) 581-4128; fax (573) 581-4461; e-mail mail@continentalproducts.com; web site www.continentalproducts.com
Vice Pres., Sales/Mktg.–Vince Fuemmeler
Mgr., Sales–Don Price
Industry: Circulation Equipment & Supplies; Newspaper Bags; Tubes, Racks (Includes Racks: Motor Route Tubes);

Continental Solid State Services, Inc.
930 Linden Ave., San Francisco, CA, 94080; tel N/A

Control Engineering Co.
2306 Newport Blvd., Costa Mesa, CA, 92627; tel (714) 535-5590; fax (714) 535-0625; e-mail ccarrillo@controlengineering.com; web site www.controlengineering.com
Engineering Mgr.–Carlos Carrillo
Industry: Cabinets; Conveyors; Material Handling Equipment: Automatic Guided Vehicles; Material Handling Equipment: Truck Loaders; Newsprint Handeling Equipment; Paper Handeling Equipment;

Controls Group, Inc.
5060 27th Ave., Rockford, IL, 61109-1711; tel (815) 227-0027; fax (815) 227-0025; web site www.controlsgroupinc.com
Pres.–Richard Atwater
Vice Pres., Sales–Darrell Hinson
Vice Pres.–Mike Hatlak
Industry: Ink Controls, Computerized; Ink Pumping Systems;

Craftsman Newspaper Production Systems
5205 S. County Rd. 25A, Ste. C, Tipp City, OH, 45371; tel (937) 669-2255; fax (937) 669-2266; e-mail perrmill@juno.com; web site www.craftsmansystems.com
Pres.–Richard Higgins
Vice Pres.–Roger Miller
Sales Mgr.–Jim Davis
Industry: Conveyors; Inserting Equipment (Includes Stuffing Machines); Material Handling Equipment: Palletizing Machines;

Craftsmen Machinery Co., Inc.
PO Box 38, Millis, MA, 02054; tel (508) 376-2001; fax (508) 376-2003
Pres./Chief Exec. Officer–Sherwin Marks
Industry: Core Cutters, Restorers, Rounders; Dark Room Equipment; Densitometers; Folder Knives; Gauges, Measuring; Presses: Offset;

Creative Brilliance Advertising, Marketing & Public Relation
PO Box 44237, Madison, WI, 53744; tel (608) 827-6483
Pres.–Naomi K. Shapiro
Industry: Consulting Services: Advertising; Consulting Services: Circulation; Training: Sales & Marketing;

Creative Circle Media Solutions
52 Amaral Street, East Providence, RI, 02915, USA; tel (401) 272-1122; fax (401) 272-1150; e-mail info@creativecirclemedia.com; web site www.creativecirclemedia.com; www.adqic.com
President & CEO–Bill Ostendorf
Design director–Lynn Rognsvoog
IT director–Tim Benson
Industry: Software: Advertising (Includes Display; Classified)

Creative House Print Media Consultants
PO Box 160, Sheldon, IA, 51201-0160, United State; tel (712) 324-5347; fax (712) 324-2345; e-mail pww@iowainformation.com
Pres.–Peter W. Wagner
Vice Pres.–Connie Wagner
Sec./Treasurer–Jeff Wagner
Industry: Consulting Services: Advertising; Consulting Services: Circulation; Consulting Services: Computer; Consulting Services: Editorial; Consulting Services: Financial; Consulting Services: Marketing; Consulting Services: Production;

Creo
3 Federal St., Billerica, MA, 01821; tel (978) 439-7000; fax (781) 275-3430; web site www.creo.com
Pres., Creo Americas–Larry Letteney
CEO–Amos Michelson
Vice Pres.-HR–Darcy O'Grady
Vice Pres., Global Mktg.–Boudewijn Neijens
Industry: Color Proofing; Color Seperation Scanners; Computers: Hardware & Software Integrators;

Cribb, Greene & Associates
104 E. Main St., Ste. 402, Bozeman, MT, 59715; tel (406) 586-6621; fax (406) 586-6774; e-mail jcribb@cribb.com; web site www.cribb.com
MD.–John T. Cribb
MD.–Gary Greene
Market Analyst–Bill Wilke
Industry: Brokers & Appraisers

Cryogenesis (A Div. of WM & C Services, Inc.)
2140 Scranton Rd., Cleveland, OH, 44113; tel (216) 696-8797; fax (216) 696-8794; e-mail cryogen@cryogenesis-usa.com; web site www.cryogenesis-usa.com
Pres.–James Becker
Vice Pres., Sales–John R. Whalen
Industry: Cleaners & Solvents; Roll Cleaning Equipment;

Cyber Age Technologies
5440 Cherokee Ave., Ste. 200, Alexandria, VA, 22312; tel (703) 750-1740; fax (703) 750-1710; e-mail info@cyberagetech.com; web site www.cyberagetech.com
Pres.–Marc Beaudoin
Industry: Consulting Services: Computer; Consulting Services: Editorial; Consulting Services: Equipment;

Cygnet Storage Solutions, Inc.
2560 Junction Ave., San Jose, CA, 95134-1902; tel (800) 7-CYGNET; fax (408) 954-9017; e-mail waynea@cygnet.com
Vice Pres., Mktg.–Wayne Augsburger
Industry: Archiving Systems; Disk Drive Sales/Repair; Files, Storage; Library Retrieval Systems; Software: Asset Management; Storage Retrieval Systems;

Cymbolic Sciences International Ltd.
13231 Delf Pl., Ste.501, Richmond, BC, V6V 2C3, Canada; tel (604) 273-7730; fax (604) 273-2775; e-mail ge@cymbolic.com; web site www.cymbolic.com
Pres.–Dan Whittle
Mktg. Dir.–Neena Rahemtulla
Industry: Platemakers: Offset (Computer to Plate)

D

DAC Systems
4 Armstrong Park Rd., Bldg II, Shelton, CT, 06484; tel (203) 924-7000; fax (203) 944-1618; e-mail sales@dacsystems.com; web site www.dacsystems.com
Pres.–Mark Nickson
Industry: Audiotex Systems & Software; Facsimilie/Fax Transmission Systems; Integrated Fax Servers; Optical Character Recognition (OCR); Speech Recognition; Telecommunications;

DM Graphics System
31 W. 331 Schoger Dr., Naperville, IL, 60564-4652; tel (630) 851-8386; fax (630) 851-4197
Pres.–David Mukenschnabl
Industry: Consulting Services: Equipment; Cylinder Repair; Equipment Dealers (New); Equipment Dealers (Used); Erectors & Riggers; Press Rebuilding; Press Repairs; Presses: Offset; Training: Press Operation & Maintenance; Web Press - Special Equipment

D & R Engineering
12693 Crenshaw Blvd., Hawthorne, CA, 90250; tel (310) 676-4896; fax (310) 676-3420
Owner–Daws Waffer
Industry: Counting, Stacking, Bundling Machines; Gluing Systems; Web Cleaners; Web Offset Remoisturizers; Web Press - Special Equipment;

DYC Supply Co.
5740 Bayside Rd., Virginia Beach, VA, 23455; tel (800) 446-8240; fax (757) 486-5689; e-mail marcb@dynaric.com; web site www.dynaric.com
Pres.–Joseph Martinez
Asst. Mktg. Mgr.–Marc Banks
Industry: Blankets; Offset Blankets, Blanket Wash;

Daige Products, Inc.
1 Albertson Ave., Ste. 5, Albertson, NY, 11507; tel (516) 621-2100; fax (516) 621-1916; e-mail info@daige.com; web site www.daige.com
Pres.–Ike Harris
Industry: Adhesive Wax Coaters; Adhesives;

Dail Advertising Service
PO Box 10278, Goldsboro, NC, 27532, USA; tel (919) 736-0447; fax (919) 736-0483; e-mail dailadvertising@bellsouth.net
Nat'l Rep.–Annette W. Dail
Industry: Consulting Services: Advertising

Dan-Bar, Inc.
2440 Dinnen Ave., Orlando, FL, 32804-4206; tel (407) 292-0600; fax (407) 292-0602; e-mail dcmdanbar@aol.com; contact@danbarinc.com; web site www.danbarinc.com
Pres.–Dan Baratta
Industry: Automatic Plastic Bagging Equipment; Baling Machines; Collating Equipment; System Installations;

Danfoss Graham
PO Box 245041, Milwaukee, WI, 53223; tel (414) 355-8800; fax (414) 355-6117; web site www.danfoss.com
Pres.–Arnoldo Ricca
Industry: Drives & Controls; Motors;

Dario Designs, Inc.
29 Bartlett St., Marlborough, MA, 01752; tel (508) 877-4444; fax (508) 877-4474; e-mail dario@dariodesigns.com; web site www.dariodesigns.com
Pres.–Dario Dimare
Vice Pres.–David Ehrhardt
Industry: Architects/Engineers (Includes Design/Construction Firms)

Data Engineering Ltd.
Sorvaajankatu 13, Helsinki, N/A, 00880, Finland; tel 358 9 759 1988; fax 358 9 786 626; e-mail data@dataengineering.fi; web site www.dataengineering.fi
Mgr.–Marco Aueinen
Industry: Ink Controls, Computerized; Proofing Systems;

SAXOTECH Circulation
14900 Sweitzer Ln., Ste. 200, Laurel, MD, 20707; tel (301) 957-0100; fax (301) 957-0111; e-mail info@saxotech.com; web site www.saxotech.com
Pres.–Mark J. Ganslaw
Director of Ciculation–Daniel C. Martini
Industry: Computers: Hardware & Software Integrators; Computers: Laptop & Portable; Computers: Storage Devices; Consulting Services: Advertising; Consulting Services: Circulation; Consulting Services: Computer; Software: Advertising (Includes Display; Classified); Software: Circulation; Speech Recognition;

Datafest Technologies, Inc.
5961 S. Redwood Rd., Salt Lake City, UT, 84123-5261; tel (801) 261-4608; fax (801) 261-3857; e-mail sales@datafest.com; web site www.datafest.com
Pres.–Scott A. Clawson
Industry: Software: Advertising (Includes Display; Classified); Software: Business (Includes Administration/Accounting);

Day-Glo Color Corp.
4515 St. Clair Ave., Cleveland, OH, 44103; tel (216) 391-7070; fax (216) 391-7751; e-mail dayglo@dayglo.com; web site www.dayglo.com
Vice Pres., Sales–Mark Wright
Industry: Inks

Day International
15151 Prater Dr., Unit L, Covington, GA, 30014; tel (770) 787-5080; fax (770) 787-4589; web site www.rotadyne.com
Mgr., Customer Serv.–Rita Harper
Industry: Blanket Mounting and Bars

Day International
1333 N. Kirk Rd., Batavia, IL, 60510-1444; tel (630) 526-9903; fax (630) 526-9926
Industry: Chemicals: Pressroom; Chemicals: Roller Cleaning; Cleaners & Solvents; Dampening Systems; Offset Chemicals & Supplies; Offset Fountain Solutions; Offset Prevention-Materials & Equipment; Plate Cleaners; Press Accessories, Parts & Supplies; Rollers: Dampening;

Dean Machinery International, Inc.
6855 Shiloh Rd. E., Alpharetta, GA, 30005; tel (678) 947-8550; fax (678) 947-8554; e-mail sales@deanmachinery.com; web site www.deanmachinery.com
Pres.–Walter Dean
Industry: Adhesive Wax Coaters; Brokers & Appraisers; Equipment Dealers (Used); Label Printing Machines; Presses: Flexographic; Presses: Offset; Presses: Rotogravure;

Decisionmark Corp.
818 Dows Rd. SE, Cedar Rapids, IA, 52403-7000; tel (319) 365-5597; fax (319) 365-5694; e-mail sales@decisionmark.com; web site www.decisionmark.com
Pres./CEO–Jack Perry
Vice Pres., Pdct. Devel.–Mick Rinehart
Vice Pres., Opns.–Herb Skoog
Industry: Software: Advertising (Includes Display; Classified); Software: Circulation; Software: Editorial;

Dee-Paul Graphic Services
12629 Crenshaw Blvd., Hawthorne, CA, 90250; tel (310) 676-2806; fax (310) 676-3420
Pres.–Diana Howard
Nat'l Sales Mgr.–Art Contreras

Dematics
507 Plymouth Ave. NE, Grand Rapids, MI, 49505; tel (616) 913-7700; fax (616) 913-7701; web site www.dematic.us
Pres.–John Baysore
Vice Pres., Field Sales–S. Buccella
Mgr., Purchasing–R. Klaasen
Industry: Conveyors; Material Handling Equipment: Automatic Guided Vehicles; Material Handling Equipment: Truck Loaders;

Denex, Inc.
135 W. Illionis Ave., Southern Pines, NC, 28387; tel (910) 692-5463; fax (910) 222-3100; e-mail gcarroll@denexinc.com; web site www.denex.se; www.denex.com
Pres.–Gary J. Carroll
Industry: Laser Printers

Descartes Systems Group
120 Randall Dr., Waterloo, ON, N2V 1C6, Canada; tel (519) 746-8110; fax (519) 747-0082; e-mail info@descartes.com; web site www.descartes.com
CEO–Arthur Mesher
CFO–Stephanie Ratza
Exec. Vice Pres., Solutions/Servs.–Chris Jones
Exec. Vice Pres., Cor. Devel./Gen. Counsel–Scott J. Pagan
Exec. Vice Pres., Global Field Opns.–Edward J. Ryan
Exec. Vice Pres., Information Servs.–Raimond Diederik
Industry: Computers: Hardware & Software Integrators

Design Science, Inc.
140 Pine Ave., 4th Fl., Long Beach, CA, 90802; tel (562) 432-2920; fax (562) 432-2857; e-mail sales@dessci.com; web site www.dessci.com
Pres.–Paul Topping
Industry: Input & Editing Systems; Type, Fonts;

DeskNet, Inc.
83 Maiden Ln., 9th Fl., New York, NY, 10038; tel (212) 343-9800; fax (212) 343-9857; web site www.desknetinc.com
Pres.–Brian Fitzsimons
Vice Pres.-Mktg./Sales–Thomas C. Triumph
Industry: Software: Asset Management; Software: Design/Graphics; Software: Editorial; Software: Electronic Data Interchange; Software: Pagination/Layout; Software: Workflow Management/Tracking; System Integration Services;

Devin
5051 Peachtree Corners Cir., Norcross, GA, 30092; tel (770) 239-4000; fax (770) 239-4444; web site www.devine.com
Chrmn./CEO–Andrew Filipowski
Vice Pres./Gen. Mgr.–Joe Forgione
Industry: Telecommunications

Devlin Electronics Ltd.
D1 Grafton Way, Basingstoke, Basingstoke, N/A, RG22 6HZ, United Kingdom; tel +44 1256 467 367; fax +44 1256 840 048; e-mail sales@devlin.co.uk; web site www.devlin.co.uk
Mng. Dir.–Martin Baker
Industry: Composing Room Equipment & Supplies; Interfaces;

A.B. Dick Co.
7400 Caldwell Ave., Niles, IL, 60714; tel (800) 752-5139; fax (847) 647-6940 (Sales/Mktg.); web site www.abdick.com
Pres./CEO–Brian Long
COO–Ken Newton
Industry: Platemakers: Offset (Computer to Plate); Plates: Offset (Computer to Plate); Press Accessories, Parts & Supplies; Press Repairs; Presses: Offset; Processors: Film & Paper; Proofing Systems; Punching Equipment; Training: Post Press; Training: Pre Press;

Dienamic Microprint
71 King St., Ste.3024, Saint Catharines, ON, L2R 3H7, Canada; tel (905) 688-5593; fax (905) 688-6132; e-mail microprint@vaxxine.com; web site www.dienamicmis.com
Pres.–Mark Porter
Vice Pres.-Finance–Lori Walsh
Industry: Mailroom Systems & Equipment

Digital Collections
312 Elm Street, 20th Floor, Cincinnati, OH, 45202, USA; tel (800) 801-3771; fax (513) 768-8958; e-mail gmti-info@gmti.gannett.com; web site www.gmti.com
Pres./CEO–Steve Fuschetti
Vice Pres., Installations/Support–Bill Mahlock
Dir., Sales & Marketing–Michael Tucker
Industry: Archiving Systems; Computers: Hardware & Software Integrators; Library Retrieval Systems; Photo Archiving; Software: Asset Management; Storage Retrieval Systems; System Installations; System Integration Services;

Digital Information Group
PO Box 110235, Stamford, CT, 06911-0235; tel (203) 840-0045; e-mail infoib@aol.com
Pub.–Jeff Silverstein
Industry: Consulting Services: Computer; Consulting Services: Financial;

Digital Technology International
2611 Hamline Ave. N., Ste. 100, Saint Paul, MN, 55113; tel (651) 639-0662; fax (651) 639-0306; e-mail info@dtint.com; web site www.dtint.com
Vice president, marketing–Steve Nilan
Exec. Vice Pres.–Bud DePietto
Vice Pres., Opns.–Mary Olson
Industry: Software: Advertising (Includes Display; Classified); Software: Business (Includes Administration/Accounting); Software: Circulation;

Digital Technology International
1180 N. Mountain Springs Pkwy., Springville, UT, 84663; tel (801) 853-5000; e-mail info@dtint.com; web site www.dtint.com
Pres./CEO–Don Oldham
COO–Jeff Carpenter
Industry: Software: Advertising (Includes Display; Classified); Software: Business (Includes Administration/Accounting); Software: Pagination/Layout;

Digital Technology International
1180 N. Mountain Springs Pkwy., Springville, UT, 84663; tel (801) 853-5000; fax (801) 853-5001; e-mail dtinfo@dtint.com; web site www.dtint.com
Pres./COO–Jeff Carpenter
CEO–Don Oldham
CFO–Geoff Walker
Vice Chrmn.–Levor Oldham
Technical Dir.–Jim Knudsen
Industry: Archiving Systems; Software: Advertising (Includes Display; Classified); Software: Asset Management; Software: Business (Includes Administration/Accounting); Software: Circulation; Software: Design/Graphics; Software: Editorial; Software: Pagination/Layout; System Integration Services

Direct Reproduction Corp.
34 Macquesten Pkwy. S., Mount Vernon, NY, 10550-1704; tel (914) 665-6515; fax (914) 665-6518; e-mail drcmap@aol.com
Pres.–Ronald L. Russo
Industry: Color Proofing; Color Registration; Masking Materials; Offset Negative Masking Paper; Prepress Color Proofing Systems;

Dirks, Van Essen & Murray
119 E. Marcy St., Ste. 100, Santa Fe, NM, 87501-2902; tel (505) 820-2700; fax (505) 820-2900; web site www.dirksvanessen.com
Pres.–Owen D. Van Essen
Exec. Vice Pres.–Philip W. Murray
Vice Pres.–Sara April
Sr. Vice Pres.–James H. Oldershaw
Industry: Brokers & Appraisers; Consulting Services: Financial;

Diversified Photo/Graphics Supply
333 W. Alondra Blvd., Unit C, Gardena, CA, 90248; tel (800) 544-1609; fax (310) 328-8518; e-mail orders@diversifiedimaging.net; web site www.diversifiedimaging.net
Pres.–Darrell Benton
Opns. Mgr.–Bruce Benton
Industry: Automatic Film Processors; Cameras & Accessories; Chemicals: Photographic; Enlargers (Photographic); Equipment Dealers (New); Film & Paper: Filters (Photographic); Inks; Lenses (Camera); Photography: Digital/Electronic Cameras; Processors: Film & Paper;

Domino Amjet, Inc.
1290 Lakeside Dr., Gurnee, IL, 60031-2400; tel (847) 244-2501; fax (847) 244-1421; e-mail marketing@dominoamjet.com; web site www.domino-printing.com
Industry: Addressing Machines; Label Printing Machines; Laser Printers; Numbering Machines

Domtar, Inc.
395 de Maisonneuve Blvd. W., Montreal, QC, H3A 1L6, Canada; tel (514) 848-5400; fax (514) 848-6878; web site www.domtar.com
Chrmn.–Brian Levitt
Pres./CEO–Raymond Royer
Industry: Paper: Specialty Printing Paper

Douthitt Corp.
245 Adair St., Detroit, MI, 48207-4287; tel (313) 259-1565; fax (313) 259-6806; e-mail em@douthittcorp.com; web site www.douthittcorp.com

Int'l Sales–Mark W. Diehl
Industry: Controls: Exposure; Exposure Lamps; Layout Tables, Light Tables & Workstations; Light Integrators; Offset Plate-Making Service & Equipment; Pin Register Systems; Plate Exposure Units; Platemakers: Flexographic (Traditional); Platemakers: Offset (Computer to Plate); Vacuum Frames;

Dover Diversified
2607 N. Grandview Blvd., Ste. 105, Unknown, WI, 99999; tel N/A

Dover Technologies
Somewhere in NYC, New York, NY, 66666; tel N/A

The Dow Chemical Co.
2030 Dow Ctr., Midland, MI, 48674; tel (989) 636-1000; fax (989) 636-3518; e-mail dowmedia.relations@dow.com; web site www.dow.com
Chrmn./Pres./CEO–Andrew Liveris
Vice Pres., Global Pub. Aff.–Matt Davis
Vice Pres./Treasurer–Fernando Ruiz
Industry: Adhesives; Cleaners & Solvents;

Drake Communications, Inc.
2435 Squire Pl., Ste. 400, Dallas, TX, 75234; tel (972) 243-2500; fax (972) 247-2872
Pres.–Cecil Drake
Vice Pres.–L.G. Drake
Industry: Telecommunications

E.I. du Pont de Nemours & Co.
1007 Market St., Wilmington, DE, 19898-0001; tel (302) 774-1000; fax (302) 355-4013; e-mail contactus@dupont.com; web site www2.dupont.com
Chrmn./Pres./CEO–Ellen J. Kullman
Exec., Vice Pres./CFO–Jeffrey L. Keefer
Exec. Vice Pres./Chief Innovation Officer–Thomas M. Connelly
Exec. Vice Pres./COO–Richard R. Goodmanson
Exec. Vice Pres./Human Resources–W. Donald Johnson
Grp. Vice Pres., Chief Mktg./Sales Officer–Diane H. Gulyas
Vice Pres./Controller–Barry J. Niziolek
Vice Pres., DuPont Sales Effectiveness–Harry Parker
Vice Pres./Treasurer–Susan M. Stalnecker
Vice Pres./CMO/Chief Sales Officer–Cynthia C. Green
Industry: Color Analyzers; Color Proofing; Color Registration; Color Seperation Scanners; Color Viewing Equipment; Controls: Register; Phototypesetting Interface Equipment; Prepress Color Proofing Systems; Press Control Systems;

Dunhill International List Co., Inc.
6400 Congress Ave #1750, Boca Raton, FL, 33487, USA; tel (561) 998-7800; fax (561) 998-7880; e-mail cindy@dunhills.com; web site www.dunhills.com
Pres.–Robert Dunhill
Vice Pres.–Candy Dunhill
Vice Pres.–Cindy Dunhill
Industry: Mailing List Compiler

William Dunkerley Publishing Consultant
275 Batterson Dr., New Britain, CT, 06053; tel (860) 827-8896; fax (508) 507-3021; e-mail wdpc@publishinghelp.com; web site www.publishinghelp.com/consultants
Consultant–William Dunkerley
Industry: Consulting Services: Advertising; Consulting Services: Editorial; Consulting Services: Financial; Consulting Services: Marketing; Market Research

Dunning Photo Equipment, Inc.
605 W. Needles St., Bixby, OK, 74008; tel (918) 366-4917; fax (918) 366-4918; e-mail ernie@dunningphoto.com; web site www.dunningphoto.com
Pres.–Ernie Dunning
Industry: Dark Room Equipment; Processors: Film & Paper;

Duostat Co. (Affiliated with VGC Corp.)
Three Luger Rd., Denville, NJ, 07834; tel (800) 524-2140; fax (973) 586-2585; web site www.graphline.com
CEO/Pres.–Michael Ostroff
Exec. Vice Pres.–Ray Domis
Sales Mgr.–Bob Gibson
Industry: Chemicals: Pressroom; Color Proofing; Color Seperation Scanners; Computers: Hardware & Software Integrators; Dampening Systems; Densitometers; Equipment Dealers (New); Film & Paper: Film Processing Machines; Laser Printers; Layout Tables, Light Tables & Workstations;

Dynalith, Inc.
PO Box 440, Easton, MD, 21601; tel (410) 822-4400; fax (410) 820-8649
Comptroller–Christy Brinsfield
Mgr., Sales–Lila Simmons
Nat'l Sales–Connie Prue
Newspaper Sales–Connie Coughenour
Industry: Chemicals: Plate Processing; Environmental Control Systems; Equipment Dealers (New); Film & Paper: Filters (Photographic); Offset Chemicals & Supplies; Plate Exposure Units; Plate Processors; Platemakers: Offset (Conventional); Plates: Offset (Computer to Plate); Plates: Offset (Conventional)

Dynaric, Inc.
5740 Bayside Rd., Virginia Beach, VA, 23455; tel (800) 526-0827; fax (757) 363-8016; web site www.dynaric.com
Pres.–Joseph Martinez
Asst. Mktg. Mgr.–Marc Banks

E

EAM-Mosca Corp.
675 Jaycee Dr., Valmont Industrial Pk., Hazle Township, PA, 18202-1155; tel (570) 459-3426; fax (570) 455-2442; e-mail info@eammosca.com; web site www.eammosca.com
Pres.–Ralph Morini
Sales Admin.–Pam Kuzmak
Vice President, Sales–Edward Martin
Sales Mgr.–Randy Wright
Industry: Bundling and Tying Machines; Strapping Machines;

ECRM
554 Clark Rd., Tewksbury, MA, 01876, USA; tel (978) 851-0207; fax (978) 851-7016; e-mail sales@ecrm.com; web site www.ecrm.com
President&CEO–Richard Black
Industry: Imagesetters; Platemakers: Offset (Computer to Plate); Prepress Color Proofing Systems; Processors: Film & Paper; Proofing Systems;

e/Doc Systems
6949 Appling Farms Pkwy., Memphis, TN, 38133; tel (901) 367-9500; fax (901) 367-9510; web site www.edocsystems.com
Pres.–Tom Pease
Industry: Facsimilie/Fax Transmission Systems; Laser Printers;

Earmark
1125 Dixwell Ave., Hamden, CT, 06514; tel (203) 777-2130; fax (203) 777-2886; e-mail staff@earmark.com; web site www.earmark.com
Pres.–Mitch Slater
Industry: Telecommunications

Eastman Kodak Co.
343 State St., Rochester, NY, 14650; tel (800) 698-3324; fax (585) 724-1089; web site www.kodak.com
Chrmn./CEO–Antonio Perez
Pres./COO–Philip J. Faraci
Exec. Vice Pres./CFO–Frank Sklarsky
Vice Pres., Global Logistics–Etienne Bourgeois
Vice Pres./Dir., Brand/Market Devel.–Claude H. Denker
Vice Pres./Chief Diversity Officer–Essie L. Calhoun
Vice Pres./Dir., Health/Safety/Environment–David Kiser
Dir., Cor. Media Rel.–Gerard Meuchner
Dir., Interactive Mktg./Convergence–Thomas Hoehn
Mgr., Film/Worldwide Strategic Prdct. Grp.–Larry Morgan
Industry: Cameras & Accessories; Film & Paper: Contact; Film & Paper: Filters (Photographic); Film & Paper: Phototypesetting; Microfilming; Offset Plate-Making Service & Equipment; Photo Proofing Papers; Plate Processors; Plates: Offset (Conventional); Processors: Film & Paper;

The Eclectic Co., Inc.
PO Box 277, Lebanon, OH, 45036; tel (937) 371-2920; e-mail eclectic@earthlink.net; web site www.eclectic-co.com
Pres.–Ronald W. Wantz
Industry: Ink De-Misting Systems; Ink Recovery Systems; Noise Control;

Eclipse Services (Div. of Quadrivium, Inc.)
41 Erna Court, Millbourne, PA, 19082, USA; tel 484-462-4300; e-mail sales@eclipseservices.com; web site www.eclipseservices.com
President–Jeanette MacNeille
Industry: Software: Advertising (Includes Display; Classified); Software: Business (Includes Administration/Accounting);

Edgil Associates, Inc.
6 Fortune Dr., Ste. 201, Billerica, MA, 01821, USA; tel (800) 457-9932; fax (978) 667-6050; e-mail sales@edgil.com; web site www.edgil.com
Dir., Sales–Sean Callahan

Editor & Publisher Magazine
200 W. Jackson Blvd., Ste. 2700, Chicago, IL, 60606-6943; tel (312) 583-5522; fax (312) 583-5504; e-mail edpub@editorandpublisher.com; web site www.editorandpublisher.com
Editor–Mark Fitzgerald

Editor & Publisher Magazine
770 Broadway, 7th Fl., New York, NY, 10003-9595; tel (646) 654-5000; e-mail edpub@editorandpublisher.com; web site www.editorandpublisher.com
Pub.–Charles McKeown
Ed.–Greg Mitchell
Industry: Trade Publications

Editorial Management Strategies
2073 Marshall Avenue , Saint Paul , MN, 55104, United States; tel (651) 210-4313; fax 651-602-9099; e-mail editstrat@aol.com
Pres.–Rita Stollman
Industry: Consulting Services: Editorial

EDIWISE
2227 S. Millway, Ste. 200, Mississauga, ON, L5L 3R6, Canada; tel (905) 820-3084; fax (905) 820-1498; e-mail ericw@ediwise.com; web site www.ediwise.comEric Wee
Pres.–Susan Sulman
Industry: Computers: Hardware & Software Integrators; Newsprint; Newsprint Handeling Equipment; Paper Handeling Equipment; Software: Asset Management; Software: Business (Includes Administration/Accounting); Software: Electronic Data Interchange

Egenolf Machine, Inc. (Egenolf Contracting & Rigging)
2916 Bluff Rd., Indianapolis, IN, 46225; tel (317) 787-5301; fax (317) 787-5018; e-mail egenolfma@aol.com
Pres.–James Egenolf
Industry: Press Rebuilding; Press Repairs;

eGIX, Inc.
11550 N. Meridian St., Ste. 500, Carmel, IN, 46032; tel (317) 816-5100; fax (317) 816-5115; e-mail voice-net@voicenet1.com; web site www.egix.com
Pres./CEO–Steve Johns
Vice Pres., Mktg.–Andy Gorogiani
Industry: Data Communication; System Integration Services; Telecommunications

ELAPLAN Buchholz GmbH & Co.
D-24217, Schonberg, N/A, N/A, Germany; tel +49 4344 309 158; fax +49 4344 309 172; e-mail hj@elaplan.de; web site www.elaplan.de
Mng. Dir.–Hans-Herbert Buchholz
Industry: Facsimilie/Fax Transmission Systems; Press Control Systems;

Elcorsy Technology, Inc.
4405 Poirier Blvd., Saint Laurent, QC, H4R 2A4, Canada; tel (888) 352-6779; fax (514) 337-0042; e-mail marketing@elcorsy.com; web site www.elcorsy.com
Vice Pres., Mktg.–Pierre Castegnier
Sales Rep.–Robert Jollet
Industry: Inks; Presses: DiLitho;

Electronic Specialists, Inc.
PO Box 389, Natick, MA, 01760-0389; tel (508) 655-1532; fax (508) 653-0268; e-mail esp@elect-spec.com; web site www.elect-spec.com
Pres.–F.J. Stifter
Vice Pres. Mktg.–A. Brown
Industry: Business Computers; Data Communication; Noise Control; Telecommunications;

Electronic Systems Engineering Co.
One Eseco Rd., Cushing, OK, 74023; tel (918) 225-1266; fax (918) 225-1284; e-mail wallace@eseco-speedmaster.com; web site www.eseco-speedmaster.com
CFO–Ed Handlin
Pres.–Wallace Hallman
Industry: Color Analyzers; Dark Room Equipment; Densitometers; Enlargers (Photographic); Film & Paper: Film Processing Machines;

Electronic Tele-Communications, Inc.
1915 MacArthur Rd., Waukesha, WI, 53188; tel (262) 542-5600; fax (262) 542-1524; web site www.etcia.com
Pres./CEO–Dean W. Danner
Vice Pres., Sales–Joseph A. Voight
Industry: Telecommunications

Engineering Products Co., Inc.
309 N. Meadow Ln., Plainfield, IL, 60544; tel (815) 726-8640; fax (815) 726-3253
Gen. Mgr.–Sharon A. Fazio
Vice Pres., Sales–Robert Herman
Industry: Conveyors

Ergotron, Inc.
1181 Trapp Rd., Saint Paul, MN, 55121-1248; tel (651) 681-7600; fax (651) 681-7715; e-mail sales@ergotron.com; web site www.ergotron.com
Pres.–Joe Hazzard
Industry: Cabinets; Computers: Local Area Network (LANS); Computers: Storage Devices; Consulting Services: Ergonomics;

Esko-Graphics
721 Crossroads Ct., Vandalia, OH, 45377; tel (937) 454-1721; fax (937) 454-1522; web site www.esko.com
Division Mgr., Printers Systems–Tony Wiley
Mktg. Commun. Mgr.–Carrie Woryk
Industry: Software: Design/Graphics

Esko-Graphics
721 Crossroads Ct., Vandalia, OH, 45377; tel (770) 427-5700; fax (937) 454-1522; e-mail infousa@eskographics.com; web site www.esko.com
Pres./CEO–Carsten Knudsen
Industry: Software: Design/Graphics

Essex Products Group
PO Box 307, Centerbrook, CT, 06409; tel (860) 767-7130; fax (860) 767-9137; e-mail sales@epg-inc.com; web site www.epg-inc.com
Pres.–Peter Griffin
Sales Mgr.–Peter Alfano
Industry: Ink Controls, Computerized

Ewert America Electronics Ltd.
869 Pickens Industrial Dr. NE, Ste. 12, Marietta, GA, 30062; tel (770) 421-0774; fax (770) 421-0731; e-mail ceickhoff@eaeusa.com; web site

www.eaeusa.com
CM, COO–Chris Eickhoff
Industry: Computers: Hardware & Software Integrators; Drives & Controls; Press Control Systems; Software: Workflow Management/Tracking; System Installations; System Integration Services; Training: Press Operation & Maintenance;

Extratec Corp.
5930 Muncaster Mill Rd., Rockville, MD, 20855; tel (301) 924-5150; fax (301) 924-5151; e-mail extratec@starpower.com
Pres.–Regis E. Finn
Industry: Environmental Control Systems

F

F & F Printing Ink
14-16 Delaware Dr., Salem, NH, 03079; tel (800) 824-4030; fax (603) 894-4384
Gen. Mgr.–Peter Vonfiglio
Comptroller–Kevin Price
Industry: Inks

FMC Technologies
400 Highpoint Dr., Chalfont, PA, 18914; tel (215) 822-4300; fax (215) 822-4553; e-mail sgv.sales@fmcti.com; web site www.fmcsgvs.com
Mktg. Mgr.–Mark Longacre
Industry: Material Handling Equipment: Automatic Guided Vehicles; Newsprint Handeling Equipment; Paper Handeling Equipment; Roll Handeling Equipment; Roll Preparation Equipment; Software: Workflow Management/Tracking; System Integration Services;

Fake Brains, Inc.
791 SouthPark Dr., Ste. 300, Littleton, CO, 80120-6401; tel (303) 791-3301; fax (303) 470-5218; e-mail sales@fakebrains.com; web site www.fakebrains.com
Pres.–Pat Pfeifer
Vice Pres./Sales Dir.–Lisa Pfeifer
Industry: Software: Advertising (Includes Display; Classified); Software: Business (Includes Administration/Accounting); Software: Circulation;

FANUC Robotics America, Inc.
3900 W. Hamlin Rd., Rochester Hills, MI, 48309; tel (248) 377-7000; fax (248) 377-7362; e-mail marketing@fanucrobotics.com; web site www.fanucrobotics.com
Sr. Mktg. Analyst–Cathy Powell
Industry: Conveyors; Material Handling Equipment: Palletizing Machines; Newsprint Handeling Equipment; Paper Handeling Equipment; Roll Handeling Equipment;

FELINS, Inc.
8306 W. Parkland Ct., Milwaukee, WI, 53223; tel (414) 355-7747; fax (414) 355-7559; e-mail salesteam@felins.com; web site www.felins.com
Industry: Bundling and Tying Machines; Mailroom Systems & Equipment; Strapping Machines;

Ferag Americas
3150 Brunswick Pike, Ste. 220, Lawrenceville, NJ, 08648; tel (856) 842-0600; fax (856) 842-0989; e-mail barry.evans@ferag-americas.com; web site www.ferag-americas.com
CEO & President–Joseph Colletti
Vice Pres.–Barry Evans
Industry: Bundling and Tying Machines; Conveyors; Delivery Equipment; Inserting Equipment (Includes Stuffing Machines); Storage Retrieval Systems;

Fiberweb
100 ISO Pkwy., Gray Court, SC, 29645; tel (864) 967-5600; fax (864) 962-2034; e-mail sdavis@fiberweb.com; web site www.fiberwebgraphics.com
Area Mgr.–Shawn Davis
Industry: Cleaners & Solvents; Plate Cleaners; Press Accessories, Parts & Supplies;

Fife Corporation
PO Box 26508, Oklahoma City, OK, 73126; tel (405) 755-1600; fax (405) 755-8425; e-mail fife@fife.com; web site www.fife.com
Mgr.–Marcel Hage
Industry: Visual Display Terminals; Web Break Detector; Web Guides; Web Press - Special Equipment;

Fincor Automation, Inc.
3750 E. Market St., York, PA, 17402-2765; tel (717) 751-4300; fax (717) 751-4263
Sales Mgr., Printing–Lee Hankey
Industry: Drives & Controls; Press Control Systems;

The Findlay Group
7870 W. 118th Pl., Overland Park, KS, 66210-2545, USA; tel (913) 491-4353; fax (913) 491-4353; e-mail efindlay@hotmail.com
Pres.–Ted Findlay
Industry: Consulting Services: Editorial

FKI Logistex
9301 Olive Blvd., Saint Louis, MO, 63132; tel (314) 993-4700; fax (314) 995-2400; web site www.fkilogistex.com
Industry: Material Handling Equipment: Palletizing Machines; Remanufactures Equipment

Fleming Enterprises
928 Blue Mound Rd., Fort Worth, TX, 76131; tel (817) 232-9575; fax (817) 847-6705; web site www.flemingenterprises.net
Owner–Jeff M. Fleming
Industry: Drives & Controls; Drying Systems; Equipment Dealers (Used); Erectors & Riggers; Feeder Press; Feeding, Folding, Delivery Equipment; Produciton Control Systems; Roll Handeling Equipment; Roller Grinders; Tension & Web Controls;

Flexo Printing Equipment Corp.
416 Hayward Ave., N., Oakdale, MN, 55128; tel (651) 731-9499; fax (651) 731-0525
Pres.–E.W. Lidell
Office Mgr.–Nancy Bailey
Industry: Conversion Equipment; Equipment Dealers (New); Flexogrpahic Press Conversion; Label Printing Machines; Presses: Flexographic; Rewinders;

Flexographic Technical Association
3920 Veterans Memorial Hwy Ste 9, Bohemia, NY, 11716-1074; tel (631) 737-6020; fax (631) 737-6813; e-mail membership@flexography.org; web site www.flexography.org
President–Mark Cisternino
Pub.–Robert Moran
Dir., Bus. Devel.–Jay Kaible
Industry: Consulting Services: Production; Flexogrpahic Press Conversion; Hazardous Waste Disposal Services; Trade Publications; Training: Post Press; Training: Pre Press; Training: Press Operation & Maintenance;

Flint Group
14909 N. Beck Rd., Plymouth, MI, 48170-2411; tel (734) 781-4600; fax (734) 781-4699; e-mail info@na.flintgrp.com; web site www.flintgrp.com
Pres., North Amer.–Bill Miller
Vice Pres./Gen. Mgr., News Ink/Pub. Div.–Mike Green
Vice Pres., Bus./Technical Devel.–Norm Harbin
Industry: Ink Pumping Systems; Ink Storage Tanks; Inks;

Flint Group.
PO Box 338, Dayton, OH, 45401-0338; tel (937) 224-4000; fax (937) 226-1466; e-mail info@day-intl.com; web site www.day-intl.com
Pres./CEO–Dennis R. Wolters
Regl. Dir., Sales–Bill Smals
Vice Pres.–Mike Neroni
Mktg. Mgr.–Denise Fourmier
Industry: Blanket Mounting and Bars; Chemicals: Pressroom; Chemicals: Roller Cleaning; Offset Blankets, Blanket Wash; Offset Chemicals & Supplies;

Fluorographic Services & CP Collier Technologies
622 Olive St., Santa Barbara, CA, 93101; tel (805) 962-7615; fax (805) 564-7829
Gen. Mgr.–Sandra N. Stites
Technical Rep.–Charles P. Collier
Industry: Masking Materials; 159;

Flynn Burner Corp.
PO Box 431, New Rochelle, NY, 10802-0431; tel (914) 636-1320; fax (914) 636-3751; web site www.flynnburner.com
Pres.–Julian Modzeleski
Vice Pres.–Dom Medina
Industry: Web Press - Special Equipment

Foley, Torregiani & Associates, Inc.
24 Ellery Ln., West Port, CT, 06880; tel (410) 992-5071; fax (203) 227-8225; web site www.northwoodpublishing.com
Pres.–James Torregiani
Vice Pres., Sales–Ray Mancini
Industry: Phototypesetting Interface Equipment; Software: Advertising (Includes Display; Classified); Software: Pagination/Layout; Software: Workflow Management/Tracking; Training: Pre Press;

Forrest Consulting
725 Kenilworth Ave., Glen Ellyn, IL, 60137-3805; tel (630) 730-9619; web site www.strategicbusinessleader.com
Pres.–Lee Crumbaugh
Industry: Consulting Services: Advertising; Consulting Services: Circulation; Consulting Services: Financial; Consulting Services: Marketing;

Fortec, Inc.
3831 W. Wells St., Milwaukee, WI, 53208-3167; tel (414) 344-1900; fax (414) 935-3309; e-mail email@fortec.com; web site www.fortec.com
Pres.–Jack Olson
Industry: Newspaper Dispensers (Mechanical/Electronic); Tubes, Racks (Includes Racks: Motor Route Tubes);

Fortfiber Corp., Paper Mill Packaging Grp.
1008 Trident St., Hanahan, SC, 29406; tel (888) 847-4448; fax (843) 746-2010; web site www.fortiwrap.com
Bus. Unit Leader–Michael Johnson
Industry: Grater Wrap-Roller Covering; Newsprint; Paper: Coated Groundwood Offset; Paper: Groundwood Specialties; Paper: Specialty Printing Paper; Shrink Wrapping Equipment;

Forum Architectural Services, LLC
Playhouse Sq., 1240 Huron Rd., Cleveland, OH, 44115-1702; tel (216) 363-0000; fax (216) 363-1990; e-mail info@forumarc.com; web site www.forumarc.com
Pres.–Peter F. Spittler
Dir., Newspaper Grp.–Steve Barber
Dir., Architecture–Chuck Rosati
Industry: Architects/Engineers (Includes Design/Construction Firms)

Foster Mfg. Co.
905 Louis Dr., Warminster, PA, 18974; tel (215) 442-1700; fax (215) 442-1313; e-mail information@fostermfg.com; web site www.fostermfg.com
Pres.–Ted Borowsky
Industry: Archiving Systems; Art & Layout Equipment and Services; Cabinets; Color Viewing Equipment; Composing Room Equipment & Supplies; Cutters & Trimmers; Cutting Tools; Dark Room Equipment; Files, Storage; Layout Tables, Light Tables & Workstations; Offset Plate Files; Photo Archiving; Plastic Folders; Prepress Color Proofing Systems; Proofing Systems; Storage Retrieval Systems; Tables (Dot, Etch, Opaquing, Register, Retouching, Stripping)

John Foust Training
PO Box 97606, Raleigh, NC, 27624, USA; tel (919) 848-2401; e-mail jfoust@mindspring.com
Owner–John Foust
Industry: Consulting Services: Advertising

Fox Bay Industries, Inc.
4150 B Pl. NW, Ste. 101, Auburn, WA, 98001; tel (253) 941-9155; fax (253) 941-9197; e-mail info@foxbay.com; sales@foxbay.com; web site www.foxbay.com
Pres.–Ladele Walker
Sales Mgr.–Wayne Walker
Industry: Consulting Services: Ergonomics

Franklin Wire Works, Inc.
910 E. Lincoln Ave., Belvidere, IL, 61008; tel (815) 544-6676; fax (815) 547-5356; web site www.franklindisplay.com
Sales Mgr.–Dick Boyett
Industry: Circulation Equipment & Supplies

Barry French
3 Ashlawn Rd., Assonet, MA, 02702; tel (508) 644-5772
Dir., Mktg.–Barry French
Industry: Brokers & Appraisers; Consulting Services: Financial;

Fry Communications
800 W. Church Rd., Mechanicsburg, PA, 17055; tel (717) 766-0211; fax (717) 691-0341; e-mail info@frycomm.com; web site www.frycomm.com
Vice President, Sales–Stephen Grande
Pres.–Henry Fry
Industry: Publishing Systems; Trade Publications;

Fujifilm Hunt Chemicals U.S.A., Inc.
40 Boroline Rd., Allendale, NJ, 07401; tel (800) 526-0851; fax (201) 995-2299; web site www.fujihuntusa.com
Vice Pres.–Scott Clouston
Pres.–Albert Adrts
Industry: Chemicals: Photographic; Chemicals: Pressroom;

Fuji Photo Film USA/Graphic Systems Div.
850 Central Ave., Hanover Park, IL, 60103; tel (312) 924-5800; fax (630) 259-7898; web site www.fujifilm.com
Pres., Industrial Imaging Markets Grp.–Tim Combs
Sr. Vice Pres./Gen. Mgr., PhotoImaging Grp.–Bill Diminno
Industry: Chemicals: Plate Processing; Color Proofing; Film & Paper: Contact; Film & Paper: Duplicating; Film & Paper: Filters (Photographic); Imagesetters; Plates: Offset (Computer to Plate); Proofing Systems; Plates: Offset (Conventional); Scanners: Color B & W, Plates, Web;

Fujifilm Graphic Systems USA, Inc.
2507 W. Erie Dr., Ste. 103, Tempe, AZ, 85282; tel (602) 437-4944; web site www.fujifilmgs.com
Reg'l Sales Mgr.–Richard Pyane

Fujifilm Graphic Systems USA, Inc.
200 Summit Lake Dr., Valhalla, NY, 10595; tel (914) 749-4800; web site www.fujifilmgs.com
Mktg. Mgr.–Tim Combs
Industry: Blankets; Chemicals: Pressroom; Color Management Software; Imagesetters; Inks; Offset Chemicals & Supplies; Platemakers: Flexographic (Computer to Plate); Plates: Offset (Conventional); Proofing Systems; Software: Press/Post Press;

Fujifilm Graphic Systems USA, Inc.
8680 Greenwood Pl., Savage, MD, 20763; tel (301) 362-2640; fax (301) 317-7480; e-mail jchumley@fujifilmgs.com; web site www.fujifilmgs.com
Reg'l Sales Mgr.–Rod Ambrose

Fujifilm Graphic Systems USA, Inc.
147 W. Airport Rd., Lititz, PA, 17543; tel (717) 569-4582; fax (717) 581-3460
Reg'l Sales Mgr.–Paul Voll

Fujifilm Graphic Systems USA, Inc.
4245 S. 143rd St., Southwestern Plz., Ste. 6, Omaha, NE, 68137; tel (402) 731-6258; fax (402) 731-6280; web site www.fujifilmgs.com
Reg'l Sales Mgr.–Bob Bloemer

Fujifilm Graphic Systems USA, Inc.
211 Vanbruggen, Galesburg, MI, 49053; tel (269) 381-2640; fax (269) 381-9428; web site www.fujifilmgs.com
Reg'l Sales Mgr.–Paul Caruso

Fujifilm Graphic Systems USA, Inc.
10920 W. Sam Houston Pkwy. N, Houston, TX, 77064; tel (281) 955-5240
Reg'l Sales Mgr.–Craig Robillo

Fujifilm Graphic Systems USA, Inc.
1312 Crossbeam Dr., Charlotte, NC, 28217; tel (704) 357-3094; fax (704) 357-6281
Reg'l Sales Mgr.–Bill O'Day

Fujifilm Graphic Systems USA, Inc.
1808 N. Corrington Ave., Kansas City, MO, 64120; tel (816) 241-2782; fax (816) 241-3232; web site www.fujifilmgs.com
Reg'l Sales Mgr.–Richard H. Brown

Fujifilm Graphic Systems USA, Inc.
3926 Willow Lake Blvd., Memphis, TN, 38118; tel (901) 363-6260; fax (901) 345-5820; web site www.fujifilmgs.com
Reg'l Sales Mgr.–Tommy Greene

Fujifilm Graphic Systems USA, Inc.
6601 Lyons Rd., Ste. A, Coconut Creek, FL, 33073; tel (954) 427-1470
Reg'l Sales Mgr.–Greg Furlong

Fujifilm Graphic Systems USA, Inc.
11150 Hope St., Cypress, CA, 90630; tel (714) 933-3300; web site www.fujifilmgs.com
Reg'l Sales Mgr.–Richard Payne

Fujifilm Graphic Systems USA, Inc.
30962 San Benito St., Hayward, CA, 94544; tel (510) 259-7100; web site www.fujifilmgs.com
Reg'l Sales Mgr.–Richard Cay

Fujifilm Graphic Systems USA, Inc.
3926 Willow Lake Blvd., Memphis, TN, 38118; tel (901) 363-6260; fax (901) 345-5820; web site www.fujifilmgs.com
Reg'l Sales Mgr.–Tommy Greene

Fujifilm Graphic Systems USA, Inc.
3425 Gilchrist Rd., Mogadore, OH, 44260; tel (330) 628-0601; fax (330) 628-0607
Reg'l Sales Mgr.–Kurt Paskert

Fujifilm Graphic Systems USA, Inc.
436 Hayden Station Rd., Windsor, CT, 06095; tel (860) 298-0509; fax (860) 298-0296; web site www.fujifilmgs.com
Reg'l Sales Mgr.–Tony Aquino

Fujifilm North America Corporation
850 Central Avenue, Hanover Park, IL, 60133, USA; tel 866.378.1429; fax 765-482-0288; e-mail seattlecs@fujifilmgs.com; web site www.fujifilmusa.com
Vice President, Newspaper Sales–Lane Palmer
Newspaper Account Manager, SE Region–Al Barnard
Newspaper Account Manager, NE Region–Lorna Borghese
Newspaper Account Manager, West Region–Bob Veyera
Newspaper Support Specialist–Michael Mossman

Fujifilm Graphic Systems USA, Inc.
8777 N. Purdue Rd., Ste. 205, Indianapolis, IN, 46268; tel (317) 334-0460; fax (317) 334-0468; web site www.fujifilmgs.com
Reg'l Sales Mgr.–Mike Nagle

Fujifilm Graphic Systems USA, Inc.
897 Fee Fee Rd., Maryland Heights, MO, 63043; tel (314) 453-9292
Reg'l Sales Mgr.–Mike Chastain

Fujifilm Graphic Systems USA, Inc.
1650 Magnolia Dr., Cincinnati, OH, 45215; tel (513) 563-6700; fax (513) 563-0377; web site www.fujifilmgs.com
Reg'l Sales Mgr.–Kurt Paskert

Fujifilm Graphic Systems USA, Inc.
4103 SE International Way, Portland, OR, 97222; tel (503) 353-7468; fax (503) 353-7470
Reg'l Sales Mgr.–Les Natzel

Fujifilm Graphic Systems USA, Inc.
5165 S. Towne Dr., New Berlin, WI, 53151; tel (262) 796-8721; fax (262) 796-9589; web site www.fujifilmgs.com
Reg'l Sales Mgr.–Mark Harpke

Fujifilm Graphic Systems USA, Inc.
850 Central Ave., Hanover Park, IL, 60133; tel (630) 259-7200; fax (630) 259-7078; web site www.fujifilmgs.com
Reg'l Sales Mgr.–John Briar

Fujifilm Graphic Systems USA, Inc.
330 Westway Pl., Ste. 446, Arlington, TX, 76018; tel (817) 784-6474; fax (817) 467-7351; web site www.fujifilmgs.com
Reg'l Sales Mgr.–Randy Sullivan

Fujifilm Graphic Systems USA, Inc.
1005 Satellite Blvd., Ste. 200, Suwanee, GA, 30024; tel (770) 279-8900; fax (678) 804-5195; web site www.fujifilmgs.com
Reg'l Sales Mgr.–Bruce Simon

Fulco, Inc.
30 Broad St., Denville, NJ, 07834, USA; tel (973) 627-2427; fax (973) 627-5872; e-mail support@fulcoinc.com; web site www.fulcoinc.com
Owner/President–Jim Duffy
Industry: Subscription Fulfillment Software

Ralph Fusco, Inc.
30 Fern Dr., Commack, NY, 11725-4104; tel (631) 864-1352; fax (631) 864-1352
Pres.–Ralph Fusco
Industry: Architects/Engineers (Includes Design/Construction Firms); Consulting Services: Equipment;

GE Instrument Control Systems, Inc.
PO Box 7126, Pensacola, FL, 32534; tel (850) 474-4646; fax (850) 968-0563
Sales–Sharon Stall
Industry: Architects/Engineers (Includes Design/Construction Firms); Controls: Exposure; Controls: Photo Electric; Controls: Register;

GP Plastics Corp.
PO Box 560584, Dallas, TX, 75356-0584; tel (800) 527-9459; fax (214) 689-3920; e-mail sherryb@gpplastics.com
Pres.–Bob Baumgarner
Industry: Circulation Equipment & Supplies

G

GSP, Inc.
PO Box 2358, Westerly, RI, 02891; tel (401) 348-0210; fax (401) 348-0689; e-mail gspmystic@gsptoday.com; web site www.gsptoday.com
Pres.–Jens E. Ljungberg
Vice Pres.–Maurice Blanchet
Treasurer–Maija L. Ljungberg
Industry: Presses: Offset; Web Press - Special Equipment;

G.T. Specialties
PO Box 6383, Albuquerque, NM, 87197; tel (505) 343-0600; fax (505) 343-0606; e-mail pressgripper@earthlink.net; web site www.gt-specialties.com
Owner–Louis Nunez
Industry: Press Accessories, Parts & Supplies

Gammerler AG
Lietenstr. 26, Geretsried-Gelting, N/A, D-82538, Germany; tel +49 8171 404-326; fax +49 8171 404-244; e-mail dietrich.lauber@gammerler.de; web site www.gammerler.com
Sales Mgr.–Dietrich Lauber

Gammerler (US) Corp.
431 Lakeview Ct., Mt. Prospect, IL, 60056; tel (224) 361-8300; e-mail marketing@gammerler.com; web site www.gammerler.com
CEO–Clay Bruneman
Industry: Conveyors; Counting, Stacking, Bundling Machines; Cutters & Trimmers; Feeding, Folding, Delivery Equipment; Gluing Systems; In-Line Trimming Systems; Mailroom Systems & Equipment; Material Handling Equipment: Palletizing Machines; Material Handling Equipment: Pallets & Palletizers;

Gannett Media Technologies International (GMTI)
151 W. Fourth St., Ste. 201, Cincinnati, OH, 45202, USA; tel (513) 665-3777; fax (513) 241-7219; e-mail gmti-info@gmti.gannett.com; web site www.gmti.com
Pres./CEO–Steve Fuschetti
Industry: Archiving Systems; Computers: Hardware & Software Integrators; Library Retrieval Systems; Marketing Database Design and Implementation; Photo Archiving; Software: Advertising (Includes Display; Classified); Storage Retrieval Systems;

Gazette Communications, Inc.
PO Box 511, Cedar Rapids, IA, 52406, USA; tel (319) 398-8211; fax (319) 398-5846; web site www.thegazette.com
Chrmn.–Joe Hadky

General Binding Corp.
300 Tower Pkwy., Lincolnshire, IL, 60069; tel (847) 541-9500; fax (847) 478-0073; web site www.gbc.com
Industry: Paper Shredders

General DataComm, Inc.
6 Rubber Ave., Naugatuck, CT, 06770; tel (203) 729-0271; fax (203) 723-2883; web site www.gdc.com
CFO–William Henry
Industry: Computers: Hardware & Software Integrators; Telecommunications;

GeoRack, Inc.
1372 Anderson Rd., Clawson, MI, 48017; tel (248) 435-7720; fax (248) 435-7920; e-mail sales@georack.com; web site www.georack.com
Pres.–Andrew Franklin
Gen. Sales Mgr.–Norman L. Schmitt
Industry: Circulation Equipment & Supplies; Newspaper Dispensers (Mechanical/Electronic); Tubes, Racks (Includes Racks: Motor Route Tubes);

Georgia-Pacific Corp.
133 Peachtree St. NE, Atlanta, GA, 30303-1808; tel (404) 652-4000; fax (404) 230-1674; e-mail gpfinance@gapac.com; web site www.gp.com
Chrmn.–Dave Robertson
Pres./CEO–Jim Hannan
Pres., Recycled Fibers–Simon H. Davies
Pres., N. American Retail Bus.–John P. O'-Donnell
Pres., Chemicals–Richard G. Urschel
Pres., Dixie–Sean R. Fallmann
Exec. Vice Pres., Global Consumer Pdcts.–Kathleen A. Walters
Exec. Vice Pres., Wood Pdcts.–Ronald L. Paul
Sr. Vice Pres., Commun. government and Pub. Aff.–Sheila M. Weidman
Vice Pres., Mktg. Commun.–Rob Lorys
Dir., Mktg. Servs.–Chris Beyer
Brand Mktg. Dir., Brawny–Gino Biondi
Vice Pres., Information Resources/CIO–H. James Dallas
Industry: Photostat: Paper

Gerrard Ovalstrapping
735 Oval Ct., Burlington, ON, L7L 6A9, Canada; tel (905) 632-3662; fax (905) 639-2290; web site www.goval.com
Natl. Accts./Equipment Mgr.–Dan Crespi
Industry: Baling Machines; Bundling and Tying Machines; Conveyors; Counting, Stacking, Bundling Machines; Flooring; Mailroom Systems & Equipment; Roll Handeling Equipment; Strapping Machines;

Gerrard Ovalstrapping
4020 Gault Ave. S., Fort Payne, AL, 35967-7567; tel (256) 845-1928; fax (256) 845-1490; e-mail usa_info@goval.com; web site www.goval.com
Mgr.–Neena Wilson
Industry: Strapping Machines

Gilbane Building Co.
7 Jackson Walkway, Providence, RI, 02903; tel (401) 456-5800; fax (401) 456-5930; web site www.gilbaneco.com
Chrmn./CEO–Paul J. Choquette
Pres./COO–Thomas F. Gilbane
Exec. Vice Pres.–William Gilbane
Sr. Vice Pres.-Mktg./Sales–Alfred K. Potter
Sr. Vice Pres./Mgr.-Central Reg.–Walter Mckelvey
Sr. Vice Pres./Mgr., Southwest–Wandell Holmes
Sr. Vice Pres./Mgr., Mid Atlantic–Bruce Hoffman
Sr. Vice Pres./Mgr.-North East Reg.–George Cavallo
Industry: Architects/Engineers (Includes Design/Construction Firms)

William Ginsberg Associates
420 E. 55th St., New York, NY, 10022; tel (212) 888-1956; fax (212) 888-1957; e-mail rkgwga@aol.com
Pres.–R.K. Ginsberg
Industry: Architects/Engineers (Includes Design/Construction Firms); Consulting Services: Equipment; Consulting Services: Production; Controllers: Press; Newsprint Handeling Equipment; Noise Control; Paper Handeling Equipment;

Global Press Management Services, LLC.
63 Coryell St., Lambertville, NJ, 08530; tel (609) 773-0401; fax (609) 773-0403; e-mail epadilla@globalpressmanagement.com; web site www.globalpressmanagement.com
CEO–Edward R. Padilla
Industry: Consulting Services: Equipment; Folding Machines; Press Accessories, Parts & Supplies; Press Engineers; Press Rebuilding; Web Width Changer;

Global Turnkey Systems, Inc.
2001 Rt. 46, Ste. 203, Parsippany, NJ, 07054; tel (973) 331-1010; fax (973) 331-0042; e-mail sales@gtsystems.com; web site www.gtsystems.com
Pres./CEO–Al Alteslane
Industry: Computers: Hardware & Software Integrators; Computers: Local Area Network (LANS); Consulting Services: Circulation; Consulting Services: Computer; Software: Circulation; Software: Electronic Data Interchange; Subscription Fulfillment Software; System Installations; System Integration Services;

Globix Corp.
95 Christopher Columbus Dr., 16th Fl., Jersey City, NJ, 07302; tel (212) 334-8500; fax (212) 625-8650; e-mail support@qualitytech.com; web site www.qualitytech.com
Pres./CEO/COO–Kurt Van Wagenen
Gen. Mgr.–Shelagh Montgomery
Industry: Computers: Hardware & Software Integrators; Computers: Laptop & Portable; Computers: Local Area Network (LANS); Computers: Storage Devices;

Glunz & Jensen, Inc.
12633 Industrial Dr., Granger, IN, 46530; tel (574) 272-9950; fax (574) 272-6566; e-mail sales-usa@glunz-jensen.com; web site www.glunz-jensen.dk
Gen. Mgr.–Kent Deal

Industry: Processors: Film & Paper

Go Plastics/StreetSmart LLC
515 Brown Industrial Pkwy., Canton, GA, 30114; tel (866) 366-6166; fax (877) 894-9966; e-mail inquiries@goplastics.com; web site www.goplastics.com
Dir.-Sales/Mktg.–Brian Bauman
Adv. Customer Info Serv.–Michelle Gollob
Industry: Circulation Equipment & Supplies; Newspaper Dispensers (Mechanical/Electronic);

M. Golda Engineering
433 Solano Dr., Benicia, CA, 94510; tel (707) 745-6073; fax (707) 745-6073
Industry: Drives & Controls; Ink Controls, Computerized; Ink Pumping Systems; Ink Recovery Systems; Interfaces; Newsprint Handeling Equipment; Paper Handeling Equipment; Testing Instruments; Web Break Detector; Web Guides;

Goss International Corporation
3 Territorial Ct., Bolingbrook, IL, 60440-3557; tel (630) 755-9300; fax (630) 755-9301; e-mail info@gossinternational.com; web site www.gossinternational.com
Chrmn.–Ed Padilla
CEO–Jochen Meissner
CFO–Joseph Gaynor
Sr. Vice Pres., Global Sales–Richard Schultz
Mktg. Mgr.–Cecilia Chou
Industry: Press Accessories, Parts & Supplies; Press Rebuilding; Press Repairs; Presses: Offset;

Lissom Corp. Inc.
PO Box 441, Bronxville, NY, 10708; tel (914) 761-6360; fax (914)761-6360; e-mail hank@lissomcorp.com; web site www.weboffsetpress.comHank F. Damhuis
Industry: Presses: Offset

grafikAmerica
1285 W. King St., York, PA, 17404; tel (717) 843-3183; fax (717) 845-8828; e-mail sales@grafikam.com
Pres.–Ward Walsh
Industry: Blanket Cleaner/Washer (Automatic); Color Registration; Controls: Register; Ink Controls, Computerized; Tension & Web

Graphic Arts Blue Book Online
2000 Clearwater Dr., Oak Brook, IL, 60523, US; tel 800/323-4958, x8333; fax 678/680-1667; e-mail info@gabb.com; web site www.gabb.com
Global Marketing Director–Mary Miller
Industry: Trade Publications

Graphic Machine Sales, Inc.
8917 Hickory Ln, Wonder Lake, IL, 60097, USA; tel (815) 382-1914; e-mail graphic@stans.net; web site www.graphicmachinesales.com
Pres.–James Anzelmo
Industry: Dampening Systems

Graphic Printing Roller Ltd.
343 Rodick Rd., Unit 6, Markham, ON, L6G 1B1, Canada; tel (800) 265-7418; fax (905) 475-3421; e-mail bvenis@graphicroller.com; web site www.graphicroller.com
Pres.–Brian Venis
Industry: Grater Wrap-Roller Covering; Ink Fountains & Accessories; Press Accessories, Parts & Supplies; Roller Grinding Services; Rollers; Rollers: Dampening;

Graphic Publishing Systems, Inc.
PO Box 1216, Clinton, MS, 39056; tel (601) 924-0405; fax (601) 924-4769; e-mail graphic@graphicpub.com
Pres.–Bob Gilmore
Industry: Computers: Hardware & Software Integrators; Computers: Local Area Network (LANS); Film & Paper: Film Processing Machines; Film & Paper: Phototypesetting; Imagesetters; Laser Printers; Raster Image Processors; Typesetters: Laser;

Graphic System Services, Inc.
1201 Ardmore Ave., Itasca, IL, 60143; tel (630) 860-5959; fax (630) 860-6515; e-mail info@jardis.com; web site www.jardis.com
Pres.–Allan Jardis
Mgr.–Gary Klawinski
Industry: Architects/Engineers (Includes Design/Construction Firms); Consulting Services: Equipment; Ink Pumping Systems; Pasters; Press Accessories, Parts & Supplies; Pumps (Air, Ink, Vacuum); Remanufactures Equipment; Splicers, Automatic; Tension & Web Controls; Web Press - Special Equipment;

Graphic Technology, Inc. (GTI)
PO Box 3138, Newburgh, NY, 12550; tel (845) 562-7066; fax (845) 562-2543; e-mail sales@gtilite.com; web site www.gtilite.com
Pres.–Frederic McCurdy
Vice Pres., Sales/Mktg.–Robert McCurdy
Sales/Mktg Coord.–Linda Sutherland
Industry: Art & Layout Equipment and Services; Color Viewing Equipment; Layout Tables, Light Tables & Workstations; Lighting Equipment; Press Accessories, Parts & Supplies;

Graphics Microsystems, Inc.
1655 Science Pl., Rockwall, TX, 75032-6202; tel (972) 290-3120; fax (972) 722-1128; e-mail avt@avt-inc.com; web site www.avt-inc.com
Southern Regional Sales Mgr.–Bill Fleck
Industry: Color Registration; Controls: Register; Densitometers; Ink Controls, Computerized; Press Control Systems;

GraphLine
1100 International Pkwy., Sunrise, FL, 33323, USA; tel (800) 998-3200; fax (954) 724-2255; e-mail marketing@graphline.com; web site www.graphline.com
Pres./CEO–Michael Ostroff
Exec. Vice Pres./CFO–Ray Domis
Vice Pres.,Marketing/Operations–Ralph Theile
Dir., Mktg.–Tom Brancato
Industry: Chemicals: Photographic; Chemicals: Plate Processing; Film & Paper: Contact; Densitometers; Film & Paper: Duplicating; Film & Paper: Film Processing Machines; Imagesetters; Laser Printers; Platemakers: Direct;

GraphX, Inc.
444 E. Susquehanna St., Allentown, PA, 18103-5144; tel (610) 797-5515; fax (610) 797-8740; e-mail sales@adtaker.com; web site www.adtaker.com
Pres.–Douglas S. Turner
Vice Pres.-Systems–James B. Pfeiffer
Opns. Mgr.–Kelly Fost
Industry: Software: Advertising (Includes Display; Classified)

Great Southern Corp. (Sirco Div.)
PO Box 18710, Memphis, TN, 38181; tel (901) 365-1611; fax (901) 365-4498; e-mail sales@greatsoutherncorp.com; web site www.greatsoutherncorp.com
Pres.–Scott Vaught
Industry: Circulation Equipment & Supplies; Newspaper Bags;

Grimes, W.B. & Co.
24212 Muscari Court, Gaithersburg, MD, 20882-3804, United States; tel (301) 253-5016; fax (240) 358-0790; e-mail lgrimes@mediamergers.com; web site www.mediamergers.com
President–Larry Grimes
Founder–Walter Grimes
Senior Associate-Midwest–Julie Bergman
Senior Associate-Northeast/New England–John Szefc
Senior Associate- Mid-Atlantic/Southeast–David Slavin
Senior Associate- Southeast/South–Mark Laskowski
Senior Associate- South–Dennis Richardson
Director-Southwest/Plains/West–Rollie Hyde
Associate- Western States–Jay Harn
Senior Associate-Trade and Consumer Magazines; Digital Media–John McGovern
Industry: Brokers & Appraisers; Consulting Services: Advertising; Consulting Services: Financial; Consulting Services: Human Resources; Consulting Services: Marketing;

Group 1 Software, Inc.
4200 Parliament Pl., Ste. 600, Lanham, MD, 20706-1844; tel (301) 731-2300; fax (301) 731-0360; e-mail info@g1.com; pr@g1.com; web site www.g1.com
Vice Chrmn./CEO–Robert S. Bowen
Pres./COO/Acting Vice Pres., Sales–Ronald F. Friedman
Exec. Vice Pres./CFO–Mark D. Funston
Exec. Vice Pres., Ent. Solutions Div. Sales/Cor. Mktg.–Andrew W. Naden
Exec. Vice Pres., Sales/Mktg., DOC1 Div.–Elizabeth Walter
Vice Pres., Sales–Brian Borda
Gen. Mgr.–Steve Bebee
Dir., Tech Servs.–Ray Chin
Industry: Mailroom Systems & Equipment

Gulf Coast System Design Co.
1940 N. Gate Blvd., Ste. B6, Sarasota, FL, 34234; tel (941) 358-6020
Pres.–D.G.B. Lindsay
Industry: Business Computers; Computers: Hardware & Software Integrators; Consulting Services: Computer;

Gutenberg Printing Press Co.
2830 Habersham Rd. NW, Atlanta, GA, 30305; tel (404) 841-0102; fax (404) 842-0525; e-mail press@gutenberg-press.com; web site www.gutenberg-press.com
Pres.–Durelle Boles
Industry: Equipment Dealers (New); Equipment Dealers (Used); Flying Pasters; Remanufactures Equipment; Presses: Offset; Splicers, Automatic

Norman X Guttman, Inc.
135 Green St., Woodbridge, NJ, 07095-2961; tel (732) 636-8671; fax (732) 636-8673; web site www.advertoon.com
Pres.–Daniel Guttman
Industry: Inks; Roll Converters; Roller Grinding Services; Rollers; Rollers: Dampening; Tension & Web Controls;

HFW Industries
PO Box 8, Buffalo, NY, 14207; tel (716) 875-3380; fax (716) 875-3385; web site www.hfwindustries.com
Pres.–John Watson
Industry: Remanufactures Equipment

H

HK Systems
2855 S. James Dr., NewBurlin, WI, 53151; tel (262) 860-7000; fax (262) 860-7020; e-mail info@hksystems.com; web site www.hksystems.com
Pres.–John W. Splude
Sr. Vice Pres., Sales–Mike Kotecki
Vice Pres., Mktg.–Cheryl Falk
Industry: Consulting Services: Production; Conveyors; Material Handling Equipment: Automatic Guided Vehicles; Material Handling Equipment: Palletizing Machines; Shrink Wrapping Equipment; Software: Press/Post Press; Storage Retrieval Systems;

H & M Paster Sales & Service, Inc.
21828 87th Ave SE, Suite D, Woodinville, WA, 98072, United States of America; tel 425-892-1093; fax 425-892-1096; e-mail steve@bjmach.com; web site www.bjmach.com
Pres.–Steven Bjorklund
Industry: Adhesives; Gluing Systems; Pasters; Web Press - Special Equipment;

Haas & Associates
9438 Briar Forest Dr., Houston, TX, 77063; tel (713) 977-8955; fax (713) 977-9656
Pres.–Ron Haas
Industry: Consulting Services: Human Resources

Hadronics
4570 Steel Pl., Cincinnati, OH, 45209, U.S.A; tel (513) 321-9350; fax (513) 321-9377; e-mail sales@hadronics.com; web site www.hadronics.com
Vice Pres., Sales–Jeff McCarty
Industry: Copper Plating Drums; Cylinder Repair; Dampening Systems; Ink Fountains & Accessories; Roller Grinding Services; Rollers; Rollers: Dampening;

Hall Contracting Services, Inc.
33530 Pin Oak Pkwy., Avon Lake, OH, 44012-2320; tel (440) 930-0050; fax (440) 930-0025; e-mail hcs@hallcontractingservices.com; web site www.hallcontractingservices.com
President & CEO–Richard F. Palmer
Director of Sales–Sam Pernice
CEO–Graham Hall
Sr. Vice Pres.-Finance/Admin.–Dennis E. Bushman
Vice Pres.-Engineering–Devin Hogan
Vice Pres.-Press Servs.–A. Pat Jarrell
Industry: Conveyors; Equipment Dealers (Used); Erectors & Riggers; Press Engineers; Press Rebuilding; Press Repairs; Remanufactures Equipment; Web Width Changer;

Hamada of America, Inc.
22675-F Savi Ranch Pkwy., Yorba Linda, CA, 92887; tel (714) 637-3844; fax (714) 637-7490; e-mail marketing@hamadaoamerica.com; web site www.hamadaoamerica.com
Industry: Presses: Offset

Hamilton Circulation Supplies Co.
PO Box 398, Beecher, IL, 60401, USA; tel (708) 946-2208; fax (708) 946-3733; e-mail info@hamiltoncirculation.com; web site www.theservicechamps.com
Pres.–Joseph M. Beaudry
Vice Pres.–Thomas P. Hamilton
Office Mgr.–Pat Stein
Industry: Adhesives; Circulation Equipment & Supplies; Delivery Equipment; Material Handling Equipment: Pallets & Palletizers; Newspaper Bags; Newspaper Dispensers (Mechanical/Electronic); Newspaper Marketing; Rack Display Cards; Software: Circulation; Tubes, Racks (Includes Racks: Motor Route Tubes);

Hare Associates, Inc.
62 Black Walnut Dr., Rochester, NY, 14615-1259; tel (585) 621-6873; fax (585) 621-4197
Pres.–Richard L. Hare
Industry: Brokers & Appraisers; Consulting Services: Advertising; Consulting Services: Editorial; Research Studies;

Harland Simon
Windsor Office Plz., 210 W. 22nd St., Ste. 134, Oak Brook, IL, 60523; tel (630) 572-7650; fax (630) 572-7653; e-mail sales@harlandsimon.com; web site www.harlandsimon.com
Sr. Vice Pres., Sales–John Staiano
Industry: Color Proofing; Drives & Controls; Ink Controls, Computerized; Mailroom Systems & Equipment; Inserting Equipment (Includes Stuffing Machines); Press Control Systems; Press Data Accumulators; Produciton Control Systems; Software: Pagination/Layout; Software: Press/Post Press; Software: Workflow Management/Tracking;

Harper Corp. of America (Anilox Roll Supplier)
PO Box 38490, Charlotte, NC, 28278-0369; tel (704) 588-3371; fax (704) 588-3819; web site www.harperimage.com
Pres.–Margaret Harper Kluttz
Mgr., Gen. Sales–Peter Hartman
Industry: Rollers

Harris Corp.
1025 W. Nasa Blvd., Melbourne, FL, 32919; tel (321) 727-9100; fax (321) 726-4527; web site www.harris.com
Pres./CEO/Chrmn.–Howard L. Lance
COO–Robert K. Henry

Sr. Vice Pres./CFO–Gary L. McArthur
Vice Pres., Investor Rel.–Pamela Padgett
Treasurer–Charles J. Greene
Industry: Business Computers; Data Communication; Facsimilie/Fax Transmission Systems; Pagination Systems; Input & Editing Systems; Press Control Systems; Publishing Systems; Visual Display Terminals;

Hart Industries
43 Doran St., East Haven, CT, 06512; tel (203) 469-6344; fax (203) 469-6592; e-mail smancuso@hartindus.com
Pres.–Steve Mancuso
Industry: Dark Room Equipment; Environmental Control Systems; Silver Recovery; Wastewater Treatment;

Hart Industries/Metafix Compliance Systems
43 Doran St., East Haven, CT, 06512-2212; tel (203) 469-6344; fax (203) 469-6592
Owner–Steve Mancuso
Industry: Dark Room Equipment; Environmental Control Systems; Silver Recovery; Wastewater Treatment;

The Haskell Co.
PO Box 44100, Jacksonville, FL, 32231-4100; tel (904) 791-4500; fax (904) 791-4699; web site www.thehaskellco.com
Pres.–Steve Halverson
Resource Center Administrator–Sara Guthrie
Industry: Architects/Engineers (Includes Design/Construction Firms); Consulting Services: Equipment;

Headline Memories
PO Box 54, Safety Harbor, FL, 34695; tel (727) 726-8431; fax (727) 725-5186; e-mail info@headlinememories.com; web site www.headlinememories.com
Pres.–Wayne Matthews
Industry: Consulting Services: Circulation

Heat and Control, Inc.
21121 Cabot Blvd., Hayward, CA, 94545-1132; tel (510) 259-0500; fax (510) 259-0600; e-mail info@heatandcontrol.com; web site www.heatandcontrol.com
Chrmn./CEO–Andy Caridis
Pres.–Tony Caridis
Dir., Mktg.–Audrey Waidelich
Industry: Counting, Stacking, Bundling Machines

Heidelberg USA, Inc.
1000 Gutenberg Dr. NW, Kennesaw, GA, 30144; tel (888) 472-9655; fax (770) 419-6625; web site www.heidelberg.com
Pres.–James Donn
Sr. Vice Pres., Sheetfed/Opns.–Steen Jensen
Sr. Vice Pres., HR/Gen. Counsel–Susan Nofi
Sr. Vice Pres., Finance–Thomas Topp
Sr. Vice Pres., Mktg. Commun.–James Martin
Industry: Cutters & Trimmers; Platemakers: Letterpress; Presses: Letterpress; Presses: Offset;

Heidelberger Druckmaschinen AG
Kurfuersten Anlage 52-60, Heidelberg, N/A, 69115, Germany; tel +49 6221-9200; fax +49 6221-9269-99; e-mail hddteam@heidelberg.com; web site www.heidelberg.com; www.de.heidelberg.com
CEO–Bernhard Schreier
Mktg. Mgr.–Dietmar Walz

Heitz Service Corp.
34-11 62nd St., Woodside, NY, 11377; tel (718) 565-0004; fax (718) 565-2582; e-mail karlheitz@compuserve.com
Pres.–Karl Heitz
Vice Pres.–Loretta Rosas
Industry: Cameras & Accessories; Lenses (Camera);

Herco Graphic Products
PO Box 369, Wauconda, IL, 60084; tel (847) 526-1300; fax (815) 578-9593; e-mail hercographics@aol.com; web site www.hercographics.com
Dir. Sales–Christine Polanzi
Industry: Roll Coverings; Rollers;

Hewlett-Packard Co.
3000 Hanover St., Palo Alto, CA, 94304-1185; tel (650) 857-1501; fax (650) 857-5518; e-mail hp-leads@hp.com; web site www.hp.com
Chrmn./Pres./CEO–Mark Hurd
CMO–Michael Mendenhall
Exec. Vice Pres., Enterprise Bus.–Ann Livermore
Exec. Vice Pres., Worldwide Mktg., Personal Systems Grp.–Richard Gerstein
Vice Pres., Mktg.–Tariq Hassan
Vice Pres., Brand Strategy–Glenna Patton
Dir., Mktg., Small/Midsize Bus.–Brian Burch

Hewlett-Packard Co.
11311 K-Tel Dr., Minnetonka, MN, 55343; tel (952) 944-9330; fax (952) 943-8622; e-mail info@colorspan.com; web site www.colorspan.com
Dir., Mktg.–Bruce Butler
Industry: Inks

Hexagon Metrology, Inc.
250 Circuit Dr., North Kingstown, RI, 02852-0700; tel (401) 886-2000; fax (401) 886-2762; web site www.hexagonmetrology.com
Adv. Mgr.–William Fetter
Industry: Gauges, Measuring

Hitachi Printing Solutions
1757 Tapo Canyon Rd., Simi Valley, CA, 93063; tel (805) 578-4000; fax (805) 578-4001; web site www.hitachi-printingsolutions.us
Pres./CEO, HPSA–Yasuo Kikuchi
Mktg. Dir., Worldwide Printers–Gary Coon
Mktg. Dir., Supplies–Jeff Sampson
Industry: Laser Printers

Honeywell, Inc.
101 Columbia Rd., Morristown, NJ, 07962; tel (973) 455-6768; fax (973) 455-4002; e-mail lois.sills@honeywell.com; web site www.honeywell.com
CEO–Dave Cote
Industry: Fire Protection; Humidifiers; Press Control Systems;

Horizons, Inc.
18531 S. Miles Rd., Cleveland, OH, 44128; tel (216) 475-0555; fax (216) 475-6507; e-mail sales@horizonsisg.com; web site www.horizonsisg.com
Pres.–Herb Wainer
Vice Pres., Mktg.–Wayne Duignan
Industry: Adhesives; Chemicals: Photographic; Input & Editing Systems; Label Printing Machines;

Howtek
98 Spit Brook Rd., Ste. 100, Nashua, NH, 03062; tel (603) 882-5200; fax (603) 880-3843; e-mail sales@icadmed.com; web site www.icadmed.com
Pres.–Ken Ferry
Industry: Color Seperation Scanners

Hudson-Sharp
975 Lombardi Ave., Green Bay, WI, 54304; tel (920) 494-4571; fax (920) 496-1322; web site www.hudsonsharp.com
CEO–Rod Drummond
Industry: Automatic Plastic Bagging Equipment

Hughes Electronics Corp.
200 N. Sepulveda Blvd., El Segundo, CA, 90245-0956; tel N/A

Hurletron, Inc.
1820 Tempel Dr., Libertyville, IL, 60048; tel (847) 680-7022; fax (847) 680-7338; e-mail sales@hurletron.com; web site www.hurletron.com
Gen. Mgr.–Steve J. Siler
Sales,Service,Marketing–Charles R. Conover
Industry: Adhesives; Controls: Register;

IGS Knives, Inc.
760 W. Wallick Ln., Red Lion, PA, 17356-8859; tel (717) 244-6753; fax (717) 244-6529; e-mail info@igsknives.com; web site www.igsknives.com
Pres./Treasurer–David Herrick
Vice Pres./Sec.–Kay Herrick
Industry: Web Press - Special Equipment

I

IMC America
PO Box 2771, York, PA, 17405; tel (717) 845-4807; fax (717) 845-8828; e-mail imcsales@imcamerica.com; web site www.imcamerica.com
Pres.–Ward Walsh
Vice Pres., Mktg./Sales–Ric Mayle
Industry: Blanket Cleaner/Washer (Automatic); Conveyors; Counting, Stacking, Bundling Machines; Cutters & Trimmers; In-Line Trimming Systems; Material Handling Equipment: Automatic Guided Vehicles; Material Handling Equipment: Palletizing Machines; Paper Handeling Equipment; Roll Handeling Equipment;

IMSI
25 Leveroni Ct, Novato, CA, 94949; tel (415) 878-4000; fax (415) 897-2544; e-mail sales@imsisoft.com; web site www.imsidesign.com
Chrmn./CEO–Royal Farros
COO–Robert Mayer
Industry: Software: Design/Graphics; Software: Electronic Data Interchange; Software: Pagination/Layout;

I-many, Inc.
399 Thornall St., 12th Fl., Edison, NJ, 08837; tel (800) 832-0228; e-mail info@imany.com; web site www.imany.com
Pres./CEO–John A. Rade
Industry: Consulting Services: Financial

IPC
144 Triple Diamond Blvd., Ste. C, North Venice, FL, 34275; tel (941) 484-3622; fax (941) 484-0828; e-mail charlie@ipcpoly.com; web site www.ipcpoly.com
Pres.–Charlie Hencye
Asst. Mgr.–Cheryl Hencye
Industry: Circulation Equipment & Supplies; Consulting Services: Circulation; Consulting Services: Human Resources; Consulting Services: Marketing; Newspaper Bags; Promotion Services; Rack Display Cards;

ITW Packaging Brands
2601 Westinghouse Blvd., Charlotte, NC, 28273; tel (704) 588-2510; fax (704) 588-8795; web site www.strapex.com
Mgr.–Glen Boyd
Industry: Strapping Machines

ICANON Associates, Inc.
2321 N. Penn Rd., Hatfield, PA, 19440, USA; tel (215) 822-5519; fax (215) 822-5523; e-mail sales@icanon.com; web site www.newzware.com
Pres.–Joe Lewinski
Dir., Mktg.–Gary Markle
Engineering–Mike Hanson
Industry: Computers: Hardware & Software Integrators; Consulting Services: Computer; Consulting Services: Financial; Software: Advertising (Includes Display; Classified); Software: Business (Includes Administration/Accounting); Software: Circulation; Software: Editorial; Software: Pagination/Layout;

IdeaFisher Systems, Inc.
23072 Lake Ctr., Ste. 203, Lake Forest, CA, 92630; tel (949) 903-1987; fax (949) 474-1778; e-mail info@ideafisher.com; web site www.ideafisher.com
CEO–Marsh Fisher
Industry: Software: Advertising (Includes Display; Classified)

IKS Klingelnberg GmbH
In der Fleute 18, 42897 Remscheid, N/A, N/A, Germany; tel +49 2191 969-0; fax +49 2191 969-111; e-mail info@interknife.com; web site www.interknife.com
Pres./CEO–Thomas Meyer

Imapro Corp.
85 Pond St., Rockcliffe, ON, K1L 8J1, Canada; tel (613) 738-3000; e-mail sales@imapro.com; web site www.imapro.com
Pres.–Fred Andreone
Industry: Computers: Hardware & Software Integrators; Computers: Local Area Network (LANS); Disk Drive Sales/Repair; Dryers: Film and Papers; Software: Pagination/Layout;

Impact Racks, Inc.
12 Wheatland Dr., Mechanicsburg, PA, 17050; tel (717) 200-1213; fax (717) 918-4854; e-mail impactracks@aol.com
Pres.–John Knowles
Vice President–Stefan knowles
Industry: Circulation Equipment & Supplies; Newspaper Dispensers (Mechanical/Electronic); Remanufactures Equipment; Strapping Machines; Tubes, Racks (Includes Racks: Motor Route Tubes);

Impak (A Div. of Pakon, Inc.)
5950 Clearwater Dr., Ste. 100, Minnetonka, MN, 55345-5961; tel (952) 936-9500; fax (952) 936-9509; e-mail salesinfo@pakon.com; web site www.pakon.com
Sales/Mktg. Mgr.–Juan Palacios
Industry: Scanners: Color B & W, Plates, Web

Industrial Acoustics Co.
1160 Commerce Ave., Bronx, NY, 10462; tel (718) 931-8000; fax (718) 863-1138; e-mail info@industrialacoustics.com; web site www.industrialacoustics.com
Pres.–Kenneth Delasho
Industry: Environmental Control Systems

Industrial Noise Control, Inc.
401 Airport Rd., North Aurora, IL, 60542; tel (630) 844-1999; fax (630) 966-9710; e-mail sales@industrialnoisecontrol.com; web site www.industrialnoisecontrol.com
Pres.–Mark Rubino
Industry: Architects/Engineers (Includes Design/Construction Firms); Noise Control;

Infocom Systems
1721 central Ave S., Ste A2, Kent, WA, 98032-5875; tel (253) 859-0700; fax (253) 867-5474; e-mail infosys@aol.com
CEO/Dir., Pdct. Devel.–Robert R. Lewis
Industry: System Integration Services

Informatica Dalai SA de CV
Prolongacion A. Reyes 4508, Col. Villa del Rio, Monterrey, N/A, 64850, Mexico; tel +52 81 365-4077; fax +52 81 365-5990; web site www.dalai.com
Devel. Mgr.–Gerardo Trevino
Mng. Dir.–Juan Lauro Aguirre
Adv. Mgr.–David Valdez
Industry: Pagination Systems; Software: Advertising (Includes Display; Classified); Software: Asset Management; Software: Editorial;

Ingersoll-Rand-Aro Fluid Product Div.
PO Box 151, Bryan, OH, 43506-1100; tel (419) 636-4242; fax (419) 633-1674; e-mail arowebleads@irco.com; web site www.ingersollrandproducts.com
Chrmn./Pres.–Herbert L. Henkel
Industry: Ink Bleeding Equipment; Ink Pumping Systems; Pumps (Air, Ink, Vacuum);

Inland Industries, Inc.
PO Box 15999, Lenexa, KS, 66215; tel (913) 492-9050; web site www.inlandnews.com
Sales Sec.–Ann Campbell

Inland Newspaper Machinery LLC
PO Box 15999, Lenexa, KS, 66285-5999, USA; tel (913) 492-9050; fax (913) 492-6217; e-mail inmc1@inlandnews.com; web site www.inlandnews.com

Pres.–Beau Campbell
Sales Admin.–Ann Campbell
Industry: Brokers & Appraisers; Consulting Services: Equipment; Equipment Dealers (New); Equipment Dealers (Used); Press Rebuilding; Press Repairs; Presses: Offset; Remanufactures Equipment;

Innotek Corporation
9140 Zachary Ln., Maple Grove, MN, 55369; tel (763) 493-2810; fax (763) 493-2809; e-mail sales@innotek-ep.com; web site www.innotek-ep.com
Pres./CEO–Dennis Burns
Vice Pres., Finance–David Kalina
Vice Pres., Sales–Lynn Hughes
Industry: Press Accessories, Parts & Supplies

Innovative Systems Design, Inc.
222 Brunswick Blvd., Pointe-Claire, QC, H9R 1A6, Canada; tel (514) 459-0200; fax (514) 459-0300; e-mail sales@isd.ca; web site www.isd.ca
Sales Mgr.–D'arcy Tierney
Sales Coord.–Monica Steibelt
Manager Sales & Operations–Robert Dumas
Industry: Telecommunications

Insert East, Inc.
7045 Central Hwy., Pennsauken, NJ, 08109; tel (856) 663-8181; fax (856) 663-3288; web site www.insertseast.com
Owner–Gino Maiale
Pres.–Nick Maiale
Plant Mgr.–Frank Oliveti
Industry: Circulation Equipment & Supplies

Insurance Specialties Services, Inc.
2370 York Rd., Commonwydds, Ste. D4, Jamison, PA, 18929, USA; tel (800) 533-4579; fax (215) 918-0507; e-mail kensmith@issisvs.com; web site www.issisvs.com
Pres.–Kenneth P. Smith
Sales–Kathy Liney
Industry: Insurance

Integrated Newspaper Systems, Inc.
50 W. State St., Ste. 1202, Trenton, NJ, 08608-1298; tel (609) 393-9293; fax (609) 393-9391
Exec. Vice Pres.–Jean B. Clifton
Vice Pres., Techn.–Allen J. Mailman
Mktg. Mgr.–Randy Notter
Industry: Business Computers; Consulting Services: Advertising; Consulting Services: Circulation; Consulting Services: Financial;

Inter-Continental Graphics, Inc.
11351 Bent Pine Dr., Fort Myers, FL, 33913; tel (239) 561-6401; fax (239) 561-6402; e-mail inter2003@embarqmail.com
Pres.–Judith E. Wenzel
Dir., Sales–John F. Velilla
Industry: Blankets; Counting, Stacking, Bundling Machines; Plates: Offset (Conventional); Press Accessories, Parts & Supplies; Press Control Systems; Presses: Offset; Reels & Tensions; Rollers; Splicers, Automatic;

Interactive Data Real-Time Services, Inc.
100 Hillside Ave., White Plains, NY, 10603; tel (800) 431-2602; fax (914) 313-4805; e-mail sales.us@interactivedata.com; web site www.interactivedata-rts.com
Pres.–Mark Hopsworth
Mktg. Mgr.–Azriane Carnan
Industry: Consulting Services: Financial

Intercontinental Engineering Co.
25944 Northline Rd., Taylor, MI, 48180; tel (734) 946-9931; fax (734) 946-9992
Pres.–Michael Schwartz
Dir.–Somendra Khosla
Industry: Presses: Offset

Interlink
PO Box 207, Berrien Springs, MI, 49103-0207; tel (269) 473-3103; fax (206) 984-2240; web site www.ilsw.com
Founder–William E. Garber
Industry: Software: Advertising (Includes Display; Classified); Software: Circulation;

The International School For Pressroom Management
3526 Raymond Ave., Brookfield, IL, 60513; tel (708) 485-6973; fax (708) 485-1019; e-mail drazan1@aol.com
Pres.–Frank Drazan
Industry: Consulting Services: Equipment; Consulting Services: Ergonomics; Consulting Services: Financial; Consulting Services: Production; Controllers: Press; Fluid Handeling: Pressroom; Trade Publications; Training: Keyboard Operation;

International Trademark Association
655 3rd Ave., 10th Fl., New York, NY, 10017-5617; tel (212) 642-1700; fax (212) 768-7796; e-mail info@inta.org; web site www.inta.org
Exec. Dir.–Alan Drewsen

Interstate Distributor Co.
N/A, N/A, N/A, N/A; tel (253) 537-9455; fax (800) 795-1075; e-mail web_info@intd.com; web site www.intd.com
President & CEO–George Payne
Pres.–Gary McLean
Sec.–Dolores Fitzerald
Sr. Vice Pres., Sales/Mktg.–Peter M. Carlander

InterVoice-Brite, Inc.
17811 Waterview Pkwy., Dallas, TX, 75252; tel (972) 454-8000; fax (972) 454-8707; web site www.convergys.com
Pres.–Mike Betzer
Industry: Consulting Services: Advertising; Consulting Services: Marketing; Interfaces; Promotion Services; Speech Recognition; Telecommunications;

Intralox, LLC
201 Laitram Ln., Harahan, LA, 70123; tel (504) 733-0463; fax (504) 734-0063; web site www.intralox.com
Sales Mgr.–Edel Blanks
Industry: Conveyors

INX International Ink Co.
150 N. Martingale Rd., Ste. 700, Schaumburg, IL, 60173-2009; tel (630) 682-1800; fax (847) 969-9758; e-mail general@inxinternational.com; info@inxintl.com; web site www.inxinternational.com
Chrmn.–M. Matsuzawa
Pres./CEO–Richard Clendenning
Sr. Vice Pres., Product/Mfg. Technology–Joe Cichon
Sr. Vice Pres.-Gen. Affairs/Admin.–John Carlson
Sr. Vice Pres.-Liquid Div.–Charles Weinholzer
Sr. Vice Pres.-Metal Div.–Kenneth O'-Callaghan
Sr. Vice Pres.-Offset Div./COO–George Polasik
Dir., PR–Betty Leavitt
Industry: Chemicals: Pressroom; Cleaners & Solvents; Consulting Services: Marketing; Ink Bleeding Equipment; Ink Fountains & Accessories; Ink Pumping Systems; Ink Storage Tanks; Inks;

INX International Ink Co.
3257 Middle Rd., Dunkirk, NY, 14048; tel (716) 366-6010; fax (716) 366-2820; web site www.inxinternational.com
Product Mgr.–Don Szwejbka
Industry: Inks

ITW Hobart Brothers Co.
400 Trade Sq. E., Troy, OH, 45373-2975; tel (937) 332-4000; fax (937) 332-5224; web site www.hobartbrothers.com
Welding Equip. Mgr.–Dean Phillips
Adv./Commun. Mgr.–Debbie Doench
Industry: Motors

J

JFM Machine Co., Inc.
PO Box 16, Beacon Falls, CT, 06403; tel (203) 888-4744; fax (203) 888-2807; e-mail info@jfmmachine.com; web site www.jfmmachine.com
Pres.–Joe Moroz
Industry: Dampening Systems

JP Media Partners
604 Sutter Street, Suite 394, Folsom, CA, 95630, USA; tel (916) 673-9779; fax (888) 933-0807; e-mail jeff@jpmediapartners.com; web site www.jpmediapartners.com
Principal–Jeffrey Potts
Industry: Brokers & Appraisers

Jardis Industries, Inc.
1201 W. Ardmore Ave., Itasca, IL, 60143; tel (630) 860-5959; fax (630) 860-6515; e-mail info@jardis.com; web site www.jardis.com
Pres.–Alan W. Jardis
Dir., Sales–Gary Klawinski
Industry: Dryers: Film and Papers; Drying Systems; Erectors & Riggers; Flying Pasters; Pasters; Reels & Tensions; Reels (Inlcudes Paper Reels); Remanufactures Equipment;

Johnstone Engineering & Machine Co.
11 High St, Christiana, PA, 17509; tel 610-593-6350; fax 610-593-2172; e-mail jemco2@comcast.net
Sales Mgr.–Raymond E. Sullivan
President–Bill Haag
Industry: Reels & Tensions; Reels (Inlcudes Paper Reels); Rewinders; Roll Handeling Equipment;

John Juliano Computer Services Co.
2152 Willive Pl., Decatur, GA, 30033; tel (404) 327-6010; e-mail jjcs@jjcs.com; web site www.jjcs.com
Pres.–John Juliano
Industry: Consulting Services: Advertising; Consulting Services: Computer; Consulting Services: Marketing; Software: Editorial; Software: Pagination/Layout; Software: Workflow Management/Tracking;

Jupiter Images Corp.
6000 N. Forest Park Dr., Peoria, IL, 61614, USA; tel (309) 688-8800; fax (309) 688-5873; e-mail sales@jupiterimages.com; web site www.jupiterimages.com
Vice Pres., Opns.–Mark Nickerson
Industry: Software: Design/Graphics; Trade Publications;

Just Normlicht, Inc.
2000 Cabot Blvd. W., Ste. 120, Langhorne, PA, 19047-2408; tel (267) 852-2200; fax (267) 852-2207; e-mail sales@justnormlicht.com; web site www.justnormlicht.com
Vice President–Eric Dalton
Industry: Color Proofing; Color Viewing Equipment;

K

KBA North America, Inc. (Koenig & Bauer AG)
2555 Regent Blvd, Dallas, TX, 75261; tel 469-532-8000; fax ; e-mail namarketing@kba,com; web site www.kba.com
Pres./CEO–Mark Hischar
Vice Pres., Finance–Gerrit Zwergel
Vice Pres., Mktg.–Eric Frank
Vice Pres., Servs./Opns.–Tim McKeon
Dir., Sales–Jason Maurice
Industry: Flexogrpahic Press Conversion; Flying Pasters; Pasters; Presses: Flexographic; Presses: Offset; Reels & Tensions; Reels (Inlcudes Paper Reels); Tension & Web Controls;

K & F International, Inc.
12633 Industrial Park Dr., Granger, IN, 46530; tel (574) 272-9950; fax (574) 277-6566; e-mail sales@k-f.com; web site www.k-f.com
Gen. Mgr.–Kent Deal
Vice Pres., Sales–Al Brunner
Mktg. Coord.–Tim Scott
Coord., Int'l Sales–Linda Vervaet
Industry: Color Registration; Offset Plate-Making Service & Equipment; Pin Register Systems; Plate Bending Systems; Plate Processors; Platemakers: Offset (Conventional); 281;

K-Jack Engineering Co., Inc.
PO Box 2320, Gardena, CA, 90249; tel (310) 327-8389; fax (310) 769-6997; e-mail kjack@kjack.com; web site www.kjack.com
Pres.–Jack S. Chalabian
Vice Pres.–Jacqueline Chalabian-Jernigan
Vice Pres., Sales–Steven H. Chalabian
Industry: Cart Distribution Systems; Circulation Equipment & Supplies; Delivery Equipment; Newspaper Dispensers (Mechanical/Electronic); Software: Circulation; Tubes, Racks (Includes Racks: Motor Route Tubes);

K & M Newspaper Services, Inc.
45 Gilbert St. Extension, Monroe, NY, 10950; tel (845) 782-3817; fax (845) 783-2972; e-mail info@kmnewspaper.com; web site www.kmnewspaper.com
Pres.–Mark Jacobs
Controller–Micki Jacobs
Office Mgr.–Karla Hahan
Vice Pres., Sales–Rick Walter
Industry: Belts, Belting, V-Belts; Controls: Photo Electric; Conveyors; Mailroom Systems & Equipment; Motors; Remanufactures Equipment;

Kaim & Associates International Marketing, Inc.
102 Industrial Park Rd., Lodi, WI, 53555-1374; tel (608) 592-7404; fax (608) 592-7404; e-mail info@kaiminc.com; web site www.kaiminc.com
Pres.–Wayne Kaim
Industry: Color Registration; Controls: Register; Paper Shredders; Pasters; Reels & Tensions; Roll Cleaning Equipment; Rollers; Tension & Web Controls; Web Break Detector; Web Cleaners;

Kamen & Co. Group Services
626 RXR Plaza, Uniondale, NY, 11556, USA; tel (516) 379-2797; fax (516) 379-3812; e-mail info@kamengroup.com; web site www.kamengroup.com
Pres./CEO–Kevin B. Kamen
Vice Pres.–Celeste Myers
Industry: Architects/Engineers (Includes Design/Construction Firms); Brokers & Appraisers; Circulation Equipment & Supplies; Consulting Services: Advertising; Consulting Services: Circulation; Consulting Services: Financial; Consulting Services: Human Resources; Consulting Services: Marketing; Training: Sales & Marketing; Tubes, Racks (Includes Racks: Motor Route Tubes);

Kanaly Trust Co.
5555 San Felipe, Ste. 200, Houston, TX, 77056; tel (713) 626-9483; fax (713) 877-8744; e-mail kanaly@kanaly.com; web site www.kanaly.com
Chairman/CEO–Drew Kanaly
Industry: Consulting Services: Financial

Kansa Technology, LLC
3700 Oakes Dr., Emporia, KS, 66801; tel (620) 343-6700; fax (620) 343-2108; e-mail marketing@kansa.com; web site www.kansa.com
CEO–Jerry Waddell
Controller–Juanita White
Opns. Mgr.–Lonnie Worthington
Industry: Addressing Machines; Collating Equipment; Conveyors; Counting, Stacking, Bundling Machines; Feeding, Folding, Delivery Equipment; Folding Machines; Infeed Stackers; Inserting Equipment (Includes Stuffing Machines); Mailroom Systems & Equipment; Remanufactures Equipment;

Kaspar Wire Works, Inc./Sho-Rack
PO Box 1127, Shiner, TX, 77984; tel (361)

594-2911; fax (361) 594-4264; e-mail cust-serv@shorack.com; web site www.shorack.com
Inside Sales Mgr.–Chris Stluka
Sales-AL, FL, MS, LA, TN, AR–Gary Grosz
Sales-KY, IL, OH, IN, WI, MO–Bob Sanders
President–David Kaspar
Sales-KS, OK–Frank Dromgoole
Sales-NJ, PA, MD, DE–Robert Jarjisian
Industry: Cabinets; Cart Distribution Systems; Circulation Equipment & Supplies; Cleaners & Solvents; Delivery Equipment; Mailroom Systems & Equipment; Newspaper Dispensers (Mechanical/Electronic); Paper Handeling Equipment; Software: Circulation;

Katahdin Paper Company LLC
50 Main St., Millinocket, ME, 04430; tel (207) 723-2351; fax (207) 723-2200
Prodn. Mgr., East–Jim Cornell
Industry: Newsprint; Paper: Groundwood Specialties; Paper: Specialty Printing Paper;

K-Cor, Inc.
1885 Main St., Pittsburgh, PA, 15215; tel N/A

The Keenan Group, Inc.
PO Box 458, Pleasant View, TN, 37146-0458, USA; tel (615) 746-2443; fax (615) 746-2270; e-mail info@keenangroup.com; web site www.keenangroup.com
Pres.–Robert P. Keenan
Vice Pres., Sales/Mktg.–Debra B. Keenan
Industry: Consulting Services: Advertising; Consulting Services: Circulation; Consulting Services: Equipment; Consulting Services: Marketing; Consulting Services: Production; Newspaper Bags; Newspaper Dispensers (Mechanical/Electronic); Newspaper Marketing;

Keene Technology, Inc. (KTI)
14357 Commercial Pkwy., South Beloit, IL, 61080; tel (815) 624-8989; fax (815) 624-4223; e-mail info@keenetech.com; web site www.keenetech.com
Office Mgr.–Kery Wallace
Industry: Rewinders; Splicers, Automatic;

Keister Williams Newspaper Services, Inc.
PO Box 8187, Charlottesville, VA, 22906, USA; tel (434) 293-4709; fax (434) 293-4884; e-mail ky@kwnews.com; web site www.kwnews.com
Pres./Treasurer–Walton C. (Ky) Lindsay
Vice Pres., Mktg.–Meta L. Nay
Admin.–Carol Lindsay
Pres.–Walton Lindsay
Industry: Consulting Services: Advertising; Consulting Services: Marketing;

Kepes, Inc.
9016 58th pl., Kenosha, WI, 53144; tel (262) 652-7889; fax (262) 652-7787; e-mail inquire@kepes.com; web site www.kepes.com
Pres./Sales Mgr.–Wayne Pagel
Mktg. Mgr.–John Slanchik
Industry: Equipment Dealers (Used); Feeding, Folding, Delivery Equipment; Gluing Systems; Remanufactures Equipment; Roll Handeling Equipment; Rollers;

Kidder, Inc.
270 Main St., Agawam, MA, 01001; tel (413) 786-8692; fax (413) 786-8785; e-mail kidderpress@worldnet.att.net; web site www.kidderpress.com
Pres.–Charles Rae
CFO–Thomas K. Trant
Vice Pres.-HR–John Rico
Vice Pres.-Engineering–Harris Barnard
Mktg. Mgr.–Cheryl N. Smith
Industry: Dryers: Film and Papers; Ink Fountains & Accessories; Presses: Flexographic; Rewinders;

Kimoto Tech
1850 Howard St., Ste. G, Elk Grove Village, IL, 60007; tel (847) 640-8022; fax (847) 640-7942; e-mail kimofilms@aol.com; web site www.kimototech.com
Sales Supvr.–Alex Jasinowski
Industry: Film & Paper: Filters (Photographic); Film & Paper: Phototypesetting;

Kinetic Corporation
200 Distillery Commons, Ste. 200, Louisville, KY, 40206-1990, USA; tel (502) 719-9500; fax (502) 719-9569; e-mail info@theTechnologyAgency.com; web site www.theTechnologyAgency.com
Pres.–G. Raymond Schuhmann
Chief Brand Strategist–Cindi Ramm
Industry: Consulting Services: Production; Photo Archiving; Preprint Service & Production; Software: Asset Management; Software: Design/Graphics; Software: Pagination/Layout; Software: Workflow Management/Tracking;

Kirk-Rudy, Inc.
125 Lorraine Pkwy., Woodstock, GA, 30188; tel (770) 427-4203; fax (770) 427-4036; web site www.kirkrudy.com
Pres.–Rick Marshal
Industry: Addressing Machines; Inserting Equipment (Includes Stuffing Machines); Mailroom Systems & Equipment;

Kodak GCG
401 Merritt 7, Norwalk, CT, 06851-1000; tel (203) 845-7115; fax (203) 845-7173; web site www.kodak.com
Sr. Cor. Vice Pres.–Andrew Copley
Industry: Chemicals: Photographic; Chemicals: Plate Processing; Color Management Software; Color Proofing; Film & Paper: Contact; Film & Paper: Duplicating; Film & Paper: Filters (Photographic); Offset Plate-Making Service & Equipment; Plates: Offset (Computer to Plate); Plates: Offset (Conventional);

Koenig & Bauer Aktiengesellschaft (KBA)
Postfach 6060, Wuerzburg, N/A, D 97010, Germany; tel +49 931 909 4336; fax +49 931 909 6015; e-mail kba-wuerzburg@kba-print.de; web site www.kba-print.de
Pres.–Helge Hansen
Dir., Mktg.–Klaus Schmidt
Industry: Flexogrpahic Press Conversion; Flying Pasters; Press Control Systems; Presses: Flexographic; Presses: Offset; Presses: Rotogravure; Reels & Tensions; Roll Handeling Equipment; Roll Preparation Equipment; Web Press - Special Equipment;

Kolbus America, Inc.
812 Huron Rd., E. Ste.750, Cleveland, OH, 44115-1126; tel (216) 931-5100; fax (216) 931-5101; e-mail robert.shafer@kolbus.com; web site www.kolbus.com
Office Mgr.–Ruth Wilson
Pres./Dir., Sales/Distr. Americas–Robert Shafer
Industry: Counting, Stacking, Bundling Machines; Cutters & Trimmers; Material Handling Equipment: Palletizing Machines;

Komori America Corp.
5520 Meadowbrook Industrial Ct., Rolling Meadows, IL, 60008-3800; tel (847) 806-9000; fax (847) 806-9038; e-mail komori.american@attglobal.net; contact@komori-america.com; web site www.komori.com; www.komori-america.us
Pres./COO, Komori America Cor.–Kosh Miyao
Pdct. Mgr.–Doug Schardt
Industry: Presses: Offset; Proofing Systems;

Konica Minolta Graphic Imaging USA
5800 Foremost Dr. SE, Grand Rapids, MI, 49546; tel (616) 575-2800; fax (800) 204-4291; web site www.gi.konicaminolta.us
Sr. Vice Pres.–Wayne Bell
Industry: Color Proofing; Proofing Systems;

Konica Minolta Printing Solutions
PO Box 81250, Mobile, AL, 36689; tel (251) 633-4300; fax (251) 633-4460; e-mail stephanie.ryan@bpus.konicaminolta.us; web site www.konicaminolta.us; www.printer.konicaminolta.net
Chrmn./CEO–Shoei Yamana
Pres./COO–Stephen Fletcher
Inside Sale Dir.–Rick Gable
Corporate Contact–Stephanie Ryan
Industry: Laser Printers

Krause Newspaper Systems, Inc.
3585 Mystac Pointe Dr., Ste. A, Aventura, FL, 33180; tel (305) 792-2720; fax (305) 792-2719; e-mail krausenctb@bellsouth.net
Gen. Mgr., Newspaper–Richard Reipke
Vice Pres., Sales/Mktg.–Peter Lingat
Vice Pres., Sales/Mktg.–Manuel Hiraldo
Industry: Equipment Dealers (New)Pin Register Systems; Plate Processors; Platemakers: Direct; Platemakers: Offset (Computer to Plate); Platemakers: Offset (Conventional);

Krohm International Ltd.
4450 S. Noland Rd., Ste. C, Independence, MO, 64055-4766; tel (816) 373-7828; e-mail gary@krohm.com; web site www.krohm.com
Mgr., Mktg.–Gary Krohm
Industry: Typesetting Programs; Word Processing System;

Kubra
5050 Tomken Rd., Mississauga, ON, L4W 5B1, Canada; tel (905) 624-2220; fax (905) 624-2886; web site www.kubra.com
Pres./CEO–Rick Watkin
Vice Pres., Opns.–Robert Iantorno
Vice Pres., Sales/Mktg.–Rick Huff
Sr. Vice Pres., Bus. Devel.–Mark Visic

KYE International Corp.
12675 Colony, Pomona, CA, 91766; tel (909) 923-3510; fax (909) 923-1469; e-mail ddang@genius-kye.com; web site www.genius-kye.com
Pres.–Geoffrey Lin
Sales/Mktg. Mgr.–Duc Dang
Industry: Computers: Hardware & Software Integrators; Computers: Local Area Network (LANS); Scanners: Color B & W, Plates, Web;

L

Lankford Engineering, Inc.
PO Box 80335, Lafayette, LA, 70503-2506; tel (337) 267-3131; fax (337) 261-2332; e-mail infol@lankfordengr.com; web site www.lankfordengr.com
Mgr.–Greg Laurent
Industry: Architects/Engineers (Includes Design/Construction Firms); Consulting Services: Production; Flying Pasters; Maintenance, Plant & Equipment; Pasters; Reels & Tensions; Tension & Web Controls;

Lasalle Papers, Inc.
987 1st Ave., Sainte-Catherine, QC, J5C 1C5, Canada; tel (450) 635-5005; fax (450) 635-0462; web site www.lasallepapers.com
Pres.–Michel Lefort
Industry: Newsprint

Laser Products Technologies
3936 Circle Dr., Holmen, WI, 54636; tel (608) 781-1606; fax (608) 781-1626; e-mail lpt@centurytel.net; info@lptnow.com; web site www.lptnow.com
Pres.–Michael Marty
Vice Pres.–Bob King
Industry: Laser Printers

Latin American Div./Flint Ink
9100 S. Dadeland Blvd., Ste. 1800, Miami, FL, 33156; tel (305) 670-0066; fax (305) 670-0060; web site www.flintink.com
Pres.–Jerko E. Rendic
Bus. Mgr.–Claudia Anderson
Regl. Sales Mgr., Brazil–Paul Chmielewicz
Regl. Sales Mgr., South America–Fernando Tavara
Regl. Sales Mgr., Central America/Caribbean–Nestor Porto
Technical Serv. Mgr.–Al Miller
Industry: Blankets; Chemicals: Plate Processing; Chemicals: Pressroom; Chemicals: Roller Cleaning; Ink Pumping Systems; Ink Recovery Systems; Inks; Plates: Offset (Conventional); Presses: Offset;

Latran Technologies
31 Olympia Ave., Woburn, MA, 01801-1402; tel (800) 228-0979; fax (781) 932-1368; e-mail contact.latran@latran.com; web site www.latran.com
Chrmn./CEO–Anthony P. Crupi
GM/CTO–David McCarthy
Vice Pres., Sales–Jim McElhenny
Industry: Color Management Software; Color Proofing; Prepress Color Proofing Systems; Proofing Systems;

Lauterbach Group
W.222 N.5710 Millerway, Sussex, WI, 53089; tel (800) 558-2126; fax (800) 784-2591; e-mail mascinfo@masclabels.com; web site www.masclabels.com
Pres.–Shane Lauterbach

Vice Pres. Mktg.–Rebecca Kerschinske
Bus. Mgr.–Elaine Schnier
Industry: Label Printing Machines

Lazer-fare Media Services Ltd.
PO Box 48114, RPO Lakewood, Winnipeg, MB, R2J 4A3, Canada; tel (204) 452-5023; fax (204) 272-3499; e-mail inquires@lazerfare.com; sales@lazerfare.com; web site www.lazerfare.com
Pres.–Kelly Armstrong
Industry: Archiving Systems; Calibration Software/Hardware; Computers: Hardware & Software Integrators; Consulting Services: Advertising; Consulting Services: Computer; Consulting Services: Editorial; Consulting Services: Equipment;

Learning Tree International
400 Continental Blvd., Ste. 150, El Segundo, CA, 90245-0028; tel (310) 417-9700; fax (310) 410-2952; e-mail uscourses@learningtree.com; web site www.learningtree.com
Chrmn.–David Collins
Pres./CEO–Nicholas Schacht
Industry: Training: Keyboard Operation

LEXIS-NEXIS
PO Box 933, Dayton, OH, 45401, USA; tel (937) 865-6800; fax (937) 865-1583; e-mail bookstore.support@lexisnexis.com; web site www.lexisnexis.com
CEO, Lexis-Nexis Grp.–Andrew Prozes
Pres./CEO, Cor. & Fed. Mkts.–Kurt Sanford
Pres./CEO, U.S. Legal Mkts.–Michael Walsh
CEO, Risk Mgmt.–James M. Peck

Lincoln Industrial
1 Lincoln Way, Saint Louis, MO, 63120-1578; tel (314) 679-4200; fax (800) 424-5359; web site www.lincolnindustrial.com
Pres.–Bart Aitken
Vice Pres., Finance–Phillip Garton
Dir., Product Mgmt.–Pete Laucis
Vice Pres., Sales/Mktg.–Jim Hawk
Mgr., Mktg. Serv.–Roy Lotspeich
Industry: Lubricants; Pumps (Air, Ink, Vacuum);

Linde Lift Truck Corp.
PO Box 2400, Summerville, SC, 29484-2400; tel (843) 875-8000; fax (843) 875-8362; web site www.lmh-na.com; www.lindelifttruck.com
Pres.–Brian Butler
Mktg. Dir.–Mark Rossler
Industry: Material Handling Equipment: Automatic Guided Vehicles; Material Handling Equipment: Truck Loaders; Material Handling Equipment: Vehicle Loading;

Litco International, Inc.
PO Box 150, Vienna, OH, 44473-9600; tel (330) 539-5433; fax (330) 539-5388; e-mail info@litco.com; info-websales@litco.com; web site www.litco.com
Pres.–Gary L. Trebilcock
CEO–Lionel F. Trebilcock
Vice Pres.–Gary A. Sharon
Industry: Material Handling Equipment: Pallets & Palletizers

Lithco Inc.
PO Box 8, East Syracuse, NY, 13057; tel (800) 454-8426; fax (315) 656-2004; e-mail lithco@lithcoinc.com; web site www.lithco-inc.com
Pres.–Gerald Gaebel
Office Mgr.–Sheila Martin
Industry: Gauges, Measuring; Layout Tables, Light Tables & Workstations; Optical Products; Prepress Color Proofing Systems; Rules;

Litho Research, Inc.
1621 W. Carroll Ave., Chicago, IL, 60612-2595; tel (312) 738-0292; fax (312) 738-2386
Pres.–Michael T. Miske
Industry: Environmental Control Systems; Offset Blankets, Blanket Wash; Offset Chemicals & Supplies; Plate Cleaners; Roll Cleaning Equipment; Static Eliminators;

LogEtronics Corp.
6521 Arlington Rd., Ste. 210, Falls Church, VA, 22042; tel (703) 912-7745; fax (703) 912-7610; e-mail loge@starpower.net
Pres.–Raymond Luca
Industry: Film & Paper: Film Processing Machines; Film & Paper: Film Roll Dispensers; Plate Coating Machines; Plate Exposure Units; Plate Processors; Plate Scanning Systems; Processors: Diffusion Transfer; Processors: Film & Paper; Remanufactures Equipment;

Logic Associates, Inc.
221 Christian St., White River Junction, VT, 05001; tel (802) 295-5661; fax (802) 295-5512; e-mail jimd@zlogic.com; web site www.zlogic.com
Dir.-Sales–Jim Downey
Sales–Frank Gorski
Sales Administrator–Barb Ritchotte
Industry: Consulting Services: Production; Drives & Controls; System Integration Services; Totalizing Systems;

Lorentzen & Wettre
1055 Windward Ridge Pkwy., Ste. 160, Alpharetta, GA, 30005; tel (770) 442-8015; fax (770) 442-6792; e-mail usa@lorentzen-wettre.com; web site www.lorentzen-wettre.com
Pres.–Phillip Westmoreland
Industry: Consulting Services: Production; Maintenance, Plant & Equipment; Paper Testing Instruments;

Lyon Enterprises
4305 Cloud Dance, Santa Fe, NM, 87507; tel (505) 473-1775; fax (505) 471-1665; e-mail info@lyonenterprises.com; web site www.lyonenterprises.com
Pres.–Ray Lyon
Industry: Circulation Equipment & Supplies; Tubes, Racks (Includes Racks: Motor Route Tubes);

MBG Telecom Software, Inc.
370 Lexington Ave., 23rd Fl., New York, NY, 10017; tel (212) 822-4400; fax (212) 822-4499; e-mail info@mbg-inc.com; web site www.mbgtelecom.com
Pres.–Michael Greenspan
Industry: Software: Design/Graphics; Telecom

M

MBM Corp.
PO Box 40249, North Charleston, SC, 29418; tel (843) 552-2700; fax (843) 552-2974; e-mail sales@mbmcorp.com; web site www.mbmcorp.com
Pres.–Ned Ginsburg
Industry: Cutters & Trimmers; Cutting Tools; Feeding, Folding, Delivery Equipment; Folding Machines; In-Line Trimming Systems;

McCrrory Publishing
P.O. Box 5218, Fort Wayne, IN, 46895; tel 260-485-1812; e-mail info@mccpub.com; web site www.mccpub.com
Industry: Computers: Hardware & Software Integrators; Consulting Services: Computer; Consulting Services: Editorial; Software: Advertising (Includes Display; Classified); Software: Editorial; Software: Electronic Data Interchange; Software: Pagination/Layout; System Integration Services;

MCI
22001 Loudoun County Pkwy., Ashburn, VA, 20147, USA; tel (703) 206-5600; fax (703) 206-5601; e-mail info@mci.com; web site www.mci.com
Chrmn./CEO–Ivan Siedenberg
Pres., Opns./Tech.–Fred Briggs
Exec. Vice Pres./CFO–Robert Blakely
Exec. Vice Pres., HR–Daniel Casaccia
Exec. Vice Pres., Strategy/Cor. Devel.–Jonathan Crane
Sr. Vice Pres., Commun.–Grace Chentent
Sr. Vice Pres., Mktg./CMO–Nancy B. Gofus
Industry: Data Communication

MGI International, Inc.
1800 Chapman Ave., Rockville, MD, 20852; tel (301) 881-4242; fax (301) 881-9121; e-mail mgiahamlin@aol.com
Pres.–Arthur Hamlin
Industry: Environmental Control Systems; Ink Controls, Computerized; Ink De-Misting Systems; Ink Recovery Systems; Wastewater Treatment;

MPC LLC
906 East Karcher Rd., Nampa, ID, 83687; tel (800) 776-4516; fax (208) 893-8720; web site www.mpccorp.com
Exec. Vice Pres., Sales/Mktg.–Ross Ely
Industry: Computers: Hardware & Software Integrators

MPC Computers, LLC
906 E. Karcher Rd., Nampa, ID, 83687-3045; tel (208) 893-3434; fax (208) 893-7215; e-mail pr@mpccorp.com; web site www.mpccorp.com
CEO–John P. Yeros
COO–Jeff Fillmore
Vice Pres., Cor. Mktg./PR–Ross Ely
Industry: Computers: Hardware & Software Integrators

MSP Communications
220 S. 6th St., Ste. 500, Minneapolis, MN, 55402-4507; tel (612) 339-7571; fax (612) 339-5806; e-mail edit@mspmag.com; web site www.mspmag.com
Pres.–Gary Johnson
Ed. in Chief–Brian Anderson
Industry: Trade Publications

Mac Dermid Autotype Inc.
1675 Winnetka Cir., Rolling Meadows, IL, 60008; tel (847) 818-8262; fax (847) 818-8280; e-mail info@autotypeamerica.com; web site www.macdermidautotype.com
Pres.–Peter Levinsohn
Industry: Chemicals: Photographic; Masking Materials; Plates: Offset (Computer to Plate)

MacDermid Printing Solutions
260 S. Pacific St., San Marcos, CA, 92069; tel (760) 510-6277; fax (760) 471-6982; web site www.macdermid.com/printing
Pres.–Stephen Largan
Publication Mktg. Mgr.–Tom Moore
Industry: Cleaners & Solvents; Color Management Software; Platemakers: Flexographic (Traditional); Platemakers: Letterpress; Plates: Flexographic (Conventional);

MacDermid Printing Solutions
245 Freight St., Waterbury, CT, 06702-1818; tel (203) 575-5700; fax (203) 575-5916; web site www.macdermid.com/printing
CEO–Dan Leever
Mgr., Nat'l Sales–Timothy Sener
Industry: Blanket Mounting and Bars; Blankets; Platemakers: Direct; Platemakers: Flexographic (Computer to Plate); Platemakers: Flexographic (Traditional); Platemakers: Letterpress; Plates: Flexographic (Conventional); Plates: Letterpress; Plates: Offset (Computer to Plate);

MacDonald Advertising Services
302 Ferry St., Lafayette, IN, 47901-1185; tel (765) 742-9012; fax (765) 742-2843; e-mail info@macdonaldclassified.com; web site www.gomacdonald.com
Pres.–Patrick McDonald
Mng. Ed.–Andrew McGlothlen
Industry: Art & Layout Equipment and Services; Consulting Services: Advertising; Software: Design/Graphics; Trade Publications;

Magnetic Power Systems, Inc.
22 W. Memorial Rd., Oklahoma, OK, 73114; tel (405) 755-1600; fax (405) 755-8425; e-mail magpowr@magpowr.com; web site www.magpowr.com
Industry: Drives & Controls; Reels & Tensions; Tension & Web Controls;

MAH Machine Co., Inc.
3301 S. Central Ave., Cicero, IL, 60804; tel (708) 656-1826; fax (708) 656-4152; e-mail info@mahmachine.com; web site www.mahmachine.com
Pres.–Martin Hozjan
Industry: Cylinder Repair; Equipment Dealers (New); Equipment Dealers (Used); Feeding, Folding, Delivery Equipment; Presses: Offset; Roller Grinding Services; Rollers; Rollers: Dampening;

Malow Corp.
100 E. Progress Rd., Lombard, IL, 60148; tel (847) 956-0200; fax (847) 956-0935; web site www.malow.com
Sales Mgr.–Terry Luzader
Industry: Automatic Plastic Bagging Equipment; Bundling and Tying Machines; Strapping Machines;

Manroland Inc.
800 E. Oak Hill Dr., Westmont, IL, 60559, USA; tel (630) 920-2000; fax (630) 920-9146; e-mail marketing@mru.com; web site www.manroland.us.com
CEO–Vincent Lapinski
Marketing & CRM Specialist–Denise Lease
Industry: Material Handling Equipment: Automatic Guided Vehicles; Newsprint Handeling Equipment; Press Accessories, Parts & Supplies; Press Control Systems; Presses: Flexographic; Presses: Offset; Reels (Inlcudes Paper Reels); Roll Cleaning Equipment;

Managing Editor, Inc.
610 Old York Rd., Ste. 250, Jenkintown, PA, 19046; tel (215) 886-5662; fax (215) 886-5681; e-mail info@maned.com; web site www.maned.com
Pres.–Dennis McGuire
Vice Pres., Sales–Steven Haught
Vice Pres., Bus. Devel.–Mark Leister
Vice Pres., Pdct. Devel.–Bob Baldwin
Industry: Pagination Systems; Preprint Service & Production; Software: Advertising (Includes Display; Classified); Software: Editorial; Software: Pagination/Layout; Software: Workflow Management/Tracking;

Manassy Sales Inc.
6861 Yellowstone Blvd., Forest Hills, NY, 11375, USA; tel (718) 544-4739; fax (347) 642 8060; e-mail manassyparts@yahoo.com
Pres.–Joel Marcus
Industry: Press Accessories, Parts & Supplies; Rollers;

Manistique Papers, Inc.
453 S. Mackinac Ave., Manistique, MI, 49854; tel (906) 341-2175; fax (906) 341-5635; e-mail info@manistiquepapers.com; web site www.manistiquepapers.com
Gen. Mgr.–Jon Johnson
Comptroller–Linda Benedetto
Prodn. Mgr.–Tony Martin
Industry: Newsprint; Paper: Groundwood Specialties;

Manugraph DGM, Inc.
PO Box 573, Elizabethville, PA, 17023; tel (717) 362-3243; fax (717) 362-0978; web site www.dauphingraphic.com
CEO–Chris Lunt
Pres.–Brian LaBine
Vice Pres., Sales/Mktg.–David Moreland
Mgr., Inside Sales/Mktg.–David Lucas
Industry: Press Repairs; Presses: Offset; Remanufactures Equipment; Software: Workflow Management/Tracking; Training: Press Operation & Maintenance;

Maratek Environmental Technologies, Inc.
60 Healey Rd., Unit 8, Bolton, ON, L7E 5A5, Canada; tel (905) 857-2738; fax (905) 857-2764; e-mail mchouinard@maratek.com; web site www.maratek.com/stor.pdf
Pres.–Colin Darcel
Mktg. Mgr.–Michelle Chouinard
Industry: Environmental Control Systems; Equipment Dealers (New); Fluid Handeling: Pressroom; Ink Recovery Systems; Silver Recovery; Wastewater Treatment; Solvent Recovery Systems;

Markem-Imaje
1650 Airport Rd., Ste. 101, Kennesaw, GA, 30144-7017; tel (770) 421-7700; fax (770) 421-7702; e-mail custsvc@markem-imaje.com; web site www.imaje.com; www.markem-imaje.com
President–Omar Kerbage
Gen. Mgr.–Jacques Desroches
Mgr., Mktg.–Alisha Howard
Industry: Addressing Machines; Inks; Label Printing Machines; Mailroom Systems & Equipment;

Marketing Plus, Inc.
135 Green St., Woodbridge, NJ, 07095-2961; tel (732) 694-1020; fax (732) 602-9090; e-mail mpi@marketingplusinc.com; web site www.marketingplusinc.com
Pres./CEO–Monty Cerasani
Gen. Mgr.–Susan Taylor
Office Mgr.–John Saparito
HR Mgr.–Karen Marov
Vice Pres., Bus. Devel.–John Lederer
IT Mgr.–Phil Lyman
Industry: Consulting Services: Marketing; Market Research;

Marketing Research Associates, Inc.
3511 W. 55th St., Minneapolis, MN, 55410; tel 612-414-4672; e-mail asday65@gmail.com; web site www.retail-promotions.com
CEO–Adam Scott Day
Industry: Consulting Services: Advertising; Consulting Services: Circulation; Consulting Services: Marketing; Newspaper Marketing; Software: Advertising (Includes Display; Classified); Training: Sales & Marketing;

Marketing Strategies Incorporated
90 Libbey Pkwy., Ste. 101, Weymouth, MA, 02189; tel (781) 340-6640; fax (781) 340-7640; e-mail info@marketingstrategies.org; web site www.marketingstrategies.org
Industry: Consulting Services: Advertising; Consulting Services: Marketing;

Markzware Software, Inc.
1805 E. Dyer Rd., Ste. 101, Santa Ana, CA, 92705-5742; tel (949) 756-5100; fax (949) 756-5108; e-mail info@markzware.com; web site www.markzware.com
Pres./CEO–Patrick Marchese
PR–Mary Gay
Public Relations–Mary Gay Marchese
Industry: Software: Editorial; Software: Electronic Data Interchange;

Martin Automatic, Inc.
1661 Northrock Ct., Rockford, IL, 61103; tel (815) 654-4800; fax (815) 654-4810; e-mail info@martinauto.com; web site www.martin-auto.com
Vice Pres., Sales–David A. Wright
Contract Admin.–Bob Sanderson
Contract Admin.–Tim Delhotal
Mktg. Mgr.–Tim Ward
Industry: Conversion Equipment; Flying Pasters; Newsprint Handeling Equipment; Pasters; Press Accessories, Parts & Sup-

plies; Rewinders; Web Guides;

Martin Yale, Inc.
251 Wedcor Ave., Wabash, IN, 46992; tel (260) 563-0641; fax (260) 563-4575; e-mail info@martinyale.com; web site www.martinyale.com
Pres.–Greg German
Industry: Cutters & Trimmers; Folding Machines; Label Printing Machines; Paper Handeling Equipment; Paper Shredders;

Master Flo Technology
1233 Tessier St., Hawkesbury, ON, K6A 3R1, Canada; tel (613) 636-0539; fax (613) 636-0762; e-mail info@mflo.com; web site www.mflo.com
President–Edward Desaulniers
Vice Pres., Opns–Tim Duffy
Industry: Circulation Equipment & Supplies; Dampening Systems; Delivery Equipment; Feeding, Folding, Delivery Equipment; Ink Fountains & Accessories; Inserting Equipment (Includes Stuffing Machines); Material Handling Equipment: Pallets & Palletizers; Offset Fountain Controls; Press Accessories, Parts & Supplies; Recirculators;

Masthead International, Inc.
2020 W. Pinnacle Peak Rd., Phoenix, AZ, 85027; tel (623) 780-0005; fax (623) 780-0020; e-mail steve.stone@masthead.net; web site www.masthead.net
Branch Mgr.–Steve Stone
Bus. Devel. Mgr.–Kent Kraft
Industry: Controllers: Press; Drives & Controls; Erectors & Riggers; Pasters; Press Parts; Press Rebuilding; Press Repairs; Presses: Flexographic; Presses: Letterpress; Presses: Offset; Tension & Web Controls; Training: Press Operation & Maintenance; Web Width Changer;

Masthead International, Inc.
1504 Harrell St., LaVergne, TN, 37086; tel (615) 287-1330; fax (615) 287-1335; web site www.masthead.net
Proj. Mgr./Estimator–Joel Birket

Matthews International Corp.
2 North Shore Ctr., Pittsburgh, PA, 15206-4407; tel (412) 665-2550; fax (412) 365-2055; e-mail info@matw.com; web site www.matthewsmarking.com; www.matw.com
Pres./CEO–Joseph C. Bartolacci
Industry: Laser Printers

Maxcess
PO Box 26508, Oklahoma City, OK, 73126; tel (405) 755-1600; fax (405) 755-8425; e-mail sales@maxcessintl.com; web site www.maxcessintl.com
Brand Manager–Kasey Morales
Dir., Mktg./Sales–Stephanie Millman
Industry: Chemicals: Chuck (Paper Roll); Cutters & Trimmers; Cutting Tools; Drives & Controls; Reels & Tensions; Tension & Web Controls; Visual Display Terminals; Web Break Detector; Web Guides; Web Press - Special Equipment;

MAXX Material Handling LLC
315 E. St., Hampton, VA, 23661; tel (757) 825-8100; fax (757) 825-8800; e-mail mhogan@maxxmh.com; web site www.maxxmh.com
Pres.–Randy Gilliland
Vice Pres.–Mark Hogan
Industry: Material Handling Equipment: Truck Loaders; Material Handling Equipment: Vehicle Loading;

McCain Bindery Systems
15454 Edison Drive, New Lenox, IL, 60451; tel 815-462-1129; fax 815-462-1471; e-mail mccainbind@earthlink.net; web site www.mccainbindery.com
Pres.–Nancy Jones
Sales Manager–Bill Whitehead
National Service/ Product Manager–Chester Zurek
Vice Pres./Gen. Mgr.–Dennis Keem
Industry: Inserting Equipment (Includes Stuffing Machines); Mailroom Systems & Equipment;

McCain Printing Co.
PO Box 3443, Danville, VA, 24543; tel (434) 792-1331; fax (434) 793-5473; e-mail efsounders@mccainprint.com; web site www.mccainprint.com
Owner–Eugene Sounders

McGrann Paper Corp.
2101 Westinghouse Blvd., Charlotte, NC, 28273; tel (704) 583-2101; fax (704) 369-2229; web site www.mcgrann.com
Owner–Karl McGrann
Sr. Vice Pres., Sales–Keith Castle
Customer Serv. Rep.–Candice Sheehy
Industry: Newsprint; Paper: Coated Groundwood Offset; Paper: Groundwood Specialties; Paper: Specialty Printing Paper;

McGrann Paper East
22476 Fisher Rd., Watertown, NY, 13601; tel (315) 788-4090; fax (315) 788-3388

McGrann Paper West
10865 Jersey Blvd, Rancho Cucamonga, CA, 91768; tel (909) 595-2727; fax (909) 595-2247; web site www.mcgrann.com
Pres.–Anthony V. Nanna

J. Thomas McHugh Co., Inc.
12931 Ford Dr., Fishers, IN, 46038; tel (317) 577-2121; fax (317) 577-2125; e-mail tbryant@jtmchugh.com; web site www.jtmchugh.com
Owner/CEO–Thomas J. Bryant
Vice Pres./Gen. Mgr.–Bill Vincent
Industry: Blanket Mounting and Bars; Blankets; Offset Blanket Thickness Gauge; Offset Blankets, Blanket Wash;

Media America Brokers
3137 E. Shadowlawn Ave., NE, Atlanta, GA, 30305-2405, USA; tel (404) 869-8686; fax (404) 869-9595; e-mail lonwwilliams@aol.com
Owner–Lon Williams
Industry: Brokers & Appraisers

Media Consultants, Inc.
3904 Central Ave., Ste. A140, Cheyenne, WY, 82001; tel (509)248-5860; web site www.mediaconsultants.com
Co-Owner–Michael Lindsey
Pres.–Pat Lindsey
Industry: Brokers & Appraisers

Media Consultants, Inc.
5132 Saint Andrews Dr., Loveland, CO, 80537-7954; tel (970) 215-4897; e-mail tslicence@comcast.netTerry Licence

Media Cybernetics LP
4340 East-West Hwy., Ste. 400, Bethesda, MD, 20814; tel (301) 495-3305; fax (301) 495-5964; e-mail info@mediacy.com; web site www.mediacy.com
Pres.–Doug Paxson
Industry: Optical Character Recognition (OCR)

Media Data Technology, Inc. (MDTI)
439 Grandy Rd., Ste. 1, South Hadley, MA, 01075; tel (413) 534-3307; e-mail jpeters@mediadatatech.com
Pres.–John Peters
Industry: Software: Advertising (Includes Display; Classified)

Media Marketing, Inc.
10955 Westmoor Dr. 4th Fl., Westminster, CO, 80021, USA; tel (303) 440-7855; fax 303-440-8035; e-mail info@immediate.com; sales@immediate.com; web site www.immediate.com
Pres./CEO–James Theall
VP, Solutions–Charles Mauldin
VP, Sales–Patti Theall
Industry: Consulting Services: Advertising; Consulting Services: Marketing; Software: Advertising (Includes Display; Classified); Training: Sales & Marketing;

Media Monitors, Inc.
445 Hamilton Ave., 7th Fl., White Plains, NY, 10601; tel (914) 428-5971; fax (914) 259-4541; web site www.mediamonitors.com
Pres.–Philippe Generali
Sales–John L. Selig
Industry: Consulting Services: Advertising

Media Professional Insurance
2 Pershing Sq., 2300 Main St., Ste. 800, Kansas City, MO, 64108-2404; tel (816) 471-6118; fax (816) 471-6119; e-mail marketing@mediaprof.com; web site www.mediaprof.com
Sr. Vice Pres., Underwriting–Mary Schust
Industry: Insurance

MediaSpan Group Inc.
2725 S. Industrial Hwy Suite 100, Ann Arbor, MI, 48104; tel (734) 887-4400; fax (734) 887-4401; e-mail marketing@mediaspangroup.com; web site www.mediaspangroup.com
Coord., Domestic Sales–Kim Anderson
Industry: Consulting Services: Circulation; Consulting Services: Editorial; Consulting Services: Production; Library Retrieval Systems; Pagination Systems; Publishing Systems; Software: Circulation; Software: Editorial; Software: Pagination/Layout; Training: Design & Layout

MediaSpan Group, Inc.
PO Box 97308, Raleigh, NC, 27624, USA; tel (321) 242-5000; web site www.mediaspangroup.com
CEO–F.R. Campagnoni
CMO–Mark S. Zagorski
Publishing Div. Contact–Peter Cooper
Industry: Software: Advertising (Includes Display; Classified); Software: Circulation; Software: Design/Graphics; Software: Editorial; Software: Pagination/Layout;

MediaSpan Media Software
300 North Dr., Ste. 1, Melbourne, FL, 32934; tel (734) 887-4400; fax (321) 242-5298; web site www.mediaspansoftware.com
Vice Pres., Mktg.–Ken Freedman
Exec. Vice Pres.–Dan Roberts
Vice Pres., Customer Servs.–Carla A. Green
Industry: Software: Advertising (Includes Display; Classified); Software: Circulation; Software: Design/Graphics; Software: Editorial; Software: Pagination/Layout; Software: Press/Post Press;

Meena Advertising Copy & Layout
200 Distillery Commons, Ste. 100, Louisville, KY, 40206; tel (800) 818-1181; fax (800) 818-8329; e-mail lynnemeena@aol.com
Pres.–Lynne Meena
Industry: Consulting Services: Advertising; Training: Design & Layout;

L
ynne Meena Co.
97 Warrior Rd., Louisville, KY, 40207; tel (800) 818-1181; fax (502) 897-3019

Megadata Corp.
35 Orville Dr., Bohemia, NY, 11716-2598; tel (631) 589-6800; fax (631) 589-6858; web site www.passur.com
CEO–James Barry
Pres.–Beck Gilbert
Industry: Data Communication; Input & Editing Systems;

Megasys International, Inc.
45 H Industrial Park Rd. W., Tolland, CT, 06084; tel (860) 871-8713; fax (860) 871-8710; e-mail megasysint@aol.com; web site megasysinternational.com
Pres.–Fred McNutt
Industry: Bundling and Tying Machines; Composing Room Equipment & Supplies; Equipment Dealers (New); Equipment Dealers (Used); Folding Machines; Label Printing Machines; Paper Shredders; Photostat: Machines;

MEGTEC Systems
PO Box 5030, De Pere, WI, 54115-5030; tel (920) 336-5715; fax (920) 339-2793; e-mail info@megtec.com; web site www.megtec.com
Mktg. Mgr.–Mary Van Vonderen
Industry: Dryers: Film and Papers; Drying Systems; Environmental Control Systems; Flying Pasters; Roll Handeling Equipment;

Louis Melind Co.
PO Box 1112, Skokie, IL, 60076; tel (847) 581-2500; fax (847) 581-2531; e-mail JustRiteLM@aol.com; web site members.aol.com/justritelm
Pres.–David B. Sterrett
Vice Pres., Mktg.–Donald M. Dowd
Mktg. Mgr.–Chip Sterrett
Industry: Cleaners & Solvents; Fixing & Stop Baths; Inks; Numbering Machines; Plate Exposure Units; Platemakers: Flexographic (Traditional); Platemakers: Offset (Conventional); Plates: Flexographic (Conventional);

Mercer Human Resource Consulting
720 Bausch & Lomb Pl., Rochester, NY, 14604; tel (585) 325-2870; fax (585) 325-2091; web site www.mercerhr.com
Mktg. Rep.–Jim Hardesty

MerlinOne, Inc.
17 Whitney Rd., Quincy, MA, 02169; tel (617) 328-6645; fax (617) 328-9845; e-mail info@merlinone.com; web site www.merlinone.com
Pres./CEO–David M. Tenenbaum
Merlin Senior Account Representative–Rande Simpson
Vice President of IT & Managed Services–Jeff Seidensticker
Dir., Cust. Support–Michael Kullen
Industry: Archiving Systems; Photo Archiving; Software: Asset Management;

Merrimac Software Associates
PO Box 28, South Tamworth, NH, 03883-0028, USA; tel 603-323-5077; fax (603) 218-2140; e-mail sales@merrsoft.com; web site www.merrsoft.com
Owner–Tom Vachon
Support Manager–Sabrina Fobes
Technical Support–Michael Davidson
Industry: Software: Advertising (Includes Display; Classified); Software: Business (Includes Administration/Accounting); Software: Circulation; Software: Pagination/Layout;

Mesa Corp.
4546 S. 86th St., Ste. B, Lincoln, NE, 68526; tel (402) 489-9303; fax (402) 489-7524; e-mail info@mesacorp.com; sales@mesacorp.com; web site www.mesacorp.com
Vice Pres.-Sales/Mktg.–Thomas Manning
Industry: Storage Retrieval Systems

Metafix, Inc.
1925 46th Ave., Montreal, QC, H8T 2P1, Canada; tel (514) 633-8663; fax (514) 633-1678; e-mail sales@metafix.com; web site www.metafix.com
Industry: Environmental Control Systems; Silver Recovery;

Metals Recovery Service
1660 Georgesville Rd., Columbus, OH, 43228-3620; tel (614) 870-0400; fax (614) 878-6000; web site www.msitarget.com
Vice Pres.–Steven P. Dahms
Industry: Silver Recovery

Metro Creative Graphics, Inc.
519 Eighth Ave., 18th Fl., New York, NY, 10018, USA; tel (212) 947-5100; fax (212) 967-4602; e-mail service@metro-email.com; web site www.metrocreativeconnection.com
Pres./CEO–Robert Zimmerman
Exec. Vice Pres./Mktg. Dir.–Debra Weiss
Mktg. Mgr.–Lauren Lekoski
Industry: Art & Layout Equipment and Services; Consulting Services: Advertising; Consulting Services: Editorial; Software: Design/Graphics; Software: Editorial;

Metroland Printing/Publishing & Distributing Ltd.

3125 Wolfedale Rd., Mississauga, ON, L5C 1W1, Canada; tel (905) 279-0440; fax (905) 279-7763; web site www.metroland.com
Vice Pres., HR–Brenda Biller
Industry: Presses: Offset; Publishing Systems;

Metso Paper
PO Box 2771, York, PA, 17405; tel (717) 845-4807; fax (717) 845-8828; e-mail imc-sales@imcamerica.com
Pres.–Ward Walsh
Vice Pres., Sales./Mktg.–Ric Mayle
Industry: Newsprint Handeling Equipment; Paper Handeling Equipment; Roll Handeling Equipment;

Micro Systems Specialists, Inc. (MSSI)
PO Box 347, Millbrook, NY, 12545-0347; tel (845) 677-6150; fax (845) 677-6620; e-mail mssisoftware@cs.com; web site www.mssi-software.com
Pres.–Catherine M. Culkin
Sec./Treasurer–Judy M. Bruning
Vice Pres., Mktg.–Dawn M. Roeller
Industry: Software: Advertising (Includes Display; Classified); Software: Business (Includes Administration/Accounting); Software: Circulation;

Microfilm Products Co.
157 Avalon Gardens Dr., Nanuet, NY, 10954-7417; tel (845) 371-3700; fax (845) 371-3780; e-mail info@microfilmproducts.com; web site www.microfilmproducts.com
Pres.–Gary Moelis
Industry: Addressing Machines; Bundling and Tying Machines; Equipment Dealers (New); Equipment Dealers (Used); Folding Machines;

Microtek
16941 Keegan Ave., Carson, CA, 90746; tel (310) 687-5800; fax (310) 687-5984; e-mail sales@microtek.com; web site www.microtekusa.com
Dir., Mktg.–Mary Ann Whitlock
Industry: Color Seperation Scanners; Scanners: Color B & W, Plates, Web;

Mid-America Graphics, Inc.
PO Box 466, Harrisonville, MO, 64701; tel (816) 887-2414; fax (816) 887-2762; e-mail sales@midamericagraphics.com; web site www.midamericagraphics.com
Pres.–Charles George
Exec. Vice Pres.–William David George
Gen. Mgr.–Dan George
Sec.–Terri Widdle
Industry: Conveyors; In-Line Trimming Systems; Infeed Stackers; Inserting Equipment (Includes Stuffing Machines); Newsprint Handeling Equipment;

MidLantic Equipment Co., Inc.
567 Wyckoff Ave., Wyckoff, NJ, 07481; tel (201) 891-1448; fax (201) 891-2664; e-mail midequip@yahoo.com; web site www.agfa-imagesetters.com
Mktg. Mgr.–Arlene Vanderweert
Industry: Imagesetters

Midsystems Technology Ltd.
125 Kensington High St., London, N/A, W8 5SF, United Kingdom; tel +44 2073 682 300; fax +44 2073 682 400; e-mail sales@midsys.co.uk; web site www.misys.co.uk
Mng. Dir.–John Sussens
Industry: Produciton Control Systems

Midwest Publishers Supply Co.
4640 N. Olcott Ave., Harwood Heights, IL, 60706-4604; tel (708) 867-4646; fax (708) 867-6954; e-mail info@mps-co.com
Pres.–James Rezabek
Industry: Art & Layout Equipment and Services; Blankets; Blue Line Grids; Chemicals: Pressroom; Composing Room Equipment & Supplies; Lift Trucks; Mailroom Systems & Equipment; Offset Chemicals & Supplies; Press Accessories, Parts & Supplies;

Miles 33
40 Richards Ave, Norwalk, CT, 06854, USA; tel (203) 838-2333; fax (203) 838-4473; e-mail info@miles33.com; web site www.miles33.com
Sr. VP. Sales–Don Sullivan
Industry: Consulting Services: Advertising; Consulting Services: Editorial; Software: Advertising (Includes Display; Classified); Software: Circulation; Software: Workflow Management/Tracking;

Miles 33 International
40 Richards Ave., Norwalk, CT, 06854, USA; tel (203) 838-2333; fax (203) 838-4473; e-mail info@miles33.com; web site www.miles33.com
Pres.–Chris Habasinski
Sr. VP Sales & Mkg–Don Sullivan
Industry: Computers: Hardware & Software Integrators; Consulting Services: Advertising; Consulting Services: Editorial; Software: Advertising (Includes Display; Classified); Software: Asset Management; Software: Editorial; Software: Pagination/Layout; Software: Workflow Management/Tracking;

Miller-Cooper Co.
5187 Merriam Dr., Merriam, KS, 66203-2167; tel (913) 312-5020; e-mail info@mcink.com; web site www.mcink.com
Pres.–Debbie Nylund
Industry: Adhesives; Blankets; Chemicals: Pressroom; Inks;

Simon Miller Sales Co.
1218 Chestnut St., Philadelphia, PA, 19107; tel (215) 923-3600; fax (215) 923-1173; e-mail info@simonmiller.com; web site www.simonmiller.com
Pres.–Joseph Levit
COO–Henri C. Levit
Vice Pres., Mktg.–David Donde
Industry: Newspaper Couter; Newspaper Marketing; Newsprint; Paper: Coated Groundwood Offset; Paper: Groundwood Specialties; Paper: Specialty Printing Paper; Roll Converters;

Minnesota Opinion Research, Inc. (MORI)
8500 Normandale Lake Blvd., Ste. 630, Minneapolis, MN, 55437-3809; tel (952) 835-3050; fax (952) 835-3385; web site www.moriresearch.com
Pres.–Ron Mulder
Vice Pres., Research–Brent Stahl
Industry: Consulting Services: Advertising; Consulting Services: Circulation; Consulting Services: Editorial; Consulting Services: Marketing; Market Research; Newspaper Marketing; Research Studies;

Mirachem Corp.
PO Box 14059, Phoenix, AZ, 85063-4059; tel (602) 415-9262; fax (602) 353-1411; e-mail cservice@mirachem.com; web site www.mirachem.com
COO–Pat Doughty
Sales Mgr.–Bob Boyle
Industry: Chemicals: Pressroom; Chemicals: Roller Cleaning; Cleaners & Solvents;

Miracle Industries, Inc.
259 Great Hill Rd., Naugatuck, CT, 06770; tel (203) 723-0928; fax (203) 723-0394
Pres.–John Chabot
Vice Pres., Sales/Mktg.–Phyllis Fennlly
Industry: Motors; Press Accessories, Parts & Supplies; Press Control Systems; Press Engineers; Presses: Offset; Roller Grinding Services; Web Break Detector; Web Press - Special Equipment;

Miracom Computer Corp.
PO Box 44, Eastchester, NY, 10709, USA; tel (888) 309-0639; fax (888)309-0639; e-mail info@miracomcomputer.com; web site www.miracomcomputer.com
CEO–Judah Holstein
Vice President–Bill Harley
Director, Customer Service–Tom Whelan
Field Application Engineer–Ralph Valero
Industry: Produciton Control Systems

Missouri Press Service, Inc.
802 Locust St., Columbia, MO, 65201; tel (573) 449-4167; fax (573) 874-5894; e-mail dcrews@socket.net; web site www.mopress.com
Exec. Dir.–Doug Crews
Industry: Consulting Services: Advertising; Consulting Services: Editorial;

Mitchell's
PO Box 2431, JAF Sta., New York, NY, 10116; tel (212) 594-6426; fax (212) 594-7254; e-mail menewman@mitchellsny.com; web site www.mitchellsny.com
–Mitchell Newman
–Roy NewmanOwners
Industry: Delivery Equipment

Mo-Money Associates, Inc.
3838 N. Palafox St., Pensacola, FL, 32505; tel (850) 432-6301; fax (850) 434-5645; e-mail momoney@momoney.com; web site www.momoney.com
Pres.–Cliff Mowe
Mktg. Mgr.–Tom McVoy

Mobile Computing Corporation USA
PO Box 5223, Charlottesville, VA, 22905-5223; tel (434) 977-2732; fax (434) 295-7414; web site www.mobilecom.com
Sales Rep.–Les Feasey
Industry: Business Computers; Computers: Hardware & Software Integrators; Consulting Services: Circulation; Consulting Services: Computer; Software: Circulation;

Mobile Reclamation System/MRS (Div. of Marpax)
1115 Shore St., West Sacramento, CA, 95691; tel (713) 621-1874; fax (713) 621-1878; e-mail gregpope1@compuserve.com
Division Pres.–Greg Pope
Industry: Ink Recovery Systems

Mohr Enterprise
15 E. Palatine Rd., Ste. 108, Prospect Heights, IL, 60070-1898, USA; tel (847) 465-0048; fax (847) 465-0044; e-mail info@vastechusa.com; sales@vastechusa.com; service@vastechusa.com; web site www.vastechusa.com; www.mohrpro.com
Pres.–G. Robert Jackson
Industry: Chemicals: Photographic; Cleaners & Solvents; Cutters & Trimmers; Processors: Film & Paper;

Monaco Systems, Inc.
100 Burtt Rd., Ste. 203, Andover, MA, 01810; tel (978) 749-9944; fax (978) 749-9977; e-mail info@monacosys.com; web site www.monacosys.com
Dir.-Mktg.–Bonnie Fladung
Industry: Color Management Software; Software: Workflow Management/Tracking;

Morcor Solutions, Inc.
232 Dundas St. W., Ste. 201, Napanee, ON, K7R 2A8, Canada; tel (613) 354-2912; e-mail info@morcor.com; web site www.morcor.com
Pres.–Kenn Morrison
Industry: Software: Asset Management; Software: Workflow Management/Tracking; Training: Design & Layout; Training: Keyboard Operation; Training: Pre Press;

Motterstitch Company, Inc.
PO Box 1301, Charlestown, RI, 02813, US; tel 401-364-6061; fax 401-364-6063; e-mail tom@motterstitch.com; web site www.motterstitch.com
President–Thomas Northup
Vice President–Roland Johnsen
Office Administrator–Linda Northup
Consultant–Roland Reuterfors
Consultant Engineer–Bengt Magnusson
Industry: Stitchers

Mouser Institute School of Advertising
PO Box 86, Nottoway, VA, 23955; tel (434) 292-1604; fax (434) 292-6672; e-mail cm@mouserinstitute.com; web site www.mouserinstitute.com
Pres.–Charles Mouser
Industry: Trade Publications

Moving Bytes
5858 Horton St., Ste. 101, Emeryville, CA, 94608; tel (510) 985-1175; fax (877) 252-0361; e-mail info@movingbytes.com; web site www.movingbytes.com
Pres.–Mark Smith
CEO–J. Erik Mustad
Industry: Facsimilie/Fax Transmission Systems

Muller Martini
Untere Bruhlstrasse 13, Zofingen, N/A, CH-4800, Switzerland; tel 41 62 745 4575; fax 41 62 751 5550; e-mail info@mullermartini.com; web site www.mullermartini.com

Muller Martini Corp.
PO Box 18020, Hauppauge, NY, 11788; tel (631) 582-4343; fax (631) 582-1961; e-mail info@mullermartiniusa.com; web site www.mullermartiniusa.com
Pres./CEO–Werner Naegeli
Vice Pres., Sales–Roger Bilodeau
Industry: Bundling and Tying Machines; Counting, Stacking, Bundling Machines; Cutters & Trimmers; Inserting Equipment (Includes Stuffing Machines); Mailroom Systems & Equipment; Material Handling Equipment: Palletizing Machines; Newsprint Handeling Equipment; Paper Handeling Equipment; Shrink Wrapping Equipment; Storage Retrieval Systems;

Muller Martini Mailroom Systems, Inc.
4444 Innovation Way, Allentown, PA, 18109-9404; tel (610) 266-7000; fax (610) 231-3990; e-mail info@mullermartinims.com; web site www.mullermartinims.com
Vice Pres., Contracts–Timothy Adams
Vice Pres., Sales/Mktg.–Gary Owen
Dir., Integrated Systems Engineering–Hal Thomas
Dir., Inserting–Dan Cropley
Dir., Regl. Sales (Mid-Atlantic States)–Eric Rosner
Parts Mgr.–Cathy Roberts
Mgr., Mktg.–Mathew McKittrick
Industry: Automatic Plastic Bagging Equipment; Bundling and Tying Machines; Conveyors; Inserting Equipment (Includes Stuffing Machines); Mailroom Systems & Equipment; Material Handling Equipment: Palletizing Machines; Remanufactures Equipment; Software: Press/Post Press; Storage Retrieval Systems; Training: Post Press;

MultiAd Services, Inc.
1720 W. Detweiller Dr., Peoria, IL, 61615-1612; tel 800-245-9278; e-mail info@multiad.com; web site www.multiad.com
Marketing Manager–Rachel McMenimen
Marketing Coordinator–Jill Brown
VP Product Development–Brian Dickerson
Call Center Manager–Nicole Schmidt
Pres.–Larry Clore
Sr. Vice Pres.–Jill Addy
Vice Pres., Opns.–Brian Dickerson
Industry: Consulting Services: Advertising; Software: Advertising (Includes Display; Classified); Software: Asset Management; Software: Design/Graphics; Software: Pagination/Layout;

Myrtle Beach, Inc.
2294 John Henry Ln., Myrtle Beach, SC, 29579; tel (843) 903-1515; fax (843) 903-1510; e-mail myrtlebeachinc@worldnet.att.net
Adv. Mgr.-Sales–Ralph C. Meadows
Industry: Circulation Equipment & Supplies; Mailroom Systems & Equipment; Newspaper Bags;

N

NB Finishing, Inc.
1075 Morse Ave., Schaumburg, IL, 60193-

4503; tel (847) 895-0900; fax (847) 895-0999; e-mail info@nbfinishing.com; web site www.nbfinishing.com
Pres.–Bruce Nichols
Mgr., Opns.–Dave Nichols
Industry: Plate Processors; Roller Grinding Services;

NDI (Morway Div.)
4801 W. 160th St., Cleveland, OH, 44135; tel (216) 267-8820; fax (216) 267-2905; e-mail sharrison@ndiww.com; web site www.dayintl.com
Pres.–D. Scott Morrison
Industry: Blanket Mounting and Bars; Blankets; Chemicals: Pressroom; Chemicals: Roller Cleaning; Cleaners & Solvents; Offset Blanket Thickness Gauge; Offset Blankets, Blanket Wash; Offset Chemicals & Supplies; Offset Fountain Solutions;

N & L Enterprises, Inc.
306 Wynn Dr. NW, Huntsville, AL, 35805; tel (256) 883-8700; fax (256) 880-8800; web site www.nlisc.com
Pres.–Bill Serrell
Industry: Composing Room Equipment & Supplies; Equipment Dealers (New); Equipment Dealers (Used); Facsimilie/Fax Transmission Systems; Proofing Systems;

NRD LLC
PO Box 310, Grand Island, NY, 14072; tel (716) 773-7634; fax (716) 773-7744; e-mail sales@nrdinc.com; web site www.nrdinc.com
Pres./CEO–Doug Fiegle
Industry: Static Eliminators

N/S Corporation
235 W. Florence Ave., Inglewood, CA, 90301; tel (310) 412-7074; fax (310) 673-0276; e-mail info@nswash.com; web site www.nswash.com
CEO–Thomas Ennis
Pres.–Thomas G. Ennis
Mktg. Mgr.–Gary Avrech
Industry: Conveyors; Drying Systems; Environmental Control Systems;

NUS Consulting Group
PO Box 712, Park Ridge, NJ, 07656-0712; tel (201) 391-4300; fax (201) 391-8158; e-mail contact@nusconsulting.com; web site www.nusconsulting.com
–Gary Soultanian
–Richard SoultanianCo-Pres.s
Industry: Telecommunications

Nama Graphics E, LLC
15751 Annico Dr., Homer Glen, IL, 60491; tel (630) 668-6262; fax 9262) 966-3852; e-mail rsnama@wi.rr.com; web site www.namagraphicse.com
–John Griffin
–Rick SmithOwners
Industry: Environmental Control Systems; Flying Pasters; Ink Fountains & Accessories; Rollers: Dampening;

National Graphic Supply Corp.
226 N. Allen St., Albany, NY, 12206; tel (518) 438-8411; fax (518) 438-0940; e-mail mail@ngscorp.com; web site www.ngscorp.com
Vice Pres.-Nat'l Accts./Opns.–Roberta Berkowitz
Industry: Blankets; Cameras & Accessories; Chemicals: Photographic; Chemicals: Pressroom; Color Management Software; Film & Paper: Contact; Film & Paper: Duplicating; Film & Paper: Filters (Photographic); Film & Paper: Phototypesetting; Lenses (Camera);

National Media Associates
PO Box 849, Ada, OK, 74821-0849; tel (580) 421-9600; fax (580) 421-9966; e-mail bolitho@nationalmediasales.com; web site www.nationalmediasales.com
–Thomas C. Bolitho
–Edward M. AndersonPres.s
Industry: Brokers & Appraisers; Consulting Services: Financial

National Media Associates
PO Box 849, Ada, OK, 74821; tel (580) 421-9600; fax (580) 421-9960; e-mail bolitho@bolitho.com; web site www.nationalmediasales.com
–Thomas C. Bolitho
–Edward M. AndersonBrokers
Industry: Brokers & Appraisers; Consulting Services: Financial;

National Media Associates
PO Box 2001, Branson, MO, 65615; tel (417) 336-3457; fax (417) 336-5717; web site www.nationalmediasales.com
Owner–Edward M. Anderson
Industry: Brokers & Appraisers; Consulting Services: Financial;

National Newspaper Association Publishers' Auxiliary
PO Box 7540, Columbia, MO, 65205-7540; tel (573) 777-4980; fax (573) 777-4985; e-mail pubaux@nna.org; web site www.nna.org
Communications Director–Stan Schwartz
Publisher–Tonda Rush
Industry: Trade Publications

National Newsvend
3257 E. 26th St., Los Angeles, CA, 90023; tel (323) 981-8585; fax (323) 981-8588; e-mail nationalnewsvend@mcmillinmfg.com
Pres.–Bruce Goodman
Industry: Circulation Equipment & Supplies; Newspaper Dispensers (Mechanical/Electronic); Rack Display Cards; Tubes, Racks (Includes Racks: Motor Route Tubes);

National Soy Ink Information Center
4554 NW 114th St., Urbandale, IA, 50322-5410; tel (515) 251-8640; fax (515) 251-8657; e-mail soyink@soyink.com; web site www.soyink.com
Coord., Soy Ink–Elaine Kenney
Mktg./Promo.–Karen Anderson-Shank
Industry: Inks

Neasi-Weber International
25115 Avenue Stanford, Ste. A300, Valencia, CA, 91355; tel (818) 895-6900; fax (818) 830-0889; web site www.nwintl.com
Pres.–Jim S. Weber
CEO–Dennis J. Neasi
Industry: Mailroom Systems & Equipment; Software: Advertising (Includes Display; Classified); Software: Circulation;

NELA
610 Whitetail Blvd., River Falls, WI, 54022-5209; tel (715) 425-1900; fax (751) 425-1901; e-mail info@nela-usa.com; web site www.nela-usa.com
Pres.–David Klein
Mgr., Engineering–Bob Deis
Pdct. Mgr., Web & Sheetfed–Taag Erickson
Sales Dir.–Jurgen Gruber
Mktg. Mgr.–Katharina Gruber
Industry: Color Registration; Controls: Register; Offset Plate-Making Service & Equipment; Pin Register Systems; Plate Bending Systems; Plate Mounting & Register Systems; Press Accessories, Parts & Supplies; Punching Equipment; Web Press - Special Equipment;

NENSCO
PO Box 348, Millbury, MA, 01527; tel (508) 865-0800; fax (508) 865-0811; e-mail dmacaruso@buynensco.com; web site www.buynensco.com
Pres.–Larry Erwin
CEO–Brad Beaton
Adv. Mgr.–Diana Macaruso-Carignan
Bus. Mgr., Pre Press Prodn.–David Vito
Industry: Blanket Cleaner/Washer (Automatic); Chemicals: Pressroom; Chemicals: Roller Cleaning; Circulation Equipment & Supplies; Flying Pasters; Material Handling Equipment: Pallets & Palletizers; Plates: Offset (Conventional); Press Accessories, Parts & Supplies; Rollers;

net-linx AG
Kathe-Kollwitz-Ufer 76-79, Dresden, N/A, 01309, Germany; tel +49 351 3187 5888; fax +49 351 3187 5550; e-mail nxinfo@net-linx.com; web site www.net-linx.com
Pres.–Holm Hallbauer

Network Newspaper Advertising, Inc.
23811 Chagrin Blvd., Ste. LL25, Cleveland, OH, 44122-5525; tel (216) 595-3990; fax (216) 595-3992; e-mail cccamh@aol.com
Pres.–Charles Hickman
Industry: Consulting Services: Advertising

New Consolidated International Corp.
4801 S. Whipple St., Chicago, IL, 60632-2025; tel (773) 376-5600; fax (773) 376-5835; e-mail info@consolidateddoorintl.com; web site www.consolidateddoorintl.com
Contact–R. Persa
Industry: Cameras & Accessories; Collating Equipment; Cutters & Trimmers; Cutting & Creasing Presses; Dark Room Equipment; Enlargers (Photographic); Equipment Dealers (New); Offset Camera, Darkroom Equipment; Presses: Offset; Step & Repeat Systems;

The Newark Group
312 E. Ellawood Dr., Cedartown, GA, 30125; tel (770) 748-3715; fax (770) 748-7414
Vice Pres.–Mickey Thompson
Sales Mgr.–Randy Tillery
Industry: Newsprint Handeling Equipment

Newman International, LLC
4121 W. 83rd St., Ste. 155, Prairie Village, KS, 66208; tel (913) 648-2000; fax (913) 648-7750; e-mail j.newman@att.net
Pres.–John T. Newman
Vice Pres.–Mary C. Newman
Industry: Presses: Offset; Web Press - Special Equipment;

Newscolor, LLC
P.O. Box 802, Silverton, OR, 97381, USA; tel (503) 873-2414; fax (503) 873-3333; e-mail sales@newscolor.com; web site www.newscolor.com
Mng. Dir.–Ron LaForge
Sales Dir.–Karen Barr
Industry: Color Proofing

NewsCurrents
PO Box 52, Madison, WI, 53701; tel (608) 661-5666; fax (800) 618-1570; e-mail support@newscurrents.com; web site www.newscurrents.com
Mktg. Mgr.–Matt Tivula
Industry: Consulting Services: Marketing

NewsEngin, Inc.
15560 Golden Ridge Ct., Chesterfield, MO, 63017-5124; tel (636) 537-8548; fax (636) 532-9408; web site www.newsengin.com
CEO–Jim Mosley
Pres.–George Landau
CTO–Virgil Tipton
Industry: Archiving Systems; News Wire Capture Systems; Software: Editorial; Software: Pagination/Layout;

Newspaper Electronics Corp.
5737 Swope Pkwy., Kansas City, MO, 64130-4224; tel (816) 523-5993; fax (816) 523-2820; e-mail sales@ne-corp.com; web site www.ne-corp.com
Pres.–Kelvin W. Perry
Dir., Special Markets–Vincent P. Jacks
Industry: Business Computers; Computers: Hardware & Software Integrators; Computers: Laptop & Portable; Computers: Local Area Network (LANS); Computers: Storage Devices; Consulting Services: Computer; Integrated Fax Servers;

Newspaper Services of America
3025 Highland Pkwy., Ste. 700, Downers Grove, IL, 60515-7063; tel (630) 729-7500; fax (630) 241-7223; web site www.nsamedia.com
Industry: Consulting Services: Advertising

Newspaper Space Bank
32680 N. 70 St., Scotsdale, AZ, 85262; tel (602) 595-2899; fax (602) 595-1059; e-mail sbnsb@mindspring.com
CEO–Peter Anderson
Regl. Sales Mgr.–Susan Butash
Industry: Consulting Services: Advertising; Electronic Ad Delivery; 282; Software: Advertising (Includes Display; Classified);

N
ewspaper Technologies, Inc. (NTI)
3100 500 4th Ave. SW, Calgary, AB, T2P 2V6, Canada; tel (403) 234-0230; fax (403) 234-7897; e-mail marketing@nti.ca; web site www.nti.ca
Pres.–Donald Chapman
CEO–Ron Newman
Sales Exec.–Leslie Templeton
Mktg. Coord.–Jacqueline Schledt
Industry: Marketing Database Design and Implementation; Software: Advertising (Includes Display; Classified); Software: Circulation;

Newsprint Sales Co.
PO Box 5224, Charlottesville, VA, 22905; tel (434) 972-7712; fax (434) 977-5902; e-mail rswift@brant-allen.com
Gen. Mgr.–Jacques Beauchesne
Gen. Sales Mgr.–Richard P. Swift
Industry: Newsprint

Newsprint South, Inc.
460 Briarwood Dr., Ste. 505, Jackson, MS, 39206; tel (601) 952-0900; fax (601) 957-6182
Pres./CEO–Don W. Westfall
Adv. Cor. Sr. Vice Pres./Pres.-Sales–Bob Reynolds
Cor. Sr. Vice Pres./Gen. Mgr.–Stewart Thomas
Vice Pres.-Finance–Tony Bond
Industry: Newsprint

Newstech Co. (Div. of Rovinter, Inc.)
675 NW 97th St., Miami, FL, 33150-1562; tel (305) 757-5577; fax (305) 757-2255; e-mail e-mail@newstech.com; web site www.newstech.com
Pres.–Oscar Rovito
Vice Pres.–Diego A. Rovito
Industry: Blankets; Film & Paper: Phototypesetting; Inks; Offset Chemicals & Supplies; Plate Mounting & Register Systems; Plate Processors; Plates: Offset (Computer to Plate); Plates: Offset (Conventional); Press Parts; Rollers;

News-Type Service, Inc.
PO Box 1809, Glendale, CA, 91209; tel (818) 247-7821; fax (818) 247-9331
Pres.–Jeff Jutras
Office Mgr.–Barbara Pallone
Industry: Newsprint

NewsView Solutions
143 S. Main St., 8th Flr., Salt Lake City, UT, 84111; tel (800) 897-3271; fax (801) 257-8818; e-mail info@newsviewsolutions.com; web site www.newsviewsolutions.com
Dir.-Sales–Mike Venso
Dir.-Tribune Solutions–Tony Semerad
Dir.-Mktg.–Kim McDaniel
Industry: Archiving Systems; Software: Asset Management; Software: Electronic Data Interchange; Software: Workflow Management/Tracking; Storage Retrieval Systems;

Nikon, Inc.
1300 Walt Whitman Rd., Melville, NY, 11747-3064; tel (631) 547-4200; fax (631) 547-0299; web site www.nikonusa.com
Pres./CEO–Nobuyoshi Gokyu
Sr. Vice Pres.–David Lee
Gen. Mgr., Mktg. Pro Pdcts./Digital SLR Systems/Speedlights–Steve Heiner
Nat'l Mktg. Mgr., Nikon USA–William Giordano
Communications Coordinator–Kristina Kurtzke

Nisus Software, Inc.
PO Box 1300, Solana Beach, CA, 92075-1900; tel (858) 481-1477; fax (858) 764-

0573
Industry: Word Processing System

Nomads, Inc.
807 Edgewood Blvd., papillion, NE, 68046; tel (402) 391-3110; fax (402) 391-8906
Contact–Rodney Kading
Industry: Software: Advertising (Includes Display; Classified); Software: Editorial; Software: Pagination/Layout;

North Atlantic Publishing Systems, Inc.
66 Commonwealth Ave., Concord, MA, 01742-2974; tel (978) 371-8989; fax (978) 371-5678; e-mail naps@napsys.com; xthelp@napsys.com; web site www.napsys.com
Retail Sales Mgr.–Andrew W. Koppel
Industry: Consulting Services: Editorial; Software: Asset Management; Software: Editorial; Software: Pagination/Layout; Software: Workflow Management/Tracking;

North Shore Consultants, Inc.
4910 N. Monitor Ave., Chicago, IL, 60630; tel (773) 286-7245; fax (773) 286-1974; e-mail nsc@enescee.com; web site www.enescee.com
Pres.–Audrey Mysliwiec
Mgr.–Dennis B. Wojtecki
Industry: Adhesives; Flying Pasters; Splicers, Automatic; Tape Splicing Equipment;

Northeast Industries, Inc.
2965 Tolemac Way, Prescott, AZ, 86305; tel 800-821-6257; fax (928) 443-0851; e-mail sam@neiinc.com; web site www.neiinc.com
Pres.–Sam W. Boyles
Industry: Consulting Services: Equipment; Presses: DiLitho; Presses: Flexographic; Presses: Letterpress; Presses: Offset;

Northern Graphic Supply
64 Hardy Dr., Sparks, NV, 89431; tel (775) 359-6466; fax (775) 359-6966; e-mail 4ngs@sbcglobal.net
Pres.–Barbara Gouldstone
Industry: Newspaper Marketing

Northwest Publishers, Inc.
PO Box 275, Spirit Lake, IA, 51360-0275; tel (712) 336-3085; fax (712) 336-0611; e-mail johnvan@rconnect.com
Broker–John E. van der Linden
Industry: Brokers & Appraisers

Norwood Paper
7001 W. 60th St., Chicago, IL, 60638-3101; tel (773) 788-1508; fax (773) 788-1528; e-mail sales@norwoodpaper.com; web site www.norwoodpaper.com
President–Laura Martin
Vice President–Robert Zeman
Chrmn.–Robert Zeman
COO–Kathleen Zemen
Industry: Newsprint; Paper: Coated Groundwood Offset; Paper: Groundwood Specialties; Paper: Specialty Printing Paper; Rewinders;

NoteAds.com, Inc./Post-it Note Advertising
PO Box 3806, Lacey, WA, 98509; tel (360) 705-4548; fax (800) 309-7503; e-mail john@noteads.com; web site www.noteads.com
President–John Grantham
Sales–Diana Lofflin
Industry: Consulting Services: Advertising

Nuance
One Wayside Rd., Burlington, MA, 01803; tel (781) 565-5000; fax (781) 565-5000; e-mail info@dragonsys.com; web site www.nuance.com
Mgr., Cor. Commun.–Renee Blodgett
Industry: Speech Recognition

Nuance Communications Inc.
1 Wayside Rd., Burlington, MA, 01803; tel (781) 565-5000; fax (781) 565-5001; web site www.nuance.com
Chrmn./CEO–Paul Ricci
Exec. Vice Pres./CFO–Thomas Beaudoin
Sr. Vice Pres., Cor. Devel.–Richard Palmer
Sr. Vice Pres., Mktg.–Robert Weideman
Vice Pres., Opns.–Rick Broyles
Sr. Vice Pres., Worldwide Sales–Steve Chambers
Vice Pres., HR–Dawn Howarth

NuArc Co., Inc.
6200 W. Howard St., Niles, IL, 60714; tel (847) 967-4400; fax (847) 967-9664; e-mail nuarc@ccm.net; web site www.mrprint.com
Industry: Cameras & Accessories; Color Printing Frames; Controls: Exposure; Dark Room Equipment; Diffusion Transfer Processors; Offset Plate-Making Service & Equipment; Plate Exposure Units; Platemakers: Offset (Conventional); Processors: Diffusion Transfer; Proofing Systems;

Offset Services Ink
9851 Dino Dr., Elk Grove, CA, 95624; tel (916) 686-0643; fax (916) 686-2726; e-mail offsetservices@aol.com
Owner–Russ Syracuse
Industry: Press Accessories, Parts & Supplies

O

OLEC
1850 East St., Andrew Pl., Santa Ana, CA, 92705-5043; tel (714) 258-5600; fax (714) 258-5601; e-mail sales@olec.com; web site www.olec.com
Mng. Dir.–Don Ohlig
Sales Mgr.–Al Mora
Vice Pres.,Electronics Sales–Gordon Quinn
Industry: Produciton Control Systems

Olympus America, Inc.
3500 Corporate Pkwy., Center Valley, PA, 18034-0610; tel (484) 896-5000; fax (484) 896-7115; e-mail info@olympusamerica.com; web site www.olympusamerica.com
Pres./COO–F. Mark Gumz
Exec. Dir., Brand Devel.–Mark Huggins
Sr. PR Mgr.–Elizabeth Sullivan
Vice Pres., Mktg.–Michael J. Hunter

Omicron Media
201-2630 116th Ave. NE, Bellevue, WA, 98004; tel (604) 632-3350; fax (604) 632-3351; e-mail cbaker@omicronconsulting.com; web site www.omicronconsulting.com
Principal–Tim Loo
Industry: Architects/Engineers (Includes Design/Construction Firms); Consulting Services: Computer; Consulting Services: Equipment; Consulting Services: Ergonomics; Consulting Services: Production; Training: Post Press; Training: Pre Press; Training: Press Operation & Maintenance;

ONE Corp.
455 E. Paces Ferry Rd., Ste. 350, Atlanta, GA, 30305-3315; tel (404) 842-0111; fax (404) 848-0822; e-mail presses@onecorp.com; web site www.onecorp.com; www.webpresses.com
Pres.–Durelle Boles
CFO–Jennifer Dwyer
Industry: Equipment Dealers (New); Equipment Dealers (Used); Flying Pasters; Gluing Systems; Presses: Offset; Remanufactures Equipment; Splicers, Automatic;

Outsourcing USA
1200 Memorial Hwy., Dallas, PA, 18612-9157; tel (570) 674-5600; e-mail info@outsourcingusa.net; web site www.outsourcingusa.net
CEO–Lynn Banta
VP Business Development–Maureen Missal
Industry: Art & Layout Equipment and Services

Overland Storage, Inc.
4820 Overland Ave., San Diego, CA, 92123; tel (858) 571-5555; fax (858) 571-3664; e-mail sales@overlandstorage.com; web site www.overlandstorage.com
Pres–Eric Kelly
Vice Pres., HR–Veritta Wells
Vice Pres., Opns.–Mike Gawarecki
Vice Pres., Sales–Ravi Pendekanti
Industry: Computers: Storage Devices

P

PC Industries
176 Ambrogio Dr., Gurnee, IL, 60031-3373; tel (847) 336-3300; fax (847) 336-3232; e-mail sales@pcindustries.com; web site www.pcindustries.com
Pres./Sales Mgr.–John Woolley
Industry: Cameras & Accessories; Color Registration; Controls: Register; Optical Character Recognition (OCR); Press Control Systems; Proofing Systems;

PDI Plastics
5037 Pine Creek Dr., Westerville, OH, 43081; tel (614) 890-0343; fax (614) 890-0467; e-mail sales@pdisaneck.com; web site www.newsbags.com
Pres.–Frank Cannon
Industry: Circulation Equipment & Supplies

ppi Media GmbH
Hindenburgstrasse 49, Hamburg, N/A, D-22297, Germany; tel +49 40 2274 3360; fax +49 40 2276 33666; e-mail media@ppimedia.de; web site www.ppimedia.de
CEO–Norbert Ohl
US Market Consultant–Steve Nilan
Sales Mgr.–Christian Finder
Product Mgr.–Jorg Kruse
Industry: Mailroom Systems & Equipment; Output Management and Preflight Software; Pagination Systems; Produciton Control Systems; Software: Advertising (Includes Display; Classified); Software: Pagination/Layout; Software: Workflow Management/Tracking; System Integration Services;

PSC Flo-Turn, Inc.
1050 Commerce Ave., Union, NJ, 07083-5087; tel (908) 687-3225; fax (908) 687-1715; e-mail info@pscturn.com; web site www.pscturn.com
Pres.–Rod Chrysler
Industry: Conveyors

Pacesetter Graphic Service Corp.
PO Box 499, Acworth, GA, 30101; tel (800) 241-7970; fax (770) 975-3511; web site www.pacesetterusa.com
Pres.–Robert Allen
Exec. Vice Pres.–Jeri Hammond
Industry: Blankets; Rollers; Rollers: Dampening;

PAGE
700 American Ave., Ste. 101, King of Prussia, PA, 19406; tel (610) 687-3778; fax (610) 592-0647; web site www.pagecooperative.com
CEO–John Snyder
Office Mgr.–Evelyn Jayne
Industry: Composing Room Equipment & Supplies; Inks; Newsprint; Paper: Groundwood Specialties; Plates: Offset (Conventional);

PALOS Software
9606 Aero Dr., San Diego, CA, 92123; tel (858) 836-4444; fax (858) 836-4401; e-mail marketing@palos.com; web site www.palos.com
Pres.–David Altomare
Industry: Software: Pagination/Layout

Pamarco Global Graphics
235 E. 11th Ave., Roselle, NJ, 07203-0215; tel (908) 241-1200; fax (908) 241-4009; web site www.pamarcoglobal.com
Pres./CEO–Terry Ford
Industry: Rollers

Pamarco Global Graphics
150 Marr Ave., Marietta, GA, 30060; tel (770) 795-8556; fax (770) 795-8943; e-mail info@pamarcoglobal.com; web site www.pamarcoglobal.com
Vice Pres., Mfg.–James Miller
Vice Pres., Sales/Mktg.–Greg Anderson
Industry: Press Accessories, Parts & Supplies; Presses: Offset; Rollers; Rollers: Dampening;

Pan American Papers, Inc.
5101 NW 37th Ave., Miami, FL, 33142; tel (305) 635-2534; fax (305) 635-2538; e-mail panampap@bellsouth.net; web site www.panampap.com
Sr. Vice Pres.–Jesus A. Roca
Industry: Newsprint; Paper: Specialty Printing Paper;

Pantone, Inc.
590 Commerce Blvd., Carlstadt, NJ, 07072; tel (201) 935-5500; fax (201) 935-3338; e-mail support@pantone.com; web site www.pantone.com
Pres.–Ron Potesky
Industry: Color Management Software; Software: Design/Graphics;

Papier Masson Ltee
2 Montreal Rd. W., Masson-Angers, QC, J8M 2E1, Canada; tel (819) 986-4300; fax (819) 986-7331; web site www.papiermasson.com
Vice Pres., Sales/Mktg.–William Raby
Industry: Newsprint

Papiers Stadacona
181 University Ave., St. 1610, Toronto, ON, M5H 3M7, Canada; tel (416) 862-5000; fax (416) 862-7051
Vice Pres., Sales–Roland J. Holub
Dir., Technical Sales/Serv.–David Baker
Exec. Sec.–Doris McDougall
Industry: Newsprint

Paragon Technologies Inc.
600 Kuebler Rd., Easton, PA, 18040-9201; tel (610) 252-7321; fax (610) 252-3102; e-mail info@sihs.com; sales@sihs.com; web site www.sihs.com
Chrmn.–Theodore W. Myers
Industry: Conveyors; Mailroom Systems & Equipment; Material Handling Equipment: Automatic Guided Vehicles;

Parascan Technologies, Inc.
PO Box 712, Monrovia, CA, 91017; tel (775) 358-6446; e-mail sales@parascan.com; web site www.parascan.com
Pres.–Martin Butler
Mgr.–Steve Miller
Industry: Color Proofing; Ink Controls, Computerized; Input & Editing Systems; Prepress Color Proofing Systems; Proofing Systems;

Parsons, Inc.
100 W. Walnut St., Pasadena, CA, 91124; tel (626) 440-2000; fax (626) 440-2630; web site www.parsons.com
CEO–Charles Harrington
Pres./COO–John A. Scott
PR–Erin Kuhlman
Industry: Architects/Engineers (Includes Design/Construction Firms); Environmental Control Systems; Ink Recovery Systems;

Paste-Up Supply
10930 1/2 Grand Ave., Temple City, CA, 91780; tel (626) 351-8184; fax (626) 305-4072
Owner–Pat Treanor
Industry: Adhesive Wax Coaters

Pemco, Inc.
3333 Crocker Ave., Sheboygan, WI, 53081; tel (920) 458-2500; fax (920) 458-1265; e-mail sales@pemco.kpl.net; web site www.pemco.kpl.net
Technical Sales Dir.–Jeff Bogel
Industry: Conversion Equipment; Conveyors; Cutters & Trimmers; Photostat: Paper; Reels & Tensions; Reels (Inlcudes Paper Reels); Roll Handeling Equipment; Splicers, Automatic; Tension & Web Controls; Web Guides;

Penco Products
PO Box 158, Skippack, PA, 19474; tel (610) 666-0500; fax (610) 666-7561; e-mail general@pencoproducts.com; web site www.pencoproducts.com
Pres.–Greg Grogan
Mktg. Mgr.–Philip H. Krugler
Industry: Cabinets; Storage Retrieval Systems;

Performance Contracting Group
PO Box 20512, Phoenix, AZ, 85036-0512; tel (623) 780-0101; fax (623) 780-0020; e-mail helpdesk.press@masthead.net; web site www.pcg.com

Perma-Fix Environmental Services
8302 Dunwoody Pl., Ste. 250, Atlanta, GA, 30350; tel (770) 587-9898; fax (770) 587-9937; e-mail corporate@perma-fix.com; web site www.perma-fix.com
Pres./CEO–Lou Centofanti
Mgr.–Pam Ittah
Industry: Environmental Control Systems

Perretta Graphics Corp.
46 Violet Ave., Poughkeepsie, NY, 12601-1521; tel (845) 473-0550; fax (845) 454-7507; e-mail mailbox@perretta.com; service@perretta.com; web site www.perretta.com
Pres.–Lawrence Perretta
Bus. Mgr., Int'l Sales–Bruce Quilliam
Vice Pres., Sales/Mktg.–Bruce L. Quilliam
Sales Mgr.–Jean Laird
Serv. Mgr.–Paul Jorde
Asst. Serv. Mgr.–Jordan Terziyski
Industry: Controls: Register; Ink Controls, Computerized; Keyless Inking Conversion & Addons; Web Press - Special Equipment;

Petco Roller Co.
28041 N. Bradley Rd., Lake Forest, IL, 60045; tel (847) 362-1820; fax (847) 362-1833; e-mail mail@petcorolls.com; web site www.petcorolls.com
Sales Mgr.–Dale Glen
Industry: Roll Coverings; Rollers; Rollers: Dampening;

Phelps, Cutler & Associates
P.O. Box 15847, Savannah, GA, 31416; tel (912) 351-9122; e-mail phelpscutler@aol.com; web site www.phelpscutlerconsulting.com
Pres.–Louise D. Phelps
Industry: Brokers & Appraisers; Consulting Services: Advertising; Consulting Services: Circulation; Consulting Services: Editorial; Consulting Services: Financial; Consulting Services: Human Resources; Consulting Services: Marketing;

Photo Systems, Inc.
7200 Huron River Dr., Dexter, MI, 48130; tel (734) 426-4646; fax (734) 426-3780; e-mail sales@photosys.com; web site www.photosys.com
Pres.–Alan Fischer
Sales Mgr.–Nikki Calloway
Industry: Chemicals: Photographic; Chemicals: Plate Processing; Chemicals: Pressroom; Chemicals: Roller Cleaning; Film & Paper: Film Processing Machines;

PhotoSource International
Pine Lake Farm, 1910 35th Rd., Osceola, WI, 54020; tel (715) 248-3800; fax (715) 248-3800; e-mail info@photosource.com; web site www.photosource.com
Pub.–Rohn Engh
Mng. Ed.–Angie Dober
Industry: Photography: Digital/Electronic Cameras; Trade Publications;

Pitman Co.
721 Union Blvd., Totowa, NJ, 07512-2207; tel (973) 812-0400; fax (973) 812-1630; web site www.pitman.com
Pres.–Peter J. Moore
Industry: Color Proofing; Color Registration; Color Seperation Scanners; Color Viewing Equipment; Dark Room Equipment; Plate Exposure Units; Plate Processors; Plates: Offset (Conventional); Scanners: Color B & W, Plates, Web;

Pitman Photo Supply
13911 S. Dixie Hwy., Miami, FL, 33176-7234; tel (305) 256-9558; fax (800) 835-3995; e-mail pitmanphoto@att.net; web site www.pitmanphotosupply.com
Pres.–Michael Werner
Sales Mgr.–Lowell H. Elsea
Industry: Cameras & Accessories; Chemicals: Photographic; Dark Room Equipment; Dryers: Film and Papers; Enlargers (Photographic); Film & Paper: Film Roll Dispensers; Film & Paper: Filters (Photographic); Fixing & Stop Baths; Lenses (Camera); Photography: Digital/Electronic Cameras;

Pixo Arts Corp.
2000 Bridge Parkway, Ste. 202, Redwood City, CA, 94065; tel (650) 637-1889; fax (650) 637-1899; e-mail info@pixoarts.com; web site www.pixoarts.com
Pres.–Cliv Liu
Industry: Software: Advertising (Includes Display; Classified)

Plumtree Co.
PO Box 14216, Savannah, GA, 31416-1216; tel (912) 354-5155; fax (912) 354-1375; e-mail email@plumtreecompany.com; web site www.plumtreecompany.com
Pres.–Tim Cooper
Vice Pres., Sales–Julian Cooper
Industry: Consulting Services: Production; Mailroom Systems & Equipment; Newspaper Couter; Newspaper Marketing; Newsprint Handeling Equipment; Promotion Services; Software: Press/Post Press; Software: Workflow Management/Tracking; Totalizing Systems;

Polaroid Holding Co.
300 Baker Ave., Concord, MA, 01742-2131; tel (781) 386-2000; fax (781) 386-6243; web site www.polaroid.com
CEO–Mary L. Jeffries
Vice Pres., Product Mgmt.–Jim Koestler
Vice Pres./Gen. Mgr., Digital Imaging–Jon Pollock
Vice Pres., Mktg.–Cheryl Mau
Media Rel.–Lorrie Parent

Polkadots Software Inc.
2501 Ave. Dollard, LaSalle, QC, H8N 1S2, Canada; tel (514) 595-6866; fax (514) 595-6012; e-mail info@polkadots.ca; web site www.polkadots.ca
President–Gilles Duhamel
VP–Sylvain Audet
Director Sales–Ariane Samson
Mktg./Sales Mgr.–Robert Dumas
Industry: Prepress Color Proofing Systems

Poolside Lithographic Supply, Inc.
14126 Gannet St., Ste. 104, Santa Fe Springs, CA, 90670; tel (562) 921-5545; fax (562) 921-6238; e-mail plsupply@gte.net
Pres./Mgr., Sales–Robert P. Pursel
Industry: Chemicals: Plate Processing; Offset Fountain Solutions; 185; Plate Cleaners; 220; Plate Processors; Platemakers: Offset (Computer to Plate); Platemakers: Offset (Conventional); Plates: Offset (Computer to Plate); Plates: Offset (Conventional);

Portage Newspaper Supply Co.
PO Box 5500, Akron, OH, 44334-0500; tel (877) 907-6397; fax (877) 806-6397; e-mail info@portagegraphic.com; web site www.portagegraphic.com
Pres.–Robert Belter
Industry: Cutters & Trimmers

Poyry Management Consulting (USA) Inc.
52 Vanderbilt Aveue, Suite 1005, New York, NY, 10017, USA; tel (646) 651-1547; fax (212) 661-3830; web site www.poyry.us
Director–Soile Kilpi
Industry: Consulting Services: Ergonomics; Consulting Services: Human Resources;

Praxair, Inc.
39 Old Ridgebury Rd., Danbury, CT, 06810-5113; tel (716) 879-4077; fax (716) 879-2040; e-mail info@praxair.com; web site www.praxair.com
Chrmn./Pres./CEO–Stephen F. Angel
Exec. Vice Pres.–Ricardo Malfitano
Sr. Vice Pres./CFO–James Sawyer
Vice Pres., Procuremenet/Materials Mgmt.–John Stevens
Vice Pres., Strategic Planning/Mktg.–Sunil Mattoo
Vice Pres., Commun./Pub. Rel.–Nigel Muir
Industry: Rollers

Precision Pressroom Products, Inc.
PO Box 349, Harrisonville, MO, 64701; tel (816) 887-5831; fax (816) 887-5834; e-mail pppoffice@aol.com; web site www.precision-pressroom.com
Pres./CEO–Michael E. McCarty
Vice Pres.–Shannon Kash
Industry: Blankets; Chemicals: Pressroom; Gauges, Measuring; Ink Page Pac Reconditioning ; Rollers;

PrePRESS DIRECT
10 Columbia Dr., Amherst, NH, 03031; tel (603) 689-1101; fax (603) 689-1190; e-mail catalog@prepress.pps.com; web site www.prepress.pps.com
Industry: Film & Paper: Phototypesetting; Imagesetters; Laser Printers; Processors: Film & Paper; Raster Image Processors; Software: Pagination/Layout; System Integration Services; Training: Keyboard Operation; Typesetters: Laser;

Press and Bindery Systems, Inc.
7005 Spinnaker Ln., Oklahoma City, OK, 73116-1649; tel (405) 842-6034; fax (405) 842-8513; e-mail bob-orner@msn.com; web site www.orner.com
Pres.–Robert Orner
Industry: Mailroom Systems & Equipment; Output Management and Preflight Software; Pagination Systems; Produciton Control Systems; Software: Advertising (Includes Display; Classified); Software: Pagination/Layout; Software: Workflow Management/Tracking; System Integration Services;

Press-Enterprise, Inc. (Color Graphics Dept.)
3185 Lackawanna Ave., Bloomsburg, PA, 17815; tel (570) 784-2121; fax (570) 784-9226; web site www.pressenterpriseonline.com
Prodn. Mgr., Color Graphics–Bill Bason
Industry: Color Proofing; Color Seperations, Positives; Electronic Pre-Scan Systems; Input & Editing Systems;

Press Rubber Co., Inc.
10925 Stephen Ct., Mokena, IL, 60448; tel (708) 479-1810; fax (708) 479-7712
Chairwoman–Carolyn R. Wagenaar
Mgr.–Boyd A. Wagenaar
Industry: Cutters & Trimmers; Cutting & Creasing Presses; Cutting Tools; Folder Knives; Gauges, Measuring;

Pressline Services, Inc.
9711 Green Pk., Industrial Dr., Saint Louis, MO, 63123; tel (314) 533-0080; fax (314) 533-6944; web site www.pressline.info; www.presslineservices.com
Pres.–Steve N. Brown
Vice Pres., /GM–Jim Gore
Vice Pres., Prodn.–Wayne Geske
Industry: Consulting Services: Equipment; Cylinder Repair; Press Rebuilding; Press Repairs; Web Width Changer;

Pressroom Cleaners
5709 S. 60th St., Omaha, NE, 68117, United States; tel (402) 597-3199; fax (402) 597-8765; e-mail theresa@pressroomcleaners.com; web site www.pressroomcleaners.com
Co-Owner (President)–Roy R. Lilledahl
Co-Owner (Vice President)–Steve Lilledahl
Mgr. Special Projects (CFO)–Theresa Frangoulis
Office Mgr.–Angie Clarke
Industry: Cleaners & Solvents

Presteligence
8328 Cleveland Ave. NW, North Canton, OH, 44720-8080, United States; tel (330) 305-6960; fax (330) 497-5562; e-mail info@presteligence.com; web site www.presteligence.com
President–Bob Behringer
Controller–Melissa McBride
Dir., Mktg.–Denise Fedder
Vice Pres., Opns.–Randy Plant
Industry: Calibration Software/Hardware; Color Proofing; Multiplexers/Routers; Ink Controls, Computerized; Output Management and Preflight Software; Prepress Color Proofing Systems; Software: Advertising (Includes Display; Classified); Software: Press/Post Press; Software: Workflow Management/Tracking; System Integration Services;

Prim Hall Enterprises, Inc.
11 Spellman Rd., Plattsburgh, NY, 12901; tel (518) 561-7408; fax (518) 563-1472; e-mail sales@primhall.com; primhall@primhall.com; web site www.primhall.com
Pres.–John E. Prim
Vice Pres.–David E. Hall
Vice Pres., Opns.–Pamela K. Prim
Mktg. Coord.–Matt Demers
Industry: Collating Equipment; Conveyors; Mailroom Systems & Equipment; Paper Handeling Equipment; Three Knife Trimmer;

Primark Tool Group
1800 W. Central Rd., Mount Prospect, IL, 60056; tel (224) 232-2000; fax (224) 232-4828; web site www.primarktoolgroup.com
Gen. Mgr.–Ralph Cox
Sales Mgr.–Fran Wesloy
Mktg. Dir.–Sal Locascio
Mgr.-Plant–Dave Gentry
Industry: Cutters & Trimmers; Cutting Tools;

Print Marketing Concepts, Inc.
10590 Westoffice Dr., Ste. 100, Houston, TX, 77042, USA; tel (713) 780-7055; fax (713) 780-9731; e-mail rgoodpmc@aol.com; web site www.printmkt.com
Pres.–Sue Beck
Pres.–Sue Beck
Sr. Vice Pres.–Robin L. Good
Sr. Vice Pres.–Robin L. Good
Sr. Vice Pres., Nat'l Adv. Sales–Robin Good
Vice Pres.–Greg Wickliff
Vice Pres.–Greg Wickliff
Industry: Consulting Services: Advertising; Consulting Services: Financial; Pagination Systems;

Printers House Americas LLC
530 Saddle Creek Circle, Roswell, GA, 30076; tel N/A

Printers' Service/Prisco/PriscoDigital
26 Blanchard St., Newark, NJ, 07105; tel (973) 589-7800; fax (973) 589-3225; e-mail inquiries@prisco.com; web site www.prisco.com
Chrmn.–Richard B. Liroff
Pres.–Bruce Liroff
CFO–Russ Mantione
Vice Pres., Research/Technology–David Gerson
Vice Pres., Mktg.–Eric A. Gutwillig
Vice Pres., Prodn./Mfg.–Joe Schleck
Exec. Vice Pres.–Barry Kronman
Industry: Chemicals: Pressroom; Circulation Equipment & Supplies; Cleaners & Solvents; Lubricants; Offset Blankets, Blanket Wash; Offset Chemicals & Supplies; Offset Fountain Solutions; Plate Cleaners; Press Accessories, Parts & Supplies; Solvent Recovery Systems;

Printex Products
PO Box 31515, Rochester, NY, 14603-1515; tel (800) 836-1627; fax (585) 336-2357; web

site www.rochestermidland.com
Pres./CEO–H.D. Calkins
Exec. Vice Pres.–Bradley Calkins
Vice Pres., Printex Prod. Div.–Katherine Calkins
Industry: Scanners: Color B & W, Plates, Web; Cameras & Accessories; Chemicals: Photographic; Dark Room Equipment; Dryers: Film and Papers; Enlargers (Photographic); Film & Paper: Film Roll Dispensers;

Printing Press Services, Inc.
Sellers St. Works, Preston Lancs, N/A, PR1 5EU, United Kingdom; tel +44 1772 797 050; fax +44 1772 705 761; e-mail stephenm@ppsi.co.uk; web site www.ppsi.co.uk
Pres.–Joe McManamon
Mng. Dir.-Press Division–Stephen McManamon
Mng. Dir.-Inking Systems Division–David McManamon
Office Mgr.–Marilyn Lloyd
Industry: Conversion Equipment; Drives & Controls; Equipment Dealers (New); Equipment Dealers (Used); Erectors & Riggers; Ink Controls, Computerized; Ink Fountains & Accessories; Presses: Offset; Splicers, Automatic;

Printing Technology, Inc.
1016 Katy Rd., Keller, TX, 76248-4520; tel (817) 431-0132; fax (817) 431-0270; e-mail bissatpti@aol.com; web site www.webpressparts.com
Bus. Mgr.–Leigh Ann Bissbort
Industry: Cylinder Repair; Equipment Dealers (Used); Folder Knives; Ink Fountains & Accessories; Press Accessories, Parts & Supplies; Press Rebuilding; Press Repairs; Presses: Offset; Rollers; Rollers: Dampening;

Printmark
432 Johnson Rd., East Montpelier, VT, 05651-4250; tel (802) 229-9743; fax (802) 229-9746
Dir., Prodn.–Alex Brown
Industry: Consulting Services: Computer; Consulting Services: Editorial; Consulting Services: Production;

Printronix, Inc.
14600 Myford Rd., Irvine, CA, 92606-1005; tel (714) 368-2300; fax (714) 368-2600; e-mail info@printronix.com; sales@printronix.com; web site www.printronix.com
Industry: Computers: Hardware & Software Integrators

Printsoft Americas, Inc.
500 Park Blvd., Ste. 270, Itasca, IL, 60143-3121; tel (630) 625-5400; fax (630) 625-5401; e-mail sales@printsoftamericas.com; web site www.printsoft.com
Nat'l Sales Mgr.–Daniel Sheedy
Industry: Laser Printers; Software: Circulation;

Printware
2935 Waters Rd., Ste. 160, Saint Paul, MN, 55121; tel (651) 456-1400; fax (651) 454-3684; e-mail sales@printwarellc.com; web site www.printwarellc.com
Pres.–Stan Goldberg
Vice Pres.-Sales/Mktg.–Tim Murphy
Industry: Offset Plate-Making Service & Equipment; Plate Processors; Platemakers: Offset (Conventional); Plates: Offset (Conventional);

Pro Starts
46 Ravenna St., Ste. B-1, Hudson, OH, 44236; tel (330) 650-5678; fax (330) 650-6898; e-mail tzgonc@prostarts.com; web site www.prostarts.com
Pres.–Tom Zgonc
Industry: Consulting Services: Circulation

ProImage America, Inc.
103 Carnegie Ctr., Ste. 300, Princeton, NJ, 08540; tel (609) 844-7576; e-mail pia@proimage.co.il; web site www.newproimage.com
Pres.–John J. Ialacci
Industry: Calibration Software/Hardware; Color Viewing Equipment; Consulting Services: Production; Software: Electronic Data Interchange; Software: Pagination/Layout; Software: Workflow Management/Tracking; Training: Pre Press;

ProQuest LLC
PO Box 1346, Ann Arbor, MI, 48106-1346; tel (734) 761-4700; e-mail info@proquest.com; web site www.proquest.com
CEO–Marty Kahn
Sr. Vice Pres., Global Sales–Simon Beale
Sr. Vice Pres., Mktg.–Lynda James-Gilboe
Industry: Archiving Systems

Publishers Idea Exchange
PO Box 1408, Miami, OK, 74355; tel (918) 541-1934; fax (918) 541-1939; e-mail jerryturner@familymediainc.com; web site www.publishersideaexchange.com
Gen. Mgr.–Jerry Turner
Industry: Consulting Services: Advertising

Publishing House Research LLC
215 E. 15th St., Ste. 43, New York, NY, 10003-3701; tel (212) 946-4352; e-mail research@publishinghouseresearch.com; web site www.publishinghouseresearch.com
Dir.–Steve Greechie
Industry: Consulting Services: Editorial; Newspaper Marketing; Research Studies;

Pulse Research, Inc.
1200 NW Naito Pkwy., Ste. 290, Portland, OR, 97209-2831; tel (503) 626-5224; fax (503) 277-2184; e-mail info@pulsesearch.com; support@pulseresearch.com; web site www.pulseresearch.com
CEO–John W. Marling
CIO–John Bertoglio
Vice Pres., Sales–Denice Nichols
Industry: Consulting Services: Advertising; Consulting Services: Circulation; Consulting Services: Marketing;

Q

QMS, Inc.
1 Magnum Pass, Mobile, AL, 36618; tel (251) 633-4300; fax (251) 633-0013; e-mail info@qms.com; web site www.qms.com
Vice Pres.-Sales/Mktg.–Richard Bowles
Industry: Laser Printers

Quad Tech
N64 W23110 Main St., Sussex, WI, 53089-5301; tel (414) 566-7500; fax (414) 566-9670; e-mail info@qtiworld.com; web site www.qtiworld.com
Pres.–Karl Fritchen
Vice Pres.,Sales–Randy Freeman
Industry: Color Registration; Controls: Register; Ink Controls, Computerized; Press Control Systems; Web Break Detector;

QuadTech
N64 W23110 Main St., Sussex, WI, 53089; tel (414) 566-7500; fax (414) 566-9670; e-mail info@quadtechworld.com; web site www.quadtechworld.com
Pres.–Karl Fritchen
Vice Pres., Bus. Devel.–Randy Freeman
Dir., Engineering/Gen. Mgr.,Commercial/Newspaper–Vince Balistrieri
Dir., Material Mgmt.–Jeff Karch
Dir., Manufacturing/Field Servs./Gen. Mgr., Support Bus. unit–Dan Piergies
Dir., Finance–Lisa Hansen
Dir., Sales/Int'l Opns.–Chris Thompson
Industry: Color Registration; Controls: Register; Ink Controls, Computerized; Press Control Systems; Web Break Detector;

Quark, Inc.
1800 Grant St., Denver, CO, 80203; tel (303) 894-8888; fax (303) 894-3399; e-mail quarkxpress@quark.com; web site www.quark.com
Pres./CEO–Kamar Aulakh
Industry: Software: Asset Management; Software: Design/Graphics; Software: Editorial; Software: Pagination/Layout;

Quebecor World
980 Washington St., Ste. 222, Dedham, MA, 02026; tel (781) 410-2000; fax (781) 410-2192; e-mail contact.us@quebecorusa.com; web site www.quebecorworld.com
Pres./CEO–Charles Cavell
Exec. Vice Pres., Sales–Brian Freschi
Dir. Cor. Commun.–Jeremy Roberts
Industry: Consulting Services: Production; Input & Editing Systems; Preprint Service & Production; Presses: Rotogravure;

Quickwire Labs
2-558 Upper Gage Ave., Ste. 409, Hamilton, ON, L8V 4J6, Canada; tel (905) 785-0748; fax (905) 383-3200; e-mail bmiller@quickwire.com; web site www.quickwire.com
Gen. Mgr.–Bill Miller
Quicktrac Developer–Paul Medland
Integrator–Richard Bliss
Industry: Software: Advertising (Includes Display; Classified); Software: Editorial; Software: Pagination/Layout;

Quipp
4800 NW 157th St., Miami, FL, 33014; tel (305) 623-8700; fax (305) 623-0980; e-mail info@quipp.com; web site www.quipp.com
Mktg. Mgr.–Leticia Gostisa
Industry: Mailroom Systems & Equipment

Quipp System, Inc.
4800 NW 157th St., Miami, FL, 33014-6434; tel (305) 623-8700; fax (305) 623-0980; e-mail info@quipp.com; web site www.quipp.com
Vice Pres., Sales.–Angel Arrabal
Vice Pres., Opns.–David Switalski
Industry: Conveyors; Material Handling Equipment: Pallets & Palletizers; Material Handling Equipment: Truck Loaders; Software: Press/Post Press; System Installations; System Integration Services; Training: Post Press;

R

RAK Systems, Inc.
670 Zeigler Circle W. Suite H, Mobile, AL, 36608; tel (251) 653-4080; fax (251) 653-1014; e-mail info@raksystems.com; web site www.raksystems.com
Pres.–Richard Kitzmann
Mktg. Dir.–Pamela Davis
Industry: Circulation Equipment & Supplies; Newspaper Bags; Newspaper Dispensers (Mechanical/Electronic); Rack Display Cards; Tubes, Racks (Includes Racks: Motor Route Tubes);

R.B. Intermark, Inc.
15 Kirkland Blvd., Ste. 108, Kirkland, QC, H9J 1N2, Canada; tel (514) 695-7172; fax (514) 695-2108; e-mail digitron.brimo@sympatico.ca
Pres.–Rene J. Brimo
Industry: Silver Recovery; Solvent Recovery Systems; Wastewater Treatment; Water Management Systems;

R.C. Anderson Associates, Inc.
PO Box 300, Pittsford, NY, 14534; tel (585) 248-5385; fax (585) 248-9551; e-mail rander5165@aol.com
Chrmn.–Ronald C. Anderson
Pres.–Roger Scalzo
Bus. Mgr.–Dawn Jones
Industry: Promotion Services; Trade Publications

RFC Wire Forms
525 W. Brooks St., Ontario, CA, 91762; tel (909) 984-5500; fax (909) 984-2322; e-mail rfccompany@aol.com; web site www.rfcwireforms.com
Pres.–Don Kemby
Gen. Mgr.–Greg Lunsmann
Industry: Rack Display Cards

R.R. Donnelley & Sons Co.
111 S. Wacker Dr., Chicago, IL, 60606; tel (312) 326-8000; fax (312) 326-8543; e-mail info@rrd.com; web site www.rrdonnelley.com
Pres./CEO–Thomas J. Quinlan
COO–John R. Paloian
Sr. Vice Pres., Mktg./Commun.–Douglas Fitzgerald

RTP Technical Specialists
18217 Wolbrette Circle, Port Charlotte, FL, 33948; tel (941) 743-5676; fax (941) 743-6576; e-mail billspells@att.net
Owner–William C. Spells
Industry: Consulting Services: Production; Flying Pasters; Press Accessories, Parts & Supplies; Press Control Systems; Press Rebuilding; Press Repairs; Reels & Tensions; Splicers, Automatic; Tension & Web Controls; Training: Press Operation & Maintenance;

Random Access
62 Birdsall St., Greene, NY, 13778; tel (607) 656-7584; e-mail marsland@aol.com
Pres.–William Marsland
Industry: Consulting Services: Computer; System Integration Services;

Ranger Data Technologies Inc.
210 E. 3rd St., Ste. 208, Royal Oak, MI, 48067, USA; tel (248) 336-7300; fax (248) 336-8775; e-mail info@rangerdata.com; web site www.rangerdata.com
Chrmn./CEO–George Willard
Pres./COO–Tony Marsella
Sr. VP of Operations–George Willard
Director of Marketing & Customer Service–Grace Shields
National Director of Sales & Marketing–Dolores Gauthier
Industry: Software: Advertising (Includes Display; Classified)

Ramsey (A Thermo Sentron Co.)
501 90th Ave. NW, Minneapolis, MN, 55433; tel (763) 783-2500; fax (763) 783-2525; e-mail sales@ramseytsr.com
Product Dir.–Paul Barker
Mktg. Commun. Mgr.–Don Bina
Industry: Belts, Belting, V-Belts; Conveyors;

Moss Reck & Associates, Inc.
15W700 N. Frontage Rd., Ste. 116, Burr Ridge, IL, 60527; tel (800) 826-1357 (Western U.S.); fax (630) 655-9890
Pres.–Moss Reck
Industry: Belts, Belting, V-Belts; Blanket Mounting and Bars; Chemicals: Chuck (Paper Roll); Copper Plating Drums; Cylinder Repair;

Reed Brennan Media Associates, Inc.
628 Virginia Dr., Orlando, FL, 32803-1858; tel (407) 894-7300; fax (407) 894-7900; e-mail rbma@rbma.com; web site www.rbma.com
Vice Pres.–Jeff Talbert
Mgr., Mktg.–Timothy Brennan
Industry: Input & Editing Systems; Pagination Systems;

Reeves Brothers, Inc.
PO Box 1531, Spartanburg, SC, 29304-1531; tel (864) 576-1210; fax (864) 595-2270; web site www.trelleborg.com
CEO–Keith Dye
Industry: Blanket Mounting and Bars; Blankets;

Republic Roller Corp.
PO Box 330, Three Rivers, MI, 49093-0330; tel (800) 765-5377; fax (269) 273-7655; e-mail bestroll@aol.com; web site www.republicroller.com
Pres.–G.L. Umphrey

Sales Mgr.–Bill Gross
Industry: Roll Coverings; Roller Grinding Services; Rollers; Rollers: Dampening;

Republic Service Co.
415 S. Lively Blvd., Elk Grove Village, IL, 60007-2011; tel (847) 640-7567; fax (847) 640-7586
Pres.–John Morez
Industry: Newsprint Handeling Equipment; Paper Handeling Equipment;

Research USA, Inc.
180 N.Wacker Dr., Ste. 202, Chicago, IL, 60606-1600; tel (847) 762-7850; fax (847) 762-7889; e-mail info@researchusainc.com; hr@researchusainc.com; web site www.researchusainc.com
Vice Pres., Mktg.–Chris Mink
Industry: Market Research

Revere Graphics Worldwide
5 Boundary St., Plymouth, MA, 02360; tel (508) 746-1000; fax (508) 747-4589; e-mail info@etchrevere.com; web site www.etchrevere.com
Dir., Mktg.–Steve Swindell

Richard Mfg. Co., Inc.
PO Box 1080, Fernandina Beach, FL, 32035; tel (904) 261-4075; fax (904) 261-9736
Pres.–J. Carter Fletcher
Industry: Dark Room Equipment; Developing and Processing;

Richmond/Graphic Products, Inc.
20 Industrial Dr., Smithfield, RI, 02917-1502; tel (401) 233-2700; fax (401) 233-0179; e-mail info@richmond-graphic.com; web site www.richmond-graphic.com
CEO–Hugh C. Neville
Controller–P.J. Griffee
Vice Pres., Sales/Mktg.–Frank Ragazzo
Industry: Art & Layout Equipment and Services; Exposure Lamps; Film & Paper: Film Processing Machines; Layout Tables, Light Tables & Workstations; Offset Plate-Making Service & Equipment; Plate Processors; Processors: Diffusion Transfer; Processors: Film & Paper; Tables (Dot, Etch, Opaquing, Register, Retouching, Stripping); Vacuum Frames;

Rickenbacher Media
6731 Desco Dr., Dallas, TX, 75225; tel (214) 265-9300; fax (214) 369-6496; e-mail rmedia@msn.com; web site www.rickenbacher-media.com
Pres./Exec. Dir.–Ted Rickenbacher
Western States Dir.–Jim Afinowich
Industry: Brokers & Appraisers

Ricoh Corp.
5 Dedrick Pl., West Caldwell, NJ, 07006-6304; tel (973) 882-2000; fax (973) 808-7555; web site www.ricoh-usa.com
Pres.–Martin Brodigan

Robertson Equipments
1301 Maiden Ln., Joplin, MO, 64801; tel (800) 288-1929; fax (417) 781-3704; e-mail sales@robertsonpress.com; web site www.robertsonpress.com
Owner–Bob Robertson
Pres.–Charles J. Robertson
Dir., Mktg.–Jason Bard
Parts Mgr.–Dave Reddick
Industry: Consulting Services: Computer; System Integration Services; Conveyors; Material Handling Equipment: Automatic Guided Vehicles; Material Handling Equipment: Truck Loaders;

Robertson Press Machinery Co., Inc.
1301 S. Maiden Ln., Joplin, MO, 64801; tel (417) 673-1929; fax (417) 781-3704; e-mail sales@robertsonpress.com; web site www.robertsonpress.com
Pres.–Charles Robertson
Industry: Color Registration; Dampening Systems; Equipment Dealers (New); Equipment Dealers (Used); Press Accessories, Parts & Supplies; Press Rebuilding; Presses: Offset; Remanufactures Equipment; Tension & Web Controls; Web Press - Special Equipment;

Rochester Institute of Technology
69 Lomb Memorial Dr., Rochester, NY, 14623-5603; tel (585) 475-2728; fax (585) 475-7029; e-mail spmofc@rit.edu; web site www.rit.edu
Admin. Chair–Patricia Sores
Industry: Abrasives; Cameras & Accessories; Consulting Services: Computer; Consulting Services: Equipment; Consulting Services: Production;

AD-A-NOTE
1000 Rockpoint Blvd., Pittsburgh, PA, 15084; tel 800-724-8746; e-mail Bruce@ad-a-note.com; web site www.ad-a-note.com
Executive Vice President –Bruce Barna
Industry: Counting, Stacking, Bundling Machines; Gluing Systems; In-Line Trimming Systems; Roll Handeling Equipment; Three Knife Trimmer;

Rockwell Automation
PO Box 760, Milwaukee, WI, 53304; tel (262) 512-8200; fax (262) 512-8579; web site www.rockwellautomation.com
Mktg. Commun. Specialist–Michael Faase
Industry: Controllers: Press; Drives & Controls; Press Control Systems;

Roconex Corp.
20 S. Marybill Dr., Troy, OH, 45373; tel (937) 339-2616; fax (937) 339-1470; e-mail info@roconex.com; web site www.roconex.com
Pres.–Tyrone Spear
Industry: Art & Layout Equipment and Services; Cabinets; Cutters & Trimmers; Files, Storage; Layout Tables, Light Tables & Workstations; Offset Plate Holders; Plate Exposure Units; Platemakers: Offset (Conventional); Storage Retrieval Systems; Tables (Dot, Etch, Opaquing, Register, Retouching, Stripping);

Rogersol, Inc.
5538 N. Northwest Hwy., Chicago, IL, 60630; tel (773) 735-5100; fax (773) 775-9414; web site www.rogersol.com
Mgr.–Mark Desandi
Industry: Blanket Cleaner/Washer (Automatic); Chemicals: Roller Cleaning; Cleaners & Solvents;

R
oggen Management Consultants, Inc.
223 Egremont Plain Rd #603, North Egremont, MA, 01230; tel (413) 528-2300; fax (413) 528-2300; e-mail mark.roggen@roggenconsultants.com; mn-roggen@aol.com; web site www.roggenconsultants.com
Pres.–Mark N. Roggen

Roll-Crafters
3902 E. 16th St., Indianapolis, IN, 46201-1500; tel (317) 359-2776; fax (317) 359-3983
Pres.–Duane Henry
Industry: Roll Coverings; Roller Grinding Services; Rollers; Rollers: Dampening;

Rollem Corp. of America
43 Polk Ave., Hempstead, NY, 11550; tel (516) 485-6655; fax (516) 485-5936; e-mail info@rollemusa.com; web site www.rollemusa.com
Vice Pres., Sales–Richard Nigro
Industry: Numbering Machines

Roosevelt Paper
1 Roosevelt Dr., Mount Laurel, NJ, 08054; tel (856) 303-4100; fax (856) 642-1949; e-mail info@rooseveltpaper.com; web site www.rooseveltpaper.com
Pres.–David Kosloff
Vice Pres., Sales/Mktg.–Eric Conine
Mktg. Dir.–Lynn Perce
Industry: Newsprint; Paper: Coated Groundwood Offset; Paper: Specialty Printing Paper;

Rosback Co.
125 Hawthorne Ave., Saint Joseph, MI, 49085; tel (269) 983-2582; fax (269) 983-2516; e-mail rosbacksales@qtm.net; web site www.qtm.net/rosback
Pres.–Larry R. Bowman
Vice Pres., Sales/Mktg.–Ron F. Bowman
Industry: Adhesives; Collating Equipment; Equipment Dealers (New); Folding Machines;

RotaDyne Corp.
8140 Cass Ave., Darien, IL, 60561-5013; tel (630) 769-9700; fax (630) 769-9255; e-mail rotadynecorp@rotadyne.com; web site www.rotadyne.com
Vice Pres., OEM Sales–John A. Costello
Vice Pres. Industrial Sales–John Kaminski
Vice Pres. Graphic Sales–John Breau
Industry: Blankets; Roll Coverings; Rollers; Rollers: Dampening;

Rotoflex Mark Andy Canada, Inc.
420 Ambassador Dr., Mississauga, ON, L5T 2R5, Canada; tel (905) 670-8700; fax (905) 670-3402; e-mail sales@rotoflex.com; web site www.rotoflex.com
Vice Pres., Finance–Rod Allen
Dir., Mfg.–Brian Nicoll
Gen. Mgr./Vice Pres., Sales/Mktg.–Val Rimas
Industry: Conversion Equipment; Dies (Perforating and Slitting); Rewinders;

Rowlett Advertising Service, Inc.
PO Box 50, Goodlettsville, TN, 37070-0050; tel (615) 859-6609; fax (615) 851-7187; e-mail rowlettadvertising@att.net; rowlettadvertising@worldnet.att.net; web site www.rowlettadv.com
Pres.–Richard Rowlett
Sec./Treasurer–Mary Belcher
Industry: Consulting Services: Advertising

Richard S Rowse & Associates
1 Blueberry Lane, Norfolk, MA, 02056; tel (508) 520-8329; fax (508) 520-8347
Pres.–Richard S. Rowse
Industry: Architects/Engineers (Includes Design/Construction Firms); Consulting Services: Equipment; Consulting Services: Production; Conveyors; Infeed Stackers; Inserting Equipment (Includes Stuffing Machines); Mailroom Systems & Equipment; Material Handling Equipment: Palletizing Machines; Newsprint Handeling Equipment;

Royal Consumer Information Products, Inc.
2 Riverview Dr., 3rd Fl., Sommerset, NJ, 08873; tel (732) 627-9977; fax (800) 232-9769; e-mail info@royalsupplies.com; web site www.royal.com
Pres.–Salomon Suwalsky
Vice Pres., Sales (Royal)–Terry Setar
Mgr., Sales/Supplies–Wendy Donnelly
Industry: Facsimilie/Fax Transmission Systems; Laser Printers;

Royal Graphics
138 N. Forest Ave., Hartwell, GA, 30643; tel (706) 376-2919; fax (706) 376-8136; e-mail royalgraphics@hartcom.net
CEO/Sales–Curt Robison
CFO–Linda Staffort
Sec./Treasurer–Gloria Robison
Vice Pres., Sales–Ted Robison
Industry: Blankets; Chemicals: Plate Processing; Chemicals: Pressroom; Chemicals: Roller Cleaning; Densitometers; Offset Chemicals & Supplies; Platemakers: Offset (Conventional); Plates: Offset (Conventional); Press Accessories, Parts & Supplies; Rollers;

Bill Rudder & Associates, Inc.
4486 Posterity Ct., Gastonia, NC, 28056-8432; tel (704) 824-7865; fax (704) 824-2043
Pres.–Bill Rudder
Vice Pres., Sales–Fred Rudder
Industry: Offset Blanket Thickness Gauge; Rewinders; Tension & Web Controls;

Rycoline Products, Inc.
5540 N. Northwest Hwy., Chicago, IL, 60630; tel (773) 775-6755; fax (773) 775-9414; web site www.rycoline.com
Gen. Mgr.–Mike Dodd
Industry: Blankets; Chemicals: Plate Processing; Chemicals: Pressroom; Circulation Equipment & Supplies; Cleaners & Solvents; Offset Blanket Thickness Gauge; Offset Blankets, Blanket Wash; Offset Chemicals & Supplies; Offset Fountain Solutions;

Ryder System, Inc.
11690 NW 105th St., Miami, FL, 33178; tel (305) 500-3726; fax (305) 500-4339; web site www.ryder.com
Chrmn./Pres./CEO–Gregory Swienton
Sr. Vice Pres., Sales/Mktg.–Thomas Renehan
Industry: Lift Trucks

S

SAP America, Inc.
3999 West Chester Pk., Newtown Square, PA, 19073, USA; tel (610) 661-1000; web site www.sap.com
CFO–Mark White
Vice Pres., Global Adv./Branding–Costanza Tedesco
Sr. Dir., Social Media Mktg.–Brian Ellefritz
Industry: Software: Advertising (Includes Display; Classified); Software: Circulation;

SCA Promotions, Inc.
3030 LBJ Frwy., Ste. 300, Dallas, TX, 75234; tel (214) 860-3700; fax (214) 860-3480; e-mail info@scapromo.com; web site www.scapromotions.com
Pres.–Robert D. Hamman
Vice Pres., Sales–Shiela Bryan
Industry: Insurance; Newspaper Marketing; Promotion Services;

SKO Brenner American
841 Merrick Rd., CS9320, Baldwin, NY, 11510; tel (516) 771-4400; fax (516) 771-7810; e-mail stu@skobrenner.com; web site www.skobrenner.com
CEO–Stuart Brenner
COO–Jon R. Lunn
Sr. Vice Pres.–Jim Graziano
Industry: Credit & Collections

SP Newsprint Co.
245 Peachtree Center Ave. NE, Ste. 1800, Atlanta, GA, 30303-1231; tel (404) 979-6600; fax (404) 979-6615; e-mail corp@sp-newsprint.com
Gen. Mgr.–Michael Thornhill
Industry: Newsprint

SRDS, a Kantar Media Company
1700 Higgins Rd., Des Plaines, IL, 60018-5605, United States; tel (847) 375-5000; fax (847) 375-5001; e-mail contact@srds.com; web site www.srds.com
CFO–Kevin McNally
President–Stephen Davis
Vice Pres., HR–Valerie LaMorte
VP, Information Sales & Client Service–Trish DeLaurier
Vice Pres., Pdct. Opns.–Gayle Paprocki
Vice Pres., Mktg./Bus. Devel.–Dave Kostolansky
Mktg. Commun. Dir.–Lindsay Morrison
VP & Publisher–Joseph Hayes
Director, Data Services–June Levy
Industry: Trade Publications

STM Networks
Two Faraday, Irvine, CA, 92618; tel (949) 753-7864; fax (949) 273-6020; e-mail info@stmi.com; web site www.stmi.com
Chrmn.–Emil Youssefzadeh
COB–Faramarz Youssefzadeh
Vice Pres., Sales–Umar Javed
Vice Pres., Mktg.–Rick Forberg

Industry: Facsimilie/Fax Transmission Systems; Interfaces;

St. Louis Journalism Review
PO Box 12474, Saint Louis, MO, 63132-0174; tel (314) 991-1699; fax (314) 963-6104; e-mail sjreview@sbcglobal.net; web site www.sjreview.org
Ed.–Ed Bishop
Asst. Gen. Mgr.–Erica Burleson
Industry: Consulting Services: Editorial

Sakurai USA
1700 N. Basswood Rd., Schaumburg, IL, 60173-5318; tel (847) 490-9400; fax (847) 490-4200; e-mail sales@sakurai.com; info@sakurai.com; inquiry@sakurai.com; web site www.sakurai.com
Vice Pres., Sales–Don Bence
Industry: Presses: Offset

Sales Development Services
600 N. Cleveland Ave., Ste. 260, Westerville, OH, 43082-7265; tel (614) 794-0500; fax (614) 961-3268; e-mail info@salesdevelopment.com; web site www.sdsinc.com
Vice Pres., Opns.–Christine Hunt
Industry: Consulting Services: Advertising; Consulting Services: Computer; Consulting Services: Marketing; Facsimilie/Fax Transmission Systems; Integrated Fax Servers; Market Research; Marketing Database Design and Implementation; Software: Advertising (Includes Display; Classified); Trade Publications;

Sales Training Consultants, Inc.
7900 Glades Rd., Ste. 430, Boca Raton, FL, 33434; tel (561) 482-8801; fax (561) 482-8210; e-mail akemper@salestrainingconsultants.com; web site www.newspapertraining.com
Pres.–Alice Kemper
Consultant/Trainer–Diane Rossi
Consultant/Trainer–Denise Zagnoli
Consultant/Trainer–Margo Berman
Consultant/Trainer–Ed Baron
Consultant/Trainer–Anne Stein
Industry: Consulting Services: Advertising; Consulting Services: Circulation; Training: Sales & Marketing;

Samuel Strapping System
1401 Davey Rd., Ste. 300, Woodridge, IL, 60517; tel (800) 323-4424; fax (630) 783-8901; e-mail info@samuelsystem.com; web site www.samuelsystems.com
Industry: Bundling and Tying Machines; Strapping Machines;

Sappi Fine Paper
225 Franklin St., 28th Fl., Boston, MA, 02110-2889; tel (617) 423-7300; fax (617) 423-5494; e-mail info@sappi.com; web site www.sappi.com
Pres./CEO–Mark Gardner
Vice Pres., Finance/CFO–Annette Luchene
Vice Pres., Sales–Bob Forsberg
Industry: Paper: Coated Groundwood Offset; Paper: Groundwood Specialties; Paper: Specialty Printing Paper; Photostat: Paper;

Saxmayer Corp.
PO Box 10, Blissfield, MI, 49228; tel (517) 486-2164; fax (517) 486-2055; e-mail info@saxmayercorp.com; web site www.erichbaumeister.com
Pres., Mktg./Sales–Michael Vennekotter
Vice Pres., Engineering/Mfg.–James Fischer
Process Supvr., Information Technology–Jeremy Sell
Industry: Newsprint Handeling Equipment; Strapping Machines;

Saxotech
360 Rt. 101, Ste. 1302 C, Bedford, NH, 03110; tel (603) 472-5825; fax (603) 472-3082; e-mail ussales@saxotech.com; web site www.ckp.com; www.saxotech.com
Pres.–Pat Stewart
Mng. Partner/CFO–Dick Mooney
Vice Pres., Opns.–James Mooney
Dir., Sales–Jeff Rapson
Industry: Pagination Systems; Software: Advertising (Includes Display; Classified); Software: Editorial; Software: Pagination/Layout;

SAXOTECH
302 Knights Run Avenue, Tampa, FL, 33602, USA; tel 813-221-1600; fax 813-221-1604; e-mail info@saxotech.com; web site www.saxotech.com
CEO–Anders Christiansen

SAXOTECH, Inc.
302 Knights Run Ave., Ste. 1150, Tampa, FL, 33602-5974; tel (813) 221-1600; fax (813) 221-1604; e-mail info@saxotech.com; ussales@saxotech.com; web site www.saxotech.com
CEO/Pres.–Anders Christiansen
Director of Marketing–Robert Payne
Vice Pres., Cor. Mktg.–Paul Harris
Industry: Archiving Systems; News Wire Capture Systems; Pagination Systems; Photo Archiving; Publishing Systems; Software: Asset Management; Software: Editorial; Software: Pagination/Layout; Software: Workflow Management/Tracking;

Scarborough Research
770 Broadway, New York, NY, 10003-9595; tel (646) 654-8400; fax (646) 654-8440; e-mail info@scarborough.com; web site www.scarborough.com
Pres./CEO–Robert L. Cohen
Exec. Vice Pres./Dir., Sales–Steven Seraita
Vice Pres., Mktg./Commun.–Deirdre McFarland
Industry: Consulting Services: Advertising; Consulting Services: Marketing; Market Research; Newspaper Marketing; Research Studies; Software: Advertising (Includes Display; Classified); Training: Keyboard Operation;

Ernest Schaefer, Inc.
731 Lehigh Ave., Union, NJ, 07083, U.S.A.; tel (908) 964-1280; fax (908) 964-6787; e-mail eschaefe@aol.com; web site www.ernestschaeferinc.com
Pres.–Ernest Schaefer
Industry: Type, Fonts

Schaefer Machine Co., Inc.
200 Commercial Dr., Deep River, CT, 06417; tel (860) 526-4000; fax (860) 526-4654; e-mail schaefer01@snet.net; web site www.schaeferco.com
Pres.–Bob Gammons
Vice Pres.–Virginia Gammons
Industry: Adhesives; Gluing Systems;

Schawk
225 W. Superior St., Chicago, IL, 60610; tel (312) 943-0400; fax (312) 943-2450; web site www.schawk.com
Sales Mgr.–Jamie Mandarion
Industry: Color Management Software; Library Retrieval Systems; Preprint Service & Production; Storage Retrieval Systems;

Schermerhorn Bros. Co.
340 Eisenhower Ln. N, Lombard, IL, 60148; tel (630) 627-9860; fax (630) 627-1178; web site www.schermerhornbrosco.com
Sales Contact–Dennis Jenkins
Industry: Circulation Equipment & Supplies

Schlenk-Both Industries
40 Nickerson Rd., Ashland, MA, 01721; tel (508) 881-4100; fax (508) 881-1278; e-mail customer.service@schlenkboth.com; web site www.schlenk-both.com/
Pres.–Brian Kelly
Industry: Inks

Schur International a/s
J.W. Schurs Vej 1, DK-8700 Horsens, N/A, N/A, Denmark; tel +45 7627 2727; fax +45 7627 2700; e-mail sin@schur.com; web site www.schur.com
Owner–Hans Schur

Schur Packaging Systems, Inc.
165 E. Commerce Dr., Ste. 105, Schaumburg, IL, 60173; tel (847) 619-0068; fax (847) 619-0353; e-mail spi@schur.com; web site www.schur.com
Parts/Serv. Dir.–Magnus Wall
Dir., Sales–Dan Kemper
Technical Sales Dir.–Gert Jensen
Dir. Tech. Sales–Gert Jensen
Industry: Consulting Services: Circulation; Insurance; Presses: Flexographic; Presses: Rotogravure; Adhesives; Mailroom Systems & Equipment;

SCREEN (USA)
5110 Tollview Dr., Rolling Meadows, IL, 60008; tel (847) 870-7400; fax (847) 870-0149; e-mail rsiwicki@screenusa.com; web site www.screenusa.com
Pres–Mike Fox
CFO–Robert Bernstein
Application Support Mgr.–Richard Siwicki
Opns. Mgr.–Edvardo Navarro
Industry: Color Proofing; Color Seperation Scanners; Imagesetters; Proofing Systems; Raster Image Processors; Software: Pagination/Layout; Tables (Dot, Etch, Opaquing, Register, Retouching, Stripping);

Seidel Enterprises
805 Canal St., Easton, PA, 18042; tel (610) 252-9000; fax (610) 252-9898; e-mail info@seidelenterprises.com; web site www.seidelenterprises.com
Pres.–Randy Seidel
Industry: Conveyors; Counting, Stacking, Bundling Machines; Delivery Equipment; Inserting Equipment (Includes Stuffing Machines); Mailroom Systems & Equipment;

Semler Industries, Inc. (Pressroom Fluids Equipment Div.)
3800 N. Carnation St., Franklin Park, IL, 60131-1205; tel (847) 671-5650; fax (847) 671-7686; e-mail semler@semlerindustries.com; web site www.semlerindustries.com
Pres.–Loren H. Semler
Dir. Sales–William E. Schulz
Industry: Circulation Equipment & Supplies; Fluid Handeling: Pressroom; Ink Recovery Systems; Ink Storage Tanks; Wastewater Treatment;

The Seybold Report
PO Box 682, Gilbertsville, PA, 19525; tel (610) 327-3958; fax (888) 463-4814; e-mail seybold@thejossgroup.com; web site www.seyboldreports.com
Publisher, Editor, Owner–Molly Joss
Industry: Trade Publications

Shoom, Inc.
6345 Balbow Blvd., Ste. 247, Incino, CA, 91316; tel (800) 446-6646; fax (818) 755-9943; e-mail info@shoom.com; web site www.shoom.com
Vice Pres., Customer Serv.–Sharon Ryoji
Industry: Software: Electronic Data Interchange

Shreve Systems
1200 Marshall St., Shreveport, LA, 71101; tel (318) 424-9791; fax (318) 424-9771; e-mail ssystems@bellsouth.net; web site www.shrevesystems.com
Pres.–Rich Harold
Industry: Computers: Hardware & Software Integrators

David A. Shulda Enterprises, Inc.
PO Box 8984, Fountain Valley, CA, 92728-8984; tel (949) 361-5167
Consultant–David A. Shulda
Industry: Consulting Services: Equipment; Environmental Control Systems; Ink Bleeding Equipment; Ink Recovery Systems; 243;

Shuttleworth, LLC
10 Commercial Rd., Huntington, IN, 46750, USA; tel (260) 356-8500; fax (260) 359-7810; e-mail inc@shuttleworth.com; web site www.shuttleworth.com
Industry: Conveyors; Masking Materials; Paper Handeling Equipment; Roll Handeling Equipment;

Siebert, Inc.
8134 W. 47th St., Lyons, IL, 60534; tel (708) 442-2010; fax (708) 447-9353; e-mail customerservice@siebertinc.com; web site www.siebertinc.com
Pres.–J.P. Mulcahy
Industry: Chemicals: Roller Cleaning; Cleaners & Solvents;

Siemens Communications Group
900 Broken Sound Pkwy., Boca Raton, FL, 33487-3527; tel (561) 923-5000; web site www.siemens.com
CFO/CIO–Michael Kutschenreuter
Media Rel.–Bill Makley
Sr. Vice Pres., Sales/Serv.–J. Licata
Industry: Telecommunications

Signode Corp.
3600 W. Lake Ave., Glenview, IL, 60026; tel (847) 724-7500; fax (847) 657-4261; web site www.itw.com
Pres.–David Steer
Vice Pres.–R. Flaum
Dir., Mktg. Commun.–Jim Fallon
Industry: Strapping Machines

Siix USA Corp.
651 Bonnie Ln., Elk Grove Village, IL, 60007; tel (847) 593-3211; fax (847) 364-5290; e-mail bpusczan@siix-usa.com; web site www.siix.co.jp
Mgr., Sales/Engineering–Steve Swanson
Industry: Scanners: Color B & W, Plates, Web

Silverman Newspaper Management Consultants
2841 Golden Rain Rd., Walnut Creek, CA, 94595-1949; tel (925) 939-3030; fax (925) 937-6143
Owner–Herman Silverman
Industry: Consulting Services: Advertising; Consulting Services: Circulation; Consulting Services: Editorial; Consulting Services: Financial; Consulting Services: Marketing; Market Research; Promotion Services; Training: Keyboard Operation; Training: Press Operation & Maintenance;

Simco Industrial Static Control Products
2257 N. Penn Rd., Hatfield, PA, 19440-1906; tel (215) 822-6401; fax (215) 822-3795; e-mail simcoind@itw.com; customerservice@simcomail.com; sales@simco.biz; web site www.simco-static.com
Customer Serv. Mgr.–Ed Huber
Technical Rep.–Brian Mininger
Industry: Inserting Equipment (Includes Stuffing Machines); Paper Cleaners; Press Accessories, Parts & Supplies; Static Eliminators; Testing Instruments;

SITMA USA, Inc.
45 Empire Dr., Saint Paul, MN, 55103-1586; tel (651) 222-2324; fax (651) 222-4652; e-mail sitmausa@sitma.com; web site www.sitma.com
Mktg. Mgr.–Ann Butzer
Industry: Automatic Plastic Bagging Equipment; Collating Equipment; Conveyors; Counting, Stacking, Bundling Machines; Feeding, Folding, Delivery Equipment; Folding Machines; Inserting Equipment (Includes Stuffing Machines); Mailroom Systems & Equipment; Remanufactures Equipment; Shrink Wrapping Equipment;

Skyline Graphic Services, LLC
755 Hwy. 105, Ste. 2F, Palmer Lake, CO, 80133; tel (719) 481-9993; fax (719) 481-2232; e-mail jmb@skylinegraphicservices.com; web site www.skylinegraphicservices.com
CEO–Bob Bowers
Gen. Mgr.–Josh Bowers
Sales Rep.–Jason Bowers
Industry: Press Control Systems; Press Re-

building;

H.R. Slater Co., Inc.
2050 W. 18th St., Chicago, IL, 60608; tel (312) 666-1855; fax (312) 666-1856; e-mail hrslatercompany@aol.com
Pres.–Robert Kurzka
Office Mgr.–William C. St. Hilaire
Industry: Delivery Equipment; Gauges, Measuring; Mailroom Systems & Equipment; Newsprint Handeling Equipment; Paper Handeling Equipment;

Smart Storage, Inc.
100 Burtt Rd., Andover, MA, 01810; tel (888) 479-0100; fax (978) 623-3310; e-mail sales@smartstorage.com; info@smartstorage.com; web site www.smartstorage.com
Marcon Specialist–Donna Mentlick
Pub. Rel. Mgr.–Christian Simko
Industry: Files, Storage; Storage Retrieval Systems;

Smith PPI Inc.
15019 W. 95th St., Lenxa, KS, 66215; tel (913) 888-0695; fax (913) 888-0699; e-mail info@smithrpm.com; web site www.smithrpm.com
Pres.–Dennis Schupp
Engineer–Jessie Brunk
Industry: Blanket Cleaner/Washer (Automatic); Dampening Systems;

Smith Pressroom Products, Inc.
15019 W 95th St., Lenexa, KS, 66215-1038; tel (913) 888-0695; fax (913) 888-0699; e-mail info@smithrpm.com; web site www.smithrpm.com
Pres.–Dennis Schupp
Vice Pres., Sales/Mktg.–Paul W. Geralds
Industry: Blanket Cleaner/Washer (Automatic); Dampening Systems; Offset Fountain Controls; Offset Fountain Solutions; Pumps (Air, Ink, Vacuum); Recirculators; Solvent Recovery Systems; Wastewater Treatment; Water Management Systems; Web Offset Remoisturizers;

Snap-on Business Solutions
3900 Kinross Lakes Pkwy., Richfield, OH, 44286; tel (330) 659-1600; fax (330) 659-1601; e-mail info@snaponbusinesssolutions.com; web site www.snaponbusinesssolutions.com
Pres.–Mary Beth Siddons
Industry: Computers: Storage Devices; Developing and Processing

Software Business Systems
7401 Metro Blvd., Ste. 550, Edina, MN, 55439-3033; tel (952) 835-0100; fax (952) 835-7504; e-mail admin@sbsweb.com
Pres.–Curtis Cerf
Vice Pres., Software–Mary K. Brennan
Industry: Software: Business (Includes Administration/Accounting); System Installations; System Integration Services;

The Software Construction Co.
3810 Hamby Rd., Alpharetta, GA, 30004; tel (770) 751-8500; fax (770) 772-6800; e-mail sales@sccmediaserver.com; web site www.sccmediaserver.com
CEO–Rick Marucci
Vice Pres.–Lee Funnell
Industry: Software: Asset Management; Software: Design/Graphics; Software: Editorial; Software: Workflow Management/Tracking;

Software Consulting Services
630 Selzaggio Dr., Ste. 420, Nazareth, PA, 18064; tel (610) 746-7700; fax (610) 746-7900; e-mail sales@newspapersystems.com; web site www.newspapersystems.com
Pres.–Richard J. Cichelli
Vice Pres., Opns.–Curtis Jackson
Mktg. Dir.–Martha J. Cichelli
Industry: Consulting Services: Computer; Consulting Services: Marketing; Facsimilie/Fax Transmission Systems; Integrated Fax Servers; Market Research; Marketing Database Design and Implementation; Software: Advertising (Includes Display; Classified); Trade Publications;

Solar Systems
8134 304th Ave. SE, Bldg. 3, Preston, WA, 98050; tel (425) 270-6100; fax (425) 270-6150; e-mail info@solarsystems.com; web site www.solarsystems.com
CFO–Jean McCall
Industry: Computers: Hardware & Software Integrators; Remanufactures Equipment; Storage Retrieval Systems;

Solna Offset AB
Veddestavagen 13, Box 582, Jarfalla, N/A, SE-175 26, Sweden; tel +46 8 708 212 426; fax +46 8 621 24 97; e-mail info@solna.com; web site www.solnaoffset.com
Gen. Mgr.–Janeric Akerlund
Contact–Alf Nilsson

Solna Web USA, Inc.
PO Box 15066, Lenexa, KS, 66285-5066; tel (913) 492-9925; fax (913) 492-0170; e-mail rkerns@solnaweb.com; web site www.solnaweb.com
Pres.–Richard Kerns
Industry: Presses: Offset

Sonoco Products Co.
PO Box 160, Hartsville, SC, 29550; tel (843) 383-7000; fax (843) 383-7008; web site www.sonoco.com
Pres.–Harris Deloach
Division Vice Pres., Sales–Don Gore
Industry: Newspaper Bags; Recycling Newsprint; Tubes, Racks (Includes Racks: Motor Route Tubes);

Sonoran Scanners, Inc.
2302 N. Forbes Blvd., Tucson, AZ, 85745; tel (520) 617-0072; fax (520) 617-0806; e-mail sales@sonoranscanners.com
Vice Pres.–Norm Bogen
Industry: Platemakers: Flexographic (Computer to Plate); Platemakers: Offset (Conventional);

South Bend Lathe Corp.
1735 N. Bendix Dr., South Bend, IN, 46628; tel (574) 289-7771; fax (574) 236-1210; e-mail sales@southbendlathe.com; web site www.southbendlathe.com
Pres.–Carmine Martino
Vice Pres.–Joseph Mittiga
Industry: Roller Grinders

Southern Lithoplate, Inc.
PO Box 9400, Wake Forest, NC, 27588; tel (919) 556-9400; fax (919) 556-1977; web site www.slp.com
Chrmn./CEO–Edward A. Casson
Pres./COO–Clark A. Caston
Nat'l Sales Mgr.–Brandon A. Casson
Vice Pres., Sales/Mktg.–Steve Mattingly
Industry: Chemicals: Plate Processing; Chemicals: Pressroom; Film & Paper: Film Processing Machines; Film & Paper: Filters (Photographic); Offset Chemicals & Supplies; Offset Film; Offset Fountain Solutions; Plate Processors; Plates: Offset (Computer to Plate); Plates: Offset (Conventional);

Southwest Alabama Radio Resources Bureau
2665 Pleasant Valley Rd., Mobile, AL, 36606; tel (251) 473-3946
Assoc. Ed.–Roy E. Kadel
Industry: Research Studies

Spartanics
3605 Edison Pl., Rolling Meadows, IL, 60008; tel (847) 394-5700; fax (847) 394-0409; e-mail sales@spartanico.com; web site www.spartanics.com
VP., Sales/Mktg.–Mike Bacon
Industry: Counting, Stacking, Bundling Machines; Paper Handeling Equipment;

Spectra Logic
1700 N. 55th St., Boulder, CO, 80301; tel (303) 449-6400; fax (303) 939-8844; e-mail sales@spectralogic.com; web site www.spectralogic.com
Dir., Cor. Mktg.–Molly Rector
Industry: Computers: Hardware & Software Integrators; Library Retrieval Systems;

Spectrecom Corporation
PO Box 950096, Mission Hills, CA, 91395; tel (818) 832-4111; fax (818) 832-8111; e-mail info@spectrecom.com; web site www.spectrecom.com
Pres.–Terry Allen
Vice Pres.–Sandra Allen
Industry: Consulting Services: Advertising; Consulting Services: Marketing; Market Research; Newspaper Marketing; Research Studies; Software: Advertising (Includes Display; Classified); Training: Keyboard Operation;

SPECTRUM Human Resource Systems Corp.
707 17th St., Ste. 3800, Denver, CO, 80202-3438; tel (303) 592-3200; fax (303) 595-9970; e-mail info@spectrumhr.com; web site www.spectrumhr.com
Pres.–Sybll Romley
Exec. Vice Pres.–Matthew Keitlen
Industry: Software: Asset Management; Software: Business (Includes Administration/Accounting);

Standard Electric and Engineering Co.
150 W. Harris Ave., South San Francisco, CA, 94080; tel (650) 952-6500; fax (650) 952-0102; e-mail ssummert@seeco.org; web site ^www.seeco.org
Pres.–Steve Summer
Industry: Consulting Services: Equipment; Consulting Services: Production; Controllers: Press; Dampening Systems; Drives & Controls; Maintenance, Plant & Equipment; Motors; System Installations; System Integration Services;

Stanford Products
PO Box 578, Salem, IL, 62881; tel (618) 548-2600; fax (618) 548-6782; web site www.stanfordproductsllc.com
Customer Serv. Mgr.–Deann Sager
Sales Mgr.–Tim Andrews
Sales Mgr.–Larry Boyles
Industry: Rewinders

Star Vend
PO Box 1176, Corona, CA, 92878-1176; tel (951) 734-4585; fax (951) 734-9814; e-mail starvend@sbcglobal.net
Industry: Circulation Equipment & Supplies; Cleaners & Solvents; Newspaper Dispensers (Mechanical/Electronic); Newspaper Marketing; Rack Display Cards;

Stauffer Media Systems
PO Box 1330, Joplin, MO, 64802; tel (417) 782-0280; fax (417) 782-1282; e-mail patch@stauffergold.com; web site www.stauffergold.com
Sales Mgr.–Keith Wood
Sales Rep.–Kim Sexton
Sales Rep.–Harry Stewart
Mgr., Pdct. Devel.–Lynn Grantham
Dir., Audiotex Tech.–Chris Waage
Industry: Business Computers; Computers: Hardware & Software Integrators; Consulting Services: Circulation; Consulting Services: Editorial; Input & Editing Systems; Library Retrieval Systems; Publishing Systems; Software: Circulation; Software: Editorial; Software: Pagination/Layout;

Steel City Corp.
1000 Hedstrom Drive, Ashland, OH, 44805; tel 800-321-0350; fax (330) 797-2947; e-mail jsmith@scity.com; web site www.scity.com
Nat'l Sales Mgr.–Jim Smith
Industry: Circulation Equipment & Supplies

Stepper, Inc.
PO Box 1126, Olathe, KS, 66051-1126; tel (913) 782-2584; fax (913) 782-2441; e-mail stepper@bigstuff-stepper.com
Pres.–Warren Hannon
Industry: Feeding, Folding, Delivery Equipment

Sterling Packaging Systems
6275 Heisley Rd., Mentor, OH, 44060-1858; tel (440) 358-7060; fax (440) 358-7061; web site www.polychem.com
Gen. Mgr.–Mihia Cojocaru
Industry: Bundling and Tying Machines; Consulting Services: Equipment; Conveyors; Mailroom Systems & Equipment; Remanufactures Equipment;

Sterling Type Foundry
PO Box 50234, Indianapolis, IN, 46250, USA; tel (317) 849-5665; fax (317) 849-1616; web site www.sterlingtype.com
Works Mgr.–David C. Churchman
Industry: Platemakers: Letterpress; Presses: Letterpress; Type, Fonts;

Stewart Glapat Corp.
PO Box 3030, Zanesville, OH, 43702-3030; tel (740) 452-3601; fax (740) 452-9140; e-mail sglapat@adjustoveyor.com; web site www.adjustoveyor.com
Pres.–Charles T. Stewart
Sales Mgr.–C. Dutch Lewis
Industry: Material Handling Equipment: Truck Loaders

Herman H. Sticht Co., Inc.
45 Main St., Ste. 701, Brooklyn, NY, 11201; tel (718) 852-7602; fax (718) 852-7915; e-mail stichtco@aol.com; web site www.stichtco.com
Pres.–Paul H. Plotkin
Industry: Static Eliminators

Stoesser Register Systems
2440 Leghorn St., Mountain View, CA, 94043; tel (650) 969-1020; fax (650) 967-5963; e-mail bills@stoesser.com; rcust@stoesser.com; web site www.olec.com
Vice Pres.–Bill J. Stoesser
Controller–Jasvir Bassi
Industry: Color Registration; Controls: Register; Cutters & Trimmers; Exposure Lamps; Pin Register Systems; Plate Bending Systems; Plate Exposure Units; Plate Mounting & Register Systems; Platemakers: Offset (Conventional); Punching Equipment;

StoraEnso
6 Landmark Sq., 4th Fl., Stamford, CT, 06901; tel (203) 359-5707; fax (203) 359-5858; web site www.storaenso.com
Mgr., Mktg.–Paul Lukaszewski
Industry: Paper: Coated Groundwood Offset

Dennis Storch Co.
175 W. 72nd St., Ste. 8G, New York, NY, 10023; tel (212) 877-2622; fax (212) 724-3824; e-mail dstorch@aol.com; web site www.dennis-storch.com
Pres.–Dennis Storch
Industry: Consulting Services: Equipment; Dark Room Equipment; Equipment Dealers (Used); Platemakers: Offset (Conventional); Presses: Offset; Processors: Film & Paper; Raster Image Processors; Training: Pre Press; Typesetters: Laser;

Strategic Telemedia
PO Box 1162, New York, NY, 10014; tel (212) 366-0895; fax (212) 366-0897; e-mail plakias@tiac.com; web site www.teamtelemedia.com
Gen. Mgr.–Mark Plakias
Industry: Consulting Services: Marketing; Market Research;

Summit Media Partners LLC
23454 Waynes Way, Golden, CO, 80401-9155; tel (303) 526-7906; fax (303) 526-2568; e-mail info@smpllc.com; info@summitmediapartners.com
Pres.–Carmen Lamar
Industry: Consulting Services: Advertising; Consulting Services: Circulation; Consulting Services: Computer; Consulting Services: Editorial; Consulting Services: Equipment; Consulting Services: Marketing; Consulting Services: Production;

Sun Graphic, Inc.
1820 NW 21st St., Pompano Beach, FL, 33069; tel (954) 974-0217; fax (954) 974-0304; web site www.rycoline.com
Chrmn./Owner–Charles Palmer
Pres.–Norman Nichol
Vice Pres./Gen. Mgr.–Ron Askin
Industry: Blanket Mounting and Bars; Offset Blankets, Blanket Wash;

SunShine Paper Co.
12601 E. 33rd Ave., Ste. 109, Aurora, CO, 80011-1839; tel (303) 341-2990; fax (303) 341-2995; e-mail mgsunpco@aol.com; web site www.sunshinepaper.com
Vice Pres., Sales/Mktg.–Michael S. Gallagher
Adv. Customer Info Serv.–Geri Hancock
Industry: Offset Blanket Thickness Gauge; Offset Chemicals & Supplies;

Superior Handling Equipment, Inc.
8 Aviator Way, Ormond Beach, FL, 32174-2983; tel (800) 221-4339; fax (386) 677-0022; e-mail info@superiorlifts.com; web site www.superiorlifts.com
Pres.–Pete Dilella
Industry: Material Handling Equipment: Truck Loaders; Material Handling Equipment: Vehicle Loading; Paper Handeling Equipment;

Superior Lithoplate of Indiana, Inc.
PO Box 192, Rockville, IN, 47872-0192; tel (765) 569-2094; fax (765) 569-2096; web site www.superiorlithoplate.com
Pres.–Robert T. Blane
Vice Pres.–Steven C. Blane
Office Mgr.–Miriam Blane
Nat'l Sales Mgr.–Thomas J. Casson
Industry: Chemicals: Plate Processing; Chemicals: Pressroom; Offset Chemicals & Supplies; Plate Cleaners; Platemakers: Offset (Conventional);

Support Products, Inc.
PO Box 1185, Effingham, IL, 62401-1185; tel (217) 536-6171; fax (217) 536-6828; e-mail supprot@supportproducts.com; custserv@supportproducts.com; sales@supportproducts.com; web site www.supportproducts.com
CEO–Jim Calhoon
Dir., Sales–Rob Bradshaw
Industry: Adhesives; Chemicals: Roller Cleaning; Composing Room Equipment & Supplies; Ink Fountains & Accessories; Layout Tables, Light Tables & Workstations; Masking Materials; Offset Blanket Thickness Gauge; Plate Cleaners; Rules; Static Eliminators;

Support Systems International Corp.
136 S. 2nd St., Richmond, CA, 94804-2110; tel (510) 234-9090; fax (510) 233-8888; e-mail info@support-systems-intl.com; web site www.support-systems-intl.com
Pres.–Ben Parsons
Industry: Computers: Local Area Network (LANS); Telecommunications;
Syntellect, Inc.
16610 N. Black Canyon Hwy., Ste. 100, Phoenix, AZ, 85053, USA; tel (602) 789-2800; fax (602) 789-2899; e-mail info@syntellect.com; web site www.syntellect.com
Pres.–Steve Dodenhoff
Vice Pres., Sales Americas–Keith Gyssler
Industry: Computers: Hardware & Software Integrators; Computers: Local Area Network (LANS); Consulting Services: Advertising; Consulting Services: Circulation; Consulting Services: Equipment; Consulting Services: Marketing; Speech Recognition; Subscription Fulfillment Software; System Integration Services; Telecommunications;

System Facilities, Inc.
PO Box 4970, Syracuse, NY, 13221-4970; tel (315) 234-2348; fax (315) 234-3652; e-mail sfi@scotsmanpress.com; web site www.systemfacilities.com
Bus. Mgr.–William Veit
Industry: Laser Printers; Phototypesetting Interface Equipment; Scanners: Color B & W, Plates, Web; Typesetting Programs;
Systems Technology, Inc.
1351 E. Riverview Dr., San Bernardino, CA, 92408; tel (909) 799-9950; fax (909) 796-8297; e-mail info@systems-technology-inc.com; web site www.systems-technology-inc.com
Pres.–John St. John
Exec. Asst.–Sheila Barnett
Industry: Bundling and Tying Machines; Counting, Stacking, Bundling Machines; Cutters & Trimmers; In-Line Trimming Systems; Material Handling Equipment: Palletizing Machines; Strapping Machines

T

TALX Corp.
11432 Lackland Dr., Saint Louis, MO, 63146; tel (314) 214-7000; fax (314) 214-7588; e-mail moreinfo@talx.com; web site www.talx.com
CEO–William Canfield
Vice Pres., Market Devel.–Michael Smith
Industry: Speech Recognition

TKM United States, Inc.
PO Box 75015, Cincinnati, OH, 45275; tel (859) 689-7094; fax (859) 689-7565; e-mail sales@tkmus.com; web site www.tkmus.com
Market Mgr.–Michael Clark
Industry: Cutters & Trimmers

TKS (USA), Inc.
9155 Sterling St., Ste. 100, Irving, TX, 75063; tel (972) 983 0600; fax (972) 870-5857; e-mail sales@tkspress.com; web site www.tksusa.com
Director of Sales and Marketing–Mike Shafer
Sales Mgr.–Yuri Kopchenko
Industry: Presses: Offset

TNS
11 Madison Ave., 12th Flr., New York, NY, 10010, USA; tel (212) 991-6000; e-mail info-us@tns-global.com; web site www.tns-us.com
Industry: Consulting Services: Advertising; Consulting Services: Marketing; Market Research;

TNS Media Intelligence
100 Park Ave., 4th Fl., New York, NY, 10017; tel (212) 991-6000; fax (212) 949-1942; web site www.tns-mi.com
Pres.–Mark Nesbitt
Industry: Consulting Services: Advertising

TRX Interactive Communications, Inc.
400 E. 59th St., 12th Fl., New York, NY, 10022, USA; tel (212) 355-4565; e-mail info@trxinteractive.com; sales@trxinteractive.com; web site www.trxinteractive.com
Pres./CEO–Roger Vitkansas

TSA
2050 W. Sam Houston Pkwy. N., Houston, TX, 77043; tel (713) 935-1500; fax (713) 935-1555; e-mail info@tsa.com; web site www.tsa.com
Pres.–William C. Smith
Sales Mgr.–Steven Perry
Servs. Devel. Mgr.–Rick Valanta
Industry: Computers: Hardware & Software Integrators; Equipment Dealers (New); Equipment Dealers (Used);

TSI International Software Ltd.
45 Danbury Rd., Wilton, CT, 06897; tel (203) 761-8600; fax (203) 762-9677; e-mail dpower@tsisoft.com; web site www.tsisoft.com
Pres.–Constance Galley
Vice Pres.-Mktg.–Robert Bouton
Industry: Software: Electronic Data Interchange

Taft Contracting Co. (not affiliated w/Taft Eqpt. Co.)
9000 67th St., Hodgkins, IL, 60525-5185; tel (708) 656-7500; fax (708) 656-8945; e-mail info@taftcontracting.com; web site www.taftcontracting.com
CEO–Richard J. Walsh
Pres., Sales–Michael Walsh
Vice Pres., Field Servs.–John Bianchi
Industry: Erectors & Riggers

Tally Genicom
14600 Myford Rd., Irvine, CA, 92606-1005; tel (714) 368-2300; fax (714) 368-2335; e-mail info@printronix.com; web site www.tallygenicom.com
CEO–Randy Eisendach
Dir., Mktg.–Karen Jensen
Industry: Laser Printers

TALX Corp.
11432 LackLand Dr., Saint Louis, MO, 63146; tel (314) 214-7000; fax (314) 214-7588; e-mail moreinfo@talx.com; web site www.talx.com
CEO–William Canfield
Vice Pres.-Market Devel.–Michael Smith
Industry: Speech Recognition

Taylor Made Digital Systems
288 Lindbergh Ave., Livermore, CA, 94550-9512; tel (925) 245-9500; fax (925) 245-9400; web site www.taylormadedigital.com
Vice Pres., Major Accts.–Dave Ruotolo
Vice Pres., Sales–Clint Taylor
Vice Pres., Serv.–Tom Gernhardt
Customer Serv. Mgr.–Chuck Smith
Industry: Facsimilie/Fax Transmission Systems

Tech-Energy Co.
1111 Schneider Dr., Cibolo, TX, 78108; tel (210) 658-0614; fax (210) 658-0653; e-mail techenergy@techenergy.com; web site www.techenergy.com
Pres.–John E. Pickard
Vice Pres.–Beth Benke
Sec.–Phyllis Pickard
Treasurer–Teresa Moeller
Serv. Mgr.–Louis Benke
Int'l Sales Mgr.–Rachel Bell
Nat'l Sales Mgr.–David N. Moeller
Industry: Blanket Mounting and Bars; Blankets; Ink Fountains & Accessories; Press Accessories, Parts & Supplies; Press Engineers; Press Rebuilding; Press Repairs; Presses: Letterpress; Presses: Offset; Rollers;

T
echnidyne Corp.
100 Quality Ave., New Albany, IN, 47150-2272; tel (812) 948-2884; fax (812) 945-6847; e-mail spectrum@technidyne.com; web site www.technidyne.com
Pres./CEO–M. Todd Popson
Bus. Dir.–Paul M. Crawford
Vice Pres., Sales/Mktg.–Thomas Crawford
Mgr., Technical Servs.–Patrick Robertson
Industry: Color Analyzers; Color Management Software; Equipment Dealers (New); Equipment Dealers (Used); Paper Testing Instruments;

Technology Integrators
PO Box 334, Effingham, IL, 62401-0334; tel (217) 342-3981; fax (217) 342-1286; web site www.technologyintegrators.net; www.airstamping.com
Sales Engineer–Gene Williams
Sales Engineer–Troy Ramey
Acct. Exec.–Kim Schmidt
Industry: Press Accessories, Parts & Supplies; Vacuum Frames;

Technotrans America, Inc.
1050 E. Business Center Dr., Mount Prospect, IL, 60056; tel (847) 227-9200; fax (847) 227-9400; e-mail ttasales@technotrans.com; info@technotrans.com; web site www.technotrans.com
Vice Pres.–Thomas Carbery
Sales Admin.–Victoria Moore
Technical Sales Mgr.–Marty Kaczmarek
Industry: Blanket Cleaner/Washer (Automatic); Dampening Systems; Dies (Perforating and Slitting); Water Management Systems; Web Offset Remoisturizers;

Tek-Tools, Inc.
4040 McEwen Rd., Ste. 240, Dallas, TX, 75244-5032; tel (972) 980-2890; fax (972) 866-0714; e-mail contact@tek-tools.com; web site www.tek-tools.com
Pres./CEO–Ken Barth
Dir., Sales–Cindy Whitley
Dir., Mktg.–Stephen Harding
Industry: Software: Advertising (Includes Display; Classified); Software: Editorial; Software: Electronic Data Interchange; Software: Workflow Management/Tracking;

Tel-Aire Publications, Inc.
3105 E. Carpenter Frwy., Irving, TX, 75062-4933; tel (972) 438-4111; fax (972) 579-7483; e-mail sales@tel-aire.com; web site www.tel-aire.com
Pres.–David McGee
Industry: Trade Publications

Tel-Management, Inc.
2337 Lemoine Ave., Fort Lee, NJ, 07024; tel (201) 224-6510; fax (201) 363-9591
Regl. Mgr.–Dave Tirpak
Industry: Computers: Hardware & Software Integrators; Equipment Dealers (New); Facsimilie/Fax Transmission Systems; Integrated Fax Servers; Software: Electronic Data Interchange;

TeleDirect International, Inc.
17255 N. 82nd St., Scottsdale, AZ, 85255; tel (480) 585-6464; fax (480) 585-3373; e-mail sales@tdiinc.com; web site www.tdi-inc.com
Pres./CEO–Kathleen Kelly
COO–Rita Dearing
CFO–Jay S. Mayne
CTO–Mark M. Moore
Vice Pres., Sales/Mktg.–Christopher Saulkner
Industry: Telecommunications

Telesonic Packaging Corp., Ames Engineering Div.
805 E. 13th St., Wilmington, DE, 19802; tel (302) 658-6945; fax (302) 658-6946; e-mail telesonics@aol.com; web site www.telesoniconline.com
Pres.–Bernard Katz
Industry: Automatic Plastic Bagging Equipment; Bundling and Tying Machines; Shrink Wrapping Equipment;

TeleType Co.
20 Park Plz., Boston, MA, 02116; tel (617) 542-6220; fax (617) 542-6289; e-mail info@teletype.com; web site www.teletype.com
–Marlene Winer
–Edward FreemanMktg. Mgr.s
Industry: Publishing Systems

Tembec, Paper Group
405 The West Mall, Ste. 800, Etobicoke, ON, M9C 5J1, Canada; tel (416) 775-2801; fax (416) 621-4303; web site www.tembec.ca
Pres./Exec. Vice Pres.–Chris Black
Industry: Newsprint

Tensor Group, Inc.
10351 Rising Ct., Woodridge, IL, 60517-4930; tel (630) 739-9600; fax (630) 739-9339; e-mail mruda@ustensor.com; web site www.tensorgroup.com
Chrmn./Pres.–Martin Hozjan
Exec. Vice Pres.–Martina Hozjan Ruda
Int'l Sales–Michael Pavone
Mktg. Mgr./Sales Admin.–Karin Arlt
Industry: Presses: Offset

Tera D.P. S.r.l.
Viale Certosa, 148, Milano, N/A, 20156, Italy; tel 39 02 380 9871; fax 39 02 380 08119; web site ^www.teradp.com
Founder/CEO–Michele Mottini
MD–Franz Rossi
Mgr., Mktg./Reseller Relations–John Juliano

Industry: Consulting Services: Advertising

Teufelberger GmbH
Vogelweiderstrasse 50, Wels, N/A, 4600, Austria; tel 43 7242 4130; fax 43 7242 413100; e-mail fibersplastics@teufelberger.com; mailbox@teufelberger.com; web site www.teufelberger.com
Owner–Teufel Berger
Mgr., Mktg./Sales Agriculture–Harald Katzinger
Industry: Bundling and Tying Machines; Counting, Stacking, Bundling Machines; Strapping Machines;

Thompson Cabinet Co.
PO Box 588, Ludington, MI, 49431; tel (231) 843-7000; fax (231) 843-4200; e-mail requestinfo@thompsoncabinet.com; web site www.thompsoncabinet.com
Vice Pres./Sales Mgr.–Edward Thompson
Industry: Cabinets; Composing Room Equipment & Supplies; Computers: Storage Devices; Tables (Dot, Etch, Opaquing, Register, Retouching, Stripping);

Thought Equity Management, Inc.
1530 16th St., 6th Fl., Denver, CO, 80202; tel (720) 382-2869; fax (720) 382-2719; e-mail sales@thoughtequity.com; web site www.thoughtequity.com
Founder/CEO–Kevin Schaff
CTO–Mark Lemmons
Vice Pres., Mktg.–Mike Emerson
Vice Pres., Bus. Devel.–Frank Cardello
Industry: Electronic Ad Delivery

Tidland Corp.
2305 SE Eighth Ave., Camas, WA, 98607; tel (360) 834-2345; fax (360) 834-5865; e-mail tidland@tidland.com; web site www.tidland.com
Media Mgr.–Kasey Morales
Mktg. Commun.–Michelle Pass
Industry: Chemicals: Chuck (Paper Roll); Consulting Services: Equipment; Conversion Equipment; Core Cutters, Restorers, Rounders; Cutters & Trimmers; Cutting Tools; Reels & Tensions; Reels (Inlcudes Paper Reels); Tension & Web Controls; Web Press - Special Equipment;

Tilt-Lock
12070 43rd St. NE, St. Michael, MN, 55376; tel (800) 999-8458; fax (763) 497-7046; e-mail sales@tiltlock.com; web site www.tiltlock.com
Sales Mgr.–Jerry Morton
Industry: Chemicals: Chuck (Paper Roll); Roll Handeling Equipment;

TKS Ltd.
26-24 Shiba 5-Chome Minato-Ku, Tokyo, N/A, 108-8375, Japan; tel +81 3 3451-8141; fax +81 3 3451-7425; e-mail overseas@tks-net.co.jp; web site www.tks-net.co.jp
Pres.–Noriyuki Shiba
Sales Chief Officer–Osamu Kurata

Tobias Associates, Inc.
PO Box 2699, Ivyland, PA, 18974-0347; tel (800) 877-3367; fax (215) 322-1504; e-mail sales@tobiasinc.com; web site www.densitometer.com
Vice Pres.–Eric M. Tobias
Sales Mgr.–William D. Bender
Industry: Calibration Software/Hardware; Color Analyzers; Dark Room Equipment; Densitometers; Electronic Pre-Scan Systems; Press Accessories, Parts & Supplies; Testing Instruments;

Tolerans AB Sweden
P.O Box 669, Tyreso, N/A, 135 26, Sweden; tel +46 8 4487030; fax +46 8 4487040; e-mail info@tolerans.com; web site www.tolerans.com
President–Jan Melin
Vice Pres. Sales & Mktg.–Olof Aurell

Total Mailroom Support, Inc. (TMSI)
6800 Lake Abram Dr., Middleburg Heights, OH, 44130; tel (440) 239-9000; fax (440) 239-9006; e-mail info@thetotalmailroom.com; web site www.thetotalmailroom.com
Pres.–Micheal McGeady
Vice Pres.–Anthony Skerl
Nat'l Sales Mgr.–Tim Higgins
Mgr., Western Regl. Sales–Patrick McGeady
Mgr., Southern Regl. Sales–David Admire
Mgr., Eastern Regl. Sales–Wayne Anderson
Sales/Mktg. Administrator–Wendy Silvis
Mgr., Parts/Serv.–Paul Cook
Industry: Belts, Belting, V-Belts; Conveyors; Erectors & Riggers; Mailroom Systems & Equipment; Material Handling Equipment: Truck Loaders; Remanufactures Equipment; Software: Press/Post Press; System Installations; Training: Post Press;

Tower Products, Inc.
PO Box 3070, Palmer, PA, 18043, USA; tel (610) 253-6206; fax (610) 258-9695; e-mail info@towerproducts.com; web site www.towerproducts.com
President & CEO–Richard Principato
Industry: Chemicals: Pressroom; Chemicals: Roller Cleaning; Cleaners & Solvents;

Transportation Consultants, Inc.
8302 Dunwoody Pl., Ste. 352, Atlanta, GA, 30350; tel (404) 250-0100; fax (404) 250-0253; e-mail tci@transpconsult.com; web site www.transpconsult.com
Pres.–Paul Gold
Industry: Consulting Services: Circulation

Trauner Consulting Services, Inc.
1617 JFK Blvd., Ste. 600, Philadelphia, PA, 19103; tel (215) 814-6400; fax (215) 814-6440; e-mail philadelphia@traunerconsulting.com; web site www.traunerconsulting.com
Mgr., New Bus.–Russ Thomas
Industry: Architects/Engineers (Includes Design/Construction Firms); Training: Keyboard Operation;

Tribune Media Services
333 Glen St., Glens Falls, NY, 12801; tel (518) 792-9914; fax (518) 761-7118; e-mail tvdata@tvdata.com; web site www.tvdata.com; www.clicktv.com
Pres.-Publishing Division–Roger Moore
CFO/Sr. Vice Pres.-New Bus. Devel.–Kenneth Carter
Sr. Vice Pres.-Sales–Kathleen Tolstrup
Sr. Vice Pres.-Info Systems–James McCormick
Vice Pres.-Opns.–John McVay
Vice Pres.-Newspaper/Sales–Cameron Yung
Vice Pres.-Newspaper Grp. Sales–Bill Callahan
Vice Pres.-Metro Newspaper Sales–John Dodds
Vice Pres.-Editorial–Rob Plocharczyk
Dir., Regl. Sales–Bill Ranney
Mgr.-Online Product–Kevin Joyce
Industry: Software: Pagination/Layout; Training: Design & Layout;

Trumatch, Inc.
PO Box 501, Water Mill, NY, 11976-0501, USA; tel (631) 204-9100; fax (631) 204-0002; e-mail info@trumatch.com; web site www.trumatch.com
Pres.–Steven J. Abramson
Vice Pres.–Jane E. Nichols
Office Mgr.–Joan Dalessandro
Industry: Color Management Software; Color Seperation Guides;

Truproof Ltd.
Unit 7 Bldg. B Faircharm Trading Estate, London, N/A, SE8 3DX, United Kingdom; tel +44 181 694-8588; fax +44 181 443-288; e-mail info@truproof.co.uk; sales@truproof.co.uk
Mng. Dir.–G.M. Walden
Industry: Cabinets; Color Proofing; Color Viewing Equipment; Densitometers; Laser Printers; Layout Tables, Light Tables & Workstations; Prepress Color Proofing Systems; Storage Retrieval Systems;

U

UMI
2821 A Worth Ave., Englewood, FL, 34224; tel (941) 475-1313; fax (941) 475-1404; e-mail info@umipressparts.com
Pres.–Bob MacKenzie
Industry: Equipment Dealers (Used); Folder Knives; Press Repairs;

US Ink
651 Garden St., Carlstadt, NJ, 07072; tel (201) 935-8666; fax (201) 933-3728; web site www.usink.com
Vice Pres., Opns.–Lawrence J. Lepore
Vice Pres., Sales–John C. Corcoran
Technical Dir.–Peter I. Ford
Industry: Inks

U.S. Petrolon Industrial
11442 Queens Dr., Omaha, NE, 68164; tel (402) 445-8600; fax (402) 445-8608; e-mail al@uspetrolon.com; web site www.uspetrolon.com
Regl. Distributor–Al Harrell
Industry: Fluid Handeling: Pressroom

U.S. Suburban Press (USSPI)
428 E. State Pkwy., Ste. 226, Schaumburg, IL, 60173; tel (847) 490-6000; fax (847) 843-9058; web site www.usspi.com
CEO–Phil Miller
CFO–Sandy Smith
Pres., Sales–Frank O'Connell
Mktg./PR Dir.–Rick Baranski
Industry: Consulting Services: Advertising; Newspaper Marketing

UVP, Inc.
2066 W. 11th St., Upland, CA, 91786; tel (909) 946-3197; fax (909) 946-3597; e-mail uvp@uvp.com; web site www.uvp.com
Pres.–Leighton Smith
Vice Pres., Mktg./Sales–Alex Waluszko
Commun. Mktg. Serv.–Kathy Buckman
Industry: Exposure Lamps; Inks;

UV Process Supply, Inc.
1229 W. Cortland St., Chicago, IL, 60614-4805; tel (773) 248-0099; fax (773) 880-6647; e-mail info@uvps.com; web site www.uvprocess.com
Pres.–Stephen Siegel
Industry: Color Analyzers; Drying Systems; Ink Bleeding Equipment; Ink Fountains & Accessories; Ink Pumping Systems; Ink Storage Tanks; Lubricants; Offset Chemicals & Supplies; Pumps (Air, Ink, Vacuum); Static Eliminators;

UMAX Technologies, Inc.
10460 Brockwood Rd., Dallas, TX, 75238; tel (214) 342-9799; fax (214) 342-9046; e-mail sales@umax.com; web site www.umax.com
Vice Pres., Mktg.–Tenny Sin
Sr. Line Mgr.–Linn Lin
Industry: Color Seperation Scanners; Scanners: Color B & W, Plates, Web;

Unicom, Inc.
PO Box 92730, Anchorage, AK, 99518; tel (907) 561-1674; fax (907) 563-3185; e-mail unicom@unicom-alaska.com; web site www.unicom-alaska.com
Vice Pres./Gen. Mgr.–Rob Taylor
Industry: Telecommunications

Union Rubber, Inc.
PO Box 1040, Trenton, NJ, 08606-1040; tel (609) 396-9328; fax (609) 396-3587; e-mail contact@best-testproducts.com; web site papercement.com
Pres.–Paul Neiber
Industry: Adhesives

Unique Photo
123 US Hwy, 46 W., Fairfield, NJ, 07004; tel (973) 377-5555; fax (973) 377-8800; e-mail info@uniquephoto.com; sales@uniquephoto.com; web site www.uniquephoto.com
COO–Matthew Sweetwood
CFO–Jonathon Sweetwood
Industry: Cameras & Accessories; Chemicals: Photographic; Cutters & Trimmers; Dark Room Equipment; Developing and Processing; Film & Paper: Film Roll Dispensers; Film & Paper: Filters (Photographic); Lenses (Camera); Photography: Digital/Electronic Cameras; Photostat: Chemicals;

Unisys Corp.
Unisys Way, Blue Bell, PA, 19424-0001, USA; tel (215) 986-6999; fax (215) 986-2312; e-mail info@unisys.com; investor@unisys.com; web site www.unisys.com
Chrmn./CEO–J. Edward Coleman
Sr. Vice Pres./CFO–Janet Brutschea Haugen
Vice Pres./Treasurer–Scott A. Battersby
Industry: Archiving Systems; Computers: Hardware & Software Integrators; Electronic Ad Delivery; Software: Advertising (Includes Display; Classified); Software: Business (Includes Administration/Accounting); Software: Editorial; Software: Pagination/Layout; Software: Workflow Management/Tracking; System Integration Services;

United Paper Mills Kymmene, Inc.
1270 Avenue of the Americas, Ste. 203, New York, NY, 10020-1700; tel (212) 218-8232; fax (212) 218-8240; web site www.upm.com
Pres.–Tapio Korpeinen
Exec. Vice Pres./CFO–Jyrki Salo
Industry: Newsprint

United States Postal Service
475 L'Enfant Plz. SW, Washington, DC, 20260-0010; tel (202) 268-2500; fax (202) 268-5211; web site www.usps.gov; www.usps.com; www.usps.com/mailingonline
Chrmn.–James C. Miller
Postmaster General/CEO–John Potter
Deputy Postmaster General–Patrick R. Donahoe
Exec. Vice Pres./CFO–Harold Walker
CMO–Anita J. Bizzotto
Exec. Vice Pres./Chief HR Officer–Anthony Vegliante
Sr. Vice Pres., Mktg. Devel.–John R. Wargo
Vice Pres., Product Devel.–Nicholas F. Barranca
Vice Pres./Treasurer–Robert Peterson
Mgr., Product Mktg.–Larry M. Speakes
Mgr., USPS Adv. Program/Media Planning–Al Gilbert
Industry: Mailroom Systems & Equipment

Utilimaster
PO Box 585, Wakarusa, IN, 46573-0585; tel (574) 862-4561; fax (574) 862-4517; e-mail info@utilimaster.com; web site www.utilimaster.com
Sr. Vice Pres., Sales/Mktg.–John Marshall
Industry: Delivery Equipment

V

Valco Sales, Inc.
3491 Delaware Ave., Ste. 210, Buffalo, NY, 14217; tel (716) 873-2266; fax (716) 873-8970
Pres.–Barbara Vanyo
Industry: Consulting Services: Marketing; Market Research;

Valley Remanufacturing Co.
777 E. Fairmont St., Allentown, PA, 18109-3382; tel (610) 820-9669; fax (610) 820-0738
Owner–Bruce L. Seidel
Industry: Conveyors; Counting, Stacking, Bundling Machines; Equipment Dealers (New); Equipment Dealers (Used); Inserting Equipment (Includes Stuffing Machines);

Mailroom Systems & Equipment; System Integration Services;

Value Checks
15880 SW Barnard Ct., Beaverton, OR, 97007; tel (503) 643-1827; fax (503) 641-0900; e-mail luman@teleport.com
Pres./Mktg. Mgr.–David Luman
Industry: Promotion Services

Van Son Holland Ink Corp. of America
185 Oval Dr., Islandia, NY, 11749; tel (800) 645-4182; fax (800) 442-8744; e-mail info@vansonink.com; web site www.vansonink.com
Pres.–Joseph Bendowski
Industry: Inks

Vegra USA
1621 W. Carroll Ave., Chicago, IL, 60612-2501; tel (312) 733-3400; fax (312) 738-2386; e-mail info@vegra.de; web site www.vegra.de
Vice Pres., Sales–Michael Miske
Industry: Chemicals: Pressroom; Core Strippers & Seperators; Dies (Perforating and Slitting); Offset Blankets, Blanket Wash; Offset Chemicals & Supplies; Offset Fountain Solutions; Static Eliminators;

Ver-A-Fast Corp.
20545 Center Ridge Rd., Ste. 300, Rocky River, OH, 44116-3430; tel (440) 331-0250; fax (440) 331-2701; web site www.verafast.com
Pres.–Robert Bensman
Exec. Vice Pres.–Cathy Soprano
Vice Pres., Mktg./Devel.–Nanette Kubera
Mktg. Devel. Mgr.–James Tanner
Prodn. Mgr.–Carol Tanner
Computer Servs. Mgr.–Kim Taraba
Industry: Consulting Services: Circulation; Market Research; Research Studies; Telecommunications;

Verity, Inc.
5758 W. Losposits Blvd., Ste. 100, Pleasanton, CA, 94588; tel (408) 982-4230; fax (408) 654-9302
Pres. / CEO–Sttouffer Eagan
PR Mgr.–Winifred Shum
Industry: Library Retrieval Systems; Software: Electronic Data Interchange; Storage Retrieval Systems;

Versar Inc.
6850 Versar Ctr., Springfield, VA, 22151; tel (703) 750-3000; fax (703) 642-6807; e-mail info@versar.com; web site www.versar.com
Pres./CEO–Theodore M. Prociv
Industry: Architects/Engineers (Includes Design/Construction Firms); System Installations;

Vertis
250 W. Pratt St., Baltimore, MD, 21201; tel (410) 528-9800; fax (410) 528-9289; e-mail info@vertisinc.com; web site www.vertisinc.com; www.vertis.co.uk
Industry: Software: Advertising (Includes Display; Classified)

Vexure Logistic Company
13901 Sutton Park Dr., S., Jacksonville, FL, 32224; tel (800) 874-3315; fax (904) 249-7299; web site www.vexure.com
CEO–Allen J. Steele
Pres./COO–Tom Piatak
Sr. Vice Pres./Gen. Mgr.–David Stonier
Bookkeeping–Gene Wood
Dispatcher–Lorrie Chauncey
Dispatcher–Nancy Hillier
Industry: Delivery Equipment

VIDAR Systems Corp.
365 Herndon Pkwy., Herndon, VA, 20170; tel (703) 471-7070; fax (703) 471-1165; e-mail medical@vidar.com; web site www.vidar.com
Industry: Scanners: Color B & W, Plates, Web

Video Jet Technologies
1500 Mittel Blvd., Wood Dale, IL, 60191-1073; tel (630) 860-7300; fax (630) 616-3623; e-mail information_center@marconidata.com; web site www.videojet.com
Sr. Mktg. Communication Specialist–Theresa DiCanio
Industry: Addressing Machines; Inks; Label Printing Machines; Mailroom Systems & Equipment;

Vijuk Equipment
715 Church Rd., Elmhurst, IL, 60126; tel (630) 530-2203; fax (630) 530-2245; e-mail info@vijukequip.com; web site www.vijukequip.com
Pres.–Joseph Vijuk
Sales–Luis Campos
Industry: Cutters & Trimmers; Folding Machines;

Vision Data Equipment Corp.
1377 3rd St., Rensselaer, NY, 12144; tel (518) 434-2193; fax (518) 434-3457; e-mail sales@vdata.com; web site www.vdata.com
Pres.–Thomas Dempsey
Adv. Contact–Amy Weaver
Industry: Business Computers; Software: Advertising (Includes Display; Classified); Software: Business (Includes Administration/Accounting); Software: Circulation; Software: Electronic Data Interchange; Software: Pagination/Layout; Software: Workflow Management/Tracking;

VoCal Telecommunications
1815 S. Mayflower Ave., Monrovia, CA, 91016, USA; tel (626) 357-2449; e-mail r.emerling@ieee.org
Pres.–Ron Emerling
Industry: Computers: Hardware & Software Integrators; Telecommunications;

Voice Connexion
2324 N. Batavia St., Ste. 105, Orange, CA, 92865; tel (714) 685-1066; fax (714) 685-1070; e-mail voicecnx@aol.com; web site www.voicecnx.com
Vice Pres., Sales/Mktg.–Shirlee Dworak
Mktg.–Sharla Cartwright
Industry: Speech Recognition

VoiceWorld, Inc.
11201 N. 70th St., Scottsdale, AZ, 85254-5183; tel (718) 252-3153; fax (480) 922-5572; e-mail prospects@voiceworld.com; web site www.voiceworld.com
Pres./Founder–Brian L. Berman
Industry: Business Computers; Consulting Services: Circulation; Telecommunications;

WIFAG Press Co.
1901 St. Ives Dr., Birmingham, AL, 25242; tel (205) 980-0748; fax (205) 980-0645; e-mail thomas.stuart@wifag.ch; web site www.wifag.ch
Vice Pres., Sales–Thomas S. Stuart
Industry: Presses: Offset; Training: Press Operation & Maintenance;

W

WPC Machinery Corp.
1600 Downs Dr., Ste. 4, West Chicago, IL, 60185-1888; tel (630) 231-7721; fax (630) 231-7827
Prodn. Mgr., Press Servs.–Ron Dewall
Industry: Consulting Services: Production; Cylinder Repair; Drives & Controls; Erectors & Riggers; Ink Fountains & Accessories; Paper Handeling Equipment; Press Rebuilding; Press Repairs; Rollers;

WRH Marketing
Industriesse 1, Hinwil, Zurich, N/A, CH 8340, Switzerland; tel 41 44 938 7000; fax 41 44 938 7070; e-mail info@wrh-marketing.com; web site www.wrh-marketing.com

WRH Marketing Americas, Inc.
3150 Brunswick Pike, Ste. 220, Lawrenceville, NJ, 08648, USA; tel (856) 842-0600; fax (856) 842-0989; e-mail barry.evans@ferag-americas.com; web site www.ferag-americas.com
Pres.–Joseph Colletti
Vice Pres.–Barry Evans
Industry: Bundling and Tying Machines; Conveyors; Delivery Equipment; Inserting Equipment (Includes Stuffing Machines); Storage Retrieval Systems;

Walter Meier Climate (USA), Inc.
PO Box 698, Ogdensburg, NY, 13669; tel (315) 425-1255; fax (613) 822-7964; e-mail nortec@humidity.com; web site www.humidity.com
Pres.–Urs Schenk
Vice Pres., Sales–Gary Berlin
Vice Pres., Mktg.–Mike Hurley
Mktg. Coord.–Naomi Cassidy
Industry: Humidifiers

Walterry Insurance Brokers
7411 Old Branch Ave., Clinton, MD, 20735-0128; tel (301) 868-7200; fax (301) 868-2611; e-mail insurance@walterry.com; web site www.walterry.com
Dir., Mktg.–Walter J. Coady
Industry: Insurance

Weatherline, Inc.
12119 St. Charles Rock Rd., Saint Louis, MO, 63044; tel (314) 291-1000; fax (314) 291-3226; e-mail info@weatherline.com; web site www.weatherline.com
Pres.–Richard H. Friedman
Exec. Vice Pres.–Michelle Parent
Sr. Vice Pres.–Nancy J. Friedman
Sr. Vice Pres.–Martha Murphy
Sr. Vice Pres.–Stephen L. Smith
Industry: Consulting Services: Advertising; Consulting Services: Marketing; Promotion Services;

Web Printing Controls
23872 N. Kelsey Rd., Barrington, IL, 60010-1563; tel (847) 382-7970; fax (847) 382-2348; e-mail sales@webprintingcontrols.com; web site www.wpcteam.com
Pres.–Herman Gnuechtel
Vice Pres.–James Tasch
Industry: Controls: Register; Numbering Machines; Press Control Systems; Tension & Web Controls; Web Break Detector; Web Guides;

Jervis B. Webb Co.
34375 W. Twelve Mile Rd., Farmington Hills, MI, 48331-3375; tel (248) 553-1000; fax (248) 553-1228; e-mail info@jerviswebb.com; web site www.jervisbwebb.com
Pres./CEO–Brian G. Stewart
Sr. Vice Pres./CFO–John S. Doychich
Industry: Computers: Hardware & Software Integrators; Consulting Services: Equipment; Conveyors; Mailroom Systems & Equipment; Material Handling Equipment: Automatic Guided Vehicles; Material Handling Equipment: Vehicle Loading; Newsprint Handeling Equipment; Paper Handeling Equipment; Roll Handeling Equipment; Storage Retrieval Systems;

Bob Weber, Inc.
23850 Commerce Park Rd., Cleveland, OH, 44122, United States; tel 8003994294; fax 8008378973; e-mail sales@bob-weber.com; web site www.bob-weber.com
President–Bob Weber
Marketing Manager–Leslie Schmidt
Mgr., Prodn.–Steve Fondriest
Sales Manager–Jennifer Klett
Vice President–Betty Weber
Industry: Color Seperation Scanners; Densitometers; Equipment Dealers (Used); Imagesetters; Plate Processors; Prepress Color Proofing Systems; Processors: Film & Paper; Proofing Systems; Raster Image Processors; Scanners: Color B & W, Plates, Web;

Weber Systems, Inc.
23850 Commerce Park Rd., Ste. 108, Beachwood, OH, 44122-5829; tel (432) 687-5445; fax (432) 687-5445; web site www.jefweber.net
Pres.–Jeff Weber
Industry: Prepress Color Proofing Systems; Storage Retrieval Systems; Computers: Hardware & Software Integrators; Equipment Dealers (New); Equipment Dealers (Used); Software: Pagination/Layout;

WebPress, LLC
P. O. Box 2274, Tacoma, WA, 98401, USA; tel 253-620-4747; fax 253-722-0378; e-mail info@webpressllc.com; web site www.webpressllc.com
Operations Manager–Rick Guinn
President–Brian Haun
Customer Service/Parts–Brian Hilsendager
Sales–Jim Merek
Industry: Folding Machines; Presses: Offset; Remanufactures Equipment; Roll Handeling Equipment; Web Press - Special Equipment;

The Wellmark Company
1903 SE 29th St., Oklahoma City, OK, 73129; tel (405) 672-6660; fax (405) 672-6661; e-mail twc@wellmarkco.com; web site www.wellmarkco.com
Pres.–Dick Pfieffer
VP Sales/Mktg.–Steve Lawson
Industry: Gauges, Measuring; Ink Storage Tanks;

J.N. Wells & Co., Inc.
534 Gamble Dr., Lisle, IL, 60532-2404; tel (630) 852-2215; fax (630) 852-2215
Pres.–Jonathan (Scott) Wells
Industry: Brokers & Appraisers; Consulting Services: Financial;

Wesco Graphics
410 E. Grant Line Rd., Ste. B, Tracy, CA, 95376; tel (209) 832-1000; fax (209) 832-7800; e-mail jim@wescographics.com; web site www.wescographics.com
Pres.–Jim Estes
Vice Pres.–Betty Estes
Industry: Consulting Services: Equipment; Equipment Dealers (Used); Erectors & Riggers; Inserting Equipment (Includes Stuffing Machines); Press Rebuilding; Press Repairs; Presses: Offset; Reels & Tensions; Roll Handeling Equipment; Web Press - Special Equipment;

West Coast Computer Systems
2010 N. Wilson Way, Stockton, CA, 95205; tel (209) 948-5499; e-mail sales@wccsys.com; web site www.wccsys.com
Sales/Mktg. Mgr.–Ed Kobrin
Application Software Mgr.–Simon Young
System Software Mgr.–Jim Ponder
Industry: Ink Storage Tanks; Lubricants; Offset Chemicals & Supplies; Pumps (Air, Ink, Vacuum); Static Eliminators; Consulting Services: Marketing; Market Research;

Westburg Media Capital
PO Box 4225, Incline Village, NV, 89450; tel (206) 774-1801; fax (775) 833-1136; e-mail john.hansen@westburg.com; web site www.westburg.com
Pres.–David B. Westburg
Dir.–John S. Hansen
Industry: Consulting Services: Financial

Western LithoTech
2625 N. Neergard, Springfield, MO, 65803; tel (800) 421-0051; fax (417) 831-0142; web site www.westernlithotech.com
Mktg. Mgr.–Keith Walker
OEM Sales Mgr., Machinery Division–Tony Petersen

Western LithoTech
3433 Tree Court Industrial Blvd., Saint Louis, MO, 63122; tel (800) 325-3310; fax (636) 825-4681; e-mail kathy_may@westernlitho.com
Pres./CEO–William Streeter
Sr. Vice Pres., Sales/Mktg.–Lane Palmer
Vice Pres., Machinery Division–John Powers

Mgr., Nat'l Sales–Todd Socia
Mgr., Int'l Sales–Ernie Stokes
Mgr., US/Int'l Mktg.–Kathryn May
Prodn. Mgr., Newspaper Product–Keith Walker
Industry: Chemicals: Plate Processing; Offset Plate-Making Service & Equipment; Plate Cleaners; Plate Processors; Platemakers: Flexographic (Traditional); Platemakers: Letterpress; Platemakers: Offset (Computer to Plate); Platemakers: Offset (Conventional); Plates: Offset (Computer to Plate); Plates: Offset (Conventional);

Western Printing Machinery
9229 Ivanhoe St., Schiller Park, IL, 60176; tel (847) 678-1740; fax (847) 678-6176; e-mail kmarkovich@wpm.com; web site www.wpm.com
Industry: Counting, Stacking, Bundling Machines; Cutters & Trimmers; Dies (Perforating and Slitting); Web Press - Special Equipment;

Western Quartz Products, Inc.
2432 Spring St., Paso Robles, CA, 93446; tel (805) 238-3524; fax (805) 238-6811; e-mail info@westernquartz.com; web site www.westernquartz.com
Pres.–Jon Dallons
CFO–Katy Wetterstrand
Industry: Exposure Lamps

Western Roller Corp.
63393 Nels Anderson Rd., Bend, OR, 97701; tel (541) 382-5643; fax (541) 382-0159; web site www.westernroller.com
Owner–Doug Collver
Industry: Delivery Equipment; Mailroom Systems & Equipment; Web Press - Special Equipment;

White Birch Paper
80 Field Point Rd., Greenwich, CT, 06830; tel (203) 661-3344; fax (203) 661-3349; web site www.whitebirchpaper.com
Chrmn./CEO–Peter M. Brant
Sr. Vice Pres./CFO–Edward D. Sherrick
President & COO–Christopher M. Brant
Sr. Vice Pres., Sales–Russel Lowder
Industry: Newsprint; Paper: Groundwood Specialties;

Whiting Technologies
646 Executive Dr., Willowbrook, IL, 60527; tel (630) 850-9680; fax (630) 850-9580; e-mail info@whitingtech.com; web site www.whitingtech.com
Chief Engineer–Fred Whiting
Sr. Engineer–Griffin Doak

Whitney Worldwide, Inc.
553 Hayward Ave., N. Ste.250, Saint Paul, MN, 55128; tel (800) 597-0227; fax (651) 748-4000; e-mail whitney@whitneyworld.com; web site www.whitneyworld.com
CEO–Les Layton
Industry: Consulting Services: Circulation; Consulting Services: Marketing; Mailing List Compiler; Market Research; Newspaper Marketing;

Whitworth Knife Company
508 Missouri Ave., Cincinnati, OH, 45226; tel (513) 321-9177; fax (513) 321-9938; web site www.whitworthknifecompany.com
Pres.–Ray Whitworth
Industry: Consulting Services: Production; Core Cutters, Restorers, Rounders; Core Strippers & Seperators; Cutters & Trimmers; Cutting Tools; Dies (Perforating and Slitting); Folder Knives; In-Line Trimming Systems; Ink Fountains & Accessories; Roller Grinders;

Wilson Gregory Agency, Inc.
PO Box 8, Camp Hill, PA, 17001-0008; tel (717) 730-9777; fax (717) 730-9328; e-mail info@wilsongregory.com; web site www.wilsongregory.com
Chrmn./CEO–Ted Gregory
Pres.–Richard Hively
Vice Pres.–Todd Gregory
Vice Pres., Opns.–Mark Gregory
Industry: Consulting Services: Circulation; Insurance;

Windmoeller and Hoelscher Corp.
23 New England Way, Lincoln, RI, 02865-4252; tel (401) 333-2770; fax (401) 333-6491; e-mail info@whcorp.com; web site www.whcorp.com
Pres.–Hans Deamer
Vice Pres.–Andrew Wheeler
Industry: Presses: Flexographic; Presses: Rotogravure;

Chauncey Wing's Sons, Inc.
PO Box 420, Marion, MA, 02738; tel 508-748-1680; e-mail info@chaunceywing.com; web site www.chaunceywing.com
Pres.–Donald Wing
Vice Pres.–Paul Sevrens
Mktg. Mgr.–Anne C. Wing
Industry: Adhesives; Mailroom Systems & Equipment;

Winton Engineering Co.
2303 W. 18th St., Chicago, IL, 60608; tel (312) 733-5200; fax (312) 733-0446; e-mail d.allison@w-rindustries.com; web site ^www.w-rindustries.com
Vice Pres.–David Allison
Industry: Chemicals: Pressroom; Chemicals: Roller Cleaning; Cleaners & Solvents; Offset Chemicals & Supplies; Press Accessories, Parts & Supplies;

Witte Energy Management
PO Box 10566, Midland, TX, 79702; tel (432) 685-1878; fax (432) 685-1883; e-mail wittrich@aol.com
Pres.–Richard Earl Witte
Industry: Maintenance, Plant & Equipment

Wolk Advertising, Inc. (Retail Carpet Ad Service)
920 E Lincoln St., Birmingham, MI, 48009, USA; tel (248) 540-5980; e-mail wolkadv@earthlink.net; web site www.flooringads.com
Pres.–Erv Wolk
Industry: Art & Layout Equipment and Services; Consulting Services: Advertising; Training: Design & Layout;

WordMark International Corp.
1400 Coleman Ave., Ste. F16, Santa Clara, CA, 95050-4321; tel (800) 835-2400; fax (408) 975-1111; e-mail info@multivalue.com
Pres.–Jeff Weidler
Industry: Computers: Local Area Network (LANS); Word Processing System;

Wrubel Communications
12-32 River Rd., Fair Lawn, NJ, 07410-1802; tel (201) 796-3331; fax (201) 796-5083
Pres.–Charles Wrubel
Industry: Consulting Services: Advertising; Consulting Services: Circulation; Consulting Services: Editorial; Consulting Services: Financial; Consulting Services: Marketing;

X

X-Rite Inc.
4300 44th St SE., Grand Rapids, MI, 49512-4009; tel (616) 803-2100; fax (888) 826-3061; e-mail info@xrite.com; investor@xrite.com; customerservice@xrite.com; web site www.xrite.com
Pres./CEO/COO–Thomas J. Vacchiano
Exec. Vice Pres./CFO–Raj Shah
CTO–Francis Lamy
Industry: Color Analyzers; Color Proofing; Color Viewing Equipment; Densitometers; Ink Controls, Computerized; Lighting Equipment; Photo Proofing Systems; Proofing Systems; Testing Instruments;

Xerium Technologies Inc.
14101 Capital Blvd, Ste 201, Youngsville, NC, 27596, United States; tel 919-556-7235; fax 919-556-1063
Vice Pres., Sales–Kevin Frank
Industry: Roll Coverings; Roller Grinding Services; Rollers;

Xerox (Corp. Headquarters)
PO Box 1600, Stamford, CT, 06904-1600; tel (800) ASK-XEROX (275-9376)
Chrmn. of the Bd./Chrmn.-Exec. Committee–Paul Allaire
Pres./CEO–Anne Mulcahy
Industry: Scanners: Color B & W, Plates, Web

Xerox Corp.
6336 Austin Center Blvd., Ste.300, Austin, TX, 78729; tel (512) 343-5600; fax (512) 343-5635; e-mail marketing@omnifax.xerox.com; web site www.omnifax.com
Mgr.–Erin Hunt
Industry: Facsimilie/Fax Transmission Systems

Xerox Corp.
PO Box 4505, Norwalk, CT, 06856-4505; tel (203) 968-3000; e-mail info@xerox.com; ethics@xerox.com; web site www.xerox.com
Chrmn.–Anne Mulcahy
Pres./CEO–Ursula M. Burns
Pres., N. American Channels Grp.–Russell Peacock
Pres., N. American Solutions Grp.–Doug Lord
Sr. Vice Pres./Pres., Global Servs.–Thomas J. Dolan
Sr. Vice Pres./CFO–Lawrence Zimmerman
CMO–Christa Carone
Vice Pres., HR–Patricia M. Nazemetz
Pres., Global Accts./Mktg. Opns.–Michael C. Mac Donald
Vice Pres., Mktg.–Valerie Mason-Cunningham
Vice Pres., Brand Mktg./Adv.–Richard Wergan
Pres., Cor. Opns.–James Firestone

Xerox Corp.
45 Glover Avenue, Norwalk, CT, 06856-4505; tel (800) 275-9376; web site www.xerox.com
Chairman and CEO–Ursula Burns
Industry: Facsimilie/Fax Transmission Systems; Input & Editing Systems; Laser Printers; Scanners: Color B & W, Plates, Web;

Xitron
4880 Venture Drive, Suite 500, Ann Arbor, MI, 48108; tel (734) 913-8080; fax (734) 913-8088; e-mail xitronsales@xitron.com; web site www.xitron.com
Director of Marketing–Bill Owens
Vice Pres., Sales–Patrick French
Industry: Archiving Systems; Calibration Software/Hardware; Color Proofing; Imagesetters; Phototypesetting Interface Equipment; Raster Image Processors; Typesetters: Laser;

Xpedx Printing Technologies
6285 Tri-Ridge Blvd., Loveland, OH, 45140-8318; tel (513) 965-2900; fax (901) 214-9674; web site www.xpedx.com
Pres.–Mary Laschinger
Vice Pres./Gen. Mgr.–John Torrey
Industry: Cutters & Trimmers; Paper Handeling Equipment; Presses: Offset;

X-Rite, Inc.
4300 44th St SE, Grand Rapids, MI, 49512; tel (616) 534-7663; fax (616) 534-8960; e-mail info@xrite.com; web site www.xrite.com
CEO/Pres.–Thomas J. Vacchiano
CFO–Mary E Chowning
CTO–Francis Lamy
Industry: Densitometers; Optical Products; Silver Recovery;

XYonicz
6754 Martin St., Rome, NY, 13440; tel (315) 334-4214; fax (315) 336-3177
Pres./Mgr., Mktg.–Ed Zionc
Industry: Equipment Dealers (New); Feeding, Folding, Delivery Equipment; Mailroom Systems & Equipment; Material Handling Equipment: Truck Loaders; Newsprint Handeling Equipment;

Y

Yale Materials Handling Corp.
1400 Sullivan Dr., Greenville, NC, 27834-9007; tel (800) 233-9253; fax (252) 931-7873; e-mail ayinfo@yale.com; web site www.yale.com
Pres.–Don Chance
Dir., Financial Servs.–Tina Goodwin
Vice Pres., Aftermarket Sales–Jay Costello
Dir., Dealer Devel.–Walt Nawicki
Industry: Lift Trucks

CATEGORIES OF EQUIPMENT, SUPPLIES AND SERVICES

ABRASIVES
Rochester Institute of Technology

ACID DISPENSING SYSTEMS
Arch Chemicals, Inc.

ADDRESSING MACHINES
Automated Mailing Systems Corp.
Domino Amjet, Inc.
Markem-Imaje
Kansa Technology, LLC
Kirk-Rudy, Inc.
Microfilm Products Co.
Video Jet Technologies
Brock Solutions U.S. Inc.

ADHESIVE WAX COATERS
Allpress Equipment, Inc.
Daige Products, Inc.
Dean Machinery International, Inc.
Paste-Up Supply

ADHESIVES
Adhesives Research, Inc.
Daige Products, Inc.
BASF Corp.
Hamilton Circulation Supplies Co.
H & M Paster Sales & Service, Inc.
Herco Graphic Products
Horizons, Inc.
Hurletron, Inc.
North Shore Consultants, Inc.
Rosback Co.
Schaefer Machine Co., Inc.
Support Products, Inc.
Union Rubber, Inc.
Chauncey Wing's Sons, Inc.
The Dow Chemical Co.
Miller-Cooper Co.

ARCHITECTS/ENGINEERS (INCLUDES DESIGN/CONSTRUCTION FIRMS)
AEC, Inc.
The Austin Company
B E & K, Inc.
Carlson Design Construct
Chemetron Fire Systems
Applied Industrial Machinery
Dario Designs, Inc.
Ralph Fusco, Inc.
GE Instrument Control Systems, Inc.
Gilbane Building Co.
William Ginsberg Associates
Graphic System Services, Inc.
Versar Inc.
Forum Architectural Services, LLC
The Haskell Co.
Industrial Noise Control, Inc.
Kamen & Co. Group Services
Lankford Engineering, Inc.
Ch2MHill Lockwood Greene
AECOM
Omicron Media
Parsons, Inc.
Richard S Rowse & Associates
Trauner Consulting Services, Inc.

ARCHIVING SYSTEMS
AccuDocs LLC
Autologic Information International
Cygnet Storage Solutions, Inc.
Digital Collections
Digital Technology International
Foster Mfg. Co.
Gannett Media Technologies International (GMTI)
Lazer-fare Media Services Ltd.
NewsEngin, Inc.
SAXOTECH, Inc.
MerlinOne, Inc.
NewsView Solutions
Xitron
Unisys Corp.
ProQuest LLC

ART & LAYOUT EQUIPMENT AND SERVICES
Brady & Paul Communications
Foster Mfg. Co.
Graphic Technology, Inc. (GTI)
Metro Creative Graphics, Inc.
Midwest Publishers Supply Co.
Richmond/Graphic Products, Inc.
Roconex Corp.
Wolk Advertising, Inc. (Retail Carpet Ad Service)
MacDonald Advertising Services
Publication Design, Inc.
Outsourcing USA

AUDIOTEX SYSTEMS & SOFTWARE
American International Communications, Inc.
DAC Systems
FANUC Robotics America, Inc.

AUTOMATIC FILM PROCESSORS
Diversified Photo/Graphics Supply

AUTOMATIC PLASTIC BAGGING EQUIPMENT
Hudson-Sharp
Buhrs Americas, Inc.
Dan-Bar, Inc.
Muller Martini Mailroom Systems, Inc.
Malow Corp.
SITMA USA, Inc.
Telesonic Packaging Corp., Ames Engineering Div.
Schur Packaging Systems, Inc.

BALING MACHINES
Balemaster
Dan-Bar, Inc.
Dynaric, Inc.
Gerrard Ovalstrapping

BELTS, BELTING, V-BELTS
A-American Machine & Assembly (Press Parts Div.)
Arco Engineering, Inc. (Newspaper Div.)
Ashworth Brothers, Inc.
Baumfolder Corp.
Belt Corporation of America
Belting Industries Co., Inc.
Central Graphics
Clipper Belt Lacer Co.
K & M Newspaper Services, Inc.
Ramsey (A Thermo Sentron Co.)
Moss Reck & Associates, Inc.
Robertson Equipments
Total Mailroom Support, Inc. (TMSI)

BLANKET CLEANER/WASHER (AUTOMATIC)
grafikAmerica
IMC America
NENSCO
Baldwin Oxy-Dry Americas
Smith Pressroom Products, Inc.
Printex Products
Rogersol, Inc.
Technotrans America, Inc.
Smith PPI Inc.

BLANKET MOUNTING AND BARS
Flint Group.
Day International
J. Thomas McHugh Co., Inc.
NDI (Morway Div.)
MacDermid Printing Solutions
Moss Reck & Associates, Inc.
Reeves Brothers, Inc.
Sun Graphic, Inc.
Tech-Energy Co.

BLANKETS
Inter-Continental Graphics, Inc.
Fujifilm Graphic Systems USA, Inc.
J. Thomas McHugh Co., Inc.
Midwest Publishers Supply Co.
NDI (Morway Div.)
National Graphic Supply Corp.
Newstech Co. (Div. of Rovinter, Inc.)
Pacesetter Graphic Service Corp.
MacDermid Printing Solutions
Precision Pressroom Products, Inc.
Reeves Brothers, Inc.
Latin American Div./Flint Ink
RotaDyne Corp.
Royal Graphics
Rycoline Products, Inc.
Tech-Energy Co.
DYC Supply Co.
Miller-Cooper Co.

BLUE LINE GRIDS
Base-Line, Inc.
Midwest Publishers Supply Co.

BROKERS & APPRAISERS
C. Berky & Associates, Inc.
Cribb, Greene & Associates
National Media Associates
Rickenbacher Media
National Media Associates
Dean Machinery International, Inc.
Dirks, Van Essen & Murray
Barry French
Grimes, W.B. & Co.
Hare Associates, Inc.
Inland Newspaper Machinery LLC
Kamen & Co. Group Services
Media Consultants, Inc.
Northwest Publishers, Inc.
Phelps, Cutler & Associates
Press and Bindery Systems, Inc.
J.N. Wells & Co., Inc.
JP Media Partners
National Media Associates
Media America Brokers

BUNDLING AND TYING MACHINES
Arpac Group
Automated Mailing Systems Corp.
Systems Technology, Inc.
B.H. Bunn Co.
EAM-Mosca Corp.
FELINS, Inc.
Ferag Americas
Gerrard Ovalstrapping
Muller Martini Mailroom Systems, Inc.
Malow Corp.
Megasys International, Inc.
Microfilm Products Co.
Muller Martini Corp.
Samuel Strapping System
Sterling Packaging Systems
Telesonic Packaging Corp., Ames Engineering Div.
Teufelberger GmbH
WRH Marketing Americas, Inc.

BUSINESS COMPUTERS
Auto-Grafica Corp.
BMF Newspaper Accounting Systems
Electronic Specialists, Inc.
Gulf Coast System Design Co.
Harris Corp.
Integrated Newspaper Systems, Inc.
Mobile Computing Corporation USA
Newspaper Electronics Corp.
Stauffer Media Systems
Vision Data Equipment Corp.
VoiceWorld, Inc.

CABINETS
Control Engineering Co.
Consolidated Storage Cos.
Ergotron, Inc.
Foster Mfg. Co.
Kaspar Wire Works, Inc./Sho-Rack
Penco Products
Roconex Corp.
Thompson Cabinet Co.
Truproof Ltd.

CALIBRATION SOFTWARE/HARDWARE
Baton Lock & Hardware Co., Inc.
Beta Screen Corp.
Presteligence
Lazer-fare Media Services Ltd.
ProImage America, Inc.
Tobias Associates, Inc.
Xitron

CAMERAS & ACCESSORIES
AAA Press International
Automatic Newsstand, Inc. (ANI Promotions)
CHF Foto Supply
CK Optical Co., Inc.
Diversified Photo/Graphics Supply
Heitz Service Corp.
National Graphic Supply Corp.
New Consolidated International Corp.
NuArc Co., Inc.
PC Industries
Pitman Photo Supply
Rochester Institute of Technology
Unique Photo
Eastman Kodak Co.

CART DISTRIBUTION SYSTEMS
Baird Manufacturing
Cannon Equipment
Kaspar Wire Works, Inc./Sho-Rack
K-Jack Engineering Co., Inc.

CHEMICALS: CHUCK (PAPER ROLL)
Maxcess
Moss Reck & Associates, Inc.
Tidland Corp.
Tilt-Lock

CHEMICALS: PHOTOGRAPHIC
Mac Dermid Autotype Inc.
Berkshire/Westwood Graphics Group, Inc.
ByChrome Ltd.
Cachet Fine Art Photographic Paper
Diversified Photo/Graphics Supply
Fujifilm Hunt Chemicals U.S.A., Inc.
GraphLine
Horizons, Inc.
Kodak GCG
Mohr Enterprise
National Graphic Supply Corp.
Photo Systems, Inc.
Pitman Photo Supply
Unique Photo

CHEMICALS: PLATE PROCESSING
Anocoil Corporation
Base-Line, Inc.
Berkshire/Westwood Graphics Group, Inc.
ByChrome Ltd.
Citiplate, Inc.
Coast Graphic Supply
Dynalith, Inc.
Fuji Photo Film USA/Graphic Systems Div.
GraphLine
Kodak GCG
Arch Chemicals, Inc.
Photo Systems, Inc.
Poolside Lithographic Supply, Inc.
Latin American Div./Flint Ink
Royal Graphics
Rycoline Products, Inc.
Southern Lithoplate, Inc.
Spectrecom Corporation
Superior Lithoplate of Indiana, Inc.
Western LithoTech

CHEMICALS: PRESSROOM
Base-Line, Inc.
Berkshire/Westwood Graphics Group, Inc.
Coast Graphic Supply
Flint Group.
Duostat Co. (Affiliated with VGC Corp.)
Fujifilm Hunt Chemicals U.S.A., Inc.
INX International Ink Co.
Base-Line, Inc.
Fujifilm Graphic Systems USA, Inc.

Midwest Publishers Supply Co.
Mirachem Corp.
NDI (Morway Div.)
National Graphic Supply Corp.
NENSCO
Arch Chemicals, Inc.
Photo Systems, Inc.
Precision Pressroom Products, Inc.
Printers' Service/Prisco/PriscoDigital
Printex Products
Latin American Div./Flint Ink
Royal Graphics
Rycoline Products, Inc.
Southern Lithoplate, Inc.
Spectrecom Corporation
Superior Lithoplate of Indiana, Inc.
Tower Products, Inc.
Day International
Vegra USA
Winton Engineering Co.
Miller-Cooper Co.

CHEMICALS: ROLLER CLEANING
Flint Group.
Base-Line, Inc.
Mirachem Corp.
NDI (Morway Div.)
NENSCO
Photo Systems, Inc.
Printex Products
Latin American Div./Flint Ink
Rogersol, Inc.
Royal Graphics
Siebert, Inc.
Support Products, Inc.
Tower Products, Inc.
Day International
Winton Engineering Co.

CIRCULATION EQUIPMENT & SUPPLIES
AAA Press International
Alliance Rubber Co.
American International Communications, Inc.
ANewStartGuy.com
AWS, A Thermal Care Division
Baldwin Americas Corp.
Bellatrix Systems, Inc.
Cannon Equipment
Circulation Solutions, Inc.
Continental Products
Franklin Wire Works, Inc.
GeoRack, Inc.
Go Plastics/StreetSmart LLC
GP Plastics Corp.
Great Southern Corp. (Sirco Div.)
Hamilton Circulation Supplies Co.
Impact Racks, Inc.
Insert East, Inc.
IPC
Kamen & Co. Group Services
Kaspar Wire Works, Inc./Sho-Rack
K-Jack Engineering Co., Inc.
Lyon Enterprises
Master Flo Technology
Myrtle Beach, Inc.
National Newsvend
NENSCO
PDI Plastics
Printers' Service/Prisco/PriscoDigital
RAK Systems, Inc.
Rycoline Products, Inc.
Schermerhorn Bros. Co.
Semler Industries, Inc. (Pressroom Fluids Equipment Div.)
Star Vend
Steel City Corp.

CLEANERS & SOLVENTS
ARC International
Cold Jet, Inc.
Cryogenesis (A Div. of WM & C Services, Inc.)
INX International Ink Co.
Base-Line, Inc.
Kaspar Wire Works, Inc./Sho-Rack
Louis Melind Co.
Mirachem Corp.
Mohr Enterprise
NDI (Morway Div.)
MacDermid Printing Solutions
Pressroom Cleaners
Printers' Service/Prisco/PriscoDigital
Printex Products
Rogersol, Inc.
Rycoline Products, Inc.
Siebert, Inc.
Star Vend
Tower Products, Inc.
Day International
Fiberweb
Winton Engineering Co.
The Dow Chemical Co.

COLLATING EQUIPMENT
Baumfolder Corp.
Dan-Bar, Inc.
Kansa Technology, LLC
New Consolidated International Corp.
Prim Hall Enterprises, Inc.
Rosback Co.
SITMA USA, Inc.

COLOR ANALYZERS
Electronic Systems Engineering Co.
X-Rite Inc.
Technidyne Corp.
Tobias Associates, Inc.
UV Process Supply, Inc.
E.I. du Pont de Nemours & Co.

COLOR MANAGEMENT SOFTWARE
BST Pro Mark
Kodak GCG
Fujifilm Graphic Systems USA, Inc.
Monaco Systems, Inc.
MacDermid Printing Solutions
National Graphic Supply Corp.
Pantone, Inc.
Latran Technologies
Schawk
Spectrecom Corporation
Technidyne Corp.
Trumatch, Inc.

COLOR PRINTING FRAMES
NuArc Co., Inc.

COLOR PROOFING
All Systems Color, Inc.
Auto-Grafica Corp.
Beta Screen Corp.
Burgess Industries, Inc.
Direct Reproduction Corp.
Duostat Co. (Affiliated with VGC Corp.)
Fuji Photo Film USA/Graphic Systems Div.
Presteligence
X-Rite Inc.
Harland Simon
Just Normlicht, Inc.
Kodak GCG
alfaQuest Technologies
Parascan Technologies, Inc.
Pitman Co.
Latran Technologies
Press-Enterprise, Inc. (Color Graphics Dept.)
Creo
SCREEN (USA)
Newscolor, LLC
Truproof Ltd.
Weber Systems, Inc.
Xitron
E.I. du Pont de Nemours & Co.
Konica Minolta Graphic Imaging USA

COLOR REGISTRATION
BST Pro Mark
Burgess Industries, Inc.
Direct Reproduction Corp.
Taylor Made Digital Systems
grafikAmerica
Graphics Microsystems, Inc.
Kaim & Associates International Marketing, Inc.
K & F International, Inc.
PC Industries
Pitman Co.
QuadTech
Quad Tech
Robertson Press Machinery Co., Inc.
Robertson Equipments
Stoesser Register Systems
NELA
E.I. du Pont de Nemours & Co.

Color Seperation Guides
Trumatch, Inc.

Color Seperation Scanners
All Systems Color, Inc.
Duostat Co. (Affiliated with VGC Corp.)
Howtek
Microtek
Pitman Co.
Creo
SCREEN (USA)
UMAX Technologies, Inc.
Bob Weber, Inc.
E.I. du Pont de Nemours & Co.

COLOR SEPERATIONS, POSITIVES
All Systems Color, Inc.
Press-Enterprise, Inc. (Color Graphics Dept.)

COLOR VIEWING EQUIPMENT
Beta Screen Corp.
BST Pro Mark
Foster Mfg. Co.
Graphic Technology, Inc. (GTI)
X-Rite Inc.
Just Normlicht, Inc.
Pitman Co.
ProImage America, Inc.
Truproof Ltd.
E.I. du Pont de Nemours & Co.

COMPOSING ROOM EQUIPMENT & SUPPLIES
Alteneder, Theo & Sons
Berkshire/Westwood Graphics Group, Inc.
Coast Graphic Supply
Devlin Electronics Ltd.
Foster Mfg. Co.
Megasys International, Inc.
Midwest Publishers Supply Co.
N & L Enterprises, Inc.
PAGE
Support Products, Inc.
Thompson Cabinet Co.

COMPUTERS: HARDWARE & SOFTWARE INTEGRATORS
Abelson Communications, Inc.
Advanced Technical Solutions, Inc.
All Systems Go
Auto-Grafica Corp.
Autologic Information International
Bruce Bell & Associates
BMF Newspaper Accounting Systems
Bottom Line Industries
Burt Technologies, Inc.
CE Engineering
Celebro
Computer Tree
SAXOTECH Circulation
Flint Group.
Descartes Systems Group
Digital Collections
Duostat Co. (Affiliated with VGC Corp.)
EDIWISE
Ewert America Electronics Ltd.
Gannett Media Technologies International (GMTI)
General DataComm, Inc.
Global Turnkey Systems, Inc.
Globix Corp.
Graphic Publishing Systems, Inc.
Gulf Coast System Design Co.
ICANON Associates, Inc.
Imapro Corp.
KYE International Corp.
Lazer-fare Media Services Ltd.
McCrrory Publishing
MPC LLC
Miles 33 International
Mobile Computing Corporation USA
alfaQuest Technologies
Newspaper Electronics Corp.
Printronix, Inc.
Creo
Shreve Systems
Software Consulting Services
Solar Systems
Spectra Logic
Stauffer Media Systems
Syntellect, Inc.
Buffalo Technology Inc.
Tel-Management, Inc.
TSA
VoCal Telecommunications
Jervis B. Webb Co.
West Coast Computer Systems
MPC Computers, LLC
Unisys Corp.

COMPUTERS: LAPTOP & PORTABLE
Acer America
All Systems Go
Bruce Bell & Associates
SAXOTECH Circulation
Globix Corp.
Newspaper Electronics Corp.

COMPUTERS: LOCAL AREA NETWORK (LANS)
Advanced Graphic Systems (AGS)
Applied Creative Technologies
Computer Tree
Ergotron, Inc.
Global Turnkey Systems, Inc.
Globix Corp.
Graphic Publishing Systems, Inc.
Imapro Corp.
KYE International Corp.
Newspaper Electronics Corp.
Support Systems International Corp.
Syntellect, Inc.
Buffalo Technology Inc.
WordMark International Corp.

COMPUTERS: STORAGE DEVICES
All Systems Go
ADI/PDM Trade Group
Snap-on Business Solutions
SAXOTECH Circulation
Consolidated Storage Cos.
Ergotron, Inc.
Globix Corp.
Newspaper Electronics Corp.
Overland Storage, Inc.
Buffalo Technology Inc.
Thompson Cabinet Co.

CONSULTING SERVICES: ADVERTISING
Dail Advertising Service
Abelson Communications, Inc.
Advertising Data Scan/Adspies.com
All Systems Go
U.S. Suburban Press (USSPI)
American Consulting Services
American Newspaper Representatives
American Opinion Research
Arrow Printing Co.
ASTech InterMedia
Ed Baron & Associates, Inc.
Bruce Bell & Associates
Berting Communications
M.W. Burke & Associates, Inc.
Communications Service Co.
TNS Media Intelligence
ComPlan Associates
Creative Brilliance Advertising, Marketing & Public Relation
Creative House Print Media Consultants
SAXOTECH Circulation
William Dunkerley Publishing Consultant
Ewert America Electronics Ltd.
Forrest Consulting
John Foust Training
Grimes, W.B. & Co.
Hare Associates, Inc.
Integrated Newspaper Systems, Inc.
InterVoice-Brite, Inc.
John Juliano Computer Services Co.
Kamen & Co. Group Services
The Keenan Group, Inc.
Lazer-fare Media Services Ltd.
Atex North America
Marketing Research Associates, Inc.
Media Marketing, Inc.
Media Monitors, Inc.
Meena Advertising Copy & Layout
Metro Creative Graphics, Inc.
Miles 33 International
Minnesota Opinion Research, Inc. (MORI)
Missouri Press Service, Inc.
MultiAd Services, Inc.
Network Newspaper Advertising, Inc.

Newspaper Space Bank
NoteAds.com, Inc./Post-it Note Advertising
Phelps, Cutler & Associates
Print Marketing Concepts, Inc.
Publishers Idea Exchange
Pulse Research, Inc.
Rowlett Advertising Service, Inc.
Sales Development Services
Sales Training Consultants, Inc.
Scarborough Research
Silverman Newspaper Management Consultants
Summit Media Partners LLC
Syntellect, Inc.
Miles 33
Weatherline, Inc.
West Coast Computer Systems
Keister Williams Newspaper Services, Inc.
Wolk Advertising, Inc. (Retail Carpet Ad Service)
Wrubel Communications
AIM Group / Classified Intelligence
MacDonald Advertising Services
Marketing Strategies Incorporated
TNS
Newspaper Services of America
ChannelNet
Classifieds Plus, Inc.
Tera D.P. S.r.l.

CONSULTING SERVICES: CIRCULATION

Abelson Communications, Inc.
Advantex Marketing International, Inc.
All Systems Go
American International Communications, Inc.
American Opinion Research
ANewStartGuy.com
Ashcraft Consulting
ASTech InterMedia
Ed Baron & Associates, Inc.
MediaSpan Group Inc.
M.W. Burke & Associates, Inc.
Church Rickards, Whitlock & Co., Inc.
Circulation Development, Inc.
Circulation Solutions, Inc.
Circulation III Promotions, Inc.
Communications Management Service, Inc.
Communications Service Co.
ComPlan Associates
Creative Brilliance Advertising, Marketing & Public Relation
Creative House Print Media Consultants
SAXOTECH Circulation
Ewert America Electronics Ltd.
Forrest Consulting
Global Turnkey Systems, Inc.
Integrated Newspaper Systems, Inc.
IPC
Kamen & Co. Group Services
The Keenan Group, Inc.
Marketing Research Associates, Inc.
Marketing Research Associates, Inc.
Headline Memories
Minnesota Opinion Research, Inc. (MORI)
Mobile Computing Corporation USA
Phelps, Cutler & Associates
Pulse Research, Inc.
Sales Training Consultants, Inc.
Silverman Newspaper Management Consultants
Stauffer Media Systems
Summit Media Partners LLC
Syntellect, Inc.
Transportation Consultants, Inc.
Ver-A-Fast Corp.
VoiceWorld, Inc.
Whitney Worldwide, Inc.
Wilson Gregory Agency, Inc.
Wrubel Communications
Pro Starts

CONSULTING SERVICES: COMPUTER

Abelson Communications, Inc.
Agfa Monotype Corporation
All Systems Go
Ashcraft Consulting
ASTech InterMedia
The Business Scribe, Inc.
CE Engineering
ComPlan Associates
Computer Tree
Controls Group, Inc.
Creative House Print Media Consultants
Cyber Age Technologies
SAXOTECH Circulation
Digital Information Group
Ewert America Electronics Ltd.
Global Turnkey Systems, Inc.
Gulf Coast System Design Co.
ICANON Associates, Inc.
John Juliano Computer Services Co.
Lazer-fare Media Services Ltd.
McCrrory Publishing
Mobile Computing Corporation USA
Newspaper Electronics Corp.
Omicron Media
Printmark
Random Access
Rochester Institute of Technology
Sales Development Services
Summit Media Partners LLC

CONSULTING SERVICES: EDITORIAL

American Opinion Research
Ashcraft Consulting
MediaSpan Group Inc.
Brady & Paul Communications
The Business Scribe, Inc.
CE Engineering
ComPlan Associates
Creative House Print Media Consultants
Cyber Age Technologies
William Dunkerley Publishing Consultant
Editorial Management Strategies
Ewert America Electronics Ltd.
The Findlay Group
St. Louis Journalism Review
Hare Associates, Inc.
Lazer-fare Media Services Ltd.
Marketing Research Associates, Inc.
McCrrory Publishing
Metro Creative Graphics, Inc.
Miles 33 International
Minnesota Opinion Research, Inc. (MORI)
Missouri Press Service, Inc.
North Atlantic Publishing Systems, Inc.
Phelps, Cutler & Associates
Printmark
Silverman Newspaper Management Consultants
Stauffer Media Systems
Summit Media Partners LLC
Miles 33
West Coast Computer Systems
Wrubel Communications
Publishing House Research LLC

CONSULTING SERVICES: EQUIPMENT

Advanced Control Technologies, Inc.
All Systems Go
The Austin Company
Chuck Blevins & Assoc.
Boles, Morgan & Canino, Inc.
Canadian Web Consultants Ltd.
Capital Track Co.
CE Engineering
ComPlan Associates
Cyber Age Technologies
DM Graphics System
Consolidated Storage Cos.
Ewert America Electronics Ltd.
Ralph Fusco, Inc.
William Ginsberg Associates
Global Press Management Services, LLC.
Graphic System Services, Inc.
The Haskell Co.
Inland Newspaper Machinery LLC
The International School For Pressroom Management
The Keenan Group, Inc.
Lazer-fare Media Services Ltd.
AECOM
Northeast Industries, Inc.
Omicron Media
Pressline Services, Inc.
Reeves Brothers, Inc.
Rochester Institute of Technology
Richard S Rowse & Associates
David A. Shulda Enterprises, Inc.
Standard Electric and Engineering Co.
Sterling Packaging Systems
Dennis Storch Co.
Summit Media Partners LLC
Syntellect, Inc.
Tidland Corp.
Jervis B. Webb Co.
Wesco Graphics

CONSULTING SERVICES: ERGONOMICS

Applied Learning Corp.
Chuck Blevins & Assoc.
Consolidated Storage Cos.
Ergotron, Inc.
Ewert America Electronics Ltd.
Fox Bay Industries, Inc.
The International School For Pressroom Management
Omicron Media
Poyry Management Consulting (USA) Inc.

CONSULTING SERVICES: FINANCIAL

National Media Associates
Ashcraft Consulting
The Austin Company
Ed Baron & Associates, Inc.
Boles, Morgan & Canino, Inc.
National Media Associates
I-many, Inc.
ComPlan Associates
Creative House Print Media Consultants
Digital Information Group
Dirks, Van Essen & Murray
William Dunkerley Publishing Consultant
Ewert America Electronics Ltd.
Forrest Consulting
Barry French
Grimes, W.B. & Co.
ICANON Associates, Inc.
Integrated Newspaper Systems, Inc.
The International School For Pressroom Management
Kamen & Co. Group Services
Kanaly Trust Co.
Marketing Research Associates, Inc.
Phelps, Cutler & Associates
Print Marketing Concepts, Inc.
Silverman Newspaper Management Consultants
Interactive Data Real-Time Services, Inc.
J.N. Wells & Co., Inc.
Westburg Media Capital
Wrubel Communications
National Media Associates

CONSULTING SERVICES: HUMAN RESOURCES

Church Rickards, Whitlock & Co., Inc.
Ewert America Electronics Ltd.
Grimes, W.B. & Co.
Haas & Associates
IPC
Kamen & Co. Group Services
Marketing Research Associates, Inc.
Phelps, Cutler & Associates
Poyry Management Consulting (USA) Inc.

CONSULTING SERVICES: MARKETING

Abelson Communications, Inc.
Advantex Marketing International, Inc.
Advertising Data Scan/Adspies.com
All Systems Go
American Opinion Research
ANewStartGuy.com
ASTech InterMedia
The Austin Company
Ed Baron & Associates, Inc.
Bruce Bell & Associates
Berting Communications
The Business Scribe, Inc.
Circulation Development, Inc.
Claritas
Communications Management Service, Inc.
ComPlan Associates
Creative House Print Media Consultants
William Dunkerley Publishing Consultant
Ewert America Electronics Ltd.
Forrest Consulting
Grimes, W.B. & Co.
InterVoice-Brite, Inc.
INX International Ink Co.
IPC
John Juliano Computer Services Co.
Kamen & Co. Group Services
The Keenan Group, Inc.
Marketing Research Associates, Inc.
Marketing Research Associates, Inc.
Media Marketing, Inc.
Minnesota Opinion Research, Inc. (MORI)
NewsCurrents
Phelps, Cutler & Associates
Pulse Research, Inc.
Sales Development Services
Scarborough Research
Silverman Newspaper Management Consultants
Strategic Telemedia
Summit Media Partners LLC
Syntellect, Inc.
Valco Sales, Inc.
Weatherline, Inc.
Whitney Worldwide, Inc.
Keister Williams Newspaper Services, Inc.
Wrubel Communications
Marketing Strategies Incorporated
TNS
Marketing Plus, Inc.

CONSULTING SERVICES: PRODUCTION

'Ataboy, Inc.
The Austin Company
MediaSpan Group Inc.
Chuck Blevins & Assoc.
Boles, Morgan & Canino, Inc.
M.W. Burke & Associates, Inc.
Canadian Web Consultants Ltd.
CNI Corp.
ComPlan Associates
Creative House Print Media Consultants
Ewert America Electronics Ltd.
Flexographic Technical Association
William Ginsberg Associates
HK Systems
The International School For Pressroom Management
The Keenan Group, Inc.
Lankford Engineering, Inc.
Logic Associates, Inc.
Lorentzen & Wettre
AECOM
Omicron Media
Plumtree Co.
Printmark
ProImage America, Inc.
Quebecor World
Reeves Brothers, Inc.
Rochester Institute of Technology
Richard S Rowse & Associates
RTP Technical Specialists
Standard Electric and Engineering Co.
Summit Media Partners LLC
Whitworth Knife Company
WPC Machinery Corp.
Kinetic Corporation
Brock Solutions U.S. Inc.

CONTROLLERS: PRESS

AirSystems, Inc.
William Ginsberg Associates
The International School For Pressroom Management
Masthead International, Inc.
Rockwell Automation
Standard Electric and Engineering Co.

CONTROLS: EXPOSURE

Burgess Industries, Inc.
Douthitt Corp.
GE Instrument Control Systems, Inc.
NuArc Co., Inc.

CONTROLS: PHOTO ELECTRIC

Advanced Graphic Systems (AGS)
Baumer Electric Ltd.
GE Instrument Control Systems, Inc.
K & M Newspaper Services, Inc.

CONTROLS: REGISTER

Burgess Industries, Inc.
GE Instrument Control Systems, Inc.
grafikAmerica
Graphics Microsystems, Inc.
Hurletron, Inc.
Kaim & Associates International Marketing, Inc.
PC Industries
Perretta Graphics Corp.
QuadTech
Quad Tech

Stoesser Register Systems
NELA
Web Printing Controls
E.I. du Pont de Nemours & Co.

CONVERSION EQUIPMENT
Charles Beck Machine Corp.
Flexo Printing Equipment Corp.
Martin Automatic, Inc.
Printing Press Services, Inc.
Rotoflex Mark Andy Canada, Inc.
Tidland Corp.
Pemco, Inc.

CONVEYORS
Arpac Group
Ashworth Brothers, Inc.
'Ataboy, Inc.
Butler Automatic
Cannon Equipment
Control Engineering Co.
Craftsman Newspaper Production Systems
Engineering Products Co., Inc.
FANUC Robotics America, Inc.
Ferag Americas
Gammerler (US) Corp.
Gerrard Ovalstrapping
Muller Martini Mailroom Systems, Inc.
Hall Contracting Services, Inc.
HK Systems
IMC America
Intralox, LLC
K & M Newspaper Services, Inc.
Kansa Technology, LLC
Mid-America Graphics, Inc.
N/S Corporation
Prim Hall Enterprises, Inc.
PSC Flo-Turn, Inc.
Quipp System, Inc.
Ramsey (A Thermo Sentron Co.)
Dematics
Richard S Rowse & Associates
Shuttleworth, LLC
Paragon Technologies Inc.
SITMA USA, Inc.
Sterling Packaging Systems
Seidel Enterprises
Total Mailroom Support, Inc. (TMSI)
Valley Remanufacturing Co.
Jervis B. Webb Co.
Pemco, Inc.
Schur Packaging Systems, Inc.
WRH Marketing Americas, Inc.

COPPER PLATING DRUMS
A-American Machine & Assembly (Press Parts Div.)
Aaro Roller Corp.
Central Graphics
Hadronics
Moss Reck & Associates, Inc.

CORE CUTTERS, RESTORERS, ROUNDERS
Craftsmen Machinery Co., Inc.
Tidland Corp.
Whitworth Knife Company

CORE STRIPPERS & SEPERATORS
Vegra USA
Whitworth Knife Company

COUNTING, STACKING, BUNDLING MACHINES
Advance Graphics Equipment of York, Inc.
ADI/PDM Trade Group
'Ataboy, Inc.
Systems Technology, Inc.
Baumfolder Corp.
Butler Automatic
D & R Engineering
Gammerler (US) Corp.
Gerrard Ovalstrapping
Heat and Control, Inc.
IMC America
Inter-Continental Graphics, Inc.
Kansa Technology, LLC
Kolbus America, Inc.
Muller Martini Corp.
AD-A-NOTE
SITMA USA, Inc.
Spartanics
Teufelberger GmbH
Seidel Enterprises
Valley Remanufacturing Co.
Western Printing Machinery
Schur Packaging Systems, Inc.

CREDIT & COLLECTIONS
SKO Brenner American

CUTTERS & TRIMMERS
Advanced Control Technologies, Inc.
Advance Graphics Equipment of York, Inc.
Colter Peterson
Systems Technology, Inc.
Baumfolder Corp.
Charles Beck Machine Corp.
Blower Application Co., Inc.
Butler Automatic
Foster Mfg. Co.
Gammerler (US) Corp.
Heidelberg USA, Inc.
IMC America
Kolbus America, Inc.
Martin Yale, Inc.
Maxcess
MBM Corp.
Mohr Enterprise
Muller Martini Corp.
New Consolidated International Corp.
Portage Newspaper Supply Co.
Press Rubber Co., Inc.
Primark Tool Group
Roconex Corp.
Stoesser Register Systems
Tidland Corp.
Bruno Knives USA
Unique Photo
Vijuk Equipment
Western Printing Machinery
Whitworth Knife Company
Pemco, Inc.
Xpedx Printing Technologies
TKM United States, Inc.

CUTTING & CREASING PRESSES
New Consolidated International Corp.
Press Rubber Co., Inc.

CUTTING TOOLS
A-American Machine & Assembly (Press Parts Div.)
Clipper Belt Lacer Co.
Foster Mfg. Co.
Maxcess
MBM Corp.
Press Rubber Co., Inc.
Primark Tool Group
Tidland Corp.
Whitworth Knife Company

CYLINDER REPAIR
Brodie System, Inc.
Brown's Web Press Service & Machine Shop
Central Graphics
DM Graphics System
Hadronics
MAH Machine Co., Inc.
Pressline Services, Inc.
Printing Technology, Inc.
Moss Reck & Associates, Inc.
Robertson Equipments
WPC Machinery Corp.

DAMPENING SYSTEMS
Baldwin Americas Corp.
BESCO Graphic Systems Corp.
Chapel Hill Manufacturing Co.
Clark-Cutler-McDermoth Co. (Air-Loc Div.)
JFM Machine Co., Inc.
Duostat Co. (Affiliated with VGC Corp.)
Graphic Machine Sales, Inc.
Hadronics
Base-Line, Inc.
Master Flo Technology
Smith Pressroom Products, Inc.
Printex Products
Robertson Press Machinery Co., Inc.
Technotrans America, Inc.
Smith PPI Inc.
Standard Electric and Engineering Co.
Day International

DARK ROOM EQUIPMENT
Beta Screen Corp.
Cachet Fine Art Photographic Paper
Craftsmen Machinery Co., Inc.
Electronic Systems Engineering Co.
Foster Mfg. Co.
Hart Industries
Hart Industries/Metafix Compliance Systems
Dunning Photo Equipment, Inc.
New Consolidated International Corp.
NuArc Co., Inc.
Pitman Co.
Pitman Photo Supply
Richard Mfg. Co., Inc.
Dennis Storch Co.
Tobias Associates, Inc.
Unique Photo

DATA COMMUNICATION
AccuDocs LLC
AdStar, Inc.
eGIX, Inc.
CNI Corp.
Electronic Specialists, Inc.
Harris Corp.
MCI
Megadata Corp.

DELIVERY EQUIPMENT
'Ataboy, Inc.
Baumfolder Corp.
Ferag Americas
Hamilton Circulation Supplies Co.
Kaspar Wire Works, Inc./Sho-Rack
K-Jack Engineering Co., Inc.
Master Flo Technology
Mitchell's
H.R. Slater Co., Inc.
Vexure Logistic Company
Seidel Enterprises
Utilimaster
Western Roller Corp.
WRH Marketing Americas, Inc.

DENSITOMETERS
Beta Screen Corp.
Caprock Developments, Inc.
Coast Graphic Supply
Craftsmen Machinery Co., Inc.
Duostat Co. (Affiliated with VGC Corp.)
Electronic Systems Engineering Co.
Graphics Microsystems, Inc.
GraphLine
X-Rite Inc.
Reeves Brothers, Inc.
Royal Graphics
Tobias Associates, Inc.
Truproof Ltd.
Bob Weber, Inc.
Weber Systems, Inc.
X-Rite, Inc.

DEVELOPING AND PROCESSING
Snap-on Business Solutions
Richard Mfg. Co., Inc.
Unique Photo

DIES (PERFORATING AND SLITTING)
Rotoflex Mark Andy Canada, Inc.
Technotrans America, Inc.
Vegra USA
Western Printing Machinery
Whitworth Knife Company

DIFFUSION TRANSFER PROCESSORS
NuArc Co., Inc.

DISK DRIVE SALES/REPAIR
Cygnet Storage Solutions, Inc.
Imapro Corp.

DRIVES & CONTROLS
ABB, Inc. (Printing Systems)
Allpress Equipment, Inc.
Baldor Electric Co.
Brown's Web Press Service & Machine Shop
Danfoss Graham
Ewert America Electronics Ltd.
Fincor Automation, Inc.
Fleming Enterprises
M. Golda Engineering
Harland Simon
Logic Associates, Inc.
Magnetic Power Systems, Inc.
Masthead International, Inc.
Maxcess
Printing Press Services, Inc.
Rockwell Automation
Standard Electric and Engineering Co.
WPC Machinery Corp.
ABB Inc.

DRYERS: FILM AND PAPERS
Advance Systems, Inc.
Imapro Corp.
Jardis Industries, Inc.
Kidder, Inc.
MEGTEC Systems
Pitman Photo Supply

DRYING SYSTEMS
Advance Systems, Inc.
Baldwin Americas Corp.
BESCO Graphic Systems Corp.
Fleming Enterprises
Jardis Industries, Inc.
MEGTEC Systems
N/S Corporation
Baldwin Oxy-Dry Americas
UV Process Supply, Inc.

ELECTRONIC AD DELIVERY
AdStar, Inc.
Alpha-Omega Color Graphics, Inc.
Celebro
Newspaper Space Bank
Unisys Corp.
Thought Equity Management, Inc.

ELECTRONIC PRE-SCAN SYSTEMS
Flint Group.
Press-Enterprise, Inc. (Color Graphics Dept.)
Tobias Associates, Inc.

ENLARGERS (PHOTOGRAPHIC)
Diversified Photo/Graphics Supply
Electronic Systems Engineering Co.
New Consolidated International Corp.
Pitman Photo Supply

ENVIRONMENTAL CONTROL SYSTEMS
Baldwin Americas Corp.
Dynalith, Inc.
Extratec Corp.
Hart Industries
Hart Industries/Metafix Compliance Systems
Industrial Acoustics Co.
Litho Research, Inc.
Maratek Environmental Technologies, Inc.
MEGTEC Systems
Metafix, Inc.
MGI International, Inc.
Nama Graphics E, LLC
N/S Corporation
Parsons, Inc.
Perma-Fix Environmental Services
David A. Shulda Enterprises, Inc.

EQUIPMENT DEALERS (NEW)
AAA Press International
ALTA- Al Taber - PHA
Arco Engineering, Inc. (Newspaper Div.)
Auto-Grafica Corp.
Charles Beck Machine Corp.
Berkshire/Westwood Graphics Group, Inc.
Clark Material Handling Co.
Applied Industrial Machinery
Diversified Photo/Graphics Supply
DM Graphics System
Duostat Co. (Affiliated with VGC Corp.)
Dynalith, Inc.
Flexo Printing Equipment Corp.
Gutenberg Printing Press Co.
Inland Newspaper Machinery LLC
Krause Newspaper Systems, Inc.
MAH Machine Co., Inc.
Maratek Environmental Technologies, Inc.
Megasys International, Inc.
Microfilm Products Co.
N & L Enterprises, Inc.
New Consolidated International Corp.
ONE Corp.
Printing Press Services, Inc.

Robertson Press Machinery Co., Inc.
Rosback Co.
Spectrecom Corporation
Technidyne Corp.
Tel-Management, Inc.
TSA
Valley Remanufacturing Co.
XYonicz

EQUIPMENT DEALERS (USED)
AAA Press International
Allpress Equipment, Inc.
ALTA- Al Taber - PHA
American Graphic Arts, Inc.
Arco Engineering, Inc. (Newspaper Div.)
'Ataboy, Inc.
Brown's Web Press Service & Machine Shop
Central Graphics
Clark Material Handling Co.
Dean Machinery International, Inc.
DM Graphics System
Fleming Enterprises
Gutenberg Printing Press Co.
Hall Contracting Services, Inc.
Inland Newspaper Machinery LLC
Kepes, Inc.
MAH Machine Co., Inc.
Megasys International, Inc.
Microfilm Products Co.
N & L Enterprises, Inc.
ONE Corp.
Press and Bindery Systems, Inc.
Printing Press Services, Inc.
Printing Technology, Inc.
Robertson Press Machinery Co., Inc.
Dennis Storch Co.
Technidyne Corp.
TSA
UMI
Valley Remanufacturing Co.
Bob Weber, Inc.
Weber Systems, Inc.
Wesco Graphics

ERECTORS & RIGGERS
Brown's Web Press Service & Machine Shop
Canadian Web Consultants Ltd.
DM Graphics System
Fleming Enterprises
Hall Contracting Services, Inc.
Jardis Industries, Inc.
Masthead International, Inc.
Printing Press Services, Inc.
Taft Contracting Co. (not affiliated w/Taft Eqpt. Co.)
Total Mailroom Support, Inc. (TMSI)
Wesco Graphics
WPC Machinery Corp.

Exposure Lamps
Amergraph Corporation
Caprock Developments, Inc.
Douthitt Corp.
Richmond/Graphic Products, Inc.
Stoesser Register Systems
UVP, Inc.
Western Quartz Products, Inc.

FACSIMILIE/FAX TRANSMISSION SYSTEMS
Autologic Information International
e/Doc Systems
DAC Systems
Taylor Made Digital Systems
ELAPLAN Buchholz GmbH & Co.
Moving Bytes
Harris Corp.
N & L Enterprises, Inc.
Royal Consumer Information Products, Inc.
Xerox Corp.
Sales Development Services
STM Networks
Tel-Management, Inc.
Xerox Corp.

FEEDER PRESS
Fleming Enterprises

FEEDING, FOLDING, DELIVERY EQUIPMENT
Advance Graphics Equipment of York, Inc.
ADI/PDM Trade Group
Baumfolder Corp.
Buhrs Americas, Inc.
Applied Industrial Machinery
Fleming Enterprises
Gammerler (US) Corp.
Kansa Technology, LLC
Kepes, Inc.
MAH Machine Co., Inc.
Master Flo Technology
MBM Corp.
SITMA USA, Inc.
Stepper, Inc.
XYonicz

FILES, STORAGE
Cygnet Storage Solutions, Inc.
Consolidated Storage Cos.
Foster Mfg. Co.
Roconex Corp.
Smart Storage, Inc.

FILM & PAPER: CONTACT
ByChrome Ltd.
Coast Graphic Supply
Fuji Photo Film USA/Graphic Systems Div.
GraphLine
Kodak GCG
National Graphic Supply Corp.
Eastman Kodak Co.

FILM & PAPER: DUPLICATING
AbitibiBowater Pulp and Paper Canada, Inc.
ByChrome Ltd.
Fuji Photo Film USA/Graphic Systems Div.
GraphLine
Kodak GCG
National Graphic Supply Corp.

FILM & PAPER: FILM PROCESSING MACHINES
Amergraph Corporation
Duostat Co. (Affiliated with VGC Corp.)
Electronic Systems Engineering Co.
Graphic Publishing Systems, Inc.
GraphLine
LogEtronics Corp.
Photo Systems, Inc.
Richmond/Graphic Products, Inc.
Southern Lithoplate, Inc.
Weber Systems, Inc.

FILM & PAPER: FILM ROLL DISPENSERS
LogEtronics Corp.
Pitman Photo Supply
Unique Photo

FILM & PAPER: FILTERS (PHOTOGRAPHIC)
AbitibiBowater Pulp and Paper Canada, Inc.
Cachet Fine Art Photographic Paper
CHF Foto Supply
Diversified Photo/Graphics Supply
Dynalith, Inc.
Fuji Photo Film USA/Graphic Systems Div.
Kimoto Tech
Kodak GCG
National Graphic Supply Corp.
Photo Systems, Inc.
Pitman Photo Supply
Southern Lithoplate, Inc.
Unique Photo
Agfa, Inc.
Eastman Kodak Co.

Film & Paper: Phototypesetting
Alpha-Omega Color Graphics, Inc.
ByChrome Ltd.
Coast Graphic Supply
Graphic Publishing Systems, Inc.
Kimoto Tech
National Graphic Supply Corp.
Newstech Co. (Div. of Rovinter, Inc.)
PrePRESS DIRECT
Eastman Kodak Co.

FIRE PROTECTION
Badger Fire Protection
Chemetron Fire Systems
Honeywell, Inc.

FIXING & STOP BATHS
Louis Melind Co.
Pitman Photo Supply

FLEXOGRPAHIC PRESS CONVERSION
Flexo Printing Equipment Corp.
Flexographic Technical Association
KBA North America, Inc. (Koenig & Bauer AG)
Koenig & Bauer Aktiengesellschaft (KBA)

FLOORING
Barry French
Gerrard Ovalstrapping

FLUID HANDELING: PRESSROOM
Baldwin Americas Corp.
The International School For Pressroom Management
Maratek Environmental Technologies, Inc.
Semler Industries, Inc. (Pressroom Fluids Equipment Div.)
U.S. Petrolon Industrial

FLYING PASTERS
Advanced Graphic Systems (AGS)
Butler Automatic
Gutenberg Printing Press Co.
Jardis Industries, Inc.
KBA North America, Inc. (Koenig & Bauer AG)
Koenig & Bauer Aktiengesellschaft (KBA)
Lankford Engineering, Inc.
Martin Automatic, Inc.
MEGTEC Systems
Nama Graphics E, LLC
NENSCO
North Shore Consultants, Inc.
ONE Corp.
RTP Technical Specialists

FOLDER KNIVES
A-American Machine & Assembly (Press Parts Div.)
Allpress Equipment, Inc.
Central Graphics
Craftsmen Machinery Co., Inc.
Press Rubber Co., Inc.
Printing Technology, Inc.
Robertson Equipments
UMI
Bruno Knives USA
Whitworth Knife Company

FOLDING MACHINES
Advance Graphics Equipment of York, Inc.
ADI/PDM Trade Group
Baumfolder Corp.
Buhrs Americas, Inc.
Applied Industrial Machinery
Global Press Management Services, LLC.
Kansa Technology, LLC
Martin Yale, Inc.
MBM Corp.
Megasys International, Inc.
Microfilm Products Co.
Rosback Co.
SITMA USA, Inc.
Vijuk Equipment
WebPress, LLC

GAUGES, MEASURING
A-American Machine & Assembly (Press Parts Div.)
Arco Engineering, Inc. (Newspaper Div.)
Beta Screen Corp.
Hexagon Metrology, Inc.
Caprock Developments, Inc.
Craftsmen Machinery Co., Inc.
Lithco Inc.
Precision Pressroom Products, Inc.
Press Rubber Co., Inc.
H.R. Slater Co., Inc.
The Wellmark Company

GLUING SYSTEMS
American Graphic Arts, Inc.
D & R Engineering
Gammerler (US) Corp.
H & M Paster Sales & Service, Inc.
Kepes, Inc.
ONE Corp.
AD-A-NOTE
Schaefer Machine Co., Inc.

GRATER WRAP-ROLLER COVERING
Fortfiber Corp., Paper Mill Packaging Grp.
Graphic Printing Roller Ltd.

HAZARDOUS WASTE DISPOSAL SERVICES
Commodity Resource & Environment
Flexographic Technical Association

HUMIDIFIERS
Honeywell, Inc.
Walter Meier Climate (USA), Inc.

IMAGESETTERS
AAA Press International
All Systems Go
Auto-Grafica Corp.
Berkshire/Westwood Graphics Group, Inc.
Computer Tree
Taylor Made Digital Systems
Fuji Photo Film USA/Graphic Systems Div.
Graphic Publishing Systems, Inc.
GraphLine
Fujifilm Graphic Systems USA, Inc.
MidLantic Equipment Co., Inc.
alfaQuest Technologies
ECRM
PrePRESS DIRECT
alfa CTP Systems LLC
SCREEN (USA)
Bob Weber, Inc.
Weber Systems, Inc.
Xitron

INFEED STACKERS
Kansa Technology, LLC
Mid-America Graphics, Inc.
Richard S Rowse & Associates

INK BLEEDING EQUIPMENT
Amergraph Corporation
BEK Systems, Inc.
Ingersoll-Rand-Aro Fluid Product Div.
INX International Ink Co.
David A. Shulda Enterprises, Inc.
UV Process Supply, Inc.

INK CONTROLS, COMPUTERIZED
Baldwin Americas Corp.
B.G. Industrial, Inc.
Controls Group, Inc.
Data Engineering Ltd.
Essex Products Group
M. Golda Engineering
grafikAmerica
Presteligence
Graphics Microsystems, Inc.
X-Rite Inc.
Harland Simon
MGI International, Inc.
Parascan Technologies, Inc.
Perretta Graphics Corp.
QuadTech
Printing Press Services, Inc.
Quad Tech

INK DE-MISTING SYSTEMS
The Eclectic Co., Inc.
MGI International, Inc.

INK FOUNTAINS & ACCESSORIES
Allpress Equipment, Inc.
AWS, A Thermal Care Division
BEK Systems, Inc.
Brodie System, Inc.
Graphic Printing Roller Ltd.
Hadronics
INX International Ink Co.
Kidder, Inc.
Master Flo Technology
Nama Graphics E, LLC
Printing Press Services, Inc.
Printing Technology, Inc.
Support Products, Inc.
Tech-Energy Co.
UV Process Supply, Inc.
Whitworth Knife Company
WPC Machinery Corp.

INK PAGE PAC RECONDITIONING
Precision Pressroom Products, Inc.

INK PUMPING SYSTEMS
Allpress Equipment, Inc.
Amergraph Corporation
AWS, A Thermal Care Division
BEK Systems, Inc.
B.G. Industrial, Inc.
Controls Group, Inc.
Flint Group
M. Golda Engineering
Graphic System Services, Inc.
Ingersoll-Rand-Aro Fluid Product Div.
INX International Ink Co.
Latin American Div./Flint Ink
UV Process Supply, Inc.

INK RECOVERY SYSTEMS
BEK Systems, Inc.
The Eclectic Co., Inc.
M. Golda Engineering
Maratek Environmental Technologies, Inc.
MGI International, Inc.
Mobile Reclamation System/MRS (Div. of Marpax)
Parsons, Inc.
Latin American Div./Flint Ink
Semler Industries, Inc. (Pressroom Fluids Equipment Div.)
David A. Shulda Enterprises, Inc.

INK STORAGE TANKS
B.G. Industrial, Inc.
Flint Group
INX International Ink Co.
Semler Industries, Inc. (Pressroom Fluids Equipment Div.)
UV Process Supply, Inc.
The Wellmark Company

INK TANK MONITORS
B.G. Industrial, Inc.

INKS
AirSystems, Inc.
Allpress Equipment, Inc.
American Ink Jet Corp.
Hewlett-Packard Co.
INX International Ink Co.
Day-Glo Color Corp.
Diversified Photo/Graphics Supply
Elcorsy Technology, Inc.
F & F Printing Ink
Flint Group
Norman X Guttman, Inc.
Markem-Imaje
INX International Ink Co.
Fujifilm Graphic Systems USA, Inc.
Louis Melind Co.
National Soy Ink Information Center
Newstech Co. (Div. of Rovinter, Inc.)
PAGE
Latin American Div./Flint Ink
US Ink
UVP, Inc.
Van Son Holland Ink Corp. of America
Video Jet Technologies
Schlenk-Both Industries
Miller-Cooper Co.

IN-LINE TRIMMING SYSTEMS
Advance Graphics Equipment of York, Inc.
Systems Technology, Inc.
Blower Application Co., Inc.
Applied Industrial Machinery
Gammerler (US) Corp.
IMC America
MBM Corp.
Mid-America Graphics, Inc.
AD-A-NOTE
Whitworth Knife Company

INPUT & EDITING SYSTEMS
Advanced Technical Solutions, Inc.
CNI Corp.
Computerease Software, Inc.
Conley Publishing Systems
Design Science, Inc.
Harris Corp.
Horizons, Inc.
Kubra
Megadata Corp.
Parascan Technologies, Inc.
Press-Enterprise, Inc. (Color Graphics Dept.)
Quebecor World
Reed Brennan Media Associates, Inc.
Stauffer Media Systems
West Coast Computer Systems
Xerox Corp.

INSERTING EQUIPMENT (INCLUDES STUFFING MACHINES)
Advance Graphics Equipment of York, Inc.
Automated Mailing Systems Corp.
Baumfolder Corp.
Buhrs Americas, Inc.
Burt Technologies, Inc.
Craftsman Newspaper Production Systems
Ferag Americas
Muller Martini Mailroom Systems, Inc.
Harland Simon
Kansa Technology, LLC
Kirk-Rudy, Inc.
Master Flo Technology
MBM Corp.
McCain Bindery Systems
Mid-America Graphics, Inc.
Muller Martini Corp.
Richard S Rowse & Associates
Simco Industrial Static Control Products
SITMA USA, Inc.
Seidel Enterprises
Valley Remanufacturing Co.
Wesco Graphics
Schur Packaging Systems, Inc.
WRH Marketing Americas, Inc.

INSURANCE
American Fidelity Assurance Co.
Church Rickards, Whitlock & Co., Inc.
Insurance Specialties Services, Inc.
Media Professional Insurance
SCA Promotions, Inc.
Walterry Insurance Brokers
Wilson Gregory Agency, Inc.

INTEGRATED FAX SERVERS
DAC Systems
Newspaper Electronics Corp.
Sales Development Services
Tel-Management, Inc.

INTERFACES
AdStar, Inc.
Applied Creative Technologies
Burt Technologies, Inc.
Devlin Electronics Ltd.
M. Golda Engineering
InterVoice-Brite, Inc.
alfaQuest Technologies
STM Networks

KEYLESS INKING CONVERSION & ADD-ONS
Perretta Graphics Corp.

LABEL PRINTING MACHINES
Dean Machinery International, Inc.
Domino Amjet, Inc.
Flexo Printing Equipment Corp.
Horizons, Inc.
Markem-Imaje
Lauterbach Group
Martin Yale, Inc.
Megasys International, Inc.
Press and Bindery Systems, Inc.
Video Jet Technologies
Schur Packaging Systems, Inc.
ACCUFAST Package Printing Systems
Accraply, Inc.

LASER PRINTERS
Coast Graphic Supply
e/Doc Systems
Hitachi Printing Solutions
Denex, Inc.
Domino Amjet, Inc.
Duostat Co. (Affiliated with VGC Corp.)
Tally Genicom
Graphic Publishing Systems, Inc.
GraphLine
Laser Products Technologies
Matthews International Corp.
alfaQuest Technologies
Royal Consumer Information Products, Inc.
PrePRESS DIRECT
Printsoft Americas, Inc.
QMS, Inc.
System Facilities, Inc.
Truproof Ltd.
Xerox Corp.
Konica Minolta Printing Solutions

Layout Tables, Light Tables & Workstations
Beta Screen Corp.
Douthitt Corp.
Duostat Co. (Affiliated with VGC Corp.)
Foster Mfg. Co.
Lithco Inc.
Graphic Technology, Inc. (GTI)
Richmond/Graphic Products, Inc.
Roconex Corp.
Support Products, Inc.
Truproof Ltd.

Lenses (Camera)
CK Optical Co., Inc.
Diversified Photo/Graphics Supply
Heitz Service Corp.
National Graphic Supply Corp.
Pitman Photo Supply
Unique Photo

LIBRARY RETRIEVAL SYSTEMS
Advertising Checking Bureau, Inc.
MediaSpan Group Inc.
Cygnet Storage Solutions, Inc.
Digital Collections
Gannett Media Technologies International (GMTI)
Schawk
Spectra Logic
Stauffer Media Systems
Verity, Inc.

LIFT TRUCKS
Berlee Vacuum Systems
Clark Material Handling Co.
Midwest Publishers Supply Co.
Ryder System, Inc.
Yale Materials Handling Corp.

LIGHT INTEGRATORS
Burgess Industries, Inc.
Douthitt Corp.

LIGHTING EQUIPMENT
Atlas Specialty Lighting
Bulbtronics
Caprock Developments, Inc.
Graphic Technology, Inc. (GTI)
X-Rite Inc.

LUBRICANTS
Herco Graphic Products
Lincoln Industrial
Printers' Service/Prisco/PriscoDigital
UV Process Supply, Inc.

MAILING LIST COMPILER
Dunhill International List Co., Inc.
Whitney Worldwide, Inc.

MAILROOM SYSTEMS & EQUIPMENT
The Austin Company
Automated Mailing Systems Corp.
Bell & Howell Scanners
Bowe Bell + Howell
Bishamon Industries Corp.
Chuck Blevins & Assoc.
Buhrs Americas, Inc.
Burt Technologies, Inc.
Cannon Equipment
FELINS, Inc.
Gammerler (US) Corp.
Gerrard Ovalstrapping
Muller Martini Mailroom Systems, Inc.
Group 1 Software, Inc.
Harland Simon
Markem-Imaje
K & M Newspaper Services, Inc.
Kansa Technology, LLC
Kaspar Wire Works, Inc./Sho-Rack
Kirk-Rudy, Inc.
Kubra
McCain Bindery Systems
Dienamic Microprint
Midwest Publishers Supply Co.
Muller Martini Corp.
Myrtle Beach, Inc.
Neasi-Weber International
Quipp
ppi Media GmbH
Plumtree Co.
Prim Hall Enterprises, Inc.
Richard S Rowse & Associates
Paragon Technologies Inc.
SITMA USA, Inc.
H.R. Slater Co., Inc.
Sterling Packaging Systems
Seidel Enterprises
Total Mailroom Support, Inc. (TMSI)
Valley Remanufacturing Co.
Video Jet Technologies
Jervis B. Webb Co.
Western Roller Corp.
Chauncey Wing's Sons, Inc.
XYonicz
United States Postal Service
Schur Packaging Systems, Inc.
ACCUFAST Package Printing Systems
Aragon System Products

MAINTENANCE, PLANT & EQUIPMENT
A-American Machine & Assembly (Press Parts Div.)
The Austin Company
Lankford Engineering, Inc.
Lorentzen & Wettre
Standard Electric and Engineering Co.
Witte Energy Management

MARKET RESEARCH
A & A Research
Advertising Checking Bureau, Inc.
Claritas
William Dunkerley Publishing Consultant
Minnesota Opinion Research, Inc. (MORI)
Research USA, Inc.
Sales Development Services
Scarborough Research
Silverman Newspaper Management Consultants
Strategic Telemedia
Valco Sales, Inc.
Ver-A-Fast Corp.
Whitney Worldwide, Inc.
TNS
Marketing Plus, Inc.

MARKETING DATABASE DESIGN AND IMPLEMENTATION
AccuDocs LLC
Alaska Information Marketing (AIM)
ASTech InterMedia
Gannett Media Technologies International (GMTI)
Newspaper Technologies, Inc. (NTI)
Sales Development Services

MASKING MATERIALS
Mac Dermid Autotype Inc.
Base-Line, Inc.
Direct Reproduction Corp.
Fluorographic Services & CP Collier Technologies
Shuttleworth, LLC
Support Products, Inc.

MATERIAL HANDLING EQUIPMENT: AUTOMATIC GUIDED VEHICLES
ADI/PDM Trade Group
Control Engineering Co.
FMC Technologies
HK Systems
IMC America
Linde Lift Truck Corp.
Ch2MHill Lockwood Greene
Manroland Inc.
Ramsey (A Thermo Sentron Co.)
Dematics
Paragon Technologies Inc.
Jervis B. Webb Co.

MATERIAL HANDLING EQUIPMENT: PALLETIZING MACHINES
FKI Logistex
ADI/PDM Trade Group
Systems Technology, Inc.

Butler Automatic
Clark Material Handling Co.
Craftsman Newspaper Production Systems
FANUC Robotics America, Inc.
Gammerler (US) Corp.
Muller Martini Mailroom Systems, Inc.
HK Systems
IMC America
Kolbus America, Inc.
Muller Martini Corp.
Richard S Rowse & Associates
Schur Packaging Systems, Inc.

MATERIAL HANDLING EQUIPMENT: PALLETS & PALLETIZERS
ADI/PDM Trade Group
Clark Material Handling Co.
Gammerler (US) Corp.
Hamilton Circulation Supplies Co.
Litco International, Inc.
Master Flo Technology
NENSCO
Quipp System, Inc.
Schur Packaging Systems, Inc.

MATERIAL HANDLING EQUIPMENT: TRUCK LOADERS
Cascade Corp.
Clark Material Handling Co.
Control Engineering Co.
Stewart Glapat Corp.
Linde Lift Truck Corp.
MAXX Material Handling LLC
Quipp System, Inc.
Dematics
Superior Handling Equipment, Inc.
Total Mailroom Support, Inc. (TMSI)
XYonicz

MATERIAL HANDLING EQUIPMENT: VEHICLE LOADING
Bishamon Industries Corp.
Clark Material Handling Co.
Linde Lift Truck Corp.
MAXX Material Handling LLC
Superior Handling Equipment, Inc.
Jervis B. Webb Co.

MICROFILMING
Eastman Kodak Co.

MOTORS
A-American Machine & Assembly (Press Parts Div.)
Baldor Electric Co.
Baumuller
Bodine Electric
Danfoss Graham
ITW Hobart Brothers Co.
K & M Newspaper Services, Inc.
Miracle Industries, Inc.
Standard Electric and Engineering Co.

MULTIPLEXERS/ROUTERS
Autologic Information International
Presteligence
alfaQuest Technologies

NEWS WIRE CAPTURE SYSTEMS
Automatic Newsstand, Inc. (ANI Promotions)
NewsEngin, Inc.
SAXOTECH, Inc.

NEWSPAPER BAGS
Automatic Newsstand, Inc. (ANI Promotions)
Continental Products
Great Southern Corp. (Sirco Div.)
Hamilton Circulation Supplies Co.
IPC
The Keenan Group, Inc.
Myrtle Beach, Inc.
RAK Systems, Inc.
Sonoco Products Co.

NEWSPAPER COUTER
Baumer Electric Ltd.
Buhrs Americas, Inc.
Simon Miller Sales Co.
Plumtree Co.
Ramsey (A Thermo Sentron Co.)

NEWSPAPER DISPENSERS (MECHANICAL/ELECTRONIC)
AG Industries, Inc.
Automatic Newsstand, Inc. (ANI Promotions)
Bellatrix Systems, Inc.
Fortec, Inc.
GeoRack, Inc.
Go Plastics/StreetSmart LLC
Hamilton Circulation Supplies Co.
Impact Racks, Inc.
Kaspar Wire Works, Inc./Sho-Rack
The Keenan Group, Inc.
K-Jack Engineering Co., Inc.
National Newsvend
RAK Systems, Inc.
Star Vend

NEWSPAPER MARKETING
AdStar, Inc.
U.S. Suburban Press (USSPI)
ANewStartGuy.com
Circulation Solutions, Inc.
Claritas
Communications Management Service, Inc.
Hamilton Circulation Supplies Co.
The Keenan Group, Inc.
Marketing Research Associates, Inc.
Simon Miller Sales Co.
Minnesota Opinion Research, Inc. (MORI)
Northern Graphic Supply
Plumtree Co.
SCA Promotions, Inc.
Scarborough Research
Star Vend
Whitney Worldwide, Inc.
Publishing House Research LLC

NEWSPRINT
AbitibiBowater Inc.
Newsprint Sales Co.
Behrens International Ltd.
Bender Machine, Inc.
Katahdin Paper Company LLC
AbitibiBowater Inc.
Abi Bow US Inc.
AbitibiBowater Pulp and Paper Canada, Inc.
Papiers Stadacona
EDIWISE
Catalyst Paper (USA), Inc.
Fortfiber Corp., Paper Mill Packaging Grp.
Lasalle Papers, Inc.
Manistique Papers, Inc.
McGrann Paper Corp.
Simon Miller Sales Co.
White Birch Paper
Newsprint South, Inc.
News-Type Service, Inc.
Norwood Paper
PAGE
Pan American Papers, Inc.
Papier Masson Ltee
Roosevelt Paper
Blue Heron Paper Co.
SP Newsprint Co.
Tembec, Paper Group
United Paper Mills Kymmene, Inc.

NEWSPRINT HANDELING EQUIPMENT
The Austin Company
Bender Machine, Inc.
Bishamon Industries Corp.
Capital Track Co.
Control Engineering Co.
EDIWISE
FANUC Robotics America, Inc.
FMC Technologies
William Ginsberg Associates
M. Golda Engineering
Manroland Inc.
Martin Automatic, Inc.
Mid-America Graphics, Inc.
Muller Martini Corp.
The Newark Group
Plumtree Co.
Republic Service Co.
Richard S Rowse & Associates
Saxmayer Corp.
H.R. Slater Co., Inc.
Metso Paper
Jervis B. Webb Co.
XYonicz

NOISE CONTROL
Airloc Products
Arco Engineering, Inc. (Newspaper Div.)
The Eclectic Co., Inc.
Electronic Specialists, Inc.
William Ginsberg Associates
Industrial Noise Control, Inc.

NUMBERING MACHINES
Advance Graphics Equipment of York, Inc.
Domino Amjet, Inc.
Louis Melind Co.
Rollem Corp. of America
Web Printing Controls

OFFSET BLANKET THICKNESS GAUGE
Caprock Developments, Inc.
J. Thomas McHugh Co., Inc.
NDI (Morway Div.)
Bill Rudder & Associates, Inc.
Rycoline Products, Inc.
SunShine Paper Co.
Support Products, Inc.

OFFSET BLANKETS, BLANKET WASH
Flint Group.
Litho Research, Inc.
J. Thomas McHugh Co., Inc.
NDI (Morway Div.)
Printers' Service/Prisco/PriscoDigital
Printex Products
Rycoline Products, Inc.
Sun Graphic, Inc.
Vegra USA
DYC Supply Co.

OFFSET CAMERA, DARKROOM EQUIPMENT
Arrow Printing Co.
CK Optical Co., Inc.
New Consolidated International Corp.

OFFSET CHEMICALS & SUPPLIES
Base-Line, Inc.
Berkshire/Westwood Graphics Group, Inc.
Citiplate, Inc.
Flint Group.
Dynalith, Inc.
Base-Line, Inc.
Litho Research, Inc.
Fujifilm Graphic Systems USA, Inc.
Midwest Publishers Supply Co.
NDI (Morway Div.)
Newstech Co. (Div. of Rovinter, Inc.)
Printers' Service/Prisco/PriscoDigital
Printex Products
Royal Graphics
Rycoline Products, Inc.
Southern Lithoplate, Inc.
SunShine Paper Co.
Superior Lithoplate of Indiana, Inc.
UV Process Supply, Inc.
Day International
Vegra USA
Winton Engineering Co.

OFFSET FILM
Southern Lithoplate, Inc.

OFFSET FOUNTAIN CONTROLS
BEK Systems, Inc.
Master Flo Technology
Smith Pressroom Products, Inc.

OFFSET FOUNTAIN SOLUTIONS
Base-Line, Inc.
Burnishine Products
NDI (Morway Div.)
Poolside Lithographic Supply, Inc.
Smith Pressroom Products, Inc.
Printers' Service/Prisco/PriscoDigital
Printex Products
Rycoline Products, Inc.
Southern Lithoplate, Inc.
Day International
Vegra USA

OFFSET NEGATIVE MASKING PAPER
Base-Line, Inc.
Direct Reproduction Corp.

OFFSET PLATE FILES
Arrow Printing Co.
Foster Mfg. Co.

OFFSET PLATE HOLDERS
Roconex Corp.

OFFSET PLATE-MAKING SERVICE & EQUIPMENT
Amergraph Corporation
Douthitt Corp.
Herco Graphic Products
K & F International, Inc.
Kodak GCG
NuArc Co., Inc.
Printware
Richmond/Graphic Products, Inc.
NELA
Western LithoTech
Eastman Kodak Co.

OFFSET PREVENTION-MATERIALS & EQUIPMENT
Baldwin Oxy-Dry Americas
Day International

OPTICAL CHARACTER RECOGNITION (OCR)
CNI Corp.
DAC Systems
Media Cybernetics LP
PC Industries

OPTICAL PRODUCTS
Beta Screen Corp.
Caprock Developments, Inc.
Lithco Inc.
X-Rite, Inc.

OUTPUT MANAGEMENT AND PREFLIGHT SOFTWARE
Presteligence
alfaQuest Technologies
ppi Media GmbH

PAGINATION SYSTEMS
MediaSpan Group Inc.
Brainworks Software Development Corp.
Saxotech
CNI Corp.
Computer Tree
Conley Publishing Systems
Informatica Dalai SA de CV
Harris Corp.
Managing Editor, Inc.
ppi Media GmbH
Print Marketing Concepts, Inc.
Reed Brennan Media Associates, Inc.
SAXOTECH, Inc.
West Coast Computer Systems

PAPER CLEANERS
Herco Graphic Products
Simco Industrial Static Control Products

PAPER HANDELING EQUIPMENT
Bishamon Industries Corp.
Capital Track Co.
Cascade Corp.
Control Engineering Co.
EDIWISE
FANUC Robotics America, Inc.
FMC Technologies
William Ginsberg Associates
M. Golda Engineering
IMC America
Kaspar Wire Works, Inc./Sho-Rack
Martin Yale, Inc.
Muller Martini Corp.
Prim Hall Enterprises, Inc.
Republic Service Co.
Shuttleworth, LLC
H.R. Slater Co., Inc.
Spartanics
Superior Handling Equipment, Inc.
Metso Paper
Jervis B. Webb Co.
WPC Machinery Corp.
Xpedx Printing Technologies

PAPER SHREDDERS
Blower Application Co., Inc.
General Binding Corp.
Kaim & Associates International Marketing, Inc.
Martin Yale, Inc.
Megasys International, Inc.

PAPER TESTING INSTRUMENTS
Caprock Developments, Inc.
Lorentzen & Wettre
Technidyne Corp.

PAPER: COATED GROUNDWOOD OFFSET
AbitibiBowater Inc.
Behrens International Ltd.
Catalyst Paper (USA), Inc.
Fortfiber Corp., Paper Mill Packaging Grp.
McGrann Paper Corp.
Simon Miller Sales Co.
Norwood Paper
Roosevelt Paper
Sappi Fine Paper
StoraEnso

PAPER: GROUNDWOOD SPECIALTIES
AbitibiBowater Inc.
Behrens International Ltd.
Katahdin Paper Company LLC
Catalyst Paper (USA), Inc.
Fortfiber Corp., Paper Mill Packaging Grp.
Manistique Papers, Inc.
McGrann Paper Corp.
Simon Miller Sales Co.
White Birch Paper
Norwood Paper
PAGE
Sappi Fine Paper

PAPER: SPECIALTY PRINTING PAPER
AbitibiBowater Inc.
Anchor Paper Corp.
Katahdin Paper Company LLC
Domtar, Inc.
Catalyst Paper (USA), Inc.
Fortfiber Corp., Paper Mill Packaging Grp.
McGrann Paper Corp.
Simon Miller Sales Co.
Norwood Paper
Pan American Papers, Inc.
Roosevelt Paper
Sappi Fine Paper

PASTERS
Arco Engineering, Inc. (Newspaper Div.)
Butler Automatic
Graphic System Services, Inc.
H & M Paster Sales & Service, Inc.
Jardis Industries, Inc.
Kaim & Associates International Marketing, Inc.
KBA North America, Inc. (Koenig & Bauer AG)
Lankford Engineering, Inc.
Martin Automatic, Inc.
Masthead International, Inc.

PHOTO ARCHIVING
Digital Collections
Foster Mfg. Co.
Gannett Media Technologies International (GMTI)
alfaQuest Technologies
SAXOTECH, Inc.
MerlinOne, Inc.
Kinetic Corporation

PHOTO PROOFING PAPERS
Eastman Kodak Co.

PHOTO PROOFING SYSTEMS
Arrow Printing Co.
BESCO Graphic Systems Corp.
X-Rite Inc.

PHOTOGRAPHY: DIGITAL/ELECTRONIC CAMERAS
Applied Graphics Technologies
Flint Group.
Diversified Photo/Graphics Supply
PhotoSource International
Pitman Photo Supply
Unique Photo

PHOTOSTAT: CHEMICALS
Unique Photo

PHOTOSTAT: MACHINES
Megasys International, Inc.

PHOTOSTAT: PAPER
AbitibiBowater Pulp and Paper Canada, Inc.
Sappi Fine Paper
Pemco, Inc.
Georgia-Pacific Corp.

PHOTOTYPESETTING FONTS
Conley Publishing Systems

PHOTOTYPESETTING INTERFACE EQUIPMENT
Foley, Torregiani & Associates, Inc.
System Facilities, Inc.
Xitron
E.I. du Pont de Nemours & Co.

PIN REGISTER SYSTEMS
Central Graphics
Douthitt Corp.
Taylor Made Digital Systems
K & F International, Inc.
Krause Newspaper Systems, Inc.
Stoesser Register Systems
NELA

PLASTIC FOLDERS
Base-Line, Inc.
Foster Mfg. Co.

PLATE BENDING SYSTEMS
Burgess Industries, Inc.
Taylor Made Digital Systems
K & F International, Inc.
Robertson Equipments
Stoesser Register Systems
NELA

PLATE CLEANERS
Base-Line, Inc.
Burnishine Products
Litho Research, Inc.
Poolside Lithographic Supply, Inc.
Printers' Service/Prisco/PriscoDigital
Superior Lithoplate of Indiana, Inc.
Support Products, Inc.
Day International
Fiberweb
Western LithoTech

PLATE COATING MACHINES
LogEtronics Corp.

PLATE EXPOSURE UNITS
Amergraph Corporation
Berkshire/Westwood Graphics Group, Inc.
Douthitt Corp.
Dynalith, Inc.
LogEtronics Corp.
Louis Melind Co.
NuArc Co., Inc.
Pitman Co.
Roconex Corp.
Stoesser Register Systems

PLATE MOUNTING & REGISTER SYSTEMS
AAA Press International
Burgess Industries, Inc.
Taylor Made Digital Systems
Newstech Co. (Div. of Rovinter, Inc.)
Stoesser Register Systems
NELA
Acutech LLC

PLATE PROCESSORS
Amergraph Corporation
Auto-Grafica Corp.
Dynalith, Inc.
Herco Graphic Products
K & F International, Inc.
Krause Newspaper Systems, Inc.
LogEtronics Corp.
NB Finishing, Inc.
Newstech Co. (Div. of Rovinter, Inc.)
Pitman Co.
Poolside Lithographic Supply, Inc.
Printware
Richmond/Graphic Products, Inc.
Southern Lithoplate, Inc.
Bob Weber, Inc.
Western LithoTech
Eastman Kodak Co.

PLATE SCANNING SYSTEMS
LogEtronics Corp.

Platemakers: Direct
Auto-Grafica Corp.
Autologic Information International
GraphLine
Krause Newspaper Systems, Inc.
MacDermid Printing Solutions

PLATEMAKERS: FLEXOGRAPHIC (COMPUTER TO PLATE)
ARC International
Autologic Information International
Fujifilm Graphic Systems USA, Inc.
MacDermid Printing Solutions
Sonoran Scanners, Inc.

PLATEMAKERS: FLEXOGRAPHIC (TRADITIONAL)
Douthitt Corp.
Louis Melind Co.
MacDermid Printing Solutions
MacDermid Printing Solutions
Western LithoTech

PLATEMAKERS: LASER
ARC International
alfaQuest Technologies

PLATEMAKERS: LETTERPRESS
Heidelberg USA, Inc.
Herco Graphic Products
MacDermid Printing Solutions
MacDermid Printing Solutions
Sterling Type Foundry
Western LithoTech

PLATEMAKERS: OFFSET (COMPUTER TO PLATE)
Amergraph Corporation
Cymbolic Sciences International Ltd.
A.B. Dick Co.
Douthitt Corp.
Krause Newspaper Systems, Inc.
ECRM
Poolside Lithographic Supply, Inc.
Spectrecom Corporation
Western LithoTech

PLATEMAKERS: OFFSET (CONVENTIONAL)
Arrow Printing Co.
Citiplate, Inc.
Dynalith, Inc.
K & F International, Inc.
Krause Newspaper Systems, Inc.
Louis Melind Co.
NuArc Co., Inc.
Poolside Lithographic Supply, Inc.
Printware
Roconex Corp.
Royal Graphics
Sonoran Scanners, Inc.
Stoesser Register Systems
Dennis Storch Co.
Superior Lithoplate of Indiana, Inc.
Western LithoTech

PLATES: FLEXOGRAPHIC (CONVENTIONAL)
Louis Melind Co.
MacDermid Printing Solutions
MacDermid Printing Solutions

PLATES: LETTERPRESS
ByChrome Ltd.
Herco Graphic Products
MacDermid Printing Solutions
MacDermid Printing Solutions

PLATES: OFFSET (COMPUTER TO PLATE)
Anocoil Corporation
Mac Dermid Autotype Inc.
ByChrome Ltd.
A.B. Dick Co.
Dynalith, Inc.
Fuji Photo Film USA/Graphic Systems Div.
Kodak GCG
Newstech Co. (Div. of Rovinter, Inc.)
MacDermid Printing Solutions
Poolside Lithographic Supply, Inc.
alfa CTP Systems LLC
Southern Lithoplate, Inc.
Spectrecom Corporation
Western LithoTech

PLATES: OFFSET (CONVENTIONAL)
Anocoil Corporation
Arrow Printing Co.
Base-Line, Inc.
Berkshire/Westwood Graphics Group, Inc.
ByChrome Ltd.
Citiplate, Inc.
Coast Graphic Supply
Dynalith, Inc.
Fuji Photo Film USA/Graphic Systems Div.
Inter-Continental Graphics, Inc.
Kodak GCG
Fujifilm Graphic Systems USA, Inc.
NENSCO
Newstech Co. (Div. of Rovinter, Inc.)
PAGE
Pitman Co.
Poolside Lithographic Supply, Inc.
Printware
Latin American Div./Flint Ink
Royal Graphics
Southern Lithoplate, Inc.
Superior Lithoplate of Indiana, Inc.
Western LithoTech
Eastman Kodak Co.

PREPRESS COLOR PROOFING SYSTEMS
All Systems Color, Inc.
Arrow Printing Co.
Auto-Grafica Corp.
M.W. Burke & Associates, Inc.
CNI Corp.
Direct Reproduction Corp.
Foster Mfg. Co.
Lithco Inc.
Presteligence
ECRM
Parascan Technologies, Inc.
Latran Technologies
Truproof Ltd.
Bob Weber, Inc.
E.I. du Pont de Nemours & Co.
Polkadots Software Inc.

PREPRINT SERVICE & PRODUCTION
Managing Editor, Inc.
Quebecor World
Schawk
Kinetic Corporation

PRESS ACCESSORIES, PARTS & SUPPLIES
AAA Press International
A-American Machine & Assembly (Press Parts Div.)
Aaro Roller Corp.
AEC, Inc.
ALTA- Al Taber - PHA
AWS, A Thermal Care Division
Baldwin Americas Corp.
Brodie System, Inc.
BST Pro Mark
Central Graphics
Pamarco Global Graphics
A.B. Dick Co.
Global Press Management Services, LLC.
Goss International Corporation
Graphic Printing Roller Ltd.
Graphic System Services, Inc.
Graphic Technology, Inc. (GTI)
G.T. Specialties
Innotek Corporation

Inter-Continental Graphics, Inc.
Base-Line, Inc.
Manassy Sales Inc.
Manroland Inc.
Martin Automatic, Inc.
Master Flo Technology
Midwest Publishers Supply Co.
Miracle Industries, Inc.
NENSCO
Baldwin Oxy-Dry Americas
PAGE
Printers' Service/Prisco/PriscoDigital
Printing Technology, Inc.
Robertson Press Machinery Co., Inc.
Royal Graphics
Robertson Equipments
RTP Technical Specialists
Simco Industrial Static Control Products
Tech-Energy Co.
Technology Integrators
NELA
Tobias Associates, Inc.
Day International
Fiberweb
Winton Engineering Co.
Offset Services Ink
American Ultraviolet Co., Inc.

PRESS CONTROL SYSTEMS

ABB, Inc. (Printing Systems)
Advanced Control Technologies, Inc.
ELAPLAN Buchholz GmbH & Co.
Ewert America Electronics Ltd.
Fincor Automation, Inc.
Graphics Microsystems, Inc.
Harland Simon
Harris Corp.
Honeywell, Inc.
Inter-Continental Graphics, Inc.
Koenig & Bauer Aktiengesellschaft (KBA)
Manroland Inc.
Miracle Industries, Inc.
PC Industries
QuadTech
Quad Tech
Bosch Rexroth
Rockwell Automation
RTP Technical Specialists
Web Printing Controls
E.I. du Pont de Nemours & Co.
ABB Inc.
Skyline Graphic Services, LLC

PRESS DATA ACCUMULATORS

Harland Simon

PRESS ENGINEERS

Chuck Blevins & Assoc.
Global Press Management Services, LLC.
Hall Contracting Services, Inc.
Miracle Industries, Inc.
Tech-Energy Co.

PRESS PARTS

Masthead International, Inc.
Newstech Co. (Div. of Rovinter, Inc.)

PRESS REBUILDING

A-American Machine & Assembly (Press Parts Div.)
Brown's Web Press Service & Machine Shop
DM Graphics System
Egenolf Machine, Inc. (Egenolf Contracting & Rigging)
Global Press Management Services, LLC.
Goss International Corporation
Hall Contracting Services, Inc.
Inland Newspaper Machinery LLC
Masthead International, Inc.
Pressline Services, Inc.
Printing Technology, Inc.
Robertson Press Machinery Co., Inc.
RTP Technical Specialists
Tech-Energy Co.
Wesco Graphics
WPC Machinery Corp.
Skyline Graphic Services, LLC

PRESS REPAIRS

Brown's Web Press Service & Machine Shop
Manugraph DGM, Inc.
A.B. Dick Co.
DM Graphics System
Egenolf Machine, Inc. (Egenolf Contracting & Rigging)
Goss International Corporation
Hall Contracting Services, Inc.
Inland Newspaper Machinery LLC
Masthead International, Inc.
Pressline Services, Inc.
Printing Technology, Inc.
RTP Technical Specialists
Tech-Energy Co.
UMI
Wesco Graphics
WPC Machinery Corp.

PRESSES: DILITHO

Elcorsy Technology, Inc.
Northeast Industries, Inc.
Press and Bindery Systems, Inc.

PRESSES: FLEXOGRAPHIC

AAA Press International
ADI/PDM Trade Group
Dean Machinery International, Inc.
Flexo Printing Equipment Corp.
KBA North America, Inc. (Koenig & Bauer AG)
Kidder, Inc.
Koenig & Bauer Aktiengesellschaft (KBA)
Manroland Inc.
Masthead International, Inc.
Northeast Industries, Inc.
Press and Bindery Systems, Inc.
Windmoeller and Hoelscher Corp.

PRESSES: LETTERPRESS

Heidelberg USA, Inc.
Masthead International, Inc.
Northeast Industries, Inc.
Sterling Type Foundry
Tech-Energy Co.

PRESSES: OFFSET

Allpress Equipment, Inc.
ALTA- Al Taber - PHA
Arrow Printing Co.
'Ataboy, Inc.
B & L Machine & Design
Brown's Web Press Service & Machine Shop
Central Graphics
Craftsmen Machinery Co., Inc.
Manugraph DGM, Inc.
Dean Machinery International, Inc.
Pamarco Global Graphics
A.B. Dick Co.
DM Graphics System
Goss International Corporation
Lissom Corp. Inc.
GSP, Inc.
Gutenberg Printing Press Co.
Hamada of America, Inc.
Heidelberg USA, Inc.
Ingersoll-Rand-Aro Fluid Product Div.
Inland Newspaper Machinery LLC
Intercontinental Engineering Co.
Inter-Continental Graphics, Inc.
KBA North America, Inc. (Koenig & Bauer AG)
Koenig & Bauer Aktiengesellschaft (KBA)
Komori America Corp.
MAH Machine Co., Inc.
Manroland Inc.
Masthead International, Inc.
Metroland Printing/Publishing & Distributing Ltd.
Miracle Industries, Inc.
New Consolidated International Corp.
Newman International, LLC
Northeast Industries, Inc.
ONE Corp.
Press and Bindery Systems, Inc.
Printing Press Services, Inc.
Printing Technology, Inc.
Reeves Brothers, Inc.
Latin American Div./Flint Ink
Robertson Press Machinery Co., Inc.
Sakurai USA
Solna Web USA, Inc.
Dennis Storch Co.
Tech-Energy Co.
Tensor Group, Inc.
TKS (USA), Inc.
WebPress, LLC
Wesco Graphics
WIFAG Press Co.
Xpedx Printing Technologies

PRESSES: ROTOGRAVURE

Dean Machinery International, Inc.
Koenig & Bauer Aktiengesellschaft (KBA)
Press and Bindery Systems, Inc.
Quebecor World
Windmoeller and Hoelscher Corp.

PROCESSORS: DIFFUSION TRANSFER

LogEtronics Corp.
NuArc Co., Inc.
Richmond/Graphic Products, Inc.

PROCESSORS: FILM & PAPER

Amergraph Corporation
Arrow Printing Co.
Auto-Grafica Corp.
Carnfeldt America
A.B. Dick Co.
Diversified Photo/Graphics Supply
Glunz & Jensen, Inc.
Herco Graphic Products
Dunning Photo Equipment, Inc.
LogEtronics Corp.
Mohr Enterprise
ECRM
PrePRESS DIRECT
Richmond/Graphic Products, Inc.
Dennis Storch Co.
Bob Weber, Inc.
Weber Systems, Inc.
Eastman Kodak Co.

PRODUCITON CONTROL SYSTEMS

'Ataboy, Inc.
BST Pro Mark
Fleming Enterprises
Harland Simon
Midsystems Technology Ltd.
Miracom Computer Corp.
OLEC
ppi Media GmbH

PROMOTION SERVICES

Advantex Marketing International, Inc.
R.C. Anderson Associates, Inc.
ANewStartGuy.com
InterVoice-Brite, Inc.
IPC
Plumtree Co.
SCA Promotions, Inc.
Silverman Newspaper Management Consultants
Value Checks
Weatherline, Inc.

PROOFING SYSTEMS

AAA Press International
BESCO Graphic Systems Corp.
Burgess Industries, Inc.
Data Engineering Ltd.
A.B. Dick Co.
Foster Mfg. Co.
Fuji Photo Film USA/Graphic Systems Div.
X-Rite Inc.
Komori America Corp.
Fujifilm Graphic Systems USA, Inc.
N & L Enterprises, Inc.
NuArc Co., Inc.
ECRM
Parascan Technologies, Inc.
PC Industries
Latran Technologies
alfa CTP Systems LLC
SCREEN (USA)
Spectrecom Corporation
Bob Weber, Inc.
Weber Systems, Inc.
Konica Minolta Graphic Imaging USA
Anygraaf USA

PUBLISHING SYSTEMS

AdStar, Inc.
Advanced Technical Solutions, Inc.
Autologic Information International
MediaSpan Group Inc.
Bell & Howell Scanners
CNI Corp.
Computerease Software, Inc.
Computer Tree
Conley Publishing Systems
Fry Communications
Harris Corp.
Metroland Printing/Publishing & Distributing Ltd.
SAXOTECH, Inc.
Stauffer Media Systems
TeleType Co.

PUMPS (AIR, INK, VACUUM)

Baumfolder Corp.
Busch, Inc.
Graphic System Services, Inc.
Ingersoll-Rand-Aro Fluid Product Div.
Lincoln Industrial
Smith Pressroom Products, Inc.
David A. Shulda Enterprises, Inc.
UV Process Supply, Inc.

PUNCHING EQUIPMENT

A.B. Dick Co.
Taylor Made Digital Systems
Stoesser Register Systems
NELA

RACK DISPLAY CARDS

Hamilton Circulation Supplies Co.
IPC
National Newsvend
RAK Systems, Inc.
RFC Wire Forms
Star Vend

RASTER IMAGE PROCESSORS

Graphic Publishing Systems, Inc.
alfaQuest Technologies
PrePRESS DIRECT
SCREEN (USA)
Spectrecom Corporation
Dennis Storch Co.
Bob Weber, Inc.
Xitron

RECIRCULATORS

AEC, Inc.
Baldwin Americas Corp.
Master Flo Technology
Smith Pressroom Products, Inc.

RECYCLING NEWSPRINT

Atex North America
Moss Reck & Associates, Inc.
Sonoco Products Co.

REELS & TENSIONS

Advanced Graphic Systems (AGS)
Arco Engineering, Inc. (Newspaper Div.)
'Ataboy, Inc.
Inter-Continental Graphics, Inc.
Jardis Industries, Inc.
Johnstone Engineering & Machine Co.
Kaim & Associates International Marketing, Inc.
KBA North America, Inc. (Koenig & Bauer AG)
Koenig & Bauer Aktiengesellschaft (KBA)
Lankford Engineering, Inc.
Magnetic Power Systems, Inc.
Maxcess
RTP Technical Specialists
Tidland Corp.
Wesco Graphics
Pemco, Inc.

REELS (INLCUDES PAPER REELS)

Advanced Graphic Systems (AGS)
Arco Engineering, Inc. (Newspaper Div.)
Jardis Industries, Inc.
Johnstone Engineering & Machine Co.
KBA North America, Inc. (Koenig & Bauer AG)
Manroland Inc.
Tidland Corp.
Pemco, Inc.

REMANUFACTURES EQUIPMENT

FKI Logistex
'Ataboy, Inc.
Manugraph DGM, Inc.
Muller Martini Mailroom Systems, Inc.
Graphic System Services, Inc.
Gutenberg Printing Press Co.
Hall Contracting Services, Inc.
HFW Industries

Impact Racks, Inc.
Inland Newspaper Machinery LLC
Jardis Industries, Inc.
K & M Newspaper Services, Inc.
Kansa Technology, LLC
Kepes, Inc.
LogEtronics Corp.
ONE Corp.
Robertson Press Machinery Co., Inc.
SITMA USA, Inc.
Solar Systems
Sterling Packaging Systems
Total Mailroom Support, Inc. (TMSI)
WebPress, LLC

RESEARCH STUDIES
A & A Research
Advertising Checking Bureau, Inc.
CK Optical Co., Inc.
Hare Associates, Inc.
Minnesota Opinion Research, Inc. (MORI)
Scarborough Research
Southwest Alabama Radio Resources Bureau
Ver-A-Fast Corp.
Publishing House Research LLC

REWINDERS
AAA Press International
Flexo Printing Equipment Corp.
Johnstone Engineering & Machine Co.
Keene Technology, Inc. (KTI)
Kidder, Inc.
Martin Automatic, Inc.
Norwood Paper
Rotoflex Mark Andy Canada, Inc.
Bill Rudder & Associates, Inc.
Stanford Products

ROLL CLEANING EQUIPMENT
A-Korn Roller, Inc.
Cryogenesis (A Div. of WM & C Services, Inc.)
Kaim & Associates International Marketing, Inc.
Litho Research, Inc.
Manroland Inc.

ROLL CONVERTERS
Charles Beck Machine Corp.
Norman X Guttman, Inc.
Simon Miller Sales Co.
Norwood Paper

ROLL COVERINGS
A-Korn Roller, Inc.
American Roller Co.
ARC International
Herco Graphic Products
Base-Line, Inc.
Petco Roller Co.
Republic Roller Corp.
Roll-Crafters
RotaDyne Corp.
Robertson Equipments
Xerium Technologies Inc.

ROLL HANDELING EQUIPMENT
The Austin Company
Butler Automatic
Capital Track Co.
FANUC Robotics America, Inc.
Fleming Enterprises
FMC Technologies
Gerrard Ovalstrapping
IMC America
Johnstone Engineering & Machine Co.
Kepes, Inc.
Koenig & Bauer Aktiengesellschaft (KBA)
MEGTEC Systems
AD-A-NOTE
Shuttleworth, LLC
H.R. Slater Co., Inc.
Seidel Enterprises
Tilt-Lock
Metso Paper
Jervis B. Webb Co.
WebPress, LLC
Wesco Graphics
Pemco, Inc.
XYonicz

ROLL PREPARATION EQUIPMENT
FMC Technologies
Koenig & Bauer Aktiengesellschaft (KBA)

ROLLER GRINDERS
A-Korn Roller, Inc.
Bender Machine, Inc.
Capco Machinery Systems, Inc.
Fleming Enterprises
South Bend Lathe Corp.
Whitworth Knife Company

ROLLER GRINDING SERVICES
Aaro Roller Corp.
A-Korn Roller, Inc.
Bender Machine, Inc.
Brodie System, Inc.
Brown's Web Press Service & Machine Shop
Central Graphics
Graphic Printing Roller Ltd.
Norman X Guttman, Inc.
Hadronics
MAH Machine Co., Inc.
Miracle Industries, Inc.
NB Finishing, Inc.
Republic Roller Corp.
Roll-Crafters
Robertson Equipments
Xerium Technologies Inc.

ROLLERS
Aaro Roller Corp.
A-Korn Roller, Inc.
Allpress Equipment, Inc.
American Roller Co.
ARC International
Bottcher America Corp.
Brodie System, Inc.
Pamarco Global Graphics
Graphic Printing Roller Ltd.
Norman X Guttman, Inc.
Hadronics
Harper Corp. of America (Anilox Roll Supplier)
Herco Graphic Products
Inter-Continental Graphics, Inc.
Jardis Industries, Inc.
Base-Line, Inc.
Kaim & Associates International Marketing, Inc.
Kepes, Inc.
MAH Machine Co., Inc.
Manassy Sales Inc.
NENSCO
Newstech Co. (Div. of Rovinter, Inc.)
Pacesetter Graphic Service Corp.
Pamarco Global Graphics
Petco Roller Co.
Praxair, Inc.
Praxair, Inc.
Precision Pressroom Products, Inc.
Printing Technology, Inc.
Republic Roller Corp.
Roll-Crafters
RotaDyne Corp.
Royal Graphics
Xerium Technologies Inc.
Tech-Energy Co.
WPC Machinery Corp.

ROLLERS: DAMPENING
Aaro Roller Corp.
A-Korn Roller, Inc.
American Roller Co.
Brodie System, Inc.
Central Graphics
Pamarco Global Graphics
Graphic Printing Roller Ltd.
Norman X Guttman, Inc.
Hadronics
Base-Line, Inc.
MAH Machine Co., Inc.
Nama Graphics E, LLC
Pacesetter Graphic Service Corp.
Petco Roller Co.
Praxair, Inc.
Printing Technology, Inc.
Moss Reck & Associates, Inc.
Republic Roller Corp.
Roll-Crafters
RotaDyne Corp.
Day International

RULES
Alteneder, Theo & Sons
Lithco Inc.
Support Products, Inc.

SCANNERS: COLOR B & W, PLATES, WEB
Arco Engineering, Inc. (Newspaper Div.)
Arrow Printing Co.
Auto-Grafica Corp.
Autologic Information International
Fuji Photo Film USA/Graphic Systems Div.
Impak (A Div. of Pakon, Inc.)
KYE International Corp.
Microtek
Pitman Co.
Siix USA Corp.
System Facilities, Inc.
UMAX Technologies, Inc.
VIDAR Systems Corp.
Bob Weber, Inc.
Weber Systems, Inc.
Xerox (Corp. Headquarters)
Xerox Corp.

SHRINK WRAPPING EQUIPMENT
APS Packaging Systems
Arpac Group
Fortfiber Corp., Paper Mill Packaging Grp.
HK Systems
Muller Martini Corp.
SITMA USA, Inc.
Telesonic Packaging Corp., Ames Engineering Div.

SILVER RECOVERY
Commodity Resource & Environment
Hart Industries
Hart Industries/Metafix Compliance Systems
Maratek Environmental Technologies, Inc.
Metafix, Inc.
R.B. Intermark, Inc.
Metals Recovery Service
X-Rite, Inc.

SOFTWARE: ADVERTISING (INCLUDES DISPLAY; CLASSIFIED)
Vertis
AdStar, Inc.
Advanced Publishing Technology
Advanced Technical Solutions, Inc.
Advertising Data Scan/Adspies.com
Atex North America
Autologic Information International
Bruce Bell & Associates
BMF Newspaper Accounting Systems
Brainworks Software Development Corp.
CCI Europe, Inc.
CE Engineering
Celebro
Cenosis
Saxotech
Computerease Software, Inc.
Computer Tree
Conley Publishing Systems
Informatica Dalai SA de CV
Datafest Technologies, Inc.
SAXOTECH Circulation
Decisionmark Corp.
Digital Technology International
Eclipse Services (Div. of Quadrivium, Inc.)
Fake Brains, Inc.
Foley, Torregiani & Associates, Inc.
Gannett Media Technologies International (GMTI)
Atex North America
Presteligence
GraphX, Inc.
MediaSpan Media Software
ICANON Associates, Inc.
IdeaFisher Systems, Inc.
Digital Technology International
Interlink
Atex North America
Managing Editor, Inc.
Marketing Research Associates, Inc.
McCrrory Publishing
Media Data Technology, Inc. (MDTI)
Media Marketing, Inc.
Merrimac Software Associates
Micro Systems Specialists, Inc. (MSSI)
Miles 33 International
MultiAd Services, Inc.
Neasi-Weber International
Newspaper Space Bank
Newspaper Technologies, Inc. (NTI)
Nomads, Inc.
ppi Media GmbH
Pixo Arts Corp.
Digital Technology International
Quickwire Labs
Sales Development Services
Scarborough Research
Software Consulting Services
Miles 33
Tek-Tools, Inc.
Vision Data Equipment Corp.
West Coast Computer Systems
MediaSpan Group, Inc.
SAP America, Inc.
Unisys Corp.
ChannelNet
Ranger Data Technologies Inc.
Creative Circle Media Solutions

SOFTWARE: ASSET MANAGEMENT
Atex North America
CCI Europe, Inc.
Cygnet Storage Solutions, Inc.
Informatica Dalai SA de CV
DeskNet, Inc.
Digital Collections
Digital Technology International
EDIWISE
Miles 33 International
Morcor Solutions, Inc.
MultiAd Services, Inc.
North Atlantic Publishing Systems, Inc.
Quark, Inc.
SAXOTECH, Inc.
The Software Construction Co.
SPECTRUM Human Resource Systems Corp.
MerlinOne, Inc.
NewsView Solutions
Kinetic Corporation

SOFTWARE: BUSINESS (INCLUDES ADMINISTRATION/ACCOUNTING)
Brainworks Software Development Corp.
CCI Europe, Inc.
Datafest Technologies, Inc.
Digital Technology International
Eclipse Services (Div. of Quadrivium, Inc.)
EDIWISE
Fake Brains, Inc.
Atex North America
ICANON Associates, Inc.
Digital Technology International
Atex North America
Merrimac Software Associates
Micro Systems Specialists, Inc. (MSSI)
Digital Technology International
Software Business Systems
SPECTRUM Human Resource Systems Corp.
Vision Data Equipment Corp.
Unisys Corp.

SOFTWARE: CIRCULATION
Advanced Publishing Technology
Advanced Technical Solutions, Inc.
ASTech InterMedia
Atex North America
MediaSpan Group Inc.
SAXOTECH Circulation
Decisionmark Corp.
Digital Technology International
Fake Brains, Inc.
Atex North America
Global Turnkey Systems, Inc.
Hamilton Circulation Supplies Co.
MediaSpan Media Software
ICANON Associates, Inc.
Interlink
Kaspar Wire Works, Inc./Sho-Rack
K-Jack Engineering Co., Inc.
Merrimac Software Associates
Micro Systems Specialists, Inc. (MSSI)
Mobile Computing Corporation USA
Neasi-Weber International
Newspaper Technologies, Inc. (NTI)
Printsoft Americas, Inc.
Digital Technology International
Software Consulting Services
Stauffer Media Systems

Miles 33
Vision Data Equipment Corp.
MediaSpan Group, Inc.
SAP America, Inc.

SOFTWARE: DESIGN/GRAPHICS
Agfa Monotype Corporation
All Systems Go
Artbeats
Esko-Graphics
Brainworks Software Development Corp.
CCI Europe, Inc.
Conley Publishing Systems
Flint Group.
DeskNet, Inc.
Digital Technology International
Jupiter Images Corp.
MediaSpan Media Software
IMSI
MBG Telecom Software, Inc.
Metro Creative Graphics, Inc.
MultiAd Services, Inc.
Pantone, Inc.
Esko-Graphics
Quark, Inc.
The Software Construction Co.
Software Consulting Services
Kinetic Corporation
MediaSpan Group, Inc.
MacDonald Advertising Services

SOFTWARE: EDITORIAL
Advanced Publishing Technology
Advanced Technical Solutions, Inc.
Agile Enterprise
Atex North America
MediaSpan Group Inc.
Brainworks Software Development Corp.
CCI Europe, Inc.
CE Engineering
Cenosis
Saxotech
Computerease Software, Inc.
Conley Publishing Systems
Informatica Dalai SA de CV
Decisionmark Corp.
DeskNet, Inc.
Digital Technology International
Atex North America
MediaSpan Media Software
ICANON Associates, Inc.
John Juliano Computer Services Co.
Managing Editor, Inc.
Markzware Software, Inc.
McCrrory Publishing
Metro Creative Graphics, Inc.
Miles 33 International
NewsEngin, Inc.
Nomads, Inc.
North Atlantic Publishing Systems, Inc.
Quark, Inc.
Quickwire Labs
SAXOTECH, Inc.
The Software Construction Co.
Software Consulting Services
Stauffer Media Systems
Tek-Tools, Inc.
West Coast Computer Systems
MediaSpan Group, Inc.
Unisys Corp.

SOFTWARE: ELECTRONIC DATA INTERCHANGE
Shoom, Inc.
Autologic Information International
CCI Europe, Inc.
CE Engineering
Celebro
Cenosis
ColorVision, Inc.
Computerease Software, Inc.
Computer Talk Technology, Inc.
Comtel Instruments Co.
Flint Group.
DeskNet, Inc.
EDIWISE
Global Turnkey Systems, Inc.
IMSI
Markzware Software, Inc.
McCrrory Publishing
ProImage America, Inc.
Tek-Tools, Inc.
Tel-Management, Inc.
NewsView Solutions
TSI International Software Ltd.
Verity, Inc.
Vision Data Equipment Corp.

SOFTWARE: PAGINATION/LAYOUT
Advanced Publishing Technology
Agile Enterprise
Atex North America
MediaSpan Group Inc.
Brainworks Software Development Corp.
CCI Europe, Inc.
CE Engineering
Cenosis
Saxotech
Computerease Software, Inc.
Conley Publishing Systems
DeskNet, Inc.
Digital Technology International
Foley, Torregiani & Associates, Inc.
Capita Technologies
Atex North America
Harland Simon
MediaSpan Media Software
ICANON Associates, Inc.
Imapro Corp.
IMSI
Digital Technology International
John Juliano Computer Services Co.
Managing Editor, Inc.
McCrrory Publishing
Merrimac Software Associates
Miles 33 International
MultiAd Services, Inc.
NewsEngin, Inc.
Nomads, Inc.
North Atlantic Publishing Systems, Inc.
PALOS Software
ppi Media GmbH
PrePRESS DIRECT
alfa CTP Systems LLC
ProImage America, Inc.
Quark, Inc.
Quickwire Labs
SAXOTECH, Inc.
SCREEN (USA)
Software Consulting Services
Stauffer Media Systems
Tribune Media Services
Vision Data Equipment Corp.
West Coast Computer Systems
Kinetic Corporation
MediaSpan Group, Inc.
Unisys Corp.

SOFTWARE: PRESS/POST PRESS
Advanced Technical Solutions, Inc.
Buhrs Americas, Inc.
Burt Technologies, Inc.
Muller Martini Mailroom Systems, Inc.
Presteligence
Harland Simon
MediaSpan Media Software
HK Systems
Fujifilm Graphic Systems USA, Inc.
Plumtree Co.
Quipp System, Inc.
Total Mailroom Support, Inc. (TMSI)
MediaSpan Group, Inc.

SOFTWARE: WORKFLOW MANAGEMENT/TRACKING
Advanced Publishing Technology
CCI Europe, Inc.
Manugraph DGM, Inc.
DeskNet, Inc.
Ewert America Electronics Ltd.
FMC Technologies
Foley, Torregiani & Associates, Inc.
Presteligence
Harland Simon
John Juliano Computer Services Co.
Managing Editor, Inc.
Miles 33 International
Monaco Systems, Inc.
Morcor Solutions, Inc.
North Atlantic Publishing Systems, Inc.
ppi Media GmbH
Plumtree Co.
ProImage America, Inc.
SAXOTECH, Inc.
The Software Construction Co.
Miles 33
Tek-Tools, Inc.
NewsView Solutions
Vision Data Equipment Corp.
Kinetic Corporation
Unisys Corp.

SOLVENT RECOVERY SYSTEMS
ADI/PDM Trade Group
Baldwin Americas Corp.
Chemical Management Technology, Inc.
Maratek Environmental Technologies, Inc.
Baldwin Oxy-Dry Americas
Smith Pressroom Products, Inc.
Printers' Service/Prisco/PriscoDigital
R.B. Intermark, Inc.

SPEECH RECOGNITION
DAC Systems
SAXOTECH Circulation
Nuance
FANUC Robotics America, Inc.
InterVoice-Brite, Inc.
Syntellect, Inc.
TALX Corp.
Voice Connexion
TALX Corp.

SPLICERS, AUTOMATIC
Allpress Equipment, Inc.
Butler Automatic
Graphic System Services, Inc.
Gutenberg Printing Press Co.
Inter-Continental Graphics, Inc.
Jardis Industries, Inc.
Keene Technology, Inc. (KTI)
MEGTEC Systems
North Shore Consultants, Inc.
ONE Corp.
Press and Bindery Systems, Inc.
Printing Press Services, Inc.
RTP Technical Specialists
Pemco, Inc.

STATIC ELIMINATORS
Beta Screen Corp.
Burgess Industries, Inc.
Litho Research, Inc.
Martin Yale, Inc.
NRD LLC
ECRM
Simco Industrial Static Control Products
Herman H. Sticht Co., Inc.
Support Products, Inc.
UV Process Supply, Inc.
Vegra USA
Winton Engineering Co.

STEP & REPEAT SYSTEMS
Taylor Made Digital Systems
New Consolidated International Corp.

STITCHERS
Motterstitch Company, Inc.

STORAGE RETRIEVAL SYSTEMS
Cygnet Storage Solutions, Inc.
Digital Collections
Consolidated Storage Cos.
Ferag Americas
Foster Mfg. Co.
Gannett Media Technologies International (GMTI)
Muller Martini Mailroom Systems, Inc.
HK Systems
Mesa Corp.
Mobile Computing Corporation USA
Muller Martini Corp.
Penco Products
Roconex Corp.
Schawk
Smart Storage, Inc.
Solar Systems
NewsView Solutions
Truproof Ltd.
Verity, Inc.
Jervis B. Webb Co.
WRH Marketing Americas, Inc.

STRAPPING MACHINES
Automated Mailing Systems Corp.
Systems Technology, Inc.
B.H. Bunn Co.
Dynaric, Inc.
EAM-Mosca Corp.
FELINS, Inc.
Gerrard Ovalstrapping
Impact Racks, Inc.
Malow Corp.
Gerrard Ovalstrapping
Samuel Strapping System
Saxmayer Corp.
Signode Corp.
Sterling Packaging Systems
ITW Packaging Brands
Teufelberger GmbH

SUBSCRIPTION FULFILLMENT SOFTWARE
ANewStartGuy.com
Fulco, Inc.
Global Turnkey Systems, Inc.
Syntellect, Inc.

SYSTEM INSTALLATIONS
Blower Application Co., Inc.
CE Engineering
Chemetron Fire Systems
Computer Tree
Dan-Bar, Inc.
Digital Collections
Ewert America Electronics Ltd.
Global Turnkey Systems, Inc.
Versar Inc.
Quipp System, Inc.
Software Business Systems
Software Consulting Services
Standard Electric and Engineering Co.
Total Mailroom Support, Inc. (TMSI)

SYSTEM INTEGRATION SERVICES
ABB, Inc. (Printing Systems)
eGIX, Inc.
The Austin Company
Brainworks Software Development Corp.
CCI Europe, Inc.
CE Engineering
Chemetron Fire Systems
Computer Talk Technology, Inc.
Computer Tree
DeskNet, Inc.
Digital Collections
Digital Technology International
Ewert America Electronics Ltd.
FMC Technologies
Capita Technologies
Global Turnkey Systems, Inc.
Presteligence
Infocom Systems
Logic Associates, Inc.
McCrrory Publishing
ppi Media GmbH
PrePRESS DIRECT
Quipp System, Inc.
Random Access
Software Business Systems
Software Consulting Services
Standard Electric and Engineering Co.
Syntellect, Inc.
Valley Remanufacturing Co.
Unisys Corp.
AdMission Corp.
Aragon System Products
ABB Inc.

TABLES (DOT, ETCH, OPAQUING, REGISTER, RETOUCHING, STRIPPING)
Beta Screen Corp.
Foster Mfg. Co.
Richmond/Graphic Products, Inc.
Roconex Corp.
SCREEN (USA)
Thompson Cabinet Co.

TAPE SPLICING EQUIPMENT
Cariweb Products
North Shore Consultants, Inc.

TELECOMMUNICATIONS
Advanced Graphic Systems (AGS)
ALLTEL Communications Products
Alpha-Omega Color Graphics, Inc.
eGIX, Inc.

Applied Graphics Technologies
Chemetron Fire Systems
Computerease Software, Inc.
DAC Systems
Drake Communications, Inc.
Earmark
Electronic Specialists, Inc.
Electronic Tele-Communications, Inc.
Devin
FANUC Robotics America, Inc.
General DataComm, Inc.
Innovative Systems Design, Inc.
InterVoice-Brite, Inc.
MBG Telecom Software, Inc.
NUS Consulting Group
Support Systems International Corp.
Syntellect, Inc.
TeleDirect International, Inc.
Tel-Management, Inc.
NewsView Solutions
Unicom, Inc.
Ver-A-Fast Corp.
VoCal Telecommunications
VoiceWorld, Inc.
Advanced Telecom Services, Inc.
Siemens Communications Group

TENSION & WEB CONTROLS
Advanced Graphic Systems (AGS)
Arco Engineering, Inc. (Newspaper Div.)
Butler Automatic
Fleming Enterprises
grafikAmerica
Graphic System Services, Inc.
Norman X Guttman, Inc.
Kaim & Associates International Marketing, Inc.
KBA North America, Inc. (Koenig & Bauer AG)
Lankford Engineering, Inc.
Magnetic Power Systems, Inc.
Masthead International, Inc.
Maxcess
Robertson Press Machinery Co., Inc.
RTP Technical Specialists
Bill Rudder & Associates, Inc.
Tidland Corp.
Web Printing Controls
Pemco, Inc.

TESTING INSTRUMENTS
Advanced Graphic Systems (AGS)
Caprock Developments, Inc.
M. Golda Engineering
X-Rite Inc.
Simco Industrial Static Control Products
Technidyne Corp.
Tobias Associates, Inc.

THREE KNIFE TRIMMER
Advance Graphics Equipment of York, Inc.
Applied Industrial Machinery
Prim Hall Enterprises, Inc.
AD-A-NOTE

TOTALIZING SYSTEMS
Baumer Electric Ltd.
Logic Associates, Inc.
Plumtree Co.

TRADE PUBLICATIONS
Alpha-Omega Color Graphics, Inc.
R.C. Anderson Associates, Inc.
Artbeats
Drake Communications, Inc.
Jupiter Images Corp.
Editor & Publisher Magazine
Flexographic Technical Association
Fry Communications
Graphic Arts Blue Book Online
The International School For Pressroom Management
Mouser Institute School of Advertising
MSP Communications
National Newspaper Association Publishers' Auxiliary
PhotoSource International
Sales Development Services
The Seybold Report
Tel-Aire Publications, Inc.
MacDonald Advertising Services
SRDS, a Kantar Media Company

TRAINING: DESIGN & LAYOUT
Alpha-Omega Color Graphics, Inc.
ANewStartGuy.com
MediaSpan Group Inc.
Meena Advertising Copy & Layout
Morcor Solutions, Inc.
Tribune Media Services
Wolk Advertising, Inc. (Retail Carpet Ad Service)

TRAINING: KEYBOARD OPERATION
Applied Learning Corp.
CCI Europe, Inc.
CNI Corp.
Computer Tree
The International School For Pressroom Management
Learning Tree International
Morcor Solutions, Inc.
PrePRESS DIRECT
Scarborough Research
Silverman Newspaper Management Consultants
Trauner Consulting Services, Inc.

TRAINING: POST PRESS
Burt Technologies, Inc.
A.B. Dick Co.
Flexographic Technical Association
Muller Martini Mailroom Systems, Inc.
Omicron Media
Quipp System, Inc.
Total Mailroom Support, Inc. (TMSI)

TRAINING: PRE PRESS
Alpha-Omega Color Graphics, Inc.
A.B. Dick Co.
Flexographic Technical Association
Foley, Torregiani & Associates, Inc.
Morcor Solutions, Inc.
Omicron Media
ProImage America, Inc.
Reeves Brothers, Inc.
Dennis Storch Co.

TRAINING: PRESS OPERATION & MAINTENANCE
'Ataboy, Inc.
B & L Machine & Design
Manugraph DGM, Inc.
DM Graphics System
Ewert America Electronics Ltd.
Flexographic Technical Association
Masthead International, Inc.
Omicron Media
Reeves Brothers, Inc.
RTP Technical Specialists
Silverman Newspaper Management Consultants
WIFAG Press Co.

TRAINING: SALES & MARKETING
ASTech InterMedia
Ed Baron & Associates, Inc.
Berting Communications
Creative Brilliance Advertising, Marketing & Public Relation
Kamen & Co. Group Services
Marketing Research Associates, Inc.
Media Marketing, Inc.
Sales Training Consultants, Inc.

TUBES, RACKS (INCLUDES RACKS: MOTOR ROUTE TUBES)
Continental Products
Fortec, Inc.
GeoRack, Inc.
Hamilton Circulation Supplies Co.
Impact Racks, Inc.
Kamen & Co. Group Services
K-Jack Engineering Co., Inc.
Lyon Enterprises
National Newsvend
RAK Systems, Inc.
Sonoco Products Co.

TYPE, FONTS
Agfa Monotype Corporation
Bishamon Industries Corp.
Design Science, Inc.
Ernest Schaefer, Inc.
Sterling Type Foundry

TYPESETTERS: LASER
Autologic Information International
Berkshire/Westwood Graphics Group, Inc.
CNI Corp.
Graphic Publishing Systems, Inc.
PrePRESS DIRECT
alfa CTP Systems LLC
Dennis Storch Co.
Xitron

TYPESETTING PROGRAMS
Conley Publishing Systems
Krohm International Ltd.
System Facilities, Inc.

VACUUM FRAMES
Amergraph Corporation
Burgess Industries, Inc.
Douthitt Corp.
Richmond/Graphic Products, Inc.
Technology Integrators

VISUAL DISPLAY TERMINALS
Fife Corporation
Harris Corp.
Maxcess

WASTEWATER TREATMENT
Beckart Environmental, Inc.
Hart Industries
Hart Industries/Metafix Compliance Systems
Maratek Environmental Technologies, Inc.
MGI International, Inc.
Smith Pressroom Products, Inc.
R.B. Intermark, Inc.
Semler Industries, Inc. (Pressroom Fluids Equipment Div.)

WATER MANAGEMENT SYSTEMS
Alar Engineering Corp.
Baldwin Americas Corp.
MGI International, Inc.
Smith Pressroom Products, Inc.
R.B. Intermark, Inc.
Technotrans America, Inc.

WEB BREAK DETECTOR
Baumer Electric Ltd.
Fife Corporation
M. Golda Engineering
Kaim & Associates International Marketing, Inc.
Maxcess
Miracle Industries, Inc.
QuadTech
Quad Tech
Web Printing Controls

WEB CLEANERS
BST Pro Mark
D & R Engineering
Kaim & Associates International Marketing, Inc.
Simco Industrial Static Control Products

WEB GUIDES
BST Pro Mark
Fife Corporation
M. Golda Engineering
Martin Automatic, Inc.
Maxcess
QuadTech
Quad Tech
Web Printing Controls
Pemco, Inc.

WEB OFFSET REMOISTURIZERS
D & R Engineering
grafikAmerica
Smith Pressroom Products, Inc.
Technotrans America, Inc.

WEB PRESS - SPECIAL EQUIPMENT
Advanced Control Technologies, Inc.
Advance Graphics Equipment of York, Inc.
ALTA- Al Taber - PHA
BLK Ltd.
Applied Industrial Machinery
D & R Engineering
DM Graphics System
Fife Corporation
Flynn Burner Corp.
Graphic System Services, Inc.
GSP, Inc.
H & M Paster Sales & Service, Inc.
IGS Knives, Inc.
Koenig & Bauer Aktiengesellschaft (KBA)
Maxcess
Miracle Industries, Inc.
Newman International, LLC
Perretta Graphics Corp.
Robertson Press Machinery Co., Inc.
NELA
Tidland Corp.

INTERACTIVE PRODUCTS AND SERVICES COMPANIES SERVING THE NEWSPAPER INDUSTRY

A

ABC INTERACTIVE
900 N. Meacham Rd., Schaumburg, IL, 60173, USA (847) 605-0909; fax (847) 605-0483; web site www.accessabc.com
Product or Service: Web Site Auditor
Pres./MD–Michael Lavery
Vice Pres., Auditing Servs.–Scott Hanson

ACT TELECONFERENCING, INC.
1526 Cole Blvd., Ste. 300, Golden, CO, 80401, USA (303) 235-9000; web site www.acttel.com
Product or Service: Multimedia/Interactive Products
Pres.–Peter Salas

APCO WORLDWIDE
700 12th St. NW, Ste. 800, Washington, DC, 20005-3545, USA (202) 778-1000; fax (202) 466-6002; e-mail information@apcoworldwide.com; web site www.apcoworldwide.com
Product or Service: Advertising/Marketing Agency, Consultants

ARC RESEARCH
14 Commerce Dr., Cranford, NJ, 07016, USA (908) 276-6300; fax (908) 276-1301; web site www.arcresearch.com
Product or Service: Advertising/Marketing Agency, Consultants
Pres.–Sallie Bernard
Vice Pres.–Douglas Belt

AT&T, INC.
175 E. Houston St., San Antonio, TX, 78205-2233, USA (210) 821-4105; fax (210) 351-2071; web site www.att.com

Product or Service: Telecommunications/Service Bureaus
Chrmn./CEO–Randall L. Stephenson
Pres./CEO, AT&T Directory Opns.–Dennis M. Payne
Sr. Exec. Vice Pres./CMO–Lea Ann Champion
SVP/Global Mktg. Officer–Cathy Coughlin

ACCUWEATHER, INC.
385 Science Park Rd., State College, PA, 16803, USA (814) 235-8600; fax (814) 235-8609; e-mail sales@accuweather.com; info@accuwx.com; web site www.accuweather.com
Product or Service: Online Service Provider and Internet Hosts
President and Founder–Dr. Joel N. Myers
Exec. Vice Pres.–Barry Lee Myers
Sr. Vice Pres.–Elliot Abrams
Sr. Vice Pres.–Joseph P. Sobel
Sr. Vice Pres.–Evan A. Myers
Sr. Vice Pres.–Michael A. Steinberg
Vice Pres., New Media–James Candor
Mktg. Dir.–R. Lee Rainey
Sr. Sales Mgr.–Brian Kisslak
Mktg. Asst.–Felisha Dib
Vice President/Mktg.–Lee Rainey
Vice Pres. Sales–Brian Kisslack
Sr. Vice Pres.–Michael Steinberg
Dir., New Media Sales–Jim Candor

ACES RESEARCH, INC.
40087 Mission Blvd., Ste. 175, Fremont, CA, 94538, USA (510) 364-5870; fax (510) 683-8875; e-mail info@acesxprt.com; web site www.acesxprt.com
Product or Service: CD-ROM Designer/Manufacturer
Pres.–Allan Kwang

ACTIVE DATA EXCHANGE
190 Broadhead Rd., Ste. 300, Lehigh Valley Industrial Pk. IV, Bethlehem, PA, 18017-8617, USA (610) 997-8100; fax (610) 866-7899; e-mail info@activedatax.com; web site www.activedatax.com
Product or Service: Publisher/Media
Pres./CEO–Susan C. Yee
COO–Kendra Hollinger

ADAPTIVE OPTICS ASSOCIATES, INC., A UNITED TECHNOLOGIES CO.
10 Wilson Rd., Cambridge, MA, 02138, USA (617) 806-1400; fax (617) 806-1899; e-mail info@aoainc.com; web site www.northrop-grumman.com
Product or Service: Hardware/Software Supplier
Pres.–Jeff Yourz

ADOBE SYSTEMS, INC.
345 Park Ave., San Jose, CA, 95110-2074, USA (408) 536-6000; fax (408) 537-6000; web site www.adobe.com
Product or Service: Hardware/Software Supplier
Sr. Vice Pres., Global Mktg.–Ann Lewnes
Dir., Worldwide Adv.–Jennifer Reynolds

ADSTAR, INC.
13428 Maxella Ave., Ste. 261, Marina del Rey, CA, 90929, USA (310) 577-8255; fax (888) 872-7981; e-mail info@adstar.com; web site www.adstar.com
Product or Service: Hardware/Software Supplier
Pres./CEO–Leslie Bernhard
Exec. Vice Pres./CTO–Eli Rousso
Sr. Vice Pres./COO–Jeffrey Baudo

ADSTREAM AMERICA
845 3rd Ave., New York, NY, 10022, USA (845) 496-8283; fax (845) 496-8037; e-mail info@adstream.com; web site www.adstream.com
Product or Service: Hardware/Software Supplier
Pres.–Michael Palmer
Business Mgr.–Kirk Brauch

ADTRAN
901 Explorer Blvd., Huntsville, AL, 35806-2807, USA (256) 963-8000; fax (256) 963-8030; e-mail info@adtran.com; web site www.adtran.com
Product or Service: Hardware/Software Supplier
PR Dir.–Tammie Dodson

ADVANCE INTERNET, INC.
30 Journal Sq., Ste. 400, Jersey City, NJ, 07306-4101, USA (201) 459-2888; fax (201) 653-1189; web site www.advance.net
Product or Service: Publisher/Media
Pres.–Peter Weinberger
Admin–Johanna Dell'Aquila

ADVANCED COMMUNICATION DESIGN, INC.
7901 12th Ave. S., Minneapolis, MN, 55425-1017, USA (952) 854-4000; fax (952) 854-5774; e-mail sales@acdstar.com; web site www.acdstar.com
Product or Service: Multimedia/Interactive Products
Pres./CEO–Marco Scibora
Customer Serv.–Geri Charleston

ADVANCED PUBLISHING TECHNOLOGY
123 S. Victory Blvd., Burbank, CA, 91502, USA (818) 557-3035; fax (818) 557-1281; e-mail info@advpubtech.com; web site www.advpubtech.com
Product or Service: Hardware/Software Supplier
Pres.–David Kraai
Vice Pres.–Ken Barber
Vice Pres., Sales-Central US–Mike Seller

ADVANCED PUBLISHING TECHNOLOGY
123 S Victory Blvd, Burbank, CA, 91502, USA (818) 557-3035; fax (818) 557-1281; e-mail aptsales@advpubtech.com; web site www.advpubtech.com
Product or Service: Hardware/Software Supplier
Pres.–David Kraai
Vice Pres., Sales–Mike Seller
Vice Pres., Opns.–Ken Barber
Sr Product Manager–Wolfi Frank
Vice Pres., Devel.–David Bridges
Sls. Mgr.–Joanne Froelich

ADVANCED TELECOM SERVICES, INC. (CANADA)
996 Old Eagle School Rd., Wayne, PA, 19087, USA (610) 688-6000; fax (610) 964-9117; e-mail sales@advancedtele.com; web site ^www.advancedtele.com
Product or Service: Telecommunications/Service Bureaus
Director of Marketing–Bob Bentz

ADVANCED TELECOM SERVICES, INC. (U.K.)
213 St. John St., London, ENG, 07054, United Kingdom 7608 7787; fax 7608 7788; e-mail uksales@advancedtele.co.uk; web site www.advancedtele.com
Product or Service: Telecommunications/Service Bureaus
Mng. Dir./Gen. Mgr.–Ian Scott
Dir., Sales–Cindy Aspland

ADVANCED TELECOM SERVICES, INC.
996 Old Eagle School Rd., Ste. 1105, Wayne, PA, 19087-1806, USA (610) 688-6000; fax (610) 964-9117; e-mail sales@advancedtele.com; web site www.advancedtele.com
Product or Service: Telecommunications/Service Bureaus
Regional Sales Manager–Scott Bronenberg

ADVERTISING AGE
711 3rd Ave., New York, NY, 10017-4036, USA (212) 210-0100; fax (212) 210-0200; e-mail editor@adage.com; web site www.adage.com
Product or Service: Publisher/Media
Pub.–Allison Price Arden

AGENCY.COM
488 Madison Ave., 4th Fl., New York, NY, 10022, USA (212) 358-2600; fax (212) 358-2604; e-mail info@agency.com; web site www.agency.com
Product or Service: Consultants

AGENCY.COM
7850 N. Belt Line Rd., 4th Fl., Irving, TX, 75063-6092, USA (972) 831-2100; fax (972) 831-2140; e-mail info.dallas@agency.com; web site www.agency.com
Product or Service: Advertising/Marketing Agency

AGENCY.COM
55 Union St., 3rd Fl., San Francisco, CA, 94111, USA (415) 817-3800; fax (415) 817-3801; e-mail info@agency.com; web site www.agency.com
Product or Service: Consultants

AGILITY
15900 Morales Rd., Houston, TX, 77032, USA (281) 227-0077; fax (281) 227-3641; e-mail info@wtsinc.com; web site www.wtsinc.com
Product or Service: Telecommunications/Service Bureaus
Sales–Pam Holdrup

AI MULTIMEDIA
2340 Stanley Hills Dr., Hollywood, CA, 90046, USA (323) 656-2185; fax (323) 656-6194; e-mail aimulti@aimultimedia.com; web site www.aimultimedia.com
Product or Service: Online Service Provider and Internet Hosts
Pres.–Mark Hanau
Vice Pres.–Tom Wood
Technical Dir.–John McNair

AIM GROUP / CLASSIFIED INTELLIGENCE
402 Spring Valley Rd., Altamonte Springs, FL, 32714-5845, USA (407) 788-2780; fax 866-611-6551; e-mail info@aimgroup.com; web site www.aimgroup.com
Product or Service: Consultants, Publisher/Media
Founding principal–Peter M. Zollman
Editorial director–Jim Townsend
Europe Director–Katja Riefler
Asia-Pacific Director–Emma Sorenson
MD–Bruce Annan

THE AKER PARTNERS, INC.
2801 M St., NW, Washington, DC, 20007, USA (202) 223-4889; fax (202) 789-1818; e-mail aker@akerpartners.com; web site www.akerpartners.com
Product or Service: Advertising/Marketing Agency
Mng. Partner–G. Colburn Aker

AMASIS
1538 W. Cullerton St., Chicago, IL, 60608, USA (312) 850-9459; fax (312) 850-9459; e-mail amasis@amasis.com; web site www.amasis.com
Product or Service: Graphic/Design Firm
Head Designer–Tamara Manning

AMERICA ONLINE DIGITAL CITY, INC.
22000 AOL Way, Dulles, VA, 20166, USA (877) 265-5622; web site www.aol.com
Product or Service: Publisher/Media
Pres./CEO–Ray Oglethrepe
Dir., Bus. Devel.–Bill McIntosh

AMERIKIDS USA
10 Leonard St., Ste. 3SW, New York, NY, 10013-2929, USA (212) 941-8461; e-mail developer@amerikids.com; web site www.amerikids.com
Product or Service: CD-ROM Designer/Manufacturer
CEO–Lynn Rogoff
Media Producer–Mark Tabashnick

AMPLIFIED.COM, INC.
1465 Northside Dr. NW, Ste. 110, Atlanta, GA, 30318, USA (404) 351-0600; fax (404) 351-0645; e-mail parker@amplified.com
Product or Service: Publisher/Media
Pres.–Wayne Parker

ANIMATED SOFTWARE CO.
PO Box 1936, Carlsbad, CA, 92018-1936, USA (760) 720-7261; e-mail rhoffman@animatedsoftware.com; web site www.animatedsoftware.com
Product or Service: Multimedia/Interactive Products
Owner/Chief Programmer–Ace Hoffman

ANODE, INC.
N/A N/A
Product or Service: Multimedia/Interactive Products

THE ANSWER TEAM NETWORKS
PO Box 1284, Menlo Park, CA, 94026-1284, USA (650) 204-4068; e-mail BBagent@getansr.com
Product or Service: Advertising/Marketing Agency
Exec. Coord.–Emmett T. Pickett

ANSWERS MEDIA INC.
400 W. Erie St., Chicago, IL, 60654, USA (312) 421-0113; fax (312) 421-1457; e-mail info@answersmediainc.com; web site www.answersmediainc.com
Product or Service: Multimedia/Interactive Products
Pres.–Jeff Bohnson

APPLE, INC.
1 Infinite Loop, Cupertino, CA, 95014, USA (408) 996-1010; fax (408) 996-0275; web site www.apple.com; www.musicfan.com
Product or Service: Hardware/Software Supplier
CEO/Dir.–Steven P. Jobs
Sr. Vice Pres., Worldwide Pdct. Mktg.–Philip W. Schiller

APDI-APPLICATION PROGRAMMING & DEVELOPMENT, INC.
1282 Smallwood Dr. W, Ste. 276, Waldorf, MD, 00603-4732, USA (301) 893-9115; fax (301) 645-5035; web site www.apdi.net
Product or Service: Online Service Provider and Internet Hosts
Pres./CEO–Mark Burnett

APPLIED ART & TECHNOLOGY
2430 106th St., Des Moines, IA, 50322-3763, USA (515) 331-7400; fax (515) 331-7401; e-mail mail@appliedart.com; info@appliedart.com; web site www.appliedart.com
Product or Service: Multimedia/Interactive Products
Media Mgr.–Jeanie Jorgensen

APTAS
1221 Auraria Pkwy., Denver, CO, 80204-1836, USA (303) 572-1122; fax (303) 572-1123; e-mail info@aptas.com; web site www.localmatters.com
Product or Service: Hardware/Software Supplier, Multimedia/Interactive Products, Publisher/Media
CEO–Perry Evans

THE ARBITRON CO.
142 W. 57th St., New York, NY, 10019-3300, USA (212) 887-1300; fax (212) 887-1401; web site www.arbitron.com
Product or Service: Telecommunications/Service Bureaus
Pres.–Steve Morris
Pres., Opns./Technology/Research/Devel.–Owen Charlebois
Gen. Mgr./Domestic Radio–Brad Kelly
Vice Pres., Sales, Advertiser/Agency Servs.–Carol Edwards
Pres., Sales/Mktg.–Pierre Bouvard

ARCH COMMUNICATIONS, INC.
1327 Hampton Ave., Saint Louis, MO, 63139, USA (314) 645-8000; fax (314) 781-7148; e-mail archcom37@aol.com; web site www.archcom.net
Product or Service: Telecommunications/Service Bureaus
Pres.–David Brandstetter

ARIZONA REPUBLIC DIGITAL MEDIA
200 E. Van Buren St., Phoenix, AZ, 85004,

USA (602) 444-8000; fax (602) 444-8044; web site www.azcentral.com
Product or Service: Publisher/Media
Exec. Vice Pres., Digital Media–Mike Coleman

ARLEN COMMUNICATIONS LLC
7315 Wisconsin Ave., Ste. 805, Bethesda, MD, 20814, USA (301) 656-7940; e-mail info@arlencom.com; web site www.arlencom.com
Product or Service: Consultants
Pres.–Gary Arlen

ASBURY PARK PRESS
3601 Hwy. 66, Neptune, NJ, 07754, USA (732) 922-6000; fax (732) 922-0783; e-mail kstetter@app.com; web site www.app.com
Product or Service: Multimedia/Interactive Products
Online Adv.–Kevin Stetter

ASCENT ENTERTAINMENT GROUP, INC.
4610 S. Ulster St., Sixth Fl., Denver, CO, 80237-4324, USA (720) 873-3200; web site www.lodgenet.com
Product or Service: Multimedia/Interactive Products
CEO–Scott C. Petersen

ASPECT COMMUNICATIONS
140 Baytech Dr., San Jose, CA, 95134-2302, USA (978) 250-7900; fax (408) 325-2260; web site www.aspect.com
Product or Service: Hardware/Software Supplier
Pres./CEO/Dir.–James D. Foy
Exec. Vice Pres., Finance/CFO–Michael J. Provenzano
Sr. Vice Pres., Mktg.–Laurie Cairns

ASSIGNMENT DESK
820 N. Orleans, Ste. 205, Chicago, IL, 60610, USA (312) 464-8600; fax (312) 464-8605; e-mail cya@assignmentdesk.com; web site www.assignmentdesk.com
Product or Service: Multimedia/Interactive Products, Telecommunications/Service Bureaus
Bus. Mgr.–Evelyn Beldam

ASSOCIATED PRESS INFORMATION SERVICES
450 W. 33rd St., New York, NY, 10001, USA (212) 621-1585; fax (212) 621-7520; e-mail apif@ap.org; web site www.ap.org
Product or Service: Publisher/Media
Dir. Sales–Ted Mendelsohn

ASTECH INTERMEDIA
999 18th St., Ste. 2240, Denver, CO, 80202-2442, USA (303) 296-9966; fax (303) 296-9969; e-mail ter@astech-intermedia.com; web site www.smartfocus.com
Product or Service: Online Service Provider and Internet Hosts
Pres./CEO–Tom Ratkovich
Dir., Client Servs.–Tia Talbert

ATEX NORTH AMERICA
5 Burlington Woods, Ste. 100, Burlington, MA, 01803, USA (781) 685-3240; fax (781) 685-3276; e-mail info@atex.com; web site www.atex.com
Product or Service: Hardware/Software Supplier
CEO–John Hawkins
CEO, North America–Scott Roessler
CEO, NEMEA–David Hall
CEO, Asia Pacific–Ross Wood
COO–Alan Reardon
Sr. Vice Pres./Chief Integration Officer–Peter Marsh
Sr. Vice Pres., Sales Americas–Malcolm McGrory

ATOMIC IMAGING, INC.
1501 N. Magnolia Ave., Chicago, IL, 60622, USA (312) 649-1800; fax (312) 642-7441; e-mail info@atomicimaging.com; web site www.atomicimaging.com
Product or Service: Graphic/Design Firm
Pres.–Ari Golan
Commun. Consultant–Nick Brown
Producer–Aigar Dombrouskis
Interactive Design–Jim Abreu

AUDIO SERVICE AMERICA PRODUCTIONS
28 Ten Eyck Ave., Albany, NY, 12209, USA (800) 723-4272; fax (760) 406-5800; e-mail holdit@4asap.com; web site www.4asap.com
Product or Service: Advertising/Marketing Agency, CD-ROM Designer/Manufacturer, Consultants, Graphic/Design Firm, Hardware/Software Supplier, Multimedia/Interactive Products, Online Service Provider and Internet Hosts, POP/Kiosk Designer, Telecommunications/Service Bureaus, Web Site Auditor
Pres.–Kevin Childs
Mktg. Dir.–T. Raymond Gruno

AUTHORLINK
755 Laguna, Irving, TX, 75039-3218, USA (972) 402-0101; fax (866) 381-1587; e-mail dbooth@authorlink.com; web site www.authorlink.com
Product or Service: Multimedia/Interactive Products
Ed. in Chief–Doris Booth

AUTOMATED GRAPHIC SYSTEMS
4590 Graphics Dr., White Plains, MD, 20695, USA (800) 678-8760; fax (301) 843-6339; e-mail info@ags.com; web site www.ags.com
Product or Service: CD-ROM Designer/Manufacturer
Pres.–Dustin Graupman
Controller–Teresa Willingham
Dir., New Technology–Mark Czajka

AUTOMEDIA, INC.
345 Ocean Dr., Ste. 614, Miami Beach, FL, 33139, USA (305) 531-9000
Product or Service: Consultants
Pres.–Stephanie Sladon

AUTONOMY, INC.
1 Market Plz. 19th Fl., San Francisco, CA, 94105, USA (415) 243-9955; fax (415) 243-9984; e-mail autonomy@autonomy.com; web site www.autonomy.com
Product or Service: Multimedia/Interactive Products
CEO–Michael Lynch
CTO–Richard Gaunt

B

BKJ PRODUCTIONS
22 Pleasant St., Malden, MA, 02148, USA (781) 393-9600; e-mail info@bkjproductions.com; web site www.bkjproductions.com
Product or Service: Multimedia/Interactive Products
Pres.–Brian K. Johnson

BKR STUDIO, INC.
110 E. Madison St., South Bend, IN, 46601-1224, USA (574) 245-9576; e-mail info@bkrstudio.com; web site www.bkrstudio.com
Product or Service: Multimedia/Interactive Products
Pres.–Brian Rideout
Office Mgr.–Tina Merrill

B-LINKED, INC.
PO Box 3721, Chapel Hill, NC, 27515, USA (800) 254-6533; e-mail tmelet@b-linked.com; web site www.adtransit.com
Product or Service: Online Service Provider and Internet Hosts
Pres.–Todd Melet

BMC GROUP, INC.
875 3rd Ave., 5th Fl., New York, NY, 10022, USA (212) 310-5900; fax (212) 644-4552; web site www.bmcgroup.com
Product or Service: Hardware/Software Supplier
Sales Contact–Matt Morris

BACKE DIFITAL BRAND MARKETING
100 Matsonford Rd Building 3 Suite 101, Radnor, PA, 19087, USA (610) 947-6900; fax (610) 896-9242; e-mail info@backemarketing.com; web site www.backemarketing.com
Product or Service: Advertising/Marketing Agency
Pres./CEO–John E. Backe
Sr. Vice Pres.–Malcolm Brown

BACKWEB
2077 Gateway Pl., Ste. 500, San Jose, CA, 95110, USA (408) 933-1700; fax (408) 933-1800; e-mail pr@backweb.com; web site www.backweb.com
Product or Service: Hardware/Software Supplier
Vice Pres., Mktg./Pdct. Mgmt.–Yishay Yovel

BAILEY BROADCASTING SERVICES
655 N. Central Ave., 17th. Fl., Glendale, CA, 91203, USA (818) 649-7865; fax (818) 647-7501; e-mail BBSRADIO@LEEBAILEY.COM; web site www.leebailey.com
Product or Service: Publisher/Media
Pres.–Lee Bailey
Ed., RadioScope–Kim Cohn
Asst. Ed., RadioScope–Janice Little John

BEATLEY GRAVITT COMMUNICATIONS
9A W Grace St., Richmond, VA, 23226, USA (888) 355-9151; fax (804) 359-5261; web site www.beatleygravitt.com
Product or Service: Graphic/Design Firm
Pres./Dir., Mktg.–Ed Lacy

BENDER/HELPER IMPACT
11500 W. Olympic Blvd., Ste. 655, Los Angeles, CA, 90064, USA (310) 473-4147; fax (310) 478-4727; e-mail info@bhimpact.com; web site www.bhimpact.com
Product or Service: Advertising/Marketing Agency
Pres.–Lee Helper
Partner–Dean Bender
Sr. Vice Pres.–Shawna Lynch

BERSEARCH INFORMATION SERVICES
PO Box 2429, Breckenridge, CO, 80424-2429, USA (970) 547-1071; fax (970) 547-1072; e-mail sales@bersearch.com; web site www.bersearch.com
Product or Service: Graphic/Design Firm
Pres.–Tom Bernard

BIAKELSEY
600 Executive Dr., Princeton, NJ, 08540-1528, USA (609) 921-7200; fax (609) 921-2112; e-mail tkg@kelseygroup.com; web site www.kelseygroup.com
Product or Service: Publisher/Media
CEO–Neal Polachek

BLACK STAR PUBLISHING CO., INC.
116 E. 27th St., New York, NY, 10016, USA (212) 679-3288; fax (212) 447-9732; e-mail sales@blackstar.com; research@blackstar.com; ben@blackstar.com; web site www.blackstar.com
Product or Service: Advertising/Marketing Agency
Pres.–Ben Chapnick
Vice Pres.–John P. Chapnick

BLASS COMMUNICATIONS
17 Drowne Rd., Old Chatham, NY, 12136-3006, USA (518) 766-2222; fax (518) 766-2445; e-mail info@blasscommunications.com; web site www.blasscommunications.com
Product or Service: Advertising/Marketing Agency

BLUECIELO ECM SOLUTIONS
2400 Lake Park Dr., Ste. 450, Atlanta, GA, 30080-8982, USA (404) 634-3302; fax (404) 633-4604; e-mail info@bluecieloecm.com; web site www.bluecieloecm.com
Product or Service: Hardware/Software Supplier
Contact–Karen Rhymer

BORGHETTI CONSULTING GROUP
PO Box 20790, Charleston, SC, 29413, USA (801) 599-3183; fax (888) 771-7180; e-mail info@beicommunications.com
Product or Service: Consultants
Pres.–Frank R. Borghetti
Bus. Developer–Charles Stier
Administrative Assistant–Mendy Goodwin

BRANFMAN & ASSOCIATES
708 Civic Ctr. Dri., Oceanside, CA, 92054, USA (858) 481-5800; fax (760) 687-7421; e-mail info@branfman.com; web site www.branfman.com
Product or Service: Consultants
Owner–David Branfman
Assoc.–Mark Reichenthal

AL BREDENBERG CREATIVE SERVICES
71 Franklin St., Danbury, CT, 06810, USA (203) 791-8204; e-mail ab@copywriter.com; web site www.copywriter.com
Product or Service: Advertising/Marketing Agency
Contact–Al Bredenberg

BREZE, INC.
3625 Quakerbridge Rd., Hamilton, NJ, 08619, USA (609) 587-4200; fax (609) 936-9077; e-mail mail@breze.com; web site www.breze.com
Product or Service: Multimedia/Interactive Products
Vice Pres.–Jerry Konecny

BROADCAST PRODUCTION GROUP (BPG)
1901 S. Bascom Ave., 9th Fl., Campbell, CA, 95008-2215, USA (408) 559-6300; fax (408) 559-6382; e-mail info@bpgnet.com
Product or Service: Multimedia/Interactive Products
Pres./CEO–Ephraim Lindenbaum
Vice Pres., Bus. Devel.–Daniel Fortune
Mktg./Pub. Rel.–Stacy Evensen
Vice Pres., Interactive Multimedia–Edward Olsen

BROADVISION
75 3rd Ave., Waltham, MA, 02451, USA (781) 290-0710; fax (781) 290 5379; e-mail jean.mccorthy@broadvision.com; web site www.broadvision.com
Product or Service: Hardware/Software Supplier
Dir.–Jean Mc Corthy

BROADXENT, INC.
188 Topaz St., Milpitas, CA, 95035, USA (408) 719-5100; fax (408) 262-1390; e-mail info@broadxent.com; web site www.broadxent.com
Product or Service: Hardware/Software Supplier
Pres.–Joseph Liow
CFO–Tang Kee Fei
CTO–Tan Hock Guan
Vice Pres., Sales/Mktg.–Bryan Chan
Vice Pres., Engineering–Ching-Kay Chow

BROADXENT PTE. LTD.
31 International Business Park, Creative Resource, Singapore, 609921, Singapore 6890-5200; fax 6890-5269; web site www.broadxent.com
Pres.–Joseph Liow

BUSINESS WIRE - NEW YORK, NY
40 E. 52nd St., 14th Fl., New York, NY, 10022, USA (800) 221-2462, (212) 752-9600; fax (212) 752-9698; web site www.businesswire.com
Product or Service: Online Service Provider and Internet Hosts
Vice Pres., New York Reg.–Phyllis Dantuono
Pres./CEO–Cathy Baron Tamraz

C

CD TECHNOLOGY
1112 Walsh Ave., Santa Clara, CA, 95050-2646, USA (408) 982-0990; fax (408) 982-

0991; web site www.cdtechnology.com
Product or Service: CD-ROM Designer/Manufacturer
Pres.–William W. Liu

C-T INNOVATIONS
11001 Bluegrass Pkwy., Ste. 300, Louisville, KY, 40299-2368, USA (502) 814-5100; fax (502) 814-5110; web site www.ct-innovations.com
Product or Service: Telecommunications/Service Bureaus
Pres.–Robert Flynn

CABLEFAX DAILY LLC
4 Choke Cherry Rd., 2nd Fl., Rockville, MD, 20850, USA (301) 354-2000; fax (301) 738-8453; e-mail sarenstein@accessintel.com; web site www.cablefax.com
Product or Service: Online Service Provider and Internet Hosts
Editorial Dir.–Seth Arenstein

CABLEVISION SYSTEMS CORPORATION
1111 Stewart Avenue, Bethpage, NY, 11714, USA (516) 803-2300; web site www.cablevision.com
Product or Service: Telecommunications/Service Bureaus
Chairman–Charles F. Dolan
President and CEO–James L. Dolan
Vice Chairman–Hank Ratner
COO–Tom Rutledge
President, Cable & Communications–John Bickham
Executive Vice President & General Counsel–David Ellen
Executive Vice President & CFO–Gregg Seibert
President, Local Media–Tad Smith
Sr. Advisor, Engineering/Technology–Wilt Hildenbrand

CAPTURED IMAGES, INC.
919 Lawrence Dr., Newbury Park, CA, 91320, USA (805) 499-7333; fax (805) 499-7332; e-mail info@capturedimages.com; web site www.capturedimages.com
Product or Service: Telecommunications/Service Bureaus
Pres./Dir., Mktg.–John Bird

CASCADE TECHNOLOGIES, INC.
1075 Eastern Ave., Somerset, NJ, 08873-2220, USA (732) 560-9908; fax (908) 626-1209; e-mail info@cascadetechnologies.com; web site www.cascadetechnologies.com
Product or Service: Telecommunications/Service Bureaus
Pres.–Vigdis Austad
Vice Pres.-Technology–Frank Joicy
Sales–Barbara Bishop
Mktg. Assoc.–Janice Harrison

CATALYST INTERNATIONAL, INC.
8989 N. Deerwood Dr., Milwaukee, WI, 53223, USA (414) 362-6800; fax (414) 362-6794; e-mail info@ctcsoftware.com; web site www.ctcsoftware.com
Product or Service: Hardware/Software Supplier
Contact–Mark Shupac

CBS MAXPREPS, INC.
4080 Plz. Goldorado Cir., Ste. A, Cameron Park, CA, 95682, USA (800) 329-7324; fax (530) 672-8559; e-mail sales@maxpreps.com; web site www.maxpreps.com
Product or Service: Multimedia/Interactive Products, Online Service Provider and Internet Hosts
Pres.–Andy Beal
Vice Pres., Sales–Kelly Groth
Vice Pres., Opns.–Kyle Smith

CELEBRO
151 W. Fourth St., Ste. 201, Cincinnati, OH, 45202, USA (513) 665-3777; fax (513) 241-7219; e-mail info@celebro.com; web site www.gmti.com
Product or Service: Hardware/Software Supplier
Pres./CEO–Steve Fuschetti
Vice Pres., Celebro Opns.–Tom Foster
Dir., Implementation Servs.–Michael Hibert

CENTURYTEL INTERACTIVE
8750 N. Central Expwy., Ste. 720, Dallas, TX, 75231, USA (214) 360-6280; fax (972) 996-0868; e-mail jd@centuryinteractive.com; web site www.centuryinteractive.com
Product or Service: Telecommunications/Service Bureaus
COO–Jack Doege

CHANNELNET
100 Shoreline Hwy., Bldg. B, Ste. 300, Mill Valley, CA, 94941-3653, USA (415) 332-4704; fax (415) 332-1635; e-mail info@channelnet.com; web site www.softad.com; www.channelnet.com
Product or Service: Consultants, Hardware/Software Supplier
Founder/CEO–Paula George Tompkins
CFO–Kevin Kelly
Sr. Dir., Professional Servs.–Mike Behr

CHASE BOBKO, INC.
750 N. 34th St., Seattle, WA, 98103, USA (206) 547-4310; fax (206) 548-0749; e-mail information@chasebobko.com
Product or Service: Multimedia/Interactive Products
Pres.–Bob Boiko
CEO–Jayson Antonoff
Vice Pres.–Patricia Chase

CHRIS BAKER & ASSOCIATES LTD.
14465 29A Ave., South Surrey, BC, V4P 1P7, Canada (604) 536-1132
Product or Service: Consultants
Pres.–Chris Baker

CIBER, INC.
6363 S. Fiddler's Green Circle, Greenwood Village, CO, 80111, USA (303) 220-0100; fax (303) 220-7100; web site www.ciber.com
Product or Service: Consultants
COO–Peter Cheesbrough

CINEMAN SYNDICATE
31 Purchase St., Ste. 203, Rye, NY, 10580-3013, USA (914) 582-8906; e-mail cinemansyndicate@verizon.net; web site www.minireviews.com
Product or Service: Publisher/Media
Ed.–John P. McCarthy

CITYSEARCH.COM
8833 W. Sunset Blvd., West Hollywood, CA, 90069, USA (310) 360-4500; e-mail contactus@citysearch.com; web site www.citysearch.com
Product or Service: Multimedia/Interactive Products
CEO–Jay Herratti

CLASSIFIED VENTURES, INC.
175 W. Jackson Blvd., Ste. 800, Chicago, IL, 60604, USA (312) 601-5000; fax (312) 601-5755; e-mail dburke@classifiedventures.com; web site www.classifiedventures.com
Product or Service: Multimedia/Interactive Products
Sr. Vice Pres., Admin./Cor. Devel.–Richard Burke

COBBEY & ASSOCIATES FULL SERVICE MARKETING RESEARCH
PO Box 12, Carson City, NV, 89440, USA (877) 433-3242; fax (775) 847-0327; e-mail cobbey@cobbey.com; web site www.cobbey.com
Product or Service: Consultants

COGENT COMMUNICATIONS, INC.
1015 31st St. NW, Washington, DC, 20007-4406, USA (202) 295-4200; fax (202) 338-8798; e-mail info@cogentco.com; web site www.cogentco.com
Product or Service: Online Service Provider and Internet Hosts
Founder/CEO–Dave Schaeffer
Pres./COO–Reed Harrison
CFO–Tad Weed

COLLEGE PUBLISHER, INC.
675 Massachussets Ave., 6th Fl., Cambridge, MA, 02139, USA (617) 354-2038; web site cpsite.collegepublisher.com
Product or Service: Hardware/Software Supplier
Contact–Chris Gillon

COMMGRAPHICS INTERACTIVE, INC.
9259 Pioneer Ct., Lincoln, NE, 68520, USA (402) 484-8118; e-mail nwineman@commgraphics.com; web site www.commgraphics.com
Product or Service: Multimedia/Interactive Products
New Bus. Dir.–Neil Wineman

COMMUNICATION DESIGN
1606 Hodges Ct., Marina, CA, 93933, USA (831) 582-9876; fax (831) 883-1463; e-mail john@csumb.edu; web site www.theidealab.com
Product or Service: Multimedia/Interactive Products
Contact–John C. Ittelson
Project Mgr.–Bobbi Kamil
Webmaster–Brendan Ittelson

COMMUNITECH, INC.
1260 Mark St., Bensenville, IL, 60106-1022, USA (888) 795-7222; fax (630) 521-9493; e-mail info@communitech.com; headsets@communitech.com
Product or Service: Telecommunications/Service Bureaus
Mktg. Dir.–Chris Ganjani

COMMUNITECH SERVICES INC.
2340 S. Arlington Heights Rd., Ste. 360, Arlington Heights, IL, 60005, USA (847) 981-1200; fax (847) 981-9085; e-mail info@communitechservices.com; web site www.communitechservices.com
Product or Service: Telecommunications/Service Bureaus
Vice Pres.–Barb Gendes Shact

COMMUNITY NEWSPAPERS CO. INTERACTIVE MEDIA GROUP
254 Second Ave., Needham, MA, 02194, USA (781) 433-6700; fax (781) 433-7888; web site ; www.wickedlocal.com
Product or Service: Publisher/Media
Ed.–Wayne Braverman

COMPETENCE SOFTWARE
500 N. Osceola Ave., Ste. 605, Clearwater, FL, 33757-3939, USA (727) 298-0341; fax (727) 444-4449; web site www.competencesoftware.net
Product or Service: Multimedia/Interactive Products
Founder–Larry Byrnes
Vice Pres., Devel.–Mary Lou Dewyngaert
Vice Pres., Mkt. Devel.–Shannon Byrnes
Asst. to CEO–Jessica Byrnes

COMPETITIVEDGE LEARNING
201 E. 66th St., New York, NY, 10021, USA (212) 861-8432; e-mail info@competitivedgelearning.com; web site www.competitivedgelearning.com
Product or Service: Multimedia/Interactive Products

COMPUSERVE INTERACTIVE SERVICES, INC.
5000 Arlington Ctr. Blvd., Columbus, OH, 43220-2913, USA (614) 457-8600; fax (614) 457-0348
Product or Service: Online Service Provider and Internet Hosts
Vice Pres., Adv. Sales–Ron Bernstein

COMPUTER TALK TECHNOLOGY, INC.
225 E. Beaver Creek Rd., Ste. 310, Richmond Hill, ON, L4B 3P4, Canada (905) 882-5000; fax (905) 882-5501; e-mail info@icescape.com; web site www.computer-talk.com
Product or Service: Hardware/Software Supplier
Mktg. Dir.–Robert Moore
Pres./CEO–Mandle Cheung
Mktg. Mgr.–Lindsay Aitken

COMTEX NEWS NETWORK
625 N. Washington St., Ste. 301, Alexandria, VA, 22314, USA (703) 820-2000; fax (703) 820-2005; e-mail sales@comtexnews.net; web site www.comtex.com
Product or Service: Online Service Provider and Internet Hosts
Chrmn./Interim CEO–C.W. Gillmly
Pres.–Chip Brian
Vice Pres., Content–Kathy Ballard
Dir.–Pieter VanBennekom

CONGRESSIONAL QUARTERLY, INC.
77 K Street NE, Washington, DC, 20002, USA 202-650-6500; fax 650-6741; web site www.cq.com
Product or Service: Publisher/Media
Editorial Director–Mike Mills
Sr Vice pres./CFO–Douglas Wallen
Sr. Vice Pres., Sales–Jim Gale
Executive Vice President and Managing Director–Keith White
SVP, Advertising–Mark Walters
SVP, legislative services and publisher–Meg Hargreaves
Vice President and Publisher, advocacy, state and transcripts –Barkley Kern
Exec. Ed., News–Susan Benkelman

CONSERVIT CORPORATION
1914 E. Grand Ave., Ste. 1, Lindenhurst, IL, 60046-7822, USA (847) 629-5567; fax (847) 265-4915; e-mail sales@conservit.com; web site www.conservit.com
Product or Service: Telecommunications/Service Bureaus
Pres.–Peter F. Theis

CONVERGENT MEDIA SYSTEMS
190 Bluegrass Valley Pkwy., Alpharetta, GA, 30005, USA (770) 369-9000; fax (770) 369-9100; e-mail convergent@convergent.com; web site www.convergent.com
Product or Service: Multimedia/Interactive Products
CEO–Bryan Allen
Vice Pres., Mktg.–Rick Hutcheson

CONVERGYS
41 Village Sq., Hazelwood, MO, 63042, USA (314) 506-8400; e-mail marketing@convergys.com; web site www.convergys.com
Product or Service: Multimedia/Interactive Products
Sr. Dir., Mktg.–Keith Wolters

COPIA INTERNATIONAL LTD.
1342 Avalon Ct., Wheaton, IL, 60189, USA (630) 388-6900; fax (630) 778-8848; e-mail sales@copia.com; web site www.copia.com
Product or Service: Hardware/Software Supplier
President–Steve Hersee
Vice Pres., Mktg.–Dorothy Gaden-Flanagan
Vice Pres., Engineering–Terry Flanagan

COREL
1600 Carling Ave., Ottawa, ON, K1Z 8R7, Canada (613) 728-8200; fax (613) 728-9790; web site www.corel.com
Product or Service: Hardware/Software Supplier
Sr. Vice Pres., Sales/Mktg.–Kevin Thornton

CORPORATE DISK COMPANY
4610 Prime Pkwy., McHenry, IL, 60050, USA (815) 331-6000; fax (815) 331-6030; e-mail info@disk.com; web site www.disk.com
Product or Service: CD-ROM Designer/Manufacturer
Pres.–William Mahoney

COSMOS COMMUNICATIONS, INC.
11-05 44th Dr., Long Island City, NY, 11101, USA (718) 482-1800; fax (718) 482-1968; web site www.cosmoscommunications.com
Product or Service: Graphic/Design Firm

Pres.–Arnold Weiss

CRAMP + TATE, INC.
230 S. 15th St., 2nd Floor, Philadelphia, PA, 19102-3837, USA (215) 893-0500; fax (215) 893-0543; e-mail jeff.cramp@cramp.com; web site www.cramp.com
Product or Service: Advertising/Marketing Agency

CREATIVE CIRCLE MEDIA SOLUTIONS
52 Amaral Street, East Providence, RI, 02915, USA (401) 272-1122; fax (401) 272-1150; e-mail info@creativecirclemedia.com; web site www.creativecirclemedia.com; www.adqic.com
Product or Service: Consultants, Hardware/Software Supplier
President & CEO–Bill Ostendorf
Design director–Lynn Rognsvoog
IT director–Tim Benson

CREATIVE DIRECT
10 Schalks Crossing Rd., Ste. 501, Plainsboro, NJ, 08536, USA (908) 239-8965
Product or Service: Advertising/Marketing Agency

THE CREATORS MEDIA GROUP
415 Bedford Rd., Pleasantville, NY, 10570, USA (914) 769-0676; fax (914) 769-0763; e-mail trama@creatorsmedia.com; web site www.creatorsmedia.com
Product or Service: Multimedia/Interactive Products
CEO–Anthony Trama

CSTV ONLINE, INC.
2035 Corte del Nogal, Ste. 250, Carlsbad, CA, 92011, USA (760) 431-8221; fax (760) 431-8108; e-mail customersupport@cstv.com; web site www.cstv.com
Product or Service: Multimedia/Interactive Products
Vice Pres., Sales–Tim Rivere
Dir., Finance–George Scott
Exec. Producer–Tom Keyes

CUSTOMER COMMUNICATIONS GROUP
12600 W. Cedar Ave., Denver, CO, 80228, USA (303) 986-3000; fax (303) 989-4805; e-mail info@customer.com; web site www.customer.com
Product or Service: Advertising/Marketing Agency
Pres.–Sandra Gudat

CYBER SALES ONE, INC.
PO Box 84., Bronxville, NY, 10708, USA (917) 250-6074; e-mail albertcran@aol.com
Product or Service: Advertising/Marketing Agency
Pres./CEO–Albert H. Crane

CYBERCON.COM
210 N. Tucker Blvd., 7th Fl., Saint Louis, MO, 63101, USA (314) 621-9991; fax (314) 241-1777; e-mail staff@cybercon.com; web site www.cybercon.com
Product or Service: Online Service Provider and Internet Hosts
Pres.–Joshua Chen

THE CYBERMEDIA GROUP
10410 San Fernando Ave., Cupertino, CA, 95014-2867, USA (408) 255-5007; fax (408) 255-5730; e-mail CM2001@cybrmda.com
Product or Service: Consultants
Chrmn./Chief Futurist–Kenneth T. Lim
Exec. Vice Pres./Dir. Research–Peter Teige

CYBERTECH, INC.
935 Horsham Rd., Horsham, PA, 19044, USA (215) 957-6220; fax (215) 674-8515; e-mail sales@cbrtech.com; web site www.cbrtech.com
Product or Service: Hardware/Software Supplier, Multimedia/Interactive Products, POP/Kiosk Designer
Pres.–Ronald Schmidt

Sec./Treasurer–Lloyd Barnett

CYWAYS, INC.
19 Westchester Rd., Newton, MA, 02458, USA (617) 796-8995; fax (617) 796-8997; e-mail support@cyways.com; web site www.cyways.com
Product or Service: Online Service Provider and Internet Hosts
Pres.–Peter H. Lemieux

D

DAC SYSTEMS
4 Armstrong Park Rd., Shelton, CT, 06484, USA (203) 924-7000; fax (203) 944-1618; e-mail sales@dacsystems.com; web site www.dacsystems.com
Product or Service: Telecommunications/Service Bureaus
Pres.–Mark Nickson

D & H INFORMATION SERVICES, INC.
5720 Osuna Rd. NE, Albuquerque, NM, 87109, USA (505) 888-3620; fax (505) 888-3722; e-mail dhinfo@dhinfo.com; web site www.dhinfo.com

DLS DESIGN
232 Madison Ave., Ste. 800, New York, NY, 10016-2901, USA (212) 255-3464; e-mail info@dlsdesign.com; web site www.dlsdesign.com
Product or Service: Graphic/Design Firm
Pres.–David Schiffer

D-SQUARED STUDIOS, INC.
4312 Elm St., Dallas, TX, 75226, USA (214) 746-6336; fax (214) 746-6338; web site www.d2studios.net
Product or Service: Multimedia/Interactive Products
Pres.–Doug Davis

DANA COMMUNICATIONS
2 E. Broad St., Hopewell, NJ, 08525, USA (609) 466-9187; fax (609) 466-0285; e-mail bprewitt@danacommunications.com; web site www.danacommunications.com
Product or Service: Advertising/Marketing Agency

DANIEL LAMPERT COMMUNICATIONS CORP.
PO Box 151719, Altamonte Springs, FL, 32715-1085, USA (407) 327-7000; fax (407) 695-9014; e-mail sales@dlc2.com; web site www.dlc2.com
Product or Service: Multimedia/Interactive Products
Pres.–Dan Lampert

DATAVOICE TECHNOLOGY
4919 LaMonte, Houston, TX, 77092-5639, USA (713) 783-0123; fax (713) 783-9538; web site ^www.datavoicetechnology.com
Product or Service: Telecommunications/Service Bureaus
Pres.–Ralph Hayes

DESIGN MEDIA, INC.
650 Alabama St., San Francisco, CA, 94110-2039, USA (415) 641-4848; fax (415) 641-5245; e-mail info@designmedia.com; web site www.designmedia.com
Product or Service: Multimedia/Interactive Products
Pres./CEO–Pamela May
Sr. Project Mgr.–Marlita Kahn
Sr. Project Mgr.–Barbara Berry
Project Mgr.–Wallace Murray
Project Mgr.–Alison DeGrassi
Office Mgr.–Cori Freeland
Sr. Web Developer–Rylan North

DESKNET, INC.
10 Exchange Pl., 20th Fl., Jersey City, NJ, 07302, USA (201) 946-7080; e-mail sales@desknetinc.com; web site www.desknetinc.com

Product or Service: Consultants
Co-CEO–Michael Fitzsimons

DEX MEDIA
1001 Winsted Dr., Cary, NC, 27513, USA (919) 297-1600; web site www.dexmedia.com
Chrmn./CEO, Qwest–Richard C. Notebaert
Vice Chrmn./CFO–Oren G. Shaffer
Pres./CEO, Qwest Dex–George Burnett
Exec. Vice Pres., Finance–Robin R. Szeliga
Sr. Vice Pres., Cor. Commun.–Joan H. Walker

DEX ONE CORP.
1001 Winstead Dr., Cary, NC, 27513, USA (919) 297-1600; fax (919) 297-1285; e-mail info@dexone.com; web site www.dexone.com
Product or Service: Publisher/Media
Exec. Vice Pres./CFO–Steven M. Blondy
Sr. Vice Pres./CMO–Maggie LeBeau

DIALOG CORP.
2250 Perimeter Park Dr., Ste. 300, Morrisville, NC, 27560-8893, USA (919) 804-6400; fax (919) 804-6410; e-mail customer@dialog.com; web site www.dialog.com
Product or Service: Multimedia/Interactive Products
Gen. Mgr.–Suzanne BeDell
Vi ce Pres., Mktg.–Libby Trudell

DIALOGIC COMMUNICATIONS CORP.
730 Cool Springs Blvd., Ste. 300, Franklin, TN, 37067, USA (615) 790-2882; fax (615) 790-1329; e-mail sales@dccusa.com; bcarman@dccusa.com; web site www.dccusa.com
Product or Service: Telecommunications/Service Bureaus
Sales Rep.–Bill Carman

DIALOGIC CORP.
1515 Rte. 10, Parsippany, NJ, 84111-2753, USA (800) 755-4444; fax (973) 993-3093; e-mail sales@dialogic.com; web site www.dialogic.com
Product or Service: Telecommunications/Service Bureaus
Pres./CEO–Howard Bubb
Contact–Athena Mandros

DIGITAL COLLECTIONS
312 Elm Street, 20th Floor, Cincinnati, OH, 45202, USA (800) 801-3771; fax (513) 768-8958; e-mail gmti-info@gmti.gannett.com; web site www.gmti.com
Product or Service: Consultants, Hardware/Software Supplier, Publisher/Media
Pres./CEO–Steve Fuschetti
Vice Pres., Installations/Support–Bill Mahlock
Dir., Sales & Marketing–Michael Tucker

DIGITAL DESIGN GROUP LIMITED
955 Milton St., Pittsburgh, PA, 15218-1031, USA (412) 243-9119; fax (412) 243-2285; e-mail rob@ddg-designs.com; web site www.ddg-designs.com
Product or Service: Multimedia/Interactive Products

DIGITAL SCRIBE
67-71 Yellowstone Blvd., #6D, Forest Hills, NY, 20725-1241, USA (718) 268-1493; e-mail harry@digitalscribe.com
Product or Service: Multimedia/Interactive Products
Pres.–Harry Widoff

DIGITAL SYMPHONY
1011 W. Alameda, Ste. F, Burbank, CA, 91506, USA (818) 973-7600; fax (818) 238-9600; e-mail bbenedetti@digitalsymphony.net
Product or Service: Multimedia/Interactive Products
Vice Pres. Client Servs.–Ben Benedetti

DIRECT IMAGES INTERACTIVE, INC.
1933 Davis St., Ste. 314, San Leandro, CA, 94577, USA (510) 613-8299; e-mail info@directimages.com; web site www.directimages.com
Product or Service: Multimedia/Interactive Products
Producer/Dir.–Bill Knowland
Art Dir.–Beverly Knowland

DOUBLECLICK
111 8th Ave., 10th Fl., New York, NY, 10011, USA (212) 271-2542; fax (212) 287-1203; e-mail publicrelations@doubleclick.net; web site www.doubleclick.com
Product or Service: Advertising/Marketing Agency

DOW JONES INTERACTIVE PUBLISHING
4300 N. Rte. 1, South Brunswick, NJ, 08852, USA (609) 520-4000; fax (609) 520-4662; e-mail marianne.krafinski@dowjones.com; web site www.dowjones.com
Product or Service: Multimedia/Interactive Products
CEO–Les Hinton

DREAMSCAPE DESIGN, INC.
125 S. Wacker Dr., Chicago, IL, 60606-4424, USA (217) 359-8484; fax (217) 356-3378; web site www.dreamscapedesign.com
Product or Service: Graphic/Design Firm
Bus. Devel. Mgr.–Amy Moushon

DREAMSCAPE DESIGN, INC.
10 Henson Pl., Ste. A, Champaign, IL, 61820, USA (217) 359-8484; fax (217) 239-5858; e-mail info@dreamscapedesign.com; web site www.dreamscapedesign.com
Product or Service: Advertising/Marketing Agency, CD-ROM Designer/Manufacturer, Consultants, Graphic/Design Firm, Multimedia/Interactive Products, POP/Kiosk Designer, Web Site Auditor

D3, INC.
4200 Pennsylvania, Ste. 250, Kansas City, MO, 64111, USA (816) 471-7373; fax (816) 471-4223; e-mail webmaster@d3design.com
Product or Service: Graphic/Design Firm
Partner–Dave Svet

DUNN SOLUTIONS GROUP
5550 W. Touhy Ave., Skokie, IL, 60077, USA (847) 673-0900; fax (847) 673-0904; web site www.dunnsolutions.com
Product or Service: Multimedia/Interactive Products
Pres.–David Skwarczek

E

EBT
299 Promenade St., Providence, RI, 02908, USA (401) 752-4400; fax (401) 752-4444; e-mail info@ebt.com; web site www.ebt.com
Product or Service: Hardware/Software Supplier
Pres./CEO–James Ringrose
Vice Pres., Worldwide Sales–Michael Nawrocki
Vice Pres., Worldwide Mktg.–Jean Boulet
Vice Pres., Engineering–George Chitouras
Vice Pres., Cor. Devel.–William Stone
Vice Pres./Gen. Mgr., European Opns.–Christopher Codrington
Vice Pres., HR–Patricia Duarte
PR Mgr.–Susan Carroll

EDR/BEACHWOOD STUDIOS
23330 Commerce Park Rd., Beachwood, OH, 44122, USA (216) 292-7300; fax (216) 292-0545; e-mail staff@edr.com; web site www.edr.com
Product or Service: CD-ROM Designer/Manufacturer, Multimedia/Interactive Products, POP/Kiosk Designer
CEO–Peter Vrettas
Office Mgr.–Darcy Angell

E AND E DISPLAY GROUP
910 E. 29th St., Lawrence, KS, 66046, USA (800) 456-7679; fax (785) 843-9288
Product or Service: POP/Kiosk Designer
Chrmn.–Edward White
Pres./CEO–Daryl Morgison
Vice Pres., Finance–Brian Iverson
Vice Pres., Research–Keith White
Acct. Exec.–Don Kelly

ETC, INC.
1915 MacArthur Rd., Waukesha, WI, 53188, USA (262) 542-5600; fax (262) 542-1524; e-mail etcmkt@etcia.com
Product or Service: Telecommunications/Service Bureaus
Pres./CEO–Dean W. Danner
Vice Pres., Sales–Joseph A. Voight

EUR/ELECTRONIC URBAN REPORT
PO Box 412081, Los Angeles, CA, 90041-9801, USA (323) 254-9599; fax (323)-421-9383; e-mail info@eurweb.com; web site www.eurweb.com
Product or Service: Publisher/Media
Pub.–Lee Bailey

EASE CT SOLUTIONS
5995 Windward Pkwy., Alphretta, GA, 30005-4184, USA (404) 338-2241; fax (404) 338-6101
Product or Service: Hardware/Software Supplier

EDGIL ASSOCIATES, INC.
6 Fortune Dr., Ste. 201, Billerica, MA, 01821, USA (800) 457-9932; fax (978) 667-6050; e-mail sales@edgil.com; web site www.edgil.com
Product or Service: Hardware/Software Supplier
Dir., Sales–Sean Callahan

EDITOR & PUBLISHER INTERACTIVE
770 Broadway, New York, NY, 10003-9595, USA (646) 654-5000; fax (646) 654-5360; e-mail edpub@editorandpublisher.com; web site www.editorandpublisher.com
Product or Service: Publisher/Media
Pub.–Charles McKeown
Admin.–David Maddux
Adv. Dir.–Betsy Maloney
Online Ed.–Shawn Moynihan
Online Pdct. Mgr.–Kathleen Ehrlich

EDS (ELECTRONIC DATA SYSTEMS)
5400 Legacy Dr., Plano, TX, 75024, USA (212) 403-6000; fax (212) 703-5110; e-mail info@eds.com; web site www.eds.com
Product or Service: Publisher/Media
Chrmn./CEO–Richard H. Brown
Chief Mktg. Officer–Bob Segert

ELFWORKS 3D CONSTRUCTION CO.
1421 Page St., Alameda, CA, 94501-3822, USA (510) 769-9391; e-mail erik@elfworks.com; web site www.elfworks.com
Product or Service: Graphic/Design Firm
Owner–Erik Flom

EMERGENCE LABS, INC.
5150 N. Royal Atlanta Dr., Tucker, GA, 30084-3407, USA (770) 908-5650; fax (770) 908-5673; web site www.emergencelabs.com
Product or Service: Advertising/Marketing Agency

EMPIRE INFORMATION SERVICES
418 Broadway, Albany, NY, 12207, USA (518) 429-2800; fax (518) 429-2801; e-mail customerservice@eisinc.com; web site www.readmedia.com
Product or Service: Graphic/Design Firm
CEO/Pres.–Colin Mathews

EN TECHNOLOGY CORP.
322 N. Main St., Newport, NH, 03773, USA (603) 863-8102; fax (603) 863-7316; e-mail sales@entechnology.com; web site www.entechnology.com
Product or Service: Telecommunications/Service Bureaus
Chrmn. of the Bd.–David Hall
Pres.–Patricia Gallup
Opns. Mgr.–Matt Cookson

ENIGMA
200 Wheeler Rd., Burlington, MA, 01803, USA (781) 273-3600; fax (781) 273-4400; e-mail infous@enigma.com; web site www.enigma.com
Product or Service: Hardware/Software Supplier
Chrmn./CEO–Johathan Yaron
Vice Pres., Mktg.–John Snow

ENVISION INTERACTIVE
520 Pike St. Ste. 1600, Seattle, WA, 98101, USA (206) 225-0800; fax (206) 225-0801; e-mail sales@envisioninc.com; web site www.envisioninc.com
Product or Service: Multimedia/Interactive Products

EPIC SOFTWARE GROUP, INC.
701 Sawdust Rd., The Woodlands, TX, 77380, USA (281) 363-3742; fax (281) 419-4509; e-mail epic@epicsoftware.com; web site www.epicsoftware.com
Product or Service: Multimedia/Interactive Products
Pres.–Vic Cherubini

EPSILON
601 Edgewater Dr., Wakefield, MA, 01880, USA (781) 685-6000; fax (781) 685-0830; web site www.epsilon.com
Product or Service: Advertising/Marketing Agency

EPSILON INTERACTIVE
11 W. 19th St., 9th Fl., New York, NY, 10011, USA (212) 995-7500; fax (212) 457-7040; e-mail info@epsilon.com; web site www.epsilon.com
Product or Service: Advertising/Marketing Agency

ESOFT
295 Interlocken Blvd., Ste. 500, Broomfield, CO, 80021-8002, USA (303) 444-1600; fax (303) 444-1640; e-mail info@esoft.com; web site www.esoft.com
Product or Service: Hardware/Software Supplier
CEO/Pres.–Jeff Finn
CTO–Patrick Walsh
Dir., Finance–Tim Olson
Vice Pres., Opns.–Jason Rollings

ET SRL ELETTRONICA TELECOMUNICAZIONI
Viale Veneto 4, Cinisello Balsamo, Milan, 20092, Italy 660 331
Product or Service: Hardware/Software Supplier
Mgr., Projects/Devel.–Marco Prandi
Commercial Mgr.–Massimo Fiocchi

F

FLI, INCORPORATED
400 Palisades Ave., Santa Monica, CA, 90402, USA (310) 451-3307; fax (310) 451-3107; e-mail jcwills@fliinc.com; web site www.fliinc.com
Product or Service: Consultants
President/CEO–John Wills
Vice President–Jane Wills
Dir., Bus. Devel.–Susan Moore

FAMILY FEATURES EDITORIAL SYNDICATE, INC.
5825 Dearborne St., Mission, KS, 66202-2745, USA (913) 722-0055, (800) 800-5579; fax (913) 789-9228; e-mail support@familyfeatures.com, wmacdonald@familyfeatures.com; web site www.culinary.net; www.familyfeatures.com
Product or Service: Multimedia/Interactive Products
Owner–Dianne Hogerty
President–Brian Agnes
Director of Media–Wendy MacDonald
Pres.–Dena Klein
CEO–Diane Hogerty

FAST CHANNEL NETWORK
70 Walnut St., Wellesley, MA, 02481, USA (617) 928-3000; fax (617) 928-3001; e-mail info@dgfastchannel.com; web site www.fastchannel.com
Product or Service: Online Service Provider and Internet Hosts
Dir., Mktg.–Kim Vranas

FILESTREAM, INC.
PO Box 93, Glen Head, NY, 11545-0093, USA (516) 759-4100; fax (516) 759-3011; e-mail info@filestream.com ; support@filestream.com; server@filestream.com; reseller@filestream.com; web site www.filestream.com
Product or Service: Hardware/Software Supplier
Chrmn./CEO–Yao Chu

FILM ARTISTS ASSOCIATES
21044 Ventura Blvd., Ste 215, Woodland Hills, CA, 91364-6501, USA (818) 883-5008; fax (818) 386-9363
Product or Service: Advertising/Marketing Agency
Contact–Chris Dennis

THE FINDLAY GROUP
7870 W. 118th Pl., Overland Park, KS, 66210-2545, USA (913) 491-4353; fax (913) 491-4353; e-mail efindlay@hotmail.com
Pres.–Ted Findlay

FIRST DATA VOICE SERVICES
10910 Mill Valley Rd., Omaha, NE, 68154-3930, USA (402) 777-2100; fax (402) 222-7910; e-mail fdvsinfo@firstdata.com; web site www.callit.com/FDVSSite/contact.aspx
Product or Service: Telecommunications/Service Bureaus
Vice Pres., Devel.–James Harvey
Vice Pres., Sales–Bob Van Stry

FISHER PHOTOGRAPHY
2234 Cathedral Ave. NW, Washington, DC, 20008-1504, USA (202) 232-3781; web site www.fisherphoto.com
Product or Service: Graphic/Design Firm
Owner–Patricia Fisher
Contact–Wayne W. Fisher

FLIP YOUR LID
3049 Blazing Star Dr., housand Oaks, CA, 91362, USA (818) 307-4165; e-mail jay@flipyourlid.com; web site www.flipyourlid.com
Product or Service: Multimedia/Interactive Products
Pres./CEO–Jay Jacoby

FOUR PALMS, INC.
11260 Roger Bacon Dr., 4th Fl., Reston, VA, 20190-5203, USA (703) 834-0200; fax (703) 834-0219; e-mail info@fourpalms.com; web site www.fourpalms.com
Product or Service: Multimedia/Interactive Products
Pres.–Pat Buteux

FUJITSU TEN CORP. OF AMERICA
19600 S. Vermont Ave., Torrance, CA, 90502, USA (310) 327-2151; fax (310) 767-4355; e-mail info@lao.ten.fujitsu.com
Product or Service: Multimedia/Interactive Products
Mktg., Dir.–Michael West

FUSEBOX, INC.
36 W. 20th St., 11th Fl., New York, NY, 10011, USA (212) 929-7644; fax (212) 929-7947; e-mail info@fusebox.com; web site www.fusebox.com
Product or Service: Graphic/Design Firm

G

GCN PUBLISHING
37 N. Ave., Ste. 105, Norwalk, CT, 06851, USA (203) 665-6211; fax (203) 665-6212; e-mail info@gcnpublishing.com; web site www.gcnpublishing.com
Product or Service: Multimedia/Interactive Products
Vice Pres., Technology–Sean Fulton
Creative Dir.–Joanne Persico

G2 DIRECT & DIGITAL
777 3rd Ave., New York, NY, 10017, USA (212) 537-3700; fax (212) 537-3737; web site www.g2.com
Product or Service: Advertising/Marketing Agency

GANNETT MEDIA TECHNOLOGIES INTERNATIONAL (GMTI)
151 W. Fourth St., Ste. 201, Cincinnati, OH, 45202, USA (513) 665-3777; fax (513) 241-7219; e-mail gmti-info@gmti.gannett.com; web site www.gmti.com
Pres./CEO–Steve Fuschetti

GATEHOUSE MEDIA, INC.
1101 W 31st St., Ste 185, Downers Grove, IL, 60515, USA 630-348-3373; fax 630-348-3355

GAZETTE COMMUNICATIONS, INC.
500 3rd Ave. SE, Cedar Rapids, IA, 52401, USA (319) 398-8211; fax (319) 398-5846; web site www.thegazette.com
Chrmn.–Joe Hadky

GODFREY
40 N. Christian St., Lancaster, PA, 17602, USA (717) 393-3831; fax (717) 393-1403; e-mail curt@godfrey.com; web site www.godfrey.com
Product or Service: Advertising/Marketing Agency

GREAT!
3527 Knollhaven Dr. NE, Atlanta, GA, 30319-1908, USA (404) 303-7311; fax (404) 252-0697; e-mail dan@greattv.com; web site www.greattv.com
Product or Service: Telecommunications/Service Bureaus
CEO/Chief Creative Officer–Dan Smigrod

GRIFFIN CHASE OLIVER, INC.
25262 Monte Verde Dr., Laguna Niguel, CA, 92677-1535, USA (949) 495-1144; fax (815) 366-3885; e-mail info@griffinchaseoliver.com; web site www.griffinchaseoliver.com
Product or Service: POP/Kiosk Designer
CEO–Jim Redfield

GTEK
399 Hwy. 90, Bay Saint Louis, MS, 39520, USA (228) 467-8048; fax (228) 467-0935; e-mail spot@gtek.com; deb@gtek.com; web site www.gtek.com
Product or Service: Hardware/Software Supplier
Pres.–Bill Groves
Sales Mgr.–Tracey Higgins

H

HEC READING HORIZONS
60 N. Cutler Dr., Ste.101, North Salt Lake, UT, 84054, USA (801) 295-7054; fax (801) 295-7088; e-mail info@readinghorizons.com; web site www.readinghorizons.com
Product or Service: Publisher/Media
Pres.–Tyson Smith

HTS INTERACTIVE HEALTH CARE
434 NW 6th Ave., Ste. 202, Portland, OR, 11375, USA (503) 241-9315; fax (503) 241-8466; e-mail info@htshealthcare.com; web site www.htshealthcare.com
Product or Service: Multimedia/Interactive Prod-

ucts
Mng. Dir./Vice Pres.–Harvey Smythe
Creative Dir.–Charlie Levinson

HARRIS & BASEVIEW
3900 Dow Rd., Ste. D, Melbourne, FL, 32934, USA (734) 662-5800; fax (734) 662-5204; e-mail marketing@harrisbaseview.com; web site www.mediaspanonline.com
Product or Service: Hardware/Software Supplier
Creative/Mktg. Dir.–Peter Cooper

HARRIS PUBLISHING SYSTEMS
505 N. John Rodes Blvd., Melbourne, FL, 32934, USA (321) 242-5000; fax (321) 242-4074; e-mail pweber@harris.com; web site www.harris.com
Product or Service: Hardware/Software Supplier
Pres.–G. Briggs Kilborne
Vice Pres., Sales–John MacEwen

HEALTHSTREAM
209 10th Ave. S., Ste. 450, Nashville, TN, 37203, USA (615) 248-4848; fax (615) 301-3200; e-mail contact@healthstream.com; web site www.healthstream.com
Product or Service: Multimedia/Interactive Products
CEO–Robert A. Frist
Sr. Vice Pres., Finance–Arthur E. Newman

HEWLETT-PACKARD CO.
5400 Legacy Dr., Plano, TX, 75024-3199, USA (972) 604-6000; web site www.hp.com
Product or Service: Publisher/Media

HITCHCOCK FLEMING AND ASSOCIATES, INC.
500 Wolf Ledges Pkwy., Akron, OH, 44311-1080, USA (330) 376-2111; fax (330) 376-2808; e-mail jdeleo@teamhfa.com; web site www.teamhfa.com
Product or Service: Advertising/Marketing Agency

HOLDCOM
955 Lincoln Ave., Glen Rock, NJ, 07452, USA (201) 444-6488; fax (201) 445-4653; e-mail info@holdcom.com; web site www.holdcom.com
Product or Service: Advertising/Marketing Agency
Pres.–Neil Fishman
CEO–Harvey Edelman

HOSKYNS & ASSOCIATES
3038 E. Cactus Rd., Phoenix, AZ, 85032, USA (602) 867-1324; fax (602) 867-3673; web site www.hot4spots.com; www.hometowntv.com
Product or Service: Multimedia/Interactive Products
Pres.–Donald Hoskyns
Creative Dir.–Curtiss Prickett

HOTWAX MULTIMEDIA, INC.
16 Stoney Brook Court, Ramsey, NJ, 07446, USA 201-818-0001; e-mail info@hotwax.com; web site www.hotwax.com
Product or Service: Multimedia/Interactive Products
Owner–David R. Huber

HTI VOICE & INTERNET SOLUTIONS, INC.
Two Mount Royal, Marlborough, MA, 01752, USA (508) 485-8400; fax (508) 485-9584; e-mail hr@htivs.com
Product or Service: Telecommunications/Service Bureaus
CEO–Peter Keenan
Vice Pres., Sales–David Baker
Vice Pres., Bus. Devel.–Ted Davenport
Vice Pres., Tech. Servs.–Todd Palumbo

HUTCHINSON ASSOCIATES, INC.
822 Linden Ave, Suite 200, Oak Park, IL, 60302, USA (312) 455-9191; fax (312) 455-9190; e-mail hutch@hutchinson.com; web site www.hutchinson.com
Product or Service: Advertising/Marketing Agency, Consultants, Graphic/Design Firm
Pres.–Jerry Hutchinson

I

IBM CORP.
Rte. 100, Somers, NY, 10589-3202, USA (914) 766-1900; fax (914) 499-5099; e-mail migr8te@us.ibm.com; web site www.ibm.com
Product or Service: Hardware/Software Supplier
Chrmn./Pres./CEO–Samuel J. Palmisano
Sr. Vice Pres./Grp. Exec., Sales–Frank Kern
Sr. Vice Pres., Strategy–J. Bruce Harreld
Vice Pres., Worldwide media/digital media–Marianne Caponnetto
Sr. Vice Pres., Dir. of Research–John E. Kelly III
Sr. Vice Pres., HR–J. Randall Macdonald
Sr. Vice Pres., Cor. Commun./Mktg.–Jon C. Iwata
Sr. Vice Pres./CFO–Mark Loughridge
Sr. Vice Pres., Enterprise Bus. Servs., IBM Global Servs.–Virginia M. Rometty
Sr. Vice Pres., Information Technology Servs., IBM Global Servs.–Michael E. Daniels
Sr. Vice Pres., Systems/Technology Grp.–Robert W. Moffatt
Vice Pres., Worldwide Adv.–Deirdre Bigley
Vice Pres., Mktg., IBM Global Servs.–Mary Garrett
Vice Pres., Worldwide Integrated Mktg. Commun.–Diane Brink
Vice Pres., Integrated Mktg. Commun., IBM Software Grp.–Mark A. Rosen
Gen. Mgr., Internet Application Servs.–John E. Patrick
Exec. Dir., Adv./Cor. Mktg.–Roger W. Adams
Dir., Media Opns.–J. Kosanke
Program Dir., GLBT Supplier Rel./Procurement–Irwin Drucker
Program Dir., GLBT Sales/Talent–Joseph Bertolotti

IBM CORP.
6303 Barfield Rd., Atlanta, GA, 30328, USA (404) 236-2600; fax (404) 236-2626; e-mail sales@iss.net; web site www.iss.net
Product or Service: Hardware/Software Supplier

ICENI TECHNOLOGY
Sackville Place 44-48 Magdalen St., Norwich, NR3 1JV, United Kingdom 603-628-289; fax 603-627-415; e-mail sales@iceni.com; web site www.iceni.com
Product or Service: Multimedia/Interactive Products
Dir.–Simon Crowfoot

ICONNICHOLSON
295 Lafayette St., New York, NY, 10012, USA (212) 274-0470; fax (212) 274-0380; web site www.iconnicholson.com
Product or Service: Multimedia/Interactive Products
CEO–Tom Nicholson

IDEALWORKS PRESENTATIONS
1 Westinghouse Plz., Hyde Park, MA, 02136, USA (617) 879-4800; fax (617) 969-3300; e-mail ideaworks@ideaology.com; web site www.ideaology.com
Product or Service: Multimedia/Interactive Products
Pres.–Charles Goldstone
Vice Pres.–Richard Goldstone

ILIO ENTERTAINMENT
PO Box 6211, Malibu, CA, 90265, USA (818) 707-7222; fax (818) 707-8552; e-mail info@ilio.com; web site www.ilio.com
Product or Service: Hardware/Software Supplier
–Shelly Williams
–Mark HiskeyCo-Owners

IMAGE ZONE, INC.
11 West 69th Street #10 - A, New York, NY, 10023, USA (212) 924-8804; e-mail mail@imagezone.com; web site www.imagezone.com
Product or Service: Multimedia/Interactive Products
MD–Doug Ehrlich
Creative Dir.–Peter Smallman

IMAGEN, INC.
PO Box 814270, Dallas, TX, 75381, USA (214) 232-3385; fax (419) 821-2047; e-mail al@imageninc.com; web site www.imageninc.com
Product or Service: Graphic/Design Firm
Pres.–Al Schmidt

IMERGY
48 W. 38th St., 6th Fl., New York, NY, 10018-0045, USA (212) 221-8585; fax (212) 869-3676
Product or Service: Multimedia/Interactive Products
Pres.–Flora W. Perskie
Vice Pres., Media Integration–Peter Mackey
Sr. Creative Dir.–Debra Leeds
Dir., Multimedia Productions–Richard Spitalny

INETUSA
PO Box 917208, Longwood, FL, 32791-1373, USA (321) 733-5391; fax (321) 723-4552; e-mail info@inetusa.com; web site www.inetusa.com
Pres.–Tim Yandell

INFOCUS CORP.
27500 SW Pkwy. Ave., Wilsonville, OR, 97070, USA (503) 685-8888; fax (503) 685-8887; e-mail info@infocus.com; web site www.infocus.com
Product or Service: Hardware/Software Supplier
Pres./CEO–John Harker
Sr. Vice Pres./Gen. Mgr., Americas–William D. Yavorsky
Vice Pres., Mktg./Strategy–Candace Petersen

INFOMEDIA, INC.
1151 Eagle Dr., Ste. 325, Loveland, CO, 80537, USA (970) 278-0011; e-mail jcomm@worldvillage.com; web site infomediainc.com
Product or Service: Publisher/Media
Pres.–Joel Comm

INFOPAGER TECHNOLOGIES, INC.
11 Rivka St., Jerusalem, 91530, Israel 672-6111; fax 972-2-671-3002; e-mail info@infopager.com; web site www.infopager.com
Product or Service: Hardware/Software Supplier
CEO–Drew Adam Tick

INFORMATION PRESENTATION TECH.
825 Buckley Rd., Ste. 200, San Luis Obispo, CA, 93401-8193, USA (805) 541-3000; fax (805) 541-3037; e-mail info@iptech.com; web site www.iptech.com
Product or Service: Multimedia/Interactive Products
Vice Pres., Sales/Mktg.–Olivia Favela

INFORONICS, INC.
25 Porter Rd., Littleton, MA, 01460-1434, USA (978) 698-7400; fax (978) 698-7500; web site www.inforonics.com
Product or Service: Multimedia/Interactive Products
Pres.–Bruce Mills
Vice Pres., Sales–Andy Kramer
Vice Pres., Opns.–Tom Pellegriti

INFOUSE
2560 Nineth St., Ste. 320, Berkeley, CA, 94710, USA (510) 549-6520; fax (510) 549-6512; e-mail info_use@infouse.com; web site www.infouse.com
Product or Service: Multimedia/Interactive Products
Pres.–Susan Stoddard

INNOVATIVE SYSTEMS DESIGN, INC.
222 Brunswick Blvd., Pointe-Claire, QC, H9R 1A6, Canada (514) 459-0200; fax (514) 459-0300; e-mail sales@isd.ca; web site www.isda.ca
Product or Service: Telecommunications/Service Bureaus
Pres.–Jeff Tierney
Sales Manager–Robert Dumas
Sales Coord.–Monica Steidelt

INTACTIX
7501 Esters Blvd., Ste. 100, Irving, TX, 75063, USA (817) 491-2435; fax (214) 277-7721; web site www.intactix.com; www.jda.com
Product or Service: Hardware/Software Supplier
Sales Mgr.–Karen Storey

INTERACTIVE CONFERENCING NETWORK
42 Oak Ave., Tuckahoe, NY, 10707, USA (914) 961-0700
Product or Service: Telecommunications/Service Bureaus
Owner–Steve Campus

INTERACTIVE EDUCATIONAL SYSTEMS DESIGN, INC.
33 W. 87th St., New York, NY, 10024-3082, USA (631) 691-2606; web site www.iesd-inc.com
Product or Service: Consultants
Pres.–Ellen Bialo
Vice Pres.–Jay Sivin Kachala

INTERACTIVE INTERNATIONAL, INC.
290 West End Ave., New York, NY, 10023-8106, USA (212) 580-5015; fax (212) 580-5017; e-mail ivie@erols.com; web site 290 West End Avenue #12D
Product or Service: Hardware/Software Supplier
Pres.–George M. Bulow

INTERACTIVE MARKETING & RESEARCH, INC.
815 E. Worthington Ave., Charlotte, NC, 28203, USA (704) 374-1333; fax (704) 376-3949; e-mail research@inter-active.com; web site www.inter-active.com
Product or Service: Consultants
Pres.–Riley Kirby
Sr. Vice Pres., Research–Sarah Monks
Vice Pres., Mktg.–Erin Gallagher

INTERACTIVE MEDIA ASSOCIATES
1719 Rte. 10, Ste. 230, Parsippany, NJ, 07054-4500, USA (973) 539-5255; fax (973) 539-5711; web site www.imediainc.com
Product or Service: Consultants
Founder–Len Muscarella
Pres.–Sally Muscarella
Vice Pres./Creative Dir.–Michelle Camaron
Vice Pres., Bus. Devel.–Anthony Zarro
Dir., Devel.–Brian McGovern
Dir., Pjct. Mgmt.–Geri Ricciani

INTERACTIVE PICTURES CORPORATION (IPIX)
Reston Executive Ctr., 12120 Sunset Hills Rd., Ste. 410, Reston, VA, 20190, USA (703) 674-4100; fax (703) 674-4101; web site www.ipix.com
Product or Service: Multimedia/Interactive Products
Contact–Mary Pam Claiborne

INTERACTIVE PUBLISHING CORP.
7639 Edarwood Cir., Boca Raton, FL, 33434, USA (561) 483-7734; e-mail vicmilt@victormilt.com; web site www.victormilt.com
Product or Service: CD-ROM Designer/Manufacturer
CEO–Kim Milt
Creative Dir.–Victor Milt
Exec. Producer–Martin Ross

INTERACTIVE STRATEGIES
957 Park Ave., New York, NY, 10028, USA (212) 737-8910; fax (212) 737-8910; e-mail info@thewritingworks.com; web site www.thewritingworks.com
Product or Service: Consultants
Contact–John K. MacKenzie

INTERACTIVE VISUALS, INC.
1434 W. Montrose Ave., Chicago, IL, 60613-1320, USA (773) 275-5039; fax (773) 275-3830; e-mail info@ivisuals.com; web site www.ivisuals.com
Product or Service: Consultants, Graphic/Design Firm, Multimedia/Interactive Products
Technical Dir.–Mark Weber
Creative Dir.–Julie Weber
Pjct. Mgr.–Justin Ziegler

INTERALIA COMMUNICATIONS
10340 Viking Dr., Ste. 135, Eden Prairie, MN, 55344-7231, USA (952) 942-6088; fax (952) 942-6172; e-mail info@interalia.com; web site www.interalia.com
Product or Service: Telecommunications/Service Bureaus
Bus. Admin. Assoc.–Mary Mcracken

INTERCOM
3 Grogans Park, Ste. 200, The Woodlands, TX, 77380, USA (800) 298-7070; fax (281) 364-7032; e-mail intercom@intercom-interactive.com; web site www.intercom-interactive.com; www.intercomtraining.com
Product or Service: Multimedia/Interactive Products
Pres.–Bob Yeager
Gen. Mgr.–Margo Pearson

INTERNATIONAL DEMOGRAPHICS/THE MEDIA AUDIT
10333 Richmond Ave., Ste. 200, Houston, TX, 77042-9956, USA (713) 626-0333; fax (713) 626-0418; e-mail tma@themediaaudit.com; web site www.themediaaudit.com
Product or Service: Advertising/Marketing Agency
Chrmn.–James B. Higginbotham
Pres.–Robert A. Jordan
Exec. Vice Pres., Sales–J. Phillip Beswick
Exec. Vice Pres./Sales Mgr.–Michael W. Bustell

INVENTURE, INC.
5102 California St., Omaha, NE, 68132, USA (402) 559-0285; fax (402) 341-2367; e-mail inventure@longshot.com; web site www.longshot.com
Product or Service: Multimedia/Interactive Products
Pres.–James Abbott
Vice Pres.–Rebecca Abbott

INVISION MARKETING
147 West Oak St., Fort Collins, CO, 80521, USA (866) 992-0500; fax (970) 225-6688; e-mail bklipps@invision1.com; web site www.invision1.com
Product or Service: Multimedia/Interactive Products
CEO–Keith Lipps
Pres./CFO–Alan Lipps

IRON DESIGN
120 N. Aurora St., Ste. 5-A, Ithaca, NY, 14850-4337, USA (607) 275-9544; fax (607) 275-0370; e-mail todd@irondesign.com; web site www.irondesign.com

ISRAEL FAXX
611 Saint Andrews Blvd, The Villages, FL, 32159, USA 352-750-9420; e-mail dcanaan@israelfaxx.com; web site www.israelfaxx.com
Product or Service: CD-ROM Designer/Manufacturer, Publisher/Media
Contact–Don Canaan

J

JDA SOFTWARE GROUP, INC.
14400 N. 87th St., Scottsdale, AZ, 85260-3649, USA (480) 308-3000; fax (480) 308-3001; e-mail info@jda.com; web site www.jda.com
Product or Service: Hardware/Software Supplier
CEO–Hamish Brewer

JLM CD-ROM PUBLISHING CO.
189 Magnolia St.,, Suite 100, San Francisco, CA, 94123, USA (415) 440-2668; fax (877) 904-3300; e-mail jlee123@earthlink.net; web site www.jlmcdpublishing.com
Product or Service: Multimedia/Interactive Products
Partner–Lorenzo Orrego
Partner–Miguel Florez
CFO–Raymond Proca
Contact–James Lee

JABLONSKI DESIGN, INC.
8 Daisy Way, Ste. B, Paramus, NJ, 07652, USA (201) 843-0228; e-mail info@jablonskidesign.com; web site www.jablonskidesign.com
Product or Service: Graphic/Design Firm
Pres.–Carl Jablonski

JUDSON ROSEBUSH CO.
630 9th Ave., Room 502, New York, NY, 10036, USA (212) 581-3000; e-mail info@rosebush.com; web site www.rosebush.com
Product or Service: Multimedia/Interactive Products
Pres.–Judson Rosebush

JUPITER IMAGES CORP.
6000 N. Forest Park Dr., Peoria, IL, 61614, USA (309) 688-8800; fax (309) 688-5873; e-mail sales@jupiterimages.com; web site www.jupiterimages.com
Product or Service: Hardware/Software Supplier
Vice Pres., Opns.–Mark Nickerson

K

KEN PETRETTI PRODUCTIONS, LLC
33 Parkway, Maywood, NJ, 07607, USA (201) 368-2296; fax (201) 368-1489; e-mail ken@kenpetretti.com; web site www.kenpetretti.com
Product or Service: Advertising/Marketing Agency, CD-ROM Designer/Manufacturer, Consultants, Graphic/Design Firm, Multimedia/Interactive Products, Online Service Provider and Internet Hosts, POP/Kiosk Designer, Publisher/Media, Web Site Auditor
Producer–Ken Petretti

KINETIC CORPORATION
200 Distillery Commons, Ste. 200, Louisville, KY, 40206-1990, USA (502) 719-9500; fax (502) 719-9569; e-mail info@theTechnologyAgency.com; web site www.theTechnologyAgency.com
Product or Service: Graphic/Design Firm
Pres.–G. Raymond Schuhmann
Chief Brand Strategist–Cindi Ramm

KING FEATURES SYNDICATE
300 W 57th St. 15th Fl., New York, NY, 10019 5238, USA (212) 969-7550; (800) 526-5464; fax (646) 280-1550; e-mail kfs-public-relations@hearst.com; web site www.kingfeatures.com
Product or Service: Publisher/Media
Pres.–T.R. Shepard, III
Vice Pres., Creative Services–Frank Caruso
Vice Pres., Gen. Mgr.–Keith McCloat
Vice Pres., North American Licensing–Ita Golzman
Vice Pres., Int'l Licensing–Cathleen Titus
Gen. Mgr., King Features Weekly Service–David Cohea
Dir., Adv./Pub. Rel.–Claudia Smith
Senior Sales Consultant/Printing & New England Newspaper Sales–Jack Walsh
Int'l Sales Mgr.–John Perry
Inside Sales Mgr.–Dennis Danko
Telemktg. Sales Rep.–Michael Mancino
Sunday Comics Mgr.–Jim Nolan
Syndication Sales Dir.–John Killian
SE Sales–Louis Albert
Sales Mgr., Western Region–Richard Heimlich
Promotions Director–Rose Croke
Editorial Dir., King Features Weekly Serv.–Jim Clarke
Mng. Ed./Dir., Publishing–Glenn Mott
Comics Editor–Brendan Burford
Director of Marketing–Mark Karlan
Director, Web Development–Michael G. Chan
Vice Pres., Worldwide Syndication Sales–George Haeberlein
Domestic Sales Coord.–Venetta Smith
Pres.–T.R. Shepard

KIOSK INFORMATION SYSTEMS
346 S. Arthur Ave., Louisville, CO, 80027, USA (303) 466-5471; fax (303) 466-6730; e-mail sales@kiosk.com; web site www.kiosk.com
Product or Service: POP/Kiosk Designer
Pres.–Rick Malone
Vice Pres., Sales/Mktg.–Tom Weaver

KNIGHT MEDIACOM
7949 E. Ridge Dri., La Mesa, CA, 91941, USA (619) 573-9919; fax (619) 338-9886; e-mail info@knightmedia.com; web site www.knightmedia.com
Product or Service: Publisher/Media
Owner–Ron Knight

KOBIE MARKETING, INC.
100 Second Ave. S., Ste. 1000, Saint Petersburg, FL, 33701, USA (727) 822-5353; fax (727) 822-5265; e-mail info@kobie.com; web site www.kobie.com
Product or Service: Advertising/Marketing Agency

L

L-SOFT INTERNATIONAL, INC.
8100 Corporate Dr., Ste. 350, Landover, MD, 20785-2231, USA (301) 731-0440; fax (301) 731-6302; e-mail pressinfo@lsoft.com; info@lsoft.com; web site www.lsoft.com
Product or Service: Hardware/Software Supplier
CEO–Eric Thomas
Vice Pres., Admin.–Donna Laster
Vice Pres., Software Eng.–Francoise Becker
Vice Pres., Computer Servs.–John Harlan

LARSON TEXTS INC
1762 Norcross Rd., Erie, PA, 16510, USA (814) 824-6365; fax (814) 824-6377; web site www.larsontexts.com
Product or Service: Multimedia/Interactive Products
Pres./CEO–R. Scott O'Neil
Owner–Jill Larson

L@IT2'D (LATITUDE)
714 N. Laurel Ave., Los Angeles, CA, 90046-7008, USA (323) 852-1425; fax (323) 856-0704; e-mail info@lati2d.com; web site www.lati2d.com
Product or Service: Graphic/Design Firm
CCO–Water Kerner

LAUNCH AGENCY
4100 Midway Rd., Ste. 2110, Carrollton, TX, 75007, USA (972) 818-4100; fax (972) 818-4101; e-mail mboone@launchagency.com; web site www.launchagency.com
Product or Service: Advertising/Marketing Agency

LAZER-FARE MEDIA SERVICES LTD.
PO Box 48114, RPO Lakewood, RPO Lakewood, Winnipeg, MB, R2J 4A3, Canada (204) 452-5023; fax (204) 272-3499; e-mail inquires@lazerfare.com; sales@lazerfare.com; web site www.lazerfare.com
Product or Service: Consultants, Hardware/Software Supplier
Pres.–Kelly Armstrong

LENDER SUPPORT SYSTEMS, INC.
13475 Danielson St., Ste.220, Poway, CA, 92024, USA (858) 268-7100; fax (858) 268-7111; web site www.lendersupport.com
Product or Service: Hardware/Software Supplier
Pres.–Kerry Burch

LEVEL X LLC
255 Old New Brunswick Rd., Ste. N320, Piscataway, NJ, 08854, USA (732) 562-9700; fax (732) 562-1632; e-mail info@levelx.com; web site www.levelx.com
Product or Service: CD-ROM Designer/Manufacturer
Chrmn.–B. Gopinath
Pres./Dir., Sales–Jane Miller

LEXIS-NEXIS
9443 Springboro Pk., Miamisburg, OH, 45342, USA (937) 865-6800; fax (937) 865-1583; e-mail bookstore.support@lexisnexis.com; web site www.lexisnexis.com
CEO, Lexis-Nexis Grp.–Andrew Prozes
Pres./CEO, Cor. & Fed. Mkts.–Kurt Sanford
Pres./CEO, U.S. Legal Mkts.–Michael Walsh
CEO, Risk Mgmt.–James M. Peck

LIEBERMAN RESEARCH WORLDWIDE
1900 Avenue of the Stars, Los Angeles, CA, 90067, USA (310) 553-0550; fax (310) 553-4607; e-mail info@lrwonline.com; web site www.lrwonline.com
Product or Service: Advertising/Marketing Agency
Pres.–Dave Sackman

LIGHT FANTASTIC STUDIOS, INC
618 Portland Ave., Baldwin, NY, 11510, USA (212) 604-0666; fax (212) 604-0666; e-mail design@lightfantasticstudios.com ; info@lightfantasticstudios.com; web site www.lightfantasticstudios.com
Product or Service: Multimedia/Interactive Products
Pres./Creative Dir.–Paul Hollett
Art Dir.–Ray Rue
Designer–Ranee Chong

LIVE WIRE PRODUCTIONS
28631 S. Western Ave., Ste. 101, Rancho Palos Verdes, CA, 90275, USA (310) 831-6227; e-mail info@livewireprod.com; web site www.livewireprod.com; www.livewirestudio.com
Product or Service: Graphic/Design Firm
Dir./Art Dir.–Scott Simmons
Sound Dir.–Dan Nienaltowski
Producer, Computer Graphics/VFX–K. Simmons

LO/AD COMMUNICATIONS
150 E. Colorado Blvd., Ste. 210, Pasadena, CA, 91105, USA (626) 304-7750; fax (626) 304-2716; e-mail loadcomm@earthlink.net; web site www.lo-ad.com
Product or Service: Telecommunications/Service Bureaus
Dir., Mktg./Sales–Kris Flynn

LOGICA, INC.
460 Totten Pond Rd., Ste. 530, Waltham, MA, 02451, USA (781) 238-6777; fax (781) 238-6781; web site www.logica.com
Product or Service: Consultants
Global Mktg. Mgr.–Jennifer Peters

LOGICAL DESIGN SOLUTIONS
200 Park Ave., Ste. 210, Florham Park, NJ, 07932-1026, USA (973) 210-6300; fax (973) 971-0103; e-mail info@lds.com; web site www.lds.com
Product or Service: Multimedia/Interactive Products
Pres./CEO–Mimi Brooks
CFO–E. Bruce Lovenberg
Sr. Vice Pres., Bus. Devel.–Mauricio Barberi
Vice Pres., Pjct. Mgmt.–Ken Kuhl
Vice Pres., Techn.–Marty Burns
Vice Pres., Sales–John Fee
Vice Pres., Mktg.–Kevin Casey
Vice Pres., Client Servs.–Eric Dalessio
Vice Pres., Opns.–Gary Sikorski

LOGOPREMIUMS.COM
PO Box 295, Mount Kisco, NY, 10549, USA (914) 244-0716; fax (914) 244-1995; e-mail info@logopremiums.com; web site www.lo-

gopremiums.com
Product or Service: Graphic/Design Firm
Project Mgr.–Jeff Levine

LOS ANGELES TIMES SYNDICATE NEW MEDIA
145 S. Spring St., 10th Fl., Los Angeles, CA, 90012, USA (213) 237-4559; fax (213) 237-0776; e-mail jeffrey.lin@latimes.com; web site www.tmsinternational.com
Product or Service: Publisher/Media
Dir., Int'l Sales–Ryan Stephens

LUMINARE
65 Norfolk, Ste. 4, San Francisco, CA, 94103-4357, USA (347) 204-7859; e-mail info@luminare.com; web site www.luminare.com
Product or Service: CD-ROM Designer/Manufacturer
Pres.–Caitlin Curtin

M

M/C/C
8131 LBJ Frwy., Ste. 275, Dallas, TX, 75251-1352, USA (972) 480-8383; fax (972) 669-8447; e-mail info@mccom.com; web site www.mccom.com
Product or Service: Advertising/Marketing Agency

MCC
8131 LBJ Freeway, Ste. 275, Dallas, TX, 75251, USA (972) 480-8383; fax (972) 669-8447; e-mail sam_watkins@mccom.com; web site www.mccom.com
Product or Service: Advertising/Marketing Agency
Pres.–Mike Crawford
Vice Pres., Creative Servs.–Greg Hansen
Vice Pres., Bus. Devel.–Pam Watkins
Vice Pres., Account Svcs.–Jim Terry
Vice Pres., Media/Prod. Svcs.–Karen Hansen
Pub. Rel. Mgr.–Michelle Metzger

MCI
22001 Loudoun County Pkwy., Ashburn, VA, 20147, USA (703) 206-5600; fax (703) 206-5601; e-mail info@mci.com; web site www.mci.com
Product or Service: Online Service Provider and Internet Hosts, Telecommunications/Service Bureaus
Chrmn./CEO–Ivan Siedenberg
Pres., Opns./Tech.–Fred Briggs
Exec. Vice Pres./CFO–Robert Blakely
Exec. Vice Pres., HR–Daniel Casaccia
Exec. Vice Pres., Strategy/Cor. Devel.–Jonathan Crane
Sr. Vice Pres., Commun.–Grace Chentent
Sr. Vice Pres., Mktg./CMO–Nancy B. Gofus

MCI ENTERPRISE HOSTING
14400 Sweitzer Ln., Laurel, MD, 20707, USA (240) 264-2000; fax (240) 456-3597; web site global.mci.com
Product or Service: Online Service Provider and Internet Hosts
Pres./CEO–George Kerns
CFO–Scott Zimmerman
Sr. Vice Pres., Sales/Mktg.–John Callari
Sr. Vice Pres., European Bus. Opns.–Thomas Davidson
Sr. Vice Pres., Serv. Delivery/Opns.–Jim McLaughlin
Sr. Vice Pres./Gen. Counsel–Bruce Metge
Sr. Vice Pres., Solutions/Servs.–Tom Walton
Sr. Vice Pres., HR/Commun.–Howard Weizermann

MPI TELEPRODUCTIONS
16101 S. 108th Ave., Orland Park, IL, 60467, USA (708) 460-0555; fax (708) 873-3177; web site www.mpimedia.com
Product or Service: Publisher/Media
Contact–Nicola Goelzhaeufer

MPS MEDIA PHONE SERVICE KG
Markenstrasse 21, Duesseldorf, D-40014, Germany 777 3237; fax 167 5994; e-mail hjkruse@mediaphone.de; web site www.mediaphone.de
Product or Service: Telecommunications/Service Bureaus
Mng. Dir.–Hans-Joachim Kruse

MRW COMMUNICATIONS, INC.
2 Fairfield St., Hingham, MA, 02043, USA (781) 740-4525; fax (617) 740-0042; e-mail jim@mrwinc.com; web site www.mrwinc.com
Product or Service: Hardware/Software Supplier

MACTECH MAGAZINE
PO Box 5200, Westlake Village, CA, 91359-5200, USA (805) 494-9797; fax (805) 494-9798; e-mail press_releases@mactech.com; web site www.mactech.com
Product or Service: Publisher/Media
Pub.–Neil Ticktin
Ed. in Chief–Dave Mark
Reviews/KoolTools Ed.–Michael R. Harvey

FRANK MAGID ASSOCIATES
1 Research Ctr., Marion, IA, 52302, USA (319) 377-7345; fax (319) 377-5861; e-mail mailia@magid.com; web site www.magid.com
Product or Service: Consultants
Pres.–Brent Magid
Sr. Vice Pres.–Bill Hague

MAGNACOM CORP.
8613 Lee Hwy., 2nd Fl., Merrifield, VA, 22031, USA (703) 564-0505; fax (703) 564-0520; e-mail general@ii1.iinfo.com
Product or Service: Telecommunications/Service Bureaus
Pres.–John Trainor

MALL MARKETING MEDIA
209 E. Gordon Ave., Layton, UT, 84041, USA (801) 927-2600; fax (801) 927-2727; e-mail michael@mallmarketingmedia.com; web site www.mallmarketingmedia.com
Product or Service: Advertising/Marketing Agency
Vice Pres.–Kayla Vigil
Sales Mgr.–Michael O'Connell

MAPS.COM
120 Cremona Dr. Ste. H, Santa Barbara, CA, 93117-3110, USA (805) 685-3100; fax (805) 685-3330; e-mail info@maps.com; web site www.maps.com
Founder/Chrmn./CEO–Robert H. Temkin
Pres.–John Serpa
Exec. Vice Pres.–Charles Regan
Vice Pres., Finance/Admin.–Anne Messner
Dir., Mktg.–Bruce Kurtz
Dir., Online Commerce–Bill Spicer
Dir., Mapping Servs.–Ed Easton
Dir., Tech./Project Devel.–Mitch McCoy
Dir., Education Mktg.–Erik Davis

MARCOLE ENTERPRISES, INC.
2920 Camino Diablo, Ste. 200, Walnut Creek, CA, 94597, USA (925) 933-9792; fax (925) 933-9795; e-mail generalinfo@marcole.com; web site www.marcole.com
Product or Service: Hardware/Software Supplier, Multimedia/Interactive Products, Online Service Provider and Internet Hosts, POP/Kiosk Designer
Vice Pres., Sales & Marketing–David Pava

AARON MARCUS AND ASSOCIATES, INC.
1196 Euclid Ave., Ste. 1F, Berkeley, CA, 94708-1640, USA (510) 601-0994; e-mail mail@amanda.com; web site www.amanda.com
Product or Service: Graphic/Design Firm
Pres.–Aaron Marcus

MARKE COMMUNICATIONS, INC.
45 W. 45th St., 16th Fl., New York, NY, 10036, USA (212) 201-0600; fax (212) 213-0785; web site www.marke.com
Product or Service: Advertising/Marketing Agency

MCCLATCHY INTERACTIVE
1100 Situs Ct., Raleigh, NC, 27606-4295, USA (919) 861-1200; fax (919) 861-1300; web site www.mcclatchyinteractive.com
Product or Service: Publisher/Media
Vice Pres.–Christian A. Hendricks
Exec. Vice Pres./Gen. Mgr.–Fraser Van Asch
Vice President Strategic Development–James Calloway
Product Management Director–Kathy Lehmen

MCMONIGLE & ASSOCIATES
818 E. Foothill Blvd., Monrovia, CA, 91016, USA (626) 303-1090; fax (626) 303-5431; e-mail jamie@mcmonigle.com; web site www.mcmonigle.com
Product or Service: Advertising/Marketing Agency

MEDFORUM
600 Druid Rd. E., Clearwater, FL, 34616, USA (727) 461-4464; fax (727) 443-1984; e-mail gpresson@sixth-estate.com
Product or Service: Online Service Provider and Internet Hosts
Pres.–Gina Presson
Project Dir.–Cheri Fazioli

MEDIA DESIGN GROUP
1353 Palmetto Ave., Ste. 120, Winter Park, FL, 32789, USA (407) 628-1755; fax (407) 647-4071; e-mail js@mediadesigngroup.com; web site www.mediadesigngroup.com
Product or Service: CD-ROM Designer/Manufacturer
CEO–John D. Slack

MEDIA DIRECT, INC.
PO Box 302, Tenafly, NJ, 07670, USA (201) 894-5548; fax (201) 894-5586
Product or Service: Multimedia/Interactive Products
Editorial Dir.–Bette Weinstein Kaplan
Technical Dir.–David Kaplan

MEDIA ENTERPRISES
1644 S. Clementine St., Anaheim, CA, 92802-2901, USA (714) 778-5336; fax (714) 778-6367; web site www.media-enterprises.com
Product or Service: Multimedia/Interactive Products

MEDIA LOGIC LLC, USA
1 Park Pl., Albany, NY, 12205, USA (518) 456-3015; fax (518) 456-4279; e-mail sgun@mlinc.com; web site www.mlinc.com
Product or Service: Multimedia/Interactive Products

MEDIA MARKETING, INC.
10955 Westmoor Dr. 4th Fl., Westminster, CO, 80021, USA (303) 440-7855; fax 303-440-8035; e-mail info@immediate.com; sales@immediate.com; web site www.immediate.com
Product or Service: Hardware/Software Supplier
Pres./CEO–James Theall
VP, Solutions–Charles Mauldin
VP, Sales–Patti Theall

MEDIABIDS, INC.
448 Main St., Winsted, CT, 06098, USA (860) 379-9602; fax (860) 379-9617; e-mail info@mediabids.com; web site www.mediabids.com
Product or Service: Multimedia/Interactive Products
President–Jedd Gould
Vice Pres.–June Peterson

MEDIAGRAPHICS-DEV.KINNEY/MEDIAGRAPHICS, INC.
717 Spring St., Memphis, TN, 38182-0525, USA (901) 324-1658; fax (901) 323-7214 (clients only); e-mail mediagraphics@devkinney.com; web site www.devkinney.com
Product or Service: Advertising/Marketing Agency
Pres.–J.D. Kinney
Vice Pres.–C.P. Kinney
Office Mgr.–Lynn Hastines

MEDIASPAN GROUP, INC.
630 Davis Rd., Ste. 220, Morrisville, NC, 27560, USA (321) 242-5000; web site www.mediaspangroup.com
Product or Service: Multimedia/Interactive Products
CEO–F.R. Campagnoni
CMO–Mark S. Zagorski
Publishing Div. Contact–Peter Cooper

MEDIASPAN ONLINE SERVICES
8687 Research Dr., Ste. 100, Irvine, CA, 92618, USA (949) 892-2928; fax (949) 892-2930; e-mail info@mediaspanonline.com; web site www.mediaspanonline.com
Product or Service: Multimedia/Interactive Products
Exec. Vice Pres./Gen. Mgr.–Dan Roberts
Exec. Vice Pres.–Steven Barth
Vice President of Sales & Marketing–Charles Whatley

MERCURY CENTER
750 Ridder Park Dr., San Jose, CA, 95190, USA (408) 920-5000; fax (408) 288-8060; e-mail tmooreland@sjmercury.com; web site www.mercurycenter.com
Product or Service: Online Service Provider and Internet Hosts
Dir., Mercury Center–Tom Mooreland

METEORLOGIX
11400 Rupp Dr., Burnsville, MN, 55337-1506, USA (781) 932-3599; web site www.dtn.com
Product or Service: Online Service Provider and Internet Hosts
CEO–Bob Gordon

METHODOLOGIE, INC.
720 3rd Ave., Ste. 800, Seattle, WA, 98104, USA (206) 623-1044; fax (206) 625-0154; e-mail info@methodologie.com; web site www.methodologie.com
Product or Service: CD-ROM Designer/Manufacturer, Graphic/Design Firm, Multimedia/Interactive Products

METRO NEWSPAPER
550 S. First St., San Jose, CA, 95113, USA (408) 298-8000; fax (408) 279-5813; e-mail press@metronews.com; web site www.metroactive.com; www.metronews.com
Product or Service: Online Service Provider and Internet Hosts
Pres.–Dan Pulcrano

MICRO PERFECT CORP.
PO Box 285, Calverton, NY, 11933-0285, USA (631) 727-9639; fax (631) 727-9638; e-mail info@microperfect.com; perfect@microperfect.com; web site www.microperfect.com
Product or Service: Hardware/Software Supplier
Mgr.–Gregory Fischer

MICROLOG CORP.
401 Professional Dr., Ste. 125, Gaithersburg, MD, 20879-3468, USA (301) 540-5500; fax (301) 330-2450; web site www.mlog.com
Product or Service: Hardware/Software Supplier
Pres./CEO/Dir.–W. Joseph Brookman
CTO–John C. Mears
Exec. Vice Pres., Worldwide Sales–Steve Feldman

MICROSOFT CORP.
1 Microsoft Way, Redmond, WA, 98052-6399, USA (425) 882-8080; fax (425) 936-7329; web site www.microsoft.com
Product or Service: Hardware/Software Supplier
Non-Exec. Chrmn.–William H. Gates
CEO–Steven A. Ballmer
COO–Kevin Turner
Chief Software Architect–Ray Ozzie
CIO–Tony Scott

CCO–Gayle Troberman
Pres., Platform Products/Servs. Div.–Kevin Johnson
Pres., Bus. Div.–Stephen Elop
Pres., Online Servs. Grp.–Qi Lu
Pres., Server/Tools Bus.–Bob Muglia
Pres., Windows Div.–Steven Sinofsky
CFO/Cor. Vice Pres., Windows Div.–Tami Reller
Cor. Vice Pres., Worldwide Retail Sales, Home Retail Div.–Mitchell Koch
Cor. Vice Pres., MSN Global Mktg.–Jane Boulware
Cor. Vice Pres., Retail Stores–David Porter
Sr. Vice Pres., Technical Strategy–Eric Rudder
Sr. Vice Pres., Cor. Mktg. Grp.–Mich Mathews
Sr. Vice Pres., Online Servs./Windows–Bill Veghte
Sr. Vice Pres./Gen. Mgr., MSN Int'l–Greg Nelson
Sr. Vice Pres., Interactive Entertainment Bus.–Don Mattrick

MICROVOICE APPLICATIONS, INC.
5100 Gamble Dr., Ste. 400, Minneapolis, MN, 55416-1587, USA (612) 373-9300; fax (612) 373-9779; e-mail sales@mva.com; web site www.mva.com
Product or Service: Telecommunications/Service Bureaus
Nat'l Sales Mgr.–Rich Berg
Int'l Sales Mgr.–Mike James

MIDWEST DIGITAL COMMUNICATIONS
701 Walsh Rd., Madison, WI, 53714, USA (608) 257-5673; fax (608) 257-5669; e-mail info@midwestdigital.com; web site www.midwestdigital.com
Product or Service: Advertising/Marketing Agency
CEO–Jay Jurado

MILES 33
40 Richards Ave, Norwalk, CT, 06854, USA (203) 838-2333; fax (203) 838-4473; e-mail info@miles33.com; web site www.miles33.com
Product or Service: Hardware/Software Supplier
Sr. VP. Sales–Don Sullivan

MILES 33 INTERNATIONAL
40 Richards Ave., Norwalk, CT, 06854, USA (203) 838-2333; fax (203) 838-4473; e-mail info@miles33.com; web site www.miles33.com
Product or Service: Hardware/Software Supplier
Pres.–Chris Habasinski
Sr. VP Sales & Mkg–Don Sullivan

MINACS WORLDWIDE, INC.
180 Duncan Mill Rd., Toronto, ON, M3B 1Z6, Canada (416) 380-3800; fax (416) 380-3830; e-mail info@minacs.com; web site www.minacs.com
Product or Service: Telecommunications/Service Bureaus
COO–Anil Bhalia
CEO–Deepak Patel

MODERN DIGITAL POST & GRAPHICS
1921 Minor Ave., Seattle, WA, 98101, USA (206) 623-3444; fax (206) 340-1548; e-mail post@moderndigital.com; web site www.moderndigital.com
Product or Service: CD-ROM Designer/Manufacturer
Vice Pres.–David Fassio

MORPACE INTERNATIONAL
31700 Middlebelt Rd., Ste. 200, Farmington Hills, MI, 48334, USA (248) 737-5300; fax (248) 737-5326; e-mail information@morpace.com; web site www.morpace.com
Product or Service: Consultants
Pres.–Jack McDonald
CEO–Francis Ward

MOTION CITY FILMS
1424 Fourth St. No.604, Santa Monica, CA, 90401, USA (310) 434-1272; e-mail editor@motioncity.com; web site www.motioncity.com
Product or Service: Multimedia/Interactive Products
Producing Dir.–G. Michael Witt
Composer/Audio Engineer–Marty Blasick

MOTOROLA PAGING
1500 Gateway Blvd., Mail Stop 64, Boynton Beach, FL, 33426-8292, USA (561) 739-2000; fax (561) 739-2341; web site www.mot.com/pagers; www.motorola.com/mims/mspg
Product or Service: Telecommunications/Service Bureaus
Contact–Steve Shapiro

MOTOROLA PERSONAL COMMUNICATIONS SECTOR
600 N. US Highway 45, Libertyville, IL, 60048, USA (847) 523-5000; fax (847) 523-8770
Product or Service: Telecommunications/Service Bureaus
Sr. Vice Pres./Gen. Mgr., North American Reg.–Tim Cawley
Sr. Vice Pres./CTO–Ralph Pini
Sr. Vice Pres., Global Devices–Terry Vega
Sr. Dir., Global Web Mktg.–Ben Hill
Global Dir.,Media Commun./Pub. Aff.–Leslie Dance
CMO, Mobile Devices–Bill Ogle
Dir., Commun./Pub. Aff.–Alan Buddendeck
Dir., Emerging Consumer Mktg.–David Rudd

MOVING GRAPHICS
2276 S. Beverly Glen Blvd., Ste. 108, Los Angeles, CA, 90064-2440, USA (310) 286-0969; fax (310) 286-0970; e-mail info@professorppt.com; web site www.professorppt.com
Product or Service: Multimedia/Interactive Products
Pres.–Tom Bunzel

MOVIUS INTERACTIVE CORPORATION
11360 Lakefield Dr., Duluth, GA, 30097, USA (770) 283-1000; fax (770) 497-3990; web site www.glenayre.com
Product or Service: Telecommunications/Service Bureaus
CEO–Oscar Rodriguez

M2 COMMUNICATIONS LTD.
PO Box 4030, Bath, ENG, BA1 0EE, United Kingdom 7047 0200; fax 7057 0200; e-mail info@m2.com; web site www.m2.com
Product or Service: Publisher/Media
Ed. in Cheif–Jamie Ayres

MULTI-MEDIA COMMUNICATIONS
81 Speen St., PO Box 27740, Natick, MA, 01760-4147, USA (508) 653-3392; fax (508) 651-9970; e-mail info@mmcom.com; web site www.mmcom.com; www.lumaglass.com
Product or Service: Multimedia/Interactive Products
Pres.–Don Baine

MULTIMEDIA RESEARCH GROUP, INC.
1754 Technology Dr., Ste. 132, San Jose, CA, 95110, USA (408) 453-5553; e-mail info@mrgco.com; web site www.mrgco.com
Product or Service: Consultants
Pres.–Gary Schultz

MULTIMEDIA RESOURCE GROUP
505 W. Olive Ave., Ste. 433, Sunnyvale, CA, 94086-7625, USA (408) 315-8720; fax (408) 277-0783; e-mail training@multigroup.com; web site www.multigroup.com
Product or Service: Consultants
Owner–Ken Durso

MURKWORKS, INC.
304 Peyton Hall, Potsdam, NY, 13676, USA (315) 268-1000; fax (315) 268-9812; e-mail info@murkworks.com; web site www.murkworks.com
Product or Service: Hardware/Software Supplier
Pres.–Brad Clements
Vice Pres.–Marsha Farr

MUSE PRESENTATION TECHNOLOGIES
3510 S. Susan St., Santa Ana, CA, 92704-6925, USA (800) 950-4955; fax (714) 850-1018; e-mail jimmuse@museprestech.com; web site www.museprestech.com
Pres.–Joyce Logan
CEO–Jim Muse
Gen. Mgr.–Wil Bigelow

N

NEC INFRONTIA, INC.
4 Forest Pkwy., Shelton, CT, 06484, USA (203) 926-5400; fax (203) 926-5458; e-mail info@necinfrontia.com; web site www.necunifiedsolutions.com
Product or Service: Telecommunications/Service Bureaus
Gen. Mgr.–Albert F. Kelly

NEC USA, INC.
395 North Service Rd., Ste. 407, Melville, NY, 11747-3143, USA (631) 753-7200; fax (631) 753-7434
Product or Service: Hardware/Software Supplier
Dir., Adv./Internet Servs.–Kenneth Vedder

NVS INTERACTIVE MEDIA
150 Essjay Rd., Ste. 200, Williamsville, NY, 14221, USA (716) 626-0100; fax (716) 626-1592; web site www.nvsmedia.com
Product or Service: Multimedia/Interactive Products, Telecommunications/Service Bureaus
Pres.–Michelle Plimpton
Dir., Opns.–Sally Stroka
Southwest Sales Mgr.–John Matyjas

NY INFORMATION TECHNOLOGY CENTER
55 Broad St., 4th Fl., New York, NY, 10004, USA (212) 482-0857; fax (212) 482-0815; e-mail nyitc@55broadst.com; web site www.55broadst.com
Product or Service: Multimedia/Interactive Products
Pres.–William C. Rudin
COO/Exec. Vice Pres.–John J. Gilbert
Dir.-Info Serv.–Jason Largever

NETVILLAGE.COM, INC.
342 Main St., Laurel, MD, 20707-7100, USA (301) 498-7797; fax (301) 498-8110; web site www.gcomm.com; www.netvillage.com
CEO–Harold Van Arnem
Pres./COO–Nathan Hammond
CTO–Stephen Bathurst
Controller–Tony Burgess

NETWORK TELEPHONE SERVICES
21135 Erwin St., Woodland Hills, CA, 91367, USA (818) 992-4300; fax (818) 992-8415; e-mail sales@nettel.com; web site www.nts.net
Product or Service: Telecommunications/Service Bureaus
Pres.–Gary Passon

NEW HORIZONS COMPUTER LEARNING CENTER
1900 S. State College Blvd., Ste. 450, Anaheim, CA, 91286-6135, USA (714) 940-8000; e-mail info.corp@newhorizons.com; web site www.newhorizons.com
Product or Service: Multimedia/Interactive Products
CEO–Mark Miller
Sr. Vice Pres., Mktg.–Heidi Rose
Vice. Pres., Mktg.–Mark Tucker

NEW MEDIA HOLLYWOOD
6150 Santa Monica Blvd., Los Angeles, CA, 90038, USA (323) 957-5000; fax (323) 957-8500; e-mail info@nmh.com; web site www.nmh.com
Product or Service: Multimedia/Interactive Products
Pres.–Chris Speer

NEWMAN BROTHERS
112 E. Pecan St., Ste. 2222, San Antonio, TX, 78205-1582, USA (210) 226-0371; fax (210) 226-6506
Product or Service: Multimedia/Interactive Products
Owner–John Newman

NEWS USA, INC.
2841 Hartland Rd., Ste. 301, Falls Church, VA, 22043, USA (703) 734-6300; fax (703) 734-6314; e-mail info@newsusa.com, YB_ASSOC_CLIPART; web site www.newsusa.com
Product or Service: Publisher/Media
Pres./CEO–Richard D. Smith
Vice Pres., Sales–Richard Rothstein
Ed.–Jacob Maurer
IT Dir.–Scott Peters
Pub.–Rick Smith
CEO–Richard Smith
Sales Rep.–John Phillips

NEWSCOM
145. S. Spring St., 10th Fl., Los Angeles, CA, 90012, USA (213) 237-4643; fax (213) 237-7914; e-mail sales@newscom.com; web site www.newscom.com
Product or Service: Telecommunications/Service Bureaus
Gen Mgr.–Jay Brodsky
IP Rel. Dir.–Melanie Rockwell
Dir., Opns.–Dan Royal
Dir., Sales/Mktg.–Diana Backlund

NEWSPHERE
12412 SE 26th Pl., Bellevue, WA, 98005-4157, USA (425) 957-0219; web site www.newsphere.org
Product or Service: Publisher/Media
Ed.–Alan Boyle

NEWSSTAND, INC.
1835 B Kramer Ln., Austin, TX, 78758, USA (512) 334-5100; fax (512) 334-5199; e-mail support@newsstand.com; web site www.newsstand.com
Product or Service: Telecommunications/Service Bureaus

NEWTON MEDIA ASSOCIATES, INC.
824 Greenbrier Pkwy., Ste. 200, Chesapeake, VA, 23320, USA (757) 547-5400; fax (757) 547-7383; e-mail info@newtonmedia.com; web site www.newtonmedia.com
Product or Service: Advertising/Marketing Agency
Pres.–Steven Newton
Media Dir.–Janet Burke
Sr. Media Consultant–Harry Weimar
Media Consultant–Aimee James
Account Executive/ Media Buyer–Aubry Winfrey

THE NEXT WAVE
100 Bonner St., Dayton, OH, 45410, USA (937) 228-4433; fax (937) 228-4111; e-mail surf@thenextwave.biz; web site www.thenextwave.biz
Product or Service: Advertising/Marketing Agency

NEXTCOM
5454 Beethoven St., Ste. 200, Los Angeles, CA, 90066, USA (310) 360-1000; fax (310) 360-5000; e-mail customercare@nextcom.net; web site www.nextcom.net
Product or Service: Telecommunications/Service Bureaus
Opns. Mgr.–David Hajian

NICHOLSON KOVAC, INC.
600 Broadway St., Kansas City, MO, 64105-1536, USA (816) 842-8881; fax (816) 842-6340; e-mail nk@nicholsonkovac.com; web site www.nicholsonkovac.com
Product or Service: Advertising/Marketing Agency

NICOLLET TECHNOLOGIES
7901 12th Ave. S., Bloomington, MN, 55425-1017, USA (952) 854-3336; fax (952) 854-

5774; e-mail info@nicollet.com; web site www.nicollet.com
Product or Service: Telecommunications/Service Bureaus
Pres.–Marco Scibora

NIELSEN
9276 Scranton Road, Suite 200, San Diego, CA, 92121, USA 800-234-5973; fax (858) 500-5800; web site www.nielsen.com
Product or Service: Advertising/Marketing Agency
Sr. Vice Pres., Data Research/Devel.–Dave Miller
President–Drake Bassett
Pres.–Matthew O'Grady

NORTEL
195 The West Mall, Toronto, ON, M9C 5K1, Canada (905) 863-7000; fax (905) 238-7350; web site www.nortel.com
Product or Service: Telecommunications/Service Bureaus

NORTH VALLEY DIVER PUBLICATIONS
585 Royal Oaks Dr., Redding, CA, 96001-0133, USA (530) 246-7755; e-mail nvdp@c-zone.net; web site www.northvalleydiver.com
Product or Service: Publisher/Media
CEO–Dan Bailey

NUANCE COMMUNICATIONS, INC., DICTAPHONE SOLUTIONS
3191 Broadbridge Ave., Stratford, CT, 06614-2559, USA (203) 381-7000; fax (203) 386-8566; web site www.nuance.com
Product or Service: Multimedia/Interactive Products
Pres.–Robert Schwager
CFO–Tim Ledwick
Sr. Vice Pres./Gen. Mgr., Int'l/Commun. Recording Systems–Ed Rucinski
Sr. Vice Pres./Gen. Mgr., Integrated Voice Systems–Bob Attanasio
Sr. Vice Pres., Mktg./Strategic Planning–Donald Fallati
Sr. Vice Pres., Worldwide Servs.–Joe Delaney
Sr. Vice Pres., Mfg./Logistics–Jim Davis

O

O'HALLORAN ADVERTISING, INC.
270 Saugatuck Ave., Westport, CT, 06880, USA (203) 341-9400; fax (203) 341-8681; e-mail inquiry@ohalloranagency.com; web site www.ohalloranagency.com
Product or Service: Advertising/Marketing Agency
CEO–James O'Halloran
Pres.–Kevin O'Halloran

O&J DESIGN, INC.
41 W. 25th St., 4th Fl., New York, NY, 10010, USA (212) 242-1080; fax (212) 242-1081; e-mail info@oandjdesign.com; web site www.oandjdesign.com
Product or Service: Multimedia/Interactive Products

TOM O'TOOLE COMMUNICATIONS GROUP
115 W. 79th St., Burr Ridge, IL, 60527, USA (630) 789-8666; e-mail toolbox@svs.com; web site www.tomotoole.com
Product or Service: Advertising/Marketing Agency
Contact–Tom O'Toole

OCTEL COMMUNICATIONS (MESSAGING DIVISION)
2 Ravinia Dr., Ste. 790, Atlanta, GA, 30346-3104, USA (770) 390-3315; fax (770) 395-1557
Product or Service: Telecommunications/Service Bureaus
Contact–Denise Reese
Sales Mgr.–Peg Nicholls

OMIX, INC. (ONLINE MARKETSPACE)
102 Vaquero Way, Redwood City, CA, 94062-3152, USA (650) 568-9800; fax (650) 368-6973; e-mail information@omix.com; web site www.omix.com
Product or Service: Online Service Provider and Internet Hosts
Pres./CTO–Terry Lillie
Vice Pres.–Kyle Hurlbut
Gen. Mgr.–Sandy Lillie
Dir., Bus. Devel.–Jim Chabrier
Dir., Mktg.–Maxine Lym
Creative Dir.–Jim Rodgers
Dir., Finance/Opns.–Gail Price

OPEN TEXT CORP.
25 Burlington Mall Rd., 4th Fl., Burlington, MA, 01803, USA (800) 933-3627; fax (781) 272-3693; e-mail info@opentext.com; web site www.opentext.com
Product or Service: Hardware/Software Supplier
CEO–John Shackleton

OPEN TEXT CORP.
275 Frank Tompa Dr., Waterloo, ON, N2L 0A1, Canada (519) 888-7111; fax (519) 888-0677; e-mail info@opentext.com; web site www.opentext.com
Product or Service: Hardware/Software Supplier
CEO–Tom Jenkins

OPENPAGES, INC.
201 Jones Rd., Waltham, MA, 02451, USA (781) 647-3800; fax (781) 647-4300; web site www.openpages.com
Product or Service: Multimedia/Interactive Products
Vice Pres., Mktg.–Gordon Burnes

ORIGIN COMMUNICATIONS, INC.
4140 Regency Dr., Colorado Springs, CO, 80906, USA (719) 785-9900; fax (719) 630-8537; e-mail info@origincom.com; web site www.origincom.com
Product or Service: Advertising/Marketing Agency
Pres.–Randel Castleberry
Acct. Servs./Media Dir.–Jil Goebel
Acct. Exec.–Jessica Seybold

P

PA-SPORTSTICKER
55 Realty Dr., Cheshire, CT, 06410, USA (203) 272-2072; e-mail sales@pa-sportsticker.com; web site www.pa-sportsticker.com
Product or Service: Multimedia/Interactive Products
Gen. Mgr.–Jim Morganthaler

PC TODAY MAGAZINE
120 W. Harvest Dr., Lincoln, NE, 68521-4408, USA (402) 479-2142; fax (402) 458-4569; web site www.pctoday.com
Product or Service: Publisher/Media
Pres.–Thomas J. Peed
Coord./Mgr.–Mark Peery

PC WORLD ONLINE SERVICES GROUP
501 Second St., Ste. 600, San Francisco, CA, 94107, USA (415) 243-0500; fax (415) 442-1891; e-mail webmaster@pcworld.com; web site www.pcworld.com
Product or Service: Publisher/Media
Assoc. Pub., PC World.com–Michael Carrol
Mgr., Online Ad Opns.–Brian Buizer
Mgr. Bus Devl–David Lake

PR & MARKETING NEWS
110 William St., 11th Fl., New York, NY, 10038, USA (212) 621-4964; web site www.prandmarketing.com
Product or Service: Publisher/Media
Vice Pres./Pub.–Diane Schwartz

PR NEWSWIRE
350 Hudson St., Ste. 300, New York, NY, 10014, USA (212) 596-1500; fax (212) 541-6414; e-mail publicrelations@prnewswire.com; media_services@prnewswire.com; web site www.prnewswire.com
Product or Service: Multimedia/Interactive Products
CEO–Charles Gregson

PTI
3786 Dekalb Technology Pkwy., Ste. 290, Atlanta, GA, 30340, USA (770) 452-1777; fax (770) 452-9887; e-mail info@galileoinc.com; web site www.pti-intl.com
Product or Service: Advertising/Marketing Agency

PAGE COOPERATIVE
700 America Ave., Ste. 101, King of Prussia, PA, 19406, USA (610) 687-3778; fax (610) 592-0647; e-mail john.snyder@pagecooperative.com; web site www.pagecooperative.com
Product or Service: Telecommunications/Service Bureaus
CEO–John Snyder
Office Mgr.–Evelyn Jayne

PAGE SYSTEMS, INC.
One Eva Rd., Ste. 416, Toronto, ON, M9C 4Z5, Canada (416) 695-2288; fax (416) 695-2290; e-mail info@pageint.com
Product or Service: Multimedia/Interactive Products
Pres.–Michael Clark
Vice Pres.–Terence Bower
Gen. Mgr.–Susan Vander Masp

PAPER.NET
10200 SW Eastridge, Ste. 230, Portland, OR, 97225, USA (503) 292-2718; fax (503) 292-3498; e-mail marling@paper.net; web site www.paper.net
Product or Service: Hardware/Software Supplier
Pres.–John W. Marling
CIO–Dan Divens

PARTSRIVER-SAQQARA
3155 Kearney St., Ste. 210, Fremont, CA, 53538, USA (510) 360-5361; fax (510) 413-0079; e-mail steve@partsriver.com; web site www.partsriver.com
Product or Service: Hardware/Software Supplier
CEO–Horacio Woolcott
Chief Devel. Officer–Steve de Laet
CTO–Rishi Agarwal
Vice Pres., Servs./Content Mgmt.–Sherry Arnold

PEARSON EDUCATION
255 Old New Brunswick Rd., Piscataway, NJ, 08854, USA (732) 981-0445; fax (732) 981-0732; e-mail info@intellipro.com; web site www.intellipro.com
Product or Service: Multimedia/Interactive Products
Dir.–Philippe Marchal

PEIRCE-PHELPS, INC.
2000 N. 59th St., Philadelphia, PA, 19131-3031, USA (215) 879-7000; fax (215) 879-5427; e-mail techhelp@peirce.com; web site www.peirce.com
Product or Service: Hardware/Software Supplier
Pres.–Brian Peirce

PENTON MEDIA
249 W. 17th St., New York, NY, 10011, USA (212) 204-4200; fax (212) 206-3622; web site www.penton.com
Product or Service: Publisher/Media

PIERIAN SPRING SOFTWARE
5200 SW Macadam Ave., Ste. 570, Portland, OR, 97201, USA (503) 222-2044; fax (503) 222-0771; e-mail info@pierian.com; jfowler@pierian.com
Product or Service: Hardware/Software Supplier
Mktg.–Dave Roth
Press Rel.–Jennifer Fowler

PIXEL TOUCH
2311 E. Locust Ct., Ontario, CA, 91761, USA (909) 923-6124; fax (909) 923-6126; e-mail sales@pixeltouch.com; web site www.pixeltouch.com
Product or Service: Multimedia/Interactive Products
Pres.–Jim Stewart

PLANET DISCOVER
2171 Chamber Center Dr., Fort Mitchell, KY, 41017, USA (859) 392-3100; fax (859) 292-5793; e-mail info@planetdiscover.com; web site www.planetdiscover.com
Product or Service: Consultants, Hardware/Software Supplier
Pres./CEO–David Lenzen

PLAY MUSIC, INC.
37152 Ila Ct., Ste. W, Fremont, CA, 94536, USA (949) 360-0865; e-mail scott@playmusic.com; info@playmusic.com
Product or Service: Multimedia/Interactive Products
Pres.–Scott Szymkowski
Vice Pres.–Dan Kessler

POLYCOM, INC.
4750 Willow Rd., Pleasanton, CA, 94588-2708, USA (925) 924-6000; fax (925) 924-6100; web site www.polycom.com
Product or Service: Telecommunications/Service Bureaus
Chrmn./Pres./CEO–Robert C. Hagerty

POWER BBS COMPUTING
35 Fox Ct., Hicksville, NY, 11801, USA (516) 938-0506; fax (516) 681-3226; e-mail d2java@yahoo.com; web site www.javadelphi.com
Product or Service: Online Service Provider and Internet Hosts
Pres.–Russell Frey

POWERONE MEDIA, INC.
99 Troy Rd., East Greenbush, NY, 12061, USA (518) 687-6000; fax (518) 687-6060; e-mail info@poweronemedia.com
Product or Service: Online Service Provider and Internet Hosts
CFO–John Lang

PRECISION ARTS ADVERTISING, INC.
57 Fitchburg Rd., Ashburnham, MA, 01430-1409, USA (978) 827-4552; e-mail sales@precisionarts.com; web site www.precisionarts.com
Product or Service: Advertising/Marketing Agency

PREMIERE GLOBAL SERVICES, INC.
3280 Peachtree Rd. NW, Ste. 1000, Atlanta, GA, 30305, USA (404) 262-8400; web site www.premiereglobal.com
Product or Service: Telecommunications/Service Bureaus
Chrmn./CEO–Boland T. Jones
Pres.–Theodore P. Schrafft
CFO–Michael E. Havener

PRESS+
25 W. 52nd St., 15th Flr., New York, NY, 10019, USA (212) 332-6405; e-mail info@mypressplus.com; web site www.mypressplus.com
Product or Service: Consultants
Co-Founder–Steven Brill
Co-Founder–Gordon Crovitz
Press Rel.–Cindy Rosenthal
Matt Skibinski
Co-Founder–Leo Hindery

PRESSTIME (NEWSPAPER ASSOCIATION OF AMERICA)
4401 Wilson Blvd., Arlington, VA, 22203, USA (703) 902-1600; fax (571) 366-1200; web site www.naa.org
Product or Service: Publisher/Media
Dir., Adv. Sales–Kevin McCourt

PROCESS SOFTWARE
959 Concord St., Framingham, MA, 01701-4682, USA (508) 879-6994; fax (508) 879-0042; e-mail info@process.com; careers@process.com;

international@process.com; web site www.process.com
Product or Service: Hardware/Software Supplier
Vice Pres., Sales–Mick McCarthy

PRODIGY, INC.
6500 Riverplace Blvd., Bldg. 3, Austin, TX, 78730, USA (512) 527-1500; fax (914) 448-8455; e-mail danlevine@prodigy.net
Product or Service: Online Service Provider and Internet Hosts
CEO–Edward Whitaker
PR–Dan Levine

PROJECTS IN KNOWLEDGE, INC.
150 Clove Rd., Little Falls, NJ, 07424, USA (973) 890-8988; fax (973) 890-8866; e-mail rstern@projectsinknowledge.com; web site www.projectsinknowledge.com
Product or Service: Multimedia/Interactive Products
Pres.–Robert Stern
Sr. Vice Pres.–Patricia Peterson
Sr. Vice Pres.–Susan Hostetler
Vice Pres., Design Servs.–Adrian Holmes

PROLINE DIGITAL
PO Box 27682, Denver, CO, 80227, USA (303) 761-3999; fax (303) 761-1818; e-mail info@prolinedigital.com; web site www.prolinedigital.com
Product or Service: CD-ROM Designer/Manufacturer
Pres.–Tony Marcon

PROXIOS
2501 Monument Ave., Richmond, VA, 23220-2618, USA (804) 342-1200; fax (804) 342-1209; e-mail info@proxios.com; web site www.proxios.com
Product or Service: Multimedia/Interactive Products
Pres.–Frank E. Butler

PUBLITECH, INC.
211 Farm Rd., Sherborn, MA, 01770, USA (508) 651-3932; fax (413) 581-0289; e-mail publisher@adcom.net
Pres./Pub.–Carl Shedd

PYRAMID STUDIOS
1710 Altamont Ave., Richmond, VA, 23230, USA (804) 353-0700; fax (804) 355-5019; web site www.pyramidstudios.com
Product or Service: Multimedia/Interactive Products
Pres.–Bruce Hornstein

R

RG CREATIONS, INC.
9638 Industrial Rd., San Carlos, CA, 94070, USA (650) 596-0123; fax (650) 596-8590; e-mail bob@rgcreations.com; web site www.rgcreations.com
Product or Service: Graphic/Design Firm
Owner–Robert G. Fuller

RISI, INC.
4 Alfred Cir., Bedford, MA, 01730-2340, USA (781) 734-8900; fax (781) 271-0337; e-mail info@risiinfo.com; info@risi.com; web site www.risiinfo.com
Product or Service: Publisher/Media
CEO–Mike Cossey

RANGER DATA TECHNOLOGIES INC.
210 E. 3rd St., Ste. 208, Royal Oak, MI, 48067, USA (248) 336-7300; fax (248) 336-8775; e-mail info@rangerdata.com; web site www.rangerdata.com
Product or Service: Hardware/Software Supplier
Chrmn./CEO–George Willard
Pres./COO–Tony Marsella
Sr. VP of Operations–George Willard
Director of Marketing & Customer Service–Grace Shields
National Director of Sales & Marketing–Dolores Gauthier

RAPP
437 Madison Ave., New York, NY, 10022-7001, USA (212) 817-6800; fax (212) 817-6750; e-mail webmaster@rappcollins.com; web site www.rapp.com
Product or Service: Advertising/Marketing Agency

RED HILL STUDIOS
2257 F. Larkspur Landing Circ., Larkspur, CA, 94939, USA (415) 464-8840; fax (415) 464-8664; e-mail info@redhillstudios.com; web site www.redhillstudios.com
Product or Service: Multimedia/Interactive Products
Creative Dir./Founder–Robert Hone
Sr. Producer–Walter Sanford

REECE & ASSOCIATES
PO Box 5309, San Jose, CA, 95150-5309, USA (408) 978-8599; fax (413) 647-8147; e-mail garyreece@aol.com
Product or Service: Multimedia/Interactive Products
–Gary Reece
–Lynda ReeceOwners

REUTERS MEDIA
3 Times Square, New York, NY, 10036, USA (1-646-223-4000); e-mail ReutersAmerica@thomsonreuters.com; web site reuters.com/newsagency
Product or Service: Multimedia/Interactive Products, Publisher/Media
Publishing Solutions Specialist–Melissa Metzger
Global Director of Marketing–Bipasha Ghosh

REZN8 PRODUCTIONS, INC.
6430 Sunset Blvd., Ste. 500, Hollywood, CA, 90028, USA (323) 957-2161; fax (323) 464-8912; e-mail sales@rezn8.com; web site www.rezn8.com
Product or Service: Graphic/Design Firm
Pres.–Paul Sidlo

RIBIT PRODUCTIONS, INC.
4287 Beltline Rd., Ste. 135, Addison, TX, 75001, USA (972) 239-8866; fax (972) 239-8788; e-mail ribit@ribit.com; web site www.ribit.com
Product or Service: Multimedia/Interactive Products
Pres./Founder–Robin Moss
Creative Dir.–Jason Landry
Multimedia Developer–Linda Krauss

RISDALL ADVERTISING
2467 15th St. NW, Saint Paul, MN, 55112-5596, USA (651) 631-2252; fax (651) 631-2561; e-mail webmaster@digitalhabitat.com
Product or Service: CD-ROM Designer/Manufacturer, Multimedia/Interactive Products, POP/Kiosk Designer
Pres./Dir.-Sales/Mktg.–Ted Risdall
CEO–John Risdall

RISDALL ADVERTISING AGENCY
550 Main St., New Brighton, MN, 55112, USA (651) 631-1098; fax (651) 631-2561; e-mail getwired@rladvert.com; web site www.risdall.com
Product or Service: CD-ROM Designer/Manufacturer, Multimedia/Interactive Products, POP/Kiosk Designer

RISDALL MARKETING GROUP
550 Main Street, Suite 100, New Brighton, MN, 55112, USA 651-286-6700; fax (651) 631-2561; e-mail info@risdall.com; web site www.risdall.com
Product or Service: Advertising/Marketing Agency, Graphic/Design Firm, POP/Kiosk Designer
Chrmn./CEO–John Risdall
Vice Pres./Dir. Web Devel.–Joel Koenigs
Chairman/President–Ted Risdall

RUNNING WITH SCISSORS (RWS)
1840 E. River Rd., Ste. 100, Tucson, AZ, 85718, USA (520) 577-0321; fax (520) 577-8670; e-mail vdesire@rspinc.com; web site www.runningwithscissors.com
Product or Service: Multimedia/Interactive Products
Pres.–Michael J. Riedel
Vice Pres.–Vince Desiderio

S

SAP AMERICA, INC.
3999 West Chester Pk., Newtown Square, PA, 19073, USA (610) 661-1000; web site www.sap.com
Product or Service: Hardware/Software Supplier
CFO–Mark White
Vice Pres., Global Adv./Branding–Costanza Tedesco
Sr. Dir., Social Media Mktg.–Brian Ellefritz

SS8 NETWORKS
91 E. Tasman Dr., San Jose, CA, 95134-1620, USA (408) 944-0250; fax (408) 428-3732; e-mail info@ss8.com; web site www.ss8.com
Product or Service: Telecommunications/Service Bureaus
Pres./CEO–Dennis Haar
CFO–Kam Wong
Sr. Vice Pres., Bus. Devel. Mgr.–Derek G. Roga
Sr. Vice Pres., Global Sales–Jim Della Chiesa
Vice Pres., Mktg.–Michele Wrath
CTO–Dr. Cemal Dikmen
Sr. Vice Pres., Engineering/Servs.–Dr. Bulent Erbilgin
Vice Pres., Pdct. Line Mgmt.–Derek Granath

SAME PAGE.COM
PO Box 325, Sanibel, FL, 33957-0325, USA (239) 395-7655; fax (239) 395-6745; e-mail press@same-page.com; web site www.same-page.com
Product or Service: Graphic/Design Firm
Pres.–Bruce Collen

SANTRONICS SOFTWARE
15600 SW 288 St., Ste. 306, Homestead, FL, 97209, USA (305) 248-3204; fax (305) 248-0394; e-mail sales@santronics.com; web site www.santronics.com
Product or Service: Hardware/Software Supplier
Pres.–Hector Santos
Dir., Mktg.–Andrea Santos

SCALA, INC.
350 Eagleview Blvd., Ste. 150, Exton, PA, 19341-1194, USA (610) 363-3350; fax (610) 363-4010; e-mail marc.rifkin@scala.com; web site www.scala.com
Product or Service: Hardware/Software Supplier
CEO–Gerard Bucas
Pres.–Robert Koolen
CFO–Anthony Maddalone
Dir. Training/Servs.–Marc Rifkin

SCRAMBL-GRAM, INC.
5225 W. Lakeshore Dr., Bldg. 340, Port Clinton, OH, 43452, USA (419) 734-2600; fax (419) 734-2868; e-mail info@scrambl-gram.com; web site www.scrambl-gram.com
Product or Service: Multimedia/Interactive Products
Co-Owner–Slate Kessler
Sales/Promo. Dir.–Mary Elum Kessler
Adv. Mgr.–Scott Bowers

SEALANDER & CO.
611 N. Buckner Blvd., Dallas, TX, 75218-2708, USA (214) 321-8612; fax (214) 328-0779; e-mail john@sealander.com; web site www.sealander.com
Product or Service: Advertising/Marketing Agency
Owner–John Sealander

SILICON GRAPHICS, INC.
46600 Landing Pkwy., Fremont, CA, 94538, USA (510) 933-8300; web site www.sgi.com
Product or Service: Hardware/Software Supplier
Pres./CEO–Mark Barrenechea
Sr. Vice Pres., Worldwide Sales/Mktg.–Tony Carrozza
Sr. Vice Pres./CFO–Jim Wheat
Vice Pres./CMO–George Skaff

SILVER OAKS COMMUNICATIONS
824 17th St., Moline, IL, 61266, USA (309) 797-9898; fax (309) 797-9653; e-mail info@silveroaks.com; web site www.silveroaks.com
Product or Service: CD-ROM Designer/Manufacturer
System Mgr.–Charles Dostale

SIMBA INFORMATION
60 Long Ridge Rd., Ste. 300, Stamford, CT, 06902-1841, USA (203) 325-8193; fax (203) 325-8975; e-mail customerservice@simbainformation.com; web site www.simbainformation.com
Product or Service: Publisher/Media
Pub.–Linda Kopp
Sr. Ed.–David Goddard
Sr. Ed.–Michael Norris
Sr. Ed.–Dan Strempel
Mng. Ed.–Kathy Mickey
Ed.–Karen Meaney

SLINGSHOT TECHNOLOGIES
1811 Chestnut St., Ste.304, Bridgeport, PA, 19103, USA (610) 277-1722; fax (610) 277-1748; e-mail csteph@genfax.com; info@genfax.com
Product or Service: Telecommunications/Service Bureaus
Pres./CEO–Christopher S. Stephano

SMARTMAX SOFTWARE, INC.
Southern Hills Tower, 2431 E. 61st St., Ste. 307, Tulsa, OK, 74136-1231, USA (918) 496-8103; fax (918) 491-0033; e-mail sales@smartmax.com; info@smartmax.com; web site www.smartmax.com
Product or Service: Hardware/Software Supplier
Pres.–Eric Weber

LAURA SMITH ILLUSTRATION
6545 Cahuenga Terrace, Hollywood, CA, 90068, USA (323) 467-1700; fax (323) 467-1700; e-mail Laura@LauraSmithArt.com; web site www.laurasmithart.com
Product or Service: Graphic/Design Firm
Contact–Laura Smith

SOCIALNET, INC.
2700 Garcia Ave., Ste. 200, Mountain View, CA, 94043, USA (650) 691-0609; fax (650) 691-0783; e-mail busdev@socialnet.com
Product or Service: Multimedia/Interactive Products
CEO–Elizabeth Kalodner
CFO–Bruce Cunningham
Vice Pres., Mktg./Membership–Niquette L. Hunt
Vice Pres., Sales–John Sieling
Vice Pres., Engineering–Greg Anderson

SOFTWARE CONSULTING SERVICES, LLC
630 Selvaggio Dr., Ste. 420, Nazareth, PA, 18064, USA (610) 746-7700; fax (610) 746-7900; e-mail sales@newspapersystems.com; web site www.newspapersystems.com
Product or Service: Hardware/Software Supplier
Pres.–Richard Cichelli
Controller–Susan Fenstermaker
Vice Pres., Opns.–Kurt M. Jackson

SOFTWARE & INFORMATION INDUSTRY ASSOCIATION
1090 Vermont Ave. NW, 6th Fl., Washington, DC, 20005, USA (202) 289-7442; fax (202) 289-7097; web site www.siia.net
Product or Service: Trade Association
Pres.–Ken Wasch

SOLO PHOTOGRAPHY, INC.
1463 NW 27th St., Miami, FL, 33142, USA (305) 634-8820; e-mail rp@solo-photography.com; web site www.solo-

photography.com
Contact–Raul Pedroso

SOURCELINK
10866 Wilshire Blvd., Ste. 700, Los Angeles, CA, 90024-4311, USA (310) 208-2024; fax (310) 208-5681; web site www.sourcelink.com
Product or Service: Advertising/Marketing Agency
Vice Pres., Interactive Servs.–Scott L. Hilchey

SPANLINK COMMUNICATIONS
605 Hwy. 169 N., Minneapolis, MN, 55441-1535, USA (763) 971-2000; fax (763) 971-2300; e-mail support@spanlink.com; web site www.spanlink.com
Product or Service: Telecommunications/Service Bureaus
CEO–Scott Christian

SPAR ASSOCIATES, INC.
927 West St., Annapolis, MD, 21401, USA (410) 263-8593; fax (410) 267-0503; e-mail info@sparusa.com; web site www.sparusa.com
Product or Service: Hardware/Software Supplier
Pres.–Laurent C. Deschamps
Vice Pres., Opns.–Charles Greenwell

SPECIALTY SYSTEMS, INC.
1451 Rte. 37 W., Toms River, NJ, 08755-4969, USA (732) 341-1011; fax (732) 341-0655; e-mail contact@specialtysystems.com; web site www.specialtysystems.com
Product or Service: Hardware/Software Supplier
Vice Pres.–Bill Cabey

THE SPORTS NETWORK
2200 ByBerry Rd., Ste. 200, Hatboro, PA, 19040, USA (215) 441-8444; fax (215) 441-5767; e-mail info@sportsnetwork.com; web site www.sportsnetwork.com
Product or Service: Multimedia/Interactive Products
Pres./CEO–Mickey Charles
Nat'l Sales Mgr.–Ken Zajac
Dir., Technical Opns.–Bruce Michaels

SPOTMAGIC, INC.
1700 California St., Ste. 430, San Francisco, CA, 94109, USA (415) 692-0117; e-mail john@spotmagic.com; web site www.spotmagic.com
Product or Service: Multimedia/Interactive Products
Founder, Affiliate Rel.–John Armstrong
Founder, Pub. Rel.–Robin Solis

SPRINT NEXTEL CORP.
2001 Edmund Halley Dr., Reston, VA, 20191-3436, USA (703) 433-4000; e-mail boardinquiries@sprint.com; web site www.sprint.com
Product or Service: Telecommunications/Service Bureaus
Non-Exec. Chrmn.–James Hance
Pres./CEO–Daniel R. Hesse
CFO–Robert Brust
Controller–William G. Arendt
CIO–Richard T.C. LeFave
Acting CMO–John Garcia
Chief Network Officer–Kathryn Walker
Sr. Vice Pres., Brand Adv.–Bill Morgan
Vice Pres./Chief Diversity Officer–David P. Thomas
Vice Pres., Cor. Mktg.–Mike Goff
Pres., Network Opns.–Steven Elfman

STAR-BYTE, INC.
611 Jeffers Cir., Exton, PA, 19341, USA (610) 884-4400; fax (610) 884-4500; e-mail starbyte@starbyte.com; edr@starbyte.com
Product or Service: CD-ROM Designer/Manufacturer
Sales Mgr.–Steven P. Derstine

STATE NET
2101 K St., Sacramento, CA, 95816, USA (916) 444-0840; fax (916) 446-5369; e-mail info@statenet.com; web site www.statenet.com
Product or Service: Online Service Provider and Internet Hosts
–Laurie Stinson
–Jud ClarkPres.s

THE STEPHENZ GROUP
75 E. Santa Clara St., Ste. 900, San Jose, CA, 95113, USA (408) 286-9899; fax (408) 286-9866; e-mail info@stephenz.com; web site www.stephenz.com
Product or Service: Advertising/Marketing Agency

THE STEPHENZ GROUP
150 Almaden Blvd., Fourth Fl., San Jose, CA, 95113, USA (408) 286-9899; fax (408) 286-9866; e-mail info@stephenz.com; web site www.stephenz.com
Product or Service: Advertising/Marketing Agency
Pres./CEO–Barbara Zenz
Vice Pres., Creative Servs.–Stephanie Paulson

STOCKALERT, INC.
201 Lloyd Rd., Bernardsville, NJ, 07924-1711, USA (908) 221-1516; fax (908) 221-0617; e-mail information@cybersmart.org; web site www.cybersmart.org
Product or Service: Multimedia/Interactive Products
–James Teicher
–Mala BawerExec. Dir.s

STOK SOFTWARE, INC.
373 Nesconset Hwy., Ste. 287, Hauppauge, NY, 11788-2516, USA (631) 232-2228; e-mail customerservice@stok.com; web site www.stok.com
Product or Service: Telecommunications/Service Bureaus
Pres./Founder–Glenn Stok

STONEMAN LAW OFFICES LTD.
3724 North 3rd Street, Suite 200, Phoenix, AZ, 85012-2601, USA (602) 263-9200; fax (602) 277-4883; e-mail request@patentdoc.com; web site www.patentdoc.com
Product or Service: Consultants
–Marty Stoneman
–Eric FishRegistered Patent Attorneys

STORMFRONT STUDIOS
4040 Civic Center Dr., San Rafael, CA, 94903, USA (415) 479-2800; fax (415) 479-2880; e-mail inquiries@stormfront.com; web site www.stormfront.com
Product or Service: Multimedia/Interactive Products
Pres.–Don Daglow

SUMERIA, INC.
100 Eucalyptus Dr., San Francisco, CA, 94132, USA (415) 586-3820; fax (415) 586-3941; e-mail info@sumeria.com
Product or Service: CD-ROM Designer/Manufacturer
Pres.–Jerry Borrell

SUMTOTAL SYSTEM INC.
110 110th Ave. NE, Ste. 700, Bellevue, WA, 98004, USA (877) 868-2527 (Technical Support); fax (425) 455 3071; e-mail sales@click2learn.com; web site www.click2learn.com; www.asymetrix.com
Product or Service: Multimedia/Interactive Products
Vice Pres., Worldwide Sales/Alliances–Gary Millrood
Vice Pres., Professional Servs.–Ray Pitts

SUN MARKETING, LLC
3233 W. Peoria Ave., Ste. 119, Phoenix, AZ, 85029, USA (602) 942-6654; fax (602) 942-8664; e-mail gklein@sunmktg.com; web site www.sunmktg.com
Product or Service: Advertising/Marketing Agency
Owner–Greg Klein

SUN MICROSYSTEMS, INC.
4150 Network Cir., Santa Clara, CA, 95054-1778, USA (650) 960-1300; fax (408) 276-3804; e-mail info@sun.com; web site www.oracle.com/us/sun/index.html
Chrmn.–Scott G. McNealy
Pres./CEO–Jonathan I. Schwartz
Exec. Vice Pres., Cor. Resources/CFO–Michael Lehman
Chief Acctg. Officer–Kalyani Chatterjee
Pres., Enterprise Servs.–Lawrence Hambly
Exec. Vice Pres., Sun Servs.–Don Grantham
Exec. Vice Pres., People/Places/Chief HR Officer–Crawford Beveridge
Exec. Vice Pres./CTO, SunLabs–Greg Papadopoulos
Exec. Vice Pres., Sun Software–Richard Green
Sr. Brand Strategist, Java–Tom Herbst
Sr. Dir., Brand Experience, Java–Rhodes Klement
Sr. Vice Pres., Brand/Global Commun./Integrated Mktg.–Ingrid van der Hoogen
Vice Pres., Client Brand Mktg./Adv.–Scott Kraft

SUNGARD SECURITIES FINANCE, INC.
45 Broadway, 10th Fl., New York, NY, 10006-3007, USA (646) 445-1000; fax (212) 406-2861; e-mail getinfo@sungard.com; web site www.sungard.com
Product or Service: Hardware/Software Supplier
Vice Pres., Mktg.–Nicole Burn
Pres.–Cristobal Conde

SUSSEX COUNTY ONLINE
PO Box 874, Ocean View, DE, 19970, USA (302) 537-4198; web site www.sussexcountyonline.com
Product or Service: Consultants
Owner/Pub.–Eric Magill
Content Ed.–Kerin Magill

SYMANTEC CORP.
3381 Steeles Ave. E., 4th Fl., Toronto, ON, M2H 3S7, Canada (416) 774-0000; fax (416) 774-0001; e-mail info@symantec.com; web site www.symantec.com
Product or Service: Online Service Provider and Internet Hosts
CMO–Suzana Correa

SYNCHRONICITY, INC.
15127 NE 24th St., Redmond, WA, 98052, USA (425) 558-7540; fax (425) 641-5341; e-mail danielw@nsynch.com
Product or Service: Online Service Provider and Internet Hosts
Mktg. Dir.–Daniel Ward

SYNTELLECT, INC.
16610 N. Black Canyon Hwy., Ste. 100, Phoenix, AZ, 85053, USA (602) 789-2800; fax (602) 789-2899; e-mail info@syntellect.com; web site www.syntellect.com
Product or Service: Telecommunications/Service Bureaus
Pres.–Steve Dodenhoff
Vice Pres., Sales Americas–Keith Gyssler

SYNTELLECT INTERACTIVE SERVICES
1000 Holcomb Woods Pky. Ste. 410A, Roswell, GA, 30076-2585, USA (770) 587-0700 ext. 75348; fax (770) 587-0589; e-mail info@syntellect.com; web site www.syntellect.com
Product or Service: Telecommunications/Service Bureaus
CFO–Peter Pamplin
Vice Pres., Pdct. Mktg.–Tricia Lester
Contact–Jackie Dasta

SYSTEM GUIDES
31 Sandpiper Strand, Coronado, CA, 92118, USA (619) 575-6974; fax (419) 844-0886
Product or Service: Hardware/Software Supplier
Mktg. Dir.–James G. Root

T

TALX CORP.
11432 Lackland Rd., Saint Louis, MO, 63146, USA (314) 214-7000; fax (314) 214-7588; e-mail moreinfo@talx.com; web site www.talx.com
Product or Service: Telecommunications/Service Bureaus
CEO–William Canfield
Vice Pres., Market Devel.–Michael Smith

TNS
11 Madison Ave., 12th Flr., New York, NY, 10010, USA (212) 991-6000; e-mail info-us@tns-global.com; web site www.tns-us.com
Product or Service: Advertising/Marketing Agency

TRX INTERACTIVE COMMUNICATIONS, INC.
400 E. 59th St., Ste. 12th Fl., New York, NY, 10022, USA (212) 355-4565; e-mail info@trxinteractive.com; sales@trxinteractive.com; web site www.trxinteractive.com
Product or Service: Multimedia/Interactive Products
Pres./CEO–Roger Vitkansas

TV DATA (TRIBUNE MEDIA SERVICES)
333 Glen St., Glens Falls, NY, 12801, USA (518) 792-9914; fax (518) 792-4414; e-mail tvdata@tvdata.com; web site www.clicktv.com; www.tvdata.com
Product or Service: Multimedia/Interactive Products
Vice Pres., Newspaper/Adv. Sales–Cameron Yung

TADIRAN TELECOM, INC.
4 Tri Harbor Ct., Port Washington, NY, 11050, USA (516) 632-7200; fax (516) 632-7210; web site www.tadiran-us.com
Product or Service: Telecommunications/Service Bureaus
CEO–David Sopko

TAM COMMUNICATIONS
5610 scotts valley Dr. Ste. B 552, Scotts Valley, CA, 95066, USA (831) 439-1500; fax (831) 439-0298; web site www.tamcomm.com
Product or Service: Advertising/Marketing Agency
Pres./CEO–Susan O'Connor Fraser

TARGETBASE
7850 N. Belt Line Rd., Irving, TX, 75063-6098, USA (972) 506-3400; fax (972) 506-3505; e-mail customer.value@targetbase.com; web site www.targetbase.com
Product or Service: Advertising/Marketing Agency

TARGETBASE
202 Centreport Dr., Greensboro, NC, 27409-9518, USA (336) 665-3800; fax (336) 665-3855; e-mail info@targetbase.com; web site www.targetbase.com
Product or Service: Advertising/Marketing Agency

TECH IMAGE LTD.
1130 Lake Cook Rd., Ste. 250, Buffalo Grove, IL, 60089, USA (847) 279-0022; fax (847) 279-8922; e-mail pr@techimage.com; web site www.techimage.com

TECHNICOLOR PACKAGED MEDIA SERVICES
3233 E. Mission Oaks Blvd., Camarillo, CA, 93012, USA (805) 445-1122; fax (805) 445-4280; e-mail info@technicolor.com
Product or Service: CD-ROM Designer/Manufacturer
Pres.–Lanny Roimondo
Vice Pres., Sales/Mktg.–Josh Pine
Plant Mgr.–Duke Potts

TELE-PUBLISHING, INC.
126 Brookline Ave., Boston, MA, 02215, USA (800) 874-2340; fax (800) 397-4444; web site www.tpigroup.com
Product or Service: Online Service Provider and Internet Hosts
Contact–Lindsey Mathison

TELECOMPUTE CORP.
1275 K St. NW, Ste. G-9, Washington, DC, 20005-4006, USA (202) 789-7860; fax (800) 872-8642; e-mail warren@telecompute.com; web site www.telecompute.com
Product or Service: Telecommunications/Service Bureaus
Pres.–Warren Miller

TELEPERFORMANCE INTERACTIVE
One Plymouth Meeting, Ste. 610, Plymouth Meeting, PA, 19462, USA (610) 684-2701; fax (610) 941-9844; e-mail mcohen@teleperformance.com; web site www.teleperformance.com
Product or Service: Telecommunications/Service Bureaus
Pres.–Marc Cohen
COO–Jeffrey Cohen
Vice Pres., Sales–Charles Dowbird

TELEPHONE DOCTOR CUSTOMER SERVICE TRAINING
30 Hollenberg Ct., Saint Louis, MO, 63044, USA (314) 291-1012; fax (314) 291-3710; e-mail info@telephonedoctor.com; web site www.telephonedoctor.com
Product or Service: Online Service Provider and Internet Hosts
Pres.–Nancy Friedman
Gen. Mgr./Vice Pres.–David Friedman

TELEQUEST
1250 E. Copeland Rd., Ste. 850, Arlington, TX, 76011, USA (817) 258-6500; fax (817) 258-6505; e-mail sales@telequest.com
Product or Service: Telecommunications/Service Bureaus
Sr. Vice Pres., Sales/Mktg.–Mark Foley
Nat'l Sales Dir.–Mike Larose

TELSPAN, INC.
101 W. Washington St., Ste. C 1200, National City Ctr., Indianapolis, IN, 46204-3413, USA (317) 631-6565; fax (317) 687-1747; e-mail info@telspan.com; web site www.telspan.com
Product or Service: Telecommunications/Service Bureaus
Chrmn.–J. Bruce Laughrey
Pres./CEO–Keith E. Locke

THOMAS TABER & DRAZEN
1610 15th St., Denver, CO, 80202-1304, USA (303) 468-3550; fax (303) 468-3551; e-mail info@ttdusa.com
Product or Service: Advertising/Marketing Agency
CEO–Bryan Thomas

3M TOUCH SYSTEMS, INC.
300 Griffin Brook Park Dr., Methuen, MA, 01844, USA (978) 659-9000; fax (978) 659-9100; web site www.3mtouch.com
Product or Service: Hardware/Software Supplier
Bus. Unit Mgr.–Chris Tsourides

THUNDERSTONE SOFTWARE LLC
815 Superior Ave E., Cleveland, OH, 44114-3909, USA (216) 820-2200; fax (216) 820-2211; e-mail info@thunderstone.com; web site www.thunderstone.com
Product or Service: Hardware/Software Supplier, Online Service Provider and Internet Hosts
CMO–Peter Thusat

TOUCH TONE SERVICES
PO Box 2994, Renton, WA, 98056, USA (425) 271-7200; fax (425) 235-8275; e-mail tbarrett@ttsfax.com; web site www.ttsfax.com
Product or Service: Telecommunications/Service Bureaus
Pres.–Thomas Barrett

TOWNNEWS.COM
1521 47th Ave., Moline, IL, 61265, USA (800) 293-9576; fax (309) 743-0830; e-mail info@townnews.com; web site www.townnews.com
Product or Service: Online Service Provider and Internet Hosts
CEO/President–Marc Wilson

TRADEWINDS PUBLISHING CO.
207 Chipman Rd., Bethpage, TN, 37022-8629, USA (615) 841-3066; fax (615) 841-3288; e-mail wgray@wgray.com
Product or Service: Publisher/Media
Ed.–William Gray

TREEHOUSEONE INTERACTIVE PRODUCTIONS
40310 Three Forks Rd., Magnolia, TX, 77354, USA (512) 682-6943; fax (512) 682-6943; e-mail treehouse1@aol.com; treehouse1@onebox.com; web site www.treehouse1.com
Product or Service: Multimedia/Interactive Products
Contact–Brian K. Hecht

TRIBAL DDB
437 Madison Ave., 8th Fl., New York, NY, 10022, USA (212) 515-8321; fax (212) 515-8660; web site www.tribalddb.com
Product or Service: Advertising/Marketing Agency

TRIBUNE MEDIA SERVICES
435 N. Michigan Ave., Ste. 1500, Chicago, IL, 60611-4012, USA (312) 222-4444; fax (312) 222-8620; e-mail asingleton@tribune.com; web site www.tms.tribune.com
Product or Service: Multimedia/Interactive Products
Pres./CEO–David D. Williams
Vice Pres., Entertainment Products–Jay Fehnel
Vice Pres., Finance/CFO–Mike Gart
Vice Pres., HR–Alexa Bazanos
Licensing Mgr.–Tom Nesis
Vice Pres., Worldwide Sales–Walter Mahoney
Vice Pres., Mktg./Licensing–Stephen Tippie
Exec. Producer–Sarah Zupko

TSANG SEYMOUR DESIGN, INC.
526 W. 26th St., Ste. 708, New York, NY, 10001-5517, USA (212) 352-0063; fax (212) 352-0067; e-mail info@tsangseymour.com; ps@tsangseymour.com; web site www.tsangseymour.com
Product or Service: Graphic/Design Firm
–Patrick Seymour
–Catarina TsangPrincipals

THE TUCKER GROUP
19 Edgewood Road, Sharon, MA, 02067-1938, USA (781) 784-0932; e-mail mtucker@tuckergroup.com
Product or Service: Advertising/Marketing Agency
Owner–Michael Tucker

24/7 REAL MEDIA, INC.
132 W. 31st St., 9th Fl., New York, NY, 10001, USA (212) 231-7100; fax (212) 760-1774; e-mail info@247realmedia.com; web site www.247realmedia.com
Product or Service: Advertising/Marketing Agency

TWO TWELVE
902 Broadway, 20th Fl., New York, NY, 10010-6002, USA (212) 254-6670; fax (212) 254-6614; e-mail info@twotwelve.com; web site www.twotwelve.com
Product or Service: Graphic/Design Firm
Founder/Principal/Pres.–David Gibson
Principal–Ann Harakawa
CMO–Sarah Haun

TYJILL ENTERPRISES, INC.
1009 E. Elmtree Rd., Rossford, OH, 43460, USA (419) 349-6513; fax (419) 666-4249; e-mail jappt@tyjill.com; web site www.tyjill.com
Product or Service: Multimedia/Interactive Products
Pres.–John J. Appt

U

USA 800, INC.
9808 E. 66th Terr., Kansas City, MO, 64133-5240, USA (816) 358-1303; fax (816) 358-8845; e-mail tdavis@usa-800.com; web site www.thecontactcenter.com
Product or Service: Telecommunications/Service Bureaus
Pres./CEO–Tom Davis
Exec. Vice Pres./CFO–Dan Quigley
Vice Pres./Dir., Techn.–Mike Langel

U.S. NETCOM CORPORATION
1531 West 32nd, Ste 209, Joplin, MO, 64804, USA (888) 910-3329; fax 877-829-8607; e-mail important@usnlive.com; web site www.usnlive.com
Product or Service: Telecommunications/Service Bureaus
Pres.–JJ Kelly
VP of Business Development–Kim Gustafson

US TELEPHONY LTD.
4250 Ferguson Dr., Ste. 100, Cincinnati, OH, 45245-1072, USA (513) 943-9000; fax (513) 943-9092; e-mail info@zimmers.com; web site www.zimmers.com
Product or Service: Multimedia/Interactive Products
Pres.–Louis E. Zimmers
Vice Pres.–Gregory P. Zimmers

ULEAD SYSTEMS, INC.
970 W. 190th St., Ste. 480, Torrance, CA, 90502, USA (510) 979-7118; fax (310) 512-6408; e-mail info@ulead.com; web site www.ulead.com
Product or Service: Hardware/Software Supplier
Vice Pres., American Sales–Mike Yanez

ULTITECH, INC.
Foot of Broad St., Stratford, CT, 06497, USA (203) 375-7300; fax (203) 375-6699; e-mail ultitech@meds.com; web site www.meds.com
Product or Service: Multimedia/Interactive Products
Pres.–William J. Comcowich
Mgr., Opns.–Laura McClatchie

UNET 2 CORPORATION
80E11st 512, New York, NY, 10003, USA N/A; e-mail sales@unet2.net; web site www.unet2.net
Product or Service: Multimedia/Interactive Products, Online Service Provider and Internet Hosts, Publisher/Media
Pres.–James Monaco

UNISYS CORP.
Unisys Way, Blue Bell, PA, 19424-0001, USA (215) 986-6999; fax (215) 986-2312; e-mail info@unisys.com; investor@unisys.com; web site www.unisys.com
Product or Service: Hardware/Software Supplier
Chrmn./CEO–J. Edward Coleman
Sr. Vice Pres./CFO–Janet Brutschea Haugen
Vice Pres./Treasurer–Scott A. Battersby

UNITED MEDIA
312 Walnut St, 28th Floor, Cincinnati, OH, 45202, USA 513-977-3000; fax 513-977-3866; e-mail vincent.marciano@scripps.com; web site www.comics.com; www.unitedmedia.com; www.unitedfeatures.com
Product or Service: Publisher/Media
General Manager - Syndicate–Vincent Marciano
Pres./CEO–Douglas R. Stern
Sr. Vice Pres., US Licensing–Joshua Kislevitz
Sr. Vice Pres., Finance/Admin.–Paul Crystal
Sr. Vice Pres., Int'l Licensing–Rita Rubin
Sr. Vice Pres./Gen. Mgr.–Lisa Klem Wilson
Vice Pres., Opns.–Peri Hochwald
Mng. Ed., Comics–Jake Morrissey
Exec. Dir., Pub. Rel.–Mary Anne Grimes
Mgr., Sales/Admin.–Susan Fine
Mgr., Regl. Sales-West–Ron O'Neal
Mgr., Regl. Sales-East–Donald Lane
Mgr., Regl. Sales-Central–Louis Albert
Mgr., Regl. Sales–Marc DeLaurentis
Mgr., Customer Rel.–Carmen Puello
Mng. Ed., Editorial–Neil Gladstone
Exec. Dir., Editorial–Marianne Goldstein

UNIVERSAL TECHNICAL SYSTEMS, INC.
202 W. State St., Ste. 700, Rockford, IL, 61101, USA (815) 963-2220; fax (815) 963-8884; e-mail sales@uts.us.com; web site www.uts.us.com
Product or Service: Hardware/Software Supplier
Pres.–Jack Marathe

UPSHAW & ASSOCIATES
14 Altamira Ave., Kentfield, CA, 94904-1407, USA (415) 785-8735; fax (415) 507-9194; e-mail upshaw@upshawmarketing.com; web site www.brandbuilding.com
Product or Service: Consultants
Principal–Lynn B. Upshaw

V

V-CHANNEL, INC.
3080 Olcott St., Ste. 130C, Santa Clara, CA, 95054-3252, USA (408) 980-9999; fax (408) 996-0961; e-mail info@vchannel.com; sales@vchannel.com; vci@vchannel.com
Product or Service: Hardware/Software Supplier
Pres.–Alan S. Yatagai

VNU EMEDIA
770 Broadway, New York, NY, 10003-9595, USA (646) 654-5550; fax (646) 654-5584; web site www.vnuemedia.com
Product or Service: Publisher/Media
Pres., eMedia/Information Mktg.–Toni Nevitt
Vice Pres., eMedia–John Lerner
Vice Pres., Technology–Christian Evans
Dir., Sales–Eileen Long
Nat'l Sales Dir.–Jeff Green
Bus. Devel. Mgr.–Evan Ambinder

V!STUDIOS
8200 Greensboro Dr., Ste. 900, McLean, VA, 22102-4931, USA (703) 760-0440; fax (703) 760-0417; e-mail operations@v-studios.com; web site www.v-studios.com
Product or Service: Online Service Provider and Internet Hosts
Vice Pres.–Cindy Benesch
Vice Pres., Promo.–Troy Benesch
Dir., Mktg./Sales–Jim Hatch

VCAMPUS CORP.
1850 Cenntenial Park Dr., Ste. 200, Reston, VA, 20191, USA (703) 893-7800; fax (703) 893-1905; e-mail info@vcampus.com; web site www.vcampus.com/webuol
Product or Service: Multimedia/Interactive Products
Chrmn.–Nat P. Kannan
Sr. Vice Pres.–Lindsay H. Miller
Sr. Vice Pres., Worldwide Sales/Mktg.–Ronald E. Freedman

VERIO, INC.
8005 S. Chester St., Ste. 200, Centennial, CO, 80112-3523, USA (303) 645-1900; fax (303) 708-2490; e-mail veriomedia@verio.net ; jobs@verio.net; web site www.verio.com
Product or Service: Online Service Provider and Internet Hosts
Pres.–Kiyoshi Maeda

VERIZON COMMUNICATIONS, INC.
140 West St., New York, NY, 10007-2141,

USA (212) 395-2121; fax (212) 719-3349; e-mail info@verizon.com; web site www.verizon.com
Product or Service: Telecommunications/Service Bureaus
Chrmn./CEO–Ivan G. Seidenberg
Vice Chrmn./Pres.–Lawrence Babbio
Grp. Pres., Int'l–Dan Petri
Exec. Vice Pres./CFO–Doreen Toben
Pres., Verizon Foundation–Patrick Gaston
Exec. Vice Pres., Pub. Affairs/Commun.–Thomas Tauke
Exec. Vice Pres., HR–Marc Reed
Exec. Vice Pres./CTO–Dick Lynch
Sr. Vice Pres., Strategy/Devel./Planning–John Diercksen
Sr. Vice Pres./Treasurer–Tom Bartlett
Sr. Vice Pres., Domestic Telecom HR–John Bell
Sr. Vice Pres., Mktg./Digital Media–John Harrobin
Sr. Vice Pres., Investor Rel.–Catherine Webster
CIO–Shaygan Kheradpir
Pres., Landline Opns.–Francis Shamoo
Pres., Wholesale Mkts.–Virginia Ruesterholz
Mgr., Hispanic Mktg.–Joe Paz

VERTICAL COMMUNICATIONS
4717 E. Hilton Ave., Ste. 400, Phoenix, AZ, 85034, USA (800) 843-4863; fax (941) 554-5053; web site www.vertical.com
Product or Service: Hardware/Software Supplier
CFO–Ken Clinebell

VERTICAL COMMUNICATIONS, INC.
10 Canal Park, Ste. 602, Cambridge, MA, 02141-2250, USA (617) 517-5470; fax (617) 517-5459; e-mail info@vertical.com; web site www.vertical.com
Product or Service: Hardware/Software Supplier
CEO–William Tauscher
Exec. Vice Pres./Gen. Mgr.–Dick Anderson
CFO–Ken Clinebell
CTO–Scott Pickett
Sr. Vice Pres., Bus. Devel./Pdct. Mgmt.–Peter H. Bailey
Sr. Vice Pres., Devel.–Chris Brookins
Vice Pres., Sales/Channel Mgmt.-SME Solutions–Jim Scanlon
Vice Pres., Sales/Channel Mgmt.-Distributed Enterprise Solutions–Ben Alves
Vice Pres., Int'l Sales–Mel Passarelli

VERVE WIRELESS, INC.
725 S. Coast Hwy. 101, Encinitas, CA, 92024-5070, USA (760) 479-0055; e-mail info@vervewireless.com; web site www.vervewireless.com
Product or Service: Multimedia/Interactive Products
CEO–Art Howe
Pres.–Tom Kenney
CMO–Greg Hallinan
CTO–Mitri Abou-Rizk

VICORP.COM
101 E. Park Blvd., Ste. 600-15, Plano, TX, 75054-5483, USA (972) 596-2969; e-mail sales@vicorp.com; info@vicorp.com; web site www.vicorp.com
Product or Service: Hardware/Software Supplier
CEO–Brendan Treacy
COO–Lee Cottle

VIDEO PIPELINE, INC.
16 S. Haddon Ave., Haddonfield, NJ, 08033, USA (856) 310-1981; fax (856) 427-9046; e-mail contact@videopipeline.com
Product or Service: Multimedia/Interactive Products
Pres.–Jed Horovitz
Gen. Mgr.–Tracy Haines
Retail Servs. Mgr.–David Onesti
Dir., Technology–Bob Kolo

VOCAL TELECOMMUNICATIONS
1815 S. Mayflower Ave., Monrovia, CA, 91016, USA (626) 357-2449; e-mail r.emerling@ieee.org
Product or Service: Telecommunications/Service Bureaus
Pres.–Ron Emerling

VOICE TECHNOLOGIES GROUP, INC.
2350 N. Forest Rd., Buffalo, NY, 14068-1296, USA (716) 689-6700 ext. 255; fax (716) 689-6800; e-mail info@vtg.com; web site www.vtg.com
Product or Service: Telecommunications/Service Bureaus
Sales Dir.–Joseph Miller
Mktg. Serv. Mgr.–Cathryn Apenowich

VOICEMAGIC, INC.
3400 Fernandina Rd., Columbia, SC, 29210, USA (803) 786-5812; fax (803) 750-7272; e-mail info@voicemagic.com; web site www.voicemagic.com
Product or Service: Telecommunications/Service Bureaus
Pres.–Dave Swetnam

VOICETEXT.COM
211 E. Seventh St., 12th Fl., Austin, TX, 78701, USA (512) 404-2300; fax (512) 479-6464; e-mail conference@voicetext.com; web site www.voicetext.com
Product or Service: Telecommunications/Service Bureaus
Pres.–Eileen Williams
Mgr., Audio Conference–Jennifer Mackin

VOICEWORLD
11201 N. 70th St., Scottsdale, AZ, 85254, USA (602) 922-5500; fax (602) 922-5572; e-mail brains@voiceworld.com; web site www.voiceworld.com
Product or Service: Hardware/Software Supplier
Pres.–Brian L. Berman

VOLT INFORMATION SCIENCES
1 Sentry Pkwy., Ste. 1000, Blue Bell, PA, 19422, USA (610) 825-7720; fax (610) 941-6874
Product or Service: Multimedia/Interactive Products
Pres.–Gerard Dipippo
Exec. Vice Pres./COO–Steven A. Shaw
Contact–John Stuart
Prodn.–Bob Epstein

VOXWARE, INC.
300 American Metro Blvd., Ste. 155, Hamilton, NJ, 08619, USA (609) 514-4100; fax (609) 514-4101; e-mail sales@voxware.com; web site www.voxware.com
Product or Service: Hardware/Software Supplier
Vice Pres., Sales/Bus. Devel.–Charlie Rafferdy

W

WPA FILM LIBRARY
16101 S. 108th Ave., Orland Park, IL, 60467, USA (708) 460-0555; fax (708) 460 0187; e-mail sales@wpafilmlibrary.com; web site www.wpafilmlibrary.com
Product or Service: Publisher/Media
Dir., Sales–Diane Paradiso

CARL WALTZER DIGITAL SERVICES, INC.
873 Broadway, Ste. 412, New York, NY, 10003-1234, USA (212) 475-8748; fax (212) 475-9359; e-mail wdigital@nyc.rr.com; web site www.waltzer.com
Product or Service: Telecommunications/Service Bureaus
Pres.–Carl Waltzer
Photographer–Bill Waltzer

WARNER MEDIA SERVICES
375 Hudson St., New York, NY, 10014, USA (212) 741-1136; fax (212) 243-8255; e-mail info@ivyhill-wms.com
Product or Service: CD-ROM Designer/Manufacturer, POP/Kiosk Designer
Exec. Vice Pres.–Arthur Kern

THE WASHINGTON TIMES CORP.
3600 New York Ave. NE, Washington, DC, 20002, USA (202) 636-3000; fax (202) 269-3419; e-mail general@washingtontimes.com; web site www.washingtontimes.com
Product or Service: Publisher/Media
Adv. Dir.–Michael R. Mahr
Circ. Dir.–Arthur D. Farber
Exec. Ed.–John F. Solomon
Mng. Ed.–Francis B. Coombs

WASHINGTONPOST.NEWSWEEK INTERACTIVE
1150 15th St., NW, Washington, DC, 20071-0001, USA (202) 334-6000; fax (703) 469-2995; web site www.washingtonpost.com
Product or Service: Publisher/Media
Exec. Ed.–Marcus Brauchli

WESSAN INTERACTIVE
3033 N. 93rd St., Omaha, NE, 68134, USA (402) 572-8200; fax (402) 572-7244; e-mail sales@wessan.com; web site www.wessan.com
Product or Service: Telecommunications/Service Bureaus
–Karen Westerfield
–Terry SanfordPres.s

WEST INTERACTIVE CORP.
11808 Miracle Hills Dr., Omaha, NE, 68154, USA (402) 963-1300; fax (402) 963-1602; e-mail sales@west.com; web site www.west.com
Product or Service: Multimedia/Interactive Products
Pres.–Nancee Berger
Vice Pres., Sales/Mktg.–Mack McKenzie

WIDECOM GROUP, INC.
7895 Tranmere Dr. Unit 207, Mississauga, ON, L5S 1V9, Canada (905) 712-0505; fax (905) 712-0506; e-mail info@widecom.com; widecom@widecom.com; web site www.widecom.com
Product or Service: Telecommunications/Service Bureaus
Vice Pres., Sales/Mktg.–Suneet Tuli

WINSTAR/NORTHWEST NEXUS, INC.
15821 NE Eighth St., Ste. W200, Bellevue, WA, 98008, USA (425) 455-5151; fax (206) 415-2500; e-mail sales@nwnexus.com; web site www.nwnexus.net
Product or Service: Online Service Provider and Internet Hosts
Pres.–Ed Morin
Vice Pres.–Ralph Sims

WIRELESS COMMUNICATIONS ASSOCIATION INTERNATIONAL
1333 H St. NW, Ste. 700 W., Washington, DC, 20005, USA (202) 452-7823; web site www.wcai.com
Product or Service: Trade Association
Pres.–Fred Cambell

WOLFF/SMG
1641 Common Pkwy., Macedon, NY, 14502, USA (315) 986-1155; fax (315) 986-1157; e-mail info@wolff-smg.com; web site www.wolff-smg.com
Product or Service: Advertising/Marketing Agency, Consultants, Graphic/Design Firm, Multimedia/Interactive Products

WOODWARD COMMUNICATIONS
801 Bluff St., Dubuque, IA, 52001, USA (563) 588-5687; fax (563) 588-5739; e-mail corpadmin@wcinet.com; web site www.wcinet.com
Product or Service: Publisher/Media
Pres.–Tom Yunt

WORLD INTERACTIVE NETWORK
3960 Broadway, 4th Fl., New York, NY, 10032-1543, USA (212) 740-4400; fax (212) 795-8553; e-mail winnet@panix.com; web site www.winglobal.com
Product or Service: Multimedia/Interactive Products
Vice Pres./Gen. Mgr.–Claudia Soifer
Exec. Producer, Multimedia–Charles David Padro

THE WRITERS ALLIANCE, INC.
12008 Golden Twig Ct., North Potomac, MD, 20878, USA (301) 926-4447; fax (301) 948-8028; e-mail john@journalist.com
Product or Service: Publisher/Media
Contact–John Makulowich

X

X'IT GROUP CREATIVE
22486 Almaden, Ste. 401, Mission Viejo, CA, 92691-1403, USA (949) 461-0358; fax (949) 830-3579; e-mail info@xgroup.com; sales@xgroup.com
Product or Service: Consultants
CEO–Ciaran Foley
Pres.–John MacDonald

XMISSION
51 E. 400 S, Ste. 200, Salt Lake City, UT, 94538, USA (801) 539-0852; fax (801) 539-0853; e-mail info@xmission.com; web site www.xmission.com
Product or Service: Online Service Provider and Internet Hosts
Founder–Howard Gordon
Pres.–Peter Ashdown
Gen. Mgr.–Sue Ashdown
Cor. Sales–Bret Jensen
Mktg. Mgr.–Bob Dobbs

XTIVIA
45 W. 25th St., 11th Fl., New York, NY, 10010, USA (212) 739-7450; e-mail nir.gryn@xtivia.com; web site www.xtivia.com
Product or Service: Consultants
CEO–Nir Gryn

Y

Y2M: YOUTH MEDIA AND MARKETING NETWORKS
100 City Hall Plz., Level 2, Boston, MA, 02108, USA (617) 248-9880; e-mail ss-rogers@y2m.com; web site www.y2m.com
Product or Service: Advertising/Marketing Agency
Vice Pres./Gen.Mgr.–Dina Witter Pradel
Dir., Strategic Devel./Opns.–Tom Peterson
Contact–Sara Steele-Rogers

YOSHO
1777 Borel Pl., Ste. 500, San Mateo, CA, 94402, USA (650) 358-5555; fax (650) 358-5556; e-mail info@yosho.com
Product or Service: Multimedia/Interactive Products
CEO–Mike McGrath
Bus. Mgr.–Elise Maramontes
Dir.-Engineering–Wallace Rutherford

Z

ZANE PUBLISHING, INC.
PO Box 1697, Woodstock, GA, 30188, USA (770) 795-9195; fax (770) 795-8495; e-mail stewart.cross@zane.com; web site www.zane.com
Product or Service: CD-ROM Designer/Manufacturer
Pres./COO–Stewart Cross

ZHIVAGO MANAGEMENT PARTNERS
381 Seaside Dr., Jamestown, RI, 02835, USA (401) 423-2400; e-mail kristin@zhivago.com; web site www.zhivago.com
Product or Service: Consultants
Pres.–Kristin Zhivago

PRIMARY CATEGORIES OF INTERACTIVE PRODUCTS AND SERVICES

ADVERTISING/MARKETING AGENCY

APCO Worldwide
ARC Research
Agency.Com
The Aker Partners, Inc.
The Answer Team Networks
Audio Service America Productions
Backe Difital Brand Marketing
Bender/Helper Impact
Black Star Publishing Co., Inc.
Blass Communications
Al Bredenberg Creative Services
Cramp + Tate, Inc.
Creative Direct
Customer Communications Group
Cyber Sales One, Inc.
Dana Communications
DoubleClick
Dreamscape Design, Inc.
Emergence Labs, Inc.
Epsilon Interactive
Film Artists Associates
G2 Direct & Digital
Godfrey
Hitchcock Fleming and Associates, Inc.
Holdcom
Hutchinson Associates, Inc.
International Demographics/The Media Audit
Ken Petretti Productions, LLC
Kobie Marketing, Inc.
Launch Agency
Lieberman Research Worldwide
M/C/C
Mall Marketing Media
Marke Communications, Inc.
McMonigle & Associates
MediaGraphics-Dev.Kinney/MediaGraphics, Inc.
Midwest Digital Communications
Newton Media Associates, Inc.
The Next Wave
Nicholson Kovac, Inc.
Nielsen
O'Halloran Advertising, Inc.
Tom O'Toole Communications Group
Origin Communications, Inc.
PTi
Precision Arts Advertising, Inc.
Rapp
Risdall Marketing Group
Sealander & Co.
SourceLink
The Stephenz Group
Sun Marketing, LLC
TNS
Tam Communications
Targetbase
Thomas Taber & Drazen
Tribal DDB
The Tucker Group
24/7 Real Media, Inc.
Wolff/SMG
Y2M: Youth Media and Marketing Networks

CD-ROM DESIGNER/MANUFACTURER

Aces Research, Inc.
Amerikids USA
Audio Service America Productions
Automated Graphic Systems
CD Technology
Corporate Disk Company
Dreamscape Design, Inc.
EDR/Beachwood Studios
interActive Publishing Corp.
Israel Faxx
Ken Petretti Productions, LLC
Level X LLC
Luminare
Media Design Group
Methodologie, Inc.
Modern Digital Post & Graphics
Proline Digital
Risdall Advertising Agency
Silver Oaks Communications
Star-Byte, Inc.
Sumeria, Inc.
Technicolor Packaged Media Services
Warner Media Services
Zane Publishing, Inc.

CONSULTANTS

APCO Worldwide
ARC Research
Agency.com
AIM Group / Classified Intelligence
Arlen Communications LLC
Audio Service America Productions
Automedia, Inc.
Borghetti Consulting Group
Branfman & Associates
ChannelNet
Chris Baker & Associates Ltd.
Ciber, Inc.
Cobbey & Associates Full Service Marketing Research
Creative Circle Media Solutions
The CyberMedia Group
DeskNet, Inc.
Digital Collections
Dreamscape Design, Inc.
FLI, Incorporated
Hutchinson Associates, Inc.
Interactive Educational Systems Design, Inc.
Interactive Marketing & Research, Inc.
Interactive Media Associates
Interactive Strategies
Interactive Visuals, Inc.
Ken Petretti Productions, LLC
Lazer-fare Media Services Ltd.
Logica, Inc.
Frank Magid Associates
Morpace International
Multimedia Research Group, Inc.
Planet Discover
Press+
Stoneman Law Offices Ltd.
Sussex County Online
Upshaw & Associates
Wolff/SMG
X'iT Group Creative
Xtivia
Zhivago Management Partners

GRAPHIC/DESIGN FIRM

Amasis
Atomic Imaging, Inc.
Audio Service America Productions
Beatley Gravitt Communications
Bersearch Information Services
Cosmos Communications, Inc.
DLS Design
Dreamscape Design, Inc.
D3, Inc.
ELFWorks 3D Construction Co.
Empire Information Services
Fisher Photography
Fusebox, Inc.
Hutchinson Associates, Inc.
Imagen, Inc.
Interactive Visuals, Inc.
Jablonski Design, Inc.
Ken Petretti Productions, LLC
Kinetic Corporation
L@IT2'D (LATITUDE)
Live Wire Productions
Logopremiums.com
Aaron Marcus and Associates, Inc.
Methodologie, Inc.
RG Creations, Inc.
Rezn8 Productions, Inc.
Risdall Marketing Group
Same Page.com
Laura Smith Illustration
Tsang Seymour Design, Inc.
Two Twelve
Wolff/SMG

HARDWARE/SOFTWARE SUPPLIER

Adaptive Optics Associates, Inc., A United Technologies Co.
Adobe Systems, Inc.
AdStar, Inc.
Adstream America
ADTRAN
Advanced Publishing Technology
Apple, Inc.
Aptas
Aspect Communications
Atex North America
Audio Service America Productions
BMC Group, Inc.
BackWeb
BlueCielo ECM Solutions
BroadVision
Broadxent, Inc.
Catalyst International, Inc.
Celebro
ChannelNet
College Publisher, Inc.
Computer Talk Technology, Inc.
Copia International Ltd.
Corel
Creative Circle Media Solutions
Cybertech, Inc.
Digital Collections
eBT
EASE CT Solutions
Edgil Associates, Inc.
Enigma
eSoft
ET Srl Elettronica Telecomunicazioni
Filestream, Inc.
GTEK
Harris & Baseview
Harris Publishing Systems
IBM Corp.
ILIO Entertainment
Infocus Corp.
infoPager Technologies, Inc.
Intactix
Interactive International, Inc.
JDA Software Group, Inc.
Jupiter Images Corp.
L-Soft International, Inc.
Lazer-fare Media Services Ltd.
Lender Support Systems, Inc.
MRW Communications, Inc.
MarCole Enterprises, Inc.
Media Marketing, Inc.
Micro Perfect Corp.
Microlog Corp.
Microsoft Corp.
Miles 33
Miles 33 International
MurkWorks, Inc.
NEC USA, Inc.
Open Text Corp.
Paper.net
PartsRiver-SAQQARA
Peirce-Phelps, Inc.
Pierian Spring Software
Planet Discover
Process Software
Ranger Data Technologies Inc.
SAP America, Inc.
Santronics Software
Scala, Inc.
Silicon Graphics, Inc.
SmartMax Software, Inc.
Software Consulting Services, LLC
Spar Associates, Inc.
Specialty Systems, Inc.
SunGard Securities Finance, Inc.
System Guides
3M Touch Systems, Inc.
Thunderstone Software LLC
Ulead Systems, Inc.
Unisys Corp.
Universal Technical Systems, Inc.
V-Channel, Inc.
Vertical Communications, Inc.
Vicorp.com
VoiceWorld
Voxware, Inc.

MULTIMEDIA/INTERACTIVE PRODUCTS

ACT Teleconferencing, Inc.
Advanced Communication Design, Inc.
Animated Software Co.
Anode, Inc.
Answers Media Inc.
Applied Art & Technology
Aptas
Asbury Park Press
Ascent Entertainment Group, Inc.
Assignment Desk
Audio Service America Productions
Authorlink
Autonomy, Inc.
BKJ Productions
BKR Studio, Inc.
Breze, Inc.
Broadcast Production Group (BPG)
CBS MaxPreps, Inc.
Chase Bobko, Inc.
citysearch.com
Classified Ventures, Inc.
CommGraphics Interactive, Inc.
Communication Design
Competence Software
CompetitivEdge Learning
Convergent Media Systems
Convergys
The Creators Media Group
CSTV Online, Inc.
Cybertech, Inc.
D-Squared Studios, Inc.
Daniel Lampert Communications Corp.
Design Media, Inc.
Dialog Corp.
Digital Design Group Limited
Digital Scribe
Digital Symphony
Direct Images Interactive, Inc.
Dow Jones Interactive Publishing
Dreamscape Design, Inc.
Dunn Solutions Group
EDR/Beachwood Studios
Envision Interactive
epic software group, Inc.
Family Features Editorial Syndicate, Inc.
Flip Your Lid
Four Palms, Inc.
Fujitsu Ten Corp. of America
GCN Publishing
HTS Interactive Health Care
HealthStream
Hoskyns & Associates
Hotwax Multimedia, Inc.
Iceni Technology
IconNicholson
Idealworks Presentations
Image Zone, Inc.
Imergy
Information Presentation Tech.
Inforonics, Inc.
InfoUse
Interactive Pictures Corporation (IPIX)
Interactive Visuals, Inc.
InterCom
Inventure, Inc.
Invision Marketing
JLM CD-ROM Publishing Co.
Judson Rosebush Co.
Ken Petretti Productions, LLC
Larson Texts Inc
Light Fantastic Studios, Inc
Logical Design Solutions
MarCole Enterprises, Inc.
Media Direct, Inc.
Media Enterprises
Media Logic LLC, USA
Mediabids, Inc.
MediaSpan Group, Inc.
MediaSpan Online Services
Methodologie, Inc.
Motion City Films
Moving Graphics
Multi-Media Communications
NVS Interactive Media

NY Information Technology Center
New Horizons Computer Learning Center
New Media Hollywood
Newman Brothers
Nuance Communications, Inc., Dictaphone Solutions
O&J Design, Inc.
OpenPages, Inc.
PA-SportsTicker
PR Newswire
Page Systems, Inc.
Pearson Education
Pixel Touch
Play Music, Inc.
Projects In Knowledge, Inc.
Proxios
Pyramid Studios
Red Hill Studios
Reece & Associates
Reuters Media
Ribit Productions, Inc.
Risdall Advertising Agency
Running With Scissors (RWS)
Scrambl-Gram, Inc.
SocialNet, Inc.
The Sports Network
SpotMagic, Inc.
Stockalert, Inc.
Stormfront Studios
Sumtotal System Inc.
TRX Interactive Communications, Inc.
TV Data (Tribune Media Services)
TreeHouseOne Interactive Productions
Tribune Media Services
TyJill Enterprises, Inc.
US Telephony Ltd.
UltiTech, Inc.
Unet 2 Corporation
VCampus Corp.
Verve Wireless, Inc.
Video Pipeline, Inc.
Volt Information Sciences
West Interactive Corp.
Wolff/SMG
World Interactive Network
Yosho

ONLINE SERVICE PROVIDER AND INTERNET HOSTS

AccuWeather, Inc.
AI Multimedia
APDI-Application Programming & Development, Inc.
ASTech InterMedia
Audio Service America Productions
B-Linked, Inc.
Business Wire - New York, NY
CableFAX Daily LLC
CBS MaxPreps, Inc.
Cogent Communications, Inc.
CompuServe Interactive Services, Inc.
Comtex News Network
Cybercon.com
Cyways, Inc.
Fast Channel Network
Ken Petretti Productions, LLC
MCI
MCI Enterprise Hosting
MarCole Enterprises, Inc.
Medforum
Mercury Center
Meteorlogix
Metro Newspaper
Omix, Inc. (Online Marketspace)
Power BBS Computing
PowerOne Media, Inc.
Prodigy, Inc.
State Net
Symantec Corp.
Synchronicity, Inc.
Tele-Publishing, Inc.
Telephone Doctor Customer Service Training
Thunderstone Software LLC
TownNews.com
Unet 2 Corporation
V!Studios
Verio, Inc.
WinStar/Northwest Nexus, Inc.
XMission

POP/KIOSK DESIGNER

Audio Service America Productions
Cybertech, Inc.
Dreamscape Design, Inc.
EDR/Beachwood Studios
E and E Display Group
Griffin Chase Oliver, Inc.
Ken Petretti Productions, LLC
Kiosk Information Systems
MarCole Enterprises, Inc.
Risdall Advertising Agency
Risdall Marketing Group
Warner Media Services

PUBLISHER/MEDIA

Active Data Exchange
Advance Internet, Inc.
Advertising Age
AIM Group / Classified Intelligence
America Online Digital City, Inc.
Amplified.com, Inc.
Aptas
Arizona Republic Digital Media
Associated Press Information Services
Bailey Broadcasting Services
BIAKelsey
Cineman Syndicate
Community Newspapers Co. Interactive Media Group
Congressional Quarterly, Inc.
Dex One Corp.
Digital Collections
EUR/Electronic Urban Report
Editor & Publisher Interactive
EDS (Electronic Data Systems)
HEC Reading Horizons
Hewlett-Packard Co.
InfoMedia, Inc.
Israel Faxx
Ken Petretti Productions, LLC
King Features Syndicate
Knight Mediacom
Los Angeles Times Syndicate New Media
MPI Teleproductions
MacTech Magazine
McClatchy Interactive
M2 Communications Ltd.
News USA, Inc.
Newsphere
North Valley Diver Publications
PC Today Magazine
PC World Online Services Group
PR & Marketing News
Penton Media
Presstime (Newspaper Association of America)
RISI, Inc.
Reuters Media
Simba Information
Tradewinds Publishing Co.
Unet 2 Corporation
United Media
VNU eMedia
WPA Film Library
The Washington Times Corp.
Washingtonpost.Newsweek Interactive
Woodward Communications
The Writers Alliance, Inc.

TELECOMMUNICATIONS/SERVICE BUREAUS

AT&T, Inc.
Advanced Telecom Services, Inc. (Canada)
Advanced Telecom Services, Inc.
Advanced Telecom Services, Inc. (U.K.)
Agility
The Arbitron Co.
Arch Communications, Inc.
Assignment Desk
Audio Service America Productions
C-T Innovations
Cablevision Systems Corporation
Captured Images, Inc.
Cascade Technologies, Inc.
CenturyTel Interactive
CommuniTech, Inc.
CommuniTech Services Inc.
Conservit Corporation
DAC Systems
Datavoice Technology
Dialogic Communications Corp.
Dialogic Corp.
ETC, Inc.
En Technology Corp.
First Data Voice Services
GREAT!
HTI Voice & Internet Solutions, Inc.
Innovative Systems Design, Inc.
Interactive Conferencing Network
Interalia Communications
LO/AD Communications
MCI
MPS Media Phone Service KG
MagnaCom Corp.
MicroVoice Applications, Inc.
Minacs Worldwide, Inc.
Motorola Paging
Motorola Personal Communications Sector
Movius Interactive Corporation
NEC Infrontia, Inc.
NVS Interactive Media
Network Telephone Services
Newscom
NewsStand, Inc.
Nextcom
Nicollet Technologies
Nortel
Octel Communications (Messaging Division)
PAGE Cooperative
Polycom, Inc.
Premiere Global Services, Inc.
SS8 Networks
Slingshot Technologies
Spanlink Communications
Sprint Nextel Corp.
Stok Software, Inc.
Syntellect, Inc.
Syntellect Interactive Services
TALX Corp.
Tadiran Telecom, Inc.
Telecompute Corp.
Teleperformance Interactive
TeleQuest
TelSpan, Inc.
Touch Tone Services
USA 800, Inc.
U.S. Netcom Corporation
Verizon Communications, Inc.
VoCal Telecommunications
Voice Technologies Group, Inc.
VoiceMagic, Inc.
VoiceText.com
Carl Waltzer Digital Services, Inc.
Wessan Interactive
WideCom Group, Inc.

TRADE ASSOCIATION

Software & Information Industry Association
Wireless Communications Association International

WEB SITE AUDITOR

ABC Interactive
Audio Service America Productions
Dreamscape Design, Inc.
Ken Petretti Productions, LLC

Section VI

Other Organizations and Industry Services

ADVERTISING/CIRCULATION NEWSPAPER PROMOTION SERVICES

CIRCULATION

CREATIVE MARKETING ASSOCIATES, INC.
3100 Broadway, Ste. 227, Kansas City, MO 64111
tel (816) 474-1400, fax (816) 753-2270
President – Maynard Small

LYON ENTERPRISES
4305 Cloud Dance, Santa Fe, NM 87507
tel (505) 473-1775, fax (505) 471-1665
e-mail: info@lyonenterprises.com
web site : http://www.lyonenterprises.com
President – Ray Lyon

PRO STARTS
46 Ravenna St. Ste B-1, Hudson OH 44236
tel (330) 650-5678; fax (330) 650-6898
e-mail: prostarts@aol.com
web site: http://www.prostarts.com
President – Tom Zgonc

SCRAMBL-GRAM, INC
5225 W Lakeshore Dr. Bldg 340, Port Clinton OH 43452
tel (419) 734-2600; fax (419) 734-2868
e-mail: info@scrambl-gram.com
web site: http://www.scrambl-gram.com
Co-Owner – Scott Bowers
Co-Owner – Slate Kessler
Sales/Promo Dir – Mary Elum Kessler
Adv. Mgr. – Scott Bowers

CONTESTS

CREATIVE MARKETING ASSOCIATES, INC
3100 Broadway, Ste. 227, Kansas City, MO 64111
tel (816) 474-1400; fax (816) 753-2270
President – Maynard Small

MARDEN-KANE, INC
36 Maple Pl, Manhasset , NY 11030-1962
tel (516) 365-3999; fax (516) 365-5520
e-mail: expert@mardenkane.com
web site: http://www.mardenkane.com
CFO – Alan Richter
Exec. Vice Pres – Leonard Bierman
Exec. Vice-Pres – Paul Goldman
Exec. Vice-Pres – Marc Wortsman
Vice-Pres – Fae Savignano
Vice-Pres – Jessie Auletti
Acct. Exec – Richard Facianella

MARKETING RESEARCH ASSOCIATES, INC.
3511 W 55th St, Minneapolis MN 55410
e-mail: asday@retailpromotions.com
web site: http://www.retailpromotions.com
CEO – Adam Scott Day

WINGO, LLC
12230 Forest Hills Blvd, Ste 110, Wellington, FL 33414
tel (561) 379-2635; fax (561) 792-8203
e-mail: sat@wingopromo.com
web site: http://www.amerimarketing.com
web site: http://wingopromo.com
President: Scott Thompson

COUPON INSERTS

FARAGO & ASSOCIATES
3240 Coolidge Hwy, Berkley MI 48072
tel (248) 546-7070; fax (248) 546-7521
President – Peter Farago
Dir. Finance – Bruce MacDonald
Dr. Operations – Scott Schofding
Production Mgr. Composing Graphics – Michael Schofding

NEWS AMERICA FSI
1185 Avenue of the Americas, 27th Floor
New York, NY 10036
tel (212) 782-8000; fax (212) 575-5847
web site: http://www.newsamerica.com
President – Chris Mixson
Sr. Vice-President – Robert Cole
Office Mgr – Maggie Smith
Sr. Vice President Marketing – Jessie Aversano
Atlanta, GA
3455 Peachtree Rd., Ste. 950, Atlanta, GA 30326
tel (404) 760-5950; fax (404) 237-0705
web site: http://www.newsamerica.com
Chicago, IL
303 E Wacker Dr., 21st Fl., Chicago IL 60601
tel (312) 540-4100; fax (312) 938-5456
web site: http://www.newsamerica.com
Dallas, TX
2626 Howell St., Ste 960, Dallas, TX 75204-2530
tel (214) 981-0800; fax (214) 953-3090
web site: http://www.newsamerica.com
Los Angeles, CA
2121 Avenue of the Stars, Los Angeles, CA 90067
tel (310) 407-2500; fax (310) 785-0862
website: http://www.newsamerica.com
Minneapolis, MN
150 S Sixth St., Ste 3400, Minneapolis MN 55402
tel (612) 395-7340; fax (612) 376-0990
web site: http://www.newsamerica.com
Wilton, CT
20 Westport Rd., Wilton, CT 06897
tel (203) 563-6600; fax (203) 845-9096
web site: http://www.newsamerica.com

VALASSIS COMMUNICATIONS, INC.
19975 Victor Pkwy, Livonia, MN 48152
tel (734) 591-3000; fax (734) 591-4503
e-mail: pr@valassis.com,
website: http://www.valassis.com
Chrmn/Pres/CEO – Alan F. Schultz
Exec Vice-Pres/CFO – Robert L. Recchia
Exec. Asst. – Mary Broaddus
Exec. Vice-Pres US Sales – Richard P Herpich
Exec. Vice-Pres Mfg/Opns – William F Hogg, Jr.
Costa Mesa, CA
1575 Corporate Dr., Costa Mesa CA 92626
tel (714) 918-5200; fax (714) 751-0584
web site: http://www.valassis.com
Dallas, TAX
600 N Cockrell Hill Rd., Dallas, TX 75211-1860
tel (214) 353-6200; fax (612) 338-3844
web site: http://www.valassis.com
Shelton, CT
6 Armstrong Rd., 2nd Fl., Shelton, CT 06484-4722
tel (203) 225-9400, website: http://www.valassis.com

EDUCATIONAL SERVICES
KNOWLEDGE UNLIMITED, INC
2310 Darwin Rd., Madison, WI 53704, P O Box 52, Madison, WI 53701
tel (608) 661-5666; fax (608) 442-1525
e-mail: csis@newscurrents.com
website: http://www.knowledgeunlimited.com
President – Judith Laitman

PROMOTIONAL MERCHANDISE

ATLAS FLAGS, INC
2010 Weems Rd., Tucker, GA 30084
tel (770) 938-0003, fax (770) 493-4083
e-mail: atlasflags@mindspring.com
web site: http://www.atlasflags.com
President – Fary Rosenthal
Vice-President /Sales Mgr – Robert Rosenthal

HOT OF FTHE PRESS PROMOTIONS, INC
P O Box 2848, New Smyrna Beach, FL 32170-2848
tel (386) 423-2396; fax (386) 423-2397
e-mail: info@hot-promos.com
web-site: http://www.hotoffthepress.com
President – Harry Campbell
Vice-President – Patricia Campbell

LYON ENTERPRISES
4305 Cloud Dance, Santa Fe, NM 87507
tel (505) 473-1775; fax 505-471-1665
e-mail: info@lyonenterprises.com
web site: http://www.lyonenterprises.com
President – Ray Lyon

RESEARCH

NADBANK-NEWSPAPER AUDIENCE DATABANK
890 Yonge St., Ste 200, Toronto, ON M4W 3P4
tel (416) 923-3569; fax (416) 923-4002
e-mail: acrassweller@nadbank.com
web site: http://www.nadbank.com
Exec. Dir. – Anne Crassweller
Client Services Dir – MeLing Johnston

SIMMONS MARKET RESEARCH BUREAU
29 Broadway, New York, NY 10006
tel (212) 863-4500; fax (212) 863-4495
web site: http://www.smrb.com
Chrmm/CEO – William Engel
Pres/COO – Chris Wilson
Exec. VP Simmons Local – Craig Harper
Acct. Mgr – Jeremy Gabor
VP Integrated Mktg/Sales – Gary Warech
Exec VP Mktg/New Bus Dev – Evan Goldfarb

SERVICES

COMMUNICATIONS SERVICE CO
P O Box 643, Antioch, IL 60002
tel (847) 395-9369; fax (847) 395-1231
President- Mark A Mehaffey

EYECATCHER PRODUCTIONS
2718 Westshire Dr., Hollywood CA 90068
tel (323) 467-7011
e-mail: frankpierson@gmail.com
Producer – Frank W Pierson

SELECTIVE MARKETING
P O Box 2956, Naples, FL 34106
tel (239) 649-0013; fax (239) 649-0013
President – John A. Mehaffey

ASSOCIATIONS, CLUBS, & PRESS CLUBS - NATIONAL & INTERNATIONAL

A

AAF College Chapters–1101 Vermont Ave. NW, Ste. 500, Washington, DC, 20005-3521 (202) 898-0089; fax (202) 898-0159; e-mail education@aaf.org; aaf@aaf.org; web site www.aaf.org
Pres./CEO James Datri
Sr. Vice Pres. Joanne Schecter
Elections held in June

Accrediting Council on Education in Journalism and Mass Communications1–Univ. of Kansas, Journalism School, Stauffer-Flint, 1435 Jayhawk Blvd., Lawrence, KS, 66045-7575 (785) 864-3973; fax (785) 864-5225; e-mail sshaw@ku.edu; web site www2.ku.edu/~acejmc
Vice. Pres. Jan Dates
Pres Peter Bhatia
Exec. Dir. Susanne Shaw

The Advertising Council, Inc.–815 2nd Ave., 9th Fl., New York, NY, 10016-2301 (212) 922-1500; fax (212) 922-1676; e-mail info@adcouncil.org; web site www.adcouncil.org

Advertising Media Credit Executives Association International–8840 Columbia 100 Pkwy., Columbia, MD, 21045 (410) 992-7609; fax (410) 740-5574; e-mail amcea@amcea.org; web site www.amcea.org
Pres. Mike Murphy
Elections held in Oct

The Advertising Research Foundation (ARF)–432 Park Ave. S., 6th Fl., New York, NY, 10016-4503 (212) 751-5656; fax (212) 319-5265; e-mail info@thearf.org; web site www.thearf.org
Elections held in March

American Advertising Federation–1101 Vermont Ave. NW, Ste. 500, Washington, DC, 20005-6306 (202) 898-0089; fax (202) 898-0159; e-mail aaf@aaf.org; web site www.aaf.org

American Association of Independent News Distributors–93 Second St., Harrison, NY, 10528-4611 (877) 462-2463; fax (914) 777-0406; e-mail info@aaind.org; web site www.aaind.org
Exec. Dir. Erik Zenhausern

American Association of Sunday and Feature Editors–1117 Journalism Bldg., College of Journalism, College Park, MD, 20742-7111 (301)

314-2631; fax (301) 314-9166; e-mail aasfe@jmail.umd.edu; web site www.aasfe.org
Pres. Denise Joyce
Exec. Dir. Kalyani Chadda
Elections held in Sept./Oct

American Business Media–675 3rd Ave., 7th Fl., New York, NY, 10017-5704 (212) 661-6360; fax (212) 370-0736; e-mail info@abmmail.com; web site www.americanbusinessmedia.com
Elections held in May

American Business Media Agricultural Council–675 Third Ave., New York, NY, 10017 (212) 661-6360; fax (212) 370-0736; e-mail info@abmmail.com; web site www.americanbusinessmedia.com
Exec. Dir. Todd Hittle

American Court & Commercial Newspapers, Inc.–484 Upland Ave., Pontiac, MI, 48340-1346 (248) 344-4329; fax (248) 334-2226
Exec. Dir. Carol Pierce
Elections held at annual meeting in fall

American Forest & Paper Association, Inc.–1111 19th St. NW, Ste. 800, Washington, DC, 20036-3562 (202) 463-2700; fax (202) 463-2040; e-mail info@afandpa.org; membership@afandpa.org; web site www.afandpa.org
Pres./CEO Donna Harman

AIGA, the professional association for design–164 Fifth Ave., New York, NY, 10010-5901; tel (001) (212) 807-1990; fax (212) 807-1799; e-mail general@aiga.org; web site www.aiga.org
COO Denise Wood
Exec. Dir. Richard Grefe
AIGA is the professional association for design, a nonprofit organization dedicated to advancing design as a professional craft, strategic tool and vital cultural force. Founded in 1914, AIGA today serves more than 22,000 members through 66 chapters and 200 student groups across the United States. AIGA stimulates thinking about design, demonstrates the value of design and empowers the success of designers at each stage of their careers.

American Jewish Press Association–1726 M St. NW, Ste. 750, Washington, DC, 20036-4573 (202) 250-6144; fax (202) 250-6151; e-mail info@aipa.org; web site www.ajpa.org
Pres Elana Kahn-Oren
Assoc. Dir. Natasha Nadel
Exec. Dir. Toby Dershowitz
Elections held in June

American Marketing Association–311 S. Wacker Dr., Ste. 5800, Chicago, IL, 60606 (312) 542-9000; fax (312) 542-9001; e-mail info@ama.org; web site www.marketingpower.com
Elections held in spring

American News Women's Club, Inc.–1607 22nd St. NW, Washington, DC, 20008 (202) 332-6770; fax (202) 265-6092; e-mail anwclub@comcast.net; web site www.anwc.org
Pres. Pam Ginsbach
Elections held in May.

American Newspaper Layout Managers Association (ANLOMA)–2442 Dr. Martin Luther King Jr. Blvd., Fort Meyers, FL, 33901-3904 (239) 335-0340; fax (239) 335-0205
Vice Pres. Jonathan Tolton
Pres. Robert Hammond
Yearly Conference - March/April

American Press Institute–11690 Sunrise Valley Dr., Reston, VA, 20191-1498 (703) 620-3611; fax (703) 620-5814; e-mail info@americanpressinstitute.org; web site www.americanpressinstitute.org
Exec. Dir./Pres. Andrew B. Davis
Vice Pres., Programming/Personnel Carol Ann Riordan
Dir., Tailored Solutions Elaine Clisham
Assoc. Dir. Mary Peskin

American Society of Journalists and Authors–1501 Broadway, Ste. 302, New York, NY, 10036-5505 (212) 997-0947; fax (212) 937-2315; e-mail staff@asja.org; web site www.asja.org
Exec. Dir. Alexandra Owens
Pres. Salley Shannon

American Society of News Editors–11690B Sunrise Valley Dr., Reston, VA, 20191-1436 (703) 453-1122; fax (703) 453-1133; e-mail asne@asne.org; web site www.asne.org
Exec. Dir. Richard Karpel
Elections held in April

Anglo-American Press Association of Paris–67 Rue Halle, Paris, 75014, France; tel (33) 1 4545 7400; e-mail axelkrause@wanadoo.fr; web site www.aapafrance.com
Sec. Gen. Axel Krause
British Co-Pres. Georgina Oliver
American Co-Pres. Gregory Viscusi

Asian American Journalists Association–5 Third Street, Suite 1108, San Francisco, CA, 94103 (415) 346-2051; fax (415) 346-6343; e-mail national@aaja.org; web site www.aaja.org
Contact Annabelle Udo-O'Malley

Associated Press Managing Editors Association–450 W. 33rd St., New York, NY, 10001-2603 (212) 621-1838; fax (212) 506-6102; e-mail apme@ap.org; web site www.apme.com
Gen. Mgr. Sally Jacobsen
Elections held in Oct

Association of Alternate Postal Systems–1725 Oaks Way, Oklahoma City, OK, 73131-1220 (405) 478-0006; e-mail aaps@cox.net; web site www.aapsinc.org
Exec. Dir. John White
Pres. Michael Lynch
Elections held at annual conference

Association of Alternative Newsmedia–1156 15th Street, NW Suite 905, Washington, DC, 20005, USA 202 289-8484; fax (202) 289-2004; e-mail web@aan.org; web site www.aan.org
Dir., Meetings/Special Projects Debra Silvestrin
Editorial Awards/Adv. Dir. Jason Zaragoza
Executive Director Tiffany Shackelford
Ed. Jon Whiten
Annual convention held in June.

Association of American Editorial Cartoonists–3899 N. Front St., Harrisburg, PA, 17110 -1583 (717) 703-3003; fax (717) 703-3008; e-mail info@pa-news.org; aaec@pa-news.org; web site www.editorialcartoonists.com
Manager Teresa Shaak
Elections held in Aug

Association of Canadian Advertisers, Inc.–95 Saint Clair Ave. W., Ste. 1103, Toronto, ON, M4V 1N6, Canada (416) 964-3805; fax (416) 964-0771; e-mail info@acaweb.ca; web site www.acaweb.ca
Vice Pres., Media/Research Bob Reaume
Pres./CEO Ron Lund
Vice Pres., Member Servs. Susan Charles
Elections held in Nov

Association for Education in Journalism and Mass Communication–234 Outlet Pointe Blvd., Ste. A, Columbia, SC, 29210-5667 (803) 798-0271; fax (803) 772-3509; e-mail aejmchq@aol.com; web site www.aejmc.org
Exec. Dir. Jennifer McGill
Bus. Mgr. Richard Burke
Elections held in March; conventions in early August.

Association of Food Journalists, Inc.–N/A, USA 505-466-4742; e-mail caroldemasters@yahoo.com; web site www.afjonline.com
Exec. Dir. Carol DeMasters
Election held in summer of even years

Association of National Advertisers, Inc.–708 Third Avenue , New York, NY, 10017 (212) 697-5950; fax (212) 687-7310; web site www.ana.net

Association of National Advertisers, Inc.–2020 K Street, NW, Suite 660 , Washington, DC, 20006 (202) 296-1883; fax (202) 296-1430; web site www.ana.net

Association of Opinion Page Editors–c/o Dept. of Public Information, Pennsylvania State University, 1 College Ave. Annex, University Park, PA, 16802 (814) 863-4717; fax (814) 869-9421; e-mail rburr@detnews.com or cfk3@psu.edu; web site www.aope.org
Or Lisa Powers Chris Koleno

Association of Schools of Journalism and Mass Communication–234 Outlet Pointe Blvd., Ste. A, Columbia, SC, 29210-5667 (803) 798-0271; fax (803) 772-3509; e-mail aejmchq@aol.com; web site www.asjmc.org
Exec. Dir. Jennifer McGill
Elections held in April

Association for Women in Communications–3337 Duke St., Alexandria, VA, 22314-5219 (703) 370-7436; fax (703) 342-4311; e-mail info@womcom.org; members@womcom.org; web site www.womcom.org
Chrmn. Judy Arent Morency
Exec. Dir. Pamela N. Valenzuela
Elections held via mail in the spring. Group and individual memberships only from all communications disciplines

Audit Bureau of Circulations (ABC)–48 W. Seegers Road, Arlington Heights, IL, 60005-3913 (224) 366-6939; fax (224) 366-6949; web site www.accessabc.com
Commun. Mgr. Kammi Altig
Vice Pres., Info Systems Kaydene Stachelski
Vice Pres., HR Laura Ferraris
Sr. Vice Pres., Mktg./Sales Mark Wachowicz
Chrmn. Merle Davidson
Pres./MD Michael J. Lavery
Sr. Vice Pres., Auditing/Technical Review Mike Moran
Sr. Vice Pres., Accounting Paul Fajnor
Sr. Vice Pres., Centralized/Electronic Auditing Scott Hanson
Vice Pres., Meetings Sue Thomas
Sr. Vice Pres., Publisher Rel./Field Auditing Teresa Perry

B

BBM Canada–1500 Don Mills Rd., 3rd Fl., Toronto, ON, M3B 3L7, Canada (416) 445-9800; fax (416) 445-8644; e-mail info@bbm.ca; web site www.bbm.ca
Vice Pres., Western Servs. Catherine Kelly
Corp. Scrvs. Dorena Noce
Exec. Vice Pres./CFO Glen Shipp
Exec. Asst. Heather Gillis
Pres./CEO Jim Mac Leod
Vice Pres., Meter Servs. Randy Missen
Vice Pres., Quebec Servs. Robert Langlois

BPA Worldwide–2 Corporate Dr., Ninth Fl., Shelton, CT, 06484-6259 (203) 447-2800; fax (203) 447-2900; web site www.bpaww.com
Chrmn. Carole A. Walker
Pres./CEO Glenn Hansen
Vice Pres., Commun. Karlene Lukeovitz
Sr. Vice Pres., Mktg. Servs. Peter D. Black
Sr. Vice Pres., Auditing Richard Murphy
Sr. Vice Pres., Mktg. Servs. Peter Black
Elections held in May

Baseball Writers Association of America–N/A (718) 767-2582; fax (718) 767-2583; e-mail bbwaa@aol.com
Secretary-Treasurer Jack O'Connell
Elections held in Oct

Business Marketing Association–1833 Center Point Cir., Ste 123, Naperville, IL, 60563-4868 (630) 544-5054; fax (630) 544-5055; e-mail info@marketing.org; web site www.marketing.org
Membership Mgr. Kelly Staley
Exec. Dir. Patrick Farrey
Elections held in June

C

Canadian Business Press–4195 Dundas St. W, Ste. 346, Toronto, ON, M8X 1Y4, Canada (416) 239-1022; fax (416) 239-1076; e-mail admin@cbp.ca; web site www.cbp.ca
Pres. Karen Dalton
Elections held in June. Will accept trade publications

Canadian Circulation Management Association–100 Belliveau Beach Rd., Pointe-Du-Chene, NB, E4P 3W6, Canada (506) 532-9186; fax (506) 855-1334; e-mail dorman@nbnet.nb.ca; web site www.ccmanet.ca
Sec. /Treasurer Dave Dorman
Elections held in June

Canadian Circulations Audit Board (CCAB, Inc.)–1 Concorde Gate Ste. 800, Toronto, ON, M3C 3N6, Canada (416) 487-2418; fax (416) 487-6405; e-mail info@bpaww.com; web site www.bpaww.com
Mktg. Mgr. Neil Ta
Elections held in April

Canadian Community Newspapers Association–890 Yonge St., Ste. 200, Toronto, ON, M4W 3P4, Canada (416) 482-1090; fax (416) 482-1908; e-mail info@ccna.ca; web site www.ccna.ca
Pres. John Hinds
Elections held in July

Canadian Newspaper Association–890 Yonge St., Ste. 200, Toronto, ON, M4W 3P4, Canada (416) 923-3567; fax (416) 923-7206; e-mail info@newspaperscanada.ca; web site www.newspaperscanada.ca
Pres./CEO John Hinds
Elections held in April.

Canadian Press, The - Toronto, ON–36 King St. E., Toronto, ON, M5C 2L9, Canada (416) 364-0321; fax (416) 364-0207; e-mail info@thecanadianpress.com; web site www.thecanadianpress.com
Chrmn. John Honderich
Pres. Eric Morrison
CFO David Ross
Chief, Ontario Servs. Wendy McCann
Vice Pres., Broadcasting Terry Scott
Vice Pres., French Servs. Jean Roy
Dir., HR Paul Woods
Office Mgr. Sharon Hockin
Exec. Dir. Philipe Mercure
Elections held in April

Canadian Printing Ink Manufacturers Association–52 Palmer Rd., Grimby, ON, L3M 5L4, Canada (905) 309-5883; fax (905) 309-5838; e-mail cpima@sympatico.ca; web site www.cpima.org
Exec. Dir./Sec./Treasurer Dorothea Nace
Pres. Neil Marshall
Vice Pres. Vivy da Costa

Elections held in Aug. for a two year term

Canadian Radio-Television News Directors Association–2175 Sheppard Ave. E., Ste. 310, Toronto, ON, M2J 1W8, Canada (416) 756-2213; fax (416) 491-1670; e-mail rtnda@taylorenterprises.com; info@rtndacanada.com; web site www.rtndacanada.com
Opns. Mgr.Sherry Denesha
Elections held in June

Catholic Press Association–205 W. Monroe St., Ste. 470, Chicago, IL, 60606-5011 (312) 380-6789; fax (312) 361-0256; e-mail cathjourn@catholicpress.org; web site www.catholicpress.org
Exec. Dir Timothy Walter
Elections held in Feb

College Media Advisers–VU Station B 351669, 2301 Vanderbilt Place, Nashville, TN, 37235-1669 (615) 322-6610; fax (615) 371-2968; e-mail chris.carroll@vanderbilt.edu; web site www.collegemedia.org
Executive Director Christopher Carroll
Elections held in Oct every two years.

Council for the Advancement of Science Writing, Inc.–PO Box 910, Hedgesville, WV, 25427-0910 (304) 754-6786; web site www.casw.org
Pres. John Lippincott
Pres. Cristine Russell
Exec. Dir. Ben Patrusky
Admin. Diane McGurgan
Elections held in May. Not a membership organization

Council for Advancement and Support of Education–1307 New York Ave. NW, Ste. 1000, Washington, DC, 20005-4726 (202) 328-2273; fax (202) 387-4973; e-mail memberservicecenter@case.org; web site www.case.org
Exec. Dir. Ben Patrusky
Pres. Cristine Russell
Admin. Diane McGurgan
Pres. John Lippincott
Elections held in July.

D

The Direct Marketing Association, Inc.–1120 Ave. of the Americas, New York, NY, 10036-6700 (212) 768-7277; fax (212) 302-6714; web site www.the-dma.org
CEO Lawrence M. Kimmel
Elections held in Oct

Dog Writers' Association of America–173 Union Rd., Coatesville, PA, 19320-1326, USA (610) 384-2436; fax (610) 384-2471; e-mail dwaa@dwaa.org; web site www.dwaa.org
Sec. Pat Santi
Pres. Dr. Carmen Battaglia
Pres. Carmen Battaglia
Elections held in Feb. Writers contest closes Sept. 1 each year

E

European Newspaper Publishers' Association–Square du Bastion 1A, Bte 3, 1050 Bruxelles, Belgium; tel (32) 2 551 0190; fax 551 0199; e-mail enpa@enpa.be; web site www.enpa.be
Dir. Valtteri Niiranen
Office Mgr. Viviane Garceau
The ENPA is an association of European daily newspaper publishers organizations

F

Foreign Press Association–333 E. 46th St., Ste. 1K, New York, NY, 10017-7426 (212) 370-1054; fax (212) 370-1058; e-mail fpanewyork@aol.com
Gen. Sec. Agnes Niemetz
Pres. Alan Capper
Vice Pres. David Michaels
Asst. Gen. Sec. Hadar Harel
Treasurer Jan Latus
Asst. Treasurer Roberto Socas
Elections held in Dec

The 4 A's–405 Lexington Ave., 18th Fl., New York, NY, 10174-1801 (212) 682-2500; fax (212) 682-8391; e-mail info@aaaa.com; web site www.aaaa.org
Election held in April

Freedom Forum–555 Pennsylvania Ave. NW, Washington, DC, 20001-2114 (202) 292-6100; e-mail news@freedomforum.org; info@newseum.org; web site www.freedomforum.org
Chrmn./CEO Charles L. Overby
Sr. Vice Pres., Int'l Programs Chris Wells
Vice Pres., Opns. James Thompson
Sr. Vice Pres., Devel. Mary Kay Blake
Sr. Vice Pres., Finance Nicole Mandeville
Vice Pres., Mktg. Susan Bennett
Not a membership organization

G

Graphic Communications Council–1899 Preston White Dr., Reston, VA, 20191-4367 (703) 264-7200; fax (703) 620-0994; e-mail npes@npes.org; web site www.npes.org
Administrator Carol J. Hurlburt
Asst. Dir., Membership Carol Lee Hawkins

Graphic Communications International Union–1900 L St. NW, Washington, DC, 20036-5080 (202) 462-1400; fax (202) 721-0600; web site www.gciu.org
Sec./Treasurer Gerald Deneau
Elections held quadrennially.

Gravure Association of America–PO Box 25617, Rochester, NY, 14625, usa (201) 523-6042; fax (201) 523-6048; e-mail gaa@gaa.org; web site www.gaa.org
Pres./CEO Bill Martin
Exec. Dir. Bernadette Carlson
Dir. Michelle Jones Aronowitz
Ed. Roger Ynosroza
Elections held in April

H

Hebdos Qu bec–538 Place St. Henri, Montreal, QC, H4C 2R9, Canada (514) 861-2088; fax (514) 861-1966; e-mail communications@hebdos.com; web site www.hebdos.com
Chair of the Board Charles couture
Exec. Dir. Gilber Paquette
Elections held in May.

I

Independent Free Papers of America–107 Hemlock Dr., Rio Grande, NJ, 08242-1731 (609) 408-8000; fax (609) 889-0141; web site www.ifpa.com
Exec. Dir. Gary Rudy
Elections held in Sept

Inter American Press Association–1801 SW 3rd Ave., 8th Fl., Miami, FL, 33129-1487 (305) 634-2465; fax (305)635-2272; e-mail info@sipiapa.org; web site www.sipiapa.org
Librarian Alfonso Juarez
Exec. Dir. Julio Munoz
Elections held in Nov

Intermarket Agency Network–5307 S. 92nd St., Hales Corners, WI, 53130-1677 (414) 425-8800; fax (414) 425-0021; web site www.intermarketnetwork.com; www.nonbox.com
Exec. Dir. Bill Eisner

International Advertising Association, Inc.–275 Madison Ave., Ste. 2102, New York, NY, 10016-1118 (212) 557-1133; fax (212) 983-0455; e-mail iaa@iaaglobal.org; membership@iaaglobal.org; web site www.iaaglobal.org
Mgr. IT. Karl Kam
Exec. Dir. Michael Lee
Elections held every two years at the IAA World-Advertising Congress. The IAA is a global partnership of advertisers, agencies, and media. The Association has 3,700 members in 95 countries, 105 corporate members, 65 organizational members and 61 chapters

International Association of Business Communicators (IABC)–1 Hallidie Plz., Ste. 600, San Francisco, CA, 94102-2842 (415) 544-4700; fax (415) 544-4747; e-mail service_centre@iabc.com; web site www.iabc.com
Pres./CEO Julie Freeman
Elections held at international conference

International Association of Sports Newspapers (IASN)–7 rue Geoffroy Saint Hilaire, Paris, 75005, France; tel (33) 1 47 42 85 29; fax 47 42 49 48; e-mail rcuccoli@press-iasn.org; web site www.press-iasn.org
Sec. Gen. Rosarita Cuccoli

International Center for Journalists–1616 H St. NW, 3rd Fl., Washington, DC, 20006 (202) 737-3700; fax (202) 737-0530; e-mail editor@icfj.org; web site www.icfj.org
Commn. Mgr. Dawn Arteaga
Treasurer Jack Hamilton
Chrmn. James F. Hoge
Pres. Joyce Barnathan
Vice Pres., Finance Nancy Frye
Vice Pres., Programs Patrick Butler
International Center for Journalists is not a membership organization. It is a nonprofit organization dedicated to improving journalism worldwide.

International Labor Communications Association AFL/CIO/CLC–815 16th St.,NW, Washington, DC, 20006-4101 (202) 637-5068; fax (202) 637-5069; e-mail ilca@aflcio.org; web site www.ilcaonline.org
Pres. Steve Stallone
Elections held biennially.

International Newspaper Marketing Association, Inc.–PO Box 740186, Dallas, TX, 75374-0186 (214) 373-9111; fax (214) 373-9112; e-mail inma@inma.org; web site www.inma.org
Exec. Dir. Earl J. Wilkinson
Elections held in May

International Prepress Association–7200 France Ave., Ste. 223, Edina, MN, 55435 (952) 896-1908; e-mail info@ipa.org; web site www.ipa.org
Exec. Asst. Donna McDevitt
Pres. Steven Bonoff
Elections held in Oct.

International Press Club of Chicago (IPCC)–5220 Ellington, Western Springs, IL, 60558-2035 (708) 246-5556; e-mail info@ipcc.org; web site www.ipcc.org
Pres. Harry Lepinske
Weekly luncheon meeting at noon every Wednesday at Tavern Club, 25th Floor, 333 N. Michigan.
Chicago Journalism Hall of Fame Dinner

International Press Institute–Spiegelgasse 2, Vienna, A-1010, Austria; tel (43) 1 512 9011; fax 512 9014; e-mail ipi@freemedia.at; web site www.freemedia.at
Dir. David Dadge
Elections held annually on a rotation basis

International Society of Weekly Newspaper Editors–Missouri Southern State Univ., 3950 E. Newman Rd., Joplin, MO, 64801-1595 (417) 625-9736; fax (417) 659-4445; e-mail stebbins-c@mssu.edu; web site www.iswne.org
Exec. Dir. Chad Stebbins
Elections held in July

Investigative Reporters and Editors (IRE)–141 Neff Annex, Columbia, MO, 65211 (573) 882-2042; fax (573) 882-5431; e-mail info@ire.org; web site www.ire.org
Exec. Dir. Mark Horvit
Elections held in June

J

Japan Newspaper Publishers & Editors Association–c/o NAA, 4401 Wilson Blvd., Ste. 900, Arlington, VA, 22203-4915 (571) 366-1180; fax (571) 366-1195; web site www.pressnet.or.jp/english/index.htm
North American Rep. Ryuta Araki

K

Kappa Alpha Mu Honorary Society in Photo Journalism–316F Lee Hills Hall, Columbia, MO, 65211-1370 (573) 882-4882; fax (573) 882-5737; web site photojournalism.missouri.edu
Chrmn. David Rees
Dir. Rick Shaw
Director of Photography, Assistant Professor Brian Kratzer
An affiliate of the National Press Photographers Association. Elections held in the fall

Kappa Tau Alpha National Honor Soc. for Journ. & Mass Comm.–Univ. of Missouri, 76 Gannett Hall, Columbia, MO, 65211-1200 (573) 882-7685; fax (573) 884-1720; e-mail umcjourkta@missouri.edu; web site www.kappataualpha.org
Exec. Dir./Treasurer Keith P. Sanders
President W. Joseph Campbell
Vice-President Peter Gade
Pres. Dr. Jane B. Singer
Pres. Jane B. Singer
Elections held every two years

L

League of Advertising Agencies, Inc.–65 Reade St., Ste. 3A, New York, NY, 10007 (212) 528-0364; fax (212) 766-1181; web site www.adagencies.org
Exec. Dir. Deana Boles
Pres. Lori Fabisiak
Treasurer Mark Levit
Sec. Mindy Gale
Vice Pres. Richard Harrow
Elections held in May

M

Marketing Advertising Global Network–1017 Perry Hwy., Ste. 5, Pittsburgh, PA, 15237 -2173, USA (412) 366-6850; fax (412) 366-6840; e-mail cheri@magnetglobal.org; web site www.magnetglobal.org
Executive Director Cheri Gmiter
Elections held in Oct

Media Alliance–1904 Franklin St., Ste. 500, Oakland, CA, 94612 (510) 832-9000; fax (510) 238-8557; e-mail information@media-alliance.org; web site www.media-alliance.org
Exec. Dir. Tracy Rosenberg
Pgm. Dir. Eloise Lee

Media Financial Management Association–550 West Frontage Road, Ste. 3600, Northfield, IL, 60093 847/716-7000; fax 847-716-7004; e-mail info@mediafinance.org; web site www.mediafinance.org
President & CEO Mary Collins
Vice Pres./Exec. Dir. Robert J. Kasabian

Media Human Resources Association–1800 Duke St., Alexandria, VA, 22314-3494 (703) 548-3440; fax (703) 739-0399; e-mail shrm@shrm.org; web site www.shrm.org
Pres. Laurence O'Neil
Elections held in June

N

NPES–1899 Preston White Dr., Reston, VA, 20191-4367 (703) 264-7200; fax (703) 620-0994; e-mail npes@npes.org; web site www.npes.org
Dir., Commun. Judy Durham
Pres. Ralph Nappi
Chrmn. Tom Saggiomo
NPES is the association for suppliers of printing, publishing and converting technologies. Elections held at fall meeting

National Association of Black Journalists–8701-A Adelphi Rd., Adelphi, MD, 20783-1716 (301) 445-7100; fax (301) 445-7101; e-mail nabj@nabj.org; web site www.nabj.org
Exec. Dir. Karen Wynn Freeman
Pres. Kathy Times
Elections held every two years

National Association of Broadcasters–1771 N St. NW, Washington, DC, 20036 (202) 429-5300; fax (202) 429-4199; e-mail nab@nab.org; web site www.nab.org
Joint Board Chrmn. Bruce T. Reese
COO/CFO Janet McGregor
Elections held once in two years.

National Association of Credit Management–8840 Columbia 100 Pkwy., Columbia, MD, 21045-2158 (410) 740-5560; fax (410) 740-5574; e-mail info@nacm.org; web site www.nacm.org
Dir., Commun. Caroline Zimmerman
Treasurer James E. Vanghel
Pres. Robin D. Schauseil
Elections held in May

National Association of Hispanic Journalists–529 14th St. NW, 1000 National Press Bldg., Washington, DC, 20045 (202) 662-7145; fax (202) 662-7144; e-mail nahj@nahj.org; web site www.nahj.org
Exec. Dir. Ivan Roman

National Association of Hispanic Publications–8400 W. Park Dr., 2nd Fl., McLean, VA, 22102 (703) 610-9000; fax (703) 610-9005; web site www.nahp.org
Exec. Dir. Kerry Stackpole
Elections held every two years

National Association of Science Writers–N/A, United States; tel ((510) 647-9500) 510647-500; e-mail director@nasw.org; web site www.nasw.org

National Association for Printing Leadership–75 W. Century Rd., Ste. 100, Paramus, NJ, 07652 (201) 634-9600; fax (201) 634-0324; e-mail info@napl.org; web site www.napl.org
Pres./CEO Joseph Truncale
Elections held in Oct

National Association of Real Estate Editors (NAREE)–1003 NW 6th Terr., Boca Raton, FL, 33486 (561) 391-3599; fax (561) 391-0099; e-mail madkimba@aol.com; web site www.naree.org
Exec. Dir. Mary Doyle-Kimball
Elections held in Oct

National Association of Real Estate Publishers–165 Jackson St., Sandusky, OH, 44870 (419) 621-2142; fax (419) 621-2134; e-mail et@adwriter.com; web site www.narep.org
Sec. Edward Toomey
Elections held in May

National Association of Science Writers–N/A; tel (1) 510-647-9500; e-mail director@nasw.org; web site www.nasw.org

National Cartoonists Society–341 N. Maiteland Ave., Ste. 130, Maiteland, FL, 32751 (407) 647-8839; fax (407) 629-2502; e-mail crowsegal@crowsegal.com; web site www.reuben.org
Pres. Jeff Keane
Elections held annually

National Conference of Editorial Writers–3899 N. Front St., Harrisburg, PA, 17110-1583 (717) 703-3015; fax (717) 703-3014; e-mail ncew@pa-news.org; web site www.ncew.org
Pres. Tom Waseleski
Elections held in Sept

National Federation of Press Women–PO Box 5556, Arlington, VA, 22205 (703) 812-9487; fax (703) 812-4555; e-mail presswomen@aol.com; web site www.nfpw.org
Pres. Marsha Shuler
Elections held odd years in June

National Lesbian and Gay Journalists Association–1420 K St. NW, Ste. 910, Washington, DC, 20005 (202) 588-9888; fax (202) 588-1818; e-mail info@nlgja.org; web site www.nlgja.org
Pres. David Barrie
Elections held annually

National Newspaper Association–134 Neff Annex, Columbia, MO, 65211-1200 (573) 882-5800; fax (573) 884-5490; e-mail info@nna.org; web site www.nna.org
Exec. Dir. Brian Steffens
Assoc. Dir. Lynn Edinger
Officer elections held in Sept during Annual Convention; annual Government Affairs Conference in March; annual Better Newspaper Contest entry deadline March 31

National Newspaper Publishers Association Black Press of America–3200 13th St. NW, Washington, DC, 20010-2410 (202) 319-1292; fax (202) 319-0963; e-mail nnpadc@nnpa.org; web site www.nnpa.org
Interim Exec. Ed. Hazel Trice Edney
Elections held every two years in June.

National Paper Trade Association, Inc.–401 N. Michigan Ave., Ste. 2200, Chicago, IL, 60611 (312) 321-4092; fax (312) 673-6736; e-mail npta@gonpta.com; web site www.gonpta.com
Pres. Newell Holt
Elections held in Oct

National Press Club–529 14th St. NW, National Press Bldg., Washington, DC, 20045 (202) 662-7500; fax (202) 662-7569; web site www.npc.press.org
Pres. Jerry Zremski
Elections held in Nov

National Press Foundation–1211 Connecticut Ave. NW, Ste. 310, Washington, DC, 20036-2709 (202) 663-7280; fax (202) 530-2855; e-mail npf@nationalpress.org; web site www.nationalpress.org
Pres. Bob Meyers

National Press Photographers Association, Inc.–3200 Croasdaile Dr., Ste. 306, Durham, NC, 27705 (919) 383-7246; fax (919) 383-7261; e-mail info@nppa.org; web site www.nppa.org
Exec. Dir. Jim Straight
Membership Dir. Mindy Hutchison
Elections held in June

National Retail Federation–325 7th St. NW, Liberty Pl., Ste. 1100, Washington, DC, 20004 (202) 783-7971; fax (202) 737-2849; web site www.nrf.com
CFO Carleen C. Kohut
Pres. Tracy Mullin
Elections held in Jan

National Scholastic Press Association–2221 University Ave. SE, Ste. 121, Minneapolis, MN, 55414 (612) 625-8335; fax (612) 626-0720; e-mail info@studentpress.org; web site www.studentpress.org
Exec. Dir. Logan Aimone

The National Society of Newspaper Columnists, Inc.–PO Box 411532, San Francisco, CA, 941410-1532 (412) 722-7030; fax (866) 635-5759; e-mail director@columnists.com; web site www.columnists.com
Exec. Dir. Luenna Kim
Annual conference held in June.

National Writers Association–10940 S. Parker Rd., Ste. 508, Parker, CO, 80134; tel (1) 303 (303) 841-0246; fax (303) 841-2607; e-mail natlwritersassn@hotmail.com; web site www.nationalwriters.com
Exec. Dir. Sandy Whelchel

Native American Journalists Association–395 W. Lindsey St., Norman, OK, 73019-4201 (405) 325-9008; fax (405) 325-7565; e-mail info@naja.com; web site www.naja.com
Pres. Cristina Azocar
Interim. Dir. Jeff Harjo
Elections held in August

NEW YORK MEDIA CREDIT GROUP–1100 MAIN STREET, BUFFALO, NY, 14209; tel (716-885-4444) 716-885-4444; e-mail info@abc-amega.com
Regional Account Manager Robert Gagliardi
Pres. Nina Link
Dir. Vaughn P. Benjamin
Elections held in March

News Limited of Australia–1211 Ave. of the Americas, 9th Floor, New York, NY, 10036 (212) 852-7600
Bureau Chief Phil Correy

Newspaper Association of America–4401 Wilson Blvd., Ste. 900, Arlington, VA, 22203-1867 (571) 366-1000; fax (571) 366-1195; e-mail sheila.owens@naa.org; web site www.naa.org
Elections held in April/May

Newspaper Association Managers, Inc.–PO Box 458, Essex, MA, 091929 (978) 210-6832; web site www.nammanagers.com
Exec. Dir. Morley Piper
Elections held in Aug

The Newspaper Guild-CWA–501 Third St. NW, 6th Fl., Washington, DC, 20001, USA (202) 434-7177; fax (202) 434-1472; e-mail guild@cwa-union.org; web site www.newsguild.org
President Bernard Lunzer
Secretary/Treasurer Carol Rothman
International Chairperson Martha Waggoner

Newspaper Purchasing Management Association, Inc.–1313 N. Market St. 10th Fl., Wilmington, DE, 19801-6101 (302) 830-9667; fax (302) 830-9982; e-mail michael_kelly@newspapersupport.com; web site www.npma.net
Pres. Mike Kelly
Elections held in May

North American Agricultural Journalists–2604 Cumberland Ct., College Station, TX, 77845 (614) 292-9637; fax (614) 292-2270; e-mail ka-phillips@tamu.edu; web site www.naaj.net
Exec. Sec./Treasurer Kathleen Phillips
Elections held in April

North American Mature Publishers Association–1140 Jupiter Rd., Camdenton, MO, 65020 (877) 466-2672; fax (573) 873-9993; e-mail kzarky@maturepublishers.com; web site www.maturepublishers.com
Exec. Dir. Karen Zarky
Election held in Nov

O

Online Publishers Association–249 W. 17th St., New York, NY, 10011 (212) 204-1488; fax (212) 204-1514; e-mail info@online-publishers.org; web site www.online-publishers.org

Organization of News Ombudsmen–c/o Jeffrey Dvorkin, 775 Manning Ave., Toronto, ON, M6G 2W7, Canada; tel (+1) 416 537-2892; e-mail jdvorkin@newsombudsmen.org; web site www.newsombudsmen.org
Exec. Dir. Jeffrey Dvorkin
Elections held in May

Outdoor Advertising Association of America (OAAA)–1850 M St. NW, Ste. 1040, Washington, DC, 20036-5803 (202) 833-5566; fax (202) 833-1522; e-mail info@oaaa.org; web site www.oaaa.org

Outdoor Writers Association of America, Inc.–121 Hickory St., Ste. 1, Missoula, MT, 59801 (406) 728-7434; fax (406) 728-7445; web site www.owaa.org
Exec. Dir. Kevin Rhoades
Elections held in Spring

Overseas Press Club of America–40 West 45 Street, New York, NY, 10036, United States of America; tel (1) 212 (212) 626-9220; fax (212) 626-9210; web site www.opcofamerica.org
Exec. Dir. Sonya K. Fry
President David Andelman
Elections held in late summer

P

PO Box 7905–N/A N/A

Printing Industries of America–200 Deer Run Rd., Sewickley, PA, 15143-2324 (412) 741-6860; fax (412) 741-2311; e-mail printing@printing.org; web site www.printing.org
Mktg. Mgr. Lisa Erdner

Printing, Publishing & Media Workers Sector-CWA–501 3rd St. NW, Ste. 950, Washington, DC, 20001-2797 (202) 434-1106; fax (202) 434-1482; e-mail bshippe@cwa-union.org; web site www.cwa-union.org
Pres. Larry Cohen
Elections to be held at CWA convention in August 2008.

Professional Football Writers of America (PFWA)–11345 Frontage Ave., Maryland Heights, MO, 63043 (314) 298-2681; e-mail hbalzer@aol.com; web site www.pfwa.org
Secretary Howard Balzer
Elections held in Jan

Promotion Marketing Association, Inc.–257 Park Ave. S., Ste. 1102, New York, NY, 10010-7304 (212) 420-1100; fax (212) 533-7622; e-mail pma@pmalink.org; web site www.pmalink.org
Elections held in June

Promotional Products Association International–3125 Skyway Cir. N., Irving, TX, 75038 (972) 252-3000; fax (972) 258-3004; e-mail pr@ppai.org; web site www.ppai.org
Vice Pres., Mktg./Commun. Paul Bellantone
Pres./CEO Steve Slagle

Public Relations Society of America, Inc.–33 Maiden Ln. 11th Fl., New York, NY, 10038 (212) 460-1400; fax (212) 995-0757; e-mail hq@prsa.org; web site www.prsa.org
Pres. Willam Murray
Elections held in October

Q

Quill and Scroll Society–Univ. of Iowa School of Journalism and Mass Comm., 100 Adler Journalism Bldg., Ste. E346, Iowa City, IA, 52242-1528 (319) 335-3457; fax (319) 335-3989; e-mail quill-scroll@uiowa.edu; web site www.uiowa.edu/~quill-sc

R

Radio Television Digital News Association–4121 Plank Rd., Ste. 512, Fredericksburg, VA, 22407 (202) 659-6510; fax (202) 223-4007; e-mail rtnda@rtdna.org; web site www.rtdna.org
Exec. Dir. Jane Nassiri

Elections held in Sept

Regional Reporters Association–529 14th St., Ste. 1255, Washington, DC, 20045-2201 (202) 408-2705; e-mail president@rra.org; web site www.rra.org
Sec. Adrianne Flynn
Pres. Suzanne Struglinski

Religion Newswriters Association–309 South State Street, Westerville, OH, 43081, US (573) 355-5201; fax 888-707-3755; e-mail debramason@rna.org; web site www.rna.org
Exec. Dir. Debra L. Mason
Bus./HR Mgr. Michelle Stacho
Assoc. Dir. Tiffany A. McCallen

Reporters Committee for Freedom of the Press–1101 Wilson Blvd., Ste. 1100, Arlington, VA, 22209-1817 (703) 807-2100; fax (703) 807-2109; e-mail rcfp@rcfp.org; web site www.rcfp.org
Exec. Committee Dahlia Lithwick
Exec. Dir. Lucy A. Dalglish
Exec. Committee Neil Lewis
Exec. Committee Tony Mauro

S

Sales and Marketing Executives International–PO Box 1390, Sumas, WA, 98295-1390 (312) 893-0751; fax (604) 855-0165; e-mail willis.turner@smei.org; web site www.smei.org
Pres./CEO Willis Turner
Elections held on a rolling basis

Society of American Business Editors and Writers, Inc.–University of Missouri, 30 Neffannex, Columbia, MO, 65211-1200 (573) 882-7862; fax (573) 884-1372; e-mail sabew@missouri.edu; web site www.sabew.org
Exec. Dir. Warrden Watson
Elections held in April

Society of American Travel Writers, Inc.–7044 S. 13th St., Oak Creek, WI, 53154 (414) 908-4949; fax (414) 768-8001; e-mail satw@satw.org; web site www.satw.org
Exec. Dir. Nancy Short

Society of Environmental Journalists (SEJ)–115 W Ave., Suite 301, Jenkintown, PA, 19046, USA (215) 884-8174; fax (215) 884-8175; e-mail sej@sej.org; web site www.sej.org
Exec. Dir. Beth Parke
Dir.,Pgm. Chris Rigel
Elections held in Oct.

Society for News Design, Inc.–424 E. Central Blvd., Ste. 406, Orlando, FL, 32801 (401) 294-5233; fax (401) 294-5238; e-mail snd@snd.org; web site www.snd.org
Exec. Dir. Stephen Komives
Elections held in fall prior to annual workshop exhibition

Society of Professional Journalists–3909 N. Meridian St., Indianapolis, IN, 46208 (317) 927-8000; fax (317) 920-4789; e-mail spj@spj.org; web site www.spj.org
Pres. Dave Aeikens
Exec. Dir. Joe Skeel
Elections held in Oct

Society of the Silurians–PO Box 1195, New York, NY, 10159, United States (212) 532-0887; fax (212) 532-0887; e-mail silurians@aol.org; web site www.silurians.com
President Tony Guida
Elections held in April

Special Libraries Association, News Division–331 S. Patrick St., Alexandria, VA, 22314-3501 (703) 647-4900; fax (703) 647-4901; e-mail sla@sla.org; web site www.sla.org
CEO Janice R. Lachance
COO/CFO Nancy A. Sansalone
Dir., Exec. Office Relations
Natasha Kenner
Elections held in May

Suburban Newspapers of America–116 Cass St., Traverse City, MI, 49684 (888) 486-2466; fax (231) 932-2985; web site www.suburban-news.org
Vice Pres., Sales/Mktg. Al Cupo
Mktg. Mgr. Kimberly Cole
Pres. Nancy Lane
Elections held in the fall

T

Technical Association of the Graphic Arts–200 Deer Run Rd., Sewickley, PA, 15143 (412) 259-1706; fax (412) 741-2311; web site www.printing.org
Managing Director Mark Bohan
Elections held in February

Trans-Canada Advertising Agency Network–504-401 Bayview Ave., Toronto, ON, M2M 3Z7, Canada (416) 221-6984; fax (416) 221-8260; e-mail marketingmonkey@sympatico.ca; wwsr@rogers.com; web site www.tcaan.ca
Exec. Dir. Alice Zaharchuk
Mng. Dir./Treasurer Bill Whitehead

U

United Nations Correspondents Association–United Nations, Rm. 326, New York, NY, 10017 (212) 963-7137; e-mail contactus@unca.com; web site www.unca.com
Pres. Giam Palo Pioli
1st Vice Pres. Louis Charbonneau
2nd Vice Pres. Masood Haider
Office Mgr. Sandra Winter
Elections held in Dec

W

Winnipeg Press Club–C/O Royal Canadian Legion Branch #4, 1755 Portage Avenue, Winnipeg, MB, R3J 0E6, Canada (204) 800-1887; e-mail info@winnipegpressclub.com; web site www.winnipegpressclub.com
President Dwight MacAulay

World Association of Newspapers and News Publishers (WAN-IFRA)–Washingtonplatz 1, Darmstadt, 64287, Germany; tel (49) 6151 7336; fax 733 800; e-mail info@wan-ifra.org; web site www.wan-ifra.org
CEO Christoph Riess

World Association of Newspapers and News Publishers (WAN-IFRA)–7 Rue Geoffroy, Saint Hilaire, Paris, 75005, France; tel (33) 1 4742 8500; fax 4742 4948; e-mail info@wan-ifra.org; web site www.wan-ifra.org
CEO Christoph Riess
Pres. Gavin O'Reilly
Dir., Commun. Larry Kilman
Dir., Global Affairs Timothy Balding
Elections held every two years in May

World Press Institute–3415 University Ave., Saint Paul, MN, 55114-1019 (651) 208-9378; e-mail info@worldpressinstitute.org; web site www.worldpressinstitute.org
Exec. Dir. David McDonald

Y

Youth Editorial Association –N/A, VA 571-366-1000; e-mail sandy.woodcock@naa.org; web site www.naafoundation.org
Director- NAA Foundation Sandy Woodcock

ASSOCIATIONS, CLUBS, & PRESS CLUBS - CITY, STATE & REGIONAL

A

The Ad Club–38 Newbury St. 5th Fl., Boston, MA, 02116; tel (617) 262-1100; fax (617) 262-0739; web site www.adclub.org
Pres. Kathy Kiely

The Ad Club–9 Hamilton Pl., Boston, MA, 02108-3210; tel (617) 262-1100; fax (617) 456-1772; e-mail newsfeed@adclub.org; web site www.adclub.org

Advertising Club of Greater New York–235 Park Ave., S., New York, NY, 10003; tel (212) 533-8080; fax (212) 533-1929; e-mail memberships@theadvertisingclub.org; web site www.theadvertisingclub.org
Exec. Dir. Gina Grillo
Elections held in July

Alabama Associated Press Managing Editors Association–201 Monroe St., RSA Tower, Ste. 1940, Montgomery, AL, 36104; tel (334) 262-5947; fax (334) 265-7177; e-mail kweaver@ap.org; web site www.ap.org/alabama
Sec. Kendal Weaver
Elections held in the spring

Alabama Baptist–3310 Independence Dr., Birmingham, AL, 35209-5602; tel (205) 870-4720; fax (205) 870-8957; web site www.thealabamabaptist.org
Pres. Bob Terry

Alabama Press Association–3324 Independence Dr., Ste. 200, Birmingham, AL, 35209-5602; tel (205) 871-7737; fax (205) 871-7740; e-mail felicia@alabamapress.org; web site www.alabamapress.org
Adv. Mgr. Brad English
Exec. Dir. Felicia Mason
Elections held in Feb

Alaska Newspaper Association–PO Box 7900, Ketchikan, AK, 99901; tel (907) 225-3157; fax (907) 225-1096; e-mail kdn@kpunet.net
Sec. Teena Williams

Alberta Weekly Newspapers Association–4445 Calgary Trail S., Ste. 800, Edmonton, AB, T6H 5R7, Canada; tel (780) 434-8746; fax (780) 438-8356; e-mail info@awna.com; web site www.awna.com
Exec. Dir. Dennis Merrell

Allied Daily Newspapers of Washington–PO Box 29, Olympia, WA, 98507-0029; tel (360) 943-9960; fax (360) 943-9962; e-mail anewspaper@aol.com
Exec. Dir. Rowland Thompson

Arizona Associated Press Managing Editors Association–1850 N. Central Ave., Ste. 640, Phoenix, AZ, 85004; tel (602) 258-8934; fax (602) 254-9573; e-mail aparizona@ap.org; web site www.ap.org/arizona
Bureau Chief Michelle Williams
Elections held in the summer

Arizona Newspapers Association–1001 N. Central Ave., Ste. 670, Phoenix, AZ, 85004-1947; tel (602) 261-7655; fax (602) 261-7525; e-mail office@ananews.com; web site www.ananews.com
Exec. Dir. Paula Casey
Elections held in Sept. Statewide and national one order/one bill advertising placement service

Arkansas Associated Press–10810 Executive Center Dr., Ste. 308, Little Rock, AR, 72211-4388; tel (501) 225-3668; fax (501) 225-3249; e-mail pebbles@ap.org
News Ed. Kelly Kessel

Arkansas Press Association–411 S. Victory St., Little Rock, AR, 72201; tel (501) 374-1500; fax (501) 374-7509; e-mail info@arkansaspress.org; web site www.arkansaspress.org
Exec. Dir. Tom Larimer
Elections held in July

Arkansas Press Women Association, Inc.–N/A; tel 501-671-2126; fax 501-671-2121; e-mail arkpresswomen@yahoo.com; web site arkpresswomen.wordpress.com
President Mary Hightower
Treasurer Terry Hawkins
Elections held in the fall of spring odd numbered years

Associated Collegiate Press–2221 University Ave. SE, Ste. 121, Minneapolis, MN, 55414; tel (612) 625-8335; fax (612) 626-0720; e-mail info@studentpress.org; web site www.studentpress.org
Exec. Dir. Logan Aimone

Associated Press/California-Nevada News Executives–221 S. Figueroa St., Ste. 300, Los Angeles, CA, 90012; tel (213) 626-1200; fax (213) 346-0200; e-mail losangeles@ap.org; web site www.ap.org/losangeles
Bureau Chief, Los Angeles Anthony Marquez
Bureau Chief, San Francisco John Raess
Reg'l Vice Pres. Newyork Sue Cross
Elections held in May

Associated Press/Oklahoma News Executives–525 Central Park Dr., Ste. 202, Oklahoma City, OK, 73105; tel (405) 525-2121; fax (405) 524-7465; e-mail apoklahoma@ap.org; web site www.ap.org/oklahoma
Bureau Chief Dale Leach

Atlantic Community Newspapers Association–7075 Bayers Rd., Ste. 216, Halifax, NS, B3L 2C2, Canada; tel (902) 832-4480; fax (902) 832-4484; web site www.acna.com
Exec. Dir. Mike Kierstead

B

British Columbia/Yukon Community Newspapers Association–1020 Mainland St., Ste. 122, Vancouver, BC, V6B 2T4, Canada; tel (604) 669-9222; fax (604) 684-4713; e-mail info@bccommunitynews.com; web site www.bccommunitynews.com
Gen. Mgr. George Affleck
Elections held in May

C

CCNMA: Latino Journalists of California–727 W. 27th St., Rm. 201, Los Angeles, CA, 90007; tel (213) 821-0075; fax (213) 743-1838; e-mail ccnmainfo@ccnma.org; web site

www.ccnma.org
Exec. Dir. Julio Moran
Office Mgr. Sylvia Wells

California Association of Newspaper Distributors–16 Santa Ana Pl., Walnut Creek, CA, 94598; tel (925) 935-2026; fax (925) 906-0922; e-mail d2@dobbsgroup.com; web site www.cand.com
Treasurer Dave Skidmore
Exec. Dir. Deborah S. Dobbs
1st Vice Pres. Jennifer Jost
Pres. Mike Heaton
2nd Vice Pres. Rick Sealy

California Newspaper Advertising Executives Association (Southern)–c/o Union-Tribune, 678 Third Ave., Ste. 101, Chula Vista, CA, 91910; tel (619) 498-6604; fax (619) 498-6680; e-mail donald.borucki@laopinion.com
Pres. Donald Borucki
Treasurer Scott Adams
Elections held in Sept

California Newspaper Publishers Association, Inc.–708 Tenth St., Sacramento, CA, 95814-1803; tel (916) 288-6000; fax (916) 288-6002; web site www.cnpa.com
Exec. Dir. Jack Bates

California Press Association–Cal. Newspr. Publs. Assoc., 708 Tenth St., Sacramento, CA, 95814-1803; tel (916) 288-6000; fax (916) 288-6002; web site www.cnpa.com
Exec. Dir. Jack Bates
Elections held in Dec

California Press Photographers Association, Inc.–3512 14th St., Riverside, CA, 92501-3878; tel (951) 684-1200; fax (951) 782-7572; web site www.cppaonline.org
1st Vice Pres. Carlos Puma
Sec. Mark Zaleski
Elections held in June every two years

Capitol Press Association–PO Box 191, Raleigh, NC, 27602; tel (919) 836-2858; e-mail smooneyh@ncinsider.com
Mgr. Scott Mooneyham
Elections held in Jan

Central States Circulation Managers Association–PO Box 229, Glasford, IL, 61533; tel N/A; e-mail cscma@aol.com; web site www.cscma.com
Pres. Bruce Tischer
Contact Joe Schaechter
President Pete Jones
Elections held in April

Colorado Associated Press Editors and Reporters–1444 Wazee St., Ste. 130, Denver, CO, 80202-1395; tel (303) 825-0123; fax (303) 892-5927; e-mail apdenver@ap.org; web site www.ap.org/colorado/
Bureau Chief Jim Clarke
Elections held in Feb

Colorado Press Association–1336 Glenarm Pl., Denver, CO, 80204; tel (303) 571-5117; fax (303) 571-1803; e-mail eotte@colopress.net; web site www.coloradopressassociation.com
Exec. Dir. Ed Otte
Elections held in Feb

Community Papers of Indiana–PO Box 1004, Crown Point, IN, 46308; tel (219) 689-6262; fax (219) 374-7558
Gen. Mgr. Shari Foreman
Elections held in April

Community Papers of Michigan–5000 Northwind Dr., Ste. 240, East Lansing, MI, 48823; tel (517) 333-3355; fax (989) 466-1313; web site www.communitypapersofmichigan.com
Exec. Dir. Jack Guza

Community Papers of Ohio & West Virginia–3500 Sullivant St., Columbus, OH, 43204; tel (614) 272-5422; fax (614) 272-0684; e-mail psd1@aol.com; web site www.paperchain-network.net

Coord. Phil Daubel

Connecticut Associated Press Managing Editors Association–10 Columbus Blvd., Hartford, CT, 06106; tel (860) 246-6876; fax (860) 727-4003; e-mail aphartford@ap.org; web site www.ap.org
Bureau Chief William Kole

Connecticut Daily Newspapers Association–15 N. River Rd., Tolland, CT, 06084; tel (860) 656-6615; web site www.ctdailynews.com
Exec. Dir. Jim Leahy
Elections held in April/May

Conseil de Presse du Quebec–1000, rue Fullum, Ste. A.208, Montreal, QC, H2K 3L7, Canada; tel (514) 529-2818; fax (514) 873-4434; e-mail info@conseildepresse.qc.ca; web site www.conseildepresse.qc.ca
Contact Guy Amyot

Cal Western Circulation Managers' Association–8345 Singh Ct., Hemet, CA, 92545, USA; tel (951) 492-9330; fax (951) 253-3437; e-mail director@cwcma.com; web site www.cwcma.com
Executive Director Charlie McManis
Election of officers is held during the annual meeting in April.

E

Eastern Ski Writers Association–120 Meeting House Ln., Cherry Hill, NJ, 08002; tel (856) 662-2779; fax (856) 662-3124; e-mail njgdesign@att.net; web site www.nasja.org
Exec. Sec. Jim Gregory

Linda–N/A; tel N/A

F

Florida Newspaper Advertising & Marketing Executives–1138 Linkside Court, Apopka, FL, 32712; tel 813-220-4402; fax (407) 703-4510; web site www.fname.org
Exec. Dir. Sandy Osteen

Florida Press Association–336 E. College Avenue, Suite 203, Tallahassee, FL, 32301; tel (850) 222-5790; fax (850) 224-6012; e-mail fpa-info@flpress.com; web site www.flpress.com
President & CEO Dean Ridings
Media Dir. Scott Harding
Vice President and Chief Sales Officer Melanie Mathewson
Chief Financial Officer Patrick Bowen
General Counsel Sam Morley
Association accepts shopper publications as members if they include editorial content.
Elections held in June

Florida Society of Newspaper Editors–336 E. College Ave. Suite 203, Tallahassee, FL, 32301; tel (850) 222-5790; fax 850-224-6012; e-mail fpa-info@flpress.com; web site www.fsne.org
Membership Coordinator Marcia Cyr
Elections held at June convention

Free Community Papers of New England–700 Main St., Willimantic, CT, 06226; tel (860) 423-6398; fax (860) 423-6391; e-mail bne@fcpne.com; web site www.communitypapersne.com
Admin. Lynn Duval

Free Community Papers of New York–750 W. Genesee St., Syracuse, NY, 13204; tel (315) 472-6007; fax (315) 472-5919; e-mail ads@fcpny.com; web site www.fcpny.org
Executive Director Dan Holmes

Freedom of Information Foundation of Texas–3001 N Lamar Blvd., Ste. 302, Austin, TX, 78705; tel (512) 377 1575; fax (512) 377 1578; e-mail foift@foift.org; web site www.foift.org
Exec. Dir. Keith Elkins

Elections held in Dec

G

Georgia Press Association–3066 Mercer University Dr., Ste. 200, Atlanta, GA, 30341-4137; tel (770) 454-6776; fax (770) 454-6778; e-mail mail@gapress.org; web site www.gapress.org
Exec. Dir. Robin Rhodes
Elections held at annual convention in June

Great Lakes/Midstates Newspaper Conference, Inc.–7500 Shotsilk Dr., Jackson, MI, 49201; tel (574) 536-8042; fax (574) 536-8042; e-mail glmsconf@comcast.net
Bus. Mgr./Sec./Treasurer Jack Gahagan
Elections held in Feb

H

Hollywood Foreign Press Association–646 N. Robertson Blvd., West Hollywood, CA, 90069-5078; tel (310) 657-1731; fax (310) 657-5576; e-mail info@hfpa.org; web site www.hfpa.org
Head, Mktg. Michael Russell
Pres. Philip Berk

Hoosier State Press Association, Inc.–41 E. Washington St., Ste. 301, Indianapolis, IN, 46204; tel (317) 803-4772; fax (317) 624-4428; web site www.hspa.com
Executive Director and General Counsel Stephen Key
Exec. Dir. David Stamps
Elections held in Jan

I

Idaho Newspaper Association, Inc.–60125 Wallowa Lake Hiway, Joseph, OR, 97846, USA; tel 541 432 7090; e-mail bobchall@idahopapers.com
Exec. Dir. Bob C. Hall

Idaho Press Club–PO Box 2221, Boise, ID, 83701-2221; tel (208) 389-2879; e-mail email@idahopressclub.org; web site www.idahopressclub.org
Exec. Dir. Martha Borchers
IPC accepts individual memberships for reporters and public information officers in several areas. Elections and awards ceremony held in the spring. One annual seminars held in spring and fall

Illinois Associated Press Editors Association–Associated Press, 10 S. Wacker Dr., Ste. 2500, Chicago, IL, 60606; tel (312) 781-0500; fax (312) 781-1989; e-mail chifax@ap.org; web site www.ap.org
Chief Of Bureau George Garties
Elections held in Sept

Illinois Press Association–900 Community Dr., Springfield, IL, 62703; tel (217) 241-1700; fax (217) 241-1701; e-mail presslines@illinoispress.org; web site www.illinoispress.org
Dir. Commun./Mktg. David Porter
Exec. Dir. Dennis DeRossett
Advertising Director Jeffrey Holman
The Illinois Press Advertising Service can place any newspaper product available in Illinois and has several well-established, low-cost networks.

Illinois Press Photographers Association–c/o Northwest Herald, 7717 S. Rte. 31, Crystal Lake, IL, 60014; tel (815) 459-4122; web site www.ippaonline.com
Vice Pres. Mark Black
Pres. Scott Strazzante
Sec. Steve Warmowski
Elections held every two years in the spring. Education Conference and Pictures of the Year contest is held in combination with the Wisconsin News Photographers Assoc. in April in Gurnee, IL. Newsletter ClipNotes published monthly

Illinois Woman's Press Association, Inc.–PO Box 438489, Chicago, IL, 60643; tel (312) 458-9151; e-mail iwpa@comcast.net; web site www.iwpa.org
Immediate Past-President, Executive Board Member Suzanne Hanney
President Marianne Wolf-Astrauskas
Editor- PenPoints, Executive Board member Rebecca Sarwte
State affiliate to the National Federation of Press Women. Elections held in May

Indiana Associated Press Managing Editors Association–251 N. Illinois St., Ste. 1600, Indianapolis, IN, 46204; tel (317) 639-5501; fax (317) 638-4611; e-mail indy@ap.org; web site www.ap.org
Chief of Bureau, Illinois and Indiana George Garties

Indianapolis Press Club Foundation–PO Box 40923, Indianapolis, IN, 46240; tel (317) 701-1130; e-mail jlabalme@indypress@att.net; web site www.indypressfoundation.org
Executive Director Jenny Labalme
Elections held in January

Inland Press Association–701 Lee St., Ste. 925, Des Plaines, IL, 60016; tel (847) 795-0380; fax (847) 795-0385; e-mail inland@inlandpress.org; web site www.inlandpress.org
HR Research Mgr. Karla Zander
Director of Membership and Programming Patty Slusher
Financial Studies Manager Tim Mather
Publications Editor Adolfo Mendez
Executive Director Tom Slaughter
Elections held in Oct

Iowa Associated Press Managing Editors Association–505 Fifth Ave., Ste. 1000, Des Moines, IA, 50309, US; tel (515) 243-3281; fax (515) 243-3884; e-mail apdesmoines@ap.org; web site www.apiowa.org
Chief of Bureau Kia Breaux
Elections held in June

Iowa Newspaper Association, Inc.–319 E. Fifth St., Des Moines, IA, 50309; tel (515) 244-2145; fax (515) 244-4855; e-mail ina@inanews.com; web site www.inanews.com
Bill Monroe
Chris MudgeExec. Dir.s
Elections held in May

K

Kansas Associated Press Managing Editors Association–Associated Press, 215 W. Pershing St., Ste. 221, Kansas City, MO, 64108; tel (816) 421-4844; fax (816) 421-3590; e-mail apkansascity@ap.org; web site www.ap.org/kansas
Bureau Chief Randy Picht
Elections held in Oct

Kansas Associated Press Publishers and Editors–Associated Press, 215 W. Pershing, Ste. 221, Kansas City, MO, 64108; tel (816) 421-4844; fax (816) 421-3590
Bureau Chief Paul Stevens
Bd. Chrmn. Tom Bell
Elections held in Dec

Kansas Press Association–5423 SW Seventh St., Topeka, KS, 66606; tel (785) 271-5304; fax (785) 271-7341; e-mail info@kspress.com; web site www.kspress.com
Exec. Dir. Doug Anstaett
Member Serv. Dir. Emily Bradbury
Dir., Gov't Affairs Richard Gannon
Administrative Assistant/Advertising Lori Jackson
Adv. Mgr. Dan Rukes
Educ. Dir. Rachel Willis

Acct. Amy Blaufelder
Represents 32 daily and 200 weekly newspapers in Kansas

Kansas Professional Communicators–1845 Fairmount Street, Wichita State University, Wichita, KS, 67260-0031; tel (316) 978-6065; e-mail kansasprocom@gmail.com; web site www.kansasprofessionalcommunicators.org
Pres. Teresa Veazey
Professor, WSU Elliott School of Communication Les Anderson
Becky Funke
Wilma Moore-Black
Miller Jill
Jennifer ????

Kentucky Associated Press Editors Association–525 W. Broadway, Louisville, KY, 40202; tel (502) 583-7718; fax (502) 589-4831; e-mail kentucky@ap.org; web site www.ap.org/kentucky
Elections held in Nov

Kentucky Press Association, Inc.–101 Consumer Ln., Frankfort, KY, 40601; tel (502) 223-8821; fax (502) 226-3867; e-mail dthompson@kypress.com; web site www.kypress.com
Executive Director David T. Thompson
Elections held in Jan

L

Legislative Correspondents Association–State Capitol Bldg., Albany, NY, 12224; tel (518) 455-2388; web site lcapressroom.blogspot.com
Treasurer Bill Hammond

Los Angeles Press Club–4773 Hollywood Blvd., Los Angeles, CA, 90027; tel (323) 669-8081; fax (323) 669-8069; e-mail info@lapressclub.org; web site www.lapressclub.org
Exec. Dir. Diana Ljungaeus
Elections held in Nov

Louisiana-Mississippi Associated Press Managing Editors Association–1515 Poydras St., Ste. 2500, New Orleans, LA, 70112; tel (504) 523-3931; fax (504) 586-0531; e-mail nrle@ap.org; web site www.ap.org
News Ed. Brian Schwaner

Louisiana Press Association–404 Europe St., Baton Rouge, LA, 70802; tel (225) 344-9309; fax (225) 344-9344; e-mail pam@lapress.com; web site www.lapress.com
Adv./Commun. Dir. Mike Rood
Exec. Dir. Pamela Mitchell-Wagner
Elections held in March/April

Louisiana Press Women, Inc.–The Advocate, 7290 Blue Bonnet Rd., Baton Rouge, LA, 70810; tel (225) 383-1111; fax (225) 388-0323; e-mail mshuler@theadvocate.com; web site www.theadvocate.com
Pres. David Manship
Elections held even years

M

Maine Daily Newspaper Publishers Association–104 Park St., Lewiston, ME, 04240; tel (207) 784-5411; e-mail scostello@sunjournal.com; web site www.sunjournal.com
Dir., Adv. Steven Costello
Elections held in June

Maine Press Association–26 Elmwood Rd., Cape Elizabeth, ME, 04107-1337; tel (866) 602-2418; fax (800) 799-6008; e-mail maine.press@verizon.net; web site www.mainepress.org
Jeff Ham
Mike LangeExec. Dir.s
Elections held in Sept

Manitoba Community Newspaper Association–943 McPhillips Street, Winnipeg, MB, R2X 2J9, Canada; tel (204) 947-1691; fax (204) 947-1919; web site www.mcna.com
Elections held at annual April convention

Maryland-Delaware-DC Press Association–2191 Defense Highway, Ste. 300, Crofton, MD, 21114; tel (410) 721-4000; fax (410) 721-4557; e-mail info@mddc.com; web site www.mddcpress.com
Exec. Dir. John J. Murphy
Elections held in Nov.

Massachusetts Newspaper Publishers Association–7 S Street Ct., Rockport, MA, 01966; tel (978) 546-3400; fax (978) 418-9161; e-mail info@masspublishers.org; web site www.masspublishers.org

Exec. Dir. Robert J. Ambrogi

Metropolitan New York Football Writers Association–USA College Sports, Inc., Roseland, NJ, 07068-0477, USA; tel (973) 983-3686; fax (973) 364-0425; e-mail collegesportsintheusa@gmail.com; web site www.mnyfwa.com
Pres. Dennis Wilson
Sec./Treasurer Phil Nardone

Michigan Associated Press Editorial Association–300 River Pl., Ste. 2400, Detroit, MI, 48207; tel (313) 259-0650; fax (313) 259-4966; e-mail apmichigan@ap.org; web site www.ap.org
Bureau Chief Charles C. Hill
Elections held in June

Michigan Press Association–827 N. Washington Ave., Lansing, MI, 48906-5199; tel (517) 372-2424; fax (517) 372-2429; e-mail mpa@michiganpress.org; web site www.michiganpress.org
Exec. Dir. Mike MacLaren
Elections held in Jan

Mid-Atlantic Circulation Managers Association–Daily Herald, PO Box 520, Roanoke Rapids, NC, 27870-0520; tel (252) 537-2505; fax (252) 537-1887; web site www.midatlanticcma.org
Sec./Treasurer Carol Moseley
Elections held in May

Mid-Atlantic Community Papers Association–150 Valley Rd., Hamburg, PA, 19526-0408; tel (610) 488-1406; fax (610) 743-8500; e-mail info@macpa.net; web site www.macpa.net
Exec. Dir. Alyse Mitten
Elections held in Oct. for the MACPA Board
Elections Held in April for the MACnet Board

Mid-Atlantic Newspaper Advertising & Marketing Executives–PO Box 31932, Raleigh, NC, 27622-1932; tel (919) 781-9284; fax (252) 977-7341; e-mail terisaylor@hotmail.com; web site www.midatlanticname.com
Exec. Dir. Terri Saylor
Elections held in March

Midwest Free Community Papers–PO Box 1350, Iowa City, IA, 52244; tel (319) 341-4352; fax (319) 341-4358; e-mail mfcp@mchsi.com; web site www.mfcp.org
Exec. Dir. Brian Gay
Office Mgr. Jori Hendon
Classified advertising for 124 publications

Midwest Travel Writers Association–PO Box 409, Fayette, MO, 65248, USA; tel 660-248-3455; e-mail sylvia@forbesfreelance.com; web site www.mtwa.org
Active Dir. Barbara Ostmann
Active Dir. Carla Waldemar
Treasurer Rich Warren
Active Dir. Susan Pollack
Administrative AssistantSylvia Forbes
Elections held in Mar or April

Minnesota Associated Press Association–511 11th Ave. S., Ste. 460, Minneapolis, MN, 55415-1568; tel (612) 332-2727; fax (612) 342-5299; e-mail apminneapolis@ap.org; web site www.apminnesota.org
Bureau Chief Dave Pyle

Minnesota Free Paper Association–21998 Hwy. 27, Little Falls, MN, 56345; tel (320) 632-4426; fax (320) 632-2348; web site www.mfpa.com
Asst. Sec./Treasurer Terry Lehrke
Pres. Trevor Slette
Elections held in Feb

Minnesota News Council–12 S. Sixth St., Ste. 927, Minneapolis, MN, 55402-1513; tel (612) 341-9357; fax (612) 341-9358; e-mail info@news-council.org; web site www.newscouncil.org
Chrmn. Tony Carideo

Minnesota Newspaper Association–12 S. Sixth St., Ste. 1120, Minneapolis, MN, 55402; tel (612) 332-8844; fax (612) 342-2958; e-mail advertising@mna.org; web site www.mna.org
Asst. Exec. Dir. Barbara Trebisovsky
Adv. Sales Dir. Lisa Hills
Represents 350 weekly and 29 daily newspapers in Minnesota. In addition, the Fargo-Moorhead (ND) Forum, Grand Forks (ND) Herald and Wahpeton-Breckenridge (ND) News are members of the MNA

Mississippi Press Association–371 Edgewood Terr., Jackson, MS, 39206-6217; tel (601) 981-3060; fax (601) 981-3676; e-mail mspress@mspress.org; web site www.mspress.org
Exec. Dir. Layne Bruce
Sales Director David Gillis
Media Buyer Andrea Ross
Elections held in June

Mississippi Valley Classified Advertising Association–1170 S. Curtis Ave., Kankakee, IL, 60901; tel (815) 935-8713; e-mail jacharbonneau@ameritech.net; web site www.mississippivalley.org
Gen. Mgr. JoAnn Charbonneau
Elections held in March

Missouri Associated Press Publishers and Editors–Associated Press, 215 W. Pershing, Ste. 221, Kansas City, MO, 64108; tel (816) 421-4844
Pres. Dan Chiodo
Elections held in Dec

Missouri Associated Press Managing Editors–Associated Press, 215 W. Pershing, Ste. 221, Kansas City, MO, 64108; tel (816) 421-4844; fax (816) 421-3590; e-mail apkansascity@ap.org; web site www.ap.org
Bureau Chief Randy Picht
Elections held in April

Missouri Press Association–802 Locust St., Columbia, MO, 65201-7799; tel (573) 449-4167; fax (573) 874-5894; web site www.mopress.com
Exec. Dir. Doug Crews
Elections held in Sep.

Missouri Press Women–528 Pamela Ln., Kirkwood, MO, 63122-1138; tel (314) 821-2462; e-mail kjkglines@aol.com; web site www.nfpw.org
Treasurer Ddee Rabey
Co-Pres. Fran Mannino
Pres. Janice Denham
Membership Dir. Suzanne Corbett

Montana Associated Press Association–825 Great Northern Blvd., Ste. 203, Helena, MT, 59601; tel (406) 442-7440; fax (406) 442-5162; e-mail apmontana@ap.org; web site www.ap.org/montana
Bureau Chief Jim Clark
Elections held in June every two years

Montana Newspaper Association–825 Great Northern Blvd., Ste. 202, Helena, MT, 59601; tel (406) 443-2850; fax (406) 443-2860; e-mail mtnews@mtnewspapers.com; web site www.mtnewspapers.com
Executive Director John Barrows
Elections held in June

Montana Newspaper Group–401 N. 28th St., Billings, MT, 59101-1243, USA; tel (406) 657-1200; fax (406) 657-1350; e-mail drussiff@billingsgazette.com; web site www.billingsgazette.com
Pub. Mike Gullidge
Adv. Dir. Dave Worstell
Nat'l Adv. Coord. Diana Russiff
Ed. Steve Prosinski

N

Nebraska Associated Press Association–Associated Press, 909 N. 96th St., Ste. 104, Omaha, NE, 68114-2497; tel (402) 391-0031; fax (402) 391-1412; e-mail omahane@ap.org; web site www.ap.org/nebraska
Bureau Chief Tina Heraldson
Elections held in Sept

Nebraska Press Association–845 S St., Lincoln, NE, 68508-1226; tel (402) 476-2851; fax (402) 476-2942; e-mail nebpress@nebpress.com; web site www.nebpress.com
Exec. Dir. Allen Beermann
Sales Mgr. Rob James
Elections held in April

Nevada Press Association, Inc.–102 N. Curry St., Carson City, NV, 89703; tel (775) 885-0866; fax (775) 885-8233; e-mail nvpress@callatg.com; web site www.nevadapress.com
Exec. Dir. Barry Smith
Elections held in Sept

Associated Press–Associated Press, 184 High St., Boston, MA, 02110; tel (617) 357-8100; fax (617) 338-8125; e-mail apboston@ap.org; web site www.ap.org/boston
Bureau Chief William Kole

New England Association of Circulation Executives–4 Trotting Rd., Chelmsford, MA, 01824; tel (978) 256-0691; fax (978) 256-4873; e-mail neace@neace.com; web site www.neace.com
Sec. William H. Hoar
Elections held in May

New England Newspaper Advertising Executives Association–370 Common St., Dedham, MA, 02026; tel (781) 320-8050; fax (781) 320-8055; web site www.nenpa.com
Exec. Dir. NENPA Dan Cotter
Elections held in Oct

New England Newspaper & Press Association, Inc.–370 Common Street, Dedham, MA, 02026; tel (781) 320-8048; fax (781) 320-8055; e-mail info@nenpa.com; web site www.nenpa.com
Executive Director Dan Cotter
Exec. Dir. Morley L. Piper
Elections held in March

New England Press Association–716 Columbus Ave., Ste. 428, Boston, MA, 02120-2111; tel (617) 373-5615; fax (617) 373-5610; e-mail info@nepa.org; web site www.nenpa.org
Exec. Dir. Brenda L. Reed
Adv. Dir. Linda Conway
Elections held at annual winter convention

New England Society of Newspaper Editors–70 Washington St., Salem, MA, 01970-3518; tel (978) 744-8940; fax (978) 744-0333; e-mail nena@nenews.org; web site www.nesne.org
Ed. George Geers
Elections held in Nov

New Jersey Associated Press Managing Editors Association–50 W. State St., Ste. 1114, Trenton, NJ, 08608; tel (609) 392-3622; fax (609) 392-3525; e-mail aptrenton@ap.org; web site www.ap.org/nj
Deputy Bureau Chief Andrew Fraser

New Jersey Legislative Correspondents Club–Hackensack Record, Trenton, NJ, 08625; tel (609) 292-5159; fax (609) 984-1888
Pres. Jim Hooker

This group accepts news organizations with correspondents based in Trenton, N.J

New Jersey Press Association–840 Bear Tavern Rd., Ste. 305, West Trenton, NJ, 08628-1019; tel (609) 406-0600; fax (609) 406-0300; e-mail njpress@njpa.org; web site www.njpa.org
Exec. Dir. John J. O'Brien

New Mexico Press Association–700 Silver SW , Albuquerque, NM, 87190-3015; tel (505) 275-1241; fax (505) 275-1449; e-mail director@nmpress.org; web site www.nmpress.org
Office Mgr. Holly Aguilar
Executive Director Philip M. Lucey
Elections held in Oct

New Mexico Press Women–256 DP Rd., Los Alamos, NM, 87544; tel (505) 662-4185; fax (505) 827-6496; e-mail lanews@lamonitor.com; web site www.newmexicopresswomen.org
Pres. Carol Clark
Elections held May 1st of even numbered years

New Orleans Press Club–203 Carondelet Ave., Ste. 415, New Orleans, LA, 70130-3029; tel (504) 383-4305; fax (504) 525-9327; web site www.pressclubneworleans.org
Exec. Dir. Bill Langkopp
Elections held in July

New York Fair Trial Free Press Conference–Bracken & Margolin, One Suffolk Sq., Ste. 300, Islandia, NY, 11722-1588; tel (631) 234-8585; fax (631) 234-8702
Exec. Dir. Gordon T. Platt
Chrmn. Judith S. Kaye
Elections held in May

New York Financial Writers Association, Inc.–PO Box 338, Ridgewood, NJ, 07451-0338; tel (201) 612-0100; fax (201) 612-9915; e-mail nyfwa@aol.com; web site www.nyfwa.org
Exec. Mgr. Jane Reilly
Elections held on fourth Wed. of Jan. Members are journalists in the business or financial media

New York Newspaper Publishers Association–291 Hudson Ave., Ste. A, Albany, NY, 12210; tel (518) 449-1667; fax (518) 449-5053; web site www.nynpa.com
Pres. Diane Kennedy

New York Press Association–1681 Western Ave., Albany, NY, 12203-4305; tel (518) 464-6483; fax (518) 464-6489; e-mail nypa@nynewspapers.com; web site www.nynewspapers.com
Exec. Dir. Michelle K. Rea
Elections held in Sept; annual convention held in April

New York Press Photographers Association, Inc.–225 E. 36th St., Ste. 1P, New York, NY, 10016-3664; tel (212) 889-6633; fax (212) 889-6634; e-mail office@nyppa.org; web site www.nyppa.org
Pres. Ray Stubblebine
Sec. Susan Markisz
Elections held every other year

New York Society of Newspaper Editors–215 University Pl., Syracuse, NY, 13244; tel (315) 443-2305; fax (315) 443-3946
Pres. Joann M. Crupi

New York State Associated Press Association–645 Albany Shaker Rd., Albany, NY, 12211; tel (518) 458-7821; fax (518) 438-5891; e-mail info@ap.org; web site www.ap.org
Bureau Chief Howard Goldberg
Elections held in Sept

New York State Circulation Managers Association–85 Civic Center Plz., Poughkeepsie, NY, 12601; tel (845) 437-4738; fax (845) 437-4902; e-mail farrellb@poughkee.gannett.com; web site www.poughkeepsiejournal.com
Board Member Bill Farrell
Elections held in May

Newspaper Association of Idaho–333 Northgate Mile, Idaho Falls, ID, 83401-2529; tel (208) 522-1800; fax (208) 529-3142; e-mail rplothow@postregister.com
Pres. Roger Plothow

Newspaper Features Council, Inc.–22 Byfield Ln., Greenwich, CT, 06830; tel (203) 661-3386; fax (203) 661-7337
Exec. Dir. Corinta Kotula
2nd Vice Pres. David D. Williams
Pres. Sid Goldberg
1st Vice Pres. Sue F. Smith
Elections held every two years

North Carolina Associated Press News Council–4800 Six Forks Rd., Ste. 210, Raleigh, NC, 27609-5245; tel (919) 510-8937
Bureau Chief Sue Price Wilson
Elections held in Nov

North Carolina Press Association–5171 Glenwood Ave., Ste. 364, Raleigh, NC, 27612-3266; tel (919) 787-7443; fax (919) 787-5302; e-mail ten@ncpress.com; web site www.ncpress.com
Exec. Dir. Beth Grace
Elections held in July

North Carolina Press Club–110 Bonnell Ct., Cary, NC, 27511; tel (919) 469-9611; e-mail ncpressclub@aol.com.; web site www.ncpressclub.org
Pres Suzy Barile
Elections held in March

North Dakota Associated Press–PO Box 1018, Bismarck, ND, 58502-5646; tel (701) 223-8450; fax (701) 224-0158; e-mail apbismarck@ap.org; web site www.ap.org/bismarck
Contact Phyllis Mensing
Elections held in Sept

North Dakota Newspaper Association–1435 Interstate Loop, Bismarck, ND, 58503-0567; tel (701) 223-6397; fax (701) 223-8185; e-mail info@ndna.com; web site www.ndna.com
Mktg. Mgr. Kelli Richey
Exec. Dir. Roger Bailey
Elections held in April

Northern Illinois Newspaper Association–Northern Illinois Univ., Dept. of Communication, Campus Life Building, Suite 130, DeKalb, IL, 60115; tel (815) 753-4239; fax (815) 753-0708; web site www.ninaonline.org
Advisor Jim Killam

Northern States Circulation Managers Association–PO Box 220, Grand Rapids, MN, 55744; tel (218) 326-6623; fax (218) 326-6627; e-mail ron.oleheiser@grandrapidsmn.com; web site www.grandrapidsmn.com
Pub. Ron Oleheiser
Elections held in Sept

Northwest International Circulation Executives–PO Box 778, La Conner, WA, 98257; tel (360) 466-2006; fax (360) 466-2006; e-mail nice@galaxynet.com; web site www.nicex.org
Sec./Treasurer Dale Irvine
Management seminars sponsored in Oct. (non-dailies welcome). Elections held at annual conference in May

O

Ohio Circulation Managers Association–4800 Tiedeman Rd., Brooklyn, OH, 44144; tel (216) 999-6672; fax (216) 999-6761; e-mail bbarker@plaind.com; web site www.ohiocirculation.com
Pres./Sec./Treasurer Brian Barker
Elections held in Oct

Ohio Newspaper Advertising Executives–1335 Dublin Rd. S., Ste. 216-B, Columbus, OH, 43215; tel (614) 486-6677; fax (614) 486-6373; e-mail mhenry@adohio.net; web site www.adohio.net
Mgr. Mark Henry
Elections held in Feb.

Ohio Newspaper Association–1335 Dublin Rd., Ste. 216, Columbus, OH, 43215; tel (614) 486-6677; fax (614) 486-4940; e-mail fdeaner@ohionews.org; web site www.ohionews.org
Exec. Dir./Sec. Frank E. Deaner
Elections held in Feb

Oklahoma Press Association–3601 N. Lincoln Blvd., Oklahoma City, OK, 73105-5499; tel (405) 524-4421; fax (405) 499-0048; e-mail lgarvin@okpress.com; web site www.okpress.com
Clipping Bureau Mgr. Louise Garvin
Exec. Dir. Mark Thomas
Adv. Mgr. Sara Barrow
Elections held in Feb

Ontario Community Newspapers Association–3050 Harvester Rd., Ste. 103, Burlington, ON, L7N 3J1, Canada; tel (905) 639-8720; fax (905) 639-6962; e-mail info@ocna.org; web site www.ocna.org
Executive Director Anne Lannan

Orange County Press Club–PO Box 19793-245, Irvine, CA, 92713; tel (714) 564-1052; fax (714) 564-1047; e-mail jopasco@sbcglobal.net; web site www.ocpressclub.org
Sec./Treasurer Jean O. Pasco
Elections held in July

Oregon Newspaper Publishers Association–7150 SW Hampton St., Ste. 111, Portland, OR, 97223-8365; tel (503) 624-6397; fax (503) 624-9811; e-mail onpa@orenews.com; web site www.orenews.com
Exec. Dir. Laurie Hieb
Elections held in June

Overseas Press Club of Puerto Rico–PO Box 12326, Loiza St. Sta., San Juan, PR, 00914-0323; tel (787) 354-4029; fax (787) 753-8343; e-mail opcpr@yahoo.com; web site www.opcpr.com
President, Overseas Press de Puerto Rico Milly Mendez
Assistant Executive Director Martha Alonso
Executive Director Gail Arenas
Elections held in Nov 2012

P

Pacific Northwest Association of Want-Ad Newspapers–626 Thain Rd., Lewiston, ID, 83501; tel (208) 746-0483; fax (208) 746-8507; web site www.pnawan.org
Coord. Tamara Byrd

Pacific Northwest Newspaper Association–708 Tenth St., Sacramento, CA, 95814; tel (888) 344-7662; fax (916) 288-6002; e-mail jack@pnna.com; web site www.pnna.com
Exec. Dir. Jack Bates
Elections held in the July

Pennsylvania Newspaper Association–3899 N. Front St., Harrisburg, PA, 17110; tel (717) 703-3000; fax (717) 703-3001; e-mail info@pa-news.org; web site www.pa-newspaper.org
President Teri Henning
Past President Timothy M. Williams
Vice President, Association Services Tricia Wright
Vice President, Advertising Lisa Knight
Represents daily, weekly, collegiate and online newspapers in Pennsylvania & the U.S.

Pennsylvania Society of Newspaper Editors–3899 N. Front St., Harrisburg, PA, 17110; tel (717) 703-3000; fax (717) 703-3001; e-mail timw@pa-news.org; web site www.pa-newspaper.org
Pres./CEO Timothy M. Williams
Elections held in May

Pennsylvania Women's Press Association–511 Lenox St., Stroudsburg, PA, 18360; tel (717) 295-7869; e-mail pwpa@lancasteronline.com; web site www.pwpa.us
Elections held in May. Organization accepts freelancers

Pittsburgh Baseball Writers Association of America–Associated Press, 11 Stanwix St., Pittsburgh, PA, 15222-1312; tel (412) 281-3747; fax (412) 281-1869; e-mail appittsburgh@ap.org
Pres. Alan Robinson
Elections held in Oct.

Press Club of Ohio–50 W. Broad St., Ste. 1622, Columbus, OH, 43215; tel (614) 464-1856
Vice Pres. Betty Clark
Pres. Mary Anne Knappne
Sec./Treasurer Ralph Krasick
Elections for trustees held in Feb., officers in March

Q

Quebec Community Newspapers Association–400 Grand Blvd., Ste. 5, Ile Perrot, QC, Canada; tel (514) 453-6300; fax (514) 453-6330; e-mail info@qcna.qc.ca; web site www.qcna.org

R

Rhode Island Press Association–University of Rhode Island, Journalism Dept., Kingston, RI, 02881; tel 401-874-2195; fax (401) 874-4450; e-mail lllevin@uri.edu; web site www.uri.edu/artsci/jor/
Treasurer Kristen Cyr
Sec. Linda Levin
Elections held in Jan

S

Saskatchewan Weekly Newspapers Association–14-401 45th St. W., Saskatoon, SK, S7L 5Z9, Canada; tel (306) 382-9683; fax (306) 382-9421; e-mail swna@swna.com; web site www.swna.com
Tech. Officer Cameron Just
Commun.Coord. Julie Schau
Office Mgr. Louise Simpson
Adv. Coord., Classified Nicole Nater
Exec. Dir. Steve Nixon

Society of Classified Advertising Managers of America, Inc.–PO Box 531335, Mountain Brook, AL, 352530-1335; tel (205) 592-0389; fax (205)599-5598; e-mail hrushing@usit.net; web site www.scama.com
Exec. Officer Hugh J. Rushing
Elections held in Feb

South Carolina Associated Press News Council–1311 Marion St., Columbia, SC, 29201; tel (803) 799-5510; fax (803) 252-2913; e-mail apcolumbia@ap.org; web site www.ap.org/southcarolina
Bureau Chief Maryann Mrowca
Elections held in Feb

South Carolina News Photographers Association–The Sun News, 914 Frontage Rd. E., Myrtle Beach, SC, 29577; tel (843) 626-8555; fax (843) 626-0208; web site www.scnpa.org
Pres. PJ Browning
Elections held in Jan.

South Carolina Press Association–421 Zimalcrest Dr., Ste. 304, Columbia, SC, 29210; tel (803) 750-9561; fax (803) 551-0903; e-mail scpress@scpress.org; web site www.scpress.org
Adv. Dir. Alanna Ritchie
Member Servs. Dir. Michelle Kerscher
Mgr., Press Servs. Randall Savely
Exec. Dir. William C. Rogers
Elections held in Feb

South Dakota Newspaper Association–1125 32nd Ave., Brookings, SD, 57006; tel (605) 692-4300; fax (605) 692-6388; e-mail sdna@sdna.com; web site www.sdna.com
Asst. Mgr. Cherie Jensen
Gen. Mgr. David Bordewyk
Sales Mgr. John Brooks
Elections held in May

Southeastern Advertising Publishers Association–319 W. Seventh St., Ste. A, Columbia, TN, 38401; tel (800) 334-0649; fax (888) 334-0649; e-mail info@sapatoday.com; web site www.sapatoday.com
Exec. Dir. Douglas Fry

Southern Circulation Managers Association–401 N. Water St., Mobile, AL, 36602-4015; tel (251) 219-5372; fax (251) 219-5398; e-mail dcasciano@press-register.com; web site www.scmaonline.net
Sec. Debra Casciano
Treasurer Glen Tabor
Elections held in April. Organization accepts shoppers as Associate Members

Southern Newspaper Publishers Association–3680 N. Peachtree Rd., Ste. 300, Atlanta, GA, 30341; tel (404) 256-0444; fax (404) 252-9135; e-mail edward@snpa.org; web site www.snpa.org
Asst ED Cindy Durham
Exec. Dir. Edward VanHorn
Office Mgr. Paulette Sheffield
Elections held at the annual convention in Nov

Southwest Classified Advertising Managers Association–Dallas Morning News, PO Box 655237, Dallas, TX, 75265-5237; tel (214) 977-8222; e-mail jmckeon@dallasnews.com; web site www.dallasnews.com
President and General Manager John Mckeon
General Manager, Recruitment, Real Estate, General Classifieds Michael Mayer

State Historical Society of Wisconsin–816 State St., Madison, WI, 53706; tel (608) 264-6534; fax (608) 264-6520; web site www.wisconsinhistory.org
Administrative Asst. Margaret T. Dwyer

T

Texas Circulation Management Association–8010 Kempwood Dr, Houston, TX, 77055, USA; tel (713) 362-5567; fax (713) 354-3099; e-mail tcma@texascma.org; web site www.texascma.org
Sec./Treasurer J W Smith
Elections and annual conference held in Oct. Training seminar held in May

Tennessee Associated Press Managing Editors–215 Centerview Dr., Ste. 110 c/o Associated Press, Brentwood, TN, 37027; tel (615) 373-9988; fax (615) 376-0947; e-mail apnashville@ap.org; web site www.ap.org/tennessee
Bureau Chief Adam Yeomans

Tennessee Press Association, Inc.–435 Montbrook Ln., Knoxville, TN, 37919-2704; tel (865) 584-5761; fax (865) 558-8687; e-mail info@tnpress.com; web site www.tnpress.com
Adv. Dir. Barry Jarrell
Exec. Dir. Greg Sherrill
Elections held in June

Tennessee Press Service, Inc.–435 Montbrook Ln., Knoxville, TN, 37919-2704; tel (865) 584-5761; fax (865) 558-8687; e-mail info@tnpress.com; web site www.tnpress.com
Adv. Dir. Barry Jarrell
Exec. Dir. Greg Sherrill
Elections held in June

Texas Associated Press Managing Editors–The Dallas Morning News, 508 Young St., Dallas, TX, 75202; tel (214) 977-8222; web site www.txapme.org
Deputy Mng. Ed. Leona Allen
Elections held in March

Texas Community Newspaper Association–7920 Kern Lane, Ft. Worth, TX, 76137; tel 817-503-8100; fax (866) 822-4920; e-mail dick.colvin@hotmail.com; web site www.tcnatoday.com
Exec. Dir. Dick Colvin

Texas Daily Newspaper Association–718 W. Fifth St., Austin, TX, 78701-2796; tel (512) 476-4351; fax (512) 476-0515; e-mail info@tdna.org; web site www.tdna.org
Member Servs. Dir. Cindy Brown
Elections held in Nov

Texas Press Association–718 W. Fifth St., Ste 100, Austin, TX, 78701-2783, United States; tel (512) 477-6755; fax (512) 477-6759; e-mail mikehodges@texaspress.com; web site www.texaspress.com
Exec. Dir. Micheal Hodges
Elections held in June

Tucson Press Club–PO Box 1469, Tucson, AZ, 85702-1469; tel N/A
Contact John Bort
Club is inactive but will respond to any inquiries.

U

University Press of Kentucky–663 S. Limestone St., Lexington, KY, 40508-4008; tel (859) 257-8432; fax (859) 323-1873; e-mail smwrin2@uky.edu; web site www.kentuckypress.com
Mktg. Dir. John Hussey
Dir. Stephen Wrinn
Elections held in spring/fall of odd numbered years

Utah-Idaho-Spokane Associated Press Association–30 E. 100 South St., Ste. 200, Salt Lake City, UT, 84111; tel (801) 322-3405; fax (801) 322-0051; e-mail apsaltlake@ap.org
Bureau Chief Jim Clarke
Elections held in June

Utah Press Association, Inc.–1521 E. 3900 S., Ste. 100, Salt Lake City, UT, 84124; tel (801) 308-0268; fax (801) 308-0269; e-mail upa@utahpress.com; web site www.utahpress.com
Exec. Dir. Michael J. Fox
Elections held in March

V

Valley Press Club, Inc.–PO Box 5475, Springfield, MA, 01101-5475; tel (413) 575-4954; fax (413) 781-3749; e-mail info@valleypressclub.com; web site www.valleypressclub.com
Pres. Charlie Bennett
Elections held in March

Vermont Press Association–St. Michael's College, Journalism Dept., Colchester, VT, 05439-0284; tel (802) 654-2442; fax (802) 654-2560; e-mail mdonoghue@smcvt.edu
Executive Director Mike Donoghue
Elections held in June

Virginia Associated Press–Associated Press, 600 E. Main St., Ste. 1250, Richmond, VA, 23219-2416; tel (804) 643-6646; fax (804) 643-6223
Bureau Chief Dorothy Abernathy
Administrative Asst. Stacey Carroll

Virginia Press Association, Inc.–11529 Nuckols Rd., Glen Allen, VA, 23059; tel (804) 521-7570; fax (804) 521-7590; web site www.vpa.net
Exec. Dir. Ginger Stanley
Elections held in April

W

Washington Associated Press Newspaper Executives Association–3131 Elliott Ave., Ste. 750, Seattle, WA, 98121; tel (206) 682-1812; fax (206) 621-1948; e-mail apseattle@ap.org; web site www.ap.org
Bureau Chief Nancy Trott
Elections held in Oct./Nov

Washington Newspaper Publishers Association, Inc.–12354 30th Ave. NE, Seattle, WA, 98125; tel (206) 634-3838; fax (206) 634-3842; e-mail bwill@wnpa.com; web site www.wnpa.com
Executive Director Bill Will
Elections held in Oct; officers installed in Oct

Washington Press Association–14243 156th Ave. SE, Renton, WA, 98059-7400; tel (425) 228-5903; e-mail nlbarba@aol.com
retired Barbara Nilson

West Texas Press Association–706 SW 10th St., Perryton, TX, 79070; tel (806) 435-3631; fax (806) 435-2420; e-mail secretary@wtpa.org; web site www.wtpa.org
Sec. Mary Dudley
Elections held at annual convention in July

West Virginia News Photographers Association–1001 Virginia St., Charleston, WV, 25301; tel (304) 348-1234
Pres. Craig Cunningham
Vice Pres. Dale Sparks
Sec./Treasurer Kenneth Kemp
Elections held in Feb

West Virginia Press Association, Inc.–3422 Pennsylvania Ave., Charleston, WV, 25302; tel (800) 235-6881; fax (800) 526-6939; e-mail wvpress@wvpress.org; web site www.wvpress.org
Exec. Dir. Gloria Flowers
Elections held in Aug

Western States Advertising Agencies Association–6404 Wilshire Blvd., Ste. 1111, Los Angeles, CA, 90048; tel (323) 655-1951; fax (323) 655-8627; e-mail adclubla@aol.com
Exec. Dir. Carol Golden

White House Correspondents Association–600 New Hampshire Ave., Ste. 800, Washington, DC, 20037; tel (202) 266-7453; fax (202) 266-7454; e-mail whca@starpower.net; web site www.whca.net
Exec. Dir. Julia Whiston
Elections held in July

White House News Photographers Association, Inc.–PO Box 7119, Washington, DC, 20044-7119; tel (202) 785-5230; e-mail info@whnpa.org; web site www.whnpa.org
Treasurer Jon Elswick
Sec. Ron Sachs
Elections held in Mar.

Wisconsin Associated Press Association–111 E. Wisconsin Ave., Ste.1925, Milwaukee, WI, 53202; tel (414) 225-3580; e-mail apmlw@ap.org; web site www.ap.org
News Ed. Roger Schneider
Elections held in May

Wisconsin Free Community Papers–101 S. Main St., Fond Du Lac, WI, 54935; tel (920) 924-2651; fax (920) 922-0861; e-mail wcp@wisad.com; web site www.wisad.com
Exec. Dir. Janelle Anderson

Wisconsin Newspaper Association–1901 Fish Hatchery Rd., Madison, WI, 53713; tel (608) 283-7620; fax (608) 283-7631; e-mail info@wnanews.com; web site www.wnanews.com
Member Servs. Mgr. Bonnie Fechtner
Exec. Dir. Peter D. Fox

Wisconsin Outdoor Communicators Association (WOCA)–917 N. Glendale Ave., Tomah, WI, 54660-1303; tel (608) 372-2640
Sec./Treasurer Eugene T. Muench
Pres. Jerry Kiesow
Elections held in Aug

Women's Press Club of Indiana–538 S. Main St., Churubusco, IN, 46723, United States; tel (260) 461-8207; e-mail vsade8@gmail.com; web site www.jg.net
Historian Jackie Davis
Pres. Vivian Sade
Elections held in March

Wyoming Associated Press–320 W. 25th St., Ste. 310, Cheyenne, WY, 82001; tel (307) 632-9351; fax (307) 637-8538; web site www.ap.org
Bureau Chief Jim Clark

Wyoming Press Association–2121 Evans Ave., Cheyenne, WY, 82001; tel (307) 635-3905; fax (307) 635-3912; e-mail wyopress@wyopress.org; web site www.wyopress.org
Exec. Dir. Jim Angell
Elections held in Jan

CIRCULATION AUDIT SERVICES

Audit Bureau of Circulations (ABC) (Est. 1914)– 48 W. Seegers Road, Arlington Heights, IL, 60005-3913; tel (224) 366-6939; fax (224) 366-6949; web site www.accessabc.com
Commun. Mgr. – Kammi Altig
Vice Pres., Info Systems – Kaydene Stachelski
Vice Pres., HR – Laura Ferraris
Sr. Vice Pres., Mktg./Sales – Mark Wachowicz
Chrmn. – Merle Davidson
Pres./MD – Michael J. Lavery
Sr. Vice Pres., Auditing/Technical Review – Mike Moran
Sr. Vice Pres., Accounting – Paul Fajnor
Sr. Vice Pres., Centralized/Electronic Auditing – Scott Hanson
Vice Pres., Meetings – Sue Thomas
Sr. Vice Pres., Publisher Rel./Field Auditing – Teresa Perry
Auditing of circulation for print and digital analytics to include web, mobile, and ad serving platforms via ABC Interactive.
Established in 1914 as a tripartite, not-for-profit media auditing organization. ABC represents the industry recognized Gold Standard in media audits.

BPA Worldwide (Est. 1930)– 100 Beard Sawmill Rd. 6th Floor, Shelton, CT, 6484; tel (203) 447-2800; fax (203) 447-2900; web site www.bpaww.com

Pres./CEO – Glenn Hansen
Sr. Vice Pres., Bus. Devel. – Peter D. Black
Sr. Vice Pres., Auditing – Richard J. Murphy

Canadian Circulations Audit Board (CCAB, Inc.) (Est. 1937)– 1 Concorde Gate Ste. 800, Toronto, ON, M3C 3N6, Canada; tel (416) 487-2418; fax (416) 487-6405; e-mail info@bpaww.com; web site www.bpaww.com
Mktg. Mgr. – Neil Ta
Bulk Distribution Audit; Select Distribution Audit.

Canadian Community Newspaper Association (Est. 1919)– 8 Market St., Ste. 300, Toronto, ON, M5E 1M6, Canada; tel (416) 482-1090; fax (416) 482-1908; e-mail info@ccna.ca; web site www.ccna.ca
Pres. – John Hinds
MD – Tina Ongkeko

Certified Audit of Circulations, Inc. (Est. 1956)– 155 Willowbrook Blvd., 4th Fl., Wayne, NJ, 7470-7032; tel (973) 785-3000; fax (973) 785-8341; e-mail esodt@certifiedaudit.com; web site www.certifiedaudit.com
Dir., Opns. – David Roe
Audit Mgr. – Debbie Maragoudakis
Dir., Mktg. – Evelina Sodt
CEO – Mark Stoecklin
Circulation Auditing Readership, Reach and Advertising Value Research

Circulation Verification Council (Est. 1992)– 338 South Kirkwood Road, Suite 102, Saint Louis, MO, 63122; tel (314) 966-7711; fax (314) 822-0666; e-mail tbingaman@cvcaudit.com; web site www.cvcaudit.com
Office Mgr. – Darlene Lucy
Audit Coord. – Deborah Tata
Audit Mgr. – Jim Kennedy
Audit Coord. – Karen Wood
Audit Coord. – Lisa Funken
Pres./CEO – Tim Bingaman
Laura Jens
Lisa Kelly

Office de la Distribution Certifiee (ODC, Inc.) (Est. 1976)– 538, Place Saint-Henri, Montreal, QC, H4C 2R9, Canada; tel (514) 393-5139; fax (514) 393-5289; e-mail info@odcinc.ca; web site www.odcinc.ca
Exec. Sec. – Louise Godon

Verified Audit Circulation (VAC) (Est. 1951)– 900 Larkspur Landing Cir., Ste. 295, Larkspur, CA, 94939; tel (415) 461-6006; fax (415) 461-6007; e-mail support@verifiedaudit.com; web site www.verifiedaudit.com
Dir., Market Research – Mike Lynch
CEO – Tim Prouty

CLIP ART SERVICES

B&B - Banker & Brisebois Advertising– 901 Tower Dr., Ste. 315, MI, 48098, USA
(248) 519-9200; fax (248) 519-9206; e-mail bbinfo@bbfurnitureadvertising.com; web site www.bbfurnitureadvertising.com
Established: 1912
Pres. – Lee Gilmore
Specializes in newspaper advertising for retail furniture dealers.
Furniture Ad Idea Services: Retail home furnishings ads available for ideas or to download online. Includes events, promotions, seasonal ads, departmental and positioning ads for lower-endto higher-end stores.

Century Features, Inc.– 1420 Centre Ave., Ste. 2213, PA, 15219-3536
(412) 471-6533; fax (412) 765-3672
Contact – Charles Reichblum
I Bet You Didn't Know: Series of sports columns leased exclusively to automobile dealers, tire dealers, men's stores, etc; Calling All Home Makers: Series of furniture columns leased to furniture stores; Interesting Facts: Leased exclusively to one sponso

Coleman Advertising– 1837 Green Jays Ct., Corpus Christi, TX, 78418
(361) 779-1580; e-mail challengeradv@aol.com; web site www.challengeradvertising.com
Established: 1958
Owner – Zack Coleman
Everyone in The Church and Support America: Advertising and selling programs with local weekly sponsorships; 3 X 4 col. SA6 proof series.

EZAdsPro– 302 Ferry St., 2nd Floor, IN, 47901, United States
(765) 742-9012; fax (765) 742-2843; e-mail perry@ezadspro.com; web site www.ezadspro.com
Managing Partner – Perry Rice
EZAdsPro Publisher: Online ad-building system exclusively designed for real estate and automotive classified advertising; Above the Fold publications: Industry news for advertising departments both in print, online and mobile.

Jupiter Images Corp.– 6000 N. Forest Park Dr., Peoria, IL, 61614, USA
(309) 688-8800; fax (309) 688-5873; e-mail sales@jupiterimages.com; web site www.jupiterimages.com
Established: 1964
Vice Pres., Opns. – Mark Nickerson
All-purpose art and idea service.

JupiterImages– 5232 E. Pima St., Ste. 200C, AZ, 85712
(520) 811-8101; fax (520) 881-1841; web site www.jupiterimages.com
Pres. – Peter Gariepy
Dir., Mktg. – Dan Burk
Clipart.com: Offers downloadable clip art via subscription.

Keister-Williams Newspaper Services, Inc.– PO Box 8187, VA, 22906
(800) 293-4709; fax (434) 293-4884; e-mail kw@kwnews.com; web site www.kwnews.com
Pres. – Walton C. Lindsay
Support the Church: Weekly series in two, three or four column glossy form. CD solicitation of sponsorship available through Keister in most states or by newspaper staff.

Metro Creative Graphics, Inc.– 519 Eighth Ave., 18th Fl., NY, 10018
(212) 947-5100; fax (212) 967-4602; e-mail service@metro-email.com; web site www.metrocreativegraphics.com
Established: 1910
Pres./CEO – Robert Zimmerman
Exec. Vice Pres./Mktg. Dir. – Debra Weiss
Mktg. Mgr. – Lauren Lekoski
Metro Creative Graphics, Inc.: Creative advertising services designed to fulfill the creative needs throughout publications and organizations. Resources available for revenue-generating ideas and concepts including: ready-to-use spec ads, campaigns, layouts, photographs, graphic illustrations, marketing programs and sales opportunities; along with ready-to-sell telemarketing promotions, reader contests, circulation-building ideas and self-promotion items. Available online and on CD-ROM.
Metro Classified Dynamics.: Innovative ads and promotions for generating classified advertising revenue. Includes art and photos for automotive, recruitment and real estate, plus, telemarketing directories, self-promotion and circulation-building ideas.
Metro Editorial Services.: Ready-to-use themed editorial sections and Timely Features (calendar, seasonal and event-related features), both focused on providing editorial material for many of the key selling opportunities each month.
Metro Holiday Advertising Service.: This annual service contains holiday art and greetings ads covering the big end-of-year sales opportunities from Thanksgiving through Christmas and New Year's.
Metro Newspaper Service.: Resource for monthly images, photos and spec ads. Creative concepts cover every saleable event and important advertiser category.
Metro Plus Business.: A forum for the exchange of creative ideas. Articles give how-to's for executing successful ad and promotion ideas already proven profitable by fellow publications.
Metro Sales Spectaculars.: This monthly service is ready-to-sell with more than 80 small space ad layouts based on popular ad themes such as bridal, home, auto services, health, seniors, and more.
MetroCreativeConnection.: Metro's online portal provides access to all service materials. Subscribers can access an expanding library of images, photos and spec ads. Search, preview, print and download directly from the site, plus, benefit from Metro's Project Organizer software.

Multi-Ad Services, Inc.– 1720 W. Detweiller Dr., IL, 61615-1695
(309) 692-1530; fax (309) 692-6566; web site www.multiad.com
Pres./CEO – James M. Douglas
Exec. Vice Pres. – John F. Kocher
Sr. Vice Pres. – Jim Garner

News USA, Inc.– 2841 Hartland Rd., Ste. 301, Falls Church, VA, 22043, USA
(703) 734-6300; fax (703) 734-6314; e-mail info@newsusa.com, YB_ASSOC_CLIPART; web site www.newsusa.com
Established: 1987
Pres./CEO – Richard D. Smith
Vice Pres., Sales – Richard Rothstein
Ed. – Jacob Maurer
IT Dir. – Scott Peters
Pub. – Rick Smith
CEO – Richard Smith
Sales Rep. – John Phillips
Features: Print features, in AP style, carry the messages of Fortune 500 companies, nonprofit organizations, public relations agencies, smaller companies and individual entrepreneurs. Byline articles, evergreen features and seasonal and timely features ar

North American Precis Syndicate, Inc.– 415 MADISON AVENUE FL 12, NY, 10017
(212) 867-9000; fax (212) 867-9010; e-mail glipton@napsnet.com; web site www.napsnet.com
Pres. – Dorothy York
Vice Pres., Media Rel. – Gary Lipton
Ed. in Chief – Candace Leiberman
Serv. Mgr. – Yauling Wagner
Featurettes (Free Filler/Feature Service): Free repro proofs, CD-ROMS or diskettes of cartoons, features and fillers from PR sources mailed once a week; free on behalf of 700 non-profit organizations, trade associations and government agencies to newspape

Syndicated Ad Features, Inc.– 1416 Providence Hwy., MA, 02062-4648
(781) 255-7773; fax (781) 255-7774; e-mail info@syndicatedadfeatures.com; web site www.syndicatedadfeatures.com
Established: 1967
Pres. – David G. Margolis
Controller – Denise Duca
Vice Pres./Western Regl. Sales Dir. – Richard Ross
Vice Pres./Eastern Regl. Sales Dir. – Bill Blumsack
Mid-Atlantic Regl. Sales Mgr. – Tim Wydro
General Office Manager – Marti Northover
Personalized Columns: Ghostwrites feature columns for businesses and medical professionals that appear under the client's picture and by-line in his or her local newspaper on an exclusive basis. The program consists of a 52-week supply of informative, fre

Thought Equity Management, Inc.– 1530 16th St., 6th Fl., CO, 80202
(720) 382-2869; fax (720) 382-2719; e-mail sales@thoughtequity.com; web site www.thoughtequity.com
Established: 2003
Founder/CEO – Kevin Schaff
CTO – Mark Lemmons
Vice Pres., Mktg. – Mike Emerson
Vice Pres., Bus. Devel. – Frank Cardello
Thought Equity Libraries: Supplier of motion content to newspaper, cable and broadcast companies. Thousands of affordable, top-quality ads and commercials are searchable and accessible online.

CLIPPING BUREAUS

Allen's Press Clipping Bureau–657 Mission St., Rm. 602, San Francisco, CA, 94105; tel (415) 392-2353; fax (415) 362-6208; web site allenspcb.com
Gen. Mgr. – John N. McCombs

Allen's Press Clipping Bureau–720 Third Ave., Ste. 1410, Seattle, WA, 98104; tel (206) 622-8312; fax (206) 622-5748; e-mail seattle@allenspcb.com; web site www.allenspcb.com
Established: 1888
Regional Manager – Grace Chrystie

Allen's Press Clipping Bureau–621 SW Alder, Rm. 540, Portland, OR, 97205-3620; tel (503) 223-7824; fax (503) 223-3819; e-mail portland@allenspcb.com; web site www.allenspcb.com
Office Mgr. – Whit Draper

Allen's Press Clipping Bureau–900 Wilson Blvd., Ste. 430, Los Angeles, CA, 90017; tel (213) 628-4214; fax (213) 627-0889; e-mail la@al-

lenspcb.com; web site www.allenspcb.com
Office Mgr – Linda Wiser

Arkansas Newspaper Clipping Service–411 S. Victory St., Ste. 201, Little Rock, AR, 72209; tel (501) 375-2757; fax (501) 375-2969; web site www.newzgroup.com
Mgr. – Shirley Anderson

BurrellesLuce–42 S. Center St., Mesa, AZ, 85210; tel (480) 834-4884; fax (480) 834-3821; web site www.burrelles.com
Pres./COO – John P. French

BurrellesLuce–75 E. Northfield Rd., Livingston, NJ, 7039; tel (973) 992-6600; fax (973) 992-7675; e-mail rwaggoner@burrellesluce.com; web site www.burrellesluce.com
Established: 1888
Chrmn./ CEO – Robert C. Waggoner

Cision AB–Linnegatan 87A, Stockholm, SE-114 88, Sweden; tel 507 410 00; fax 507 417 17; e-mail support.se@cision.com; web site www.cision.com
Pres. – Hans Gieskes
Gen. Mgr. – Magnus Thell
Commun. Mgr. – Ulrika Nyberg

Cision Canada Ltd.–150 Ferrand Dr., Ste. 1100, Toronto, ON, M3C 3E5, Canada; tel (416) 750-2220; fax (416) 750-2233; e-mail sales@cision.com; web site www.cision.com
Pres. – Phil Crompton
Gen. Mgr., Print Monitoring – Gary LaRose

Cision US, Inc.–332 S. Michigan Ave., Chicago, IL, 60604; tel (312) 922-2400; fax (312) 922-3127; web site www.cision.com
Vice Pres., Bus. Devel. – Michael Renderman
Exec.Dir. – Diana Eagen

Colorado Press Clipping Service–1336 Glenarm Pl., Denver, CO, 80204-2115; tel (303) 571-5117; fax (303) 571-1803; e-mail clips@colopress.net; web site www.coloradopressassociation.com
Exec. Dir. – Ed Otte

Clipping Serv. Mgr. – Ellen Kessler

Illinois Press Clipping Bureau–900 Community Dr., Springfield, IL, 62703; tel (217) 241-1300; fax (217) 241-1301; e-mail smulvany@il-press.com; web site www.IllinoisPress.org
Interim Exe. Dir. – Don Craven

International Press Cutting Bureau–224/236 Walworth Rd., London, ENG, SE17 1JE, United Kingdom; tel 7708 2113; fax 7701 4489; e-mail info@ipcb.co.uk; web site www.ipcb.co.uk
Sr. Partner/Gen. Mgr. – Robert Podro

Iowa Press Clipping Bureau–319 E. 5th St., Ste. 6, Des Moines, IA, 50309; tel (515) 244-8331; fax (515) 244-5118; web site www.newzgroup.com/pages/IApage.htm
Mgr. – Nancy Swinehart

Kansas Press Clipping Service–1100 SW Wanamaker Ave., Topeka, KS, 66604; tel (785) 271-0206; fax (785) 271-0220; web site www.newzgroup.com
Mgr. – Dorinda Brucken

Kentucky Press Clipping Service–1505 Twilight Trail, Frankfort, KY, 40601; tel (502) 227-0110; fax (502) 227-8888; web site www.newzgroup.com

Mgr. – Jamie Keith

Missouri Press Clipping Bureau–409 Vandiver W., Bldg. 3 Ste. 100, Columbia, MO, 65202; tel (573) 817-5832; fax (573) 442-4895; web site www.newzgroup.com/pages/MOpage.html
Exec. Dir. – Brad Buchanan
Mgr. – Lee Brooks

Mutual Press Clipping Service, Inc.–1315 Walnut St., Ste. 1500, Philadelphia, PA, 19107; tel (215) 735-7260; fax (215) 735-8510; e-mail mutualpressclipping@burrellesluce.com; web site www.mutualpressclipping.com
Gen. Mgr. – Susan R. Begley

New England Newsclip Agency, Inc.–75 East Northfield Road, Livingston, NJ, 07039; tel (508) 663-1920; fax 800-563-9725; e-mail mmckenna@burrellesluce.com; web site www.newenglandnewsclip.com
Group: BurrellesLuce.
National Sales Manager – Michael McKenna

New Mexico Press Clipping Bureau–PO Box 3015, Albuquerque, NM, 87190; tel (505) 275-1377; fax (505) 275-1449; e-mail nmpressaccounting@earthlink.net; web site www.nmpress.org
Exec. Dir. – Dana Bowley
Office Mgr. – Holly Aguilar

New York State Clipping Service, NJ; tel 800-631-1160; fax 800-563-9725; web site www.burrellesluce.com
Group: BurrellesLuce. **Established:** 1888
Established: 1888
VP, Director of National Sales – Rick Melchers

Newz Group–409 Vandiver West , Bldg. 3, Ste 100, Columbia, MO, 65201; tel (573) 474-1000; fax (573) 474-1001; e-mail info@newzgroup.com; web site www.newzgroup.com
Established: 1991
Pres. – Brad Buchanan
Vice Pres. – Scott Buchanan
Vice President – Ian Buchanan

Oklahoma Press Association–3601 N. Lincoln Blvd., Oklahoma City, OK, 73105-5499; tel (405) 524-4421; fax (405) 499-0048; e-mail lgarvin@okpress.com; web site www.okpress.com
Established: 1906
Clipping Bureau Mgr. – Louise Garvin
Exec. Dir. – Mark Thomas
Adv. Mgr. – Sara Barrow

Romeike Ltd.–Romeike House, 290-296 Green Lanes, Palmers Green, London, N13 5TP, United Kingdom; tel 882 0155; fax 882 6716; web site www.romeike.com

– Giselle Bodie
– Michael HigginsMng. Dir.s

South Carolina Press Clipping Bureau–421 Zimalcrest Dr., Ste. 304, Columbia, SC, 29210-6835; tel (803) 561-0200; fax (803) 561-0440; web site www.newzgroup.com
Mgr. – Claire Whelan

South Dakota Newspaper Association–1125 32nd Ave., Brookings, SD, 57006-8100; tel (605) 692-4300; fax (605) 692-6388; e-mail clipping@sdna.com; web site www.sdna.com
Established: 1882
Gen. Mgr. – David Bordewyk

Tennessee Press Service, Inc.–435 Montbrook Ln., Knoxville, TN, 37919-2704; tel (865) 584-5761; fax (865) 558-8687; e-mail info@tnpress.com; web site www.tnpress.com
Adv. Dir. – Barry Jarrell
Exec. Dir. – Greg Sherrill

Texas Press Clipping Service–718 W. Fifth St., Austin, TX, 78701; tel (512) 472-7299; fax (512) 472-7335; web site www.newzgroup.com
Mgr. – Lee Brooks

Virginia Clipping Service–10195 Maple Leaf Ct., Ashland, VA, 23005; tel (804) 550-5114; fax (804) 550-5116; e-mail virginiaclipping@burrellesluce.com; web site www.vaclippingservice.com
Client Servs. Mgr. – Duska Adams

West Virginia Press Clipping Bureau–3422 Pennsylvania Ave., Charleston, WV, 25302; tel (304) 346-9126; fax (304) 346-9126; web site www.newzgroup.com
Mgr. – Yvonne Cobb

Wyoming Newspaper Clipping Service–2121 Evans Ave., Cheyenne, WY, 82001-3733; tel (307) 432-9748; fax (307) 778-0601; web site www.newzgroup.com
Mgr. – Cindy Conner

ELECTRONIC CLIPPING BUREAUS

Associated Press Information Services–450 W. 33rd St. New York, NY 10001, USA; tel (212) 621-1585; fax (212) 621-7520; e-mail apif@ap.orgwww.ap.org
Dir. Sales – Ted Mendelsohn

BurrellesLuce–42 S. Center St. Mesa, AZ 85210; tel (480) 834-4884; fax (480) 834-3821www.burrelles.com
Pres./COO – John P. French

BurrellesLuce–75 E. Northfield Rd. Livingston, NJ 07039; tel (973) 992-6600; fax (973) 992-7675; e-mail rwaggoner@burrellesluce.comwww.burrellesluce.com@RecordBody:**Established:** 1888
Chrmn./ CEO – Robert C. Waggoner

Dialog Corp.–2250 Perimeter Park Dr., Ste. 300 Morrisville, NC 27560-8893, USA; tel (919) 804-6400; fax (919) 804-6410; e-mail customer@dialog.comwww.dialog.com
Gen. Mgr. – Suzanne BeDell
Vi ce Pres., Mktg. – Libby Trudell

eWatch–Two Meridian Crossings, Ste. 510 Minneapolis, MN 55423-3963; tel (612) 331-7800; fax (888) 776-6552; e-mail nancy.sells@prnewswire.comwww.ewatch.com
Vice Pres. – Nancy Sells

Infomart Ltd.–1450 Don Mills Rd. Toronto, ON M3B 2X7, Canada; tel (416) 442-2222; fax (416) 442-2968; e-mail helpdesk@infomart.cawww.infomart.ca
Pres. – Warren Cable

Wavo Corporation–375 Chipeta Way Salt Lake City, UT 84108; tel (801) 584-2800; fax (801) 584-2831; e-mail juberty@wavo.com
Dir., Mktg. – Dina Murphy

YellowBrix–500 Montgomery St., Ste. 700 Alexandria, VA 22314, USA; tel (703) 548-3300; fax (703) 548-9151; e-mail info@yellowbrix.comwww.yellowbrix.com
Founder/Pres./CEO – Jeffrey P. Massa
Adv. Mgr. – Tom Hargis

NEWSPAPER BROKERS AND APPRAISERS

AdMedia Partners, Inc.–3 Park Ave., 31st Fl., New York, NY, 10016-6903, usa; tel (212) 759-1870; fax (212) 888-4960; e-mail info@admediapartners.com; web site www.admediapartners.com
; Established 1990
Managing Director – Seth R. Alpert
Principal – Oliver Schweitzer
Managing Director (Retired) – Mark M. Edmiston
Managing Director (Retired) – Abbott C. Jones
Managing Director – Gregory C. Smith

Associated Texas Newspapers, Inc.–4100 Jackson Ave., Apt. 460, Austin, TX, 78731; tel (512) 407-8283; fax (512) 407-8289; e-mail Billberger@austin.rr.com; web site www.hondoanvilherald.com
Pres. – Bill Berger
Vice Pres. – Jeff Berger

C. Berky & Associates, Inc.–11750 Watercrest Lane, Boca Raton, FL, 33498; tel (561) 212-1219; fax (561) 852-6482; e-mail pageboca@aol.com
Pres. – H. Charles Berky

Blackburn & Co., Inc.–201 N. Union St., Ste. 340, Alexandria, VA, 22314-2642; tel (703) 519-3703; fax (703) 519-9756
Chrmn. – James W. Blackburn
Pres. – Richard F. Blackburn

CBS Associates–423 Sutton Cr., Danville, CA, 94506; tel (925) 736-6350; fax (925) 736-3034
Contact – Carl B. Shaver

Capital Endeavors, Inc.–232 W. Crogan St., Ste. C, Lawrenceville, GA, 30046; tel (770) 962-8399; fax (770) 962-8640; e-mail davidstill@capitalendeavors.com; web site www.capitalendeavors.com
Pres. – David R. Still

Cribb, Greene & Associates–104 E. Main St., Ste. 402, Bozeman, MT, 59715; tel (406) 586-6621; fax (406) 586-6774; e-mail jcribb@cribb.com; web site www.cribb.com
Managing Director – John Cribb
MD. – Gary Greene
Market Analyst – Bill Wilke

Dirks, Van Essen & Murray–119 E. Marcy St., Ste. 100, Santa Fe, NM, 87501-2092; tel (505) 820-2700; fax (505) 820-2900; web site www.dirksvanessen.com
; Established 1980
Pres. – Owen D. Van Essen

Exec. Vice Pres. – Philip W. Murray
Vice Pres. – Sara April

Fournier Media Services, Inc.–613 Seventh St., Prosser, WA, 99350; tel 206 409 9216; fax (509) 786-1779; e-mail mutinybaydad@aol.com; web site www.recordbulletin.com
; Established 1982
Pres. – John L. Fournier

French, L. Barry–3 Ashlawn Rd., Assonet, MA, 02702-1105; tel (508) 644-5772; e-mail barryfrench@yahoo.com
Pres. – Barry French

Gauger Media Service, Inc.–205 Duryea St., Ste. B, Raymond, WA, 98577, USA; tel (360) 942-3560; fax (360) 942-9896; e-mail dave@gaugermedia.com; web site www.gaugermedia.com
; Established 1987
Pres./Broker – Dave Gauger

Grimes, W.B. & Co.–276 Springbrook Trail, Sparta, NJ, 07871; tel (973) 729-2973; web site www.mediamergers.com

Grimes, W.B. & Co.–59 Manor Sq., Sparta, NJ, 07871; tel (973) 729-7299; fax (973) 729-0648; e-mail dslavin@mediamergers.com; web site www.mediamergers.com
Southeast/Mid-Atlantic Assoc. – David Slavin

Grimes, W.B. & Co.–11229 Greenbriar Chase, Oklahoma City, OK, 73170; tel (405) 735-7394; e-mail rhyde@att.net; web site www.mediamergers.com
Southwest/Mountain States Assoc. – Rollie Hyde

Grimes, W.B. & Co.–24212 Muscari Court, Gaithersburg, MD, 20882-3804, Unitred States; tel (301) 253-5016; fax (240) 358-0790; e-mail lgrimes@mediamergers.com; web site www.mediamergers.com
; Established 1959
President – Larry Grimes
Founder – Walter Grimes
Senior Associate-Midwest – Julie Bergman
Senior Associate-Northeast/New England – John Szefc
Senior Associate- Mid-Atlantic/Southeast – David Slavin
Senior Associate- Southeast/South – Mark Laskowski
Senior Associate- South – Dennis Richardson
Director-Southwest/Plains/West – Rollie Hyde
Associate- Western States – Jay Harn
Senior Associate-Trade and Consumer Magazines; Digital Media – John McGovern

Grimes, W.B. & Co.–699 Channing Way, Camden, TN, 38320; tel (731) 694-2149; fax (731) 584-4943; e-mail drichardson@mediamergers.com; web site www.mediamergers.com
South/Southwest Assoc. – Dennis Richardson

Grimes, W.B. & Co.–2533 Amelia Rd., Fernandina, FL, 32034; tel (888) 237-7244; e-mail david@wbgrimes.com; web site www.mediamergers.com
Southeast/Nat'l Grps. Assoc. – David Emmons

Grimes, W.B. & Co.–175 N. Tamarack St., Sisters, OR, 97759; tel (541) 948-9501; fax (541) 549-6170; e-mail tommauldin@iinet.com; web site www.mediamergers.com
West/Mountain States Assoc. – Tom Mauldin

Grimes, W.B. & Co.–1252 Shalem Colony Trl., Las Cruces, NM, 88005; tel (505) 524-0122; e-mail sck01@comcast.net; web site www.mediamergers.com
Southwest/West Assoc. – Steve Klinger

Grimes, W.B. & Co.–35 Ridge Rd., Goshen, NY, 10924-5300; tel (845) 291-7367; fax (845) 291-7367; e-mail jszefc@mediamergers.com; web site www.mediamergers.com
Northeast/New England Regl. Mgr. – John Szefc

Gruntal & Co., Inc.–650 Madison Ave., New York, NY, 10022; tel (212) 820-8240; fax (212) 750-5147; e-mail mccluskw@gruntal.com; web site www.gruntal.com
Mng. Dir. – William J. McCluskey

Hare Associates, Inc.–62 Black Walnut Dr., Rochester, NY, 14615-1259; tel (585) 621-6873; fax (585) 621-4197
Pres. – Richard L. Hare

Harris Williams & Co.–575 Market St., 31st Fl., San Francisco, CA, 94105; tel (415) 288-4260; fax (415) 288-4269; e-mail tarmstrong@harriswilliams.com; web site www.harriswilliams.com
Mng. Dir. – Tiff B. Armstrong

Harris Williams & Co.–2 International Pl., 24th Fl., Boston, MA, 2110; tel (617) 482-7501; fax (617) 482-7503; e-mail broman@harriswilliams.com; web site www.harriswilliams.com
Mng. Dir. – William E. Roman

Harris Williams & Co.–101 Haxall Point, 9th Fl., Richmond, VA, 23219; tel (804) 648-0072; fax (804) 648-0073; e-mail cwilliams@harriswilliams.com; web site www.harriswilliams.com
– Dena Frith Moore
– R. Giles Tucker
– Christopher H. WilliamsMng. Dir.s

Harvey, Faye–PO Box 1410, Lebanon, MO, 65536-1410; tel (417) 532-4809; e-mail f_harvey@hotmail.com
Broker – Faye Harvey

Hempstead & Co., Inc.–807 Haddon Ave., Haddonfield, NJ, 08033-1749; tel (856) 795-6026; fax (856) 795-4911; web site www.hempsteadco.com
Mng. Dir. – Mark Penny

JP Media Partners–604 Sutter Street, Suite 394, Folsom, CA, 95630, USA; tel (916) 673-9779; fax (888) 933-0807; e-mail jeff@jpmediapartners.com; web site www.jpmediapartners.com
; Established 2003
Principal – Jeffrey Potts

Jordan, Edmiston Group, Inc.–150 E. 52nd St., 18th Fl., New York, NY, 10022; tel (212) 754-0710; fax (212) 754-0337; e-mail adamg@jegi.com; web site www.jegi.com
CEO – Wilma Jordan
COO – Bill Hitzig
Mng. Dir. – Tolman Geffs
Mng. Dir. – Michael Marchesano
Mng. Dir. – Richard Mead
Mng. Dir. – Scott Peters
Vice Pres., Mktg. – Adam Gross

Kamen & Co. Group Services–626 RXR Plaza, Uniondale, NY, 11556; tel (516) 379-2797; fax (516) 379-3812; e-mail info@kamengroup.com; web site www.kamengroup.com
; Established 1993
Pres./CEO – Kevin B. Kamen
Vice Pres. – Celeste Myers

Kevin Brian Kamen & Co. (Kamen & Co. Group Services)– 626 RXR Plaza, Uniondale, NY, 11556, USA; tel (516) 379-2797; fax (516) 379-3812; e-mail info@KamenGroup.com; web site www.KamenGroup.com
; Established 1981
Pres. – Kevin Brian Kamen
Vice Pres., New York – Gary R. Kamen
Vice Pres., Tampa – Rosalyn Kamen
Vice Pres. – Celeste Myers
Gen. Mgr., Los Angeles – Mathew Kamen
Office Mgr. – Mary Hiscock
Office Mgr. – Tom Horowitz

Knowles Media Brokerage Services–PO Box 9698, Bakersfield, CA, 93389; tel (661) 833-3834; fax (661) 833-3845; e-mail gregg.knowles@netzero.com; web site www.media-broker.com
; Established 1987
Owner – Gregg Knowles

Management Planning, Inc.–77 Franklin St., 5th Fl., Boston, MA, 2110; tel (617) 482-6462; fax (617) 482-2515; e-mail jweir@mpival.com; web site www.mpival.com
Reg'l Dir. – Jeremy Weir

Management Planning, Inc.–101 Poor Farm Rd., Princeton, NJ, 8540; tel (609) 924-4200; fax (609) 924-4573; e-mail mpival.com; web site www.mpival.com
Pres. – Harry L. Curtis
Sr. Vice Pres. – Thomas A. Egan
Sr. Vice Pres. – Frank E. Koehl
Sr. Vice Pres. – Roy H. Meyers
Vice Pres. – Gerald P. Valentine

Management Planning, Inc.–300 Park Ave. S., Ste. 1700, New York, NY, 10022; tel (212) 572-6291; fax (212) 572-6499; e-mail jhardwick@mpival.com; web site www.mpival.com
Reg'l Dir. – John H. Hardwick

Management Planning, Inc.–10 Station St., Ste. 3, Simsbury, CT, 6070; tel (860) 651-8185; fax (860) 651-0032; e-mail bcranshaw@mpival.com; web site www.mpival.com
Vice Pres. – William O. Cranshaw
Gen. Mgr. – Harry.L Curtis

Management Planning, Inc.–70 W. Madison St., Ste. 1400, Chicago, IL, 60602; tel (312) 214-6141; fax (312) 214-3110; e-mail sroberts@mpival.com; web site www.mpival.com
Vice Pres. – Stephen J. Roberts

Management Planning, Inc.–5401 Kirkman Rd., Ste. 310, Orlando, FL, 32819; tel (407) 599-0060; fax (407) 641-8778; web site www.mpival.com
Vice Pres. – Joseph A. Gitto

Mayo Communications, Inc.–2576 Seaford Cir., Tampa, FL, 33682-5056; tel (813) 971-2061; fax (813) 977-1947
Pres. – Lincoln A. Mayo

McMullin, Norman R.–8613 E. Appaloosa Trail, Scottsdale, AZ, 85258-6207; tel (480) 922-3986; fax (480) 922-3986
Pres. – Norman R. McMullin

Media America Brokers–3137 E. Shadowlawn Ave., NE, Atlanta, GA, 30305-2405; tel (404) 869-8686; fax (404) 869-9595; e-mail lonwwilliams@aol.com
; Established 1989
Owner – Lon W Williams

Media Consultants, Inc.–5132 St. Andrews Dr., Loveland, CO, 80537-7954; tel (970) 215-4897

Media Consultants, Inc.–3093 Valley View Rd. NE, Lancaster, OH, 43130; tel (740) 681-9259; fax (740) 681-9440; e-mail alspach@compuserve.com
Vice Pres., Free Papers – Howard Alspach

Media Consultants, Inc.–3904 Central Ave., Ste. A140, Cheyenne, WY, 82001; tel (509)248-5860; web site www.publicationsforsale.com
; Established 1958
Co-Owner – Michael Lindsey
Pres – Pat Lindsey

Media Consultants, Inc.–8160 Piute Rd., Colorado Springs, CO, 80926; tel (719) 579-0409; e-mail mediamike1@aol.com; web site www.publicationsforsale.com
; Established 1958
Pres. – Michael D. Lindsey

Media Services Group, Inc.–3948 S. Third St., Ste. 191, Jacksonville Beach, FL, 32250; tel (904) 285-3239; fax (904) 285-5618; web site www.mediaservicesgroup.com
Mng. Dir. – George R. Reed
Dir. – William H. Lytle
Dir. – Robert J. Maccini
Dir. – Thomas McKinley
Dir. – Gregory Merrill
Dir. – William L. Whitley
Dir. – Jody McCoy
Assoc. – Eddie Esserman
Assoc. – Stephan Sloan

National Media Associates–1412 Kerr Research Drive, Ada, OK, 74821-0849; tel (580) 421-9600; fax (580) 421-9966; e-mail bolitho@nationalmediasales.com; web site www.nationalmediasales.com
; Established 1995
– Thomas Bolitho
– Edward AndersonPres.s

National Media Associates–PO Box 2001, Branson, MO, 65615; tel (417) 336-3457; fax (417) 336-5717; web site www.nationalmediasales.com
Owner – Edward M. Anderson

Northwest Publishers, Inc.–104 S. Walnut, La Crescent, MN, 55947; tel (507) 895-2900; fax (507) 895-2942
Broker Assoc. – Tom van der Linden

Northwest Publishers, Inc.–710 Lake St., Spirit Lake, IA, 51360-0275; tel (712) 336-3085; fax (712) 336-0611; e-mail johnvan@rconnect.com
; Established 1972
Broker – John E. van der Linden

Phelps, Cutler & Associates–6605 Abercorn St., Suite 208, Savannah, GA, 31405, USA; tel (912) 351-9122; fax (912) 351-9045; e-mail phelpscutler@aol.com; web site www.phelpscutlerconsulting.com
; Established 1991
Pres. – Louise D. Phelps

Phillips Properties, Inc.–1713 Giant Sycamore Ln., Baker, FL, 32531-8176; tel (850) 537-4040; fax (850) 537-4050
Chrmn. of the Bd. – Rupert Phillips

Rickenbacher Media–6731 Desco Dr., Dallas, TX, 75225; tel (214) 265-9300; fax (214) 369-6496; e-mail rmedia@msn.com; web site www.rickenbachermedia.com
; Established 1985
Pres./Exec. Dir. – Ted Rickenbacher
Western States Dir. – Jim Afinowich

Veronis Suhler Stevenson–350 Park Ave., New York, NY, 10022; tel (212) 935-4990; fax (212) 381-8168; e-mail stevensonj@vss.com; web site www.vss.com
Co-Founder/Mng. Partner/Chrmn./Co-CEO – John J. Veronis
Co-Founder/Mng. Partner – John S. Suhler
Mng. Partner/Co-CEO – Jeffrey T. Stevenson

Whitesmith Publication Services–PO Box 4487, Vancouver, WA, 98662-0487; tel (360) 892-7196; fax (360) 892-7196 (call first)
Newspaper Broker – Rod Whitesmith

NEWSPAPER REPRESENTATIVES - FOREIGN

A

AD*REACH
3050 Harvester Rd., Ste. 103, Burlington, ON, L7N 3J1, Canada
(905) 639-8720; fax (905) 639-6962; e-mail adreach@ocna.org; web site www.adreach.ca

Group:
Ontario Community Newspapers Association
Member Services Coordinator – Kelly Gorven
Executive Director – Anne Lannan

ADMARKET INTERNATIONAL (DIV. OF MARCOM INTERNATIONAL, INC.)
Marcom Group Bldg., 105 Woodrow Ave., Southport, CT, 06890-1121
(203) 319-1000; fax (203) 319-1004; e-mail info@admarketintl.com; web site www.admarketintl.com
Established: 1986
Pres./CEO – Nabil E. Fares
Acct. Exec. – Kristina Kalman
AdMarket International plans and places advertising in 15,000 media newspapers in over 200 countries worldwide

ADMAX INTERNATIONAL MEDIA
7326 McLaren Ave., West Hills, CA, 91307-2123
(818) 715-9931; fax (253) 648-4574; e-mail admax@sbcglobal.net; web site www.admaxinternational.com
Established: 1992
Pres. – Maria de los Angeles
Pres. – Edward G. Wilson
Media Dir. – Maria Teresa Perez
Acct. Exec. – Brad Brigg
Acct. Exec. – Simon English
Acct. Exec. – Larry Redd
Acct. Exec. – Julio Vender

ADVANTAGE NEWSPAPER CONSULTANTS
597 Oliver St., Fayetteville, NC, 28304, United States
(910) 323-0349; fax (910) 323-9280; e-mail info@newspaperconsultants.com; web site www.newspaperconsultants.com
Established: 1996
President – Timothy O. Dellinger
Vice President – John M. Jones
General Manager – Susan M. Jolley
Over 200 newspaper publishers use Advantage Newspaper Consultants□ selling approach, generating new revenue without incremental fulfillment cost. In less staff time than goes into a typical special section, Advantage delivers you new annually-contracted business that publishes in your core newspaper and Website without adding newsprint cost or reducing banner-ad availability. Advantage consultants customize valuable advertising packages adding technology we provide and work with your sales team to deliver year-long results serving your advertisers and readers.

ASSOCIATED NEWSPAPERS (USA) LTD.
225 Park Ave. S., New York, NY, 10003
(212) 893-2170; fax (212) 893-2178; e-mail maria.gibbs@dailymail.co.uk
Mgr. – Maria Gibbs

AXEL SPRINGER VERLAG AG
Axel Springer Platz 1, Hamburg, D-20350, Germany; tel (49) 40
34700; fax 3472 5540; web site www.asv.de
Chrmn. – Mathias Dopfner

B

BRYDSON GLOBAL MEDIA SALES
301 W. 53 St., Ste. 10E, New York, NY, 10019
(212) 586-7773; fax (212) 582-6353; e-mail brydmedia@aol.com; web site www.brydsonglobalmedia.com
Established: 1980
Pres. – David Brydson

C

CHARNEY/PALACIOS & CO.
5201 Blue Lagoon Dr., Ste. 200, Miami, FL, 33126-2065
(786) 388-6340; fax (786) 388-9113; e-mail miami@publicitas.com; web site www.publicitas.com

CEO – Grace Palacios
Sales Mktg. Mgr. – Maria Jose Torres
Charney/Palacios is a subsidiary of Publicitas

CHINA ONLINE, INC.
900 N. Michigan Ave., Ste. 2800, Chicago, IL, 60611
(312) 664-8880; fax (312) 787-0993; e-mail adnetinfo@chinaonline.com; web site www.chinaonline.com

Pres. – David Hale
Bus. Dir. – Julie Zhang
China Online also represents a host of trade journals in telecommunications, electric power, construction, machinery, building, and other industries in China

D

DICOMM MEDIA
333 W. 39th St., Ste. 602, New York, NY, 10018
(646) 536-7206; fax (973) 335-1038; e-mail info@dicommintl.com; web site www.dicommintl.com
Established: 1995
Gen. Mgr. – Thibaud Wallaert

DOW JONES INTERNATIONAL MARKETING SERVICES
1155 Avenue of the Americas, New York, NY, 10036
(212) 597-5743; fax (212) 597-5833; web site www.wsj.com
Exec. Asst. – Courtney Tate

L

LATIN ADMERICA, INC.
1260 SW First St., Miami, FL, 33135
(305) 649-2007; fax (305) 649-7733; e-mail andespacif@aol.com

Pres. – Omar Pinto

LEE & STEEL LLC
PO Box 2007, Darien, CT, 06820
(203) 445-8900; fax (203) 445-1885; e-mail michael.lee@leeandsteel.com
Established: 1991
CEO – Michael Lee

M

MARSTON WEBB INTERNATIONAL
60 Madison Ave., Ste. 1212, New York, NY, 10010
(212) 684-6601; fax (212) 725-4709; e-mail marwebint@cs.com; web site www.marston-webb.com
Established: 1981
Pres. – Victor Webb
Vice Pres. – Madlene Olson
MWI also represents South African and Middle Eastern papers

MULTIMEDIA, INC.
7061 Grand National Dr., Ste. 127, Orlando, FL, 32819-8992
(407) 903-5000; fax (407) 363-9809; e-mail info@multimediausa.com; web site www.multimediausa.com
Pres. – Fernando Mariano

P

PUBLICITAS NORTH AMERICA, INC.
330 7th Ave., 5th Fl., New York, NY, 10001-5010
(212) 599-5057; fax (212) 599-8298; e-mail newyork@publicitas.com; web site www.publicitas.com
CFO – Joseph DeFalco

NEWSPAPER REPRESENTATIVES - NATIONAL

A

AP ADVANTAGE
450 W. 33rd St., New York, NY, 10001-2603; tel (212) 621-7107; fax (212) 246-2402; web site www.ap.org; www.apads.biz
Pres. – Tom Turley

AD PLACEMENT SERVICES
24 Lakeside Ave., Pompton Lakes, NJ, 7442; tel (800) 737-9676; fax (973) 208-6687; web site www.ifpa.com
Established 1996
Mgr. – Alan Spoto
Display advertising for 220 publications nationwide, in cooperation with Independent Free Papers Association

AD REPS
51 Church St., Boston, MA, 02116-5417; tel (617) 542-6913; fax (617) 542-7227; e-mail adreps1@yahoo.com
Pres. – Steve Ganak

ADVANTAGE NEWSPAPER CONSULTANTS
597 Oliver St., Fayetteville, NC, 28304, United States; tel (910) 323-0349; fax (910) 323-9280; e-mail info@newspaperconsultants.com; web site www.newspaperconsultants.com
Established 1996
President – Timothy O. Dellinger
Vice President – John M. Jones
General Manager – Susan M. Jolley
Over 200 newspaper publishers use Advantage Newspaper Consultants□ selling approach, generating new revenue without incremental fulfillment cost. In less staff time than goes into a typical special section, Advantage delivers you new annually-contracted business that publishes in your core newspaper and Website without adding newsprint cost or reducing banner-ad availability. Advantage consultants customize valuable advertising packages adding technology we provide and work with your sales team to deliver year-long results serving your advertisers and readers.

ADVERTISING MEDIA PLUS, INC.
PO Box 1529, Ellicott, MD, 21041; tel (410) 740-5009; fax (410) 740-5888; e-mail mail@ampsinc.net; web site www.ampsinc.net
Pres. – Daniel Medinger

ALTERNATIVE WEEKLY NETWORK
1122 Del Paso Blvd, Sacramento, CA, 95815-3600; tel (916) 551-1770; fax (916) 551-1777; e-mail mark@awn.org; web site www.awn.org
Established 1996
Exec. Dir. – Mark Hanzlik
Pres. – Brian Hieggelke
Sec. – Gloria Mock
Treasurer – Everett Frukelstein
Newspaper representative for 93 alternative newsweeklies

AMALGAMATED PUBLISHERS, INC.
341 W. 38th St., New York, NY, 10036; tel (212) 904-1880; fax (212) 904-1594; e-mail mark@amalgamatedpublishers.com; web site www.apipub.com
Established 1959
MD – Mark Channing
Representatives for over 200 of the leading African-American newspapers in 100 top markets

AMERICAN NEWSPAPER REPRESENTATIVES, INC.
2075 W. Big Beaver Rd., Ste. 310, Troy, MI, 48084-3543; tel (248) 643-9910; fax (248) 643-9914; web site www.gotoanr.com
Established 1943
Pres. – John Jepsen
Exec. Vice Pres./COO – Robert Sontag
ANR represents over 9,000 daily and weekly community newspapers nationwide

AMERICAN NEWSPAPER REPRESENTATIVES, INC.
940 W. County Rd. B, Roseville, MN, 55113; tel (651) 487-5778; e-mail mcox@anrinc.net; web site www.anrinc.com
Sales Mgr. – Melanie Cox

AMERICAN PASSAGE MEDIA CORP./YOUTHSTREAM MEDIA NETWORKS
541 N. Fairbanks Ct., Ste. 1890, Chicago, IL, 60611; tel (800) 676-2838
Adv. Contact – Kelly McCabe

AMERICAN PASSAGE MEDIA CORP./YOUTHSTREAM MEDIA NETWORKS
100 W. Harrison St., Ste. 150, Seattle, WA, 98119; tel (800) 359-6676
Adv. Contact – Chris Robinson

AMERICAN PASSAGE MEDIA CORP./YOUTHSTREAM MEDIA NETWORKS
28 W. 23rd St. 6th Fl., New York, NY, 10010; tel (800) 473-6474; fax (212) 622-7331; e-mail dennisr@youthstream.com; web site www.youthstream.com
Chrmn. – Harlan Pletz
COO – Dennis Roche

Exec. Vice Pres./CFO – Irwin Engleman
Pres./Sec. – James Lucchese
Newspaper representative for the college market

AMERICAN PASSAGE MEDIA CORP./YOUTHSTREAM MEDIA NETWORKS
1950 Sawtelle Blvd., Los Angeles, CA, 90025; tel (310) 575-3900
Vice Pres., West Coast Sales – David Antisdale

AMERICAN PUBLISHERS REPRESENTATIVES LTD.
468 Queen St. E., Ste. 300, Toronto, ON, M5A 1T7, Canada; tel (416) 363-1388; fax (416) 363-2889; e-mail linda.power@publicitas.com
Established 1963
Pres./CEO – Wayne St. John

C

DAILY JOURNAL CORPORATION
915 E. 1st Street, Los Angeles, CA, 90012, USA; tel (213) 229-5530; fax (213) 229-5352; e-mail ari_gutierrez@dailyjournal.com; web site www.dailyjournal.com
Established 1888
Director of Government Advertising
Government Advertising Division
Daily Journal Corporation and
California Newspaper Service Bureau – Ari Gutierrez
The Daily Journal Corporation is a publisher of 10 legal and business publications, including the Los Angeles and San Francisco Daily Journals, distributed in major California cities.

Additionally, its in-house media buying service provides ad placement services to government agencies, attorney's and other advertisers for mandated and outreach advertising, including class action notices, in any daily, community and/or ethnic publication.

CAMPUS MEDIA GROUP, INC.
2 Appletree Sq., 4th Fl., Bloomington, MN, 55425; tel (952) 854-3100; fax (952) 854-3104; e-mail info@campusmediagroup.com; web site www.campusmediagroup.com
Established 2002
Dir., Mktg. – Jason Bakker
Dir., Media – Joel Eisfelder
College marketing agency.

CAMPUS PARTY, INC.
444 N. 3rd St., Philadelphia, PA, 19123; tel (215) 320-1810; fax (215) 320-1819; e-mail info@campusclients.com; web site www.campusclients.com
Established 1997
Pres. – Sean Sheridan
Represents more than 2,100 college newspapers

CANWEST MEDIA SALES
250 Yonge St., Ste. 1700, Toronto, ON, M5B 2L7, Canada; tel (416) 593-6556; fax (416) 593-1765; web site www.canwest.com
Established 2002
Vice Pres., Integrated Research Div. – Kathy Gardner
Exec. Asst. – Jennifer Griffith
Dir., Newspaper Sales – Quin Millar

CANWEST MEDIA SALES-VANCOUVER
1500-355 Burrard St., Vancouver, BC, V6C 2G8, Canada; tel (604) 730-7802; fax (604) 730-1253; web site www.canwest.com
Western Sales Mgr. – Alvin Chow

CANWEST PUBLISHING
1010 St. Catherine St. W., Ste. 200, Montreal, QC, H3B 5L1, Canada; tel (514) 849-9987; fax (514) 849-3422; web site www.canwest.com
Dir. Sales. – Quin Millar

CENTRO LLC
222 W. Hubbard St., Suite 400,, Chicago, IL, 60654; tel (312) 397-3330; fax (312) 670-1357; web site www.centro.net
Established 2005
Founder/CEO – Shawn Riegsecker
Mgr., Publisher Devel. – Katie Risch
Pres., Midwest Sales – Brian Berner
West Coast Acct. Exec. – Beau Lemire
West Coast Acct. Exec. – Jenny Nargi

COLLEGIATE ADVANTAGE
313 Congress St., Boston, MA, 2110; tel (617) 443-0300; fax (617) 443-4545

Pres. – Paul Tedeschi
Mgr., Media/PR – Jodi Orseberg
Represents college newspapers and their advertisers

H

HARTE-HANKS COMMUNICATIONS, INC.
200 Concord Plz. Dr., Ste. 800, San Antonio, TX, 78216; tel (210) 829-9000; fax (210) 829-9101; web site www.harte-hanks.com
Pres., Direct Mktg. – Gary Skidmore
Represents shopper publications

J

JOSEPH JACOBS ORGANIZATION
349 W. 87th St., Ste. 1, New York, NY, 10024; tel (212) 787-9400; fax (212) 787-8080; e-mail erosenfeld@josephjacobs.org; web site www.josephjacobs.org
Established 1919
Pres. – David Koch
Represents Jewish publications

L

LANCASTER NEWSPAPERS, INC.
8 W. King St., Lancaster, PA, 17608-1328, USA; tel (717) 291-8811; fax (717) 291-8653; e-mail lnp@lnpnews.com; web site www.lancasteronline.com
President & CEO – Harold E. Miller

LATINO PRINT NETWORK
2777 Jefferson St., Ste. 200, Carlsbad, CA, 92008-1743; tel (760) 434-7474; fax (760) 434-7476; web site www.latinoprintnetwork.com
Pres. – Kirk Whister
Vice Pres., Media Servs. – Laura Najera

LEE ENTERPRISES
201 N. Harrison St., Ste. 600, Davenport, IA, 52801-1924; tel (563) 383-2100; e-mail info@lee.net; web site www.lee.net
Chairman/Pres./CEO – Mary Junck
Vice Pres. Commun. – Daniel Hayes

LINGUA ADS SERVICE
101 Wingold Ave., Toronto, ON, M6B 1P8, Canada; tel (416) 922-5258; fax (416) 922-5562; e-mail lingua@linguaads.com; web site www.multimedianova.com
Pres. – Lori Abittan

MARKET PLACE MEDIA/ALLOY, INC.
104 W. Anapamu St., Santa Barbara, CA, 93101; tel (805) 968-8000; fax (805) 968-8003; e-mail info@marketmedia.com; web site www.marketmedia.com
Established 1987
Pres. – Andrew T. Sawyer
Sr. Vice Pres., Nat'l Sales – Greg Anthony
MPM specializes in the military, college, Hispanic, African-American, ethnic and senior markets. Direct enquiries to Sales Development (ext. 149)

MCGOWN INTERMAC/PUBLICITAS NORTH AMERICA, INC.
468 Queen St., Ste. 300, Toronto, ON, M4A 1T7, Canada; tel (416) 966-1622; fax (416) 966-1434; web site www.publicitas.com
Vice Pres. – Wayne St. John

MCGOWN INTERMAC/PUBLICITAS NORTH AMERICA, INC.
1281 W. Georgia St., Ste. 502, Vancouver, BC, V6E 3J7, Canada; tel (604) 688-5914; fax (604) 689-0703; web site www.publicitas.com
Vice Pres., Sales – Brenda Finn

MEDIA SPACE INC.
101 Merritt 7, 3rd Fl., Norwalk, CT, 6851; tel (203) 849-8855; fax (203) 849-5946; e-mail info@mediaspacesolutions.com; web site www.mediaspacesolutions.com
Pres. – Scott Kerr
Vice Pres., Research/Planning – Jose Rodriguez

METRO NEWSPAPER ADVERTISING SERVICES, INC.
8 W. 38th St., 4th Fl., New York, NY, 10018; tel (212) 689-8200; fax (212) 779-9795; web site www.metrosn.com
Established 1932
Chairman/CEO – Phyllis Cavaliere
President/COO – Michael Baratoff
Vice Pres., Client Servs./Info. Systems – Tack Prashad
Sr. Vice Pres., Finance – Nili DeBono
Sr. Vice Pres./Eastern Region – William Huck
Metro has been creating networks for national advertisers since 1932. It places advertising for represented newspapers through its Sunday Magazine, Metro-Puck Comics and Metro ROP Networks. Please see these entries in Section V of the Year Book.

METRO NEWSPAPER ADVERTISING SERVICES, INC.
160 Spear St., Ste. 1875, San Francisco, CA, 94105; tel (415) 227-8857; fax (415) 227-0995; e-mail info@metrosn.com; web site www.metrosn.com
Sr. Vice Pres., Wetern Sales Region – Ali Nazem

METRO NEWSPAPER ADVERTISING SERVICES, INC.
8 West 38th Street, New York, NY, 10018; tel (212) 689-8200; e-mail getinfony@metrosn.com; web site www.metrosn.com
Exec. Dir. – Tom Vorel

METRO NEWSPAPER ADVERTISING SERVICES, INC.
200 Pier Avenue, Hermosa Beach, CA, 90254; tel (310) 798-4986; web site www.metrosn.com
Mgr. – Kathy Jahns

METRO SUBURBIA, INC./NEWHOUSE NEWSPAPERS
925 S. Federal Hwy., Boca Raton, FL, 33432-6122; tel (561) 750-1700; fax (561) 998-0953
Adv. Sales Mgr. – Brenda Goodwin-Garcia

METRO SUBURBIA, INC./NEWHOUSE NEWSPAPERS
3820 Mansell Rd., Alpharetta, GA, 30022; tel (678) 352-8820
Adv. Sales Mgr. – Jon Gold

METRO SUBURBIA, INC./NEWHOUSE .-NEWSPAPERS
711 Third Ave., 15th Fl., New York, NY, 10017; tel (212) 697-8020; fax (212) 972-3146
Pres. – Robert N. Schoenbacher
New York Sales Mgr. – John A. Colombo

METRO SUBURBIA, INC./NEWHOUSE NEWSPAPERS
6300 Wilshire Blvd., Los Angeles, CA, 90048; tel (323) 965-3677; fax (323) 965-4962
Adv. Sales Mgr. – Kevin Drolet

METRO SUBURBIA, INC./NEWHOUSE NEWSPAPERS
221 E. Ontario St., Ste. 1700, Chicago, IL, 60611; tel (847) 242-0519
Adv. Sales Mgr. – Chad Johnson

METRO SUBURBIA, INC./NEWHOUSE NEWSPAPERS
37000 Grand River Rd., Ste. 330, Farmington Hills, MI, 48335; tel (248) 426-4202; fax (248) 426-4203; e-mail johnt@metrosuburbia.com; web site www.metrosuburbia.com
Adv. Sales Mgr. – John Tingwall

METROLAND MEDIA GROUP
10 Tempo Ave., Willowdale, ON, M2H 2N8, Canada; tel (416) 493-1300; fax (416) 493-0623; web site www.metroland.com
Pres. – Ian Oliver
Vice Pres. – Kathie Bride

MORRIS MULTIMEDIA, INC.
27 Abercorn St., Savannah, GA, 31401; tel (912) 233-1281; fax (912) 238-2059; e-mail info@morrismultimedia.com; web site www.morrismultimedia.com
Established 1970
Chrmn./CEO – Charles H. Morris
Vice Pres./CFO – Jeffrey R. Samuels
Secretary – Kathy Kurazawa
Morris Multimedia, Inc. owns four daily, numerous non-daily, niche and shopper publications and 14 television stations serving 6 television markets.

N

NATIONAL NEWSPAPER PLACEMENT SERVICES
766 N. Sun Drive, Suite 2000, Lake Mary, FL, 32746, United States; tel (321)283-5255; e-mail info@n2ps.com; web site www.n2ps.com
Established 1959
Pres./CEO – Dean Ridings
Vice Pres. – Melanie Mathewson
Media Dir. – Scott Harding
Account Manager – Joan Marchand
Accou8nt Manager – Carolyn Klinger
Chris Smith
Sharon Osbourne
Media Manager – Jessica Pitts

NEWSPAPER NATIONAL NETWORK
41899 Waterfall Rd., Northville, MI, 48168; tel (248) 680-4676; fax (248) 680-4667
Sales Exec. – Larry Doyle

NEWSPAPER NATIONAL NETWORK LP
20 W. 33rd St., 7th Floor, New York, NY, 10001-3305, USA; tel (866) 451-4636; fax (212) 856-6341; web site www.nnnlp.com
Established 1994
President & CEO – Jason E. Klein
Sr. Vice Pres., Bus. Devel. – Paul C. Atkinson
Vice Pres., Newspaper Rel. – Frank P. Grasso
Sr. Vice Pres., Sales – Lynn A. Lehmkuhl
Sr. Vice Pres., Mktg. – Mary Ellen Holden
Doug MacDonald
Sales Dir. – Jack Grandcolas
Sales Dir. – Mary Dowling
Sr. Vice Pres., Media/Opns. – Jerry Fragetti

NNN (NEWSPAPER NATIONAL NETWORK LP)
500 N. Michigan Ave., Ste. 2210, Chicago, IL, 60611-3776; tel (312) 644-7338; web site www.nnnlp.com
Midwest Sales Director, Digital & Print – Gary Martin

NEWSPAPER NATIONAL NETWORK LP
20 West 33rd Street, 7th Floor, New York, NY, 10001, USA; tel 856-6387; fax 856-6341; e-mail cfigueroa@nnnlp.com; web site nnnlp.com
Established 1994
President & CEO – Jason E.
Sr. Vice Pres./Dir., West Coast Sales – Jack Grandcolas

THE NEWSPAPER NETWORK (TNN)
400 Interstate N. Pkwy., Ste. 1050, Atlanta, GA, 30339; tel (770) 988-1750; fax (770) 988-1756
Vice Pres., Sales (Southern Reg.) – Ann Robb
Vice Pres., Automotive Sales – June Holmes

THE NEWSPAPER NETWORK (TNN)
3840 Rosin Court Ste. 100, Sacramento, CA, 95834; tel (916) 614-7070; fax (916) 614-7072; e-mail bhoyt@tnninc.com
Pres. – Kevin Hart
Exec. Vice Pres., Sales – Louisa Koken
Vice Pres., Mktg. – Karen Hardison
Vice Pres., Newspaper Rel. – Jeff Deitz
Vice Pres., Sales, Western Reg. – Jim McGee
Reg'l Sales Mgr. – Laura Kerbs
Administrative Mgr. – Barbara Hoyt
TNN represents 2,500 daily and weekly newspapers in the U.S.

THE NEWSPAPER NETWORK (TNN)
350 5th Ave., Rm. 1802, New York, NY, 10118; tel (212) 268-1540; fax (212) 268-1541
Regl. Sales Mgr. – Rita Jurczyk

THE NEWSPAPER NETWORK (TNN)
1010 E. North St., Ste. B, Greenville, SC, 29602; tel (864) 241-8122; fax (864) 241-8121
Regl. Sales Mgr. – Cynthia Miller
Regl. Sales Exec. – LaTrecia Hopson
Regl. Sales Exec. – Stephanie Stanton

NEWSPAPERS FIRST, INC.
5757 Wilshire Blvd., Ste. 570, Los Angeles, CA, 90036; tel (323) 549-9144; fax (323) 459-0944
Vice Pres./Sales Mgr. – Richard Riegle

NEWSPAPERS FIRST, INC.
330 Madison Ave., 11th Fl., New York, NY, 10017-5001; tel (212) 692-7100; fax (212) 286-9004; web site www.newspapersfirst.com
Established 1960
Pres./CEO – Bob Termotto
Sr. Vice Pres./CFO – Robert Termotto
Vice Pres., Southern Reg. – Darren Larson
Vice Pres., Eastern Reg. – Allen Dunstan

NEWSPAPERS FIRST, INC.
8115 Preston Rd., Ste. 640, Dallas, TX, 75225; tel (214) 696-8666; fax (214) 696-3416; web site www.newspapersfirst.com
Vice Pres./Sales Mgr. – Darren Larson

NEWSPAPERS FIRST, INC
4601 Sheridan St., Ste. 317, Hollywood, FL, 33021; tel (954) 987-8666; fax (954) 963-0921; web site www.newspapersfirst.com
Vice Pres./Sales Mgr. – Lawrence J. Malloy

NEWSPAPERS FIRST, INC.
444 N. Michigan Ave., Ste. 1100, Chicago, IL, 60611; tel (312) 822-8666; fax (312) 822-9835; web site www.newspapersfirst.com
Vice Pres./Sales Mgr. – Geoffrey Welch

P

PAXTON MEDIA GROUP LLC
201 S. Fourth St., Paducah, KY, 42003-1524, USA; tel (270) 575-8630; fax (270) 442-8188
Established 1896
Pres./CEO – David M. Paxton
Pres. & COO, Newspaper Division – Jay Frizzo
Vice Pres./CFO – Richard E. Paxton
Asst. – Milinda Harnice
Paxton Media Group LLC owns 32 daily newspapers and more than 20 non-daily publications. Paxton Media also owns and operates an NBC-affiliated television station in Paducah, KY.

PHILADELPHIA AREA NEWSPAPERS
580 W. Germantown Pk., Ste. 108, Plymouth Meeting, PA, 19462; tel (610) 941-3555; fax (610) 941-1289; e-mail brian@phillyareapapers.com; web site www.phillyareapapers.com
Established 1929
Pres. – R. Brian Hitchings
Acct. Supvr. – Donna DeFrangesco

PUBLICITAS MCGOWN INC.
8250 Decarie Blvd., Ste. 205, Montreal, QC, H4P 2P5, Canada; tel (514) 735-5191; fax (514) 342-9406; e-mail cynthia.jollymore@publicitas.com; web site www.publicitas.com
Mng. Dir. – Wayne Faint John
Vice Pres., Sales – Cynthia Jollymore
McGown/Intermac represents 25 U.S. daily newspapers

PUBLICITAS NORTH AMERICA, INC.
26234 N. 72nd Dr., Peoria, AZ, 85383; tel (623) 561-5692; fax (623) 561-5539; web site www.publicitas.com
Contact – Lisa Richmeier

PUBLICITAS NORTH AMERICA, INC.
1401 E. Broward Blvd., Ste. 204, Fort Lauderdale, FL, 33301; tel (954) 768-9323; fax (954) 768-9013
Branch Dir. – Brad Ames

PUBLICITAS NORTH AMERICA, INC.
2701 Troy Center Dr., Ste. 250, Continental Plz., Troy, MI, 48084; tel (248) 720-2456; fax (248) 404-9609
Branch Dir. – Michael May

PUBLICITAS NORTH AMERICA, INC.
50 California St., Ste. 1547, San Francisco, CA, 94111-4624; tel (415) 439-5278; fax (415) 439-5299; e-mail sanfrancisco@publicitas.com; web site www.publicitas.com
Mgr. – Humberto Najar

PUBLICITAS NORTH AMERICA, INC.
225 W. Washington Ave., Ste. 2200, Chicago, IL, 60606; tel (312) 201-9393; fax (312) 924-0273; e-mail ppn-chicago@publicitas.com
Reg'l Mgr. – Christopher Nolan

PUBLICITAS NORTH AMERICA, INC.
820 Mililani St., Ste. 700, Honolulu, HI, 96813-2937; tel (808) 587-8300; fax (808) 587-8308; e-mail ppn-honolulu@publicitas.com; honolulu@publicitas.com; web site www.publicitas.com
Branch Dir. – Gary Wiegand

PUBLICITAS NORTH AMERICA, INC.
13355 Noel Rd., Ste. 1030, 1 Galleria Tower, Dallas, TX, 75240; tel (972) 233-0567; fax (972) 233-9819; e-mail ppn-dallas@publicitas.com
Branch Dir. – Jo Neese

PUBLICITAS NORTH AMERICA, INC.
330 7th Ave., 5th Fl., New York, NY, 10001-5010; tel (212) 599-5057; fax (212) 599-8298; e-mail newyork@publicitas.com; web site www.publicitas.com
CFO – Joseph DeFalco

PUBLICITAS NORTH AMERICA, INC.
3400 Peachtree Rd., Ste. 1700, Atlanta, GA, 30326; tel (404) 262-2312; fax (404) 262-3746; e-mail ppn-atlanta@publicitas.com
Branch Dir. – Sal Zammuto

PUBLICITAS NORTH AMERICA, INC.
15043 Gilmore St., Van Nuys, CA, 91411; tel (310) 601-7618; e-mail losangeles@publicitas.com; web site www.publicitas.com
Mgr. – Shireen Stangl

PUBLISHERS REPRESENTATIVES OF FLORIDA, INC.
285 NW 199th St., Ste. 202, Miami, FL, 33169; tel (305) 652-8510; fax (305) 652-0796
Mgr. – Rick Cammack

PUBLISHERS REPRESENTATIVES OF FLORIDA, INC.
4601 W. Kennedy Blvd., Ste. 227, Tampa, FL, 33609; tel (813) 286-8299; fax (813) 287-0651
Mgr. – Jim Gundry

PUBLISHERS REPRESENTATIVES OF FLORIDA, INC.
3825 Henderson Blvd., Ste. 406, Tampa, FL, 33629; tel (813) 286-8299; fax (813) 287-0651; e-mail proftampa@aol.com
Pres. – Jim Gundry

PUBLISHERS REPRESENTATIVES OF FLORIDA, INC.
455 N. Douglas Ave., Ste. 2155-M, Altamonte Springs, FL, 32714; tel (407) 521-5587
Mgr. – Lee Knox

R

RIVENDELL MEDIA, INC.
1248 Rte. 22 W, Mountainside, NJ, 07092-2692; tel (908) 232-2021; fax (908) 232-0521; e-mail info@rivendellmedia.com; sales@rivendellmedia.com; web site www.rivendellmedia.com
Established 1979
Pres. – Todd Evans
Represents GLBT newspapers

RUXTON GROUP
185 Berry St., Ste. 3800, San Francisco, CA, 94107; tel (415) 659-5546; fax (415) 659-2499; web site www.ruxton.com
Dir., West Coast Sales – Terri Reed
Gen Mgr. – Josh Fromson

S

SENIOR PUBLISHERS MEDIA GROUP
4141 Jutland Drive, Suite 300, San Diego, CA, 92117, USA; tel (858) 272-9023; fax (858) 272-7275; e-mail marcia@spmg.com; web site www.spmg.com
Established 1977
Partner – Marcia A. Hansen
CEO – Trevor Hansen
Motivate, Inc. represents the following targets through it's divisions: SPMG/Mature Market; EPMG/Multi-Cultural Markets-Hispanic, African-American, Asian

T

TOWMAR REPRESENTACIONES S.A.FL; TEL (305) 395 7170; FAX 914 315 0324; E-MAIL JMDUGAY@TOWMAR.NET
Established 1968

TOWMAR REPRESENTACIONES S.A.
Presa de la Angostura 8, Mexico City, 11500, Mexico; tel 2122 3900; fax 5395 4985; e-mail info@towmar.net; web site www.towmar.net
Pres. – Juan Martinez Dugay
Comm. Dir. – Cesar Quijas
Admin. – Silvia Vadillo

TOWMAR REPRESENTACIONES S.A.
Cereza 37, S.M. 2-A, Cancun Q. Roo, 77500, Mexico; tel 9884-2073; fax 9884-6453
Pres. – Juan Martinez Dugay

TRADE UNION ADVERTISING
114 E. 32nd St., Ste. 906, New York, NY, 10016; tel (212) 724-0075; fax (212) 447-6628
Pres. – Alex Smith

TRIBUNE COMPANY
435 N. Michigan Ave., 2nd Fl., Chicago, IL, 60611; tel (312) 222-4150; fax (312) 222-3935; web site www.tribune.com
Chicago Mgr. – Dave Chiappe

TRIBUNE MEDIA NETWORK
12900 Preston Rd., Ste. 615, Dallas, TX, 75230-1322; tel (972) 789-6920; fax (972) 239-2737; web site www.tribunemediagroup.com
Southwestern Regl. Sales Dir. – Grant Moise

TRIBUNE MEDIA NETWORK
202 W. First St., Los Angeles, CA, 90012; tel (213) 237-2135; fax (213) 237-2007
Dir., Western Reg. – Richard Jones

TRIBUNE MEDIA NETWORK
100 Bush St., Ste. 925, San Francisco, CA, 94104-3920; tel (415) 693-5600; fax (415) 391-4992; web site www.tribunemediagroup.com
Mgr. – Neal Zimmerman

TRIBUNE 365
3107 Stirling Rd., Ste. 205, Fort Lauderdale, FL, 33312-6526; tel (954) 989-8833; fax (954) 963-3395; web site www.ctmgadvertise.com
Florida Mgr. – Berry Werblow

TRIBUNE 365
220 E. 42nd St., New York, NY, 10017; tel (212) 448-2600; fax (212) 983-0234; web site www.tribune.com
Dir., Mktg. – Irina David

TRIBUNE 365
19500 Victor Pkwy., Ste. 100, Livonia, MI, 48152; tel (734) 464-6500; fax (734) 464-7188; web site www.ctmgadvertise.com
Detroit Mgr. – Mark Barrons

TRIBUNE 365
2839 Paces Ferry Rd., Ste. 1105, Atlanta, GA, 30339; tel (770) 433-9554; fax (770) 433-1927; web site www.ctmgadvertise.com
Atlanta Mgr. – Gail Brinkman

U

U.S. SUBURBAN PRESS, INC.
428 E. State Pky., Ste. 226, Schaumburg, IL, 60173; tel (847) 490-6000; fax (847) 843-9058; e-mail rickb@usspi.com; web site www.usspi.com
Mktg. Dir. – Rick Baranski
Designs cost effective newspaper packages for national advertisers.

V

VOICE MEDIA GROUPCHICAGO, IL, 60611; TEL (312) 828-0564; FAX (312) 828-0558; WEB SITE WWW.VOICEMEDIAGROUP.COM

VOICE MEDIA GROUP
1201 E. Jefferson St., Phoenix, AZ, 85034; tel (602) 238-4800; fax (602) 238-4805; e-mail joe.larkin@voicemediagroup.com; web site www.voicemediagroup.com
Sr. Vice Pres. Sales – Joe Larkin
Vice Pres., Sales – Susan Belair
Newspaper represents for 50 alternative newsweeklies

VOICE MEDIA GROUP
36 Cooper Sq., New York, NY, 10003; tel (212) 475-2529; fax (212) 475-4566; web site www.voicemediagroup.com
Vice Pres., Sales – Susan Belair

W

WIDE AREA CLASSIFIED
113 N. Minnesota St., New Ulm, MN, 56073; tel (507) 359-7326; fax (507) 359-7166; e-mail info@wideareaclassifieds.com; web site www.wideareaclassifieds.com
Established 1986
Exec. Dir. – Shannon Reinhart
Represents shopper publications in 50 states

NEWSPAPER REPRESENTATIVES - STATE

Alabama Newspaper Advertising Service, Inc.–3324 Independence Dr., Ste. 200, Birmingham, AL, 35209-5602; tel (205) 871-7737; fax (205) 871-7740; e-mail mail@alabamapress.org; web site www.alabamapress.org
Exec. Dir. – Felicia Mason
Adv. Mgr. – Brad English

Arkansas Press Services–411 S. Victory St., Little Rock, AR, 72201-2933; tel (501) 374-1500; fax (501) 374-7509; e-mail info@arkansaspress.org; web site www.arkansaspress.org
Established: 1873
Exec. Dir. – Tom Larimer
Advertising and Marketing Director – Ashley Wimberley
Represents daily and weekly newspapers in Arkansas

ANA Advertising Services, Inc. (Arizona Newspaper Association)–1001 N. Central, Ste. 670, Phoenix, AZ, 85004; tel (602) 261-7655; fax (602) 261-7525; e-mail office@ananews.com; web site www.ananews.com
Established: 1931
Exec. Dir. – Paula Casey
Deputy Exec. Dir. – John Fearing
Network Adv. Mgr. – Sharon Schwartz
Media Buyer – Cindy Meaux
Represents daily and weekly newspapers in Arizona

CNPA Advertising Services–708 10th St., Sacramento, CA, 95814; tel (916) 288-6011; fax (916) 288-6003; web site www.cnpa.com/adserv
Exec. Dir. – Jack Bates
Dir. – Sharla Trillo
Client Rel./Sales Mgr. – Patrice Bayard-Miller

Colorado Press Service–1336 Glenarm Pl., Denver, CO, 80204; tel (303) 571-5117; fax (303) 571-1803; e-mail coloradopress@colopress.net; web site www.coloradopressassociation.com
Exec. Dir. – Ed Otte
Represents daily and weekly newspapers in Colorado

Community Papers of Florida–13405 SE Hwy. 484, Belleview, FL, 34420; tel (877) 373-3142; fax (352) 347-3384; e-mail djneuharth@aol.com; web site www.communitypapersofflorida.com
Established: 1960
Executve Director – Dave Neuharth
Administrative Asst. – Barbara Holmes
Classified Coordinator – Tiffany Clark
Florida statewide association for free papers
Classified advertising for 103 publications and display advertising for 132 shopper and community news publications in Florida.

Florida Press Service, Inc.–2636 Mitcham Dr., Tallahassee, FL, 32308; tel (850) 222-6401; fax (850) 222-4498; e-mail fps-info@flpress.com; web site www.flpress.com
Pres./CEO – Dean Riddings
Florida Press is an intergrated, full service placement, research invoicing and verification firm owned and operated by all of Florida's newspapers. Our mission is to help our client advertisors coordinate multi-market newspaper campaigns quickly, effecie
Represents 42 daily and 135 weekly newspapers in Florida

Georgia Newspaper Service, Inc.–3066 Mercer University Dr., Ste. 200, Atlanta, GA, 30341-4137; tel (770) 454-6776; fax (770) 454-6778; e-mail rrhodes@minespring.com; web site www.gapress.org
Exec. Dir. – Robin Rhodes
Represents daily and weekly newspapers in Georgia

Customized Newspaper Advertising (Iowa)–319 E. Fifth St., Des Moines, IA, 50309-1931; tel (515) 244-2145; fax (515) 244-4855; web site www.cnaads.com; www.inanews.com
Exec. Dir. – Chris Mudge
Acct. Exec. – Bryan Rohe
Sales Director – Ron Bode
Represents 302 daily and weekly newspapers in Iowa and can place advertising in any newspaper in the country.

Midwest Free Community Papers–PO Box 1350, Iowa City, IA, 52244; tel (319) 341-4352; fax (319) 341-4358; e-mail mfcp@mchsi.com; web site www.mfcp.org
Exec. Dir. – Brian Gay
Office Mgr. – Jori Hendon
Classified advertising for 124 publications

Idaho's Complete Advertising in Newspapers Network (ICANN)–6560 Emerald, Ste. 124, Boise, ID, 83704-8781; tel (208) 375-0733; fax (208) 375-0914; web site www.webdms.com
Exec. Dir./Mgr. – Bob C. Hall
Represents 52 daily and weekly newspapers in Idaho

Pacific Northwest Association of Want-Ad Newspapers–PO Box 682, Lewiston, ID, 83501-0682; tel (208) 746-0483; fax (208) 746-8507; web site www.pnawan.org
Established: 1977
Coord. – Tamara Byrd
Gen. Mgr. – Diane Thomson
Represents 28 shopper publications in Idaho, Montana, Oregon, Washington and Canada.

Illinois Press Advertising Service–900 Community Dr., Springfield, IL, 62703; tel (217) 241-1300; fax (217) 241-1301; web site www.il-press.com
Exec. Dir. – David Bennett
Dir., Commun./Mktg. – David Porter
Represents over 600 newspapers in Illinois and handles newspaper placements across the US.

Hoosier State Press Association–41 E. Washington St., Ste. 301, Indianapolis, IN, 46204; tel (317) 803-4772; fax (317) 624-4428; web site www.hspa.com
executive director and general counsel – Stephen Key
Exec. Dir. – David Stamps
Represents daily and weekly newspapers in Indiana

Kansas Press Association–5423 SW Seventh St., Topeka, KS, 66606; tel (785) 271-5304; fax (785) 271-7341; e-mail info@kspress.com; web site www.kspress.com
Established: 1863
Exec. Dir. – Doug Anstaett
Member Serv. Dir. – Emily Bradbury
Dir., Gov't Affairs – Richard Gannon
Administrative Assistant/Advertising – Lori Jackson
Adv. Mgr. – Dan Rukes
Educ. Dir. – Rachel Willis
Acct. – Amy Blaufelder
Represents 32 daily and 200 weekly newspapers in Kansas

Kentucky Press Service, Inc.–101 Consumer Ln., Frankfort, KY, 40601; tel (502) 223-8821; fax (502) 875-2624; web site www.kypress.com
Established: 1959
Exec. Dir. – David Thompson
Dir., Sales – Teresa Revlett
Represents daily and weekly newspapers in Kentucky

Louisiana Press Association–404 Europe St., Baton Rouge, LA, 70802; tel (225) 344-9309; fax (225) 344-9344; web site www.lapress.com
Exec. Dir. – Pam Wagner
Adv. Dir. – Mike Reed
Sr. Adv. Coord. – Terri Jackson
Represents daily and weekly newspapers in Louisiana

NENPA Ad Network (New England Newspaper and Press Association)–370 Common Street, Dedham, MA, 02026; tel (781) 320-8048; fax (781) 320-8055; e-mail info@nenpa.com; web site www.nenpa.com
Established: 1950
Executive Director – Dan Cotter
Advertising Director – Linda Conway
Advertising Operations Manager – Lindsey Ford
Exec. Dir. – Brenda Reed
Adv. Mgr. – Philip Lucey
Adv. Admin. – Patricia Daigle
Represents daily, weekly and specialty newspapers in the six New England states

Community Papers of Michigan, Inc.–5000 Northwind Dr., Ste.240, Eastlansing, MI, 48823-5032; tel (800) 783-0267; fax (517) 333-3322; web site www.communitypapersofmichigan.com
Pres. – Terry Roby
Exec.Dir. – Jack Guza
Office Mgr. – Stacy Kotecki
Display advertising for 90 publications in Michigan that in cooperation with Community Papers of Michigan reaches more than 2.5 million Michigan households. Classifed advertising reaches 1.7 million Michigan households

Michigan Newspapers, Inc.–827 N. Washington Ave., Lansing, MI, 48906-5199; tel (517) 372-2424; fax (517) 372-2429; e-mail mpa@michiganpress.org; web site www.michiganpress.org
Established: 1868
Exec. Dir. – Michael MacLaren
Pub. Aff. Mgr. – Lisa McGraw
Office Mgr. – Colleen Dawson
Opns. Mgr. – Linda Dancer
Represents daily and weekly newspapers in Michigan

Morning Star Publications–PO Box 766, Mount Pleasant, MI, 49734; tel (989) 732-5125; fax (989) 731-6612
Classified advertising for 90 publications in Michigan. In cooperation with Community Papers of Michigan

Minnesota Newspaper Association–12 S. Sixth St., Ste. 1120, Minneapolis, MN, 55402; tel (612) 332-8844; fax (612) 342-2958; e-mail advertising@mna.org; web site www.mna.org
Established: 1867
Asst. Exec. Dir. – Barbara Trebisovsky
Adv. Sales Dir. – Lisa Hills
One order, one bill newspaper advertising placement service. We can coordinate statewide, regional or national newspaper advertising buys. The service is free to the advertiser.
Represents 350 weekly and 29 daily newspapers in Minnesota. In addition, the Fargo-Moorhead (ND) Forum, Grand Forks (ND) Herald and Wahpeton-Breckenridge (ND) News are members of the MNA

Missouri Press Service, Inc.–802 Locust St., Columbia, MO, 65201; tel (573) 449-4167; fax (573) 874-5894; e-mail dcrews@socket.net; web site www.mopress.com
Exec. Dir. – Doug Crews
Adv. Dir. – Greg Baker
Represents daily and weekly newspapers in Missouri

Mississippi Press Services, Inc.–371 Edgewood Ter., Jackson, MS, 39206-6217; tel (601) 981-3060; fax (601) 981-3676; e-mail mspress@mspress.org; web site www.mspress.org
Exec. Dir. – Layne Bruce
Represents daily and weekly newspapers in Mississippi

Montana Newspaper Advertising Service, Inc.–825 Great Northern Blvd., Ste.202, Helena, MT, 59601; tel (406) 443-2850; fax (406) 443-2860; e-mail mtadv@mtnewspapers.com; web site www.mtnewspapers.com
Established: 1955
Adv. Coord. – Linda C. Fromm
Represents daily and weekly newspapers in Montana.

North Carolina Press Service, Inc.–5171 Glenwood Ave., Ste. 364, Raleigh, NC, 27612-3266; tel (919) 787-7443; fax (919) 787-5302; web site www.ncpress.com
Established: 1985
Exec. Dir. – Beth Grace
Network Adv. Dir. – Leta Pope
Adv. Dir. – Lindsay Webster
Represents all daily and weekly newspapers in North Carolina

North Dakota Advertising Service–1435 Interstate Loop, Bismarck, ND, 58503-0567; tel (701) 223-6397; fax (701) 223-8185; e-mail info@ndna.com; web site www.ndna.com
Exec. Dir. – Roger Bialey
Mktg. Mgr. – Kelli Richey
Advertising placed in 90 North Dakota newspapers and auxillary publications. Statewide classified advertising programs
Represents daily and weekly newspapers in North Dakota

Nebraska Press Advertising Service–845 S St., Lincoln, NE, 68508; tel (402) 476-2851; fax (402) 476-2942; e-mail nebpress@nebpress.com; web site www.nebpress.com
Established: 1879
Exec. Dir. – Allen Beermann
Sales Mgr. – Rob James
Represents daily and weekly newspapers in Nebraska

New Jersey Newspaper Network (NJNN)–840 Bear Tavern Rd., Ste. 305, West Trenton, NJ, 08628-1019; tel (609) 406-0600; fax (609) 406-0399; e-mail njnn@njpa.org; web site www.njpa.org/njnn
Established: 1991
Exec. Dir. – John O'Brien
Adv. Dir. – Amy Lear
Mktg. Mgr. – Brian Critchley
Represents daily and weekly newspapers and newspaper groups in New Jersey

New Mexico Press Association–700 Silver SW , Albuquerque, NM, 87102; tel (505) 275-1241; fax (505) 275-1449; e-mail info@nmpress.org; web site www.nmpress.org
Executive Director – Philip Lucey
Represents daily and weekly newspapers in New Mexico

Community Papers Advertising Network–PO Box

11279, Syracuse, NY, 13204; tel (315) 472-6007; fax (315) 472-5919; e-mail ads@fcpny.com; web site www.fcpny.org
Exec. Dir. – Dan Holmes
Classified and display advertising for 62 publications

New York News Publishers Association–50 Colvin Ave, Suite 102, Albany, NY, 12206, USA; tel (518) 449-1667; fax (518) 449-5053; web site www.nynpa.com
Pres. – Diane Kennedy
NIE Coord. – Mary H. Miller
Events Coord. – Don Ferlazzo
Represents daily newspapers in New York

New York Press Service–1681 Western Ave., Albany, NY, 12203-4305; tel (518) 464-6483; fax (518) 464-6489; e-mail nypa@nynewspapers.com; web site www.nynewspapers.com
Established: 1853
Adv. Rep., Classified Sales – Phil Anthony
Mktg. Dir. – Jill Van Dusen
New York Press Service is a nationwide newspaper advertising, buying and placement service. Market analysis, rate/coverage spreadsheets. Nine publications, ethnic, senior family, alternative and mainstream community newspapers. Target marketing solutions
Represents weekly newspapers in New York

OHIAD–PO Box 69, Covington, OH, 45318; tel (937) 473-2028; fax (937) 473-2500; e-mail production@woh.rr.com; web site www.arenspub.com
Secreatary/Treasurer – Gary Godfrey
Classified advertising for 16 publications. In cooperation with Community Papers of Ohio.

Ohio Newspaper Services, Inc. dba AdOhio–1335 Dublin Rd., Ste. 216B, Columbus, OH, 43215-1000; tel (614) 486-6677; fax (614) 486-4940; web site www.ohionews.org; www.adohio.net
Executive Director – Dennis Hetzel
Director of Sales – Chris Crawford
Exec. Dir./Sec. – Frank E. Deaner
Represents 86 daily and 90 weekly Ohio newspaper and affiliated websites.

Oklahoma Press Service–3601 N. Lincoln Blvd., Oklahoma City, OK, 73105-5499; tel (405) 524-4421; fax (405) 524-2201; e-mail sysop@okpress.com; web site www.okpress.com
Exec. Vice Pres. – Mark Thomas
Adv. Dir. – Brian Blansett
Represents daily and weekly newspapers in Oklahoma

Reseau Select/Select Network–2 Carlton St., Ste. 804, Toronto, ON, M5B 1J3, Canada; tel (416) 362-4488; fax (416) 362-8905; e-mail infos@selectnetwork.ca; web site www.reseauselect.com

Hitchings & Co.–Plymouth Plz., 580 W. Germantown Pk., Ste. 108, Plymouth Meeting, PA, 19462; tel (610) 941-3555; fax (610) 941-1289; e-mail brian@phillyareapapers.com; web site www.phillyareapapers.com
Pres. – Brian Hitchings
Acct. Supvr. – Donna DeFrangesco

MACNET–PO Box 408, Hamburg, PA, 19506; tel (800) 450-7227; fax (610) 743-8500; e-mail info@macpa.net; web site www.macpa.net; www.macnetonline.com
Exec. Dir. – Alyse Mitten
Classified advertising for 360 publications in PA, OH, NY, NJ, DE, MD, WV, VA, Washington DC.

MANSI Media–3899 N. Front St., Harrisburg, PA, 17110; tel (717) 703-3030; fax (717) 703-3033; e-mail sales@mansimedia.com; web site www.mansimedia.com
Vice Pres., Advertising – Lisa Knight
Represents daily and weekly newspapers in the U.S

Pennsylvania Newspaper Association–3899 N. Front St., Harrisburg, PA, 17110; tel (717) 703-3000; fax (717) 703-3001; e-mail info@pa-news.org; web site www.pa-newspaper.org
President – Teri Henning
Past President – Timothy M. Williams
Vice President, Association Services – Tricia Wright
Vice President, Advertising – Lisa Knight
Represents daily, weekly, collegiate and online newspapers in Pennsylvania & the U.S.

Reseau Select/Select Network–630 Sherbrooke W. Ste. 810, Montreal, QC, H3A 1E4, Canada; tel (514) 866-3131; fax (514) 866-3030; e-mail infos@reseauselect.com; web site www.reseauselect.com
Established: 1976
Gen. Mgr. – Lucie Leduc
Asst. Gen. Mgr. – Ginette Villeneuve
Represents more than 170 weekly French-language newspapers in Quebec, Ontario, British Columbia, Manitoba, New Brunswick and Nova Scotia

South Carolina Press Services, Inc.–PO Box 11429, Columbia, SC, 29210; tel (803) 750-9561; fax (803) 551-0903; e-mail scpress@scpress.org; web site www.scpress.org
Established: 1985
Exec. Dir. – William C. Rogers

Adv. Dir. – Alanna Ritchie
Represents all South Carolina newspapers in placement of classified and display advertising

Southeastern Advertising Publishers Association–PO Box 456, Columbia, TN, 38402; tel (800) 334-0649; fax (888) 334-0649; e-mail info@sapatoday.com; web site www.sapatoday.com
Established: 1979
Exec. Dir. – Douglas Fry
Classified advertising for 75 publications in 10 Southeastern states. Display Network also available.

TEXCAP–1440 W. Bitters Rd. Ste. 2737, San Antonio, TX, 78248-1468; tel (210) 590-4402; fax (866) 822-4920; web site www.tcnatoday.com
Established: 1964
Exec. Dir. – Dick Colvin
Classified advertising for 109 publications. In cooperation with Texas Community Newspapers Assoc

Great Northern Connection–8703 Midway Rd., Lena, WI, 54139-9769; tel (920) 829-5145; e-mail classifieds@greatnorthernconn.com; web site www.greatnorthernconn.com
Established: 1985
Adv. Contact – Char Meier
Represents 35 publications in northeastern Wisconsin and upper peninsula Michigan

Publishers Development Service–PO Box 1256, Fond du Lac, WI, 54935; tel (920) 922-4864; fax (920) 922-0861; e-mail janelle@pdsadnet.com; web site www.pdsadnet.com
Established: 1978
CEO – Janelle Anderson
Gen. Mgr. – Jeanne Schmal
Classified Sales Mgr. – Kathy Braun
Media placement firm specializing in print media in particular community papers.
Display advertising for 122 publications. In cooperation with Wisconsin Free Community Papers

Wisconsin Newspaper Association; tel (608) 283-7620; fax (608) 283-7631; web site www.wnanews.com
Established: 1853
Pres. – Andrew Johnson
First Vice Pres. – Pieter Graaskamp
Second Vice Pres. – Steve Dzubay
Third Vice Pres. – Kent Eymann
Sec. – Chris Hardie
Treasurer – Kevin Corrado
Commun. Dir. – Mary Callen
Dir., Member Servs. – Bonnie Fechtner
Third Vice President – Carol O'Leary
WNA Executive Director – Beth Bennett
Represents 33 daily and over 225 weekly and specialty newspapers

TRADE UNIONS IN THE NEWSPAPER FIELD

Communications Workers of America–501 Third St. NW, Washington, DC, 20001-2797; tel 202-434-1100; fax 202-434-1279; web site www.cwa-union.org
Pres. – Larry Cohen
Sec./Treasure – Jeffrey Rechenbach

Graphic Communications International–1900 L St. NW, Washington, DC, 20036; tel 202-721-0537; fax 202-721-0641; e-mail webmessenger@gciu.org; web site gtedeschi@gciu.org
Pres. – George Tedeschi
Vice Pres. – Robert Lacey
Executive Assistant to the President – Richard Whitworth

International Union of Operating Engineers–1125 17th St. NW, Washington, DC, 20036; tel 202-429-9100; fax 202-778-2688; web site www.iuoe.org
Gen. Pres. – Vincent J. Giblin
Gen. Sec./Treasurer – Christopher Hanley

The Laborers' International Union of North America–905 16th St. NW, Washington, DC, 20006; tel 202-737-8320; fax 202-737-2754; web site www.liuna.org
Gen. Pres. – Terence M. O'Sullivan
Gen. Sec./Treasurer – Armand E. Sabitoni

The Newspaper Guild-CWA–501 Third St. NW, 6th Fl., Washington, DC, 20001, USA; tel (202) 434-7177; fax (202) 434-1472; e-mail guild@cwa-union.org; web site www.newsguild.org
Established: 1933
President – Bernard Lunzer
Secretary/Treasurer – Carol Rothman
International Chairperson – Martha Waggoner

(Newspaper Periodical) Drivers, Chauffeurs & Helpers Union–3100 Ames Pl. NE, Washington, DC, 20018-1513
Pres. – John Catlett

Service Employees International Union, CLC–1800 Massachusetts Ave. NW, Washington, DC, 20036; tel 202-730-7000; fax 202-429-5660; web site www.seiu.org
Int'l Pres. – Andrew L. Stern
Sec./Treasurer – Anna Burger
Int'l Exec. Vice Pres. – Mary Kay Henry
Int'l Vice Pres. – Gerald Hudson
Int'l Exec. Vice Pres. – Eliseo Medina
Int'l Exec. Vice Pres. – Tom Woodruff

UNITED NATIONS CORRESPONDENTS ASSOCIATION

United Nations, New York
UNCA is a professional organization of nearly 200 journalists from dozens of countries representing scores of publications and broadcasters from all regions of the world, plus the major global news agencies.
It represents reporters in dialogues with the U.N. Secretariat to resolve problems, such as disagreements over security concerns and access to news sources.
UNCA also sponsors related briefings by sources both inside and outside the United Nations and an annual gala dinner recognizing outstanding journalism and a Citizen of the World Award. It is associated with the Dag Hammarskjold Fund for Journalists, (www.unjournalismfellowship) which sponsors journalists from developing countries for the duration of the annual General Assembly.
UNCA EXECUTIVE COMMITTEE
President – Giampaolo Pioli (Quotidiano Nazionale)
First Vice-President – Louis Charbonneau (Reuters)
Second Vice-President – Masood Haider (Dawn)
Third Vice-President – Silviane Zehil (L'Orient Le Jour)
Treasurer – Margaret Besheer (Voice of America)
Secretary – Barbara Plett (BBC)

EXECUTIVE COMMITTEE

MEMBERS AT LARGE
Nizar Abboud (Al-Akhbar, Daily- Lebanon)
Talal Al-Haj (Al-Arabiya TV)
Bouchra Benyoussef (Maghreb Arab Press)
Zhenqiu Gu (Xinhua News Agency)
Kahraman Haliselik (TRT Turkish Radio & Television)
Marcelle Hopkins (Al-Jazeera Arabic)
Flavia Drause Jackson (Bloomberg)

Matthew Russel Lee (Inner City Press)
Luiz Rampelotto (Europe Newswire)
Timothy Witcher (Agence France Presse)

REGULAR MEMBERS

Abad Jose Angel (Antena 3 TV Spain (TV))
Abbadi Abdelkader (Dossiers du TADLA; Columbia Paper)
Abboud Nizar (Alalam TV; Al-Akhbar, Beirut)
Abi Saab Nabil (Alhurra TV)
Acar Selcuk (Star Turkish Daily Newspaper; Turkish Journal)
Albayrak Nafiz (DHA (Dogan News Agency))
Al-Haj Anita (Al-Arabiya News Channel (TV))
Al-Haj Talal (Al-Arabiya News Channel (TV))
Ali Iftikhar (Associated Press of Pakistan (NA))
Alrawi Khaldoun (Associated Press)
Amaba Ayano (Nippon TV)
Ask Alf Ole (Aftenposten, Norwegian (D))
Avakian Florence (Armenian Radio)
Avdovic Erol (Webpublicapress; Radio Deutsche Welle)
Avni Benny (Kol Israel, Israel; The New York Post (D))
Bai Jie (Xinhua News Agency)
Barada Ali (An-Nahar Newspaper (Lebanon)-New York & United Nations Bureau Chief)
Baris Behzat (Cumhurriet Bizim Gazet, Istanbul (D))
Bases Daniel (Reuters, New York (NA))
Batson Roger (Nippon TV)
Baumgarten George (Jewish Newspapers)
Benyoussef Bouchra (Maghreb Arab Press Agency)
Berrocal Frances Elaine (Mainichi Newspapers)
Besheer Margaret (Voice of America (R/TV))
Bhalla Arvind (Daily Punjab Kesri, India)
Bian Chenguang (Science and Technology Daily)
Bortolaso Matteo Bosco (ANSA - Italian News Agency)
Broeker Anja (ARD/WDR German TV (TV/D))
Bryce-Pease Sherwin (South African Broadcasting "SABC NEWS")
Burtis Farida (International News Link, NY (TV))
Carriba Victor (Prensa Latina)
Cespedes Marisa (Televisa NY News Bureau(Mexican TV))
Chang Heidi Shih-hsin (Hong Kong Phoenix Satellite TV (TV))
Charbonneau Louis (Reuters (NA))
Charles Ann (Baltic Review; The Brasilians; Draugas-Lithuanian World Wide Daily (D); Travel World News (MM))
Cianfanelli Renzo (RAC Associates LLC; Il Secolo XIX (D);)
Cinar Ali (Turkish Journal (MM))
Common David (CBC News (TV/R))
Coombs Casey L. (The Diplomatic Courier)
Darabi Afshar (Islamic Republic News Agency)
Dayani Dilshad (Rhythm Broadcasting (R))
Deen Thalif (Inter Press Service News Agency; London; Sunday Times, Sri Lanka)
Dergham Raghida (Al Hayat, Columnist and Senior Diplomatic Correspondent)
Deyab Safie Eldin (Sphinx News)
DiRonza Serena (ANSA News Agency)
Donnet Pierre-Antoine ()
Dowlatshahi Tala (Talk Radio/Media News Service, UN Bureau Chief)
Droubi Hala Tarek (Al Arabiya)
Ebara Miki (NHK Japanese Broadcasting (TV))
Edwards Steven (Postmedia Network Inc., Canada - incl. National Post (D)(NA))
Eid Randa (Al Jazeera Arabic)
Elliot Joy (Carib News, New York)
Espinoza Cholene (Talk Radio/Media News Service - International Correspondent)
Faccioli Pintozzi Liliana (SKY TG24)
Falk Pamela (CBS News TV & Radio)
Farkas Alessandra (Corriere della Sera (D))
Farrell Naomi (World Union Press)
Fasulo Linda (NPR News, Washington DC (R))
Fathi Tarek (Middle East News Agency)
Figueiredo Paulo Dias (LUSA- Agencia de Noticias de Portugal (NA))
Fitzgerald Denis (Saudi Press Agency)
Font Eva (Radio Francia Internacional)
Franco Widad (NHK Japanese Broadcasting (TV))
Gabel Glenn (Al Jazeera Arabic)
Gallavin Georgia (Fujisankei Communications)
Gallego Mercedes (Vocento Media Group)
Galsim Raymund (Privilege Lifestyle Magazine (Canada) (M))
Geni Joe (Yomiuri Shimbun (D))
Goyal Raghubir (Asia Today, Washington DC (TV) (M); Asia TV Network, DC/NY (TV); India Globe, New York (WN); ATN News Service Global (NA))
Gripiotis Mihalis (Hellenic Broadcasting Corp./ERT)
Gronewold Nathanial (Environment & Energy Publishing)
Gu Zhenqiu (Xinhua News Agency)
Guaita Anna (Il Messagero)
Guerrero Maurizio (Notimex (NA))
Haider Masood (Dawn (D), Pakistan)
Haliscelik Kahraman (TRT Turkish Radio & Television)
Hashim Morad (Al Jazeera)
Hauben Ronda (taz.de (Die Tageszeitung); Telepolis)
Hernandez Daniel (Tokyo Shimbun/ Chunichi Shimbun)
Hopkins Marcelle (Al Jazeera Arabic)
Hou Minggu (China Central TV)
Houngbo Herman (LC2 TV-Benin)
Huang Jishun (China Central Television)
Hurst Whitney (CNN)
Hvistendahl Else (Norwegian American Weekly;)
Ignatiou Michail (Ethnos Newspaper- Mega TV)
Jackson Flavia (Bloomberg News)
Jendoubi Saloua (Kuwait News Agency (KUNA))
Jha Lalit K. (Pajhwok Afghan News, Afghanistan (D); The Irrawaddy, Myanmar; Press Trust of India, India)
Jiang Guangfu (Hong Kong Phoenix Satellite TV (TV))
Ji Yujie (China Central TV)
Kabbaj Abdellatif (Moroccan Press (TV/R))
Kalayci Sezai (Zaman Newspaper)
Kammerlander Annemarie (ARD German TV, New York Bureau)
Kant Ravi (TV Asia, New Jersey)
Kawaguchi Traci Yuri (Tokyo Broadcasting System Intl)
Kent Melissa (Canadian Broadcasting Corp/Radio-Canada)
Kikilo Vladimir (ITAR-TASS, Moscow (NA))
Kins Gloria Starr (Society & Diplomatic Review; Irish Connections NY (M); Irish Examiner USA (W); ELAPH)
Klein Joseph A. (Canada Free Press)
Kodani Hiromi (The Tokyo Shimbun)
Kolesa Kristina (Al-Arabiya News Channel (TV))
Konja Afaf (South South News)
Koundakjian Harry L. (Dar As Sayyad publications; Al Anwar newspapers)
Krastev Nikola (Radio Free Europe/ Radio Liberty)
Krauss Mitchell (CBS News - Retired)
Lane Thomas (BBC)
Lauria Joe (The Wall Street Journal, NY (D); The Johannesburg Star, Johannesburg (D); The Sunday Times, London (W))
de Lavarene Celhia Chaix (Radio France)
Lederer Edith (Associated Press (NA))
Lee Matthew (Inner City Press)
Leopold Evelyn (Huffington Post Contributor)
Li Wenjia (China Central TV)
Liu Chang (China Central TV)
Lurie Ranan R. (Cartoonews International Syndicate)
Macfarquhar Neil (The New York Times (D), United Nations Bureau Chief)
Magee Seana Kathleen (Kyodo News)
Mastrolilli Paolo (La Stampa)
Matsuo Michiya (Sankei Shimbun)
Melzer Chris (DPA German Press Agency)
Metzler John (Worldtribune.com, Washington DC; Korea Times, Seoul; syndicated column)
Mian Azim (GEO-TV; The News International; Daily JANG (Pakistan))
Miller William (Wahington International; Global Connections TV Prodcutions)
Miwa Atsuko (TV Asahi)
Moran Benedict (Al Jazeera English)
Moreno Elena (EFE News Agency)
Morishita Tomoya (Fujisankei Communications)
Mula Halil (RTV21 - Kosovo National TV)
Mulvoni Donatella (Quotidiano Nazionale; Il Giorno)
Mumin Md Kausar (Weekly Akhon Samoy)
Mutiasari Tia (Antara News Agency)
Nader Samar (NTV (Lebanon))
Nalavala Nosh (MediaGlobal News Service)
Nazzal Khawla (Emirates News Agency WAM; Al Qabas Newspaper (D) Kuwait)
Nguyen Thu Ding (Vietnam News Agency)
Nguyen Trung Huu (Vietnam News Agency)
Nguyen Tuan Anh (Vietnam News Agency)
Nguyen Tuyet J. (German Press Agency/DPA, Hamburg (NA))
Noain Idoya (El Periodico)
Oikawa Jun (NHK Japanese Broadcasting (TV))
Onwubuariri Peter (News Agency of Nigeria)
Orvis Patricia M. (Newport Daily News)
Oshima Michael Haruto (TV Asahi America)
Ostwald Gisela (German Press Agency/DPA, Hamburg (NA))
Pak Cia (Scannews)
Panagos Dimitrios S. (Greek American News Photos (NA))
Panayiotis Panayiotou (Athens News Agency, Greece (NA))
Pandhi Vijay (The Himachal Times (D); Business Economics (BM); Energy India (Q))
Patterson Dan (ABC News Radio)
Pavia Will (The Times of London)
Pfaeffle Walter (Austria Presse Agentur, Vienna (NA); Germerica.com (WEB))
Pioli Giampaolo (Quotidiano Nazionale, Italy (D); La Nazione; Il Resto del Carlino, Il Giorno; Quotidiano.net)
Pisik Betsy (Portfolio.com (website))
Plesea Gabriel (Freelance Reporter)
Plett Barbara (British Broadcasting Corporation (BBC))
Pontecorboli Gianna (Lettera 22 (NA))
Prengel Kate (Sankei Shimbun)
Rampelotto Luiz (Europa Newswire)
Rankin Katherine Anne (Nikkei America (D))
Ratner Ellen (Talk Radio/Media News Service, President)
Rees John (International Reports: Early Warning, WDC (BWN))
Reilly William M. (Xinhua News Agency (NA))
Richter Cristelle (ARD German Television, Producer)
Riccardi Emanuele (ANSA - Italian News Agency)
Rizvi Haider (Pacifica Radio)
Robecco Valeria (Quotidiano Nazionale (D); Quotidiano.net)
Rodriguez Carmen Maria (Radio Marti, US Office of Cuba Broadcasting)
Roth Richard (CNN (TV))
Roth Thomas Martin (ARD/WDR German TV (TV/D))
Sabet Sadegh (Scannews)
Sahin Sakar Ozlem (Anadolu Agency)
Saloomey Kristen (Al Jazeera English)
Sandrasagra Mithre J. (Inter Press Servive (IPS))
Sarre Claudia (ARD German Radio Network)
Sawa Yasuomi (Kyodo News)
Schlesinger Stephen (Freelance/ Stringer)
Schmidt Thomas (ARD German Radio Network)
Schuh Patricia (Esquire (MM))
Semprini Francesco (La Stampa)
Shakouri Ebrahim (I.R.I.B News)
Shen Hong (Xinhua News Agency)
Shen Ting (China Radio Intl)
Shibata Nobuaki (Tokyo Broadcasting Sysytem Intl)
Shoda Chizuko (Nippon TV)
Silverman Ken (Fuji TV Network News)
Sintes Fabienne (Radio France)
Smith Adele (Le Figaro (D))
Soueid Marie (Al-Arabiya News Channel (TV))
Springer Bevan (New York Amsterdam News/Caribbean Media Exchange)
Stamper Dr.Max (MaximsNews Network; Society & Diplomatic Review)
Stapp Katherine (Inter Press Service (IPS))
Stea Carla (Global Research (I))
Sun Yuting (China News Service)
Tang Yuhua (Wen Hui Daily, Shaghai CHINA)
Teramoto Atsuko (The Mainichi Newspapers (D))
Toyama Kaoru (875 third Avenue, 3rd Floor)
Trudeau Sam (Talk Radio/Media News- NOT TO BE LISTED IN DIRECTORY OR ON-LINE- just paying to be in UNCA club/newsletters)
Tsitsas Athanasios (Eleftherotypia (Greek Newspaper), Antenna (TV-Greece); Alitheia (GreekCypriot Newspaper))
Ucciardo Frank (CBS News, New York (TV); Up to The Minute)
Uluc Dogan (Hurriet, Istanbul (D); Dogan Haber Ajansi (NA))
Usher Graham (Al Ahram Weekly)
Vaccara Stefano (America Oggi (D), Oggi 7 (W); Radio Radicale)
Valenzuela David (EFE News Services)
Vyas Rohit (TV Asia)
Wachtel Jonathan (Fox News, New York (TV,Radio, Internet))
Wakaki Noriko (Fujisankei Communications TV)
Wang Tongye (China Central Television)
Warren April (The Yomiuri Shimbun (D))
Wei Wei (Xinhua News Agency)
Weschler Joanna (Security Council Report)
Williams Ian (Tribune , weekly, London UK; Deadline pundit, weblog; Foreign Policy in Focus)
Witcher Timothy (Agence France-Presse (NA))
Wu Yun (People's Daily)
Wu Zhiqiang (Xinhua News Agency (NA))
Wurst James (LGMA.TV)
Xi Laiwang (The People's Daily (D))
Yamashina Takeshi (The Mainichi Newspapers (D))
Yanagisawa Michinobu (The Yomiuri Shimbun (D))
Yoshikata Yuji (The Yomiuri Shimbun (D))
Youssef Ezzat Ibrahim (Al-Ahram (D))
Youssef Sana (Al-Akhbar, Cairo (D); Akhbar El-Yom, Cairo (WN); Akher Saa, Cairo (WN))
Yan Huan (Xinhua News Agency)
Zehil Sylviane (L'Orient Le Jour)
Zeng Hu (Xinhua News Agency)
Zoupaniotis Apostolos (Cyprus News Agency (NA); CyBC (TV); Kathimerini Newspaper Cyprus;)

Section VII

Who's Where

A

A'Hearn, Jill..........................(520) 295-4236
jahearn@azbiz.com, Adv. Dir., The Daily Territorial, AZ, Tucson
jahearn@azbiz.com, Adv. Dir., Inside Tucson Business, AZ, Tucson
jahearn@azbiz.com, Adv. Dir., Tucson Weekly, AZ, Tucson
Aaron, Charlotte
dcr@primetimenewspapers.com, Ed., The Daily Commercial Recorder
Aaron, Charlotte
vfusco@express-news.net, Gen. Mgr., Ad' Smart, TX, San Antonio
vfusco@express-news.net, Vice Pres., Classified Adv., San Antonio Express-News, TX, San Antonio
vfusco@express-news.net, Vice Pres., Classified Adv., Bulverde Community News, TX, San Antonio
vfusco@express-news.net, Vice Pres., Classified Adv., Fort Sam News Leader, TX, San Antonio
vfusco@express-news.net, Vice Pres., Classified Adv., Kelly Observer, TX, San Antonio
vfusco@express-news.net, Vice Pres., Classified Adv., Lackland Talespinner, TX, San Antonio
vfusco@express-news.net, Vice Pres., Classified Adv., Medical Patriot, TX, San Antonio
vfusco@express-news.net, Vice Pres., Classified Adv., North Central News, TX, San Antonio
vfusco@express-news.net, Vice Pres., Classified Adv., Northeast Herald, TX, San Antonio
vfusco@express-news.net, Vice Pres., Classified Adv., Northwest Weekly, TX, San Antonio
vfusco@express-news.net, Vice Pres., Classified Adv., Randolph Wingspread, TX, San Antonio
vfusco@express-news.net, Vice Pres., Classified Adv., Brooks Discovery News, TX, San Antonio
Abbey, Alan D. ...Vice Pres., Electronic Publishing
alan@jpost.co.il, The Jerusalem Post Foreign Service, Jerusalem
Abbott, Brian..........................(269) 387-2110
Western Michigan Univ., MI, Kalamazoo
Abbott, Rebecca
inventure@longshot.com, Vice Pres., Inventure, Inc., NE, Omaha
Abdon, Jim
circ@havasunews.com, Circ. Mgr., Today's News-Herald, AZ, Lake Havasu City
circ@havasunews.com, Circ. Mgr., River Extra, AZ, Lake Havasu City
Abdulwahid, Rasheed Ali
yementimes@yementimes.com, Adv. Mgr., YEMEN TIMES
Abell, Gene ....(859) 231-3237
gabell@herald-leader.com, Sports Ed., Lexington Herald-Leader, KY, Lexington
Abels, Debbie
dabels@heraldonline.com, Pub., The Herald, SC, Rock Hill
dabels@heraldonline.com, Circ. Dir., The Charlotte Observer, NC, Charlotte
Abernathy, Michael G................(502) 513-1143
mabernathy@lcni.com, President, Landmark Community Newspapers, LLC, KY, Shelbyville
Abid, Qazi Asad
ibrat@hyd.paknet.com.pk, Mng. Ed., IBRAT, Hyderabad, Hyderabad Division
Abittan, Lori
lori@multimedianova.com, Pres., Lingua Ads Service, ON, Toronto
Abraham, Paul........................(865) 342-6940
Dir., Finance, Knoxville News Sentinel, TN, Knoxville
Abrahamian, Aram
news@aravot.am, Ed. in Chief, ARAVOT, Erevan
Abramowitz, Roxanne ....(724) 626-3530
rabramowitz@tribweb.com, Mng. Ed., Daily Courier, PA, Connellsville
Abramowitz, Joe ....(724) 684-2634
jabramowitz@tribweb.com, City Ed., The Valley Independent, PA, Monessen
Abrams, Drew Dara..................(650) 949-7372
Foothill College, CA, Los Altos Hills
Abramson, Steven J.
stevea@trumatch.com, Pres., Trumatch, Inc., NY, Water Mill
Abreu, Jim
jim@atomicimaging.com, Interactive Design, Atomic Imaging, Inc., IL, Chicago
Abruzzo, James
james.abruzzo@miaminewsrecord.com, Pub., Miami News-Record, OK, Miami
james.abruzzo@miaminewsrecord.com, Prodn. Mgr., Pressroom, Neosho Daily News, MO, Neosho
Abu-Zuluf, M.
marwan@alquds.com, Ed., AL-QUDS
Acevedo, Melorie ....(415) 777-7473
macevedo@sfchronicle.com, MIS Director, San Francisco Chronicle, CA, San Francisco
Achatz, Carol..........................(360) 754-5491
cachatz@theolympian.com, Dir., HR, The Olympian, WA, Olympia
Acker, Yvonda..........................(620) 792-9239
Barton County Cmty. College, KS, Great Bend
Ackerman, Jeff ....(530) 477-4299
jeffa@theunion.com, Pub., The Union, CA, Grass Valley
Acor, Brett
bacor@postregister.com, Sales Director, Post Register, ID, Idaho Falls
Acuna, Vidi ....ext. 1023
Circ. District Mgr., The Porterville Recorder, CA, Porterville
Adachi, Yoroku
adachi@cusa.canon.com, Pres./CEO, Canon U.S.A., Inc., Canon USA, Inc., NY, Lake Success
Adadie, Chuck ....(601) 403-1312
Pearl River Cmty. College, MS, Poplarville
Adair, Shane 575-763-3431
sadair@cnjonline.com, Advertising Director, Clovis News Journal, NM, Clovis
Adame, Gustavo Salazar
puebloguerrero@yahoo.com.mx, Pres., PUEBLO, Chilpancingo, Guerrero
Adamis, Tony ....ext. 415
tadamis@freemanonline.com, Asst. Mng. Ed., Daily Freeman, NY, Kingston
Adams, Darrel ....(620) 408-9918
darrel.adams@dodgeglobe.com, Adv. Mgr., The Shopper's Weekly, KS, Dodge City
darrel.adams@dodgeglobe.com, Display Adv. Mgr., Dodge City Daily Globe, KS, Dodge City
Adams, Bob ....(270) 745-6278
Western Kentucky Univ., KY, Bowling Green
Adams, Mike
adamsm@fayettevillenc.com, Asst. Mng. Ed., The Fayetteville Observer, NC, Fayetteville
Adams, Jennifer
editor@theplainsman.com; opinion@theplainsman.com, Auburn Univ., AL, Auburn University
Adams, John
jadams@heartlandpublications.com, CFO, Heartland Publications LLC, CT, Clinton
Adams, Ben ....(432) 333-7793
ben_adams@link.freedom.com, News Ed., Odessa American, TX, Odessa
Adams, Bart S.
badams@dunndailyrecord.com, Pub., Harnett County News, Inc., NC, Lillington
badams@dunndailyrecord.com, Ed., The Daily Record, NC, Dunn
Adams, Joe ....(615) 444-3952 ext. 12
jadams@lebanondemocrat.com, Pub./Vice Pres., The Lebanon Democrat, TN, Lebanon
jadams@lebanondemocrat.com, Asst. Mng. Ed., The Florida Times-Union, FL, Jacksonville
Adams, Cecil...........................(312) 828-0350
cecil@straightdope.com, Creator/Writer, Straight Dope - Creative Loafing Media, Inc., IL, Chicago
Adams, Sarah
sadams@mckendree.edu, Editor in Chief, McKendree University, IL, Lebanon
Adams, Micki ....(651) 796-1112
adamsm@pressenter.com, Mng. Ed., Stillwater Gazette, MN, Stillwater
Adams, Sarah ....ext. 247
sadams@sharonherald.com, News Ed., The Herald, PA, Sharon
Adams, Hoover ....(910) 230-2045
hadams@dunndailyrecord.com, Travel Ed., The Daily Record, NC, Dunn
Adams, Ron ....(440) 245-6901 ext. 470
radams@morningjournal.com, CFO, The Morning Journal, OH, Lorain
Adams, Elizabeth.....................(706) 823-3348
elizabeth.adams@augustachronicle.com, Mng. Ed., The Augusta Chronicle, GA, Augusta
Adams, Elizabeth.....................(936) 631-2607
Controller, The Lufkin Daily News, TX, Lufkin
Adams, Duska..........................(804) 550-5114
virginiaclipping@burrellesluce.com, Client Servs. Mgr., Virginia Clipping Service, VA, Ashland
Adams, Ron
radams@journalregister.com, Controller, The News-Herald, OH, Willoughby
Adams, Beth ....(504) 826-3272
badams@timespicayune.com, Vice Pres., HR, The Times Picayune, LA, New Orleans
Adams, Arthur J.
aadams@theadvocate.com, Asst. Mng. Ed., Features, The Advocate, LA, Baton Rouge
Adams, James.........................(603) 668-4321
jadams@unionleader.com, Instr., Alabama State University, AL, Montgomery
jadams@unionleader.com, Prod. Mgr., The Sunday Sun, OK, Midwest City
jadams@unionleader.com, Sunday City Ed., New Hampshire Union Leader/New Hampshire Sunday News, NH, Manchester
Adamson, Pam
padamson@dailyhome.com, Adv. Dir., The Daily Home, AL, Talladega
Adamson, Donn ....ext. 143
Sports Ed., Daily Journal, MO, Park Hills
Adger, Arlene
aadger@gannett.com, HR Business Partner, The Shreveport Times, LA, Shreveport
Adkins, Allen
composing@monett-times.com, Prodn. Mgr., The Monett Times, MO, Monett
Adkins, Paul
padkins@loganbanner.com, Sports Ed., The Logan Banner, WV, Logan
Adkins, Mark...........................(415) 777-7767
madkins@sfchronicle.com, President, San Francisco Chronicle, CA, San Francisco
Adkins, Shirley ....(434) 432-1654 ext. 24
shirleyadkins@womackpublishing.com, Circ. Mgr., Womack Publishing Co., VA, Chatham
Adkins, Calvin
cadkins@dailysoutherner.com, Sports Editor, The Daily Southerner, NC, Tarboro
Adler, Al ....(248) 745-4626
al.adler@oakpress.com, Metro Ed., Projects, The Oakland Press, MI, Pontiac
Adolphe, Edgar
sentinelle@bow.intnet.mu, Prodn. Mgr., L'EXPRESS, Port Louis
Adrian, M.
whv@wz.online.de, Proprietor, Wilhelmshavener Zeitung, Wilhelmshaven
Aeikens, Dave
daeikens@spj.org, Pres., Society of Professional Journalists, IN, Indianapolis
Affleck, George
info@bccommunitynews.com, Gen. Mgr., British Columbia/Yukon Community Newspapers Association, BC, Vancouver
Afridi, Rahmat Shah
tfpost@brain.net.pk, Ed. in Chief, FRONTIER POST, Peshawar, Peshawar District
tfpost@brain.net.pk, Chief Ed., FRONTIER POST, Karachi
Afssanelkwary, Salihbin
edit@raya.com, Ed, AR-RAYAH
Agarwal, B.D.
dainikbhaskar@mantrafreenet.com, Pub., DAINIK BHASKAR, Jabalpur, Madhya Pradesh
Agarwal, Shyam G.
aajkaanand@yahoo.com, Ed. in Chief, AAJ KA ANAND, Pune, Maharashtra
Agarwal, Ramesh Chandra
editorbhaskar@bhaskar.com, Chrmn., DAINIK BHASKAR, Bhopal, Madhya Pradesh
Agarwal, Amit 94311 72015
amit1ag@yahoo.com, Resident Editor - Manager, BIHAR SAMACHAR PATRA PVT LTD, Ranchi, Jharkhand
Agarwal, Deepak.....................(312) 222-2928
dagarwal@tribune.com, Dir., Client Servs., Chicago Tribune, IL, Chicago
Aggrey, Joe
graphic@ghana.com.gh, Ed., GRAPHIC SPORTS, Accra
Agha, Reneh ....ext. 1041
ragha@portervillerecorder.com, Visuals Dir., The Porterville Recorder, CA, Porterville
Agha, Mohammad
syriatimes@tishreen.news.sy, Ed. in Chief, SYRIA TIMES
Agnes, Brian ....(913) 647-0936
bagnes@familyfeatures.com, President, Family Features Editorial Syndicate, Inc., KS, Mission
Agois Banchero, Luis 225-5656
cmanrique@epensa.com.pe, Gen. Mgr., Agois Banchero Family, Lima
cmanrique@epensa.com.pe, Gen. Mgr., Agois Banchero Family, Lima
Agois Banchero, Enrique 225-5656
vramirez@epensa.com.pe, Pres., Correo de Huancayo, Huancayo
vramirez@epensa.com.pe, Pres., Correo de Piura, Piura
vramirez@epensa.com.pe, Pres., Correo de Tacna, Tacna
vramirez@epensa.com.pe, Gen. Mgr., Agois Banchero Family, Lima
Agrawalla, Prakash Chandra
vismtra@cal2.vsnl.net.it, Ed., Vishwamitra Karyalaya, Kolkata, West Bengal
Agres, Ted ....(202) 636-3203
tagres@washingtontimes.com, Deputy Mng. Ed., Admin., The Washington Times, DC, Washington
Aguero Gomez, Frank
redac@granmai.get.cma.net, Dir., GRANMA INTERNACIONAL, Havana
Aguilar, Holly
hollya@nmpress.org, Office Mgr., New Mexico Press Association, NM, Albuquerque
Aguilar, Holly ....(505) 275-1241
nmpressaccounting@earthlink.net, Office Mgr., New Mexico Press Clipping Bureau, NM, Albuquerque
Aguilar, Miguel................................78-3251
Editorial Dir., EL ESPECTADOR, Valencia, Carabobo
Aguilera, Cesar Izquierdo 275-3582
Owner/Pres., La Palabra, Quevedo, Los Rios
Aguilera, Luis Horacio Salinas
eldiario@mexico.com, Pres., EL DIARIO DE COAHUILA, Saltillo, Coahuila
Aguirre, Martin
maguirre@adinet.com.uy, Ed., EL PAIS, Montevideo
Aguirre, Johnny ....(618) 463-2543
johnny_aguirre@thetelegraph.com, Adv. Dir., The Telegraph, IL, Alton
Aguirre, Horacio
advertising@diariolasamericas.com, Ed., Diario Las Americas, FL, Miami
Agurs, Brent............................(919) 419-6542
bagurs@heraldsun.com, Circ. Dir., The Herald-Sun, NC, Durham
Ahern, Harry.....................................ext. 1222
hahern@keenesentinel.com, Adv. Mgr., Co-op/Promo. Coord., The Keene Sentinel, NH, Keene
Ahlberg, Tibas ....(585) 258-2476
tahlberg@rocheste.gannett.com, Adv. Mgr., Retail Territories, Democrat and Chronicle.com, NY, Rochester
Ahlberg, Morgan
morgan.ahlberg@vgt.se, Ed. in Chief, SKARABORGS LANS TIDNING, Skara
morgan.ahlberg@vgt.se, Ed. in Chief, FALKOPINGS TIDNING, Falkoping
morgan.ahlberg@vgt.se, Ed. in Chief, VASTGOTA-BLADET, Tidaholm
Ahle, Dorothy
dorothyahle@hotmail.com, Artist/Owner, Dorothy Ahle Caricatures, MA, Malden
Ahle, Nathan...................................ext. 109
editor@ridgecrestca.com, Ed., The Daily Independent, CA, Ridgecrest
Ahlstrom, Per
annons.nn@vpress.se, Ed. in Chief, Vasternorrlands Press AB, Harnosand
Ahrens, Kimberly A. ....(231) 725-6550

kahrens@muskegonchronicle.com, Controller, The Muskegon Chronicle, MI, Muskegon

Aikat, Deb ....(919) 962-4090
Assoc. Prof., University of North Carolina, NC, Chapel Hill

Aikins, Glenda
gaikins@iolaregister.com, Office Mgr., Iola Register, KS, Iola

Aimone, Logan
info@studentpress.org, Exec. Dir., Associated Collegiate Press, MN, Minneapolis
info@studentpress.org, Exec. Dir., National Scholastic Press Association, MN, Minneapolis

Ainsworth, Julie
jainsworth@newcastle.fairfax.com.au, Gen. Mgr., THE NEWCASTLE HERALD

Ainsworth, Brent ....(415) 382-7356
bainsworth@marinij.com, Lifestyles Ed., Marin Independent Journal, CA, Novato

Aisberg, Mark
daily@express-k.kz, Ed. in Chief, EXPRESS K, Almaty

Ajemian, A.
alikmail@hyenet.ir, Pub., ALIK

Aker, G. Colburn ....(202) 789-2424
aker@akerpartners.com, Mng. Partner, The Aker Partners, Inc., DC, Washington

Akerlund, Janeric
info@solna.com, Gen. Mgr., Solna Offset AB, Jarfalla

Akers, Paul E..........................(540) 374-5531
pakers@freelancestar.com, Editorial Page Ed., The Free Lance-Star, VA, Fredericksburg

Akpinar, Mehmet Ali
kibris@cypronet.net, Ed., KIBRIS, Yeni Sanayi B□lgesi

Akuta, Cosmas........................(610) 399-2373
Cheyney Univ. of Pennsylvania, PA, Cheyney

Al Hamdani, Ibrahim Bin Saif
editor@omanobserver.com, Ed. in Chief, OMAN DAILY OBSERVER

Al Saqqaf, Nadia Abdulaziz
editor@yementimes.com, Pub., YEMEN TIMES

Al Tayer, Obaid Humaid
edit@gulf-news.co.ae, Mng. Dir./Ed. in Chief, GULF NEWS

Al-Aziz Al-Jarallah, Ahmed Abd
ahmedjarallah@hotmail.com, Ed. in Chief, AL-SEYASSAH

Al-Mahmoud, Abdul Latif
alsharqadv@qatar.net.qa, Gen. Mgr., AL-SHARQ

Al-Mazroui, Obeid
fajrnews@emirates.net.ae, Ed. in Chief, AL FAJR

Al-Mazroui, Obaid
obaid@alfajrnews.ae, Mng. Ed., AL FAJR

Al-Yaakoubi, Ahmad
webmaster@mincom.gov.ma, Pub./Dir., AL-ANBA'A, Rabat

Alatriste Montoto, Baraquiel
madek@pue1.telmex.net.mx, Pres., MOMENTO, Puebla, Puebla

Albano, George.......................(203) 354-1056
galbano@thehour.com, Asst. Sports Ed., The Hour Publishing Co., CT, Norwalk

Albano-Risso, Rose 209-249-3536
City Editor, Manteca Bulletin, CA, Manteca

Albarran Jaramillo, Jorge
diario21@prodigy.net.mx, Owner/Pres., Diario 21, Iguala, Guerrero

Albers, Connie
calbers@post-dispatch.com, Asst to Vice Pres., HR, St. Louis Post-Dispatch, MO, Saint Louis

Albers, Wes..........................(202) 383-6068
walbers@mctinfoservices.com, MCT Graphics Dir., McClatchy-Tribune Information Services, DC, Washington

Albert, G. Claude.....................(860) 241-6755
calbert@courant.com, Mng. Ed., The Hartford Courant, CT, Hartford

Albert, Louis ....(972) 470-9997
lalbert@unitedmedia.com, Mgr., Regl. Sales-Central, United Media, OH, Cincinnati
lalbert@unitedmedia.com, SE Sales, King Features Syndicate, NY, New York

Alberts, Jay ....(530) 752-6851
Univ. of California Davis, CA, Davis

Albertson, Keith ....(770) 718-3400
kalbertson@gainesvilletimes.com, Mng. Ed., The Times, GA, Gainesville

Albrecht, Craig
craig.albrecht@lethbridgeherald.com, City Ed., The Lethbridge Herald, AB, Lethbridge

Albrecht, Bill..........................(320) 255-8709
balbrech@stcloud.gannett.com, Pres./Pub., St. Cloud Times, MN, Saint Cloud

Albright, John..........................(903) 596-6285
jra@tylerpaper.com, Mgmt. Info Servs. Mgr., Tyler Morning Telegraph, TX, Tyler

Albright, Jodeane ....(208) 239-3123
jodyalb@journalnet.com, Community Ed., Idaho State Journal, ID, Pocatello

Albright, Mike ....(217) 421-7909
Sports Ed., Herald & Review, IL, Decatur

Alcala, Michael
malcala@ccdailyrecord.com, News Ed., The Canon City Daily Record, CO, Canon City

Alcazar Ramirez, Enrique
opinion@ulter.net, Pres., LA OPINION DE MICHOACAN, Uruapan, Michoacan

Alcorn, Bill ....(330) 747-1471 ext. 1303
balcorn@vindy.com, Health/Medical Ed., The Vindicator, OH, Youngstown

Aldacushion, Richard................(202) 334-4523
aldacushionr@washpost.com, Editorial Prodn. Mgr., The Washington Post Writers Group, DC, Washington

Aldape, Speedy........................(956) 982-6637
Adv. Mgr., Retail, The Brownsville Herald, TX, Brownsville

Alderman, Pat
aldermanp@emergencelabs.com, Pres., Emergence Creative Labs, GA, Tucker

Alderman, Larry
larry.a@gwcommonwealth.com, Adv. Mgr., The Greenwood Commonwealth, MS, Greenwood

Aldridge, Larry ....(865) 981-1115
larry.aldridge@thedailytimes.com, Exec. Ed., The Daily Times, TN, Maryville

Alexander, Mary.......................(810) 766-6381
malexander@flintjounal.com, Adv. Mgr., Grand Blanc News, MI, Flint
malexander@flintjounal.com, Adv. Dir., The Flint Journal, MI, Flint
malexander@flintjounal.com, Adv. Dir., The Flushing Observer, MI, Flint

Alexander, Tim ....(337) 289-6399
talexander@theadvertiser.com, Circ. Dir., The Star Press, IN, Muncie

Alexander, Cindy ....(530) 749-4783
cindy_alexander@link.freedom.com, Prodn. Foreman, Mailroom, Appeal-Democrat, CA, Marysville

Alexander, Jeremy....................(928) 556-2286
Circ. Mgr., Arizona Daily Sun, AZ, Flagstaff

Alexander, Dave........................(231) 725-6366
dalexander@muskegonchronicle.com, Bus./Finance Ed., The Muskegon Chronicle, MI, Muskegon

Alexander, Steven H...................(612) 673-7060
Steve.Alexander@startribune.com, Sr. Vice Pres., Circ., Star Tribune, MN, Minneapolis

Alexander, Justin
fashionshowroom@yahoo.com, Prodn. Art Dir., Fashion Syndicate Press, VT, Woodstock

Alexander, J.
jalexander@chronline.com, Ad. Mgr., The Chronicle, WA, Centralia

Alexander, Robin......................(360) 792-3332
ralexander@kitsapsun.com, Credit Mgr., Kitsap Sun, WA, Bremerton

Alexandre, Roger
info@paris-turf.com, Pub., PARIS-TURF/DIMANCHE TURF, Paris

Alexiou, George
info@neosagon.gr, Pub., NEOS AGON, Karditsa, Thessaly

Alfano, Ellen ....(817) 390-7093
ealfano@star-telegram.com, Mng. Ed., Sports, Fort Worth Star-Telegram, TX, Fort Worth

Alfano, Peter
pete.alfano@epg-inc.com, Sales Mgr., Essex Products Group, CT, Centerbrook

Alfaro, David
meridiano@tepic.megared.net.mx, Pres., MERIDIANO, Tepic, Nayarit

Alfaro, Edinson
director@eluniversal.com.co, Dir., Sociedad Anonima, Cartagena, Bolivar

Alfaro, Edgar
ealfaro@elnorte.com.ve, Ed., EL NORTE, Barcelona, Anzoategui

Alford, Nathan
alford@dnews.com, Pub., Northwest Market, ID, Moscow
alford@dnews.com, Ed., Moscow-Pullman Daily News, ID, Moscow
alford@dnews.com, Ed., Lewiston Morning Tribune, ID, Lewiston

Alford, Melissa
malford@lsj.com, Dir., HR, Lansing State Journal, MI, Lansing

Algier, Angela ....ext. 240
aalgier@thewesterlysun.com, Local News Ed., The Westerly Sun, RI, Westerly

Alhokail, Abdul Hazeez Mohammed
mail@alyaum.com, Chrmn., AL-YAUM

Ali, Alhaj Liaquat
info@purbanchal.com, Pub., DAINIK PURBANCHAL, Khulna
info@purbanchal.com, Ed., DAINIK PURBANCHAL, Khulna

Ali Al-Abdullah, Ahmad....................465 2244
alwatan_adv@yahoo.com, Ed. in Chief, AL WATTAN

Alison, Dale
dalison@thehawkeye.com, Mng. Ed., The Hawk Eye, IA, Burlington

Alizadeh, Zardusht
istiklal@ngonet.baku.az, Ed., ISTIKLAL, Baku

Aljassin, Abdukader
alwatan@gmail.com, Adv. Mgr., AL-WATAN

Alker, Dina...................(905) 752-1132 ext. 234
dina.alker@sunmedia.ca, Exec. Asst., Osprey Media Group, ON, Markham

Alkner, Lars
lars.alkner@varnamonyheter.se, Ed. in Chief, VARNAMO NYHETER, Varnamo

Alkon, Amy............................(310) 306-6160
flame777@aol.com, Self-Syndicator, The Advice Goddess-Amy Alkon, CA, Santa Monica

Allan, Susan ....(613) 596-3503
sallan@thecitizen.southam.ca, Books Ed., The Ottawa Citizen, ON, Ottawa

Allan, Stuart ....(604) 654-4447
stuart.allan@catalystpaper.com, Dir., Mktg., Catalyst Paper (USA), Inc., WA, Seattle

Allard, Louis Eric
latribune@latribune.qc.ca, Newsroom Dir., La Tribune, QC, Sherbrooke

Allbritton, Joe L.
newsroom@wenpub.com, Pres., The Westfield News, MA, Westfield

Allegretti, Anthony ....(408) 842-6400 ext. 220
aaallegretti@yahoo.com, Pres./CEO, Mainstreet Media Group, CA, Gilroy

Allen, Joseph ....(508) 862-1186
jallen@capecodonline.com, Member Servs. Mgr., Cape Cod Times, MA, Hyannis

Allen, Kirk 416-442-2190
Vice President, Advertising, National Post, ON, Toronto

Allen, Dave.............................(415) 382-4206
dallen@marinij.com, Sports Ed., Marin Independent Journal, CA, Novato

Allen, Ron..............................(573) 815-1604
rrallen@columbiatribune.com, Circ. Info Systems Mgr., Columbia Daily Tribune, MO, Columbia

Allen, John.............................(361) 886-3745
allenj@caller.com, Sports Ed., Corpus Christi Caller-Times, TX, Corpus Christi

Allen, Sandra
sandra@spectrecom.com, Vice Pres., Spectrecom Corporation, CA

Allen, Sue......................................ext. 1126
sue.allen@timesargus.com, Ed., The Times Argus, VT, Barre

Allen, David S.
dsallen@uwm.edu, Assoc. Prof./Head Grad Studies, University of Wisconsin-Milwaukee, WI, Milwaukee

Allen, Leona ....(214) 977-8942
ldallen@dallasnews.com, Deputy Mng. Ed., Local News, The Dallas Morning News, TX, Dallas

Allen, Chris
callen@heartlandpublications.com, Pub., Durant Daily Democrat, OK, Durant
callen@heartlandpublications.com, Sports Ed., The Marshall Democrat-News, MO, Marshall
callen@heartlandpublications.com, Assoc. Prof., University of Nebraska at Omaha, NE, Omaha

Allen, Craig 203-330-6254
craig.allen@scni.com, Vice Pres., Opns./Circ. Dir., The Advocate, CT, Stamford
craig.allen@scni.com, Assoc. Prof., Arizona State University, AZ, Tempe
craig.allen@scni.com, Vice Pres. Operations, Greenwich Time, CT, Greenwich

Allen, Donna ....(252) 329-9546
dallen@reflector.com, HR Dir., The Daily Reflector, NC, Greenville

Allen, Carolyn 601-961-7167
Credit Mgr., The Clarion-Ledger, MS, Jackson

Allen, J.P.....................(310) 519-1442 ext. #1
james@randomlengthsnews.com, Los Angeles Harbor College, CA, San Pedro

Allen, Sherhonda.......................(256) 740-5732
sherhonda.allen@timesdaily.com, City Ed., TimesDaily, AL, Florence

Allen, Chris 973-569-7835
Local Retail Sales Manager, North Jersey Media Group, NJ, Woodland Park

Aller, Danny.............................229-888-9306
danny.aller@albanyherald.com, Sports Editor, The Albany Herald, GA, Albany

Aller Gonzalez, Fernando
diariodeleon@lesein.es, MD, Diario De Leon, Leon

Allewelt, Kenneth.......................850-599-2185
kallewelt@tallahassee.com, Research & New Business Manager, Tallahassee Democrat, FL, Tallahassee

Alley, Joyce
dherald@verizon.net, Circ. Mgr., The Daily Herald, PA, Tyrone

Allione, Mino..................................22-941
Dir., BRESCIA OGGI, Brescia

Allison, David
d.allison@w-rindustries.com, Vice Pres., Winton Engineering Co., IL, Chicago

Allison, Dean ....(814) 472-3038
St. Francis Univ., PA, Loretto

Allman, Ron.............................(812) 941-2253
Indiana Univ. Southeast, IN, New Albany

Allmers, Elisabeth
redaktion@jeversches-wochenblatt.de, Proprietor, Jeversches Wochenblatt, Jever

Almaeena, Khaled A.
almaeena@arabnews.com, Ed. in Chief, ARAB NEWS

Almert, Dr.Boda
balmert@moz.de, MD, Markische Oderzeitung, Frankfurt an der Oder

Almquist, Terese
talmquist@newstopic.net, Pub., News-Topic, NC, Lenoir

Alnor, William M.
william.alnor@tamuk.edu, Journalism Dir., Texas A&M University-Kingsville, TX, Kingsville

Alonso, Javier
paris@efe.com, Rep., EFE News Services - Paris, France, Paris

Alonso, Martha.........................787-4083033
martharalonso@gmai;.com, Assistant Executive Director, Overseas Press Club of Puerto Rico, PR, San Juan

Alonso, Elsa..................................4349 1000
informaciongeneral@laprensa.com.ar, Adv. Mgr., La Prensa, Buenos Aires

Alpert, Seth R.
salpert@admediapartners.com, Managing Director, AdMedia Partners, Inc., NY, New York

Alsop, Jonathon ....(617) 784-7150
jalsop@invinoveritas.com, Wine Writer/Self-Syndicator, Jonathon Alsop, MA, Brookline

Alspach, Howard
alspach@compuserve.com, Vice Pres., Free Papers, Media Consultants, Inc., OH, Lancaster

Alston, Beth.....................................ext. 226
beth.alston@gaflnews.com, Mng. Ed., Americus Times-Recorder, GA, Americus

Alt, Jason
jalt@thedailyjournal.com, Local News Ed., The Daily Journal, NJ, Vineland

Altamirano Madriz, Enrique

ventas@elsalvador.com, Pres., EL DIARIO DE HOY, San Salvador
Altavilla, Mark .... ext. 2037
marka@citizensvoice.com, Adv. Dir., The Citizens' Voice, PA, Wilkes-Barre
Alter, Larry
sportsdepartment@thecourier.com, Sports Ed., The Courier, OH, Findlay
Althoff, George
galthoff@capitalnewspapers.com, Pub., Baraboo News-Republic, WI, Baraboo
Altomare, David
marketing@palos.com, Pres., PALOS Software, CA, San Diego
Altschiller, Howard .... (603) 610-1113
haltschiller@seacoastonline.com, Exec. Ed., Portsmouth Herald, NH, Portsmouth
Alustiza, Raul Chavez
deportes@eldiariodecoahuila.com.mx, Sports Ed., EL DIARIO DE COAHUILA, Saltillo, Coahuila
Alvardo, Angie
atawater@palestineherald.com, Mng. Ed., Palestine Herald-Press, TX, Palestine
Alvarez, Juan S. 420-1100
informat@lacapital.com.ar, Gen. Mgr., La Capital, Rosario, Provincia de Santa Fe
Alvarez, Soledad
efebol@entelnet.bo, Rep., EFE News Services - La Paz, Bolivia, La Paz
Alvarez Montes, Juan
elsol@omanet.com.mx, Pres., Diario de Durango, Durango, Durango
elsol@omanet.com.mx, Pres., El Sol de Durango, Durango, Durango
Alvarez del Castillo Zuloaga, Jorge
diario@informador.com.mx, Pres., El Informador, Guadalajara, Jalisco
Alves, Antonio C. 433-1022
Pres., Jornal do Comercio, Marilia, Sao Paulo
Alves, Kristen .... (203) 789-5352
kjohnson@nhregister.com, Promo. Mgr., New Haven Register, CT, New Haven
Alvey, Dan
victory@tstar.net, Co-Pub., The River Cities Sunday Tribune, TX, Marble Falls
Alvine, Ken .... (605) 336-9434
kenalvine@qwestoffice.net, Owner/Mgr., Creative Comic Syndicate, SD, Sioux Falls
Alvord, Rick .... (360) 577-2527
ralvord@tdn.com, Sports Ed., The Daily News, WA, Longview
Alvord, Karen 315-363-5100
kalvord@journalregister.com, Oneida-Madison Pennysaver, NY, Oneida
kalvord@journalregister.com, General Manager & Advertising Director, The Oneida Daily Dispatch, NY, Oneida
Alyan, Abd Al-Rahman
abs@kuwaittimes.net, Ed. in Chief, KUWAIT TIMES
Amador, Dava .... (707) 526-8517
dava.amador@pressdemocrat.com, Circ. Mgr., The Press Democrat, CA, Santa Rosa
Aman, Terry
taman@minotdailynews.com, Features Ed., Minot Daily News, ND, Minot
Amarante, Joseph .... (203) 789-5675
news@nhregister.com, Radio/Television Ed., New Haven Register, CT, New Haven
Amari, Jane .... (520) 573-4215
Vice Pres., News & Pub./Ed., Arizona Daily Star, Pulitzer Newspapers, Inc., MO, Saint Louis
Amato, Neil .... (910) 343-2261
neil.amato@starnewsonline.com, Sports Ed., Star-News, NC, Wilmington
Ambrogi, Robert J. 978-546-3400
info@masspublishers.org, Exec. Dir., Massachusetts Newspaper Publishers Association, MA, Rockport
Ambrose, Tricia
tambrose@news-herald.com, Editor, The News-Herald, OH, Willoughby
Ambrose, Kelly
info@advantex.com, Pres., Advantex Marketing International, Inc., ON, Toronto
Amdal, Rolv
ha-torget@ha-nett.no, Ed., HAMAR ARBEIDERBLAD, Hamar
Amed, Khurshid
alakhbar@yahoo.com, Ed., ALAKHBAR, Peshawar, Peshawar District
Ameden, Paul .... (585) 598-0030
CIO, GateHouse Media Inc., NY, Fairport
Amero, Jeff
jeff.amero@newschief.com, Circ. Dir., News Chief, FL, Winter Haven
Ames, Brad
bames@publicitas.com, Branch Dir., Publicitas North America, Inc., FL, Fort Lauderdale
Amey, David
damey@circlevilleherald.com, Ed., Herald, OH, Circleville
Amick, George
gamick@njtimes.com, Editorial Page Ed., The Times, NJ, Trenton
Ammerman, Robert 610-330-6501
rammerman@csci-usa.com, President, Consolidated Storage Cos., PA, Tatamy
Ammerman, Steven
stevea@wctrib.com, Pub., West Central Tribune, MN, Willmar
Ammons, Patty .... (207) 621-5732
pammons@centralmaine.com, Features Ed., Kennebec Journal, ME, Augusta
Amnon, Dankner
ads@maariv.co.il, Ed., MA'ARIV VREMIA
Amorim Sicherle, Isabel .... +55 11 3812 5588
sicheia@nytimes.com, Regional Director, Latin America, Mexico & the Caribbean, New York Times News Service, NY, New York
Amorim Sicherle, Isabel .... +55 11 3812 5588
sicheia@nytimes.com, Regional Director, Latin America, Mexico & the Caribbean, New York Times Syndicate, NY, New York
Amos, Bob .... (813) 259-7702
Controller, The Tampa Tribune, FL, Tampa
Amoss, Jim .... (504) 826-3475
jamoss@timespicayune.com, Ed., The Times Picayune, LA, New Orleans
Amudhan, B.T.
sanjayvani@gmail.com, Gen. Mgr., DINA SUDAR, Bangalore, Karnataka
Amundsen, Hans Kristian
nyheter@nordlys.no, Ed., NORDLYS, Tromsoe
Amundsen, Dan .... (425) 339-3085
amundsen@heraldnet.com, Controller/Dir., Labor Rel., The Herald, WA, Everett
Amundson, Eldon .... (306) 657-6333
eamundson@sp.canwest.com, Controller, The StarPhoenix, SK, Saskatoon
Amundson, Kenneth J. .... (970) 669-5050
kamundson@reporter-herald.com, Ed., Daily Reporter-Herald, CO, Loveland
Amundson, Kenneth J .... (970) 669-5050
kamundson@reporter-herald.com, Editorial Page Ed., Daily Reporter-Herald, CO, Loveland
Amuthan, B.T.
svani@sanjevani.com, Mng. Dir., SANJEVANI, Bangalore, Karnataka
Anam, Mahfuz
editor@thedailystar.net, Editor and Publisher, DAILY STAR, Dhaka
Anami, Arshad Majeed
commnews@fsbconceptnet.pk, Ed., COMMERCIAL NEWS, Faisalabad, Faisalabad Division
Anand, Madhusudan
madhusudan.anand@timesgroup.com, Ed. in Chief, NAVBHARAT TIMES, New Delhi
Ananda, Azrul
editor@jawapos.co.id, Ed., JAWA POS, Surabaya, East Java
Anastasia, Phil .... (856) 486-2424
panastasia@courierpostonline.com, Sports Ed., Courier-Post, NJ, Cherry Hill
Anbar, Hanna
hanna.anbar@dailystar.com, Ed., DAILY STAR
Andelman, David .... (212) 626.9220
President, Overseas Press Club of America, NY, New York
Ander, Staffan
redaktion@nwt.se, Ed., NYA VERMLANDSTIDNINGEN, Karlstad
Anders, Rob .... (724) 229-2075
randers@observer-reporter.com, National Accounts, Observer-Reporter, PA, Washington
Andersen, Paul Eric
pea@fyens.dk, Mng. Dir., FYENS STIFTSTIDENDE, Odense, Fyn
Andersen, Gary
publisher@fairmontsentinel.com, Pub., Sentinel, MN, Fairmont
Andersen, Ph.D., P. Andrew
triusmed@gateway.net, Author/Owner/Pres., Sports Adviser Features, IL, Saint Charles
Anderson, Janelle .... ext. 108
CEO, Publishers Development Service, WI, Fond du Lac
Anderson, Greg .... (617) 823-7861
grega@pamarcoglobal.com, Vice Pres., Sales/Mktg., Pamarco Global Graphics, GA, Marietta
grega@pamarcoglobal.com, Vice Pres., HR, Cascade Corp., OR, Fairview
grega@pamarcoglobal.com, Vice Pres., Engineering, SocialNet, Inc., CA, Mountain View
Anderson, Tim .... (919) 419-6534
Dir., Info Technology, The Herald-Sun, NC, Durham
Anderson, Dennis .... (785) 832-7194
danderson@ljworld.com, Mng. Ed., The World Co.- Lawrence, Kan., Journal-World, KS, Lawrence
Anderson, James T.
Jim_Anderson@tamu-commerce.edu, Instr., Texas A&M University-Commerce, TX, Commerce
Anderson, Scott .... (613) 596-8503
sanderson@thecitizen.southam.ca, Ed. in Chief, The Ottawa Citizen, ON, Ottawa
Anderson, Michele .... (360) 650-6763
Western Washington Univ., WA, Bellingham
Anderson, Kim
marketing@mediaspansoftware.com, Coord., Domestic Sales, MediaSpan Group Inc., MI, Ann Arbor
Anderson, Loraine .... (231) 933-1468
landerson@record-eagle.com, Regl. Ed., Record-Eagle, MI, Traverse City
Anderson, Jaime Mantilla
hoy@hoy.com.ec, Pub., Edimpres S.A., Quito, Pichincha
Anderson, Julia .... (360) 735-4509
julia.anderson@columbian.com, Bus. Ed., The Columbian, WA, Vancouver
Anderson, Ronald C.
rander5165@aol.com, Chrmn., R.C. Anderson Associates, Inc., NY, Pittsford
Anderson, N. Christian
canderson@exec.oregonion.com, Pres./Pub., The Oregonian, OR, Portland
Anderson, Janna
andersj@elon.edu, Assoc. Prof., Elon University, NC, Elon
Anderson, Edward M. .... (417) 336-3457
anderson@nationalmediasales.com, Owner, National Media Associates, MO, Branson
Anderson, Steve
anderssd@jmu.edu, Dir./Prof., James Madison University, VA, Harrisonburg
Anderson, Sue .... (928) 763-2505 ext. 106
suemvdn@npgcable.com, Bus. Mgr., Mohave Valley Daily News, AZ, Bullhead City
Anderson, James
janderson@wasecacountynews.com, Waseca County Area Shopper, MN, Waseca
janderson@wasecacountynews.com, Lane Cmty. College, OR, Eugene
Anderson, Karen .... (541) 383-0324
kanderson@bendbulletin.com, CFO, Western Communications, Inc., OR, Bend
Anderson, Dennis 785-832-7194
danderson@ljworld.com, The World Co.- Lawrence, Kan., Journal-World, KS, Lawrence
Anderson, Edward M. .... (417) 336-3457
anderson@nationalmediasales.com, Pres., National Media Associates, OK, Ada
anderson@nationalmediasales.com, Owner, National Media Associates, MO, Branson
anderson@nationalmediasales.com, Broker, National Media Associates, OK, Ada
Anderson, Karen .... (541) 383-0324
Dir., Finance, The Bulletin, OR, Bend
Anderson, Dennis .... (661) 267-4153
danderson@avpress.com, Ed., Antelope Valley Press, CA, Palmdale
Anderson, Sue
suemvdn@npgcable.com, Bus. Mgr., News West Publishing Company Inc., AZ, Bullhead City
Anderson, Logan .... (434) 385-5549
landerson@newsadvance.com, Editorial Page/Opinion. Ed., The News & Advance, VA, Lynchburg
Anderson, Les .... (316) 978-6065
les.anderson@wichita.edu, Professor, WSU Elliott School of Communication, Kansas Professional Communicators, KS, Wichita
Anderson, John .... (317) 444-4185
john.anderson@indystar.com, Circ Dir., Home Delivery/Transportation, The Indianapolis Star, IN, Indianapolis
Anderson, Penny .... (540) 574-6255
pander@dnronline.com, Mgmt. Info Servs. Mgr., Daily News-Record, VA, Harrisonburg
Anderson, Vern
vanderson@sltrib.com, Editorial Page Ed., The Salt Lake Tribune, UT, Salt Lake City
Anderson, Jim
janderson@ironmountaindailynews.com, News Ed., The Daily News, MI, Iron Mountain
Anderson, David E.
david.anderson@religionnews.com, Senior Editor, Religion News Service, DC, Washington
Anderson, Rodrick
swdailysports@yahoo.com, Sports Ed., Southwest Daily News, LA, Sulphur
Anderson, Jenny .... (989) 839-4260
janderson@hearstnp.com, Pub., Midland Daily News, MI, Midland
Anderson, Janelle .... ext. 105
janelle@wisad.com, Exec. Dir., Wisconsin Free Community Papers, WI, Fond Du Lac
Anderson-Shank, Karen .... (515) 251-8640
Mktg./Promo., National Soy Ink Information Center, IA, Urbandale
Andersson, Thomaz
thomas.andersson@eposten.se, Ed. in Chief, ENKOPINGS-POSTEN, Enkoping
Andino, Vicente Limaico 296-0617
Gen. Mgr., EL ESPECTADOR, Riobamba, Chimborazo
Andonie, Abraham
elndia@hondutel.hn, Pres., Editorial La Nacion S.A., San Pedro Sula
Andrade, Nelly 23-5256
Ed., El Matutino, Iquitos, Loreto
Andras, Elekes
elekes.andras@fma.plt.hu, Ed. in Chief, DUNAUJVAROSI HIRLAP, Dunaujvaros
Andre, Marilyn
marilyna@npgco.com, Office Mgr., Atchison Globe, KS, Atchison
Andreassen, Arild
redaksjonen@moss-dagblad.no, Ed., MOSS DAGBLAD, Moss
Andreasson, Gunilla
gunilla.andreasson@barometern.se, Pres., BAROMETERN med OSKARSHAMNS-TIDNINGEN, Kalmar
Andreone, Fred .... (613) 738-3000
sales@imapro.com, Pres., Imapro Corp., ON, Rockcliffe
Andreottola, Michael
info@amjet.com, Pres./CEO, American Ink Jet Corp., MA, Billerica
Andrews, Phil .... (519) 823-6050
pandrews@guelphmercury.com, Mng. Ed., The Guelph Mercury, ON, Guelph
Andrews, Susan .... ext. 1106
susan.andrews@graypub.com, Financial Dir., Gwinnette Daily Post, GA, Lawrenceville
Andrews, Connie .... (610) 371-5006
candrews@readingeagle.com, Newspapers in Educ., Reading Eagle, PA, Reading
Andrews, Jean .... (678) 804-7411
Pres., Syndicated Writers of America, GA, Suwanee
Andrews, Tom
publisher@picayuneitem.com, Pub., Picayune Item, MS, Picayune
Andrews, Caesar .... (313) 222-6821
candrews@freepress.com, Exec. Ed., Detroit Free Press, MI, Detroit
Andrews, Pat .... (954) 938-7105
pandrews@miamiherald.com, Asst. Mng. Ed., Broward, The Miami Herald, FL, Miami
Andrews-Gross, Buffy .... (717) 771-2052
buffy@ydr.com, Asst. Mng. Ed., Features/Niche, York Daily Record/York

Sunday News, PA, York
Andrus, Elyssa......................(801) 344-2553
eandrus@heraldextra.com, Lifestyle Ed., The Daily Herald, UT, Provo
Angeler, Geancarlo
direttore@prealpina.it, Dir., LA PREALPINA, Varese
Angeles, Maria de los...............(818) 715-9931
admax@sbcglobal.net, Pres., Admax International Media, CA, West Hills
Angeli, Burt
bangeli@ironmountaindailynews.com, Sports Ed., The Daily News, MI, Iron Mountain
Angeli, Gerolamo
directore@corrieremercantile.it, Dir., CORRIERE MERCANTILE, Genoa
Angelini, Erin
adreachnetwork@imvi.bls.com, Contact, BellSouth AdReach, GA, Atlanta
Angell, Jim
wyopress@wyopress.org, Exec. Dir., Wyoming Press Association, WY, Cheyenne
Angell, Darcy
angell@edr.com, Office Mgr., EDR/Beachwood Studios, OH, Beachwood
Angell, Mark
online@guardian.co.uk, Adv. Dir., THE GUARDIAN, London
Angelo, Dan...................................ext. 331
danangelo@sanduskyregister.com, Sports Ed., Sandusky Register, OH, Sandusky
Anger, Laura..........................(231) 591-2609
Ferris State Torch., MI, Big Rapids
Anger, Kimberly.......(209) 369-2761 ext. 229
kimberlya@lodinews.com, Adv. Dir., Lodi News-Sentinel, CA, Lodi
Anger, Paul...........................(313) 222-6606
panger@freepress.com, Ed., Detroit Free Press, MI, Detroit
Anger, N/A
compass@lssu.edu, Lake Superior State Univ., MI, Sault Sainte Marie
Angers, Gilles
gangers@lesoleil.com, Real Estate, Le Soleil, QC, Quebec
Anguiano, Richard....................352.867.4104
Online Community Editor, Ocala Star-Banner, FL, Ocala
Angulo Aragus, Antonio
redaccion@diariodelaltoaragon.es, MD, DIARIO DEL ALTOARAGON, Heusca
Ankney, Bernie......................(205) 726-2465
rnankney@samford.edu, Chair, Samford University, AL, Birmingham
Annan, Bruce.........................(905) 726-2642
MD, AIM Group / Classified Intelligence, FL, Altamonte Springs
Annesley, Vera
news.advert@@samoatelco.com, Pub., SAMOA NEWS, Pago Pago
Annett, Lesley...........................416-946-2297
lesley.annett@sunmedia.ca, Sales Director/Director of Promotion, The Toronto Sun, ON, Toronto
Anschutz, Philip F...................(303) 298-1000
Chrmn./CEO, The Anschutz Co., CO, Denver
Anselm, Debbie............(219) 462-5151 ext. 337
danselm@nwitimes.com, Retail Adv. Mgr., Valparaiso, The Times, IN, Munster
Anstaett, Doug........................(785) 271-5304
danstaett@kspress.com, Exec. Dir., Kansas Press Association, KS, Topeka
Antal, Roy.............................(306) 781-5233
photography@leaderpost.canwest.com, Photo Dept. Mgr., The Leader-Post, SK, Regina
Antani, Hiren
editor@gujaratsamachar.com, Ed., GUJARAT SAMACHAR, Baroda, Gujarat
Anthar Makairo, Sakir
dailymehran@hotmail.com, Ed. in Chief, MEHRAN, Hyderabad, Hyderabad Division
Anthony, Phil
nypa@nynewspapers.com, Adv. Rep., Classified Sales, New York Press Service, NY, Albany
Anthony, Bill..............................8124647477
anthonyb@courierpress.com, Finance Director, Evansville Courier & Press, IN, Evansville
Anthony, Greg
info@marketmedia.com, Sr. Vice Pres., Nat'l Sales, Market Place Media/Alloy, Inc., CA, Santa Barbara
Anthony, Clifford....................(440) 366-7729
Lorain County Cmty. College, OH, Elyria
Anthony, Robert S....................(917) 267-2493
bob@paperpc.net, Ed./Columnist, Stadium Circle Features, NY, New York
Antich, Jose
digital@vanguardia.es, Dir., La VanGuardia, Barcelona
Antisdale, David
david@youthstream.com, Vice Pres., West Coast Sales, American Passage Media Corp./Youthstream Media Networks, CA, Los Angeles
Antosiewicz, Joseph D......................ext. 1003
jantosiewicz@keenesentinel.com, Dir., Prodn. Opns., The Keene Sentinel, NH, Keene
Antoye, Xavier
redactionenchef@leprogres.fr, Ed. in Chief, LE PROGRES/LE PROGRES DIMANCHE, Lyon
Anzelmo, James
graphic@stans.net, Pres., Graphic Machine Sales, Inc., IL, Wonder Lake
Apenowich, Cathryn
info@vtg.com, Mktg. Serv. Mgr., Voice Technologies Group, Inc., NY, Buffalo
Apesteguia, Hugo E.
laopinion@bbt11.com.ar, Dir., La Opinion, Pergamino, Provincia de Buenos Aires
Apostolakis, Alexandra
tharros@kal.forthnet.gr, Pub., THARROS, Kalamata, Peloponnese
Apperson, Glenda..............................ext. 218
glenda.apperson@gaflnews.com, Prodn. Foreman, Composing, The Moultrie Observer, GA, Moultrie
Apple, Charity...........................336-506-3057
Features Ed., Times-News, NC, Burlington
Appleyard, Ernie...........(815) 625-3600 ext. 350
Prodn. Mgr., Sauk Valley Newspapers, IL, Dixon
Appt, John J...........................(419) 255-3567
jappt@tyjill.com, Pres., TyJill Enterprises, Inc., OH, Rossford
April, Sara
sara@dirksvanessen.com, Vice Pres., Dirks, Van Essen & Murray, NM, Santa Fe
April, Sara
sara@dirksvanessen.com, Vice Pres., Dirks, Van Essen & Murray, NM, Santa Fe
Apud, Salvador Kamar
editorial@lavozmva.com, Pres., LA VOZ DE MONCLOVA, Monclova, Coahuila
editorial@lavozmva.com, Owner/Pres., LA VOZ DE COAHUILA, Monclova, Coahuila
Aquino, Tony
taquino@fujifilmgs.com, Reg'l Sales Mgr., Fujifilm Graphic Systems USA, Inc., CT, Windsor
Aquino, Jose
jaquino@santamariatimes.com, Web Developer, Santa Maria Times, CA, Santa Maria
Aquino, Jennifer
jaquino@sanmateocountytimes.com, Exec. Ed., San Mateo County Times, CA, San Mateo
Aquino, Andres........................(203) 820-7927
info@usafashionshows.com, Owner, Fashion Syndicate Press, VT, Woodstock
Arambula, Odie.......................(956) 728-2561
odie@lmtonline.com, Sunday Ed., Laredo Morning Times, TX, Laredo
Araujo Paulino, Alfonso
jornaldeminas@city10.com.br, Pub., Jornal de Minas S.A., Belo Horizonte, Minas Gerais
Arcarese, Cory........................(719) 636-0396
cory.arcarese@gazette.com, Circ. Vice Pres., The Gazette, CO, Colorado Springs
Archer, Kim.............................(918) 581-8315
kim.archer@tulsaworld.com, Health/Medical Writer, Tulsa World, OK, Tulsa
Archibald, Edward
ed@daily-jeff.com, Adv. Dir., The Daily Jeffersonian, OH, Cambridge
Archibald-Russell, Kimberly........(216) 999-4074
Credit Mgr., The Plain Dealer, OH, Cleveland
Ardila, Antonio Tinoco
avillar@elperiodico.com, Dir., Periodico ExtreMadura, Caceres
Ardila Sierra, Pablo...........................410-5066
Gen. Mgr., J Ardila C & Cia, Bogota, D.C.
Ardizzone, Antonio
segretaria.direzione.gds@gestelnet.it, Dir., GIORNALE DI SICILIA, Palermo
Arellano Ontiveros, Edgar Rafael
express@foreigner.com.mx, Pres., EXPRESS, Tepic, Nayarit
Arenas, Gail...............................787-354-4029
andragale@aol.com, Executive Director, Overseas Press Club of Puerto Rico, PR, San Juan
Arenstein, Seth........................(301) 354-2000
sarenstein@accessintel.com, Editorial Dir., CableFAX Daily LLC, MD, Rockville
Arevalo, Gaby...........................(410) 455-1262
Univ. of Maryland Baltimore County, MD, Baltimore
Arevalo, Julia Rodriguez
efedelhi@gmail.com, Rep., EFE News Services - New Delhi, India, New Delhi
Arevalo Juarez, Fernando Homero
dinovedades@chisnet.com.mx, Ed., NOVEDADES DE CHIAPAS, Tuxtla Gutierrez, Chiapas
Argue, Linda
largue@lsj.com, Circulation, Portland Review & Observer, MI, Lansing
largue@lsj.com, Circ. Dir., Lansing State Journal, MI, Lansing
Arguello Oertel, Arturo
mercadeo@elmundo.com.sv, Gen. Mgr., EL MUNDO, San Salvador
Arias Vallarino, Francisco
franscco.arias@epasa.com, Pres., EL PANAMA AMERICA, Panama City
franscco.arias@epasa.com, Gen. Mgr., CRITICA LIBRE, Panama City
Arie, Mike.................................405.238.6464
marie@pvdemocrat.com, Editor, Pauls Valley Democrat, OK, Pauls Valley
Aritin, Turiy
turiy.aritin@yeniasir.com.tr, Adv. Mgr., YENI ASIR
Arke, Ed
earke@messiah.edu, Professor of Communications, Messiah College, PA, Grantham
Arlen, Gary..............................(301) 656-7940
garlen@arlencom.com, Pres., Arlen Communications LLC, MD, Bethesda
Arleth, Joe
voiceeditor@huskies.bloomu.edu, Bloomsburg Univ., PA
Arlt, Karin................................(630) 739-9600
karlt@ustensor.com, Mktg. Mgr./Sales Admin., Tensor Group, Inc., IL, Woodridge
Armendariz, Bill
barmendariz@deminghedlight.com, Ed., Deming Headlight, NM, Deming
Armengol Cardiel, Jaime
eparagon@elperiodico.com, Dir., El Periodico De Aragon, Zaragoza
Armenta Balderrama, Gerardo
informa@cybernet.com.mx, Pres., EL INFORMADOR DEL MAYO, Navojoa, Sonora
Armstong, Susan.......................(540) 213-9105
sarmstrong@newsleader.com, Admin., HR, The News Leader, VA, Staunton
Armstrong, John
jarmstrong@spotmagic.com, Founder, Affiliate Rel., SpotMagic, Inc., CA, San Francisco
Armstrong, Kelly
inquires@lazerfare.com, Pres., Lazer-fare Media Services Ltd., MB, Winnipeg
Armstrong, Rod........................(979) 731-4613
rod.armstrong@theeagle.com, Finance Dir., The Eagle, TX, Bryan
Armstrong, John
jarmstrong@bayareanewsgroup.com, Pres./Pub., Tri-Valley Herald/San Ramon Valley Herald, CA, Pleasanton
Armstrong, Terry
terry.armstrong@ok.bc.ca, Vice Pres./Grp. Pub., The Daily Courier, BC, Kelowna
Armstrong, John
jarmstrong@bayareanewsgroup.com, Pres./CEO/Pub., The Daily Review, CA, Hayward
Armstrong, John
jarmstrong@bayareanewsgroup.com, Pub., The Argus, CA, Fremont
Armstrong, Travis K...................(805) 564-5161
voices@newspress.com, Editorial Page Ed., Santa Barbara News-Press, CA, Santa Barbara
Armstrong, Tiff B......................(415) 288-4260
tarmstrong@harriswilliams.com, Mng. Dir., Harris Williams & Co., CA, San Francisco
Armstrong, Matt.......................(805) 681-5979
marmstrong@newspress.com, Prodn. Mgr., Press, Santa Barbara News-Press, CA, Santa Barbara
Armstrong, Kevin......................(918) 495-6489
warmstrong@oru.edu, Oral Roberts Univ., OK, Tulsa
Armstrong, Rachel....................(505) 835-5996
New Mexico Inst. of Mining & Technology, NM, Socorro
Arndt, Markus
redaktion@en-online.de, Ed., ELMSHORNER NACHRICHTEN, Elmshorn
Arnett, Ronald C.
arnett@duq.edu, Chair/Prof., Duquesne University, PA, Pittsburgh
Arnholt, Michael.......................(910) 486-3558
arnholtm@fayettevillenc.com, Mng. Ed., The Fayetteville Observer, NC, Fayetteville
Arning, Albert
a.arning@vkz.de, Ed., Vaihinger Kreiszeitung, Vaihingen
Arnink-Pate, Karleen.................(415) 777-7373
karnink-pate@sfchronicle.com, Director, Retail Adv., San Francisco Chronicle, CA, San Francisco
Arnold, Anthony.......................(256) 740-5758
anthony.arnold@timesdaily.com, Prodn. Mgr., Distr., TimesDaily, AL, Florence
Arnold, Ed N.
newsroom@peterboroughexaminer.com, Mng. Ed., The Peterborough Examiner, ON, Peterborough
Arnold, Bruno
redaktion@neue-uz.ch, Ed. in Chief, NEUE URNER ZEITUNG, Altdorf
Arnold, Patti.....................................ext. 311
Sports Ed., The Daily Sentinel, CO, Grand Junction
Arnold, Mike...........................(352) 563-3393
marnold@chronicleonline.com, Mng. Ed., Citrus County Chronicle, FL, Crystal River
Arnold, Steve...........................(361) 886-3624
arnolds@caller.com, Mktg. Dir., Corpus Christi Caller-Times, TX, Corpus Christi
Arnold, Bruno
redaktion@neue.ch, Ed. in Chief, NEUE URNER ZEITUNG, Altdorf
Arnold, Brian...........................(707) 427-6969
Asst. Sports Ed., Daily Republic, CA, Fairfield
Arnold, Arne............................(262) 631-1734
aarnold@journaltimes.com, Circ. Mgr., Pennysaver, The Journal Times, WI, Racine
Arnoldaussen, Dennis................(479) 784-0404
darnoldussen@swtimes.com, Circ. Dir., Times Record, AR, Fort Smith
Arocha, Marcos Lopez........................67-2918
general@el-carabobeno.com, Gen. Mgr., EL CARABOBENO, Valencia, Carabobo
Aronoff, Roger...................................ext. 109
roger@aim.org, Exec. Secretary, Accuracy in Media, DC, Washington
Aronowitz, Michelle Jones
maronowitz-jones@gaa.org, Dir., Gravure Association of America, NY, Rochester
Arora, Rajeev Kumar
gandiv@dataone.in, Ed., GANDIVA, Varanasi, Uttar Pradesh
Arpad, Farkas
haromszek@3szek.ro, Ed. in Chief, HAROMSZEK, Sepsiszentgyorgy, Covasna
Arranz, Bidal
redaccion.valladolid@el-mundo.es, Dir., El Mundo De Valladolid, Valladolid
Arrazola, Carlos
guatemala@acan-efe.com, Rep., EFE News Services - Guatemala City, Guatemala, Guatemala City
Arredondo Ortega, Felix
el_centro@infosel.net.mx, Pres., El Centro, Irapuato, Guanajuato
Arriaga Rodriguez, Raul......................472-5607
Pres., Ecos de Guerrero, Chilpancingo, Guerrero
Arrigoni, Patricia
patarrigoni@comcast.net, Pres., Arrigoni Travel Syndication, CA, Fairfax
Arroyo, Raymond.......................(413) 496-6322

Rarroyo@berkshireeagle.com, Adv. Mgr., Interactive Sales, The Berkshire Eagle, MA, Pittsfield
Arshad, Mirza
dailyaftab786@gmail.com, Publication Mgr., AFTAB, Multan
Arteaga, Dawn
darteaga@icfj.org, Commn. Mgr., International Center for Journalists, DC, Washington
Arter, Lisa..................(330) 747-1471 ext. 1214
larter@vindy.com, Adv. Mgr., Retail, The Vindicator, OH, Youngstown
Arth, Shelly
shellyarth@socket.net, Pub., The Marshall Democrat-News, MO, Marshall
Arthur, Shannon.......................(573) 815-1621
ssarthur@columbiatribune.com, Circ. Mgr., Educ./Promos. Coord., Columbia Daily Tribune, MO, Columbia
Arthur, Marvin C.
arthurintl@aol.com, Pres., Arthur's International, NV, Las Vegas
Arthur, Damon.........................(530) 225-8226
darthur@redding.com, Living/Lifestyle Ed., Record Searchlight, CA, Redding
Arvizu Negrete, Luis
panorama1@prodigy.net.mx, Pres., Panorama, Colima, Colima
Asahana, Yutaka
webmaster@mainichi.co.jp, Exec. Dir./Tokyo Head Officer, MAINICHI SHIMBUN, Tokyo
Asbach, Richard M.
raspach@westhawaiitoday.com, Pub., West Hawaii Today, HI, Kailua-Kona
Ascher, Evelyn.........................(609) 927-1842
Sec./Treasurer, Ascher Features Syndicate, NJ, Egg Harbor Township
Ascher, Sidney.........................(609) 927-1842
Pres., Ascher Features Syndicate, NJ, Egg Harbor Township
Ascoli, Ralph C. ....(603) 668-4321 ext. 240
rascoli@unionleader.com, Adv. Vice Pres., New Hampshire Union Leader/New Hampshire Sunday News, NH, Manchester
Asel, Hans-Karl
impressum@vrm.de, Ed., LAMPERTHEIMER ZEITUNG, Lampertheim
Ash, Nancy..................................ext. 238
nash@sharonherald.com, Living/Lifestyle Ed., The Herald, PA, Sharon
Ashcraft, Sheila.......................(248) 334-4329
aconsultinginc@aol.com, Dir., Mktg., Ashcraft Consulting, MI, Pontiac
Asher, Gunilla
gasher@postindependent.com, Adv. Dir., Glenwood Springs Post Independent, CO, Glenwood Springs
Ashley, Jay..............................336-506-3031
jashley@thetimesnews.com, Mng. Ed., Times-News, NC, Burlington
Ashley, Samantha.........(540) 374-5000 ext. 5550
sashley@freelancestar.com, Exec. Asst., The Free Lance-Star, VA, Fredericksburg
Ashon, Enimil
info@newtimes.com.gh, Ed., THE GHANAIAN TIMES, Accra
Ashton, Jean
jashton@stonebridgepress.com, Adv. Mgr., Stonebridge Press, Inc., MA, Southbridge
Asleson, Glen
gasleson@mankatofreepress.com, Prodn. Dir., The Free Press, MN, Mankato
Asmussen, Morten
ma@erhvervsbladet.dk, Ed., ERHVERVS-BLADET, Kobenhavn
Asper, David A.
corporateinquiries@canwest.com, Exec. Vice Pres., CanWest Global Communications Corp., MB, Winnipeg
Asper, Leonard
sfernandez@canwest.com, Pres./CEO, CanWest MediaWorks Publications, Inc., ON, Don Mills
Asper, Leonard J. ....(204) 953-7742
Pres./CEO, CanWest Global Communications Corp., MB, Winnipeg
Aspland, Cindy
cindya@advancedtele.co.uk, Dir., Sales, Advanced Telecom Services, Inc. (U.K.), ENG, London
Aspo, Marku
marku.aspo@kymensanomat.fi, Ed., KYMEN SANOMAT, Kotka
Aspuria, Ray
raspuria@times-standard.com, Sports Ed., Times-Standard, CA, Eureka
Asvat, Ebrahim
easvat@elsiglo.com, Pres., EL SIGLO, Panama City
Asvestas, Theodosios
asves196@openet.gr, Pub, Ekdoseis Poseidon A E, Kavala, Macedonia
Aswege, Scott.........................(309) 757-4934
ashwish@qconline.com, Bus. Mgr., The Dispatch, IL, Moline
At Mussen, Peter
peter.atmussen@mazonline.de, Dir., Markische Allgemeine, Potsdam
Atcheson, Denice.....................(805) 437-0404
datcheson@venturacountystar.com, Dir., Finance, Ventura County Star, CA, Camarillo
Aten, Tim
tlaten@naplesnews.com, News Ed., Naples Daily News, FL, Naples
Athanasiou, V.
info@dimokratiki.gr, Pub./Dir., DIMOKRATIKI TIS RODOU, Rhodos, Aegean Islands
Athanasiou, Evagelos
nagones@ioa.forthnet.gr, Pub., NEOI AGONES EPIROU, Ioannina, Epirus
Athar, Jamil
djurat@gmail.com, Ed. in Chief, JURAT, Rawalpindi, Rawalpindi Division
Atkins, Joan
sports@trailblazeronline.net, Morehead State Univ., KY, Morehead
Atkins, Joan...........................(606) 783-5312
Morehead State Univ., KY, Morehead
Atkins, Joan
j.atkins@moreheadstate.edu, Journalism Coord., Morehead State University, KY, Morehead
Atkins, Lisa.............................(856) 486-2477
latkins@courierpostonline.com, Living/Lifestyle Ed., Courier-Post, NJ, Cherry Hill
Atkins, Karen
news@fultonsun.com, Ed., The Fulton Sun, MO, Fulton
Atkins, Charlotte.....................(706) 290-5279
catkins@rn-t.com, Ed., Rome News-Tribune, GA, Rome
Atkins, Ralph
ralph.atkins@ft.com, Ed. in Chief, Financial Times, Frankfurt am Main
Atkinson, Catherine
catkinson@ wacotrib.com, Lifestyles Ed., Waco Tribune-Herald, TX, Waco
Atkinson, Paul C.....................(212) 856-6304
paulcatkinson@nnnlp.com, Sr. Vice Pres., Bus. Devel., Newspaper National Network LP, NY, New York
Atkinson, Dave.............(785) 822-1487 ext. 853
sjdatkinson@saljournal.com, Prodn. Dir., The Salina Journal, KS, Salina
Atler, Dick...............................(209) 667-3411
California State Univ. Stanislaus, CA, Turlock
Attanio, Maurizio
diffusione@larena.it, Dir., L'ARENA, Verona
Attard, Alex
alex.attard@media.link.com.mt, Ed., IN-NAZZJON, Pieta, Hamrun
Attaway, Mark.........................(843) 317-7363
mattaway@florencenews.com, Prodn. Foreman, Pressroom, Morning News, SC, Florence
Atwal, Kulwant.........................(250) 995-4421
katwal@te.canwest.com, Accounting Mgr., Times Colonist, BC, Victoria
Atwell, Kit.................(928) 445-3333 ext. 1070
ksoldwedel@prescottaz.com, Pub./CEO, The Daily Courier, AZ, Prescott
Atwell, Kit.................(928) 445-3333 ext. 1070
Vice Pres./CEO, Prescott Newspapers Inc., Western Newspapers, Inc., AZ, Yuma
Atwill, Kevin
kevinatwill@forsythnews.com, Ed., Forsyth County News, GA, Cumming
Atwill, Kevin
kevinatwill@forsythnews.com, Ed., Forsyth County News, GA, Cumming
Atwood, Kelly...........................601-477-4084
kelly.atwood@jcjc.edu, Newspaper Adviser, Jones County Junior College, MS, Ellisville
Aueinen, Marco
data@dataengineering.fi, Mgr., Data Engineering Ltd., Helsinki
Aughenbaugh, Cindy.......(814) 765-5581 ext. 213
Circ. Mgr., The Progress, PA, Clearfield
Augsburger, Wayne
sales@cygnet.com, Vice Pres., Mktg., Cygnet Storage Solutions, Inc., CA, San Jose
Augustine, Larry D.
augustin@susqu.edu, Chair, Susquehanna University, PA, Selinsgrove
Augustine, Grace
cairo@efe.com, Rep., EFE News Services - Cairo, Egypt, Cairo
Augusto, Kate
editor@huntington-news.com, Northeastern Univ., MA, Boston
Aulakh, Kamar.........................(303) 894-8888
quarkxpress@quark.com, Pres./CEO, Quark, Inc., CO, Denver
Auman, Richard D.....................(610) 371-5151
rauman@readingeagle.com, Circ. Dir., Reading Eagle, PA, Reading
Aumann, Michael
michaelaumann@buhrs.com, Pres., Buhrs Americas, Inc., MN, Plymouth
Aurell, Olof..................................448 70 46
olof.aurell@tolerans.com, Vice Pres. Sales & Mktg., Tolerans AB Sweden, Stockholm
Aurellano, Arnie.....................806-669-2525
editor@thepampanews.com, Managing Editor, The Pampa News, TX, Pampa
Austin, John.............................(818) 754-0751
holywood@ez2.net, Dir., Hollywood Inside Syndicate, CA, Los Angeles
Austin, Kevin...........................(229) 888-9398
kevin.austin@albanyherald.com, Advetising Director, The Albany Herald, GA, Albany
Austin, Steve...........................(270) 831-0325
saustin@thegleaner.com, Pub., The Gleaner, KY, Henderson
Austin, Steve...........................(479) 872-5100
saustin@nwaonline.net, Circ. Dir., The Morning News of Northwest Arkansas, AR, Springdale
Austin, Ronna...............................ext. 7307
Oklahoma City Cmty. College, OK, Oklahoma City
Austin, Karen
kaustin@bayareanewsgroup.com, Mgr., HR, Tri-Valley Herald/San Ramon Valley Herald, CA, Pleasanton
Avalos, Engel...........................(530) 749-4742
engel_avalos@link.freedom.com, Prodn. Foreman, Pressroom, Appeal-Democrat, CA, Marysville
Avanzado, Susan.......................(202) 383-7811
susan.avanzado@newhouse.com, Office Mgr., Newhouse News Service, DC, Washington
Avarra, Greg
info@abc.es, Mng. Dir., ABC, Sevilla
Avedikian, Hagob
azg@azg.am, Ed. in Chief, AZG, Yerevan
Aven, Sandra.............................(806) 296-1310
saven@hearstnp.com, Pub., Plainview Herald, TX, Plainview
Aven Gladych, Paula.......(303) 776-2244 ext. 414
pavengladych@lehmancomm.com, Web Ed., Times-Call, CO, Longmont
Averett, Justin.........................(205) 665-6222
Univ. of Montevallo, AL, Montevallo
Averill, David...........................(918) 581-8333
david.averill@tulsaworld.com, Editorial Page Ed., Tulsa World, OK, Tulsa
Avery, John.............................(626) 585-7979
Pasadena City College, CA, Pasadena
Avery, Judy
javery@freedomenc.com, Vice Pres., Mktg., The Sun Journal, NC, New Bern
Averyt, Libby...........................(361) 886-3681
averytl@caller.com, Gen. Mgr. Online., Corpus Christi Caller-Times, TX, Corpus Christi
Avgeris, Jeff
Jeff.Avgeris@registerguard.com, Internet Sales/Devel. Mgr., The Register-Guard, OR, Eugene
Avila, Larry
lavila@appleton.gannett.com, Bus. Ed., The Post-Crescent, WI, Appleton
Avila, Miguel Garay
xpresion@progidy.net.mx, Ed., EXPRESION, Matamoros, Tamaulipas
Avila, Noah Rodriguez
noe@diario.com.mx, Gen. Mgr., DIARIO DE JUAREZ, Ciudad Juarez, Chihuahua
Avrech, Gary
info@nswash.com, Mktg. Mgr., N/S Corporation, CA, Inglewood
Aweidha, Rashid
alwahdah@emi.ae, Owner, AL-WAHDAH
Awin, Charlie
charlie.awin@metro.lu, Publinews, Guatemala City
Awtry, Greg
greg.awtry@yorknewstime.com, Pub., York News-Times, NE, York
Axel, Elise.............................(509) 359-4317
The Easterner, WA, Cheney
Axelrad, Mitchell
mitchell.axelrad@ott.sunpub.com, News Ed., The Ottawa Sun, ON, Ottawa
Axelton, Duane...............................ext. 256
daxelton@theworldlink.com, Systems Mgr., The World, OR, Coos Bay
Ayala, Hildebrand H. Deandar
drando.deandar@latarde.com.mx, Ed., La Tarde, Reynosa, Tamaulipas
Ayala, Jorge L.........................(917) 339-0863
jorge.ayala@hoynyc.com, CEO/Pub., Hoy, NY, New York
Aydelotte, Rod
raydelotte@wacotrib.com, Chief Photographer, Waco Tribune-Herald, TX, Waco
Aydin, Nezir
ankara@milligazete.com.tr, Dir., MILLI GAZETE
Ayearst, John.........................(807) 343-6207
john.ayearst@chroniclejournal.com, Assignment Ed., The Chronicle-Journal, ON, Thunder Bay
Ayer, Tammy...........................(239) 344-4785
Lifestyles Ed., The News-Press, FL, Fort Myers
Ayers, Darryl...........................336-506-3085
dayers@thetimesnews.com, Prodn. Director, Times-News, NC, Burlington
Ayers, H. Brandt
bayers@annistonstar.com, Chrmn./Pub., The Anniston Star, AL, Anniston
Ayers, Jeff...............................(919) 718-1233
Circ. Dir., The Sanford Herald, NC, Sanford
Ayers, H. Brandt.......................(256) 235-9201
bayers@annistonstar.com, Chrmn., Consolidated Publishing Co., AL, Anniston
Ayers, Robert
ayers@publicationdesign.com, President, Publication Design, Inc., PA, Zionsville
Ayres, Jamie
jamie.ayres@m2.com, Ed. in Cheif, M2 Communications Ltd., ENG, Bath
Ayscue, Ashley Steven...............(252) 436-2842
Photo Dept. Mgr., Daily Dispatch, NC, Henderson
Ayuso Centurion, Felix
novcam@cancun.novenet.com.mx, Pres., Novedades de Campeche, Campeche, Campeche
Az-Zedjali, Ahammed
editor@timesofoman.com, Mng. Dir., TIMES OF OMAN
Azevedo, Stephanie..................(530) 749-4785
stephanie_azevedo@link.freedom.com, Adv. Mgr., Nat'l, Appeal-Democrat, CA, Marysville
Azis, Tuty
sbypost@server.indo.net.id, Pub., SURABAYA POST, Surabaya, East Java
Aziz, Abdul
online@utusan.com.my, Ed. in chief, UTUSAN MALAYSIA, Kuala Lumpur
Azmayesh, Asghar A.
info@shz.de, Bus. Mgr., Norddeutsche Rundschau, Flensburg
Azmayesh, Kessler
martina.laville@shz.de, Ed. in Chief, Schleswig-Holsteinische Landeszeitung, Rendsburg
Azmayesh, Asghar A.
info@shz.de, Bus. Mgr., FLENSBURGER TAGEBLATT, Flensburg
Azocar, Cristina
azocar@naja.com, Pres., Native American Journalists Association, OK, Norman
Azriela, Jaffe.........................(732) 985-7613
azjaffe@optonline.net, Author/Self-Syndicator,

Anchored Dreams, NJ, Highland Park

B

Babb, Andrew M.......................**(864) 583-2907**
ababb@msmgmt.com, Pres., Mid-South Management Co., Inc., SC, Spartanburg

Babb, Andrew M.
ababb@msmgmt.com, Pres., Crescent Media Group, Inc., SC, Spartanburg

Babbington, Stuart....................**(334) 380-3845**
Spring Hill College, AL, Mobile

Babbitt, Krista..........................**(616) 546-4278**
krista.babbitt@hollandsentinel.com, Presentation Team Leader, The Holland Sentinel, MI, Holland

Babbitt, Alan............................**(616) 546-4271**
alan.babbitt@hollandsentinel.com, Sports Team Leader, The Holland Sentinel, MI, Holland

Babcock, Mike..........................**406-791-1487**
mbabcock@greatfallstribune.com, Outdoor Ed., Great Falls Tribune, MT, Great Falls

Babczak, John
johnh@times-press.com, Circ. Mgr., The Times-Press, IL, Streator

Babu, Vijaya
info@andhraprabha.com, Ed., ANDHRA PRABHA, Hyderabad

Babu, Vijay
newxpres@vsnl.com, Ed. in Chief, ANDHRA PRABHA, Vijayawada, Andhra Pradesh

Bacanu, Petre Mihai
politica@romanialibera.ro, Exec. Dir., ROMANIA LIBERA, Bucharest

Bacchiocchi, Carin....................**212-969-7534**
caward@hearst.com, Domestic Sales Coordinator, North America Syndicate, NY, New York

Bach, Horst...**3871**
kontakt@echo-online.de, Proprietor, ODENWALDER ECHO, Darmstadt

Bach, Hans-Peter
kontakt@echo-online.de, Proprietor, ODENWALDER ECHO, Darmstadt
kontakt@echo-online.de, Proprietor, DARMSTADTER ECHO, Darmstadt
kontakt@echo-online.de, Proprietor, Russelsheimer Echo, Darmstadt

Bachman, Bart
bart@mountwashingtonvalley.com, Mng. Ed., The Conway Daily Sun, NH, North Conway

Bachman, Denise......................**(724) 222-2200**
dbachman@observer-reporter.com, Entertainment/Amusements Ed., Observer-Reporter, PA, Washington

Backe, John E.................................**ext. 6901**
jebacke@backemarketing.com, Pres./CEO, Backe Difital Brand Marketing, PA, Radnor

Backlund, Diana
diana@newscom.com, Dir., Sales/Mktg., Newscom, CA, Los Angeles

Bacon, Alicia..........................**(603) 543-3100**
abacon@tsvmedia.net, Online Sales, Eagle Times, NH, Claremont

Bacon, Rick..............................**910 997-3111**
rbacon@heartlandpublications.com, Pub., Richmond County Daily Journal, NC, Rockingham

Bacon, Jake.............................**(908) 556-2258**
Photo Ed., Arizona Daily Sun, AZ, Flagstaff

Bacon, Cheryl M.
cheryl.bacon@jmc.acu.edu, Chair/Prof., Abilene Christian University, TX, Abilene

Bacon, Mike.............................**(847) 394-5700**
VP., Sales/Mktg., Spartanics, IL, Rolling Meadows

Bacungan, J.
jbacungan@annarbornews.com, Asst. to Pub., The Ann Arbor News, MI, Ann Arbor

Badger, Tom............................**(262) 513-2607**
tbadger@conleynet.com, Circ. Mgr., Mktg./Promo., The Freeman, WI, Waukesha

Badman, John...........................**(618) 463-2572**
john_badman@thetelegraph.com, Photo Dept. Mgr., The Telegraph, IL, Alton

Baechtel, Mark................................**ext. 323**
mbaechtel@adn.com, Film/Theater Ed., Anchorage Daily News, AK, Anchorage

Baer, Jamie
jbaer@hjnews.com, News Ed., The Herald Journal, UT, Logan

Baer, John
baerj@phillynews.com, Columnist, News, The Philadelphia Daily News, PA, Philadelphia

Baergen, Darrel
dbaergen.comm@hsutx.edu, Chair, Hardin-Simmons University, TX, Abilene

Baggett, Debbie.......................**(530) 749-4758**
dbaggett@appealdemocrat.com, Adv. Dir., Appeal-Democrat, CA, Marysville

Baggs, Norman........................**(770) 535-6300**
nbaggs@gainesvilletimes.com, Gen. Mgr., The Times, GA, Gainesville

Bagonzi, Jolie
jbagonzi@islandpacket.com, HR Dir., The Island Packet, SC, Bluffton

Bahauddin, A.M.M.
inqilab@neksus.com, Ed., DAINIK INQILAB, Dhaka

Baiaroski, Valdemar..........................**231-3535**
Pres., Diario da Manha, Corumba, Mato Grosso

Bailey, Dan
dbailey@c-zone.net, CEO, North Valley Diver Publications, CA, Redding

Bailey, Robert
rbailey@macontel.com, Circ. Single Copy Mgr., The Telegraph, GA, Macon

Bailey, Lee
leebay@aol.com, Pres., Bailey Broadcasting Services, CA, Glendale
leebay@aol.com, Pub., EUR/Electronic Urban Report, CA, Los Angeles

Bailey, Erin............................**(631) 289-5911**
St. Josephs College, NY, Patchogue

Bailey, Donald W.
don.bailey@augustachronicle.com, Pres., The Augusta Chronicle, GA, Augusta

Bailey, Julie...........................**(818) 710-2960**
Los Angeles Pierce College, CA, Woodland Hills

Bailey, Roger
bailey@ndna.com, Exec. Dir., North Dakota Newspaper Association, ND, Bismarck

Bailey, Brad....................................**ext. 467**
bbailey@dailyitem.com, Adv. Dir., The Daily Item, PA, Sunbury

Baillie, Peter
pbaillie@tc.canwest.com, Vice Pres., Adv./Sales & Mktg., Times Colonist, BC, Victoria

Bailly, Diegou
lejour@AfricaOnline.co.ci, Dir., LE JOUR, Abidjan

Baily, Marilyn..........................**(206) 527-3645**
North Seattle Cmty. College, WA, Seattle

Bain, Michael...........................**(262) 656-6247**
mbain@kenoshanews.com, Mgr., Computer Servs., Kenosha News, WI, Kenosha

Baine, Don
dbaine@mmcom.com, Pres., Multi-Media Communications, MA, Natick

Baine, Wallace.........................**(831) 429-2427**
wbaine@santa-cruz.com, Film/Theater Ed., Santa Cruz Sentinel, CA, Scotts Valley

Baines, Pat
pat.baines@gadsdentimes.com, System Coord., The Gadsden Times, AL, Gadsden

Baines, Tim
tim.baines@ott.sunpub.com, Sports Ed., The Ottawa Sun, ON, Ottawa

Baird, David............................**(765) 641-4341**
Anderson Univ., IN, Anderson

Baird, Linda B.........................**(585) 258-2205**
lbaird@rocheste.gannett.com, Vice Pres., HR, Democrat and Chronicle.com, NY, Rochester

Baittiner, Roberto............................**25-6777**
editor@panodi.com, Dir., Diario Panorama C.A., Maracaibo, Zulia

Bajackson, Bob..........................**512.245.3408**
bobb8082002@yahoo.com, Advisor, Texas State Univ., TX, San Marcos

Bak, Robert
publicitate@cugetliber.ro, Dir., CUGET LIBER, Constanta

Bakar, Timbang Bin
pelita@brunet.bn, Ed., PELITA BRUNEI, Lapangan Terbang Lama, Berakas

Baker, Kenneth.........................**(415) 777-8445**
kbaker@sfchronicle.com, Arts Critic, San Francisco Chronicle, CA, San Francisco

Baker, Bernard...........**(434) 793-2311 ext. 3045**
bbaker@registerbee.com, Asst. City Ed., Danville Register & Bee, VA, Danville

Baker, Craig............................**(815) 220-6971**
cbaker@newstrib.com, Cor. Accounting Mgr., News-Tribune, IL, La Salle

Baker, Bridget D.
bridget.baker@registerguard.com, Cor. Dir./Sec., The Register-Guard, OR, Eugene

Baker, Dave.............................**(541) 338-2320**
dave.baker@registerguard.com, Mng. Ed., The Register-Guard, OR, Eugene

Baker, Gail.......................................**ext. 250**
g.baker@theday.com, Tourism Mktg. Specialist, The Day Publishing Company, CT, New London

Baker, Alton F..........................**(541) 338-2318**
Ed./Pub., The Register-Guard, OR, Eugene

Baker, Dan.......................................**ext. 234**
dbaker@msmgmt.com, News Ed., La Grange Daily News, GA, LaGrange

Baker, Andrew
andbaker@snu.edu, Graphic Design, Southern Nazarene University, OK, Bethany

Baker, Daleen...................................**ext. 106**
daleen@redbluffdailynews.com, Bus. Mgr., Daily News, CA, Red Bluff

Baker, Bridget..........................**(541) 338-2469**
Pub. Rels. Dir., The Register-Guard, OR, Eugene

Baker, Becky...................................**ext. 1640**
bbaker@the-daily-record.com, Copy Ed., The Daily Record, OH, Wooster

Baker, Sue...............................**(815) 439-5356**
sbaker@scn1.com, Features Ed., The Herald News, IL, Joliet

Baker, Da'Shaun........................**318-487-6388**
dbaker@thetowntalk.com, Advertising Services Manager, The Town Talk, LA, Alexandria

Baker, Nancy............................**(336) 888-3558**
nbaker@hpe.com, Controller, High Point Enterprise, NC, High Point

Baker, Andrew..........................**(619) 594-7291**
San Diego State Univ., CA, San Diego

Baker, Elaine................**(510) 658-9252 ext. 128**
elaine@inman.com, Membership Coord., Inman News, CA, Alameda

Baker, Kathy............................**(888) 217-7951**
kbaker@interest.com, Regl. Dir., Mortgage Market Information Services, IL, Villa Park

Baker, Martin
martin.baker@devlin.co.uk, Mng. Dir., Devlin Electronics Ltd., Basingstoke

Baker, Chris.............................**(604) 536-1132**
chrisbakerassociates@mac.com, Pres., Chris Baker & Associates Ltd., BC, South Surrey

Bakker, Jason
jason@campusmediagroup.com, Dir., Mktg., Campus Media Group, Inc., MN, Bloomington

Bal, Samahit
pragativadi@pragativadi.com, Ed., PRAGATIVADI, Bhubaneswar, Orissa

Balderamma, Frank...................**(310) 481-0401**
Bus. Mgr., City News Service, Inc. - Los Angeles, CA, CA, Los Angeles

Balding, Timothy
timothy.balding@wan-ifra.org, Dir., Global Affairs, World Association of Newspapers and News Publishers (WAN-IFRA), Paris

Baldwin, Mark F........................**(715) 845-0666**
mbaldwin@wdhprint.com, Exec. Ed., The Wausau Daily Herald, WI, Wausau

Baldwin, Peter
peter@starnews.com.au, Gen. Mgr., THE NORTH WEST STAR

Baldwin, Chuck
cbaldwin@hcnonline.com, CFO, Houston Community Newspapers, TX, Houston

Baldwin, Ralph.........................**(423) 252-1205**
rbaldwin@xtn.net, COO, Jones Media, Inc., TN, Greeneville

Baldwin, Chad..........................**(307) 266-0545**
chad.baldwin@trib.com, Ed., Casper Star-Tribune, WY, Casper

Balentine, Ian
ibalentine@mtdemocrat.net, Adv. Dir., Mountain Democrat, CA, Placerville

Baleschrino, Richard.................**(212) 217-4472**
Fashion Inst. of Technology, NY, New York

Balinsky, Derrick
derrickbalinsky@eveningtribune.com, Sports Ed., The Evening Tribune, NY, Hornell

Balkun, John............................**(973) 586-8178**
Director of Sports, North Jersey Media Group, NJ, Woodland Park

Balkun, John............................**(201) 646-4433**
sports@northjersey.com, Dir., Sports, Herald News, NJ, West Paterson

Ball, Peg...................................**(512) 445-3551**
pball@statesman.com, Exec. Asst. to Pub., Austin American-Statesman, TX, Austin

Ball, Katherine.........................**(831) 754-4212**
kball@salinas.gannett.com, Features Ed., The Salinas Californian, CA, Salinas

Ballah, Vedi
lacresselibereesocialiste@yahoo.fo, Ed., LE SOCIALISTE, Port Louis

Ballance, John..........................**(225) 388-0680**
jballance@theadvocate.com, Photo Dept. Mgr., The Advocate, LA, Baton Rouge

Ballantine, Richard G.
rgb@durangoherald.com, Pub., Durango Herald, CO, Durango

Ballantyne, Neil...........**(519) 894-2250 ext. 2615**
nballantyne@therecord.com, News Ed., The Record, ON, Kitchener

Ballard, Linda
advertising@kilgorenewsherald.com, Adv. Mgr., Kilgore News Herald, TX, Kilgore

Ballard, Sarah.............**(407) 328-4722 ext. 3321**
Seminole State College, FL, Sanford

Ballard, Debbie
dlogan@fortfrances.com, Adv. Mgr., Fort Frances Daily Bulletin, ON, Fort Frances

Balle, Hermann
service@idowa.de, Bus. Mgr., HALLERTAUER ZEITUNG, Mainburg

Balle, Hermann
statcree@landshuter-zeitung.de, Proprietor, LANDSHUTER ZEITUNG, Landshut

Ballestrini, Janet M..............................**ext. 309**
j.ballestrini@theday.com, Circ. Mgr., The Day Publishing Company, CT, New London

Ballmer, Steven A.
stevenb@microsoft.com, CEO, Microsoft Corp., WA, Redmond

Baltera, Savannah....................**(702) 895-4803**
Univ. of Nevada, NV, Las Vegas

Baluk, Natalia
info@wz.lviv.ua, Ed. in Chief, VYSOKIY ZAMOK, Lviv

Balzer, Howard.........................**(314) 298-2681**
hbalzer@aol.com, Secretary, Professional Football Writers of America (PFWA), MO, Maryland Heights

Balzi, Kaerim
k.balzi@todayszaman.com, Ankara Rep., ZAMAN

Bammer, Richard
features@thereporter.com, Entertainment/Amusements Ed., The Reporter, CA, Vacaville

Banda, Lynn....................................**ext. 1562**
lynn.banda@uniontrib.com, Adv. Sales Dir., Ret. Communities, The San Diego Union-Tribune, CA, San Diego

Bandiola-Cabusao, Amalia
editorial.mtimes@gmail.com, Ed. in Chief, MINDANAO TIMES, Davao City

Baneky, Bill
william.baneky@sourcemedia.com, Adv. Dir., Legal, The Bond Buyer

Bang, Derrick...........................**(530) 747-8047**
dbang@davisenterprise.net, Arts Ed., The Davis Enterprise, CA, Davis

Bangkuai, Datuk Joniston
jon@nst.com.my, Regional Head/Bureau Chief, NEW STRAITS TIMES, Kota Kinabalu, Sabah

Banish, Terrie..........................**805-781-7841**
tbanish@thetribunenews.com, Director of Advertising, The Tribune, CA, San Luis Obispo

Banisky, Sandy.........................**(410) 332-6105**
sandy.banisky@baltsun.com, Deputy Mng. Ed., Metro, The Baltimore Sun, MD, Baltimore

Banister, Auriel
depauliabusiness@gmail.com, Advertising Manager, DePaul Univ., IL, Chicago

Banks, Marc
marcb@dynaric.com, Asst. Mktg. Mgr., DYC Supply Co., VA, Virginia Beach

marcb@dynaric.com, Asst. Mktg. Mgr., Dynaric, Inc., VA, Virginia Beach
Banks, Adelle ....(202) 463-8777
adelle.banks@religionnews.comMr., Production Editor, Religion News Service, DC, Washington
Bankston, Norman ....(229) 226-2400
norman.bankston@gaflnews.com, Pub., Thomasville Times-Enterprise, GA, Thomasville
Bankston, Bill ....(225) 388-0202
bbankston@theadvocate.com, Editorial Page Ed., The Advocate, LA, Baton Rouge
Banos Loinaz, Juan Jose
infodeia@deia.com, Dir., Deia, Bilbao, Vizcaya
Banov, Jessica
banovj@fayettevillenc.com, Educ. Ed., The Fayetteville Observer, NC, Fayetteville
Banta, Lynn 570-674-5600
info@outsourcingusa.net, CEO, Outsourcing USA, PA, Dallas
Banton, Fiona 954 262 8461
Nova Southeastern Univ., FL, Fort Lauderdale
Bantz, Connie
connieb@spokesman.com, Mgr., HR, The Spokesman-Review, WA, Spokane
Baptista, Dan ....(559) 441-6039
dbaptista@fresnobee.com, Circ. Sr. Mgr., The Fresno Bee, CA, Fresno
Barackman, Carlee
cbarackman@rc.edu, Co-Editor-In-Chief, Rochester College, MI, Rochester Hills
Baraliakos, Xenoson
tharos@otenet.gr, Dir., THARROS, Kozani, Macedonia
Baran, Marcin
marcin.baran@dziennik.krakow.pl, Vice editor in Chief, DZIENNIK POLSKI, Krakow
Baranczyk, Merle
merle@mountainmail.com, Pub., The Mountain Mail, CO, Salida
Baranski, Rick ....ext. 207
rickb@usspi.com, Mktg. Dir., U.S. Suburban Press, Inc., IL, Schaumburg
Baranski, Rick ....ext. 207
rickb@usspi.com, Mktg./PR Dir., U.S. Suburban Press (USSPI), IL, Schaumburg
Baratoff, Michael.....................(212) 576-9511
michaelb@metrosn.com, President/COO, Metro Newspaper Advertising Services, Inc., NY, New York
Baratoff, Michael.....................(212) 576-9511
michaelb@metrosn.com, Exec. Vice Pres./COO, Metro-Puck Comics Network - New York, NY, NY, New York
Baratoff, Michael.....................(212) 576-9511
michaelb@metrosn.com, Pres., Metro Newspaper Advertising Services, Inc. Sunday Magazine Network - New York, NY, NY, New York
Baratta, Dan
dcmdanbar@aol.com, Pres., Dan-Bar, Inc., FL, Orlando
Barbara, Smith
bsmith@breezenewspapers.com, Circulation Director, Cape Coral Breeze, FL, Cape Coral
Barber, David ....(312) 494-8224
dave_barber@parade.com, Sr. Vice Pres., Newspaper Rel., Parade Publications, Inc. - New York, NY, NY, New York
Barber, Ken
kenb@tiac.net, Vice Pres., Advanced Publishing Technology, CA, Burbank
kenb@tiac.net, Vice Pres., Opns., Advanced Publishing Technology, CA, Burbank
Barber, Lionel
lionel.barber@ft.com, Ed., FINANCIAL TIMES, Paris
Barberi, Mauricio ....(973) 210-6318
mbarberi@lds.com, Sr. Vice Pres., Bus. Devel., Logical Design Solutions, NJ, Florham Park
Barbu, Ioan
ioanbarbu@curierul.ro, Dir., CURIERUL DE VALCEA, V□lcea
Barbuto, Dana ....(617) 786-7074
dbarbuto@ledger.com, Features Ed., The Patriot Ledger, MA, Quincy
Barclay, Becky.........................(919) 739-7837
bbarclay@newsargus.com, Society/Women's Ed., Goldsboro News-Argus, NC, Goldsboro
Barco, Manolo ....(305) 237-1255
Advisor, Miami Dade College - North Campus, FL, Miami
Barcomb, Maurice......................315-789-3333
mbarcomb@fltimes.com, Circulation Director, Finger Lakes Times, NY, Geneva
Bardonner, Sharon.....................765-659-4622
sbardonner@ftimes.com, Publisher, The Times, IN, Frankfort
Bardonner, Sharon ....(765) 420-5293
sbardonner@journalandcourier.com, Adv. Mgr., Retail, Journal and Courier, IN, Lafayette
Barend, Pete ....(419) 521-7361
pbarend@nncogannett.com, Circ. Dir., News Journal, OH, Mansfield
Bargarsen, Rogar
redaksjon@fremover.no, Gen. Mgr., FREMOVER, Narvik
Barger, Jeannine ....(814) 765-9495 ext. 222
display@theprogressnews.com, Adv. Mgr., Display, The Progress, PA, Clearfield
Barhoum, Samir
jotimes@jpf.com.jo, Ed. in Chief, JORDAN TIMES
Barile, Suzy
suzyb3@gmail.com, Pres, North Carolina Press Club, NC, Cary
Barker, Marilyn ....(231) 723-3592
advocate@pioneergroup.net, Pub., Manistee News-Advocate, MI, Manistee
Barker, Brian ....(216) 999-6762
bbarker@plaind.com, Pres./Sec./Treasurer, Ohio Circulation Managers Association, OH, Brooklyn
Barker, Hanna
hmb002@mcdaniel.edu, Co-Editor in Chief, McDaniel College, MD, Westminster
Barker, Carol
cbarker@timesanddemocrat.com, Regl. Ed., The Times and Democrat, SC, Orangeburg
Barker, Rene
adsales@lebanondailyrecord.com, Adv. Mgr., The Lebanon Daily Record, MO, Lebanon
Barker, William.......................(813) 259-7135
Vice Pres., Opns., The Tampa Tribune, FL, Tampa
Barker, Chris ....(804) 649-6614
cbarker@timesdispatch.com, Recruitment Adv. Sales Mgr., Richmond Times-Dispatch, VA, Richmond
Barker, Sean ....(203) 789-5700
Sports Ed., New Haven Register, CT, New Haven
Barker, Chris
pcbarker@douglascountysentinel.com, Paulding County News Ed., Douglas County Sentinel, GA, Douglasville
Barkin, Dan ....(919) 829-4562
dbarkin@newsobserver.com, Deputy Mng. Ed., The News & Observer, NC, Raleigh
Barkley, Greg...............................ext. 3046
gbarkley@hanfordsentinel.com, Circ. Dir., The Sentinel, CA, Hanford
Barkmeir, Steve ....(303) 954-6453
sbarkmeier@medianewsgroup.com, Vice Pres., Tax, MediaNews Group Inc, CO, Denver
Barkovich, Joe................................ext. 268
gbarkovich@wellandtribune.ca, City Ed., Welland Tribune, ON, Welland
Barlow, Keith E. ....(478) 453-1424
kbarlow@unionrecorder.com, Pub., The Union-Recorder, GA, Milledgeville
Barlow, John ....(843) 317-7360
jbarlow@florencenews.com, Prodn. Dir., Morning News, SC, Florence
Barman, Hemanta
editordj@sify.com, Ed., DAINIK JANAMBHUMI, Jorhat, Assam
Barna , Bruce 724-889-7707
Bruce@ad-a-note.com, Executive Vice President , AD-A-NOTE, PA, Pittsburgh
Barnard, Craig ....(416) 383-2315
cbarnard@nationalpost.com, Circ. Vice Pres., Reader Sales/Serv., National Post, ON, Toronto
Barnard, Sara...........................(504) 826-3500
sbarnard@timespicayune.com, Adv. Mgr., Classified, The Times Picayune, LA, New Orleans
Barnard, Jacky.........................(805) 564-5120
jbarnard@newspress.com, Customer Serv. Mgr., Santa Barbara News-Press, CA, Santa Barbara
Barnard, Al..............................860-818-3634
abarnard@fujifilm.com, Newspaper Account Manager, SE Region, Fujifilm North America Corporation, IL, Hanover Park
Barnard, Wayne
wbarnard@scsun-news.com, Gen. Mgr., Deming Headlight, NM, Deming
Barner, Craig
craig_barner@macgraw-hill.com, Ed., Dodge Construction News Chicago
Barner, Mark R.
barner@niagara.edu, Chair/Assoc. Prof., Niagara University, NY, Niagara University
Barnes, Christopher.....................876 932 6089
Managing Director, THE JAMAICA GLEANER, Kingston
Barnes, Jeff
publisher@kentontimes.com, Pub./Gen. Mgr./Purchasing Agent, The Kenton Times, OH, Kenton
Barnes, Janet ....ext. 2271
Office Mgr., Texarkana Gazette, TX, Texarkana
Barnes, Brad
bbarnes@ledger-enquirer.com, Entertainment Writer, Columbus Ledger-Enquirer, GA, Columbus
Barnes, Nancy ....(612) 673-4951
Nancy.Barnes@startribune.com, Ed./Sr. Vice Pres., Star Tribune, MN, Minneapolis
Barnes, Jeff
dcueditor@dailychiefunion.com, Mgmt. Info Servs. Mgr., The Daily Chief-Union, OH, Upper Sandusky
Barnes, Susan ....(734) 994-6842
sbarnes@annarbornews.com, Food Ed., The Ann Arbor News, MI, Ann Arbor
Barnes, Charles
kceditor@kentontimes.com, Pres., Ray Barnes Newspapers, Inc., OH, Kenton
Barnett, Doug ....(901) 529-2235
dbarnett@commercialappeal.com, Classified Transportation Mgr., The Commercial Appeal, TN, Memphis
Barnett, Brooke
bbarnett@elon.edu, Assoc. Prof., Elon University, NC, Elon
Barnett, Wren...........................(704) 698-0021
Grimes, W.B. & Co., MD, Gaithersburg
Barnett, Catherine ....(707) 521-5202
catherine.barnett@pressdemocrat.com, Exec. Ed., The Press Democrat, CA, Santa Rosa
Barnett, Sheila
info@systems-technology-inc.com, Exec. Asst., Systems Technology, Inc., CA, San Bernardino
Barney, Diane
dbarney@thereporter.com, Ed., The Reporter, CA, Vacaville
Barney, Justin ....(904) 819-3492
justin.barney@staugustinerecord.com, Sports Ed., The St. Augustine Record, FL, Saint Augustine
Barnick, Florence C...................(540) 374-5452
fbarnick@freelancestar.com, Vice President/Assoc. Pub., The Free Lance-Star, VA, Fredericksburg
Baron, Ed ....(703) 620-1725
edbaron@edbaron.com, Pres., Ed Baron & Associates, Inc., VA, Oakton
edbaron@edbaron.com, Consultant/Trainer, Sales Training Consultants, Inc., FL, Boca Raton
Barr, Wayne.............................(413) 782-1580
Western New England College, MA, Springfield
Barr, Karen..................(650) 237-2290 ext. 11
karen@newscolor.com, Sales Dir., Newscolor, LLC, OR, Silverton
Barranca, Nicholas F.
nicholas.f.barranca@usps.gov, Vice Pres., Product Devel., United States Postal Service, DC, Washington
Barraza Gonzalez, Rodolfo
cambio@cambio.com.mx, Pres., Cambio, Hermosillo, Sonora
Barraza Sanchez, Alberto
editotol@edomex1.telmex.net.mx, Ed./Dir., EL HERALDO DE TOLUCA, Toluca, Mexico
Barrena, Juan Carlos
berlin@efe.com, Rep., EFE News Services - Berlin, Germany, Berlin
Barrett, Paul M ....(315) 789-3333
pmbpub@aol.com, Publisher, Finger Lakes Times, NY, Geneva
Barrett, Thomas
tbarrett@ttsfax.com, Pres., Touch Tone Services, WA, Renton
Barrett, Donna............................334-293-5800
dbarrett@cnhi.com, Pres./CEO, Community Newspaper Holdings, Inc., AL, Montgomery
Barrett, Gretchen.......................(609) 871-8051
gbarrett@phillyburbs.com, Editorial Page Ed., Burlington County Times, NJ, Willingboro
Barrett, Suzanne............(303) 776-2244 ext. 361
sbarrett@lehmancomm.com, Mgmt. Info Servs. Mgr., Times-Call, CO, Longmont
Barrick, Rhonda ....(803) 774-1264
rhondab@theitem.com, Living/Lifestyle Ed., The Item, SC, Sumter
Barrie, David
info@nlgja.org, Pres., National Lesbian and Gay Journalists Association, DC, Washington
Barrington, Ray
ray.barrington@gogreenbay.com, News Ed., The Green Bay News-Chronicle, WI, Green Bay
Barrios, Lois Marcan 32-1175
Pub., Region, Cumana, Sucre
Barrios, George
gbarrios@globe.com, Sr. Vice Pres./CFO/Treasurer, The Boston Globe, MA, Boston
Barron, Cate ....(717) 255-8165
cbarron@patriot-news.com, Exec. Ed., The Patriot-News, PA, Mechanicsburg
Barron-Fury, Linda ....(432) 333-7736
linda_fury@link.freedom.com, Circ. Dir., Odessa American, TX, Odessa
Barrons, Mark
mbarrons@tribune.com, Detroit Mgr., Tribune 365, MI, Livonia
Barros, Laura
elsalvador@acan-efe.com, Rep., EFE News Services - San Salvador, El Salvador, San Salvador
Barrows, John 406-443-2850
mtnews@mtnewspapers.com, Executive Director, Montana Newspaper Association, MT, Helena
Barrozo, Rodrigo
rodrigo@jornaldoestado.com.br, Dir., Editora Jornal do Estado Ltd., Curitiba, Parana
Barry, Mark L. ....ext. 301
m.barry@theday.com, Circ. Dir., The Day Publishing Company, CT, New London
Barry, John
info@brainworks.com, Mgr., Brainworks Software Development Corp., NY, Sayville
Barstow, Tom 717-771-2036
News Editor, York Daily Record/York Sunday News, PA, York
Bart, Andrew
andrew.bart@pcipage.com, Pres., Publishing Connections, Inc., MD, Potomac
Bartel, Roger ....(715) 526 - 2121
rbartel@bluelinemediaholdings.com, Editorial Director, Shawano Leader, WI, Shawano
Barth, Steven.............................949-892-2929
sbarth@mediaspanonline.com, Exec. Vice Pres., MediaSpan Online Services, CA, Irvine
Barth, Ken ....(972) 980-2890
contact@tek-tools.com, Pres./CEO, Tek-Tools, Inc., TX, Dallas
Barth, Pete ....(920) 453-5156
pbarth@sheboygan.gannett.com, Sports Ed., The Sheboygan Press, WI, Sheboygan
Bartholomay, Lucy ....(617) 929-2619
bartholomay@gobe.com, Mng. Dir., Pdct. Innovation, The Boston Globe, MA, Boston
Bartholow, Jim ....(740) 376-5448
jbarthol@mariettatimes.com, Sr. Copy Ed., The Marietta Times, OH, Marietta
Bartlett, Fred
fbarlett@ccbcmd.edu, Cmty. College of Baltimore County, MD, Catonsville
Bartlett, Allen
albartlett@naplesnews.com, City Ed., Naples Daily News, FL, Naples
Bartolacci, Joseph C.
info@matw.com, Pres./CEO, Matthews Inter-

national Corp., PA, Pittsburgh
Bartoldson, Craig ....(304) 263-8931
cbartoldson@journal-news.net, Pub., The Journal, WV, Martinsburg
Barton, Tom ....(912) 652-0324
tom.barton@savannahnow.com, Editorial Page Ed., Savannah Morning News, GA, Savannah
Baru, Sanjaya
sanjaya.baru@bsmail.in, Ed. in Chief, BUSINESS STANDARD, New Delhi
Baruah, P.G
dainikasam@rediffmail.com, Mng. Dir., DAINIK ASAM, Guwahati, Assam
Baruah, P.G.
info@assamtribune.com, Mgr./Dir./Ed., ASSAM TRIBUNE, Guwahati, Assam
Baruzzi, Cara..........................(203) 789-5748
Bus. Ed., New Haven Register, CT, New Haven
Bas, Miguel
efemos@gmail.com, Rep., EFE News Services - Moscow, Russia, Moscow
Bas, Rene Q
business@manilatimes.net, Ed. in Chief, THE MANILA TIMES, Manila
Basbanes, Nicholas A.
nick@gentlymad.com, Mng. Ed./Columnist, Literary Features Syndicate, MA, North Grafton
Basbiam, Syamsir
redaksi@harianposkota.com, Ed., POS KOTA, Jakarta, Java
Baschin, Carsten
az@madsack.de, Ed. in Chief, ALLER-ZEITUNG, Gifhorn
Basilio, Teresita F.
mirror1@skyinet.net, Pub., MINDANAO MIRROR BULLETIN, Davao City
Basinger, Chris ....ext. 628
cbasinger@newtondailynews.com, Prodn. Mgr., Commercial Printing, Newton Daily News, IA, Newton
Baskin, Mike 386-681-2491
Advertising Director, Daytona Beach News-Journal, FL, Daytona Beach
Basolo, Kristy..........................(906)227-2545
kbasolo@nmu.edu, Advisor, Northern Michigan Univiversity, MI, Marquette
Bason, Bill
bill.b@pressenterprise.net, Prodn. Mgr., Color Graphics, Press-Enterprise, Inc. (Color Graphics Dept.), PA, Bloomsburg
Basse, Christian
skn.verlag@nwn.de, Bus. Mgr., Ostfriesischer Kurier, Norden
Bassett, Greg
gbassett@dmg.gannett.com, Gen. Mgr & Exec. Ed., The Daily Times, MD, Salisbury
Bast, Philip ....(519) 894-2250 ext. 2630
pbast@therecord.com, Entertainment Ed., The Record, ON, Kitchener
Bates, Carl ....(205) 325-2237
Adv. Dir., Bus. Devel., The Birmingham News, AL, Birmingham
Bates, Jack............................(916) 288-6000
jack@cnpa.com, Exec. Dir., California Newspaper Publishers Association, Inc., CA, Sacramento
jack@cnpa.com, Exec. Dir., California Press Association, CA, Sacramento
jack@cnpa.com, Exec. Dir., Pacific Northwest Newspaper Association, CA, Sacramento
Bates, Jack............................(916) 288-6006
jack@cnpa.com, Exec. Dir., CNPA Advertising Services, CA, Sacramento
Batson, Nanci.......................401.789.9744
Publisher, Southern Rhode Island Newspapers, RI, Wakefield
Batson, Nanci.......................401.789.9744
The Kent County Times, RI, West Warwick
Batson, Phil ....(864) 260-1230
batsonpr@independentmail.com, Pub., Orange & White, Anderson Independent-Mail, SC, Anderson
Battaglia, Pat ....(704) 921-1818
publisher@cleverpuzzles.com, Owner, International Puzzle Features, NC, Charlotte
Battaglia, Dr. Carmen
cbattaglia@mindspring.com, Pres., Dog Writers' Association of America, PA, Coatesville
Battaglia, Carmen
cbattaglia@mindspring.com, Pres., Dog Writers' Association of America, PA, Coatesville
Batten, Rob ....(902) 421-5815
rbatten@hfxnews.ca, Prodn. Mgr., The Daily News, NS, Dartmouth
Battersby, Mark E. ....(610) 924-9158
crcktinc@aol.com, Vice Pres./Ed., Cricket Communications, Inc., PA, Ardmore
Battista, Jocelyn ....(203) 354-1115
jbattista@thehour.com, Classified Supervisor, The Hour Publishing Co., CT, Norwalk
Battiste, Jerry
jerryb@news-banner.com, Online Ed., News-Banner, IN, Bluffton
Battles, Lori
lori@perrydailyjournal.com, Adv. Dir., Accts., The Perry Daily Journal, OK, Perry
Batts, Lisa ....(252) 265-7810
lisa@wilsondaily.com, Lifestyle Ed., The Wilson Daily Times, NC, Wilson
Bauab, Mima Cury 621-2000
Pres., Comercio do Jahu, Jau, Sao Paulo
Bauer, Frank ....(360) 754-5461
fbauer@theolympian.com, Adv. Dir., The Olympian, WA, Olympia
Bauer, James R.
jrbauer@alltel.net, Bus. Mgr., The Daily Press, PA, Saint Marys
Bauer, Tyson
rbeditor@andrew.cmu.edu, Carnegie Mellon Grad. School Bus. Admin., PA, Pittsburgh
Bauer, Traci ....(585) 258-2615
tbauer@democratandchronicle.com, Asst. Mng. Ed., Multimedia, Democrat and Chronicle.com, NY, Rochester
Bauer, Kurt
info@medianhaus-bauer.de, Ed. in Chief, Recklinghauser Zeitung, Marl
Bauer, Frank ....(253) 597-8625
frank.bauer@thenewstribune.com, Adv. Vice Pres., The News Tribune, WA, Tacoma
Bauer, Dave ....(408) 920-5323
dbauer@mercurynews.com, Vice Pres., Opns., San Jose Mercury News, CA, San Jose
Bauer, Karen ....(701) 224-5522
Advisor, Bismarck State College Mystician, ND, Bismarck
Bauer, Eric
ebauer@orangeleader.com, Pub., The Orange Leader, TX, Orange
Bauer, Marjan
andreja.anzur@delo.si, Ed. in Chief, SLOVENSKE NOVICE, Ljubljana
Baum, Margeret
sanmatean@smccd.net., College of San Mateo, CA, San Mateo
Bauman, Brian ....(866) 366-6166 ext. 223
brianb@goplastics.com, Dir.-Sales/Mktg., Go Plastics/StreetSmart LLC, GA, Canton
Bauman, Brian.........................(202) 636-4731
bbauman@washingtontimes.com, Dir., Mktg., The Washington Times, DC, Washington
Baumann, Gunther
baumann@kuhnverlag.de, Ed. in Chief, Sudwest Presse (Die Neckarquelle), Villingen-Schwenningen
Baumann, Daniel
dbaumann@dailyherald.com, Chrmn. Emeritus, Daily Herald, IL, Arlington Heights
Baumeler, Sandra
luheu@centralnet.ch, Ed. in Chief, LUZERN HEUTE, Lucerne, Luzern
Baumgarner, Bob
sherryb@gpplastics.com, Pres., GP Plastics Corp., TX, Dallas
Baumgart, Jim..........................(262) 513-2621
jbaumgart@conleynet.com, Adv. Mgr., The Freeman, WI, Waukesha
Baun, Kathy
kbaun@te.canwest.com, Promo. Mgr., Times Colonist, BC, Victoria
Baur, Hans Wilhelm 7890
vertrieb@bnn.de, Proprietor/Bus. Mgr., BADISCHE NEUESTE NACHRICHTEN, Karlsruhe
Baurkemper, Wayne
waynebaurkemper@sidneysuntelegraph.com, Gen. Mgr., Sidney Sun-Telegraph, NE, Sidney
Bauserman, Pamela ....(209) 369-7035 ext. 211
pamelab@lodinews.com, Society Page Ed., Lodi News-Sentinel, CA, Lodi
Bautsch, Florence....................(570) 628-6020
fbautsch@republicanherald.com, Editorial Page Ed., Republican Herald, PA, Pottsville
Bauza, Miguel
sramirez@losandes.com.ar, Gen. Mgr., Diario Los Andes Hermanos Calle S.A., Mendoza, Provincia de Mendoza
Bawer, Mala
mala@cybersmart.org, Exec. Dir., Stockalert, Inc., NJ, Bernardsville
Baxter, Rick ....(772) 221-4107
rick.baxter@scripps.com, Mktg. Dir., Treasure Coast News/Press-Tribune, FL, Stuart
Baxter, Robert ....(856) 486-2436
rbaxter@courierpostonline.com, Theater/Music Ed., Courier-Post, NJ, Cherry Hill
Bayard-Miller, Patrice...............(916) 288-6029
patrice@cnpa.com, Client Rel./Sales Mgr., CNPA Advertising Services, CA, Sacramento
Bayles, Jim ....(604) 654-4921
jim.bayles@catalystpaper.com, Vice Pres./Gen. Mgr. Newsprint/ Int'l, Catalyst Paper (USA), Inc., WA, Seattle
Baylet, Jean Michel.......................6211 3300
correspondants@ladepeche.com, Chrmn./MD, LA DEPECHE DU MIDI, 31095 Toulouse
Beach, Joe..................(309) 786-6441 ext. 202
jbeach@qconline.com, Metro Ed., The Dispatch, IL, Moline
Beach, Charles ....(845) 358-1710
Nyack College, NY, Nyack
Beach, Joe ....ext. 202
jbeach@qconline.com, Bus./Finance Ed., The Rock Island Argus, IL, Rock Island
Beager, Laurel
laurel@ifallsdailyjournal.com, Ed., The Daily Journal, MN, International Falls
Beagle, Ben ....ext. 129
bbeagle@batavianews.com, Living/Lifestyle Ed., The Daily News, NY, Batavia
Beagley, Harlan............(509) 765-4561 ext. 214
hbeagley@columbiabasinherald.com, Pub., Columbia Basin Herald, WA, Moses Lake
Beal, Ron ....(440) 245-6901 ext. 492
rbeal@morningjournal.com, Adv. Dir. / Gen. Mgr., The Morning Journal, OH, Lorain
Beal, Andy
andy@waveshift.com, Pres., CBS MaxPreps, Inc., CA, Cameron Park
Beale, Nick
nick.beale@ruralpress.com, Adv. Mgr., SOUTH COAST
Beals, Gregg ....ext. 701
gbeals@hutchnews.com, Prodn. Mgr., The Hutchinson News, KS, Hutchinson
Bean, Carla ....ext. 217
Adv. Mgr., West Plains Daily Quill, MO, West Plains
Bean, Ed..................................404-419-2830
ebean@alm.com, Fulton County Daily Report, GA, Atlanta
ebean@alm.com, Daily Report
Bean, Joanna ....(719) 636-0273
joanna.bean@gazette.com, Local News Editor, The Gazette, CO, Colorado Springs
Beard, Michael ....(770) 718-3402
mbeard@gainesvilletimes.com, New Media Ed., The Times, GA, Gainesville
Beard, Susan..........................(973) 569 -7670
Beard@northjersey.com, Vice Pres., HR, North Jersey Media Group, NJ, Woodland Park
Bearden, Claudia
cbearden@thedailyworld.com, Bus. Mgr., The Daily World, WA, Aberdeen
Bearden, Patti ....(205) 325-2361
Circ. Mgr., South Zone, The Birmingham News, AL, Birmingham
Beasley, H. Lone
circ@adaeveningnews.com, Pub., Ada Evening News, OK, Ada
Beasley, Stephen A.
stephen.beasley@lubbockonline.com, Pub., Lubbock Avalanche-Journal, TX, Lubbock
Beasley, Toren........................(202) 383-7824
toren.beasley@newhouse.com, Mng. Ed., Photography/Shared Content, Newhouse News Service, DC, Washington
Beaton, Brad
dmacaruso@buynensco.com, CEO, NENSCO, MA, Millbury
Beatty, Mike............................(410) 332-6041
mike.beatty@baltsun.com, Exec. Dir., Retail Sales, The Baltimore Sun, MD, Baltimore
Beatty, Glenn
glennbeatty@gmail.com, Producer/Director, Globalvision News Network, NY, New York
Beauchamp, Debbi 250-371-6115
dbeauchamp@kamloopsnews.ca, Business Manager, Kamloops Daily News, BC, Kamloops
Beauchesne, Jacques ....(804) 227-4001
Gen. Mgr., Newsprint Sales Co., VA, Charlottesville
Beaudette, Rick ....(202) 383-7850
rick.beaudette@newhouse.com, Deputy Bureau Chief, Newhouse News Service, DC, Washington
Beaudin, Matthew
editor@telluridedailyplanet.com, Ed., Telluride Daily Planet, CO, Telluride
Beaudin, Mike ....ext. 243
mbeaudin@bar.southam.ca, Mng. Ed., The Barrie Examiner, ON, Barrie
Beaudoin, Marc
info@cyberagetech.com, Pres., Cyber Age Technologies, VA, Alexandria
Beaudry, Joseph M.
jbeaudry@hamiltoncirculation.com, Pres., Hamilton Circulation Supplies Co., IL, Beecher
Beavers, Jefferson ....(559) 278-8180
California State Univ., CA, Fresno
Bebe, Jens
jensbebe@horsens-folkeblad.dk, Ed., HORSENS FOLKEBLAD, Horsens, Jutland
Bechtel, Julie ....(563) 383-2224
jbechtel@qctimes.com, Pub., Quad-City Times, IA, Davenport
Bechtle, Otto Wolfgang
info@ez-online.de, Proprietor, ESSLINGER ZEITUNG, Esslingen
Beck, Matthew
mbeck@chronicleonline.com, Photo Ed., Citrus County Chronicle, FL, Crystal River
Beck, Randell..........................(605) 331-2250
rabeck@argusleader.com, Pres./Pub., Argus Leader, SD, Sioux Falls
Beck, Sue 832-563-3633
sbeckpmc@aol.com, Pres., Print Marketing Concepts, Inc., TX, Houston
Beck, Steve ....(419) 993-2036
sbeck@limanews.com, Adv. Mgr., Regl., The Lima News, OH, Lima
Beck, Daniel 518-395-3036
dbeck@dailygazette.net, Gen. Mgr., The Daily Gazette, NY, Schenectady
Beck, Patricia
pbeck@leaderherald.com, Pub., The Leader-Herald, NY, Gloversville
Beck, John 217-351-5212
jbeck@news-gazette.com, Editor in Chief, News-Gazette Inc., IL, Champaign
Beck, Michael ....(715) 845-0622
mbeck@wdhprint.com, Pres./Pub., The Wausau Daily Herald, WI, Wausau
Beck, Gayle...................................ext. 8308
gayle.beck@cantonrep.com, Editorial Page Ed., The Repository, OH, Canton
Beck, Bill ....(574) 296-5871
bbeck@etruth.com, Sports Ed., The Elkhart Truth, IN, Elkhart
Beck, C. Arthur ....(610) 265-0500
chmc@aol.com, Pres., Charles Beck Machine Corp., PA, King of Prussia
Beck, Klaus
info@main-rheiner.de, Ed., Main-Spitze, Mainz
Beck, Sue ....(713) 780-7055 ext. 306
sueb@printmkt.com, Pres., Print Marketing Concepts, Inc., TX, Houston
Becker, David ....(780) 429-5111
dbecker@thejournal.canwest.com, Vice Pres., Finance, Edmonton Journal, AB, Edmonton
Becker, James
jbecker@cryogenesis-usa.com, Pres., Cryogenesis (A Div. of WM & C Services, Inc.), OH, Cleveland
Becker, Carol...........................(607) 274-9255
cbecker@ithaca.gannett.com, Adv. Dir., The Ithaca Journal, NY, Ithaca
Becker, Mike
editorial@jcfloridan.com, Mng. Ed., Jackson

County Floridan, FL, Marianna
Beckham, Lisa
lisa.beckham@gaflnews.com, Adv. Mgr., The Tifton Gazette, GA, Tifton
Beckley, Jean ....ext. 3314
Adv. Dir., The Chronicle, CT, Willimantic
Beckman, Linda..........(626) 962-8811 ext. 2251
linda.beckman@sgvn.com, Editorial Page Writer, The Whittier Daily News, CA, Whittier
Beckman, Dean
dbeckman@smumn.edu, Coord., St. Mary's University of Minnesota, MN, Winona
Beckman, Mary........................(805) 564-5203
mbeckman@newspress.com, Web Designer/Developer, Santa Barbara News-Press, CA, Santa Barbara
Beckner, William T.
bni@boonenewspapers.com, Sr. Vice Pres., Boone Newspapers, Inc., AL, Northport
Bedford, Michelle.....................(250) 364-1413
Circ. Mgr., Trail Daily Times, BC, Trail
Bedient, Paul
pbedient@grandhaventribune.com, Pub./Vice Pres., Grand Haven Tribune, MI, Grand Haven
Bednara, Mark
redaktion@dzonline.de, Pub., DULMENER ZEITUNG, Dulmen
Bedoya, Shari.........................(318) 487-6412
sbedoya@thetowntalk.com, Circ. Mgr., Single Copy, The Town Talk, LA, Alexandria
Beebe, Phil............................(765) 213-5863
Webmaster, The Star Press, IN, Muncie
Beeby, Dean
dbeeby@cp.org, Bureau Chief, Broadcast News Limited, NS, Halifax
dbeeby@cp.org, Bureau Chief, Canadian Press, The - Halifax, NS, NS, Halifax
Beehner, Reggie......................(859) 622-1143
Eastern Kentucky Univ., KY, Richmond
Beelman, Maud S....................(214) 977-8473
mbeelman@dallasnews.com, Deputy Mng. Ed., Projects, The Dallas Morning News, TX, Dallas
Beene, Richard........................(661) 395-7284
rbeene@bakersfield.com, Pres./CEO, The Bakersfield Californian, CA, Bakersfield
Beer, Gavin............................(902) 421-5892
gbeer@hfxnews.ca, Adv. Dir., The Daily News, NS, Dartmouth
Beermann, Allen
nebpress@nebpress.com, Exec. Dir., Nebraska Press Advertising Service, NE, Lincoln
Beermann, Allen
abeermann@nebpress.com, Exec. Dir., Nebraska Press Association, NE, Lincoln
Beeson, Frank
fbeeson@ohcommedia.com, Grp. Pub., The Sidney Daily News, OH, Sidney
Beeson, Frank
fbeeson@ohcommedia.com, Grp. Pub., Piqua Daily Call, OH, Piqua
Beeson, Frank
fbeeson@ohcommedia.com, Grp. Pub., Troy Daily News, OH, Troy
Beevor, Darren........................(408) 920-5617
dbeevor@mercurynews.com, Circ. Dir., Sales/Admin., San Jose Mercury News, CA, San Jose
Begley, Susan R.
sbegley@burrellesluce.com, Gen. Mgr., Mutual Press Clipping Service, Inc., PA, Philadelphia
Behan, Michael
mbehan@fortfrances.com, Ed., Fort Frances Daily Bulletin, ON, Fort Frances
Behr, Mike.............................(313) 253-3675
mbehr@channelnet.com, Sr. Dir., Professional Servs., ChannelNet, CA, Mill Valley
Behrens, Daniel E.....................(937) 644-9111
Editorial Page Ed., Marysville Journal-Tribune, OH, Marysville
Beideman, Jeff.........................(215) 345-3076
Sports Ed., The Intelligencer, PA, Doylestown
Beilhart, Terry L. ....(610) 371-5142
tbeilhart@readingeagle.com, Adv. Mgr., Prodn., Reading Eagle, PA, Reading
Beique, Paul............................(802) 654-6708
St. Michael's College, VT, Colchester
Beirne, Horton P..............(540) 962-2121 ext. 13
virginianreview@aol.com, News Ed., Virginian Review, VA, Covington
Beiswinger, George L..................(610) 728-5366
gb@sdlifestyle.com, Writer/Self-Syndicator, Elder Mirth, PA, Audubon
Beitler, Paul
sports@news-banner.com, Sports Ed., News-Banner, IN, Bluffton
Beitman, Sara
weeklyeditor@gmail.com, Muhlenberg College, PA, Allentown
Beitz, Mike ....(519) 271-2220 ext. 207
mbeitz@bowesnet.com, Wire Ed., The Beacon-Herald, ON, Stratford
Bekins, Hillary
bonnie@bonniechurchill.com, Pres., Communication International/National News, CA, Los Angeles
Bekke, Nathan ....(307) 266-0503
nathan.bekke@trib.com, Pub., Casper Star-Tribune, WY, Casper
Belair, Susan
sue.belair@voicemediagroup.com, Vice Pres., Sales, Voice Media Group, NY, New York
Belanger, Michele
michelebelanger@cwc4webs.com, Vice Pres., Canadian Web Consultants Ltd., ON, Port Sydney
Belcher, Steve
stevebelcher@clintondailynews.com, News Ed., The Clinton Daily News, OK, Clinton
Belcher, Ellen..........................(937) 225-2286
ebelcher@coxohio.com, Editorial Page Ed., Dayton Daily News, OH, Dayton
Belda, Fearne
fearne@epi.es, Dir., Levante-El Mercantil Valenciano, Valencia
Beldam, Evelyn
cya@assignmentdesk.com, Bus. Mgr., Assignment Desk, IL, Chicago
Bell, Brandon...........................402-444-3114
National Advg Acct Exec, Omaha World-Herald, NE, Omaha
Bell, Paul...............................(212) 659-1212
paul.bell@dowjones.com, Vice Pres., Partner Businesses, The Wall Street Journal Sunday, NY, New York
Bell, Joseph 814-773-3151
Editor, The Ridgway Record, PA, Ridgway
Bell, Wayne
kgisales@gi.konicaminolta.us, Sr. Vice Pres., Konica Minolta Graphic Imaging USA, MI, Grand Rapids
Bell, Gary...............................(617) 989-4084
Wentworth Institute of Tech., MA, Boston
Bell, Chris..............................(785) 832-7137
cbell@ljworld.com, Circ. Mgr., The World Co.-Lawrence, Kan., Journal-World, KS, Lawrence
Bell, Mike ....(575) 437-7120
mbell@alamogordonews.com, Pub., Alamogordo Daily News, NM, Alamogordo
Bell, Jason ....(204) 697-7247
Jason.Bell@freepress.mb.ca, Asst. City Ed., Winnipeg Free Press, MB, Winnipeg
Bell, Kristina
kbell@highpoint.edu, Lectr., High Point University, NC, High Point
Bell, Kathy
kbell@cp.org, Bureau Chief, Broadcast News Limited, AB, Edmonton
Bell, Amy
amy.bell@lee.net, Controller, The Columbus Telegram, NE, Columbus
Bell, Thom ....ext. 237
Circ. Dir., The Newton Citizen, GA, Covington
Bell, Ronnie E.
ronnieb@commpub.com, Pub., Harrison Daily Times, AR, Harrison
Bell, Tom.....................(785) 822-1491 ext. 753
tbell@saljournal.com, Pub., The Salina Journal, KS, Salina
Bell, Bob
bob.bell@leaderpub.com, Prodn. Mgr., Pressroom, Dowagiac Daily News, MI, Dowagiac
Bell, Todd..............................(732) 565-7253
toddbell@thnt.com, News Ed., Home News Tribune, NJ, East Brunswick
Bell, Alberta
albertabell@thegardnernews.com, Pub., The Gardner News, MA, Gardner
Bell, Wayne
runderwood@americanlitho.cc, Sales Mgr., American Litho, Inc., MI, Grand Rapids
Bell, David ....(613) 732-3692
circ@nrtco.net, Circ. Mgr., Observer, ON, Pembroke
Bell, Carol...............................312-225-2400
CFO, Dir. of Fin & Bus Op, Chicago Defender, IL, Chicago
Bell, Chris...............................785-832-7137
cbell@ljworld.com, The World Co.- Lawrence, Kan., Journal-World, KS, Lawrence
Bell, Bob
bob.bell@leaderpub.com, Prodn. Mgr., Pressroom, Niles Daily Star, MI, Niles
Bell, Lorraine ....(705) 385-8016
lorrainebell@cwc4webs.com, Office Mgr., Canadian Web Consultants Ltd., ON, Port Sydney
Bell, Bruce ....+64 21 339079
bruce.b@theguardian.co.nz, Managing Director, ASHBURTON GUARDIAN
Bella, Michael J.
mbella@salisburypost.com, Prodn. Vice Pres., Opns., Salisbury Post, NC, Salisbury
Bella, Mickey ....(843) 937-5665
mbella@postandcourier.com, Cor. Prodn. Dir., The Post and Courier, SC, Charleston
Bella, Joe..............................1-574-276-1547
jbella@acu-tech.net, Mng. Dir., Acutech LLC, IN, Elkhart
Bellaby, Mara............................321-242-3573
mbellaby@floridatoday.com, Enterprise Editor / space, family, education, Florida Today, FL, Melbourne
Bellamy, Lee
lbellamy@timesnews.net, Adv. Mgr., Classified, Kingsport Times-News, TN, Kingsport
Bellefleur, Yves.......................(418) 686-3413
ybellefleur@lesoleil.com, Librarian, Le Soleil, QC, Quebec
Belles, Mike.................(209) 722-1812 ext. 493
belles@pspub.com, Vice Pres., Circ., Pacific Sierra Publishing, Inc., CA, Merced
Bellotti, John
John_Bellotti@tamu-commerce.edu, Asst. Prof., Texas A&M University-Commerce, TX, Commerce
Belter, Robert
info@portagegraphic.com, Pres., Portage Newspaper Supply Co., OH, Peninsula
Beltrame, Agustin........................4309-7216
abeltrame@clarin-contenidos.com.ar, Ed., Clarin Contenidos, Buenos Aires
Bemis, Dave
dbemis@santamariatimes.com, Mng. Ed., Santa Maria Times, CA, Santa Maria
Benavides, M.E........................(956) 982-6622
Sports Ed., The Brownsville Herald, TX, Brownsville
Benavides, Rachel
rbenavides@link.freedom.com, Ed., El Nuevo Heraldo, TX, Brownsville
Benben, Nancy ....(860) 241-3687
nbenben@courant.com, Vice Pres., Mktg./Cor. Affairs, The Hartford Courant, CT, Hartford
Benbow, Mike..........................(425) 339-3459
benbow@heraldnet.com, Bus. Ed., The Herald, WA, Everett
Bence, Don
don@sakurai.com, Vice Pres., Sales, Sakurai USA, IL, Schaumburg
Bench, Mark
embench@wpfc.org, Exec. Dir., World Press Freedom Committee, VA, Reston
Bender, Ralph
rbender@theadvocate.com, CFO, The Advocate, LA, Baton Rouge
Bender, Valerie ....(559) 441-6766
vbender@fresnobee.com, Vice Pres., Custom Publications, The Fresno Bee, CA, Fresno
Bender, Thomas
tbender@mzv.net, Ed., ALTENAER KREISBLATT, Altena
Bender, Dean
dean_bender@bhimpact.com, Partner, Bender/Helper Impact, CA, Los Angeles
Bendheim, Anne......................(732) 565-7332
njannieb@thnt.com, Special Sections Ed., Home News Tribune, NJ, East Brunswick
Bendowski, Joseph
info@vansonink.com, Pres., Van Son Holland Ink Corp. of America, NY, Islandia
Benedetti, Ben
bbenedetti@digitalsymphony.net, Vice Pres. Client Servs., Digital Symphony, CA, Burbank
Benedetto, Linda ....(906) 341-4211
Comptroller, Manistique Papers, Inc., MI, Manistique
Benedict, Olin ....(607) 441-7204
obenedict@thedailystar.com, Prodn. Mgr., Pre Press, The Daily Star, NY, Oneonta
Benek, Christopher ....(330) 569-5203
Hiram College, OH, Hiram
Benette, Djalma L.
editor@jcruzeiro.com.br, Ed., Cruzeiro Do Sul, Sorocaba, Sao Paulo
Bengelsdorf, Peter...................(631) 843-2728
Dir., Publishing Devel., Newsday, NY, Melville
Bengtson, Ed...........................(541) 812-6052
ed.bengtson@lee.net, Controller, Albany Democrat-Herald, OR, Albany
Beni, John L.............................(210) 450-7115
john_beni@parade.com, Vice Chrmn./COO, Parade Publications, Inc. - New York, NY, NY, New York
Beniash, Michael
beniashm@caledonian-record.com, Sports Ed., The Caledonian-Record, VT, Saint Johnsbury
Benitez, Nestor O.
diarito@copesnet.com, Ed., Amanecer Nueva Epoca, Navarro, Prov. de Buenos Aires
Benitez, M.
mbenitez@voznet.com.mx, Sales Mgr., LA VOZ DE MICHOACAN, Morelia, Michoacan
Benjamin, Vaughn P.
vpbenjamin@cfoadvisors.com, Dir., NEW YORK MEDIA CREDIT GROUP, NY, Buffalo
Benjamin, Wayne ....(504) 826-3267
wbenjamin@timespicayune.com, Vice Pres., Purchasing, The Times Picayune, LA, New Orleans
Benjamin, Jim
jbenjam@utnet.utoledo.edu, Chair, University of Toledo, OH, Toledo
Benke, Louis
louis_benke@techenergy.com, Serv. Mgr., Tech-Energy Co., TX, Cibolo
Benkelman, Susan....................(202) 419-8458
sbenkelman@cq.com, Exec. Ed., News, Congressional Quarterly, Inc., DC, Washington
Benko-Wylie, Mari......................559-735-3211
Controller, Tulare Advance-Register, CA, Visalia
Benko-Wylie, Mari....................(559) 735-3211
accounting@visaliatimesdelta.com, Controller, Visalia Times-Delta, CA, Visalia
Bennett, Jon
jbennett@chronline.com, IT Director, The Chronicle, WA, Centralia
Bennett, Beverly.......................(601) 961-7144
Adv. Pre Prints, The Clarion-Ledger, MS, Jackson
Bennett, David.........................(217) 249-1300
dbennett@il-press.com, Exec. Dir., Illinois Press Advertising Service, IL, Springfield
Bennett, Kerry
kerry@gradingthemovies.com, Reviewer, One Voice Communications, AB, Calgary
Bennett, Chuck 310-540-5511 x6358
chuck.bennett@dailybreeze.com, Visuals, Daily Breeze, CA, Torrance
Bennett, Patricia Work
addup4@yahoo.com, Pres., Listening, Inc., IN, Hobart
Bennett, David.........................(860) 241-6641
dbennett@courant.com, Circ. Vice Pres., The Hartford Courant, CT, Hartford
Bennett, Patty
pbennett@dailyitem.com, Sr. Adv. Mgr., The Daily Item, PA, Sunbury
Bennett, Grace.........................(313) 222-5976
gbennett@freepress.com, Administrative Mgr., Detroit Free Press, MI, Detroit
Bennett, Beth 608-283-7621
Beth.Bennett@WNAnews.com, WNA Executive Director, Wisconsin Newspaper Association
Bennett, James........................(661) 395-7365
jbennett@bakersfield.com, Asst. Mng. Ed., Design/Prodn., The Bakersfield Californian, CA, Bakersfield
Bennett, Becky.........................(717) 262-4813
bbennett@publicopinionnews.com, Editor,

Public Opinion, PA, Chambersburg
Bennett, Mark ext. 377
mark.bennett@tribstar.com, Columnist, The Tribune Star, IN, Terre Haute
Bennett, Susan
news@freedomforum.org, Vice Pres., Mktg., Freedom Forum, DC, Washington
Bennett, Deborah (410) 332-6203
deborah.bennett@baltsun.com, Adv. Dir., Sales Devel./Target Mktg., The Baltimore Sun, MD, Baltimore
Bennett, Charlie
info@valleypressclub.com, Pres., Valley Press Club, Inc., MA, Springfield
Bennett, Brenda ext. 236
brenda.bennett@rockdalecitizen.com, Adv. Dir., The Rockdale Citizen, GA, Conyers
Bennett, Richard
listeninginc@verizon.net, Vice Pres., Listening, Inc., IN, Hobart
Bennett, Brenda ext. 236
brenda.bennett@newcitizen.com, Adv. Dir., The Newton Citizen, GA, Covington
Bennett, Deborah (613) 596-8530
dbennett@thecitizen.southam.ca, Vice Pres., HR/Finance, The Ottawa Citizen, ON, Ottawa
Bennett Harvey, Helen (203) 789-5730
State/City Ed., New Haven Register, CT, New Haven
Benninghoff, Chris
cbenninghoff@sbtinfo.com, Features Ed., South Bend Tribune, IN, South Bend
Benny, Jim
jbenny@thestar.canwest.com, Pub., The Windsor Star, ON, Windsor
Benoit, Caleb (815) 937-3391
cbenoit@daily-journal.com, Asst. Metro Ed., Sports/Innovations, The Daily Journal, IL, Kankakee
Bensman, Robert
bbensman@verafast.com, Pres., Ver-A-Fast Corp., OH, Rocky River
Benson, Randy (318) 487-6431
rbenson@thetowntalk.com, Sports Ed., The Town Talk, LA, Alexandria
Benson, Tim (401) 272-1122
IT director, Creative Circle Media Solutions, RI, East Providence
Benson, Tom (847) 929-1909
bensont@thermalcare.com, Vice Pres., Sales/Mktg., AWS, A Thermal Care Division, IL, Nile
Benson, Robert ext. 3090
rbenson@registerbee.com, Editorial Page Ed., Danville Register & Bee, VA, Danville
Bent, Kevin D. (604) 605-2480
kbent@sunprovince.com, Pres./Pub., The Province, BC, Vancouver
Bent, Rhiannon 435-652-7816
bent@dixie.edu, Dixie State College, UT, Saint George
Bentley, Don
paper@sirinet.net, Co-Ed., The Lawton Constitution, OK, Lawton
Benton, David (704) 261-2235
dbenton@theej.com, Prodn. Mgr., Pressroom, The Enquirer-Journal, NC, Monroe
Benton, Darrell (310) 328-8577
orders@diversifiedphoto.com, Pres., Diversified Photo/Graphics Supply, CA, Gardena
Benton, Melinda (541) 440-4687
Umpqua Cmty. College, OR, Roseburg
Bentz, Bob 610-254-7191
bobb@advancedtele.com, Director of Marketing, Advanced Telecom Services, Inc. (Canada), PA, Wayne
Bentzen, Claire (519) 894-2250 ext. 2503
cbentzen@therecord.com, Dir., Finance, The Record, ON, Kitchener
Bentzen, Jarle 6981 6158
smaa@online.no, Ed. in Chief, OEVRE SMAALENENE, Askim
Benz, Todd 336-506-3020
tbenz@thetimesnews.com, Circ. Dir., Times-News, NC, Burlington
Beoletto, Bernard (309) 820-3270
bbeoletto@pantagraph.com, Adv. Mgr., Classified Sales, The Pantagraph, IL, Bloomington
Berard-Quelin, Marianne
redaccom@sgpresse.fr, Pub. Ed., CORRESPONDANCE DE LA PRESSE, Paris
Berard-Quelin, Marianne
sgp@sgpresse.fr, Pres./Pub. Dir., CORRESPONDANCE ECONOMIQUE, Paris
Berard-Quelin, Marianne
mbq@sgpresse.fr, Pres., CORRESPONDANCE DE LA PUBLICITE, Paris
Berardi, Robert
robtberardi@yahoo.com, Creator/Owner, No Rodeo, NY, Brewster
Berberoglu, Enis
eberberoglu@hurriyet.com.tr, Ed. in Chief, HURRIYET
Berblinger, Gary (573) 431-2010 ext. 136
gberblinger@dailyjournalonline.com, Pub., Daily Journal, MO, Park Hills
Bercun Melnic, Mauricio
heraldoleon@heraldo-adi.com.mx, Pres., El Heraldo de Irapuato, Irapuato, Guanajuato
Bercun Melnic, Mauricio
heraldo@heraldosa.com, Pres., El Heraldo, Aguascalientes, Aguascalientes
Berczuk, Robert
rberczuk@njherald.com, Mng. Ed., New Jersey Herald, NJ, Newton
Berdayes, Manny
mberdayes@thesunnews.com, Vice Pres., Finance, The Sun News, SC, Myrtle Beach
Berenson, Kay
kberenson@recorder.com, Editorial Bd., The Recorder, MA, Greenfield
Beretownier, Jean Michel
jmberetownier@lavoixdunord.fr, Ed., LA VOIX DU NORD, Lille
Berez, Ignacio
ncdigital@nortecastilla.es, Mng. Dir., El Norte De Castilla, Valladolid
Berg, Barry (561) 820-4650
bberg@pbpost.com, Circ. Vice Pres., The Palm Beach Post, FL, West Palm Beach
Berg, Paal A.
redaksjonen@haugesunds-avis.no, Ed., HAUGESUNDS AVIS, Haugesund
Berg, Hanna Relling
hanna.relling.berg@smp.no, Ed., SUNNMORSPOSTEN, Alesund
Berg, Brandon 715-738-1641
brandon.berg@lee.net, sports editor, The Chippewa Herald, WI, Chippewa Falls
Berg, Rich
rberg@mva.com, Nat'l Sales Mgr., MicroVoice Applications, Inc., MN, Minneapolis
Berg, Carl
carlb@metrosn.com, Sr. Vice Pres./Midwest Sales Dir., Metro-Puck Comics Network - Chicago, IL, IL, Chicago
Berg, Carl (603) 578-9780
cez_berg@compuserve.com, Pres., Computerease Software, Inc., NH, Nashua
Bergdahl, Karin Rosencrantz
karin.rosencrantz@daltid.se, Ed. in Chief, NYA LUDVIKA TIDNING, Ludvika
Berge, Sara Vanden
sara.vandenberge@empiretribune.com, Mng. Ed., Stephenville Empire-Tribune, TX, Stephenville
Bergen, Lori
bergen@txstate.edu, Prof./Dir., Texas State University-San Marcos, TX, San Marcos
Berger, Betsy (206) 768-6477
South Seattle Cmty. College, WA, Seattle
Berger, Bill 512 407 8283
billberger@austin.rr.com, Pres., Associated Texas Newspapers, Inc., TX, Austin
Berger, Tim (626) 962-8811 ext. 2131
tim.berger@sgvn.com, Visuals Ed., The Whittier Daily News, CA, Whittier
Berger, Teufel
fibersplastics@teufelberger.com, Owner, Teufelberger GmbH, Wels
Berghaus, Bob (828) 232-5866
bberghau@citizen-times.com, Sports Ed., The Asheville Citizen-Times, NC, Asheville
Bergin, Mary (608) 274-8925
info@roadstraveled.com, Columnist, Midwest Features Syndicate, WI, Madison
Bergknut, Per
debatt@news.arbetet.se, Mng. Dir., Nya Arbetet AB, Goteborg
Bergmam, Sture
sture.bergmam@kuriren.com, Ed. in Chief, NORRBOTTENS-KURIREN, Lulea
Bergman, Micheal
m.bergman@parool.nl, Adv. Mgr., HET PAROOL, Amsterdam
Bergman, Julie (218) 230-8943
julie@wiktel.com, Senior Associate-Midwest, Grimes, W.B. & Co., MD, Gaithersburg
Bergmark, Torbjorn
info@vk.se, Ed. in Chief, VASTERBOTTENS-KURIREN, Umea
Bergmeier, Dave (785) 263-1000
publisher@abilene-rc.com, Editorial Page Ed., Abilene Reflector-Chronicle, KS, Abilene
Bergo, Olav Terje
bergo@ba.no, Ed. in Chief, BERGENSAVISEN, Bergen
Bergstrom, Tony
tony.bergstrom@ljp.se, Adv. Mgr., LJUSDALSPOSTEN, Ljusdal
Berkan, Ismet
ismet.berkan@radikal.com.tr, Ed., YENI ASIR, Beste
Berkowitz, Roberta
mail@ngscorp.com, Vice Pres.-Nat'l Accts./Opns., National Graphic Supply Corp., NY, Albany
Berky, H. Charles 561-212-1219
pageboca@aol.com, Pres., C. Berky & Associates, Inc., FL, Boca Raton
Berky, H. Charles
pageboca@aol.com, Pres., C. Berky & Associates, Inc., FL, Boca Raton
Berlinski, John
cotidian@moldova-suverana.md, Ed. in Chief, MOLDOVA SUVERANA, Kishinev
Bermamm Oliva, Mario Augusto 221-7008
Ed., Diario de Montes Claros, Montes Claros, Minas Gerais
Berman, Brian L.
brains@voiceworld.com, Pres./Founder, VoiceWorld, Inc., AZ, Scottsdale
Berman, Brian L.
brains@voiceworld.com, Pres., VoiceWorld, AZ, Scottsdale
Bermudez, Lendy 41-1977
elregionalredac@iamnet.com, Gen. Mgr., EL REGIONAL DEL ZULIA, Ciudad Ojeda, Zulia
Bernal, Luis Alejandro
lbernal@elimparcial.com, Gen Mgr., El Imparcial, Hermosillo, Sonora
Bernal Lozolla, Osvaldo
solmaz@red.2000.com.mx, Ed./Dir., EL SOL DEL PACIFICO, Mazatlan, Sinaloa
Bernard, Daniel
d.bernard@wsj.com, Gen Mgr., The Wall Street Journal-Eastern Edition, NY, New York
Bernard, Jim (612) 673-4477
jim.bernard@startribune.com, Sr. VP Digital, Star Tribune, MN, Minneapolis
Bernard, Daniel
d.bernard@wsj.com, Gen. Mgr., The Wall Street Journal-Central Edition, IL, Chicago
Bernard, Tom
sales@bersearch.com, Pres., Bersearch Information Services, CO, Breckenridge
Berner, Fred A.
adj@dwave.net, Ed., Antigo Daily Journal, WI, Antigo
Berner, Marie
adj@dwave.net, Pub., Antigo Daily Journal, WI, Antigo
Bernfalk, Lasse
lasse.bernfalk@kristianstadsbladet.se, Ed. in Chief, KRISTIANSTADSBLADET, Kristianstad
Bernhard, Leslie
leslie@adstar.com, Pres./CEO, AdStar, Inc., CA, Marina del Rey
Bernhardsson, Bo
centralred@arbetet.se, Ed. in Chief, Official Journal of the Labour Party, Malmo
Bernick, Bob (801) 237-2111
bbjr@desnews.com, Political Ed., Deseret News, UT, Salt Lake City
Bernier, Sandra (601) 636-4545 ext. 120
sbernier@vicksburgpost.com, Admin. Mgr., The Vicksburg Post, MS, Vicksburg
Bernstein, Dan (951) 782-7532
dbernstein@pe.com, Columnist, The Press-Enterprise, CA, Riverside
Bernstein, Ron
sales@compuserve.com, Vice Pres., Adv. Sales, CompuServe Interactive Services, Inc., OH, Columbus
Bernstein-Chargin, Jan (408) 848-4724
Gavilan College, CA, Gilroy
Bernt, Joseph (740) 593-2589
Prof./Assoc. Dir., Grad. Studies/Research, Ohio University, OH, Athens
Bernthal, Ron (845) 292-3071
ronbernthal@wjffradio.org, Self-Syndicator, Travel/Historic Preservation Audio Programs, Ron Bernthal, NY, Hurleyville
Berrian, Lisa 478-744-4245
lberrian@macon.com, Adv. Mgr., Retail, The Telegraph, GA, Macon
Berriman, Mark
mberriman@acnpapers.com, Pub., Stillwater Gazette, MN, Stillwater
Berrios, Fernando (504) 2553-3101
Carlos.Flores@elheraldo.hn, El Heraldo, San Pedro Sula
Carlos.Flores@elheraldo.hn, Diez, San Pedro Sula
Carlos.Flores@elheraldo.hn, La Prensa, San Pedro Sula
Berroa Loo, Gerardo
periodistas@laestrella.com.pa, Dir., LA ESTRELLA DE PANAMA, Panama City
Berry, Dave (903) 596-6238
dvberry@tylerpaper.com, Mng. Ed., Tyler Morning Telegraph, TX, Tyler
Berry, Peter L. (570) 420-4372
pberry@poconorecord.com, Adv. Dir., Pocono Record, PA, Stroudsburg
Berry, Lynn (575) 763-3431
lberry@cnjonline.com, Interim Circulation Director, Clovis News Journal, NM, Clovis
Berry, Dave
daveb@cpimo.com, Nixa Xpress, MT, Nixa
daveb@cpimo.com, Vice Pres., Community Publishers, Inc., AR, Bentonville
Berry, Ivy (208) 542-6710
iberry@postregister.com, Dir. Bus. Admin., Post Register, ID, Idaho Falls
Berry, Michele
editor@borgernewsherald.com, Ed., Borger News-Herald, TX, Borger
Berta, Steve (330) 996-3569
sberta@thebeaconjournal.com, Bus. Ed., Akron Beacon Journal, OH, Akron
Berta, Steve (317) 444-6280
steve.berta@indystar.com, Asst. Mng. Ed., Bus., The Indianapolis Star, IN, Indianapolis
Bertetto, Jennifer
jbertetto@tribweb.com, Adv. Dir., Valley News Dispatch, PA, Tarentum
Berthiaume, Ed ext. 213
eberthiaume@postcrescent.com, Custom Publishing Sr. Ed., The Post-Crescent, WI, Appleton
Berting, Bob (317) 536-5408
bob@bobberting.com, Pres., Berting Communications, IN, Indianapolis
Bertoglio, John
bertoglio@pulseresearch.com, CIO, Pulse Research, Inc., OR, Portland
Bertolotti, Joseph
mbertol@us.ibm.com, Program Dir., GLBT Sales/Talent, IBM Corp., NY, Somers
Berton, Paul
pberton@lfpress.com, Ed. in Chief, The London Free Press, ON, London
Bertrand, Guy (250) 364-1242 ext. 211
editor@trailtimes.ca, Editor, Trail Daily Times, BC, Trail
Berzanskis, Cheryl (806) 345-3335
cheryl.berzanskis@amarillo.com, Real Estate Ed., Amarillo Globe-News, TX, Amarillo
Bes, John
redactie@bndestem.nl, Ed., BN DESTEM, Breda
Besley, Glen
gbesley@lfpress.com, Mgmt. Info Servs. Mgr., The London Free Press, ON, London
Bessengleng, A.
a.bessengleng@brabantsdagblad.wegener.nl, Ed., BRABANTS DAGBLAD, S-Hertogenbosch
Best, Justin (425) 339-3448
jbest@heraldnet.com, Photo Ed., The Herald, WA, Everett
Best, Michael
wb@westfalen-blatt.de, Bus. Mgr., WESTFALEN-BLATT, Bielefeld

Betancor Brito, Santiago
diario@editorialprensacanaria.es, Dir., DIARIO DE LAS PALMAS, Las Palmas de Gran Canaria, Las Palmas
Betancourt, Ismael E. 257 2003
Gen. Mgr., El Mundo S.A., Loja
Betancourt, Selma ....(917) 339-0804
Dir., Commun./Mktg., Hoy, NY, New York
Betz, Emily ....(515) 628-5239
Central College, IA, Pella
Betz, Dr. Esther
info@rp-online.de, Proprietor, RHEINISCHE POST, Dusseldorf
Beveridge, Lici ....(601) 584-3104
Online Ed., Hattiesburg American, MS, Hattiesburg
Bevins, Evan
ebevins@mariettatimes.com, News Ed., The Marietta Times, OH, Marietta
Bhalia, Anil
info@minacs.com, COO, Minacs Worldwide, Inc., ON, Toronto
Bhatia, Peter..........................(503) 221-8393
pbhatia@news.oregonian.com, Ed., The Oregonian, OR, Portland
Bhatt, Nimit ....(410) 455-1261
Univ. of Maryland Baltimore County, MD, Baltimore
Bhuiyan, Serajul
sbhuiyan@lincoln.edu, Prof./Dir., Lincoln University of the Commonwealth of Pennsylvania, PA, Lincoln University
Bialey, Roger
bailey@ndna.com, Exec. Dir., North Dakota Advertising Service, ND, Bismarck
Bialo, Ellen
ebialo@iesdinc.com, Pres., Interactive Educational Systems Design, Inc., NY, New York
Biavardi, Andrea...............................77-681
Mgr., IL GIORNO, Milan
Bibs, Tom..................................(540) 374-5490
tbibs@freelancestar.com, Circ. Dir., The Free Lance-Star, VA, Fredericksburg
Bichara Nicolas, Alberto
chanarcillo@enteiney.net, Pres., Chanarcillo, Copiapo
Bickel, Mark ....(239) 344-0347
mbickel@news-press.com, Digital Ed., The News-Press, FL, Fort Myers
Bickel, Rich
rbickel@times-standard.com, Photo Ed., Times-Standard, CA, Eureka
Bickert, Tom................(724) 775-3200 ext. 155
tbickert@timesonline.com, Mng. Ed., Content, Beaver County Times, PA, Beaver
Bieberly, Clifford
cbieberl@chaminade.edu, Dir., Chaminade, University of Honolulu, HI, Honolulu
Biekkola, Jennifer...................(906) 483-2260
jennbiekkola@mininggazette.com, Circ. Mgr., The Daily Mining Gazette, MI, Houghton
Bielema, Charlene
cbielema@clintonherald.com, Ed., Clinton Herald, IA, Clinton
Biella, Antonio
cdg@corgiorno.it, MD, CORRIERE DEL GIORNO, Taranto
Biere, Steve
steve.biere@lee.net, Regional Circulation Manager, Independent Record, MT, Helena
Bierl, Chris
cbierl@minotdailynews.com, Sports Ed., Minot Daily News, ND, Minot
Biermann, Tom ....(307) 266-0526
tom.biermann@trib.com, Circ. Dir, Casper Star-Tribune, WY, Casper
Bigelow, Bill ....(541) 383-0359
bbigelow@bendbulletin.com, Sports Ed., The Bulletin, OR, Bend
Bigelow, Chandler
cbigelow@tribune.com, CFO, Tribune Co., IL, Chicago
Bigelow, Renee........................(504) 826-3121
rbigelow@timespicayune.com, Vice Pres., Mktg., The Times Picayune, LA, New Orleans
Biggam, Jamie................................ext. 1156
jamie.biggam@timesargus.com, Sports Ed., The Times Argus, VT, Barre
Biggin, Chloe
cos@thecourier.com.au, Chief of Staff, THE BALLARAT COURIER
Bilas, Francisco 266-9773
Ed., Editora Verdes Mares Ltd., Fortaleza, Ceara
Bilbney, Greg ....ext. 111
gbilbneynews@robdailynews.com, Ed., Daily News, IL, Robinson
Bilbow, Leonarda..........................ext. 2067
News Ed., The Citizens' Voice, PA, Wilkes-Barre
Bilgin, Dinc
bilgi.eser@sabah.com.tr, Pub./Owner, SABAH
bilgi.eser@sabah.com.tr, Pub., SABAH
bilgi.eser@sabah.com.tr, Pub., SABAH
bilgi.eser@sabah.com.tr, Pub./Owner, SABAH
bilgi.eser@sabah.com.tr, Pub., YENI ASIR
bilgi.eser@sabah.com.tr, Pub./Owner, YENI ASIR
Bilgin, Onay 448 8000
Pub., BUGUN
Owner/Pub., BUGUN
Pub., BUGUN
Bill, David ....(706) 208-2352
david.bill@onlineathens.com, Online Ed., Athens Banner-Herald, GA, Athens
Billesimo, Traci J.
tbillesimo@tsvmedia.net, Financial Mgr., Eagle Times, NH, Claremont
Billiel, Jeff
jbilliel@sdnccg.com, Exec. Editor, The Sidney Daily News, OH, Sidney
Billings, Robert.......................(903) 237-7774
bbillings@coxnews.com, Prodn. Dir., Longview News-Journal, TX, Longview
Billings, Melissa ....(603) 543-3100 ext. 129
mbillings@tsvmedia.net, Mktg. Mgr., Eagle Times, NH, Claremont
Billings, Glynna ....(559) 441-6260
gbillings@fresnobee.com, Controller, The Fresno Bee, CA, Fresno
Bilyeu, Hank
editor@hopewellnews.com, Sports Ed., The Hopewell News, VA, Hopewell
Bina, Don
sales@ramseytsr.com, Mktg. Commun. Mgr., Ramsey (A Thermo Sentron Co.), MN, Minneapolis
Bingaman, Tim ....(314) 966-7711
info@cvcaudit.com, Pres./CEO, Circulation Verification Council, MO, Saint Louis
Bingle, Jerry ....(574) 936-3101
jbingle@thepilotnews.com, Gen. Mgr., Pilot News, IN, Plymouth
Bintliff, Valerie ....(806) 345-3333
valerie.bentliff@amarillo.com, Personnel Dir., Amarillo Globe-News, TX, Amarillo
Biondi, Chris ....(508) 626-3923
jdwindell@cnc.com, Mng. Ed., Metrowest Daily News, MA, Framingham
Birch, Timothy J. ....ext. 4120
tbirch@phillyburbs.com, Adv. Dir., Bucks County Courier Times, PA, Levittown
Birch, Simon ....(209) 369-2761 ext. 261
projects@lodinews.com, Mgr., Internet Servs., Lodi News-Sentinel, CA, Lodi
Birch, Tonya............................(505) 564-4501
jamesw@daily-times.com, Adv. Coord., Design, The Daily Times, NM, Farmington
Bird, Micheal
post-journal@oweb.com, Pub., The Post-Journal, NY, Jamestown
Bird, Jared ....(801) 625-4388
jbird@standard.net, Adv. Mgr., Display, Standard-Examiner, UT, Ogden
Bird, Henry
rdavis@pulitzer.net, Vice Pres. & Pres./Pub., The Pantagraph, Pulitzer Newspapers, Inc., MO, Saint Louis
Birdsong, Hasanna...................(610) 867-5000
hbirdsong@express-times.com, Retail Sales Mgr., Bethlehem, The Express-Times, PA, Easton
Birkland, Jasmine....................(360) 417-7690
jasmine.birkland@peninsuladailynews.com, Circulation Marketing Assistant, Peninsula Daily News, WA, Port Angeles
Birks, Debbie ....(610) 622-8855
dbirks@journalregister.com, Controller, Delaware County Daily Times, PA, Primos
Birmingham, Patrick J................(361) 886-3780
birminghamp@caller.com, Pres./Pub., Corpus Christi Caller-Times, TX, Corpus Christi
Biro, Christoph
christoph.biro@kronezeitung.at, Ed. in Chief, STEIRERKRONE: NEUE KRONEN ZEITUNG, Graz
Birolini, John ....(617) 929-8373
j_birolini@globe.com, Adv. Div. Mgr., Automotive, The Boston Globe, MA, Boston
Birrell, Lisa ....(559) 441-6074
lbirrell@fresnobee.com, Circ. Mgr., Mktg., The Fresno Bee, CA, Fresno
Bischof, Greg..................................ext. 7244
Farm Reporter, Texarkana Gazette, TX, Texarkana
Bischos, Tre
publisher@ennisdailynews.com, Pres, Ennis Daily News, TX, Ennis
Bish, Tammy ....ext. 235
tbish@tribweb.com, Bus. Mgr., Leader Times, PA, Kittanning
Bishop, Bojinka.......................(740) 593-2675
Assoc. Prof., Ohio University, OH, Athens
Bishop, Peter
pbishop@thestar.ca, VP & CFO, Toronto Star, ON, Toronto
Bishop, Melody........................(256) 740-5800
melody.bishop@timesdaily.com, Adv. Dir., TimesDaily, AL, Florence
Bishop, Barbara ....(732) 906-2020
bbishop@cascadetechnologies.com, Sales, Cascade Technologies, Inc., NJ, Somerset
Bishop, Chris ....(609) 871-8112
cbishop@phillyburbs.com, Bus. Ed., Burlington County Times, NJ, Willingboro
Bissbort, Leigh Ann..................(817) 379-5960
bissatpti@aol.com, Bus. Mgr., Printing Technology, Inc., TX, Keller
Bissett, Kevin ....(506) 457-0746
kevin.bissett@thecanadianpress.com, New Brunswick Correspondent, Broadcast News Limited, NB, Fredericton
kevin.bissett@thecanadianpress.com, Correspondent, Canadian Press, The - Fredericton, NB, NB, Fredericton
Bittick, Paul ....(805) 756-2537
pbittick@calpoly.edu, GM, California Polytechnic State Univ., CA, San Luis Obispo
Bittner, Drew ....(419) 238-2285 ext. 215
sports@timesbulletin.com, Sports Ed., The Times Bulletin, OH, Van Wert
Bitu, Mercar
red@tribuna.ro, Ed. in Chief, TRIBUNA, Sibiu
Bitzer, John F............................(609) 272-7000
Pres./CEO, The Press of Atlantic City, NJ, Pleasantville
Bivona, Dwayne........................940-720-3491
bivonad@timesrecordnews.com, Publisher, Wichita Falls Times Record News, TX, Wichita Falls
Bizzotto, Anita J.
abizzott@emai.usps.gov, CMO, United States Postal Service, DC, Washington
Bjerager, Erik
bjerager@kristeligt-dagblad.dk, Ed., KRISTELIGT DAGBLAD, Copenhagen, Sjaelland
Bjorgulv, Braanen
bjorgulv.braanen@klassekampen.no, Pub., KLASSEKAMPEN, Oslo
Bjork, Michelle
bjorkm@phillynews.com, Asst. Mng. Ed., Opns., The Philadelphia Daily News, PA, Philadelphia
Bjork, Becky
becky.bjork@svherald.com, Adv. Dir., Sierra Vista Herald, AZ, Sierra Vista
Bjorklund, Steven ....(425) 892-1093
steve@bjmach.com, Pres., H & M Paster Sales & Service, Inc., WA, Woodinville
BjÃ£rklund, Margareta
nyheter@vasabladet.fi, Ed., VASABLADET, Vasa
Black, Jo Dee..........................406-791-6502
Business Editor, Great Falls Tribune, MT, Great Falls
Black, Roger ....(518) 565-4122
rblack@pressrepublican.com, Webmaster, Press-Republican, NY, Plattsburgh
Black, David
dblack@edmsun.com, Pub., The Edmonton Sun, AB, Edmonton
Black, Don
dblack@laramieboomerang.com, Pub., Laramie Daily Boomerang, WY, Laramie
Black, Curtis 406-243-4314
Business manager, Univ. of Montana, MT, Missoula
Black, Gordon R. ....(541) 383-0339
gblack@bendbulletin.com, Pub., The Bulletin, OR, Bend
Black, Jason ....(724) 626-3534
jblack@tribweb.com, Sports Ed., Daily Courier, PA, Connellsville
Black, Peter D...............................ext. 2802
pblack@bpaww.com, Sr. Vice Pres., Bus. Devel., BPA Worldwide, CT, Shelton
pblack@bpaww.com, Sr. Vice Pres., Mktg. Servs., BPA Worldwide, CT, Shelton
Black, Marty ....(808) 690-8849
mblack@staradvertiser.com, Production Director, Honolulu Star-Advertiser, HI, Honolulu
Black, Peter ....ext. 2802
pblack@bpaww.com, Sr. Vice Pres., Mktg. Servs., BPA Worldwide, CT, Shelton
Black, Gordon R. ....(541) 383-0339
gblack@bendbulletin.com, Pres., Western Communications, Inc., OR, Bend
Black, JoEllen
publisher@richmond-dailynews.com, Pub., The Daily News, MO, Richmond
Blackburn, Gary ....(812) 385-2525
gblack@pdclarion.com, Pub., Princeton Daily Clarion, IN, Princeton
Blackburn, Gary
gblack@pdclarion.com, Pres., Princeton Publishing Co., Inc., IN, Princeton
Blackledge, Karen
kblackledge@dailyitem.com, Reporter, The Danville News, PA, Danville
Blackman, Bob
news@muscatinejournal.com, Pub., Muscatine Journal, IA, Muscatine
Blackstock, Joe........................(909) 483-9382
j_blackstock@dailybulletin.com, Asst. City Ed., Los Angeles Co., Inland Valley Daily Bulletin, CA, Ontario
Blackwell, Mary Alice ....(434) 978-7242
mblackwell@dailyprogress.com, Features Ed., The Daily Progress, VA, Charlottesville
Blackwell, Teresa ....(804) 775-8297
Circ. Mgr., Single Copy, Richmond Times-Dispatch, VA, Richmond
Blackwell, Mike ....(805) 437-0240
mblackwell@venturacountystar.com, Asst. Mng. Ed., Ventura County Star, CA, Camarillo
Blaesser, Mike..........................(831) 429-2417
mblaesser@santacruzsentinel.com, Opns. Dir., Santa Cruz Sentinel, CA, Scotts Valley
Blagg, Brenda ....(479) 872-5189
bblagg@nwaonline.net, Political Ed., The Morning News of Northwest Arkansas, AR, Springdale
Blair, Will
will@newnan.com, Copy Ed., The Times-Herald, GA, Newnan
Blair, Skyler.............................(657) 278-5815
California State Univ., CA, Fullerton
Blair, Jerry ....(540) 574-6279
jblair@dnronline.com, Night News Ed., Daily News-Record, VA, Harrisonburg
Blair, Gary.................................(419) 724-6258
gblair@toledoblade.com, Pres., Block Communications, Inc., OH, Toledo
Blair, Kelly
sports@camdenarknews.com, Sports Ed., Camden News, AR, Camden
Blair, Kirk ....ext. 5304
kblair@texarkanagazette.com, Mktg. Dir., Texarkana Gazette, TX, Texarkana
Blair, Jan ....(815) 232-0188
jablair@rrstar.com, Circ. Mgr., The Journal-Standard, IL, Freeport
Blair, Paula ....ext. 169
paula.blair@duncanbanner.com, Adv. Mgr., Classified, The Duncan Banner, OK, Duncan
Blair, LouAnn
circulation@portsmouth-dailytimes.com, Circ. Mgr., The Portsmouth Daily Times, OH, Portsmouth
Blais, Rich
sales@beltcorp.com, Sales Mgr., Belt Corporation of America, GA, Cumming
Blake, Melissa ....(815) 825-2086 ext. 3450
Kishwaukee College, IL, Malta
Blakeley, Eddie ....(606) 326-2601
publisher@dailyindependent.com, Pub., The

Daily Independent, KY, Ashland
Blakemore, John S.
johnb@stephens.edu, Chair, Stephens College, MO, Columbia
Blakley, Stewart
sblakley@lib.brenau.edu, Chair, Brenau University, GA, Gainesville
Blanchard, Dean
dblanchard@theadvocate.com, Circ. Dir., The Advocate, LA, Baton Rouge
Blanchet, Maurice
mblanchet@gsptoday.com, Vice Pres., GSP, Inc., RI, Westerly
Blanco, Freddy 22-8817
Gen. Mgr., La Voz De Guarenas, Guarenas, Miranda
Blane, Miriam
miriam@superiorlithoplate.com, Office Mgr., Superior Lithoplate of Indiana, Inc., IN, Rockville
Blane, Robert T.
robert@superiorlithoplate.com, Pres., Superior Lithoplate of Indiana, Inc., IN, Rockville
Blane, Steven C.
steve@superiorlithoplate.com, Vice Pres., Superior Lithoplate of Indiana, Inc., IN, Rockville
Blaner, David
dblainer@acba.org, Exec. Dir., Pittsburgh Legal Journal
Blankenship, Jim....................(479) 571-6470
jblankenship@nwanews.com, Adv. Dir., Sales/Mktg., Northwest Arkansas Times, AR, Fayetteville
Blansett, Brian
bblansett@okpress.com, Adv. Dir., Oklahoma Press Service, OK, Oklahoma City
Blasco, Isaac
blasco@abc.es, Dir., ABC, Valencia
Blaser, Chris ....(415) 777-6450
Vice Pres., Circ., San Francisco Chronicle, CA, San Francisco
Blasick, Marty
mb@motioncity.com, Composer/Audio Engineer, Motion City Films, CA, Santa Monica
Blaskey, Lawrence L.
publisher@douglasdispatch.com, Editorial Page Ed., The Daily Dispatch, AZ, Douglas
Blaszkiewicz, Robert ....(219) 762-4334
robertb@nwitimes.com, Gen. Mgr., Portage, The Times, IN, Munster
Blatchford, Barbara ....(250) 368-8551 ext. 200
publisher@trailtimes.ca, Publisher, Trail Daily Times, BC, Trail
Blaufelder, Amy
ablaufelder@kspress.com, Acct., Kansas Press Association, KS, Topeka
Blevins, Ken ....(910) 343-2375
ken.blevins@starnewsonline.com, Deputy Photo Ed., Star-News, NC, Wilmington
Blevins, Lynn
lynnb@commpub.com, Television/Film Ed., Harrison Daily Times, AR, Harrison
Blevins, Kevin ....(306) 781-5408
kblevins@leaderpost.canwest.com, Deputy Ed., Online, The Leader-Post, SK, Regina
Blevins, Keith....................334-293-5800
kblevins@cnhi.com, Executive VP/COO, Community Newspaper Holdings, Inc., AL, Montgomery
Blevins, Chuck
crblevins@aol.com, Pres., Chuck Blevins & Assoc., FL, Naple
Blewett, Steve
steve.blewett@mailserver.ewu.edu, Dir./Prof., Eastern Washington University, WA, Spokane
Blick, Thomas Edward
blick@latech.edu, Head, Louisiana Tech University, LA, Ruston
Bliss, Sidney H.
sbliss@gazetteextra.com, CEO/Pub., The Janesville Gazette, WI, Janesville
Bliss, Sidney H.
sbliss@gazetteextra.com, Pres./Chrmn./CEO, Bliss Communications, Inc., WI, Janesville
Bliss, Richard
rbliss@quickwire.com, Integrator, Quickwire Labs, ON, Hamilton
Blizzard, Andy 937-225-2026
ablizzard@coxohiomedia.com, Vice President, Publishing Sales, Dayton Daily News, OH, Dayton
Block, Diana
dblock@post-gazette.com, Co-Pub., The Blade, OH, Toledo
Block, Paul....................518-454-5787
pblock@timesunion.com, Online Executive Producer, Times Union, NY, Albany
Block, Diana
dblock@post-gazette.com, Co-Pub., Pittsburgh Post-Gazette, PA, Pittsburgh
Block, John Robinson ....(419) 724-6176
johnrblock@theblade.com, Ed. in Chief, The Blade, OH, Toledo
Blonde, Scott 239-574-1110
sblonde@breezenewspapers.com, Saturday Breeze, FL, Cape Coral
sblonde@breezenewspapers.com, Publisher, Cape Coral Breeze, FL, Cape Coral
Bloom, Karen
karenb@kpcnews.net, Adv. Dir., Herald-Republican, IN, Angola
Bloom, Karen
karenb@kpcnews.net, Adv. Dir., The Star, IN, Auburn
Bloom, David ....(281) 425-8016
david.bloom@baytownsun.com, Mng. Ed., The Baytown Sun, TX, Baytown
Bloom, Bob....................(765) 420-5249
bbloom@journalandcourier.com, Copy Ed., Journal and Courier, IN, Lafayette
Bloomfield, Michelle L.....................ext. 241
News Ed., The Hickory Daily Record, NC, Hickory
Bloor, Jep ....ext. 109
advertising@sanduskyregister.com, Adv. Mgr., Retail, Sandusky Register, OH, Sandusky
Blose, F. Len....................(330) 841-1670
lenblose@tribtoday.com, Gen. Mgr., The Tribune Chronicle, OH, Warren
Blount, Christina
cblount@itemonline.com, Mailroom Manager, The Huntsville Item, TX, Huntsville
Blount, Thomas L. ....(336) 888-3543
tblount@hpe.com, Columnist, High Point Enterprise, NC, High Point
Blount, Donald W.
dblount@recordnet.com, Mng. Editor, The Record, CA, Stockton
Blubaugh, Bob ....(410) 857-7895
Sports Ed., Carroll County Times, MD, Westminster
Blum, Mark....................(717) 240-7110
mblum@cumberlink.com, Pub., The Sentinel, PA, Carlisle
Blum, Joel
info@pacedesign.com, Creative Dir., Pace Design Group, CA, San Francisco
Blumsack, Bill..............(781) 255-7773 ext. 16
billblumsack@syndicatedadfeatures.com, Vice Pres./Eastern Regl. Sales Dir., Syndicated Ad Features, Inc., MA
Bluner, Lelani....................(714) 796-3530
lbluner@ocregister.com, Vice Pres., Mktg, The Orange County Register, CA, Santa Ana
Blunt, Ann
ann.blunt@lee.net, Adv. Dir., The Columbus Telegram, NE, Columbus
Blurton, Kevin 256-740-5786
kevin.blurton@timesdaily.com, Prod. Dir., TimesDaily, AL, Florence
Blystone, Chuck ....(309) 820-3248
cblystone@pantagraph.com, Features Ed., The Pantagraph, IL, Bloomington
Blyth, Jeffrey....................(212) 873-0772
itpnyc@aol.com, Chief Ed., Interpress of London and New York, NY, New York
Boabentuda, Egivaldo
wgasino@grupoatarde.com.br, Pub., Empresa Editora A Tarde S.A., Salvador, Bahia
Board, Fred
fredboard@dailybulletin.com, Gen. Mgr., Inland Vision, CA, Woodland Hills
Boath, Kim ....(203) 330-6267
kboath@ctpost.com, Adv. Mgr., Retail, Connecticut Post, CT, Bridgeport
Bober, Andrzej
zycie@zw.com.pl, Ed. in Chief, ZYCIE WARSZAWY, Warsaw
Boberg, James
jboberg@forumcomm.com, Gen. Mgr., InForum, ND, Fargo
Boberg, Anders
anders.boberg @ folket.se, Mktg. Dir., FOLKET, Eskilstuna
Boccardo de Britos, Maria E.
hoycanelones@hoycanelones.com.uy, Pres., Hoy Canelones, Canelones
Bock, Jeff....................(310) 441-7400
jeff@ercboxoffice.com, Box Office Analyst, Exhibitor Relations Co., CA, Los Angeles
Bock, David
dbock@hawaiitribune-herald.com, Ed., Hawaii Tribune-Herald, HI, Hilo
Bodde, Bert
b.bodde@tctubantia.nl, Adv. Mgr., TWENTSCHE COURANT, Enschede
Boden, Dave
dboden@newstribune.info, Pub., Mineral Daily News-Tribune, WV, Keyser
Bodette, John L.
jbodette@stcloud.gannett.com, Mng. Ed., St. Cloud Times, MN, Saint Cloud
Bodner, Sherman 607-271-8210
sbodner@gannett.com, President & Publisher, Star-Gazette, NY, Elmira
Bodner, Sherman 607-798-1111
sbodner@gannett.com, Pub., Press & Sun-Bulletin, NY, Binghamton
Bodner, Sherman 607-274-9252
sbodner@gannett.com, Pub., The Ithaca Journal, NY, Ithaca
Boduroglu, Sevda
tana.schultheis@dogan-media.com, Mgr., MILLIYET, Walldorf
Boehne, Richard A. ....(513) 977-5150
boehne@scripps.com, Pres., E.W. Scripps, E. W. Scripps Co., OH, Cincinnati
Boer, Georg
boer@derpatriot.de, Adv. Mgr, DER PATRIOT, Lippstadt
Boermann, Johan
juan. boermann@mgl.nl, Dir., LIMBURGS DAGBLAD, Sittard
Bogaczk, Wlodzimierz
adres@gazeta.pl, Ed., GAZETA WYBORCZA, Poznan
Bogan, Mike
mbogan@hearstnp.com, Sports Ed., The Huron Daily Tribune, MI, Bad Axe
Bogart, Doug....................(219) 648-3012
dbogart@post-trib.com, Mgmt. Info Servs. Mgr., Post-Tribune, IN, Merrillville
Bogel, Jeff
sales@pemco.kpl.net, Technical Sales Dir., Pemco, Inc., WI, Sheboygan
Bogen, Norm
sales@sonoranscanners.com, Vice Pres., Sonoran Scanners, Inc., AZ, Tucson
Bogert, John....................310-540-5511 x6663
john.bogert@dailybreeze.com, Columnist, Daily Breeze, CA, Torrance
Boggs, Jerry
jboggs@news-expressky.com, Ed., The Appalachian News-Express, KY, Pikeville
Boggs, Larry..............(724) 775-3200 ext. 221
lboggs@timesonline.com, Circ. Dir., Beaver County Times, PA, Beaver
Boggs, Steve
publisher@carthagepress.com, Publisher, The Carthage Press, MO, Carthage
Bogoni, Euclides....................423-2626
Pres., Diario Noroeste, Paranavai, Parana
Bohan, Mark
mbohan@printing.org, Managing Director, Technical Association of the Graphic Arts, PA, Sewickley
Bohenkamp, John
jbohenkamp@thehawkeye.com, Sports Ed., The Hawk Eye, IA, Burlington
Bohlein, Dawn
dawn@bryantimes.com, Online Mgr., The Bryan Times, OH, Bryan
Bohler, Robert....................(817) 257-6556
Texas Christian Univ., TX, Fort Worth
Bohlke, Klaus 68860
redaktion@boyens-medien.de, Bus. Mgr., DITHMARSCHER LANDESZEITUNG, Heide
Bohn, Brenda....................ext. 1207
brenda.bohn@gwinnettdailypost.com, Adv. Dir., Retail, Gwinnette Daily Post, GA, Lawrenceville
Bohn, Sandra....................ext. 37
sbohn@delphosherald.com, Prodn. Mgr., Graphic Arts, Delphos Daily Herald, OH, Delphos
Bohrer, Dave ....(607) 274-9272
dbohrer@ithaca.gannett.com, Asst. Mng. Ed., The Ithaca Journal, NY, Ithaca
Boiko, Bob
information@chasebobko.com, Pres., Chase Bobko, Inc., WA, Seattle
Boisvert, Louis
louis.boisvert@latribune.qc.ca, Pres./Ed., La Tribune, QC, Sherbrooke
Bok, L. Chip ....(330) 996-3518
cbok@thebeaconjournal.com, Editorial Cartoonist, Akron Beacon Journal, OH, Akron
Bokamper, Jerry W.....................(214) 977-8650
jbokamper@dallasnews.com, Asst. Arts/Entertainment Ed., The Dallas Morning News, TX, Dallas
Boland, Ryan
news@fultonsun.com, Sports Ed., The Fulton Sun, MO, Fulton
Bolas, Rich
rbolas@yourwestvalley.com, Sports Ed., Daily News-Sun, AZ, Sun City
Bolerjack, Bob ....(425) 339-3466
bolerjack@heraldnet.com, Editorial Page Ed., The Herald, WA, Everett
Boles, Durelle
press@gutenberg-press.com, Pres., Gutenberg Printing Press Co., GA, Atlanta
press@gutenberg-press.com, Pres., ONE Corp., GA, Atlanta
press@gutenberg-press.com, Vice Pres., Boles, Morgan & Canino, Inc., AL, Florence
Boles, Carmen....................719-636-0279
carmen.boles@gazette.com, Dir., Interactive Content/Audience Devel., The Gazette, CO, Colorado Springs
Boles, Deana
lori@weinrichadv.com, Exec. Dir., League of Advertising Agencies, Inc., NY, New York
Boles, Lana ....(541) 463-5655
Lane Cmty. College, OR, Eugene
Bolger, Bill ....(317) 444-3889
bill.bolger@indystar.com, Prodn & IT, Vice Pres., The Indianapolis Star, IN, Indianapolis
Bolich, Matt
mbolich@lewistownsentinel.com, Adv. Dir., The Sentinel, PA, Lewistown
Bolick, Elaine ....(704) 261-2206
ebolick@theej.com, Nat'l Adv. Sales, The Enquirer-Journal, NC, Monroe
Bolinger, Vickie....................ext. 1198
vickie.bolinger@uniontrib.com, Credit Mgr., The San Diego Union-Tribune, CA, San Diego
Bolitho, Thomas C. ....(580) 421-9600
bolitho@nationalmediasales.com, Pres., National Media Associates, OK, Ada
bolitho@nationalmediasales.com, Broker, National Media Associates, OK, Ada
Bolitho, Thomas....................(580) 421-9600
bolitho@nationalmediasales.com, Pres., National Media Associates, OK, Ada
Boll, Bernhard....................2990
b.boll@solingen-online.de, Proprietor, ST SOLINGER TAGEBLATT, Solingen
Bollinger, Cory....................(812) 331-4279
cbollinger@heraldt.com, Adv. Dir., The Herald-Times, IN, Bloomington
Bollmann, Ulrich
anzeigen@der-bote.de, Proprietor, DER BOTE fur NURNBERG-LAND, Feucht
Bollmann, Rolf
redaktion@tages-anzeiger.ch, Pub., TAGES-ANZEIGER ZURICH, Zurich
Bolton, Tom....................(805) 739-2229
Exec. Ed., The Lompoc Record, CA, Lompoc
Bolton, John ....(520) 618-7868
bolton@azstarnet.com, Starnet Online Ed., Arizona Daily Star, AZ, Tucson
Bolton, Tom....................ext. 2228
tbolton@pulitzer.net, Exec. Ed., Santa Maria Times, CA, Santa Maria
Bolz, Barbara J.
bolzbj@udmercy.edu, Chair, University of Detroit Mercy, MI, Detroit
Bona, Don ....(501) 374-5103
donbona@dailydata.com, Pres, The Daily Record, AR, Little Rock
Bonanny, Brett....................(570) 740-0638
Luzerne County Cmty. College, PA, Nanticoke

Bonaros, George
george.bonaros@uniontrib.com, Dir., Mktg., The San Diego Union-Tribune, CA, San Diego
Bonavita, Dennis ....(814) 371-4200 ext. 177
dbonavita@thecourierexpress.com, Pub., The Courier-Express/Tri-County Sunday, PA, Du Bois
Bond, Jesse P............................315-789-3333
production@fltimes.com, Production Manager, Finger Lakes Times, NY, Geneva
Bond, Sally...........................(519) 823-6010
sbond@guelphmercury.com, Adv. Mgr., The Guelph Mercury, ON, Guelph
Bonde, Alysoun........................(530) 752-9888
Univ. of California Davis, CA, Davis
Bonenti, Charles ....(413) 496-6211
cbonenti@berkshireeagle.com, Features Ed., The Berkshire Eagle, MA, Pittsfield
Boner, Michelle
mboner@neondsl.com, Prodn. Mgr., Benton Evening News, IL, Benton
Bongiorni, Tami ....(330) 672-6306
Kent State Univ., OH, Kent
Bonjer, Jan
service@ad.nl, Ed., Nederlandse Dagbladunie B.V., Rotterdam, South Holland
Bonn, Jim
jbonn@oleantimesherald.com, Pub., Olean Times Herald, NY, Olean
Bonnard, Joan
redaction@nouvelliste.ch, Ed., NOUVELLISTE, Sion, Valais
Bonner, Kim
kim.bonner@dailysentinel.com, Mng. Ed., The Daily Sentinel, AL, Scottsboro
Bonoff, Steven
steve@ipa.org, Pres., International Prepress Association, MN, Edina
Bonuccelli, Patricia May-02
publicidad@opinion-bo.com, Adv. Mgr., Opinion, Cochabamba
Bonza, Ed...............................(770) 423-6470
Kennesaw State Univ., GA, Kennesaw
Book, Constance
cbook@elon.edu, Assoc. Dean/Assoc. Prof., Elon University, NC, Elon
Bookstaver, Thomas ....(417) 836-1103
Pres./Pub., Springfield News-Leader, MO, Springfield
Boone, Kenneth
kenneth.boone@alexcityoutlook.com, Pub., Alexander City Outlook, AL, Alexander City
Boonjathai, Kimberly
phoenixnews@luc.edu, Loyola Univ., IL, Chicago
Booth, Kyle...............................(941) 957-5182
kyle.booth@heraldtribune.com, News Ed., Sarasota Herald-Tribune, FL, Sarasota
Booth, Ray H.
rbooth@daily-jeff.com, Exec. Ed., The Daily Jeffersonian, OH, Cambridge
Booth, Jeanie..........................(850) 599-2356
jbooth@tallahassee.com, Community Rel. Mgr., Tallahassee Democrat, FL, Tallahassee
Booth, Jim..............................(727) 893-8420
jbooth@tampabay.com, Sr. Ed., Tampa Bay Times, FL, Saint Petersburg
Booth, Doris...........................(972) 650-1986
dbooth@authorlink.com, Ed. in Chief, Authorlink, TX, Irving
Booth, Sally.............................(734) 426-8433
Sec., Schwadron Cartoon & Illustration Service, MI, Ann Arbor
Borak, Jeffrey.........................(413) 496-6212
jborak@berkshireeagle.com, Entertainment Ed., The Berkshire Eagle, MA, Pittsfield
Borchers, Martha.....................(208) 389-2879
email@idahopressclub.org, Exec. Dir., Idaho Press Club, ID, Boise
Borden, Robert C. ....(979) 731-4621
robert.borden@theeagle.com, Editorial Page Ed., The Eagle, TX, Bryan
Borders, Gary
gborders@longview-news.com, Pub., Longview News-Journal, TX, Longview
Bordewyk, David
clipping@sdna.com, Gen. Mgr., South Dakota Newspaper Association, SD, Brookings
Bordewyk, David ....(605) 692-4300
sdna@sdna.com, Gen. Mgr., South Dakota Newspaper Association, SD, Brookings
Bordonaro, Dominick..................716-250-6884
dbordonaro@classifiedsplus.com, Executive Director, Classifieds Plus, Inc., NY, Williamsville
Bore, Geir Arne
geir.arne.bore@dt.no, Ed., DRAMMENS TIDENDE og BUSKERUDS BLAD A/S, Drammen
Boreman, Deborah..................419-281-0581
dboreman@times-gazette.com, Circulation Director, Ashland Publishing Co. LLC, OH, Ashland
Boren, James ....(559) 441-6307
jboren@fresnobee.com, Editorial Page Ed./Vice Pres., The Fresno Bee, CA, Fresno
Borer, Eric.................(909) 593-3511 ext. 4292
Univ. of La Verne, CA, La Verne
Borg, Malcolm A. ....(201) 646-4301
borgm@northjersey.com, Chrmn. of the Bd., North Jersey Media Group, Inc., NJ, Hackensack
Borg, Stephen A. ....(973) 569-7270
BorgS@northjersey.com, President & Publisher, North Jersey Media Group, NJ, Woodland Park
Borg, Jennifer A. ....(973) 569-7680
BorgJ@northjersey.com, VP/Corp Secy & Genl Counsel , North Jersey Media Group, NJ, Woodland Park
Borg, Jennifer A.......................(201) 646-4490
borgj@northjersey.com, Vice Pres./Gen. Counsel/Sec., North Jersey Media Group, Inc., NJ, Hackensack
Borg, Stephen A
borgs@northjersey.com, President./Publisher, The Record, Herald News, NJ, Woodland Park
borgs@northjersey.com, Pres., North Jersey Community Newspapers, NJ, Woodland Park
Borgardt, Jurgen 9970
bremervoerder.zeitung@t-online.de, Bus. Mgr., BREMERVOERDER ZEITUNG, Bremervoerde
Borgen, Kari ....(541) 523-3673
kborgen@bakercityherald.com, Publisher, Baker City Herald, OR, Baker City
Borges, Craig ....(508) 236-0337
news@thesunchronicle.com, Asst. Mng. Ed., News, The Sun Chronicle, MA, Attleboro
Borghese, Lorna 570-690-2344
lborghese@fujifilm.com, Newspaper Account Manager, NE Region, Fujifilm North America Corporation, IL, Hanover Park
Borghetti, Frank R.
info@beicommunications.com, Pres., Borghetti Consulting Group, SC, Charleston
Borgmeyer, Les........................(573) 815-1808
lborgmeyer@columbiatribune.com, Vice President of Sales, Columbia Daily Tribune, MO, Columbia
Borhani, Faryar........................(619) 594-4190
San Diego State Univ., CA, San Diego
Borise, Stephanie.....................203-964-2420
stephanie.borese@scni.com, Business Editior, Greenwich Time, CT, Greenwich
Borisov, Yuri
yborisov@duma.bg, Ed. in Chief, DUMA, Sofia
Born, Linda ....ext. 10
sentinelliners@sbcglobal.net, Adv. Dir., Classified, McPherson Sentinel, KS, McPherson
Bornhauser, Thomas
thomas.bornhauser@luzernerzeitung.ch, Ed. in Chief, NEUE NIDWALDNER ZEITUNG, Luzern
Bornhauser, Thomas
thomas.bornhauser@luzernerzeitung.ch, Chief-Editor, NEUE LUZERNER ZEITUNG, Lucerne, Luzern
Borom, Damon ....(216) 999-6603
Prodn. Mgr., Machinists/Engineers, The Plain Dealer, OH, Cleveland
Borowski, Neill A.....................(609) 272-7277
nborowski@pressofac.com, Exec. Ed./Content Dir., The Press of Atlantic City, NJ, Pleasantville
Borowsky, Ted
information@fostermfg.com, Pres., Foster Mfg. Co., PA, Warminster
Borquez Felix, Jose Regino
lavoz@tetakawi.net.mx, Gen. Mgr., La Voz Del Puerto, Guaymas, Sonora
Borrell, Jerry
info@sumeria.com, Pres., Sumeria, Inc., CA, San Francisco
Borrell, Esther
efered1@cantv.net, Rep., EFE News Services - Caracas, Venezuela, Caracas
Bortel, Robert..........................(419) 372-2606
Bowling Green State Univ., OH, Bowling Green
Borton, Sara Johnson
sborton@lowcountrynewspapers.com, Pres./Pub., The Beaufort Gazette, SC, Beaufort
Borton, Sara Johnson
sborton@islandpacket.com, Pub., The Island Packet, SC, Bluffton
Borucki, Donald
donald.borucki@laopinion.com, Pres., California Newspaper Advertising Executives Association (Southern), CA, Chula Vista
Borud, Haon
haon.borud@tb.no, Ed. in Chief, TONSBERGS BLAD, Tonsberg
Bosak, Chris ....(203) 354-1047
Co-Managing Editor, Bus. Ed., The Hour Publishing Co., CT, Norwalk
Bose, Jaideep
jaideep.bose@timesgroup.com, Ed. in Chief, THE TIMES OF INDIA, New Delhi
Bossey, Steve..........................(810) 762-5616
Mott Cmty. College, MI, Flint
Bostwick, Charles.....................(661) 267-4119
cbostwick@avpress.com, Mng. Ed., Antelope Valley Press, CA, Palmdale
Boswell, Sarah ....(765) 285-8249
Ball State Daily News, IN, Muncie
Botelho, Greg...........................(617) 786-7017
gbotelho@ledger.com, City Ed., The Patriot Ledger, MA, Quincy
Both, Kristene ....(973) 290-4343
College of St. Elizabeth, NJ, Morristown
Bothwell, Anne ....(214) 977-8404
abothwell@dallasnews.com, Asst. Arts/Entertainment Ed., The Dallas Morning News, TX, Dallas
Botta, Maria Cecilia
diario@elpopular.com.ar, Adv. Mgr., El Popular, Olavarria, Provincia de Buenos Aires
Bottome, Abigail ....(978) 232-2050
Endicott College, MA
Bottomly, Therese.....................(503) 221-8434
theresebottomly@news.oregonian.com, Mng. Ed., News, The Oregonian, OR, Portland
Boucar, Grmah
anfani@intnet.ne, Pub., ANFANI, Niamey
Boucher, Jody..............................ext. 101
jboucher@ricentral.com, Adv. Mgr., Display, The Kent County Times, RI, West Warwick
Boulares, Naima Nefles
redaction@jeune-independant.net, Ed., LE JEUNE INDEPENDANT, Algiers
Boulay, Patrick
patrick.boulay@legal-ledger.com, Pub., Saint Paul Legal Ledger
Boureima, Sigue Jeremie
ed.lepays@cenatrin.bf, MD, LE PAYS, Ouagadougou
Bourjaily, Gavin ....(540) 635-3229
dist@globesyndicate.com, Ed./Pub., Globe Syndicate, VA, Strasburg
Bourner, Wayne ....ext. 340
Data Processing Mgr., The Standard, ON, Saint Catharines
Bourque, Jeffrey A.
adman@mindspring.com, Pres., Hemsing Advertising, Inc., MI, Troy
Bouthas, D.
imerisia@odenet.gr, Pub., IMERISIA, Verioa, Macedonia
Bouthillette, Jean Louis
info@cenosis.com, Pres., Cenosis, QC, Laval
Boutwell, Melissa
mboutwell@postindependent.com, Circ. Coord., Glenwood Springs Post Independent, CO, Glenwood Springs
Bouvard, Pierre
pierre.bouvard@arbitron.com, Pres., Sales/Mktg., The Arbitron Co., NY, New York
Bouzin, Jean-Louis 2836 8850
libertehebdo@nordnet.fr, Ed. in Chief, LIBERTE, Lille
Bowden, Janet
janet.bowden@atnnewpapers.com.au, Sales Adv. Mgr., THE NORTHERN STAR, Goonellabah
Bowder, Mark ....(360) 735-4512
mark.bowder@columbian.com, Asst. Metro Ed., The Columbian, WA, Vancouver
Bowen, Keith............................(530) 852-0296
keithb@goldcountrymedia.com, Prodn. Mgr., Pressroom, Auburn Journal, Inc., CA, Auburn
Bowen, Patrick ....(850) 521-1182
pbowen@flpress.com, Chief Financial Officer, Florida Press Association, FL, Tallahassee
Bower, Jennifer........................(603) 594-6539
Coord., Promo., The Telegraph, NH, Hudson
Bowers, Jason
jmb@skylinegraphicservices.com, Sales Rep., Skyline Graphic Services, LLC, CO, Palmer Lake
Bowers, Scott ....(815) 987-1269
Pub., Rockford Register Star, IL, Rockford
Bowers, Kenn ....(704) 261-2233
kbowers@theej.com, Composing Supvr., The Enquirer-Journal, NC, Monroe
Bowers, Josh
josh.bowers@skylinegraphicservices.com, Gen. Mgr., Skyline Graphic Services, LLC, CO, Palmer Lake
Bowles, Eduardo
ebowles@eldia.com.bo, Dir., El Dia, Santa Cruz de la Sierra, Santa Cruz
Bowles, Richard
info@qms.com, Vice Pres.-Sales/Mktg., QMS, Inc., AL, Mobile
Bowman, Sharynn ....ext. 202
sharynn@gctelegram.com, Classifieds Mgr., The Garden City Telegram, KS, Garden City
Bowman, Serena......................336-506-3063
sbowman@thetimesnews.com, Sales Manager, Times-News, NC, Burlington
Bowman, Ron F.
rosbacksales@qtm.net, Vice Pres., Sales/Mktg., Rosback Co., MI, Saint Joseph
Bowman, Donnie ....(256) 235-9251
Circ. Mgr., The Anniston Star, AL, Anniston
Bowman, Joseph.......................(216) 999-6643
Vice President and Director of Operations, The Plain Dealer, OH, Cleveland
Bowtwell, Susan ....ext. 217
srand@vnews.com, News Ed., Valley News, VT, West Lebanon
Boyd, Lorraine
laboyd@mcleodusa.net, Ed., Daily Record
Boyd, Robert David ....(770) 253-5355
oldboyd@gmail.com, Pres., Mark-Morgan, Inc., GA, Newnan
Boyd, David ....(803) 644-2397
dboyd@aikenstandard.com, System Mgr., Aiken Standard, SC, Aiken
Boyd, Heather
heather.boyd@thecanadianpress.com, Bureau Chief, Canadian Press, The - Edmonton, AB, AB, Edmonton
Boyd, Jim...............................(865) 342-6100
Circ. Dir., Knoxville News Sentinel, TN, Knoxville
Boyens, Uwe 90080
info@eckernfoerder-zeitung.de, Proprietor, ECKERNFORDER ZEITUNG, Eckernfoerde
Boyer, Dick ....(207) 621-5646
dboyer@centralmaine.com, Prodn. Dir., Opns., Kennebec Journal, ME, Augusta
Boyer, Jeremy
jeremy.boyer@lee.net, Executive Editor, The Citizen, NY, Auburn
Boyer, Leroy............................(570) 628-6026
lboyer@republicanherald.com, Sports Ed., Republican Herald, PA, Pottsville
Boyer, Gerald
gboy@maryville.edu, PhD, Maryville University, MO, Saint Louis
Boyett, Dick
dboyett@fww.com, Sales Mgr., Franklin Wire Works, Inc., IL, Belvidere
Boyette, John ....(706) 823-3337
jboyette@augustachronicle.com, Sports Ed., The Augusta Chronicle, GA, Augusta
Boyle, Andrew
andrew.boyle@press.co.nz, Mng. Dir., THE PRESS
Boyle, Tom

tboyle@titusvilleherald.com, Reporter, The Titusville Herald, PA, Titusville
Boyle, Bob
rb026@mirachem.com, Sales Mgr., Mirachem Corp., AZ, Phoenix
Boyle, Patrick C.
info@thederrick.com, Pres., The News-Herald, PA, Oil City
Boyle, Alan
atboyle@gmail.com, Ed., Newsphere, WA, Bellevue
Boyle, Patrick C.
newsroom@usachoice.net, Ed., The Derrick, PA, Oil City
Boyles, Larry
lboyles@stanfordproductsllc.com, Sales Mgr., Stanford Products, IL, Salem
Boyles, Dana ....ext. 131
dana.boyles@duncanbanner.com, Adv. Mgr., The Duncan Banner, OK, Duncan
Boyles, Sam W.
sam@neiinc.com, Pres., Northeast Industries, Inc., AZ, Prescott
Boynton, Lois ....(919) 843-8342
Assoc. Prof., University of North Carolina, NC, Chapel Hill
Bracamontes, Ramon ....(915) 546-6352
eshugart@elpasotimes.com, Bus. Ed., El Paso Times, TX, El Paso
Bracamontes Galvez, Federico
dirgral@diariodemexico.com.mx, Pres., DIARIO DE MEXICO, Mexico City
Brachvogel, Hans
anzeigen@haller-kreisblatt.de, Bus. Mgr., Haller Kreisblatt, Halle
Brack, Votel
info@swp.de, Proprietor, SUDWEST PRESSE ULM, Ulm
Brackenbury, Mark ....(203) 789-5708
mbrackenbury@nhregister.com, Mng. Ed., New Haven Register, CT, New Haven
Bracket, Stephanie
sbrackett@edmondsun.com, Bus. Mgr., The Edmond Sun, OK, Edmond
Brackin, Becky
stnews@texaswest.com, Pub., San Angelo Standard-Times, TX, San Angelo
Brackvogel, Thomas
info@swp.de, Bus. Mgr., SUDWEST PRESSE ULM, Ulm
Brad, Mosher
sports@lagrandeobserver.com, Sports ed, The Observer, OR, La Grande
Bradbury, Shonnie
sbradbury@times-standard.com, Adv. Dir., Times-Standard, CA, Eureka
Bradbury, Emily
ebradbury@kspress.com, Member Serv. Dir., Kansas Press Association, KS, Topeka
Braddy, Leigh ....(770) 428-9411 ext. 454
Prodn. Mgr., Pre Press, Marietta Daily Journal, GA, Marietta
Braddy, Joe ....(863) 294-7731 ext. 3075
joe.braddy@newschief.com, Mng. Ed., News Chief, FL, Winter Haven
Bradford, Alissa.................................ext. 32
sicirc@intrstar.net, Circ. Dir., The Sampson Independent, NC, Clinton
Bradlee, Thomas F..........(410) 398-3311 ext. 3055
tbradlee@chespub.com, Pres./CEO, Chesapeake Publishing Corp., MD, Elkton
Bradley, Bruce R.
contactvp@pilotonline.com, Pres., The Virginian-Pilot, VA, Norfolk
Bradley, Brian ....(816) 271-8508
bbradley@npgco.com, Pres., NPG Newspapers, Inc., MO, Saint Joseph
Bradley, Michael ....(508) 563-2835
mbradley@capecod.net, Grimes, W.B. & Co., MD, Gaithersburg
Bradley, David R.
davidb@npgco.com, Pres., News-Press & Gazette Co., MO, Saint Joseph
Bradley, Joe 808-242-6305
jbradley@mauinews.com, Pub., The Maui News, HI, Wailuku
Bradley, Steve
sbradley@adirondackguide.com, Prodn. Mgr., Adirondack Daily Enterprise, NY, Saranac Lake
Bradley-Bursack, Carol
cbursack@forumcomm.com, Librarian, InForum, ND, Fargo
Bradnam, Susan
sbradnam@lfpress.com, Chief Photographer, The London Free Press, ON, London
Bradwell, Mike ....(724) 222-2200
mbradwell@observer-reporter.com, Bus. Ed., Observer-Reporter, PA, Washington
Brady, John
contact@johnbrady.info, Pres., Brady & Paul Communications, MA, Newburyport
Brady, Charles F.
sports@monett-times.com, Sports Ed., The Monett Times, MO, Monett
Brady, Timothy E. 978-946-2161
tbrady@eagletribune.com, Adv. Dir., The Eagle-Tribune, MA, North Andover
Brady, Timothy E.
tbrady@eagletribune.com, Adv. Dir., Retail, Gloucester Daily Times, MA, Gloucester
Bragg, Jeanine ....ext. 227
jbragg@monroenews.com, Adv. Dir., Sales, The Monroe Evening News, MI, Monroe
Bragg, Beth ....ext. 350
bbragg@adn.com, Columnist, Anchorage Daily News, AK, Anchorage
Braima, Mahmoud
mahmoud_braima@cxs.subr.edu, Head, Southern University and A&M College, LA, Baton Rouge
Brain, Ricardo
director@diarioelsur.cl, Sales Mgr., El Sur, Concepcion
Bramlett, Scott.............(870) 862-6610 ext. 152
Circ. Mgr., El Dorado News-Times, AR, El Dorado
Brammer, Charlie ....(210) 531-3240
St. Philip's College, TX, San Antonio
Brancaccio, Louis ....(360) 735-4505
lou.brancaccio@columbian.com, Ed., The Columbian, WA, Vancouver
Brancato, Tom ....(800) 997-3600 ext. 2166
brancatot@graphline.com, Dir., Mktg., GraphLine, FL, Sunrise
Branch, Kip..........................(252) 335-3588
Elizabeth City State Univ., NC, Elizabeth City
Branch, Jay
jbranch@broadcastnews.ca, Saskatchewan Correspondent, Broadcast News Limited, SK, Regina
Branch, Kristin........................(334) 712-7964
kbranch@dothaneagle.com, News Ed., The Dothan Eagle, AL, Dothan
Brand, Brad
brad.brand@lethbridgeherald.com, Prodn. Systems Mgr./Foreman, Composing Room, The Lethbridge Herald, AB, Lethbridge
Brander, Don ....(902) 629-6000
d.brander@theguardian.pe.ca, Pub., The Guardian, PE, Charlottetown
Brandl, Richard
redaktion@maintaltagesanzeiger.de, Bus. Mgr., MAINTAL TAGESANZEIGER, Maintal
Brandl, Tara
tbrandl@marshallindependent.com, Adv. Mgr., Independent, MN, Marshall
Brandly, Christain
redaktion@avu.ch, Ed. in Chief, ANZEIGER VON USTER, Uster, Altdorf
Brandstaetter, Richard ....(316) 875-3361
richardbrandstaetter@kleinezeitung.at, Reg'l Sales Dir., KLEINE ZEITUNG, 8010 Graz
Brandstetter, David
archcom@37.com, Pres., Arch Communications, Inc., MO, Saint Louis
Brandt, Jay ....(541) 383-0370
jbrandt@bendbulletin.com, Adv. Dir., The Bulletin, OR, Bend
Brandt, Patti ....(989) 894-9673
pbrandt@bc-times.com, Educ. Ed., The Bay City Times, MI, Bay City
Brandt, Steven R. ....(864) 298-4100
srbrandt@gannett.com, Pub., The Greenville News, SC, Greenville
Branfcomb, Max ....(619) 482-6368
Southwestern College, CA, Chula Vista
Branfman, David
dbranfman@branfman.com, Owner, Branfman & Associates, CA, Oceanside
Brannan, Dan ....(618) 463-2560
dan_brannan@thetelegraph.com, Editorial Page Ed., The Telegraph, IL, Alton
Brannon, Sue ....(386) 754-0419
sbrannon@lakecityreporter.com, Controller, Lake City Reporter, FL, Lake City
Branson, Patrick.......................(563) 588-7828
Loras College, IA, Dubuque
Branstetter, Ziva......................(918) 581-8326
ziva.branstetter@tulsaworld.com, City Ed., Tulsa World, OK, Tulsa
Brant, Lee ....(530) 477-4202
leeb@theunion.com, Prodn. Dir., The Union, CA, Grass Valley
Brantford, Keith ....(780) 468-0264
kbrantford@edmsun.com, Sports Ed., The Edmonton Sun, AB, Edmonton
Brasch, Walter.........................(570) 389-4565
brasch@bloomu.edu, Ed. in Chief, Spectrum Features, PA, Bloomsburg
Brashear, Karen ....(904) 359-4435
karen.brahear@jacksonville.com, Mgr., Promo., The Florida Times-Union, FL, Jacksonville
Brasier, Deborah ....(563) 383-2452
Bus. Ed., Quad-City Times, IA, Davenport
Brasier, John..........................(864) 260-1267
brasierjd@indpendentmail.com, Sports Ed., Anderson Independent-Mail, SC, Anderson
Brasil, Joe..............................(707) 256-2244
csutko@napanews.com, Circ. Dir., Napa Valley Register, CA, Napa
Brassard, Robbie
rharrington@berkshireeagle.com, Adv. Supvr., Sales, The Berkshire Eagle, MA, Pittsfield
Braswell, Bob ....(432) 333-7605
braz@oaoa.com, Prodn. Dir., Odessa American, TX, Odessa
Brauch, Kirk
kirkb@adstream.com, Business Mgr., Adstream America, NY, New York
Braun, Kathy ....ext. 104
classifieds@pdsadnet.com, Classified Sales Mgr., Publishers Development Service, WI, Fond du Lac
Braun, Bob ....(215) 345-3045
bbraun@phillyburbs.com, Prodn. Dir., The Intelligencer, PA, Doylestown
Braun, J.B.
jbraun@delawareonline.com, Mktg. Mgr., The News Journal, DE, New Castle
Braun, Waltraud
verlag@weissenburger-tagblatt.com, Proprietor, Weissenburger Tagblatt, Weissenburg
Braun, Chris
cbraun@therecorder.com, Pub., The Recorder
Braunschweig, Joe...................(920) 996-7298
jbraunschweig@gannett.com, Circ. Dir., The Post-Crescent, WI, Appleton
Brawdy, Bob...........................(509) 582-1548
bbrawdy@tri-cityherald.com, Chief Photographer, Tri-City Herald, WA, Kennewick
Breaux, Nona ....(215) 361-8820
nbreaux@thereporteronline.com, Exec. Ed., The Reporter, PA, Lansdale
Bredenberg, Al
ab@copywriter.com, Contact, Al Bredenberg Creative Services, CT, Danbury
Breeden, Dan ....(408) 920-5820
dbreeden@mercurynews.com, Mgr., Mktg. Commun./Special Sections, San Jose Mercury News, CA, San Jose
Breeding, Lucinda ....(940) 566-6884
Arts/Entertainment Ed., Denton Record-Chronicle, TX, Denton
Breen, Neil
neil@sundaytelegraph.com.au, Ed., SUNDAY TELEGRAPH
Brehm, Sharon ....(305) 628-6800
St. Thomas Univ., FL, Miami
Brehm, Darryl..........................(312) 421-0480
Univ. of Illinois at Chicago, IL, Chicago
Brehm, Brian..........................(540) 667-3205
bbrehm@winchesterstar.com, City Ed., The Winchester Star, VA, Winchester
Bremer, Rainer
rainer.bremer@ln-luebeck.de, Distr. Mgr., LUBECKER NACHRICHTEN/LUBECKER NACHRICHTEN AM SONNTAG, Lubeck
Brendel, Dale..........................(816)350-6365
dale.brendel@examiner.net, Gen. Mgr., The Examiner, MO, Independence
Brendergast, Nessa
nessa.brendergast@transcontinental.ca, Media Relations Dir., Transcontinental, Inc., QC, Montreal
Brendlinger, Brian....................(215) 619-7306
Montgomery County Cmty. College, PA, Blue Bell
Brennan, Steve
International Ed., The Hollywood Reporter
Brennan, Tom.........................(419) 521-7340
tbrennan@nncogannett.com, Exec. Ed., News Journal, OH, Mansfield
Brennan, Tom
tbrennan@nncogannett.com, Pub., The Marion Star, OH, Marion
Brennan, Charles
cbrennan@chronicleonline.com, Ed., Citrus County Chronicle, FL, Crystal River
Brennan, Tom
tfnews@nncogannett.com, Pub., Bucyrus TelegraphForum.com, OH, Bucyrus
Brennan, Neale
nealab@chronicleonline.com, Community Affairs Dir., Citrus County Chronicle, FL, Crystal River
Brennan, Timothy
rbma@rbma.com, Mgr., Mktg., Reed Brennan Media Associates, Inc., FL, Orlando
Brennan, Mary K.
admin@sbsweb.com, Vice Pres., Software, Software Business Systems, MN, Edina
Brenner, Elizabeth
jsedit@journalsentinel.com, Pres./Pub., Milwaukee Journal Sentinel, WI, Milwaukee
Brenner, Stuart
stu@skobrenner.com com, CEO, SKO Brenner American, NY, Baldwin
Bresett, Scott ....(518) 565-4160
sbresett@pressrepublican.com, Circ. Mgr., Press-Republican, NY, Plattsburgh
Breslauer, Irwin J. 212-580 8559
ijbnyc@aol.com, Ed., Journal Press Syndicate, NY, New York
Breslin, Tom
tbreslin@corpemail.com, Pres., AEC, Inc., IL, Schaumburg
Bressan, Nick.........................(217) 788-1358
nick.bressan@sj-r.com, Adv. Supvr., Retail, The State Journal-Register, IL, Springfield
Brett, Regina ....(216) 999-6327
Metro Columnist, The Plain Dealer, OH, Cleveland
Brewer, Dale ....ext. 211
dbrewer@heraldpalladium.com, Editorial Page Ed., The Herald-Palladium, MI, Saint Joseph
Brewer, Hamish
info@jda.com, CEO, JDA Software Group, Inc., AZ, Scottsdale
Brewer, Beth
bethtimes@twcny.rr.com, Pub., The Evening Times, NY, Herkimer
Brewer, Kay ....(501) 378-3836
Mgr., Personnel, Arkansas Democrat-Gazette, AR, Little Rock
Brewer, Mike 758 0559
enquiry@dailynews.co.nz, Mng. Dir., TARANAKI DAILY NEWS
Brewer, Paul
prbrewer@uwm.edu, Chair/Assoc. Prof., University of Wisconsin-Milwaukee, WI, Milwaukee
Brewer, Beth A. ....(315) 866-2220
beth@herkimertelegram.com, Pub., The Evening Telegram, NY, Herkimer
Brewer, John C. ....(360) 417-3500
john.brewer@peninsuladailynews.com, Publisher and Editor, Peninsula Daily News, WA, Port Angeles
Brewster, Murray
mbrewster@broadcastnews.ca, Legislative Reporter, Broadcast News Limited, NS, Halifax
Brezina, Mike
mbrezina@herald-democrat.com, Circ. Dir., Herald Democrat, TX, Sherman
Briar, John
jbriar@fujifilmgs.com, Reg'l Sales Mgr., Fujifilm Graphic Systems USA, Inc., IL, Hanover Park
Briceno, Manuel 35-2383
Gen. Mgr., ANTORCHA, El Tigre, Anzoategui
Brickley, Shari ....(941) 957-5336
shari.brickley@herladtribune.com, Asst. Adv. Dir., Sarasota Herald-Tribune, FL, Sarasota
Bridges, Janet A.
jabridges@shsu.edu, Chair/Prof., Sam Hous-

ton State University, TX, Huntsville
Bridges, David
bridges@advpubtech.com, Vice Pres., Devel., Advanced Publishing Technology, CA, Burbank
Bridges, Robert 386-754-0428
Editor, Lake City Reporter, FL, Lake City
Bridges, Lamar W.
lamar_bridges@tamu-commerce.edu, Prof., Texas A&M University-Commerce, TX, Commerce
Bridges, Vera ....(601) 961-7098
Circ. Mgr., The Clarion-Ledger, MS, Jackson
Bridges, Pat..........................(541) 957-4250
pbridges@nrtoday.com, Adv. Dir., The News-Review, OR, Roseburg
Bridges, Betty
classads@thnews.com, Classified Adv. Mgr., Times-Herald, AR, Forrest City
Bridges, Tommy ....(540) 574-6241
tbridges@dnronline.com, Circ. Dir., Daily News-Record, VA, Harrisonburg
Bridgewater, Frank
fbridgewater@starbulletin.com, Ed., Honolulu Star-Bulletin, HI, Honolulu
Bridgewater, Frank....................(808) 529-4791
fbridgewater@staradvertiser.com, Vice President / Editor, Honolulu Star-Advertiser, HI, Honolulu
Briffa, Alfred
uniprint@kemmunet.net.mt, Ed., IT-TORCA, Valletta
Briggs, Scott
sbriggs@opubco.com, Vice Pres. Administration, The Oklahoman, OK, Oklahoma City
Briggs, Stacy..........................(215) 345-3057
Features Ed., The Intelligencer, PA, Doylestown
Briggs, Alexis..........................253-535-7489
mastads@plu.edu, Business & Ad Manager, Pacific Lutheran Univ., WA, Tacoma
Briggs, Dick
rhb@teleplex.net, Principal, Briggs, Richard & Assoc., SC, Landrum
Briggs, Steve ....(916) 321-1755
sbriggs@sacbee.com, Adv. Mgr., The Sacramento Bee, CA, Sacramento
Bright, Tom 609-272-7175
tbright@pressofac.com, Operataions/Pressroom Manager, The Press of Atlantic City, NJ, Pleasantville
Brighton, James......................(717) 255-8236
jbrighton@patriot-news.com, Dir. Technology, The Patriot-News, PA, Mechanicsburg
Briley, Russ ....(805) 437-0454
rbriley@venturacountystar.com, Circ. Dir., Sales/Retention, Ventura County Star, CA, Camarillo
Brill, James ....(212) 210-2901
jbrill@nydailynews.com, Sr. Vice Pres., Circ./Distr., NY Daily News, NY, New York
Brill, Joseph A. ....ext. 2271
jbrill@registerstar.com, City Ed., Register-Star, NY, Hudson
Brilliant, Dorothy.....................(805) 682-0531
ashleigh@ashleighbrilliant.com, Vice Pres., Ashleigh Brilliant, CA, Santa Barbara
Brimley, Wendy.......................(810) 767-8922
wbrimley@flintjournal.com, Adv. Mgr., Retail Sales Initiatives, The Flint Journal, MI, Flint
Brimo, Rene J.
digitron.brimo@sympatico.ca, Pres., R.B. Intermark, Inc., QC, Kirkland
Brin, Dale ....(306) 657-6258
dbrin@sp.canwest.com, Pub., The StarPhoenix, SK, Saskatoon
Brincefield, Robert
bob.brincefield@brownwoodbulletin.com, Pub., Brownwood Bulletin, TX, Brownwood
Brinkman, Gary.......................(928) 775-3804
Asst. Prodn. Dir., The Daily Courier, AZ, Prescott
Brinkman, Gail
gbrinkman@tribune.com, Atlanta Mgr., Tribune 365, GA, Atlanta
Brinley, Jeff
jbrinley@thetribunenews.com, Circ. Dir./Vice Pres., The Tribune, CA, San Luis Obispo
Brinson, Maureen.....................(252) 335-8132
mbrinson@dailyadvance.com, Financial/Accounting Manager, The Daily Advance, NC, Elizabeth City
Briscoe, Keith W. ....ext. 155
Exec. Ed., Beaver County Times, PA, Beaver
Brittingham, Tamra ....(302) 674-3600
tbritting@aol.com, Pub., Delaware State News, DE, Dover
Brittingham, Tamra
shelclen@newszap.com, Corp. Pres., Independent Newspapers, Inc. (DE), DE, Dover
Brittingham, Susan
sbrittingham@mcalesternews.com, Living/Lifestyle Ed., McAlester News-Capital, OK, McAlester
Britton, Dora ....(419) 521-7392
dbritton@nncogannett.com, Prodn. Mgr., Plate, News Journal, OH, Mansfield
Britton, Lisa
lbritton@bakercityherald.com, Entertainment/Amusements Ed., Baker City Herald, OR, Baker City
Britton, Chuck..........................(815) 547-9393
chuck@bobray.com, Pres., Bob Ray & Associates, Inc., IL, Belvidere
Brizh, Alexander
brizh@donbass.dn.ua, Ed. in Chief, DONBASS, Donetsk
Broadbooks, Jon ....(217) 788-1505
jon.broadbooks@sj-r.com, Exec. Ed., The State Journal-Register, IL, Springfield
Broadway, Rob ....(706) 290-5287
rbroadway@npco.com, Prodn. Mgr., Press, Rome News-Tribune, GA, Rome
Broadwell, Charles W. ....(910) 486-3501
cbwell@fayobserver.com, Pres./Pub., The Fayetteville Observer, NC, Fayetteville
Broas, Steve 920-996-7219
sbroas@appleton.gannett.com, Vice President Gannett Wisconsin Media, The Post-Crescent, WI, Appleton
Brochu, Ron............................(715) 395-5029
rbrochu@superiortelegram.com, Exec. Ed., The Daily Telegram, WI, Superior
Brock, Roger
news@theherald.com.au, Ed., THE NEWCASTLE HERALD
Brock, Gary
gbrock@recordherald.com, Pub., Record Herald, OH, Washington Court House
Brock, Terry ....(731) 287-7244
tbrock@stategazette.com, Circ. Dir., State Gazette, TN, Dyersburg
Brock, Depen
depen.brock@berliner-zeitung.de, Ed. in Chief, BERLINER KURIER, Berlin
Brock, Harvey
hbrock@thedickinsonpress.com, Pub./Purchasing Agent, Dickinson Press, ND, Dickinson
hbrock@thedickinsonpress.com, The Dickinson Press (Advertizer), ND, Dickinson
Brock, Christina ....(909) 386-3844
christina.brock@sbsun.com, Editorial Page Asst., San Bernardino County Sun, CA, San Bernardino
Brockington, Wanda
wgbrockington@nsu.edu, Chair/Assoc. Prof., Norfolk State University, VA, Norfolk
Brodbeck, Stephen C. ....(217) 421-7916
Controller, Herald & Review, IL, Decatur
Brodnax, Ken ....(432) 333-7779
kbrodnax@oaoa.com, Editorial Page Ed., Odessa American, TX, Odessa
Brodt, Jay ....ext. 210
Adv. Mgr., Classified, Walla Walla Union-Bulletin, WA, Walla Walla
Broertjes, P.I. 5629111
Ed., DE VOLKSKRANT, Amsterdam
Brogdon, Mike.........................(317) 736-2782
mbrogdon@dailyjournal.net, Mgmt. Info Servs. Mgr., Daily Journal, IN, Franklin
Brokow, Lynn...........................(909) 386-3912
lynn.brokaw@sbsun.com, Circ. Mgr., Home Delivery, San Bernardino County Sun, CA, San Bernardino
Bronenberg, Scott......................610-994-1850
scottb@advancedtele.com, Regional Sales Manager, Advanced Telecom Services, Inc., PA, Wayne
Bronner, Oscar
chefredaktion@derstandard.at, Pub., DER STANDARD, A-1014 Vienna
Bronson, William
williambronson@daltoncitizen.com, Pub., The Daily Citizen, GA, Dalton
Bronson, Rhona 609-272-7105
rbronson@pressofac.com, Director of Marketing, The Press of Atlantic City, NJ, Pleasantville
Brooker, Thomas
tom.brooker@gogreenbay.com, Ed., The Green Bay News-Chronicle, WI, Green Bay
Brooker, Sally
sally.brooker@oamarumail.co.nz, Ed., THE OAMARU MAIL, Oamaru
Brooks, Dan ....(616) 632-2068
newsroom@aqsaint.com, Aquinas College, MI, Grand Rapids
Brooks, Linda ....(916) 321-1639
lbrooks@sacbee.com, Vice Pres., HR, The Sacramento Bee, CA, Sacramento
Brooks, Ben ....(540) 667-3206
bbrooks@winchesterstar.com, Sports Ed., The Winchester Star, VA, Winchester
Brooks, Steve ....(630) 368-4338
skbrooks@tribune.com, Adv. Dir., Regl. Accounts, Chicago Tribune, IL, Chicago
Brooks, Becky
news@gazettepublishingco.com, Editor, Bellevue Gazette, OH, Bellevue
Brooks, John ....(605) 692-4300
advertising@sdna.com, Sales Mgr., South Dakota Newspaper Association, SD, Brookings
Brooks, Debby
dbrooks@greenfieldreporter.com, Admin. Mgr., Daily Reporter, IN, Greenfield
Brooks, Joni
jbrooks@yumasun.com, Pub., Yuma Sun, AZ, Yuma
Brooks, Ron ....(704) 797-4221
rbrooks@salisburypost.com, Circ. Dir., Salisbury Post, NC, Salisbury
Brooks, Hubby ....(229) 219-0230 ext. 222
hubby.brooks@gaflnews.com, Vice Pres., Technology, Valdosta Daily Times, GA, Valdosta
Broome, Cindy.........................(360) 754-5477
cbroome@theolympian.com, Adv. Mgr., Classified, The Olympian, WA, Olympia
Brophy, Peter ....(609) 272-7207
pbrophy@pressofac.com, Lead Local Content Producer, The Press of Atlantic City, NJ, Pleasantville
Bross, James ....(360) 577-2517
jbross@tdn.com, Editorial Page Ed., The Daily News, WA, Longview
Brossart, Mike ....(909) 483-9359
m_brossart@dailybulletin.com, Sr. Ed./Editorial Page Ed., Inland Valley Daily Bulletin, CA, Ontario
Brosz, John 203-354-1093
VP Sales & Marketing, The Hour Publishing Co., CT, Norwalk
Brothers, Joyce
joyce@mountwashingtonvalley.com, Office Mgr., The Conway Daily Sun, NH, North Conway
Broussard, Sharon ....(216) 999-4149
Editorial Writer, The Plain Dealer, OH, Cleveland
Broussard, Terry 318-427-1204
tbroussard@thetowntalk.com, Advertising Sales Manager, The Town Talk, LA, Alexandria
Browall, Ken ....(715) 395-5009
kbrowall@superiortelegram.com, Pub., The Daily Telegram, WI, Superior
Browall, Ken
kbrowall@duluthnews.com, Pub., Duluth News Tribune, MN, Duluth
Brown, Ross ....(509) 527-2971
Walla Walla College, WA, College Place
Brown, Oby..............................(478) 744-4396
obrown@macontel.com, News Ed., The Telegraph, GA, Macon
Brown, Mandy 386-754-0405
Circulation Director, Lake City Reporter, FL, Lake City
Brown, Kelly ....(979) 731-4656
kelly.brown@theeagle.com, Mng. Ed., The Eagle, TX, Bryan
Brown, Phil
phil.brown@djc.com, Pub., Seattle Daily Journal of Commerce, WA, Seattle
Brown, L.G.
lgbrown59@gmail.com, Pres., Brown's Web Press Service & Machine Shop, MO, Mexico
Brown, Craig ....(360) 735-4514
craig.brown@columbian.com, Metro Ed., The Columbian, WA, Vancouver
Brown, Graham
gbrown@newspress.com, Dir., Community Rel., Santa Barbara News-Press, CA, Santa Barbara
Brown, Robert L. ....(775) 850-7676
COO, Swift Communications, Inc., NV, Carson City
Brown, Dave ....ext. 298
dbrown@heraldpalladium.com, Online Ed., The Herald-Palladium, MI, Saint Joseph
Brown, Howard J. ....(262) 656-6320 ext. 320
hbrown@kenoshanews.com, Pres., United Communications Corporation, WI, Kenosha
Brown, Travis ....(319) 653-2191
sports@washjrnl.com, Sports Ed., The Washington Evening Journal, IA, Washington
Brown, Cailin
chronicle@strose.edu, College of St. Rose, NY, Albany
Brown, David
bangcirc@bayareanewsgroup.com, Pres./CEO, The Oakland Tribune, CA, Oakland
Brown, Tom
tbrown@eastoregonian.com, Publisher & Editor, East Oregonian, OR, Pendleton
Brown, Paul
pbrown@theobserver.ca, Adv. Mgr., Observer, ON, Sarnia
Brown, Kathryn B.
kbbrown@eastoregonian.com, Assoc. Publisher, East Oregonian, OR, Pendleton
Brown, Gary ....ext. 8303
gary.brown@cantonrep.com, Living Section Ed., The Repository, OH, Canton
Brown, Linda 62022412422
linda.brown@mcphersonsentinel.com, Mailroom Manager, McPherson Sentinel, KS, McPherson
Brown, Josh......................................ext. 112
Sports Ed., Daily News, IL, Robinson
Brown, Martha
advertising@thedeal.com, Dir., Cor. Commun., The Daily Deal
Brown, Eric...............................(303) 892-5261
browne@rockymountainnews.com, Deputy City Ed., Rocky Mountain News, CO, Denver
Brown, Nancy ....(530) 749-4721
nancy_brown@link.freedom.com, Adv. Mgr., Classified, Appeal-Democrat, CA, Marysville
Brown, Renee 239-574-1110
rbrown@breezenewspapers.com, Adv. Dir., Cape Coral Breeze, FL, Cape Coral
Brown, Neil ....(727) 893-8441
nbrown@tampabay.com, Editor/Vice President, Tampa Bay Times, FL, Saint Petersburg
Brown, Steve N.
sjbrown@pressline.info, Pres., Pressline Services, Inc., MO, Saint Louis
Brown, David ....(501) 378-3676
Adv. Mgr., Retail Sales, Arkansas Democrat-Gazette, AR, Little Rock
Brown, Kathy ....ext. 104
Sports Ed., The News-Record, WY, Gillette
Brown, Crystal..........................(256) 340-2352
crystalvbb@aol.com, Adv. Mgr., Retail, The Decatur Daily, AL, Decatur
Brown, Melissa.........................(510) 293-2427
mabrown@angnewspapers.com, Promo. Coord., San Mateo County Times, CA, San Mateo
Brown, Michael
mbrown@detroitnews.com, Asst. Managing Editor, The Detroit News, MI, Detroit
Brown, Julie ....(608) 745-3526
jbrown@capitalnewspapers.com, Adv. Dir., Daily Register, WI, Portage
Brown, Michelle................................ext. 262
mbrown@meadvilletribune.com, Controller, The Meadville Tribune, PA, Meadville
Brown, Lee ....(717) 240-7120
lbrown@cumberlink.com, Prodn. Mgr., Pressroom, The Sentinel, PA, Carlisle
Brown, Mark
mark.brown@tulsaworld.com, Entertainment Ed., Tulsa World, OK, Tulsa

Brown, Karen ....(419) 739-3505
retailadv@wapakwdn.com, Mktg. Dir., Wapakoneta Daily News, OH, Wapakoneta
Brown, Jill
jbrown@multiad.com, Marketing Coordinator, MultiAd Services, Inc., IL, Peoria
Brown, Alex
alex@printmark.net, Dir., Prodn., Printmark, VT, East Montpelier
Brown, Josh
jbrown@tdnpublishing.com, Sports Editor, Troy Daily News, OH, Troy
Brown, Gordon
gordon.brown@dailynews.co.nz, Ed., NORTH TARANAKI MIDWEEK
Brown, Jay 208-848-2287
jbrown@lmtribune.com, Pressroom Manager, Lewiston Morning Tribune, ID, Lewiston
Brown, Nick..................................ext. 5704
nick@atomicimaging.com, Commun. Consultant, Atomic Imaging, Inc., IL, Chicago
Brown, Christine 860/701-4488
c.brown@theday.com, Advertising Services Manager, The Day Publishing Company, CT, New London
Brown, Malcolm..............................ext. 255
mbrown@backemarketing.com, Sr. Vice Pres., Backe Difital Brand Marketing, PA, Radnor
Brown, Kevin..........................(425) 339-3474
brown@heraldnet.com, Sports Ed., The Herald, WA, Everett
Brown, Kaycie
kaycie.brown@morningsun.net, Bus. Mgr., The Morning Sun, KS, Pittsburg
Brown, Chuck ....(612) 673-4760
Chuck.Brown@startribune.com, Vice Pres./Controller and Treasurer, Star Tribune, MN, Minneapolis
Brown, Janet...........................(202) 898-4825
unionnews@hotmail.com, Ed., Press Associates, Inc., DC, Washington
Brown, Roy E.
info@brownpublishing.com, Pres./CEO, Brown Publishing Co., OH, Cincinnati
Brown, M. Eileen
ebrown@dailyherald.com, Asst. Vice Pres./Dir., Innovation and Audience Development, Daily Herald, IL, Arlington Heights
Brown, Jeffrey N......................(812) 379-5615
jbrown@therepublic.com, Pres., Home News Enterprises, IN, Columbus
Brown, Ann...............................(520) 573-4201
annbrown@azstarnet.com, Editorial Page Ed., Arizona Daily Star, AZ, Tucson
Brown, Jodi
jbrown@cnhi.com, Bus. Mgr., Corsicana Daily Sun, TX, Corsicana
Brown, John
franklin.editor@wrcn.co.nz, Ed., FRANKLIN COUNTY NEWS
Brown, Alan ....(706) 208-2296
alan.brown@onlineathens.com, Adv. Mgr., Online Sales, Athens Banner-Herald, GA, Athens
Brown, Cindy
info@tdna.org, Member Servs. Dir., Texas Daily Newspaper Association, TX, Austin
Brown, Paul B.
mail@urnerbarry.com, Pres., Urner Barry's Price-Current, NJ, Toms River
Brown, Oswald
freeport@nasguard.com, Ed., THE FREEPORT NEWS, Freeport
Brown, Mark A.............(330) 747-1471 ext. 1204
markbrown@vindy.com, Vice Pres./Gen. Mgr./Sec./Asst. Treasurer, The Vindicator, OH, Youngstown
Brown, A................................(508) 655-1532
esp@elect-spec.com, Vice Pres. Mktg., Electronic Specialists, Inc., MA, Natick
Brown, Suzanne ....(303) 820-1697
sbrown@denverpost.com, Fashion/Style Ed., The Denver Post, CO, Denver
Brown, Jeff...............................(317) 398-1285
jbrown@shelbynews.com, Sports Ed., The Shelbyville News, IN, Shelbyville
Brown, David ....(417) 836-1117
dbrown@springfi.gannett.com, Circ. Dir., Springfield News-Leader, MO, Springfield
Brown, Gloria G.
gloria@perrydailyjournal.com, News Ed., The Perry Daily Journal, OK, Perry
Brown, Doug
postandmail@earthlink.net, Pub., The Post & Mail, IN, Columbia City
Brown, Carolyn
thedailyworld@cox-internet.com, Bus. Mgr., The Daily World, AR, Helena
Brown, Kim..............................(616) 222-5821
kbrown@boothmichigan.com, Sales Mgr., Booth Newspapers, Inc., MI, Grand Rapids
Brown, Michael..........................(918) 622-4996
mikeb@commpub.com, Exec. Vice Pres., Community Publishers, Inc., AR, Bentonville
Browne, Ryan
rbrowne@mines.edu, Editor-in-Chief, Colorado School of Mines, CO, Golden
Browne, Bruce ....(920) 459-4423
Univ. of Wisconsin Sheboygan, WI, Sheboygan
Browne, Maggie........................(805) 437-0453
mbrowne@venturacountystar.com, Circ. Mgr., Single Copy, Ventura County Star, CA, Camarillo
Brownell, Greg ....(518) 792-3277
brownell@poststar.com, Sports Ed., The Post-Star, NY, Glens Falls
Browning, Bruce
bbrowning@times-georgian.com, Mng. Ed., Times-Georgian, GA, Carrollton
Browning, P. J.
pbrowning@thesunnews.com, Pub., The Sun News, SC, Myrtle Beach
Browning, Donna
classified@snyderdailynews.com, Adv. Mgr., Classified, Snyder Daily News, TX, Snyder
Brownlee, Betty
bbrownlee@tdnpublishing.com, Bus. Mgr., Troy Daily News, OH, Troy
Brownlee, Betty
bbrownlee@tdnpublishing.com, Bus. Mgr., The Sidney Daily News, OH, Sidney
Brownlee, Betty
bbrownlee@tdnpublishing.com, Grp. Bus. Mgr., Piqua Daily Call, OH, Piqua
Brownlee, Phillip.......................(316) 268-6262
pbrownlee@wichitaeagle.com, Opinion Ed., The Wichita Eagle, KS, Wichita
Broyles, Pam
pbroyles@snu.edu, Speech Commun. Dept., Southern Nazarene University, OK, Bethany
Brubaker, Christine ....(706) 886-6831 ext. 5340
Toccoa Falls College, GA, Toccoa Falls
Brubaker, Moe
moeb@northwestsignal.net, Sr. Ed., Northwest Signal, OH, Napoleon
Bruce, Colin J...........................(807) 343-6201
colin.bruce@chroniclejournal.com, Pub., The Chronicle-Journal, ON, Thunder Bay
Bruce, Carol....................................ext. 210
Environmental Ed., West Plains Daily Quill, MO, West Plains
Bruce, Jeff................................(937) 225-2335
jbruce@coxohio.com, Ed., Dayton Daily News, OH, Dayton
Bruce, Layne
mspress@mspress.org, Exec. Dir., Mississippi Press Services, Inc., MS, Jackson
Bruce, Layne
lbruce@mspres.org, Exec. Dir., Mississippi Press Association, MS, Jackson
Bruck, Robert
bbruck@messenger-inquirer.com, Photo Ed., Messenger-Inquirer, KY, Owensboro
Brucken, Dorinda......................(785) 357-7031
Mgr., Kansas Press Clipping Service, KS, Topeka
Bruen, Dennis
dbruen@the-leader.com, Pub., The Leader, NY, Corning
Brumby, Otis ....(770) 428-9411
bjacoby@cherokeetribune.com, Pub., Cherokee Tribune, GA, Canton
Brumby, Otis ....(770) 428-9411 ext. 301
Pub., Times-Journal, Inc., GA, Marietta
Brumby, Otis A.............(770) 428-9411 ext. 315
tsmith@mdjonline.com, Pres., Marietta Daily Journal, GA, Marietta
Brumby, Otis A.............(770) 428-9411 ext. 301
Pub., Marietta Daily Journal, GA, Marietta
Bruna, Sergio Montivero
director@prensatocopilla.cl, Dir., La Prensa, Tocopilla
Brundo, John
brundoj@gnnewspaper.com, Adv. Dir., Tonawanda News, NY, North Tonawanda
Bruned Mompeon, Antonio
redaccion1@heraldo.es, Dir., Heraldo De Aragon, Zaragoza
Brunegard, Thomas
redaktion@gp.se, Ed. in Chief, GOTEBORGS-POSTEN, Goteborg
Bruner, Andrea
andreab@guardonline.com, Asst. Mng. Ed., Batesville Guard, AR, Batesville
Bruner, Betsey ....(928) 556-2255
Educ. Ed., Arizona Daily Sun, AZ, Flagstaff
Bruni, Sharmin 707-864-7000
Editor-In-Chief, Solano Community College, CA, Fairfield
Brunjes, Robert........................(772) 221-4273
bob.brunjes@scripps.com, Adv. Dir., Treasure Coast News/Press-Tribune, FL, Stuart
Brunner, Al
abrunner@autologic.com, Pres., Autologic Information International, CA, Thousand Oaks
abrunner@autologic.com, Vice Pres., Sales, K & F International, Inc., IN, Granger
Bruns, Andy
abruns@dailyamerican.com, Pub., Daily American, PA, Somerset
Bruns, Andy ....(301) 733-5131
President and Publisher, The Herald-Mail, MD, Hagerstown
Bruns, Tom
tomb@commpub.com, CFO, Community Publishers, Inc., AR, Bentonville
Bruns, Penny
pbruns@yourwestvalley.com, Adv. Dir., Daily News-Sun, AZ, Sun City
Brunson, Melody
mbrunson@washtimesherald.com, Editorial Page Ed., The Washington Times-Herald, IN, Washington
Brunton, Joshua ....(760) 951-6256
joshua_brunton@link.freedom.com, Mgmt. Info Servs. Mgr., Daily Press, CA, Victorville
Brunye, Shana ....(603) 594-6497
Adv. Mgr., Retail Sales, The Telegraph, NH, Hudson
Brusic, Ken..............................(714) 796-2226
kbrusic@ocregister.com, Ed., The Orange County Register, CA, Santa Ana
Brusic, Ken..............................(714) 796-2226
kbrusic@ocregister.com, Fullerton News Tribune, CA, Santa Ana
kbrusic@ocregister.com, Sr. Vice Pres./Ed., The Orange County Register, CA, Santa Ana
Bruton, Bill.......................................ext. 136
bbruton@batavianews.com, Sports Ed., The Daily News, NY, Batavia
Bruyns, Rosaline ....(519) 537-2341 ext. 264
Adv. Mgr., The Sentinel-Review, ON, Woodstock
Bryan, Harry ....(502) 582-4060
hbryan@courier-journal.com, Sports Ed., The Courier-Journal, KY, Louisville
Bryan, Mark...............................(907)-523-2253
mark.bryan@juneauempire.com, Publisher, Juneau Empire, AK, Juneau
Bryant, Charles A. ....(609) 272-7107
cbryantjr@pressofac.com, Dir., Finance/Admin., The Press of Atlantic City, NJ, Pleasantville
Bryant, Thomas J.
tbryant@jtmchugh.com, Owner/CEO, J. Thomas McHugh Co., Inc., IN, Fishers
Bryant, Cherie ....(661) 267-4127
cbryant@avpress.com, Vice Pres./Gen. Mgr., Antelope Valley Press, CA, Palmdale
Bryant, Diane
dbryant@timesrepublican.com, Adv. Dir., Times-Republican, IA, Marshalltown
Bryantt, Shelley
sbryantt@minotdailynews.com, Copy Desk Chief, Minot Daily News, ND, Minot
Bryce, Andrew ....(508) 236-0395
Sports Ed., Sunday, The Sun Chronicle, MA, Attleboro
Bryce, Richard
editor@sheppnews.com.au, Ed., THE SHEPPARTON NEWS, Shepparton
Brydson, David ....(212) 586-7773
brydmedia@aol.com, Pres., Brydson Global Media Sales, NY, New York
BrÃ£chmann, Peter
bt@bt.dk, Ed. in Chief, B.T.-DETAILHANDLERE/LANDSANNONCORER, Copenhagen, Sjaelland
Buahler, Gilbert
g.buahler@freiburger-nachrichten.ch, Ed., FREIBURGER NACHRICHTEN, Fribourg, Freiburg
Bucalo, Paul ....(360) 754-4229
pbucalo@olympia.gannett.com, Online News Ed., The Olympian, WA, Olympia
Bucci, Paul...................................604-605-2154
pbucci@vancouversun.com, Deputy Managing Editor, Digital, The Vancouver Sun, BC, Vancouver
Bucey, Tim ....(937) 328-0371
tbucey@coxohio.com, Bus. Ed., Springfield News-Sun, OH, Springfield
Buchan, Jim......................................ext. 292
jbuchan@wwub.com, Sports Ed., Walla Walla Union-Bulletin, WA, Walla Walla
Buchanan, Scott........................(573) 474-1000
sbuchanan@newzgroup.com, Vice Pres., Newz Group, MO, Columbia
Buchanan, Jim...........................(828) 232-5841
jbuchanan@citizen-times.com, Assoc. Ed., The Asheville Citizen-Times, NC, Asheville
Buchanan, Joan ....(304) 327-4186
Bluefield State College, WV, Bluefield
Buchanan, Brad
bbuchanan@newzgroup.com, Pres., Newz Group, MO, Columbia
Buchanan, Margaret E.
mbuchanan@enquirer.com, Pres./Pub., The Cincinnati Enquirer, OH, Cincinnati
Buchanan, Bruce ....(620) 694-5830
buchanan@dailynews.net, Pres./CEO, Harris Enterprises, Inc., KS, Hutchinson
Buchholz, Hans-Herbert
hj@elaplan.de, Mng. Dir., ELAPLAN Buchholz GmbH & Co., Schonberg
Buchs, Merrily
mbuchs@newburyportnews.com, Night Ed., The Daily News, MA, Newburyport
Buck, Jerry ....(719) 476-4892
jerry.buck@gazette.com, Vice Pres., Opns., The Gazette, CO, Colorado Springs
Buckey, David E. ....(772) 221-4134
david.buckey@scripps.com, Finance Dir., Treasure Coast News/Press-Tribune, FL, Stuart
Buckingham, Lisa ....(408) 920-5255
lbuckingham@mercurynews.com, Vice Pres./CFO, San Jose Mercury News, CA, San Jose
Buckler, Matt
mbuckler@journalinquirer.com, Television/Radio Ed., Journal Inquirer, CT, Manchester
Buckley, Teresa.........................(518) 454-5630
tbuckley@timesunion.com, Sr. Local News Ed., Times Union, NY, Albany
Buckmaster, Mike
mbuckmaster@dailyadvocate.com, News Ed., Daily Advocate, OH, Greenville
Bucksbaum, Robert....................(310) 441-7400
robert@reelsource.com, Pres., Exhibitor Relations Co., CA, Los Angeles
Budris, William...............................ext. 223
bbudris@timesonline.com, Circ. Mgr., Home Delivery, Beaver County Times, PA, Beaver
Buel, Bobbie Jo..........................(520) 573-4217
bjbuel@azstarnet.com, Mng. Ed., Arizona Daily Star, AZ, Tucson
Buell, Duane ....(360) 735-4606
duane.buell@columbian.com, Circ. Mgr., Transportation, The Columbian, WA, Vancouver
Buenger, Paula ....(712) 262-6610
pbuenger@spencerdailyreporter.com, Pub., The Daily Reporter, IA, Spencer
Buenker, Todd ....ext. 119
tbuenker@cnhi.com, Circ. Mgr., Effingham Daily News, IL, Effingham
Buffelli, Miguel J.
diario@laopinion-rafaela.com.ar, Pres., Buffelli y Actis S.A., Rafaela, Provincia de Santa Fe
Bugeja, Ray
daily@timesofmalta.com, Ed., THE TIMES, Valletta
Bugge, Frank
redaktion@usinger-anzeiger.de, Ed., Usinger Anzeiger, Usingen

Bujalski, Henry .... **(814) 870-1626**
hank.bujalski@timesnews.com, CFO, Erie Times-News, PA, Erie
Bukhari, Syed Sajjad
pbpisfl@brail.net.tk, Ed. in Chief, DAILY MUSAWAAT, Lahore, Lahore District
Buley, Bill .... **(208) 664-8176 ext. 2006**
bbuley@cdapress.com, News Ed., Coeur d'Alene Press, ID, Coeur d'Alene
Bull, Stevan .... **(918) 684-2952**
Prodn. Mgr., Pressroom, Muskogee Daily Phoenix & Times Democrat, OK, Muskogee
Bullis, Judy
jbullis@stcatharinesstandard.ca, Sr. Group Publisher, Niagara
Publisher, St. Catharines Standard, The Standard, ON, Saint Catharines
Bulow, George M. .... **(212) 580-5015**
george.bulow@verizon.net, Pres., Interactive International, Inc., NY, New York
Bumeder, Shawn .... **(810) 989-6284**
sbumeder@porthuro.gannett.com, Prodn. Mgr., Times Herald, MI, Port Huron
Bump, Debbie
dbump@thedailyreview.com, Circ. Dir., The Daily Review/The Sunday Review, PA, Towanda
Bumstead, Bruce .... **(204) 571-7436**
bbumstea@brandonsun.com, Photographer, Brandon Sun, MB, Brandon
Buncher, Alan
ecledger@ellwoodcityledger.com, Pub., Ellwood City Ledger, PA, Ellwood City
Buncher, Alan H. .... **(724) 775-3200 ext. 120**
abuncher@timesonline.com, Pub., Beaver County Times, PA, Beaver
Bundotich, John
jbundotich@standardmedia.co.ke, Grp. Mng. Dir., THE STANDARD, Nairobi
Bundy, Deb
dbundy@skagitpublishing.com, Adv. Mgr., Display, Skagit Valley Herald, WA, Mount Vernon
Bundy, Sam .... **(843) 317-7274**
sbundy@florencenews.com, Sports Ed., Morning News, SC, Florence
Buneci, Victor
gorjanul@intergorj.ro, Ed. in Chief, GORJANUL, Gorj
Bungart, Jack .... **(707) 553-6836**
jbungart@timesheraldonline.com, Mng. Ed., Vallejo Times-Herald, CA, Vallejo
Bunn, John R. .... **(863) 647-1555**
jbunn@bunntyco.com, Pres., B.H. Bunn Co., FL, Lakeland
Bunnell, Doug .... **(415) 382-7290**
dbunnell@marinij.com, Editorial Page Ed., Marin Independent Journal, CA, Novato
Bunte, Frank
ztg.gruppewaz@cityweb.de, Ed. in Chief, WR WESTFALISCHE RUNDSCHAU, Dortmund
Bunyan, Clytie
cbunyan@opubco.com, Bus. Ed., The Oklahoman, OK, Oklahoma City
Bunzel, Tom .... **(310) 286-0969**
tom@professorppt.com, Pres., Moving Graphics, CA, Los Angeles
Burbach, Mike **651-228-5544**
mburbach@pioneerpress.com, Editor, St. Paul Pioneer Press, MN, Saint Paul
Burbank, April
the.record@my.wheaton.edu, Editor in Chief, Wheaton College, IL, Wheaton
Burbidge, Sara .... **(760) 744-1150 ext. 2450**
Palomar College, CA, San Marcos
Burch, Kerry
cburch@lendersupport.com, Pres., Lender Support Systems, Inc., CA, Poway
Burden, Ernesto .... **(802) 479-0191 ext. 1186**
ernesto.burden@rutlandherald.com, New Media Dir., Rutland Herald, VT, Rutland
Burford, Brendan .... **(212) 969-7575**
bburford@hearst.com, Comics Ed., North America Syndicate, NY, New York
bburford@hearst.com, Comics Editor, King Features Syndicate, NY, New York
Burgard, Allen .... **(920) 453-5108**
aburgard@sheboygan.gannett.com, Transportation Supvr., The Sheboygan Press, WI, Sheboygan
Burgason, Verle .... **(515) 232-2161 ext. 440**
vburgason@amestrib.com, Chrmn., Iowa Newspapers, Inc., IA, Ames
Burgess, Dennis
djburgess@burgessind.com, Pres./CEO, Burgess Industries, Inc., MN, Plymouth
Burgess, Landra **321-242-3920**
lburgess@floridatoday.com, Assistant Controller, Florida Today, FL, Melbourne
Buri, Peter
azredaktion@azag.ch, Ed. in Chief, AARGAUER ZEITUNG, Baden
Burk, Dan .... **(520) 881-8101**
Dir., Mktg., JupiterImages, AZ
Burke, Richard
dburke@classifiedventures.com, Sr. Vice Pres., Admin./Cor. Devel., Classified Ventures, Inc., IL, Chicago
dburke@classifiedventures.com, Bus. Mgr., Association for Education in Journalism and Mass Communication, SC, Columbia
Burke, Sean
newsroom@tauntongazette.com, Pub., Taunton Daily Gazette, MA, Taunton
Burke, Daniel .... **(202) 463-8777**
daniel.burke@religionnews.com, Associate Editor, Religion News Service, DC, Washington
Burke, M.W. (Maury)
mwburke@aol.com, Pres./Chrmn., M.W. Burke & Associates, Inc., CA, Berkeley
Burke, Dyana .... **(407) 420-5272**
Compensation/Commun. Mgr., Orlando Sentinel, FL, Orlando
Burke, Bob .... **(724) 684-2631**
bburke@tribweb.com, Mng. Ed., The Valley Independent, PA, Monessen
Burke, Tim .... **(561) 820-4742**
tburke@pbpost.com, Exec. Ed./Pub., The Palm Beach Post, FL, West Palm Beach
Burke, Tim
tburke@pbpost.com, Pub., Palm Beach Newspapers, Inc., FL, West Palm Beach
Burke, Gerry
gburke@morrisdailyherald.com, Pub., Morris Daily Herald, IL, Morris
Burke, Paul .... **(208) 664-8176 ext. 3001**
pburke@cdapress.com, Adv. Dir., Coeur d'Alene Press, ID, Coeur d'Alene
Burke, Judy
burkej@caledonian-record.com, Bookkeeper, The Caledonian-Record, VT, Saint Johnsbury
Burke-Gaffney, Mike .... **(416) 947-2311**
mike.burkegaffney@sunmedia.ca, Mng. Ed., The Toronto Sun, ON, Toronto
Burkhammer, Victor .... **(304) 348-5184**
vicburkhammer@wvgazette.com, News Ed., The Charleston Gazette, Sunday Gazette-Mail, WV, Charleston
Burkhart, Libby **563-588-5719**
lburkhart@wcinet.com, Business Manager, Telegraph Herald, IA, Dubuque
Burleson, Erica .... **(314) 961-2660 ext. 7523**
review@webster.edu, Asst. Gen. Mgr., St. Louis Journalism Review, MO, Saint Louis
Burleson, John
john@akronlegalnews.com, Pres., Daily Legal News
Burleson, Marty .... **(559) 735-3282**
features@visaliatimesdelta.com, Features Ed., Visalia Times-Delta, CA, Visalia
Burman, Rick
rburman@adirondackguide.com, Pressroom Foreman, Adirondack Daily Enterprise, NY, Saranac Lake
Burn, Nicole
Nicole.burn@sungard.com, Vice Pres., Mktg., SunGard Securities Finance, Inc., NY, New York
Burnell, Gary .... **(508) 626-3803**
gburnell@cnc.com, Circ. Mgr., Transportation, Metrowest Daily News, MA, Framingham
Burner, Kim
kburner@grandcountynews.com, Pub., Sky-Hi News, CO, Granby
Burnett, Carl .... **(740) 681-4520**
cburnette@nncogannett.com, News Ed., Eagle-Gazette Media, OH, Lancaster
Burnett, Barbara
bburnett@ogd.com, Prodn. Supt., The Courier-Observer, The Journal & The Advance-News, NY, Ogdensburg
Burnett, Garthia Elena
gburnett@cdispatch.com, News Ed., The Commercial Dispatch, MS, Columbus
Burnett, Mark
mburnett@apdi.net, Pres./CEO, APDI-Application Programming & Development, Inc., MD, Waldorf
Burney, Wayne
advertising@snyderdailynews.com, Adv. Dir., Snyder Daily News, TX, Snyder
Burney, Butch
butchb@ssecho.com, Gen. Mgr., Sulphur Springs News-Telegram, TX, Sulphur Springs
Burney, Pam .... **ext. 235**
pburner@courier-herald.com, Adv. Dir., The Courier Herald, GA, Dublin
Burney, Bobby
sportsed@ssecho.com, Sports Ed., Sulphur Springs News-Telegram, TX, Sulphur Springs
Burns, Bobby .... **(252) 329-9572**
baburns@reflector.com, News Ed., The Daily Reflector, NC, Greenville
Burns, Eddie .... **(512) 445-3552**
eburns@statesman.com, Vice Pres./CFO, Austin American-Statesman, TX, Austin
Burns, Howard
hburns@lfpress.com, Today Ed., The London Free Press, ON, London
Burns, Mike
mburns@freedom.com, Interim Publisher, The Gazette, CO, Colorado Springs
Burns, Joel E.
jburns@s-t.com, Dir., HR, The Standard-Times, MA, New Bedford
Burns, Judith M.
jburns@indexjournal.com, CEO/Pub., The Index-Journal, SC, Greenwood
Burns, Dennis .... **(763) 488-9910 ext. 101**
dburns@innotek-ep.com, Pres./CEO, Innotek Corporation, MN, Maple Grove
Burns, Robert
rburns@nsb-observer.com, Ed., The Observer, FL, New Smyrna Beach
Burns, Brian **973-569-7840**
VP/Digital Sales, North Jersey Media Group, NJ, Woodland Park
Burns, Brenda .... **(937) 652-1334**
bburns@urbanacitizen.com, Ed., Urbana Daily Citizen, OH, Urbana
Burris, Tracy .... **(319) 372-6421 ext. 211**
production@dailydem.com, Prodn. Mgr., Fort Madison Daily Democrat, IA, Fort Madison
Burris, Keith C.
kburris@journalinquirer.com, Editorial Page Ed., Journal Inquirer, CT, Manchester
Burriss, Andy .... **(803) 329-4000 ext. 8380**
aburriss@heraldonline.com, Photo Ed., The Herald, SC, Rock Hill
Burroughs, Park .... **(724) 222-2200**
pburroughs@observer-reporter.com, Mng. Ed., Observer-Reporter, PA, Washington
Burrows, Kenda .... **(309) 757-4990**
burrows@qconline.com, Editorial Page Ed., The Dispatch, IL, Moline
Burrus, Bill
bburrus@gwcommonwealth.com, Sports Ed., The Greenwood Commonwealth, MS, Greenwood
Burt, Jim
info@burtmountain.com, Founder/Pres., Burt Technologies, Inc., CO, Evergreen
Burti, Alencar
dcomercio@acsp.com.br, Pub., Associacao Comercial de Sao Paulo, Sao Paulo, Sao Paulo
Burtoff, Barbara .... **(202) 966-0488**
BBapartmentlife@aol.com, Ed./Pub., Barbara Burtoff Syndicated Features, DC, Washington
Burton, Greg
grburton@delawareonline.com, Asst, Mng. Ed., The News Journal, DE, New Castle
Burton, Bruce .... **(530) 406-6236**
bburton@dailydemocrat.com, Sports Ed., The Daily Democrat, CA, Woodland
Burton, David **785-832-7231**
dburton@ljworld.com, Production Manager-prepress, The World Co.- Lawrence, Kan., Journal-World, KS, Lawrence
Burton, Bonita .... **(407) 650-6374**
bburton@orlandosentinel.com, Assoc. Mng. Ed., Photo/Design/Visuals, Orlando Sentinel, FL, Orlando
Burton, David **785-832-7231**
dburton@ljworld.com, The World Co.- Lawrence, Kan., Journal-World, KS, Lawrence
Burton, Gary
Gary_Burton@tamu-commerce.edu, Assoc. Prof., Texas A&M University-Commerce, TX, Commerce
Buryk, Alexis .... **(212) 556-4104**
Adv. Sr. Vice Pres., The New York Times, NY, New York
Busby, Christy .... **ext. 7236**
cbusby@texarkanagazette.com, City Ed., Texarkana Gazette, TX, Texarkana
Busby, Mark .... **(901) 529-2221**
busby@commercialappeal.com, Adv. Mgr., Classified, The Commercial Appeal, TN, Memphis
Buscaglia, Marco .... **(312) 222-5964**
mbuscaglia@tribune.com, Gen. Mgr., TMS Specialty Products, IL, Chicago
Buscaglia, Marco .... **(312) 222-5964**
mbuscaglia@tribune.com, Gen. Mgr., TMS Specialty Products, IL, Chicago
Buse, Dean .... **(308) 233-9749**
Audiotex Mgr., Kearney Hub, NE, Kearney
Busgos, Jose Luis **576-4111**
elglobo@infoline.wtfe.com, Gen. Mgr., EL GLOBO, Caracas, D.F.
Bush, Michael
mbush@heartlandpublications.com, President /CEO, Heartland Publications LLC, CT, Clinton
Bush, Toebe
tbush@recordgazette.net, Pub., The Record Gazette, CA, Banning
Bush, Lee
lbush3@elon.edu, Asst. Prof., Elon University, NC, Elon
Bush, Lori .... **(270) 831-8319**
lbush@thegleaner.com, Circ. Mgr., The Gleaner, KY, Henderson
Bush, Jerry .... **ext. 229**
Southern Illinois Univ., IL, Carbondale
Bush, Kent
publisher@augustagazette.com, Pub., Augusta Daily Gazette, KS, Augusta
Bushee, Ward .... **(415) 777-7757**
wbushee@sfchronicle.com, Editor/Exec. Vice Pres., San Francisco Chronicle, CA, San Francisco
Bushey, Pat .... **(541) 885-4479**
pbushey@heraldandnews.com, Opinion Ed., Herald and News, OR, Klamath Falls
Bushman, Larry D.
lbushman@messengernews.net, Pub., The Messenger, IA, Fort Dodge
Bussard, Pat .... **(540) 964-2555**
Southwest Virginia Cmty. College, VA, Richlands
Bussey, Bill .... **(864) 260-1240**
bussey@independentmail.com, IT Mgr., Anderson Independent-Mail, SC, Anderson
Bustamente Molina, Transito
administracion@lasnoticiasdevictoria.cl, Dir., Las Noticias, Victoria
Butash, Susan
sbnsb@mindspring.com, Regl. Sales Mgr., Newspaper Space Bank, AZ, Scotsdale
Butcher, Jim
editor@cj.kscoxmail.com, Ed., The Coffeyville Journal, KS, Coffeyville
Butcher, Stu
stu@chanute.com, Mng. Ed., The Chanute Tribune, KS, Chanute
Butcher, Ashley **386-754-0417**
abutcher@lakecityreporter.com, Advertising Director, Lake City Reporter, FL, Lake City
Butcher, Chris
cbutcher@perutribune.com, Sports Ed., The Peru Tribune, IN, Peru
Butcher, Warren
webmaster@liverpool.com, Adv. Dir., DAILY POST, Liverpool
Butcher, Warren
davies@liverpool.com, Adv. Dir., LIVERPOOL ECHO, Liverpool
Buteux, Pat
info@fourpalms.com, Pres., Four Palms, Inc., VA, Reston

Butkiewicz, Joe......................(570) 829-7249
jbutkiewicz@timesleader.com, Exec. Ed/Vice Pres., Times Leader, PA, Wilkes-Barre
Butler, Frank E.
fbutler@proxios.com, Pres., Proxios, VA, Richmond
Butler, David J.......................(408) 920-5456
Exec. Ed., San Jose Mercury News, CA, San Jose
Butler, Jim......................(979) 731-4635
jim.butler@theeagle.com, Entertainment Ed., The Eagle, TX, Bryan
Butler, Jim......................(867) 667-4481
editorial@whitehorsestar.com, Ed., Whitehorse Star, YT, Whitehorse
Butler, Goldie......................(202) 636-2916
gbutler@washingtontimes.com, Mgr., Research, The Washington Times, DC, Washington
Butler, Elizabeth............(229) 244-3400 ext. 256
elizabeth.butler@gaflnews.com, Lifestyle Ed., Valdosta Daily Times, GA, Valdosta
Butler, Keith............(317) 467-6010 ext. 253
kbutler@greenfieldreporter.com, Prodn. Mgr., Post Press, Daily Reporter, IN, Greenfield
Butler, Bruce......................(952) 944-9457
bruce.butler@colorspan.com, Dir., Mktg., Hewlett-Packard Co., MN, Minnetonka
Butler, Jim
jimb@ssecho.com, Vice Pres./Controller, Sulphur Springs News-Telegram, TX, Sulphur Springs
Butler, Laura......................(859) 622-1572
Eastern Kentucky Univ., KY, Richmond
Butler, David J.......................(408) 920-5456
dbutler@medianewsgroup.com, Vice Pres., News, MediaNews Group Inc, CO, Denver
Butler, Erica
managingeditor@gmail.com, Florida A&M Univ., FL, Tallahassee
Butler, III, Morgan......................ext. 204
nf-support@newsfinder.com, Admin. Mgr., Newsfinder, WI, Waukesha
Butner, Cindy......................(417) 836-1208
cbutner@news-leader.com, Dir., Market Devel., Springfield News-Leader, MO, Springfield
Butner, Cindy......................(707) 526-8577
cindy.butner@pressdemocrat.com, Dir., Mktg., The Press Democrat, CA, Santa Rosa
Butorac, Matt..............(719) 544-0166 ext. 310
circ@chieftain.com, Circ. Dir., The Pueblo Chieftain, CO, Pueblo
Butow-Gonzales, Jamie..............(559) 735-3265
news@visaliatimesdelta.com, Sr. Ed., Visalia Times-Delta, CA, Visalia
Butzer, Ann
sitmausa@sitma.com, Mktg. Mgr., SITMA USA, Inc., MN, Saint Paul
Buxton, Chuck......................(707) 521-5246
cbuxton@pressdemocrat.com, Sr. Ed., The Press Democrat, CA, Santa Rosa
Buzdo, Jozsef
szerkesztoseg@nemzetisport.hu, Ed., NEMZETI SPORT, Budapest, Pest
Buzzard, Natalie......................(419) 993-2052
nbuzzard@limanews.com, Adv. Mgr., Local, The Lima News, OH, Lima
Buzzini, Norberto......................220-2000
diario@diarioweb.com.br, Pres., Diario da Regiao, Sao Jose Do Rio Preto, Sao Paulo
Byars, Carey
cbyars@jbu.edu, Chair, John Brown University, AR, Siloam Springs
Byars, Robin
rbyars@messenger-inquirer.com, Circ. Mgr., Mktg., Messenger-Inquirer, KY, Owensboro
Bye, Jim......................(330) 996-3240
jbye@thebeaconjournal.com, Adv. Mgr., CTS, Akron Beacon Journal, OH, Akron
Byerly, Marina
mabyerly0@frostburg.edu, Editor-in-Chief, The Bottom Line, MD, Frostburg
Byers, Alex......................(202) 994-1313
George Washington Univ., DC, Washington
Byers, Karlyn......................(937) 642-6397
Society Ed., Marysville Journal-Tribune, OH, Marysville
Bykofsky, Melissa......................(607) 777-2257
SUNY/Binghamton, NY, Binghamton
Byrd, Thomas T.
news@winchesterstar.com, Pub., The Winchester Star, VA, Winchester
Byrd, Tina..................(419) 238-2285 ext. 230
tbyrd@timesbulletin.com, Market Devel. Dir., The Times Bulletin, OH, Van Wert
Byrd, Tamara
ads@pnawan.org, Coord., Pacific Northwest Association of Want-Ad Newspapers, ID, Lewiston
Byrd, Dennis M.
dbyrd@suntimes.com, Treasurer, Sun-Times Media Group Inc., IL, Chicago
Byrne, Penny......................(435) 797-3289
Assoc. Prof., Utah State University, UT, Logan
Byrne, Dean......................(435) 797-3754
Lectr., Utah State University, UT, Logan
Byrnes, Jessica......................(727) 298-0341
jessica@competencesoftware.net, Asst. to CEO, Competence Software, FL, Clearwater
Bytwerk, Randall
bytw@calvin.edu, Chair, Dept. of Commun. Arts & Sciences, Calvin College, MI, Grand Rapids
Bywater, Pat......................ext. 267
Exec. Ed., The Meadville Tribune, PA, Meadville

C

CM, Suma......................(212) 293-8725
scm@unitedmedia.com, Exec. Ed., Newspaper Enterprise Association (Div. of United Media), NY, New York
scm@unitedmedia.com, Exec. Ed., United Feature Syndicate (Div. of United Media), NY, New York
Caballero, Paloma
pekin@efe.com, Rep., EFE News Services - Beijing, China, Beijing
Caballero, Shelby
shelby.caballero@lubbockonline.com, Dir., HR, Lubbock Avalanche-Journal, TX, Lubbock
Caballero, Raul David......................257-1182
Ed., Perspectiva Sur, Quilmes, Provincia de Buenos Aires
Caballero Vela, Arturo......................482-4083
Pres./Owner, Diario Del Pacifico, Acapulco, Guerrero
Cabalo, Lanaly......................ext. 237
lcabalo@kauaipubco.com, Sports Ed., The Garden Island, HI, Lihue
Cable, Warren
helpdesk@infomart.ca, Pres., Infomart Ltd., ON, Toronto
Cabrera, Enriqueta
buzon@condor.dgsca.unam.mx, Gen. Dir., EL NACIONAL, Mexico City, Distrito Federal
Cabreros, Oscar C.......................14-7376
Ed., La Manana, Bolivar, Provincia de Buenos Aires
Caderaro, Umberto
jornal@acritica.com.br, Dir., Empresa de Jornais Calderaro, Manaus, Amazonas
Cadi, Thierry......................4017-1780
thierry.cadin@dowjones.com, Reg'l Sales Mgr., Dow Jones Newswires - Paris, France, Paris
Cadwallender, Nicholas J...........(540) 374-5454
njc@freelancestar.com, President/Publisher, The Free Lance-Star, VA, Fredericksburg
Cagle, Steve......................(252) 329-9576
scagle@reflector.com, Features Ed., The Daily Reflector, NC, Greenville
Cagle, Daryl
daryl@cagle.com, Pres./CEO, Cagle Cartoons, Inc., CA, Santa Barbara
Cagnina, James......................(805) 642-5585
jim@inksoup.com, Pres., Coast Graphic Supply, CA, Ventura
Cagnoli, Alejandro
elchubut-trelew@speedy.com.ar, Dir., Impresora Chubutense S.A., Trelew, Provincia de Chubut
Cahalan, Steve......................(608) 791-8229
scalahan@lacrossetribune.com, Bus. Ed., La Crosse Tribune, WI, La Crosse
Cahalane, Dan
info@americanroller.com, Vice Pres., Sales/Mktg., American Roller Co., WI, Union Grove
Caikada, Alexander
editorincharge@deepika.com, Ed. in Chief, DEEPIKA, Kottayam, Kerala
Caillard, Jean-Pierre
lamontagne@centrefrance.com, MD, LA MONTAGNE/LA MONTAGNE DIMANCHE, Clermont-Ferrand
Cain, Stephanie......................(225) 771-2230
Southern Univ. A&M College, LA, Baton Rouge
Cain, Tim......................(217) 421-6908
Entertainment Ed., Herald & Review, IL, Decatur
Cainas, Elena......................(901) 529-2285
cainas@commercialappeal.com, Dir., Mktg./Community Rel., The Commercial Appeal, TN, Memphis
Cains, Rich......................(219) 648-3189
rcains@post-trib.com, Adv. Supvr., Retail, Post-Tribune, IN, Merrillville
Cal Sanchez, Juan
jcal@segre.com, Mng. Dir., Segre, Lleida
Calaiacovo, William......................(216) 999-4258
Vice Pres./Dir., Labor Rel./HR, The Plain Dealer, OH, Cleveland
Calaiacovo , Bill......................(216) 999-3513
Asst. Circ. Dir., The Plain Dealer, OH, Cleveland
Calantone, Jen......................(202) 885-1402
American Univ., DC, Washington
Calchi, Joseph......................(856) 563-5215
Adv. Dir., The Daily Journal, NJ, Vineland
Caldas, Breno
correio@cpovo.net, Dir., Empresa Jornalistica Caldas Junior Ltd., Porto Alegre, Rio Grande do Sul
Calderaro, Jon......................(310) 581-0688
Dir., West Coast, Concepts Video Productions, Inc., NJ, Boonton
Calderon, Joseph......................(909) 386-3928
joe.calderon@sbsun.com, Asst. Mng. Ed., Metro, San Bernardino County Sun, CA, San Bernardino
Calderon, Bolivar Prieto..................293-0255
editorsur@eo.pro.ec, Pres., Editorial del Sur Ltda, Machala, El Oro
Caldwell, Pam
pcaldwell@mydailyregister.com, Gen. Mgr., Point Pleasant Register, WV, Point Pleasant
Caldwell, Michael
mike.caldwell@irontontribune.com, Pres./Pub., The Ironton Tribune, OH, Ironton
Caldwell, David
dcaldwell@minotdailynews.com, News Ed., Minot Daily News, ND, Minot
Caldwell, Matt......................(614) 738-2280
Adv. Contact, Capital Track Co., OH, Columbus
Caldwell, Richard......................ext. 105
CFO, Southeast Missourian, MO, Cape Girardeau
Caldwell, Debbie
newseditor@harlanonline.net, News Ed., The Harlan Daily Enterprise, KY, Harlan
Calhoon, Jim
supprod@supportproducts.com, CEO, Support Products, Inc., IL, Effingham
Calhoun, Ken
kcalhoun@elon.edu, Asst. Prof., Elon University, NC, Elon
Calhoun, Scott......................(256) 235-9290
scalhoun@annistonstar.com, Controller/Treasurer, Consolidated Publishing Co., AL, Anniston
Cali, Jeff......................(580) 332-4433
Sports Ed., Ada Evening News, OK, Ada
Call, Ravell......................(801) 236-6004
ravell@desnews.com, Photo Ed., Deseret News, UT, Salt Lake City
Call, Andrea......................(406) 758-4423
Adv. Sales Mgr., Daily Inter Lake, MT, Kalispell
Callahan, Sean
scallahan@edgil.com, Dir., Sales, Edgil Associates, Inc., MA, Billerica
Callahan, Angie
acallahan@vvdailypress.com, Adv. Dir., Daily Press, CA, Victorville
Callahan, Colleen
colleen.a.callahan@uwrf.edu, Chair, University of Wisconsin-River Falls, WI, River Falls
Callas, Peter
pcallas@njtimes.com, Mng. Ed., The Times, NJ, Trenton
Calle, Rene Toral......................288-2551
eltiempo@cue.satnet.net, Pres./Gen. Mgr., El Tiempo Cia. Ltd., Cuenca, Azuay
Calleja, Stephen
scalleja@independent.com.mt, News Room Mgr., THE MALTA INDEPENDENT, Valletta, Sliema
Callen, Mary......................(608) 283-7623
Commun. Dir., Wisconsin Newspaper Association
Calles Broca, Jorge Fausto
presente@nexus.net.mx, Pres., PRESENTE, Villahermosa, Tabasco
presente@nexus.net.mx, Pub./Mng. Dir., PRESENTE DE LA CHONTALPA, Villahermosa, Tabasco
presente@nexus.net.mx, Ed./Dir., EL VESPERTINO DE PRESENTE, Villahermosa, Tabasco
Callihan, Lisa......................(606) 326-2606
lcallihan@cnhi.com, Controller, The Daily Independent, KY, Ashland
Callinan, Tom
tcallinan@enquirer.com, Ed., The Cincinnati Enquirer, OH, Cincinnati
Calloway, James
jcalloway@mcclatchyinteractive.com, Vice President Strategic Development, McClatchy Interactive, NC, Raleigh
Calloway, Nikki
nikki@photosys.com, Sales Mgr., Photo Systems, Inc., MI, Dexter
Calos, Anne......................ext. 6239
Features Ed., Union-Sun & Journal, NY, Lockport
Calvert, Ericka......................(646) 682-9466
ecalvert@newscom.com, Mktg. Dir., Newscom, DC, Washington
Camara, Fassiri
horoya@leland-gn.org, Dir., PDG (Party-State), Conakry
Camarillo, John J
john@zumapress.com, Head of Licensing and Global Relations, ZUMA Press, Inc., CA, San Clemente
Camaron, Michelle
mcameron@imediainc.com, Vice Pres./Creative Dir., Interactive Media Associates, NJ, Parsippany
Cambell, Fred
president@wcai.com, Pres., Wireless Communications Association International, DC, Washington
Cambridge, Patricia......................(740) 593-0899
Asst. Prof., Ohio University, OH, Athens
Cameron, Ian
apimages_us@ap.org, Vice Pres., AP Images, NY, New York
Cameron, Susan......................(276) 645-2533
scameron@bristolnews.com, City Ed., Bristol Herald Courier, VA, Bristol
Cameron, Scott......................(312) 222-8697
jscameron@tribune.com, Dir., US Syndication Sales, Tribune Media Services, Inc., IL, Chicago
Camilleri, Victor
nazzjon@mbox..vol.net.mt, Ed., Independence Print, G'Mangia/Pieta, Hamrun
Camino, Juan Carlos......................565 5581
hoydigital@hoy.com.do, Gen. Mgr., HOY, Santo Domingo
Cammack, Charles
editpage@aol.com, Vice Pres., HR, The Philadelphia Inquirer, PA, Philadelphia
Camp, Tommy
tommy@newnan.com, Sports Ed., The Times-Herald, GA, Newnan
Camp, Paul A.......................(773) 728-8351
paul@contentthatworks.com, CEO, Content That Works, IL, Chicago
paul@contentthatworks.com, Gen. Mgr., Thomson Target Media, IL, Chicago
Campanini, James......................(978) 970-4621
jcampanini@lowellsun.com, Ed., The Sun, MA, Lowell
Campbell, Bill......................(903) 596-6295
bcampbell@tylerpaper.com, Asst. Circ. Mgr., Tyler Morning Telegraph, TX, Tyler
Campbell, Chad......................(815) 929-2135
ccampbell@daily-journal.com, Circ. Mgr., The Daily Journal, IL, Kankakee
Campbell, Thomas E...................(989) 725-5136

argus@chartermi.net, Pub., The Argus-Press, MI, Owosso
Campbell, Don.......................(867) 668-2002
don@whitehorsestar.com, Head Pressman, Whitehorse Star, YT, Whitehorse
Campbell, Christopher P.
christopher.campbell@usm.edu, Dir./Prof. School of Mass Commun. and Journ., University of Southerm Mississippi, MS, Hattiesburg
Campbell, Debbie...............................ext. 262
deb.campbell@sunmedia.ca, Prodn. Mgr., The Sentinel-Review, ON, Woodstock
Campbell, Lynne
lynne@mcdonoughvoice.com, Publisher. Ad Director, Macomb Journal, IL, Macomb
Campbell, Jim.........................(360) 792-9204
jcampbell@kitsapsun.com, Submitted Content Ed., Kitsap Sun, WA, Bremerton
Campbell, Linda......................(561) 820-4651
lcampbell@pbpost.com, Circ. Mgr., Admin. Servs., The Palm Beach Post, FL, West Palm Beach
Campbell, David
circ@livent.net, Circ. Mgr., The Livingston Enterprise, MT, Livingston
Campbell, Bob.........................(313) 223-4549
campbell@freepress.com, Deputy Metro Ed., Detroit Free Press, MI, Detroit
Campbell, Bryan
bryan@snsnews.com, Administrative Ed., Syndicated News Service, NY, Rochester
Campbell, Roshelle....................402-444-1150
Dir., HR, Omaha World-Herald, NE, Omaha
Campbell, Terri........................(402) 444-1422
terri.campbell@owh.com, Adv. Mgr., Employment, Omaha World-Herald, NE, Omaha
Campbell, Renee.......................(970) 875-1791
Adv. Dir., Craig Daily Press, CO, Craig
Campbell, Chastity................................ext. 11
ccampbell@adspies.com, Sales Mgr., Advertising Data Scan/Adspies.com, FL, Jacksonville
Campbell, George......................(520) 573-4173
campbell@azstarnet.com, Copy Chief, Arizona Daily Star, AZ, Tucson
Campbell, Beau
bcampbell@inlandnews.com, Pres., Inland Graphics International LC, FL, Miami
bcampbell@inlandnews.com, Pres., Inland Newspaper Machinery LLC, KS, Lenexa
Campbell, Talmage.......(626) 962-8811 ext. 2129
talmage.campbell@sgvn.com, Exec. Ed., The Whittier Daily News, CA, Whittier
Campbell, Bob...........................321-242-3554
bcampbell@floridatoday.com, Operations Production Manager, Florida Today, FL, Melbourne
Campbell, Mark..............(812) 265-3641 ext. 27
mcampbell@madisoncourier.com, News Ed., The Madison Courier, IN, Madison
Campbell, Charles.........(719) 544-3520 ext. 411
newsroom@chieftain.com, Editorial Page Ed., The Pueblo Chieftain, CO, Pueblo
Campbell, Craig..........(519) 894-2250 ext. 2418
ccampbell@therecord.com, Circ. Mgr., Systems/Admin., The Record, ON, Kitchener
Campbell, Dave........................(216) 999-4335
Asst. Sports Editor, The Plain Dealer, OH, Cleveland
Campbell, Ruth
rcampbell@fstribune.com, Managing Editor, The Fort Scott Tribune, KS, Fort Scott
Campbell, Myrna............(580) 338-3355 ext. 12
businessmanager@guymondailyherald.com, Office Mgr., Guymon Daily Herald, OK, Guymon
Campbell, Scott........................(360) 735-4500
scott.campbell@columbian.com, Pub., The Columbian, WA, Vancouver
Campi, John G.........................(212) 210-1925
Vice Pres./Dir., Promo./Community Affairs, NY Daily News, NY, New York
Campillo, Oscar
raquel.sanz@marca.com, MD, MARCA, Madrid
Campo, Charles........................(207) 990-8160
bdnlib@bangordailynews.net, Librarian, Bangor Daily News, ME, Bangor
Campomizzi-Clews, Kathryn.........(570) 628-6006
kclews@republicanherald.com, News Ed., Republican Herald, PA, Pottsville
Campuzano Gomez, Andres
reporte@dns.centrinet.com.mx, Pres., El Reportero, Chilpancingo, Guerrero
Camus, Jacques
jacquescamus@larep.com, Ed. in Chief, LA REPUBLIQUE DU CENTRE, Orleans
Canaan, Don...............................352-750-9420
dcanaan@israelfaxx.com, Contact, Israel Faxx, FL, The Villages
Canacci, Bill.............................(732) 565-7322
bcanacci@thnt.com, Teen Scene Ed., Home News Tribune, NJ, East Brunswick
Canaday, Durwood....................(919) 829-4585
dcanaday@newsobserver.com, Vice Pres., Classified Adv., The News & Observer, NC, Raleigh
Canalis, John
john.canalis@latimes.com, Ed., Daily Pilot, CA, Costa Mesa
Cander Meulen, Wouter
wouter.candermeulen@persgroep.nl, Adv. Mgr., DE VOLKSKRANT, Amsterdam
Canela Ciurana, Jorge Luis
digital@trabaja.cip.cu, Dir., LOS TRABAJADORES, Havana
Canelas, Gonzalo...............................May-61
redaccion@grupocanales.com, Gen. Mgr., Los Tiempos, Cochabamba
Canelas Tardio, Gonzalo
info@correodelsur.net, Pres., Grupo Canelas, Sucre
Canepa, Valerie
vcanepa@ledger-enquirer.com, Pres./Pub., Columbus Ledger-Enquirer, GA, Columbus
Canfield, William
moreinfo@talx.com, CEO, TALX Corp., MO, Saint Louis
moreinfo@talx.com, CEO, TALX Corp., MO, Saint Louis
moreinfo@talx.com, CEO, TALX Corp., MO, Saint Louis
Cannon, Keith...........................(704) 233-8161
Wingate Univ., NC, Wingate
Cannon, Shawn.........................(620) 408-9930
shawn.cannon@dodgeglobe.com, Website Mgr., Dodge City Daily Globe, KS, Dodge City
Cannon, Jason
jason.cannon@demopolistimes.com, Pub., Demopolis Times, AL, Demopolis
Cannon, John...........................(606) 326-2649
Opinion Page Ed., The Daily Independent, KY, Ashland
Cannon, Joseph A......................(801) 237-2176
cannon@desnews.com, Ed., Deseret News, UT, Salt Lake City
Cannon, Frank
sales@pdisaneck.com, Pres., The Cannon Group, Inc., OH, Westerville
Cannon, Frank
sales@pdisaneck.com, Pres., PDI Plastics, OH, Westerville
Cannon, Shanna
scannon@redding.com, Pres./Pub., Record Searchlight, CA, Redding
Cano, Kelsey............................(937) 229-3878
Univ. of Dayton, OH, Dayton
Cant, Sue
scant@eastoregonian.com, Circulation Manager, East Oregonian, OR, Pendleton
Cantillo, Tatiana......................(305) 348-6993
Florida International Univ., FL, Miami
Cantillon, Sheila Murphy
fiveblue@earthlink.net, Self-Syndicator/Columnist, Work It!, CA, Santa Barbara
Cantley, Rebeccah....................(850) 599-2391
rcantley@tallahassee.com, Managing Ed., Tallahassee Democrat, FL, Tallahassee
Canton Zetina, Miguel
tab-hoy@nexus.net.mx, Pres., TABASCO HOY, Villahermosa, Tabasco
Cantor, Lori..............................(330) 72-0887
Kent State Univ., OH, Kent
Cantore, Mat............................(518) 629-4998
Hudson Valley Cmty. College, NY, Troy
Cantrell, Scott.........................(214) 977-8082
scantrell@dallasnews.com, Arts/Entertainment Critic, The Dallas Morning News, TX, Dallas
Cantrell, Susan..........................785-832-6307
scantrell@ljworld.com, Vice President of Sales and Marketing, The World Co.- Lawrence, Kan., Journal-World, KS, Lawrence
Cantu, Jose Gerardo......................83421392
editorial@prodigy.net.mx, CEO, EL PORVENIR, Monterrey, Nuevo Leon
Cantwell, Rebecca....................(303) 820-1537
rcantwell@denverpost.com, Political Ed., The Denver Post, CO, Denver
Canty, Patrick
patrick_canty@link.freedom.com, Pub., Odessa American, TX, Odessa
Capers, Averil..........................(508) 793-9483
acapers@telegram.com, Dir., Research, Telegram & Gazette, MA, Worcester
Capo, Carol.............................(757) 247-2837
ccapo@dailypress.com, Assoc. Ed., Editorial Page, Daily Press, VA, Newport News
Capriles, Manuel
direccion@elsiglo.com.ve, Pres., Publicaciones Capriles, Maracay
Cara, Cass...............................(805) 564-5251
ccara@newspress.com, Librarian, Santa Barbara News-Press, CA, Santa Barbara
Caracciolo, Carlo
redazione.re@gazzettadireggio.it, Pres., GAZZETTA DI REGGIO, Reggio Emilia
Caracciolo, Carlo
lettere@ilcentro.it, Pres., IL CENTRO, Pescara
Caracciolo, Carlo...............................220-111
iltirreno@finegilpal.inet.it, Pres., IL TIRRENO, Livorno
Caracciolo, Carlo
nuovavenezia@nuovavenezia.it, Pres., LA NUOVA VENEZIA, Venice
Caraganis, Nick........................(978) 970-4641
ncaraganis@lowellsun.com, Automotive Ed., The Sun, MA, Lowell
Carbajal, Alfredo......................(469) 977-3603
acarbajal@aldiatx.com, Ed. in Chief, Al Dia, TX, Dallas
Carbery, Thomas
tcarbery@technotrans.com, Vice Pres., Technotrans America, Inc., IL, Mount Prospect
Carbone, Filippo Agusto
direttore@laprovinciapavese.it, Pres., LA PROVINCIA PAVESE, Pavia
Card, Irene C...........................(973) 492-2828
irenec@micinsurance.com, Pres./Author, MIC Insurance Services, NJ, Kinnelon
Cardello, Frank
sales@thoughtequity.com, Vice Pres., Bus. Devel., Thought Equity Management, Inc., CO
Cardello, Frank
sales@thoughtequity.com, Vice Pres., Bus. Devel., Thought Equity Management, Inc., CO, Denver
Carden, Barry
bcarden@messenger-inquirer.com, Circ. Dir., Messenger-Inquirer, KY, Owensboro
Carden, Sandy
scarden@dailyhome.com, Adv. Mgr., Retail Sales, The Daily Home, AL, Talladega
Cardenas, Rogelio
contacto@elfinanciero.com.mx, Owner/Pres., EL FINANCIERO, Puebla, Puebla
Cardenas Sarmiento, Rogelio
contacto@elfinanciero.com.mx, Owner/Pres., EL FINANCIERO, Toluca, Mexico
contacto@elfinanciero.com.mx, Owner/Pres., EL FINANCIERO, Monterrey, Nuevo Leon
contacto@elfinanciero.com.mx, Owner/Pres., EL FINANCIERO, Queretaro, Queretaro
contacto@elfinanciero.com.mx, Owner/Pres., EL FINANCIERO, Mexico City, Distrito Federal
contacto@elfinanciero.com.mx, Owner/Pres., EL FINANCIERO, Merida, Yucatan
contacto@elfinanciero.com.mx, Dir., El Financiero, Guaymas, Sonora
contacto@elfinanciero.com.mx, Owner/Pres., El Financiero, Hermosillo, Sonora
contacto@elfinanciero.com.mx, Owner/Pres., El Financiero, Cuernavaca, Morelos
Cardona, Rene.........................(956) 882-5143
Collegian Editor, Univ. of Texas at Brownsville, TX, Brownsville
Cardona Delclos, Juan
maritimas@men-car.com, Mng. Dir., DIARIO MARITIMAS, Barcelona
Cardosa, Robert...............................ext. 215
bcardosa@thewesterlysun.com, Vice Pres./Adv. Dir., The Westerly Sun, RI, Westerly
Cardwell, Joel.............................ext. 5904
Adv. Mgr., Classified, The Post and Courier, SC, Charleston
Cardwell, Jewell.......................(330) 996-3567
jcardwell@thebeaconjournal.com, Columnist, Local, Akron Beacon Journal, OH, Akron
Carey, Conell...........................(609) 272-7035
ccareyl@pressofac.com, Adv. Mgr., Reg'l, The Press of Atlantic City, NJ, Pleasantville
Carey, George B.
gbcarey@aol.com, Prodn. Foreman, Composing/Pressroom, The Daily Clintonian, IN, Clinton
Carey, Ellen.............................(718) 990-6756
St. John's Univ., NY, Queens
Carey, Bob...............................(403) 328-4003
bcarey@lethbridgeherald.com, Vice Pres./Gen. Mgr., Southern Alberta Newspaper Group, AB, Lethbridge
Carey, Bob...............................(403) 328-4003
bcarey@lethbridgeherald.com, Vice Pres./Gen. Mgr., The Lethbridge Herald, AB, Lethbridge
Carey, James...........................925432-7246
james@onthehouse.com, Pres./Co-Host, On The House Syndication, Inc., CA, Brentwood
Carey, Morris...........................(925) 432-7246
morris@onthehouse.com, Vice Pres./Co-Host, On The House Syndication, Inc., CA, Brentwood
Carey, Renee...........................(919) 739-7840
rcarey@newsargus.com, Editor, Goldsboro News-Argus, NC, Goldsboro
Carey, Angela
editassist@thecourier.com.au, Ed., THE BALLARAT COURIER
Carideo, Tony
info@news-council.org, Chrmn., Minnesota News Council, MN, Minneapolis
Carifio, Edward
ecarifio@yumasun.com, Sports Editor, Yuma Sun, AZ, Yuma
Carlbom, Herbert W.
carlbomhs@cox.net, Pres., CK Optical Co., Inc., CA
Carletta, Dennis.......................(973) 392-1705
dcarletta@starledger.com, Circ. Dir., The Star-Ledger, NJ, Newark
Carlisle, Jill
jillcarlisle@emeraldis.com, MIS Sys. Operator, The Index-Journal, SC, Greenwood
Carlos, Alvanilson.........................315-3200
diretor@omossoroense.com.br, Pres., O Mossoroense, Mossoro, Rio Grande do Norte
Carlsen, Dorthe
doca@stiften.dk, Ed. in Chief, ARHUUS STIFTSTIDENDE, Aarhus, Jutland
Carlson, Mary..........................(262) 513-2629
mcarlson@conleynet.com, Automotive Ed., The Freeman, WI, Waukesha
Carlson, Mark..........................(425) 339-3457
carlson@heraldnet.com, News Ed., The Herald, WA, Everett
Carlson, Bernadette
bcarlson@gaa.org, Exec. Dir., Gravure Association of America, NY, Rochester
Carlson, Rod...........................(541) 957-4292
rcarlson@nrtoday.com, Prodn. Mgr., The News-Review, OR, Roseburg
Carlson, Ken...........................(209) 578-2321
kcarlson@modbee.com, Health/Medical Reporter, The Modesto Bee, CA, Modesto
Carlson, Carole........................(219) 477-6011
ccarlson@post-trib.com, Porter County Ed., Post-Tribune, IN, Merrillville
Carlson, John...............(847) 981-9399 ext. 275
carlsonj@corp.inxintl.com, Sr. Vice Pres.-Gen. Affairs/Admin., INX International Ink Co., IL, Schaumburg
Carlson, D. Lee.........................717-255-8272
lcarlson@pnco.com, General Manager, The Patriot-News, PA, Mechanicsburg
Carlsson, Luf
lufcarlsson@ostran.se, Ed. in Cheif, OSTRA SMALAND/NYHETERNA, Kalmar
Carlsson, Thomas
tomas.carlsson@lt.se, Ed., LANSTIDNINGEN, Sodertalje
Carman, Bill

sales@dccusa.com, Sales Rep., Dialogic Communications Corp., TN, Franklin
Carmona de Sanchez, Irma Yolanda
tribuna@tribunacampeche.com, Gen. Mgr., Tribuna de Campeche, Campeche, Campeche
Carnan, Azriane
sales.us@interactivedata.com, Mktg. Mgr., Interactive Data Real-Time Services, Inc., NY, White Plains
Carnbro, Kjell
kjell.carnbro@st.nu, Ed. in Chief, SUNDSVALLS TIDNING, Sundsvall
Carneiro Dias, Paulo Antonio..............242-3189
Pres., Diario de Petropolis, Petropolis, Rio de Janeiro
Carney, John I. ....ext. 216
jcarney@t-g.com, City Ed., Shelbyville Times-Gazette, TN, Shelbyville
Carney, Jeff 402-444-1078
Managing Editor for Digital Development, Omaha World-Herald, NE, Omaha
Carney, Jeff 402-444-1078
Managing Editor for Digital Development, Omaha World-Herald, NE, Omaha
Carolyn, Gibson
cgibson@lagrandeobserver.com, The Observer, OR, La Grande
Caron, Glen
gcaron@esthervilledailynews.com, Pub., Estherville Daily News, IA, Estherville
Caron, Kevin ....(705) 759-3030 ext. 268
Prodn. Mgr., The Sault Star, ON, Sault Ste Marie
Carone, Aurelio Flores 213-1210
Pres., Diario de Minas, Belo Horizonte, Minas Gerais
Carpenter, Todd
todd.carpenter@natchezdemocrat.com, Pub., Natchez Newspapers, Inc., MS, Natchez
Carpenter, Jeff
info@dtint.com, Pres./COO, Digital Technology International, UT, Springville
info@dtint.com, COO, Digital Technology International, UT, Springville
Carpenter, Todd H.
todd.carpenter@natchezdemocrat.com, Pres., The Natchez Democrat, MS, Natchez
Carpenter, Bryant ....(203) 317-2204
bcarpenter@record-journal.com, Asst. Sports Ed., Record-Journal, CT, Meriden
Carpenter, Chris ....(607) 777-2515
SUNY/Binghamton, NY, Binghamton
Carpenter, Ken........................(407) 299-5000
Valencia Cmty. College, FL, Orlando
Carpenter, Chris
ccarpenter@opubco.com, Adv. Mgr., Real Estate Sales, The Oklahoman, OK, Oklahoma City
Carr, Paul..............................(254) 710-4693
Paul_Carr@baylor.edu, Dir., Mktg. Information, Baylor (University) Lariat, TX, Waco
Carr, Scott
scarr@acnpapers.com, Adv. Dir., McKinney Courier-Gazette, TX, McKinney
Carr, Gene
gcarr@acnpapers.com, Pres., Star Community Newspapers, TX, Plano
Carr, Geoff
gtcarr@nic.edu, Advisor, North Idaho College, ID, Coeur D Alene
Carr, Cindy 662-678-1534
cindy.carr@djournal.com, Classified Advertising Manager, Journal Publishing Company, MS, Tupelo
Carr, Gene ....(952) 392-6851
gcarr@mnsun.com, CEO, American Community Newspapers LLC, MN, Eden Prairie
Carr, Dan ....ext. 141
dcarr@timesonline.com, Adv. Mgr., Sales, Beaver County Times, PA, Beaver
Carranza, Rafael 305-262-7575
rcarranza@efeamerica.com, Sales and Business Development Director, EFE News Services - Washington, DC, DC, Washington
Carrasco, Sergio Rivero
cip228@cip.enet.cu, Dir., VICTORIA, Isla De La Juventud
Carrasco Jahnsen, Jorge 233 2233
redinfo@eldiario.net, Gen. Mgr., El Diario, La Paz
Carre, Karen ....(518) 483-4720
kcarre@mtelegram.com, Adv. Mgr., The Malone Telegram, NY, Malone
Carrer, Paolo. G
correo@elmundo-eldia.com, Pres., EL MUNDO/EL DIA DE BALEARES, Palma de Mallorca, Balearic Islands
Carreras, Âµngel
eladelanto@eladelanto.com, Dir., El Adelanto, Salamanca
Carretero Balboa, Jose
elbravo@riogrande.net.mx, Pres., EL BRAVO, Matamoros, Tamaulipas
elbravo@riogrande.net.mx, Pres., PM DE EL BRAVO, Matamoros, Tamaulipas
Carrier, Wayne.........................(251) 219-5305
Circ. Mgr., Home Delivery, Press-Register, AL, Mobile
Carrillo, Carlos
ccarrillo@controlengineering.com, Engineering Mgr., Control Engineering Co., CA, Costa Mesa
Carrington, Jim
sports@bemidjipioneer.com, Sports Ed., The Pioneer, MN, Bemidji
Carroll, Ellin
ecarroll@nashuatelegraph.com, Mgr., HR/Vice Pres., Admin., The Telegraph, NH, Hudson
Carroll, Rick
rcarroll@aspentimes.com, Mng. Ed., The Aspen Times, CO, Aspen
Carroll, Vincent.......................(303) 892-2477
carrollv@rockymountainnews.com, Editorial Page Ed., Rocky Mountain News, CO, Denver
Carroll, Jimmy........................(336) 888-3542
jcarroll@hpe.com, Home Furnishings Ed., High Point Enterprise, NC, High Point
Carroll, Christopher 615-322-6610
chris.carroll@vanderbilt.edu, Executive Director, College Media Advisers, TN, Nashville
Carroll, Braxton ....(805) 739-2222
IT/Web Admin., The Lompoc Record, CA, Lompoc
Carroll, Nicole ....(602) 444-8797
nicole.carroll@arizonarepublic.com, Exec. Ed., The Arizona Republic, AZ, Phoenix
Carroll, Susan
scarroll@ebt.com, PR Mgr., eBT, RI, Providence
Carroll, Stacey
scarroll@ap.org, Administrative Asst., Virginia Associated Press, VA, Richmond
Carroll, Andrew 613-933-3160
maned@standard-freeholder.com, Managing Editor, Standard-Freeholder, ON, Cornwall
Carroll, Deborah
hottopics@comcast.net, Pres., Hot Topics Publications, Inc., PA, Wyncote
Carroll, Gary J. ....(412) 369-3590
gcarroll@denexinc.com, Pres., Denex, Inc., NC, Southern Pines
Carron, Eileen Dupuch
ecarron@tribunemedia.net, Pub./Ed., NASSAU DAILY TRIBUNE, Nassau
Carson, Mary ....(414) 410-4173
Cardinal Stritch Univ., WI, Milwaukee
Carson, Clay ....(501) 378-3653
Mgr., Data Processing/Typeset, Arkansas Democrat-Gazette, AR, Little Rock
Carsten, Helen
carsten@siadvance.com, Sec., Staten Island Advance, NY, Staten Island
Carstorp, Goran
webmaster@sn.se, Ed., SODERMANLANDS NYHETER, Nykoping
Carswell, Steve........................(904) 819-3520
steve.carswell@staugustinerecord.com, Prodn. Dir., The St. Augustine Record, FL, Saint Augustine
Carter, Chris 605-886-6901
Dir., Admin., Watertown Public Opinion, SD, Watertown
Carter, Cindy ....ext. 1160
cindy.carter@gwinnettdailypost.com, Adv. Mgr., Legal Notices, Gwinnette Daily Post, GA, Lawrenceville
Carter, Lee
lcarter@standard.net, Pub. VP, Standard-Examiner, UT, Ogden
lcarter@standard.net, El Estandar, UT, Ogden
Carter, Steve
steve.carter@gaflnews.com, Sports Ed., The Tifton Gazette, GA, Tifton
Carter, Deedie
deedie.carter@troymessenger.com, Adv. Dir., The Messenger, AL, Troy
Carter, Danny ....(229) 888-9346
danny.carter@albanyherald.com, Mng. Ed., The Albany Herald, GA, Albany
Carter, Andrew
acater@mydailytribune.com, Ed., Point Pleasant Register, WV, Point Pleasant
Carter, Carl
newsroom@gladstoneobserver.com.au, Gen. Mgr., THE GLADSTONE OBSERVER
Carter, Denise ....(540) 932-3542
dcarter@newsvirginian.com, Bus. Mgr., The News Virginian, VA, Waynesboro
Carter, Donnie ....(912) 283-2244
donnie.carter@wjhnews.com, Mgr., Promo., Waycross Journal-Herald, GA, Waycross
Carthew, Renee ....(814) 532-5072
Style Ed., The Tribune-Democrat, PA, Johnstown
Carty, Paul V. ....(318) 487-6370
pcarty@thetowntalk.com, Exec. Ed., The Town Talk, LA, Alexandria
Caruso, Frank
fcaruso@hearst.com, Vice Pres., Creative Services, King Features Syndicate, NY, New York
Caruso, Glenn ....(814) 870-1755
glenn.caruso@timesnews.com, Circ. Dir., Erie Times-News, PA, Erie
Carver, Deborah.......................(509) 582-1530
librarian@tri-cityherald.com, Librarian, Tri-City Herald, WA, Kennewick
Carver, Douglas
carverdigital@earthlink.net, Contact, Carver Digital, NY, New York
Carveth, Rod
carvethr@csusys.ctstateu.edu, Chair, University of Bridgeport, CT, Bridgeport
Casale, Tony
acasale@imsworld.com, Chrmn./CEO, American Opinion Research, NJ, Princeton
Casanova, Amanda ....(979) 845-3315
Texas A&M Univ., TX, College Station
Casas, Shannon ....(770) 718-3417
scasas@gainesvilletimes.com, Asst. Life Ed., The Times, GA, Gainesville
Casciano, Debra
dcasciano@press-register.com, Sec., Southern Circulation Managers Association, AL, Mobile
Case, Lloyd ....(701) 235-7311 ext. 5404
Pres./CEO, Forum Communications Co., ND, Fargo
Casensky, Robert
mfdnes@mfdnes.cz, Ed. in Chief, MLADA FRONTA DNES, Prague
Casey, Kit..............................(203) 236-9800
Univ. of Connecticut, CT, Waterbury
Casey, Ashley.........................(315) 445-4542
dolphin@lemoyne.edu, Co-Executive Editor, The Dolphin, NY, Syracuse
Casey, William ....(319) 335-5788
Univ. of Iowa, IA, Iowa City
Casey, Paula ....(602) 261-7655 ext. 102
p.casey@ananews.com, Exec. Dir., ANA Advertising Services, Inc. (Arizona Newspaper Association), AZ, Phoenix
Casey, Mitch ....(740) 376-5468
mcasey@mariettatimes.com, Photo Ed., The Marietta Times, OH, Marietta
Casey, Wilson ....(864) 621-7129
trivguy@bellsouth.net, Trivia Guiness World Record Holder/Syndicated Columnist, Trivia Guy by Guinness Holder, SC, Spartanburg
Casey, Paula.............................602-261-7655
p.casey@ananews.com, Exec. Dir., Arizona Newspapers Association, AZ, Phoenix
Casey, Kevin ....(973) 210-6382
kcasey@lds.com, Vice Pres., Mktg., Logical Design Solutions, NJ, Florham Park
Cash, John E. ....(423) 359-3165
jcash@xtn.net, Vice Pres., Adv., Jones Media, Inc., TN, Greeneville
Cashman, Louis P. ....(601) 636-4545 ext. 122
pcashman@vicksburgpost.com, Ed., The Vicksburg Post, MS, Vicksburg
Casini, Jamie ....(650) 391-1345
jcasini@dailynewsgroup.com, Mng. Ed., Palo Alto Daily News, CA, Menlo Park
Casler, Sheila.........................(330) 580-8356
sheila.casler@cantonrep.com, Circ. Dir., The Independent, OH, Massillon
Casselton, Valerie ....(604) 605-2125
vcasselton@vancouversun.com, Exec. Ed., The Vancouver Sun, BC, Vancouver
Cassidy, Naomi.......................(315) 425-1255
nbelmar@humidity.com, Mktg. Coord., Walter Meier Climate (USA), Inc., NY, Ogdensburg
Cassidy, Craig ....ext. 580
ccassidy@uniondemocrat.com, Ed., The Union Democrat, CA, Sonora
Casson, Thomas J.
tom@superiorlihtoplate.com, Nat'l Sales Mgr., Superior Lithoplate of Indiana, Inc., IN, Rockville
Castagneto, Alfonso
estrell@entelchile.net, Dir., Empresa El Mercurio S.A.P., Valparaiso
Castaneda Perez, Manuel Angel
eco.dm@eldiariomontanes.es, Dir., El Diario Montanes, Santander, Cantabria
Castanho, Evanilton Sergio 534-9192
jornalrclaro@linkway.com.br, Pres., Jornal de Rio Claro, Rio Claro, Sao Paulo
Castano, Javier.......................(917) 339-0850
javier.castano@hoynyc.com, Ed. in Chief, Hoy, NY, New York
Castegnier, Pierre
marketing@elcorsy.com, Vice Pres., Mktg., Elcorsy Technology, Inc., QC, Saint Laurent
Castelaz, Terri
tcastelaz@ironmountaindailynews.com, Lifestyles Ed., The Daily News, MI, Iron Mountain
Castellanos, Alicia Paz 21-1811
dlandes@dlandes.com, Gen. Mgr., Casa Muchacho Hermanos C.A., Valera, Trujillo
Castilla Galindo, Armando
arcasa@vanguardia.com, Dir., VANGUARDIA, Saltillo, Coahuila
Castillo, Luis Antonio Contreras
luis-contreras-castillo@hotmail.com, Chrmn., Administrative council, DIARIO DE QUINTANA ROO, Chetumal, Quintana Roo
Castillo, Darragh Doiron ....(409) 721-2430
doiron@panews.com, Life/Entertainment Ed., Port Arthur News, TX, Port Arthur
Castillo, Owen..................................63-9761
elchino@edsport.com.pe, Ed., El Chino, Lima
Castillon, John ....(916) 321-1336
jcastillon@sacbee.com, Adv. Mgr., Classified/Real Estate, The Sacramento Bee, CA, Sacramento
Castle, John.....................................ext. 302
jcastle@johnsoncitypress.com, Opns. Mgr., Johnson City Press, TN, Johnson City
Castle, Keith
keithcastle@mcgrann.com, Sr. Vice Pres., Sales, McGrann Paper Corp., NC, Charlotte
Castleberry, Bruce ....(479) 872-5188
bcastleberry@nwaonline.net, Bus. Ed., The Morning News of Northwest Arkansas, AR, Springdale
Castor, Gary.............................573-761-0255
gary@newstribune.com, Mng. Ed., News Tribune, MO, Jefferson City
Castor, Stephen R.
worldpressusa@aol.com, Ed., World Press, MI, West Bloomfield
Castoria, Louie ....(650) 726-7973
castoria@earthlink.net, Humorist, QuipTide.com, CA, Half Moon Bay
Castrejon, Aaron ....(909) 869-3530
The Poly Post, CA, Pomona
Castro, Tony...........................(352) 544-5278
acastro@hernandotoday.com, Sports Ed., Hernando Today, FL, Brooksville
Castro, Greg................(760) 322-8889 ext. 565
gcastro@palmspri.gannett.com, Circ. Dir., The Desert Sun, CA, Palm Springs
Castro, Veronica 437-800
market@salnet.com.ar, Gen. Mgr., El Tribuno de Jujuy, San Salvador de Jujuy, Provincia de San Salvador de Jujuy
Castro Caro, Antonio
info@abc.es, Ed. in Chief, ABC, Jerez de la Frontera
Casullo, Richard ....(518) 454-5727
rcasullo@timesunion.com, Prodn. Supt., Mailroom, Times Union, NY, Albany
Catania Chiaramida, Lisa

lchiaramida@lfpress.com, Adv. Dir., The London Free Press, ON, London
Catchings, Billy
catchings@uindy.edu, Chair, University of Indianapolis, IN, Indianapolis
Cates, E. Nuel
dcr@dailycommercialrecord.com, Pub., Daily Commercial Record
Cates, Carl
ccates@valdosta.edu, Head, Valdosta State University, GA, Valdosta
Catlett, Vicki ....(251) 219-5402
Controller/Treasurer, Press-Register, AL, Mobile
Caton-Rosser, Mary ....(605) 642-6422
Black Hills State Univ., SD, Spearfish
Caton-Rosser, Mary
marycatonrosser@bhsu.edu, Asst. Prof., Mass Commun., Black Hills State University, SD, Spearfish
Catron, Derek
derek.catron@news-jrnl.com, Asst. Mng. Ed., Daytona Beach News-Journal, FL, Daytona Beach
Caudill, Tom ....(859) 231-3301
tcaudill@herald-leader.com, Asst. Mng. Ed., Local News, Lexington Herald-Leader, KY, Lexington
Caulkins, Ann
acaulkins@charlotteobserver.com, Pres./Pub., The Charlotte Observer, NC, Charlotte
Cavalier, Debbie................(402) 444-1455
deb.cavalier@owh.com, Adv. Mgr., Real Estate, Omaha World-Herald, NE, Omaha
Cavaliere, Phyllis ....(212) 576-9504
pcav@metrosn.com, CEO, Metro Newspaper Advertising Services, Inc. Sunday Magazine Network - New York, NY, NY, New York
Cavaliere, Phyllis ....(212) 576-9504
pcav@metrosn.com, Chairman/CEO, Metro Newspaper Advertising Services, Inc., NY, New York
Cavaliere, Phyllis ....(212) 576-9504
pcav@metrosn.com, Pres./CEO, Metro-Puck Comics Network - New York, NY, NY, New York
Cavallo, Carol ....ext. 4169
ccavallo@phillyburbs.com, Librarian, Bucks County Courier Times, PA, Levittown
Cavataio, Christy
orangecountyinfo@c-b.com, Contact, Carter/Burgess, Inc., CA, Santa Ana
Cavazos, Daniel R.
rdcavazos@brownsvilleherald.com, Pub., The Brownsville Herald, TX, Brownsville
Cavazos, R. Daniel
rdaniel_cavazos@link.freedom.com, Pub., El Nuevo Heraldo, TX, Brownsville
Cavone, Joseph ....(732) 643-3150
jcav1@app.com, Vice Pres., Mktg., Home News Tribune, NJ, East Brunswick
Cavone, Joseph
jcavone@gannett.com, Pres./Pub., Daily Record, NJ, Parsippany
Caywood, David................609-272-7036
Special Sections Manager, The Press of Atlantic City, NJ, Pleasantville
Cazalas, Mike................(850) 747-5094
mmcazalas@pcnh.com, Ed., The News Herald, FL, Panama City
Ceballo Bustos, Florencio
info@diarioficial.cl, Pres., Diario Oficial, Santiago
Cech, Lisa
Online Ed., editor@dln.com, The Daily Legal News and Cleveland Recorder
Cecil, Mike................(309) 686-3117
mcecil@pjstar.com, Metro Ed., Journal Star, IL, Peoria
Cederholm, Vicki................(719) 636-0307
vicki.cederholm@gazette.com, Adv. Dir., Sales Opns., The Gazette, CO, Colorado Springs
Cejas, Raul Hector................42-1857
Pub., El Orden, Coronel Pringles, Provincia de Buenos Aires
Cejudo Hidalgo, Jose
info@abc.es, Ed. in Chief, ABC, Huelva
Cekongz, Sheobanna
union@chasque.apc.org, Ed., La Union, Minas, Lavalleja
Celestino, John................(609) 272-7047
jcelestino@pressofac.com, VP Sales & Marketing, The Press of Atlantic City, NJ, Pleasantville
Centers, Joe ....ext. 234
jcenters@norwalkreflector.com, Mng. Ed., Norwalk Reflector, OH, Norwalk
Centofanti, Lou
corporate@perma-fix.com, Pres./CEO, Perma-Fix Environmental Services, GA, Atlanta
Centoni, Danielle ....(925) 416-4840
dcentoni@angnewspapers.com, Food Ed., San Mateo County Times, CA, San Mateo
Cerasani, Monty
mpi@marketingplusinc.com, Pres./CEO, Marketing Plus, Inc., NJ, Woodbridge
Cerna, Marco C.
mcerna@duarteregister.com, Latin America Sales, Duarte Register Systems, Inc., CA, Palo Alto
Cerny, Keith R................(719) 589-2553 ext. 120
krcemail@aol.com, Publisher/Adv. Dir., The Valley Courier, CO, Alamosa
Ceron, Aline Magalhaes................534-5511
alinejc@uol.com.br, Pres., Jornal Cidade, Rio Claro, Sao Paulo
Cerro Moral, Maria Ofelia
chiclayo@laindustria.com.pe, Pres., Satelite, Trujillo, La Libertad
chiclayo@laindustria.com.pe, Pres., The Cerro Family, Lima
chiclayo@laindustria.com.pe, Gen. Mgr., La Industria, Chiclayo, Lambayeque
Cerro de Burga, Isabel 23-4270
redaccion@laindustria.com, Pres., La Industria, Chiclayo, Lambayeque
redaccion@laindustria.com, Gen. Mgr., La Industria, Trujillo
redaccion@laindustria.com, Gen. Mgr., Satelite, Trujillo, La Libertad
redaccion@laindustria.com, Gen. Mgr., The Cerro Family, Lima
Cervantes, MÂ ximo HernÂ ndez
publicidad@elsoldetlaxcala.com.mx, Dir., EL SOL DE TLAXCALA, Tlaxcala, Tlaxcala
Cessna, Robert ....(979) 731-4638
robert.cessna@theeagle.com, Sports Ed., The Eagle, TX, Bryan
Chabalgoity, Ariel
aqui1952@adinet.com.uy, Pres., Aqui Esta, San Jose
Chacko, Ninan
ninan.chacko@prnewswire.com, CEO, PR Newswire - San Diego, CA, CA, San Diego
ninan.chacko@prnewswire.com, CEO, PR Newswire - Cleveland, OH, OH, Cleveland
ninan.chacko@prnewswire.com, CEO, PR Newswire - Boston, MA, MA, Boston
ninan.chacko@prnewswire.com, CEO, PR Newswire - Atlanta, GA, GA, Atlanta
ninan.chacko@prnewswire.com, CEO, PR Newswire - Charlotte, NC, NC, Charlotte
ninan.chacko@prnewswire.com, CEO, PR Newswire - Seattle, WA, WA, Seattle
ninan.chacko@prnewswire.com, CEO, PR Newswire - San Francisco, CA, CA, San Francisco
ninan.chacko@prnewswire.com, CEO, PR Newswire - New York, NY, NY, New York
ninan.chacko@prnewswire.com, CEO, PR Newswire - Philadelphia, PA, PA, Philadelphia
ninan.chacko@prnewswire.com, CEO, PR Newswire - Minneapolis, MN, MN, Minneapolis
ninan.chacko@prnewswire.com, CEO, PR Newswire - Washington, DC, DC, Washington
ninan.chacko@prnewswire.com, CEO, PR Newswire - Denver, CO, CO, Denver
ninan.chacko@prnewswire.com, CEO, PR Newswire - Los Angeles, CA, CA, Los Angeles
ninan.chacko@prnewswire.com, CEO, PR Newswire - Chicago, IL, IL, Chicago
ninan.chacko@prnewswire.com, CEO, PR Newswire - Pittsburgh, PA, PA, Pittsburgh
Chadda, Kalyani
kchadha@jmail.umd.edu, Exec. Dir., American Association of Sunday and Feature Editors, MD, College Park
Chae-Keun, Chang
webmaster@hk.co.kr, Pres., HANKOOK ILBO, Seoul
Chafai, Reda ....(773) 206-4676
DePaul Univ., IL, Chicago
Chaffin, Dan
dchaffin@dailycall.com, Prod. Mgr., Piqua Daily Call, OH, Piqua
Chaffin, Nancy
nchaffin@bakersfield.com, Vice Pres., HR, The Bakersfield Californian, CA, Bakersfield
Chafin, Kathy
kchafin@loganbanner.com, Adv. Mgr., The Logan Banner, WV, Logan
Chako, Ninan
ninan.chacko@prnewswire.com, CEO, PR Newswire - New York, NY, NY, New York
Chakraborty, Chandan
kalantar_patrika@hotmail.com, Ed., Kalantar, Kolkata, West Bengal
Chalabian, Steven H.
kjack@kjack.com, Vice Pres., Sales, K-Jack Engineering Co., Inc., CA, Gardena
Chalen, Marco 262-3052
Gen. Mgr., EL MERCURIO, Manta, Manabi
Challoner, Louise 020 701 75445
louise.challoner@informa.com, Head of Marketing, Lloyd's List, LLOYD'S OF LONDON PRESS, London
Chamberlain, Adrian ....(250) 380-5364
achamberlain@te.canwest.com, Arts/Entertainment Reporter, Times Colonist, BC, Victoria
Chambers, Emily................(937) 225-2098
echambers@coxohio.com, Regional Vice President, Human Resourcs, Dayton Daily News, OH, Dayton
Chambers, Emily................(404) 894-2831
Georgia Inst. of Technology, GA, Atlanta
Chamorro Cardenal, Xavier
ndiaro@elnuevodiario.com.ni, Pres./Owner, EL NUEVO DIARIO, Managua
Champion, Lee
lee.champion@alexcityoutlook.com, Prodn. Mgr., Alexander City Outlook, AL, Alexander City
Champion, Laurel R. ....(734) 994-6936
lchampion@annarbornews.com, Pub., The Ann Arbor News, MI, Ann Arbor
Champion, Lea Ann................(210) 821-4105
Sr. Exec. Vice Pres./CMO, AT&T, Inc., TX, San Antonio
Chan, Bryan................(408) 719-5100
sales@broadxent.com, Vice Pres., Sales/Mktg., Broadxent, Inc., CA, Milpitas
Chan, Michael G................(212) 969-7578
mchan@hearst.com, Director, Web Development, North America Syndicate, NY, New York
Chan, William
william56chan@yahoo.com, Ed., UTUSAN SARAWAK, Kuching, Sarawak
Chan, Michael G. 212-969-7578
Director, Web Development, King Features Syndicate, NY, New York
Chan-Olmsted, Sylvia ....(352) 392-6557
Prof./Assoc. Dean, Research/AI and Effie Flanagan Prof. in Journalism & Communications, University of Florida, FL, Gainesville
Chance, Don
info@yale.com, Pres., Yale Materials Handling Corp., NC, Greenville
Chandler, Becky ....(601) 636-4545 ext. 124
bchandler@vicksburgpost.com, Circ. Dir., The Vicksburg Post, MS, Vicksburg
Chandler, Robert C.
robert.chandler@pepperdine.edu, Chair, Pepperdine University, CA, Malibu
Chandler, Myriah
classified@nsb-observer.com, Circ. Mgr., The Observer, FL, New Smyrna Beach
Chandler, Ross................252-407-9942
Features Ed., Rocky Mount Telegram, NC, Rocky Mount
Chaney, Kathy 312-225-2400
Managing Editor, Chicago Defender, IL, Chicago
Chaney, Lynn................(254) 757-5783
lchaney@wacotrib.com, Human Resource Manager, Waco Tribune-Herald, TX, Waco
Chang, Yoon Young
yychang@heraldm.com, Mng. Ed., THE HERALD BUSINESS, Seoul
Chang, F. A.
cip218@cip.enet.cu, Dir., VANGUARDIA, Santa Clara
Channing, Mark
mark@amalgamatedpublishers.com, MD, Amalgamated Publishers, Inc., NY, New York
Channon, Ethel................ext. 7224
echannon@texarkanagazette.com, Mng. Ed., Texarkana Gazette, TX, Texarkana
Chantianont Wong, PattnaPong
pattnapong@bangkokpost.co.th, Ed., BANGKOK POST, Bangkok
Chaparro Espitia, Leovanny 571-0505
Gen. Mgr., DIARIO LA FRONTERA, Cucuta, Santander Del Norte
Chapin, Sonya ....(756) 285-8256
Ball State Daily News, IN, Muncie
Chapin, Rob................(413) 788-3519
rchapin@repub.com, IT Mgr., The Republican, MA, Springfield
Chapin, Tom
tchapin@punxsutawneyspirit.com, Ed., The Punxsutawney Spirit, PA, Punxsutawney
Chapman, Randy
news@postbulletin.com, Pub., Post-Bulletin, MN, Rochester
Chapman, Robert ....(979) 731-4682
robert.chapman@theeagle.com, Pressroom Mgr., The Eagle, TX, Bryan
Chapman, Paul ....(604) 605-2078
pchapman@theprovince.com, Prodn. Mgr., Post Press, The North Bay Nugget, ON, North Bay
pchapman@theprovince.com, Senior News. Ed., The Province, BC, Vancouver
Chapman, Peggy ....(760) 739-6610
pchapman@nctimes.com, HR Dir., North County Times, CA, Escondido
Chapman, Indra ....(214) 640-3118
ichapman@beldenassociates.com, Project Dir., Belden Associates, TX, Dallas
Chapman, Robert ....(413) 496-6332
rchapman@berkshireeagle.com, Adv. Mgr., The Berkshire Eagle, MA, Pittsfield
Chapman, Josie ....ext. 1061
jchapman@portervillerecorder.com, Adv. Supvr., The Porterville Recorder, CA, Porterville
Chapman, Bob
rchapman@thetranscript.com, Adv. Dir., North Adams Transcript, MA, North Adams
Chapnick, John P.
john@blackstar.com, Vice Pres., Black Star Publishing Co., Inc., NY, New York
Chapnick, Ben ....(212) 679-3288
ben@blackstar.com, Pres., Black Star Publishing Co., Inc., NY, New York
Chappell, Steven................(615) 898-2205
Middle Tennessee State Univ., TN, Murfreesboro
Charbel, Ghassan
gcharbel@alhayat.com, Ed. in Chief, AL HAYAT
Charbonneau, JoAnn ....(815) 935-8713
jacharbonneau@ameritech.net, Gen. Mgr., Mississippi Valley Classified Advertising Association, IL, Kankakee
Charette, Traci
tcharette@ironmountaindailynews.com, Adv. Dir., The Daily News, MI, Iron Mountain
Charisse, Marc ....ext. 112
mcharisse@eveningsun.com, Ed. in Chief, The Evening Sun, PA, Hanover
Charles, Susan
scharles@acaweb.ca, Vice Pres., Member Servs., Association of Canadian Advertisers, Inc., ON, Toronto
Charles, Mickey................(215) 441-8444 ext. 2100
mcharles@sportsnetwork.com, Pres./CEO, The Sports Network, PA, Hatboro
mcharles@sportsnetwork.com, Pres./CEO, The Sports Network (Div. of Computer Info. Network), PA, Hatboro
Chartrand, Keith................(352) 753-1119
keith.chartrand@thevillagesmedia.com, Sports Ed., The Villages Daily Sun, FL, The Villages
Chase, Debra 716-250-6892
dchase@classifiedsplus.com, Client Partnerships, Classifieds Plus, Inc., NY, Williamsville
Chase, Denny................(231) 933-1494
dchase@record-eagle.com, Sports Ed.,

Record-Eagle, MI, Traverse City
Chatelain, Steve
steve.chatelain@kearneyhub.com, Pres./Pub., Kearney Hub, NE, Kearney
Chatelain, Stephen ....(308) 233-9700
Ed., Kearney Hub, NE, Kearney
Chatham, Betty
editorial@eldoradonews.com, Gen. Mgr., El Dorado News-Times, AR, El Dorado
Chaudhary, Durga Prasad
daidainiknavajyothi@siffy.com, Ed. in Chief, DAINIK NAVAJYOTI, Ajmer, Rajasthan
Chaudhary, Deen Bandhu
jaipur@dainiknavajyoti.com, Pub./Ed., NAVAJYOTI, Jaipur, Rajasthan
Chaudhuri, Sushil
ganadoot@rediffmail.com, Ed., DAINIK GANADOOT, Agartala, Tripura
Chauvet, Max E.
administration@lenouvelliste.com, Dir., LE NOUVELLISTE, Port-Au-Prince
Chauvin, Jim
jchauvin@usaweekend.com, Adv. Mgr., USA WEEKEND - Troy, MI, MI, Troy
Chauvin, Jim
jchauvin@usaweekend.com, Adv. Mgr., USA WEEKEND - Troy, MI, MI, Troy
Chavez, Jeanette ....(303) 820-1800
jchavez@denverpost.com, Mng. Ed., Opns., The Denver Post, CO, Denver
Chavez, Javier Valle
javiervallechavez@eloccidental.com, Ed., El Occidental, Guadalajara, Jalisco
Cheadle, Judy ....(804) 649-6730
jcheadle@timesdispatch.com, Sales Devel. Mgr., Richmond Times-Dispatch, VA, Richmond
Cheak, Connie J.
janicep@nacms-c.com, Pub., The Daily Record
Cheatham, Kathy........................615) 259-8857
kcheatham@tennessean.com, Vice Pres., HR, The Tennessean, TN, Nashville
Cheek, Pat......................................ext. 223
Adv. Dir., Middlesboro Daily News, KY, Middlesboro
Cheeseman, Rosanne
rosanne.cheeseman@timesnews.com, CEO/Pub., Erie Times-News, PA, Erie
Cheffen, Jimmy......................(501) 370-5354
Philander Smith College, AR, Little Rock
Cheikhrouhou, R.
letemps@gnet.tn, Gen. Mgr., LE TEMPS, Tunis
Cheikhrouhou, Habib
info@assabah.com.tn, Founder, AS-SABAH, Tunis,
Chen, Hwei Ying
info@batonlockusa.com, Pres., Baton Lock & Hardware Co., Inc., CA, Garden Grove
Chen, Joshua
sales@cybercon.com, Pres., Cybercon.com, MO, Saint Louis
Chen, Angela..............................408-838-2621
Ed. in Chief, Univ. of California San Diego, CA, La Jolla
Cheng, Hong ....(740) 593-2619
Assoc. Prof., Ohio University, OH, Athens
Chengappa, Raj
letters@tribuneindia.com, Ed. in Chief, PUNJABI TRIBUNE, Chandigarh
Cherba, John.........................(317) 444-7145
john.cherba@indystar.com, Adv. Dir., Display, The Indianapolis Star, IN, Indianapolis
Cherbal, Abdelmadjid
cherbal@elmoudjahid.com, Mng. Dir., AL-MOUDJAHID, Algiers
Chermoore, Ed................(636) 207-9880 ext. 4
echermoore@plainlabelpress.com, Vice Pres./Mng. Ed., Plain Label Press, MO, Ballwin
Chernivsky, Ben ....(618) 374-4748
Principia College, IL, Elsah
Chernoff, Amy ....ext. 102
achernoff@pubgroup.com, Sr. Vice Pres./Grp. Pub., American Profile - New York, NY, NY, New York
Chernoff, Amy..............(212) 478-1900 ext. 102
achernoff@pubgroup.com, Sr. Vice Pres./Grp. Pub., American Profile - New York, NY, NY, New York
Chernoff, Amy
achernoff@pubgroup.com, Sr. Vice Pres./Grp. Pub., Relish - New York, NY, NY, New York
Cherubini, Vic ....(281) 363-3742
epic@epicsoftware.com, Pres., epic software group, Inc., TX, The Woodlands
Chesnut, Helen
hchesnut@te.canwest.com, Garden Writer, Times Colonist, BC, Victoria
Chestaro, Ivette ....(917) 339-0861
Prodn. Mgr., Hoy, NY, New York
Chester, Jr., Kenneth J.
motornewsmedia@live.com, Pres./CEO, Motor News Media Corp., IA, Grimes
Chesto, Jon ....(617) 786-7087
jchesto@ledger.com, Bus. Ed., The Patriot Ledger, MA, Quincy
Chetty, Shirley
shirley.chettty@inl.co.za, Asst. to CEO, THE STAR/WEEKEND STAR, Johannesburg, PWV
Cheung, Paul
chiefeditor@mingpao.com, Ed. in Chief, MING PAO DAILY NEWS, Hong Kong
Cheung, Mandle
info@icescape.com, Pres./CEO, Computer Talk Technology, Inc., ON, Richmond Hill
Cheung, Ariel ....(513) 556-5912
chief.newsrecord@gmail.com, Editor-in-chief, The News Record, OH, Cincinnati
Chhajlani, Abhay
editor@naidunia.com, Ed. in Chief, NAIDUNIA, Indore, Madhya Pradesh
Chiaia, Nicholas
hguerra@upi.com., Pres., United Press International, DC, Washington
Chiano, Shini
dy@yomiuri.com, Mng. Ed., THE DAILY YOMIURI, Tokyo
Chiappe, Dave
dchiappe@tribune.com, Chicago Mgr., Tribune Company, IL, Chicago
Chiappetta, Delia ....(262) 656-6227
dchiappetta@kenoshanews.com, Prodn. Mgr., Opns., Kenosha News, WI, Kenosha
Chiasson, JoAnn ....(504) 826-3509
Adv. Mgr., Real Estate, The Times Picayune, LA, New Orleans
Chiaviello, Anthony ....(713) 221-8520
Univ. of Houston Downtown, TX, Houston
Chiba, Masahiro
iwanichi@iwanichi.co.jp, Adv. Dir., IWATE NICHI-NICHI SHIMBUN, Ichinoseke City, Tohoku
Chichester, Duane L. ....(352) 544-5204
dchichester@hernandotoday.com, Pub., Hernando Today, FL, Brooksville
Chichester, Karen
kchichester@thedailystar.com, Controller, The Daily Star, NY, Oneonta
Chick Whiteside, Mary Ann..........(810) 766-6343
mwhiteside@flintjournal.com, New Media/Online Mgr., The Flint Journal, MI, Flint
Chikoto, William
william.chikoto@zimpapers.co.zw, Ed., THE HERALD/THE SUNDAY HERALD, Harare
Childers, Bobby............(601) 636-4545 ext. 148
bchilders@vicksburgpost.com, Prodn. Foreman, Pressroom, The Vicksburg Post, MS, Vicksburg
Childree, Zach.........................(256) 782-5701
Jacksonville State Univ., AL, Jacksonville
Childs, Kevin
holdit@4asap.com, Pres., Audio Service America Productions, NY, Albany
Childs, Joe ....(727) 893-8328
childs@tampabay.com, Mng. Ed., Tampa Bay, Tampa Bay Times, FL, Saint Petersburg
Chilinski, Frank
frank@stonebridgepress.com, President & Publisher, Southbridge Evening News, MA, Southbridge
Chilinski, Frank 508-909-4101
frank@stonebridgepress.com, President & Publisher, Stonebridge Press, Inc., MA, Southbridge
Chilton, Susan............(519) 894-2250 ext. 2642
schilton@therecord.com, Deputy City Ed., The Record, ON, Kitchener
Chilton, Elizabeth E. ....(304) 348-5125
echilton@wvgazette.com, Pres./Pub., The Charleston Gazette, Sunday Gazette-Mail, WV, Charleston
Chimes, Chris..........................(216) 999-4676
IT Mgr., Systems and Development, The Plain Dealer, OH, Cleveland
Chin, Dianne ....(617) 619-6219
dchin@bostonherald.com, Adv. Mgr., Market Research, Boston Herald, MA, Boston
Chiodo, Terri ....(310) 448-6700
terri.chiodo@investors.com, Vice Pres./Nat'l Adv. Dir., Investor's Business Daily, CA, Los Angeles
Chiodo, Daniel P.
emailads@joplinglobe.com, Pub./Pres., The Joplin Globe, MO, Joplin
Chisenhall, Sherry ....(316) 268-6405
schisenhall@wichitaeagle.com, Editor/Vice Pres., News, The Wichita Eagle, KS, Wichita
Chisholm, Tina
tchisholm@gfherald.com, Prodn. Mgr., Pre Press, Grand Forks Herald, ND, Grand Forks
Chitwood, Tim
tchitwood@ledger-enquirer.com, Columnist, Columbus Ledger-Enquirer, GA, Columbus
Chmelir, Rudolf
office@rundschau.co.at, Ed. in Chief, OBEROSTERREICHISCHE RUNDSCHAU, Linz
Choate, John ....(318) 487-6307
jchoate@thetowntalk.com, Dir., Information Servs., The Town Talk, LA, Alexandria
Chodosovski, V.
root@belmarket.belpak.minsk.by, Ed., BELARUSKI RYNOK, Minsk
Chon, Shiyong
sychon@heraldm.com, Mng.Ed., KOREA HERALD, Seoul
Chon, Lai Su
atimes@tm.net.my, Ed., ASIA TIMES, Kota Kinabalu, Sabah
Chong, Alina Rosell
arosell@enet.cu, Dir., CINCO DE SEPTIEMBRE, Cienfuegos
Chopra, Vijay Kumar
sales@punjabkesari.com, Ed. in Chief, PUNJAB KESARI, Jalandhar, Punjab
Chopra, Vijaya Kumar
news@punjavkesari.com, Pub., HIND SAMACHAR, Jullundur, Punjab
Chopra, Ashwini Kumar
ashwanik@nda.vsnl.net.in, Ed., PUNJAB KESARI, New Delhi
Chou, Cecilia ....(630) 922-9381
cecilia.chou@gossinternational.com, Mktg. Mgr., Goss International Corporation, IL, Bolingbrook
Chouinard, Michelle..................(905) 857-2378
mchouinard@maratek.com, Mktg. Mgr., Maratek Environmental Technologies, Inc., ON, Bolton
Chow, Alvin
achow@canwest.com, Western Sales Mgr., CanWest Media Sales-Vancouver, BC, Vancouver
Chowdhury, Manzoor A.
observer@dhaka.net, Chrmn., BANGLADESH OBSERVER, Dhaka
Chown, Jeff
jchown@niu.edu, Acting Chair, Northern Illinois University, IL, DeKalb
Chris, Ashley
editor@thetigernews.com, Clemson Univ., SC, Clemson
Christ, Dan ....(717) 255-8239
dchrist@patriot-news.com, Social Media Dir., The Patriot-News, PA, Mechanicsburg
Christ, Shelly 507-389-1079
rachelle.christ@mnsu.edu, Advertising Sales Manager, Minnesota State Univ. Mankato, MN, Mankato
Christensen, Jan
jc@fla.de, News Ed., FLENSBORG AVIS, Flensburg
Christensen, Bente....................(828) 628-1994
Bus. Mgr., Editor's Copy Syndicate, FL, Sarasota
Christensen, Bette ....(803) 329-4052
webmaster@heraldonline.com, Admin. Asst., The Herald, SC, Rock Hill
Christensen, Sandra.........(719) 539-6694 ext. 14
Circ. Mgr., The Mountain Mail, CO, Salida
Christensen, Sarah J. ....(503)725-5691
Portland State Univ., OR, Portland
Christenson, Peter ....(503) 768-7146
Lewis & Clark College, OR, Portland
Christian, Scott
support@spanlink.com, CEO, Spanlink Communications, MN, Minneapolis
Christiansen, Anders
achristiansen@saxotech.com, CEO, SAXOTECH, FL, Tampa
achristiansen@saxotech.com, CEO/Pres., SAXOTECH, Inc., FL, Tampa
Christie, Rick ....(561) 820-4476
rchristie@pbpost.com, Asst. Mng. Ed., Bus., The Palm Beach Post, FL, West Palm Beach
Christino, Scott.........................(804) 649-6437
schristino@timesdispatch.com, Classified Adv. Mgr., Richmond Times-Dispatch, VA, Richmond
Christman, Michael J.
nsnews@news-sentinel.com, CEO/President/Publisher, The News-Sentinel, IN, Fort Wayne
Christmas, Wanda ....(843) 317-7361
wchristmas@florencenews.com, Prodn. Mgr., Pre Press, Morning News, SC, Florence
Christner, Rex...........................(620) 694-5776
rchristner@harrisbusiness.com, HR Dir., The Hutchinson News, KS, Hutchinson
Christofferson, Tim ....(605) 394-8379
tim.christofferson@rapidcityjournal.com, Adv. Mgr., Retail, Rapid City Journal, SD, Rapid City
Christofides, Aris T....................(513) 761-1188
comments@critics.com, Pub./Ed., Critics, Inc., OH, Dublin
Chrysler, Rod ....(908) 687-3225
info@psctum.com, Pres., PSC Flo-Turn, Inc., NJ, Union
Chrystie, Grace
seattle@allenspcb.com, Regional Manager, Allen's Press Clipping Bureau, WA, Seattle
Chu, Yao
info@filestream.com, Chrmn./CEO, Filestream, Inc., NY, Glen Head
Chu-Hwan, Son
webmaster@seoul.co.kr, Pub./Pres., SEOUL SHINMUN, Seoul
Chua, Reginald
editor@scmp.com, Ed., SOUTH CHINA MORNING POST, Hong Kong
Chuan, Liew Chen
editorial@mail.sinchew.com.my, Ed. in Chief, SIN CHEW JIT POH, 46200 Petaling Jaya, Selangor
Chubb, Lee ....(208) 726-5232
info@intbuild.com, Pres., Interface Builders, ID, Ketchum
Chubb, Anne T. ....(610) 371-5141
achubb@readingeagle.com, Adv. Mgr., Training/Sales Support, Reading Eagle, PA, Reading
Chun, Lei Seng
mcnews@macau.ctm.net, Chm., OU MUN IAT POU, Macau
Chung, Chun Young
root@honam.co.kr, Pres., MOODEUNG ILBO, Kwangju, Gwangiu
Churchill, Lisa
lisa_churchhill@dailyjournal.com, Ed., Daily Commerce, CA, Los Angeles
Chute, Michael ....(731) 661-6594
Union Univ., TN, Jackson
Ciambrone, Ed...............................785-832-7260
eciambrone@ljworld.com, The World Co.- Lawrence, Kan., Journal-World, KS, Lawrence
Ciambrone, Ed...............................785-832-7260
eciambrone@ljworld.com, Production Director, The World Co.- Lawrence, Kan., Journal-World, KS, Lawrence
Ciampini, Helen........................(514) 987-2202
hciampini@montrealgazette.com, Exec. Asst. to Pub. & Ed. in Chief, The Gazette, QC, Montreal
Cianci, Lisa ....(407) 420-6229
lcianci@orlandosentinel.com, City Ed., Orlando Sentinel, FL, Orlando
Ciavaglia, Jo ....ext. 4181
jcialvaglia@phillyburbs.com, Reporter, Bucks County Courier Times, PA, Levittown
Cibart, Michael ....ext. 258
mcibart@ubnet.com, Circ. Mgr., Walla Walla

Union-Bulletin, WA, Walla Walla
Ciccantelli, Steve ....(262) 670-1502
sciccantelli@conleynet.com, Vice Pres., Sales/Mktg., Conley Publishing Group Ltd., WI, Beaver Dam
Ciccantelli, Steve ....(262) 670-1502
sciccantelli@conleynet.com, Pub., The Daily News, WI, West Bend
Cichelli, Richard
cichelli@newspapersystems.com, Pres., Software Consulting Services, LLC, PA, Nazareth
Cichelli, Richard J.
scs@nscs.fast.net, Pres., Software Consulting Services, PA, Nazareth
Cichon, Joe..................(913) 441-0139 ext. 109
cichonj@corp.inxintl.com, Sr. Vice Pres., Product/Mfg. Technology, INX International Ink Co., IL, Schaumburg
Cichy, Betty..................................ext. 4171
bcichy@phillyburbs.com, Food Writer, Bucks County Courier Times, PA, Levittown
Ciechon, Sharon..........(603) 668-4321 ext. 503
sciechon@unionleader.com, Vice Pres., HR, New Hampshire Union Leader/New Hampshire Sunday News, NH, Manchester
Ciliberti, Dino..............................(508) 967-3150
dciliberti@tauntongazette.com, Mng. Ed., Taunton Daily Gazette, MA, Taunton
Ciliberti, Dino
editor@wayneindependent.com, Editor, The Wayne Independent, PA, Honesdale
Cimburek, James
james.cimburek@yankton.net, Sports Ed., Yankton Daily Press & Dakotan, SD, Yankton
Cincotta, Tom..................................ext. 461
tcincotta@journalregister.com, Gen. Mgr., Daily Freeman, NY, Kingston
Cincrost, David
david.cincrost@dailyexaminer.com.au, Ed., THE DAILY EXAMINER
Cirak, Kemal
ttsgmd@tobb.org.tr, Pub., TURKIYE TICARET SICILI
Cisneros, Luis...........................(956) 982-6655
Prodn. Mgr., Pressroom, The Brownsville Herald, TX, Brownsville
Cistelbarth, Kilman
archief@stimme.de, Ed. in Chief, Heilbronner Stimme, Heilbronn
Cisternino, Mark
markc@flexography.org, President, Flexographic Technical Association, NY, Bohemia
Ciudadsa, Graficas
ciudadpulvlei@elperiodico.com, Ed., CIUDAD DE ALCOY, Alcoy
Ciuffo, Philip A. ....(212) 556-1234
Vice Pres., Internal Audit, The New York Times Co., NY, New York
Claiborne, Mary Pam
clairbornem@ipix.com, Contact, Interactive Pictures Corporation (IPIX), VA, Reston
Claiborne, Jamii ....(712) 749-1212
Buena Vista Univ., IA, Storm Lake
Clairet, Marcel
m.clairet@lapressedelamanche.fr, Pub., LA PRESSE DE LA MANCHE, Cherbourg
Clancy, Nicole ....(805) 683-3272
n.clancy@att.net, Pres., Healthy Living, CA, Santa Barbara
Clancy, Douglas ....(973) 569-7168
Assistant Managing Editor/Administration, North Jersey Media Group, NJ, Woodland Park
Clancy, Lou..............................(416) 947-2242
lou.clancy@sunmedia.ca, Ed. in Chief, The Toronto Sun, ON, Toronto
Clancy, Doug............................(201) 646-4481
Asst. Mng. Ed., Admin., Herald News, NJ, West Paterson
Clapp, Kevin............................609-272-7255
kclapp@pressofac.com, Entertainment Editor, The Press of Atlantic City, NJ, Pleasantville
Clapper, Bryan
bryan.clapper@leaderpub.com, Pub., Niles Daily Star, MI, Niles
Clapper, Bryan
bryan.clapper@leaderpub.com, Gen. Mgr., Dowagiac Daily News, MI, Dowagiac
Clarin, Paul
pclarin@keysnews.com, Pub., The Key West Citizen, FL, Key West
Clark, Michael
sales@tkmus.com, Market Mgr., TKM United States, Inc., KY, Hebron
Clark, Joe
bill@dial.pipex.com, Mgr., THE OBSERVER, ENG, London
Clark, Andrew
info@mid-atlantic.verio.net, Pres., Verio Mid-Atlantic, MD, Columbia
Clark, Randy.............................(678) 466-4724
Clayton State Univ., GA, Morrow
Clark, Cathy..............................(215) 345-3102
cclark@phillyburbs.com, Classified Adv. Dir., Burlington County Times, NJ, Willingboro
Clark, Jimmy
jclark@vicksburgpost.com, Gen. Mgr., The Vicksburg Post, MS, Vicksburg
Clark, Dave
dclark@pioneergroup.com, Editorial Page Ed., The Pioneer - Big Rapids, MI, Big Rapids
Clark, Carol.....................................ext. 21
laeditor@lamonitor.com, Mng. Ed., Los Alamos Monitor, NM, Los Alamos
Clark, Pat..................................(209) 578-2312
pclark@modbee.com, Television/Film Writer, The Modesto Bee, CA, Modesto
Clark, Ron................................(419) 448-3212
Circ. Mgr., The Advertiser-Tribune, OH, Tiffin
Clark, Jennifer
jennifer.clark@dowjones.com, Correspondent, Dow Jones Newswires - Milano, Italy, Milano
Clark, John
jclark@heartlandpublications.com, Pub., The Portsmouth Daily Times, OH, Portsmouth
jclark@heartlandpublications.com, Gen. Mgr., Ed., Spiro Graphic, OK, Spiro
Clark, Jud
info@statenet.com, Pres., State Net, CA, Sacramento
Clark, Judy
classified@mydailysentinel.com, Adv. Mgr., Classified, The Daily Sentinel/Sunday Times-Sentinel, OH, Pomeroy
Clark, Rob...............................(308) 692-6441
rob.clark@mjtimes.sk.ca, Pub., The Moose Jaw Times-Herald, SK, Moose Jaw
Clark, Terry M.
tclark@ucok.edu, Chair, University of Central Oklahoma, OK, Edmond
Clark, Darrin..................................ext. 3051
dclark@staffordgroup.com, News Ed., The Daily News, MI, Greenville
Clark, Kaleigh ....(913) 758-6147
St. Mary College, KS, Leavenworth
Clark, Rob ....(989) 894-9653
rclark@bc-times.com, Bus. Ed., The Bay City Times, MI, Bay City
Clark, Al ....(252) 329-9560
aclark@reflector.com, Exec. Ed., The Daily Reflector, NC, Greenville
Clark, Michael..................................ext. 224
info@pageint.com, Pres., Page Systems, Inc., ON, Toronto
Clark, Larry ....ext. 253
Opinion Page Ed., The Hickory Daily Record, NC, Hickory
Clark, Carol
lanews@lamonitor.com, Pres., New Mexico Press Women, NM, Los Alamos
Clark, Brian ....(209) 578-2301
bclark@modbee.com, Sports Ed., The Modesto Bee, CA, Modesto
Clark, Jim
apmontana@ap.org, Bureau Chief, Montana Associated Press Association, MT, Helena
apmontana@ap.org, Bureau Chief, Wyoming Associated Press, WY, Cheyenne
Clark, Tiffany 850-762-4086
TiffWhy1@aol.com, Classified Coordinator, Community Papers of Florida, FL, Belleview
Clark, Doug.......................................ext. 39
Asst. Ed., The Sampson Independent, NC, Clinton
Clarke, Sandra
sclarke@barbadosadvocate.com, Adv. Mgr., BARBADOS ADVOCATE/SUNDAY ADVOCATE-NEWS, Bridgetown
Clarke, Sandra 416-364-0321
sandra.clarke@thecanadianpress.com, Broadcast News Limited, ON, Toronto
Clarke, Jim
jclarke@ap.org, Bureau Chief, Colorado Associated Press Editors and Reporters, CO, Denver
jclarke@ap.org, Bureau Chief, Utah-Idaho-Spokane Associated Press Association, UT, Salt Lake City
Clarke, Jim..................800-708-7311 Ext. 251
jclarke@hearstsc.com, Editorial Director, King Features Weekly Service, North America Syndicate, NY, New York
Clarke, Oliver
ofclarke@hotmail.com, Chairman, THE JAMAICA GLEANER, Kingston
ofclarke@hotmail.com, Dir., THE DAILY STAR, Kingston
Clarke, Kevin J..........................604 247 4417
contact.us@catalystpaper.com, President & CEO, Catalyst Paper Corp., BC, Richmond
Clarke, Angie
angie@pressroomcleaners.com, Office Mgr., Pressroom Cleaners, NE, Omaha
Clarke, Brad..............................(812) 331-4272
bclarke@heraldt.com, Prodn. Dir., The Herald-Times, IN, Bloomington
Clarke, Mitch ....(770) 718-3403
mclarke@gainesvilletimes.com, Exec. Ed., The Times, GA, Gainesville
Clarke, Jim ....(407) 894-7300 ext. 251
jclarke@hearstsc.com, Editorial Dir., King Features Weekly Serv., King Features Syndicate, NY, New York
Clarkson, Maggie...........(830) 379-5441 ext. 205
maggie.clarkson@seguingazette.com, Bus. Mgr., The Seguin Gazette-Enterprise, TX, Seguin
Clarkston, Derek
sports@kodiakdailymirror.com, Ed., Kodiak Daily Mirror, AK, Kodiak
Clary, Gareth
msnews@themississippipress.com, Pub., The Mississippi Press, MS, Pascagoula
Clausen, Ron 717-262-4775
rclausen@publicopinionnews.com, Publisher, Public Opinion, PA, Chambersburg
Claussen, Nick..........................(740) 245-7521
Univ. of Rio Grande, OH, Rio Grande
Clavadetscher, Josias
redaktion@bote.ch, Ed. in Chief, BOTE DER URSCHWEIZ, Schwyz
Clawson, Doug
news@mail.estripes.osd.mil, Mng. Ed., THE STARS AND STRIPES, Kaiserslautern
Clawson, Doug
clawsond@estripes.osd.mil, Mng. Ed., STARS AND STRIPES, Tokyo
Clawson, Scott A.
sales@datafest.com, Pres., Datafest Technologies, Inc., UT, Salt Lake City
Clay, Tonya.................................904-819-3508
tonya.clay@staugustine.com, Advertising Director, The St. Augustine Record, FL, Saint Augustine
Clay, Nikki..................................(606) 326-2611
nclay@dailyindependent.com, Adv. Dir., The Daily Independent, KY, Ashland
Clay, Nancy ....(734) 994-6869
nclay@annarbornews.com, Mgr., Promo./Community Rel., The Ann Arbor News, MI, Ann Arbor
Claybourn, David ....ext. 20
dclaybourn@heraldbanner.com, Sports Ed., Herald-Banner Publications, TX, Greenville
Clayman, Arthur J..........................518-395-3133
aclayman@dailygazette.net, Editorial Page Ed., The Daily Gazette, NY, Schenectady
Clayton, Barry
barryclayton@shawcable.com, Pub., The Daily Graphic, MB, Portage la Prairie
Clayton, Darlene ....(951) 782-7654
dclayton@pe.com, Adv. Mgr., Real Estate, The Press-Enterprise, CA, Riverside
Cleetus, Francis
editor@deepika.com, Chrmn, DEEPIKA, Kottayam, Kerala
Clelan, Gary..............................(530) 477-4252
garyc@theunion.com, Prodn. Mgr., Press, The Union, CA, Grass Valley
Cleland, Robert S.
clelandrs@washpost.com, Vice Pres., Mktg./Tech., Washington Post News Service with Bloomberg News, DC, Washington
Clements, Brad
bkc@murkworks.com, Pres., MurkWorks, Inc., NY, Potsdam
Clements, Thomas H. ....ext. 207
thomas.clements@gaflnews.com, Circ. Dir., Thomasville Times-Enterprise, GA, Thomasville
Clements, Julie
editor@eldoradotimes.com, News Ed., The El Dorado Times, KS, El Dorado
Clements, Cliff
cliff.clements@baytownsun.com, Pub., The Baytown Sun, TX, Baytown
Clemmenos, Konstandinos
elefkal@otenet.gr, Pub./Dir., ELEFTHERIA, Kalamata
Clemons, Marv ....(815) 987-1390
News Ed., Rockford Register Star, IL, Rockford
Clendaniel, Sheila ....(302) 741-8259
shelclen@newszap.com, Exec. Asst., Independent Newspapers, Inc. (DE), DE, Dover
Clendenning, Richard......(847) 981-9399 ext. 205
Pres./CEO, INX International Ink Co., IL, Schaumburg
Clermont, Lois..........................(518) 565-4131
lclermont@pressrepublican.com, News Ed., Press-Republican, NY, Plattsburgh
Clermont-Anderson, Twyla ....(306) 781-5364
tclermont-anderson@leaderpost.canwest.com, Mgr., HR, The Leader-Post, SK, Regina
Cleveland, Gary ....(706) 208-2270
gary.cleveland@onlineathens.com, Prodn. Dir., Athens Banner-Herald, GA, Athens
Cleveland, Barry
advertising@carmitimes.com, Online Ed., Carmi Times, IL, Carmi
Clevenger, David
dclevenger@griffindailynews.com, Pub., Griffin Daily News, GA, Griffin
Clever, Dick
dclever@skagitpublishing.com, Mng. Ed., News, Skagit Valley Herald, WA, Mount Vernon
Click, J. William
clickw@winthrop.edu, Chair/Prof., Winthrop University, SC, Rock Hill
Clifford, Kevin
kevinc@wdtimes.com, Gen. Mgr., Watertown Daily Times, WI, Watertown
Clifford, James M.
jimc@wdtimes.com, Ed., Watertown Daily Times, WI, Watertown
Clifford, John
butler@butlerautomatic.com, Vice Pres., Engineering, Butler Automatic, MA, Middleborough
Cline, Andrew...............(603) 668-4321 ext. 305
acline@unionleader.com, Editorial Page Dir., New Hampshire Union Leader/New Hampshire Sunday News, NH, Manchester
Clinebell, Ken
kclinebell@vertical.com, CFO, Vertical Communications, AZ, Phoenix
Clinebell, Ken ....(941) 554-5000
kclinebell@vertical.com, CFO, Vertical Communications, Inc., MA, Cambridge
Clinger, Bill ....(419) 993-2075
bclinger@limanews.com, Dir., Mktg., The Lima News, OH, Lima
Clinton, Tom
tomclinton@the-messenger.com, Exec. Ed., The Messenger, KY, Madisonville
Clinton, Sharon ....ext. 43
sharon.clinton@bolivarcommercial.com, Prodn. Mgr., The Bolivar Commercial, MS, Cleveland
Clinton, Kendall ....(334) 712-7954
kclinton@dothaneagle.com, City Ed., The Dothan Eagle, AL, Dothan
Clore, Larry
lclore@multiaad.com, Pres., MultiAd Services, Inc., IL, Peoria
Closson, Stefani ....ext. 5169
stefani.closson@pharostribune.com, Dir., Mktg., Pharos-Tribune, IN, Logansport
Cloud, George W. ....(919) 962-4070
Assoc. Prof., University of North Carolina, NC, Chapel Hill
Clouston, Scott
sclouston@fujihuntusa.com, Vice Pres., Fujifilm Hunt Chemicals U.S.A., Inc., NJ, Allendale

Clubb, Angela..........................(301) 650-1490
Montgomery College, MD, Takoma Park
Clugston, Patty
pclugston@chambers.gannett.com, Prodn. Mgr., Composing/Camera, Public Opinion, PA, Chambersburg
Clutter, Dan
dclutter@nncogannett.com, Sports Ed., Bucyrus TelegraphForum.com, OH, Bucyrus
Clyde, Nelson..........................(903) 596-6245
cnciv@tylerpaper.com, Pres./Pub., Tyler Morning Telegraph, TX, Tyler
Clyde, Thomas..........................(903) 596-6239
tclyde@tylerpaper.com, CFO, Tyler Morning Telegraph, TX, Tyler
Clynes, Philip
advert@gladstoneobserver.com.au, Adv. Mgr., THE GLADSTONE OBSERVER
Coady, Walter J.
insurance@walterry.com, Dir., Mktg., Walterry Insurance Brokers, MD, Clinton
Coakley, John..........................(559) 441-6143
jcoakley@fresnobee.com, Adv. Sr. Vice Pres., Sales/Strategic Mktg., The Fresno Bee, CA, Fresno
Coates, Rusty..........................(813) 259-8353
Gen. Mgr., The Tampa Tribune, FL, Tampa
Cobb, Liz..........................(719) 636-0354
liz.cobb@gazette.com, Vice Pres., Mktg., The Gazette, CO, Colorado Springs
Cobb, Phil
publisher@maryvilledailyforum.com, Pub., The Maryville Daily Forum, MO, Maryville
Cobb, Lona D...........................(336) 750-2327
Winston-Salem State Univ., NC, Winston-Salem
Cobler, Chris
newsroom@vicad.com, Ed., Victoria Advocate, TX, Victoria
Cobo Gonzalez, Ignacio
davance@nexus.net.mx, Owner/Pres., AVANCE, Villahermosa, Tabasco
Cochran, Harrison..........................(303) 750-7555
publisher@aurorasentinel.com, Pub./Pres., Aurora Sentinel, CO, Aurora
Cochran, Terry
tcochran@ccdailyrecord.com, Gen. Mgr./Ed., The Canon City Daily Record, CO, Canon City
Cocu, Cristina
cristina.cocu@viata-libera.ro, Dir., VIATA LIBERA, Galati
Coddington, Judy..........................(732) 565-7470
jcoddington@gannett.com, Adv. Mgr., Ad Servs., Courier News, NJ, Somerville
Coder, Darlene
dcoder@alltel.net, Pub., The Daily Press, PA, Saint Marys
Coder, Darlene..........................(814) 773-3161
ridgwayrecord@shop-right.com, Pub., The Ridgway Record, PA, Ridgway
Cody, Don..........................ext. 116
dcody@uniondailytimes.com, Prodn. Mgr., Mailroom, Union Daily Times, SC, Union
Cody, Martin
mcody@havredailynews.com, Pub., The Havre Daily News, MT, Havre
Cody, Phil..........................(229) 888-9304
phil.cody@albanyherald.com, Adv. Accts. Rep., Nat'l/Major, The Albany Herald, GA, Albany
Cody, Martin..........................(641) 684-4611 ext. 341
mcody@cnhi.com, Publisher, Money Saver, IA, Ottumwa
Cody, Martin
mcody@cnhi.com, Pub., The Ottumwa Courier, IA, Ottumwa
Coello, Henry..........................(830) 625-9144 ext. 214
Prodn. Mgr., New Braunfels Herald-Zeitung, TX, New Braunfels
Coello Trejo, Roberto
edilavoz@chis1.telmex.net.mx, Pres., LA VOZ DEL SURESTE, Tuxtla Gutierrez, Chiapas
Coen, Jeremy..........................ext. 700
jcoen@hutchnews.com, Prodn. Mgr., Packaging/Distribution, The Hutchinson News, KS, Hutchinson
Coffey, Charles
ccoffey2@indy.rr.com, Contact, Leaning Tree Features, IN, Indianapolis
Coffey, Betsy..........................(660) 263-4110
Moberly Area Cmty. College, MO, Moberly
Coffman, Jason..........................(410) 228-3131 ext. 20
jcoffman@newszap.com, Circ. Mgr., The Daily Banner, MD, Cambridge
Coffman, Frank..........................(815) 921-3307
Rock Valley College, IL, Rockford
Cofre, Oscar..........................421073
clubdelectores@estrellaiquique.cl, Gen. Mgr., LA ESTRELLA DE IQUIQUE, Iquique
Coggins, Rudy..........................(919) 739-7856
rcoggins@newsargus.com, Sports Ed., Goldsboro News-Argus, NC, Goldsboro
Cogley, Colette..........................(312) 981-1747
ccogley@unitedmedia.com, Regl. Sales Mgr., Newspaper Enterprise Association (Div. of United Media), NY, New York
ccogley@unitedmedia.com, Regl. Sales Mgr., United Feature Syndicate (Div. of United Media), NY, New York
Cognetta, Gary V...........................(718) 816-2821
Dir., Adv., Staten Island Advance, NY, Staten Island
Cogswell, George H...........................(805) 437-0400
gcogswell@vcstar.com, Pres./Pub., Ventura County Star, CA, Camarillo
Cohea, David..........................(407) 894-7300 ext. 252
dcohea@hearstsc.com, Gen. Mgr., King Features Weekly Service, King Features Syndicate, NY, New York
dcohea@hearstsc.com, Gen. Mgr., King Features Weekly Service, North America Syndicate, NY, New York
Cohen, Larry..........................(202) 434-1100
lcohen@cwa-union.org, Pres., Communications Workers of America, DC, Washington
Cohen, Shelly..........................(617) 619-6492
scohen@bostonherald.com, Editorial Page Ed., Boston Herald, MA, Boston
Cohen, Hal
hcohen@alm.com, Publisher, The Legal Intelligencer
Cohen, Robert L...........................(646) 654-8411
Pres./CEO, Scarborough Research, NY, New York
Cohen, Mark
mcohen@cnc.com, Adv. Vice Pres., Metrowest Daily News, MA, Framingham
Cohen, Larry
lcohen@cwa-union.org, Pres., Printing, Publishing & Media Workers Sector-CWA, DC, Washington
Cohen, Jeffrey
jcohen@teleperformance.com, COO, Teleperformance Interactive, PA, Plymouth Meeting
Cohen, Murray..........................ext. 21
murray@delphosherald.com, Pub., Delphos Daily Herald, OH, Delphos
Cohen, Marc
mcohen@teleperformance.com, Pres., Teleperformance Interactive, PA, Plymouth Meeting
Cohen, Mark..........................(781) 433-6950
salesteam@wickedlocal.com, Vice Pres., Adv., Taunton Daily Gazette, MA, Taunton
Coile, Norma..........................(520) 573-4102
ncoile@azstarnet.com, Science/Technology Ed., Arizona Daily Star, AZ, Tucson
Coish, Gladys
gcoish@amherstdaily.com, Adv. Mgr., Amherst Daily News, NS, Amherst
Cojocaru, Mihia
mcojocaru@polychem.com, Gen. Mgr., Sterling Packaging Systems, OH, Mentor
Colacioppo, Leeann..........................(303) 820-1754
elcolacioppo@denverpost.com, City Ed., The Denver Post, CO, Denver
Colberg, Michael..........................(802) 254-2311 ext. 157
Mailroom Mgr., Brattleboro Reformer, VT, Brattleboro
Cole, Jeff..........................(419) 724-6392
jcole@toledoblade.com, Circ. Mgr., City Home Delivery, The Blade, OH, Toledo
Cole, Gail..........................(541) 737-3191
Oregon State Univ., OR, Corvallis
Cole, Dean
dcole@c-dh.net, Circ. Mgr., Columbia Daily Herald, TN, Columbia
Cole, Richard R...........................(919) 843-8289
Dean Emer./John Thomas Kerr Distinguished Prof., University of North Carolina, NC, Chapel Hill
Cole, Darrell
dcole@amherstdaily.com, Sports Ed., Amherst Daily News, NS, Amherst
Cole, Aaron..........................(303) 750-7555
acole@aurorasentinel.com, Mng. Ed., Aurora Sentinel, CO, Aurora
Cole, Kimberly..........................(610) 345-0795
kim.cole@suburban-news.com, Mktg. Mgr., Suburban Newspapers of America, MI, Traverse City
Colehower, Roger
rogerc@base-line.com, Vice Pres., Sales/Opns., Jomac Pdcts., Base-Line, Inc., PA, Warminster
Coleman, Ken..........................(204) 571-7438
kcoleman@brandonsun.com, Copy Ed., Brandon Sun, MB, Brandon
Coleman, J. Edward
info@unisys.com, Chrmn./CEO, Unisys Corp., PA, Blue Bell
Coleman, Roger F...........................ext. 2249
publisher@registerstar.com, Pub., Register-Star, NY, Hudson
Coleman, Don..........................ext. 16
Prodn. Foreman, Press/Camera, Gallipolis Daily Tribune, OH, Gallipolis
Coleman, Darrell..........................(940) 767-8341
colemand@timesrecordnews.com, Pub., Wichita Falls Times Record News, TX, Wichita Falls
Coleman, Frances..........................(251) 219-5607
fcoleman@press-register.com, Editorial Page Ed., Press-Register, AL, Mobile
Coleman, Roger F...........................(518) 943-2100
publisher@thedailymail.net, Pub., The Daily Mail, NY, Catskill
Coleman, Don..........................ext. 16
Prodn. Foreman, Pressroom, The Daily Sentinel/Sunday Times-Sentinel, OH, Pomeroy
Coleman, Zack..........................(361) 779-1580
challengeradv@aol.com, Owner, Coleman Advertising, TX, Corpus Christi
Coleman, Mike..........................602-444-8074
mcoleman@republicmedia.com, VP/Digital Media, The Arizona Republic, AZ, Phoenix
Coles, Michelle..........................(907) 564-8297
Alaska Pacific Univ., AK, Anchorage
Collen, Bruce
bcollen@same-page.com, Pres., Same Page.com, FL, Sanibel
Colletti, Joseph..........................(856) 842-0600 x 112
joseph.colletti@ferag-americas.com, CEO & President, Ferag Americas, NJ, Lawrenceville
Colletti, Joseph..........................(856) 842-0600
joseph.colletti@ferag-americas.com, Pres., WRH Marketing Americas, Inc., NJ, Lawrenceville
Colley, Tom
editor@bdtonline.com, Exec. Ed., Bluefield Daily Telegraph, WV, Bluefield
Colley, Kay..........................817-531-6525
Student Media Director, The Rambler, TX, Fort Worth
Collier, Andy..........................(662) 843-4241
sports@bolivarcommercial.com, Sports Ed., The Bolivar Commercial, MS, Cleveland
Collier, D'Lorah..........................(409) 683-5218
dlorah.collier@galvnews.com, Bus. Mgr., The Galveston County Daily News, TX, Galveston
Collier, Jana..........................(937) 225-2388
jcollier@coxohio.com, Editor in Chief, Dayton Daily News, OH, Dayton
Collier, Christy..........................(770) 478-5753
ccollier@news-daily.com, Adv. Dir., News/Daily, GA, Jonesboro
Collins, Erik..........................(803) 777-7726
Univ. of South Carolina, SC, Columbia
Collins, S. John
jcollins@bakercityherald.com, Photo Ed., Baker City Herald, OR, Baker City
Collins, Judy..........................ext. 201
Bus. Mgr., West Plains Daily Quill, MO, West Plains
Collins, Mary..........................847-716-7000
President & CEO, Media Financial Management Association, IL, Northfield
Collins, Tracy..........................(602) 444-8094
tracy.collins@pni.com, Deputy Ed., Presentation/Sports, The Arizona Republic, AZ, Phoenix
Collins, Christine
ccollins@bakercityherald.com, Health/Medical Ed., Baker City Herald, OR, Baker City
Collins, William A...........................(864) 943-2511
bcollins@indexjournal.com, Exec. Editorial Ed., The Index-Journal, SC, Greenwood
Collins, Cynthia
ccollins@hopewellnews.com, Office Mgr., The Hopewell News, VA, Hopewell
Collins, Rod..........................(804) 458-8511
rcollins@hopewellnews.com, Pub., The Hopewell News, VA, Hopewell
Collins, Lois..........................(801) 237-2180
lois@desnews.com, Health/Medical Writer, Deseret News, UT, Salt Lake City
Collins, Lawrence..........................(201) 703-0911
stepoutmag@aol.com, Publisher, Collins Communications, NJ, Fairlawn
Collins, Connie..........................ext. 210
ccollins@ant-news.com, Pub., Atlantic News-Telegraph, IA, Atlantic
ccollins@ant-news.com, Southwest Iowa Shopper, IA, Atlantic
Collums, Terri..........................(662) 328-2424 ext. 139
tcollums@cdispatch.com, Bus. Mgr./Controller, The Commercial Dispatch, MS, Columbus
Collver, Doug..........................(541) 382-5643
dcollver@westernroller.com, Owner, Western Roller Corp., OR, Bend
Colombo, Mike..........................(706) 290-5259
mcolombo@rn-t.com, Mng. Ed., Rome News-Tribune, GA, Rome
Colville, Warren T.
colville@buffnews.com, Pres., The Buffalo News, NY, Buffalo
Colvin, Dick
dick.colvin@hotmail.com, Exec. Dir., Texas Community Newspaper Association, TX, Ft. Worth
Colvin, Dick
dcolvin@gmail.com, Exec. Dir., TEXCAP, TX, San Antonio
Comas Barcelo, Pedro
redaccion@ultimahora.es, Dir., Ultima Hora, Palma de Mallorca, Baleares
Comcowich, William J.
comcowic@meds.com, Pres., UltiTech, Inc., CT, Stratford
Comm, Joel
jcomm@worldvillage.com, Pres., InfoMedia, Inc., CO, Loveland
Compton, David W.
dcompton@dailyadvocate.com, Grp. Pub., Daily Advocate, OH, Greenville
Compton, Jay..........................ext. 206
Sports Ed., Middlesboro Daily News, KY, Middlesboro
Conarroe, Doug..........................(253) 597-8567
doug.conarroe@thenewstribune.com, Asst. Mng. Ed., Online, The News Tribune, WA, Tacoma
Concilio, Joan..........................(717) 771-2084
jconcilio@ydr.com, Weekly/Web Ed., York Daily Record/York Sunday News, PA, York
Concilio, Joan..........................717-771-2084
jconcilio@ydr.com, Weekly Record Editor, Weekly Record, PA, York
Conde, Roberto
rconde@larazon.com.ar, Gen. Mgr., La Razon, Buenos Aires
Condon, Kent..........................(801) 236-6075
kcondon@desnews.com, Sports Ed., Deseret News, UT, Salt Lake City
Condon, Bob..........................(518) 792-3250
condon@poststar.com, City Ed., The Post-Star, NY, Glens Falls
Condra, Edward..........................(203) 789-5694
econdra@nhregister.com, Pub., New Haven Register, CT, New Haven
Cone, Vincent..........................(989) 671-1234
vcone@valleypublishing.com, Circ. Dir., The Bay City Times, MI, Bay City
Conerly, Robin..........................(985) 857-2270
robin.conerly@dailycomet.com, Advertising Director, The Daily Comet, LA, Thibodaux
Conerly, Robin..........................(985) 857-2270
robin.conerly@houmatoday.com, Advertising Director, The Courier, LA, Houma
Conetzkey, Chris
editor@iowastatedaily.com, Iowa State Univ., IA, Ames
Coney, Kevin..........................(479) 785-7728
kconey@swtimes.com, Mgr., Cor. Accts., Times Record, AR, Fort Smith

Coniglio, Ray ext. 127
rconiglio@batavianews.com, Bus./Finance Ed., The Daily News, NY, Batavia
Conkling, Cathy ext. 236
cdoup@mountvernonnews.com, Adv. Mgr., Classified, Mount Vernon News, OH, Mount Vernon
Conley, James E.
concept@conleynet.com, Pres., Conley Publishing Systems, WI, Beaver Dam
Conley, James E. (920) 356-6706
jconley@conleynet.com, Pres./CEO, Conley Publishing Group Ltd., WI, Beaver Dam
Conley, Fred
sports@thnews.com, Sports Ed., Times-Herald, AR, Forrest City
Connaghan, William B.
will.connaghan@molawyersmedia.com, Assoc. Ed., St. Louis Daily Record, MO, Saint Louis
Connell, Mike
sales@balemaster.com, Sales Mgr., Balemaster, IN, Crown Point
Connell, Angela
aconnell@express-times.com, Dir., HR, The Express-Times, PA, Easton
Connell, Tara
tjconnel@gannett.com, Vice Pres., Cor. Commun., Gannett Co., Inc., VA, McLean
Connelly, Mike (941) 957-5213
mike.connelly@heraldtribune.com, Exec. Ed., Sarasota Herald-Tribune, FL, Sarasota
Connelly, Bryce (540) 213-9185
bconnelly@newsleader.com, Prodn. Dir., The News Leader, VA, Staunton
Conner, Tom
news@nwfdailynews.com, Pub., Northwest Florida Daily News, FL, Fort Walton Beach
Conner, Loretta W. (864) 583-2907
lconner@msmgmt.com, Vice Pres./Sec./Treasurer, Mid-South Management Co., Inc., SC, Spartanburg
Connolly, John (780) 429-5129
jconnolly@edmontonjournal.com, Publisher, Edmonton Journal, AB, Edmonton
Connolly, Craig (856) 317-7885
cconnolly@gannett.com, Dir., Info Servs., Courier-Post, NJ, Cherry Hill
Connolly, Greg (208) 885-7825
Univ. of Idaho, ID, Moscow
Connor, Richard L. (207) 791-6925
Ed., Kennebec Journal, ME, Augusta
Connor, Richard L. (207) 791-6630
rconnor@centralmaine.mainetoday.com, Pres./Pub., Maine Today Media Inc., ME, Portland
Connor, Gary
gwconnor@cnhi.com, Pub., Palestine Herald-Press, TX, Palestine
Connor, Richard L. (570) 829-7272
rconnor@timesleader.com, Ed./Pub., Times Leader, PA, Wilkes-Barre
rconnor@timesleader.com, Fort Worth Business Press, TX, Fort Worth
Connors, Tom
tomconnors@eveningtribune.com, Pub., The Evening Tribune, NY, Hornell
Connors, Mary (773) 728-8351
mary@contentthatworks.com, Editorial Director, Content That Works, IL, Chicago
Conover, Charles R.
cconover@hurletron.com, Sales,Service,Marketing, Hurletron, Inc., IL, Libertyville
Conrad, Dianne (360) 867-6078
The Evergreen State College, WA, Olympia
Conrad, Cindy (616) 527-2100 ext. 104
publisher@sentinel-standard.com, Pub., Sentinel-Standard, MI, Ionia
Conry, Carol (617) 619-6555
cconroy@bostonherald.com, Circ. Mgr., Mktg., Boston Herald, MA, Boston
Constance, Harold 318-427-1202
hconstance@thetowntalk.com, Classified Sales Supervis, The Town Talk, LA, Alexandria
Constancio, Joe
joe.constancio@wninews.com, Prodn. Mgr., Waxahachie Daily Light, TX, Waxahachie
Constantine, Kristie (406) 496-5554
kristie.constantine@mtstandard.com, News Ed., The Montana Standard, MT, Butte
Contractor, Farzana
afternoondispatch@gmail.com, CEO, Courier Publications (Pvt.) Ltd., Mumbai, Maharashtra
Contreras, Mark G. (513) 977-3703
mark.contreras@scripps.com, Vice Pres., Newspaper Opns., Scripps Howard Newspapers, OH, Cincinnati
Contreras, Art (310) 676-2806
Nat'l Sales Mgr., Dee-Paul Graphic Services, CA, Hawthorne
Contreras, Mark G.
burleigh@scripps.com, Vice Pres., Newspapers Opns., E. W. Scripps Co., OH, Cincinnati
Contreras, Puri
info@tribuna.net, Dir., Tribuna De Salmanca, Salamanca
Convey, Kevin R. (617) 619-6403
kconvey@bostonherald.com, Ed. in Chief, Boston Herald, MA, Boston
Conway, Linda
l.conway@nepa.org, Adv. Dir., New England Press Association, MA, Boston
Conway, Linda (781) 320-8049
l.conway@nenpa.com, Advertising Director, NENPA Ad Network (New England Newspaper and Press Association), MA, Dedham
Conway, Maia (231) 933-1402
mconway@record-eagle.com, Mktg. Dir., Record-Eagle, MI, Traverse City
Conyers, Ashley M.
cnmsrbch@aol.com, Pres., Pythia Press, FL, Santa Rosa Beach
Cook, John
john.a.cook@utb.edu, Program Coord., University of Texas at Brownsville, TX, Brownsville
Cook, Montgomery
monty.cook@baltsun.com, Ed./Sr. Vice Pres., The Baltimore Sun, MD, Baltimore
Cook, Jennifer (479) 273-7600 ext. 5512
jcook@nwaonline.net, Metro Ed., The Morning News of Northwest Arkansas, AR, Springdale
Cook, Justin (928) 539-6812
jcook@yumasun.com, Manager, Human Resources, Yuma Sun, AZ, Yuma
Cook, Elizabeth G. (704) 797-4244
editor@salisburypost.com, Ed., Salisbury Post, NC, Salisbury
Cook, Kristen (520) 573-4194
kcook@azstarnet.com, Food/Home Ed., Arizona Daily Star, AZ, Tucson
Cook, John (252) 329-9540
jcook@huntingdondailynews.com, Pub., The Daily Reflector, NC, Greenville
jcook@huntingdondailynews.com, The Bargain Sheet, PA, State College
Cook, Neil
editor@gulf-times.com, Mng. Ed., DAILY GULF TIMES & WEEKLY GULF TIMES

Cook, Andrew
andrew.cook@cmdg.com, Vice Pres./Pub., Daily Commercial News and Construction Record
Cook, James A.
jcook@dailyherald.com, Asst. Vice Pres./Mgr., Mktg./Promo., Daily Herald, IL, Arlington Heights
Cook, Chuck
chuck.cook@usm.edu, News Content Adviser, Univ. of Southern Mississippi, MS, Hattiesburg
Cook, Carey Orr 772-492-9032
careycook@hotmail.com, Pres./Cartoon Ed., Sam Mantics Enterprises, FL, Vero Beach
Cook, A.J. (901) 754-8925
ajcook@pietrangelocook.com, Owner/Author, A.J. Cook, TN, Memphis
Cook, Joel
cooksreviews@optonline.net, Ed., The Agency, NY, Kings Park
Cooke, Johnson (662) 325-7907
Mississippi State Univ., MS, Mississippi State
Cooke, Gene
info@coldjet.com, Pres./CEO, Cold Jet, Inc., CA, Rancho Cucamonga
Cooke, Simon 7005 2000
webmaster@the-times.co.uk, Adv. Dir., THE INDEPENDENT, ENG, London
Cooke, J. Jefferson
jcooke@mycentraljersey.com, Assoc. Ed., Courier News, NJ, Somerville
Cooksey, Fred (413) 552-2538
Holyoke Cmty. College, MA, Holyoke
Cookson, Matt
mcookson@entechnology.com, Opns. Mgr., En Technology Corp., NH, Newport
Cooley, Jeremy
jcooley@rexburgstandardjournal.com, Audience Development Director, The Standard-Journal, ID, Rexburg
Cooley, Rosalind (601) 584-3056
Circ. Mgr., Hattiesburg American, MS, Hattiesburg
Cooley, Ronald (765) 362-1200 ext. 136
rcooley@jrpress.com, Prodn. Foreman, Lead Pressman, Journal Review, IN, Crawfordsville
Coombs, Francis B.
fcoombs@washingtontimes.com, Mng. Ed., The Washington Times Corp., DC, Washington
Coomes, Terry
tcoomes@independenttribune.com, Pub., Independent Tribune, NC, Concord
Coon, Steve
scoon@michigannewspapers.com, Mng. Ed., Morning Sun, MI, Mount Pleasant
Coon, Jim
coon@wingate.edu, Chair, Wingate University, NC, Wingate
Cooney, Stephen
editor@hofstrachronicle.com, Hofstra Univ., NY, Hempstead
Cooney, Raymond
cr_sports@earthlink.net, Sports Ed., The Commercial Review, IN, Portland
Cooper, Don
dcooper@kpcnews.net, GM/VP Sales Mktg, The News-Sun, IN, Kendallville
Cooper, Paulette
nationalpresssyndicate@aol.com, Contact, National Press Syndicate, FL, Palm Beach
Cooper, Brenda (435) 797-3253
Assoc. Prof., Utah State University, UT, Logan
Cooper, Shirley
scooper@gwcommonwealth.com, Circ. Mgr., The Greenwood Commonwealth, MS, Greenwood
Cooper, Christopher 3475495627
Editor-in-Chief, Utica College, NY, Utica
Cooper, Steve (937) 328-0357
scooper@coxohio.com, Film/Theater Ed., Springfield News-Sun, OH, Springfield
Cooper, Don
dcooper@kpcnews.net, VP of Sales/Marketing, The Star, IN, Auburn
Cooper, Tim
tsbcooper@msn.com, Pres., Plumtree Co., GA, Savannah
Cooper, Kevin 601-445-3539
kevin.cooper@natchezdemocrat.com, Publisher, Natchez Newspapers, Inc., MS, Natchez
Cooper, Peter (321) 242-4382
peter.cooper@harrisbaseview.com, Creative/Mktg. Dir., Harris & Baseview, FL, Melbourne
Cooper, Brad (540) 374-5464
bcooper@freelancestar.com, Print Advertising Manager, The Free Lance-Star, VA, Fredericksburg
Cooper, Rose (937) 382-2574
County Ed., Wilmington News Journal, OH, Wilmington
Cooper, Don
dcooper@njherald.com, Gen. Mgr., New Jersey Herald, NJ, Newton
Cooper, Peter (615) 259-8063
pcooper@tennessean.com, Music Writer, The Tennessean, TN, Nashville
Cooper, Audrey (415) 777-7112
acooper@sfchronicle.com, Metro Editor, San Francisco Chronicle, CA, San Francisco
Cooper, Brian (937) 225-2321
brian.cooper@coxinc.com, Senior Vice President, Operations, Dayton Daily News, OH, Dayton
Cooper-Chen, Anne (740) 593-2598
Prof., Ohio University, OH, Athens
Coord., Reprints (212) 293-8500
reprints@unitedmedia.com, Reprint Rights Sales, Newspaper Enterprise Association (Div. of United Media), NY, New York
Coord., Reprint Rights (212) 293-8500
reprints@unitedmedia.com, Reprint Rights Sales, United Feature Syndicate (Div. of United Media), NY, New York
Coover, Roger (209) 546-8243
coover@recordnet.com, Pub., The Record, CA, Stockton
Copeland, Mike
mcopeland@wacotrib.com, Bus./Finance Ed., Waco Tribune-Herald, TX, Waco
Copeland, Robert (863) 802-7212
robert.copeland@theledger.com, Circ. Mgr., The Ledger, FL, Lakeland
Copeland, Julie (831) 429-2467
jcopeland@santacruzsentinel.com, Bus. Ed., Santa Cruz Sentinel, CA, Scotts Valley
Copeland, Pete
news@lahontanvalleynews.com, Pub., Lahontan Valley News/Fallon Eagle Standard, NV, Fallon
Copeland, Gunter ext. 1060
gcopeland@portervillerecorder.com, Adv. Dir., The Porterville Recorder, CA, Porterville
Copeland, Peter (202) 408-2756
copelandp@shns.com, Ed./Gen. Mgr., Scripps Howard News Service, DC, Washington
Copeland, David
dcopeland@elon.edu, Prof./Fletcher Chair/Grad. Dir., Elon University, NC, Elon
Copic, Nancy
copic@up.edu, The Beacon/ Univ. of Portland, OR, Portland
Coplen, Debbie (318) 362-0204
Gen. Sales Mgr., The News-Star, LA, Monroe
Copley, David C. (858) 454-0411
Pres./CEO, Copley News Service - San Diego, CA, CA, San Diego
Coplin, Lynn
lcoplin@trcle.com, Adv. Mgr., Classified, Cleburne Times-Review, TX, Cleburne
Coppage, Mike 321-242-3544
jcoppage@floridatoday.com, Retail Sales Manager, Florida Today, FL, Melbourne
Coppler, Jeff (740) 375-5101
jcoppler@nncogannett.com, Adv. Dir., The Marion Star, OH, Marion
Corbett, Neil ext. 2063
Sports Ed., The Citizens' Voice, PA, Wilkes-Barre
Corbett, Doug
dcorbitt@minotdailynews.com, Ad. Dir., Minot Daily News, ND, Minot
Corcoran, Bruce ext. 324
Ed., The Chatham Daily News, ON, Chatham
Corcoran, James
jcorcoran@bmsvax.simmons.edu, Chair, Simmons College, MA, Boston
Corder, Charles
ccorder@gwcommonwealth.com, Mng. Ed., The Greenwood Commonwealth, MS, Greenwood
Corder, Dinah ext. 124
dcorder@robdailynews.com, Adv. Mgr., Classified, Daily News, IL, Robinson
Cordero, Benjamin
bcorderoh@yahoo.com.mx, Ed. in Chief, El Heraldo De Leon, Leon, Guanajuato
Cordero, Mario
mcordero@lahora.com.gt, Chief Ed., LA HORA, Guatemala City
Cordes, Wade 541-823-4841
wadec@argusobserver.com, Prodn. Mgr., Argus Observer, OR, Ontario
Cordo, Mario
cordom@ambito.com.ar, Ed., Editorial Amfin S.A., Buenos Aires
Cordoba, Francisco Luis
cperez@cordoba.elperiodico.com, Ed. in Chief, Cordoba, Cordoba
Cordoba, Lucio del Carmen 421-000
independ@satlink.com, Ed., El Independiente, La Rioja, Provincia de La Rioja
Cordon, Enrique
murcia@prensalibre.com.gt, Sales Mgr., PRENSA LIBRE, Guatemala City
Corell, Cindy (540) 213-9123
ccorell@newsleader.com, City Ed., The News Leader, VA, Staunton
Corey, Wes (253) 597-8875
wes.corey@thenewstribune.com, Packaging &

Dist. Manager, The News Tribune, WA, Tacoma
Corey, Scott
scorey@cctimes.com, Ed., West County Times, CA, Richmond
Corey, Christina ....(828) 236-8978
corey@citizen-times.com, Mgr., Mktg. Commun., The Asheville Citizen-Times, NC, Asheville
Corker, Ellen L.
ellen@newnan.com, News Ed., The Times-Herald, GA, Newnan
Corkery, Dan 217-351-5218
dcorkery@news-gazette.com, Managing Editor, News-Gazette Inc., IL, Champaign
Cormier, Kathy........................(337) 893-4223
amadvert@bellsouth.net, Mgr., Mktg./Promo., Abbeville Meridional, LA, Abbeville
Corneau, Colin........................(204) 571-7436
ccorneau@brandonsun.com, Photographer, Brandon Sun, MB, Brandon
Cornejo, Azenett.......................(956) 882-5142
azenett.cornejo@utb.edu, Univ. of Texas at Brownsville, TX, Brownsville
Cornelius, Steve
scornelius@somerset-kentucky.com, Sports Ed., The Commonwealth-Journal, KY, Somerset
Cornelius, Daria.........................850-599-2204
dcornelius@tallahassee.com, Circulation Sales Specialist, Tallahassee Democrat, FL, Tallahassee
Cornell, Mike..............................250-371-6145
mcornell@kamloopsnews.ca, News Editor, Kamloops Daily News, BC, Kamloops
Cornwell, Bill ....(979) 265-7411
thefacts@thefacts.com, Pub., The Facts, TX, Clute
Corrado, Kevin ....(920) 993-1000 ext. 7206
kcorrado@greenbaypressgazette.com, Pub., Green Bay Press-Gazette, WI, Green Bay
Corre, Stephane 4217 2000
mail@mondepub.fr, Mng. Dir., LE MONDE/LE MONDE DIMANCHE, Paris Cedex 13
Correa, Afranio E. 242-8363
Ed., Informe do Empresario, Salvador, Bahia
Correa, Suzana
info@symantec.com, CMO, Symantec Corp., ON, Toronto
Correa Leo, Carlos
notichis@tapachula.podernet.com.mx, Pres., NOTICIAS DE CHIAPAS, Tapachula, Chiapas
Correal, Josep
diari@diaridetarragona.com, Dir., Diari De Tarragona, Tarragona
Correia, Henrique
hcorreia@jornaldamadeira.pt, Dir., JORNAL DA MADEIRA, Funchal
Corrigan, Don
corrigdh@webster.edu, Journ. Seq., Webster University, MO, Saint Louis
Corrigan, Don..........................(314) 961-2660
Webster Univ., MO, Saint Louis
Corrigan, Steve.........................(912) 652-0312
steve.corrigan@savannahnow.com, Community Ed., Savannah Morning News, GA, Savannah
Corter, Walter ....(570) 748-6791 ext. 117
wcorter@lockhaven.com, Circ. Mgr., The Express, PA, Lock Haven
Cortes, Raul
montevideo@efe.com, Rep., EFE News Services - Montevideo, Uruguay, Montevideo
Cortez, Gustavo
gcortez@eluniverso.com, Ed., Compania Anonima El Universo, Guayaquil
Corty, Andrew P.......................(727) 893-8204
acorty@tampabay.com, Vice Pres./Sec., Tampa Bay Times, FL, Saint Petersburg
Corvi, Lawrence
lcorvi@muskogeephoenix.com, Pres./Pub., Muskogee Daily Phoenix & Times Democrat, OK, Muskogee
Corwin, Scott ....(941) 206-1501
webeditor@sun-herald.com, Internet Ed., Charlotte Sun, FL, Charlotte Harbor
Cory, Matt
mcory@gfherald.com, News Editor, Grand Forks Herald, ND, Grand Forks
Coschica, Mario
coschicam@ambito.com.ar, Pub., Editorial Amfin S.A., Buenos Aires
Cosenza, Lisa
dailypilot@latimes.com, Adv. Dir., Daily Pilot, CA, Costa Mesa
Cosner, Christina......................(317) 736-2750
ccosner@dailyjournal.net, Adv. Dir., Daily Journal, IN, Franklin
Cossey, Mike
info@risiinfo.com, CEO, RISI, Inc., MA, Bedford
Costa, Denise.........................(541) 383-0356
dcosta@bendbulletin.com, Features Ed., The Bulletin, OR, Bend
Costa, John ....(541) 383-0337
jcosta@bendbulletin.com, Ed. in Chief, The Bulletin, OR, Bend
Costa, Mat.............................(479) 571-6454
mcosta@nwanews.com, Dir., IT, Northwest Arkansas Times, AR, Fayetteville
Costello, John A.
jcostello@rotadyne.com, Vice Pres., OEM Sales, RotaDyne Corp., IL, Darien
Costello, Stephen M......(207) 784-5411 ext. 1220
scostello@sunjournal.com, Vice Pres. Adv./Mktg., Sun Journal, ME, Lewiston
Costello, Steven
scostello@sunjournal.com, Dir., Adv., Maine Daily Newspaper Publishers Association, ME, Lewiston
Costello, Vic
vcostello@elon.edu, Assoc. Prof., Elon University, NC, Elon
Costello, Carlita.......................(915) 546-6176
ccostello@elpasotimes.com, Design Ed., El Paso Times, TX, El Paso
Cote, Maria ....(303) 892-5169
cotem@rockymountainnews.com, Lifestyle Ed., Rocky Mountain News, CO, Denver
Cote, Therese.........................(418) 686-3254
tcote@lesoleil.com, Supvr., Le Soleil, QC, Quebec
Cote, Andre-Philippe
apcote@lesoleil.com, Cartoonist, Le Soleil, QC, Quebec
Cote, Dave
lois.sills@honeywell.com, CEO, Honeywell, Inc., NJ, Morristown
Cothron, Kevin.........................(217) 477-5147
kcothron@dancomnews.com, Circ. Dir., Commercial News, IL, Danville
Cothron, Kevin
advertising@parisbeacon.com, Pub., Paris Beacon-News, IL, Paris
Cottay, George........................(309) 757-5005
cottay@qconline.com, Online Ed., The Dispatch, IL, Moline
Cotter, Dan ....(781) 320-8048
d.cotter@nenpa.com, Executive Director, New England Newspaper & Press Association, Inc., MA, Dedham
Cotter, Dan
d.cotter@nenpa.com, Exec. Dir. NENPA, New England Newspaper Advertising Executives Association, MA, Dedham
Cotter, Dan ....(781) 320-8048
d.cotter@nenpa.com, Executive Director, NENPA Ad Network (New England Newspaper and Press Association), MA, Dedham
Cotter, Tim 860/701-4372
t.cotter@theday.com, Managing Editor, The Day Publishing Company, CT, New London
Cotter, William M.
bcotter@tribweb.com, Sales/Mktg. Dir., Trib Total Media
Cotters, Mary ....ext. 241
mcotters@timesonline.com, Circ. Mgr., Opns., Beaver County Times, PA, Beaver
Cottingham, James ....(580) 585-5075
tlcbus@swbell.net, Bus. Mgr., The Lawton Constitution, OK, Lawton
Cottle, Lee
sales@vicorp.com, COO, Vicorp.com, TX, Plano
Cotton, Eric..........................(203) 317-2344
ecotton@record-journal.com, City Ed., Record-Journal, CT, Meriden
Cottos, Scott ....ext. 237
scottcottos@reviewtimes.com, Sports Ed., The Review Times, OH, Fostoria
Coudurier, Edouard 9862 1133
telegramme@bretagne-online.com/telegram, Pres./MD, LE TELEGRAMME, 29205 Moriax
Coulter, Keith ....(306) 657-6365
kcoulter@sp.canwest.com, Prodn. Mgr., Pressroom, The StarPhoenix, SK, Saskatoon
Coulter, Barry...............................ext. 210
townsman@cyberlink.bc.ca, Ed., Cranbrook Daily Townsman, BC, Cranbrook
Coulter, Alexander
news@theeveningtimes.com, Pub., Times, AR, Marion
Coulter, Barry
barry@dailytownsman.com, Ed., The Kimberley Daily Bulletin, BC, Kimberley
Counts, Chris ....(850) 671-6530
ccounts@tallahassee.com, Digital Media Dir., Tallahassee Democrat, FL, Tallahassee
Courter, Cindy
cindyc@gilroydispatch.com, Adv. Mgr., Retail, The Dispatch, CA, Gilroy
Courter, Cindy.........................(408) 842-1922
cindyc@gilroydispatch.com, Adv. Servs. Mgr., Free Lance, CA, Hollister
Courtet de Barcia, Elsa......................426-164
diario@diarioelargentino.com.ar, Gen. Mgr., EL ARGENTINO, Gualeguaychu, Provincia de Entre Rios
Courtney, Mark ....(910) 343-2201
mark.courtney@starnewsonline.com, Photo Ed., Star-News, NC, Wilmington
Courtney, Bernadette
bernadette.courtney@dompost.co.nz, Ed., THE DOMINION POST
Courtney, Kevin
kcourtney@tribune.com, Commun. Mgr., Sun-Sentinel Co., FL, Fort Lauderdale
Courtney, Will
wcourtney@newburyportnews.com, City Ed., The Daily News, MA, Newburyport
Cousins, Bruce ....(250) 380-5274
bcousins@te.canwest.com, Circ. Mgr., Distr./Mktg., Times Colonist, BC, Victoria
Couto, Dan ....(518) 454-5401
dcouto@timesunion.com, Dir., Opns./Facilities Planning, Times Union, NY, Albany
Couture, Marc
mcouture@jdeq.com, Circ. Mgr., Le Journal de Quebec, QC, Vanier
Covert, Tom ....ext. 667
Mgr., Computer Serv., New Castle News, PA, New Castle
Covington, Michelle ....(616) 222-5317
mcovington@grpress.com, Adv. Mgr., Classified, The Grand Rapids Press, MI, Grand Rapids
Covington, Michelle ....(616) 222-5317
vmcreynolds@boothmichigan.com, Classified Mgr., Booth Newspapers, Inc., MI, Grand Rapids
Cowan, Bruce
bcowan@thedailypress.ca, Pub., The Daily Press, ON, Timmins
Cowan, Cindy ....(505) 564-4605
ccowan@daily-times.com, Prodn. Dir., The Daily Times, NM, Farmington
Cowan, Cale
ccowan@nanaimodailynews.com, Mng. Ed., Nanaimo Daily News, BC, Nanaimo
Cowan, Ted.............................(416) 869-4994
tcowan@torstar.com, Sales Rep., Torstar Syndication Services, ON, Toronto
Coward, John
john-coward@utulsa.edu, Chair, University of Tulsa, OK, Tulsa
Cowles, Roger........................(409) 721-2431
rcowles@panews.com, Editorial Page Ed., Port Arthur News, TX, Port Arthur
Cowley, Peter
pcrowley@adirondackguide.com, Mng. Ed., Adirondack Daily Enterprise, NY, Saranac Lake
Cowling, Randy
rcowling@claremoreprogress.com, Ed., The Claremore Daily Progress, OK, Claremore
Cox, Jim ....(360) 735-4609
jim.cox@columbian.com, Circ. Mgr., Sales/Home Delivery, The Columbian, WA, Vancouver
Cox, Rose ....ext. 469
rcox@adn.com, Community News Ed., Anchorage Daily News, AK, Anchorage
Cox, Ron......................(434) 432-1654 ext. 31
rcox@womackpublishing.com, HR Mgr., Womack Publishing Co., VA, Chatham
Cox, V. Marvin
mcox@boisestate.edu, Chrmn., Boise State University, ID, Boise
Cox, Melanie
mcox@anrinc.net, Sales Mgr., American Newspaper Representatives, Inc., MN, Roseville
Cox, Dan................................785-832-7275
dcox@mediaphormedia.com, President, Mediaphormedia LLC, The World Co.- Lawrence, Kan., Journal-World, KS, Lawrence
Cox, Dan...............................(785) 838-7275
dcox@ljworld.com, Pres., Mediaphormedia, The World Co.- Lawrence, Kan., Journal-World, KS, Lawrence
Cox, Bob
bob.cox@freepress.mb.ca, Pub., Winnipeg Free Press, MB, Winnipeg
Cox, Rich ....(574) 753-0137 ext. 224
rich.cox@pharostribune.com, Prodn. Mgr., Pre Press, Pharos-Tribune, IN, Logansport
Cox, Melanie..........................(651) 487-5778
mcox@anrinc.net, Regl. Sales Mgr., Minneapolis, American Newspaper Representatives, MI, Troy
Cox, Jackie............................(717) 240-7107
jcox@cumberlink.com, Adv. Sales Mgr., The Sentinel, PA, Carlisle
Cox, Wendy
wendy.cox@thecanadianpress.com, Bureau Chief, Canadian Press, The - Vancouver, BC, BC, Vancouver
Cox, Ralph ....(502) 625-2133
Gen. Mgr., Primark Tool Group, IL, Mount Prospect
Coyne, Brian
bcoyne@journalinquirer.com, Sports Ed., Journal Inquirer, CT, Manchester
Cozby, Julie ....(360) 501-2705
jcozby@tdn.com, Copy Ed., The Daily News, WA, Longview
Crabtree, Larry L.
publisher@vernonrecord.com, Pres./Pub., The Vernon Daily Record, TX, Vernon
Crabtree, Sharlene...................(541) 383-0327
scrabtree@bendbulletin.com, Dir., HR, The Bulletin, OR, Bend
Craft, Michael ....(318) 869-0115
jmichaelcraft@bellsouth.net, Sr. Newspaper Consultant, The Austin Company, OH, Cleveland
Craft, Lisa
publisher@monett-times.com, Pub., The Monett Times, MO, Monett
Craft, Dan ....(309) 820-3259
dcraft@pantagraph.com, Entertainment Ed., The Pantagraph, IL, Bloomington
Crage, Jerry
jgrage@northumberlandtoday.com, Adv. Dir., Port Hope Evening Guide, ON, Port Hope
Craig, Brian ....(209) 369-7035 ext. 225
bcraig@lodinews.com, News Ed., Lodi News-Sentinel, CA, Lodi
Craig, Frank L.........................(412) 320-7816
fcraig@tribweb.com, Ed., Pittsburgh, Tribune-Review, PA, Pittsburgh
Craig, Richard ....(408) 924-3270
San Jose State Univ., CA, San Jose
Craig, M. Joseph ....(910) 739-4322 ext. 101
jcraig@robesonian.com, Pub., The Robesonian, NC, Lumberton
Craine, Charlie ....(801) 236-6082
ccraine@desnews.com, Dir., Interactive Media, Deseret News, UT, Salt Lake City
Cramer, George
gcramer@arglobal.com, Vice Pres., Commercial Devel., Adhesives Research, Inc., PA, Glen Rock
Cramer, Kristi ....(717) 334-1131 ext. 290
kristic@gburgtimes.com, Pre Press Opns. Mgr., Gettysburg Times, PA, Gettysburg
Crandall, Margaret...................(740) 654-1321
mcrandall@nncogannett.com, Sec., Ohio Newspaper Women's Association, OH, Enon
Crandell, Scott.......................(406) 758-4430
newsed@dailyinterlake.com, News Ed., Daily Inter Lake, MT, Kalispell
Crane, Leonard
lcrane@news-daily.com, Prodn. Mgr., Mailroom/Distr., News/Daily, GA, Jonesboro
Cranshaw, William O.

bcranshaw@mpival.com, Vice Pres., Management Planning, Inc., CT, Simsbury
Crawford, Donald ....(979) 731-4686
donald.crawford@theeagle.com, Mailroom Mgr., The Eagle, TX, Bryan
Crawford, Nancy J. ....(410) 398-3311 ext. 3055
ncrawford@chespub.com, Exec. Asst., Chesapeake Publishing Corp., MD, Elkton
Crawford, William..........(808) 935-6621 ext. 236
bcrawford@hawaiitribune-herald.com, Circ. Dir., Hawaii Tribune-Herald, HI, Hilo
Crawford, Carolyn....................(215) 949-4017
ccrawford@calkins-media.com, Sec. to Pres., Calkins Media, PA, Levittown
Crawford, Paul.......................(256) 340-2370
paul.crawford@decaturdaily.com, Online Dir., TimesDaily, AL, Florence
Crawford, Paul M.....................(502) 644-5650
paulc@technidyne.com, Bus. Dir., Technidyne Corp., IN, New Albany
Crawford, Karen
sjackson@greenfieldreporter.com, Mng. Ed., Daily Reporter, IN, Greenfield
Crawley, David
d.crawley@womackpublishing.com, Grp. Pub., Womack Publishing Co., VA, Chatham
Crawley, Nancy........................(616) 222-5452
ncrawley@grpress.com, Bus. Ed., The Grand Rapids Press, MI, Grand Rapids
Crawley, Phillip
comments@globeandmail.ca, Pub./CEO, The Globe and Mail, ON, Toronto
Crawley, Matthew.....................(979) 731-4663
matthew.crawley@theeagle.com, Dir., Internet/New Media, The Eagle, TX, Bryan
Crea, Joe..............................(216) 999-4873
Food Editor, The Plain Dealer, OH, Cleveland
Creasy, Roger..........................336-506-3089
New Media Director, Times-News, NC, Burlington
Creer, J.D.
jdcreer@salemnews.net, Ed., Salem News, OH, Salem
Creighton, Bill........................(202) 383-6058
bcreighton@newscom.com, Gen. Mgr., Newscom, DC, Washington
Cremonese, Socieca
ctosi@cremononline.it, Ed. in Chief, LA PROVINCIA, Cremona
Crenshaw, Richard....................662-678-0550
richard.crenshaw@journalinc.com, Advertising and Marketing Director, Journal Publishing Company, MS, Tupelo
Crespo, Emilio
lisboa@efe.com, Rep., EFE News Services - Lisbon, Portugal, Lisbon
Crevier, Guy
gcrevier@lapresse.ca, Pub., La Presse, QC, Montreal
Crews, Doug
dcrews@socket.net, Exec. Dir., Missouri Press Association, MO, Columbia
Crews, Doug
dcrews@socket.net, Exec. Dir., Missouri Press Service, Inc., MO, Columbia
Crews, Doug..........................(573) 449-4167
dcrews@socket.net, Exec. Dir., Missouri Press Service, Inc., MO, Columbia
Cribb, John..........................(406) 586-6621
jcribb@cribb.com, Managing Director, Cribb, Greene & Associates, MT, Bozeman
Cribb, John T........................(406) 586-6621
jcribb@cribb.com, MD., Cribb, Greene & Associates, MT, Bozeman
Cribb, Vince................(229) 219-0230 ext. 202
vince.cribb@gaflnews.com, Vice Pres., Prodn., Valdosta Daily Times, GA, Valdosta
Crichfield, Beverly
bcrichfield@skagitpublishing.com, Features Ed., Skagit Valley Herald, WA, Mount Vernon
Crider, Dennis...................................ext. 215
Farm Ed., West Plains Daily Quill, MO, West Plains
Crigger, David........................(276) 645-2535
dcrigger@bristolnews.com, Chief Photographer, Bristol Herald Courier, VA, Bristol
Criscoe, Ray..........................(336) 626-6115
rcriscoe@courier-tribune.com, Ed., The Courier-Tribune, NC, Asheboro
Crisp, Bob
bcrisp@dailyhome.com, Photo Ed., The Daily Home, AL, Talladega
Crisp, Dale
dcrisp@dcn.com.au, Ed., DAILY COMMERCIAL NEWS
Crisp, John.............................419-724-6491
jcrisp@toledoblade.com, Director of Advertising and New Media, The Blade, OH, Toledo
Criss, Leslie...........................662-678-1584
leslie.criss@journalinc.com, Lifestyles Editor, Journal Publishing Company, MS, Tupelo
Crist, Mike.............................(610) 622-8819
Asst. City Ed., Night, Delaware County Daily Times, PA, Primos
Crist, Steven
(212) 366-7791, Pub., Daily Racing Form
Critchley, Brian
njnn@njpa.org, Mktg. Mgr., New Jersey Newspaper Network (NJNN), NJ, West Trenton
Critchlow, David
dgc@ucmessenger.com, Pres./Pub., The Messenger, TN, Union City
Crivellone, Jim
jimcriv@cgipressparts.com, Pres., Central Graphics, IL, Romeoville
Crockett, Tammy............(250) 368-8551 ext 205
accounting@trailtimes.ca, accounting, Trail Daily Times, BC, Trail
Crofoot, Art...........................(202) 636-3062
acrofoot@washingtontimes.com, Adv. Mgr., Major Accts., The Washington Times, DC, Washington
Crofoot, Patrick.......................(202) 636-3026
pcrofoot@washingtontimes.com, Mgr., Art Graphics, The Washington Times, DC, Washington
Croft, Mary Lou.......................(902) 426-1133
mcroft@herald.ca, Dir., Cor. Admin., The Chronicle Herald, NS, Halifax
Croft, Charles.........................(251) 434-8620
ccroft@mobileregister.com, Farm/Agriculture Ed., Press-Register, AL, Mobile
Croft, Margaret.......................(318) 362-0308
Photography Ed., The News-Star, LA, Monroe
Croke, Rose............................(212) 969-7594
rmcroke@hearst.com, Promotions Director, North America Syndicate, NY, New York
rmcroke@hearst.com, Promotions Director, King Features Syndicate, NY, New York
Croley, Tina...........................(313) 222-8774
croley@freepress.com, Features Ed., Detroit Free Press, MI, Detroit
Cromeens, Barton.....................(325) 670-5213
cromeensb@reporternews.com, Ed., Abilene Reporter-News, TX, Abilene
Crompton, Dave...............................ext. 304
david.crompton@ok.bc.ca, Sports Ed., Penticton Herald, BC, Penticton
Cronick, Scott..........................609-272-7017
scronick@pressofac.com, Local Content Producer/News, The Press of Atlantic City, NJ, Pleasantville
Cronin, Steve...........................609-272-7242
scronin@pressofac.com, Local Content Producer/Features, The Press of Atlantic City, NJ, Pleasantville
Cronin, Daniel..............(515) 232-2160 ext. 314
dcronin@amestrib.com, Circ. Dir., Iowa Newspapers, Inc., IA, Ames
Cronin, Dennis..........................402-4441482
Dir., Circulation, Omaha World-Herald, NE, Omaha
Cronin, Dennis.........................402-444-1482
Dir., Circulation, Omaha World-Herald, NE, Omaha
Cronk, Alan............................(336) 727-7406
Exec. Ed., Star Watch, NC, Winston-Salem
Cronk, Alan............................(336) 727-7406
Bus. Mgr., Spotlight, NC, Winston-Salem
Cronk, Dale..................................ext. 2388
dcronk@wdt.net, Prodn. Mgr., Watertown Daily Times, NY, Watertown
Cronk, Alan............................(336) 727-7406
Bus. Mgr., Spotlight, NC, Winston-Salem
Cronk, Donna...............(765) 593-2459 ext. 232
dcronk@thecouriertimes.com, Neighbors Ed., The Courier-Times, IN, New Castle
Crook, David..........................(212) 416-3375
david.crook@dowjones.com, Ed., The Wall Street Journal Sunday, NY, New York
Croom, Larry..........................(352) 753-1119
larry.croom@thevillagesmedia.com, Exec. Ed., The Villages Daily Sun, FL, The Villages
Cropley, Dan
dcropley@mullermartinims.com, Dir., Inserting, Muller Martini Mailroom Systems, Inc., PA, Allentown
Crosbie, Kevin B...........................ext. 3313
editor@thechronicle.com, Purchasing Agent, The Chronicle, CT, Willimantic
Cross, Tom
tom@register-pajaronian.com, Pub., Register-Pajaronian, CA, Watsonville
Cross, Pete............................(561) 820-4466
pcross@pbpost.com, Asst. Mng. Ed., Photo, The Palm Beach Post, FL, West Palm Beach
Cross, Dale
edalecross@desototimes.com, Adv. Dir., DeSoto Times Today, MS, Hernando
Cross, Lynnette........................419-281-0581
lcross@times-gazette.com, Business Manager, Ashland Publishing Co. LLC, OH, Ashland
Cross, Sue
scross@ap.org, Reg'l Vice Pres. Newyork, Associated Press/California-Nevada News Executives, CA, Los Angeles
Cross, Stewart........................(770) 795-9195
stewart.cross@zane.com, Pres./COO, Zane Publishing, Inc., GA, Woodstock
Crossley, Gay Lynn...................(317) 955-6397
Marian College, IN, Indianapolis
Crosthwaite, Fred....................(530) 896-7751
fcrosthwaite@chicoer.com, Online Dir., Chico Enterprise-Record, CA, Chico
Crouse, Katelyn.......................(252) 328-9249
editor@theeastcarolinian.com, The East Carolinian, NC, Greenville
Crow, Peter M.........................(918) 786-9051
editor@grovesun.com, Pres., Grove Sun Daily, OK, Grove
Crowe, J.D.............................(251) 219-5676
jdcrowe@press-register.com, Self-Syndicator, staff editorial cartoonist, Mobile Press-Register, J.D. Crowe, AL, Mobile
Crowe, Diane
diane.crowe@journal-register.com, Pub., The Journal-Register, NY, Medina
Crowe, Diane
diane.crowe@lockportjournal.com, Pub., Union-Sun & Journal, NY, Lockport
Crowell, Jeff...........................(517) 768-4850
jcrowell@citpat.com, Distribution Mgr., The Jackson Citizen Patriot, MI, Jackson
Crowfoot, Simon
sales@iceni.com, Dir., Iceni Technology, Norwich
Crowley, Tom..........................(206) 838-2014
tom.crowley@catalystpaper.com, Sr. Vice Pres. Sales/Mktg., Catalyst Paper (USA), Inc., WA, Seattle
Crowley, Kevin..........(519) 894-2250 ext. 2624
kcrowley@therecord.com, Bus. Ed., The Record, ON, Kitchener
Crowther-Barnes, Wendy
wendy.crowther-barnes@thevillagesmedia.com, CSR Mgr., The Villages Daily Sun, FL, The Villages
Cruce, Joyce............................575-763-3431
jcruce@cnjonline.com, Human Resources Director, Clovis News Journal, NM, Clovis
Cruden, Alex..........................(313) 223-4702
cruden@freepress.com, Copy Desk Chief, Detroit Free Press, MI, Detroit
Cruickshank, John
jcruickshank@thestar.ca, Publisher, Toronto Star, ON, Toronto
Crumbaugh, Lee
leepublish@aol.com, Pres., Forrest Consulting, IL, Glen Ellyn
Crump, Ardell
acrump@njtimes.com, Circ. Mgr., Home Delivery, The Times, NJ, Trenton
Crupi, Joann M........................(518) 454-5470
jcrupi@timesunion.com, Opinion Pages Ed., Times Union, NY, Albany
Cruz, Debra Renee...................(215) 849-9016
fashionnnb@aol.com, Fashion/Beauty/Lifestyles Ed., National News Bureau, PA, Philadelphia
Cruz, Paula
paulacruz@uze.com.br, Sales Mgr., Folha de Boa Vista, Boa Vista, Roraima
Cruz Flores, Gilberto........................232 4424
Pres., DIARIO DE PUEBLA, Puebla, Puebla
Cryder, Chris
ccryder@daily-jeff.com, Circ. Dir., The Daily Jeffersonian, OH, Cambridge
Crystal, Paul..........................(212) 293-8670
pcrystal@unitedmedia.com, Sr. Vice Pres., Finance/Admin., United Media, OH, Cincinnati
Csaba, Nyerges
szerkesztoseg@delmagyar.hu, Ed. in Chief, DELVILAG, Szeged, Csongrad
Csaba, Nyerges
kisalfold@kisafold.hu, Ed. in Chief, KISALFOLD, Gyor, Gyor-Sopron
Cubbal, Kayleen..............................ext. 617
Sports Ed., New Castle News, PA, New Castle
Cube, Christine
christine.cube@prnewswire.com, Audience Development, PR Newswire - Washington, DC, DC, Washington
Cuccoli, Rosarita
rcuccoli@press-iasn.org, Sec. Gen., International Association of Sports Newspapers (IASN), Paris
Cueva, Hector.........................(479) 634-5504
hcueva@nwanews.com, Circ. Dir., Northwest Arkansas Times, AR, Fayetteville
Cueva, Hernan
hernan@hoy.com.ec, VP., Adv., Edimpres S.A., Quito, Pichincha
Culbertson, Kay H.
kculbertson@mountvernonnews.com, Pres./Pub., Mount Vernon News, OH, Mount Vernon
Cullen, Julie..........................(616) 222-5819
jcullen@grpress.com, Adv. Dir., Sales, The Grand Rapids Press, MI, Grand Rapids
Cullen, Jackie.........................(608) 822-3262
Southwest Wisconsin Tech. College, WI, Fennimore
Cullinan, Thomas....................(559) 441-6290
tcullinan@fresnobee.com, Circ. Vice Pres., The Fresno Bee, CA, Fresno
Cullis, Christopher
christopher@bryantimes.com, Chrmn./Pres./Pub., Bryan Publishing Co., OH, Bryan
Cullis, Christopher
christopher@bryantimes.com, Chrmn./Pres./Pub., The Bryan Times, OH, Bryan
Cullis, Christopher
president@bryantimes.com, Pres./Pub., Northwest Signal, OH, Napoleon
Culp, Ph.D., Mildred L.
culp@workwise.net, Dir., Passage Media, IL, Crete
Cumiskey, Gail.......................(904) 819-3518
gail.cumiskey@staugustinerecord.com, Special Projects Dir., The St. Augustine Record, FL, Saint Augustine
Cumming, James R.
jcumming@fortfrances.com, Pub., Fort Frances Daily Bulletin, ON, Fort Frances
Cummings, Frank....................(205) 664-8660
spaztik@earthlink.net, Owner/Creator, Frank Cummings Illustration, AL, Montevallo
Cummings, Dale......................(204) 697-7043
Dale.Cummings@freepress.mb.ca, Cartoonist, Winnipeg Free Press, MB, Winnipeg
Cummings, Bill................................ext. 381
bcummings@johnsoncitypress.com, Adv. Sales Mgr., Johnson City Press, TN, Johnson City
Cummings, Michael
michael.cummings@msl.co.nz, Ed., MANAWATU STANDARD
Cummins, Gregg..............................ext. 120
Prodn. Foreman, Press, Daily News, IL, Robinson
Cuneo, Kevin.........................(814) 870-1701
kevin.cuneo@timesnews.com, Lifestyle Ed., Erie Times-News, PA, Erie
Cuniberti, Betty......................(314) 340-8383
bcuniberti@post-dispatch.com, Columnist, St. Louis Post-Dispatch, MO, Saint Louis
Cunningham, Rusty
rusty.cunningham@lee.net, Pub., Winona Daily News, MN, Winona
Cunningham, Bill
sjdailycourier@sbcglobal.net, Ed., St. Joseph Daily Courier
Cunningham, Lee

lee.cunningham@lee.net, Creative Services Mgr., The Citizen, NY, Auburn
Cunningham, Laura..................(561) 820-4939
lcunningham@pbpost.com, Dir., Mktg. Servs., The Palm Beach Post, FL, West Palm Beach
Cunningham, Craig..................(304) 348-1234
Pres., West Virginia News Photographers Association, WV, Charleston
Cunningham, Bill
sjdailycourier@sbcglobal.net, Pres./Pub., St. Joseph Daily Courier
Cunningham, Linda G................(815) 987-1355
Exec. Ed., Rockford Register Star, IL, Rockford
Cunningham, Lynn....................(504) 826-3345
lcunningham@timespicayune.com, Online Ed., The Times Picayune, LA, New Orleans
Cunningham, Rusty..................(608) 791-8285
rusty.cunningham@lacrossetribune.com, Pub., La Crosse Tribune, WI, La Crosse
Cunningham, Ben....................(256) 235-3542
bcunningham@annistonstar.com, Metro Ed., The Anniston Star, AL, Anniston
Cunningham, Bill
sjdailycourier@sbcglobal.net, Prodn. Mgr., St. Joseph Daily Courier
Cunningham, Bob....................(660) 263-4123
advertising@moberlymonitor.com, Pub., Moberly Monitor-Index & Evening Democrat, MO, Moberly
Cuomo, Brenda C......................(609) 871-8085
bcuomo@phillyburbs.com, Retail Adv. Mgr., Burlington County Times, NJ, Willingboro
Cupo, Al
al.cupo@suburban-news.org, Vice Pres., Sales/Mktg., Suburban Newspapers of America, MI, Traverse City
Curbelo, Carlos.......................(305) 346-6647
ccurbelo@alm.com, Director of Products, Miami Daily Business Review, FL, Miami
Curbelo, Carlos.......................(305) 347-6647
ccurbelo@alm.com, Director of Products, Palm Beach Daily Business Review, FL, West Palm Beach
Curet, Monique.......................(251) 434-8604
wrabb@mobileregister.com, Health/Medical Reporter, Press-Register, AL, Mobile
Curran, Tom............................(973) 392-4003
tcurran@starledger.com, Assoc. Ed., The Star-Ledger, NJ, Newark
Curran, Jay.............................(661) 940-5361
jcurran@avpress.com, Adv. Dir., Retail, Antelope Valley Press, CA, Palmdale
Curry, John.............................(706) 208-2265
john.curry@onlineathens.com, Photo Dir., Athens Banner-Herald, GA, Athens
Curry, Travis
editor@spencereveningworld.com, Editor, Spencer Evening World, IN, Spencer
Curry, Vanessa........................(903) 565-5617
Univ. of Texas, TX, Tyler
Curry, Kim
kcurry@sharonherald.com, Educ. Ed., The Herald, PA, Sharon
Curtin, Christine.......................(212) 210-1907
ccurtin@nydailynews.com, Vice Pres., Mktg., NY Daily News, NY, New York
Curtin, Josh............................(229) 931-2035
Georgia Southwestern State Univ., GA, Americus
Curtin, Jack............................(407) 420-5270
jcurtin@orlandosentinel.com, Adv. Sr. Mgr., Delivery, Orlando Sentinel, FL, Orlando
Curtin, Caitlin
info@luminare.com, Pres., Luminare, CA, San Francisco
Curtis, Harry.L
hcurtis@mpival.com, Gen. Mgr., Management Planning, Inc., CT, Simsbury
Curtis, John
john.curtis@shelbyvilledailyunion.com, Sports Ed., Daily Union, IL, Shelbyville
Curtis, Harry L.
hcurtis@mpival.com, Pres., Management Planning, Inc., NJ, Princeton
Curtis, Steve...........................(209) 249-3508
scurtis@mantecabulletin.com, Prodn. Mgr., Manteca Bulletin, CA, Manteca
Curtis, Opal............................(540) 374-5471
ocurtis@freelancestar.com, Classified Call Ctr. Sales Mgr., The Free Lance-Star, VA, Fredericksburg
Curtis, Andy..................................ext. 691
Prodn. Mgr., Bldg., The Jackson Sun, TN, Jackson
Curtis, Dean............................(417) 836-1182
dcurtis@news-leader.com, Photo Ed., Springfield News-Leader, MO, Springfield
Curtis, Jasper..........................(903) 596-6200
Adv. Mgr., Opns., Tyler Morning Telegraph, TX, Tyler
Cusac, Bill...............................(810) 989-6286
wrcusac@porthuro.gannett.com, Pre Press Mgr., Times Herald, MI, Port Huron
Cusato, Michael........................(808) 525-7643
Circ. Vice Pres., Honolulu Star-Advertiser, HI, Honolulu
Cushing, Marie
letters@jhunewsletter.com, The Johns Hopkins News-Letter, MD, Baltimore
Cuslidge, Tara
tcuslidge@recordnet.com, Online Editor, The Record, CA, Stockton
Custeau, Andre..........................819 566-8022
andre.custeau@latribune.qc.ca, Nouvelle de Sherbrooke, QC, Sherbrooke
andre.custeau@latribune.qc.ca, Circ. Mgr., La Tribune, QC, Sherbrooke
Cutillo, Michael J.......................315-789-3333
mcutillo@fltimes.com, Executive Editor, Finger Lakes Times, NY, Geneva
Cutshall, Brian.........................(423) 359-3109
brian.cutshall@jonesmedia.biz, Gen. Mgr., GreenevilleSun.com, The Greeneville Sun, TN, Greeneville
Cuturi, R.A.
redaktion@nachrichten.at, Pub., OBEROSTERREICHISCHE NACHRICHTEN, Linz, Upper Austria
Cyr, Kristen
spickering@eastbaynewspapers.com, Treasurer, Rhode Island Press Association, RI, Kingston
Cyr, Marcia..............................850-521-1165
mcyr@flpress.com, Membership Coordinator, Florida Society of Newspaper Editors, FL, Tallahassee
Czajka, Mark..................................ext. 479
mczajka@ags.com, Dir., New Technology, Automated Graphic Systems, MD, White Plains

D

D'Adamo, Gene.........................(602) 444-8078
gene.dadamo@pni.com, Vice Pres., Community Rel., The Arizona Republic, AZ, Phoenix
D'Alessandro, Matt
matt@fnanews.com, Photo Bureau Chief, FNA News, UT, Salt Lake City
D'Alessandro, George S.
gdales1680@aol.com, Vice Pres., All-Sports Publications, NY, Carmel
D'Alessio, Marietta
marietta.d'alessio@ott.sunpub.com, Adv. Mgr., Classified, The Ottawa Sun, ON, Ottawa
D'Alessio, Jeff..................................ext. 290
jdalessio@thenewsenterprise.com, News Ed., The News Enterprise, KY, Elizabethtown
D'Alio, Cindy............................(570) 628-6015
Special Sections Ed., Republican Herald, PA, Pottsville
D'Angelo, Chris.........................(330) 841-1620
cdangelo@tribtoday.com, Dir., Sales/Mktg., The Tribune Chronicle, OH, Warren
D'Arconte, Oreste......................(508) 236-0394
darconte@thesunchronicle.com, Pub., The Sun Chronicle, MA, Attleboro
D'Atri de Santesteban, Rosalba............433-733
arena@cpsarg.com, Pres., La Arena, Santa Rosa, Provincia de La Pampa
D'Avila, Wanderley Rossilho................22-2400
Pres., Jornal da Manha Regional, Marilia, Sao Paulo
D'Hooge, Edward.......................(928) 556-2284
edhooge@azdailysun.com, Prodn. Dir., Arizona Daily Sun, AZ, Flagstaff
D'Onofrio, John................................ext. 6247
Sports Ed., Union-Sun & Journal, NY, Lockport
D'Souza, Wilfred
contact@navabharat.com, Mgr., NAVA BHARAT, Bhopal
D'Vari, Marisa
mdvari@deg.com, Pres./Writer, Deg Syndication, NY, new york
DAmore, Laurie..........................978-946-2113
ldamore@eagletribune.com, Director of Humas Resources, The Eagle-Tribune, MA, North Andover
DEBORAH, ANDERSON..................816-234-4088
danderson@kcstar.com, CLASSIFIED CALL CENTER MANAGER, The Olathe News, MO, Kansas City
DaRosa, Antonio H......................(508) 236-0368
tdarosa@thesunchronicle.com, Bus. Mgr., The Sun Chronicle, MA, Attleboro
Daar, Adina..............................(904) 620-2727
Univ. of North Florida, FL, Jacksonville
Dabaji, Michel
service.client@lesechos.com, Ed. in Chief, LES ECHOS, Paris
Dabin, Dominique
redacchef@nicematin.fr, Ed. in Chief, MONACO-MATIN, Monaco
Dabney, Bailey
bdabney@claremoreprogress.com, Pub., The Claremore Daily Progress, OK, Claremore
Dacosta Gomez, Willem
directie@amigoearuba.aw, Gen. Mgr., AMIGOE, Oranjestad
Dadge, David
ipi@freemedia.at, Dir., International Press Institute, Vienna
Dae-Sung, Kim
cjnews@chejunews.co.kr, Pres., CHEJU DAILY NEWS, Cheju
Dae-jung, Kim
kwangju@kwangju.co.kr, Ed., KWANGJU ILBO, Kwangju, Gwangiu
Daenzer, Jeana.........................(231) 933-1437
jdaenzer@record-eagle.com, Adv. Mgr., Classified, Record-Eagle, MI, Traverse City
Dafoe, Dave..............................(807) 343-6206
dave.dafoe@chroniclejournal.com, Prodn. Mgr., The Chronicle-Journal, ON, Thunder Bay
Daglow, Don
ddaglow@stormfront.com, Pres., Stormfront Studios, CA, San Rafael
Dagostino, Bob.........................(216) 999-4921
Prepress Mgr., Commercial & Quality Assurance, The Plain Dealer, OH, Cleveland
Dahl, Michael
mdahl@lz-online.de, Ed., LIPPISCHE LANDES-ZEITUNG, Detmold
Dahlman, Jim............................(423) 461-8995
Milligan College, TN, Milligan College
Dahlman, Simon J.
sjdahlman@milligan.edu, Chair, Milligan College, TN, Milligan College
Dahms, Steven P........................(614) 870-9444
sales@msitarget.com, Vice Pres., Metals Recovery Service, OH, Columbus
Dail, Annette W.........................(919) 736-0447
dailadvertising@bellsouth.net, Nat'l Rep., Dail Advertising Service, NC, Goldsboro
Dailey, Gary
sales@star-teck.com, Mktg. Mgr., DayStar Digital, Inc./Star-Teck, GA, Norcross
Dailey, Marc.............................(360) 735-4601
marc.dailey@columbian.com, Circ. Dir., The Columbian, WA, Vancouver
Dailey, Kelly.............................(912) 489-9473
kdailey@statesboroherald.com, Print Adv. Mgr., Statesboro Herald, GA, Statesboro
Dakin, David.............................(559) 441-6160
ddakin@fresnobee.com, Adv. Dir., Display, The Fresno Bee, CA, Fresno
Dalal, Pinky
samachar.bombay@gmail.com, Ed., BOMBAY SAMACHAR, Bombay, Maharashtra
Dale, Peggy..............................(760) 337-3447
ceditor@ivpressonline.com, News Ed., Imperial Valley Press, CA, El Centro
Dale, Kevin..............................(303) 820-1578
kdale@denverpost.com, Sports Ed., The Denver Post, CO, Denver
Dalgleish, Jim..................................ext. 219
jdalgleish@heraldpalladium.com, City Ed., The Herald-Palladium, MI, Saint Joseph
Dalglish, Lucy A.
rcfp@rcfp.org, Exec. Dir., Reporters Committee for Freedom of the Press, VA, Arlington
Dall, Ole
ole.dall@skivefolkeblad.dk, Ed., SKIVE FOLKEBLAD, Skive, Jutland
Dallas, Ann..............................(203) 789-5645
Graphics Ed., New Haven Register, CT, New Haven
Dallons, Jon
jon@westernquartz.com, Pres., Western Quartz Products, Inc., CA, Paso Robles
Dalton, Karen
kdalton@cbp.ca, Pres., Canadian Business Press, ON, Toronto
Dalton, Eric
edalton@justnormlicht.com, Vice President, Just Normlicht, Inc., PA, Langhorne
Dalton, Dan..............................(909) 793-9890
dan@contentthatworks.com, Vice Pres., Sales, Content That Works, IL, Chicago
Dalton, Debby
deb@bryantimes.com, Prodn. Mgr., The Bryan Times, OH, Bryan
Daly, Michael...........................(203) 330-6394
mdaly@ctpost.com, Editorial Page Ed., Connecticut Post, CT, Bridgeport
Dalziel, Graham.........................(780) 408-0107
gdalziel@edmsun.com, Ed. in Chief, The Edmonton Sun, AB, Edmonton
Damboa, Gerardo Garcia
claudia@novenet.com.mx, Pres., NOVEDADES DE QUINTANA ROO, Cancun, Quintana Roo
Damhuis, Hank F.
hank@lissomcorp.com, Lissom Corp. Inc., NY, Bronxville
Damish, Steven.........................(508) 427-4023
sdamish@enterprisenews.com, Mng. Ed., The Enterprise, MA, Randolph
Damron, Paul
ndamron@hopewellnews.com, Adv. Mgr., The Hopewell News, VA, Hopewell
Damron, Beth
bdamron@dispatch.com, Adv. Mgr., Nat'l, The Columbus Dispatch, OH, Columbus
Dan, McDonald................906-786-2021 ext 101
dmcdonald@dailypress.net, Publisher, Daily Press, MI, Escanaba
Dance, Leslie...........................(847) 523-2226
leslie.dance@motorola.com, Global Dir.,Media Commun./Pub. Aff., Motorola Personal Communications Sector, IL, Libertyville
Dancer, Linda
linda@michiganpress.org, Opns. Mgr., Michigan Newspapers, Inc., MI, Lansing
Daneliuk, Randy
reminder@mb.sympatico.ca, Prodn. Foreman, Pressroom, The Reminder, MB, Flin Flon
Danforth, David N.
ddanforth@aol.com, Owner, Aspen Daily News, CO, Aspen
Dang, Jennifer..........................(808) 525-7660
jdang@honolulu.gannett.com, Circ. NIE Coord., Honolulu Star-Advertiser, HI, Honolulu
Dang, Duc
ddang@genius-kye.com, Sales/Mktg. Mgr., KYE International Corp., CA, Pomona
Daniel, Ted..............................(404) 262-3121
Kansas State Univ. Engineering School, GA, Snellville
Daniel, Lasael
valladolid@abc.es, Ed. in Chief, ABC, Valladolid
Daniel, Richard J........................(617) 383-2258
Pres., Boston Globe, The New York Times Co., NY, New York
Daniels, Doug
ddaniels@onecliq.net, Prodn. Mgr., Du Quoin Evening Call, IL, Du Quoin
Daniels, Rick...........................(781) 433-6720
Regional VP - New England, GateHouse Media Inc., NY, Fairport
Daniels, Ted.............................419-281-0581
tdaniels@times-gazette.com, Editor and General Manager, Ashland Publishing Co. LLC, OH, Ashland
Daniels, Ashley..........................610-996-9356
danielaj@eckerd.edu, Editor-in-Chief, The Current - Eckerd College, PA, Saint Petersburg
Daniels, Ted
atg@bright.net, Mng. Ed., Ashland Times-Gazette, OH, Ashland
Daniels, Broderick.....................(479) 571-6404
bdaniels@nwanews.com, Dir., HR, Northwest

Arkansas Times, AR, Fayetteville
Danio, Maria Antonio
madario@folhaderegiao.com.br, Mgr., Editora Folha da Regiao da Aracatuba Ltd., Aracatuba, Sao Paulo
Danko, Dennis ....(877) 658-2424
ddanko@hearst.com, Inside Sales Mgr., King Features Syndicate, NY, New York
ddanko@hearst.com, Inside Sales Mgr., North America Syndicate, NY, New York
Dannels, Cheri 212-556-5924
cheri.dannels@nytimes.com, Marketing Manager, New York Times News Service, NY, New York
Dannels, Cheri 212-556-5924
cheri.dannels@nytimes.com, Marketing Manager, New York Times Syndicate, NY, New York
Dannoin, Alide
alide.dannoin@inl.co.za, Ed., THE CAPE TIMES, Cape Town
Dantas, Maria Helena Silva 211-8833
gazetase@netdados.com.br, Pres., Gazeta de Sergipe, Aracaju, Sergipe
Dantuono, Phyllis
phyllis.dantuono@businesswire.com, Vice Pres., New York Reg., Business Wire - New York, NY, NY, New York
Dantzler, Gayle
gdantzler@sbtinfo.com, Editorial Page Ed., South Bend Tribune, IN, South Bend
Danzoll, Graham ....(970) 748-2949
gdanzoll@vaildaily.com, Sales Mgr., Vail Daily, CO, Vail
Daoura, Saedou
onep@intnet.ne, Pub. Dir., LE SAHEL, Niamey
Daravanis, Scott ....(928) 445-3333
City Ed., The Daily Courier, AZ, Prescott
Darcy, Jeff ....(216) 999-4445
Editorial Cartoonist, The Plain Dealer, OH, Cleveland
Darda, Vijay
lokmat@bom2.vsnl.net.in, Ed. in Chief, LOKMAT, Nagpur, Maharashtra
Darga, Otto
webmaster@bekes.hungary.net, Ed., BEKES MEGYEI HIRLAP, Bekescsaba, Bekes
Dark, Joy ....(678) 804-7411
joy.dark@buystory.com, Opns. Mgr., Syndicated Writers of America, GA, Suwanee
Darr, Ron ....(203) 330-6528
rdarr@newstimes.com, Director of Operations, The News-Times, CT, Danbury
Darrow, Dennis ....(719) 544-3520 ext. 471
ddarrow@chieftain.com, Bus. Ed., The Pueblo Chieftain, CO, Pueblo
Dart, Les
ldart@snu.edu, Broadcasting, Southern Nazarene University, OK, Bethany
Das, Bhaskar
etbom@timesgroup.com, Mgr., THE ECONOMIC TIMES, Kolkata, West Bengal
Dasambiagio, Tirreno
diario@odiariodemogi.com.br, Pub., Diario de Mogi Empresa Jornalistica S.A., Mogi Das Cruzes, Sao Paulo
Dasch, Max
service@salzburg.com, Pub./Bus. Mgr., SALZBURGER NACHRICHTEN, Salzburg, Salzburg
Dasgupta, Ashok
aajkaal@cal.vsnl.net.in, Ed. in Chief, AAJKAAL, Kolkata, West Bengal
Dasta, Jackie
info@syntellect.com, Contact, Syntellect Interactive Services, GA, Roswell
Daswani, Roger
ammnews@amm.com, American Metal Market
Datta Bhowmick, Pradip
dainikphoto@yahoo.com, Pub., DAINIK SAMBAD, Agartala, Tripura West
Daubel, Phil
psd1@aol.com, Coord., Community Papers of Ohio & West Virginia, OH, Columbus
Dauber, Carol ....(203) 330-6440
cdauber@ctpost.com, Online Mgr., Connecticut Post, CT, Bridgeport
Daudinhan, Catherine
redacciondo@alsapresse.com, Ed., LE PAYS DE FRANCHE-COMTE, Montbeliard
Daus, Keye ....(216) 999-6642
Asst. Director of Operations, The Plain Dealer, OH, Cleveland
David, Irina
idavid@tribune.com, Dir., Mktg., Tribune 365, NY, New York
David, Reuben ....(612) 343-4727
North Central Univ., MN, Minneapolis
David D., N/A ....Pres./CEO
Tribune Media Services TV Log - Chicago, IL, IL, Chicago
Davidson, Donna ....(941) 206-1124
ddavidson@sun-herald.com, Features Ed., Charlotte Sun, FL, Charlotte Harbor
Davidson, Donna 941-206-1164
Features Editor, Charlotte Sun, FL, Charlotte Harbor
Davidson, Bob ....(785) 822-1404 ext. 155
sjbdavidson@saljournal.com, Sports Ed., The Salina Journal, KS, Salina
Davidson, Todd ....(812) 349-1415
tdavidson@heraldt.com, Online Mgr., The Herald-Times, IN, Bloomington
Davidson, Art
artd@cnc.com, Sports Ed., Milford Daily News, MA, Milford
Davidson, Ron
ron.davidson@staugustine.com, Publisher, The St. Augustine Record, FL, Saint Augustine
Davidsson, Mona
mona.davidsson@laholmstidning.se, Ed., LAHOLMS TIDNING, Laholm
Davies, Steve
sdavies@circlevilleherald.com, Pub., Herald, OH, Circleville
Davies, Dave ....(530) 896-7779
ddavies@chicoer.com, Sports Ed., Chico Enterprise-Record, CA, Chico
Davila Velasquez, Vicente 4-0752
Ed., Pagina 20, Sucre, Chuquisaca
Davis, Karen ....ext. 223
kdavis@thewesterlysun.com, Adv. Mgr., Classified, The Westerly Sun, RI, Westerly
Davis, Joanie ....(270) 783-3205
jdavis@bgdailynews.com, Adv. Mgr., Nat'l, Daily News, KY, Bowling Green
Davis, Jamie
editor@bannernews.net, Mng. Ed., Banner-News, AR, Magnolia
Davis, Doug
doug.davis@d2studios.net, Pres., D-Squared Studios, Inc., TX, Dallas
Davis, Jim
permmill@juno.com, Sales Mgr., Craftsman Newspaper Production Systems, OH, Tipp City
Davis, Shawn
sdavis@fiberweb.com, Area Mgr., Fiberweb, SC, Gray Court
Davis, Jennifer ....(309) 686-3249
jdavis@pjstar.com, Lifestyles Ed., Journal Star, IL, Peoria
Davis, Paul
pdavis@hjnews.com, Prodn. Mgr., Systems, The Herald Journal, UT, Logan
Davis, Anita ....(661) 395-7437
adavis@bakersfield.com, Adv. Mgr., Display, The Bakersfield Californian, CA, Bakersfield
Davis, Russ
rdavis@hjnews.com, Circ. Mgr., The Herald Journal, UT, Logan
Davis, Stephen 646-895-8424
stephen.davis@srds.com, President, SRDS, a Kantar Media Company, IL, Des Plaines
Davis, Erik ....ext. 125
davise@maps.com, Dir., Education Mktg., Maps.com, CA, Santa Barbara
Davis, Dan ....ext. 217
ddavis@tribtown.com, Ed., The Tribune, IN, Seymour
Davis, Murdoch
mdavis@southtownstar.com, Pres./Pub., SouthtownStar, IL, Tinley Park
Davis, Alan ....(334) 792-3141
adavis@alsmg.com, Vice Pres., Opelika-Auburn News, AL, Opelika
Davis, Peter
tribnews@nn.independent.co.za, Ed., SUNDAY TRIBUNE, Durban, Kwazulu & Natal
Davis, Jim ....(937) 335-5634
davis@tdnpublishing.com, Copy Ed., Troy Daily News, OH, Troy
Davis, Debbie ....(530) 756-0800 ext. 254
ddavis@davisenterprise.net, Political/Gov't Ed., The Davis Enterprise, CA, Davis
Davis, Jim ....ext. 111
jimdavis@dnj.com, Chief Photographer, The Daily News Journal, TN, Murfreesboro
Davis, Tom
tdavis@usa-800.com, Pres./CEO, USA 800, Inc., MO, Kansas City
Davis, P.
ceo@parwell.hypermart.net, Pres./Chrmn., Parwell-Davis Features, IN, Lagro
Davis, Andrew B.
adavis@americanpressinstitute.org, Exec. Dir./Pres., American Press Institute, VA, Reston
Davis, Lerecia ....(707) 553-6825
Librarian, Vallejo Times-Herald, CA, Vallejo
Davis, Pamela ....(251) 653-4080
info@raksystems.com, Mktg. Dir., RAK Systems, Inc., AL, Mobile
Davis, Lisa ....(256) 235-3555
ldavis@annistonstar.com, Features Ed., The Anniston Star, AL, Anniston
Davis, Richard ....(812) 523-7050
rdavis@tribtown.com, Pub., The Tribune, IN, Seymour
Davis, Pamela J.
pdavis@dailyprogress.com, Bus. Mgr., The Daily Progress, VA, Charlottesville
Davis, Steve ....(616) 222-5565
sdavis@boothmichigan.com, Sales Mgr., Booth Newspapers, Inc., MI, Grand Rapids
Davis, Kirk
kdavis@ledger.com, Pub., The Patriot Ledger, MA, Quincy
Davis, Catherine ....(540) 374-5453
catherined@freelancestar.com, Graphics/Design Dir., The Free Lance-Star, VA, Fredericksburg
Davis, Tim ....(434) 432-1654 ext. 18
tim.davis@womackpublishing.com, Editorial Dir., Womack Publishing Co., VA, Chatham
Davis, Brent 501-315-8228
501-315-1920, Editor, The Saline Courier, AR, Benton
Davis, Rita ....(301) 696-3641
Hood College, MD, Frederick
Davis, Jay
jay.davis@selmatimesjournal.com, Vice Pres./Bus. Mgr., The Selma Times-Journal, AL, Selma
Davis, Dennis ....(307) 754-6438
Northwest College, WY, Powell
Davis, David
managingeditor@clevelandbanner.com, Mng. Ed., Cleveland Daily Banner, TN, Cleveland
Davis, Joe
jdavis@mariettatimes.com, Sports Ed., The Marietta Times, OH, Marietta
Davis, Kristen ....(216) 999-6163
Asst. Sports Editor, The Plain Dealer, OH, Cleveland
Davis, Perk
pdavis@cnc.com, Pub., Metrowest Daily News, MA, Framingham
Davis, Kirk
kdavis@gatehousemediane.com, Pres./CEO/Pub., Community Newspaper Co., MA, Framingham
Davis, Mike ....(479) 784-0441
mdavis@swtimes.com, Dir., Promo., Times Record, AR, Fort Smith
Davis, Robin A. ....(314) 340-8437
rdavis@pulitzer.net, Vice Pres./CFO, Pulitzer Newspapers, Inc., MO, Saint Louis
Davis, Gwen ....(252) 407-9900
gdavis@rmtelegram.com, Mgr., HR, Rocky Mount Telegram, NC, Rocky Mount
Davis, Kevin ....(209) 722-1812 ext. 402
kdavis@pspub.com, Vice Pres., Adv., Pacific Sierra Publishing, Inc., CA, Merced
Davis, Harry ....(512) 445-3758
hdavis@statesman.com, Vice Pres., Circ., Austin American-Statesman, TX, Austin
Davis, Kirk ....(617) 786-7018
Pres./COO, GateHouse Media Inc., NY, Fairport
Davis, Chanel ....(336) 888-3657
khayes@hpe.com, Davidson/Randolph counties, High Point Enterprise, NC, High Point
Davis, Andrew ....(904) 822-7224
Stetson Univ., FL, Deland
Davis, Douglas R.
doug.davis@news-jrnl.com, Circ. Dir., Daytona Beach News-Journal, FL, Daytona Beach
Davis, Bill ....(209) 954-5286
San Joaquin Delta College, CA, Stockton
Davis, David H.
davehdavis@bellsouth.net, Sec., Fackelman Newspapers, FL
Davis, Lonnie ....(810) 766-6298
ldavis@flintjournal.com, Prodn. Asst. Mgr., Pressroom, The Flint Journal, MI, Flint
Davis, Anita 951-368-9207
adavis@pe.com, Director Gen and Major Accounts, The Press-Enterprise, CA, Riverside
Davis, M. Lynn ....(302) 324-2740
ldavis@wilmingt.gannett.com, Circ. Mgr., Single Copy, The News Journal, DE, New Castle
Davison, Matt
mdavison@kvnews.com, Pub., Daily Record, WA, Ellensburg
Davison, Pat ....(919) 962-4073
Assoc. Prof., University of North Carolina, NC, Chapel Hill
Davison, Nick 630-942-2683
editor@cod.edu, Editor-in-chief, College of DuPage, IL, Glen Ellyn
Davisson, Brandie
bdavisson@nncogannett.com, Adv. Dir., Times Recorder, OH, Zanesville
Davner, Aliza
davaliz@lycoming.edu, Editor-in-chief, Lycoming College, PA, Williamsport
Davy, James L. ....(949) 498-0833
jldavy@sbcglobal.net, Owner, Davy Associates Media Features, CA, San Clemente
Davy, Kent ....(760) 740-5401
kdavy@nctimes.com, Ed., North County Times, CA, Escondido
Dawkins, Stephen ....ext. 20
stephen.dawkins@clantonadvertiser.com, Sports Ed., The Clanton Advertiser, AL, Clanton
Dawn, Keith L. ....(609) 272-7101
kdawn@pressofac.com, Exec. Vice Pres./COO/Pub., The Press of Atlantic City, NJ, Pleasantville
Dawson, Anastasia ....(813) 974-5190
Univ. of South Florida, FL, Tampa
Dawson, Fabian ....(604) 605-2858
fdawson@theprovince.com, Deputy Ed., The Province, BC, Vancouver
Dawson, Carol ....(501) 918-4522
Adv. Mgr., Retail Sales, Arkansas Democrat-Gazette, AR, Little Rock
Dawson, Ed
editor@herald-dispatch.com, Pub., The Herald-Dispatch, WV, Huntington
Dawson, Hugh ....(604) 605-2170
hdawson@png.canwest.com, Bus. Ed., The Vancouver Sun, BC, Vancouver
Dawson, Colleen
colleen@michiganpress.org, Office Mgr., Michigan Newspapers, Inc., MI, Lansing
Dawson, Matt ....(902) 563-3888
Circ. Mgr., Promotional, The Cape Breton Post, NS, Sydney
Dawson, David ....(217) 421-7980
Mng. Ed., Herald & Review, IL, Decatur
Dawson, Dave ....(217) 421-7980
Opinion Page Ed., Herald & Review, IL, Decatur
Dawson, Donna ....(951) 782-7743
ddawson@pe.com, Mgr., Promo., The Press-Enterprise, CA, Riverside
Dawson Bartley, Cari ....(800) 696-7561
cari@cagle.com, Exec. Ed./Mktg. Dir., Cagle Cartoons, Inc., CA, Santa Barbara
Day, Cassandra
cday@middletownpress.com, Features Ed., The Middletown Press, CT, Middletown
Day, Adam Scott
aday@newspaperpromotions.com, CEO, Marketing Research Associates, Inc., MN, Minneapolis
Day, Jerome ....(603) 656-6063
St. Anselm College, NH, Manchester
Day, Chris
cday@coxnc.com, Asst. News Ed., The Daily Advance, NC, Elizabeth City

Dayberry, John ....ext. 275
Bus. Ed., The Hickory Daily Record, NC, Hickory
Days, Michael
daysm@phillynews.com, Ed., The Philadelphia Daily News, PA, Philadelphia
De Both, James R.
gregz@interest.com, Pres., Mortgage Market Information Services, IL, Villa Park
De Caires, David
stabroeknews@stabroeknews.com, Ed. in Chief, STABROEK NEWS, Georgetown
De L'Estrac, Jean-Claude
sentinelle@intnet.mu, Dir., L'EXPRESS, Port Louis
De Lemos, Nancy........................50622580016
ndelemos@acan-efe.com, Director, EFE News Services - San Jose, Costa Rica, San Jose
De Marco, Jim ....(262) 656-6216
jdemarco@kenoshanews.com, Prodn. Mgr., Distr., Kenosha News, WI, Kenosha
De Palma, Frank..............................ext. 0277
fdepalma@herald.ca, Asst. Dir., Newsroom, The Chronicle Herald, NS, Halifax
De Salakar, Jose Martinez
redaccion@diariojerez.es, Ed. in Chief, DIARIO DE JEREZ, Jerez de la Frontera, Cadiz
De Silva, Indra
desilva@Xavier.edu, Chair, Xavier University, OH, Cincinnati
De Silva, Charles Rex
brupress@brunet.bn, Ed., BORNEO BULLETIN, Bandar Seri Begawan
De Tomaso, Giuseppe
redazione.internet@gazzettamezzogiorno.it, Mng. Dir., LA GAZZETTA DEL MEZZOGIORNO, Bari
De beer, Shilo
shilo@yedioth.co.il, Ed. in Chief, YEDIOTH AHARONOTH
DeAngelis, Bernard...................(215) 361-8803
bdeangelis@journalregister.com, Controller/Purchasing Agent, The Reporter, PA, Lansdale
DeAugustine, John......................203-330-6211
john.deaugustine@ctpost.com, Group Publisher, Greenwich Time, CT, Greenwich
DeBartolo, Mike
det_sales@parade.com, Vice Pres., Adv., Parade Publications, Inc. - Bloomfield Hills, MI, MI, Bloomfield Hills
DeBolt, Vernon
vdebolt@freedomenc.com, Pub., The Sun Journal, NC, New Bern
DeBono, Nili ....(212) 576-9505
debonon@metrosn.com, Vice Pres., Finance/Admin., Metro Newspaper Advertising Services, Inc. Sunday Magazine Network - New York, NY, NY, New York
DeBono, Nili ....(212) 576-9505
debonon@metrosn.com, Sr. Vice Pres., Finance, Metro Newspaper Advertising Services, Inc., NY, New York
DeBono, Nili ....(212) 576-9505
debonon@metrosn.com, Vice Pres., Finance/Admin., Metro-Puck Comics Network - New York, NY, NY, New York
DeBoth, James R.
rateguy@interest.com, Pres./Columnist, Mortgage Market Information Services, IL, Villa Park
DeChantal, Rick.......................(312) 222-4544
rdechantal@tribune.com, MCT Sales Mgr., McClatchy-Tribune Information Services, DC, Washington
rdechantal@tribune.com, Sales Mgr., McClatchy-Tribune Information Services, Tribune Media Services, Inc., IL, Chicago
DeCicco, Nick..........................(707) 427-6966
Tailwind Ed., Daily Republic, CA, Fairfield
DeCoursey, Sarah.........(800) 255-6734 ext. 7335
sdecoursey@amuniversal.com, Licensing Dir., Universal Uclick, MO, Kansas City
DeFalco, Joseph
joseph.defalco@publicitas.com, CFO, Publicitas North America, Inc., NY, New York
DeFillipo, James F.
jdefillipo@sjnewsco.com, Adv. Dir., The News of Cumberland County, NJ, Bridgeton
DeFranco, Robert J. ....(561) 630-2400
bdefranco@bankrate.com, Sr. Vice Pres., Finance/CFO, Bankrate.com, FL, North Palm Beach
DeFrangesco, Donna
donna@phillyareapapers.com, Acct. Supvr., Hitchings & Co., PA, Plymouth Meeting
DeGrado, John ....ext. 627
jdegrado@newtondailynews.com, Prodn. Mgr., Newton Daily News, IA, Newton
DeGrado, Mari Jo ....ext. 530
mdegrado@newtondailynews.com, Prodn. Supvr., Composing Room, Newton Daily News, IA, Newton
DeGroff, Ray ....(410) 749-7171 ext. 540
rdegroff@smgpo.gannett.com, Prodn. Dir., The Daily Times, MD, Salisbury
DeGurse, Carl...........................(204) 697-7292
Carl.DeGurse@freepress.mb.ca, Asst. City Ed., Winnipeg Free Press, MB, Winnipeg
DeLaurentis, Marc ....(212) 293-8610
mdelaurentis@unitedmedia.com, Mgr., Regl. Sales, United Media, OH, Cincinnati
DeLaurier, Trish.........................386-760-1035
trish.delaurier@srds.com, VP, Information Sales & Client Service, SRDS, a Kantar Media Company, IL, Des Plaines
DeLeon, Lucia ....(415) 514-2141
Univ. of California, CA, San Francisco
DeLong, Paula...........................(252) 407-9931
pdelong@rmtelegram.com, Mktg. Mgr., Rocky Mount Telegram, NC, Rocky Mount
DeLuca, Matt ....(617) 552-2223
editor@bcheights.com, Boston College, MA, Chestnut Hill
DeLuca, Joe..............................(727) 322-6777
jdeluca@tampabay.com, Vice Pres./Pub., Tampa, Tampa Bay Times, FL, Saint Petersburg
DeLuca, Jim ....(330) 996-3485
jdeluca@thebeaconjournal.com, Circ. Dir., Akron Beacon Journal, OH, Akron
DeMark, Steve Van
vandemark@crescent-news.com, Gen. Mgr., Defiance Publishing LLC, OH, Defiance
DeMasters, Carol
caroldemasters@yahoo.com, Exec. Dir., Association of Food Journalists, Inc.
DeMeglio, Linda ....(610) 622-8817
newsroom@delcotimes.com, Mng. Ed., Delaware County Daily Times, PA, Primos
DeMontis, Rita ....(416) 947-2247
rita.demontis@sunmedia.ca, Lifestyle/Food Ed., The Toronto Sun, ON, Toronto
DePaola, Paolo
p.depaola@tuttosport.com, Dir., TUTTOSPORT, Turin
DeParis, Marie ....(212) 210-2163
mdeparis@nydailynews.com, Sr. Vice Pres., Strategic Mktg./Sales, NY Daily News, NY, New York
DeRienzo, Matt.........................(860) 489-1877
mderienzo@journalregister.com, Pub., The Register Citizen, CT, Torrington
DeRose, Dena
dderose@dailytidings.com, Adv. Dir., The Ashland Daily Tidings, OR, Ashland
DeRossett, Dennis
dennis.derossett@thesouthern.com, Pub., The Southern Illinoisan, IL, Carbondale
DeRossett, Dennis
dderossett@illinoispress.org, Exec. Dir., Illinois Press Association, IL, Springfield
DeSalvo, James........................(617) 619-6502
jdesalo@bostonherald.com, Circ. Asst. Dir., Boston Herald, MA, Boston
DeSchriver, Thomas J. ....(570) 420-4358
tdeschriver@poconorecord.com, Prodn. Ed., Pocono Record, PA, Stroudsburg
DeVarenne, Maria......................(951) 248-7620
mdevarenne@pe.com, Vice Pres., News/Exec. Ed., The Press-Enterprise, CA, Riverside
DeWeese, Shawn ....(937) 754-2504
sdeweese@coxohio.com, Circ. Dir., Sales, Dayton Daily News, OH, Dayton
DeWitt, Blake ....(928) 783-3311 ext. 103
bdewitt@westernnewspapers.com, Sr. Vice Pres., Western Newspapers, Inc., AZ, Yuma
DeYoung, Matt.................................ext. 228
mdeyoung@grandhaventribune.com, Sports Ed., Grand Haven Tribune, MI, Grand Haven
Deakin, Erika Stutzman ....(303) 473-1354
stutzmane@dailycamera.com, Features Ed., Daily Camera, CO, Boulder
Deal, Kent
sales-usa@glunz-jensen.com, Gen. Mgr., Glunz & Jensen, Inc., IN, Granger
Deamer, Hans
info@whcorp.com, Pres., Windmoeller and Hoelscher Corp., RI, Lincoln
Dean, Walter...........................(678) 947-8550
sales@deanmachinery.com, Pres., Dean Machinery International, Inc., GA, Alpharetta
Dean, James L.
james.dean@lee.net, Mng. Ed., The Columbus Telegram, NE, Columbus
Dean, Irving..............................518-395-3103
dean@dailygazette.net, City Ed., The Daily Gazette, NY, Schenectady
Dean, Matthew ....(212) 854-5833
Columbia Univ. Law School, NY, New York
Deandar, Tomas Orlando Martinez
elmananarey@infosel.net.mx, Pres., La Tarde, Reynosa, Tamaulipas
Deandar Martinez, Ninfa
ninfa.deandar@elmanana.com.mx, Pres., EL MANANA, Nuevo Laredo, Tamaulipas
Deaner, Frank E.
fdeaner@ohionews.org, Exec. Dir./Sec., Ohio Newspaper Services, Inc. dba AdOhio, OH, Columbus
Deaner, Frank E.
fdeaner@ohionews.org, Exec. Dir./Sec., Ohio Newspaper Association, OH, Columbus
Dearing, Robin.............(970) 242-5050 ext. 251
rdearing@gjds.com, Exec. Sec., The Daily Sentinel, CO, Grand Junction
Dearman, Tim
tdearman@hickoryrecord.com, Regl. Pub., The Hickory Daily Record, NC, Hickory
Dearman, Tim
tdearman@statesville.com, Pub., Statesville Record & Landmark, NC, Statesville
Deason, Randy
publisher@bdtonline.com, Pub., Bluefield Daily Telegraph, WV, Bluefield
Deaton, Dell ....(734) 668-2001
dell@divorcebalance.com, Divorce Mediator, Divorce Reality Group, MI, Saline
Deaton, Tona............................(706) 290-5318
tdeaton@npco.com, Prodn. Dir., Dispatch, Rome News-Tribune, GA, Rome
Deaton, Mike ....(706) 290-5283
mdeaton@npco.com, Data Processing Mgr., Rome News-Tribune, GA, Rome
Deaton, Janice.............(740) 353-3101 ext. 248
Prodn. Mgr., Mailroom, The Portsmouth Daily Times, OH, Portsmouth
Deaver, Rick
rdeaver@coxnews.com, Circ. Dir., Waco Tribune-Herald, TX, Waco
Debatin, Bernhard ....(740) 593-9809
Assoc. Prof./Dir. Studies, Honors Tutorial College, Ohio University, OH, Athens
Debbrecht, Micki ....(316) 268-6466
mdebbrecht@wichitaeagle.com, Vice Pres., HR, The Wichita Eagle, KS, Wichita
Debord, Matt............................(706) 290-5322
mdebord@npco.com, Dir., Information Technology, Rome News-Tribune, GA, Rome
Debrdder, Vadeenna
vadeenna.debrdder@concentra.be, Adv.Mgr., GAZET VAN ANTWERPEN, Antwerp
Debski, Wieslaw
redakcja@trybuna.com.pl, Ed. in Chief, TRYBUNA, Warsaw
Deburro, Joe ....(413) 788-1117
jdeburro@repub.com, Sports Ed., The Republican, MA, Springfield
Decherd, Robert W.
blc@belo.com, Chrmn. of the Bd./CEO, A. H. Belo Corp., TX, Dallas
Decker, Caron 717-262-4790
cdecker@publicopinionnews.com, Controller, Public Opinion, PA, Chambersburg
Decker, Lisa.....................................ext. 102
Credit Mgr., The Courier-Observer, The Journal & The Advance-News, NY, Ogdensburg
Deeds, Anne ....(901) 529-2611
deeds@commercialappeal.com, Budget/Gen. Acctg. Mgr., The Commercial Appeal, TN, Memphis
Deegan, Jim...................................ext. 3638
jdeegan@express-times.com, Mng. Ed., The Express-Times, PA, Easton
Deegan, Joanne.........................(978) 970-4634
jdeegan@lowellsun.com, Lifestyle Copy Ed., The Sun, MA, Lowell
Deegan, Suzanne ....(916) 321-1400
sdeegan@sacbee.com, Adv. Mgr., Nat'l, The Sacramento Bee, CA, Sacramento
Deeks, Gordon...........................(780) 429-5577
gdeeks@thejournal.canwest.com, Adv. Mgr., Sales Planning/Nat'l Sales, Edmonton Journal, AB, Edmonton
Deepak, Tilak
d_tilak@hotmail.com, Mgr., KESARI, Pune, Maharashtra
Degerman, Eric.........................(509) 582-1404
edegerman@tri-cityherald.com, Online Mng. Ed., Tri-City Herald, WA, Kennewick
Deggendorf, Steve
sdeggendorf@thehawkeye.com, Prodn. Mgr., Packaging, The Hawk Eye, IA, Burlington
Degive, Rich
rdegive@hanfordsentinel.com, Sports Ed., The Sentinel, CA, Hanford
Degtyare, Peter
stroygaz@mtu-net.ru, Ed. in Chief, STROITELNAYA GAZETA, Moscow
Dehnel, Chris
cdehnel@journalinquirer.com, Town News Ed., Ellington/Stafford, Journal Inquirer, CT, Manchester
Deibele, James
info@teleport.com, Contact, Teleport Internet Services, OR, Portland
Deibert, Kendra ....(605) 692-6271
registerdesign@brookingsregister.com, Mgr., Brookings Register, SD, Brookings
Deis, Bob
bob_deis@nela-usa.com, Mgr., Engineering, NELA, WI, River Falls
Deitz, Harry J. ....(610) 371-5004
hdeitz@readingeagle.com, Ed., Reading Eagle, PA, Reading
Dejonge, Peter
p.dejonge@ad.nl, Ed. in Chief, ROTTERDAMS DAGBLAD, Rotterdam, South Holland
Del-Riccio, Ana 4314-8788
ana.del-riccio@dowjones.com, Sales Exec., Dow Jones Newswires - Buenos Aires, Argentina, Buenos Aires
DelMauro, John
john.delmauro@sourcemedia.com, Pub., American Banker, NY, 1 State Street Plz.
DelRe, Stefano
s.delre@lanuovasardegna.it, Mgr., LA NUOVA SARDEGNA, Sassari
Delaney, Suzanne ....(360) 417-3540
ads@peninsuladailynews.com, Advertising Director, Peninsula Daily News, WA, Port Angeles
Delaney, Ellen
edelaney@journalsentinel.com, Asst. to Ed., Milwaukee Journal Sentinel, WI, Milwaukee
Delaney, Robert ....(850) 747-5003
rdelaney@pcnh.com, Regl. Controller/FP&A, The News Herald, FL, Panama City
Delano Brown, Jane ....(919) 962-4089
Prof./James L. Knight, University of North Carolina, NC, Chapel Hill
Delaplace, Fredrick
fredrick.delapalace@media.fin, Ed. in Chief, L'ECHO, Brussels
Delasho, Kenneth
info@industrialacoustics.com, Pres., Industrial Acoustics Co., NY, Bronx
Deleu, Kevin
kevin@telluridedailyplanet.com, Prodn. Mgr., Telluride Daily Planet, CO, Telluride
Delgado, Enrique 43-5555
Editorial Dir., Vanguardia, San Cristobal, Tachira
Delgado, Anjanette ....(831) 754-4281
areiger@salinas.gannett.com, Mng. Ed., The Salinas Californian, CA, Salinas
Delhawe, Thirrw
havierlamberg@sudpresse.be, Ed., LA MEUSE, Liege, Liege
Dell, Cheryl ....(916) 321-1885
cdell@sacbee.com, Pres./Pub., The Sacramento Bee, CA, Sacramento
Dell'Aquila, Johanna ....(201) 459-2836
Admin, Advance Internet, Inc., NJ, Jersey City
Dellenbach, Cory.......................(715) 526-7019

sports@shawanoleader.com, Community News Editor, Shawano Leader, WI, Shawano
Dellinger, Timothy O.
tim@newspaperconsultants.com, President, Advantage Newspaper Consultants, NC, Fayetteville
Delp, Johann
Windsheimer-Zeitung@odn.de, Proprietor, Windsheimer Zeitung, Bad Windsheim
Delso, Nick..................(318) 362-0234
Asst. Mng. Ed., Online/Sports, The News-Star, LA, Monroe
Deluna, Diana..................(214) 691-4103
deluna@amconmedia.com, Dir., Payroll/HR, American Consolidated Media, TX, Dallas
Demagistris, John..................(585) 258-2373
jdemagis@rocheste.gannett.com, Circ. Div. Mgr., Democrat and Chronicle.com, NY, Rochester
Demarest, Dusti..................253-274-7380
ddemarest@theolympian.com, Team Leader, The Olympian, WA, Olympia
Demeer, Andrea..................ext. 241
Pub., The Sentinel-Review, ON, Woodstock
Demers, Matt..................(518) 561-7408
mattdemers@primhall.com, Mktg. Coord., Prim Hall Enterprises, Inc., NY, Plattsburgh
Demidov, Yuri..................(973) 569-7744
VP/Internet Technology, North Jersey Media Group, NJ, Woodland Park
Demir, GÃ£ray
g.demir@zaman.com.tr, Pub., ZAMAN
Demirkent, Didem
didem.demirkent@dunyagazetesi.com, Ed. in Chief, DUNYA
Demirkent, Didem
didem.demirkent@dunyagazetesi.com, Ed. in Chief, DUNYA
Demirkent, Didem
didem.demirkent@dunyagazetesi.com, Ed. in Chief, DUNYA
Demjanik, Daniel..................(888) 942-3253
Regl. Mgr., Church Rickards, Whitlock & Co., Inc., IL, Westchester
Demko Ph.D., David J...................(561) 866-8251
demko@ageventurenewsservice.com, Gerontologist/Ed., Demko Publishing/Age Venture News Service, FL, Boca Raton
Dempsey, Carla..................(508) 676-2581
cdempsey@heraldnews.com, Life Ed., The Herald News, MA, Fall River
Dempsey, Thomas
sales@vdata.com, Pres., Vision Data Equipment Corp., NY, Rensselaer
Dempsey, Shawn..................(517) 356-9021
Alpena Cmty. College, MI, Alpena
Dempsey, John Mark
John_Dempsey@tamu-commerce.edu, Assoc. Prof., Texas A&M University-Commerce, TX, Commerce
Demuth, Gary..................(785) 822-1405 ext. 109
sjgdemuth@saljournal.com, Society Ed., The Salina Journal, KS, Salina
Denbrock, Cam..................ext. 8363
cam.denbrock@cantonrep.com, Circ. Sales/Mktg. Mgr., The Repository, OH, Canton
Denesha, Sherry
sherry@rtndacanada.com, Opns. Mgr., Canadian Radio-Television News Directors Association, ON, Toronto
Dengler, John..................(417) 836-1206
jdengler@news-leader.com, Graphics Ed., Springfield News-Leader, MO, Springfield
Denker, Vicki..................(402) 444-1243
vicki.denker@owh.com, Adv. Mgr., Local Retail Sales, Omaha World-Herald, NE, Omaha
Dennehy, Sharon..................(214) 785-7661
Paris Junior College, TX, Paris
Denning, W. Mitchel
mitch.denning@jacksonville.com, Controller, Div., The Florida Times-Union, FL, Jacksonville
Dennis, Pat
pdennis@opubco.com, Vice Pres. Operations, The Oklahoman, OK, Oklahoma City
Dennis, Yvonne
dennisy@phillynews.com, Deputy City Ed., The Philadelphia Daily News, PA, Philadelphia
Dennis, Joan
sales@alliance-rubber.com, Mktg. Servs. Mgr., Alliance Rubber Co., AR, Hot Springs
Dennis, Sarah..................(902) 426-3345
sdennis@herald.ca, Pub./CEO/Vice Pres., The Chronicle Herald, NS, Halifax
Dennis, Andy..................(270) 783-3235
malexieff@bgdailynews.com, Managing Editor, Daily News, KY, Bowling Green
Dennis, Craig..................548 7079
nml@nelsonmail.co.nz, Mng. Dir., THE NELSON MAIL
Dennis, Tom
tdennis@gfherald.com, Editorial Page Ed., Grand Forks Herald, ND, Grand Forks
Dennis, Bob
bob.dennis@register-news.com, Pub., Register-News, IL, Mount Vernon
Dennison, Brad..................(630) 368-1100
Vice Pres., Content/News Opns., GateHouse Media Inc., NY, Fairport
Denniston, Pam..................(541) 617-7817
pdenniston@bendbulletin.com, Circ. Mktg. Mgr., The Bulletin, OR, Bend
Deno, Chris..................(765) 420-5277
cdeno@journalandcourier.com, Controller, Journal and Courier, IN, Lafayette
Denson, Sandy..................281.425.8003
Business Manager/HR, The Baytown Sun, TX, Baytown
Dente, Jim
jdente@njherald.com, Sports/Night Ed., New Jersey Herald, NJ, Newton
Denton, Frank
frank.denton@jacksonville.com, Ed., The Florida Times-Union, FL, Jacksonville
Deobald, Lonny..................(306) 765-1301
ldeobald@paherald.sk.ca, Bus. Mgr., Prince Albert Daily Herald, SK, Prince Albert
Depuoz, Thomas
thomas.depuoz@corbis.com, Office Mgr., Corbis, NY, New York
Dergez, Kevin..................2503716128
National Advertising, Special Publications and Online Sales Manager, Kamloops Daily News, BC, Kamloops
Dermisis, George
pier-antil@kat.forthnet.gr, Pub., PIERIKOI ANTILALOI, Katerini
Derringer, Alan
aderringer@detroitnews.com, Auto Editor, The Detroit News, MI, Detroit
Derry, Mark
editor@garlic.com, Exec. Ed., The Dispatch, CA, Gilroy
Dershowitz, Toby
toby@ajpa.org, Exec. Dir., American Jewish Press Association, DC, Washington
Derstine, Steven P.
steved@starbyte.com, Sales Mgr., Star-Byte, Inc., PA, Exton
Dery, Matthew R...................ext. 232
m.dery@theday.com, Circ. Mgr., Sales, The Day Publishing Company, CT, New London
DesJardins, Marc..................(831) 429-2445
mdesjardins@santacruzsentinel.com, Copy Desk Chief, Santa Cruz Sentinel, CA, Scotts Valley
Desai, Bharat
bharat.desai@timesgroup.com, Ed., THE TIMES OF INDIA, Ahmedabad, Gujarat
Desch, Larry..................(920) 683-4731
Univ. of Wisconsin Center, WI, Manitowoc
Deschamps, Laurent C.
info@sparusa.com, Pres., Spar Associates, Inc., MD, Annapolis
Descoteaux, Bernard
bdescoteaux@ledevoir.com, Pub., Le Devoir, QC, Montreal
Deselms, Jen..................(361) 886-3627
deselmsj@caller.com, News Ed., Corpus Christi Caller-Times, TX, Corpus Christi
Deshong, Martha..................(585) 258-2525
mdeshong@rocheste.gannett.com, Vice Pres., Finance, Democrat and Chronicle.com, NY, Rochester
Desiderio, Vince
vdesire@rspinc.com, Vice Pres., Running With Scissors (RWS), AZ, Tucson
Desmond, Kevin..................(612) 673-8710
Kevin.Desmond@startribune.com, Sr. Vice Pres., Opns., Star Tribune, MN, Minneapolis
Desmond, Richard..................211 7760
communications@unitedbusinessmedia.com, CEO, DAILY EXPRESS, ENG, London
Desroches, Jacques..................(770) 421-7700
Gen. Mgr., Markem-Imaje, GA, Kennesaw
Dethleffsen, A.
info@shz.de, Proprietor, MARNER ZEITUNG, Flensburg
Devally, Adriana..................(956) 728-2511
adriana@lmtonline.com, Adv. Mgr., Laredo Morning Times, TX, Laredo
Devaraja, V.
advertising@virakesari.lk, Ed. in Chief, VIRAKESARI, Colombo
Devine, Kevin..................(734) 487-1026
editor@easternecho.com, Eastern Michigan Univ., MI, Ypsilanti
Devlin, Sherry..................406-523-5250
sherry.devlin@missoulian.com, Editor, Missoulian, MT, Missoula
Devlin, Michelle
mdevlin@highpoint.edu, Admin. Asst., High Point University, NC, High Point
Devnath, Chitta
satyajug_2000@yahoo.com, Mng. Dir., SATYAJUG, Calcutta
Dewaele, Lou..................406-791-6543
Circulation Sale Specialist (West Group), Great Falls Tribune, MT, Great Falls
Dewalt, Gregg..................(256) 740-5748
gregg.dewalt@timesdaily.com, Sports Ed., TimesDaily, AL, Florence
Dewitt, Larry
info@creweb.com, Pres., Commodity Resource & Environment, CA, Burbank
Dey, Jim..................217-351-5369
jdey@news-gazette.com, Opinions Page Editor, News-Gazette Inc., IL, Champaign
Dezam, Anthony..................(541) 383-0344
Circ. Mgr., Single Copy/Transportation, The Bulletin, OR, Bend
Dhattani, Tarun
lokasatta@sambhaav.com, Ed., Traders (Pvt.) Ltd., Ahmedabad, Gujarat
Di Pietro, Sylvia..................(212) 255-4059
femalelitigator@yahoo.com, Self-Syndicator, Sylvia Di Pietro, NY, New York
DiAngelis, Dawna..................ext. 8472
dawna.diangelis@cantonrep.com, Prodn. Mgr., Pre Press, The Repository, OH, Canton
DiCanio, Theresa
information_center@marconidata.com, Sr. Mktg. Communication Specialist, Video Jet Technologies, IL, Wood Dale
DiChiara, Thomas..................973-569-7850
Automotive Sales Manager, North Jersey Media Group, NJ, Woodland Park
DiGioia, Robert J.
bob@roammedia.net, Pres./CEO, Interactive Media System, PA, Pittsburgh
DiMambro, John..................(303) 776-2244 ext. 293
jdimambro@times-call.com, Adv. Dir., Times-Call, CO, Longmont
DiMenna, Hernan..................4309-7216
hdimenna@clarin-contenidos.com.ar, Ed., Clarin Contenidos, Buenos Aires
DiPoce, Lora..................(416) 507-2129
lora.dipoce@canadianpress.com, Admin. Asst., Press News Ltd., ON, Toronto
DiPreta, Mike..................(212) 930-8244
Adv. Mgr., Research, New York Post, NY, New York
DiPrince, Chad..................(303) 443-6272 ext. 110
diprince@coloradodaily.com, Pre Press/Systems Mgr., Colorado Daily, CO, Boulder
DiSandro, Deb..................(815) 439-1172
deb@slightlyoff.com, Author/Owner, Slightly Off!, IL, Plainfield
DiSanto, Laura
laura@thetriangle.org, Staff Manager, Drexel Univ., PA, Philadelphia
DiSpigno, Vincent
amyh@pwrsystems.com, Pres./CEO, Vizacom, Inc., NY, New York
DiStaso, John..................(603) 668-4321 ext. 343
jdistaso@unionleader.com, Columnist, New Hampshire Union Leader/New Hampshire Sunday News, NH, Manchester
Diadiun, Ted..................(216) 999-4408
Reader Rep, The Plain Dealer, OH, Cleveland
Diah, Herawati
indonesian-observer@indoexchange.com, Pub., INDONESIAN OBSERVER, Jakarta, Java
Dianda, Mario..................(650) 391-1342
mdianda@dailynewsgroup.com, Exec. Ed., Palo Alto Daily News, CA, Menlo Park
Diaz, Lisset..................(714) 992-7156
Fullerton College, CA, Fullerton
Diaz, Iris..................(469) 977-3723
idiaz@aldiatx.com, Mktg. Exec., Al Dia, TX, Dallas
Diaz, Mauro..................(469) 977-3677
mdiaz@aldiatx.com, Sports Ed., Al Dia, TX, Dallas
Diaz, Jim..................303-566-4070
jdiaz@ccnewspapers.com, President & CEO, ASP Westward LP, CO, Englewood
jdiaz@ccnewspapers.com, Castle Rock News Press, CO, Englewood
jdiaz@ccnewspapers.com, Highland Ranch Herald, CO, Englewood
Diaz Martinez, Jose Guadalupe
elgrafico@infosel.net.mx, Pres., El Grafico, Ciudad Victoria, Tamaulipas
Diaz Redondo, Regino
foro@excelsior.com.mx, Pres./Gen. Dir., Cia. Editorial, S.C. de R.L., Mexico City, Distrito Federal
Dib, Felisha..................(814) 235-0309 ext. 7633
dib@accuwx.com, Mktg. Asst., AccuWeather, Inc., PA, State College
Dichand, H.
ooe@kronezeitung.at, Pub., OBEROSTERREICHISCHE NEUE KRONEN ZEITUNG, Linz, Upper Austria
Dichand, Hans
krone@krone.at, Pub., NEUE KRONEN-ZEITUNG, Vienna
Dick, Jeff..................ext. 230
jeffdick@qconline.com, Action Line Ed., The Rock Island Argus, IL, Rock Island
Dick, Brad..................(607) 337-3034
subscribe@evesun.com, Circ. Mgr., The Evening Sun, NY, Norwich
Dickens, David..................ext. 257
Prodn. Mgr., Admin., The News Enterprise, KY, Elizabethtown
Dickens, Julie..................(270) 783-3225
jdickens@bgdailynews.com, Adv. Mgr., Classified, Daily News, KY, Bowling Green
Dickerman, Morgan Paul..................(252) 265-7802
mpd@wilsontimes.com, Pres./Pub., The Wilson Daily Times, NC, Wilson
Dickerson, Brian
briandickerson@multiaad.com, Vice Pres., Opns., MultiAd Services, Inc., IL, Peoria
Dickerson, Brian
bdickerson@multiad.com, VP Product Development, MultiAd Services, Inc., IL, Peoria
Dickey, James
jdickey@yourwestvalley.com, Prodn. Mgr., Press, Daily News-Sun, AZ, Sun City
Dickey, Robert J.
gcishare@gannett.com, Pres., Gannett US Community Publishing, Gannett Co., Inc., VA, McLean
Dickinson, John
jon@cnicorp.com, Pres., CNI Corp., NH, Milford
Dickman, Ed..................(406) 758-4480
Prodn. Foreman, Pressroom, Daily Inter Lake, MT, Kalispell
Dickson, Gary D.
gdickson@record-bee.com, Pub., Lake County Record-Bee, CA, Lakeport
Didato, Salvatore
svdidato@frognet.com, Principal/Ed., Didato Associates, NY, Ossining
Didriksen, Per
per.h.didriksen@l-a.no, Adv. Mgr., LINDESNES, Mandal
Dieffenbacher, Amy..................(315)445-4542
dolphin@lemoyne.edu, The Dolphin, NY, Syracuse
Diehl, Mark W.
mark@douthittcorp.com, Int'l Sales, Douthitt Corp., MI, Detroit
Diehl, Becky..................(573) 882-6288
Univ. of Missouri, MO
Diekmann, Kai..................34700
Ed. in Chief, BILD, Berlin
Dielessen, G.
info@wegener.nl, Ed., ARNHEMSE

COURANT, Apeldoorn
Diels, Sarah..........................(920) 356-6719
sdiels@conleynet.com, Commun. Coord., Conley Publishing Group Ltd., WI, Beaver Dam
Diemand, Robert......................(413) 585-5341
rdiemand@gazettenet.com, Prodn. Mgr., Distr. Ctr., Daily Hampshire Gazette, MA, Northampton
Dietmann, Carsten
sz.geschaeftsfuehrung@dd-v.de, Bus. Mgr., DRESDNER MORGENPOST, Dresden
Dietrich, Matthew.....................(217) 788-1509
matt.dietrich@sj-r.com, Editorial Page Ed., The State Journal-Register, IL, Springfield
Dietz, Bernie..............(617) 779-8900 ext. 2112
bdietz@domania.com, Vice Pres., Sales, Domania, Inc., MA, Watertown
Diggs, Angel..........................(203) 789-5642
Librarian, New Haven Register, CT, New Haven
Digiacinto, Corey......................(206) 464-2227
Cor. Commun. Mgr., Seattle Times Co., WA, Seattle
Dijkstra, G..................................4842842
redactye@tubantia.wegener.nl, Ed. in Chief, DAGBLAD TUBANTIA/TWENTSCHE COURANT, Enschede
Dikaiou, Koinonia Astikou
estianews@otenet.gr, Pub., ESTIA, Athens, Central Greece
Dilella, Pete
info@superiorlifts.com, Pres., Superior Handling Equipment, Inc., FL, Ormond Beach
Dillaway, Warren..............................ext. 235
Photographer, Star Beacon, OH, Ashtabula
Dille, Penny...............(303) 776-2244 ext. 445
pdille@times-call.com, Adv. Mgr., Display, Times-Call, CO, Longmont
Dillena, Giancarlo
cdt@cdt.ch, Ed., CORRIERE DEL TICINO, Muzzano, Ticino
Dillon, Jason..........................(843) 317-7232
jdillon@florencenews.com, Adv. Dir., Morning News, SC, Florence
Dillon, John..............................541-832-4830
johnd@argusobserver.com, Pub., Argus Observer, OR, Ontario
Dillon, William.......................(507) 333-3133
Mng. Ed., Faribault Daily News, MN, Faribault
Dillon, Jim............................(937) 225-7311
jdillon@coxohio.com, Bus. Ed., Dayton Daily News, OH, Dayton
Dillon, Karen..........................(804) 649-6242
kdillon@timesdispatch.com, Mgr., Pre Press Design Servs., Richmond Times-Dispatch, VA, Richmond
Dillon, Kim..................................ext. 5121
kim.dillon@cnhiindiana.com, Gen. Mgr, Pharos-Tribune, IN, Logansport
Dimare, Dario
dario@dariodesigns.com, Pres., Dario Designs, Inc., MA, Marlboro
Dimesio, Rose................................ext. 294
Morton College, IL, Cicero
Dimichele, Amie
editor@etownian.edu, Elizabethtown College, PA, Elizabethtown
Dimitrakopoulou, Danay
info@eleftheria.gr, Pub., ELEFTHERIA, Larissa, Thessaly
Dimmitt, Craig..............................ext. 1011
cdimmitt@portervillerecorder.com, Bus. Mgr., The Porterville Recorder, CA, Porterville
Dimock, Donna.......................(805) 737-1031
Bus. Mgr., The Lompoc Record, CA, Lompoc
Dinan, Stephen
sdinan@washingtontimes.com, Capitol Hill Bureau Chief, The Washington Times, DC, Washington
Dinan, John...........................(214) 352-1123
jdinan@circulationiii.com, Owner/Pres., Circulation III Promotions, Inc., TX, Dallas
Dinardo, Victor A.
vdinardo@telegram.com, Dir., HR, Telegram & Gazette, MA, Worcester
Ding, Zuang Ming
editor@siongpo.com, Ed., Yuyitung Communications, Inc., Manila
Dinh, Chris............................(702) 895-3878
Univ. of Nevada, NV, Las Vegas
Dinis, Jose Rocha
jtm@yp.com.mo, Ed., TRIBUNA DE MACAU, Macau
Diotte, Kerry..........................(780) 425-9130
kdiotte@edm.sunpub.com, Columnist, The Edmonton Sun, AB, Edmonton
Dipolt, Walter
w.dipolt@volksblatt.at, CEO, NEUES VOLKSBLATT, Linz, Upper Austria
Dirking, Brian
info@infoaccess.com, Mktg. Dir., InfoAccess, Inc., MN, Eden Prairie
Dirks, Michael.........................(828) 694-7863
michael.dirks@hendersonvillenews.com, Chief Photographer, Times-News, NC, Hendersonville
Dishmon, Banks.........................405.238.6464
bdishmon@pvdemocrat.com, Publisher, Pauls Valley Democrat, OK, Pauls Valley
Dissanayaka, Sujeewa
lakjanatha@lakehouse.lk, Ed. in Chief, LAKJANATHA, Colombo
Distelhorst, Mike
mike.distelhorst@amarillo.com, Adv. Dir., Amarillo Globe-News, TX, Amarillo
Dithurbida, Ana Lina.............................2227
lamanana@ciudad.com.ar, Gen. Mgr., La Manana, Veinticinco de Mayo, Provincia de Buenos Aires
Dittelbach, Sven
sven.dittelbach@dk-online.de, Adv. Mgr., DELMENHORSTER KREISBLATT, Delmenhorst
Ditzen-Blanke, Roswitha
nzbremerhaven@nordsee-zeitung.de, Proprietor, NORDSEE-ZEITUNG, Bremerhaven
Ditzen-Blanke, Joachim
nordenham.redaktion@kreiszeitung-wesermarsch.de, Proprietor, Kreiszeitung Wesermarsch, Nordenham
Ditzler, Joe
jditzler@eastoregonian.com, City Editor, East Oregonian, OR, Pendleton
Dix, Andrew S.
asdix@dixcom.com, Pub., The Daily Jeffersonian, OH, Cambridge
Dix, Andrew S.
asdix@dixcom.com, Publisher, Jeffersonian Co. LLC, OH, Cambridge
Dix, David E...............................ext. 1280
Pub., Record-Courier, OH, Ravenna
Dix, Troy...................................419-281-0581
tadix@dixcom.com, Publisher, Ashland Publishing Co. LLC, OH, Ashland
Dix, David E.
dedix@dixcom.com, Sec., Dix Communications, OH, Wooster
Dix, G. Charles
gcdixii@the-reviewcom, Pub., The Review, OH, Alliance
Dix, Andrew R...............................ext. 2209
ardix@dixcom.com, Dir., Web, Record-Courier, OH, Ravenna
Dix, Troy
tdix@times-gazette.com, Pub., Ashland Times-Gazette, OH, Ashland
Dix Maenza, Ann
admaenza@state-journal.com, Publisher, Frankfort Publishing Co., KY, Frankfort
Dixon, Rod.............................(660) 646-2411
rdixon@chillicothenews.com, Pub./Purchasing Agent, Constitution-Tribune, MO, Chillicothe
Dixon, Rod
rdixon@chillicothenews.com, Pub., Linn County Leader, MO, Brookfield
Dixon, Chris
cdixon@advertiser-tribune.com, Adv. Mgr., The Advertiser-Tribune, OH, Tiffin
Dixon, David..........................(330) 471-8212
Malone College, OH, Canton
Dixon, Ted E.
tdixon@hawaiitribune-herald.com, Pub., Hawaii Tribune-Herald, HI, Hilo
Dixon, Shane...........................860/701-4387
s.dixon@theday.com, Director of Information Technology, The Day Publishing Company, CT, New London
Dixon, David..........................(270) 831-8333
ddixon@thegleaner.com, Ed., The Gleaner, KY, Henderson
Djakovic, Pedja
pdjakovic@praguepost.com, Adv. Dir., Lion's Share Group, Prague
Djqde, Amung
tips@dn.no, Ed., DAGENS NAERINGSLIV, Oslo
Do, Hai..................................(914) 694-5055
Photo Ed., The Journal News, NY, White Plains
Doaei, Seyyed Mahmud
email@ettelaat.com, Ed., ETTELA'AT
Doak, Griffin
griffin@whitingtech.com, Sr. Engineer, Whiting Technologies, IL, Willowbrook
Doane, Patrick.........................(717) 240-7123
pdoane@cumberlink.com, Prodn. Mgr., Opns., The Sentinel, PA, Carlisle
Doane, Carol...........................(360) 735-4474
carol.doane@columbian.com, Adv. Sales Mgr., The Columbian, WA, Vancouver
Dobbs, Deborah S.
d2@dobbsgroup.com, Exec. Dir., California Association of Newspaper Distributors, CA, Walnut Creek
Dobbyn, Karen.........................(207) 621-5741
HR Dir., Morning Sentinel, ME, Waterville
Dobler, Ewald...................................80020
Pub./MD, ALFELDER ZEITUNG, Alfeld
Doblin, Alfred..........................(973) 569-7084
Editorial Page Editor, North Jersey Media Group, NJ, Woodland Park
Dobrenski, Julie
jdobrenski@marshallindependent.com, Circ. Mgr., Independent, MN, Marshall
Dobson, Byron.........................(850) 599-2256
bdobson@tallahassee.com, Metro Ed., Tallahassee Democrat, FL, Tallahassee
Dobson, Jana...........................(512) 912-2525
jdobson@statesman.com, Circ. Dir., Austin American-Statesman, TX, Austin
Dobson, Kathy.........................(314) 340-8460
kdobson@post-dispatch.com, Credit Mgr., St. Louis Post-Dispatch, MO, Saint Louis
Dockendorf, Randy
randy.dockendorf@yankton.net, City Ed., Yankton Daily Press & Dakotan, SD, Yankton
Dockery, Sherrie.......................(336) 888-3539
sdockery@hpe.com, News Ed., High Point Enterprise, NC, High Point
Dockham, Janice.......................(306) 781-5378
jdockham@leaderpost.canwest.com, Ed. in Chief, The Leader-Post, SK, Regina
Dodd, Mike
mike.dodd@sunchemical.com, Gen. Mgr., Rycoline Products, Inc., IL, Chicago
Dodds, Don..............................805-781-7980
ddodds@thetribunenews.com, VP/Production, The Tribune, CA, San Luis Obispo
Dodge, Rose
bds@berlindailysun.com, Mng. Ed., The Berlin Daily Sun, NH, Berlin
Dodson, Richard.......................(865) 981-1146
News Ed., The Daily Times, TN, Maryville
Dodson, Tammie.......................(256) 963-6739
tammie.dodson@adtran.com, PR Dir., ADTRAN, AL, Huntsville
Doeden, Dennis
ddoeden@bemidjipioneer.com, Pub., The Pioneer, MN, Bemidji
Doege, Cindy...........................(612) 673-4142
Cindy.Doege@startribune.com, Circ. Vice Pres., Star Tribune, MN, Minneapolis
Doege, Jack
jd@centuryinteractive.com, COO, CenturyTel Interactive, TX, Dallas
Doench, Debbie..............................ext. 5635
doencde@hobartbrothers.com, Adv./Commun. Mgr., ITW Hobart Brothers Co., OH, Troy
Dogan, Aydin
aydin.dogan@milliyet.com.cr, Pub., MILLIYET
Dogan, Aydin
webadmin@milliyet.com.tr, Pub., MILLIYET
Doherty, Brad..........................(956) 982-6626
brad_doherty@link.freedom.com, Photo Ed., El Nuevo Heraldo, TX, Brownsville
Doherty, Brad..........................(956) 982-6626
Photo Dept. Mgr., The Brownsville Herald, TX, Brownsville
Doherty, Phil...........................(312) 222-3117
pdoherty@tribune.com, Vice Pres., Finance/CFO, Chicago Tribune, IL, Chicago
Doherty, Donna........................(203) 789-5672
ddoherty@nhregister.com, Arts/Travel Ed., New Haven Register, CT, New Haven
Doherty, Rod.................................ext. 5100
Exec. Ed., Foster's Daily Democrat, NH, Dover
Dolan, Mary............................(914) 694-5070
Lifestyles Ed., The Journal News, NY, White Plains
Dolan, Jennifer C.......................(212) 556-1234
Vice Pres., Forest Pdct., The New York Times Co., NY, New York
Dolan, John................(802) 747-6121 ext. 2221
john.dolan@rutlandherald.com, Mng. Ed., Rutland Herald, VT, Rutland
Dolan, Scott............................(508) 676-2532
sdolan@heraldnews.com, City Ed., The Herald News, MA, Fall River
Dolan, Thomas J.
thomas.dolan@usa.xerox.com, Sr. Vice Pres./Pres., Global Servs., Xerox Corp., CT, Norwalk
Doland, Ross..............................337-371-3301
rdoland@theadvertiser.com, Production Director, The Town Talk, LA, Alexandria
Doll, Dennis
press@natchitochestimes.com, Systems Mgr., Natchitoches Times, LA, Natchitoches
Doll, Julie................................(765) 420-5242
jdoll@journalandcourier.com, Exec. Ed., Journal and Courier, IN, Lafayette
Doll Pinto, David................................342535
editor@estrellaloa.cl, Dir., La Estrella Del Loa, Calama
Dolley, Steve.............................(419) 724-6234
sdolley@toledoblade.com, Controller, The Blade, OH, Toledo
Dolny, Jim................................(724) 226-7760
jdolny@tribweb.com, Prodn. Mgr., Mailroom, Valley News Dispatch, PA, Tarentum
Domador, Alfredo
adomador@b2bportables.com, Vice Pres., Opns., Artes Graficas (A Vertical Community of B2B Portales), FL, Miami
Domaingue, Edward C......(603) 668-4321 ext. 302
edomaingue@unionleader.com, Vice Pres., News, New Hampshire Union Leader/New Hampshire Sunday News, NH, Manchester
Domash, Harry...........................(831) 685-1932
hdomash@winninginvesting.com, Self-Syndicator, Newsletters Plus, CA, Aptos
Dombrouskis, Aigar......(312) 649-1800 ext. 5720
aigar@atomicimaging.com, Producer, Atomic Imaging, Inc., IL, Chicago
Dombrowski, Jim...........(734) 240-5708 ext. 249
jimd@monroewnews.com, Creative Serv./Alt Pub Mgr., The Monroe Evening News, MI, Monroe
Dombrowski, Chip................................ext. 243
cdombrowski@theworldlink.com, Entertainment Ed., The World, OR, Coos Bay
Domenick, Jeff..........................(724) 226-4687
jdomenick@tribweb.com, Mng. Ed., Valley News Dispatch, PA, Tarentum
Domet, Gary..............................(402) 444-1406
gary.domet@owh.com, Mgr., Training, Omaha World-Herald, NE, Omaha
Dominguez, Rosy
rosy_dominguez@pulsoslp.com.mx, Asst. Dir., PULSO, San Luis Potosi, San Luis Potosi
Dominici, Emily
edom@timesleaderonline.com, Online Mgr., The Times Leader, OH, Martins Ferry
Domis, Ray................................(954) 722-3000
Exec. Vice Pres./CFO, GraphLine, FL, Sunrise
DomÃ¡nguez, MarÃ¡a Elvira
diario@elpais.com.co, Owner, El Pais Ltda., Cali
Donahoe, Patrick R.
pdonahoe@email.usps.gov, Deputy Postmaster General, United States Postal Service, DC, Washington
Donahoo, Malcolm.....................(707) 553-6843
malcolm@timesheraldonline.com, Copy Ed., Vallejo Times-Herald, CA, Vallejo
Donahue, Jim....................................ext. 223
jdonahue@adn.com, Credit Mgr., Anchorage Daily News, AK, Anchorage
Donahue, Gail
gail.donahue@sbsun.com, Adv. Acct. Exec., New Media, San Bernardino County Sun, CA, San Bernardino
Donato, Andrew.........................(416) 947-2253
andy.donato@sunmedia.ca, Cartoonist, The Toronto Sun, ON, Toronto
Dondoneau, Dave.......................(808) 525-8048
ddondoneau@honoluluadvertiser.com, Deputy

City Ed., Honolulu Star-Advertiser, HI, Honolulu
Dong, Qingwen ....(209) 946-2505
qdong@uop.edu, Chair, University of the Pacific, CA, Stockton
Donker, Birgig
nrc@nrc.nl, Ed. in Chief, NRC HANDELSBLAD, Amsterdam
Donnellon, Bill ....(973) 569-7071
Business Editor, North Jersey Media Group, NJ, Woodland Park
Donnelly, Scott ....(518) 792-3322
donnelly@poststar.com, Asst. City Ed., The Post-Star, NY, Glens Falls
Donnelly, Doug ....ext. 318
doug@monroenews.com, Local Ed., The Monroe Evening News, MI, Monroe
Donnelly, Jerry
jerryd@mail.nwmissouri.edu, Chair, Northwest Missouri State University, MO, Maryville
Donnelly, John Thomas
tom@westwardstudio.com, CEO, Westward Studio, BC, Victoria
Donnelly, Michael....................(760) 740-5408
mdonnelly@nctimes.com, Asst. Mng. Ed., Online, North County Times, CA, Escondido
Donnelly, Michael J.....................(724) 465-5555
gazedit@indianagazette.net, Pres./Pub., The Indiana Gazette, PA, Indiana
Donoghue, Dennis 518-395-3055
ddonoghue@dailygazette.net, Circulation Mgr/Mailroom, The Daily Gazette, NY, Schenectady
Donoghue, Mike
mdonoghue@smcvt.edu, Executive Director, Vermont Press Association, VT, Colchester
Donoghue, James
spotnews@priority.dowjones.com, Vice Pres., Sales/Mktg., Dow Jones Newswires - New York, NY, NY, New York
Donovan, Jim
jdonovan@acnpapers.com, Sports Ed., McKinney Courier-Gazette, TX, McKinney
Donovan, Donna M.....................(315) 792-5002
ddonovan@uticaod.com, Pres./Pub., Observer-Dispatch, NY, Utica
Donovan, Suzanne ....(912) 652-0414
suzanne.donovan@savannahnow.com, Justice Ed., Savannah Morning News, GA, Savannah
Doolittle, Todd
tdoolittle@njtimes.com, Circ. Asst. Dir., The Times, NJ, Trenton
Doorne, Bart Van
bert.van.doorne@demorgen.be, Ed., DE MORGEN, 1000 Brussels
Dopfner, Mathias
info@asv.de, Chrmn., Axel Springer Verlag AG, Hamburg
Dora, Christopher
victoria@theaustralian.com.au, Ed., THE AUSTRALIAN, Southbank
Dorger, Samanda 707-864-7000
Journalism Advisor, Solano Community College, CA, Fairfield
Doring, Pierre
redaktion@stz-online.de, Mktg. Mgr., Sudthuringer Zeitung, Bad Salzungen
Dorji, Kinley
editor@kuensel.com, Ed. in Chief, KUENSEL, Thimphu
Dorksen, Aaron ....ext. 1621
adorksen@the-daily-record.com, Sports Ed., The Daily Record, OH, Wooster
Dorman, Bill
bill.dorman@millersville.edu, Chair, Millersville University, PA, Millersville
Dorman, Dave
dorman@nbnet.nb.ca, Sec. /Treasurer, Canadian Circulation Management Association, NB, Pointe-Du-Chene
Dormann, Henry O.
sipa@sipausa.com, Chrmn./Ed. in Chief, Sipa News Service, NY, New York
Dormien, Ursula
brasilpost@brasilpost.com.br, Pub., Editora Brazil-Post, Sao Paulo, Sao Paulo
Dorn, Jennie
law.commentator@nyu.edu, New York Univ. Law School, NY, New York
Dorr, Joe
breezecourier@ctitech.com, Online Mgr., Breeze-Courier, IL, Taylorville
Dorries, Bruce
bdorries@mbc.edu, Chair, Mary Baldwin College, VA, Staunton
Dorries, Bruce ....(540) 887-7112
Mary Baldwin College, VA, Staunton
Dorsch, Vicki
vdorsch@bentoncourier.com, Bus. Mgr., The Saline Courier, AR, Benton
Dorschner, Larry
news@mojonews.com, Pub., Morning Journal, OH, Lisbon
Dorsey, Patrick E. ....(850) 599-2124
pdorsey@tallahassee.com, Pres. & Publisher, Tallahassee Democrat, FL, Tallahassee
Dorsey, Steve ....(313) 222-6792
sdorsey@freepress.com, Asst. Mng. Ed., Presentation, Detroit Free Press, MI, Detroit
Dorsey, Tom ....(785) 822-1406 ext. 123
sjphoto@saljournal.com, Chief Photograher, The Salina Journal, KS, Salina
Dortch, Sebastian ....(727) 893-8084
sdortch@tampabay.com, Dir., HR/Diversity Officer, Tampa Bay Times, FL, Saint Petersburg
Dorton, Chris ....(276) 645-2548
cdorton@bristolnews.com, Circ. Dir., Audience Growth, Bristol Herald Courier, VA, Bristol
Dosa, Don ....(360) 792-8569
ddosa@kitsapsun.com, Nat'l Adv. Mgr., Co-op, Kitsap Sun, WA, Bremerton
Dosch, Scott
sdosch@parisbeacon.com, Sports Ed., Paris Beacon-News, IL, Paris
Doser, Alfons
info@ovb.net, Proprietor, Oberbayerisches Volksblatt, Rosenheim
Dottolo, Reinhold
kaernten@kleinezeitung.at, Ed. in Chief, KLEINE ZEITUNG, Klagenfurt
Doty, Clayton
daily@rensselaerrepublican.com, Exec. Ed., Republican, IN, Rensselaer
Dougal, Kirk ....(419) 238-2285 ext. 210
kdougal@timesbulletin.com, Ed., The Times Bulletin, OH, Van Wert
Dougherty, Patrick
pdougherty@skagitpublishing.com, Interactive Media Mgr., Skagit Valley Herald, WA, Mount Vernon
Dougherty, Patrick..........(907) 257-4303 ext. 303
pdougherty@adn.com, Ed., Anchorage Daily News, AK, Anchorage
Dougherty, Diane 703-955-6130
Editor-in-Chief, Old Dominion Univ., VA, Norfolk
Doughton, James E.
jim.doughton@gvillesun.com, Pub., The Gainesville Sun, FL, Gainesville
Doughty, Pat
pd025@mirachem.com, COO, Mirachem Corp., AZ, Phoenix
Douglas, Bruce ....(216) 368-2916
Case Western Reserve Univ., OH, Cleveland
Douglas, Donnie
ddouglas@robesonian.com, Editorial Page Ed., The Robesonian, NC, Lumberton
Douglas, Brian....................(415) 435-4541
brian@autoeditor.com, Ed./Pub., Autoeditor Syndication, CA, Tiburon
Douglas, Michael ....(330) 996-3514
mdouglas@thebeaconjournal.com, Editorial Page Ed., Akron Beacon Journal, OH, Akron
Douglass, Brenda ....(319) 291-1404
brenda.douglass@wcfcourier.com, Admin. Asst., The Courier, IA, Waterloo
Dove, Jim ....(915) 546-6332
jdove@elpasotimes.com, Circ. Dir., El Paso Times, TX, El Paso
Dovichi, Larry....................(209) 385-2499
ldovichi@mercedsun-star.com, Adv. Dir., Merced Sun-Star, CA, Merced
Dowaliby, Chazy....................(617) 786-7013
chazy@ledger.com, Ed., The Patriot Ledger, MA, Quincy
Dowaliby, Chazy....................(508) 427-4036
cdowaliby@enterprisenews.com, Ed., The Enterprise, MA, Randolph
Dowdell, Kenneth L.....................(262) 656-6249
kdowdell@kenoshanews.com, Vice President, United Communications Corporation, WI, Kenosha
Dowdell, Kenneth L.....................(262) 656-6249
kdowdell@kenoshanews.com, Publisher, Kenosha News, WI, Kenosha
Dowell, Ken
ken.dowell@prnewswire.com, Exec. Vice Pres., PR Newswire - New York, NY, NY, New York
Dowling, Mary
mdowling@nnnlp.com, Sales Dir., Newspaper National Network LP, NY, New York
Downes, Stephen ....(808) 535-8066
sdownes@honoluluadvertiser.com, Database/Special Projects Ed., Honolulu Star-Advertiser, HI, Honolulu
Downey, Kevin
dailynews@vipowernet.net, Adv. Dir., DAILY NEWS, Saint Croix
Downey, Jim
jimd@zlogic.com, Dir.-Sales, Logic Associates, Inc., VT, White River Junction
Downing, Charles ....(541) 338-2204
chuck.downing@registerguard.com, Circ. Dir., The Register-Guard, OR, Eugene
Downs, Peter ....ext. 250
Health Ed., The Standard, ON, Saint Catharines
Downs, John ....(518) 565-4142
jdowns@pressrepublican.com, Design/Systems Ed., Press-Republican, NY, Plattsburgh
Dowse, Rod ....(530) 842-5777
publisher@siskiyoudaily.com, Pub., Siskiyou Daily News, CA, Yreka
Doxee, Sharon....................ext. 343
CFO, The Pioneer - Big Rapids, MI, Big Rapids
Doyle, Patrick ....1-907-257-4210 -direct
pdoyle@adn.com, Pub./Pres., Anchorage Daily News, AK, Anchorage
Doyle, Kevin
news@pnj.com, Pub./Pres., Pensacola News Journal, FL, Pensacola
Doyle, Chris
info@naplesnews.com, Pres./Pub., Naples Daily News, FL, Naples
Doyle, Rick ....(509) 525-3300 ext. 249
rdoyle@ubnet.com, Ed., Walla Walla Union-Bulletin, WA, Walla Walla
Doyle-Kimball, Mary
madkimba@aol.com, Exec. Dir., National Association of Real Estate Editors (NAREE), FL, Boca Raton
Dozier, Bobi
world@npgco.com, Adv. Mgr., Hiawatha World, KS, Hiawatha
Dozier, Van ....(334) 826-6847
van@circulationsolutions.com, Pres., Circulation Solutions, Inc., AL, Auburn
Dragin, Burt ....(510) 464-3459
Laney College, CA, Oakland
Drago, Mike ....(214) 977-8731
mdrago@dallasnews.com, Asst. Mng. Ed., Local News, The Dallas Morning News, TX, Dallas
Dragon, Jennifer ....(404) 572-1957
jdragon@coxnews.com, Contact, COXnet (Cox Newspapers' Wide Area Network/Cox News Service), GA, Atlanta
Dragotescu, Laurentiu
laurentiu.ciocazanu@adevarul.ro, Ed. in Chief, ADEVARUL, Bucharest
Draheim, Brenda....................402-444-1644
Treasurer & Controller, Omaha World-Herald, NE, Omaha
Draheim, Brenda....................402-444-1644
Treasurer & Controller, Omaha World-Herald, NE, Omaha
Drahos, Marta Hepler ....(231) 933-1487
mdrahos@record-eagle.com, Assoc. Ed., Record-Eagle, MI, Traverse City
Drain, Christina ....(850) 484-1374
Pensacola Junior College, FL, Pensacola
Drake, Cecil....................(972) 243-2500
Pres., Drake Communications, Inc., TX, Dallas
Drake, Shelly....................62022412422
shelly.drake@thekansan.com, Controller, McPherson Sentinel, KS, McPherson
Drake, Carolyn....................(902) 629-6036
gdnlifestyles@chg.southam.ca, Features Ed., The Guardian, PE, Charlottetown
Drake, Shelly 316-283-1500
shelly.drake@thekansan.com, Controller, Wellington Daily News, KS, Wellington
Draper, Monte
mdraper@bemidjipioneer.com, Photo Ed., The Pioneer, MN, Bemidji
Draper, Whit
portland@allenspcb.com, Office Mgr., Allen's Press Clipping Bureau, OR, Portland
Draughn, Kim ....(843) 792-4107
Medical Univ. of South Carolina, SC, Charleston
Drazan, Frank....................(708) 485-6973
drazan1@aol.com, Pres., The International School For Pressroom Management, IL, Brookfield
Dreiling, Janell ....ext. 25
mcpproduction1@sbcglobal.net, Prodn. Mgr., McPherson Sentinel, KS, McPherson
Drescher, John....................(919) 829-4515
drescher@newsobserver.com, Mng. Ed., The News & Observer, NC, Raleigh
Dressler, Rolf
wb@westfalen-blatt.de, Ed. in Chief, Weinheimer Nachrichten, Bielefeld
Dressler, Dawn ....(806) 345-3365
dawn.dressler@amarillo.com, Exec. Ed., Amarillo Globe-News, TX, Amarillo
Dressman, Dennis L.....................(303) 892-2527
dressmand@rockymountainnews.com, Assoc. Mng. Ed., Admin., Rocky Mountain News, CO, Denver
Drew, Duchesne....................(612) 673-7111
duchesne.drew@startribune.com, Managing Editor, Operations, Star Tribune, MN, Minneapolis
Drewry, Bryan....................Sports Ed.
Times Colonist, BC, Victoria
Drewry, Dan
ddrewry@hagadone.com, Pub., Shoshone News-Press, ID, Kellogg
Drewsen, Alan
info@inta.org, Exec. Dir., International Trademark Association, NY, New York
Drexel, Robert C.....................(610) 371-5216
rdrexel@readingeagle.com, Building Supvr., Reading Eagle, PA, Reading
Driscoll, Ellen
edriscoll@keenesentinel.com, Interactive Media, The Keene Sentinel, NH, Keene
Driscoll, Lorinda ....(810) 989-6236
advdirector@thetimesherald.com, Adv. Dir., Times Herald, MI, Port Huron
Dritschel, Steve
agcorp4usa@aol.com, Mgr.-Opns., Auto-Grafica Corp., NJ, River Vale
Driver, Di
ddriver@nbr.co.nz, Adv. Mgr., NATIONAL BUSINESS REVIEW
Droege, LuAnn....................(618) 532-5601
ldroege@morningsentinel.com, Sr. Ed., Morning Sentinel, IL, Centralia
Drolet, Kevin
kevind@metrosuburbia.com, Adv. Sales Mgr., Metro Suburbia, Inc./Newhouse Newspapers, CA, Los Angeles
Drolet, Jamie ....(843) 937-5904
Adv. Mgr., Retail, The Post and Courier, SC, Charleston
Dromgoole, Frank....................(800) 527-1134
fdromgoole@shorack.com, Sales-KS, OK, Kaspar Wire Works, Inc./Sho-Rack, TX, Shiner
Drownell, Malcolm
malcom.drownell@jacksonville.com, Circ. Dir., The Florida Times-Union, FL, Jacksonville
Drozdowski, Stanislaw
poczta@mediaexpress.pl, Ed. in Chief, Media Express Sp. z o.o, Warsaw
Druck, M.A.
english@hamodia.co.il, Ed., HAMODI'A
Drucker, Irwin
drucker@us.ibm.com, Program Dir., GLBT Supplier Rel./Procurement, IBM Corp., NY, Somers
Drummond, John
info.office@atlantis.co.ac, Ed., ST. HELENA NEWS, Jamestown
Drummond, Rod
roddrummond@hudsonsharp.com, CEO, Hudson-Sharp, WI, Green Bay
Drummond, Mike
clearcreekrancher@yahoo.com, Author/Self-Syndicator/Pub., Clear Creek Features, CA, Grass Valley

Dryden, Lee ....**(248) 745-4641**
lee.dryden@oakpress.com, Metro Ed., Community/Sunday, The Oakland Press, MI, Pontiac
Du Plessis, Johan
johan.duplessis@inl.co.za, Ed., DIAMOND FIELDS ADVERTISER, Kimberley, Northern Cape
DuMont, Alfred **2240**
redaktion@express.de, Proprietor, EXPRESS, Koln
DuMont, Alfred Neven **13930**
duesseldorf@express.de, Proprietor, DUSSELDORF EXPRESS, Dusseldorf
DuMont, Alfred Neven
mhalle@mz-web.de, Proprietor, MITTELDEUTSCHE ZEITUNG, Halle
DuMont, Alfred Neven...........................**2240**
Proprietor, KOLNER STADT-ANZEIGER, Koln
Dua, H.K.
letters@tribuneindia.com, Ed. in Chief, DAINIK TRIBUNE, Chandigarh
Duarte, Waldemar.......................**232-3176**
Ed., A Voz Do Vale Do Pariabo, Taubate, Sao Paulo
Dubberly, Debbie
ddubberly@nujournal.com, Mgr., Mgmt. Info Servs., The Journal, MN, New Ulm
Dubovik, Sergey
root@republ.belpak.minsk.by, Ed., RESPUBLIKA, Minsk
Dubowitz, Nicole.......................**202-955-9010**
nicole@washingtonmonthly.com, Business Manager, The Washington Monthly LLC, DC, Washington
Duca, Denise ....**(781) 255-7773 ext. 12**
deniseduca@syndicatedadfeatures.com, Controller, Syndicated Ad Features, Inc., MA
Duchek, Dennis
dduchek@eastoregonian.com, Lead Pressman, East Oregonian, OR, Pendleton
Duchemin, Bob ....**(902) 563-3886**
b.duchemin@cbpost.com, Sports Ed., The Cape Breton Post, NS, Sydney
Ducker, Penny ....**ext. 456**
pducker@freemanonline.com, Adv. Mgr., Classified, Daily Freeman, NY, Kingston
Duddy, Curt............................**(250) 729-4211**
cduddy@nanaimodailynews.com, Pub., Nanaimo Daily News, BC, Nanaimo
Duddy, Curt
cduddy@nanaimodailynews.com, Gen. Mgr., Alberni Valley Times, BC, Port Alberni
Dudek, Matthew.........................**(585) 258-2223**
mdudek@democratandchronicle.com, Asst. Mng. Ed., Admin., Democrat and Chronicle.com, NY, Rochester
Dudgeon, Thom ....**(251) 434-8478**
tdudgeon@mobileregister.com, Graphics Ed., Press-Register, AL, Mobile
Dudiek, Brian ....**(570) 829-7168**
briand@timesleader.com, Mgmt. Info Servs. Mgr., Times Leader, PA, Wilkes-Barre
Dudley, Mary
secretary@wtpa.org, Sec., West Texas Press Association, TX, Perryton
Dudley, Lynette........................**(843) 626-0289**
ldudley@thesunnews.com, Prodn. Mgr., The Sun News, SC, Myrtle Beach
Dudrick, Darian
editor.plainsman@midconetwork.com, Ed., Huron Plainsman, SD, Huron
Duerr, Sandra...........................**(805) 781-7901**
sduerr@thetribunenews.com, VP/Executive Editor, The Tribune, CA, San Luis Obispo
Duff, Kathleen ....**(970) 224-7733**
kathleenduff@coloradoan.com, Editorial Page Ed., The Coloradoan, CO, Fort Collins
Duff, Sean...............................**(970) 224-7750**
seanduff@coloradoan.com, Sports Ed., The Coloradoan, CO, Fort Collins
Duffey, Katie
kduffey@thehj.com, Mng. Ed., Herald Journal, IN, Monticello
Duffy, Jim...................**(973) 627-2427 ext. 108**
jduffy@fulcoinc.com, Owner/President, Fulco, Inc., NJ, Denville
Duffy, Shana ....**(262) 513-2618**
sduffy@conleynet.com, Editorial Page Ed., The Freeman, WI, Waukesha
Duffy, Tim ....**(613) 636-0539**
info@mflo.com, Vice Pres., Opns, Master Flo Technology, ON, Hawkesbury
Dugan, Pamela ....**(205) 325-3449**
Asst. Mng. Ed., The Birmingham News, AL, Birmingham
Dugan, Chris..............**(724) 222-2200 ext. 2431**
dugan@observer-reporter.com, Sports Ed., Observer-Reporter, PA, Washington
Dugay, Juan Martinez
jmdugay@towmar.net, Pres., Towmar Representaciones S.A., Mexico City
Duignan, Wayne
sales@horizonsisg.com, Vice Pres., Mktg., Horizons, Inc., OH, Cleveland
Duke, Oak
oduke51895@aol.com, Adv. Dir., Wellsville Daily Reporter, NY, Wellsville
Dulhunt, Simon
shdmedia@fairfaxmedia.com.au, Ed., THE SUN HERALD
Dulley, James T. ....**(513) 231-6034**
dulley@dulley.com, Pres., Starcott Media Services, Inc., OH, Cincinnati
Dumanli, Ekren
e.dumanli@zaman.com.tr, Gen. Dir., ZAMAN
Dumas, Robert
info@polkadots.ca, Mktg./Sales Mgr., Polkadots Software Inc., QC, LaSalle
Dumas, Robert
robd@isd.ca, Sales Manager, Innovative Systems Design, Inc., QC, Pointe-Claire
Dumas, Maurice
mdumas@lesoleil.com, Sports Dir., Le Soleil, QC, Quebec
Dumitru, Teodorescu
contact@crainou.ro, Ed. in Chief, CRAI NOU, Suceava
Dumont, Mike..........................**(330) 416-4822**
mdumont@independentcollegian.com, Sales Manager, Univ. of Toledo-Independent Collegian, OH, Toledo
Dunacason, Blythe
tcnews@tcway.tc, Adv. Mgr., TURKS and CAICOS NEWS, Grand Turk, Grand Turk Islands
Dunagan, Christopher ....**(360) 792-9207**
cdunagan@kitsapsun.com, Environmental/Tech. Writer, Kitsap Sun, WA, Bremerton
Dunbar, Steve...........................**(319) 653-2191**
prod@washjrnl.com, Prodn. Mgr., The Washington Evening Journal, IA, Washington
Duncan, Craig
sbrady@c-dh.net, Adv. Mgr., Columbia Daily Herald, TN, Columbia
Duncan, James.........................**(864) 231-2000**
Anderson Univ., SC, Anderson
Duncan, Susan
susan.duncan@tribstar.com, News Ed., The Tribune Star, IN, Terre Haute
Duncan, Lisa
duncan@knews.com, Mktg. Dir., Knoxville News Sentinel, TN, Knoxville
Duncan-Bush, Joan ....**(760) 335-4643**
graphics@ivpressonline.com, Graphics Ed., Imperial Valley Press, CA, El Centro
Dunesme, Philippe
pdunesme@nicematin.fr, Adv. Mgr., NICE-MATIN, Nice
Dungca, Jessica ....**(559) 735-3303**
jdungca@visalia.gannett.com, Circ. Sales/Opns. Mgr., Visalia Times-Delta, CA, Visalia
Dunhill, Robert ....**(800) 386-4455**
robert@dunhills.com, Pres., Dunhill International List Co., Inc., FL, Boca Raton
Dunhill, Cindy ....**(800) 386-4455**
cindy@dunhills.com, Vice Pres., Dunhill International List Co., Inc., FL, Boca Raton
Dunhill, Candy.........................**(800) 386-4455**
candy@dunhills.com, Vice Pres., Dunhill International List Co., Inc., FL, Boca Raton
Dunivan, Chris........................**(479) 872-4708**
cdunivan@nwaonline.net, Mgmt. Info Servs. Mgr., The Morning News of Northwest Arkansas, AR, Springdale
Dunkel, Bob.............................**(202) 253-3899**
dunkelratings@msn.com, Co-Ed./Co-Owner, Dunkel Sports Research Service, VA, Mount Vernon
Dunkerley, William
wd@publishinghelp.com, Consultant, William Dunkerley Publishing Consultant, CT, New Britain
Dunkle, Dirk............................**(573) 815-1608**
dadunkle@columbiatribune.com, Circ. Dir., Columbia Daily Tribune, MO, Columbia
Dunkmann, Robert **17080**
info@on-online.de, Bus. Mgr., OSTFRIESISCHE NACHRICHTEN, Aurich
Dunlap, Joe ....**(309) 686-3127**
jdunlap@pjstar.com, Credit Mgr., Journal Star, IL, Peoria
Dunn, Carole...........................**(816) 271-8673**
caroledunn@npgco.com, Mktg. Dir., St. Joseph News-Press, MO, Saint Joseph
Dunn, Anita ....**ext. 8475**
anita.dunn@cantonrep.com, Circ. Mgr., District Sales, The Repository, OH, Canton
Dunn, Angie
advertising@ssecho.com, Adv. Dir., Sulphur Springs News-Telegram, TX, Sulphur Springs
Dunn, Dennis
ddunn@annistonstar.com, Circ. Dir., The Anniston Star, AL, Anniston
Dunn, Bill................................**(308) 381-5431**
bill.dunn@theindependent.com, Community Conversation Ed., The Grand Island Independent, NE, Grand Island
Dunn, Alan
alan.dunn@inl.co.za, Ed., THE DAILY NEWS, Greyville
Dunn-Rankin, Debbie **941-206-1500**
debbiedr@sun-herald.com, VP of Marketing, Charlotte Sun, FL, Charlotte Harbor
Dunn-Rankin, David ....**(941) 206-1003**
daviddr@sun-herald.com, President, Sun Coast Media Group, Inc./Sun Newspapers/Pub., Charlotte Sun, FL, Charlotte Harbor
Dunning, Ernie
ernie@dunningphoto.com, Pres., Dunning Photo Equipment, Inc., OK, Bixby
Dunning, Joe
jdunning@the-leader.com, Mng. Ed., The Leader, NY, Corning
Dunsford, Deborah
dj-king@tamu.edu, Program Coord., Texas A&M University, TX, College Station
Dunstan, Allen
adunstan@newspapersfirst.com, Vice Pres., Eastern Reg., Newspapers First, Inc., NY, New York
Dunwoody, Brian ....**ext. 30**
Prodn. Mgr., Los Alamos Monitor, NM, Los Alamos
Dupre, Crystal
cdupre@themeridianstar.com, Pub., The Meridian Star, MS, Meridian
Dupre, Bret
bdupre@theadvocate.com, Production Director, The Advocate, LA, Baton Rouge
Dupree, Jimmy ....**(919) 419-6674**
jdupree@heraldsun.com, Sports Ed., The Herald-Sun, NC, Durham
Dupree, Cheryl
cheryldk@aol.com, Ed., International Photo News, FL, West Palm Beach
Dupue, Linda
ldepue@winchestersun.com, Sec., The Winchester Sun, KY, Winchester
Duque Rengifo, Maximiliano
prensa@diariodelhuila.com, Gen. Mgr., DIARIO DEL HUILA, Huila, Neiva
Duran, Michael.........................**662-678-1548**
michael.duran@journalinc.com, Interactive Director, Journal Publishing Company, MS, Tupelo
Duray, Christopher..................**(860) 486-6141**
Univ. of Connecticut, CT, Storrs
Durazo, Armando V. ....**(915) 546-6124**
adurazo@elpasotimes.com, City/Metro Ed., El Paso Times, TX, El Paso
Durfey, Jim
ads@livent.net, Adv. Dir., The Livingston Enterprise, MT, Livingston
Durgaprasad, A.
durga_prasad9@rediff.com, Gen. Mgr., EENADU, Vijayawada, Andhra Pradesh
Durham, Cindy ....**ext. 15**
cindy@snpa.org, Asst ED, Southern Newspaper Publishers Association, GA, Atlanta
Durham, Judy
jdurham@npes.org, Dir., Commun., NPES, VA, Reston
Durkin, Margaret ....**(312) 222-3684**
mdurkin@tribune.com, Adv. Dir., Planning/Analysis, Chicago Tribune, IL, Chicago
Durkin, John
jdunkin@landonmedia.com, Acct. Exec., Landon Media Group LLC, NJ, Marlton
Durocher, Claudette..................**(603) 594-6411**
durocher@telegraph-nh.com, Editorial Page Ed., The Telegraph, NH, Hudson
Durso, Ken
kdurso@multigroup.com, Owner, Multimedia Resource Group, CA, Sunnyvale
Duso, Kim
publisher@borgernewsherald.com, Pub., Borger News-Herald, TX, Borger
Dustin, Mark
mark.dustin@latimes.com, Photo Ed., Daily Pilot, CA, Costa Mesa
Dutt, Balbir
editor@ranchiexpress.com, Ed., RANCHI EXPRESS, Ranchi, Jharkhand
Duval, Lynn
bne@fcpne.com, Admin., Free Community Papers of New England, CT, Willimantic
Dvorkin, Jeffrey **416-537-2892**
jdvorkin@newsombudsmen.org, Exec. Dir., Organization of News Ombudsmen, ON, Toronto
Dworak, Shirlee
voicecnx@aol.com, Vice Pres., Sales/Mktg., Voice Connexion, CA, Orange
Dwyer, Timothy **860/701-4379**
t.dwyer@theday.com, Executive Editor, The Day Publishing Company, CT, New London
Dye, Keith
keith.dye@trelleborg.com, CEO, Reeves Brothers, Inc., SC, Spartanburg
Dyer, Dery
ddyer@ticotimes.net, Owner/Publisher, THE TICO TIMES, San Jose
Dyke, Justin.............................**850-561-1606**
jdyke@fsview.com, Content Supervisor, FSView & Florida Flambeau, FL, Tallahassee
Dykes, Steven J.
sd@kingsportdailynews.com, Adv. Mgr., Daily News, TN, Kingsport
Dykes, David
localnews@greenvillenews.com, Farm/Agriculture Ed., The Greenville News, SC, Greenville
Dykstra, Dave ....**(250) 364-1416 ext 203**
d.dykstra@trailtimes.ca, sales, Trail Daily Times, BC, Trail
Dyslin, Amanda
adyslin@mankatofreepress.com, Features Ed., The Free Press, MN, Mankato
Dzubay, Steve..........................**(715) 425-1561**
publish@rivertowns.net, Second Vice Pres., Wisconsin Newspaper Association
Dzwonkowski, Ron ....**(313) 222-6583**
dzwonk@freepress.com, Editorial Page Ed., Detroit Free Press, MI, Detroit
DÂ£ffert, Thomas
duffert.thomas@dd-v.de, Bus. Mgr., SACHSISCHE ZEITUNG, Dresden

E

E., Jason **212-856-6387**
jklein@nnnlp.com, President & CEO, Newspaper National Network LP, NY, New York
ESPINOZA, RICHARD **816-234-7738**
respinoza@kcstar.com, EDITOR, The Olathe News, MO, Kansas City
Eade, Ron ....**(613) 596-3793**
reade@thecitizen.southam.ca, Food Ed., The Ottawa Citizen, ON, Ottawa
Eads, Andy
hpnews@h-ponline.com, Pub., Huntington Herald-Press, IN, Huntington
Eagle, Nathan ....**ext. 224**
neagle@kauaipubco.com, Asst. Ed., The Garden Island, HI, Lihue
Eagles, Dana...........................**(407) 420-5427**
deagles@orlandosentinel.com, Ed., Recruitment/Staff Devel., Orlando Sentinel, FL, Orlando
Eans, Greg ....**(252) 329-9584**

geans@reflector.com, Photography/Graphics Ed., The Daily Reflector, NC, Greenville
Earle, Rosalie ....**(304) 348-5115**
earle@wvgazette.com, Lifestyles Ed., The Charleston Gazette, Sunday Gazette-Mail, WV, Charleston
Earley, Brenda
bearley@timesgazette.com, Circ. Mgr., Times-Gazette, OH, Hillsboro
Earley, Kathy
kearley@scn1.com, HR Dir., The Beacon News, IL, Aurora
Earnest, Jon
jearnest@hanfordsentinel.com, City Ed., The Sentinel, CA, Hanford
Earnheardt, Mary Beth ....**(330) 742-3095**
Youngstown State Univ., OH, Youngstown
Easterbrook, Cathryn ....**(905) 526-3491**
Adv. Mgr., Servs., The Hamilton Spectator, ON, Hamilton
Easterly, Jim ....**(530) 852-0224**
jime@goldcountrymedia.com, Gen. Mgr., Print Div., Auburn Journal, Inc., CA, Auburn
Eastman, Augustin Edwards
redaccio@elmercurio.cl, Pres., EL MERCURIO, Santiago
Eastman, Agustin Edwards
ultimas.noticias@lun.cl, Pres., El Mercurio S.A., Santiago
Easttom, Holly ....**(405) 878-2236**
Oklahoma Baptist Univ., OK, Shawnee
Eaton, Eddie ....**(731) 989-6000**
Freed-Hardeman Univ., TN, Henderson
Eberhardt, Eric P.......................**(215) 345-3124**
eeberhardt@phillyburbs.com, Mktg. Dir., The Intelligencer, PA, Doylestown
Eberle, Terry ....**(239) 335-0280**
teberle@fortmyer.gannett.com, Exec. Ed./Vice Pres., News, The News-Press, FL, Fort Myers
Ebert, Pam ....**(202) 659-1921**
Ed., Global Horizons, DC, Washington
Ebihara, Fumisato
ecntct@nikkei.co.jp, Sapporo Head Officer, NIHON KEIZAI SHIMBUN, Sapporo, Hokkaido
Ebner, Toni
toniebner@athesia.it, Mgr., DOLOMITEN, Bolzano
Eby, John
john.eby@leaderpub.com, Mng. Ed., Dowagiac Daily News, MI, Dowagiac
Eby, John ....**(217) 351-2278**
Parkland College, IL, Champaign
Echarri, Carmen
ceuta@grupofaro.es, Chief Ed., El Faro De Ceuta, Ceuta, Cadiz
Echegaray, Laurentzi Odriozola
webnotitarde@gmail.com, Ed., Corporacin Noti-Libre C.A., Valencia, Carabobo
Echols, Tonya D. ....**(404) 572-1814**
techols@coxnews.com, Finance/Bus. Opns. Mgr., COXnet (Cox Newspapers' Wide Area Network/Cox News Service), GA, Atlanta
Eck, Chris.............................**(781) 433-6751**
Online Adv. Mgr., Taunton Daily Gazette, MA, Taunton
Eck, Christopher.......................**(781) 433-6751**
ceck@cnc.com, Online Adv. Mgr., Milford Daily News, MA, Milford
Eckenrode, Ray.........................**(814) 946-7463**
reckenrode@altoonamirror.com, Gen. Mgr., Altoona Mirror, PA, Altoona
Eckert, Michael........................**(810) 989-6264**
meckert@gannett.com, Graphics Ed., Times Herald, MI, Port Huron
Eckert, Theodor
info@vsonline.ch, Ed. in Chief, SOLOTHURNER ZEITUNG, Solothurn
Eckert, Diane ....**(866) 805-1327**
deckert@dbrmedia.com, Vice Pres., Opns., DBR Media, FL, Orlando
Eckstrom, Kevin ....**(202) 463-8777**
kevin.eckstrom@religionnews.com, Editor-in-Chief, Religion News Service, DC, Washington
Edde, Michel
administration@lorientlejour.com, Pres., L'ORIENT/LE JOUR
Eddings, Christopher A.......................**ext. 102**
chris.eddings@thedailyrecord.com , President, The Daily Record
Eddins, David ....**(901) 529-2825**
eddins@commercialappeal.com, Circ. Mgr., Metro, The Commercial Appeal, TN, Memphis
Eddy, Debbie
debbie.eddy@dodgeglobe.com, Bus. Mgr./Personnel Mgr., Dodge City Daily Globe, KS, Dodge City
Edelman, Andy ....**(215) 849-9016**
nnbfeature@aol.com, Features Ed., National News Bureau, PA, Philadelphia
Edgar, Mark ....**(214) 977-8970**
medgar@dallasnews.com, Deputy Mng. Ed., Local News, The Dallas Morning News, TX, Dallas
Edge, Malcolm **419-724-6295**
malcolm@toledoblade.com, Dir., Info Technology, The Blade, OH, Toledo
Edgren, Charlie........................**(915) 546-6121**
cedgren@elpasotimes.com, Editorial Page Ed., El Paso Times, TX, El Paso
Edinger, Lynn
lynnedinger@nna.org, Assoc. Dir., National Newspaper Association, MO, Columbia
Edlund, Ronald
ronald.edlund@folkbladt.nu, Ed. in Chief/ Adv. Mgr., VASTERBOTTENS FOLKBLAD, Umea
Edmisten, Jason.......................**(423) 359-3149**
jason.edmisten@jonesmedia.biz, CFO, Jones Media, Inc., The Greeneville Sun, TN, Greeneville
Edmiston, Mark M.
medmiston@admediapartners.com, Managing Director (Retired), AdMedia Partners, Inc., NY, New York
Edmondson, Aimee ....**(740) 597-3336**
Asst. Prof., Ohio University, OH, Athens
Edney, Hazel Trice
Hazel@nnpa.org, Interim Exec. Ed., National Newspaper Publishers Association Black Press of America, DC, Washington
Edri, George
erancourt@shani.co.il, Ed., VIATA-NOASTRA
Edshaw, Robert.........................**(902) 563-3846**
Adv. Dir., Serv., The Cape Breton Post, NS, Sydney
Edu, Martin O.
edum@gram.edu, Acting Head, Grambling State University, LA, Grambling
Edwards, Kevin
kevsports7@hotmail.com, Sports Editor, The Wayne Independent, PA, Honesdale
Edwards, Jerry.........................**(864) 882-3272**
Owner, Daily Journal/Messenger, SC, Seneca
Edwards, Robert
news@southtownstar.com, Circ. Dir., SouthtownStar, IL, Tinley Park
Edwards, Danny ....**(661) 395-4344**
Bakersfield College, CA, Bakersfield
Edwards, Jim
jime@camdenarknews.com, Mng. Ed., Camden News, AR, Camden
Edwards, Kim ....**(863) 802-7381**
kim.edwards@theledger.com, Adv. Mgr., Classified/Display, The Ledger, FL, Lakeland
Edwards, Mark..........................**(256) 304-2461**
mark.edwards@decaturdaily.com, Sports Writer, The Decatur Daily, AL, Decatur
Edwards, Tracy ....**ext. 650**
design650@svherald.com, Prodn. Mgr., Composing, Sierra Vista Herald, AZ, Sierra Vista
Edwards, Bethany.....................**(508) 634-7567**
bedwards@cnc.com, Mng. Ed., Milford Daily News, MA, Milford
Edwards, Thomas
editor@thepicayune.com, Ed., The River Cities Sunday Tribune, TX, Marble Falls
Edwards, James
jedwards@hendersondispatch.com, Pub., Daily Dispatch, NC, Henderson
Edwards, Vanya ....**(212) 727-8170**
vanya@sovfoto.com, Dir., Sovfoto/Eastfoto, NY, New York
Edwards, Bruce...........**(802) 747-6121 ext. 2220**
bruce.edwards@rutlandherald.com, Bus. Ed., Rutland Herald, VT, Rutland
Edwards, Richard
edwards@xtn.net, Mng. Ed., The Daily Post-Athenian, TN, Athens
Edwards, John
je@punchin.com, Contributing Writer, Punch In Travel, Food, Wine & Entertainment News Syndicate, NY, New York
Edwards, Jay
jedwards@dailydata.com, Adv./Mktg. Dir., The Daily Record, AR, Little Rock
Edwards, Dr. Robert M.
red@drawnandquartered.com, Pres./CEO, Drawn & Quartered, PA, Sewickley
Edwards, Nancy ....**(360) 577-2544**
nedwards@tdn.com, Regl. Ed., The Daily News, WA, Longview
Effenberger, Pat........................**651-228-5016**
peffenberger@pioneerpress.com, Commun. Mgr., St. Paul Pioneer Press, MN, Saint Paul
Egan, Thomas A.
tegan@mpival.com, Sr. Vice Pres., Management Planning, Inc., NJ, Princeton
Egenolf, James
egenolfma@aol.com, Pres., Egenolf Machine, Inc. (Egenolf Contracting & Rigging), IN, Indianapolis
Egger, Terrance C.Z...................**(216) 999-4216**
Pres./Pub., The Plain Dealer, OH, Cleveland
Egger, Jim
dsnews@europa.com, Pub., Daily Shipping News
Eggers, David.................................**ext. 234**
deggers@hickoryrecord.com, Circ. Dir., The Hickory Daily Record, NC, Hickory
Eggers, Tom...........................**(541) 957-4220**
teggers@nrtoday.com, Sports Ed., The News-Review, OR, Roseburg
Egli, Monika
m.egli@appon.ch, Adv. Mgr., APPENZELLER ZEITUNG, Herisau, Aargau
Ehrenklau, Martin
vertrieb@oz.ehrenklau.de, Proprietor, OBERHESSISCHE ZEITUNG, Alfeld
Ehret, Chad............................**(605) 394-8341**
chad.ehret@rapidcityjournal.com, IT Systems Support Mgr., Rapid City Journal, SD, Rapid City
Ehrhardt, David
dehrhardt@dariodesigns.com, Vice Pres., Dario Designs, Inc., MA, Marlboro
Ehrhardt, Phil..........................**(504) 826-3680**
pehrhardt@timespicayune.com, Vice Pres., Circ., The Times Picayune, LA, New Orleans
Ehrhardt, Philip
pehrhardt@timespicayune.com, Vice Pres./Circ. Dir., The Times Picayune, LA, New Orleans
Ehrlich, Doug...........................**201 741 8901**
dehrlich@imagezone.com, MD, Image Zone, Inc., NY, New York
Ehrmantraut, Sarah
sehrmantraut@heraldextra.com, Adv. Dir., The Daily Herald, UT, Provo
Eiasonidou, Eleni
empros@ixanthi.gr, Pub., EMPROS, Xanthi, Thrace
Eicher, Bob ....**ext. 239**
Mgr., Mgmt. Info Servs., The Daily Sentinel, CO, Grand Junction
Eichorn, Jennifer.....................**(941) 957-5239**
jennifer.eichorn@heraldtribune.com, Circ. Mgr., Retention, Sarasota Herald-Tribune, FL, Sarasota
Eickhoff, Chris........................**(678) 996-2411**
ceickhoff@eaeusa.com, CM, COO, Ewert America Electronics Ltd., GA, Marietta
Eid, Nadia.......................................**464 646**
Adv. Mgr., Chamber of Commerce & Industry, Santa Cruz de la Sierra, Sant Cruz
Eik, James ....**(509) 359-6737**
easterner.editor@gmail.com, The Easterner, WA, Cheney
Eikenberry, Kent.......................**(479) 872-5080**
keikenberry@nwaonline.net, Adv. Dir., The Morning News of Northwest Arkansas, AR, Springdale
Eilertsen, Trine
trine.eilertsen@bt.no, Editor in Chief, BERGENS TIDENDE, Bergen
Eisele, Sandy ....**(517) 768-4853**
sandye@citpat.com, Circ. Mgr., The Jackson Citizen Patriot, MI, Jackson
Eisenhut, Markus
markus.eisenhut@tages-anzeiger.ch, Ed. in Chief, TAGES-ANZEIGER ZURICH, Zurich
Eisenmenger, Anne
aeisenmenger@wickedlocal.com, Website Mgr., Taunton Daily Gazette, MA, Taunton
Eisner, Bill................................**(414) 425-8800**
bille@nonbox.com, Exec. Dir., Intermarket Agency Network, WI, Hales Corners
Eke, Ocek
oeke@elon.edu, Asst. Prof., Elon University, NC, Elon
Ekhaml, Pam...........................**(651) 796-1115**
pekhaml@pressenter.com, Adv. Acct. Exec., Stillwater Gazette, MN, Stillwater
Eklund, Bo
bo.eklund@smt.se, MD, SMALANDS-TIDNINGEN, Eksjo
El-Bardissi, Ahmed
ask@progres.net.eg, Ed. in Chief, LE PROGRES EGYPTIEN/LE PROGRES DIMANCHE, Cairo
El-Hasan, Muhammed **310-540-5511 x6175**
Business, Daily Breeze, CA, Torrance
Elbel, Jennifer..........................**(303) 750-7555**
jelbel@aurorasentinel.com, Prodn. Supvr., Aurora Sentinel, CO, Aurora
Elbel, Gus ....**(830) 625-5232**
Pressroom Supvr., New Braunfels Herald-Zeitung, TX, New Braunfels
Elchert, John...........................**(505) 564-4510**
jelchert@daily-times.com, Pub., The Daily Times, NM, Farmington
Elchert, John
advertising@timesobserver.com, Pub., Times-Observer, PA, Warren
Elder, Dave ....**(407) 420-5149**
delder@orlandosentinel.com, Circ. Mgr., Subscriber Servs., Orlando Sentinel, FL, Orlando
Eldridge, David ....**(202) 636-3214**
deldridge@washingtontimes.com, Online Mng. Ed., The Washington Times, DC, Washington
Eldridge, Dave
deldridge@winchestersun.com, Pub., The Winchester Sun, KY, Winchester
Elekes, Andras
elekes.andras@fmh.plt.hu, Ed. in Chief, FEJER MEGYEI HIRLAP, Szekesfehervar, Fejer
Elerte, Sarmite
diena@diena.lv, Ed. in Chief, DIENA, Riga
Elhart, Maurice ....**(303) 776-2244 ext. 304**
melhart@lehmancomm.com, Circ. Dir., Cor., Times-Call, CO, Longmont
Eli, Jack C.
jack.eli@angelo.edu, Prof./Head, Angelo State University, TX, San Angelo
Elias, Lieso
liesoe@dispatch.co.za, Adv. Mgr., DAILY DISPATCH, East London, Eastern Cape
Elias, Thomas ....**(310) 452-3918**
tdelias@aol.com, Author, Southern California Focus, CA, Santa Monica
Elias Valencia, Francisco
colatino@es.com.sv, Ed., CO LATINO, San Salvador
Elie, Lolis Eric
lelie@timespicayune.com, Columnist, The Times Picayune, LA, New Orleans
Elizondo, Alejandro Junco de la Vega
nacional@reforma.com.mx, Dir., REFORMA, Mexico City, Distrito Federal
Elkins, Arron ....**(202) 994-7079**
George Washington Univ., DC, Washington
Ellerbach, Susan
susan.ellerbach@tulsaworld.com, Mng. Ed., Tulsa World, OK, Tulsa
Ellinston, Randy.......................**(514) 954-2100**
Vice Pres.-Domestic Sales, AbitibiBowater Pulp and Paper Canada, Inc., QC, Montreal
Elliott, April ....**(440) 245-6901 ext. 571**
aelliott@morningjournal.com, Mng. Ed., The Morning Journal, OH, Lorain
Elliott, Claudia ....**ext. 1040**
celliott@portervillerecorder.com, Ed., The Porterville Recorder, CA, Porterville
Elliott, Nancy ....**(217) 333-8618**
Univ. of Illinois, IL, Champaign
Elliott, Donna ....**ext. 103**
delliott@batavianews.com, Mgr., Bus. Dept., The Daily News, NY, Batavia
Elliott, Darrell ....**(912) 489-9425**
delliott@statesboroherald.com, Circ. Mgr., Statesboro Herald, GA, Statesboro
Elliott, Bo

bo.elliott@irontontribune.com, Pressroom Foreman, The Ironton Tribune, OH, Ironton
Elliott, Brian
brianelliott@reviewatlas.com, Circ. Mgr., Daily Review Atlas, IL, Monmouth
Ellis, Lorraine....................................ext. 1202
lellis@keenesentinel.com, Adv. Mgr., Classified, The Keene Sentinel, NH, Keene
Ellis, Milton
publisha@standard-freeholder.southam.ca, Purchasing Agent, Standard-Freeholder, ON, Cornwall
Ellis, Gene ....(717) 871-2102
Millersville Univ. of Pennsylvania, PA, Millersville
Ellis, Sheryl
sellis@kentuckynewera.com, Bus. Mgr., Kentucky New Era, KY, Hopkinsville
Ellis, Stanley M.....................(609) 871-8000
sellis@phillyburbs.com, Vice Pres./Dir., Strategy, Burlington County Times, NJ, Willingboro
Ellis, Peter ....(904) 819-3517
peter.ellis@staugustinerecord.com, Ed., The St. Augustine Record, FL, Saint Augustine
Ellis, Elizabeth S. ....(860) 646-0500
eellis@journalinquirer.com, Pub., Journal Inquirer, CT, Manchester
Ellis, Michael..........................580-765-3311
mdellis@poncacitynews.com, Comptroller, The Ponca City News, OK, Ponca City
Ellis, Jim
jellis@hartmannews.com, Alvin Advertiser, TX, Alvin
jellis@hartmannews.com, Alvin Sun, TX, Alvin
jellis@hartmannews.com, Alvin Sun-Advertiser, TX, Alvin
jellis@hartmannews.com, Circ. Mgr., Fort Bend Herald, TX, Rosenberg
Ellison, Fred ....(901) 529-2235
ellison@commercialappeal.com, Nat'l/Major Acct. Mgr., The Commercial Appeal, TN, Memphis
Ellman, Kenneth......................(973) 896-8284
ke@kennethellman.com, Pub., Public Service News, Kenneth Ellman, NJ, Newton
Ellwanger, Woldgang
woldgang.ellwanger@ellwanger-online.de, Proprietor, NORDBAYERISCHER KURIER, Bayreuth
Elmatti, Heather......................(352) 323-3652
Lake Sumter Cmty. College, FL, Leesburg
Elooey, David
mail.ndl@ruralpress.com, Ed., THE NORTHERN DAILY LEADER
Elpers, Scott ....(316) 978-6918
Wichita State Univ., KS, Wichita
Elsinger, Raener
info@mm-zeitung.de, Mgr., Memminger Zeitung, Memmingen
Elson, Bryon
bryonelson@dbrmedia.com, Pres., DBR Media, FL, Orlando
Elson, Brad
bradelson@dbrmedia.com, Opns./Sales Dir., DBR Media, FL, Orlando
Elson, Mary ....(312) 222-4423
melson@tribune.com, Mng. Ed., TMS Specialty Products, IL, Chicago
melson@tribune.com, Mng. Ed., News/Features, Tribune Media Services, Inc., IL, Chicago
Elson, Mary ....(312) 222-4423
melson@tribune.com, Mng. Ed., TMS Specialty Products, IL, Chicago
Elstermann, Hermann
redaktion@neue-oz.de, Pub./Bus. Mgr., Neue Oz Osnabrucker Zeitung, Osnabruck
Elswick, Jon
info@whnpa.org, Treasurer, White House News Photographers Association, Inc., DC, Washington
Eltantawy, Nahed
neltante@highpoint.edu, Asst. Prof., High Point University, NC, High Point
Elton, Al
brunoungerusa@yahoo.com, Owner, Bruno Knives USA, KS, Overland Park
Elyazghi, Mohamed
ail@menara.ma, Dir., AL ITTAHID AL ICHTIRAKI, Casablanca
Emanuel, Dr. Juliet ....(212) 406-3972
Borough of Manhattan Cmty. College, NY, New York
Emberger, Edward E. ....(215) 949-4021
eemberger@calkins-media.com, Dir., Information Servs., Calkins Media, PA, Levittown
Embry, Scott ....ext. 202
sembry@tribtown.com, Adv. Dir., The Tribune, IN, Seymour
Embry, Scott
sembry@freedomenc.com, Ad director, The Sun Journal, NC, New Bern
Embry, Eugene
eembry@messenger-inquirer.com, Copy Ed., Messenger-Inquirer, KY, Owensboro
Embs, Merrilee ....(937) 864-1136
membs@tcnewsnet.com, Vice Pres., Ohio Newspaper Women's Association, OH, Enon
Emden, Christie ....(212) 450-7049
mediarelations@parade.com, Vice Pres., Commun., Parade Publications, Inc. - New York, NY, NY, New York
Emendoerfer, Gan
redaktion@ostee-zeitung.de, Ed. in Chief, Ostsee-Zeitung, Rostock
Emerling, Ron
r.emerling@ieee.org, Pres., VoCal Telecommunications, CA, Monrovia
Emery, Sherry.........................(509) 582-1557
semery@tri-cityherald.com, Graphics Ed., Tri-City Herald, WA, Kennewick
Emery, Tracey.........................(208) 735-3240
tracey.emery@lee.net, Online Ed., The Times-News, ID, Twin Falls
Emmerich, Michael
info@tiff-q.de, Circ. Mgr., Giebener Anzeiger, Giessen
Emmerich, J. Wyatt........(601) 957-1122 ext. 992
wyatt@northsidesun.com, Pres./CEO, Emmerich Newspapers Inc, MS, Jackson
Emmons, Mary Frances ....(407) 420-5671
memmons@orlandosentinel.com, Arts/Entertainment Ed., Orlando Sentinel, FL, Orlando
Emmons, David.......................(888) 237-7244
david@wbgrimes.com, Southeast/Nat'l Grps. Assoc., Grimes, W.B. & Co., FL, Fernandina
Emsley, Bruce ....(408) 278-3413
bemsley@mercurynews.com, Circ. Mgr., Single Copy, San Jose Mercury News, CA, San Jose
Enberg, Martin
martin.enberg@vlt.se, Mng. Ed., VESTMANLANDS LANS TIDNING, Vasteras
Enbom, Mary...........................(707) 553-6840
mary@timesheraldonline.com, City Ed., Vallejo Times-Herald, CA, Vallejo
Encina Undurraga, Juan Carlos
cartasdirector@mercuriovalp.cl, Sales Mgr., EL MERCURIO DE VALPARAISO, Valparaiso
Enderle, Marvin ....(704) 261-2200
menderle@theej.com, Pub., The Enquirer-Journal, NC, Monroe
Enders, Kathy ....(860) 241-3380
kenders@courant.com, Adv. Mgr., Courant Direct Sales, The Hartford Courant, CT, Hartford
Engbeers, Alex
v.doorn@wugo.wegener.nl, Ed., APELDOORNSE COURANT, Apeldoorn
Engberg, M.D., Karen M.
kengbergmd@aol.com, Self-Syndicator, Karen M. Engberg, M.D., CA, Goleta
Engbers, Alex
deventer@destentor.nl, Ed., DEVENTER DAGBLAD, Deventer, Overijssel
Engelman, Ralph ....(718) 488-1009
ralph.engelman@liu.edu, Dept. Chair, Long Island University - The Brooklyn Campus, NY, Brooklyn
Engh, Rohn ....(715) 248-3800
info@photosource.com, Pub., PhotoSource International, WI, Osceola
Engh, Jeri
DAISY@photosource.com, Editorial Dir., PhotoSource International, WI, Osceola
Engles, Matt
mengles@islandpacket.com, Audiotex Mgr., The Island Packet, SC, Bluffton
English, Brad
brad@alabamapress.org, Adv. Mgr., Alabama Press Association, AL, Birmingham
English, Brad
brad@alabamapress.org, Adv. Mgr., Alabama Newspaper Advertising Service, Inc., AL, Birmingham
English, James ....(435) 674-6246
jenglish@thespectrum.com, Adv. Dir., The Spectrum, UT, Saint George
English, Dewey ....(251) 219-5612
denglish@press-register.com, Mng. Ed., Press-Register, AL, Mobile
English, Leah
leah.english@oakpress.com, Editorial Asst., The Oakland Press, MI, Pontiac
Englram, Paul
penglram@beksystems.com, Pres., BEK Systems, Inc., IL, Oak Park
Engstrom, Margaretha
margaretha.engstrom@allehandasyd.se, Ed. in Chief, TRELLEBORGS ALLEHANDA, Trelleborg
Engstrom, Margaretha 0411 55 78 51
margaretha.engstrom@ystadsallehanda.se, Ed. in Chief, YSTADS ALLEHANDA, Ystad
Enoch, David.............(330) 747-1471 ext. 1228
denouch@vindy.com, Circ. Dir., The Vindicator, OH, Youngstown
Enrietto, John.................................ext. 241
Sports Ed., Butler Eagle, PA, Butler
Enriquez, Manuel Villanueva
publicidad@dqr.com.mx, Adv. Mgr., DIARIO DE QUINTANA ROO, Chetumal, Quintana Roo
Ensley, Ronald........................(507) 444-2367
rensley@owatonna.com, Publisher/Editor, Owatonna People's Press, MN, Owatonna
Ensley, Ron ....(507) 444-2367
rensley@owatonna.com, Sr. Vice Pres., Huckle Media, LLC, MI, Traverse City
Ensley, Debbie.......................(507) 444-2386
densley@owatonna.com, Advertising Director, Owatonna People's Press, MN, Owatonna
Entrup, Matt
mentrup@eastoregonian.com, Sports Editor, East Oregonian, OR, Pendleton
Epperly, Dianna
depperly@wapakwdn.com, Pub., Wapakoneta Daily News, OH, Wapakoneta
Epps, Richard
repps@detroitnews.com, Presentation Editor, The Detroit News, MI, Detroit
Epstein, Warren ....(719) 636-0270
warren.epstein@gazette.com, Entertainment Ed., The Gazette, CO, Colorado Springs
Epstein-Shepherd, Dr. Bee ....(831) 625-3188
drbeemm@aol.com, Mental Skills Coach/Writer, Dr. Bee Epstein-Shepherd, CA, Carmel
Erbach, Michael
michael.erbach@pnn.de, Ed. in Chief, Potsdamer Neueste Nachrichten, Potsdam
Erdner, Lisa
lerdner@printing.org, Mktg. Mgr., Printing Industries of America, PA, Sewickley
Ericksen-Mendoza, Carlos
charlie@hispaniclink.org, Pub., Hispanic Link News Service, DC, Washington
Erickson, Taag
taag_erickson@nela-usa.com, Pdct. Mgr., Web & Sheetfed, NELA, WI, River Falls
Erickson, Nicole ....(509) 359-6270
The Easterner, WA, Cheney
Erickson, Kurt.........................(217) 782-1249
kerickson@springnet1.com, Capitol Bureau Chief, The Pantagraph, IL, Bloomington
Erickson, John ....(937) 225-2266
jerickson@coxohio.com, Environmental Ed., Dayton Daily News, OH, Dayton
Erickson, Brenda
brenda.erickson@gogreenbay.com, Features Ed., The Green Bay News-Chronicle, WI, Green Bay
Erickson, John ....(937) 225-2266
jerickson@coxohio.com, Assistant Managing Editor, Content, Dayton Daily News, OH, Dayton
Erickson, Brett.......................(402) 461-7338
Hastings College, NE, Hastings
Eriksen, Charlotte ....(248) 396-1806
DePaul Univ., IL, Chicago
Eriksson, Karin
karin.eriksson@mariestadstidningen.se, Ed. in Chief, MARIESTADS-TIDNINGEN, Mariestad
Eriksson, Jan-Erik
bjorn.johansson@ingress.se, Ed. in Chief, ARBOGA TIDNING, Arboga
Erlacher, Brandon ....(574) 296-5845
berlacher@etruth.com, Publisher, The Elkhart Truth, IN, Elkhart
Ermeland, Mari
vetlandared@smt.se, Ed. in Chief, VETLANDA-POSTEN, Vetlanda
Ermen, Don
don.ermen@ott.sunpub.com, City Ed., The Ottawa Sun, ON, Ottawa
Ernesto, John M. ....(610) 371-5056
jernesto@readingeagle.com, Dir., Mktg./Promo., Reading Eagle, PA, Reading
Ernst, Charles A. S. ....(716) 649-7900 ext. 315
Hilbert College, NY, Hamburg
Ernst, Eric ....(941) 627-7584
eric.ernst@heraldtribune.com, Columnist, Charlotte, Sarasota Herald-Tribune, FL, Sarasota
Erskine, Robin.........................415-850-1268
rerskine@sfchronicle.com, Production Operations Manager, San Francisco Chronicle, CA, San Francisco
Erstad, Rolf A.
rolfae@online.no, Mgr., TROMS FOLKEBLAD, Finnsnes
Erwin, Sheila
newseditor@douglascountysentinel.com, News Ed., Douglas County Sentinel, GA, Douglasville
Erwin, Denise...................................ext. 209
derwin@dglobe.com, Circ. Mgr., The Daily Globe, MN, Worthington
Erzigkeit, Ullrich
redaktion@otz.de, Ed. in Chief, Ostthuringer Zeitung, Gera
Escabar, Mimi
mescabar@mtdemocrat.net, Features Ed., Mountain Democrat, CA, Placerville
Escalante, Faustino Felix
tribuna@tribuna.com.mx, Pres., Tribuna del Yaqui, Ciudad Obregon, Sonora
Escobedo, Frank 951-368-9913
fescobedo@pe.com, General Manager/Hispanic Media, The Press-Enterprise, CA, Riverside
Escobedo, Gilbert ....(317) 444-3555
gilbert.escobedo@indystar.com, Prodn. Dir., Printing/Packaging, The Indianapolis Star, IN, Indianapolis
Escudero Marquez, Josefina
elpuerto@publicacionesdelsur.net, Ed. in Chief, INFORMACION EL PUERTO, El Puerto De Santa Maria, Cadiz
Esis, Atilio Yanez 51-8667
Pub., La Manana, Coro, Falcon
Eskil, Rick.......................................ext. 271
reskil@wwub.com, Editorial Page Ed., Walla Walla Union-Bulletin, WA, Walla Walla
Esmaeili, Parviz
esmaeili@tehrantimes.com, Mng. Dir., TEHERAN TIMES
Espejo Gonzalez, Juan
diariojaen@interbook.net, Dir., Jaen, Jaen
Esper, Mark ....(406) 758-4442
mesper@dailyinterlake.com, Wire Ed., Daily Inter Lake, MT, Kalispell
Esper, Roberto 831-1517
libertad@metrotel.net.co, Editorial Dir., Esper Editores S.A., Barranquilla, Atlantico
Espetia, Tony..........................(305) 376-3543
tespetia@miamiherald.com, Dir., Int'l Edition, The Miami Herald, FL, Miami
Espinar Sanchez, Laura
lespinar@lanzadigital.com, MD, Lanza-Ciudad Real, Ciudad Real
Espinosa, Bobbie ....ext. 2001
bobbie.espinosa@uniontrib.com, Vice Pres., HR, The San Diego Union-Tribune, CA, San Diego
Espinosa, Maritza 427-6455
direccion@hoyperu.com.pe, Ed., Hoy, Lima
Espinoza, Josh.........................(970) 392-9327
Univ. of Northern Colorado, CO, Greeley
Esposito, Carl ....(276) 645-2552
cesposito@bristolnews.com, Regl. Pub., Bristol Herald Courier, VA, Bristol
Esposito, Martha ....(609) 871-8074
mesposito@phillyburbs.com, Mng. Ed., Burlington County Times, NJ, Willingboro

Esposito, Richard B. ....(530) 344-5055
resposito@mtdemocrat.net, Publisher, Mountain Democrat, CA, Placerville
Esposito, Carl..........................865-981-1137
carl.esposito@thedailytimes.com, Publisher, The Daily Times, TN, Maryville
Esselstein, Lisa
info@zip2.com, Contact, Zip2 Corp., CA, Mountain View
Esser, Peter
peter.esser@@mittlebayerische.de, Bus. Mgr., MITTLEBAYERISCHE ZEITUNG, Regensburg
Esser, Peter
on@donau.de, Bus. Mgr., Oberpfalzer Nachrichten, Weiden in der Oberpfalz
Esserman, Eddie ....(912) 634-6575
edwesser@bellsouth.com, Assoc., Media Services Group, Inc., FL, Jacksonville Beach
Esslinger-Kiefer, Albert
webmaster@pz-news.de, Pub./Bus. Mgr., Pforzheimer Zeitung, Pforzheim
Essman, Joseph...............................ext. 207
jessman@athensmessenger.com, Circ. Mgr., The Athens Messenger, OH, Athens
Estes, Jim
jim@wescographics.com, Pres., Wesco Graphics, CA, Tracy
Estes, Bruce..........................(607) 274-9242
bestes@ithaca.gannett.com, Mng. Ed./General Manager, The Ithaca Journal, NY, Ithaca
Estes, Robby..................................ext. 296
restes@paxtonmedia.com, Controller, The Herald-Palladium, MI, Saint Joseph
Estrada, Rich ....(209) 578-2316
restrada@modbee.com, Farm/Agriculture Writer, The Modesto Bee, CA, Modesto
Estrada Elizondo, Mario
uniomor@infosel.net.mx, Pres./Gen. Dir., La Union de Morelos, Cuernavaca, Morelos
Estrada Pinuelas, Salvador...............122-8181
peninsul@bcs1.telmex.net.mx, Pres., Diario Peninsular, La Paz, Baja California Sur
Etchevehere, Arturo R.
arturoetchevehere@eldiarioentrerios.com.ar, Prodn. Mgr., El Diario, Parana, Provincia de Entre Rios
Etienne, Larry..........................(402) 444-1408
larry.etienne@owh.com, Adv. Mgr., Classified, Omaha World-Herald, NE, Omaha
Etnyre, Geoffrey ....(202) 636-3280
getnyre@washingtontimes.com, Asst. Mng. Ed., News, The Washington Times, DC, Washington
Ettenhofer, Connie ....(906) 786-2021
cettenhofer@dailypress.net, Bus. Mgr., Daily Press, MI, Escanaba
Etwell, Hieve
layout@thechronicle.com.au, Ed., THE CHRONICLE
Eubank, Clay..........................(530) 896-7719
ceubank@chicoer.com, Circ. Dir., Chico Enterprise-Record, CA, Chico
Eugene, N/A.......................Adv. Mgr., Design
Herald-Standard, PA, Uniontown
Eure, Julian
jeure@coxnc.com, News Ed., The Daily Advance, NC, Elizabeth City
Evans, Diane..........................(330) 996-3513
devans@thebeaconjournal.com, Columnist, Bus., Akron Beacon Journal, OH, Akron
Evans, Todd
todd@rivendellmedia.com, Pres., Rivendell Media, Inc., NJ, Mountainside
Evans, Jeffrey N.
jevans@ludingtondailynews.com, Pub., Daily News, MI, Ludington
Evans, Thomas
tevans@nccu.edu, Coord., North Carolina Central University, NC, Durham
Evans, Leah...........................(252) 329-9616
levans@reflector.com, Commercial Print Sales Mgr., The Daily Reflector, NC, Greenville
Evans, Christopher....................(216) 999-6139
Editorial Writer, The Plain Dealer, OH, Cleveland
Evans, Cari............................(850) 599-2189
clevans@tallahassee.com, Retail Adv. Mgr., Tallahassee Democrat, FL, Tallahassee
Evans, Dee
devans@starcourier.com, Pub., Star-Courier, IL, Kewanee
Evans, Barry ....(856) 842-0600
barry.evans@ferag-americas.com, Vice Pres., Ferag Americas, NJ, Lawrenceville
Evans, Larry
chesstours@cs.com, Author/Owner, Chesstours, NV, Reno
Evans, Barry ....(856) 842-0600
barry.evans@ferag-americas.com, Vice Pres., WRH Marketing Americas, Inc., NJ, Lawrenceville
Evans, Wendy.........................(703) 469-3155
Dir., Recruitment Adv., The Washington Post, DC, Washington
Evans, Mary...........................(408) 920-5477
mevans@mercurynews.com, Adv. Dir., Opns., San Jose Mercury News, CA, San Jose
Evans, Daniel F.
devans@sunmulti.com, Ed., The Houston Home Journal, GA, Perry
Evans, David B........................(413) 788-1119
devans@repub.com, Controller, The Republican, MA, Springfield
Evans, Tom.............................(917) 368-8600
tevans@bankrate.com, Pres./CEO, Bankrate.com, FL, North Palm Beach
Evans, Andrea
adreps@chanute.com, Display Adv. Rep., The Chanute Tribune, KS, Chanute
Evans, Beth ....(717) 815-1312
York College of Pennsylvania, PA, York
Evans, Perry
pevans@aptas.com, CEO, Aptas, CO, Denver
Evans, Molly
molly.evans@dowjones.com, Senior VP, Advertising Sales, Dow Jones Local Media Group, NY, Middletown
Evans, Mark.............................520-573-4614
mevans@tucsoncitizen.com, Administrator/Editor, TucsonCitizen.com, AZ, Tucson
Evans, Tanna
tevans@rc.edu, Co-Editor-in-Chief, Rochester College, MI, Rochester Hills
Evavold, Ross 715-738-1606
ross.evavold@lee.net, Editor, The Chippewa Herald, WI, Chippewa Falls
Evelyn, Gwendolyn...................(767) 448-6661
General Manager / Editor, THE CHRONICLE, Roseau
Even, Jan...............................(541) 617-7849
jeven@bendbulletin.com, New Media Dir., Western Communications, Inc., OR, Bend
Even, Jan...............................(541) 617-7849
jeven@bendbulletin.com, New Media Dir., The Bulletin, OR, Bend
Evens, Robert ....(607) 432-1000 ext. 235
Adv. Mgr., Sales, The Daily Star, NY, Oneonta
Evensen, Stacy
info@bpgnet.com, Mktg./Pub. Rel., Broadcast Production Group (BPG), CA, Campbell
Evensen, Jay..........................(801) 237-2185
even@desnews.com, Editorial Page Ed., Deseret News, UT, Salt Lake City
Everett, Renee
renee.everett@eku.edu, Chair, Eastern Kentucky University, KY, Richmond
Everhart, William ....(413) 496-6271
weverhart@berkshireeagle.com, Editorial Page Ed., The Berkshire Eagle, MA, Pittsfield
Everidge, Frank
feveridge@lagrandeobserver.com, Operations. Dir., The Observer, OR, La Grande
Everidge, Frank
production@neobserver.com, Prodn. Mgr., Baker City Herald, OR, Baker City
Everly, Lori ....(570) 628-6036
leverly@republicanherald.com, Bus. Office Mgr., Republican Herald, PA, Pottsville
Everman, David ....(410) 770-4107
Special Sections Ed., The Star-Democrat, MD, Easton
Evers, Byron
bevers@mesastate.edu, Dir., Mesa State College, CO, Grand Junction
Ewell, Stephanie
stephaniea@guardonline.com, Photo Ed., Batesville Guard, AR, Batesville
Ewig, Steve S. ....(920) 453-5118
sewig@sheboygan.gannett.com, Home Delivery Mgr., The Sheboygan Press, WI, Sheboygan
Ewig, Steve
sewig@minotdailynews.com, Circ. Dir., Minot Daily News, ND, Minot
Ewing, Thomas M. ....ext. 1001
Pub., The Keene Sentinel, NH, Keene
Eymann, Kent D. ....(608) 364-9211
keymann@beloitdailynews.com, Pub., Beloit Daily News, WI, Beloit
Eymann, Kent..........................(608) 365-8811
keymann@beloitdailynews.com, Third Vice Pres., Wisconsin Newspaper Association

F

Faase, Michael........................(262) 512-8456
Mktg. Commun. Specialist, Rockwell Automation, WI, Milwaukee
Faber, Adrian
editor@expressandstar.co.uk, Ed., EXPRESS & STAR, Wolverhampton, West Midlands
Fabisiak, Lori
lori@weinrichadv.com, Pres., League of Advertising Agencies, Inc., NY, New York
Fabrizio, Rick.........................(603) 610-1193
rfabrizio@seacoastonline.com, Sunday Ed., Portsmouth Herald, NH, Portsmouth
Faddis, Jim ....(308) 381-9413
jim.faddis@theindependent.com, Mng. Ed., The Grand Island Independent, NE, Grand Island
Fadula Suhaimi, Mustafa
corpcomm@utusan.com.my, Ed., UTUSAN ZAMAN, Cheras
Fagan, Cathy...................................ext. 202
cfagan@hickoryrecord.com, Adv. Dir., The Hickory Daily Record, NC, Hickory
Fagan, David 1300 30 40 20
mailman@qnp.newsltd.com.au, Ed., THE COURIER-MAIL, Bowen Hills
Fagundes de Oliveira, Omair
paulo@bjd.com.br, Pub., BRAGANCA JORNAL DIARIO, Braganca Paulista, Sao Paulo
Fahrney, Lance ....(970) 748-2946
lfahrney@vaildaily.com, Adv. Dir., Vail Daily, CO, Vail
Faigin, Doug ....(310) 481-0401
Pres., City News Service, Inc. - Los Angeles, CA, CA, Los Angeles
Fain, Ferris H.
ffain@coxnews.com, Pres./Gen. Mgr., The Daily Sentinel, TX, Nacogdoches
Fain, Sandy ....(919) 836-5630
sfain@newsobserver.com, Local Adv. Mgr., The News & Observer, NC, Raleigh
Fair, Charles
fair@umco.edu, Chair, University of Central Missouri, MO, Warrensburg
Falcone, Michael......................(609) 272-7018
mfalcone@pressofac.com, Adv. Mgr., Nat'l/Major, The Press of Atlantic City, NJ, Pleasantville
Falduto, Anthony ....(609) 272-7038
afalduto@pressofac.com, Digital Sales Strategy Manager, The Press of Atlantic City, NJ, Pleasantville
Falk, Cheryl ....(262) 860-6715
cheryl.falk@hksystems.com, Vice Pres., Mktg., HK Systems, WI, NewBurlin
Falk, Thomas G.........................(607) 441-7244
tomfalk@thedailystar.com, Circ. Mgr., The Daily Star, NY, Oneonta
Falkenstein, Sophie ....(856) 486-2527
sfalkenstein@gannett.com, Mgr., Nat'l Adv., Courier-Post, NJ, Cherry Hill
Fallati, Donald.........................(203) 381-7000
Sr. Vice Pres., Mktg./Strategic Planning, Nuance Communications, Inc., Dictaphone Solutions, CT, Stratford
Fallding, Helen ....(204) 697-7292
Helen.Fallding@freepress.mb.ca, Asst. City Ed., Winnipeg Free Press, MB, Winnipeg
Fallesen, Leif Beck
lbf@borsen.dk, Ed. in Chief, BORSEN, Copenhagen, Sjaelland
Fallon, Greg............................(765) 231-5810
Sports Ed., The Star Press, IN, Muncie
Fallon, Jim
jfallon@itw.com, Dir., Mktg. Commun., Signode Corp., IL, Glenview
Fallon, Helen
hfallon@pointpark.edu, Chair/Prof., Point Park University, PA, Pittsburgh
Fallstrom, Robert ....(217) 421-7981
Reporter, Herald & Review, IL, Decatur
Falzone, James 978-946-2349
jfalzone@eagletribune.com, Director of Operations, The Eagle-Tribune, MA, North Andover
Fan, Zhang
info@targetnewspapers.com, CEO, TARGET FINANCIAL SERVICE, Hong Kong
Fancher, Don
dfancher@memphisdailynews.com, Adv. Mgr., The Daily News
Fanfanis, Stazros
xronos@otenet.gr, Dir., HRONOS, Komotini, Thrace
Fanlund, Paul.........................(608) 252-6210
pfanlund@madison.com, Ed., Capital Newspapers, WI, Madison
Fanshier, Brad........................(785) 832-7204
bfanshier@ljworld.com, IT Dir., The World Co.-Lawrence, Kan., Journal-World, KS, Lawrence
Fanshier, Brad..........................785-832-7204
bfanshier@ljworld.com, The World Co.-Lawrence, Kan., Journal-World, KS, Lawrence
Fantasia, Ruth.........................(518) 454-5362
rfantasia@timesunion.com, Features Ed., Times Union, NY, Albany
Fantle, David
davereel@execpc.com, Creator/Writer, Reel to Real Celebrity Profiles, WI, Bayside
Farber, Arthur D. ....(202) 636-3360
afarber@washingtontimes.com, Circ. Dir., The Washington Times Corp., DC, Washington
Fardal, Jan Inge
jani@sognavis.no, Ed., SOGN AVIS, Leikanger
Fares, Nabil E.
info@admarketintl.com, Pres./CEO, Admarket International (Div. of Marcom International, Inc.), CT, Southport
Faricy, Bob ....(615) 729-8909
bfaricy@tennessean.com, Market Devel. Dir., The Tennessean, TN, Nashville
Farina, Robert ....(920) 453-5190
rfarina@sheboygan.gannett.com, Presentation Ed., The Sheboygan Press, WI, Sheboygan
Farkas, Tim ....(413) 496-6205
tfarkas@berkshireeagle.com, Exec. Ed., The Berkshire Eagle, MA, Pittsfield
Farley, Tom.............................(262) 631-1723
tfarley@journaltimes.com, News Ed., The Journal Times, WI, Racine
Farmer, Helmuth Young
dr.jungbauer@fraenkischer-tag.de, Pub., COBURGER TAGEBLATT, Coburg
Farmer, Lisa ....(910) 230-2028
lfarmer@dunndailyrecord.com, Online Ed., The Daily Record, NC, Dunn
Farmer, Emily.........................(607) 441-7216
efarmer@thedailystar.com, Community Ed., The Daily Star, NY, Oneonta
Farmer, Paul ....(707) 425-4646 ext. 264
Sports Ed., Daily Republic, CA, Fairfield
FarnStrand, Juan
juan.farnstrand@promedia.se, Dir., VESTMANLANDS LANS TIDNING, Vasteras
Farooq, Tahir
editor_iddehad@yahoo.com, Ed., JIHAD, Peshawar, Peshawar District
Farr, Sheila............................(206) 464-2270
Arts Critic/Visual Arts Reporter, Seattle Post-Intelligencer/Seattle Times, WA, Seattle
Farr, Marsha ....(315) 268-1000
marsha@murkworks.com, Vice Pres., MurkWorks, Inc., NY, Potsdam
Farrell, Cathleen
marissa.rodriguez@vistamagazine.com, Ed. Dir., Vista - The Magazine for All Hispanics - Miami Beach, FL, FL, Miami Beach
Farrell, Bill..............................845-437-4738
farrellb@poughkee.gannett.com, Board Member, New York State Circulation Managers Association, NY, Poughkeepsie
Farrell, Bill............................(845) 437-4738
farrellb@poughkee.gannett.com, Circ. Mgr., Poughkeepsie Journal, NY, Poughkeepsie
Farrell, John
jfarrell@brodiesystem.com, Prodn. Mgr., Opns., Brodie System, Inc., NJ, Linden
Farrell, John R........................(908) 709-7550

Vice Pres., Union County College, NJ, Cranford
Farrey, Patrick
pfarrey@marketing.org, Exec. Dir., Business Marketing Association, IL, Naperville
Farros, Royal
sales@imsisoft.com, Chrmn./CEO, IMSI, CA, Novato
Farrow, Ross................(209) 369-7035 ext. 219
rossf@lodinews.com, Religion Page Ed., Lodi News-Sentinel, CA, Lodi
Farrugia, Gary..........................860/701-4202
g.farrugia@theday.com, Publisher, The Day Publishing Company, CT, New London
Fasano Mertens, Federico
redaccion@diariorepublica.com, Pres., La Republica, Montevideo
Fasbender, Anita
anita.fasbender@lee.net, Regional Marketing Manager, Independent Record, MT, Helena
Fasol, Tara............................(618) 985-3741
John A. Logan College, IL, Carterville
Fasugba, Seyi
letters@champion-newspapers.com, Ed., DAILY CHAMPION/SUNDAY CHAMPION, Ilasamaja, Mushin
Fathi, Hussan
hossan@alwatan.com.kw, Ed. in Chief, AL-WATAN
Faulk, Bitsy...........................(817) 257-6274
Texas Christian Univ., TX, Fort Worth
Faulk, James
jfaulk@times-standard.com, City Ed., Times-Standard, CA, Eureka
Faulkner, Lori
lfaulkner@digitalcourier.com, Adv. Dir., The Daily Courier, NC, Forest City
Faulkner, Vern........................(306) 765-1302
vfaulkner@paherald.sk.ca, Mng. Ed., Prince Albert Daily Herald, SK, Prince Albert
Faupel, Gunther
redaktion@rheiderland.de, Ed. in Chief, Rheiderland Zeitung, Weener
Faust, Michele........................(231) 725-6316
Circ. Supvr., Pre Print, The Muskegon Chronicle, MI, Muskegon
Faust, Ray.............................(612) 673-4899
ray.faust@startribune.com, V.P. National Sales, Star Tribune, MN, Minneapolis
Faust, Susan..........................(860) 241-6235
sfaust@courant.com, Adv. Mgr., Regl. Sales, The Hartford Courant, CT, Hartford
Favale, Susanne
sfavale@legalnews.com, Pub., Detroit Legal News
Favela, Olivia
info@iptech.com, Vice Pres., Sales/Mktg., Information Presentation Tech., CA, San Luis Obispo
Fawcett, Dave.........................(703) 878-8052
dfawcett@potomacnews.com, Sports Ed., Manassas Journal Messenger, VA, Manassas
Fawcett, Dave.........................(703) 878-8052
dfawcett@potomacnews.com, Sports Ed., News & Messenger, VA, Woodbridge
Fazioli, Cheri
gpresson@sixth-estate.com, Project Dir., Medforum, FL, Clearwater
Fazzone, Mark...............................ext. 1010
mfazzone@portervillerecorder.com, Editor and Publisher, The Porterville Recorder, CA, Porterville
Feasey, Mike
willowsix@aol.com, Pres., WillowSix, Inc., CA, San Clemente
Feather, Carl...................................ext. 297
Lifestyle Ed., Star Beacon, OH, Ashtabula
Febres, Luis Natera.............................23-4170
info@correodelcaroni.com, Pres./Gen. Mgr., Editorial Roderick, Puerto Ordaz, Bolivar
Fechtner, Bonnie
bonnie.fechtner@wnanews.com, Dir., Member Servs., Wisconsin Newspaper Association
Fechtner, Bonnie...............................ext. 12
bonnie.fechtner@wnanews.com, Member Servs. Mgr., Wisconsin Newspaper Association, WI, Madison
Fecioru, Narcisa
narcisa.fecioru@desteptarea.ro, Mgr., DESTEPTAREA, Bacau, Bacau
Fedder, Denise.............(330) 305-6960 ext. 714
doates@prestilgence.com, Dir., Mktg., Presteligence, OH, North Canton
Fedesco, Frederick..................(413) 788-1191
ffedesco@repub.com, Vice Pres./Gen. Mgr., The Republican, MA, Springfield
Fedoroff, Vince.......................(867) 668-2060
vince@whitehorsestar.com, Photo Ed., Whitehorse Star, YT, Whitehorse
Fedrigon, Dan
inbox@beckart.com, Mgr., Mktg./Sales, Beckart Environmental, Inc., WI, Kenosha
Fedrigon, Thomas M........(262) 656-7680 ext. 115
tfedrigon@beckart.com, Pres., Beckart Environmental, Inc., WI, Kenosha
Fee, John..............................(973) 210-6393
jfee@lds.com, Vice Pres., Sales, Logical Design Solutions, NJ, Florham Park
Fee, Frank..............................(919) 962-4071
Assoc. Prof., University of North Carolina, NC, Chapel Hill
Feeley, Michael........................(717) 255-8228
mfeeley@patriot-news.com, Asst. Managing Ed., The Patriot-News, PA, Mechanicsburg
Feeney, Richard S....................(860) 241-6321
rfeeney@courant.com, Vice Pres./CFO, The Hartford Courant, CT, Hartford
Feeney, Tom...........................(352) 563-3275
tfeeney@chronicleonline.com, Prodn. Mgr., Citrus County Chronicle, FL, Crystal River
Feeney, Joe............................(336) 888-3537
jfeeney@hpe.com, City Ed., High Point Enterprise, NC, High Point
Feisal, Marcia
mfeisal@snu.edu, Yearbook, Southern Nazarene University, OK, Bethany
Feld, Karen.............................(202) 337-2044
karen@karenfeld.com, Columnist/Owner, Capital Connections, DC, Washington
Feldman, Steve
stevef@mlog.com, Exec. Vice Pres., Worldwide Sales, Microlog Corp., MD, Gaithersburg
Feldman, Jeremy
classified@jamestownsun.com, Circ. Mgr., The Jamestown Sun, ND, Jamestown
Felix, Gina.............................(918) 225-3333
ads@cushingdaily.com, Adv. Mgr., Cushing Daily Citizen, OK, Cushing
Fellers, Kent
arrow@arrowprintco.com, Pres., Arrow Printing Co., KS, Salina
Fellman, Peter
peter.fellman@di.se, Ed. in Chief, DAGENS INDUSTRI, Stockholm
Fellone, Frank........................(501) 378-3475
frank-fallone@adg.ardemgaz.com, Deputy Ed., Arkansas Democrat-Gazette, AR, Little Rock
Felten, Ralph
rfelten@asltg2.com, Mgr., Atlas Specialty Lighting, FL, Tampa
Feltus, Vallerie
vfeltus@skagitpublishing.com, Adv. Dir., Skagit Valley Herald, WA, Mount Vernon
Fender, Mike...........................(317) 444-6444
mike.fender@indystar.com, Photography Dir., The Indianapolis Star, IN, Indianapolis
Fenger, Darin
dfenger@yumasun.com, Features Editor, Yuma Sun, AZ, Yuma
Fennell, Dan...........................(724) 223-2633
dfennell@observer-reporter.com, Systems Mgr., Observer-Reporter, PA, Washington
Fennell, Peter
pfennell@times-standard.com, Circ./Mktg. Dir., Times-Standard, CA, Eureka
Fennerssy, David.......................412-664-9161
dfennessy@tribweb.com, News Editor, The Daily News, PA, McKeesport
Fenske, Bruce.............(507) 359-2911 ext. 130
bfenske@nujournal.com, Pub., The Journal, MN, New Ulm
Fenstermaker, Susan
scf@nscs.fast.net, Controller, Software Consulting Services, LLC, PA, Nazareth
Fenton, Lois..........................(914-698-0721)
lois.fenton@prodigy.net, Columnist/Advice, Men's Business & Social Dress Consultant/Men's Personal Shopper, Blogger, Male Call, NY, Mamaroneck
Fenton, Kevin
kfenton@reviewonline.com, Circ. Mgr., The Review, OH, East Liverpool
Fenton, Heidi..........................(989) 774-4343
Central Michigan Univ., MI, Mount Pleasant
Feorino, Lu.............................(413) 788-1216
lfeorino@repub.com, City Ed., Night, The Republican, MA, Springfield
Ference, Jim...........................(724) 684-2638
jference@tribweb.com, Chief Photographer, The Valley Independent, PA, Monessen
Ferguson, Anthony
aferguson@cfal.com, Pres., THE NASSAU GUARDIAN, Nassau
Ferguson, Carole.....................(530) 225-8232
cferguson@redding.com, Mng. Ed., Record Searchlight, CA, Redding
Ferguson, Mike........................(702) 383-0211
fergy@stephensmedia.com, Chief Executive Officer, Stephens Media LLC, NV, Las Vegas
Ferguson, Carol
cferguson@heraldbanner.com, Features Ed., Herald-Banner Publications, TX, Greenville
Ferguson, Jerry
jferguson@theintermountain.com, Circ. Mgr., The Inter-Mountain, WV, Elkins
Ferguson, Sharon C...................(203) 330-6212
sferguson@ctpost.com, Mgr., HR, Connecticut Post, CT, Bridgeport
Ferguson, Denise P.
denise.ferguson@indwes.edu, Chair, Indiana Wesleyan University, IN, Marion
Ferguson, Jim..........................(419) 521-7286
jferguson@nncogannett.com, Prodn. Dir., News Journal, OH, Mansfield
Ferko, Katrena
katrena@delo.si, Mktg. Mgr., DELO, Ljubljana
Ferlazzo, Don
dferlazzo@nynpa.com, Events Coord., New York News Publishers Association, NY, Albany
Fernandes, Jose Manuel
publico@publico.pt, Dir., PUBLICO, Lisbon
Fernandez, Bernie.....................253-597-8504
bfernandez@theolympian.com, Major Accounts Rep, The Olympian, WA, Olympia
Fernandez, Gabriel
gfernandez@adradio.ad, Ed., DIARI D'ANDORRA, Andorra la Vella
Fernandez, Lynne.....................(209) 588-4573
lfernandez@uniondemocrat.com, Bus. Mgr., The Union Democrat, CA, Sonora
Fernandez, Paul
redaccaocm@mail.telepac.pt, Chrmn., CORREIO DA MANHA, Lisbon
Fernandez, Lydia......................(585) 258-2292
lfernand@democratandchronicle.com, Asst. Features Ed., Democrat and Chronicle.com, NY, Rochester
Fernandez, Phil........................(828) 232-5839
pfernand@citizen-times.com, Mng. Ed., The Asheville Citizen-Times, NC, Asheville
Fernandez Cabeza de Vaca, Leopoldo
info@teideradio.com, Dir., Diario De Avisos, Santa Cruz de Tenerife
Fernandez Lasalvia, Fernando
accion@internet.com.uv, Pres., Accion, Mercedes, Soriano
Fernandez Pichardo, Benjamin
el_imparcial@infosel.net.mx, Dir., EL IMPARCIAL, Oaxaca, Oaxaca
Fernandez Pichardo, Benjamin
imparoax@prodigy.net.mx, Pres., EL IMPARCIAL DEL ISTMO, Salina Cruz, Oaxaca
Ferrand Bullock, Cathy..............(435) 797-1412
Assoc. Prof., Utah State University, UT, Logan
Ferrari, Jerrod.........................203-354-1044
Co-Managing Editor, The Hour Publishing Co., CT, Norwalk
Ferraz, Benedito A..........................361-5838
Pres., Jornal do Dia, Cuiaba, Mato Grosso
Ferre, Maria Eugenia
meferre@elnuevodia.com, Pres., EL NUEVO DIA, PR, San Juan
Ferreira, Izabel M...........................273-1370
Ed., Comunicacao Jornal, Sumare, Sao Paulo
Ferreira Diniz, Maria E.....................222-8244
Pres., Jornal do Piaui, Teresina, Piaui
Ferreira Levy, Luiz Fernando.............5547-3133
red@gazetamercantil.com.br, Pres., GAZETA MERCANTIL, Sao Paulo
Ferreiro Regueiro, Manuel
director@elidealgallego.com, MD, El Ideal Gallego, Mesoiro, La Coruna
Ferrell, Jennifer.......................(202) 334-5042
ferrelljf@washpost.com, Sales Rep., North America, The Washington Post Writers Group, DC, Washington
Ferriss, Susan...............................55497329
Mexico City Correspondent, Cox Newspapers, Inc. - Mexico City, Mexico, Mexico City
Ferro, David
david.ferro@hillsdale.net, Pub., Hillsdale Daily News, MI, Hillsdale
Ferro, David R................(517) 278-2318 ext. 28
dferro@thedailyreporter.com, Adv. Dir., The Daily Reporter, MI, Coldwater
Ferrucci, Patrick......................(203) 789-5678
news@nhregister.com, Entertainment Ed., New Haven Register, CT, New Haven
Ferry, Michael..........................(216) 999-6572
Asst. Circ. Dir., Retail Sales/Mktg., The Plain Dealer, OH, Cleveland
Ferson, Jerome
jerome.ferson@theledger.com, Pub./Pres., The Ledger, FL, Lakeland
Ferstel, Vicki...........................(225) 388-0641
vferstel@theadvocate.com, Metro Ed., The Advocate, LA, Baton Rouge
Fettin, Carol............................(308) 233-9727
Religion Ed., Kearney Hub, NE, Kearney
Feulner, Brian...............(209) 369-7035 ext. 276
brianf@lodinews.com, Photo Ed., Lodi News-Sentinel, CA, Lodi
Few, Jenel..............................(912) 652-0345
jenel.few@savannah.com, Educ. Reporter, Savannah Morning News, GA, Savannah
Fey, J.T..................................605-886-6901
Online Mgr., Watertown Public Opinion, SD, Watertown
Fibich, Linda...........................(202) 383-7850
linda.fibich@newhouse.com, Bureau Chief/Ed., Newhouse News Service, DC, Washington
Ficcara, Mark
ptnews@presstelegram.com, Pub., Press-Telegram, CA, Long Beach
Fideles, Fabiano..............................212-2900
otriang@triang.com.br, Pres., O Triangulo, Uberlandia, Minas Gerais
Fidler, Eric J.....................................ext. 247
Southern Illinois Univ., IL, Carbondale
Fiegle, Doug............................(716) 773-7634
sales@nrdinc.com, Pres./CEO, NRD LLC, NY, Grand Island
Field, Irene.............................(850) 522-5111
ifield@pcnh.com, Regl. Classified Dir., The News Herald, FL, Panama City
Field, Malena...........................(915) 546-6254
mfield@elpasotimes.com, Dir., HR, El Paso Times, TX, El Paso
Fielder, Jeff
sports@starherald.com, Sports Ed., Star-Herald, NE, Scottsbluff
Fields, Nell
(510) 465-1576, Pub., The Inter-City Express
Fields, Amy.............................(815) 937-3353
amyf@daily-journal.com, Mktg. Mgr., The Daily Journal, IL, Kankakee
Fields, Reginald.......................(614) 228-8200
Columbus Bureau Chief, The Plain Dealer, OH, Cleveland
Fields, Ron
rfields@dailynews.net, Mng. Ed., The Hays Daily News, KS, Hays
Figueroa Ewachyna, Esteban
editora@correo.chiapas.com, Pres., LA REPUBLICA EN CHIAPAS, Tuxtla Gutierrez, Chiapas
Fike, David.............................(410) 770-4040
stardem@chespub.com, Gen. Mgr., The Star-Democrat, MD, Easton
Fike, Kevin A.........................(410) 770-4066
Mktg. Mgr., The Star-Democrat, MD, Easton
Filardo, Francisco............................33-0394
Pres., LAS NOTICIAS DE COJEDES, San Carlos, Cojedes
Filho, Americo Martins......................221-1616
Pres., Jornal Do Norte, Montes Claros, Minas Gerais
Filip, Joe...............................(412) 320-7831
jfilip@tribweb.com, Night City Ed., Tribune-Review, PA, Pittsburgh
Filip, Gheorghe
etl@starnets.ro, Ed. in Chief, TELEORMANUL LIBER, Alexandria, Teleorman

Filipek, Kori..........................(562) 938-4284
Long Beach City College, CA, Long Beach
Filippi, Andrea
direzione@messaggeroveneto.it, Dir., MESSAGGERO VENETO, Udine
Filippini, Anibal
nuevaera@infovia.com.ar, Ed., Nueva Era, Tandil, Provincia de Buenos Aires
Filizola Gonzalez, Francisco
redaccion@eldiariodevictoria.com.mx, Ed., El Diario, Ciudad Victoria, Tamaulipas
Fillmore, Ken
kenf@kpcnews.net, Sports Ed., Herald-Republican, IN, Angola
Finch, Bill..........................(251) 434-8535
bfinch@mobileregister.com, Growth/Environmental Ed., Press-Register, AL, Mobile
Finch, Tony..........................(662) 720-7304
Northeast Mississippi Cmty. College, MS, Booneville
Finder, Christian
finder@ppimedia.de, Sales Mgr., ppi Media GmbH, Hamburg
Findlay, Ted
efindlay@hotmail.com, Pres., The Findlay Group, KS, Overland Park
Fine, Susan..........................(212) 293-8602
sfine@unitedmedia.com, Mgr., Sales/Admin., United Media, OH, Cincinnati
Fingeroot, Randy..........................(850) 599-2141
rfingeroot@tallahassee.com, Prepress, Postpress, IT Mgr, Tallahassee Democrat, FL, Tallahassee
Fink, Beverly..........................(419) 739-3501
circulation@wapakwdn.com, Circ. Mgr., Wapakoneta Daily News, OH, Wapakoneta
Fink, Christine..........................(256) 740-5726
christine.fink@timesdaily.co, Night Ed., TimesDaily, AL, Florence
Fink, Tom..........................(918) 341-0220
County Ed., The Claremore Daily Progress, OK, Claremore
Finkelstein, Gary..........................(508) 427-4057
gfinkelstein@enterprisenews.com, Editorial Page Ed., The Enterprise, MA, Randolph
Finley, Paris..........................(413) 585-5363
ismgr@gazettenet.com, Info Servs. Mgr., Daily Hampshire Gazette, MA, Northampton
Finley, Nicole
nicole.finley@gwinnettdailypost.com, Graphics Ed., Gwinnette Daily Post, GA, Lawrenceville
Finley, Laurie..........................(204) 697-7164
laurie.finley@freepress.mb.ca, Adv. Dir., Sales/Mktg., Winnipeg Free Press, MB, Winnipeg
Finley, John..........................(703) 878-8023
jfinley@potomacnews.com, Circ. Mgr., Home Delivery, News & Messenger, VA, Woodbridge
Finley, Nolan
nfinley@detroitnews.com, Editorial Page Editor, The Detroit News, MI, Detroit
Finn, Jeff
jfinn@esoft.com, CEO/Pres., eSoft, CO, Broomfield
Finn, Brenda
bfinn@mcgown.com, Vice Pres., Sales, McGown Intermac/Publicitas North America, Inc., BC, Vancouver
Finn, Regis E.
extratec@starpower.com, Pres., Extratec Corp., MD, Rockville
Finney, Mark..........................(719) 587-7494
Adams State College, CO, Alamosa
Fioravanti, Federico..........................52-731
Pres., CORRIERE DELL'UMBRIA, Perugia
Firestone, Joanna
jfirestone@detroitnews.com, Business Editor, The Detroit News, MI, Detroit
Fischer, Werner
redaktion@faz.de, Distr. Mgr., Frankfurter Allgemeine, Frankfurt am Main
Fischer, George..........................(805) 739-2234
Prodn. Mgr., The Lompoc Record, CA, Lompoc
Fischer, Thomas
Kreisblatt@t-online.de, Ed., Gandersheimer Kreisblatt, Bad Gandersheim
Fischer, Charles
cfischer@roswell-record.com, Pub., Roswell Daily Record, NM, Roswell
Fischer, Peter
redaktion@emderzeitung.de, Bus. Mgr., EMDER ZEITUNG, Emden
Fischer, Alan..........................(734) 426-4646
fischer@photosys.com, Pres., Photo Systems, Inc., MI, Dexter
Fischer, James
jimf@saxmayercorp.com, Vice Pres., Engineering/Mfg., Saxmayer Corp., MI, Blissfield
Fischer, Gregory..........................(631) 727-9639
perfect@microperfect.com, Mgr., Micro Perfect Corp., NY, Calverton
Fischer-Huettner, Suzanne
suzanne.huettner@thedailyrecord.com, Publisher, The Daily Record
Fischman, Gerald..........................ext. 5917
gfischman@capitalgazette.com, Editorial Page Ed., The Capital, MD, Annapolis
Fish, Eric
eric@patentdoc.com, Registered Patent Attorney, Stoneman Law Offices Ltd., AZ, Phoenix
Fisher, Deborah..........................(615) 664-2156
dfisher@tennessean.com, Asst. Mng. Ed., Business, The Tennessean, TN, Nashville
Fisher, Scott..........................(717) 771-2049
sfisher@ydr.com, Editorial Ed., York Daily Record/York Sunday News, PA, York
Fisher, Robert
bob@ecdailynews.com, Mng. Ed., Elk City Daily News, OK, Elk City
Fisher, Sara..........................405.238.6464
sfisher@pvdemocrat.com, Advertising Account Executive, Pauls Valley Democrat, OK, Pauls Valley
Fisher, Grace Simmons..........................601-961-7250
gsimmons@jackson.gannett.com, Metro Ed., The Clarion-Ledger, MS, Jackson
Fisher, Jim..........................(505) 277-5656
Univ. of New Mexico, NM, Albuquerque
Fisher, Coreen
cfisher@greenvillenews.com, Adv. Vice Pres./Dir., The Greenville News, SC, Greenville
Fisher, Loren..........................(732) 565-7251
lfisher@mycentraljersey.com, Digital Ed., Courier News, NJ, Somerville
Fisher, Jamie..........................620-241-2422
circulation@mcphersonsentinel.com, Circulation Manager, McPherson Sentinel, KS, McPherson
Fisher, Marsh
marsh@ideafisher.com, CEO, IdeaFisher Systems, Inc., CA, Lake Forest
Fisher, Gordon..........................416-.442-2905
gfisher@nationalpost.com, President, National Post, ON, Toronto
Fishman, Neil
neilf@holdcom.com, Pres., Holdcom, NJ, Glen Rock
Fissolo, Maureen..........................(707) 427-6995
Design Ed., Daily Republic, CA, Fairfield
FitzSimmons, Cal..........................(360) 577-2579
cfitzsimmons@tdn.com, Mng. Ed., The Daily News, WA, Longview
Fitzgerald, Joe
jfitzgerald@theguardsman.com, Editor-in-chief, City College of San Francisco, CA, San Francisco
Fitzgerald, Mark
mfitzgerald@editorandpublisher.com, Editor, Editor & Publisher Magazine, IL, Chicago
Fitzgerald, Todd..........................(508) 626-3983
Opns. Dir., Distr./Post Press, Metrowest Daily News, MA, Framingham
Fitzgerald, Shane..........................(361) 886-3681
Ed., Corpus Christi Caller-Times, TX, Corpus Christi
Fitzhenry, Lester..........................(775) 881-1235
lfitzhenry@sierranevadamedia.com, Circ. Mgr., Nevada Appeal, NV, Carson City
Fitzhenry, Jim..........................(920) 426-6672
Mng. Ed., Oshkosh Northwestern, WI, Oshkosh
Fitzpatrick, John
johnf@robertstock.com, Vice Pres., Sales, Robertstock/Classicstock, PA, Philadelphia
Fitzsimmons, Robert
robert_fitzsimmons@link.freedom.com, Bus. Mgr., Daily Press, CA, Victorville
Fitzsimons, Michael
mfitz@desknetinc.com, Co-CEO, DeskNet, Inc., NJ, Jersey City
Fivian, Christine
redaktion@zuonline.ch, Ed. in Chief, ZURCHER UNTERLANDER, Dielsdorf
Fladung, Bonnie
info@monacosys.com, Dir.-Mktg., Monaco Systems, Inc., MA, Andover
Fladung, Thomas..........................(216) 999-4068
Managing Editor, The Plain Dealer, OH, Cleveland
Flagg, James..........................ext. 3547
letters@express-times.com, Editorial Page Ed., The Express-Times, PA, Easton
Flagg, Linda..........................(603) 352-1234 ext. 1601
lflagg@keenesentinel.com, Bus. Mgr., The Keene Sentinel, NH, Keene
Flagstad, Tim..........................(208) 239-3124
Sports Ed., Idaho State Journal, ID, Pocatello
Flaherty, Ed..........................(603) 610-1182
eflaherty@seacoastonline.com, Sports Ed., Portsmouth Herald, NH, Portsmouth
Flaherty, Sharon..........................(978) 970-4623
sflaherty@lowellsun.com, Editorial Page Ed., The Sun, MA, Lowell
Flaherty, Alan
alanflaherty@fuse.net, Principal, ComPlan Associates, OH, Cincinnati
Flaig, Michael..........................860/701/4234
m.flaig@theday.com, Commercial Print Sales Manager, The Day Publishing Company, CT, New London
Flanagan, Michael..........................(617) 929-2137
m_flanagan@globe.com, Adv. Dir., Cross Media Sales, The Boston Globe, MA, Boston
Flanagan, Mark..........................(508) 236-0331
opinion@thesunchronicle.com, Editorial Page Ed., The Sun Chronicle, MA, Attleboro
Flanagan, Terry..........................(630) 388-6901
tflanagan@copia.com, Vice Pres., Engineering, Copia International Ltd., IL, Wheaton
Flanigan, Meg
meg@accufastpps.com, Mgr., ACCUFAST Package Printing Systems, NY, Troy
Flannery, Mary Ann
mflannery@jcu.edu, Chair/Assoc. Prof., John Carroll University, OH, University Heights
Flannery, Dan..........................(920) 993-7104 ext. 282
dflannery@appleton.gannett.com, Exec. Ed., The Post-Crescent, WI, Appleton
Flanzraich, Annie..........................(530) 542-8006
aflanz@tahoedailytribune.com, Ed., Tahoe Daily Tribune, CA, South Lake Tahoe
Flatt, Steve..........................(309) 757-4911
sflatt@qconline.com, Mgr., Promo./Special Projects, The Rock Island Argus, IL, Rock Island
Flatt, Steve..........................(309) 757-4911
sflatt@qconline.com, Dir., Promos./Special Projects, The Dispatch, IL, Moline
Flattau, Edward..........................(202) 966-8636
edflattau@msn.com, Pres., Global Horizons, DC, Washington
Flaum, Randy
rflaum@yorkdispatch.com, Asst. Mng. Ed., Visuals, The York Dispatch, PA, York
Flavell, John
jflavell@dailyindependent.com, Photo Dept. Mgr., The Daily Independent, KY, Ashland
Fleck, Robert..........................(312) 222-6691
rfleck@tribune.com, Adv. Sr. Vice Pres., Chicago Tribune, IL, Chicago
Fleet, William..........................(559) 441-6060
publisher@fresnobee.com, Pres./Pub., The Fresno Bee, CA, Fresno
Fleet, Bob..........................(405) 523-2000
bob.fleet@af-group.com, Div. Mktg. Mgr., American Fidelity Assurance Co., OK, Oklahoma City
Fleishman, Paul..........................(631) 843-4097
Vice Pres., Mktg., Newsday, NY, Melville
Fleisig, Dr. Wayne..........................(205) 969-2963
wfleisig@hotmail.com, Writer/Self-Syndicator, Healthy Minds, AL, Birmingham
Fleming, Christina..........................416-947-3170
christina.fleming@sunmedia.ca, Executive Assistant to the Publisher, The Toronto Sun, ON, Toronto
Fleming, Mike..........................(419) 521-7297
mfleming@nncogannett.com, Circ. Opns. Mgr., News Journal, OH, Mansfield
Fleming, Mike..........................(419) 521-7297
mfleming@nncogannett.com, Circ. Mgr., The Marion Star, OH, Marion
Fleming, Carl..........................(902) 421-5811
cfleming@hfxnews.ca, Sports Ed., The Daily News, NS, Dartmouth
Flemington, Jan..........................(800) 255-6734
jflemington@amuniversal.com, Sales Admin., Eastern USA/Canada, Universal Uclick, MO, Kansas City
Flemmer, Kevin
kflemmer@mitchellrepublic.com, Adv. Mgr., The Daily Republic, SD, Mitchell
Flemming, Paul..........................(850) 671-6550
pflemming@tallahassee.com, State Editor, Tallahassee Democrat, FL, Tallahassee
Fletcher, Lynne..........................ext. 114
Prodn. Mgr., St. Albans Messenger, VT, Saint Albans
Fletcher, Cheryl..........................661-267-4146
cfletcher@avpress.com, Marketing Director, Antelope Valley Press, CA, Palmdale
Fletcher, Stephen..........................(251) 633-4300
Pres./COO, Konica Minolta Printing Solutions, AL, Mobile
Fletcher, Gloria..........................(405) 880-6153
Regional VP - Midwest, GateHouse Media Inc., NY, Fairport
Fletcher, Carlton..........................229-888-9360
carlton.fletcher@albanyherald.com, Metro Editor, The Albany Herald, GA, Albany
Fletcher, Chris
cfletcher@c-dh.net, Ed., Columbia Daily Herald, TN, Columbia
Fletcher, Cheryl..........................661-267-4146
cfletcher@avpress.com, Marketing Director, Antelope Valley Press, CA, Palmdale
Flick, Bill..........................(309) 820-3221
flick@pantagraph.com, Columnist/Online Producer, The Pantagraph, IL, Bloomington
Flikke, Gunnar
redaksjonen.faxmottak@adresseavisen.no, Ed., ADRESSEAVISEN, Trondheim
Flint, Connie..........................ext. 12
officemgr@themonroetimes.com, Office Mgr., The Monroe Times, WI, Monroe
Flippen, Charles
cflippen@towson.edu, Chair, Towson University, MD, Towson
Flippin, William S...........................(610) 371-5000
wflippin@readingeagle.com, Pres./Pub., Reading Eagle, PA, Reading
Flippin, James C...........................(610) 371-5202
jflippin@readingeagle.com, Vice Pres./Sec., Reading Eagle, PA, Reading
Flom, Erik
erik@elfworks.com, Owner, ELFWorks 3D Construction Co., CA, Alameda
Flood, Pat..........................ext. 296
Photo Dept. Mgr., The Reporter, WI, Fond du Lac
Flores, Carlos Roberto
tribuna@latribuna.hn, Pres., LA TRIBUNA, Tegucigalpa
Flores, Eric
sports@alamosanews.com, Sports Editor, The Valley Courier, CO, Alamosa
Flores, Roberto..........................422-112
el-norte@el-norte.com.ar, Gen. Mgr., El Norte, San Nicolas, Provincia de Buenos Aires
Flores Acosta, Gustavo
publicidad@noticiasdelsoldelalaguna.com.mx, Dir., NOTICIAS DEL SOL DE LA LAGUNA, Torreon, Coahuila
Florez, Sergio..........................(212) 556-1658
florez@nytimes.com, Managing Editor/Images, NYT Graphics Service, NY, New York
florez@nytimes.com, Dir., Photos/Graphics News Servs., NYT Photo Service, NY, New York
Florman, Katherine..........................(719) 636-0308
kflorman@freedom.com, Regional Director HR, The Gazette, CO, Colorado Springs
Floss, Dennis..........................(585) 258-2242
dfloss@democratandchronicle.com, Gen. Mgr., Specialty Publications, Democrat and Chronicle.com, NY, Rochester
Floto, Barbara
bfloto@owensoundsuntimes.com, Adv. Supvr., Classified, The Sun Times, ON, Owen Sound
Flowers, Rick
rflowers@evtrib.com, Publisher, East Valley

Tribune, AZ, Tempe
Flowers, Gloria
gloriaflowers@wvpress.org, Exec. Dir., West Virginia Press Association, Inc., WV, Charleston
Fluker, Cassandra....................(313) 845-9838
Henry Ford Cmty. College, MI, Dearborn
Flynn, Kris............................(626) 304-7750
loadcomm@earthlink.net, Dir., Mktg./Sales, LO/AD Communications, CA, Pasadena
Flynn, Robert
rflynn@ct-innovations.com, Pres., C-T Innovations, KY, Louisville
Flynn, Adrianne
aflynn@jmail.umd.edu, Sec., Regional Reporters Association, DC, Washington
Flyte, Rebecca........................(814) 444-5900
beckyf@dailyamerican.com, Data Processing Mgr., Daily American, PA, Somerset
Flyvholm, Mogens
mf@nortvest.dk, Ed. in Chief, HOLBAEK AMTS VENSTREBLAD, Holbaek, Sjaelland
Fobes, Jon ....(216) 999-4877
Night Photo Editor, The Plain Dealer, OH, Cleveland
Fockler, Ingo
ingo.fockler@thevillagesmedia.com, Prodn. Mgr., Opns., The Villages Daily Sun, FL, The Villages
Foderaro, Jane
equinox30@hotmail.com, Fairleigh Dickinson Univ., NJ, Teaneck
Foges, Ernest
management@amigoe.com, Dir., AMIGOE DI CURACAO, Willemstad, Curacao
Foglesong, Sam W....................(814) 444-5915
samf@dailyamerican.com, Circ. Mgr., Daily American, PA, Somerset
Foiles, Roland ....ext. 250
rfoiles@msmgmt.com, Prodn. Mgr., La Grange Daily News, GA, LaGrange
Folan, Thomas P......................(617) 929-7176
t_folan@globe.com, Adv. Dir., Serv., The Boston Globe, MA, Boston
Foley, Larry
lfoley@ledger-enquirer.com, News Ed., Columbus Ledger-Enquirer, GA, Columbus
Foley, Mark
sales@telequest.com, Sr. Vice Pres., Sales/Mktg., TeleQuest, TX, Arlington
Foley, Pat.............................(814) 444-5910
patf@dailyamerican.com, Adv. Mgr., Classified, Daily American, PA, Somerset
Foley, Marietta ....(616) 222-5576
mfoley@grpress.com, Mgr., HR, The Grand Rapids Press, MI, Grand Rapids
Fondriest, Steve
sfondriest@bob-weber.com, Mgr., Prodn., Bob Weber, Inc., OH, Cleveland
Fong, David
fong@tdnpublishing.com, Exec. Ed., Troy Daily News, OH, Troy
Fong, Katherine ....(408) 278-3448
kfong@mercurynews.com, Deputy Mng. Ed., Convergence, San Jose Mercury News, CA, San Jose
Fonseca, Edgar
efonseca@aldia.co.cr, Dir., AL DIA, San Jose
Fontenot, Amy ....(970) 824-2600
Circ. Mgr., Craig Daily Press, CO, Craig
Fonticiella, Nelson
nfonticiella@herald-leader.com, Circ. Dir., Lexington Herald-Leader, KY, Lexington
Foos, Kim
kimfoos@thecourier.com, Circ. Mgr., The Courier, OH, Findlay
Foote, Joe
jfoote@ou.edu, Dean/Prof., University of Oklahoma, OK, Norman
Foran, Mike
mforan@arcinternational.com, Pres., ARC International, NC, Charlotte
Forberg, Rick
info@stmi.com, Vice Pres., Mktg., STM Networks, CA, Irvine
Forbes, Sylvia 660-248-3455
sylvia@forbesfreelance.com, Administrative Assistant, Midwest Travel Writers Association, MO, Fayette
Ford, Pam ....(810) 989-6212
pamford@porthuro.gannett.com, Sr. Adv. Sales Mgr., Times Herald, MI, Port Huron
Ford, Amber...........................(208) 467-8656
Northwest Nazarene Univ., ID, Nampa
Ford, Alan
alanford@shelbystar.com, Sports Ed., The Star, NC, Shelby
Ford, Lindsey ....(781) 320-8052
l.ford@nenpa.com, Advertising Operations Manager, NENPA Ad Network (New England Newspaper and Press Association), MA, Dedham
Ford, Robert D..........................860/701-4279
r.ford@theday.com, Post-Press/Distribution Operations Manager, The Day Publishing Company, CT, New London
Ford, Stephen..........................(502) 582-4230
sford@courier-journal.com, Editorial Page Ed., The Courier-Journal, KY, Louisville
Ford, Cynthia A.......................(717) 339-2040
corp@gburgtimes.com, Pres./Pub., Gettysburg Times, PA, Gettysburg
Ford, Tony
info@alfactp.com, Gen. Mgr., alfa CTP Systems LLC, NH, Amherst
Ford, Thomas
tford@gburgtimes.com, Systems Analyst/Online Mgr., Gettysburg Times, PA, Gettysburg
Ford, Chris..................................ext. 5157
Adv. Dir., Pharos-Tribune, IN, Logansport
Ford, Wayne ....(706) 208-2218
wayne.ford@onlineathens.com, Oconee Ed., Athens Banner-Herald, GA, Athens
Ford, Michael..........................(904) 819-3525
Prodn. Superintendent, Mailroom, The St. Augustine Record, FL, Saint Augustine
Ford, John
jford@neoshodailynews.com, Online Mgr./Mgmt. Info Servs. Mgr., Neosho Daily News, MO, Neosho
Ford, Terry
sales@pamarcoinc.com, Pres./CEO, Pamarco Global Graphics, NJ, Roselle
Foreman, Shari
shari@familyflyer.com, Gen. Mgr., Community Papers of Indiana, IN, Crown Point
Foreman, Chris.......................(317) 398-1274
cforeman@shelbynews.com, Bus. Mgr., The Shelbyville News, IN, Shelbyville
Foreman, John
jforeman@news-gazette.com, Publisher, News-Gazette Inc., IL, Champaign
Foreman, Tamara......................209-249-3504
tforeman@mantecabulletin.com, Business Manager, Manteca Bulletin, CA, Manteca
Forman, Elaine
starcity@midrivers.com, News Ed., Miles City Star, MT, Miles City
Forness, Roger........................(808) 529-4312
rforness@staradvertiser.com, Vice President / Technology, Honolulu Star-Advertiser, HI, Honolulu
Forrest, Sandra ....ext. 5085
HR, Pharos-Tribune, IN, Logansport
Forrest, H. Miles.....................(985) 850-1100
miles.forrest@dailycomet.com, Pub., The Daily Comet, LA, Thibodaux
Forrest, H. Miles.....................(985) 850-1100
miles.forrest@houmatoday.com, Publisher, The Courier, LA, Houma
Forrest, Ron............................(706) 208-2343
ron.forrest@onlineathens.com, Circ. Dir., Athens Banner-Herald, GA, Athens
Forro, Tamas
vg@vilaggazdasag.hu, Pub./Ed., VILAGGAZDASAG, Budapest, Pest
Forster, Cathy
cforster@lfpress.com, Adv. Mgr., Bus. Devel., The London Free Press, ON, London
Forsythe, Frank.......................(610) 436-4975
Systems Engineer, Alternative Learning Solutions, PA, West Chester
Fort, Frankie ....(912) 652-0261
frankie.fort@savannahnow.com, HR Dir., Savannah Morning News, GA, Savannah
Foss, Lennart
lennart.foss@nt.se, Dir., NORRKOPINGS TIDNINGAR, Norrkoping
Fossett, Christine 360-807-8242
cfossett@chronline.com, Publisher, The Chronicle, WA, Centralia
Foster, Beth ....(303) 914-6371
Red Rocks Cmty. College, CO, Lakewood
Foster, Michael........................(410) 651-7956
Univ. of Maryland Eastern Shore, MD, Princess Anne
Foster, Jeffrey
info@dailycourt.com, Pres./Pub., Daily Court Reporter, OH, Dayton
Foster, Clay 662-678-1505
clay.foster@journalinc.com, CEO/Publisher/President, Journal Publishing Company, MS, Tupelo
Foster, Simon
albrightian@albright.edu, Albright College, PA, Reading
Foster, Clay 662-678-1505
clay.foster@journalinc.com, CEO/Publisher/President, Journal Publishing Company, MS, Tupelo
Foster, Cecil ....ext. 249
rclark@richmondregister.com, Circ. Mgr., The Richmond Register, KY, Richmond
Foster, Patrice...........................6037424455
pfoster@fosters.com, Pres./Pub., Foster's Daily Democrat, NH, Dover
Foster, Skip
skipfoster@shelbystar.com, Pub., The Star, NC, Shelby
Foster, Lisa.............................(609) 871-8137
lfoster@phillyburbs.com, Adv. Team Leader, Burlington County Times, NJ, Willingboro
Foster, Tom............................(513) 587-2944
tfoster@gmti.gannett.com, Vice Pres., Celebro Opns., Celebro, OH, Cincinnati
Foster, Randy
rfoster@freedomenc.com, Mng. Ed., The Sun Journal, NC, New Bern
Foster, Tracie
tracie.foster@shj.com, Dir., HR, Herald-Journal, SC, Spartanburg
Foster, J. Todd.......................(276) 645-2513
jfoster@bristolnews.com, Mng. Ed., Bristol Herald Courier, VA, Bristol
Foster-Manning, Michelle ....(506) 859-7126
Reader Sales/Servs., Times & Transcript, NB, Moncton
Fotes, Jim ....(559) 441-6277
jfotes@fresnobee.com, Circ. Mgr., Systems, The Fresno Bee, CA, Fresno
Foudy, James T.......................(413) 585-5250
jfoudy@gazettenet.com, Ed., Daily Hampshire Gazette, MA, Northampton
Foulon, Jeanine ....(519) 354-2000
jfoulon@chathamdailynews.ca, Adv. Mgr., The Chatham Daily News, ON, Chatham
Fourmier, Denise
info@day-intl.com, Mktg. Mgr., Flint Group., OH, Dayton
Foust, Courtney
courtneyf@northwestsignal.net, Education/Health Ed., Northwest Signal, OH, Napoleon
Foust, John
jfoust@mindspring.com, Owner, John Foust Training, NC, Raleigh
Foutz, Keith ....(541) 385-5805
kfoutz@bendbulletin.com, Prodn. Dir., Opns., WESCOM, The Bulletin, OR, Bend
Fowkes, Kate
kfowkes@highpoint.edu, Prof., High Point University, NC, High Point
Fowler, Jennifer
info@pierian.com, Press Rel., Pierian Spring Software, OR, Portland
Fowler, Jeff.................(830) 625-9144 ext. 228
Circ. Mgr., New Braunfels Herald-Zeitung, TX, New Braunfels
Fowler, Ed ....(256) 235-9203
efowler@annistonstar.com, Vice Pres., Opns., Consolidated Publishing Co., AL, Anniston
Fowler, Kim ....(605) 394-8372
kim.fowler@rapidcityjournal.com, Director of Audience Development
Interim Publisher, Rapid City Journal, SD, Rapid City
Fowler, Ed
efowler@annistonstar.com, Vice Pres., Opns., The Anniston Star, AL, Anniston
Fox, Harry ....(276) 645-4801
hfox@bristolnews.com, Regl. Creative Servs. Mgr., Bristol Herald Courier, VA, Bristol
Fox, Kathy ....(937) 652-1334
kfox@urbanacitizen.com, Asst. Ed, Urbana Daily Citizen, OH, Urbana
Fox, Jeff ....(816)350-6313
jeff.fox@examiner.net, Editorial Page Ed., The Examiner, MO, Independence
Fox, Katie 860/701-4221
k.fox@theday.com, Membership Marketing Manager, The Day Publishing Company, CT, New London
Fox, Carey
redwood17257@yahoo.com, Sports Ed., The Brazil Times, IN, Brazil
Fox, Michael J.
michaeljfox@utahpress.com, Exec. Dir., Utah Press Association, Inc., UT, Salt Lake City
Fox, Bob ....ext. 124
bfox@robdailynews.com, Circ. Mgr., Promo., Daily News, IL, Robinson
Fox, Carolyn ....(818) 990-5945
editor@newscalendar.com, Ed. in Chief, Hollywood News Service, CA, Sherman Oaks
Fox, Marjorie
foxm@uc.edu, Journalism Coord., University of Cincinnati, OH, Cincinnati
Fox, Jerry D............................(260) 461-8620
jerrydfox@verizon.net, Sec./Treasurer, The Journal Gazette, IN, Fort Wayne
Fox, Peter D.
peter.fox@wnanews.com, Exec. Dir., Wisconsin Newspaper Association, WI, Madison
Fox, Sue ....(847) 635-1678
Oakton Cmty. College, IL, Des Plaines
Fpitzhorn, Tobias
fpitzhorn.tobias@dd-v.de, Adv. Mgr., SACHSISCHE ZEITUNG, Dresden
Fracassa, Hawke
avanti1054@aol.com, Editorial Dir./Columnist, Avanti NewsFeatures, MI, Clinton Township
Fragetti, Jerry
gfragetti@nnnlp.com, Sr. Vice Pres., Media/Opns., Newspaper National Network LP, NY, New York
Frailly, Ron
ron.frailly@indeonline.com, Pub., The Independent, OH, Massillon
Francis, Rob ....ext. 241
rfrancis@grandhaventribune.com, Adv. Dir., Grand Haven Tribune, MI, Grand Haven
Francis, David ....(504) 826-3176
tpdfrancis@gmail.com, Vice Pres./Bus. Mgr., The Times Picayune, LA, New Orleans
Francis, Mark..........................(352) 753-1119
mark.francis@thevillagesmedia.com, Opinion Page Ed., The Villages Daily Sun, FL, The Villages
Francis, Dennis.......................(808) 529-4700
dfrancis@staradvertiser.com, President and Publisher, Honolulu Star-Advertiser, HI, Honolulu
Francis, Dennis
dfrancis@starbulletin.com, Pres./Pub., Honolulu Star-Bulletin, HI, Honolulu
Francisco, Jose
jcanla@laprensa.hn, Dir., LA PRENSA, San Pedro Sula
Franeschi, Bruno
contact@sudouest.com, Dir., SUD-OUEST/SUD-OUEST DIMANCHE, 33094 Bordeaux
Frangoulis, Theresa ....(800) 657-2110
theresa@pressroomcleaners.com, Mgr. Special Projects (CFO), Pressroom Cleaners, NE, Omaha
Franjul, Miguel 686 6688
m.franjul@listin.com.do, Ed., LISTIN DIARIO, Santo Domingo
Frank, Martin ....ext. 231
Editorial Page Ed., Valley News, VT, West Lebanon
Frank, Eric.............................(469) 532-8040
eric.frank@kba.com, Vice Pres., Mktg., KBA North America, Inc. (Koenig & Bauer AG), VT
Frank, Peter...........................(920) 431-8301
pfrank@greenbaypressgazette.com, News Ed., Green Bay Press-Gazette, WI, Green Bay
Frank, Kevin
kevin.frank@stowewoodward.com, Vice Pres., Sales, Xerium Technologies Inc., NC
Frank, Robert L.
bfrank@berry.edu, Chair, Berry College, GA, Mount Berry
Frank, Marilyn
bmfi@aol.com, Mgr., BMF Newspaper Ac-

counting Systems, TX, Temple
Frank, Robert ....(425) 339-3426
frank@heraldnet.com, City Ed., The Herald, WA, Everett
Frankenberg, Lisa L.
frankenberg@praguepost.cz, Pres./Pub., Lion's Share Group, Prague
Franklin, Teryl ....(608) 252-6155
tfranklin@madison.com, Managing Editor, Wisconsin State Journal, WI, Madison
Franklin, Douglas
Doug.Franklin@coxinc.com, Exec. Vice. Pres., Cox Newspapers, Inc., GA, Atlanta
Franklin, Joy ....(828) 232-5895
jfrankli@citizen-times.com, Editorial Page Ed., The Asheville Citizen-Times, NC, Asheville
Franks, Bob ....(541) 957-4245
rfranks@nrtoday.com, Circ. Dir., The News-Review, OR, Roseburg
Frankscoviak, Karen
kfranscoviak@thehj.com, Gen. Mgr., Herald Journal, IN, Monticello
Franscell, Ann
publisher@gillettenewsrecord.com, Editorial Page Ed., The News-Record, WY, Gillette
Frasca, Ralph
ralph.frasca@marymount.edu, Mass Commun. Coord., Marymount University, VA, Arlington
Fraser, Jayme 406-243-2394
Editor, Univ. of Montana, MT, Missoula
Fraser, Andrew
aptrenton@ap.org, Deputy Bureau Chief, New Jersey Associated Press Managing Editors Association, NJ, Trenton
Fraser, Don....................ext. 231
Bus. Ed., The Standard, ON, Saint Catharines
Fraser, Judith C.....................(413) 788-1026
jfraser@repub.com, Dir., HR, The Republican, MA, Springfield
Fraser, Susan O'Connor
susan@tamcom.com, Pres./CEO, Tam Communications, CA, Scotts Valley
Frasz, Krista ....(250) 470-0761
krista.frasz@ok.bc.ca, Advertising Dir., The Daily Courier, BC, Kelowna
Frate, Elisabeth
verlagsleitung@tagblatt.de, Proprietor, Sudwest Presse (Schwabisches Tagblatt), Tubingen
Frattura, Al ....(989) 779-6000
afrattura@journalregister.com, Pub., Morning Sun, MI, Mount Pleasant
afrattura@journalregister.com, Clare County Buyers Guide, MI, Mount Pleasant
afrattura@journalregister.com, Grand Traverse Insider , MI, Mount Pleasant
afrattura@journalregister.com, Northeastern Shopper South, MI, Mount Pleasant
afrattura@journalregister.com, Morning Star Publishing Co - Adwrap North, MI, Mount Pleasant
afrattura@journalregister.com, Morning Star Publishing Co - Adwrap South, MI, Mount Pleasant
Fray, Peter
smh@access.fairfax.com.au, Ed., THE SYDNEY MORNING HERALD, Pyrmont
Fraze, Kathy....................(330) 996-3867
kfraze@thebeaconjournal.com, Asst. Mng. Ed., Features, Akron Beacon Journal, OH, Akron
Frazier, Greg....................(650) 391-1330
gfrazier@dailynewsgroup.com, Sports Ed., Palo Alto Daily News, CA, Menlo Park
Fredel, Jill
jfredel@delawareonline.com, Asst. Mng. Ed., The News Journal, DE, New Castle
Frederick, Sharon....................ext. 265
Adv. Mgr., The Pioneer - Big Rapids, MI, Big Rapids
Frederick, Karl....................(262) 656-6276
kfrederick@kenoshanews.com, Mng. Ed., Kenosha News, WI, Kenosha
Frederick, Sherman
sfrederick@reviewjournal.com, Pub., Las Vegas Review-Journal, NV, Las Vegas
Fredericks, Trevor 416-386-2853
VP, Reader Sales and Service, National Post, ON, Toronto
Fredericks, Doug ....(508) 967-3140
subscriptions@tauntongazette.com, Circ. Mgr., Taunton Daily Gazette, MA, Taunton
Fredette, Bob ....(802) 747-6121 ext. 2210
bob.fredette@rutlandherald.com, Sports Ed., Rutland Herald, VT, Rutland
Fredly, Jan Eivind
jan.eivind.fredly@lofotposten.no, Ed. in Chief, LOFOTPOSTEN, Svolvaer
Fredricks, Jim
jfredricks@hcnonline.com, Grp. Pub., Courier, TX, Conroe
Free, Ginny....................ext. 109
pryclass@swbell.net, Classified Mgr., The Daily Times, OK, Pryor
Freedman, Ronald E.
sales@vcampus.com, Sr. Vice Pres., Worldwide Sales/Mktg., VCampus Corp., VA, Reston
Freedman, Ken
Kfreedman@mediaspansoftware.com, Vice Pres., Mktg., MediaSpan Media Software, FL, Melbourne
Freels, Larry W. ....(660) 665-2808
kvnews@sbcglobal.net, Pub./Bus. Mgr., Kirksville Daily Express, MO, Kirksville
Freeman, Scott ....(508) 862-1188
sfreeman@capecodonline.com, Bldg. Mgr., Cape Cod Times, MA, Hyannis
Freeman, Henry ....(914) 694-5002
Vice Pres./Exec. News Ed., The Journal News, NY, White Plains
Freeman, Rebecca K. ....(772) 221-4131
becky.freeman@scripps.com, Vice Pres./Gen. Mgr., Treasure Coast News/Press-Tribune, FL, Stuart
Freeman, Randy
info@quadtechworld.com, Vice Pres., Bus. Devel., QuadTech, WI, Sussex
Freeman, Richard....................(707) 553-6820
richardf@timesheraldonline.com, Community Ed., Vallejo Times-Herald, CA, Vallejo
Freeman, Julie
jfreeman@iabc.com, Pres./CEO, International Association of Business Communicators (IABC), CA, San Francisco
Freeman, Karen Wynn
kfreeman@nabj.org, Exec. Dir., National Association of Black Journalists, MD, Adelphi
Freemyer, Jordan ....(970) 392-9341
Univ. of Northern Colorado, CO, Greeley
Freider, Neil ....ext. 257
Ed., Star Beacon, OH, Ashtabula
Freiha, Bassam
alanwar@alanwar.com.lb, Gen. Mgr., Al Anwar
Freker, Stephen
editor@maldennews.com, Sports Ed., The Evening News-Mercury, MA, Malden
Fremgen, James ....(707) 521-5204
jfremgen@pressdemocrat.com, News Ed., The Press Democrat, CA, Santa Rosa
French, Virginia ....(310) 914-2064
Grp. Vice Pres., The New York Times, NY, New York
French, Patrick
xitronsales@xitron.com, Vice Pres., Sales, Xitron, MI, Ann Arbor
French, Barry
barryfrench@yahoo.com, Dir., Mktg., Barry French, MA, Assonet
French, Barry
barryfrench@yahoo.com, Pres., French, L. Barry, MA, Assonet
French, Randy
bdasun@mail.ibl.bm, Pub., BERMUDA SUN, Hamilton
French, John P.....................(480) 834-4884
Pres./COO, BurrellesLuce, AZ, Mesa
Frenya, James G. ....(518) 565-4190
jfrenya@pressrepublican.com, Circ. Dir., Press-Republican, NY, Plattsburgh
Freud, Chris....................(970) 748-2934
cfreud@vaildaily.com, Sports Ed., Vail Daily, CO, Vail
Freudensprung, Kelly....................(870) 508-8075
addir@baxterbulletin.com, Online Adv. Mgr./Adv. Dir., The Baxter Bulletin, AR, Mountain Home
Frey, Russell
d2java@yahoo.com, Pres., Power BBS Computing, NY, Hicksville
Frey, Chad
cfrey@thekansan.com, Educ./Features Ed., The Newton Kansan, KS, Newton
Frey, Mike ....(815) 937-3343
mfrey@daily-journal.com, Metro Ed., The Daily Journal, IL, Kankakee
Frias Ruiz, Jose Antonio
surdigital@diariosur.es, MD, Sur, Malaga
Frick, Kelly Adrian ....(989) 894-9632
kfrick@bc-times.com, Metro Ed., The Bay City Times, MI, Bay City
Friday, Rufus M....................(509) 582-1443
rfriday@tricityherald.com, Pub., Tri-City Herald, WA, Kennewick
Fried, Jeff ....(305) 347-6615
jfried@alm.com, Associate Publisher/Chief Financial Officer , Miami Daily Business Review, FL, Miami
Fried, Jeff ....(305) 347-6615
jfried@alm.com, Associate Publisher/Chief Financial Officer , Palm Beach Daily Business Review, FL, West Palm Beach
Friedlander, Sharon
sfriedlander@journal-advocate.com, Adv. Dir., Journal-Advocate, CO, Sterling
Friedman, David
david@telephonedoctor.com, Gen. Mgr./Vice Pres., Telephone Doctor Customer Service Training, MO, Saint Louis
Friedman, Richard H.
info@weatherline.com, Pres., Weatherline, Inc., MO, Saint Louis
Friedmann, Anneliese 23770
info@abendzeitung.de, Proprietor, ABENDZEITUNG, Munchen
Friedrich, Karl
redaction@flz.de, Ed., FRANKISHE LANDESZEITUNG, Ansbach
Friend, Nan
nfriend@marshallnewsmessenger.com, Adv. Mgr., Marshall News Messenger, TX, Marshall
Friend, Cecilia
cfriend@utica.edu, Dir./Prof., Utica College of Syracuse University, NY, Utica
Friend, Nanya
nanyaf@dailymail.com, Ed., Charleston Daily Mail, WV, Charleston
Friend, Chuck ....(919) 419-6788
cfriend@heraldsun.com, Prodn. Dir., The Herald-Sun, NC, Durham
Friesner, Karen ....(303) 776-2244 ext. 353
kfriesner@times-call.com, Promos./Community Servs. Coord., Times-Call, CO, Longmont
Frink, Clayton....................(608) 252-6402
cfrink@madison.com, Pres./Pub., Capital Newspapers, WI, Madison
Frink, Clayton
cfrink@madison.com, Pub., The Capital Times, WI, Madison
Frisch, Kevin M. ....(585) 394-0770 ext. 257
kfrisch@messengerpostmedia.com, Mng. Ed., Daily Messenger, NY, Canandaigua
Frischkorn, Jeff....................ext. 625
Environmental Writer, The News-Herald, OH, Willoughby
Frisneda, Ramon....................(917) 339-0857
Mng. Ed., Hoy, NY, New York
Fritch, John
john.fritch@uni.edu, Dept. Chair, University of Northern Iowa, IA, Cedar Falls
Fritchen, Karl ....(414) 566-7500
info@qtiworld.com, Pres., Quad Tech, WI, Sussex
Frith, Stefanie ....(818) 719-6492
frithsa@piercecollege.edu, Adviser to the Roundup newspaper, Los Angeles Pierce College, CA, Woodland Hills
Frith, Cary....................(740) 593-9581
Asst. Prof., Ohio University, OH, Athens
Frith Moore, Dena
dmoore@harriswilliams.com, Mng. Dir., Harris Williams & Co., VA, Richmond
Fritsche, Lydia....................(920) 356-6720
lfritsche@conleynet.com, Employment Manager, Conley Publishing Group Ltd., WI, Beaver Dam
Fritz, Marsha....................ext. 240
marsha.fritz@lee.net, Circ. Mgr., The Ledger Independent, KY, Maysville
Fritz, Gunther
fritz@medienhaus.li, Ed., LIECHTENSTEINER VATERLAND, Vaduz
Fritz, Dena
dfritz@journalregister.com, Pub., The Reporter, PA, Lansdale
Fritz, Keith ....(610) 371-5181
kfritz@readingeagle.com, Adv. Dir., Reading Eagle, PA, Reading
Fritz, David....................(540) 213-9116
dfritz@newsleader.com, Exec. Ed., The News Leader, VA, Staunton
Frobe, Bill....................(607) 778-5110
Broome Cmty. College, NY, Binghamton
Froelich, Joanne
aptsales@advpubtech.com, Sls. Mgr., Advanced Publishing Technology, CA, Burbank
Frohlich, Susan
susan.frohlich@afp.com, Admin., Agence France-Presse - Montreal, QC, QC, Montreal
Frolik, Joe ....(216) 999-4548
Chief Editorial Writer, The Plain Dealer, OH, Cleveland
Fromm, Linda C. ....(406) 443-2850
mtomgr@mtnewspapers.com, Adv. Coord., Montana Newspaper Advertising Service, Inc., MT, Helena
Frontani, Michael
mfrontani@elon.edu, Assoc. Prof., Elon University, NC, Elon
Frontczak, Michal....................637 74 01
frontczak@express.lodz.pl, Dir., Adv. Sales, EXPRESS ILUSTROWANY, Lodz
Fruit, Jeff
jfruit@kent.edu, Dir./Prof., Kent State University, OH, Kent
Frukelstein, Everett....................(401) 273-6397
efrukelstein@phx.com, Treasurer, Alternative Weekly Network, CA, Sacramento
Frund, Rudiger
redaktion-std@tageblatt.de, Bus. Mgr., BUXTEHUDER TAGEBLATT, Stade
Frungillo, John
johnfrungillo@eveningtribune.com, Mktg. Dir., The Evening Tribune, NY, Hornell
Frustere, Jim
elooman@suite224.net, Pub., Star Beacon, OH, Ashtabula
Fry, Matt....................(352) 753-1119
matt.fry@thevillagesmedia.com, Mng. Ed., The Villages Daily Sun, FL, The Villages
Fry, Douglas
info@sapatoday.com, Exec. Dir., Southeastern Advertising Publishers Association, TN, Columbia
Fry, Sonya K.
sonya@opcofamerica.org, Exec. Dir., Overseas Press Club of America, NY, New York
Fry, Douglas
info@sapatoday.com, Exec. Dir., Southeastern Advertising Publishers Association, TN, Columbia
Fryer, Bob ....(412) 320-7916
bfryer@tribweb.com, Mng. Ed., Pittsburgh, Tribune-Review, PA, Pittsburgh
Fryette, Mike....................(479) 785-7762
mfryette@swtimes.com, Prodn. Mgr., Pressroom, Times Record, AR, Fort Smith
Fryman, John
rob@bryantimes.com, Sports Ed., The Bryan Times, OH, Bryan
Fuentes, Angie ....(432) 333-7631
angie_fuentes@link.freedom.com, Adv. Mgr., Classified, Odessa American, TX, Odessa
Fuentes, Manuel....................5545 8256
redaccion@agenciaefe.tie.cl, Rep., EFE News Services - Santiago, Chile, Santiago
redaccion@agenciaefe.tie.cl, Rep., EFE News Services - Mexico City, Mexico, Mexico City
Fugslang, Ross ....(712) 274-5129
Morningside College, IA, Sioux City
Fujimoto, Troy ....(808) 695-6322
tfujimoto@staradvertiser.com, Director of Digital Media, Honolulu Star-Advertiser, HI, Honolulu
Fujimura, Keigo
hensyu@higashi.co.jp, Pres., HIGASHI-AICHI SHIMBUN, Toyohashi City, Chubu
Fujiyoshi, Toshio
webmaster@nikkan.co.jp, Chrmn., NIKKAN KOGYO SHIMBUN, Tokyo
Fuke, Richard....................(808) 525-7442
Vice Pres., Finance, Honolulu Star-Advertiser, HI, Honolulu
Fukunaga, Katsuya

osaka@mdx.mainichi.co.jp, Mng. Ed., THE MAINICHI DAILY NEWS, Osaka, Osaka
Fulcher, Kathy..............(603) 543-3100 ext. 143
kfulcher@tsvmedia.net, Web Coord., Eagle Times, NH, Claremont
Fulcher, Michelle......................(303) 820-1577
mfulcher@denverpost.com, Nat'l Ed., The Denver Post, CO, Denver
Fulk, Scott..............................(219) 980-6792
Indiana Univ. Northwest, IN, Gary
Fuller, Richard...........................419-724-6314
dfuller@toledoblade.com, Circ. Dir., The Blade, OH, Toledo
Fuller, George............................717-262-4731
gfuller@publicopinionnews.com, Circulation Director, Public Opinion, PA, Chambersburg
Fuller, Dick..............................(937) 754-2515
dfuller@coxohio.com, Circ. Dir., Retail Sales, Dayton Daily News, OH, Dayton
Fuller, Robert G.
bob@rgcreations.com, Owner, RG Creations, Inc., CA, San Carlos
Fulton, Susan Dagg
susan.fulton@ott.sunpub.com, Mktg. Dir., Commercial Sales/Promos., The Ottawa Sun, ON, Ottawa
Funabashi, Yoichi
newsroom@emb.asahi-np.co.jp, Ed. in Chief, ASAHI SHIMBUN, Sapporo, Hokkaido
Fung, Brian..............................(802) 443-4827
Middlebury College, VT, Middlebury
Funk, Warren C.........................(901) 529-2631
funk@commercialappeal.com, HR Dir./Gen. Counsel, The Commercial Appeal, TN, Memphis
Funke, Becky............................(316) 942-5385
bfunke@activeagingonline.com, Kansas Professional Communicators, KS, Wichita
Funnell, Lee
sales@sccmediaserver.com, Vice Pres., The Software Construction Co., GA, Alpharetta
Furio, Brian
bfurio@ycp.edu, Chair, York College of Pennsylvania, PA, York
Furler, Mark
mark.furler@scnews.com.au, Ed. in Chief, SUNSHINE COAST DAILY
Furry, Lucy..............................(310) 306-6100
Vice Pres., Syndication, The Advice Goddess-Amy Alkon, CA, Santa Monica
Furst von Waldburg zu Zeil, Georg
info@all-in.de, Proprietor, ALLGAUER ZEITUNG, Marktoberdorf
Fuschetti, Steve
info@celebro.com, Pres./CEO, Celebro, OH, Cincinnati
Fuschetti, Steve........................(513) 587-2934
sfuschetti@gmti.gannett.com, Pres./CEO, Gannett Media Technologies International (GMTI), OH, Cincinnati
Fusfeld, Ira..................................ext. 534
ifusfeld@journalregister.com, Pub., Daily Freeman, NY, Kingston
Futrell, Ashley B.......................(252) 946-9797
news@wdnweb.com, Pres./Pub., Washington Daily News, NC, Washington

G

Gabordi, Bob..............................(850) 599-2177
bgabordi@tallahassee.com, Exec. Ed., Tallahassee Democrat, FL, Tallahassee
Gabriel, Kelle............................(740) 375-5145
kgabriel@nncogannett.com, Conversation Ed., The Marion Star, OH, Marion
Gaccak, Salem
salem.gaccak@dailystar.com, Circ. Mgr., DAILY STAR
Gadd, Brian...............................(740) 450-6758
Reporter., Times Recorder, OH, Zanesville
Gaddy, Joy
advertising@griffindailynews.com, Adv. Dir., Griffin Daily News, GA, Griffin
Gaden-Flanagan, Dorothy...........(630) 388-6903
dorothy@copia.com, Vice Pres., Mktg., Copia International Ltd., IL, Wheaton
Gaebel, Gerald
sales@lithcoinc.com, Pres., Lithco Inc., NY, East Syracuse
Gaetano, Rizzuto...............................393-939
info@liberta.it, Mgr., LIBERTA, Piacenza
Gage, Ralph
rgage@ljworld.com, The World Co.- Lawrence, Kan., Journal-World, KS, Lawrence
Gage, Ralph...............................(785) 832-7125
rgage@ljworld.com, Special Projects Dir., The World Co.- Lawrence, Kan., Journal-World, KS, Lawrence
Gage, Ralph D.
rgage@ljworld.com, Cor. Sec., WorldWest LLC, KS, Lawrence
Gage, Bob.................................(361) 886-3730
gageb@caller.com, Circ. Opns. Mgr., Corpus Christi Caller-Times, TX, Corpus Christi
Gagen, Jay
jay@rpmassoc.com, Acct. Mgr., Vista - The Magazine for All Hispanics - Pontiac, MI, MI, Pontiac
Gagen, Jay
jay@rpmassoc.com, Acct. Mgr., Vista - The Magazine for All Hispanics - Pontiac, MI, MI, Pontiac
Gagnon, John
john.gagnon@thevillagesmedia.com, Circ. Dir., The Villages Daily Sun, FL, The Villages
Gahagan, Jack
glmsconf@comcast.net, Bus. Mgr./Sec./Treasurer, Great Lakes/Midstates Newspaper Conference, Inc., MI, Jackson
Gaier, Paul................................(920) 996-7213
pgaier@appleton.gannett.com, Adv. Dir., The Post-Crescent, WI, Appleton
Gaines, Steve............................270-781-1700
sgaines@bgdailynews.com, Editorial Page Ed., Daily News, KY, Bowling Green
Gaines, John
jgaines@thehawkeye.com, Photo Dept. Mgr., The Hawk Eye, IA, Burlington
Gaines, Mary.............................(270) 783-3206
mgaines@bgdailynews.com, Co-Owner, Daily News, KY, Bowling Green
Gaines, John..............................(270) 783-3208
pgaines@bgdailynews.com, Pub./Pres., Daily News, KY, Bowling Green
Gaines, Scott.............................(270) 781-1700
sgaines@bgdailynews.com, Mgr., Promo., Daily News, KY, Bowling Green
Gainey, Jim...................................ext. 189
jgainey@nvdaily.com, Adv. Dir., Northern Virginia Daily, VA, Strasburg
Gaitan, Adrian...........................(657) 278-4411
California State Univ., CA, Fullerton
Galant, Richard..........................(631) 843-3274
Mng. Ed., News, Newsday, NY, Melville
Galant, Mark..............................(413) 585-5336
mgalant@gazettenet.com, Circ. Asst. Mgr., Daily Hampshire Gazette, MA, Northampton
Galantis, Jim
jgalantis@sharonherald.com, Adv. Mgr., Retail, The Herald, PA, Sharon
Galati, K.J...................................ext. 3581
kjgalati@express-times.com, Adv. Coord., Special Sections, The Express-Times, PA, Easton
Galbincea, Barbara....................(216) 999-4185
Deputy Metro Editor, The Plain Dealer, OH, Cleveland
Galbraith, Dan
angelah@npgco.com, Mng. Ed., Atchison Globe, KS, Atchison
Gale, Jim...................................(202) 650-6406
jgale@cq.com, Sr. Vice Pres., Sales, Congressional Quarterly, Inc., DC, Washington
Galetano, James J.
jgaletano@dailyherald.com, Circ. Vice Pres., Daily Herald, IL, Arlington Heights
Gall, Steven................................253-597-8625
steve.gall@thenewstribune.com, VP/Advertising, The News Tribune, WA, Tacoma
Gallagher, Becky........................(205) 325-2108
Pub. Serv. Dir., Birmingham Post-Herald, AL, Birmingham
Gallagher, Ronnie.......................(704) 797-4287
rgallagher@salisburypost.com, Sports Ed., Salisbury Post, NC, Salisbury
Gallagher, Tim
tgallagher@siouxcityjournal.com, Society/Women's Ed., Sioux City Journal, IA, Sioux City
Gallagher, Amanda
agallagher3@elon.edu, Asst. Prof., Elon University, NC, Elon
Gallagher, Ursla........................(757) 247-7472
ugallagher@dailypress.com, Target Mktg. Mgr., Daily Press, VA, Newport News
Gallagher, Kristin.......................660-543-4051
The Muleskinner, Univ. of Central Missouri, MO, Warrensburg
Gallagher, Donald.........................Mng. Ed.
donald.gallagher@nielsen.com, Nielsen Entertainment News Wire, MA, Boston
Gallagher, Phil................................9282 3415
afreditor@afr.com, Adv. Mgr., AUSTRALIAN FINANCIAL REVIEW
Gallagher, Michael S.
mgallagher@sunshinepaper.com, Vice Pres., Sales/Mktg., SunShine Paper Co., CO, Aurora
Gallardo, Margaret.....................915-546-6166
mgallardo@elpasotimes.com, Sports Editor , El Paso Times, TX, El Paso
Gallegos, Nelson Castillo...................295-5495
editores@imbanet.net, Gen. Mgr., DIARIO DEL NORTE, Ibarra, Imbabura
Galli, Roberto..................................434-511
direttore@laprovinciapavese.it, Mgr., LA PROVINCIA PAVESE, Pavia
Galligan, Cindy.................................ext. 438
cgalligan@thenewsdispatch.com, Adv. Mgr., Nat'l Rep., News Dispatch, IN, Michigan City
Gallimore, Joe...........................(941) 206-1316
igallimore@sun-herald.com, Circ. Dir., Charlotte Sun, FL, Charlotte Harbor
Gallman, Vanessa......................(859) 231-1393
vgallman@herald-leader.com, Editorial Page Ed., Lexington Herald-Leader, KY, Lexington
Galloway, Rob
rgalloway@sierranevadamedia.com, Adv. Mgr., Nevada Appeal, NV, Carson City
Galloway, Debra.........................(850) 599-2292
dgalloway@tallahassee.com, News Ass't, Tallahassee Democrat, FL, Tallahassee
Gallup, Larry.....................................ext. 297
lgallup@appleton.gannett.com, Community Conversation Sr. Ed., The Post-Crescent, WI, Appleton
Galvin, Rita
rgalvin@interest.com, Gen. Mgr., Mortgage Market Information Services, IL, Villa Park
Galvin, Rita P.............................(925) 398-0839
rgalvin@interest.com, Gen. Mgr., West, Mortgage Market Information Services, IL, Villa Park
Gamage, Peter H................................ext. 311
news@itemlive.com, Pres./Pub./Dir., The Daily Item, MA, Lynn
Gambescia, Paolo
multimedia@mclink.it, Mgr., L'Unita Editrice Multimediale SpA, Rome
Gambill, George (Buzz)
editor@thevalleybreeze.com, Creator/Owner/Artist, Gambill Arts & Graphix Syndicate, CA, Desert Hot Springs
Gamble, Karen.............(601) 636-4545 ext. 131
kgamble@vicksburgpost.com, Mng. Ed., The Vicksburg Post, MS, Vicksburg
Gamble, Speed..............................ext. 1020
sgamble@portervillerecorder.com, Prodn. Mgr., The Porterville Recorder, CA, Porterville
Gamble, Phonda.........................(937) 225--0550
pgamble@coxohio.com, Vice President, Circulation, Dayton Daily News, OH, Dayton
Gamboa, Eric...............................951-827-3459
News Editor, Univ. of California, Riverside Highlander Newspaper, CA, Riverside
Gambrell, Mandy
mgambrell@coxohio.com, Lifestyle Ed., JournalNews, OH, Hamilton
Gamell, Nomagroma
nomagroma@diarisabadell.com, Chief Dir., DIARI DE SABADELL, Sabadell, Barcelona
Gammons, Bob
schaefer01@snet.net, Pres., Schaefer Machine Co., Inc., CT, Deep River
Ganak, Steve
adreps1@yahoo.com, Pres., Ad Reps, MA, Boston
Gandat, N/A.....................................323 223
Ed., UNEN, Ulaanbaatar
Gandhi, Rakesh
rakesh.gandhi@epatrika.com, Ed., RAJASTHAN PATRIKA, Kota, Rajasthan
Gandhi, Rakesh
info@rajasthanpatrika.com, Ed., RAJASTHAN PATRIKA, Udaipur, Rajasthan
Gandola, Georgeo
g.gandola@laprovincia.it, Dir., LA PROVINCIA DI COMO, Como
Gandy, Terry E.
tgandy@kdhnews.com, Gen. Mgr., Killeen Daily Herald, TX, Killeen
Ganjani, Chris
chrisg@communitech.com, Mktg. Dir., CommuniTech, Inc., IL, Bensenville
Gannon, Kate
kategannon@coloradoan.com, Online Sales Mgr., The Coloradoan, CO, Fort Collins
Gannon, Richard
rgannon@kspress.com, Dir., Gov't Affairs, Kansas Press Association, KS, Topeka
Gans, Maureen...........................(250) 380-5230
mgans@te.canwest.com, Credit Mgr., Times Colonist, BC, Victoria
Gant, Kelly................................(541) 338-2254
kelly.gant@registerguard.com, Adv. Mgr., The Register-Guard, OR, Eugene
Gant, Kelly................................(541) 338-2254
kelly.gant@registerguard.com, Classified Adv. Mgr., The Register-Guard, OR, Eugene
Gao, Teri...................................(310) 337-7003
tgao@creators.com, Office Mgr., Creators Syndicate, CA, Los Angeles
Garber, William E........................269-473-3103
Founder, Interlink, MI, Berrien Springs
Garceau, Viviane
viviane.garceau@enpa.be, Office Mgr., European Newspaper Publishers' Association, 1050 Bruxelles
Garcia, Javier
javiergarcia@efe.com, Rep., EFE News Services - Algiers, Algeria, Algiers
Garcia, Carmen Sara
cgarcia@sagrado.edu, Dir., University of the Sacred Heart, PR, San Juan
Garcia, Luiz Alberto.........................218-7888
correio@triang.com.br, Pres., Correio de Uberlandia, Uberlandia, Minas Gerais
Garcia, Jesus P.
editorial@sunstar.com.ph, Chrmn., SUN-STAR DAILY, Cebu City
Garcia, Arnold...........................(512) 445-3667
agarcia@statesman.com, Editorial Page Ed., Austin American-Statesman, TX, Austin
Garcia, Guillermo......................(305) 347-6658
ggarcia@alm.com, Director of Operations & MIS, Miami Daily Business Review, FL, Miami
Garcia, Roel...............................(616) 546-4219
roel.garcia@hollandsentinel.com, News Team Asst. Leader, The Holland Sentinel, MI, Holland
Garcia, Hector............................(302) 324-2744
Circ. Mgr., Opns., The News Journal, DE, New Castle
Garcia, Kay................................(209) 249-3549
composing@mantecabulletin.com, Composing & Commercial Print Mgr., Manteca Bulletin, CA, Manteca
Garcia, Arturo
agarcia@tribuna.com.mx, Sports Ed., Tribuna del Yaqui, Ciudad Obregon, Sonora
Garcia, Robert...................................ext. 226
Graphics Ed./Art Dir., The Daily Sentinel, CO, Grand Junction
Garcia , Paz...............................(915) 546-6387
pgarcia@elpasotimes.com, Information Technolgy Dir., El Paso Times, TX, El Paso
Garcia Alvarez, Edber Arturo...............554-3864
zihua@cdnet.com.mx, Pres., Diario de Zihuatanejo, Zihuatanejo, Guerrero
Garcia Avalos, Sandra Luz
sgarcia@elsiglodetorreon.com.mx, Sales Mgr., EL SIGLO DE TORREON, Torreon, Coahuila
Garcia Gamboa, Gerardo
ggg@cancun.novenet.com, Gen. Mgr., NOVEDADES DE YUCATAN, Merida, Yucatan
Garcia Gomez, Juan B.
opinion1@tamps1.telmex.net.mx, Pres./Gen. Dir., Cia. Editora La Opinion de Tamaulipas, S.A., Matamoros, Tamaulipas
Garcia Raja, Pedro
laopiniondecartagena@ebi.es, Dir., La Opinion De Cartagena, Cartagena, Murcia
Garcia , Mabel Guerra

cip222@cip.enet.cu, Ed. in Chief, ADELANTE, Camaguey
Gard, Richard
richard.gard@molawersmedia.com, Pub., The St. Louis Countian
Gard, Richard
richard.gard@thedailyrecord.com, Pub., St. Louis Daily Record, MO, Saint Louis
Gard, Richard
richard.gard@molawyersmedia.com, Pub., The Daily Record
Gardener, Donna ....(905) 526-2485
dgardener@hamiltonspectator.com, Adv. Mgr., Retail Sales, The Hamilton Spectator, ON, Hamilton
Gardiner, Wyatt........................(360) 577-2570
wgardiner@tdn.com, Cir. Dir., Audience, The Daily News, WA, Longview
Gardner, Ann..........................(785) 832-7153
agardner@ljworld.com, Editorial Page Ed., The World Co.- Lawrence, Kan., Journal-World, KS, Lawrence
Gardner, Rex.................................6230 0651
Mng. Dir., THE MERCURY
Gardner, Robert ....(530) 896-7703
rgardner@chicoer.com, Controller, Chico Enterprise-Record, CA, Chico
Gardner, Nanette
ngardner@alamogordonews.com, Office Mgr., Alamogordo Daily News, NM, Alamogordo
Gardner, Ann..............................785-832-7153
agardner@ljworld.com, Editorial Page Editor, The World Co.- Lawrence, Kan., Journal-World, KS, Lawrence
Gardner, Rex
mercuryedletter@dbl.newsltd.com.au, Mng. Dir., THE SUNDAY TASMANIAN
Gardner, Karie ....(801) 625-4394
Adv. Supvr., Classified Telephone Sales, Standard-Examiner, UT, Ogden
Garey, Ashley
agarey@trcle.com, Graphics Ed./Art Dir., Cleburne Times-Review, TX, Cleburne
Garfias Ruiz, Rogelio
noticiasqro@prodigy.net.mx, Owner/Pres., NOTICIAS, Queretaro, Queretaro
Gargano, Frank
fgargano@sjnewsco.com, Vice Pres./Pub., The Gloucester County Times, NJ, Woodbury
Gargasz, Steve ....(724) 588-5000
sgargasz@therecordargus.com, Pres./Pub., The Record-Argus, PA, Greenville
Garibaldi, Roberto
info@diarioelaccionista.com.ar, Owner/Dir./Ed., EL ACCIONISTA, Buenos Aires
Garland, Frank.........................(814) 871-5808
Gannon Univ., PA, Erie
Garlinghouse, Paul ....(718) 575-4314
CUNY School of Law/Queens College, NY, Flushing
Garman, Shannon.....................(717) 255-8205
sgarman@patriot-news.com, Adv. Sales Asst., Nat'l, The Patriot-News, PA, Mechanicsburg
Garman, Barbara ....(814) 765-5535 ext. 210
classifieds@theprogressnews.com, Adv. Mgr., Classified, The Progress, PA, Clearfield
Garmon, Ryan
rgarmon@forsythnews.com, Adv. Mgr., Forsyth County News, GA, Cumming
Garneau, Richard
contactus@catalystpaper.com, Pres., Catalyst Paper Corp., BC, Richmond
Garrahan, John
djopinion@thedailyjournal.com, Editorial Page Ed., The Daily Journal, NJ, Vineland
Garrett, Harry L.
hgarrett@indexjournal.com, Exec. Mktg. Dir., The Index-Journal, SC, Greenwood
Garrett, Lee ....(770) 428-9411 ext. 302
lgarrett@mdjonline.com, HR Mgr., Marietta Daily Journal, GA, Marietta
Garrett, Jim ....(580) 585-5101
Adv. Dir., The Lawton Constitution, OK, Lawton
Garris, Kevin 651-228-2028
kgarris@pioneerpress.com, Vice Pres. Production, St. Paul Pioneer Press, MN, Saint Paul
Garrison, Matt.............(618) 985-2828 ext. 8387
John A. Logan College, IL, Carterville
Garrison, Ron..........................(859) 231-1601
rgarrison@herald-leader.com, Photo Dir., Lexington Herald-Leader, KY, Lexington
Garrison, Homer
hdnadv@sbcglobal.net, Prodn. Mgr., Hugo Daily News, OK, Hugo
Garrison, Terresa.....................(903) 237-7787
Prodn. Mgr., Post Press, Longview News-Journal, TX, Longview
Garritano, Tom..........................(312) 222-3185
tgarritano@tribune.com, Sr. Mgr., Multimedia Mktg., Chicago Tribune, IL, Chicago
Garrity, Maureen ....(530) 896-7752
mgarrity@chicoer.com, Dir., HR, Chico Enterprise-Record, CA, Chico
Garske, Monica
monica@flashnews.com, Sr. Ed., Wireless Flash News, Inc., CA, San Diego
Garson, Arnold
publisher@courier-journal.com, Pres./Pub., The Courier-Journal, KY, Louisville
Garthe, Michael
rheinpfalz@rheinpfalz.de, Ed. in Chief, DIE RHEINPFALZ, Ludwigshafen am Rhein
Garties, George
ggarties@ap.org, Chief Of Bureau, Illinois Associated Press Editors Association, IL, Chicago
Garties, George
ggarties@ap.org, Chief of Bureau, Illinois and Indiana, Indiana Associated Press Managing Editors Association, IN, Indianapolis
Garvin, Felecia ....(903) 813-2296
Austin College, TX, Sherman
Garwood, Eric 321-242-3759
egarwood@floridatoday.com, Delivery News Editor, Florida Today, FL, Melbourne
Gary, Bob
doug_hanes@notes.freedom.com, Mgr., Mktg. Communication, The Orange County Register, CA, Santa Ana
Gary, Greene...............................(910) 343-2380
gary.greene@starnewsonline.com, News Ed., Star-News, NC, Wilmington
Garza Elizondo, Felix Mario
prensare@tamps1.telmex.net.mx, Pres., PRENSA DE REYNOSA, Reynosa, Tamaulipas
Gaskill, Debra K........................(937) 864-2798
dgaskill@woh.rr.com, Pres., Ohio Newspaper Women's Association, OH, Enon
Gass, Doug................................(815) 987-1366
Asst. Mng. Ed., Rockford Register Star, IL, Rockford
Gassaway, Melinda............................ext. 225
Editorial Page Ed., The Sentinel-Record, AR, Hot Springs
Gassman, W.
abo@bielertagblatt.ch, Pub., BIELER TAGBLATT, Biel
Gates, Ernie..............................(757) 247-4628
egates@dailypress.com, Vice Pres./Ed., Daily Press, VA, Newport News
Gates, Jill ....(573) 815-1814
jgates@columbiatribune.com, Adv. Major Acct./Pre Print Coord., Columbia Daily Tribune, MO, Columbia
Gatewood, Sondra ....(503) 843-4555
binky@acmefeatures.com, Editorial Dir., Acme Features Syndicate, OR, Sheridan
Gatti, Maria ....(202) 334-4466
gattimn@washpost.com, Sales Mgr., Spanish Language Servs., The Washington Post Writers Group, DC, Washington
Gatto, Patricia
patricia.gatto@dowjones.com, Vice Pres., HR, Dow Jones Local Media Group, NY, Middletown
Gauger, Jim
sports@njtimes.com, Exec. Sports Ed., The Times, NJ, Trenton
Gauger, Dave
dave@gaugermedia.com, Pres./Broker, Gauger Media Service, Inc., WA, Raymond
Gaugh, Catherine ....(626) 962-8811 ext. 2479
catherine.gaugh@sgvn.com, Features Ed., The Whittier Daily News, CA, Whittier
Gaul, Lou ....(609) 871-8055
lgaul@phillyburbs.com, Entertainment Ed., Burlington County Times, NJ, Willingboro
Gauld, Natlie
natlie.gauld@tweednews.com.au, Ed., TWEED DAILY NEWS
Gault, Albert E. ....ext. 2363
bgault@wdt.net, Exec. Ed., Watertown Daily Times, NY, Watertown
Gauslaa, Stein
agderposten@agderposten.no, Ed., AGDERPOSTEN, Arendal
Gauthier, Tom.............................(978) 970-4867
tgauthier@lowellsun.com, Circ. Mgr., Systems, The Sun, MA, Lowell
Gauthier, Dolores.........................248-336-7300
dgauthier@rangerdata.com, National Director of Sales & Marketing, Ranger Data Technologies Inc., MI, Royal Oak
Gavira, Jose Antonio
diariodeandalucia@svqservicom.es, Dir., Diario 16 Andalucia, Seville
Gaviria Echeverri, Guillermo
direccion@elmundo.com, Pres., Gaviria Family Group, Medellin, Antioquia
Gawron, Daren.............(780) 743-8186 ext. 248
dgawron@bowesnet.com, Adv. Mgr., Fort McMurray Today, AB, Fort McMurray
Gay, David
dgay@ccstrexcom.com, Inside Sales Mgr., Computer Communications Specialists, Inc., GA, Norcross
Gay, Gregory ....ext. 2377
ggay@wdt.net, Sports Ed., Watertown Daily Times, NY, Watertown
Gay, Mary
pr@markzware.com, PR, Markzware Software, Inc., CA, Santa Ana
Gay, Brian
bgmfcp@mchsi.com, Exec. Dir., Midwest Free Community Papers, IA, Iowa City
Gay, Kathy................................(248) 745-4608
kathy.gay@oakpress.com, News Ed., The Oakland Press, MI, Pontiac
Gaydou, Danny R.......................(616) 222-5818
dgaydou@grpress.com, Pub., The Grand Rapids Press, MI, Grand Rapids
Gayheart, Tina ....ext. 29
tgayheart@news-expressky.com, Prodn. Mgr., The Appalachian News-Express, KY, Pikeville
Gayle, Barbara Mae
gayle@uofport.edu, Chair, University of Portland, OR, Portland
Gaynor, Joseph..........................(630) 755-9330
joe.gaynor@gossinternational.com, CFO, Goss International Corporation, IL, Bolingbrook
Gear, Sharmaine 5480 4214
production@gympietimes.com, Prodn, Mgr., THE GYMPIE TIMES
Geary, Joseph L.
jlgeary@indianagazette.net, Gen. Mgr., The Indiana Gazette, PA, Indiana
Geary, Ray
rgeary@delphosherald.com, Bus. Mgr., Delphos Daily Herald, OH, Delphos
Gebhardt, Ellyn.........................(303) 750-7555
egebhardt@aurorasentinel.com, Adv. Dir., Aurora Sentinel, CO, Aurora
Gebhart, Michael.......................(229) 438-3219
mike.gebhart@albanyherald.com, President/Publisher, The Albany Herald, GA, Albany
Gebhart, Michael
mike.gebhart@triplecrownmedia.com, Pres./CEO/Dir., Triple Crown Media, GA, Lawrenceville
Gebis, Wayne S.
wgebis@dailyherald.com, Circ. Mgr., New Bus., Daily Herald, IL, Arlington Heights
Geer, Rhonda..................................ext. 1653
rgeer@dixcom.com, Adv. Dir., The Daily Record, OH, Wooster
Geeraerts, Dirk 285-0151
dirk.geeraerts@dowjones.com, Acct. Mgr., Dow Jones Newswires - Brussels, Belgium, Brussels
Geers, George
george@nenews.org, Ed., New England Society of Newspaper Editors, MA, Salem
Geese, Terry.................(618) 253-7146 ext. 243
tgeese@yourclearwave.com, Mng. Ed., Eldorado Daily Journal, IL, Harrisburg
Geffen, Fmoenke.........................4618082050
Adv. Mgr., Schleswig-Holsteinische Landeszeitung, Rendsburg
Geffert, Kimberly
kimberlygeffert@npgco.com, Lifestyles Ed., Atchison Globe, KS, Atchison
Geffre, Anita
ageffre@gfherald.com, Director of Finance, Grand Forks Herald, ND, Grand Forks
Geffs, Tolman
tolmang@jegi.com, Mng. Dir., Jordan, Edmiston Group, Inc., NY, New York
Gehl, Robert...................................602-677-2831
rgehl@asu.edu, Editor-in-chief, @west news
Gehle, Janice ....(941) 957-5136
jan.gehle@heraldtribune.com, News Bus. Mgr., Sarasota Herald-Tribune, FL, Sarasota
Gehring, Fried 730
gehring@die-glocke.de, Ed. in Chief, DIE GLOCKE, Oelde
Geier, Leslie 618-393-2931
accounting@olneydailymail.com, Office Mgr., Olney Daily Mail, IL, Olney
Geier, Emil
info@schifferstadter-tagblatt.de, Ed., SCHIFFERSTADTER TAGBLATT, Schifferstadt
Geier, Susanne
anzeigen@schifferstadter-tagblatt.de, Distr. Mgr., SCHIFFERSTADTER TAGBLATT, Schifferstadt
Geiger, Benjamin
bgeiger@zsz.ch, Ed. in Chief, ZURICHSEE-ZEITUNG, Stafa, Zurich
Geiger, Bob...............................(813) 259-7494
Adv. Vice Pres., Sales, The Tampa Tribune, FL, Tampa
Geisler, Kristy J.
kjo@rexburgstandardjournal.com, Publisher, The Standard-Journal, ID, Rexburg
Geiss, Mike
mgeiss@couriernews.com, Circ. Mgr., The Courier, AR, Russellville
Geissler, Kyle.............................262-472-1426
geisslek@uww.edu, Adviser, Univ. of Wisconsin Whitewater, WI, Whitewater
Gelakis, Bagelis 332 0800
Adv. Mgr., RIZOSPASTIS, Athens, Central Greece
Gelfand, Jeff
jeff.gelfand@us.abb.com, Nat'l Sales/Mktg. Dir., ABB Inc., TX, Dallas
Gelfand, Jeffrey ....(214) 328-1202
jeff.gelfand@us.abb.com, Nat'l Sales/Mktg. Dir.-Printing Systems, ABB, Inc. (Printing Systems), WI, New Berlin
Gellar, David 860/701-4291
d.gellar@theday.com, Sales Development Manager, The Day Publishing Company, CT, New London
Gelman, Bernard
bernardgelman@aol.com, Owner/Ed., The Gelman Feature Syndicate, NY, Roscoe
Gelmi di Caporiacco, Sergio
p.geovarnette@ladige.it, Pres., L'ADIGE, Trent
Geloff, Peter ....(360) 735-4625
peter.geloff@columbian.com, Circ. Mgr., Single Copy, The Columbian, WA, Vancouver
Gemmiti, Jamie
jamieg@mountwashingtonvalley.com, Photography Ed., The Conway Daily Sun, NH, North Conway
Gendelman, George J.
george.gendelman@presscopyright.com, Pres., International Press Syndicate, Paris
Gendes Shact, Barb
info@communitechservices.com, Vice Pres., CommuniTech Services Inc., IL, Arlington Heights
Gennario, Chris..........................(631) 843-4744
Adv. Administrator, Newsday.com Bus., Newsday, NY, Melville
Gentry, James K........................(785) 864-4755
jschool@ku.edu, Prof., University of Kansas, KS, Lawrence
Gentry, Jim................................(252) 329-9594
jgentry@reflector.com, Sports Ed., The Daily Reflector, NC, Greenville
Genung, Jack ....(732) 565-7231
jgenung@thnt.com, Sports Ed., Home News Tribune, NJ, East Brunswick
Genung, Jeffrey ....(607) 337-3070
jeff@evesun.com, Mng. Ed., The Evening Sun, NY, Norwich
George, Charles
sales@midamericagraphics.com, Pres., Mid-

America Graphics, Inc., MO, Harrisonville
George, Hunter........................(205) 325-2295
Exec. Ed., The Birmingham News, AL, Birmingham
George, Beverly................................ext. 130
bgeorge@nvdaily.com, Prodn. Mgr., Mailroom, Northern Virginia Daily, VA, Strasburg
George, Cindy
cmgeorge@fremont.gannett.com, Pub., News-Herald, OH, Port Clinton
George, P.J.
editorial@mm.co.in, News Ed., MALAYALA MANORAMA, Cochin, Kerala
George, Amy............................217-373-7453
ageorge@news-gazette.com, Director of Market Development, News-Gazette Inc., IL, Champaign
George, Kandi
kgeorge@dailyhome.com, Circ. Mgr., The Daily Home, AL, Talladega
Georgiadis, N.
agonas@xan.forthnet.gr, Pub., AGONAS, Xanthi, Thrace
Geosits, Stephanie....................(617) 495-5969
Harvard Univ./JFK School of Gov't, MA, Cambridge
Geppert, Dennis........................(616) 546-4277
dennis.geppert@hollandsentinel.com, Photo/Video Team Leader, The Holland Sentinel, MI, Holland
Geraghty, Pat..........................(651) 322-6342
Nat'l Sales Mgr./Newspaper Handling Systems, Cannon Equipment, MN, Rosemount
Geralds, Paul W.
pgeralds@earthlink.net, Vice Pres., Sales/Mktg., Smith Pressroom Products, Inc., KS, Lenexa
Gerard, Gary
ggerard@timesuniononline.com, General Manager, Times-Union, IN, Warsaw
Gerardi, Charles........................(561) 820-4125
cgerardi@pbpost.com, Vice Pres./Gen. Mgr., The Palm Beach Post, FL, West Palm Beach
Gerardi, Charles
charles_gerardi@palmbeachpost.com, Gen. Mgr., Palm Beach Interactive, FL, West Palm Beach
Gerber, Dale E.
dgerber@dixcom.com, CFO, Dix Communications, OH, Wooster
Gerber, Rebecca........................(620) 408-9924
rebecca.gerber@dodgeglobe.com, Classified Adv. Mgr., Dodge City Daily Globe, KS, Dodge City
Gerds, Warren..........................(920) 431-8352
wgerds@greenbaypressgazette.com, Film/Theater Ed., Green Bay Press-Gazette, WI, Green Bay
Gerhart, Lori E...........................(610) 371-5103
lgerhart@readingeagle.com, Adv. Mgr., Sales, Reading Eagle, PA, Reading
Geringer, Dan
geringd@phillynews.com, Columnist, News, The Philadelphia Daily News, PA, Philadelphia
Gerke, Julie..............................(309) 820-3256
jgerke@pantagraph.com, Mng. Ed., The Pantagraph, IL, Bloomington
Gerken, Bob..............................(402) 444-1449
bob.gerken@owh.com, Adv. Mgr., Major Accts., Omaha World-Herald, NE, Omaha
Gerl, Ellen................................(740) 597-3136
Asst. Prof., Ohio University, OH, Athens
Gerlach, Michele
editor@andalusiastarnews.com, Pub., Andalusia Star-News, AL, Andalusia
Germain, Jean
info@leparisien.fr, MD, LE PARISIEN, Paris
German, Greg
info@martinyale.com, Pres., Martin Yale, Inc., IN, Wabash
Germann, Chris..........................941-206-1435
cgermann@suncoastpress.com, Press Room Manager, Charlotte Sun, FL, Charlotte Harbor
Germann, Eric............................(419) 993-2190
egermann@limanews.com, Systems Integrated Mgr., The Lima News, OH, Lima
Germano, Andrea.........(718) 981-1234 ext. 2550
Adv. Mgr., Serv., Staten Island Advance, NY, Staten Island
Germuska, Tom..........................(260) 461-8428
tgermuska@jg.net, Asst. Mng. Ed., Metro, The Journal Gazette, IN, Fort Wayne
Gerry, Kristy..............................402-444-3129
Dir., Production, Omaha World-Herald, NE, Omaha
Gerry, Kristy..............................402-444-3129
Dir., Production, Omaha World-Herald, NE, Omaha
Gerstenberg, Dr. Bruno
vertrieb@gerstenberg.com, Proprietor, Hildesheimer Allgemeine Zeitung, Hildesheim
Gerstmyer, Tim..........................973-569-7845
Director, Real Estate and Corporate Advertising, North Jersey Media Group, NJ, Woodland Park
Gerzanics, Janine......................(408) 741-4073
West Valley College, CA, Saratoga
Gesell, Michelle
admin@thisisstaffordshire.co.uk, Adv. Mgr., EVENING SENTINEL, Stoke-On-Trent, Staffordshire
Gesler, Josh......................................ext. 237
Systems Specialist, Walla Walla Union-Bulletin, WA, Walla Walla
Gess, Joe..................................(813) 259-7447
Adv. Mgr., Majors/National, The Tampa Tribune, FL, Tampa
Getertz, Boine
redaktionen@hn.se, MD, HALLANDS NYHETER, Falkenberg
Getler, Al....................................978-946-2110
agetler@eagletribune.com, Pub., The Eagle-Tribune, MA, North Andover
agetler@eagletribune.com, Pub., Carriage Towne News, NH, Kingston
Gets, Erik..................................(419) 521-7374
egets@nncogannett.com, Grp. Consumer Mktg. Mgr., News Journal, OH, Mansfield
Gett, Sam..................................(507) 645-1112
sgett@northfieldnews.com, Vice Pres. of Develop., Huckle Media, LLC, MI, Traverse City
Gettinger, Tom P.
publisher@sullivan-times.com, Gen. Mgr., The Sullivan Daily Times, IN, Sullivan
Gettman, Tracy..................................ext. 241
Circ. Mgr., The Daily Sentinel, CO, Grand Junction
Getts, Matt....................(260) 347-0400 ext. 127
mattg@kpcnews.net, Senior Reporter, The News-Sun, IN, Kendallville
Geurts, Jimmy............................(813) 974-5190
Univ. of South Florida, FL, Tampa
Geyer, Debby..............................(419) 724-6157
dgeyer@toledoblade.com, Circ. Coord., Newspapers in Educ., The Blade, OH, Toledo
Ghanem, Salma
ghanem@panam.edu, Chair, University of Texas-Pan American, TX, Edinburg
Ghezzi, Paolo......................................990-711
Dir., IL MATTINO DI BOLZANO E PROVINCIA, Bolzano
Ghisani, Rodrigo..............................4253-3320
rodrigoghisani@elsolquilmes.com.ar, Pres., El Sol S.A., Quilmes, Provincia de Buenos Aires
Gholdston, John..........................435-586-7751
gholdston@suu.edu, Southern Utah Univ., UT, Cedar City
Gholson, Nick..............................(940) 720-3470
gholsonn@wtr.com, Sports Ed., Wichita Falls Times Record News, TX, Wichita Falls
Ghosh, Bipasha............................6462234000
Bipasha.Ghosh@thomsonreuters.com, Global Director of Marketing, Reuters Media, NY, New York
Giambruno, Michelle
mngiambruno0@frostburg.edu, Manging Editor, The Bottom Line, MD, Frostburg
Giametta, Jim..............................(903) 596-6281
ajg@tylerpaper.com, Exec. Ed., Tyler Morning Telegraph, TX, Tyler
Giang, Nhat
email@chieuduong.com.au, Ed. in Chief, CHIEU DUONG
Giannonccaro, Catherine
cgiannoccaro@newburyportnews.com, Adv. Mgr., The Daily News, MA, Newburyport
Gibb, Steve..................................(306) 657-6315
sgibb@sp.canwest.com, Ed., The StarPhoenix, SK, Saskatoon
Gibb Guerrero, Raul
redaccion@laopinion.com.mx, Owner/Pres., LA OPINION, Poza Rica, Veracruz
Gibbard, Jerry
jgibbard@nbearstnp.com, Prodn. Mgr., The Huron Daily Tribune, MI, Bad Axe
Gibbens, Mark............................(605) 394-8390
mark.gibbens@rapidcityjournal.com, Prodn. Dir., Rapid City Journal, SD, Rapid City
Gibbons, Mike............................(803) 644-2381
mgibbons@aikenstandard.com, News Ed., Aiken Standard, SC, Aiken
Gibbons, Kathy............................(231) 933-1452
kgibbons@record-eagle.com, Features Ed., Record-Eagle, MI, Traverse City
Gibbs, Maria..............................(212) 893-2170
maria.gibbs@dailymail.co.uk, Mgr., Associated Newspapers (USA) Ltd., NY, New York
Gibens, Guillermo......................(641) 673-2170
William Penn Univ., IA, Oskaloosa
Giblin, Patrick............................(209) 578-2347
pgiblin@modbee.com, Technology Writer, The Modesto Bee, CA, Modesto
Gibney, Shannon........................(763) 488-0497
North Hennepin Cmty. College, MN, Brooklyn Park
Gibney, Charles W.......................(201) 646-4303
gibney@northjersey.com, Exec. Vice Pres./CFO/Treasurer, North Jersey Media Group, Inc., NJ, Hackensack
Gibson, Robin............................(765) 213-5855
rgibson@thestarpress.com, Asst. Metro Ed., The Star Press, IN, Muncie
Gibson, Candice..........................(318) 678-6364
Bossier Parish Cmty. College, LA, Bossier City
Gibson, Enrique Zileri
info@caretas.com.pe, Ed., CARETAS, Lima
Gibson, Malcolm..........................(785) 864-7667
mgibson@kansan.com, Gen. Mgr./News Advisor, The University Daily Kansan, KS, Lawrence
Gibson, Jim..............................(250) 380-5357
jgibson@te.canwest.com, Columnist, Times Colonist, BC, Victoria
Gibson, David
dgibson@twotwelve.com, Founder/Principal/Pres., Two Twelve, NY, New York
Gibson, Nevil
ngibson@nbr.co.nz, Ed. in Chief, NATIONAL BUSINESS REVIEW
Gibson, Jill
jlgibson@actx.edu, Broadcast and Online Adviser, Amarillo College, TX, Amarillo
Giddens, Tharon........................(706) 823-3347
feature@augustachronicle.com, Features Ed., The Augusta Chronicle, GA, Augusta
Giebel, Heinz-Ludwig
redaktion@schwarzwaelder-bote.de, Mgr., Der Enztaler, Neuenburg
Giebel, Heinz-Ludwig
service@schwarzwaelder-bote.de, Bus. Mgr., Schwarzwalder Bote, Oberndorf
Gieneart, Kathryn......................8124611238
gieneartk@courierpress.com, Dir., Mktg., Evansville Courier & Press, IN, Evansville
Gieseke, Bridget........................(707) 526-8590
bridget.gieseke@pressdemocrat.com, Adv. Mgr., The Press Democrat, CA, Santa Rosa
Gieseking, Hal
halron8@yahoo.com, Pres., The Business Scribe, Inc., VA, Williamsburg
Gieskes, Hans
hans.gieskes@cision.com, Pres., Cision AB, Stockholm
Giffels, David............................(330) 996-3572
dgiffels@thedeaconjournal.com, Columnist, Local, Akron Beacon Journal, OH, Akron
Giglio, Susan............................(970) 224-7773
Circ. Mgr., Opns., The Coloradoan, CO, Fort Collins
Gil, Raul....................................(805) 564-5185
rgil@newspress.com, Dir., Systems, Santa Barbara News-Press, CA, Santa Barbara
Gilbert, Miriam..........................(215) 596-8769
Univ. of the Sciences in Philadelphia, PA, Philadelphia
Gilbert, Glenn
glenn.gilbert@oakpress.com, Exec. Ed., The Oakland Press, MI, Pontiac
Gilbert, Holly............................(248) 370-4138
Oakland Univ., MI, Rochester
Gilbert, Karl D.
k.gilbert24@hotmail.com, Pres., Golf Publishing Syndicate, PA, Allentown
Gilbert, Michael..........................(615) 418-9154
Lipscomb Univ., TN, Nashville
Gilbert, Anne..............................(561) 364-5798
antique2@bellsouth.net, Pres./Writer, Antique Detective Syndicate, FL, Boynton Beach
Gilbert, Tyger
tylergilbert@azwebads.com, Webmaster, Mountain Media, NV, Las Vegas
Gilchrest, Ryan..........................(478) 744-4364
rgilchrest@macon.com, Interactive Mgr., The Telegraph, GA, Macon
Gilchrist, Guy............................(860) 693-0587
gilchristguy@yahoo.com, Self Syndicator, Gilchrist Features, CT, Simsbury
Gilchrist, Tracy..........................250-371-6143
tgilchrist@kamloopsnews.ca, City Editor, Kamloops Daily News, BC, Kamloops
Gilchrist, David..........................(509) 582-1460
dgilchrist@tri-cityherald.com, Adv. Dir., Tri-City Herald, WA, Kennewick
Giles, Donnell............................(910) 343-2330
donnell.giles@starnewsonline.com, Circ. Opns. Dir., Star-News, NC, Wilmington
Giles, Tammi..............................(405) 379-5411
holdenvillenews@itlnet.net, Prodn. Mgr., Pre Press, Holdenville News, OK, Holdenville
Giles, Charlie E...........................(757) 247-4844
cgiles@dailypress.com, Financial Planning Mgr., Daily Press, VA, Newport News
Gilkay, Julie..ext. 319
jgilkay@appleton.gannett.com, Custom Publishing Asst. Ed., The Post-Crescent, WI, Appleton
Gill, Pam Wier..................................ext. 5641
Mgr., Bus./Accounting, The Post and Courier, SC, Charleston
Gill, Carrie..................................609-272-7337
cgill@pressofac.com, Circulation Sales Development Manager, The Press of Atlantic City, NJ, Pleasantville
Gill, Regina
regina.gill@ft.com, Adv. Mgr., Financial Times, Frankfurt am Main
Gill, Susan
advertising@bannernews.net, Gen. Mgr., Banner-News, AR, Magnolia
Gillaspy, John A.........................(812) 829-2255
Gen. Mgr., Spencer Evening World, IN, Spencer
Gilles, Sandy..............................(873) 986-5514
Adv. Dir., The Beaufort Gazette, SC, Beaufort
Gillespie, Jeff......................................ext. 238
jeff.gillespie@rockdalecitizen.com, Sports Ed., The Rockdale Citizen, GA, Conyers
Gillespie, Kim
editor@dailypost.co.nz, Ed., DAILY POST
Gillespie, Scott............................(612) 673-4516
Scott.Gillespie@startribune.com, Ed./VP Editorial Pages, Star Tribune, MN, Minneapolis
Gillespie, Carla..........................(205) 722-0116
carla.gillespie@tuscaloosanews.com, HR/Administrative Asst., The Tuscaloosa News, AL, Tuscaloosa
Gillet, Claude
infolj@actu24.be, Ed. in Chief, LE JOUR/LE COURRIER, Verviers, Heusy
Gilley, Mary Lou..........................(707) 256-2273
mgilley@napanews.com, Prodn. Foreman, Composing, Napa Valley Register, CA, Napa
Gilliam, Chris
cgilliam@bannernews.net, Sports Ed., Banner-News, AR, Magnolia
Gilliam, Dona
gilliadj@jmu.edu, Prof., James Madison University, VA, Harrisonburg
Gillies, Iain
editorial@gisborneherald.co.nz, Ed., GISBORNE HERALD
Gilligan, Tom............................(907) 459-7528
circulation@newsminer.com, Circ. Dir., Fairbanks Daily News-Miner, AK, Fairbanks
Gillis, Heather..........................(416) 847-2092
hgillis@bbm.ca, Exec. Asst., BBM Canada, ON, Toronto
Gillis, Paula..............................609-272-7236
pgillis@pressofac.com, Local Content Producer/Hyperlocal, The Press of Atlantic City, NJ, Pleasantville
Gillis, David

dgillis@mspress.org, Sales Director, Mississippi Press Association, MS, Jackson
Gillis, Tamara L.
GILLISTL@etown.edu, Chair/Assoc. Prof., Elizabethtown College, PA, Elizabethtown
Gillispie, Jay
jgillispie@chicoer.com, Circulation Director, Chico Enterprise-Record, CA, Chico
Gillmly, C.W.
sales@comtexnews.net, Chrmn./Interim CEO, Comtex News Network, VA, Alexandria
Gillon, Chris ....**ext. 236**
Contact, College Publisher, Inc., MA, Cambridge
Gills, Sandy...............**(843) 706-8160 ext. 8160**
sgillis@islandpacket.com, Adv. Dir., The Island Packet, SC, Bluffton
Gilmore, Bob
graphic@graphicpub.com, Pres., Graphic Publishing Systems, Inc., MS, Clinton
Gilmore, Guy **651-228-5404**
ggilmore@pioneerpress.com, Pres./Pub., St. Paul Pioneer Press, MN, Saint Paul
Gilmore, Lee..........................**(248) 519-9200**
bbinfo@bbfurnitureadvertising.com, Pres., B&B - Banker & Brisebois Advertising, MI
Gilpin, Keith ....**(714) 796-3578**
kgilpin@ocregister.com, Vice Pres., Adv. Dist., The Orange County Register, CA, Santa Ana
Gilroy, Joseph ....**(570) 629-9128**
Prodn. Mgr., Mailroom, Pocono Record, PA, Stroudsburg
Gilroy, Herb ....**(814) 870-1851**
herb.gilroy@timesnews.com, HR Dir., Erie Times-News, PA, Erie
Gilroy, Joe
jgilroy@njherald.com, Post Press Foreman, New Jersey Herald, NJ, Newton
Gimenez, Nelson
gimenez@jcomm.com.br, Gen. Mgr., Jornal do Comercio, Rio De Janeiro
Ginat, Goman
hazofe@zahav.net.il, Ed., National Religious Front
Ginepi, Mauricio
mginepi@jcom.com.br, Pres., Jornal do Comercio, Rio De Janeiro
Ginfrida, Kimberly ....**(843) 317-7285**
kginfrida@florencenews.com, News Ed., Morning News, SC, Florence
Gingles, Keenan
kgingles@hammondstar.com, Pub., The Daily Star, LA, Hammond
Ginsbach, Pam
anwclub@comcast.net, Pres., American News Women's Club, Inc., DC, Washington
Ginsberg, R.K.
rkgwga@aol.com, Pres., William Ginsberg Associates, NY, New York
Ginsburg, Ned
sales@mbmcorp.com, Pres., MBM Corp., SC, North Charleston
Ginter, Barry ....**(360) 754-5423**
bginter@olympia.gannett.com, City Ed., The Olympian, WA, Olympia
Giomi, Staci...........................**(720) 222-2222**
sgiomi@aurorasentinel.com, Classified Mgr., Aurora Sentinel, CO, Aurora
Giordano, Mario
sigreterio@ilgiornale, Ed. in Chief, IL GIORNALE, Milan
Giorgios, George
mail@simerini.com.cy, Ed. in Chief, SIMERINI, Nicosia
Girardet, Michael
wz.razinfki@p-online.de, Pub., WZ WESTDEUTSCHE ZEITUNG, Dusseldorf
Girdler, Jim
circulation@somerset-kentucky.com, Circ. Mgr., The Commonwealth-Journal, KY, Somerset
Giri, Hardev
lokasatta@rediffmail.com, Ed., LOKASATTA-JANASATTA, Baroda, Gujarat
Giroir, Chris ....**(256) 740-4716**
chris.giroir@timesdaily.com, Dir., ITS/Pre Press Serv., TimesDaily, AL, Florence
Gisclair, Jessica
jgisclair@elon.edu, Assoc. Prof., Elon University, NC, Elon
Gismondi, Mario
pubblicita@sigma86.it, MD, PUGLIA, Bari
Gitahi, Linus
lgitahi@nation.co.ke, CEO, DAILY NATION, Nairobi
Gitosardjono, H. Sukamdani S.
pda_bisnis@bisnis.co.id, Ed., BISNIS INDONESIA, Jakarta, Java
Gittens, Vivian Anne
nationnews@sunbeach.net, Pub., THE DAILY NATION/THE WEEKEND NATION/THE SUNDAY SUN, Bridgetown
Gittens, Jim ....**ext. 2053**
Editorial Page Ed., The Citizens' Voice, PA, Wilkes-Barre
Gittleman, Linda ....**(989) 463-6071**
lgittleman@michigannewspapers.com, Mng. Ed., Alma, Morning Sun, MI, Mount Pleasant
Gitto, Joseph A.
jgitto@mpival.com, Vice Pres., Management Planning, Inc., FL, Orlando
Giz, Alvaro
agiz@ultimasnoticias.com.uy, Dir., Impresora Polo Ltd., Montevideo
Giza, Roger **847-274-4231**
President, Burnishine Products, IL
Gjolme, Andreas
andreas.gjolme@budstikka.no, Ed. in Chief, BUDSTIKKE, Billingstad
Gjoulosku, Mikai
argesul@gmail.com, Mgr., ARGESUL LIBER, Arges, Pitesti
Gjurich, Louis.........................**(814) 532-5110**
Controller, The Tribune-Democrat, PA, Johnstown
Glad, Geir
geir.glad@helgeland-arbeiderblad.no, Ed., HELGELAND ARBEIDERBLAD, Mosjoeen
Gladstone, Neil ....**(212) 293-8725**
ngladstone@unitedmedia.com, Mng. Ed., Editorial, United Media, OH, Cincinnati
Gladys, Niki ....**(775) 881-1269**
ngladys@nevadaappeal.com, Pub., Nevada Appeal, NV, Carson City
Glancey, Christine
editor@wsj.com, Mng. Ed., WALL STREET JOURNAL, Hong Kong
Glantz, Gordon ....**ext. 212**
gglantz@timesherald.com, Mng. Ed., The Times Herald, PA, Norristown
Glasar, Stefan
info@bietigheimerzeitung.de, Proprietor, BIETIGHEIMER ZEITUNG, Bietigheim-Bissingen
Glaser, Susan..........................**(216) 999-4240**
Travel Editor, The Plain Dealer, OH, Cleveland
Glasier, David S. ....**ext. 551**
Radio/Television Writer, The News-Herald, OH, Willoughby
Glass, Sarah ....**(913) 530-0854**
saglass@mnu.edu, Editor-in-Chief, MidAmerica Nazarene University, KS, Olathe
Glasser, Selma ....**(818) 769-4774**
Pres./Ed., Glasserfide Directory, CA, Toluca Lake
Glastris, Paul..........................**202-955-9010**
glastris@washingtonmonthly.com, Ed. in Chief, The Washington Monthly LLC, DC, Washington
Gleason, Brian **941-206-1133**
Viewpoint Editor, Charlotte Sun, FL, Charlotte Harbor
Gleeson, Peter
peter.gleeson@townsvillebulletin.com.au, Ed., TOWNSVILLE BULLETIN
Gleich, Marta
marta.gleich@zerohora.com.br, Ed. in Chief, Zero Hora, Porto Alegre, Rio Grande do Sul
Gleim, Jim
jgleim@bayareanewsgroup.com, Pub., The Daily Democrat, CA, Woodland
Glen, Dale
mail@petcorolls.com, Sales Mgr., Petco Roller Co., IL, Lake Forest
Glenas, Orcutt
gorcutt@lagrandeobserver.com, Adv. dir., The Observer, OR, La Grande
Glencross, Dorothy
dorothyg@dailyinterlake.com, Bus. Mgr., Daily Inter Lake, MT, Kalispell
Glende, Phil............................**(608) 252-6117**
pglende@madison.com, City Ed., Wisconsin State Journal, WI, Madison
Glendenning, Lauren ....**(970) 748-2983**
lglendenning@vaildaily.com, Community Ed., Vail Daily, CO, Vail
Glenen, Dave ....**(902) 752-3000**
dglenen@ngnews.ca, Mng. Ed., The News, NS, New Glasgow
Glenn, Barry ....**(407) 420-5497**
bglenn@orlandosentinel.com, Lifestyles Ed., Orlando Sentinel, FL, Orlando
Glick, Jeff ....**(615) 881-7601**
jglick@tennessean.com, Dir/Design Studio, The Tennessean, TN, Nashville
Glick, Damian
dglick@recordnet.com, Prodn. Dir., Opns., The Record, CA, Stockton
Glick, Albert....................................**ext. 248**
aglick@theworldlink.com, Circ. Dir., The World, OR, Coos Bay
Glickman, Caroline ....**(434) 385-5552**
cglickman@newsadvance.com, City Ed., The News & Advance, VA, Lynchburg
Glidewell, Jim...............**(434) 432-1654 ext. 11**
jglidewell@womackpublishing.com, Accounting Mgr., Womack Publishing Co., VA, Chatham
Glines, Walt............................**(408) 842-5359**
wglines@svnewspapers.com, Circ. Mgr., Free Lance, CA, Hollister
Glines, Sara...........................**(303) 954-6463**
sglines@medianewsgroup.com, Vice President of Field Operations, MediaNews Group Inc, CO, Denver
Glink, Ilyce R. ....**(847) 835-3450**
ilyce@thinkglink.com, Pub., Think Glink Inc., IL, Chicago
Glitman, Russell.............................**ext. 2120**
russell.glitman@rutlandherald.com, Digital Media Dir., The Times Argus, VT, Barre
Gloster, Steve..........................**(613) 732-3373**
ads@thedailyobserver.ca, Pub., Observer, ON, Pembroke
Glynn, Carroll J.
glynn.14@osu.edu, Dir./Prof., Ohio State University, OH, Columbus
Glynn, John ....**(800) 255-6734**
jglynn@amuniversal.com, Vice Pres., Acquisitions/Rights, Universal Uclick, MO, Kansas City
Glynn, Patrick..................................**ext. 161**
pglynn@flashnews.com, Mng. Ed., Wireless Flash News, Inc., CA, San Diego
Gmur, Heinc
h.gmur@sarganserlander.ch, Ed. in Chief, SARGANSERLANDER, Mels, St. Gallen
Gneiser, Jonathan
areanews@marshfieldnewsherald.com, General manager/editor, Marshfield News-Herald, WI, Marshfield
Gnuechtel, Herman
sales@webprintingcontrols.com, Pres., Web Printing Controls, IL, Barrington
Gober, Dee Dee........................**(559) 735-3224**
tech@visaliatimesdelta.com, Dir., Information Systems, Visalia Times-Delta & Tulare Advance-Register, CA, Visalia
Gober, Deanne.........................**(559) 735-3224**
tech@visaliatimesdelta.com, Dir., Info Technology, Visalia Times-Delta, CA, Visalia
Gocke, Martin "MJ".....................**559-735-3355**
Media Sales Manager, Visalia Times-Delta, CA, Visalia
Goddard, Jillian ....**(416) 947-3123**
jgoddard@sunpub.com, Photo Reprint Sales, Sun Media Corporation/Toronto Sun Syndicate Sales, ON, Toronto
Godfrey, Gary
production@woh.rr.com, Secreatary/Treasurer, OHIAD, OH, Covington
Godon, Louise ....**(514) 393-5139**
info@odcinc.ca, Exec. Sec., Office de la Distribution Certifiee (ODC, Inc.), QC, Montreal
Goebel, Jenn............................**(508) 520-1714**
jenn@contentthatworks.com, COO, Content That Works, IL, Chicago
Goebel, Jil ....**(719) 785-9900**
jil.goebel@origincom.com, Acct. Servs./Media Dir., Origin Communications, Inc., CO, Colorado Springs
Goeckner, Ken ....**ext. 140**
kgoeckner@cnhi.com, Adv. Dir., Effingham Daily News, IL, Effingham
Goeken, Debrah ....**(303) 892-5443**
goekend@rockymountainnews.com, Mng. Ed., Rocky Mountain News, CO, Denver
Goelzhaeufer, Nicola
nicola@mpimedia.com, Contact, MPI Teleproductions, IL, Orland Park
Goenka, Vivek
feedback@expressindia.com, Mng. Ed., INDIAN EXPRESS, New Delhi
Goenka, Vivek
editor@expressindia.com, Mng. Ed., FINANCIAL EXPRESS, Chennai, Tamil Nadu
Goens, Mike ....**(256) 740-5740**
mike.goens@timesdaily.com, Mng. Ed., TimesDaily, AL, Florence
Goetz, Paul
pgoetz@themountainmail.com, Mng. Ed., The Mountain Mail, CO, Salida
Goetz, Devon P. **805-781-7805**
dgoetz@thetribunenews.com, VP/Human Resources, The Tribune, CA, San Luis Obispo
Goetz, Bob..............................**(518) 565-4124**
bgoetz@pressrepublican.com, Sports Ed., Press-Republican, NY, Plattsburgh
Gofus, Nancy B. ....**(703) 206-5600**
info@mci.com, Sr. Vice Pres., Mktg./CMO, MCI, VA, Ashburn
Gogick, John ....**(706) 823-3450**
jgogick@augustachronicle.com, News Ed., The Augusta Chronicle, GA, Augusta
Gogol, Frank ....**(732) 263-5711**
Monmouth Univ., NJ, West Long Branch
Goheen, Mike...........................**(937) 225-2219**
mgoheen@coxohio.com, Assistant Managing Editor, Production & Online, Dayton Daily News, OH, Dayton
Golan, Haggai
hagaig@globes.co.il, Ed. in Chief, GLOBES
Golan, Ari
ari@atomicimaging.com, Pres., Atomic Imaging, Inc., IL, Chicago
Gold, Anita ....**(773) 267-9773**
thecapecod@aol.com, Author/Creator/Owner, Antiques & Collectible Self-Syndicated Column, IL, Chicago
Gold, Paul
gold@transpconsult.com, Pres., Transportation Consultants, Inc., GA, Atlanta
Gold, Jon
jgold@metrosuburbia.com, Adv. Sales Mgr., Metro Suburbia, Inc./Newhouse Newspapers, GA, Alpharetta
Goldberg, Elliot
egoldberg@sjnews.com, Editorial Page Ed., The Gloucester County Times, NJ, Woodbury
Goldberg, Howard
info@ap.org, Bureau Chief, New York State Associated Press Association, NY, Albany
Goldberg, Ron ....**(312) 222-3911**
rgoldberg@tribune.com, Adv. Dir., Network, Chicago Tribune, IL, Chicago
Goldberg, Stan
sales@printwarellc.com, Pres., Printware, MN, Saint Paul
Goldberg, Larry
info@betascreen.com, Contact, Beta Screen Corp., NJ, Carlstadt
Goldberger, Richard ....**(801) 355-3336**
richard@fnanews.com, Mng. Ed., FNA News, UT, Salt Lake City
Golden, Jill..................**(814) 765-7813 ext. 234**
news@theprogressnews.com, Ed., The Progress, PA, Clearfield
Golden, Todd
todd.golden@tribstar.com, Sports Ed., The Tribune Star, IN, Terre Haute
Golden, Mike **605-331-2258**
mgolden@argusleader.com, IT Manager, Argus Leader, SD, Sioux Falls
Golden, Cory............................**(530) 747-8046**
cgolden@davisenterprise.net, Religion Ed., The Davis Enterprise, CA, Davis
Golden, Michael........................**(212) 556-1234**
Vice Chrmn., New England Newspaper Group, NY, New York
Vice Chrmn., The New York Times Co./Pub., International Herald Tribune, The New York Times Co., NY, New York
Golder, Ed ....**(616) 222-5613**
egolder@grpress.com, Editorial Page Ed., The Grand Rapids Press, MI, Grand Rapids
Golding, Mark ....**ext. 301**
markgolding@forsythnews.com, Circ. Dir.,

Forsyth County News, GA, Cumming
Golding, Mark ....ext. 301
markgolding@forsythnews.com, Circ. Dir., Forsyth County News, GA, Cumming
Goldman, Scott ....(317) 444-6085
scott.goldman@indystar.com, Asst. Mng. Ed., Visuals, The Indianapolis Star, IN, Indianapolis
Goldstein, Marianne ....(212) 293-8784
mgoldstein@unitedmedia.com, Exec. Dir., Editorial, United Media, OH, Cincinnati
Goldstein, Lorrie ....(416) 947-2212
lorrie.goldstein@sunmedia.ca, Sr. Assoc. Ed., The Toronto Sun, ON, Toronto
Goldstein, Norm
ngoldstein@ap.org, Special Projects Dir., Associated Press, AP Newsfeatures, NY, New York
Goldstone, Richard
ideaworks@ideaology.com, Vice Pres., Idealworks Presentations, MA, Hyde Park
Goldy, Andrea 518-395-3008
agoldy@dailygazette.net, Credit Mgr., The Daily Gazette, NY, Schenectady
Gollop, Howard ....(440) 245-6901 ext. 671
arcade@morningjournal.com, Entertainment/Amusements Ed., The Morning Journal, OH, Lorain
Golzman, Ita ....(212) 969-7584
igolzman@hearst.com, Vice Pres., North American Licensing, King Features Syndicate, NY, New York
igolzman@hearst.com, Vice Pres., North American Licensing, North America Syndicate, NY, New York
Gombach, Jennifer ....(317) 444-6667
jennifer.gombach@indystar.com, Brand Mgr., The Indianapolis Star, IN, Indianapolis
Gomez, Enrique
egomez@am.com.mx, Dir., AM, Leon, Guanajuato
Gomez, Jose
jgomez@el-mexicano.com.mx, Adv. Mgr., EL MEXICANO, Tijuana, Baja California Norte
Gomez Amado, Jose Antonio
director@grupodiarioarea.info, Dir., AREA CAMPO DE GILBRALTAR Y COSTA DEL SOL, La Linea de la Concepcion, Cadiz
Gomez Junco, Enrique
diariomty@hotmail.com, Gen. Mgr., EXTRA, Monterrey, Nuevo Leon
Gomez Nucamendi, Ericel
noticias@noticias-oax.com.mx, Pres., NOTICIAS, Oaxaca, Oaxaca
Gomez Orozco, Enrique
guanajuato@am.com.mx, Gen. Dir., AM DE SAN FRANCISCO, Altos
Gomez Orozco, Enrique
amcelaya@celaya.podernet.com.mx, Owner/Pres., Am, Celaya, Guanajuato
Gomoll, Kim
library@lnpnews.com, Librarian, Intelligencer Journal/Lancaster New Era/Sunday News, PA, Lancaster
Gonyaw, Michael
gonyawm@caledonian-record.com, Advertising Director/Online Mgr., The Caledonian-Record, VT, Saint Johnsbury
Gonzales, Victor ....(650) 508-3677
Notre Dame De Namur University, CA, Belmont
Gonzales, Victor ....(650) 391-1334
vgonzales@dailynewsgroup.com, Asst. City Ed., Palo Alto Daily News, CA, Menlo Park
Gonzales, Frank
fgonzales@sanmarcosrecord.com, Prodn. Foreman, Pressroom, San Marcos Daily Record, TX, San Marcos
Gonzales, Leticia ....(509) 577-7721
lgonzales@yakima-herald.com, HR Mgr., Yakima Herald-Republic, WA, Yakima
Gonzales, Randy
randyg_news@dailynews.net, Sports Ed., The Hays Daily News, KS, Hays
Gonzalez, Hector ....(562) 698-0955 ext. 3027
hector.gonzalez@sgvn.com, City Ed., The Whittier Daily News, CA, Whittier
Gonzalez, John ....(616) 222-5685
jgonzalez@grpress.com, Entertainment Ed., The Grand Rapids Press, MI, Grand Rapids
Gonzalez, Luis Miguel
lmgonzalez@eleconomista.com.mx, Ed., EL ECONOMISTA, Mexico City, Distrito Federal
Gonzalez, Humberto Villalobos
publicidad@hidrocalidodigital.com, Adv. Mgr., Hidrocalido, Aguascalientes, Aguascalientes
Gonzalez, Pedro J. 422-227
el-litoral@compunort.com.ar, Gen. Mgr., El Litoral, Corrientes, Provincia de Corrientes
Gonzalez, Mario
tribuna@latribuna.com.ni, Gen. Mgr., LA TRIBUNA, Managua
Gonzalez, Francisco A.
laopinion@opinion.com.mx, Pres., Medios Estrella de Oro, S.A. de C.V., Torreon, Coahuila
Gonzalez, Fernando
fgonzalez@cronista.com, Ed., El Cronista, Buenos Aires
Gonzalez, Yadira ....(214) 977-7214
ygonzalez@aldiatx.com, Cliente Serv. Coord., Al Dia, TX, Dallas
Gonzalez, Jorge A.
ecosdelvalle@hotmail.com, Pres., ECOS DEL VALLE, Cintalapa, Chiapas
Gonzalez Jerez, Antonio
toledo@abc.es, Dir., ABC, Toledo
Gonzalez Menendez, Marcelino
elcomercio@elcomercio-sa.es, Ed. in Chief, El Comercio, Gijon, Asturias
Gonzalez Perez, Arturo
soltij@oem.com.mx, Dir., EL SOL DE TIJUANA, Tijuana, Baja California
Gonzalez Ramos, Maria Eugenia
diario@diariodetampico.com, Pres., EXTRA, Tampico, Tamaulipas
Gonzalez Valdez, Jorge Luis
tribuna@tribunacampeche.com, Pres., Tribuna del Carmen, Ciudad del Carmen, Campeche
Gonzalo, Mar 305-262-7575
mgonzalo@efe.com, Bureau Chief-Miami, EFE News Services - Washington, DC, DC, Washington
Gooch, Cheryl R.
cgooch@claflin.edu, Chair/Prof., Claflin University, SC, Orangeburg
Good, Robin 281-660-5405
rgoodpmc@aol.com, Sr. Vice Pres., Nat'l Adv. Sales, Print Marketing Concepts, Inc., TX, Houston
Good, Dominic
letters.editor@ft.com, Adv. Dir., FINANCIAL TIMES, ENG, London
Good, Robin L. 281-660-5405
rgoodpmc@aol.com, Sr. Vice Pres., Print Marketing Concepts, Inc., TX, Houston
Good, Dan 609-272-7203
dgood@pressofac.com, Asst. Local Content Producer/Digital, The Press of Atlantic City, NJ, Pleasantville
Good, Jeffrey ....ext. 222
Ed., Valley News, VT, West Lebanon
Good, Robin L. ....(713) 780-7055 ext. 318
rgoodpmc@aol.com, Sr. Vice Pres., Print Marketing Concepts, Inc., TX, Houston
Goodhand, Margo
Margo.Goodhand@freepress.mb.ca, Ed., Winnipeg Free Press, MB, Winnipeg
Goodin, Rex
grex@alamogordonews.com, Circ. Mgr., Alamogordo Daily News, NM, Alamogordo
Goodlin, Lori
lgoodlin@yorkdispatch.com, Ed., The York Dispatch, PA, York
Goodman, Jeannie 951-368-9311
jgoodman@pe.com, Recruitment/SMB Sales Mgr, The Press-Enterprise, CA, Riverside
Goodman, Elaine
egoodman@tahoedailytribune.com, Mng. Ed., Tahoe Daily Tribune, CA, South Lake Tahoe
Goodman, Mike
mgoodman@coxnc.com, Editor/Editorial Page Editor, The Daily Advance, NC, Elizabeth City
Goodman, Hays ....(262) 670-1521
hgoodman@conleynet.com, Online/Mgmt. Info Servs. Mgr., The Freeman, WI, Waukesha
Goodman, Bruce ....(323) 981-8585
newsracks@earthlink.net, Pres., National Newsvend, CA, Los Angeles
Goodman, Jim
jgoodman@highpoint.edu, Asst. Prof., High Point University, NC, High Point
Goodrich, Teresa ....(248) 745-4526
Adv. Dir., The Oakland Press, MI, Pontiac
Goodrich, Dan
news@mydailyregister.com, Pub., Point Pleasant Register, WV, Point Pleasant
Goodrich, Robbie
rgoodrich@coxnews.com, Mng. Ed., The Daily Sentinel, TX, Nacogdoches
Goodsell, Jeff ....(205) 985-7021
jeffgoodsell@bellsouth.net, Webmaster, Frank Cummings Illustration, AL, Montevallo
Goodwin, Andrew ....(415) 422-6680
goodwina@usfca.edu, Chair, University of San Francisco, CA, San Francisco
Goodwin, Dave ....(305) 865 0158
davegoodwi@aol.com, Author/Owner, Dave Goodwin & Associates, FL, Miami Beach
Goodwin, Jerry ....(918) 595-7388
Tulsa Cmty. College, OK, Tulsa
Goodwin, Brooke ....(309) 438-5929
Daily Vidette, IL, Normal
Goodwin, Nathan
ngoodwin@starhq.com, Pub., Elizabethton Star, TN, Elizabethton
Goodwin-Garcia, Brenda
bgoodwin@metrosuburbia.com, Adv. Sales Mgr., Metro Suburbia, Inc./Newhouse Newspapers, FL, Boca Raton
Goossen, John
jgoossen@amestrib.com, Pub., The Tribune, IA, Ames
Goossen, John
jgoossen@amestrib.com, Pres., Iowa Newspapers, Inc., IA, Ames
Gopinath, B. ....ext. 612
bg@levelx.com, Chrmn., Level X LLC, NJ, Piscataway
Gorby, Marshall ....(937) 328-0340
mgorby@coxohio.com, Photo Ed., Springfield News-Sun, OH, Springfield
Gorczyca, Rob ....ext. 384
rob@monroenews.com, New Media Mgr., Web, The Monroe Evening News, MI, Monroe
Gordon, Robert 212-239-8714
robert.gordon@am-ny.com, Retail Advertising Director , amNew York, NY, New York
Gordon, Tracy 502-419-0919
tracy.gordon@religionnews.com, Editorial/Publishing Consultant, Religion News Service, DC, Washington
Gordon, Mel ....(303) 954-6433
mgordon@medianewsgroup.com, Vice President, IT, MediaNews Group Inc, CO, Denver
Gordon, Paul ....(206) 838-2016
paul.gordon@catalystpaper.com, Vice Pres./Gen. Mgr. Directory Paper, Catalyst Paper (USA), Inc., WA, Seattle
Gordon, Paul ....(309) 686-3288
pgordon@pjstar.com, Bus. Ed., Journal Star, IL, Peoria
Gordon, Anne ....(215) 854-4682
Mng. Ed./Vice Pres., The Philadelphia Inquirer, PA, Philadelphia
Gore, Kevin
kgore@coxnews.com, Sports Ed., The Daily Sentinel, TX, Nacogdoches
Gore, Don
don.gore@sonoco.com, Division Vice Pres., Sales, Sonoco Products Co., SC, Hartsville
Gorham, Christine
cgorham@lockhaven.com, Advertising Sales Manager, The Express, PA, Lock Haven
Gorman, Mike ....(985) 448-7612
mike.gorman@dailycomet.com, Editorial Page Editor, The Daily Comet, LA, Thibodaux
Gorman, Doug ....ext. 280
dgorman@news-daily.com, Sports Ed., News/Daily, GA, Jonesboro
Gorman, Fred
fgorman@reddeeradvocate.com, Pub., Red Deer Advocate, AB, Red Deer
Gorman, Robert D. ....ext. 2359
bgorman@wdt.net, Mng. Ed., Watertown Daily Times, NY, Watertown
Gormley, Mike ....(937) 376-6491
Central State Univ., OH, Wilberforce
Gorogiani, Andy
voice-net@voicenet1.com, Vice Pres., Mktg., eGIX, Inc., IN, Carmel
Gorski, Steve
info@alarcorp.com, Sales Mgr., Alar Engineering Corp., IL, Mokena
Gort, Den
redactie@nd.nl, MD, NEDERLANDS DAGBLAD, Barneveld
Gorven, Kelly
k.gorven@ocna.org, Member Services Coordinator, Ad*Reach, ON, Burlington
Goss, Nathan R. ....(770) 534-6162
Brenau Univ., GA, Gainesville
Goss, Nancy
ngoss@news-expressky.com, Everyday Living Ed., The Appalachian News-Express, KY, Pikeville
Goss, Dick ....(815) 729-6040
dgoss@scnl.com, Sports Ed., The Herald News, IL, Joliet
Goss, Aron
arongoss@shelbystar.com, Adv. Dir., The Star, NC, Shelby
Gossert, Shirley
classified@therecordherald.com, Adv. Mgr., Classified, The Record Herald, PA, Waynesboro
Gossett, Dave ....(478) 744-4210
dgossett@macon.com, Circ. Vice Pres., The Telegraph, GA, Macon
Gostisa, Leticia
info@quipp.com, Mktg. Mgr., Quipp, FL, Miami
Gotcher, Mike
gotcherm@apsu.edu, Chair, Austin Peay State University, TN, Clarksville
Gothie, Frank
fgothie@delcotimes.com, Pub., Delaware County Daily Times, PA, Primos
Gottlieb, Dr. Claus
info@teckbote.de, Bus. Mgr., DER TECKBOTE, Kirchheim Unter Teck
Gottlieb, Paul ....(360) 417-3536
paul.gottlieb@peninsuladailynews.com, Letters to Editors/Commentary, Peninsula Daily News, WA, Port Angeles
Gottus, Tina ....(863) 386-5811
tgottus@highlandstoday.com, Pub., Highlands Today, FL, Sebring
Gotwals, Ed ....(717) 262-4755
egotwals@publicopinionnews.com, Sports Editor, Public Opinion, PA, Chambersburg
Gouger, Marta ....(570) 420-4343
mgouger@poconorecord.com, Lifestyle Ed., Pocono Record, PA, Stroudsburg
Gould, Gary ....(248) 745-4668
gary.gould@oakpress.com, Metro Ed., Nights, The Oakland Press, MI, Pontiac
Gould, Dave ....(615) 259-8822
Vice Pres., Adv., The Tennessean, TN, Nashville
Gould, Wayne ....(603) 383-6729
wayne.gould@sudoku.com, Dir., Pappocom, NH, Glen
Gould, Jedd 860-379-9602
jgould@mediabids.com, President, Mediabids, Inc., CT, Winsted
Gould, Scott
scott@waynegouldpuzzles.com, Mgr., Pappocom, NH, Glen
Gould, Harriet E.
gould@globe.com, Vice Pres., Employee Rel., The Boston Globe, MA, Boston
Goulding, John
johng@greystar.co.nz, GM, THE GREYMOUTH EVENING STAR
Gouldstone, Barbara
4ngs@sbcglobal.net, Pres., Northern Graphic Supply, NV, Sparks
Gouvellis, Jim ....(941) 206-1136
gouvellis@sun-herald.com, Exec. Ed., Charlotte Sun, FL, Charlotte Harbor
Govang, Don
govangd@lincolnu.edu, Dept. Head/Assoc. Prof., Lincoln University, MO, Jefferson City
Gove, Scott M. ....(419) 342-4276
globe@sdgnewsgroup.com, Pres./Pub., Daily Globe, OH, Shelby
Gove, Chris ....(432) 333-7791
chris_gove@link.freedom.com, Sports Ed., Odessa American, TX, Odessa
Govette, Julie ....(209) 369-2761 ext. 226
comp@lodinews.com, Composing Mgr., Lodi News-Sentinel, CA, Lodi
Graaskamp, Daniel ....(715) 830-5821
dan.graaskamp@ecpc.com, Adv. Dir., Leader-Telegram, WI, Eau Claire
Graaskamp, Pieter ....ext. 3277

pieter.graaskamp@ecpc.com, Pres./CEO, Leader-Telegram, WI, Eau Claire
Graaskamp, Pieter....................(715) 833-9200
pieter.graaskamp@ecpc.com, First Vice Pres., Wisconsin Newspaper Association
Grabmuller, Thomas.............................8080
redaktion@trostberger-tagblatt.de, Ed., TROSTBERGER TAGBLATT, Trostberg
Grace, Jo-Ann W.
news@metnews.com, Co-Pub., Metropolitan News-Enterprise
Grace, Beth...........................(919) 789-2090
beth@ncpress.com, Exec. Dir., North Carolina Press Service, Inc., NC, Raleigh
Grace, Beth
beth@ncpress.com, Exec. Dir., North Carolina Press Association, NC, Raleigh
Graczyk, Mark.................................ext. 126
mgraczyk@batavianews.com, Mng. Ed., The Daily News, NY, Batavia
Gradin, Jonathan.....................(208) 769-3388
North Idaho College, ID, Coeur D Alene
Gradwohl, Colette
redaktion@landbote.ch, Ed., DER LANDBOTE, Winterthur, Zurich
Grady, Don
gradyd@elon.edu, Assoc. Prof./Dept. Chair, Elon University, NC, Elon
Grady, Robert.........................(518) 565-4148
bgrady@pressrepublican.com, Ed., Press-Republican, NY, Plattsburgh
Graells, Uwe
sn@madsack.de, Bus. Mgr., SN Schaumburger Nachrichten, Stadthagen
Grafe, Mike...........................(406) 791-6516
mgrafe@greatfal.gannett.com, Production Operations Dir., Great Falls Tribune, MT, Great Falls
Graff, Tim J............................(509) 837-4500
tgraff@sunnewspapers.com, Pub., Daily Sun News, WA, Sunnyside
Graff, Gary.............................(703) 878-8031
ggraff@insidenova.com, Adv. Dir., Manassas Journal Messenger, VA, Manassas
Gragg, Drew............................(613) 596-3799
dgragg@thecitizen.southam.ca, Bus. Ed., The Ottawa Citizen, ON, Ottawa
Graham, Cristal
cgraham@robesonian.com, Mgmt. Info Servs. Mgr., The Robesonian, NC, Lumberton
Graham, Patrick
pgraham@theparisnews.com, Ed., The Paris News, TX, Paris
Graham, John
leader@leaconet.com, Ed., Lovington Leader, NM, Lovington
Graham, John
jgraham@dailyherald.com, Mgr., Mktg. and Research Servs., Daily Herald, IL, Arlington Heights
Graham, Trish
tgraham@timesleaderonline.com, Lifestyles Ed., The Times Leader, OH, Martins Ferry
Graham, Patricia
pgraham@vancouversun.com, Ed. in Chief, The Vancouver Sun, BC, Vancouver
Graham, Pat............................(703) 878-8030
pgraham@insidenova.com, Circ. Dir., Manassas Journal Messenger, VA, Manassas
Graham, Ronda
grahamr@fayettevilleObserver.com, Controller, The Fayetteville Observer, NC, Fayetteville
Graham, Keith..............(724) 282-8000 ext. 204
kgraham@butlereagle.com, Adv. Dir., Butler Eagle, PA, Butler
Graham, Patricia..................................ext. 121
pgraham@potomacnews.com, Circ. Dir., Culpeper Star-Exponent, VA, Culpeper
Graham, Larry..........................(501) 378-3604
lgraham@ardemgaza.com, Circ. Dir., Arkansas Democrat-Gazette, AR, Little Rock
Graham, Gary...........................(705) 259-5811
Prodn. Foreman, Pressroom, The Sault Star, ON, Sault Ste Marie
Graham, Sandy
circulation@altustimes.com, Circ. Dir., Altus Times, OK, Altus
Graham, Keith...........................724-282-8000
kgraham@butlereagle.com, Director of advertising, Eagle Printing Co., PA, Butler
Graham, Stephanie
info@thecanadianpress.com, Correspondent, Canadian Press, The - Regina, SK, SK, Regina
Graham, Deborah.......................707-864-7000
tempest@solano.edu, Online Editor, Solano Community College, CA, Fairfield
Graham, Scott
Ed. in Chief, The Recorder
Grahn, Kari
kari.grahn@forssanlehti.fi, Ed. in Chief, FORSSAN LEHTI, Forssa
Grams, David...........................(815) 937-3338
dgrams@daily-journal.com, Prodn. Foreman, Press (Day), The Daily Journal, IL, Kankakee
Gramsch, Rudiger
nwz.anzeigen@swp.de, Ed., NWZ Goppinger Kreisnachrichten, Goppingen
Gran, Dana
dgran@santamariatimes.com, Features Ed., Santa Maria Times, CA, Santa Maria
Granatstein, Rob......................(416) 947-8359
rob.granatstein@sunmedia.ca, Editor, The Toronto Sun, ON, Toronto
Granda, Leonard V.
granda@focusweb.com, Pres., Focus Interactive Technology, Inc., NY, Troy
Grandcolas, Jack
jgrandcolas@nnnlp.com, Sales Dir., Newspaper National Network LP, NY, New York
Grandcolas, Jack.....................(415) 713-6568
jgrandcolas@nnnlp.com, Sr. Vice Pres./Dir., West Coast Sales, Newspaper National Network LP, NY, New York
Grande, Stephen
info@frycomm.com, Vice President, Sales, Fry Communications, PA, Mechanicsburg
Grande, Pam
pam@herkimertelegram.com, Adv. Mgr., The Evening Telegram, NY, Herkimer
Grandy, James..........................518-395-3094
jgrandy@dailygazette.net, Prodn. Mgr., The Daily Gazette, NY, Schenectady
Granerud, Terje
terje.granerud@eub.no, Ed. in Chief, EIDSVOLD BLAD/ULLENSAKER BLAD, Eidsvoll
Granger, Randy........................(251) 219-5370
rgranger@press-register.com, Dir., Mktg./Promo., Press-Register, AL, Mobile
Granier, Frank.............(208) 664-8176 ext. 1008
fgranier@cdapress.com, Bus. Mgr./Purchasing Agent, Coeur d'Alene Press, ID, Coeur d'Alene
Grant, Mischelle
mgrant@alm.com, Adv. Dir., Daily Report
Grantham, John..........................360-705-4585
john@noteads.com, President, NoteAds.com, Inc./Post-it Note Advertising, WA, Lacey
Granville, Charles
sales@capita.com, CEO, Capita Technologies, CA, Irvine
Graser, Tom..............................(740) 375-5107
tgraser@nncogannett.com, Mng. Ed., The Marion Star, OH, Marion
Graslie, Serri
editor@hamlineoracle.com, Hamline Univ., MN, Saint Paul
Grasso, Frank P.
fgrasso@nnnlp.com, Vice Pres., Newspaper Rel., Newspaper National Network LP, NY, New York
Gratten, Jim..............................(204) 571-7448
Prodn. Foreman, Mail Room (Night), Brandon Sun, MB, Brandon
Gratzfeld, Wilfried
mail@butzbacher-zeitung.de, Mng. Ed., BUTZBACHER ZEITUNG, Butzbach
Grauls, Marcel
hbvlsecretariaat@concentra.be, Project Mgr., HET BELANG VAN LIMBURG, 3500 Hasselt
Graupman, Dustin
dgraupman@ags.com, Pres., Automated Graphic Systems, MD, White Plains
Gravel, Vaughn M....................(570) 420-4380
vgravel@poconorecord.com, Prodn. Dir., Pocono Record, PA, Stroudsburg
Graveland, Bill..........................403-543-7238
bill.graveland@thecanadianpress.com, National Correspondent, Canadian Press, The - Calgary, AB, AB, Calgary
bill.graveland@thecanadianpress.com, National Correspondent, Canadian Press, The - Calgary, AB, AB, Calgary
Graves, Monica
lcldelivery@shighway.com, Circ. Mgr., Linn County Leader, MO, Brookfield
Graves, Tina............................(248) 745-4536
tina.graves@oakpress.com, Circ. Mgr., Single Copy, The Oakland Press, MI, Pontiac
Graves, Jeanna........................(662) 263-5352
Wood College, MS, Mathiston
Gravir, Sondre
sondre.gravir@bt.no, CEO, BERGENS TIDENDE, Bergen
Gravois, John...........................(817) 390-7734
grav@star-telegram.com, Asst. Mng. Ed., Gov't Affairs, Fort Worth Star-Telegram, TX, Fort Worth
Graxiola, Mike.........................(830) 257-0330
mike.graxiola@dailytimes.com, Ed., Kerrville Daily Times, TX, Kerrville
Gray, Janie..............................(281) 425-8000
Publisher, The Baytown Sun, TX, Baytown
Gray, Mark...............................(985) 857-2236
mark.gray@houmatoday.com, Operations Manager, The Courier, LA, Houma
Gray, Andy.......................................ext. 752
grayareas@tribtoday.com, Entertainment/Amusements Reporter, The Tribune Chronicle, OH, Warren
Gray, Dana
grayd@caledonian-record.com, Exec. Ed., The Caledonian-Record, VT, Saint Johnsbury
Gray, Jana
jana.gray@austindailyherald.com, Adv. Dir., Austin Daily Herald, MN, Austin
Gray, Bill
news@mpnews.net, Pub., Mt. Pleasant News, IA, Mount Pleasant
Gray, Lloyd...............................662-678-1579
lloyd.gray@journalinc.com, Executive Editor, Journal Publishing Company, MS, Tupelo
Gray, Lisa..ext. 220
Circ. Mgr., Middlesboro Daily News, KY, Middlesboro
Gray, TC...................................(808) 529-4832
tcgray@staradvertiser.com, Controller, Honolulu Star-Advertiser, HI, Honolulu
Gray, Mark...............................(985) 857-2236
mark.gray@houmatoday.com, Operations Manager, The Daily Comet, LA, Thibodaux
Gray, Matt
mgray@sjnewsco.com, Music Ed., The News of Cumberland County, NJ, Bridgeton
Gray, Lisa................................(202) 636-3379
lgray@washingtontimes.com, Circ. Mgr., Systems, The Washington Times, DC, Washington
Gray, Brian
tgray@coxnc.com, Creative Services Manager, The Daily Advance, NC, Elizabeth City
Graziano, Richard....................(860) 241-6780
rgraziano@Tribune.com, Pres./Pub./CEO, The Hartford Courant, CT, Hartford
Graziano, Dan...........................860-425-4322
Advertising Director, The Bulletin, CT, Norwich
Grech, Joe.................................(734) 994-6866
jgrech@annarbornews.com, Adv. Dir., Sales/Mktg., The Ann Arbor News, MI, Ann Arbor
Greco, Marcus...........................321-242-3512
mgreco@floridatoday.com, Packaging Center Manager, Florida Today, FL, Melbourne
Greco, Mike.......................................ext. 237
mgreco@norwalkreflector.com, Sports Ed., Norwalk Reflector, OH, Norwalk
Greechie, Steve.........................(212) 946-4352
sgreechie@publishinghouseresearch.com, Dir., Publishing House Research LLC, NY, New York
Green, John.................(620) 694-5700 ext. 311
jgreen@hutchnews.com, Reporter, The Hutchinson News, KS, Hutchinson
Green, Susan............................(843) 706-8201
sgreen@islandpacket.com, Adv. Mgr., Classified, The Island Packet, SC, Bluffton
Green, Kevin.............................(765) 932-2222
rushvillerepublican@rushvillerepublican.com, Mng. Ed., Rushville Republican, IN, Rushville
Green, William B.......................(956) 728-2501
bill@lmtonline.com, Pub., Laredo Morning Times, TX, Laredo
Green, Scott......................................ext. 670
scott.green@wickcommunications.com, Prodn. Mgr., Bisbee Daily Review, AZ, Bisbee
Green, Linda............................(559) 735-3268
news@visaliatimesdelta.com, Exec. Ed., Visalia Times-Delta & Tulare Advance-Register, CA, Visalia
Green, Bill................................(540) 665-4945
bgreen@winchesterstar.com, Circ. Mgr., The Winchester Star, VA, Winchester
Green, Mike.....................................ext. 3036
mgreen@dailytidings.com, Content Ed., The Ashland Daily Tidings, OR, Ashland
Green, Jason.............................(650) 391-1337
jgreen@dailynewsgroup.com, City Ed., Palo Alto Daily News, CA, Menlo Park
Green, Kevin.............................(903) 237-7792
kgreen@coxnews.com, Chief Photographer, Longview News-Journal, TX, Longview
Green, Michael
chf@chffoto.com, Co-Owner, CHF Foto Supply, NJ, South Hackensack
Green, Lisa...............................(260) 461-8200
lgreen@jg.net, Bus. Ed., The Journal Gazette, IN, Fort Wayne
Green, Tiffany
tgreen@pubgroup.com, Partner Services Coordinator, Hometown Content, TN, Franklin
Green, Leslie
lgreen@detroitnews.com, Arts/Entertainment Ed., The Detroit News, MI, Detroit
Green, Jennifer.........................(317) 444-6245
jennifer.green@indystar.com, Mng. Ed., The Indianapolis Star, IN, Indianapolis
Green, Carla A.
cgreen@mediapsansoftware.com, Vice Pres., Customer Servs., MediaSpan Media Software, FL, Melbourne
Green, Linda..............................559-735-3268
Executive Editor, Tulare Advance-Register, CA, Visalia
Green, Joe
paperman@gbpnews.com, The Banner Gazette, IN, Pekin
paperman@gbpnews.com, Circ. Mgr., The Times-Mail, IN, Bedford
Green, Andi
adverts@athensreview.com, Adv. Dir., Athens Daily Review, TX, Athens
Green, Linda............................(559) 735-3268
news@visaliatimesdelta.com, Exec. Ed., Visalia Times-Delta, CA, Visalia
Green, Janice...........................(772) 221-4102
janice.green@scripps.com, Dir., HR, Treasure Coast News/Press-Tribune, FL, Stuart
Green, Kevin L.
kevin.green@indianamediagroup.com, Regl. Mng. Ed., Greensburg Daily News, IN, Greensburg
Green, Carl
cgreen@edwpub.net, Managing editor, Edwardsville Intelligencer, IL, Edwardsville
Greenberg, Allen..............................ext. 5538
Deputy Mng. Ed., The Post and Courier, SC, Charleston
Greenberg, Heywood
greenberg_h@mail.lynchburg.edu, Dena/Prof., Journ., Lynchburg College, VA, Lynchburg
Greenberg, Howard
hgreenberg@sunsentinel.com, Pub., Orlando Sentinel, FL, Orlando
Greene, Aaron...........................(260) 481-6584
contact@ipfwcommunicator.org, Indiana-Purdue Univ., IN, Fort Wayne
Greene, Wayne
wayne.greene@tulsaworld.com, Editorial Writer, Tulsa World, OK, Tulsa
Greene, Rustin
greenerp@jmu.edu, Prof., James Madison University, VA, Harrisonburg
Greene, Donna..................................ext. 205
Teen-Age/Youth Ed., Middlesboro Daily News, KY, Middlesboro
Greene, Gary
ggreene@cribb.com, MD., Cribb, Greene & Associates, MT, Bozeman
Greene, Gary
ggreene@cribb.com, MD., Cribb, Greene & Associates, MT, Bozeman
Greene, Karen H........................(202) 334-4511

greenek@washpost.com, Opns. Mgr., The Washington Post Writers Group, DC, Washington
Greenspun, Barbara ....(702) 259-4050
barbara@lasvegassun.com, Pub., Las Vegas Sun, NV, Henderson
Greenstreet, Robert
bgrnst@ecok.edu, Chair, East Central University (Oklahoma), OK, Ada
Greenwald, Marilyn....................(740) 593-4387
Prof., Ohio University, OH, Athens
Greenwood, Penny
penny.greenwood@awp.ch, Sr. Acct. Mgr., Dow Jones Newswires - Zurich, Switzerland, Zurich
Greenwood, Alan......................(603) 594-6427
alang@telegraph-nh.com, Sports Ed., The Telegraph, NH, Hudson
Greer, Bill ....(561) 820-4530
bgreer@pbpost.com, Asst. Mng. Ed., Projects, The Palm Beach Post, FL, West Palm Beach
Greer, Daniel..........................(870) 508-8040
online@baxterbulletin.com, Online Mgr., The Baxter Bulletin, AR, Mountain Home
Greer, Bill ....(615) 259-8889
bgreer@tennessean.com, Asst. Features Ed., Presentation, The Tennessean, TN, Nashville
Greer, Bobby
bgreer@dailystatesman.com, Assistant Publisher, The Daily Statesman, MO, Dexter
Greer, Charles R.
sales@bgitex.com, Pres., B.G. Industrial, Inc., TX, Deer Park
Greer, Tom
tgreer@messenger-inquirer.com, Circ. Mgr., Home Delivery, Messenger-Inquirer, KY, Owensboro
Greeson, Ron
rgreeson@dailyadvocate.com, Sports Ed., Daily Advocate, OH, Greenville
Grefe, Richard ....ext. 3100
grefe@aiga.org, Exec. Dir., AIGA, the professional association for design, NY, New York
Gregersen, Arni ....+298 79 02 34
arni@dimma.fo, Managing editor, DIMMALAETTING, T□rshavn
Gregg, Janet..............................903-586-2236
publisher@jacksonvilleprogress.com, Publisher / Editor, Jacksonville Daily Progress, TX, Jacksonville
Gregory, Becky
bgregory@wacotrib.com, Mng. Ed., Waco Tribune-Herald, TX, Waco
Gregory, Jim
njgdesign@att.net, Exec. Sec., Eastern Ski Writers Association, NJ, Cherry Hill
Gregory, John ....ext. 2570
IT/Prodn. Dir., The Daily News, MA, Newburyport
Gregory, Thom..........................615/259-8881
tgregory@tennessean.com, Production Director, The Tennessean, TN, Nashville
Gregory, Wendy
wgregory@dunndailyrecord.com, Prodn. Mgr., Post Press, The Daily Record, NC, Dunn
Gregory, Pamela ....(850) 747-5005
phgregory@pcnh.com, Adv. Dir., The News Herald, FL, Panama City
Gregory, John 978-946-2150
jgregory@eagletribune.com, Director of IT, The Eagle-Tribune, MA, North Andover
Gregory, Melissa.......................(318) 487-6330
mgregory@thetowntalk.com, Multimedia Ed., The Town Talk, LA, Alexandria
Gregory, Ted ....(717) 901-0758
ted@wilsongregory.com, Chrmn./CEO, Wilson Gregory Agency, Inc., PA, Camp Hill
Gregory, Todd..........................(717) 901-0757
todd@wilsongregory.com, Vice Pres., Wilson Gregory Agency, Inc., PA, Camp Hill
Gregory, Mark
mark@wilsongregory.com, Vice Pres., Opns., Wilson Gregory Agency, Inc., PA, Camp Hill
Gregory, James.........................(856) 486-2640
jgregory@gannett.com, Circ. Dir., Courier-Post, NJ, Cherry Hill
Gregory, Dawn..........................(212) 293-8603
dgregory@unitedmedia.com, Customer Serv. Rep, United Feature Syndicate (Div. of United Media), NY, New York
Greider, Goran
redaktion@daladem.se, Ed. in Chief, DALA-DEMOKRATEN, Falun
Greiling, David ....(801) 625-4224
dgreiling@standard.net, Metro Ed., Standard-Examiner, UT, Ogden
Greis, Engelbert
kr.narichten@skr-runvschau.de, Ed. in Chief, KOLNISCHE RUNDSCHAU, Koln
Grell, Manfred
manfred.grell@fehmarnsches-tageblatt.de, Bus. Mgr., FEHMARNSCHES TAGEBLATT, Burg
Gremillion, Robert........(954) 356-4000 ext. 4305
Pres., Sun-Sentinel Co., FL, Fort Lauderdale
Greminger, Sherry ....ext. 115
Wire Ed., Daily Journal, MO, Park Hills
Grenzow, Mary Jane ....ext. 22
editor@themonroetimes.com, Editorial Page Ed., The Monroe Times, WI, Monroe
Gresenberg, Ana 3842-1151
ana.gresenberg@dowjones.com, Sales Exec., Dow Jones Newswires - Sao Paulo, Brazil, Sao Paulo
Gresham, Michael ....(972) 563-6476
publisher@terrelltribune.com, Interim Pub., The Terrell Tribune, TX, Terrell
Gresko, Dale...............(330) 747-1471 ext. 1321
dgresko@vindy.com, Adv. Mgr., Classified, The Vindicator, OH, Youngstown
Grethe, Michael
michael.grethe@frankischenachrichten.de, Bus. Mgr., Frankische Nachrichten, Tauberbischofsheim
Greyowl, Wendy
editor@dailyevents.com, Ed., The Daily Events, MO, Springfield
Gribbin, William
wgribbin@Liberty.edu, Dean, School of Commun., Liberty University, VA, Lynchburg
Griep, John..............................(410) 770-4094
Chief Copy Ed., The Star-Democrat, MD, Easton
Griffin, Sarah
sarahgriffin@npgco.com, Circ. Mgr., Atchison Globe, KS, Atchison
Griffing, Jeff ....(612) 673-4901
jeff.griffing@startribune.com, Chief Revenue Officer, Star Tribune, MN, Minneapolis
Griffith, Laura..........................(618) 463-2556
Online Ed., The Telegraph, IL, Alton
Griffith, Ed
director@strategic-images.tv, Pres., Strategic Images, TN, Cordova
Grigoli, John ....(216) 999-4474
Prepress Director, The Plain Dealer, OH, Cleveland
Grigorjev, Sergei
info@moles.ee, MOLODEZH ESTONII, Tallinn
Grijelmo, Alejandro ....+34-91-346-7100
President, EFE News Services - Washington, DC, DC, Washington
Grijelmo, Alexandro
agrijelmo@efe.es, Pres., EFE News Services - Madrid, Spain, Madrid
Grillo, Gina
gina@theadvertisingclub.org, Exec. Dir., Advertising Club of Greater New York, NY, New York
Grim, Hubert.............................(540) 213-9131
hgrimiii@newsleader.com, Sports Ed., The News Leader, VA, Staunton
Grimes, Lorraine ....(850) 747-5002
lgrimes@pcnh.com, Regl. HR Dir., The News Herald, FL, Panama City
Grimes, Larry ....(301) 253-5016
lgrimes299@comcast.net, Grimes, W.B. & Co., MD, Gaithersburg
Grimes, Larry ....(301) 253-5016
lgrimes299@comcast.net, Grimes, W.B. & Co., MD, Gaithersburg
Grimes, Larry ....(301) 253-5016
lgrimes@mediamergers.com, President, Grimes, W.B. & Co., MD, Gaithersburg
Grimes, Mary Anne ....(212) 293-8626
magrimes@unitedmedia.com, Exec. Dir., Pub. Rel., Newspaper Enterprise Association (Div. of United Media), NY, New York
magrimes@unitedmedia.com, Exec. Dir., Pub. Rel., United Feature Syndicate (Div. of United Media), NY, New York
Grimes, Larry
lgrimes299@comcast.net, Grimes, W.B. & Co., MD, Gaithersburg
Grimes, Mary Anne ....(212) 293-8626
magrimes@unitedmedia.com, Exec. Dir., Pub. Rel., United Media, OH, Cincinnati
Grimes, David ....(941) 957-5209
david.grimes@heraldtribune.com, Columnist, Sarasota Herald-Tribune, FL, Sarasota
Grimminck, Jerry ....ext. 250
Press Foreman/Supvr., Grand Haven Tribune, MI, Grand Haven
Grinde, Kevin
kgrinde@gfherald.com, Mng. Ed., Grand Forks Herald, ND, Grand Forks
Grindstaff, Robert P.
grindstaffr@stripes.osd.mil, Exec. Ed., STARS AND STRIPES, Tokyo
Grinstead, Jeanne 727.893.8769
jgrinstead@tampabay.com, Deputy Managing Editor, Features, Tampa Bay Times, FL, Saint Petersburg
Grissom, Whitney.......................(405) 491-6382
Southern Nazarene Univ., OK, Bethany
Grist, Stephanie
advertising@henryettanewspaper.com, Adv. Dir., Henryetta Free-Lance, OK, Henryetta
Griteman, Brenna
brennag@northwestsignal.net, Bus./Farm Ed., Northwest Signal, OH, Napoleon
Grizzard, Mike ....(252) 329-9580
mgrizzard@reflector.com, Bus. Ed., The Daily Reflector, NC, Greenville
Grnuoneorg, Sven
grnuoneorg@horsens-folkeblad.dk, Adv. Mgr., HORSENS FOLKEBLAD, Horsens, Jutland
Grob, James
sports@ottumwacourier.com, Sports Ed., The Ottumwa Courier, IA, Ottumwa
Grobman, Beth ....(408) 864-8588
De Anza College, CA, Cupertino
Groch, Laura ....(760) 739-6658
lgroch@nctimes.com, Features Ed., North County Times, CA, Escondido
Groenke, Sharon ....(262) 656-6259
sgroenke@kenoshanews.com, Adv. Customer Serv. Mgr., Kenosha News, WI, Kenosha
Grosam, Steve
sgrosam@nujournal.com, Circ. Mgr., The Journal, MN, New Ulm
Groskreutz, Stuart......................(651) 796-1107
gztsport@pressenter.com, Sports Ed., Stillwater Gazette, MN, Stillwater
Gross, Adam ....(212) 754-0710
adamg@jegi.com, Vice Pres., Mktg., Jordan, Edmiston Group, Inc., NY, New York
Gross, George ....(416) 947-3115
Cor. Sports Ed., The Toronto Sun, ON, Toronto
Gross, Liza ....(305) 376-3415
lgross@miamiherald.com, Mng. Ed., Presentations/Opns., The Miami Herald, FL, Miami
Grossman, Gary
ggrossman@dailyitem.com, Pub., The Danville News, PA, Danville
Grossman, Gary
ggrossman@dailyitem.com, Pub., The Daily Item, PA, Sunbury
Grossman, Andrew.......................(757) 220-3076
andrew@cartoonresource.com, Creative Dir., Cartoon Resource, MI, Grand Rapids
Grosz, Gary................................(251) 423-6688
gwgrosz@aol.com, Sales-AL, FL, MS, LA, TN, AR, Kaspar Wire Works, Inc./Sho-Rack, TX, Shiner
Groth, Kelly.................(530) 676-7440 ext. 220
Vice Pres., Sales, CBS MaxPreps, Inc., CA, Cameron Park
Groves, Roberta
robertag@classicstock.com, Vice Pres., Creative, Robertstock/Classicstock, PA, Philadelphia
Groza, Michael
informatiahr@gmail.com, Ed. in Chief, ADEVARUL HARGHITEI, Miercurea Ciuc, Harghita
Grubaugh, Dennis........................(618) 463-2576
dennis_grubaugh@thetelegraph.com, News Ed., The Telegraph, IL, Alton
Grubb, Jere ....(425) 339-3411
grubb@heraldnet.com, Circ. Opns. Mgr., The Herald, WA, Everett
Gruber, Chuck
info@cannonequipment.com, Pres., Cannon Equipment, MN, Rosemount
Gruber, Russel
russel.gruber@aliceechonews.com, Classified Sales Mgr., Alice Echo-News Journal, TX, Alice
Gruber, Katharina ....(651) 407-4863
katharina_gruber@nela-usa.com, Mktg. Mgr., NELA, WI, River Falls
Gruber, Jurgen
jurgen_gruber@nela-usa.com, Sales Dir., NELA, WI, River Falls
Gruder, Liz.................................(504) 826-3080
Adv. Mgr., Creative Servs., The Times Picayune, LA, New Orleans
Gruenberg, Mark J. ....(202) 898-4825
press_associates@yahoo.com, Ed. in Chief, Press Associates, Inc., DC, Washington
Grunder, Eric
egrunder@recordnet.com, Editorial Page Ed., The Record, CA, Stockton
Grundmann, Mike
grundmmj@jmu.edu, Asst. Prof., James Madison University, VA, Harrisonburg
Grundy, Michael.........................(250) 470-0776
michael.grundy@ok.bc.ca, Office/Financial Mgr., The Daily Courier, BC, Kelowna
Grunwald, Gray..........................(704) 261-2215
ggrunwald@theej.com, Circ. Dir., The Enquirer-Journal, NC, Monroe
Gruter, Stephen
redaktion@marchanzeiger.ch, Ed. in Chief, MARCH-ANZEIGER, Lachen
Gryka, John ....(951) 782-7660
jgryka@pe.com, Mng. Ed., The Press-Enterprise, CA, Riverside
Gryn, Nir
nir.gryn@xtivia.com, CEO, Xtivia, NY, New York
Grzella, Paul
pgrzella@mycentraljersey.com, Mng. Ed., Courier News, NJ, Somerville
Guajardo Adame, Sergio Enrique
sguajardo@elsiglodetorreon.com.mx, Ed./Dir., EL SIGLO DE TORREON, Torreon, Coahuila
Guarini, Michael
guariniasid@msn.com, Author, Interior Design Teacher, NJ, Lakewood
Guarnieri, Damion ....(770) 428-9411 ext. 231
Photo Dept. Mgr., Marietta Daily Journal, GA, Marietta
Gudat, Sandra
info@customer.com, Pres., Customer Communications Group, CO, Denver
Guerard, Marsha ....ext. 5515
Deputy Mng. Ed., The Post and Courier, SC, Charleston
Guerke, Gwen
tell2gwen@aol.com, Entertainment Ed., Delaware State News, DE, Dover
Guernsey, Dean ....(541) 419-8057
dguernsey@bendbulletin.com, Photo Ed., The Bulletin, OR, Bend
Guerra, Raul
gallardo@adinet.com.uy, Gen. Mgr., Forgold S.A., Maldonado
Guerra Galaz, Edmund
info@elproa.cl, Dir., Proa Regional, San Antonio
Guerreo, Debbie
dmarez@eaglenewspapers.com, Circ. Mgr., Daily Sun News, WA, Sunnyside
Guerrero, Bob...............(303) 750-7555 ext. 220
bobguerrero@aurorasentinel.com, Circ. Dir., Aurora Sentinel, CO, Aurora
Guerrero, Juan Jose Briceno
nacionales@elregional.net.ve, Pres., EL REGIONAL, Araure, Portuguesa
Guerrero Gijon, Esther
eguerrero@heraldo.es, Dir., Soria 7 Dias, Soria
Guerringue, Mark
dailysun@mountwashingtonvalley.com, Circ. Mgr., The Conway Daily Sun, NH, North Conway
Guerringue, Mark
dailysun@mountwashingtonvalley.com, Pub., The Berlin Daily Sun, NH, Berlin
Guevara, Carmen 65-4344
el.tiempo@eldish.net, Gen. Mgr., EL TIEMPO, Puerto La Cruz, Anzoategui
Guevara Monosalva, Luis 41-4762
Pub., EL SOL DE MATURIN, Maturin, Mona-

gas
Guggi, Ros ....(604) 605-2005
rguggi@theprovince.com, Deputy Ed., The Province, BC, Vancouver
Gugliotta, William ....(216) 999-6124
Dir. Photography, The Plain Dealer, OH, Cleveland
Gugliotto, Mike
mgugliotto@pioneernewspapers.com, Pres., Pioneer Newspapers Inc, WA, Seattle
Guida, Tony ....(212) 288-2258
tony@tonyguida.com, President, Society of the Silurians, NY, New York
Guidarelli, Audrey ....(847) 929-1950
aguidarelli@thermalcare.com, Mktg. Servs. Mgr., AWS, A Thermal Care Division, IL, Nile
Guidry, Joe ....(813) 259-7673
jjguidry@tampatrib.com, Editor, Opinions, The Tampa Tribune, FL, Tampa
Guilfoyle, Christine
christine_guilfoyle@condenast.com, Pub., Women's Wear Daily, NY, New York
Guimaraes, Antonio Costa
director@correiodominho.com, Dir., CORREIO DO MINHO, Braga
Guimarin, Kimberly
kimberly.guimarin@inlandnewspapers.com, Senior Editor, San Bernardino County Sun, CA, San Bernardino
Guiniven, John
guinivje@jmu.edu, Assoc. Prof., James Madison University, VA, Harrisonburg
Guinn, Rick............................(253) 620-4747
Rickg@webpressllc.com, Operations Manager, WebPress, LLC, WA, Tacoma
Guinn, Jordan ....(209) 369-7035 ext. 256
jordang@lodinews.com, Bus. Page Ed., Lodi News-Sentinel, CA, Lodi
Guinta, Peter............................(904) 819-3493
peter.guints@staugustinerecord.com, Assignment Ed., The St. Augustine Record, FL, Saint Augustine
Guiot, Shanna
office@chanute.com, Pub., The Chanute Tribune, KS, Chanute
Gulig, Joe ....(920) 453-5191
jgulig@sheboygan.gannett.com, Editorial Page Ed., The Sheboygan Press, WI, Sheboygan
Gulla, Tim ....ext. 2052
tgulla@citizensvoice.com, Bus. Ed., The Citizens' Voice, PA, Wilkes-Barre
Gullberg, Ron..........................(307) 266-0560
ron.gulberg@trib.com, Online Dir., Casper Star-Tribune, WY, Casper
Gulledge, Michael R..................(406) 657-1225
mgulledge@billingsgazette.com, Vice Pres./Pub., Billings Gazette, MT, Billings
Gullifor, Paul
pfg@bradley.edu, Chair/Prof., Bradley University, IL, Peoria
Gullixson, Paul ....(707) 526-8651
paul.gullixson@pressdemocrat.com, Editorial Page Ed., The Press Democrat, CA, Santa Rosa
Gulzar, Muhammed Humayun
daily_sayadat_vwp@hotmail.com, Ed., SAYADAT, Bahawalpur, Bahawalpur Division
Gun, Milton J.
nenewsnow@yahoo.com, Pub./Ed., Travel & Leisure Features, MA, Newton
nenewsnow@yahoo.com, Bureau Chief, New England News Service, Inc., MA, Newton
Gunderman, Mark.....................715-738-1607
mark.gunderman@lee.net, Business editor, The Chippewa Herald, WI, Chippewa Falls
Gundersen, Dave.......................(612) 673-4819
David.Gundersen@startribune.com, Dir., Sales Mktg./Research, Star Tribune, MN, Minneapolis
Gunderson, Marsha
mgunderson@gfherald.com, Circ. Sales/Mktg., Grand Forks Herald, ND, Grand Forks
Gunn, James
sales@arcoengineering.com, Pres., Arco Engineering, Inc. (Newspaper Div.), KY, Louisville
Gunn, Drew ....(205) 348-8995
Univ. of Alabama, AL, Tuscaloosa
Gunther, John ....ext. 241
jgunther@theworldlink.com, Sports Ed., The World, OR, Coos Bay
Gupta, Shardul Vikram
ajvaranasi@rediffmail.com, Ed., AJ, Varanasi, Uttar Pradesh
Gupta, Rajiv Mohan
bhopal@bpl.jagran.com, Ed., DAILY JAGRAN, Bhopal, Madhya Pradesh
Gupta, Sanjay
jpl@jagran.com, Ed., DAILY JAGRAN, Kanpur, Uttar Pradesh
Gupta, Shekhar
feedback@expressindia.com, Ed. in Chief, INDIAN EXPRESS, New Delhi
Gupta, M. Mohan
jagran@lw1.vsnl.net.in, Mng. Dir., DAINIK JAGRAN, Kanpur, Uttar Pradesh
Gupta, Sekar
sekar.gupta@expressindia.com, Ed., INDIAN EXPRESS, Mumbai, Maharashtra
Gupta, Shardul Vikram
patnaaj@gmail.com, Ed., AJ, Patna, Bihar
Gurley, Georgia.......................(919) 739-7811
ggurley@newsargus.com, Adv. Mgr., Nat'l, Goldsboro News-Argus, NC, Goldsboro
Gursha, Rob ....(612) 673-4040
rob.gursha@startribune.com, VP, Consumer Marketing, Star Tribune, MN, Minneapolis
Guseinov, Gary
gary@directsynergy.com, Pres./Chief Technical Officer, Synergy Ventures, CA, Encino
Guske, Sheri ....(810) 989-6200
sguske@porthuro.gannett.com, Circ. Opns. Mgr., Times Herald, MI, Port Huron
Gust, Kelly
vtletters@cctimes.com, Ed., Valley Times, CA, Pleasanton
Gustafson, Kim.........................888-910-3329
VP of Business Development, U.S. Netcom Corporation, MO, Joplin
Gustafson, David
david.gustafson@valleynewstoday.com, Pub., Valley News Today, IA, Shenandoah
Gustafson, Donald.....................630 238 4817
donald.gustafson@baldwintech.com , Vice President, Baldwin Americas Sales & Marketing, Baldwin Americas Corp., IL, Addison
Gustafson, Donna
donna@gradingthemovies.com, Reviewer, One Voice Communications, AB, Calgary
Gustafson, Rod ....(800) 565-4661
rod@parentpreviews.com, Pres./Sr. Reviewer, One Voice Communications, AB, Calgary
Gustafsson, Christer
christer.gustafsson@smalanningen.se, Ed. in Chief, SMALANNINGEN, Ljungby
Gustafzon, Helge
redaktion@stenungsundsposten.se, Ed. in Chief, STENUNGSUNDS-POSTEN med ORUST-TJORN, Stenungsund, Lysekil
Gustafzon, Helge
redaktion@lysekilsposten.se, MD/Ed. in Chief, LYSEKILSPOSTEN, Lysekil
Guszynski, Jan
JGuszynski@Tribune.com, Dir., Mktg., News/Features Worldwide, McClatchy-Tribune Information Services, Tribune Media Services, Inc., IL, Chicago
Guthard, Lori.........................(308) 233-9701
Adv. Mgr., Sales, Kearney Hub, NE, Kearney
Gutierrez, Ari 213-220-5530
ari_gutierrez@dailyjournal.com, Director of Government Advertising
Government Advertising Division
Daily Journal Corporation and
California Newspaper Service Bureau, Daily Journal Corporation, CA, Los Angeles
Gutierrez, Monica
monica@deminghe adlight.com, Mktg. Consultant, Deming Headlight, NM, Deming
Gutkowski, Phil
pgutkowski@wacotrib.com, Prodn. Mgr., Systems, Waco Tribune-Herald, TX, Waco
Guttenplan, Dan
dguttenplan@newburyportnews.com, Sports Ed., The Daily News, MA, Newburyport
Guttman, Jeannine A.
jguttman@pressherald.com, Vice Pres., Portland Press Herald/Maine Sunday Telegram, ME, Portland
Guttman, Daniel
dan@stemsystems.com, Pres., Norman X Guttman, Inc., NJ, Woodbridge
Gutwillig, Eric A.
inquiries@prisco.com, Vice Pres., Mktg., Printers' Service/Prisco/PriscoDigital, NJ, Newark
Gutzmer, Jim..........................(620) 624-2541
Pub., Southwest Daily Times, KS, Liberal
Guy, Greg...............................(902) 426-3039
gguy@herald.ca, Entertainment Ed., The Chronicle Herald, NS, Halifax
Guy, Ginny..............................(800) 282-4833
printing@ct.net, Prodn. Mgr., Pressroom, Okeechobee News, FL, Okeechobee
Guyon, Jacques
j.guyon@charentelibre.fr, Dir., LA CHARENTE LIBRE, Angouleme
Guza, Jack...............................(517) 333-3355
jackguza@cpapersmi.com, Exec.Dir., Community Papers of Michigan, Inc., MI, Eastlansing
Guzman, J.M. Feb-08
Editorial Dir., EL EXPRESO, Ciudad Bolivar, Bolivar
Guzzo, Maria............................(412) 765-2585
mguzzo@amm.com , Americas Steel News Ed., American Metal Market
Gwin, Harold..............(330) 747-1471 ext. 1259
gwin@vindy.com, Education Ed., The Vindicator, OH, Youngstown
Gwinnup, Jason 419-281-0581
jgwinnup@times-gazette.com, Advertising Director, Ashland Publishing Co. LLC, OH, Ashland
Gyllenhaal, Anders ....(305) 376-3790
andersg@miamiherald.com, Vice Pres./Exec. Ed., The Miami Herald, FL, Miami

H

HOUSE, GINGER 816-234-4247
ghouse@kcstar.com, FINANCIAL ANALYST/CIRCULATION, The Olathe News, MO, Kansas City
Haapaoja, Dave
dave.haapaoja@prnewswire.com, Sr. Vice Pres., Opns., PR Newswire - New York, NY, NY, New York
Haar, Dennis
info@ss8.com, Pres./CEO, SS8 Networks, CA, San Jose
Haas, Jim
jhaas@pekintimes.com, Sports Ed., Pekin Daily Times, IL, Pekin
Haas, Ron ....(713) 977-8955
rhaas@rhaas.com, Pres., Haas & Associates, TX, Houston
Haas, Mark ....ext. 3909
marcus@ecol.net, Circ./Promo. Mgr., Leader-Telegram, WI, Eau Claire
Haas, Wally ....(815) 987-1359
Editorial Page Ed., Rockford Register Star, IL, Rockford
Habara, Kiyomasa
newsroom@emb.asahi-np.co.jp, Bd. Dir./Seibu Head Officer, ASAHI SHIMBUN, Kita-Kyushu, Kyushu
Habasinski, Chris
chrish@miles33.com, Pres., Miles 33 International, CT, Norwalk
Habbe, John ....(978) 970-4808
jhabbe@lowellsun.com, CFO, The Sun, MA, Lowell
Haberman, Shir ....(603) 610-1161
shaberman@seacoastonline.com, Editorial Page Ed., Portsmouth Herald, NH, Portsmouth
Habermann, Antje
vertreieb@np-coburg.de, Adv. Mgr, NEUE PRESSE, Coburg
Habets, Jerry ....(406) 791-5231
Univ. of Great Falls, MT, Great Falls
Habib, Ghassane ....(559) 441-6229
ghabib@fresnobee.com, Mgr., Research, The Fresno Bee, CA, Fresno
Habis, Yikki
yikki.habis@milliyet.com.tr, Adv. Mgr, MILLIYET
Habrat, David
dhabrat@mankatofreepress.com, Adv. Dir., The Free Press, MN, Mankato
Hachigian, Niky
niky.hachigian@macombdaily.com, Lifestyles Editor, The Macomb Daily, MI, Mount Clemens
Hacker, Kristina
khacker@turlockjournal.com, Ed., Turlock Journal, CA, Turlock
Hacker, John
jhacker@carthagepress.com, Mng. Ed., The Carthage Press, MO, Carthage
Hackett, David ....(941) 486-3071
david.hackett@heraldtribune.com, Venice Bureau Ed., Sarasota Herald-Tribune, FL, Sarasota
Hackett, Jan 419-734-7505
jhackett@gannett.com, ACcount Executive, News-Herald, OH, Port Clinton
Hackett, Richard...........(303) 776-2244 ext. 229
rhackett@times-call.com, Chief Photographer, Times-Call, CO, Longmont
Hackett, Derick ....(225) 771-2230
Southern Univ. A&M College, LA, Baton Rouge
Hackett, Jim ....(212) 450-7125 ext. 7125
jim_hackett@parade.com, Sr. Vice Pres., Mktg., Parade Publications, Inc. - New York, NY, NY, New York
Hackmack, Ulrich
vertrieb@bremer-nachrichten.de, Proprietor, BREMER NACHRICHTEN, Bremen
Hackney, Joanne ....(941) 207-1640
jhackney@scmginc.com, Data Processing Mgr., Charlotte Sun, FL, Charlotte Harbor
Hackworth, John ....(941) 206-1147
hackworth@sun-herald.com, Managing Editor, Charlotte Sun, FL, Charlotte Harbor
Haddix, Paulette ....(219) 648-3158
phaddix@post-trib.com, Exec. Ed., Post-Tribune, IN, Merrillville
Haddrall, Lynn............(519) 894-2250 ext. 2606
lhaddrall@therecord.com, Ed. in Chief, The Record, ON, Kitchener
Hader, Lolly............................406-791-1468
lhader@greatfallstribune.com, Literacy Outreach Coordinator, Great Falls Tribune, MT, Great Falls
Hadjinakos, Lazaros
vellidis@hyper.gr, Dir., Publishing Co. of Northern Greece SA, Thessaloniki, Macedonia
Hadky, Joe ....(319) 398-8207
Chrmn., Gazette Communications, Inc., IA, Cedar Rapids
Hadley, Roger
roger.hadley@okbu.edu, Chair, Oklahoma Baptist University, OK, Shawnee
Hadley, Graham
ghadley@dailyhome.com, City Ed., The Daily Home, AL, Talladega
Haeberle, G.
ghaeberle@bergstraesser-anzeiger.de, Bus. Mgr., BA BERGSTRABER ANZEIGER, Bensheim
Haeberlein, George..................(212) 969-7586
ghaeberlein@hearst.com, Vice Pres., Worldwide Syndication Sales, North America Syndicate, NY, New York
ghaeberlein@hearst.com, Vice Pres., Worldwide Syndication Sales, King Features Syndicate, NY, New York
Haekenkamp, Kevin ....(507) 333-3110
khaekenkamp@fairbault.com, Controller, Faribault Daily News, MN, Faribault
Haekenkamp, Kevin 507-333-3110
khaekenkamp@faribault, Controller, Owatonna People's Press, MN, Owatonna
Haezebroeck, Kevin..................(248) 745-4501
kevin.haezebroeck@oakpress.com, Pub. & Sr. Vice Pres., Michigan Papers, The Oakland Press, MI, Pontiac
Haff, Jeff 518-395-3123
jhaff@dailygazette.net, Online Ed., The Daily Gazette, NY, Schenectady
Hagdag, Rola
rola.hagdag@dailystar.com, Pub. Asst, DAILY STAR
Hage, Marcel
fife@fife.com, Mgr., Fife Corporation, OK, Oklahoma City
Hagemeyer, Seanne ....(651) 796-1117
gazads@pressenter.com, Prodn. Mgr., Stillwater Gazette, MN, Stillwater
Hagen, Kit...............................907-257-4289
Classified Manager, Anchorage Daily News, AK, Anchorage

Hager, Annie
ahager@washingtonexaminer.com, Sr. Vice Pres., Sales/Mktg., The Washington Examiner, VA, Springfield
Hager, Annie ....(410) 332-6039
annie.hager@baltsun.com, Adv. Dir., Local Retail/Multimedia/Creative, The Baltimore Sun, MD, Baltimore
Hagerty, Vaughn......................(910) 343-2217
vaughn.hagerty@starnewsonline.com, City Ed., Star-News, NC, Wilmington
Haggerty, James D.
news@woburnonline.com, Ed., Daily Times Chronicle, MA, Woburn
Haggerty, Sandra......................(740) 593-2604
Assoc. Prof., Ohio University, OH, Athens
Haggerty, Kenneth ....(781) 433-6797
Telecom Mgr., Metrowest Daily News, MA, Framingham
Haggerty, Mathew E.
mhaggerty@timesshamrock.com, Pub., The Times-Tribune, PA, Scranton
Hagin, Bob ....(925) 228-1410
bobhagin@juno.com, CEO/Gen. Mgr./Ed./Writer, Pacheco Research and Development Co., CA, Concord
Haheen, Zaan
bayan@albayan.ae, Gen. Mgr., AL-BAYAN
Hahn, Arthur
arthur@brenhambanner.com, News Ed., Brenham Banner-Press, TX, Brenham
Hahn, Mark............................(847) 818-1100
mark.hahn@aaapress.com, Vice Pres., Sales/Mktg., AAA Press International, IL, Arlington Heights
Hahn, Terri ....(308) 381-9463
terri.hahn@theindependent.com, Women's Ed., The Grand Island Independent, NE, Grand Island
Haidari, Leila
forum@thetartan.org, Carnegie Mellon Univ., PA, Pittsburgh
Haidet, Doug..........................419-281-0581
dhaidet@times-gazette.com, Sports Editor, Ashland Publishing Co. LLC, OH, Ashland
Haile, Mike 217-351-5349
mitm@news-gazette.com, VP: General Manager Radio Center, News-Gazette Inc., IL, Champaign
Haines, Tom..................................ext. 4201
thaines@phillyburbs.com, Life Ed., Bucks County Courier Times, PA, Levittown
Haines, Tracy................(856) 427-9799 ext. 10
tracyh@videopipeline.com, Gen. Mgr., Video Pipeline, Inc., NJ, Haddonfield
Haitz, Henry
publisher@thestate.com, Pres./Pub., The State, SC, Columbia
Hajian, David
david@nextcom.net, Opns. Mgr., Nextcom, CA, Los Angeles
Hajostek, John ....(701) 235-7311 ext. 5499
CFO, Forum Communications Co., ND, Fargo
Hakala, Bruce
bhakala@kpcnews.net, Circ. Dir., The Star, IN, Auburn
Hakala, Bruce
bhakala@kpcnews.net, Circ. Dir., Herald-Republican, IN, Angola
Hakansson, Lennart
lennart.hakansson@nsd.se, Ed., NORRLANDSKA SOCIALDEMOKRATEN, Lulea
Hakkarainen, Sinikka 348 1730
paatoimittaja@pieksamaenlehti.fi, Ed., PIEKSAMAEN LEHTI, Pieksamaki
Haldane, Neal
nhaldane@madonna.edu, Dir., Madonna University, MI, Livonia
Hale, JeAlison.......................(303) 820-1358
jhale@denverpost.com, Photo Assignment Ed., The Denver Post, CO, Denver
Hale, Caitlin ....(205) 328-9249
Editor, The East Carolinian, NC, Greenville
Hale, Terri
thale@bdtonline.com, Adv. Dir., Bluefield Daily Telegraph, WV, Bluefield
Hale, David
adnetinfo@chinaonline.com, Pres., China Online, Inc., IL, Chicago
Hale, Angie 765-659-4622
ahale@ftimes.com, Classified/Retail Inside Sales, The Times, IN, Frankfort

Haley, Eric............................(479) 770-8462
ehaley@ardemgaz.com, Prodn. Mgr., Plant, Northwest Arkansas Times, AR, Fayetteville
Haley, Tom...............(802) 747-6121 ext. 2209
tom.haley@rutlandherald.com, Asst. Sports Ed., Rutland Herald, VT, Rutland
Halkiadakis, I.
info@rethnea.gr, Dir., RETHYMNIOTIKA NEA, Rethymnon, Crete
Hall, Larry.....................................ext. 553
jhall@heraldpalladium.com, Mgr., Opns., The Herald-Palladium, MI, Saint Joseph
Hall, Sharon ....(816) 350-6312
sharon.hall@examiner.net, Bus. Mgr., The Examiner, MO, Independence
Hall, David E..................................ext. 112
davehall@primhall.com, Vice Pres., Prim Hall Enterprises, Inc., NY, Plattsburgh
Hall, John ....(770) 887-3126
johnhall@forsythnews.com, Pub., Forsyth County News, GA, Cumming
Hall, Mark ....(770) 718-3456
mhall@gainesvilletimes.com, Prodn. Dir., The Times, GA, Gainesville
Hall, Cheryl
chall@tdnpublishing.com, Circ. Mgr., Piqua Daily Call, OH, Piqua
Hall, David
david.hall@atex.com, CEO, NEMEA, Atex North America, MA, Burlington
Hall, Bob C.
bobchall@idahopapers.com, Exec. Dir., Idaho Newspaper Association, Inc., OR, Joseph
Hall, Linda ....ext. 230
lhall@the-daily-record.com, Educ. Ed., The Daily Record, OH, Wooster
Hall, Kersh ....(870) 543-1457
khall@pbcommercial.com, Regl. Ed., Pine Bluff Commercial, AR, Pine Bluff
Hall, Charlotte H. ....(407) 420-5195
editor@orlandosentinel.com, Ed., Orlando Sentinel, FL, Orlando
Hall, Richard.........................(801) 237-2110
rhall@desnews.com, Mng. Ed., Deseret News, UT, Salt Lake City
Hall, Debbie
manager.kansascity@americanclassifieds.com, Thrifty Nickel - Kansas City - East, MO, Kansas City
manager.kansascity@americanclassifieds.com, Thrifty Nickel - Kansas City - Kansas, MO, Kansas City
manager.kansascity@americanclassifieds.com, Thrifty Nickel - Kansas City - North, MO, Kansas City
manager.kansascity@americanclassifieds.com, Prodn. Mgr., Composing, The Terrell Tribune, TX, Terrell
Hall, Carla
chall@timesanddemocrat.com, Mktg./Promo., The Times and Democrat, SC, Orangeburg
Hall, Danny ....(276) 645-2564
dhall@bristolnews.com, Prodn. Mgr., Bristol Herald Courier, VA, Bristol
Hall, Dorothy.........................(860) 647-8266
dhall@record-journal.com, Artist, Amanda y Rocinante, CT, Bolton
Hall, Donna ....(937) 259-2025
donna.hall@cmgohio.com, Senior Vice President, Marketing & Client Solutions, Dayton Daily News, OH, Dayton
Hall, John ....(770) 887-3126
johnhall@forsythnews.com, Pub., Forsyth County News, GA, Cumming
Hall, Bob C.
bobchall@aol.com, Exec. Dir./Mgr., Idaho's Complete Advertising in Newspapers Network (ICANN), ID, Boise
Hall, Cheryl
chall@tdnpublishing.com, Circ. Mgr., Troy Daily News, OH, Troy
Hall, Andrea
ahall@gwcommonwealth.com, Lifestyles Ed., The Greenwood Commonwealth, MS, Greenwood
Hall, Mike ....(325) 670-5245
hallm@reporternews.com, Prodn. Dir., Opns., Abilene Reporter-News, TX, Abilene
Hall, Terry ....(804) 649-6030
thall@timesdispatch.com, Telephone Sales Mgr., Richmond Times-Dispatch, VA, Richmond

Hall, Steve ....(251) 219-5503
shall@press-register.com, Adv. Mgr., Retail, Press-Register, AL, Mobile
Hall, Gene A.
genehall@charlescitypress.com, Pub./President/Owner, Charles City Press, IA, Charles City
Hallbauer, Holm
nxinfo@net-linx.com, Pres., net-linx AG, Dresden
Hallgren, Elaine
fashionshowroom@yahoo.com, Ed., Fashion Syndicate Press, VT, Woodstock
Halling, Gregory.....................(574) 296-5937
ghalling@etruth.com, Mng. Ed., The Elkhart Truth, IN, Elkhart
Hallion, Kathleen ....(518) 454-5568
khallion@timesunion.com, Adv. Vice Pres., Times Union, NY, Albany
Hallman, Wallace
wallace@eseco-speedmaster.com, Pres., Electronic Systems Engineering Co., OK, Cushing
Halmo, Bruce ....(920) 453-5131
bhalmo@sheboygan.gannett.com, Photo Lab, The Sheboygan Press, WI, Sheboygan
Halpern, Kevin ....ext. 304
online@dnj.com, Online Servs. Dir., The Daily News Journal, TN, Murfreesboro
Ham, Jeff ....(800) 799-6008
maine.press@verizon.net, Exec. Dir., Maine Press Association, ME, Cape Elizabeth
Ham, Larry ....(317) 477-3247
lham@greenfieldreporter.com, Prodn. Dir., Daily Reporter, IN, Greenfield
Hamann, Didier
didier.hamann@lesoir.be, Ed., LE SOIR, Wavre, Brabant
Hamar, Bob............................(308) 381-9417
bob.hamar@theindependent.com, Sports Ed., The Grand Island Independent, NE, Grand Island
Hamburger, Jared....................(845) 451-4508
jhamburg@poughkee.gannett.com, Multimedia Web Developer, Poughkeepsie Journal, NY, Poughkeepsie
Hameed, Tariq
editorial@asharqalawsat.com, Ed., ASHARQ ALAWSAT
Hamel, Kerri ....(403) 528-5692
khamel@medicinehatnews.com, City Ed., Medicine Hat News, AB, Medicine Hat
Hamid Rao, Mumtaz
TimesGroup@hotmail.com, Ed. in Chief, PAKISTAN TIMES, Islamabad
Hamill, Blair ....(303) 820-1923
Graphics Dir., The Denver Post, CO, Denver
Hamilton, Fred
fred.hamilton@inlandnewspapers.com, Pub./CEO, San Bernardino County Sun, CA, San Bernardino
Hamilton, Lynn ....(501) 378-3464
lhamilton@ardemgaz.com, Vice Pres., Opns., Arkansas Democrat-Gazette, AR, Little Rock
Hamilton, Malcolm 9022 0523
malcolm.hamilton@kalminer.com.au, Accountant, KALGOORLIE MINER
Hamilton, Thomas P.
thamilton@hamiltoncirculation.com, Vice Pres., Hamilton Circulation Supplies Co., IL, Beecher
Hamilton, David
dhamilton@heralddispatch.com, Production Director, The Herald-Dispatch, WV, Huntington
Hamilton, Brittney ....(301) 733-5131
Advertising Director, The Herald-Mail, MD, Hagerstown
Hamilton, June ....(705) 475-2171
jhamilton@nugget.ca, Purchasing Agent, The North Bay Nugget, ON, North Bay
Hamilton, Brian ....(530) 477-4240
brian@theunion.com, Sports Ed., The Union, CA, Grass Valley
Hamilton, Devin.....................(740) 852-1616
dhamilton@madison-press.com, Publisher, The Madison Press, OH, London
Hamilton, Fred
fred.hamilton@inlandnewspapers.com, CEO/Pub., Inland Valley Daily Bulletin, CA, Ontario
Hamlan, Sheila
sheila@trinidadchroniclenews.com, Prodn. Mgr., The Chronicle-News, CO, Trinidad
Hamlin, Anita ....(757) 221-3271
College of William and Mary, VA, Williamsburg
Hamlin, Arthur
mgiahamlin@aol.com, Pres., MGI International, Inc., MD, Rockville
Hamlin Smith, Emily ....(216) 999-4152
Deputy Features Editor, The Plain Dealer, OH, Cleveland
Hamm, Sandy ....ext. 205
nf-support@newsfinder.com, Gen. Mgr., Newsfinder, WI, Waukesha
Hammarqvist, Johan
chefred@nsk.se, Ed. in Chief, NORRA SKANE, Hassleholm
Hammel, Cathy ....(318) 678-6000
Bossier Parish Cmty. College, LA, Bossier City
Hammer, Randy
rhammer@ashevill.gannet.com, Pres./Pub., The Asheville Citizen-Times, NC, Asheville
Hammerback, John
jhammerb@csuhayward.edu, Interim Chair, California State University, Hayward, CA, Hayward
Hammerstrom, Richard J. ....(540) 374-5414
rhammer@freelancestar.com, Local News Ed., The Free Lance-Star, VA, Fredericksburg
Hammett, Glenn......................(661) 395-7467
ghammett@bakersfield.com, Design Ed., The Bakersfield Californian, CA, Bakersfield
Hammond, Robert
hammore@nytimes.com, Pres., American Newspaper Layout Managers Association (ANLOMA), FL, Fort Meyers
Hammond, Bill
whammond@dailynews.com, Treasurer, Legislative Correspondents Association, NY, Albany
Hammond, Wayne 605-886-6901
News Ed., Watertown Public Opinion, SD, Watertown
Hammond, Bruce.....................(503) 221-8525
bhammond@news.oregonian.com, Bus. Ed., The Oregonian, OR, Portland
Hammond, Kate ....(610) 499-4000
Widener Univ., PA, Chester
Hammond, Dan.......................(940) 566-6830
Circ. Dir., Denton Record-Chronicle, TX, Denton
Hammond, Kathy
khammond@messengerpostmedia.com, Pub./Gen. Mgr., Daily Messenger, NY, Canandaigua
Hammons, Gale ....(951) 782-7768
ghammons@pe.com, Editorial Ed., The Press-Enterprise, CA, Riverside
Hammons, Kathy
kathy.hammons@augustachronicle.com, Credit Mgr., The Augusta Chronicle, GA, Augusta
Hammons, Dean ....ext. 227
dean.hammons@mountvernonnews.com, Pressroom Mgr., Mount Vernon News, OH, Mount Vernon
Hamner, Elise...............................ext. 239
ehamner@theworldlink.com, City Ed., The World, OR, Coos Bay
Hampton, David.......................601-961-7240
dhampton@jackson.gannett.com, Editorial Page Ed., The Clarion-Ledger, MS, Jackson
Hamrin, Lovisa
lovisa.hamrin@herenco.com, MD, JONKOPINGS-POSTEN/SMALANDS ALLEHANDA, Jonkoping
Hanada, Tsutomu
kokoku@mimpo.np.jp, Chrmn., FUKUSHIMA MIMPO, Fukushima, Tohoku
Hanafin, John C.
lfdnews@litchfieldil.com, Bus. Mgr., News-Herald, IL, Litchfield
Hanau, Mark
aimulti@aimultimedia.com, Pres., AI Multimedia, CA, Hollywood
Hanauer, Joe F.
corporateinfo@move.com, Chrmn., Move, Inc., CA, Westlake Village
Hanbury, Sophie
sophie.hanbury@telegraph.co.uk, Syndication Dir., Telegraph Media Group, London
Hancks, Murray ....ext. 210
hancks@qconline.com, Editorial Page Ed.,

The Rock Island Argus, IL, Rock Island
Hancock, Joan ....ext. 660
joan.hancock@svherald.com, Bus. Mgr., Bisbee Daily Review, AZ, Bisbee
Hancock, Marilyn ....(508) 427-4025
mhancock@enterprisenews.com, Asst. Metro Ed., The Enterprise, MA, Randolph
Hancock, Lura
lhancock@coxnews.com, Dir., HR, Waco Tribune-Herald, TX, Waco
Hancock, Caitlin........................(812) 237-4344
Indiana State Univ., IN, Terre Haute
Hancock, Joan ....ext. 660
Data Processing Mgr., Sierra Vista Herald, AZ, Sierra Vista
Hancq, Laura
laura.c.hancq@gmail.com, editor, Cabrini College Loquitur, PA, Radnor
Hand, Jim ....(508) 236-0399
Politics Reporter, The Sun Chronicle, MA, Attleboro
Hand, Jeff ....(505) 646-6397
New Mexico State Univ., NM, Las Cruces
Handayani, Primastuti
yani@thejakartapost.com, Mng. Ed., JAKARTA POST, Jakarta, Java
Handelman, Jay.......................(941) 957-5294
jay.handelman@heraldtribune.com, Critic, Theater/Television, Sarasota Herald-Tribune, FL, Sarasota
Handke, Lisa.....................660-543-4050 ext 1
The Muleskinner, Univ. of Central Missouri, MO, Warrensburg
Handy, Stephanie Y.
shandy@bhamnews.com, Research Mgr., The Birmingham News, AL, Birmingham
Hanel, Thomas
fp-redaktion@frankenpost.de, Author., Frankenpost, Hof
Hanes, Karen E........................(850) 747-5001
kehanes@pcnh.com, Division Vice Pres./Pub., The News Herald, FL, Panama City
Hangguman, Willy
pembaru@suarapembaruan.com, Ed., SUARA PEMBARUAN, Jakarta, Java
Hanjore, Mary
manjore@limanews.com, Administrative Asst., The Lima News, OH, Lima
Hankey, Lee
lhankey@emersonct.com, Sales Mgr., Printing, Fincor Automation, Inc., PA, York
Hann, Kevin...........................(416) 947-2211
kevin.hann@sunmedia.ca, City Ed., The Toronto Sun, ON, Toronto
Hannaford, Tom
75561.3535@compuserve.com, Pres., Visual Solutions, GA, Atlanta
Hannah, Evin
hannah@ntnews.com.au, Gen. Mgr., NORTHERN TERRITORY NEWS
Hannah, Deborah D....................(360) 577-2534
dhannah@tdn.com, Prodn. Mgr., Mailroom, The Daily News, WA, Longview
Hannell, Nancy.......................(530) 747-8032
nhannell@davisenterprise.net, Adv. Dir., The Davis Enterprise, CA, Davis
Hanner, Rich ....(209) 369-7035 ext. 215
richardh@lodinews.com, City Ed., Lodi News-Sentinel, CA, Lodi
Hanner, Richard ....(209) 369-7035 ext. 215
richardh@lodinews.com, Ed., Lodi News-Sentinel, CA, Lodi
Hanners, John
john_hanners@tamu-commerce.edu, Head/Prof., Texas A&M University-Commerce, TX, Commerce
Hanney, Suzanne
suzannestreetwise@yahoo.com, Immediate Past-President, Executive Board Member, Illinois Woman's Press Association, Inc., IL, Chicago
Hannon, Warren
stepper@bigstuff-stepper.com, Pres., Stepper, Inc., KS, Olathe
Hansen, Helge
helge.hansen@kba.com, Pres., Koenig & Bauer Aktiengesellschaft (KBA), Wuerzburg
Hansen, Glenn
ghansen@bpaww.com, Pres./CEO, BPA Worldwide, CT, Shelton
Hansen, Dave
sales@accraply.com, Vice Pres., Sales, Accraply, Inc., MN, Minneapolis
Hansen, Chris..........................(770) 806-6760
Circ. Gen. Mgr., Atlanta, USA TODAY, VA, McLean
Hansen, Elizabeth.....................(207) 990-8278
Dir., Mktg. Servs., Bangor Daily News, ME, Bangor
Hansen, Wendie.......................(509) 577-7710
whansen@yakima-herald.com, Finance Dir., Yakima Herald-Republic, WA, Yakima
Hansen, Karen..........................(309) 820-3236
khansen@pantagraph.com, Bus. Ed., The Pantagraph, IL, Bloomington
Hansen, Marcia A......................858-272-9023
marcia@spmg.com, Partner, Senior Publishers Media Group, CA, San Diego
Hansen, Glenn ....ext. 2801
ghansen@bpaww.com, Pres./CEO, BPA Worldwide, CT, Shelton
Hansen, Trevor.........................858-272-9023
trevor@epmg360.com, CEO, Senior Publishers Media Group, CA, San Diego
Hansen, Heidi ....(928) 913-8652
Classified Adv. Dir., Arizona Daily Sun, AZ, Flagstaff
Hansen, Kare M.
kare.m.hansen@l-a.no, Ed., LINDESNES, Mandal
Hansen, Jonny
jonny.hansen@itromso.no, Ed. in Chief, TROMSOE, Tromsoe
Hansen, Bonnie
bhansen@postregister.com, Asst. to the Publisher, Post Register, ID, Idaho Falls
Hansen, Barbara ....(928) 445-3333
Personnel Dir., The Daily Courier, AZ, Prescott
Hansen, Judi...........................(479) 785-7759
jhansen@swtimes.com, City Ed., Times Record, AR, Fort Smith
Hansen, Ben ....(928) 445-3333
Ed., The Daily Courier, AZ, Prescott
Hansen, John S.
john.hansen@westburg.com, Dir., Westburg Media Capital, NV, Incline Village
Hanson, V.H............................(205) 325-3126
Pub., The Birmingham News, AL, Birmingham
Hanson, Dennis ....(970) 375-4536
dhanson@durangoherald.com, Dir., Adv./Mktg., Durango Herald, CO, Durango
Hanson, Debra.........................(203) 354-1012
dhanson@thehour.com, Advertising Director, The Hour Publishing Co., CT, Norwalk
Hanson, Carmela
carmela@focus-news.com, Adv. Mgr., Best Southwest Focus, TX, DeSoto
Hanson, Scott..........................(847) 879-8418
hansonsj@accessabc.com, Vice Pres., Auditing Servs., ABC Interactive, IL, Schaumburg
Hanson, Bob 414-297-7824
Faculty Adviser, Milwaukee Area Tech. College, WI, Milwaukee
Hanson, Marlon ....(972) 223-9175
focusnews@wans.net, Pub., Best Southwest Focus, TX, DeSoto
Hanson, Bill
bhanson@thetimestribune.com, Pub., Times-Tribune, KY, Corbin
Hanssen, Jan-Eirik
jeh@an.no, Ed., AVISA NORDLAND, Bodo
Hanzlik, Mark...........................(916) 551-1770
mark@awn.org, Exec. Dir., Alternative Weekly Network, CA, Sacramento
Hapney, Terry..........................(740) 351-4778
Shawnee State Univ., OH, Portsmouth
Happychuk, Tim
thappy@wpgsun.com, Mgmt. Info Servs. Mgr., The Winnipeg Sun, MB, Winnipeg
Harada, Hainichi
info@hokkaido-np.co.jp, Mgr., HOKKAIDO SHIMBUN, Hakodate, Hokkaido
Harakawa, Ann
aharakawa@twotwelve.com, Principal, Two Twelve, NY, New York
Harbert, Tom...........................530-477-4257
tomh@theunion.com, Mgmt. Info Servs./Online Mgr., The Union, CA, Grass Valley
Harbin, Norm
info@na.flintgrp.com, Vice Pres., Bus./Technical Devel., Flint Group, MI, Plymouth
Harbison, Steven K. ....(423) 359-3110
steve.harbison@greenevillesun.com, Gen. Mgr., The Greeneville Sun, TN, Greeneville
Harbison, Steven K. ....(423) 359-3110
sharbison@xtn.net, Vice Pres., Special Projects, Jones Media, Inc., TN, Greeneville
Harbor, Kingsley O....................(256) 782-5300
kharbor@jsu.edu, Chair/Prof., Jacksonville State University, AL, Jacksonville
Harbour, Alison...............................ext. 141
Photographer, The Sentinel-Record, AR, Hot Springs
Harbron, Chris ....(306) 781-5228
editorial@leaderpost.canwest.com, News Coord., The Leader-Post, SK, Regina
Hardee, Gary...........................(817) 548-5401
ghardee@star-telegram.com, Pub., Arlington Star-Telegram, Fort Worth Star-Telegram, TX, Fort Worth
Hardfeldt, Ake
akehardfeldt@dagbladet.se, Ed., DAG-BLADET/NYA SAMHALLET, Sundsvall
Hardgrave, Johnie
johnie@ssecho.com, Adv. Mgr., Sulphur Springs News-Telegram, TX, Sulphur Springs
Hardie, Chris...........................(608) 791-8223
chris.hardie@lee.net, Tri-County Foxxy Shopper East, WI, La Crosse
chris.hardie@lee.net, Ed., La Crosse Tribune, WI, La Crosse
Harding, Shane
shane.harding@nqo.com, Advertising Manager, OXFORD MAIL, Oxford, Oxfordshire
Harding, Stephen ....ext. 229
sharding@tek-tools.com, Dir., Mktg., Tek-Tools, Inc., TX, Dallas
Harding, Cathie.......................(580) 310-5250
East Central University, OK, Ada
Harding, Sally ....(212) 431-2851
New York Law School, NY, New York
Harding, Scott
sharding@flpress.com, Media Dir., Florida Press Association, FL, Tallahassee
Harding, Scott
sharding@n2ps.com, Media Dir., National Newspaper Placement Services, FL, Lake Mary
Hardison, Karen
kardison@tnninc.com, Vice Pres., Mktg., The Newspaper Network (TNN), CA, Sacramento
Hardisty, Dianne ....(661) 395-7414
dhardisty@bakersfield.com, Editorial Page Ed., The Bakersfield Californian, CA, Bakersfield
Hardoin, Jacques
sport@nordeclair.fr, Dir., NORD-ECLAIR, Roubaix
Hardwick, John H.
jhardwick@mpival.com, Reg'l Dir., Management Planning, Inc., NY, New York
Hardwig, Greg
gshardwig@naplesnews.com, Sports Ed., Naples Daily News, FL, Naples
Hardy, Conna ....(478) 744-4292
chardy@macontel.com, CFO, The Telegraph, GA, Macon
Hardy, Sandra C. ....Sec.
Herald-Standard, PA, Uniontown
Hardy, Tracy...........................(707) 256-2207
thardee@pulitzer.net, Bus. Mgr., Napa Valley Register, CA, Napa
Hare, Doug
advert@bowesnet.com, Assoc. Pub., Daily Herald-Tribune, AB, Grande Prairie
Hare, Richard L.
mmhare@frontiernet.net, Pres., Hare Associates, Inc., NY, Rochester
Hargis, Amanda
ahargis@onecliq.net, Adv. Mgr., Classified, Du Quoin Evening Call, IL, Du Quoin
Hargreaves, Meg.......................202-650-6680
meghargreaves@cqrollcall.com, SVP, legislative services and publisher, Congressional Quarterly, Inc., DC, Washington
Harjo, Jeff
harjo@naja.com, Interim. Dir., Native American Journalists Association, OK, Norman
Harke, Peter
redaktion@ahlener-zeitung.de, Ed., AHLENER ZEITUNG, Ahlen
Harker, John
info@infocus.com, Pres./CEO, Infocus Corp., OR, Wilsonville
Harkins, Joe ....(201) 985-2105
joe@travelthenet.com, Self-Syndicator, Joe Harkins, NJ, Jersey City
Harknett, Rich ....(212) 210-2271
rharknett@nydailynews.com, Circ. Vice Pres., NY Daily News, NY, New York
Harlan, Scott...........................(920) 453-5114
sharlan@sheboygan.gannett.com, Adv. Dir., The Sheboygan Press, WI, Sheboygan
Harley, Bill ....(888)309-0639
bharley@miracomcomputer.com, Vice President, Miracom Computer Corp., NY, Eastchester
Harman, Donna
sharon_ashley@afandpa.org, Pres./CEO, American Forest & Paper Association, Inc., DC, Washington
Harmon, Leland...........(250) 372-2331 ext. 6164
Prodn. Mgr., Pressroom, Kamloops Daily News, BC, Kamloops
Harmon, Brian
bharmon@greenfieldreporter.com, Sports Ed., Daily Reporter, IN, Greenfield
Harmon, Tim
tharmon@sbtinfo.com, Mng. Ed., South Bend Tribune, IN, South Bend
Harmon, Clinton L.....................(918) 496-1679
clintoons@aol.com, Pres., Clintoons Features, OK, Tulsa
Harmon, Karlie
kharmon@okcu.edu, Chair, Oklahoma City University, OK, Oklahoma City
Harmon, Greg...........................(415) 566-4348
gharmon@beldenassociates.com, Dir., Bus. Devel., Belden Associates, TX, Dallas
Harmon, Brad ....(585) 298-0030
Vice Pres., Sales & Marketing, GateHouse Media Inc., NY, Fairport
Harms, Laura
business@taylordailypress.net, Bus. Mgr., Taylor Daily Press, TX, Taylor
Harms, Joni......................................ext. 208
jharms@dglobe.com, Pub., The Daily Globe, MN, Worthington
jharms@dglobe.com, Worthington Daily Globe, MN, Worthington
Harn, Jay ....(661) 857-4595
jayharn@sbcglobal.net, Associate- Western States, Grimes, W.B. & Co., MD, Gaithersburg
Harnack, Kevin ....(262) 513-2652
kharnack@conleynet.com, Photo Ed., The Freeman, WI, Waukesha
Harnice, Milinda
mharnice@paxtonmedia.com, Asst., Paxton Media Group LLC, KY, Paducah
Haro, V. Richard......................(970) 224-7734
richardharo@coloradoan.com, Chief Photographer, The Coloradoan, CO, Fort Collins
Harold, Rich
ssystems@bellsouth.net, Pres., Shreve Systems, LA, Shreveport
Harper, Stephanie
sharper@skagitpublshing.com, Adv. Mgr., Majors/Natl. Accts., Skagit Valley Herald, WA, Mount Vernon
Harper, Ann ....(208) 677-8734
alharper@southidahopress.com, Bus. Mgr., South Idaho Press, ID, Burley
Harper, Howard
howardh@base-line.com, Owner, Base-Line, Inc., IL, Gurnee
Harpine, William
williamh@usca.edu, Chair, University of South Carolina, Aiken, SC, Aiken
Harr, Gregg.............................(561) 820-4647
gharr@pbpost.com, Adv. Dir., Opns., The Palm Beach Post, FL, West Palm Beach
Harral, Paul K..........................(817) 390-7836
harral@star-telegram.com, Vice Pres./Editorial Dir., Fort Worth Star-Telegram, TX, Fort Worth
Harreld, J. Bruce......................(914) 499-5433
harreld@us.ibm.com, Sr. Vice Pres., Strategy, IBM Corp., NY, Somers
Harriger, Ginny ....(717) 262-4710
gharriger@mediaonepa.com, Advertising Director, Public Opinion, PA, Chambersburg
Harring, Valarie........................239-574-1110
vharring@breezenewspapers.com, Editorial Dir., Cape Coral Breeze, FL, Cape Coral
Harrington, Craig......................(530) 225-4929

Shasta College, CA, Redding
Harrington, Zach
zharrington@times-standard.com, Display Adv. Dir., Times-Standard, CA, Eureka
Harris, Kandace L.
klharris@jcsu.edu, Interim Dept. Chair, Johnson C. Smith University, NC, Charlotte
Harris, Jean ....(845) 437-4712
harrisje@poughkee.gannett.com, Mktg. Mgr., Poughkeepsie Journal, NY, Poughkeepsie
Harris, Sheryl ....(216) 999-4409
Consumer Reporter, The Plain Dealer, OH, Cleveland
Harris, Michael..........................(615) 790-2570
harris16464@bellsouth.net, Ed., The Plant Man, TN, Franklin
Harris, Susan ....(252) 335-8077
sharris@dailyadvance.com, Customer Service/Classified Managr, The Daily Advance, NC, Elizabeth City
Harris, Ike
info@daige.com, Pres., Daige Products, Inc., NY, Albertson
Harris, Frank............................(203) 392-5804
Southern Connecticut State Univ., CT, New Haven
Harris, Tom ....ext. 373
tharris@johnsoncitypress.com, Dir., Sales/Mktg., Johnson City Press, TN, Johnson City
Harris, Clint.............................(807) 343-6219
clint.harris@chroniclejournal.com, Dir., Mktg./Sales, The Chronicle-Journal, ON, Thunder Bay
Harris, Karen ....(540) 368-5006
kharris@freelancestar.com, Bus. Mgr., The Free Lance-Star, VA, Fredericksburg
Harris, Kay..................(229) 244-3400 ext. 280
kay.harris@gaflnews.com, Mng. Ed., Valdosta Daily Times, GA, Valdosta
Harris, Franklin.........................(256) 340-2394
franklin@decaturdaily.com, Asst. Metro Ed., The Decatur Daily, AL, Decatur
Harris, Inez..............................(217) 788-1482
inez.harris@sj-r.com, HR Mgr., The State Journal-Register, IL, Springfield
Harris, Christy...........................405.238.6464
charris@pvdemocrat.com, Classified & Legal Account Rep, Pauls Valley Democrat, OK, Pauls Valley
Harris, Matthew
sales@bychrome.com, Gen. Mgr., ByChrome Ltd., OH, Springfield
Harris, Paul
pharris@saxotech.com, Vice Pres., Cor. Mktg., SAXOTECH, Inc., FL, Tampa
Harris, W. Russell ....(760) 745-3521
rharris@nctimes.com, Mng. Ed., North County Times, CA, Escondido
Harris, Michelle
michelle@couriernews.com, Adv. Dir., The Courier, AR, Russellville
Harris, Nicol
nicol.harris@pressdemocrat.com, Online Adv., The Press Democrat, CA, Santa Rosa
Harris Lipschultz, Jeremy
jlipschultz@mail.unomaha.edu, Dir./Prof., University of Nebraska at Omaha, NE, Omaha
Harrison, Caroline Diamond.........(718) 981-1234
harrison@siadvance.com, Pub., Staten Island Advance, NY, Staten Island
Harrison, Chad ....(434) 369-6688
chadjourn@yahoo.com, Grp. Pub, Womack Publishing Co., VA, Chatham
Harrison, Jeremy.......................(253) 597-8278
jeremy.harrison@thenewstribune.com, Photography Dir., The News Tribune, WA, Tacoma
Harrison, Shawn
sharrison@hjnews.com, Sports Ed., The Herald Journal, UT, Logan
Harrison, Vicki..........................(828) 232-5993
vharriso@citizen-times.com, Prodn. Mgr., The Asheville Citizen-Times, NC, Asheville
Harrow, Richard
rharrow@msn.com, Vice Pres., League of Advertising Agencies, Inc., NY, New York
Hart, Earnest
ehart@jackson.gannett.com, Assistant Managing Editor/Multimedia, The Clarion-Ledger, MS, Jackson
Hart, Scott ....(765) 593-2459 ext. 218
shart@thecouriertimes.com, Adv. Mgr., The Courier-Times, IN, New Castle
Hart, Patti ....(518) 454-5067
phart@timesunion.com, Interactive Gen. Mgr., Times Union, NY, Albany
Harter, Lee
lharter@timesanddemocrat.com, Editorial Page Ed., The Times and Democrat, SC, Orangeburg
Harter, Kristina ....(308) 432-6304
ads@csceagle.com, Advertising Director, The Eagle, NE, Chadron
Hartgrave, Greg ....(360) 735-4603
greg.hartgrave@columbian.com, Circulation Systems Administrator, The Columbian, WA, Vancouver
Hartgrove, Rhett ....ext. 671
rhett.hartgrove@svherald.com, Prodn. Foreman, Press/Camera, Sierra Vista Herald, AZ, Sierra Vista
Hartley, Bill
bhartley@my403.com, Prodn. Mgr., Commercial Print, The Lethbridge Herald, AB, Lethbridge
Hartley, Susan
shartely@dailycall.com, Exec. Ed., Piqua Daily Call, OH, Piqua
Hartley, Jeff
jeff.hartley@augustachronicle.com, Circ. Mgr., The Augusta Chronicle, GA, Augusta
Hartley, Russell..................................ext. 259
rhartley@thworldlink.com, Prodn. Foreman, Mailroom, The World, OR, Coos Bay
Hartman, Philip ....(732) 565-7310
phartman@thnt.com, Editorial Page Ed., Home News Tribune, NJ, East Brunswick
Hartman, Julie..........................(801) 625-4329
Adv. Mgr., Major/Nat'l, Standard-Examiner, UT, Ogden
Hartman, Michelle..............................ext. 270
mhartman@mountvernonnews.com, NIE Coord., Mount Vernon News, OH, Mount Vernon
Hartman, Peter
petehartman@harperimage.com, Mgr., Gen. Sales, Harper Corp. of America (Anilox Roll Supplier), NC, Charlotte
Hartman, Michelle L...........................ext. 270
mhartman@mountvernonnews.com, Vice Pres., Mount Vernon News, OH, Mount Vernon
Hartman, Harry.........................603-581-1977
Publisher, Citizen, NH, Laconia
Hartman, Fred B........................(281) 342-8691
Vice Chairman, Hartman Newspapers LP, TX, Rosenberg
Hartmann, R.L.B.
rlb@wombania.com, Ed., Wombania, ON, Hamilton
Hartmann, Bruce ....(865) 523-3131
news@knews.com, Pres./Pub., Knoxville News Sentinel, TN, Knoxville
Harton, Greg ....(479) 571-6429
editor@nwarktimes.com, Exec. Ed., Northwest Arkansas Times, AR, Fayetteville
Hartung, Raymond.....................(412) 380-5612
rhartung@tribweb.com, Sr. Vice. Pres./CFO, Tribune-Review Publishing Co., PA, Greensburg
Hartwell, Jay.............................(808) 956-3217
hartwell@hawaii.edu, Ed. Advisor, Univ. of Hawaii Manoa, Ka Leo O Hawaii, HI, Honolulu
Harty, Ken
kenh@wahpetondailynews.com, Pub., The Daily News, ND, Wahpeton
kenh@wahpetondailynews.com, Wahpeton Daily News, ND, Wahpeton
Harty, Tim ....ext. 204
City Ed., The Daily Sentinel, CO, Grand Junction
Hartzell, Ted ....ext. 293
thartzell@heraldpalladium.com, Metro Ed., The Herald-Palladium, MI, Saint Joseph
Harvey, Carol ....(507) 444-1561
charvey@owatonna.com, Circ. Mgr., Owatonna People's Press, MN, Owatonna
Harvey, Brian ....ext. 315
News Ed., The Daily Sentinel, CO, Grand Junction
Harvey, Christine Lynn ....(631) 751-8819
charvey@newliving.com, Pub./Ed. in Chief, New Living Syndicate, NY, Patchogue
Harvey, Alyssa..........................(270) 783-3257
aharvey@bgdailynews.com, Living/Lifestyle Ed., Daily News, KY, Bowling Green
Harvey, Faye
f_harvey@hotmail.com, Broker, Harvey, Faye, MO, Lebanon
Harvey, James
fdvs_info@firstdatacorp.com, Vice Pres., Devel., First Data Voice Services, NE, Omaha
Harvill, Jerry
jharvill@timesanddemocrat.com, Mgmt. Info Servs. Mgr., The Times and Democrat, SC, Orangeburg
Harville, Kelly ....(415) 777-7337
kharville@sfchronicle.com, Vice Pres., Marketing, San Francisco Chronicle, CA, San Francisco
Harwood, Michael ....(508) 427-5009
mharwood@enterprisenews.com, Adv. Dir., Retail, The Enterprise, MA, Randolph
Haselden, Mark ....(843) 317-7271
mhaselden@florencenews.com, Asst. Sports Ed., Morning News, SC, Florence
Hasenorhl, Hans-Peter
hans-peter.hasenoehrl@kronanzaetunt.at, Ed. in Chief, SALZBURG KRONE: NEUE KRONEN ZEITUNG, Salzburg
Hashii, Shoroku
master@kochinews.co.jp, Chrmn., KOCHI SHIMBUN, Kochi, Shikoku
Hashmi, Ahtar
jasarat@cyber.net.pk, Ed., JASARAT, Karachi
Haskell, Robert H.
info@martinsvillebulletin.com, Pres./Pub., Martinsville Bulletin, VA, Martinsville
Haskell, Scott............................(207) 990-8164
bdnphoto@bangordailynews.net, Photo Ed., Bangor Daily News, ME, Bangor
Haskell, Sabina ....(802) 747-6121 ext. 2223
sabina.haskell@rutlandherald.com, Asst. Mng. Ed., Rutland Herald, VT, Rutland
Haskins, Rhonda ....ext. 1025
Circ. District Mgr., The Porterville Recorder, CA, Porterville
Haskmack, Ulrech
vertrieb@weser-kurier.de, Proprietor, WESER-KURIER, Bremen
Haslag, Jane ....(573) 761-0270
jane@newstribune.com, Advertising Manager, News Tribune, MO, Jefferson City
Hasse, Ron..................................(818) 713-3101
ron.hasse@langnews.com, Vice Pres., Consumer Mktg., Daily Breeze, CA, Torrance
Hassing, Geoff...........................(253) 503-7573
geofftoons@comcast.net, Cartoonist, Travelin' Light, IN, Muncie
Hastbacka, Borje
borje.hastbacka@ot.fi, Ed. in Chief, OESTERBOTTNINGEN, Karleby
Hasten, Mike
mhasten@gannett.com, Bureau Chief, Gannett News Service - Baton Rouge, LA, LA, Baton Rouge
Hastings, Mark L. ....(620) 365-2111
registerdisplay@gmail.com, Adv. Mgr., Iola Register, KS, Iola
Hastings, Catherine....................(570) 372-4298
Susquehanna Univ., PA, Selinsgrove
Hasty, J.D.
publisher@brooklyneagle.net, Pub., Brooklyn Daily Eagle & Daily Bulletin, 30 Henry St.
Hatayama, Hiroshi
osaka@nnn.co.jp, Ed., OSAKA NICHI-NICHI SHIMBUN, Osaka Bakuromachi
Hatch, Danielle..........................(309) 686-3262
dhatch@pjstar.com, Entertainment Ed., Journal Star, IL, Peoria
Hatch, Jim
marketing@v-studios.com, Dir., Mktg./Sales, V!Studios, VA, McLean
Hatcher, Anthony
ahatcher@elon.edu, Assoc. Prof., Elon University, NC, Elon
Hatfield, Abby
abbyhatfield@thesouthern.com, Opns. Mgr., The Southern Illinoisan, IL, Carbondale
Hatfield, David ....(520) 295-4237
dhatfield@azbiz.com, Ed., The Daily Territorial, AZ, Tucson
Hatfield, Ken.............................(559) 441-6302
khatfield@fresnobee.com, Vice Pres., Community Rel./Sr. Circ. Mgr., The Fresno Bee, CA, Fresno
Hatley, Trip
thatley@robesonian.com, Adv. Dir., The Robesonian, NC, Lumberton
Haudsrjerd, Hilde
hilde.haudsrjerd@aftenposten.no, Ed. in Chief, AFTENNUMMER, Oslo
Haufe, William ....(410) 770-4095
Sports Ed., The Star-Democrat, MD, Easton
Haug, Glenn................................(306) 691-1277
glenn.haug@mjtimes.sk.ca, Adv. Mgr., The Moose Jaw Times-Herald, SK, Moose Jaw
Haught, Betsy............................(304) 367-2535
bchaught@timeswv.com, Circ. Dir., Times West Virginian, WV, Fairmont
Haught, James A. ....(304) 348-5199
haught@wvgazette.com, Ed., The Charleston Gazette, Sunday Gazette-Mail, WV, Charleston
Haugsgjerd, Hilde
hilde.haudsrjerd@aftenposten.no, Ed. in Chief, AFTENPOSTEN, Oslo
Hauke, Angelika
info@mt-news.de, Ed. in Chief, MUNSTERLANDISCHE TAGESZEITUNG, Cloppenburg
Haun, Brian ....(253) 620-4747
Brianh@webpressllc.com, President, WebPress, LLC, WA, Tacoma
Haun, Sarah...............................(212) 254-6670
shaun@twotwelve.com, CMO, Two Twelve, NY, New York
Haus, Keith
khaus@gfherald.com, Prodn. Mgr., Pressroom, Grand Forks Herald, ND, Grand Forks
Hauser, Bea
sh-az@bluewin.ch, Ed. in Chief, SCHAFFHAUSER AZ, Schaffhausen
Hausfeld, Kevin
advertising@lanthorn.com, Grand Valley State Univ., MI, Allendale
Hausler, Steve
steveh_news@dailynews.net, Photo Ed., The Hays Daily News, KS, Hays
Haver, Sharon
information@focusonstyle.com, Syndicated Columnist, Newspaper/Online, Focus On Style, NY, New York
Haward, Steve
gcbmarketing@gcb.newsltd.com.au, MD, THE GOLD COAST BULLETIN, Molendinar
Hawes, Kelly ....ext. 5155
kelly.hawes@pharostribune.com, Mng. Ed., Pharos-Tribune, IN, Logansport
Hawk, Jim
jhawk@lincolnindustrial.com, Vice Pres., Sales/Mktg., Lincoln Industrial, MO, Saint Louis
Hawk, Rochelle
rhawk@logandaily.com, Mng. Ed., Logan Daily News, OH, Logan
Hawkins, Alecia ....(616) 647-8865
ahawkins@grpress.com, Circ. Mgr., Single Copy, The Grand Rapids Press, MI, Grand Rapids
Hawkins, Iyvonne ....(605) 331-2326
cbaldwin@argusleader.com, Editorial Page Ed., Argus Leader, SD, Sioux Falls
Hawkins, Bill..............................(843) 937-5665
bhawkins@postandcourier.com, Exec. Ed., The Post and Courier, SC, Charleston
Hawkins, Tom............................(937) 328-0343
thawkins@coxohio.com, Graphics Ed./Art Dir., Springfield News-Sun, OH, Springfield
Hawkins, Terry
thawkins@centurytel.net, Treasurer, Arkansas Press Women Association, Inc.
Hawkins, Brian
sdneditor@starkvilledailynews.com, Online Ed., Starkville Daily News, MS, Starkville
Hawkins, Carol Lee ....(703) 264-7211
clhawkins@nes.org, Asst. Dir., Membership, Graphic Communications Council, VA, Reston
Hawkins, James E.
james.hawkins@famu.edu, Dean, Florida A&M University, FL, Tallahassee
Hawkley, John ....(707) 256-2293
jhawkley@pulitzer.net, Prodn. Foreman, Pressroom/Platemaking, Napa Valley Regis-

ter, CA, Napa
Hawn, Sherrie ....ext. 247
cwilliams@richmondregister.com, Adv. Dir., The Richmond Register, KY, Richmond
Hay, Shannon
shay@pubgroup.com, Adv. Dir., American Profile - New York, NY, NY, New York
Hay, Ellen
ellenhay@augustana.edu, Chair, Augustana College, IL, Rock Island
Hay, Shannon
shay@pubgroup.com, Adv. Dir., Relish - New York, NY, NY, New York
Hay, Shannon
shay@pubgroup.com, Adv. Dir., American Profile - New York, NY, NY, New York
Hayashi, Hiroshi
info@kachimai.co.jp, Pres., TOKACHI MAINICHI SHIMBUN, Obihiro, Hokkaido
Hayden, Jim ....(616) 546-4274
jim.hayden@holldandsentinel.com, News Team Leader, The Holland Sentinel, MI, Holland
Hayden, Tom..........................(239) 344-4621
Cape Coral Ed., The News-Press, FL, Fort Myers
Hayes, Taylor Wood
twhayes@kentuckynewera.com, Publisher, Kentucky New Era, KY, Hopkinsville
Hayes, Patty ....(707) 521-5296
phayes@pressdemocrat.com, Books Ed., The Press Democrat, CA, Santa Rosa
Hayes, Rockford M....................(505) 887-5501
rhayes@currentargus.com, Pub., Current-Argus, NM, Carlsbad
Hayes, Kristie..........................(580) 765-3311
news@poncacitynews.com, Mng. Ed, The Ponca City News, OK, Ponca City
Hayes, Ralph
ralph@datavoicetechnology.com, Pres., Datavoice Technology, TX, Houston
Hayes, Bob
bhayes@artbeats.com, Dir., Tech., Artbeats, OR, Myrtle Creek
Hayes, Daniel
info@lee.net, Vice Pres. Commun., Lee Enterprises, IA, Davenport
Hayes, Sandy
shayes@thesuntimes.ca, Coord., Computer Servs., The Sun Times, ON, Owen Sound
Hayes, Daniel K. ....(563) 383-2163
dan.hayes@lee.net, Vice Pres., Commun., Lee Enterprises, Inc., IA, Davenport
Hayes, Kathleen
michael.pppost@worldmail.com.kh, Mng. Dir., PHNOM PENH POST, Bangkok
Hayes, Joseph..........................646-895-8421
joseph.hayes@srds.com, VP & Publisher, SRDS, a Kantar Media Company, IL, Des Plaines
Hayes, Pete ....(618) 463-2565
pete_hayes@thetelegraph.com, Sports Ed., The Telegraph, IL, Alton
Hayes, Kristi
circmgr@ssecho.com, Circ. Mgr., Sulphur Springs News-Telegram, TX, Sulphur Springs
Hayley, Randy
randy.hayley@ott.sunpub.com, Circ. Dir., The Ottawa Sun, ON, Ottawa
Haynes, Mike ....(806) 371-5293
jmhaynes@actx.edu, Advisor, Amarillo College, TX, Amarillo
Haynes, Lori 805-781-7818
lhaynes@thetribunenews.com, Advertising Manager, The Tribune, CA, San Luis Obispo
Haynes, Stephen C....................(785) 475-2206
s.haynes@nwkansas.com, Pres., Haynes Publishing Co., KS, Oberlin
Hays, Jean 316-268-6557
jhays@wichitaeagle.com, Investigations Editor, The Wichita Eagle, KS, Wichita
Hays, Rob ....(610) 861-5372
Northampton Cmty. College, PA, Bethlehem
Hays, Linda ....(573) 815-1841
lhays@columbiatribune.com, Mktg./Promo. Mgr., Columbia Daily Tribune, MO, Columbia
Hays, Debbie
dhays@timesonline.com, Credit Mgr., Beaver County Times, PA, Beaver
Hayt, Teri ....(520) 573-4226
thayt@azstarnet.com, Asst. Mng. Ed., Arizona Daily Star, AZ, Tucson
Haytslt, F.
ringkoebing@bergske.dk, Ed., DAGBLAD RINGKOBING SKYERN, Ringkobing, Jutland
Hazarian, Tony
tonyh@goldcountrymedia.com, Pub., Auburn Journal, Inc., CA, Auburn
Hazarian, Tommy
auburnjournal@goldcountrymedia.com, Pub., Auburn Journal, Inc., CA, Auburn
Hazell, Naedine ....(860) 241-3745
nhazell@courant.com, Interim Ed., The Hartford Courant, CT, Hartford
Hazelwood, Mary......................(530) 852-0251
maryh@goldcountrymedia.com, Prodn. Supvr., Imaging, Auburn Journal, Inc., CA, Auburn
Hazle, Maline
mhazle@redding.com, City Ed., Record Searchlight, CA, Redding
Hazzard, Joe
sales@ergotron.com, Pres., Ergotron, Inc., MN, Saint Paul
Heacock, Lesa
ktimesadv@dbscorp.net, Adv. Mgr., The Kenton Times, OH, Kenton
Heacox, Frank ....(252) 265-7860
heacox@wilsondaily.com, Circ. Mgr., The Wilson Daily Times, NC, Wilson
Headrick, Doug
dheadrick@xtn.net, Editorial Writer, The Daily Post-Athenian, TN, Athens
Healy, Jean ....(605) 331-2369
jhealy@argusleader.com, Principal HR Business Partner, Argus Leader, SD, Sioux Falls
Healy, John F.
jfhealy@elimparcial.com, Pres./CEO, El Imparcial, Hermosillo, Sonora
Hearing, Carl C...............(608) 328-4202 ext. 15
chearing@themonroetimes.com, Vice Pres./Gen. Mgr., The Monroe Times, WI, Monroe
Hearst, George R.......................(518) 454-5555
ghearst@timesunion.com, Pub./CEO, Times Union, NY, Albany
Heasley, Jim ....(724) 543-1303 ext. 215
jheasley@tribweb.com, News Ed., Leader Times, PA, Kittanning
Heasley, Dan
circulation@redlandsdailyfacts.com, Circ. Dir., Redlands Daily Facts, CA, Redlands
Heastings, David...............................ext. 266
News Ed., Butler Eagle, PA, Butler
Heaston, Sally
ads@northwestsignal.net, Adv./Mktg. Dir., Northwest Signal, OH, Napoleon
Heater, Jay ....(765) 362-1200 ext. 119
jheater@jrpress.com, Mng. Ed., Journal Review, IN, Crawfordsville
Heater, Jay..............................661-267-4143
jheater@avpress.com, Sports Editor, Antelope Valley Press, CA, Palmdale
Heater, Jay..............................661-267-4143
jheater@avpress.com, Sports Editor, Antelope Valley Press, CA, Palmdale
Heatherly, Roy
rheatherly@jacksonsun.com, Pub./Pres., The Jackson Sun, TN, Jackson
Heaton, Betty Jo......................(775) 881-1240
bjheaton@sierranevadamedia.com, Prodn. Mgr., Nevada Appeal, NV, Carson City
Hebrero, Virginia
ginebra@efe.com, Rep., EFE News Services - Geneva, Switzerland, Geneva
Hecht, Brian K.
treehouse1@aol.com, Contact, TreeHouse-One Interactive Productions, TX, Magnolia
Heck, Matt..................(770) 428-9411 ext. 400
mheck@mdjonline.com, Circ. Mgr., Cherokee Tribune, GA, Canton
Heck, Matt.......................................ext. 406
Prodn. Mgr., Distr., Marietta Daily Journal, GA, Marietta
Heckel, Sherri
sheckel@messenger-inquirer.com, Librarian, Messenger-Inquirer, KY, Owensboro
Heckel, Dan
dheckel@messenger-inquirer.com, Ed., Messenger-Inquirer, KY, Owensboro
Hecker, TJ ....(253) 579-4235
Pacific Lutheran Univ., WA, Tacoma
Heckler, Sharon 850-747-5049
sheckler@flafreedom.com, Regional Circulation Director, The News Herald, FL, Panama City
Hedge, Dave 8124647640
hedged@courierpress.com, Advertising Director, Evansville Courier & Press, IN, Evansville
Heekin-Canedy, Scott.................(212) 556-1234
Pres., New York Times, The New York Times Co., NY, New York
Heeschen, Paula C.....................(570) 420-4348
pheeschen@poconorecord.com, Editorial Page Ed., Pocono Record, PA, Stroudsburg
Hefflinger, Bruce ....ext. 226
hefflinger@crescent-news.com, Sports Ed., Defiance Publishing LLC, OH, Defiance
Hegarty, Erin.............................847-951-8018
ehegarty@vikings.northpark.edu, Editor-In-Chief, North Park Univ., IL, Chicago
Hegglin, Markus
verlag@tagblatt-zverich.ch, Ed. in Chief, Berichthaus Verlag, Zurich
Hegna, Jason
jhegna@dailyherald.com, Asst. V.P., Adv. Dir., Daily Herald, IL, Arlington Heights
Hehir, Scott..............................(715) 845-0654
shehir@wdhprint.com, Adv. Mgr., Retail/Classified/Nat'l, The Wausau Daily Herald, WI, Wausau
Heichel, Steve ....(814) 765-5581 ext. 224
shop@theprogressnews.com, Prodn. Supt., Plant, The Progress, PA, Clearfield
Heidbreder, Paul J.
paulheidbreder@lenconnect.com, Pub., The Daily Telegram, MI, Adrian
paulheidbreder@lenconnect.com, Access Shoppers' Guide, MI, Adrian
Heide, Ruth
news@alamosanews.com, Editor, The Valley Courier, CO, Alamosa
Heidman, Bruce ....(705) 674-5271 ext. 269
editorial@thesudburystar.com, Sports Ed., The Sudbury Star, ON, Sudbury
Heilman, Dan
dheilman@computeruser.com, Ed., ComputerUser, MN, Minneapolis
Heim, Mike.......................................ext. 820
mheim@hutchnews.com, Prodn. Mgr., Pressroom, The Hutchinson News, KS, Hutchinson
Heimgartner, Janna
jheimgartner@eastoregonian.com, Business Office Manager, East Oregonian, OR, Pendleton
Heimlich, Richard.....................(760) 804-1641
rheimlich@hearst.com, Sales Mgr., Western Region, King Features Syndicate, NY, New York
rheimlich@hearst.com, Sales Mgr., Western Reg., North America Syndicate, NY, New York
Heine, Kurt
heinek@phillynews.com, City Ed., The Philadelphia Daily News, PA, Philadelphia
Heinemann, Juergen
service@kieler-nachrichten.de, Ed. in Chief, Kieler Nachrichten, Kiel
Heinemann, Wilfred
haz@madsack.de, Mng. Ed., Hannoversche Allgemeine Zeitung, Hannover
Heintzelman, Andrew ....ext. 241
andy_h@newsitem.com, Exec. Ed., The News-Item, PA, Shamokin
Heinz, Eric..............................(970) 392-9341
Univ. of Northern Colorado, CO, Greeley
Heirtzler, William C...................(318) 487-6450
bheirtzler@thetowntalk.com, Adv. Dir., The Town Talk, LA, Alexandria
Heisel, Scott ....(360) 501-2708
sheisel@tdn.com, Online Ed., The Daily News, WA, Longview
Heithaus, Harriet Howard
hkheithaus@naplesnews.com, Homes/Ambience Ed., Naples Daily News, FL, Naples
Heitz, Karl..............................(212) 303-0004
karlheitz@compuserve.com, Pres., Heitz Service Corp., NY, Woodside
Held, Jon ....(602) 444-8566
jon.held@pni.com, Exec. Vice Pres./CFO, The Arizona Republic, AZ, Phoenix
Helems, Jerry
jhelems@poncacitynews.com, Prodn. Mgr., The Ponca City News, OK, Ponca City
Helguero, Luz Maria
lmhelguero@eltiempo.com.pe, Pub., El Tiempo, Piura
Helicke, James ....(724) 222-2200
pressroom@observer-reporter.com, Prodn. Mgr./Foreman, Pressroom, Observer-Reporter, PA, Washington
Helin, Jan
jan.helin@aftonbladet.se, Ed., AFTONBLADET, Stockholm, Globen
Helle, Lars
lahe@dagbladet.no, Ed. in Chief, DAGBLADET, Oslo
Helliker, Kevin........................(312) 750-4124
Bureau Chief, Chicago, The Wall Street Journal, NY, New York
Helling, Thomas.......................(212) 556-4164
Adv. Vice Pres., The New York Times, NY, New York
Hellner, Oren...........................(212) 944-1060
editor@featurephoto.com, Pres./CEO, Feature Photo Service, Inc., NY, New York
Helm, Elaine ....(847) 491-7206
Northwestern Univ., IL, Evanston
Helm, Steve..............................(314) 340-8800
shelm@post-dispatch.com, Circ. Vice Pres./Dir., St. Louis Post-Dispatch, MO, Saint Louis
Helm, Denise ....(250) 380-5334
dhelm@te.canwest.com, Web Ed., Times Colonist, BC, Victoria
Helmchen, Scott.......................(815) 459-4122
Features Ed., Northwest Herald, IL, Crystal Lake
Helms, Kay
khelms@trcle.com, Adv. Dir., Cleburne Times-Review, TX, Cleburne
Helms, Deneal..........................(540) 374-5533
dhelms@freelancestar.com, Mktg. Dir., The Free Lance-Star, VA, Fredericksburg
Helms, Patrick..............(423) 623-6171 ext. 3128
pat.helms@newportplaintalk.com, Circ. Mgr., Newport Plain Talk, TN, Newport
Helnen, Helmut
bonner.rundschau@kr-redaktion.de, Proprietor, BONNER RUNDSCHAU, Bonn
Heltsley, Randy...............................ext. 6510
Adv./Classified Dir., Pasadena Star-News, CA, Pasadena
Heminger, Karl L. ....(419) 427-8081
karlheminger@thecourier.com, Pres., The Review Times, OH, Fostoria
Heminger, Karl L. ....(419) 427-8081
karlheminger@thecourier.com, Pres./Pub./Treasurer, The Courier, OH, Findlay
Heminger, Karl L. ....(419) 427-8081
karlheminger@thecourier.com, Pres./Treasurer, The Findlay Publishing Co., OH, Findlay
Hemmerich, Stephanie...............(305) 347-6623
shemmerich@alm.com, Director of Client Development, Palm Beach Daily Business Review, FL, West Palm Beach
Hemmerich, Stephanie...............(305) 347-6623
shemmerich@alm.com, Director of Client Development, Miami Daily Business Review, FL, Miami
Hemmingsson, Bjorn
redaktionen@ltz.se, Mgr. Dir., LANSTIDNINGEN, Ostersund
Hencye, Charlie
charlie@ipcpoly.com, Pres., IPC, FL, North Venice
Henderson, Thad
thenderson@hawaiitribune-herald.com, Cir Dir, Hawaii Tribune-Herald, HI, Hilo
Henderson, Mark.......................(318) 362-0350
News Ed., The News-Star, LA, Monroe
Henderson, Jane ....(314) 340-8222
jhenderson@post-dispatch.com, Books Ed., St. Louis Post-Dispatch, MO, Saint Louis
Henderson, Charles A.
chenderson@kentuckynewera.com, Pres./Gen. Mgr., Kentucky New Era, KY, Hopkinsville
Henderson, Jose
cariwebproducts@aol.com, Pres., Cariweb Products, TX, Harlingen
Henderson, Tanya.....................(804) 649-6709

thenderson@timesdispatch.com, Market Devel. Mgr., Richmond Times-Dispatch, VA, Richmond
Henderson, Felecia
fhenderson@detroitnews.com, Asst. Managing Editor, The Detroit News, MI, Detroit
Hendon, Jori ....(319) 341-4352
mfcp@mchsi.com, Office Mgr., Midwest Free Community Papers, IA, Iowa City
Hendricks, Jim ....(229) 888-9352
jim.hendricks@albanyherald.com, Editor, The Albany Herald, GA, Albany
Hendricks, William
circulation@hopewellnews.com, Circ. Mgr., The Hopewell News, VA, Hopewell
Hendricks, Karen
karenh@standard-journal.com, Bus. Mgr., The Standard-Journal, PA, Milton
Hendrickson, John ....(415) 565-4786
Hastings College of Law, CA, San Francisco
Hendrickson, Robert L.....(606) 564-9091 ext. 291
bob.hendrickson@lee.net, Pub., The Ledger Independent, KY, Maysville
Hendrix, Arnold
ahendrix@registerbee.com, Ed., Danville Register & Bee, VA, Danville
Hengel, Michael.......................(870) 534-1428
mhengel@pbcommercial.com, Pub., Pine Bluff Commercial, AR, Pine Bluff
Henke, Bruce
bruceh@jamestownsun.com, Pub., The Jamestown Sun, ND, Jamestown
Henkel, Herbert L.
irworks@irco.com, Chrmn./Pres., Ingersoll-Rand-Aro Fluid Product Div., OH, Bryan
Henley, Linda ....(405) 366-3542
lhenley@normantranscript.com, City Ed., Norman Transcript, OK, Norman
Henley, Brian
bhenley@capitalonline.com, Online Ed., The Capital, MD, Annapolis
Hennessey, Robert..................(814) 870-1646
robert.hennessey@timesnews.com, Adv. Mgr., Classified, Erie Times-News, PA, Erie
Henney, Spencer.......................321-242-3520
shenney@floridatoday.com, Automotive Manager, Florida Today, FL, Melbourne
Henning, Teri ....(717) 703-3076
terih@pa-news.org, President, Pennsylvania Newspaper Association, PA, Harrisburg
Henningsen, Ronald A.
lhenningsen@omahadailyrecord.com, Pres./Pub., Daily Record
Henningsen, Lynda K.
dailyrecord@mcleodusa.net, Assoc. Pub., Daily Record
Henrikson, John.........................253-597-8651
john.henrikson@thenewstribune.com, AME online, The News Tribune, WA, Tacoma
Henry, Lois ....(661) 395-7373
lhenry@bakersfield.com, Asst. Mng. Ed., Projects, The Bakersfield Californian, CA, Bakersfield
Henry, Mark
mark@themexianews.com, Publisher, The Mexia Daily News, TX, Mexia
Henry, Tedda.........................(207) 621-5643
thenry@centralmaine.com, Community Ed., Kennebec Journal, ME, Augusta
Henry, Mark
mhenry@adohio.net, Mgr., Ohio Newspaper Advertising Executives, OH, Columbus
Henry, Gary
ghenry@parisbeacon.com, School Ed., Paris Beacon-News, IL, Paris
Henry, Pat ....(202) 383-7878
pat.henry@newhouse.com, Night Copy Ed., Newhouse News Service, DC, Washington
Henry, Ken
khenry@messengerpostmedia.com, Vice Pres., Adv., Daily Messenger, NY, Canandaigua
Henschen, Mark......................(760) 739-6630
mhenschen@nctimes.com, Circ. Dir., North County Times, CA, Escondido
Hensley, Phil.................................ext. 310
phensley@johnsoncitypress.com, Circ. Dir., Johnson City Press, TN, Johnson City
Hensley, Dean ....(828) 694-7868
dean.hensley@hendersonvillenews.com, Sports Ed., Times-News, NC, Hendersonville
Hensley, Richard ....(863) 386-5843
rhensley@highlandstoday.com, Ed., Highlands Today, FL, Sebring
Hensley, Dennis E.
dnhensley@tayloru.edu, Prof., English/Dir., Professional Writing Major, Taylor University, Fort Wayne Campus, IN, Fort Wayne
Henson, John
editor@harlanonline.net, Mng. Ed., The Harlan Daily Enterprise, KY, Harlan
Henson, Richard ....ext. 28
Prodn. Mgr., Pressroom, McPherson Sentinel, KS, McPherson
Henson, Steve ....(719) 544-3520 ext. 410
shenson@chieftain.com, Mng. Ed., News, The Pueblo Chieftain, CO, Pueblo
Henton, John 438 2399
daily@northernadvocate.co.nz, Mng. Dir., THE NORTHERN ADVOCATE
Hepperla, Rick
rick.hepperla@abb.com, Vice Pres.-Paper Drives Systems/Printing, ABB, Inc. (Printing Systems), WI, New Berlin
Heraande, Felipe
direction@eltiempo.com.ec, Editorial Dir., El Tiempo Cia. Ltd., Cuenca, Azuay
Heraldson, Tina
omahane@ap.org, Bureau Chief, Nebraska Associated Press Association, NE, Omaha
Herbig, Donna ....(309) 757-4920
dherbig@qconline.com, Dir., HR, The Dispatch, IL, Moline
Herbig, Terry..........................(309) 757-4993
therbig@qconline.com, Photo Dir., The Dispatch, IL, Moline
Heredia, Rosario ....(469) 977-2816
rheredia@aldiatx.com, Circ. Dir., Al Dia, TX, Dallas
Herics, Werner
werner.herics@politika.rs, Dir., POLITIKA, Belgrade
Hering, Hasso ....(541) 812-6097
hasso.hering@lee.net, Editorial Page Ed., Albany Democrat-Herald, OR, Albany
Herl, Terry
circulation@wellingtondailynews.com, Circ. Mgr., Wellington Daily News, KS, Wellington
Herligz, Guneilla
guneilla.herligz@dn.se, Ed., DAGENS NYHETER, Stockholm
Herlin, Lars
redaktion@gotlandsallehanda.se, MD, GOTLANDS ALLEHANDA, Visby, Gotland County
Herman, Brian ....(724) 684-2667
bherman@tribweb.com, Sports Ed., The Valley Independent, PA, Monessen
Herman, Gary..........................(856) 486-2905
gherman@gannett.com, Prodn. Opns. Mgr., Courier-Post, NJ, Cherry Hill
Hermansson, Tommy
tommy.hermansson@ttela.se, Executive Director, TTELA, Trollh□ttan
Hernandez, Alex......................(972) 273-3057
North Lake College, TX, Irving
Hernandez, Tony
editor@swdtimes.com, Mng. Ed., Southwest Daily Times, KS, Liberal
Hernandez, Patsy ....(915) 546-6182
phernandez@elpasotimes.com, VP of Production, El Paso Times, TX, El Paso
Hernandez, Tony
composing@bigspringherald.com, Prodn. Mgr., Big Spring Herald, TX, Big Spring
Hernandez, John ....(305) 347-6642
jhernandez@alm.com, Web Adminstrator, Miami Daily Business Review, FL, Miami
Hernandez, John ....(305) 347-6642
jhernandez@alm.com, Web Administrator, Palm Beach Daily Business Review, FL, West Palm Beach
Hernandez Salas, Jose Luis
redaccio@independiente.com.mx, Pres., El Independiente, Hermosillo, Sonora
Herppich, Steven.....................(360) 754-5467
Photo Ed., The Olympian, WA, Olympia
Herrado, Leonardo
leonardh@diario.net, Ed., EL DIARIO DE NUEVO LAREDO, Nuevo Laredo, Tamaulipas
Herranz Cano, Carlos
adelantado@eladelantado.com, Dir., El Adelantado De Segova, Segovia
Herratti, Jay
contactus@citysearch.com, CEO, citysearch.com, CA, West Hollywood
Herrell, Keith
kherrell@cincypost.com, Sports Ed., The Kentucky Post, OH, Cincinnati
Herrera, Francisco 220-1100
garciam@granasa.com.ec, Gen. Mgr., EXTRA, Guayaquil, Guayas
Herrera, Romulo Apr-45
Editorial Dir., AVANCE, Los Teques, Miranda
Herres, Dan
dherres@postandcourier.com, Pres., Evening Post Community Publications Grp., Evening Post Community Publications Group, Inc., SC, Charleston
Herrick, David ....(717) 244-6753
info@igsknives.com, Pres./Treasurer, IGS Knives, Inc., PA, Red Lion
Herrick, Christina...........................ext. 1642
cherrick@the-daily-record.com, Copy Ed., The Daily Record, OH, Wooster
Herrin, Jeff.............................252-407-9943
Editor, Rocky Mount Telegram, NC, Rocky Mount

Herring, Dal M.
dherring@usi.edu, Prof. Emer., University of Southern Indiana, IN, Evansville
Herron, Steve
bleath@minotdailynews.com, Pub., Minot Daily News, ND, Minot
Hersant, Philippe
lnc@canl.nc, Pub., LES NOUVELLES CALEDONIENNES, Noumea
Herschberger, Pete ....(408) 271-3637
pherschberger@mercurynews.com, Adv. Dir., Classified, San Jose Mercury News, CA, San Jose
Hersee, Steve..........................(630) 388-6901
shersee@copia.com, President, Copia International Ltd., IL, Wheaton
Hersey, Michael ....(207) 621-5625
Adv. Mgr., Classified Sales, Morning Sentinel, ME, Waterville
Hershberger, Forrest
fhershberger@journal-advocate.com, Ed., Journal-Advocate, CO, Sterling
Hertz, Kelly
kelly.hertz@yankton.net, Mng. Ed., Yankton Daily Press & Dakotan, SD, Yankton
Hertz, Michael...............................ext. 675
mhertz@medicinehatnews.com, Sr. Vice Pres./Grp. Pub., Southern Alberta, Medicine Hat News, AB, Medicine Hat
Hertzberg, Mark ....(262) 631-1719
mhertzberg@journaltimes.com, Photo Dir., The Journal Times, WI, Racine
Hertzberg, Philippe ....+33 1 41 43 97 66
hertzberg@nytimes.com, Director, International Sales, New York Times News Service, NY, New York
Hertzberg, Philippe ....+33 1 41 43 97 66
hertzberg@nytimes.com, Director, International Sales, New York Times Syndicate, NY, New York
Hervieu, Bruno
info@jir.fr, Dir., JOURNAL DE L'ILE DE LA REUNION, Saint-Denis
Heryford, Shauna
sheryford@edmsun.com, Mgr., Promo., The Edmonton Sun, AB, Edmonton
Herzog, Karen ....(701) 250-8267
krherzog@ndonline.com, Religion Reporter, The Bismarck Tribune, ND, Bismarck
Herzog, Tilo
redaktion@svz.de, Mng. Ed., Norddeutsche Neueste Nachrichten, Rostock
Herzog, Dennis ....ext. 221
Ed., The Daily Sentinel, CO, Grand Junction
Heskes, L.M. 487444
Ed., RIJN EN GOUWE, Alphen aan den Rijn
Hespenhide, Melissa ....(757) 247-4918
mhespenhide@dailypress.com, Dir., Commun./Community Rel., Daily Press, VA, Newport News
Hess, Andreas
andreas.hess@ln-luebeck.de, Mng. Ed., LUBECKER NACHRICHTEN/LUBECKER NACHRICHTEN AM SONNTAG, Lubeck
Hess, Samantha
publisher@poteaudailynews.com, Pub., Poteau Daily News, OK, Poteau
Hesse, Steve ....(303) 954-6369
shesse@medianewsgroup.com, Sr. Vice President Circulation, MediaNews Group Inc, CO, Denver
Hesson, Gary ....(432) 333-7635
gary_hesson@link.freedom.com, Prodn. Foreman, Mailroom, Odessa American, TX, Odessa
Hetland, Tom
privatannonser@aftenbladet.no, Ed., STAVANGER AFTENBLAD, Stavanger
Hettinga, Don ....(616) 526-6520
Prof., Dept. of English, Calvin College, MI, Grand Rapids
Hetzler, John...........................229.888.9319
john.hetzler@albanyherald.com, General Manager, The Albany Herald, GA, Albany
Hew, Shirley 63198340
shew@sph.com.sg, Executive Director, BERITA HARIAN, Singapore
Hewitt, Roy............................(216) 999-4101
Sports Editor, The Plain Dealer, OH, Cleveland
Heymen, Anne ....(904) 819-3486
anne.heymen@staugustinerecord.com, Features Ed., The St. Augustine Record, FL, Saint Augustine
Heyser, Holly
editor@statehornet.com, California State Univ. Sacramento, CA, Sacramento
Hiam, N/A ....N. American Adv. Dir.
(212) 226-1940, The Jerusalem Post Foreign Service, Jerusalem
Hibert, Michael
mhibert@gmti.gannett.com, Dir., Implementation Servs., Celebro, OH, Cincinnati
Hickey, Tom ....(815) 987-1492
thickey@rockford.gannett.com, Prodn. Mgr., Bldg. Serv./Distr. Ctr., Rockford Register Star, IL, Rockford
Hicklin, M.
redaktion@baz.ch, Mng. Ed., BASLER ZEITUNG, Basel, Basel-Stadt
Hickman, Matt ....ext. 619
sports@svherald.com, Sports Ed., Sierra Vista Herald, AZ, Sierra Vista
Hickman, Gerald ....(724) 222-2200
mailroom@observer-reporter.com, Prodn. Mgr., Mailroom, Observer-Reporter, PA, Washington
Hickman, Matt ....ext. 614
sports@svherald.com, Sports Ed., Bisbee Daily Review, AZ, Bisbee
Hickman, Charles
cccamh@aol.com, Pres., Network Newspaper Advertising, Inc., OH, Cleveland
Hicks, Catherine ....ext. 270
cjhicks@wwub.com, Wire Ed., Walla Walla Union-Bulletin, WA, Walla Walla
Hicks, Everett ....(618) 463-2594
everett_hicks@thetelegraph.com, Mgmt. Info Servs. Mgr., The Telegraph, IL, Alton
Hicks, Judy ....(309) 686-3109
jhicks@pjstar.com, Head Librarian, Journal Star, IL, Peoria
Hickson, Fern
fhickson@bowesnet.com, Adv. Mgr., Nat'l, Daily Herald-Tribune, AB, Grande Prairie
Hidek, Jeff ....(910) 343-2371
jeff.hidek@starnewsonline.com, Asst. Features Ed., Star-News, NC, Wilmington
Hidlay, William C.
shidlay@mycentraljersey.com, Pres./Pub., Home News Tribune, NJ, East Brunswick
Hidlay, William C. ....(732) 565-7317
shidlay@mycentraljersey.com, Pres./Pub., Courier News, NJ, Somerville
Hidook, Kevin.........................(518) 565-4118
khidook@pressrepublican.com, Press, Night Supvr., Press-Republican, NY, Plattsburgh
Hieb, Laurie
onpa@orenews.com, Exec. Dir., Oregon Newspaper Publishers Association, OR, Portland
Hieb, Gene 406-791-1499
Production Mgr., Mailroom, Great Falls Tribune, MT, Great Falls
Hieggelke, Brian ....(312) 243-8786 ext. 29
brian@newcitynet.com, Pres., Alternative Weekly Network, CA, Sacramento
Hielscher, Michael

michael .hielscher@oranienburger-generalanzeiger.de, Ed., Oranienburger Generalanzeiger, Oranienburg

Hiemenz, Bob........................(618) 662-2108
bhiemenz@bspeedy.com, Adv. Mgr., The Clay County Advocate-Press, IL, Flora

Hiemstra, Doug.......................(402) 444-1172
doug.hiemstra@owh.com, Vice Pres., Opns., Omaha World-Herald, NE, Omaha

Higehisa, Watanabe
watanabe@shinmai.co.jp, Ed. in Chief, SHINANO MAINICHI SHIMBUN, Nagano, Chubu

Higgins, Tracey
spot@gtek.com, Sales Mgr., GTEK, MS, Bay Saint Louis

Higgs, Robert..........................(216) 999-4407
Politifact Editor, The Plain Dealer, OH, Cleveland

Higgs, Chuck 209-249-3505
Advertising Director, Manteca Bulletin, CA, Manteca

High, Kristina.........................(330) 721-4001
Adv. Dir., Sales, The Medina County Gazette, OH, Medina

Highfill, Bob
bhighfill@recordnet.com, Sports Editor, The Record, CA, Stockton

Highland, William
whighland@exponent-telegram.com, Pres./Pub., The Exponent Telegram, WV, Clarksburg

Highsmith, Shawn
shawn.highsmith@gaflnews.com, Circ. Dir., The Moultrie Observer, GA, Moultrie

Hight, Joe
jhight@opubco.com, Database Mgr, The Oklahoman, OK, Oklahoma City

Hightower, Mary
mhightower@uaex.edu, President, Arkansas Press Women Association, Inc.

Hightower, Sam ....(804) 649-6603
shightower@timesdispatch.com, Vice Pres., Opns., Richmond Times-Dispatch, VA, Richmond

Hiha, Skippy
shiha@laurelleadercall.com, Business Manager, Laurel Leader-Call, MS, Laurel

Hildebrand, Greg
ghildebrand@thepilotnews.com, Prodn. Foreman, Composing, Pilot News, IN, Plymouth

Hildebrandt, Beth ....(217) 238-6857
bhildebrandt@jg-tc.com, Features Ed., Times-Courier, IL, Mattoon

Hildner, Judy...............(719) 544-3520 ext. 450
jhildner@chieftain.com, Sports Ed., The Pueblo Chieftain, CO, Pueblo

Hildreth, Chris........................(812) 320-0144
Indiana Univ. Kelley School of Bus., IN, Bloomington

Hildreth, Shannon.....................(903) 596-6369
shildreth@tylerpaper.com, Adv. Mgr., Classified, Tyler Morning Telegraph, TX, Tyler

Hile, Sally.............................(800) 255-6734
shile@amuniversal.com, Sales Admin., Western USA, Universal Uclick, MO, Kansas City

Hileman, Jeff ....(814) 870-1734
jeff.hileman@timesnews.com, Mng. Ed., New Media, Erie Times-News, PA, Erie

Hilfrink, Michael B.
mhilfrink@whig.com, Gen. Mgr., The Quincy Herald-Whig, IL, Quincy

Hill, Veronica ....(760) 241-7744
Features Ed., Daily Press, CA, Victorville

Hill, Dennis ....(919) 739-7834
dhill@newsargus.com, Mng. Ed., Goldsboro News-Argus, NC, Goldsboro

Hill, Harvey ....(410) 332-6474
harvey.hill@baltsun.com, Dir., Nat'l Adv., The Baltimore Sun, MD, Baltimore

Hill, Charles C.
apmichigan@ap.org, Bureau Chief, Michigan Associated Press Editorial Association, MI, Detroit

Hill, Harvey
hhill@tsvmedia.net, Pub., Eagle Times, NH, Claremont

Hill, Carl...............................(724) 684-2633
chill@tribweb.com, News Ed., The Valley Independent, PA, Monessen

Hill, Diane ....(740) 446-2342 ext. 24
dhill@mydailytribune.com, Purchasing Agent, The Daily Sentinel/Sunday Times-Sentinel, OH, Pomeroy

Hill, Murray ....(306) 657-6206
mhill@sp.canwest.com, Prodn. Mgr., Pre Press, The StarPhoenix, SK, Saskatoon

Hill, Candi
editor@lajuntatribunedemocrat.com, Ed., La Junta Tribune-Democrat, CO, La Junta

Hill, Sue
sue.hill@stl.co.nz, Ed., THE MIRROR

Hill, Steve
steve@newnan.com, Tech. Mgr., The Times-Herald, GA, Newnan

Hill, James S. ....(202) 334-6376
hilljs@washpost.com, Mng. Ed., The Washington Post Writers Group, DC, Washington

Hill, Mary
mhill@titusvilleherald.com, Reporter, The Titusville Herald, PA, Titusville

Hill, Julie ....(541) 863-4429 ext. 304
jhill@artbeats.com, Adv./Mktg. Mgr., Artbeats, OR, Myrtle Creek

Hill, Michael.........................229-438-3213
michael.hill@albanyherald.com, Circulation Director, The Albany Herald, GA, Albany

Hill, Mark
mhill@postregister.com, Advertising Manager, Post Register, ID, Idaho Falls

Hill, David
dhill@greenfieldreporter.com, Ed., Daily Reporter, IN, Greenfield

Hill, John ....(919) 508-2214
Peace College, NC, Raleigh

Hill, Dave..............................(209) 578-2336
dhill@modbee.com, Work/Money Team Leader, The Modesto Bee, CA, Modesto

Hill, Diane ....ext. 24
dhill@mydailytribune.com, Controller, Gallipolis Daily Tribune, OH, Gallipolis

Hillebrand, Melissa..................(402) 280-4058
editor@creightonian.com, Creighton Univ., NE, Omaha

Hilliard, David R.
dhilliard@dailyitem.com, Mng. Ed., News, The Daily Item, PA, Sunbury

Hilliard, Bronson ....(303) 443-6272 ext. 113
Mng. Ed., Colorado Daily, CO, Boulder

Hillibish, James ....ext. 8324
Online Mgr., The Repository, OH, Canton

Hillrichs, Emke
dizpost@t-online.de, Proprietor, DEISTERLEINE-ZEITUNG, Barsinghausen

Hills, Curt ....(352) 753-1119
curt.hills@thevillagesmedia.com, Asst. Mng. Ed., The Villages Daily Sun, FL, The Villages

Hilsendager, Brian ....(253) 620-4747
Bhilsendager@webpressllc.com, Customer Service/Parts, WebPress, LLC, WA, Tacoma

Hilt, Sandy ....(937) 512-4523
sandy.hilt@sinclair.edu, Advisor, Sinclair Cmty. College, OH, Dayton

Hilton, Fred
sports@poncacitynews.com, Sports Ed., The Ponca City News, OK, Ponca City

Hilts, Rod
rhilts@theobserver.ca, Managing Editor, Observer, ON, Sarnia

Hinchey, Timothy.......................860/701-4344
t.hinchey@theday.com, Accounting Manager, The Day Publishing Company, CT, New London

Hinde, Tom..ext. 229
thinde@columbiabasinherald.com, Circ. Dir., Columbia Basin Herald, WA, Moses Lake

Hinds, John ....(416) 482-1090
jhinds@ccna.ca, Pres., Canadian Community Newspaper Association, ON, Toronto

Hinds, John
info@cna-acj.ca, Pres./CEO, Canadian Association of Newspaper Editors, ON, Toronto

Hinds, John
info@ccna.com, Pres., Canadian Community Newspapers Association, ON, Toronto

Hinds, John
info@newspaperscanada.ca, Pres./CEO, Canadian Newspaper Association, ON, Toronto

Hiner, John P.........................(989) 894-9629
jhiner@bc-times.com, Ed., The Bay City Times, MI, Bay City

Hines, Martha ....(616) 222-5759
mhines@grpress.com, Circ. Dir., The Grand Rapids Press, MI, Grand Rapids

Hines, Ryan
sports@dailystandard.com, Sports Ed., The Daily Standard, OH, Celina

Hinick, Walter ....(406) 496-5509
walt.hinick@mtstandard.com, Photo Ed., The Montana Standard, MT, Butte

Hinkle, Kurt ....(970) 392-9286
Univ. of Northern Colorado, CO, Greeley

Hinshaw, Wayne ....(704) 797-4296
whinshaw@salisburypost.com, Photo Dept. Mgr., Salisbury Post, NC, Salisbury

Hinshaw, Joe
hinshamj@jmu.edu, Assoc. Prof., James Madison University, VA, Harrisonburg

Hinson, Darrell
dhinson@controlsgroupinc.com, Vice Pres., Sales, Controls Group, Inc., IL, Rockford

Hinterlong, Anne
anneh@times-press.com, Adv. Mgr., The Times-Press, IL, Streator

Hinton, Alan..........................(601) 584-3136
Asst. Sports Ed., Hattiesburg American, MS, Hattiesburg

Hinton, Sue ....(405) 682-1611
Shinton@occc.edu, Oklahoma City Cmty. College, OK, Oklahoma City

Hinton, Jim.............................(541) 338-2426
Targeted Media Mgr., The Register-Guard, OR, Eugene

Hinton, Leslie
les.hinton@dowjones.com, CEO, Dow Jones & Company, NY, New York

Hintze, Lynnette ....(406) 758-4421
lhintze@dailyinterlake.com, Features Ed., Daily Inter Lake, MT, Kalispell

Hinueber, Mark A......................(702) 477-3830
mhinueber@stephensmedia.com, Vice Pres./Gen. Counsel, Director-Human Resources, Stephens Media LLC, NV, Las Vegas

Hiott, Debbie
dhiott@statesman.com, Mng. Ed., Austin American-Statesman, TX, Austin

Hirai, Takushi
hostmaster@shikoku-np.co.jp, Owner/Chrmn., SHIKOKU SHIMBUN, Takamatsu City, Shikoku

Hiraldo, Manuel
hiraldo@gate.net, Vice Pres., Sales/Mktg., Krause Newspaper Systems, Inc., FL, Aventura

Hirko, Cathy...........................(717) 771-2027
chirko@ydr.com, Bus. Ed., York Daily Record/York Sunday News, PA, York

Hiro, Erin ....(760) 744-1150
Palomar College, CA, San Marcos

Hirsch, Rick ....(305) 376-3504
rhirsch@miamiherald.com, Mng. Ed., Multimedia, The Miami Herald, FL, Miami

Hirschler, Becky ....ext. 5138
becky.hirschler@pharostribune.com, Customer Serv. Mgr., Pharos-Tribune, IN, Logansport

Hirshan, Adam
adam@mountwashingtonvalley.com, Ed., The Conway Daily Sun, NH, North Conway

Hischar, Mark..........................(469) 532-8000
mark.hischar@kba.com, Pres./CEO, KBA North America, Inc. (Koenig & Bauer AG), VT

Hiser, Margie
mhiser@uniondemocrat.com, Mng. Ed., Features, The Union Democrat, CA, Sonora

Hitchings, Don
bhayden@imageinc.com, Sales Dir., IMAGE, Inc., NY, New York

Hitchings, Brian
brian@phillyareapapers.com, Pres., Hitchings & Co., PA, Plymouth Meeting

Hitchings, R. Brian
brian@phillyareapapers.com, Pres., Philadelphia Area Newspapers, PA, Plymouth Meeting

Hite, Sandy
sandyhite@pressregister.com, Office Mgr., The Clarksdale Press Register, MS, Clarksdale

Hite, Tom
thite@opubco.com, Adv. Mgr., Classified, The Oklahoman, OK, Oklahoma City

Hite-Wadler, Lisa ....(317) 444-7144
lisa.hitewadler@indystar.com, Adv. Dir., Opns., The Indianapolis Star, IN, Indianapolis

Hittle, Todd
info@abmmail.com, Exec. Dir., American Business Media Agricultural Council, NY, New York

Hitzeroth, Dr. Wolfram
info@op-marburg.de, Proprietor, OBERHESSISCHE PRESSE, Marburg

Hitzig, Bill
billh@jegi.com, COO, Jordan, Edmiston Group, Inc., NY, New York

Hively, Richard ....(717) 901-0770
rick@wilsongregory.com, Pres., Wilson Gregory Agency, Inc., PA, Camp Hill

Hladky, Greg ....(860) 524-0719
Capitol Bureau Chief, New Haven Register, CT, New Haven

Ho, Hwee-Kun ....(65) 6415-4200
hweekun.ho@dowjones.com, Regl. Sales Mgr., Dow Jones Newswires - Singapore, Singapore, Singapore

Hoar, William H.
neacesecretary@aol.com, Sec., New England Association of Circulation Executives, MA, Chelmsford

Hoare, Eva ....(902) 426-3088
ehoare@herald.ca, Assignment Ed., Night, The Chronicle Herald, NS, Halifax

Hoarty, John ....(617) 619-6500
jhoarty@bostonherald.com, Circ. Vice Pres., Boston Herald, MA, Boston

Hobbs, Woody
orders@pumatech.com, Pres./CEO, Puma Technology, CA, San Jose

Hobbs, Chris ....ext. 245
Sports Ed., The Hickory Daily Record, NC, Hickory

Hobin, Keith
keith@thetriangle.org, Managing Editor, Drexel Univ., PA, Philadelphia

Hobson, Staci..........................(800) 255-6734
shobson@amuniversal.com, Digital Rep., Western USA/Pagination Sales, Universal Uclick, MO, Kansas City

Hocher, Rainer
info@hallertagblatt.de, Ed., HALLER TAGBLATT, Schwabisch-Hall

Hochwald, Peri ....(212) 293-8530
phochwald@unitedmedia.com, Vice Pres., Opns., United Media, OH, Cincinnati

Hockin, Sharon ....(416) 364-0321
info@thecanadianpress.com, Office Mgr., Canadian Press, The - Toronto, ON, ON, Toronto

Hodeige, Christian H.
redaktion@badische-zeitung.de, Proprietor/Publisher, BADISCHE ZEITUNG

Hodge, John................(765) 593-2459 ext. 221
ncspts@thecouriertimes.com, News Ed., The Courier-Times, IN, New Castle

Hodge, Kelly ....ext. 340
khodge@johnsoncitypres.com, Sports Ed., Johnson City Press, TN, Johnson City

Hodgens, Stephen
shodgens@syracuse.com, Mktg. Commun. Mgr., The Post-Standard, NY, Syracuse

Hodges, Micheal
mikehodges@texaspress.com, Exec. Dir., Texas Press Association, TX, Austin

Hodges, Wayne...............................ext. 120
Prodn. Foreman, Pressroom, The Daily Corinthian, MS, Corinth

Hodges, Dave..........................(850) 599-2321
dhodges@tallahassee.com, Bus. Ed., Tallahassee Democrat, FL, Tallahassee

Hodo, Lela ....ext. 219
Circ. Mgr., West Plains Daily Quill, MO, West Plains

Hodson, Doug
dhodson@nsb-observer.com, Gen. Mgr., Sales/Mktg., The Observer, FL, New Smyrna Beach

Hodson, Thomas ....(740) 593-2550
Dir./Assoc. Prof., Ohio University, OH, Athens

Hoe, Koh Lin
kohlh@sph.com.sg, Ed., SHIN MIN DAILY NEWS, Singapore

Hoeflich, Charlene
hoeflich@mydailysentinel.com, News Ed., The Daily Sentinel/Sunday Times-Sentinel, OH, Pomeroy

Hoeft, Randy 928-539-6869
rhoeft@yumasun.com, Special Content Editor, Yuma Sun, AZ, Yuma
Hoel, Arne L. ....(775) 850-2281
Pres./CEO, Swift Communications, Inc., NV, Carson City
Hoemann, Darrell ....(217) 351-5603
dhoemann@news-gazette.com, Photo Editor, News-Gazette Inc., IL, Champaign
Hoepli, Gottlieb
gf.hoepli@tagblatt.ch, Ed., ST GALLER TAGBLATT, Saint Gallen
Hoesli, Eric
eric.hoesli@edipresse.ch, Pub., 24 HEURES, Lausanne, Vaud
Hoff, Steve ....(402) 444-1734
steve.hoff@owh.com, Cor. HR Mgr., Omaha World-Herald, NE, Omaha
Hoffman, Brooke 856-308-9022
bhoffma1@gccnj.edu, Advisor, Gloucester County College, NJ, Sewell
Hoffman, Marsha ....(712) 325-5730
mhoffman@nonpareilonline.com, Internet Coord./New Media Ed., The Daily Nonpareil, IA, Council Bluffs
Hoffman, Fred ....ext. 28
fhoffman@mydailytribune.com, Prodn. Mgr., Gallipolis Daily Tribune, OH, Gallipolis
Hoffman, Dirk ....ext. 125
dhoffman@batavianews.com, News Ed., The Daily News, NY, Batavia
Hoffman, Ann
ahoffman@dailyadvance.com, Pub., The Daily Advance, NC, Elizabeth City
Hoffman, Ace
rhoffman@animatedsoftware.com, Owner/Chief Programmer, Animated Software Co., CA, Carlsbad
Hoffman, Eric
mayfieldmessenger@newwavecomm.net, Pub., The Mayfield Messenger, KY, Mayfield
Hoffmeister, Hans
chefredaktion@tlz.de, Ed. in Chief, TLZ Weimar Thuringische Landeszeitung, Weimar
Hofmann, Eberhard
aznews@iafrica.com.na, Ed. in Chief, ALLGEMEINE ZEITUNG, Windhoek
Hofmann, Carol 203-354-1002
Copy Editor, Religion Ed., The Hour Publishing Co., CT, Norwalk
Hofmann, Dietmar
verlagsleitung@baumann-online.de, News Ed., Baumann Verlag, Kulmbach
Hogan, Mark
mhogan@maxxmh.com, Vice Pres., MAXX Material Handling LLC, VA, Hampton
Hogan, Shannon
hogan@thereporter.com, HR Dir., The Reporter, CA, Vacaville
Hogan, Randy
editorial@helena-arkansas.com, Mng. Ed., The Daily World, AR, Helena
Hogan, Al ....(506) 859-7120
Mng. Ed., Times & Transcript, NB, Moncton
Hogan, Joseph
engage.abb@ch.abb.com, CEO, ABB Ltd., Zurich
Hogan, Patrick
phogan@daily-times.com, Online Ed., The Daily Times, NM, Farmington
Hogben, Andrea ....(216) 999-4951
Adv. Vice Pres., Display and Mktg., The Plain Dealer, OH, Cleveland
Hogerty, Dianne ....(913) 722-0055 ext. 234
Owner, Family Features Editorial Syndicate, Inc., KS, Mission
Hogue, Glen ....(479) 785-7860
ghogue@swtimes.com, Circ. Mgr., Times Record, AR, Fort Smith
Hogue-Heiby, Claire
chogue@mariettatimes.com, Copy Ed., The Marietta Times, OH, Marietta
Hohlstein, Rebecca ....(608) 836-4505
bhohlstein@aol.com, Independent Consultant/Author/Speaker, RBH Food Safety/Education & Consultation, WI, Madison
Hohlt, Rick ....(318) 255-4353
rick@rustonleader.com, Publisher, Ruston Daily Leader, LA, Ruston
Hoilman, Josie ....(404) 471-6000
Agnes Scott College, GA, Decatur
Hoisington, Mary
mhioisington@gbtribune.com, Pub., Great Bend Tribune, KS, Great Bend
Hojnacki, Stan ....(704) 261-2220
shojnacki@theej.com, Mng. Ed., The Enquirer-Journal, NC, Monroe
Holcher, Molly ....(308) 381-9435
molly.holcher@theindependent.com, HR Mgr., The Grand Island Independent, NE, Grand Island
Holcomb, Lori
lholcomb@wnewsj.com, Circ. Dir., Wilmington News Journal, OH, Wilmington
Holcomb, Jody ....(818) 677-3140
California State University, Northridge - Daily Sundial, CA, Northridge
Holda, Margaret Bielecka
margeretta.vielckaholda@lubline.pl, Ed. in Chief, GAZETA W LUBLINIE, Lublin
Holden, Mary Ellen
meholden@nnnlp.com, Sr. Vice Pres., Mktg., Newspaper National Network LP, NY, New York
Holden, Tom
tom.holden@dailytimes.com, Photographer, Kerrville Daily Times, TX, Kerrville
Holden, Ben ....(706) 571-8560
bholden@ledger-enquirer.com, Exec. Ed., Columbus Ledger-Enquirer, GA, Columbus
Holder, Thomas ....(903) 237-7780
tholder@longview-news.com, Prodn. Asst. Mgr., Longview News-Journal, TX, Longview
Holder, Tim
tholder@joplinglobe.com, Adv. Dir., The Joplin Globe, MO, Joplin
Holdrup, Pam
sales@wtsinc.com, Sales, Agility, TX, Houston
Holeva, Larry ....ext. 2064
lholeva@citizensvoice.com, Mng. Ed., The Citizens' Voice, PA, Wilkes-Barre
Holgate, David
dholgate@theh-p.com, Publisher, The Herald-Palladium, MI, Saint Joseph
Holguin, Sergio ....(805) 781-7880
sholguin@thetribunenews.com, VP/Online and Marketing, The Tribune, CA, San Luis Obispo
Holhut, Randy ....(802) 254-2311 ext. 160
Night News Ed., Brattleboro Reformer, VT, Brattleboro
Holla, Balakrishna
holla@manipalmedia.com, Ed., UDAYAVANI, Manipal, Karnataka
Holland, Jim
jim.holland@starherald.com, Vice Pres./Pub., Star-Herald, NE, Scottsbluff
Holland, Liam
editorial@irish-times.com, Adv. Mgr., THE IRISH TIMES, Dublin
Holland, Shani
shani@edge.net, Contact, EdgeNet Media, TN, Brentwood
Holland, Don
don_holland@link.freedom.com, Ed., Daily Press, CA, Victorville
Holland, Gunter 96050
druck@schnitzer-azmod.de, Proprietor, ALLGAUER ZEITUNG, Marktoberdorf
Holland, Ellinor
desk@augsburger-allgemeine.de, Proprietor, LANDSBERGER TAGBLATT, Augsburg
Holland, Gunter 2060
azv@azv.de, Proprietor, ALLGAUER ZEITUNG, Kempten
Holland, Stephanie ....(951) 222-8495
Riverside Cmty. College, CA, Riverside
Holland, Ellinor
100443.1674@compuserve.com, Proprietor, AUGSBURGER ALLGEMEINE, Augsburg
Holland, G.
info@allgauer-anzeigeblatt.de, Proprietor, ALLGAUER ANZEIGEBLATT, Immenstadt
Hollaway, Jim ....(316) 268-6200
jhollaway@wichitaeagle.com, Prodn. Mgr., Bldg., The Wichita Eagle, KS, Wichita
Hollenbaugh, Lindsey ....(607) 274-3208
Ithaca College, NY, Ithaca
Hollett, Paul
phollett@lightfantasticstudios.com, Pres./Creative Dir., Light Fantastic Studios, Inc, NY, Baldwin
Holley, Kenny
kholley@hopewellnews.com, Webmaster, The Hopewell News, VA, Hopewell
Holliday, Guy D. ....(212) 556-8090
Adv. Vice Pres., Sales, The New York Times, NY, New York
Hollifield, Laura
lhollifield@artbeats.com, COO, Artbeats, OR, Myrtle Creek
Hollinger, Berni ....(715) 526 - 7003
bhollinger@shawanoleader.com, Group Controller, Shawano Leader, WI, Shawano
Hollinger, Kendra
info@activedatax.com, COO, Active Data Exchange, PA, Bethlehem
Hollinger, Bernadette
wpeters@bluelinemediaholdings.com, Group Controller, BlueLine Media Holdings, WI, Neenah
Hollingsworth, Christina ....(770) 287-3798
commfeat@charter.net, Co-Owner, Community Features, GA, Gainesville
Hollingsworth, Laura ....(515) 284-8041
Pres./Pub./Gen. Mgr., The Des Moines Register, IA, Des Moines
Hollis, Todd ....(203) 330-6480
thollis@ctpost.com, Asst. Mng. Ed., Prodn., Connecticut Post, CT, Bridgeport
Hollis, Donnie ....(870) 777-8841
Circ. Mgr., Arkadelphia Siftings Herald, AR, Arkadelphia
Hollon, Jay ....ext. 297
jhollon@monroenews.com, CFO, The Monroe Evening News, MI, Monroe
Holloway, Rachel L.
rhollowa@vt.edu, Head, Virginia Polytechnic Institute and State University, VA, Blacksburg
Holloway, Rita J. ....(508) 427-4063
rholloway@enterprise.com, Controller, The Enterprise, MA, Randolph
Holloway, Brent ....(770) 718-3406
bholloway@gainesvilletimes.com, Sports Ed., The Times, GA, Gainesville
Holm, Jim ....(765) 420-5272
jholm@journalandcourier.com, Adv. Dir., Journal and Courier, IN, Lafayette
Holm, Den
editor@theaustralian.com.au, Tasmanian Correspondent, THE AUSTRALIAN
Holman, Denise L. ....(314) 340-8575
dholman@post-dispatch.com, Adv. Vice Pres., Sales-Major Accts./Autos/Nat'l/Real Estate, St. Louis Post-Dispatch, MO, Saint Louis
Holman, Jeffrey 217-241-1700
jholman@illinoispress.org, Advertising Director, Illinois Press Association, IL, Springfield
Holmann Chamorro, Hugo
hholman@laprensa.com, Gen. Mgr., LA PRENSA, Managua
Holmberg, Jukka
jukka.holmberg@sss.fi, Ed., SALON SEUDUN SANOMAT, Salo
Holmberg, Charlene ....(208) 465-8196
cholmberg@idahopress.com, Prodn., Post Press, Idaho Press-Tribune, ID, Nampa
Holmes, Yasha 317-444-7097
Class Adv Director, The Indianapolis Star, IN, Indianapolis
Holmes, Mark
adman@nfreview.com, Adv. Mgr., Niagara Falls Review, ON, Niagara Falls
Holmes, Dan
ads@fcpny.com, Exec. Dir., Community Papers Advertising Network, NY, Syracuse
Holmes, Angela
angelah@npgco.com, News Ed., Atchison Globe, KS, Atchison
Holmes, Barbara 352-347-3384
CPFDisplayAds@aol.com, Administrative Asst., Community Papers of Florida, FL, Belleview
Holmes, Anita ....ext. 207
aholmes@dglobe.com, Bus. Mgr., The Daily Globe, MN, Worthington
Holmes, Rick ....(508) 626-3932
Editorial Page Ed., Metrowest Daily News, MA, Framingham
Holmes, Bruce ....(613) 739-7100
bruce.holmes@ott.sunpub.com, Adv. Dir., The Ottawa Sun, ON, Ottawa
Holmes, Dan
ads@fcpny.com, Executive Director, Free Community Papers of New York, NY, Syracuse
Holmes, Jennifer ....(207) 990-8216
bdnhr@bangordailynews.net, HR Mgr., Bangor Daily News, ME, Bangor
Holmes-Greeley, Paula ....(231) 725-6353
pholmes@muskegonchronicle.com, News Ed., The Muskegon Chronicle, MI, Muskegon
Holmstrom, Stefan ....+358207568666
stefan.holmstrom@bbl.fi, Vice Editor-In-Chief, Borgabladet, Borga
Holstein, Judah ....(888)309-0639
judah@miracomcomputer.com, CEO, Miracom Computer Corp., NY, Eastchester
Holt, Newell
npta@gonpta.com, Pres., National Paper Trade Association, Inc., IL, Chicago
Holt, J. Tim ....(252) 329-9510
tholt@reflector.com, Gen. Mgr., The Daily Reflector, NC, Greenville
Holtkamp, Michele ....(317) 736-2774
mholtkamp@dailyjournal.net, Asst. Mng. Ed., Daily Journal, IN, Franklin
Holtzhausen, Derina
derina.holtzhausen@okstate.edu, Dir., Oklahoma State University, OK, Stillwater
Holway, Linda ....(603) 610-1177
lholway@seacoastonline.com, Adv. Dir., Portsmouth Herald, NH, Portsmouth
Holze, Todd ....(203) 746-1012
tholze@classifiedguys.com, Co-Pres., The Classified Guys, CT, Danbury
Holzer, Elmar 3990
info@westallgaeuer-zeitung.de, Proprietor, DER WESTALLGAUER, Weiler-Simmerberg
Hombach, Bodo
kontakt@waz-mediengruppe.de, Bus. Mgr., WESTDEUTSCHE ALLGEMEINE WAZ, Essen
Honald, Michelle ....(740) 593-0093
Asst. Prof., Ohio University, OH, Athens
Hone, Robert
bobh@redhillstudios.com, Creative Dir./Founder, Red Hill Studios, CA, Larkspur
Honea, Bob ....(907)-523-2223
Production Director, Juneau Empire, AK, Juneau
Hong, Seok-Hyun
feedback@joongang.co.kr, Pres./Pub., JOONG-ANG ILBO, Seoul
Honig, Robin
ANIpromo@aol.com, Vice Pres., Automatic Newsstand, Inc. (ANI Promotions), NY, Monsey
Honig, Tom ....(831) 423-4242 ext. 444
thonig@santacruzsentinel.com, Ed., Santa Cruz Sentinel, CA, Scotts Valley
Honkanaa, Tapio
tapio.honkanaa@lansi-savo.fi, Ed., LANSI-SAVO, Mikkeli
Hood, Aileen
aileen@trinidadchroniclenews.com, Pub., The Chronicle-News, CO, Trinidad
Hood, Jeffrey
jhood@pioneernewspapers.com, CFO, Pioneer Newspapers Inc, WA, Seattle
Hood, Steve ....(317) 736-2711
shood@dailyjournal.net, Circ. Dir., Daily Journal, IN, Franklin
Hooper, Rick
rick.hooper@newportplaintalk.com, Mng. Ed., Newport Plain Talk, TN, Newport
Hooper, Trish
thooper@tribweb.com, COO, Tribune-Review Publishing Co., PA, Greensburg
Hooton, Tom
thooton@lagrandeobserver.com, Circ. Dir., Baker City Herald, OR, Baker City
Hoover, Rick 605-886-6901
Managing Ed., Watertown Public Opinion, SD, Watertown
Hope, Sandra ....(870) 543-1407
shope@pbcommercial.com, City/Metro Ed., Pine Bluff Commercial, AR, Pine Bluff
Hope, William
whope@capitalgazette.com, Prodn. Mgr., The Capital, MD, Annapolis
Hopesto, Manuel
redacao@ji.com.br, Ed., Jornal de Itatiba, Itatiba, Sao Paulo
Hopkins, Niki 509-574-6870
nhopkins@yvcc.edu, Ed., Yakima Valley Cmty.

College, WA, Yakima
Hopkinson, Bianca 9022 0552
bianca.hopkinson@kalminer.com.au, Circulation & Administration Manager, KALGOORLIE MINER
Hoppenjans, Dan
dhoppenjans@dcherald.com, Distribution Manager, The Herald, IN, Jasper
Hopperton, Jodie....................+33 141 43 97 69
jodie.hopperton@nytimes.com, Regional Director, Northern, Eastern & Central Europe, New York Times Syndicate, NY, New York
Hopperton, Jodie....................+33 141 43 97 69
jodie.hopperton@nytimes.com, Regional Director, Northern, Eastern & Central Europe, New York Times News Service, NY, New York
Hopwood, Howard
howardhopwood@yahoo.com, Self-Syndicator, The Media Maven, GA, Carrollton
Horan, Linda ....(912) 652-0491
linda.horan@savannahnow.com, Adv. Mgr., Real Estate, Savannah Morning News, GA, Savannah
Horan, John F.
jhoran@nvdaily.com, Editorial Page Ed., Northern Virginia Daily, VA, Strasburg
Horling, Lennart
post@nlt.se, Ed., NYA LANS-TIDNINGEN, Lidkoping
Horn, Brant...........................(406) 758-4490
bhorn@dailyinterlake.com, Circ. Mgr., Daily Inter Lake, MT, Kalispell
Horn, Richard A. ....(620) 326-3326
rickhorn@wellingtondailynews.com, Pub., Wellington Daily News, KS, Wellington
Hornbaker, Thomas
thornbaker@ljworld.com, The World Co.- Lawrence, Kan., Journal-World, KS, Lawrence
Hornbaker, Tom.......................(785) 832-7175
thornbaker@ljworld.com, CFO, The World Co.- Lawrence, Kan., Journal-World, KS, Lawrence
Horne, Terry...........................(714) 796-7740
thorne@ocregister.com, Pres./Pub., The Orange County Register, CA, Santa Ana
Horning, Clay ....(405) 366-3526
cfhorning@normantranscript.com, Sports Ed., Norman Transcript, OK, Norman
Horovitz, Jed
jedh@videopipeline.com, Pres., Video Pipeline, Inc., NJ, Haddonfield
Horovitz, David
davidh@jpost.com, Ed. in Chief, JERUSALEM POST
Horowitz, Rick ....(414) 963-9333
rickhoro@execpc.com, Self-Syndicator, Rick Horowitz, WI, Shorewood
Horrock, Nicholas
nhorrock@dcexaminer.com, Mng. Ed., The Examiner, VA, Alexandria
Horst, Gustavo
jmanha@terra.com.br, Pub., Jornal da Manha, Mar¡lia
Horstman, Barbara....................(618) 463-2511
barb_horstman@thetelegraph.com, Circ. Mgr., The Telegraph, IL, Alton
Horton, Les
lhorton@gdn.com.bh, Deputy Ed., GULF DAILY NEWS
Horton, Rick.................................ext. 227
Prodn. Mgr., Pressroom, Columbia Basin Herald, WA, Moses Lake
Horton, Ron ....(209) 588-4574
rhorton@uniondemocrat.com, Pub., The Union Democrat, CA, Sonora
Horton, Charles
chorton@kitsapsun.com, President & Publisher, Kitsap Sun, WA, Bremerton
Horvath, Laura
circulation@azbiz.com, Circ. Dir., The Daily Territorial, AZ, Tucson
Horvath, Alex ....(661) 395-7403
ahorvath@bakersfield.com, Photo Dir., The Bakersfield Californian, CA, Bakersfield
Horvath, Frank ....ext. 1606
frank.horvath@uniontrib.com, Circ. Dir., Sales, The San Diego Union-Tribune, CA, San Diego
Horvit, Mark
mark@ire.org, Exec. Dir., Investigative Reporters and Editors (IRE), MO, Columbia
Hosein, Mainul
editor@nation-online.com, Pub., NEW NATION, Dhaka
Hossain, Mia Musa
patrika@citechco.net, Pub./Ed. in Chief, Dainik Patrika, Dhaka
Host, Dennis
dhost@stcloud.gannett.com, Mktg. Devel. Dir., St. Cloud Times, MN, Saint Cloud
Hostetter, Lance.......................(719) 587-7904
Adams State College, CO, Alamosa
Hosto, Sue
circ@oelweindailyregister.com, Circ. Mgr., The Oelwein Daily Register, IA, Oelwein
Hota, Himanshu
himanshu@dharitri.com, Dir. Mktg., DHARITRI, Bhubaneswar, Orissa
Hotvet, Owen ....(605) 331-2240
ohotvet@argusleader.com, Circulation Director, Argus Leader, SD, Sioux Falls
Houchens, Chris........................270-781-1700
chouchens@bgdailynews.com, Online Mgr., Daily News, KY, Bowling Green
Houck, Jim ....(559) 735-3276
news@visaliatimesdelta.com, City Ed., Visalia Times-Delta, CA, Visalia
Houck, Jim ....(559) 735-3276
editorial@visaliatimesdelta.com, City Ed., Visalia Times-Delta & Tulare Advance-Register, CA, Visalia
Houk, Robert....................................ext. 325
rhouk@johnsoncitypress.com, Editorial Page Ed., Johnson City Press, TN, Johnson City
Houle, Randy...............(574) 753-0137 ext. 222
randy.houle@pharostribune.com, Prodn. Mgr., Pre/Post Press, Pharos-Tribune, IN, Logansport
Houlton, Elizabeth ....(973) 569-7133
Director of News Production, North Jersey Media Group, NJ, Woodland Park
House, Judy.............................(559) 737-3889
College of the Sequoias, CA, Visalia
House, Michael 312-225-2400
President, Chicago Defender, IL, Chicago
Householder, Lorri
lhouseholder@jonesborosun.com, Circulation Director, The Jonesboro Sun, AR, Jonesboro
Houseman, Alex.......................(616) 331-2486
business@lanthorn.com, Grand Valley State Univ., MI, Allendale
Housh, David
david.housh@tulsaworld.com, Graphics Ed., Tulsa World, OK, Tulsa
Housholder, Terry
terryh@kpcnews.net, Pres./CEO/Pub., Herald-Republican, IN, Angola
Housholder, Terry ....(260) 347-0400 ext. 176
terryh@kpcnews.net, Pres./CEO/Pub., The Star, IN, Auburn
Housholder, Terry
terryh@kpcnews.net, Pres./CEO/Pub., KPC Media Group Inc., IN, Kendallville
Housholder, Terry ....(260) 347-0400 ext. 176
terryh@kpcnews.net, Pres./CEO/Pub., The News-Sun, IN, Kendallville
Houslet, Travis........................(608) 745-3518
thouslet@capitalnewspapers.com, Sports Ed., Daily Register, WI, Portage
Houston, Kristin ....(707) 526-8665
kristin.houston@pressdemocrat.com, Innovation Dir., The Press Democrat, CA, Santa Rosa
Houtman, Jennifer ....(740) 376-5437
jhoutman@mariettatimes.com, Ed., The Marietta Times, OH, Marietta
Hove, Odd Sverre
odd.sverre.hove@dagen.no, Ed. in Chief, DAGEN, Bergen
Howard, Julie...........................(252) 407-9915
Controller, Rocky Mount Telegram, NC, Rocky Mount
Howard, Pat.............................(814) 870-1721
pat.howard@timesnews.com, Mng. Ed., Erie Times-News, PA, Erie
Howard, Josephine..........(802) 254-2311 ext. 161
Wire Ed., Brattleboro Reformer, VT, Brattleboro
Howard, Henry.........................(765) 420-5262
hhoward@journalandcourier.com, Mng. Ed., Journal and Courier, IN, Lafayette
Howard, Glenn
ghoward@dunndailyrecord.com, Prodn. Mgr., The Daily Record, NC, Dunn
Howard, Alisha ....(770) 421-7700 ext. 174
ahoward@imageamericas.com, Mgr., Mktg., Markem-Imaje, GA, Kennesaw
Howard, Mari ....(401) 274-2149
staff@whitegatefeatures.com, Office Mgr., Whitegate Features Syndicate, RI, Providence
Howard, Judith ....(303) 820-1480
jhoward@denverpost.com, Features Ed., The Denver Post, CO, Denver
Howarth, Dawn
dfournier@scansoft.com, Vice Pres., HR, Nuance Communications Inc., MA, Burlington
Howe, Russell Warren ....(202) 337-1560
Author, Don't Laugh, You're Next, DC, Washington
Howe, Andrea
andrea@pdclarion.com, Ed., Princeton Daily Clarion, IN, Princeton
Howe, Kevin R.
admin@cortlandstandard.net, Pub., Cortland Standard, NY, Cortland
Howe, Alan
sundayha@hwt.newsltd.com.au, Ed., THE SUNDAY HERALD SUN
Howe, Art
info@vervewireless.com, CEO, Verve Wireless, Inc., CA, Encinitas
Howell, Victoria ....(205) 325-3559
Recruitment Team Leader, The Birmingham News, AL, Birmingham
Howell, Andy............................(801) 625-4288
Graphics Ed., Standard-Examiner, UT, Ogden
Howell, Brian ....(303) 776-2244 ext. 298
bhowell@times-call.com, Sports Ed., Times-Call, CO, Longmont
Howell, Scott...............(209) 369-7035 ext. 221
scotth@lodinews.com, Sports Ed., Lodi News-Sentinel, CA, Lodi
Hower, Kurt...............................(717) 255-8434
khower@patriot-news.com, Circ. Dir., The Patriot-News, PA, Mechanicsburg
Howes, Adam ....(44 20)78429550
adam.howes@dowjones.com, Regl. Sales Mgr., Dow Jones Newswires - London, United Kingdom, London
adam.howes@dowjones.com, Regl. Sales Mgr., Dow Jones Newswires - London, United Kingdom, London
Howie, Staurt
editor@illawarramercury.com.au, Ed., ILLAWARRA MERCURY
Howie, Mike ....(217) 351-5211
mhowie@news-gazette.com, Online Editor, News-Gazette Inc., IL, Champaign
Howitt, John ....(902) 426-0478
jhowitt@herald.ca, Asst. Dir., Design, The Chronicle Herald, NS, Halifax
Howry, Joe R.............................(805) 437-0200
jhowry@venturacountystar.com, Vice Pres./Ed., Ventura County Star, CA, Camarillo
Howsare, Timothy.......................(352) 544-5284
thowsare@hernandotoday.com, Community News Ed., Hernando Today, FL, Brooksville
Howse, Robert.........................(902) 426-3098
bhowse@herald.ca, Editorial Page Ed., The Chronicle Herald, NS, Halifax
Hoxter, Betsy
bhoxter@gannett.com, Systems Mgr., Poughkeepsie Journal, NY, Poughkeepsie
Hoxter, Betsy.............................(406) 791-6504
boxter@greatfal.gannett.com, Info Technology Dir., Great Falls Tribune, MT, Great Falls
Hoying, Dave................(419) 586-2371 ext. 235
business@dailystandard.com, Bus. Mgr., The Daily Standard, OH, Celina
Hoyos, Carlos
choyos@elmundo.com, Adv. Mgr., Gaviria Family Group, Medellin, Antioquia
Hoyos, Jorge M. De...................316) 978-6908
Wichita State Univ., KS, Wichita
Hoyt, Barbara
bhoyt@tnninc.com, Administrative Mgr., The Newspaper Network (TNN), CA, Sacramento
Hozjan, Martin
info@mahmachine.com, Pres., MAH Machine Co., Inc., IL, Cicero
Hozjan, Martin
mhozjan@ustensor.com, Chrmn./Pres., Tensor Group, Inc., IL, Woodridge
Hozjan Ruda, Martina.......................ext. 2120
mruda@ustensor.com, Exec. Vice Pres., Tensor Group, Inc., IL, Woodridge
Hrabal, Don
donh@times-press.com, Mng. Ed., The Times-Press, IL, Streator
Hrettac, Constantine
constantine.hrettac@ziaruldeiasi.ro, Ed. in. Chief, ZIARUL DE IASI, Iasi
Hsu, C.J.
e-member@taitra.org.tw, Ed. in Chief, TRADERS EXPRESS, Taipei
Huang, Roger
info@ausdaily.com.au, Pub., CHINESE HERALD, Surry Hills
Huang, Tom ....(214) 977-8635
thuang@dallasnews.com, Asst. Mng. Ed./Sunday Ed., The Dallas Morning News, TX, Dallas
Huang, Jack
cpost@msl.hinet.net, Pub./Ed., CHINA POST, Taipei
Huay, Chonchau
chon@guangming.com.my, Ed., GUANG MING DAILY, Pulau Pinang
Hubartt, Kerry..........................(260) 461-8471
khubartt@news-sentinel.com, Sr. Ed., The News-Sentinel, IN, Fort Wayne
Hubbard, Leeann.......................(508) 967-3124
lhubbard@tauntongazette.com, Lifestyles Ed., Taunton Daily Gazette, MA, Taunton
Hubbard, Charles G.
chubbard@baldor.com, Cor. Commun. Dir., Baldor Electric Co., AR, Fort Smith
Hubbard, Todd ....(757) 247-4843
thubbard@dailypress.com, Circ. Mgr., Daily Press, VA, Newport News
Hubbard, Jon B.
news@examiner.org, Vice Pres., Bellefontaine Examiner, OH, Bellefontaine
Hubbell, Linda
linda_hubbell@dailyjournal.com, Adv. Dir., San Francisco Daily Journal
Hubbell, Linda
linda_hubbell@dailyjournal.com, Ed., San Francisco Daily Journal
Hubbell, Linda
linda_hubbell@dailyjournal.com, Pub., San Francisco Daily Journal
Hubble, Melissa.......................(580) 235-1456
East Central University, OK, Ada
Hubele, Don.............................(601) 968-8702
Belhaven College, MS, Jackson
Huber, Mark..............................937-382-2574
mhuber@wnewsj.com, Online Ed., Wilmington News Journal, OH, Wilmington
Huber, Ed
customerservice@simcomail.com, Customer Serv. Mgr., Simco Industrial Static Control Products, PA, Hatfield
Huber, David R.
info@hotwax.com, Owner, Hotwax Multimedia, Inc., NJ, Ramsey
Hubrain, Patrick
patrick.hubrain@lesoir.be, Pres., LE SOIR, 1000 Brussels
Huck, Bill ....(212) 576-9510
billh@metrosn.com, Vice Pres./Eastern Adv. Dir., Metro-Puck Comics Network - New York, NY, NY, New York
Huck, Bill ....(212) 576-9510
billh@metrosn.com, Sr. Vice Pres., Eastern Adv., Metro Newspaper Advertising Services, Inc. Sunday Magazine Network - New York, NY, NY, New York
Huck, William ....(212) 576-9510
billh@metrosn.com, Sr. Vice Pres./Eastern Region, Metro Newspaper Advertising Services, Inc., NY, New York
Huckast, Ali
ahuckast@zlv.lu, Ed., ZEITUNG VUM LETZEBURGER VOLLEK, Luxembourg
Huckfeldt, Katie
khuckfel@mines.edu, Managing Editor, Colorado School of Mines, CO, Golden
Huckle, T. Chris ....(231) 775-6565
huckle@cadillacnews.com, Pres./Pub., Cadillac News, MI, Cadillac
huckle@cadillacnews.com, Northern Michigan News, MI, Cadillac

Huckle Mittelstaedt, Renee 507-645-1102
rhmittelstaedt@charter.net, Pres./CEO, Huckle Media, LLC, MI, Traverse City
Huddleston, Joe
jhuddleston@mountvernonnews.com, Sports Ed., Mount Vernon News, OH, Mount Vernon
Hudelson, Donna
dhudelson@yorkdispatch.com, Food Ed., The York Dispatch, PA, York
Hudler, Carol..........................615/259-8303
publisher@tennessean.com, President & Publisher, The Tennessean, TN, Nashville
Hudler, Carol..........................615/259-8303
publisher@tennessean.com, President & Publisher, The Tennessean, TN, Nashville
Hudleson, Richard
dickh@commpub.com, Circ. Mgr., Harrison Daily Times, AR, Harrison
Hudnutt, Cooper
ctnews@chronicletelegram.com, Pub., Chronicle-Telegram, OH, Elyria
Hudnutt, George D.
ghudnutt@ohio.net, Pub., The Medina County Gazette, OH, Medina
Hudon, Joe..........................(951) 587-3111
jhudon@pe.com, Adv. Mgr., Regl., The Press-Enterprise, CA, Riverside
Hudson, Bob................(719) 544-3520 ext. 511
bhudson@chieftain.com, Adv. Mgr., Display, The Pueblo Chieftain, CO, Pueblo
Hudson, Jeff..........................(530) 747-8055
jhudson@davisenterprise.net, Educ./Schools Ed., The Davis Enterprise, CA, Davis
Hudson, Jerry C.
jerry.hudson@ttu.edu, Dean/Prof., Texas Tech University, TX, Lubbock
Hudson, Stacey..........................706-721-4410
smcgowen@georgiahealth.edu, Communications Coordinator
Editor, The Connection (formerly the Beeper), Georgia Health Sciences University (formerly Medical College of Georgia), GA
Hudson, Tim
keyesa@mail.ecu.edu, Dir., East Carolina University, NC, Greenville
Hudson, David..........................(651) 523-2893
Hamline Univ., MN, Saint Paul
Hudson, Gene
dailysoutherner@gmail.com, Advertising Sales Manager, The Daily Southerner, NC, Tarboro
Hudson, Melodie..........................ext. 1177
melody.hudson@timesargus.com, Circ. Mgr., The Times Argus, VT, Barre
Hudson, Lugene..........................ext. 620
Educ. Rep., New Castle News, PA, New Castle
Huebert, Ellen
ellen.huebert@thecanadianpress.com, News Editor, Broadcast News Limited, ON, Toronto
ellen.huebert@thecanadianpress.com, News Editor, Canadian Press, The - Toronto, ON, ON, Toronto
Huebscher, Don..........(715) 833-9216 ext. 3216
don.huebscher@ecpc.com, Ed., Leader-Telegram, WI, Eau Claire
Huening, Adam
adam.huening@greensburgdailynews.com, News Ed., Greensburg Daily News, IN, Greensburg
Huerta, Juan Ramon
barricada@ibw.com.ni, Ed., Editorial El Amanecer, Managua
Huff, Kevin..........................615/881-7014
khuff@tennessean.com, VP/Finance, The Tennessean, TN, Nashville
Huff, Kevin..........................(302) 324-2519
khuff@delawareonline.com, Controller, The News Journal, DE, New Castle
Huff, Katheryn..........................(540) 574-6276
khuff@dnronline.com, Features Ed., Daily News-Record, VA, Harrisonburg
Huffer, J.B.
buchverlag@aschendorff.de, Bus. Mgr., Westfalische Nachrichten/Zeno Zeitungen, Munster, Westfalen
Huffman, Faith
faith@ssecho.com, News Ed., Sulphur Springs News-Telegram, TX, Sulphur Springs
Huffman, Jess
jhuffman@freedomenc.com, Sports Ed., The Sun Journal, NC, New Bern
Hug, Michael
werbung@espace.ch, Ed., BERNER ZEITUNG BZ, Bern
Hug, Charles..........................(518) 454-5070
chug@timesunion.com, Dir., Technical Servs., Times Union, NY, Albany
Hug, Jerry..........................907-257-4219
Finance, Anchorage Daily News, AK, Anchorage
Hug, Gerald..........................(509) 582-1499
jhug@tri-cityherald.com, Dir., Finance, Tri-City Herald, WA, Kennewick
Huggard, Shannon..........................ext. 309
Circ. Mgr., Penticton Herald, BC, Penticton
Huggins, Paul..........................(256) 340-2395
paul.huggins@decaturdaily.com, Environmental Writer, The Decatur Daily, AL, Decatur
Hughes, Laura..........................ext. 24
lhughes@themonroetimes.com, Adv. Mgr., Retail, The Monroe Times, WI, Monroe
Hughes, Butch..........................ext. 279
hughesb@independentmail.com, Pres./Pub., Anderson Independent-Mail, SC, Anderson
Hughes, Lynn..........................ext. 130
lhughes@innotek-ep.com, Vice Pres., Sales, Innotek Corporation, MN, Maple Grove
Hughes, Julie
jhughes@pioneernewspapers.com, Information Systems Mgr., Pioneer Newspapers Inc, WA, Seattle
Hughes, John..........................(204) 571-7445
jhughes@brandonsun.com, Sunday Ed., Brandon Sun, MB, Brandon
Hughes, Autumn
autumnh@xtn.net, Lifestyles Ed., The Daily Post-Athenian, TN, Athens
Hughes, John C.
pub@thedailyworld.com, Ed., The Daily World, WA, Aberdeen
Hughes, Bayne..........................(256) 340-2432
bhughes@decaturdaily.com, Educ. Writer, The Decatur Daily, AL, Decatur
Hughes, Cathy C.
chughes@timesanddemocrat.com, Pub., The Times and Democrat, SC, Orangeburg
Hughes, William..........................(718) 262-2492
York College of CUNY, NY, Jamaica
Hughes, Clark M...........................(989) 894-9631
chughes@bc-times.com, Editorial Page Ed., The Bay City Times, MI, Bay City
Hughes, Kathy
hugheska@jmu.edu, Asst. Prof., James Madison University, VA, Harrisonburg
Huidan, Eduard
gazeta.transilvania@brasovia.ro, Ed. in Chief, GAZETA DE TRANSILVANIA, Brasov, Brasov
Hukel, Danny
danny@brenhambanner.com, Gen. Mgr., Brenham Banner-Press, TX, Brenham
Hulac, Kari..........................(650) 348-4333
alarson@angnewspapers.com, Lifestyle Ed., San Mateo County Times, CA, San Mateo
Hulen, David..........................ext. 596
dhulen@adn.com, City Ed., Anchorage Daily News, AK, Anchorage
Hulin, Kelly..........................(405) 339-3413
hulin@heraldnet.com, Mktg. Dir., The Herald, WA, Everett
Huls, Steve..........................(605) 331-2390
shuls@argusleader.com, Pressroom Mgr., Argus Leader, SD, Sioux Falls
Hultgren, Randal
hultgren@crookstontimes.com, Pub., Crookston Daily Times, MN, Crookston
Humanes, Carlos
carloshumanes@elboletin.com, Dir., EL BOLETIN DE LA TARDE, Madrid
Hummel, Kent..........................(915) 546-6258
khummel@elpasotimes.com, Mktg. Dir., El Paso Times, TX, El Paso
Hummel, Marci
marci@bryantimes.com, Bus. Ed., The Bryan Times, OH, Bryan
Hummels, Jill..........................(785) 864-2934
Univ. of Kansas Engineering School, KS, Lawrence
Humphrey, William E...........................(318) 487-6409
ehumphrey@thetowntalk.com, Pres./Pub., The Town Talk, LA, Alexandria
Humphrey, Janice
jhumphrey@bowesnet.com, Credit Mgr., The Beacon-Herald, ON, Stratford
Humphreys, Robert..........................ext. 128
rhumphreys@starexponent.com, Mng. Ed., Culpeper Star-Exponent, VA, Culpeper
Hundt, David..........................(508) 862-1132
dhundt@capecodonline.com, Controller, Cape Cod Times, MA, Hyannis
Hundt, Camilla
st@mzv.net, Distr. Mgr., Suderlander Tageblatt, Plettenberg
Hunt, Bud
bhunt@dddnews.com, Mgr., Mktg./Promo., The Daily Dunklin Democrat, MO, Kennett
Hunt, Steve..............(626) 962-8811 ext. 2125
steve.hunt@sgvn.com, Mng. Ed., The Whittier Daily News, CA, Whittier
Hunt, Christine..........................ext. 109
christine@sdsinc.com, Vice Pres., Opns., Sales Development Services, OH, Westerville
Hunt, Fay
fhunt@c-dh.net, IT Dir., Columbia Daily Herald, TN, Columbia
Hunt, Brian
brian.hunt@djcoregon.com, Pub., Daily Journal of Commerce, OR, Portland
Hunt, Jill..................(405) 372-5000 ext. 264
ads@newspress.com, Adv. Dir., The News Press, OK, Stillwater
Hunt, Craig..........................(717) 257-4748
chunt@patriot-news.com, Systems Ed., The Patriot-News, PA, Mechanicsburg
Hunt, Cortland..........................(559) 735-3325
chunt@visalia.gannett.com, Prodn. Dir., Visalia Times-Delta, CA, Visalia
Hunt, Bud
bhunt@dddnews.com, Pub., The Daily Statesman, MO, Dexter
Hunt, Brian
advertising@djc-or.com, Ed., Daily Journal of Commerce, OR, Portland
Hunt, Jack..........................(419) 993-2122
jhunt@limanews.com, Prodn. Supvr., Press, The Lima News, OH, Lima
Hunter, Scott B...........................(813) 644-2345
shunter@aikenstandard.com, Pres./Pub., Aiken Standard, SC, Aiken
Hunter, Jon M.
jon@madisondailyleader.com, Editorial Writer, The Madison Daily Leader, SD, Madison
Hunter, Jennifer..........................(650) 813-0100
jennifer@bonus.com, Traffic Admin., Headbone Interactive, CA, Palo Alto
Hunter, Joan..........................(814) 532-5120
Personnel Mgr., The Tribune-Democrat, PA, Johnstown
Hunter, Scott B.
shunter@aikenstandard.com, Pub., Aiken Communications, Inc., SC, Aiken
Hunter, Viv..........................(406) 791-1415
vhunter@greatfal.gannett.com, Acct. Mgr., Great Falls Tribune, MT, Great Falls
Hunter, Bob
bhunter@dailytidings.com, Ed., The Ashland Daily Tidings, OR, Ashland
Hunting, Paul..........................(816)350-6353
paul.hunting@examiner.net, Prodn. Mgr., The Examiner, MO, Independence
Huntington, Linn Ann
lhunting@fhsu.edu, Dir., Fort Hays State University, KS, Hays
Hunton, Kaye..........................(479) 571-6435
kayeh@nwarktimes.com, Adv. Mgr., Classified, Northwest Arkansas Times, AR, Fayetteville
Hurbain, Patrick
gazette@charline.be, MD, LA NOUVELLE GAZETTE, Charleroi, Hainault
Hurd, Don L.
dhurd@intranix.com, Pub., Republican, IN, Rensselaer
Hurd, Brad
brad.hurd@lee.net, Pub., The Times-News, ID, Twin Falls
Hurd, Don
dongo75@aol.com, Pub., Times-Republic, IL, Watseka
Hurley, Garth..........................(902) 629-6032
Sports Ed., The Guardian, PE, Charlottetown
Hurley, Deborah C.
hurleyd@mscd.edu, Chair, Metropolitan State College of Denver, CO, Denver
Hurley, Paul..........................(559) 735-3277
editorial@visaliatimesdelta.com, Opinion Page Ed., Visalia Times-Delta, CA, Visalia
Hurley, Sandy
shurley@heartlandpublications.com, Pub., The Sampson Independent, NC, Clinton
Huron, Elliott
ehuron@ctpost.com, Adv. Dir., Connecticut Post, CT, Bridgeport
Hurrle, Larry..........................541-823-4818
Editor, Argus Observer, OR, Ontario
Hurst, Leslie..........................601-961-7066
publisher@clarionledger.com, Publisher, The Clarion-Ledger, MS, Jackson
Hurst, Leslie J.
news@dailyworld.com, Pres./Pub., The Daily World, LA, Opelousas
Hurst, Leslie J.
news@dailyworld.com, Pres./Pub., The Daily Advertiser, LA, Lafayette
Hurtado, Luis..........................35-9027
Editorial Dir., Repuestos Petroleros S.A., El Tigre, Anzoategui
Hurwitz, Michael
mhurwitz@usaweekend.com, USA WEEKEND - Los Angeles, CA, CA, Los Angeles
Husar, Calin
abonamente@cotidianul.ro, Dir., COTIDIANUL, Bucharest
Huskey, Stan..........................ext. 215
shuskey@timesherald.com, Ed., The Times Herald, PA, Norristown
Huss, Mary
mhuss@advertiser-tribune.com, Bus. Mgr., The Advertiser-Tribune, OH, Tiffin
Hussain, Anwar
dailybtz@yahoo.com, Mgr., BALOCHISTAN TIMES, Quetta, Quetta Division
Hussain Manju, Anwar
webguru@daily-ittefaq.com, Pub./Ed., ITTEFAQ, Dhaka
Hussey, John
jphuss2@uky.edu, Mktg. Dir., University Press of Kentucky, KY, Lexington
Hussman, Walter E.
whussman@arkansasonline.com, Pub., Arkansas Democrat-Gazette, AR, Little Rock
Hussman, Cassie..........................(479) 571-6481
cassiec@nwarktimes.com, Features Ed., Northwest Arkansas Times, AR, Fayetteville
Hussman, Walter E...........................Ed.
Jr., Texarkana Gazette, TX, Texarkana
Hussman, Walter E.
news@arkansasonline.com, Owner/Pub., Wehco Media, Inc., AR, Little Rock
Husso, Simo..........................1066 55114
simo.husso@sps.fi, Ed., PYHAJOKISEUTU, Oulainen
Hustasffon, Rene
rene.hustasffon@ingress.se, Adv. Mgr., AVESTA-TIDNING, Avesta
Hutcheson, Jack..........................ext. 5179
Circ. Mgr., Pharos-Tribune, IN, Logansport
Hutcheson, Rick
convergent@convergent.com, Vice Pres., Mktg., Convergent Media Systems, GA, Alpharetta
Hutchinson, Cam..........................(306) 657-6402
chutchinson@sp.canwest.com, Mng. Ed., The StarPhoenix, SK, Saskatoon
Hutchinson, Jeff
jhutchinson@heralddispatch.com, Operations manager, The Herald-Dispatch, WV, Huntington
Hutchinson, Linda..........................(724) 684-2624
lhutchison@tribweb.com, Circ. Dir., The Valley Independent, PA, Monessen
Hutchinson, Jerry
hutch@hutchinson.com, Pres., Hutchinson Associates, Inc., IL, Oak Park
Hutchison, Jim..........................(705) 475-2187
sports@nugget.ca, Sports Ed., The North Bay Nugget, ON, North Bay
Hutchison, Mindy
info@nppa.org, Membership Dir., National Press Photographers Association, Inc., NC, Durham
Hutchison, Patricia..........................(780) 498-5743
phutchinson@thejournal.canwest.com, Vice Pres., Mktg., Edmonton Journal, AB, Edmonton
Hutchison, Earl R.

ehutch@tntech.edu, Dir., Tennessee Technological University, TN, Cookeville
Hutchison, Laura ....(540) 374-5485
lhutchison@freelancestar.com, Local News Ed., The Free Lance-Star, VA, Fredericksburg
Hutchison, Nathan ....ext. 242
sports@richmondregister.com, Sports Ed., The Richmond Register, KY, Richmond
Huthins, Virginia ....(208) 734-3242
virginia.huthins@lee.net, Features Ed., The Times-News, ID, Twin Falls
Hutiel, Daniel
dj@courrier-piccard.fr, Ed., LE COURRIER PICARD, Amiens
Hutin, Francois-Regis 9932 6000
actualite@france-ouest.com, Chrmn., OUEST-FRANCE, 35051 Rennes Cedex 9
Hutton, Jeff
jeff@ottumwacourier.com, Editor, The Ottumwa Courier, IA, Ottumwa
Huxman, Susan
susan.huxman@wichita.edu, Assoc. Prof./Dir., Wichita State University, KS, Wichita
Hwa-Yang, Kim
hykim@kyeongin.com, Ed. in Chief, KYEONGIN ILBO, Suwon
Hwan-Chai, Hwang
webman@segye.com, Pres., SEGYE TIMES, Seoul
Hyde, Rollie............................(405) 735-7394
rhyde@att.net, Director-Southwest/Plains/West, Grimes, W.B. & Co., MD, Gaithersburg
Hyde, Evan X.
russell@btl.net, Ed., AMANDALA, Belize City
Hyde, Rollie............................(405) 788-5597
rhyde@att.net, Southwest/Mountain States Assoc., Grimes, W.B. & Co., OK, Oklahoma City
Hyden, Shirley..................................ext. 223
shirley@monroenews.com, Sec./HR Dir., The Monroe Evening News, MI, Monroe
Hyeon, Sang
southern@daejonilbo.com, Planning Mgr., TAEJON DAILY NEWS, Taejon
Hyland, Theresa E...........................ext. 2257
thyland@registerstar.com, Ed., Register-Star, NY, Hudson
Hynes, Terry ....(352) 392-0466
Dean Emerita/Prof., University of Florida, FL, Gainesville
Hynum, Erin
erin@carnfeldt.com, Dir., Sales/Mktg., Carnfeldt America, WI, Fort Atkinson
Hyska, Blaine
bhyska@ironmountaindailynews.com, Editorial Page Ed., The Daily News, MI, Iron Mountain
Hyytinen, Pekka..............................717 6230
pekka.hyytinen@sps.fi, Ed. in Chief, KOILLISHAME, J□ms□

I

Iacuessa, Mark ....(413) 585-5275
melliott@gazettenet.com, Adv. Dir., Daily Hampshire Gazette, MA, Northampton
Ialacci, John J.
pia@proimage.co.il, Pres., ProImage America, Inc., NJ, Princeton
Ibanez, Enrique
redacquito@efe.com, Rep., EFE News Services - Quito, Ecuador, Quito
Ibrahim, Adel ....(719) 636-0120
adel.ibrahim@gazette.com, Circ. Dir., Consumer Sales, The Gazette, CO, Colorado Springs
Icart, Melodye Hecht
namegameco@aol.com, Pres., The Name Game International, Inc., FL, Plantation
Iceman, Deborah 419-281-0581
diceman@times-gazette.com, Composing Manager, Ashland Publishing Co. LLC, OH, Ashland
Ichiriki, Kazuo
kahoku@po.kahoku.co.jp, Owner, KAHOKU SHIMPO, Sendai City, Tohoku
Ickes, Dave
dickes@theintermountain.com, Prodn. Press Mgr., The Inter-Mountain, WV, Elkins

Iglesias Barca, Jose Eduardo
diariomallorca@diariodemallorca.es, Dir., Diario De Mallorca, Palma de Mallorca, Baleares
Ignacio, Guillermo Anibal
ecosventas@infovia.com.ar, Pres., Ecos Diarios, Necochea, Provincia de Buenos Aires
Ikeakanam, Tony
info@nigerianobservernews.com, Ed., NIGERIAN OBSERVER, Benin City
IldikÃ¢, Ã©jvÂ ri
office@szabadsag.ro, Ed. in Chief, SZABADSAG, Cluj-Napoca, Cluj
Ilelga, Matt
redaktionen@pitea-tidningen.se, Ed., PITEA-TIDNINGEN, Pitea
Illman, Art..............................(508) 626-3875
Photo Dept. Mgr., Metrowest Daily News, MA, Framingham
Imel, Joe ....(270) 783-3292
adennis@bgdailynews.com, Asst. Mgr./Photo Editor, Daily News, KY, Bowling Green
Imel, Joe ....(270) 783-3248
jimel@bgdailynews.com, Photo Ed., Daily News, KY, Bowling Green
Imes, Birney ....ext. 163
birney@cdispatch.com, Gen. Mgr., The Commercial Dispatch, MS, Columbus
Immelt, Devon
dimmelt@delgazette.com, Editor, The Delaware Gazette, OH, Delaware
Imoni, James
airiloc@ma.ultranet.com, Vice Pres., Mktg., Clark-Cutler-McDermoth Co. (Air-Loc Div.), MA, Franklin
Imrie, Chris ....(519) 823-6025
cimrie@guelphmercury.com, Prodn. Mgr., Pre Press, The Guelph Mercury, ON, Guelph
Infantino, Stella Maris 44-2160
Adv. Mgr., El Fenix, Benito Juarez, Provincia de Buenos Aires
Infinger, Steven............................ext. 9275
steven.infinger@thevillagesmedia.com, Dir., Opns., The Villages Daily Sun, FL, The Villages
Ingalls, Charlotte A. ....(603) 668-4321 ext. 270
cingalls@unionleader.com, Adv. Mgr., Classified, New Hampshire Union Leader/New Hampshire Sunday News, NH, Manchester
Ingberg, Pia
pia.ingberg@tribune.com, Dir., European Opns., Tribune Media Services International, London
Ingram, Sean
managingeditor@couriernews.com, Mng. Ed., The Courier, AR, Russellville
Ingrassia, Leonard M.
lingrassia@dailyitem.com, Ed., The Daily Item, PA, Sunbury
Ingvarsson, Anders
anders.ingvarsson@ljp.se, Ed. in Chief, LJUSDALS-POSTEN, Ljusdal
Inmon, Nick
nick.inmon@dailyexaminer.com.au, Adv. Mgr., THE DAILY EXAMINER
Inskeep, Julie
jinskeep@jg.net, Vice Pres./Pub., The Journal Gazette, IN, Fort Wayne
Intagliata, Clara ....(419) 724-6306
cintagliata@toledoblade.com, Circ. Mgr., Direct Sales, The Blade, OH, Toledo
Ippen, Dirk
info@hna.de, Proprietor, HNA HESSISCHE/NIEDERSACHSISCHE ALLGEMEINE, Kassel
Ippen, Dirk
dirk.ippen@merkur-online.de, Proprietor/Pub., TZ, Munich
Ippen, Dirk 8080
info@cbeckers.de, Proprietor, ALLGEMEINE ZEITUNG DER LUNEBURGER HEIDE, Uelzen
Ippen, D.
info@merkur-online.de, Proprietor, MUNCHNER MERKUR, Munich
Ipsan, Matthew........................334-293-5800
mipsan@cnhi.com, Chief Digital Officer , Community Newspaper Holdings, Inc., AL, Montgomery
Irausquin, R.
romulo@laprensacur.com, Dir., LA PRENSA, Willemstad, Curacao

Irby-Jones, Mary ....(937) 225-7311
mirby@coxohio.com, Assistant Managing Editor, Assignment Desk, Dayton Daily News, OH, Dayton
Ireland, Barbara......................(410) 332-6713
barbara.ireland@baltsun.com, Dir., Budgets/Finance Planning, The Baltimore Sun, MD, Baltimore
Ireland, Joe
envoyeditor@gmail.com, Hunter College/CUNY, NY, New York
Irigoyen, Victoriano Raul 422-814
eltiempo@satlink.com.ar, Adv. Mgr., El Tiempo, Azul, Provincia de Buenos Aires
Irion, Christoph
christoph.irion@gea.de, Ed. in Chief, Reutlinger General-Anzeiger, Reutlingen
Iroku, Tammy
tammy@thegreenmconsulting.com, Webmaster and Graphics Specialist, Heart Tones, MO, Kansas City
Irvine, Donald K...............................ext. 110
Chrmn., Accuracy in Media, DC, Washington
Irvine, Frances ....(432) 333-7640
frances_irvine@link.freedom.com, Bus. Mgr., Odessa American, TX, Odessa
Irvine, Dale
nice@galaxynet.com, Sec./Treasurer, Northwest International Circulation Executives, WA, La Conner
Irwin, Barbara
irwin@canisius.edu, Chair, Canisius College, NY, Buffalo
Irwin, Dan ....ext. 621
Religion Ed., New Castle News, PA, New Castle
Irwin, Debbie ....ext. 100
dirwin@hutchnews.com, Circ. Mgr., Opns., The Hutchinson News, KS, Hutchinson
Irwin, Simon
tmbully@capnews.com.au, Gen. Mgr., THE MORNING BULLETIN
Irwin, Heather
heather.irwin@pressdemocrat.com, Ed., The Press Democrat, CA, Santa Rosa
Isaacs, Brad....................................ext. 660
Prodn. Servs. Mgr., The Jackson Sun, TN, Jackson
Isaksen, Judy
jisaksen@highpoint.edu, Assoc. Prof., High Point University, NC, High Point
Iseli, Claire ....(202) 955-9010
claire@washingtonmonthly.com, VP Cir., The Washington Monthly LLC, DC, Washington
Iseli, Carl..............................202-955-9010
carl@washingtonmonthly.com, VP, Operations & Marketing, The Washington Monthly LLC, DC, Washington
Isenberg-O'Loughlin, Jo ....(646) 274-6230
jisenberg@amm.com, Mng. Ed., American Metal Market
Islam, Arife
life@arife.net, Pub., DAILY LIFE, Chittagong
Ismail, Mohammed
ismmailjhan@dawn.com, Ed., DAWN, Peshawar
Isom, Paul............................(252) 328-9234
Advisor, The East Carolinian, NC, Greenville
Isomatsu, Koji
newsroom@emb.asahi-np.co.jp, Hokkaido Office Dir., ASAHI SHIMBUN, Sapporo, Hokkaido
Israel, Gunilla
gunilla@aspentimes.com, Adv. Dir., The Aspen Times, CO, Aspen
Istvan, Stefka
stefka.istvan@magyarhirlap.hu, Dir., MAGYAR HIRLAP, Budapest, Pest
Ittelson, John C.
john@csumb.edu, Contact, Communication Design, CA, Marina
Ivanov, Vjatsheslav
kron.est@estpak.estnet.ee, Pub., ESTONIJA, Tallinn
Ives, Gerald ....ext. 140
gives@hearstnp.com, Circulation Dir., The Huron Daily Tribune, MI, Bad Axe
Ivory, Bennie L. ....(502) 582-4295
bivory@courier-journal.com, Exec. Ed./Vice Pres., News, The Courier-Journal, KY, Louisville
Iwasaki, Scott..........................(801) 236-6014
scott@desnews.com, Music Ed., Deseret News, UT, Salt Lake City
Iwata, Jon C.............................(914) 499-6630
iwata@us.ibm.com, Sr. Vice Pres., Cor. Commun./Mktg., IBM Corp., NY, Somers
Izarra, Josean
elmundo@elmundo.com, Dir., EL MUNDO DEL PAIS VASCO, Bilbao, Vizcaya
Izeze, Emeka
editday@ngrguardiannews.com, Ed., THE GUARDIAN, Lagos

J

Jaan, Rene
redaktion@rva.ch, Ed. in Chief, RHEINTALISCHE VOLKSZEITUNG, Altstaetten, St. Gallen
Jablonski, Carl
carl@jablonskidesign.com, Pres., Jablonski Design, Inc., NJ, Paramus
Jabotte, Denise
info@oxydry.com, Sales Contact, Baldwin Oxy-Dry Americas, IL, Wood Dale
Jacinto, Jonamar 209-249-3538
Sports Editor, Manteca Bulletin, CA, Manteca
Jack-Romero, Kathy ....(970) 416-3989
kathyjackromero@coloradoan.com, Circ. Dir., The Coloradoan, CO, Fort Collins
Jackimowicz, Ron..........................ext. 238
rjackimowicz@theworldlink.com, Cuisine Ed., The World, OR, Coos Bay
Jackoway, Richard
rick.jackoway@thedailyrecord.com, St. Louis Daily Record, MO, Saint Louis
Jackson, Jeffrey ....(507) 444-2371
jjackson@owatonna.com, Mng. Ed., Owatonna People's Press, MN, Owatonna
Jackson, Lori
ljackson@kspress.com, Administrative Assistant/Advertising, Kansas Press Association, KS, Topeka
Jackson, Gloria
gjackson@times-journal.com, Adv. Mgr., The Times-Journal, AL, Fort Payne
Jackson, Rachel ....ext. 1641
rjackson@the-daily-record.com, Copy Ed., The Daily Record, OH, Wooster
Jackson, Fred..........................(902) 563-3843
maned@cbpost.com, Mng. Ed., The Cape Breton Post, NS, Sydney
Jackson, Shirley......................(410) 770-4079
Composition Mgr., The Star-Democrat, MD, Easton
Jackson, Robert 256-235-9220
Assistant VP for Operations, The Anniston Star, AL, Anniston
Jackson, Tracee
info@hearttones.com, Public Relations Director, Heart Tones, MO, Kansas City
Jackson, Lynda ....(478) 453-1442
ljackson@unionrecorder.com, Bus. Mgr., The Union-Recorder, GA, Milledgeville
Jackson, Freida
fjackson@wacotrib.com, Systems Ed., Waco Tribune-Herald, TX, Waco
Jackson, Kurt M.
kurt@nscs.fast.net, Vice Pres., Opns., Software Consulting Services, LLC, PA, Nazareth
Jackson, Richard
rjackson@emeraldis.com, Exec. Controller, The Index-Journal, SC, Greenwood
Jackson, Jackie ....(202) 636-4946
jjackson@washingtontimes.com, Circ. Mgr., Customer Serv., The Washington Times, DC, Washington
Jacob, Cheryl ....(352) 564-2909
cjacob@chronicleonline.com, Chief Copy Desk Ed., Citrus County Chronicle, FL, Crystal River
Jacob, Steve ....(817) 685-3955
sjacob@star-telegram.com, Pub., Northeast Tarrant Star-Telegram, Fort Worth Star-Telegram, TX, Fort Worth
Jacobs, Judy ....ext. 2434
jjacobs@wdt.net, Currents/Society Ed., Watertown Daily Times, NY, Watertown
Jacobs, Micki ....(800) 828-0242
info@kmnewspaper.com, Controller, K & M Newspaper Services, Inc., NY, Monroe

Jacobs, Jane W.........................**(812) 265-3641**
jwjacobs@madisoncourier.com, Pres./Pub., The Madison Courier, IN, Madison
Jacobs, Michael
mjacobs@gfherald.com, Pub., Grand Forks Herald, ND, Grand Forks
Jacobs, Wanda Heary
whjmsps@aol.com, Pub., The Mississippi Press, MS, Pascagoula
Jacobs, Mike
mjacobs@gfherald.com, Executive Editor, Grand Forks Herald, ND, Grand Forks
Jacobs, Janice..........................**(312) 222-2122**
jjacobs@tribune.com, Vice Pres., HR, Chicago Tribune, IL, Chicago
Jacobs, Mindelle......................**(780) 468-0274**
mindy.jacobs@edm.sunpub.com, Columnist, The Edmonton Sun, AB, Edmonton
Jacobs, Wanda..........................**(228) 934-1417**
wjacobs@press-register.com, Adv. Mgr., Nat'l, Press-Register, AL, Mobile
Jacobs, Mark
mjacobs@kmnewspaper.com, Pres., K & M Newspaper Services, Inc., NY, Monroe
Jacobs, Eric.................**(215) 898-6581 ext. 100**
The Daily Pennsylvanian, PA, Philadelphia
Jacobs, Laura............................**(630) 782-4386**
ljacobs@interest.com, Sr. Ed., Mortgage Market Information Services, IL, Villa Park
Jacobsen, Sally
sjacobsen@ap.org, Gen. Mgr., Associated Press Managing Editors Association, NY, New York
Jacobson, Julie........................**(248) 745-4632**
julie.jacobson@oakpress.com, Local News Ed., The Oakland Press, MI, Pontiac
Jacobson, Ruben
mats.amvall@ljusnan.se, Mng. Ed., LJUSNAN, Bollnas
Jacobson, John
john_jacobson@nac.net, Pres., American Graphic Arts, Inc., NJ, Elizabeth
Jacobson, Bryce........................**(970) 875-1788**
bjacobson@craigdailypress.com, Pub., Craig Daily Press, CO, Craig
Jacobson, Bryce........................**970-875-1788**
bjacobson@craigdailypress.com, Publisher - Craig Daily Press, WorldWest LLC, KS, Lawrence
Jacobsson, Ruben
redaktion@ht.se, Mng. Dir., HUDIKSVALLS TIDNING (med HALSINGLANDS TIDNING), Hudiksvall
Jacobsson, Ruben
ruben.jacobsson@ht.se, Ed., HALSINGE KURIREN, Soderhamn
Jacobucci, Justin......................**(316) 321-1120**
Prodn. Mgr., The Derby Reporter, KS, Derby
Jacoby, Jay.............................**(818) 595-1122**
jay@flipyourlid.com, Pres./CEO, Flip Your Lid, CA, housand Oaks
Jacoby, Jayson
jjacoby@bakercityherald.com, News Ed., Baker City Herald, OR, Baker City
Jacoby, Barbara
bjacoby@cherokeetribune.com, Ed., Cherokee Tribune, GA, Canton
Jacomet, Bret
bretj@kpcnews.net, Adv. Vice Pres., Sales/Mktg., The Star, IN, Auburn
Jacquart, Paul..........................**(902) 426-2873**
pjacquart@herald.ca, Adv. Mgr., Retail Sales, The Chronicle Herald, NS, Halifax
Jaeger, Jan
jjaeger@thehawkeye.com, Mgr., HR, The Hawk Eye, IA, Burlington
Jaffe, Chuck A.........................**(781) 383-6688**
jfeatures@aol.com, Columnist, J Features, MA, Cohasset
Jagan, Janet
news@guyana.net.gy, Ed., New Guyana Co. Ltd., Georgetown
Jagnow, Betty H. Brown .(330) 747-1471 ext. 1203
bjagnow@vindy.com, Pres./Pub./Treasurer, The Vindicator, OH, Youngstown
Jahilo, Marika
marika.jahilo@postimees.ee, Adv. Mgr., POSTIMEES, Tartu
Jahn, Steve
steve.jahn@finance-commerce.com, Vice Pres./Pub., Finance and Commerce
Jahns, Kathy............................**(713) 417-7615**
getinfony@metrosn.com, Mgr., Metro Newspaper Advertising Services, Inc., CA, Hermosa Beach
Jain, Trilok
adhuniks_news@yahoo.co.in, Ed. in Chief, ADHUNIK RAJASTHAN, Ajmer, Rajasthan
Jain, K.C.
vishwa_pariwar@yahoo.com, Pub., DAINIK VISHWA PARIWAR, Jhansi, Uttar Pradesh
Jain, Ashok
lokmat@bom2.vsnl.net.in, Adv. Mgr., LOKMAT, Nagpur, Maharashtra
Jakiela, Lori............................**(724) 836-7481**
Univ. of Pittsburgh/Greensburg, PA, Greensburg
Jallaluddin, Mohammed
rozanahind_99@yahoo.co.in, Ed., ROZANA HIND, Kolkata, West Bengal
Jallow, Baba Galleh
adverts@observer.gm, Ed., THE DAILY OBSERVER, Banjul
Jamerson, Terry........................**(434) 385-5570**
tjamerson@newsadvance.com, Pub., The News & Advance, VA, Lynchburg
James, Michael L.
james@harding.edu, Dean/Prof., Harding University, AR, Searcy
James, George..........................**(706) 208-2282**
george.james@onlineathens.com, Mktg. Dir., Athens Banner-Herald, GA, Athens
James, Teri...............................**(831) 754-4212**
tjames@thecalifornian.com, Dir., HR/Community Aff., The Salinas Californian, CA, Salinas
James, William E.
billjames@npgco.com, Pub., The Daily Star-Journal, MO, Warrensburg
James, Sardathisa
sph@tm.net.my, Ed. in Chief, DAILY EXPRESS, Kota Kinabalu, Sabah
James, Bill...............................**(707) 427-6983**
bjames@dailyrepublic.net, Pub., Daily Republic, CA, Fairfield
James, Gary
garyjames111@hotmail.com, Pres./Self-Syndicator, Gary James, NY, East Syracuse
James, Rob
rj@nebpress.com, Sales Mgr., Nebraska Press Advertising Service, NE, Lincoln
James, Rob
rj@nebpress.com, Sales Mgr., Nebraska Press Association, NE, Lincoln
Jameson, Stephanie L.
sjameson@americanhometownpublishing.com, Vice President HR, American Hometown Publishing, TN, Franklin
Janendo, Janice........................**(212) 626-7685**
janice.janendo@investors.com, Adv. Mgr., Opns. (E. Coast), Investor's Business Daily, CA, Los Angeles
Janesh, Barbara........................**(920) 431-8325**
bjanesh@greenbaypressgazette.com, Mng. Ed., Green Bay Press-Gazette, WI, Green Bay
Jang, Phillip...........................**News Ed., Night**
(250) 380-5353, Times Colonist, BC, Victoria
Janigian, Laura........................**(559) 441-6243**
ljanigian@fresnobee.com, Vice Pres., HR, The Fresno Bee, CA, Fresno
Janik, Melinda A.......................**(585) 598-0030**
Sr. Vice Pres./CFO, GateHouse Media Inc., NY, Fairport
Jankowski, Carol..........**(519) 894-2250 ext. 2640**
cjankowski@therecord.com, Lifestyle Ed., The Record, ON, Kitchener
Jannings, Jodi
jjannings@landonmedia.com, Acct. Exec., Landon Media Group LLC, CA, Benicia
Janos, John G.
jjanos@dailyherald.com, Circ. Mgr., Daily Herald, IL, Arlington Heights
Janos, Gyarmath
rmsz@com.pcnet.ro, Ed. in Chief, ROMANIAI MAGYAR SZO, Bucharest
Janos, Ban
ujneplap@axels.hu, Dir., UJ NEPLAP, Szolnok, Szolnok
Jansen, Peter
redactie@pzc.nl, Ed., PROVINCIALE ZEEUWSE COURANT, Goes
Janus, William..........................**(410) 332-6438**
bill.janus@baltsun.com, Dir., Classified Adv., The Baltimore Sun, MD, Baltimore
Janviroj, Pana
bangna@nationgroup.com, Ed., THE NATION, Bangkok
Jaramillo, Eleazar..............................**292725**
ejaramillo@australtemuco.cl, Sales Mgr., Sociedad Periodistica Araucania S.A., Temuco
Jarden, Andy.................................**349 0710**
carol.grinstead@wanganuichronicle.co.nz, Gen. Mgr., WANGANUI CHRONICLE
Jardim, Murilo................................**332-5643**
Pres., Lavoura E Comercio, Uberaba, Minas Gerais
Jaros, Michal
mjaros@perex.sk, Key Accts. Mgr., PRAVDA, Bratislava
Jarosh, Andrew..........................**(239) 335-0299**
Asst. Metro Ed., The News-Press, FL, Fort Myers
Jaroslavsky, Gracia...........................**42-1113**
lamanana@arnet.com.ar, Ed., La Manana, Victoria, Provincia de Entre Rios
Jarrach, Robert
bjarrach@njtimes.com, Prodn. Dir., Opns., The Times, NJ, Trenton
Jarrell, Rosemary........................**662-678-1515**
rosemary.jarrell@journalinc.com, Director of Finance, Journal Publishing Company, MS, Tupelo
Jarrell, Barry..................................**ext. 108**
bjarrell@tnpress.com, Adv. Dir., Tennessee Press Association, Inc., TN, Knoxville
bjarrell@tnpress.com, Adv. Dir., Tennessee Press Service, Inc., TN, Knoxville
Jarret, Pam...............................**(561) 439-8064**
Palm Beach Cmty. College, FL, Lake Worth
Jarvis, Charles..............**(730) 841-1600 ext. 660**
charlesjarvis@tribtoday.com, Pub., The Tribune Chronicle, OH, Warren
Jarvis, Steven...........................**(479) 571-6494**
stevenj@nwanews.com, Online Mgr., Northwest Arkansas Times, AR, Fayetteville
Jarvis, Lori
djliving@thedailyjournal.com, Features Ed., The Daily Journal, NJ, Vineland
Jasinowski, Alex
ajasinowski@kimototech.com, Sales Supvr., Kimoto Tech, IL, Elk Grove Village
Jaunzems, Andris...............................**ext. 253**
ajaunzems@pulitzer.net, Prodn. Foreman, Composing, The World, OR, Coos Bay
Javed-ur-Rehman, Mir
groupeditor@janggroup.com.pk, Ed., DAILY JANG, Rawalpindi, Rawalpindi Division
Jaworski, Mark..........................**(260) 461-8260**
mjaworksi@jg.net, Sports Ed., The Journal Gazette, IN, Fort Wayne
Jaworski, Randy........................**(530) 852-0255**
randyj@goldcountrymedia.com, Prodn. Mgr., Post Press, Auburn Journal, Inc., CA, Auburn
Jayarajan, E.T.
kochi@deshabhimani.com, Gen. Mgr., DESHABHIMANI, Cochin, Kerala
Jayaraman, C.
no1thanthi@yahoo.co.in, Ed., DAILY THANTHI, Vellore, Tamil Nadu
Jayne, Greg..............................**(360)735-4531**
greg.jayne@columbian.com, Sports Ed, The Columbian, WA, Vancouver
Jayne, Evelyn
evelyn.jayne@pagecooperative.com, Office Mgr., PAGE Cooperative, PA, King of Prussia
Jean, Patrick..................................**ext. 237**
City Ed., The Hickory Daily Record, NC, Hickory
Jeanty, David
david@lematinhaiti.com, Mgr., LE MATIN, Port-Au-Prince
Jebailey, Heissam...........**(407) 447-4555 ext. 102**
Univ. of Central Florida, FL, Orlando
Jebson, Donna...........................**(757) 247-4943**
djebson@dailypress.com, Adv. Dir., Key Accts. Sales, Daily Press, VA, Newport News
Jeevaratnam, Karunanidhi
karuna@sph.com.sg, Adv. Mgr, TAMIL MURASU, Singapore
Jeffcoat, David
david.jeffcoat@yankton.net, Circ. Dir., Yankton Daily Press & Dakotan, SD, Yankton
Jefferson, Letitia......................**(803) 644-2344**
ljefferson@aikenstandard.com, Customer Serv. Mgr., Aiken Standard, SC, Aiken
Jeffery, Estel..........................**(501) 378-3545**
estel@ardemgaz.com, Dir., Promo., Arkansas Democrat-Gazette, AR, Little Rock
Jeffries, Jina.....................................**ext. 27**
jjeffries@stategazette.com, Bus. Mgr., State Gazette, TN, Dyersburg
Jeffus, Jeff..............................**(479) 442-1705**
publisher@nwarktimes.com, Pub., Northwest Arkansas Times, AR, Fayetteville
Jelks, Lo..................................**(404) 523-6136**
Atlanta Univ. Center, GA, Atlanta
Jem, Harad
np@madsack.de, Ed., Neue Presse, Hannover
Jenkins, Joel
jjenkins@cninewspapers.com, Corporate Marketing Director / Major Account Manager, Community Newspapers, Inc., GA, Athens
Jenkins, John...........................**540-645-5950**
jjenkins@printinnovators.com, Operations Director , The Free Lance-Star, VA, Fredericksburg
Jenkins, Alan
alanjenkins@shelbystar.com, Mng. Ed., The Star, NC, Shelby
Jenkins, Eva.............................**(803) 329-4087**
ejenkins@heraldonline.com, Adv. Mgr., Nat'l/Preprint, The Herald, SC, Rock Hill
Jenkins, Tom
info@opentext.com, CEO, Open Text Corp., ON, Waterloo
Jenkins, Phil.............................**(540) 374-5422**
pjenkins@freelancestar.com, Mng. Ed., The Free Lance-Star, VA, Fredericksburg
Jenkins, Donna Pipes................**(856) 486-2408**
djenkins@courierpostonline.com, Metro Ed., Courier-Post, NJ, Cherry Hill
Jenkins, Judy..............**(270) 831-8339 ext. 8339**
jjenkins@thegleaner.com, Health/Medical Ed., The Gleaner, KY, Henderson
Jenkinson, Mike........................**(780) 468-0226**
mike.jenkinson@edm.sunpub.com, Editorial Page Ed., The Edmonton Sun, AB, Edmonton
Jenner, Mike.............................**(661) 395-7387**
mjenner@bakersfield.com, Vice Pres./Exec. Ed., The Bakersfield Californian, CA, Bakersfield
Jennex, Ken..............................**(902) 426-2886**
kjennex@herald.ca, Purchasing, The Chronicle Herald, NS, Halifax
Jenney, Rob
robjenney@thecourier.com, Circ. Mgr., Sales, The Courier, OH, Findlay
Jennings, Mary..........................**(256) 765-4363**
Univ. of North Alabama, AL, Florence
Jennings, Stacy.........................**(912) 652-0236**
stacy.jennings@savannahnow.com, Dir., Mktg./Promo., Savannah Morning News, GA, Savannah
Jennings, Brad..........................**(717) 771-2061**
bjennings@ydr.com, Photo Ed., Weekly Record, PA, York
Jennings, Brad..........................**(717) 771-2061**
bjennings@ydr.com, Visual Ed., York Daily Record/York Sunday News, PA, York
Jensen, John.............................**(319) 472-2311**
editor@cedarvalleydailytimes.com, News Ed., Cedar Valley Daily Times, IA, Vinton
Jensen, Jens O.
jens.olai.jenssen@oa.no, Ed. in Chief, OPPLAND ARBEIDERBLAD, Gjovik
Jensen, Tom..............................**(415) 382-7341**
tjensen@marinij.com, Prodn. Mgr., Opns., Marin Independent Journal, CA, Novato
Jensen, Gert..............................**(847) 466-1243**
gli@schur.com, Technical Sales Dir., Schur Packaging Systems, Inc., IL, Schaumburg
Jensen, Nels..............................**(951) 782-7550**
njensen@pe.com, Deputy Mng. Ed., The Press-Enterprise, CA, Riverside
Jensen, Carsten Boe
cje@ccieurope.com, President, CCI US, CCI Europe, Inc., GA, Kennesaw
Jensen, Cherie
cheriej@sdna.com, Asst. Mgr., South Dakota Newspaper Association, SD, Brookings
Jensen, Amy
amy@chanute.com, Circ. Mgr., The Chanute Tribune, KS, Chanute

Jensen, Karen
kjensen@printronix.com, Dir., Mktg., Tally Genicom, CA, Irvine
Jensen, Peter Orry......................+45 2060 4501
por@jv.dk, Dir./Ed., JYDSKE VESTKYSTEN, Esbjerg, Jutland
Jensen, Michael L.
mjensen@standard-democrat.com, Co-Owner/Pub., Standard Democrat, MO, Sikeston
Jensen, Ian..........................(306) 765-1300
ian.jensen@paherald.sk.ca, Adv. Mgr., Prince Albert Daily Herald, SK, Prince Albert
Jensen, Gert..............................847 558 5039
Glj@ schur.com, Dir. Tech. Sales, Schur Packaging Systems, Inc., IL, Schaumburg
Jensen, Randy
randy.jensen@lethbridgeherald.com, News Desk Ed., The Lethbridge Herald, AB, Lethbridge
Jepsen, John
jjepsen@gotoanr.com, Pres., American Newspaper Representatives, Inc., MI, Troy
Jernigan, Floyd
news@therolladailynews.com, Pub., Rolla Daily News, MO, Rolla
Jerome, Kelly L. ....ext. 106
kjerome@hearstnp.com, Ed., The Huron Daily Tribune, MI, Bad Axe
Jesionowski, Kendrick
ktsports@kentontimes.com, Sports Ed., The Kenton Times, OH, Kenton
Jeske, Jeff 336-316-2216
jjeske@guilford.edu, Guilford College, NC, Greensboro
Jeter, Phillip
jeterph@wssu.edu, Chair/Prof., Winston-Salem State University, NC, Winston-Salem
Jetter, Klaus 2660
zak@zak.de, Proprietor, ZOLLERN-ALB KURIER, Balingen
Jewell, Paul..............................(901) 529-2219
jewell@commercialappeal.com, Mgr., Mktg., The Commercial Appeal, TN, Memphis
Jewell, Steve ....ext. 229
sjewell@heraldpalladium.com, News Ed., The Herald-Palladium, MI, Saint Joseph
Jill, Miller ....(316) 841-8927
jilldm@swbell.net, Kansas Professional Communicators, KS, Wichita
Jim, Furley...............................920-563-5553
jfurley@dailyunion.com, Circulation Manager, Daily Jefferson County Union, WI, Fort Atkinson
Jimenez, Terry A.
terry.jimenez@newsday.com, President, Newsday, NY, Melville
Jimenez Hernandez, Agustin
publicidad@elsoldetampico.com.mx, Dir., EL SOL DE TAMPICO, Tampico, Tamaulipas
Jimenez Horna, Carlos..........................65-1283
Gen. Mgr., El Callao, Lima
Jimison, Jon
jonjimison@shelbystar.com, Ed., The Star, NC, Shelby
Jimmar, Renita..........................(256) 740-5815
renita.jimmar@timesdaily.com, Adv. Mgr., Display, TimesDaily, AL, Florence
Joachim, Jean ....(212) 799-6416
moviechoices@cs.com, Writer, Movie Choices for Kids, NY, New York
Joensen, Oliver
oliver@nordlysid.fo, Ed., NORDLYSID, Klaksvik
Joentausta, Jouko
jouko.joentausta@kansanuutiset.fi, Ed. in Chief, KANSAN UUTISET, Helsinki
Joffrin, Laurent
joffrin@liberation.fr, Dir., LIBERATION, Paris Cedex 03
Johal, Hardip ....(604) 605-2782
hjohal@theprovince.com, Lifestyles Ed., The Province, BC, Vancouver
Johanek, John
johanek@publicationdesign.com, Partner, Ayers/Johanek Publication Design, Inc., MT, Bozeman
Johannessen, Matthias
ritstjorn@mbl.is, Ed., MORGUNBLADID, Reykjavik
Johansson, Borje
borje.johansson@vgt.se, Contact, FALKOPINGS TIDNING, Falkoping
Johansson, Jan A.
jan_a_johansson@skd.se, Ed., SKANSKA DAGBLADET, Malmo
Johansson, Wolf
na@na.se, Ed. in Chief, NERIKES ALLEHANDA, Orebro
Johansson, Goran
info@hallandsposten.se, MD, HALLANDSPOSTEN, Halmstad
Johansson, Sven 15 93 00
sven.johansson@arbetarbladet.se, Pub., ARBETARBLADET, Gavle
Johansson, Uls
mt@motalatidning.se, MD, MOTALA TIDNING MED VADSTENA TIDNING, Motala
John, India
johni@beloit.edu, Co Editor-in-Chief , Beloit College, WI, Beloit
John, Open inch rate $25.20 ....Pub.
The Daily Journal
Johns, Amy
ajohns@mcalesternews.com, Pub., McAlester News-Capital, OK, McAlester
Johns, Michael..........................573-761-0261
mjohns@newstribune.com, Circ. Mgr. , News Tribune, MO, Jefferson City
Johns, Philomena..............................ext. 226
pjohns@timesherald.com, Lifestyle Ed., The Times Herald, PA, Norristown
Johns, Arlene ....(814) 532-5065
City Ed., The Tribune-Democrat, PA, Johnstown
Johnsen, Roland 401-364-6061
roland@motterstitch.com, Vice President, Motterstitch Company, Inc., RI, Charlestown
Johnson, Scott.........................(570) 748-6791
sjohnson@lockhaven.com, Online Mgr., The Express, PA, Lock Haven
Johnson, Dave
nbhcn@triton.net, Harbor Country News Ed., News Dispatch, IN, Michigan City
Johnson, Bill
bjohnson@grcnet.net, Circ. Mgr., Blackwell Journal-Tribune, OK, Blackwell
Johnson, Gita
registercirculation@yahoo.com, Circ. Mgr., Iola Register, KS, Iola
Johnson, Michael
mjohnson@alamogordonews.com, Mng. Ed., Alamogordo Daily News, NM, Alamogordo
Johnson, Kristin
kristin.johnson@kokomotribune.com, Adv. Dir., Kokomo Tribune, IN, Kokomo
Johnson, John ....(316) 782-1000
jbj@wdt.net, General Manager, Watertown Daily Times, NY, Watertown
Johnson, Leigh
leigh@alternet.org, Bus. Mgr., AlterNet, CA, San Francisco
Johnson, Sally..........................(906) 497-5652
sjohnson@powersprinting.net, Prodn. Mgr., Mailroom, The Daily News, MI, Iron Mountain
Johnson, Ken
kjohnson@ledger.com, Online Ed., The Enterprise, MA, Randolph
Johnson, Mans
redaktion@sla.se, Ed., SKARABORG LANS ALLEHANDA, Skovde, Erling Ekelund
Johnson, Kent
kjohnson@dailyherald.com, Sr. Vice Pres./Treasurer, Daily Herald, IL, Arlington Heights
Johnson, Elmore ....ext. 225
ejohnson@wdt.net, Prodn. Foreman, Pressroom, The Courier-Observer, The Journal & The Advance-News, NY, Ogdensburg
Johnson, Vicki
vickij@northwestsignal.net, Family/Evening Ed., Northwest Signal, OH, Napoleon
Johnson, Kathy ....(909) 386-3809
Finance Dir., San Bernardino County Sun, CA, San Bernardino
Johnson, Ken ....(617) 786-7052
kjohnson@ledger.com, Online Ed., The Patriot Ledger, MA, Quincy
Johnson, Lowell
ljohnson@htrnews.com, General Manager / Advertising Director, Herald Times Reporter, WI, Manitowoc
Johnson, Robert J......................(906) 774-2772
bjohnson@ironmountaindailynews.com, Pub., The Daily News, MI, Iron Mountain
Johnson, Rhonda.........................(574) 224-5324
rjohnson@rochsent.com, Lifestyles Ed., The Rochester Sentinel, IN, Rochester
Johnson, David ....(843) 317-7301
djohnson@florencenews.com, Circ. Dir., Morning News, SC, Florence
Johnson, Jason
jljohnson@hearstnp.com, Online Mgr., Plainview Herald, TX, Plainview
Johnson, Dan ....(705) 674-5271 ext. 216
danjohnson@thesudburystar.com, Mgmt. Info Servs. Mgr., The Sudbury Star, ON, Sudbury
Johnson, Tamara
tamjohns@thnews.com, Mng. Ed., Times-Herald, AR, Forrest City
Johnson, Henry
hjohnson@journalnet.com, Office Mgr., Idaho State Journal, ID, Pocatello
Johnson, Randy ....(715) 395-5031
rjohnson@superiortelegram.com, Adv. Dir., The Daily Telegram, WI, Superior
Johnson, Tom.............................(630) 978-8421
News Ed., The Beacon News, IL, Aurora
Johnson, Scott
scottj@npgco.com, Design Ed., Atchison Globe, KS, Atchison
Johnson, David ....(202) 408-2717
johnsond@shns.com, Chief Tech. Officer/Webmaster, Scripps Howard News Service, DC, Washington
Johnson, Nila ....ext. 102
nila@press-herald.com, Pres./Gen. Mgr., Minden Press-Herald, LA, Minden
Johnson, Deb
dkjohnson@marshallindependent.com, Prodn. Mgr., Pre Press, Independent, MN, Marshall
Johnson, Sheila 405.238.6464
sjohnson@pvdemocrat.com, Office Manager, Pauls Valley Democrat, OK, Pauls Valley
Johnson, Jon.............................(334) 712-7965
jjohnson@dothaneagle.com, Sports Ed., The Dothan Eagle, AL, Dothan
Johnson, Dan ....(705) 475-2192 ext. 705
Pub., The North Bay Nugget, ON, North Bay
Johnson, Ric
bac@bloapco.com, Mgr., Sales, Blower Application Co., Inc., WI, Germantown
Johnson, Joshua 9722232998
Editor, Best Southwest Focus, TX, DeSoto
Johnson, Peter
economia@buenosairesherald.com, Ed., Buenos Aires Herald Ltda. S.A., Buenos Aires
Johnson, Charles R.
charles.johnson@mx3.com, Pres./CEO, Superior Publishing Corp., WI, Superior
Johnson, Jeanie
addirector@register-pajaronian.com, Mgr., Nat'l Adv., Register-Pajaronian, CA, Watsonville
Johnson, Kent ....(714) 796-5005
kjohnson@ocregister.com, Vice Pres., Adv., The Orange County Register, CA, Santa Ana
Johnson, Jeffry ....(904) 819-3526
jeffry.johnson@staugustinerecord.com, Prodn. Superintendent, Pressroom, The St. Augustine Record, FL, Saint Augustine
Johnson, John B.
jbjjr@wdt.net, Chrmn. of the Bd./CEO, Johnson Newspaper Corp., NY, Watertown
Johnson, Kyle
kj@parenttoparent.com, Personal Assistant Assistant Editor, Parent to Parent, MO, Wildwood
Johnson, Tom
bleader@latimes.com, Gen. Mgr., Times Community News (TCN), CA, Glendale
Johnson, Cedric..........................321-242-3856
cjohnson@floridatoday.com, Distribution Operations Manager, Florida Today, FL, Melbourne
Johnson, Andrew.........................(920) 533-8338
johnson@mayvillenews.com, Pres., Wisconsin Newspaper Association
Johnson, Jon.............................(906) 341-4204
info@manistiquepapers.com, Gen. Mgr., Manistique Papers, Inc., MI, Manistique
Johnson, Chad
cjohnson@metrosuburbia.com, Adv. Sales Mgr., Metro Suburbia, Inc./Newhouse Newspapers, IL, Chicago
Johnson, Gary...................................ext. 3211
gary.johnson@ecpc.com, Local Ed., Leader-Telegram, WI, Eau Claire
Johnson, Ryan ....(701) 231-8994
ad.manager@ndsuspectrum.com, North Dakota State Univ., ND, Fargo
Johnson, Gary
edit@mspmag.com, Pres., MSP Communications, MN, Minneapolis
Johnson, Marilou
johnsomx@jmu.edu, Prof., James Madison University, VA, Harrisonburg
Johnson, Patrick
pat@zumapress.com, CTO, ZUMA Press, Inc., CA, San Clemente
Johnson, George
johnsogc@jmu.edu, Prof., James Madison University, VA, Harrisonburg
Johnson, Harold B...........(315) 782-1000 ext. 279
hbj@wdt.net, Pres./COO, Johnson Newspaper Corp., NY, Watertown
Johnson, Tiffany..........................(937) 775-5534
Wright State Univ., OH, Dayton
Johnson, Brian K.
bkj@bkjproductions.com, Pres., BKJ Productions, MA, Malden
Johnson, Haylley ....(802) 656-8482
Univ. of Vermont, VT, Burlington
Johnson, Ruth 406-243-6646
Office manager, Univ. of Montana, MT, Missoula
Johnson, Maurice ....(281) 369-4016
bizniz@biznizweb.com, Bus. Mgr., DynaPortal Software Co., TX, The Woodlands
Johnson, Sean.............................(530) 896-7799
sjonhson@chicoer.com, Prodn. Foreman, Pressroom, Chico Enterprise-Record, CA, Chico
Johnson, Randy ....(815) 877-4044 ext. 54
Gen. Mgr., Belvidere Republican, IL, Belvidere
Johnson, D.J. ....(928) 783-3311 ext. 105
djjohnson@westernnewspapers.com, Vice Pres./Dir., HR, Western Newspapers, Inc., AZ, Yuma
Johnsrud, Mathew
math.johnsrud@journaltimes.com, Circ. Mgr., The Journal Times, WI, Racine
Johnsson, Robert
robert.johnsson@norrteljetidning.se, Ed., NORRTALJE TIDNING, Norrtalje
Johnston, Richard.........................(309) 820-3213
Pub., The Pantagraph, IL, Bloomington
Johnston, Bill
bjohnston@madison.com, Pub., Wisconsin State Journal, WI, Madison
Johnston, Karen
advertising@dailytownsman.com, Publisher, Cranbrook Daily Townsman, BC, Cranbrook
Johnston, Eric ....(209) 578-2149
ejohnston@modbee.com, Online Dir., The Modesto Bee, CA, Modesto
Johnston, Anne ....(919) 962-4286
Prof./Assoc. Dean for Grad. Studies, University of North Carolina, NC, Chapel Hill
Johnston, Jim.............................(734) 994-6884
jjohnston@annarbornews.com, Mgr., Systems, The Ann Arbor News, MI, Ann Arbor
Johnston, Norman ....ext. 2320
njohnston@wdt.net, Photo Ed., Watertown Daily Times, NY, Watertown
Johnstone, Bruce.........................(306) 781-5304
bjohnstone@leaderpost.canwest.com, Finance Ed., The Leader-Post, SK, Regina
Jollet, Robert ....(514) 337-1974 ext. 270
rjollet@elconsy.com, Sales Rep., Elcorsy Technology, Inc., QC, Saint Laurent
Jolley, Susan M.
susan@newspaperconsultants.com, General Manager, Advantage Newspaper Consultants, NC, Fayetteville
Jollymore, Cynthia
cynthia@mcgown.com, Vice Pres., Sales, Publicitas McGown Inc., QC, Montreal
Jones, Ken
publisher@pryordailytimes.com, Pub., The Daily Times, OK, Pryor
Jones, Steve
steve@landsteward.org, Author, The Plant Man, TN, Franklin
Jones, Janeen ....(717) 771-2036
jjones@ydr.com, News Ed., York Daily

Record/York Sunday News, PA, York
Jones, Gregg K. ....(423) 359-3122
gregg.jones@jonesmedia.biz, Co-Pub., The Greeneville Sun, TN, Greeneville
Jones, Max ....(812) 231-4336 ext. 336
max.jones@tribstar.com, Ed., The Tribune Star, IN, Terre Haute
Jones, Tim
tjones@ashwoth.com, Mktg. Mgr., Ashworth Brothers, Inc., VA, Winchester
Jones, James
jjones@sanmarcosrecord.com, Adv. Dir., San Marcos Daily Record, TX, San Marcos
Jones, Rich ....(423) 359-3138
rich.jones@greenevillesun.com, Asst. Mng. Ed., The Greeneville Sun, TN, Greeneville
Jones, Gary ....(706) 272-7709
jeffmutter@daltoncitizen.com, Adv. Dir., The Daily Citizen, GA, Dalton
Jones, Richard
rljones@tribune.com, Dir., Western Reg., Tribune Media Network, CA, Los Angeles
Jones, Pat
news@guardonline.com, Gen. Mgr., Batesville Guard, AR, Batesville
Jones, Nate 620-326-3326
nate.jones@wellingtondailynews.com, managing Editor, Wellington Daily News, KS, Wellington
Jones, Darrell ....(901) 529-2640
djones@commercialappeal.com, Circ. Dir., The Commercial Appeal, TN, Memphis
Jones, Abbott C.
ajones@admediapartners.com, Managing Director (Retired), AdMedia Partners, Inc., NY, New York
Jones, Edward W. ....(540) 374-5401
edjones@freelancestar.com, Editor, The Free Lance-Star, VA, Fredericksburg
Jones, Dorian ....(773) 602-5000
Kennedy-King College, IL, Chicago
Jones, Maurice 757-446-2631
maurice.jones@pilotonline.com, President and Publisher, The Virginian-Pilot, VA, Norfolk
Jones, Margaret 937-382-2574
mjones@wnewsj.com, Assistant Editor, Wilmington News Journal, OH, Wilmington
Jones, Chuck ....ext. 292
cjones@thenewsenterprise.com, Sports Ed., The News Enterprise, KY, Elizabethtown
Jones, Andrea ....631) 913.4257
andrea.jones@libn.com, Long Island Business News, NY, Ronkonkoma
andrea.jones@libn.com, West Texas A&M Univ., TX, Canyon
Jones, Jana ....(727) 893-8634
jljones@tampabay.com, Vice Pres./CFO, Tampa Bay Times, FL, Saint Petersburg
Jones, Pete 217-351-5327
pjones@news-gazette.com, Circulation Director, News-Gazette Inc., IL, Champaign
Jones, Tracy ....(239) 335-0236
tjones@news-press.com, Grandeur Ed., The News-Press, FL, Fort Myers
Jones, Dan
djones@crain.com, Editorial Asst., Crain News Service (includes Automotive News Syndicate), MI, Detroit
Jones, Brian
brian.jones@wninews.com, Circ. Mgr., Waxahachie Daily Light, TX, Waxahachie
Jones, Deidre 903-675-6397
dbjones@tvcc.edu, Media Instructor/Adviser, Trinity Valley Cmty. College, TX, Athens
Jones, Harold ....(719) 275-7565
hjones@ccdailyrecord.com, Circ. Mgr., The Canon City Daily Record, CO, Canon City
Jones, Leween 321-242-3541
ljones3@floridatoday.com, Retail Sales Manager, Florida Today, FL, Melbourne
Jones, Hugh
hjones@t-g.com, Pub., Shelbyville Times-Gazette, TN, Shelbyville
Jones, Pete
pjones@news-gazette.com, President, Central States Circulation Managers Association, IL, Glasford
Jones, John M. ....(423) 359-3129
john.jones@jonesmedia.com, Ed., The Greeneville Sun, TN, Greeneville
Jones, Gregg K.
gjones@xtn.net, President and CEO, Jones Media, Inc., TN, Greeneville
Jones, Earl ....(757) 934-9607
Adv. Dir., Suffolk News-Herald, VA, Suffolk
Jones, Christopher ....(225) 771-2464
Southern Univ. A&M College, LA, Baton Rouge
Jones, Howard
hjones@news-banner.com, Prodn. Supt., News-Banner, IN, Bluffton
Jones, John M.
john@newspaperconsultants.com, Vice President, Advantage Newspaper Consultants, NC, Fayetteville
Jones, Trevor ....(740) 450-6766
Photo Ed., Times Recorder, OH, Zanesville
Jones, Rita
ritaj@npgco.com, Prodn. Foreman, Paste-Up, Atchison Globe, KS, Atchison
Jones, Paula
pjones@thetimestribune.com, Data Processing Mgr., Times-Tribune, KY, Corbin
Jones, Sam ....(770) 253-1576
sam@newnan.com, Pub., The Times-Herald, GA, Newnan
Jones, Chris ....(417) 667-3344 ext. 20
Prodn. Mgr., The Nevada Weekend Herald-Tribune, MO, Nevada
Prodn. Mgr., The Nevada Daily Mail, MO, Nevada
Jones, Robbie ....(901) 529-2751
jones@commercialappeal.com, Mgr., Purchasing, The Commercial Appeal, TN, Memphis
Jones, Sue ....(412) 320-7946
sjones@tribweb.com, News Ed., Pittsburgh, Tribune-Review, PA, Pittsburgh
Jones, Ester ....(903) 237-7797
ejones@longview-news.com, Prodn. Mgr., Mailroom, Longview News-Journal, TX, Longview
Jones, Erin ....(616) 222-5680
ejones@grpress.com, Adv. Coord., Interactive Sales, The Grand Rapids Press, MI, Grand Rapids
Jones, Mark ....(204) 571-7448
Prodn. Foreman, Mail Room (Day), Brandon Sun, MB, Brandon
Jones, Mike ....(479) 271-3724
aronline@arkansasonline.com, Ed., Benton County Daily Record, AR, Bentonville
Jones, William
wjones@adspies.com, Pres., Advertising Data Scan/Adspies.com, FL, Jacksonville
Jones, Sherrie ....(770) 535-6304
sjones@gainesvilletimes.com, Adv. Dir., The Times, GA, Gainesville
Jonker, Ulko
ujonker@fd.nl, Ed., HET FINANCIEELE DAGBLAD, Amsterdam
Jordan, Annette ....(336) 626-6140
ajordan@courier-tribune.com, News Ed., The Courier-Tribune, NC, Asheboro
Jordan, Phil ....(309) 686-3026
pjordan@pjstar.com, Mgr., Mktg./Pub. Affairs, Journal Star, IL, Peoria
Jordan, Adam ....(501) 378-4579
ajordan@ardemgaz.com, Mgr., Accounting, Arkansas Democrat-Gazette, AR, Little Rock
Jordan, Wilma
wilmaj@jegi.com, CEO, Jordan, Edmiston Group, Inc., NY, New York
Jordan, Pat ....(580) 765-3311
ads@poncacitynews.com, Adv. Mgr., The Ponca City News, OK, Ponca City
Jordan, Robert A.
bjordan@themediaaudit.com, Pres., International Demographics/The Media Audit, TX, Houston
Jorde, Paul
pjorde@perretta.com, Serv. Mgr., Perretta Graphics Corp., NY, Poughkeepsie
Jorgensen, Jeanie
jjorgensen@appliedart.com, Media Mgr., Applied Art & Technology, IA, Des Moines
Jorgenson, Vickie 605-394-8303
vickie.jorgenson@rapidcityjournal.com, Controller, Rapid City Journal, SD, Rapid City
Jose Torres, Maria
maria-jose.torres@publicitas.com, Sales Mktg. Mgr., Charney/Palacios & Co., FL, Miami
Joseph, Jason
jjoseph@yourwestvalley.com, Pub., Daily News-Sun, AZ, Sun City
jjoseph@yourwestvalley.com, Ahwatukee Foothills News, AZ, Phoenix
jjoseph@yourwestvalley.com, Glendale-Peoria Today , AZ, Sun City
Joseph, Tracy
info@interactivepartner.com, Contact, Interactive Media Partners, CA, Fountain Valley
Josh, Pradeep
info@jaihindnewspaper.com, Adv. Mgr., JAI HIND, Rajkot, Gujarat
Joshi, Ravi
rjoshi@expressbuzz.com, Ed., INDIAN EXPRESS, Bangalore, Karnataka
Joshi, Rahul
rahul.joshi@timesgroup.com, Ed. in Chief, THE ECONOMIC TIMES, New Delhi
Joshi, Rahul
rahul.joshi@timesgroup.com, Exec. Ed., THE ECONOMIC TIMES, Mumbai, Maharashtra
Joshua, P.J.
editorial@mm.co.in, Ed., MALAYALA MANORAMA, Calicut, Kerala
Joslin, Jean
sales@trginc.com, Dir., TRG, Inc., NC, Raleigh
Joslin, Jan ....(843) 863-8042
Charleston Southern Univ., SC, Charleston
Joslin, Ben ....(617) 779-8900 ext. 2123
bjoslin@domania.com, Vice Pres., Mktg., Domania, Inc., MA, Watertown
Joss, Molly 484-529-95472
Publisher, Editor, Owner, The Seybold Report
Jost, Shannon ....(712) 546-7031 ext. 28
dsprepress@frontier.net, Composition Mgr., Le Mars Daily Sentinel, IA, Le Mars
Jost, Monte ....(712) 546-7031 ext. 31
mjost@lemarscomm.net, Mktg. Dir., Le Mars Daily Sentinel, IA, Le Mars
Jouahri, Mohamed
m.jouahri@lematin.ma, Dir., LE MATIN DU SAHARA ET DU MAGHREB, Casablanca
Joubert, Anthony 613-933-3160
readersales@standard-freeholder.com, Circ. Dir., Standard-Freeholder, ON, Cornwall
Jovanovic, Bojan
cws@cartoonweb.com, Assoc. Ed., Cartoonists & Writers Syndicate/Cartoon Arts International - Rancho Palos Verdes, CA, CA, Rancho Palos Verdes
Jow, Lauren
editor@media.ucla.edu, Ed. in Chief, Univ. of California Los Angeles, CA, Los Angeles
Joyce, Marion
marion.joyce@verizon.net, Pres., Marion Joyce, NY, Bronxville
Joyce, Denise
djoyce@tribune.com, Pres., American Association of Sunday and Feature Editors, MD, College Park
Joyce, Michael A. ....(570) 628-6049
mjoyce@republicanherald.com, Adv. Dir., Republican Herald, PA, Pottsville
Joyce, Mike ....ext. 222
mike_j@newsitem.com, Adv. Dir., The News-Item, PA, Shamokin
Joyce, Janet ....(570) 628-6145
jjoyce@republicanherald.com, Dir., Mktg./Community Serv., Republican Herald, PA, Pottsville
Joyce, Dennis ....(520) 573-4224
djoyce@azstarnet.com, Asst. Mng. Ed., Arizona Daily Star, AZ, Tucson
Jozsef, Mihovics
zalaihirlap@zh.plt.hu, Mgr., ZALAI HIRLAP, Zalaegerszeg, Zala
Juagardo, Carlos
redaccion1@diariojornada.com, Ed., Diario Jornada, Trelew, Provincia de Chubut
Juarez, Alfonso
info@sipiapa.org, Librarian, Inter American Press Association, FL, Miami
Juaristi, Francisco 844 438 1800
fjuaristi@hotmail.com, Presidente y Director General, ZOCALO, Saltillo, Coahuila
Judah, Glenn
gjudah@mysanfordherald.com, Ed., Sanford Herald, FL, Sanford
Judd, Don ....ext. 677
it@svherald.com, IT Mgr., Sierra Vista Herald, AZ, Sierra Vista
Judd, Sara ....(314) 935-6713
Washington Univ., MO, Saint Louis
Judge, Bernie ....(312) 644-7800
displayads@lbpc.com, Consultant , Chicago Daily Law Bulletin
Judson, David
david.judson@tdn.co.tr, Ed., TURKISH DAILY NEWS
Judson, David
david.judson@hurriyet.com.tr, Ed. in Chief, HURRIYET
Judson, David
tdn@tdn.com.tr, Ed., HURRIYET DAILY NEWS
Juett, Cindy
cjuett@winchestersun.com, Adv. Mgr., The Winchester Sun, KY, Winchester
Juillier, Patrice
patricejuillier@courrier-ouest.com, Chief Ed., LE COURRIER DE L'OUEST, Angers
Julian, William
ahnews@awink.com, Adv. Mgr., Alaska Highway Daily News, BC, Fort Saint John
Julian, William
publisher@prbn.ca, Pub., Dawson Creek Daily News, BC, Dawson Creek
Julian, William
publisher@princerupertdailynews.ca, Pub., The Daily News, BC, Prince Rupert
Juliano, John
john.juliano@teradp.com, Mgr., Mktg./Reseller Relations, Tera D.P. S.r.l., Milano
Juliano, John
john@jjcs.com, Pres., John Juliano Computer Services Co., GA, Decatur
Julien, Aaron
ajulien@gazettenet.com, Pres./Pub., Daily Hampshire Gazette, MA, Northampton
Jumonville, Judy ....(225) 388-0304
jjumonville@theadvocate.com, Librarian, The Advocate, LA, Baton Rouge
Junco de la Vega, Alejandro
marpha.tarvino@elnorte.com, Pres., EL NORTE, Monterrey, Nuevo Leon
Jung, Mike
mjung2@santacruzsentinel.com, Pub., Santa Cruz Sentinel, CA, Scotts Valley
Jung, Pam ....(530) 477-4232
pamj@theunion.com, Entertainment Ed., The Union, CA, Grass Valley
Jungbauer, Dr. Helmuth
redaktion@fraenkischer-tag.de, Proprietor, FRANKISCHER TAG, Bamberg
Jungels, Allen 605-331-2399
ajungels@argusleader.com, Production Manager, Argus Leader, SD, Sioux Falls
Junger, Dr. Richard
richard.junger@wmich.edu, Prog. Dir., Western Michigan University, MI, Kalamazoo
Jungfer, Sigfried
redaktion@harzkurier.de, Proprietor, Harz Kurier, Osterode
Jurado, Jay
info@midwestdigital.com, CEO, Midwest Digital Communications, WI, Madison
Jurczyk, Rita ....ext. 1424
rita.jurczyk@uniontrib.com, Adv. Dir., Major Media Sales, The San Diego Union-Tribune, CA, San Diego
Jurkonis, Mary
mjurkonis@tahoedailytribune.com, Pub., Tahoe Daily Tribune, CA, South Lake Tahoe
Jurvelin, Markku
markku.jurvelin@kaleva.fi, Circ. Dir., KALEVA, Oulu
Just, Cameron ....(306) 651-6307
Tech. Officer, Saskatchewan Weekly Newspapers Association, SK, Saskatoon
Justegard, Jan
jan@tranasposten.se, Pub./Ed., TRANAS-POSTEN, Tranas
Justesen, DeAnn ....(805) 437-0207
dajustesen@venturacountystar.com, Asst. Mng. Ed., Ventura County Star, CA, Camarillo
Justin, Heela ....(212) 790-0283
Cardozo School of Law/Yeshiva, NY, New York
Juul, Torben
tj@ccieurope.com, Vice Pres., Mktg., CCI Europe, Inc., GA, Kennesaw

K

Kabat, Bruce
bkabat@wacotrib.com, Asst. Mng. Ed., Waco Tribune-Herald, TX, Waco
Kabir, Ahmadul
sangbad@gononet.com, Ed., SANGBAD, Dhaka
Kachala, Jay Sivin
jsivinkachala@iesdinc.com, Vice Pres., Interactive Educational Systems Design, Inc., NY, New York
Kacich, Tom ....(217) 351-5221
tkacich@news-gazette.com, Columnist, News-Gazette Inc., IL, Champaign
Kaczmarek, Jackie
jkaczmarek@hanfordsentinel.com, Mng. Ed., The Sentinel, CA, Hanford
Kaczmarek, Marty
mkaczmarek@technotrans.com, Technical Sales Mgr., Technotrans America, Inc., IL, Mount Prospect
Kada, Yasuhidea
c-nippon@j-link.ne.jp, Pres., CHIBA NIPPO, Chiba, Kanto
Kader, Ramadan Abdel
gazette-editor@hotmail.com, Ed. in Chief, AL MISSA', Cairo
Kaggwa, Lawrence
lkaggwa@howard.edu, District Chronicles, DC, Washington
lkaggwa@howard.edu, Prof., Howard University, DC, Washington
Kahan, Jonathan
jonathan.kahan@dowjones.com, CFO, Dow Jones Local Media Group, NY, Middletown
Kahana, Leslie 423.757.6514
lkahana@timesfreepress.com, Advertising Director, Chattanooga Times Free Press, TN, Chattanooga
Kahn, A. David
kahn@artistmarket.com, CEO/Ed., ArtistMarket.com, MI, Farmington Hills
Kahoun, Jane ....(216) 999-4824
Deputy Metro Editor State, The Plain Dealer, OH, Cleveland
Kaija, Barbara
bkaija@newvision.co.ug, Ed. in Chief, NEW VISION, Kampala
Kaim, Wayne...........................(608) 592-7404
Mktg., Advanced Graphic Systems (AGS), CA, Grass Valley
Kaim, Wayne
wayne@kaiminc.com, Pres., Kaim & Associates International Marketing, Inc., WI, Lodi
Kaiser, Gina 321-242-3740
gkaiser@floridatoday.com, Strategic Marketing Solutions Director, Florida Today, FL, Melbourne
Kaiser, Howard A.......................(906) 632-2235
enpub@sooeveningnews.com, Pub., The Evening News, MI, Sault Sainte Marie
Kaiser, Mike
mkaiser@cincypost.com, Asst. Mng. Ed., News, The Kentucky Post, OH, Cincinnati
Kaiser, Glenn ....(780) 468-0259
glenn.kaiser@edm.sunpub.com, Info. Serv. Mgr., The Edmonton Sun, AB, Edmonton
Kaitouni, Muhammad Idrissi
lopinion@lopinion.ma, Dir., L'OPINION, Rabat
Kajihara, Sumitsugu
newsroom@emb.asahi-np.co.jp, Nagoya Head Officer, ASAHI SHIMBUN, Nagoya, Chubu
Kajunori, Aray
k.arai@sankei.co.jp, Asst. Dir., NIHON KOGYO SHIMBUN, Tokyo
Kalaitzakis, John
info@kritet.gr, Pub., KRITIKI EPITHEORISSIS, Rethymnon, Crete
Kalbfleisch, Eric.......................(613) 596-8596
ekalbfleisch@thecitizen.southam.ca, Adv. Mgr., Classified/Career/Category Sales, The Ottawa Citizen, ON, Ottawa
Kalenak, JoeAnn
hcnsyndicate@hcnsyndicate.org, Syndicate Representative, High Country News, CO, Paonia
Kalich, Tim
tkalich@gwcommonwealth.com, Editorial Page Ed., The Greenwood Commonwealth, MS, Greenwood
Kalina, David ....ext. 320
dkalina@innotek-ep.com, Vice Pres., Finance, Innotek Corporation, MN, Maple Grove
Kalinaki, Daniel
dkalinaki@ug.nationmedia.com, Mng. Ed., THE MONITOR, Kampala
Kalinowski, Linda ....ext. 201
Acct. Mgr., Newsfinder, WI, Waukesha
Kalivouris, Pierre
info@proodos.net, Pub,/Dir., PROODOS, Rhodos, Aegean Islands
Kalkowski, Jens
j.kalkowski@han-online.de, Ed. In Cheif, Harburger Anzeigen und Nachrichten, Hamburg
Kalkowski, Elizabeth..................(217) 337-8365
Univ. of Illinois, IL, Champaign
Kallan, Richard A.
rakallan@csupomona.edu, Chair, California State Polytechnic University, Pomona, CA, Pomona
Kallmayer, Morten
morten.kallmayer@jp.dk, Adv. Mgr., MORGENAVISEN JYLLANDS-POSTEN, Viby, Jutland
Kallstrom, Anders
anders.kallstrom@allehanda.se, Mgr., ORNSKOLDSVIKS ALLEHANDA, Ornskoldsvik
Kalmann, Arjeh
a.kalmann@ad.nl, Ed. in Chief, UTRECHTS NIEUWSBLAD/DAGBLAD RIVERENLAND, Houten, Utrecht
Kalmann, A.
un.redactie@ad.nl, Ed., AMERSFOORTSE COURANT/UTRECHTS NIEUWSBLAD, Houten
Kalmbach, Fred ....(225) 388-0313
fkalmbach@theadvocate.com, Mng. Ed., The Advocate, LA, Baton Rouge
Kalyango, Yusuf.......................(740) 597-3335
Asst. Prof./Dir., Inst. for Int'l Journalism, Ohio University, OH, Athens
Kam, Karl ....(212) 557-1133 ext. 13
karl.kam@iaaglobal.org, Mgr. IT., International Advertising Association, Inc., NY, New York
Kamage, Paul J. ....ext. 12
pkamage@brodiesystem.com, Plant Mgr., Brodie System, Inc., NJ, Linden
Kamal, Mustapha
mustaphakamal@nstp.com.my, Ed. in Chief, BUSINESS TIMES, Kuala Lumpur
Kamarul Baid, Datuk Mior
mkamarul@nstp.com.my, Ed., BERITA HARIAN, Kuala Lumpur
Kamen, Kevin B. ....(516) 379-2797
info@kamengroup.com, Pres./CEO, Kamen & Co. Group Services, NY, Uniondale
Kamen, Kevin B. ....(516) 379-2797
info@kamengroup.com, Pres./CEO, Kamen & Co. Group Services, NY, Uniondale
Kamen, Kevin Brian 516-379-2797
info@KamenGroup.com, Pres., Kevin Brian Kamen & Co. (Kamen & Co. Group Services), NY, Uniondale
Kamen, Charles ....(303) 954-6396
ckamen@medianewsgroup.com, Vice Pres., HR, MediaNews Group Inc, CO, Denver
Kaminishi, Akio
webmaster@mainichi.co.jp, Mng. Dir./Seibu Head Officer, MAINICHI SHIMBUN, Kitakyushu, Kyushu
Kaminski, Robert ....ext. 208
Press. Mgr., The Pioneer - Big Rapids, MI, Big Rapids
Kamperos, Theodoros
news@imeranews.gr, Ed. in Chief, IMERA, Patras, Peloponnese
Kampman, Kevin
kevin.kampman@cantonrep.com, Pub., The Repository, OH, Canton
Kampman, Kevin......................(330) 580-8451
Regional VP - Great Lakes, GateHouse Media Inc., NY, Fairport
Kanaly, Drew
kanaly@kanaly.com, Chairman/CEO, Kanaly Trust Co., TX, Houston
Kane, Michael S.......................(302) 324-2738
mkane@delawareonline.com, Vice Pres., Circ., The News Journal, DE, New Castle
Kane, Liz
lkane@mtdemocrat.net, Sports Ed., Mountain Democrat, CA, Placerville
Kane, Michael
michael.kane@indystar.com, Pres./Pub., The Indianapolis Star, IN, Indianapolis
Kanelis, John ....(806) 345-3358
john.kanelis@amarillo.com, Editorial Page Ed., Amarillo Globe-News, TX, Amarillo
Kaney, Georgia M.
georgia.kaney@news-jrnl.com, Pres./CEO/Pub., Daytona Beach News-Journal, FL, Daytona Beach
Kang, Chua Chim
chuackg@sph.com.sg, Ed., LIANHE WANBAO, Singapore
Kang, Kuik Cheng
editorial@mail.sinchew.com.my, Deputy Exe. Ed. in Chief, SIN JEW JIT PHO, Petaling Jaya
Kang, Tricia ....(212) 556-5156
tricia.kang@nytimes.com, Mktg. Mgr., New York Times News Service, NY, New York
tricia.kang@nytimes.com, Mktg. Mgr., New York Times Syndicate, NY, New York
Kangas, Seppo
seppo.kangas@kalajokilaakso.fi, Mgr., KALAJOKILAAKSO, Ylivieska
Kanick, Robert W.
rwkanick@indianagazette.net, Controller, The Indiana Gazette, PA, Indiana
Kannapan, S.
dinamalarnews@gmail.com, Mng. Ed., DINAMALAR, Erode, Tamil Nadu
Kannberg, Daryl ....(216) 999-4865
Deputy Managing Editor, The Plain Dealer, OH, Cleveland
Kaori, Koji tail
bunsha@naigai-times.net, Pres./CEO, NAIGAI TIMES, Tokyo
Kaplan, Adam..........................(305) 347-6680
akaplan@alm.com, Audience Development Manager, Palm Beach Daily Business Review, FL, West Palm Beach
Kaplan, Thomas
editor@yaledailynews.com, Yale Univ., CT, New Haven
Kaplan, Susan
susank@abelson.com, Vice Pres., Abelson Communications, Inc., NY, Rockville Centre
Kaplan, Adam..........................(305) 347-6680
akaplan@alm.com, Audience Development Manager, Miami Daily Business Review, FL, Miami
Kaplan, Jackie........................(305) 376-2398
miamisales@miamiherald.com, Interactive Sales Mgr., The Miami Herald, FL, Miami
Kappel, Joanne............(864) 370-1800 ext. 2738
Bob Jones Univ., SC, Greenville
Kapperman, Christine
ckapperman@reporter-herald.com, Mng. Ed., Daily Reporter-Herald, CO, Loveland
Kappes, John ....(216) 999-4724
Deputy Features Editor, The Plain Dealer, OH, Cleveland
Kapral, Robert
bkapral@timesleaderonline.com, Mng. Ed., The Times Leader, OH, Martins Ferry
Karaffa, Eric
chi_sales@parade.com, Vice Pres./Mid-Western Mgr., Parade Publications, Inc. - Chicago, IL, IL, Chicago
Karafin, Ron ....(856) 486-2450
rkarafin@courierpostonline.com, Photo Ed., Courier-Post, NJ, Cherry Hill
Karapanayiotis, Leon
tanea@dolnet.gr, Dir., TA NEA, Athens, Central Greece
Karg y de Juamblez, Alfonzo Gonzalez
agkarg@elsiglodetorreon.com.mx, Asst. Pub., EL SIGLO DE TORREON, Torreon, Coahuila
Karger, Claude
journal@journal.lu, Ed. in Chief, LETZEBUERGER JOURNAL, Luxembourg
Karim, Zeenat
jayzedkay@yahoo.com, Owner, THE INDEPENDENT, Blantyre
Karis, Kostas
k.karis@avgi.gr, Ed., AVGI, Athens, Central Greece
Karius, Joe ....(906) 932-2211 ext. 111
jkarius@chartermi.net, Pub., The Daily Globe, MI, Ironwood
Karl, Heidi
heidik@hollistercreative.com, Art Dir., Hollister Kids, PA, Wynnewood
Karlan, Mark............................212-969-7572
mkarlan@hearst.com, Director of Marketing, King Features Syndicate, NY, New York
Karlinsey, Kay
kkarlinsey@eastoregonian.com, Production Manager, East Oregonian, OR, Pendleton
Karlon, Marty ....(603) 594-6400
karlonm@telegraph-nh.com, Sunday Ed., The Telegraph, NH, Hudson
Karlovec, Lucien B.
editor@dln.com, Chrmn./Pres./Pub., The Daily Legal News and Cleveland Recorder
Karlsen, Sveim
svein.karlsen@namdalsavisa.no, Ed., NAMDALS-AVISA A/S, Namsos
Karlson, Bruce..........................937-225-2249
bkarlson@coxohiomedia.com, Sales Manager - National/Major, Dayton Daily News, OH, Dayton
Karlson, Bruce........................(937) 225-2249
bkarlson@coxohiomedia.com, Sales Manager - National/ Major, Dayton Daily News, OH, Dayton
Karlsson, Magnus
magnus.karlsson@smp.se, Ed., SMALANDSPOSTEN, Vaxjo
Karlsson, Peter
peter.karlsson@dt.se, Adv. Mgr, FALU KURIREN, Falun
Karnen, Rusan
runarusan@yahoo.com, Ed., CUVANTUL LIBERTATII, Craiova, Dolj
Karnes, Cheryl
ckarnes@times-standard.com, Copy Desk Chief, Times-Standard, CA, Eureka
Karpel, Richard
rkarpel@asne.org, Exec. Dir., American Society of News Editors, VA, Reston
Karpen, Jim ....(641) 472-0778
jkarpen@mum.edu, Maharishi Univ. of Mgmt., IA, Fairfield
Karpenko, Vitaliy
office@vechirniykyiv.com, Ed. in Chief, VECHIRNIY KYIV, Kiev, Ukraine
Karst, Mary..................(785) 628-1081 ext. 118
maryk_ads@dailynews.net, Adv. Dir., The Hays Daily News, KS, Hays
Karstensen, Kari
kk@finnmarken.no, Ed., FINNMARKEN, Vadsoe
Kart, Jeff...............................(989) 894-9639
jkart@bc-times.com, Political/Gov't Ed., The Bay City Times, MI, Bay City
Kartha, Hari S.
janmabhumi97@rediffmail.com, Ed.-in-Cheif, JANMABHUMI, Cochin, Kerala
Kartis, Ray
rkartis@scnl.com, Circ. Mgr., Regl., The Herald News, IL, Joliet
Karununean, Lilian..........................885-0288
Lilian.Karununean@dowjones.com, Correspondent, Dow Jones Newswires - Manila, Philippines, Manila
Karwaki, Taduz
arabtimes@arabtimesonline.com, Mng. Ed., ARAB TIMES
Karwath, Rob
karwath@duluthnews.com, Exec. Ed., Duluth News Tribune, MN, Duluth
Kasabian, Robert J. ....ext. 104
bkasabian@infe.org, Vice Pres./Exec. Dir., Media Financial Management Association, IL, Northfield
Kasate, Teresa........................(314) 340-8922
tkasate@post-dispatch.com, Purchasing Mgr., St. Louis Post-Dispatch, MO, Saint Louis
Kasbohm, Paul ....(612) 673-7207
Paul.Kasbohm@startribune.com, Adv. Vice Pres., Sales, Star Tribune, MN, Minneapolis
Kash, Shannon ....(816) 887-5831
pppoffice@aol.com, Vice Pres., Precision Pressroom Products, Inc., MO, Harrisonville
Kaskan, Mary ....ext. 2397
mkaskan@wdt.net, Sunday Ed., Watertown Daily Times, NY, Watertown
Kaskovich, Steve ....(817) 390-7773
skaskovich@star-telegram.com, Asst. Mng. Ed., Bus., Fort Worth Star-Telegram, TX, Fort Worth
Kaspar, Michael
mkaspar@zsz.ch, Dir., LINTH ZEITUNG, Rapperswil
Kaspar, David...........................(361)594-2911

dckaspar@shorack.com, President, Kaspar Wire Works, Inc./Sho-Rack, TX, Shiner
Kasper, Dr. Jeffrey S.........(925) 798-0896 ext. 15
jk@service-quality.com, Pres., ServiceQuality.US, CA, Concord
Kasper, Valerie ....(352) 588-8294
St. Leo Univ., FL, Saint Leo
Kasper, Rita
rksh@vrm.de, Sec., ALLGEMEINE ZEITUNG, Mainz
Kaspryzk, Joseph ....ext. 244
Editorial Writer., Butler Eagle, PA, Butler
Kasten, Judy
jkasten@strato.net, Adv. Dir., Okeechobee News, FL, Okeechobee
Kasten, Daniel............(330) 747-1471 ext. 1215
dkasten@vindy.com, Adv. Dir., The Vindicator, OH, Youngstown
Kastner, John ....(519) 271-2220 ext. 202
jkastner@gbowesnet.com, Mng. Ed., The Beacon-Herald, ON, Stratford
Kastner, Jill Watry ....(310) 825-9437
Univ. of California Law School, CA, Los Angeles
Kastrup, Thom ....(402) 444-1429
thom.kastrup@owh.com, Adv. Dir., Omaha World-Herald, NE, Omaha
Katajamaki, Pasi
pasi.katajamaki@raplamaasuomi.fi, Ed. in Chief, LANSI-SUOMI, Rauma
Katsiabas, Elias L.
erevna@otenet.gr, Pub., EREVNA, Trikala, Thessaly
Katsipanelis, D.
vima_pr@otenet.gr, Pub., VIMA TIS PREVEZAS, Preveza, Epirus
Katz, Bernard ....(302) 658-6945
telesonics@aol.com, Pres., Telesonic Packaging Corp., Ames Engineering Div., DE, Wilmington
Katz, Harry Jay ....(215) 849-9016
hjaykatz@aol.com, Pub./Ed. in Chief, National News Bureau, PA, Philadelphia
Katz, Linda
marketing@buschinc.com, Mktg. Specialist, Busch, Inc., VA, Virginia Beach
Katzeff, Dottie ....(415) 338-3133
San Francisco State Univ., CA, San Francisco
Katzinger, Harald
hka@teufelberger.com, Mgr., Mktg./Sales Agriculture, Teufelberger GmbH, Wels
Kauffman, Bette J.
kauffman@ulm.edu, Dept. Head/Assoc. Prof., University of Louisiana at Monroe, LA, Monroe
Kauffman, Kermit ....(813) 259-7700
Vice Pres., Admin., The Tampa Tribune, FL, Tampa
Kauffman, Diane ....(916) 278-6583
California State Univ. Sacramento, CA, Sacramento
Kausler, Donald H....................(864) 260-1249
kauslerdh@independentmail.com, Ed., Anderson Independent-Mail, SC, Anderson
Kavanaugh, James....................(330) 996-3853
jkavanagh@thebeaconjournal.com, Copy Desk Chief, Akron Beacon Journal, OH, Akron
Kay, Ron ....(307) 266-0506
ron.kay@trib.com, Controller, Casper Star-Tribune, WY, Casper
Kay, Richard ....(850) 599-2231
rkay@tallahassee.com, Circ. Mgr., Tallahassee Democrat, FL, Tallahassee
Kaylor, Steve
skaylor@reidsvillereview.com, Pub., The Eden Daily News, NC, Reidsville
Kaylor, Steven K.
skaylor@reidsvillereview.com, Pub., The Reidsville Review, NC, Reidsville
Kays, Mike ....(918) 684-2904
mkays@muskogeephoenix.com, Sports Ed., Muskogee Daily Phoenix & Times Democrat, OK, Muskogee
Kazarian-Hodder, Loise
lkazarian@thesuntimes.ca, Adv. Dir., The Sun Times, ON, Owen Sound
Kazek, Kelly
kelly@athensnews-courier.com, Mng. Ed., The News-Courier, AL, Athens
Kazibut, Elzibieta 358 2104
redakcja@dz.com.pl, Ed. in Chief, DZIENNIK ZACHODNI, Katowice
Kazismierczak, Zbigniew
info@mediatel.pl, Pres., SZTANDAR MLODYCH, Warsaw
Kazuo, Furukawa
surukawa@shinmai.co.jp, Adv. Mgr., SHINANO MAINICHI SHIMBUN, Nagano, Chubu
Kealing, Jonathan 785-832-7221
jkealing@ljworld.com, The World Co.- Lawrence, Kan., Journal-World, KS, Lawrence
Keane, Jeff
crowsegal@crowsegal.com, Pres., National Cartoonists Society, FL, Maitleand
Keane, Connie ....(302) 998-1650
keane@motormatters.biz, President, AutoWriters Associates, Inc. (dba Motor Matters), DE, Wilmington
Keane, Robert ....(631) 843-2781
Vice Pres./Mng. Ed., Newsday, NY, Melville
Keane, Kevin...........................(415) 777-8443
kkeane@sfchronicle.com, Business Editor, San Francisco Chronicle, CA, San Francisco
Kearney, J. Michael ....(207) 990-8212
Adv. Mgr., Sales, Bangor Daily News, ME, Bangor
Kearsey, David ....(709) 637-4670
dkearsey@thewesternstar.com, Sports Ed., The Western Star, NL, Corner Brook
Kearsley, Kelly ....(253) 597-8573
kelly.kearsley@thenewstribune.com, Trade/Ports/Jobs Reporter, The News Tribune, WA, Tacoma
Keating, Kevin ....(415) 331-7700
Author, Silver Bird Travel Features, CA, Sausalito
Keckeisen, Kevin......................951-827-3460
Managing Editor, Univ. of California, Riverside Highlander Newspaper, CA, Riverside
Kee, Chua
uniteddailynews@yahoo.com, Ed., United Daily News, Inc., Manila
Keebaugh, Kent............(780) 532-1110 ext. 274
kentk@bowesnet.com, Pub., Daily Herald-Tribune, AB, Grande Prairie
Keeble, Jim ....(205) 325-3214
Circ. Asst. Dir., The Birmingham News, AL, Birmingham
Keegan, Tom...........................785-832-7147
tkeegan@ljworld.com, Sports Editor, The World Co.- Lawrence, Kan., Journal-World, KS, Lawrence
Keegan, Tom...........................(785) 832-7147
tkeegan@ljworld.com, Sports Ed., The World Co.- Lawrence, Kan., Journal-World, KS, Lawrence
Keeley, Roger
roger_keeley@atlantic.ca, Mktg. Mgr., Atlantic Packaging Products Ltd., ON, Scarborough
Keem, Dennis..........................(708) 824-9600
mccainbind@earthlink.net, Vice Pres./Gen. Mgr., McCain Bindery Systems, IL
Keena, Brian ....(813) 259-7438
Circ. Mgr., Systems, The Tampa Tribune, FL, Tampa
Keenan, Diane.........................(910) 343-2321
diane.keenan@starnewsonline.com, Adv. Dir., Star-News, NC, Wilmington
Keenan, Debra B.
debbi@keenangroup.com, Vice Pres., Sales/Mktg., The Keenan Group, Inc., TN, Pleasant View
Keenan, Robert P......................615-945-5698
Pres., The Keenan Group, Inc., TN, Pleasant View
Keenan, Peter
hr@htivs.com, CEO, HTI Voice & Internet Solutions, Inc., MA, Marlborough
Keep, Paul M. ....(616) 222-5508
pkeep@grpress.com, Ed., The Grand Rapids Press, MI, Grand Rapids
Keever, Paul
speedyon@aol.com, Pres./CEO, American International Communications, Inc., CA, Long Beach
Kehias, Jonell ....(309) 820-3350
jkehias@pantagraph.com, Mktg. Servs. Mgr., The Pantagraph, IL, Bloomington
Kehl, Lisa ....(740) 376-5426
lkehl@mariettatimes.com, Classified Inside Sales Mgr., The Marietta Times, OH, Marietta
Keim, Henry
hkeim@breezenewspapers.com, Prodn. Mgr., Press, Cape Coral Breeze, FL, Cape Coral
Keim, Julie
jkeim@oleantimesherald.com, Adv. Mgr., Nat'l, Olean Times Herald, NY, Olean
Keister, Hilda L...............................ext. 149
dkeister@nvdaily.com, Sec., Northern Virginia Daily, VA, Strasburg
Keisuke, Hama
info@nagano-np.co.jp, Dir./Advisor, NAGANO NIPPO, Suwa, Chubu
Keith, Janice
jkeith@dailyhome.com, Assoc. Ed., The Daily Home, AL, Talladega
Keith, Debbie ....(409) 683-5240
debbie.keith@galvnews.com, Adv. Mgr., Retail, The Galveston County Daily News, TX, Galveston
Keitlen, Matthew
info@spectrumhr.com, Exec. Vice Pres., SPECTRUM Human Resource Systems Corp., CO, Denver
Kellagher, Robert R...................(215) 269-5054
bkellagher@phillyburbs.com, Dir., Interactive Media, Calkins Media, PA, Levittown
Kellam, Gary ....(909) 888-6511
San Bernardino Valley College, CA, San Bernardino
Kellar, Patrick
pkellar@heraldargus.com, Pub., Herald-Argus, IN, La Porte
Kelleher, John ....(603) 543-3100 ext. 112
jkelleher@tsvmedia.net, Mng. Ed., Eagle Times, NH, Claremont
Keller, Gene
jsadvertising@daktel.com, Adv. Dir., The Jamestown Sun, ND, Jamestown
Keller, Mitch 212-556-4410
mikell@nytimes.com, Managing Editor News Services, New York Times News Service, NY, New York
Keller, Mark J.
mark@bryantimes.com, Circ. Mgr., The Bryan Times, OH, Bryan
Keller, James
info@lexeme.com, Vice Pres., LeXeme, Inc., MA, Cambridge
Keller, Mark ....(815) 965-0882
mark@a-americancompanies.com, Pres., A-American Machine & Assembly (Press Parts Div.), IL, Rockford
Keller, Mark............................301-733-5131
Sports Editor, The Herald-Mail, MD, Hagerstown
Keller, Kai
k.keller@marbacher-zeitung.zgs.de, Proprietor, MARBACHER ZEITUNG, Marbach
Keller, Jessica..........................541-823-4822
News Editor, Argus Observer, OR, Ontario
Keller, Teresa
tkeller@ehc.edu, Chair, Emory and Henry College, VA, Emory
Keller, Mark
mkeller@bryantimes.com, Circ. Mgr., Bryan Publishing Co., OH, Bryan
Keller, Bill
keller@nytimes.com, Exec. Ed., New England Newspaper Group, NY, New York
Kelley, Tracy
TracyK@lodinews.com, Ad Director, Lodi News-Sentinel, CA, Lodi
Kelley, Tim ....(608) 252-6115
tkelley@madison.com, On-Line Director, Wisconsin State Journal, WI, Madison
Kelley, Tracy
tkelley@ivpressonline.com, Adv. Dir., Imperial Valley Press, CA, El Centro
Kelley, Michael R.
mike.kelley@clantonadvertiser.com, Pres./Pub., The Clanton Advertiser, AL, Clanton
Kelley, Retta ....(519) 912-2959
rkelley@statesman.com, Dir., InfoVentures/Commun., Austin American-Statesman, TX, Austin
Kelley, Stuart
leaseguy@waymark.net, Contact, ACS Capital, TX, North Richland Hills
Kelley, Michael J.....................(702) 259-4181
kelley@lasvegassun.com, Mng. Ed., Las Vegas Sun, NV, Henderson
Kelley, Edgar
sports@theintermountain.com, Sports Ed., The Inter-Mountain, WV, Elkins
Kelling, Patrick ....(970) 521-6671
Northeastern Junior College, CO, Sterling
Kelly, Ray ....(413) 788-1291
Mng. Ed., Lifestyle, The Republican, MA, Springfield
Kelly, John 321-242-3660
jkelly@floridatoday.com, Local Editor, Florida Today, FL, Melbourne
Kelly, Kathy
kathy.kelly@news-jrnl.com, Asst. Mng. Ed., Metro, Daytona Beach News-Journal, FL, Daytona Beach
Kelly, Carolyn
ckelly@seattletimes.com, Pres./COO, Seattle Post-Intelligencer/Seattle Times, WA, Seattle
Kelly, Sheila Rouse ....ext. 11
skelly@stategazette.com, Pub., State Gazette, TN, Dyersburg
Kelly, Marguerite......................(202) 544-5698
marguerite.kelly@verizon.net, Self-Syndicator, Family Almanac, DC, Washington
Kelly, Doug...............................416-383-2482
Publisher, National Post, ON, Toronto
Kelly, Brian
customer.service@schlenkboth.com, Pres., Schlenk-Both Industries, MA, Ashland
Kelly, Tom ....(714) 796-3860
tkelly@ocregister.com, Vice Pres., Adv., The Orange County Register, CA, Santa Ana
Kelly, Timothy M. ....(859) 231-3100
hlnews@herald-leader.com, Pub./Pres., Lexington Herald-Leader, KY, Lexington
Kelly, Charles W.
ckelly@odg.com, Ed., The Courier-Observer, The Journal & The Advance-News, NY, Ogdensburg
Kelly, Charles W.
ckelly@ogd.com, Pub., The Malone Telegram, NY, Malone
Kelly, Kathleen
kathleen.kelly@tdirect.com, Pres./CEO, TeleDirect International, Inc., AZ, Scottsdale
Kelly, Mike
michael_kelly@newspapersupport.com, Pres., Newspaper Purchasing Management Association, Inc., DE, Wilmington
Kelly, Catherine ....(604) 249-3500
ckelly@bbm.ca, Vice Pres., Western Servs., BBM Canada, ON, Toronto
Kelly, Bob...................(785) 822-1483 ext. 505
bkelly@saljournal.com, Systems Mgr., The Salina Journal, KS, Salina
Kelly, Albert F.
info@necinfrontia.com, Gen. Mgr., NEC Infrontia, Inc., CT, Shelton
Kelly, Ruthie ....(619) 594-3906
San Diego State Univ., CA, San Diego
Kelly, Laurence A.
lk@maine.rr.com, Pres., Small Talk, MA, Boston
Kelly, Don ....(785) 843-9240
edwhite@eandedisplay.com, Acct. Exec., E and E Display Group, KS, Lawrence
Kelly, Carolyn S. ....(206) 464-2329
kcoughlin@seattletimes.com, Pres./COO, Seattle Times Co., WA, Seattle
Kelly, Ron ....(902) 629-6031
ron.kelly@theguardian.pe.ca, Controller, The Guardian, PE, Charlottetown
Kelly, Josh ....(308) 381-9471
josh.kelly@theindependent.com, Info Tech Mgr., The Grand Island Independent, NE, Grand Island
Kelly-Goss, Robert
rkelly-goss@coxnc.com, Albemarle Life Ed., The Daily Advance, NC, Elizabeth City
Kelsey, Stephen ....(801) 344-2912
skelsey@heraldextra.com, Circ. Dir., The Daily Herald, UT, Provo
Kelsh, James
jkelsh@capitolnewspapers.com, Pub., Daily Citizen, WI, Beaver Dam
jkelsh@capitolnewspapers.com, Beaver Dam - Monday Mini, WI, Beaver Dam
jkelsh@capitolnewspapers.com, Beaver Dam - Tri County, WI, Beaver Dam
Kelso, David ....(570) 420-4400
dkelso@poconorecord.com, Mgmt. Info Servs.

Mgr., Pocono Record, PA, Stroudsburg
Kemby, Don
rfccompany@aol.com, Pres., RFC Wire Forms, CA, Ontario
Kemp, Denise
dkemp@timesrepublican.com, Marketing Director, Times-Republican, IA, Marshalltown
Kemper, Alice
akemper@salestrainingconsultants.com, Pres., Sales Training Consultants, Inc., FL, Boca Raton
Kemper, Dan ....(847) 506-1942
dmk@schur.com, Dir., Sales, Schur Packaging Systems, Inc., IL, Schaumburg
Kempton, Austin
akempton@delgazette.com, Circulation Manager, The Delaware Gazette, OH, Delaware
Kendall, Don
jeff.ross@kcjn.com, Gen. Mgr., King County Publications, WA, Bellevue
Kendall, Joel..........................(580) 774-3083
The Southwestern, OK, Weatherford
Kendrick-Holmes, Dimon
dkholmes@ledger-enquirer.com, Metro Ed./Planning, Columbus Ledger-Enquirer, GA, Columbus
Kenedy, Beverly
circulation@vernonrecord.com, Circ. Coord., The Vernon Daily Record, TX, Vernon
Kenemer, Steve.......................(616) 546-1741
steve.kenemer@hollandsentinel.com, Circ. Mgr., The Holland Sentinel, MI, Holland
Kennard, David ....(419) 521-7204
chunnell@nncogannett.com, Mng. Ed., News Journal, OH, Mansfield
Kennedy, Maureen
moreinfo@ttmedia.com, Mktg. Dir., Thomson Target Media, IL, Chicago
Kennedy, Michael ....(502) 852-0663
Univ. of Louisville, KY, Louisville
Kennedy, Diane
dianenynpa@aol.com, Pres., New York Newspaper Publishers Association, NY, Albany
Kennedy, Michael D. ....(308) 432-6047
Advisor, The Eagle, NE, Chadron
Kennedy, Peter
peterk@bendigoadvertiser.com.au, Ed., BENDIGO ADVERTISER
Kennedy, Joyce Lain..................(760) 431-1660
jlk@sunfeatures.com, Pres., Sun Features, Inc., CA, Cardiff
Kennedy, Lesley......................(303) 892-5460
kennedyl@rockymountainnews.com, Fashion Ed., Rocky Mountain News, CO, Denver
Kennedy, Michelle ....ext. 235
Retail Sales Rep., The Barrie Examiner, ON, Barrie
Kennedy, Dave
dkennedy@starbulletin.com, Vice Pres., Mktg., Honolulu Star-Bulletin, HI, Honolulu
Kennedy, Chris.......................(715) 526 - 7006
ckennedy@shawanoleader.com, Regional Advertising Director, Shawano Leader, WI, Shawano
Kennedy, Natalie
nkennedy@therecordargus.com, Ed., The Record-Argus, PA, Greenville
Kennedy, Rick
rkennedy@record-bee.com, Ed., Lake County Record-Bee, CA, Lakeport
Kennedy, Eileen ....(603) 594-6499
kennedye@telegraph-nh.com, Bus. Ed., The Telegraph, NH, Hudson
Kennedy, Jason
jkennedy@times-standard.com, Prodn. Dir., Times-Standard, CA, Eureka
Kennedy, Dave.........................(808) 529-4818
dkennedy@staradvertiser.com, Senior Vice President, Marketing, Honolulu Star-Advertiser, HI, Honolulu
Kennedy, Jim
jkennedy@cvcaudit.com, Audit Mgr., Circulation Verification Council, MO, Saint Louis
Kennedy, William T.
william.kennedy@dowjones.com, COO, Dow Jones Local Media Group, NY, Middletown
Kenner, Natasha
nkenner@sla.org, Dir., Exec. Office Relations, Special Libraries Association, News Division, VA, Alexandria
Kenner, Herschel.....................(408) 278-3478
hkenner@mercurynews.com, Asst. Mng. Ed., Editing, San Jose Mercury News, CA, San Jose
Kenney, Elaine
soyink@soyink.com, Coord., Soy Ink, National Soy Ink Information Center, IA, Urbandale
Kenney, Trevor
trevor.kenney@lethbridgeherald.com, Sports Ed., The Lethbridge Herald, AB, Lethbridge
Kenniston, Betsy ....(419) 724-6312
bkenninston@toledoblade.com, Circ. Mgr., Single Copy, The Blade, OH, Toledo
Kenny, Jim ....(205) 391-2278
Shelton State Cmty. College, AL, Tuscaloosa
Kenny, Michael.........................(574) 224-5314
mkenny@rochsent.com, Photo Dept. Mgr., The Rochester Sentinel, IN, Rochester
Kenoly, Deitra 209-546-8238
Adv. Dir., The Record, CA, Stockton
Kent, Paul
paul.kent@scnews.com.au, Gen. Mgr., SUNSHINE COAST DAILY
Kent, Jill ....(602) 589-2569
Grand Canyon Univ., AZ, Phoenix
Kent, Scott ....(850) 747-5093
skent@pcnh.com, Editorial Page Ed., The News Herald, FL, Panama City
Kent, Scott ....(912) 652-0345
scott.kent@savannahnow.com, Editorial Writer, Savannah Morning News, GA, Savannah
Keough, Winfred 609-272-7238
wkeough@pressofac.com, Local Content Producer/News, The Press of Atlantic City, NJ, Pleasantville
Kepler, Peg ....(814) 837-6000
krnews1@verizon.net, Mgmt. Info Servs. Mgr., The Kane Republican, PA, Kane
Keplinger, Teresa ....(360) 735-4470
teresa.keplinger@columbian.com, Adv. Dir., The Columbian, WA, Vancouver
Kerkemeyer, Terra ....(618) 438-5611
terrak@clearwave.com, Adv. Mgr., Retail, Benton Evening News, IL, Benton
Kerkhov, Pascal
gvaredactie@concentra.be, Ed. in Chief, GAZET VON ANTWERPEN, Antwerpen
Kerkhove, Pascal
pkerkhove@concentra.be, Ed. in Chief, GAZET VAN ANTWERPEN, 2050 Antwerp
Kern, John P.
jkern@southtownstar.com, Sr. Vice Pres., SouthtownStar, IL, Tinley Park
Kern, Barkley 202-650-6414
bkern@cq.com, Vice President and Publisher, advocacy, state and transcripts
, Congressional Quarterly, Inc., DC, Washington
Kern, Frank
frankkern@us.ibm.com, Sr. Vice Pres./Grp. Exec., Sales, IBM Corp., NY, Somers
Kern, Arthur
info@ivyhill-wms.com, Exec. Vice Pres., Warner Media Services, NY, New York
Kerner, Water
info@lati2d.com, CCO, L@IT2'D (LATITUDE), CA, Los Angeles
Kerns, Mary Ann ....ext. 270
mary.kearns@lee.net, Ed., The Ledger Independent, KY, Maysville
Kerns, Richard
rkerns@solnaweb.com, Pres., Solna Web USA, Inc., KS, Lenexa
Kerntopf, Willy ....(250) 470-0705
willy.kerntopf@ok.bc.ca, Prodn. Vice Pres., Opns., The Daily Courier, BC, Kelowna
Kerr, Alec
alec@mountwashingtonvalley.com, Wire/Entertainment Ed., The Conway Daily Sun, NH, North Conway
Kerr, Scott
info@mediaspacesolutions.com, Pres., Media Space Inc., CT, Norwalk
Kerr, George "Buddy" ....(813) 259-7896
Mgr., Pressroom, The Tampa Tribune, FL, Tampa
Kerr, Susan.............................(860) 241-3730
skerr@courant.com, Circ. Mgr., Retail Sales, The Hartford Courant, CT, Hartford
Kerr, Alan...............................(215) 345-3049
Editorial Page Ed., The Intelligencer, PA, Doylestown
Kerr, John 951-368-5191
jkerr@pe.com, Dir Multimedia Sales Dev, The Press-Enterprise, CA, Riverside
Kerrigan, Pat..........................(608) 796-3041
Viterbo College, WI, La Crosse
Kerschinske, Rebecca
mascinfo@masclabels.com, Vice Pres. Mktg., Lauterbach Group, WI, Sussex
Kersey, Sharon
skersey@wnewsj.com, Adv. Dir., Wilmington News Journal, OH, Wilmington
Kershner, James ....(508) 362-2131 ext. 4734
jkershner@capecod.edu, Cape Cod Cmty. College, MA, West Barnstable
Kessel, Laura
lkessel@news-herald.com, Mng. Ed., The News-Herald, OH, Willoughby
Kessler, Slate ....(419) 734-2600
slate@parkpressdirect.com, Co-Owner, Scrambl-Gram, Inc., OH, Port Clinton
Kessler, Thomas
info@shz.de, Bus. Mgr., Stormarner Tageblatt, Badoldeslod
Kesterson, Tom.................................ext. 214
tkesterson@tribtown.com, Circ. Dir., The Tribune, IN, Seymour
Ketcham, Julie ....(804) 649-6014
jketcham@timesdispatch.com, South Zone Mgr., Richmond Times-Dispatch, VA, Richmond
Ketkar, Kumar
kumar.ketkar@expressindia.com, Ed., LOKASATTA, Mumbai, Maharashtra
Ketonen, Keijo
keijo.ketonen@ts.fi, MD, TURUN SANOMAT, Turku, Abo
Kevin, Torbjorn..............................274 9930
torbjorn.kevin@fabsy.fi, Ed. in Chief, ABO UNDERRATTELSER, Turku, Abo
Key, Stephen..........................(317) 624-4427
skey@hspa.com, Executive Director and General Counsel, Hoosier State Press Association, Inc., IN, Indianapolis
Key, Stephen..........................(317) 624-4427
skey@hspa.com, executive director and general counsel, Hoosier State Press Association, IN, Indianapolis
Keyes, David ....(208) 263-9534
dkeyes@cdapress.com, Pub., Bonner County Daily Bee, ID, Sandpoint
Keys, Scott ....(903) 885-8663
scott@ssecho.com, Pres./Pub., Sulphur Springs News-Telegram, TX, Sulphur Springs
Khader, Mohamed
yementimes@yementimes.com, Ed., YEMEN TIMES
Khahaifa, Avido........................(407) 420-5341
akhahaifa@orlandosentinel.com, Sr. Vice Pres./Gen. Mgr., Orlando Sentinel Communications, Orlando Sentinel, FL, Orlando
Khairat, Abdelhadi
liberation@mis.net.ma, Dir., LIBERATION, Casablanca
Khan, Kay ....(202) 383-7865
kay.khan@newhouse.com, Admin. Asst., Newhouse News Service, DC, Washington
Khan, Zahid Ali
siasat.daily@yahoo.com, Ed., SIASAT DAILY, Hyderabad, Andhra Pradesh
Khan, Maria
maria.khan@pakistantimes.net, Adv. Mgr., PAKISTAN TIMES, Islamabad
Khare, Harish
khare@hindu.co.in, Sr. Assoc. Ed., THE HINDU, Chennai
Khartoum, Dar El
technical_dept@khartoumnewspaper.com, Pub., AL KHARTOUM, Khartoum
Khatri, Kirtin Jayant
kirtikhatri@hotmail.com, Ed., KUTCHMITRA, Bhuj, Gujarat
Khawar, Saeed
saeed.khawar@hotmail.com, Ed., NAWA-E-WAQT, Karachi
Khorashadi-Zadeh, Marjan ....(310) 243-2312
California State Univ. Dominguez, CA, Carson
Kiczales, Ken ....(212) 930-8228
Adv. Mgr., Nat'l, New York Post, NY, New York
Kidder, Nancy
nancy@cheboygantribune.com, Adv. Mgr., Cheboygan Daily Tribune, MI, Cheboygan
Kidwell, David S.......................(570) 420-4499
dkidwell@poconorecord.com, Chief Photographer, Pocono Record, PA, Stroudsburg
Kieffer, Myra
myra.kieffer@macombdaily.com, Promotions Manager, The Macomb Daily, MI, Mount Clemens
Kiel, Jeff
jkiel@mercurynews.com, Chrmn./Pub., San Jose Mercury News, CA, San Jose
Kiely, Kathy 617-262-1100
kathy@adclub.org, Pres., The Ad Club, MA, Boston
Kienzler, Mike ....(217) 788-1519
mike.kienzler@sj-r.com, Night Metro Ed., The State Journal-Register, IL, Springfield
Kier, Brian ....(309) 686-3195
lkoenig@pjstar.com, Controller, Journal Star, IL, Peoria
Kiffer, Lecile
subscribe@ketchikandailynews.com, Circ. Mgr., Ketchikan Daily News, AK, Ketchikan
Kikuchi, Ikuo
info@hokkaido-np.co.jp, Chrmn., HOKKAIDO SHIMBUN, Sapporo, Hokkaido
Kilborne, G. Briggs
briggs.kilborne@harrisbaseview.com, Pres., Harris Publishing Systems, FL, Melbourne
Kilgallon, Patrick.....................(814) 870-1778
patrick.kilgallon@timesnews.com, Tech. Serv. Mgr., Erie Times-News, PA, Erie
Kilgore, Vickie ....(360) 754-4223
vkilgore@theolympian.com, Exec. Ed., The Olympian, WA, Olympia
Kilian, Dan ....(314) 340-8585
dkilian@post-dispatch.com, Adv. Dir., Admin., St. Louis Post-Dispatch, MO, Saint Louis
Killam, Jim
jkillam@niu.edu, Advisor, Northern Illinois Newspaper Association, IL, DeKalb
Killam, Jim.............................(815) 753-4239
Northern Illinois Univ., IL, Dekalb
Killgallon, David 252-407-9905
dkillgallon@rmtelegram.com, Circulation Sales & Marketing Mgr., Rocky Mount Telegram, NC, Rocky Mount
Killian, Rebecca.......................(724) 226-4669
rkillian@tribweb.com, Lifestyle Ed., Valley News Dispatch, PA, Tarentum
Killian, Michael F. ....(203) 317-2380
mkillian@record-journal.com, Sr. Vice Pres., Sales/Mktg., The Record-Journal Publishing Co., CT, Meriden
Killian, Emily
emilykillian@shelbystar.com, Online Ed., The Star, NC, Shelby
Killian, John ....(262) 521-9222
jkillian@hearst.com, Syndication Sales Dir., North America Syndicate, NY, New York
jkillian@hearst.com, Syndication Sales Dir., King Features Syndicate, NY, New York
Killian, Michael ....(203) 317-2380
mkillian@record-journal.com, Sr. Vice Pres., Sales/Mktg., Record-Journal, CT, Meriden
Killion, Sherri....................................ext. 225
Southern Illinois Univ., IL, Carbondale
Killon, Steele
reception@geelongadvertiser.com.au, Ed., GEELONG ADVERTISER
Killoy, Dan ....(406) 234-0450
dkilloy@midrivers.com, Pub., Miles City Star, MT, Miles City
Kilman, Larry
larry.kilman@wan-ifra.org, Dir., Commun., World Association of Newspapers and News Publishers (WAN-IFRA), Paris
Kilpatrick, Troy ....(605) 394-8331
troy.kilpatrick@rapidcityjournal.com, Adv. Dir., Rapid City Journal, SD, Rapid City
Kilpatrick, Kent A.
kent_kilpatrick@link.freedom.com, Pub., Jacksonville Journal-Courier, IL, Jacksonville
Kilpatrick, Amy ....(205) 934-8043
Univ. of Alabama at Birmingham, AL, Birmingham
Kilz, Hans-Werner
verlag@sueddeutsche.de, Ed. in Chief, Suddeutsche Zeitung, Munich
Kim, Luenna
director@columinists.com, Exec. Dir., The National Society of Newspaper Columnists, Inc., CA, San Francisco
Kim, Jae-ho

newsroom@dong.com, Pres., DONG-A ILBO, Seoul
Kimbel, John..........................(276) 645-2565
jkimbel@bristolnews.com, Regl. Adv. Dir., Bristol Herald Courier, VA, Bristol
Kimbro, Jeff N. ....(901) 529-2650
kimbro@commercialappeal.com, Circ. Mgr., Administrative, The Commercial Appeal, TN, Memphis
Kimmel , Lawrence M.
ceo@the-dma.org, CEO , The Direct Marketing Association, Inc., NY, New York
Kimmes, Amy.........................(715) 845-0658
akimmes@wdhprint.com, Lifestyle Ed., The Wausau Daily Herald, WI, Wausau
Kincy, Gene ....(479) 785-7702
gkincy@swtimes.com, Pub., Times Record, AR, Fort Smith
Kindeall, Aaron
akindeall@ccac.edu, Cmty. College Allegheny County South, PA, West Mifflin
Kindelspire, Tony..........(303) 776-2244 ext. 291
tkindelspire@times-call.com, Bus. Ed., Times-Call, CO, Longmont
King, Anna ....(509) 582-1537
aking@tri-cityherald.com, Agriculture, Tri-City Herald, WA, Kennewick
King, Stacia
sking@lsj.com, Adv. Dir., Lansing State Journal, MI, Lansing
King, John..............................(973) 586-8018
Director of Manufacturing , North Jersey Media Group, NJ, Woodland Park
King, William
wking@beaufortgazette.com, Prodn. Dir., The Beaufort Gazette, SC, Beaufort
King, Lau Kung
kklau@uniteddaily.co.my, Ed., THE MIRI DAILY NEWS, Miri, Sarawak
King, Jason
jason.king@fairfax.com.au, Adv. Sales Mgr., THE NEWCASTLE HERALD
King, Elliot
eking@loyola.edu, Journ./PR, Loyola College, MD, Baltimore
King, Darrick..........................(574) 296-5917
dking@etruth.com, Data Processing Mgr., The Elkhart Truth, IN, Elkhart
King, Michael...........................662-678-1634
michael.king@journalinc.com, Circulation - Delivery Manager
, Journal Publishing Company, MS, Tupelo
King, David
kingd@theaustralian.com.au, Chief of Staff, THE AUSTRALIAN, Surry Hills
King, Larry.............................402-444-1003
VP, News & Content, Omaha World-Herald, NE, Omaha
King, William
wking@islandpacket.com, Prodn. Dir., The Island Packet, SC, Bluffton
King, Marshall........................(574) 296-5805
mking@etruth.com, Fun Writer, The Elkhart Truth, IN, Elkhart
King, Buddy..............(903) 794-3311 ext. 1362
classifieds@texarkanagazette.com, Pub., Texarkana Gazette, TX, Texarkana
King, Peggy
peggy.king@gaflnews.com, Mng. Ed., Cordele Dispatch, GA, Cordele
King, Michelle........................(530) 896-7772
mking@chicoer.com, News Ed., Chico Enterprise-Record, CA, Chico
King, Clyde C..........................(281) 232-3737
cking@herald-coaster.com, Pres., Fort Bend Herald, TX, Rosenberg
King, Paul ....(902) 563-3837
Prodn. Mgr., Pressroom, The Cape Breton Post, NS, Sydney
King, Jim...............................575-763-3431
jking@cnjonline.com, Production Manager, Clovis News Journal, NM, Clovis
King, Tracey ....(902) 426-2811 ext. 3360
tking@herald.ca, Research Analyst/ROP Specialist, The Chronicle Herald, NS, Halifax
King, Larry.............................402-444-1003
VP, News & Content, Omaha World-Herald, NE, Omaha
King, Larry.............................(815) 937-3338
lking@daily-journal.com, Prodn. Foreman, Press (Night), The Daily Journal, IL, Kankakee
King, Lee
lee.king@helenair.com, Production Manager, Independent Record, MT, Helena
King, Kevin
cesales@ceengineering.com, Mktg. Dir., CE Engineering, CA, Loomis
Kingman, Matt...............................ext. 608
Mgr., Educ. Serv., New Castle News, PA, New Castle
Kinney, Bill ....(770) 428-9411 ext. 516
Columnist, Marietta Daily Journal, GA, Marietta
Kinney, J.D.
mediagraphics@devkinney.com, Pres., Media-Graphics-Dev.Kinney/MediaGraphics, Inc., TN, Memphis
Kinney, James........................(413) 788-1298
Bus. Ed., The Republican, MA, Springfield
Kinsey, Michelle ....(765) 213-5822
mkinsey@thestarpress.com, Arts/Entertainment Reporter, The Star Press, IN, Muncie
Kinter, Hastie D.
hastie@indianagazette.net, Sec., The Indiana Gazette, PA, Indiana
Kinzel, Robert F.
rfkinzel@toshiba-machine.com, HR, Toshiba Machine Co. America, IL, Elk Grove Village
Kipamura, Masato
webmaster@mainichi.co.jp, Chmn., MAINICHI SHIMBUN, Tokyo
Kirby, Bill..............................(706) 823-3344
bkirby@augustachronicle.com, Metro Ed., The Augusta Chronicle, GA, Augusta
Kirby, Mike.............................(508) 236-0335
mkirby@thesunchronicle.com, Ed., The Sun Chronicle, MA, Attleboro
Kirby, Nancy ....(630) 637-5283
North Central College, IL, Naperville
Kirby, Tim ....(386) 754-0421
tkirby@lakecityreporter.com, Sports Ed., Lake City Reporter, FL, Lake City
Kirby, Riley............................(704) 374-1333
orileyk@inter-active.com, Pres., Interactive Marketing & Research, Inc., NC, Charlotte
Kirby, Joe.......................................ext. 229
Editorial Page Ed., Marietta Daily Journal, GA, Marietta
Kirby, Mary Ann 601-360-4637
mkirby@jackson.gannett.com, Sales and Marketing Manager, The Clarion-Ledger, MS, Jackson
Kirch, Raimund
nz-redaktion@pressenetz.de, Ed. in Chief, NZ Nurnberger Zeitung, Nurnberg
Kirchman, Steve......................(920) 431-8389
skirchman@greenbaypressgazette.com, Travel Ed., Green Bay Press-Gazette, WI, Green Bay
Kirchner, James ....(502) 582-4180
jkirchner@courier-journal.com, Opns. News Mgr., The Courier-Journal, KY, Louisville
Kirchoff, Aaron................................ext. 7006
Sports Ed., Greensburg Daily News, IN, Greensburg
Kireowz, Koerarz
redakcja@kurierlubelski.pl, Ed. in Chief, KURIER LUBELSKI, Lublin
Kirk, Ray................................(530) 896-7782
rkirk@chicoer.com, Systems Mgr., Chico Enterprise-Record, CA, Chico
Kirk, Rebecca.........................(918) 542-8441
Northeastern Oklahoma A&M College, OK, Miami
Kirk, Mike ....(402) 444-1589
mike.kirk@owh.com, Finance Dir./Controller, Omaha World-Herald, NE, Omaha
Kirkley, Karin ....Prodn. Mgr., Composing
Minden Press-Herald, LA, Minden
Kirkman, David B......................(804) 775-2702
dkirkman@timesdispatch.com, Vice Pres., Circ., Richmond Times-Dispatch, VA, Richmond
Kirkman, Susan ....(330) 996-3886
skirkman@thebeaconjournal.com, Asst. Mng. Ed., Photos/Graphics, Akron Beacon Journal, OH, Akron
Kirkpatrick, John A...................(717) 255-8178
jkirkpatrick@patriot-news.com, Pres./Pub., The Patriot-News, PA, Mechanicsburg
Kirkwood, R. Cort.....................(540) 574-6289
kirkwood@dnronline.com, Mng. Ed., Daily News-Record, VA, Harrisonburg
Kirsh, Julie..........................(416) 947-2257
julie.kirsh@sunmedia.ca, Electronic Information Dir., Sun Media Corporation/Toronto Sun Syndicate Sales, ON, Toronto
Kirsh, Julie..........................(416) 947-2257
julie.kirsh@sunmedia.ca, News Research Dept., The Toronto Sun, ON, Toronto
Kirtley, Matthew.......................(503)725-5686
Portland State Univ., OR, Portland
Kise, Lars
lars.kise@varden.no, Ed. in Chief, VARDEN, Skien
Kiser, Rob
rkiser@dailycall.com, Sports Ed., Piqua Daily Call, OH, Piqua
Kish, Ken
ken.kish@macombdaily.com, Mng. Ed., News, The Macomb Daily, MI, Mount Clemens
Kish, Peter ....(203) 354-1028
pkish@thehour.com, Bus. Systems Mgr., The Hour Publishing Co., CT, Norwalk
Kislevitz, Joshua ....(212) 293-8522
jkislevitz@unitedmedia.com, Sr. Vice Pres., US Licensing, United Media, OH, Cincinnati
Kislingbury, Graham.................(541) 812-6111
graham.kislingbury@lee.net, Online Ed., Albany Democrat-Herald, OR, Albany
Kisliuk, Bill
bkisliuk@napanews.com, Mng. Ed., Napa Valley Register, CA, Napa
Kiss, Tony ....(828) 232-5855
tkiss@citizen-times.com, Entertainment Ed., The Asheville Citizen-Times, NC, Asheville
Kissel, Mary
mkissel@messenger-inquirer.com, Copy Ed., Messenger-Inquirer, KY, Owensboro
Kissoon, Grenfell
letters@ttol.co.tt, Dir., TRINIDAD GUARDIAN/SUNDAY GUARDIAN, Port-of-Spain
Kitazume, Takashi
kitazume.takashi@japantimes.co.jp, Managing editor, JAPAN TIMES, Tokyo
Kitchell, David ....ext. 5130
david.kitchell@pharostribune.com, Editorial Page Ed., Pharos-Tribune, IN, Logansport
Kitsch, LeDonna.......................(319) 758-8114
lkitsch@thehawkeye.com, Bus. Mgr., The Hawk Eye, IA, Burlington
Kizzia, Kevin ....(918) 684-2960
Prodn. Mgr., Mailroom, Muskogee Daily Phoenix & Times Democrat, OK, Muskogee
Kizziar, Sherry
skkizziar@yahoo.com, Adv. Mgr., Arkadelphia Siftings Herald, AR, Arkadelphia
Klaff, Alan
alexklaff@adnat.com, Pres., Ad National Yellow Pages, MD, Columbia
Klapper, Fred
fred.klapper@shj.com, Dir., Finance Serv., Herald-Journal, SC, Spartanburg
Klatt, Manfred
info@a-beig.de, Bus. Mgr., WEDEL-SCHULAUER TAGEBLATT, Pinneberg
Klawinski, Gary
gklawinski@jardis.com, Mgr., Graphic System Services, Inc., IL, Itasca
Klawinski, Gary
info@jardis.com, Dir., Sales, Jardis Industries, Inc., IL, Itasca
Klein, Kevin
kevin.klein@sunmedia.ca, Pub., The Winnipeg Sun, MB, Winnipeg
Klein, Greg
gklein@sunmktg.com, Owner, Sun Marketing, LLC, AZ, Phoenix
Klein, Dee
dee.klein@nptelegraph.com, Dir., Sales (NPC), The North Platte Telegraph, NE, North Platte
Klein, Jason E. ....(212) 856-6380
jklein@nnnlp.com, President & CEO, Newspaper National Network LP, NY, New York
Klein, Kimberly........................(248) 745-4505
kimberly.kelin@oakpress.com, Dir., Mktg., The Oakland Press, MI, Pontiac
Klein, Michael
michael.klein@pm-zw.de, Ed. in Chief, Pfaalzischer Merkur, Zweibrucken
Kleine, Kevin ....(706) 236-2294
Berry College, GA, Mount Berry
Kleinschmidt, Vitto ....(907)-523-2222
Circulation/Mailroom Director, Juneau Empire, AK, Juneau
Kleist, Trina ....(530) 477-4230
trinak@theunion.com, City Ed., The Union, CA, Grass Valley
Klemm, Hans.......................................850
info@zeitung.org, Ed. in Chief, DER NEUE TAG, Weiden
Kless, Richard F. ....(401) 865-2214
Providence College, RI, Providence
Kletke, Walt............................(559) 441-6441
wkletke@modbee.com, Regl. Vice. Pres., Finance, The Fresno Bee, CA, Fresno
Klett, Jennifer 8003994294
sales@bob-weber.com, Sales Manager, Bob Weber, Inc., OH, Cleveland
Kline, Daniel...........................(917) 523-3496
dan@notastep.com, Columnist, Daniel Kline Newspaper Column, CT, Newington
Kline, Karen E.
kkline@lhup.edu, Chair, Lock Haven University, PA, Lock Haven
Kline, Kay
kaykline@southwesttimes.com, Pub., The Southwest Times, VA, Pulaski
Kline, Dave.............................(610) 371-5200
dkline@readingeagle.com, Chief Sales/Mktg. Officer, Reading Eagle, PA, Reading
Klingensmith, Michael
Michael.Klingensmith@startribune.com, Publisher and CEO, Star Tribune, MN, Minneapolis
Klinger, Stephen......................(505) 524-0122
sklinger@zignet.com, Grimes, W.B. & Co., MD, Gaithersburg
Klinger, Teresa ....(608) 745-3565
tklinger@capitalnewspapers.com, Circ. Dir, Daily Register, WI, Portage
Klinger, Steve..........................(505) 524-0122
sck01@comcast.net, Southwest/West Assoc., Grimes, W.B. & Co., NM, Las Cruces
Klingsporn, Katie
katie@telluridedailyplanet.com, Asst. Ed., Telluride Daily Planet, CO, Telluride
Klink, J. Bruce.........................(317) 444-8005
bruce.klink@indystar.com, Vice Pres., Finance, The Indianapolis Star, IN, Indianapolis
Klint, Jonas
jonas.klint@karlskogatidning.se, Ed. in Chief, KARLSKOGA TIDNING, Karlskoga
Klipper, Leslie........................(858) 536-7000
San Diego Miramar College, CA, San Diego
Klocke, Mike..............................209-546-8250
mklocke@recordnet.com, Editor, The Record, CA, Stockton
Klockow, Birgit
nnn@nnn.de, Branch Office Mgr., Norddeutsche Neueste Nachrichten, Rostock
Klopfenstein, Suzanne ....(937) 225-9870
sklopfenstein@coxohiomedia.com, Senior Director, Local Accounts, Dayton Daily News, OH, Dayton
Klopfenstein, Suzanne 937-225-9870
sklopfenstein@coxohiomedia.com, Senior Director, Local Sales, Dayton Daily News, OH, Dayton
Kluetzmann, Judy A.
judyk@wdtimes.com, Adv. Dir., Retail/Nat'l, Watertown Daily Times, WI, Watertown
Kluever, Sheila..............................ext. 201
skluever@dglobe.com, Adv. Supvr., Classified, The Daily Globe, MN, Worthington
Klugman, Craig.......................(260) 461-8853
cklugman@jg.net, Ed., The Journal Gazette, IN, Fort Wayne
Klunder, Jack
jack.klunder@dailynews.com, Pub./Pres., California Newspapers Partnership, CA, Woodland Hills
Klunder, Jack 310-540-5511
Publisher, Daily Breeze, CA, Torrance
Klurfeld, James ....(631) 843-2908
Vice Pres./Editorial Page Ed., Newsday, NY, Melville
Klutts, Charlotte
advertising@tahlequahdailypress.com, Pub., Tahlequah Daily Press, OK, Tahlequah
Klyne, Marty
mklyne@leaderpost.canwest.com, Pub., The Leader-Post, SK, Regina
Klypchak, Carrie Lee

Carrie_klypchak@tamu-commerce.edu, Asst. prof., Texas A&M University-Commerce, TX, Commerce
Kmiecik, Betsy
bkmiecik@dailyherald.com, Vice Pres./Dir., HR, Daily Herald, IL, Arlington Heights
Knape, Steve ....(209) 333-1400 ext. 240
stevek@lodinews.com, Circ. Mgr., Lodi News-Sentinel, CA, Lodi
Knape, Steve ....(231) 933-1420
sknape@record-eagle.com, Circ. Mgr., Record-Eagle, MI, Traverse City
Knapp, Julie ....(480) 423-6410
Scottsdale Cmty. College, AZ, Scottsdale
Knappe, Mario
info@dnn.de, Distr. Mgr., DRESDNER NEUESTE NACHRICHTEN, Dresden
Knarr, Glenn ....ext. 245
nisysmgr@ptd.net, Systems Mgr., The News-Item, PA, Shamokin
Knarr, Glenn A. ....ext. 7
omar_k@newsitem.com, Prodn. Foreman, Composing, The News-Item, PA, Shamokin
Knauss, Chris ....(410) 770-4099
Bus. Ed., The Star-Democrat, MD, Easton
Knechtel, Jamie ....ext. 14
Office Mgr., The Latrobe Bulletin, PA, Latrobe
Kneer, Mark ....ext. 120
Circ. Dir., Southeast Missourian, MO, Cape Girardeau
Kneib, Bruce ....(816) 271-8651
brucek@npgco.com, Controller, St. Joseph News-Press, MO, Saint Joseph
Knepper, Ken
kenneth.knepper@thekansan.com, Pub., McPherson Sentinel, KS, McPherson
Knerler, John
johnk@magicvalley.com, Controller, The Times-News, ID, Twin Falls
Kniceley, Andrew B.
timeswv@timeswv.com, Pub., Times West Virginian, WV, Fairmont
Knight, Ed
eknight@robesonian.com, Circ. Dir., The Robesonian, NC, Lumberton
Knight, Sheila
sknight@claremoreprogress.comt, HR Mgr., The Claremore Daily Progress, OK, Claremore
Knight, Michael G.
michael_knight@tamu-commerce.edu, Asst. Prof., Texas A&M University-Commerce, TX, Commerce
Knight, Ron
info@knightmedia.com, Owner, Knight Mediacom, CA, La Mesa
Knight, Lisa 717-703-3043
lisak@mansimedia.com, Vice Pres., Advertising, MANSI Media, PA, Harrisburg
Knight, Bridget ....(940) 763-7535
knightb@wtr.com, Society/Women's Ed., Wichita Falls Times Record News, TX, Wichita Falls
Knight, Lisa ....(717) 703-3043
lisak@mansimedia.com, Vice President, Advertising, Pennsylvania Newspaper Association, PA, Harrisburg
Knipe-Brown, Julie
knipej@phillynews.com, Asst. City Ed., The Philadelphia Daily News, PA, Philadelphia
Knoblock, Lawrence...................985-857-2245
lawrence.knoblock@houmatoday.com, Packaging / Circulation Manager, The Courier, LA, Houma
Knochen, Jorg Peter
info@ov-online.de, Bus. Mgr., Oldenburgische Volkszeitung, Vechta
Knopfler, Vicki ....(336) 888-3601
vknopfler@hpe.com, Radio/Television Ed., High Point Enterprise, NC, High Point
Knopsnyder, Eric ....(814) 532-5085
Sports Ed., The Tribune-Democrat, PA, Johnstown
Knorr, Winfried
rnz-kontaktrnz.de, Proprietor, Rhein-Neckar-Zeitung, Heidelberg
Knowland, Beverly
bev@directimages.com, Art Dir., Direct Images Interactive, Inc., CA, San Leandro
Knowland, Bill
bill@directimages.com, Producer/Dir., Direct Images Interactive, Inc., CA, San Leandro
Knowles, Gregg ....(661) 333-9516
gregg.knowles@netzero.com, Owner, Knowles Media Brokerage Services, CA, Bakersfield
Knowles, John
impactracks@aol.com, Pres., Impact Racks, Inc., PA, Mechanicsburg
Knowles, Barbara ....ext. 1300
barbara.knowles@newtoncitizen.com, City Ed., The Newton Citizen, GA, Covington
Knowles, Clayton P...................(212) 289-6139
knowlaw@earthlink.net, Attorney, The Law Offices of Clayton P. Knowles, NY, New York
Knowlton, John ....(253) 833-9111
Green River Cmty. College, WA, Auburn
Knox, Jack ....(250) 380-5206
jknox@te.canwest.com, Columnist, Times Colonist, BC, Victoria
Knudsen, Carsten
infousa@eskographics.com, Pres./CEO, Esko-Graphics, OH, Vandalia
Knudsen, SÃ£ren
sorenknudsen@folketidende.dk, Ed., FOLKETIDENDE, Nykobing, Llolland-Falster
Knudson, Charles C.
zarmel@juno.com, Pres., Core-Concepts, FL, Homosassa
Knuth, Michael ....(920) 453-5128
mknuth@sheboygan.gannett.com, Ed., The Sheboygan Press, WI, Sheboygan
Knuth, Mike
mknuth@gannett.com, The Shoreline Chronicle, WI, Sheboygan
mknuth@gannett.com, Editor
, Herald Times Reporter, WI, Manitowoc
Knutsen, Peter 488 4106
peter.knutsen@inl.co.za, Display Adv. Mgr., CAPE ARGUS, Cape Town
Kobayashi, Senzo
mail@isenp.co.jp, Pres., ISE SHIMBUN, Tsu, Kinki
Kobernus, Klaire ....(808) 529-4899
kkobernus@starbulletin.com, Admin. Asst., Honolulu Star-Bulletin, HI, Honolulu
Kobrin, Ed
sales@wccsys.com, Sales/Mktg. Mgr., West Coast Computer Systems, CA, Stockton
Koch, Kevin
composing@standard-journal.com, Prodn. Mgr., The Standard-Journal, PA, Milton
Koch, Mark C..........................(203) 354-1080
Vice Pres., Opns., The Hour Publishing Co., CT, Norwalk
Koch, David
erosenfeld@josephjacobs.org, Pres., Joseph Jacobs Organization, NY, New York
Kochakian, Charles P. ....(203) 789-5635
letters@nhregister.cocm, Editorial Page Ed., New Haven Register, CT, New Haven
Kocher, Douglas J.
douglas.kocher@valpo.edu, Chair, Valparaiso University, IN, Valparaiso
Kodama, Lester ....(808) 525-7628
lkodama@honolulu.gannett.com, Circ. Mgr., Single Copy, Honolulu Star-Advertiser, HI, Honolulu
Koehl, Frank E.
fkoehl@mipval.com, Sr. Vice Pres., Management Planning, Inc., NJ, Princeton
Koehler, Boyd ....(612) 330-1018
Augsburg College, MN, Minneapolis
Koeller, Brian
briank@northwestsignal.net, News Ed., Northwest Signal, OH, Napoleon
Koenders, Denny
dkoenders@laurinburgexchange.com, Pub., The Laurinburg Exchange, NC, Laurinburg
Koenig, Roman ....(619) 388-3880
San Diego City College, CA, San Diego
Koenigs, Joel 651-286-6700
Vice Pres./Dir. Web Devel., Risdall Marketing Group, MN, New Brighton
Koesema, Michelle ....(361) 886-3601
koesemam@caller.com, CFO, Corpus Christi Caller-Times, TX, Corpus Christi
Koester, Mattheis
info@hallertagblatt.de, Pub., HALLER TAGBLATT, Schwabisch-Hall
Koesters, Aloif
aloifkoesters@mittelhessen.de, Ed. in Chief, Wetzlarer Neue Zeitung, Wetzlar
Koff, Steve ....(202) 638-1366
Washington Bureau Chief, The Plain Dealer, OH, Cleveland
Kogler, David ....(507) 933-7636
Gustavus Adolphus College, MN, Saint Peter
Kohl, Todd ....ext. 145
tkohl@ccdailyrecord.com, Lead Press Operator, The Canon City Daily Record, CO, Canon City
Kohut, Carleen C.
kohutc@nrf.com, CFO, National Retail Federation, DC, Washington
Koivisto, Katarina
katarina.koivisto@hbl.fi, news editor, HUFVUDSTADSBLADET, Helsingfors, Uusima
Koivula, Mai
mai.koivula@warkaudenlehti.fi, Ed. in Chief., WARKAUDEN LEHTI, Varkaus
Koivula, Mai
maikoivula@iisalmensanomat.fi, Ed. in Chief, IISALMEN SANOMAT, Iisalmi, Kuopio
Koivuma, Pasi
pasi.koivuma@karjalainen.fi, Ed., KARJALAINEN, Joensuu, Pohjois-Karjala
Kokae, Peter
katirna@magyarszo.com, Ed. in Chief, MAGYAR SZO, Novi Sad, Vojvodina
Kokou, Prosper
editogo@cafe.tg, Dir., TOGO-PRESSE, Lome
Kolanski, Kevin
timesleader@timesleaderonline.com, Adv. Dir., The Times Leader, OH, Martins Ferry
Kolb, David ....(231) 725-6354
dkolb@muskegonchronicle.com, Editorial Page Ed., The Muskegon Chronicle, MI, Muskegon
Kole, William
apboston@ap.org, Bureau Chief, Connecticut Associated Press Managing Editors Association, CT, Hartford
apboston@ap.org, Bureau Chief, Associated Press, MA, Boston
Koleno, Chris
cfk3@psu.edu or lmr8@psu.edu, Or Lisa Powers , Association of Opinion Page Editors, PA, University Park
Kolkman, Richard ....(317) 858-0630
protista1@aol.com, Cartoonist, Seriocomics Features, IN, Fort Wayne
Kollbaum, Kristin ....(712) 324-5061
Northwest Iowa Cmty. College, IA, Sheldon
Kolo, Bob ....(856) 427-9799 ext. 14
bobk@videopipeline.com, Dir., Technology, Video Pipeline, Inc., NJ, Haddonfield
Kolodziej, Tim ....ext. 614
Television/Film Ed., New Castle News, PA, New Castle
Kolsky, Charles ....(314) 340-8897
Vice Pres., Mktg./Research & E-Media, Pulitzer Newspapers, Inc., MO, Saint Louis
Kolsti, Paul
pkolsti@optonline.net, Illustrator, Pen Tip, NJ, Parsippany
Komar, Debbie
debbie.komar@macombdaily.com, Features/Entertainment Ed., The Macomb Daily, MI, Mount Clemens
Komatsubara, Motoko ....(661) 395-7211
Sr. Vice Pres./CFO, The Bakersfield Californian, CA, Bakersfield
Komatsuzaki, Kazuo
webmaster@yomiuri.co.jp, Hokuriku Head Officer, YOMIURI SHIMBUN, Takaoka City, Hokuriku
Komidar, Travis.......................(765) 420-5224
tkomidar@journalandcourier.com, Opns. Dir., Journal and Courier, IN, Lafayette
Komives, Stephen
skomives@snd.org, Exec. Dir., Society for News Design, Inc., FL, Orlando
Komives, Stephen....................(912) 652-0316
skomives@savannahnows.com, News Planning Ed., Savannah Morning News, GA, Savannah
Konate, Hamidou
jamana@jamana.org, Mng. Dir., LES ECHOS, Bamako
Kondylis, S.
elthraki@otenet.gr, Pub., ELEFTHERI THRAKI, Alexandroupolis, Thrace
Konecny, Jerry
jkonecny@breze.com, Vice Pres., Breze, Inc., NJ, Hamilton
Konig, Jim 239-574-1110
jkonig@breezenewspapers.com, Advertisng Director, Cape Coral Breeze, FL, Cape Coral
Konig, Bob ....(973) 586-8117
VP/Manufacturing, North Jersey Media Group, NJ, Woodland Park
Konrad, Jim.............................860-425-4201
Exec. Editor, The Bulletin, CT, Norwich
Konte, Joe ....(415) 382-7386
jkonte@marinij.com, Page One Ed., Marin Independent Journal, CA, Novato
Konz, Michael ....(308) 233-9720
Features Ed., Kearney Hub, NE, Kearney
Kooistra, L..................................2987654
t.milgen@friesch-dagblad.nl, Ed., FRIESCH DAGBLAD, Leeuwarden
Koomar, Susan ....(570) 420-4341
skoomar@poconorecord.com, Bus. Ed., Pocono Record, PA, Stroudsburg
Koon, Scott
skoon@cantondailyledger.com, Pub., Daily Ledger, IL, Canton
Koonce, Jill
kooncej@fayettevillenc.com, Credit Mgr., The Fayetteville Observer, NC, Fayetteville
Koones, Charles C.
ckoones@variety.cahners.com, Grp. Vice Pres./Pub., Daily Variety
Koorberg, Vaino 372 614 4085
vaino.koorberg@ohtuleht.ee, Ed. in Chief, OHTULEHT, Tallinn
Kopeck, John ....(780) 429-5652
jkopeck@thejournal.canwest.com, Adv. Mgr., Local Territory, Edmonton Journal, AB, Edmonton
Kopecky, Tina..........................(573) 248-2710
Dir., Sales/Mktg., Hannibal Courier-Post, MO, Hannibal
Kopitch, Louise.......................(909) 386-3802
kopitch.louise@sbsun.com, Vice Pres., HR, San Bernardino County Sun, CA, San Bernardino
Kopitch, Louise.......................(909) 386-3802
kopitch.louise@sbsun.com, Vice Pres., HR, Inland Vision, CA, Woodland Hills
Kopli, Merit
merit.kopli@postimees.ee, Ed. in Chief, POSTIMEES, Tartu
Kopoulos, Genni
proini3@otonet.gr, Pub., PROINI, Kavala
Kopp, Linda
lkopp@simbainformation.com, Pub., Simba Information, CT, Stamford
Koppe, Olaf
o.koppe@nd-online.de, CEO - Chief Executive Manager, NEUES DEUTSCHLAND, Berlin
Koppel, Andrew W.
naps@napsys.com, Retail Sales Mgr., North Atlantic Publishing Systems, Inc., MA, Concord
Koppelmann, Ken ....ext. 446
kenk@ftimes.com, Prodn. Mgr., The Times, IN, Frankfort
Koppenhofer, Tom....................(814) 444-5922
tomk@dailyamerican.com, Adv. Mgr., Daily American, PA, Somerset
Kopper, W.
ejz@ejz.de, Bus. Mgr., ELBE-JEETZEL-ZEITUNG, Luchow
Kordalski, David......................(216) 999-4721
Chief Librarian, The Plain Dealer, OH, Cleveland
Kordalski, David ....(216) 999-4721
Asst. Managing Editor/Visuals, The Plain Dealer, OH, Cleveland
Koren, Michael
a-kornroller@a-kornroller.com, Pres., A-Korn Roller, Inc., IL, Chicago
Koren, Michael J. ....(303) 954-6466
mkoren@medianewsgroup.com, Vice Pres./Controller, MediaNews Group Inc, CO, Denver
Korimbao, Daniel
korimbo@thenational.com.pg, Ed., THE NATIONAL, Boroko, NCD
Korman, Chris ....(812) 331-4353
ckorman@heraldt.com, Sports Ed., The Herald-Times, IN, Bloomington
Kornet, W.
ensign@alliedpress.co.nz, Pub./Ed., THE ENSIGN

Kornmiller, Debbie....................(520) 573-4127
kornmiller@azstarnet.com, Reader Advocate, Arizona Daily Star, AZ, Tucson
Koroi, Mesake
info@fijidailypost.com, Ed., FIJI DAILY POST, Vatuwaqa, Suva
Koromilis, John
ol-bhma@odenet.gr, Ed., Ekdotiki Enimerotiki-Ikoromilos A E, Katerini
Kortink, Cheryl
news@dompost.co.nz, Adv. Mgr., THE DOMINION POST
Kosaka, Kensuke
center@shinmai.co.jp, Pres., SHINANO MAINICHI SHIMBUN, Nagano, Chubu
Koschmieder, Dietmar
redaktion@jungewelt.de, Bus. Mgr., JUNGE WELT, Berlin
Koshimune, Takamasa
s-net@mxa.mesh.ne.jp, Pres., SANYO SHIMBUN, Okayama, Chugoku
Kosmicki, Kollin.......................(831) 637-5566
kkosmicki@freelancenews.com, Ed., Free Lance, CA, Hollister
Kosnac, Erin...........................(601) 584-3070
Metro Ed., Hattiesburg American, MS, Hattiesburg
Kossag, Claus
redaktion@@ivz-online.de, Pub., Ibbenburener Volkszeitung, Ibbenburen
Kostarellas, Nikos
xronos@hol.gr, Pub., HRONOS, Kozani, Macedonia
Kostecka, Norma......................(707) 256-2228
nkostecka@pulitzer.net, Adv. Dir., Napa Valley Register, CA, Napa
Kostich, Drago
dkostich@eldiariolaprensa.com, Prodn. Dir., El Diario La Prensa, NY, Brooklyn
Kostolansky, Dave
dkost@srds.com, Vice Pres., Mktg./Bus. Devel., SRDS, a Kantar Media Company, IL, Des Plaines
Koszegi, Ferenc
mainap@mail.datanet.hu, Ed. in Chief, MAI NAP, Budapest, Pest
Kotarek, Aaron.............................951-368-9796
akotarek@pe.com, VP Circulation and Distribution, The Press-Enterprise, CA, Riverside
Kotecki, Stacy
slkotecki@cpapersmi.com, Office Mgr., Community Papers of Michigan, Inc., MI, East-lansing
Kotecki, Mike
mike.kotecki@hksystems.com, Sr. Vice Pres., Sales, HK Systems, WI, NewBurlin
Kothari, Gulab
gulabkothari@rajasthanpatrika.com, Ed., RAJASTHAN PATRIKA, Jaipur, Rajasthan
Kothari, Gulab
gulabkothari@rajasthanpatrika.com, Ed. in Chief, RAJASTHAN PATRIKA, Jaipur, Rajasthan
Kott, Doug..............................(605) 692-6271
dkott@brookingsregister.com, News Ed., Brookings Register, SD, Brookings
Kotta, N/A..Ed.
DAILY THANTHI, Bangalore, Karnataka
Kottke, Penny..........................(920) 356-6739
pkottke@conleynet.com, CFO, Conley Publishing Group Ltd., WI, Beaver Dam
Kotwasinski, Bob.........................602-444-8211
VP/Production, The Arizona Republic, AZ, Phoenix
Kotz, Geraldine.........................(904) 359-4309
geri.kotz@jacksonville.com, Adv. Dir., Classified, The Florida Times-Union, FL, Jacksonville
Kotz, Geri..................................941-429-3108
gkotz@sun-herald.com, Class/Telmktg Manager, Charlotte Sun, FL, Charlotte Harbor
Kotzer, Peter............................(416) 947-2354
peter.kotzer@sunmedia.ca, Credit Mgr., The Toronto Sun, ON, Toronto
Kouame, Michel
fratmat@AfricaOnline.co.ci, Gen. Dir., FRATERNITE-MATIN, Abidjan
Kountourantzi, D.
enimerossi@gmail..com, Pub., ENIMEROSSI, Ioannina, Epirus
Koupal, Ray..............................(518) 454-5328
rkoupal@timesunion.com, CFO, Times Union, NY, Albany
Kourajian, Chad
chad.kourajian@bismarktribune.com, HR Mgr., The Bismarck Tribune, ND, Bismarck
Kouri, Tony...............................(940) 720-3467
kourit@wtr.com, Adv. Mgr., Internet, Wichita Falls Times Record News, TX, Wichita Falls
Kourpanidis, Wanda
wKourpanidis@mysanfordherald.com, Circ. Mgr., Sanford Herald, FL, Sanford
Koutsoliontos, Vas
vkoutsoliontos@proinoslogos.gr, Owner/Pub./Dir., PROINOS LOGOS, Ioannina, Epirus
Kovacs, Zoltan
office@agenda.ro, Dir., AGENDA, Timisoara
Kovacs, Peter...........................(504) 826-3350
pkovacs@timespicayune.com, Mng. Ed., The Times Picayune, LA, New Orleans
Kovalainen, Irpa
irpa.kovalainen@kansantahto.fi, Mng. Dir., KANSAN TAHTO, Oulu
Kovatch, John...........................(330) 996-3190
jkovatch@thebeaconjournal.com, Vice Pres., Admin./Finance, Akron Beacon Journal, OH, Akron
Kowalczyk, Marcin
kowalczyk@express.lodz.pl, Ed. in Chief, EXPRESS ILUSTROWANY, Lodz
Kowalski, Sheldon.......................419-724-6382
skowalski@toledoblade.com, Adv. Mgr., Sales Devel., The Blade, OH, Toledo
Koyama, Ken
kkoyama@wellandtribune.ca, Pub., Welland Tribune, ON, Welland
Koyama, Yohachiro
agara-km@mb.aikis.or.jp, Pres., KII MINPO, Tanabe City, Akitsu Town Minpo
Koyano, Keith...........................(909) 624-1887
Claremont Colleges, CA, Claremont
Kozakewicz, Ray
rkozakewicz@mediageneral.com, Mgr., Cor. Commun., Media General, Inc., VA, Richmond
Kozen, Bernard..........................(570) 420-4310
bkozen@poconorecord.com, Prodn. Mgr., Distr., Pocono Record, PA, Stroudsburg
Kozerski, Randy................................ext. 221
rkozerski@kauaipubco.com, Pres./Pub., The Garden Island, HI, Lihue
Koziol, Timothy
tkoziol@cet.com, Mktg. Dir., Wally Pike's Outdoor Features, WA, Spokane
Kraai, David
kraai@advpubtech.com, Pres., Advanced Publishing Technology, CA, Burbank
Kraai, David
kraai@advpubtech.com, Pres., Advanced Publishing Technology, CA, Burbank
Kraemer, Wendy S......................(570) 420-4414
wkraemer@poconorecord.com, Prodn. Mgr., Creative Servs., Pocono Record, PA, Stroudsburg
Kraft, Kent..ext. 202
kent.kraft@masthead.net, Bus. Devel. Mgr., Masthead International, Inc., AZ, Phoenix
Kragh, Hans Peter
hans.peter.kragh@nordjyske.dk, Ed., THISTED DAGBLAD, Thisted, Jutland
Kraiselburd, Raul
editor@eldia.com, Ed., El Dia, Gualeguaychu, Provincia de Entre Rios
Kralinger, Thomas
thomas.kralinger@mediabring.at, Pub., KURIER, Vienna
Kramer, Jack.............................(203) 789-5601
jkram@nhregister.com, Ed., New Haven Register, CT, New Haven
Kramer, Cecil V.
cvkramer@liberty.edu, Jr. Assoc. Dean, Liberty University, VA, Lynchburg
Kramer, Jonathan
jkramer@njtimes.com, Adv. Mgr., Nat'l/Co-Op, The Times, NJ, Trenton
Krarup, Poul
krarup@sermitsiaq.gl, Ed., Sermitsiaq, Nuuk
Kraske, Karyn
kkraske@dailyherald.com, Adv. Mgr., Div. Sales, Daily Herald, IL, Arlington Heights
Kratzer, Brian
kratzerb@missouri.edu, Director of Photography, Assistant Professor, Kappa Alpha Mu Honorary Society in Photo Journalism, MO, Columbia
Kratzmann, Torsten
redaktion@zevener-zeitung.de, Ed., Zevener Zeitung, Zeven
Kraus, Ann S.............................(212) 556-1234
Vice Pres., Compensation/Benefits, The New York Times Co., NY, New York
Krause, Don...............................(573) 248-2758
don.krause@courierpost.com, Mng. Ed., Hannibal Courier-Post, MO, Hannibal
Krause, Axel
axelkrause@wanadoo.fr, Sec. Gen., Anglo-American Press Association of Paris, Paris
Krauskopf, Achim
kf@shz.de, Ed., OSTHOLSTEINER ANZEIGER, Eutin
Krauth, Gerald
redaktion@eberbacher-zeitung.de, Bus. Mgr., EBERBACHER ZEITUNG, Eberbach
Kravetz, Jay N...........................(561) 683-9090
jay@jaykravetz.com, Ed., International Photo News, FL, West Palm Beach
Krebs, Joegen
post@fynsamtsavis.dk, Ed. in Chief, FYNS AMTS AVIS, Svendborg, Fyn
Krebs, Randy............................(320) 255-8762
rkrebs@stcloud.gannett.com, Editorial Page Ed., St. Cloud Times, MN, Saint Cloud
Krebs, Adam...ext. 33
sportseditor@themonroetimes.com, Sports Ed., The Monroe Times, WI, Monroe
Krecklow, Robert..........(419) 238-2285 ext. 202
rkrecklow@timesbulletin.com, Pub., The Times Bulletin, OH, Van Wert
Kreibel, Dave............................(610) 371-4818
dkreibel@readingeagle.com, Circ. Mgr., Sales, Reading Eagle, PA, Reading
Kreiser, Mike............................(951) 782-7782
mkreiser@pe.com, Circ. Mgr., Home Delivery, The Press-Enterprise, CA, Riverside
Kreisler, Kevin..........................(760) 778-4568
kkreisler@palmspri.gannett.com, Circ. Mgr., Home Delivery, The Desert Sun, CA, Palm Springs
Krejlgaard, Chris..........(705) 674-5271 ext. 234
editorial@thesudburystar.com, News Ed., The Sudbury Star, ON, Sudbury
Kreppert, Mike...........................(217) 788-1492
mike.kreppert@sj-r.com, Director of operations, The State Journal-Register, IL, Springfield
Kreps, Rick A.
rkreps@thepilotnews.com, Pub., Pilot News, IN, Plymouth
Kresl, Lisa................................(214) 977-8807
lkresl@dallasnews.com, Deputy Mng. Ed., Lifestyles, The Dallas Morning News, TX, Dallas
Kreten, Peter.............................(773) 298-3375
pkreten@sxu.edu , Asst. Dir, Saint Xavier University, IL, Chicago
Kretschmer, Mark.......................(262) 656-6211
Circ. Asst. Mgr., Delivery/Collections, Kenosha News, WI, Kenosha
Kreuz, Joao.....................................252-3222
Pres., Jornal Do Oeste, Toledo, Parana
Krichenbauer, Monika
forum@ntz.de, Proprietor, Nurtinger Zeitung, Nurtingen
Krieghoff, Lothar
anzeigen@kreiszeitung.de, Proprietor, Kreiszeitung fur die Landkreise Diepholz und Verden, Syke
Krigar, Martin
lokales@mendener-zeitung.de, Ed. in Chief, Mendener Zeitung, Menden
Kriluck, Audrea..................................ext. 367
akriluck@stcatharinesstandard.ca, Mng. Ed., The Standard, ON, Saint Catharines
Krisher, Bernard
editor@cambodia.daily.com, Pub., CAMBODIA DAILY, Phnom Penh
Krishnamoorthy, R.
dmrcni@dinamalar.com, Ed., DINAMALAR, Chennai, Tamil Nadu
Kristian Myhre, Nils
nilskristianmyhre@ostlentingen.no, Ed.in Chief, OESTLENDINGEN/HAMAR/OESTLENDINGEN SOLOER-ODAL, Elverum
Kristjansson, Jonas
dvdreif@ff.is, Ed., DAGBLADID/VISIR, Reykjavik
Kroeger, Terry J.........................(402) 444-1179
kroeger@owh.com, Pub./CEO, Omaha World-Herald, NE, Omaha
Kroemer, James D..........(574) 533-2151 ext. 301
jim.kroemer@goshennews.com, Pub., The Goshen News, IN, Goshen
Krohm, Gary
gary@krohm.com, Mgr., Mktg., Krohm International Ltd., MO, Independence
Kroke, Karlheinz
verlagsleitung@fr-online.de, Bus. Mgr., FRANKFURTER RUNDSCHAU, Frankfurt am Main
Kroll, John................................(216) 999-4117
Online Editor, The Plain Dealer, OH, Cleveland
Kromer, Miroslaw Marek
boslupsk@op.p, Ed. in Chief, Dziennikarska Oficyna Wydawnieza Rondo, Slupsk
Kronvall-Jordan, Kim.....(708) 596-2000 ext. 2426
South Suburban College, IL, South Holland
Kropper, Steve
kropper@domania.com, CEO/Co-Founder, Domania, Inc., MA, Watertown
Kroshus, Brian
brian.kroshus@bismarcktribune.com, Publisher, The Bismarck Tribune, ND, Bismarck
Krost, Maggie............................(205) 325-3344
Vice Pres., Sales/Mktg., The Birmingham News, AL, Birmingham
Krough, Tom...............(303) 776-2244 ext. 235
tgkrough@lehmancomm.com, Dir., Cor. Relations, Lehman Communications Corp., CO, Longmont
Krough, Tom...............(303) 776-2244 ext. 235
tgkrough@lehmancomm.com, Dir., Cor. Finance, Times-Call, CO, Longmont
Krpalek, Michele.........................(616) 471-3385
Andrews Univ., MI, Berrien Springs
Kruckemyer, Gene
gkruckemyer@mysanfordherald.com, Pub., Sanford Herald, FL, Sanford
Krucker, Kelsey
advertising@universitychronicle.net, St. Cloud State Univ., MN, Saint Cloud
Krueger, Ralph H.
ralphk@wdtimes.com, Treasurer/Bus. Mgr., Watertown Daily Times, WI, Watertown
Krueger, Margaret A.
marg@wdtimes.com, Sec., Watertown Daily Times, WI, Watertown
Krueger, Ron..............................(810) 766-6117
rkrueger@flintjournal.com, Food Writer, The Flint Journal, MI, Flint
Kruger, Eden
news@lagrandeobserver.com, News assistant, The Observer, OR, La Grande
Krugler, Philip H.................................ext. 201
general@pencoproducts.com, Mktg. Mgr., Penco Products, PA, Skippack
Krugman, Milt.....................................ext. 4171
mkrugman@phillyburbs.com, Religion Ed., Bucks County Courier Times, PA, Levittown
Krull, Maria................................(815) 753-0707
Northern Illinois Univ., IL, Dekalb
Krumel, Jim...............................(419) 993-2076
jkrumel@limanews.com, Ed., The Lima News, OH, Lima
Kruppa, Rudiger
ruddiger.kruppa@ln-luebeck.de, Adv. Mgr., LUBECKER NACHRICHTEN/LUBECKER NACHRICHTEN AM SONNTAG, Lubeck
Kruse, Hans-Joachim
hjkruse@mediaphone.de, Mng. Dir., MPS Media Phone Service KG, Duesseldorf
Kruse, Jorg
joerg.kruse@ppimedia.de, Product Mgr., ppi Media GmbH, Hamburg
Kruszewski, Konrad
kkruszewski@wspolczesna.pl, Ed. in Chief, GAZETA WSPOLCZESNA, Bialystok
Kruzel, Bettina...........................(303) 473-1518
kruzelb@dailycamera.com, Prodn. Mgr., Pre Press, Daily Camera, CO, Boulder
Krygiel, Chris............................(416) 947-2057
chris.krygiel@sunmedia.ca, Cor. Dir., HR, The Toronto Sun, ON, Toronto
Krygier, Michael.........................(989) 671-1235
mkrygier@valleypublishing.com, Circ. Mgr., The Bay City Times, MI, Bay City
Kryk, John.................................(416) 947-2118

john.kryk@sunmedia.ca, Corporate Entertainment Editor, The Toronto Sun, ON, Toronto
Kubera, Nanette
nkubera@verafast.com, Vice Pres., Mktg./Devel., Ver-A-Fast Corp., OH, Rocky River
Kubik, John M.
kubikjohn@fotopressnews.org, Opns. Dir., Fotopress Independent News Service International, ON, Peterborough
Kubilius, Ausra
a.kubilius@snhu.edu, Chair, Southern New Hampshire University, NH, Manchester
Kubinski, Chris
ckubinski@lfpress.com, Adv. Mgr., Auto/Real Estate, The London Free Press, ON, London
Kuchenberg, Alfred
info@grenzecho.be, MD, GRENZ-ECHO, Saint Vith, Liege
Kudri, Abdo Aref 362-2233
diario@diariopopular.com.br, Pub., Diario Popular, Curitiba, Parana
Kuehl, Mark D.
markk@wdtimes.com, Circ. Dir., Watertown Daily Times, WI, Watertown
Kuehner, Elmer
ekuehner@infoblvd.net, Circ. Dir., The Leader, NY, Corning
Kueter, Maricarrol....................(605) 331-2332
mkueter@argusleader.com, Executive Editor, Argus Leader, SD, Sioux Falls
Kuhlman, Steve
steve.kuhlman@agfamonotype.com, Mgr., Sales/Mktg., Agfa Monotype Corporation, IL, Elk Grove Village
Kuhlman, Erin
erin.kuhlman@parsons.com, PR, Parsons, Inc., CA, Pasadena
Kuhlman, Fred G. ....(308) 762-3060
fredk@alliancetimes.com, Exec. Vice Pres./Pub./Sec./Treasurer, Alliance Times-Herald, NE, Alliance
Kuhn, Mary Ann
mkuhn@dcexaminer.com, Virginia Ed., The Examiner, VA, Alexandria
Kuhn, Michele J. ....(732) 565-7249
mjkuhn@thnt.com, Community Ed., Home News Tribune, NJ, East Brunswick
Kuhn, Lynn ....(724) 836-5569
lkuhn@tribweb.com, Food Ed., Tribune-Review, PA, Pittsburgh
Kuhnle, Otto
info@bb-live.de, News Ed., KREISZEITUNG, Boeblingen
Kuhns, Michael D. ....(570) 420-4389
mkuhns@poconorecord.com, Sports Ed., Pocono Record, PA, Stroudsburg
Kuhns, John
jkuhns@cmonitor.com, Chrmn., Newspapers of New England, NH, Concord
Kuhr, Peggy
peggy.kuhr@umontana.edu, Dean, The University of Montana, MT, Missoula
Kukic, Goran
redakcija@novilist.hr, Ed., NOVI LIST, Rijeka
Kukis, Kelly ....(916) 789-2699
Sierra College, CA, Rocklin
Kulak, Mary....................630-978-8020
mkulak@stmedianetwork.net, Advertising Sales Manager, The Naperville Sun, IL, Aurora
Kullen, Michael
mkullen@merlinone.com, Dir., Cust. Support, MerlinOne, Inc., MA, Quincy
Kumar, Ravindra
calaal12@giascl01.vsnl.net.in, Ed., THE STATESMAN, New Delhi
Kumar, Ramesh
dmrmdu@dinamalar.in, Ed. in Chief, DINAMALAR, Madurai, Tamil Nadu
Kumar, Ravindra
rk.statesman@gmail.com, Mng. Dir., THE STATESMAN, Kolkata, West Bengal
Kund, Nagy Miklos
nepujsag@e-nepujsag.ro, Ed. in Chief, NEPUJSAG, Targu Mures, Mures
Kundanis, Rose
rkundani@keene.edu, Prof., Keene State College of the University System of New Hampshire, NH, Keene
Kunerth, Bill ....(208) 232-4161
bkunerth@journalnet.com, Pub., Idaho State Journal, ID, Pocatello
Kunken, Darrell....................(916) 321-1594
dkunken@sacbee.com, Adv. Mgr., Market Analysis, The Sacramento Bee, CA, Sacramento
Kunkle, Deb
news@oelweindailyregister.com, City Ed., The Oelwein Daily Register, IA, Oelwein
Kunn, Christian
redaktiontg@tagblatt.ch, Ed. in Chief, TAGBLATT THURGAU, Arbon, Thurgau
Kuntz, Lothar
uprkaus@springer.com, Bus. Mgr., Arzte Zeitung, Neu-Isenburg
Kuntz, J. Fred
fkuntz@guelphmercury.com, Pub., The Guelph Mercury, ON, Guelph
Kuntz, Katy ....(406) 791-6520
kkuntz@greatfal.gannett.com, Adv. Mgr., Classified, Great Falls Tribune, MT, Great Falls
Kunz, Amy ....(808) 525-7618
Controller, Honolulu Star-Advertiser, HI, Honolulu
Kuperman, Amanda
akuperman@jpost.com, Adv. Mgr., JERUSALEM POST
Kuprionis, M. Denise....................(513) 977-3835
kuprionis@scripps.com, Vice Pres./Sec., E. W. Scripps Co., OH, Cincinnati
Kurani, Edison ....+355682054752
edisonkurani@kohajone.com, Ed., KOHA JONE, Tirana
Kurasiewicz, Dale....................ext. 211
dkurasiewicz@batavianews.com, Prodn. Mgr., The Daily News, NY, Batavia
Kurata, Osamu
o_kurata@tks-net.co.jp, Sales Chief Officer, TKS Ltd., Tokyo
Kurazawa, Kathy 912-233-1281
Secretary, Morris Multimedia, Inc., GA, Savannah
Asst. to President , Morris Multimedia, Inc., GA, Savannah
Kurdy, Tom ....(406) 755-7000
tkurdy@dailyinterlake.com, Pub., Daily Inter Lake, MT, Kalispell
Kurosawa, Yusuke
info@yamagata-np.jp, Owner, YAMAGATA SHIMBUN, Yamagata, Tohoku
Kursman, Seth....................(514) 394-2398
seth.kursman@abitibibowater.com, Vice Pres., Pub. Aff./Sustainability/Environment, Abitibi-Bowater Inc., QC, Montreal
Kurtz, Dave....................(260) 925-2611 ext. 46
dkurt@kpcnews.net, Ed., The Star, IN, Auburn
Kurtz, Bruce ....(805) 685-3100 ext. 136
kurtzb@maps.com, Dir., Mktg., Maps.com, CA, Santa Barbara
Kurtz, Tim
tkurtz@oskyherald.com, Pub., Oskaloosa Herald, IA, Oskaloosa
tkurtz@oskyherald.com, Oskaloosa Shopper, IA, Oskaloosa
Kurtz, David
dkurtz@kpcnews.net, executive editor, The News-Sun, IN, Kendallville
Kurtzke, Kristina
kkurtzke@nikon.net, Communications Coordinator, Nikon, Inc., NY, Melville
Kuryla, Charles
panchokuryla@inlandnews.com, Dir.-Int'l Sales, Inland Graphics International LC, FL, Miami
Kurz, Jeffery ....(203) 317-2213
jkurz@record-journal.com, Sr. Writer, Record-Journal, CT, Meriden
Kusch, Michael
michael.kusch@mittlebayerische.de, Adv. Mgr, MITTLEBAYERISCHE ZEITUNG, Regensburg
Kushnier, Joanne....................(807) 343-6215
joanne.kushnier@chroniclejournal.com, News Ed., The Chronicle-Journal, ON, Thunder Bay
Kuster, Steve....................(805) 681-5969
skuster@newspress.com, Prodn. Mgr., Distr., Santa Barbara News-Press, CA, Santa Barbara
Kuta, Dave
dkuta@times-standard.com, Pub., Times-Standard, CA, Eureka
Kutnick, Geoffry ....(562) 985-7410
California State Univ. Long Beach, CA, Long Beach
Kuykendall, Debra
dkuykendall@mercedsun-star.com, Pub., Merced Sun-Star, CA, Merced
Kuzinski, Karen
advert@fultonsun.com, Prodn. Mgr., Pre Press, The Fulton Sun, MO, Fulton
Kuzmak, Pam
sales@eammosca.com, Sales Admin., EAM-Mosca Corp., PA, Hazle Township
Kvarnstrom, Peter....................(250) 371-6100
pk@glaciermedia.ca, Pub., Kamloops Daily News, BC, Kamloops
Kwak, Dr. Chung Hwan
info@upi.com, Chrmn./Pres., United Press International, DC, Washington
Kwang, Allan
allan@acesxprt.com, Pres., Aces Research, Inc., CA, Fremont
Kwang-Suc, Song
songs@kyeongin.com, Chrmn., KYEONGIN ILBO, Suwon, Kyonggi
Kwong, Ngai Kai
localnews@singpao.com.hk, Ed. in Chief, SING PAO DAILY NEWS, Hong Kong
Kyse, Bruce
bruce.kyse@pressdemocrat.com, Pub., The Press Democrat, CA, Santa Rosa
Kyu Park, Nam
nkpark@chosun.com, Adv. Mgr., SPORTS CHOSUN, Seoul

L

L'Ecluse, Kathleen ....(707) 427-6933
Online/Projects Ed., Daily Republic, CA, Fairfield
La Arin, Lea
mail@epl.ee, Ed. in Chief, PAEVALEHT, Tallinn
La Barth, Len ....(831) 427-2411
llabarth@santacruzsentinel.com, City Desk, Santa Cruz Sentinel, CA, Scotts Valley
La Prade, Konrad....................(410) 770-4049
Adv. Mgr., The Star-Democrat, MD, Easton
La Rocque, Mike ....(517) 768-4895
mlarocque@citpat.com, Adv. Sales Mgr., The Jackson Citizen Patriot, MI, Jackson
LaBell, Dave ....(727) 893-8523
dlabell@tampabay.com, Community/Events Mgr., Tampa Bay Times, FL, Saint Petersburg
LaBrake, Brenda
blabrake@ogd.com, Bus. Mgr., St. Lawrence Newspapers, The Malone Telegram, NY, Malone
LaBrie, Brad ....(360) 417-3525
brad.labrie@peninsuladailynews.com, Sports Ed., Peninsula Daily News, WA, Port Angeles
LaForge, Ron
ron@newscolor.com, Mng. Dir., Newscolor, LLC, OR, Silverton
LaFuria, Scott....................(850) 599-2130
slafuria@tallahassee.com, Controller, Tallahassee Democrat, FL, Tallahassee
LaMorte, Valerie
vlamo@srds.com, Vice Pres., HR, SRDS, a Kantar Media Company, IL, Des Plaines
LaPierre, Jim ....ext. 3031
jlapierre@herald.ca, Circ. Mgr., District, The Chronicle Herald, NS, Halifax
LaPointe, Rom
info@vucom.com, Pres., VuCom newMedia, Inc., MI, Troy
LaPrade, Darel
deelap@aol.com, Adv. Vice Pres., Delaware State News, DE, Dover
LaVigne, Nikki
nlavigne@dmg.gannett.com, Circ. Mgr., The Daily Times, MD, Salisbury
LaVo, Carl ....ext. 4227
clavo@phillyburbs.com, Asst. Mng. Ed., Content, Bucks County Courier Times, PA, Levittown
LaVoie, Terry W. ....(915) 937-3350
tlavoie@daily-journal.com, Prodn. Mgr., Distr., The Daily Journal, IL, Kankakee
Laakkola, Heikki
heikki.laakkola@pohjolansanomat.fi, Ed. in Chief, POHJOLAN SANOMAT, Kemi, Vaihde
Laaninen, Timo
latomo@suomenmaa.fi, Ed. in Chief, SUOMENMAA, Oulu
Labalme, Jenny 317-701-1130
jlabalme.indypress@att.net, Executive Director, Indianapolis Press Club Foundation, IN, Indianapolis
Labat, Russell D.....................(507) 537-1551 ext. 107
rlabat@marshallindependent.com, Pub., Independent, MN, Marshall
Labelle, Matt ....(703) 282-5491
Radford Univ., VA, Radford
Labrador, Jorge....................(702) 895-3889
Univ. of Nevada, NV, Las Vegas
Lacaeyse, Joseph E.....................(815) 937-3311
joel@daily-journal.com, Vice Pres., Finance, The Daily Journal, IL, Kankakee
Lacaillade, Ray....................(508) 236-0342
rlacaillade@thesunchronicle.com, Mktg./Promo. Mgr., The Sun Chronicle, MA, Attleboro
Lacava, Tony....................(661) 395-7393
tlacava@bakersfield.com, Sports Ed., The Bakersfield Californian, CA, Bakersfield
Lacey, Herb
circulation@clevelandbanner.com, Circ. Dir., Cleveland Daily Banner, TN, Cleveland
Lachance, Janice R.
janice@sla.org, CEO, Special Libraries Association, News Division, VA, Alexandria
Lacher, Doug....................(651) 796-1114
dlacher@pressenter.com, Adv. Acct. Exec., Stillwater Gazette, MN, Stillwater
Laciura, Phil
placiura@detroitnews.com, Sports Editor, The Detroit News, MI, Detroit
Lackey, Brad ....(318) 362-0214
Adv. Dir., The News-Star, LA, Monroe
Lacroixe, Sonya ....(780) 743-8186 ext. 230
Circ. Mgr., Fort McMurray Today, AB, Fort McMurray
Lacy, Carrie
clacy@greenfieldreporter.com, Adv. Mgr., Commercial Sales, Daily Reporter, IN, Greenfield
Lacy, Ed
ed.lacy@beatleygravitt.com, Pres./Dir., Mktg., Beatley Gravitt Communications, VA, Richmond
Lacy, Drew....................321-987-5989
lacyd2010@my.fit.edu, Editor-in-Chief, Florida Institute of Technology, FL, Melbourne
Ladendorf, Pete
pladendorf@minotdailynews.com, Online Ed., Minot Daily News, ND, Minot
Ladendorf, Peter
pladendorf@minotdailynews.com, MIS/Online Mgr., Minot Daily News, ND, Minot
Laderer, Jeff ....(574) 296-5898
jladerer@etruth.com, Controller, The Elkhart Truth, IN, Elkhart
Lafferty, Walt
wlafferty@courierpostonline.com, Pub., Courier-Post, NJ, Cherry Hill
Lafferty, Walt T. ....(217) 788-1500
walt.lafferty@sj-r.com, Publisher, The State Journal-Register, IL, Springfield
Laffoon, Polk
plaffoon@knightridder.com, Vice Pres., Cor. Relations, Knight Ridder, CA, San Jose
Laflin, John ....(605) 256-5278
Dakota State Univ., SD, Dakota State University
Lafontaine, Raymond Ozier
france.guyane@media-antilles.fr, Dir., France-Guyane, Cayenne
Lage, Wally
wlage@semissourian.com, Vice Pres./COO, Rust Communications, MO, Cape Girardeau
Lago, Amy....................(202) 334-6510
lagoa@washpost.com, Comics Ed., The Washington Post Writers Group, DC, Washington
Lagrenade, Alberto M. 23115
Pres., El Debate-Pregon, Gualeguay, Provincia de Entre Rios
Lahr, Steve ....(309) 820-3344
slahr@pantagraph.com, Adv. Mgr., Majors/Nat'l, The Pantagraph, IL, Bloomington
Lahr-Smith, Diane 315-789-3333

dlahr@fltimes.com, Advertising Director, Finger Lakes Times, NY, Geneva
Lair, William ....(217) 238-6865
blair@jg-tc.com, Mng. Ed., Times-Courier, IL, Mattoon
Laird, Jean
jlaird@perretta.com, Sales Mgr., Perretta Graphics Corp., NY, Poughkeepsie
Laird, John ....(360) 735-4564
john.laird@columbian.com, Editorial Page Ed., The Columbian, WA, Vancouver
Lajara, Ivan ....ext. 502
ilajara@freemanonline.com, Preview, Daily Freeman, NY, Kingston
Lake, Kari ....(218) 855-5807
kari.lake@brainerddispatch.com, Controller/HR Dir., Brainerd Dispatch, MN, Brainerd
Lake, Chris ....(408) 842-6400 ext. 250
clake@mainstreetmg.com, CFO, Mainstreet Media Group, CA, Gilroy
Lake, John
jlake@dailystandard.com, Adv. Mgr., The Daily Standard, OH, Celina
Lake, David
david@pcworld.com, Mgr. Bus Devl, PC World Online Services Group, CA, San Francisco
Lakey, Pat
plakey@mtdemocrat.net, Mng. Ed., Mountain Democrat, CA, Placerville
Lalley, Patrick ....(605) 331-2291
plalley@argusleader.com, Managing Editor, Argus Leader, SD, Sioux Falls
Lally, John
jlally@alfaquest.com, Sr. Vice Pres., Sales, alfaQuest Technologies, IL, Rolling Meadows
Lalonde, Claire-Anne
claire-anne.lalonde@ott.sunpub.com, Prodn. Dir., Mfg., The Ottawa Sun, ON, Ottawa
Lam, Shan-muk
hkej@netvigator.com, Ed., HONG KONG ECONOMIC JOURNAL, Hong Kong
Lam, Steve ....(765) 213-5712
Dir., Finance, The Star Press, IN, Muncie
Lamar, Carmen
clamar@summitmediapartners.com, Pres., Summit Media Partners LLC, CO, Golden
Lamar, Jim ....(850) 599-2297
jhlamar@tallahassee.com, Sports Ed., Tallahassee Democrat, FL, Tallahassee
Lamar, Scott ....(703) 878-8063
slamar@insidenova.com, Photo Ed., Manassas Journal Messenger, VA, Manassas
Lamb, John
jlamb@forumcomm.com, Features Ed., InForum, ND, Fargo
Lamb, Madelyn ....(225) 388-0314
mlamb@theadvocate.com, People Ed., The Advocate, LA, Baton Rouge
Lamb, Brenda ....ext. 618
Bus. Mgr., Newton Daily News, IA, Newton
Lamb, Rob ....ext. 12
Prodn. Mgr., IT/Composition, Los Alamos Monitor, NM, Los Alamos
Lambarg, Ulrike
redaktion@lahrer-zeitung.de, MD, LAHRER ZEITUNG, Lahr
Lamberg, Gary
ads@cheboygantribune.com, Pub., Cheboygan Daily Tribune, MI, Cheboygan
Lambert, Steve
slambert@broadcastnews.ca, Manitoba Correspondent, Broadcast News Limited, MB, Winnipeg
slambert@broadcastnews.ca, Manitoba Correspondent, Canadian Press, The - Winnipeg, MB, MB, Winnipeg
Lambert, Steve ....(909) 386-3840
steve.lambert@sbsun.com, Ed., San Bernardino County Sun, CA, San Bernardino
Lambert, Karen
klambert@metrowestnewspaper.com, Pub., Landmark Metro West Newspapers, CO, Brighton
Lambert, Brad
blambert@highpoint.edu, Asst. Prof., High Point University, NC, High Point
Lambert, Deborah ....ext. 108
deb@aim.org, Special Projects Dir., Accuracy in Media, DC, Washington
Lambert, Jennie
gastongazette@link.freedom.com, Pub., The Gaston Gazette, NC, Gastonia
Lambert, Cynthia Royle ....(914) 694-5099
Sr. Mng. Ed., The Journal News, NY, White Plains
Lambert, Steve
news.tribune@sgvn.com, Pub., San Gabriel Valley Tribune, CA, West Covina
Lambrakis, C.
info@tanea.gr, Pub., NEA, Athens, Central Greece
Lampert, Dan
sales@dlc2.com, Pres., Daniel Lampert Communications Corp., FL, Altamonte Springs
Lampi, Niklas
niklas.lampi@alandstidningen.ax, Ed. in Chief, ALAND, Mariehamn
Lancaster, Brent 336-506-3040
blancaster@thetimesnews.com, News Ed., Times-News, NC, Burlington
Lancaster, Cory
cory.lancaster@news-jrnl.com, Mng. Ed., Daytona Beach News-Journal, FL, Daytona Beach
Lancaster, Charles W.
mschuver@lminews.com, Pres., Lancaster Management, Inc., AL, Gadsden
Land, Robin ....(903) 596-6244
Adv. Mgr., Nat'l, Tyler Morning Telegraph, TX, Tyler
Land, Marilyn
marilyn.land@rushvillerepublican.com, Adv. Mgr., Rushville Republican, IN, Rushville
Land, Mary Jean
maryjean.land@gcsu.edu, Chair/Prof., Georgia College & State University, GA, Milledgeville
Landau, George ....(636) 537-8548
george@newsengin.com, Pres., NewsEngin, Inc., MO, Chesterfield
Landers, Mary ....(912) 652-0337
mary.landers@savannahnow.com, Environmental Reporter, Savannah Morning News, GA, Savannah
Landis, Tim ....(217) 788-1536
tim.landis@sj-r.com, Bus. Ed., The State Journal-Register, IL, Springfield
Landon, Owen E.
olandon3@landonmedia.com, Exec. Vice Pres., Landon Media Group LLC, MA, North Scituate
Landon, Mark ....(310) 342-1300
mlandon@landonmedia.com, Exec. Vice Pres., Landon Media Group LLC, CA, Rolling Hills Estates
Landon, Owen E. ....(212) 826-1113
olandonjr@landonmedia.com, Chrmn./CEO, Landon Media Group LLC, NY, New York
Landry, Kim
kiml@hollistercreative.com, Pres., Hollister Kids, PA, Wynnewood
Landry, Peter ....(877) 643-5437
peterl@hollistercreative.com, Vice Pres., Hollister Kids, PA, Wynnewood
Landsberg, David A.
dlandsberg@miamiherald.com, Pres./Pub., The Miami Herald, FL, Miami
Lane, Nancy ....(610) 361-9234
nancylanesna@aol.com, Pres., Suburban Newspapers of America, MI, Traverse City
Lane, Laurel ....(814) 878-1967
llane@goerie.com, Vice Pres., Interactive Media, Erie Times-News, PA, Erie
Lane, Richard D. ....(617) 779-8900 ext. 2111
rlane@domania.com, Pres., Domania, Inc., MA, Watertown
Lane, Brian
bryan.lane@tribstar.com, Prodn. Dir., The Tribune Star, IN, Terre Haute
Lane, Donald ....(919) 846-5881
dlane@unitedmedia.com, Mgr., Regl. Sales-East, United Media, OH, Cincinnati
Laney, Nina
nlaney@wapakwdn.com, Prodn. Mgr., Composing/Printing, Wapakoneta Daily News, OH, Wapakoneta
Laney, William ....(419) 739-3515
blaney@wapakwdn.com, Exec. Ed., Wapakoneta Daily News, OH, Wapakoneta
Lang, Mike ....(941) 957-5232
mike.lang@heraldtribune.com, Photo Dir., Sarasota Herald-Tribune, FL, Sarasota
Lang, Thompson H. ....(505) 823-7777
journal@abqjournal.com, Pres./Pub., Albuquerque Journal, NM, Albuquerque
Lang, John
info@poweronemedia.com, CFO, PowerOne Media, Inc., NY, East Greenbush
Lang, Stew ....(250) 380-5275
slang@te.canwest.com, Bus./Finance Reporter, Times Colonist, BC, Victoria
Lange, Klaus
anzeigen@volksstimme.de, Bus. Mgr., MAGDEBURG VOLKSSTIMME, Magdeburg
Lange, Steffen
slange@midtjyllandsavis.dk, Ed. in Chief, MIDTJYLLANDS AVIS, Silkeborg, Jutland
Lange, Michael
gt-anzeigen@tagespost.de, Ed. in Chief, GMUNDER TAGESPOST, Schwabisch-Gmund
Langer, Markus
markus.langer@badisches-tagblatt.de, Ed. in Chief, BADISCHES TAGBLATT, Baden-Baden
Langford, David
dlangford@lfpress.com, Sports Ed., The London Free Press, ON, London
Langkopp, Bill
pressclub_no@hotmail.com, Exec. Dir., New Orleans Press Club, LA, New Orleans
Langley, Greg ....(225) 388-0199
glangley@theadvocate.com, News Features Editor, The Advocate, LA, Baton Rouge
Langley, Greg
glangley@theadvocate.com, Entertainment/TV Ed., The Advocate, LA, Baton Rouge
Langlois, Robert ....(514) 878-9711
rlanglois@bbm.ca, Vice Pres., Quebec Servs., BBM Canada, ON, Toronto
Langman, William 860/701-4283
b.langman@theday.com, Director of Operations, The Day Publishing Company, CT, New London
Langton, Trent ....(734) 240-5789
trent@monroenews.com, Opns. Dir., Systems, The Monroe Evening News, MI, Monroe
Lanier, David ....ext. 1411
dlanier@keenesentinel.com, Sports Ed., The Keene Sentinel, NH, Keene
Lankford, Jennifer ....(970) 542-3170
Morgan Cmty. College, CO, Fort Morgan
Lannan, Anne
a.lannan@ocna.org, Executive Director, Ad*Reach, ON, Burlington
Lannan, Anne ....ext. 228
a.lannan@ocna.org, Executive Director, Ontario Community Newspapers Association, ON, Burlington
Lannero, Dan
dan.lannero@unt.se, CEO, UPSALA NYA TIDNING, Uppsala
Lanthier, Maggie
mlanthier@ironmountaindailynews.com, Online Mgr., The Daily News, MI, Iron Mountain
Lanthier, Marguerite
mlanthier@ironmountaindailynews.com, Entertainment/Amusements Ed., The Daily News, MI, Iron Mountain
Laperle, Alice ....ext. 1180
alice.laperle@timesargus.com, Prodn. Coord., The Times Argus, VT, Barre
Lapinski, Vincent ....(630) 920-5856
vince.lapinski@manroland.us, CEO, Manroland Inc., IL, Westmont
Laraway, Cindy ....(757) 247-7466
claraway@dailypress.com, Admin./Planning Mgr., Daily Press, VA, Newport News
Larcombe, Butch
Butch.larcombe@helenair.com, Managing Editor, Independent Record, MT, Helena
Larcombe, Butch
blarcombe@greatfal.gannett.com, Bus. Ed., Great Falls Tribune, MT, Great Falls
LardizÂ bal, Oscar
diario@lacapitalnet.com.ar, Ed. in Chief, La Capital, Mar del Plata, Provincia de Buenos Aires
Largan, Stephen
info@nappsystems.com, Pres., MacDermid Printing Solutions, CA, San Marcos
Large, Jodi
jodi.large@shelbyvilledailyunion.com, Circ. Mgr., Daily Union, IL, Shelbyville
Largever, Jason
nyitc@55broadst.com, Dir.-Info Serv., NY Information Technology Center, NY, New York
Larimer, Tom
tom@arkansaspress.org, Exec. Dir., Arkansas Press Services, AR, Little Rock
Larimer, Tom 501-374-1500
tom@arkansaspress.org, Exec. Dir., Arkansas Press Association, AR, Little Rock
LariviÃ£££Ã£Â¯Ã£Â¿Ã£Â½re, Natalie ......(514) 392-9000
Pres., Trancontinental Media Inc., Transcontinental, Inc., QC, Montreal
Larkey, Wayne
wlarkey@clintonherald.com, Adv. Dir., Clinton Herald, IA, Clinton
Larkin, Joe
joe.larkin@voicemediagroup.com, Sr. Vice Pres. Sales , Voice Media Group, AZ, Phoenix
Larmer, Paul
paul@hcn.org, Exec. Dir., High Country News, CO, Paonia
Larocca, Umberto
avvisatore@publerama.it, Dir., L'AVVISATORE MARITTIMO, Genova
Larrain Wormald, Juan Carlos
lacuarta@copesa.cl, Gen. Mgr., LA CUARTA, Santiago
Larrinaga, Amanda ....(406) 994-2224
editor@exponent.montana.edu, Montana State Univ. Bozeman, MT, Bozeman
Larsen, Linda
llarsen@reporter-herald.com, Mgr., Mktg./Promo., Daily Reporter-Herald, CO, Loveland
Larsen, Tom
tlarsen@skagitpublshing.com, Prodn. Dir., Skagit Valley Herald, WA, Mount Vernon
Larsen, Flemming
hf@herningfolkeblad.dk, Ed., HERNING FOLKEBLAD, Herning, Jutland
Larsen, Sharon ....ext. 124
slarsen@batavianews.com, Editorial Page Ed., The Daily News, NY, Batavia
Larson, Jayson ....(909) 675-5626
editor@athensreview.com, Ed., Athens Daily Review, TX, Athens
Larson, Kathy
kathy.larson@yorknewstimes.com, Adv. Sales Mgr., York News-Times, NE, York
Larson, Richard K.
dlarson@swiftcom.com, Chrmn., Bd., Swift Communications, Inc., NV, Carson City
Larson, Rick ....(509) 582-1522
rlarson@tri-cityherald.com, Mng. Ed., Tri-City Herald, WA, Kennewick
Larson, Darren
dlarson@newspapersfirst.com, Vice Pres./Sales Mgr., Newspapers First, Inc., TX, Dallas
Larson, Tim
tim@kansasmediaone.com, Pub., The Leavenworth Times, KS, Leavenworth
Larson, Craig ....(508) 626-3987
metrowest.sports@cnc.com, Sports Ed., Metrowest Daily News, MA, Framingham
Larsson, Bengt
reklamation@vlt.se, Mng. Dir., BARGSLAGSBLADET, Koping
Las Heras, Hugo Horacio 453-3851
Pres., El Diario del Sur de Cordoba, Villa Maria, Provincia de Cordoba
Lasak, Ed ....(951) 368-9702
elasak@pe.com, SVP Finance and Publishing Ops, The Press-Enterprise, CA, Riverside
Laskey, Kristen
lacommunity@lamonitor.com, Community Ed., Los Alamos Monitor, NM, Los Alamos
Laskowski, Mark ....(843) 317-7200
mlaskowski@florencenews.com, Pub., Morning News, SC, Florence
Laskowski, Mark ....(843) 601-2780
mlaskowski@bellsouth.net, Senior Associate-Southeast/South, Grimes, W.B. & Co., MD, Gaithersburg
Lasley, James ....(864) 260-1401
lasleyjc@independentmail.com, Vice Pres., Opns., Anderson Independent-Mail, SC, Anderson
Lasley, Tom ....(815) 987-1321
tlasley@rockford.gannett.com, Gen. Mgr., Rockford Register Star, IL, Rockford

Lasseigne, Marcie ....(956) 982-6624
Features Ed., The Brownsville Herald, TX, Brownsville
Laster, David ....ext. 27
advertising@bolivarcommercial.com, Adv. Mgr., The Bolivar Commercial, MS, Cleveland
Lastinger, Mark................................ext. 206
mark.lastinger@gaflnews.com, Mng. Ed., Thomasville Times-Enterprise, GA, Thomasville
Latham, Phil
platham@marshallnewsmessenger.com, Ed., Marshall News Messenger, TX, Marshall
Latham, Anna...................................ext. 294
alatham@wellandtribune.ca, Office Mgr., Welland Tribune, ON, Welland
Latif, Shaib
inquilab@mid-day.com, Ed., INQUILAB, Mumbai, Maharashtra
Latour, Almar
editor@wsj.com, Ed. in Chief, WALL STREET JOURNAL ASIA, Wan Chai
Laub, Val J............................(724) 439-7519
vlaub@heraldstandard.com, Pub., Herald-Standard, PA, Uniontown
Laubach, Edward ....ext. 3573
sports@express-times.com, Sports Ed., The Express-Times, PA, Easton
Lauber, Dietrich
dietrich.lauber@gammerler.de, Sales Mgr., Gammerler AG, Geretsried-Gelting
Lauenstein, Allison ....(518) 454-5338
alauenstein@timesunion.com, Mktg. Dir., Times Union, NY, Albany
Laugesen, Wayne
wayne.laugesen@gazette.com, Editorial Page Ed., The Gazette, CO, Colorado Springs
Laughlin, Nancy ....(313) 222-6494
laughlin@freepress.com, Asst. Mng. Ed., Web, Detroit Free Press, MI, Detroit
Laughrey, J. Bruce
info@telspan.com, Chrmn., TelSpan, Inc., IN, Indianapolis
Laumanns, Reinhard............................20100
redaktion@derpatriot.de, Proprietor, DER PATRIOT, Lippstadt
Laurel, Alyssa ....(559) 737-4856
College of the Sequoias, CA, Visalia
Laurence, Ann
ann@athensnews-courier.com, Pub., The News-Courier, AL, Athens
Laurencio, Shelley...................(978) 970-4862
slaurencio@lowellsun.com, Circ. Mgr., Telemktg./Promo., The Sun, MA, Lowell
Laurent, Greg
infol@lankfordengr.com, Mgr., Lankford Engineering, Inc., LA, Lafayette
Laurin, Ron
rlaurin@thewhig.com, Pub., The Kingston Whig-Standard, ON, Kingston
Lauro Aguirre, Juan
juan@dalai.com, Mng. Dir., Informatica Dalai SA de CV, Monterrey
Laut, Marvin..............(719) 544-3520 ext. 202
mlautjr@chieftain.com, Gen. Mgr., The Pueblo Chieftain, CO, Pueblo
Lavender, Roxzie
rlavender@mysanfordherald.com, Adv. Dir./Classified Mgr., Sanford Herald, FL, Sanford
Lavery, Michael J.
laverymj@accessabc.com, Pres./MD, Audit Bureau of Circulations (ABC), IL, Arlington Heights
Lavery, Michael
abci@accessabc.com, Pres./MD, ABC Interactive, IL, Schaumburg
Lavery, Roger.........................(765) 285-8200
Prof./Dean, Ball State University, IN, Muncie
Lavigne, Ray ....(705) 674-5271 ext. 250
advertising@thesudburystar.com, Adv. Mgr., The Sudbury Star, ON, Sudbury
Lavin, Carl ....(215) 854-4562
Deputy Mng. Ed., News, The Philadelphia Inquirer, PA, Philadelphia
Lavin, Chris..................................ext. 1303
chris.lavin@uniontrib.com, Adv. Mgr., Bus. Channels/Gen. Mgr., Lifestyles/Entertainment, The San Diego Union-Tribune, CA, San Diego
Lavine, Alan ....(561) 640-6098
mwliblav@aol.com, Chrmn./Pres., Alan Lavine, Inc., FL, Palm Beach Gardens
Lawhead, Donna ....(256) 740-5763
donna.lawhead@timesdaily.com, Controller, TimesDaily, AL, Florence
Lawhorn, Chad 785-832-6362
clawhorn@ljworld.com, The World Co.- Lawrence, Kan., Journal-World, KS, Lawrence
Lawhorn, Chad 785-832-6362
clawhorn@ljworld.com, Business Editor, The World Co.- Lawrence, Kan.- Journal-World, KS, Lawrence
Lawler, Holly...........................(352) 753-1119
holly.lawler@thevillagesmedia.com, Lifestyles Ed., The Villages Daily Sun, FL, The Villages
Lawley, Joe ....(724) 357-1306
Indiana Univ. of Pennsylvania, PA, Indiana
Lawrence, Misty
mistyl@northwestsignal.net, Public Record/Church Ed., Northwest Signal, OH, Napoleon
Lawrence, Mala 973-569-7305
lawrence@northjersey.com, VP/Circulation, North Jersey Media Group, NJ, Woodland Park
Lawrence, Gary
glawrence@heartlandpublications.com, Pub., Mount Airy News, NC, Mount Airy
Lawrence, Ted
tedl@cpimo.com, Adv./Mktg. Mgr., Community Publishers, Inc., AR, Bentonville
Lawrence, James ....(585) 258-2415
jlawrence@democratandchronicle.com, Editorial Page Ed., Democrat and Chronicle.com, NY, Rochester
Lawrence, Gary
glawrence@heartlandpublications.com, COO, Heartland Publications LLC, CT, Clinton
Lawrence, Mark
mlawrence@sun-herald.com, Deputy Sports Editor, Charlotte Sun, FL, Charlotte Harbor
Lawrence, Dan ....(617) 450-2662
lawrenced@csmonitor.com, Bus. Mgr., The Christian Science Monitor News Service, MA, Boston
Lawrence, Mala K....................(201) 646-4281
lawrence@northjersey.com, Asst. Pub., North Jersey Media Group, Inc., NJ, Hackensack
Lawrence, Jim.........................(209) 578-2072
jlawrence@modbee.com, Graphics Dir., The Modesto Bee, CA, Modesto
Lawrence, Dennis
dennislawrence@clarkmhc.com, Pres., Clark Material Handling Co., KY, Lexington
Lawrence, Mike ....(270) 831-8346 ext. 8346
mlawrence@thegleaner.com, Photo Ed., The Gleaner, KY, Henderson
Lawson, Eric ....(506) 458-6435
eric.lawson@brunswicknews.com, Co-Pub., Brunswick News, Inc., NB, Moncton
Lawson, Gary ....(940) 720-3446
lawsong@wtr.com, Photo Dept. Mgr., Wichita Falls Times Record News, TX, Wichita Falls
Lawson, Mike
mlawson@njherald.com, Circ. Dir., New Jersey Herald, NJ, Newton
Lawson, Steve
slawson@wellmarkco.com, VP Sales/Mktg., The Wellmark Company, OK, Oklahoma City
Lawson, Carol
caroll@commpub.com, Bus. Mgr., Harrison Daily Times, AR, Harrison
Lawson, George
lawsong@unk.edu, Chair, University of Nebraska-Kearney, NE, Kearney
Lawson, Charles
clawson@hearstnp.com, Prodn. Mgr., Mailroom, Plainview Herald, TX, Plainview
Lawson, Eric
info@timestranscript.com, Pub., Times & Transcript, NB, Moncton
Lawson, Eric
lawson.eric@dailygleaner.com, Pub., The Daily Gleaner, NB, Fredericton
Lay, Lydia ....(901) 435-1309
LeMoyne-Owen College, TN, Memphis
Lay, Pat
patlay@harlanonline.net, Pub., The Harlan Daily Enterprise, KY, Harlan
Layng Rosner, Terre
trosner@stfrancis.edu, Chair, University of St. Francis, IL, Joliet
Layton, Les
llayton@whitneyworld.com, CEO, Whitney Worldwide, Inc., MN, Saint Paul
Le Hyaric, Patrick 4922 7272
humanite@humanite.presse.fr, Pres./Pub., L'HUMANITE/L'HUMANITE DIMANCHE, Saint-Denis
Le Sache, Francois
redaction@lest-eclair.fr, Dir., L'EST ECLAIR, Troyes
LeBar, Bob..............................(570) 629-9128
Prodn. Foreman, Pressroom, Pocono Record, PA, Stroudsburg
LeBeau, Maggie
info@dexone.com, Sr. Vice Pres./CMO, Dex One Corp., NC, Cary
LeBeau, Wade ....(815) 937-3315
wlebeau@daily-journal.com, Dir., Network Opns. Ctr., The Daily Journal, IL, Kankakee
LeBlanc, Gerry........................(413) 585-5295
director@gazettenet.com, Online/New Media Mgr., Daily Hampshire Gazette, MA, Northampton
LeClaire, Nick
nick@telluridedailyplanet.com, Retail Adv., Telluride Daily Planet, CO, Telluride
LeFort, Michael ....(605) 394-8314
michael.lefort@rapidcityjournal.com, Ed., Rapid City Journal, SD, Rapid City
LeJeune, Tom
abrunner@autologic.com, Mktg. Mgr., Autologic Information International, CA, Thousand Oaks
LePorin, Eliza........................(850) 561-1600
eleporin@fsview.com, FSView Gen. Mgr., Tallahassee Democrat, FL, Tallahassee
LePorin, Eliza 850-561-1600
eleporin@fsview.com, General Manager, FSView & Florida Flambeau, FL, Tallahassee
Lea, Nat
nwlea@wehco.com, Gen. Mgr., The Sentinel-Record, AR, Hot Springs
Leach, Dean
dleach@sanmarcosrecord.com, Bus. Mgr., San Marcos Daily Record, TX, San Marcos
Leach, Leah ....(36) 417-3531
leah.leach@peninsuladailynews.com, Managing Editor, Peninsula Daily News, WA, Port Angeles
Leahy, Jim
cdna@djstrat.com, Exec. Dir., Connecticut Daily Newspapers Association, CT, Tolland
Leake, Teresa
ads@fmtimes.com, Adv. Mgr., Fort Morgan Times, CO, Fort Morgan
Leander, Tom
tom.leander@informa.com, Editor and Chief, Lloyd's List Asia, LLOYD'S OF LONDON PRESS, London
Leano Reyes, Gonzalo
ocho@foreigner.class.udg.mx, Pres., Ocho Columnas, Guadalajara, Jalisco
Lear, Amy ....ext. 15
aclear@njpa.org, Adv. Dir., New Jersey Newspaper Network (NJNN), NJ, West Trenton
Leary, Sean ....ext. 293
ferris@qconline.com, Film/Theater Ed., The Rock Island Argus, IL, Rock Island
Lease, Denise ....(630) 920-3574
denise.lease@manroland.us, Marketing & CRM Specialist, Manroland Inc., IL, Westmont
Leasor, Lydia...............(270) 769-1200 ext. 270
lleasor@thenewsenterprise.com, Adv. Graphic Design Team Leader, The News Enterprise, KY, Elizabethtown
Leath, O. Scott.......................(804) 649-6613
sleath@timesdispatch.com, Sr. Vice Pres./Bus. Mgr., Richmond Times-Dispatch, VA, Richmond
Leath, Susan D. ....(814) 238-5000
sleath@centredaily.com, Pres./Pub., Centre Daily Times, PA, State College
Leatherdale, Linda..................(416) 947-2332
linda.leatherdale@sunmedia.ca, Bus./Finance Ed., The Toronto Sun, ON, Toronto
Leau, Janet ....(65) 6415-4200
janet.leau@dowjones.com, Acct. Mgr., Dow Jones Newswires - Kuala Lumpur, Malaysia, Kuala Lumpur
Leavitt, Betty
leavittb@corp.inxintl.com, Dir., PR, INX International Ink Co., IL, Schaumburg
Leavy, Buff ....(912) 265-8320
editor@thebrunswicknews.com, Ed., The Brunswick News, GA, Brunswick
Lebedoff, Randy......................(612) 673-7133
randy.lebedoff@startribune.com, Sr. V.P. General Counsel, Star Tribune, MN, Minneapolis
Lebensohn, Hector............................44 4408
Ed., Democracia, Junin, Provincia de Buenos Aires
Leblanc, Roger 902-432-8212
rleblanc@journalpiuoneer.com, Managing Editor, The Journal Pioneer, PE, Summerside
Lebolte, Fred
flebolt@suntimes.com, Pres./Pub., The Beacon News, IL, Aurora
Lebzelter, Bob ....ext. 275
Special Sections Ed., Star Beacon, OH, Ashtabula
Lechner, Kerry ....(715) 845-0657
klechner@wdhprint.com, Presentation Ed., The Wausau Daily Herald, WI, Wausau
Lechtanski, Ken
klechtanski@enterprisenews.com, Online Sports Ed., The Enterprise, MA, Randolph
Lechter, Mattheas
lechter@gn-online.de, Adv. Mgr., Grafschafter Nachrichten, Nordhorn
Ledbetter, Eddie.......................(912) 489-9403
eledbetter@statesboroherald.ncom, Asst. Ed., Statesboro Herald, GA, Statesboro
Ledbetter, Wendy
wendylledbetter@gmail.com, News Ed,, Arkadelphia Siftings Herald, AR, Arkadelphia
Lederman, Ron ....(419) 993-2078
rlederman@limanews.com, Editorial Page Ed., The Lima News, OH, Lima
Ledford, David ....(302) 324-2860
dledford@delawareonline.com, Vice Pres., News/Exec. Ed., The News Journal, DE, New Castle
Leduc, Lucie
lleduc@reseauselect.com, Gen. Mgr., Reseau Select/Select Network, QC, Montreal
Lee, Jane ....ext. 430
jlee@adn.com, Mktg. Mgr., Anchorage Daily News, AK, Anchorage
Lee, Chrstian 253-597-8725
christian.lee@thenewstribune.com, VP of Circulation, The News Tribune, WA, Tacoma
Lee, Amy
alee@glasgowdailytimes.com, Adv. Dir., Glasgow Daily Times, KY, Glasgow
Lee, Michael
medialee@aol.com, CEO, Lee & Steel LLC, CT, Darien
Lee, Thomas ....(520) 294-1200
editorial@azbiz.com, Pub., The Daily Territorial, AZ, Tucson
Lee, Chin-Yong
sahb2@joongboo.com, Ed. in Chief, JOONG BOO ILBO, Suwon, Kyonggi
Lee, Stephen
slee@scu.edu, Head, Santa Clara University, CA, Santa Clara
Lee, Sammy.....................................ext. 3328
Prodn. Mgr., Press, Texarkana Gazette, TX, Texarkana
Lee, Jae-won
j.lee@csuohio.edu, Div. Dir., Cleveland State University, OH, Cleveland
Lee, Dee...............................541-823-4804
Bus Mgr., Argus Observer, OR, Ontario
Lee, Joseph B.
joelee3@aol.com, Pub., The Daily Star, MS, Grenada
Lee, Katherine.........................(205) 722-0202
katherine.lee@tuscaloosanews.com, City Ed., The Tuscaloosa News, AL, Tuscaloosa
Lee, Pat ....(302) 629-5505 ext. 3005
adsales@newszap.com, Adv. Dir., Regl., The Daily Banner, MD, Cambridge
Lee, Byung
byunglee@elon.edu, Assoc. Prof., Elon University, NC, Elon
Lee, David.............................(404) 572-1977
dlee@coxnews.com, Opns. Dir., COXnet (Cox Newspapers' Wide Area Network/Cox News Service), GA, Atlanta
Lee, Daryl 575-356-4481

dlee@pntonline.com, Prodn. Mgr. - Freedom Printing, Clovis News Journal, NM, Clovis
Lee, Christian 253-597-8725
clee@theolympian.com, VP Circulation, The Olympian, WA, Olympia
Lee, Jerry
jerry@smdailyjournal.com, Pub., San Mateo Daily Journal, CA, San Mateo
Lee, Don..ext. 318
donlee@sanduskyregister.com, Editorial Page Ed., Sandusky Register, OH, Sandusky
Lee, Amy
alee@itemonline.com, Publisher, The Huntsville Item, TX, Huntsville
Lee, Steve
slee@gfherald.com, Religion Reporter, Grand Forks Herald, ND, Grand Forks
Lee, James..........................(415) 440-2668
jlee123@earthlink.net, Contact, JLM CD-ROM Publishing Co., CA, San Francisco
Lee, Michael
michael.lee@iaaglobal.org, Exec. Dir., International Advertising Association, Inc., NY, New York
Lee, Helen J. ....(949) 215-3751
hlee@wwmedia.net, Licensing Dir., WorldWide Media, CA, Aliso Viejo
Leech, Melissa
subscribe@monett-times.com, Circ. Dir., The Monett Times, MO, Monett
Leewe, Jim..........................(904) 359-4350
jim.leewe@jacksonville.com, Adv. Mgr., Nat'l Accts., The Florida Times-Union, FL, Jacksonville
Lefkofrydis, John
dimonews@dimoprasion.gr, Managing Dir., EPHIMERIS DIMOPRASION & PLEISTIRIASMON, Athens, Central Greece
Lefkow, Mike
mlefkow@bayareanewsgroup.com, Sports Ed., The Argus, CA, Fremont
Lefort, Michel..........................(450) 443-8330
Pres., Lasalle Papers, Inc., QC, Sainte-Catherine
Leftridge, Danny ....ext. 217
Prodn. Mgr., Distr., The Sentinel-Record, AR, Hot Springs
Legatz, Alan W...........................(941) 434-5555
alanlegatz@globalwealthstrategists.com, Pres., The Strategist, FL, Naples
Legault, Tracey
tracey.legault@ott.sunpub.com, Prodn. Mgr., The Ottawa Sun, ON, Ottawa
Leger, Dan..ext. 3340
dleger@herald.ca, Dir., News Content, The Chronicle Herald, NS, Halifax
Legrand, Gera ....ext. 109
Adv. Dir., Southeast Missourian, MO, Cape Girardeau
Legutko, Piotr
piotr.legutko@dziennik.krakow.pl, Ed. in Chief, DZIENNIK POLSKI, Krakow
Lehman, Dean G.............(303) 776-2244 ext. 310
dlehman@lehmancomm.com, Pres., Lehman Communications Corp., CO, Longmont
Lehman, Christy
clehman@dailycitizen.com, Adv. Mgr., The Evening World, IN, Linton
Lehman, Edward
elehman@lehmancomm.com, Pub., Lehman Communications Corp., CO, Longmont
Lehman, Dean G.............(303) 776-2244 ext. 310
dlehman@lehmancomm.com, Pres./Ed., Times-Call, CO, Longmont
Lehman, Dean ....(303) 776-2244
Publisher, The Canon City Daily Record, CO, Canon City
Lehman, Edward............(303) 776-2244 ext. 210
elehman@lehmancomm.com, Pub., Times-Call, CO, Longmont
Lehmkuhl, Lynn A. ....(212) 856-6329
llehmkuhl@nnnlp.com, Sr. Vice Pres., Sales, Newspaper National Network LP, NY, New York
Lehrke, Terry
terry@littlefalls.net, Asst. Sec./Treasurer, Minnesota Free Paper Association, MN, Little Falls
Leibold, Kelly..........................(530) 852-0203
kellyl@goldcountrymedia.com, Circulation Dir., Auburn Journal, Inc., CA, Auburn
Leidholdt, Alex
leidhoas@jmu.edu, Prof., James Madison University, VA, Harrisonburg
Leif, Bangsund
lb@glomdalen.no, Managing director, GLOMDALEN, Kongsvinger
Leifeld, Ellen
publisher@tennessean.com, Pres./Pub., The Tennessean, TN, Nashville
Leifeste, Terry ....ext. 205
tleifeste@ricentral.com, Pub., The Kent County Times, RI, West Warwick
Leifeste, Terri 501-315-8228
tleifeste@ricentral.com, Publisher, The Saline Courier, AR, Benton
Leinonen, Hannu
hannu.leinonen@kauppalethi.fi, Ed. in Chief, KAUPPALEHTI, Helsinki
Leister, Mark..........................(215) 886-5662
info@maned.com, Vice Pres., Bus. Devel., Managing Editor, Inc., PA, Jenkintown
Leiva Concha, Jorge..........................453 601
jleiva@mercurio.cl, Gen. Mgr., La Estrella del Norte, Antofagasta
Lejrand, Chip
lejrand@theaustralian.com.au, Ed. in Chief, THE AUSTRALIAN, Southbank
Lekoski, Lauren
llekoski@metro-email.com, Mktg. Mgr., Metro Creative Graphics, Inc., NY
Lekoski, Lauren
llekoski@metro-email.com, Mktg. Mgr., Metro Creative Graphics, Inc., NY, New York
Lemaster, Milton ....(972) 931-0711
milton@ghosting.com, Pres., AirSystems, Inc., TX, Addison
Lembeke, Denise ....ext. 213
dlembeke@columbiabasinherald.com, Bus. Mgr., Columbia Basin Herald, WA, Moses Lake
Lemieux, Jacques
jacques.lemieux@afp.com, Bureau Chief, Agence France-Presse - Montreal, QC, QC, Montreal
Lemieux, Peter H.
support@cyways.com, Pres., Cyways, Inc., MA, Newton
Lemire, Don..........................(302) 324-2466
dlemire@delawareonline.com, Vice Pres., Finance, The News Journal, DE, New Castle
Lemon, Claudette
clemon@times-standard.com, Controller, Times-Standard, CA, Eureka
Lempke, Georg
lempke@tageblatt.de, Bus. Mgr., Stader Tageblatt, Stade
Lendan, Lesa
lesa.lendan@oskarshamns.se, Mgr., OSKARSHAMNS - TIDNINGEN, Kalmar
Lenhoff, Alyssa
alenhoff@ysu.edu, Dir., Journalism, Youngstown State University, OH, Youngstown
Lenihan, Kevin ....(845) 437-4834
klenihan@poughkee.gannett.com, City Ed., Poughkeepsie Journal, NY, Poughkeepsie
Lensing-Wolff, Lambert
rn@westline.de, Proprietor, RUHR NACHRICHTEN, Dortmund
Lensing-Wolff, Florian
dorothee.ecgling@mehl.de, Proprietor, EMSDETTENER VOLKSZEITUNG, Emsdetten
Lensink, Gijs 5844106
gijs.lensink@ndcmediagroup.nl, Dir., DAGBLAD van het NOORDEN, Groningen
Lentz, Betty ....ext. 231
blentz@crescent-news.com, Circ. Mgr., Defiance Publishing LLC, OH, Defiance
Lenzen, David
david@planetdiscover.com, Pres./CEO, Planet Discover, KY, Fort Mitchell
Leon Morgado, Jose Joaquin
redaccion@diariodecadiz.com, Dir., Diario De Cadiz, Cadiz
Leon-Cains, Isis..................................ext. 410
icains@thenewsdispatch.com, Adv. Dir., News Dispatch, IN, Michigan City
Leonard, Kathleen J. ....(609) 272-7103
kleonard@pressofac.com, Dir., HR, The Press of Atlantic City, NJ, Pleasantville
Leonard, Gladys
advertising@thewesternstar.com, Bus. Mgr./Accountant, The Western Star, NL, Corner Brook
Leonard, Suzy 321-242-3614
sleonard@floridatoday.com, Custom Content Editor, Florida Today, FL, Melbourne
Leonard, Cathy ....(276) 645-4415
cleonard@bristolnews.com, Prodn. Mgr., Mailroom, Bristol Herald Courier, VA, Bristol
Leong, Joe ....(808) 695-6318
jleong@staradvertiser.com, Director of Consumer Sales/Retention, Honolulu Star-Advertiser, HI, Honolulu
Leonte, Mirela
bzb@bzb.ro, Mng. Ed., BUNA ZIUA BRASOV, Brasov, Brasov
Lepinske, Harry
lepinske@sbcglobal.net, Pres., International Press Club of Chicago (IPCC), IL, Western Springs
Leposky, George ....(305) 285-2200
amprsnd@aol.com, Ed., Ampersand Communications, FL, Miami
Leposky, Rosalie E.
amprsnd@aol.com, Mng. Partner, Ampersand Communications, FL, Miami
Lepovac, Sanny
slepovac@srtesse-normandie.com, Adv. Rep., PARIS-NORMANDIE, Deville-les-Rouen
Leppert, Dale ....(303) 473-1552
leppertd@dailycamera.com, Prodn. Mgr., Pressroom, Daily Camera, CO, Boulder
Leritz, Heidi..........................406-657-2193
editor@msubretort.org, Editor-in-Chief, Montana State Univ. Billings, MT, Billings
Lerner, John
jlerner@vnuemedia.com, Vice Pres., eMedia, VNU eMedia, NY, New York
Leroux-Lanthier, Sylvia 613-933-3160
accounts@standard-freeholder.com, Office Mgr., Standard-Freeholder, ON, Cornwall
Lerseth, Lisa..........................(707) 553-6853
llerseth@timesheraldonline.com, Pre Press Mgr., Vallejo Times-Herald, CA, Vallejo
Lesco, Deana
deana.lesco@thefacts.com, Adv. Mgr., Retail, The Facts, TX, Clute
Leshico, Thabo..........................280 3000
editor@sowetan.co.za, Ed., THE SOWETAN, Johannesburg, PWV
Leskaj, Arben
adn@albnet.net, Ed., ALBANIAN DAILY NEWS, Tirana
Lesko, Robert
sales@amergraph.com, Pres., Amergraph Corporation, NJ, Sparta
Leslie, Keith ....(416) 325-7843
keith.leslie@thecanadianpress.com, Legislature Correspondent, Canadian Press, The - Toronto, ON, ON, Toronto
Leslie, Melissa
melissa_leslie@mcgraw-hill.com, Ed., The Daily Journal
Lesnick, Dave..........................(406) 758-4426
dlesnick@dailyinterlake.com, Sports Ed., Daily Inter Lake, MT, Kalispell
Lessa, Geraldo
redacao@tribunadealagoas.com.br, Dir., Jornal de Alagoas, Maceio, Alagoas
Lessersohn, James C.................(212) 556-1234
Vice Pres., Finance/Cor. Devel., The New York Times Co., NY, New York
Lester, Mary ....(408) 257-9567
Pub., Lester Syndicate, CA, Cupertino
Letheby, Pete ....(308) 381-9468
pete.letheby@theindependent.com, Assoc. Ed., The Grand Island Independent, NE, Grand Island
Lett, Dan..........................(204) 697-7257
Dan.Lett@freepress.mb.ca, Columnist, Winnipeg Free Press, MB, Winnipeg
Letterman, Gretchen..................(727) 892-2203
letterman@tampabay.com, Dir., Editorial/Creative, Times Targeted Media, Tampa Bay Times, FL, Saint Petersburg
Lev, Deborah..........................(908) 852-1400
Centenary College, NJ, Hackettstown
Levesque, Joyce M..............(603) 668-4321 ext. 401
jlevesque@unionleader.com, New Hampshire Union Leader/New Hampshire Sunday News, NH, Manchester
Levey, Brian
info@colovision.com, Vice Pres. Mktg./Sales, ColorVision, Inc., NJ, Lawrenceville
Levin, Linda
lllevin@uri.edu, Sec., Rhode Island Press Association, RI, Kingston
Levin, Deborah
deblevin@aol.com, Pres., Levin Represents, CA, Santa Monica
Levine, Jeff ....(860) 241-3931
jlevine@courant.com, Dir., Content, The Hartford Courant, CT, Hartford
Levine, Jason
jlevine@delawareonline.com, Sports Ed., The News Journal, DE, New Castle
Levine, Jeff
info@logopremiums.com, Project Mgr., Logopremiums.com, NY, Mount Kisco
Levine, Michael..................................ext. 252
mlevine@kauaipubco.com, Asst. Ed., The Garden Island, HI, Lihue
Levine, Charisse ....(704) 463-1360
Pfeiffer Univ., NC, Misenheimer
Levine, Edward
nlevine@firebrand.com, Pres., Firebrand, RI, Providence
Levinsohn, Peter
info@autotypeamerica.com, Pres., Mac Dermid Autotype Inc., IL, Rolling Meadows
Levinson, Paul
paullevinson1@cs.com, Chair, Fordham University, NY, Bronx
Levit, Joseph
info@simonmiller.com, Pres., Simon Miller Sales Co., PA, Philadelphia
Levit, Henri C.
info@simonmiller.com, COO, Simon Miller Sales Co., PA, Philadelphia
Levy, Jay R. ....(212) 686-6850
news@blackradionetwork.com, Pres., Black Press Service, Inc., NY, New York
Levy, Michael
info@arpacgroup.com, Pres., Arpac Group, IL, Schiller Park
Levy, June..........................847-375-5183
june.levy@srds.com, Director, Data Services, SRDS, a Kantar Media Company, IL, Des Plaines
Levy, Pat..........................(775) 788-6475
plevy@rgj.com, IT Mgr., Reno Gazette-Journal, NV, Reno
Levy, Alan
alevy@praguepost.com, Ed. in Chief, Lion's Share Group, Prague
Lewers, Jim
newsroom@press-citizen.com, Mng. Ed., Iowa City Press-Citizen, IA, Iowa City
Lewey, Weston McCollum ..(570) 633-3130 ext. 14
wlewey@thnews.com, Pub., Times-Herald, AR, Forrest City
Lewis, C. Dutch..........................(740) 452-3601
sglapat@adjustoveyor.com, Sales Mgr., Stewart Glapat Corp., OH, Zanesville
Lewis, Wayne
wlewis@franciscan.edu, Chair, Franciscan University of Steubenville, OH, Steubenville
Lewis, Nicholas ....ext. 231
nlewis@richmondregister.com, Pub., The Richmond Register, KY, Richmond
Lewis, Zachary ....(216) 999-4632
Classical Music Critic, The Plain Dealer, OH, Cleveland
Lewis, Julie..........................(607) 441-7212
jlewis@thedailystar.com, Photo Dept. Mgr., The Daily Star, NY, Oneonta
Lewis, Sheri ....(806) 742-3349
Asst. Dir./Editorial/Broadcasting Advisor, Texas Tech. Univ., TX, Lubbock
Lewis, Tim 87241505
tim@tbw.com.au, Gen. Mgr., BORDER WATCH
Lewis, Judy
judy.lewis@dailyexaminer.com.au, Gen. Mgr., THE DAILY EXAMINER
Lewis, Kevin
kevin@plainviewdailyherald.com, Editorial Page Ed., Plainview Herald, TX, Plainview
Lewis, Charles J.
chuck@hearstdc.com, Senior Editor, Hearst News Service, DC, Washington
Lewis, Francesca ....(916) 321-1703
flewis@sacbee.com, Adv. Sr. Vice Pres., The Sacramento Bee, CA, Sacramento
Lewis, Robert R.
infosys@aol.com, CEO/Dir., Pdct. Devel., Info-

com Systems, WA, Kent
Lewis, Kathleen
news@robdailynews.com, Pub., Lewis Newspapers, IL, Robinson
Lewis, Francesca ....(805) 437-0086
flewis@venturacountystar.com, Adv. Sr. Vice Pres., Ventura County Star, CA, Camarillo
Lewis, Kathleen
lawnews@lawdailyrecord.com, Pub., Daily Record, IL, Lawrenceville
Lewis, Jennifer ....(912) 489-9439
jlewis@morrismultimedia.com, Regl. Controller, Statesboro Herald, GA, Statesboro
Lewis, Danny
dlewis@eprisenow.com, Mng. Ed., The Enterprise Ledger, AL, Enterprise
Lewnes, Ann
jwarnock@adobe.com, Sr. Vice Pres., Global Mktg., Adobe Systems, Inc., CA, San Jose
Lewthwaite, Jim.....................(204) 571-7433
jlewthwa@brandonsun.com, News Ed., Brandon Sun, MB, Brandon
Leyshon, Maryanne
mleyshon@yourwestvalley.com, Ed., Daily News-Sun, AZ, Sun City
Liakounakos, Th.
kerdos@kerdos.gr, Pub., KERDOS, Athens, Central Greece
Liang, Lin
feedback@mail.mdnkids.com, Pub., MANDARIN DAILY NEWS, Taipei
Liang, Lin
feedback@mail.mdnkids.com, Pub., GWOYEU RYHBAW, Taipei
Liantonio, Collette
collette@conceptstv.com, Contact, Concepts Video Productions, Inc., NJ, Boonton
Libien Kaui, Naim
artardecer@prodigy.net.mx, Pres., ATARDECER, Toluca, Mexico
Libien Kaui, Naim
nlkmx@yahoo.com.mx, Pres., AMANECER, Toluca, Mexico
Libien Kaui, Miled
miled1@mail.miled.com, Pres., EL MANANA, Toluca, Mexico
Licence, Terry
tslicence@comcast.net, Media Consultants, Inc., CO, Loveland
Lickers, Lynn ....ext. 256
Mktg. Dir., The Daily Sentinel, CO, Grand Junction
Licklider, Debi
licklid@phillynews.com, Features Ed., The Philadelphia Daily News, PA, Philadelphia
Lid, Eivind
eal@glomdalen.no, Chief Editor, GLOMDALEN, Kongsvinger
Lieb, William ....(724) 684-2651
blieb@tribweb.com, Prodn. Dir., The Valley Independent, PA, Monessen
Liebana, Estrada
lacronica@dvnet.es, Dir., LA CRONICA 16 DE LEON, Leon
Liebelt, David.....................(920) 453-5120
dliebelt@sheboygan.gannett.com, Retail Adv. Mgr., The Sheboygan Press, WI, Sheboygan
Liebermann, Carlos
redaccion@elheraldo.com.ar, Pres., El Heraldo, Concordia, Provincia de Entre Rios
Liebman, Seymour
sliebman@cusa.canon.com, Exec. Vice Pres./Gen. Counsel Admin./Reg'l Opns., Canon USA, Inc., NY, Lake Success
Lifton, Tyler ....(434) 982-2395
Colgate Darden Grad. School of Bus., VA, Charlottesville
Liggett, Dan.....................937-382-2574
dliggett@wnewsj.com, Editor, Wilmington News Journal, OH, Wilmington
Ligomeka, Brian.....................+265 888 476 035
brianligo@bnltimes.com, DAILY TIMES, Blantyre
Likan, Aaron
mail.liberal@ruralpress.com, Pub./Ed., DAILY LIBERAL
Liles, Vince ....(863) 386-5808
vliles@highlandstoday.com, Circ. Dir., Highlands Today, FL, Sebring
Lilje, Kathy.....................ext. 315
kathylilje@sanduskyregister.com, Features Ed., Sandusky Register, OH, Sandusky
Lillagore, Jim.....................ext. 389
Prodn. Mgr., The Hickory Daily Record, NC, Hickory
Lillie, Sandy
information@omix.com, Gen. Mgr., Omix, Inc. (Online Marketspace), CA, Redwood City
Lilly, John ....(308) 381-9440
john.lilly@theindependent.com, Prodn. Dir., Opns., The Grand Island Independent, NE, Grand Island
Lim, Kenneth T.
klim@cybrmda.com, Chrmn./Chief Futurist, The CyberMedia Group, CA, Cupertino
Lima, John
edletters@sharon-herald.com, Pub., The Herald, PA, Sharon
Lima, Carlos
clima@lacronica.com, Ed., LA CRONICA, Mexicali, Baja California Norte
Limon, Jose Angel Martinez
publicidad@elsoldesanluis.com.mx, Dir., EL SOL DE SAN LUIS, San Luis Potosi, San Luis Potosi
Limongi, Eugenio.....................222-5402
Gen. Mgr., La Ciudad, Avellaneda, Provincia de Buenos Aires
Limtiaco, Rindraty Celes
enery@guam.gannett.com, Pub., PACIFIC DAILY NEWS/SUNDAY NEWS, Hagatna
Lin, Jong-Gun
imjk@sed.co.kr, Pres., SEOUL KYUNGJE SHINMUN, Seoul
Lind, Raymond
ral@rogalandsavis.no, Adv. Mgr., ROGALANDS AVIS, Stavanger
Lindemann, Bill ....(940) 720-3492
lindemannb@wtr.com, Dir., Information Systems, Wichita Falls Times Record News, TX, Wichita Falls
Linden, Michael ....ext. 280
mlinden@sharonherald.com, Circ. Dir., The Herald, PA, Sharon
Linden, Thomas R.....................(919) 962-4078
Glaxo Wellcome Distinguished Prof. of Medical Journalism, University of North Carolina, NC, Chapel Hill
Linden, Brian ....ext. 220
Univ. of Central Florida, FL, Orlando
Lindenberg, Maria Antonietta Queiroz
aure@redegazeta.com.br, Pres., A Gazeta, Vitoria, Espirito Santo
Linder, Peter
linderpeter@nmhu.edu, Chair, New Mexico Highlands University, NM, Las Vegas
Lindgren, Dawn 651-228-5018
dlindgren@pioneerpress.com, Credit Mgr., St. Paul Pioneer Press, MN, Saint Paul
Lindley, Doug ....(208) 239-3138
douglind@journalnet.com, Photo Ed., Idaho State Journal, ID, Pocatello
Lindley, Mary Ann.....................(850) 599-2178
mlindley@tallahassee.com, Community Conversation/Editorial Page Ed., Tallahassee Democrat, FL, Tallahassee
Lindley, Donald
don.lindley@news-jrnl.com, Ed., Daytona Beach News-Journal, FL, Daytona Beach
Lindner, Christian
christian.lindner@rhein-zeitung.net, Ed. in Chief, RHEIN-ZEITUNG, Koblenz
Lindoo, Ed.....................(772) 221-4123
ed.lindoo@scripps.com, IT Dir., Treasure Coast News/Press-Tribune, FL, Stuart
Lindsay, Walton
ky@kwnews.com, Pres., Keister Williams Newspaper Services, Inc., VA, Charlottesville
Lindsay, Walton C.
ky@kwnews.com, Pres., Keister-Williams Newspaper Services, Inc., VA
Lindsay, Walton C. (Ky)
ky@kwnews.com, Pres./Treasurer, Keister Williams Newspaper Services, Inc., VA, Charlottesville
Lindsay, Debbie
debbiel@brehmmail.com, Executive Assistant, Brehm Communications, Inc., CA, San Diego
Lindsey, Michael ....(307) 772-0003
mediamike@earthlink.net, Co-Owner, Media Consultants, Inc., WY, Cheyenne
Lindsey, Michael ....(307) 772-0003
mediamike@earthlink.net, Co-Owner, Media Consultants, Inc., WY, Cheyenne
Lindsey, Michael D.
mediamike1@aol.com, Pres., Media Consultants, Inc., CO, Colorado Springs
Lindus, Linda ....(562) 499-1422
linda.lindus@presstelegram.com, Publisher, Press-Telegram Publications, Inc., CA, Long Beach
linda.lindus@presstelegram.com, Pub., Press Telegram, CA, Long Beach
Linebarger, Les
leslinebarger@hendersondailynews.com, Pub., Henderson Daily News, TX, Henderson
Linehan, Gary
glinehan@uniondemocrat.com, Theater/Music Ed., The Union Democrat, CA, Sonora
Linenberger, Lori.....................(316) 268-6321
llineberger@wichitaeagle.com, Features Ed., The Wichita Eagle, KS, Wichita
Linette, Jim.....................239-574-1110
jlinette@breezenewspapers.com, Sports Ed., Cape Coral Breeze, FL, Cape Coral
Linex, Raymond
rlinex@corsicanadailysun.com, Mng. Ed., Corsicana Daily Sun, TX, Corsicana
Lingelbach, Dene ....(780) 429-5173
dlingelbach@thejournal.canwest.com, Adv. Local Online Sales Specialist, Edmonton Journal, AB, Edmonton
Linhares, Emerson
editor@omossoreonse.com.br, Ed. in Chief, O Mossoroense, Mossoro, Rio Grande do Norte
Link, John ....(918) 256-6422
vdj@cableone.net, Pub., The Vinita Daily Journal, OK, Vinita
Linker, Erich.....................(212) 807-4791
erich.linker@impremedia.com, Sr. Vice Pres., Sales, impreMedia LLC, NY, Brooklyn
Linsner, Dawn ....(804) 947-4299
Randolph-Macon Woman's College, VA, Lynchburg
Lint, Bea.....................(760) 256-4140
blint@desertdispatch.com, Adv. Dir., Desert Dispatch, CA, Barstow
Liow, Joseph.....................6890-5200
info@broadxent.com, Pres., Broadxent Pte. Ltd., Singapore
Lippincott, John
lippincott@case.org, Pres., Council for Advancement and Support of Education, DC, Washington
Lippincott, John
lippincott@case.org, Pres., Council for the Advancement of Science Writing, Inc., WV, Hedgesville
Lippoldt, Keith
publisher@pratttribune.com, Pub., The Pratt Tribune, KS, Pratt
Lipps, Keith
bklipps@invision1.com, CEO, Invision Marketing, CO, Fort Collins
Lippus, Mike.....................ext. 225
mikelippus@sanduskyregister.com, Prodn. Foreman, Mailroom, Sandusky Register, OH, Sandusky
Lipsey, Stanford
webmaster@buffalo.com, Pub., The Buffalo News, NY, Buffalo
Lipsey, Jeff
jlipsey@cdispatch.com, Prodn. Mgr., The Commercial Dispatch, MS, Columbus
Lipshetz, Terry
tlipshet@appleton.gannett.com, Digital Opns. Ed., The Post-Crescent, WI, Appleton
Lipsky, Seth.....................ext. 688
lipsky@nysun.com, Ed., The New York Sun, NY, New York
Lipson, Jenifer ....(508) 626-3826
Entertainment Ed., Milford Daily News, MA, Milford
Liptak, Cynthia J. ....(815) 673-3771
cindyl@times-press.com, Gen. Mgr., The Times-Press, IL, Streator
Liptak, Cindy.....................(815) 937-3310
cliptak@daily-journal.com, Bus. Mgr., The Daily Journal, IL, Kankakee
Lipton, Gary ....(800) 222-5551 ext. 107
gary@napsnet.com, Vice Pres., Media Rel., North American Precis Syndicate, Inc., NY, New York
Lipton, Gary.....................ext. 107
gary@napsnet.com, Vice Pres., Media Rel., North American Precis Syndicate, Inc., NY
Liscia, Richard
redaction@quoti.med.com, Ed. in Chief, LE QUOTIDIEN DU MEDECIN, Paris
List, Randy
rlist2@hotmail.com, Pub., The Evening World, IN, Linton
List, Karen
klist@journ.umass.edu, Dir., University of Massachusetts, MA, Amherst
List, Randy
rlist2@hotmail.com, Pub., The Brazil Times, IN, Brazil
List, Randy E.
rlist2@hotmail.com, Pub., Banner-Graphic, IN, Greencastle
List, Randy ....(812) 847-4487
Pub., Greene County Daily World, IN, Linton
Lister, Gwen
gwen@namibian.com.na, Ed., THE NAMIBIAN, Windhoek
Listopad, Steve.....................(701) 252-3467
Jamestown College, ND, Jamestown
Lisuzzo, Josephine.....................(312) 321-3232
jlisuzzo@suntimes.com, Strategic Mktg. Mgr., Chicago Sun-Times, IL, Chicago
Liter, Hannah ....(208) 885-5780
Univ. of Idaho, ID, Moscow
Little, David.....................(530) 896-7793
dlittle@chicoer.com, Ed., Chico Enterprise-Record, CA, Chico
Little, Mike.....................336-506-3061
GM/Adv. Director, Times-News, NC, Burlington
Littlepage, Deborah
debbielittlepage@the-messenger.com, Adv. Dir., The Messenger, KY, Madisonville
Littler, Janet ....(704) 261-2205
jlittler@theej.com, Adv. Dir., The Enquirer-Journal, NC, Monroe
Litty, Jamie
jamie.litty@uncp.edu, Chair, University of North Carolina at Pembroke, NC, Pembroke
Litzel, Dianna
adreps@chanute.com, Display Adv. Rep., The Chanute Tribune, KS, Chanute
Liu, Dejun
dejun_liu@pvamu.edu, Head, Prairie View A&M University, TX, Prairie View
Liu, Cliv
info@pixoarts.com, Pres., Pixo Arts Corp., CA, Redwood City
Liu, William W.
bill@cdtechnology.com, Pres., CD Technology, CA, Santa Clara
Liveris, Andrew
dowmedia.relations@dow.com, Chrmn./Pres./CEO, The Dow Chemical Co., MI, Midland
Livernois, Joe
jlivernois@montereyherald.com, Exec. Ed., The Monterey County Herald, CA, Monterey
Livingston, JoAnn
joann@wninews.com, Mng. Ed., Waxahachie Daily Light, TX, Waxahachie
Lizotte, Mary.....................(603) 543-3100 ext. 161
mlizotte@tsvmedia.net, Nat'l Adv. Mgr., Eagle Times, NH, Claremont
LiÂ£vana de Camargo, Danilo
diario.votup@votuporanga.com.br, Dir., Diario De Votuporanga, Votuporanga, Sao Paulo
Ljungaeus, Diana
diana@lapressclub.org, Exec. Dir., Los Angeles Press Club, CA, Los Angeles
Llewellyn, Lynne
generalmanager@thebraziltimes.com, Gen. Mgr., The Brazil Times, IN, Brazil
Llorca Llinares, Vicente
redaccion@canarias7.es, Asst. Dir., Canarias 7, Las Palmas de Gran Canaria, Las Palmas
Lloyd, Lynn
lynn.lloyd@mtstandard.com, Interim Pub., The Montana Standard, MT, Butte
Lloyd, Nicholas ....ext. 16
nlloyd@brodiesystem.com, Engineer, Brodie System, Inc., NJ, Linden
Lloyd, Jared 801-344-2555
Sports Editor, The Daily Herald, UT, Provo
LoCascio, Chris 951-827-2105
Editor-in-Chief, Univ. of California, Riverside

Highlander Newspaper, CA, Riverside
LoPilato, Joseph J. ....(617) 619-6221
jlopilato@bostonherald.com, Adv. Dir., Classified, Boston Herald, MA, Boston
LoPresti, Brittny
editor@keenequinox.com, Keene State College, NH, Keene
LoScalzo, Mary Beth ....ext. 258
mbloscalzo@sharonherald.com, Coord., Educ. Serv., The Herald, PA, Sharon
Lobanov, Igor ....(858) 270-9002
Travel Ed., Mature Life Features, CA, San Diego
Lobas, Jim ....(920) 431-8371
jlobas@greenbay.gannett.com, Adv. Mgr., Nat'l, Green Bay Press-Gazette, WI, Green Bay
Lobb, William J. ....(610) 371-5158
blobb@readingeagle.com, Circ. Mgr., Single Copy, Reading Eagle, PA, Reading
Lobeck, Linda
lobeck@ironmountaindailynews.com, Bus./Finance Ed., The Daily News, MI, Iron Mountain
Lobecker, William B. ....(215) 345-3034
blobecker@phillyburbs.com, Circ. Dir., The Intelligencer, PA, Doylestown
Loberstein, Adam ....(530) 752-9887
Univ. of California Davis, CA, Davis
Lochthofen, Sergej
redaktion@thueringer-allgemeine.de, Ed. in Chief, THURINGER ALLGEMEINE, Erfurt
Lock, Yet...............................(310) 481-0401
yet@socalnews.com, Vice Pres., City News Service, Inc. - Los Angeles, CA, CA, Los Angeles
Lockhart, Lee
leel@wyodaily.com, Educ. Ed., Northern Wyoming Daily News, WY, Worland
Lodge, Richard ....(508) 626-3871
News Ed., Metrowest Daily News, MA, Framingham
Lodge, Richard ....(508) 626-3871
rlodge@cnc.com, Exec. Ed., Milford Daily News, MA, Milford
Lodge Kopenhaver, Lillian
kopenhav@fiu.edu, Prof./Dean, Florida International University, FL, North Miami
Lodovic, Joseph J. ....(303) 820-1619
jlodovic@medianewsgroup.com, Pres., MediaNews Group Inc, CO, Denver
Lodunis, Kimsoi
kimsoi@nstp.com.my, Adv. Mgr., NEW STRAITS TIMES, Kota Kinabalu, Sabah
Loeberg, Arve..........................+4741100110
arve.loberg@t-a.no, CEO, TROENDER-AVISA, Steinkjer
Loehr, Tom
tloehr@shc.edu, Chair, Spring Hill College, AL, Mobile
Loenborg, B.
redaktion@flensborg-avis.de, Bus. Mgr., FLENSBORG AVIS, Flensburg
Loera, Juan Fernando Healy
jfhealy@lacronica.com, Pres./CEO, LA CRONICA, Mexicali, Baja California Norte
Loerts-Sabin, Helmut 9890
anzeiger@ost-friesland.de, Bus. Mgr., ANZEIGER FUR HARLINGERLAND, Wittmund
Lofdahl, Duane ....(404) 564-3968
duane.lofdahl@theaustin.com, Vice Pres., Planning/Design, The Austin Company, OH, Cleveland
Loffley, Paul
paul@times.co.sz, Pub., TIMES OF SWAZILAND, Mbabane
Loftis, Rachael
rachael.loftis@wninews.com, Bus. Mgr., Waxahachie Daily Light, TX, Waxahachie
Logan, Casey ....(239) 344-4721
Lehigh Ed., The News-Press, FL, Fort Myers
Logan, Nicki ....(806) 296-1362
nicki@plainviewdailyherald.com, Lifestyle Ed., Plainview Herald, TX, Plainview
Loh, Sharon ....(203) 576-4382
Univ. of Bridgeport, CT, Bridgeport
Lohmann, Carsten 882 252
Publishing Dir., MINDENER TAGEBLATT, Minden
Loi, Ho Quing
quingloi@hanoimoi.com.vn, Ed. in Chief, HANOI MOI, Hanoi
Lomax, Glynda ....(580) 303-4381
glyndalomax@gmail.com, Author, Glynda Lomax, TX, Princeton
Lonborg, Bjarne
bl@flensborg-avis.de, Ed.-in-Chief, FLENSBORG AVIS, Flensburg
Lonchar, Donna.......................(479) 872-3032
dlonchar@nwaonline.net, Metro Ed., The Morning News of Northwest Arkansas, AR, Springdale
Londono Riani, Ana Maria
gerencia@elliberal.com.co, Pres., Editorial El Liberal S.A., Popayan, Cauca
Long, Nancy...........................(314) 340-8904
nlong@post-dispatch.com, Mgr., Consumer Mktg., St. Louis Post-Dispatch, MO, Saint Louis
Long, Harry F. ....ext. 172
hlong@nvdaily.com, Opns. Mgr., Northern Virginia Daily, VA, Strasburg
Long, Matt...............................(919) 836-5670
mlong@newsobserver.com, Adv. Prodn. Mgr., The News & Observer, NC, Raleigh
Long, Marian ....(985) 857-2291
marian.long@houmatoday.com, Inside Sales / Class Manager, The Courier, LA, Houma
Long, Marian ....(985) 857-2291
marian.long@houmatoday.com, Inside Sales Manager, The Daily Comet, LA, Thibodaux
Long, Helen
hlong@punxsutawneyspirit.com, Circ. Mgr., The Punxsutawney Spirit, PA, Punxsutawney
Long, Ita Mari
classified@decaturdailydemocrat.com, Adv. Mgr., Classified, Decatur Daily Democrat, IN, Decatur
Long, Joel ....(402) 444-1493
joel.long@owh.com, Dir., Communications, Omaha World-Herald, NE, Omaha
Long, Karen...........................(216) 999-4410
Book Editor, The Plain Dealer, OH, Cleveland
Long, Gary ....(956) 982-6674
gary_long@link.freedom.com, News Ed., El Nuevo Heraldo, TX, Brownsville
Long, Steven..........................(806) 291-1084
longs@wbu.edu, Wayland Baptist Univ., TX, Plainview
Long, Sandra D........................(215) 854-4515
Mng. Ed., The Philadelphia Inquirer, PA, Philadelphia
Longacre, Mark
mark.longacre@jbtc.com, Mktg. Mgr., FMC Technologies, PA, Chalfont
Longley, Rob..........................(540) 574-6281
rlongley@dnronline.com, Day News Ed., Daily News-Record, VA, Harrisonburg
Loo, Tim ....(604) 632-3355
tloo@omicronconsulting.com, Principal, Omicron Media, WA, Bellevue
Loomis, Robert.......................(619) 232-4381
editor@sddt.com, Pub./CEO, The Daily Transcript, CA, San Diego
Loomis, Robert
editor@sddt.com, Pub., The Daily Transcript, CA, San Diego
Loose, Holger
redaktion.neumunster@shz.de, Ed. in Chief, Holsteinischer Courier, Neumunster
Lopez, Jessica........................(864) 294-2077
Furman Univ., SC, Greenville
Lopez, Raul ....(305) 376-5187
rlopez@miamiherald.com, Gen. Mgr., Miami-Herald.com, The Miami Herald, FL, Miami
Lopez, Rosa ....ext. 2364
Dir., Finance, Pasadena Star-News, CA, Pasadena
Lopez, Miguel Angel Capriles 596-1911
edrangel@la-cadena.com, Pres., Publicaciones Capriles, Caracas, D.F.
Lopez, Miguel 39-2115
uhora@caoba.entelnet.bo, Gen. Mgr., Ultima Hora, La Paz
Lopez, Larry................(719) 544-3520 ext. 413
llopez@chieftain.com, City Ed., The Pueblo Chieftain, CO, Pueblo
Lopez, Michelle ....(928) 913-8624
Gen. Mgr., Electronic Media, Arizona Daily Sun, AZ, Flagstaff
Lopez Morales, Oscar
loddim@pue1.telmex.net.mx, Pres., LA OPINION, Puebla, Puebla
Lopez Saldana, Maria Eugenia
eltiempo@infosel.net.mx, Gen. Mgr., EL TIEMPO, Monclova, Coahuila
Lord, Kristina ....(509) 582-1481
klord@tri-cityherald.com, Asst. City Ed., Tri-City Herald, WA, Kennewick
Lord, Debbie ....(251) 219-5705
dlord@mobileregister.com, Features Ed., Press-Register, AL, Mobile
Lord, Bill ....(201) 646-4361
Dir., Consumer Sales, Herald News, NJ, West Paterson
Lorenzen, Robin......................(508) 626-4331
rlorenzen@cnc.com, Vice Pres., Promo., Metrowest Daily News, MA, Framingham
Lorenzen, Robin
rlorenzin@cnc.com, Vice Pres. Promos./Mktg., Community Newspaper Co., MA, Framingham
Lorton, Robert ....(918) 581-8450
Pub., Tulsa World, OK, Tulsa
Losness, Jon ....(262) 656-6270 ext. 270
jlosness@kenoshanews.com, Ed., Kenosha News, WI, Kenosha
Lotridge Levin, Linda
llevin@uri.edu, Chair, University of Rhode Island, RI, Kingston
Lott, Rick
rick.lott@leaderpub.com, Distr. Mgr., Dowagiac Daily News, MI, Dowagiac
Lott, Michele
mlott@nsb-observer.com, Owner/Pub., The Observer, FL, New Smyrna Beach
Lott, Tim...............................(512) 912-2510
tlott@statesman.com, Gen. Mgr., statesman.com, Austin American-Statesman, TX, Austin
Louage, Jaki
hetvolk@hetvolk.be, Mng. Ed., Dagblad Het Volk NV, Gent, East Flanders
Loubert, Joel
redaction.sports@lyonne-republicaine.fr, Pres., L'YONNE REPUBLICAINE, Auxerre
Louder, Jon
jlouder@mitchellrepublic.com, Circ. Mgr., The Daily Republic, SD, Mitchell
Lough, Michael.......................(478) 744-4626
mlough@macontel.com, Sports Columnist, The Telegraph, GA, Macon
Louie, David ....ext. 131
dslouie@flashnews.com, Sales/Mktg. Mgr., Wireless Flash News, Inc., CA, San Diego
Lourenco, Jose
np21na@mail.telepac.pt, Dir., DIARIO INSULAR, Angra do Heroismo, Azores
Lovang, Magnus
magnus.lovang@na.se, Adv. Mgr, NERIKES ALLEHANDA, Orebro
Lovas, Anne
anne.lovas@nopg.com, Gen. Mgr., Daily Journal of Commerce
Love, Lorie ....ext. 259
editor@richmondregister.com, Ed., The Richmond Register, KY, Richmond
Love, Jason...........................(805) 271-9560
yours@jasonlove.com, Sole Proprietor, JasonLove.com (Humor Features), CA, Port Hueneme
Love, Gary.............................(765) 420-5288
glove@journalandcourier.com, Dir., Information Sys., Journal and Courier, IN, Lafayette
Love, Beryl ....(775) 788-6596
blove@rgj.com, Exec. Ed., Reno Gazette-Journal, NV, Reno
Lovegrove, David............................ext. 4235
Bob Jones Univ., SC, Greenville
Lovejoy, Bill...........................(831) 429-2445
blovejoy@santacruzsentinel.com, Photo Ed., Santa Cruz Sentinel, CA, Scotts Valley
Lovejoy, Steve.........................(262) 631-1722
slovejoy@journaltimes.com, Ed., The Journal Times, WI, Racine
Lovejoy, Andrea ....ext. 237
alovejoy@msmgmt.com, Ed., La Grange Daily News, GA, LaGrange
Lovelace, Allan.......................(909) 222-8488
Riverside Cmty. College, CA, Riverside
Lovelady, Jay ....(559) 737-4866
College of the Sequoias, CA, Visalia
Loveless, Diana ....(519) 271-2220 ext. 204
Editorial Page Ed., The Beacon-Herald, ON, Stratford
Loveless, Beth.........................(540) 374-5538
bloveless@freelancestar.com, Adv. Team Leader, The Free Lance-Star, VA, Fredericksburg
Lovell, Paula...........................(920) 832-2649
University of Wisconsin, Fox Valley, WI, Menasha
Lovely, Randy 602-444-8790
rlovely@republicmedia.com, SVP/News and Audience Development, The Arizona Republic, AZ, Phoenix
Lovett, Genia ....ext. 201
publisher@postcrescent.com, Pres./Pub., The Post-Crescent, WI, Appleton
Lovin, Claudia
clovin@newsrepublican.com, Pub., Boone News-Republican, IA, Boone
clovin@newsrepublican.com, Boone County Shopping News, IA, Boone
Loving, Jim ....(507) 285-7204
Rochester Cmty. Tech. College, MN, Rochester
Loving, Bill
lovibill@isu.edu, Chair, Idaho State University, ID, Pocatello
Lovisa, Hector 425-614
Gen. Mgr., La Calle, Concepcion del Uruguay, Provincia de Entre Rios
Low, Trinnique
info@connectinc.com, Contact, ConnectInc.com, CA, Mountain View
Lowe, Frances C............(540) 667-3200 ext. 265
flowe@winchesterstar.com, Life Ed., The Winchester Star, VA, Winchester
Lowe, Patrick..........................609-272-7170
plowe@pressofac.com, Packaging & Distribution Manager, The Press of Atlantic City, NJ, Pleasantville
Lowe, James ....ext. 1154
james.lowe@timesargus.com, Arts Ed., The Times Argus, VT, Barre
Lowe, Kenneth W......................(513) 977-3028
lowe@scripps.com, Pres., Scripps Network Interactive, E. W. Scripps Co., OH, Cincinnati
Lowe-Guzman, Debbie ....(559) 735-3240
classified@visaliatimesdelta.com, Adv. Mgr., Classified Inside Sales, Visalia Times-Delta, CA, Visalia
Lowell, Brad
bladeempire@nckcn.com, Ed., Concordia Blade-Empire, KS, Concordia
Lowen, Marke
publisher@news.vu, Pub., VANUATU NEWS, Port Vila
Lowenstein, Adam.....................321-242-3654
alowenst@floridatoday.com, Business Editor, Florida Today, FL, Melbourne
Lowenthal, Maria ....(650) 688-3840
Chair, Menlo College, CA, Atherton
Lowery, D.J.
djlowery@npgco.com, Adv. Mgr., Promo., The Daily Star-Journal, MO, Warrensburg
Lowrey, Pat
mikec_news@dailynews.net, Editorial Writer, The Hays Daily News, KS, Hays
Lowry, Pat
patl_news@dailynews.net, Ed., The Hays Daily News, KS, Hays
Lozano, Jose ....(212) 807-4770
jose.lozano@impremedia.com, Vice Chrmn., impreMedia LLC, NY, Brooklyn
Lozano, Monica ....(213) 896-2153
monica.lozano@laopinion.com, CEO & Pub./CEO, La Opinion, impreMedia LLC, NY, Brooklyn
Lozino, Josh
redkaction@lindependant.com, Adv. Mgr, L'INDEPENDANT, Rivesaltes
Lubar, Jose 275 0444
Pres., ECOS DE QUEVEDO, Quevedo, Los Rios
Lubbes, Sara...........................(314) 889-4550
Fontbonne College, MO, Clayton
Lubell, Mark
photography@magnumphotos.com, Cultural Projects Dir., Magnum Photos, Inc., NY, New York
Lublin, Steve ....ext. 1070
slublin@portervillerecorder.com, IT Mgr., The Porterville Recorder, CA, Porterville
Luca, Raymond.......................(703) 912-7745

loge@starpower.net, Pres., LogEtronics Corp., VA, Falls Church
Lucas, Adriano Calle
diariodeleiria@diariodeleiria.pt, Dir., DIARIO DE LEIRIA, Leiria
Lucas, Mitch
sports@kilgorenewsherald.com, Sports Ed., Kilgore News Herald, TX, Kilgore
Lucas, Merilee ....(808) 525-8694
mlucas@honolulu.gannett.com, Circ. Mgr., Customer Serv., Honolulu Star-Advertiser, HI, Honolulu
Lucas, Guy
glucas@mediageneral.com, Ed., Media General News Service, VA, Richmond
Lucas, David ....(717) 362-3243 ext. 301
dlucas@dauphingraphic.com, Mgr., Inside Sales/Mktg., Manugraph DGM, Inc., PA, Millersburg
Lucas, Adriano Mario
redac@diariocoimbra.pt, Mng. Dir., DIARIO DE COIMBRA, Coimbra
Lucato, Robert
gazeta@limeira.com.br, Pres., Gazeta de Limeira, Limeira, Sao Paulo
Luce, Patrick..........................(508) 676-2538
pluce@heraldnews.com, Editorial Page Ed., The Herald News, MA, Fall River
Lucey, William F.............(401) 849-3300 ext. 204
Lucey@NewportRI.com, Pub., The Newport Daily News, RI, Newport
Lucey, Philip..................................505-275-1377
director@nmpress.org, Executive Director , New Mexico Press Association, NM, Albuquerque
Lucey, Philip M.
director@nmpress.org, Executive Director , New Mexico Press Association, NM, Albuquerque
Luchini, Eric ....(916) 321-1434
eluchini@sacbee.com, Adv. Mgr., Reg'l, The Sacramento Bee, CA, Sacramento
Lucht, Becky ....(918) 684-2815
blucht@muskogeephoenix.com, Dir., Market Devel., Muskogee Daily Phoenix & Times Democrat, OK, Muskogee
Luciani, Jerry.........................(973) 569-7166
News Graphics Director, North Jersey Media Group, NJ, Woodland Park
Lucke, Lutz
lutz.luecke@volksstimme.de, Distr. Mgr., MAGDEBURG VOLKSSTIMME, Magdeburg
Ludlow, Shawna......................(217) 788-1359
shawna.ludlow@sj-r.com, Adv. Mgr., Outside Sales, The State Journal-Register, IL, Springfield
Ludovici, Lisa
lludovici@reviewonline.com, Adv. Dir., The Review, OH, East Liverpool
Ludwig, Robert D.
bob.ludwig@htimes.com, Pres./Pub., The Huntsville Times, AL, Huntsville
Ludwig, Jack
jack.ludwig@aaapress.com, Pres., AAA Press International, IL, Arlington Heights
Luecke, John
jluecke@highpoint.edu, Assoc. Prof., High Point University, NC, High Point
Luedi, Urs
redaktion@thurgauerzeitung.ch, Ed. in Chief, THURGAUER ZEITUNG, Weinfelden, Thurgau
Luik, Mark
sleht@ruuter.sl.ee, Ed. in Chief, SONUMILEHT, Tallinn
Luis Correa, Juan
gerencia@laestrella.com.pa, Gen. Mgr., LA ESTRELLA DE PANAMA, Panama City
Lujan, Rafael
diari@diaridebarcelona.com, Ed., DIARI DE BARCELONA, Barcelona
Lujano, Jose Antonio
jlujano@lacronicabc.com, Prodn. Mgr., LA CRONICA, Mexicali, Baja California Norte
Lukas, Mark............................(860) 241-6319
mlukas@courant.com, Adv. Dir., Regl./Major, The Hartford Courant, CT, Hartford
Lukaszewski, Paul ....(203) 256-2304
paul.lukaszewski@storaenso.com, Mgr., Mktg., StoraEnso, CT, Stamford
Lukens, Erik............................(541) 617-7816
elukens@bendbulletin.com, Editorial Page Ed., The Bulletin, OR, Bend
Luksza, Rick
rick@mountwashingtonvalley.com, Display Adv. Sales Mgr., The Conway Daily Sun, NH, North Conway
Luman, David
luman@teleport.com, Pres./Mktg. Mgr., Value Checks, OR, Beaverton
Lumbye, Betsy........................(559) 441-6207
blumbye@fresnobee.com, Exec. Ed./Sr. Vice Pres., The Fresno Bee, CA, Fresno
Lumsden, Carolyn..........(86) 241-6200 ext. 3698
clumsden@courant.com, Vice Pres./Editorial Page Ed., The Hartford Courant, CT, Hartford
Luna, Bridget ....(480) 898-6415
bluna@aztrib.com, Adv. Mgr., Nat'l, East Valley Tribune, AZ, Tempe
Luna, Judy
jluna@lcsun-news.com, HR Mgr., Deming Headlight, NM, Deming
Lund, Shauna..........................(801) 625-4281
slund@standard.net, Davis Co. Ed./Bureau Chief, Standard-Examiner, UT, Ogden
Lund, Rolf Edmund
rolf@altaposten.no, Ed. in Chief, ALTAPOSTEN, Alta
Lund, Steve.............................(262) 656-6283
slund@kenoshanews.com, Editorial Page Ed., Kenosha News, WI, Kenosha
Lund, Ron..................(416) 964-3805 ext. 228
rlund@acaweb.ca, Pres./CEO, Association of Canadian Advertisers, Inc., ON, Toronto
Lundberg, Goran
at.redaktionen@ingress.se, Dir., AVESTA-TIDNING, Avesta
Lundberg, Goran
sa.info@ingress.se, Dir., SALA ALLEHANDA-OSTRA LANSTIDNINGEN, Sala
Lunders, Staci ....(402) 473-7349
ssand@journalstar.com, Circ. Mgr., Customer Serv., Lincoln Journal Star, NE, Lincoln
Lundquist, Jeff
news@metc.net, Ed., Atlantic News-Telegraph, IA, Atlantic
Lundquist, Derek
kross@amm.com, Pricing Dir., American Metal Market
Lundy, Jeff ....ext. 215
jlundy@thewhig.com, Circ. Mgr., Reader Sales, The Kingston Whig-Standard, ON, Kingston
Luneau, Domeinique
domeinique.luneau@presse-ocean.com, Mgr., PRESSE-OCEAN, Nantes
Lunn, Alice..............................724-421-2200
alunn@butlereagle.com, Circulation Director, Eagle Printing Co., PA, Butler
Lunn, Alice ....(724) 431-2200 ext. 231
alunn@butlereagle.com, Circ. Dir., Butler Eagle, PA, Butler
Lunzer, Bernard 202-434-7175
bernielunzer@gmail.com, President, The Newspaper Guild-CWA, DC, Washington
Lupo, Lee..................................(231) 725-6362
llupo@muskegonchronicle.com, Online Ed., The Muskegon Chronicle, MI, Muskegon
Lusarrata, Esabel
redaccion@lavozdelanzarote.com, Dir., LA VOZ DE LANZAROTE, Arrecife Lanzarote, Las Palmas
Lusk, Julie 321-242-3753
jlusk@floridatoday.com, VP/South Region, HR Business Partner Team, Florida Today, FL, Melbourne
Lussier, John H........................(608) 252-6403
Chrmn., Board, Capital Newspapers, WI, Madison
Lutwick, Elizabeth ....ext. 224
lutwick@mountvernonnews.com, Sec./Treasurer/Asst. Pub., Mount Vernon News, OH, Mount Vernon
Lybrand, Kathy........................(803) 644-2343
Mgr., Mailroom, Aiken Standard, SC, Aiken
Lyder, Omatie
express@trinidadexpress.com, Ed., TRINIDAD EXPRESS/SUNDAY EXPRESS, Port-Of-Spain
Lyford, Kirk
kirk@phototune.com, Owner, Vivid Details, CA, Penn Valley
Lyle, David F. ....(724) 223-2624
dlyle@observer-reporter.com, CFO, Observer-Reporter, PA, Washington
Lyle, Colin R....................................ext. 1201
rlyle@keenesentinel.com, Audiotex Mgr., The Keene Sentinel, NH, Keene
Lyman, Shelby..........................(607) 775-0587
slyman@tds.net, Pres., Basic Chess Features, NY, Windsor
Lynch, Corinne ....ext. 1400
corinne.lynch@uniontrib.com, Adv. Gen. Mgr., SD Marketplace (Class.), The San Diego Union-Tribune, CA, San Diego
Lynch, Michael
info@cipsmarketing.com, Pres., Association of Alternate Postal Systems, OK, Oklahoma City
Lynch, Lloyd
llynch@state-journal.com, Adv. Dir., The State Journal, KY, Frankfort
Lynch, Shannon
shannon@thesandspur.org, Managing Editor, The Sandspur, FL, Winter Park
Lynch, Tim ....(617) 471-8733
Pres./Pub./Ed., New Wave Syndication, MA, North Quincy
Lynch, Michael
autonomy@autonomy.com, CEO, Autonomy, Inc., CA, San Francisco
Lynch, Peter
lynchp@caledonian-record.com, Picture Ed., The Caledonian-Record, VT, Saint Johnsbury
Lynch-Hudson, Regina ....(770) 998-9911
thewritepublicist@earthlink.net, Creator/Writer, Doing Biz In, GA, Roswell
Lynett, W. Scott..............................ext. 2095
slynett@citizensvoice.com, Pub., The Citizens' Voice, PA, Wilkes-Barre
Lynn, Jodie
editor@parenttoparent.com, Owner, Parent to Parent, MO, Wildwood
Lynn, Richard J........................(260) 782-2345
parwell@email.com, Author/Illustrator/Cartoonist/Historian/Speaker, Parwell-Davis Features, IN, Lagro
Lynn, Michelle..........................(360) 417-3510
michelle.lynn@peninsuladailynews.com, Director of Circulation , Peninsula Daily News, WA, Port Angeles
Lynn, Emerson
news@samessenger.com, Editorial Page Ed., St. Albans Messenger, VT, Saint Albans
Lynn, Suzanne..................................ext. 106
suzanne@samessenger.com, Bus. Mgr./Controller, St. Albans Messenger, VT, Saint Albans
Lyon, Dave ....(810) 989-6765
dlyon@gannett.com, Prodn. Mgr., Mailroom, Times Herald, MI, Port Huron
Lyon, Allen
alyon@meadvilletribune.com, Prodn. Mgr., Mailroom, The Meadville Tribune, PA, Meadville
Lyon, Ray..................................(505) 473-1775
info@lyonenterprises.com, Pres., Lyon Enterprises, NM, Santa Fe
Lyon, Jeff..................................312-369-8903
jlyon@colum.edu, Faculty advisor, Columbia College, IL, Chicago
Lyons, David ....(305) 347-6694
dlyons@alm.com, Editor-in-Chief, Miami Daily Business Review, FL, Miami
Lyons, David ....(305) 347-6694
dlyons@alm.com, Editor-in-Chief, Palm Beach Daily Business Review, FL, West Palm Beach
Lyons, Pam...............................(856) 486-2447
plyons@courierpostonline.com, Food Ed., Courier-Post, NJ, Cherry Hill
Lyons, Tom ....(941) 957-5367
tom.lyons@heraldtribune.com, Columnist, Sarasota Herald-Tribune, FL, Sarasota
Lyons, Kevin....................................ext. 4571
klyons@nwherald.com, Prodn. Mgr., Pressroom, Northwest Herald, IL, Crystal Lake
Lytle, Denise.............................(214) 691-4061
lytle@amconmedia.com, Sr. Vice Pres./CFO, American Consolidated Media, TX, Dallas
Lytle, William H. ....(913) 498-0040
billlytle8@cs.com, Dir., Media Services Group, Inc., FL, Jacksonville Beach
Lytle, Dean ....(204) 697-7464
dean.lytle@freepress.mb.ca, Circ. Dir., Winnipeg Free Press, MB, Winnipeg
Lytle, Regina.............................(252) 329-9643
rlytle@reflector.com, Pre Press Mgr., The Daily Reflector, NC, Greenville
Lytle, Jeffrey
jflytle@naplesnews.com, Editorial Page Ed., Naples Daily News, FL, Naples

M

M'membe, Fred
post@zamnet.zm, Ed. in Chief, THE POST, Lusaka
MENDEZ, MIGUEL
webmaster@prensalibre.com.gt, Editorial Director, Prensa Libre, Guatemala, Guatemala
Ma, Sonic
sonictkp@gmail.com, Adv. Mgr., TA KUNG PAO, Hong Kong
Maack, Lebrecht
redaktion@winsener-anzeiger.de, Bus. Mgr., Winsener Anzeiger, Winsen
Maas, Duke ....(813) 259-7753
Managing Editor, The Tampa Tribune, FL, Tampa
Maass, Wolfgang
anzeigen@gelnhaeuser-tageblatt.de, Bus. Mgr., Gelnhauser Tageblatt, Gelnhaeusen
Mac Leod, Jim...........................(416) 847-2001
jmacleod@bbm.ca, Pres./CEO, BBM Canada, ON, Toronto
MacAfee, Michelle
michelle.macafee@thecanadianpress.com, Correspondent, Canadian Press, The - Saint John's, NL, Saint John's
MacAulay, Dwight......................204-945-3939
dwight.macaulay@leg.gov.mb.ca, President, Winnipeg Press Club, MB, Winnipeg
MacCormack, Bruce......(902) 426-2811 ext. 2847
bmaccormack@herald.ca, Vice Pres., Bus. Devel., The Chronicle Herald, NS, Halifax
MacDonald, Charles H.
cmacdonald@sjnews.com, Controller, The Gloucester County Times, NJ, Woodbury
MacDonald, Jim
jmacdonald@broadcastnews.ca, Contact, Broadcast News Limited, AB, Edmonton
MacDonald, Charles
cmacdonald@sjnewsco.com, Controller, The News of Cumberland County, NJ, Bridgeton
MacDonald, Joanne ....(416) 869-4989
Sales Asst., Torstar Syndication Services, ON, Toronto
MacDonald, Dan
dan@skagitpublishing.com, Info Systems Mgr., Skagit Valley Herald, WA, Mount Vernon
MacDonald, Don............(705) 674-5271 ext. 232
editorial@thesudburystar.com, City Ed., The Sudbury Star, ON, Sudbury
MacDonald, John
info@xgroup.com, Pres., X'iT Group Creative, CA, Mission Viejo
MacDonald, Wendy.......................913-647-0940
wmacdonald@familyfeatures.com, Director of Media, Family Features Editorial Syndicate, Inc., KS, Mission
MacDonald, Roseanne ....(902) 629-6051
letters@cjg.southam.ca, Editorial Page Ed., The Guardian, PE, Charlottetown
MacDougall, Gary J....................(902) 629-6039
gmacdougall@chg.southam.ca, Mng. Ed., The Guardian, PE, Charlottetown
MacDougall, Gary.......................(902) 629-6045
gmacdougall@chg.southam.ca, Online Ed., The Guardian, PE, Charlottetown
MacEwen, John
john_macewen@baseview.com, Vice Pres., Sales, Harris Publishing Systems, FL, Melbourne
MacInnes, Chuck
cmacinnes@amherstdaily.com, Circ. Mgr., Amherst Daily News, NS, Amherst
MacKay, Margaret ....(902) 426-1143
mmackay@herald.ca, Lifestyle Ed., The Chronicle Herald, NS, Halifax
MacKenzie, John K.
jkm3@pipeline.com, Contact, Interactive Strategies, NY, New York
MacKenzie, Heather

webmaster@cbpost.com, Online Mgr., The Cape Breton Post, NS, Sydney
MacKenzie, Bob
info@umipressparts.com, Pres., UMI, FL, Englewood
MacKinnon, Doyle
dmackinnon@lethbridgeherald.com, Mng. Ed., The Lethbridge Herald, AB, Lethbridge
MacLaren, Mike
mike@michiganpress.org, Exec. Dir., Michigan Press Association, MI, Lansing
MacLaren, Michael
mike@michiganpress.org, Exec. Dir., Michigan Newspapers, Inc., MI, Lansing
MacLeod, Brian............(705) 674-5271 ext. 240
Editorial Page Ed., The Sudbury Star, ON, Sudbury
MacLeod, Sandy........................416 869 4654
416 865 3606, Vice Pres., Mktg., Toronto Star, ON, Toronto
MacNaull, Steve
steve.macnaull@ok.bc.ca, Bus. Ed., The Daily Courier, BC, Kelowna
MacNeille, Jeanette
sales@eclipseservices.com, President, Eclipse Services (Div. of Quadrivium, Inc.), PA, Millbourne
Macaruso-Carignan, Diana
dmacaruso@buynensco.com, Adv. Mgr., NENSCO, MA, Millbury
Macasaet, Allen A.
abantetonite@gmail.com, Pub., ABANTE, Manila
Maccini, Robert J. ....(401) 454-3130
rmaccini@cox.net, Dir., Media Services Group, Inc., FL, Jacksonville Beach
Mace, Dave ....(800) 255-6734
dmace@amuniversal.com, Asst. Vice Pres., Sales, Western USA, Universal Uclick, MO, Kansas City
Mace, Tony.............................(212) 669-6400
tony@marketnews.com, Mng. Ed., Market News International, NY, New York
Mace, Michael.........................(518) 454-5746
mmace@timesunion.com, Prodn. Mgr., Times Union, NY, Albany
Macedo, Carlos Antonio Campos.........2221-2926
confidenc@uol.com.br, Ed., Jornal dos Sports, Rio De Janeiro
Macedo Gutierrez, Daniel 21-1500
Pres., Editorial Arequipa S.A., Arequipa
Macfarlane, William..................(413) 496-6280
wmacfarlane@berkshireeagle.com, Dir., Systems, The Berkshire Eagle, MA, Pittsfield
Machan, Randy........................(419) 352-4421
subscriptions@sentinel-tribune.com, Circ. Dir., Sentinel Company, OH, Bowling Green
Machesic, Dale........................(215) 345-3018
dmachesic@phillyburbs.com, Adv. Mgr., Classified/Retail, The Intelligencer, PA, Doylestown
Maciel, Cheryl.........................(559) 441-6219
cmaciel@fresnobee.com, Circ. Mgr., Sales, The Fresno Bee, CA, Fresno
Maciel, Enrique 430-680
redaccion@lavozdelpueblo.com.ar, Pres., Maciel Hermanos S.A.E.C.I., Tres Arroyos, Provincia de Buenos Aires
Macintyre, Kevin ....(250) 368-8551 ext 209
ads@trailtimes.ca, production manager, Trail Daily Times, BC, Trail
Macisse Uribe, Anuar
eldiario@netspace.com.mx, Owner/Pres., El Noticiero, Toluca, Mexico
Maciuliene, Tekle
redakcija@kaunodiena.lt, Ed. in Chief, KAUNO DIENA, Kaunas
MaciÂ, Gaspar
elche.lv@laverdad.es, Dir., La Verdad De Elche, Elche, Alicante
Mack, J.
drukkerei-mack@t-online.de, Proprietor, Mack Verlag, Mellrichstadt
Mack, Dennis
dmack@thedailycourier.com, Pub., Daily Courier, OR, Grants Pass
Mack, Tyler............................(541) 338-2291
tyler.mack@registerguard.com, Digital Media Director, The Register-Guard, OR, Eugene
Macke, Rich............................(805) 739-2147
Circ. Dir., The Lompoc Record, CA, Lompoc
Macke, Rich 580-256-2200
Pub., Woodward News, OK, Woodward
Macke, Rich
rmacke@santamariatimes.com, Circ. Dir., Santa Maria Times, CA, Santa Maria
Mackeler, Manfred
ldz-anzeigen@leinetal-online.de, Distr. Mgr., Leine Deister Zeitung, Gronau
Mackenzia, David
david.mackenzia@bayofplentytimes.co.nz, Gen. Mgr., BAY OF PLENTY TIMES
Mackey, Jim
jmackey@reviewonline.com, Mng. Ed., The Review, OH, East Liverpool
Macknicki, Jim ....ext. 453
jmacknicki@adn.com, Copy Desk Chief, Anchorage Daily News, AK, Anchorage
Macomber, Aletha....................(360) 650-3171
Western Washington Univ., WA, Bellingham
Macone, John ....ext. 3255
jmacone@newburyportnews.com, Ed., The Daily News, MA, Newburyport
Macor, Alida ....(908) 722-5676
Pres./Author, And Sew On, NJ, Martinsville
Macovei, Vlad
vlad.macovei@evz.ro, Ed. in Chief, EVENIMENTUL ZILEI, Bucharest
Macy, Robert..........................(702) 228-9110
Author, Dateline Las Vegas, NV, Las Vegas
Madden, Doreen ....(860) 241-6424
dmadden@courant.com, Mktg. Mgr., The Hartford Courant, CT, Hartford
Madden, Lance........................(520) 621-7579
Univ. of Arizona, AZ, Tucson
Maddox, Terry
stnnews@wickcommunications.com, Pub., Slidell Sentry-News, LA, Slidell
Maddux, Jason ....(608) 745-3517
jmaddux@capitalnewspapers.com, Ed., Daily Register, WI, Portage
Maddux, David
dmaddux@editorandpublisher.com, Admin., Editor & Publisher Interactive, NY, New York
Madigan, Jamie
jmadigan@messenger-inquirer.com, Copy Ed., Messenger-Inquirer, KY, Owensboro
Madigan, Terri
tmadigan@surview.com, Opns. Dir., Bruce Bell & Associates, CO, Canon City
Madill, John ....ext. 204
jmadill@heraldpalladium.com, Photo Ed., The Herald-Palladium, MI, Saint Joseph
Madray, Janet
janetmadray2@yahoo.com, Circ. Mgr., Okeechobee News, FL, Okeechobee
Madsen, Paul
paul.madsen@ep.dk, Ed. in Chief, EKSTRA BLADET-VESTUDGAVE, Copenhagen, Sjaelland
Madsen, Paul
paul.madsen@ep.dk, Ed.-in-Cheif, EKSTRA BLADET, Copenhagen, Sjaelland
Maduro, Grace Mary
bondia.aruba@gmail.com, Gen. Mgr., ARUBA TODAY/BON DIA ARUBA, Oranjestad
Maeda, Kiyoshi
veriomedia@verio.net, Pres., Verio, Inc., CO, Centennial
Maenza, Ann Dix ....(502) 227-4556
admaenza@state-journal.com, Pub., The State Journal, KY, Frankfort
Maeshiro, Karen
kmaeshiro@avpress.com, Special Sections Ed., Antelope Valley Press, CA, Palmdale
Magee, Amy ....(804) 649-6478
amagee@timesdispatch.com, Real Estate Mgr., Richmond Times-Dispatch, VA, Richmond
Magel, Robert ....(717) 291-8731
bmagel@lnpnews.com, Mgr., Mktg., Intelligencer Journal/Lancaster New Era/Sunday News, PA, Lancaster
Magid, Brent
bmagid@magid.com, Pres., Frank Magid Associates, IA, Marion
Magill, Keith ....(985) 857-2201
keith.magill@houmatoday.com, Executive Editor, The Daily Comet, LA, Thibodaux
Magill, Eric
emagill@scdel.net, Owner/Pub., Sussex County Online, DE, Ocean View
Magill, Keith ....(985) 857-2201
news@houmatoday.com, Executive Editor, The Courier, LA, Houma
Magnuson, Doug
magnuson@hagadone.com, CFO, Hagadone Corp., ID, Coeur d'Alene
Magnuson, Karen M. ....(585) 258-2220
kmagnuso@democratandchronicle.com, Vice Pres., News/Ed., Democrat and Chronicle.com, NY, Rochester
Magram, Jeffrey......................(617) 619-6300
jmagram@bostonherald.com, Vice Pres., Finance, Boston Herald, MA, Boston
Mah, Cindy ....(780) 429-5320
cmah@thejournal.canwest.com, Mktg. Research Mgr., Edmonton Journal, AB, Edmonton
Mahagan, Mark 270-781-1700
mmahagan@bgdailynews.com, Adv. Mgr., Daily News, KY, Bowling Green
Mahajan, Sudhir
lokmat@bom2.vsnl.net.in, Ed., LOKMAT, Jalgaon, Maharashtra
Maher, John ....(314) 340-8974
jmaher@post-dispatch.com, Vice Pres./Dir., Mktg., St. Louis Post-Dispatch, MO, Saint Louis
Maheshwari, P.K.
editor@centralchronicle.com, Pub., MADHYA PRADESH CHRONICLE, Bhopal, Madhya Pradesh
Maheswari, Vinod
editor.nagpur@navabharat.biz, Ed., NAVA BHARAT, Nagpur, Maharashtra
Mahfoudh, Mohamed
contact@lapresse.tn, Pub., AS-SAHAFA, Tunis
Mahle, Kim............................(828) 232-6018
kmahle@citizen-times.com, Circ. Mgr., Single Copy Sales, The Asheville Citizen-Times, NC, Asheville
Mahler, Donald ....ext. 225
sports@vnews.com, Sports Ed., Valley News, VT, West Lebanon
Mahoney, Buck ....(308) 233-9750
Sports Ed., Kearney Hub, NE, Kearney
Mahoney, William
wmahoney@disk.com, Pres., Corporate Disk Company, IL, McHenry
Mahoney, Mark ....(518) 792-3220
mahoney@poststar.com, Editorial Page Ed., The Post-Star, NY, Glens Falls
Mahoney, Walter F. ....(312) 222-6698
wmahoney@tribune.com, Vice Pres., Global Sales, McClatchy-Tribune Information Services, DC, Washington
wmahoney@tribune.com, Vice Pres., Sales, News/Features Worldwide, McClatchy-Tribune Information Services, Tribune Media Services, Inc., IL, Chicago
Mahony, Paul
pmahony@mantecabulletin.com, Pub., Manteca Bulletin, CA, Manteca
Mahr, Michael R......................(202) 636-3079
mmahr@washingtontimes.com, Adv. Dir., The Washington Times Corp., DC, Washington
Maiden, Lisa ....(508) 862-1331
lmaiden@capecodonline.com, Adv. Mgr., Cape Cod Times, MA, Hyannis
Maier, Timothy W.
tmaier@dcexaminer.com, Maryland Ed., The Examiner, VA, Alexandria
Main, Fred ....ext. 284
fmain@mountvernonnews.com, City Ed., Mount Vernon News, OH, Mount Vernon
Main, Jim
jmain@pubgroup.com, Auto Adv. Mgr., Relish - Northville, MI, MI, Northville
Main, Jim ....(248) 477-5508
jmain@pubgroup.com, Auto Adv. Mgr., American Profile - Northville, MI, MI, Northville
Main, Jim ....(248) 477-5508
jmain@pubgroup.com, Auto Adv. Mgr., American Profile - Northville, MI, MI, Northville
Mainor, Robert P.
cs@xpedite.com, Pres./CEO, Xpedite, NJ, Tinton Falls
Majeske, Jeff ....(219) 648-3138
jmajeske@post-trib.com, Sports Ed., Post-Tribune, IN, Merrillville
Majoor, J.G.C.
stadsredactie@leidschdagblad.nl, Ed., LEIDSCH DAGBLAD, Leiden, South Holland
Major, Mark
mmajor@cninewspapers.com, CFO, Community Newspapers, Inc., GA, Athens
Major, Dwight.........................(248) 745-4540
dwight.major@oakpress.com, Circ. Mgr., Home Delivery, The Oakland Press, MI, Pontiac
Makemson, Harlen
hmakemson@elon.edu, Assoc. Prof., Elon University, NC, Elon
Maki, Greg ....(410) 770-4104
Entertainment Ed., The Star-Democrat, MD, Easton
Maki, Brian 715-738-1614
brian.maki@lee.net, advertising director, The Chippewa Herald, WI, Chippewa Falls
Makings, Vicki ....(303) 820-1691
vmakings@denverpost.com, Editorial Librarian, The Denver Post, CO, Denver
Makley, Bill ....(561) 923-5000
Media Rel., Siemens Communications Group, FL, Boca Raton
Makulowich, John
john@journalist.com, Contact, The Writers Alliance, Inc., MD, North Potomac
Malave-Baber, Lourdes ....(757) 247-4992
lmalave@dailypress.com, Adv. Dir., Key Accts. Sales, Daily Press, VA, Newport News
Malayandy, M.
news@nanban.com.my, Ed. in Chief, MALAYSIAN NANBAN, Kuala Lumpur
Malbu, Paulo A.
redacao@santa.com.br, Dir., Empresa Editora Jornal de Santa Catarina Ltd., Blumenau, Santa Catarina
Maldonado, Persio
redaccionnd@verizon.net.do, Dir., EL NUEVO DIARIO, Santo Domingo
Male, Helen...........................(306) 657-6290
hmale@sp.canwest.com, Admin. Asst., The StarPhoenix, SK, Saskatoon
Malek, Abdul
azadi@dainikazadi.net, Pub., DAINIK AZADI, Chittagong
Maletz, Jon
jmaletz@aspentimes.com, Sports Ed., The Aspen Times, CO, Aspen
Malihabadi, Ahmad
azadhinddaily@hotmail.com, Pub./Ed., AZAD HIND, Kolkata, West Bengal
Malik, Sanjay
smalik@gulfnews.com, Circ. Mgr., GULF NEWS
Malik, Zahid
observer@pakobserver.net, Ed. in Chief, PAKISTAN OBSERVER, Islamabad
Malinowski, Mark (Scoop)...........(201) 833-2350
mrbiofile@aol.com, Ed., Biofile, NJ, Teaneck
Malkin, James
john.delmauro@sourcemedia.com, CEO, American Banker, NY, 1 State Street Plz.
Malkovich, Daniel
demalkov@clearwave.com, Pub., Benton Evening News, IL, Benton
Mallou DÂ¡az, Jose Antonio
jerez@publicacionesdelsur.net, Dir., INFORMACION JEREZ, Jerez de la Frontera, Cadiz
Malloy, Lawrence J.
lmalloy@newspapersfirst.com, Vice Pres./Sales Mgr., Newspapers First, Inc, FL, Hollywood
Malmgren, Jeanne...................(864) 260-1254
Lifestyle Ed., Anderson Independent-Mail, SC, Anderson
Malone, Brian S.
bmalone@njtimes.com, Ed., The Times, NJ, Trenton
Malone, Richard ....(312) 222-2400
dmalone@tribune.com, Sr. Vice Pres./Gen. Mgr., Chicago Tribune, IL, Chicago
Maloney, E. Mayer...................(812) 331-4251
mmaloney@heraldt.com, Pub./Purchasing Agent, The Herald-Times, IN, Bloomington
Maloney, James V....................(314) 340-2402
jmaloney@pulitzer.net, Cor. Sec./Dir., Investor Realtions, Pulitzer, Inc., MO, Saint Louis
Maloney, Mayer
mmaloney@reportert.com, Pub., The Reporter-Times, IN, Martinsville
Malott, Adele
maturetrav@aol.com, Ed./Pub., The Mature Traveler, NV, Reno

Malpica de Ahued, Bertha Rosalia
eldictamen@infosel.net.mx, Pres., El Dictamen, Veracruz, Veracruz
Mamontov, Vladimir
info1@izvestia.ru, Ed. in Chief, IZVESTIYA, Moscow
Man, Yip Yui
zbhk01@netvigator.com, Ed. in Chief, LIANHE ZAOBAO, Hong Kong
Manaila, Mioara
mioara@viata-libera.ro, Adv. Mgr., VIATA LIBERA, Galati
Manastarni, Ulrich
hagen@westfalenpost.de, Ed. in Chief, WP Westfalenpost, Hagen
Manchester, Jon......................**(250) 470-0741**
jon.manchester@ok.bc.ca, Mng. Ed., The Daily Courier, BC, Kelowna
Mancini, Ray..............................**(410) 992-5071**
Vice Pres., Sales, Foley, Torregiani & Associates, Inc., CT, West Port
Mancino, Michael.....................**(212) 969-7593**
mmancino@hearst.com, Telemktg. Sales Rep., King Features Syndicate, NY, New York
mmancino@hearst.com, Inside Sales Rep, North America Syndicate, NY, New York
Mancuso, Tony **217-351-5219**
tmancuso@news-gazette.com, Features Editor, News-Gazette Inc., IL, Champaign
Mancuso, Steve
smancuso@hartindus.com, Pres., Hart Industries, CT, East Haven
Mandel, Melis
melis.mandel@aripaev.ee, Ed. in Chief, ARIPAEV, Tallinn
Mandl, Donna..........................**(717) 771-2065**
dmandl@ydr.com, Exec. Asst. to Pub., Weekly Record, PA, York
Mandl, Donna..........................**(717) 771-2065**
dmandl@ydr.com, Exec. Asst. to Pub., York Daily Record/York Sunday News, PA, York
Mandros, Athena
sales@dialogic.com, Contact, Dialogic Corp., NJ, Parsippany
Manes, Nancy ....**ext. 586**
nmanes@adn.com, Dir., Organizational Devel., Anchorage Daily News, AK, Anchorage
Maness, Michael L......................**(302) 324-2577**
mmaness@delawareonline.com, Vice Pres., Innovation/Design, Gannett Co., Inc., VA, McLean
Mangan, Dennis..........**(330) 747-1471 ext. 1289**
mangan@vindy.com, Editorial Page Ed., The Vindicator, OH, Youngstown
Mangar, Andree
andreem@zetagestion.com, Intl Adv./Sales, El Periodico De Catalunya, Barcelona
Mangiantini, Dean
dean.mangiantini@peninsuladailynews.com, Director of Production, Peninsula Daily News, WA, Port Angeles
Manilla, Kathy..........................**(312) 222-2499**
kmanilla@tribune.com, Adv. Dir., Devel., Chicago Tribune, IL, Chicago
Mann, Les
lmann@norfolkdailynews.com, Gen. Mgr., Norfolk Daily News, NE, Norfolk
Mann, Mark.....................................**ext. 239**
news@butlereagle.com, Mng. Ed., Butler Eagle, PA, Butler
Mann, Chris....................................**ext. 203**
chris.mann@gaflnews.com, Adv. Dir., Cordele Dispatch, GA, Cordele
Mann, Mark **724-282-8000**
mmann@butlereagle.com, Managing Editor, Eagle Printing Co., PA, Butler
Mann, Exra..............................**405.238.6464**
emann@pvdemocrat.com, Reporter, Pauls Valley Democrat, OK, Pauls Valley
Manna, John K. ....**ext. 624**
Political Ed., New Castle News, PA, New Castle
Manni, Jessica ....**(724) 830-4791**
Seton Hill University, PA, Greensburg
Manning, Jennifer L. ....**(812) 379-5614**
jmanning@therepublic.com, Dir., HR, Home News Enterprises, IN, Columbus
Manning, Tamara
amasis@amasis.com, Head Designer, Amasis, IL, Chicago
Manning, Timothy......................**(563) 588-7954**
Loras College, IA, Dubuque
Manning, Thomas
info@mesacorp.com, Vice Pres.-Sales/Mktg., Mesa Corp., NE, Lincoln
Manning, Mark ....**(949) 731-4671**
mark.manning@theeagle.com, Prodn. Dir., The Eagle, TX, Bryan
Manrique, Carlos
editoraperu@editoraperu.com.pe, Ed., Peruvian Government, Lima
Manrique Romero, Adan.....................**32-4410**
Pres., El Imparcial, Huancho
Mansch, Scott **406-791-1481**
Sports Editor, Great Falls Tribune, MT, Great Falls
Mansell, Melvin
mailedit@sundaymail.com.au, Ed., THE ADELAIDE ADVERTISER
Manship, David C.
david.manship@theadvocate.com, Pub., The Advocate, LA, Baton Rouge
Manship, David
david.manship@theadvocate.com, Pres., Louisiana Press Women, Inc., LA, Baton Rouge
Mansur, Jossy M.
arubadaily@yahoo.com, Ed. in Cheif, DIARIO, Oranjestad
Manzi, Al
manzia@dailycamera.com, Pub., Daily Camera, CO, Boulder
Manzullo, Brain ....**(989) 774-4338**
Central Michigan Univ., MI, Mount Pleasant
Manzur Maron, Antonio
mundo@interxcable.net.mx, Pres., EL MUNDO, Tampico, Tamaulipas
Maoualr, Virginia
avesohe@adinet.com.uy, Adv. Mgr., El Heraldo S.A., Florida
Maphumulo, Amos
cindyd@nu.independent.co.za, Ed., ILANGA, Durban, Kwazulu & Natal
Mara, Jamie ....**ext. 298**
jmara@appleton.gannett.com, Mng. Ed., The Post-Crescent, WI, Appleton
Maraccini, Terry
tmaraccini@kenohsanews.com, Web Servs. Supvr., Kenosha News, WI, Kenosha
Maragoudakis, Debbie ....**ext. 123**
dmaragoudakis@certifiedaudit.com, Audit Mgr., Certified Audit of Circulations, Inc., NJ, Wayne
Maran, Kalanidhi
dinakarannew@gmail.com, Chrmn., DINAKARAN, Chennai, Tamil Nadu
Marathe, Jack
sales@uts.us.com, Pres., Universal Technical Systems, Inc., IL, Rockford
Marc, Glasanar
wort@wort.lu, Ed. in Chief, LUXEMBURGER WORT, Luxembourg
Marcano, Ray...........................**(937) 225-2323**
rmarcano@coxohio.com, Deputy Mng. Ed., Dayton Daily News, OH, Dayton
Marcase, John.............................**318-487-6490**
jmarcase@thetowntalk.com, Asst. Managing Editor, The Town Talk, LA, Alexandria
Marcel, Amanda **765-659-4622**
amarcel@ftimes.com, Circulation Director, The Times, IN, Frankfort
Marcelino, Joao
joao.marcelino@dn.pt, Dir., DIARIO DE NOTICIAS, Lisbon
March, Nancy
nmarch@pottsmerc.com, Ed., The Mercury, PA, Pottstown
Marchand, Dernarg
dernarg.marchand@rossel.be, Dir., LA CAPITALE, Brussels, Brabant
Marchek, Mike
mmarchek@timesbulletin.com, Circ. Mgr., The Times Bulletin, OH, Van Wert
Marchese, Mary Gay...................**949 756 5100**
pr@markzware.com, Public Relations, Markzware Software, Inc., CA, Santa Ana
Marchese, Patrick
sales@markzwarwe.com, Pres./CEO, Markzware Software, Inc., CA, Santa Ana
Marciano, Vincent **513-977-3949**
vincent.marciano@scripps.com, General Manager, United Media, United Media/EW Scripps, OH, Cincinnati
Marciano, Vincent **513-977-3949**
vincent.marciano@scripps.com, General Manager - Syndicate, United Media, OH, Cincinnati
Marcil, William C.
wmarcil@forumcomm.com, Pub., Forum Communications Co., ND, Fargo
Marcil, William C. ....**(701) 235-7311**
wmarcil@forumcomm.com, Pub./Chrmn./CEO, InForum, ND, Fargo
Marciniaik, Judith....................**(773) 702-9555**
Univ. of Chicago, IL, Chicago
Marcink, Robert..........................**815-280-2313**
rmarcink@jjc.edu, Advisor, Joliet Junior College, IL, Joliet
Marcon, Tony
info@prolinedigital.com, Pres., Proline Digital, CO, Denver
Marcum, Kim ....**(407) 420-5082**
kmarcum@orlandosentinel.com, Assoc. Mng. Ed., Features, Orlando Sentinel, FL, Orlando
Marcum, Bill
bmarcum@eastoregonian.com, Advertising Director, East Oregonian, OR, Pendleton
Marcus, Aaron
aaron.marcus@amanda.com, Pres., Aaron Marcus and Associates, Inc., CA, Berkeley
Marcus, Joel
manassyparts@yahoo.com, Pres., Manassy Sales Inc., NY, Forest Hills
Marcus, Larry...........................**(212) 210-1806**
lmarcus@nydailynews.com, Vice Pres./Gen. Counsel, NY Daily News, NY, New York
Marcus, Ed ....**(724) 684-2655**
emarcus@tribweb.com, Prodn. Mgr., Mailroom, The Valley Independent, PA, Monessen
Marek, Cynthia M.
cindym@wyomingnews.com, Nat'l Adv. Mgr., Wyoming Color Comic Group, WY, Cheyenne
Marek, Joseph M.
jmarek@dailyherald.com, Circ. Mgr., Single Copy Sales, Daily Herald, IL, Arlington Heights
Mares, Marco Antonio
marcomares@eleconomista.com.mx, Dir. Gen., EL ECONOMISTA, Mexico City, Distrito Federal
Margolis, David G.
davidmargolis@syndicatedadfeatures.com, Pres., Syndicated Ad Features, Inc., MA
Margoreeth, Jeanine.........**(250) 368-8551 ext 204**
nationals@trailtimes.ca, classifieds, Trail Daily Times, BC, Trail
Marian, Boris **233 605**
tis@nm.mid.net.com, Ed., NEZAVISIMAYA MOLDOVA, Chisinau
Mariani-Belding, Jeanne ....**(808) 535-2445**
jmbelding@honoluluadvertiser.com, Editorial/Opinion Ed., Honolulu Star-Advertiser, HI, Honolulu
Mariano, Andrea **212-556-5162**
andrea.mariano@nytimes.com, Regional Manager, Southern Region, New York Times Syndicate, NY, New York
Mariano, Andrea **212-556-5162**
andrea.mariano@nytimes.com, Regional Manager, Southern Region, New York Times News Service, NY, New York
Mariano, Fernando
info@multimediausa.com, Pres., Multimedia, Inc., FL, Orlando
Mariea, Fred
fmariea@newspress.com, Adv. Dir., Santa Barbara News-Press, CA, Santa Barbara
Marietta, Roger ....**(912) 430-6808**
Darton College, GA, Albany
Marimow, William K.
bmarimow@phillynews.com, Ed./Exec. Vice Pres., The Philadelphia Inquirer, PA, Philadelphia
Marin, Jose luis
sistemas@mediterraneo.elperiodico.com, Prodn., Mediterranio, Castellon
Marin, Mar
redaccion@efe.com.ar, Rep., EFE News Services - Havana, Cuba, Havana
redaccion@efe.com.ar, Rep., EFE News Services - Buenos Aires, Argentina, Buenos Aires
Marin, David...........................**(408) 842-5755**
dmarin@mainstreetmg.com, Vice. Pres., Adv., Free Lance, CA, Hollister
Marinacci, Peter ....**(905) 544-6174**
pdm@wombania.com, Owner/Cartoonist, Wombania, ON, Hamilton
Marini, Wilson
atribuna@atribuna.com.br, Ed. in Chief, A Tribuna, Santos, Sao Paulo
Marino, Marie ....**(703) 854-5866**
mmarino@gns.gannett.com, Office Mgr., Gannett News Service - McLean, VA, VA, McLean
Marino, Rob ....**(352) 854-2322 ext. 1364**
Central Florida Cmty. College, FL, Ocala
Marino Vasquez, Segundo
lavozdeltajo@lavozdeltajo.com, Dir., LA VOZ DEL TAJO, Toledo
Mario Pumarejo, Alberto **349-309**
elheraldo@metrotel.net.co, Gen. Mgr., El Heraldo Ltd., Barranquilla, Atlantico
Markevicz, George ....**(251) 219-5300**
gmarkevicz@press-register.com, Circ. Dir., Press-Register, AL, Mobile
Markham, William C...................**(661) 273-2700**
Pub., Antelope Valley Press, CA, Palmdale
Markisz, Susan
secretary@nyppa.org, Sec., New York Press Photographers Association, Inc., NY, New York
Markle, Gary ....**(215) 822-5519 ext. 103**
gmarkle@icanon.com, Dir., Mktg., ICANON Associates, Inc., PA, Hatfield
Markoe, Lauren ....**(202) 463-8777**
lauren.markoe@religionnews.com, National Correspondent, Religion News Service, DC, Washington
Markowitz, Kelly
kelly.markowitz@news-jrnl.com, Deputy Mng. Ed., Visuals, Daytona Beach News-Journal, FL, Daytona Beach
Markowski, Denise ....**(920) 431-8268**
dmarkowski@greenbaypressgazette.com, Prodn. Mgr., Pre Press, Green Bay Press-Gazette, WI, Green Bay
Marks, Andy **352.867.4143**
eric.barnes@starbanner.com, Sports Ed., Ocala Star-Banner, FL, Ocala
Marks, Ted ....**(207) 389-2620**
tmarks@mfamedia.com, Pres., Marks & Frederick Assoc., LLC, ME, Phippsburg
Marks, Lori.................................**(216) 999-6442**
Circ. Mgr., Educational Servs., The Plain Dealer, OH, Cleveland
Marks, Ted ....**(860) 927-3948**
tmarks@mfamedia.com, Pres., Marks & Frederick Associates LLC., ME, Sebasco Estates
Markussen, Inga Dora
inga@ag.gl, Ed., AG ATUAGAGDLIUTIT/GRONLANDSPOSTEN, Nuuk
Markward, Philip
phil.markward@thevillages.com, Pub., The Villages Daily Sun, FL, The Villages
Marlett, Matt.............................**(262) 542-2501**
mmarlett@conleynet.com, VP of Media Operations, Conley Publishing Group Ltd., WI, Beaver Dam
Marling, John W.
marling@pulseresearch.com, CEO, Pulse Research, Inc., OR, Portland
Marling, John W.
marling@paper.net, Pres., Paper.net, OR, Portland
Marlowe, Michelle....................**(843) 294-8424**
amarlowe@wbtw.com, Adv. Mgr., Interactive Sales, Morning News, SC, Florence
Maroo, Manish
manish@ranchiexpress.com, Circ. Mgr., RANCHI EXPRESS, Ranchi, Jharkhand
Marquardt, Tom
tmarquardt@capitalgazette.com, Exec. Ed., The Capital, MD, Annapolis
Marquart, Pam ....**(701) 642-8585**
ads@wahpetondailynews.com, Adv. Mgr., The Daily News, ND, Wahpeton
Marquez, Anthony
amarquez@ap.org, Bureau Chief, Los Angeles, Associated Press/California-Nevada News Executives, CA, Los Angeles
Marquez, Israel **406-4111**
imarquez@dearmas.com, Editorial Dir., Editorial Santiago de Leon, Caracas, D.F.

Marr, Robert L. ....ext. 216
bmarr@thewesterlysun.com, Asst. Sports Ed., The Westerly Sun, RI, Westerly
Marra, David....(716) 282-2311 ext. 2242
marrad@gnnewspaper.com, Graphics Ed., Niagara Gazette, NY, Niagara Falls
Marran, David ....(262) 656-6294
dmarran@kenoshanews.com, Sports Ed., Kenosha News, WI, Kenosha
Marroquin, Oscar Clemente
ocmarroq@lahora.com.gt, Pres./CEO, LA HORA, Guatemala City
Marroquin, Pedro Pablo
pmarroquin@lahora.com.gt, Dir., LA HORA, Guatemala City
Marrs, Krista
kmarrs@citizen.com, Features Ed., Citizen, NH, Laconia
Marsala, Robert....203-354-1076
Production Director, The Hour Publishing Co., CT, Norwalk
Marsh, Greg....(403) 528-5632
gmarsh@medicinehatnews.com, Online Ed., Medicine Hat News, AB, Medicine Hat
Marsh, Peter....(781) 266-1616
pmarsh@atex.com, Sr. Vice Pres./Chief Integration Officer, Atex North America, MA, Burlington
Marshal, Rick
rick@kirkrudy.com, Pres., Kirk-Rudy, Inc., GA, Woodstock
Marshall, John
info@utilimaster.com, Sr. Vice Pres., Sales/Mktg., Utilimaster, IN, Wakarusa
Marshall, Loraine....(203) 731-3328
lmarshall@hearstmediact.com, Multimedia Sales Manager, The News-Times, CT, Danbury
Marshall, Melanie ....(760) 901-4079
mmarshall@nctimes.com, City Ed., Coastal, North County Times, CA, Escondido
Marshall, Michael ....(251) 219-5674
mmarshall@press-register.com, Vice Pres., News/Ed., Press-Register, AL, Mobile
Marshall, Sherrie ....(478) 744-4340
smarshall@macontel.com, Exec. Ed., The Telegraph, GA, Macon
Marshall, Howard....(202) 994-7079
George Washington Univ., DC, Washington
Marshall, Marlon....(306) 781-5241
mmarshall@leaderpost.canwest.com, Assoc. Ed., The Leader-Post, SK, Regina
Marshall, Woody....(478) 744-4233
wmarshall@macontel.com, Chief, Photography, The Telegraph, GA, Macon
Marshall, Sue....(306) 781-5234
Librarian, The Leader-Post, SK, Regina
Marshall, Anita
dqbee@ipa.net, Pub., De Queen Daily Citizen, AR, De Queen
Marshall, Alex
amarshall@heraldstaronline.com, Pub., Herald-Star, OH, Steubenville
Marshall, Brad....(217) 421-6955
Tech. Servs. Mgr., Herald & Review, IL, Decatur
Marshall, David ....(780) 429-5144
dmarshall@thejournal.canwest.com, Credit Mgr., Edmonton Journal, AB, Edmonton
Marshall, Deborah
deborah@boonvilledailynews.com, Pub., Boonville Daily News, MO, Boonville
Marshall, Wayne ....(205) 325-2212
Art Dir., The Birmingham News, AL, Birmingham
Marsland, Kevin....(603) 610-1224
kmarsland@secoastonline.com, Circ. Mgr., Retail Sales, Portsmouth Herald, NH, Portsmouth
Marthoz, Jean-Paul 211.27.77
llb.direction@saipm.com, Ed. in Chief, LA LIBRE BELGIQUE, 1000 Brussels
Martin, Becca....(479) 872-5054
bmartin@nwaonline.net, Entertainment Ed., The Morning News of Northwest Arkansas, AR, Springdale
Martin, Elizabeth
emartin@seeitfirst.com, Cor. Commun., SeeltFirst.com, CA, Sausalito
Martin, Hernan
panama@acan-efe.com, Rep., EFE News Services - Panama City, Panama, Panama City
Martin, Susan....(717) 771-2039
susan@ydr.com, Asst. Mng. Ed., Metro, York Daily Record/York Sunday News, PA, York
Martin, Rita J. ....(413) 788-1065
rmartin@repub.com, Adv. Mgr., Major Accts., The Republican, MA, Springfield
Martin, Hans Nikolaus
verlag@viernheimertageblatt.de, Proprietor, Viernheimer Tageblatt, Viernheim
Martin, Jason
jason.martin@newschief.com, Sports Ed., News Chief, FL, Winter Haven
Martin, Tony....(906) 341-4234
Prodn. Mgr., Manistique Papers, Inc., MI, Manistique
Martin, Gary
gmartin@herald-coaster.com, Sports Ed., Fort Bend Herald, TX, Rosenberg
Martin, Bill
bmartin@gaa.org, Pres./CEO, Gravure Association of America, NY, Rochester
Martin, Samuel
dgoddard@gannett.com, President & Publisher, Montgomery Advertiser, AL, Montgomery
Martin, Thomas
tribuna@tribunacampeche.com, Dir., TRIBUNA DE YUCATAN, Merida, Yucatan
Martin, Mike
manoim@e-mg.co.za, CEO, MAIL & GUARDIAN, Braamfontein
Martin, Annalisa 406-523-5206
annalisa.martin@lee.net, Controller, Missoulian, MT, Missoula
Martin, Cal ....(306) 781-5219
cmartin@leaderpost.canwest.com, Prodn. Foreman, Pre Press, The Leader-Post, SK, Regina
Martin, Ed ....(804) 649-6615
emartin@timesdispatch.com, Research Mgr., Richmond Times-Dispatch, VA, Richmond
Martin, Buddy....(941) 206-1123
martin@sun-herald.com, Mng. Ed., Charlotte Sun, FL, Charlotte Harbor
Martin, Paul ....(440) 329-7101
pmartin@chroniclet.com, President and CEO, Lorain County Printing & Publishing Corp., OH, Elyria
Martin, Diane....ext. 254
d.martin@theday.com, Adv. Mgr., Retail, The Day Publishing Company, CT, New London
Martin, Robin
newsroom@sfnewmexican.com, Pub., The Santa Fe New Mexican, NM, Santa Fe
Martin, Heidi....(252) 407-9902
hmartin@rmtelegram.com, Opns. Mgr., Rocky Mount Telegram, NC, Rocky Mount
Martin, Andre
andre.martin@pentictonherald.ca, Gen. Mgr., Penticton Herald, BC, Penticton
Martin, Doug
dmartin@benderus.com, Acct. Mgr., Bender Machine, Inc., CA, Los Angeles
Martin, Robert E.....(904) 359-4629
robert.martin@jacksonville.com, Gen. Mgr., The Florida Times-Union, FL, Jacksonville
Martin, Sheila
sheila@gaebel.com, Office Mgr., Lithco Inc., NY, East Syracuse
Martin, Gary
gmartin@nnnlp.com, Midwest Sales Director, Digital & Print, NNN (Newspaper National Network LP), IL, Chicago
Martin, Frank L. ....ext. 216
Editorial Page Ed., West Plains Daily Quill, MO, West Plains
Martin, Debbie ....(706) 864-1468
North Georgia College, GA, Dahlonega
Martin, Donald
herald@cins.co.uk, Ed. in Chief, The Herald, Glasgow, Strathclyde
Martin, Jackie 217-351-5275
jmartin@news-gazette.com, Advertising Sales Manager & National Sales, News-Gazette Inc., IL, Champaign
Martin, Wolfgang
verlag@mopo-speyer.de, Ed. in Chief, SPEYERER MORGENPOST, Speyer
Martin, Roger
redaktion@obermain.de, Ed. in Chief, OBERMAIN-TAGBLATT, Lichtenfels
Martin, Ralph ....(412) 320-7977
rmartin@tribweb.com, Chrmn./Pres., Tribune-Review Publishing Co., PA, Greensburg
Martin, Julie ....(910) 343-2383
julie.martin@starnewsonline.com, Mng. Ed., Star-News, NC, Wilmington
Martin, Matt....(814) 870-1704
matt.martin@timesnews.com, Sports Ed., Erie Times-News, PA, Erie
Martin, Bob
bmartin@winchestersun.com, Circ. Dir., The Winchester Sun, KY, Winchester
Martin, Ryne R. ....ext. 229
rmartin@ogd.com, Mng. Ed., Courier-Observer, The Courier-Observer, The Journal & The Advance-News, NY, Ogdensburg
Martin, Marione ....(580) 327-2202
alvareview@aol.com, Ed., Alva Review-Courier, OK, Alva
Martin, Harold
hmartin@messenger-inquirer.com, Sports Copy Ed., Messenger-Inquirer, KY, Owensboro
Martin, Josh....(717) 334-1134 ext. 254
jmartin@gburgtimes.com, Sports Ed., Gettysburg Times, PA, Gettysburg
Martin, Candace
cmartin@theadvocate.com, HR Dir., The Advocate, LA, Baton Rouge
Martin-Streeby, Michelle ....(530) 225-8239
mmstreeby@redding.com, Dir., Mktg./Convergence, Record Searchlight, CA, Redding
Martindale, Carolyn ....(403) 314-4326
cmartindale@reddeeradvocate.com, City Ed., Red Deer Advocate, AB, Red Deer
Martinez, Lluis
lmartinez@avui.cat, Ed., AVUI, Barcelona
Martinez, Joseph ....(201) 692-7700 ext. 122
joem@dynaric.com, Pres., Dynaric, Inc., VA, Virginia Beach
Martinez, Melissa....(915) 546-6345
mmartinez@elpasotimes.com, Features Ed., El Paso Times, TX, El Paso
Martinez, Joseph ....(201) 692-7700 ext. 122
joem@dynaric.com, Pres., DYC Supply Co., VA, Virginia Beach
Martinez, Johnny....(765) 973-4545
Adv. Mgr., Classified Sales, Palladium-Item, IN, Richmond
Martinez, Annette....(305) 347-6670
amarinez@alm.com, Group Subscriptions Manager, Palm Beach Daily Business Review, FL, West Palm Beach
Martinez, Philadelphus
nicaragua@acan-efe.com, Rep., EFE News Services - Managua, Nicaragua, Managua
Martinez, Luis
luis_martinez@elsur.com.mx, Sr., El Sur, Campeche, Campeche
Martinez, Annette ....(305) 347-6670
amartinez@alm.com, Group Subscriptions Manager, Miami Daily Business Review, FL, Miami
Martinez, Max 302-530-6007
martinpm@eckerd.edu, Managing Editor, The Current - Eckerd College, PA, Saint Petersburg
Martinez De La Rosa, Armando
ecos01@volcan.ucol.mx, Pres., Ecos de la Costa, Colima, Colima
Martinez Hidalgo, Rafael....45-1487
Pub., Medano, Punto Fijo, Falcon
Martinez Jimenez, Alonso
elsureste@mail.ccsnet.net.mx, Editorial Coord., Ediciones Empresariales del Sureste, S.A. de C.V., Villahermosa, Tabasco
Martinez Perez, Simon
diariola.regio001@chilnet.cl, Gen. Mgr., La Region, San Fernando
Martinez Rodriguez, Isidro
elfaro@astorga.com, Dir., El Faro Astorgano, Astorga, Leon
Martinez Tecco, Luis E.....495-0783
Gen. Mgr., Editorial El Atlantico S.A., Mar del Plata, Provincia de Buenos Aires
Martini, Daniel C.....(702) 837-4946
martini187@aol.com, Director of Ciculation, SAXOTECH Circulation, MD, Laurel
Martino, Sam ....(262) 472-5100
Univ. of Wisconsin Whitewater, WI, Whitewater
Martino, Carmine
southbendlathe@att.net, Pres., South Bend Lathe Corp., IN, South Bend
Martoccia, Mike....(803) 329-4031
mmartoccia@heraldonline.com, Dir., New Media, The Herald, SC, Rock Hill
Marton, George
george.marton@bowebellhowell.com, Pres., Bell & Howell Scanners, IL, Wheeling
Martsev, P.
edit@bdg.belpak.minsk.by, Ed., BELORUSSKAYA DELOVAYA GAZETA, Minsk
Marturello, Michael
mikem@kpcnews.net, Ed., Herald-Republican, IN, Angola
Marty, Michael ....(608) 781-1606
lpt@centurytel.net, Pres., Laser Products Technologies, WI, Holmen
Martz, Linda ....(419) 521-7229
lmartz@nncogannett.com, Educ. Reporter, News Journal, OH, Mansfield
Maruyama, Akira
soumu@saitama-np.co.jp, Pres., SAITAMA SHIMBUN, Saitama City, Kita-ku
Marwick, Sandra....ext. 253
Features Ed., Butler Eagle, PA, Butler
Marx, John....ext. 291
johnny@qconline.com, Columnist, The Rock Island Argus, IL, Rock Island
Marx, Linda
classifieds@madiosn-press.com, Adv. Mgr., Classified, The Madison Press, OH, London
Mascolo, Antonio 247-311
Mgr., NUOVA GAZZETTA DI MODENA, Modena
Mascorro, Yvonne
yvonne.mascorro@galvnews.com, Circ. Mgr., The Galveston County Daily News, TX, Galveston
Masegosa, Alberto
administracion@efejerusalen.com, Rep., EFE News Services - Jerusalem, Israel, Jerusalem
Maser, Peter ....(780) 429-5399
pmaser@thejournal.canwest.com, City Ed., Edmonton Journal, AB, Edmonton
Masingale, Bob....(760) 739-6673
bmasingale@nctimes.com, City Ed., Inland, North County Times, CA, Escondido
Maslund, Lars
gt.se@gt.se, Ed. in Chief, GT (GOTEBORG TIDNINGEN), Goteborg
Mason, Felicia
felicia@alabamapress.org, Exec. Dir., Alabama Newspaper Advertising Service, Inc., AL, Birmingham
Mason, Debra L.
masondl@rna.org, Exec. Dir., Religion Newswriters Association, OH, Westerville
Mason, Shelagh ....ext. 19
Mgr., Accounting, The Lebanon Democrat, TN, Lebanon
Mason, Daniel....(570) 662-4986
Mansfield Univ. of Pennsylvania, PA, Mansfield
Mason, Felicia
felicia@alabamapress.org, Exec. Dir., Alabama Press Association, AL, Birmingham
Mason, Julie
julie@zumapress.com, CFO, ZUMA Press, Inc., CA, San Clemente
Mason, Rachel
rmason@nanaimodailynews.com, Bus. Mgr., Nanaimo Daily News, BC, Nanaimo
Mason, Stephen....5208931
steve.mason@marlexpress.co.nz, Editor, THE MARLBOROUGH EXPRESS, Blenheim
Mason, Joan ....(856) 486-2502
Mgr., Retail Adv., Courier-Post, NJ, Cherry Hill
Mason-Cunningham, Valerie
info@xerox.com, Vice Pres., Mktg., Xerox Corp., CT, Norwalk
Masotta, Richard....(617) 929-2279
masotta@globe.com, Adv. Dir., Opns., The Boston Globe, MA, Boston
Masquelier, Sibyl ....(207) 871-5527
sibyl@mediahunter.com, I permanently disabled and is no longer a headhunter., Executive Resource Group, Inc. is closed, ME, Portland
Massa, Jeffrey P.....(703) 548-3300
info@yellowbrix.com, Founder/Pres./CEO, YellowBrix, VA, Alexandria

Massett, Ray ....(504) 826-3179
rmassett@bellsouth.net, Vice Pres./Gen. Mgr., The Times Picayune, LA, New Orleans
Massey, Thomas ....(919) 419-5128
tmassey@heraldsun.com, Mrktg. Mgr., The Herald-Sun, NC, Durham
Massey, Cal
cal.massey@news-jrnl.com, Deputy Mng. Ed., News, Daytona Beach News-Journal, FL, Daytona Beach
Massey, Kristi
kmassey@turlockjournal.com, Gen. Mgr., Turlock Journal, CA, Turlock
Masslich, Hugo ....(212) 681-3451
hmasslich@nydailynews.com, Circ. Promos. Vice Pres., NY Daily News, NY, New York
Massoth, Michele ....(815) 987-1320
Adv. Mgr., Classified, Rockford Register Star, IL, Rockford
Massott, Jackie ....ext. 4189
jmassott@phillyburbs.com, Content Ed., Bucks County Courier Times, PA, Levittown
Mast, Greg
sports@ottowaherald.com, Sports Ed., The Ottawa Herald, KS, Ottawa
Masterman, Christine ....(519) 894-2250 ext. 2695
cmasterman@therecord.com, Librarian, The Record, ON, Kitchener
Masters, Tim
tmasters@masterpiecemedia.com, Pres., Masterpiece Media Design, NJ, Farfield
Masterson, Bill
bill.masterson@nwitimes.com, Pub., The Times, IN, Munster
Mastin, Dan ....(252) 329-9654
dmastin@reflector.com, Dir., Opns., The Daily Reflector, NC, Greenville
Masucger, Andrea
andrea.masucger@suedostschweiz.ch, Ed., DIE SU DOSTSCHWEIZ, Chur, Graubunden/Grisons
Masuda, Hiroshi
hiroshi.masuda@jijiusa.com, Pres., Jiji Press America Ltd., NY, New York
Masueter, Andrea
amasueger@suedostschweiz.ch, Ed. in Chief/Adn. Mgr., SUEDOSTSCHWEIZ, Uznach
Mata, Francisco ....ext. 2342
francisco.mata@uniontrib.com, Pub., Enlace, The San Diego Union-Tribune, CA, San Diego
Matea, Dan
danmatea@yahoo.com, Ed. in Chief, CRISANA, Bihor, Oradea
Matejczyk, Lon ....(719) 634-1048
lon.matejczyk@csbj.com, Pub., Daily Transcript, CO, Colorado Springs
Matejczyk, Lon ....(719) 634-1048
editorial@csbj.com, Adv. Mgr., Daily Transcript, CO, Colorado Springs
Mateo Sahuquillo, Santiago
mateo.santiago@grupo-eldia.net, Dir., EL DIA DE CUENCA, Cuenca
Mathema, Puskar
trn@gorkhapatra.org.np, Ed. in Chief, THE RISING NEPAL, Kathmandu
Mathers, Margaret
mmathers@daily-times.com, Sr. Copy Ed., The Daily Times, NM, Farmington
Matheson, Andrew ....(831) 637-5566
amatheson@freelancenews.com, Sports Ed., Free Lance, CA, Hollister
Matheson, Keith ....ext. 265
Prodn. Mgr., Mailroom, The Standard, ON, Saint Catharines
Mathew, Mammen
kijames@mm.co.in, Mng. Dir./Ed., MALAYALA MANORAMA, Kottayam, Kerala
Mathews, Jackie
crosspuzz@aol.com, Ed., Puzzle Features Syndicate, WA, Lynnwood
Mathews, Colin
customerservice@eisinc.com, CEO/Pres., Empire Information Services, NY, Albany
Mathews, Gregory ....(417) 836-1195
gmatthews@news-leader.com, Online Ed., Springfield News-Leader, MO, Springfield
Mathewson, Melanie ....(321) 283-5259
mmathewson@flpress.com, Vice President and Chief Sales Officer, Florida Press Association, FL, Tallahassee
Mathewson, Melanie
mmathewson@n2ps.com, Vice Pres., National Newspaper Placement Services, FL, Lake Mary
Mathieu, Bernd
chefredaktion@mail.an-online.de, Ed. in Chief, AACHENER NACHRICHTEN, Aachen
Mathieu, Bernd
verlagsleitung@zeitungsverlang-aachen.de, Ed. in Chief, AACHENER ZEITUNG, Aachen
Mathis, Pearl A.
edinrev@aol.com, Pres./Pub., Edinburg Review, TX, Edinburg
Mathison, Lindsey
lmathison@people2people.com, Contact, Tele-Publishing, Inc., MA, Boston
Matia, Liza 814-765-7813
news@theprogressnews.com, Assistant Editor, The Progress, PA, Clearfield
Matilla, Arnaldo Cesar 421-854
director@lareformaonline.com.ar, Dir., La Reforma, General Pico, Provincia de La Pampa
Matlok, Siegfried
redaktion@nordschleswiger.dk, Ed., NORDSCHLESWIGER, Aabenraa, Jutland
Maton, Leeann
phoenixnews@luc.edu, Loyola Univ., IL, Chicago
Matos Solorzano, Roberto 225-8501
sintesis@amauta.rcp.net.pe, Gen. Mgr., Sintesis, Lima
Matsui, Jun
webmaster@sbs-np.co.jp, Pres., SHIZUOKA SHIMBUN, Shizuoka, Chubu
Matsuzawa, M. ....(847) 981-9399 ext. 210
Chrmn., INX International Ink Co., IL, Schaumburg
Matt, Judy ....ext. 26
jmatt@adspies.com, Gen. Mgr./Controller, Advertising Data Scan/Adspies.com, FL, Jacksonville
Matteau, Michel
michel.matteau@afp.com, Bureau Chief, Agence France-Presse - Montreal, QC, QC, Montreal
Matteo, Leonardo Di
ldimatteo@clarin.com, Ed., Clarin Contenidos, Buenos Aires
Matthews, Blair
bmatthews@alm.com, Pub., Daily Report
Matthews, Allen.......................(415)777-8890
amatthews@sfchronicle.com, Editorial Operations, San Francisco Chronicle, CA, San Francisco
Matthews, Wayne
info@headlinememories.com, Pres., Headline Memories, FL, Safety Harbor
Matthews, Cheri
cherim@tracypress.com, Ed., Tracy Press, CA, Tracy
Matthews, Sherry...............................ext. 23
smatthews@intrstar.net, Ed., The Sampson Independent, NC, Clinton
Matthews, Dena
dmatthews@thefacts.com, Adv. Mgr., Classified, The Facts, TX, Clute
Matthews, Robert S..................(209) 835-3030
rsm@tracypress.com, Pres./Pub., Tracy Press, CA, Tracy
Matthey, Patrice
lematin@edipresse.ch, Mktg. Dir., LE MATIN, Lausanne, Vaud
Matticks, Angie
amatticks@timesgazette.com, Composing Mgr., Times-Gazette, OH, Hillsboro
Mattingly, Steve
steve@slp.com, Vice Pres., Sales/Mktg., Southern Lithoplate, Inc., NC, Wake Forest
Mattress, Willie ....(864) 260-1274
mattresswm@independentmail.com, Ed., HomeTowner, Anderson Independent-Mail, SC, Anderson
Matts-Sprague, Jennifer
jmatts-sprague@theolympian.com, VP Finance, The Olympian, WA, Olympia
Mattson, Thomas
thomas.mattson@expressen.se, Ed. in Chief/Pub., EXPRESSEN, Stockholm
Matusoka, Yoshiaki
info@hokkaido-np.co.jp, Kushiro Head Officer, HOKKAIDO SHIMBUN, Kushiro, Hokkaido
Matyas, Jaroslav
jmatyas@pravda.sk, Online Ed., PRAVDA, Bratislava
Matyjas, John
jmatyjas@nvsmedia.com, Southwest Sales Mgr., NVS Interactive Media, NY, Williamsville
Mauer, Jennifer
jmauer@nydailynews.com, Vice Pres., Commun., NY Daily News, NY, New York
Mauger, Steve
gpads@guernsey-press.com, Adv. Dir., GUERNSEY PRESS & STAR, ENG, Vale, Guernsey
Mauldin, Charles
charliem@immediatesfa.com, VP, Solutions, Media Marketing, Inc., CO, Westminster
Mauldin, Tom ....(541) 948-9501
tommauldin@iinet.com, West/Mountain States Assoc., Grimes, W.B. & Co., OR, Sisters
Maulucci, Lou ....(705) 759-5810
lmaulucci@saultstar.com, Publisher, General Manager, The Sault Star, ON, Sault Ste Marie
Maune, Dietrich
maunedx@jmu.edu, Asst. Dir./Prof., James Madison University, VA, Harrisonburg
Mauney, Paul 336-506-3002
pmauney@thetimesnews.com, Publisher, Times-News, NC, Burlington
Maureen M., N/A ....Adv. Dir.
Herald-Standard, PA, Uniontown
Maureen M., N/A ....Dir., Mktg.
Herald-Standard, PA, Uniontown
Maurer, Konrad................................828 81 18
k.maurer@bom.ch, CEO, THUNER TAGBLATT, Thun, Bern
Maurer, Konrad
redaktion-tt@bom.ch, Bus. Mgr., BERNER OBERLANDER, Thun
Maurer, Jerry ....(937) 328-0387
jmaurer@coxohio.com, Prodn. Supvr., Bldg., Springfield News-Sun, OH, Springfield
Maurice, Jason
sales@kba-usa.com, Dir., Sales, KBA North America, Inc. (Koenig & Bauer AG), VT
Mauritson, Martha
marthamauritson@currentargus.com, Mng. Ed., Current-Argus, NM, Carlsbad
Mauro, Ezio...49-821
e.mauro@repubblica.it, Ed. in Chief, LA REPUBBLICA, Rome
Mauser, Michael
info@murrhardter-zeitung.de, Distr. Mgr., MURRHARDTER ZEITUNG, Murrhardt
Mauser, Robin
kingmannewspaper@mcimail.com, Pub., Kingman Daily Miner, AZ, Kingman
Mauser, Ken.............................(309) 686-3005
kmauser@pjstar.com, Vice Pres./Gen. Mgr., Journal Star, IL, Peoria
Maxey, Brian...........................(559) 278-5732
California State Univ., CA, Fresno
Maxfield, Dennis C...................(585) 396-0027
tns@fats-and-oils.com, Sr. Ed., Trade News Service (Fats And Oils), NY, Canandaigua
Maxwell, Scotty 270-590-2647
smaxwell@glasgowdailytimes, General Manager, Glasgow Daily Times, KY, Glasgow
Maxwell, Becky
iowegianpublisher@mchsi.com, Circ. Mgr., Ad Express & Daily Iowegian, IA, Centerville
Maxwell, Tim ....(334) 737-2557
Prodn. Mgr., Opelika-Auburn News, AL, Opelika
Maxwell, Brenda ....(937) 644-9111
Adv. Mgr., Classified, Marysville Journal-Tribune, OH, Marysville
May, Roy ....(228) 934-1412
rmay@themississippipress.com, Adv. Mgr., The Mississippi Press, MS, Pascagoula
May, Pamela......................................ext. 139
pmay@designmedia.com, Pres./CEO, Design Media, Inc., CA, San Francisco
May, David
editor@mineralwellsindex.com, Ed., Mineral Wells Index, TX, Mineral Wells
May, Jerry..................(334) 749-6271 ext. 2555
jmay@oanow.com, Circ. Dir., Opelika-Auburn News, AL, Opelika
May, Michael
mmay@publicitas.com, Branch Dir., Publicitas North America, Inc., MI, Troy
May, Joe ....(573) 581-1111
jmay@mail.itwebs.com, Pub., Mexico Ledger, MO, Mexico
May, Gary ....(813) 627-1309
Circ. Opns. Mgr., Metro, The Tampa Tribune, FL, Tampa
Mayberry, Jason
jmayberry@heraldstaronline.com, Adv. Dir., Herald-Star, OH, Steubenville
Mayberry, David
david.mayberry@trib.com, Sports/City Ed., Casper Star-Tribune, WY, Casper
Mayborn, Sue..........................(254) 778-4444
tdtads@temple-telegram.com, Ed., Temple Daily Telegram, TX, Temple
Mayborn, Anyse Sue
tdt@temple-telegram.com, Pres., Frank Mayborn Enterprises, Inc., TX, Temple
Mayer, Chris
smt@globe.com, Pres., The Boston Globe, MA, Boston
Mayer, Michael
mmayer@dallasnews.com, General Manager, Recruitment, Real Estate, General Classifieds, Southwest Classified Advertising Managers Association, TX, Dallas
Mayer, Allan ....(780) 429-5201
amayer@thejournal.canwest.com, Ed. in Chief, Edmonton Journal, AB, Edmonton
Mayer, Tom...............................(386) 754-0428
Ed., Lake City Reporter, FL, Lake City
Mayes, Malcolm ....(780) 471-6112
mmayes@artizans.com, Pres., Artizans.com Syndicate, AB, Edmonton
Mayeux, Debra
dmayeux@daily-times.com, Features Ed., The Daily Times, NM, Farmington
Mayfield, Trevis
tmayfield@svnmail.com, Pub., Sauk Valley Media, IL, Sterling
Mayfield, Erica ....(256) 740-4733
erica.mayfield@timesdaily.com, Adv. Mgr., Classified Call Ctr., TimesDaily, AL, Florence
Mayfield, Trevis
tmayfield@svnmail.com, Pub., Sauk Valley Newspapers, IL, Dixon
Mayger, Janine...............................9326 8404
Mktg. Servs. Mgr., SUNDAY TIMES
Maynard, Mark ....(606) 326-2648
mmaynard@dailyindependent.com, Mng. Ed., The Daily Independent, KY, Ashland
Mayo, Ron..................................(303) 954-6464
rmayo@medianewsgroup.com, Vice Pres./CFO, MediaNews Group Inc, CO, Denver
Mazanec, Greg 651-228-5315
gmazanec@pioneerpress.com, Vice Pres., Adv., St. Paul Pioneer Press, MN, Saint Paul
Maze, Brent..ext. 19
brent.maze@clantonadvertiser.com, Mng. Ed., The Clanton Advertiser, AL, Clanton
Mazumdar, Saurav
iemumbai@express.indexp.co.in, Ed., FINANCIAL EXPRESS, Mumbai, Maharashtra
Mazur, Bob ....(216) 999-5694
IT Mgr., Infrastructure and Opns., The Plain Dealer, OH, Cleveland
Mazurier, Luis A.
correo@diarioelsol.com.ar, Pres., Cooperativa de Trabajo Obrera, Concordia, Provincia de Entre Rios
Mazzapica, Gina 661-940-5352
gmazzapica@avpress.com, Classified Advertising Director, Antelope Valley Press, CA, Palmdale
Mazzapica, Gina 661-940-5352
gmazzapica@avpress.com, Classified Advertising Director, Antelope Valley Press, CA, Palmdale
Mazzara, Sam...............(256) 734-2131 ext. 238
smazzara@cullmantimes.com, Circ. Mgr., The Cullman Times, AL, Cullman
Mazzarri, Clara 431-0246
Sales Mgr., Publicaciones Obelisco C.A., Barquisimeto, Lara
Mazzarri, Clara..................................May-56
buzon@eltiempo.com.ve, Sales Mgr., EL TIEMPO, Valera, Trujillo
Mazzarri, Clara....................................53-1832
Sales Mgr., EL PERIODICO DE OCCIDENTE, Guanare, Portuguesa
Mbenekos, Versilees

vanetol@odenet.gr, Ed., Panaetoliki Etairia, Agrinion, Aetolia & Acarnania
Mbingo, Mbongeni
editor@times.co.sz, Mng. Ed., TIMES OF SWAZILAND, Mbabane
Mbodj, Ibrahima 859 5940
Ed. in Chief, LE SOLEIL, Dakar
Mc Corkle, Mary ....(805) 546-3288
Cuesta College, CA, San Luis Obispo
Mc Corthy, Jean
jean.mccorthy@broadvision.com, Dir., BroadVision, MA, Waltham
Mc Dowell, Pam
publisher@pontiacdailyleader.com, Pub., The Daily Leader, IL, Pontiac
McAbee, Michelle 203-316-2044
michelle.mcabee@scni.com, Publisher, Greenwich Time, CT, Greenwich
McAbee, Michelle
michelle.mcabee@scni.com, Pub., The Advocate, CT, Stamford
McAden, Fitz ....(843) 706-8110 ext. 8105
fmcaden@islandpacket.com, Exec. Ed., The Island Packet, SC, Bluffton
McAdler, Sandy ....(707) 526-8589
sandy.mcadler@pressdemocrat.com, Controller, The Press Democrat, CA, Santa Rosa
McAfee, Paul 951-368-5160
pmcafee@pe.com, Interactive Development Director, The Press-Enterprise, CA, Riverside
McAlexander, W. Scott ....(541) 343-3029
scottm@landmarkdesigns.com, Chrmn./Pres., Landmark Designs, Inc., OR, Eugene
McAlpin, Leslie ....ext. 288
lmcalpin@glasgowdailytimes.com, Circ. Mgr., Glasgow Daily Times, KY, Glasgow
McAnally, Neil
Neil.mcanally@latimes.com, Opns. Mgr., Times Community News (TCN), CA, Glendale
McAnulty, Drew
drew.mcanulty@ott.sunpub.com, Entertainment Ed., The Ottawa Sun, ON, Ottawa
McAuley, Lynn ....(613) 596-8567
lmcauley@thecitizen.southam.ca, Citizen Weekly Magazine Style Ed., The Ottawa Citizen, ON, Ottawa
McAuslin, Chris 684 4129
editor@timaruherald.co.nz, Gen Mgr., THE TIMARU HERALD
McAvoy, Doug 574-296-5934
dmcavoy@etruth.com, Audience Development Director, The Elkhart Truth, IN, Elkhart
McBride, Nadine 860-425-4351
nmcbride@norwichbulletin.com, Controller/Director of Operations, The Bulletin, CT, Norwich
McBride, Mike
mcbride@lmtribune.com, Circ. Mgr., Moscow-Pullman Daily News, ID, Moscow
McBride, Roland ....(618) 993-1711
Exec. Vice Pres./CFO, Horizon Publications, IL, Marion
McBride, Carolyn N.
dailynews@netride.net, Weekender Ed., The Anadarko Daily News, OK, Anadarko
McBride, Michael ....(208) 743-9600 ext. 220
mcbride@lmtribune.com, Circ. Dir., Lewiston Morning Tribune, ID, Lewiston
McCabe, Jeremoy
mccabej@avusa.co.za, Ed. In Cheif, THE HERALD, Port Elizabeth, Eastern Cape
McCabe, Jeremy
mccabe@avusa.co.za, Ed. in Chief, POST/WEEKEND POST, Port Elizabeth, Eastern Cape
McCaffery, Deb ....(607) 441-7219
dmccaffery@thedailystar.com, Librarian, The Daily Star, NY, Oneonta
McCall, Jeffrey M.
jeffmccall@depauw.edu, Chair, DePauw University, IN, Greencastle
McCall, Jean
info@solarsystems.com, CFO, Solar Systems, WA, Preston
McCallen, Tiffany A.
mccallen@rna.org, Assoc. Dir., Religion Newswriters Association, OH, Westerville
McCance, McGregor ....(434) 978-7283
cmccance@dailyprogress.com, Mng. Ed., The Daily Progress, VA, Charlottesville
McCanless, George
gmccanless@macontel.com, Pres./Pub., The Telegraph, GA, Macon
McCann, Pat ....(850) 747-5068
pmccann@pcnh.com, Exec. Sports Ed., The News Herald, FL, Panama City
McCann, Gary ....(803) 329-4074
gmccann@heraldonline.com, Sports Ed., The Herald, SC, Rock Hill
McCarthy, Stephen ....(973) 569-7111
hncitydesk@northjersey.com, Ed., Herald News, NJ, West Paterson
McCarthy, Brett
brett.mccarthy@wanews.com.au, Ed., THE WEST AUSTRALIAN, Osborne Park
McCarthy, Dan
dmccarthy@yourwestvalley.com, Exec. Ed., Daily News-Sun, AZ, Sun City
McCarthy, Michael 540-654-1033
Advisor, University of Mary Washington, VA, Fredericksburg
McCarthy, Randy ....(253) 597-8277
randy.mccarthy@thenewstribune.com, Crime/Breaking News Team Leader, The News Tribune, WA, Tacoma
McCarthy, Carol 860/701-4352
c.mccarthy@theday.com, Deputy Managing Editor/News Operations, The Day Publishing Company, CT, New London
McCarthy, Mick
info@process.com, Vice Pres., Sales, Process Software, MA, Framingham
McCarthy, John P.
cinemansyndicate@verizon.net, Pub./Ed./Co-Owner, Cineman Syndicate LLC, NY, Rye
McCarthy, John P.
cinemansyndicate@verizon.net, Ed., Cineman Syndicate, NY, Rye
McCarthy, John 321-752-5018
jmccarthy@floridatoday.com, Enterprise Editor/county, state, environment, Florida Today, FL, Melbourne
McCarthy , Stephen
stephen.mccarthy@am-ny.com, Marketing Director , amNew York, NY, New York
McCarty, Jeff 513-403-4198
jeffmccarty@hadronics.com, Vice Pres., Sales, Hadronics, OH, Cincinnati
McCauley, Byron ....(318) 274-2560
Grambling State Univ., LA, Grambling
McClain, Cindy ....(989) 779-6130
cmcclain@michigannewspapers.com, Prodn. Mgr., Composing, Morning Sun, MI, Mount Pleasant
McClain, Randy ....(615) 259-8284
rmcclain@tennessean.com, Asst. Bus. Ed., The Tennessean, TN, Nashville
McClain, David
dmcclain@journal-advocate.com, Pub., Journal-Advocate, CO, Sterling
McClanahan, Jenny
jmcclanahan@coxohio.com, Prodn. Mgr., Pre Press, Middletown Journal, OH, Middletown
McClary, Kevin
news@recordernews.com, Pub., The Recorder, NY, Amsterdam
McClary, Emmett H. 662-254-3458
Mississippi Valley State Univ., MS, Itta Bena
McCleary, Mike ....(701) 250-8265
mmccleary@ndonline.com, Photographer, The Bismarck Tribune, ND, Bismarck
McClellan, Philip
pmcclellan@iht.com, Deputy Mng. Ed., INTERNATIONAL HERALD TRIBUNE, Hong Kong
McClellan, Linnea ....(334) 712-7902
lmclellan@dothaneagle.com, Lifestyle Ed., The Dothan Eagle, AL, Dothan
McClelland, Art ....(903) 596-6269
amcclelland@tylerpaper.com, Vice Pres., Sales/Mktg., Tyler Morning Telegraph, TX, Tyler
McClesky, Pat ....(770) 428-9411 ext. 401
Prodn. Mgr., Mailroom, Marietta Daily Journal, GA, Marietta
McClintock, Robert ....ext. 537
bmcclintock@journalregister.com, Controller, Daily Freeman, NY, Kingston
McClintock, Ron ....(519) 354-2000
circmgr@chathamdailynews.ca, Circ. Mgr., The Chatham Daily News, ON, Chatham
McCloat, Keith ....(212) 969-7595
kmccloat@hearst.com, Vice Pres./Gen. Mgr., North America Syndicate, NY, New York
kmccloat@hearst.com, Vice Pres., Gen. Mgr., King Features Syndicate, NY, New York
McCloskey, Robyn ....ext. 5133
robyn.mccloskey@indianamediagroup.com, Pub., Pharos-Tribune, IN, Logansport
McCloskey, Brian ....(440) 951-0000 ext. 611
bmccloskey@news-herald.com, GM, The News-Herald, OH, Willoughby
McCloskey, Robyn
robyn.mccloskey@kokomotribune.com, Pub., Kokomo Tribune, IN, Kokomo
McCloud, Ken ....(239) 335-0230
Circ. Dir., The News-Press, FL, Fort Myers
McClure, Jim ....(919) 836-2822
jmcclure@newsobserver.com, Vice Pres., Display Adv., The News & Observer, NC, Raleigh
McClure, James ....(717) 771-2011
jem@ydr.com, Ed., York Daily Record/York Sunday News, PA, York
McClure, John ....(336) 888-3545
lwagner@hpe.com, Adv. Dir., High Point Enterprise, NC, High Point
McClure, Julie ....(765) 420-5226
jmcclure@journalandcourier.com, Features Ed., Journal and Courier, IN, Lafayette
McCluskey, William J. ....(212) 407-0500
mccluskw@gruntal.com, Mng. Dir., Gruntal & Co., Inc., NY, New York
McCluskey, Brooke ....(812) 349-1400
bmccluskey@heraldt.com, Mktg. Mgr., The Herald-Times, IN, Bloomington
McCollum, Charles
cmccollum@hjnews.com, Editorial Page Ed., The Herald Journal, UT, Logan
McCollum, Trent Bonner
thpub@thnews.com, Pub. Emer., Times-Herald, AR, Forrest City
McConnell, Kevin
udjpublisher@pacific.net, Pub., Ukiah Daily Journal, CA, Ukiah
McConnell, Gregg ....(530) 896-7708
gmcconnell@chicoer.com, Pub., Chico Enterprise-Record, CA, Chico
McConnell, Lawrence ....(434) 978-7200
lmcconnell@dailyprogress.com, Pub., The Daily Progress, VA, Charlottesville
McConnell, Catherine ....(250) 995-4426
cmcconnell@te.canwest.com, Dir., Finance, Times Colonist, BC, Victoria
McConnell, Justin ....(309) 686-3069
jmcconnell@pjstar.com, Asst. Gen. Mgr., Journal Star, IL, Peoria
McCool, Elizabeth C. ....(541) 383-0374
Chrmn. of the Bd., Western Communications, Inc., OR, Bend
McCorkle, Brenda ....(360) 577-2515
brendamc@tdn.com, Community Ed., The Daily News, WA, Longview
McCormack, Don ....ext. 298
Sports Ed., Star Beacon, OH, Ashtabula
McCormick, Robin ....(757) 247-4735
rmccormick@dailypress.com, Mng. Ed., Print, Daily Press, VA, Newport News
McCormick, Beth ....(217) 421-7928
Online Mgr., Herald & Review, IL, Decatur
McCormick, Joye ....(850) 522-5113
jmccormick@pcnh.com, Adv. Mgr., Creative Servs., The News Herald, FL, Panama City
McCormick, Carol ....(563) 383-2241
Controller, Quad-City Times, IA, Davenport
McCormick, Mack ....(919) 836-5621
mmccormi@newsobserver.com, Adv. Mgr., Regl., The News & Observer, NC, Raleigh
McCormick, Keith
circulation@herald-citizen.com, Circ. Mgr., Herald-Citizen, TN, Cookeville
McCormick, Teri 940-552-5454
Classified & New Media Director, The Vernon Daily Record, TX, Vernon
McCormick, Bret 940-552-5454
publisher@vernonrecord.com, President / Publisher, The Vernon Daily Record, TX, Vernon
McCoshen, Jeff
jmccoshen@bowesnet.com, Mng. Ed., Daily Herald-Tribune, AB, Grande Prairie
McCourt, Kevin
kevin.mccourt@naa.org, Dir., Adv. Sales, Presstime (Newspaper Association of America), VA, Arlington
McCoy, John ....(607) 441-7245
jmccoy@thedailystar.com, Prodn. Mgr., Pressroom, The Daily Star, NY, Oneonta
McCoy, Kathleen ....ext. 330
kmccoy@adn.com, Features Ed., Anchorage Daily News, AK, Anchorage
McCoy, Jody ....(719) 630-3111
jbmccoy@adelphia.net, Dir., Media Services Group, Inc., FL, Jacksonville Beach
McCrabb, Rick ....(513) 422-3611
rmccrabb@coxohio.com, Treasurer, Ohio Newspaper Women's Association, OH, Enon
McCrabb, Rick
rmccrabb@coxohio.com, Features Ed., Middletown Journal, OH, Middletown
McCracken, Ian ....(410) 263-2212
St. Johns College, MD, Annapolis
McCraken, L. Michael ....(307) 633-3140
mikem@wyomingnews.com, Pres./Pub., Wyoming Tribune-Eagle, WY, Cheyenne
McCraken, L. Michael ....(307) 633-3140
news@wyomingnews.com, Pres., Wyoming Newspaper Group, WY, Cheyenne
McCraven, Dennis ....(706) 208-2382
dennis.mccraven@onlineathens.com, Prodn. Mgr., Mailroom, Athens Banner-Herald, GA, Athens
McCray, Janet ....ext. 1214
janet.mccray@gwinnettdailypost.com, Adv. Mgr., Major Accts., Gwinnette Daily Post, GA, Lawrenceville
McCrory, Sean
smccrory@thetowntalk.com, Deputy Dir., The Town Talk, LA, Alexandria
McCullen, Brenda ....ext. 15
siclass@intrstar.net, Adv. Dir., Classified, The Sampson Independent, NC, Clinton
McCulligh, Carolyn ....(707) 526-8563
carolyn.mcculligh@pressdemocrat.com, Adv. Dir., The Press Democrat, CA, Santa Rosa
McCulloch, Sue ....ext. 122
smcculloch@ccdailyrecord.com, Prodn. Mgr., Pre Press, The Canon City Daily Record, CO, Canon City
McCullough, Joyce ....(815) 220-6929
joyce@newstrib.com, Pub., News-Tribune, IL, La Salle
McCullough, Shelly ....(707) 553-6811
smccullough@timesheraldonline.com, Adv. Dir., Vallejo Times-Herald, CA, Vallejo
McCullough, Nate ....ext. 1315
nate.mccullough@gwinnettdailypost.com, Copy Desk Chief, Gwinnette Daily Post, GA, Lawrenceville
McCullough, Gwendolyn ....ext. 5936
gmccullough@postandcourier.com, Dir., HR, The Post and Courier, SC, Charleston
McCumber, David 203-964-2465
david.mccumber@scni.com, Editor, Greenwich Time, CT, Greenwich
McCune, Robert ....ext. 3210
robert.mccune@indeonline.com, Ed., The Independent, OH, Massillon
McCurdy, Don ....(519) 894-2250 ext. 2693
dmccurdy@therecord.com, Mng. Ed., The Record, ON, Kitchener
McCurdy, Mary Liz ....(650) 721-5803
Stanford Univ., CA, Stanford
McCurdy, Frederic
fmccurdy@gtilite.com, Pres., Graphic Technology, Inc. (GTI), NY, Newburgh
McCurdy, Robert
rmccurdy@gtilite.com, Vice Pres., Sales/Mktg., Graphic Technology, Inc. (GTI), NY, Newburgh
McCurry-Ross, Cindy ....(239) 344-4812
cmcross@news-press.com, Sr. Mng. Ed., The News-Press, FL, Fort Myers
McCusker, Kevin ....(559) 735-3288
news@visaliatimesdelta.com, Sports Ed., Visalia Times-Delta & Tulare Advance-Register, CA, Visalia
McDaniel, Polly ....(828) 232-5834
pmcdanie@citizen-times.com, Features Ed., The Asheville Citizen-Times, NC, Asheville
McDaniel, Jayna ....(614) 233-7404
jmcdaniel@nncogannett.com, Dir., Online Servs., News Journal, OH, Mansfield
McDermand, David ....(979) 731-4658
dave.mcdermand@theeagle.com, Photo Dept.

Mgr., The Eagle, TX, Bryan
McDermott, Kaitie ....(386) 801-9546
Lipscomb Univ., TN, Nashville
McDermott, Larry A. ....(413) 788-1312
lmcdermott@repub.com, Pub./CEO, The Republican, MA, Springfield
McDermott, Russell
rmcdermott@texarkanagazette.com, Editorial Page Ed., Texarkana Gazette, TX, Texarkana
McDevitt, Donna
donna@ipa.org, Exec. Asst., International Prepress Association, MN, Edina
McDivitt, Krista...........................8124647680
mcdivittk@courierpress.com, I.T. Director, Evansville Courier & Press, IN, Evansville
McDonald, Maria 416-442-5626
Director of Sales, National Post, ON, Toronto
McDonald, Susan ....(541) 338-2543
NIE Coord., The Register-Guard, OR, Eugene
McDonald, Tom.........................(505) 425-6796
optic@lasvegasoptic.com, Ed., Las Vegas Optic, NM, Las Vegas
McDonald, Sean
smcdonald@mediaonene.com, Pub., Sentinel & Enterprise, MA, Fitchburg
McDonald, David
info@worldpressinstitute.org, Exec. Dir., World Press Institute, MN, Saint Paul
McDonald, Jack
jmcdonald@morpace.com, Pres., Morpace International, MI, Farmington Hills
McDonald, Jim
jlmcd1492@aol.com, Pres., ADI/PDM Trade Group, GA, Slyvania
McDonald, John
john.mcdonald@ok.bc.ca, Westside Ed., The Daily Courier, BC, Kelowna
McDonald, Belinda
info@infosiscorp.com, Dir., Mktg., Infosis Corp., MA, Quincy
McDonald, Jonathan.................(604) 605-2462
jmcdonald@theprovince.com, Sports Ed., The Province, BC, Vancouver
McDonnell, Jenna
newsroom@s-t.com, Controller, The Standard-Times, MA, New Bedford
McDonough, Doug ....(806) 296-1350
dmcdonough@hearstnp.com, News/Wire Ed., Plainview Herald, TX, Plainview
McDougal, Audrey
editorinchief@clarknews.org, Clark College, WA, Vancouver
McDougald, James ....(303) 954-6450
jmcdougald@medianewsgroup.com, Treasurer, MediaNews Group Inc, CO, Denver
McDougall, Doris ....(416) 862-5000
Exec. Sec., Papiers Stadacona, ON, Toronto
McDowell, Brian ....(315) 684-6169
Morrisville State College, NY, Morrisville
McDowell, Marshall ....(559) 441-6292
mmcdowell@fresnobee.com, Circ. Mgr., Home Delivery, The Fresno Bee, CA, Fresno
McDowell, Raymond ....(804) 649-6240
rmcdowell@timesdispatch.com, Controller, Richmond Times-Dispatch, VA, Richmond
McDowell, Pam
pam@mcdonoughvoice.com, Pub., Macomb Journal, IL, Macomb
McElhenny, Jim
contact.latran@latran.com, Vice Pres., Sales, Latran Technologies, MA, Woburn
McElhinny, Brad
dmnews@dailymail.com, City Ed., Charleston Daily Mail, WV, Charleston
McElroy, Jack...........................(865) 342-6300
Ed., Knoxville News Sentinel, TN, Knoxville
McElwain, Charles........(617) 779-8900 ext. 2142
cmcelwain@domania.com, Exec. Dir., Engineering, Domania, Inc., MA, Watertown
McElwee, John ....(843) 317-7203
jmcelwee@florencenews.com, Controller, Morning News, SC, Florence
McElyea, Faye
faye@athensnews-courier.com, Adv. Mgr., Classified, The News-Courier, AL, Athens
McEnery, Brian ....(860) 241-6219
lmcenery@courant.com, Circ. Mgr., Opns., The Hartford Courant, CT, Hartford
McEwen, Craig
cmcewen@forumcomm.com, Bus. Ed., InForum, ND, Fargo
McEwen, Ken ....(405) 366-3570
kmcewen@normantranscript.com, Circ. Dir., Norman Transcript, OK, Norman
McFadden, John ....ext. 2443
jmcfadden@wdy.net, Editorial Page Ed., Watertown Daily Times, NY, Watertown
McFadden, Marsha ....(808) 535-2426
mmcfadden@honoluluadvertiser.com, Mng. Ed., Content, Honolulu Star-Advertiser, HI, Honolulu
McFadden, Andrew 951-368-5153
amcfadden@pe.com, Mgr Innovation/Business Dev, The Press-Enterprise, CA, Riverside
McFarland, Deirdre ....(646) 654-8434
Vice Pres., Mktg./Commun., Scarborough Research, NY, New York
McFarland, Donna
donna.mcfarland@wninews.com, Adv. Mgr., Waxahachie Daily Light, TX, Waxahachie
McFarlin, Diane ....(941) 361-4571
diane.mcfarlin@heraldtribune.com, Publisher, Sarasota Herald-Tribune, FL, Sarasota
McFerren, Robert ....(330) 747-1471 ext. 1380
mcferren@vindy.com, Graphics Ed./Art Dir., The Vindicator, OH, Youngstown
McGee, Tammy.........................(360) 754-5438
tmcgee@theolympianc.com, Librarian, The Olympian, WA, Olympia
McGee, David
sales@tel-aire.com, Pres., Tel-Aire Publications, Inc., TX, Irving
McGee, Brian
mcgeeb@cofc.edu, Chair, College of Charleston, SC, Charleston
McGee, Doug ....(902) 563-3878
letters@cbpost.com, Editorial Page Ed., The Cape Breton Post, NS, Sydney
McGee, Trevan 785-832-7178
tmcgee@ljworld.com, The World Co.- Lawrence, Kan., Journal-World, KS, Lawrence
McGee, Trevan 785-832-7178
tmcgee@ljworld.com, Entertainment Editor, The World Co.- Lawrence, Kan., Journal-World, KS, Lawrence
McGeoghie, Craig
courier@dcthomson.co.uk, Adv. Mgr., COURIER & ADVERTISER, SCO, Dundee, Tayside
McGhee, Richard.......................(219) 648-3098
rmcghee@post-trib.com, Telecom Mgr., Post-Tribune, IN, Merrillville
McGhee, Libby 512-912-2989
Manager, Human Resources, Austin American-Statesman, TX, Austin
McGihon, Errol
errol.mcgihon@ott.sunpub.com, Photo Ed., The Ottawa Sun, ON, Ottawa
McGill, Carol
cmcgill@hearstnp.com, Prodn. Supvr., Pre Press, Plainview Herald, TX, Plainview
McGill, Jennifer ....(803) 798-0271
aejmchq@aol.com, Exec. Dir., Association for Education in Journalism and Mass Communication, SC, Columbia
McGill, Jennifer
jennifer@aejmchq.org, Exec. Dir., Association of Schools of Journalism and Mass Communication, SC, Columbia
McGinley, Lisa...........................860/701-4334
l.mcginley@theday.com, AME/Reporters, The Day Publishing Company, CT, New London
McGinnis, Judith ....(940) 763-7534
mcginnisj@wtr.com, Food Ed., Wichita Falls Times Record News, TX, Wichita Falls
McGinnis, Sharon
smcginnis@poconorecord.com, Mgr., HR, Pocono Record, PA, Stroudsburg
McGinnis, Mary-Jane 860/701-4238
mj.mcginnis@theday.com, Chief, Staff/Dir., HR, The Day Publishing Company, CT, New London
McGirt, Tonyia 803-774-1227
tmcgirt@theitem.com, Item Sunday, SC, Sumter
tmcgirt@theitem.com, Managing Editor, The Item, SC, Sumter
McGivney, Betsy.........................(518) 483-4700
bmcgivney@mtelegram.com, Bus. Mgr., The Malone Telegram, NY, Malone
McGlamery, Joe ....(912) 489-9432
joe@morrisnews.com, Pres., Statesboro Herald, GA, Statesboro
McGlocklin, Susan ....(812) 855-0766
Indiana Univ., IN, Bloomington
McGlothlen, Andrew
info@macdonaldclassified.com, Mng. Ed., MacDonald Advertising Services, IN, Lafayette
McGlynn, Michael ....ext. 2069
Wire Ed., The Citizens' Voice, PA, Wilkes-Barre
McGonigle, Marcia ....(541) 885-4419
mmcgonigle@heraldandnews.com, Lifestyle Ed., Herald and News, OR, Klamath Falls
McGovern, Brian
bmcgovern@imediainc.com, Dir., Devel., Interactive Media Associates, NJ, Parsippany
McGovern, John ....(212) 255-9700
John@McGovernLLC.com, Senior Associate-Trade and Consumer Magazines; Digital Media, Grimes, W.B. & Co., MD, Gaithersburg
McGowan, Linda ....(719) 540-7480
Pikes Peak Cmty. College, CO, Colorado Springs
McGowan, Jim 406-523-5201
jim.mcgowan@lee.net, Publisher, Missoulian, MT, Missoula
McGrann, Karl
kmcgrann@mcgrann.com, Owner, McGrann Paper Corp., NC, Charlotte
McGrath, Kevin ....(316) 268-6680
kmcgrath@wichitaeagle.com, Night city editor, The Wichita Eagle, KS, Wichita
McGrath, Cindy.........................(925) 439-2181
Los Medanos College, CA, Pittsburg
McGrath, Mike
info@yosho.com, CEO, Yosho, CA, San Mateo
McGraw, Charlene ....(207) 621-5659
cmcgraw@centralmaine.com, Circ. Mgr., Sales/Retention, Kennebec Journal, ME, Augusta
McGraw, Lisa
lisa@michiganpress.org, Pub. Aff. Mgr., Michigan Newspapers, Inc., MI, Lansing
McGraw, James
james_mcgraw@mcgraw-hill.com, Pub., Dodge Construction News Greensheet
McGregor, Janet
nab@nab.org, COO/CFO, National Association of Broadcasters, DC, Washington
McGregor, Andrew
mcgregora@caledonian-record.com, City/Metro Ed., The Caledonian-Record, VT, Saint Johnsbury
McGregory, Malcom
mmcgregory@atex.com, Sales Mgr., Atex North America, FL, Tampa
McGrory, Malcolm
mmcgrory@atex.com, Sr. Vice Pres., Sales Americas, Atex North America, MA, Burlington
McGuffin, Michelle ....ext. 210
mmcguffin@thenewsenterprise.com, Classified Adv. Mgr., The News Enterprise, KY, Elizabethtown
McGuire, Muriel Elliott..............(214) 640-3105
mmcguire@beldenassociates.com, Vice Pres., Belden Associates, TX, Dallas
McGurgan, Diane
diane@nasw.org, Admin., Council for Advancement and Support of Education, DC, Washington
McGurgan, Diane
diane@nasw.org, Admin., Council for the Advancement of Science Writing, Inc., WV, Hedgesville
McGurk, John ....ext. 2017
Prodn. Mgr., Mailroom, The Citizens' Voice, PA, Wilkes-Barre
McHardy, Tom
mchardtj@jmu.edu, Assoc. Prof., James Madison University, VA, Harrisonburg
McHarg, Nev 5480 4210
Ed., THE GYMPIE TIMES
McHugh, Brien.........................(800) 735-7500
Univ. of St. Francis, IL, Joliet
McInally, Mike
news@gtconnect.com, Pub., Corvallis Gazette-Times, OR, Corvallis
McIntosh, Ed..............................941-206-1446
emcintosh@sun-herald.com, Systems Manager, Charlotte Sun, FL, Charlotte Harbor
McIntosh, Bill
dciadvertising@aol.com, Dir., Bus. Devel., America Online Digital City, Inc., VA, Dulles
McIntosh, Tammie
tmcintosh@reviewonline.com, Pub., The Review, OH, East Liverpool
McIntyre, Jeff ....(256) 740-5737
jeff.mcintyre@timesdaily.com, Asst. Sports Ed., TimesDaily, AL, Florence
McIntyre, Bill ....(515) 576-2571
Iowa Central Cmty. College, IA, Fort Dodge
McIver, Rose ....ext. 4207
rmclver@phillyburbs.com, Mng. Ed., Content, Bucks County Courier Times, PA, Levittown
McJunkins, James
olafjames@earthlink.net, Chair, Clark Atlanta University, GA, Atlanta
McJunkins, James.......................770-941-7089
jamesolaf@comcast.net, Advisor, Clark Atlanta Univ., GA, Atlanta
McKean, Matthew T. ....(256) 740-5753
matt.mckean@timesdaily.com, Photo Ed., TimesDaily, AL, Florence
McKean, Patrick.........................(562) 938-4282
Long Beach City College, CA, Long Beach
McKee, Sally..............................(309) 686-3157
smckee@pjstar.com, Asst. Mng. Ed., Sunday Features/Servs., Journal Star, IL, Peoria
McKee, Rick ....(706) 823-3369
graphix@augustachronicle.com, Editorial Cartoonist, The Augusta Chronicle, GA, Augusta
McKeel, Jim ....(251) 219-5351
Circ. Mgr., Single Copy, Press-Register, AL, Mobile
McKeen, William.......................(352) 392-0500
Prof./Chair, Dept. of Journalism, University of Florida, FL, Gainesville
McKeenan, Ryan ....(717) 240-7121
rmckeenan@cumberlink.com, Prodn. Foreman, Mailroom, The Sentinel, PA, Carlisle
McKeithen, Tracy
dnadvertising@edailynews.info, Adv. Dir., Daily News, LA, Bogalusa
McKelley, Michelle ....ext. 3317
michelle.mckelley@indeonline.com, Prodn. Mgr., The Independent, OH, Massillon
McKenen, Ken
kmckenen@acnpapers.com, Circ. Dir., McKinney Courier-Gazette, TX, McKinney
McKenna, Frank ....(413) 496-6309
fmckenna@berkshireeagle.com, Controller, The Berkshire Eagle, MA, Pittsfield
McKenna, Michael ....(508) 663-1920
mmckenna@burrellesluce.com, National Sales Manager, New England Newsclip Agency, Inc., NJ, Livingston
McKennon, Teresa 575-763-3431
tmckennon@cnjonline.com, Business Manager, Clovis News Journal, NM, Clovis
McKenzie, Peggy........................(901) 529-2341
mckenziep@commercialappeal.com, Asst. Mng. Ed., Features, The Commercial Appeal, TN, Memphis
McKenzie, Bob..........................(250) 380-5202
bmckenzie@te.canwest.com, Pub., Times Colonist, BC, Victoria
McKenzie, Mack
sales@west.com, Vice Pres., Sales/Mktg., West Interactive Corp., NE, Omaha
McKeon, Tim..............................(469) 532-8120
tim.mckeon@kba.com, Vice Pres., Servs./Opns., KBA North America, Inc. (Koenig & Bauer AG), VT
McKeon, John ....(214) 977-8467
jmckeon@dallasnews.com, Pres./Gen. Mgr., The Dallas Morning News, TX, Dallas
McKeown, Charles
cmckeown@editorandpublisher.com, Pub., Editor & Publisher Magazine, NY, New York
McKeown, Charles.......................(646) 654-5120
cmckeown@editorandpublisher.com, Pub., Editor & Publisher Interactive, NY, New York
McKey, Tucky ....(707) 704-2086
kango@pacbell.net, Pub., King & Kango Komix & Illustrations, CA, Vallejo
McKibben, Christy
christym@npgco.com, Adv. Mgr., Atchison Globe, KS, Atchison
McKiel, Julie
jschulz@heraldargus.com, Circ. Mgr., Herald-

Argus, IN, La Porte
McKiernan, Jim ....ext. 236
Adv. Dir., Columbia Basin Herald, WA, Moses Lake
McKiernan, Scott ....(212) 924-8123
scott@keystone.com, Dir., Keystone Pictures, CA, San Clemente
McKiernan, Scott
scott@zumapress.com, CEO/Founder, ZUMA Press, Inc., CA, San Clemente
McKillip, Michael ....(256) 740-4726
mike.mckillip@timesdaily.com, Circ. Dir., TimesDaily, AL, Florence
McKinley, Thomas ....(415) 382-8367
rtmck2515@aol.com, Dir., Media Services Group, Inc., FL, Jacksonville Beach
McKinney, William C. ....(330) 287-1601
wcm@dixcom.com, Gen. Mgr., The Daily Record, OH, Wooster
McKinney, William C. ....(330) 287-1601
wcm@dixcom.com, Gen. Mgr., Wooster Republican Printing Co., OH, Wooster
McLamb, Lynn
lmclamb@heartlandpublications.com, Pub., La Grange Daily News, GA, LaGrange
McLanahan, Joyce ....ext. 202
Prodn. Mgr., Distr., Columbia Basin Herald, WA, Moses Lake
McLarty, Dianne
dmclarty@amm.com, Assoc. Ed., American Metal Market
McLaughlin, Scott ....(716) 879-4077
Nat'l Sales Mgr., Praxair Surface Technologies, Inc., CT, Danbury
McLaughlin, Roberta ....ext. 275
r.mclaughling@theday.com, Adv. Mgr., Classified/Telephone Sales, The Day Publishing Company, CT, New London
McLaughlin, Joe ....(403) 314-4328
jmclaughlin@reddeeradvocate.com, Mng. Ed., Red Deer Advocate, AB, Red Deer
McLaughlin, Carol ....ext. 242
carol@norwalkreflector.com, Data Processing Mgr., Norwalk Reflector, OH, Norwalk
McLaughlin, Bob ....(209) 722-1812 ext. 405
bmac@pspub.com, Vice Pres., Mktg., Pacific Sierra Publishing, Inc., CA, Merced
McLean, Chris ....(719) 544-3520 ext. 490
pics@chieftain.com, Photo Dir., The Pueblo Chieftain, CO, Pueblo
McLean, Judith ....(810) 989-6255
jmclean@gannett.com, Mng. Ed., Times Herald, MI, Port Huron
McLean, Gary
web_info@intd.com, Pres., Interstate Distributor Co., Tacoma
McLean, Alisdair
alisdair.mclean@tweednews.com.au, Gen. Mgr., TWEED DAILY NEWS
McLeod, Tommie 813-259-7435
tmcleod@tampatrib.com, Circulation Director, The Tampa Tribune, FL, Tampa
McLeroy, Kathy ....(256) 734-2131 ext. 229
kathym@cullmantimes.com, Adv. Dir., The Cullman Times, AL, Cullman
McLoone, Pat
mcloonep@phillynews.com, Mng. Ed., The Philadelphia Daily News, PA, Philadelphia
McMacken, William ....(605) 692-6271
registeradvertising@brookingsregister.com, Adv. Dir., Brookings Register, SD, Brookings
McMahon, Todd
todd.mcmahon@gogreenbay.com, Sports Ed., The Green Bay News-Chronicle, WI, Green Bay
McMahon, Kathleen ....(508) 862-1136
kmcmahon@capecodonline.com, Adv. Dir., Cape Cod Times, MA, Hyannis
McManamon, Joe
joem@ppsi.co.uk, Pres., Printing Press Services, Inc., Preston Lancs
McManamon, Stephen
stephenm@ppsi.co.uk, Mng. Dir.-Press Division, Printing Press Services, Inc., Preston Lancs
McManis, Charlie 951-926-2388
chazmcmanis@hotmail.com.com, Executive Director, Cal Western Circulation Managers' Association, CA, Hemet
McManus, Greg ....(207) 990-8065
gmcmanus@bangordailynews.net, Copy Desk Ed., Bangor Daily News, ME, Bangor
McMenemy, Jeff ....(978) 343-6911 ext. 214
jmcmenemy@sentinelandenterprise.com, Ed., Sentinel & Enterprise, MA, Fitchburg
McMenemy, Cheryl
cmcmenemy@owensoundsuntimes.com, Pub., The Sun Times, ON, Owen Sound
McMenimen, Rachel
rmcmenimen@multiad.com, Marketing Manager, MultiAd Services, Inc., IL, Peoria
McMillan, Malcolm 407 2743
northernnews.editor@snl.co.nz, Editor, NORTHERN NEWS
McMillan, Betty ....(423) 623-6171 ext. 3104
betty.mcmillian@newportplaintalk.com, Adv. Mgr., Newport Plain Talk, TN, Newport
McMillin, Sue ....(719) 636-0251
sue.mcmillin@gazette.com, Local News Editor, The Gazette, CO, Colorado Springs
McMullen, Cathy ....(218) 299-3994
Concordia College, MN, Moorhead
McMullen, Arthur ....(724) 838-5165
amcmullen@tribweb.com, Gen. Mgr., Westmoreland, Tribune-Review, PA, Pittsburgh
McMullin, Norman R.
nrmcmullin@cox.net, Pres., McMullin, Norman R., AZ, Scottsdale
McMurtrie, Rhonda
rmcmurtrie@idahopress.com, Bus. Mgr., Idaho Press-Tribune, ID, Nampa
McNally, Kevin
kmcna@srds.com, CFO, SRDS, a Kantar Media Company, IL, Des Plaines
McNamara, Tom ....(215) 854-2549
Deputy Mng. Ed., Sunday, The Philadelphia Inquirer, PA, Philadelphia
McNamee, Chris ....(203) 625-4425
chris.mcnamee@scni.com, Sports Editor, Greenwich Time, CT, Greenwich
McNaughton, Burt ....(530) 747-8030
bmcnaughton@davisenterprise.net, Pub./Vice Pres./Sec., The Davis Enterprise, CA, Davis
McNaughton, Foy ....(707) 427-6962
fmcnaughton@dailyrepublic.com, Pres./CEO, Daily Republic, CA, Fairfield
fmcnaughton@dailyrepublic.com, Pres./CEO, McNaughton Newspapers, CA, Fairfield
McNaughton, R. ....(530) 756-0800
bmcnaughton@davisenterprise.net, Vice Pres., McNaughton Newspapers, CA, Fairfield
McNeal, Quasha ....(252) 407-9961
qmcneal@rmtelegram.com, Classified Adv. Mgr., Rocky Mount Telegram, NC, Rocky Mount
McNeal, Craig A.
cgnews@cgtelco.net, Ed., Council Grove Republican, KS, Council Grove
McNealy, Scott G.
info@sun.com, Chrmn., Sun Microsystems, Inc., CA, Santa Clara
McNeely, Jack
jmcneely@somerset-kentucky.com, Pub., The Commonwealth-Journal, KY, Somerset
McNeely, Joanna ....ext. 252
jmcneely@theworldlink.com, Adv. Mgr., Classified, The World, OR, Coos Bay
McNeile, Dan ....(309) 820-3261
dmcneile@pantagraph.com, Asst. News Ed., The Pantagraph, IL, Bloomington
McNichols, Michael ....ext. 232
mike.mcnichols@mountvernonnews.com, Circ./MIDS Mgr., Mount Vernon News, OH, Mount Vernon
McNickle, Colin ....(412) 320-7836
cmcnickle@tribweb.com, Editorial Page Ed., Tribune-Review, PA, Pittsburgh
McNiff, Tom 352.8674013
tom.mcniff@starbanner.com, Managing Editor, Ocala Star-Banner, FL, Ocala
McNulty, Kendrick D. ....(540) 574-6298
kmcnulty@dnronline.com, Asst. to Gen. Mgr., Daily News-Record, VA, Harrisonburg
McNulty, Tami ....(202) 319-4690
Columbus School of Law, DC, Washington
McNutt, Fred
mcmeganutt@aol.com, Pres., Megasys International, Inc., CT, Tolland
McPaul, F. Steve 334-293-5800
smcphaul@cnhi.com, Executive VP of Corporate Operations, Community Newspaper Holdings, Inc., AL, Montgomery
McPherson, Eric
eric.mcpherson@tribune.com, Dir., Opns., Tribune Media Services International Syndication, Kowloon
McQuade, Mike ....(920) 453-5141
mmcquade@sheboygan.gannett.com, Mng. Ed., The Sheboygan Press, WI, Sheboygan
McQuaid, Joseph W. ....(603) 668-4321 ext. 200
jmcquaid@unionleader.com, Pres./Pub., New Hampshire Union Leader/New Hampshire Sunday News, NH, Manchester
McQuaid, Brendan
bmcquaid@unionleader.com, Vice President of New Media, New Hampshire Union Leader/New Hampshire Sunday News, NH, Manchester
McQueen, Kelli ....(334) 712-7955
kmcqueen@dothaneagle.com, Online Adv. Mgr, The Enterprise Ledger, AL, Enterprise
McQueen, Mariann ....(252) 329-9550
mmcqueen@reflector.com, CFO, The Daily Reflector, NC, Greenville
McQueen, Roy ....(915) 573-5486
publisher@snyderdailynews.com, Pres./Pub., Snyder Daily News, TX, Snyder
McQuilkin, Steve ....(239) 335-0352
Bus. Ed., The News-Press, FL, Fort Myers
McQuillen, Patti ....(502) 213-2249
Jefferson Community and Technical College, KY, Louisville
McSwain, Dan ....(760) 839-3323
dmcswain@nctimes.com, Mng. Ed., North County Times, CA, Escondido
McTermott, Micheal
mmctermott@airloc.com, Vice Pres., Mktg., Airloc Products, MA, Franklin
McVoy, Tom
momoney@momoney.com, Mktg. Mgr., Mo-Money Associates, Inc., FL, Pensacola
McWilliams, Avery 432-552-2659
mesajournal@utpb.edu, Editor, Univ. of Texas Permian Basin, TX, Odessa
Mccaffrey, Ed
emccaffrey@sparkstribune.net, Pub., The Daily Sparks Tribune, NV, Sparks
Mccaw, Wendy
wmccaw@newspress.com, Co-Pub., Santa Barbara News-Press, CA, Santa Barbara
Mccoy, Helen ....(902) 563-3845
Adv. Mgr., Classified, The Cape Breton Post, NS, Sydney
Mcdaniel, Steve ....ext. 276
Online Mgr., The World, OR, Coos Bay
Mcgee, Adrienne ....(419) 993-2072
Lifestyle Ed., The Lima News, OH, Lima
Mckeon, John 214-977-8467
jmckeon@dallasnews.com, President and General Manager, Southwest Classified Advertising Managers Association, TX, Dallas
Mctuire, Bill
info@brocksolutions.com, Project Mgr., Brock Solutions U.S. Inc., TX, Irving
Mead, Richard
richardm@jegi.com, Mng. Dir., Jordan, Edmiston Group, Inc., NY, New York
Meade, Richard 020 701 74636
richard.meade@informa.com, Editor, Lloyd's List, LLOYD'S OF LONDON PRESS, London
Meador, Cherie ....(312) 935-4217
Robert Morris College, IL, Chicago
Meadows, David
dmeadows@couriernews.com, Pub., The Courier, AR, Russellville
Meadows, Sheila
smeadows@freedomenc.com, Circ. Dir., The Sun Journal, NC, New Bern
Meaney, Karen
kmeaney@marketresearch.com, Ed., Simba Information, CT, Stamford
Means, Dan ....(941) 206-1121
dmeans@sun-herald.com, Bus. Ed., Charlotte Sun, FL, Charlotte Harbor
Meaux, Cindy ....ext. 112
Media Buyer, ANA Advertising Services, Inc. (Arizona Newspaper Association), AZ, Phoenix
Mechanic, Barry
bmechanic@pawtuckettimes.com, Pub., The Times, RI, Pawtucket
Mechanic, Barry 401-767-8572
bmechanic@woonsocketcall.com, Publisher, The Call, RI, Woonsocket
Medina, Dom ....ext. 32
domm@flynnburner.com, Vice Pres., Flynn Burner Corp., NY, New Rochelle
Medina, Jim ....(805) 437-0238
jmedina@venturacountystar.com, Bus. Ed., Ventura County Star, CA, Camarillo
Medina Robles, Miguel
miguelmedina@voznet.com.mx, Ed./Dir., LA VOZ DE MICHOACAN, Morelia, Michoacan
Medinger, Daniel
mail@ampsinc.net, Pres., Advertising Media Plus, Inc., MD, Ellicott
Medland, Paul
pmedland@quickwire.com, Quicktrac Developer, Quickwire Labs, ON, Hamilton
Meece, Mickey ....(502) 852-6727
Univ. of Louisville, KY, Louisville
Meehan, Bonnie ....(360) 417-3501
bonnie.meehan@peninsuladailynews.com, Bus./Finance Dir., Peninsula Daily News, WA, Port Angeles
Meena, Lynne
lynnemeena@aol.com, Pres., Meena Advertising Copy & Layout, KY, Louisville
Meenahan, Andrew
andrew.meenahan@ruralpress.com, Gen. Mgr., CENTRAL WESTERN DAILY
Meese, Ray ....(805) 437-0287
rmeese@venturacountystar.com, Photography Dir., Ventura County Star, CA, Camarillo
Meesey, Jeff 321-242-3572
jmeesey@floridatoday.com, Multimedia Editor, Florida Today, FL, Melbourne
Mehalack, Susan ....(518) 454-5470
smahelack@timesunion.com, City Ed., Times Union, NY, Albany
Mehle, Michael ....(303) 892-5346
mehlem@rockymountainnews.com, Asst. Entertainment Ed., Rocky Mountain News, CO, Denver
Mehtala, Anssi
anssi.mehtala@lansi-savo.fi, Ed., LANSI-SAVO, Mikkeli
Mei Yu, Wang
editorplan@mail.chinatimes.com.tw, Ed. in Chief, CHINA TIMES, Taipei
Meier, Char 920-829-5145
meier.char@yahoo.com, Adv. Contact, Great Northern Connection, WI, Lena
Meilach, Dona Z. ....(760) 436-1402
dmeilach@msn.com, Pres., Dona Z. Meilach Features, CA, Carlsbad
Meissner, Jochen ....(630) 755-9320
jochen.meissner@gossinternational.com, CEO, Goss International Corporation, IL, Bolingbrook
Meissner, Dirk 250-384-4912
dirk.meissner@thecanadianpress.com, Correspondent, Canadian Press, The - Victoria, BC, BC, Victoria
Meistes, Ralf
herforder@westfalen-blatt.de, Ed., Herforder Kreisblatt, Herford
Meiswinkle, Bruce ....(518) 943-6953
Prodn. Foreman, Press, The Daily Mail, NY, Catskill
Meitus, Marty ....(303) 892-5229
meitusm@rockymountainnews.com, Food Ed., Rocky Mountain News, CO, Denver
Mejia, Luis Fernando Baena 335-4666
webmaster@latarde.com.co, Gen. Mgr., Comunicadores del Risaralda Ltd., Pereira, Risaralda
Melbourne, Allan ....(403) 314-4304
amelbourne@reddeeradvocate.com, Circ. Mgr., Red Deer Advocate, AB, Red Deer
Melcher, Iris
info@berchtesgadener-anzeiger.de, Ed., BERCHTESGADENER ANZEIGER, Berchtesgaden
Melcher, Joe ....(504) 485-5096
jmelcher@xula.edu, PD, Xavier University of Louisiana, LA, New Orleans
Melchers, Rick 973-251-3034
rmelchers@burrellesluce.com, VP, Director of National Sales, New York State Clipping Service, NJ
Meldonian, Susan ....(561) 820-4251
Credit Mgr., The Palm Beach Post, FL, West Palm Beach
Melendez, Alberto Santeliz Feb-35
Pres., Editorial Sabana C.A., Barinas, Barinas

Melet, Todd
tmelet@b-linked.com, Pres., B-Linked, Inc., NC, Chapel Hill

Melhorn, Mark..........................609-272-7179
mmelhorn@pressofac.com, Local Content Producer/Sports, The Press of Atlantic City, NJ, Pleasantville

Melin, Jon..............................(309) 757-5023
jmelin@qconline.com, Adv. Mgr., Nat'l, The Rock Island Argus, IL, Rock Island

Mellingen, Ove
ove.mellingen@ta.no, Ed. in Chief, TELE-MARKSAVISA A/S, Skien

Mellis, Gregory A.
gmellis@rhinelanderdailynews.com, COO/Pub., The Daily News, The Daily News, WI, Rhinelander

Mellis, Greg..........................(715) 526 - 7016
gmellis@bluelinemediaholdings.com, COO/Publisher, Shawano Leader, WI, Shawano

Mello, Amateur
jb@jb.com.br, Ed., Jornal do Brasil, Rio De Janeiro

Mellott, Jeff...........................(540) 574-6290
jmellott@dnronline.com, Educ. Ed., Daily News-Record, VA, Harrisonburg

Melon, Mary...........................(405) 278-2815
mary.melon@journalrecord.com, Pub., The Journal Record, OK, Oklahoma City

Melton, Valerie
marketing@kilgorenewsherald.com, Mktg. Mgr., Kilgore News Herald, TX, Kilgore

Melton, Jan.............................(912) 489-9401
jmelton@statesboroherald.com, Adv. Dir., Statesboro Herald, GA, Statesboro

Melvin, Richard
sports@clevelandbanner.com, Sports Ed., Cleveland Daily Banner, TN, Cleveland

Melvin, Linda
linda.melvin@mchsi.com, Prodn. Mgr., The Daily Leader, IL, Pontiac

Membrino, John........................(202) 383-7839
john.membrino@newhouse.com, News Servs. News Ed., Newhouse News Service, DC, Washington

Menard, Vicki..........................(541) 957-4203
vmenard@nrtoday.com, Editorial Writer, The News-Review, OR, Roseburg

Menard, Dave...........................(586) 530-0650
Sr. Ed., Avanti NewsFeatures, MI, Clinton Township

Mendell, Ron...........................(316) 688-1233
rmendell@tribune.com, Nat'l Acct. Exec., McClatchy-Tribune Information Services, Tribune Media Services, Inc., IL, Chicago

Mendelsohn, Ted
apif@ap.org, Dir. Sales, Associated Press Information Services, NY, New York

Mendelson, Jorge..........................149 1160
azuccolillo@abc.com.py, Gen. Mgr., ABC Color, Asuncion

Mendes, Andrea........................(978) 970-4739
amendes@lowellsun.com, Adv. Mgr., New Media, The Sun, MA, Lowell

Mendez, Milly.............................787-721-2300
millymendez@gmail.com, President, Overseas Press de Puerto Rico, Overseas Press Club of Puerto Rico, PR, San Juan

Mendiratta, Rajesh
rajesh.mendiratta@bsmail.in, Gen. Mgr., BUSINESS STANDARD, New Delhi

Mendive, Santigo
huesca@heraldo.es, Dir., HERALDO DE HUESCA, Huesca

Mendives, Sue.........................(202) 414-0555
sue.mendives@afp.com, Sr. Mktg. Mgr., Agence France-Presse - Washington, DC, DC, Washington

Mendler, Skip
circulation@wayneindependent.com, Circulation Manager, The Wayne Independent, PA, Honesdale

Menendez Rodriguez, Mario Renato
poresto@prodigy.com.net.mx, Pres., POR ESTO, Merida, Yucatan

Meng, Chiang Sao
vakiopou@macau.ctm.net, Mng. Dir., VA KIO POU, Macau

Menicucci, Piero........................416-947-3115
piero.menicucci@sunmedia.ca, Vice President, Finance, The Toronto Sun, ON, Toronto

Menlrd, Hans Peter
hanspetermenlrd@tagespost.de, Adv. Mgr, GMUNDER TAGESPOST, Schwabisch-Gmund

Mennenga, Gary R.
alphagr839@aol.com, Owner, Alpha-Omega Color Graphics, Inc., IL, Mount Morris

Mensing, Phyllis
apbismarck@ap.org, Contact, North Dakota Associated Press, ND, Bismarck

Mentlick, Donna
sales@smartstorage.com, Marcon Specialist, Smart Storage, Inc., MA, Andover

Mentzer, Michael..............................ext. 247
mmentzer@fdlreporter.com, Mng. Ed., The Reporter, WI, Fond du Lac

Meranus, Rachel.......................(201) 360-6776
rachel.meranus@prnewswire.com, Vice Pres., Mktg./PR, PR Newswire - New York, NY, NY, New York

Mercado, Pedro Rivero
web@eldeber.com.bo, Dir., Editorial Oriente, Santa Cruz De La Sierra

Mercer, Michael L.....................(210) 829-6069
Univ. of the Incarnate Word, TX, San Antonio

Mercer, Robert.........................(937) 328-0240
rmercer@coxohio.com, Adv. Dir., Springfield News-Sun, OH, Springfield

Merchan, Doris..............................281-1723
redaccion@elmercurio.com.ec, Gen. Mgr., Compania Ltd., Cuenca, Azuay

Merchant, Jim.............................941-206-1117
jmerchant@sun-herald.com, Charlotte Sun Systems Editor, Charlotte Sun, FL, Charlotte Harbor

Mercure, Philipe
phillipe.mercure@thecanadianpress.com, Exec. Dir., Canadian Press, The - Toronto, ON, ON, Toronto

Meredith, Rick.................................ext. 5324
rmeredith@texarkanagazette.com, Adv. Sales Mgr., Texarkana Gazette, TX, Texarkana

Merek, Jim...............................(253) 620-4747
Jmarek@webpressllc.com, Sales, WebPress, LLC, WA, Tacoma

Merino, Jose.............................(520) 573-4187
jmerino@azstarnet.com, Graphics Ed., Arizona Daily Star, AZ, Tucson

Merkle, Juergen
juergen.merkle@lkz.de, Adv. Mgr., LUDWIGSBURGER KREISZEITUNG, Ludwigsburg

Merkley, Mark
mmerkley@postregister.com, Commercial Printing Mgr., Post Register, ID, Idaho Falls

Merle, Henri
regaction@leveil.fr, Pub., L'EVEIL DE LA HAUTE-LOIRE/L'EVEIL DU DIMANCHE, Le Puy

Merphy, Tim
newsdesk@nzherald.co.nz, Ed. in Chief, THE NEW ZEALAND HERALD

Merrell, Gary................(740) 592-6612 ext. 242
gmerrell@brownpublishing.com, Pub., The Delaware Gazette, OH, Delaware

Merrell, Jesse H.......................(202) 265-1925
jessemerrell@comcast.net, Pres., Merrell Enterprises, DC, Washington

Merrell, Dennis
dennis@awna.com, Exec. Dir., Alberta Weekly Newspapers Association, AB, Edmonton

Merriam, Roger........................605-886-6901
Sports Ed., Watertown Public Opinion, SD, Watertown

Merrick, Ed.............................(503) 221-8482
Transportation/Real Estate Mgr., The Oregonian, OR, Portland

Merrick, Rick...........................(805) 564-5171
MIS Mgr., Santa Barbara News-Press, CA, Santa Barbara

Merrill, Gregory........................(435) 753-8090
99m@cache.net, Dir., Media Services Group, Inc., FL, Jacksonville Beach

Merriman, Ed
emerriman@bakercityherald.com, Farm/Agriculture Ed., Baker City Herald, OR, Baker City

Merritt, Mimi...........................(276) 326-3682
Bluefield College, VA, Bluefield

Merritt, Sage...........................(540) 932-3559
smerritt@newsvirginian.com, Features Ed., The News Virginian, VA, Waynesboro

Merritt, Jeff............................(603) 594-6433
news@telegraph-nh.com, City Ed., The Telegraph, NH, Hudson

Mervola, Pekka
pekka.mervola@keski.suomalainen.fi, Ed., KESKISUOMALAINEN, Jyvaskyla, Keski-Suomi

Mesaros, Stefan
redakcia@narodnaobroda.sk, Ed. in Chief, NARODNA OBRODÁ, Bratislava

Meschinelli, Jennifer.................(518) 565-4183
jmeschinelli@pressrepublican.com, Special Sections Ed., Press-Republican, NY, Plattsburgh

Mesher, Arthur
info@descartes.com, CEO, Descartes Systems Group, ON, Waterloo

Messenger, Jane.......................(612) 673-7327
Jane.Messenger@startribune.com, Creative Director, Star Tribune, MN, Minneapolis

Messer, Michael...............................ext. 3201
michael.messer@indeonline.com, Prodn./IT Dir., The Independent, OH, Massillon

Messick, David.........................(757) 247-7469
dmessick@dailypress.com, Dir., Consumer Mktg., Daily Press, VA, Newport News

Messick, Steve
smessick@republican-eagle.com, Pub., Republican Eagle, MN, Red Wing

Messina, Charles......................(416) 507-2021
charles.messina@thecanadianpress.com, Sales/Mktg. Dir., Broadcast News Limited, ON, Toronto

Messinger, Kelly.......................(614) 236-6567
Capital Univ., OH, Columbus

Meszoros, Mark
mmeszoros@news-herald.com, Entertainment Ed., The News-Herald, OH, Willoughby

Metcalfe, Jim.....................................ext. 33
jmetcalfe@delphosherald.com, Sports Ed., Delphos Daily Herald, OH, Delphos

Metea, Rachel
depauliaeic@gmail.com, Editor in Chief, DePaul Univ., IL, Chicago

Metrick, Gene..........................(252) 407-9944
gmetrick@rmtelegram.com, Content Ed., Rocky Mount Telegram, NC, Rocky Mount

Mets, Margus
margus.m@postimees.prn.ee, Pub., PARNU POSTIMEES, Parnu

Metz, Eddy...............................(479) 784-0455
emetz@swtimes.com, Prodn. Mgr., Times Record, AR, Fort Smith

Metz, Jenn...............................(574) 631-4542
Univ. of Notre Dame, IN, Notre Dame

Metzdorf, Ken...................................ext. 236
kmetzdorf@grandhaventribune.com, Circ. Dir., Grand Haven Tribune, MI, Grand Haven

Metzger, Melissa..........................6462234000
Publishing Solutions Specialist, Reuters Media, NY, New York

Metzger, Juli............................(317) 444-6168
juli.metzger@indystar.com, Exec. Ed., The Indianapolis Star, IN, Indianapolis

Metzler, John J.
jjmcolumn@earthlink.net, Ed., Worldwatch/Foreign Affairs Syndicate, NY, Jamaica

Meyer, Peter D.........................(508) 862-1111
pmeyer@capecodonline.com, Pres./Pub., Cape Cod Times, MA, Hyannis

Meyer, Tim
tmeyers@capitalnewspapers.com, Prodn. Mgr., Daily Register, WI, Portage

Meyer, Thierry
thierry.meyer@edipresse.ch, Ed., 24 HEURES, Lausanne, Vaud

Meyer, Thomas
info@interknife.com, Pres./CEO, IKS Klingelnberg GmbH

Meyer, Nancy A...........(860) 241-6225 ext. 6225
nmeyer@courant.com, Vice Pres., Adv., The Hartford Courant, CT, Hartford

Meyer, Bobbi...........................(951) 782-7661
bmeyer@pe.com, Adv. Mgr., Display, The Press-Enterprise, CA, Riverside

Meyer, Amy
easterner.editor@gmail.com, Editor-in-chief, The Easterner, WA, Cheney

Meyer, Tonda
tonda.meyer@helenair.com, Advertising Manager, Independent Record, MT, Helena

Meyer-Bohm, Michael
michael.meyer-bohm@morgenpost.de, Bus. Mgr., BERLINER MORGENPOST, Berlin

Meyer-Bohm, M.
m.bayer@abendblatt.de, Bus. Mgr., Hamburger Abendblatt, Hamburg

Meyering, Carl E.
cmeyering@ameritech.net, Ed., Business Newsfeatures, MI, Grosse Pointe Farms

Meyers, Cory...........................(605) 331-2202
cbeck@argusleader.com, Online Content Ed., Argus Leader, SD, Sioux Falls

Meyers, Bob....................................ext. 101
bob@nationalpress.org, Pres., National Press Foundation, DC, Washington

Meyers, Dan............................(303) 820-1555
dmeyers@denverpost.com, Nat'l Foreign Ed., The Denver Post, CO, Denver

Meyers, Roy H.
rmeyers@mpival.com, Sr. Vice Pres., Management Planning, Inc., NJ, Princeton

Meyers, Sherrie.........................(360) 577-2587
sherrie.meyers@tdn.com, Adv. Mgr., Classified, The Daily News, WA, Longview

Meyers, Matt...............................608-745-3571
mmeyers@capitalnewspapers.com, Shopper Stopper - Columbia, WI, Portage
mmeyers@capitalnewspapers.com, Shopper Stopper - Sauk, WI, Portage
mmeyers@capitalnewspapers.com, Shopper Stopper Extra - Sauk, MI, Portage
mmeyers@capitalnewspapers.com, General Manager, Baraboo News-Republic, WI, Baraboo

Miami, Jari
internet@iha.ess.fi, Ed. in Chief, ITA-HAME, Heinola

Micale, Anthony.......................(781) 239-4229
Babson College, MA, Babson Park

Michael, N/A..................................Sports Ed.
Herald-Standard, PA, Uniontown

Michael, Hearn.........................(419) 521-7412
mhearn@nncogannett.com, Adv. Dir., News Journal, OH, Mansfield

Michaels, Bruce
bmichaels@sportsnetwork.com, Dir., Technical Opns., The Sports Network, PA, Hatboro

Michaels, Bruce........................(215) 441-8444
bmicheals@sportsnetwork.com, Technical Opns. Dir., The Sports Network (Div. of Computer Info. Network), PA, Hatboro

Michalak, Kathy
kathy.michalak@inlandnewspapers.com, Circ. Vice Pres., Inland Valley Daily Bulletin, CA, Ontario

Michnik, Adam
redakcja_portalu@agora.pl, Ed. in Chief, GAZETA WYBORCZA, Warsaw

Mick, Andrew
amick@berkshireeagle.com, Pres./Pub., The Berkshire Eagle, MA, Pittsfield

Mick, Andy...............................(413) 496-6310
amick@berkshireeagle.com, Pres./Pub., New England Newspapers, Inc., MA, Pittsfield

Mick, Barbara
reviewgraphics@reviewonline.com, Prodn. Supvr., Graphics, The Review, OH, East Liverpool

Mickey, Kathy
kmickey@marketresearch.com, Mng. Ed., Simba Information, CT, Stamford

Mickey, Betty Grace...................(970) 224-7745
bettygracemickey@coloradoan.com, Online Content Ed., The Coloradoan, CO, Fort Collins

Mickey, William........................(216) 999-4004
Vice Pres. and Dir., Information Technology, The Plain Dealer, OH, Cleveland

Mickler, Jeannetta....................(541) 812-6120
jeannettia.mickler@lee.net, Circ. Mgr., Albany Democrat-Herald, OR, Albany

Midani, Moetaz
mmidani@assafir.com, Exec. Ed., AS-SAFIR

Middlebrook, Walter
wmiddlebrook@detroitnews.com, Asst. Managing Editor, The Detroit News, MI, Detroit

Midkiff, Ron
publisher@bigspringherald.com, Pub., Big Spring Herald, TX, Big Spring

Miele, Frank............................(406) 758-4447
edit@dailyinterlake.com, Online Ed., Daily Inter Lake, MT, Kalispell

Miguel, Dawne
advmgr@mauinews.com, Adv. Mgr., Retail, The Maui News, HI, Wailuku
Mihalache, Dan
dan.mihalache@cronicaromana.ro, Mktg. Mgr., CRONICA ROMANA, Bucharest
Mihalyo, John
jmihalyo@dailytidings.com, Circ. Dir., The Ashland Daily Tidings, OR, Ashland
Mihlar, Fazil............................(604) 605-2185
Editorial Page Ed., The Vancouver Sun, BC, Vancouver
Mikkelson, Jorn
jp@jp.dk, Ed. in Chief, MORGENAVISEN JYLLANDS-POSTEN, Viby, Jutland
Miklos, Toth
petofinepe@axels.hu, Gen. Dir., PETOFI NEPE, Kecskemet
Miklos, Kopka
kopkam@szdsz.hu, Ed.-in-Cheif, NOGRAD MEGYEI HIRLAP, Salgotarjan, Nograd
MiklÂ¢s, HalmÂ gyi
vasnepe@vn.plt.hu, Mgr., VAS NEPE, Szombathely, Vas
Miko, Robert J.........................(203) 829-5613
bmiko@pacificdialogue.com, Ed., Miko's Pacific News Service, CT, Stratford
Mikolajczak, Joanna.................(972) 273-3057
North Lake College, TX, Irving
Mikolajczyk, Mark 321-242-3777
mmikol@floridatoday.com, President and Publisher, Florida Today, FL, Melbourne
Mikulak, Ron............................(502) 582-4203
rmikulak@courier-journal.com, Food Ed., The Courier-Journal, KY, Louisville
Milano, Tracy............................(509) 335-4573
Washington State Univ., Daily Evergreen, WA, Pullman
Miles, Chris................(207) 729-3311 ext. 3204
cmiles@timesrecord.com, Pub., The Times Record, ME, Brunswick
Miles, Gary
gmiles@detroitnews.com, Deputy Managing Editor, The Detroit News, MI, Detroit
Milet, Jean-Pierre
redaction@laprovence-presse.fr, MD, LA PROVENCE, Marseille
Milheiser, Pam
pmilheiser@gazetteextra.com, Sec., The Janesville Gazette, WI, Janesville
Milks, Gary
publisher@dailydem.com, Pub., Fort Madison Daily Democrat, IA, Fort Madison
Millar, Quin ....(416) 593-2035
qmillar@canwest.com, Dir., Newspaper Sales, TVtimes, ON, Toronto
Millar, Quin ....(416) 593-2035
qmillar@canwest.com, Dir., Newspaper Sales, CanWest Media Sales, ON, Toronto
Millar, Quin
qmillar@canwest.com, Dir. Sales., CanWest Publishing, QC, Montreal
Millare, Nora
nora.millare@dowjones.com, Mgmt., Sec., The Wall Street Journal-Western Edition, CA, Palo Alto
Millbern, Tim
pressroom@ottowaherald.com, Prodn. Mgr., The Ottawa Herald, KS, Ottawa
Millegan, Lisa ....(209) 578-2313
lmillegan@modbee.com, Theater/Music Writer, The Modesto Bee, CA, Modesto
Millener, George ....(707) 521-5244
gmillener@pressdemocrat.com, Sr. Ed., Presentation, The Press Democrat, CA, Santa Rosa
Miller, Larry 803-774-1277
lmiller@theitem.com, General Manager, The Item, SC, Sumter
Miller, Tony
tmiller@thehawkeye.com, Prodn. Mgr., Systems, The Hawk Eye, IA, Burlington
Miller, Rachel 212-239-3485
rachel.miller@am-ny.com, National and Image Advertising Director, amNew York, NY, New York
Miller, Ric.......................................ext. 206
ricmiller@sanduskyregister.com, Prodn. Foreman, Pressroom, Sandusky Register, OH, Sandusky
Miller, Gary ....(973) 569-7042
News Editor, North Jersey Media Group, NJ, Woodland Park
Miller, Kathy
krmiller@ottowaherald.com, Data Processing Mgr., The Ottawa Herald, KS, Ottawa
Miller, Dave...........................(231) 933-1441
dmiller@record-eagle.com, Editorial Page Ed., Record-Eagle, MI, Traverse City
Miller, Robert
robert.miller@tribstar.com, Adv. Dir., The Tribune Star, IN, Terre Haute
Miller, Jeff..............................(610) 622-8820
Political/Gov't Ed., Delaware County Daily Times, PA, Primos
Miller, April ....(508) 862-1128
aprilm@capecodonline.com, Classified Adv. Mgr., Cape Cod Times, MA, Hyannis
Miller, Debbie ....(479) 872-5029
dmiller@nwaonline.net, Living Ed., The Morning News of Northwest Arkansas, AR, Springdale
Miller, Tim ....(508) 862-1140
tmiller@capecodonline.com, Entertainment Ed., Cape Cod Times, MA, Hyannis
Miller, Rich..............................(407) 420-5706
akmiller@orlandosentinel.com, Adv. Mgr., Bus., Orlando Sentinel, FL, Orlando
Miller, Roger............................(309) 820-3233
rmiller@pantagraph.com, Night City Ed., The Pantagraph, IL, Bloomington
Miller, Mary.............................(417) 837-1353
mfmiller@news-leader.com, Prodn. Mgr., Distr. Ctr., Springfield News-Leader, MO, Springfield
Miller, Bill................................(905) 645-2086
bmiller@quickwire.com, Gen. Mgr., Quickwire Labs, ON, Hamilton
Miller, Jeffery..........................(605) 274-4423
Augustana College, SD, Sioux Falls
Miller, Max B.
entertainment@earthlink.net, Pub., Fotos International, CA, Los Angeles
Miller, Anita
amiller@sanmarcosrecord.com, News Ed., San Marcos Daily Record, TX, San Marcos
Miller, Marcus
info@pvr.com, Dir., Sales/Mktg., Pacific Video Resources/PVR Labs, CA, San Francisco
Miller, Tom..............................(509) 323-6875
Gonzaga Univ., WA, Spokane
Miller, Scott
webmaster@yorkdispatch.com, Mgmt. Info Servs./Online Mgr., The York Dispatch, PA, York
Miller, Thomas
thomas.miller@traunsteiner-tagblatt.de, Bus. Mgr., Traunsteiner Tagblatt, Traunstein
Miller, Matt...............................(724) 225-2073
mtmiller@observer-reporter.com, Adv. Dir., Observer-Reporter, PA, Washington
Miller, Lisa ....ext. 18
circulation@laurelleadercall.com, Circ. Mgr., Laurel Leader-Call, MS, Laurel
Miller, Mark F.
miller@news-banner.com, Pres./Pub., News-Banner, IN, Bluffton
Miller, Tim ....(937) 642-6397
Sports Ed., Marysville Journal-Tribune, OH, Marysville
Miller, Scott..............................(970) 748-2930
smiller@vaildaily.com, Bus. Ed., Vail Daily, CO, Vail
Miller, Kristin
kmiller@thenewsdispatch.com, Lifestyle Ed., News Dispatch, IN, Michigan City
Miller, Morgan...........................(863) 386-5810
cmiller@highlandstoday.com, Adv. Dir., Highlands Today, FL, Sebring
Miller, Lisa
lcm@cisunix.unh.edu, Dir., University of New Hampshire, NH, Durham
Miller, Lisa...............................(419) 521-7240
lkmiller@nncogannett.com, Bus. Writer, News Journal, OH, Mansfield
Miller, Chris.............................(801) 625-4261
cmiller@standard.net, Sports Ed., Standard-Examiner, UT, Ogden
Miller, Mike ....(850) 747-5049
mmiller@pcnh.com, Circ. Dir., Regl., The News Herald, FL, Panama City
Miller, Robin
citydesk@thereporter.com, City Ed., The Reporter, CA, Vacaville
Miller, Steve ....(607) 274-9266
Circ. Dir., The Ithaca Journal, NY, Ithaca
Miller, Paul A. ....ext. 1401
pmiller@keenesentinel.com, Mng. Ed., The Keene Sentinel, NH, Keene
Miller, Barbara
barbara_miller@link.freedom.com, Promo. Sales Mgr., Daily Press, CA, Victorville
Miller, Marsha..........................(580) 221-6529
News Ed., The Daily Ardmoreite, OK, Ardmore
Miller, Terry
news@ketchikandailynews.com, Mng. Ed., Ketchikan Daily News, AK, Ketchikan
Miller, David ....(254) 501-7543
Asst. Mng. Ed., Killeen Daily Herald, TX, Killeen
Miller, Rudy ....ext. 3612
rmiller@express-times.com, Easton Ed., The Express-Times, PA, Easton
Miller, Lowell
lowell.miller@owh.com, Retail Sales Mgr., Omaha World-Herald, NE, Omaha
Miller, Bill...................................214-361-2276
Pres., North Amer., Flint Group, MI, Plymouth
Lone Star Outdoor News, TX, Dallas
Miller, Robert G. ....(802) 775-5511
bob.miller@rutlandherald.com, Audiotex Mgr., Rutland Herald, VT, Rutland
Miller, Susan................(725) 775-3200 ext. 119
smiller@timesonline.com, Exec. Sec., Beaver County Times, PA, Beaver
Miller, Shawn...........................(707) 427-6958
News Ed., Daily Republic, CA, Fairfield
Miller, James ....(770) 795-8556
jimmym@pamarcoglobal.com, Vice Pres., Mfg., Pamarco Global Graphics, GA, Marietta
Miller, David ....(618) 374-4415
Principia College, IL, Elsah
Miller, Phil
pmiller@altmarknet.com, CEO, U.S. Suburban Press (USSPI), IL, Schaumburg
Miller, Curt...................................949-451-9050
curt.miller@theaustin.com, Gen. Mgr., The Austin Company, OH, Cleveland
Miller, Shannon ....(604) 605-2026
smiller@theprovince.com, Metro Ed., The Province, BC, Vancouver
Miller, Steve
sales@parascan.com, Mgr., Parascan Technologies, Inc., CA, Monrovia
Miller, Randy
rmiller@thehawkeye.com, News Ed., The Hawk Eye, IA, Burlington
Miller, Jay K.
jmiller@ursinus.edu, Chair, Ursinus College, PA, Collegeville
Miller, Steve ....(541) 885-4437
smiller@heraldandnews.com, Ed., Herald and News, OR, Klamath Falls
Miller, Colleen..........................(248) 370-4268
Oakland Univ., MI, Rochester
Miller, Gaylord (Rick)
rick@gazettepublishingco.com, Publisher, The Bellevue Gazette, OH, Bellevue
Miller, Dave
dmiller@claritas.com, Sr. Vice Pres., Data Research/Devel., Nielsen, CA, San Diego
Miller, David.................................580-765-3311
sports@poncacitynews.com, Sports reporter, The Ponca City News, OK, Ponca City
Miller, Warren
warren@telecompute.com, Pres., Telecompute Corp., DC, Washington
Miller, Mark...............................(254) 501-7563
Sports Ed., Killeen Daily Herald, TX, Killeen
Miller-Carl, Michelle ....(530) 852-0235
michellem@goldcountrymedia.com, News Ed., Auburn Journal, Inc., CA, Auburn
Milles, Erin..............................(616) 957-7031
Calvin College, MI, Grand Rapids
Millhouse, Tom
tmillhouse@dailycall.com, News Ed., Piqua Daily Call, OH, Piqua
Milliman, Dirk
publisher@threeriversnews.com, Pub., Three Rivers Commercial-News, MI, Three Rivers
Millis, Kristen ....(206) 543-7666
Univ. of Washington, WA, Seattle
Millman, Stephanie
mktg@maxcessintl.com, Dir., Mktg./Sales, Maxcess, OK, Oklahoma City
Millner, Frazier........................(804) 649-6085
Promo. Mgr., Richmond Times-Dispatch, VA, Richmond
Millrood, Gary
sales@click2learn.com, Vice Pres., Worldwide Sales/Alliances, Sumtotal System Inc., WA, Bellevue
Mills, Therese
newsday@newsday.co.tt, CEO, NEWSDAY, Port-of-Spain
Mills, Mike.....................................202-650-6535
mikemills@cqrollcall.com, Editorial Director, Congressional Quarterly, Inc., DC, Washington
Mills, Amy..................................(901) 333-2036
mills.amy@desotoappeal.com, Adv. Sales Mgr., DeSoto Appeal, The Commercial Appeal, TN, Memphis
Mills, Rick
rmills@michigannewspapers.com, Exec. Ed., Morning Sun, MI, Mount Pleasant
Millsap, David M........................(276) 645-2526
dmillsap@bristolnews.com, Grp. Adv. Mgr., Bristol Herald Courier, VA, Bristol
Millsaps, Eric......................................ext. 388
emillsaps@hickoryrecord.com, Ed., The Hickory Daily Record, NC, Hickory
Milone, Steve............................(978) 946-2000
smilone@eagletribune.com, Directr of Circulation., Gloucester Daily Times, MA, Gloucester
Milt, Victor ....(561) 483-7734
vicmilt@victormilt.com, Creative Dir., interActive Publishing Corp., FL, Boca Raton
Mimai, Tonia
enquiries@nisyndication.com, Syndication Sales Mgr., NISyndication, ENG, London
Mims, Scott..ext. 28
scott.mims@clantonadvertiser.com, News Ed., The Clanton Advertiser, AL, Clanton
Min, Shin Sang
ssm11@hankyung.com, Pres., KOREA ECONOMIC DAILY, Seoul
Mina, Frank ....(415) 777-7221
fminna@sfchronicle.com, Asst. Mng. Editor, Presentation, San Francisco Chronicle, CA, San Francisco
Minemyer, Chip..........................(814) 532-5091
Ed., The Tribune-Democrat, PA, Johnstown
Minford, Chris
cminford@mauinews.com, Circ. Mgr., The Maui News, HI, Wailuku
Minge, Harald
ham@rogalandsavis.no, Ed. in Chief, ROGALANDS AVIS, Stavanger
Miniard, Wylene
advertising@harlanonline.net, Adv. Mgr., The Harlan Daily Enterprise, KY, Harlan
Minichino, Adam
aminichino@cdispatch.com, Sports Ed., The Commercial Dispatch, MS, Columbus
Minick, Jane
janem@kpcnews.net, Composing Mgr., The Star, IN, Auburn
Mininger, Brian..........................(215) 997-3447
bmininger@simcomail.com, Technical Rep., Simco Industrial Static Control Products, PA, Hatfield
Mink, Chris...............................(847) 762-7855
cmink@researchusainc.com, Vice Pres., Mktg., Research USA, Inc., IL, Chicago
Mink, Eric ....(314) 340-8391
emink@post-dispatch.com, Commentary Page Ed., St. Louis Post-Dispatch, MO, Saint Louis
Minor, Les ....ext. 7256
lminor@texarkanagazette.com, Ed., Texarkana Gazette, TX, Texarkana
Minsaoo, Melvin
tiser@adv.newsltd.com.au, Ed., THE ADELAIDE NEWS
Minton, Brenda..........................(813) 259-7705
Adv. Mgr., NW Regl. Sales, The Tampa Tribune, FL, Tampa
Minton, Meta.............................(352) 753-1119
meta.minton@thevillagesmedia.com, Mng. Ed., The Villages Daily Sun, FL, The Villages
Minton, Tammy
bizoffice@jacksonvilleprogress.com, Office Mgr., Jacksonville Daily Progress, TX, Jacksonville
Minty, Dawn

dminty@ledger-enquirer.com, Features Ed., Columbus Ledger-Enquirer, GA, Columbus
Mintz, Yvonne
kelly.hawes@thefacts.com, Mng. Ed., The Facts, TX, Clute
Mio, Peter
peter.mio@niagara-gazette.com, Pub., Niagara Gazette, NY, Niagara Falls
Miraglia, Mindy
mindymiraglia@uswest.net, Vice Pres.-Sales/Mktg., ARC Research, AZ, Scottsdale
Miralles Bova, Marcelo 525-0761
info@lapatria.com.bo, Pres./Ed., La Patria, Oruro, Oruro
Miranda, Carlos
redaccion@el-siglo.com.ar, Sales Mgr., Siglo XXI S.A., San Miguel de Tucuman, Provincia de Tucuman
Miranda Ester, Jose Carlos
jcmiranda@segre.com, Dir., Segre, Lleida
Mirquez Rochyn, Jayma
opinionapatzingan@gmail.com, Dir., La Opinion De Apatzingan, Apatzingan, Michoacan
Mirrington, Andrew ....(303) 443-6272 ext. 131
mirrington@coloradodaily.com, Adv. Dir., Colorado Daily, CO, Boulder
Mirrington, Andrew
publisher@telluridenews.com, Pub., Telluride Daily Planet, CO, Telluride
Misarski, Michael ....(203) 317-2241
mmisarski@record-journal.com, News Ed., Record-Journal, CT, Meriden
Mishra, Veer Bhadra
vbmganga@satyam.net.in, Pub., SANMARG, Varanasi, Uttar Pradesh
Miske, Michael
info@vegra.com, Vice Pres., Sales, Vegra USA, IL, Chicago
Misra, Sarat
samaj@orissanews.com, Exec. Ed., THE SAMAJ, Cuttack, Orissa
Missakian, A.
jharatch@aol.com, Pub., HARATCH, Paris
Missal, Maureen 570-674-5600
mmissal@outsourcingsua.net, VP Business Development, Outsourcing USA, PA, Dallas
Missen, Randy ....(416) 289-6566
rmissen@bbm.ca, Vice Pres., Meter Servs., BBM Canada, ON, Toronto
Missler, Sherry
smissler@timesbulletin.com, Ed., The Times Bulletin, OH, Van Wert
Mitchel, Barbara ....(707) 526-8525
barbara.mitchel@pressdemocrat.com, Adv. Mgr., Nat'l, The Press Democrat, CA, Santa Rosa
Mitchell, Bill ....(904) 819-3444
bill.r.mitchell@staugustinerecord.com, Circ. Dir., The St. Augustine Record, FL, Saint Augustine
Mitchell, Jason
pwallner@heraldpalladium.com, Sports Ed., The Herald-Palladium, MI, Saint Joseph
Mitchell, Dick ....(630) 245-0316
dmitchell@landonmedia.com, Sr. Vice Pres., Landon Media Group LLC, IL, Naperville
Mitchell, Randy ....(260) 563-2131
rmitchell@paxtonmedia.com, Pub., Wabash Plain Dealer, IN, Wabash
Mitchell, Chris
editor@theaustralian.com.au, Ed. in Chief, THE AUSTRALIAN
Mitchell, Billy ....(770) 428-9411 ext. 207
Mng. Ed., Marietta Daily Journal, GA, Marietta
Mitchell, Chris
act@theaustralian.com.au, Ed. in Chief, THE AUSTRALIAN
Mitchell, Chris
editor@theaustralian.com.au, Ed. in Chief, THE AUSTRALIAN
Mitchell, Bill ....(352) 753-1119
bill.mitchell@thevillagesmedia.com, Photo Ed., The Villages Daily Sun, FL, The Villages
Mitchell, Sara ....(661) 763-3171
editor@bay.rr.com, Sports Ed., Daily Midway Driller, CA, Taft
Mitchell, T.C. ....ext. 348
Food Ed., Anchorage Daily News, AK, Anchorage
Mitchell, R. John ....(802) 479-4039 ext. 1133
john.mitchell@rutlandherald.com, Pres./Pub., The Times Argus, VT, Barre
Mitchell, Randy ....(765) 473-6641
rmitchell@paxtonmedia.com, Pub., The Peru Tribune, IN, Peru
Mitchell, Trisha ....(208) 735-3327
tmitchell@magicvalley.com, Circ. Dir., The Times-News, ID, Twin Falls
Mitchell, Charles D. ....(601) 636-4545 ext. 123
post@vicksburg.com, Exec. Ed., The Vicksburg Post, MS, Vicksburg
Mitchell, R. John ....(802) 747-6121 ext. 2202
john.mitchell@rutlandherald.com, Pres./Pub., Rutland Herald, VT, Rutland
Mitchell, Sara ....(540) 231-9867
Virginia Polytechnic Institute, VA, Blacksburg
Mitchell, Nancy ....(303) 892-5245
mitchelln@rockymountainnews.com, Educ. Ed., Suburban Schools, Rocky Mountain News, CO, Denver
Mitchell, Elena
elena.mitchell@savannahnow.com, Acct. Mgr., Savannah Morning News, GA, Savannah
Mitchell, Michelle ....(727) 893-8363
mmitchell@tampabay.com, Adv. Mgr., Classified, Tampa Bay Times, FL, Saint Petersburg
Mitchell, Linda ....ext. 520
lmitchell@reporter-herald.com, Librarian, Daily Reporter-Herald, CO, Loveland
Mitchell, Catherine ....(204) 697-7041
Catherine.Mitchell@freepress.mb.ca, Columnist, Winnipeg Free Press, MB, Winnipeg
Mitchell, Colleen
colleen@newnan.com, Sales/Mktg. Dir., The Times-Herald, GA, Newnan
Mitchell, Randy 316-641-4200
randy.mitchell@mcphersonsentinel.com, Publisher, McPherson Sentinel, KS, McPherson
Mitchell, Sheila ....ext. 107
smitchell@batavianews.com, Adv. Dir., The Daily News, NY, Batavia
Mitchell, Randy 316-641-4200
publisher@wellingtondailynews.com, Publisher, Wellington Daily News, KS, Wellington
Mitchell-Wagner, Pamela
pam@lapress.com, Exec. Dir., Louisiana Press Association, LA, Baton Rouge
Mitra, Chandan
pioneer@del2.vsnl.net.in, Ed., PIONEER, New Delhi
Mittelstaedt, Rob 507-645-1118
rjmittelstaedt@charter.net, CFO, Huckle Media, LLC, MI, Traverse City
Mitten, Alyse ....(610) 562-5480 ext. 12
alyse.mitten@gmail.com, Exec. Dir., Mid-Atlantic Community Papers Association, PA, Hamburg
Mitten, Alyse
alyse.mitten@gmail.com, Exec. Dir., MACNET, PA, Hamburg
Miura, Hiroshi
center@iwate-np.co.jp, Pres., IWATE NIPPO, Morioka City, Tohoku
Miyake, Riichiro
info@the-miyanichi.co.jp, Pres., MIYAZAKI NICHI-NICHI SHIMBUN, Miyazaki, Kyushu
Miyamoto, Tomoharu
henshu@tomamin.co.jp, Ed. in Chief, TOMAKOMAI MIMPO, Tomakomai, Hokkaido
Mizak, Michael J. ....(610) 371-5204
mmizak@readingeagle.com, CFO/Treasurer/Assoc. Pub., Reading Eagle, PA, Reading
Mizami, Najeeb
editor@nation.com.pk, Ed. in Chief, THE NATION, Islamabad
Mizukami, Ken-ya
webmaster@yomiuri.co.jp, Chrmn., YOMIURI SHIMBUN, Tokyo
Mkhuma, Zingisa
9zingisa.mkhuma@inl.co.za, Ed., THE PRETORIA NEWS, Pretoria, PWV
Mlokdecki, Dan ....(506) 859-4875
Mgmt. Info Servs. Mgr., Times & Transcript, NB, Moncton
Moats, David ....(802) 747-6121 ext. 2204
david.moats@rutlandherald.com, Editorial Page Ed., Rutland Herald, VT, Rutland
Mobbs, John ....(501) 378-3437
jmobbs@ardemgaz.com, Adv. Dir., Arkansas Democrat-Gazette, AR, Little Rock
Mobley, Chris ....(305) 347-6612
cmobley@alm.com, Group Publisher, FL/GA/TX, Palm Beach Daily Business Review, FL, West Palm Beach
Mobley, Chris ....(305) 347-6612
cmobley@alm.com, Group Publisher, FL/GA/TX, Miami Daily Business Review, FL, Miami
Moctezuma, Sabrena
sabrenam@forsythnews.com, Office Mgr., Forsyth County News, GA, Cumming
Moctezuma, Sabrena
sabrenam@forsythnews.com, Office Mgr., Forsyth County News, GA, Cumming
Modestino, Lou
lmodestino@hotmail.com, Author, TV Times/New England Motorsports Syndication, MA, Sharon
Moe, Jeff ....(573) 815-1522
jmoe@columbiatribune.com, Chief Financial Officer, Columbia Daily Tribune, MO, Columbia
Moe, Eirik
eirik.moe@sa.no, Ed., SARPSBORG ARBEIDERBLAD, Sarpsborg
Moe, Mitsy
mmoe@willistonherald.com, Pub., Williston Daily Herald, ND, Williston
Moelis, Gary
garym@microfilmproducts.com, Pres., Microfilm Products Co., NY, Nanuet
Moffitt, Michael
moffittm@dbl.newsltd.com.au, Adv. Dir., THE MERCURY
Mohamed Khan, Khan Lateef
munsifdaily@eth.net, Ed. in Chief, MUNSIF, Hyderabad
Mohammed Isa, Zainul Arifin
zainul@nstp.com.my, Mng. Ed. (Grp.), NEW STRAITS TIMES & NEW SUNDAY TIMES, Kuala Lumpur
Mohan Gupta, Madhan
madhanmohan.jagran@gmail.com, Pub., DAINIK JAGRAN, Indore, Madhya Pradesh
Mohlin, Lars
lars.mohlin@kvp.se, Ed. /Pub., KVALL-SPOSTEN, Malmo
Mok, Andrew 651-228-5149
amok@pioneerpress.com, Vice Pres., Circ., St. Paul Pioneer Press, MN, Saint Paul
Mokhtarrozaidi, Mohammad 4023 6753
Ed. in Chief, HARAKAH, Kuala Lumpur
Molas, Cesar Atilio 343-6666
redaccion@launiononline.com.ar, Ed., La Union, Catamarca, Provincia de Catamarca
Moldovan, Ioana 0040 21 317 89 16
Marketing and Media Relations, ALLGEMEINE DEUTSCHE ZEITUNG FÃ£R RUMÃ£NIEN, Bucuresti
Moldovan, Dragos
dra.moldovan@gmail.com, Ed. in Chief, CRONICA ROMANA, Bucharest
Molenar, Roxanne ....(928) 539-6862
rmolenar@yumasun.com, Assignments Editor, Yuma Sun, AZ, Yuma
Molina de la Torre, Samuel
momento@www.teqcorp.com/mx, Pres., Editora Regional del Centro, S.A., San Luis Potosi, San Luis Potosi
Molitor, Wolfgang
leserport@stn.zgs.de, Ed., Stuttgarter Nachrichten, Stuttgart
Moll, Oliva
info@goettinger-tageblatt.de, Circ. Mgr., Gottinger Tageblatt, Gottingen
Moller, Wolfgang 419090
nb@moellerdruck.de, Proprietor, DER NORDBERLINER, Berlin
Molley, John
jmolley@johnsoncitypress.com, Mng. Ed., Johnson City Press, TN, Johnson City
Moloney, Mike ....(216) 999-6586
Circ. Mgr., Transportation, The Plain Dealer, OH, Cleveland
Molossi, Giuliano 2251
Mgr., GAZZETTA DI PARMA, Parma
Mominee, Thomas 8124647463
momineet@courierpress.com, HR Dir., Evansville Courier & Press, IN, Evansville
Momot, Kevin
kevin.momot@nydailyrecord.com, Vice Pres./Pub., The Daily Record, NY, New York
Mona, Tuck
mtuck@lagrandeobserver.com, Office mgr, The Observer, OR, La Grande
Monaco, Alberto
larazon@chivilcoy.com.ar, Pres., La Razon de Chivilcoy S.A., Chivilcoy, Provincia de Buenos Aires
Monaco, James
jmonaco@unet2.net, Pres., Unet 2 Corporation, NY, New York
Monaghan, David ....(815) 439-5302
dmonaghan@scn1.com, Mng. Ed., The Herald News, IL, Joliet
Monahan, Ronald
rmonahan@times-news.com, Pub./Gen. Mgr., The Cumberland Times-News, MD, Cumberland
Monbarren, Dennis ....ext. 1660
dennism@dixcom.com, Mgmt. Info Servs. Mgr., The Daily Record, OH, Wooster
Mondragon, Jaime Gaez 294-0100
enrsan@eltiempo.com.co, Gen. Mgr., Editorial El Tiempo Ltd., Bogota, D.C.
Mondt, Dave ....(941) 206-1000
dmondt@sun-herald.com, Asst. Sports Ed., Charlotte Sun, FL, Charlotte Harbor
Monestier, Omar
mattino@mattinopadova.it, MD, IL MATTINO DI PADOVA, Padova
Money, Sarah
sarah.money@dowjones.com, Sales Mgr., Dow Jones Newswires - London, United Kingdom, London
Mong, Robert ....(214) 977-6828
bmong@dallasnews.com, Ed., The Dallas Morning News, TX, Dallas
Monghyri, Karim Raza 09433778776
akkas@cal3.vsnl.net.in, Pub., AKKAS DAILY, Kolkata, West Bengal
Monico, Nick ....(614) 403-7501
Div. Mgr., North, Leader Times, PA, Kittanning Regional VP - Western, GateHouse Media Inc., NY, Fairport
Monico, Nickolas F.
nmonico@tribweb.com, COO, Tribune-Review Publishing Co., PA, Greensburg
Moniz, Manuel
moniz@diariodosacores.pt, Ed., DIARIO DOS ACORES, Ponta del Gada
Monroe, Marilyn
sdneditorial@yahoo.com, Ed., Southwest Daily News, LA, Sulphur
Monroe, Bill
bmonroe@inanews.com, Exec. Dir., Iowa Newspaper Association, Inc., IA, Des Moines
Monsalve, Alcides 21-3787
monsalvea@telcel.net.ve, Pres., Ediciones Occidente C.A., Merida
Monsalve, Patricia 571-9999
director@laopinion.com.co, Gen. Mgr., La Opinion, Cucuta
Monscour, Mike ....(239) 335-0284
Vice Pres., Opns., The News-Press, FL, Fort Myers
Monson, Lynn ....(734) 994-6828
lmonson@annarbornews.com, Environmental Ed., The Ann Arbor News, MI, Ann Arbor
Monson, Kristi ....(218) 477-2110
Minnesota State Univ. Moorhead, MN, Moorhead
Montague, Brad ....(306) 781-5260
bmontague@leaderpost.canwest.com, Prodn. Mgr., Bldg., The Leader-Post, SK, Regina
Montague, Bill ....(705) 759-3030 ext. 271
jthompson@saultstar.com, City Ed., The Sault Star, ON, Sault Ste Marie
Monteiro, Claudio 371-1875
Ed., Jornal do Poste, Sao Joao Del Rei, Minas Gerias
Montell, Gabriella ....(617) 349-8501
Lesley University, MA, Cambridge
Montemurro, Ronald J. ....(262) 656-6301
rmontemurro@kenoshanews.com, Gen. Mgr., Kenosha News, WI, Kenosha
Montemurro, Ronald J. ....(262) 656-6301 ext. 301
rmontemurro@kenoshanews.com, Vice President, United Communications Corporation, WI, Kenosha
Montero, Elena
emontero@efe.com, Bureau Chief, EFE News Services - New York, NY, NY, New York
Montes, Francisco J.

direcciondc@diariodecuyo.com.ar, Dir., Francisco Salvador Montes S.A., San Juan, Provincia de San Juan

Montgomery, David ....(928) 783-3311 ext. 109
Vice Pres./CFO, Western Newspapers, Inc., AZ, Yuma

Montgomery, John ....ext. 400
jmont@hutchnews.com, Ed./Pub., The Hutchinson News, KS, Hutchinson

Montgomery, Barb ....(734) 994-6876
bmontgomery@annarbornews.com, Adv. Mgr., Retail/Nat'l/Co-op, The Ann Arbor News, MI, Ann Arbor

Montgomery, Shelagh
support@qualitytech.com, Gen. Mgr., Globix Corp., NJ, Jersey City

Montgomery, Mary Lou ....(573) 248-2750
marylou.montgomery@courierpost.com, Ed., Hannibal Courier-Post, MO, Hannibal

Montgomery, Mark....................(916) 321-1648
mmontgomery@sacbee.com, Audience Devel./Membership Servs. Mgr., Admin./Opns., The Sacramento Bee, CA, Sacramento

Montgomery, Brenda ....(815) 937-3300
bmontgomery@daily-journal.com, Administrative Asst., Small Newspaper Group, Inc., IL, Kankakee

Montgomery, John......................620-694-5700
Vice President, Harris Enterprises, Inc., KS, Hutchinson

Montgomery, John Grey.............(785) 762-5000
j.montgomery@thedailyunion.net, Pres./ceo, The Daily Union, KS, Junction City

Monti, Andra
amonti@rcs.it, Dir., LA GAZZETTA DELLO SPORT, Milan

Montoya, Sam
samm@gilroydispatch.com, Prodn. Mgr., Pressroom, The Dispatch, CA, Gilroy

Montri, Ron ....ext. 321
sports@monroenews.com, Sports Ed., The Monroe Evening News, MI, Monroe

Montuori, Vincent....................(212) 930-8000
editor@nypost.com, Vice Pres., Promo./Mktg., New York Post, NY, New York

Montz, Dora ....(505) 391-5415
administration@hobbsnews.com, Admin. Asst., Hobbs News-Sun, NM, Hobbs

Moo Jong, Park
moojong@koreatimes.co.kr, Pres., KOREA TIMES, Seoul

Moody, Linda
lmoody@dailyadvocate.com, Asst. Ed., Daily Advocate, OH, Greenville

Moon, Lane ....(937) 652-1331
Publisher/Adv Dir, Urbana Daily Citizen, OH, Urbana

Mooney, Marysue ....(413) 788-1220
Adv. Mgr., Classified, The Republican, MA, Springfield

Mooney, Dick ....(603) 472-5825 ext. 11
dick.mooney@ckp.com, Mng. Partner/CFO, Saxotech, NH, Bedford

Mooney, Bob ....ext. 302
bobm@thepublicopinion.com, City Ed., Watertown Public Opinion, SD, Watertown

Mooney, James
james.mooney@ckp.com, Vice Pres., Opns., Saxotech, NH, Bedford

Mooneyham, Scott
smooneyh@ncinsider.com, Mgr., Capitol Press Association, NC, Raleigh

Moore, Chris
kemoore@mckendree.edu, Associate Editor, McKendree University, IL, Lebanon

Moore, Kristie
kmoore@hopewellnews.com, Acctg. Mgr., The Hopewell News, VA, Hopewell

Moore, Ruby ....(252) 335-8082
rmoore@dailyadvance.com, Advertising Director , The Daily Advance, NC, Elizabeth City

Moore, Billy..........................(252) 527-3191
bmoore@freedomenc.com, Adv. Dir., The Free Press, NC, Kinston

Moore, Don
dmoore@highpoint.edu, Opns. Mgr., High Point University, NC, High Point

Moore, Patricia................................ext. 280
patty.moore@lee.net, Adv. Mgr., The Ledger Independent, KY, Maysville

Moore, Jim
jmoore@epi-net.com, Gen. Mgr., EPI Communications, MD, Rockville

Moore, Carrie........................(801) 237-2144
carrie@desnews.com, Religion Ed., Deseret News, UT, Salt Lake City

Moore, Robert ....ext. 126
info@icescape.com, Mktg. Dir., Computer Talk Technology, Inc., ON, Richmond Hill

Moore, Kellie ....ext. 1150
kellie.moore@gwinnettdailypost.com, Adv. Mgr., Classified, Gwinnette Daily Post, GA, Lawrenceville

Moore, Paul...........................(410) 332-6679
paul.moore@baltsun.com, Deputy Mng. Ed., News, The Baltimore Sun, MD, Baltimore

Moore, Phyllis........................(919) 739-7828
pmoore@newsargus.com, Educ./Health Ed., Goldsboro News-Argus, NC, Goldsboro

Moore, Jason
editorial@majorcadailybulletin.es, Ed., Majorca Daily Bulletin, Palma de Mallorca, Baleares

Moore, Stephen ....(858) 677-9634
Dir., Public Rel., Claritas, CA, San Diego

Moore, Shirley
moore_sw@tsu.edu, Chair, Texas Southern University, TX, Houston

Moore, Donna ....(850) 599-2345
dsmoore@tallahassee.com, Adv. Dir., Tallahassee Democrat, FL, Tallahassee

Moore, Ivy.............................(803) 774-1221
ivym@theitem.com, Features Ed., The Item, SC, Sumter

Moore, John ....(805) 437-0201
jmoore@venturacountystar.com, Mng. Ed., Ventura County Star, CA, Camarillo

Moore, Bruce ....(573) 882-5742
mooreba@missouri.edu, Production Manager, Columbia Missourian, MO, Columbia

Moore, Catherine
adenews@adirondackguide.com, Adv. Mgr., Adirondack Daily Enterprise, NY, Saranac Lake

Moore, Gatha
gmoore@yourclearwave.com, Prodn. Mgr., The Daily Register, IL, Harrisburg

Moore, Michael ....(360) 377-3711
mmoore@kitsapsun.com, Entertainment Writer, Kitsap Sun, WA, Bremerton

Moore, Gregory.......................(303) 954-1400
gmoore@denverpost.com, Ed., The Denver Post, CO, Denver

Moore, Danny..........................(903) 237-7780
dmoore@longview-news.com, Prodn. Asst. Mgr., Longview News-Journal, TX, Longview

Moore, Tom ....(831) 429-2417
tmoore@santacruzsentinel.com, Sports Ed., Santa Cruz Sentinel, CA, Scotts Valley

Moore, Holly..........................(850) 599-2179
htmoore@tallahassee.com, Digitial Communities Ed./Photo Ed., Tallahassee Democrat, FL, Tallahassee

Moore, Troy
troy.moore@news-jrnl.com, Sr. Mng. Ed., Daytona Beach News-Journal, FL, Daytona Beach

Moore, Brenda
bmoore@register-news.com, Bus. Mgr., Register-News, IL, Mount Vernon

Moore, Kay............................(208) 677-8738
kmoore@southidahopress.com, Prodn. Supvr., South Idaho Press, ID, Burley

Moore-Black, Wilma.................(316) 978-6113
wilma.black@wichita.edu, Kansas Professional Communicators, KS, Wichita

Moore-Macias, Kimi ....ext. 1776
kimi.macias@uniontrib.com, Adv. Dir., Bus. Channels/Opns., The San Diego Union-Tribune, CA, San Diego

Moore-Yount, Jeanne................(814) 870-1650
jeanne.yount@timesnews.com, Adv. Mgr., Display, Erie Times-News, PA, Erie

Mooreland, Tom
tmooreland@sjmercury.com, Dir., Mercury Center, Mercury Center, CA, San Jose

Moorhead, Ron C.
glenmoorent@yahoo.com, Gen. Mgr., Glenmoor Enterprise Media Group, CA, Willits

Moorhouse, Ginger F.
gmoorhouse@bakersfield.com, Chrmn. of the Board/Pub., The Bakersfield Californian, CA, Bakersfield

Moorman, J.R.
moorman-j@mail.mssc.edu, Head, Missouri Southern State University, MO, Joplin

Mora, Al ....(562) 841-6672
almora@olec.com, Sales Mgr., OLEC, CA, Santa Ana

Morales, Kasey..........................3608345756
Brand Manager, Maxcess, OK, Oklahoma City

Morales, Kristen ....(770) 718-3427
kmorales@gainesvilletimes.com, Sr. Design Ed., The Times, GA, Gainesville

Morales, Kasey
tidland@tidland.com, Media Mgr., Tidland Corp., WA, Camas

Morales, Melinda.....................559-735-3278
Daily Editor, Visalia Times-Delta, CA, Visalia

Morales, Rogue ....(559) 737-4856
College of the Sequoias, CA, Visalia

Morales, Roberto..............................264-0335
laverdad@im.pro.ec, Gen. Mgr., La Verdad, Ibarra, Imbabura

Morales Carillo, Miguel Angel
tribuna@df1.telmex.mx, Pres., TRIBUNA, Mexico City, Distrito Federal

Moran, Julio ....(213) 821-0075
juliomoran@ccnma.org, Exec. Dir., CCNMA: Latino Journalists of California, CA, Los Angeles

Moran, Tim............................(209) 578-2349
tmoran@modbee.com, Wine Writer, The Modesto Bee, CA, Modesto

Moran, Lee Ann ....ext. 575
lmoran@news-herald.com, Prodn. Mgr., Pre Press, The News-Herald, OH, Willoughby

Moran, Mike ....moranmk@accessabc.com
Sr. Vice Pres., Auditing/Technical Review, Audit Bureau of Circulations (ABC), IL, Arlington Heights

Moran, Jose Agustin 45-0396
eloeste@teletel.com.ar, Ed., El Oeste, Esquel, Provincia de Chubut

Moran, Tom
tmoran@starledger.com, Editorial Page Ed., The Star-Ledger, NJ, Newark

Morano, John ....(732) 571-4424
Monmouth Univ., NJ, West Long Branch

Morash, John...........................250-371-6172
jmorash@kamloopsnews.ca, Director of Advertising, Kamloops Daily News, BC, Kamloops

Morbach, Fern
telecran@isp.lu, Mng. Ed., TELECRAN, Luxembourg

Mordhorst, Todd.......................(530) 852-0240
atoddm@goldcountrymedia.com, Sports Ed., Auburn Journal, Inc., CA, Auburn

Moreau, Michael......................(818) 551-5214
mmoreau@glendale.edu, Glendale Cmty. College, CA, Glendale

Moree, Hans
redaktionen.skaraborg@sr.se, MD, SKOVDE NYHETER (SKARABORGS TIDNINGEN), Skovde

Moreland, David
dmoreland@dauphingraphic.com, Vice Pres., Sales/Mktg., Manugraph DGM, Inc., PA, Millersburg

Morelli, Joe...........................(410) 617-2867
Loyola College, MD, Baltimore

Morem, Bill
letters@thetribunenews.com, Editorial Page Ed., The Tribune, CA, San Luis Obispo

Morency, Judy Arent
judy@womcom.org, Chrmn., Association for Women in Communications, VA, Alexandria

Moreno, Pinky ....(956) 982-6653
Asst. Pre Press Mgr., The Brownsville Herald, TX, Brownsville

Moreno, Alexandra 31-1008
Gen. Mgr., La Region, Los Teques, Miranda

Moreno, Elena........................212-867-5757
efenyc@efeamerica.com , Bureau Chief- New York, EFE News Services - Washington, DC, DC, Washington

Moreno, Sebastian
smoreno@elimparcial.com, Reporter, El Imparcial, Hermosillo, Sonora

Moreo, Chip...........................(419) 993-2108
cmoreo@limanews.com, Prodn. Supt., Bldg., The Lima News, OH, Lima

Moretz, Brian
bmoretz@equipto.com, Mktg. Lead, Consolidated Storage Cos., PA, Tatamy

Morgan, Judy ....ext. 7202
Features Ed., Texarkana Gazette, TX, Texarkana

Morgan, Shannon
editor@arbiteronline.com, Boise State Univ., ID, Boise

Morgan, Bill
bmorgan@cullmantimes.com, Pub., The Cullman Times, AL, Cullman

Morgan, Lori ....(416) 386-2707
VP, Marketing, National Post, ON, Toronto

Morgan, Kevin ....(317) 444-6292
kevin.morgan@indystar.com, Suburban Ed., The Indianapolis Star, IN, Indianapolis

Morgan, Karen.........................(757) 247-4757
kmorgan@dailypress.com, Features Ed., Daily Press, VA, Newport News

Morgan, James........................805-781-7856
jmorgan@thetribunenews.com, Pre-Press Manager, The Tribune, CA, San Luis Obispo

Morgan, Veda..........................(502) 582-4215
vmorgan@courier-journal.com, Suburban Ed., The Courier-Journal, KY, Louisville

Morgante, Giovanni 2261
Pres., GAZETTA DEL SUD, Messina

Morganthaler, Jim
jim.morganthaler@pa-sportsticker.com, Gen. Mgr., PA-SportsTicker, CT, Cheshire

Morgenweck, Fred.....................609-272-7117
fmorgenweck@pressofac.com, IT Manager, The Press of Atlantic City, NJ, Pleasantville

Morgenweck, Fred.....................609-272-7117
fmorgenweck@pressofac.com, PrePress Manager, The Press of Atlantic City, NJ, Pleasantville

Morgnanesi, Lanny ....(215) 345-3075
lmorganesi@phillyburbs.com, Exec. Ed., The Intelligencer, PA, Doylestown

Morhart, Claus
info@main-netz.de, Ed. in Chief, MAIN-ECHO, Aschaffenburg

Mori, Michael 419-724-6380
mmori@toledoblade.com, Adv. Director, Majors/Nat'l Sales, The Blade, OH, Toledo

Moriarty, Daniel A.
dmoriarty@journalregister.com, Pub., The Middletown Press, CT, Middletown

Moriarty, Wayne......................(604) 605-2968
wmoriarty@theprovince.com, Ed. in Chief, The Province, BC, Vancouver

Morin, Tom
editor@dailycourtreview.com, Pub., Daily Court Review, TX, Houston

Morin, Ed
sales@nwnexus.com, Pres., WinStar/Northwest Nexus, Inc., WA, Bellevue

Morin, Leonel...................................563-0600
lareligion@cantv.net, Gen. Mgr., La Religion, Caracas, D.F.

Morini, Ralph
ralph.morini@eammosca.com, Pres., EAM-Mosca Corp., PA, Hazle Township

Mork, Karen ....(419) 625-5500 ext. 176
karenmork@sanduskyregister.com, Online Ed., Sandusky Register, OH, Sandusky

Morkem, Anders
anders.morken@avisa-st.no, Ed. in Chief, SOER-TROENDELAG, Orkanger

Morkved, Lars
lars.morkved@namdalsavisa.no, News Ed,, NAMDALS-AVISA A/S, Namsos

Morley, Sam ....(850) 521-1199
smorley@flpress.com, General Counsel, Florida Press Association, FL, Tallahassee

Morlock, Jerry ....(231) 725-6361
jmorlock@muskegonchronicle.com, City Ed., The Muskegon Chronicle, MI, Muskegon

Moroney, James M.
jmoroney@dallasnews.com, Pub./CEO, The Dallas Morning News, TX, Dallas

Moroz, Joe
info@jfmmachine.com, Pres., JFM Machine Co., Inc., CT, Beacon Falls

Morris, Scott ....(256) 740-5721
scott.morris@timesdaily.com, Exec. Ed., TimesDaily, AL, Florence

Morris, Bob
bmorris@messenger-inquirer.com, Pub., Messenger-Inquirer, KY, Owensboro

Morris, Debbie Wachter ....ext. 631
Reporter, New Castle News, PA, New Castle

Morris, Phillip ....(216) 999-4070
Metro Columnist, The Plain Dealer, OH, Cleveland
Morris, Faye ....(843) 317-7201
fmorris@florencenews.com, Adv. Mgr., Nat'l Classified, Morning News, SC, Florence
Morris, Charles H. 912-233-1281
chm@morrismultimedia.com, Chrmn./CEO, Morris Multimedia, Inc., GA, Savannah
Morris, Saundra ....(405) 366-3554
saundra@normantranscript.com, Adv. Dir., Norman Transcript, OK, Norman
Morris, Tony...........................(361) 664-6588
tony.morris@aliceechonews.com, Adv. Dir., Alice Echo-News Journal, TX, Alice
Morris, Richard
morris@sentinel-tribune.com, Vice Pres./Gen. Mgr., Sentinel Company, OH, Bowling Green
Morris, William S.
morris@morris.com, Chrmn./CEO, Morris Communications Co. LLC, GA, Augusta
Morris, William ....(514) 954-2100
Vice Pres.-Int'l Sales, AbitibiBowater Pulp and Paper Canada, Inc., QC, Montreal
Morris, Jack ....(785) 827-5541 ext. 5227
Kansas Wesleyan Univ., KS, Salina
Morris, Kim Taylor
lmorris@eaglenewspapers.com, Prodn. Mgr., Daily Sun News, WA, Sunnyside
Morris, John
jlmorris@adams.edu, Program Head, Adams State College, CO, Alamosa
Morris, Steve 800-451-9753
smorris606@aol.com, President and CEO, Bellatrix Systems, Inc., OR, Bend
Morrison, Josh
josh.morrison@irontontribune.com, Circ. Dir., The Ironton Tribune, OH, Ironton
Morrison, Mike ....(518) 565-4179
mmorrison@pressrepublican.com, Adv. Sales Mgr., Press-Republican, NY, Plattsburgh
Morrison, Lindsay ....(800) 851-7737 ext. 5123
lmorr@srds.com, Mktg. Commun. Dir., SRDS, a Kantar Media Company, IL, Des Plaines
Morrison, Joshua
webmaster@mountvernonnews.com, Web Ed., Mount Vernon News, OH, Mount Vernon
Morrison, Windy
office@age.co.nz, Mng. Dir., WAIRARAPA TIMES-AGE
Morrison, D. Scott
sharrison@ndiww.com, Pres., NDI (Morway Div.), OH, Cleveland
Morrison, Kenn
kmorrison@morcor.com, Pres., Morcor Solutions, Inc., ON, Napanee
Morrison, Eric ....(416) 364-0321
eric.morrison@thecanadianpress.com, Pres., Canadian Press, The - Montreal, QC, QC, Montreal
eric.morrison@thecanadianpress.com, Pres., Canadian Press, The - Toronto, ON, ON, Toronto
Morrissey, Liisa ....(303) 750-7555
lmorrissey@aurorasentinel.com, Bus. Mgr., Aurora Sentinel, CO, Aurora
Morrissey, Jake ....(212) 293-8640
jmorrissey@unitedmedia.com, Mng. Ed., Comics, United Media, OH, Cincinnati
Morrow, Rhonda ....ext. 7257
rmorrow@texarkanagazette.com, Religion Ed., Texarkana Gazette, TX, Texarkana
Morrow, Mike ....(615) 259-8027
mmorrow@tennessean.com, Editorial Writer, The Tennessean, TN, Nashville
Morrow, Michael J. ....(717) 255-8275
mmorrow@patriot-news.com, Controller, The Patriot-News, PA, Mechanicsburg
Morse, Heather.........................(541) 957-4208
hmorse@nrtoday.com, Entertainment/N. County Reporter, The News-Review, OR, Roseburg
Mortensen, Michael
mikem@citizen.com, Editorial Page Ed., Citizen, NH, Laconia
Morton, Jerry
sales@tiltlock.com, Sales Mgr., Tilt-Lock, MN, St. Michael
Morton, Dana
dmorton@marshallnewsmessenger.com, Bus. Mgr., Marshall News Messenger, TX, Marshall
Morton, Bjorn ....(850) 599-2257
bmorton@tallahassee.com, Digital/Systems Ed., Tallahassee Democrat, FL, Tallahassee
Morton, Meredith Jean
meredith.morton@newschief.com, Lifestyle Ed., News Chief, FL, Winter Haven
Morton, Randy...........................(912) 489-9431
randy@statesboroherald.com, Pub., Statesboro Herald, GA, Statesboro
Morwick, Rick...........................(317) 736-2715
rmorwick@dailyjournal.net, Sports Ed., Daily Journal, IN, Franklin
Mosconi, Toni
circulation@leaderherald.com, Circ. Dir./Promo. Mgr., The Leader-Herald, NY, Gloversville
Moseley, Carol
carolmosely@rrdailyherald.com, Sec./Treasurer, Mid-Atlantic Circulation Managers Association, NC, Roanoke Rapids
Moseley, John A.
johnmosley@bigspringherald.com, Ed., Big Spring Herald, TX, Big Spring
Moseley, Davy
davy@ssecho.com, MIS Mgr./Websmaster, Sulphur Springs News-Telegram, TX, Sulphur Springs
Moseman, Gary 406-791-1465
gmoseman@greatfallstribune.com, Managing Ed., Great Falls Tribune, MT, Great Falls
Moser, Sandro
cronaca@tribunatreviso.it, Ed., LA TRIBUNA DI TREVISO, Treviso
Moser, Ralf
redaktions@ktz.at, Ed., KARNTNER TAGESZEITUNG, Klagenfurt
Moser, Charles
cmoser@brenhambanner.com, Brenham Banner Extra, TX, Brenham
cmoser@brenhambanner.com, Editorial Writer, Political, Brenham Banner-Press, TX, Brenham
Moses, Lori ....(585) 292-3122
Monroe Cmty. College, NY, Rochester
Moses, John ....(907)-523-2265
john.moses@juneauempire.com, Managing Editor, Juneau Empire, AK, Juneau
Moses, Paul............................(718) 951-5302
CUNY/Brooklyn College, NY, Brooklyn
Mosesso, David
dmosesso@jonesborosun.com, Pub., The Jonesboro Sun, AR, Jonesboro
Moskowitz, Gary
gavriael@aol.com, Pres./Ed./Columnist, Moskowitz News and Learning Network, NY, Kew Gardens
Mosley, Jim
jim@newsengin.com, CEO, NewsEngin, Inc., MO, Chesterfield
Moss, Robin ....(972) 239-8866
robin@ribit.com, Pres./Founder, Ribit Productions, Inc., TX, Addison
Moss, Joe ....(510) 642-7480
Univ. of California Bus. School, CA, Berkeley
Moss, Doug.................(203) 854-5559 ext. 106
doug@emagazine.com, Pub./Exec. Ed., Earth Talk: Questions & Answers About Our Environment, CT, Norwalk
Moss, Elizabeth ....(828) 694-7896
elizabeth.moss@hendersonvillenews.com, TN Weekly/Assoc. Magazine Ed., Times-News, NC, Hendersonville
Moss, Dick ....(585) 258-2549
dmoss@democratandchronicle.com, News Ed., Democrat and Chronicle.com, NY, Rochester
Moss, William..........................(828) 694-7876
william.moss@blueridgenow.com, Exec. Ed., Times-News, NC, Hendersonville
Mossiah, Karen.........................(310) 243-1060
California State Univ. Dominguez, CA, Carson
Mossman, Michael 765-336-4454
mmossman@fujifilm.com, Newspaper Support Specialist, Fujifilm North America Corporation, IL, Hanover Park
Mote, Zuhair
quami@hotmail.com, Gen. Mgr., QAUMI AKHBAR, Karachi
Motsch, Gunther
gmotsch@edmsun.com, Controller, The Edmonton Sun, AB, Edmonton
Mott, Glenn ....(212) 969-7597
gmott@hearst.com, Mng. Ed./Dir., Publishing, North America Syndicate, NY, New York
gmott@hearst.com, Mng. Ed./Dir., Publishing, King Features Syndicate, NY, New York
Motta, Bernardo........................540-828-5758
bmotta@bridgewater.edu, Assistant Professor of Communication Studies, Bridgewater College, VA, Bridgewater
Moulton, David ....(888) 684-0084
info@greatplans.com, Pres., Syndication Associates, Inc., QC, Beaconsfield
Moura, Carlos
geral@oprimeirodejaneiro.pt, Dir., O PRIMEIRO DE JANEIRO, Porto
Mouser, Charles........................(800) 448-8595
cm@mouserinstitute.com, Pres., Mouser Institute School of Advertising, VA, Nottoway
Mouser, Shelly
smouser@logandaily.com, Bus. Mgr., Logan Daily News, OH, Logan
Mousseau, Christine.......(800) 336-5096 ext. 218
christine.mousseau@nora.com, Mktg. Specialist, nora systems, Inc., MA, Lawrence
Mouton, Wanda
wmouton@sfasu.edu, Interim Chair, Stephen F. Austin State University, TX, Nacogdoches
Mowbray, Kevin
kmowbray@post-dispatch.com, Pub., St. Louis Post-Dispatch, MO, Saint Louis
Mowbray, Kevin ....(563) 383-2195
Vice Pres., Publishing, Lee Enterprises, Inc., IA, Davenport
Mowery, David..........................(610) 371-5011
dmowery@readingeagle.com, Mng. Ed., Reading Eagle, PA, Reading
Mowry, Paul............................(512) 445-3717
pmowry@statesman.com, Dir., Info/Technology Servs., Austin American-Statesman, TX, Austin
Moxley, Donna ....ext. 1406
dmoxley@keenesentinel.com, Features Ed., The Keene Sentinel, NH, Keene
Moyer, Amy ....(570) 742-9671
amym@standard-journal.com, Adv. Mgr., The Standard-Journal, PA, Milton
Moyo, Debayo R.
dmoyo@rustcollege.edu, Chair, Rust College, MS, Holly Springs
Moyo, Debayo ....(662) 252-8000 ext. 4553
dmoyo@rustcollege.edu, The Rustorian, Rust College, MS, Holly Springs
Mozarsky, Scott
scott.mozarsky@prnewswire.com, Exec. Vice Pres./Chief Devel. Officer, PR Newswire - New York, NY, NY, New York
Mozer, Mindy ....(585) 258-2214
mmozer@democratandchronicle.com, Asst. Metro Ed., Democrat and Chronicle.com, NY, Rochester
Mroue, Jamil K.
editorial@dailystar.com.lb, Pub./Ed. in Chief, DAILY STAR
Muccilli, Keith ....(732) 565-7280
kmuccill@thnt.com, Photo Ed., Home News Tribune, NJ, East Brunswick
Muchmore, Tom ....(580) 765-3311
tmuch@poncacitynews.com, Editor/Publisher, The Ponca City News, OK, Ponca City
Muck, Rob.......................................ext. 245
Prodn. Foreman, Pressroom, The Daily Globe, MN, Worthington
Mudge, Chris
cmudge@cnaads.com, Exec. Dir., Customized Newspaper Advertising (Iowa), IA, Des Moines
Mueller, Donna ....(262) 631-1709
dmueller@journaltimes.com, Adv. Mgr., Classified, The Journal Times, WI, Racine
Mueller, Konrad
redaktion@zol.ch, Pub., ZURCHER OBERLANDER, Wetzikon, Zurich
Mueller, Andreas
andreas.mueller@nora.com, Pres, nora systems, Inc., MA, Lawrence
Muenzenberger, Charolette ....ext. 1645
Agriculture Ed., The Daily Record, OH, Wooster
Mugueta San Martin, Luis
vozredaccion@elperiodico.com, Dir., El Periodico-La Voz De Asturias, Lugones-Siero
Muharrem, Dean ....(519) 354-4781
dmuharrem@chathamdailynews.ca, Pub., The Chatham Daily News, ON, Chatham
Muhleck, Claus Peter
tauber-zeitung@t-online.de, Ed. in Chief, Tauber-Zeitung, Bad Mergentheim
Muhleman, Ron ....(360) 792-3355
rmuhleman@kitsapsun.com, Opns. Dir., Kitsap Sun, WA, Bremerton
Muilenburg, Robert...................361/698-1246
rmuilenburg@delmar.edu, Advisor, Del Mar College Foghorn, TX, Corpus Christi
Muir, Michael 869 0600
info@gisborneherald.co.nz, Mng. Dir., GISBORNE HERALD
Muir, Nigel
info@praxair.com, Vice Pres., Commun./Pub. Rel., Praxair, Inc., CT, Danbury
Muir, Sandy ....(416) 947-8357
sandy.muir@sunmedia.ca, Adv. Vice Pres., Sales, The Toronto Sun, ON, Toronto
Mujika, Jose Gabriel
redaccion@diariovasco.com, Dir., EL DIARIO VASCO, San Sebastian, Guipuzcoa
Mukenschnabl, David
david@dmgraphic.com, Pres., DM Graphics System, IL, Naperville
Muladzhanov, Shod
newspaper@mospravda.ru, Ed., MOSKOVSKAYA PRAVDA, Moscow
Mulcahy, James........................(814) 781-7535
Sports Ed., The Daily Press, PA, Saint Marys
Mulcahy, J.P.
siebert123@msn.com, Pres., Siebert, Inc., IL, Lyons
Mulchinock, Jack..........(905) 752-1132 ext. 235
jack.mulchinock@sunmedia.ca, Vice Pres., Technology, Osprey Media Group, ON, Markham
Mulder, Ron
rmulder@moriresearch.com, Pres., Minnesota Opinion Research, Inc. (MORI), MN, Minneapolis
Mulgrew, Tom ....(615) 661-6123
Southeast Reg. Mgr., Business Wire, TN, Brentwood
Mulholland, Frank
frank.mulholland@shelbyvilledailyunion.com, Mng. Ed., Daily Union, IL, Shelbyville
Mulick, Chris...........................(360) 753-0862
cmulick@tri-cityherald.com, Political Ed., Tri-City Herald, WA, Kennewick
Mullaney, Paul ....(219) 933-3239
mullaney@nwitimes.com, Mng. Ed., News, The Times, IN, Munster
Mullen, William
wmullen@Liberty.edu, Chrmn., Liberty University, VA, Lynchburg
Mullen, Rodger
mullenr@fayettevillenc.com, Columnist, The Fayetteville Observer, NC, Fayetteville
Mullen, Steve
smullen@cdispatch.com, Mng. Ed., The Commercial Dispatch, MS, Columbus
Mullen, Steve...........................(661) 395-7365
smullen@bakersfield.com, Mng. Ed., The Bakersfield Californian, CA, Bakersfield
Mullen, Jennifer
jen.mullen@colostate-pueblo.edu, Chair, Colorado State University, Pueblo, CO, Pueblo
Mullen, Patrick ....(570) 420-4386
pmullen@poconorecord.com, Online Dir., Pocono Record, PA, Stroudsburg
Mullen, Neil 651-228-5132
nmullen@pioneerpress.com, CFO, St. Paul Pioneer Press, MN, Saint Paul
Muller, Scott ....(973) 569-7153
News Editor, North Jersey Media Group, NJ, Woodland Park
Muller, Jan
mjan@sosialurin.fo, Ed., SOSIALURIN, Torshavn
Muller, William........................(609) 272-7342
wmuller@pressofac.com, Circ. Mgr., Sales, The Press of Atlantic City, NJ, Pleasantville
Muller, Scott ....(973) 569-7124
News Ed., Herald News, NJ, West Paterson
Mulligan, Gerry.........................(352) 563-3222
gmulligan@chronicleonline.com, Pub., Citrus County Chronicle, FL, Crystal River
Mullin, Deborah ....(561) 820-2069
dmullin@alm.com, Vice President/Broward & Palm Beach Legals, Palm Beach Daily Busi-

ness Review, FL, West Palm Beach
Mullin, Beckie
bm@bulbtronics.com, Mgr., Mktg., Bulbtronics, NY, Farmingdale
Mulliner, Michelle ....(231) 933-1492
mmulliner@record-eagle.com, Prodn. Dir., Record-Eagle, MI, Traverse City
Mullins, Jack ....(480) 461-7270
Mesa Community College, AZ, Mesa
Mullins, Theresa ....(559) 735-3326
Prodn. Mgr., Pre Press, Visalia Times-Delta & Tulare Advance-Register, CA, Visalia
Mullins, Steve ....ext. 5700
Mng. Ed., The Post and Courier, SC, Charleston
Mumert, Tommy.......................(501) 968-0284
Arkansas Tech. Univ., AR, Russellville
Mumme, Gerhard
redaktion@fsd.de, Ed. in Chief, Frankfurter Neue Presse, Frankfurt am Main
Munday, Patrick ....(406) 496-4461
Montana Tech. Univ., MT, Butte
Mundo Catalan, Arturo
diaguero@dns.pentrinex.com.mx, Pres., Diario de Guerrero, Chilpancingo, Guerrero
Mundschenk, Wolff Martin
bohme-zeitung@mundschenk.de, Bus. Mgr., Bohme-Zeitung, Soltau
Munjoy, Kenneth......................(815) 937-3346
kmunjoy@daily-journal.com, Gen. Mgr., The Daily Journal, IL, Kankakee
Munk, Melanie ....(425) 339-3430
munk@heraldnet.com, Features/Food Ed., The Herald, WA, Everett
Munn, Pam
pmunn@fortfrances.com, Circ. Mgr., Fort Frances Daily Bulletin, ON, Fort Frances
Munoz, Sara
badalona@elpunt.cat, MD, EL PUNT BARCELONES NORD, Badalona, Barcelona
Munoz, Luis 223 0266
lmunoz@larepublica.net, Dir., LA REPUBLICA, San Jose
Munoz, Julio
jmunoz@sipiapa.org, Exec. Dir., Inter American Press Association, FL, Miami
Munoz Nunez, Anna
anna.m@diariterrassa.es, Dir., DIARI DE TERRASSA, Terrassa, Barcelona
Munro, Harold ....(604) 605-2985
hmunro@png.canwest.com, Deputy Mng. Ed., The Vancouver Sun, BC, Vancouver
Munson, Beverly ....(562) 985-5736
California State Univ. Long Beach, CA, Long Beach
Munson, Jeff...........................(530) 542-8012
jmunson@tahoedailytribune.com, Mulitmedia Ed., Tahoe Daily Tribune, CA, South Lake Tahoe
Munson, Jim............................323.343.4220
jmunson@cslanet.calstatela.edu, Business, Advt. Mgr., California State Univ., CA, Los Angeles
Murayama, Michiko
newsroom@emb.asahi-np.co.jp, Owner, ASAHI SHIMBUN, Tokyo
Murdoch, Scott ....(508) 427-6821
smurdoch@enterprisenews.com, Circ. Mgr., The Enterprise, MA, Randolph
Murdoch, Rupert
webmaster@the-times.co.uk, Chrmn., Sunday Times, ENG, London
Murdoch, Rupert
webmaster@the-times.co.uk, Chrmn., The Times, ENG, London
Murdock, Tina ....(937) 382-2574
tmurdock@wnewsj.com, Graphics Mgr., Wilmington News Journal, OH, Wilmington
Murdock, Mark
markm@kpcnews.net, Sports Ed., The Star, IN, Auburn
Muria, Gino
gino@uai.com.br, Sales Mgr., Estado de Minas, Belo Horizonte, Minas Gerais
Murphy, Patrick
editor@thesheridanpress.com, Sheridan Press, WY, Sheridan
editor@thesheridanpress.com, Editorial Writer, The Sheridan Press, WY, Sheridan
Murphy, Daniel
danmurphy@starledger.com, Deputy Editorial Page Ed., The Star-Ledger, NJ, Newark
Murphy, Jim
jimmurphy@journalregister.com, Pub., The Record, NY, Troy
Murphy, John J.
info@mddc.com, Exec. Dir., Maryland-Delaware-DC Press Association, MD, Crofton
Murphy, John ....(617) 786-7076
jmurphy@ledger.com, Editorial Page Ed., The Patriot Ledger, MA, Quincy
Murphy, Mike
publisher@thedailycitizen.com, Pub., Daily Citizen, AR, Searcy
Murphy, Mary ....(919) 660-7888
Duke Univ. Fuqua Bus. School, NC, Durham
Murphy, Richard J.
rmurphy@bpaww.com, Sr. Vice Pres., Auditing, BPA Worldwide, CT, Shelton
Murphy, Erich
ldreditor@mchsi.com, News Ed./Sports Ed., The Daily Leader, IL, Pontiac
Murphy, Joe
journal@ntamar.net, Pub., THE MASHALL ISLANDS JOURNAL, Majuro
Murphy, J.K.................................ext. 1300
jk.murphy@gwinnettdailypost.com, Pub., Gwinnette Daily Post, GA, Lawrenceville
Murphy, Mike
mmurphy@charlotteobserver.com, Pres., Advertising Media Credit Executives Association International, MD, Columbia
Murphy, Dan
sports@siskiyoudaily.com, Sports Ed., Siskiyou Daily News, CA, Yreka
Murphy, Richard ....ext. 2805
Sr. Vice Pres., Auditing, BPA Worldwide, CT, Shelton
Murphy, Dina
juberty@wavo.com, Dir., Mktg., Wavo Corporation, UT, Salt Lake City
Murphy, Mark ....(401) 273-2201
editor@pbn.com, Editor, Providence Business News, RI, Providence
editor@pbn.com, News Ed., The Capital, MD, Annapolis
Murphy, Myles ....ext. 3024
mmurphy@dailytidings.com, City Ed., The Ashland Daily Tidings, OR, Ashland
Murphy, Linda ....(561) 820-4143
lmurphy@pbpost.com, Vice Pres., HR, The Palm Beach Post, FL, West Palm Beach
Murphy, Darren..........................416-947-8357
darren.murphy@sunmedia.ca, Vice President, Advertising Sales, The Toronto Sun, ON, Toronto
Murphy, Pat
murfman@cgipressparts.com, Sales/Opns. Mgr., Central Graphics, IL, Romeoville
Murphy, Tim
sales@printwareinc.com, Vice Pres.-Sales/Mktg., Printware, MN, Saint Paul
Murray, Philip W. ....(505) 820-2700
phil@dirksvanessen.com, Exec. Vice Pres., Dirks, Van Essen & Murray, NM, Santa Fe
Murray, Brian D.......................(913) 492-9050
inmc1@inlandnews.com, Chrmn. of the Bd., Inland Industries, Inc., KS, Lenexa
Murray, Andrea ....(812) 331-4351
amurray@heraldt.com, Mng. Ed., The Herald-Times, IN, Bloomington
Murray, Carolyn ....(843) 626-0319
cmurray@thesunnews.com, Mng. Ed., The Sun News, SC, Myrtle Beach
Murray, Kathy..........................(310) 448-6700
kathy.murray@investors.com, Adv. Mgr., Opns. (W. Coast), Investor's Business Daily, CA, Los Angeles
Murray, Philip W. ....(505) 820-2700
phil@dirksvanessen.com, Exec. Vice Pres., Dirks, Van Essen & Murray, NM, Santa Fe
Murray, Michael D.
murraymd@umsl.edu, UM Board of Curators' Distinguished Prof., University of Missouri-St. Louis, MO, Saint Louis
Murray, Wayne P.
publisher@privacyalert.us, Pub., Mountain Media, NV, Las Vegas
Murray, Craig ....(508) 427-4059
cmurray@enterprisenews.com, Photo Dir./Ed., The Enterprise, MA, Randolph
Murray, Kathleen..............................ext. 273
kmurray@thewesterlysun.com, Controller, The Westerly Sun, RI, Westerly
Murray, Bill
bill_murray@parade.com, Adv. Contact, Parade Publications, Inc. - San Francisco, CA, CA, San Francisco
Murray, William T.
bmurray@journalregister.com, Pub., The Trentonian, NJ, Trenton
Murry, Faye
fmurry@messenger-inquirer.com, Adv. Dir., Messenger-Inquirer, KY, Owensboro
Murthy, Ramachandra
editor@andhrajyothy.com, Ed. in Chief, ANDHRA JYOTI, Vijayawada, Andhra Pradesh
Musante, Allison ....(607) 274-3208
Ithaca College, NY, Ithaca
Muscarella, Sally
smuscarella@imediainc.com, Pres., Interactive Media Associates, NJ, Parsippany
Muscarella, Len
len@imediainc.com, Founder, Interactive Media Associates, NJ, Parsippany
Muse, Jim
jimmuse@museprestech.com, CEO, Muse Presentation Technologies, CA, Santa Ana
Muse Abernathy, Penelope ....(919) 843-4910
Prof./Knight Chair in Journ. and Digital Media Economics, University of North Carolina, NC, Chapel Hill
Mustafayev, A.
azerbaijan_newspaper@azeronline.com, Ed. in Chief, AZERBAIJAN, Baku
Muszak, Susan
smuszak@lfpress.com, Pub./CEO, The London Free Press, ON, London
Muthler, Lana.................................ext. 132
News Ed., The Express, PA, Lock Haven
Muya, Gabby
newsdesk@dailynews-tsn.com, Mng. Ed., DAILY NEWS, Dar Es Salaam
Muzik, Vladimir
blesk@blesk.cz, Ed., BLESK, Prague
Myers, Eva
pressroom@ottowaherald.com, Prodn. Mgr., Mailroom, The Ottawa Herald, KS, Ottawa
Myers, Cory ....(605) 331-2389
ctmyers@argusleader.com, Digital Media Manager, Argus Leader, SD, Sioux Falls
Myers, Brett
sports@cedarvalleydailytimes.com, Sports Ed., Cedar Valley Daily Times, IA, Vinton
Myers, Jim ....(318) 487-6322
jmyers@thetowntalk.com, Controller, The Town Talk, LA, Alexandria
Myers, Stan..................................ext. 8409
stan.myers@cantonrep.com, Photo Ed., The Repository, OH, Canton
Myers, Kathy..........................(540) 213-9140
kmyers@newsleader.com, Circ. Dir., The News Leader, VA, Staunton
Myers, Sherry..........................(859) 422-6400
brianbutler@clarkmhc.com, Dir., HR, Clark Material Handling Co., KY, Lexington
Myers, Gary ....(905) 526-3381
Vice Pres., Circ./Mktg., The Hamilton Spectator, ON, Hamilton
Myers, Bruce A...............(800) 939-6367 ext. 110
bruce@newspapercharts.com, CEO, The National Financial News Service, PA, West Chester
Myers, Theodore W.
info@sihs.com, Chrmn., Paragon Technologies Inc., PA, Easton
Myers, Bruce..........................(360) 577-2548
bmyers@tdn.com, Prodn. Mgr., Pressroom, The Daily News, WA, Longview
Myers, Dave 717-262-4781
Production Director, Public Opinion, PA, Chambersburg
Myers, Drew 573-815-1960
admyers@columbiatribune.com, IT Director, Columbia Daily Tribune, MO, Columbia
Myhre, Joel
joel.myhre@fergusfallsjournal.com, Adv. Mgr., Classified, Fergus Falls Daily Journal, MN, Fergus Falls
Mykoniatis, A.
patris@patris.gr, Pub., PATRIS, Irakliou, Crete

N

Nabors, Nancy ....(865) 342-6454
Adv. Mgr., Retail, Knoxville News Sentinel, TN, Knoxville
Nace, Dorothea
cpima@sympatico.ca, Exec. Dir./Sec./Treasurer, Canadian Printing Ink Manufacturers Association, ON, Grimby
Nadel, Natasha
natasha@ajpa.org, Assoc. Dir., American Jewish Press Association, DC, Washington
Nadell, Deborah A. ....(757) 247-4891
dnadell@dailypress.com, Adv. Gen. Mgr., Real Estate, Daily Press, VA, Newport News
Nadell, Deborah.......................(757) 247-4891
dnadell@dailypress.com, Interim Adv. Dir., Daily Press, VA, Newport News
Nadha, K.
balipost@indo.net.id, Ed., HARIAN PAGI UMUM, Denpasar, Bali
Nading, Brad
photo@gctelegram.com, Photo Dept. Mgr., The Garden City Telegram, KS, Garden City
Naeem, Nafees
nafeeszar@yahoo.com, Ed., THE LEADER, Karachi
Naegeli, Werner
info@mullermartiniusa.com, Pres./CEO, Muller Martini Corp., NY, Hauppauge
Nagano, Takeshi
hori@oita-press.co.jp, Pres., OITA GODO SHIMBUN, Oita, Kyushu
Nagano, Mitsuya
staff@kumanichi.co.jp, Chrmn., KUMAMOTO NICHI-NICHI SHIMBUN, Kumamoto, Kyushu
Nagel, Bill ....ext. 1601
bill.nagel@uniontrib.com, Sr. Vice Pres., Bus. Channels, The San Diego Union-Tribune, CA, San Diego
Nagel, Rick............................(630) 844-5840
rnagel@scn1.com, Ed., The Beacon News, IL, Aurora
Nagle, Mike
mnagle@fujifilmgs.com, Reg'l Sales Mgr., Fujifilm Graphic Systems USA, Inc., IN, Indianapolis
Nagy, John ....(807) 343-6285
john.nagy@chroniclejournal.com, Sports Ed., The Chronicle-Journal, ON, Thunder Bay
Nahalka, Robert
rnahalka@perex.sk, Sales Devel. Mgr., PRAVDA, Bratislava
Naik, Suresh
editor@deinikgomantak.com, Ed., GOMANTAK, Panaji, Panjim
Naime, Ignacio
eldiario@netspace.com.mx, Prodn. Mgr., EL DIARIO, Toluca, Mexico
Nair, Shankaran
sn@expressbuzz.com, Pub., INDIAN EXPRESS, Bangalore, Karnataka
Najar, Humberto
humberto.najar@publicitas.com, Mgr., Publicitas North America, Inc., CA, San Francisco
Najera, Laura
laura@latinoprintnetwork.com, Vice Pres., Media Servs., Latino Print Network, CA, Carlsbad
Nakao, Seiichiro
webmaster@saga-s.co.jp, Pres., SAGA SHIMBUN, Saga, Kyushu
Nakhshkaryan, Flora
gonline@arminco.com, Ed., GOLOS ARMENII, Yerevan
Nalamwar, Kranti Keshavrao
mahavidarbha@gmail.com, Ed., MAHAVIDRABHA, Nagpur, Maharashtra
Nale, Dwight...................................ext. 410
dnale@appleton.gannett.com, Multimedia Sr. Ed., The Post-Crescent, WI, Appleton
Nally, Tracy 217-351-5375
tnally@news-gazette.com, VP: Director of Human Resources, News-Gazette Inc., IL, Champaign
Nam, Kok
info@sadirectory.co.za, Dir., SAVANA, Maputo
Nam, Tok-U
tradenews@tradenews.net, Pub., DAILY TRADE NEWS, Seoul
Nam, Chong Choong
cnchong@nanyang.com.my, Ed. in Chief,

NANYANG SIANG PAU, Petaling Jaya
Namanny, Beth ext. 227
brickers@dglobe.com, Lifestyle Ed., The Daily Globe, MN, Worthington
Namini, Yasmin
yasmin.namini@nytimes.com, Sr. Vice Pres., Mktg./Circ., The New York Times, NY, New York
Nangle, William (219) 933-3327
nangle@nwitimes.com, Exec. Ed., The Times, IN, Munster
Nanna, Anthony V. 704-369-8217
tnanna@mcgrann.com, Pres., McGrann Paper West, CA, Rancho Cucamonga
Napier, Paul 0113 2388984
eped@ypn.co.uk, Ed., YORKSHIRE EVENING POST, Leeds, West Yorkshire
Napoletino, Roberto
robertonapoletino@ilmessagero.it, Mgr., IL MESSAGGERO, Rome
Naranjo, Antonio R.
redaccion@diariodelhenares.com, Dir., Diario De Alcala, Alcal de Henares
Narayan, Sanjoy
feedback@hindustantimes.com, Ed. in Chief, HINDUSTAN TIMES EVENING NEWS, New Delhi
Narce, Mark
regio7@regio7.com, Dir., Regio 7 Informativo Intercomarcal, Manresa, Barcelona
Nardo, Perry A.
pnardo@theintelligencer.net, Gen. Mgr., The Intelligencer/Wheeling News-Register, WV, Wheeling
Narendra, K.
dailypratap@gmail.com, Ed., DAILY PRATAP, New Delhi
Narkevich, Uladizimir B.
reklama@zvyazda.minsk.by, Ed., ZVYAZDA, Minsk
Narron, Worth (919) 829-4715
wnarron@newsobserver.com, Circ. Mgr., State, The News & Observer, NC, Raleigh
Narumi, Seiji
narumi1130@toonippo.co.jp, Ed., TO-O NIPPO, Aomori, Tohoku
Nase, Dan (740) 681-4333
dnase@nncogannett.com, Adv. Dir., Eagle-Gazette Media, OH, Lancaster
Nash, Steve
snash@richmond.edu, Journ. Chair, University of Richmond, VA, Richmond
Nash, Robert L.
tiptontribune@elwoodpublishing.com, Pub., Tipton County Tribune, IN, Tipton
Nash, John 203-354-1051
Managing Sports Editor, The Hour Publishing Co., CT, Norwalk
Nash, Bob
elpub@elwoodpublishing.com, Pub., Elwood Publishing Co., Inc., IN, Elwood
Nasir, Abbas
abbas.nasir@dawn.com, Ed., DAWN, Karachi
Naslund, Jimmie
jimmie.naslund@allehanda.se, Editor in Chief, TIDNINGEN ANGERMANLAND, Ornskoldsvik
Naso, Jon (973) 569-7141
Director of Photography, North Jersey Media Group, NJ, Woodland Park
Nassar, Douglas 432-0394
Editorial Dir., DIARIO DE SUCRE, Carupano, Sucre
Nassiri, Jane
janen@rtnda.org, Exec. Dir., Radio Television Digital News Association, VA, Fredericksburg
Natecz, Krzysztof
krzysztof.natecz@mediaregionalne.pl, Dir., GLOS KOSZALINSKI, Koszalin
Natera, Alvaro Feb-34
Editorial Dir., EL BOLIVARENSE, Ciudad Bolivar, Bolivar
Nathan, Vaithya
info@newindpress.com, Ed., DINAMANI, Chennai, Tamil Nadu
Nathan, Dominic
dominic@sph.com.sg, Ed., THE NEW PAPER, Singapore
Nation, Laura
lnation@dailyhome.com, Lifestyles Ed., The Daily Home, AL, Talladega
Nations, Jeff (540) 465-5137
jnations@nvdaily.com, Sports Ed., Northern Virginia Daily, VA, Strasburg
Naughton, John 928-474-5251
jnaughton@payson.com, Publisher - Payson Roundup, WorldWest LLC, KS, Lawrence
Nauman, Barbara (401) 277-7623
bnauman@projo.com, Vice Pres., Circ., The Providence Journal, RI, Providence
Nauss, Don
don.nauss@detroitnews.com, Managing Editor, The Detroit News, MI, Detroit
Nauss-Redden, Pam (902) 426-1134
pnauss@herald.ca, Mktg. Mgr., The Chronicle Herald, NS, Halifax
Nava, Antonio (213) 291-9986
antonio@agenciapi.com, Ed., Agencia Prensa Internacional Inc., CA, Los Angeles
Nava Stenner, Juan G.
lavozdedurango@yahoo.com.mx, Dir., La Voz de Durango, Durango, Durango
Navarrete, Carlos R. Menendez
diario@megamedia.com.mx, Gen. Mgr., DIARIO DE YUCATAN, Merida, Yucatan
Navas, Luis 31-1811
informad@telcel.net.ve, Gen. Mgr., EL INFORMADOR, Barquisimeto, Lara
Nay, Meta L.
meta@kwnews.com, Vice Pres., Mktg., Keister Williams Newspaper Services, Inc., VA, Charlottesville
Naymik, Mark (216) 999-4849
Political Writer, The Plain Dealer, OH, Cleveland
Nazem, Ali (415) 293-8464
info@metrosn.com, Sr. Vice Pres., Wetern Sales Region, Metro Newspaper Advertising Services, Inc., CA, San Francisco
Nazem, Ali (415) 293-8464
ali@metrosn.com, Sr. Vice Pres., Metro-Puck Comics Network - San Francisco, CA, CA, San Francisco
Nazem, Ali
ali@metrosn.com, Sr. Vice Pres., Western Sales, Metro Newspaper Advertising Services, Inc. Sunday Magazine Network - San Francisco, CA, CA, San Francisco
Nazemetz, Patricia M.
patricia.nazemetz@usa.xerox.com, Vice Pres., HR, Xerox Corp., CT, Norwalk
Ndembiyembe, Paul C.
cameroon-tribune@cameroon-tribune.cm, MD, CAMEROON TRIBUNE, Yaounde
Ndlangamandla, Musa
chiefeditor@observer.org.sz, Ed. in Chief, SWAZI OBSERVER, Mbabane
NeCastro, Joseph G. (513) 977-3833
joe.necastro@scripps.com, Exec. Vice Pres., Scripps Network Interactive, E. W. Scripps Co., OH, Cincinnati
NeSmith, William H. Dink
dnesmith@cninewspapers.com, Pres., Community Newspapers, Inc., GA, Athens
Neal, Dennis (540) 213-9128
dneal@newsleader.com, Editorial Page Ed., The News Leader, VA, Staunton
Neal, Jeff
jneal@somerset-kentucky.com, News Ed., The Commonwealth-Journal, KY, Somerset
Neale, Guy 830930
Adv. Mgr., DORSET ECHO, Weymouth, Dorset
Nealy-Brown, Jounice (727) 893-8289
nealy@tampabay.com, Staff-Commun. Mgr., Tampa Bay Times, FL, Saint Petersburg
Necaelsan, Board
bni@nt.nl, Ed., HARSTAD TIDENDE, Harstad
Nedbalek, Wayne (979) 731-4684
wayne.nedbalek@theeagle.com, Direct Mail Mgr., The Eagle, TX, Bryan
Nedeljkovic, Nebojsa
borba@bitsyu.net, Ed. in Chief, BORBA, Belgrade
Nedved, Marissa
mknedved0@frostburg.edu, Business Manager, The Bottom Line, MD, Frostburg
Needham, Bob (734) 994-6841
bneedham@annarbornews.com, Film/Theater Ed., The Ann Arbor News, MI, Ann Arbor
Neely, Richard A. (804) 775-2723
rneely@timesdispatch.com, Circ. Mgr., Sales/Serv., Richmond Times-Dispatch, VA, Richmond
Neese, Jo
jneese@publicitas.com, Branch Dir., Publicitas North America, Inc., TX, Dallas
Negrea, Ruxandra
ruxandra.negrea@azi.ro, Ed. in Chief, AZI, Bucharest
Neiber, Paul
contact@best-testproducts.com, Pres., Union Rubber, Inc., NJ, Trenton
Neilsen, Brian (217) 238-6856
bneilsen@jg-tc.com, Sports Ed., Times-Courier, IL, Mattoon
Neilson, Tony
tony.neilson@oamarumail.co.nz, Gen. Mgr., THE OAMARU MAIL, Oamaru
Neininger, Norbert
neininger@shn.ch, Ed. in Chief, SCHAFFHAUSER NACHRICHTEN, Schaffhausen
Neira Ruiz, Reinaldo
rneira@mercurio.cl, Dir., La Estrella de Arica, Arica
Nelke, Mark (208) 664-0239
sports@cdapress.com, Sports Ed., Coeur d'Alene Press, ID, Coeur d'Alene
Nellessen-Lara, Lisa
news@stevenspointjournal.com, Editorial Page Ed., Stevens Point Journal, WI, Stevens Point
Nelson, John (845) 437-4836
jrnelson@poughkee.gannett.com, Local Ed., Poughkeepsie Journal, NY, Poughkeepsie
Nelson, Michael
mnelson@journalstar.com, Ed., Lincoln Journal Star, NE, Lincoln
Nelson, Wayne
wnelson@gfherald.com, Sports Ed., Grand Forks Herald, ND, Grand Forks
Nelson, Todd
tnelson@hanfordsentinel.com, Prodn. Mgr., Mailroom, The Sentinel, CA, Hanford
Nelson, Pam
prnelson@cnhi.com, Pub., The News Press, OK, Stillwater
Nelson, Catherine (802) 775-5511
Gen. Mgr., Rutland Herald, VT, Rutland
Nelson, Don (706) 208-2214
don.nelson@onlineathens.com, Bus./Finance Ed., Athens Banner-Herald, GA, Athens
Nelson, DuWayne ext. 602
Circ. Mgr., New Castle News, PA, New Castle
Nelson, Clay
bgchief@isu.edu, Idaho State Univ., ID, Pocatello
Nelson, Catherine (802) 479-0191 ext. 1131
catherine.nelson@timesargus.com, Gen. Mgr., The Times Argus, VT, Barre
Nelson, Paula (352) 544-5203
pnelson@hernandotoday.com, Special Sections Ed., Hernando Today, FL, Brooksville
Nelson, Shelley (715) 395-5022
snelson@superiortelegram.com, Asst. Ed., The Daily Telegram, WI, Superior
Nelson, Lauren (209) 369-7035 ext. 216
laurenn@lodinews.com, Lodi Living Ed., Lodi News-Sentinel, CA, Lodi
Nelson, Loren (760) 740-3551
lnelson@nctimes.com, Sports Ed., North County Times, CA, Escondido
Nelson, David (360) 377-3711
dnelson@kitsapsun.com, Ed., Kitsap Sun, WA, Bremerton
Nelson, Kathy Webb (416) 947-2258
Asst. Mgr., News Research, Sun Media Corporation/Toronto Sun Syndicate Sales, ON, Toronto
Nelson, Leah (907)-523-2274
leah.nelson@juneauempire.com, Advertising Manager, Juneau Empire, AK, Juneau
Nelson, DeAnna (573) 471-1137
dnelson@standard-democrat.com, Adv. Mgr., Standard Democrat, MO, Sikeston
Nelson, Tom
nelsont@elon.edu, Assoc. Prof., Elon University, NC, Elon
Nelson, Jim (641) 792-3121 ext. 612
jnelson@newtondailynews.com, Pub., Newton Daily News, IA, Newton
Nelson, Dean
deannelson@pointloma.edu, Journalism Dir., Point Loma Nazarene University, CA, San Diego
Nelson, Marietta
nelson@pdclarion.com, Bus. Mgr., Princeton Daily Clarion, IN, Princeton
Nelson, Patricia (260) 563-2131
Bus. Mgr., The Peru Tribune, IN, Peru
Nelson, Paul E.
paul.nelson.1@ndsu.edu, Prof./Head, North Dakota State University, ND, Fargo
Nelson, Scott (203) 575-8040
Naugatuck Valley Cmty. Tech. College, CT, Waterbury
Nelson, Ken 951-368-9201
knelson@pe.com, SVP Advertising and Interactive Dev, The Press-Enterprise, CA, Riverside
Nelson-Hutchinson, Angelyn (801) 237-2132
angie@desnews.com, Features Ed., Deseret News, UT, Salt Lake City
Nemec, Nancy
nnemec@greeleytrib.com, Editorial Page Ed., Greeley Daily Tribune, CO, Greeley
Nemesio, Jorge Ricardo 431-400
eldiario@infovia.com.ar, Ed., El Diario, Santa Rosa, Provincia de La Pampa
Nemeth, Peter
nemethp@nepszava.hu, Ed. in Chief, NEPSZAVA, Budapest, Pest
Nemeth, Mike (831) 754-4280
mnemeth@salinas.gannett.com, Sr. News Ed., The Salinas Californian, CA, Salinas
Nephew, Jim
jnephew@aztrib.com, Local Sales Manager, East Valley Tribune, AZ, Tempe
Ner, Tick
mail.mercury@ruralpress.com, Ed., MAITLAND MERCURY
Nergaard, Richard
richard.nergaard@rbt.no, Ed., ROMSDALS BUDSTIKKE, Molde
Nesbitt, Mark
mark.nesbitt@tns-mi.com, Pres., TNS Media Intelligence, NY, New York
Nesis, Tom
tnesis@tribune.com, Licensing Mgr., Tribune Media Services, IL, Chicago
Ness, Douglas (360) 735-4502
doug.ness@columbian.com, CFO, The Columbian, WA, Vancouver
Nessel, Lee 321-242-3640
lnessel@floridatoday.com, Enterprise Editor/breaking news, military, religion, Florida Today, FL, Melbourne
Nethercutt, Judy (501) 378-3430
jnethercutt@wehco.com, Bus. Mgr., Arkansas Democrat-Gazette, AR, Little Rock
Neuharth, Dave (877) 373-3142
djneuharth@aol.com, Executve Director, Community Papers of Florida, FL, Belleview
Neuhaus, Eric (212) 362-4739
eric_neuhaus@yahoo.com, Rep., Get Fit with The World's Fittest Man, NY, New York
Nevarez, Manny
mnevarez@skagitpublshing.com, Circ. Dir., Skagit Valley Herald, WA, Mount Vernon
Neves, Christine 860/701-4250
c.neves@theday.com, Director of Advertising, The Day Publishing Company, CT, New London
Neville, Hugh C.
hugh.neville@richmond-graphic.com, CEO, Richmond/Graphic Products, Inc., RI, Smithfield
Neville, Bill (205) 934-6691
Univ. of Alabama at Birmingham, AL, Birmingham
Neville, Scott (318) 487-6467
sneville@thetowntalk.com, Prodn. Mgr., The Town Talk, LA, Alexandria
Nevling, Tonya J. (717) 291-8680
humanresources@lnpnews.com, Mgr., HR, Intelligencer Journal/Lancaster New Era/Sunday News, PA, Lancaster
Newby, John
ha@heraldargus.com, Pub., The Times, IL, Ottawa
Newby, John (309) 797-0322
jnewby@qconline.com, Circ. Dir., The Rock Island Argus, IL, Rock Island
Newcom, Scot (803) 644-2350
snewcom@aikenstandard.com, Circ. Dir., Aiken Standard, SC, Aiken

Newcom, Amy..............................ext. 5163
amy.newcomb@pharostribune.com, Prodn. Graphic Artist, Pharos-Tribune, IN, Logansport
Newell, Ben..........................(202) 319-5779
editor@cuatower.com, Catholic Univ. of America, DC, Washington
Newell, Pat............................(607) 337-3078
pat@evesun.com, Sports Ed., The Evening Sun, NY, Norwich
Newfield, Amanda..................(909) 869-3530
The Poly Post, CA, Pomona
Newgate, J. Baxter
megalomedia@lawtv.com, Pres., Megalo Media, NY, New York
Newhouse, Robyn A. ....(413) 788-1021
rnewhouse@repub.com, Asst. to Pub., The Republican, MA, Springfield
Newhouse, John
jnewhouse@hearstnp.com, Pub., The Beaumont Enterprise, TX, Beaumont
Newhouse, Donald E.
dnewhouse@boothmichigan.com, Pres., Booth Newspapers, Inc., MI, Grand Rapids
Newhouse, David ....(717) 255-8299
dnewhouse@patriot-news.com, Editor., The Patriot-News, PA, Mechanicsburg
Newland, Mike ....(563) 588-5629
mnewland@wcinet.com, Circ. Mgr., Telegraph Herald, IA, Dubuque
Newman, John T.
j.newman@att.net, Pres., Newman International, LLC, KS, Prairie Village
Newman, Mitchell
menewman@mitchellsny.com, Owner, Mitchell's, NY, Long Island City
Newman, Chuck
cnewma17@jaguar.com, Webmaster, Global Information Network, NY, New York
Newman, Julie ....(479) 785-7704
jnewman@swtimes.com, Adv. Mgr., Classified, Times Record, AR, Fort Smith
Newman, Stanley
snpuzz@aol.com, Pres./Ed. in Chief, American Crossword Federation, NY, Massapequa Park
Newman, Arthur E.
arthur.newman@healthstream.com, Sr. Vice Pres., Finance, HealthStream, TN, Nashville
Newman, Dan...........................(734) 764-0558
Univ. of Michigan, MI, Ann Arbor
Newman, David ....(801) 625-4374
dnewman@standard.net, Adv. Mgr., Classified, Standard-Examiner, UT, Ogden
Newman, Harry 330-298-2002
hnewman@recordpub.com, Marketing Director, Record Publishing Co., OH, Ravenna
Newman, Brant......................(724)222-2200
bnewman@observer-reporter.com, Asst. News Ed., Observer-Reporter, PA, Washington
Newman, Harry E...........................ext. 3109
Adv. Dir., Record-Courier, OH, Ravenna
Newman, Ian...........................(780) 429-5575
inewman@thejournal.canwest.com, Adv. Mgr., Retail Multi-Market Sales, Edmonton Journal, AB, Edmonton
Newman, Tom..............................ext. 3043
Prodn. Foreman, Pressroom, The Intelligencer, PA, Doylestown
Newton, Steven......................(757) 547-5400
info@newtonmedia.com, Pres., Newton Media Associates, Inc., VA, Chesapeake
Newton, Dawn ....(252) 329-9601
dnewton@reflector.com, Creative Servs. Mgr., The Daily Reflector, NC, Greenville
Newton, Gail...........................(501) 378-3562
Adv. Supvr., Opns., Arkansas Democrat-Gazette, AR, Little Rock
Ney, Bill ....ext. 123
billney@sanduskyregister.com, Circ. Dir., Sandusky Register, OH, Sandusky
Ng, Jeffrey
djnews.hk@dowjones.com, Correspondent, Dow Jones Newswires - Hong Kong, Hong Kong, Hong Kong
Nguba, Saidi
uhuru@intafrica.com, Mng. Ed., UHURU/MZALENDO, Dar Es Salaam
Ngugi, Michael
mngugi@nation.co.ke, Adv. Mgr., DAILY NATION, Nairobi
Nguyen, Anne..........................(609) 272-7430
anguyen@pressofac.com, Marketing Manager, The Press of Atlantic City, NJ, Pleasantville
Nguyen, J. Tuyet
natuyet@aol.com, English Correspondent United Nations and New York, German Press Agency, NY, New York
NiYamoto, Akahiko
ecntct@nikkei.co.jp, Ed., NIHON KEIZAI SHIMBUN, Nagoya, Chubu
Nicado, Idelle.........................(530) 406-6220
dnicado@dailydemocrat.com, Circ. Mgr., The Daily Democrat, CA, Woodland
Nicholas, Tim..........................(601) 925-3462
Mississippi College, MS, Clinton
Nicholas, Betty 708-909-5809
bnicholas@specializedmediaservices.net, Self-Syndicator, The Usual Suspects/Mystery Fiction Lineup, IL, Libertyville
Nicholls, Murray
mail.westernadvocate@ruralpress.com, Ed., WESTERN ADVOCATE
Nichols, Peggy
pnichols@artbeats.com, Global Dist. Mgr., Artbeats, OR, Myrtle Creek
Nichols, Dave
nbfdavid@sbcglobal.net, Mgr., Opns., NB Finishing, Inc., IL, Schaumburg
Nichols, Skip
snichols@eastoregonian.com, Managing Editor, East Oregonian, OR, Pendleton
Nichols, Daniel
news@morningsentinel.com, Adv. Mgr., Morning Sentinel, IL, Centralia
Nichols, Denice
info@pulsesearch.com, Vice Pres., Sales, Pulse Research, Inc., OR, Portland
Nick, Michael
lortiz@pentawave.com, Vice Pres., Sales, Pentawave, AZ, Scottsdale
Nickels, Mary
mary@bryantimes.com, Adv. Mgr., Nat'l, The Bryan Times, OH, Bryan
Nickerson, Glen ....(941) 206-1262
gnickerson@sun-herald.com, Advertising Director, Charlotte Sun, FL, Charlotte Harbor
Nickles, Brenda ....(518) 943-6953
bnickles@resgisterstar.com, Prodn. Mgr., Mailroom, Register-Star, NY, Hudson
Nicks, Nicholas.......................(608) 791-8337
nnicks@lacrossetribune.com, Circ. Dir., La Crosse Tribune, WI, La Crosse
Nickson, Mark............(203) 924-7000 ext. 4374
mnickson@dacsystems.com, Pres., DAC Systems, CT, Shelton
Nickson, Mark............(203) 924-7000 ext. 4374
mnickson@dacsystems.com, Pres., DAC Systems, CT, Shelton
Nicolas, Lola
lolanicholas@dgabc.com.br, Ed., Diario do Grande ABC, Santo Andre, Sao Paulo
Niebel, Kelly L...................................ext. 106
Features Ed., The Huron Daily Tribune, MI, Bad Axe
Nielsen, Kirsti
kirsti.nielsen@ranablad.no, Ed. in Chief, RANA BLAD, Mo
Nielsen, Thomas W.
tnielsen@brodiesystem.com, Pres., Brodie System, Inc., NJ, Linden
Nielsen, Roger ....(706) 208-2225
roger.nielsen@onlineathens.com, Metro Ed., Athens Banner-Herald, GA, Athens
Nielsen, Alvin
alvin@thesheridanpress.com, Prodn. Mgr., Systems, The Sheridan Press, WY, Sheridan
Nielsen, Bruce.........................(309) 686-3175
bnielsen@pjstar.com, Circ. Mgr., Journal Star, IL, Peoria
Niemann, Paul..........................(217) 653-7058
niemann7@aol.com, Syndicated Columnist, Red, White & True Mysteries, IL, Quincy
Niemetz, Agnes 646-367-4782
aginiemetz@aol.com, Gen. Sec., Foreign Press Association, NY, New York
Niemeyer, Gunther
schaumburger-zeitung@t-online.de, Proprietor, SCHAUMBURG-LIPPISCHE LANDES-ZEITUNG, Buckeburg
Niemeyer, Diane
dniemeyer@dailyunion.com, Mktg. Dir., Daily Jefferson County Union, WI, Fort Atkinson
Niemeyer, Julia
j.niemeyer@dewezet.de, Ed. in Chief, DEISTER-und WESERZEITUNG, Hameln
Nieporte, Monica
info@logandaily.com, Ed., Logan Daily News, OH, Logan
Nieri Boggiano, Atilio 232 112
lavozica1918@yahoo.es, Dir., La Voz de ICA, Ica
Nierman, Dennis E.
dnierman@alfaquest.com, Pres., alfaQuest Technologies, IL, Rolling Meadows
Nigro, Richard ....(516) 485-6655
info@rollemusa.com, Vice Pres., Sales, Rollem Corp. of America, NY, Hempstead
Niiranen, Valtteri
valtteri.niiranen@enpa.be, Dir., European Newspaper Publishers' Association, 1050 Bruxelles
Nikpour, Katie..........................(501) 378-3845
Adv. Mgr., Classified Inside Sales, Arkansas Democrat-Gazette, AR, Little Rock
Nilan, Steve
steve.nilan@dtint.com, Vice president, marketing, Digital Technology International, MN, Saint Paul
Nilson, Barbara
nlbarba@aol.com, retired, Washington Press Association, WA, Renton
Nilsson, Charli
charli.nilsson@vt.se, Ed. in Chief, VASTERVIKS-TIDNINGEN, Vastervik
Nilsson, Alf
alf.nilsson@solna.com, Contact, Solna Offset AB, Jarfalla
Nilsson, Lars
lars.nilsson@unt.se, Ed., UPSALA NYA TIDNING, Uppsala
Nilsson, Charli
charli.nilsson@nt.se, Ed., NORRKOPINGS TIDNINGAR, Norrkoping
Nimrodi, Offer
inbal@ildc.co.il, Pub., MA'ARIV EVENING
Ninestine, Tom
tomninestine@pensacolanewsjournal.com, Content Ed., Pensacola News Journal, FL, Pensacola
Nirmala, M.
mnirmala@sph.com.sg, Ed., TAMIL MURASU, Singapore
Nisenholtz, Martin A.................(212) 556-1234
Sr. Vice Pres., Digital Opns., The New York Times Co., NY, New York
Nistor, Catalin
contact@evenimentul.ro, Ed., EVENIMENTUL, Iasi
Nix, Dusty
dnix@ledger-enquirer.com, Assoc. Ed., Columbus Ledger-Enquirer, GA, Columbus
Nixon, Charity ....(912) 226-1621
Thomas College, GA, Thomasville
Nixon, Maggie
mnixon@thepilotnews.com, Mng. Ed., Pilot News, IN, Plymouth
Nixon, Steve ....(306) 651-6301
swna@swna.com, Exec. Dir., Saskatchewan Weekly Newspapers Association, SK, Saskatoon
Nizami, Arif
editor@nation.com.pk, Ed., THE NATION, Lahore, Lahore District
Nizami, Majid
mnizami@nawaiwaqt.com.pk, Ed., NAWA-I-WAQT, Lahore, Lahore District
Nobel, Carl............................(479) 785-7760
cnobel@swtimes.com, IT Dir., Times Record, AR, Fort Smith
Noble, Kim ....(215) 345-3088
knoble@phillyburbs.com, Adv. Dir., The Intelligencer, PA, Doylestown
Noble, Kim
knoble@calkins-media.com, Dir., Adv./Mktg., Calkins Media, PA, Levittown
Noble, Kim ....(215) 949-4120
knoble@phillyburbs.com, Adv. Dir., Burlington County Times, NJ, Willingboro
Nobles, Doug ....(318) 362-0238
dnobles@thenewsstar.com, Prodn. Dir., The News-Star, LA, Monroe
Noce, Dorena ....(416) 847-2013
dnoce@bbm.ca, Corp. Scrvs., BBM Canada, ON, Toronto
Nocito, Marge
atlanticcapereview9@gmail.com, Atlantic Cape Cmty. College, NJ, Mays Landing
Noda, Debbie ....(209) 578-2322
dnoda@modbee.com, Chief Photographer, The Modesto Bee, CA, Modesto
Noe, Mike ....(303) 892-2436
noem@rockymountainnews.com, Internet News Ed., Rocky Mountain News, CO, Denver
Noel, Jon 252-407-9931
jnoel@rmtelegram.com, Retail Sales & Marketing Mgr., Rocky Mount Telegram, NC, Rocky Mount
Noel, Sharrye..........................270-783-3265
Mgr., Educ. Serv., Daily News, KY, Bowling Green
Noel, Jon M.
jnoel@brownpublishing.com, Pub., Fairborn Daily Herald, OH, Xenia
Noftle, Randy ....(336) 727-7330
rnoftle@wsjournal.com, Dir., HR, Winston-Salem Journal, NC, Winston-Salem
Noguchi, Eiichi
staff@sannichi-ybs.co.jp, Pres., YAMANASHI NICHI-NICHI SHIMBUN, Kofu City, Chubu
Noguera, Yanancy
ynoguera@nacion.com, Dir., LA NACION, San Jose
Nohejl, Denise........................(352) 544-5206
dnohejl@hernandotoday.com, Office Mgr., Hernando Today, FL, Brooksville
Nolan, Christopher
chris.nolan@publicitas.com, Reg'l Mgr., Publicitas North America, Inc., IL, Chicago
Nolan, Jim ....(303) 892-2900
jnolan@denvernewspaperagency.com, Dir., Commun., Rocky Mountain News, CO, Denver
Nolan, Jim ....(212) 969-7599
jdnolan@hearst.com, Sunday Comics Mgr., King Features Syndicate, NY, New York
jdnolan@hearst.com, Sunday Comics Mgr., North America Syndicate, NY, New York
Nolan, William 419-724-6207
bnolan@toledoblade.com, Director of HR and Labor Relations, The Blade, OH, Toledo
Nolen, Wes.............................(270) 745-5044
Western Kentucky Univ., KY, Bowling Green
Noone, Dennis..........................775-881-1221
dnoone@nevadaappeal.com, Editor, Nevada Appeal, NV, Carson City
Norbert, Molnar
redakcia@ujszo.com, Ed. in Chief, UJ SZO, Bratislava 1
Nordahl, Karl-Einar
karl-einar@blv.no, Ed. in Chief, BLADET VESTERALEN, Sortland
Norden, Kevin ....(815) 937-3342
knorden@daily-journal.com, Prodn. Dir., The Daily Journal, IL, Kankakee
Norden, Chris ....ext. 5605
Promo. Coord., The Post and Courier, SC, Charleston
Norder, Lois
lnorder@star-telegram.com, Mng. Ed., Investigations, Fort Worth Star-Telegram, TX, Fort Worth
Nordmark, Frode
frode@ba-avis.no, Adv. Mgr., BROENNOEYSUND AVIS, Broennoeysund
Nordstrom, Deborah
dnordstrom@cctimes.com, Mktg., The Argus, CA, Fremont
Norlock, George
george.norlock@ott.sunpub.com, Circ. Mgr., The Ottawa Sun, ON, Ottawa
Norman, Don...........................(662) 323-1642
sdnpub@starkvilledailynews.com, Mgr., Mktg./Promo., Starkville Daily News, MS, Starkville
Norman, Dean
dnorman@bge.net, Artist/Owner, Beaver Creek Features, OH, Cleveland
Norman, Jeremy
sports@southwesttimes.com, Sports Ed., The Southwest Times, VA, Pulaski
Norman, Don...........................(662) 323-1642
sdnpub@bellsouth.net, Pub., Daily Times Leader, MS, West Point
Norman, Michael......................(216) 999-4109
Online Entertainment Editor, The Plain Dealer,

OH, Cleveland
Norrgrann, Stefan
stefan.norrgrann@nyan.ax, Adv. Mgr., NYA ALAND, Mariehamn
Norris, Michael
mnorris@marketresearch.com, Sr. Ed., Simba Information, CT, Stamford
Norris, Bob ....(865) 981-1143
City/Metro Ed., The Daily Times, TN, Maryville
Norris, Jane Dunlap ....(434) 978-7249
jnorris@dailyprogress.com, Entertainment Ed., The Daily Progress, VA, Charlottesville
Northern, Reginald ....(615) 726-8962
rnorthern@tennessean.com, Research Mgr., The Tennessean, TN, Nashville
Northington, Richard ....(870) 543-1435
dnorthington@pbcommercial.com, Prodn. Foreman, Composing, Pine Bluff Commercial, AR, Pine Bluff
Northover, Marti
mnorthover@syndicatedadfeatures.com, General Office Manager, Syndicated Ad Features, Inc., MA
Northrop, Thomas P...................(724) 223-2626
tnorthrop@observer-reporter.com, Pres./Pub., Observer-Reporter, PA, Washington
Northrop, Lucy S. ....(724) 222-2200
lnorthrop@observer-reporter.com, Director of News, Observer-Reporter, PA, Washington
Northup, Thomas.......................401-225-6061
tom@motterstitch.com, President, Motterstitch Company, Inc., RI, Charlestown
Northup, Linda 401-364-6061
linda@motterstitch.com, Office Administrator, Motterstitch Company, Inc., RI, Charlestown
Norton, Mindy
mnorton@michigannewspapers.com, Sunday Ed., Morning Sun, MI, Mount Pleasant
Norton, Will
wnorton1@unl.edu, Dean/Prof., University of Nebraska-Lincoln, NE, Lincoln
Norton, John
jnorton@pioneergroup.com, Pub., The Pioneer - Big Rapids, MI, Big Rapids
Norton, Barbara ....ext. 554
bnorton@freemanonline.com, Adv. Dir., Daily Freeman, NY, Kingston
Norup, Lars
lars@bergske.dk, Ed., VIBORG STIFTS FOLKEBLAD, Viborg, Jutland
Norwood, Kim..............(785) 822-1442 ext. 209
knorwood@saljournal.com, Adv. Mgr., The Salina Journal, KS, Salina
Noseworthy, Al ....(909) 489-9443
a_noseworthy@dailybulletin.com, Automotive Ed., Inland Valley Daily Bulletin, CA, Ontario
Nostrand, Tim..........................(973) 569-7117
Projects Editor, North Jersey Media Group, NJ, Woodland Park
Nothaft, Keira..........................(602) 444-4850
keira.nothaft@arizonarepublic.com, Deputy Mng. Ed., Page One, The Arizona Republic, AZ, Phoenix
Notter, Randy
rnotter@journalregister.com, Pub., Daily Local News, PA, West Chester
Notter, Randy ....(215) 854-4194
rnotter@phillynews.com, Adv. Sales Devel./Mktg. Dir. (Philadelphia Newspapers Inc.), The Philadelphia Inquirer, PA, Philadelphia
Novak, Kim.............................(519) 426-5710
Women's/Society Ed., The Simcoe Reformer, ON, Simcoe
Novak, Scott
scott.novak@leaderpub.com, Sports Ed., Dowagiac Daily News, MI, Dowagiac
Novo, Juan Martinez
redacciontf@lagacetadecanarias.com, Dir., La Gaceta De Canarias, Los Majuelos, Santa Cruz de Tenerife
Nowicki, Helen
retail@brenhambanner.com, Adv. Mgr., Retail, Brenham Banner-Press, TX, Brenham
Noziska, Natalie.......................(530) 896-7707
nnoziska@chicoer.com, Asst. to Pub., Chico Enterprise-Record, CA, Chico
Nufer, Kathy..................................ext. 290
knufer@appleton.gannett.com, School Ed., The Post-Crescent, WI, Appleton
Nugent, Wendy
wnugent@thekansan.com, Food/Lifestyle Ed., The Newton Kansan, KS, Newton
Nunez, Louis
pressgripper@earthlink.net, Owner, G.T. Specialties, NM, Albuquerque
Nunez de Leon, Gonzalo
nunezdiaz@infosel.net.mx, Ed./Dir., EL SOL DE CHIAPAS, Tuxtla Gutierrez, Chiapas
Nunn, Chuck ....(208) 677-8786
cnunn@southidahopress.com, Sports Ed., South Idaho Press, ID, Burley
Nurmela, Makko
makko.nurmela@kansanuutiset.fi, Adv. Mgr., KANSAN UUTISET, Helsinki
Nusbaum, Mark E.
mark.nusbaum@cjonline.com, Pub., The Topeka Capital-Journal, KS, Topeka
Nussbaum, Kim 316-268-6503
knussbaum@wichitaeagle.com, Pres. and publisher, The Wichita Eagle, KS, Wichita
Nussbaum, Kim
nussbaumk@reporternews.com, Pres./Pub., Abilene Reporter-News, TX, Abilene
Nusser, Nancy
nussernl@jmu.edu, Asst. Prof., James Madison University, VA, Harrisonburg
Nusunginya, Vincent
webmaster@peninsulaclarion.com, New Media Dir., Peninsula Clarion, AK, Kenai
Nusz, Nancy ....(530) 406-6224
Pre Press Mgr., The Daily Democrat, CA, Woodland
Nutt, Charles W.
classified@thedailyjournal.com, Ed., The Daily Journal, NJ, Vineland
Nuzum, Scott
snuzum@fstribune.com, Sports Ed., The Fort Scott Tribune, KS, Fort Scott
Nyce, Henry
hnyce@newsitem.com, Pub., The News Item, PA, Shamokin
Nydick, David ....(516) 921-4611
danynews@aol.com, Pres./Ed., DANY News Service, NY, New York
Nyland, Anders
anders.nyland@ba.no, Ed., BERGENS ARBEIDERBLAD, Bergen
Nyland, Anders
anders.nyland@ba.no, Ed. in Chief, BERGENSAVISEN, Bergen
Nylund, Debbie
info@mcink.com, Pres., Miller-Cooper Co., KS, Merriam
Nysko, Sheila.............(201) 440-2500 ext. 7042
sheila.nysko@agfa.com, Dir. Bus. Dev., Agfa, Inc., NJ, Ridgefield Park

O

O'Briant, Tim..........................(803) 644-2380
tobriant@aikenstandard.com, Mng. Ed., Aiken Standard, SC, Aiken
O'Brien, Neal ....(570) 628-6117
Home Delivery Mgr., Republican Herald, PA, Pottsville
O'Brien, Michael........................312-321-7760
mpobrien@usaweekend.com, Senior VP/Advertising, USA WEEKEND - McLean, VA, VA, McLean
O'Brien, John...................................ext. 13
jjobrien@njpa.org, Exec. Dir., New Jersey Newspaper Network (NJNN), NJ, West Trenton
O'Brien, John J.
jjobrien@njpa.org, Exec. Dir., New Jersey Press Association, NJ, West Trenton
O'Brien, Kevin ....(216) 999-4146
Chief Editorial Writer, The Plain Dealer, OH, Cleveland
O'Brien, Michael
mpobrien@usaweekend.com, Midwest Adv. Dir., USA WEEKEND - Chicago, IL, IL, Chicago
O'Brien, Beth...........................(530) 852-0225
betho@goldcountrymedia.com, Adv. Mgr., Auburn Journal, Inc., CA, Auburn
O'Brien, Michael
mpobrien@usaweekend.com, Midwest Adv. Dir., USA WEEKEND - Chicago, IL, IL, Chicago
O'Brien, Dan ....(978) 970-4642
dobrien@lowellsun.com, Bus. Ed., The Sun, MA, Lowell
O'Brien, Gerry
gerry.o'brien@lee.net, Regional Editor, Independent Record, MT, Helena
O'Brien, Dave ....(204) 943-6548
Dave.Obrien@freepress.mb.ca, Columnist, Winnipeg Free Press, MB, Winnipeg
O'Brien, Bill ....(231) 933-1493
bobrien@record-eagle.com, Bus. Ed., Record-Eagle, MI, Traverse City
O'Callaghan, Kenneth .....(847) 981-9399 ext. 204
ocallagk@corp.inxintl.com, Sr. Vice Pres.-Metal Div., INX International Ink Co., IL, Schaumburg
O'Callahan, Patrick ....(253) 597-8639
patrick.ocallahan@thenewstribune.com, Editorial Page Editor, The News Tribune, WA, Tacoma
O'Connell, Maureen ....(808) 525-8053
moconnell@honoluluadvertiser.com, Asst. City Ed., Honolulu Star-Advertiser, HI, Honolulu
O'Connell, Jim..........................(719) 636-0263
jim.oconnell@gazette.com, Sports Ed., The Gazette, CO, Colorado Springs
O'Connell, John ....(208) 239-3128
joconnell@journalnet.com, City Ed., Idaho State Journal, ID, Pocatello
O'Connell, Anne
aoconnell@dmg.gannett.com, Bus. Mgr., The Daily Times, MD, Salisbury
O'Connell, Kevin ....(541) 383-0398
Classified Adv. Mgr., The Bulletin, OR, Bend
O'Connell, Jack.........................(718) 767-2582
bbwaa@aol.com, Secretary-Treasurer, Baseball Writers Association of America
O'Connell, Frank ....(847) 490-6000
hollyv@usspi.com, Pres., Sales, U.S. Suburban Press (USSPI), IL, Schaumburg
O'Connell, Michael
michael@mallmarketingmedia.com, Sales Mgr., Mall Marketing Media, UT, Layton
O'Connor, Lona ....(561) 487-5104
lona_oconnor@pbpost.com, Author, journalist, Lona O'Connor, FL, Boca Raton
O'Connor, James
joconnor@brandonsun.com, Mng. Ed., Brandon Sun, MB, Brandon
O'Connor, Trisha.......................(843) 626-0316
toconnor@thesunnews.com, Ed., The Sun News, SC, Myrtle Beach
O'Connor, Mike ....(806) 345-3270
mike.oconnor@amarillo.com, Prodn. Dir., Opns., Amarillo Globe-News, TX, Amarillo
O'Connor, Clint ....(216) 999-4456
Movie Critic, The Plain Dealer, OH, Cleveland
O'Connor, Rory ....(212) 246-0202 ext. 3024
editorial@globalvision.org, CEO/Ed. in Chief, Globalvision News Network, NY, New York
O'Connor, Tom
oconnotp@jmu.edu, Assoc. Prof., James Madison University, VA, Harrisonburg
O'Connor, Rosie
roconnor@chronline.com, HR Dir., The Chronicle, WA, Centralia
O'Donnell, Colin
codonnell@dailyherald.com, Sr. Vice Pres., Director of Content and Strategic Planning, Daily Herald, IL, Arlington Heights
O'Donovan, Betsy ....(704) 261-2223
bodonovan@theej.com, City Ed., The Enquirer-Journal, NC, Monroe
O'Dowd, Nora
features@njtimes.com, Features Ed., The Times, NJ, Trenton
O'Farrill, Romulo
pubcomercial@novedades.com.mx, Pres., THE NEWS, Mexico City, Distrito Federal
O'Farrill, Romulo
editor@aca-novenet.com.mx, Pres./Gen. Dir., Novedades de Acapulco, Acapulco, Guerrero
O'Grady, Patrick ....(603) 543-3100 ext. 111
pogrady@tsvmedia.net, Local News Editor, Eagle Times, NH, Claremont
O'Grady, Beth ....(617) 619-6275
bogrady@bistonherald.com, Adv. Mgr., Classified, Boston Herald, MA, Boston
O'Halloran, James
inquiry@ohalloranagency.com, CEO, O'Halloran Advertising, Inc., CT, Westport
O'Hare, Amy
graphics@neagle.com, Graphics Manager, The Wayne Independent, PA, Honesdale
O'Hare, Michael ....(724) 543-1303 ext. 213
mohare@tribweb.com, Mng. Ed., Leader Times, PA, Kittanning
O'Hearn, Frank
fohearn@alfaquest.com, Dir., Systems Tech., alfaQuest Technologies, IL, Rolling Meadows
O'Keefe, Terry ....ext. 309
terryo@thepublicopinion.com, Farm Ed., Watertown Public Opinion, SD, Watertown
O'Leary, Bob ....(845) 437-4755
boleary@poughkee.gannett.com, Adv. Mgr., Retail, Poughkeepsie Journal, NY, Poughkeepsie
O'Leary, Mike ....(772) 408-5315
mike.oleary@scripps.com, Prodn. Dir., Opns., Treasure Coast News/Press-Tribune, FL, Stuart
O'Loughlin, John
john.oloughlin@latimes.com, EVP/Advertising, Los Angeles Times, CA, Los Angeles
O'Neal, Dori ....(509) 582-1514
doneal@tri-cityherald.com, Arts/Entertainment Ed., Tri-City Herald, WA, Kennewick
O'Neal, Ron ....(818) 788-1488
roneal@unitedmedia.com, Regl. Sales Mgr., Newspaper Enterprise Association (Div. of United Media), NY, New York
roneal@unitedmedia.com, Regl. Sales Mgr., United Feature Syndicate (Div. of United Media), NY, New York
O'Neal, Shawn..........................(208) 885-7825
Univ. of Idaho, ID, Moscow
O'Neal, Patricia ....(620) 408-9906
patricia.oneal@dodgeglobe.com, Circ. Mgr., Dodge City Daily Globe, KS, Dodge City
O'Neal, Ron ....(818) 788-1488
roneal@unitedmedia.com, Mgr., Regl. Sales-West, United Media, OH, Cincinnati
O'Neil, Terry...................................ext. 3060
toneil@herald.ca, Dir., News Admin., The Chronicle Herald, NS, Halifax
O'Neil, Laurence
laurence.oneil@shrm.org, Pres., Media Human Resources Association, VA, Alexandria
O'Neil, Mark ....(978) 970-4807
moneil@lowellsun.com, Pres./Pub., The Sun, MA, Lowell
O'Neil, Melissa ....(509) 582-1554
moneil@tri-cityherald.com, Coord., Promo./Mktg., Tri-City Herald, WA, Kennewick
O'Neill, Alice...........................(847) 446-4082
lafs@aol.com, Mng. Ed., L. A. Features Syndicate, IL, Winnetka
O'Reilly, Kerry
koreilly@tampabay.com, Mgr., Creative Strategy, Tampa Bay Times, FL, Saint Petersburg
O'Rourke, James.......................(617) 224-2344
Regional VP - Atlantic, GateHouse Media Inc., NY, Fairport
O'Rourke, Jennie.......................(518) 445-7200
Albany College of Pharmacy, NY, Albany
O'Sullivan, Michael F.
mosullivan@journalregister.com, Pub., The Saratogian, NY, Saratoga Springs
O'Toole, Tom............................(630) 789-8666
toolbox@svs.com, Contact, Tom O'Toole Communications Group, IL, Burr Ridge
O'Toole, Thomas J.
traveljournalists@hotmail.com, Journalist/Photographer, Tom & Joanne O'Toole, Travel Journalists/Photographers, OH, Willoughby
O'dell, Andrew..........................(314) 935-6713
Washington Univ., MO, Saint Louis
Oakes, Courtney........................(303) 750-7555
coakes@aurorasentinel.com, Sports Ed., Aurora Sentinel, CO, Aurora
Oakland, Mike ....(360) 754-5464
moakland@theolympian.com, Editorial Page Ed., The Olympian, WA, Olympia
Oakley, Karol
production@durantdemocrat.com, Prodn. Mgr., Composing/Pre Press, Durant Daily Democrat, OK, Durant
Oates, Sean ....(973) 569-7159
Web Editor, North Jersey Media Group, NJ, Woodland Park
Oathout, Doug ....(814) 870-1698
doug.oathout@timesnews.com, Mng. Ed.,

News, Erie Times-News, PA, Erie
Obee, Dave............................(250) 380-5201
dobee@te.canwest.com, Editorial Page Ed., Times Colonist, BC, Victoria
Obenchain, Bryan L...................(701) 857-1959
editor@ndweb.com, Ed., Minot Daily News, ND, Minot
Oberlin, Amy
amyo@kpcnews.net, News Ed., Herald-Republican, IN, Angola
Obeso Garcia, Jesus
liberal@moomsa.com.mx, Gen. Mgr., El Liberal del Sur, Coatzacoalcos, Veracruz
Obley, Pat................................941-206-1122
pobley@sun-herald.com, Sports Editor, Charlotte Sun, FL, Charlotte Harbor
Obriqewitsch, Jerry
roadvertising@thedicksonpress.com, Adv. Mgr., Dickinson Press, ND, Dickinson
Oby, Mortan
mortan.oby@amta.no, Ed., AKERSHUS AMTSTIDENDE, Droebak
Ocampo, Nancy
nocampo@latarde.com.co, Ed., Comunicadores del Risaralda Ltd., Pereira, Risaralda
Ockerbloom, Peter...................(617) 929-2104
ockerbloom@globe.com, Adv. Dir., Retail, The Boston Globe, MA, Boston
Oden, Jim
billwesa@circulation.net, Pres., Circulation Development, Inc., MO
Odindo, Joseph
jodindo@nation.co.ke, Ed. Dir. (Grp.), DAILY NATION, Nairobi
Odom, Rod..................1155 Peachtree St., Ste.
Pres.-BellSouth Systems, BellSouth Business, GA, Atlanta
Odom, Marianne.......................210-486-1786
modom@alamo.edu, Advisor, San Antonio College, TX, San Antonio
Odyniec, Fran.................(740) 852-1616 ext. 21
editor@madison-press.com, Mng. Ed., The Madison Press, OH, London
Oelrich, Stacey........................(715) 389-6545
Univ. of Wisconsin Marshfield, WI, Marshfield
Oetama, Jakob
kompas@kompas.com, Pub., KOMPAS, Jakarta, Java
Oetzel, John
joetzel@unm.edu, Chair, University of New Mexico, NM, Albuquerque
Ofakunrin, Remi
infoadvert@punchontheweb.com, Adv. Mgr., THE PUNCH, Lagos
Ogasawara, Toshiaki
jtinter@japantimes.co.jp, Chrmn./Pub., JAPAN TIMES, Tokyo
Ogata, Wendy..........................(801) 237-2128
ogata@desnews.com, Asst. Mng. Ed., Deseret News, UT, Salt Lake City
Ogawara, Tamotsu
oogawr.t@chunichi.co.jp, Pres., NIKKAN KENMIN FUKUI, Fukui, Hokuriku
Ogle, Mark.............................(541) 338-2513
mark.ogle@registerguard.com, Circ. Asst. Dir., The Register-Guard, OR, Eugene
Ogolo, Celesbin
contact@thetidenews.com, Ed., NIGERIAN TIDE/SUNDAY TIDE, Port Harcourt, Rivers
Ogrodnek, Vernon.......................609-272-7222
vogrodnek@pressofac.com, Local Content Producer/Photo, The Press of Atlantic City, NJ, Pleasantville
Ogurcak, Janice.......................(570) 326-1921
jogurcak@LittleLeague.org, Advisor, Lycoming College, PA, Williamsport
Ogurlic, Goran
redakcija@vecernji.net, Ed. in Chief, VECERNJI LIST, Zagreb
Ohlig, Don.............................(714) 258-5600
dohlig@olec.com, Mng. Dir., OLEC, CA, Santa Ana
Ohlman, Tim.............................402 643 7330
Tim.Ohlman@cune.edu, The Sower - Concordia University-Nebraska, NE, Seward
Ohlson, Andreas
andreas.ohlson@metro.se, Mng. Dir., METRO, Stockholm
Ohlsson, Per
sydsvenskan@sydsvenska.se, Ed., SYDSVENSKA DAGBLADET, Malmo
Ojeda Camacho, Armando
webmaster@noroeste.com.mx, Ed./Dir., NOROESTE, Guamuchil, Sinaloa
Ojeda Gonzalez, Francisco
estrategia@edgestion.cl, Sales Mgr., Estrategia, Santiago
Okada, Yuko
okada@shizuokaonline.com, Sec., SHIZUOKA SHIMBUN, Shizuoka, Chubu
Oke, Babafunmilayo..................(212) 237-8308
John Jay College of Criminal Justice, NY, New York
Okeowo, David........................(334) 229-4493
dokeowo@asunet.alasu.edu, Prof./Chair, Alabama State University, AL, Montgomery
Oksanen, Juha
juha.oksanen@@kymensanomat.fi, Ed. in Chief, KYMEN SANOMAT, Kotka
Oksenhorn, Stewart
stewart@aspentimes.com, Arts Ed., The Aspen Times, CO, Aspen
Okuda, Toshiko
info@hokkaido-np.co.jp, Asahikawa Head Officer, HOKKAIDO SHIMBUN, Asahikawa City, Hokkaido
Oladru, Magdlaena
magdlaena.oladru@ziaruldeiasi.ro, Mktg. Asst., ZIARUL DE IASI, Iasi
Older, Mary
circulation@dailydem.com, Bus. Mgr., Fort Madison Daily Democrat, IA, Fort Madison
Oldershaw, James H...................(505) 820-2700
james@dirksvanessen.com, Sr. Vice Pres., Dirks, Van Essen & Murray, NM, Santa Fe
Oldham, Levor
dtinfo@dtint.com, Vice Chrmn., Digital Technology International, UT, Springville
Oldham, Don
info@dtint.com, Pres./CEO, Digital Technology International, UT, Springville
Oldham, R. Troy.......................(435) 797-3279
Lectr., Utah State University, UT, Logan
Oleheiser, Ron
ron.oleheiser@grandrapidsmn.com, Pub., Northern States Circulation Managers Association, MN, Grand Rapids
Olesin, Nancy..........................(508) 626-3928
Features Ed., Metrowest Daily News, MA, Framingham
Oleson, Tom.............................(204) 697-7038
Tom.Oleson@freepress.mb.ca, Columnist, Winnipeg Free Press, MB, Winnipeg
Oliver, Ian
ioliver@thespec.com, Pres., The Hamilton Spectator, ON, Hamilton
Oliver, Chris
coliver@wacotrib.com, Radio/Television Ed., Waco Tribune-Herald, TX, Waco
Oliver, Ian
ioliver@thespec.com, Pres., Metroland Media Group, ON, Mississauga
Oliveri, Elena...............................241-2039
Gen. Mgr., Pregon, Lanus Oeste, Provincia de Buenos Aires
Ollove, Steve..........................(978) 468-2632
sportsbuff.features@comcast.net, Ed., Sportsbuff Features, MA, Hamilton
Olsen, Sandy
solsen@forumcomm.com, Adv. Mgr., Inside Sales, InForum, ND, Fargo
Olson, Mary
marketing@dtint.com, Vice Pres., Opns., Digital Technology International, MN, Saint Paul
Olson, Kent..............................(701) 857-1954
kolson@ndweb.com, Asst. Ed., Minot Daily News, ND, Minot
Olson, Jack.................(262) 544-4300 ext. 103
jbo@fortec.com, Pres., Fortec, Inc., WI, Milwaukee
Olson, Tammy P........................(207) 947-9624
info@practicalpantry.com, Writer, The Practical Pantry, ME, Veazie
Olszak, Mitch....................................ext. 628
Mng. Ed., New Castle News, PA, New Castle
Olszewski, Gary........................(410) 332-6239
gary.olszewski@baltsun.com, Circ. Dir., Mktg./Retail Sales, The Baltimore Sun, MD, Baltimore
Olufsen, Bernt
annonser@vg.no, Ed. in Chief, VERDENS GANG, Oslo
Omori, Dale.............................(216) 999-4425
Deputy Dir. Photography, The Plain Dealer, OH, Cleveland
Omoto, Loren..........................(813) 259-8048
Dir., Content (TBO), The Tampa Tribune, FL, Tampa
Omvik, Erling
tips@f-b.no, Ed. in Chief, FREDRIKSTAD BLAD, Fredrikstad
Onesti, David.................(856) 427-9799 ext. 16
davido@videopipeline.com, Retail Servs. Mgr., Video Pipeline, Inc., NJ, Haddonfield
Oney, Bob..............................(919) 836-5622
boney@newsobserver.com, Dir., Mktg./Research, The News & Observer, NC, Raleigh
Ongis, Ettore
sesaab@eco.bg.it, MD, L'ECO DI BERGAMO, Bergamo
Ongkeko, Tina....................................ext. 25
MD, Canadian Community Newspaper Association, ON, Toronto
Ongley, Christina
christina.ongley@news-mail.com.au, Ed., NEWS-MAIL
Ongsansoy, Hans.......................604-605-2649
hongsansoy@theprovince.com, Entertainment Ed., The Province, BC, Vancouver
Ontiveros, Mario......................(915) 546-6178
montiveros@elpasotimes.com, Online Sales Mgr., El Paso Times, TX, El Paso
Ooton, Jenn.................(303) 776-2244 ext. 295
jooton@times-call.com, Editorial Page Ed., Times-Call, CO, Longmont
Opatz, Jarred............................419-281-0581
jopatz@times-gazette.com, Special Projects Editor, Ashland Publishing Co. LLC, OH, Ashland
Opel, Paula..............................(518) 395-3058
popel@dailygazette.net, Bus. Mgr., The Daily Gazette, NY, Schenectady
Opfer, Steven E...........................757-823-2444
Advisor, Norfolk State University, VA, Norfolk
Opperman, Nathaniel.................(612) 336-9231
nopperman@keypromedia.com, Vice Pres., Publishing, ComputerUser, MN, Minneapolis
Oppmann, Andrew
aoppmann@dnj.com, Pres./Pub., The Daily News Journal, TN, Murfreesboro
Oravec, Bernard
boravec@sungazette.com, Publisher, Williamsport Sun-Gazette, PA, Williamsport
Oravecz, John..........................(412) 320-7882
joravecz@tribweb.com, Bus. Ed., Tribune-Review, PA, Pittsburgh
Orban, Jim
jorban@thecitizen.canwest.com, Pres./Pub., The Ottawa Citizen, ON, Ottawa
Orce, Annuar
pregon@imagine.com.ar, Ed., Pregon, San Salvador de Jujuy, Provincia de Jujuy
Orcutt, Jamie...........................(715) 845-0603
jorcutt@wdhprint.com, Home Ed., The Wausau Daily Herald, WI, Wausau
Ordemann, Herbert C...........................36710
vertrieb@bremer-nachrichten.de, Proprietor, BREMER NACHRICHTEN, Bremen
Ordonez, Isabel
isabel.ordonez@ dowjones.com, Reg. Sales Mgr., Dow Jones Newswires - Stockholm, Sweden, Stockholm
Orduno Gonzalez, Luis
diario@mail.internexos.net, Gen. Dir., Editorial Diario de la Frontera, S.A. de C.V., Nogales, Sonora
Ordway, Chris...................................ext. 202
cordway@thenewsenterprise.com, Pub., The News Enterprise, KY, Elizabethtown
Orf, Steve
steveo@allsystemscolour.com, Gen. Mgr., All Systems Color, Inc., OH, West Carrollton
Orfeo, Mario....................................794-7111
posta@ilmattino.it, Mgr., IL MATTINO, Naples
Orfinger, Becky........................(607) 255-3312
Cornell Univ. Engineering School, NY, Ithaca
Orlando, Staci..........................(530) 852-0257
stacio@goldcountrymedia.com, Bus. Dir., Auburn Journal, Inc., CA, Auburn
Ormsbee, Tracy........................(518) 454-5486
tormsbee@timesunion.com, Sr. Features Ed., Times Union, NY, Albany
Orner, Robert...........................(405) 842-6034
bob-orner@msn.com, Pres., Press and Bindery Systems, Inc., OK, Oklahoma City
Orosz, Craig.............................(419) 993-2057
corosz@limanews.com, Photo Ed., The Lima News, OH, Lima
Orozco, Enrique Gomez
egomez@am.com.mx, Dir. Gen., Am Guanajuato, Guanajuato, Guanajuato
Orr, Cynthia A..........................(989) 894-9674
corr@bc-times.com, Adv. Dir., The Bay City Times, MI, Bay City
Orr, Erin.................................(217) 788-1512
erin.orr@sj-r.com, Mng. Ed., Content, The State Journal-Register, IL, Springfield
Orr, Cynthia.............................(989) 894-9674
corr@bc-times.com, Mgr., Mktg./Promo., The Bay City Times, MI, Bay City
Ortega, Solorsano
direction@diariodelistmo.com, Adv. Mgr., DIARIO DEL ISTMO, Coatzacoalcos, Veracruz
Ortega, Jaime
jortega@efe.com, Rep., EFE News Services - Brasilia, Brazil, Brasilia
jortega@efe.com, Rep., EFE News Services - Rio de Janeiro, Brazil, Rio de Janeiro
Ortega CastaÃeda, Clovis
cip217@cip.enet.cu, Dir., GIRON, Matanzas
Ortego Elvira, Juan Carlos
redaccion@menorca.info, Ed. in Chief, Menorca, Mahon, Balearic Islands
Ortiz, Jose Maria
sudafrica@efe.com, Rep., EFE News Services - Johannesburg, South Africa, Johannesburg
Ortiz, Juan Francisco Ealy
redaccio@aguila.el-universal.com.mx, CEO, EL UNIVERSAL, Mexico City, Distrito Federal
Ortiz, Elizabeth............(610) 437-4471 ext. 3429
Cedar Crest College, PA, Allentown
Orty, Patti................................(315) 498-2278
Onondaga Cmty. College, NY, Syracuse
Orwig, Christy...................................ext. 250
corwig@aberdeennews.com, Adv. Dir., American News, SD, Aberdeen
Osborne, Rodney
osborne@cherokee@nsuok.ed, Chair, Northeastern State University (Oklahoma), OK, Tahlequah
Osborne, Erika.........................(502) 452-8157
Bellarmine College, KY, Louisville
Osborne, Jeff
newsroom@herald-coaster.com, News Ed., Fort Bend Herald, TX, Rosenberg
Osborne, Rachael......................(518) 565-4136
Asst. News Ed., Press-Republican, NY, Plattsburgh
Osborne, J.
dailyregister@ntin.net, Mng. Ed., Gainesville Daily Register, TX, Gainesville
Osborne, Jeff
josborne@wacotrib.com, Asst. City Ed., Waco Tribune-Herald, TX, Waco
Osbourne, Wayne.........(931) 684-1200 ext. 227
printing@t-g.com, Prodn. Dir., Commercial Printing, Shelbyville Times-Gazette, TN, Shelbyville
Oshima, Hirohiko
webmaster@chunichi.co.jp, Chrmn., CHUNICHI SHIMBUN, Nagoya, Chubu
Oshima, Torao
taiko@tokyo-np.co.jp, Tokyo Head Officer, TOKYO SHIMBUN, Tokyo
Oshino, Shinya
ecntct@nikkei.co.jp, Staff writer, NIHON KEIZAI SHIMBUN, Tokyo
Oshiro, Sandra S........................(808) 525-8063
soshiro@honoluluadvertiser.com, Mng. Ed., Digital/Multimedia, Honolulu Star-Advertiser, HI, Honolulu
Osmundson, Paul.......................(803) 329-4061
posmundson@heraldonline.com, Ed., The Herald, SC, Rock Hill
Osorio, Andres Mata.........................561-6016
mata@eud.com, Owner/Pres., Editorial Ambos Mundos C.A., Caracas, D.F.
Osteen, Jack.............................(803) 774-1238
jack@theitem.com, Vice Pres./Publisher, The Item, SC, Sumter
Osteen, Sandy...........................(813) 220-4402
sandy@fname.org, Exec. Dir., Florida Newspaper Advertising & Marketing Executives, FL, Apopka
Osteen, Kyle.............................(803) 774-1254
kosteen@theitem.com, Co-Pres., The Item,

SC, Sumter
Osteen, Graham
graham@theitem.com, Co-Pres., The Item, SC, Sumter
Osteen, Hubert D.
hubert@theitem.com, Editor and Chairman, The Item, SC, Sumter
Osteen, Jim............................352.374.5035
Executive Editor, Ocala Star-Banner, FL, Ocala
Ostendorf, Bill.......................(401) 455-1555
bill@creativecirclemedia.com, President, Creative Circle Media Syndication, RI, East Providence
Ostendorf, Bill..........................401-455-1555
bill@creativecirclemedia.com, President & CEO, Creative Circle Media Solutions, RI, East Providence
Osting, Leila..........................(419) 993-2074
losting@limanews.com, Dir., HR, The Lima News, OH, Lima
Ostos, Marina Rivas........................43-2015
Gen. Mgr., Diocese of San Cristobal, San Cristobal, Tachiro
Ostroff, Michael
ostroffm@graphline.com, Pres./CEO, GraphLine, FL, Sunrise
Ostroff, David..........................(352) 392-2081
Prof./Chair, Dept. of Telecommunication, University of Florida, FL, Gainesville
Ostroski, Drew
ostroski@newszap.com, Asst. Mng. Ed., Delaware State News, DE, Dover
Ota, Daisuke
kni@kyodonews.com, Sales Mgr., Kyodo News International, Inc., NY, New York
Otamendi, Martxelo
egunkaria@egunkaria.info, MD, Euskaldunon Egunkaria, Andoain, Guipuzcoa
Otazu, Javier
lima@efe.com, Rep., EFE News Services - Lima, Peru, Lima
Otero, Jorge
joterom@adinet.com.uy, Ed., EL DIARIO, Montevideo
Otero, Jose Calvo..........................408-3111
jcalvo@el-nacional.com, Pres., Editora El Nacional S.A., Caracas, D.F.
Othman, Henrik
henrik.othman@ot.fi, Asst. Ed., OSTERBOTTENS TIDNING, Jakobstad, Jakobstad
Otte, Ed......................(303) 571-5117 ext. 11
eotte@colopress.net, Exec. Dir., Colorado Press Service, CO, Denver
Otte, Ed
eotte@colopress.net, Exec. Dir., Colorado Press Association, CO, Denver
Otto, John K...........................(262) 513-2687
jotto@conleynet.com, Prodn. Mgr., Facility, The Freeman, WI, Waukesha
Otto, Christian
anzeigen@goslarsche-zeitung.de, Ed. in Chief, Goslarsche Zeitung, Goslar
Otto, Chris
cotto@ydr.com, Sports Ed., Weekly Record, PA, York
Otto, Chris..............................(717) 771-2064
cotto@ydr.com, Asst. Mng. Ed., Sports, York Daily Record/York Sunday News, PA, York
Oudsema, Mary.......................(269) 388-8255
moudsema@boothmichigan.com, Mgr., Mktg./Promo., The Grand Rapids Press, MI, Grand Rapids
Ouedraogo, Daouda Emile
daouda.ouedraogo@sidwaya.bf, Ed. in Chief, SIDWAYA, Ouagadougou
Ouedraogo, Edouard
lobservateur@zcp.bf, Dir., OBSERVATEUR PAALGA, Ouagadougou
Ouellett, Martin
mouellett@ntr.ca, Correspondent, Broadcast News Limited, QC, Quebec City
Ouellette, Phil...........................781-593-7700
pouellette@itemlive.com, General Manager, Hastings & Sons Publishing Co.d/b/a The Daily Item, MA, Lynn
Ousmane, Malle
ccim@cefip.com, Ed., BULLETIN QUOTIDIEN, Bamako
Outeirino Rodrguez, Jose Luis
jlo@laregion.net, Ed., LA REGION INTERNACIONAL, Ourense
Outing, Steve
steve@content-exchange.com, Pres., Content Exchange LLC, CO, Boulder
OuÃ£draogo, Edouard
lobs@fasonet.bf, Dir., L'OBSERVATEUR, Ouagadougou
Ovalle, Nathan........................(518) 565-4157
novalle@pressrepublican.com, Night Ed., Press-Republican, NY, Plattsburgh
Overduin, Henry
hover@mcneese.edu, Head/Prof., McNeese State University, LA, Lake Charles
Overmyer, Jack K.
jover@aol.com, Pres., The Rochester Sentinel, IN, Rochester
Oviatt, Tim..................................605-886-6901
tim.oviatt@thepublicopinion.com, Adv. Mgr., Watertown Public Opinion, SD, Watertown
Owen, Howard...........................(540) 374-5539
howen@freelancestar.com, Bus. Ed., The Free Lance-Star, VA, Fredericksburg
Owens, Joseph P................................ext. 3535
jowens@express-times.com, Ed., The Express-Times, PA, Easton
Owens, Bill..................................734-794-1315
Director of Marketing, Xitron, MI, Ann Arbor
Owens, Margot.................................ext. 103
circulation@prbn.ca, Circ. Mgr., Dawson Creek Daily News, BC, Dawson Creek
Owens, Alisha..............................609-272-7100
aowens@pressofac.com, Director of Advertising, The Press of Atlantic City, NJ, Pleasantville
Owens, Brian............................(928) 539-6837
nationals@yumasun.com, National Advertising Sales Representative, Yuma Sun, AZ, Yuma
Owens, Alexandra
staff@asja.org, Exec. Dir., American Society of Journalists and Authors, NY, New York
Owensby, Mike
mowensby@lawton-constitution.com, Gen. Mgr., The Lawton Constitution, OK, Lawton
Owensby, Sonia...................................ext. 129
Online Ed., Daily News, CA, Red Bluff
Owings, Wanda.........................(864) 298-4277
lifestyle@greenvillenews.com, Food Ed., The Greenville News, SC, Greenville
Oyama, Takaaki
ooyama@jmd.co.jp, Pres., NIHON KAIJI SHIMBUN, Tokyo
Oyhamburu, Terry...........................406-791-1434
toyhambu@greatfallstribune.com, Consumer & Business Dev. Director, Great Falls Tribune, MT, Great Falls

P

Paans, M.
m.paans@brabantsdagblad.wegener.nl, CEO, BRABANTS DAGBLAD, S-Hertogenbosch
Paari, Vell
mytamilnesan@yahoo.com, Mng. Dir., TAMIL NESAN, Kuala Lumpur
Pablo, Valladares
local@sanluishoy.com.mx, Pres., SAN LUIS HOY, San Luis Potosi, San Luis Potosi
Pacetti, Diane..........................(419) 993-2084
dpacetti@limanews.com, Mng. Ed., The Lima News, OH, Lima
Pacheco, Michael......................(508) 676-2559
mpacheco@heraldnews.com, News Ed., The Herald News, MA, Fall River
Pacitto, John
jpacitto@lfpress.com, Dir., Opns., The London Free Press, ON, London
Pack, Amy L...........................(559) 735-3201
apack@visalia.gannett.com, Pres./Pub., Visalia Times-Delta, CA, Visalia
Pack, Amy.....................................559-735-3202
President & Publisher, Tulare Advance-Register, CA, Visalia
Pack, Amy L...........................(559) 735-3201
apack@visalia.gannett.com, Pres./Pub., Visalia Times-Delta & Tulare Advance-Register, CA, Visalia
apack@visalia.gannett.com, El Sol - Visalia, CA, Visalia
Packard, Gabriel.......................(212) 244-3123
globalnews@earthlink.net, News Ed., Global Information Network, NY, New York
Packard, Linda
adsolutions@sbcglobal.net, Adv. Dir., Hugo Daily News, OK, Hugo
Packham, Amy
amy.packham@lee.net, Circ. Mgr., Elko Daily Free Press, NV, Elko
Padbury, Peter...........................613-933-3160
adman@standard-freeholder.com, Adv. Dir., Standard-Freeholder, ON, Cornwall
Padden, Marty..........................(410) 332-6437
marty.padden@baltsun.com, Adv. Dir., Major Retail/Food, The Baltimore Sun, MD, Baltimore
Paddock, Robert Y.
rpaddockjr@dailyherald.com, Vice Chrmn./Exec. Vice Pres., Daily Herald, IL, Arlington Heights
Padgett, George
padgettg@elon.edu, Assoc. Prof., Elon University, NC, Elon
Padgett, Beth..........................(864) 298-4321
nwsltrs@greenville.infi.net, Editorial Page Ed., The Greenville News, SC, Greenville
Padilla, Augustine Morales
director@hidrocalidodigital.com, Pres./CEO, Hidrocalido, Aguascalientes, Aguascalientes
Padilla, Edward R...........................609-773-0401
epadilla@globalpressmanagement.com, CEO, Global Press Management Services, LLC., CO, Vail
Padilla Cruz, Guillermo
miled1@mail.miled.com, Dir., ABC, Toluca, Mexico
Padrick, Roy
rcpadrick@nsb-observer.com, Prodn. Dir., The Observer, FL, New Smyrna Beach
Padro, Charles David.................(212) 740-4400
winnet@panix.com, Exec. Producer, Multimedia, World Interactive Network, NY, New York
Paes Barreto, Denis
denispb@libnet.com.br, Pub., Delta Publicidade S.A., Belem, Para
Pafford, Jeremy.........................(949) 731-4649
News Ed., The Eagle, TX, Bryan
Pagan, Virginia
v.pagan@elcaribecdn.com.do, Adv. Mgr., EL CARIBE, Santo Domingo
Pagani, Ken
kpagani@the-review.com, Circ. Dir., The Review, OH, Alliance
Page, Phil.................................(262) 387-4830
ppaige@conleynet.com, Grp. Pub., Conley Publishing Group Ltd., WI, Beaver Dam
Page, Dave.................................(651) 450-8563
Inver Hills Cmty. College, MN, Inver Grove Heights
Page, Steve...............................(705) 475-2198
spage@nugget.ca, Adv. Assoc. Mgr., Sales, The North Bay Nugget, ON, North Bay
Page, Bill
bill.page@atusa.com, Exec. Vice Pres., Advanced Technical Solutions, Inc., MA, Acton
Paige, Bob
rpaige@culver.edu, Interpersonal Head, Culver-Stockton College, MO, Canton
Paige, Phil................(262) 375-5100 ext. 4830
ppaige@conleynet.com, Grp. Pub., The Freeman, WI, Waukesha
Painter, Amelia
amelia@agfeatures.com, Sales/Mktg., Ag Features, IA, Fostoria
Painter, Len......................................ext. 232
lpainter@grandhaventribune.com, Mng. Ed., Grand Haven Tribune, MI, Grand Haven
Pais, Albino Bento
clarim@macau.ctm.net, Director, O CLARIM, Macau
Palacios, Juan
salesinfo@pakon.com, Sales/Mktg. Mgr., Impak (A Div. of Pakon, Inc.), MN, Minnetonka
Palacios, Grace........................(828) 963-9731
grace.palacios@publicitas.com, CEO, Charney/Palacios & Co., FL, Miami
Palen, Ann
annpalen@mac.com, Office Mgr., Stampede Features, WY, Saratoga
Palen, Jerry..............................(307) 326-9852
Pres., Stampede Features, WY, Saratoga
Palisa, Abelardo................................42-2868
Dir., Primera Hora, Goya, Provincia de Corrientes
Pallavera, Ferruccio
redacionen@ilcittadino.it, Dir., IL CITTADINO, Lodi
Palm, Erik
ep@fd.no, Ed. in Chief, FINMARK DAGBLAD, Hammerfest
Palmer, Nicholas......................(604) 605-2167
npalmer@vancouversun.com, Sr. Ed., The Vancouver Sun, BC, Vancouver
Palmer, Thomas.......................(518) 454-5461
tpalmer@timesunion.com, Art Dir., Times Union, NY, Albany
Palmer, Shawn..........................(203) 731-3401
spalmer@newstimes.com, Publisher, The News-Times, CT, Danbury
Palmer, Karen..........................(419) 521-7224
kpalmer@nncogannett.com, Religion Writer, News Journal, OH, Mansfield
Palmer, Vickie K.
vpalmer@suncommercial.com, Pub., Vincennes Sun-Commercial, IN, Vincennes
Palmer, Shawn E.................................ext. 264
s.palmer@theday.com, Adv. Dir., The Day Publishing Company, CT, New London
Palmer, John............................(617) 619-6506
jpalmer@bostonherald.com, Circ. Mgr., Single Copy Sales, Boston Herald, MA, Boston
Palmer, Dennis
dennis.palmer@selmatimesjournal.com, Pres./Pub., The Selma Times-Journal, AL, Selma
Palmer, Andy
display@fultonsun.com, Adv. Mgr., Display, The Fulton Sun, MO, Fulton
Palmer, R.L.
dailytribune@bluebonnet.net, Ed., Mount Pleasant Daily Tribune, TX, Mount Pleasant
Palmer, Richard
rpalmer@scansoft.com, Sr. Vice Pres., Cor. Devel., Nuance Communications Inc., MA, Burlington
Palmer, Lane...............................636-346-3074
lpalmer@fujifilm.com, Vice President, Newspaper Sales, Fujifilm North America Corporation, IL, Hanover Park
Palmer, Denise E.......................(813) 259-7424
dpalmer@tampatrib.com, Pres./Pub., The Tampa Tribune, FL, Tampa
Palmer, Mark............................(931) 388-6464
mpalmer@c-dh.net, Pub., Columbia Daily Herald, TN, Columbia
Paloian, John R.
info@rrd.com, COO, R.R. Donnelley & Sons Co., IL, Chicago
Palomino, Josefina
perioam@infosel.net.mx, Gen. Mgr., AM DE LEON, Leon, Guanajuato
Palomino, Josephine
spalomino@am.com.mx, Gen. Mgr., Am Guanajuato, Guanajuato, Guanajuato
Pande, H. R.
sanmarg@sanmarghindi.com, Ed., SANMARG, Kolkata, West Bengal
Pandey, Suresh Chandra
sureshchandra.pandey@esakal.com, Ed. in Chief, SAKAL/SUNDAY SAKAL, Pune, Maharashtra
Pandey, Jaishree Khadilkar
navakal@vsnl.com, Ed., NAVAKAL, Mumbai
Pandit, Girish............................(775) 881-1228
gpandit@sierranevadamedia.com, Prodn./Opns. Dir., Nevada Appeal, NV, Carson City
Panerai, Paulo
ppanerai@class.it, Pub., ITALIA OGGI, Milan
Panigutti, Alessandro
redazione@latinaoggi.net, Dir., LATINA OGGI, Latina
Panigutti, Alessandro
apanigutti@libero.it, Dir., CIOCIARIA OGGI, Frosinone
Papadopoulos, Greg
greg.papadopoulos@sun.com, Exec. Vice Pres./CTO, SunLabs, Sun Microsystems, Inc., CA, Santa Clara
Papanikolaou, N.
geniki@otenet.gr, Pub., GENIKI DIMOPRASION, Athens, Central Greece
Pape, Richard
pape@allsysgo.com, Pres., All Systems Go, MA, Woburn
Papert, S.W. (Sammy)...............(214) 640-3103

samiii@beldenassociates.com, Chrmn./CEO, Belden Associates, TX, Dallas
Papetti, Roberto
segredazione@gazzettino.it, Dir., IL GAZZETTINO, Venice
Papile, Cyndi
cpapile@ledger.com, Mgr., HR, The Patriot Ledger, MA, Quincy
Papineau, Claude
claude.papineau@thecanadianpress.com, Vice Pres.-French Serv., Canadian Press, The - Montreal, QC, QC, Montreal
Pappas, Nick
pappasn@telegraph-nh.com, Ed. in Chief, The Telegraph, NH, Hudson
Pappas, Carol
cpappas@dailyhome.com, Ed., The Daily Home, AL, Talladega
Pappas, Steve....................................ext. 1151
steve.pappas@timesargus.com, Deputy Ed., The Times Argus, VT, Barre
Paprocki, Gayle
gpapr@srds.com, Vice Pres., Pdct. Opns., SRDS, a Kantar Media Company, IL, Des Plaines
Paquett, Jim ....(916) 321-1460
jpaquett@sacbee.com, Adv. Mgr., Retail Territories, The Sacramento Bee, CA, Sacramento
Paquette, Gilber
gpaquette@hebdos.com, Exec. Dir., Hebdos Qu□bec, QC, Montreal
Paradis, Tom...........................(951) 782-7688
tparadis@pe.com, Adv. Mgr., Major Accts., The Press-Enterprise, CA, Riverside
Paradiso, Diane
sales@wpafilmlibrary.com, Dir., Sales, WPA Film Library, IL, Orland Park
Pardo-Figueroa, Cesar........................26-4676
amiroque@comercio.com.pe, Gen. Mgr., El Comercio, Lima
Pardon, Daniel
redaction@france-antilles.pf, Ed. in Chief, SOCIETE OCEANIENNE DE COMMUNICATION, Papeete
Pare, David ....(203) 317-2366
dpare@record-journal.com, Circ. Dir., Record-Journal, CT, Meriden
Parent, Rob ....(610) 622-8884
Sports Ed., Delaware County Daily Times, PA, Primos
Parent, Lorrie.........................(952) 936-5000
lorrie.parent@polaroid.com, Media Rel., Polaroid Holding Co., MA, Concord
Parham, Maria ....(520) 573-4116
parham@azstarnet.com, Entertainment/Features/Travel Ed., Arizona Daily Star, AZ, Tucson
Paris, Daniel ....(208) 465-8152 ext. 135
dparis@idahopress.com, Prodn. Dir., Press, Idaho Press-Tribune, ID, Nampa
Parisi, Mark...........................(781) 665-4442
markparisi@aol.com, Pres., Atlantic Feature Syndicate, MA, Melrose
Parisse, Samuel L.
sparisse@indianagazette.net, Prodn. Mgr., Post Press, The Indiana Gazette, PA, Indiana
Parke, Beth 215-884-8178
bparke@sej.org, Exec. Dir., Society of Environmental Journalists (SEJ), PA, Jenkintown
Parker, Randy..........................(717) 771-2012
rparker@ydr.com, Mng. Ed., Weekly Record, PA, York
Parker, Wayne
parker@amplified.com, Pres., Amplified.com, Inc., GA, Atlanta
Parker, Alan...........................(416) 947-2243
alan.parker@sunmedia.ca, Deputy Mng. Ed., The Toronto Sun, ON, Toronto
Parker, Jim ....ext. 5594
Automotive Ed., The Post and Courier, SC, Charleston
Parker, Jack...........................(830) 257-0305
jack.parker@dailytimes.com, Circ. Dir., Kerrville Daily Times, TX, Kerrville
Parker, Glen...........................(204) 571-7424
gparker@brandonsun.com, Sales Mgr., Brandon Sun, MB, Brandon
Parker, Kathy ....ext. 119
kparker@pryordailytimes.com, Ed., The Daily Times, OK, Pryor
Parker, Randy..........................(717) 771-2012
rparker@ydr.com, Mng. Ed., York Daily Record/York Sunday News, PA, York
Parker, Preston ....(435) 797-3259
Lectr., Utah State University, UT, Logan
Parker, Steve..........................(314) 340-8290
sparker@post-dispatch.com, Asst. Mng. Ed., News, St. Louis Post-Dispatch, MO, Saint Louis
Parker, Kelvin 603-570-2171
kparker@seacoastonline.com, SEACOAST SUNDAY, NH, Portsmouth
kparker@seacoastonline.com, Circ. Dir., Portsmouth Herald, NH, Portsmouth
Parker, Jo Alyson
jparker@sju.edu, Chair, Saint Joseph's University, PA, Philadelphia
Parks, Tonya
tparks@keysnews.com, Circ. Manager, The Key West Citizen, FL, Key West
Parks, Robert W. ....(518) 565-4130
bparks@pressrepublican.com, Pub., Press-Republican, NY, Plattsburgh
Parks, Bill ....(510) 659-6075
Ohlone College, CA, Fremont
Parks, Will ....(309) 797-0302
wparks@qconline.com, Adv. Mgr., Retail, The Rock Island Argus, IL, Rock Island
Parma, Pavel
slovo@svobodne-slovo.anet.cz, Ed. in Chief, SVOBODNE SLOVO, Prague
Parmelee, Lisa
lparmelee@postindependent.com, Classified Adv. Sup., Glenwood Springs Post Independent, CO, Glenwood Springs
Parnass, Larry ....(413) 585-5248
lparnass@gazettenet.com, Mng. Ed., News, Daily Hampshire Gazette, MA, Northampton
Paroby, Johnathon ....(570) 628-6033
foto1@republicanherald.com, Photo Ed., Republican Herald, PA, Pottsville
Parra, Ron ....ext. 1147
ron.parra@uniontrib.com, Budget/Analysis Mgr., The San Diego Union-Tribune, CA, San Diego
Parra, Alberto Gonzalez
cuestion@compuserve.com, Pres., Cuestion, Mexico City, Distrito Federal
Parral, Leonard Teran
lteran@eluniverso.com, Gen. Mgr., Compania Anonima El Universo, Guayaquil
Parreira, Nelson
nparreira@lfpress.com, Adv. Mgr., Natl./Major Retail/Inserts, The London Free Press, ON, London
Parrish, Mi-Ai
publisher@idahostatesman.com, Pres., The Idaho Statesman, ID, Boise
Parry, Dale ....(313) 222-6549
dparry@freepress.com, Deputy Mng. Ed., Detroit Free Press, MI, Detroit
Parshall, Margaret....................(517) 768-4885
mparshall@citpat.com, Adv. Dir., The Jackson Citizen Patriot, MI, Jackson
Parson, Brian ....(479) 571-6475
bparson@nwanews.com, Adv. Mgr., Retail, Northwest Arkansas Times, AR, Fayetteville
Parsons, Allen..........................352.867.4020
allen.parsons@starbanner.com, Publisher, Ocala Star-Banner, FL, Ocala
Parsons, Paul
parsons@elon.edu, Dean/Prof., Elon University, NC, Elon
Parsons, Jackie
jackie_parsons@link.freedom.com, Circ. Mgr., Daily Press, CA, Victorville
Parsons, Tim...........................(530) 542-8033
tparsons@tahoedailytribune.com, Action Ed., Tahoe Daily Tribune, CA, South Lake Tahoe
Parsons, Ben
info@support-systems-intl.com, Pres., Support Systems International Corp., CA, Richmond
Parsons, Mike 321-242-3576
mparsons@floridatoday.com, Sports Editor, Florida Today, FL, Melbourne
Partlow, John ....ext. 264
jpartlow@wwub.com, Prodn. Mgr., Walla Walla Union-Bulletin, WA, Walla Walla
Partridge, Bruce
bruce.partridge@news-mail.com.au, Adv. Mgr., NEWS-MAIL
Pasco, Jean O.
jopasco@sbcglobal.net, Sec./Treasurer, Orange County Press Club, CA, Irvine
Passafiume, Josie ....(216) 999-4992
Asst. Circ. Dir., Sales Devel., The Plain Dealer, OH, Cleveland
Passmore, Michelle
mpassmore@the-leader.com, Adv. Dir., The Leader, NY, Corning
Passmore, Michelle 207-282-1535
mpassmore@journaltribune.com, General Manager, Journal Tribune, ME, Biddeford
Passon, Gary
gpasson@nts.net, Pres., Network Telephone Services, CA, Woodland Hills
Pastorica, Sose
lri@laregion.net, Dir., LA REGION INTERNACIONAL, Ourense
Pastorino, Mike ....(810) 766-6143
Circ. Mktg. Mgr., The Flint Journal, MI, Flint
Pastrana, Guy 609-272-7044
gpastrana@pressofac.com, Digital Technical Team Manager, The Press of Atlantic City, NJ, Pleasantville
Pate, Jack 812-461-0770
patej@courierpress.com, Pres./Pub., Evansville Courier & Press, IN, Evansville
Patel, Falgunbhai C.
sandesh@sandesh.com, Chrmn./MD, SANDESH, Ahmedabad, Gujarat
Patel, Nikunj
english@westerntimes.co.in, Mng. Ed./Ed. in Chief, WESTERN TIMES, Ahmedabad, Gujarat
Patel, D.C.
nayapadkar@gmail.com, Mng. Ed., NAYA PADKAR, Anand, Gujarat
Patel, Niloufer
gm.circ@dawn.com, Dir. Circ., DAWN, Karachi
Patellis, Dan 321-242-3552
dpatellis@floridatoday.com, Systems Manager, Florida Today, FL, Melbourne
Paterno, Francesco
demafone@ilmanifesto.it, Journalist, IL MANIFESTO, Rome
Paterson, Bob
bpaterson@edmsun.com, Adv. Mgr., Classified, The Edmonton Sun, AB, Edmonton
Paterson, David J.
david.paterson@abitibibowater.com, Pres./CEO, AbitibiBowater Inc., QC, Montreal
Pathadan, Varghese 9349599162
rmtcr@deepika.com, Resident Manager, DEEPIKA, Trichur, Kerala
Patino, Jorge Castro 293 0375
Gen. Mgr., Graficos Orenses C.A., Machala, El Oro
Patino, Jorge Castro 241-2032
Gen. Mgr., El Heraldo C.A., Ambato, Tungurahua
Patnaik, B.K.
srp@orissasambad.com, Pub., SAMBAD, Bhubaneswar, Orissa
Paton, John ....(212) 807-4640
john.paton@impremedia.com, Chrmn./CEO, impreMedia LLC, NY, Brooklyn
Patozi, Astrit
gazetard@albaniaonline.net, Ed. in Chief, RILINDJA DEMOKRATIKE, Tirana
Patrick, Jan ....(276) 645-2515
jpatrick@bristolnews.com, Features Ed., Bristol Herald Courier, VA, Bristol
Patrick, Anna
aptrick@westliberty.edu, Editor, West Liberty University, WV, West Liberty
Patrick, Judith 518-395-3101
jpatrick@dailygazette.net, Mng. Ed., The Daily Gazette, NY, Schenectady
Patrick, Wendy ....(530) 406-6251
wpatrick@dailydemocrat.com, Bus. Mgr., The Daily Democrat, CA, Woodland
Patrick, Perry ....(404) 572-1912
ppatrick@coxnews.com, Pagination Dir., COXnet (Cox Newspapers' Wide Area Network/Cox News Service), GA, Atlanta
Patrick, John E.........................(614) 659-7253
jepatri@us.ibm.com, Gen. Mgr., Internet Application Servs., IBM Corp., NY, Somers
Patrick, Randy
rpatrick@winchestersun.com, Mng. Ed., The Winchester Sun, KY, Winchester
Patrick, Mike
mpatrick@cdapress.com, Editorial Page Ed., Coeur d'Alene Press, ID, Coeur d'Alene
Patrick, Charlotte ....(812) 379-5656
cpatrick@therepublic.com, Administrative Mgr., The Republic, IN, Columbus
Patrick, Scott ....(406) 657-1217
spatrick@billingsgazette.com, Controller, Billings Gazette, MT, Billings
Patrudkar, Sunil
sakal@vsnl.in, Ed., MUMBAI SAKAL, Navi Mumbai, Maharashtra
Patrusky, Ben
bpatrusky@aol.com, Exec. Dir., Council for the Advancement of Science Writing, Inc., WV, Hedgesville
Patrusky, Ben
bpatrusky@aol.com, Exec. Dir., Council for Advancement and Support of Education, DC, Washington
Patten, Sharon
sharon@bryantimes.com, Women's Ed., The Bryan Times, OH, Bryan
Patterson, Bill ....(940) 566-6808
bpatterson@dentonrc.com, Pub., Denton Record-Chronicle, TX, Denton
Patterson, Sue.........................(309) 686-3099
spatterson@pjstar.com, Adv. Mgr., Retail, Journal Star, IL, Peoria
Patterson, Oscar
opatters@unf.edu, Chair, University of North Florida, FL, Jacksonville
Patterson, Pat ....(717) 762-2151
pat@therecordherald.com, Pub., The Record Herald, PA, Waynesboro
Patterson, Keesha ....(856) 468-5000
Gloucester County College, NJ, Sewell
Patterson, Linda
lpatterson@avtimes.net, Pub., Alberni Valley Times, BC, Port Alberni
Pattichis, Nicole
mailbox@phileleftheros.com, MD, PHILELEFTHEROS, Nicosia
Pattison, Ian ....(807) 343-6203
ian.pattison@chroniclejournal.com, Editorial Page Ed., The Chronicle-Journal, ON, Thunder Bay
Pattison, Neal ....(425) 339-3480
npattison@heraldnet.com, Exec. Ed., The Herald, WA, Everett
Patton, Tyler ....ext. 250
tylerp@valleystar.com, Gen. Mgr./Pub., Valley Morning Star, TX, Harlingen
Patton, Patti............................(740) 376-5420
ppatton@mariettatimes.com, Office Mgr., The Marietta Times, OH, Marietta
Patton, Paula ....(507) 333-3105
ppatton@faribault.com, Ed., Faribault Daily News, MN, Faribault
Patton, Meredith V.
mvpatton@observertoday.com, Adv. Dir., Observer, NY, Dunkirk
Patton, Geoff...........................(215) 361-8825
gpatton@thereporteronline.com, Chief Photographer, The Reporter, PA, Lansdale
Patton, Beth
bpatton@islandpacket.com, Mktg./Promo. Dir., The Island Packet, SC, Bluffton
Paturat Romero, Mario
correotac@epensa.com.pe, Gen. Mgr., Correo de Tacna, Tacna
Paul, Anne
apaul@standard.net, Exec. Asst. to the Pub., Standard-Examiner, UT, Ogden
Paul, Nathanael ....(305) 626-3102
Florida Memorial College, FL, Miami
Paul, Patricia ....(610) 367-6041 ext. 243
ppaul@journalregister.com, Pub., The Phoenix, PA, Phoenixville
Paul, John M...........................(650) 254-1900
info@netscape.com, Sr. Vice Pres./Gen. Mgr., Server Pdcts., Netscape Communications Corp., CA, Mountain View
Paul, Hallie
hpaul@express-news.net, Asst. Mng. Ed., Graphics/Design/Photo, Randolph Wingspread, TX, San Antonio
hpaul@express-news.net, Asst. Mng. Ed., Graphics/Design/Photo, Brooks Discovery News, TX, San Antonio
hpaul@express-news.net, Asst. Mng. Ed., Graphics/Design/Photo, Bulverde Community News, TX, San Antonio

hpaul@express-news.net, Asst. Mng. Ed., Graphics/Design/Photo, Fort Sam News Leader, TX, San Antonio
hpaul@express-news.net, Asst. Mng. Ed., Graphics/Design/Photo, Kelly Observer, TX, San Antonio
hpaul@express-news.net, Asst. Mng. Ed., Graphics/Design/Photo, Lackland Talespinner, TX, San Antonio
hpaul@express-news.net, Asst. Mng. Ed., Graphics/Design/Photo, Medical Patriot, TX, San Antonio
hpaul@express-news.net, Asst. Mng. Ed., Graphics/Design/Photo, North Central News, TX, San Antonio
hpaul@express-news.net, Asst. Mng. Ed., Graphics/Design/Photo, Northeast Herald, TX, San Antonio
hpaul@express-news.net, Asst. Mng. Ed., Graphics/Design/Photo, Northwest Weekly, TX, San Antonio
hpaul@express-news.net, Asst. Mng. Ed., Graphics/Design/Photo, San Antonio Express-News, TX, San Antonio

Paulk, Kevin ....(615) 259-8226
kpaulk@tennessean.com, Asst. Mng. Ed., Nights, The Tennessean, TN, Nashville

Paulsen, Rich................................ext. 230
publisher@crestonnews.com, Pub., Creston News Advertiser, IA, Creston

Paulson, Adam ....(218) 683-8733
Northland Cmty. & Tech. College, MN, Thief River Falls

Paulson, Jon
mcgavin_l@utpb.edu, Area Coord., University of Texas of the Permian Basin, TX, Odessa

Paulson, Jill ....(605) 668-1293
Mt. Marty College, SD, Yankton

Paulson, Stephanie
info@stephenz.com, Vice Pres., Creative Servs., The Stephenz Group, CA, San Jose

Paulu, Tom ....(360) 577-2540
tpaulu@tdn.com, Outdoors Ed., The Daily News, WA, Longview

Paulus, Shawn
jdolley@observertoday.com, Circ. Mgr., Observer, NY, Dunkirk

Paunescu, Valentin
curiernr@bx.logicnet.ro, Dir., CURIERUL NATIONAL, Bucharest

Paupore, Jason.......................(219) 464-5271
Valparaiso Univ., IN, Valparaiso

Pautrat Calderon, Mario
correoaqp@epensa.com.pe, Gen. Mgr., Correo de Arequipa, Arequipa

Pautrat Calderon, Mario 32-3610
piured@correoperu.com.pe, Gen. Mgr., Correo de Piura, Piura

Pava, David
dpava@marcole.com, Vice Pres., Sales & Marketing, MarCole Enterprises, Inc., CA, Walnut Creek

Pavey, Rob ....(706) 868-1222 ext. 119
rpavey@augustachronicle.com, Outdoors Ed., The Augusta Chronicle, GA, Augusta

Pavich, Bill ....(760) 740-5495
bpavich@nctimes.com, IT Mgr., North County Times, CA, Escondido

Pavlik, John
jpavlik@rutgers.edu, Chair/Prof., Rutgers University, NJ, New Brunswick

Pavone, Michael
mpavone@ustensor.com, Int'l Sales, Tensor Group, Inc., IL, Woodridge

Pawloski, Stan
spawloski@timesleaderonline.com, Wire News Ed., The Times Leader, OH, Martins Ferry

Pawlowski, Adam
a.pawlowski @ glos.com, Ed. in Chief, GAZETA POZNANSKA, Poznan

Pawlowski, Adam
a.pawlowski@glos.com, Ed. in Chief, GLOS WIELKOPOLSKI, Poznan

Paxson, Doug
info@mediacy.com, Pres., Media Cybernetics LP, MD, Bethesda

Paxton, Jim
jpaxton@paducahsun.com, Ed., The Paducah Sun, KY, Paducah

Payer, Zach.................................ext. 5444
Adv. Mgr., Charleston.Net, The Post and Courier, SC, Charleston

Payne, Robert 813-314-2413
Director of Marketing, SAXOTECH, Inc., FL, Tampa

Payne, Cynthia
newstimes@comcast.net, Pub., News-Times, IN, Hartford City

Payne, Joe ....ext. 274
joepayne@qconline.com, Features Ed., The Rock Island Argus, IL, Rock Island

Payne, Vince.................................ext. 116
vince@colterpeterson.com, Mktg. Mgr., Colter Peterson, IA, Des Moines

Payne, Debbie
dpayne@news-leader.com, HR Dir., Springfield News-Leader, MO, Springfield

Payson, David
dpayson@keene.edu, Assoc. Prof., Keene State College of the University System of New Hampshire, NH, Keene

Paz, Nestor Ramirez.........................21-1144
Pres., Lalano Adentro, Acarigua, Portuguesa

Pazos, Alberto 4309 7500
lectores@clarin.com.ar, Sales Mgr., Clarin, Buenos Aires

Pearce, David
editorial@bdtruth.com.au, Ed., BARRIER DAILY TRUTH

Pearce, Frazer
frazer.pearce@capnews.com.au, Ed., THE MORNING BULLETIN

Pearlman, Gene ....(909) 386-3947
gene.pearlman@sbsun.com, Adv. Dir., San Bernardino County Sun, CA, San Bernardino

Pearlman, Gene
gene.pearlman@inlandnewspapers.com, Adv. Vice Pres., Inland Valley Daily Bulletin, CA, Ontario

Pears, Joy
newsexaminer@newsexaminer.com, Gen. Mgr., Connersville News-Examiner, IN, Connersville

Pearson, Lynn 334-293-5800
lpearson@cnhi.com, Executive VP/CFO, Community Newspaper Holdings, Inc., AL, Montgomery

Pearson, Margo............(291) 298-1010 ext. 103
margo@intercom-interactive.com, Gen. Mgr., InterCom, TX, The Woodlands

Pearson, Jean 651-228-5306
jpearson@pioneerpress.com, Dir., Market Research/Info., St. Paul Pioneer Press, MN, Saint Paul

Pearson, Mike ....(800) 535-4425
pearsmh@nytimes.com, Sales Exec., Western US, New York Times Syndicate, NY, New York

Pearson, Dianna ....(423) 585-6816
Walters State Cmty. College, TN, Morristown

Pearson, Eva Marie..................(870) 543-1418
epearson@pbcommercial.com, Travel Ed., Pine Bluff Commercial, AR, Pine Bluff

Pearson, Tammy...........(402) 873-3334 ext. 102
tpearson@ncnewspress.com, Exec. Ed., Nebraska City News-Press, Inc., NE, Nebraska City

Pearson, Mike ....(303) 892-2592
pearsonm@rockymountainnews.com, Features Ed., Rocky Mountain News, CO, Denver

Pease, Edward C. ....(435) 797-3293
Prof./Grad. Coord., Utah State University, UT, Logan

Pease, Tom
tpease@corporatecopy.com, Pres., e/Doc Systems, TN, Memphis

Peattie, Earl
epeat@mortgagenews.com, Pres./Author, Mortgage News Company, CT, Cromwell

Pecci, Jose Luis 129-2721
director@diarionoticias.com.py, Gen. Mgr., Editorial Continental S.A., Asuncion

Pech, Ian
wseditor@standard.fairfax.com.au, Sub Ed, THE STANDARD

Pechek, Jay ....(512) 349-1333
jayp@buffalotech.com, PR, Buffalo Technology Inc., TX, Austin

Peck, Steven R.
ranger@wyoming.com, Columnist/Editorial Page Ed., The Riverton Ranger, WY, Riverton

Peck, Chris ....(901) 529-2390
peck@commercialappeal.com, Ed., The Commercial Appeal, TN, Memphis

Peck, Thomas H. ....(212) 210-1810
tpeck@nydailynews.com, CFO, NY Daily News, NY, New York

Pedersen, Gus
pedersen@cycube.com, Pres., CEC Corp. (CyCube), NY, City Island

Pederson, Gary ....(253) 597-8564
gary.pederson@thenewstribune.com, Mgr., Research, The News Tribune, WA, Tacoma

Pedigo, Bill ....(425) 339-3046
pedigo@heraldnet.com, Librarian/TV Ed., The Herald, WA, Everett

Pedigo, Wendell......................(615) 259-8844
Adv. Mgr., Nat'l, The Tennessean, TN, Nashville

Pedrosa, Ignacio
publicidad@minidiario.com, Dir., Finance, MINI DIARIO VALENCIA, Valencia

Pedroso, Raul ....(305) 634-8820
rp@solo-photography.com, Contact, Solo Photography, Inc., FL, Miami

Peeler, Jodie..........................(803) 321-5225
Newberry College, SC, Newberry

Peeples, Michael ....(618) 437-5321
Rend Lake College, IL, Ina

Peery, Mark
mark-peery@sandhills.com, Coord./Mgr., PC Today Magazine, NE, Lincoln

Pegoboulos, Kanasis
etegomail@enet.gr, Ed. in Chief, KYRIAKATIKI ELEFTHEROTYPIA, Athens, Central Greece

Pehrson, Greg
greg.pherson@lee.net, Circ. Dir., The Columbus Telegram, NE, Columbus

Peinazo Pleguezuelos, Antonio
redaccion@huelvainformacion.es, Chief Ed., Huelva Informacion, Huelva

Peirce, Brian
techhelp@peirce.com, Pres., Peirce-Phelps, Inc., PA, Philadelphia

Pekala, Gary ....ext. 1141
gary.pekala@uniontrib.com, Controller/Mgr., Bus. Servs., The San Diego Union-Tribune, CA, San Diego

Pelaez Gularte, Wilfredo 31-2405
Gen. Mgr., Diario de Chimbote, Chimbote, Ancash

Pelchar, Joseph ....(610) 371-5156
jpelchar@readingeagle.com, Circ. Mgr., Home Delivery, Reading Eagle, PA, Reading

Pele, Philippe
philippe.pele@ouest-france.fr, Sales Mgr., PRESSE-OCEAN, Nantes

Pelisson, Maureen
maureen@telluridedailyplanet.com, Adv. Mgr., Telluride Daily Planet, CO, Telluride

Pellegrene, Tom........................(260) 461-8377
tpellegrene@jg.net, News Technology Mgr., The Journal Gazette, IN, Fort Wayne

Pelleschi, Kathy........................(570) 970-7293
kpelleschi@leader.net, Adv. Mgr., Retail, Times Leader, PA, Wilkes-Barre

Pelletier, Pierre
publisher@shawcable.com, Interim Pub., The Kimberley Daily Bulletin, BC, Kimberley

Pelline, Jeff...........................(530) 477-4235
jeffp@theunion.com, Ed., The Union, CA, Grass Valley

Pellman, Mark
baumfolder@baumfolder.com, Dir., Sales/Mktg., Baumfolder Corp., OH, Sidney

Peltonen, Juha
juha.peltonen@demari.fi, Editor, UUTISPAIVA DEMARI, Helsinki, Uusima

Pemberton, Bill.......................(972) 392-0888
bpemberton@wieck.com, Sales Mgr., Wieck Media, TX, Dallas

Pen, Albert
echohebd@cancom.net, Dir., L'ECHO des CAPS, Saint-Pierre

Pena, Dr. Ramon Morales Agustin
agustin@hidrocalidodigital.com, Asst. Gen. Mgr., Hidrocalido, Aguascalientes, Aguascalientes

Pena, Denny ....(212) 807-4618
dpena@eldiariolaprensa.com, Circ. Dir., El Diario La Prensa, NY, Brooklyn

Penfold, Judy
judy.penfold@coxnews.com, Admin. Coord., COXnet (Cox Newspapers' Wide Area Network/Cox News Service), GA, Atlanta

Pennell, Debbie M. ....(919) 739-7905
dpennel@newsargus.com, Mgr., HR, Goldsboro News-Argus, NC, Goldsboro

Pennington, Gary.......................(715) 682-2313
gary.pennington@mx3.com, Pub., The Daily Press, WI, Ashland

Penny, Mark
jmpenny@hempsteadco.com, Mng. Dir., Hempstead & Co., Inc., NJ, Haddonfield

Penny, Trent
tpenny@annistonstar.com, Photo Ed., The Anniston Star, AL, Anniston

Pensaari, Jouko
jouko.pensaari @ kokkolalehti.fi, Ed. in Chief, KESKIPOHJANMAA, Kokkola, Vaasa

Pensiero, F. James ....(609) 520-7487
Vice Pres., News Projects, The Wall Street Journal, NY, New York

Pentikainen, Mikael
mikael.pentikainen@sanoma.fi, Pub., HELSINGIN SANOMAT, Sanoma

Pepe, Joseph
linda.key@commercialappeal.com, Pres./Pub., The Commercial Appeal, TN, Memphis

Pepper, Christopher..........................882 248
chp@mt-online.de, Ed. in Chief, MINDENER TAGEBLATT, Minden

Peppler-Moyer, Lonnie.......................ext. 221
lonnie@monroenews.com, Pres./Pub., The Monroe Evening News, MI, Monroe

Peraca, Elizabeth
elizabeth@noroeste.com, Sales Mgr., NOROESTE, Mazatlan, Sinaloa

Peralta de Ana, Eduardo
eperalta@ideal.es, Dir., IDEAL, Peligros, Granada

Perce, Lynn
info@rooseveltpaper.com, Mktg. Dir., Roosevelt Paper, NJ, Mount Laurel

Perea, Abel Ramos 23-3352
comercio@telser.com.pe, Dir., El Comercio, Cuzco

Peregrin, Patrick ....(317) 444-7145
patrick.peregrin@indystar.com, Sales & Marketing, Vice Pres., The Indianapolis Star, IN, Indianapolis

Pereira, Damiao
chfe_redaccao@diariodominho.pt, Ed. in Chief, DIARIO DO MINHO, Braga

Pereira, Carlos Marques 442-5944
Ed.., Folha Do Povo, Tupa, Sao Paulo

Pereira, Jose Miguel
director@diariodominho.pt, Dir., DIARIO DO MINHO, Braga

Pereira, Jose Leite
noticias@noticias.pt, Dir., JORNAL DE NOTICIAS, Porto

Pereira, Maria Emilia Lopes...............321-6214
gazeta@nextway.com.br, Gen. Mgr., Gazeta de Oeste, Mossoro, Rio Grande do Norte

Pereiro, Marisol
admonad@atlantico.net, Administrator, Atlantico Diario, Vigo, Pontevedra

Perel, Erica 919-962-4215
Univ. of North Carolina - The Daily Tar Heel, NC, Chapel Hill

Perez, Sylvia
perezs@caller.com, Exec. Sec., Corpus Christi Caller-Times, TX, Corpus Christi

Perez, Linda ....(909) 869-5483
The Poly Post, CA, Pomona

Perez, Rodolfo Abel..........................447-2160
redaccion@elpatagonico.net, Pres., El Patagonico, Comodoro Rivadavia, Provincia de Chubut

Perez, Jesus.................................541-5211
enpais@telcel.net.ve, Gen. Mgr., EL NUEVO PAIS, Caracas, D.F.

Perez Ansotegui, Jordi
manyana@lleida.net, Dir., LA MANANA-DIARI DE PONENT, Lleida

Perez Oliva, Milagros
publicidad@elpais.es, Ed. in Chief, El Pais, Barcelona

Perez Puche, Francisco
cartas@lasprovincias.es, Dir., LAS PROVINCIAS, Valencia

Perez Rocha, Jaime

info@debate.com.mx, Ed./Dir., EL DEBATE, Los Mochis, Sinaloa
Perez Soler, Pilar
correo@diariodesoria.com, Ed. in Chief, Diario De Soria, Soria
Perfecto, Elizabeth.....................(218) 681-0819
Northland Cmty. & Tech. College, MN, Thief River Falls
Perinciolli, Hector Mario......................420 185
laopinion@laopinionaustral.com, Pres., La Opinion Austral, Rio Gallegos, Provincia de Santa Cruz
Perini, Bob...........................(715) 526 - 7002
rperini@shawanoleader.com, vice president production, Shawano Leader, WI, Shawano
Perkins, Dan...........................(718) 768-2522
tomtomorrow@ix.netcom.com, Creator, This Modern World, NY, Brooklyn
Perkins, Connie.......................(337) 433-3000
cperkins@americanpress.com, Classified Mgr., Shearman Corporation, LA, Lake Charles
Perkins, Connie.......................(337) 433-3000
cperkins@americanpress.com, Classified Adv. Mgr., American Press, LA, Lake Charles
Perkins, Penny..........................518-244-2016
perkip@sage.edu, Russell Sage College, NY, Troy
Perkins, Charlotte.............................ext. 234
cperkins@evansnewspapers.com, Lifestyle Ed., The Houston Home Journal, GA, Perry
Perkins, Howard
editor@lamaruniversitypress.com, Lamar Univ., TX, Beaumont
Perkins, Nena.................................ext. 1222
nperkins@vindy.com, Promo. Mgr., The Vindicator, OH, Youngstown
Perkins, Scott..........................(870) 239-8562
sperkins@paragoulddailypress.com, Pub., Paragould Daily Press, AR, Paragould
Perkins, William........................(334) 712-7901
bperkins@dothaneagle.com, Editorial Page Ed., The Dothan Eagle, AL, Dothan
Perkinson, Elizabeth...................580-225-3000
President, Elk City Daily News, OK, Elk City
Perla, Giovanni........................(917) 339-0789
giovanni.perla@hoynyc.com, Adv. Mgr., General Sales, Hoy, NY, New York
Perlberg, Richard
rperlberg@gannett.com, Gen. Mgr., The Livingston County Daily Press & Argus, MI, Howell
Perlmutter, Mark.............................ext. 8056
News Graphics, Burlington County Times, NJ, Willingboro
Permutter, Dave........................(413) 585-5292
dpermutter@gazettenet.com, Adv. Mgr., Retail, Daily Hampshire Gazette, MA, Northampton
Pero, David...........................(541) 338-2312
david.pero@registerguard.com, COO, The Register-Guard, OR, Eugene
Perona, Robert.........................(216) 999-4172
Circ. Vice Pres./Dir., The Plain Dealer, OH, Cleveland
Perozek, Dave
dperozek@chronicletelegram.com, Editorial Page Ed., Chronicle-Telegram, OH, Elyria
Perricone, Mike........................(404) 526-5256
mperricone@ajc.com, Adv. Vice Pres., Retail, Atlanta Journal-Constitution, GA, Atlanta
Perron, John...........................(508) 626-4434
jperron@cnc.com, Site Mgr., Metrowest Daily News, MA, Framingham
Perrone, Carlo..................................53-881
info@ilsecoloxix.it, Pres., IL SECOLO XIX, Genova
Perrota, Michael.......................(914) 674-7422
Mercy College, NY, Dobbs Ferry
Perrotto, Larry J............(618) 937-6412 ext. 102
Chrmn./Pres./CEO, Community Media Group, IL, West Frankfort
Perry, Steven
info@tsa.com, Sales Mgr., TSA, TX, Houston
Perry, D. Gaither
dgperry@heartlandpublications.com, Pres./Pub., Williamson Daily News, WV, Williamson
Perry, Peary...................(512) 653-8545 ext. 14
pperry@austin.rr.com, Self-Syndicator/Columnist, Peary Perry Enterprises, TX, Austin
Perry, Bobby...................................ext. 6306
Circ. Mgr., Texarkana Gazette, TX, Texarkana
Perry, Scott
scott.perry@lee.net, Bus. Ed., Herald & Review, IL, Decatur
Perry, Lynette
lperry@bakercityherald.com, Mgr., Promo., Baker City Herald, OR, Baker City
Perry, Samantha
sperry@bdtonline.com, Mng. Ed., Bluefield Daily Telegraph, WV, Bluefield
Perry, John.............................(407) 894-6610
jperry@hearstsc.com, Int'l Sales Mgr., King Features Syndicate, NY, New York
jperry@hearstsc.com, Int'l Sales Mgr., North America Syndicate, NY, New York
Perry, Bruce
info@bendermachine.com, Mktg. Mgr., Bender Machine, Inc., CA, Los Angeles
Perry, Captain Christopher..........(540) 464-7326
Virginia Military Institute, VA, Lexington
Perry, Wayne
wperry@cincypost.com, Features Ed., The Kentucky Post, OH, Cincinnati
Perry, Dave.............................(303) 750-7555
dlperry@aurorasentinel.com, Ed., Aurora Sentinel, CO, Aurora
Perry, Kelvin W.................................ext. 13
sales@ne-corp.com, Pres., Newspaper Electronics Corp., MO, Kansas City
Persa, R.
info@consolidateddoorintl.com, Contact, New Consolidated International Corp., IL, Chicago
Persico, Joanne
info@gcnpublishing.com, Creative Dir., GCN Publishing, CT, Norwalk
Persily, Larry..................................ext. 439
lpersily@adn.com, Editorial Page Ed., Anchorage Daily News, AK, Anchorage
Persinger, Joanne.............................ext. 219
jpersinger@tribtown.com, Commun./Copy Ed., The Tribune, IN, Seymour
Perskie, James........................609-272-7267
jperskie@pressofac.com, Editorial Page Editor, The Press of Atlantic City, NJ, Pleasantville
Peschka, Darrin.......................(805) 437-0222
dpeschka@venturacountystar.com, News Ed., Ventura County Star, CA, Camarillo
Pesci, Valentino...............................214-211
Mgr., LA NUOVA FERRARA, Ferrara
Pesek, Peter
pes@aci.cvut.cz, Mgr., LIDOVE NOVINY, Prague
Peshave, Manohar...................91233-2311015
mpeshave@yahoo.com, MANAGER, LOKMANYA TRUST, Sangli, Maharashtra
Pesznecker, Katie............................ext. 589
kpesznecker@adn.com, Educ. Reporter, Anchorage Daily News, AK, Anchorage
Petapov, Aleksandr S.
trud1@co.ru, Ed., Publimedia, Moscow
Petermann, Eric........................(815) 232-0117
epetermann@journalstandard.com, Mng. Ed., The Journal-Standard, IL, Freeport
Petermann, Eric
eric.petermann@svherald.com, Managing Editor, Sierra Vista Herald, AZ, Sierra Vista
Peters, Mike...........................(937) 225-2289
Cartoonist, Dayton Daily News, OH, Dayton
Peters, John
jpeters@mediadatatech.com, Pres., Media Data Technology, Inc. (MDTI), MA, South Hadley
Peters, Karen..........................(724) 684-2639
kpeters@tribweb.com, Copy Ed., The Valley Independent, PA, Monessen
Peters, Karen..........................(902) 629-6045
Prodn. Mgr., Pre Press, The Guardian, PE, Charlottetown
Peters, Susan................................ext. 7014
Prodn. Dir., Graphic Arts, Greensburg Daily News, IN, Greensburg
Peters, Scott
scottp@jegi.com, Mng. Dir., Jordan, Edmiston Group, Inc., NY, New York
Peters, Chuck..........................(319) 398-8211
chuck.peters@gazettecommunications.com, Pres., The Gazette, IA, Cedar Rapids
Peters, Scott...........................(703) 462-2049
IT Dir., News USA, Inc., VA, Falls Church
Peters, Martin A.......................(650) 493-0174
mpeters@duarteregister.com, Pres., Duarte Register Systems, Inc., CA, Palo Alto
Petersen, Jeff
jpetersen@lagrandeobserver.com, A&E editor, The Observer, OR, La Grande
Petersen, Ted
tpetersen@fit.edu, Adviser, Florida Institute of Technology, FL, Melbourne
Peterson, Per
phpeterson@marshallindependent.com, News Ed., Independent, MN, Marshall
Peterson, Amanda....................(205) 348-6144
Univ. of Alabama, AL, Tuscaloosa
Peterson, Jeff...........................508.236.0314
jpeterson@thesunchronicle.com, General Manager, The Sun Chronicle, MA, Attleboro
Peterson, Ron..........................(712) 293-4250
ron.peterson@lee.net, Pub., Sioux City Journal, IA, Sioux City
Peterson, Paul..........................(641) 422-4304
North Iowa Area Cmty. College, IA, Mason City
Peterson, Susan.......................(806) 742-3388
Student Media Dir., Texas Tech. Univ., TX, Lubbock
Peterson, Theresa
tpeterson@ironmountaindailynews.com, Photo Ed., The Daily News, MI, Iron Mountain
Peterson, Jason..............................ext. 1048
jpeterson@portervillerecorder.com, Asst. Sports Ed., The Porterville Recorder, CA, Porterville
Peterson, Christine...................(661) 395-7418
cpeterson@bakersfield.com, News Ed., The Bakersfield Californian, CA, Bakersfield
Peterson, Craig.........................(306) 657-6336
cpeterson@sp.canwest.com, Mgr., Promotions, The StarPhoenix, SK, Saskatoon
Peterson, June
jpeterson@mediabids.com, Vice Pres., Mediabids, Inc., CT, Winsted
Peterson, Karen........................(253) 597-8434
karen.peterson@thenewstribune.com, Exec. Ed., The News Tribune, WA, Tacoma
Peterson Arnold, Mary
mary.arnold@sdstate.edu, Head, South Dakota State University, SD, Brookings
Petracci, John
jpetracci@sjnews.com, Circ. Dir., The Gloucester County Times, NJ, Woodbury
Petracci, John
jpetracci@sjnewsco.com, Circ. Dir., The News of Cumberland County, NJ, Bridgeton
Petrak, Michael........................(303) 954-6462
mpetrak@medianewsgroup.com, Vice Pres. of Sales, MediaNews Group Inc, CO, Denver
Petretti, Ken
ken@kenpetretti.com, Producer, Ken Petretti Productions, LLC, NJ, Maywood
Petrich, Bernie........................(813) 259-8056
Dir., Ad Ops, The Tampa Tribune, FL, Tampa
Petrichev, Angel
office@narodnodelo.bg, Ed. in Chief, NARODNO DELO, Varna
Petrie, Jay
jpetrie@starledger.com, Adv. Dir., Display, The Star-Ledger, NJ, Newark
Petrie, Bob.............................(920) 453-5143
bpetrie@sheboygan.gannett.com, City Gov't, The Sheboygan Press, WI, Sheboygan
Petrillo, Richard
news@herkimertelegram.com, Mng. Ed., The Evening Telegram, NY, Herkimer
Petroff, Karen
kspetroff@punxsutawneyspirit.com, Prodn. Supvr., Composing, The Punxsutawney Spirit, PA, Punxsutawney
Petrovits, Nicholas...................(414) 277-7255
Milwaukee School of Engineering, WI, Milwaukee
Petrowich, Tim
editor@dailyrepublicannews.com, Mng. Ed., The Marion Daily Republican, IL, Marion
Petroziello, Guy.............................ext. 4162
gpetroziello@phillyburbs.com, Editorial Page Ed., Bucks County Courier Times, PA, Levittown
Pett, Joel...............................(859) 231-3443
jpett@herald-leader.com, Cartoonist, Lexington Herald-Leader, KY, Lexington
Pettengill, Carol
cpettengill@staffordgroup.com, Circ. Dir, The Daily News, MI, Greenville
Pettit, Leann................(610) 933-8926 ext. 627
lpettit@phoenixvillenews.com, Ed., The Phoenix, PA, Phoenixville
Petty, Matthew.........................(415) 777-7983
mpetty@sfchronicle.com, Sr. Art Dir., San Francisco Chronicle, CA, San Francisco
Petty, David B..........................(318) 362-0345
dpetty@thenewsstar.com, Pres./Pub., The News-Star, LA, Monroe
Petykiewicz, Sandy...................(517) 768-4810
publisher@citpat.com, Pub., The Jackson Citizen Patriot, MI, Jackson
Petykiewicz, Ed........................(734) 994-6870
editor@annarbornews.com, Ed., The Ann Arbor News, MI, Ann Arbor
Peveto, Suzanne
speveto@gatehousemedia.com, Pub., Southwest Daily News, LA, Sulphur
Peyrat, Anne............................(805) 564-5244
apeyrat@newspress.com, Spec. Sections Ed., Santa Barbara News-Press, CA, Santa Barbara
Pezzano, Jeff............................419-724-6280
jpezzano@toledoblade.com, Adv. Mgr., Retail, The Blade, OH, Toledo
Pfeifer, John
john.pfeifer@lee.net, Adv. Dir., The Times-News, ID, Twin Falls
Pfeifer, Lisa
info@fakebrains.com, Vice Pres./Sales Dir., Fake Brains, Inc., CO, Littleton
Pfeiffer, Ursula
nav@pressenetz.de, Proprietor, Hersbrucker Zeitung, Hersbruck
Pfingsten, Ernst Andreas..........................9900
verlag@cellesche-zeitung.de, Proprietor, CELLESCHE ZEITUNG, Celle
Pfortner, Martin
m.pfortner@verlagshaus-jaumann.de, Bus. Mgr., OBERBADISCHES VOLKSBLATT, Lorrach
Pfromm, Markus
anzeigen@hersfelder-zeitung.de, Bus. Mgr., Hersfelder Zeitung, Bad Hersfeld
Phaneuf, Wayne E......................(413) 788-1315
wphaneuf@repub.com, Exec. Ed., The Republican, MA, Springfield
Phares, Douglas D.
dougphares@sanduskyregister.com, Vice Pres./Pub., Sandusky Register, OH, Sandusky
Phelps, Dan.............................(978) 970-4640
dphelps@Lowellsun.com, Columnist/Copy Ed., The Sun, MA, Lowell
Phelps, Dale............................(253) 597-8681
dale.phelps@thenewstribune.com, Mng. Ed., The News Tribune, WA, Tacoma
Phelps, Michael
mphelps@washingtonexaminer.com, CEO/Pub., The Washington Examiner, VA, Springfield
Phelps, Ashton.........................(504) 826-3170
aphelps@aol.com, Publisher, The Times Picayune, LA, New Orleans
Phelps, Louise D........................912-220-2759
phelpscutler@aol.com, Pres., Phelps, Cutler & Associates, GA, Savannah
Phelps, Louise D.
phelpscutler@aol.com, Pres., Phelps, Cutler & Associates, GA
Philipps, Mike
mphillips@cincypost.com, Ed., The Kentucky Post, OH, Cincinnati
Phillips, Stu
news@seminoleproducer.com, Science/Technology Ed., The Seminole Producer, OK, Seminole
Phillips, Bruce.........................(978) 970-4638
bphillips@lowellsun.com, Copy Ed., The Sun, MA, Lowell
Phillips, Tom...........................(951) 782-7696
tphillips@pe.com, PR Mgr., The Press-Enterprise, CA, Riverside
Phillips, Fred..........................(318) 362-0256
Multimedia Ed., The News-Star, LA, Monroe
Phillips, Bob...........................(415) 382-7334
bphillips@marinij.com, Prodn. Mgr., Pressroom, Marin Independent Journal, CA, Novato
Phillips, Sarah
sphillips@olivetcollege.edu, Editor, Olivet College, MI, Olivet
Phillips, Bradley......................(541) 338-2215

Controller, The Register-Guard, OR, Eugene
Phillips, Kathleen
ka-phillips@tamu.edu, Exec. Sec./Treasurer, North American Agricultural Journalists, TX, College Station
Phillips, Dan..............(208) 664-0220 ext. 5001
dphillips@cdapress.com, Circ. Dir., Coeur d'Alene Press, ID, Coeur d'Alene
Phillips, Greg 401 0123
northern.news@icn.co.nz, Mng. Dir., NORTHERN NEWS
Phillips, Julie..........................(706) 208-2221
julie.phillips@onlineathens.com, Arts/Entertainment Ed., Athens Banner-Herald, GA, Athens
Phillips, Ann ....ext. 321
ann.phillips@muscatinejournal.com, Features Ed., Muscatine Journal, IA, Muscatine
Phillips, Valerie.......................(801) 236-6099
vphillips@desnews.com, Food Ed., Deseret News, UT, Salt Lake City
Phillips, Dean...............................ext. 5084
phillde@hobartbrothers.com, Welding Equip. Mgr., ITW Hobart Brothers Co., OH, Troy
Phillips, Judy..................................ext. 241
jphillips@msmgmt.com, Bus. Mgr., La Grange Daily News, GA, LaGrange
Phillips, Dale ....(734) 994-6968
dphillips@annarbornews.com, Controller, The Ann Arbor News, MI, Ann Arbor
Phillips, Suzanne H...................(214) 640-3104
sphillips@beldenassociates.com, Sr. Vice Pres., Belden Associates, TX, Dallas
Phillips, Jan ....(864) 298-4294
lifestyle@greenvillenews.com, Books Ed., The Greenville News, SC, Greenville
Phillips, Tim
timphillips@oxfordeagle.com, Pres./Pub., The Oxford Eagle, MS, Oxford
Phillips, Glenna...............................ext. 143
gphillips@ccdailyrecord.com, Bus. Mgr., The Canon City Daily Record, CO, Canon City
Phillips, Larry ....(419) 521-7238
lbphillips@nncogannett.com, Sports Ed., News Journal, OH, Mansfield
Phillips-Long, Barbara ....(717) 240-7125 ext. 231
bphillips@cumberlink.com, Assoc. Ed., The Sentinel, PA, Carlisle
Philpott, Tom..........................(703) 830-6863
tomphilpott@militaryupdate.com, Self-Syndicator, Military Update, VA, Centreville
Pi-Ly, Wang
news@udn.com, Pub., ECONOMIC DAILY NEWS, Taipei
Piaggio, Griselda 425 0101
gpiaggio@eldia.com, Gen. Mgr., El Dia, La Plata, Buenos Aires
Piao, Liang Guo
ycwbic@ycwb.com.cn, Pres., YANGCHENG WANBAO, Guangzhou, Guangzhou
Picardi, Jennifer ....(508) 427-4012
jpicardi@enterprisenews.com, Adv. Coord., Nat'l/Preprint, The Enterprise, MA, Randolph
Picarra, Manuel Madeira
publicidade@diariodosul.com.pt, MD, DIARIO DO SUL, Evora
Piccato, Franco
fpiccato@lavozdelinterior.com.ar, Ed., La Voz del Interior, Cordoba, Provincia de Cordoba
Piccola, Janelle........................303-431-5909
janellepiccola@aol.com, Mktg. Mgr., Chuck Blevins & Assoc., FL, Naple
Picht, Randy
rpicht@ap.org, Bureau Chief, Kansas Associated Press Managing Editors Association, MO, Kansas City
rpicht@ap.org, Bureau Chief, Missouri Associated Press Managing Editors, MO, Kansas City
Pickard, John E.......................(210) 658-0614
techenergy@techenergy.com, Pres., Tech-Energy Co., TX, Cibolo
Pickens, Jim
jpickens@messenger-inquirer.com, Sports Ed., Messenger-Inquirer, KY, Owensboro
Pickering, Jane........................(309) 820-3408
jpickering@pantagraph.com, Day Desk Ed., The Pantagraph, IL, Bloomington
Pickering, Mark ....(309) 820-3252
mpickering@pantagraph.com, Ed., The Pantagraph, IL, Bloomington
Pickering, Vernon W.
issun@candwbvi.net, Ed., THE ISLAND SUN, Tortola
Pickett, Emmett T. ....(650) 204-4068
emmett@locationgreen.us, Exec. Coord., The Answer Team Networks, CA, Menlo Park
Pickett, Britt...........................(251) 219-5003
bpickett@press-register.com, Adv. Mgr., Classified, Press-Register, AL, Mobile
Pico, Kelli ....(209) 722-1812 ext. 506
kellis@pspub.com, Controller, Pacific Sierra Publishing, Inc., CA, Merced
Piech, Gary.............................(209) 588-4560
gpiech@uniondemocrat.com, Adv. Dir., The Union Democrat, CA, Sonora
Pierard, Louis
editor@hbtoday.co.nz, Ed., HAWKE'S BAY TODAY
Pierce, Michele ....(867) 668-2060
michele@whitehorsestar.com, Adv. Mgr., Whitehorse Star, YT, Whitehorse
Pierce, Bill ....(416) 947-2021
bill.pierce@sunmedia.ca, Sports Ed., The Toronto Sun, ON, Toronto
Pierce, David ....(603) 594-6443
News Ed., The Telegraph, NH, Hudson
Pierce, Michael G.....................(440) 544-2607
mike.pierce@theaustin.com, Sr. Vice Pres., Sales/Mktg. Gen. Mgr., The Austin Company, OH, Cleveland
Pierce, Scott ....(801) 237-2146
pierce@desnews.com, Television Ed., Deseret News, UT, Salt Lake City
Pierce, Jackie ....(867) 668-2063
jackie@whitehorsestar.com, Pres./Pub., Whitehorse Star, YT, Whitehorse
Pierce, Rebecca........................(269) 388-8421
rpierce@kalamazoogazette.com, Ed., Kalamazoo Gazette, MI, Kalamazoo
Piercy, Janet ....(503) 244-7426
jcpclemens@yahoo.com, Pres., Piercy & Barclay Designers, Inc., OR, Portland
Pieronek, Cathy ....(574) 631-4385
Univ. of Notre Dame Engineering School, IN, Notre Dame
Pierquet, Chelly ....(920) 468-5477
cmp@advancesystems.com, Office Mgr., Advance Systems, Inc., WI, Green Bay
Pierre, Leslie
gvoice@caribsurf.com, Pub./Mng. Ed., THE GRENADIAN VOICE, Saint Georges
Pieters Mayfield, Nancy
nmayfield@smwc.edu, Chair, Saint Mary-of-the-Woods College, IN, Saint Mary-of-the-Woods
Pietrafesa, Dan........................(845) 437-4849
dpietraf@poughkee.gannett.com, Sports Ed., Poughkeepsie Journal, NY, Poughkeepsie
Pietrafesa, Nora.......................(845) 437-4758
npietraf@poughkee.gannett.com, HR Mgr., Poughkeepsie Journal, NY, Poughkeepsie
Pietrangelo, Pete ....(906) 483-2216
ppietrangelo@mininggazette.com, Sports Ed., The Daily Mining Gazette, MI, Houghton
Pietropaolo, Janet ....(717) 255-8130
pietropaolo@pnco.com, Adv. Mgr., Classified, The Patriot-News, PA, Mechanicsburg
Pietrowicz, Peggy
ppietrowicz@uniondemocrat.com, Adv. Mgr., Classified, The Union Democrat, CA, Sonora
Pigden, Richard 873-3671
photosynd@ft.com, Picture Synd., Financial Times, ENG, London
Pignone, Ray ....ext. 3326
Ed., The Daily Mail, NY, Catskill
Piirainen, Matti
toimitus@kainuunsanomat.fi, Ed. in Chief, KAINUUN SANOMAT, Kajaani, Oulu
Pike, Daniel.............................270-783-3276
dpike@bgdailynews.com, City Ed., Daily News, KY, Bowling Green
Piller, Cindy ....(303) 776-2244 ext. 338
cpiller@times-call.com, NIE Coord., Times-Call, CO, Longmont
Pilvelis, Algirdas 261 0544
centr@aidas.lt, Ed., LIETUVOS AIDAS, Vilnius
Pinder, Susan 352.867.4060
susan.pinder@gvillesun.com, Advertising Director, Ocala Star-Banner, FL, Ocala
Ping, Jiang
webmaster@zjnews.com.cn, Ed. in Chief, ZHEJIANG RIBAO, Hangzhou, Zhejiang
Pinheiro, Walter
tribunadabahia@tribunadabahia.com.br, Pres., Tribuna da Bahia, Salvador, Bahia
Pinto, Dolores ....(302) 324-2450
dpinto@delawareonline.com, Vice Pres., HR, The News Journal, DE, New Castle
Pinto, Omar
andespacif@aol.com, Pres., Latin Admerica, Inc., FL, Miami
Pinzon, Mario Rodriguez....................410-5066
sredacc@cc-net.net, Gen. Mgr., Sociedad Anonima, Bogota, D.C.
Piontkowski, Jamie ....(920) 453-5130
jpiontkowski@sheboygan.gannett.com, Online Ed., The Sheboygan Press, WI, Sheboygan
Piotrowski, Mariusz
mariusz.piotrowski@krakow.agora.pl, Sales Dir., GAZETA W KRAKOWIE, Krakow
Piper, Morley L.
mlp@nenews.org, Exec. Dir., New England Newspaper & Press Association, Inc., MA, Dedham
Piper, Winnie ....ext. 119
wpiperads@robdailynews.com, Data Processing Mgr., Daily News, IL, Robinson
Piper, Morley 978-338-2555
mlpiper52@comcast.net, Exec. Dir., Newspaper Association Managers, Inc., MA, Essex
Pippin, Martin
marin.pippin@augustachronicle.com, CFO, The Augusta Chronicle, GA, Augusta
Pirch, Hans 725660
hans.pirch@bergedorfer-zeitung.de, Bus. Mgr., BERGEDORFER ZEITUNG, Hamburg
Pirovano Pena, Javier 603 400
Pres., Diario Popular, Asuncion
Pirthauer, Johann
johann.pirthauer@frankenpost.de, Ed. in Chief, SELBER TAGBLATT FRANKEN-POST, Hof
Pisani, Italo
redaccion@rionegro.com.ar, Ed., Rio Negro, General Roca, Provincia de Rio Negro
Pisarik, Kris............................(978) 970-4637
kpisarik@lowellsun.com, Asst. Mng. Ed., Local News, The Sun, MA, Lowell
Piscia, Jason ....(217) 788-1525
jason.piscia@sj-r.com, Online Ed., The State Journal-Register, IL, Springfield
Pistello, Michael.....................239-574-1110
mpistello@breezenewspapers.com, Photo Dept. Mgr., Cape Coral Breeze, FL, Cape Coral
Pitlo, Stan
stan.pitlo@peninsulaclarion.com, Pub., Peninsula Clarion, AK, Kenai
Pitlo, Stan
pitlo@alaska.net, Pub., Southeastern Newspapers, Inc., AK, Kenai
Pitluck, Steven
office@ponyexpress.net, CEO, Brown Mannschreck Business System, MO, Saint Joseph
Pitrone, James...............................ext. 5051
dralis@phillyburbs.com, Mng. Ed., Presentation, Bucks County Courier Times, PA, Levittown
Pittman, Charles V. ....(574) 236-1768
cpittman@schurz.com, Sr. Vice Pres., Newspaper Opns., The Reporter-Times, IN, Martinsville
Pittman, Ronald ....(740) 593-2612
Assoc. Prof., Ohio University, OH, Athens
Pittman, John S. ....(864) 298-4165
jpittman@greenvil.gannett.com, Sr. Vice Pres./Exec. Ed., The Greenville News, SC, Greenville
Pittman, Daniel.........................(336) 888-3651
dpittman@hpe.com, Circ. Dir., High Point Enterprise, NC, High Point
Pittman, Garth
pittman@sou.edu, Chair, Southern Oregon University, OR, Ashland
Pitts, Mac ....(404) 894-7732
Georgia Inst. of Technology, GA, Atlanta
Pitts, Jim
jpitts@als4business.com, Pres., Alternative Learning Solutions, PA, West Chester
Pitts, Gary ....(916) 321-1418
gpitts@sacbee.com, Audience Devel./Membership Servs. Mgr., Opns., The Sacramento Bee, CA, Sacramento
Pizarro, Mariano Cervantes
editorial@periodicovictoria.com.mx, Ed., Victoria de Durango, Durango, Durango
Placak, Marlene ....(951) 782-7758
mplacak@pe.com, Adv. Mgr., Regl., The Press-Enterprise, CA, Riverside
Plakias, Mark
plakias@tiac.com, Gen. Mgr., Strategic Telemedia, NY, New York
Planakis, Beth ....(561) 630-2400
bplanakis@bankrate.com, Mktg. Dir., Bankrate.com, FL, North Palm Beach
Plath, Debra ....(319) 335-5786
Univ. of Iowa, IA, Iowa City
Platt, Eric................................(517) 750-1200
Spring Arbor Univ., MI, Spring Arbor
Platt, John...............................(574) 296-5882
jplatt@etruth.com, Prodn. Mgr., Pressroom, The Elkhart Truth, IN, Elkhart
Platt, Pam ....(502) 582-4578
pplatt@courier-journal.com, Editorial Writer, The Courier-Journal, KY, Louisville
Platte, Mark.............................(808) 535-8203
mplatte@honoluluadvertiser.com, Ed., Honolulu Star-Advertiser, HI, Honolulu
Plazas, David ....(239) 335-0224
dplazas@news-press.com, Editorial/Community Conversation Ed., The News-Press, FL, Fort Myers
Plenke, Mark.............................(952) 358-8716
mark.plenke@normandale.edu, Advisor, Normandale Community College, MN, Bloomington
Plessis, Tim Du
timdup@beeld.com, Ed., BEELD, Auckland Park, Johannesburg
Pletcher, James................................Bus. Ed.
Herald-Standard, PA, Uniontown
Pletsch, Karen
kpletsch@chroniclenewsgroup.com, Adv. Dir., Kane County Chronicle, IL, Saint Charles
Plevka, John ....(309) 686-3159
jplevka@pjstar.com, Mng. Ed., Journal Star, IL, Peoria
Plimpton, Michelle
mplimpton@nvsmedia.com, Pres., NVS Interactive Media, NY, Williamsville
Ploenges, Demi
distrubtion@tbw.com.au, Circ. Mgr., BORDER WATCH
Plog, Kari...............................(253) 535-7494
Pacific Lutheran Univ., WA, Tacoma
Plombat, Alain
redac.ig@midilibre.com, MD, MIDI LIBRE/MIDI LIBRE DIMANCHE, Montpellier
Plooster, Matthew.....................(208) 239-3140
Circ. Mgr., Newspapers in Educ./Sales, Idaho State Journal, ID, Pocatello
Plothow, Roger ....(208) 500-1800
rplothow@postregister.com, Editor and Publisher, Post Register, ID, Idaho Falls
Plothow, Roger
rplothow@postregister.com, Pres., Newspaper Association of Idaho, ID, Idaho Falls
Plotkin, Paul H.
stichtco@aol.com, Pres., Herman H. Sticht Co., Inc., NY, Brooklyn
Plumley, Monique.....................(864) 599-4124
mplumlwy@lg.com, Contact, Ch2MHill Lockwood Greene, SC, Spartanburg
Plunkett, Bob ....(501) 425-9737
carnews@aol.com, Ed. in Chief, New Car News Syndicate, AR, Little Rock
Ply, Michael P..........................(616) 222-5444
mply@grpress.com, Dir., Finance/HR, The Grand Rapids Press, MI, Grand Rapids
Plyler, Tami.................(603) 668-4321 ext. 321
tplyler@unionleader.com, Vice Pres., New Media, New Hampshire Union Leader/New Hampshire Sunday News, NH, Manchester
Plyler, Tami
tplyler@unionleader.com, Vice President of News, New Hampshire Union Leader/New Hampshire Sunday News, NH, Manchester
Pobre, Hermogenes P.
editorial@mb.com.ph, Pub., BALITA, Manila
Pocchiola, Andres M.
prensita@teletel.com.ar, Pub., La Prensita, City of Buenos Aires
Pochat Alurralde, Jose 484-2200
redaccion@lagaceta.com.ar, Gen. Mgr., La Gaceta, San Miguel de Tucuman, Provincia de Tucuman

Podro, Robert
info@ipcb.co.uk, Sr. Partner/Gen. Mgr., International Press Cutting Bureau, ENG, London
Poe, Pat ....(870) 543-1435
ppoe@pbcommercial.com, Mgmt. Info Servs./Online Mgr., Pine Bluff Commercial, AR, Pine Bluff
Poepping, Don ....(408) 278-3450
dpoepping@mercurynews.com, Adv. Dir., Targeted Delivery, San Jose Mercury News, CA, San Jose
Pogue, Greg....................................ext. 170
pogue@dnj.com, Exec. Sports Ed., The Daily News Journal, TN, Murfreesboro
Pohjonen, Ville
ville.pohjonen@sss.fi, Editor-in-Chief, SALON SEUDUN SANOMAT, Salo
Pohly, George
george.pohly@macombdaily.com, Sports Ed., The Macomb Daily, MI, Mount Clemens
Poignant, Gary.........................(780) 468-0276
gary.poignant@edm.sunpub.com, Wire Ed., The Edmonton Sun, AB, Edmonton
Poirier, Kevin
kpoirier@kenoshanews.com, Chief Photographer, Kenosha News, WI, Kenosha
Poirier, Alan.............................(403) 528-5691
apoirier@medicinehatnews.com, Mng. Ed., Medicine Hat News, AB, Medicine Hat
Poirier, John
dicircmgr@bellsouth.net, Circ. Dir., The Daily Iberian, LA, New Iberia
Pokas, Betty
bpokas@timesleaderonline.com, News Ed., The Times Leader, OH, Martins Ferry
Polachek, Neal
tkg@kelseygroup.com, CEO, BIAKelsey, NJ, Princeton
Polanco Fuentes, Rogelio
jrebelde@teleda.get.cma.net, Dir., JUVENTUD REBELDE, Havana
Polaneczky, Ronnie
polaner@phillynews.com, Columnist, News, The Philadelphia Daily News, PA, Philadelphia
Polasik, George ....(847) 981-9399
polasikg@corp.inxintl.com, Sr. Vice Pres.-Offset Div./COO, INX International Ink Co., IL, Schaumburg
Polcyn, Dave...........................(419) 521-7218
dpolcyn@nncogannett.com, Photo Ed., News Journal, OH, Mansfield
Polden, Adam 715-738-1642
adam.polden@lee.net, Circ. District Mgr., The Chippewa Herald, WI, Chippewa Falls
Poling, Martha
mpoling@news-banner.com, Controller, News-Banner, IN, Bluffton
Polk, Richard ....(410) 770-4078
Online Ed., The Star-Democrat, MD, Easton
Polk, Alan
apolk@ccdailyrecord.com, Prodn. Mgr., The Canon City Daily Record, CO, Canon City
Pollak, Richard A.
support@emergingtechnology.com, CEO, Emerging Technology Consultants, Inc., MN, Saint Paul
Pollak, Sam...............................(607) 441-7208
spollak@thedailystar.com, Ed., The Daily Star, NY, Oneonta
Pollak, William L.
cservice@nylj.com, Pres./CEO, New York Law Journal
Pollard, Pamela........................(912) 489-9420
ppollard@statesboroherald.com, Adv. Mgr., Classified, Statesboro Herald, GA, Statesboro
Pollard, Robert....................................ext. 41
Pressroom Mgr., State Gazette, TN, Dyersburg
Pollard, Linda
lpollard@ravallirepublic.com, Bus. Mgr., Ravalli Republic, MT, Hamilton
Pollio, Luis Mario 662 4036
Gen. Mgr., Diario El Liberal, Balcarce, Provincia de Buenos Aires
Pollock, Jennifer.......................(815) 987-1379
jpollock@rrstar.com, Asst. Mng. Ed., Rockford Register Star, IL, Rockford
Polo, Gabriele
gpolo@ilmanifesto.it, Adv. Mgr, IL MANIFESTO, Rome
Polodna, Duane ....(402) 444-1480
duane.polodna@owh.com, CFO/Sr. Vice Pres., Omaha World-Herald, NE, Omaha
Pomeroy, Courtney....................(706) 208-2215
Features Ed., Athens Banner-Herald, GA, Athens
Pona, Steve ....(204) 697-7264
Steve.Pona@freepress.mb.ca, Bus. Ed., Winnipeg Free Press, MB, Winnipeg
Ponce, Hernan...........................(415) 777-6826
Adv. Vice Pres., Nat'l, San Francisco Chronicle, CA, San Francisco
Pond, Jerry
jerry.ponde@cheboygantribune.com, Prodn. Mgr., Pressroom, Cheboygan Daily Tribune, MI, Cheboygan
Ponder, Keith
kponder@glasgowdailytimes.com, Pub., Glasgow Daily Times, KY, Glasgow
Ponder, Brian ....(828) 232-5883
bponder@citizen-times.com, Metro Ed., The Asheville Citizen-Times, NC, Asheville
Ponder, Doug ....(859) 622-1489
Eastern Kentucky Univ., KY, Richmond
Pons, Robert
sales@smartserv.com, Pres./CEO, SmartServ Online, PA, Plymouth Meeting
Ponte, Jean Viansson
bienpublic@lebienpublic.fr, Gen. Dir., LE BIEN PUBLIC, 21000 Dijon
Pontius, Harry ....(760) 951-6224
Prodn. Dir., Daily Press, CA, Victorville
Ponton, Bev ....(519) 631-2790
tj_mail@sympatico.ca, Adv. Mgr., St. Thomas Times-Journal, ON, Saint Thomas
Ponzio, Melvina ....(408) 920-5435
mponzio@mercurynews.com, Circ. Mgr., Home Delivery, San Jose Mercury News, CA, San Jose
Poobalan, Afhley
poobalana@avusa.co.za, Adv. Mgr, THE HERALD, Port Elizabeth, Eastern Cape
Poole, Brenda ....(540) 665-4948
bpoole@winchesterstar.com, Prodn. Mgr., The Winchester Star, VA, Winchester
Pooley, J.D.
jdpooley@sentinel-tribune.com, Photo Ed., Sentinel Company, OH, Bowling Green
Pooley, Eduardo 339 1070
epooley@df.cl, Gen. Mgr., Ediciones Financieras S.A., Las Condes
Poorman, Kyle
kyle.poorman@tribstar.com, Circ. Mgr., Single Copy, The Tribune Star, IN, Terre Haute
Pop, Adrian
renasterea@renasterea.ro, Ed. in Chief, RENASTEREA BANATEANA, Timisoara
Pope, Steve
spope@hucklemedia.com, COO, Huckle Media, LLC, MI, Traverse City
Pope, Greg
gregpope1@compuserve.com, Division Pres., Mobile Reclamation System/MRS (Div. of Marpax), CA, West Sacramento
Pope, Eric ....(248) 204-2210
epope@ltu.edu, Lawrence Technological Univ., MI, Southfield
Pope, Kathy ....(910) 230-2021
kpope@dunndailyrecord.com, Adv. Dir., The Daily Record, NC, Dunn
Pope, Leta.................................(919) 789-2084
leta@ncpress.com, Network Adv. Dir., North Carolina Press Service, Inc., NC, Raleigh
Pope Robbins, Laura ....(631) 244-5023
Dowling College, NY, Oakdale
Popejoy, Richard
rpopejoy@mitchellrepublic.com, Prodn. Foreman, Pressroom, The Daily Republic, SD, Mitchell
Popham, Lynne 405 2744
lynne.popham@snl.co.nz, Northern Regional Manager, NORTHERN NEWS
Popiel, David ....(423) 623-6171 ext. 3110
dpopiel@xtn.net, Ed., Newport Plain Talk, TN, Newport
Popkins, Ned............................(407) 420-5051
npopkins@orlandosentinel.com, Bus. News Ed., Orlando Sentinel, FL, Orlando
Porcsin, Zsolt
naplo@iscomp.hu, Ed. in Chief, HAJDU-BIHARI NAPLO, Debrecen, Hajdu-Bihar
Porras, Andres Marsano
elsol@amauta.rcp.net.pe, Pres., EL SOL, Lima 14
Port, Robert ....(518) 454-5064
bport@timesunion.com, Sr. Investigations Ed., Times Union, NY, Albany
Portas, Steve
steve.portas@qt.com.au, Gen. Mgr., THE QUEENSLAND TIMES, West Ipswich
Portela Medrano, Jesus
local.faro@epi.es, Ed., FARO DE VIGO, Vigo, Pontevedra
Porter, Mark
microprint@vaxxine.com, Pres., Dienamic Microprint, ON, Saint Catharines
Porter, Chris.............................(941) 206-1134
porter@sun-herald.com, Executive Editor The Sun, Charlotte Sun, FL, Charlotte Harbor
Porter, Andy......................................ext. 282
aporter@wwub.com, Political Ed., Walla Walla Union-Bulletin, WA, Walla Walla
Porter, Carol
cporter@courier-herald.com, Gen. Mgr., The Courier Herald, GA, Dublin
Porter, Wayne
wporter@bottcher.com, Vice Pres., Mktg., Bottcher America Corp., MD, Belcamp
Porter, Shane ....(580) 221-6531
sporter@ardmoreite.com, Online Ed., The Daily Ardmoreite, OK, Ardmore
Porter, Bill................................(303) 820-1755
bporter@denverpost.com, Asst. Entertainment Ed., The Denver Post, CO, Denver
Porter, Don ....(801) 625-4205
dporter@standard.net, Editorial Page Ed., Standard-Examiner, UT, Ogden
Porter, Jim......................................ext. 8351
jim.porter@cantonrep.com, Circ. Dir., The Repository, OH, Canton
Porter, David..............................217-241-1300
dporter@ilinoispress.com, Dir. Commun./Mktg., Illinois Press Association, IL, Springfield
Porter, Glen ....(256) 549-2010
glen.porter@gadsdentimes.com, Pub., The Gadsden Times, AL, Gadsden
Porter, Brian 308 2470
brian.porter@inl.co.za, Joint GM: Revenue, THE MERCURY, Greyville
Porter, Jean ....(502) 582-4244
jporter@courier-journal.com, Mng. Ed., The Courier-Journal, KY, Louisville
Porterfield, Barry 405.238.6464
bporterfield@pvdemocrat.com, News Ed., Pauls Valley Democrat, OK, Pauls Valley
Porto, Marisa ....(757) 247-4766
mporto@dailypress.com, Mng. Ed., Digital, Daily Press, VA, Newport News
Portwood, Gina ....(859) 622-1881
Eastern Kentucky Univ., KY, Richmond
Porubsky, Juraj
jporubsky@perex.sk, Ed. in Chief, PRAVDA, Bratislava
Posavetz, Dave
dave.posavetz@macombdaily.com, Photo Dept. Mgr., The Macomb Daily, MI, Mount Clemens
Posner, Jack ....(954) 427-8068
Self-Syndicator/Writer, Jack Posner Syndicate, FL, Deerfield Beach
Possamai, Paolo
segreteria.redazione@ilpiccolo.it, Dir., IL PICCOLO, Trieste
Post, Gary...................................785-832-7168
gpost@ljworld.com, The World Co.- Lawrence, Kan., Journal-World, KS, Lawrence
Post, Connie ....(937) 225-2441
cpost@coxohio.com, Fashion/Style Ed., Dayton Daily News, OH, Dayton
Post, Kevin ....(609) 272-7250
kpost@pressofac.com, Local Content Producer/Business, The Press of Atlantic City, NJ, Pleasantville
Post, Dave
dpost@morning-times.com, Sports Ed., Morning Times, PA, Sayre
Post, Gary...................................785-832-7168
gpost@ljworld.com, Production Manager-Press, The World Co.- Lawrence, Kan., Journal-World, KS, Lawrence
Post, Connie ....(937) 225-2441
cpost@coxohio.com, Fashion/Style Ed., Dayton Daily News, OH, Dayton
Postigo, Carmen
eferoma@efe.it, Rep., EFE News Services - Rome, Italy, Rome
Potesky, Ron
support@pantone.com, Pres., Pantone, Inc., NJ, Carlstadt
Potter, Dan ....(573) 882-5707
potterds@missouri.edu, General Manager, Columbia Missourian, MO, Columbia
Potter, Jim................................(617) 619-6245
jpotter@bostonherald.com, Design/Prodn. Ed., Boston Herald, MA, Boston
Potter, Bruce ....(703) 878-8006
bpotter@insidenova.com, Pub., News & Messenger, VA, Woodbridge
Potter, Lori ....(308) 233-9730
Farm/Agriculture Ed., Kearney Hub, NE, Kearney
Potter, Jon ....(802) 254-2311 ext. 149
Arts/Entertainment Ed., Brattleboro Reformer, VT, Brattleboro
Potter, Elliott
cepotter@jdnews.com, Political/Gov't Ed., The Daily News, NC, Jacksonville
Potter, Bruce ....(703) 878-8006
bpotter@insidenova.com, Pub., Manassas Journal Messenger, VA, Manassas
Potter, Skip...............................(703) 680-4733
spotter@cinecom.com, Pres., Cinecom Corp., VA, Woodbridge
Pottorff, Tom
tpottorff@news-herald.com, Circ. Mgr., The News-Herald, OH, Willoughby
Pottorff, Thomas ....(518) 792-3213
sara@poststar.com, Circ. Dir., The Post-Star, NY, Glens Falls
Potts, Jeffrey
jeff@jpmediapartners.com, Principal, JP Media Partners, CA, Folsom
Potts, Keith...............................(757) 247-4940
kpotts@dailypress.com, HR Dir., Daily Press, VA, Newport News
Potts, Jeffrey
jeff@jpmediapartners.com, Principal, JP Media Partners, CA, Folsom
Potts, Joe...................................(610) 622-8840
Circ. Dir., Delaware County Daily Times, PA, Primos
Poulson, Thad
sitkanews@hotmail.com, Exec. Ed., The Daily Sitka Sentinel, AK, Sitka
Pound, Josh
joshp@npgco.com, Sports Ed., Atchison Globe, KS, Atchison
Povey, Fred ....(202) 383-6089
fpovey@mctinfoservices.com, Dir., News Servs., McClatchy-Tribune Information Services, DC, Washington
Pow, Ewan
epow@brandonsun.com, Pub., Brandon Sun, MB, Brandon
Powell, Rusty ....(770) 428-9411 ext. 400
rpowell@mdjonlin.com, Circ. Mgr., Times-Journal, Inc., GA, Marietta
Powell, Todd......................................ext. 224
Features Ed., The Daily Sentinel, CO, Grand Junction
Powell, Jeree ....(409) 721-2443
Bus. Mgr., Port Arthur News, TX, Port Arthur
Powell, Chris ....ext. 307
cpowell@journalinquirer.com, Mng. Ed./Vice Pres., News, Journal Inquirer, CT, Manchester
Powell, Cory ....(612) 673-7421
cory.powell@startribune.com, Mng. Ed., Presentation/Innovation, Star Tribune, MN, Minneapolis
Powell, Cathy ....(248) 377-7570
cathy.powell@fanucrobotics.com, Sr. Mktg. Analyst, FANUC Robotics America, Inc., MI, Rochester Hills
Power, Ted
tpower@theadvertiser.com, Pub., Reno Gazette-Journal, NV, Reno
Power, Mike
news@thebarrieexaminer.com, Pub., The Barrie Examiner, ON, Barrie
Power, Andrew.......................Features Ed.
andrew.power@nielsen.com, Features Ed., Nielsen Entertainment News Wire, MA, Boston

Powers, Arthur S.............(423) 929-3111 ext. 346
publisher@johnsoncitypress.com, Pub., Johnson City Press, TN, Johnson City
Powers, John
info@chemetron.com, Mgr., Chemetron Fire Systems, IL, Matteson
Powers, Brook........................(616) 222-5780
bpowers@grpress.com, Circ. Mgr., Sales/Mktg., The Grand Rapids Press, MI, Grand Rapids
Powers, Ted..........................(708) 608-4177
Moraine Valley Cmty. College, IL, Palos Hills
Pozo, Mendez
redaccioncr@diariolatribuna.com, Ed., La Tribuna De Ciudad Real, Ciudad Real
Pozzi, Mike
mpozzi@sbtinfo.com, Adv. Dir., Flagship, South Bend Tribune, IN, South Bend
Pozzi, Maria Julia
m.pozzi@iltempo.it, Mgr., IL TEMPO, Rome
Pradhan, Prateek
prateek@kantipur.com.np, Ed., THE KATHMANDU POST, Kathmandu
Prahl, Jack............................(800) 255-6734
jflemington@amuniversal.com, Asst. Vice Pres., US/Canadian Non-Daily Newspapers, Universal Uclick, MO, Kansas City
Prahlad, Kate.........................(540) 574-6277
kprahlad@dnronline.com, Bus. Ed., Daily News-Record, VA, Harrisonburg
Prakash, Anil
vyasumashanker@gmail.com, Ed., NAVA BHARAT, Raipur, Madhya Pradesh
Prashad, Tack.........................(212) 576-9547
prashadt@metrosn.com, Vice Pres., Client Servs./Information Servs., Metro-Puck Comics Network - New York, NY, NY, New York
Prashad, Tack.........................(212) 576-9547
prashadt@metrosn.com, Vice Pres., Client Servs./Info. Systems, Metro Newspaper Advertising Services, Inc., NY, New York
Prashad, Tack.........................(212) 576-9547
prashadt@metrosn.com, Sr. Vice Pres., Client Servs., Metro Newspaper Advertising Services, Inc. Sunday Magazine Network - New York, NY, NY, New York
Pratt, Jeff.............................(717) 240-7112
jpratt@cumberlink.com, Mng. Ed., The Sentinel, PA, Carlisle
Pratt, Milka
mpratt@amuniversal.com, Mng. Dir., Latin America, Universal Uclick International Division, MO, Kansas City
Pratt, Bonnie...................................ext. 235
bpratt@news-daily.com, Pub., News/Daily, GA, Jonesboro
Preece, Gordon.......................(204) 697-7140
Gordon.Preece@freepress.mb.a, Art Dir., Winnipeg Free Press, MB, Winnipeg
Prell, Marla
mceditor@midrivers.com, Ed., Miles City Star, MT, Miles City
Prescott, Diane.......................(631) 287-8239
Southampton College, NY, Southampton
Presley, Stephanie
spresely@dailychronicle.com, Pub./Pres., Bozeman Daily Chronicle, MT, Bozeman
Press, Aric
apress@amlaw.com, Editorial Dir., ALM, NY, New York
Preston, Jim..........................(410) 332-6846
jim.preston@baltsun.com, Asst. Mng. Ed., Photo, The Baltimore Sun, MD, Baltimore
Prewitt, Chuck........................(415) 543-4806
chuck@wunderground.com, Vice Pres., Sales/Mktg., Weather Underground, Inc., The, CA, San Francisco
chuck@wunderground.com, Vice Pres. Sales/Mktg., The Weather Underground, Inc., CA, San Francisco
Pribble, Randall......................806-669-2525
rpribble@thepampanews.com, Publisher, The Pampa News, TX, Pampa
Pribble, Sue...........................806-669-2525
spribble@thepampanews.com, Advertising Representative, The Pampa News, TX, Pampa
Price, Debra...........................(803) 644-2377
dprice@aikenstandard.com, Adv. Mgr., Major Accts./Nat'l/Co-op, Aiken Standard, SC, Aiken
Price, Keisha.........................(773) 995-2313
Chicago State Univ., IL, Chicago
Price, Bob
bprice@njherald.com, Bus./Entertainment Ed., New Jersey Herald, NJ, Newton
Price, Earl T.
earl@ags-gv.com, Pres., Advanced Graphic Systems (AGS), CA, Grass Valley
Price, James..........................(707) 453-8173
jprice@timesheraldonline.com, Interactive Mgr., Vallejo Times-Herald, CA, Vallejo
Price, James..........................(707) 453-8173
jprice@thereporter.com, Internet Mgr., The Daily Democrat, CA, Woodland
Price, Julian..........................321-242-3807
jprice@floridatoday.com, National / Majors Manager, Florida Today, FL, Melbourne
Price, Chip............................(573) 815-1702
cprice@columbiatribune.com, Copy Chief, Columbia Daily Tribune, MO, Columbia
Price, Michelle................................ext. 12
Circ. Dir., The Clanton Advertiser, AL, Clanton
Price, Kevin
kprice@ledger-enquirer.com, Sports Ed., Columbus Ledger-Enquirer, GA, Columbus
Price Arden, Allison
publisher@adage.com, Pub., Advertising Age, NY, New York
Price-Stalides, Kylie.................(800) 481-2242
Shawnee Cmty. College, IL, Ullin
Prichard, Dr. Robert
rprichard@torstar.ca, Pres./CEO, Torstar, ON, Toronto
Prichard, Janice
janicep@nacms-c.com, Mng. Ed., The Daily Record
Pride, Linwood.........................334-293-5800
lpride@cnhi.com, VP of Circulation, Community Newspaper Holdings, Inc., AL, Montgomery
Priest, Kyle............................(972) 855-8000
sales@eadstelecom-na.com, Vice Pres., Mktg., Aastra Technologies Ltd., TX, Frisco
Priest, Ellen C........................(803) 644-2333
epriest@aikenstandard.com, Bus. Mgr., Aiken Standard, SC, Aiken
Priester, Brian
bpriester@lsj.com, Pres./Pub., Lansing State Journal, MI, Lansing
bpriester@lsj.com, Clinton County News, MI, Lansing
bpriester@lsj.com, Delta Waverly Community News, MI, Lansing
bpriester@lsj.com, Dewitt Bath Review, MI, Lansing
bpriester@lsj.com, Grand Ledge Independent, MI, Lansing
bpriester@lsj.com, Holt Community News, MI, Lansing
bpriester@lsj.com, Lansing City Community News, MI, Lansing
bpriester@lsj.com, Publisher, Portland Review & Observer, MI, Lansing
Prieto, Marixi R.
feedback@inquirer.com.ph, Chrmn., PHILIPPINE DAILY INQUIRER, Makati City
Prill, Aileen...................................ext. 131
ashedd@hearstnp.com, Digital Media Dir., The Huron Daily Tribune, MI, Bad Axe
Prill, Sharon...........................509-577-7700
sprill@yakimaherald.com, Publisher, Yakima Herald-Republic, WA, Yakima
Prim, Pamela K.
pamprim@primhall.com, Vice Pres., Opns., Prim Hall Enterprises, Inc., NY, Plattsburgh
Prim, John E...................................ext. 111
johnprim@primhall.com, Pres., Prim Hall Enterprises, Inc., NY, Plattsburgh
Prince, Melissa
mprince@landonmedia.com, Acct. Exec., Landon Media Group LLC, TX, Plano
Prince, Ronald.........................(901) 529-2217
prince@commercialappeal.com, Retail Adv. Mgr., The Commercial Appeal, TN, Memphis
Principato, Richard..................610-991-5016
rick@towerproducts.com, President & CEO, Tower Products, Inc., PA, Easton
Pringle, Christine....................(814) 532-5045
Classified Sales Mgr., The Tribune-Democrat, PA, Johnstown
Pritchard, Rita
rpritchard@nncogannett.com, Prodn. Asst., Creative Serv., Bucyrus TelegraphForum.com, OH, Bucyrus
Pritchard, Andrew......................701-231-8221
andrew.pritchard@my.ndsu.edu, North Dakota State Univ., ND, Fargo
Pritchard, Harvey A.
hpritchard@starhq.com, Assoc. Pub., Elizabethton Star, TN, Elizabethton
Pritsiolas, Juan
redaccion-critica@epasa.com, Dir., CRITICA LIBRE, Panama City
Pritts, Ronald..........................(814) 444-5926
ronp@dailyamerican.com, Sports Ed., Daily American, PA, Somerset
Privett, Thomas E.....................(864) 260-1225
Major/Nat'l Adv. Mgr., Anderson Independent-Mail, SC, Anderson
Prociv, Theodore M.
info@versar.com, Pres./CEO, Versar Inc., VA, Springfield
Proctor, Darrell........................(303) 892-5242
proctord@rockymountainnews.com, Asst. Bus. Ed., Rocky Mountain News, CO, Denver
Proctor, Stephen.......................(415) 777-8772
Managing Editor, San Francisco Chronicle, CA, San Francisco
Proctor, Colleen.......................860/701-4241
c.proctor@theday.com, Product Manager, The Day Publishing Company, CT, New London
Proefe, Frank
frank.proefe@op-online.de, Ed. in Chief, Offenbach-Post, Offenbach
Profitt, Jeff
dqsports@onecliq.net, Sports Ed., Du Quoin Evening Call, IL, Du Quoin
Profitt, Jennifer.......................(989) 284-5109
Univ. of Michigan, MI, Flint
Pronovost, Paul.......................(508) 862-1166
ppronovost@capecodonline.com, Ed., Cape Cod Times, MA, Hyannis
Pronovost, Jacques
ledroit@ledroit.com, Pub., Le Droit, ON, Ottawa
Propp, Lyn..............................(780) 429-5264
lpropp@thejournal.canwest.com, Adv. Mgr., Servs., Edmonton Journal, AB, Edmonton
Prosinski, Steve........................(406) 657-1289
sprosinski@billingsgazette.com, Ed., Billings Gazette, MT, Billings
Proskuryakova, Mariya..............(907) 786-4690
Univ. of Alaska Anchorage, AK, Anchorage
Protz, Brenda..........................(217) 786-2589
brenda.protz@llcc.edu, Lincoln Land Cmty. College, IL, Springfield
Proudfoot, Rona
rproudfoot@chroniclet.com, Web Ed., Chronicle-Telegram, OH, Elyria
Prouty, Tim.....................................ext. 215
support@verifiedaudit.com, CEO, Verified Audit Circulation (VAC), CA, Larkspur
Provenzo, Matt.........................(724) 226-4686
mprovenzo@tribweb.com, City Ed., Valley News Dispatch, PA, Tarentum
Provost, Robert C.....................(973) 392-1892
rprovost@starledger.com, Director of Marketing., The Star-Ledger, NJ, Newark
Provost, Roger.........................(817) 390-7185
rprovost@star-telegram.com, Vice Pres./CFO, Fort Worth Star-Telegram, TX, Fort Worth
Provost, Olivier
oprovost@latribune.fr, Ed., LA TRIBUNE, Paris
Provost, John..........................(352) 563-3240
jprovost@chronicleonline.com, Adv. Dir., Citrus County Chronicle, FL, Crystal River
Provost, Adam..........................(203)-272-2072
adam.provost@pa-sportsticker.com, Consumer Mktg./Commun. Mgr., ESPN/SportsTicker, NY, New York
Prowd, Lisa
lisa.prowd@news-mail.com.au, Circ. Mgr., NEWS-MAIL
Pruett, Chris
cpruett@dailycitizen.com, Ed., The Evening World, IN, Linton
Pruett, Chris
chris_pruett@dailycitizen.com, Online Ed., Greene County Daily World, IN, Linton
Pruitt, Derek...........................(518) 792-3229
pruitt@poststar.com, Photography Dir., The Post-Star, NY, Glens Falls
Pruitt, Connie..........................(505) 564-4571
cpruitt@daily-times.com, Adv. Mgr., The Daily Times, NM, Farmington
Prusen de Blas, Jose Luis
redaccion@larioja.com, Dir., LA RIOJA, Logrono, La Rioja
Prutsok, Andy..................................ext. 223
aprutsok@norwalkreflector.com, Pub., Norwalk Reflector, OH, Norwalk
Pryor, Travis................(303) 776-2244 ext. 212
tpryor@times-call.com, Day Ed., Times-Call, CO, Longmont
Prysazniuk, Harold...................(204) 697-7130
Credit Mgr., Winnipeg Free Press, MB, Winnipeg
Psycharis, Stavros R.
tovima@dolnet.gr, Ed., TO VIMA, Athens, Central Greece
Puadia, Jason
news@theadvocate.com.au, Ed., THE ADVOCATE
Pucci, Amanda.......................(716) 6140-6259
Niagara County Cmty. College, NY, Sanborn
Puchalski, Bernie..............................ext. 295
bpuchalski@stcatharinesstandards.ca, Sports Ed., The Standard, ON, Saint Catharines
Puckett, Jeffrey.......................(502) 582-4160
jpuckett@courier-journal.com, Music Critic, The Courier-Journal, KY, Louisville
Puckett, Ann
advertising@helena-arkansas.com, Display Adv. Mgr., The Daily World, AR, Helena
Puckett, Carmel...........................9022 0541
carmel.puckett@kalminer.com.au, Deputy Editor, KALGOORLIE MINER
Puello, Carmen.........................(212) 293-8602
cpuello@unitedmedia.com, Sales/Admin. Mgr., Newspaper Enterprise Association (Div. of United Media), NY, New York
cpuello@unitedmedia.com, Sales/Admin. Mgr., United Feature Syndicate (Div. of United Media), NY, New York
Puello, Carmen.........................(212) 293-8602
cpuello@unitedmedia.com, Mgr., Customer Rel., United Media, OH, Cincinnati
Puga Rodriguez, Antonio
director@diarioeldia.cl, Pres., EL DIA, La Serena
Pugh, Kari...............................(703) 878-8056
kpugh@insidenova.com, Copy Ed., Features, Manassas Journal Messenger, VA, Manassas
Pugh, Mitch.............................(712) 293-4201
Ed., Sioux City Journal, IA, Sioux City
Pulaski, Jeff
Jeff@acu-tech.net, Sales Coord., Acutech LLC, IN, Elkhart
Pulcrano, Dan..................................ext. 1301
press@metronews.com, Pres., Metro Newspaper, CA, San Jose
Puleo, Sam..............................(312) 915-7898
Loyola Univ. Law School, IL, Chicago
Pulliam, Russell B....................(317) 444-6001
russell.pulliam@indystar.com, Assoc. Ed., The Indianapolis Star, IN, Indianapolis
Pulsifer, Rich..........................805-739-2147
rpulsifer@santamariatimes.com, LOMPOC RECORD, CA, Lompoc
Purcell, Patrick J.....................(617) 619-6320
ppurcell@bostonherald.com, Owner/Pres./Pub., Boston Herald, MA, Boston
Purcell, Patrick J.......................617-619-6320
ppurcell@bostonherald.com, Pres./Pub., Herald Media, Inc., MA, Boston
Purcell, Patrick.......................(617) 619-6235
ppurcell@bostonherald.com, Adv. Mgr., Display, Boston Herald, MA, Boston
Purcell, Patrick J.......................617-619-6320
ppurcell@bostonherald.com, Pres./Pub., Herald Media, Inc., MA, Boston
Purdy, Racine..........................(248) 745-4692
racine.purdy@oakpress.com, Adv. Mgr., New Media, The Oakland Press, MI, Pontiac
Purdy, Michael
m-purdy@govst.edu, Program Coord., Governors State University, IL, University Park
Puri, Shamlal..........................(020) 7368-3306
info@adlinkinternational.co.uk, Mng. Ed., Newslink Africa Ltd., ENG, London
Pursel, Robert P........................(562) 921-5545
plsupply@gte.net, Pres./Mgr., Sales, Poolside Lithographic Supply, Inc., CA, Santa Fe

Springs
Purvis, Cal ....ext. 5650
Credit Mgr., The Post and Courier, SC, Charleston
Puryear, James ....(919) 829-4727
jpuryear@newsobserver.com, Vice Pres., Circ., The News & Observer, NC, Raleigh
Pusateri, Diana ....ext. 321
dianepusateri@sanduskyregister.com, Circ. Coord., Newspapers in Educ., Sandusky Register, OH, Sandusky
Puschmann, D.
nz-redaktion@pressenetz.de, Bus. Mgr., NZ Nurnberger Zeitung, Nurnberg
Pustet, Wulf 955
info@suedostbayerische-rundschau.de, Bus. Mgr., SUDOSTBAYERISCHE RUNDSCHAU, Tittmoning
Putt, Judy 662-678-1594
judy.putt@journalinc.com, Radio/Television Ed., Journal Publishing Company, MS, Tupelo
Putz, W.
redaction@rga-online.de, Proprietor, Remscheider General-Anzeiger, Remscheid
Pyane, Richard
rpayne@fujifilmgs.com, Reg'l Sales Mgr., Fujifilm Graphic Systems USA, Inc., AZ, Tempe
Pye, Jerry
jerrypye@bastropenterprise.com, Pub., Bastrop Daily Enterprise, LA, Bastrop
Pyle, Dave ....(612) 332-2727
apminneapolis@ap.org, Bureau Chief, Minnesota Associated Press Association, MN, Minneapolis
Pyun, Yong Sik
yspyun@chosun.com, Pub., CHOSUN ILBO, Seoul
PÃ£rez, Elizabeth Santiesteban
cip227@cip.enet.cu, Dir., VENCEREMOS, Guantanamo

Q

Qeitzau, Dan
redaktion@bornholmstidende.dk, Ed. in Chief, BORNHOLMS TIDENDE, Ronne, Bornholm
Quaderer, Daniel
dquaderer@medienhaus.li, Pub., LIECHTENSTEINER VATERLAND, Vaduz
Quaife, Steve ....(360) 577-2559
squaife@tdf.com, Adv. Mgr., Retail, The Daily News, WA, Longview
Quaintance, John ....(419) 993-2024
jquaintance@limanews.com, Circ. Mgr., The Lima News, OH, Lima
Qualls, Lori ....(989) 839-4237
lqualls@mdn.net, Lifestyle Ed., Midland Daily News, MI, Midland
Qualtrough, Alan
wmnadmin@westcountrypublications.co.uk, Ed. in Chief, WESTERN MORNING NEWS, Plymouth, Devon
Quarles, Orage ....(919) 829-4659
oquarles@newsobserver.com, Pres./Pub., The News & Observer, NC, Raleigh
Quast, Travis ....(208) 377-6305
tquast@idahostatesman.com, Vice Pres., Sales/Mktg., The Idaho Statesman, ID, Boise
Queen, Alice ....(770) 787-7303
alice.queen@newtoncitizen.com, Ed., The Newton Citizen, GA, Covington
Queen, Alice
alice.queen@rockdalecitizen.com, Pub., The Rockdale Citizen, GA, Conyers
Query, Howard
howard_query@globegazette.com, Prodn. Coord., New Media, Globe-Gazette, IA, Mason City
Quigley, Kathryn ....(856) 256-4713
Rowan Univ., NJ, Glassboro
Quillen, Kim 504-826-3416
kquillen@timespicayune.com, Bus. Ed., The Times Picayune, LA, New Orleans
Quillen, Rick ....(209) 532-7151
RQuillen@uniondemocrat.com, Prodn. Mgr., Opns./Press, The Union Democrat, CA, Sonora
Quilliam, Bruce L.
bquilliam@perretta.com, Vice Pres., Sales/Mktg., Perretta Graphics Corp., NY, Poughkeepsie
Quilliam, Bruce
bquilliamjr@perretta.com, Bus. Mgr., Int'l Sales, Perretta Graphics Corp., NY, Poughkeepsie
Quillon, Robin
rquillon@tribdem.com, Pub., The Tribune-Democrat, PA, Johnstown
Quinell, Scott ....(315) 386-7315
SUNY College of Technology/Canton, NY, Canton
Quinly, Pat
pquinly@centurytel.net, Pub., Macon Chronicle-Herald, MO, Macon
Quinn, Christopher ....(216) 999-4604
Asst. Managing Editor/Metro, The Plain Dealer, OH, Cleveland
Quinn, Rod
editors.assistant@canberratimes.com.au, Ed., THE CANBERRA TIMES, Fyshwick
Quinn, Jerry
jquinn@examiner-enterprise.com, Pub., Examiner-Enterprise, OK, Bartlesville
Quinn, Terry 302 1300
feedback@star-times.co.nz, Mng. Dir., SUNDAY STAR-TIMES
Quinn, Brian
brian.quinn@wsj.com, Vice Pres. Adv. Sales, The Wall Street Journal-Eastern Edition, NY, New York
Quinn, Gordon ....(949) 300-4800
gquinn@olec.com, Vice Pres.,Electronics Sales, OLEC, CA, Santa Ana
Quinn, Terry 302 1300
editor@sunday-news.co.nz, Mng. Dir., SUNDAY NEWS
Quinn, Mike
quinn@havasunews.com, Pub., Today's News-Herald, AZ, Lake Havasu City
Quinn, Sally ....(412) 320-7885
squinn@tribweb.com, Deputy Mng. Ed., Features, Tribune-Review, PA, Pittsburgh
Quint, Heath
hquint@theintermountain.com, Local Ed., The Inter-Mountain, WV, Elkins
Quintana, Shasta
circ@alamosanews.com, Circ. Mgr., The Valley Courier, CO, Alamosa
Qureshi, Arun
kteditor@emirates.net.ae, Dir. Mktg., KHALEEJ TIMES
Qureshi, Anwar Hussain 501 1560
Ed., AACHARAN, Gwalior, Madhya Pradesh
Qureshi, Mushtaq Ahmed
thair@cyber.net.pk, Ed. in Chief, ACTION, Karachi

R

RON, CIANI 816-234-4440
rciani@kcstar.com, RETAIL ADVERTISING, The Olathe News, MO, Kansas City
Raafat, Hassan
abudhabi@khaleejtimes.com, Bureau Chief, KHALEEJ TIMES
Rabago, Joaquin
efelondon@btclick.com, Rep., EFE News Services - London, United Kingdom, London
Rabalais, Sterling
strabalais@theadvocate.com, Asst. Production Director, The Advocate, LA, Baton Rouge
Raby, William ....(819) 986-4390
Vice Pres., Sales/Mktg., Papier Masson Ltee, QC, Masson-Angers
Rackers, Tom 573-761-0256
trackers@newstribune.com, Sports Ed., News Tribune, MO, Jefferson City
Rackovic, Andrija
glavni.urednik@pobjeda.cg.yu, Ed. in Chief, Socialist Alliance of the Working People of Montenegro, Podgorica
Radbourne, Brent ....(519) 376-4303
bradbourne@owensoundsuntimes.com, Circ. Mgr., The Sun Times, ON, Owen Sound
Rade, John A.
info@imany.com, Pres./CEO, I-many, Inc., NJ, Edison
Radeanu, Stefan 599 5520
stefan.radeanu@curierulnational.ro, Ed. in Chief, CURIERUL NATIONAL, Bucharest
Rademakers, Luc
gvainfocenter@concentra.be, Ed. in Chief, GAZET VAN ANTWERPEN, Antwerp
Radford, Bill 719-636-0272
bill.radford@gazette.com, Business Editor, The Gazette, CO, Colorado Springs
Radon, Uwe
anzaegan@burstadter-zeitung.de, Ed. in Chief, BURSTADTER ZEITUNG, Burstadt
Radziewicz, Bob 305-284-3709
Faculty editorial adviser, Univ. of Miami, FL, Coral Gables
Rae, Charles
kidderpress@worldnet.att.net, Pres., Kidder, Inc., MA, Agawam
Raee, Nasheed
quamiaawaz@gmail.com, Ed., QUAMI AWAZ, Multan City, Multan District
Raese, Kathleen A.
administration@dominionpost.com, Assoc. Pub., The Dominion Post, WV, Morgantown
Raffel, John ....ext. 3035
jraffel@staffordgroup.com, Sports Ed., The Daily News, MI, Greenville
Rafferdy, Charlie
sales@voxware.com, Vice Pres., Sales/Bus. Devel., Voxware, Inc., NJ, Hamilton
Rafferty, Renata J.
rrafferty@raffertyconsulting.com, Pres., Rafferty Consulting Group, CA, Indian Wells
Raffety, Michael
mraffety@mtdemocrat.net, Online Contact, Mountain Democrat, CA, Placerville
Raffone, Keith ....(919) 829-4646
kraffone@newsobserver.com, Controller, The News & Observer, NC, Raleigh
Ragazzo, Frank 908-658-5992
frank@richmond-graphic.com, Vice Pres., Sales/Mktg., Richmond/Graphic Products, Inc., RI, Smithfield
Raghav, Ramvir Singh
info@vyaparbharti.com, MD, VYAPAR BHARATI, New Delhi
Raghuvanshi, Chandramani
bijnor_times@yahoo.co.in, Pub., BIJNOR TIMES, Bijnor, Uttar Pradesh
Ragle, Laurie ....(812) 331-4291
Advertising Director, The Herald-Times, IN, Bloomington
Rahemtulla, Neena
ge@cymbolic.com, Mktg. Dir., Cymbolic Sciences International Ltd., BC, Richmond
Rahiman, Mariam
mariam.rahiman@inl.co.za, Adv. Mgr., THE MERCURY, Greyville
Rahlf, Rona
rona.rahlf@lee.net, Pres./Pub., The Daily Herald, UT, Provo
Rahman, Tarique
dinkalnews@gmail.com, Pub., DAINIK DINKAL, Dhaka
Rahman, Mir Shakil
editor.internet@janggroup.com.pk, Ed. in Chief, THE NEWS INTERNATIONAL, Karachi
Rahman, Anwar Mohammad Abdul
akadvt@batelco.com.bh, Chrmn., AKHBAR AL KHALIJ
Raia, James ....(916) 455-8389
james@byjamesraia.com, Self-Syndicator, James Raia, CA, Sacramento
Raines, Ben ....(251) 439-7159
braines@mobileregister.com, Environmental Reporter, Press-Register, AL, Mobile
Raines, Elaine ....(520) 573-4164
eraines@azstarnet.com, News/Research Servs. Dir., Arizona Daily Star, AZ, Tucson
Rainey, James W.
jrainey@oanow.com, Pub., Opelika-Auburn News, AL, Opelika
Rainey, Lee
rainey@accuweather.com, Vice President/Mktg., AccuWeather, Inc., PA, State College
Rainnoni, Heather ....ext. 1251
Mng. Ed., Record-Courier, OH, Ravenna
Raj, Selva
mgrdtcdl@gmail.com, Mgr., DAILY THANTHI, Cuddalore, Tamil Nadu
Rakotoarivelo, Juliana Andriambelo
midi@midi-madagasikara.mg, Gen. Mgr., MIDI-MADAGASIKARA, Antananarivo
Raley, Erin
erinraley@hotmail.com, Photo Ed., Telluride Daily Planet, CO, Telluride
Ralis, David ....ext. 5051
dralis@phillyburbs.com, Online Ed., Bucks County Courier Times, PA, Levittown
Ramadan, Alan ....(415) 252-2000
pr@macromedia.com, Exec. Vice Pres., Mktg., Macromedia, Inc., CA, San Francisco
Ramadge, Paul
inquiries@theage.com.au, Ed. in Chief, THE AGE
Ramberg, Anders ....(541) 383-0373
aramberg@bendbulletin.com, Presentation Ed., The Bulletin, OR, Bend
Ramert, Cindy ....ext. 238
cramert@dglobe.com, Prodn. Mgr., Composing, The Daily Globe, MN, Worthington
Ramey, Troy
t.ramey@technologyintegrators.net, Sales Engineer, Technology Integrators, IL, Effingham
Ramhoff, Richard A.
rramhoff@palmspri.gannett.com, Pres./Pub., The Desert Sun, CA, Palm Springs
Ramirez, Alejandro Galvis 633-4000
publicidadccp@gmail.com, Owner/Gen. Mgr., VANGUARDIA LIBERAL, Bucaramanga, Santander
Ramirez, Carlos Valdez
bonetinaco@gmail.com, Pres., El Noticiero de Colima, Colima, Colima
Ramirez Codina, Pedro J.
lector@elmundo.es, MD, El Mundo, Madrid
Ramm, Cindi
cindi@thetechnologyagency.com, Chief Brand Strategist, Kinetic Corporation, KY, Louisville
Ramos, George ....(805) 756-2508
Chair/Prof., California Polytechnic State Universtiy, CA, San Luis Obispo
Ramos Santos, Jose Isabel
redaccion@debate.com.mx, Gen. Mgr., El Debate, Guamuchil, Sinaloa
Ramos Santos, Jose Isabel
info@debate.com, Gen. Mgr., El Debate, Guasave, Sinaloa
Ramos Santos, Jose Isabel
redaccion@debate.com.mx, Mgr./Dir., El Debate de Culiacan, Culiacan, Sinaloa
Ramotar, Mark
markramotar@gmail.com, Ed. in Chief, Guyana National Newspapers Ltd., Georgetown
Ramsay, Paul 902-432-8238
pramsay@journalpioneer.com, Adv. Mgr., The Journal Pioneer, PE, Summerside
Ramsey, Betty
jbyrd@tryondailybulletin.com, Publsiher, The Tryon Daily Bulletin, NC, Tryon
Ramsey, Paula
advertising@devilslakejournal.com, Adv. Mgr., Retail, Devils Lake Journal, ND, Devils Lake
Ramsey, Marshall
mramsey@jackson.gannett.com, Editorial Cartoonist, The Clarion-Ledger, MS, Jackson
Ramsower, Vernah ....(806) 296-1320
vramsower@hearstnp.com, Adv. Mgr., Retail, Plainview Herald, TX, Plainview
Rana, Mario Vazquez
solcel@oem.com.mx, Pres., El Sol del Bajio, Celaya, Guanajuato
Rana, Divesh
divesh@mos.com.np, Gen Mgr., GORKHAPATRA, Kathmandu
Rana, Mario Vazquez
oemenlinea@oem.com.mx, Pres., ESTO, Mexico City, Distrito Federal
Rana, Mario Vazquez
publicidad@eloccidental.com.mx, Pres., El Occidental, Guadalajara, Jalisco
Rana, Mario Vazquez
publicidad@elheraldodechihuahua.com.mx, Pres., El Heraldo de La Tarde, Chihuahua, Chihuahua
Rana, Mario Vazquez
publicidad@elsoldeirapuato.com.mx, Pres., El Sol de Irapuato, Irapuato, Guanajuato
Rana, Mario Vazquez
publicidad@elsoldesanjuandelrio.com.mx, Pres., EL SOL DE SAN JUAN DEL RIO, San Juan Del Rio, Queretaro
Rana, Mario Vazquez
publicidad@elsoldecuernavaca.com.mx,

Pres., El Sol de Cuautla, Cuaulta, Morelos
Rana, Mario Vazquez
publicidad@elheraldodechihuahua.com.mx, Pres., El Heraldo, Chihuahua
Rand, Michael ....(815) 562-2061 ext. 132
Controller, News Media Corp., IL, Rochelle
Randall, Christine ....ext. 5703
Amusements Ed., The Post and Courier, SC, Charleston
Randall, Sean ....(508) 862-1591
srandall@capecodonline.com, Cape Cod View/Primetime Mgr., Cape Cod Times, MA, Hyannis
Randall, Myron W.
mrandall@newspost.com, President, The Frederick News-Post, MD, Frederick
Randall, Debbie........................703-986-0171
debrandall68@gmail.com, Executive Dir, World Images News Service, VA, Woodbridge
Randolph, Shawn
shawn.randolph@irontontribune.com, Adv. Mgr., The Ironton Tribune, OH, Ironton
Randsen, Olaf
olaf@themonitor.com, Pub., The Monitor, TX, McAllen
Ranes, Doug ....(760) 739-6681
dranes@nctimes.com, Prodn. Dir., North County Times, CA, Escondido
Raney, Rachael........................(317) 398-1276
rraney@shelbynews.com, Pub., The Shelbyville News, IN, Shelbyville
Ranganathan, N.
support@dt.co.in, Mgr., DAILY THANTHI, Coimbatore, Tamil Nadu
Ranker, M.
mranker@bergstraesser-anzeiger.de, Ed., BA BERGSTRABER ANZEIGER, Bensheim
Rankin, Katie 405.238.6464
krankin@pvdemocrat.com, Advertising Account Executive, Pauls Valley Democrat, OK, Pauls Valley
Rankin, Florence..............................ext. 209
flo.rankin@gaflnews.com, Mng. Ed., The Tifton Gazette, GA, Tifton
Rankov, Suzana
suzana.rankov@dnevnik.si, Ed. in Chief, DNEVNIK, Ljubljana
Ranney, Arthur........................(608) 342-1471
Univ. of Wisconsin Platteville, WI, Platteville
Ransick, Chris
aspeditor@arapahoe.edu, Arapahoe Cmty. College, CO, Littleton
Ransier, Shelley......................(509) 582-1570
sjones@tri-cityherald.com, Adv. Mgr., Sales, Tri-City Herald, WA, Kennewick
Ransom, Dale ....(508) 236-0348
dransom@thesunchronicle.com, Sports Ed., The Sun Chronicle, MA, Attleboro
Rao, Ramoji
editor@eenadu.net, Ed. in Chief, EENADU, Hyderabad
Rao, Ramakrishna
hyd@epmltd.com, Gen. Mgr., INDIAN EXPRESS, Hyderabad, Andhra Pradesh
Raper, Jeff............................(603) 610-1155
jraper@seacoastonline.com, Online Mgr., Portsmouth Herald, NH, Portsmouth
Rapoport, Roger......................(510) 595-0595
roger@rdrbooks.com, Chrmn., RDR Books, MI, Muskegon
Rapson, Jeff ....(603) 650-1119
jeff.rapson@ckp.com, Dir., Sales, Saxotech, NH, Bedford
Raquet, Murf
mraquet@dnews.com, City Ed., Moscow-Pullman Daily News, ID, Moscow
Raquet, Murf
murf@dnews.com, Opinion Page Ed., Moscow-Pullman Daily News, ID, Moscow
Rasmountry, Savankhon
vttimes@hotmail.com, Ed. in chief, VIENTIANE TIMES, Vientiane
Rasmussen, Al.............(920) 432-2941 ext. 120
chronicle@gogreenbay.com, Gen. Mgr., The Green Bay News-Chronicle, WI, Green Bay
Rasnic, Eric ....(202) 636-2904
erasnic@washingtontimes.com, Adv. Mgr., Interactive, The Washington Times, DC, Washington
Rasor, Rob ....(405) 366-3588
rrasor@normantranscript.com, Prodn. Mgr., Norman Transcript, OK, Norman
Rassenfoss, Joe......................(303) 892-5410
rassenfossj@rockymountainnews.com, Entertainment Ed., Rocky Mountain News, CO, Denver
Rassi, Raja
raja@alhayat.com, Gen. Mgr., AL HAYAT
Ratajek, Bonnie L....................(715) 395-5725
bonnie.ratajek@mx3.com, HR Mgr., Superior Publishing Corp., WI, Superior
Ratcliff, Genevieve.....................Editorial Mgr.
recorder@flash.net, Commercial Recorder, TX, Fort Worth
Ratcliff, Marianne......................(805) 437-0250
mratcliff@venturacountystar.com, Opinion Page Ed., Ventura County Star, CA, Camarillo
Ratcliff, Genevieve
recorder@flash.net, Pres./Pub., Commercial Recorder, TX, Fort Worth
Ratcliffe, Jerry.......................(434) 978-7251
jratcliffe@dailyprogress.com, Sports Ed., The Daily Progress, VA, Charlottesville
Rath, Marc
marc.rath@cbeckers.de, Ed. in Chief, ALTMARK ZEITUNG, Salzwedel
Rathbun, Chuck............(928) 763-2505 ext. 109
chuckr@npgcable.com, Pub., Mohave Valley Daily News, AZ, Bullhead City
Rathbun, Chuck............(928) 763-2505 ext. 109
chuck@npgcale.com, Pub., News West Publishing Company Inc., AZ, Bullhead City
Rathgeber, Bob ....(239) 335-0354
brathgeber@news-press.com, Digest Ed., The News-Press, FL, Fort Myers
Rathgeber, Darrell ....(306) 765-1304
drathgeber@paherald.sk.ca, Circ./Mktg. Mgr., Prince Albert Daily Herald, SK, Prince Albert
Ratkovich, Tom..............(303) 296-9966 ext. 11
ter@astech-intermedia.com, Pres./CEO, ASTech InterMedia, CO, Denver
Ratliff, Jeff
jeffr@northwestsignal.net, Sports Ed., Northwest Signal, OH, Napoleon
Ratliff, Gregg
gratliff@pekintimes.com, Pub., Pekin Daily Times, IL, Pekin
Ratliff, Chris
cratliff@salisburypost.com, Dir., Sales/Mktg., Salisbury Post, NC, Salisbury
Rattray, Paula ....(404) 526-5990
prattray@ajc.com, Vice Pres., Strategic Mktg., Atlanta Journal-Constitution, GA, Atlanta
Ratzky, Harlan
harlan.ratzy@investors.com, Vice Pres., Internet Mktg., Investor's Business Daily, CA, Los Angeles
Rau, David
davidarau@aol.com, Chrmn./Pres./CEO, Sandusky Newspapers, Inc., SC, Hilton Head Island
Raut, Bharat Kumar
bharat.raut@timesgroup.com, Ed. in Chief, MAHARASHTRA TIMES, Mumbai, Maharashtra
Raven, William
braven@bellatrix.net, Sr. Vice Pres., Sales/Mktg., Bellatrix Systems, Inc., OR, Bend
Ravera, Maria ....(916) 321-1690
mravera@sacbee.com, Audience Devel. Dir., The Sacramento Bee, CA, Sacramento
Ravi, M.S.
desk@keralakaumudi.com, Pub., KERALA KAUMUDI, Trivandrum, Kerala
Ravi, Deepu
deepu@ekaumudi.com, Mng. Ed., KERALA KAUMUDI, Calicut, Kerala
Ravi, Rajesh
rajesh.ravi@expressindia.com, Principal Correspondent, The Financial Express, Cochin, Kerala
Rawlings, Robert H.
pueblo@chieftain.com, Ed., The Pueblo Chieftain, CO, Pueblo
Rawlinson, Adrian
webmaster@ecn.co.uk, Adv. Dir., EAST ANGLIAN DAILY TIMES, ENG, Ipswich, Suffolk
Ray, Douglas K.
dray@dailyherald.com, Chairman/Pub./President/CEO, Daily Herald, IL, Arlington Heights
Ray, Bruce 805-781-7825
bray@thetribunenews.com, President and Publisher, The Tribune, CA, San Luis Obispo
Ray, Eddie
eray@gwcommonwealth.com, Bus. Mgr., The Greenwood Commonwealth, MS, Greenwood
Ray, Rowe H.
rray@sanmarcosrecord.com, Editorial Page Ed., San Marcos Daily Record, TX, San Marcos
Ray, Peter
pray@broadcastnews.ca, Quebec Correspondent, Broadcast News Limited, QC, Montreal
Ray, Karen
kray@sanmarcosrecord.com, Prodn. Supvr., San Marcos Daily Record, TX, San Marcos
Ray, Joyce M.
jray@dmreg.com, Vice Pres., HR, The Des Moines Register, IA, Des Moines
Raybon, Otis M. ....(706) 290-5281
oraybon@npco.com, Pub., Rome News-Tribune, GA, Rome
Rayburn, Ted..........................(615) 259-8063
trayburn@tennessean.com, News Ed., The Tennessean, TN, Nashville
Raykie, Jim ....ext. 230
jraykie@sharonherald.com, Ed., The Herald, PA, Sharon
Raymer, John ....(413) 585-5350
Prodn. Mgr., Pressroom, Daily Hampshire Gazette, MA, Northampton
Raymond, Steve
steve.raymond@effinghamdailynews.com, Pub., Effingham Daily News, IL, Effingham
Raymond, L.
cartoonews@aol.com, Vice Pres., Sales, Cartoonews, Inc., NY, New York
Raymond, Mike.......................(410) 704-5153
Towson Univ., MD, Towson
Raymond, Mark ....(541) 957-4263
mraymond@nrtoday.com, Pub., The News-Review, OR, Roseburg
Rayo, Carol ....(580) 338-3355 ext. 13
Adv. Mgr., Classified, Guymon Daily Herald, OK, Guymon
Rayos, Gail............................(407) 420-5582
grayos@orlandosentinel.com, Assoc. Mng. Ed., Bus., Orlando Sentinel, FL, Orlando
Rea, Michelle K.
mkrea@nynewspapers.com, Exec. Dir., New York Press Association, NY, Albany
Read, Linda ....(814) 765-7813 ext. 233
news@theprogressnews.com, Asst. Ed., The Progress, PA, Clearfield
Read, Jeremy.....................................ext. 104
ads@samessenger.com, Adv. Dir., St. Albans Messenger, VT, Saint Albans
Reader, Bill ....(740) 597-1294
Asst. Prof., Ohio University, OH, Athens
Reagan, Michael
ads@dailynews.com, Adv. Vice Pres., Daily News, CA, Woodland Hills
Reagan, Gail...............................214-536-9399
nreagan@aol.com, Columnist, Have Fun at the Movies, TX, Dallas
Reagan, Dann ....(325) 670-5213
reagand@reporternews.com, Online Dir., Abilene Reporter-News, TX, Abilene
Reagen, James E. ....ext. 114
jreagen@ogd.com, Mng. Ed., Journal/Advance News, The Courier-Observer, The Journal & The Advance-News, NY, Ogdensburg
Ream, Stacey..........................(432) 333-7750
sream@oaoa.com, Adv./Mktg. Dir., Odessa American, TX, Odessa
Reardon, Alan
areardon@atex.com, COO, Atex North America, MA, Burlington
Reardon, Emily.........................508 213-2275
emily.reardon@nichols.edu, Assistant Director of Admissions / International Students Counselor, Nichols College, MA, Dudley
Reaume, Bob...............(416) 964-3805 ext. 224
breaume@acaweb.ca, Vice Pres., Media/Research, Association of Canadian Advertisers, Inc., ON, Toronto
Reaves, Ron ....(256) 549-2048
ron.reaves@gadsdentimestoday.com, Exec. Ed., The Gadsden Times, AL, Gadsden
Rebmann, Dr. Richard
leserpost@stn.zgs.de, CEO, Filder-Zeitung, Stuttgart
Rebollo, Esther
efecol@efebogota.com.co, Rep., EFE News Services - Bogota, Colombia, Bogota
Rech, Missy D..............(402) 371-1080 ext. 252
mbryde@norfolkdailynews.com, Circ. Mgr., Norfolk Daily News, NE, Norfolk
Rechenbach, Jeffrey
jrechenbach@cwa-union.org, Sec./Treasure, Communications Workers of America, DC, Washington
Recker, Pete ....(319) 335-5783
Univ. of Iowa, IA, Iowa City
Rector, Jenny ....(434) 978-7253
jrector@dailyprogress.com, News Ed., The Daily Progress, VA, Charlottesville
Rector, Molly
sales@spectralogic.com, Dir., Cor. Mktg., Spectra Logic, CO, Boulder
Rector, Todd...........................(312) 222-4974
trector@tribune.com, Art Dir., TMS Specialty Products, IL, Chicago
Rector, Todd...........................(312) 222-4974
trector@tribune.com, Art Dir., TMS Specialty Products, IL, Chicago
Rector, Bill F.
wfr@ipa.net, Pub., The Daily Record, AR, Little Rock
Reda, Lou ....ext. 251
lreda@norwalkreflector.com, Photo Ed., Norwalk Reflector, OH, Norwalk
Reddick, David
david@reddickulous.com, Cartoonist, Seriocomics Features, IN, Fort Wayne
Redding, Micheal ....(386) 252-9921
CEO, HarborPoint Media Group, FL, Daytona Beach
Redding, Alesia
aredding@sbtinfo.com, Asst. Editorial Page Ed., South Bend Tribune, IN, South Bend
Redding, Michael.......................386-681-2509
michael.redding@news-jrnl.com, New Smyrna Pennysaver, FL, New Smyrna Beach
michael.redding@news-jrnl.com, CEO & Publisher, Halifax Media, Daytona Beach News-Journal, FL, Daytona Beach
Reddy, Bob ....(941) 206-1166
breddy@sun-herald.com, Asst. City Ed., Charlotte Sun, FL, Charlotte Harbor
Reddy, T. Venkatram
bhoomi@deccanmail.com, Owner, ANDHRA BHOOMI, Secunderabad, Andhra Pradesh
Reddy, Venkattram
deccan@hdl.vsnl.net.in, Pub., DECCAN CHRONICLE, Secunderabad, Andhra Pradesh
Redecker, Jerre.......................(360) 754-5422
jredecker@theolympian.com, Day City Editor, The Olympian, WA, Olympia
Redfearn, Kelly.......................(605) 331-2356
kredfearn@argusleader.com, Advertising Director, Argus Leader, SD, Sioux Falls
Redfern, Ronald ....(951) 794-6937
publisher@pe.com, CEO/Publisher, The Press-Enterprise, CA, Riverside
Redfield, Jim
jimredfield@griffinchaseoliver.com, CEO, Griffin Chase Oliver, Inc., CA, Laguna Niguel
Redford, Brad.................................ext. 217
sports@columbiabasinherald.com, Sports Ed., Columbia Basin Herald, WA, Moses Lake
Redman, Carl(225) 388-0277; (225) 931-6530 (cell)
credman@theadvocate.com, Exec. Ed., The Advocate, LA, Baton Rouge
Reece, Gary
garyreece@aol.com, Owner, Reece & Associates, CA, San Jose
Reed, Steve ....(602) 444-4464
steve.reed@pni.com, Circ. Opns. Mgr., The Arizona Republic, AZ, Phoenix
Reed, Donna M.......................(804) 649-6107
dreed@mediageneral.com, Vice Pres., Content, Media General News Service, VA, Richmond
Reed, Marc
ezra.singer@verizon.com, Exec. Vice Pres., HR, Verizon Communications, Inc., NY, New York
Reed, Maryanne......................(304) 293-3505
pireed@mail.wvu.edu, Dean/Prof., West Virginia University, WV, Morgantown

Reed, Sandy ....(609) 272-7318
sreed@pressofac.com, NIE Coord., The Press of Atlantic City, NJ, Pleasantville
Reed, Lindsey ....(989) 774-6682
Central Michigan Univ., MI, Mount Pleasant
Reed, Brenda L.
b.reed@nepa.org, Exec. Dir., New England Press Association, MA, Boston
Reed, John..............................217-351-5230
jreed@news-gazette.com, VP: Chief Financial Officer, News-Gazette Inc., IL, Champaign
Reed, Robert...................................ext. 2483
bobbo.reed@scni.com, Prodn. Supvr., Pagination-Night, The Advocate, CT, Stamford
Reed, Howard F...............................ext. 1113
howard.reed@gwinnettdailypost.com, Tech. Dir./Online Mgr., Gwinnette Daily Post, GA, Lawrenceville
Reed, Mike
mike@lapress.com, Adv. Dir., Louisiana Press Association, LA, Baton Rouge
Reed, Matt..............................321-242-3631
mreed@floridatoday.com, Public Interest Editor, Florida Today, FL, Melbourne
Reed, Craig ....(541) 957-4210
creed@nrtoday.com, Features Ed., The News-Review, OR, Roseburg
Reed, Michael E.......................(585) 598-0030
CEO, GateHouse Media Inc., NY, Fairport
Reed, Brenda
nena@nenews.org, Exec. Dir., NENPA Ad Network (New England Newspaper and Press Association), MA, Dedham
Reed, Terri
terri.reed@ruxton.com, Dir., West Coast Sales, Ruxton Group, CA, San Francisco
Reed, George R. ....(904) 285-3239
reedmsconsulting@cs.com, Mng. Dir., Media Services Group, Inc., FL, Jacksonville Beach
Reel, Guy 803-323-4531
reelg@winthrop.edu, Faculty Adviser, The Johnsonian, SC, Rock Hill
Reen, Christopher
creen@opubco.com, President & Publisher, The Oklahoman, OK, Oklahoma City
Rees, David
reesd@missouri.edu, Chrmn., Kappa Alpha Mu Honorary Society in Photo Journalism, MO, Columbia
Rees, Jay..............................(305) 347-6627
jrees@alm.com, Business Editor, Miami Daily Business Review, FL, Miami
Rees, Jay..............................(305) 347-6627
jrees@alm.com, Business Editor, Palm Beach Daily Business Review, FL, West Palm Beach
Rees, Brent
brent.rees@coffscoastadvocate.com.au, Ed., THE ADVOCATE
Reese, Lisa
lreese@timesonline.com, Controller, Beaver County Times, PA, Beaver
Reese, Denise........................(770) 390-3309
Contact, Octel Communications (Messaging Division), GA, Atlanta
Reeves, Glenn........................(650) 348-4345
greeves@angnewspapers.com, Sports Ed., San Mateo County Times, CA, San Mateo
Reeves, Wendy........................(919) 829-4694
wreeves@newsobserver.com, Circ. Mgr., Sales/Mktg., The News & Observer, NC, Raleigh
Reeves, Richard 850-599-2345
rreeves@tallahassee.com, Sales and Marketing Director, Tallahassee Democrat, FL, Tallahassee
Reeves, Tim
leesha.faulkner@selmatimesjournal.com, Editor, The Selma Times-Journal, AL, Selma
Reeves, Bill...........................(607) 432-1000
Hartwick College, NY, Oneonta
Reeves, Jeffrey.......................(760) 754-2891
jreeves@u-bild.com, Features Ed., U-Bild Newspaper Features, CA, Oceanside
Reevs, James A. ....(906) 228-2500
jreevs@miningjournal.net, Pub., The Mining Journal, MI, Marquette
Regan, Trace
tregan@cc.owu.edu, Chair/Prof., Ohio Wesleyan University, OH, Delaware
Regan, Charles ....(805) 685-3100 ext. 124
reganc@maps.com, Exec. Vice Pres., Maps.com, CA, Santa Barbara
Regan, Bill ....(603) 668-4321 ext. 324
bregan@unionleader.com, Deputy Mng. Ed., Bus., New Hampshire Union Leader/New Hampshire Sunday News, NH, Manchester
Reggae, Thomas
thomas.reggae@frankenpost.de, Ed. in Chief, Munchberg-Helmbrechster Zeitung, Hof
Rehm, Barbara A. ....Ed. in Chief
American Banker, NY, 1 State Street Plz.
Reiber, Marge
mreiber@reporter-herald.com, HR Coord., Daily Reporter-Herald, CO, Loveland
Reichenthal, Mark
markr@branfman.com, Assoc., Branfman & Associates, CA, Oceanside
Reichert, Uwe
u.reichert@kornwestheimer-zeitung.zgs.de, Bus. Mgr., KORNWESTHEIMER ZEITUNG, Kornwestheim
Reid, Phillip R.
vdjnews@cableone.net, Pres., The Vinita Daily Journal, OK, Vinita
Reid, Debbie
debreid@alberni.net, Mgmt. Info Servs. Mgr., Alberni Valley Times, BC, Port Alberni
Reid, Michael D. ....(250) 380-5365
mreid@te.canwest.com, Arts/Entertainment Reporter, Times Colonist, BC, Victoria
Reid, Phillip ....(580) 336-2222
gloria@perrydailyjournal.com, Owner/Pub., The Perry Daily Journal, OK, Perry
Reid, Phillip R.
wdn@wdnonline.com, Columnist, Weatherford Daily News, OK, Weatherford
Reifert, Elizabeth
ereifert@dailyherald.com, Adv. Mgr., Nat'l Sales, Daily Herald, IL, Arlington Heights
Reiff, Peter.......................................8040
Proprietor, ACHER-RENCH-ZEITUNG, Oberkirch
Reiff, Peter
info@reiff.de, Proprietor, Offenburger Tageblatt, Offenburg
Reigler, Hunter
hreigler@messenger-inquirer.com, News Ed., Messenger-Inquirer, KY, Owensboro
Reilly, Tom...........................(508) 236-0332
treilly@thesunchronicle.com, Sunday Ed., The Sun Chronicle, MA, Attleboro
Reilly, Mike............................402-444-1277
Executive Editor, Omaha World-Herald, NE, Omaha
Reilly, John P...........................203-354-1048
Editor Emeritus, The Hour Publishing Co., CT, Norwalk
Reilly, Jane............................201-612-0100
nyfwa@aol.com, Exec. Mgr., New York Financial Writers Association, Inc., NJ, Ridgewood
Rein, Mark..............................308-635-6057
mrein@wncc.net, Adv. Mgr., Western Nebraska Community College, NE, Scottsbluff
Reina, Fernando
diario@microcad.es, Dir., Diario Malaga-Costa Del Sol, Malaga
Reinecke, Sheila.....................(231) 725-6312
sreinecke@muskegonchronicle.com, Adv. Dir., Nat'l Sales, The Muskegon Chronicle, MI, Muskegon
Reineking, Stefan
schaumburger-zeitung@t-online.de, Bus. Mgr., Schaumburger Zeitung, Rinteln
Reinertson, Ray
rreino@aol.com, Pres., Rein Tech, Inc. (Printing Systems Technology), MI, Sturgis
Reinhard, Michael
redaktion@mainpost.de, Ed. in Chief, Main Post, Wurzburg
Reinhart, Bethany....................(312) 369-8959
Columbia Chronicle Newspaper, IL, Chicago
Reinhart, Shannon
info@wideareaclassifieds.com, Exec. Dir., Wide Area Classified, MN, New Ulm
Reinschmidt, Paul C...................605-886-6901
Circ. Mgr., Watertown Public Opinion, SD, Watertown
Reitan, Claus
anzeigen@tt.com, Ed. in Chief, TIROLER TAGESZEITUNG, A-6021 Innsbruck
Reitenga, Mark........................(248) 745-4663
mark.reitenga@oakpress.com, Adv. Mgr., Automotive, The Oakland Press, MI, Pontiac
Reiter, Amanda.......................(805) 437-0224
areiter@venturacountystar.com, News Ed., Ventura County Star, CA, Camarillo
Reitz, Bob
breitz@lmtribune.com, Adv. Dir., Lewiston Morning Tribune, ID, Lewiston
Relayo, Michael.......................(650) 391-1028
mrelayo@dailynewsgroup.com, Adv. Mgr., Classified, Palo Alto Daily News, CA, Menlo Park
Reliford, Michael D...................(606) 326-2647
mreliford@dailyindependent.com, Ed., The Daily Independent, KY, Ashland
Relis, Jamie
jrelis@pubgroup.com, Acct. Mgr., Relish - Los Angeles, CA, CA, Los Angeles
Relkow, Dan ....(403) 314-4312
drelkow@reddeeradvocate.com, Bus. Mgr., Red Deer Advocate, AB, Red Deer
Relph, Tracee..............................90220524
tracee.relph@kalminer.com.au, General Manager, KALGOORLIE MINER
Rem, Kathryn..........................(217) 788-1520
kathryn.rem@sj-r.com, Food Ed., The State Journal-Register, IL, Springfield
Remchukov, Konstantin
info@ng.ru, Ed. in Chief, NEZAVISIMAYA GAZETA, Moscow
Remitz, Ed
sanmatean@smccd.net., College of San Mateo, CA, San Mateo
Remmerie, Dirk
nbantwerpen@nieuwsblad.be, Ed. in Chief, HET VOLK, Groot-Bijgaarden
Remmerie, Dirk
nvcrebactie@nieuwsblad.be, Ed., HET VOLK, Bagaarden
Rempel, Christian
mailmaster@mdv-online.de, Pub., Giebener Allgemeine, Giessen
Renaud, John................................ext. 198
Prodn. Coord., Southeast Missourian, MO, Cape Girardeau
Renberg, Werner
werren@att.net, Self-Syndicator, Werner Renberg, NY, Chappaqua
Renderman, Michael
michael.renderman@cision.com, Vice Pres., Bus. Devel., Cision US, Inc., IL, Chicago
Rene, Joseth Etienne
joseth@lematinhaiti.com, Mgr., LE MATIN, Port-Au-Prince
Renfeld, Lori..........................(406) 265-4112
Montana State Univ. Northern, MT, Havre
Renfro, Julia C.
news@arubatoday.com, Ed. in Chief, ARUBA TODAY/BON DIA ARUBA, Oranjestad
Renfroe, Sandy........................(479) 872-5060
srenfroe@nwaonline.net, Bus. Mgr., The Morning News of Northwest Arkansas, AR, Springdale
Rengifo de Sanchez, Fidelia 57-8220
Gen. Mgr., Diario Impetu, Pucallpa, Ucayali
Renneau, Lani..........................(262) 656-6243
lrenneau@kenoshanews.com, Adv. Dir., Kenosha News, WI, Kenosha
Renneisen, Beth.......................(415) 382-7351
Graphics Design Ed., Marin Independent Journal, CA, Novato
Renner, Debbie........................(605) 394-8366
debbie.renner@rapidcityjournal.com, Adv. Mgr., Online, Rapid City Journal, SD, Rapid City
Rennie, Doug..........................(215) 898-7483
Univ. of Pennsylvania Law School, PA, Philadelphia
Reno, Kim...............................(301) 791-7897
Controller, The Herald-Mail, MD, Hagerstown
Renteria, Mario ....(760) 337-3434
mrenteria@ivpressonline.com, Sports Ed., Imperial Valley Press, CA, El Centro
Reos, Ardo
areos@eleconmista.com, Sales Mgr., LA JORNADA, Mexico City, Distrito Federal
Rep, Susan
srep@therepublic.com, Exec. Asst., Home News Enterprises, IN, Columbus
Reshamwala, B.P.
gujaratmitrasurat@yahoo.com, Ed., GUJARATMITRA & GUJARATDARPAN, Surat, Gujarat
Rethi, Donna
drethi@verizon.net, Prodn. Mgr., Pre Press, The Indiana Gazette, PA, Indiana
Retief, Christo
republkn@iwwn.com.na, Ed. (acting), DIE REPUBLIKEIN, Windhoek
Retsinas, Greg........................(707) 526-8662
greg.retsinas@pressdemocrat.com, Online Ed., The Press Democrat, CA, Santa Rosa
Rettig, Gregg
sports@circlevilleherald.com, Sports Ed., Herald, OH, Circleville
Rettig, Gregg ....(740) 852-1616 ext. 18
sports@madison-press.com, Sports Ed., The Madison Press, OH, London
Reunert, Thomas
red.iserlohn@ikz-online.de, News Ed., ISERLOHNER KREISANZE UND ZEITUNG, Iserlohn
Reuteman, Rob........................(303) 892-5177
reutemanr@rockymountainnews.com, Bus. Ed., Rocky Mountain News, CO, Denver
Reuterfors, Roland 908-216-8142
Consultant, Motterstitch Company, Inc., RI, Charlestown
Reverchon, Richard
r.reverchon_lantenne.com@lantenne.com, Dir., L'ANTENNE, Marseille, Cedex 16
Revlett, Teresa
trevlett@kypress.com, Dir., Sales, Kentucky Press Service, Inc., KY, Frankfort
Rey Novoa, Jose Manuel
josemanuelrey@lcorreo.es, Dir., El Correo Gallego, Santiago de Compostela, La Coruna
Reyes, Carlos..........................(212) 244-2630
Circ. Dir., Hoy, NY, New York
Reyes, Fernando
diarioel.ranca001@chilnet.cl, Gen. Mgr., El Rancaguino, Rancagua
Reyes, German
honduras@acan-efe.com, Rep., EFE News Services - Tegucigalpa, Honduras, Tegucigalpa
Reyes, Zuriel...............(770) 428-9411 ext. 359
Online Mgr., Marietta Daily Journal, GA, Marietta
Reyes, Becci
breyes@aldiatx.com, Adv. Mgr., Nat'l Sales, Al Dia, TX, Dallas
Reyes Brambila, Luis
vtaopina@puerto-vallarta.com.mx, Owner/Pres., VALLARTA OPINA, Puerto Vallarta, Jalisco
Reynolds, Marie......................(516) 484-2000
mreynolds@citiplate.com, Customer Serv. Mgr., Citiplate, Inc., NY, Westbury
Reynolds, Jennifer
jennifer@adobe.com, Dir., Worldwide Adv., Adobe Systems, Inc., CA, San Jose
Reynolds, Laurie.............................ext. 278
Adv. Dir., Regl., The World, OR, Coos Bay
Reynolds, Kevin
reynolkj@jmu.edu, Assoc. Prof., James Madison University, VA, Harrisonburg
Reynolds, Jerry........................(205) 325-2194
Circ. Mgr., State, The Birmingham News, AL, Birmingham
Reynolds, Timothy....................(207) 990-8122
Controller, Bangor Daily News, ME, Bangor
Reynolds, Lin..........................(256) 740-5787
lin.reynolds@timesdaily.com, Prodn. Mgr., Pre Press, TimesDaily, AL, Florence
Reynolds, Lindor......................(204) 697-7272
Lindor.Reynolds@freepress.mb.ca, Columnist, Winnipeg Free Press, MB, Winnipeg
Reynolds, Ray.........................(843) 317-7362
rreynolds@florencenews.com, Prodn. Foreman, Mailroom, Morning News, SC, Florence
Reynolds, Fiona
mail@examiner.com.au, Ed., THE EXAMINER
Reynolds-Soucie, Rachael ....(815) 937-3351
rachaelr@daily-journal.com, Asst. Metro Ed., The Daily Journal, IL, Kankakee
Rezabek, James
info@mps-co.com, Pres., Midwest Publishers Supply Co., IL, Harwood Heights
Reznick, Lynn...........................(781) 665-4442
lynn@offthemarkcartoons.com, Mktg. Dir., Atlantic Feature Syndicate, MA, Melrose
Rhoades, Rex
rrhoades@sunjournal.com, Exec. Ed., Sun

Journal, ME, Lewiston
Rhoades, Kevin
krhoades@owaa.org, Exec. Dir., Outdoor Writers Association of America, Inc., MT, Missoula
Rhoades, Cher ....ext. 217
Adv. Dir., The News-Record, WY, Gillette
Rhoades, John
Rhoades, Adv. Dir., The Daily Journal
Rhodes, Veronica ....(306) 781-5300
vrhodes@leaderpost.canwest.com, City Coord., The Leader-Post, SK, Regina
Rhodes, Robin
rrhodes@minespring.com, Exec. Dir., Georgia Newspaper Service, Inc., GA, Atlanta
Rhodes, Mel
mrhodes@cnhi.com, Pub., Mineral Wells Index, TX, Mineral Wells
Rhodes, Robin
mail@gapress.org, Exec. Dir., Georgia Press Association, GA, Atlanta
Rhodin, Tony ....ext. 3465
arhodin@express-times.com, Asst. Mng. Ed., The Express-Times, PA, Easton
Rhoten, Janet
jrhoten@circlevilleherald.com, Bus. Mgr., Herald, OH, Circleville
Rhymer, Karen
info@bluecieloecm.com, Contact, BlueCielo ECM Solutions, GA, Atlanta
Ricci, Paul
pricci@scansoft.com, Chrmn./CEO, Nuance Communications Inc., MA, Burlington
Ricciani, Geri
gricciani@imediainc.com, Dir., Pjct. Mgmt., Interactive Media Associates, NJ, Parsippany
Ricciardi, Theresa ....(617) 929-2182
t_ricciardi@globe.com, Adv. Div. Mgr., Commun., The Boston Globe, MA, Boston
Rice, Stanley
autospec@cruzio.com, Contact, Autospec, Inc., CA, Santa Cruz
Rice, Frankie
frankierice@shelbystar.com, Prodn. Dir., Mailroom, The Star, NC, Shelby
Rice, Steve ....(519) 271-2220 ext. 205
srice@bowesnet.com, Sports Ed., The Beacon-Herald, ON, Stratford
Rice, Micah ....(360) 735-4548
micah.rice@columbian.com, News Ed., The Columbian, WA, Vancouver
Rice, Donna ....(617) 929-2146
drice@globe.com, Adv. Div. Mgr., Cor., The Boston Globe, MA, Boston
Rice, Pat 386-681-2222
Editor, Daytona Beach News-Journal, FL, Daytona Beach
Rice, Patrick ....(850) 747-5092
patr@flafreedom.com, Regl. Dir., Content, The News Herald, FL, Panama City
Rice, Jackie 406-791-1486
Food Ed., Great Falls Tribune, MT, Great Falls
Rice, Barry
brice@colum.edu, Acting Chair, Columbia College Chicago, IL, Chicago
Rice, Vicki ....(308) 233-9747
Educ. Ed., Kearney Hub, NE, Kearney
Rich, Linda
lrich@pubgorup.com, Assoc. Ed., Direct Response, Relish - New York, NY, NY, New York
Rich, Linda
lrich@pubgroup.com, Assoc. Ed., Direct Response, American Profile - New York, NY, NY, New York
Rich, Linda
lrich@pubgroup.com, Assoc. Ed., Direct Response, American Profile - New York, NY, NY, New York
Rich, Sherry ....(910) 343-2250
sherry.rich@starnewsonline.com, Dir., HR, Star-News, NC, Wilmington
Richard, Kevin ....(518) 565-4114
krichard@pressrepublican.com, Mgr., Mgmt. Info Servs., Press-Republican, NY, Plattsburgh
Richards, Harley ....(403) 314-4337
life@reddeeradvocate.com, Red Deer Life Ed., Red Deer Advocate, AB, Red Deer
Richards, Craig ....(304) 367-2515
carichards@timeswv.com, Adv. Dir., Times West Virginian, WV, Fairmont
Richardson, Susan 336-506-3004
srichardson@thetimesnews.com, Controller, Times-News, NC, Burlington
Richardson, Dennis ....(731) 694-2149
dennisr@usit.net, Senior Associate- South, Grimes, W.B. & Co., MD, Gaithersburg
Richardson, Patricia
pat.richardson@carrollcountytimes.com, Pub., Carroll County Times, MD, Westminster
Richardson, Chad ....(404) 526-5125
crichardson@ajc.com, Controller, Atlanta Journal-Constitution, GA, Atlanta
Richardson, Terri ....(260) 461-8304
trich@jg.net, Features Ed., The Journal Gazette, IN, Fort Wayne
Richardson, Charles ....(478) 744-4342
crichardson@macontel.com, Editorial Columnist, The Telegraph, GA, Macon
Richardson, Wayne ....(609) 871-8060
Sports Ed., Burlington County Times, NJ, Willingboro
Richardson, Denise ....(607) 441-7211
drichardson@thedailystar.com, News Ed., The Daily Star, NY, Oneonta
Richardson, Kevin
kerichardson@jackson.gannett.com, Bus. Ed., The Clarion-Ledger, MS, Jackson
Richardson, Valerie ....(303) 470-7078
Denver Bureau Chief, The Washington Times, DC, Washington
Richardson, Dennis ....(731) 694-2149
drichardson@mediamergers.com, South/Southwest Assoc., Grimes, W.B. & Co., TN, Camden
Richelderfer, Jessica
jrichelderfer@times-standard.com, Copy Ed., Times-Standard, CA, Eureka
Richerson, Brittney ....(806) 371-5209
Editor, Amarillo College, TX, Amarillo
Richert, Chris
crichert@chroniclemail.com, General Manager, Columbia Chronicle Newspaper, IL, Chicago
Richey, Kelli
kellir@ndna.com, Mktg. Mgr., North Dakota Newspaper Association, ND, Bismarck
Richey, Gary ....ext. 237
grichey@crescent-news.com, Pressroom/Mailroom Mgr., Defiance Publishing LLC, OH, Defiance
Richieri, Kenneth A. ....(212) 556-1234
Vice Pres./Deputy Gen. Counsel, The New York Times Co., NY, New York
Richman, Shira ....(303) 273-3484
srichman@mines.edu, Faculty Advisor, Colorado School of Mines, CO, Golden
Richmeier, Lisa
lrichmeier@publicitas.com, Contact, Publicitas North America, Inc., AZ, Peoria
Richmond, Ann
ann.richmond@dailyreporter.com, Vice Pres./Pub., The Daily Reporter, WI, Milwaukee
Richter, S.
info@shz.de, Ed. in Chief, Wilstersche Zeitung, Flensburg
Richter, William
Richter@lrc.edu, Chair, Lenoir-Rhyne College, NC, Hickory
Richter, Gerd
redaktion@rotenburger-kreiszeitung.de, Bus. Mgr., Rotenburger Kreiszeitung, Rotenburg, Lower Saxony
Richter, Tammie
trichter@bemidjipionner.com, Bus. Mgr., The Pioneer, MN, Bemidji
Rickenbacher, Ted ....(214) 265-9300
rmedia@msn.com, Pres./Exec. Dir., Rickenbacher Media, TX, Dallas
Rickenbacher, Ted ....(214) 265-9300
rmedia@msn.com, Pres./Exec. Dir., Rickenbacher Media, TX, Dallas
Ricker, Fred E. ....(262) 656-6310
fricker@kenoshanews.com, Bus. Mgr., Kenosha News, WI, Kenosha
Rickert, Wolfgang
verlag@borkenerzeitung.de, Bus. Mgr., BORKENER ZEITUNG, Borken
Rickman, Randy ....(406) 447-4002
randy.rickman@lee.net, Regional Publisher, Independent Record, MT, Helena
Ridder, Lynn 229-888-9387
lynn.ridder@albanyherald.com, Director of Operations, The Albany Herald, GA, Albany
Riddings, Dean
fps-info@flpress.com, Pres./CEO, Florida Press Service, Inc., FL, Tallahassee
Riddle, W. Curtis
jtaylor@delawareonline.com, Pres./Pub., The News Journal, DE, New Castle
Riddle, Lyn ....(864) 298-4301
localnews@greenvillenews.com, City Ed., The Greenville News, SC, Greenville
Rideout, Brian
info@bkrstudio.com, Pres., BKR Studio, Inc., IN, South Bend
Rider, Joshua ....(510) 655-3951
Univ. of California-Berkeley Law School, CA, Berkeley
Ridinger, Christy
ridingerc@wtr.com, Adv. Dir., Wichita Falls Times Record News, TX, Wichita Falls
Ridings, Dean
deanr@n2ps.com, Pres./CEO, National Newspaper Placement Services, FL, Lake Mary
Ridings, Dean ....(850) 521-1162
deanr@flpress.com, President & CEO, Florida Press Association, FL, Tallahassee
Rieckman, Stewart ....(920) 426-6691
srieckman@smgpo.gannett.com, Gen Mgr., Oshkosh Northwestern, WI, Oshkosh
Riefler, Katja 49 (89) 6-214-6044
Europe Director, AIM Group / Classified Intelligence, FL, Altamonte Springs
Rieger, Andy ....(405) 366-3543
editor@normantranscript.com, Exec. Ed., Norman Transcript, OK, Norman
Riegle, Richard
rriegle@newspapersfirst.com, Vice Pres./Sales Mgr., Newspapers First, Inc., CA, Los Angeles
Ries, Richard ....(812) 265-6313
rries@bigringwriting.com, Dir., Big Ring Media Team, Inc., IN, Madison
Ries, Julie ....(812) 265-6313
julie.ries@bigringwriting.com, Admin. Asst., Big Ring Media Team, Inc., IN, Madison
Riess, Christoph
christoph.riess@wan-ifra.com, CEO, World Association of Newspapers and News Publishers (WAN-IFRA), Paris
Riess, Christoph
martina.damiche@wan-ifra.org, CEO, World Association of Newspapers and News Publishers (WAN-IFRA), Darmstadt
Riesterer, Ron ....(925) 416-4829
rriesterer@angnewspapers.com, Photo Ed., San Mateo County Times, CA, San Mateo
Riesz, Charles ....(910) 343-2385
chuck.riesz@starnewsonline.com, Editorial Page Ed., Star-News, NC, Wilmington
Rifanburg, Michael 315-253-5311
michael.rifanburg@lee.net, Publisher, Auburn Publishers, Inc., NY, Auburn
Rife, Susan ....(941) 957-5271
susan.rife@heraldtribune.com, Books Ed., Sarasota Herald-Tribune, FL, Sarasota
Riffe, Daniel ....(919) 962-4082
Prof./Richard Cole Eminent Prof., University of North Carolina, NC, Chapel Hill
Riffle, Rich
rriffle@timesonline.com, Adv. Opns. Mgr., Beaver County Times, PA, Beaver
Rifkin, Marc
marc.rifkin@scala.com, Dir. Training/Servs., Scala, Inc., PA, Exton
Rifkin, Don ....(201) 646-4050
Mktg. Dir., Herald News, NJ, West Paterson
Rigel, Chris ....(215) 884-8177
crigel@sej.org, Dir.,Pgm., Society of Environmental Journalists (SEJ), PA, Jenkintown
Riggenbach, Don ....(712) 527-9517
don@riggenbach.info, Mgr., Jandon Features, IA, Glenwood
Riggs, Brett ....ext. 234
riggs@gctelegram.com, Bus. Ed., The Garden City Telegram, KS, Garden City
Righi, Jane ....(419) 625-5500 ext. 327
janerighi@sanduskyregister.com, Mgr., Bus. Office, Sandusky Register, OH, Sandusky
Righter, Julie
jrighter@nevadadailymail.com, Publisher, The Fort Scott Tribune, KS, Fort Scott
Rika, Metani
editor@fijitimes.com.fj, Ed. in Chief, FIJI TIMES, Suva
Riley, William (B.J.) ....(812) 231-4297
bj.riley@tribstar.com, Pub., The Tribune Star, IN, Terre Haute
Riley, Larry ....(714) 796-6864
lriley@ocregister.com, Vice Pres., Circ., The Orange County Register, CA, Santa Ana
Riley, Denise ....(410) 770-4088
Exec. Ed., The Star-Democrat, MD, Easton
Riley, Steve ....(919) 836-4940
sriley@newsobserver.com, Deputy Mng. Ed., The News & Observer, NC, Raleigh
Riley, Deanna ....(303) 776-2244 ext. 276
driley@times-call.com, Mgr., HR, Times-Call, CO, Longmont
Riley-Gordon, Donna ....ext. 125
driley-gordon@cnhi.com, Mng. Ed., Effingham Daily News, IL, Effingham
Rimas, Val
sales@rotoflex.com, Gen. Mgr./Vice Pres., Sales/Mktg., Rotoflex Mark Andy Canada, Inc., ON, Mississauga
Rinaldi, Sev ....(203) 330-6309
srinaldi@ctpost.com, Features Ed., Connecticut Post, CT, Bridgeport
Rindels, Michelle ....(562) 903-4880
Biola Univ., CA, La Mirada
Rindfleisch, Terry ....(608) 791-8227
trindfleisch@lacrossetribune.com, Health Reporter, La Crosse Tribune, WI, La Crosse
Rindo, John Michael ....(305) 347-6622
jrindo@alm.com, Director of Creative Services, Miami Daily Business Review, FL, Miami
Rindos, Daniel F.
dan@bargainnews.com, Vice Pres., Communications Management Service, Inc., CT, Trumbull
Rineholts, Josh ....(703) 369-7195
jrineholts@insidenova.com, Controller, News & Messenger, VA, Woodbridge
Ringel, Jonathan
jringel@alm.com, Mng. Ed., Daily Report
Ringenberg, John ....ext. 230
jringenberg@norwalkreflector.com, Adv. Dir., Norwalk Reflector, OH, Norwalk
Ringler, Larry ....ext. 763
lringler@tribtoday.com, Bus. Ed., The Tribune Chronicle, OH, Warren
Ringrose, James
sgottfried@inso.com, Pres./CEO, eBT, RI, Providence
Rini, Alan
iberianadmgr@bellsouth.net, Adv. Mgr., The Daily Iberian, LA, New Iberia
Rink, Ellen ....(661) 392-5732
erink@bakersfield.com, Circ. Mgr., Single Copy, The Bakersfield Californian, CA, Bakersfield
Rinker, Rudy ....(417) 836-1204
rrinker@news-leader.com, Circ. Mgr., Single Copy, Springfield News-Leader, MO, Springfield
Rinks, J. Wayne
wrinks@usi.edu, Chair/Assoc. Prof., University of Southern Indiana, IN, Evansville
Rintoul, Mary ....(620) 694-5700 ext. 310
mrintoul@hutchnews.com, Mng. Ed., The Hutchinson News, KS, Hutchinson
Rios, Jimmie ....(830) 257-0302
jimmie.rios@dailytimes.com, Prodn. Mgr., Press, Kerrville Daily Times, TX, Kerrville
Rios, Letty ....(956) 982-6630
Adv. Mgr., Classified, The Brownsville Herald, TX, Brownsville
Rios Chacon, Jaime 248-8163
cartas@jornadanet.com, Pres., Aurelios S.R.L., La Paz
Riotta, Gianni 655-8111
direzionegenerale@lastampa.it, Mgr., LA STAMPA, Torino
Riotto, James ....(570) 628-6053
jriotto@republicanherald.com, Adv. Mgr., Classified, Republican Herald, PA, Pottsville
Rioux, Larry ....(207) 861-9156
lrioux@centralmaine.com, Adv. Mgr., Retail Sales, Kennebec Journal, ME, Augusta
Ripley, Mike ....(360) 735-4472
mike.ripley@columbian.com, Adv. Mgr., Classified, The Columbian, WA, Vancouver
Ripley, Stephen

sripley@wpgsun.com, Ed. in Chief, The Winnipeg Sun, MB, Winnipeg
Risdall, Ted ....ext. 2
webmaster@digitalhabitat.com, Pres./Dir.-Sales/Mktg., Risdall Advertising, MN, Saint Paul
Risdall, Ted 651-286-6700
ted@risdall.com, Chairman/President, Risdall Marketing Group, MN, New Brighton
Risdall, John ....ext. 3
CEO, Risdall Advertising, MN, Saint Paul
Risdall, John 651-286-6700
Chrmn./CEO, Risdall Marketing Group, MN, New Brighton
Riski, Rich ....(360) 417-6469
Peninsula College, WA, Port Angeles
Risling, Catherine ....(310) 243-2313
California State Univ. Dominguez, CA, Carson
Ritanburg, Michael
michael.ritanburg@lee.net, Publisher, The Citizen, NY, Auburn
Ritchie, Alanna
aritchie@scpress.org, Adv. Dir., South Carolina Press Services, Inc., SC, Columbia
Ritchie, Brian ....(216) 999-6456
IT Mgr., Product Development, The Plain Dealer, OH, Cleveland
Ritter, Kristi ....(303) 776-2244 ext. 275
kkritter@times-call.com, Special Sections Ed., Times-Call, CO, Longmont
Ritter, K.J. ....(303) 776-2244 ext. 213
kritter@times-call.com, News Ed., Times-Call, CO, Longmont
Ritter, John ....(305) 372-0933 ext. 226
jar@rrzlawyers.com, Pres./Writer, Legal & Word Briefs, FL, Miami
Ritterbusch, Robert D. ....(216) 999-4596
Adv. Vice Pres., Classified, The Plain Dealer, OH, Cleveland
Riva Rey, Alvaro
arivarey@adinet.com.uy, Director Responsable, El Heraldo S.A., Florida
Rivard, Robert
rrivard@express-news.net, Ed., Randolph Wingspread, TX, San Antonio
rrivard@express-news.net, Ed., Brooks Discovery News, TX, San Antonio
rrivard@express-news.net, Ed., Bulverde Community News, TX, San Antonio
rrivard@express-news.net, Ed., Fort Sam News Leader, TX, San Antonio
rrivard@express-news.net, Ed., Kelly Observer, TX, San Antonio
rrivard@express-news.net, Ed., Lackland Talespinner, TX, San Antonio
rrivard@express-news.net, Ed., Medical Patriot, TX, San Antonio
rrivard@express-news.net, Ed., North Central News, TX, San Antonio
rrivard@express-news.net, Ed., Northeast Herald, TX, San Antonio
rrivard@express-news.net, Ed., Northwest Weekly, TX, San Antonio
rrivard@express-news.net, Ed., San Antonio Express-News, TX, San Antonio
Rivas, Roxana
roxana.rivas@vistamagazine.com, Acct. Mgr., Vista - The Magazine for All Hispanics - New York, NY, NY, New York
Rivera, Patsy ....(602) 444-8133
patsy.rivera@pni.com, Admin. Asst., The Arizona Republic, AZ, Phoenix
Rivera, Jorge 425.339.3415
jrivera@weeklyherald.com, Edmonds Enterprise, WA, Lynnwood
jrivera@weeklyherald.com, Weekly Herald, WA, Lynnwood
jrivera@weeklyherald.com, Director of Circulation and Operations, The Herald, WA, Everett
Rivera Urrutia, Gustavo
nacion01@reuna.cl, Gen. Mgr., La Nacion, Santiago
Rivero, Andelels
pam@lne.es, Dir., La Nueva Espana, Oviedo, Asturias
Rivero, Pedro Osvaldo 42-4665
Gen. Mgr., El Tiempo, Pergamino, Provincia de Buenos Aires
Rivers, Stephanie ....(973) 569-7072
Director of Features, North Jersey Media Group, NJ, Woodland Park
Rivers, Ulysses ....(973) 569-7104
Editorial Page Ed., Herald News, NJ, West Paterson
Rives, Jerry ....(903) 596-6219
jri@tylerpaper.com, Circ. Dir., Tyler Morning Telegraph, TX, Tyler
Rives, Allan
rives@riverinmediagroup.com.au, Adv. Mgr., THE DAILY ADVERTISER
Rivet, Jacques
jrivet@intnet.mu, Dir., LE MAURICIEN, Port Louis
Rivkin, Fran ....(617) 779-8900 ext. 2110
frivkin@domania.com, CFO, Domania, Inc., MA, Watertown
Rixon, Jeffrey ....(508) 862-1122
jrixon@capecodonline.com, Adv. Mgr., Cape Cod Times, MA, Hyannis
Rizk, Chris
crizk@detroitnews.com, City Ed., Night, The Detroit News, MI, Detroit
Rizos, D.
lamiakos@gmail.com, Pub./Dir., LAMIAKOS TYPOS, Lamia, Central Greece
Rizos, Dimitris
adesmeytostypos@aias.gr, Pub., ADESMEYTOS TYPOS, Kalithea, Central Greece
Roach, Rick
photo@thereporter.com, Photo Ed., The Reporter, CA, Vacaville
Roach, Dan ....(231) 933-1439
droach@record-eagle.com, Adv. Mgr., Special Projects, Record-Eagle, MI, Traverse City
Roaldseth, Jan
redaksjonen@sb.no, Dir., SANDEFJORDS BLAD, Sandefjord
Roane, Sean ....(814) 532-5062
Mng. Ed., The Tribune-Democrat, PA, Johnstown
Robanske, Eric
erobanske@thereporter.com, Circ. Mgr., The Reporter, CA, Vacaville
Robb, Diane ....(920) 431-8362
drobb@greenbaypressgazette.com, Librarian, Green Bay Press-Gazette, WI, Green Bay
Robb, Jack 334-293-5800
jrobb@cnhi.com, VP of Revenue, Community Newspaper Holdings, Inc., AL, Montgomery
Robb, Gary
grobb@santamariatimes.com, Online Ed., Santa Maria Times, CA, Santa Maria
Robbins, Jason
dailynews@vipowernet.net, Pub., VIRGIN ISLANDS DAILY NEWS, VI, Saint Thomas
Robbins, Dana ....(905) 526-3482
drobbins@thespec.com, Ed. in Chief, The Hamilton Spectator, ON, Hamilton
Robedeau, Kim 321-752-5001
krobedea@floridatoday.com, Multi Media Advertising Manager, Florida Today, FL, Melbourne
Robert, Charlene
crobert@theadvocate.com, Mktg. Mgr., The Advocate, LA, Baton Rouge
Roberts, Lorraine ....(941) 206-1168
lroberts@sun-herald.com, Deputy City Ed., Charlotte Sun, FL, Charlotte Harbor
Roberts, Dan
droberts@mediaspanonline.com, Exec. Vice Pres./Gen. Mgr., MediaSpan Online Services, CA, Irvine
Roberts, Stephen J. ....(312) 214-6141
sroberts@mpival.com, Vice Pres., Management Planning, Inc., IL, Chicago
Roberts, H. Armstrong
info@robertstock.com, Pres., Robertstock, Robertstock/Classicstock, PA, Philadelphia
Roberts, Cathy
croberts@mullermartinims.com, Parts Mgr., Muller Martini Mailroom Systems, Inc., PA, Allentown
Roberts, Angelia
news@guardonline.com, Mng. Ed., Batesville Guard, AR, Batesville
Roberts, Jeremy
contact.us@quebecorusa.com, Dir. Cor. Commun., Quebecor World, MA, Dedham
Roberts, Tim ....(972) 392-0888
tim@wieck.com, Pres., Wieck Media, TX, Dallas
Roberts, Nancy L.
nroberts@albany.edu, Prof./Dir., Journ. Prog., State University of New York at Albany, NY, Albany
Roberts, Dave ....(810) 766-6308
droberst@flintjournal.com, Prodn. Mgr., The Flint Journal, MI, Flint
Roberts, Dan
droberts@mediaspansoftware.com, Exec. Vice Pres., MediaSpan Media Software, FL, Melbourne
Roberts, Criss
croberts@thehawkeye.com, Features Ed., The Hawk Eye, IA, Burlington
Roberts, Charles
Robertsc@etsu.edu, Chair, East Tennessee State University, TN, Johnson City
Roberts, Neal ....(212) 556-1234
Vice Pres., Orgn./Devel., The New York Times Co., NY, New York
Roberts, Marc
mroberts@theobserver.ca, Circ. Mgr., Observer, ON, Sarnia
Robertson, Bradley I.
brobertson@bfp.burlingtonfreepress.com, Pres./Pub., The Burlington Free Press, VT, Burlington
Robertson, Charles
sales@robertsonpress.com, Pres., Robertson Press Machinery Co., Inc., MO, Joplin
Robertson, Jim ....(573) 815-1728
jerobertson@columbiatribune.com, Managing Editor/Editorial Page Ed., Columbia Daily Tribune, MO, Columbia
Robertson, Terry
troberts@usd.edu, Chair, University of South Dakota, SD, Vermillion
Robertson, Ken ....(509) 582-1520
krobertson@tri-cityherald.com, Exec. Ed., Tri-City Herald, WA, Kennewick
Robertson, Ashley ....(662) 846-4715
Delta State Univ., MS, Cleveland
Robillard, Yvonne ....(906) 483-2220
yrobillard@mininggazette.com, Adv. Dir., The Daily Mining Gazette, MI, Houghton
Robinette, Eric
erobinette@coxohio.com, Entertainment Ed., Middletown Journal, OH, Middletown
Robinson, LeCrete ....(318) 487-6419
lrobinson@thetowntalk.com, Features Ed., The Town Talk, LA, Alexandria
Robinson, Bob
brobinson@dailyadvocate.com, Ed., Daily Advocate, OH, Greenville
Robinson, Janet
jrobinson@examiner-enterprise.com, Adv. Acct. Exec., Examiner-Enterprise, OK, Bartlesville
Robinson, Cindy ....ext. 235
crobinson@smgpo.gannett.com, Style Ed., The Daily Times, MD, Salisbury
Robinson, Lilian ....(845) 758-6822
Bard College, NY, Annandale
Robinson, Jerry ....(212) 362-9256
cwss@cartoonweb.com, Pres., Cartoonists & Writers Syndicate/Cartoon Arts International - New York, NY, NY, New York
cwss@cartoonweb.com, Pres., Cartoonists & Writers Syndicate/Cartoon Arts International - Rancho Palos Verdes, CA, CA, Rancho Palos Verdes
Robinson, Dave ....(313) 222-6457
robinson@freepress.com, Deputy Mng. Ed., Detroit Free Press, MI, Detroit
Robinson, Greg ....(605) 331-2280
grobinso@argusleader.com, Dir., Admin./Controller, Argus Leader, SD, Sioux Falls
Robinson, Teresa ....(603) 668-4321 ext. 506
trobinson@unionleader.com, Community Relations Mgr., New Hampshire Union Leader/New Hampshire Sunday News, NH, Manchester
Robinson, Gregory ....(413) 788-3588
grobinson@repub.com, Adv. Servs. Mgr., The Republican, MA, Springfield
Robinson, Carla Kimbrough ....(303) 820-1914
Assoc. Ed., Staff Devel., The Denver Post, CO, Denver
Robinson, Shaw ....(902) 564-5451
Bus. Mgr., The Cape Breton Post, NS, Sydney
Robinson, Frank ....ext. 735
frobinson@tribtoday.com, Ed., The Tribune Chronicle, OH, Warren
Robinson, Tim
trobinson@ht.homecomm.net, Sports Ed., The Livingston County Daily Press & Argus, MI, Howell
Robinson, Janet L. ....(212) 556-1234
Pres./CEO, The New York Times Co., NY, New York
Robinson, Cheryl ....(508) 626-3984
crobinso@cnc.com, Display Adv. Mgr., Milford Daily News, MA, Milford
Robinson, Rodney ....(253) 597-8739
rodney.robinson@thenewstribune.com, Info. Systems Dir., The News Tribune, WA, Tacoma
Robinson, Jack ....(559) 441-6410
jrobinson@fresnobee.com, Mng. Ed., The Fresno Bee, CA, Fresno
Robinson, Keith
krobinson@makingit.com, Cartoonist/Owner, Making It Productions, CA, Manhattan Beach
Robinson, Alan
appittsburgh@ap.org, Pres., Pittsburgh Baseball Writers Association of America, PA, Pittsburgh
Robinson, Robin ....(416) 947-2285
robin.robinson@sunmedia.ca, Travel Ed., The Toronto Sun, ON, Toronto
Robinson, Jens
jens@cartoonweb.com, Vice Pres./Ed., Cartoonists & Writers Syndicate/Cartoon Arts International - Rancho Palos Verdes, CA, CA, Rancho Palos Verdes
Robinson, Pat ....(303) 954-1952
probinson@medianewsgroup.com, Assistant to the CEO / Corp. Sec., MediaNews Group Inc, CO, Denver
Robipaille, Lyne
lrobipaille@journalmtl.com, Pres./Pub., Le Journal de Montreal, QC, Montreal
Robison, Ted
curt@hartcom.net, Vice Pres., Sales, Royal Graphics, GA, Hartwell
Robledo, Roberto ....(831) 754-4269
rrobledo@salinas.gannett.com, Editorial Page Ed., The Salinas Californian, CA, Salinas
Robotta, Jens
jens.robotta@tagesspiegel.de, Adv. Mgr., DER TAGESSPIEGEL, Berlin
Roby, Mark S. ....(605) 886-6901
Pub., Watertown Public Opinion, SD, Watertown
Roby, Terry ....(989) 875-4151 ext. 105
troby@gcherald.com, Pres., Community Papers of Michigan, Inc., MI, Eastlansing
Roca, Jesus A.
jroca@panampap.com, Sr. Vice Pres., Pan American Papers, Inc., FL, Miami
Roca, Miguel
mwroca@vocero.com, Pres., EL VOCERO DE PUERTO RICO, PR, San Juan
Rocha, Joe ....(262) 513-2659
jrocha@conleynet.com, Prodn. Coord., Mailroom, The Freeman, WI, Waukesha
Rocha ChavarrÃ¡a, Juan Carlos
larazon@la-razon.com, Dir., Grupo Garafulic, La Paz
Roche, Matt ....ext. 238
mroche@norwalkreflector.com, News Ed., Norwalk Reflector, OH, Norwalk
Roche, Dennis
dennisr@youthstream.com, COO, American Passage Media Corp./Youthstream Media Networks, NY, New York
Rochel, Thomas
verlag@sz-sb.de, Bus. Mgr., Saarbrucker Zeitung, Saarbrucken
Rochester, Sharon ....(864) 260-1201
rochestersr@scripps.com, Vice Pres., Finance, Anderson Independent-Mail, SC, Anderson
Rochette, Marc
marc.rochette@lenouvelliste.qc.ca, Ed., Le Nouvelliste, QC, Trois-Rivieres
Rock, George ....(518) 565-4151
grock@pressrepublican.com, Mktg. Dir., Press-Republican, NY, Plattsburgh
Rock, Steve ....(815) 987-1491
srock@rockford.gannett.com, Prodn. Mgr., Press Opns., Rockford Register Star, IL, Rockford
Rockwell, Michele ....(209) 533-4013
mrockwell@uniondemocrat.com, Circ. Dir.,

The Union Democrat, CA, Sonora
Rodgers, Cheryl Kehoe ....ext. 209
City Ed., The Times Herald, PA, Norristown
Rodgers, Jeff ....(410) 961-2336
jrodgers@landonmedia.com, Vice Pres., Newpaper Strategist, Landon Media Group LLC, NY, New York
Rodgers, Douglas ....(202) 806-6631
Howard Univ. Engineering, DC, Washington
Rodi, Bob ....(419) 993-2104
brodi@limanews.com, Prodn. Mgr., Opns., The Lima News, OH, Lima
Rodregues, Sandra
diarioviseu@diarioregional.pt, Ed., DIARIO VISEU, Viseu
Rodreguez, Sernin
srodreguez@dearmas.com, Sales Mgr., Bloque de Armas Publicaciones, Caracas
Rodrick, Richard
rodrick.rich@uwlax.edu, Chair, University of Wisconsin-La Crosse, WI, La Crosse
Rodrigue, Darlene ....(985) 857-2220
darlene.rodrigue@houmatoday.com, Controller, The Courier, LA, Houma
Rodrigue, Darlene ....(985) 857-2220
darlene.rodrigue@dailycomet.com, Controller, The Daily Comet, LA, Thibodaux
Rodrigues, Jose Barbosa 742-6090
diretoria@correiodoestado.com.br, Pres., Correio do Estado, Campo Grande, Mato Grosso
Rodrigues, Rod ....(973) 569-7830
National Avertising Sales Manager, North Jersey Media Group, NJ, Woodland Park
Rodrigues, Neva T. 232-2480
Ed., Diario De Taubate, Taubate, Sao Paulo
Rodrigues, Antonio Joao Hugo 721-3030
Pres., Diario da Serra, Campo Grande, Mato Grosso
Rodrigues Ferreira, Jose Guillermo
dcomercio@acsp.com.br, Ed. in Chief, Diario do Comercio, Sao Paulo
Rodriguez, Nate ....(805) 437-0389
nrodriguez@venturacountystar.com, Adv. Mgr., Classified, Multimedia, Ventura County Star, CA, Camarillo
Rodriguez, Margarita
eldiascl@albec.net.mx, Gen. Mgr., El Dia, Mexico City, Distrito Federal
Rodriguez, Alfonso
redacpr@est.es, Ed., EFE News Services - Santurce, PR, PR, Santurce
Rodriguez, Cristian Bofill
latercera@latercera.cl, Dir., La Tercera, Santiago
Rodriguez, Carlos A. 75-3668
Ed., La Voz de Rojas, Rojas, Provincia de Buenos Aires
Rodriguez, Eolo Ernesto Pacheco
publicidadelregionaldelsur@yahoo.com.mx,, Pres., El Regional del Sur, Cuernavaca, Morelos
Rodriguez, Anthony
anthony.rodriguez@theledger.com, Dir., HR, The Ledger, FL, Lakeland
Rodriguez, Victoria ....(630) 715-2037
Ed., Elgin Community College, IL, Elgin
Rodriguez, Marissa 3054164644
marissa.rodriguez@vistamagazine.com, Editor, Vista - The Magazine for All Hispanics - Miami Beach, FL, FL, Miami Beach
Rodriguez, Jose
redaccion@correoandalucia.es, Pres., EL CORREO DE ANDALUCIA, Sevilla
Rodriguez, Alberto Jose 422-037
Pres., El Diario de La Republica, San Luis, Provincia de San Luis
Rodriguez, Pablo
advertising@sweetwaterreporter.com, Composing Mgr., Sweetwater Reporter, TX, Sweetwater
Rodriguez Borunda, Osvaldo...............429 0700
Owner, Diario de Chihuahua, Chihuahua, Chihuahua
Rodriguez Borunda, Osvaldo
djuarez@diario.com.mx, Pres., DIARIO DE JUAREZ, Ciudad Juarez, Chihuahua
Rodriguez Jimenez, Osvaldo
orj@diario.com.mx, Adv. Mgr., DIARIO DE JUAREZ, Ciudad Juarez, Chihuahua
Rodriguez Nunez, Teresiano
hoyredaccion@audinex.es, Dir., HOY-DIARIO DE EXTREMADURA, Badajoz
Rodriguez Orozco, Carlos Alfonso 741-1030
cronica@armenia.multi.net.co, Gen. Mgr., La Cronica del Quindio, Armenia, Quindio
Rodriguez Ramirez, Jose
produccion@eldia.es, Dir., El Dia, Santa Cruz de Tenerife
Rodriguez Terron, Jose Carlos
solcul@oem.com.mx, Gen. Mgr., El Sol de Culiacan, Culiacan, Sinaloa
Rodriguez Torres, Gabriela
avanhgo@prodigy.net.mx, Pres., AVANZANDO, Pachuca, Hidalgo
Rodriguez Zorrilla, Ramon
diaridesbd@cempresarial.com, Dir., DIARI DE SABADELL, Sabadell, Barcelona
Rodriguezr, Silveria Cruz
scruz@tribuna.com.mx, Prodn. Mgr., Tribuna del Yaqui, Ciudad Obregon, Sonora
RodrÃ¡guez, Leonardo
hlrodriguez@elespectador.com, Ed. Gen., El Espectador (Comunican S.A.), Bogota
Roe, John ....(519) 894-2250 ext. 2610
jroe@therecord.com, Editorial Page Ed., The Record, ON, Kitchener
Roe, Tim
sports@thereporter.com, Sports Ed., The Reporter, CA, Vacaville
Roe, David
droe@certifiedaudit.com, Dir., Opns., Certified Audit of Circulations, Inc., NJ, Wayne
Roe, Gary................................(574) 224-5311
production@rochsent.com, Circ. Mgr., The Rochester Sentinel, IN, Rochester
Roegner, Kim
kimroegner@coloradoan.com, Pres./Pub., The Coloradoan, CO, Fort Collins
Roehling, Rolf
redaktion@a-beig.de, Ed., Pinneberger Tageblatt, Pinneberg
Roehrman, Michael 316-269-6753
mroehrman@wichitaeagle.com, Deputy Ed., News Desk, The Wichita Eagle, KS, Wichita
Roeller, Dawn M.
mssisoftware@cs.com, Vice Pres., Mktg., Micro Systems Specialists, Inc. (MSSI), NY, Millbrook
Roe-er, Bob ....(928) 539-6902
broeser@yumasun.com, Circ. Dir., Yuma Sun, AZ, Yuma
Roeske, Keith ....(847) 427-8872
kroeske@alfaquest.com, Dir., Opns., alfaQuest Technologies, IL, Rolling Meadows
Roessler, Scott
adbase.support-services.us@atex.com, CEO of North America, Atex North America, FL, Melbourne
Roger, Claudia C. 420-993
diario@dechivilcoy.com.ar, Pres., La Campana, Chivilcoy, Provincia de Buenos Aires
Rogers, Tony..........................215-968-8165
rogerst@bucks.edu, Bucks County Cmty. College, PA, Newtown
Rogers, Ken ....(701) 250-8250
ken.rogers@bismarktribune.com, Mng. Ed., The Bismarck Tribune, ND, Bismarck
Rogers, Jeffery B.....................(812) 379-5670
jrogers@therepublic.com, CFO, Home News Enterprises, IN, Columbus
Rogers, Benny
sportseditor@athensreview.com, Sports Ed., Athens Daily Review, TX, Athens
Rogers, Alice ....(713) 313-1976
Texas Southern Univ., TX, Houston
Rogers, Craig ....ext. 5428
Dir., Mktg., The Post and Courier, SC, Charleston
Rogers, Mark 250-371-6142
mrogers@kamloopsnews.ca, New Media Editor, Kamloops Daily News, BC, Kamloops
Rogers, Rick
rrogers@neoshodailynews.com, Pub., Neosho Daily News, MO, Neosho
Rogers, Laura...............(229) 244-3400 ext. 253
laura.rogers@gaflnews.com, Adv. Mgr., Nat'l/Major, Valdosta Daily Times, GA, Valdosta
Rogers, Helen ....(203) 789-5214
hrogers@nhregister.com, Credit Mgr., New Haven Register, CT, New Haven
Rogers, William C.
brogers@scpress.org, Exec. Dir., South Carolina Press Services, Inc., SC, Columbia
Rogers, Peter
progers@nptelegraph.com, Pub., The North Platte Telegraph, NE, North Platte
Rogers, Adam ....(330) 941-1807
Youngstown State Univ., OH, Youngstown
Rogers, William C. ....(803) 750-9561
brogers@scpress.org, Exec. Dir., South Carolina Press Association, SC, Columbia
Rogers, Elizabeth ....(724) 222-2200
lrogers@observer-reporter.com, City/Metro Ed., Observer-Reporter, PA, Washington
Rogers, Bob
borogers@camden.gannett.com, News Ed., Courier-Post, NJ, Cherry Hill
Rogers, Don............................(970) 748-2920
drogers@vaildaily.com, Ed./Pub., Vail Daily, CO, Vail
Rogers, Stephen A.
letters@syracuse.com, Pub., The Post-Standard, NY, Syracuse
Rogers, Mark
mark.rogers@miaminewsrecord.com, Adv. Mgr., Display, Miami News-Record, OK, Miami
Rogers, Pam
news@timesrepublican.com, Television/Film Ed., Times-Republican, IA, Marshalltown
Rogers, Brad............................352.867.4101
brad.rogers@starbanner.com, Editorial Page Ed., Ocala Star-Banner, FL, Ocala
Rogers, Doug ....(919) 836-5658
dougr@newsobserver.com, Adv. Mgr., Direct Mktg., The News & Observer, NC, Raleigh
Roggen, Mark N. ....(413) 528-2300
mark.roggen@roggenconsultants.com, Pres., Roggen Management Consultants, Inc., MA, North Egremont
Roghaar, Brad ....(801) 625-4558
Mgr., Creative, Standard-Examiner, UT, Ogden
Roghaar, Bradley N. ....(801) 625-4310
broghaar@standard.net, Dir., Sales, Standard-Examiner, UT, Ogden
Rognsvoog, Lynn.....................(401) 272-1122
Design director, Creative Circle Media Solutions, RI, East Providence
Rogo, Gary ....(203) 330-6223
grogo@ctpost.com, Sports Ed., Connecticut Post, CT, Bridgeport
Rogoff, Lynn ....(212) 941-8461
director@amerikids.com, CEO, Amerikids USA, NY, New York
Rogus, Mary ....(740) 593-2606
Assoc. Prof., Ohio University, OH, Athens
Roguski, Randy ....(216) 999-4886
Bus. Editor, The Plain Dealer, OH, Cleveland
Roherty, Dan ....ext. 284
droherty@appleton.gannett.com, Print Opns. Ed., The Post-Crescent, WI, Appleton
Rohm, Wolfgang
redaktion@szbz.de, Proprietor, SZ Sindelfinger Zeitung, Sindelfingen
Rohr, Rob...............................(937) 225-6938
Senior Vice President, Sales, Dayton Daily News, OH, Dayton
Rohr, Karen ....ext. 251
karen.rohr@rockdalecitizen.com, Features Ed., The Rockdale Citizen, GA, Conyers
Rohrbein, Martin
walsroderzeitung@wz-net.de, Proprietor, Walsroder-Zeitung, Walsrode
Rohrhoser, Werner
w.rohrhoser@volksblatt.at, Ed. in chief, NEUES VOLKSBLATT, Linz, Upper Austria
Rohrman, Paul ....(215) 345-3125
Systems Mgr., The Intelligencer, PA, Doylestown
Roimondo, Lanny
info@technicolor.com, Pres., Technicolor Packaged Media Services, CA, Camarillo
Rojas, Selene 496-261
selenr@uhora.com.py, Mktg. Mgr., Ultima Hora, Asuncion
Rojas, Javier...........................(213) 804-4071
javier@agenciapi.com, Media Mgr., Agencia Prensa Internacional Inc., CA, Los Angeles
Roknick, Michael ....ext. 241
mroknick@sharonherald.com, Bus. Ed., The Herald, PA, Sharon
Rokyta, Devin
skelly@dnews.com, Sports Ed., Moscow-Pullman Daily News, ID, Moscow
Roland, Tore
redaksjonen@ringblad.no, Ed., RINGERIKES BLAD, Sentrum
Roldan Zimbron, Daniel
laextra@lapaz.cromwell.com.mx, Ed./Dir., La Extra, La Paz, Bajo California Sur
Rolfsen, Erik ....(604) 605-2079
erolfsen@theprovince.com, News Ed. - Online, The Province, BC, Vancouver
Rolley, Bob ....(570) 748-6791 ext. 114
brolley@lockhaven.com, Pub., The Express, PA, Lock Haven
Rollin, K. Ann.........................(916) 321-1495
arollin@sacbee.com, Adv. Mgr., Retail Sales, The Sacramento Bee, CA, Sacramento
Rollinger, Daniela
anzeigen@die-kitzinger.de, Ed. in Chief, DIE KITZINGER, Kitzingen
Rollins, Jess ....(417) 836-5272
Missouri State Univ., MO, Springfield
Rollins, Ron ....(937) 225-2165
rrollins@coxohio.com, Associate Editor, Dayton Daily News, OH, Dayton
Rollins, Ron............................(937) 225-2165
rrollins@coxohio.com, Asst. Mng. Ed., Features/Entertainment, Dayton Daily News, OH, Dayton
Roman, William E....................(617) 482-7501
broman@harriswilliams.com, Mng. Dir., Harris Williams & Co., MA, Boston
Roman, Ivan
iroman@nahj.org, Exec. Dir., National Association of Hispanic Journalists, DC, Washington
Romano, Marilyn
mromano@newsminer.com, Pub., Fairbanks Daily News-Miner, AK, Fairbanks
Romano, Maria Christina
info@eldebate.com.ar, Gen. Mgr., Grupo Serpein S.A., Zarate
Romantic, Bob ....(480) 898-6532
bromantic@aztrib.com, Mng. Ed., East Valley Tribune, AZ, Tempe
Romero, Oscar 428 204
oromero@diarionorte.com.ar, Gen. Mgr., Editorial Chaco S.A., Resistencia, Provincia de Chaco
Romero, Marcela 305-262-7575
mromero@efeame, Marketing Coordinator, EFE News Services - Washington, DC, DC, Washington
Romero Caro, Oscar 446-1554
gestion@gestion.com.pe, Gen. Mgr., Gestion, Lima
Romkey, Mike ....(309) 757-4988
romkey@qconline.com, Assoc. Mng. Ed., The Rock Island Argus, IL, Rock Island
Romkey, Mike ....(309) 757-4981
romkey@qconline.com, Assoc. Mng. Ed., The Dispatch, IL, Moline
Rommelmeyer, Karen ....(864) 260-1226
rommelmeyerks@independentmail.com, Adv. Mgr., Retail Sales, Anderson Independent-Mail, SC, Anderson
Ronai, Balazs
bronai@napi.hu, Mng. Dir., NAPI GAZDASAG, Budapest, Pest
Ronco, Robert ....(706) 290-5240
rronco@npco.com, Circ. Dir., Rome News-Tribune, GA, Rome
Rondeau, Mark ....ext. 113
mrondeau@benningtonbanner.com, Local News Ed., Bennington Banner, VT, Bennington
Ronquist, Niel
nronquist@paxtonmedia.com, Pub., Chronicle-Tribune, IN, Marion
Rood, Mike
mike@lapress.com, Adv./Commun. Dir., Louisiana Press Association, LA, Baton Rouge
Rood, Mark............................(800) 597-9798
info@toma.com, Pres., American Consulting Services, WA, Camas
Rooney, Sean ....(403) 528-5688
srooney@medicinehatnews.com, Sports Ed., Medicine Hat News, AB, Medicine Hat
Roosenraad, Jon A...................(352) 392-1124
Prof./Asst. Dean, Student Servs., University of Florida, FL, Gainesville
Roosevelt, Pam ....(562) 947-8755

Southern California Univ. of Health Sciences, CA, Whittier
Root, Jon ....(508) 676-2575
jroot@heraldnews.com, Mng. Ed., The Herald News, MA, Fall River
Root, Don..............................(520) 515-5984
don.root@wickcommunications.com, CFO, Wick Communications Co Inc, AZ, Sierra Vista
Ropeik, Annie
dfpeditor@gmail.com, Boston Univ., MA, Boston
Ropp, Darlene ....(519) 667-4694
dropp@lfpress.com, Asst. to Pub., The London Free Press, ON, London
Roque, Robert
bulletin@mb.com.ph, Ed. in Chief, TEMPO, Manila
Rorie, Kelley...........................336-506-3098
krorie@thetimesnews.com, Prodn. Mgr., Mailroom, Times-News, NC, Burlington
Rosado, Rossana
rossana.rosado@eldiariony.com, CEO/Pub., El Diario La Prensa, NY, Brooklyn
Rosario, Jose
jrosario@eldiariolaprensa.com, Photo Ed., El Diario La Prensa, NY, Brooklyn
Rosati, Chuck
crosati@forumarc.com, Dir., Architecture, Forum Architectural Services, LLC, OH, Cleveland
Rosato-Taylor, Andrea
arosato-taylor@nanaimodailynews.com, Adv. Mgr., Nanaimo Daily News, BC, Nanaimo
Roschewski, Marybeth........................ext. 108
Circ. Mgr., McCook Daily Gazette, NE, McCook
Rose, Helen M.
sales@farsystems.com, Gen. Mgr., FAR Systems, Inc., WI, Fort Atkinson
Rose, Amie..............................(801) 344-2530
arose@heraldextra.com, Metro Ed., The Daily Herald, UT, Provo
Rose, John ....(540) 574-6211
Graphics Ed./Art Dir., Daily News-Record, VA, Harrisonburg
Rose, Beth ....(508) 427-4042
brose@enterprisenews.com, Librarian, The Enterprise, MA, Randolph
Rose, Rebekah.................................ext. 18
rrose@ironmountaindailynews.com, Circulation Sales and Marketing Director, The Daily News, MI, Iron Mountain
Rose, Bill..............................(561) 820-4449
brose@pbpost.com, Mng. Ed., The Palm Beach Post, FL, West Palm Beach
Rose, Kelly.............................(504) 826-3070
krose@timespicayune.com, Vice Pres., Adv., The Times Picayune, LA, New Orleans
Rose, Robert...........................(404) 865-4350
Bureau Chief, Atlanta, The Wall Street Journal, NY, New York
Rose, Rachel ....(360) 735-4605
rachel.rose@columbian.com, Circ. Mgr., Promo./Sales, The Columbian, WA, Vancouver
Rose, Rod ....ext. 127
Farm Ed., The Reporter, IN, Lebanon
Rose, Bob ....(314) 340-8333
brose@post-dispatch.com, Asst. Mng. Ed., Presentation, St. Louis Post-Dispatch, MO, Saint Louis
Roseberry, Bill
broseberry@edwpub.net, Sports editor, Edwardsville Intelligencer, IL, Edwardsville
Rosebush, Judson ....(212) 581-3000
judson@rosebush.com, Pres., Judson Rosebush Co., NY, New York
Rosen, Mark A. ....(914) 766-4773
rosenm@us.ibm.com, Vice Pres., Integrated Mktg. Commun., IBM Software Grp., IBM Corp., NY, Somers
Rosen, Cheryl ....ext. 206
Gen. Mgr., Printing, The Pioneer - Big Rapids, MI, Big Rapids
Rosen, Derek
drosen@uniondemocrat.com, Coord., Systems/Web, The Union Democrat, CA, Sonora
Rosen, Jay ....(212) 998-7980
Chair, New York University, NY, New York
Rosenauer, Ken
klr9015@griffon.mwsc.edu, Chair, Missouri Western State College, MO, Saint Joseph
Rosenberg, Tracy
tracy@media-alliance.org, Exec. Dir., Media Alliance, CA, Oakland
Rosenberry, Dena ....(719) 636-0278
dena.rosenberry@gazette.com, Local News Editor, The Gazette, CO, Colorado Springs
Rosenburgh, Scott 978-970-4760
srosenburgh@mediaonene.com, VP Advertising, The Sun, MA, Lowell
Rosenbush, Rich
editor@drf.com, Ed. in Chief, Daily Racing Form
Rosengarten, Susie...................(419) 993-2038
srosengarten@limanews.com, Adv. Mgr., Servs., The Lima News, OH, Lima
Rosenthal, Dr. Robert
rrosenth@suffolk.edu, Chair, Suffolk University, MA, Boston
Rosenthal, Carlos
carlos@continental.hn, Pres., TIEMPO, San Pedro Sula, Cortes
Rosenthal, Cindy......................(212) 332-6406
cindy.rosenthal@journalismonline.com, Press Rel., Press+, NY, New York
Rosido, Armando 443-610
laverdad@satlink.com, Ed., La Verdad, Junin, Provincia de Buenos Aires
Roskam, T...494911
t.roskam@bdu.nl, Co-CEO, BARNEVELDSE KRANT, Barneveld
Rosner, Ron...................................ext. 477
rrosner@freemanonline.com, Sports Ed., Daily Freeman, NY, Kingston
Rosner, Eric
erosner@mullermartinims.com, Dir., Regl. Sales (Mid-Atlantic States), Muller Martini Mailroom Systems, Inc., PA, Allentown
Rosner, Rhonda..............................ext. 1642
rrosner@the-daily-record.com, Copy Ed., The Daily Record, OH, Wooster
Ross, Jeff
jeff.ross@kcjn.com, Circ. Mgr., King County Publications, WA, Bellevue
Ross, Terry L.
tross@yumasun.com, Editor, Yuma Sun, AZ, Yuma
Ross, Donald M. ....(917) 368-8600
rstalzer@bankrate.com, Sr. Vice Pres./Chief Revenue Officer, Bankrate.com, FL, North Palm Beach
Ross, David ....(416) 364-0321
dross@cp.org, CFO, Broadcast News Limited, ON, Toronto
dross@cp.org, CFO, Canadian Press, The - Toronto, ON, ON, Toronto
Ross, Andrea
aross@mspress.org, Media Buyer, Mississippi Press Association, MS, Jackson
Ross, Bruce ....(530) 225-8342
bross@redding.com, Editorial Page Ed., Record Searchlight, CA, Redding
Ross, Roxana ....(910) 630-7292
Methodist College, NC, Fayetteville
Ross, Kendrick
kendrick.ross@jjournal.com, Pub., The Jersey Journal, NJ, Jersey City
Ross, Alan..............................(520) 432-5146
alanross_sports@yahoo.com, Pres., Sportland Content, AZ, Bisbee
Ross, Paul
pross@standardspeaker.com, Adv. Dir., Standard-Speaker, PA, Hazleton
Ross, Richard ....(781) 255-7773 ext. 28
richardross@syndicatedadfeatures.com, Vice Pres./Western Regl. Sales Dir., Syndicated Ad Features, Inc., MA
Ross, Jim 352.671.6412
Assistant Managing Editor, Ocala Star-Banner, FL, Ocala
Rossi, Peter
news@wakefielditem.com, Ed., Wakefield Daily Item, MA, Wakefield
Rossiter, David
david.rossiter@lethbridgeherald.com, Photo Dept. Mgr., The Lethbridge Herald, AB, Lethbridge
Rossler, Mark
trucksales@lmh-na.com, Mktg. Dir., Linde Lift Truck Corp., SC, Summerville
Rossow, Jim ....(217) 351-5231
jrossow@news-gazette.com, Sports Editor, News-Gazette Inc., IL, Champaign
Rost, Peter
prost@registerstar.com, Bus. Mgr., Register-Star, NY, Hudson
Roth, Marilyn
tdchron@eaglenewspapers.com, Pub., The Dalles Daily Chronicle, OR, The Dalles
Roth, Horst
chefredaktion@mamo.de, Ed. in Chief, MANNHEIMER MORGEN, Mannheim
Rothacker, Robert F. ....ext. 3504
rrothacker@express-times.com, Circ. Vice Pres., Opns., The Express-Times, PA, Easton
Rothchild, Andrea.....................(631) 843-3063
Adv. Dir., Classified, Newsday, NY, Melville
Rothe, Deric ....(530) 852-0205
dericr@goldcountrymedia.com, Ed., Auburn Journal, Inc., CA, Auburn
Rothenburger, Mel.....................250-371-6152
mrothenburger@kamloopsnews.ca, Editor, Kamloops Daily News, BC, Kamloops
Rothfeld, Barry
brothfeld@poughkee.gannett.com, Pub., Poughkeepsie Journal, NY, Poughkeepsie
Rothmaler, W.
sekretariat@siegener-zeitung.de, Proprietor, Siegener Zeitung, Siegen
Rothman, Carol 202-434-1261
crothman@cwa-union.org, Secretary/Treasurer, The Newspaper Guild-CWA, DC, Washington
Rothrock, Edwin......................(785) 832-7233
erothrock@ljworld.com, The World Co.- Lawrence, Kan., Journal-World, KS, Lawrence
Rothrock, Edwin.........................785-832-7233
erothrock@ljworld.com, Director of Market Strategies, The World Co.- Lawrence, Kan., Journal-World, KS, Lawrence
Rothstein, Richard
rrothstein@newsusa.com, Vice Pres., Sales, News USA, Inc., VA, Falls Church
Rotter, Gerhard
Rhoen-Spiegel@t-online.de, Ed. in Chief, Rhon und Saalepost, Bad Neustadt
Rotter, John ....(805) 437-0452
jrotter@venturacountystar.com, Circ. Dir., Home Delivery, Ventura County Star, CA, Camarillo
Rounce, Robert R. ....(860) 241-6329
rrounce@courant.com, Controller, The Hartford Courant, CT, Hartford
Rounds, David ....(925) 935-2525
Pub., Contra Costa Times, CA, Walnut Creek
Rounds, David ....(408) 920-5674
drounds@mercurynews.com, Circ. Vice Pres., San Jose Mercury News, CA, San Jose
Rouse, David ....(919) 739-7870
drouse@newsargus.com, Mgmt. Info Servs. Mgr., Goldsboro News-Argus, NC, Goldsboro
Rouse, Alice.......................................ext. 11
arouse@murrayledger.com, Pub., The Murray Ledger & Times, KY, Murray
Roush, Sue.............................(800) 255-6734
sroush@amuniversal.com, Vice Pres./Mng. Ed., Universal Uclick, MO, Kansas City
Rousmaniere, James A....................ext. 1002
Pres., The Keene Sentinel, NH, Keene
Rousmaniere, James A....................ext. 1002
jrousmaniere@keenesentinel.com, Ed., The Keene Sentinel, NH, Keene
Rousseau, David M. ....(603) 668-4321 ext. 241
drousseau@unionleader.com, Adv. Mgr., Retail, New Hampshire Union Leader/New Hampshire Sunday News, NH, Manchester
Rove, Olaf...............................(360)735-4445
olaf.rove@columbian.com, IT Manager, The Columbian, WA, Vancouver
Rovira, Miguel Frau
manila@efe.com, Bureau Chief, EFE News Services - Manila, Philippines, Manila
Rovito, Diego A.
dierev@newstech.com, Vice Pres., Newstech Co. (Div. of Rovinter, Inc.), FL, Miami
Rowan, Andrew........................(718) 289-5445
Bronx Cmty. College, NY, Bronx
Rowan, Jane ....(760) 951-6206
jane_rowan@link.freedom.com, New Media Mgr., Daily Press, CA, Victorville
Rowe, John ....(920) 993-7143
jrowe@appleton.gannett.com, Adv. Dir., Grp. Majors, The Post-Crescent, WI, Appleton
Rowe, Charles ....ext. 5528
Asst. Ed., The Post and Courier, SC, Charleston
Rowe, Kermit ....(937) 328-0364
krowe@coxohio.com, Sports Ed., Springfield News-Sun, OH, Springfield
Rowell, Phil.......................................ext. 214
prowell@ricentral.com, Circ. Dir., The Kent County Times, RI, West Warwick
Rowland, Mary Pat...........................ext. 5210
Mng. Ed., Foster's Daily Democrat, NH, Dover
Rowlett, Richard
rowlettadvertising@att.net, Pres., Rowlett Advertising Service, Inc., TN, Goodlettsville
Rowley, Don
drowley@pulitzer.net, Vice Pres. & Pres./Pub., The Arizona Daily Sun, Pulitzer Newspapers, Inc., MO, Saint Louis
Rowley, Don ....(928) 556-2240
drowley@azdailysun.com, Pres./Pub., Arizona Daily Sun, AZ, Flagstaff
Roy, Carolyn
carolyn@natchitochestimes.com, Ed., Natchitoches Times, LA, Natchitoches
Roy, Richard ....(416) 947-7503
richard.roy@sunmedia.ca, VP, Info Serv., The Toronto Sun, ON, Toronto
Roy, Jami
jroy@ccdailyrecord.com, Adv. Dir., The Canon City Daily Record, CO, Canon City
Roy, Jean.................................(514) 849-7693
Vice Pres., French Servs., Canadian Press, The - Toronto, ON, ON, Toronto
Roy-Bornstein, Carolyn ....(978) 476-9121
pediatricpoints@comcast.net, MD, Pediatric Points, MA, Newburyport
Royer, Raymond
raymond.royer@domtar.com, Pres./CEO, Domtar, Inc., QC, Montreal
Royse, Pat
proyse@dailystandard.com, Mng. Ed., The Daily Standard, OH, Celina
Royseon, Brian ....(765) 213-5852
Bus./Finance Ed., The Star Press, IN, Muncie
Rozak, Bill
brozak@uniondemocrat.com, Sports Ed., The Union Democrat, CA, Sonora
Rozen, Lee
lrozen@dnews.com, Managing Editor, Moscow-Pullman Daily News, ID, Moscow
Roznovsky, Ann
aroznovsky@coxnews.com, Mktg. Dir., Waco Tribune-Herald, TX, Waco
Rubel, Jeffrey...........................(716) 878-4531
SUNY College/Buffalo, NY, Buffalo
Rubens, Gunter
verlag@hellwegeranzeiger.de, Proprietor, Hellweger Anzeiger, Unna
Rubens, Gunter.......................................71940
daanzeigen@aol.com, Proprietor, DOBELNER ANZEIGER, Dobeln
Rubido, Bieito
redac@lavoz.com, Dir., La Voz De Galicia, La Coruna
Rubin, Rita ....(212) 293-8521
rrubin@unitedmedia.com, Sr. Vice Pres., Int'l Licensing, United Media, OH, Cincinnati
Rubin, Saul 310-434-3537
rubin_saul@smc.edu, Santa Monica College, CA, Santa Monica
Rubin, Kerry 973-569-7496
Director, Advertising TeleCenter, North Jersey Media Group, NJ, Woodland Park
Rubin, Dan
drubin@dcexaminer.com, Sports Ed., The Examiner, VA, Alexandria
Rubino, Mark ....(630) 844-1999
mrubino@industrialnoisecontrol.com, Pres., Industrial Noise Control, Inc., IL, North Aurora
Rubio, Enrique
efe@menara.ma, Rep., EFE News Services - Rabat, Morocco, Rabat
Ruby, Wheeler.........................(573) 815-1853
rgwheeler@columbiatribune.com, Adv. Mgr., Classified, Columbia Daily Tribune, MO, Columbia
Ruch, Karl-Heinez
redaktion@taz.de, Bus. Mgr., Die

Tageszeitung, Berlin
Rudawsky, Gil ....(303) 892-2562
rudawskyg@rockymountainnews.com, Deputy Bus. Ed., Rocky Mountain News, CO, Denver
Rudback, Frederick
webmaster@fti.se, Mng. Dir., FINANS TIDNINGEN, Stockholm
Ruddiman, Susan ....(228) 934-1419
msfeatures@themississippipress.com, Features Ed., The Mississippi Press, MS, Pascagoula
Ruddy, Bill ....(306) 781-5364
bruddy@leaderpost.canwest.com, Prodn. Mgr., Pressroom/Distr., The Leader-Post, SK, Regina
Ruder, Steve
stever_prod@dailynews.net, Prodn. Mgr., Opns., The Hays Daily News, KS, Hays
Rudge, Brenda T.
webmaster@newsquest.co.uk, Mng. Dir., LANCASHIRE TELEGRAPH, Blackburn, Lancashire
Rudon, Michael
belizetime@btl.net, Ed., THE BELIZE TIMES, Belize City
Rudy, Gary ....(609) 886-0141
gary@ifpa.com, Exec. Dir., Independent Free Papers of America, NJ, Rio Grande
Rudy-James, Holly
advertising@humboldtsun.com, Adv. Mgr., Sales, The Humboldt Sun, NV, Winnemucca
Ruebsamen, Jim ....(661) 259-7800
College of the Canyons, CA, Santa Clarita
Rueda, Jim
jrueda@mankatofreepress.com, Sports Ed., The Free Press, MN, Mankato
Rueda Cazares, Blanca Estela
laverdadmich@prodigy.net.mx, Exec. Dir., LA VERDAD, Zitacuaro, Michoacan
Rueda Coba, Jorge
jrueda@elsur.com.mx, Sr., El Sur, Campeche, Campeche
Rueda Prada, Antonio Maria 642-5369
Gen. Mgr., Comunicaciones Melodia El Frente S.A., Bucaramanga, Santander
Ruef, Randy..........................(815) 987-1203
Sports Ed., Rockford Register Star, IL, Rockford
Ruelas, Miguel Angel
durango@elsiglo.com.mx, Gen. Mgr., El Siglo de Durango, Durango, Durango
Ruelas Talamantes, Miguel Angel
elsiglo@elsiglodetorreon.com.mx, Gen. Mgr., EL SIGLO DE TORREON, Torreon, Coahuila
Ruemenapp, Dirk F.........(603) 668-4321 ext. 501
druemenapp@unionleader.com, Exec. Vice Pres., New Hampshire Union Leader/New Hampshire Sunday News, NH, Manchester
Ruemenapp, Dirk
druemenapp@unionleader.com, Executive Vice President, New Hampshire Union Leader/New Hampshire Sunday News, NH, Manchester
Ruetschi, Pierre
news@tdg.ch, Ed., TRIBUNE DE GENEVE, Geneva
Ruff, Dale ....(413) 788-1045
druff@repub.com, Photo Ed., The Republican, MA, Springfield
Rugen, Deborah......................(214) 640-3108
drugen@beldenassociates.com, Sr. Project Dir., Belden Associates, TX, Dallas
Ruggiero, Stella
sruggiero@titusvilleherald.com, Mng. Ed., The Titusville Herald, PA, Titusville
Ruis, Betty
betty.ruis@gaflnews.com, Prodn. Compositor, Cordele Dispatch, GA, Cordele
Ruiz, Miguel Angel..........................424-0000
marketing@eltribuno.com.ar, Gen. Mgr., El Tribuno, Salta, Provincia de Salta
Ruiz, Fernando
gmerszei@dow.com, Vice Pres./Treasurer, The Dow Chemical Co., MI, Midland
Ruiz Quirrin, Francisco Javier
authentic@son1.telmex.net.mx, Ed./Dir., Primera Plana, Hermosillo, Sonora
Ruk, Barbara..........................(724) 226-7773
bruk@tribweb.com, Mgmt. Info Servs. Analyst, Valley News Dispatch, PA, Tarentum
Rukes, Dan
drukes@kspress.com, Adv. Mgr., Kansas Press Association, KS, Topeka
Rumbach, Dan E.
drumbach@dcherald.com, Co-president; co-publisher, The Herald, IN, Jasper
Rumbach, Justin
justin.rumbach@dcherald.com, Managing Editor, The Herald, IN, Jasper
Rumer, Pam...........................(760) 740-3501
prumer@nctimes.com, Adv. Dir., North County Times, CA, Escondido
Rumpeltin, Christian
info@dieharke.de, Proprietor, DIE HARKE, Nienburg
Rundle, Sandy........................(902) 432-8203
srundle@journalpioneer.com, Pub., The Journal Pioneer, PE, Summerside
Runnels, Sheila
srunnels@theadvocate.com, Adv. Dir., The Advocate, LA, Baton Rouge
Runyon, Keith.........................(502) 582-4594
krunyon@courier-journal.com, Opinion Pages Ed., The Courier-Journal, KY, Louisville
Rupnow, Darnell ....(414) 224-2746
Circ. Asst. Dir., Distr., Milwaukee Journal Sentinel, WI, Milwaukee
Rusch, Markus
m.rusch@dav.ch, Ed. in Chief, APPENZELLER VOLKSFREUND, Appenzell
Ruscitti, Joe
jruscitti@lfpress.com, Mng. Ed., The London Free Press, ON, London
Rush, Tonda 703-237-9802
tonda@nna.org, Publisher, National Newspaper Association Publishers' Auxiliary, MO, Columbia
Rushing, S. Kittrell
kitrushing@cecasun.utc.edu, Head/Frank McDonald Prof., University of Tennessee at Chattanooga, TN, Chattanooga
Rushing, Bill..........................(806) 296-1330
bjr@plainviewdailyherald.com, Prodn. Foreman, Pressroom, Plainview Herald, TX, Plainview
Rushing, Eleanor.....................(318) 362-0263
Asst. Mng. Ed., Local, The News-Star, LA, Monroe
Rushing, Hugh J.......................(205) 873-0924
hrushing@usit.net, Exec. Officer, Society of Classified Advertising Managers of America, Inc., AL, Mountain Brook
Rushmore, Valerie
vrushmore@njtimes.com, Mgr., Promo., The Times, NJ, Trenton
Rushton, Cindy
cindy.rushton@morningsun.net, Adv. Dir., The Morning Sun, KS, Pittsburg
Russ, Eugen A.
eugenruss@medienhaus.at, Pub., VORARLBERGER NACHRICHTEN, Schwarzach
Russ, Bob....................................ext. 8490
bob.russ@cantonrep.com, Suburban Ed., The Repository, OH, Canton
Russ, Douglas
redaktion@azonline.de, Pub., ALLGEMEINE ZEITUNG, Coesfeld
Russ, Carey
careyruss@earthlink.net, Ed., Syndicated Automotive News Service, CA, Walnut Creek
Russell, Richard
rrussell@ngnews.ca, Pub., Amherst Daily News, NS, Amherst
Russell, John ....(630) 844-5902
jrussell@scn1.com, Assoc. Ed., The Beacon News, IL, Aurora
Russell, Richard ....ext. 228
rrussell@norwalkreflector.com, Bus. Mgr., Norwalk Reflector, OH, Norwalk
Russell, Richard
rrussell@ngnews.ca, Pub., The News, NS, New Glasgow
Russell, Mark..........................(407) 420-5467
mrussell@orlandosentinel.com, Mng. Ed., Orlando Sentinel, FL, Orlando
Russell, Leslie........................13056720071
leslie@grouprussell.com, Sales Director, Vista - The Magazine for All Hispanics - Miami Beach, FL, FL, Miami Beach
Russell, Michael ....(310) 939-9024
mrussell@michaelrussellgroup.com, Head, Mktg., Hollywood Foreign Press Association, CA, West Hollywood
Russell, Leslie
leslie@grouprussell.com, Acct. Mgr., Vista - The Magazine for All Hispanics - Miami Beach, FL, FL, Miami Beach
Russell, Richard ....(902) 893-9405
rrussell@ngnews.ca, Pub., The Daily News, NS, Truro
Russell, Todd C.......................(419) 993-2025
trussell@limanews.com, Circ. Dir., The Lima News, OH, Lima
Russell, Vicki S.......................(573) 815-1565
vrussell@columbiatribune.com, Treasurer/Publisher, Columbia Daily Tribune, MO, Columbia
Russette, Chris ....(630) 782-4350
crussette@interest.com, Opns. Mgr., Mortgage Market Information Services, IL, Villa Park
Russin, Dean ....(607) 441-7215
drussin@thedailystar.com, Sports Ed., The Daily Star, NY, Oneonta
Russo, Ronald L.
drcmap@aol.com, Pres., Direct Reproduction Corp., NY, Mount Vernon
Russo, Tom..................(317) 467-6010 ext. 210
trusso@greenfieldreporter.com, Photo Ed., Daily Reporter, IN, Greenfield
Russo, Robert
rob.russo@thecanadianpress.com, Bureau Chief, Broadcast News Limited, ON, Ottawa
rob.russo@thecanadianpress.com, Bureau Chief, Canadian Press, The - Washington, DC, DC, Washington
rob.russo@thecanadianpress.com, Bureau Chief, Canadian Press, The - Ottawa, ON, ON, Ottawa
Rust, Jon K. ....(573) 335-6611 ext. 103
jrust@semissourian.com, Pub., Southeast Missourian, MO, Cape Girardeau
Rust, Jon K...................(573) 335-6611 ext. 103
jrust@semissourian.com, Co-Pres./Pub., Rust Communications, MO, Cape Girardeau
Rust, Rex D....................(573) 335-6611 ext. 108
rrust@semissourian.com, Co-Pres., Rust Communications, MO, Cape Girardeau
Rustowski, Tom......................(61 2) 8272 4600
tomasz.rustowski@dowjones.com, Regl. Sales Mgr., Dow Jones Newswires - Sydney, Australia, Sydney
Ruthemeyer, Dan
druthemeyer@skagitpublishing.com, Sports Ed., Skagit Valley Herald, WA, Mount Vernon
Rutherford, Chuck....................(217) 421-6943
Prodn. Mgr., Press, Herald & Review, IL, Decatur
Rutherford, Marjorie 217-238-7957
mrutherford@jg-tc.com, Circ. Mgr., Times-Courier, IL, Mattoon
Rutherford, Joe.........................662-678-1597
joe.rutherford@journalinc.com, Editorial Page Editor, Journal Publishing Company, MS, Tupelo
Ruthhart, Roger ....ext. 228
riroger@qconline.com, Mng. Ed., The Rock Island Argus, IL, Rock Island
Rutkowski, Gary...............................ext. 121
Bus. Ed., St. Albans Messenger, VT, Saint Albans
Ruud, Candice.........................(541) 737-2232
Oregon State Univ., OR, Corvallis
Ruzgar, Michelle ....(561) 820-3912
mruzgar@pbpost.com, Internet Mktg. Mgr., The Palm Beach Post, FL, West Palm Beach
Ruzicka, Lora ....(308) 381-9461
lora.ruzicka@theindependent.com, Creative Dir., The Grand Island Independent, NE, Grand Island
Ryall, Zach ....(512) 445-3685
zryall@statesman.com, Photo Dir., Austin American-Statesman, TX, Austin
Ryan, Tim ....(203) 317-2430
tryan@record-journal.com, Sr. Vice Pres., Record-Journal, CT, Meriden
Ryan, Timothy
timothy.ryan@baltsun.com, Pres./Pub./CEO, The Baltimore Sun, MD, Baltimore
Ryan, Tim
tryan@thewesterlysun.com, Pres./Pub., The Westerly Sun, RI, Westerly
Ryan, Mike ....(602) 444-5810
mike.ryan@pni.com, Gen. Mgr., Scottsdale Republic, The Arizona Republic, AZ, Phoenix
Ryan, Russ ....(304) 485-1891
rryan@mariettatimes.com, Info. Systems Mgr., The Marietta Times, OH, Marietta
Ryan, Charles ....ext. 3324
cryan@thechronicle.com, Ed., The Chronicle, CT, Willimantic
Ryan, Terry.............................(617) 786-7051
tryan@ledger.com, Mng. Ed., The Patriot Ledger, MA, Quincy
Ryan, David ....ext. 219
dryan@adn.com, Dir., Finance, Anchorage Daily News, AK, Anchorage
Ryan, Stefanie...................................ext. 111
sryan@benningtonbanner.com, Arts/Entertainment Ed., Bennington Banner, VT, Bennington
Ryan, Tim ....(607) 334-3276
Prodn. Mgr., Pressroom, The Evening Sun, NY, Norwich
Ryan, Mark.......................................ext. 214
cnads@crescent-news.com, Adv. Mgr., Defiance Publishing LLC, OH, Defiance
Ryan, Tom
tryan@carlson-dc.com, Vice Pres., Mktg, Carlson Design Construct, CA, Irvine
Ryan, Lorraine Earle..................(239) 262-8400
wstobb@yahoo.com, Sec., Advanced Control Technologies, Inc., FL, Naples
Ryan, Jack
news@enterprise-journal.com, Ed., Enterprise-Journal, MS, McComb
Ryan, Timothy...........................610-820-6500
publisher@mcall.com, Publisher, President and CEO, The Morning Call, PA, Allentown
Ryan, Shaun ....(904) 819-3503
shaun.ryan@staugustinerecord.com, Health Ed., The St. Augustine Record, FL, Saint Augustine
Ryan, Stephanie
stephanie.ryan@bpus.konicaminolta.us, Corporate Contact, Konica Minolta Printing Solutions, AL, Mobile
Ryan, Debi
dryan@coxnews.com, News Ed., The Daily Sentinel, TX, Nacogdoches
Ryan, Tim ....(203) 317-2430
tryan@record-journal.com, Sr. Vice Pres., The Record-Journal Publishing Co., CT, Meriden
Ryba, Jacki..................(785) 822-1493 ext. 759
jryba@salina.com, Bus./HR Dir., The Salina Journal, KS, Salina
Ryder, Karen ....(508) 862-1108
kryder@dowjones.com, Sales Mktg./Collateral Mgr., Cape Cod Times, MA, Hyannis
Ryder, Phillip A.........................(850) 484-8622
thejoker@thefunnypages.com, Creator, The Funny Pages, FL, Pensacola
Rye, Beth
beth.rye@yankton.net, New Media Dir., Yankton Daily Press & Dakotan, SD, Yankton
Ryerson, Dennis R. ....(317) 444-6169
dennis.ryerson@indystar.com, Vice Pres./Ed., The Indianapolis Star, IN, Indianapolis
Ryoji, Sharon
sharon@shoom.com, Vice Pres., Customer Serv., Shoom, Inc., CA, Incino
Ryong, Chang
jcy@msnet.co.kr, Ed., MAEIL SHINMUN, Daegu
Ryzewicz, Keith
kryzewicz@mycentraljersey.com, Editorial Page Ed., Courier News, NJ, Somerville

S

Sa'ad, Abdallah
shoura@y.net.ye, Ed., ASH SHURA
Saal, Rich ....(217) 788-1475
rich.saal@sj-r.com, Photo Ed., The State Journal-Register, IL, Springfield
Sabalewski, Glenn ....(603) 610-1139
gsabalewski@seacoastonline.com, Prodn. Ed., Portsmouth Herald, NH, Portsmouth
Sabin, Jim................................(740) 681-4344
jsabin@nncogannett.com, Editorial Page Ed., Eagle-Gazette Media, OH, Lancaster
Sabuncu, Mehmet
sabuncu@aydinlik.com.tr, Pub., AYDINLIK
Sacash, David ....(843) 661-1682

Francis Marion Univ., SC, Florence
Sacco, Jim ....(540) 932-3557
jsacco@newsvirginian.com, Sports Ed., The News Virginian, VA, Waynesboro
Sackman, Dave
info@lrwonline.com, Pres., Lieberman Research Worldwide, CA, Los Angeles
Sadah, Ibrahim Abu
akhbarelyom@akhbarelyom.org, Chrmn., AL AKHBAR, Cairo
Sade, Vivian
vrosswurm@aol.com, Pres., Women's Press Club of Indiana, IN, Churubusco
Sadeoja, Tapio
tapio.sadeoja@sanoma.fi, Ed. in Chief, ILTA-SANOMAT, Sanoma
Sagasti Redondo, Jose Antonio
info@oem.com.mx, Gen. Mgr., El Sol del Centro, Cordoba, Veracruz
Sage, Meagan ....(401) 232-6896
Bryant College, RI, Smithfield
Sage, Robert...........................(657) 278-4275
Bus. Mgr., California State Univ., CA, Fullerton
Sager, Martin ....(201) 342-2985
Bus. Mgr., Newsportraits Syndicate, NJ, Hackensack
Sagerstrom, Tar
tar.sagerstrom@dt.se, CEO, FALU KURIREN, Falun
Said, Tribuana
indotimes@indocon.com, Ed., INDONESIA TIMES, Jakarta, Java
Saifi, Khaliq-ur-Rehman
rizwan01@fsd.comset.pk, Pub., SAADAT, Faisalabad, Faisalabad Division
Saint Cricq, Olivier
nr.redactionenchef@nrco.fr, Pub., LA FRANCE-LA NOUVELLE REPUBLIQUE, Tours cedex 1
Saito, Yoshio
iba-news@mbf.sphere.ne.jp, Bd. Dir./Mng. Ed., IBARAKI SHIMBUN, Mito, Kanto
Saito, Osamu
kpdesk@mb.kyoto-np.co.jp, Pres., KYOTO SHIMBUN, Kyoto, Kinki
Saiwo, Siu
stltor@singtaotor.com, Ed. in Chief, SING TAO DAILY, Shaukei wan
Sajidi, Anwar
editor@dailyintekhab.com.pk, Ed., DAILY INTEKHAB, Lasbella
Sakasegawa, Naohumi
webmaster@373news.com, Ed. in Chief, MINAMI-NIPPON SHIMBUN, Kagoshima, Kyushu
Sakellariou, Tony 845-331-5000
tsakellariou@freemanonline.com, Controller, Daily Freeman, NY, Kingston
Sakowski, Robert
r.sakowski@dziennik.lodz.pl, Ed. in Chief, DZIENNIK LODZKI, Lodz
Sakya, Subha Luxmi
mrshakya@wlink.com.np, Pub., DAILY NEWS, Kathmandu
Sala, Katie ....(631) 843-2170
katie.sala@newsday.com, Mktg. Mgr., Newsday.com, Newsday, NY, Melville
Salada, Matt..............................423.757.6379
msalada@timesfreepress.com, HR Director, Chattanooga Times Free Press, TN, Chattanooga
Salah, Marie
msalah@hfxnews.ca, Online Ed., The Daily News, NS, Dartmouth
Salamone, Gary P. ....(858) 492-8696
continentalnewsservice@yahoo.com, Pres./Ed. in Chief, Continental Features/Continental News Service, Inc., CA, San Diego
Salamone, Joe ....(410) 385-7011
joe.salamone@baltsun.com, Circ. Mgr., Distr./Fleet, The Baltimore Sun, MD, Baltimore
Salas, Kent..............................(909) 483-9348
k_salas@dailybulletin.com, Online Ed., Inland Valley Daily Bulletin, CA, Ontario
Salas, Osvaldo A. 475-7200
Gen. Mgr., La Voz del Interior, Cordoba, Provincia de Cordoba
Salazar, Jennifer
jennifersalazar@coloradoan.com, Controller, The Coloradoan, CO, Fort Collins
Salazar, Roddy 212-556-7201
roddy.salazar@nytimes.com, Regional Manager, Western Region & Canada, New York Times Syndicate, NY, New York
Salazar, Antonio Melo
elnuevodia@elnuevodia.com.co, Editorial Dir., Sociedad Anonima, Ibague, Tolima
Salazar, Roddy 212-556-7201
roddy.salazar@nytimes.com, Regional Manager, Western Region & Canada, New York Times News Service, NY, New York
Saldivar, Olga.........................(956) 982-6648
Bus. Mgr., The Brownsville Herald, TX, Brownsville
Saldivar, Bobbie.......................(956) 982-6653
Prodn. Mgr., Mailroom, The Brownsville Herald, TX, Brownsville
Salem, Lee...............................(800) 255-6734
ljordan@amuniversal.com, Pres./Ed., Universal Uclick, MO, Kansas City
Salerno, Richard ....(718) 816-3162
salerno@siadvance.com, Circ. Mgr., Staten Island Advance, NY, Staten Island
Salfino, Catherine.....................(201) 939-7875
catherinesalfino@comcast.net, Pres., Meadowlands Media Group, NJ, Rutherford
Salfino, Michael........................(201) 939-7875
salfino@comcast.net, Columnist, Meadowlands Media Group, NJ, Rutherford
Salierno, Rich 785-832-7225
rsalierno@ljworld.com, Production Manager-Distribution, The World Co.- Lawrence, Kan., Journal-World, KS, Lawrence
Salierno, Rich 785-832-7225
rsalierno@ljworld.com, The World Co.- Lawrence, Kan., Journal-World, KS, Lawrence
Salinas, Sergio ....(915) 546-6159
ssalinas@elpasotimes.com, CEO/President & Publisher, El Paso Times, TX, El Paso
Sallmen, Shirley ....(330) 747-1471 ext. 1225
ssallmen@vindy.com, Garden Ed., The Vindicator, OH, Youngstown
Salman, Talal
talal@assafir.com, Ed., AS-SAFIR
Salminen, Seppo
seppo.salminen@koillissanomat.fi, Ed., KOILLISSANOMAT, Kuusamo
Saloway, Tony ....(780) 468-0170
tony.saloway@edm.sunpub.com, News Ed., The Edmonton Sun, AB, Edmonton
Salter, Donna ....(806) 371-5290
drsalter@actx.edu, Math Com Asst., Amarillo College, TX, Amarillo
Saltz, Donald
mbds@erols.com, Gen. Mgr., Quiz Features, DC, Washington
Saltz, Howard...........................(303) 820-1303
hsaltz@denverpost.com, Online Ed., The Denver Post, CO, Denver
Salvati, Carmen
carman@circulation.net, Mktg. Dir., Circulation Development, Inc., MO
Salvioni, Giacomo
info@laregione.ch, Ed., LA REGIONE, Bellinzona, Ticino
Salzman, Gerald L. ....(213) 229-5300
gerald_salzman@dailyjournal.com, Pub., Daily Commerce, CA, Los Angeles
Salzman, Jerry
daily_recorder@dailyjournal.com, Pres./Pub., The Daily Recorder, CA
Salzman, Gerald
gerald_salzman@dailyjournal.com, Pub., The Los Angeles Daily Journal
Samanez, Jose.................................427-6455
lwebmaster@libero.com.pe, Gen. Mgr., Libero, Lima
Samanez, Jose.................................426-3550
Gen. Mgr., El Popular, Lima
Samanez Acebo, Jose 427-6455
director@larepublica.com.pe, Gen. Mgr., La Republica, Lima
Sami, Kotta
neditordtbgl@gmail.com, Ed., DAILY THANTHI, Tiruchirapalli, Tamil Nadu
Sample, George R.
corryjournal@tbscc.com, Pub., The Journal, PA, Corry
Sample, Michael
msample@titusvilleherald.com, Adv. Dir., The Titusville Herald, PA, Titusville
Samrov, Adam ....ext. 114
asamrov@benningtonbanner.com, Mng. Ed., Bennington Banner, VT, Bennington
Samson, Michel
msamson@lesoleil.com, Online Ed., Le Soleil, QC, Quebec
Samuels, Jeffrey R. 912-233-1281
info@morrismultimedia.com, Vice Pres./CFO, Morris Multimedia, Inc., GA, Savannah
Samuelsson, Lena K
lena.k.samuelsson@svd.se, Ed. in Chief, SVENSKA DAGBLADET, Stockholm
Samyn, Paul ....(204) 697-7292
Paul.Samyn@freepress.mb.ca, City Ed., Winnipeg Free Press, MB, Winnipeg
San Martin Montilla, Eduardo
lectores@laverdad.com, Dir., La Verdad De Murcia, Murcia
San Miguel, Joe.........................(830) 775-1551
joe.sanmiguel@delrionewsherald.com, Circ. Mgr., Del Rio News-Herald, TX, Del Rio
Sanchez, Rene...........................(612) 673-1731
rene.sanchez@startribune.com, Mng. Ed., News, Star Tribune, MN, Minneapolis
Sanchez, Matilde
msanchez@clarin.com, Ed., Clarin Contenidos, Buenos Aires
Sanchez, Melony
msanchez@appealdemocrat.com, Asst. to Pub., Appeal-Democrat, CA, Marysville
Sanchez, Francisco
francisco.sanchez@elnorte.com, Mktg. Asst., METRO, Monterrey, Nuevo Leon
Sanchez, Alex...........................(469) 977-3602
asanchez@aldiatx.com, Gen. Mgr., Al Dia, TX, Dallas
Sanchez, Carlos
csanchez@coxnews.com, Ed., Waco Tribune-Herald, TX, Waco
Sanchez, Steve ....(508) 967-3125
sports@tauntongazette.com, Sports Ed., Taunton Daily Gazette, MA, Taunton
Sanchez de la Madrid, Manuel
elmundo@hotmail.com, Pres., El Mundo desde Colima, Colima, Colima
Sanchis, Vicent
pub@avui.cat, Pres., AVUI, Barcelona
Sancho, Jose Afonso.........................247-3066
tribuna@baydenet.com.br, Pres., Tribuna do Ceara, Fortaleza, Ceara
Sand, Linda............................(909)-537-5815
California State Univ., CA, San Bernardino
Sandberg, Christer
redaktion@folkbladet.se, Ed. in Chief, FOLKBLADET, Norrkoping
Sandberg, Matt
msandberg@summitdaily.com, Publisher, Summit Daily News, CO, Frisco
Sanders, Bob ....(888) 942-0330
shorackms@aol.com, Sales-KY, IL, OH, IN, WI, MO, Kaspar Wire Works, Inc./Sho-Rack, TX, Shiner
Sanders, Robert
Robert_Sanders@tamu-commerce.edu, Prof., Texas A&M University-Commerce, TX, Commerce
Sanders, Peggy
psanders@examiner-enterprise.com, Adv. Mgr., Classified, Examiner-Enterprise, OK, Bartlesville
Sanders, Carl P.
carl@thesheridanpress.com, Exec. Vice Pres./Pub., The Sheridan Press, WY, Sheridan
Sanders, Bob Ray ....(817) 390-7775
bobray@star-telegram.com, Vice Pres./Assoc. Ed., Fort Worth Star-Telegram, TX, Fort Worth
Sanders, Sandy.............(229) 244-3400 ext. 244
ssanders@cnhi.com, Pub., Valdosta Daily Times, GA, Valdosta
Sanders, Donna
dsanders@news-daily.com, Bus. Mgr., News/Daily, GA, Jonesboro
Sanders, Carla...........................(909) 386-3862
carla.sanders@dailybulletin.com, Features Ed., San Bernardino County Sun, CA, San Bernardino
Sanders, Keith P.
umcjourkta@missouri.edu, Exec. Dir./Treasurer, Kappa Tau Alpha National Honor Soc. for Journ. & Mass Comm., MO, Columbia
Sanderson, Greta ....(765) 482-4650
greta.sanderson@reporter.net, Ed., The Reporter, IN, Lebanon
Sandford, Jason ....(828) 232-5928
jsanford@citizen-times.com, Deputy Mng. Ed., The Asheville Citizen-Times, NC, Asheville
Sandlin, Darrell R......................(256) 740-4711
darrell.sandlin@timesdaily.com, Pub., TimesDaily, AL, Florence
Sandlin, Evelyn.........................(865) 981-1152
evelyn.sandlin@thedailytimes.com, Adv. Dir., The Daily Times, TN, Maryville
Sandlund, Elisabeth
ellisabet.sanclund@dagen.se, Ed., DAGEN, Stockholm
Sandmann, Christoph
redaktion@westline.de, Bus. Mgr., Munstersche Zeitung, Munster, Westfalen
Sandoval, Carlos Manzur 232-0635
tecnico@teleconet.net, Gen. Mgr., Carlos Mansur, Guayaquil, Guayas
Sandoval, Sergio Santa 884-6572
Gen. Mgr., NUEVO DIARIO OCCIDENTE, Cali
Sandoval Jara, Pablo
psandoval@australtemuco.cl, Dir., Diario Renacer, Angol
Sands, Rory
rory.sands@shelbyvilledailyunion.com, Adv. Mgr., Daily Union, IL, Shelbyville
SandstrÂ£m, Daniel
daniel.sandstrom@sydsvenskan.se, Ed. in Chief, SYDSVENSKAN, Malmo
Sandvig, Denise........................(360) 735-4441
denise.sandvig@columbian.com, HR Mgr., The Columbian, WA, Vancouver
Sanford, Doug 253-597-8607
Prod. & OP maint. manager, The News Tribune, WA, Tacoma
Sanford, Terry
sales@wessan.com, Pres., Wessan Interactive, NE, Omaha
Sanford, Kurt
bill.pardue@lexisnexis.com, Pres./CEO, Cor. & Fed. Mkts., LEXIS-NEXIS, OH, Miamisburg
Sang-Hoon, Bang
nkpark@chosun.com, Ed. in Chief, SPORTS CHOSUN, Seoul
Sang-Kin, Kim
sckkim@yeongnam.com, Asst. Mgr., YEONGNAM ILBO, Taegu
Sangare, Abou Drahamane
webmaster@africaonline.co.ci, Dir., LA VOIE, Abidjan
Sanguinetti, Phillip A.................(256) 235-9202
psanguinetti@annistonstar.com, Pres., The Anniston Star, AL, Anniston
Sanguinetti, Phillip A.................(256) 235-9202
psanguinetti@annistonstar.com, Pres., Consolidated Publishing Co., AL, Anniston
Sans Werner, Claudia M. ....(202) 463-8777
csans@religionnews.com, Bus./Sales Mgr., Religion News Service, DC, Washington
Sansalone, Nancy A.
nsansalone@sla.org, COO/CFO, Special Libraries Association, News Division, VA, Alexandria
Sansone, Chris
csansone@herald-coaster.com, Online Ed., Fort Bend Herald, TX, Rosenberg
Sant, Rick ....(714) 796-7717
rsant@ocregister.com, Vice Pres., Print Opns., The Orange County Register, CA, Santa Ana
Santamaria, John.......................516-589-1615
Editor in Chief, New York Institute of Technology, NY, Old Westbury
Santamaria, Joseba
cad@noticiasdenavarra.com, Dir., Diario Noticias, Huarte, Navarra
Santamaria, Jose Miguel
direccion@diario-elcorreo.es, Asst. Dir., El Correo Espanol/El Pueblo Vasco, Bilbao, Vizcaya
Santarelli, Denny 217-351-5299
dsantare@news-gazette.com , Customer Care Center Manager, News-Gazette Inc., IL, Champaign
Santaularia, Ramon
viena@efe.com, Rep., EFE News Services - Vienna, Austria, Vienna
Santi, Pat
rhydowen@aol.com, Sec., Dog Writers' Asso-

ciation of America, PA, Coatesville
Santiago, Howard 209-249-3575
Pressroom Manager, Manteca Bulletin, CA, Manteca
Santipongchai, Lee
singpau@loxinfo.co.th, Pub., Sin Poh (Thailand) Ltd., Bangkok
Santori, Jim
jsantori@mankatofreepress.com, Pub., The Free Press, MN, Mankato
Santos, Cuate
cuate@lmtonline.com, Photo Dept. Mgr., Laredo Morning Times, TX, Laredo
Santos, Andrea
sales@santronics.com, Dir., Mktg., Santronics Software, FL, Homestead
Santos, Francisco Juaristi
zocalo@infosel.net.mx, Pres., ZOCALO, Saltillo, Coahuila
Sanz, José Manuel 202-7457692
jm.sanz@efe.com, Editorial Vice President - USA and Canada, EFE News Services - Washington, DC, DC, Washington
Sanz, Jose Manuel
bruselas@efe.com, Rep., EFE News Services - Brussels, Belgium, Brussels
Saoenvagovec, Veldana
info@obodjenje.net, Ed. in Chief, OSLOBODJENJE, Sarajevo
Saozone, Jim................................ext. 2249
Vice Pres., Opns., The Daily News, MA, Newburyport
Sapp, Norma
norma.sapp@sbsun.com, Adv. Exec., Employment Classifieds, San Bernardino County Sun, CA, San Bernardino
Saquier, Julio
jsaquier@lanacionnewspaper.com, Pres., La Nacion, Buenos Aires
Saracevic, Alan.......................(415) 777-7928
asaracevic@sfchronicle.com, Sports Ed., San Francisco Chronicle, CA, San Francisco
Saracogiu, Zeki
haber@ortadogugazetesi.net, Pub., ORTADOGU
Saragoza, J. 42-9175
Pub., EL DIARIO, Maturin, Monagas
Sargent, Karie ....(419) 521-7269
ksargent@nncogannett.com, Classified Sales Ctr. Mgr., News Journal, OH, Mansfield
Sargis, Adam ....(212) 822-7800
info@myfootage.com, Vice Pres., Mktg./Sales, Footage Central, NY, New York
Sarkar, Aveek
ttcal@cal.vsnl.net.in, Ed., THE TELEGRAPH, Kolkata, West Bengal
Sarkar, Aveek
anandabazar@abpmail.com, Ed., RAVIVAR, Calcutta
Sarkar, Aveek
anandabazar@abpmail.com, Ed., ANANDA BAZAR PATRIKA, Kolkata, West Bengal
Sarkar, Aveek
anandabazar@abpmail.com, Ed., HINDUSTAN STANDARD, Calcutta
Sarr, Sam
foroyaa@commit.gm, Ed., THE FOROYAA, Banjul
Sarver, Jody Stephenson
jsarver@wsjournal.com, Sales Agent, Spotlight, NC, Winston-Salem
Sarver, Jody Stephenson
jsarver@wsjournal.com, Sales Agent, Spotlight, NC, Winston-Salem
Sarver, Jody Stephenson
jsarver@wsjournal.com, Sales Agent, Star Watch, NC, Winston-Salem
Sarwte, Rebecca
bdiva88@msn.com, Editor- PenPoints, Executive Board member, Illinois Woman's Press Association, Inc., IL, Chicago
Sass, Max
editor@hofstrachronicle.com, The Hofstra Chronicle, NY, Hempstead
Sasser, Dorothy.........................(318) 487-6447
dsasser@thetowntalk.com, Prodn. Dir., The Town Talk, LA, Alexandria
Sasser, Mark............................(561) 820-4952
msasser@pbpost.com, Dir., Sales/Mktg./Single Copy, The Palm Beach Post, FL, West Palm Beach
Sasso, Antonio
antonio.sasso@ilroma.net, Dir., IL GIORNALE DI NAPOLI, Naples
Sataloff, Ronald A.
info@worldfeatures.com, Ed., World Features Syndicate, CA, La Jolla
Saternow, Lynn...............................ext. 250
lsaternow@sharonherald.com, Sports Ed., The Herald, PA, Sharon
Satinssky, Thomas
online-redaktion@suedkurier.de, Ed. in Chief, Sudkurier, Konstanz
Sato, Satzo
tkahod11@chunichi.co.jp, Ed., CHUNICHI SHIMBUN, Hamamatsu City, Chubu
Satpathy, Tathagata 258 0348
advt@dharitri.com., Ed., DHARITRI, Bhubaneswar, Orissa
Satterwhite, John H.
info@bradfordera.com, Pres., Bradford Publishing Co., PA, Bradford
Sattler, Dena..................................ext. 201
denas@gctelegram.com, Editorial Page Ed., The Garden City Telegram, KS, Garden City
Sauer, Matt............................(941) 957-5191
matt.sauer@heraldtribune.com, Bus. Ed., Sarasota Herald-Tribune, FL, Sarasota
Sauer, Terry ....(612) 673-4460
terry.sauer@startribune.com, Asst. Mng. Ed., Continuous News, Star Tribune, MN, Minneapolis
Sauers, Barbara ....(410) 770-4090
Mng. Ed., The Star-Democrat, MD, Easton
Saul, Robin ....(336) 373-7255
rsaul@news-record.com, Pres./Pub., News & Record, NC, Greensboro
Saul, Deborah ....ext. 289
saul@monroenews.com, Ed., The Monroe Evening News, MI, Monroe
Saul, Deb......................................ext. 289
saul@monroenews.com, Editorial Page Ed., The Monroe Evening News, MI, Monroe
Saunders, Adam
asaunders@robesonian.com, Bus. Mgr., The Robesonian, NC, Lumberton
Saunders, Richard J.....................716-250-6891
rsaunders@classifiedsplus.com, Vice Pres., Sales, Classifieds Plus, Inc., NY, Williamsville
Saunders, Barry ....902.426.2811 x 3006
Director of Sales, The Chronicle Herald, NS, Halifax
Saunders, Jack........................(602) 444-8322
jack.saunders@pni.com, Circ. Asst. Dir., The Arizona Republic, AZ, Phoenix
Sauve, Ann..............................(989) 894-9630
asauve@bc-times.com, Librarian, The Bay City Times, MI, Bay City
Savage, Dan
dsavage@wacotrib.com, Interim Pub., Waco Tribune-Herald, TX, Waco
Savage, Drew............................209-249-3525
Circulation Director, Manteca Bulletin, CA, Manteca
Savage-York, Sandy 304-696-2273
sandy.york@marshall.edu, Adv. Mgr., Marshall University, WV, Huntington
Savastra, Andrea..........(860) 241-3934 ext. 3934
asavastra@courant.com, Cor. Affairs/Commun. Consultant, The Hartford Courant, CT, Hartford
Savely, Randall........................(803) 750-9561
Mgr., Press Servs., South Carolina Press Association, SC, Columbia
Savoye, Craig...........................(618) 374-5415
Principia College, IL, Elsah
Sawaneh, Ebrina
ebousawaneh@yahoo.com, Ed., THE POINT, Banjul
Sawyer, Lee M..........................(816) 271-8601
lsawyer@npgco.com, Gen. Mgr., St. Joseph News-Press, MO, Saint Joseph
Sawyer, Lee M..........................(816) 271-8601
lsawyer@npgco.com, Exec. Vice President, NPG Newspapers, Inc., MO, Saint Joseph
Sawyer, Gary...........................(217) 421-6975
Ed., Herald & Review, IL, Decatur
Saye, Wade ....(865) 342-6880
Ed., Special Publications, Knoxville News Sentinel, TN, Knoxville
Sayer, James
james.sayer@wright.edu, Chair, Wright State University, OH, Dayton
Sayers, Rick ....(814) 870-1742
rick.sayers@timesnews.com, Exec. Ed., Erie Times-News, PA, Erie
Sayler, Bruce...........................(406) 496-5544
bruce.sayler@mtstandard.com, Sports Ed., The Montana Standard, MT, Butte
Sayles, Frank ....ext. 201
fesayles@cnhi.com, Pub., The Tifton Gazette, GA, Tifton
Saylor, Terri
terisaylor@hotmail.com, Exec. Dir., Mid-Atlantic Newspaper Advertising & Marketing Executives, NC, Raleigh
Scacht, Brenda
bscacht@globeandmail.com, Vice Pres., HR, The Globe and Mail, ON, Toronto
Scaglione, Cecil F.....................(858) 483-3412
Ed. in Chief/Financial Ed., Mature Life Features, CA, San Diego
Scaife, Richard M.....................(412) 321-6460
adserve@tribweb.com, Chrmn./Pub., Tribune-Review, PA, Pittsburgh
Scaife, Richard M.
mcknews@dailynewsemail.com, Pub., The Daily News, PA, McKeesport
Scalf, Delaney
dscalf@starhq.com, Prodn. Supt., Elizabethton Star, TN, Elizabethton
Scalf, Kathy
kscalf@starhq.com, Circ. Mgr., Elizabethton Star, TN, Elizabethton
Scanlon, Donna............(260) 347-0400 ext. 178
dscanlon@kpcnews.com, CFO, Herald-Republican, IN, Angola
Scanlon, Donna............(260) 347-0400 ext. 178
dscanlon@kpcnews.net, CFO, The News-Sun, IN, Kendallville
Scanlon, Donna
dscanlon@kpcnews.net, CFO, KPC Media Group Inc., IN, Kendallville
Scanlon, Donna ....(260) 347-0400
dscanlon@kpcnews.net, CFO, The Star, IN, Auburn
Scanzi, Giacomo
info@giornaledibrescia.it, Dir., GIORNALE DI BRESCIA, Brescia
Scarritt, Thomas V. ....(205) 325-2205
Ed., The Birmingham News, AL, Birmingham
Scarvey, Katie ....(704) 797-4265
kolsen@salisburypost.com, Teen-Age/Youth Ed., Salisbury Post, NC, Salisbury
Scauzillo, Steve...........(626) 962-8811 ext. 2237
steve.scauzillo@sgvn.com, Opinions Ed., The Whittier Daily News, CA, Whittier
Schabo, Wolfgang
ln@lnnz.de, Distr. Mgr., Suderlander Volksfreund, Ludenscheid
Schacht, Nicholas
uscourses@learningtree.com, Pres./CEO, Learning Tree International, CA, El Segundo
Schade, Hans Georg
info@main-rheiner.de, Pub., ALLGEMEINE ZEITUNG, Mainz
Schading, Chuck 315-789-3333
cschading@fltimes.com, Managing Editor, Finger Lakes Times, NY, Geneva
Schaechter, Joe
jschaechter@qconline.com, Contact, Central States Circulation Managers Association, IL, Glasford
Schaefer, Heather
hschaefer@pulitzer.net, Community Ed., The Daily News, WI, Rhinelander
Schaefer, William
wschaefer@gvc.edu, Chair, Grand View College, IA, Des Moines
Schaefer, Kevin
klschaefer@mckendree.edu, Web/Design Editor, McKendree University, IL, Lebanon
Schaefer, Ernest
eschaferinc@aol.com, Pres., Ernest Schaefer, Inc., NJ, Union
Schaefer, Lindsey.......................316-268-6244
lschaefer@wichitaeagle.com, Circulation Director, The Wichita Eagle, KS, Wichita
Schaeffer, Dave
info@congentco.com, Founder/CEO, Cogent Communications, Inc., DC, Washington
Schaeffer, Eric ....(610) 371-5129
eschaeffer@readingeagle.com, Manager, Internet Services Operations, Reading Eagle, PA, Reading
Schaess, George
george.schaess@donaukurier.de, Adv. Mgr., DONAUKURIER, Ingolstadt
Schafer, Bob ....(612) 673-7155
bob.schafer@startribune.com, Asst. Mng. Ed., Admin., Star Tribune, MN, Minneapolis
Schafer, Waldemar
handelsblatt@vhb.de, Ed. in Chief, HANDELSBLATT, Dusseldorf
Schaffer, Bill...........................(831) 750-4805
adigest@iname.com, Pres., Auto Digest Syndicate, WA, Washougal
Schaffer, Jim...........................(402) 465-2352
Nebraska Wesleyan Univ., NE, Lincoln
Schaffner, Victor.......................(734) 994-6764
vschaffner@annarbornews.com, Editorial Page Ed., The Ann Arbor News, MI, Ann Arbor
Schaible, Linda.........................(407) 420-5776
lschaible@tribune.com, Vice Pres., Interactive, Orlando Sentinel, FL, Orlando
Schaper, Ellen 7890
fotosatz@ndz.de, Proprietor, NEUE DEISTER ZEITUNG, Springe
Schardl, Kati............................(850) 599-2149
kschardl@tallahassee.com, Features/Custom Content Ed., Tallahassee Democrat, FL, Tallahassee
Schardt, Doug
komori.american@attglobal.net, Pdct. Mgr., Komori America Corp., IL, Rolling Meadows
Schatz, Carolyn........................(909) 386-3845
carolyn.schatz@sbsun.com, Editorial Page Ed., San Bernardino County Sun, CA, San Bernardino
Schau, Julie.............................(306) 651-6305
Commun.Coord., Saskatchewan Weekly Newspapers Association, SK, Saskatoon
Schaub, Tom ....(231) 725-6313
tschaub@muskegonchronicle.com, Mktg. Mgr., The Muskegon Chronicle, MI, Muskegon
Schaub, Dan ....(916) 321-1615
dschaub@sacbee.com, Audience Devel./Membership Servs. Sr. Vice Pres., The Sacramento Bee, CA, Sacramento
Schauseil, Robin D.
robins@nacm.org, Pres., National Association of Credit Management, MD, Columbia
Schechter, Claire ....ext. 2056
cschechter@citizensvoice.com, Asst. Mng. Ed., The Citizens' Voice, PA, Wilkes-Barre
Schecter, Joanne
jschecter@aaf.org, Sr. Vice Pres., AAF College Chapters, DC, Washington
Schell, Jeff ....(248) 745-4749
jeff.schell@oakpress.com, Vice Pres., Circ., The Oakland Press, MI, Pontiac
Schell, Jeff
jschell@news-herald.com, Adv. Dir., The News-Herald, OH, Willoughby
Schellenbach, Tricia..................(216) 368-6949
Case Western Reserve Univ., OH, Cleveland
Scheller, Fred
fscheller@dailyitem.com, Circ. Dir., The Daily Item, PA, Sunbury
Schelling, Ameena......................610 389 3897
amschelling@gmail.com, Editor-in-Chief, The Daily Princetonian, NJ, Princeton
Schensul, Jill ....(201) 753-0580
Travel Editor, North Jersey Media Group, NJ, Woodland Park
Scherban, Debra ....(413) 585-5229
dscherban@gazettenet.com, Mng. Ed., Features, Daily Hampshire Gazette, MA, Northampton
Schermer, Greg P.......................(563) 383-2194
Vice Pres., Interactive Media/Cor. Counsel, Lee Enterprises, Inc., IA, Davenport
Schexnayder, Bryan....................(504) 826-3030
awimberly@timespicayune.com, Adv. Asst. Dir., The Times Picayune, LA, New Orleans
Schicker, Paul ....(920) 453-5193
pschicker@sheboygan.gannett.com, Mgmt. Info Servs. Mgr., The Sheboygan Press, WI, Sheboygan
Schiefelbein, Jack ....(308) 381-9436
jack.schiefelbein@theindependent.com, Controller, The Grand Island Independent, NE, Grand Island
Schieffer, Gary..........................(217) 788-1517
gary.schieffer@sj-r.com, Metro Ed., The State

Journal-Register, IL, Springfield
Schievelbein, Micki
michele.schievelbein@yankton.net, Adv. Dir., Yankton Daily Press & Dakotan, SD, Yankton
Schiff, Damien........................(619) 260-4600
Univ. of San Diego School of Law, CA, San Diego
Schiffer, David........................(212) 255-3464
david@dlsdesign.com, Pres., DLS Design, NY, New York
Schiffres, Jeremy..............................ext. 410
jschiffres@freemanonline.com, City Ed., Daily Freeman, NY, Kingston
Schild, Tonya
tonya.schild@yankton.net, Bus. Mgr., Yankton Daily Press & Dakotan, SD, Yankton
Schildkraut, Dana....................(914) 323-5447
Manhattanville College, NY, Purchase
Schilter, Joe
advertising@theeasterner.info, Advertising Manager, The Easterner, WA, Cheney
Schindler, Stephen
info@wlz-fz.de, Bus. Mgr., WALDECKSICHE LANDESZEITUNG, Korbach
Schlagheck, Carol
carol.schlagheck@emich.edu, Journ. Program Coord., Eastern Michigan University, MI, Ypsilanti
Schlechter, Deon
advertsr@iwwn.com.na, Ed., John Meinert (Pty.) Ltd., Windhoek
Schleier, Curt..........................(201) 391-7135
writa1@verizon.net, Pres./Ed., Curt Schleier Reviews, NJ, River Vale
Schleifer, Loretta......................(856) 485-2540
lschleif@gannett.com, Mgr., Classified Adv., Courier-Post, NJ, Cherry Hill
Schleihs, Janice
news@eagleherald.com, Bus. Mgr., Eagle-Herald, WI, Marinette
Schlesinger, Mike...............................ext. 243
trpub@timesrepublican.com, Pub., Times-Republican, IA, Marshalltown
Schlichenmeyer, Terri................(608) 782-2665
bookwormsez@yahoo.com, Book Reviewer, The Bookworm Sez, LLC, WI, La Crosse
Schlicht, Suzanne.......................785-832-7208
sschlicht@ljworld.com, COO, The World Co.-Lawrence, Kan., Journal-World, KS, Lawrence
Schlicht, Suzanne
sschlicht@steamboatpilot.com, Pub., Steamboat Today, CO, Steamboat Springs
Schlicht, Suzanne.......................785-832-7208
sschlicht@ljworld.com, COO, The World Co.-Lawrence, Kan., Journal-World, KS, Lawrence
Schlicht, Suzanne
sschlicht@steamboatpilot.com, COO, The World Company, Steamboat Pilot & Today, CO, Steamboat Springs
Schlickman, Joe........................(815) 987-1427
jschlickman@rrstar.com, Circ. Mgr., Opns., Rockford Register Star, IL, Rockford
Schliske, Rosalind....................(307) 778-1304
Laramie County Cmty. College, WY, Cheyenne
Schlitt, Jon...............................785-864-7666
jschlitt@kansan.com, Sales and Marketing Adviser, The University Daily Kansan, KS, Lawrence
Schlosberg, Drew.............................ext. 2165
drew.schlosberg@uniontrib.com, Mgr., Community Pub. Rel., The San Diego Union-Tribune, CA, San Diego
Schmal, Jeanne..................................ext. 105
jeanne@pdsadnet.com, Gen. Mgr., Publishers Development Service, WI, Fond du Lac
Schmeltzer, Scott
scott.schmeltzer@albertleatribune.com, Pub., Albert Lea Tribune, MN, Albert Lea
Schmid, Joe
paige.jessie@lee.net, Controller, The Citizen, NY, Auburn
Schmidt, Kim
k.schmidt@technologyintegrators.net, Acct. Exec., Technology Integrators, IL, Effingham
Schmidt, Burckhardt
bschmidt@wa.de, Bus. Mgr., MEINERZHAGENER ZEITUNG, Ludenscheld
Schmidt, Leslie............................8003994294
lschmidt@bob-weber.com, Marketing Manager, Bob Weber, Inc., OH, Cleveland
Schmidt, Burckhardt
bschmidt@wa-online.de, Bus. Mgr., LUDENSCHEIDER NACHRICHTEN, Ludenscheid
Schmidt, Rick...............(307) 672-2431 ext. 122
rick@thesheridanpress.com, Prodn. Mgr., Pre Press, The Sheridan Press, WY, Sheridan
Schmidt, Kathy
kmschmidt@appleton.gannett.com, Sales Mgr., The Green Bay News-Chronicle, WI, Green Bay
Schmidt, Al............................(214) 232-3385
al@imageninc.com, Pres., Imagen, Inc., TX, Dallas
Schmidt, Dan
dschmidt@forumcomm.com, Adv. Mgr., Outside Sales, InForum, ND, Fargo
Schmidt, Burckhardt
ln@come-on.de, Bus. Mgr, ALLGEMEINER ANZEIGER, Ludenscheid
Schmidt, Nicole
nschmidt@multiad.com, Call Center Manager, MultiAd Services, Inc., IL, Peoria
Schmidt, Jorg
j.schmidt@paz-online.de, Ed. in Chief, Peiner Allgemeine Zeitung, Peine
Schmidt, Burckhardt
sekretariat@wa-online.de, Bus. Mgr., Soester Anzeiger, Soest
Schmidt, Paul.........................(941) 206-1153
schmidt@sun-herald.com, Photo Ed., Charlotte Sun, FL, Charlotte Harbor
Schmitt, Michael
verlag@parzeller.de, Bus. Mgr., Fuldaer Zeitung, Fulda
Schmitt, Norman L.
sales@georack.com, Gen. Sales Mgr., Geo-Rack, Inc., MI, Clawson
Schnabel, Mark
nksports@thekansan.com, Audiotex Mgr., The Newton Kansan, KS, Newton
Schnars, Rich..........................(561) 820-4657
rschnars@pbpost.com, Circ. Mgr., Opns., The Palm Beach Post, FL, West Palm Beach
Schneider, John.......................(800) 255-6734
jschneider@amuniversal.com, Sales Mgr., Eastern USA, Universal Uclick, MO, Kansas City
Schneider, Wolfgang
info@rotabene.de, Proprietor, FRANKISCHER ANZEIGER, Rothenburg
Schneider, Bryan.......................(216) 999-5474
Asst. Circ. Dir., Home Delivery, The Plain Dealer, OH, Cleveland
Schnell, Bruno
nav@pressenetz.de, Proprietor, PEGNITZ-ZEITUNG, Nurnberg
Schnell, Bruno
nav@pressenetz.de, Proprietor, NURNBERGER NACHRICHTEN, Nurnberg
Schnell, Bruno
nav@pressenetz.de, Proprietor, SCHWABACHER TAGBLATT, Nurnberg
Schnell, Bruno..50080
verlag@altmuehl-bote.de, Proprietor, ALTMUHL-BOTE, Gunzenhausen
Schnell, Bruno
nav@pressenetz.de, Proprietor, ERLANGER NACHRICHTEN, Nurnberg
Schnell, Caramie.....................(970) 748-2984
cschnell@vaildaily.com, Arts/Entertainment Ed., Vail Daily, CO, Vail
Schnell, Bruno
verlag@roth-hilpoltsteiner-volkszeitung.de, Proprietor, Roth-Hilpoltsteiner Volkszeitung, Roth
Schnuecker, Hans
wt-buergerfreund@vrm.de, Bus. Mgr., Wiesbadener Tagblatt, Wiesbaden
Schnuecker, Hans
kurier-lokales@vrm.de, Bus. Mgr., Wiesbadener Kurier, Wiesbaden
Schocken, Amos
amoss@haaretz.co.il, Pub., HA'ARETZ
Schoebel, Barbara S..................(570) 420-4330
bschoebel@poconorecord.com, Adv. Mgr., Sales, Pocono Record, PA, Stroudsburg
Schoeder, Alebert
anzeigen@nez.de, Ed., Niederelbe-Zeitung, Otterndorf
Schoelles, Marjorie..................(850) 599-2232
mschoelles@tallahassee.com, Mktg & Nondaily Mgr., Tallahassee Democrat, FL, Tallahassee
Schoenberger, Wally.................(216) 999-6651
Prodn. Mgr., Printing/Night Operations, The Plain Dealer, OH, Cleveland
Schoffel, Ira............................(850) 599-2316
ischoffel@tallahassee.com, Sports Ed., Tallahassee Democrat, FL, Tallahassee
Schofield, Jennie M.
apreeq@aol.com, Pres., Allpress Equipment, Inc., FL, Orlando
Schollkopf, Rainer
anzeigen@gaeubote.de, Bus. Mgr., Gaubote, Herrenberg
Scholz, Jane............................(202) 383-6085
jscholz@mctinfoservices.com, Ed., McClatchy-Tribune Information Services, DC, Washington
jscholz@mctinfoservices.com, Ed., McClatchy-Tribune Information Services, Tribune Media Services, Inc., IL, Chicago
Schomaker, H.
i.zoldosmuhr@swp.de, Bus. Mgr., ALB BOTE, Munsingen
Schomaker, Helmut
folksblatnt@swp.de, Ed. in Chief, REUTLINGER NACHRICHTEN, Reutlingen
Schonwetter, Wendy.................(253) 838-5704
Vice Pres., Mktg., Nasco Products Co., KS, Overland Park
Schoonover, Steve....................(530) 896-7750
sschoonover@chicoer.com, City Ed., Chico Enterprise-Record, CA, Chico
Schott, Ron.............................(573) 248-2730
ron.schott@courierpost.com, Circ. Dir., Hannibal Courier-Post, MO, Hannibal
Schouten, Sir Gerardus J.
thenewsaruba@setarnet.aw, Pub., THE NEWS, Oranjestad
Schrader, Rusty............(563) 263-2331 ext. 225
rusty.schrader@muscatinejournal.com, News Ed., Muscatine Journal, IA, Muscatine
Schrafel, Daniel.......................(516) 299-2619
Long Island Univ./C.W.Post, NY, Brookville
Schrag, Jeff
editor@dailyevents.com, Adv. Dir., The Daily Events, MO, Springfield
Schrag, Jeff
editor@dailyevents.com, Prodn. Mgr., The Daily Events, MO, Springfield
Schrag, Jeff
editor@dailyevents.com, Pub., The Daily Events, MO, Springfield
Schreiber, Helmut
ga@ga-online.de, Bus. Mgr., GENERAL-ANZEIGER, Rhauderfehn
Schreiner, Susan......................(814) 870-1642
susan.schreiner@timesnews.com, Adv. Supvr., Inside Sales, Erie Times-News, PA, Erie
Schreppel, Ed...........................(570) 628-6003
eschreppel@republicanherald.com, Asst. Mng. Ed., Republican Herald, PA, Pottsville
Schrieber, Don
caradv@imsinternet.net, Pub., Daily American Republic, MO, Poplar Bluff
Schroder, Phil...........................(478) 744-4443
pschroder@macon.com, Circ. Mgr., The Telegraph, GA, Macon
Schroeder, Heather..............................ext. 486
Mount Mary College, WI, Milwaukee
Schroeder, Michael E.
mschroeder@newbritainherald.com, Pub., The Herald, CT, New Britain
Schroeder, Angela....................(218) 739-7288
Fergus Falls Cmty. College, MN, Fergus Falls
Schropp, Lisa...............(570) 748-6791 ext. 137
lschropp@lockhaven.com, Mktg. Mgr., The Express, PA, Lock Haven
Schubert, Suzanne
schuberts@fayettevillenc.com, Graphics Dir., The Fayetteville Observer, NC, Fayetteville
Schuelke, Anne.........................(507) 389-1079
Minnesota State Univ. Mankato, MN, Mankato
Schuey, Tammy............................724-282-8000
tschuey@butlereagle.com, Director of Technology, Eagle Printing Co., PA, Butler
Schuey, Tammy..................................ext. 218
tschuey@butlereagle.com, Mgr., Mgmt. Info Servs., Butler Eagle, PA, Butler
Schuhmann, G. Raymond
info@thetechnologyagency.com, Pres., Kinetic Corporation, KY, Louisville
Schulte, Chris..........................(715) 845-0701
cschulte@wdhprint.com, Sports Ed., The Wausau Daily Herald, WI, Wausau
Schulte Strathaus, Dirk
vertrieb@dk-online.de, Proprietor, DELMENHORSTER KREISBLATT, Delmenhorst
Schultz, Connie........................(216) 999-4854
Metro Columnist, The Plain Dealer, OH, Cleveland
Schultz, Susy............................(815) 937-3330
sschultz@daily-journal.com, Mng. Ed., The Daily Journal, IL, Kankakee
Schultz, Gary
info@mrgco.com, Pres., Multimedia Research Group, Inc., CA, San Jose
Schultz, Richard......................(630) 755-9370
richard.schultz@gossinternational.com, Sr. Vice Pres., Global Sales, Goss International Corporation, IL, Bolingbrook
Schultz, David
daves@news-banner.com, Asst. Ed., News-Banner, IN, Bluffton
Schultz, Dieter
lr@lr-online.de, Ed. in Chief, LAUSITZER RUNDSCHAU, Cottbus
Schultz, Thomas L.
toms@wdtimes.com, Editorial Page Ed., Watertown Daily Times, WI, Watertown
Schultz, Sonya.........................(308) 381-9426
sonya.schultz@theindependent.com, Adv. Dir., The Grand Island Independent, NE, Grand Island
Schultz-Homberg, Thomas
sz.geschaeftsfuehrung@dd-v.de, Ed., SACHSISCHE ZEITUNG, Dresden
Schulz, Sally............................(707) 453-8109
sally@timesheraldonline.com, Classified Mgr., Vallejo Times-Herald, CA, Vallejo
Schulze, Johannes...................................6560
die.tageszeitung@freiepresse.de, Bus. Mgr., FREIE PRESSE, Chemnitz
Schumacher, Michael................(806) 345-3445
michael.schumacher@amarillo.com, Photo Dept. Mgr., Amarillo Globe-News, TX, Amarillo
Schumacher, Andrew................(337) 230-3179
vermilion.adspace@gmail.com, Business manager, Univ. of Louisiana at Lafayette The Vermilion, LA, Lafayette
Schunck, Thomas
info@svz.de, Ed. in Chief, SCHWERINER VOLKSZEITUNG, Schwerin
Schunk, Christa
redaktion@mainpost.de, Proprietor, Bote vom Grabfeld, Wurzburg
Schuonengh, Daniel
servicecenter@westfalischer-anzeiger.de, Pub., Westafalischer Anzeiger, Hamm
Schupp, Dennis
info@smithrpm.com, Pres., Smith PPI Inc., KS, Lenxa
Schupp, Dennis
sschupp@rpm.com, Pres., Smith Pressroom Products, Inc., KS, Lenexa
Schur, Cynthia
cschur@santamariatimes.com, Publisher, The Lompoc Record, CA, Lompoc
Schur, Hans
hsc@schur.com, Owner, Schur International a/s, Dk-8700 Horsens
Schurter, Ted...........................(217) 788-1476
ted.schurter@sj-r.com, Asst. Photo Ed., The State Journal-Register, IL, Springfield
Schurz, Scott C.
tmnews@tmnews.com, Ed. in Chief, The Times-Mail, IN, Bedford
Schurz, Mary
advocate@amnews.com, Chrmn., The Advocate-Messenger, KY, Danville
Schurz, Scott C........................(812) 331-4250
htnews@heraldt.com, Ed. in Chief, The Herald-Times, IN, Bloomington
Schurz, Franklin D...................(574) 287-2257
fschurz@schurz.com, Chrmn., Schurz Communications Inc, IN, Mishawaka
Schussel, Dr. Wolfgang
leser@wienerzeitung.at, Pub., WIENER ZEITUNG, 1040 Vienna
Schust, Mary
mary.schust@mediaprof.com, Sr. Vice Pres., Underwriting, Media Professional Insurance,

MO, Kansas City
Schuster, Margo
margo.schuster@investors.com, Vice Pres., Customer Rel., Investor's Business Daily, CA, Los Angeles
Schutz, Bernie ....(719) 544-3520 ext. 510
Adv. Dir., Mktg./Online Publishing, The Pueblo Chieftain, CO, Pueblo
Schutz, Bernie ....(918) 581-8509
bernie.schutz@tulsaworld.com, Adv. Dir., Tulsa World, OK, Tulsa
Schuuring, Michel
info@lloyd.be, Dir., LE LLOYD, Antwerp
Schuver, Michael F.
mschuver@lminews.com, Vice Pres., Lancaster Management, Inc., AL, Gadsden
Schuver, Mike
publisher@bransontrilakesnews.com, Pub., Branson Tri-Lakes Daily News, MO, Hollister
Schwadron, Harley ....734 665 8272 tel/fax
schwaboo@comcast.net, Ed., Schwadron Cartoon & Illustration Service, MI, Ann Arbor
Schwaller, Jeff.........................(906) 497-5652
jschwaller@powersprinting.net, Prodn. Mgr., Pressroom, The Daily News, MI, Iron Mountain
Schwanbeck, Brad ....(419) 724-6320
ssecord@toledoblade.com, Circ. Mgr., Distr., The Blade, OH, Toledo
Schwartz, Diane
dschwartz@accessintel.com, Vice Pres./Pub., PR & Marketing News, NY, New York
Schwartz, Sharon ....ext. 108
s.schwartz@ananews.com, Network Adv. Mgr., ANA Advertising Services, Inc. (Arizona Newspaper Association), AZ, Phoenix
Schwartz, Sandy
sandy.schwartz@coxinc.com, Pres., Cox Newspapers, Inc., GA, Atlanta
Schwartz, Howard
schwartzh@enigma.rider.edu, Chair, Rider University, NJ, Lawrenceville
Schwartz, Leland
editor@states.com, Ed., States News Service (NY Times Subscriber Service), DC, Washington
Schwartz, Alan........................(973) 267-9292
info@caprockdev.com, President, Caprock Developments, Inc., NJ, Morris Plains
Schwartz, Stan........................(573) 777-4981
Communications Director, National Newspaper Association Publishers' Auxiliary, MO, Columbia
Schwartzkopf, Susan ....(864) 298-4360
sschwart@greenvil.gannett.com, Vice Pres., Market Devel., The Greenville News, SC, Greenville
Schwartzkopf, Marie.................(830) 257-0301
marie.schwartzkopf@dailytimes.com, Adv. Dir., Kerrville Daily Times, TX, Kerrville
Schwarz, Ingeborg
ingeborg.schwarz@shz.de, Adv. Mgr., Wilstersche Zeitung, Flensburg
Schwarz, Ingeborg
ingeborg.schwarz@shz.de@shz.de, Adv. Mgr., Norddeutsche Rundschau, Flensburg
Schweitzer, Oliver
oschweitzer@admediapartners.com, Principal, AdMedia Partners, Inc., NY, New York
Schwensen, Dave ....(440) 967-0293
dave@northshorepublishing.com, Author/Award-Winning Humor Columnist, DSEntertainment/North Shore Publishing, OH, Vermilion
Schwer, Bernd
info@zvw.de, Bus. Mgr., Welzheimer Zeitung, Waiblingen
Schwer, Bernd
info@zvw.de, Bus. Mgr., WAIBLINGER KREISZEITUNG, Waiblingen
Schwien, Nick
nicks_news@dailynews.net, Asst. Sports Ed., The Hays Daily News, KS, Hays
Schwing, John ....(203) 330-6248
jschwing@ctpost.com, Metro Ed., Connecticut Post, CT, Bridgeport
Schwizer, Thomas
t.schwizer@wundo.ch, Ed. in Chief, WERDENBERGER UND OBERTOGGENBURGER, Buchs, St. Gallen
Sciacqua, Toni 310-540-5511 x6436
toni.sciacqua@dailybreeze.com, Editor, Daily Breeze, CA, Torrance
Scibora, Marco
info@nicollet.com, Pres., Nicollet Technologies, MN, Bloomington
Scibora, Marco
marco@acdstar.com, Pres./CEO, Advanced Communication Design, Inc., MN, Minneapolis
Scites, Courtney......................(703) 878-8084
cscites@insidenova.com, Religion Ed., Manassas Journal Messenger, VA, Manassas
Scobey, Mike ....(215) 949-4067
mscobey@phillyburbs.com, Pub., Burlington County Times, NJ, Willingboro
Scobey, Michael
mscobey@calkins-media.com, COO, Calkins Media, PA, Levittown
Scobey, Mike ....(215) 345-3095
mscobey@phillyburbs.com, Pub., The Intelligencer, PA, Doylestown
Scobey, Mike
mscobey@phillyburbs.com, Pub., Bucks County Courier Times, PA, Levittown
Scoder, Dennis Van ....ext. 225
dvan@crescent-news.com, Ed., Defiance Publishing LLC, OH, Defiance
Scopin, Joseph W. ....(202) 636-3128
scopin@washingtontimes.com, Asst. Mng. Ed., Graphics, The Washington Times, DC, Washington
Scott, Sara 768-4983
sscott@citpat.com, Associate Editor/Content , The Jackson Citizen Patriot, MI, Jackson
Scott, Tim ....ext. 122
tscott@k-f.com, Mktg. Coord., K & F International, Inc., IN, Granger
Scott, Duncan...................................ext. 555
duncan_scott@news-herald.com, Photo Dept. Mgr., The News-Herald, OH, Willoughby
Scott, Michael ....(906) 483-2230
mscott@mininggazette.com, Pub., The Daily Mining Gazette, MI, Houghton
Scott, Jerry...........................(817) 390-7519
jescott@star-telegram.com, Vice Pres., Mktg., Fort Worth Star-Telegram, TX, Fort Worth
Scott, Tony
tscott@register-mail.com, Pub., The Register-Mail, IL, Galesburg
Scott, Rob
rscott@dmg.gannett.com, Adv. Dir., The Daily Times, MD, Salisbury
Scott, Fred
fred.scott@selmatimesjournal.com, Prodn. Mgr., The Selma Times-Journal, AL, Selma
Scott, Rod J.
mail@examiner.com.au, Ed., THE SUNDAY EXAMINER
Scott, Sherri
sobrien@lfpress.com, Circ. Dir., Reader Sales/Serv./Mktg., The London Free Press, ON, London
Scott, Ian
ians@advancedtele.co.uk, Mng. Dir./Gen. Mgr., Advanced Telecom Services, Inc. (U.K.), ENG, London
Scott, Tony
tscott@gatehousemedia.com, Gen. Mgr., Daily Review Atlas, IL, Monmouth
Scott, Jonathan.......................(519) 823-6030
jscott@guelphmercury.com, Prodn. Mgr., Opns., The Guelph Mercury, ON, Guelph
Scott, Terry...........................(416) 507-2126
terry.scott@thecanadianpress.com, Gen. Exec./Client Liaison, Broadcast News Limited, ON, Toronto
terry.scott@thecanadianpress.com, Vice Pres., Broadcasting, Canadian Press, The - Toronto, ON, ON, Toronto
Scott, Clay.............................(615) 230-3361
Volunteer State Cmty. College, TN, Gallatin
Scott, Chris...........................(978) 970-4648
cscott@lowellsun.com, City Ed., The Sun, MA, Lowell
Scott-Bertling, Terry
tbertling@express-news.net, Asst. Mng. Ed., Features, Randolph Wingspread, TX, San Antonio
tbertling@express-news.net, Asst. Mng. Ed., Features, Brooks Discovery News, TX, San Antonio
tbertling@express-news.net, Asst. Mng. Ed., Features, Bulverde Community News, TX, San Antonio
tbertling@express-news.net, Asst. Mng. Ed., Features, Fort Sam News Leader, TX, San Antonio
tbertling@express-news.net, Asst. Mng. Ed., Features, Kelly Observer, TX, San Antonio
tbertling@express-news.net, Asst. Mng. Ed., Features, Lackland Talespinner, TX, San Antonio
tbertling@express-news.net, Asst. Mng. Ed., Features, Medical Patriot, TX, San Antonio
tbertling@express-news.net, Asst. Mng. Ed., Features, North Central News, TX, San Antonio
tbertling@express-news.net, Asst. Mng. Ed., Features, Northeast Herald, TX, San Antonio
tbertling@express-news.net, Asst. Mng. Ed., Features, Northwest Weekly, TX, San Antonio
tbertling@express-news.net, Asst. Mng. Ed., Features, San Antonio Express-News, TX, San Antonio
Screaux, Sarah ....(781) 280-3769
Middlesex Cmty. College, MA, Bedford
Scroggins, Josh ....(207) 941-7016
Husson College, ME, Bangor
Scrum, Tia ....ext. 2248
Bus. Mgr., The Daily Mail, NY, Catskill
Sealander, John
john@sealander.com, Owner, Sealander & Co., TX, Dallas
Searano, Gil ....(213) 736-8117
Loyola Law School of Los Angeles, CA, Los Angeles
Seares, Pachico A.
freeman@mozcom.com, Ed., THE FREEMAN, Cebu City
Searl, Scott ....(402) 444-1726
scott.searl@owh.com, Vice Pres./Gen. Counsel, Omaha World-Herald, NE, Omaha
Searl, Scott 402-4441726
VP & General Counsel, Omaha World-Herald, NE, Omaha
Sears, Todd 608-252-6374
tsears@madison.com, Advertising Director, Wisconsin State Journal, WI, Madison
Sease, Brian 301-733-5131
Production and pagination manager, The Herald-Mail, MD, Hagerstown
Sease, Cindy..........................(406) 758-4410
csease@dailyinterlake.com, Adv. Dir., Daily Inter Lake, MT, Kalispell
Seaton, Donald R.
drs@hastingstribune.com, Pub., Hastings Tribune, NE, Hastings
Seaton, Frederick D.
dseaton@winfieldcourier.com, Editorial Page Ed., Winfield Daily Courier, KS, Winfield
Seaton, Edward L.
nseaton@themercury.com, Ed. in Chief, The Manhattan Mercury, KS, Manhattan
Seckar, Ron
circulation@indianagazette.net, Circ. Mgr., The Indiana Gazette, PA, Indiana
Sederberg, Deborah ....ext. 467
dsederberg@thenewsdispatch.com, Education/Lifestyles Columnist, News Dispatch, IN, Michigan City
Seeber, Mike..........................(920) 993-7138
mseeber@appleton.gannett.com, Vice Pres., Finance, The Post-Crescent, WI, Appleton
Seeburger, John
rob@chapelhillmfg.com, Pres./Vice Pres., Mktg., Chapel Hill Manufacturing Co., PA, Oreland
Seeger, Mel ....ext. 299
m.seeger@theday.com, Purchasing Agent, The Day Publishing Company, CT, New London
Seelheim, Rolf
familienanzeigen@nordwest-zeitung.de, Ed. in Chief, Nordwest Zeitung, Oldenburg
Seewald, Mario
m.seewald@npv.de, Distribution Mgr., Passauer Neue Presse, Passau
Segel, Dani
dsegel@volksblatt.li, Proprietor, LIECHTENSTEINER VOLKSBLATT, Schaan
Segovia, Jamie Cruz.........................275-1572
Gen. Mgr., Cruz Segovia Family, Quevedo, Los Rios
Seibert, Tom
tseibert@thehawkeye.com, Circ. Mgr., The Hawk Eye, IA, Burlington
Seidel, Randy
info@seidelenterprises.com, Pres., Seidel Enterprises, PA, Easton
Seidenfaden, Toger
chefredaktionen@pol.dk, Ed. in Chief, POLITIKEN-DETAILHANDLERE/LANDSANNONCORER, Copenhagen, Sjaelland
Seidensticker, Jeff 617-328-6645
jeff@merlinone.com, Vice President of IT & Managed Services, MerlinOne, Inc., MA, Quincy
Seidman, Dan ....(847) 359-7860
Dan@GotInfluenceInc.com, Founder/Self-Syndicator/Columnist, Got Influence? Publishing, IL, Barrington
Seifert, David ....(540) 458-4060
Washington and Lee Univ., VA, Lexington
Seifert, Joel ....(231) 725-6391
jseifert@muskegonchronicle.com, Circ. Mgr., Zone, The Muskegon Chronicle, MI, Muskegon
Seiki, Nakada
nakada@ryukyushimpo.co.jp, Chief, RYUKYU SHIMPO, Naha (Okinawa I.), Kyushu
Seiler, Christina ....(574) 224-5327
christinas@rochsent.com, News Ed., The Rochester Sentinel, IN, Rochester
Seiler, Casey..........................(518) 454-5619
cseiler@timesunion.com, State Ed., Times Union, NY, Albany
Seitz, Virginia A.
tlnmain@buckeye-express.com, Pub., Toledo Legal News
Seiwert, Dale ....(316) 268-6285
dseiwert@wichitaeagle.com, Vice Pres., Finance, The Wichita Eagle, KS, Wichita
Sekella, Richard M. ....ext. 1281
Gen. Mgr., Record-Courier, OH, Ravenna
Sekella, Richard M.
rsekella@recordpub.com, Gen. Mgr., Record Publishing Co., OH, Ravenna
Selcuk, Ilhan
adana@cumhuriyet.com.tr, Pub., CUMHURIYET
Self, Jennifer ....(661) 395-7434
jself@bakersfield.com, Lifestyles Ed., The Bakersfield Californian, CA, Bakersfield
Selig, John L. ....(800) 676-3342
jselig@mediamonitors.com, Sales, Media Monitors, Inc., NY, White Plains
Selim, Tamar ....(319) 335-1538
Univ. of Iowa Engineering School, IA, Iowa City
Seline, Rex.............................(817) 390-7729
rseline@star-telegram.com, Mng. Ed., News, Fort Worth Star-Telegram, TX, Fort Worth
Sell, Jeremy
jeremy@saxmayercorp.com, Process Supvr., Information Technology, Saxmayer Corp., MI, Blissfield
Sell, Steve ....ext. 19
Sports Ed., McPherson Sentinel, KS, McPherson
Sell, T.M...................(206) 878-3710 ext. 3292
tsell@highline.edu, Advisor, The Thunderword , WA, Des Moines
Seller, Mike
mikeseller@advpubtech.com, Vice Pres., Sales, Advanced Publishing Technology, CA, Burbank
Sellman, Nina
redaktion@nyan.ax, Ed. in Chief, NYA ALAND, Mariehamn
Sells, Nancy ....(651) 293-7000
nancy.sells@prnewswire.com, Vice Pres., eWatch, MN, Minneapolis
Selviano, Aine
aine@folhaderegiao.com.br, Ed., Editora Folha da Regiao da Aracatuba Ltd., Aracatuba, Sao Paulo
Sembos, Evangelos
oraspor@otenet.gr, Dir., ORA GIA SPOR, Athens, Central Greece
Semegen, Robin ....(253) 597-8467
robin.semegen@thenewstribune.com, Prodn. Dir., Opns., The News Tribune, WA, Tacoma
Semler, Loren H.
semler@semlerindustries.com, Pres., Semler Industries, Inc. (Pressroom Fluids Equipment Div.), IL, Franklin Park

Semple, Elizabeth......................(252) 329-9513
esemple@reflector.com, Dir., Mktg./Bus. Devel./Customer Care, The Daily Reflector, NC, Greenville
Semple, Paul
paul.semple@shelbyvilledailyunion.com, Pub., Daily Union, IL, Shelbyville
Seng, Cheong Yip
straits@cyberway.com.sg, Ed. in Chief, SUNDAY TIMES, Singapore
Senger, John
jsenger@greenfieldreporter.com, Adv. Dir., Daily Reporter, IN, Greenfield
Sengupta, Arindam
arindam.sengupta@timesgroup.com, Ed. in Chief, SANDHYA TIMES, New Delhi
Seraita, Steven........................(646) 654-8400
sseraita@scarborough.com, Exec. Vice Pres./Dir., Sales, Scarborough Research, NY, New York
Serban, George
graiul@graiul.ro, Ed. in Chief, GRAIUL MARAMURESULUI, Baia Mare, Maramures
Serfoss, Rod..........................(580) 323-5151
rodserfoss@clintondailynews.com, Ed., The Clinton Daily News, OK, Clinton
Sergeyev, Sergei
moles@teleport.ee, Ed. in Chief, ME, Tallinn
Serino, Stephanie......................212-556-3780
serino@nytimes.com, Director, Domestic Sales & Licensing, New York Times News Service, NY, New York
Serino, Michael........................(607) 274-1618
Ithaca College, NY, Ithaca
Serino, Stephanie......................212-556-3780
serino@nytimes.com, Director, Domestic Sales & Licensing, New York Times Syndicate, NY, New York
Sernoe, Jim
jim.sernoe@mwsu.edu, Chair/Assoc. Prof., Midwestern State University, TX, Wichita Falls
Serpa, John.................(805) 685-3100 ext. 122
serpaj@maps.com, Pres., Maps.com, CA, Santa Barbara
Serpe, Dennis..........................(262) 656-6255
dserpe@kenoshanews.com, Asst. Adv. Dir., Kenosha News, WI, Kenosha
Serra, Pedro
master@diaridebalears.com, Pres., BALEARS, Palma de Mallorca, Baleares
Serra Tur, Joan
diariodeibiza@epi.es, Dir., DIARIO DE IBIZA, Ibiza, Baleares
Serrano Alvarez, Jose Manuel
diario.avila@tsai.es, Dir., El Diario De Avila, Avila
Sessler, Michael
anzeigen@redaktion.zvw.de, Adv. Mgr., Winnender Zeitung, Waiblingen
Setar, Terry..........................(732) 627-9977
info@royalsupplies.com, Vice Pres., Sales (Royal), Royal Consumer Information Products, Inc., NJ, Sommerset
Seto, Linda.....................................ext. 698
lseto@nysun.com, Circ. Dir., The New York Sun, NY, New York
Seto, Jack............................(800) 387-9010
jseto@masterfile.com, Infringement Researcher, Masterfile (Stock Color Photo Library), ON, Toronto
Severns, Matt..........................(701) 231-8629
editor@ndsuspectrum.com, North Dakota State Univ., ND, Fargo
Seveska, Paul
pseveska@bluelinemediaholdings.com, CEO/President BlueLine Media Holdings, Shawano Leader, WI, Shawano
Seveska, Paul
pseveska@bluelinemediaholdings.com, Pres./CEO/Pub., The Shawano Leader, BlueLine Media Holdings, WI, Neenah
Seward, Matthew.......................(231) 779-4126
mseward@cadillacnews.com, Mng. Ed., Northern Michigan News, MI, Cadillac
mseward@cadillacnews.com, Editorial Page Ed., Cadillac News, MI, Cadillac
Sewell, Michael
msewell@txwes.edu, Chair, Texas Wesleyan University, TX, Fort Worth
Sexton, Jill...........................(940) 720-3441
sextonj@wtr.com, Librarian, Wichita Falls Times Record News, TX, Wichita Falls
Seymour, Patrick.......................(212) 352-0063
ps@tsangseymour.com, Principal, Tsang Seymour Design, Inc., NY, New York
Seymour, Chris
chris.seymour@news-jrnl.com, Deputy Mng. Ed., Prodn., Daytona Beach News-Journal, FL, Daytona Beach
Shaak, Teresa..........................717-703-3003
teresas@pa-news.org, Manager, Association of American Editorial Cartoonists, PA, Harrisburg
Shabazz, Thysha.......................(804) 524-5991
Virginia State Univ., VA, Petersburg
Shabram, Jeff..........................(402) 444-1018
jeff.shabram@owh.com, Adv. Dir., Online/Digital, Omaha World-Herald, NE, Omaha
Shackelford, Tiffany
tiffany@aan.org, Executive Director, Association of Alternative Newsmedia, DC, Washington
Shackford, Scott.......................(760) 256-4104
sshackford@desertdispatch.com, Ed. in Chief, Desert Dispatch, CA, Barstow
Shafer, Mike
sales@tkspress.com, Director of Sales and Marketing, TKS (USA), Inc., TX, Irving
Shafer, Robert
bshafer@kolbus.com, Pres./Dir., Sales/Distr. Americas, Kolbus America, Inc., OH, Cleveland
Shaffer, Robert C......................(330) 821-1200
rshaffer@the-review.com, Gen. Mgr., The Review, OH, Alliance
Shaffer, Leisha........................(610) 622-8871
Adv. Mgr., Classified, Delaware County Daily Times, PA, Primos
Shaffer, Barbara..........(330) 747-1471 ext. 1282
bshaffer@vindy.com, Living/Lifestyle Ed., The Vindicator, OH, Youngstown
Shafter, Cameron D.
cameronshafter@juno.com, Writer, Pacheco Research and Development Co., CA, Concord
Shah, Bahubali
advertise@gujaratsamachar.com, MD, GUJARAT SAMACHAR, Mumbai, Maharashtra
Shah, Shreyans
editor@gujaratsamachar.com, Mng. Ed., GUJARAT SAMACHAR, Ahmedabad, Gujarat
Shah, Istikhar
editor@nawaiwaqt.com.pk, Circ. Mgr., NAWA-I-WAQT, Lahore, Lahore District
Shah, Pradeep
sanjsamachar@gmail.com, Ed., SANJ SAMACHAR, Gujarat, Rajkot
Shah, Y.N.
info@jaihinddaily.com, Mng. Ed., JAI HIND, Ahmedabad, Gujarat
Shah, Prathap
saurashtrasamachar@vsnl.net, Ed., SAURASHTRA SAMACHAR, Bhavnagar, Gujarat
Shaheen, Joe...................................ext. 3237
joe.shaheen@indeonline.com, Mng. Ed., The Independent, OH, Massillon
Shaheen, Daen
bayan@albayan.ae, Ed., AL-BAYAN
Shain, Michael
mshain@jonesborosun.com, Controller, The Jonesboro Sun, AR, Jonesboro
Shain, Russell E.
rshain@astate.edu, Dean/Prof., Arkansas State University, AR, Jonesboro
Shakil-ur-Rahman, Mir
editorjang@jang.com.pk, Ed. in Chief, JANG, Karachi
Shalaway, Scott........................304-686-2630
Nature Writer, The Wild Side, WV, Cameron
Shambo, Leslie
lshambo@kcchronicle.com, Mktg. Coord., Kane County Chronicle, IL, Saint Charles
Shami, UmerMujib
umershami@yahoo.com, Adv. Mgr., DAILY PAKISTAN, Lahore, Lahore District
Shamsi, Javed Mehr................92 071 5627833
kaleemsukkur@yahoo.com, Ed. in Chief, KALEEM, Sukkur, Khairpur Division
Shane, Dave............................(989) 894-9635
dshane@bc-times.com, News Ed., The Bay City Times, MI, Bay City
Shank, Alinda..........................(413) 496-6305
ashank@berkshireeagle.com, Mgr., HR, The Berkshire Eagle, MA, Pittsfield
Shank, John
nleditor@rochellenews-leader.com, Gen. Mgr., News Media Corp., IL, Rochelle
Shanks, Amy............................(765) 677-2745
Indiana Wesleyan Univ., IN, Marion
Shannon, Brad..........................(360) 753-1688
bshannon@theolympian.com, Political Ed., The Olympian, WA, Olympia
Shannon, Kelly.........................(312) 222-4569
kshannon@tribune.com, Dir., Brand Mktg., Chicago Tribune, IL, Chicago
Shannon, Mr. Neil......................(815) 937-3303
nshannon@daily-journal.com, Adv. Dir., The Daily Journal, IL, Kankakee
Shannon, Mike
mshannon@opubco.com, Mng. Ed., The Oklahoman, OK, Oklahoma City
Shapcott, Carol........................(215) 949-4072
cshapcott@phillyburbs.com, Mktg. Mgr., Burlington County Times, NJ, Willingboro
Shapcott, Carol...............................ext. 4072
cshapcott@phillyburbs.com, Mgr., Promo., Bucks County Courier Times, PA, Levittown
Shapiro, Naomi K.
cre8vads@cheq.net, Pres., Creative Brilliance Advertising, Marketing & Public Relation, WI, Madison
Shapleigh, Katherine...................(540) 374-5461
kshapleigh@freelancestar.com, Life Ed., The Free Lance-Star, VA, Fredericksburg
Sharbal, Ghassan
information@alhayat.com, Ed. in Chief, AL-HAYAT
Shariatmadari, Hossein
kayhan@kayhannews.ir, Mng. Ed., KAYHAN INTERNATIONAL
Shariatmadari, Hossein
www.kayhannews.ir, Ed. in Chief, KAYHAN
Sharkey, Sabrina.......................315-363-5100
Circulation Supervisor, The Oneida Daily Dispatch, NY, Oneida
Sharkey, Brian.........................(262) 656-6282
bsharkey@kenoshanews.com, Get Out Ed., Kenosha News, WI, Kenosha
Sharkey, Richard.......................318-487-6390
rsharkey@thetowntalk.com, Asst. Managing Editor, The Town Talk, LA, Alexandria
Sharma, Vishnu................................2450604
adhikarpatrika@yahoo.com, Pub., ADHIKAR, Jaipur, Rajasthan
Sharma, Nidhi
nidhi.sharma3@timesgroup.com, Adv.Mgr, THE ECONOMIC TIMES, New Delhi
Sharma, Somesh
rastrdut@sancharnet.in, CEO, RASHTRADOOT, Jaipur, Rajasthan
Sharma, Brijesh Chand......................263 5695
bcsharma@swatantrachetna.com, Bureau Chief, SWATANTRA CHETNA, Gorakhpur, Uttar Pradesh
Sharon, Gary A.........................(330) 539-5433
gary@litco.com, Vice Pres., Litco International, Inc., OH, Vienna
Sharp, Jeanny J.
jsharp@ottawaherald.com, Editorial Page Ed., The Ottawa Herald, KS, Ottawa
Sharpe, Leslie.........................(505) 564-4555
lsharpe@daily-times.com, Mgmt. Info Servs. Mgr., The Daily Times, NM, Farmington
Sharpnack, Joe.........................(313) 512 9705
sharptoons@yahoo.com, Self-Syndicator, Sharpnack, Joe, IA, Iowa City
Shashack, Greg.........................(618) 463-2565
Asst. Sports Ed., The Telegraph, IL, Alton
Shattil, Daniel........................(402) 472-1769
Daily Nebraskan, Univ. of Nebraska, NE, Lincoln
Shaver, Gary
garyshaver@eveningtribune.com, Prodn. Mgr., The Evening Tribune, NY, Hornell
Shaver, Judi..................................ext. 2099
jshaver@citizensvoice.com, Coord., The Citizens' Voice, PA, Wilkes-Barre
Shaver, Mary Alice
mshaver@mail.ucf.edu, Prof., University of Central Florida, FL, Orlando
Shaw, Brad.............................(719) 476-1635
brad.shaw@gazette.com, Dir., IT, The Gazette, CO, Colorado Springs
Shaw, Donald L.........................(919) 962-4087
Kenan Prof., University of North Carolina, NC, Chapel Hill
Shaw, David............................(202) 463-8777
david.shaw@religionnews.com, Bus. Coord., Religion News Service, DC, Washington
Shaw, Rick
shawrf@missouri.edu, Dir., Kappa Alpha Mu Honorary Society in Photo Journalism, MO, Columbia
Shaw, Maria
mshaw@courier-tribune.com, Office Mgr., The Courier-Tribune, NC, Asheboro
Shaw, Susanne
sshaw@ku.edu, Exec. Dir., Accrediting Council on Education in Journalism and Mass Communications, KS, Lawrence
Shaw, Tom
tshaw@shawmedia.com, Pres./CEO, Shaw Media, IL, Dixon
Shaw, Kevin
kshaw@sbtinfo.com, Circ. Dir., Subscriber Servs./Alternate Delivery, South Bend Tribune, IN, South Bend
Shaw, Jim.......................310-540-5511 x6634
jim.shaw@dailybreeze.com, VP Advertising, Daily Breeze, CA, Torrance
Shaw, Jeremy
jshaw@new.rr.com, Web Page Ed., The Green Bay News-Chronicle, WI, Green Bay
Shaw-Lan, Wang
news@udn.com, Pub., MIN SHENG DAILY, Taipei
Shay, James............................(203) 330-6242
jshay@ctpost.com, Facility Mgr., Connecticut Post, CT, Bridgeport
Shea, Dan..............................(504) 826-3391
dshea@timespicayune.com, Mng. Ed., The Times Picayune, LA, New Orleans
Shea, Leslie...................................ext. 200
lshea@hutchnews.com, Adv. Dir., The Hutchinson News, KS, Hutchinson
Shea, Lorraine
jbarrett@timesonline.com, Mgr., Educ. Serv., Beaver County Times, PA, Beaver
Sheaffer, Pepper
judylane@earthlink.net, Bus. Mgr., Life in the Judy Lane, CA, San Diego
Sheaffer, Liz..........................(330) 721-4060
managed@ohio.net, Mng. Ed., The Medina County Gazette, OH, Medina
Shearer, Alan..........................(202) 334-6377
shearera@washpost.com, Editorial Dir./Gen. Mgr., The Washington Post Writers Group, DC, Washington
Shearer, Lisa
lshearer@edmondsun.com, News Ed., The Edmond Sun, OK, Edmond
Shearer, Michael
mshearer@nncogannett.com, Editorial Page Ed., The Advocate, OH, Newark
Shearman, Thomas B.
tshearman@americanpress.com, Pub., American Press, LA, Lake Charles
Shedd, Carl
publisher@adcom.net, Pres./Pub., Publitech, Inc., MA, Sherborn
Sheedy, Daniel
sales@printsoftamericas.com, Nat'l Sales Mgr., Printsoft Americas, Inc., IL, Itasca
Sheehan, Gayle
gsheehan@ledger.com, Exec. Office Mgr., The Patriot Ledger, MA, Quincy
Sheehan, Michael.......................(603) 594-6442
Circ. Mgr., The Telegraph, NH, Hudson
Sheehan, Mike..........................978-970-4855
msheehan @lowellsun.com, VP Circulation, The Sun, MA, Lowell
Sheehy, Candice
candicemcgrann@aol.com, Customer Serv. Rep., McGrann Paper Corp., NC, Charlotte
Sheeran, Pat..............(603) 668-4321 ext. 322
psheeran@unionleader.com, Mng. Ed., Opns., New Hampshire Union Leader/New Hampshire Sunday News, NH, Manchester
Sheets, Jocelyn
jocelynsheets@yahoo.com, Photo Ed., Iola Register, KS, Iola
Sheffield, Paulette...............................ext. 18
paulette@snpa.org, Office Mgr., Southern Newspaper Publishers Association, GA, Atlanta
Shelburne, Anita.......................(434) 978-7269

ashelburne@dailyprogress.com, Editorial Page Ed., The Daily Progress, VA, Charlottesville

Sheler, Patty
patty@ottowaherald.com, Prodn. Coord., Adv. Servs., The Ottawa Herald, KS, Ottawa

Shelnut, Adam ....(757) 247-7434
ashelnut@dailypress.com, Adv. Gen. Mgr., Automotive/Recruitment, Daily Press, VA, Newport News

Shelton, Clint ....(256) 340-2465
clint.shelton@decaturdaily.com, Gen. Mgr., The Decatur Daily, AL, Decatur

Shelton, David
classified@herald-citizen.com, Adv. Mgr., Herald-Citizen, TN, Cookeville

Shelton, Melinda......................(504) 520-5096
mshelton@xula.edu, Advisor, Xavier Univ. of Louisiana--Xavier Herald, LA, New Orleans

Shelton, Stacey........................(703) 878-8059
sshelton@potomacnews.com, Health Ed., Manassas Journal Messenger, VA, Manassas

Shelton, Barrett C.
barrett.shelton@decaturdaily.com, Pres./Pub., The Decatur Daily, AL, Decatur

Shelton, Heather
hshelton@times-standard.com, Lifestyle Ed., Times-Standard, CA, Eureka

Shelton, Clint
clint.shelton@decaturdaily.com, Gen. Mgr., Tennessee Valley Printing Co., Inc., AL, Decatur

Shelton Jr., Barrett C.
barrett.shelton@decaturdaily.com, Pres./Pub., Tennessee Valley Printing Co., Inc., AL, Decatur

Shemanske, Susan ....(262) 634-3322
sshemanske@journaltimes.com, Sports Ed., The Journal Times, WI, Racine

Shen, Jason...........................(650) 721-5801
Stanford Univ., CA, Stanford

Sheneman, Drew......................(973) 392-5937
dsheneman@starledger.com, Editorial Cartoonist, The Star-Ledger, NJ, Newark

Shepard, Ginger...............................ext. 273
Page Design Ed., The World, OR, Coos Bay

Shepard, III, T.R.......................(212) 969-7547
trshepard@hearst.com, Pres., King Features Syndicate, NY, New York
trshepard@hearst.com, Pres., North America Syndicate, NY, New York

Shepherd, Linda......................(617) 786-7324
lshepherd@ledger.com, Local News Ed., The Patriot Ledger, MA, Quincy

Shepherd, Patricia
patricia.shepherd@laopinion.com, Executive Assistant / Admin, La Opinion, CA, Los Angeles

Sheppard, Lesley ....(306) 691-1262
lsheppard@mjtimes.sk.ca, Mng. Ed., The Moose Jaw Times-Herald, SK, Moose Jaw

Sher, Gerald...........................(617) 619-6509
gsher@bostonherald.com, Circ. Mgr., Home Delivery, Boston Herald, MA, Boston

Sher, Louis Y.
care@kaidy.com, Owner/Pres., The Witzzle Co., TX, Plano

Sherblom, John C.
john@maine.edu, Chair/Prof., University of Maine, ME, Orono

Sherer, Valerie ....(256) 740-5755
valerie.sherer@timesdaily.com, News Asst., TimesDaily, AL, Florence

Sheridan, Sean
scs@campusclients.com, Pres., Campus Party, Inc., PA, Philadelphia

Sherih, Dmitry
post@spbvedomosti.ru, Ed. in Chief, SANKT-PETERBURGSKIYE VEDOMOSTI, Saint Petersburg

Sherk, Chris................(803) 329-4000 ext. 8390
csherk@heraldonline.com, News Ed., The Herald, SC, Rock Hill

Sherman, Brad................................ext. 33
bsherman@mydailytribune.com, Sports Ed., Gallipolis Daily Tribune, OH, Gallipolis

Sherman, Dan ....(775) 746-2946
dan@danshermanonline.com, Columnist, Dan Sherman's Humor Column, NV, Reno

Sherman, Charlie ....(404) 849-1086
Georgia Perimeter College, GA, Clarkston

Sherman, Darwin K. ....(319) 653-2191
pub@washjrnl.com, Ed., The Washington Evening Journal, IA, Washington

Shermeyer, Pam
Pam.Shermeyer@detroitnews.com, Online Content Dir., The Detroit News, MI, Detroit

Sherrill, Greg
gsherrill@tnpress.com, Exec. Dir., Tennessee Press Association, Inc., TN, Knoxville
gsherrill@tnpress.com, Exec. Dir., Tennessee Press Service, Inc., TN, Knoxville

Sherrill, Susan ....(973) 569-7075
Food Editor, North Jersey Media Group, NJ, Woodland Park

Sherry, Cheryl
csherry@appleton.gannett.com, Religion Ed., The Post-Crescent, WI, Appleton

Shertizinger, Bailey 850-561-1612
Editor-in-Chief, FSView & Florida Flambeau, FL, Tallahassee

Sherwin, Stuart
stuart.sherwin@qt.com.au, Ed., THE QUEENSLAND TIMES, West Ipswich

Sherwood, Courtney..................(360)735-4561
courtney.sherwood@columbian.com, Business/Features Editor, The Columbian, WA, Vancouver

Sheth, Suresh
indoresmschr@rediffmail.com, Pub., INDORE SAMACHAR, Indore, Madhya Pradesh

Shiba, Noriyuki
overseas@tks-net.co.jp, Pres., TKS Ltd., Tokyo

Shield, Fox
info@mzbern.ch, Ed., BERNER RUNDSCHAU/LANGENTHALER TAGBLATT, Langenthal, Bern

Shields, Grace.........................248-336-7300
gshields@rangerdata.com, Director of Marketing & Customer Service, Ranger Data Technologies Inc., MI, Royal Oak

Shields, Rose ....ext. 8083
rshields@phillyburbs.com, Photo Ed., Burlington County Times, NJ, Willingboro

Shields, Randall
rdshields@greenfieldreporter.com, Pub./Vice Pres., Daily Reporter, IN, Greenfield

Shifflet, Mark L.
dt4@evansville.edu, Prof./Chair, University of Evansville, IN, Evansville

Shillingburg, Dan
danshill@sourcenews.com, Vice Pres./Pub., The Daily Reporter

Shillings, Lauri
lauri@jrpress.com, Prodn. Mgr., Composing Room, Journal Review, IN, Crawfordsville

Shimizu, Hikaru
media@nishinippon.co.jp, Pres., NISHI-NIPPON SHIMBUN, Fukuoka, Kyushu

Shimojima, Andy.......................541-826-4832
andys@argusobserver.com, Adv. Mgr., Retail, Argus Observer, OR, Ontario

Shine, Tom ....(316) 268-6268
tshine@wichitaeagle.com, Deputy Ed., News, The Wichita Eagle, KS, Wichita

Shing, Fung Kon
merkk@tm.net.my, Ed. in Chief, MERDEKA DAILY NEWS, Sandakan, Sabah

Shingler, Mark
marks@wdtimes.com, Adv. Mgr., Classified, Watertown Daily Times, WI, Watertown

Shinn, Kami
ngadvertising@comcast.net, Pub., The News-Gazette, IN, Winchester

Shinske, Stuart ....(845) 437-4802
sshinske@poughkee.gannett.com, Exec. Ed., Poughkeepsie Journal, NY, Poughkeepsie

Shiplett, David H. ....(540) 574-6257
shiplett@dnronline.com, Prodn. Dir., Daily News-Record, VA, Harrisonburg

Shipley, Tonya ....(740) 450-6767
Educ. Ed., Times Recorder, OH, Zanesville

Shipman, Cheri........................(979) 458-1207
Texas A&M Univ., TX, College Station

Shipman, Gwen
gshipman@greenvillenews.com, Office Mgr., The Greenville News, SC, Greenville

Shipp, Glen ....(416) 847-2004
mjohnston@bbm.ca, Exec. Vice Pres./CFO, BBM Canada, ON, Toronto

Shirley, Loretta
advertising@taylordailypress.net, Adv. Dir., Taylor Daily Press, TX, Taylor

Shirley, Candice
classified@punxsutawneyspirit.com, Adv. Mgr., Classified, The Punxsutawney Spirit, PA, Punxsutawney

Shirley, Daniel.........................(478) 744-4227
dshirley@macon.com, Sports Ed., The Telegraph, GA, Macon

Shirley, Andy...........................(985) 384-8370
andy@daily-review.com, Gen. Mgr., Morgan City Newspapers LLC., LA, Morgan City

Shirley, Steve
steve@daily-review.com, News Ed., The Daily Review, LA, Morgan City

Shitut, Prashant B......................(570) 829-7158
prash@timesleader.com, Sr. Vice Pres., Opns., Times Leader, PA, Wilkes-Barre

Shivley, JoAnne............(770) 428-9411 ext. 350
Accounting Mgr., Marietta Daily Journal, GA, Marietta

Shmidheiser, Ken
kshmidheiser@somerset-kentucky.com, Grp. Ed., The Commonwealth-Journal, KY, Somerset

Shobe, James
jshobe@advertiser-tribune.com, Photo Ed., The Advertiser-Tribune, OH, Tiffin

Shockey, Dennis
advertising@therecordherald.com, Adv. Mgr., The Record Herald, PA, Waynesboro

Shoemaker, Gerald 518-395-3002
mailroom@dailygazette.net, Prodn. Foreman, Mailroom, The Daily Gazette, NY, Schenectady

Shoriki, Toru
webmaster@yomiuri.co.jp, Pub., YOMIURI SHIMBUN, Tokyo

Short, Nancy
satw@satw.org, Exec. Dir., Society of American Travel Writers, Inc., WI, Oak Creek

Short, Evelyn..........................(215) 361-8810
eshort@thereporteronline.com, Night Ed., The Reporter, PA, Lansdale

Short, James...........................(304) 367-2563
jeshort@timeswv.com, Prodn. Mgr., Times West Virginian, WV, Fairmont

Shorts, T. Mark ....ext. 296
mshorts@starbeacon.com, Circ. Mgr., Star Beacon, OH, Ashtabula

Shoults, Tim 250-371-6100
tshoults@kamloopsnews.ca, Publisher, Kamloops Daily News, BC, Kamloops

Showstack, Cheryl ....(508) 427-6856
cshowstack@enterprisenews.com, Circ. Coord., Newspapers in Educ., The Enterprise, MA, Randolph

Shrader, James E. ....(618) 463-2580
publisher@thetelegraph.com, Pub., The Telegraph, IL, Alton

Shrader, Greg..........................(936) 631-2602
gshrader@lufkindailynews.com, Pub., The Lufkin Daily News, TX, Lufkin

Shreve-Gilbert, Holly
shreve@oakland.edu, Co-Dir., Oakland University, MI, Rochester

Shrewsbury, Walt ....(843) 626-0363
wshrewsb@thesunnews.com, Prodn. Mgr., Packaging, The Sun News, SC, Myrtle Beach

Shrull, Dale
dshrull@postindependent.com, Mng. Ed., Glenwood Springs Post Independent, CO, Glenwood Springs

Shulda, David A. ....(949) 361-5167
Consultant, David A. Shulda Enterprises, Inc., CA, Fountain Valley

Shuler, Marsha
mshuler@theadvocate.com, Pres., National Federation of Press Women, VA, Arlington

Shull, Lindsay
lshull@nipublishing.net., Fin. Dir., Daily Chronicle, IL, DeKalb

Shults, Lana Sweeten ....(940) 720-3462
lshults@wf.scripps.com, Radio/Television Ed., Wichita Falls Times Record News, TX, Wichita Falls

Shum, Winifred........................(408) 542-2363
wshum@verity.com, PR Mgr., Verity, Inc., CA, Pleasanton

Shupac, Mark
mshupac@ctcsoftware.com, Contact, Catalyst International, Inc., WI, Milwaukee

Shupe, Andy ....(479) 571-6448
photo@nwarktimes.com, Photo Dept., Northwest Arkansas Times, AR, Fayetteville

Shurett, Brad
brad.shurett@dailysentinel.com, Pub., The Daily Sentinel, AL, Scottsboro

Shurley, Richard
rshurley@theadvocate.com, CTO, The Advocate, LA, Baton Rouge

Shurman, Mark.........................(727) 445-4144
mshurman@tampabay.com, Adv. Mgr., Tampa Bay Times, FL, Saint Petersburg

Shurtleff, Andrew ....(434) 978-7278
ashurtleff@dailyprogress.com, Chief Photographer, The Daily Progress, VA, Charlottesville

Siah, Francis
tribune@po.jaring.my, Ed., THE SARAWAK TRIBUNE/SUNDAY TRIBUNE, Kuching, Sarawak

Sian, Aw
info@singtao.com, Dir., SING TAO LI CHUNG, Hong Kong

Sian, Sally Aw
editorial@singtao.com.au, Dir., SING TAO JIH PAO, Sydney

Sibbet, Doug ....(403) 314-4302
circulation@reddeeradvocate.com, Circ. Supvr., Sales, Red Deer Advocate, AB, Red Deer

Sible, Nancy................(260) 347-0400 ext. 173
nancys@kpcnews.net, Mgr., HR, The News-Sun, IN, Kendallville

Sible, Nancy................(206) 347-0400 ext. 173
nancys@kpcnews.net, Mgr., HR, The Star, IN, Auburn

Sible, Nancy................(260) 347-0400 ext. 173
nancys@kpcnews.net, Mgr., HR, Herald-Republican, IN, Angola

Siburt, Debra ....(715) 845-0602
dsiburt@wdhprint.com, Librarian, The Wausau Daily Herald, WI, Wausau

Sickle, David...........................(570) 628-6150
dsickle@republicanherald.com, Dir., Circ., Republican Herald, PA, Pottsville

Sickle, David...........................(570) 628-6150
dsickle@republicanherald.com, Dir., Circ., The News-Item, PA, Shamokin

Sidaras, Christina ....(417) 268-6017
Baptist Bible College, MO, Springfield

Siddall, Pam ....(316) 268-6503
psiddall@wichitaeagle.com, Pres./Pub., The Wichita Eagle, KS, Wichita

Siddiqi, Mohammad
m-siddiqi@wiu.edu, Prof./Dir., Journ. Program/Advisor, PRSSA, Western Illinois University, IL, Macomb

Siddle, Ron ....(661) 267-4134
Photo Ed., Antelope Valley Press, CA, Palmdale

Siddons, Brad
bsiddons@lewistownsentinel.com, Online Mgr., The Sentinel, PA, Lewistown

Siddons, Mary Beth
info@snaponbusinesssolutions.com, Pres., Snap-on Business Solutions, OH, Richfield

Sidell, Katie...........................(989) 774-6682
editor@cm-life.com, Central Michigan Univ., MI, Mount Pleasant

Sidlo, Steve ....(937) 225-2224
ssidlo@coxohio.com, Mng. Ed., Dayton Daily News, OH, Dayton

Sidlo, Steve
ssidlo@coxohio.com, Pub., Springfield News-Sun, OH, Springfield

Sidlo, Paul
sales@rezn8.com, Pres., Rezn8 Productions, Inc., CA, Hollywood

Siebenaler, Joni...............................ext. 226
Circ. Dir., The News-Record, WY, Gillette

Siebler, Connie
info@internetigroup.com, Contact, Internet International Group, MO, Saint Louis

Siegel, Stephen
sbsiegel@uvps.com, Pres., UV Process Supply, Inc., IL, Chicago

Siegel, Randy ....(212) 450-0980 ext. 0980
randy_siegel@parade.com, Pres., Parade Publications, Inc. - New York, NY, NY, New York

Siegel, Gary ....(724) 537-3351 ext. 19
garysiegel1@verizon.net, Adv. Dir., The La-

trobe Bulletin, PA, Latrobe
Siegel, Debbie
debbie@bba-la.com, Adv Sales Rep., American Profile - Los Angeles, CA, CA, Los Angeles
Siegel, Marshall 972-238-6068
Adv. Mgr., Richland College, TX, Dallas
Siegler, Lucille ....(207) 780-4084
The Free PressUniv. of Southern Maine Student Newspaper, ME, Portland
Sieling, John
busdev@socialnet.com, Vice Pres., Sales, SocialNet, Inc., CA, Mountain View
Siemers, Mick ....(765) 420-5208
msiemers@journalandcourier.com, Circ. Dir., Journal and Courier, IN, Lafayette
Siemers, Linda ....(508) 427-4070
lsiemers@enterprisenews.com, Adv. Mgr., Classified, The Enterprise, MA, Randolph
Siemon, Kathy ....(216) 999-4027
Deputy Metro Editor, The Plain Dealer, OH, Cleveland
Sienkiewicz, Joe ....(920) 426-6632
Chief Photographer, Oshkosh Northwestern, WI, Oshkosh
Sierra, Ric..............................(813) 259-7473
Mgr., Human Resources, The Tampa Tribune, FL, Tampa
Sigale, Merwin ....(305) 237-2261
mdc.catalyst@gmail.com, Miami-Dade Cmty. College Kendall, FL, Miami
Sigel, Ellen..............................(212) 313-9044
esigel@alm.com, Vice Pres., Licensing/Bus. Devel., ALM, NY, New York
Sigg, Meinrad
info@rems-zeitung.de, Ed. in Chief, REMS-ZEITUNG, Schwabisch-Gmund
Sigler, Rob
editor@laurelleadercall.com, Ed., Laurel Leader-Call, MS, Laurel
Sigvardsson, Ola
privatannons@corren.se, Pub., OSTGOTA CORRESPONDENTEN, Linkoping
Sikop, David A. ....(413) 585-5200
rsikop@gazettenet.com, Adv. Mgr., Classified, Daily Hampshire Gazette, MA, Northampton
Silberman, Steve
ssilberman@statesmanjournal.com, Pub., Statesman Journal, OR, Salem
Silbernagel, Bob ....ext. 236
Editorial Page Ed., The Daily Sentinel, CO, Grand Junction
Siler, Steve J.
sales@hurletron.com, Gen. Mgr., Hurletron, Inc., IL, Libertyville
Sill, Melanie ....(919) 829-8986
msill@newsobserver.com, Sr. Vice Pres./Exec. Ed., The News & Observer, NC, Raleigh
Silliman, Sue
ssilliman@wehco.com, Gen. Mgr., Camden News, AR, Camden
Silva, Filomena
asemana@mail.cvtelecom.cv, Ed., A SEMANA, Praia
Silva, Matt..................(209) 369-2761 ext. 252
matts@lodinews.com, Mgr., Opns., Lodi News-Sentinel, CA, Lodi
Silver, Sheryl ....(954) 647-5995
sgsilver2002@yahoo.com, Owner/Author, Career Source/Column, FL, Hallandale
Silverberg, Melissa..................(217) 337-8343
Univ. of Illinois, IL, Champaign
Silverman, Rick ....(607) 255-0565
Cornell Law School, NY, Ithaca
Silvers, Gary ....ext. 4212
gsilvers@phillyburbs.com, Sports Ed., Bucks County Courier Times, PA, Levittown
Silverstein, Jeff
infoib@aol.com, Pub., Digital Information Group, CT, Stamford
Silverstein, Arthur
silverstein@siadvance.com, Controller, Staten Island Advance, NY, Staten Island
Silvester, J.A.
gm@telegraph.co.nz, Gen. Mgr., DAILY TELEGRAPH
Silvestri, Thomas A. ....(804) 649-6121
tsilvestri@timesdispatch.com, Pres./Pub., Richmond Times-Dispatch, VA, Richmond
Silvestrin, Debra
web@aan.org, Dir., Meetings/Special Projects, Association of Alternative Newsmedia, DC, Washington
Silvis, Wendy ....(440) 239-9000
info@thetotalmailroom.com, Sales/Mktg. Administrator, Total Mailroom Support, Inc. (TMSI), OH, Middleburg Heights
Simango, Charles
dailytimes@mailexcite.com, Ed. in Chief, DAILY TIMES, Blantyre
Simes, Libby..............................(701) 250-8202
libby@ndonline.com, Controller, The Bismarck Tribune, ND, Bismarck
Simmonds, Bob
bsimmonds@indexjournal.com, Web Page Ed., The Index-Journal, SC, Greenwood
Simmonds, Jason........................902-432-8211
jpsports@journalpioneer.com, Sports Ed., The Journal Pioneer, PE, Summerside
Simmons, Beau
sports@durantdemocrat.com, Sports Ed., Durant Daily Democrat, OK, Durant
Simmons, Nicole........................(508) 626-3923
nsimmon@cnc.com, Website Mgr., Milford Daily News, MA, Milford
Simmons, Chris ....(540) 574-6260
csimmons@dnronline.com, Sports Ed., Daily News-Record, VA, Harrisonburg
Simmons, Debra Adams ....(216) 999-4737
Editor, The Plain Dealer, OH, Cleveland
Simmons, Erin
esimmons@unionrecorder.com, Adv. Dir., The Union-Recorder, GA, Milledgeville
Simmons, Toni ....ext. 212
tsimmons@lagrangenews.com, Graphics Mgr., La Grange Daily News, GA, LaGrange
Simmons, Barb
barbsimmons@reviewatlas.com, Prodn. Mgr., Daily Review Atlas, IL, Monmouth
Simmons, Scott ....(310) 831-6227
info@livewireprod.com, Dir./Art Dir., Live Wire Productions, CA, Rancho Palos Verdes
Simmons, Tony ....(850) 747-5080
tsimmons@pcnh.com, Online Ed., The News Herald, FL, Panama City
Simoes, Renato..............................200-1234
atarde@atarde.com.br, Pres., A Tarde, Salvador, BA
Simon, Hiam..............................(212) 226-1940
lhiam1@aol.com, N. American Adv. Dir., The Jerusalem Post Foreign Service, Jerusalem
Simon, James
jsimon@mail.fairfield.edu, Chair/Fac., Fairfield University, CT, Fairfield
Simon, Carl ....(262) 634-3322
csimon@journaltimes.com, Prodn. Supvr., Pressroom, The Journal Times, WI, Racine
Simon, Celeste P.
csimon@stcloud.gannett.com, Adv. Mgr., Classified, St. Cloud Times, MN, Saint Cloud
Simon, Martin
martin.simon@dill.de, Proprietor/Adv. Mgr., DILL-ZEITUNG, Dillenburg
Simonnen, Helge
simon@vl.no, Ed., VART LAND, Oslo
Simons, Dan
dsimons@ljworld.com, Owner, WorldWest LLC, KS, Lawrence
Simons, Dolph.............................785-832-7159
simons@ljworld.com, The World Co.- Lawrence, Kan., Journal-World, KS, Lawrence
Simons, Dan...............................785-832-7176
dsimons@ljworld.com, The World Co.- Lawrence, Kan., Journal-World, KS, Lawrence
Simons, Dolph.............................785-832-7122
dsimonsjr@ljworld.com, Chairman, The World Co.- Lawrence, Kan., Journal-World, KS, Lawrence
Simons, Dan ....(785) 832-7176
dsimons@ljworld.com, Pres., Electronics Div., The World Co.- Lawrence, Kan., Journal-World, KS, Lawrence
Simons, Dolph.............................785-832-7122
dsimonsjr@ljworld.com, Editor, The World Co.- Lawrence, Kan., Journal-World, KS, Lawrence
Simons, Dolph C. ....(785) 832-7123
dsimonsjr@ljworld.com, Editor and Chairman, The World Co.- Lawrence, Kan., Journal-World, KS, Lawrence
Simons, Patricia ....(803) 329-4053
psimons@heraldonline.com, Prodn. Dir., The Herald, SC, Rock Hill
Simons, Dolph C. ....(785) 832-7159
simons@ljworld.com, Pres., Newspapers Div., The World Co.- Lawrence, Kan., Journal-World, KS, Lawrence
Simons, Dolph C.
simons@ljworld.com, Co-Mgr., WorldWest LLC, KS, Lawrence
Simpson, Shannon....................(306) 657-6387
ssimpson@sp.canwest.com, Circ. Dir., The StarPhoenix, SK, Saskatoon
Simpson, Rande
rsimpson@merlinone.com, Merlin Senior Account Representative, MerlinOne, Inc., MA, Quincy
Simpson, Les
les.simpson@amarillo.com, Pub., Amarillo Globe-News, TX, Amarillo
Simpson, Marie ....(708) 488-5106
Dominican Univ., IL, River Forest
Simpson, Roseann
rasimpso@poughkee.gannett.com, Asst. to Pub., Poughkeepsie Journal, NY, Poughkeepsie
Simpson, Larry...........................270-781-1700
lsimpson@bgdailynews.com, Prodn. Mgr., Daily News, KY, Bowling Green
Simpson, Theresa.......................(559) 735-3305
circulation@visaliatimesdelta.com, Circ. Distr. Mgr., Visalia Times-Delta & Tulare Advance-Register, CA, Visalia
Simpson, Julie
jsimpson@nevadadailymail.com, Pub., The Nevada Weekend Herald-Tribune, MO, Nevada
jsimpson@nevadadailymail.com, Pub., The Nevada Daily Mail, MO, Nevada
Simpson, Richard.......................(919) 962-5177
Prof., University of North Carolina, NC, Chapel Hill
Sims, Edward H. ....(941) 366-2169
Ed./Pub., Editor's Copy Syndicate, FL, Sarasota
Sims, Patsy
patsy1@pitt.edu, Coord., University of Pittsburgh, PA, Pittsburgh
Simson, Cynthia.........................(413) 788-1214
csumison@repub.com, Mng. Ed., Special Projects, The Republican, MA, Springfield
Simunek, Petr
petr.simunek@economia.cz, Ed. in Chief, HOSPODARSKE NOVINY, Prague
Sin, Tenny
sales@umax.com, Vice Pres., Mktg., UMAX Technologies, Inc., TX, Dallas
Sin Teck, Goh
gohst@sph.com.sg, Editor, Lianhe Zaobao, LIANHE ZAOBAO, Singapore
Sinclair, Gordon ....(204) 697-7255
Gordon.Sinclair@freepress.mb.ca, Columnist, Winnipeg Free Press, MB, Winnipeg
Sinclair, Paula...........................416-869-4046
psinclair@torstar.ca, CIO, Metroland & Star Media Group, Group IT, Torstar Corporation, Toronto Star, ON, Toronto
Sindleri, Steve...........................(814) 532-5180
Prodn. Dir., The Tribune-Democrat, PA, Johnstown
Sines, Scott ....(901) 529-5843
sines@commercialappeal.com, Mng. Ed., The Commercial Appeal, TN, Memphis
Singer, Jane B.
jane-singer@uiowa.edu, Pres., Kappa Tau Alpha National Honor Soc. for Journ. & Mass Comm., MO, Columbia
Singer, Dr. Jane B.
jane-singer@uiowa.edu, Pres., Kappa Tau Alpha National Honor Soc. for Journ. & Mass Comm., MO, Columbia
Singer, Drew ....(412) 648-7985
Univ. of Pittsburgh, PA, Pittsburgh
Singh, Guna
neditordttry@gmail.com, Ed., DAILY THANTHI, Tiruchirapalli, Tamil Nadu
Singh, Suresh
ajvaranasi@rediffmail.com, Circ. Mgr., AJ, Varanasi, Uttar Pradesh
Singh, Gurmit
ajit@jla.vsnl.net.in, Circ. Mgr., AJIT, Jullundur, Punjab
Singh, Prabhat
editor@brn.amarujala.com, Ed., AMAR UJALA, Bareilly, Uttar Pradesh
Singh Chouan, Daulat
info@rajasthanpatrika.com, Ed., RAJASTHAN PATRIKA, Jodhpur, Rajasthan
Singletary, James Grady ....ext. 3035
gsingletary@mailtribune.com, Pub., The Ashland Daily Tidings, OR, Ashland
Singletary, James Grady
gsingletary@dailytidings.com, Pub., Mail Tribune, OR, Medford
Singleton, William Dean.............(303) 954-1959
deansingleton@medianewsgroup.com, Vice Chrmn./CEO, MediaNews Group Inc, CO, Denver
Singleton, David 305-292-7777
dsingleton@keysnews.com, Advertising Director, The Key West Citizen, FL, Key West
Sinha, Arun
navhind@navhindtimes.com, Ed. in Chief, NAVHIND TIMES, Panaji, Panjim
Sinnett, David ....(850) 522-5136
dsinnett@pcnh.com, IT Servs., The News Herald, FL, Panama City
Sinno, Abdul Karim
abdul.sinno@clarke.edu, Chair, Clarke College, IA, Dubuque
Sirany, Adrienne ....(612) 673-4076
adrienne.sirany@startribune.com, Vice President, HR, Star Tribune, MN, Minneapolis
Sirotsky, Nelson Pacheco..................3218-4400
editorias@zerohora.com.br, Pres., Zero Hora, Porto Alegre, Rio Grande do Sul
Sissing, Mike ....ext. 260
woodstockcirc@bowesnet.com, Circ. Mgr, The Sentinel-Review, ON, Woodstock
Sivitz, Adam ....(909) 607-1647
Claremont McKenna College, CA, Claremont
Sivret, Tom ....ext. 1162
tom.sivret@timesargus.com, News Ed., The Times Argus, VT, Barre
Siwicki, Richard
rsiwicki@screenusa.com, Application Support Mgr., SCREEN (USA), IL, Rolling Meadows
Sizemore, Almetha
asizemore@cnhi.com, Bus. Mgr., The Claremore Daily Progress, OK, Claremore
Sizemore, Melisa ....(770) 535-6344
msizemore@gainesvilletimes.com, Adv. Supvr., New Bus.Devel., The Times, GA, Gainesville
Sjogren, Erika ....(847) 317-8155
Trinity International Univ., IL, Deerfield
Skaggs, Steve ....(352) 365-8240
Adv. Dir., The Daily Commercial, FL, Leesburg
Skaggs, Steve 336-249-3981
steve.skaggs@the-dispatch.com, Publisher, The Dispatch, NC, Lexington
Skaggs, Mary ....(941) 206-1005
mskaggs@sun-herald.com, Mgr., HR, Charlotte Sun, FL, Charlotte Harbor
Skalkos, Theo
greek@foreignlanguage.com.au, Pub., GREEK HERALD, Glebe
Skeels, Dave..............................609-272-7123
dskeels@pressofac.com, User Support Manager, The Press of Atlantic City, NJ, Pleasantville
Skelton, Matt
press@wayneindependent.com, Production Mgr., The Wayne Independent, PA, Honesdale
Skidmore, Linda
lhskidmore@theintermountain.com, Ed., The Inter-Mountain, WV, Elkins
Skinner, Winston
winston@newnan.com, Assignment Ed., The Times-Herald, GA, Newnan
Skinner, Mary Ann ....(631) 843-2335
Asst. Mng. Ed., Admin., Newsday, NY, Melville
Skinner, Anne.................................90220543
anne.skinner@kalminer.com.au, Editor, KALGOORLIE MINER
Skipper, Mike
mskipper@robesonian.com, Prodn. Mgr., Pressroom, The Robesonian, NC, Lumberton
Skipper, Debbie 601-961-7101
dskipper@jackson.gannett.com, Asst. Managing Editor/News & Business, The Clarion-Ledger, MS, Jackson
Skoch, Tom..................(440)245-6901 ext. 536
tskoch@morningjournal.com, Ed., The Morn-

ing Journal, OH, Lorain
Skog, Dave ....(520) 807-8465
dskog@azstarnet.com, Radio/Television Ed., Arizona Daily Star, AZ, Tucson
Skoglund, Dennis ....(413) 585-5335
dskoglund@gazettenet.com, Circ. Dir., Daily Hampshire Gazette, MA, Northampton
Skonie, Marissa
mskonie@st.kishwaukeecollege.edu, Ed. In Chief, Kishwaukee College, IL, Malta
Skoog, Herb
sales@decisionmark.com, Vice Pres., Opns., Decisionmark Corp., IA, Cedar Rapids
Skotnicki, Monica
mskotnicki@tribune.com, Dir., Features, Tribune Media Services, CA, Los Angeles
Skoulika, V.
kagoris@proinoslogos.gr, Gen. Mgr., PROINOS LOGOS, Ioannina, Epirus
Skoyteris, Chris
korimera@otenet.gr, Pub., KORINTHIAKI IMERA, Korinthos, Peloponnese
Skrdlant, Tammy ....(308) 233-9728
Regl. Ed., Kearney Hub, NE, Kearney
Skufca, Sherry........................(260) 461-8201
sskufca@jg.net, Mng. Ed., The Journal Gazette, IN, Fort Wayne
Skulimma, Peter
peter.skulimma@berlinzeitung.de, Bus. Mgr., BERLINER ZEITGUNG, Berlin
Skupinska, Bozena
kpkurier@kurier.pl, Ed., Kurier Polski Sp. zo.o., Warsaw
Skwarczek, David
streams@streams.com, Pres., Dunn Solutions Group, IL, Skokie
Skyberg, Carol........................(865) 220-5540
cskyberg@oakridger.com, Bus. Mgr., The Oak Ridger, TN, Oak Ridge
Slaattelid, Kari
kari@avisa-valdres.no, Mgr., VALDRES, Fagernes
Slabaugh, Ryan ....(530) 542-8009
rslabaugh@tahoedailytribune.com, Exec. Ed., Tahoe Daily Tribune, CA, South Lake Tahoe
Slack, John D. ....(407) 628-1755 ext. 111
js@mediadesigngroup.com, CEO, Media Design Group, FL, Winter Park
Slagle, Kerry ....(816) 581- 7340
kslagle@amuniversal.com, Pres., Universal Uclick International Divison, MO, Kansas City
kslagle@amuniversal.com, Vice Pres., Int'l Sales, Universal Uclick, MO, Kansas City
Slagle, Steve ....(972) 258-3090
steves@ppa.org, Pres./CEO, Promotional Products Association International, TX, Irving
Slanchik, John
inquire@kepes.com, Mktg. Mgr., Kepes, Inc., WI, Kenosha
Slat, Charles..................................ext. 313
cslat@monroenews.com, Bus. Ed., The Monroe Evening News, MI, Monroe
Slater, Mitch
staff@earmark.com, Pres., Earmark, CT, Hamden
Slater, Brad ....(605) 394-8301
brad.slater@rapidcityjournal.com, Pub., Rapid City Journal, SD, Rapid City
Slater, Nick............................(847) 491-3924
Kellogg Grad. School of Mgmt., IL, Evanston
Slater, Nathan ....(208) 239-3143
nslater@journalnet.com, Circ. Dir., Idaho State Journal, ID, Pocatello
Slattery, Jim
james.slattery@prnewswire.com, CIO, PR Newswire - New York, NY, NY, New York
Slattery, Jack
jacks@americanultraviolet.com, Sales Rep., American Ultraviolet Co., Inc., IN, Lebanon
Slattery Hall, Kathleen..............(408) 920-5095
kslattery@mercurynews.com, Vice Pres., HR/Labor, San Jose Mercury News, CA, San Jose
Slavin, David ....(973) 729-7299
David8371@aol.com, Senior Associate- Mid-Atlantic/Southeast, Grimes, W.B. & Co., MD, Gaithersburg
Slavin, David
dslavin@mediamergers.com, Southeast/Mid-Atlantic Assoc., Grimes, W.B. & Co., NJ, Sparta
Slayton, Jack
jacks@xtn.net, Sports Ed., The Daily Post-Athenian, TN, Athens
Sledge, Alice
asledge@hawaiitribune-herald.com, Adv. Dir., Hawaii Tribune-Herald, HI, Hilo
Slevin, Jonathan
jslevin@washingtontimes.com, Acting Pres./Pub., The Washington Times, DC, Washington
Sloan, Stephan ....(401) 454-3130
scs@scsloan.com, Assoc., Media Services Group, Inc., FL, Jacksonville Beach
Sloca, John ....(262) 656-6321
jsloca@kenoshanews.com, Asst. Mng. Ed., Nights, Kenosha News, WI, Kenosha
Slotkin, Jason ....(360) 867-6213
The Evergreen State College, WA, Olympia
Sly, Judy..............................(209) 578-2317
jsly@modbee.com, Editorial Page Ed., The Modesto Bee, CA, Modesto
Small, Andrew.........................(334) 712-7953
asmall@dothaneagle.com, Asst. Mng. Ed., The Dothan Eagle, AL, Dothan
Small, Len Robert....................(815) 937-3399
Pub., The Daily Journal, IL, Kankakee
Small, B.J. ....(717) 334-1131 ext. 245
editor@gburgtimes.com, Ed., Gettysburg Times, PA, Gettysburg
Small, Len ....(815) 937-3399
President, Small Newspaper Group Inc, IL, Kankakee
Smalley, John ....(608) 252-6104
jsmalley@madison.com, Ed., Wisconsin State Journal, WI, Madison
Smalley, Richard.....................(403) 314-4373
rsmalley@reddeeradvocate.com, Adv. Mgr., Major Accts., Red Deer Advocate, AB, Red Deer
Smart, Jim ....(909) 537-7429
California State Univ., CA, San Bernardino
Smathers, Randal.........(802) 747-6121 ext. 2279
randal.smathers@rutlandherald.com, Ed., Rutland Herald, VT, Rutland
Smidt, Mark
dgcsmidt@dailygate.com, Pub., Daily Gate City, IA, Keokuk
Smigrod, Dan ....(404) 303-7311
dan@greattv.com, CEO/Chief Creative Officer, GREAT!, GA, Atlanta
Smilie, Jim..............................(318) 487-6348
jsmilie@thetowntalk.com, Audience Development Director, The Town Talk, LA, Alexandria
Smilovitz, Jacob......................(734) 647-3336
Univ. of Michigan, MI, Ann Arbor
Smist, Erik
erik.smist@baltsun.com, Controller, The Baltimore Sun, MD, Baltimore
Smith, Claudia........................(212) 969-7542
cmsmith@hearst.com, Dir., Adv./Pub. Rel., King Features Syndicate, NY, New York
cmsmith@hearst.com, Adv./PR Dir., North America Syndicate, NY, New York
Smith, Sandra (Sissy) ....ext. 220
display@t-g.com, Display Adv. Mgr., Shelbyville Times-Gazette, TN, Shelbyville
Smith, Richard D.......................703 462 2700
RSmith@newsusa.com, Pres./CEO, News USA, Inc., VA, Falls Church
Smith, Edward ....(303) 820-1789
esmith@denverpost.com, Entertainment Ed., The Denver Post, CO, Denver
Smith, Michael
moreinfo@talx.com, Vice Pres., Market Devel., TALX Corp., MO, Saint Louis
Smith, Kenneth P. ....(800) 533-4579
kensmith@issisvs.com, Pres., Insurance Specialties Services, Inc., PA, Jamison
Smith, Mark.............................(510) 985-1175
info@movingbytes.com, Pres., Moving Bytes, CA, Emeryville
Smith, Clark
publisher@helena-arkansas.com, Pub., The Daily World, AR, Helena
Smith, Michael
moreinfo@talx.com, Vice Pres., Market Devel., TALX Corp., MO, Saint Louis
Smith, Daryl C.............(519) 344-3641 ext. 2242
dsmith@theobserver.ca, Pub., Observer, ON, Sarnia
Smith, Leo 310-540-5511 x6617
leo.smith@dailybreeze.com, Features Editor, Daily Breeze, CA, Torrance
Smith, Colleen
colleen.almeida@tulsaworld.com, Night Ed., Tulsa World, OK, Tulsa
Smith, Rick
aln97@apk.net, Ed., Akron Legal News, 60 S. Summit St.
Smith, Kenneth J. ....(814) 643-4040
ksmith@huntingdondailynews.com, Purchasing Agent, The Daily News, PA, Huntingdon
Smith, Evan
evan.smith@ads24.co.za, Adv. Mgr., DIE BURGER, Cape Town, Western Cape
Smith, Cindy ....(615) 259-8098
csmith@tennessean.com, Asst. Mng. Ed., Davidson A.M., The Tennessean, TN, Nashville
Smith, Justin..........................(208) 239-3150
jtsmith@journalnet.com, Dir., Info Tech Servs., Idaho State Journal, ID, Pocatello
Smith, Steve ....(417) 837-1937
ssmith@news-leader.com, Prodn. Mgr., Pressroom, Springfield News-Leader, MO, Springfield
Smith, Thomas R.
sales@gazettepublishingco.com, Pres./Pub., The Bellevue Gazette, OH, Bellevue
Smith, Clark
editor@stuttgartdailyleader.com, Pub., Stuttgart Daily Leader, AR, Stuttgart
Smith, Michael R.
smithm@campbell.edu, Chair, Campbell University, NC, Buies Creek
Smith, Kathy
csmith@lfpress.com, Adv. Mgr., Classified, The London Free Press, ON, London
Smith, Melissa
melissa@chanute.com, Asst. Mng. Ed., The Chanute Tribune, KS, Chanute
Smith, Rick
rsnama@wi.rr.com, Owner, Nama Graphics E, LLC, IL, Homer Glen
Smith, Dona H. ....(337) 824-3011
jdnpublisher@bellsouth.net, Pub., Jennings Daily News, LA, Jennings
Smith, Paula...................................ext. 254
p.smith@thedailyitemoflynn.com, Adv. Coord., The Daily Item, MA, Lynn
Smith, Malcolm 9921 1200
manager@geraldtonguardian.com.au, Gen. Mgr., GERALDTON GUARDIAN
Smith, Betty
bsmith@dailyastorian.com, Adv. Mgr., The Daily Astorian, OR, Astoria
Smith, Kevin..............(626) 962-8811 ext. 2701
kevin.smith@sgvn.com, Bus. Ed., The Whittier Daily News, CA, Whittier
Smith, Daniel ....(440) 245-6901 ext. 535
djpsmith@morningjournal.com, Television Ed., The Morning Journal, OH, Lorain
Smith, Todd M.
news@caledonian-record.com, Editorial Page Ed., The Caledonian-Record, VT, Saint Johnsbury
Smith, William ....(928) 556-2292
Prodn. Mgr., Pressroom, Arizona Daily Sun, AZ, Flagstaff
Smith, Max..............................(406) 791-1453
maxsmith@greatfal.gannett.com, Adv. Dir., Great Falls Tribune, MT, Great Falls
Smith, Ellen............................(419) 521-7206
ecsmith@nncogannett.com, Librarian, News Journal, OH, Mansfield
Smith, Anthony ....(309) 686-3258
asmith@pjstar.com, City Ed., Night, Journal Star, IL, Peoria
Smith, Griffin ....(501) 378-3610
Exec. Ed., Arkansas Democrat-Gazette, AR, Little Rock
Smith, Tyson
tyson@readinghorizons.com, Pres., HEC Reading Horizons, UT, North Salt Lake
Smith, Kevin ....(816) 271-8620
kevins@npgco.com, Circ. Dir., St. Joseph News-Press, MO, Saint Joseph
Smith, Danny P.
dannyp@cdispatch.com, Asst. Sports Ed., The Commercial Dispatch, MS, Columbus
Smith, Cynthia........................(804) 649-6743
cgsmith@timesdispatch.com, Credit Mgr., Richmond Times-Dispatch, VA, Richmond
Smith, Carl ....(662) 325-7905
Mississippi State Univ., MS, Mississippi State
Smith, Andrew
asmith@gympietimes.com, Gen. Mgr., THE GYMPIE TIMES
Smith, Jeff ....(818) 240-1000
Glendale Cmty. College, CA, Glendale
Smith, Ron
editor@recordgazette.net, Record Gazette, CA, Yucaipa
editor@recordgazette.net, Prodn. Dir., Opns., The News Herald, FL, Panama City
Smith, Barbara
basmith@messenger-inquirer.com, Adv. Mgr., Servs., Messenger-Inquirer, KY, Owensboro
Smith, William P. ....(540) 374-5470
bsmith@freelancestar.com, Adv. Dir., The Free Lance-Star, VA, Fredericksburg
Smith, Michael J. ....(865) 908-4368
mjsmith@xtn.net, Vice Pres., Tourism, Jones Media, Inc., TN, Greeneville
Smith, Larry
lsmith@dancomnews.com, Ed., Commercial News, IL, Danville
Smith, Jon
smith_jo@suu.edu, Chair, Southern Utah University, UT, Cedar City
Smith, Sandy ....(231) 779-4133
ssmith@cadillacnews.com, Mgr., Bus./Personnel, Cadillac News, MI, Cadillac
Smith, Amy..............................(540) 213-9173
asmith@newsleader.com, Adv. Servs. Mgr., The News Leader, VA, Staunton
Smith, Todd ....(802) 748-8121
smitht@caledonian-record.com, Publisher/Vice President, The Caledonian-Record, VT, Saint Johnsbury
Smith, Dave.............................(765) 420-5295
dsmith@journalandcourier.com, Enterprise Ed., Journal and Courier, IN, Lafayette
Smith, Rosie830-980-2860/603-444-7141/802-748-8121
chalouxr@caledonian-record.com, Educ. Services Director, The Caledonian-Record, VT, Saint Johnsbury
Smith, Barry
nvpress@callatg.com, Exec. Dir., Nevada Press Association, Inc., NV, Carson City
Smith, Thomas C.....................(804) 775-2704
tsmith@timesdispatch.com, Circ. Mgr., Metro, Richmond Times-Dispatch, VA, Richmond
Smith, Nicole ....(507) 389-5454
Minnesota State Univ. Mankato, MN, Mankato
Smith, Bruce K.
bsmith@hjnews.com, Pres./Pub., The Herald Journal, UT, Logan
Smith, J W
tcma@texascma.org, Sec./Treasurer, Texas Circulation Management Association, TX, Houston
Smith, Tim D...........................(812) 331-4203
tsmith@heraldt.com, Circ. Dir., The Herald-Times, IN, Bloomington
Smith, Ron
rsmith@dmg.gannett.com, Operations Dir., The Daily Times, MD, Salisbury
Smith, George
gsmith731@aol.com, Columnist, The Anniston Star, AL, Anniston
Smith, Gayle
gjsmith@gannett.com, Adv. Dir., The Asheville Citizen-Times, NC, Asheville
Smith, R. Ashley ....(208) 735-3251
ashley.smith@lee.net, Photo Dept. Mgr., The Times-News, ID, Twin Falls
Smith, Ron ....(812) 254-0480 ext. 114
rsmith@washtimesherald.com, Pub., The Washington Times-Herald, IN, Washington
Smith, Steve ....(413) 788-1303
City Ed., Day, The Republican, MA, Springfield
Smith, Jim
jsmith@scity.com, Nat'l Sales Mgr., Steel City Corp., OH, Ashland
Smith, Mark M.830-980-2860/603-444-7141/802-748-8121
smithm@caledonian-record.com, Pres., The Caledonian-Record, VT, Saint Johnsbury
Smith, Rachael
editor@nyunews.com, New York Univ., NY, New York
Smith, Becky...........................(937) 498-5980
bsmith@sdnccg.com, Adv. Dir., The Sidney

Daily News, OH, Sidney
Smith, Jim ....(530) 406-6230
news@dailydemocrat.com, Ed., The Daily Democrat, CA, Woodland
Smith, Venetta..........................(212) 969-7539
vsmith@hearst.com, Domestic Sales Coord., King Features Syndicate, NY, New York
vsmith@hearst.com, Domestic Sales Coord., North America Syndicate, NY, New York
Smith, Carol
csmith@sbtinfo.com, Adv. Dir., South Bend Tribune, IN, South Bend
Smith, Jeff
info@beltingindustries.com, Sales Mgr., Belting Industries Co., Inc., NJ, Kenilworth
Smith, Bart
bsmith@greeleytribune.com, Pub., Greeley Daily Tribune, CO, Greeley
Smith, Randy ....(204) 571-7408
rsmith@brandonsun.com, Prodn. Foreman, Pressroom, Brandon Sun, MB, Brandon
Smith, Cory ....ext. 252
Sports Ed., The Sentinel-Review, ON, Woodstock
Smith, Melanie.........................(256) 304-2468
melanie.smith@decaturdaily.com, Religion Ed., The Decatur Daily, AL, Decatur
Smith, Ken
klsmith@uwyo.edu, Chair, University of Wyoming, WY, Laramie
Smith, Deneen..........................(262) 656-6287
dsmith@kenoshanews.com, Bus. Writer, Kenosha News, WI, Kenosha
Smith, Clark
hopestar71802@yahoo.com, Pub., Hope Star, AR, Hope
Smith, Christine................................ext. 154
csmith@batavianews.com, Circ. Dir., The Daily News, NY, Batavia
Smith, Kurt.......................................ext. 266
ksmith@njherald.com, Pressroom Foreman, New Jersey Herald, NJ, Newton
Smith, Steve
ssmith@thereporter.com, Pub., The Reporter, CA, Vacaville
Smith, Sean
ssmith@jrpress.com, Pub., Journal Review, IN, Crawfordsville
Smith, Janet..........(843) 706-8114 ext. 8114
jsmith@islandpacket.com, Editorial Page Ed., The Island Packet, SC, Bluffton
Smith, Deirdre Parker................(704) 792-4252
dp1@salisburypost.com, Books Ed., Salisbury Post, NC, Salisbury
Smith, Ceil
csmith@sjnewsco.com, Pub., Today's Sunbeam, NJ, Salem
Smith, Debbie...........................(716) 645-2152
SUNY/Buffalo, NY, Buffalo
Smith, Austin L..........................(937) 225-2479
asmith@coxohio.com, Vice Pres., Circ., Dayton Daily News, OH, Dayton
Smith, Martha
msmith@tribweb.com, Exec. Asst. to Pres., Tribune-Review, PA, Pittsburgh
Smith, Julian C. S......................64 3 477 4760
corporate@alliedpress.co.nz, Managing Director, OTAGO DAILY TIMES
Smith, James....................................ext. 282
Exec. Ed., Parkersburg News & Sentinel, WV, Parkersburg
Smith, Kris ....(815) 987-1462
kasmith@rockford.gannett.com, Prodn. Dir., Rockford Register Star, IL, Rockford
Smith, Michael A.
michael.smith@galvnews.com, Assoc. Ed., The Galveston County Daily News, TX, Galveston
Smith, Kyle..................(530) 672-6440 ext. 220
Vice Pres., Opns., CBS MaxPreps, Inc., CA, Cameron Park
Smith, Val ....(916) 278-5340
valsmith@saclink.csus.edu, Chair, California State University, Sacramento, CA, Sacramento
Smith, Peter ....(502) 582-4469
psmith@courier-journal.com, Religion Writer, The Courier-Journal, KY, Louisville
Smith, Mike
advertising@guardonline.com, Adv. Dir./Promo. Mgr., Batesville Guard, AR, Batesville
Smith, Donald S........................(308) 381-9410
donald.smith@theindependent.com, Pub./Pres., The Grand Island Independent, NE, Grand Island
Smith, Brenda ....(801) 237-2192
bsmith@desnews.com, NIE Ed., Deseret News, UT, Salt Lake City
Smith, Gregory C.
gsmith@admediapartners.com, Managing Director, AdMedia Partners, Inc., NY, New York
Smith, Donald
publisher@theintermountain.com, Pub., The Inter-Mountain, WV, Elkins
Smith, Gail..................................843-937-5405
Ad Director, The Post and Courier, SC, Charleston
Smith, Steve
ssmith@timesheraldonline.com, Pub., Vallejo Times-Herald, CA, Vallejo
Smith, Samuel
samuel.smith@smail.astate.edu, Student Editor, Arkansas State Univ., AR, State University
Smith, Angela ....(706) 208-2288
angela.smith@onlineathens.com, Adv. Dir., Athens Banner-Herald, GA, Athens
Smith, Art ....(304) 485-1891
asmith@oweb.com, Online Mgr., The Marietta Times, OH, Marietta
Smith, Richard ....(703) 734-6300
rsmith@newsusa.com, CEO, News USA, Inc., VA, Falls Church
Smith, Dennis A.
dsmith@eaglenewspapers.com, Chrmn., Eagle Newspapers, Inc., OR, Salem
Smith, Patricia ....(479) 571-6459
patricias@nwarktimes.com, Admin. Asst., Northwest Arkansas Times, AR, Fayetteville
Smith, R. Terry
tsmith@mdjonline.com, Pres., Times-Journal, Inc., GA, Marietta
Smith, Steven A. ....(805) 437-0450
ssmith@venturacountystar.com, Circ. Vice Pres., Opns., Ventura County Star, CA, Camarillo
Smith, Jean
editor@siskiyoudaily.com, Circ. Mgr., Siskiyou Daily News, CA, Yreka
Smith, Michael J.................................ext. 217
msmith@thewesterlysun.com, Circ. Dir., The Westerly Sun, RI, Westerly
Smith, Jacqueline.....................(203) 731-3369
Managing Editor, The News-Times, CT, Danbury
Smith, Casey.............................(206) 543-2700
Univ. of Washington, WA, Seattle
Smith, Mike ....ext. 43
msmith@stategazette.com, Sports Ed., State Gazette, TN, Dyersburg
Smith, Rex ....(518) 454-5040
rsmith@timesunion.com, Ed./Vice Pres., Times Union, NY, Albany
Smith, Kevin
kevin.smith@leaderpub.com, Adv. Dir., Dowagiac Daily News, MI, Dowagiac
Smith, Linda
lindasmith@rrdailyherald.com, Office Mgr., Daily Herald, NC, Roanoke Rapids
Smith, Bernice
bernice.mcalpinesmith@demopolistimes.com, Gen. Mgr., Demopolis Times, AL, Demopolis
Smith, Ronald D.
smithrd@buffalostate.edu, Chair, Buffalo State College, NY, Buffalo
Smith-Hupp, Karen ....(301) 934-2251
College of Southern Maryland, MD, La Plata
Smitherman, Lamar
osmitherman@morganton.com, Pub., The News Herald, NC, Morganton
Smitherman, Lamar
news@mcdowellnews.com, Pub., The McDowell News, NC, Marion
Smoot, Elizabeth ....(540) 465-5137 ext. 156
esmoot@nvdaily.com, Gen. Mgr., Northern Virginia Daily, VA, Strasburg
Smoots MD, Elizabeth S. ....(425) 486-9131
doctor@practicalprevention.com, Self-Syndicator, Elizabeth S. Smoots, WA, Seattle
Smothers, Jim
jsmothers@dailyhome.com, Webpage Coord., The Daily Home, AL, Talladega
Smyth, Joe
jsmyth@newszap.com, Chrmn. of the Bd./CEO, Independent Newspapers, Inc. (DE), DE, Dover
Smythe, Harvey
info@htshealthcare.com, Mng. Dir./Vice Pres., HTS Interactive Health Care, OR, Portland
Snead, Brett..............................(402) 444-1425
brett.snead@owh.com, Adv. Mgr., Auto Sales, Omaha World-Herald, NE, Omaha
Sneed, Mitch 770-942-6571
Editor, Douglas County Sentinel, GA, Douglasville
Sneed, Jo Ann ....(417) 837-1127
jsneed@news-leader.com, Prodn. Supvr., Composing (Day), Springfield News-Leader, MO, Springfield
Sneed, Mitch
msneed@starexponent.com, Pub., Culpeper Star-Exponent, VA, Culpeper
Sneider, Andrew........................(405) 878-5441
St. Gregory's College, OK, Shawnee
Snelgrove, Stephen....................(604) 605-2615
ssnelgrove@png.canwest.com, Weekend Review Ed., The Vancouver Sun, BC, Vancouver
Snellings, Tom..............(703) 368-3101 ext. 140
tsnellings@potomacnews.com, Circ. Mgr., News & Messenger, VA, Woodbridge
Snider, Marie ....(316) 283-2309
thisside60@aol.com, Self-Syndicator, This Side of 60, KS, North Newton
Snider, Betty ....(540) 374-5427
bsnider@freelancestar.com, Assistant Managing Editor, The Free Lance-Star, VA, Fredericksburg
Snijder, Hans 058-2845406
hans.snijder@lc.nl, editor in chief, LEEUWARDER COURANT, Leeuwarden
Snodgress, David ....(812) 331-4365
dsnodgress@heraldt.com, Photo Dept. Mgr., The Herald-Times, IN, Bloomington
Snow, John
infous@enigma.com, Vice Pres., Mktg., Enigma, MA, Burlington
Snow, Jerry ....(704) 261-2225
jsnow@theej.com, Sports Ed., The Enquirer-Journal, NC, Monroe
Snyder, Frank M.
fsnyder@dailystandard.com, Pub., The Daily Standard, OH, Celina
Snyder, Sandra ....(570) 970-7383
ssnyder@timesleader.com, Features Ed., Times Leader, PA, Wilkes-Barre
Snyder, Kirstie...........................(937) 229-3813
Univ. of Dayton, OH, Dayton
Snyder, Richard
dsnyder@evesun.com, Pub., The Evening Sun, NY, Norwich
Snyder, John
john.snyder@pagecooperative.com, CEO, PAGE, PA, King of Prussia
Snyder, Ted.................................(330) 841-1718
tsnyder@tribtoday.com, Circ. Dir., The Tribune Chronicle, OH, Warren
Snyder, Steven R.
srsnyder@hbu.edu, Chair/Assoc. Prof./Photography, Houston Baptist University, TX, Houston
Snyder, John ....(800) 468-9568
john.snyder@pagecooperative.com, CEO, PAGE Cooperative, PA, King of Prussia
Sobczyk, Mike
businessreporter@thecourier.com, Bus./Finance Reporter, The Courier, OH, Findlay
Soberanis Rodriguez, Virgilio S.
contacto@cronicacampeche.com, Pres., Cronica, San Francisco de Campeche
Sobrinho, Ilidio Coelho......................623-3322
Ilidio@ilustrado.com.br, Pres., Umuarama Ilustrado, Umuarama, Parana
Socas, Roberto ....(212) 866-0248
Asst. Treasurer, Foreign Press Association, NY, New York
Socha, Edward
socha@standardspeaker.com, Asst. Sunday Ed., Standard-Speaker, PA, Hazleton
Soderberg, Jeffrey
jsoderberg@times-standard.com, Interactive Mgr., Times-Standard, CA, Eureka
Sodt, Evelina................(973) 785-3000 ext. 124
esodt@certifiedaudit.com, Dir., Mktg., Certified Audit of Circulations, Inc., NJ, Wayne
Soenksen, Roger
soenksra@jmu.edu, Prof., James Madison University, VA, Harrisonburg
Sofaly, Bob
bsofaly@beaufortgazette.com, Photographer, The Beaufort Gazette, SC, Beaufort
Sofradzija, Omar
omars@msu.edu, Advisor, The State News/Michigan State University, MI, East Lansing
Sohn, Ardyth
ardyth.sohn@unlv.edu, Dir./Prof., University of Nevada, Las Vegas, NV, Las Vegas
Soifer, Claudia
winnet@panix.com, Vice Pres./Gen. Mgr., World Interactive Network, NY, New York
Solan, Alan
asolan@dnews.com, News Ed., Moscow-Pullman Daily News, ID, Moscow
Solan, Alan
asolan@dnews.com, Arts Ed., Moscow-Pullman Daily News, ID, Moscow
Solares, Hernan 224-4154
hoy@wara.bolnet.bo, Gen. Mgr., Hoy, La Paz
Soldwedel, Joseph E........(928) 783-3311 ext. 102
jsoldwedel@westernnews.com, Pres./CEO, Western Newspapers, Inc., AZ, Yuma
Solheim, Dag
dag.solheim@firda.no, Mgr., FIRDA, Foerde
Solinsky, Maryellen 860/701-4218
m.solinsky@theday.com, Accounting Manager, The Day Publishing Company, CT, New London
Solliday, Nancy.........................(239) 335-0252
nsolliday@fortmyer.gannett.com, Adv. Sr. Vice Pres., Sales/Mktg., The News-Press, FL, Fort Myers
Solomon, Digby ....(757) 247-4612
dsolomon@dailypress.com, Pres./Pub./CEO, Daily Press, VA, Newport News
Solomon, Fran...........................(813) 259-7376
Mktg. Mgr., The Tampa Tribune, FL, Tampa
Solomon, Felix ....(510) 464-3460
Laney College, CA, Oakland
Solomon, Goody L. ....(202) 723-2477
goody.solomon@verizon.net, Owner/Exec. Ed./Author, Food Nutrition Health News Service, DC, Washington
Solomon, John F.
general@washingtontimes.com, Exec. Ed., The Washington Times Corp., DC, Washington
Solt, Tim.....................................(877) 334-8613
Reg. Mgr., Church Rickards, Whitlock & Co., Inc., IL, Westchester
Solt, Tim.....................................(203) 789-5350
Circ. Mgr., New Haven Register, CT, New Haven
Soltanifar, Mohammad
info@irannewsdaily.com, MD, IRAN NEWS
Soluri, Giuseppe 792-793
redazione@giornaledicalabria.net, Dir., IL GIORNALE DI CALABRIA, Catanzaro
Sominski, Stacy ....ext. 291
stacy@monroenews.com, Presentation Ed., The Monroe Evening News, MI, Monroe
Sommerfeld, Franz
retine.leuker@mds.de, Ed. in Chief, KOLNER STADT-ANZEIGER, Koln
Son-Chol, Shin
webmaster@kgib.co.kr, Chrmn., KYEONGGI ILBO, Suwon, Kyonggi
Sondrup, Brett...........................(760) 739-6698
bsondrup@nctimes.com, Online Dir., North County Times, CA, Escondido
Sones, Bill ....(440) 460-0330
strangetrue@compuserve.com, Co-Author, Strange But True, OH, Lyndhurst
Sonnenberg, Andrea
asonnenberg@pioneerlocal.com, Adv. Dir., The Lake County News-Sun, IL, Waukegan
Sonntag, Patti 212-556-5135
sonntpe@nytimes.com, Managing Editor NYT Syndicate, New York Times Syndicate, NY, New York
Sontag, Robert ....(248) 643-9910 ext. 12
rsontag@anrinc.net, Exec. Vice Pres./COO, American Newspaper Representatives, MI, Troy
Sontag, Robert ....(248) 643-7766
rsontag@anrinc.net, Exec. Vice Pres./COO, American Newspaper Representatives, Inc.,

MI, Troy
Soppe, John............................(212) 969-7535
jsoppe@hearst.com, Mng. Dir., King Digital, North America Syndicate, NY, New York
Soprano, Cathy
csoprano@verafast.com, Exec. Vice Pres., Ver-A-Fast Corp., OH, Rocky River
Sorensen, Hogens
fd@fredericiadagblad.dk, Ed. in Chief, FREDERICIA DAGBLAD, Fredericia, Jutland
Sores, Patricia
spmofc@rit.edu, Admin. Chair, Rochester Institute of Technology, NY, Rochester
Sorg, Sharon
ssorg@meadvilletribune.com, Pub., The Meadville Tribune, PA, Meadville
Sorger, Pat............................(231) 779-4123
psorger@cadillacnews.com, Adv. Leader, Cadillac News, MI, Cadillac
Sorgi, Marcello
marcello.sorgi@lastampa.it, Mgr., LA STAMPA, Torino
Soriani, Hugo..............................4334-2334
comerc@pagina12.com.ar, Gen. Mgr., Clarin, Buenos Aires
Soriano Guerrero, Javier
solaca@oem.com.mx, Gen. Mgr., El Sol de Acapulco, Acapulco, Guerrero
Sorrell, Deb............................(765) 213-5853
Features Ed., The Star Press, IN, Muncie
Sorter, Dave
dsorter@acnpapers.com, Mng. Ed., McKinney Courier-Gazette, TX, McKinney
Sorza, Selveo
lavoce@edit.hr, Ed., LA VOCE DEL POPOLO, Rijeka
Soto, Christina.........................(410) 772-4937
Howard Cmty. College, MD, Columbia
Sotomayor, Gecia P.........................227-2857
Pres., Jornal Da Manha, Sao Paulo
Soucie, Christine......................(902) 426-1146
csoucie@herald.ca, Books Ed., The Chronicle Herald, NS, Halifax
Souffront, Jose E.........................593-7281
e.informacion@codetel.net.do, Gen. Mgr., LA INFORMACION, Santiago de los Caballeros
Soulliere, Jeremy......................203-354-1065
Regional Editor - The Stamford Times & Wilton Villager, The Hour Publishing Co., CT, Norwalk
Soultanian, Gary
gsoultaniant@nusconsulting.com, Co-Pres., NUS Consulting Group, NJ, Park Ridge
Soultanian, Richard
rsoultanian@nusconsulting.com, Co-Pres., NUS Consulting Group, NJ, Park Ridge
Sounders, Eugene
efsounders@mccainprint.com, Owner, McCain Printing Co., VA, Danville
South, John
hello@bighand.com, CEO/Creative Dir., Rare Medium, TX, Dallas
Southard, Doug
dsouthard@starherald.com, Adv. Dir., Star-Herald, NE, Scottsbluff
Southard, Donna L....................(703) 370-2130
photoeditor@winsphoto.com, Photo Ed., World Images News Service, VA, Woodbridge
Southards, Sandy......................(336) 888-3567
ssouthards@hpe.com, Adv. Mgr., Major Accts., High Point Enterprise, NC, High Point
Southerland, Richard.................(423) 359-3128
richard.southerland@greenevillesun.com, Adv. Mgr., Major Accts., The Greeneville Sun, TN, Greeneville
Southworth, Ginny....................(803) 644-2394
gsouthworth@aikenstandard.com, Photo Ed., Aiken Standard, SC, Aiken
Souza, Joe....................................ext. 5912
jsouza@citizen.com, Sports Ed., Citizen, NH, Laconia
Souza, Patricia
efetokio@cello.ocn.ne.jp, Rep., EFE News Services - Tokyo, Japan, Tokyo
Souza, Chip.............................(479) 872-5131
csouza@nwaonline.net, Sports Ed., The Morning News of Northwest Arkansas, AR, Springdale
Sova, Jerry..............................(517) 768-4985
jsova@citpat.com, Assoc. Ed. Online/Print Production, The Jackson Citizen Patriot, MI, Jackson
Sovell, Jane
jsovell@marshallindependent.com, Bus. Mgr., Independent, MN, Marshall
Sozzi, Gary..............................(212) 210-2988
gsozzi@nydailynews.com, Adv. Vice Pres., Opns., NY Daily News, NY, New York
Spaeder, Jerry..........................(386) 754-0424
Mng. Ed., Lake City Reporter, FL, Lake City
Spahr, Steve............................(479) 872-5129
sspahr@nwaonline.net, Data Processing Mgr., The Morning News of Northwest Arkansas, AR, Springdale
Spain, Michael V.......................(518) 454-5060
mspain@timesunion.com, Assoc. Ed., Times Union, NY, Albany
Spangler, Todd........................(313) 222-6521
spangler@freepress.com, Deputy Metro Ed., Detroit Free Press, MI, Detroit
Spangler, Christine
dailyunion@dailyunion.com, Features Ed., Daily Jefferson County Union, WI, Fort Atkinson
Spanner, James T.
jspanner@newsandsentinel.com, Pub., Parkersburg News & Sentinel, WV, Parkersburg
Spargur, Tom
tspargur@heartlandpublications.com, Pub., Middlesboro Daily News, KY, Middlesboro
Sparks, Martha
msparks@loganbanner.com, Webmaster, The Logan Banner, WV, Logan
Sparrow, Colleen..............................ext. 767
csparrow@princegeorgecitizen.com, Circ. Dir., Reader Sales/Serv., The Prince George Citizen, BC, Prince George
Spaulding, Jon
jspaulding@palltimes.com, Pub., The Palladium-Times, NY, Oswego
Spaulding, Joann.....................765-659-4622
jspaulding@ftimes.com, Accounting Clerk, The Times, IN, Frankfort
Speakes, Larry M.
lspeakes@email.usps.gov, Mgr., Product Mktg., United States Postal Service, DC, Washington
Speaks, Edward........................(606) 326-2627
nlewis@dailyindependent.com, Circ. Dir., The Daily Independent, KY, Ashland
Spear, Glen..............................(270) 783-3254
Prodn. Mgr., Pressroom, Daily News, KY, Bowling Green
Spear, Tyrone...........................(937) 339-2616
info@roconex.com, Pres., Roconex Corp., OH, Troy
Spear, Joe
jspear@mankatofreepress.com, Mng. Ed., The Free Press, MN, Mankato
Spears, Res
news@suffolknewsherald.com, Ed., Suffolk News-Herald, VA, Suffolk
Spears, Barb...............(716) 693-1000 ext. 121
spearsb@gnnewspaper.com, Prodn. Mgr., Mailroom, Tonawanda News, NY, North Tonawanda
Spears, Jim
jspears@timesanddemocrat.com, Prodn. Mgr., The Times and Democrat, SC, Orangeburg
Specht, Wilke..................................91240
verlag@borkumer-zeitung.de, Ed. in Chief, BORKUMER ZEITUNG und BADEZEITUNG, Borkum
Speck, John.............................(479) 785-7726
jspeck@swtimes.com, Adv. Dir., Times Record, AR, Fort Smith
Spector, Mike..........................(602) 444-4348
mike.spector@pni.com, Dir., HR, The Arizona Republic, AZ, Phoenix
Spector, Joe
jspector@gannett.com, Bureau Chief, Gannett News Service - Albany, NY, NY, Albany
Spedale, Colleen......................(503) 370-6447
Willamette Univ., OR, Salem
Speer, Chris
info@nmh.com, Pres., New Media Hollywood, CA, Los Angeles
Speicher, Barbara L.
bspeciche@depaul.edu, Chair, DePaul University, IL, Chicago
Speicher, Gregory
wvs@iwaynet.net, Sr. Vice Pres., Worthington Voice Services, Inc., OH, Worthington
Speirs, Julie............................(308) 233-3790
Vice Pres., Mktg., Kearney Hub, NE, Kearney
Speirs, Dan..............................(308) 233-9721
News Ed., Kearney Hub, NE, Kearney
Speller, Cherie.........................(252) 329-9569
Asst. Mng. Ed., The Daily Reflector, NC, Greenville
Spells, William C.....................(941) 743-5676
billspells@att.net, Owner, RTP Technical Specialists, FL, Port Charlotte
Spence, Tony
cns@catholicnews.com, Dir./Ed. in Chief, Catholic News Service, DC, Washington
Spence, Joedie........................(919) 836-5782
jspence@newsobserver.com, Circ. Mgr., Distr., The News & Observer, NC, Raleigh
Spence, Maureen
mspence@wpgsun.com, Adv. Mgr., Classified Sales, The Winnipeg Sun, MB, Winnipeg
Spencer, Nancy
nspencer@delphosherald.com, Ed., Delphos Daily Herald, OH, Delphos
Spencer, T. Floyd......................(804) 649-6641
fspencer@timesdispatch.com, Mktg. Mgr., Richmond Times-Dispatch, VA, Richmond
Spencer, Halinka......................(585) 586-2525
Nazareth College of Rochester, NY, Rochester
Spencer, Matt...........................(978) 970-4619
mspencer@lowellsun.com, Copy Ed., The Sun, MA, Lowell
Spencer, Rob...............(303) 776-2244 ext. 221
rspencer@times-call.com, City Ed., Times-Call, CO, Longmont
Spencer, Mark..........................416-869-4140
mspencer@thestar.ca, Advertising Director, Toronto Star, ON, Toronto
Spessard, Bob.............(785) 822-1472 ext. 315
bspessard@saljournal.com, Circ. Dir., The Salina Journal, KS, Salina
Speth, Brenda
napanews@napanews.com, Pub., Napa Valley Register, CA, Napa
Spevak, Jeff.............................(585) 258-2452
jspevak@democratandchronicle.com, Pop Music/Nite Scene Reporter, Democrat and Chronicle.com, NY, Rochester
Spicer, Frank L........................(304) 645-1206
WVDN2@aol.com, Vice Pres./Pub., Moffitt Newspapers, VA, Roanoke
Spiegel, Kevin.............(215) 441-8444 ext.1108
kspiegel@sportsnetwork.com, Content Devel. Dir., The Sports Network (Div. of Computer Info. Network), PA, Hatboro
Spieker-Martin, Debbie.............(775) 850-2286
Cor. Dir., Swift Communications, Inc., NV, Carson City
Spierdigk, William
w.spierdigk@hdcmedia.nl, Ed., HAARLEMS DAGBLAD, Haarlem, North Holland
Spina, Anthony..............................ext. 3588
tspina@express-times.com, Major Accts. Sales Mgr., The Express-Times, PA, Easton
Spittler, Peter F.
pspittler@forumarc.com, Pres., Forum Architectural Services, LLC, OH, Cleveland
Spitz, Jill.................................(520) 573-4177
jspitz@azstarnet.com, Bus. Ed., Arizona Daily Star, AZ, Tucson
Spivey, Christopher...................(717) 255-8257
cspivey@patriot-news.com, Dir., Operations, The Patriot-News, PA, Mechanicsburg
Splain, Cheryl................................ext. 248
csplain@mountvernonnews.com, Ed., Mount Vernon News, OH, Mount Vernon
Sponenberg, David..................(603) 369-3268
dsponenberg@cmonitor.com, Controller/Co-Gen. Mgr., Concord Monitor, NH, Concord
Sponenberg, Tracie
hr@cmonitor.com, Mgr., HR, Concord Monitor, NH, Concord
Spoon, Doug.................................ext. 2731
doug.spoon@sgvn.com, Sports Ed., The Whittier Daily News, CA, Whittier
Spoon, Doug.............................(909) 869-3540
The Poly Post, CA, Pomona
Spoto, Alan
alan@adplacementservices.com, Mgr., Ad Placement Services, NJ, Pompton Lakes
Spotswood, Paul........................6620 0500
paul.spotswood@northernstar.com.au, Gen. Mgr., THE NORTHERN STAR, Goonellabah
Spreemann, Jorg
kurier-verlag@nordkurier.de, Ed. in Chief, Nordkurier, Neubrandenburg
Sprengelmeyer, Julie
pgreen@journalinquirer.com, State Ed., Journal Inquirer, CT, Manchester
Sprimont, Leigh.......................(941) 429-3006
lsprimont@sun-herald.com, Buzz Ed., Charlotte Sun, FL, Charlotte Harbor
Sprung, Jim
jim.sprung@thevillagesmedia.com, Gen. Mgr., The Villages Daily Sun, FL, The Villages
Sprung, Dan
dan.sprung@thevillagesmedia.com, Adv. Mgr., Sales/Mktg., The Villages Daily Sun, FL, The Villages
Spurgeon, Thomas J........................ext. 4066
tspurgeon@phillyburbs.com, Gen. Mgr., Bucks County Courier Times, PA, Levittown
Spychalla, Craig........................(608) 745-3516
cspychalla@capitalnewspapers.com, Lifestyle Ed., Daily Register, WI, Portage
Sranpanaria, Aoseva
redaccion@noticiasdenavarra.com, Dir., Diario De Noticias, Huarte, Navarra
Sricharatchanya, Paisal
advertising@bangkokpost.co.th, Mng. Dir., SIAM POST, Klong Toey, Bangkok
Srivastava, K.K.
sbharats@satyam.net.in, Chrmn./ MD/ Ed., SWATANTRA BHARAT, Lucknow, Uttar Pradesh
Srivastu Nilu, Dilip
aj_ranchi@rediffmail.com, Ed., BIHAR SAMACHAR PATRA PVT LTD, Ranchi, Jharkhand
Srutkowski, Tomasz
redakcja@gazetaolsztynska.pl, Ed. in Chief, GAZETA OLSZTYNSKA, Olsztyn
St. Amand, Charles....................(978) 970-4638
cstamand@lowellsun.com, Mng. Ed., The Sun, MA, Lowell
St. Claire, Allison....................(303) 355-3882
clearmountain@tde.com, Pub./Ed., Senior Wire News Service, CO, Denver
St. Germain, Brent...................(985) 857-2239
brent.stgermain@houmatoday.com, Sports Ed., The Daily Comet, LA, Thibodaux
St. Germain, Brent...................(985) 857-2239
brent.stgermain@houmatoday.com, Sports Editor, The Courier, LA, Houma
St. Hilaire, William C.
hrslatercompany@aol.com, Office Mgr., H.R. Slater Co., Inc., IL, Chicago
St. James, Jessica
jessica.stjames@irontontribune.com, Photo Ed., The Ironton Tribune, OH, Ironton
St. John, Wayne
lkelly@aprcanada.com, Pres./CEO, American Publishers Representatives Ltd., ON, Toronto
St. John, Wayne
wayne.stjohn@publicitas.com, Vice Pres., McGown Intermac/Publicitas North America, Inc., ON, Toronto
St. Lawrence, Joe......................(807) 343-6228
joe.stlawrence@chroniclejournal.com, Prodn. Foreman, Pressroom, The Chronicle-Journal, ON, Thunder Bay
St. Louis, Jill
jstlouis@cp.org, Bureau Chief, Broadcast News Limited, BC, Vancouver
Stabell, Shawn............(802) 479-0191 ext. 1170
shawn.stabell@timesargus.com, Prodn. Dir., Rutland Herald, VT, Rutland
Stabell, Shawn...............................ext. 1170
shawn.stabell@timesargus.com, Prodn. Dir., The Times Argus, VT, Barre
Stacho, Michelle
stacho@rna.org, Bus./HR Mgr., Religion Newswriters Association, OH, Westerville
Stachow, Yousuf............................629 5200
yousuf.stachow@krakow.agora.pl, Ed. in Chief, GAZETA W KRAKOWIE, Krakow
Stackhouse-Hite, Anita....................ext. 1043
astackhouse-hite@portervillerecorder.com, Asst. Mng. Ed., Features, The Porterville Recorder, CA, Porterville
Stackpole, Kerry
kstackpole@nahp.org, Exec. Dir., National Association of Hispanic Publications, VA, McLean
Stacy, Renee.....................................ext. 117

Health/Medical Ed., Daily Journal, MO, Park Hills
Stafford, Jim ....(765) 420-5235
jstafford@journalandcourier.com, Sports Ed., Journal and Courier, IN, Lafayette
Stafford, Rob ....ext. 3053
rstafford@staffordgroup.com, Pres./Gen. Mgr., Publications, The Daily News, MI, Greenville
Stahl, Brent
bstahl@moriresearch.com, Vice Pres., Research, Minnesota Opinion Research, Inc. (MORI), MN, Minneapolis
Stahl, Jerry............................(989) 779-6083
jstahl@michigannewspapers.com, Prodn. Mgr., Pre Press, Morning Sun, MI, Mount Pleasant
Stahl, Beverly.................................ext. 215
bev@crescent-news.com, Prepress Mgr., Defiance Publishing LLC, OH, Defiance
Staiano, John
john.staiano@harlandsimon.com, Sr. Vice Pres., Sales, Harland Simon, IL, Oak Brook
Stainer, Maria ....(202) 636-3265
mstainer@washingtontimes.com, Asst. Mng. Ed, Spec. Section Features, The Washington Times, DC, Washington
Stairs, Robert W........................(207) 990-8223
rstairs@bangordailynews.net, Vice Pres., Admin., Bangor Daily News, ME, Bangor
Stalcup, Anthony ....ext. 1318
anthony.stalcup@gwinnettdailypost.com, Photo Ed., Gwinnette Daily Post, GA, Lawrenceville
Stalcup, Mark
mstalcup@vinu.edu, Dir., Vincennes University, IN, Vincennes
Stalcup, Jeff ....(360)735-4428
jeff.stalcup@columbian.com, Production Director, The Columbian, WA, Vancouver
Staley, Kelly
kstaley@marketing.org, Membership Mgr., Business Marketing Association, IL, Naperville
Stallbaumer, Tom ....(479) 872-5002
tstallbaumer@nwaonline.net, Pub., The Morning News of Northwest Arkansas, AR, Springdale
Stallings, Walt........................(214) 977-8973
wstallings@dallasnews.com, Sr. Deputy Mng. Ed., News Mgmt., The Dallas Morning News, TX, Dallas
Stallone, Albert A. ....(610) 236-4745
astallone@readingeagle.com, Packaging/Distr. Dir., Reading Eagle, PA, Reading
Stallone, Steve
steve.stallone@ilwu.org, Pres., International Labor Communications Association AFL/CIO/CLC, DC, Washington
Staloch, Stephen ....(408) 842-6400 ext. 200
sstaloch@mainstreetmg.com, Pub., Morgan Hill Times, CA, Morgan Hill
sstaloch@mainstreetmg.com, Sr. Vice Pres./COO, Mainstreet Media Group, CA, Gilroy
Staloch, Stephen P.
sstaloch@mainstreetmg.com, Pub., Free Lance, CA, Hollister
Staloch, Stephen
sstaloch@gilroydispatch.com, Pub., The Dispatch, CA, Gilroy
Stalter, Mike ....(703) 878-8024
mstalter@insidenova.com, Adv. Sales Mgr., Manassas Journal Messenger, VA, Manassas
Stamm, Patricia ....(403) 314-4318
prstamm@reddeeradvocate.com, Adv. Mgr., Classified, Red Deer Advocate, AB, Red Deer
Stamper, Stan
editor@sbcglobal.net, News Ed., Hugo Daily News, OK, Hugo
Stamps, David
dstamps@hspa.com, Exec. Dir., Hoosier State Press Association, IN, Indianapolis
Stamps, David
dstamps@hspa.com, Exec. Dir., Hoosier State Press Association, Inc., IN, Indianapolis
Stancampiano, Louis..................973-192-4188
lstancampiano@starledger.com, Advertising Director, The Star-Ledger, NJ, Newark
Stancavage, John
john.stancavage@tulsaworld.com, Bus. Ed., Tulsa World, OK, Tulsa
Stanciu, Sorin Stefan
dimineata@kappa.ro, Dir., DIMINEATA, Bucharest
Standfield, Mary
mbstandfield@cnhi.com, Bus. Mgr., Herald-Banner Publications, TX, Greenville
Standridge, Karen
kstandridge@coxnews.com, Data Processing Mgr., The Daily Sentinel, TX, Nacogdoches
Standring, Chris......................(780) 429-5112
cstandring@thejournal.canwest.com, At Home/Look Ed., Edmonton Journal, AB, Edmonton
Stanford, Scott 970-871-4202
sstanford@steamboatpilot.com, General Manager - Steamboat Pilot & Today, WorldWest LLC, KS, Lawrence
Stanford, Bill...........................(570) 494-6789
wildbill@wildbillsartshow.net, Creator/Self-Syndicator, Wild Bill's Cartoon Show!, PA, Montoursville
Stanford, Scott...........................970 871-4202
sstanford@SteamboatToday.com, General Manager, Steamboat Pilot & Today, CO, Steamboat Springs
Stangl, Shireen
shireen.stangl@publicitas.com, Mgr., Publicitas North America, Inc., CA, Van Nuys
Stangl, Tom ....(712) 546-7031 ext. 40
tstangl@lemarscomm.net, Pub., Le Mars Daily Sentinel, IA, Le Mars
Stanley, Monty
mstanley@gosanangelo.com, HR Dir., San Angelo Standard-Times, TX, San Angelo
Stanley, Monica ....(231) 941-1574
Prodn. Mgr., Mailroom, Record-Eagle, MI, Traverse City
Stanley, Don ....ext. 207
donstanley@sanduskyregister.com, Circ. Asst. Dir., Sandusky Register, OH, Sandusky
Stanley, Ginger.........................804-521-7575
gingers@vpa.net, Exec. Dir., Virginia Press Association, Inc., VA, Glen Allen
Stanton, Michael
michael.stanton@sourcemedia.com, Pub., The Bond Buyer
Stapleton, Libby ....(936) 633-5288
lstapleton@angelina.edu, Advisor, Angelina College, TX, Lufkin
Stapleton, Sally 860/701-4256
s,stapleton@theday.com, Managing Editor/Multimedia, The Day Publishing Company, CT, New London
Stapley, Charles
chuck.stapley@ott.sunpub.com, Prodn. Dir., The Ottawa Sun, ON, Ottawa
Star, Darryl.................................6024 0505
darryl.star@bordermail.com.au, Nat'l Adv. Mgr., THE BORDER MAIL
Stark, Jackie............................(919) 829-4771
jstark@newsobserver.com, Vice Pres., HR, The News & Observer, NC, Raleigh
Stark, Chuck ....(360) 792-8566
cstark@kitsapsun.com, Sports Ed., Kitsap Sun, WA, Bremerton
Stark, Carol
cstark@joplinglobe.com, Ed., The Joplin Globe, MO, Joplin
Starkes, Glenda
glenda.starkes@gisborneherald.co.nz, Adv. Mgr., GISBORNE HERALD
Starkey, Mike ....(216) 999-4764
Deputy Sports Editor, The Plain Dealer, OH, Cleveland
Starkey, Vickie.........................(770) 934-7380
vstarkey@wdfarmerplans.com, Pres., W.D. Farmer Residence Designer, Inc., GA, Lilburn
Starnes, Judy
judy.starnes@thefacts.com, Gen. Mgr., The Facts, TX, Clute
Starr, Rusty
rstarr@palatkadailynews.com, Pub., Palatka Daily News, FL, Palatka
Stasney, Ted ....(813) 259-7766
Dir., Market Devel., The Tampa Tribune, FL, Tampa
Staszkow, Craig
cstaszkow@dnews.com, Adv. Mgr., Moscow-Pullman Daily News, ID, Moscow
Staton, Heather.........................(828) 694-7840
heather.staton@hendersonvillenews.com, Adv. Mgr., Times-News, NC, Hendersonville
Staub, Joel ....(318) 487-6425
jstaub@thetowntalk.com, Circ. Mgr., The Town Talk, LA, Alexandria
Stautberg, Timothy E. ....(513) 977-3826
stautberg@scripps.com, Sr. Vice Pres./CFO, E. W. Scripps Co., OH, Cincinnati
Stavrakas, Scott ....(815) 220-6945
addir@newstrib.com, Adv. Dir., News-Tribune, IL, La Salle
Stearns, John
jstearns@bendbulletin.com, Bus. Ed., The Bulletin, OR, Bend
Stebbins, Chad
stebbins-c@mssu.edu, Exec. Dir., International Society of Weekly Newspaper Editors, MO, Joplin
Stedham, Mike ....(256) 782-5713
Jacksonville State Univ., AL, Jacksonville
Steed, Camille...........................(712) 325-3725
Iowa Western Cmty. College, IA, Council Bluffs
Steele, Roger ....ext. 25
Gen. Mgr., Alexander City Outlook, AL, Alexander City
Steele, Judy
wvdailynews@suddenlinkmail.com, Pub., West Virginia Daily News, WV, Lewisburg
Steele, Margaret
msteele@bowesnet.com, Office Mgr., Daily Herald-Tribune, AB, Grande Prairie
Steele, Gerry
gsteele@bakercityherald.com, Sports Ed., Baker City Herald, OR, Baker City
Steele, Matt..............................(559) 441-6085
msteele@fresnobee.com, Circ. Mgr., Single Copy, The Fresno Bee, CA, Fresno
Steele, Jim
jsteele@greenfieldreporter.com, Prodn. Mgr., Pre Press, Daily Reporter, IN, Greenfield
Steele-Rogers, Sara ....ext. 327
ssrogers@y2m.com, Contact, Y2M: Youth Media and Marketing Networks, MA, Boston
Steelman, Ben...........................(910) 343-2208
ben.steelman@starnewsonline.com, Book Critic, Star-News, NC, Wilmington
Steenkamp, Floris
ntimes@iway.na, Ed. In Cheif, NAMIB TIMES, Walvis Bay
Stefan, Regina
rstefan@tribweb.com, Administrative Asst., The Valley Independent, PA, Monessen
Steffenhagen, Tami ....(503) 977-4184
Portland Cmty. College, OR, Portland
Steffens, Brian
briansteffens@nna.org, Exec. Dir., National Newspaper Association, MO, Columbia
Stegman, Chris..........................602-444-3902
cstegman@republicmedia.com, Director/Retail & National Advertising, The Arizona Republic, AZ, Phoenix
Steibelt, Monica
monicas@isd.ca, Sales Coord., Innovative Systems Design, Inc., QC, Pointe-Claire
Steiger, Carol ....(609) 272-7317
csteiger@pressofac.com, Circ. Systems & Acquisition/Retention Mgr., The Press of Atlantic City, NJ, Pleasantville
Stein, Tim
postphotos@cincypost.com, Photo Ed., The Kentucky Post, OH, Cincinnati
Stein, Naomi.............................(715) 395-5051
nstein@superiortelegram.com, Circ. Dir., The Daily Telegram, WI, Superior
Stein, Richard ....ext. 254
rstein@kauaipubco.com, Prodn. Mgr., The Garden Island, HI, Lihue
Stein-Burbach, Ellen..................(216) 999-4546
Asst. Managing Editor/Medical, The Plain Dealer, OH, Cleveland
Steinbeck, Laura ....(563) 589-3369
Univ. of Dubuque, IA, Dubuque
Steinberg, Jim..........................(909) 386-3855
jim.steinberg@inlandnewspapers.com, Rialto/Fontana reporter, San Bernardino County Sun, CA, San Bernardino
Steiner, Marcel
redaktion@appon.ch, Pub., APPENZELLER ZEITUNG, Herisau, Aargau
Steinig, Norbert 360010
Bus. Mgr., BUERSCHE ZEITUNG, Gelsenkirchen
Steinmoen, Jorn
jorn.steinmoen@laagendalsposten.no, Ed., LAAGENDALSPOSTEN, Kongsberg
Steitz, Marjorie ....(202) 882-8882
srcmarjorie@aol.com, Mng. Ed., Artists and Writers Syndicate, DC, Washington
Steitz, Philip
srcmarjorie@aol.com, Pres./Exec. Ed., Artists and Writers Syndicate, DC, Washington
Stemmermann, Don
dstemmermann@landonmedia.com, Vice Pres., Landon Media Group LLC, MI, Troy
Stennes, John
jstennes@gfherald.com, Photo Ed., Grand Forks Herald, ND, Grand Forks
Stepankowsky, Andre ....(360) 577-2520
andre@tdn.com, City Ed., The Daily News, WA, Longview
Stephanandreas, Dasgorss
dasgorss.stephanandreas@tagesspiegel.de, Ed., DER TAGESSPIEGEL, Berlin
Stephani, Will ....(780) 468-0144
wil.stephani@edm.sunpub.com, Prodn. Dir., The Edmonton Sun, AB, Edmonton
Stephano, Christopher S.
csteph@genfax.com, Pres./CEO, Slingshot Technologies, PA, Bridgeport
Stephens, Lois
webmaster@aliceechonews.com, Webmaster, Alice Echo-News Journal, TX, Alice
Stephens, Ryan.........................(213) 237-4559
ryan.stephens@latsi.com, Dir., Int'l Sales, Los Angeles Times Syndicate New Media, CA, Los Angeles
Stephens, Sean
seanstephens@clintondailynews.com, Sports Ed., The Clinton Daily News, OK, Clinton
Stephens, Emily ....(212) 293-8597
estephens@unitedmedia.com, Sales Mgr., Int'l/E-Rights, Newspaper Enterprise Association (Div. of United Media), NY, New York
estephens@unitedmedia.com, Sales Mgr., Int'l/E-rights, United Feature Syndicate (Div. of United Media), NY, New York
Stephens, Ryan.........................(312) 222-8682
rstephens@tribune.com, Int'l Sales Dir., News/Features, McClatchy-Tribune Information Services, Tribune Media Services, Inc., IL, Chicago
Stephenson, Carolyn N.
Cstevenson@kaplan.edu, Academic. Prog. Dir., Kaplan University, FL, Fort Lauderdale
Stephenson, Thomas A.
tstephen@express-news.net, Pres./Pub., San Antonio Express-News, TX, San Antonio
tstephen@express-news.net, Pres./Pub., Brooks Discovery News, TX, San Antonio
tstephen@express-news.net, Pres./Pub., Bulverde Community News, TX, San Antonio
tstephen@express-news.net, Pres./Pub., Fort Sam News Leader, TX, San Antonio
tstephen@express-news.net, Pres./Pub., Kelly Observer, TX, San Antonio
tstephen@express-news.net, Pres./Pub., Lackland Talespinner, TX, San Antonio
tstephen@express-news.net, Pres./Pub., Medical Patriot, TX, San Antonio
tstephen@express-news.net, Pres./Pub., North Central News, TX, San Antonio
tstephen@express-news.net, Pres./Pub., Northeast Herald, TX, San Antonio
tstephen@express-news.net, Pres./Pub., Northwest Weekly, TX, San Antonio
tstephen@express-news.net, Pres./Pub., Randolph Wingspread, TX, San Antonio
Stephenson, David
david.stephenson@thetriangle.org, Editor in Chief, Drexel Univ., PA, Philadelphia
Stephenson Sarver, Jodi ....(800) 457-1156
jsarver@wsjournal.com, Rep., Media General Syndication Services, NC, Winston-Salem
Sterkel, Mark ....(432) 333-7774
mark_sterkel@link.freedom.com, Photo Dept. Mgr., Odessa American, TX, Odessa
Sterling, Robert ....(415) 382-7294
rsterling@marinij.com, City Ed., Marin Independent Journal, CA, Novato
Stern, Andrew L.
andy.stern@feiu.org, Int'l Pres., Service Employees International Union, CLC, DC, Washington

Stern, Elliott
estern@santamariatimes.com, Sports Ed., Santa Maria Times, CA, Santa Maria
Stern, Robert
rstern@projectsinknowledge.com, Pres., Projects In Knowledge, Inc., NJ, Little Falls
Stern, Elliott ....(805) 739-2235
Sports Ed., The Lompoc Record, CA, Lompoc
Stern, Thomas von
service@nt-anzeigen.de, Ed., NIEDERSACHSISCHES TAGEBLATT, Luneburg
Stern, Mitchell 949-253-2300
jryan@freedom.com, CEO, Freedom Communications, Inc., CA, Irvine
Steven, Jamie ....(740) 375-5146
jsteven@nncogannett.com, Local Content Ed., The Marion Star, OH, Marion
Stevens, Matthew
mstevens@sun-herald.com, Asst Sports Editor, Charlotte Sun, FL, Charlotte Harbor
Stevens, Randy
rstevens@sanmarcosrecord.com, Sports Ed., San Marcos Daily Record, TX, San Marcos
Stevens, Jane 785-832-7215
jstevens@ljworld.com, Director of Media Strategies, The World Co.- Lawrence, Kan., Journal-World, KS, Lawrence
Stevens, Kathy
kstevens@njherald.com, Lifestyle Ed., New Jersey Herald, NJ, Newton
Stevens, Bill ....(727) 869-6250
stevens@tampabay.com, Ed., North Suncoast, Tampa Bay Times, FL, Saint Petersburg
Stevens, Mike ....(360) 792-3350
mstevens@kitsapsun.com, Dir., Adv./Mktg., Kitsap Sun, WA, Bremerton
Stevens, Cindy..........................(207) 621-5632
cynsteve@centralmaine.com, Adv./Promo. Dir., Kennebec Journal, ME, Augusta
Stevens, David ....(575) 763-3431
dstevens@cnjonline.com, Ed., Clovis News Journal, NM, Clovis
Stevenson, Jan..............(734) 293-7200 ext. 22
janstevenson@pridesource.com, CFO, Q Syndicate, MI, Livonia
Stevenson, Bill..........................ext. 226
editor@columbiabasinherald.com, Mng. Ed., Columbia Basin Herald, WA, Moses Lake
Stevenson, Robert ....(864) 388-8210
Lander Univ., SC, Greenwood
Stevenson, Suzanne ....(916) 774-7955
suzannes@goldcountrymedia.com, Adv. Dir., Classified, Auburn Journal, Inc., CA, Auburn
Stevenson, Jeffrey T. ....(212) 935-4990
stevensonj@vss.com, Mng. Partner/Co-CEO, Veronis Suhler Stevenson, NY, New York
Stewart, Kathie ....(352) 563-3234
kstewart@chronicleonline.com, Circ. Dir., Citrus County Chronicle, FL, Crystal River
Stewart, Don
dstewart@fmarion.edu, Chair, Francis Marion University, SC, Florence
Stewart, Brian G.
info@jerviswebb.com, Pres./CEO, Jervis B. Webb Co., MI, Farmington Hills
Stewart, Ruaridh
ruaridh@zumapress.com, News Dir./Picture Desk Mgr., ZUMA Press, Inc., CA, San Clemente
Stewart, John ....(403) 314-4342
editorial@reddeeradvocate.com, News Ed., Red Deer Advocate, AB, Red Deer
Stewart, Martin
mstewart@njtimes.com, Controller, The Times, NJ, Trenton
Stewart, Jim
sales@pixeltouch.com, Pres., Pixel Touch, CA, Ontario
Stewart, James L.
james.stewart@nicholls.edu, Head/Assoc. Prof., Nicholls State University, LA, Thibodaux
Stewart, Betty
bstewart@c-dh.net, Office Mgr., Columbia Daily Herald, TN, Columbia
Stewart, George ....(270) 783-3253
gstewart@bgdailynews.com, Mailroom Mgr., Daily News, KY, Bowling Green
Stewart, Russ ....(951) 487-2299
rstewart@pe.com, Adv. Mgr., Regl., The Press-Enterprise, CA, Riverside
Stewart, Alasdair ....ext. 272
Asst. News Ed., Walla Walla Union-Bulletin, WA, Walla Walla
Stewart, Amy ....(801) 625-4229
astewart@standard.net, Educ. Ed., Standard-Examiner, UT, Ogden
Stewart, Robert..........................(740) 593-2601
Prof./Assoc. Dir., Ohio University, OH, Athens
Stewart, Pat..................(603) 472-5825 ext. 12
pat.stewart@ckp.com, Pres., Saxotech, NH, Bedford
Stewart, Steve ....(334) 670-3328
stewart@jschool.troy.edu, Advisor, The Tropolitan, AL, Troy
Stewart, Carole C. ....(412) 787-2881
carole.stewart@homeimprovementtime.com, Vice Pres., Home Improvement Time, Inc., PA, Oakdale
Stewart, Robert..........................(512) 445-3570
rstewart@statesman.com, Controller, Austin American-Statesman, TX, Austin
Stewart, Fred
Fred_Stewart@tamu-commerce.edu, Instr./Publications Advisor, Texas A&M University-Commerce, TX, Commerce
Stewart, Fred ....(903) 886-5231
Texas A&M Univ. Commerce, TX, Commerce
Stewart, Leiann
lstewart@dailycall.com, Adv. Dir., Piqua Daily Call, OH, Piqua
Stewart, Jeff 412-787-2881
Website Marketing Manager, Home Improvement Time, Inc., PA, Oakdale
Stewart, Leiann
lstewart@dailycall.com, Adv. Mgr., Troy Daily News, OH, Troy
Stewart III, Mizell..........................8124610799
stewartm@courierpress.com, Editor, Evansville Courier & Press, IN, Evansville
Stickel, James E..........................(509) 577-7731
jstickel@yakima-herald.com, Adv. Dir., Yakima Herald-Republic, WA, Yakima
Stickel, Glen ....(540) 665-4954 ext. 284
Prodn. Foreman, Pressroom, The Winchester Star, VA, Winchester
Stickney, Ken ....(318) 362-0230
kstickney@thenewsstar.com, Mng. Ed., The News-Star, LA, Monroe
Stiles, Bill ....(717) 292-9183 ext. 226
bstiles@ageyork.com, Sales Mgr., Advance Graphics Equipment of York, Inc., PA, Dover
Still, David R...........................(770) 962-8399
davidstill@capitalendeavors.com, Pres., Capital Endeavors, Inc., GA, Lawrenceville
Stilley, Ricky
rstilley@times-georgia.com, Systems Mgr., Douglas County Sentinel, GA, Douglasville
Stillman, Marcus
m.stillman@nzz.ch, Ed. in Chief, NEUE ZURCHER ZEITUNG, Zurich
Stine, Scott..........................(501) 378-3558
Adv. Dir., Classified, Arkansas Democrat-Gazette, AR, Little Rock
Stineman, Terry ....(216) 999-4035
Mgr. of Facilities and Fleet Opns., The Plain Dealer, OH, Cleveland
Stineman, Shirley..........................(216) 999-4242
Adv. Dir., Mktg./Community Affairs, The Plain Dealer, OH, Cleveland
Stinson, Barrett..........................(308) 381-9420
barrett.stinson@theindependent.com, Photo Ed., The Grand Island Independent, NE, Grand Island
Stinson, Laurie
info@statenet.com, Pres., State Net, CA, Sacramento
Stinton, Camille..........................(860) 241-3181
cstinton@courant.com, Circ. Mgr., Single Copy, The Hartford Courant, CT, Hartford
Stiver, Wendy..........................ext. 130
Community Ed., The Express, PA, Lock Haven
Stluka, Chris..........................ext. 167
chriss@shorack.com, Inside Sales Mgr., Kaspar Wire Works, Inc./Sho-Rack, TX, Shiner
Stmyer, Kara ....(765) 213-5841
pmiller@thestarpress.com, Design Ed., The Star Press, IN, Muncie
Stock, Michael..........................(808) 984-3445
Maui Cmty. College, HI, Kahului
Stockard, Sam..........................ext. 165
stockard@dnj.com, News Ed., The Daily News Journal, TN, Murfreesboro
Stockmier, Kathleen ....(972) 273-3498
North Lake College, TX, Irving
Stockton, Cindy
cstockton@thepilotnews.com, Adv. Mgr., Mktg., Pilot News, IN, Plymouth
Stockton, Sandy ....(530) 852-0238
sandys@goldcountrymedia.com, Bus. Opns. Mgr., Auburn Journal, Inc., CA, Auburn
Stockton, Dennis ....(770) 535-6302
dstockton@gainesvilletimes.com, Pub., The Times, GA, Gainesville
Stoddard, Phil 608-252-6357
pstoddard@madison.com, Circulation Director, Wisconsin State Journal, WI, Madison
Stoddard, Susan
info_use@infouse.com, Pres., InfoUse, CA, Berkeley
Stoeckle, Jan
jstoeckle@hearstnp.com, Pub., The Huron Daily Tribune, MI, Bad Axe
Stoecklin, Mark ....ext. 131
mstoecklin@certifiedaudit.com, CEO, Certified Audit of Circulations, Inc., NJ, Wayne
Stoesser, Bill J.
bstoesser@olec.com, Vice Pres., Stoesser Register Systems, CA, Mountain View
Stoffer, Gary ....(765) 671-2239
gstoffer@marion.gannett.com, Dir., Systems, Chronicle-Tribune, IN, Marion
Stok, Glenn
customerservice@stok.com, Pres./Founder, Stok Software, Inc., NY, Hauppauge
Stoker, Kevin L. ....(801) 422-1222
Assoc. Prof./Assoc. Chair, Grad. Studies, Brigham Young University, UT, Provo
Stokstad, Are
are.stokstad@op.no, Dir., OSTLANDS-POSTEN, Larvik
Stolar, Rebecca..........................(808) 529-4845
rstolar@staradvertiser.com, Human Resources Director, Honolulu Star-Advertiser, HI, Honolulu
Stolar, David ....(814) 870-1745
dave.stolar@timesnews.com, Opns. Dir., Erie Times-News, PA, Erie
Stolk, Vanessa
vanessa.stolk@dowjones.com, Rep., Dow Jones Newswires - Brussels, Belgium, Brussels
Stoll, Ira
istoll@nysun.com, Mng. Ed., The New York Sun, NY, New York
Stolley, Theresa
techts@dailydem.com, Data Processing Mgr., Fort Madison Daily Democrat, IA, Fort Madison
Stolley, Roger ....(507) 645-1150
rstolley@cannonvalleyprinting.com, Prodn. Mgr., Owatonna People's Press, MN, Owatonna
Stolley, Roger ....(507) 645-1150
rstolley@cannonvalleyprinting.com, Prodn. Mgr., Faribault Daily News, MN, Faribault
Stollman, Rita
editstrat@aol.com, Pres., Editorial Management Strategies, MN, Saint Paul
Stoltzfus, Duane
dstoltzfus@goshen.edu, Assoc. Prof., Goshen College, IN, Goshen
Stone, Kitty..........................ext. 226
kitty.stone@gaflnews.com, Adv. Mgr., Retail Sales, The Tifton Gazette, GA, Tifton
Stone, Steve ....(602) 323-0490
steve.stone@masthead.net, Branch Mgr., Masthead International, Inc., AZ, Phoenix
Stone, Scott
sstone@dailyherald.com, Sr. Vice Pres., Gen. Mgr. and Dir. of Sales, Daily Herald, IL, Arlington Heights
Stoneburner, Mary Lou..............(860) 241-6241
mstoneburner@courant.com, Adv. Dir., Classified, The Hartford Courant, CT, Hartford
Stoneman, Marty
marty@patentdodc.com, Registered Patent Attorney, Stoneman Law Offices Ltd., AZ, Phoenix
Stoneman, Susan ....(360) 417-3555
susan.stoneman@peninsuladailynews.com, Adv Ops Manager, Peninsula Daily News, WA, Port Angeles
Stoner, Edward ....(970) 748-2929
estoner@vaildaily.com, Asst. Mng. Ed., Vail Daily, CO, Vail
Storch, Dennis
dstorch@aol.com, Pres., Dennis Storch Co., NY, New York
Storey, Bob..........................ext. 185
rstorey@nvdaily.com, Mgmt. Info Servs. Mgr., Northern Virginia Daily, VA, Strasburg
Storey, Ronald
publisher@decaturdailydemocrat.com, Pub., Decatur Daily Democrat, IN, Decatur
Storm, Kelly..........................(405) 325-2722
kstorm@ou.edu, Staff Asst., Advertising Workshop, OK, Norman
Storring, Dwight...........(519) 894-2250 ext. 2280
dstorring@therecord.com, Online Ed., The Record, ON, Kitchener
Storseth, Tone
tone.storseth@kv.no, Editor in Chief and General Manager, KRAGEROE BLAD, Krageroe
Storvik, Kaia
kaia.storvik@dagsavisen.no, Foreign Ed., DAGSAVISEN, Oslo
Story, Bob
bstory@eaglenewspapers.com, News Ed., Daily Sun News, WA, Sunnyside
Stottmeister, Janet
jstottmeister@thehawkeye.com, Adv. Dir., The Hawk Eye, IA, Burlington
Stouff, Charles..........................(717) 284-0199
charlesstouff@comcast.net, Writer/Illustrator, Domestic World Cartoons, PA, Pequea
Stout, Jennica ....(937) 564-1136
jstout@tcnews.net, Contest Chrmn., Ohio Newspaper Women's Association, OH, Enon
Stout, Jim 580-327-2200
jimstout@alvareviewcourier.net, News Editor, Alva Review-Courier, OK, Alva
Stout, Kim
circulation@washjrnl.com, Circ. Dir., The Washington Evening Journal, IA, Washington
Stout, Devon ....ext. 231
dstout@meadvilletribune.com, Circulation Director, The Meadville Tribune, PA, Meadville
Stout, Steve ....(937) 652-1337
sstout@urbanacitizen.com, Sports Ed., Urbana Daily Citizen, OH, Urbana
Stover, Bob..........................321-242-3607
bstover@floridatoday.com, Executive Editor, Florida Today, FL, Melbourne
Strabala, Rob..........................608-252-6316
rstrabala@madison.com, Operations Director, Wisconsin State Journal, WI, Madison
Strachan, Jeannie
jshort@examiner-enterprise.com, Adv. Acct. Exec., Examiner-Enterprise, OK, Bartlesville
Strain, Scott..........................(510) 323-5111
Laney College, CA, Oakland
Strange, Jim ....(217) 342-3918
Prodn. Mgr., Mfg., B & L Machine & Design, IL, Effingham
Strasner, Jay
jstrasner@thedailycitizen.com, Ed., Daily Citizen, AR, Searcy
Strasner, Jay
publisher@pressregister.com, Pub., The Clarksdale Press Register, MS, Clarksdale
Strassburg, Colette ....(928) 717-7678
Yavapai College, AZ
Strattan, Lisa ....(508) 676-2534
editor@heraldnews.com, Ed. in Chief, The Herald News, MA, Fall River
Stratton, Judy
stratton@mail.sum.edu, Administrator, Southern Methodist University, TX, Dallas
Straughan, Dulcie..........................(919) 962-9002
Prof./Sr. Assoc. Dean, University of North Carolina, NC, Chapel Hill
Straumanis, Andris
andris.straumanis@uwrf.edu, Advisor, Student Voice, WI, River Falls
Strauss, John ....(765) 285-8218
Ball State Daily News, IN, Muncie
Strauss, James..........................(406) 791-1435
jstrauss@greatfallstribune.com, Pres./Pub./Editor, Great Falls Tribune, MT, Great Falls
Stravolemos, Jill ....(303) 473-1420
stravolemosj@dailycamera.com, Mgr., Mktg./Promo./New Media, Daily Camera, CO, Boulder
Strazzante, Scott
scott@ippaonline.com, Pres., Illinois Press

Photographers Association, IL, Crystal Lake
Strean, Linda ....(805) 564-5214
Mng. Ed., Santa Barbara News-Press, CA, Santa Barbara
Street, Jody ....(317) 398-1264
jstreet@shelbynews.com, Adv. Dir., The Shelbyville News, IN, Shelbyville
Strehle, Andreas
andreas.strehle@tages-anzeiger.ch, Ed. in Chief, TAGES-ANZEIGER ZURICH, Zurich
Streitenberger, Keith ....(937) 328-0376
kstreitenberger@coxohio.com, Editorial Page Ed., Springfield News-Sun, OH, Springfield
Strempel, Dan
dstrempel@marketresearch.com, Sr. Ed., Simba Information, CT, Stamford
Strescino, Peter ....(719) 544-3520 ext. 425
pstress@chieftain.com, Lifestyle Ed., The Pueblo Chieftain, CO, Pueblo
Streuli, Ted
ted.streuli@journalrecord.com, Editor, The Journal Record, OK, Oklahoma City
Stricker, Pamela.......................(937) 382-2574
pstricker@brownpublishing.com, Publisher, Wilmington News Journal, OH, Wilmington
Strickland, Bence 860/701-4254
b.strickland@theday.com, Classified Advertising Manager, The Day Publishing Company, CT, New London
Strickland, Lynda
lstrickland@lakecityreporter.com, Adv. Dir., Lake City Reporter, FL, Lake City
Strickland, Terrell......................(501) 378-3551
tstrickland@ardemgaz.com, Controller, Arkansas Democrat-Gazette, AR, Little Rock
Strickland, Karen.......................(724) 787-7432
kstrickland@tribweb.com, Adv. Dept. Mgr., Daily Courier, PA, Connellsville
Strickland, Karen.......................(724) 684-2609
kstrickland@tribweb.com, Adv. Dept. Mgr., The Valley Independent, PA, Monessen
Strickland, Margaret..................(251) 580-2100
James Faulkner State Cmty. College, AL, Bay Minette
Strine, Chris 239-574-1110
cstrine@breezenewspapers.com, Mng. Ed., Cape Coral Breeze, FL, Cape Coral
Stringer, David R. ....(405) 366-3590
publisher@normantranscript.com, Pub., Norman Transcript, OK, Norman
Stringfellow, Lee ....(251) 219-5070
lstringfellow@press-register.com, Dir., HR, Press-Register, AL, Mobile
Stroh, W.
info@bkz-online.de, Proprietor, BACKNANGER KREISZEITUNG, Backnang
Strohm, Gary..............................(217) 826-3600
stromnews@joink.com, Pub., Marshall Advocate, IL, Marshall
Stroka, Sally
sstroka@nvsmedia.com, Dir., Opns., NVS Interactive Media, NY, Williamsville
Stromsodt, Kirsten
kstromsodt@gfherald.com, Assigning Ed., Grand Forks Herald, ND, Grand Forks
Strong, Stacey 9022 0505
stacey.strong@kalminer.com.au, Front Office Manager, KALGOORLIE MINER
Strong, Gary ....(916) 321-1520
gstrong@sacbee.com, Sr. Vice Pres., Finance, The Sacramento Bee, CA, Sacramento
Strother, William.......................(812) 331-4361
bstrother@heraldt.com, Features/Lifestyle Ed., The Herald-Times, IN, Bloomington
Stroud, Larry
larrydstroud@yahoo.com, Assoc. Ed., Batesville Guard, AR, Batesville
Strout, Lew.................................(207) 621-5670
lstrout@centralmaine.com, Circ. Mgr., Single Copy, Kennebec Journal, ME, Augusta
Strroner, Victor
v.strroner@ntz.de, Adv. Mgr, Nurtinger Zeitung, Nurtingen
Strub, Denise ....(662) 843-4241
news@bolivarcommercial.com, Mng. Ed., The Bolivar Commercial, MS, Cleveland
Strubinger, Ryan ....(573) 248-2744
ryan.strubinger@courierpost.com, Technology Dir., Hannibal Courier-Post, MO, Hannibal
Struck, Paul
pauls@ctimes.biz, Co-Assoc. Pub., Chronicle Times, IA, Cherokee
Struck, Myron....................................ext. 266
Mng. Ed., States News Service (NY Times Subscriber Service), DC, Washington
Struglinski, Suzanne
president@rra.org, Pres., Regional Reporters Association, DC, Washington
Struman, Maryann
mstruman@detroitnews.com, Deputy Metro Editor, The Detroit News, MI, Detroit
Strunk, Ella
estrunk@sdnccg.com, Circ. Mgr., The Sidney Daily News, OH, Sidney
Stry, Bob Van
robert.vanstry@firstdata.com, Vice Pres., Sales, First Data Voice Services, NE, Omaha
Stuart, Doug ....(802) 747-6121 ext. 2138
doug.stuart@rutlandherald.com, Bus. Mgr., Rutland Herald, VT, Rutland
Stuart, Maria
mstuart@ht.homecomm.net, Mng. Ed., The Livingston County Daily Press & Argus, MI, Howell
Stuart, Lauretta.........................(856) 486-2952
lstuart@courierpostonline.com, Fashion Ed., Courier-Post, NJ, Cherry Hill
Stuart, John
info@voltdirectory.com, Contact, Volt Information Sciences, PA, Blue Bell
Stuart, Thomas S.
thomas.stuart@wifag.ch, Vice Pres., Sales, WIFAG Press Co., AL, Birmingham
Stubblebine, Ray
president@nyppa.org, Pres., New York Press Photographers Association, Inc., NY, New York
Stubler, Paul
gmnewswest@npgcable.com, Gen. Mgr., Mohave Valley Daily News, AZ, Bullhead City
Stuckey, John ....(867) 667-4774
circulation@whitehorsestar.com, Circ. Mgr., Whitehorse Star, YT, Whitehorse
Studt, Bill..ext. 527
bstudt@freemanonline.com, Prodn. Dir., Daily Freeman, NY, Kingston
Stulce, Corey ....(618) 463-2553
corey_stulce@thetelegraph.com, Medical/Hospital Ed., The Telegraph, IL, Alton
Stull, Jennifer
jenn@thesandspur.org, Editor-in-Chief, The Sandspur, FL, Winter Park
Sturgeon, Bryan ....(317) 444-4152
bryan.sturgeon@indystar.com, Circ. Mgr., Mktg./Admin., The Indianapolis Star, IN, Indianapolis
Sturges, Worsgang
verlag@intrinet.de, Bus. Mgr., Trierischer Volksfreund, Trier
Sturtevant, Ben ....(206) 621-5515
bsturtevant@centralmaine.com, Sports Ed., Kennebec Journal, ME, Augusta
Stusse, Sue ....(712) 293-4292
Controller, Sioux City Journal, IA, Sioux City
Stutesman, Jeff
mercercountychronicle@bright.net, Gen. Mgr., Mercer County Chronicle, OH, Coldwater
mercercountychronicle@bright.net, Adv. Dir., The Noblesville Daily Times, IN, Noblesville
Stutsman, Beth ....(574) 237-4325
Indiana Univ., IN, South Bend
Styczinski, Mike
mstyczinski@times-standard.com, Mailroom Mgr., Times-Standard, CA, Eureka
Suarez, Cecil 22-3884
Gen. Mgr., Tipografia La Columna CA, Maracaibo, Zulia
Suarez, Ronald
cip216@cip.enet.cu, Dir., GUERRILLERO, Pinar Del Rio
Subramaniam, Siva
sivamkv@gmail.com, Ed. in Chief, THINAKARAN, Colombo
Subramanya, Shiva
shivasubramanya@kannadaprabha.com, Ed., KANNADA PRABHA, Bangalore, Karnataka
Sucher, Elizabeth.......................(617) 929-8641
esucher@globe.com, Adv. Div. Mgr., Amusement, The Boston Globe, MA, Boston
Sucupira, Walter 622-2083
redacao@atribunaonline.com.br, Pres., A Tribuna Do Povo, Umuarama, Parana
Sudbrook, Jeff
jsudbrook@journalregister.com, Pub., The News-Herald, OH, Willoughby
Sudbrook, Jeff
jsudbrook@morningjournal.com, Pub., The Morning Journal, OH, Lorain
Suffolk, Ted E. ....(330) 747-1471 ext. 1263
tsuffolk@vindy.com, Asst. Gen. Mgr., The Vindicator, OH, Youngstown
Sugg, Marvine
msugg@c-dh.net, Society Ed., Columbia Daily Herald, TN, Columbia
Suggett, Mary ....(800) 255-6734 ext. 7394
msuggett@amuniversal.com, Permissions Dir., Universal Uclick, MO, Kansas City
Sugiura, Wataru
info@bishamon.com, Pres., Bishamon Industries Corp., CA, Ontario
Suhaimi, Abdul Jabbar
alalam@alalam.ma, Dir., AL ALAM, Rabat
Suisman, Gary
gsuisman@journalandcourier.com, Pres./Pub., Journal and Courier, IN, Lafayette
Suitt, Sande.......................................ext. 160
suitt@dnj.com, Lifestyles Ed., The Daily News Journal, TN, Murfreesboro
Sujimoto, Igsuro
tokyo@jmd.co.jp, Ed. in Chief, NIHON KAIJI SHIMBUN, Tokyo
Sulayman At-Tai, Muhammad Bin
alwatan@gto.net.om, Ed. in Chief, AL-WATAN
Sullivan, Stacy ....(602) 444-8749
stacy.sullivan@arizonarepublic.com, A & E Rep. Ed., The Arizona Republic, AZ, Phoenix
Sullivan, John ....(406) 222-2000
enterprise@livent.net, Publisher, The Livingston Enterprise, MT, Livingston
Sullivan, John
enterprise@livent.net, Pres., Yellowstone Newspapers, MT, Livingston
Sullivan, Tisha..........................(928) 539-6831
tsullivan@yumasun.com, Adv. Mgr., Classified, Yuma Sun, AZ, Yuma
Sullivan, Mark Joseph................(617) 929-2152
ma_sullivan@globe.com, Adv. Div. Mgr., City Weekly, The Boston Globe, MA, Boston
Sullivan, Glenda ....(850) 747-5024
gsullivan@pcnh.com, Adv. Mgr., Classified, The News Herald, FL, Panama City
Sullivan, Randy
randy.sullivan@fujifilmgs.com, Reg'l Sales Mgr., Fujifilm Graphic Systems USA, Inc., TX, Arlington
Sullivan, Ray
pnt@yucca.net, Pub., Portales News-Tribune, NM, Portales
Sullivan, Lynne.........................(508) 676-2571
lsullivan@heraldnews.com, Features Ed., The Herald News, MA, Fall River
Sullivan, John
jsullivan@griffindailynews.com, Sports Ed., Griffin Daily News, GA, Griffin
Sullivan, Katie..........................(410) 770-4110
Community Ed., The Star-Democrat, MD, Easton
Sullivan, Mike ....(413) 532-1735
sales@bwgg.com, Pres., Berkshire/Westwood Graphics Group, Inc., MA, Holyoke
Sullivan, R. Joe ....ext. 252
Ed., Southeast Missourian, MO, Cape Girardeau
Sullivan, Maureen ....(413) 788-1192
msullivan@repub.com, Mktg. Dir., The Republican, MA, Springfield
Sullivan, Don ....(203) 838-2333
info@miles33.com, Sr. VP. Sales, Miles 33, CT, Norwalk
Sullivan, Denver..............................ext. 7005
Dir., Info Servs./Tech, Greensburg Daily News, IN, Greensburg
Sullivan, Elizabeth
elizabeth.sullivan@olympus.com, Sr. PR Mgr., Olympus America, Inc., PA, Center Valley
Sullivan, Michael ....(718) 960-4966
CUNY Schools, NY, Bronx
Sullivan, Ray ....(575) 763-3431
rsullivan@cnjonline.com, Pub., Clovis News Journal, NM, Clovis
Sullivan, Alana ....(603) 610-1158
asullivan@seacoastonline.com, Systems Mgr., Portsmouth Herald, NH, Portsmouth
Sullivan, Lisa ....(512) 445-3860
lsullivan@statesman.com, Vice Pres., Mktg., Austin American-Statesman, TX, Austin
Sullivan, Elizabeth....................(216) 999-6153
Editorial Page Editor, The Plain Dealer, OH, Cleveland
Sullivan, Nancy
nancy.sullivan@latimes.com, VP, Communications, Los Angeles Times Media Group, CA, Los Angeles
Sultze, Kimberly
ksultze@smcvt.edu, Chair/Assoc. Prof., St. Michael's College, VT, Colchester
Sulzberger, Arthur O. ....(212) 556-1234
Chrmn., The New York Time Co./ Pub., The New York Times, The New York Times Co., NY, New York
Sulzberger, Arthur Ochs ....nytnews@nytimes.com
Chrmn./Pub., The New York Times, NY, New York
New England Newspaper Group, NY, New York
Sumber, Darren D.....................(918) 224-5185
publisher@sapulpaheraldonline.com, Pub., Sapulpa Daily Herald, OK, Sapulpa
Summer, Steve
customersupport@seeco.org, Pres., Standard Electric and Engineering Co., CA, South San Francisco
Summers, Michelle...................(530) 752-9877
Univ. of California Davis, CA, Davis
Summers, Nancy.......................(813) 259-7984
Adv. Mgr., Telesales, The Tampa Tribune, FL, Tampa
Summers, Phil..............(618) 262-5144 ext. 135
psummers@mtcarmelregister.com, Pub., Daily Republican Register, IL, Mount Carmel
Sumner, Dan..............................605-886-6901
Prodn. Mgr., Press, Watertown Public Opinion, SD, Watertown
Sumpter, Randall S.
r-sumpter@tamu.edu, Dir., Journ. Studies/Assoc. Prof., Commun., Texas A&M University, TX, College Station
Sunderashan, K.
marketing@dt.co.in, Ed., DAILY THANTHI, Chennai, Tamil Nadu
Sunderland, John ....(303) 820-1266
jsunderland@denverpost.com, Photography Dir., The Denver Post, CO, Denver
Sundermeyer, Katie
ksundermeyer@skagitpublshing.com, Adv. Mgr., Co-op, Skagit Valley Herald, WA, Mount Vernon
Sunthorn, Pithoon
newmedia@thairath.co.th, Ed., THAI RATH, Bangkok
Suparno, Riyadi
riyadi@thejakartapost.com, Mng. Ed., JAKARTA POST, Jakarta, Java
Supin, Jeanne ....(828) 773-3481
info@supin.com, Author/Consultant, Watauga Consulting, Inc., NC, Boone
Suprynowicz, Vin......................(702) 656-3285
vin@privacyalert.us, Pres./Ed., Mountain Media, NV, Las Vegas
Suraci, Frank 310-540-5511 x6621
frank.suraci@dailybreeze.com, City Editor, Daily Breeze, CA, Torrance
Surber, Jim
advertising@vernonrecord.com, Adv. Dir., The Vernon Daily Record, TX, Vernon
Surgenor, Matt
matt.surgenor@dailynews.co.nz, Adv. Mgr., NORTH TARANAKI MIDWEEK
Suri, Navin 233 17651
Ed. in Chief, DAILY MILAP, New Delhi
Suri, Punam
editor@milap.com, Mng. Ed., DAILY MILAP, New Delhi
Surjanor, Mett
enquiry@dailynews.co.nz, Adv Mgr, TARANAKI DAILY NEWS
Surmen, Sabahattin
s.surmen@zaman.com.tr, Adv. Mgr., ZAMAN
Surphils, Pat.............................(416) 947-2103
pat.surphils@sunmedia.ca, Dir., Promos., The Toronto Sun, ON, Toronto
Surra de Carulla, Nelly Ruth 421 204
info@elpueblo.com.ar, Gen. Mgr., El Pueblo, Villaguay, Provincia de Entre Rios
Suryodiningrat, Meidyatama

editorial@thejakartapost.com, Deputy Chief Ed., JAKARTA POST, Jakarta, Java
Suson, Elizabeth..............................**ext. 4227**
l.suson@theday.com, Circ. Mgr., Special Prog., The Day Publishing Company, CT, New London
Sussens, John
sales@midsys.co.uk, Mng. Dir., Midsystems Technology Ltd., London
Sutch, Nedra................**(724) 282-8000 ext. 211**
nsutch@butlereagle.com, Adv. Mgr., Classified, Butler Eagle, PA, Butler
Sutherland, Patrick J.
psutherl@bethanywv.edu, Chair/Assoc. Prof., Bethany College, WV, Bethany
Sutherland, Randy S.
rsutherl@poughkee.gannett.com, Controller, Poughkeepsie Journal, NY, Poughkeepsie
Sutherland, Scott.......................**(250) 386-2552**
ssutherland@broadcastnews.ca, Legislative Reporter, Broadcast News Limited, BC, Victoria
Sutherland, Linda.....................**(845) 562-7066**
lsutherland@gtilite.com, Sales/Mktg Coord., Graphic Technology, Inc. (GTI), NY, Newburgh
Sutherland, John C....................**(352) 392-4046**
Prof./Chair, Dept. of Adv., University of Florida, FL, Gainesville
Sutherland, Bob.......................**(239) 335-0247**
Circ. Vice Pres., The News-Press, FL, Fort Myers
Sutter, Peter............................**(520) 454-9245**
Central Arizona College, AZ, Coolidge
Sutton, David............................**(559) 735-3256**
Prodn. Mgr., Opns., Visalia Times-Delta, CA, Visalia
Sutton, David............................**559-735-3263**
Operations Manager, Tulare Advance-Register, CA, Visalia
Sutton, Dan
dan.sutton@gaflnews.com, Pub., Americus Times-Recorder, GA, Americus
Sutton, Bob..............................**336-506-3050**
Sports Ed., Times-News, NC, Burlington
Sutton, Deb Holbert..........................**ext. 202**
Mng. Ed., The News-Record, WY, Gillette
Sutton, Kim.............................**(812) 331-4253**
ksutton@heraldt.com, Dir., HR, The Herald-Times, IN, Bloomington
Suzuki, Tamizo
ewbmstr@nikkei.co.jp, Dir., NIHON KEIZAI SHIMBUN, Fukuoka, Kyushu
Svendgard, Brady......................**(402) 473-7200**
bsvendgard@journalstar.com, Circ. Dir., Lincoln Journal Star, NE, Lincoln
Svensson, Lars
lars.svensson@hd.se, MD, NORDVASTRA SKANES TIDNINGAR, Helsingborg
Svensson, Lars
lars.svensson@hd.se, Dir., HELSINGBORGS DAGBLAD, Helsingborg
Sverkunou, S.
vm@nsys.by, Ed., VECHERNII MINSK, Minsk
Svet, Dave
svetdave@3design.com, Partner, D3, Inc., MO, Kansas City
Svidal, Kathy
kathys@devilslakejournal.com, Gen. Mgr., Devils Lake Journal, ND, Devils Lake
Svihlik, Susan.........................**(703) 878-8090**
ssvihlik@potomacnews.com, Exec. Ed., Manassas Journal Messenger, VA, Manassas
Svihlik, Susan.........................**(703) 878-8090**
ssvihlik@potomacnews.com, Exec. Ed., News & Messenger, VA, Woodbridge
Svihovec, Steve..............................**ext. 3257**
steves@ecol.net, Circ. Dir., Leader-Telegram, WI, Eau Claire
Swain, Bruce
bswain@uwf.edu, Chair, University of West Florida, FL, Pensacola
Swain, Robert............................**9066352551**
compass@lssu.edu, Editor-in-Chief, Lake Superior State Univ., MI, Sault Sainte Marie
Swaney, Garry
gswaney@dancomnews.com, Prodn. Dir., Commercial News, IL, Danville
Swanson, Lori............................**651-228-5086**
ljswanson@pioneerpress.com, Dir., Mktg., St. Paul Pioneer Press, MN, Saint Paul
Swanson, Sam...........................**218 855 5841**
VP of Revenue Development, Brainerd Dispatch, MN, Brainerd
Swanson, Jack
editor@oelweindailyregister.com, Mng. Ed., The Oelwein Daily Register, IA, Oelwein
Swanson, Christie.....................**(479) 571-6463**
managingeditor@nwarktimes.com, Mng. Ed., Northwest Arkansas Times, AR, Fayetteville
Swanson, Jim..................................**ext. 400**
sports@princegeorgecitizen.com, Sports Ed., The Prince George Citizen, BC, Prince George
Swanson, Steve
bpusczan@siix-usa.com, Mgr., Sales/Engineering, Siix USA Corp., IL, Elk Grove Village
Swanson, Barbara.....................**(312) 222-4041**
bswanson@tribune.com, Adv. Dir., Classified, Chicago Tribune, IL, Chicago
Swanson, Debbie.....................**(208) 459-5508**
College of Idaho, ID, Caldwell
Swarens, Tim..........................**(317) 444-6176**
tim.swarens@indystar.com, Asst. Editorial Page Ed./copydesk Ed., The Indianapolis Star, IN, Indianapolis
Swarts, Greta
gswarts@dailycall.com, Grp. Graphics Mgr., Piqua Daily Call, OH, Piqua
Swartz, Jack...........................**(573) 882-5748**
swartzj@missouri.edu, Advertising Director, Columbia Missourian, MO, Columbia
Swartz, Steven R.
sswartz@hearst.com, Pres., Hearst Newspapers, The Hearst Corporation, NY, New York
Swartz, David
editor@esthervilledailynews.com, Sports Ed., Estherville Daily News, IA, Estherville
Swartzlander, David..................**(402) 826-8269**
Doane College, NE
Swaters, Renee........................**(417) 836-1213**
rswaters@news-leader.com, Adv. Bus. Analyst, Springfield News-Leader, MO, Springfield
Swayze, Kevin
news@Cambridge-Reporter.com, Mng. Ed., The Cambridge Reporter, ON, Cambridge
Swearingen, Roger
rswearingen@pontiacdailyleader.com, Circ. Mgr., The Daily Leader, IL, Pontiac
Sweeney, John..........................**(302) 324-2906**
jsweeney@delawareonline.com, Editorial Page Ed., The News Journal, DE, New Castle
Sweeney, Tom...........................**(818) 965-0882**
toms@a-americanpressparts.com, Vice Pres., Opns., A-American Machine & Assembly (Press Parts Div.), IL, Rockford
Sweeney, John..........................**(919) 962-4074**
Distinguished Prof. in Sports Commun., University of North Carolina, NC, Chapel Hill
Sweet, Kelly
kelly.sweet@gogreenbay.com, Adv. Supvr., Classified, The Green Bay News-Chronicle, WI, Green Bay
Sweetapple, Ray.......................**(709) 637-4663**
rsweetapple@thewesternstar.com, Editorial Page Ed., The Western Star, NL, Corner Brook
Sweetman, Keri........................**(780) 429-5346**
ksweetman@thejournal.canwest.com, Culture Ed., Edmonton Journal, AB, Edmonton
Sweetser, Kim..........................**(308) 381-9434**
kim.sweetser@theindependent.com, Adv. Mgr., Retail, The Grand Island Independent, NE, Grand Island
Sweetwood, Matthew
info@uniquephoto.com, COO, Unique Photo, NJ, Fairfield
Sweetwood, Mark
msweetwood@vindy.com, Mng. Ed., The Vindicator, OH, Youngstown
Swenson, Brad
bswenson@bemidjipioneer.com, Political Ed., The Pioneer, MN, Bemidji
Swetnam, Dave
info@voicemagic.com, Pres., VoiceMagic, Inc., SC, Columbia
Swick, Heather..........................**630-201-3905**
hswick@mail.bradley.edu, Editor, Bradley Univ., IL, Peoria
Swiech, Paul............................**(309) 820-3275**
pswiech@pantagraph.com, Health Ed., The Pantagraph, IL, Bloomington
Swift, Richard P.
rswift@bi.brant.allen.com, Gen. Sales Mgr., Newsprint Sales Co., VA, Charlottesville
Swift, Hannah
associateeditor@universitychronicle.net, Associate Editor, St. Cloud State Univ., MN, Saint Cloud
Swihart, Ric
ric.swihart@lethbridgeherald.com, Agriculture Ed., The Lethbridge Herald, AB, Lethbridge
Swill, Craig
sales@bocanews.com, Pub., Boca Raton News, FL, Boca Raton
Swincher, Mark
mswincher@shelbynews.com, Asst. Ed., The Shelbyville News, IN, Shelbyville
Swindell, Steve
info@etchrevere.com, Dir., Mktg., Revere Graphics Worldwide, MA, Plymouth
Switalski, David
info@quipp.com, Vice Pres., Opns., Quipp System, Inc., FL, Miami
Swofford, Robert......................**(707) 521-5251**
bob.swofford@pressdemocrat.com, Mng. Ed., The Press Democrat, CA, Santa Rosa
Swoger, MaryBeth.....................**(814) 878-2201**
marybethswoger@timesnews.com, Adv. Coord., Co-op, Erie Times-News, PA, Erie
Swoope, Jan
jswoope@cdispatch.com, Lifestyle Ed., The Commercial Dispatch, MS, Columbus
Sword, Lewis...........................**(540) 574-6283**
Wire Ed., Daily News-Record, VA, Harrisonburg
Swoveland, Julie......................**(260) 726-8141**
gpcbusiness@embarqmail.com, Bus. Mgr., The Commercial Review, IN, Portland
Syaredzitch, Iosif
nv@promedia.by, Ed., NARODNAYA VOLYA, Minsk
Sydow, Dena................**(231) 439-9313 ext. 313**
dsydow@petoskeynews.com, Circ. Mgr., Promo., Petoskey News-Review, MI, Petoskey
Sydow, Carey...........................**(815) 987-1463**
csydow@rockford.gannett.com, Prodn. Mgr., Rockford Register Star, IL, Rockford
Sykes, Jack.............................**(703) 380-2808**
bureauchief@winsphoto.com, CEO/Chief Photographer, World Images News Service, VA, Woodbridge
Sykes, Deirdre.........................**(973) 569-7112**
Director of News Assignments, North Jersey Media Group, NJ, Woodland Park
Sylla, Abdula
modibosylla@yahoo.fr, Dir., THE SEYCHELLES NATION, Victoria, Mahe
Sylla, Abdulla
modibosylla@yahoo.fr, Ed., THE SEYCHELLES NATION, Victoria, Mahe
Sylvester, Maureen...................**(978) 970-4880**
Circ. Mgr., Alternate Delivery, The Sun, MA, Lowell
Sylvia, Vin...................**(603) 668-4321 ext. 460**
vsylvia@unionleader.com, Deputy Mng. Ed., Sunday, New Hampshire Union Leader/New Hampshire Sunday News, NH, Manchester
Symonds, Robert............................**ext. 1806**
Prodn. Mgr., Mailroom, The Keene Sentinel, NH, Keene
Symons, Betty................................**ext. 1421**
betty.symons@uniontrib.com, Adv. Budget Mgr., The San Diego Union-Tribune, CA, San Diego
Sypek, Robert...........................**(508) 862-1225**
rsypek@capecodonline.com, Member Servs. Dir., Cape Cod Times, MA, Hyannis
Sypher, Mike..................................**ext. 3343**
sports@thechronicle.com, Sports Ed., The Chronicle, CT, Willimantic
Sypher, Howard E.
hsypher@purdue.edu, Head, Purdue University, IN, West Lafayette
Syracuse, Russ
offsetservices@aol.com, Owner, Offset Services Ink, CA, Elk Grove
Syse, Scarlet..............................**(317) 736-2749**
ssyse@dailyjournal.net, Ed., Daily Journal, IN, Franklin
Szabrak, Rick............................**(740) 681-4517**
rszabrak@mncogannett.com, Pub./Gen. Mgr., Eagle-Gazette Media, OH, Lancaster
Szachara, Bernie
bszachara@denverpost.com, Exec VP of Strategy OPS & IT, The Denver Post, CO, Denver
Szadziewicz, Sherry...................**605-331-2276**
sszadzie@argusleader.com, Marketing Director, Argus Leader, SD, Sioux Falls
Szalay, Zoltan
zoltan.szalay@axelspringer.hu, Ed. in Chief, HEVES MEGYEI HIRLAP, Eger, Heves
Szczesny, Joseph......................**(248) 745-4650**
joseph.szcesny@oakpress.com, Automotive Ed., The Oakland Press, MI, Pontiac
Szczurek, Marian
mszczurek@nto.pl, Pres., NOWA TRYBUNA OPOLSKA, Opole
Szefc, John.............................**(845) 291-7367**
jszefc@mediamergers.com, Northeast/New England Regl. Mgr., Grimes, W.B. & Co., NY, Goshen
Szefc, John.............................**(845) 291-7367**
Jszefc@hvc.rr.com, Senior Associate-Northeast/New England, Grimes, W.B. & Co., MD, Gaithersburg
Szefe, John.............................**(845) 291-7367**
Grimes, W.B. & Co., MD, Gaithersburg
Szerdahelyi, Csaba
csaba.szerdahelyi@axelspringer.hu, Ed. in Chief, 24 ORA, Tatabanya, Komarom
Szold, Charlie...........................**(202) 885-1409**
American Univ., DC, Washington
Szostak, Janusz
janusz@exmedia.pl, Ed. in Chief, EXPRESS WIECZORNY, Warszawa
Szudlo, Betty...........................**(330) 721-4055**
sports@ohio.net, Sports Ed., The Medina County Gazette, OH, Medina
Szvetitz, Mike.............**(337) 749-6271 ext. 3146**
gmorgan@oanow.com, Sports Ed., Opelika-Auburn News, AL, Opelika
Szwejbka, Don..........................**(716) 366-6010**
szwejbled@corp.inxintl.com, Product Mgr., INX International Ink Co., NY, Dunkirk
Szymanski, Ed..........................**(308) 233-9718**
Prodn. Mgr., Distr., Kearney Hub, NE, Kearney
Szymanski, Jim.........................**(360) 754-5403**
jszymanski@olympia.gannett.com, Bus. Ed., The Olympian, WA, Olympia
Szymkowski, Scott
scott@playmusic.com, Pres., Play Music, Inc., CA, Fremont

T

Taber, Kim................................**501-337-7523**
Bus. Mgr., Malvern Daily Record, AR, Malvern
Taber, Albert
altaeq@aol.com, Pres., ALTA- Al Taber - PHA, GA, Roswell
Tabor, John
publisher@seacoastonline.com, Pub., Portsmouth Herald, NH, Portsmouth
Tackett, Dan
dan.tackett@lincolncourier.com, News Ed., The Courier, IL, Lincoln
Tadlock, Donna
dtadlock@coxnews.com, Controller, Waco Tribune-Herald, TX, Waco
Tafelski, Scott..........................**(312) 222-3159**
stafelski@tribune.com, Dir., Technical Devel., Chicago Tribune, IL, Chicago
Tafoya, Diane
dianet@chieftain.com, Mgr., Bus. Office/Purchasing Agent, The Pueblo Chieftain, CO, Pueblo
Taglauer, Denise......................**(989) 894-9677**
dtaglauer@bc-times.cocm, Adv. Nat'l Classified Mgr., The Bay City Times, MI, Bay City
Takahashi, Hiroshi
webmaster@mainichi.co.jp, Mng. Ed., THE MAINICHI DAILY NEWS, Tokyo
Takashi, Yamakoshi
sino2056@yomiuri.com, Ed., YOMIURI SHIMBUN, Sapporo, Hokkaido
Takeuchi, Masashi
masashi.takeuchi@dowjones.com, Sales Mgr., Dow Jones Newswires - Tokyo, Japan, Tokyo
Talbert, Lee.....................................**ext. 349**
Photo Dept. Mgr., Johnson City Press, TN,

Johnson City
Talbert, Tia ....ext. 21
tjt@astech.intermedia.com, Dir., Client Servs., ASTech InterMedia, CO, Denver
Talerico, Matt..........................(724) 225-2621
mtalerico@observer-reporter.com, Retail Sales Mgr., Observer-Reporter, PA, Washington
Tallackson, Andrew
atallackson@thenewsdispatch.com, Entertainment Ed., News Dispatch, IN, Michigan City
Talley, Lucy
lucy.talley@jacksonville.com, Pub., The Florida Times-Union, FL, Jacksonville
Tallmadge, David..........(770) 428-9411 ext. 464
Prodn. Mgr., Marietta Daily Journal, GA, Marietta
Tam, Shirley
stam@thecitizen.southam.ca, Controller, The Ottawa Citizen, ON, Ottawa
Tamas, Vasile
rasunetu@bistrita.astral.ro, Ed. in Chief, RASUNETUL, Bistrita, Brista-Nasaud
Tamayo, Ron
abantetonite@gmail.com, Adv. Mgr., ABANTE, Manila
Tamberj, Terje
terje.tamberj@budstikka.no, Adv.Mgr., BUDSTIKKE, Billingstad
Tambling, Richard
rtambling@journalinquirer.com, Living Section Ed., Journal Inquirer, CT, Manchester
Tamman, Jennifer.....................(941) 957-5324
jennifer.tamman@heraldtribune.com, Adv. Mgr., Nat'l, Sarasota Herald-Tribune, FL, Sarasota
Tamraz, Cathy Baron........................Pres./COO
Business Wire - San Francisco, CA, CA, San Francisco
Pres./COO, Business Wire - Boston, MA, MA, Boston
Tan, Whye-Ko..........................+65 6723 8150
whye-ko.tan@nytimes.com, Regional Director, Asia Pacific, New York Times Syndicate, NY, New York
Tan, Alexis S...........................(509) 335-8535
Prof., Washington State University, WA, Pullman
Tan, Whye-Ko..........................+65 6723 8150
whye-ko.tan@nytimes.com, Regional Director, Asia Pacific, New York Times News Service, NY, New York
Tanabe, Katsuji
keiei-kikaku@agrinews.co.jp, Chrmn., NIHON NOGYO SHIMBUN, Tokyo
Tanaka, Shigeru
hostmaster@shikoku-np.co.jp, Exec. Officer, SHIKOKU SHIMBUN, Takamatsu City, Shikoku
Tanaka, Kazuomi
dai-ad@tokyo-sports.co.jp, Osaka Head Officer, OSAKA SPORTS, Osaka, Osaka
Tanksley, Fia...............(434) 793-2311 ext. 3116
ftanksley@registerbee.com, Distr. Mgr., Danville Register & Bee, VA, Danville
Tanner, Jetty ....ext. 200
jetty.tanner@gaflnews.com, Office Mgr., The Tifton Gazette, GA, Tifton
Tanner, Rachel
dixiesun@dixie.edu, Dixie State College, UT, Saint George
Tanner, Hal H.......................(919) 739-7906
htanner3@newsargus.com, Publisher, Goldsboro News-Argus, NC, Goldsboro
Tanner, James
jtanner@verafast.com, Mktg. Devel. Mgr., Ver-A-Fast Corp., OH, Rocky River
Tanoos, Keith ....(775) 882-2111
ktanoos@sierranevadamedia.com, Circ. Dir., Nevada Appeal, NV, Carson City
Tant, Greg
greg.tant@coxinc.com, Dir., Newsprint Supply, Cox Newspapers, Inc., GA, Atlanta
Tapia, Roberto
oescamilla@diariodelsur.com.mx, Gen. Mgr., DIARIO DEL SUR, Tapachula, Chis
Tarabini, Laura................................ext. 1484
laura.tarabini@uniontrib.com, Dir., Direct Mktg., The San Diego Union-Tribune, CA, San Diego
Taraska, Morey ....(217) 224-3403
mtaraska@qni.biz, Asst. to Pres./CEO, Quincy Newspapers, Inc., IL, Quincy
Tarica, Joe 805-781-7911
jtarica@thetribunenews.com, Presentation Editor, The Tribune, CA, San Luis Obispo
Tarnowski, Lynn ....(715) 395-5010
ltarnowski@superiortelegram.com, Prodn. Mgr., The Daily Telegram, WI, Superior
Tarot, Gilles..........................(202) 414-0637
gilles.tarot@afp.com, Mktg./Sales Dir., North America, Agence France-Presse - Washington, DC, DC, Washington
Tarquinio, Marco
segr.direttore@avvenire.it, Ed., AVVENIRE, Milano
Tarr, Ashley...............................(607) 777-2244
SUNY/Binghamton, NY, Binghamton
Tash, Paul ....(727) 893-8887
ptash@tampabay.com, Chrmn./CEO/Ed., Tampa Bay Times, FL, Saint Petersburg
Tate, Tom ....(417) 836-1175
ttate@news-leader.com, Prodn. Dir., Springfield News-Leader, MO, Springfield
Tate, Jennifer ....(937) 229-3211
Univ. of Dayton Law School, OH, Dayton
Tate, Byron ....(479) 784-0444
btate@swtimes.com, Exec. Ed., Times Record, AR, Fort Smith
Tate, Lorie
lori.tate@augustachronicle.com, Adv. Acct. Mgr., The Augusta Chronicle, GA, Augusta
Tate, Frances ....(940) 720-3490
tatef@wtr.com, Books Ed., Wichita Falls Times Record News, TX, Wichita Falls
Tate, Sean...............................(541) 383-0386
state@bendbulletin.com, Adv. Mgr., The Bulletin, OR, Bend
Tate, Tom
jttate@gannett.com, Gen. Mgr., The Baxter Bulletin, AR, Mountain Home
Tate, Suzanne..........................(276) 645-2534
state@bristolnews.com, Opinion Ed., Bristol Herald Courier, VA, Bristol
Tatina, Lisa
ltatina@post-trib.com, Pub., Post-Tribune, IN, Merrillville
Tatum, Bill.............................(417) 836-1185
btatum@news-leader.com, City Ed., Springfield News-Leader, MO, Springfield
Tavey, Debra
director@thereporter.com, Adv. Dir., The Reporter, CA, Vacaville
Tawie, Sulok
stawie@nstp.com.my, Bureau Chief, THE NEW STRAITS TIMES, Kuching, Sarawak
Taxa, Martin
martin.taxa@kleinezeitung.at, Circ. Mgr., KLEINE ZEITUNG, 8010 Graz
Tay, Alvin
alvintay@sph.com.sg, Ed., BUSINESS TIMES, Singapore
Taylerson, Beth........................(803) 329-4048
btaylerson@heraldonline.com, Dir., HR, The Herald, SC, Rock Hill
Taylor, Vicki
vtaylor@brownpublishing.com, Pub., The Galion Inquirer, OH, Galion
Taylor, Monica..........................785-832-6389
mtaylor@ljworld.com, Marketing Director, The World Co.- Lawrence, Kan., Journal-World, KS, Lawrence
Taylor, David
dtaylor@hcnonline.com, Mng. Ed., Pasadena Citizen, TX, Pasadena
Taylor, Jon
jtaylor@portervillerecorder.com, New Media Mgr., The Porterville Recorder, CA, Porterville
Taylor, Rob ....(907) 561-1674
unicom@unicom-alaska.com, Vice Pres./Gen. Mgr., Unicom, Inc., AK, Anchorage
Taylor, Larry...........................(803) 644-2396
ltaylor@aikenstandard.com, Sports Ed., Aiken Standard, SC, Aiken
Taylor, Becky...........................(765) 420-5387
btaylor@journalandcourier.com, Adv. Mgr., Classified, Journal and Courier, IN, Lafayette
Taylor, Abigail
ads.wheatonrecord@gmail.com, Advertising Manager, Wheaton College, IL, Wheaton
Taylor, Dan ....(707) 521-5243
dtaylor@pressdemocrat.com, Entertainment Ed., The Press Democrat, CA, Santa Rosa
Taylor, Anne...........................(425) 564-2434
Bellevue Cmty. College, WA, Bellevue
Taylor, Heber..........................(409) 683-5239
heber.taylor@galvnews.com, Ed., The Galveston County Daily News, TX, Galveston
Taylor, Davis...........................559-735-3230
Advertising Director, Tulare Advance-Register, CA, Visalia
Taylor, Kevin ....(760) 754-2891
ktaylor@u-bild.com, Pres., U-Bild Newspaper Features, CA, Oceanside
Taylor, Ray
ray.taylor@svherald.com, Circ. Mgr., Sierra Vista Herald, AZ, Sierra Vista
Taylor, Keith
ktaylor@winchestersun.com, Sports Ed., The Winchester Sun, KY, Winchester
Taylor, Davis...........................559-735-3230
Advertising director, Visalia Times-Delta, CA, Visalia
Taylor, Bill.............................(850) 599-2337
btaylor@tallahassee.com, Opns./Circ. Dir., Tallahassee Democrat, FL, Tallahassee
Taylor, Beverly 806-669-2525
classified@thepampanews.com, Classified Sale Representative, The Pampa News, TX, Pampa
Taylor, Angela ....(409) 683-5239
angela.taylor@galvnews.com, Community News Editor, The Galveston County Daily News, TX, Galveston
Taylor, Barbara
btaylor@lfpress.com, News Ed., The London Free Press, ON, London
Taylor, Billie ....(252) 265-7838
Adv. Mgr., Creative Servs., The Wilson Daily Times, NC, Wilson
Taylor, Madison 336-506-3030
mtaylor@thetimesnews.com, Ed., Times-News, NC, Burlington
Taylor, Dee ....(803) 644-2371
deetaylor@aikensstandard.com, Adv. Mgr., Aiken Standard, SC, Aiken
Taylor, Harvey ....(519) 894-2250 ext. 2678
htaylor@therecord.com, City Ed., The Record, ON, Kitchener
Taylor, Jeff ....(904) 819-3527
jeff.taylor@staugustinerecord.com, Prodn. Superintendent, Pre Press, The St. Augustine Record, FL, Saint Augustine
Taylor, Brian ....(301) 733-5131
IT Director, The Herald-Mail, MD, Hagerstown
Taylor, Keith...........................(919) 739-7833
ktaylor@newsargus.com, Online Ed., Goldsboro News-Argus, NC, Goldsboro
Taylor, Art
ataylor@journal-news.net, Prodn. Mgr., Opns., The Journal, WV, Martinsburg
Taylor, Gerald J.
press@qconline.com, Pub., The Dispatch, IL, Moline
Taylor, Daryl
dtaylor@bannergraphic.com, Gen. Mgr., Banner-Graphic, IN, Greencastle
Taylor, Jeff ....(313) 222-5150
jtaylor@freepress.com, Deputy Mng. Ed., Detroit Free Press, MI, Detroit
Taylor, Bridgett ....(802) 468-5611
Castleton State College, VT, Castleton
Taylor, Monica..........................785-832-6389
mtaylor@ljworld.com, Marketing Director, The World Co.- Lawrence, Kan., Journal-World, KS, Lawrence
Taylor, Karen..........................(615) 329-8706
Fisk Univ., TN, Nashville
Taylor, Gerald J.
gjtaylor@qconline.com, Ed., The Rock Island Argus, IL, Rock Island
Tchounkeu, Severin
lanouvelleexpression2005@yahoo.fr, Ed., LA NOUVELLE EXPRESSION, Douala
Tebbe, Jay
letters@bnd.com, Pres./Pub., Belleville News-Democrat, IL, Belleville
Techaira, Patricia
patricia.techaira@sddt.com, Mgr., HR, The Daily Transcript, CA, San Diego
Tedeschi, George.....................(202) 462-1400
gtedeschi@gciu.org, Pres., Graphic Communications International, DC, Washington
Tedrick, Ben...........................(979) 731-4679
william.tedrick@theeagle.com, Mgmt. Info Servs. Mgr., The Eagle, TX, Bryan
Tedrick, Brian..........................301-733-5131
Circulation Director, The Herald-Mail, MD, Hagerstown
Tegopoulos, Chr
elef@enet.gr, Pub., ELEFTHEROTYPIA, Athens, Central Greece
Teheux, Michelle
mteheux@pekintimes.com, Ed., Pekin Daily Times, IL, Pekin
Teicher, James
jim@cybersmart.org, Exec. Dir., Stockalert, Inc., NJ, Bernardsville
Teisenhanslueke, Ralf
r.teisenhanslueke@schwaebische-zeitung.de, Ed. in Chief, SCHWABISCHE ZEITUNG, Leutkirch
Teitgen, Robert.......................(585) 258-2381
bteitgen@rocheste.gannett.com, Adv. Dir., Display, Democrat and Chronicle.com, NY, Rochester
Teixeira, Demostenes
redacao@correiodabahia.com.br, Ed., Empresa Baiana de Jornalismo (a member of Rede Bahia de Comunicacao), Salvador, Bahia
Teixidor, Jordi XargayÂ¢ i
diaridegirona@epi.es, Dir., Diari De Girona, Fornells de la Selva, Girona
Tejada, Sergio Pablo
stejada@am.com.mx, Adv. Mgr., Am Guanajuato, Guanajuato, Guanajuato
Telfer, John H. ....(989) 839-4240
jtelferii@mdn.net, Ed., Midland Daily News, MI, Midland
Temple, Darlene 203-354-1079
Asst. Circulation Director, The Hour Publishing Co., CT, Norwalk
Temple, Ron ....ext. 672
Prodn. Mgr., Mailroom, Bisbee Daily Review, AZ, Bisbee
Temple, John ....(303) 892-5102
editor@rockymountainnews.com, Ed., Rocky Mountain News, CO, Denver
Ten Dam, Geert................................5196196
directie@hdcmedia.nl, Ed., NOORDHOLLANDS DAGBLAD, Alkmaar
Tena, Ulpiano R. Sortillon
suscripciones@periodicovictoria.com.mx, Circ. Mgr., Victoria de Durango, Durango, Durango
Tenemark, Martin
martin.tenemark@economia.cz, Mgr., HOSPODARSKE NOVINY, Prague
Tenenbaum, David M.
dmt@merlinone.com, Pres./CEO, MerlinOne, Inc., MA, Quincy
Teni, Nandakumar
ng_teni@rediffmail.com, Ed. in Chief, DESHDOOT/SUNDAY DESHDOOT, Nashik, Maharashtra
Tennyson, David
dtennyson@couriernews.net, Pub., Blytheville Courier News, AR, Blytheville
Tenorio, Miguel Angel Castorena
vertice@prodigy.net.mx, Pres./Dir., VERTICE, Chilpancingo, Guerrero
Teoh, Jun-Kai..........................732-690-2233
editor@universitychronicle.net, Editor-in-Chief, St. Cloud State Univ., MN, Saint Cloud
Ter Meer, Sheila K. ....ext. 221
sheila.termeer@tribstar.com, Online Ed., The Tribune Star, IN, Terre Haute
Teran, Jamie
redaccion@telegrafo.com.ec, Dir., El Telegrafo CA, Guayaquil, Guayas
Terenzio, Matt 203-354-1087
Web Development Director, The Hour Publishing Co., CT, Norwalk
Tergeoglou, Tim.........................845-331-5000
ttergeoglou@freemanonline.com, Sales Manager, Daily Freeman, NY, Kingston
Terheyden, Jorg
verlag@bbv-net.de, Proprietor, BOCHOLTER-BORKENER VOLKSBLATT, Bocholt
Termini, Deanne L. ....(214) 640-3107
dtermini@beldenassociates.com, Pres., Belden Associates, TX, Dallas
Terrell, Scott
sterrell@skagitpublishing.com, Photo Ed., Skagit Valley Herald, WA, Mount Vernon
Terry, Bob

bterry@thealabamabaptist.org, Pres., Alabama Baptist, AL, Birmingham
Terry, Michele 336-506-3071
mterry@thetimesnews.com, Mgr., Mktg./Promo., Times-News, NC, Burlington
Terry, Reese
rterry@dailycorinthian.com, Pub., The Daily Corinthian, MS, Corinth
Terry, Michael ....(352) 544-5201
Online Mgr., Hernando Today, FL, Brooksville
Terziyski, Jordan
jterziyski@perretta.com, Asst. Serv. Mgr., Perretta Graphics Corp., NY, Poughkeepsie
Tesch, Susie ....(979) 830-4286
Blinn College, TX, Brenham
Tessier, Jordon ....(508) 967-3120
Adv. Mgr., Taunton Daily Gazette, MA, Taunton
Tew, James
jamest@kpcnews.net, Online Ed., Herald-Republican, IN, Angola
Tews, Monica
mtews@ottumwacourier.com, Adv. Dir., The Ottumwa Courier, IA, Ottumwa
Texter, Lynne
texter@lasalle.edu, Chair, La Salle University, PA, Philadelphia
Thacker, Brett
bthacker@express-news.net, Mng. Ed., Randolph Wingspread, TX, San Antonio
bthacker@express-news.net, Mng. Ed., Brooks Discovery News, TX, San Antonio
bthacker@express-news.net, Mng. Ed., Bulverde Community News, TX, San Antonio
bthacker@express-news.net, Mng. Ed., Fort Sam News Leader, TX, San Antonio
bthacker@express-news.net, Mng. Ed., Kelly Observer, TX, San Antonio
bthacker@express-news.net, Mng. Ed., Lackland Talespinner, TX, San Antonio
bthacker@express-news.net, Mng. Ed., Medical Patriot, TX, San Antonio
bthacker@express-news.net, Mng. Ed., North Central News, TX, San Antonio
bthacker@express-news.net, Mng. Ed., Northeast Herald, TX, San Antonio
bthacker@express-news.net, Mng. Ed., Northwest Weekly, TX, San Antonio
bthacker@express-news.net, Mng. Ed., San Antonio Express-News, TX, San Antonio
Thakur, Kiran D.
tarunad@rediffmail.com, Pub., TARUN BHARAT, Belgaum, Karnataka
Thangal, M. I.
knr@chandrika.net, Ed., CHANDRIKA DAILY, Kannur Rd., Kerala
Thatcher, Mollie ....(650) 254-8029
mollie.thatcher@dialog.com, Office Admin., Dialog Corp., CA, Mountain View
Thayer, Daniel L. ....(518) 565-4140
dthayer@pressrepublican.com, Prodn. Dir., Press-Republican, NY, Plattsburgh
The Huynh, Dinh
toasoan@nhandan.org.vn, Ed. in Chief, NHAN DAN, Hanoi
Theall, James ....(303) 440-7855
sales@immediate.com, Pres./CEO, Media Marketing, Inc., CO, Westminster
Theall, Patti 303-997-1350
Patti.theall@immediate.com, VP, Sales, Media Marketing, Inc., CO, Westminster
Thedford, Tommy
tommy@wieck.com, Network Mgr., Wieck Media, TX, Dallas
Theile, Ralph ....(954) 724-2181
theiler@graphline.com, Vice Pres.,Marketing/Operations, GraphLine, FL, Sunrise
Theis, Peter F.
sales@conservit.com, Pres., Conservit Corporation, IL, Lindenhurst
Theiss, Bernhard
info@sdz-medien.de, MD, SCHWABISCHE POST, Aalen
Thell, Magnus
magnus.thell@cision.com, Gen. Mgr., Cision AB, Stockholm
Therien, Mike
mike.therien@ott.sunpub.com, Ed. in Chief, The Ottawa Sun, ON, Ottawa
Therrien, James ....ext. 110
jtherrien@benningtonbanner.com, Ed., Bennington Banner, VT, Bennington
Thibodeaux, Shane ....(985) 850-1141
shane.thibodeaux@houmatoday.com, Lifestyles Editor, The Courier, LA, Houma
Thilak Kumar, K.N.
editor@deccanherald.co.in, Ed. in Chief, DECCAN HERALD, Bangalore, Karnataka
Thilak Kumar, K.N.
editor@decanherald.co.in, Ed. in Chief, PRAJAVANI, Bangalore, Karnataka
Thoma, Caroline
caroline.thoma@ringier.ch, CEO, BLICK, Zurich
Thomas, Bryan
bryant@ttdusa.com, CEO, Thomas Taber & Drazen, CO, Denver
Thomas, Mark ....(414) 224-2201
Circ. Sr. Vice Pres., Milwaukee Journal Sentinel, WI, Milwaukee
Thomas, Mark ....(405) 524-4421
mpace@okpress.com, Exec. Dir., Oklahoma Press Association, OK, Oklahoma City
Thomas, Donna ....(662) 620-5258
Dir., PR, Itawamba Cmty. College, MS, Fulton
Thomas, Michele
mthomas@triplicate.com, Pub., The Daily Triplicate, CA, Crescent City
Thomas, Jeff ....(719) 636-0384
jeff.thomas@gazette.com, Vice Pres./Ed., The Gazette, CO, Colorado Springs
Thomas, Eric
info@lsoft.com, CEO, L-Soft International, Inc., MD, Landover
Thomas, Douglas ....(312) 222-3915
dthomas@tribune.com, Adv. Vice Pres., Sales, Chicago Tribune, IL, Chicago
Thomas, Michael ....(508) 676-2530
mthomas@heraldnews.com, Sports Ed., The Herald News, MA, Fall River
Thomas, Mark
mthomas@okpress.com, Exec. Vice Pres., Oklahoma Press Service, OK, Oklahoma City
Thomas, Timothy
kteditor@kentontimes.com, Wire Ed., The Kenton Times, OH, Kenton
Thomas, Lovan
lthomas@natchitochestimes.com, Pres./Pub., Natchitoches Times, LA, Natchitoches
Thomas, Ms. Rosalina ...(646) 223-4000 ext. 5457
rosalina.thomas@thomsonreuters.com, Vice Pres./Head of Sales - The Americas, Reuters News Agency, Thomson Reuters, Reuters Media, NY, New York
Thomas, Russ
russ.thomas@traunerconsulting.com, Mgr., New Bus., Trauner Consulting Services, Inc., PA, Philadelphia
Thomas, Bill ....(231) 933-1467
bthomas@record-eagle.com, Exec. Ed., Record-Eagle, MI, Traverse City
Thomas, Mr. Richard G.
info@voterama.info, Pub./Ed., Voterama in Congress - Thomas Voting Reports, VA, Washington
Thomas, Marie
mthomas@sentinel-tribune.com, Educ. Ed., Sentinel Company, OH, Bowling Green
Thomas, Hal
hthomas@mullermartinims.com, Dir., Integrated Systems Engineering, Muller Martini Mailroom Systems, Inc., PA, Allentown
Thomas, David ....(757) 247-4715
dthomas@dailypress.com, Creative Servs. Mgr., Daily Press, VA, Newport News
Thomas-Anderson, Gloria, LMSW ...913-433-3877
gloria@hearttones.com, Pres./Founder, Heart Tones, MO, Kansas City
Thomason, Craig
cthomason@express-news.net, Asst. Mng. Ed., News, Randolph Wingspread, TX, San Antonio
cthomason@express-news.net, Asst. Mng. Ed., News, Brooks Discovery News, TX, San Antonio
cthomason@express-news.net, Asst. Mng. Ed., News, Bulverde Community News, TX, San Antonio
cthomason@express-news.net, Asst. Mng. Ed., News, Fort Sam News Leader, TX, San Antonio
cthomason@express-news.net, Asst. Mng. Ed., News, Kelly Observer, TX, San Antonio
cthomason@express-news.net, Asst. Mng. Ed., News, Lackland Talespinner, TX, San Antonio
cthomason@express-news.net, Asst. Mng. Ed., News, Medical Patriot, TX, San Antonio
cthomason@express-news.net, Asst. Mng. Ed., News, North Central News, TX, San Antonio
cthomason@express-news.net, Asst. Mng. Ed., News, Northeast Herald, TX, San Antonio
cthomason@express-news.net, Asst. Mng. Ed., News, Northwest Weekly, TX, San Antonio
cthomason@express-news.net, Asst. Mng. Ed., News, San Antonio Express-News, TX, San Antonio
Thomasson, Jana M.
jthomasson@themountainpress.com, Pub., The Mountain Press, TN, Sevierville
Thomasson, William W.
colleen@newnan.com, Pres., The Times-Herald, GA, Newnan
Thome, John
sales@bstpromark.com, Vice Pres., Mktg., BST Pro Mark, IL, Elmhurst
Thompsen, Philip ....(610) 436-2283
The Quad (West Chester University), PA, West Chester
Thompson, Rowland
anewspaper@aol.com, Exec. Dir., Allied Daily Newspapers of Washington, WA, Olympia
Thompson, Chris
chris.thomson@dailyreporter.com, Ed., The Daily Reporter, WI, Milwaukee
Thompson, Chip
editor@redbluffdailynews.com, Ed., Daily News, CA, Red Bluff
Thompson, David
dthompson@kypress.com, Exec. Dir., Kentucky Press Service, Inc., KY, Frankfort
Thompson, Edward
requestinfo@thompsoncabinet.com, Vice Pres./Sales Mgr., Thompson Cabinet Co., MI, Ludington
Thompson, Katie ....(877) 639-2232
katie@agfeatures.com, Ed., Ag Features, IA, Fostoria
Thompson, Tim 205-722-0115
tim.thompson@tuscaloosanews.com, Pub., The Tuscaloosa News, AL, Tuscaloosa
Thompson, Karen Fox ....(812) 379-5679
kfox@therepublic.com, Dir., Info. Servs., Home News Enterprises, IN, Columbus
Thompson, Becky ....(208) 465-8131
bthompson@idahopress.com, Adv. Supvr., Classified, Idaho Press-Tribune, ID, Nampa
Thompson, Andy
andythompson@eveningtribune.com, Mng. Ed., The Evening Tribune, NY, Hornell
Thompson, Donna
trends@herkimertelegram.com, Trends Ed., The Evening Telegram, NY, Herkimer
Thompson, Joyce 336-506-3003
jthompson@thetimesnews.com, HR Manager, Times-News, NC, Burlington
Thompson, Michael ....(734) 994-6854
mthompson@annarbornews.com, Nat'l Ed., The Ann Arbor News, MI, Ann Arbor
Thompson, Amie 406-791-6536
Specialty Publication Editor, Great Falls Tribune, MT, Great Falls
Thompson, Tim ....(248) 745-4655
tim.thompson@oakpress.com, Photo Ed., The Oakland Press, MI, Pontiac
Thompson, David T. ....(502) 223-8821
dthompson@kypress.com, Executive Director, Kentucky Press Association, Inc., KY, Frankfort
Thompson, Lisa ....(479) 872-5168
lthompson@nwaonline.net, Mng. Ed., The Morning News of Northwest Arkansas, AR, Springdale
Thompson, James ....(208) 664-8176 ext. 1001
Pub., Coeur d'Alene Press, ID, Coeur d'Alene
Thompson, Dennis ....(603) 610-1121
dthompson@seacoastonline.com, Circ. Mgr., Home Delivery, Portsmouth Herald, NH, Portsmouth
Thompson, Clara
composing@jacksonvilleprogress.com, Composing Mgr., Jacksonville Daily Progress, TX, Jacksonville
Thompson, Liz ....(301) 733-5131
Digital Director, The Herald-Mail, MD, Hagerstown
Thompson, Brad
bthomps@linfield.edu, Chair, Linfield College, OR, McMinnville
Thompson, Cliff
cthompson@thetribunenews.com, Circ. Mgr., Customer Serv., The Tribune, CA, San Luis Obispo
Thompson, Bill ....ext. 5707
Books Ed., The Post and Courier, SC, Charleston
Thompson, John ....(519) 894-2250 ext. 2372
jthompson@therecord.com, Adv. Mgr., Nat'l/Multi-Market, The Record, ON, Kitchener
Thompson, Sandra ....(479) 571-6432
sandyt@nwarktimes.com, Dir., Finance, Northwest Arkansas Times, AR, Fayetteville
Thompson, Nancy
nthompson@journalinquirer.com, Town News Ed., E. Windsor/Manchester/S. Windsor/Windsor/Windsor Locks, Journal Inquirer, CT, Manchester
Thompson, Terry ....(352) 544-5250
Circ. Mgr., Hernando Today, FL, Brooksville
Thompson, Terry ....(813) 259-7435
Circ. Mgr., Mktg., The Tampa Tribune, FL, Tampa
Thompson, Scott ....(561) 379-2635
sat@wingopromo.com, Pres., Wingo, LLC, FL, Wellington
Thompson, Dean
dthompson@cybermesa.com, Ed., Silver City Daily Press & Independent, NM, Silver City
Thompson, Jim ....(706) 208-2222
jim.thompson@onlineathens.com, Editorial Page Ed., Athens Banner-Herald, GA, Athens
Thompson-Kolar, Mark ....(734) 994-6790
mthompson@annarbornews.com, Graphics Ed./Art Dir., The Ann Arbor News, MI, Ann Arbor
Thoms, Sue ....(616) 222-5863
sthoms@grpress.com, Books Ed., The Grand Rapids Press, MI, Grand Rapids
Thomsen, Claus
ct@mf.dk, Ed., MORSO FOLKEBLAD, Nykobing, Llolland-Falster
Thomson, T.J. ....(303) 432-6303
editor@csceagle.com, Executive Editor, The Eagle, NE, Chadron
Thomson, Diane
ads@moneysav.com, Gen. Mgr., Pacific Northwest Association of Want-Ad Newspapers, ID, Lewiston
Thomson, John ....(937) 225-2397
jthomson@coxohio.com, Administrative Ed., Dayton Daily News, OH, Dayton
Thomson, Max ....(724) 654-6651 ext. 648
mwthomson@cnhi.com, Pub., New Castle News, PA, New Castle
Thorn, Patti ....(303) 892-5419
thornp@rockymountainnews.com, Books Ed., Rocky Mountain News, CO, Denver
Thorn, Martha ....(410) 293-1536
US Naval Academy, MD, Annapolis
Thornburg, Ron ....(801) 625-4504
Circ. Dir., Standard-Examiner, UT, Ogden
Thornhill, Michael
corp@spnewsprint.com, Gen. Mgr., SP Newsprint Co., GA, Atlanta
Thornhill, David
dthornhill@acnpapers.com, Prodn. Supt., McKinney Courier-Gazette, TX, McKinney
Thornton, Gregory L.
tthornton@globe.com, Sr. Vice Pres., Employee Rel., The Boston Globe, MA, Boston
Thornton, Penny ....ext. 111
pthornton@wehco.com, Adv. Dir., The Sentinel-Record, AR, Hot Springs
Thornton, Teri T. ....(256) 740-5742
teri.thomason@timesdaily.com, Lifestyle Ed., TimesDaily, AL, Florence
Thorpe, Keith ....(360) 417-3524
Photo Chief, Peninsula Daily News, WA, Port Angeles
Thorson, Jared ....(262) 656-6209
jthorson@kenoshanews.com, Mgr., Sales/Mktg., Kenosha News, WI, Kenosha
Thorstensson, Anna-Karin 280 144

nyhet@corren.se, News Mgr., OSTGOTA CORRESPONDENTEN, Linkoping
Thrams, Gregory J.
gregt@wdtimes.com, Prodn. Mgr., Watertown Daily Times, WI, Watertown
Thrasher, Bonnie ....(870) 972-3075
Arkansas State Univ., AR, State University
Threde, Jill ....(916) 321-1469
jthrede@sacbee.com, Adv. Dir., Major Accts., The Sacramento Bee, CA, Sacramento
Threet, Kelli
kthreet@turlockjournal.com, Circ. Mgr., Turlock Journal, CA, Turlock
Throlson, Scott
sports@jamestownsun.com, Sports Ed., The Jamestown Sun, ND, Jamestown
Thul, Walter
redaktion@rhein-zeitung.net, Bus. Mgr., RHEIN-ZEITUNG, Koblenz
Thul, Valter
redaktion@rhein-zeitung.net, Bus. Mgr., Rhein-Hunsruck Zeitung, Koblenz
Thurman, Susan
sthurman@c-dh.net, Photo Dept. Mgr., Columbia Daily Herald, TN, Columbia
Thurmond, Jason......................(937) 339-5563
Prodn. Dir., Troy Daily News, OH, Troy
Thurston, Dee Dee ....(985) 850-1149
deedee.thurston@houmatoday.com, City Editor, The Courier, LA, Houma
Thurston, Dayla ....(317) 398-1291
photog@shelbynews.com, Chief Photographer, The Shelbyville News, IN, Shelbyville
Thusat, Peter
peter.thusat@thunderstone.com, CMO, Thunderstone Software LLC, OH, Cleveland
Thwaites, Bob
news@thestarcanwest.com, Dir., Mktg./Reader Sales, The Windsor Star, ON, Windsor
Thyken, Bill
wthyken@ubnet.com, Controller, Walla Walla Union-Bulletin, WA, Walla Walla
Tian, Cheng Xi
hkness@hkcd.com.hk, Ed. in Chief, HONG KONG COMMERCIAL DAILY, Hong Kong
Tick, Drew Adam
info@infopager.com, CEO, infoPager Technologies, Inc., Jerusalem
Ticktin, Neil
press_releases@mactech.com, Pub., MacTech Magazine, CA, Westlake Village
Tidrick, Dennis...............................ext. 2216
dennis.tidrick@scni.com, Prodn. Mgr., Pre Press, The Advocate, CT, Stamford
Tiedeman, Jeff
jtiedeman@gfherald.com, Food Columnist, Grand Forks Herald, ND, Grand Forks
Tiedemann, Paul ....(575) 763-3431
ptiedemann@cnjonline.com, Info Systems Mgr., Clovis News Journal, NM, Clovis
Tiedemann, Wally.....................(415) 382-7270
wtiedemann@marinij.com, Circ. Dir., Marin Independent Journal, CA, Novato
Tierney, Brian
btierney@phillynews.com, Pres./CEO, The Philadelphia Daily News, PA, Philadelphia
Tierney, D'arcy ....(604) 538-5501
darcyt@isd.ca, Sales Mgr., Innovative Systems Design, Inc., QC, Pointe-Claire
Tierno, Anthony F......................(303) 563-6360
tonytierno@medianewsgroup.com, Sr. Vice Pres., Opns., MediaNews Group Inc, CO, Denver
Tighe, Timothy 860/701-4242
t.tighe@theday.com, Press Manager, The Day Publishing Company, CT, New London
Tilcock, Wayne ....(530) 747-8060
photo@davisenterprise.net, Photo Ed., The Davis Enterprise, CA, Davis
Till, Martin K.
mtill@express-times.com, Pub./CEO/Pres., The Express-Times, PA, Easton
Tiller, Rosemary.......................(910) 343-2300
rosemary.tiller@starnewsonline.com, Deputy News Ed., Star-News, NC, Wilmington
Tiller, Martha ....(541) 633-2193
mtiller@bendbulletin.com, Special Projects Mgr., The Bulletin, OR, Bend
Tillotson, Dolph
dolph.tillotson@galvnews.com, Pres./Pub., The Galveston County Daily News, TX, Galveston
Timmer, Lori ....(615) 546-4262
lori.timmer@hollandsentinel.com, Community Content Team Leader, The Holland Sentinel, MI, Holland
Timmerman, Kelsey ....(937) 423-3517
kelsey@travelin-light.com, Writer/Photographer, Travelin' Light, IN, Muncie
Timney, Mark
mtimney@keene.edu, Asst. Prof., Keene State College of the University System of New Hampshire, NH, Keene
Tindal, Debbie ....ext. 145
mkeeler@thewhig.com, Adv. Supvr., Special Sections, The Kingston Whig-Standard, ON, Kingston
Ting, Ching Yi
cyting@taipei.org, Contact, Taipei Economic & Cultural Office, Information Division - New York, NY, NY, New York
Tingle, Bobby ....ext. 155
Circ. Dir., The Commercial Dispatch, MS, Columbus
Tingle, Kip.............................(970) 748-2976
ktingle@vaildaily.com, Circ. Mgr., Vail Daily, CO, Vail
Tingley, Ken............................(518) 792-3225
tingley@poststar.com, Mng. Ed., The Post-Star, NY, Glens Falls
Tingwall, John
johnt@metrosuburbia.com, Adv. Sales Mgr., Metro Suburbia, Inc./Newhouse Newspapers, MI, Farmington Hills
Tinkel, Janice
jant_bus@dailynews.net, Bus. Mgr., The Hays Daily News, KS, Hays
Tinsley, Garry.........................(770) 535-6353
gtinsley@gainesvilletimes.com, Circ. Dir., The Times, GA, Gainesville
Tinsley, Anita
atinsley@americanpress.com, Bus. Mgr., Shearman Corporation, LA, Lake Charles
Tirey, Spencer ....(479) 872-5038
stirey@nwaonline.net, Photo Ed., The Morning News of Northwest Arkansas, AR, Springdale
Tischer, Bruce
btischer@gannett.com, Pres., Central States Circulation Managers Association, IL, Glasford
btischer@gannett.com, Appleton Post Crescent West, WI, Appleton
Titos, Athanasiabis
titos@apogevmatini.gr, Ed. in Chief, APOYEVMATINI, Athens, Central Greece
Titus, Sandra
stitus@seacoastonline.com, Adv. Mgr., Classified/Sales, Portsmouth Herald, NH, Portsmouth
Titus, Cathleen ....(212) 969-7537
ctitus@hearst.com, Vice Pres., Int'l Licensing, King Features Syndicate, NY, New York
ctitus@hearst.com, Vice Pres., Int'l Licensing, North America Syndicate, NY, New York
Tivula, Matt
tivula@newscurrent.com, Mktg. Mgr., News-Currents, WI, Madison
Tjitroseowarno, Soeharmono
info@pikiranrakyat.com, Dir., PIKIRAN RAKYAT, Bandung, West Java
Tobias, Eric M.
sales@tobiasinc.com, Vice Pres., Tobias Associates, Inc., PA, Ivyland
Tobin, Paulette
ptobin@gfherald.com, Entertainment Writer, Grand Forks Herald, ND, Grand Forks
Tobin, Jeff ....(712) 293-4207
Mng. Ed., Sports, Sioux City Journal, IA, Sioux City
Tobin, Tom ....(585) 258-2260
ttobin@democratandchronicle.com, Deputy Editorial Page Ed., Democrat and Chronicle.com, NY, Rochester
Tobita, Hidekazu
adm@hokkoku.co.jp, Pres./Ed. in Chief, HOKKOKU SHIMBUN, Kanazawa City, Hokuriku
Todd, Alan..............................(903) 237-7730
atodd@coxnews.com, Adv. Dir., Longview News-Journal, TX, Longview
Todd, Steven F. ....(609) 871-8022
stodd@phillyburbs.com, Circ. Dir., Burlington County Times, NJ, Willingboro
Todd, legals@tacomadailyindex.com ....Ed.
Tacoma Daily Index, WA, Tacoma
Todd, Wendy
wendytodd@reviewatlas.com, Adv. Mgr., Daily Review Atlas, IL, Monmouth
Todd, Michael..........................(801) 237-2117
mtodd@desnews.com, CFO, Deseret News, UT, Salt Lake City
Todd, Keven ....ext. 29
keven.todd@lamonitor.com, Publisher, Los Alamos Monitor, NM, Los Alamos
Toettrup, Claus
cmn@licitationen.dk, Ed., LICITATIONEN, Herlev
Tokie, Terry............................(740) 450-6778
Adv. Mgr., Display Sales, Times Recorder, OH, Zanesville
Tolentino, Eddie
etolentino@tngus.com, Vice Pres., Recycled Fibers (A Div. of The Newark Group), CA, Stockton
Toler, Jim...............................(518) 744-5211
jtoler@unitedmedia.com, Regl. Sales Mgr., Newspaper Enterprise Association (Div. of United Media), NY, New York
jtoler@unitedmedia.com, Regl. Sales Mgr., United Feature Syndicate (Div. of United Media), NY, New York
Tolis, K.
tolis@cosmoslarrissa.gr, Pub., ENIMEROSI, Trikala, Thessaly
Tolle, Jody 937-382-2574
jtolle@wnewsj.com, Business Office, Wilmington News Journal, OH, Wilmington
Tollefsen, Jan
jan.tollefsen@moss-avis.no, Ed., MOSS AVIS, Moss
Tollefson, Daniel J.
tollefson@sturgisjournal.com, Pub., Sturgis Journal, MI, Sturgis
Tolontan, Catalin
catalin.tolonton@gsp.ro, Ed. in Chief, GAZETA SPORTURILOR, Bucharest
Tolstrup, Kathleen
tvdata@tvdata.com, Sr. Vice Pres.-Sales, Tribune Media Services, NY, Glens Falls
Tolstrup, Kathleen ....(518) 792-9914 ext. 2200
kftolstrup@tribune.com, Gen. Mgr., Sales/Mktg., Tribune Media Services Entertainment Products, NY, Queensbury
Tomaselli, Ralph ....(203) 317-2220
rtomaselli@record-journal.com, Mng. Ed., Record-Journal, CT, Meriden
Tomasik, Mark
mark.tomasik@scripps.com, Ed., Treasure Coast News/Press-Tribune, FL, Stuart
Tomaske, Gordon
Gordon.tomaske@latimes.com, CFO, Times Community News (TCN), CA, Glendale
Tomczak, Gerry........................(951) 737-1313
gtomczak@pe.com, Adv. Mgr., Regl., The Press-Enterprise, CA, Riverside
Tomek, Phil 402-444-1047
Dir., IT, Omaha World-Herald, NE, Omaha
Tomek, Phil 402-444-1047
Dir., IT, Omaha World-Herald, NE, Omaha
Tomino, Steve ....(808) 525-8697
stomino@honolulu.gannett.com, Circ. Mgr., Home Delivery, Honolulu Star-Advertiser, HI, Honolulu
Tomino, Steve ....(808) 690-8864
stomino@staradvertiser.com, Circulation Director, Honolulu Star-Advertiser, HI, Honolulu
Tomlin, Jimmy.........................(336) 888-3578
jtomlin@hpe.com, Columnist, High Point Enterprise, NC, High Point
Tomlinson, Christopher ....ext. 354
Photo Ed., The Daily Sentinel, CO, Grand Junction
Tomlinson, Bruce
btomlinson@njherald.com, Ed., New Jersey Herald, NJ, Newton
Toms, Kati
ktoms@tricityherald.com, Exec. Ast, Tri-City Herald, WA, Kennewick
Toney, Douglas ....(830) 625-9144 ext. 201
doug.toney@herald-zeitung.com, Ed., New Braunfels Herald-Zeitung, TX, New Braunfels
Tong, Daniel
info@aucd.com.au, Ed., THE AUSTRALIAN CHINESE DAILY
Tong, Ivan
editor@thestandard.com.hk, Ed. in Chief, THE STANDARD, Hong Kong
Tonsing, Julie
fmtimes@fmtimes.com, Gen Mgr., Fort Morgan Times, CO, Fort Morgan
Toole, Scott...................................ext. 3488
news@express-times.com, Copy Desk News Ed., The Express-Times, PA, Easton
Toole, John ....(603) 668-4321 ext. 320
jtoole@unionleader.com, City Ed., New Hampshire Union Leader/New Hampshire Sunday News, NH, Manchester
Toomey, Edward
et@adwriter.com, Sec., National Association of Real Estate Publishers, OH, Sandusky
Topping, Julie..........................(313) 222-8850
Deputy Mng. Ed., Detroit Free Press, MI, Detroit
Topping, Paul
pault@mathtype.com, Pres., Design Science, Inc., CA, Long Beach
Tore Hamnoy, Jan
jan.tore.hamnoy@h-avis.no, MD, HAUGESUNDS AVIS, Haugesund
Torjussen, Lars Erik
03811@fvn.no, Ed., FAEDRELANDSVENNEN, Kristiansand
Tormeno, Mark ....(937) 754-2506
mtormeno@coxohio.com, Circ. Dir., Retention, Dayton Daily News, OH, Dayton
Toro, Alejandro
atoro@laprensaaustral.cl, Dir., LA PRENSA AUSTRAL, Punta Arenas
Toro, Alexandro
atoro@laprensaaustral.cl, Dir., Empresa Publicidad de La Prensa Austral Ltd., Punta Arenas
Torok, Jackie...........................(843) 317-7284
jtorok@florencenews.com, Metro Ed., Morning News, SC, Florence
Torpey, Mark
mtorpey@ledger.com, Sports Ed., The Enterprise, MA, Randolph
Torregrosa, Aixa.......................(215) 361-8824
atorregrosa@thereporteronline.com, Lifestyles Ed., The Reporter, PA, Lansdale
Torres, Melinda ....ext. 329
mtorres@redlandsdailyfacts.com, Adv. Rep, Classified, Redlands Daily Facts, CA, Redlands
Torres, Joe ....(870) 543-1434
jtorres@pbcommercial.com, Photo Ed., Pine Bluff Commercial, AR, Pine Bluff
Torres, Jason ....(718) 405-3471
College of Mt. St. Vincent, NY, Riverdale
Torrey, John
john.torrey@xpedx.com, Vice Pres./Gen. Mgr., Xpedx Printing Technologies, OH, Loveland
Tortolano, Jim ....(714) 895-8256
Advisor, Golden West College, CA, Huntington Beach
Toshev, Tosho
trud@zgb.bg, Ed. in Chief, TRUD, Sofia
Totanto, Christopher
leser@kurier.at, Ed. in Chief, KURIER, Vienna
Toth, Larry..............................(580) 585-5159
Circ. Dir., The Lawton Constitution, OK, Lawton
Toth, Levente
tothl@nepszabadsag.hu, Int. Editor in Chief, NEPSZABADSAG, Budapest, Pest
Touchberry, Bobby ....(803) 774-1252
bobbyt@theitem.com, Classified, The Item, SC, Sumter
Toulouse, Jorge Castro
jcastro@elimparcial.com, Dir., Opns, El Imparcial, Hermosillo, Sonora
Touney, Jan ....(563) 383-2264
Exec. Ed., Quad-City Times, IA, Davenport
Tousignant, Robert......................860/701-4479
b.tousignant@theday.com, Dir., Finance, The Day Publishing Company, CT, New London
Toutziaridou, Maria
elevima@otenet.gr, Dir., Thrakikes Ekdoseis Co., Komotini, Thrace
Touvell, Jim.............................(260) 461-8629
jtouvell@jg.net, Design Ed., The Journal Gazette, IN, Fort Wayne
Towery, Jennifer.......................(309) 686-3119

jtowery@pjstar.com, Neighbors Ed., Journal Star, IL, Peoria
Town, Lacey
ltown@ubnet.com, Mgr., HR, Walla Walla Union-Bulletin, WA, Walla Walla
Towner, Jim
jtowner@timesshamrock.com, Gen. Mgr., Times-Shamrock Communications, PA, Scranton
Towns, Stuart
townsws@appstate.edu, Chair, Appalachian State University, NC, Boone
Townsend, Jimmy..............................ext. 228
jtownsend@evansnewspapers.com, Prodn. Mgr., Mailroom, The Houston Home Journal, GA, Perry
Townsend, Billy ....ext. 236
btownsend@evansnewspapers.com, Prodn. Mgr., Opns., The Houston Home Journal, GA, Perry
Townsend, Debbie
debbie.townsend@bellinghamherald.com, Managing Editor, The Bellingham Herald, WA, Bellingham
Townsend, Candace ....(337) 317-1009
McNeese State Univ., LA, Lake Charles
Townsley, Steven.....................(212) 597-5733
steven.townsley@dowjones.com, Dir., Sales, The Wall Street Journal Sunday, NY, New York
Tracy, James F.
jftracyjr@sanpatpublishing.com, Ed., San Patricio County News, TX, Sinton
Tracy, Belinda 361-528-2515
Edtior, San Patricio County News, TX, Sinton
Trafton, Nancy Jo......................(765) 420-5265
ntrafton@journalandcourier.com, Dir., Market Devel., Journal and Courier, IN, Lafayette
Tragarz, Tina..........................(408) 920-5568
ttragarz@mercurynews.com, Dir., Acctg., San Jose Mercury News, CA, San Jose
Trahan, Brian
ldleader@cebridge.net, Ed., The Leesville Daily Leader, LA, Leesville
Trahan, Lucien G. ....(603) 668-4321 ext. 206
ltrahan@unionleader.com, Circ. Dir., Opns., New Hampshire Union Leader/New Hampshire Sunday News, NH, Manchester
Traini, Paolo
direttore@corriereadriatico.it, Mgr., CORRIERE ADRIATICO, Ancona
Trainor, John
general@ii1.iinfo.com, Pres., MagnaCom Corp., VA, Merrifield
Trama, Anthony
trama@creatorsmedia.com, CEO, The Creators Media Group, NY, Pleasantville
Tramazo, Rob ....(970) 748-2909
rtramazzo@vaildaily.com, Bus. Mgr., Vail Daily, CO, Vail
Trammell, Jim
jtrammel@highpoint.edu, Asst. Prof., High Point University, NC, High Point
Trammell, Janice
jtrammell@wichitaeagle.com, Asst. to the Pub., The Wichita Eagle, KS, Wichita
Tran, Vi ....(626) 395-6154
California Inst. of Technology, CA, Pasadena
Tran, Christine
tran@sddt.com, Dir., Mktg., The Daily Transcript, CA, San Diego
Tran, Ue Tsi-Ngoc
ly@saigon.teitic.com.vn, Ed. in Chief, SAIGON TIMES, Ho Chi Minh City
Tranquill, Joseph......................(740) 376-5412
Circ. Dir., The Marietta Times, OH, Marietta
Transmondi, Lori ....(856) 486-2590
lctrasmo@gannett.com, Dir., HR, Courier-Post, NJ, Cherry Hill
Trapani, Charlie ....(570) 628-6059
ctrapani@republicanherald.com, Sales Mgr., Republican Herald, PA, Pottsville
Trares, Ryan ....(317) 736-2727
rtrares@dailyjournal.net, Features Writer, Daily Journal, IN, Franklin
Traud, Steve 8124647503
trauds@courierpress.com, Director/Circulation Sales, Evansville Courier & Press, IN, Evansville
Trautman, Mike........................(502) 582-4226
mtroutmanr@courier-journal.com, Metro Ed., The Courier-Journal, KY, Louisville
Trautner, Laurie
ltrautner@thehawkeye.com, Adv. Mgr., Classified, The Hawk Eye, IA, Burlington
Travadiakis, Mike ....ext. 270
Prodn. Mgr., Pressroom, The World, OR, Coos Bay
Travis, Mark
mtravis@vnews.com, Pub., Valley News, VT, West Lebanon
Travis, Greg ....ext. 21
editor@murrayledger.com, Mng. Ed., The Murray Ledger & Times, KY, Murray
Traynor, Michael
michael.traynor@savannahnow.com, Pub., Savannah Morning News, GA, Savannah
Treadwell, Kent
ktreadwell@opubco.com, Financial Mgr., The Oklahoman, OK, Oklahoma City
Treadwell, Jaine
jaine.treadwell@troymessenger.com, Features Ed., The Messenger, AL, Troy
Treanor, Pat ....(626) 351-8184
Owner, Paste-Up Supply, CA, Temple City
Trebisovsky, Barbara ....(612) 278-0240
barbaratrebisovsky@mna.org, Asst. Exec. Dir., Minnesota Newspaper Association, MN, Minneapolis
Treinen, Mark..........................(715) 845-0655
mtreinen@wdhprint.com, Mng. Ed., The Wausau Daily Herald, WI, Wausau
Treise, Debbie...........................(352) 392-6557
Prof./Assoc. Dean, Grad. Studies/Research/Al and Effie Flanagan Prof. in Journalism & Communication, University of Florida, FL, Gainesville
Trejo, Anthony ....(469) 977-3696
atrejo@aldiatx.com, Online Ed., Al Dia, TX, Dallas
Tremaine, Kelly.........................(203) 789-5402
ktremaine@nhregister.com, Display Adv. Dir., New Haven Register, CT, New Haven
Tremaine, Kelly.........................(203) 731-3427
ktremaine@hearstmediact.com, Multimedia Sales Director, The News-Times, CT, Danbury
Tremblay, Wilfrid
wtremblay@highpoint.edu, Dir./Prof., High Point University, NC, High Point
Trenary, Cindy...........................316-269-6768
ctrenary@wichitaeagle.com, VP/Operations, The Wichita Eagle, KS, Wichita
Trevathan, Kim ....(865) 981-8241
Maryville College, TN, Maryville
Trevisani, Milena ....+39 347 0970225
trevisani@nytimes.com, Regional Director, Southern Europe, Middle East & Africa, New York Times News Service, NY, New York
Trevisani, Milena ....+39 347 0970225
trevisani@nytimes.com, Regional Director, Southern Europe, Middle East & Africa, New York Times Syndicate, NY, New York
Trexler, Frank...........................(865) 981-1139
frank.trexler@thedailytimes.com, Mng. Ed., The Daily Times, TN, Maryville
Trezise, Damian.........................03 58 203 151
damian.trezise@sheppnews.com.au, Chief Executive Officer, THE SHEPPARTON NEWS, Shepparton
Tribble, Michael........................(216) 999-4303
Dir. Design & Graphics, The Plain Dealer, OH, Cleveland
Trifunov, Dave
Dave.Trifunov@ok.bc.ca, Sports Ed., The Daily Courier, BC, Kelowna
Trillini, Jose Omar 445-9000
info@lanueva.com, Mktg. Mgr., La Nueva Provincia, Bahia Blanca, Provincia de Buenos Aires
Trillo, Sharla...........................(916) 288-6011
sharla@cnpa.com, Dir., CNPA Advertising Services, CA, Sacramento
Trillo, Manuel
zaragoza@abc.gr, Dir., ABC, Zaragoza
Trillos, Gabriel
gtrillos@laprensa.com.sv, News Editor, LA PRENSA GRAFICA, Cuscatlan, La Libertad
Trimble, Bernice
btrimble@ntin.net, Bus. Mgr., Gainesville Daily Register, TX, Gainesville
Trimble, Wally
wally.trimble@lehigh.edu, Head, Lehigh University, PA, Bethlehem
Trinko, David...........................(419) 993-2063
News Ed., The Lima News, OH, Lima
Tripathy, S.P.
sachindratripathi@timesofindia.com, Ed., NAVBHARAT TIMES, Bombay, Maharashtra
Tripp, Josie.............................(518) 565-4165
jtripp@pressrepublican.com, Controller, Press-Republican, NY, Plattsburgh
Tristan Pimienta, Angel
laprovincia@editorialprensacanaria.es, Dir., La Provincia, Las Palmas de Gran Canaria, Las Palmas
Trong, Vuong
sggponline@sggp.org.vn, Ed. in Chief, SAI GON GIAI PHONG, Ho Chi Minh City
Trosley, Steve
strosley@journalstandard.com, Pub., The Journal-Standard, IL, Freeport
Trott, Teresa R..........................(540) 374-5523
ttrott@freelancestar.com, HR Dir., The Free Lance-Star, VA, Fredericksburg
Troupe, Mary Jude
mjtroupe@punxsutawneyspirit.com, Adv. Dir., The Punxsutawney Spirit, PA, Punxsutawney
Troutman, Gary........................(501) 378-3825
Adv. Mgr., Recruitment, Arkansas Democrat-Gazette, AR, Little Rock
Trow, Lisa
ltrow@itemonline.com, Managing Editor, The Huntsville Item, TX, Huntsville
Trowbridge, Caroline...................785-832-7154
ctrowbridge@ljworld.com, Community Editor, The World Co.- Lawrence, Kan., Journal-World, KS, Lawrence
Trowbridge, Caroline ....(785) 832-7154
ctrowbridge@ljworld.com, Community Editor, The World Co.- Lawrence, Kan., Journal-World, KS, Lawrence
Truitt, Lamar
lamar@newnan.com, Adv. Mgr., The Times-Herald, GA, Newnan
Trujillo, Vernon
ads@alamosanews.com, Prodn. Foreman, Pressroom, The Valley Courier, CO, Alamosa
Truler, Juergen
sz-redaktion@schwetzinger-zeitung.de, Dir., Schwetzinger Zeitung, Schwetzingen
Truncale, Joseph
info@napl.org, Pres./CEO, National Association for Printing Leadership, NJ, Paramus
Truyts, Philippe
philippe.truyts@pressgroup.be, Contact, HET LAATSTE NIEUWS, Antwerp, Antwerp
Tryon, Thomas Lee...................(941) 957-5225
tom.tryon@heraldtribune.com, Editorial Page Ed., Sarasota Herald-Tribune, FL, Sarasota
Tsaganelis, N.
editor@imerisia.gr, Dir., IMERISIA, Athens, Central Greece
Tsaknakis, Efth
tsaknakis@fora.gr, Pub., PROINI, Grevena
Tsang, Kokan
tkp@takungpao.com, Ed., TA KUNG PAO, Hong Kong
Tsarouchas, Michalis
plogos@otenet.gr, Pub., PROINOS LOGOS, Trikala, Thessaly
Tshansavak, Tarinya
naewna@naewna.com, Ed., NAEW NA, Bangkok
Tsopanaki, Ivi-Alexandra.......................24610
ivi@rodiaki.gr, Editor, co-owner, RODIAKI, Rhodos, Aegean Islands
Tsoutsouris, Val ....(574) 224-5326
valsports@rochsent.com, Sports Ed., The Rochester Sentinel, IN, Rochester
Tsunekawa, Masahisa
m-houdo@shinmai.co.jp, Dir., SHINANO MAINICHI SHIMBUN, Matsumoto, Chubu
Tubbs, Kevin
akinfo@alaska.net, Pres., Alaska Information Marketing (AIM), AK, Anchorage
Tuca, Marius
marius.tuca@jurnalul.ro, Dir., JURNALUL NATIONAL, Bucharest
Tuccio-Koonz, Linda ....(203) 731-3330
ltuccio-koonz@newstimes.com, Entertainment Ed., The News-Times, CT, Danbury
Tuck, Deborah ....(252) 436-2821
advertising@hendersondispatch.com, Adv. Dir., Daily Dispatch, NC, Henderson
Tuck, Ken ....(334) 712-7960
ktuck@dothaneagle.com, Mng. Ed., The Dothan Eagle, AL, Dothan
Tucker, Ben
btucker@wayneindependent.com, Advertising Manager, The Wayne Independent, PA, Honesdale
Tucker, Rosalind C............................ext. 2102
roz@sportsnetwork.com, Vice Pres., Admin., The Sports Network (Div. of Computer Info. Network), PA, Hatboro
Tucker, R. Giles
gtucker@harriswilliams.com, Mng. Dir., Harris Williams & Co., VA, Richmond
Tucker, Diane Straus 202-955-9010
dstraustucker@washingtonmonthly.com, Pres./Pub., The Washington Monthly LLC, DC, Washington
Tucker, David ....(973) 392-1755
dtucker@starledger.com, Mng. Ed., The Star-Ledger, NJ, Newark
Tucker, Joanne..........................(562) 985-7998
California State Univ. Long Beach, CA, Long Beach
Tucker, Bill
btucker@theintelligencer.com, Assistant Editor, Edwardsville Intelligencer, IL, Edwardsville
Tucker, John
john.tucker@lakesunonline.com, Pub., Lake Sun Leader, MO, Camdenton
Tucker, Bob...........................(512) 445-3722
btucker@statesman.com, Prodn. Vice Pres., Opns., Austin American-Statesman, TX, Austin
Tucker, Michael........................(781) 784-0932
mtucker@tuckergroup.com, Owner, The Tucker Group, MA, Sharon
Tucker, Michael........................(513) 768-8938
mtucker@gmti.gannett.com, Dir., Sales & Marketing, Digital Collections, OH, Cincinnati
Tucker, Mark
mark.tucker@newhorizons.com, Vice. Pres., Mktg., New Horizons Computer Learning Center, CA, Anaheim
Tudor, Don..............................(740) 375-5144
dtudor@nncogannett.com, Presentation Ed., The Marion Star, OH, Marion
Tudor, Valentin
valentin.tudor@gds.ro, Deputy Chief Ed., GAZETA DE SUD, Craiova, Dolj
Tudose, Vasile
redactie@ziarulceahlaul.ro, Dir., CEAHLAUL, Neamt
Tuell, Tom ....ext. 205
ttuell@keysnews.com, Ed., The Key West Citizen, FL, Key West
Tueni, Ghassan
ghassan.tueni@annahar.com.lb, Pub./Pres., AN-NAHAR
Tuggle, Charles A. ....(919) 962-5694
Prof., University of North Carolina, NC, Chapel Hill
Tulett, Fred
executive@stl.co.nz, Ed., THE SOUTHLAND TIMES
Tuleya, R. Jonathan ....(610) 622-8812
Asst. City Ed., Day, Delaware County Daily Times, PA, Primos
Tuli, Suneet
info@widecom.com, Vice Pres., Sales/Mktg., WideCom Group, Inc., ON, Mississauga
Tullis, Candice..........................(316) 978-6905
Wichita State Univ., KS, Wichita
Tupper, Mark.............................(217) 421-7983
Exec. Sports Ed., Herald & Review, IL, Decatur
Turberville, Kim ....(856) 486-2943
kturber@gannett.com, Dir., Online, Courier-Post, NJ, Cherry Hill
Turcotte, Paul 212-239-7732
paul.turcotte@am-ny.com, Publisher, amNew York, NY, New York
Turcotte, Rita ....(413) 585-5288
rturcotte@gazettenet.com, Adv. Prodn. Mgr., Daily Hampshire Gazette, MA, Northampton
Turk, Jeff ....ext. 234
jturk@sharonherald.com, Religion Ed., The Herald, PA, Sharon
Turley, Mike............................(217) 788-1506
mike.turley@sj-r.com, Mng. Ed., Digital Deliv-

ery, The State Journal-Register, IL, Springfield
Turnbull, Thomas ....(585) 343-8000
tturnbull@batavianews.com, Publisher, The Daily News, NY, Batavia
tturnbull@batavianews.com, The Drummer Pennysaver, NY, Batavia
Turner, Charles
turnercc@jmu.edu, Prof., James Madison University, VA, Harrisonburg
Turner, K.A. ....(251) 219-5644
kturner@press-register.com, Bus./Finance Ed., Press-Register, AL, Mobile
Turner, Karl ....(216) 999-4262
Metro Editor, The Plain Dealer, OH, Cleveland
Turner, Jerry ....(918) 541-1934
jerryturner@familymediainc.com, Gen. Mgr., Publishers Idea Exchange, OK, Miami
Turner, Molly ....(312) 553-3191
mturner@ccc.edu, Faculty Advisor, Harold Washington College, IL, Chicago
Turner, Martha ....(202) 898-4825
Accounting, Press Associates, Inc., DC, Washington
Turner, Gina ....(318) 487-6481
gturner@thetowntalk.com, Mktg. Mgr., The Town Talk, LA, Alexandria
Turner, Danny ....ext. 278
dturner@athensmessenger.com, Prodn. Supvr., The Athens Messenger, OH, Athens
Turner, Dudley B.
dbturner@uakron.edu, Dir., University of Akron, OH, Akron
Turner, Mark
mturner@bendbulletin.com, Mgmt. Info Serv. Mgr., Baker City Herald, OR, Baker City
Turner, Steven
sturner@dnronline.com, Adv. Dir., Daily News-Record, VA, Harrisonburg
Turner, Mark ....(330) 996-3018
mturner@thebeaconjournal.com, Exec. News Ed., Akron Beacon Journal, OH, Akron
Turner, Sandy ....(816)350-6340
sandy.turner@examiner.net, Dir., Mktg., The Examiner, MO, Independence
Turner, Mark ....(541) 633-2105
mturner@bendbulletin.com, IT Dir., The Bulletin, OR, Bend
Turner, Greg ....(508) 626-3909
gturner@cnc.com, Bus. Ed., Metrowest Daily News, MA, Framingham
Turner, Troy
tturner@daily-times.com, Ed., The Daily Times, NM, Farmington
Turner, David 609-272-7411
dturner@pressofac.com, Lead Local Content Producer/Night, The Press of Atlantic City, NJ, Pleasantville
Turner, Rusty ....(479) 872-5026
rturner@nwaonline.net, Ed., The Morning News of Northwest Arkansas, AR, Springdale
Turner, Willis ....(312) 893-0751
willis.turner@smei.org, Pres./CEO, Sales and Marketing Executives International, WA, Sumas
Turner, Scott
marketing@bowebellhowell.com, Vice Pres., Sales, Bowe Bell + Howell, NC, Durham
Turpin, Michael ....(408) 920-5455
mturpin@mercurynews.com, Adv. Dir., Retail, San Jose Mercury News, CA, San Jose
Tuttle, Amanda ....(614) 236-6011
Capital Univ. Law School, OH, Columbus
Tuttle, Tom ....(925) 416-4852
ttuttle@angnewspapers.com, Editorial Page Ed., San Mateo County Times, CA, San Mateo
Tuttle, Heather ....(801) 236-6087
heather@desnews.com, Graphics Dir., Deseret News, UT, Salt Lake City
Tuttle, Thomas ....(919) 419-6704
ttuttle@heraldsun.com, Adv. Dir., The Herald-Sun, NC, Durham
Tweddle, Stephen
stevetweddle@cwc4webs.com, Pres., Canadian Web Consultants Ltd., ON, Port Sydney
Tweddle, Stephen ....(340) 778-9246
cariboffice@cwc4webs.com, Pres., Canadian Web Consultants Ltd., St Croix, Christiansted
Twichell, Tonia ....(303) 892-5223
twichellt@rockymountainnews.com, City Ed., Rocky Mountain News, CO, Denver
Tyler, Scott
styler@palestineherald.com, Sports Ed., Palestine Herald-Press, TX, Palestine
Tyler, Betty ....ext. 316
btyler@redlandsdailyfacts.com, News Ed., Redlands Daily Facts, CA, Redlands
Tyler, Gary ....(217) 788-1350
gary.tyler@sj-r.com, Adv. Dir., Sales, The State Journal-Register, IL, Springfield
Tym, Tina ....(570) 628-6250
ttym@republicanherald.com, Features Ed., Republican Herald, PA, Pottsville
Tyndall, Nancy
ntyndall@lfpress.com, Dir., HR, The London Free Press, ON, London
Tynen, James E. ....(801) 344-2544
Editorial Page Ed., The Daily Herald, UT, Provo
Tyree, Mike ....(231) 933-1472
mtyree@record-eagle.com, News Ed., Record-Eagle, MI, Traverse City
Tyrock, Andreas
verlag@ga-bonn.de, Ed. in Chief, GENERAL ANZEIGER, Bonn
Tzalla, Lucia
info@epirotikosagon.gr, Pub., EPIROTIKOS AGON, Ioannina, Epirus
Tzevelikas, I.
news@otenet.gr, Pub./Dir., ELEFTHERIA, Corfu

U

Udo-O'Malley, Annabelle
events@aaja.org, Contact, Asian American Journalists Association, CA, San Francisco
Udovic, Dusan
direktor@primorski.eu, Dir., PRIMORSKI DNEVNIK, Trieste
Uebel, Cecilia ....(915) 546-6250
cuebel@elpasotimes.com, Senior VP of Advertising and Marketing, El Paso Times, TX, El Paso
Uehara, Toro
kiji@okinawatimes.co.jp, Ed., OKINAWA TIMES, Naha (Okinawa I.), Kyushu
Uemura, Sara 808.529.4703
Mktg. Mgr., Honolulu Star-Bulletin, HI, Honolulu
Uffelman, Fred ....(717) 771-2066
fuffelman@ync.com, Pub., Weekly Record, PA, York
Uffelman, Fred ....(717) 767-6397
fuffelman@ydr.com, Publisher, York Daily Record/York Sunday News, PA, York
Ugar, Mark ....(415) 777-7244
mugar@sfgate.com, Vice Pres.- Digital, San Francisco Chronicle, CA, San Francisco
Ulery, Jack ....(812) 265-3641
julery@madisoncourier.com, Prodn. Mgr., The Madison Courier, IN, Madison
Ulfat, Hafeez
dailysarhad@yahoo.com, Ed., SARHAD, Peshawar, Peshawar District
Ulloth, Dana
dulloth@bloomu.edu, Chair, Bloomsburg University, PA, Bloomsburg
Ulm, Gerry
gulm@mtdemocrat.net, Circ. Mgr., Mountain Democrat, CA, Placerville
Ulmer, Gerhard
redaktion@lkz.de, Bus. Mgr., LUDWIGSBURGER KREISZEITUNG, Ludwigsburg
Ulon, Heloisa
hulon@ccm.agtnet.com, Exec-Newspaper Digital Servs. Grp., Applied Graphics Technologies, NY, New York
Umphrey, G.L. ....(800) 765-5377
bestroll@aol.com, Pres., Republic Roller Corp., MI, Three Rivers
Underation, Chris 419-434-4442
underation@findlay.edu, Advisor, The Pulse/University of Findlay, OH, Findlay
Underdonk, Carol ....ext. 216
cunderdonk@thenewsenterprise.com, Mgr., Bus. Office, The News Enterprise, KY, Elizabethtown
Underwood, Roger
runderwood@panes.com, Pub., Port Arthur News, TX, Port Arthur
Underwood, Jerry ....(205) 325-3250
Bus./Finance Ed., The Birmingham News, AL, Birmingham
Underwood, Craig ....(530) 477-4214
craigu@theunion.com, Circ. Dir., The Union, CA, Grass Valley
Unger, Dawn ....(708) 456-0300
Triton College, IL, River Grove
Unger-Poole, Jacki ....(863) 291-6115 ext. 3041
jacki.poole@newschief.com, Classified Adv. Mgr., News Chief, FL, Winter Haven
Unknown, Unknown ....(312) 503-4714
Northwestern Univ. School of Law, IL, Chicago
Upshaw, Lynn B.
upshaw@upshawmarketing.com, Principal, Upshaw & Associates, CA, Kentfield
Ur-Rehman, Shakeer
thenewslhr@hotmail.com, Ed. in Chief, JANG LAHORE, Lahore, Lahore
Urbaneja, Maria Di Mase 576-9078
econohoy@telcel.net.ve, Pres., Comunicaciones Corporatives CCD, C.A., Caracas, D.F.
Urbina, Gustavo 42-6339
Pub., EL ORIENTAL, Maturin, Monagas
Urbish, Steve ....(302) 324-2739
Circ. Mgr., Sales/Mktg., The News Journal, DE, New Castle
Urlaub, Mike ....ext. 230
Prodn. Mgr., The News-Record, WY, Gillette
Urquhart, Bruce ....ext. 248
Mng. Ed., The Sentinel-Review, ON, Woodstock
Ursini, Lisa
lursini@yourdailyglobe.com, Publisher, Daily Globe, Inc., MI, Ironwood
Usmanov, Abbas Hon
pvbox@mail.ru, Ed., PRAVDA VOSTOKA, Tashkent, Uzbekistan
Usner, Dave ....(504) 826-3046
dusner@timespicayune.com, Adv. Mgr., Auto, The Times Picayune, LA, New Orleans
Utaka, Asahina
osaka@mdx.mainichi.co.jp, Pres./Osaka Head Officer, MAINICHI SHIMBUN, Osaka, Osaka
Uusi-Kilponen, Pauli
pauli.uusi-kilponen@hameensanomat.fi, Ed. in Chief, HAMEEN SANOMAT, Hame
Uzkan, Sarp ....(312) 222-6541
suzkan@tribune.com, Dir., Technical Opns./Help Desk, Chicago Tribune, IL, Chicago
Uzzell, Brian
brian@cfp.ky, Pub., CAYMANIAN COMPASS, George Town, Grand Cayman

V

Vacar, Vaughn ....ext. 244
vvacar@timesonline.com, Circ. Mgr., Mktg., Beaver County Times, PA, Beaver
Vacchiani, Stephan
redactiondl@dordogne.com, Pub., LA DORDOGNE LIBRE, Perigueux
Vacchiano, Thomas J.
info@xrite.com, Pres./CEO/COO, X-Rite Inc., MI, Grand Rapids
Vacchiano, Thomas J.
info@xrite.com, CEO/Pres., X-Rite, Inc., MI, Grand Rapids
Vachon, Arthur ....(617) 619-6507
avachon@bostonherald.com, Circ. Coord., Boston Herald, MA, Boston
Vachon, Tom
sales@merrsoft.com, Owner, Merrimac Software Associates, NH, South Tamworth
Vad Scautt, Christina
gefle.dagblad@gd.se, Ed., GEFLE DAGBLAD, Gavle
Vadnie, Michael ....(320) 308-3943
St. Cloud State Univ., MN, Saint Cloud
Vadodaria, Kiran
lokasatta@rediffmail.com, Pub., LOKASATTA-JANASATTA, Baroda, Gujarat
Vahey, Linda ....(508) 626-3838
mypaper@cnc.com, Circ. Mgr., Milford Daily News, MA, Milford
Vahldiek, Lissa Walls......(713) 266-5481 ext. 202
lvahldiek@sninews.com, Vice Pres./Sec./COO & Owner-Times Journal (AL), Southern Newspapers, Inc., TX, Houston
Vahlenkamp, John ....(303) 776-2244 ext. 239
jvahlenkamp@times-call.com, Mng. Ed., Times-Call, CO, Longmont
Vainauskas, Gedvydas
daily@lrytas.lt, Ed. in Chief, LIETUVOS RYTAS, Vilnius
Vaivoda, Sarah
customerservice@syrlang.com, Mktg. Mgr., Syracuse Language Systems, Inc., NY, Syracuse
Vakalis, Joni 907-257-4458
Retail Ad Manager, Anchorage Daily News, AK, Anchorage
Valade, Mary ....(705) 674-5271 ext. 271
Office Mgr., The Sudbury Star, ON, Sudbury
Valadez, Lesley ....(870) 673-8533 ext. 212
editor@stuttgartdailyleader.com, Mng. Ed., Stuttgart Daily Leader, AR, Stuttgart
Valate, Marriette ....ext. 229
Dir., Mktg./Promo., The Sudbury Star, ON, Sudbury
Valdez, Carmen ....(626) 584-5430
Fuller Theological Seminary, CA, Pasadena
Valdez Vilchis, Pedro Julio
elsolchipo@yahoo.com.mx, Pres., EL SOL DE CHILPANCINGO, Chilpancingo, Guerrero
Valdivia, Sandra ....ext. 127
production@redbluffdailynews.com, Prodn. Mgr., Daily News, CA, Red Bluff
Valencia Alonso, Eligio
evalencia@el-mexicano.com.mx, Dir., EL MEXICANO, Tijuana, Baja California Norte
Valencia Roque, Eligio
evalencia-evr@el-mexicano.com.mx, Gen. Mgr., EL MEXICANO, Tijuana, Baja California Norte
Valencia Roque, Eligio
elmextj@telnor.net, Pres., SEGUNDA EDICION, Tijuana, Baja California
Valenta, Tony ....(607) 274-9285
tvalenta1@ithaca.gannett.com, Mktg. Devel. Dir., The Ithaca Journal, NY, Ithaca
Valentin, Eric
dhnet@saipm.com, Mng. Ed., LA DERNIERE HEURE-LES SPORTS, Brussels
Valentine, Gerald P.
jvalentine@mpival.com, Vice Pres., Management Planning, Inc., NJ, Princeton
Valenzuela, Pamela N.
info@womcom.org, Exec. Dir., Association for Women in Communications, VA, Alexandria
Valero, Ralph ....(888)309-0639
ralph@miracomcomputer.com, Field Application Engineer, Miracom Computer Corp., NY, Eastchester
Valeskini, Gerhard 875 3333
gerhard.valeskini@kleinezeitung.at, Adv. Dir., KLEINE ZEITUNG, 8010 Graz
Valette, Eric
e.valette@agefi.com, Dir., L'AGEFI, Lausanne
Valiante, Chet 203-354-1010
cvaliante@thehour.com, Pub./COO, The Hour Publishing Co., CT, Norwalk
Valintinelli, Monica
mvalentinelli@gmail.com, Bus. Mgr., Dork Storm Press/Shetland Productions, WI, Madison
Valkaer, Jorgen 615 495 7266
info@ccieurope.com, Sales, CCI Europe, Inc.-Georgia Branch, GA, Kennesaw
Valker, Jorgen
jv@ccieurope.com, Vice Pres., Project Sales, CCI Europe, Inc., GA, Kennesaw
Valladares Garcia, Miguel F.
pulso@slp.intermex.com.mx, Pres., PULSO, San Luis Potosi, San Luis Potosi
Vallery, Janet
jvallery@advertiser-tribune.com, Prodn. Mgr., The Advertiser-Tribune, OH, Tiffin
Valley, John
elpuntdigital@elpunt.com, Dir., El Punt Comarques Gironnes, Girona
Valli, Gail ....ext. 8438
gail.valli@cantonrep.com, Adv. Mgr., Classified, The Repository, OH, Canton
Vallieu, Melody ....(937) 335-5634
vallieu@tdnpublishing.com, City Ed., Troy Daily News, OH, Troy
Valpy, Robert ....(780) 429-5148
rvalpy@thejournal.canwest.com, Adv. Local Online Sales Specialist, Edmonton Journal,

AB, Edmonton
Valvatchov, A.
dima@gazetbel.belpak.minsk.by, Ed., BE-LORUSSKAYA GAZETA, Minsk
Van Arnem, Harold
sales@gcomm.com, CEO, netVillage.com, Inc., MD, Laurel
Van Dusen, Mike ....(616) 222-5550
Adv. Mgr., Prodn., The Grand Rapids Press, MI, Grand Rapids
Van Essen, Owen D. ....(505) 820-2700
owen@dirksvanessen.com, Pres., Dirks, Van Essen & Murray, NM, Santa Fe
Van Essen, Owen D. ....(505) 820-2700
owen@dirksvanessen.com, Pres., Dirks, Van Essen & Murray, NM, Santa Fe
Van Hine, Michael ....(810) 766-6399
mvanhine@flintjournal.com, Info. Systems Mgr., The Flint Journal, MI, Flint
Van Hook, Bill ....(251) 219-5302
bvanhook@press-register.com, Circ. Mgr., Opns., Press-Register, AL, Mobile
Van Leeuwen, Osvaldo Carlos.............714-1144
Ed., O Informativo do Vale, Lajeado, Rio Grande do Sul
Van Sickle, Sonya.....................(803) 329-4085
svansickle@heraldonline.com, Outside Sales Mgr., The Herald, SC, Rock Hill
Van Tassel, Debbie ....(216) 999-4405
Asst. Managing Editor/Features, The Plain Dealer, OH, Cleveland
Van Vonderen, Mary..................(920) 339-2787
mvanvonderen@megtec.com, Mktg. Mgr., MEGTEC Systems, WI, De Pere
Van Wyke, Jill ....(515) 271-2295
Drake Univ., IA, Des Moines
VanAernam, Tim
tim@lhprint.com, Prodn. Mgr., Mailroom, The Leader-Herald, NY, Gloversville
VanDemark, Steve ....(419) 784-5441 ext. 205
vandemark@crescent-news.com, Gen. Mgr., The Crescent-News, OH, Defiance
VanHoesen, Jill ....ext. 2571
CIO, Watertown Daily Times, NY, Watertown
VanHorn, Edward
edward@snpa.org, Exec. Dir., Southern Newspaper Publishers Association, GA, Atlanta
VanLaningham, Kelly.................(309) 686-3185
kvanlaningham@pjstar.com, News Ed., Journal Star, IL, Peoria
VanMoorsel, Greg
gvanmoorsel@lfpress.com, City Ed., The London Free Press, ON, London
Vance, Teri ....(775) 881-1272
tvance@nevadaappeal.com, Features Ed., Nevada Appeal, NV, Carson City
Vance, Tricia ....(910) 343-2310
tricia.vance@starnewsonline.com, Deputy Editorial Page Ed., Star-News, NC, Wilmington
Vance, Carolyn ....(217) 351-5228
cvance@news-gazette.com, Librarian, News-Gazette Inc., IL, Champaign
Vance, Loretta ....(309) 820-3331
lvance@pantagraph.com, Adv. Dir., The Pantagraph, IL, Bloomington
Vance, Kenneth R. ....ext. 3508
kvance@express-times.com, Controller, The Express-Times, PA, Easton
Vandenberg, Lee ....(319) 372-6421 ext. 234
composing@dailydem.com, Prodn. Mgr., Composing, Fort Madison Daily Democrat, IA, Fort Madison
VanderPas, Dan
dvanderp@appleton.gannett.com, Asst. Sports Ed., The Post-Crescent, WI, Appleton
Vanderbeck, Jeff..................................ext. 52
jvanderbeck@news-expressky.com, Pub., The Appalachian News-Express, KY, Pikeville
Vanderhoff, Larry ....(216) 999-4170
Asst. Circ. Dir., Customer Rel./Systems, The Plain Dealer, OH, Cleveland
Vanderhoof, Joe
jvanderhoof@th-record.com, Pres., Pocono Record, PA, Stroudsburg
Vandermeersch, Peter......................467.22.11
peter.vandermeersch@standaard.be, Ed. in Chief, DE STANDAARD, Groot Bijgaarden
Vandermeersch, Peter
nieuwsblad@vum.be, Ed. in Chief, HET NIEUWSBLAD/DE GENTENAAR, Groot Bijgaarden
Vanderweert, Arlene
midequip@yahoo.com, Mktg. Mgr., MidLantic Equipment Co., Inc., NJ, Wyckoff
Vanderzee, Karin...............................ext. 271
kvanderzee@wellandtribune.ca, Circ. Mgr., Welland Tribune, ON, Welland
Vangelos, Nick.........................(216) 999-6531
Prodn. Tech. Service Mgr., The Plain Dealer, OH, Cleveland
Vanhooser, Terri.......................(405) 278-2810
terri.vanhooser@journalrecord.com, Gen. Mgr., The Journal Record, OK, Oklahoma City
Vankrinkelveldt, Ralph
ralph.vankrinkelveldt@dh.be, Ed. in Chief, LA DERNIERE HEURE, Brussels
Vanlandingham, Gary ....ext. 556
Prodn. Mgr., Pressroom, The Herald-Palladium, MI, Saint Joseph
Vann, Ruby
circulation@adirondackguide.com, Circ. Dir., Adirondack Daily Enterprise, NY, Saranac Lake
Vanstone, Rob ....(306) 781-5215
rvanstone@leaderpost.canwest.com, Sports Ed., The Leader-Post, SK, Regina
Vanweert, Henk 233 6336
opinie@ed.nl, Ed. in Chief, EINDHOVENS DAGBLAD, Eindhoven
Vanzomeren, Jon......................(616) 222-5651
jvanzomeren@grpress.com, Circ. Opns. Mgr., The Grand Rapids Press, MI, Grand Rapids
Varga, Ken ....(406) 758-4461
kvarga@dailyinterlake.com, Prodn. Mgr., Daily Inter Lake, MT, Kalispell
Vargas, Jorge C. Mojica
direccion@periodicovictoria.com.mx, Dir. Gen, Victoria de Durango, Durango, Durango
Vargas, William GÃ£Â¢mez
plibre@prensalibre.co.cr, Pres., LA PRENSA LIBRE, San Jose
Varghese, Sunio........................(512) 708-9357
Univ. of Texas College of Bus., TX, Austin
Vargo, Becky
bvargo@grandhaventribune.com, News Ed., Grand Haven Tribune, MI, Grand Haven
Vargo, Shawn
svargo@the-leader.com, Sports Ed., The Leader, NY, Corning
Varney, Julie ....(978) 556-3633
Northern Essex Cmty. College, MA, Haverhill
Varouxis, E.
leonca@otenet.gr, Pub., PATRIS, Pyrgos, Peloponnese
Vartabedian, Sonya
svartabedian@newburyportnews.com, Features Ed., The Daily News, MA, Newburyport
Vasala, Pekka
pekka.vasala@kainuunsanomat.fi, Mng. Ed., KAINUUN SANOMAT, Kajaani, Oulu
Vasche, Mark ....(209) 578-2351
mvasche@modbee.com, Exec. Ed., The Modesto Bee, CA, Modesto
Vasher, Andy
avasher@autonet.net, Mktg. Mgr., Autonet (Div. of Weston Information Technologies), MI, Ann Arbor
Vasquez, Rachel A.
rachel.vasquez@sgvn.com, HR/Admin. Mgr., San Gabriel Valley Tribune, CA, West Covina
Vasquez, Rachel A. ....ext. 2304
rachel.vasquez@sgvn.com, HR/Admin. Mgr., Pasadena Star-News, CA, Pasadena
Vasquez, Rachel A. ....ext. 2304
rachel.vasquez@sgvn.com, HR/Admin. Mgr., The Whittier Daily News, CA, Whittier
Vasquez, Erwin
eknohr@elherlado.net, Pub., El Heraldo S.A., San Jose
Vasquez, Tina..........................(361) 886-3741
vasquezt@caller.com, Television Ed., Corpus Christi Caller-Times, TX, Corpus Christi
Vasquez Rana, Mario 818-3000
sgg@xal.megared.net.mx, Pres., Diario de Xalapa, Xalapa, Veracruz
Vaughan, Cinda
addir@claremoreprogress.com, Adv. Dir., The Claremore Daily Progress, OK, Claremore
Vaughn, John 928-539-6850
jvaughn@yumasun.com, Editor, Bajo El Sol, Yuma Sun, AZ, Yuma
Vaught, Scott
sales@greatsoutherncorp.com, Pres., Great Southern Corp. (Sirco Div.), TN, Memphis
Vaz, Valerie ....(559) 441-6127
vvaz@fresnobee.com, Adv. Dir., Classified, The Fresno Bee, CA, Fresno
Vaz Figueroa, Jose Miguel
editor@lanacion.com, Pres., LA NACION, Santo Domingo
Vazquez, Oscar
ovazquez@redaccion.diario.com.mx, Ed., DIARIO DE JUAREZ, Ciudad Juarez, Chihuahua
Vazquez, Raul Velasco
elcorreo@gro1.telmex.net.mx, Owner/Pres., El Correo, Iguala, Guerrero
Vazquez Rana, Mario
heraldo@oem.com.mx, Pres., El Heraldo de Chihuahua, Chihuahua, Chihuahua
Vazquez Rana, Mario
lavoz@oem.com.mx, Pres., LA VOZ DE LA FRONTERA, Mexicali, Baja California Norte
Vazquez Rana, Mario
oemenlinea@oem.com.mx, Pres., LA PRENSA, Mexico City, Distrito Federal
Vazquez Rana, Mario
diarioqro@ciateq.mx, Pres./Gen. Dir., DIARIO DE QUERETARO, Queretaro, Queretaro
Vazquez Rana, Mario
publicidad@elsoldecuernavaca.com.mx, Pres., El Sol de Cuernavaca, Cuernavaca, Morelos
Vazquez Rana, Mario
publicidad@elsoldeparral.com.mx, Pres./Gen. Dir., EL SOL DE PARRAL, Parral, Chihuahua
Vazquez Rana, Mario
publicidad@elsudcaliforniano.com.mx, Pres., Sudcaliforniano, La Paz, Bajo California Sur
Vazquez Rana, Mario
publicidad@elsoldehidalgo.com.mx, Pres., EL SOL DE TULANCINGO, Tulancingo, Hidalgo
Vazquez Rana, Mario
solpue@oem.com.mx, Pres., EL SOL DE PUEBLA, Puebla, Puebla
Vazquez Rana, Mario
publicidad@periodicoelmexicano.com.mx, Pres., El Mexicano, Ciudad Juarez, Chihuahua
Vazquez Rana, Mario
publicidad@tribunadesanluis.com.mx, Pres/Owner, TRIBUNA DE SAN LUIS, San Luis Rio Colorado, Sonora
Vazquez Rana, Mario
info@oem.com.mx, Pres., EL SOL DE ORIZABA, Orizaba, Veracruz
Vazquez Rana, Mario
publicidad@elsoldelcentro.com.mx, Pres., El Sol Del Centro, Aguascalientes
Vazquez Rana, Mario
raguilar@oem.com.mx, Pres./Gen. Dir., Cia. Periodistica del Sol de Mexico, S.A. de C.V., Mexico City, Distrito Federal
Vazquez Rana, Mario
publicidad@elsoldehidalgo.com.mx, Pres., EL SOL DE HIDALGO, Pachuca, Hidalgo
Vazquez Rana, Mario
solger@prodigy.net.mx, Pres., LA VOZ DE PUEBLA, Puebla, Puebla
Vazquez Rana, Mario
publicidad@elsoldesalamanca.com.mx, Pres., EL SOL DE SALAMANCA, Salamanca, Guanajuato
Vazquez Rana, Mario
publicidad@elsoldesinaloa.com.mx, Pres., El Sol de Sinaloa, Culiacan, Sinaloa
Vazquez Rana, Mario
publicidad@elsoldemorelia.com.mx, Pres., EL SOL DE MORELIA, Morelia, Michoacan
Vazquez Rana, Mario
info@oem.com.mx, Pres./Gen. Dir., EL SOL DE LOS MOCHIS, Los Mochis, Sinaloa
Vazquez Rana, Mario
publicidad@elsoldeleon.com.mx, Pres., El Sol de Leon, Leon, Guanajuato
Vazquez Rana, Mario
publicidad@elsoldezamora.com.mx, Pres., EL SOL DE ZAMORA, Zamora, Michoacan
Vazquez Rana, Mario
soltam@oem.com.mx, Pres., EL SOL DE LA TARDE, Tampico, Tamaulipas
Vazquez Rana, Mario
publicidad@elsoldetoluca.com.mx, Pres., EL SOL DE TOLUCA, Toluca
Veasey, John...........................(304) 367-2541
jcveasey@timeswv.com, Community Ed., Times West Virginian, WV, Fairmont
Veazey, Teresa
teresa.veazey@fhscom.com, Pres., Kansas Professional Communicators, KS, Wichita
Vedder, Kenneth.......................(516) 753-7213
vedderk@necusa.com, Dir., Adv./Internet Servs., NEC USA, Inc., NY, Melville
Vega, Philip ....(520) 458-9440 ext. 605
philip.vega@svherald.com, Sierra Vista Herald Sunday, AZ, Sierra Vista
philip.vega@svherald.com, Pub., Sierra Vista Herald, AZ, Sierra Vista
Vega, Philip ....(520) 458-9440
philip.vega@svherald.com, Pub., Bisbee Daily Review, AZ, Bisbee
Vega, Frank ....(415) 777-7522
fvega@sfchronicle.com, Publisher & Chairman, San Francisco Chronicle, CA, San Francisco
Veit, William
sfi@scotsmanpress.com, Bus. Mgr., System Facilities, Inc., NY, Syracuse
Velazquez, Gabriel Alarcon
heraldo@iwm.com.mx, Pres., EL HERALDO DE MEXICO, Mexico City, Distrito Federal
Veley, Cathy 805-781-7891
cveley@thetribunenews.com, Home Delivery Manager, The Tribune, CA, San Luis Obispo
Velez, Cesar Enrique........................296-5900
Pres., El Libertador, Riobamba, Chimborazo
Velilla, John F.
inter2003@embarqmail.com, Dir., Sales, Inter-Continental Graphics, Inc., FL, Fort Myers
Vellanti, Sue ....ext. 202
Prodn. Mgr., Distr., The Pioneer - Big Rapids, MI, Big Rapids
Velsand, Mari
mari.velsand@nationen.no, Ed. in Chief, NATIONEN, Oslo
Velton, Ron............................(903) 463-8755
Grayson County College, TX, Denison
Velu, Kanda
dknmdu@yahoo.co.in, Ed., DINAKARAN, Madurai, Tamil Nadu
Velvin, Randy ....(434) 447-3178
r.velvin@womackpublishing.com, Press Opns. Mgr., Womack Publishing Co., VA, Chatham
Venderkooi, Bart
venderkooi@friesch-dagblad.nl, Mktg. Mgr., FRIESCH DAGBLAD, Leeuwarden
Venegas Ruz, Rene
rvenegas@australosorno.cl, Gen. Mgr., Sociedad Periodista Araucania S.A., Osorno
Venema, Sheri 410-777-1947
sbvenema@aacc.edu, Advisor, Anne Arundel Cmty. College Campus Current, MD, Arnold
Venis, Brian............................(905) 475-2357
bvenis@graphicroller.com, Pres., Graphic Printing Roller Ltd., ON, Markham
Venkatesh, Venky
feedback@htclassifieds.biz, Bus. Head/Circ/SEAL, THE HINDUSTAN TIMES, New Delhi
Vennekotter, Michael.................(517) 486-2164
michael@saxmayercorp.com, Pres., Mktg./Sales, Saxmayer Corp., MI, Blissfield
Venrondhand, Zohra
contact@lapresse.tn, Dir., LA PRESSE DE TUNISIE, Tunis
Venso, Mike.............................(801) 257-8806
mvenso@newsviewsolutions.com, Dir.-Sales, NewsView Solutions, UT, Salt Lake City
Ventura, Luciano
redazione@quotidianodibari.it, Dir., IL QUOTIDIANO DI FOGGIA, Foggia
Ventura, Luciano
pubblicita@quotidianodibari.it, Dir., IL QUOTIDIANO, Bari
Veon, Greg R...........................(563) 383-2169
Vice Pres., Publishing, Lee Enterprises, Inc., IA, Davenport
Verbeke, Eric
apspkg@aol.com, Vice Pres., Sales, APS Packaging Systems, NJ, Fairfield
Verdeyen, Guido
gentenaar@vum.be, Gen. Dir., DE GENTENAAR, Ghent, East Flanders
Vergara, Tilar

redaccion@lasegunda.cl, Dir., El Mercurio S.A., Santiago
Verghe, Dirk
dirk.velghe@mediafin.be, CEO, DE FINANCIEEL ECONOMISCHE TIJD, Brussel
Vergu, Beatrice
beatrice.vergu@buzau.ro, Adv. Mgr., OPINIA, Buzau
Vermillion, Barry......................(940) 566-6890
Librarian, Denton Record-Chronicle, TX, Denton
Vermon, Cheril
cvernon@palestineherald.com, Features Ed., Palestine Herald-Press, TX, Palestine
Verner, Chris..............................(704) 797-4262
cverner@salisburypost.com, Editorial Page Ed., Salisbury Post, NC, Salisbury
Veroba, Polly..............................(306) 691-1253
pveroba@mjtimes.sk.ca, Bus. Mgr., The Moose Jaw Times-Herald, SK, Moose Jaw
Verrest, A.A.M.................................5312200
redactie@bndestem.nl, CEO, BN DE STEM, Breda
Verrico, Kurt....................................ext. 199
kverrico@timesonline.com, Circ. Mgr., Distr., Beaver County Times, PA, Beaver
Verso, Fabio Lo
abo@lecourrier.ch, Ed. in Chief, LE COURRIER, Geneva
Verticchio, Lu....................................ext. 757
lverticchio@princegeorgecitizen.com, Adv. Dir., The Prince George Citizen, BC, Prince George
Vervaet, Linda...................................ext. 112
lvervaet@k-f.com, Coord., Int'l Sales, K & F International, Inc., IN, Granger
Vetter, Kathy.............................(817) 390-7380
vetter@star-telegram.com, Mng. Ed., Enterprise, Fort Worth Star-Telegram, TX, Fort Worth
Veyera, Bob.................................860-867-6895
bveyera@fujifilm.com, Newspaper Account Manager, West Region, Fujifilm North America Corporation, IL, Hanover Park
Vezza, Richard...........................(973) 392-4161
rvezza@starledger.com, Pub., The Star-Ledger, NJ, Newark
Vian, Giovanni Maria
ornet@ossrom.va, Ed. in Chief, L'OSSERVATORE ROMANO
Viansson Ponte, Jean
infos@lejsl.fr, Dir., LE JOURNAL DE SAONE-ET-LOIRE, Chalon-sur-Saone
Vice, Jeff..................................(801) 236-6019
jeff@desnews.com, Film Critic, Deseret News, UT, Salt Lake City
Vicinanza, Luigi
l.vicinanza@ilcentro.it, Dir., IL CENTRO, Pescara
Vick, Patty
burnishine@aol.com, Graphic Arts, Vice Pres., Burnishine Products, IL
Vicker, Lauren
lvicker@sjfc.edu, Chair/Prof., St. John Fisher College, NY, Rochester
Victor, Beaux
bdnews-beaux@suddenlinkmail.com, Pub., Beauregard Daily News, LA, De Ridder
Vidlak, Pablo.............................(216) 999-6611
Prodn. Mgr., Packaging, The Plain Dealer, OH, Cleveland
Viegas, Theodorico Luiz....................421-7843
Pres., Folha de Dourados, Dourados, Mato Grosso do Sul
Vierra, Arlan
avierra@hawaiitribune-herald.com, Prodn. Mgr., Pre Press, Hawaii Tribune-Herald, HI, Hilo
Vignali, Sharon..........................(919) 829-4615
svignali@newsobserver.com, Employee Rel. Mgr., The News & Observer, NC, Raleigh
Vijuk, Joseph
info@vijukequip.com, Pres., Vijuk Equipment, IL, Elmhurst
Vilela Conde, Xose Luis
redac@lavoz.com, Asst. Dir.-Information, La Voz De Galicia, La Coruna
Vilencia, Bridget........................(724) 223-2635
bvilenica@observer-reporter.com, Circ. Dir., Observer-Reporter, PA, Washington
Villacorta, Alberto..............................444-7088
publicidad@expreso.com.pe, Gen. Mgr., Expreso, Lima
Villalpando, Carlina.....................(830) 257-0337
carlina.villalpando@dailytimes.com, Mng. Ed., Kerrville Daily Times, TX, Kerrville
Villani, Dan...............................(541) 338-2229
dan.villani@registerguard.com, Creative Servs. Mgr., The Register-Guard, OR, Eugene
Villanueva, Augusto
journal@journal.com.ph, Ed. in Chief, PEOPLE TONIGHT, Makati City
Villanueva, Augusto
journal@journal.com.ph, Ed. in Chief, PEOPLE'S JOURNAL, Manila
Villanueva, Agusto
journal@journal.com.ph, Ed. in Chief, TALIBA, Makati City
Villanueva, Augusto
journal@journal.com.ph, Ed. in Chief, PEOPLES JOURNAL, Makati City
Villareal Marroquin, Marco G.
marco@diario.net, Ed., EL DIARIO DE NUEVO LAREDO, Nuevo Laredo, Tamaulipas
Villarreal, Debra........................(361) 886-3604
Credit Mgr., Corpus Christi Caller-Times, TX, Corpus Christi
Villarreal, Phil...........................(520) 573-4130
prv@azstarnet.com, Film Critic, Arizona Daily Star, AZ, Tucson
Villarreal Saldivar, Antonio
editora@elmercurio.com.mx, Pres., El Mercurio, Ciudad Victoria, Tamaulipas
Villasana Lopez, Rodrigo
heraldo@orb.org.mx, Owner/Pres., EL HERALDO, Zacatecas, Zacatecas
Villasana Mena, Alejandro
heraldosl@s.l.p.1.telmex.net.mx, Pres., EL HERALDO, San Luis Potosi,
Villeneuve, Ginette.........(514) 866-3131 ext. 229
Asst. Gen. Mgr., Reseau Select/Select Network, QC, Montreal
Villeneuve, Pierre
promotion@jdeq.com, Mgr., Promo., Le Journal de Quebec, QC, Vanier
Villinger, Ullrich
info@zvw.de, Proprietor, SCHORNDORFER NACHRICHTEN, Waiblingen
Villlenuev, Augusto B
veliba@journal.com.ph, Ed. in Chief, PEOPLE'S BAGONG TALIBA, Manila
Vincent, Bill..............................(317) 577-2121
bvincent@jtmchugh.com, Vice Pres./Gen. Mgr., J. Thomas McHugh Co., Inc., IN, Fishers
Vincente, Evaldo A.
evaldo@tribunatp.com.br, Pub., Tribuna Piracicabana Jornal e Grafica Ltd., Piracicaba, Sao Paulo
Vinciguerra, Mark........................(518) 454-5703
mvinciguerra@timesunion.com, Dir of Audience Development, Times Union, NY, Albany
Vineberg, Andy.................................ext. 4213
avineberg@phillyburbs.com, Life/Reality Writer, Bucks County Courier Times, PA, Levittown
Vingle, Mitch.............................(304) 348-4827
mitchv@wvgazette.com, Sports Ed., The Charleston Gazette, Sunday Gazette-Mail, WV, Charleston
Vinker, Luis
lvinker@larazon.com.ar, Ed., La Razon, Buenos Aires
Vins, John
john.vins@agileenterprise.com, Dir. Technical Support, Agile Enterprise, NH, Bedford
Vinyard, Valerie.........................(520) 573-4131
vvinyard@azstarnet.com, Books Ed., Arizona Daily Star, AZ, Tucson
Virag, Jeff
starbiz@midrivers.com, Circ. Mgr., Miles City Star, MT, Miles City
Vis, Andre
redactieonline@tubantia.wegener.nl, Ed. in Chief, TWENTSCHE COURANT, Enschede
Vish, Andre
redactye@tubantia.wegener.nl, Mng. Ed., DAGBLAD TUBANTIA/TWENTSCHE COURANT, Enschede
Visic, Mark
mvisic@kubra.com, Sr. Vice Pres., Bus. Devel., Kubra, ON, Mississauga
Visser, B.
bvisser@refdag.nl, CEO, REFORMATORISCH DAGBLAD, Apeldoorn
Vita, Jim...........................310-540-5511 x6668
jim.vita@dailybreeze.com, Circ. Mgr., Customer Serv., Daily Breeze, CA, Torrance
Vitienes, Ernesto..................................688-3361
uh.redacc@codetel.net.do, Gen. Mgr., ULTIMA HORA, Santo Domingo
Vitkansas, Roger.........................(212) 355-4565
vitkansas@trxinteractive.com, Pres./CEO, TRX Interactive Communications, Inc., NY, New York
Vito, Marie
mvito@sjnewsco.com, Adv. Mgr., Classified, The News of Cumberland County, NJ, Bridgeton
Vito, David
dvito@buynensco.com, Bus. Mgr., Pre Press Prodn., NENSCO, MA, Millbury
Vito, Marie
mvito@sjnews.com, Adv. Mgr., Classified, The Gloucester County Times, NJ, Woodbury
Vittachi, Imran
imran.vittachi@latimes.com, City Ed., Daily Pilot, CA, Costa Mesa
Vittori, Gustavo Jose
litoral@litoral.com, Pres., El Litoral S.R.L., Santa Fe, Provincia de Santa Fe
Vittori, Gustavo
direccion@elliberal.com.ar, Dir., Editorial El Liberal S.R.L., Santiago del Estero
Vivanco, Gabriela
gvivanco@lahora.com.ec, Editorial VP, LA HORA, Quito
Vivanco, Gladis
gventas@lahora.com.ec, Sales Mgr., LA HORA, Quito
Vivanco Riofrio, Francisco
secretaria@lahora.com.ec, National President / Publisher, LA HORA, Quito
Viveiros, Paulo
jornal@diariodosacores.pt, MD, DIARIO DOS ACORES, Ponta del Gada
Viveisrros, Americo
jornal@diariodosacores.pt, CEO, DIARIO DOS ACORES, Ponta del Gada
Vives, Lisa..................................(212) 244-3123
ipsgin@igc.org, Exec. Dir., Global Information Network, NY, New York
Vivio, Michael............................(512) 445-3500
mvivio@statesman.com, Pub., Austin American-Statesman, TX, Austin
Vivion, Mike...............................(573) 761-0234
mvivion@newstribune.com, Gen. Mgr., News Tribune, MO, Jefferson City
Vivona, John...............................(800) 255-6734
msharp@amuniversal.com, Vice Pres., Sales, Universal Uclick, MO, Kansas City
Vizzini, John...................................321-242-3850
jvizzini@floridatoday.com, Operations Director, Florida Today, FL, Melbourne
Vladimirovich, Vladimir
veche@ng-daily.by, Ed. in Chief, NARODNAYA HAZETA, Minsk
Vobejda, Bill
bill.vobedja@lee.net, Pub., The Columbus Telegram, NE, Columbus
Vobejda, Bill
bill.vobejda@lee.net, Pub., Fremont Tribune, NE, Fremont
Vocate, Donna R.
dvocate@atu.edu, Head/Prof., Arkansas Tech University, AR, Russellville
Voccio, Chris..............................(217) 477-5111
cvoccio@dancomnews.com, Pub., Commercial News, IL, Danville
Vodenichar, Ronald....................724-282-8000 x
rvodenichar@butlereagle.com, Publisher and general manager, Eagle Printing Co., PA, Butler
Vodenichar, Ronald A.......(724) 282-8000 ext. 258
ravgm@butlereagle.com, Dir., Mktg./Promo., Butler Eagle, PA, Butler
Vogel, Artur
artur.vogel@derbund.ch, Ed, DER BUND, Berne
Vogl-Bauer, Sally
voglbaus@uww.edu, Contact, University of Wisconsin-Whitewater, WI, Whitewater
Voight, Joseph A.
etcmkt@etcia.com, Vice Pres., Sales, ETC, Inc., WI, Waukesha
Voigt, Thomas
tom@bryantimes.com, Mgr., Mktg./Promo., The Bryan Times, OH, Bryan
Voigt, Samantha..........................(906) 483-2206
svoigt@mininggazette.com, City Ed., The Daily Mining Gazette, MI, Houghton
Voigt, Thomas.............................(419) 636-1111
tom@bryantimes.com, Vice Pres./Gen. Mgr., Bryan Publishing Co., OH, Bryan
Voinea, Ina
ina@gds.ro, Ed. in Chief, GAZETA DE SUD, Craiova, Dolj
Voisard, Michel
michel.voisard@lqj.ch, Dir., LE QUOTIDIEN JURASSIEN, Delemont, Jura
Vojtasek, Karen...........................(574) 224-5323
karenv@rochsent.com, Adv. Dir., The Rochester Sentinel, IN, Rochester
Volcek, Joe
circulation@nptelegraph.com, Circ. Dir., The North Platte Telegraph, NE, North Platte
Voll-Leggo, Lisa
lvollleggo@therecord.com, HR, The Record, ON, Kitchener
Volland, Stan..............................(813) 259-7876
Mgr., Packaging & Transportation, The Tampa Tribune, FL, Tampa
Vollmer, Ted...............................(707) 553-6827
tvollmer@timesheraldonline.com, Ed., Vallejo Times-Herald, CA, Vallejo
Volosin, Beth...................................330-332-4601
bvolosin@salemnews.net, Pub., Salem News, OH, Salem
Vonderahe, Melinda.....................(920) 993-7193
mvondera@appleton.gannett.com, Mktg. Dir., The Post-Crescent, WI, Appleton
Voorhees, Gerald
gvoorhee@highpoint.edu, Asst. Prof., High Point University, NC, High Point
Vorel, Tom
tomv@metrosn.com, Adv. Dir., Midwest Sales Reg., Metro Newspaper Advertising Services, Inc. Sunday Magazine Network - Chicago, IL, IL, Chicago
Vorel, Tom
getinfony@metrosn.com, Exec. Dir., Metro Newspaper Advertising Services, Inc., NY, New York
Vorontsov, Andrei
info@mk.ru, Ed. in Chief, MOSKOVSKII KOMSOMOLETS, Moscow
Voros, Drew
avoros@bayareanewsgroup.com, Bus. Ed., The Argus, CA, Fremont
Voros, Drew...............................(925) 416-4811
dvoros@angnewspapers.com, Bus. Ed., San Mateo County Times, CA, San Mateo
Vortherms, Micheal.....................(860) 241-6783
mvortherms@courant.com, Circ. Mgr., Strategic Planning/Finance, The Hartford Courant, CT, Hartford
Vos, Kathy
kvos@mankatofreepress.com, News Ed., Day, The Free Press, MN, Mankato
Vosburg, Cindy
cvosburg@triplicate.com, Adv. Mgr., The Daily Triplicate, CA, Crescent City
Vosburg, Mike
mvosburg@forumcomm.com, Photo Ed., InForum, ND, Fargo
Vosburgh, Mark...........................(216) 999-5519
Deputy Metro Editor, The Plain Dealer, OH, Cleveland
Vosloo, John
wes@beeld.com, Bus. Mgr., BEELD, Auckland Park, Johannesburg
Voss, Mike..................................(815) 935-4639
mvoss@daily-journal.com, Chief Photographer, The Daily Journal, IL, Kankakee
Vranas, Kim
kvranas@dgfastchannel.com, Dir., Mktg., Fast Channel Network, MA, Wellesley
Vreeken, Stacy...........................(831) 429-2451
Features Ed., Santa Cruz Sentinel, CA, Scotts Valley
Vriea, Daoud
daoud@namibian.com.na, Mng. Ed., THE NAMIBIAN, Windhoek
Vris, D.
kerix@otenet.gr, Pub., IMERISSIOS KERIX PATROM, Patras, Peloponnese

Vrooman, Steven S.
svrooman@tlu.edu, Chair, Texas Lutheran University, TX, Seguin
Vusotskaya, E.
edit@workpr.minsk.by, Ed., Imya, Minsk
Vyas, Kundan
jbhoomi@yahoo.com, Ed., JANMABHOOMI, Mumbai, Maharashtra
Vyas, Shailesh
mail@jairajasthan.com, Ed. in Chief, JAI RAJASTHAN, Udaipur, Rajasthan
Vyash, Kundan
jbhoomi@yahoo.com, Ed., PRAVASI, Mumbai, Maharashtra

W

Waack, Peter 3154432315
pwaack@dailyorange.com, Advisor/Gen. Mgr., Daily Orange at Syracuse Univ., NY, Syracuse
Wachowicz, Mark
wachowicztm@accessabc.com, Sr. Vice Pres., Mktg./Sales, Audit Bureau of Circulations (ABC), IL, Arlington Heights
Wachter, Blythe ....ext. 3828
blythe.wachter@ecpc.com, Food Ed., Leader-Telegram, WI, Eau Claire
Waclawek, Nancy ....(727) 893-8780
nwaclawek@tampabay.com, Dir., Cor. Giving, Tampa Bay Times, FL, Saint Petersburg
Waddell, David ....(530) 898-4782
California State Univ., CA, Chico
Waddell, Bruce
editor@features.sundaymail.co.uk, Ed. in Chief, SUNDAY MAIL, Glasgow, Strathclyde
Waddle, Chris..........................(256) 235-3590
cwaddle@annistonstar.com, Vice Pres., Consolidated Publishing Co., AL, Anniston
Wadi, M. Kheir
tnp@mail.sy, Ed. in Chief, TISHRIN
Wadson, Dave ....(807) 343-6264
dave.wadson@chroniclejournal.com, Prodn. Foreman, Composing Room, The Chronicle-Journal, ON, Thunder Bay
Waess, Andreas
andreas.waess@kurier.tmt.de, Adv. Mgr., NORDBAYERISCHER KURIER, Bayreuth
Waeyenberge, Patrick Van
patrick.van.waeyenberge@perdgroep.be, Adv. Contact, HET LAATSTE NIEUWS, 1730 Kobbegem
Waffer, Daws
dwaffer@aol.com, Owner, D & R Engineering, CA, Hawthorne
Wagar, Michael
mwagar@chronline.com, Exec. Ed., The Chronicle, WA, Centralia
Wagenlander, Steve.......................ext. 5746
Audience Devel. Dir., The Post and Courier, SC, Charleston
Waggener, Donna
dwaggener@memphisdailynews.com, The Memphis News, TN, Memphis
dwaggener@memphisdailynews.com, Marketing Director, The Daily News
Waggoner, Robert C.
rwaggoner@burrellesluce.com, Chrmn./ CEO, BurrellesLuce, NJ, Livingston
Waggoner, Robert C.
rwaggoner@burrellesluce.com, Chrmn./ CEO, BurrellesLuce, NJ, Livingston
Wagholikar, S.
dainiklokmat@sancharnet.in, Ed. in Chief, DAINIK LOKMAT, Aurangabad, Maharashtra
Wagimin, Reginia
r.wagimin@dwt.net, Ed., DE WARE TIJD, Paramaribo
Wagle, Narayan
narayan@kantipur.com.np, Ed. in Chief, KANTIPUR DAILY, Kathmandu
Wagman, Les ....(306) 781-5239
lwagman@leaderpost.canwest.com, Adv. Dir., The Leader-Post, SK, Regina
Wagner, Sarah
swagner@alm.com, Office Mgr., Daily Report
Wagner, Jennifer......................(617) 786-7284
Photo/Graphics Ed., The Patriot Ledger, MA, Quincy
Wagner, Gerhard
redaktion@boyens-medien.de, Ed. in Chief, DITHMARSCHER LANDESZEITUNG, Heide
Wagner, Adrianne.....................(928) 539-6805
awagner@yumasun.com, Marketing Manager, Yuma Sun, AZ, Yuma
Wagner, Denise ....ext. 254
dwagner@appleton.gannett.com, Librarian, The Post-Crescent, WI, Appleton
Wagner, Peter W............(712) 324-5347 ext. 113
pww@iowainformation.com, Pres., Creative House Print Media Consultants, IA, Sheldon
pww@iowainformation.com, The Golden Shopper, IA, Sheldon
Wagner, Steve
jmail@bemidjipioneer.com, Daily Pioneer, MN, Bemidji
jmail@bemidjipioneer.com, Circ. Mgr., Laramie Daily Boomerang, WY, Laramie
Wagner, Paul ....(260) 461-8631
pwagner@jg.net, Systems Ed., The Journal Gazette, IN, Fort Wayne
Wagner, Marsha..............................ext. 229
marsha@mountvernonnews.com, Adv. Design Mgr., Mount Vernon News, OH, Mount Vernon
Wagner, Michelle ....ext. 110
mwagnernews@robdailynews.com, Social Ed., Daily News, IL, Robinson
Wahbeh, Ica
ica.wahbeh@jordantimes.com, Mng. Ed., JORDAN TIMES
Waidelich, Audrey
info@heatandcontrol.com, Dir., Mktg., Heat and Control, Inc., CA, Hayward
Wainwright, Nigel....................(780) 468-0344
nwainwright@edmsun.com, Circ. Dir., The Edmonton Sun, AB, Edmonton
Wainwright, Rachel
rachel.wainwright@gaflnews.com, Circ. Mgr., The Tifton Gazette, GA, Tifton
Wake, Bev ....(604) 605-2744
bwake@vancouversun.com, Projects Editor, The Vancouver Sun, BC, Vancouver
Wakefield, Jerry......................(360) 754-5440
jwakefield@theolympian.com, Mng. Ed., The Olympian, WA, Olympia
Walck, Pamela E. ....(912) 652-0299
pamela.walck@savannahnow.com, Gov't/Bus. Ed., Savannah Morning News, GA, Savannah
Walden, Cynthia......................(541) 338-2201
Personnel/HR Mgr., The Register-Guard, OR, Eugene
Walden, Ruth ....(919) 962-4088
James Howard & Hallie McLean Parker Distinguished Prof., University of North Carolina, NC, Chapel Hill
Walden, Paula
pwalden@gfherald.com, Adv. Mgr., Classified, Grand Forks Herald, ND, Grand Forks
Walden, Dwain ....(229) 985-4545 ext. 214
dwain.walden@gaflnews.com, Mng. Ed., The Moultrie Observer, GA, Moultrie
Walden, G.M.
info@truproof.co.uk, Mng. Dir., Truproof Ltd., London
Waldenmaier, Gerd
sog-nachrichten@merkur-online.de, Bus. Mgr., SCHONGAUER NACHRICHTEN, Schongau
Waldroff, Wayne ....(416) 507-2123
wwaldroff@cp.org, Gen. Mgr./Vice Pres., Broadcasting (CP), Press News Ltd., ON, Toronto
Walischmiller, Heinrich
service@idowa.de, Ed., DINGOLFINGER ANZEIGER, Dingolfing
Walk, Dan
sports@punxsutawneyspirit.com, Sports Ed., The Punxsutawney Spirit, PA, Punxsutawney
Walker, Douglas......................(765) 213-5851
dwalker@thestarpress.com, Metro Ed., The Star Press, IN, Muncie
Walker, Wayne ....(253) 941-9155
sales@foxbay.com, Sales Mgr., Fox Bay Industries, Inc., WA, Auburn
Walker, Scott...........................(205) 325-2100
Asst. Mng. Ed., The Birmingham News, AL, Birmingham
Walker, Sharon
swalker@nncogannett.com, Mktg. Research Analyst, Times Recorder, OH, Zanesville
Walker, Ken ....ext. 1278
ken.walker@gwinnettdailypost.com, Prodn. Mgr., Distribution, Gwinnette Daily Post, GA, Lawrenceville
Walker, Mark..........................(603) 543-3100
mwalker@tsvmedia.net, Prodn. Coord., Eagle Times, NH, Claremont
Walker, Keith ....(703) 369-6751
insidenova@potomacnews.com, Manassas Ed., Manassas Journal Messenger, VA, Manassas
Walker, Lisa...........................(603) 594-6493
Circ. Mgr., Home Delivery, The Telegraph, NH, Hudson
Walker, Beth ....ext. 723
Prodn. Mgr., Commercial Print Shop, The Jackson Sun, TN, Jackson
Walker, Scott P. ....(307) 634-3361 ext. 3150
scott@wyomingnews.com, Vice Pres., Mktg./Opns., Wyoming Color Comic Group, WY, Cheyenne
Walker, Donna ....(864) 298-4473
dwalker@greenvillenews.com, Film Writer, The Greenville News, SC, Greenville
Walker, Keith
kathy_may@westernlitho.com, Prodn. Mgr., Newspaper Product, Western LithoTech, MO, Saint Louis
Walker, Jessica ....ext. 1117
jessica.walker@uniontrib.com, Vice Pres./CFO, The San Diego Union-Tribune, CA, San Diego
Walker, William
sports@owensoundsuntimes.com, Sports Ed., The Sun Times, ON, Owen Sound
Walker, Tom...........................(810) 989-6278
twalker@gannett.com, Editorial Page Ed., Times Herald, MI, Port Huron
Walker, Harry ....(202) 383-3736
hwalker@mctinfoservices.com, Photo Servs. Dir., McClatchy-Tribune Information Services, DC, Washington
Walker, Wade..........................(205) 325-2287
Mgr., Purchasing, The Birmingham News, AL, Birmingham
Walker, Patricia S. Meagher...............ext. 4160
pwalker@phillyburbs.com, Exec. Ed., Bucks County Courier Times, PA, Levittown
Walker, Ana Pecina ....(903) 232-7225
awalker@coxnews.com, Ed., Longview News-Journal, TX, Longview
Walker, Daniel
editor@heraldbanner.com, Ed., Herald-Banner Publications, TX, Greenville
Walker, Philip
editor@examiner.co.uk, Adv. Dir., HUDDERSFIELD DAILY EXAMINER, Huddersfield, West Yorkshire
Walker, Pat.............................(215) 949-4160
pwalker@phillyburbs.com, Exec. Ed., Burlington County Times, NJ, Willingboro
Walker, Gregory ....ext. 1805
Prodn. Foreman, Pressroom, The Keene Sentinel, NH, Keene
Walker, Axel
redaktion@nw.owl-online.de, Bus. Mgr., NEUE WESTFALISCHE, Bielefeld
Walker, Tom...........................(303) 820-1624
twalker@denverpost.com, Book Ed., The Denver Post, CO, Denver
Walker, Bill 978-772-0777
bwalker@mnprintingdevens.com, Director Of Operations, The Sun, MA, Lowell
Walker, Paul David
egazzette@valu-line.com, Pres., The Emporia Gazette, KS, Emporia
Walker, Jeff
jwalker@sanmarcosrecord.com, Neighbors Ed., San Marcos Daily Record, TX, San Marcos
Walker, Steve
swalker@chronline.com, CFO, The Chronicle, WA, Centralia
Walker, Leeanna ....(479) 619-2527
lwalker@nwaonline.net, Metro Ed., The Morning News of Northwest Arkansas, AR, Springdale
Walker, James
jim.walker@irontontribune.com, Sports Ed., The Ironton Tribune, OH, Ironton
Walkling, Jennifer ....(810) 766-6241
jwalking@flintjournal.com, Home Section Ed., The Flint Journal, MI, Flint
Wall, Jim ....(801) 237-2187
jmwall@desnews.com, Pres./Pub., Deseret News, UT, Salt Lake City
Wall, Magnus ....(847) 558 5041
mwl@schur.com, Parts/Serv. Dir., Schur Packaging Systems, Inc., IL, Schaumburg
Wall, Robert
rwall@scn1.com, Adv. Vice Pres., The Beacon News, IL, Aurora
Wall, Andrew ....(563) 383-2478
Dir., HR, Quad-City Times, IA, Davenport
Wallace, Cathy ....(919) 836-5665
cwallace@newsobserver.com, Adv. Mgr., Grp. Adv., The News & Observer, NC, Raleigh
Wallace, Robert J. ....(715) 395-5725
robert.wallace@mx3.com, CFO/Treasurer, Superior Publishing Corp., WI, Superior
Wallace, Jason
editor@tbw.com.au, Ed., BORDER WATCH
Wallace, Bob 214-540-6314
wallace@amconmedia.com, Vice Pres., Accounting, American Consolidated Media, TX, Dallas
Wallace, Ron
ronwallace@dailycommercial.com, Pub., The Daily Commercial, FL, Leesburg
Wallace, James.........................416-947-2119
james.wallace@sunmedia.ca, Editor-in-Chief, The Toronto Sun, ON, Toronto
Wallace, Julia ....(937) 225-6907
julia.wallace@cmgohio.com, Market Vice President, Dayton Daily News, OH, Dayton
Wallace, Stanley ....(410) 822-1500
Treasurer, Chesapeake Publishing Corp., MD, Elkton
Wallace, Jeffrey B. ....(803) 644-2400
jwallace@aikenstandard.com, Ed., Aiken Standard, SC, Aiken
Wallace, Kendall M..................(978) 970-4801
kwallace@lowellsun.com, Chrmn., The Sun, MA, Lowell
Wallace, Debra........................(707) 468-3096
Mendocino College, CA, Ukiah
Wallaert, Thibaud
twallaert@dicommintl.com, Gen. Mgr., Dicomm Media, NY, New York
Wallberg, Bill ....(252) 329-9628
Info Systems Mgr., The Daily Reflector, NC, Greenville
Wallen, Elizabeth ....(651) 796-1113
ewallen@pressenter.com, Adv. Acct. Exec., Stillwater Gazette, MN, Stillwater
Wallen, Douglas 202-650-6509
cwallen@cq.com, Sr Vice pres./CFO, Congressional Quarterly, Inc., DC, Washington
Waller, Dennis R.
drwaller@chronline.com, CEO, The Chronicle, WA, Centralia
Waller, Deb ....(239) 335-0251
community@news-press.com, Exec. Asst. Pres./Pub., The News-Press, FL, Fort Myers
Waller, Dennis R.
drwaller@chronline.com, Pub., The Chronicle, WA, Centralia
Wallick, Steve ....(701) 250-8247
stevew@ndonline.com, News Ed., The Bismarck Tribune, ND, Bismarck
Wallick, Merritt.........................(302) 324-2856
mwallick@delawareonline.com, Bus. Ed., The News Journal, DE, New Castle
Wallingford, Jim ....(360) 575-6202
jim.wallingford@tdn.com, Mgr., Systems, The Daily News, WA, Longview
Wallis, David ....(212) 924-2283
sales@featurewell.com, Founder/CEO, Featurewell.com, NY, New York
Walls, Martha Ann ....(713) 266-5481
mwalls@sninews.com, Chrmn. of the Bd./Pres./CEO, Southern Newspapers, Inc., TX, Houston
Walls, C. Lee ....(205) 870-1684
Pres./CEO, Cleveland Newspapers, Inc., AL, Birmingham
Walls, Louis............................(410) 770-4071
Distr. Mgr., The Star-Democrat, MD, Easton
Walsh, Ward
sales@grafikam.com, Pres., grafikAmerica, PA, York
Walsh, Ward ....(717) 845-4807
imcsales@imcamerica.com, Pres., Metso Paper, PA, York

Walsh, Ward
imcsales@imcamerica.com, Pres., IMC America, PA, York
Walsh, Mike
mwalsh@theexpositor.com, Pub., The Expositor, ON, Brantford
Walsh, Jack ....(603) 627-6493
jwalsh@hearst.com, Senior Sales Consultant/Printing & New England Newspaper Sales, King Features Syndicate, NY, New York
jwalsh@hearst.com, Senior Sales Consultant/Printing and New England Newspaper Sales, North America Syndicate, NY, New York
Walsh, Steve
steve.walsh@ott.sunpub.com, Dir., Computer Servs., The Ottawa Sun, ON, Ottawa
Walsh, John G.
jwalsh@palmcoastobserver.com, Palm Coast Observer, FL, Palm Coast
jwalsh@palmcoastobserver.com, Sarasota Observer, FL, Sarasota
jwalsh@palmcoastobserver.com, Sr. Vice Pres., Circ., The Dallas Morning News, TX, Dallas
Walsh, Robert ....(203) 330-6450
bwalsh@ctpost.com, IT Dir., Connecticut Post, CT, Bridgeport
Walter, Timothy
cathjourn@catholicpress.org, Exec. Dir, Catholic Press Association, IL, Chicago
Walter, Andy
awalter@newszap.com, Sports Ed., Delaware State News, DE, Dover
Waltermeyer, Lacy...................(360) 754-5417
lwalterm@olympia.gannett.com, Adv. Mgr., Retail Territory, The Olympian, WA, Olympia
Walters, Tim............................321-242-3681
twalters@floridatoday.com, Visuals Editor, Florida Today, FL, Melbourne
Walters, Paul
pwalters@theadvocate.com, Online Ed., The Advocate, LA, Baton Rouge
Walters, Mark 202-650-6814
markwalters@cqrollcall.com, SVP, Advertising, Congressional Quarterly, Inc., DC, Washington
Walton, Georgianne ....(803) 533-5518
gwalton@timesanddemocrat.com, Data Processing Mgr., The Times and Democrat, SC, Orangeburg
Waltzer, Carl
wdigital@nyc.rr.com, Pres., Carl Waltzer Digital Services, Inc., NY, New York
Waluszko, Alex
uvp@uvp.com, Vice Pres., Mktg./Sales, UVP, Inc., CA, Upland
Walworth, Clark
cwalworth@theworldlink.com, Ed., The World, OR, Coos Bay
Walworth, Carl
editorial@jg-tc.com, Pub., Times-Courier, IL, Mattoon
Walworth, Carl
cwalworth@jg-tc.com, Pub., Journal-Gazette, IL, Mattoon
Walz, Dietmar
dietmar.walz@heidelberg.com, Mktg. Mgr., Heidelberger Druckmaschinen AG, Heidelberg
Wamsley, Jay..........................(435) 797-1757
Utah State Univ., UT, Logan
Wang, Alan ....(603) 543-3100 ext. 150
awang@tsvmedia.net, IT Dir., Eagle Times, NH, Claremont
Wang, Virginia........................(216) 999-4461
Vice Pres./Dir., Finance/Acct., The Plain Dealer, OH, Cleveland
Wang, Alice
plaffoon@knightridder.com, Vice Pres., Cor. Devel., Knight Ridder, CA, San Jose
Wanjohi, Elsie ....(386) 481-2707
Bethune-Cookman College, FL, Daytona Beach
Wannemacher, Kevin ......(419) 238-2285 ext. 228
kwannemacher@timesbulletin.com, Bus. Mgr., The Times Bulletin, OH, Van Wert
Wanner, Peter
peter.wanner@azag.ch, Pub., Buchdruckerei Baden AG, Baden, Aargau
Wantz, Ronald W.
eclectic@your-net.com, Pres., The Eclectic Co., Inc., OH, Lebanon
Warburton, Wendy ....(613) 596-8598
fashion@thecitizen.southam.ca, Fashion Ed., The Ottawa Citizen, ON, Ottawa
Ward, Lee ....(606) 326-2661
lward@dailyindependent.com, Lifestyles Ed., The Daily Independent, KY, Ashland
Ward, Daniel
danielw@nsynch.com, Mktg. Dir., Synchronicity, Inc., WA, Redmond
Ward, Jeff ....(765) 213-5854
Editorial Page Ed., The Star Press, IN, Muncie
Ward, Brian ....(902) 426-3088
brward@herald.ca, Assignment Ed., Day, The Chronicle Herald, NS, Halifax
Ward, Heidi ....(262) 631-1742
hward@journaltimes.com, Adv. Mgr., Retail, The Journal Times, WI, Racine
Ward, William ....(212) 681-3429
wward@nydailynews.com, Circ. Dir., Nat'l Sales, NY Daily News, NY, New York
Ward, Katie ....(618) 374-4258
Principia College, IL, Elsah
Ward, Terry
tward@ftimes.com, Pub., The Times, IN, Frankfort
Ward, Kevin
kward@cp.org, European Correspondent, Broadcast News Limited, London
Ward, Jannice 9022 0532
jannice.ward@kalminer.com.au, Senior Sales Excutive, KALGOORLIE MINER
Ward-Johnson, Frances
fward2@elon.edu, Assoc. Prof., Elon University, NC, Elon
Wardenfelt, Diane
dwardenfelt@newspost.com, Dir., HR, The Frederick News-Post, MD, Frederick
Wardle, Andrew ....ext. 286
andrew.wardle@gaflnews.com, Vice Pres., Circ., Valdosta Daily Times, GA, Valdosta
Wardrop, Bob ....(951) 248-6185
bwardrop@pe.com, Online Ed., The Press-Enterprise, CA, Riverside
Wareham, Fraser.....................(306) 694-8342
fraserw@mjtimes.sk.com, Prodn. Mgr., Pressroom, The Moose Jaw Times-Herald, SK, Moose Jaw
Wareham Best, Jennifer ....(707) 965-6437
Chair, Pacific Union College, CA, Angwin
Wargo, John R.
jwargo@email.usps.gov, Sr. Vice Pres., Mktg. Devel., United States Postal Service, DC, Washington
Warhover, Tom ....(573) 882-5734
warhovert@missouri.edu, Executive Editor, Columbia Missourian, MO, Columbia
Warmouth, Lee ....(734) 994-6352
lwarmouth@annarbornews.com, Circ. Dir., The Ann Arbor News, MI, Ann Arbor
Warneke, Kent
editor@norfolkdailynews.com, Ed., Norfolk Daily News, NE, Norfolk
Warner, Rob
rwarner@thecitizen.southam.ca, City Ed., The Ottawa Citizen, ON, Ottawa
Warner, Tracy ....(260) 461-8113
twarner@jg.net, Editorial Page Ed., The Journal Gazette, IN, Fort Wayne
Warner, Gary..........................(479) 524-7255
John Brown Univ., AR, Siloam Springs
Warnock, Dan.........................(813) 948-4227
Circ. Opns. Mgr., State, The Tampa Tribune, FL, Tampa
Warren, Rich 402-4441204
Dir., Marketing, Omaha World-Herald, NE, Omaha
Warren, Rich 402-444-1204
Dir., Marketing, Omaha World-Herald, NE, Omaha
Warren, Melissa......................(918) 684-2957
Prodn. Mgr., Pre Press, Muskogee Daily Phoenix & Times Democrat, OK, Muskogee
Warren, Colin 789 7319
westport.news@xtra.co.nz, Managing direcctor MD, THE WESTPORT NEWS
Warren, Hillary ....(614) 823-1159
Otterbein College, OH, Westerville
Warren, Richard J....................(207) 990-8000
bdnmail@bangordailynews.net, Ed., Bangor Daily News, ME, Bangor
Warren, Kira Lisa
liwarren@coxohio.com, Ed., JournalNews, OH, Hamilton
Warren, Troy ....(270) 783-3260
twarren@bgdailynews.com, Circ. Mgr., Daily News, KY, Bowling Green
Warren, Steve ....(609) 272-7278
swarren@pressofac.com, Deputy Content Dir., Digital, The Press of Atlantic City, NJ, Pleasantville
Warren, Wendy
wwarren@phillynews.com, Ed., Philly.com/Vice Pres., The Philadelphia Daily News, PA, Philadelphia
Warren, Bobby........................(972) 392-0888
bobby@wieck.com, Client Servs. Mgr., Wieck Media, TX, Dallas
Warren, Tim............................(772) 408-5308
tim.warren@scripps.com, Prodn. Mgr., Post Press, Treasure Coast News/Press-Tribune, FL, Stuart
Wartinger, John
john.wartinger@inlandnewspapers.com, Prodn. Vice Pres., Inland Valley Daily Bulletin, CA, Ontario
Wasch, Ken.................................ext. 1310
ken.wasch@siia.net, Pres., Software & Information Industry Association, DC, Washington
Waseleski, Tom
twaseleski@post- gazette.com, Pres., National Conference of Editorial Writers, PA, Harrisburg
Wash, Paul............................(540) 932-3570
pwash@newsvirginian.com, Circ. Dir., The News Virginian, VA, Waynesboro
Washburn, Patrick ....(740) 593-2593
Prof., Ohio University, OH, Athens
Washington, Julie....................(216) 999-4539
Home Editor, The Plain Dealer, OH, Cleveland
Wasielewski, Stacey ....(828) 232-5887
swasielewski@citizen-times.com, Info Tech. Dir., The Asheville Citizen-Times, NC, Asheville
Wasmund, Jessica R......................ext. 2226
jessye.wasmund@journal-register.com, City Ed., The Journal-Register, NY, Medina
Wass, Douglas........................(780) 498-5716
dwass@thejournal.canwest.com, Circ. Vice Pres., Reader Servs., Edmonton Journal, AB, Edmonton
Wassmann, Jerome
jasper@mountaineagle.com, Ed., Daily Mountain Eagle, AL, Jasper
Watali, Nobuo
iht-asahi@asahi.com, MD, ASAHI EVENING NEWS, Tokyo
Waterhouse, Steve
swaterhouse@bayareanewsgroup.com, Ed., The Argus, CA, Fremont
Waterman, Don
don.waterman@dowjones.com, SVP, Printing & Distribution, Dow Jones Local Media Group, NY, Middletown
Waters, George.......................(626) 568-9894
george@georgewaters.net, Humor Columnist, George Waters, CA, San Marino
Waters, John
info@watersdesign.com, Owner, Waterdesign Associates, NY, New York
Waters, Russell ....(386) 754-0407
rwaters@lakecityreporter.com, Circ. Dir., Lake City Reporter, FL, Lake City
Waters, Bill J. ....(775) 850-2285
Cor. Controller, Swift Communications, Inc., NV, Carson City
Waters, Alyssa
alyssa.waters@ecpc.com, Religion Ed., Leader-Telegram, WI, Eau Claire
Waters, Henry J. ....(573) 815-1560
hwaters@columbiatribune.com, Editorial Writer, Columbia Daily Tribune, MO, Columbia
Waters, John
beneditorial@newsquest.co.uk, Mng. Dir., BOLTON NEWS, Bolton, Lancashire
Watkins, Lynne
lwatkins@dailyadvance.com, IS Manager, The Daily Advance, NC, Elizabeth City
Watkins, John ....ext. 101
dipub@ridgecrestca.com, Pub., The Daily Independent, CA, Ridgecrest
Watkins, Patsy
pwatkins@uark.edu, Chair/Assoc. Prof., University of Arkansas, AR, Fayetteville
Watkins, Pam ....(972) 480-8383
pam_watkins@mccom.com, Vice Pres., Bus. Devel., MCC, TX, Dallas
Watkins, Betty
bwatkins@dailystatesman.com, Ad manager, The Daily Statesman, MO, Dexter
Watkins, Thomas H.
challengegroup@yahoo.com, Pub., The Daily Challenge, NY, Brooklyn
Watley, Sylvia ....(601) 979-2167
Jackson State Univ., MS, Jackson
Watson, Vanessa 5208924
vanessam@marlexpress.co.nz, General Manager, THE MARLBOROUGH EXPRESS, Blenheim
Watson, Phil
pwatson@charterminternet.com, Mng. Ed., The Daily Globe, MI, Ironwood
Watson, William J. ....(570) 420-4484
wwatson@poconorecord.com, Exec. Ed., Pocono Record, PA, Stroudsburg
Watson, John ....(716) 875-3380
jwatson@hfwindustries.com, Pres., HFW Industries, NY, Buffalo
Watson, Mark
news@bhpioneer.com, Ed., Black Hills Pioneer, SD, Spearfish
Watson, Chris...............(831) 423-4242 ext. 263
cwatson@santacruzsentinel.com, Books Ed., Santa Cruz Sentinel, CA, Scotts Valley
Watson, Dan
dwatson@santamariatimes.com, Asst. Sports Ed., Santa Maria Times, CA, Santa Maria
Watson, Randi.........................(360) 405-9161
rwatson@kitsapsun.com, Pre Press Mgr., Kitsap Sun, WA, Bremerton
Watson, Greg...........................321-242-3927
gwatson@floridatoday.com, Sales and Marketing Director, Florida Today, FL, Melbourne
Watson, Eric ....(484) 365-7524
Lincoln Univ., PA, Lincoln University
Watson, Sam ....ext. 328
swatson@johnsoncitypress.com, Educ./School Ed., Johnson City Press, TN, Johnson City
Watson, Douglas......................(423) 359-3157
doug.watson@greenevillesun.com, Mng. Ed., The Greeneville Sun, TN, Greeneville
Waugh, Diane E.
dwaugh@mikes.net, Sec./Treasurer, The Daily Clintonian, IN, Clinton
Waugh, Neil............................(780) 427-4206
Columnist, The Edmonton Sun, AB, Edmonton
Waxelbaum, Steve....................(561) 820-3405
swaxelbaum@pbpost.com, Adv. Mgr., Retail, Bureau Offices, The Palm Beach Post, FL, West Palm Beach
Wayne, Robert N. ....(813) 259-7622
Asst. Controller, The Tampa Tribune, FL, Tampa
Wayne, Rick
slustar@candw.lc, Owner/Pub./Ed., ST. LUCIA STAR, Castries
Wear, Kimberly
kwear@times-standard.com, Mng. Ed., Times-Standard, CA, Eureka
Wearing, Ben ....(785) 822-1421 ext. 113
bwearing@salina.com, Exec. Ed., The Salina Journal, KS, Salina
Weatherred, Jenna
jweatherred@postindependent.com, Pub., Glenwood Springs Post Independent, CO, Glenwood Springs
Weatherred, Jenna
mail@aspentimes.com, Pub., The Aspen Times, CO, Aspen
Weaver, Timothy J. ....(215) 345-3099
tweaver@phillyburbs.com, Controller, The Intelligencer, PA, Doylestown
Weaver, Bill
bweaver@acnpapers.com, Grp. Pub., McKinney Courier-Gazette, TX, McKinney
Weaver, Edie...........................(217) 788-1356
edie.weaver@sj-r.com, Audience Devel. Mgr., The State Journal-Register, IL, Springfield
Weaver, Tom
sales@kiosk.com, Vice Pres., Sales/Mktg., Kiosk Information Systems, CO, Louisville
Weaver, Steve

sweaver@greeleytribune.com, Grp. Pub., Greeley Daily Tribune, CO, Greeley
Weaver, Kendal
kweaver@ap.org, Sec., Alabama Associated Press Managing Editors Association, AL, Montgomery
Weaver, Curt ....ext. 207
production@columbiabasinherald.com, Prodn. Supt., Columbia Basin Herald, WA, Moses Lake
Weaver, Rob
rweaver@advertiser-tribune.com, News Ed., The Advertiser-Tribune, OH, Tiffin
Weaver, Rebecca ....ext. 3611
rweaver@express-times.com, Credit Mgr., The Express-Times, PA, Easton
Weaver, Mike ....(352) 563-3275
mweaver@chronicleonline.com, Prodn. Mgr., Pressroom, Citrus County Chronicle, FL, Crystal River
Weavers, Bill
bweavers@acnpapers.com, Pres./Pub., Plano Star Courier, TX, Plano
Webb, Victor
marwebint@cs.com, Pres., Marston Webb International, NY, New York
Webb, Penny ....(940) 720-3466
webbp@wtr.com, Adv. Coord., Nat'l, Wichita Falls Times Record News, TX, Wichita Falls
Webb, James ....(252) 329-9665
Facilities Mgr., The Daily Reflector, NC, Greenville
Webb, Bryan
bwebb@islandpacket.com, Mgmt. Info Servs. Mgr., The Island Packet, SC, Bluffton
Webb, Michael ....(919) 462-0900
michael@theromantic.com, Writer, The RoMANtic Syndicated Column, NC, Cary
Webb, Joe................................715-738-1624
joe.webb@lee.net, Prodn. Mgr., The Chippewa Herald, WI, Chippewa Falls
Webb, Tam ....(402) 444-3125
tam.webb@owh.com, Adv. Mgr., Custom Publishing/Events, Omaha World-Herald, NE, Omaha
Webber, Suzanne......................(219) 785-5213
Purdue Univ. North Central, IN, Westville
Webber, Barry
bwebber@demingheadlight.com, Circ. Mgr., Deming Headlight, NM, Deming
Webber, Lee P. ....(808) 525-7440
lwebber@honoluluadvertiser.com, Pres./Pub., Honolulu Star-Advertiser, HI, Honolulu
Weber, Christine
cweber@scn1.com, Mgr., Promo., The Beacon News, IL, Aurora
Weber, Anthony........................(937) 335-5634
weber@tdnpublishing.com, Chief Photographer, Troy Daily News, OH, Troy
Weber, Betty 2168310480
bettyweber@bob-weber.com, Vice President, Bob Weber, Inc., OH, Cleveland
Weber, Mark ....(713) 275-5039 ext. 1#
Technical Dir., Interactive Visuals, Inc., IL, Chicago
Weber, Julie ....(713) 275-5039 ext. 2#
jbw@ivisuals.com, Creative Dir., Interactive Visuals, Inc., IL, Chicago
Weber, G.
redaktion@schiltzer-bote.de, Distr. Mgr., SCHLITZER BOTE, Schlitz
Weber, Bob..............................8003884294
bweber@bob-weber.com, President, Bob Weber, Inc., OH, Cleveland
Weber, Tad 805-781-7906
tweber@thetribunenews.com, Managing Editor, The Tribune, CA, San Luis Obispo
Weber, Jeff
jeff@jeffweber.net, Pres., Weber Systems, Inc., OH, Beachwood
Weber, Phyllis ....(408) 920-2791
pweber@mercurynews.com, Adv. Dir., Nat'l, San Jose Mercury News, CA, San Jose
Weber, Eric.............................(918) 496-8103
sales@smartmax.com, Pres., SmartMax Software, Inc., OK, Tulsa
Weber, Thomas E. ....(772) 221-4134
tom.weber@scripps.com, Pres., Treasure Coast News/Press-Tribune, FL, Stuart
Webster, Doug ....(870) 508-8025
dwebster@baxterbulletin.com, Dir., Opns., The Baxter Bulletin, AR, Mountain Home
Webster, Angela
angela@newnan.com, Coweta Close-Up Ed., The Times-Herald, GA, Newnan
Webster, Andrew
websteran@tcp.newsltd.com.au, Ed., CAIRNS POST
Webster, Mark ....(843) 626-0272
mwebster@thesunnews.com, Prodn. Dir., Opns., The Sun News, SC, Myrtle Beach
Wechsler, Elizabeth ....ext. 1140
elizabeth.wechsler@timesargus.com, Bus. Office Mgr., The Times Argus, VT, Barre
Weddell, Jim...........................(915) 546-6370
jweddell@elpasotimes.com, VP of Online/Digital, El Paso Times, TX, El Paso
Weddle, Tim ....(816) 271-8510
tweddle@npgco.com, Adv. Dir., St. Joseph News-Press, MO, Saint Joseph
Wedel, Dave
dwedel@hearstnp.com, Pub., Midland Reporter-Telegram, TX, Midland
Wedel, Helge
red@sj-medier.dk, Ed. in Cheif, SJAELLANDS TIDENDE, Slagelse, Sjaelland
Wedge, Maureen......................(207) 689-2911
mwedge@sunjournal.com, Vice Pres., HR, Sun Journal, ME, Lewiston
Wee, Eric
ericw@ediwise.com, EDIWISE, ON, Mississauga
Weeks, Colette
cweeks@skagitpublishing.com, Mng. Ed., Administration, Skagit Valley Herald, WA, Mount Vernon
Weeks, Roland ....(205) 325-2424
Adv. Dir., The Birmingham News, AL, Birmingham
Weeks, John ....(909) 386-3858
john.weeks@inlandnewspapers.com, Columnist, San Bernardino County Sun, CA, San Bernardino
Weeks, Roland ....(601) 961-7143
rweeks@jackson.gannett.com, Adv. Dir., The Clarion-Ledger, MS, Jackson
Wegman, Lora ....(573) 815-1716
lewegman@columbiatribune.com, City Ed., Columbia Daily Tribune, MO, Columbia
Wegmann, Juergen
gn@gn-online.de, Pub., Grafschafter Nachrichten, Nordhorn
Wehenkel, Arthur D. ....(423) 359-3160
artie.wehenkel@greenevillesun.com, Adv. Dir., The Greeneville Sun, TN, Greeneville
Wehle, Greg 712-263-2122
greg.wehle@bulletinreview.com, Pub., Denison Bulletin and Review, IA, Denison
Wei, Simone
chinews@tpts1.seed.net.tw, Chrmn./Pub., CHINA NEWS, Taipei
Wei, Simone
cdns@ms1.hinet.net, Pub., CHINA DAILY NEWS, Taipei
Weidler, Jeff
info@multivalue.com, Pres., WordMark International Corp., CA, Santa Clara
Weidman, Sheila M.
sweidman@gapac.com, Sr. Vice Pres., Commun. government and Pub. Aff., Georgia-Pacific Corp., GA, Atlanta
Weigel, Deb
debweigel@oelweindailyregister.com, Pub., The Oelwein Daily Register, IA, Oelwein
Weikel, Dave...........................(360) 417-3516
IT/Tech. Servs. Dir., Peninsula Daily News, WA, Port Angeles
Weil, Tamara ....(910) 343-2020
tamara.weil@starnewsonline.com, Adv. Mgr., Classified, Star-News, NC, Wilmington
Weil, Robert
rweil@mcclatchy.com, Vice President, Operations, The McClatchy Company, CA, Sacramento
Wein, Dave
dave.wein@prnewswire.com, CFO, PR Newswire - New York, NY, NY, New York
Weinberg, Ann.........................(239) 335-0288
aweinberg@news-press.com, Vice Pres., HR, The News-Press, FL, Fort Myers
Weinberg, Al
weinberg@hood.edu, Dir./Prof. of Journalism, Hood College, MD, Frederick
Weinerth, Jerry...........................8083750111
aphonecardguy@aol.com, President, ANewStartGuy.com, HI, Kailua
Weingarten, Randi
online@aft.org, Pres., American Federation of Teachers, DC, Washington
Weinholzer, Charles ....(651) 483-2300
weinholc@corp.inxintl.com, Sr. Vice Pres.-Liquid Div., INX International Ink Co., IL, Schaumburg
Weinstock, C..............(805) 654-6400 ext. 1228
Ventura College, CA, Ventura
Weir, Jeremy...........................(617) 482-6462
jweir@mpival.com, Reg'l Dir., Management Planning, Inc., MA, Boston
Weis, Palle
i@information.dk, Journalist, INFORMATION, Copenhagen, Sjaelland
Weisburgh, Cecily ....ext. 1437
cweisburgh@keenesentinel.com, Local News Ed., The Keene Sentinel, NH, Keene
Weiss, Steven ....(718) 853-5435
Mgr., Rothco Cartoons, NY, Brooklyn
Weiss, Gary L.........................(989) 894-9613
gweiss@bc-times.com, Controller, The Bay City Times, MI, Bay City
Weiss, Arnold.................................ext. 273
Pres., Cosmos Communications, Inc., NY, Long Island City
Weiss, Debra
mes@metro-email.com, Vice Pres./Mktg. Dir., Metro Editorial Services, NY, New York
Weiss, Vicky ....(701) 250-8242
vicky.weiss@bismarcktribune.com, Librarian, The Bismarck Tribune, ND, Bismarck
Weissler, Mindy
sales@acbcoop.com, Dir., Mktg., Advertising Checking Bureau, Inc., NY, New York
Weitman, Gary 312-222-3394
SVP/Corporate Relations, Tribune Co., IL, Chicago
Welbon, Yvonne......................(336) 517-2306
Bennett College, NC, Greensboro
Welborn, Laura
laura.welborn@indianamediagroup.com, Regl. Pub., Greensburg Daily News, IN, Greensburg
Welch, Rick
rwelch@the-messenger.com, Pub., The Messenger, KY, Madisonville
Welch, Debi
welchd@knews.com, Dir., HR, Knoxville News Sentinel, TN, Knoxville
Welch, Bill 814-824-3362
wwelch@mercyhurst..edu, Mercyhurst College, PA, Erie
Welch, Geoffrey
gwelch@newspapersfirst.com, Vice Pres./Sales Mgr., Newspapers First, Inc., IL, Chicago
Welch, Donnie
dwelch@thespectrum.com, Pres./Pub., The Spectrum, UT, Saint George
Weld, Andy
aweld@couriernews.net, Ed., Blytheville Courier News, AR, Blytheville
Weldon, Tom...........................(408) 920-5846
tweldon@mercurynews.com, Circ. Mgr., Transportation, San Jose Mercury News, CA, San Jose
Wells, Chuck
cwells@therepublic.com, Pub., The Republic, IN, Columbus
Wells, Pam
pwells@madison.com, CFO, Capital Newspapers, WI, Madison
Wells, Rob ....(202) 862-9272
rob.wells@dowjones.com, Bureau Chief, Dow Jones Newswires - Washington, DC, DC, Washington
Wells, Ken
kwells@newportdailyadv.com, Pub., The Newport Daily Express, VT, Newport
Wells, Sylvia ....(213) 821-0075
sylvia@ccnma.org, Office Mgr., CCNMA: Latino Journalists of California, CA, Los Angeles
Wells, Chuck...........................(317) 736-2744
cwells@dailyjournal.net, Pub., Daily Journal, IN, Franklin
Wells, Martha.........................(541) 812-6125
martha.wells@lee.net, Pub., Albany Democrat-Herald, OR, Albany
Wells, Keith
keith.wells@indianamediagroup.com, Adv. Dir., Regl., Greensburg Daily News, IN, Greensburg
Wells, John ....(661) 395-7227
jwells@bakersfield.com, Vice Pres., Sales/Circ./Mktg./Opns., The Bakersfield Californian, CA, Bakersfield
Welty, Cheryl ....(937) 644-9111
cw@marysvillejt.com, Accounting Exec., Marysville Journal-Tribune, OH, Marysville
Welvaert, Brandy ....(309) 786-6441 ext. 261
bwelvaert@qconline.com, Food Ed., The Dispatch, IL, Moline
Wen-Shun, Yen
letters@taipeitimes.com, Pub., LIBERTY TIMES, Taipei City
Wendelken, Dave
wendeldh@jmu.edu, Assoc. Prof., James Madison University, VA, Harrisonburg
Wendt, Kevin
kevin.wendt@htimes.com, Ed., The Huntsville Times, AL, Huntsville
Wenrick, Laura ....(360) 735-4474
laura.wenrick@columbian.com, Advertising Sales Mgr, The Columbian, WA, Vancouver
Wensel, Diane
diane.wensel@sunmedia.ca, Mktg. Mgr., The Calgary Sun, AB, Calgary
Wenske, Ernst-Jurgen
anzeigen@kreiszeitung.de, Bus. Mgr., Wildeshauser Zeitung, Syke
Werblin, Cathy........................(714) 432-5094
Orange Coast College, CA, Costa Mesa
Werling, Jason ....ext. 303
jasonwerling@sanduskyregister.com, Chief Photographer, Sandusky Register, OH, Sandusky
Werling, Glen
glenw@news-banner.com, Mng. Ed., News-Banner, IN, Bluffton
Wermser, Jurgen
redaktion@neue-oz.de, Ed. in Chief, Neue Oz Osnabrucker Zeitung, Osnabruck
Werner, Genine............................9022 0557
genine.werner@kalminer.com.au, Production Manager, KALGOORLIE MINER
Werner, Michael
pitmanphoto@att.net, Pres., Pitman Photo Supply, FL, Miami
Werrell, James ....(803) 329-4081
jwerrell@heraldonline.com, Editorial Page Ed., The Herald, SC, Rock Hill
Werth, Darren ....ext. 210
dwerth@hutchnews.com, Adv. Supvr., Sales, The Hutchinson News, KS, Hutchinson
Wertman, Michael..........................ext. 2228
mike.wertman@journal-register.com, Sports Ed., The Journal-Register, NY, Medina
Werts, Marcia 316-269-6762
mwerts@wichitaeagle.com, Metro Ed., The Wichita Eagle, KS, Wichita
Wesa, David
davidwesa@circulation.net, Dir., Info. Servs., Circulation Development, Inc., MO
Wescott, Robert
rob@wimgo.com, Chief Product Officer, Wimgo, The Oklahoman, OK, Oklahoma City
Wessel, Chris
chriswessel@npgco.com, Pub., Atchison Globe, KS, Atchison
Wessel, Chris
cwessels@hernandotoday.com, Ed., Hernando Today, FL, Brooksville
West, Jill.....................(678) 804-7411 ext. 704
jill.west@buystory.com, Vice Pres./Mng. Ed., Syndicated Writers of America, GA, Suwanee
West, Andrew ....(302) 741-8204
awest@newszap.com, Chief Ed., The Daily Banner, MD, Cambridge
West, Amy S.
asw@capcomachinery.com, Vice Pres., Finance, Capco Machinery Systems, Inc., VA, Roanoke
West, Michael
west@lao.ten.fujitsu.com, Mktg., Dir., Fujitsu Ten Corp. of America, CA, Torrance
West, Tina
twest@thecouriertimes.com, Pub., The Courier-Times, IN, New Castle

West, Andrew
awest@newszap.com, Mng. Ed., Delaware State News, DE, Dover
West, Mark D.
west@unca.edu, Chair, University of North Carolina-Asheville, NC, Asheville
West, Larry..................(609) 272-7002
lwest@pressofac.com, Adv. Mgr., Classified, The Press of Atlantic City, NJ, Pleasantville
West, Robert..................(205) 325-2345
Mktg. Dir., The Birmingham News, AL, Birmingham
West, Bob..................(409) 721-2432
rdwest@usa.net, Sports Ed., Port Arthur News, TX, Port Arthur
West-Ravenell, Barbara
bwestravenell@timesanddemocrat.com, Prodn. Mgr., Distr., The Times and Democrat, SC, Orangeburg
Westerlund, Tommy
tommy.westerlund@vastranyland.fi, Ed. in Chief, VASTRA NYLAND, Ekenas, Turku-Pori
Westfall, Patricia..................(740) 593-2595
Prof., Ohio University, OH, Athens
Westmoreland, Phillip
usa@lorentzen-wettre.com, Pres., Lorentzen & Wettre, GA, Alpharetta
Weston, Chris..................(864) 298-4471
cweston@greenvillenews.com, Mng. Ed., The Greenville News, SC, Greenville
Westover, Angel..................(509) 582-1465
awestover@tri-cityherald.com, Online Mktg./Sales, Tri-City Herald, WA, Kennewick
Westphal, Steven..................(616) 222-5656
swestphal@grpress.com, Gen. Mgr., The Grand Rapids Press, MI, Grand Rapids
Westphal, Steve
stevewestphal@muskegonchronicle.com, Gen. Mgr., The Muskegon Chronicle, MI, Muskegon
Wetel, Helt
helt.wetel@sj-medier.dk, Ed., SJAELLANDSKE, Naestved, Sjaelland
Wetjen, Andre
andre.wetjen@eventpub.com, Coming Events Ed., The Daily Courier, BC, Kelowna
Wetterstrand, Katy..................(805) 238-3524
katy@westernquartz.com, CFO, Western Quartz Products, Inc., CA, Paso Robles
Wetzel-Handle, Brigitte
info@muehlacker-tagblatt.de, Proprietor, Muhlacker Tagblatt, Muhlacker
Weybret, Marty..........(209) 369-2761 ext. 205
martw@lodinews.com, Pub., Lodi News-Sentinel, CA, Lodi
Weydert, Debra..................732-390-4480
weyded@nytimes.com, Regional Manager, Eastern & Southeastern Region, New York Times News Service, NY, New York
Weydert, Debra..................732-390-4480
weyded@nytimes.com, Regional Manager, Eastern & Southeastern Region, New York Times Syndicate, NY, New York
Weydert, Debra..................(732) 390-4480
weyded@nytimes.com, Sales Exec., US/Canadian One-Shots, New York Times Syndicate, NY, New York
Whalen, John R.
cryogen@cryogenesis-usa.com, Vice Pres., Sales, Cryogenesis (A Div. of WM & C Services, Inc.), OH, Cleveland
Whalen, Scott..................(617) 619-6212
swhalen@bostonherald.com, Adv. Dir., Display, Boston Herald, MA, Boston
Whalen, John M...........(603) 668-4321 ext. 552
jwhalen@unionleader.com, Circ. Dir., Newspaper Sales/Mktg., New Hampshire Union Leader/New Hampshire Sunday News, NH, Manchester
Whalen, David..................(845) 451-1406
Culinary Institute of America, NY, Hyde Park
Whalen, John
jwhalen@unionleader.com, Director, Newspaper Sales & Marketing, New Hampshire Union Leader/New Hampshire Sunday News, NH, Manchester
Whaley, Mary
mwhaley@cheboygantribune.com, Circ. Mgr., Cheboygan Daily Tribune, MI, Cheboygan
Whaley, Joi
jwhaley@themountainpress.com, Adv. Dir., The Mountain Press, TN, Sevierville
Whatley, Charles..................949-892-2928
awhatley@mediaspanonline.com, Vice President of Sales & Marketing, MediaSpan Online Services, CA, Irvine
Wheat, Anessa
circ@fultonsun.com, Circ. Mgr., The Fulton Sun, MO, Fulton
Wheatcroft, Patience
patience.wheatcroft@dowjones.com, Ed. in Chief, WALL STREET JOURNAL EUROPE, ENG, London
Wheatley, Guy..................ext. 3363
gwheatley@texarkanagazette.com, Technical Serv. Administrator, Texarkana Gazette, TX, Texarkana
Wheaton, Mark..................ext. 1184
mark.wheaton@timesargus.com, Prodn. Supvr., Mailroom, The Times Argus, VT, Barre
Wheeler, Kelly..................(619) 231-9097
Bureau Chief, City News Service, Inc. - San Diego, CA, CA, San Diego
Wheeler, Vince..................(336) 888-3517
vwheeler@hpe.com, Editorial Page Ed., High Point Enterprise, NC, High Point
Wheeler, Simon..................(607) 274-9211
swheeler@ithaca.gannett.com, Photo Ed., The Ithaca Journal, NY, Ithaca
Wheitley, Kevin
kevin.wheitley@tweednews.com.au, Adv. Mgr., TWEED DAILY NEWS
Whelan, Raymond D.
rayw@globephotos.com, Vice Pres., Globe Photos, Inc., NY, West Islip
rayw@globephotos.com, Mgr., Ipol, Inc., NY, Babylon
Whelan, Marybeth
marybethw@globephotos.com, Mgr., Ipol, Inc., NY, Babylon
Whelan, Mary Beth..................(631) 661-3131
marybethw@globephotos.com, Pres., Globe Photos, Inc., NY, West Islip
Whelan, Tom..................(888)309-0639
twhelan@miracomcomputer.com, Director, Customer Service, Miracom Computer Corp., NY, Eastchester
Whelchel, Sandy..................(303) 841-0246
authorsandy@hotmail.com, Exec. Dir., National Writers Association, CO, Parker
Whetmore, Edward
ewhetmore@csudh.edu, Chair, California State University, Dominguez Hills, CA, Carson
Whetten, Bruce
bwhetten@douglasdispatch.com, Sports Ed., The Daily Dispatch, AZ, Douglas
Whister, Kirk
kirk@whisler.com, Pres., Latino Print Network, CA, Carlsbad
Whiston, Julia
whca@starpower.net, Exec. Dir., White House Correspondents Association, DC, Washington
Whitacre, Ann..................(540) 665-4949
awhitacre@winchesterstar.com, Adv. Mgr., Classified, The Winchester Star, VA, Winchester
Whitaker, Bill
bwhitaker@wacotrib.com, City Ed., Waco Tribune-Herald, TX, Waco
Whitaker, Edward..................(512) 527-1500
danlevine@prodigy.net, CEO, Prodigy, Inc., TX, Austin
Whitaker, John R...................(573) 248-2701
jack.whitaker@courierpost.com, Pub., Hannibal Courier-Post, MO, Hannibal
White, Candice..................715-738-1610
life@chippewa.com, Community Ed., The Chippewa Herald, WI, Chippewa Falls
White, Micheal
mwhite@calkins-media.com, Sr. Vice Pres., Calkins Media, PA, Levittown
White, Phyllis..................(501) 378-3460
Adv. Supvr., Customer Sales, Arkansas Democrat-Gazette, AR, Little Rock
White, Alan..................978-946-2479
awhite@eagletribune.com, Editor, The Eagle-Tribune, MA, North Andover
White, Jackie..................ext. 8027
Systems Mgr., Burlington County Times, NJ, Willingboro
White, Don
dwhite@capitalgazette.com, Prodn. Mgr., Distr., The Capital, MD, Annapolis
White, John..................(204) 697-7585
John.White@freepress.mb.ca, Deputy Ed., Online, Winnipeg Free Press, MB, Winnipeg
White, Chris..................ext. 210
chris.white@gaflnews.com, Adv. Dir., Thomasville Times-Enterprise, GA, Thomasville
White, Graham
admis@thisisstaffordshire.co.uk, Adv. Mgr., Sentinel Sunday, ENG, Stoke-On-Trent, Staffordshire
White, Edward
edwhite@eandedisplay.com, Chrmn., E and E Display Group, KS, Lawrence
White, Timothy
whitet@fayettevillenc.com, Editorial Page Ed., The Fayetteville Observer, NC, Fayetteville
White, Lance..................ext. 1636
lwhite@the-daily-record.com, Mng. Ed., The Daily Record, OH, Wooster
White, Wanda..................(306) 691-1271
wanda.white@mjtimes.sk.ca, Prodn. Mgr., Pre Press, The Moose Jaw Times-Herald, SK, Moose Jaw
White, Larry
star2020@time-data.com, Dir., Time Data Syndicate, NH, Manchester
White, Robert D...................(810) 766-6229
bwhite@flintjournal.com, Opns. Dir., The Flint Journal, MI, Flint
White, Woody..................(864) 298-4490
rwwhite@greenvillenews.com, Bus. Ed., The Greenville News, SC, Greenville
White, Keith..................(202) 650-6605
kwhite@cq.com, Executive Vice President and Managing Director, Congressional Quarterly, Inc., DC, Washington
White, Randy
sports@news-expressky.com, Sports Ed., The Appalachian News-Express, KY, Pikeville
White, Jenny..................(252) 407-9966
jwhite@rmtelegram.com, Online Ed., Rocky Mount Telegram, NC, Rocky Mount
White, Neal..................(972) 937-3310
neal.white@wninews.com, Ed., Waxahachie Daily Light, TX, Waxahachie
White, Chris..................ext. 211
Fashion Ed., West Plains Daily Quill, MO, West Plains
White, Eliot C...................(203) 317-2350
ewhite@record-journal.com, Pres./Pub., The Record-Journal Publishing Co., CT, Meriden
White, Marcia..................ext. 3541
today@express-times.com, Features Ed., The Express-Times, PA, Easton
White, Bill..................ext. 311
bwhite@adn.com, Bus. Ed., Anchorage Daily News, AK, Anchorage
White, Eric..................(517) 768-4830
ewhite@citpat.com, Pre Press Supvr., The Jackson Citizen Patriot, MI, Jackson
White, Robert M...................ext. 4080
rwhite@phillyburbs.com, Controller, Bucks County Courier Times, PA, Levittown
White, Adam..................ext. 120
awhite@benningtonbanner.com, Sports Ed., Bennington Banner, VT, Bennington
White, Meredith..................(415) 777-7676
Deputy Mng. Ed., Features, San Francisco Chronicle, CA, San Francisco
White, Diane C...........(434) 432-1654 ext. 30
dwhite5276@aol.com, Pres./COO, Womack Publishing Co., VA, Chatham
White, Rick..................(575) 763-3431
rwhite@cnjonline.com, Mng. Ed., Clovis News Journal, NM, Clovis
White, Eliot C...................(203) 317-2350
ewhite@record-journal.com, Ed., Record-Journal, CT, Meriden
White, Monica..................(805) 437-0444
mwhite@venturacountystar.com, Dir., Mktg., Ventura County Star, CA, Camarillo
Whitehead, Bill
billwwsr@rogers.com, Mng. Dir./Treasurer, Trans-Canada Advertising Agency Network, ON, Toronto
Whitehead, Bill..................937-609-1678
bwmccain@yahoo.com, Sales Manager, McCain Bindery Systems, IL
Whitehead, Bryan..................(913) 288-7237
Kansas City Cmty. College, KS, Kansas City
Whitehouse, Virginia
gwhitehouse@whitworth.edu, Chair, Whitworth University, WA, Spokane
Whitehurst, Tom..................(361) 886-3662
whitehurstt@caller.com, Bus. Ed., Corpus Christi Caller-Times, TX, Corpus Christi
Whitfield, Robert..................(941) 206-1289
rgw@sun-herald.com, Vice Pres., Mktg., Charlotte Sun, FL, Charlotte Harbor
Whitfield, Chris
argusnews@ctn.independent.co.za, Ed., CAPE ARGUS, Cape Town
Whiting, Gail..................(541) 338-2259
gail.whiting@registerguard.com, Adv. Dir., The Register-Guard, OR, Eugene
Whiting, Richard..................(864) 943-2522
rwhiting@indexjournal.com, Exec. News Ed., The Index-Journal, SC, Greenwood
Whiting, Fred
fred@whitingtech.com, Chief Engineer, Whiting Technologies, IL, Willowbrook
Whiting, Vicki..................(707) 996-6077
vicki@kidscoop.com, Pres./CEO, Kid Scoop, CA, Sonoma
Whitley, William L...................(972) 231-4500
whitleytx@cs.com, Dir., Media Services Group, Inc., FL, Jacksonville Beach
Whitley, Scott T...................ext. 1500
scott.whitley@uniontrib.com, Vice Pres./Chief Revenue Officer, The San Diego Union-Tribune, CA, San Diego
Whitlock, Mary Ann..................(310) 687-5800
whitlock@microtek.com, Dir., Mktg., Microtek, CA, Carson
Whitman, Scott..................ext. 8547
scott.whitman@cantonrep.com, Mgr., Info. Technology, The Repository, OH, Canton
Whitmire, Donald
don.w@pressenterprise.net, Circ. Mgr., Press Enterprise, PA, Bloomsburg
Whitmore, Deanna..................(209) 578-2209
dwhitmore@modbee.com, Adv. Mgr., Inside Sales, The Modesto Bee, CA, Modesto
Whitmore, Brian..................ext. 111
bwhitmore@uniondailytimes.com, Sports Ed., Union Daily Times, SC, Union
Whitney, Stu..................(605) 977-3922
swhitney@argusleader.com, Sports Editor, Argus Leader, SD, Sioux Falls
Whitsitt, Cheryl..................(417) 836-1115
cwhitsitt@news-leader.com, Mng. Ed., Springfield News-Leader, MO, Springfield
Whittaker, Paul
paul.whittaker@theaustralian.com.au, Ed., THE AUSTRALIAN
Whittaker, Paul
news@theaustralian.com.au, Ed., THE AUSTRALIAN
Whittamore, June
jwhittamore@h-ponline.com, Online Adv. Mgr., Huntington Herald-Press, IN, Huntington
Whitten, Aubra..................(662) 325-7906
Mississippi State Univ., MS, Mississippi State
Whittiken, Paul
whittikenp@theaustralian.com.au, Ed., THE AUSTRALIAN, Surry Hills
Whittington, James
jwhittington@daily-times.com, Circ. Dir., The Daily Times, NM, Farmington
Whitton, Brett..................203-354-1040
President, The Hour Publishing Co., CT, Norwalk
Whittum, Jim..................(334) 792-3141
jwhittum@dothaneagle.com, Pub., The Enterprise Ledger, AL, Enterprise
Whittum, Jim..................(334) 792-3141
jwhittum@dothaneagle.com, Pub., The Dothan Eagle, AL, Dothan
Whitworth, Richard
rwhitworth@gciu.org, Executive Assistant to the President, Graphic Communications International, DC, Washington
Whitworth, Ray
ray@whitworthknifecompany.com, Pres., Whitworth Knife Company, OH, Cincinnati
Whitworth, Steve..................(618) 463-2515
steve_whitworth@thetelegraph.com, Asst. City Ed., The Telegraph, IL, Alton
Whorton, Jay..........(770) 428-9411 ext. 510
Assoc. Pub., Marietta Daily Journal, GA, Mari-

etta
Whyte, Jeff
star@alliedpress.co.nz, Mng. Ed., DUNEDIN STAR WEEKENDER
Wiant, Jessica
jwiant@nvdaily.com, Special Sections Ed., Northern Virginia Daily, VA, Strasburg
Wick, Patricia..............................**ext. 604**
pat.wick@wickcommunications.com, Dir., Mktg., Sierra Vista Herald, AZ, Sierra Vista
Wick, Patricia..............................**ext. 604**
Dir., Mktg., Bisbee Daily Review, AZ, Bisbee
Wickenberg, Ken......................**(780) 429-5168**
kwickenberg@thejournal.canwest.com, Vice Pres., HR, Edmonton Journal, AB, Edmonton
Wicker, Beau..............................**ext. 5180**
Sports Ed., Pharos-Tribune, IN, Logansport
Wickes, Sally..........................**(541) 338-2620**
Mktg. Mgr., The Register-Guard, OR, Eugene
Wickliff, Greg...............**(713) 780-7055 ext. 304**
gregw@printmkt.com, Vice Pres., Print Marketing Concepts, Inc., TX, Houston
Wickliff, Greg..............................**ext. 304**
gregw@printmkt.com, Vice Pres., Print Marketing Concepts, Inc., TX, Houston
Widdle, Terri..........................**(816) 887-2414**
terri@midamericagraphics.com, Sec., Mid-America Graphics, Inc., MO, Harrisonville
Widmer, Franz C.
franz.c.widmer@bz-ag.ch, Ed. in Chief, BASELLANDSCHAFTLICHE ZEITUNG, Liestal, Baselland
Widoff, Harry
harry@digitalscribe.com, Pres., Digital Scribe, NY, Forest Hills
Wieck, James..........................**(972) 392-0888**
jwieck@wieck.com, Chrmn., Wieck Media, TX, Dallas
Wieckowska-Machay, Anna
redakcja@kurier.szczecin.pl, Ed. in Chief, KURIER SZCZECINSKI, Szczecin
Wiedemann, Petra
redaktion.reichenhall@bgl-median.de, Bus. Mgr., Reichenhaller Tagblatt, Bad Reichenhall
Wiederaenders, Tim..................**(928) 445-3333**
Mng. Ed., The Daily Courier, AZ, Prescott
Wieding, Frank
f.wieding@mopo.de, Ed., Hamburger Morgenpost, Hamburg
Wiegand, Gary
gary.wiegand@publicitas.com, Branch Dir., Publicitas North America, Inc., HI, Honolulu
Wiegel, Robert
bobw@dailynews.net, Circ. Mgr., The Hays Daily News, KS, Hays
Wiegenstein, Steve
swiegenstein@culver.edu, Journalism/PR Head, Culver-Stockton College, MO, Canton
Wiethaupt, Mark.......................**573-761-0211**
mwiethaupt@newstribune.co,, Prodn. Mgr., Pressroom, News Tribune, MO, Jefferson City
Wigginton, Mosby L.
cwigginton@dailysoutherner.com, Editor and Publisher, The Daily Southerner, NC, Tarboro
Wiginton, Ron..........................**(630) 617-3321**
Elmhurst College, IL, Elmhurst
Wilburn, Gloria........................**(870) 543-1471**
Prodn. Foreman, Mailroom, Pine Bluff Commercial, AR, Pine Bluff
Wilcox, Mark...........................**(906) 483-2205**
mwilcox@mininggazette.com, News Ed., The Daily Mining Gazette, MI, Houghton
Wilcox, Jim
jwilcox@snu.edu, Newspaper, Southern Nazarene University, OK, Bethany
Wild, Fredric M.
wild@lycoming.edu, Chair, Lycoming College, PA, Williamsport
Wilde, Tim.............................**(214) 221-4224**
info@connexperts.com, Pres., Applied Creative Technologies, TX, Dallas
Wilder, Marty Robacker
martyw@bradfordera.com, Mng. Ed., The Bradford Era, PA, Bradford
Wildsmith, Steven....................**(865) 981-1165**
Entertainment/Amusements Ed., The Daily Times, TN, Maryville
Wile, Jaclyn
columbiajournaleditor@gmail.com, Columbia Union College, MD, Takoma Park
Wiley, Tony
tonywiley@esko.com, Division Mgr., Printers Systems, Esko-Graphics, OH, Vandalia
Wiley, Marilyn................................**ext. 133**
mwiley@hearstnp.com, Controller, The Huron Daily Tribune, MI, Bad Axe
Wiley, Michael................................**ext. 579**
mwiley@adn.com, Adv. Mgr., Retail, Anchorage Daily News, AK, Anchorage
Wiley, Harold.........................**(317) 444-6392**
Features Wire Ed., The Indianapolis Star, IN, Indianapolis
Wilhoite, Marion
mwilhoite@c-dh.net, Sports Ed., Columbia Daily Herald, TN, Columbia
Wilhoyte, Tanya......................**(812) 231-4226**
tanya.wilhoyte@tribstar.com, Adv. Mgr., Retail, The Tribune Star, IN, Terre Haute
Wilkerson, Raymond.................**(972) 721-4070**
Univ. of Dallas, TX, Irving
Wilkie, Jim................................**(304) 457-6271**
Alderson-Broaddus College, WV, Philippi
Wilkinson, Kathy
k.wilkinson@postandcourier.com, Vice Pres., Evening Post Community Publications Grp., Evening Post Community Publications Group, Inc., SC, Charleston
Wilkinson, Barb.......................**(780) 429-5374**
bwilkinson@thejournal.canwest.com, Deputy Ed., Readership/Features, Edmonton Journal, AB, Edmonton
Wilkinson, Signe
wilkins@phillynews.com, Cartoonist, The Philadelphia Daily News, PA, Philadelphia
Wilkinson, Lisa........................**(580) 221-6513**
ddietz@ardmoreite.com, Adv. Dir., The Daily Ardmoreite, OK, Ardmore
Wilkinson, Earl J.
inma@inma.org, Exec. Dir., International Newspaper Marketing Association, Inc., TX, Dallas
Will, Bill
bwill@wnpa.com, Executive Director, Washington Newspaper Publishers Association, Inc., WA, Seattle
Willard, Jessica.......................**(425) 339-3006**
willard@heraldnet.com, HR Mgr., The Herald, WA, Everett
Willard, George.........................**248-336-7300**
gwillardsr@rangerdata.com, Chrmn./CEO, Ranger Data Technologies Inc., MI, Royal Oak
Willard, George.........................**248-336-7300**
gwillardjr@rangerdata.com, Sr. VP of Operations, Ranger Data Technologies Inc., MI, Royal Oak
Willard, Michael
onepublisher@charter.net, Pub., The Observer-News-Enterprise, NC, Newton
Willcox, Suzanne.......................**(561) 820-4930**
swillcox@pbpost.com, Mgr., Research/Sales Presentations, The Palm Beach Post, FL, West Palm Beach
Willemin, Nicolas
nwillemin@lexpress.ch, Ed. in Chief, L'IMPARTIAL, La Chaux-de-Fonds , Neuchatel
Willenbrink, Bob
bobw@mail.uca.edu, Chair, University of Central Arkansas, AR, Conway
Willes, Mark H.........................**(801) 323-4232**
Chrmn., Deseret News, UT, Salt Lake City
Willett, Janet..........................**(573) 248-2700**
janet.willett@courierpost.com, Controller/Dir., HR, Hannibal Courier-Post, MO, Hannibal
Williams, Stephen M.................**(760) 241-7744**
Editorial Page Ed., Daily Press, CA, Victorville
Williams, Lew
lpub@ketchikandailynews.com, Co-Pub., Ketchikan Daily News, AK, Ketchikan
Williams, Corrin......................**(314) 935-6713**
Washington Univ., MO, Saint Louis
Williams, Ralph W.
rwilliams@journalinquirer.com, Asst. Mng. Ed./News Ed., Journal Inquirer, CT, Manchester
Williams, Ellen.........................**(205) 325-2217**
Dir., HR, The Birmingham News, AL, Birmingham
Williams, Terrence L.................**(603) 594-6472**
terryw@telegraph-nh.com, Pub., The Telegraph, NH, Hudson
Williams, Nicola.......................**(203) 776-2985**
Yale Univ. Law School, CT
Williams, Lon W.......................**(404) 869-8686**
lonwwilliams@aol.com, Owner, Media America Brokers, GA, Atlanta
Williams, Daniel........................**860/701-4207**
d.williams@theday.com, Director of Audience Development, The Day Publishing Company, CT, New London
Williams, Gene
g.williams@technologyintegrators.net, Sales Engineer, Technology Integrators, IL, Effingham
Williams, Joanne......................**(269) 749-6630**
Olivet College, MI, Olivet
Williams, Timothy M.................**(717) 703-3060**
timw@pa-news.org, Pres./CEO, Pennsylvania Society of Newspaper Editors, PA, Harrisburg
timw@pa-news.org, Past President, Pennsylvania Newspaper Association, PA, Harrisburg
Williams, Christopher H.............**(804) 648-0072**
cwilliams@harriswilliams.com, Mng. Dir., Harris Williams & Co., VA, Richmond
Williams, Kevin........................**(800) 245-7515**
kwilliams@oasisnewsfeatures.com, Exec. Ed., Oasis Newsfeatures, Inc., OH, Middletown
Williams, Lee
lwilliams@njherald.com, Promo./Special Projects Mgr., New Jersey Herald, NJ, Newton
Williams, Michael
mwilliams@coxohio.com, Editorial Page Ed., Middletown Journal, OH, Middletown
Williams, Denice......................**(503) 221-8514**
Adv. Mgr., Retail, The Oregonian, OR, Portland
Williams, Elizabeth..................**(803) 329-4058**
ewilliams@heraldonline.com, Dir., Finance, The Herald, SC, Rock Hill
Williams, Hannah
hwilliams1@vikings.northpark.edu, Online Editor, North Park Univ., IL, Chicago
Williams, Laurie.......................**(509) 582-1523**
lwilliams@tri-cityherald.com, Asst. Mng. Ed., Tri-City Herald, WA, Kennewick
Williams, Mark
mark.williams@bolivarcommercial.com, Pub., The Bolivar Commercial, MS, Cleveland
Williams, Vern.........................**(203) 789-5643**
photo@nhregister.com, Photo Ed., New Haven Register, CT, New Haven
Williams, David........................**(607) 735-1815**
Elmira College, NY, Elmira
Williams, Elisa.........................**(360) 735-4561**
elisa.williams@columbian.com, Features Ed., The Columbian, WA, Vancouver
Williams, Maggie.....................**(601) 266-6746**
Univ. of Southern Mississippi, MS, Hattiesburg
Williams, Wanda
advertising@hastingstribune.com, Adv. Mgr., Sales, Hastings Tribune, NE, Hastings
Williams, Irene..............................**ext. 2004**
iwilliams@citizensvoice.com, Bus. Office Mgr., The Citizens' Voice, PA, Wilkes-Barre
Williams, Lon...........................**(404) 995-7088**
lonwwilliams@aol.com, Owner, Media America Brokers, GA, Atlanta
Williams, Deb..........................**(715) 395-5007**
dwilliams@superiortelegram.com, Bus. Mgr., The Daily Telegram, WI, Superior
Williams, Martin
martinw@citizen.co.za, Ed. in Chief, THE CITIZEN, Johannesburg, PWV
Williams, Art...........................**(805) 437-0374**
awilliams@venturacountystar.com, Adv. Mgr., Sales, Ventura County Star, CA, Camarillo
Williams, Moegsien
moegsien.williams@inl.co.za, Ed., THE STAR/WEEKEND STAR, Johannesburg, PWV
Williams, Theresa....................**(902) 426-1103**
hr@herald.ca, HR Mgr., The Chronicle Herald, NS, Halifax
Williams, Betty........................**(252) 329-9511**
bwilliams@reflector.com, Display Adv. Dir., The Daily Reflector, NC, Greenville
Williams, Roger L.
roger.williams@wjhnews.com, Pub., Waycross Journal-Herald, GA, Waycross
Williams, Tena
tpub@ketchikandailynews.com, Co-Pub., Ketchikan Daily News, AK, Ketchikan
Williams, Sookie.......................**(305) 347-6664**
swilliams@alm.com, Vice President/Miami-Dade Legal & Court Relations, Miami Daily Business Review, FL, Miami
Williams, Nancy M....................**(435) 797-3299**
Asst. Prof., Utah State University, UT, Logan
Williams, Bob
bob.williams@thesouthern.com, Publisher, The Southern Illinoisan, IL, Carbondale
Williams, Celeste.....................**(817) 390-7697**
cxwilliams@star-telegram.com, Asst. Mng. Ed., Sports, Fort Worth Star-Telegram, TX, Fort Worth
Williams, Alan..........................**(813) 259-8234**
Telemarketing Mgr., The Tampa Tribune, FL, Tampa
Williams, Gloria...............................**ext. 112**
gwilliams@starexponent.com, Adv. Mgr., Culpeper Star-Exponent, VA, Culpeper
Williams, Eileen........................**(512) 404-2300**
conference@voicetext.com, Pres., VoiceText.com, TX, Austin
Williams, Michelle
aparizona@ap.org, Bureau Chief, Arizona Associated Press Managing Editors Association, AZ, Phoenix
Williams, Teena
kdn@kpunet.net, Sec., Alaska Newspaper Association, AK, Ketchikan
Williams, Berk..........................**(920) 453-5129**
bwilliams@sheboygan.gannett.com, State Ed., The Sheboygan Press, WI, Sheboygan
Williams, Jane...........................**512-445-3555**
jwilliams@statesman.com, Publisher, Austin American-Statesman, TX, Austin
Williams, Bonnie.......................**(864) 260-1344**
williamsbc@independentmail.com, Editorial Page Ed., Anderson Independent-Mail, SC, Anderson
Williams, Robert H....................**(703) 370-2130**
newseditor@winsphoto.com, News Ed., World Images News Service, VA, Woodbridge
Williams, Joyce.........................**(540) 665-4959**
jwilliams@winchesterstar.com, Systems Mgr., The Winchester Star, VA, Winchester
Williams, Shelly
ilioinfo@ilio.com, Co-Owner, ILIO Entertainment, CA, Malibu
Williams, George
george@gulf-daily-news.com, Ed. in Chief, GULF DAILY NEWS
Williams, Graham.............................**ext. 109**
gwilliams@uniondailytimes.com, Women's Ed., Union Daily Times, SC, Union
Williams, Evonne......................**(731) 642-1162**
evonne@parispi.net, Bus. Mgr., The Paris Post-Intelligencer, TN, Paris
Williamson, Greg.....................**(706) 208-2334**
greg.williamson@onlineathens.com, Controller, Division, Athens Banner-Herald, GA, Athens
Williamson, Samantha
swilliamson@cdispatch.com, Asst. Adv. Dir., The Commercial Dispatch, MS, Columbus
Williamson, Rusty
rustywilliamson@forsythnews.com, Adv. Dir., Forsyth County News, GA, Cumming
Williamson, Tonya
twilliamson@timesfreepress.com, Executive Assistant, Chattanooga Times Free Press, TN, Chattanooga
Williamson, Chad.....................**(937) 642-6397**
Mng. Ed., Marysville Journal-Tribune, OH, Marysville
Williford, Joy L........................**(318) 487-6406**
jwillford@thetowntalk.com, Dir., Personnel, The Town Talk, LA, Alexandria
Williford, Mindy........................**(800) 255-6734**
mwilliford@amuniversal.com, Digital Rep., Eastern USA, Universal Uclick, MO, Kansas City
Willingham, Teresa
twillingham@ags.com, Controller, Automated Graphic Systems, MD, White Plains
Willingham, Bruce....................**(580) 286-3321**
paper@mccurtain.com, Ed., McCurtain Daily Gazette, OK, Idabel
Willis, Rachel
rwillis@kspress.com, Educ. Dir., Kansas Press Association, KS, Topeka

Willis, Jim
jwillis@postherald.com, Ed./Pub./Pres., Birmingham Post-Herald, AL, Birmingham
Willis, Bob ....(901) 678-5474
Univ. of Memphis, TN, Memphis
Willis, Stewart
swillis@recordnet.com, Dir., Info Tech, The Record, CA, Stockton
Willis, Dawn ....(863) 802-7400
dawn.willis@theledger.com, Adv. Dir., The Ledger, FL, Lakeland
Willis, Edward ....(910) 343-2213
ed.willis@starnewsonline.com, Dir., Info Systems, Star-News, NC, Wilmington
Willison, Joan ....ext. 121
jwillison@thewhig.com, Promo./Community Serv./Mktg., The Kingston Whig-Standard, ON, Kingston
Willms, Molly
managingeditor@universitychronicle.net, Managing Editor, St. Cloud State Univ., MN, Saint Cloud
Wills, John ....(310) 451-3307
jcwills@fliinc.com, President/CEO, FLI, Incorporated, CA, Santa Monica
Wills, Jane ....(310) 451-3307
jhwills@fliinc.com, Vice President, FLI, Incorporated, CA, Santa Monica
Wills, David 501-993-6284
dwills@bentoncourier.com, Addvertising Director, The Saline Courier, AR, Benton
Wilmore, Sharon ....(313) 222-8773
wilmore@freepress.com, Asst. Mng. Ed., Features, Detroit Free Press, MI, Detroit
Wilpula, Nicki ....ext. 251
Communities Ed., Star Beacon, OH, Ashtabula
Wilson, James B.
general@carrollspaper.com, Pres./Pub./Treasurer, Daily Times Herald, IA, Carroll
Wilson, John
jwilson@tracypress.com, Prodn. Mgr., Pressroom, Tracy Press, CA, Tracy
Wilson, George Q...........(618) 253-7146 ext. 236
gwilson@yourclearwave.com, Pub., Eldorado Daily Journal, IL, Harrisburg
Wilson, Jim
jwilson@lindenwood.edu, Dean, Lindenwood University, MO, Saint Charles
Wilson, Randy ....ext. 1630
rwilson@the-daily-record.com, Nat'l Adv. Sales, The Daily Record, OH, Wooster
Wilson, Michael.......................(512) 445-3715
michaelwilson@statesman.com, Adv. Vice Pres., Austin American-Statesman, TX, Austin
Wilson, Dr. Ralph F.
rfwilson@wilsonweb.com, Dir./Columnist, Wilson Internet Services, CA, Rocklin
Wilson, Dave ....(954) 538-7130
dwilson@miamiherald.com, Mng. Ed., News, The Miami Herald, FL, Miami
Wilson, Randy.........................(928) 556-2254
rwilson@azdailysun.com, Editorial Page Ed., Arizona Daily Sun, AZ, Flagstaff
Wilson, Robin...............(603) 668-4321 ext. 246
rwilson@unionleader.com, Adv. Servs. Mgr., New Hampshire Union Leader/New Hampshire Sunday News, NH, Manchester
Wilson, Keith D........................(423) 246-8121
kwilson@timesnews.net, Pub./Vice Pres./Treasurer, Kingsport Times-News, TN, Kingsport
Wilson, Kevin
kevinw@wdtimes.com, Sports Ed., Watertown Daily Times, WI, Watertown
Wilson, Gerald L. ....(205) 380-2800
glwilson@usouthal.edu, Prof./Chair, University of South Alabama, AL, Mobile
Wilson, Thomas G. ....(828) 264-3612
twilson@xtn.net, Vice Pres., Western North Carolina Div., Jones Media, Inc., TN, Greeneville
Wilson, Geordie
gwilson@fredericknewspost.com, Publisher, The Frederick News-Post, MD, Frederick
Wilson, Todd...........................(386) 754-0418
twilson@lakecityreporter.com, Publisher, Lake City Reporter, FL, Lake City
Wilson, Matthew ....(415) 382-7297
mwilson@marinij.com, Exec. Ed., Marin Independent Journal, CA, Novato
Wilson, Doris ....(618) 253-7146 ext. 229
dwilson@yourclearwave.com, Mktg. Dir., Eldorado Daily Journal, IL, Harrisburg
Wilson, Allen ....(406) 657-1471
awilson@billingsgazette.com, Circ. Dir., Billings Gazette, MT, Billings
Wilson, Lisa Klem ....(212) 293-8612
lwilson@unitedmedia.com, Sr. Vice Pres./Gen. Mgr., United Media, OH, Cincinnati
Wilson, Doris A.
dwilson@yourclearwave.com, Adv. Mgr., The Daily Register, IL, Harrisburg
Wilson, Ann B..........................(757) 247-4864
awilson@dailypress.com, CFO/Vice Pres., Finance, Daily Press, VA, Newport News
Wilson, Cathy...............................ext. 328
cwilson@redlandsdailyfacts.com, Adv. Rep, Classified, Redlands Daily Facts, CA, Redlands
Wilson, Charles ....(813) 259-7736
Credit Mgr., The Tampa Tribune, FL, Tampa
Wilson, Rex ....(360) 417-3530
rex.wilson@peninsuladailynews.com, Executive Editor, Peninsula Daily News, WA, Port Angeles
Wilson, Catherine.....................(305) 347-6611
cwilson@alm.com, Law Editor, Miami Daily Business Review, FL, Miami
Wilson, Brian ....(419) 521-7364
bwilson@nncogannett.com, Prodn. Mgr., Distr. Ctr., News Journal, OH, Mansfield
Wilson, William S.....................(574) 224-5329
wsw@rochsent.com, Ed., The Rochester Sentinel, IN, Rochester
Wilson, Matt
news-mwilson@lebanondailyrecord.com, Sports Ed., The Lebanon Daily Record, MO, Lebanon
Wilson, Cathy...........................(305) 347-6611
cwilson@alm.com, Law Editor, Palm Beach Daily Business Review, FL, West Palm Beach
Wilson, Marc 309 743-0816
mwilson@townnews.com, CEO/President, TownNews.com, IL, Moline
Wilson, Lois 607-271-8284
lowilson@gannett.com, General Manager & Managing Editor, Star-Gazette, NY, Elmira
Wilson, Mark ....(252) 407-9922
mwilson@rmtelegram.com, Adv. Dir., Rocky Mount Telegram, NC, Rocky Mount
Wilson, Kelly
kewilson@davidson.edu, Coeditor-in-Chief, Davidson College, NC, Davidson
Wilson, Tommy
tommy.wilson@dailypostathenian.com, Pub., The Daily Post-Athenian, TN, Athens
Wilson, Kristin.........................(701) 250-8285
kristin.wilson@bismarktribune.com, Adv. Sales Mgr., The Bismarck Tribune, ND, Bismarck
Wilson, Jim
news@theeagle.com, Pub., The Eagle, TX, Bryan
Wilson, Mike.............................(727) 892-2924
mwilson@tampabay.com, Mng. Ed., Enterprise, Tampa Bay Times, FL, Saint Petersburg
Wilson, Lisa Klem ....(212) 293-8612
lwilson@unitedmedia.com, Sr. Vice Pres./Gen. Mgr., Newspaper Enterprise Association (Div. of United Media), NY, New York
lwilson@unitedmedia.com, Sr. Vice Pres./Gen. Mgr., United Feature Syndicate (Div. of United Media), NY, New York
lwilson@unitedmedia.com, Sales & Mktg. Contact/Sr. Vice Pres. & Gen. Mgr., United Media, Scripps Howard News Service, DC, Washington
Wilson, Alisha.............................662-678-1635
alisha.wilson@journalinc.com, Circulation - Sales Manager, Journal Publishing Company, MS, Tupelo
Wilson, Sarah Overmyer............(574) 224-5331
news@rochsent.com, Pub., The Rochester Sentinel, IN, Rochester
Wilson, Cynthia ....(361) 886-3719
wilsonc@caller.com, Features Ed., Corpus Christi Caller-Times, TX, Corpus Christi
Wilson, Dennis ....(973) 364-0605
collegesportsintheusa@gmail.com, Pres., Metropolitan New York Football Writers Association, NJ, Roseland
Wilson, Melissa ....(217) 788-1370
melissa.wilson@sj-r.com, Adv. Supvr., Classified Sales, The State Journal-Register, IL, Springfield
Wilson, Carroll ....(940) 720-3435
wilsonc@wtr.com, Ed., Wichita Falls Times Record News, TX, Wichita Falls
Wilson, Patti..................................ext. 344
HR Mgr., The Pioneer - Big Rapids, MI, Big Rapids
Wilson, Bradley ....(919) 515-2411
Advisor, North Carolina State Univ., NC, Raleigh
Wilson, Neena..........................(256) 845-1914
nwilson@goval.com, Mgr., Gerrard Ovalstrapping, AL, Fort Payne
Wilson, George Q. ....(618) 253-7146
gwilson@yourclearwave.com, Online Mgr., The Daily Register, IL, Harrisburg
Wilson, Geordie ....(603) 224-5301 ext. 269
Pub., Newspapers of New England, NH, Concord
Wilson, Gail 609-272-7212
gwilson@pressofac.com, Asst. Entertainment Editor, The Press of Atlantic City, NJ, Pleasantville
Wimberley, Ashley.......................501-374-1500
ashley@arkansaspress.org, Advertising and Marketing Director, Arkansas Press Services, AR, Little Rock
Winckler, Terry ....(650) 348-4323
twinckler@angnewspapers.com, Ed., San Mateo County Times, CA, San Mateo
Wind, Jorgen
jw@kj-avis.dk, Adv. Mgr., KJERTEMINDE AVIS, Kerteminde, Fyn
Wind-Hansen, Jorgen
jw@kj-avis.dk, Ed. in Chief, KJERTEMINDE AVIS, Kerteminde, Fyn
Winders, Jason.........................(706) 208-2216
jason.winders@onlineathens.com, Exec. Ed., Athens Banner-Herald, GA, Athens
Windrow, John.........................(808) 525-8019
jwindrow@honoluluadvertiser.com, Asst. City Ed., Honolulu Star-Advertiser, HI, Honolulu
Winegarden, Dave.......................209-249-3503
Group Publisher, Manteca Bulletin, CA, Manteca
Wineka, Mark...........................(704) 797-4263
mwineka@salisburypost.com, Political Ed., Salisbury Post, NC, Salisbury
Wineman, Neil
nwineman@commgraphics.com, New Bus. Dir., CommGraphics Interactive, Inc., NE, Lincoln
Winer, Marlene
info@teletype.com, Mktg. Mgr., TeleType Co., MA, Boston
Wines, Elise
ewines@sanmarcosrecord.com, Circ. Dir., San Marcos Daily Record, TX, San Marcos
Winey, Leslie ....(574) 235-6363
lwiney@sbtinfo.com, Purchasing Agent, South Bend Tribune, IN, South Bend
Wing, Anne C.
cws@mechwb.com, Mktg. Mgr., Chauncey Wing's Sons, Inc., MA
Winge, Todd.............................(573) 882-7351
winge@missouri.edu, Photo Dir., Columbia Missourian, MO, Columbia
Wingen, John
sales@trginc.com, Pres., TRG, Inc., NC, Raleigh
Winger, Barry..................................ext. 300
bwwinger@sharonherald.com, Prodn. Mgr., Systems/Pre Press, The Herald, PA, Sharon
Wingert, Stephan
stephan_wingert@link.freedom.com, Pub., Desert Dispatch, CA, Barstow
Wingert, Stephan T.
stephan_wingert@link.freedom.com, Pub., Daily Press, CA, Victorville
Winges, Bruce ....(330) 996-3858
bwinges@thebeaconjournal.com, Night Mng. Ed., Akron Beacon Journal, OH, Akron
Wingler, Sharon B.
editor@travelaloneandloveit.com, Pres., Travel Alone & Love It, IL, Willowbrook
Wingragh, Kylie
class@fultonsun.com, Adv. Mgr., Classified, The Fulton Sun, MO, Fulton
Winkler, Michael
mwinkler@meielenhaun.li, Ed., LIECHTENSTEINER WOCHENZEITUNG, Vaduz
Winner, Christopher
cpwinner@praguepost.com, Exec. Ed., Lion's Share Group, Prague
Winslow, Bud..................................ext. 280
Circ. Dir., Opns., The Daily Sentinel, CO, Grand Junction
Winslow, Susan ....(707) 427-6955
Copy Ed., Daily Republic, CA, Fairfield
Winsor, Deborah ....(941) 957-5157
deb.winsor@heraldtribune.com, Asst. Mng. Ed., Sarasota Herald-Tribune, FL, Sarasota
Winter, Sabine..........................(972) 860-7290
Eastfield College, TX, Mesquite
Winter, Ken..............................(231) 347-2554
kwint@petoskeynews.com, Pres., Northern Michigan Review, Inc., MI, Petoskey
Winter, Daniel
redaktion@limmattalerzeitung.ch, Ed. in Chief, LIMMATTALER TAGBLATT, Dietikon
Winter, Sandra
contactus@unca.com, Office Mgr., United Nations Correspondents Association, NY, New York
Winterland, Barry L...................(309) 820-3205
bwinterland@pantagraph.com, Gen. Mgr., The Pantagraph, IL, Bloomington
Winters, Hans-Christian 5850
redaktion@cuxonline.de, Ed. in Chief, CUXHAVENER NACHRICHTEN, Cuxhaven
Winther, Pent
pewi@information.dk, Ed. in Chief, INFORMATION, Copenhagen, Sjaelland
Wioskowski, Ashley ....(269) 387-2097
Western Michigan Univ., MI, Kalamazoo
Wirski, Jim
addept@thnews.com, Adv. Mgr., Times-Herald, AR, Forrest City
Wirth, Hans ....(262) 785-3241
hans.wirth@us.abb.com, Mgr.-Sales Applications/Printing Drives Systems, ABB, Inc. (Printing Systems), WI, New Berlin
Wirth, Eileen M.
emw@creighton.edu, Chair/Prof., Creighton University, NE, Omaha
Wirtz, Ralph E. ....(989) 839-4241
ralphewirtz@mdn.net, Editorial Page Ed., Midland Daily News, MI, Midland
Wise, Georgiana ....(864) 622-1715
wisegy@independentmail.com, Dir., Mktg. Servs., Anderson Independent-Mail, SC, Anderson
Wise, Corby.......................................ext. 244
cwise@mountvernonnews.com, Adv. Mgr., Mount Vernon News, OH, Mount Vernon
Wise, Vernon L................................ext. 200
vernwise3@butlereagle.com, Pres., Butler Eagle, PA, Butler
Wiseman, Robert ....(330) 747-1471 ext. 1331
bwiseman@vindy.com, Personnel Mgr./Labor Rel., The Vindicator, OH, Youngstown
Wishart, John...........................(506) 859-7124
Bus. Ed., Times & Transcript, NB, Moncton
Wishart, Gordon
tele@dcthomson.co.uk, Ed., EVENING TELEGRAPH, SCO, Dundee, Tayside
Wisner, Tedd
circulation@bemidjipioneer.com, Circ. Dir., The Pioneer, MN, Bemidji
Wissinger, Bruce ....(814) 532-5076
Editorial Page Ed., The Tribune-Democrat, PA, Johnstown
Wistbacka, Krister
redaktion@kkuriren.se, Ed., KATRINEHOLMS-KURIREN, Katrineholm
Wiste, Gary ....(608) 785-9465
Western Wisconsin Tech. College, WI, La Crosse
Witcomb, Bill ....(506) 458-6482
News Ed., The Daily Gleaner, NB, Fredericton
Witt, Heiko
redaktion@fehmarnsches-tageblatt.de, Ed. in Chief, FEHMARNSCHES TAGEBLATT, Burg
Witt, G. Michael
witt@motioncity.com, Producing Dir., Motion City Films, CA, Santa Monica
Witt, Connie
connie@athensnews-courier.com, Circ. Mgr., The News-Courier, AL, Athens
Witt, Jim..................................(817) 390-7704
jwitt@star-telegram.com, Sr. Vice Pres./Exec. Ed., Fort Worth Star-Telegram, TX, Fort

Worth
Witt, Hilary
hwitt@postregister.com , Classified Ad. Mgr., Post Register, ID, Idaho Falls
Witte, John............................**(404) 572-1910**
jwitte@coxnews.com, Creative Dir., COXnet (Cox Newspapers' Wide Area Network/Cox News Service), GA, Atlanta
Witwer, George B.
gwitwer@news-banner.com, Chrmn., News-Banner, IN, Bluffton
Witwer, George O.
gowitwer@kpcnews.net, Principal Owner, KPC Media Group Inc., IN, Kendallville
Witz, Alain
redaction.temoignages@wanadoo.fr, Ed., TEMOIGNAGES, Le Port
Woare, Karen..........................**(217) 421-6917**
Data Processing Supvr., Herald & Review, IL, Decatur
Woehlk, Heinz D.
heinz@truman.edu, Contact, Truman State University, MO, Kirksville
Woelfel, Anne..........................**(570) 970-7232**
awoelfel@timesleader.com, News Ed., Times Leader, PA, Wilkes-Barre
Woelfel, Bob
bwoelfel@timesonline.com, Adv. Dir., Beaver County Times, PA, Beaver
Wohlfort, Craig..........................**512-445-3567**
Controller, Austin American-Statesman, TX, Austin
Wojciekiewicz, Tomasz..............**(052) 32-26-201**
zarzad@nowosci.com.pl, Chrmn., NOWOSCI, Torun
Woje, Thor
thwo@rb.no, Ed. in Chief, Romerikes Blad, Kjeller/Lillestrom
Wojtecki, Dennis B.
dennis@enescee.com, Mgr., North Shore Consultants, Inc., IL, Chicago
Wolcott, Howard.......................**(718) 670-7814**
hwolcott@nydailynews.com, Circ. Dir., City Sales, NY Daily News, NY, New York
Wolcott, Bill............................**(716) 286-8512**
Niagara Univ., NY, Niagara University
Wold, Knut
knutwold@ostlentingen.no, Adv. Mgr., OESTLENDINGEN/HAMAR/OESTLENDINGEN SOLOER-ODAL, Elverum
Wolf, Philip
PWolf@nanaimodailynews.com, Deputy Ed., Nanaimo Daily News, BC, Nanaimo
Wolf, Ted..............................**(217) 788-1522**
ted.wolf@sj-r.com, Day News Ed., The State Journal-Register, IL, Springfield
Wolf, Katie............................**(248) 370-2537**
Oakland Univ., MI, Rochester
Wolf, Kristy............................**(262) 306-1516**
kwolf@conleynet.com, Adv. Supvr., Classified, The Freeman, WI, Waukesha
Wolf-Astrauskas, Marianne...........**312 259-5467**
President, Illinois Woman's Press Association, Inc., IL, Chicago
Wolfe, Jennifer.......................**(843) 317-7211**
jwolfe@florencenews.com, Mgmt. Info Servs. Mgr., Morning News, SC, Florence
Wolfe, Mitch
minerandnews@bowes.com, Pub., Daily Miner & News, ON, Kenora
Wolfe, Bob
bob.wolfe@standardspeaker.com, Mng. Ed., Standard-Speaker, PA, Hazleton
Wolfe, Charlotte........................**662-678-1656**
charlotte.wolfe@journalinc.com, Associate Publisher - Human Resources/Community Newspapers, Journal Publishing Company, MS, Tupelo
Wolfe, Adam.............................**3153123269**
Editor-in-Chief, SUNY College/Oswego, NY, Oswego
Wolfe, Charlotte........................**662-678-1656**
charlotte.wolfe@journalinc.com, Associate Publisher - Human Resources/Community Newspapers, Journal Publishing Company, MS, Tupelo
Wolff, Kelly............................**(540) 231-9864**
Virginia Polytechnic Institute, VA, Blacksburg
Wolff, Shar.............................**(757) 825-2775**
Thomas Nelson Cmty. College, VA, Hampton
Wolff, Jeff..............................**(319) 398-5871**
jeff.wolff@gazettecommunications.com, Dir., Market Research/Adv. Servs., The Gazette, IA, Cedar Rapids
Wolfram, Manfred K.
wolframk@uc.edu, Chair, University of Cincinnati, OH, Cincinnati
Wolfrath, Fabien
info@lexpress.ch, MD, L'EXPRESS, Neuchatel
Wolk, Erv
wolkadv@earthlink.net, Pres., Wolk Advertising, Inc. (Retail Carpet Ad Service), MI, Birmingham
Wollney, John.........................**(630) 368-4046**
jwollney@tribune.com, Adv. Dir., Preprint, Chicago Tribune, IL, Chicago
Wollschlanger, Arnim
vertriev@kreiszeitung.de, Adv. Mgr., ACHIMER-KREISBLATT, Achim
Wolman, Jonathan
jon.wolman@detroitnews.com, Editor and Publisher, The Detroit News, MI, Detroit
Wolter, Doug
dwolter@mankatofreepress.com, News Ed., Night, The Free Press, MN, Mankato
Wolters, Keith
marketing@convergys.com, Sr. Dir., Mktg., Convergys, MO, Hazelwood
Womack, Deanna F.
dwomack@stonehill.edu, Chair, Stonehill College, MA, Easton
Womack, Charles Zan.......**(434) 432-1654 ext. 15**
zanwomack@womackpublishing.com, Chrmn., Womack Publishing Co., VA, Chatham
Womack, Charles
obxnews@aol.com, Pres., Womack Newspapers Inc., Womack Publishing Co., VA, Chatham
Womack, Jerry P...............................**ext. 207**
Mng. Ed., West Plains Daily Quill, MO, West Plains
Womer, Jake............................**(301) 733-5131**
Executive Editor, The Herald-Mail, MD, Hagerstown
Wong, Matt.............................**(212) 854-8396**
Columbia Univ. Bus. School, NY, New York
Wong, Stuart...........................**(719) 636-0245**
stuart.wong@gazette.com, Photo Dir., The Gazette, CO, Colorado Springs
Wood, Leighton P.
lpwood@skagitpublshing.com, Pres., Skagit Valley Herald, WA, Mount Vernon
Wood, Cy
advertising@valleytimes-news.com, Ed., The Valley Times-News, AL, Lanett
Wood, Frank
fwood@register-herald.com, Pub., The Register Herald, WV, Beckley
Wood, Gary
gary.wood@yankton.net, Owner, Yankton Daily Press & Dakotan, SD, Yankton
Wood, Terry...........................**(479) 571-6419**
sports@nwarktimes.com, Sports Ed., Northwest Arkansas Times, AR, Fayetteville
Wood, Keith
sales@stauffergold.com, Sales Mgr., Stauffer Media Systems, MO, Joplin
Wood, Janet...........................**(865) 482-7355**
janet.woood@oakridger.com, Adv. Dir., The Oak Ridger, TN, Oak Ridge
Wood, Tom
twood@cninewspapers.com, Chrmn., Community Newspapers, Inc., GA, Athens
Wood, Roy.............................**(780) 498-5668**
rwood@thejournal.canwest.com, Deputy Ed., News, Edmonton Journal, AB, Edmonton
Wood, Len.............................**(805) 564-5128**
lwood@newspress.com, Photo/Graphics Ed., Santa Barbara News-Press, CA, Santa Barbara
Wood, Jen.............................**(314) 340-8520**
jwood@post-dispatch.com, Adv. Vice Pres., Sales-Recruitment/Classified/Retail Territories/Bus./Health Care, St. Louis Post-Dispatch, MO, Saint Louis
Wood, Denise................................**ext. 3135**
COO, AIGA, the professional association for design, NY, New York
Wood, Stedem.........................**(360) 424-3251**
swood@skagitpublishing.com, Pub., Skagit Valley Herald, WA, Mount Vernon
Wood, Len
lwood@santamariatimes.com, Asst. Mng. Ed., Santa Maria Times, CA, Santa Maria
Wood, Ross
rwood@atex.com, CEO, Asia Pacific, Atex North America, MA, Burlington
Woodall, Bill
bwoodall@kilgorenewsherald.com, Mng. Ed., Kilgore News Herald, TX, Kilgore
Woodard, Stephanie..................**(760) 739-6692**
swoodard@nctimes.com, Prodn. Mgr., North County Times, CA, Escondido
Woodard, Doug...............................**ext. 127**
dwoodard@benningtonbanner.com, Adv. Sales Mgr., Bennington Banner, VT, Bennington
Woodcock, Sandy
sandy.woodcock@naa.org, Director- NAA Foundation, Youth Editorial Association , VA
Woodell, A.J...........................**(252) 436-2801**
ajwoodell@hendersondispatch.com, Circ. Mgr., Daily Dispatch, NC, Henderson
Woodford, Marie...........**(937) 642-5656 ext. 140**
mariew@marysvillejt.com, Adv. Dir., Marysville Journal-Tribune, OH, Marysville
Woodhams, Mark.....................**(520) 621-3408**
Univ. of Arizona, AZ, Tucson
Woodin, Rip............................**(252) 446-5161**
rwoodin@rmtelegram.com, Pub., Rocky Mount Telegram, NC, Rocky Mount
Woodka, Chris..............**(719) 544-3520 ext. 415**
cwoodka@chieftain.com, Mng. Ed., Prodn., The Pueblo Chieftain, CO, Pueblo
Woodland, Linda.............................**ext. 235**
lindawoodland@reviewtimes.com, News Ed., The Review Times, OH, Fostoria
Woodrow, Randy
rwoodrow@elkodaily.com, Prodn. Mgr., Elko Daily Free Press, NV, Elko
Woods, ReDonn.............................**669-2525**
rwoods@thepampanews.com, Advertising Manager, The Pampa News, TX, Pampa
Woods, Kim
kimyoung-taylor@heraldonline.com, Adv. Dir., Sales, The Herald, SC, Rock Hill
Woods, John
editor@cookislandnews.com, Ed., COOK ISLANDS NEWS, Rarotonga
Woods, Paul..........................**(416) 507-2133**
pwoods@cp.org, Dir., HR, Canadian Press, The - Toronto, ON, ON, Toronto
Woods, Edward
ewoods@benningtonbanner.com, Pub., Bennington Banner, VT, Bennington
Woods, Steven
steven.woods@owh.com, Credit Dept. Mgr., Omaha World-Herald, NE, Omaha
Woods, Tim............................**(530) 542-8040**
twoods@tahoedailytribune.com, Circ. Mgr., Tahoe Daily Tribune, CA, South Lake Tahoe
Woods, Dan...........................**(808) 525-5441**
dwoods@honoluluadvertiser.com, Asst. City Ed., Honolulu Star-Advertiser, HI, Honolulu
Woods, Rufus.................................**ext. 162**
rwoods@wenworld.com, Ed., The Wenatchee World, WA, Wenatchee
Woods, Gordon
gwoods@clintondailyjournal.com, Ed., Clinton Journal, IL, Clinton
Woods, Eileen
ewoods@skagitpublishing.com, NIE Mgr., Skagit Valley Herald, WA, Mount Vernon
Woods, Edward L.
ewoods@reformer.com, Pub., Brattleboro Reformer, VT, Brattleboro
Woodside, Jason
jason.woodside@thesouthern.com, Advertising Director, The Southern Illinoisan, IL, Carbondale
Woodside, Gary.......................**(559) 735-3299**
tech@visaliatimesdelta.com, Data Processing Mgr., Visalia Times-Delta & Tulare Advance-Register, CA, Visalia
Woodside, Trisha
trisha.woodside@thesouthern.com, Marketing & Circulation Director, The Southern Illinoisan, IL, Carbondale
Woodward, DeJuan..................**(770) 535-3464**
dwoodard@gainesvilletimes.com, Mgmt. Info Servs. Mgr., The Times, GA, Gainesville
Woodward, Earle.....................**(803) 774-1259**
earlew@theitem.com, Circ. Dir., The Item, SC, Sumter
Woodworth, Seth.......................**(509) 762-6248**
Big Bend Cmty. College, WA, 7662 Chanue St., Bldg. 1500
Woody, John
woodyjm@jmu.edu, Prof., James Madison University, VA, Harrisonburg
Woody, Stanley
tfrantz@fbherald.com, Pub., Fort Bend Herald, TX, Rosenberg
Woody, Frances........................**336-506-3033**
Asst. Mng. Ed., Times-News, NC, Burlington
Woolf, Greg................**(617) 779-8900 ext. 2166**
gwoolfe@domania.com, Vice Pres., Finance, Domania, Inc., MA, Watertown
Woolley, Kristine.....................**(505) 473-6980**
College of Santa Fe, NM, Santa Fe
Woolley, John
sales@pcindustries.com, Pres./Sales Mgr., PC Industries, IL, Gurnee
Woolman, Ron................................**ext. 214**
Educ. Ed., West Plains Daily Quill, MO, West Plains
Woolsey, Leonard.....................**(770) 834-6631**
publisher@times-georgian.com, Pub., Times-Georgian, GA, Carrollton
Woolwine, Walter W..................**(610) 371-5102**
wwoolwine@readingeagle.com, Adv. Sr. Dir., Key Acct. Mgmt., Reading Eagle, PA, Reading
Woosley, David...............................**ext. 112**
Asst. Mng. Ed., Idaho Press-Tribune, ID, Nampa
Wooten, Bob
bwooten@nvdaily.com, News Ed., Northern Virginia Daily, VA, Strasburg
Wooten, Frank...............................**ext. 5710**
Asst. Ed., The Post and Courier, SC, Charleston
Workman, Chris
chrisworkman@shelbystar.com, Bus. Mgr., The Star, NC, Shelby
Workman, Wayne.....................**(330) 721-4030**
Circ. Mgr., The Medina County Gazette, OH, Medina
Worley, Kathy.........................**(580) 221-6545**
kworley@ardmoreite.com, Data Processing Mgr., The Daily Ardmoreite, OK, Ardmore
Worley, Joe
joe.worley@tulsaworld.com, Exec. Ed., Tulsa World, OK, Tulsa
Worstell, Dave.......................**(406) 657-1352**
dworstell@billingsgazette.com, Adv. Dir., Sales/Mktg., Billings Gazette, MT, Billings
Wortel, Gary
gwortel@star-telegram.com, Pres./Pub., Fort Worth Star-Telegram, TX, Fort Worth
Wortman, Meg........................**(970) 871-4218**
Prodn. Mgr., Craig Daily Press, CO, Craig
Wosco, Ana Maria
info@launion.com.ar, Dir./Ed., La Union, Lomas De Zamora, Provincia de Buenos Aires
Wright, Clero..........................**(478) 744-4252**
cwright@macon.com, Adv. Mgr., Classified, The Telegraph, GA, Macon
Wright, Gary..........................**(978) 970-4882**
grwright@lowellsun.com, Circ. Mgr., Home Delivery, The Sun, MA, Lowell
Wright, Adam..........................**209-249-3555**
I.T. Manager, Manteca Bulletin, CA, Manteca
Wright, Randy........................**(801) 344-2913**
rwright@heraldextra.com, Exec. Ed., The Daily Herald, UT, Provo
Wright, David A.
info@martinautomatic.com, Vice Pres., Sales, Martin Automatic, Inc., IL, Rockford
Wright, Debbie........................**(901) 529-2604**
wright@commercialappeal.com, Credit Mgr., The Commercial Appeal, TN, Memphis
Wright, Jason Ashley
jason.wright@tulsaworld.com, Fashion/Style Ed., Tulsa World, OK, Tulsa
Wright, Tom...........................**(256) 340-2430**
tom.wright@decaturdaily.com, Editorial Page Ed., The Decatur Daily, AL, Decatur
Wright, Tricia.........................**(717) 703-3070**
triciaw@pa-news.org, Vice President, Association Services, Pennsylvania Newspaper Association, PA, Harrisburg
Wright, Regina........................**(256) 340-2439**
regina.wright@decaturdaily.com, Metro Ed., The Decatur Daily, AL, Decatur

Wright, Heidi ....(541) 885-4465
hwright@heraldandnews.com, Pub., Herald and News, OR, Klamath Falls
Wright, Dalton C.......................(417) 532-9131
editor@lebanondailyrecord.com, Pres./Pub., The Lebanon Daily Record, MO, Lebanon
Wright, John P.
jwright@herald-democrat.com, Pub., Herald Democrat, TX, Sherman
Wright, Mark
mwright@dayglo.com, Vice Pres., Sales, Day-Glo Color Corp., OH, Cleveland
Wright, Lili ....(765) 658-5977
editor@ddepauw.com, DePauw Univ., IN, Advisor
Wright, Randy
randy.wright@eammosca.com, Sales Mgr., EAM-Mosca Corp., PA, Hazle Township
Wright, Debbie
dwright@dddnews.com, Office Mgr., The Daily Dunklin Democrat, MO, Kennett
Wrinn, Stephen
smwrin2@email.uky.edu, Dir., University Press of Kentucky, KY, Lexington
Wrobel, Stanislaw
listy@echodnia.eu, Ed. in Chief, ECHO DNIA, Kielce
Wrubel, Charles
chasnews@aol.com, Pres., Wrubel Communications, NJ, Fair Lawn
Wuertenberg, Nathan
npw001@mcdaniel.edu, McDaniel College, MD, Westminster
Wuest, Joseph..............................(780) 429-5474
jwuest@thejournal.canwest.com, Adv. Mgr., Classified, Edmonton Journal, AB, Edmonton
Wuetcher, Sue ....(716) 645-4612
University at Buffalo Law School- SUNY, NY, Amherst
Wuffli, Rene
wuffli@rdv.ch, Gen. Mgr., DER RHEINTALER, Berneck St. Gallen
Wulff, Hans Christian
info@segeberger-zeitung.de, Proprietor, SZ Segeberger Zeitung, Bath Segeberg
Wunstel, Linda
lwunstel@theadvocate.com, Mktg. Dir., The Advocate, LA, Baton Rouge
Wyatt, Don ....(417) 836-1111
dwyatt@news-leader.com, Exec. Ed., Springfield News-Leader, MO, Springfield
Wyatt, Dennis...........................209-249-3519
Editorial Page Ed., Manteca Bulletin, CA, Manteca
Wyatt, Jim..................................(239) 335-0315
Retail Sales Mgr., The News-Press, FL, Fort Myers
Wyckoff, Mark ....(805) 437-0246
mwyckoff@venturacountystar.com, Entertainment Ed., Ventura County Star, CA, Camarillo
Wykle, Nancy ....(919) 419-6644
nwykle@heraldsun.com, Exec. Ed., The Herald-Sun, NC, Durham
Wysocki, Jean
jwysocki@camden.gannett.com, Controller, The Daily Journal, NJ, Vineland
Wysocki, Jean ....(856) 486-2610
jwysocki@gannett.com, Controller, Courier-Post, NJ, Cherry Hill
Wyson, Karisue...........................(202) 334-7209
wysonkm@washpost.com, Mktg. Mgr., The Washington Post Writers Group, DC, Washington
Wyss, Belinda ....(765) 973-8258
Indiana Univ. East, IN, Richmond

X

Xose Martinez, Pastoriza
info@laregion.es, Dir., La Region, Orense

Y

Yade, Vincent ....ext. 2402
vincent.yade@scni.com, Mgr., Mktg. Serv., The Advocate, CT, Stamford
Yaeger, Steve ....(612) 673-4256
steve.yaeger@startribune.com, Director of Marketing, Star Tribune, MN, Minneapolis
Yagimuma, Yukio
lomu@minyu.net.com, Ed. in Chief, FUKUSHIMA MINYU, Fukushima, Tohoku
Yagle, Mandy
madami@sdnccg.com, Classified Dir., The Sidney Daily News, OH, Sidney
Yahaya, Yushaimi
yushem@mmail.com.my, Exec. Ed., MALAY MAIL, Kuala Lumpur
Yainio, Kari
kari.vainio@ts.fi, Ed. in Chief, TURUN SANOMAT, Turku, Abo
Yakle, Richard
ryakle@examiner-enterprise.com, Circ. Dir., Examiner-Enterprise, OK, Bartlesville
Yakubovich, Pavel
sb@sovbel.belpak.minsk.by, Ed., SOVETSKAYA BELORUSSIYA, Minsk
Yamaguchi, Andy.......................(808) 525-8049
ayamaguchi@honoluluadvertiser.com, Asst. City Ed., Honolulu Star-Advertiser, HI, Honolulu
Yamamoto, Jiro
denshi@hiroshima-cdas.or.jp, Chrmn., CHUGOKU SHIMBUN, Hiroshima, Chugoku
Yandell, Tim ....(321) 733-5391
info@inetusa.com, Pres., inetUSA, FL, Longwood
Yanez, Ivan Cardozo 64-5522
elsol@telcel.net.ve, Pres., EL SOL DE MARGARITA, Porlamar, Margarita
Yanez, Mike
info@ulead.com, Vice Pres., American Sales, Ulead Systems, Inc., CA, Torrance
Yanez, Ramon 32-0736
Pub., Provincia, Cumana, Sucre
Yang, Philip...........................866-2-2397-0180
ttonline@mail.gio.gov.tw, TAIPEI JOURNAL, Taipei
Yanick, Lisa
lyanick@michigannewspapers.com, Photo Ed., Mt. Pleasant, Morning Sun, MI, Mount Pleasant
Yanick, Randy
ryanick@tsvmedia.net, Circ. Dir., Eagle Times, NH, Claremont
Yaqub Al-Hamer, Nabil
alayam@batelco.com.bh, Chrmn., AL AYAM
Yarborough, Ramon L.
foto@fayobserver.com, Chrmn., The Fayetteville Observer, NC, Fayetteville
Yardley, Donna ....(360) 577-2511
library@tdn.com, Librarian, The Daily News, WA, Longview
Yaroch, Victoria ....ext. 119
vyaroch@hearstnp.com, Adv. Dir., The Huron Daily Tribune, MI, Bad Axe
Yasir, David
tdnizm@tdn.com.tr, Ed., TURKISH DAILY NEWS
Yasuhara, Margaret...................(808) 455-0603
Leeward Cmty. College, HI, Pearl City
Yasunari, Nagiko
suikei@nisty.ne.jp, Pres., SUISAN KEIZAI SHIMBUN, Tokyo
Yatagai, Alan S.
info@vchannel.com, Pres., V-Channel, Inc., CA, Santa Clara
Yates, Peter S.........................(540) 574-6297
pyates@dnronline.com, Ed., Daily News-Record, VA, Harrisonburg
Yates, Peter S.........................(540) 574-6200
pyates@dnronline.com, Gen. Mgr., Byrd Newspapers, VA, Harrisonburg
Yates, Phillip ....(803) 644-2332
pyates@aikenstandard.com, Prodn. Dir., Aiken Standard, SC, Aiken
Yates, Bob.................................(214) 977-8260
byates@dallasnews.com, Deputy Mng. Ed., Sports, The Dallas Morning News, TX, Dallas
Yates, Peter S.
pyates@dnronline.com, Gen. Mgr., Rockingham Publishing Co., VA, Harrisonburg
Yauger, Shawn.........................(724) 684-2653
syauger@tribweb.com, Prodn. Mgr., Pre Press, The Valley Independent, PA, Monessen
Yeager, M. E................(316) 284-5271 ext. 271
Bethel College, KS, North Newton
Yeager, Milicent.........................(205) 325-3155
Credit Mgr., The Birmingham News, AL, Birmingham
Yearty, Kit ....(512) 445-3820
kyearty@statesman.com, Prodn. Dir., Austin American-Statesman, TX, Austin
Yeater, Laura
press@qconline.com, Librarian, The Dispatch, IL, Moline
Yemma, John
yemmaj@csmonitor.com, Ed., The Christian Science Monitor, MA, Boston
Yenne, John
jyenne@citizen-times.com, New Media Dir., The Asheville Citizen-Times, NC, Asheville
Yeomans, Adam
ayeomans@ap.org, Bureau Chief, Tennessee Associated Press Managing Editors, TN, Brentwood
Yero, Mark ....(941) 206-1317
myero@sun-herald.com, Circulation Director, Charlotte Sun, FL, Charlotte Harbor
Yilbiz, Ibrahim
iyilbiz@cumhuriyet.com.tr, Ed. in Chief, CUMHURIYET
Yildiz, Ibrahim
iyildiz@cumhuriyet.com.tr, Ed. in Chief, CUMHURIYET
Yingling, Steve ....(530) 542-8010
syingling@tahoedailytribune.com, Sports Ed., Tahoe Daily Tribune, CA, South Lake Tahoe
Yingling, Jaclyn ....(814) 765-7813 ext. 240
sports@theprogressnews.com, Sports Ed., The Progress, PA, Clearfield
Yingst, Cindy.............................(360) 754-5425
cyingst@olympia.gannett.com, City Ed., Night, The Olympian, WA, Olympia
Ynosroza, Roger
rynostroza@gaa.org, Ed., Gravure Association of America, NY, Rochester
Yocum, Mark A. ....ext. 122
markyocum@sanduskyregister.com, Adv. Dir., Sandusky Register, OH, Sandusky
Yoder, Donald D.
Donald.yoder@notes.udayton.edu, Chair, University of Dayton, OH, Dayton
Yoder, Josh.......................................ext. 256
Lifestyle Ed., The Hickory Daily Record, NC, Hickory
Yoder, Ben ....(478) 744-4326
byoder@macontel.com, News Ed., The Telegraph, GA, Macon
Yonan, Alan ....(808) 535-2448
ayonan@honoluluadvertiser.com, Asst. Bus. Ed., Honolulu Star-Advertiser, HI, Honolulu
Yonko, Tony.............................814-870-1765
tony.yonko@timesnews.com, Director of Finance, Erie Times-News, PA, Erie
Yontz, Joyce
joyce@daily-jeff.com, Controller, The Daily Jeffersonian, OH, Cambridge
Yopp, Jan...................................(919) 962-4083
Walter Spearman Prof., University of North Carolina, NC, Chapel Hill
Yorganciogiu, Ozkan
yeniduze@north-cyprus.net, Ed., YENI DUZEN, Nicosia
York, Angela ....(408) 920-5686
ayork@mercurynews.com, Mgr., Research, San Jose Mercury News, CA, San Jose
York, Peter ....(760) 740-5403
peter.york@lee.net, Pub., North County Times, CA, Escondido
York, Angie
ayork@messenger-inquirer.com, Bus. Mgr., The Messenger, KY, Madisonville
Yorth, Bill...................................(262) 513-2671
byorth@conleynet.com, Ed., The Freeman, WI, Waukesha
Yoshida, Kayo
yoshida-k@sponichi.co.jp, Sec, SPORTS NIPPON, Tokyo
Yoshida, Kosuke
fprs@fukuishimbun.co.jp, Pres., FUKUI SHIMBUN, Fukui, Hokuriku
Yoshida, Shinichi
newsroom@emb.asahi-np.co.jp, Gen. Mgr., ASAHI SHIMBUN, Tokyo
Yoshioka, Toshikata
info@nnn.co.jp, Owner/Pres., NIHONKAI SHIMBUN, Tottori, Chugoku
Yost, Tim
circ@madison-press.com, Circ. Mgr., The Madison Press, OH, London
Young, Nerissa ....(304) 696-2273
Marshall University, WV, Huntington
Young, Leith ....(508) 862-1137
lyoung@capecodonline.com, Member Servs. Systems Mgr., Cape Cod Times, MA, Hyannis
Young, Keith ....(864) 583-2907
kyoung@msmgmt.com, Technology Systems Dir., Mid-South Management Co., Inc., SC, Spartanburg
Young, Laura
editor@poteaudailynews.com, Mng. Ed., Poteau Daily News, OK, Poteau
Young, Gloria ....(530) 852-0234
gloriay@goldcountrymedia.com, Bus./Finance Ed., Auburn Journal, Inc., CA, Auburn
Young, Phil
webmaster@thisisleicestershire.co.uk, Adv. Dir., LEICESTER MERCURY, Leicester, Leicestershire
Young, Richard ....ext. 237
ryoung@sharonherald.com, Travel Ed., The Herald, PA, Sharon
Young, Dorothy ....ext. 1161
dorothy.young@uniontrib.com, Purchasing Mgr., The San Diego Union-Tribune, CA, San Diego
Young, Bob
bobyoungjr@computertree.com, Pres., Computer Tree, NC, Winston-Salem
Young, Joe 336-768-9820
jyoung@computertree.com, Vice President, Computer Tree, NC, Winston-Salem
Young, Ann ....(815) 232-0162
ayoung@journalstandard.com, Adv. Mgr., Display, The Journal-Standard, IL, Freeport
Young, Kelley
advertising@neoshodailynews.com, Ad Director, The Carthage Press, MO, Carthage
Young, Paul 3817 1817
paul.young@qt.com.au, Adv. Mgr., THE QUEENSLAND TIMES, West Ipswich
Young, Hope ....(318) 362-0278
Accent Ed., The News-Star, LA, Monroe
Young, Mark
myoung@gfherald.com, IT Dir., Grand Forks Herald, ND, Grand Forks
Young Seong, Song
yssong@kyunghyang.com, Pres., KYUNGHYANG SHINMUN, Seoul
Youngblood, Alan
alan.youngblood@starbanner.com, Photo Editor, Ocala Star-Banner, FL, Ocala
Youngman, Owen ....(312) 222-4179
oyoungman@tribune.com, Vice Pres., Devel., Chicago Tribune, IL, Chicago
Youngwood, Susan......................(802) 485-2763
Norwich Univ., VT, Northfield
Yount, Jean ....(803) 644-2362
jyount@aikenstandard.com, Adv. Mgr., Composition, Aiken Standard, SC, Aiken
Yount, Martin
myount@highpoint.edu, Video Producer, High Point University, NC, High Point
Younus, Mohammad
dsangram@gmail.com, Chrmn., DAINIK SANGRAM, Dhaka
Yourz, Jeff
info@aoainc.com, Pres., Adaptive Optics Associates, Inc., A United Technologies Co., MA, Cambridge
Youssef, Amre ....(973) 569-7760
Director of Digital Assets, North Jersey Media Group, NJ, Woodland Park
Yovel, Yishay ....(408) 933-1732
pr@backweb.com, Vice Pres., Mktg./Pdct. Mgmt., BackWeb, CA, San Jose
Yrausquin, R.
aziso@extra.an, Dir., EXTRA, Korsou
Yshai, Ron Ben
shimoni@globes.co.il, Ed., Histadrut (Labour Federation) Davar Ltd.
Yucqing, Dai
gzdaily@public.guangzhou.gd.cn, Dir., GUANGZHOU RIBAO, Guangzhou, Guangzhou
Yung, Cameron
tvdata@tvdata.com, Vice Pres., Newspaper/Adv. Sales, TV Data (Tribune Media Services), NY, Glens Falls
Yung, Cameron ....(312) 527-8111

cyung@tribune.com, Exec. Dir., Newspapers, Tribune Media Services Entertainment Products, NY, Queensbury
Yunt, Tom
tyunt@wcinet.com, Pres., Woodward Communications, IA, Dubuque
Yuravich, Albert 203-625-4470
albert.yuravich@scni.com, Managing Editor, Greenwich Time, CT, Greenwich
Yuri Ceballos, Margo
diaro@eltrabajo.cl, Dir., El Trabajo, San Felipe
Yusupov, Ingalill
ingalill.sundhade@bohuslaningens.se, Ed., BOHUSLANINGEN med DALS DAGBLAD, Uddevalla
Yznaga, Bob....................(805) 681-5879
byznaga@newspress.com, Prodn. Dir., Santa Barbara News-Press, CA, Santa Barbara

Z

Zabaleta, Marco
manila@efe.com, Ed., EFE News Services - Manila, Philippines, Manila
Zabel, Matt....................(940) 566-6884
City Ed., Denton Record-Chronicle, TX, Denton
Zachariassen, Siri
siri.zachariassen@oblad.no, Ed., OEST-LANDETS BLAD, Ski
Zaffke, Gary
gzaffke@jacksongraphics.com, Nat'l Sales Mgr., Jackson Graphics, Inc., WI, Richfield
Zagorski, Mark S.
mark.zagorski@mediaspangroup.com, CMO, MediaSpan Group, Inc., NC, Morrisville
Zaharchuk, Alice....................(416) 483-2430
marketingmonkey@sympatico.ca, Exec. Dir., Trans-Canada Advertising Agency Network, ON, Toronto
Zahrt, Chris....................(231) 725-6333
czahrt@muskegonchronicle.com, Mktg. Promo. Mgr., The Muskegon Chronicle, MI, Muskegon
Zajac, Ken....................(215) 441-8444
kzajac@sportsnetwork.com, Sales Dir., The Sports Network (Div. of Computer Info. Network), PA, Hatboro
Zajac, Ken
kzajac@sportsnetwork.com, Nat'l Sales Mgr., The Sports Network, PA, Hatboro
Zajac, Chris....................(203) 317-2297
cfrench@record-journal.com, Chief Photographer, Record-Journal, CT, Meriden
Zakhariya, Claudette
rzakhari@interserv.com, Vice Pres.-Mktg., Better Web Bureau, CA, Valley Center
Zaki, Oka
okazaki@nissenmedia.com, Ed. in Chief, NIHON SEN-I SHIMBUN, Tokyo
Zalabak, Tom....................217-351-5285
tzalabak@news-gazette.com, Advertising Director, News-Gazette Inc., IL, Champaign
Zalaznick, Matt....................(970) 748-2926
mzalaznick@vaildaily.com, Mng. Ed., Vail Daily, CO, Vail
Zaleski, Jack
jzaleski@forumcomm.com, Editorial Page Ed., InForum, ND, Fargo
Zaltsberg, Robert....................(812) 331-4364
bzaltsberg@heraldt.com, Editorial Page Ed., The Herald-Times, IN, Bloomington
Zaluski, Mariusz
m.zaluski@express.bydgoski.pl, Ed., EXPRESS BYDOGSKI, Bydgoszcz
Zamberlan, Jim....................(734) 994-6728
jzamberlan@annarbornews.com, Adv. Mgr., Classified, The Ann Arbor News, MI, Ann Arbor
Zambrano, MarÂ¡a Victoria
vzambrano@eldiario.com.ec, Gen. Mgr., Sociedad Anonima, Portoviejo, Manabi
Zamit, Diego
diariocronica@diariocronica.com.ar, Dir., Cronica, Comodoro Rivadavia, Provincia de Chubut
Zammuto, Sal
szammuto@publicitas.com, Branch Dir., Publicitas North America, Inc., GA, Atlanta
Zanca, Bruce
bzanca@bankrate.com, Sr. Vice Pres./Chief Mktg./Commun. Officer, Bankrate.com, FL, North Palm Beach
Zankel, Erwin....................316 875 4010
anzeigen.graz@kleinezeitung.at, Ed. in Chief, KLEINE ZEITUNG, 8010 Graz
Zanki, Tom....................ext. 3630
tzanki@express-times.com, Bus. Ed., The Express-Times, PA, Easton
Zanmiller, Pete
pzanmill@gannett.com, Pub., The Shreveport Times, LA, Shreveport
Zanolli, Vittoriano
litrovitia@cremonaonline.it, Dir., LA PROVINCIA DI CREMONA, Cremona
Zanotelli, Cheri....................(719) 544-3520 ext. 495
cheriz@chieftain.com, Radio/Television Ed., The Pueblo Chieftain, CO, Pueblo
Zapcic, William....................(732) 565-7345
bzapcic@thnt.com, Online Ed., Home News Tribune, NJ, East Brunswick
Zappa, Arthur....................(803) 644-2360
azappa@aikenstandard.com, Adv. Dir., Aiken Standard, SC, Aiken
Zariff, George....................(203) 330-6422
gzariff@ctpost.com, Adv. Mgr., Art Servs., Connecticut Post, CT, Bridgeport
Zarkin, Kimberly
kzarkin@westminstercollege.edu, Westminster College, UT, Salt Lake City
Zarky, Karen
kzarky@maturepublishers.com, Exec. Dir., North American Mature Publishers Association, MO, Camdenton
Zarpa, Jose....................31-4437
Gen. Mgr., EL NACIONALISTA, San Juan Los Morros, Guarico
Zarro, Anthony
azarro@imediainc.com, Vice Pres., Bus. Devel., Interactive Media Associates, NJ, Parsippany
Zarzalejos, Jose Antonio
info@abc.es, Dir., ABC, Madrid
Zarzalejos, Jose Antonio
spromozionez@abc.es, Ed., ABC, Madrid
Zarzana, Brandon....................(360) 735-4431
brandon.zarzana@columbian.com, Controller, The Columbian, WA, Vancouver
Zaun, Peter-Georg
info@tageblatt-online.de, Ed., Tageblatt fur den Kreis Steinfurt, Ochtrup
Zavala, Joe
jzavala@dailytidings.com, Sports Ed., The Ashland Daily Tidings, OR, Ashland
Zavarise, Dean....................905-850-6509
dzavarise@torstar.ca, EVP-Torstar Printing Group, Toronto Star, ON, Toronto
Zavodny, Barbara....................(713) 266-5481 ext. 230
bzavodny@sninews.com, Treasurer, Southern Newspapers, Inc., TX, Houston
Zavoina, Susan
zavoina@unt.edu, Chair/Assoc. Prof./Coord., Photo seq., University of North Texas, TX, Denton
Zawada, Kim
news@marquettetribune.org, Marquette Univ., WI, Milwaukee
Zawadzka, Elzbieta
elzbieta.zawadzka@gs24.pl, Dir., GLOS SZCZECINSKI, Szczecin
Zbiciak, Nancy....................(810) 766-6260
nzbiciak@flintjournal.com, Adv. Coord., Pre Print, The Flint Journal, MI, Flint
Zebora, James....................ext. 2420
jim.zebora@scni.com, Bus. Ed., The Advocate, CT, Stamford
Zechman, Martha....................609-272-7265
mzechman@pressofac.com, Librarian, The Press of Atlantic City, NJ, Pleasantville
Zedaker, Carol....................(989) 894-9675
czedaker@bc-times.com, Lifestyle Ed., The Bay City Times, MI, Bay City
Zeeck, David A.....................(253) 597-8554
david.zeeck@thenewstribune.com, Pres./Pub., The News Tribune, WA, Tacoma
Zegelat, Abdul Wahab
te@alrai.com, Ed. in Chief, AL RAI
Zellars, Courtney....................(812) 231-4264
courtney.zellars@tribstar.com, Mktg. Dir., The Tribune Star, IN, Terre Haute
Zelz, Eric....................(270) 990-8262
ezelz@bangordailynews.net, Graphics/Design Ed., Bangor Daily News, ME, Bangor
Zeman, Ann....................(206) 652-6918
azeman@seattletimes.com, Adv. Mgr., Mktg., Seattle Post-Intelligencer/Seattle Times, WA, Seattle
Zeman, Robert....................ext. 205
Chrmn., Norwood Paper, IL, Chicago
Zenhausern, Erik
erikz@aaind.org, Exec. Dir., American Association of Independent News Distributors, NY, Harrison
Zenor, Mary
mzenor@sbtinfo.com, Adv. Mgr., Classified, South Bend Tribune, IN, South Bend
Zepeda, Jorge
siglo21@foreigner.class.udg.mx, Dir., Siglo 21, Guadalajara, Jalisco
Zepezauer, Keven....................(252) 329-9516
kzepezauer@reflector.com, Circ. Dir., The Daily Reflector, NC, Greenville
Zerbey, Joseph H.....................(419) 724-6217
jzerbey@toledoblade.com, Pres./Gen. Mgr., The Blade, OH, Toledo
Zernechel, Denise
dzernechel@mankatofreepress.com, Circ. Dir., The Free Press, MN, Mankato
Zesk, Richard....................ext. 285
r.zesk@theday.com, Adv. Mgr., Classified, The Day Publishing Company, CT, New London
Zettler, Linda....................(615) 259-8232
lzettler@tennessean.com, Entertainment Ed., The Tennessean, TN, Nashville
Zewicky, Dave
dzewick@monroenews.com, Circ. Mgr., The Monroe Evening News, MI, Monroe
Zgonc, Tom....................(330) 650-5678
tzgonc@prostarts.com, Pres., Pro Starts, OH, Hudson
Zhao, Xinshu....................(919) 962-1465
Prof., University of North Carolina, NC, Chapel Hill
Zhivago, Kristin
kristin@zhivago.com, Pres., Zhivago Management Partners, RI, Jamestown
Zhu, Ling
cdweb@chinadaily.net, Ed., ZHONGGUO RIBAO, Beijing
Zidich, John....................(602) 444-8162
john.zidich@pni.com, Pres./Pub., The Arizona Republic, AZ, Phoenix
Zieco, Aitor
azieco@elvigia.com, Ed./Dir, EL VIGIA, Barcelona
Ziegler, Justin....................(713) 275-5039 ext. 5
jtz@ivisuals.com, Pjct. Mgr., Interactive Visuals, Inc., IL, Chicago
Ziegler, H.U.
redaktion@kuhnverlag.de, Proprietor, Sudwest Presse (Die Neckarquelle), Villingen-Schwenningen
Zielinska, Iwona
iZielinska@gazetalubuska.pl, Ed., GAZETA LUBUSKA, Zielona Gora
Zielinski, Andrzej....................826 4311
marketing@rynkizagraniczne.pl, Ed. in Chief, RYNKI ZAGRANICZNE, Warszawa
Zieman, Mark
zieman@kcstar.com, Pres./Pub., The Kansas City Star, MO, Kansas City
Ziemba, Denielle....................(607) 441-7259
dziemba@thedailystar.com, Features Ed., The Daily Star, NY, Oneonta
Zier, Frank
fzier@pubgroup.com, Nashville/West Coast Assoc. Pub., American Profile - Franklin, TN, TN, Franklin
Zier, Frank
fzier@pubgroup.com, Nashville/West Coast Assoc. Pub., Relish - Franklin, TN, TN, Franklin
Zier, Frank
fzier@pubgroup.com, Nashville/West Coast Assoc. Pub., American Profile - Franklin, TN, TN, Franklin
Zilar, Tim....................(509) 582-1423
tzilar@tri-cityherald.com, Circ. Mgr., Tri-City Herald, WA, Kennewick
Zimmer, Teresa....................(760) 337-3460
tzimmer@ivpressonline.com, Pres./Pub., Imperial Valley Press, CA, El Centro
Zimmerman, Neal
nzimmerman@tribune.com, Mgr., Tribune Media Network, CA, San Francisco
Zimmerman, Chris....................620-429-2773
Publisher, Cherokee County News-Advocate, KS, Columbus
Zimmerman, Cathy....................(360) 577-2541
zimmerman@tdn.com, Features Ed., The Daily News, WA, Longview
Zimmerman, Lawrence
lawrence.zimmerman@usa.xerox.com, Sr. Vice Pres./CFO, Xerox Corp., CT, Norwalk
Zimmerman, Michelle Deal....................(410) 332-6199
michelle.deal@baltsun.com, Asst. Mng. Ed., Graphics, The Baltimore Sun, MD, Baltimore
Zimmerman, Tammy....................(979) 731-4680
tammy.zimmerman@theeagle.com, Pre Press Mgr., The Eagle, TX, Bryan
Zimmers, Louis E.
info@zimmers.com, Pres., US Telephony Ltd., OH, Cincinnati
Zimney, Dawn
dzimney@gfherald.com, Circ. Dir., Grand Forks Herald, ND, Grand Forks
Zinck, Frank....................(902) 421-5805
fzinick@hfxnews.ca, Mgmt. Info Servs. Mgr., The Daily News, NS, Dartmouth
Zinke, Nikki
trpub@daktel.com, Pub., Valley City Times-Record, ND, Valley City
Ziobro, Alexis....................(302) 324-2743
aziobro@wilmingt.gannett.com, Circ. Mgr., Home Delivery Sales, The News Journal, DE, New Castle
Zipp, Fred....................(512) 912-2983
fzipp@statesman.com, Ed., Austin American-Statesman, TX, Austin
Zisman, Lawrence H.
marketplacepoll@aol.com, Pres., The Marketplace Poll, NJ, East Windsor
Zmeyushenko, Vladmir
gudok@css-rzd.ru, Ed. in Chief, GUDOK, Moscow
Zoeckler, Eric L.
mrscribe@aol.com, Columnist, Taming The Workplace, WA, Seattle
Zoeller, Chris....................(979) 731-4738
chris.zoeller@theeagle.com, Asst. Adv. Dir., The Eagle, TX, Bryan
Zohoori, Ali
zohoori@bradley.edu, Prof., Bradley University, IL, Peoria
Zoibi, Ali
azoibi@rocheste.gannett.com, Pres./Pub., Democrat and Chronicle.com, NY, Rochester
Zoldan, Sheldon....................(239) 335-0560
Asst. Mng. Ed., The News-Press, FL, Fort Myers
Zollinger, Robert C.
gallpind@cia-g.com, Vice Pres./Pub., Gallup Independent, NM, Gallup
Zollman, Joseph
joezoll183@aol.com, Author/Owner, Stamping Grounds, FL, Altamonte Springs
Zollman, Peter M.
pzollman@aimgroup.com, Founding principal, AIM Group / Classified Intelligence, FL, Altamonte Springs
Zoltan, Arpasi
somogyihirlap@axels.hu, Dir., SOMOGYI HIRLAP, Kaposvar, Somogy
Zorzi, Norberto....................424-5544
sanjusto@solsoft.com.ar, Gen. Mgr., La Voz de San Justo S.R.L., San Francisco, Provincia de Cordoba
Zremski, Jerry
jzremski@press.org, Pres., National Press Club, DC, Washington
Zuberi, Wamiq
editor@brecorder.com, Ed., BUSINESS RECORDER, Karachi
Zubkov, Vladimir
post@vm.ru, Chrmn., VECHERNYAYA MOSKVA, Moscow
Zuchelli, Mark....................ext. 224
mzuchelli@timesonline.com, Circ. Mgr., Home Delivery, Beaver County Times, PA, Beaver
Zuckerman, Mortimer B.....................(212) 326-4010
Chrmn./Pub., NY Daily News, NY, New York
Zuehls, Glenn....................(808) 529-4704
gzuehls@staradvertiser.com, Senior Vice President, Advertising, Honolulu Star-Advertiser, HI, Honolulu
Zuerker, Dawn....................(806) 742-3384
Asst. Dir./Adv. Mgr., Texas Tech. Univ., TX,

Lubbock
Zuill, William J.
wjszuill@theroyalgazette.bm, Ed. in Chief, ROYAL GAZETTE/MID OCEAN NEWS, Hamilton
Zukrow, Susan.........................(312) 222-3921
szukrow@tribune.com, Adv. Dir., Devel., Chicago Tribune, IL, Chicago
Zullo, Robert...........................(985) 448-7614
robert.zullo@dailycomet.com, City Editor, The Daily Comet, LA, Thibodaux
Zuloaga Lopez, Carlos
redaccion@latribunadealbacete.es, Ed. in Chief, La Tribuna De Albacete, Albacete
Zumwalt, Barbara
azumwalt@recordnet.com, Metro Ed., The Record, CA, Stockton
Zuppa, Tom.............................(978) 970-4643
tzuppa@lowellsun.com, Asst. Mng. Ed., Local News-Weekend, The Sun, MA, Lowell
Zuraw, Cathy...........................(203) 330-6498
czuraw@ctpost.com, Photo/Graphics Ed., Connecticut Post, CT, Bridgeport
Zurek, Chester..........................815-462-1129
czmccainbind@earthlink.net, National Service/Product Manager, McCain Bindery Systems, IL
Zurek, Jerome
zurek@cabrini.edu, Chair, Cabrini College, PA, Radnor
Zweerink, Brad.........................(707) 427-6991
Photo Ed., Daily Republic, CA, Fairfield
Zwergel, Gerrit........................(469) 532-8050
gerrit.zwergel@kba.com, Vice Pres., Finance, KBA North America, Inc. (Koenig & Bauer AG), VT
Zwerling, Elizabeth.......(909) 593-3511 ext. 4293
Univ. of La Verne, CA, La Verne
Zwez, Deb
publisher@theeveningleader.com, Pub., The Evening Leader, OH, Saint Marys
Zwickel, Steven.........................608 262-5172
Advisor, Wisconsin Engineer Magazine, WI, Madison
auvaa, Terry
auvaa@terri@samoanews.com, Gen. Mgr., SAMOA NEWS, Pago Pago
axelsson, Soren
soren.axelsson@ekurirens.com.se, Mng. Dir., ESKILSTUNA-KURIREN med STRENGNAS TIDNING, Eskilstuna
da Camara, Jose Bettencourt
internet@dnoticias.pt, Dir., DIARIO DE NOTICIAS DO FUNCHAL, Funchal
da Costa, Camilo Teixeira..................237-5000
jbosco@uai.com.br, Pres., Estado de Minas, Belo Horizonte, Minas Gerais
da Cunha Losso Pe, Antonietta Rosalina .430-4000
jp@jpjornal.com.br, Pres., Jornal de Piracicaba, Piracicaba, Sao Paulo
da Silva, Jose Carlos
jpb@openline.com.br, Pub., Editora Jornal da Paraiba S.A., Campina Grande, Paraiba
de Abreu, Esmail Texeira...................263-2081
Pres., Jornal de Paraiba do Sul, Paraiba Do Sul, Rio de Janeiro
de Acquaviva, Guadalupe Mantilla
redaccion@elcomercio.com, Gen. Dir., Compania Anonima El Comercio, Quito, Pichincha
de Araujo, Paulo Cabral....................425-7666
diario@dpnet.com.br, Pres., Diario de Pernambuco, Recife, Pernambuco
de Avelar, Sergio F.
gazetavga@varginha.com.br, Ed., Gazeta De Varginha, Bairro Santa Maria
de Barros, Luiz Antonio Montero...........322-1090
Pres., O Diario, Barretos, Sao Paulo
de Bedout Hernandez, Luis Miguel........331 5252
elcolombiano@elcolombiano.com.co, Gen. Mgr., Empresa El Colombiano Ltd., Envigabo
de Camargo Gabas, Jose Gerson
presidencia@fm.com.br, Pub., Empresa de Publicidade Catanduva Ltd., Catanduva, Sao Paulo
de Camargo Moquenco, Jandyra..........634-2549
Pres., A Cidade, Ribeirao Preto, Sao Paulo
de Carvalho, Henrique
anoticia@an.com.br, Adv. Mgr., A Noticia, Joinville, Santa Catarina
de Castro, Viviano Leite....................742-1822
Ed., Gazeta De Teresopolis, Teresopolis, Rio De Janeiro
de Castro Filho, Mucio......................313-6266
redacao@onacional.com.br, Pres., O Nacional, Passo Fundo, Rio Grande do Sul
de Conti, Maria Dolores E. 442-471
tribuno@fairweb.com.ar, Pres., El Tribuno, Dolores, Provincia de Buenos Aires
de Cortez, Gloria Nino.........................46-2367
lanacion@telcel.net.com, Gen. Mgr., La Nacion, San Cristobal, Tachira
de Faria, Pedro Magalhaes.................222-6969
jagora@jagora.com.br, Pres., Jornal Agora, Divinopolis, Minas Gerais
de Freitas, Luiz A.V. 721-1021
Ed., O Avare, Avare, Sao Paulo
de Godoy Neto, Sylvino
cpopular@cpopular.com.br, Pres., Correio Popular, Campinas, Sao Paulo
de Jesus Lopez Rodriguez, Felipe
lavoz@telnor.net, Pres., EL CENTINELA, Mexicali, Baja California Norte
de Jong, W.M.C...............................3789911
info@sdu.nl, Ed., NEDERLANDS STAATSCOURANT, The Hague
de Laet, Steve
steve@partsriver.com, Chief Devel. Officer, PartsRiver-SAQQARA, CA, Fremont
de Lima, Rosselita F. 263-5840
Pres., Diario das Concorrencias, Rio De Janeiro
de Mattos, Cezar Augusto...................601-7272
redacao@jornalsg.com.br, Pres., O Sao Goncalo, Sao Goncalo, Rio de Janeiro
de Mello, Fernando Collor
gazn01@nornet.com.br, Pub., Jornal Gazeta de Alagoas Ltd., Maceio, Alagoas
de Oliveira, Joao N...........................431-2160
Ed., Jornal da Praca, Ponta Pora, Mato Grosso
de Orleans e Braganca, Francisco.........242-5122
fob@e-tribuna.com.br, Pres., Tribuna de Petropolis, Petropolis, Rio de Janeiro
de Paolo, Virginia 420-855
lavoz@arnet.com.ar, Ed., La Voz de Zarate, Zarate, Provincia de Buenos Aires
de Pelaez, Belkis Blondell....................61-0713
Gen. Mgr., Diario Caribazo, Porlamar, Nueva Esparta
de Perez, Herminia E.P. 452-100
elterritorio@elterritorio.com.ar, Pres., El Territorio, Posadas, Provincia de Misiones
de Piedra, Ana Aguirre 275-0105
Gen. Mgr., EL SIGLO, Loja
de Pinto, Petra Acosta 31-3214
Gen. Mgr., Yaracuy Al Dia, San Felipe, Yaracuy
de Rengifo, Martha ....(57 1) 623-5020
datanewsdj@hotmail.com, Sales Exec., Dow Jones Newswires - Bogota, Colombia, Bogota
de Salas, Christian Gonzalez.................52-5510
Gen. Mgr./Sales Mgr., Empresa El Vigilante, Merida, Merida
de Sousa, Luiz Carlos
editor@jornalonorte.com.br, Ed., O Norte, Joao Pessoa, Paraiba
de Souza Cruz, Getulio Alberto.............623-8806
folhabv@technet.com.br, Pres., Folha de Boa Vista, Boa Vista, Roraima
de Vogelaere, Jean-Philippe
jeanphilippe.devogelaere@lesoir.com, Mgr., LE SOIR, Wavre, Brabant
de la Cruz Alonso, Pedro Manuel
pmanuel@lavozdealmeria.com, Dir., La Voz De Almeria, Almeria
de la Huerta de Arroniz, Clementina
mundo@cordoba.rp.com.mx, Pres., El Mundo de Cordoba, Cordoba, Veracruz
de la Isla Ortiz, Carlos.......................313-0534
diario@internexos.net, Ed., DIARIO DE NOGALES, Nogales, Sonora
de la Torre, Art
adelatorre@theadvocate.com, Classified Adv./Bus. Dev. Mgr., The Advocate, LA, Baton Rouge
de los Reyes, Joy C.
malayanews@yahoo.com, Ed. in Chief, MALAYA, Manila
deBrito, Sophie.............................7775-6248
sophie.debrito@ft.com, Synd. Mgr., Financial Times, ENG, London
dePyssler, Dr. Bruce.................(919) 530-7116
North Carolina Central Univ., NC, Durham
deSouza, Bertram.........(330) 747-1471 ext. 1280
desouza@vindy.com, Editorial Writer, The Vindicator, OH, Youngstown
del Toro, Rafael..............................683-8360
editora@elcaribe.com.do, Pres., EL CARIBE, Santo Domingo
delToro, Peggy
peggy.deltoro@inlandnewspapers.com, Gen. Mgr., Inland Valley Daily Bulletin, CA, Ontario
der Parthogh, Masis
finmir@logos.cy.net, Dir., THE CYPRUS FINANCIAL MIRROR, Nicosia
do Amaral Torres, Adiles....................421-4123
progresso@zaz.com.br, Pres., O Progresso, Dourados, Mato Grosso do Sul
farac, Sorin
sorin.farac@tribuna.ro, Adv. Mgr., TRIBUNA, Sibiu
gomez, lary 2547-9300
xquiros@diarioextra.com, Gerente Genaeral, DIARIO EXTRA, San Jose
johnson, stephen.......................419-233-3622
sjohnson@timesbulletin.com, group publisher, The Times Bulletin, OH, Van Wert
kendle, Jeanine..............................ext. 1659
Wire Ed., The Daily Record, OH, Wooster
le Roux, Greg
greg.leroux@inl.co.za, Joint GM: Finance, THE MERCURY, Greyville
mohsin, syed mohammed
admin@dailypratap.com, general manager, DAILY PRATAP, New Delhi
van Dongen, Mario....................(707) 963-2731
mvandongen@marinij.com, Pres./Pub., Marin Independent Journal, CA, Novato
van der Linden, John E.
johnvan@rconnect.com, Broker, Northwest Publishers, Inc., IA, Spirit Lake
van der Linden, John E...............(712) 336-2806
johnvan@rconnect.com, Broker, Northwest Publishers, Inc., IA, Spirit Lake
von Wiesenberger, Arthur
avw@newspress.com, Co-Pub., Santa Barbara News-Press, CA, Santa Barbara
von Ziehlberg, Lebrecht
info@uena.de, Proprietor, UETERSENER NACHRICHTEN, Uetersen
vonHassel, Kirsten......................973-569-7540
vonhassel@northjersey.com, VP/Marketing, North Jersey Media Group, NJ, Woodland Park
white, liz 203 317 2226
lwhite@record-journal.com, vp new media, The Record-Journal Publishing Co., CT, Meriden
white, elizabeth 203 317-2226
lwhite@record-journal.com, vp/new media, Record-Journal, CT, Meriden
µlvarez, Jes£s
redaccion@efe.com.py, Rep., Agencia EFE, Assumption

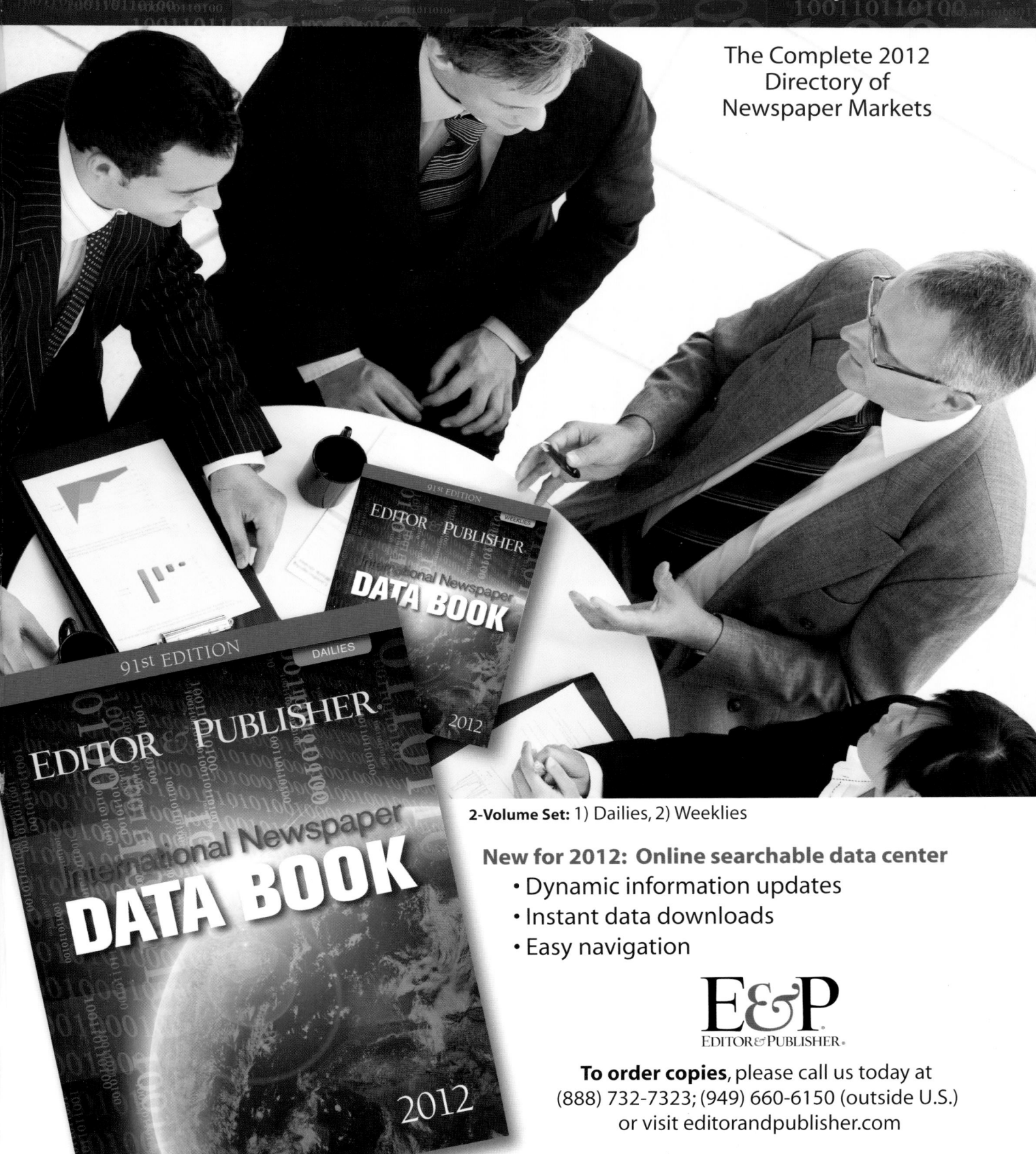

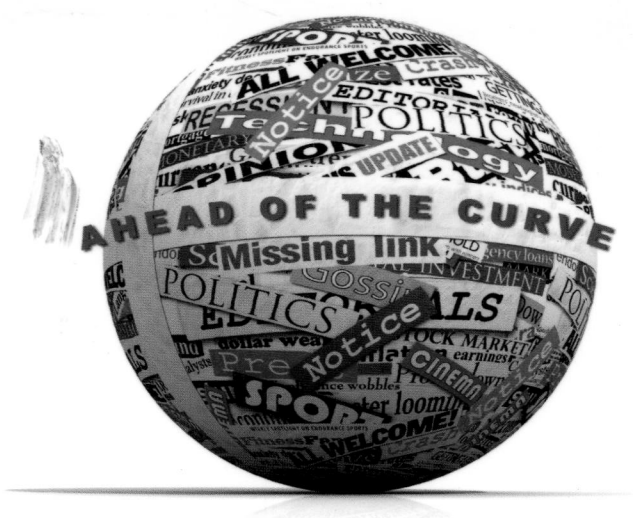

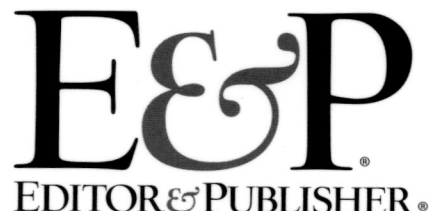